[redacted]

FIRE PROTECTION HANDBOOK®

Twentieth Edition

VOLUME II

Arthur E. Cote, P.E.
Editor-in-Chief

Casey C. Grant, P.E. ❑ **John R. Hall, Jr., Ph.D.** ❑ **Robert E. Solomon, P.E.**
Associate Editors

Pamela A. Powell
Managing Editor

Ronald L. Alpert, Sc.D.
Robert P. Benedetti, P.E.
Shane M. Clary, Ph.D.
Mark T. Conroy
Richard L. P. Custer, M.Sc.
Christian Dubay, P.E.
John A. Granito, Ed.D.
David R. Hague, P.E.
John R. Hall, Jr., Ph.D.
Gregory E. Harrington, P.E.
Edward Kirtley, M.A.
L. Jeffrey Mattern
Guylène Proulx, Ph.D.
Milosh T. Puchovsky, P.E.
Carl H. Rivkin, P.E.
Steven F. Sawyer
Robert E. Solomon, P.E.
Amy Beasley Spencer
Gary Tokle
Robert J. Vondrasek, P.E.

Section Editors

NFPA

National Fire Protection Association®
Quincy, Massachusetts

Editor-in-Chief:	Arthur E. Cote, P.E.
Associate Editors:	Casey C. Grant, P.E. John R. Hall, Jr., Ph.D. Robert E. Solomon, P.E.
Managing Editor:	Pamela A. Powell
Senior Developmental Editor:	Robine J. Andrau
Developmental Editor:	Betsey Henkels
Permissions Editor:	Michael Gammell
Project Editor:	Irene Herlihy
Editorial-Production Services:	Omegatype Typography, Inc.
Interior Design:	Cheryl Langway
Cover Design:	Greenwood Associates
Manufacturing Manager:	Ellen J. Glisker
Printer:	Courier/Westford

Notice Concerning Liability: Publication of this work is for the purpose of circulating information and opinion among those concerned for fire and electrical safety and related subjects. While every effort has been made to achieve a work of high quality, neither NFPA® nor the authors and other contributors to this work guarantee the accuracy or completeness of or assume any liability in connection with the information and opinions contained in this work. The NFPA and the authors and other contributors in no way shall be liable for any personal injury, property, or other damages of any nature whatsoever, whether special, indirect, consequential, or compensatory, directly or indirectly resulting from the publication, use of, or reliance upon this work.

This work is published with the understanding that the NFPA and the authors and other contributors to this work are supplying information and opinion but are not attempting to render engineering, design, legal, or other professional services. If such services are required, the assistance of an appropriate professional should be sought.

The NFPA codes and standards reproduced or referenced in this book are made available for use subject to Important Notices and Legal Disclaimers, which can be viewed at http://www.nfpa.org/disclaimers.

The following are trademarks and registered trademarks of the National Fire Protection Association:

National Fire Protection Association®
NFPA®
Fire Protection Handbook®
FPH™
Building Construction and Safety Code® and NFPA 5000®
Learn Not to Burn®
Life Safety Code® and 101®
National Electrical Code® and NEC®
National Fire Codes®
National Fire Alarm Code® and NFPA 72®
Risk Watch®
Sparky®

NFPA No.: FPH2008
ISBN-10: 0-87765-758-0
ISBN-13: 978-0-87765-758-3
Library of Congress Control No.: 2007928644

Printed in the United States of America

08 09 10 11 12 5 4 3 2 1

Dedication

In recognition of his extraordinary service as founder and professor of the fire protection engineering program at the University of Maryland, as chairman of the NFPA Board of Directors, as chairman of the NFPA Standards Council, as leader and mentor, this handbook is dedicated to Dr. John L. Bryan.

Contents

SECTION 3
Information and Analysis for Fire Protection 3-1

SECTION 4
Human Factors in Emergencies 4-1

SECTION 5
Fire and Life Safety Education 5-1

SECTION 8 Special Equipment 8-1

SECTION 9 Processes and Facilities 9-1

SECTION 10 Building Services 10-1

SECTION 11 Fire Prevention Practices 11-1

SECTION 12 Non-Emergency Fire Department Functions 12-1

SECTION 13
Organizing for Public Sector Emergency Response 13-1

SECTION 14
Detection and Alarm 14-1

SECTION 15 Water Supplies for Fixed Fire Protection 15-1

SECTION 16 Water-Based Fire Suppression Equipment 16-1

SECTION 17 Fire Suppression Systems and Portable Fire Extinguishers 17-1

SECTION 21 Transportation Fire Safety 21-1

Preface

The *Fire Protection Handbook*®—there is no other fire protection reference quite like it. For more than a century, the *FPH*™ has been *the* compilation of fire protection data and best practices. This 20th edition honors the traditions of thoroughness and accuracy that make this handbook so central to any fire protection library. At the same time, this edition includes new and expanded information throughout. For example, there are 25 new chapters and more than 500 new figures and tables. The pool of authors grew from 247 in the 19th edition to our current 260.

FPH users face a unique challenge: navigating quickly though such a wealth of information. This edition includes several new features to make it easier for readers to find the information they need. The most obvious change is the use of a second color to highlight important information such as subheads and expanded cross references to related chapters.

Other changes include the following:

- The addition of new features such as "Key Terms" and "Chapter Contents"—tools to help make the information easier to find
- The reorganization of the sections, so that each section contains fewer chapters

Clearly, a big team participated in creating the *FPH.* The authors are at the center of that team—and I'm particularly grateful for the evening and weekend time they devoted to their chapters. The authors were unfailingly cheerful and were marvelous at fitting the *FPH* into their busy lives and careers.

The section editors recruited authors, reviewed draft material, and resolved technical differences. They were simultaneously diplomats and technical taskmasters responsible for as many as 24 chapters. Their job was far from simple. The three associate editors completed a particularly important job in reviewing new chapters.

Special places in heaven are reserved for my colleagues, Robine Andrau (who timed her retirement to accommodate the *FPH* schedule), Betsey Henkels, and Michael Gammell. They faced a huge manuscript—a stack of paper and electronic files equivalent to 12,000 pages and 2,500 illustrations—and tamed it, one page at a time.

Many other people contributed to this handbook in large and small ways. We all share a simple goal of making our world a bit safer. I tip my hat to you all.

Pam Powell
Managing Editor and Senior Product Manager

Introduction

This is the 20th edition of the *Fire Protection Handbook®*. It has changed significantly since its inception in 1896 as the *Handbook of the Underwriter's Bureau of New England.*

The original author, Everett U. Crosby, was manager of the Underwriter's Bureau and one of the stock fire insurance company executives who came together to develop a consistent set of sprinkler rules in 1895 that led to the formation of NFPA. He also became the first secretary of NFPA, serving from 1896 to 1903, and was chairman of the executive committee from 1903 to 1907. Henry A. Fiske, who later succeeded Crosby as manager of the Underwriter's Bureau, joined Crosby as co-editor of the second edition in 1901. The third edition in 1904 was called the *Handbook of Fire Protection for Improved Risks,* and the fourth edition in 1909 became known as the *Crosby-Fiske Handbook of Fire Protection,* the title used until the 10th edition in 1948. H. Walter Forster, chair of NFPA's Safety to Life Committee, joined the editorial team in 1918 and became an editor for the sixth edition in 1921.

In 1935, Crosby, Fiske, and Forster donated all rights to their handbook to NFPA, which published the eighth and all subsequent editions. By the 11th edition, in 1954, the work was entitled the *NFPA Handbook of Fire Protection.* From the 12th edition in 1962 to this 20th edition, the handbook has been known simply as the *Fire Protection Handbook.*

The explosion of fire-related technology and fire protection knowledge during the last quarter of the twentieth century and into the beginning of the twenty-first century has driven exhaustive changes in the format and content of the *FPH*™. The original 5" × 7" pocket handbook is now a two-volume 8½" × 11" set.

As the most pressing concerns of fire protection have evolved—from property protection concerns of the late 1800s, through life safety concerns for public occupancies in the beginning of the 1900s, to the computer-modeled, risk assessment–based systems approach in use today—the number of subjects covered by the *FPH* has increased greatly.

Creation of the *Fire Protection Handbook* through 20 editions and 111 years has involved literally thousands of fire protection experts from within and without NFPA. It is their expertise that has established the *Fire Protection Handbook* as *the* reference source for fire protection practitioners worldwide.

Every effort has been made to make the content consistent with the best available information on current fire protection practices. If readers discover errors or omissions, the editors would appreciate those shortcomings being called to their attention. In offering this edition of the *Fire Protection Handbook,* the editors solicit suggestions for improvements to make future editions increasingly useful.

Arthur E. Cote, P.E., FSPE
Editor-in-Chief
NFPA Executive Vice-President and Chief Engineer (retired)

SECTION 12

Non-Emergency Fire Department Functions

John A. Granito

Section 12 of the *Fire Protection Handbook*® presents, in nineteen chapters, an overview of the policy, planning, organizational, and management issues that are basic—and often most challenging—to fire department, municipal, and corporate officials as they strive to keep their people, property, and environments safe by maintaining effective fire-rescue organizations. Chapters 2, 3, 12, and 13 are new; other chapters have been significantly revised.

The purpose of Chapter 1, "Planning for Public Fire-Rescue Protection," is to demonstrate that adequate fire protection and related public safety services are essential and that both the level and types of services provided should be carefully considered choices based on adequate information. Topics covered include integrated risk management, planning processes, evaluation as part of planning, and public protection classifications.

Chapter 2, "Organizational Benchmarking and Performance Evaluation," examines organizational benchmarking and performance evaluation from a systems perspective in order to include the key elements of success for a fire department performance management system. Steps to implement a new system are discussed.

The purpose of Chapter 3, "Needs Assessment and Hazard Analysis," is to demonstrate the interrelationship of numerous routine or special activities that can be conducted as a component of a comprehensive needs assessment and hazard analysis—that is, the identification of the challenges faced and the resources needed to manage these challenges.

Chapter 4, "Managing Fire-Rescue Departments," provides an overview of the elements involved in organizing, administering, and managing agencies that provide fire and rescue response services.

Chapter 5, "Information Management and Computer Technology," introduces information technology and networks, as well as their application to management, emergency response and operations, and internal and public communications. Systems integration is also discussed.

Chapter 6, "Liability of Fire Service Organizations for Negligent Fire Fighting," explains legal concepts such as discretionary functions immunity, governmental immunity, liability, limited damages, negligence, public duty rule, punitive damages, and tort claims act. The chapter applies these legal concepts to the fire service environment.

Chapter 7, "Safety, Medical, and Health Issues and Programs," outlines the history of safety and health legislation as it applies to fire departments and describes relevant NFPA standards and

---

John A. Granito, Ed.D., is a consultant in fire-rescue services and former coordinator of NFPA's Urban Fire Forum. He is a professor emeritus and former vice-president for Public Service and External Affairs, State University of New York, Binghamton, New York.

requirements within the context of that history. The chapter concludes with a description of the risk management program that is detailed in NFPA 1500, *Standard on Fire Department Occupational Safety and Health Program.*

The next three chapters relate to fire fighter safety. As presented in Chapter 8, "Effect of Building Construction and Fire Protection Systems on Fire Fighter Safety," fire department personnel have a very strong interest in building construction. The chapter outlines simplified principles of building construction, building codes, and building construction classification, as well as specific concerns such as building collapse.

Chapter 9, "Fire and Emergency Services Protective Clothing and Protective Equipment," describes NFPA and OSHA involvement in standards for personal protective equipment, discusses third-party certification, and offers guidelines for cleaning and maintaining personal protective equipment. Chapter 10, "Training Programs for Fire and Emergency Service Personnel," is an overview of the broad challenge of providing training for fire and emergency service personnel. The chapter presents information on the need for training, organization of training delivery, ensuring quality instruction, internal and external training programs, training safety, and records.

Chapter 11, "Industrial Fire Loss Prevention," examines the need to minimize fire loss from the corporate perspective. Topics addressed in this chapter include emergency management, fire prevention, fire risk management, hazard identification, and the role of industrial fire brigades.

Chapter 12, "Disaster Planning and Response Services," outlines the phases of emergency preparedness, techniques for a hazard vulnerability analysis, and identification of critical facilities and infrastructure. Continuity of government and continuity of operations are among the other subjects presented.

Chapter 13, "GIS for Fire Station Locations and Response Protocols," explains the use of geographic information systems in fire station location planning and site selection factors. GIS response protocols are introduced.

The next three chapters address fire department resources. Chapter 14, "Fire Rescue Stations and Fire Service Training Centers," provides a general overview of the steps necessary to develop fire stations and fire training centers. Chapter 15, "Public Emergency Services Alarm, Dispatch, and Communications Systems," provides an overview of public emergency services communication systems. This chapter addresses issues related to the design, installation, operation, maintenance, and management of such systems and the facilities that house and support them.

Chapter 16, "Fire Department Apparatus and Equipment," contains information on the standards used and procurement policies that should be followed in specifying and acquiring apparatus and equipment. The chapter discusses inspection, maintenance, testing, and retirement of apparatus and equipment.

The next two chapters address pre-incident planning. Chapter 17, "Pre-Incident Planning for Industrial and Municipal Emergency Response," defines pre-incident planning, introduces the process, and identifies data needed for pre-incident planning. Chapter 18, "Pre-Incident Planning for Emergency Response," explains how pre-incident planning allows fire-fighting personnel to view conditions within a structure or site, evaluate what these conditions are likely to develop into in the event of an emergency, and then develop strategies for dealing with the potential problems.

Chapter 19, "Community Risk Reduction," presents components and fundamentals of a community risk reduction initiative, outlines risk reduction strategies, and discusses the roles of leadership and community engagement in the community risk reduction process.

Chapter 1

Planning for Public Fire-Rescue Protection

John A. Granito

The purposes of this chapter are to demonstrate that adequate fire protection and related public safety services are essential components of any community and that both the level and types of services provided should be conscious and carefully considered choices of the community, which are made with, and based on, adequate information. As adequate public protection is designed, careful planning needs to be done to ensure that fire fighter safety is not compromised. Objective planning and evaluation can ensure that a community's desire for a stipulated level of protection is being met in as cost-effective a manner as possible.

Certain NFPA publications, including a number of codes, standards, and recommended practices, contain information that is related to this chapter. Many of these publications are listed in the bibliography at the end of this chapter.

Several other chapters in Section 12 provide information useful in the self-assessment of a public fire protection system: Chapter 2, "Organizational Benchmarking and Performance Evaluation"; Chapter 3, "Needs Assessment and Hazards Analysis"; Chapter 5, "Information Management and Computer Technology"; Chapter 7, "Safety, Medical, and Health Issues and Programs"; Chapter 12, "Disaster Planning and Response Services"; Chapter 18, "Pre-Incident Planning for Municipal Emergency Response"; and Chapter 19, "Community Risk Reduction."

Chapter Contents

Key Terms

benchmarking, deployment, emergency medical services, fire prevention, Fire Suppression Rating Schedule (FSRS), Insurance Services Office (ISO) grading schedule, master planning, needs assessment, public fire protection, risk management, rural fire protection, technical rescue, urban fire protection

INTEGRATED RISK MANAGEMENT

Growing national and international awareness of the staggering costs, both in life and dollars, of fire fighter line-of-duty deaths and injuries has given rise to the development of a newer, more comprehensive planning approach. Developed first in the United Kingdom, it is termed *integrated risk management.* This refers to a planning methodology that recognizes that citizen fire safety, plus the protection of property and the environment from fire and related causes, must include provisions for the reasonable safety of emergency responders. Chief Fire Officer Paul Young summarized the 2003 UK government white paper entitled *Integrated Risk Management and Firefighter Safety in the United Kingdom* as follows:

> Mandated Integrated Risk Management in the UK Fire and Rescue Service means that suppression resources are to be allocated on the basis of risk rather than the number of buildings in an area. This means assessing the risks faced, taking preventative action, and deploying the right resources in the right place at the right time.
>
> Far too few resources were devoted to residential areas, where most fire deaths occur, and too many resources were devoted to business districts where fewer deaths occur. Fire and rescue authorities must create local plans for fire and other emergency incidents based on local risks. There is much greater flexibility in managing risk this way, rather than under the old national standardization of response.

John A. Granito, Ed.D., is a consultant in fire-rescue services and former coordinator of NFPA's Urban Fire Forum. He is professor emeritus and former vice-president for public service and external affairs, State University of New York, Binghamton, New York.

A modern and effective fire and rescue service should serve all sections of our society fairly and equitably by:

- Reducing the number of fires and other emergency incidents
- Reducing loss of life in fires and accidents
- Reducing the number and severity of injuries in fires and other emergency incidents
- Reducing the commercial, economic, and social impact of fires and other emergency incidents
- Safeguarding the environment and heritage (both built and natural)
- Providing true value for money spent

A very important by-product of reducing the number of fires and other incidents is a reduction in the exposure of fire fighters to risk, thus improving their safety. Fewer incidents mean fewer road accidents and fewer fire fighter fatalities and injuries at the scene. The integrated risk management program (IRMP) should also ensure that the optimum operational response is made to any given incident to reduce deaths and injuries among the public. However, to do that, the response needs to be operationally effective, and that means that fire fighter crewing levels need to be adequate and, therefore, safe for the tasks. Inadequate crewing levels are not only unacceptable on the grounds of fire-fighter safety, but on the grounds of public safety as well.

In addition, fire-fighter safety depends on individual competence. Investigations into fire-fighter deaths have demonstrated often that there was no objective way of demonstrating that the fire fighters were competent to carry out the role they were performing at the time. That they had been trained did not mean that they had demonstrated their competence in a way that could be validated.

Because of this, the Integrated Personal Development System is introducing into the UK Fire and Rescue Service a competence-based training and development process that seeks to ensure that all members of the workforce can demonstrate that they are competent to carry out their role. You cannot be safe if you are not competent.

The IRMP drives the planning process for not only vehicle and equipment requirements, but also crewing arrangement, training and development, and many other factors. In short, it provides that an evidence-based approach to the management and delivery of fire and rescue Services.

BACKGROUND ISSUES CONCERNING FIRE PROTECTION

Because the safety of people, property, and the environment is so vital, questions that focus on the organization and deployment of fire-fighting resources are especially important to communities. Prompted by escalating costs, issues relating to fire suppression have attracted a great deal of public attention, even though fire fighting is but one part of what constitutes community fire protection. Although fire prevention and fire protection engineering efforts are typically less costly in the long run than fire fighting, questions relating to the appropriate size, deployment, and response protocols of fire-fighting forces remain paramount.

Financial, Technical, and Responsibility Issues

Nevertheless, governmental and public concerns that focus exclusively on emergency response issues to the exclusion of adequate provisions for the prevention of fire and other emergencies are more costly and less effective. A total fire and related protection program, which includes the application of resources to comprehensive fire prevention and life safety, provides the most effective and efficient means of saving lives, property, and the environment, plus increases the operational safety of fire fighters.

The first issue is created by the relatively high cost of fire stations, fire apparatus and equipment, on-duty personnel, and line-of-duty deaths and injuries. A second set of issues is technical in nature, dealing with the number of responders necessary to be on duty and to be dispatched, with what should be the maximum allowable time for response, and with other related technical and operational questions including the necessity for safety officers and rapid intervention teams.

The third issue considers what the process should be for determining the answers to the following technical, operational, and safety questions:

- Should communities assess their own needs and resources and provide individualized answers, or should national standards be applied?
- How should national standards and recommended practices be formulated?
- Should noncompliance with a national or industry standard expose officials to penalties?
- Should fire chiefs be obligated to inform fully their local officials concerning local hazards, risk levels, and levels of service actually available?
- Should local officials keep citizens fully informed concerning available emergency service capabilities?

These and similar questions have generated much debate about the processes of planning and evaluating community fire and rescue defenses.

Unfortunately, it appears possible that even those who are genuinely concerned with evaluating and planning for local fire, rescue, and emergency medical services may blend together the issues of cost, technical correctness, safety, and responsibility for resource decisions. When this happens, communities cannot be sure that the resulting delivery system is the most appropriate obtainable for the available financial resources.

Of course, there are multiple demands for local municipal funds. Thus, emergency protection must be fitted into a larger community priority listing of needs and desires. However, proper placement in the listing requires that a true and accurate description be publicized of existing capability compared with accurately described community hazards, response history, and call demand predictions. When the issues are erroneously blended together, citizens may believe that adequate, timely, and safe response is available when indeed it is not and may give higher budget priority to another community interest. Or citizens may be unduly anxious over erroneous observations that fire defenses are much too meager and that even more resources must be allocated. In addition, official planning and community concern may ignore the vital issues of hazard mitigation, comprehensive prevention, and life safety education.

Publicizing the Need for Prevention Programs

Citizens are often subjected to opposing budget arguments concerning protection levels and frequently lack the knowledge necessary to arrive at sound conclusions. This understandable lack of technical expertise underscores the necessity for accurate, well-balanced, and forthright information to be widely disseminated among those who will both receive and pay for service delivery. Hazard analysis and risk assessment are extremely important.

Partly because the benefits of active comprehensive prevention programs, public safety education, and fire protection engineering efforts are not well advertised, there often is little pressure exerted on their behalf. Thus, relatively few resources are allocated to these efforts in many communities when compared with allocations for suppression work. Even though it certainly is true that the least harmful fires are those that never occur, most communities fail to consider a total fire protection plan as a wise and cost-saving instrument. The benefits of residential and high-rise fire sprinklers are well documented, for example, yet conflicting pressures have often curtailed their use. The funds allocated to fight the fires that do start, however, can be quite high. Much more emphasis is needed on the total protection program if communities and their fire fighters are to be made reasonably safe at reasonable costs. The evaluation and planning of public fire protection, then, must consider total protection efforts. Benchmarking and performance evaluation play key roles in the planning process. Efforts certainly must include provisions for emergency response, but also such efforts as locally adopted codes and ordinances, built-in structural protection, inspection programs, public education for all groups, building plan reviews, and so on must be included. The same concept, of course, applies both to the preventive and emergency-type prehospital medical services fire departments often provide.

Developing a Prevention Plan

A practical approach to the development of a community's mid- to long-range plan is first to generate a view of what the community will be by the time of the planning horizon. That information comes from an analysis of past development combined with projections of demographic changes, economic development or decline, major roadway programs, annexations, significant building projects, and so on.

The second step is to assess realistically the strengths and weaknesses of the existing fire protection system, including codes, standards, and ordinances relating to safety, fire prevention efforts, public safety education programs, and emergency response capability. This is an important facet of the risk management process.

Answering the question of what the response strength should be involves an honest assessment of stations and their locations, vehicles and equipment, staffing numbers and provisions, breadth and depth of the various service delivery areas, training and other support activities, success rate in handling emergencies, mutual-aid arrangements, dispatch and communication provisions, and response times.

In 2001 the NFPA consensus standard building process produced two new standards, one for substantially career fire departments (NFPA 1710, *Standard for the Organization and Deployment of Fire Suppression Operations, Emergency Medical Operations, and Special Operations to the Public by Career Fire Departments*) and the other for substantially volunteer departments (NFPA 1720, *Standard for the Organization and Deployment of Fire Suppression Operations, Emergency Medical Operations, and Special Operations to the Public by Volunteer Fire Departments*).

Applying NFPA Standards

NFPA 1710 (2004 edition) deals with the time frame for response to fire and medical incidents for the first-due engine company, for the entire first alarm assignment, and for the first level, basic, and advanced emergency medical responders. The number of fire fighters necessary for initial suppression attack and their roles are specified in the standard, as are other aspects of organization, suppression, operations, emergency medical and other responses, special services, staffing, and so on.

NFPA 1720 (2004 edition) addresses the organization, operation, and deployment of those departments that are substantially volunteer in staffing. Recognizing the response time differences that often occur between in-station responders and volunteers who likely are not at the station, NFPA 1720 calls for minimum numbers of fire fighters depending on local population density per square mile, and differing maximum response times, which are also related to population density.

The third step is to project the needed capabilities and capacity of the fire protection system and its vitally important fire department component as the community changes. Any additional needs of the system and the fire department, so that they can meet the projected demands, represent the content components of the plan. How that plan may be financed and implemented, and the time and timing required constitute the strategic and tactical planning necessary for success.

A major challenge in this "discovery" process often lies in assessing the existing protection system and its fire department, and in determining the steps needed to bring both to the strength required by projected demands. Additionally, tests of efficiency, cost-effectiveness, economies of scale, and other sound business practices must be applied.

The following basic questions are to be raised concerning this entire process:

- What types and levels of protection does this community need both now and to meet the upcoming community profile?

- How are the details of these needs best determined?
- What process and whose expertise should be used to arrive at the answers?
- Is fire fighter safety carefully considered?
- How may the correctness of the answers be tested?
- Are the answers as cost-effective as possible?
- How can any needed improvements best be funded?
- What should be done during and after the planning process to win the support of those directly affected by changes and those who will have to pay for any improvement?
- How and when should the plan be updated?

STEPS IN PLANNING

Public fire protection, emergency medical services, and technical rescue provisions need to be carefully planned and require that certain logical steps be taken to achieve a comprehensive, acceptable, and workable plan. There are two important aspects to any good plan: (1) the plan itself, which must be feasible and directed toward clear goals; and (2) the process by which the plan is developed, which must ensure that all major goals are considered and every constituency to be affected by the plan is reasonably involved in the planning process or made well aware of its consequences prior to plan approval.

Without adequate involvement of the necessary constituencies, implementation of the plan may likely fail because of a lack of cooperation and commitment. For a satisfactory plan to evolve, the planners must decide the end results they wish to achieve (goals), determine the status of the fire protection system in relation to those goals (evaluation), and calculate how much and what kinds of progress actually can take place over a certain period of time (objectives, tactics, time frame). Each of these three steps—setting goals, evaluating, working out the details—requires the collection and analysis of relevant information. Broad goals are achieved through planned strategies and precise objectives are achieved through implemented tactics. Each must be relevant to the other. Local data collection and information management systems are vital to planning.

Careful consideration of these important factors, which will vary considerably from one community to another and which must take into account assets, liabilities, challenges, and available resources, leads to what is often referred to as a *strategic plan.*

Evaluation of Fire Protection Services

Because some degree of public fire protection is almost always in place, it is common for the entire process to begin with both a local hazards analysis and risk assessment, plus an evaluation of the fire protection that is already available. See Section 12, Chapter 3, "Needs Assessment and Hazards Analysis." The information obtained from the evaluation, when analyzed in terms of broad, generally recognized public fire protection goals, identifies needs and provides responsible community officials with the approximate parameters of the plan to be developed.

It is important to take into consideration those fire protection and other public safety services that may be provided by a fire/rescue department and that will meet specific local needs. Examples of this are hospital transportation by a fire department ambulance and responsibility for emergency management and disaster services.

Typical fire department services include fire prevention programs—such as code administration and enforcement through plans review, inspection services, and public education—as well as fire suppression, technical rescue, emergency medical, hazardous materials response, and disaster response. Various other public services, such as health screening programs, are conducted more and more often by progressive departments. This approach to broad-based community safety service takes advantage of departmental resources, such as neighborhood fire stations and on-duty personnel, experience in public service and education, and the typically high regard in which fire departments are held by citizens.

Community Involvement

As already noted, the plan cannot be developed without the involvement of a wide variety of community groups. Even if the various constituencies seem willing to allow fire protection officials to develop and write the comprehensive plan without their consultation, the fire officials should be cautious; the citizens eventually must be willing to accommodate and pay for the implementation. Because a comprehensive plan envisions a larger group or system of integrated parts, a number of organizations and agencies outside the fire department will need to play important roles in implementation of the plan. Local elected officials typically play key roles in plan approval, implementation, and funding.

Modern practices make it necessary for fire departments to work cooperatively with a variety of agencies and organizations. These range, for example, from the local building code enforcement staff to the U.S. Coast Guard for hazardous materials spills near navigable waterways. Good planning requires consultation with all operational components on a continuing basis. A good plan today is better than a perfect plan that might be developed tomorrow.

As noted, one basic aspect of a comprehensive public fire protection plan is the concept that it is infinitely better for a community to prevent fires altogether, or to mitigate them automatically through fire safety education and built-in fire protection features, than to depend solely on the fire suppression capabilities of the community's fire department. The goal of reducing the incidence and effects of fire involves all aspects of fire prevention. Historically, much more energy and many more resources have been devoted to evaluating, planning, and implementing fire suppression/fire-fighting capabilities than fire prevention capabilities. Simply stated, the United States as a whole has focused more on "fire engines and fire fighters" than on public awareness and built-in mitigation features. That focus is still necessary and exceedingly important, but effort must also be placed on measures that do not depend solely on fire suppression personnel to reduce the toll of fire. Planning groups often have difficulty, however, in evaluating the degree of effectiveness of such multifaceted fire protection programs.

Number of Resources Dispatched	Confirmed Working Single-Family-Dwelling Fire
Chief(s)	
Aides or incident command technicians	
Company officers	
Fire fighters, including "flying squads"	
Single-purpose emergency medical technicians (EMTs)	
Standard pumpers	
Quints	
Aerials	
Ladder tenders	
Ambulances	
Heavy (technical/urban) rescues	
Light/medium rescues	
Mini/midi attack pumpers	
Special operations (air, lighting, etc.) units	
"Flying squad" vehicles	
Mobile command vehicles	
Safety officer	
Rapid intervention team	
Other (types)	

FIGURE 12.1.1 Typical, Actual, First-Alarm Fire Attack Assignment

mation concerning all applicable federal (national), state, and provincial requirements, as well as applicable NFPA codes, standards, and recommended practices, as issued from time to time.

Rural Fire Protection

One principal difference between operation of rural and urban fire departments is that rural departments must deal with water supply issues with a broader variety of solutions than most urban departments. Rural fire department operations and apparatus emphasize not only fire-fighting requirements but also the provision of water for fire fighting. Rural fire apparatus must have large water tanks to permit effective initial attack on fires while supplementary water supplies are being brought into action. Supplementary water supplies include drafting sources on or adjacent to rural properties, and mobile water tanker vehicles for transporting water from more distant sources. Also in use are portable folding canvas tanks into which tank trucks quickly discharge their water supply through special dump valves. Rural fire departments often use apparatus and hose to relay water from sources several thousand feet (1000 ft equals 304.8 m) from the emergency. Initial response of pumpers, tankers, and auxiliary apparatus should be adequate for a quick attack on the burning property. With adequate highways and well-designed apparatus, it is often possible to bring substantial fire-fighting forces to an emergency in rural areas in sufficient time for a properly planned and executed initial fire attack operation to be effective, even though many of the personnel may arrive in private automobiles. Many rural properties are now located in areas that enjoy some level of fire protection. Some properties, of course, may have to depend entirely on their own private fire protection and whatever help they may obtain from forestry agencies or distant fire departments.

Newer approaches to fire insurance rating give "protected" status to property without a municipal water supply system if a fire station is within five travel miles and a stipulated gallons per minute flow can be maintained by the local department, as mentioned later in this chapter.

Fire-Fighting Apparatus. Minimum protection for a rural area would include a pumper with a large water tank and a water tank vehicle responding on an initial alarm. Properly designed tanks should be able to transport water from a source 1 mi (1.6 km) from the scene so a minimum of 250 gpm (946.25 L/min) can be pumped at the fire scene by the pumper. Because a larger flow is often required to provide adequate fire protection services, additional tankers must be used, or drafting sources within reasonable distance of the fire scene must be identified. Programs that encourage the construction of year-round rural drafting sites are to be encouraged. Rural apparatus should carry 3½-in. (89-mm) or larger supply hose to provide adequate water supply at the fire scene. It is always advisable to lay large-diameter fire hose from the water supply source to as near the fire scene as possible in order to avoid extensive friction loss. At the emergency, large-diameter hose is sometimes connected into smaller handlines, or used more often to supply another pumper from which handlines are extended. Other pieces of equipment, such as rescue and aerial ladder vehicles, should be provided as needed to carry out the mission. Elevated master streams are not needed extensively in rural operations, and sometimes ladder truck equipment for rescue, forcible entry, ventilation, and salvage operations is carried on pumpers and equipment vehicles.

To be even minimally effective in controlling a fire, the initial responding apparatus should reach the emergency scene before very rapid fire spread. As is the case in urban fire fighting, this move is termed "initial attack" and is aimed at stopping the fire as close to the point of origin as possible. So-called "sustained attack" attempts to reduce the loss to the exposed adjoining or nearby property. Because of longer response times, rural departments may find themselves in the sustained attack, or "defensive," mode on arrival. Unless sufficient water can be made available within a short time frame, the British thermal units (Btu) generated by the burning material cannot be absorbed so the temperature is not reduced sufficiently to extinguish the fire. Successful rural protection planning generally boils down to response times and water availability.

Hazardous Materials and Structures. Of special concern are the sometimes extensive supplies of fertilizer and pesticides located on rural properties. Response crews must be alert also to the possibility of above- and below-ground storage tanks for fuel and other products. The safe operations guidelines for hazardous materials response are applicable in rural as well as urban areas.

Another concern for rural fire protection exists because so many large and diverse types of structures are located in rural areas. These structures include warehouses, truck centers, product distribution facilities, processing plants, storage buildings, centralized schools, churches, trailer parks, and others.

In addition, the extension of existing housing developments and the construction of new residential and commercial structures immediately adjacent to wildland areas, or in the midst of such areas, have brought about a significant increase in wildland–urban interface fires, which present new challenges to both urban and rural fire departments.

However, it is possible to give such counsel if one can make certain assumptions that may be controlled by the community. These assumptions relate primarily to the presence of appropriately placed smoke detectors and other types of fire detection devices and a means to relay that alarm to the fire suppression agency, but they also include the existence of enforced building codes that provide some degree of resistance to fire spread from the room of origin, rural sprinkler systems, home escape plans, and so on.

Urban Fire Protection

In urban areas, inadequate fire department response to initial alarms can be a major factor in fire losses due to high population and structural densities. The number of simultaneous fire-fighting operations that may need to be conducted at the incident also dictates the total amount of personnel and equipment needed to provide effective fire-fighting operations. In any "working" structural fire, several operations must be carried on simultaneously and the fire attack must be made from several points. This attack cannot be accomplished by the crew of a single fire apparatus. Multiple apparatus must be positioned properly, and adequate waterflow made available to cope with the amount of fuel (fire load) involved or exposed.

Structural Fire Suppression. In simplest terms, structural fire suppression in an urban setting involves the accomplishment of at least the following tasks, many of which must occur almost simultaneously to ensure effective and safe operations (the proper sequence will vary, depending on circumstances, as will additional tasks):

- Command, control, and coordination of the incident (to ensure both effectiveness and safety of the fire fighters)
- Adequate on-scene radio communication among attack forces
- Application of water in appropriate quantities (dependent on the fire environment and other factors)
- Provision of appropriate source of water supply for above
- Ventilation of smoke and other hazardous products of combustion from the fire area to the outside
- Search for and rescue of fire victims
- Forcible entry
- Control of utilities
- Salvage and other property conservation operations
- Standby rapid intervention/fire fighter rescue
- Provisions for emergency medical services

At large-structure fires, additional fire-fighting personnel are needed to cover the various points of fire attack. In some cases various functions can be handled more efficiently by specially trained crews such as rescue companies and hazardous material teams operating from specially equipped apparatus.

Determination of Required Equipment and Personnel. The number of personnel and equipment necessary to accomplish the above will vary with a number of factors (i.e., the expectations placed on the mobile suppression group, the material burning, the construction of the building, the type of built-in protection provided, separation between buildings, availability of water supply, the number and physical and emotional condition of persons in the fire building, the type of equipment available to fire fighters, the level of proficiency of the fire suppression crew [including the commanders], etc.). Hence, it is difficult to determine a minimum number of fire fighters or equipment required without careful, objective planning, and without considering the important variables. Obviously, personnel needs will differ significantly between a small detached structure fire and a high-rise fire. Pre-incident planning is essential. Some general considerations may, however, be listed as follows:

- The more arduous the expectations placed on the mobile fire suppression crew, the greater the required resources. (For example, the community that expects its fire department to contain fires to the room of origin should expect to provide more fire suppression resources than the community that expects its fire department only to prevent the spread of fire from one building to another. Given the same level of protection demands, the community that leaves all fire protection to the mobile fire suppression force will require a more extensive suppression force than the community that requires a high level of built-in protection.
- The more extensive the concentrated fire potential, the greater the required fire suppression resources. For example, given the same expectations of its mobile fire suppression force, a community having high-rise buildings, a high population density, and extensive industrial risks will normally require greater fire suppression resources than a largely residential community.
- The broader the services provided by a fire protection agency, the greater the need for resources. For example, a fire agency providing emergency medical services will, given the same level of expectations for its mobile suppression forces, re-

quire more resources than an agency providing only fire protection services, assuming a significantly increased *total* workload demand, including a significant increase in simultaneous calls.

- The greater the geographic area protected, the greater the resource requirement of the mobile fire suppression forces. That is, given the same service level expectations, a community providing service to 20 mi^2 (52 km^2) will require more resources than a community providing protection to only 10 mi^2 (26 km^2); this is caused by the need for timely arrival at the scene of fire, medical, or environmentally threatening incidents. Computerized geographic information systems and accompanying computerized response maps have the powerful ability to demonstrate visually the response effectiveness of various station locations.

In most smaller and medium-size communities, all initial-response (first-alarm) apparatus will not arrive at the fire scene simultaneously. In many departments with on-duty personnel, apparatus have to respond from more than one station, and some apparatus have longer travel times to the fire scene. In volunteer departments, personnel must travel varying distances to get to the fire station or the fire scene, and, thus, all apparatus cannot go into operation at the same time. Those fire fighters and vehicles that cannot arrive at the fire scene within the first critical time period have limited impact on the initial attack, regardless of the department's response assignment ("running card"). Communities may have a false sense of security in this regard, until actual response times are tested and working initial-attack personnel counted.

Minimum Manning. The critical numbers for policy makers to use in planning related to staffing of shifts and apparatus crews—sometimes termed "minimum manning"—are those that describe how many trained personnel can arrive within a stipulated initial attack time frame. Ideally, all or most will arrive as composite crews and not as individuals.

The total minimum fire force recommended for any community is necessarily dependent on community hazards and the expectations of the community and the members of the mobile fire force. Objective planning and evaluation are necessary to determine the resources required for effective and safe fire suppression operations that will meet community requirements.

Some fire agencies are addressing the suppression challenge with different arrangements of fire crews within the communities than were heretofore generally accepted (e.g., use of multipurpose apparatus task force assignments and differential staffing). It is important to note that, although these different approaches may augment flexibility, they do not appear to reduce the number of suppression personnel required to carry out fire-fighting operations safely.

It does seem reasonable to say that not fewer than two fire suppression vehicles and a command officer should respond to any structure fire and that the number of personnel responding should be sufficient to carry out the tasks indicated above, and whatever else is typically necessary in local operations, in a timely fashion. Normative data are available from some cities. It is relevant to note that, in a broad spectrum of environments that are protected by numerous urban departments, as observed by evaluation teams, between 19 and 23 personnel typically constitute the first alarm assignment to a confirmed single-family-dwelling fire.

Where necessitated by fire frequency or response distances, additional pumpers, ladder trucks, and tankers may be needed. Reserve apparatus is desirable not only to permit the repair of first-line equipment without reducing available fireground forces but also to provide additional fire-fighting units during major emergencies. Specialized vehicles for hazardous materials response, heavy-duty and specialized rescue—including boats—lighting equipment, breathing apparatus bottles, emergency medical response, and so on, also must be planned for. If these cannot be made available locally, then mutual-aid arrangements are needed. Different types of vehicles may be necessary for the various levels of emergency medical response: first responder or basic life support, advanced life support, and hospital transport. Commercial, industrial, and mercantile areas generally require additional apparatus, or more, in response to the initial alarm. If properties with considerable life hazard are involved (schools, hospitals, nursing homes, etc.) additional resources should be considered for initial alarms. Especially large numbers of personnel are needed for search and rescue operations in these properties, with several fire fighters required to "sweep and search" each floor (Table 12.1.1).

The required fire-fighting units should arrive on scene close enough in time after the initial alarm to operate as an effective fire-fighting unit following planned tactical procedures.

Operating Personnel Safety Concerns

Over the past several years, prompted by continuing line-of-duty fire fighter deaths and injuries, additional safety protocols have been instituted by OSHA, NFPA, the National Fallen Fire Fighters Foundation Initiative, various state agencies, fire departments, labor organizations, and other groups. These protocols call for on-scene safety officers, incident command teams, rapid intervention teams for fire fighter rescue, personnel accountability systems, plus other provisions to increase responder safety. Other provisions focus on the safety of emergency medical responders, technical rescue specialists, hazardous materials responders, and so on. All of these imply that the necessary additional personnel will be present at incidents in addition to those needed to conduct typical operations.

Evaluating Workload. In evaluating the adequacy of fire protection in any given area, planners must give major consideration to the ability of the fire department to handle efficiently any reasonably anticipated workload. This assessment requires an evaluation of the possibility of simultaneous working fires and other emergencies; weather factors that may contribute to the spread of fire, the delay in response, or the possibility of slow operations at the scene; and other demographic or geographic conditions that might affect the frequency, severity, and spread of fire occurrence and the response time of initial fire-fighting units.

Where fire frequency is such that any fire company may expect two or three working fires per day, or where structures to be protected require a heavy initial response, closer geographic spacing of or increased personnel assigned to individual fire companies may be necessary. The number of other fire-fighting or related operations such as grass, brush, rubbish, and automobile

TABLE 12.1.1 Typical Initial Attack Response Capability Assuming Interior Attack and Operations Plus Command Capability

	Description	*Personnel and Apparatus*
High-hazard occupancies	Schools, hospitals, nursing homes, explosives plants, refineries, high-rise buildings, and other high life hazard or large fire potential occupancies	At least 4 pumpers, 2 ladder trucks (or combination apparatus with equivalent capabilities), 2 chief officers, and other specialized apparatus as may be needed to cope with the combustible involved; not fewer than 24 fire fighters and 2 chief officers. Extra staffing of units first due to high-hazard occupancies is advised. One or more safety officers and a rapid intervention team(s) are also necessary.
Medium-hazard occupancies	Apartments, offices, mercantile, and industrial occupancies not normally requiring extensive rescue or fire-fighting forces	At least 3 pumpers, 1 ladder truck (or combination apparatus with equivalent capabilities), 1 chief officer, and other specialized apparatus as may be needed or available; not fewer than 16 fire fighters and 1 chief officer, plus a safety officer and a rapid intervention team.
Low-hazard occupancies	One-, two-, or three-family dwellings and scattered small businesses and industrial occupancies	At least 2 pumpers, 1 ladder truck (or combination apparatus with equivalent capabilities), 1 chief officer, and other specialized apparatus as may be needed or available; not fewer than 14 fire fighters and 1 chief officer, plus a safety officer and a rapid intervention team.
Rural operations	Scattered dwellings, small businesses, and farm buildings	At least 1 pumper with a large water tank (500 gal [1.9 m^3] or more), one mobile water supply apparatus (1000 gal [3.78 m^3] or larger), and such other specialized apparatus as may be necessary to perform effective initial fire-fighting operations; at least 12 fire fighters and 1 chief officer, plus a safety officer and a rapid intervention team.
Additional alarms		At least the equivalent of that required for rural operations for second alarms; equipment as may be needed according to the type of emergency and capabilities of the fire department. This may involve the immediate use of mutual-aid companies until local forces can be supplemented with additional off-duty personnel. In some communities, single units are "special called" when needed, without always resorting to a multiple alarm. Additional units also may be needed to fill at least some empty fire stations.

fires and emergency rescue operations may also require greater-than-normal staffing of equipment and closer spacing of fire companies. Major structural fires may result when the normal first-alarm coverage in a district is depleted through coverage of these other emergencies, making remaining fire-fighting forces inadequate. Staffing fire apparatus at a level below minimum requirements can result in less effective and less safe fire-fighting performance. This factor also has an adverse effect on the number of required fire companies for various alarms, because additional fire companies must be dispatched to the scene of an emergency to provide adequate total staffing.

Effective Pumper Companies. The desirable practice of assigning emergency medical responsibility to the fire department must be calculated into the staffing formula. It is also difficult to obtain effective teamwork and coordination with understrength crews. Some fire departments have attempted to solve this problem by supplementing their crews with part-time or volunteer fire fighters, or by providing off-duty fire fighters with tone-activated radio receivers and paying them for overtime when they respond to a fire. The on-duty personnel make the initial fire attack and holding action whereas off-duty personnel provide the additional assistance needed for continuing fire-fighting operations. Although useful and possibly less costly in the short run, efficiency is lost, and increased fire losses can be expected with this arrangement. Such protection should not be relied on to replace adequately the required staffing and equipment needed immediately at the scene for initial attack and rescue.

Personnel requirements are not merely a matter of numerical strength, but are also based on the establishment of a well-trained and coordinated team necessary to utilize complicated and specialized equipment under the stress of emergency conditions. Attempting to operate more fire companies than can be effectively staffed, even if some response distances must be somewhat increased, most often is less desirable than fewer but appropriately staffed companies. The effectiveness of pumper companies must be measured by their ability to get required hose streams into service quickly and efficiently. NFPA 1410, *Standard on Training for Initial Emergency Scene Operations,* should be used as a guide in measuring this ability. Seriously understaffed fire companies are generally limited to the use of small hose streams until additional help arrives. This action may be totally ineffective in containing even a small fire and in conducting effective rescue operations.

Supplementing Fire Protection Coverage. Consideration must be given also to maintaining an adequate concentration of additional forces to handle multiple alarms at the same fire, while still providing minimum fire protection coverage for the other areas under fire department protection. If available personnel prove adequate for routine fires but inadequate for major emergencies, arrangements should be made to supplement the fire protection coverage by calling back the off-shift personnel and by promptly calling nearby fire departments for mutual aid. Off-shift personnel may operate reserve apparatus or relieve or supplement personnel on the fireground. Fire companies not dispatched or utilized on the fire scene should be repositioned throughout the remaining area of the jurisdiction to ensure minimum response times to other alarms.

Reserve apparatus should be properly maintained and equipped, and when placed in service should be staffed to a degree commensurate with standard fire apparatus requirements. Because it may take up to 30 minutes or more to place reserve units in service with personnel recalled in an emergency, these reserve units should not be completely relied on to immediately provide an adequate level of fire protection services.

Concern must be shown, under legislation and local policy, for the health and safety of fire fighters and others, for environmental protection, and for the rights of those being served. Officials must demonstrate reasonable and prudent action with establishment of incident command systems, for example, and the appointment of qualified safety officers and rapid intervention team protocols.

Cooperation Among Fire Departments

In cases in which several fire departments occupy adjacent or contiguous territories, arrangements (often termed "line response") should be made for joint response along common boundaries to high-risk hazards and for assistance in covering vacant fire stations at times of major fires. In areas where the nearest fire station or mobile unit to the incident address is not a part of the fire department district to which the address belongs, the nearest station or unit—by prearrangement—may still be dispatched to save time. This methodology is termed "closest station response." Mutual aid or mutual response should not be relied on for routine emergencies, because there could be times when local commitments will preclude the anticipated assistance. Mutual-aid agreements do not reduce the responsibility of each jurisdiction to maintain adequate facilities to handle normal fire protection needs. It also must be assumed that teamwork and tactical efficiency at a fire will be somewhat less than that expected of equal units from the same department under a united command. Often, however, specialized units (such as hazardous materials response teams) are organized to protect larger areas encompassing several fire departments.

Fairly often, consideration is given in the evaluation and planning process to the concept of merging or consolidating with one or more other departments. This unification is viewed as a possible way to attain economies of scale and to increase the breadth of service delivery to the combined area. On occasion, merging has been necessary because one district has insufficient funds available to retain viability. Other times a volunteer department may not have sufficient available personnel. Although the official combining of two or more departments may be wise, careful consideration must be given to the possible gains and losses and to the understanding that the combination of two very weak departments does not typically result in a new, strong department.

Two or more departments and often a significant number of departments in a large area—such as a county or region—may benefit greatly from what is termed "functional consolidation." This concept does not have the various departments relinquishing individual autonomy but rather cooperating and, thus, achieving economies of scale and service increases. Functional consolidation ranges from joint dispatch and stations to group purchasing and training, and from regional special response teams to combined fire prevention. Intergovernmental service contracts can facilitate these cooperative ventures.

Planning for volunteer departments in which there is a scarcity of response personnel may involve the addition of full-time or part-time personnel to carry part of the workload. So-called combination departments appear more and more necessary as community demographics change and workload increases. Various methodologies are used to produce response crews. These plans include using students and others as station "bunkers," rotating volunteer-duty shifts, using on-call personnel, and making automatic mutual-aid agreements.

Basing Response Requirements on Waterflow

In the past it was a common practice to relate the number of pumping engines and their pumping capacity, and other apparatus personnel requirements, to the population to be protected. With the industrialization of many areas and the construction of commercial shopping centers, hospitals, schools, and nursing homes in residential areas, it is possible that concentrations of life hazard and property value in areas of small or large populations may require substantial fire-fighting forces. Those with the responsibility for providing public fire protection must be prepared to cope with fire potential in any location in the jurisdiction. Fire department response requirements are now based on the waterflow in gpm (L/min) that may have to be applied. A rule of thumb is to provide one company for each 250 gpm (946.25 L/min) that may be needed in an interior attack, plus personnel for rescue and other operations that need to be performed simultaneously with the advancing of hose lines.

Some may argue that it is not the public's responsibility to provide adequate fire protection to high-hazard risks that should have built-in fire protection systems. However, failure to attempt to provide fire protection for large taxable values on which the economy of a community may be based would place the community's fiscal viability at risk. Burned-out businesses may not rebuild, and then local people will lose employment. Also, fire spread to other properties is possible.

Setting Time Requirements

Time is another critical factor in the evaluation of public fire protection. It is generally considered that the first-arriving piece of apparatus should be at the emergency scene in 5 minutes of the sounding of the alarm at the fire station, because additional minutes are needed to size up the situation, deploy hose lines, initiate search and rescue, and so on. In dense urban settings the desired response time is often shorter, and 4 minutes for the first-responding pumper is a rule-of-thumb maximum time for 90 percent of an urban area. An old adage says that the first 5 minutes of most fires is the determining factor as to whether that fire will remain a small fire or become a large fire. Although this may not always be true, delays in sounding an alarm obviously must be minimized or eliminated, as well as delays in responding and initiating rescue and attack. Time, however, cannot become the all-important factor at the expense of safety. In the interest of safety, some departments have responding vehicles run to certain calls without the use of warning devices and obeying all traffic laws ("run silent alarms").

Specialized Apparatus

There are numerous instances in which highly specialized apparatus and equipment must be available to municipalities. One category of specialization concerns apparatus designed to handle hazardous materials, including spills of petroleum products and other chemicals that require special extinguishing agents such as foams or dry powders, and special equipment to apply these agents. These dangerous substances may be present because of airports, marinas, manufacturing or storage facilities, or transportation routes in the district. Another category of specialization includes apparatus and equipment needed because of particular structures or facilities such as research laboratories, hospitals, high-rise buildings, oil and gas wells, and seaports. In some communities, fire departments are expected to conduct specialized functions such as extricating at automobile wrecks and performing water and mountain rescue, as well as providing emergency medical services. These services also require special equipment and possibly special vehicles. The necessity for many departments to deliver at least first-responder emergency medical service, and for the delivery of a wide variety of technical rescue and disaster response services, cannot be overlooked.

As with standard fire-fighting equipment and apparatus, specialized tools cannot be used effectively and safely unless personnel are highly trained in their use under a wide variety of circumstances. Whether personnel are volunteer or career, in rural or urban areas, no plan can be implemented and no reasonable level of protection afforded to the community unless well-designed and well-managed training programs are carried out.

Progressive departments of all types and sizes also concentrate on providing a broad range of community-oriented services.

Fire Prevention

The term *fire prevention* as used here generally includes inspections, education, and equipment meant to reduce the occurrence of fire and to mitigate the effects of that fire prior to the arrival of the mobile suppression force. As an example, the installation of a sprinkler system is not designed to prevent fire but to control it in its very early stages; the "Stop, Drop, and Roll" message of the NFPA's *Learn Not to Burn*® program is clearly a mitigation rather than a prevention effort. Other education efforts, such as NFPA's *Risk Watch*® program, are directed at stopping the occurrence of fire and in promoting a wide range of safe behaviors. See Section 12, Chapter 19, "Community Risk Reduction."

Evaluating Prevention Activities. As noted previously, fire prevention activities are somewhat difficult to evaluate. In a real sense, if prevention activities are effective, fires and fire-related tragedies occur with less frequency. There is a reduction or absence of fire activity, and these results are statistically evident although they do not appear in dramatic news clips and photographs. Some departments do report not only dollar amounts of fire loss but also the value of structures that were threatened by fire and thus "saved." Without careful and systematic long-term record keeping concerning the incidence of fires, fire losses, and related tragedies, the effect of prevention programs cannot be documented. Inability of fire officials to demonstrate the value of committing some additional community resources to the broad range of possible prevention activities may well result in a withdrawal of resources from prevention programs and a subsequent increase in the need for a much larger suppression budget. Rational decisions and sound recommendations concerning evaluation and planning cannot be made unless fire officials learn what changes there can be to total fire cost by reallocating resources applied to the total fire defense system.

Planning requires recognition of the component and integrated parts of a fire prevention system. Until recent years prevention was often greatly limited or nonexistent in most smaller communities. In urban areas it was limited frequently to the periodic inspection of certain types of buildings. More modern approaches to fire prevention recognize that a comprehensive program includes all organized activities, other than suppression, that reduce the incidence of fire and fire-related losses. Ideally, these activities would be carried out in communities of every size, whether rural or urban, with appropriate adjustments made for community size, type, location, and fire history. Community- and neighborhood-based focus programs, often emanating from the local station, appear to have excellent effects.

Categorizing Prevention Activities. Prevention activities may be categorized in several ways, but it is usually helpful to group them as follows:

- Activities that relate to construction, such as building codes, the approval of building and facility plans, and occupancy certification and recertification for new occupants; also included may be a sign-off for the presence of smoke detectors when new or old properties are sold
- Activities that relate to the enforcement of codes and regulations, such as inspections of certain occupancies, the licensure of certain hazardous facilities, the design of new regulations and codes, and legislation to adopt existing model codes
- Activities that relate to the reduction of arson, such as fire investigation, the collection of information, public education, and data related to setting fires; included may be arson investigation and related court proceedings, and programs such as counseling for juvenile firesetters
- Activities that relate to the collection of data helpful in improving fire protection, such as standardized fire reporting, case histories, and fire research
- Activities that relate to public education and training, including fire prevention safeguards, evacuation and per-

sonal safety steps, plant protection training for industrial and other work groups, hazardous materials and devices safeguards, and encouragement to install early warning and other built-in signaling and extinguishing devices; very popular are programs for school children, such as NFPA's *Learn Not to Burn* curriculum and self-help classes such as water safety, urban survival, and similar "Stay Alive 'Til We Arrive" projects

An analysis of the community's fire history, conducted during the evaluation phase of the fire protection plan, will usually indicate to fire experts and citizen groups which categories need strengthening. Comparing the number of fires and fire-related incidents, plus fire loss (property, life, injury) statistics over several years as more prevention activities are phased in, provides an assessment of program effectiveness. Calculating the total cost of fire to a community (fire loss plus prevention costs plus suppression costs plus fire insurance costs) will enable the fire department and the community to estimate the efficiency or cost-effectiveness of a proposed prevention program.

PUBLIC PROTECTION CLASSIFICATIONS

Fire Department Service-Level Analysis

The public, fire and other government administrators, organized labor, fire protection organizations, and the fire service in general have for many years sought to find a generally accepted method for the evaluation of services provided to a community by its fire protection agency. The approaches have been as varied as the fire service agencies being evaluated and the parties doing the evaluation. This has resulted in the application of inconsistent methodology and criteria.

For many years material developed by NFPA has been used in the analysis of services provided by fire protection organizations. However, the application of NFPA materials has been inconsistent. The fire department accreditation program is entirely voluntary, and Insurance Services Office (ISO) reviews are typically conducted whenever there is an indication that changes have occurred that would point toward a potential revision to the classification number.

Insurance Services Office (ISO) Fire Suppression Rating Schedule (FSRS)

Although not all states in the United States use the latest edition of the Insurance Services Office (ISO) grading schedule, and it is not used in other nations, it is applied to public fire departments in 48 states. (Two states—Louisiana and Washington—use an earlier edition of the grading schedule.) The purpose is to aid in the calculation of fire insurance rates and is not for property loss prevention or life safety purposes.

The service focus of ISO has broadened considerably over the past few years. The ISO prepares Public Protection Classification (PPC) reports for over 43,000 fire protection districts in the United States. In addition ISO has created a Building Code Effectiveness Grading Schedule to determine how well a municipality enforces its building code.

Furthermore, the new ISO Community Outreach Program collects information on essential fire protection features within a community. This information will lead to sound benchmarking data, permitting individual communities to better assess their own safety level and to respond accurately when completing the Commission on Fire Accreditation International's self-assessment forms.

In a January 2001 survey of 502 U.S. fire chiefs and fire department officials, 92 percent responded that their ISO Public Protection Classification number is a direct reflection of the improvements made in their community. They reported that important local uses of the ISO PPC program are as follows:

- Helping save lives and property (90%)
- Helping save money on fire insurance (67%)
- Planning for and budgeting for changes in community fire protection (61%)

The older form of the grading schedule (1974) contains more categories and more items than the schedule in current use. However, the older form is still applied in two states and is still used by some community officials as a reference tool in self-evaluations.

In Section I of the ISO grading schedule, the result and classification apply to properties with a needed fire waterflow of 3500 gpm (13,248 L/min) or less. Private and public properties with larger needed flows are individually evaluated in the grading schedule. The result and classification apply to properties with a needed fire waterflow of 3500 gpm (13,248 L/min) (134 Section II).

With improved ratings, fire insurance companies that subscribe to the ISO rating system usually lower commercial and residential fire insurance premiums to reflect the projected decrease in loss severity. At least one insurance company is using a somewhat broader approach to determine premium costs for residential properties, by reviewing total insurance costs for all hazards across zip code or other defined areas and evaluating the fire exposure separately.

The *Grading Schedule for Municipal Fire Protection,* developed originally by the National Board of Fire Underwriters (NBFU) and continued by its successor, the American Insurance Association, and then by the ISO, has provided a guideline for municipalities to classify their fire defenses and physical conditions. The gradings obtained under the schedule are used in establishing base rates for fire insurance purposes. The schedule has been subject to change with the state of the art, and sweeping changes were made in the 1980 edition with the development of a revised FSRS, and with additional changes in 1995, 1998, and 2003. Other changes will continue to be made as warranted. With the 2003 revisions (under certain circumstances), credit for a minimal water supply (4000 gallons [15,140 L]) may now be given for property within 5 road miles (8 km) of a fire station, even though a municipal water supply system is lacking.

The current ISO grading schedule reviews and correlates those features of public fire protection that have a significant effect on minimizing fire damage. Credit is given for existing fire protection, instead of debit for what is not in place.

The Fire Suppression Rating Schedule (FSRS) produces 10 different Public Protection Classifications, with Class 1, representing an exemplary fire suppression delivery system, and Class 10, not meeting FSRS criteria. The FSRS simply defines different levels of public fire suppression capabilities that are credited in the individual property fire insurance rate relativities.

Starting in 1975, on a state-by-state basis following Insurance Department approval, ISO implemented the Commercial Fire Rating Schedule (CFRS), which was a major revision to the method used to develop individual property rate relativities. The CFRS was later replaced by the Specific Commercial Property Evaluation Schedule (SCOPES). The SCOPES reviews and correlates the construction, occupancy, exposures, and private and public fire protection (represented by the Public Protection Classification number). This correlation allows development of an equitable rate relativity applicable to the individual property. To this rate relativity, affiliated companies add their cost of doing business and profit margins to produce the applicable fire insurance rate. The FSRS represents a revision in the method used to derive the Public Protection Classification number used in the SCOPES. The Public Protection Classification number is also used as a rate relativity variable for most class-related properties, in addition to construction and occupancy variables.

The *Grading Schedule for Municipal Fire Protection,*[1] although a much-improved system from previous editions, was not developed as an integral part of the individual property rating system. The previous schedules were somewhat independent primarily due to their historical development by the National Board of Fire Underwriters (NBFU), which was not an insurance rating organization. The previous schedules were used more to quantify underwriting information but did define different levels of public fire protection that could be used for a specific rating.

The FSRS is designed to assist in an objective review of those features of available public fire protection that have a significant influence on minimizing damage once a fire has occurred. This revision ties logically to the review of contributive and causative hazards that can be identified using the SCOPES.

FSRS Class Groupings

As stated earlier, the ISO prepares Public Protection Classification (PPC) reports for over 43,000 fire protection districts in the United States. Districts include political jurisdictions identified as counties, cities, towns, villages, municipalities, and fire districts. A district may support an organized fire department or contract with an existing fire department for fire suppression services. Each PPC report is prepared using an information base established from a city grading evaluation conducted by one of ISO's regional field representatives, who are highly trained in the application of the FSRS. ISO conducts municipal surveys in 45 of the 50 states. Mississippi and Washington State have elected to use the 1974 edition of the FSRS. Hawaii, Idaho, and Louisiana administer the current edition of the FSRS through state rating organizations. The District of Columbia and New York City are not graded using the FSRS.

The scope, objectives, and methods of application for the current FSRS are significantly different from previous grading schedule documents. Technological change in the real world is reflected in all elements of the current grading schedule pertaining to the three major items of coverage, which are as follows:

- Receiving and handling fire alarms
- Fire department
- Water supply

Today, the FSRS provides an objective tool for the review of city public fire suppression facilities, equipment, and programs. Credits are assigned for specific fire protection features covered by the grading schedule. Calculating deficiencies on individual items has been dropped; the percentage of adequacy is now determined for each item. Each grading schedule survey involves an extensive review of fire department records, field surveys of the city, and the testing of fire protection equipment and municipal water-supply systems.

Information gathered during the field survey is applied to the individual items in the grading schedule using quantitative analysis. The city's fire suppression potential capability is then assigned a Public Protection Classification number according to the following class groupings:

- Classes 1 through 8 are the protected property classification. All properties assigned a Class 1 through 8 have a recognized fire department with engine company response limited to 5 travel miles (8 km) in most states and a recognized water delivery system. The minimum water supply from each credited fire hydrant is 250 gpm (946 L/min) for a 2-hour duration; therefore, a recognized water system must also deliver the same minimum flow and duration.
- Class 8B recognizes a fire protection delivery system that is superior to Class 8 except for a lack of water supply system capable of the minimum Fire Suppression Rating Schedule (FSRS) fire flow criteria of 250 gpm (946 L/min) for 2 hours.
- Class 9 is the semiprotected property classification. All properties assigned a Class 9 have a recognized fire department generally limited to 5 travel miles (8 km). However, structural property is beyond 1000 feet (305 m) of a recognized water supply. The current FSRS provides a documented method for fire departments to deliver adequate water to fire sites using mobile water tankers to permit structural property in Class 9 areas to qualify for a protected property classification (Classes 1 through 8). Water delivery demonstration projects have improved Class 9 PPC districts all the way to a Class 4.
- Class 10 is the unprotected property classification for structural property. Class 10 property is generally located beyond 5 travel miles (8 km) of a recognized fire station, regardless of available water supply. Only a selected few insurers will write insurance policies for Class 10 property. When available, the insurance rates are very high compared to other property classes.

Scope and Content of the FSRS

The grading schedule is divided into two major sections: the public fire suppression and the individual property fire suppression.

Section I: Public Fire Suppression. This section is applied to develop a Public Protection Classification (PPC) for all class-rated properties and for specifically rated properties in a city

[redacted]

with a needed fire flow (NFF_i) of 3500 gpm (13,249 L/min) or less. The section is, in turn, divided into three major items for evaluation, which are as follows:

1. *Section 400: receiving and handling fire alarms.* Ten percent of a city's overall grading is based on how well the alarms are received and the fire department is dispatched. ISO evaluates the alarm-dispatch center by looking at the telephone service capability, the number of telephone lines coming into the center, the listing of emergency numbers in the area telephone book, and the number of operators on duty in the center at all times. The ISO review also examines all dispatch circuits and the electronic methods used to notify fire fighters of the location of fire incidents. The ISO uses NFPA 1221, *Standard for the Installation, Maintenance, and Use of Emergency Services Communications Systems,* as a guide for grading public sector fire alarm systems.

2. *Section 500: fire department.* Fifty percent of the city's overall grading is based on the fire department evaluation. The grading schedule considers a first-alarm assignment to be a minimum of two engine companies and one ladder-service company to all structure fires. ISO evaluates the distribution of engine companies and ladder-service companies for response areas of the city in accordance with whether the built-on area of the city has a first-due engine company within 1.5 mi (2.4 km) and a ladder-service company within 2.5 mi (4 km).

ISO also checks to determine whether the permanently mounted pumps on the fire apparatus are tested regularly and inventories are taken of each engine company's complement of fire hose, nozzles, self-contained breathing apparatus (SCBA), and small equipment items. Furthermore, ISO checks on the number and type of ladders, including both ground and aerial ladders, plus service equipment that includes salvage covers, power saws, ventilation equipment, and lighting equipment. Finally, ISO reviews fire company records to determine the following:

- Extent of structural fire suppression training provided to fire company personnel
- Actual personnel who participate in training programs
- Number of fire fighters who respond to structure fires
- Level of building familiarization and documented prefire planning conducted by fire personnel

ISO references several NFPA standards in the evaluation process of fire departments.

3. *Section 600: water supply.* Forty percent of the grading is based on the city's water supply. ISO examines the following three components of each water system to assure that sufficient water capacity, flow rate in gallons (liters) per minute, and pressure at 20 psi (138 kPA) residual pressure, are available at selected sites throughout the city:

- Water-supply works
- Water-supply mains feeding fire hydrants
- Fire hydrant installation, maintenance, and inspection; the water-supply works and pipe distribution system account for 35 percent of the entire city grading. To accomplish an analysis of a given water system, the ISO field representative does the following:
  - Examines whether sufficient water is available for fire suppression beyond the city's maximum daily consumption
  - Surveys all components of the water supply system, including stationary pumps, filtration capacity to provide potable water, and potable water storage to supply water mains
  - Observes fire-flow tests at representative locations in the city to determine the rate of flow provided by water mains
  - Counts the distribution of fire hydrants up to 1000 feet (305 m) from representative categories of property throughout the city; the classes of property evaluated include but are not limited to industrial, commercial, educational, religious, health care, and residential
  - Considers the size, type, and installation of fire hydrants, along with the operating condition of all fire hydrants

Fire hydrants should receive semiannual inspection, as outlined in the American Water Works Association Manual 17, *Installation, Field Testing, and Maintenance of Fire Hydrants.*

Section II: Individual Property Fire Suppression. This section develops Public Protection Classification for specifically rated properties that have a needed fire flow greater than 3500 gpm (134,248 L/min). The following are supporting topics on Public Protection Classification:

1. *Preparing for an ISO grading evaluation.* A city can maximize earned credits through a systematic and proper preparation for an ISO grading evaluation. Doing so involves having in place current maps, inventories, equipment test records, and personnel reports for the ISO field representative to review and evaluate in accordance with each item documented in the FSRS. The chief executive officer (e.g., mayor, city manager) of a city can request from ISO (or obtain from its website http://www.isomitigation.com) a presurvey information packet that details the information requested when an ISO field representative visits a city.

2. *Impact of a city's public protection class on fire insurance premiums.* Theoretically, the better a city's classification, with Class 1 being the best class, the lower will be both insurance rates and insurance premiums when compared to a higher class number. This is generally true for a commercial property that is specifically rated by the insurance industry. Other factors, however, enter into the premium calculation, including the following:

- Fire protection equipment such as installed fire extinguishers, early warning detection and fire alarm systems, smoke control systems in some occupancies, and, most importantly, the installation of automatic sprinkler systems
- Fire loss, or loss costs, to the insurance industry in the city or county where the building risk is located

It needs to be recognized that individual insurance companies may file with state insurance commissions for "rate deviations" from "standard rates" for specific classes of property based on that company's loss experience and insurance reserves. This practice underscores the highly competitive nature of the property insurance industry today.

PLANNING PROCESSES

Whenever a community—rural, suburban, or urban—considers its fire defenses, it must scrutinize the past and present and make predictions or forecasts for the future. Reviewing the past is called *data analysis* and depends on good record keeping. *Evaluation,* which is looking at the present, requires the ability to examine a situation objectively. The process of forecasting future conditions and preparing for them requires that a planning process be followed. This *planning* process results in a plan and its implementation, so that future challenges to the community are met. As the plan is implemented, the process must include the establishment of a *feedback loop,* providing a continuing assessment of how well the plan is contributing to successful completion of goals and objectives, and feeding revised data back into the plan so continuing redesign occurs.

Fire protection organizations, and especially fire departments, need to develop several kinds of plans related to fire prevention and fire suppression. These plans should be quite specific, directed at clearly defined goals, and operational over a relatively brief time period (usually from 1 to 5 years). Typically, such plans are internal to the department and do not involve broad-based planning groups from the outside. Examples of these types of plans, which are most often technical in nature, are apparatus replacement plans, training program plans, revised initial-response plans, plans for a special hazardous-materials attack unit, and plans for adapting fireground procedures to incorporate the use of larger-diameter hose. However, once department planning begins to consider aspects of fire protection and other related operations that will have an impact on external groups, those groups will need to be consulted and incorporated into the planning process. Fire department planning, for example, must consider land-use planning (zoning), water department planning, building code enforcement, emergency management, and possible terrorist activities.

Examples of fire department planning that require the early involvement of other groups are station relocations or closings, building inspection programs, public education programs, and changes in the scheduling of work platoons. These plans, although involving some other groups, are still fairly narrow in scope and usually can be formulated over a relatively short time.

A third type of planning, often called comprehensive, master, or strategic planning, addresses the total community fire protection problem, incorporating both prevention and suppression, and obviously involves many community agencies and organizations and, today, county, state, and federal agencies. Comprehensive planning is a necessity for communities and is aimed at integrating all community efforts at prevention, suppression, disaster response, and improving efficiency and cost-effectiveness of those activities. Improved total community protection is the goal of this planning. Its degree of success must be measured by figures relating to the total cost of fire to the community, and not just in gains for one subsystem. Comprehensive plans often consist of a number of subplans from various agencies that are developed at the same time as part of a larger, total process, and that fit together to make a comprehensive and integrated plan.

Comprehensive plans have clearly stated goals with agreed-on ways of measuring their attainment. These overall goals are reached through overall strategies acceptable to all involved agencies and to the citizens who must pay for the fire protection system. Each goal is composed of some number of subgoals or objectives, and for each objective there are tactics designed to reach that objective. All objectives lead to the accomplishment of the overall strategies. When the objectives and tactics are laid out on a time line, the overall time required to implement the comprehensive plan is then known, and the timing for attaining each objective is apparent.

Fire protection has been largely a local responsibility, and for good reasons it seems destined to remain so.*

Each community has a set of conditions unique to itself. To be adequate, the fire protection system must respond to local conditions and especially to changing conditions. Planning is the key: without local-level planning, the fire protection system is apt to be ill-suited to local needs and unadaptable to the changing needs of the community.

Excellent fire protection (for example, in the form of automatic extinguishing systems such as residential sprinklers or in the form of technically advanced and trained fire-fighting forces) is technically available and certainly can be provided with the resources of most communities. Even with considerable public support, however, this protection may require several years to attain. In the meantime, in every fire jurisdiction (whether a municipality, county, or region), fire protection goals must be set and plans made to achieve those goals. The issues below discuss some of the concepts to be defined in setting these standards.

Goal-Setting Concepts

Adequate Level of Fire Protection. The question of "adequacy" is addressed not only in day-to-day needs but also in major contingencies that can be anticipated for future needs. A definition of "optimal" protection is needed—in contrast to "minimal" protection, which fails to meet contingencies and future needs, and "maximal" protection, which is usually more expensive than a community can afford.

Comprehensive planning must include contingencies drawn from an analysis of community hazards. This process of hazard identification and analysis is crucial to fire department planning.

Reasonable Community Costs. Fire, both as threat and reality, has its costs, including deaths, injuries, property losses, hospital bills, and lost tax revenues, plus the costs of maintaining fire departments, paying fire insurance premiums, and providing built-in fire protection. Each community must decide on an ap-

*Some of the information that follows in this chapter has been extracted in whole and in part from *America Burning*[2] and *America Burning Revisited.*[3]

propriate level of investment in fire protection. Some costs that are beyond the public's willingness to bear may be transferred to the private sector (as when buildings over a certain size or height or with a certain occupancy are required to have automatic extinguishing systems).

Acceptable Risk. A certain level of fire loss must be accepted as tolerable simply because of limited resources of a community. Conditions that endanger the safety of citizens and fire fighters beyond the acceptable risk must be identified as targets for mitigation.

Consideration of these matters helps to determine what functions and emphasis should be assigned to the fire department, other municipal departments, and the private sector both now and in the future. It helps to define new policies, laws, or regulations that may be needed. Most importantly, consideration of these matters makes it clear that fire safety is a responsibility shared by the public and private sectors. Because the fire department cannot prevent all fire losses, formal obligations to have built-in fire protection fall on owners of certain kinds of buildings. For the same reason, private citizens have an obligation to exercise prudence with regard to fire in their daily lives. But prudence also requires education in fire safety, and the obligation to provide that education appropriately falls in the public sector, chiefly the fire department. The public sector (again, chiefly the fire and building code enforcement departments) also has an obligation to see that requirements for built-in protection in the private sector are being met. A fire department, then, has more than one responsibility—and the aforementioned responsibilities are not exhaustive.

Functions of Fire Protection Agencies

The following are significant functions for which fire protection agencies typically have primary or significant roles.

Fire Suppression. Fire fighters need proper training and adequate equipment to save lives, to extinguish fires quickly, and to ensure their own safety.

Specialized Emergency and Disaster Services. These situations include hazardous materials incidents, floods, earthquakes, multiple-vehicle accidents, cave-ins, collapsed buildings, volcanic eruptions, searches for lost persons, attempted suicides, a variety of specialized technical rescue services, weapons of mass destruction training, and so on.

Emergency Medical Services. Capabilities needed during fires and other emergencies include first aid, resuscitation, and possibly advanced life support (paramedical services). (The term *paramedical services* means emergency treatment beyond ordinary first aid, performed by fire service personnel under supervision—through radio communication and preapproved treatment protocols, for example—of a physician.)

Fire Prevention. This prevention includes approval of building plans and actual construction; inspection of buildings, their contents, and their fire protection equipment; and investigation of fire cause and spread to guide future fire prevention priorities and determine when the crime of arson has been committed.

Fire Safety and Dangerous-Situation Education. Fire departments have an obligation to bring fire safety and dangerous-situation education not only into schools and private homes but also into occupancies such as restaurants, hotels, hospitals, and nursing homes that have a greater-than-average fire potential or life safety hazard. These programs may include such topics as swimming pool safety, babysitter training, latchkey child safety, and so on. See Section 5, Chapter 2, "Fire and Life Safety Education Messages."

Deteriorated Building Hazards. In coordination with other municipal departments, fire departments can work to abate serious hazards to health and safety caused by deteriorated structures or abandoned buildings.

Regional Coordination. Major emergencies can exceed the capabilities of a single fire department, and neighboring fire jurisdictions should have detailed plans for coping with such emergencies. But effectiveness may also be improved through sharing of day-to-day operations—such as, for example, an area-wide communication and dispatch network or a joint training facility.

Data Development. Knowledge of fire department performance and how practices should change to improve performance depends on adequate record keeping. Computers and information management systems play a key role in fire protection and emergency management planning. See Section 12, Chapter 5, "Information Management and Computer Technology."

Community Relations. Fire departments are representative of the local community that supports them. The impression they make on citizens affects how citizens view their government. Volunteer departments dependent on private donations must, of course, also be concerned with community relations. Moreover, because fire stations are strategically located throughout the community, they can serve as referral or dispensing agencies for a wide range of municipal services.

As communities set out to improve their fire protection, they must not consider the fire department alone. The police have a role in reporting fires and in handling traffic and crowds during fires. The cooperation of the building department is needed to enforce the fire safety provisions of building codes. The work of the water department in maintaining the water system is vital to fire suppression. In fire safety education, the public schools, the department of recreation, and the public library can augment the work of the fire department. Future community development and planning will influence the location of new fire stations and how they will be equipped.

These nine functions are just the obvious examples of interdependence. Although it may seem trivial, the manner in which house numbers are assigned and posted, for example, can affect the ability of a fire department to respond quickly and effectively to emergencies, as do many other seemingly unrelated topics.

Master Planning

Fire protection is only one of many community services. Not only must it compete for dollars with other municipal needs such as the education system and the police department, but in planning for future growth the fire protection system must account for the changes in progress elsewhere in the community. For example, if a deteriorated area is to be torn down and replaced with high-rise apartment buildings, the fire protection needs of that area will change. Changes in zoning maps will also change the fire protection needs in different parts of the community.

To cope with future growth, local administrators are turning increasingly to the concept of master (comprehensive) planning of municipal functions. Such plans include an examination of existing programs, a projection of future needs of the community, and a determination of methods to fill those needs. They seek the most cost-effective allocations of resources to help ensure that the needs will be met.

A major section of a community's general plan of land use should be a master plan for fire protection, which should be written chiefly by fire department managers. This plan should, first of all, be consistent with and reinforce the goals of a city's overall general plan and its time frame. For example, managers need to plan the deployment of personnel and equipment according to the kind of growth and the specific areas of growth that the community foresees. It is critical that the comprehensive plan determine and set goals and objectives for the fire protection system and the fire department in terms that are understandable to the citizens being protected.

Having established goals, the department officers should use the plan to establish some form of management systematic and quality assurance within the fire department. Management is most effective when each person is aware of how tasks fit into the overall goals and is committed to getting specific jobs done in a specified time.

Because fire departments exist in a real world where a variety of purposes must be served with a limited amount of money, it is important that every dollar be invested for maximum return on investment. The fire protection master plan not only should seek to provide the maximum cost-benefit ratio for fire protection expenditures but also should establish a framework for measuring the effectiveness of these expenditures. Last, the plan must clarify the fire protection responsibility for other groups, both governmental and private, in the community.

Often, as the result of a comprehensive planning effort, a community will formulate a "developmental plan." This document provides a schedule for implementing those changes in the fire protection system deemed appropriate by the community.

Key questions for developmental plans include the following:

- What are the fire protection, rescue, emergency medical, disaster response, and safety education needs?
- What organizational structure and what resources are currently available to meet those needs?
- Is there a disparity between what is available and what is needed?
- What will the community profile be like in 5 to 10 years?
- What will be needed then to provide adequate protection?
- What is and what will be the financial resource base?
- What options are and will be available to enhance protection, or to keep it at an adequate level?
- How can changes be phased in to gain community goals and cost-effectiveness?

Devising a Fire Protection Plan

The following are key questions to be asked by those planning for fire protection:

- Why is planning necessary for us at this time?
- What do we need to start the process, and are the necessary groups committed to the process?
- What are the necessary steps in the planning process?
- How will the plan be financed and implemented?
- Are all aspects of the plan legally possible and enforceable?
- How will the plan be evaluated? Will it be a part of the integrated emergency management plan of the community?
- How will feedback be gathered and the plan modified and updated?

In *Introductory Summary: Fire Prevention and Control Master Planning,* the U.S. Fire Administration[4] underscored the following still very useful set of steps in its overview of the planning process.

Master planning is a participative process that should result in the establishment of a fire prevention and control system that is goal-oriented, long term, and comprehensive; provides known cost/loss performance; and adapts continually to the changing needs of your community. Master planning involves the following:

- Master planning should consider all community elements related to fire prevention and control system elements.
- Master planning involves the participation of all parties interested in the development of a defined cost/loss relationship.
- Master planning allows you to systematically analyze fire prevention and control through commonsense procedures.

Master planning has three phases: preplanning, planning, and implementation. The preplanning phase gets necessary commitments, committees, estimates and schedules, and go-ahead approvals. The planning phase gathers and analyzes data, sets goals and objectives, determines an acceptable level of fire protection service, identifies alternatives, and constructs the plan. The implementation phase never ends, because the plan is ongoing and always being revised and updated.

The following can serve as guidelines to fire department administrators for developing and presenting a master fire protection plan as part of the comprehensive master plan outlined earlier:

Phase I

1. Identify the fire protection problems of the jurisdiction.
2. Identify the best combination of public resources and built-in protection required to manage the fire problem; within acceptable limits:
   a. Specify current capabilities of and future needs for public resources.
   b. Specify current capabilities and future requirements for built-in protection.

3. Develop alternative methods that will result in trade-offs between benefits and risks.
4. Establish a system of goals, programs, and cost estimates to implement the plan:
   a. Develop department goals and programs, including maximum possible participation of fire department personnel of all ranks.
   b. Provide goals and objectives for all divisions, supportive of the overall goals of the department.
   c. Strive to develop management development programs that increase acceptance of authority and responsibility by all fire officers as they strive to accomplish established objectives and programs.

Phase II

1. Develop a definition of the roles of other government agencies in the fire protection process.
2. Present the proposed municipal fire protection system to the city administration for review.
3. Present the proposed system for adoption as the fire protection element of the jurisdiction's general plan. The standard process for development of a general plan provides the fire department administrator an opportunity to inform the community leaders of the fire protection goals and system and to obtain their support.

Phase III

In considering the fire protection element of the general plan, the governing body of the jurisdiction will have to pay special attention to the following:

1. Short- and long-range goals
2. Long-range staffing and capital improvement plans
3. Code revisions required to provide fire loss management

Phase IV

The fire loss management system must be reviewed and updated as budget allocations, capital improvement plans, and code revisions occur. Continuing review of results should concentrate on the following areas:

1. Did fires remain within estimated limits?
2. Should limits be changed?
3. Did losses prove to be acceptable?
4. Could resources be decreased, or should they be increased?

SUMMARY

Public fire protection should consist of a broad range of safeguards, programs, and activities ranging from plan review and code enforcement to provisions for fire suppression and public safety education. Careful consideration of local hazards and demographics, plus analysis of data related to protection and suppression are necessary for the design and maintenance of an effective, cost-effective system. Further, provisions must exist within the plan to promote and assure adequate health and safety levels of its fire fighters. See Section 12, Chapter 7, "Safety, Medical, and Health Issues and Programs." This results in an integrated risk management system.

Local conditions, regulatory orders, and national standards dictate the type and level of prevention and suppression/rescue provisions necessary and appropriate for a community. The time required for response and the number and types of emergency responders and vehicles should match local needs and conform to legal and industry standard requirements. Judgments about the adequacy of local prevention and emergency response provisions can be made by local authorities, Insurance Services Office (ISO) representatives, fire department accreditation teams, or other experts. Fire insurance premiums for residential and commercial property most often reflect periodic assessments of local fire protection provisions.

Municipal planning for fire protection, fire department–based emergency medical services, hazardous materials incident response, and technical rescue services requires a review of past and present data, plus knowledge-based predictions of community change and development. Agreements concerning the level of local emergency service required then lead to decisions concerning the type, size, and deployment of suppression/rescue forces.

BIBLIOGRAPHY

References Cited

1. Insurance Services Office, *Grading Schedule for Municipal Fire Protection,* Insurance Services Office, New York, 1974; ISO, *Fire Suppression Rating Schedule (FSRS),* Insurance Services Office, New York, 1998.
2. NCFPC, *America Burning,* U.S. Fire Administration, Washington, DC, 1974.
3. United States Fire Academy, *America Burning Revisited,* U.S. Fire Administration, Washington, DC, 1987.
4. National Fire Safety and Research Office, *Introductory Summary: Fire Prevention and Control Master Planning,* U.S. Department of Commerce, National Fire Safety and Research Office, Washington, DC.

NFPA Codes, Standards, and Recommended Practices

Reference to the following NFPA codes, standards, and recommended practices will provide further information on planning public fire-rescue protection discussed in this chapter. (See the latest version of The NFPA Catalog *for availability of current editions of the following documents.)*

NFPA 13E, *Recommended Practice for Fire Department Operations in Properties Protected by Sprinkler and Standpipe Systems*
NFPA 402, *Guide for Aircraft Rescue and Fire Fighting Operations*
NFPA 403, *Standard for Aircraft Rescue and Fire-Fighting Services at Airports*
NFPA 414, *Standard for Aircraft Rescue and Fire-Fighting Vehicles*
NFPA 471, *Recommended Practice for Responding to Hazardous Materials Incidents*
NFPA 472, *Standard for Professional Competence of Responders to Hazardous Materials Incidents*
NFPA 901, *Standard Classifications for Incident Reporting and Fire Protection Data*
NFPA 1001, *Standard for Fire Fighter Professional Qualifications*
NFPA 1002, *Standard for Fire Apparatus Driver/Operator Professional Qualifications*
NFPA 1003, *Standard for Airport Fire Fighter Professional Qualifications*
NFPA 1006, *Standard for Rescue Technician Professional Qualifications*

NFPA 1021, *Standard for Fire Officer Professional Qualifications*
NFPA 1031, *Standard for Professional Qualifications for Fire Inspector and Plan Examiner*
NFPA 1033, *Standard for Professional Qualifications for Fire Investigator*
NFPA 1035, *Standard for Professional Qualifications for Public Fire and Life Safety Educator*
NFPA 1041, *Standard for Fire Service Instructor Professional Qualifications*
NFPA 1051, *Standard for Wildland Fire Fighter Professional Qualifications*
NFPA 1061, *Standard for Professional Qualifications for Public Safety Telecommunicator*
NFPA 1071, *Standard for Emergency Vehicle Technician Professional Qualifications*
NFPA 1143, *Standard for Wildland Fire Management*
NFPA 1201, *Standard for Providing Emergency Services to the Public*
NFPA 1221, *Standard for the Installation, Maintenance, and Use of Emergency Services Communications Systems*
NFPA 1401, *Recommended Practice for Fire Service Training Reports and Records*
NFPA 1402, *Guide to Building Fire Service Training Centers*
NFPA 1403, *Standard on Live Fire Training Evolutions*
NFPA 1410, *Standard on Training for Initial Emergency Scene Operations*
NFPA 1452, *Guide for Training Fire Service Personnel to Conduct Dwelling Fire Safety Surveys*
NFPA 1500, *Standard on Fire Department Occupational Safety and Health Program*
NFPA 1521, *Standard for Fire Department Safety Officer*
NFPA 1670, *Standard on Operations and Training for Technical Search and Rescue Incidents*
NFPA 1710, *Standard for the Organization and Deployment of Fire Suppression Operations, Emergency Medical Operations, and Special Operations to the Public by Career Fire Departments*
NFPA 1720, *Standard for the Organization and Deployment of Fire Suppression Operations, Emergency Medical Operations, and Special Operations to the Public by Volunteer Fire Departments*
NFPA 1901, *Standard for Automotive Fire Apparatus*
NFPA 1911, *Standard for Service Tests of Fire Pump Systems on Fire Apparatus*
NFPA 1932, *Standard on Use, Maintenance, and Service Testing of In-Service Fire Department Ground Ladders*
NFPA 1961, *Standard on Fire Hose*
NFPA 1962, *Standard for the Inspection, Care, and Use of Fire Hose, Couplings, and Nozzles and the Service Testing of Fire Hose*
NFPA 1964, *Standard for Spray Nozzles*
NFPA 1971, *Standard on Protective Ensembles for Structural Fire Fighting and Proximity Fire Fighting*
NFPA 1975, *Standard on Station/Work Uniforms for Fire and Emergency Services*
NFPA 1981, *Standard on Open-Circuit Self-Contained Breathing Apparatus for Fire and Emergency Services*
NFPA 1982, *Standard on Personal Alert Safety Systems (PASS)*
NFPA 1983, *Standard on Life Safety Rope and Equipment for Emergency Services*
NFPA 1991, *Standard on Vapor-Protective Ensembles for Hazardous Materials Emergencies*
NFPA 1992, *Standard on Liquid Splash-Protective Ensembles and Clothing for Hazardous Materials Emergencies*

Reference

Hickey, H., *Fire Suppression Rating Schedule Handbook,* Society of Fire Protection Engineers, Bethesda, MD, 2002.

Chapter 2

Organizational Benchmarking and Performance Evaluation

Dorinda Cline

Chapter Contents

Key Terms

benchmarking, emergency management, evaluating, Government Accounting Standards Board (GASB), performance-based budget, performance management system

Evaluating and benchmarking are not new concepts to fire service professionals. They are inherent in the daily operations of a fire department. From fighting fire to patient care, the actions taken while performing the tasks at hand are measured and judged using a standard of service. Those actions directly and indirectly affect the outcome of the operation.

Evaluating and benchmarking result in quantifying and qualifying organizational performance. *Evaluating* is the process of measuring and judging performance as progress toward a defined standard of service. *Benchmarking* is the process of selecting the appropriate standard of service to use. Combined, evaluating and benchmarking provide information about performance that can be communicated. In this format, performance information can be used to obtain resources necessary to provide services, acknowledge performance success, and improve performance. Effective communication about performance creates the ability to efficiently manage performance on an organizational level.

To elevate performance management from a task level to an organizational level requires a systems approach. The organization is one system with one mission to fulfill. Within that one system are multiple subsystems that interrelate to fulfill a specific role. There are many examples of this concept in everyday life. Our vehicles have brake, electrical, and air bag systems. Our bodies have digestive, respiratory, and nervous systems. These analogies are common and may be useful in referencing this type of management approach. Whichever analogy works for the organization is the one to use; the critical importance resides in the perspective.

This chapter examines organizational benchmarking and performance evaluation from a systems perspective, to include the key elements of success for a fire department performance management system. Steps to implement a new system are discussed in each section. Based on a belief that the key elements already exist in the organization, the implementation is simplified to linking existing responsibilities and processes to communicate performance. With the perspective that a fire department is one system, performance management processes are integrated as a subsystem within the organization.

The first section discusses the factors that affect organizational acceptance of performance management concepts and a formal system. These factors are based on member recognition, education, and participation. The term "member" is used to represent those individuals who have a defined reporting relationship to the organization. It is intended to be inclusive of employees and volunteers, both sworn and civilian.

The second section is focused on the performance management system, as an integrated subsystem within the organization. The overall framework and data flow is charted, with roles and responsibilities defined. The organizational, financial, planning, and operational structures of a working fire department are examined to highlight the existing elements of performance

Dorinda Cline holds an associate's degree in accounting and a bachelor's degree in municipal operations management from Arizona State University. She has served as an accountant and senior manager at the Mesa, Arizona, fire department and is a charter member of the Scottsdale, Arizona, fire department, where she served on the transition team to convert fire protection services from a private provider to a municipal department. She provides administrative, financial, and budgetary consulting services to municipal fire departments including the Phoenix, Arizona, fire department.

management. The benefit to a centralized database is discussed and consideration is given to a performance-based budget development model.

The third section contains a sample performance report template and recommended reporting cycles. Performance reporting is categorized into three "*p*'s": *p*rogram descriptors, *p*erformance information, and *p*lanning objectives.

The fourth and final section examines how measurements begin with a count (a number) and combine with benchmarks to provide meaningful performance information. Included are examples and a list of data categories to consider.

See the following chapters in Section 12 for related topics: Chapter 1, "Planning for Public Fire-Rescue Protection"; Chapter 4, "Managing Fire-Rescue Departments"; Chapter 17, "Pre-Incident Planning for Industrial and Municipal Emergency Response"; and Chapter 18, "Pre-Incident Planning for Emergency Response."

ORGANIZATIONAL ACCEPTANCE

Organizational acceptance is necessary to realize the full potential of performance management concepts. Ways to enhance acceptance are based on member recognition, education, and participation. Recognizing member contributions and connecting them to organizational success is proposed to create a positive connotation to measuring performance. With clear direction and established goals and objectives, a team approach to integrating a system can increase member participation. The use of professional resources and a common language creates an environment in which everyone has a level of understanding and enables each to make a positive contribution.

Contribution Connection

Performance management concepts and words, such as *measuring* and *judging,* often have a negative connotation for the members of an organization. That connotation can be made positive when the standards of service that exist in everyday operations are used to demonstrate a contribution towards performance success for the whole organization. A formal performance management system has the ability to provide that connection and recognition.

Successfully integrating performance measures in an organization begins with recognizing that they already exist in every organization; they are blended into the culture. They exist in the thought processes and everyday actions of those who deliver the services, those who manage the operations, and those who make policy decisions. A performance management system should be designed to provide the connection between individual contributions and the shared mission and goals. In essence, every task is connected to a strategic goal. Every strategic goal is connected to service delivery in the community. The organization becomes one system, with many moving parts, working toward achieving defined standards of service to the customers.

A performance management system provides acknowledgment for the service delivery success that has existed all along. In addition, the measurements create the ability to communicate performance through data-based analysis, which is an excellent catalyst to obtaining resources. For all members, it can create a sense of contribution and connection to the whole system, a sense of belonging to something bigger than themselves, a sense of why and how their work affects the customers. For the customers, it can create a sense of confidence in the quality of service provided.

The integration of performance measures into the management process does not have to have a negative connotation. When combined with intuition, judgment, and experience, performance measures can significantly improve decision making that directly affects the members' ability to successfully perform their work for the customers. Like any other management concept, the key to organizational acceptance is the spirit in which it is presented and used.

Inclusive Participation

Member participation is a key to organizational acceptance. Members will actively participate in management efforts when their contributions are acknowledged as a vital component to success. They are already experts in performing the work associated with delivering services. All they need is the opportunity to understand the concepts and speak the language to make a positive contribution. As they participate, a sense of ownership is created. They are vested in making it work and become champions of success. With their participation, crafting a system to monitor and report performance represents building a useful tool to deliver the best services possible. We all appreciate good tools, like the computer that does the math for us and the vehicle that gets us to our destination. A performance management system has the potential to be a very valuable tool. Just like the computer or vehicle, the amount of appreciation it receives is directly dependent upon the extent to which it supports the members in providing quality services to the customer.

Purpose and Direction

To be a valuable tool, a performance management system must have a purpose, a reason to exist. A purpose is often best illustrated and communicated through established goals and objectives. The progress toward meeting objectives will evaluate the system itself to ensure it is functioning appropriately. Success of the system is critical to ensure the organization reports and acts on credible information. Once everyone understands why a performance management system exists, each member can make that positive contribution to its success. In order for the system to be useful and fulfill its purpose, it must provide information that guides the organization in the right direction. By nature, it must provide accurate and meaningful data that achieves the following:

Direction

- *D*irectly relates to operational and strategic goals
- *I*mproves decision making
- *R*espects professional judgment and technical expertise
- *E*ducates customers
- *C*elebrates accomplishments
- *T*imely reports activities
- *I*mproves processes
- *O*ffers benchmark opportunities with *no* duplication of effort for the members

Team Approach

A proven method of inclusive participation is through the use of cross-functional project teams. According to Dennis Compton, author of *When in Doubt, Lead!,*[1] teams "enhance a sense of ownership and help foster responsibility and accountability within the organization." In his book, there is a team profile template with helpful guidance to ensure a team's effectiveness.

The cross-functional project team approach has many benefits. All service areas of the organization are represented. The scope of work is well documented and understood. Decisions and activities are communicated throughout the organization as work progresses. Once the team develops a performance management system, its effectiveness is tested and reported prior to implementation. As the first phase of implementation, the responsibility of project team members may include the development and delivery of an educational program or it may be passed on to a training staff. By definition, once the project is completed, this team is disbanded. At the same time, a standing team may be established to periodically test and improve the ongoing functionality of the product of the team's efforts.

Cross-functional teams complement the operational structure of the organization. To develop a performance management system, each operational service area should have at least one representative on the team. In addition, at least one operational manager and one senior manager should serve on the team. These individuals act as liaisons between the team and their respective work groups. The goal is representation for all the services provided by the organization as well as three levels of organizational performance: strategic, operational, and task. Once achieved, the chain of command is inherently represented, which empowers the team to work on behalf of the entire organization. In other words, if the senior manager on the team approves the work, then approval from all the senior managers is implied. This streamlines the effectiveness of the team. At the same time, it places a great deal of responsibility on the team members to effectively communicate the team's actions to the rest of the organization. In addition, team members must ensure the project stays within the defined scope of work, on time, and within budget.

Team members become system experts. They are responsible for selecting the appropriate resources and for designing the overall framework for a system that is useful to the organization. They develop report templates and define reporting cycles to bring consistency within the organization. They become the facilitators within their own service area as measurements and benchmarks are selected. All of these performance management aspects are discussed later in the chapter. It is important to note that these responsibilities are different from the responsibilities of an operational manager. Once the system is developed, as illustrated later in this chapter, it is the operational managers who are responsible for evaluating the performance of services delivered.

One of the most important roles of a team member is to champion the "systems" perspective. The individual services provided by a fire department complement each other or share overlapping objectives toward the shared mission. Many customers receive multiple services from a fire department. One of the worst impressions to leave with a customer is that the right hand does not know what the left hand is doing. If innovative ideas and lessons learned about the performance in each service area are shared on an organizational level, all the service areas will benefit and the customer will see cohesive performance from the organization. The project team members have the opportunity to set the stage for cohesive performance by designing a system that fosters collaborative analysis and centralized oversight for all services.

The potential benefits of this team approach are directly related to the team's profile. The keys to successfully realizing benefits reside in a carefully defined scope of work and appropriate representation from within the organization.

Professional Resources

Professional resources are used for educational purposes and universal recognition. Lessons learned from mature systems are used to avoid pitfalls. National databases and surveys are used to identify service norms. A multitude of agencies provide performance management information, ranging from conceptual models to technical standards. The best professional resources to use are those that match the philosophy, culture, and mission of the organization. Fire departments already interact with many of these agencies, seeking technical guidance and best practices, as well as national perspectives on service-related issues. Commonly referenced agencies include the following:

- National Fire Protection Association (NFPA): Provides consensus-based codes and standards for fire and life safety, as well as research, training, and education.
  http://www.nfpa.org
- Insurance Services Office, Inc. (ISO): Provides a Fire Suppression Rating Schedule that measures the major elements of a community's fire suppression system.
  http://www.iso.com
- Center for Public Safety Excellence: Provides a comprehensive system of fire and emergency service evaluation that can help local governments determine their risks and fire safety needs, evaluate the performance of the organizations involved, and provide a method for continuous improvement.
  http://www.publicsafetyexcellence.org
- International City/County Management Association (IMCA), Center for Performance Measurement (CPM): Assists counties, cities, and towns of all sizes with the collection, analysis, and application of performance information.
  http://www1.icma.org
- Governmental Accounting Standards Board (GASB), Service Efforts and Accomplishments (SEA) research project: Provides research to address the needs of state and local governments trying to develop performance measures.
  http://www.seagov.org

In addition, the experiences of other fire departments serve as useful "lessons learned" in managing performance. Municipalities commonly referenced as progressive in the performance management field are Phoenix, Arizona; Austin, Texas; and Charlotte, North Carolina.

Effective Communication

A common language is essential to communicate effectively about organizational performance. The performance measured and reported may be specific to the fire service. Whether the measurement is an input, output, or outcome, it must have a universal meaning. Many professional resources provide a glossary of performance management terms. A comprehensive example is found in a Government Accounting Standards Board (GASB) special report, *Reporting Performance Information: Suggested Criteria for Effective Communication.*[2]

An advantage to using language published by a national standards agency such as GASB is that the scope of effective communication widens. In addition to the members of the fire department, more customers and partners in performance understand the language. The barriers created by service-specific acronyms are minimized. When the fire department is working with local government services, such as the water or police departments, or is presenting funding requests to elected officials in a public forum, a common language and defined terminology increases the effectiveness of communication. Adoption of a common language is a key step to integrating a new performance management system. To create a common language for this chapter, definitions of the terms used are listed in Table 12.2.1.

PERFORMANCE MANAGEMENT SYSTEM

A successful performance management system is recognized by every member of the organization. It is charted, accessible, and easy to understand. Members know its purpose and use, as well as their roles within the system. These types of system charts are not commonly published, even though key performance measurements are published in most fire department annual reports. For the members of the organization, the visual link between daily operations and published results must exist to connect their contributions to organizational performance. The link improves understanding in how their work affects the customers and becomes an excellent basis for processing improvements.

To integrate a new system, the overall framework and data flow must be charted. An efficient process involves conducting a self-analysis of how the organization currently functions. With the belief that performance evaluation already exists in the organization, it is reasonable to assume the key elements are fragmented within existing operations. In conjunction with reviewing how the organization functions, additional steps can be identified to continue with the process of integrating a new system.

The following series of conceptual charts are derived from organizational charts provided by the Mesa Fire Department,[3] a municipal career department in Arizona. Each chart highlights how the organization functions and how the functions relate to performance management. Included is a transitional model from the organization's operational chart to visually document the integrated performance management system.

The Mesa Fire Department is managed as a system, with three levels of performance. The comprehensive body of work introducing this management concept is *Improving Performance: How to Manage the White Space on the Organization Chart,*[4] by Geary A. Rummler and Alan P. Brache. This book offers charts, checklists, hands-on tools, and case studies to demonstrate implementation of the concept.

Defined Roles and Responsibilities

A successful performance management system has top-down value. Impacts to performance are considered in the decision-making processes at all levels of the organization. Each level of authority has a role and responsibility in organizational performance. A coordinated effort from each level of the organization provides the policy decisions, operational management, and service delivery tasks that contribute to success. A review of the organizational chart shown in Figure 12.2.1 defines these levels of responsibility, with each level of authority having a role and responsibility in organizational performance.

As shown in Figure 12.2.1, the fire department's organizational chart is similar to many organizations. Direct lines of authority are established through a division of labor and reporting relationships. Commonly referred to as the *chain of command,* these lines of authority are primarily used for human resource and fiscal management. Services are not actually delivered through the lines of authority. However, the organizational chart contains key elements to performance success—that is, defined leadership and accountability.

Leaders lead by example. If their actions and language demonstrates that they value performance results, so will the rest of the organization. Holding themselves and others accountable for their role in organizational performance shows top-down value. Performance results should not be punitive. If the results are not quite where they should be, they should serve as a catalyst to ensure resources have been appropriately aligned with service delivery expectations. Processes may need to be improved. New or advanced training may be in order. Equipment may need to be replaced or technology updated. When leaders react with a holistic approach to the factors that contribute to performance success, they demonstrate universal accountability for performance results.

Resources Linked to Performance

Resources used linked to services delivered represent the ins and outs of performance. Resources used represent the inputs to performance. As shown in Figure 12.2.2, a review of the fire department's financial structure reveals the process of documenting the cost of resources used. As expenditures occur, the amount of resources used (inputs) is documented and then summarized on each level of fiscal management.

Typically, a financial structure is an accounting system aligned with the organizational chart. Generally speaking, the budget is developed and financial transactions are captured in a series of revenue and expenditure accounts. In government accounting, fire department revenue and the budget (funding allocated) are not the same. The budget is usually developed by projecting expenditures. Then, actual expenditures are recorded, as they occur, over the course of the fiscal year.

Actual expenditures are the primary focus of a performance management system. As expenditures occur, the amount of resources used (inputs) is documented. These inputs include the following:

TABLE 12.2.1 Common Performance Management System Terms

Common Terms	*Definitions*
Accountability	• Responsibility of one party to another party; in government, responsibility of elected and appointed officials to those who elected or chose them or who provide resources with which services are provided • Being obliged to explain one's actions, to justify what one does; requires government to answer to the citizenry to justify the raising of public resources and explain purposes for which they are used; governmental accountability is based on the belief that the citizenry has a "right to know"
Benchmark	• In the context of outcomes and performance discussion, refers to desired program results • May include a target or standard for the program to achieve • Denotes best practices
Budget	• A quantitative plan of activities and programs expressed in terms of assets, liabilities, revenues, expenses (or expenditures), and in some cases outputs or outcomes • A performance-based budget may express the organizational goals in terms of specific financial and operating objectives
Effectiveness	• Producing a desired result • An ends-oriented concept that measures degree to which predetermined goals and objectives for a particular activity or program are achieved; both intended and unintended results of a program may be included as part of the measurement of effectiveness
Efficiency	• Relationship between efforts (or inputs) to outputs or outcomes; measured by indicators of the resources used or cost per unit of output or outcome • Resource-usage concept, also with a least-cost notion, that is concerned with maximizing outputs or outcomes at a minimal cost or using minimum resources
Explanatory factors	• Includes a variety of information about the environment and other factors that might affect an organization's performance; they can be either factors substantially outside the control of the entity, such as environmental and demographic characteristics, or factors over which the entity has some control, such as staffing patterns
Goal	• Condition or state that one is striving to achieve • Usually long term and may be beyond what might reasonably be expected to be achieved
Input	• Amount of financial and nonfinancial resources (in terms of money, material, etc.) that are applied to producing a product or providing a service (output)
Mission	• Charge, assignment, or purpose of an organization or some part of that organization
Objective	• Statement of the condition one expects to achieve; an objective should be realistic, measurable, generally within the control of the organization, and time constrained
Outcome	• Basic unit of measurement of progress toward achieving an objective; at the least, an outcome may be initial, intermediate, or long term
Output	• Measure of the quantity of a service or product provided (may include a quality component)
Performance measure	• Quantifiable indicator of progress, achievement, and efficiency that includes outcome, output, input, efficiency, and explanatory indicators
Strategy	• Based on goals and objective, a means for transforming inputs into outputs, and ultimately outcomes, through planned use of budgetary and other resources
Target	• Organization's intended results for a program or service

Source: Definitions based on those used in GASB special report, *Reporting Performance Information: Suggested Criteria for Effective Communication.*[2]

- Employee labor and related employer expenses (payroll)
- Services provided by other departments (internal service charges)
- Services provided by outside agencies (invoices/payables)
- Commodities used in service delivery (purchase orders/payables)
- Capital equipment outlay

Linking expenditures to service delivery on an ongoing basis captures meaningful data about performance.

In government accounting, expenditures are typically recorded in cost centers that group like (related) activities. Expenditures, which are initially reported on the cost center level, are compiled into summaries for each level of fiscal management in the organization. These summaries can be useful in connecting

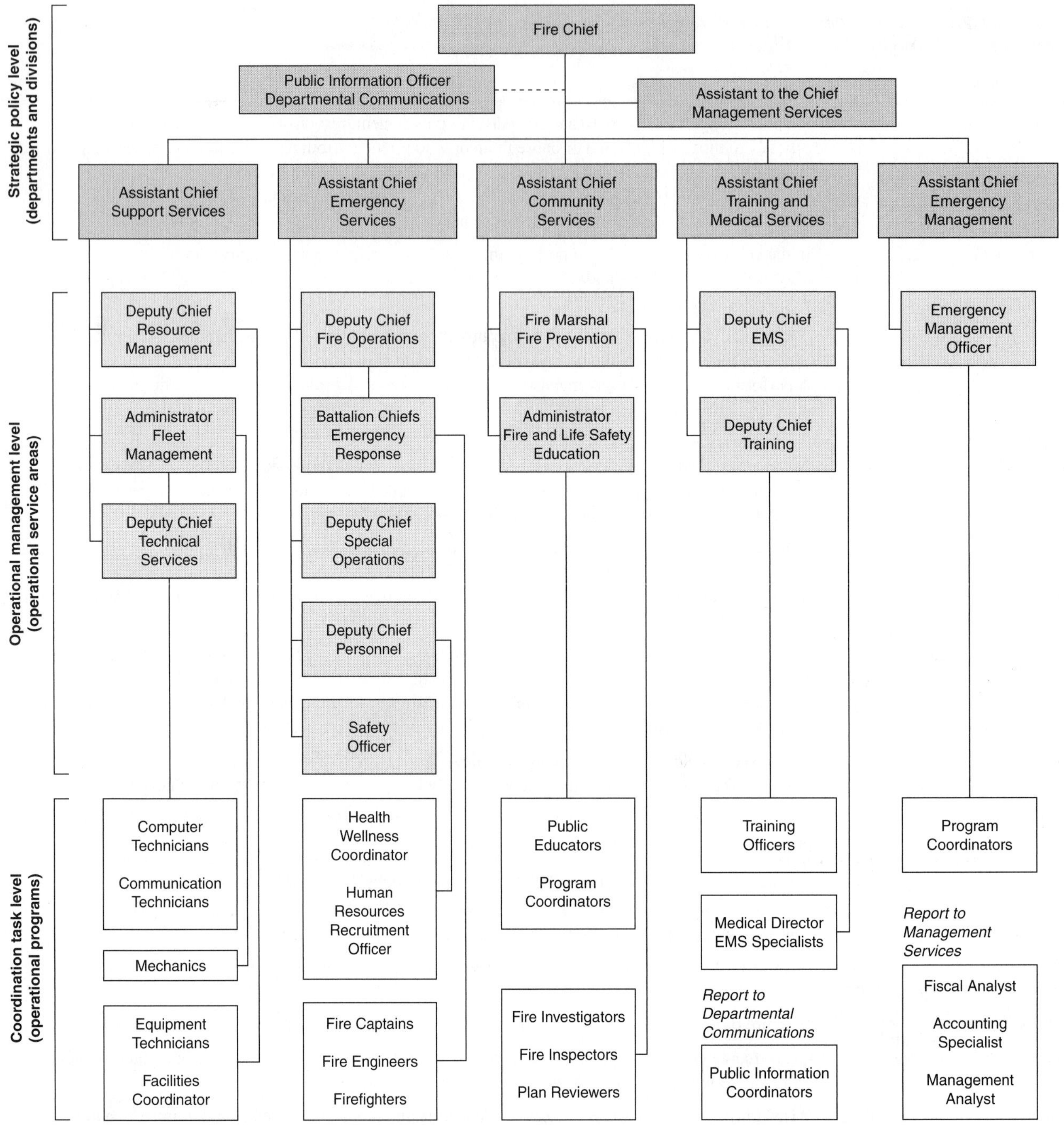

FIGURE 12.2.1 Fire Department Organizational Chart

the resources used (inputs) with the service delivered (outputs). In this type of accounting system, selecting the appropriate level cost centers will increase the usefulness of the summary reports.

One of the most common challenges in selecting the appropriate level to summarize financial data is when recording payroll (time dedicated to service delivery). Since fire department labor is the primary input to performance, this can become a significant challenge. Members may dedicate their time to multiple operational programs. Establishing a cost center for each one may, therefore, create a system that is cumbersome and difficult to use. At the same time, operational managers need detailed information about how much time is dedicated to which services. This information helps determine the efficiency of services, such as turnaround time for customers. In these cases, a cost accounting system embedded in the financial system is the most effective mechanism to use.

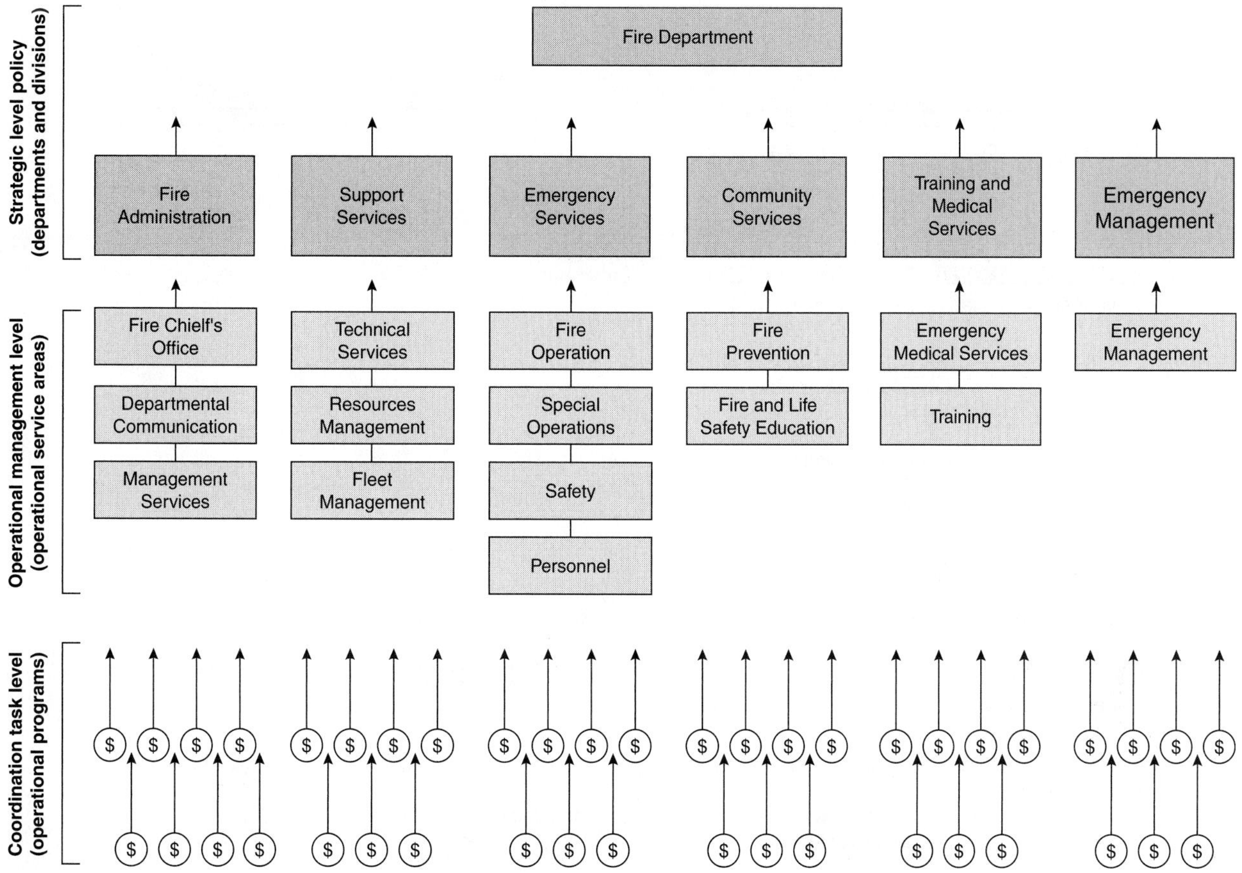

FIGURE 12.2.2 Fire Department Financial Structure

Other challenges may occur when linking an accounting system to a performance management system. A recent survey conducted by researchers at Georgia State University and the Governmental Accounting Standards Board (GASB) specifically addressed this issue with local governments. Results published in *Performance Measurement at the State and Local Levels: A Summary of Survey Results*[5] indicate that most respondents "feel there is an inadequate link between the performance measurement database and the accounting/budget database systems. . . . Nearly 80 percent of respondents from each group indicated that this is somewhat of a problem or is a significant problem."

No matter what financial structure is established or what level of automation is achieved, the key element of performance management remains the accounting of expenditures. The link between expenditures (inputs) and service delivery (outputs) must be established to calculate efficiency measures. Once calculated, they provide meaningful information that is useful to improve performance and justify budget requests.

Direct Relationship to Operational and Strategic Goals

Performance evaluation measures the success toward achieving operational and strategic goals. Planning documents contain a multitude of performance data, such as the strategic and operational goals, activity statistics, and service benchmarks. They represent valuable mediums for communicating a shared vision of performance success.

With an integrated performance management system to collect data, the process of planning is simplified and focused. Operational managers contribute the vast majority or performance data using short-range documents. With the data collected, reporting for multiple uses and to diverse audiences is quicker and easier. A review of the planning and reporting chart (Figure 12.2.3) shows the opportunities to link performance data with planning activities, which is a key step to integrating a new system.

As shown in Figure 12.2.3 the fire department's planning and reporting chart represents an inclusive tiered approach to developing and publishing the organization's mission, vision, goals, and accomplishments. Long-range, strategic-level documents include a 25 year infrastructure plan and a 10 year strategic plan. Shorter-range, management-level documents include a 5 year operating plan, 5 year reaccreditation plan with annual updates, and a 2 year financial (budget) plan. Short-range operational documents include an annual report, 6 month activity plans, program management guides, and project action plans. Operational managers contribute the vast majority of data using short-range documents, which provides the opportunity to link performance data to planning activities.

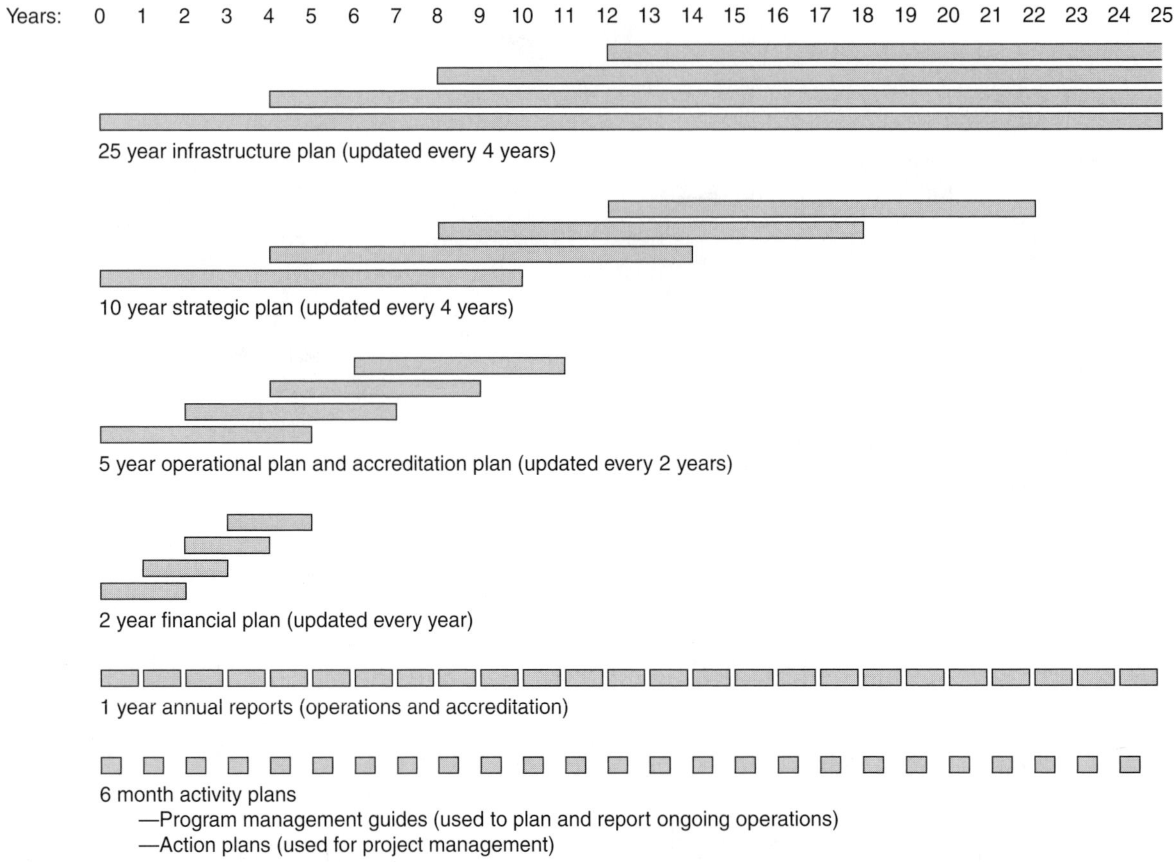

FIGURE 12.2.3 Fire Department Planning and Reporting Chart

Customer Focused Service Delivery

The performance management system quantifies how organizational efforts impact customers. When combined with professional judgment and technical expertise, it guides the organization towards performance success. The fire department's operational chart (see Figure 12.2.4) represents service delivery to the customers. In a circular model, the roles and responsibilities of each service area center around and focus on customers, both internal and external.

As shown in Figure 12.2.4, operational programs are grouped into service areas, which are grouped into divisions based on related roles in the fire department mission. All divisions have a senior manager in the leadership role. The senior managers work as a team, with the fire chief as the team leader, to develop policy and provide consistent cohesive leadership to the organization.

The operational chart is meant to capture the lateral interfaces between operational areas. This cross-functional cooperation is critical in cohesive consistent service delivery to the customers. In contrast, the traditional organizational chart as shown in Figure 12.2.1 captures interfaces vertically, aligned with the chain of command. White space exists between the divisions creating a type of silo effect. If service is delivered by following the traditional chart, a risk of critical components of service falling between the silos into the white space exists. We have all heard the expression of things falling through the cracks in an organization. Creating operational charts that manage lateral interfaces (the white space) minimizes that risk.

According to Rummler and Brache in *Improving Performance: How to Manage the White Space on the Organization Chart,*[4] "the greatest opportunities for performance improvement often lie in the functional interfaces—those points at which the baton is being passed from one department to another." With this in mind, the operational chart is the ideal framework for an integrated performance management system that maintains a focus on customers. Based on performance information, effective and efficient processes that create cross-functional responsibilities can be developed and maintained. In addition, operational managers will be able to respond quickly to customer needs identified in the performance evaluation process.

System Framework

In the transitional model shown in Figure 12.2.5, the operational chart is the starting point of a new performance management flowchart. Performance data must be captured at the point of service delivery. To integrate a performance management system, a linear flowchart was created to represent the transmission of performance data from the point of service delivery. In essence, the organizational chart was turned upside down to create a flow of information from the staff responsible for specific

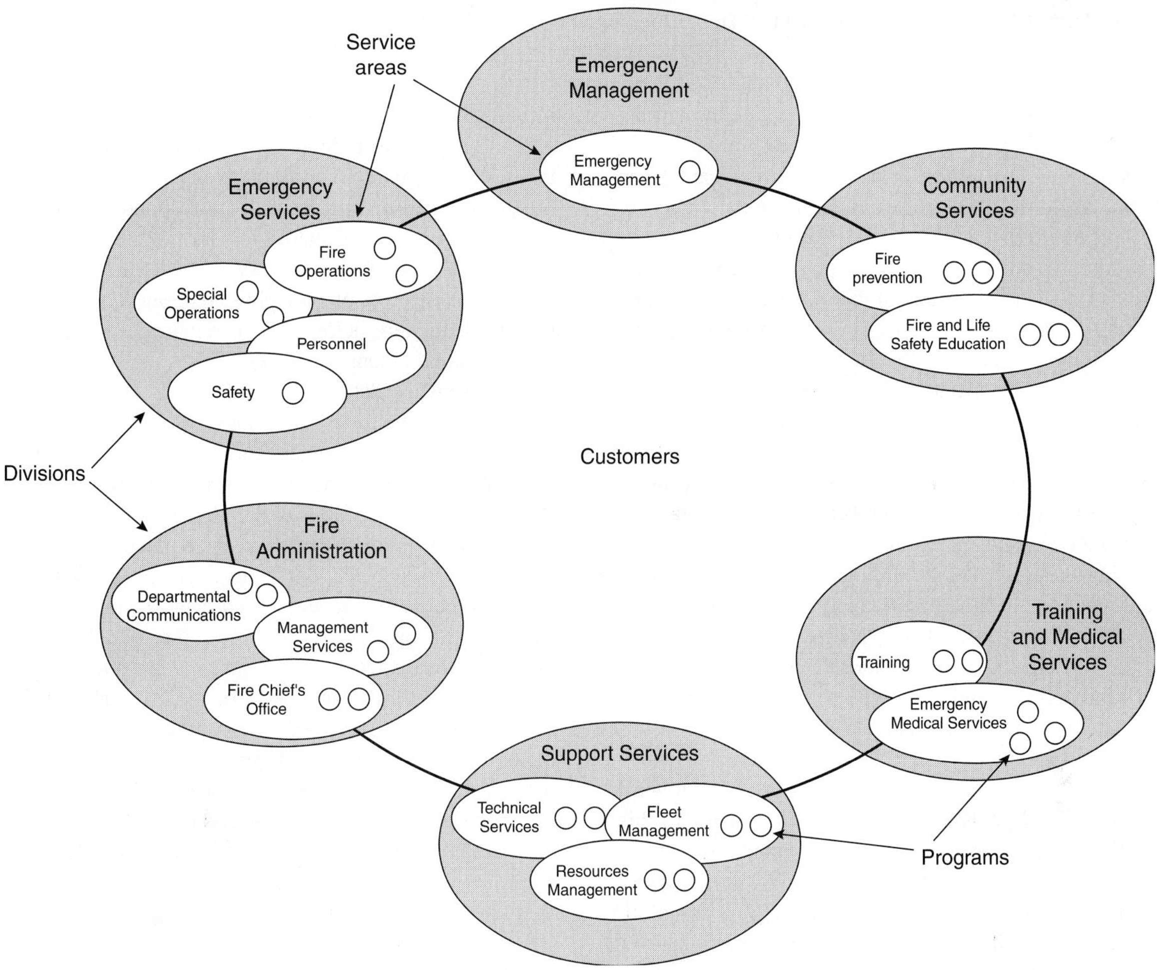
Service areas
Emergency Management
Emergency Management
Community Services
Fire prevention
Fire and Life Safety Education
Emergency Services
Fire Operations
Special Operations
Personnel
Safety
Divisions
Customers
Fire Administration
Departmental Communications
Management Services
Fire Chief's Office
Training and Medical Services
Training
Emergency Medical Services
Support Services
Technical Services
Fleet Management
Resources Management
Programs

FIGURE 12.2.4 Fire Department Operational Chart

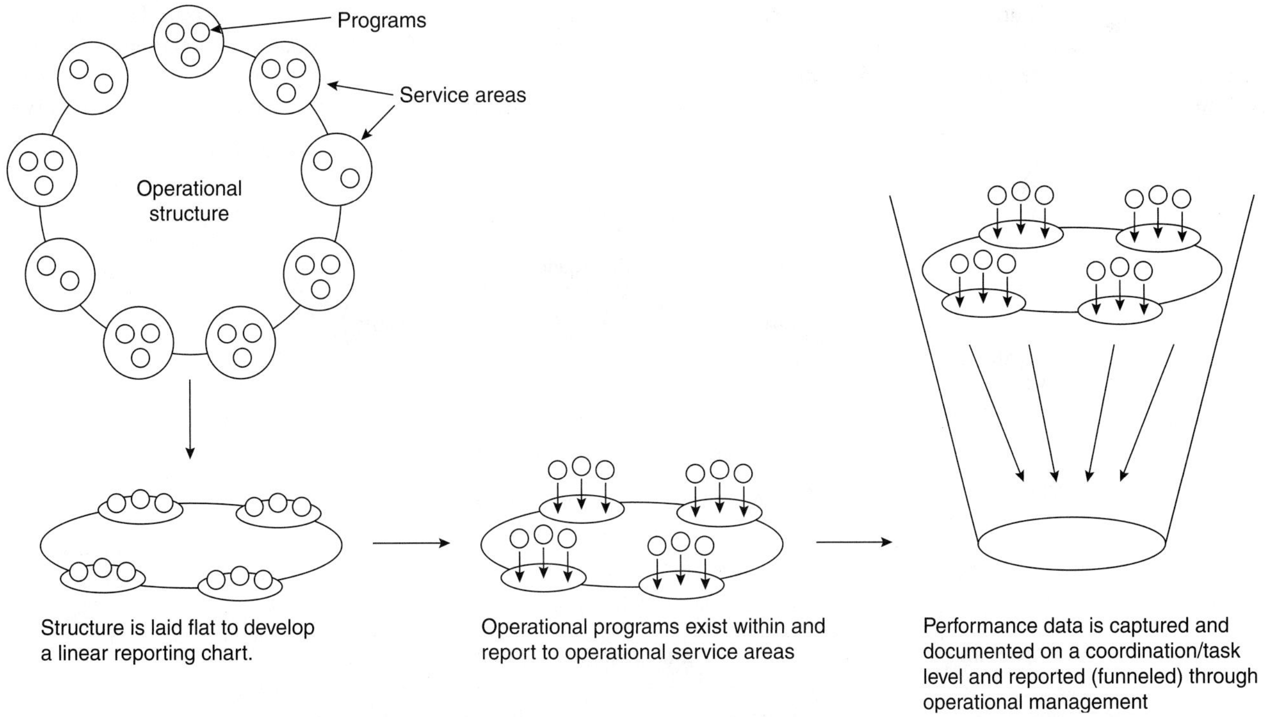
Programs
Service areas
Operational structure
Structure is laid flat to develop a linear reporting chart.
Operational programs exist within and report to operational service areas
Performance data is captured and documented on a coordination/task level and reported (funneled) through operational management

FIGURE 12.2.5 Transitional Model

services to those who manage the organization. The result is a flowchart that resembles the shape of a funnel.

In this model, a collection of individual facts can create a useful context for analysis. For example, a specific measure such as emergency response times may be placed in context with the number of calls for service or population as it flows through the system. In addition, numbers collected from various service areas may be aligned to determine relationships. For example, the number of traffic calming devices installed, media releases on pulling over for fire trucks, or the location of new housing developments may have a relationship with emergency response times. These individual facts might be captured by different service areas but they end up in the same flow of information within a system that compiles and funnels data to an operational and division/department level for analysis.

Following the flow of data through the system (funnel), operational managers are the first to analyze performance data and apply the results to operations. The process of analyzing data includes participation from the coordinators and those who accomplish the tasks related to service delivery. With a direct customer relationship, actions taken at this level will have an immediate effect on customer service.

At the operational service area level, progress toward achieving operational goals is evaluated. An advantage to this process is the ability to apply professional judgment and expertise in the first review of performance data. With the volume of data to be summarized, computer technology is essential. Computer programs will process data consistently in whatever manner they are designed to do. However, data entry is subject to human behavior, which is not quite as consistent.

Whether the technology used is a computer-aided dispatch system, incident reporting system, or spreadsheet software, it is subject to human error. An extra zero here, a dash there, or the push of a button a little differently each time, can skew performance reports. A good operational manager will be able to review data and know when something is just not quite right. Based on the goal of gaining customer confidence, it is very important for all data to be evaluated by those who manage daily operations prior to public release. At the very least, if there is unusual performance data for a given period of time, the operational manager will be prepared to respond to inquiries about the activity. Also, explanatory factors can be documented to accompany the data through the system.

The next level of data flow, moving through the system (down the funnel), is the division/department level. The leader for each area, a senior manager, is responsible to ensure that the performance data is reported appropriately. At this level, the data from individual programs is grouped into operational service areas and compiled to summarize collective progress toward achieving strategic goals. Specific program flowcharts, as shown in Figures 12.2.6 and 12.2.7, may be helpful to visualize the transmission of data through each division.

After the data is processed through the division/department level, it continues to a centralized database moving toward the small central base of the funnel. Figure 12.2.8 illustrates the flow of performance data through the department.

The most important aspect of the performance data flowchart is the evaluation process that occurs as data moves through the organization (down the funnel). By following this path and the associated processes, performance data is converted into performance *information.* Data such as individual facts about specific events, community statistics, and service delivery counts are collectively studied and benchmarked to create messages about how the organization is performing.

Centralized Database

When performance data reaches the centralized database, it has been converted from just numbers into information. Performance information is best centralized within the organization, with a designated custodian. The centralized database should be the sole source of all performance information used or published. One of the quickest ways to lose customer confidence is to publish conflicting information about service delivery. If

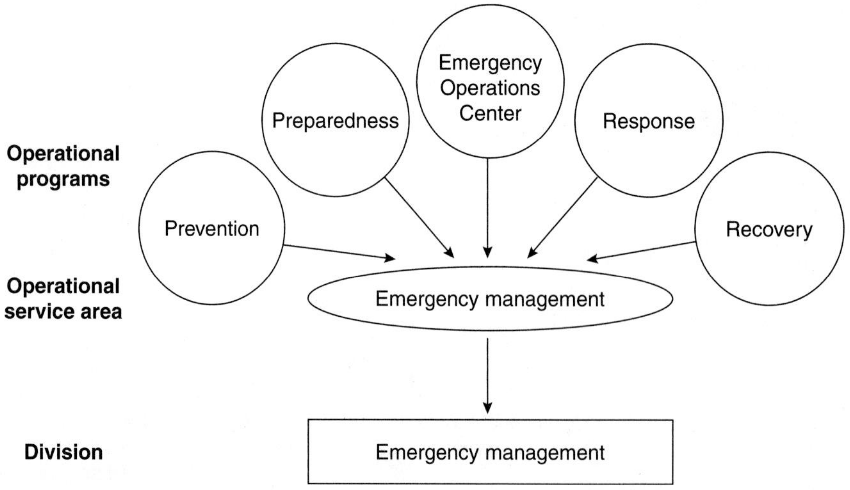

FIGURE 12.2.6 Flowchart for Emergency Management Programs

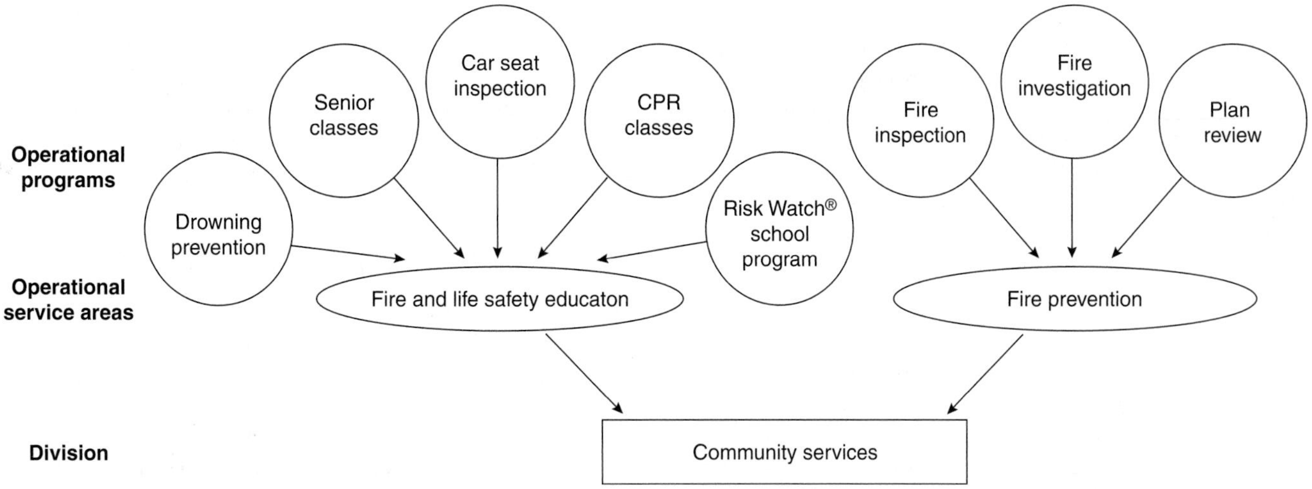

FIGURE 12.2.7 Flowchart for Community Services Programs

an existing system is not producing the information needed to manage operations, then the system should be changed. The alternative of creating multiple sources of information is not a viable option for success. A service measure as simple as the number of fire fighters on duty can vary. For example, one area may publish the people count and another area may publish the position count (to include vacancies). If an organization cannot publish consistent numbers about how many fire fighters are on duty, the credibility of more complex measures is compromised.

The ideal location for the centralized database within the organization varies. The decision depends on the staffing available and the organization's commitments to report performance. The key to successfully selecting the appropriate location is to match the custodianship with similar internal services. Planning and research, technical services, or management services

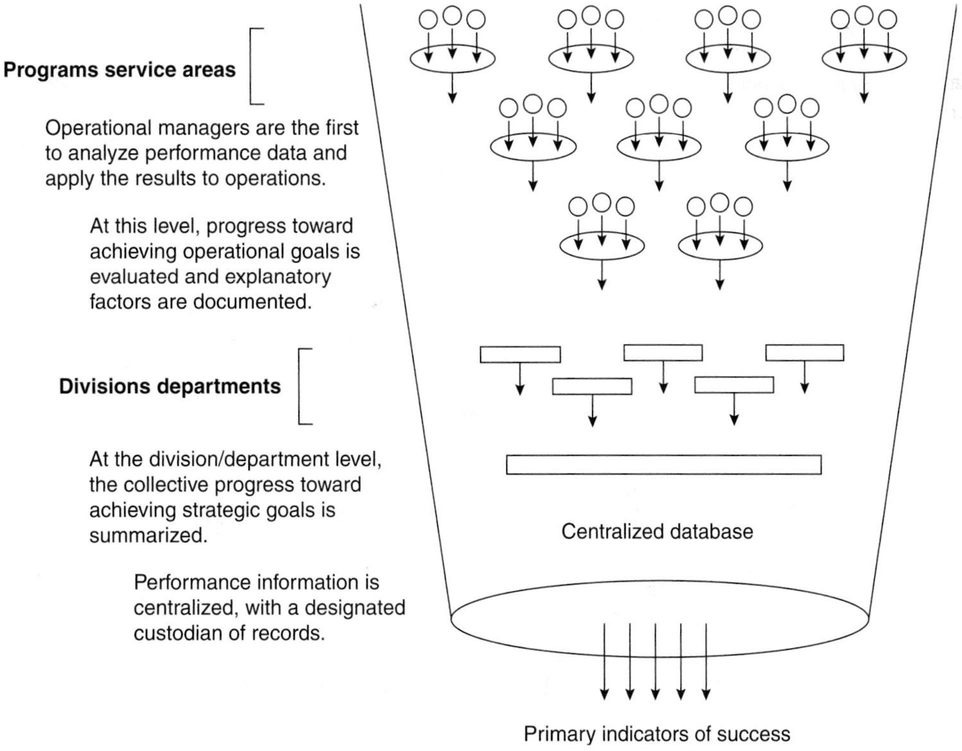

FIGURE 12.2.8 Fire Department Performance Management Flowchart

are excellent candidates. These areas may already coordinate department-wide, data-based programs, such as strategic planning, accreditation, and budget development. These internal service areas may also provide historical statistical information for process improvements and management reports. The opportunity to eliminate duplication of efforts and streamline processes resides in the selection of the centralized database location. This selection represents another step to integrating a new system.

Performance-Based Budget

Many local governments require budget documents to include performance measurements. Funding allocations are quantified to show the impact of service delivery to the community. (If operational programs are not fully funded, they will not be able to meet performance expectations). For government and community leaders, this adds value to their decision-making process. For publicly funded fire departments, accounting for resources becomes critical to maintaining funding for services. The process of budget adoption is open to the public and is participative, which provides an excellent forum for educating customers. In this environment, integrating the centralized performance database with fiscal management maximizes the opportunities to obtain resources and gain customer confidence.

Fiscal management typically resides in an administrative area, such as management services. Common fiscal management includes developing and monitoring the budget. When integrated with administrative information from multiple stakeholders and sources, such as policies, surveys, and planning documents, budget development becomes an inclusive participative process in which financial resource needs are applied to performance expectations (Figure 12.2.9). This process is commonly referred to as performance-based budgeting.

REPORTS AND REPORTING CYCLES

A standard report template streamlines the process of compiling, analyzing, and reporting data. An electronic format streamlines the transmission of data, as well as the ability to index and sort the data for multiple purposes. A fully integrated system connects service levels (outputs) with operational goals (targets), strategic goals (outcomes), and resources used (inputs). Using a report format, programs are set up by operational managers, who populate program descriptions, targets, and outcomes. The report is populated with outputs and inputs by selected criteria from other technological databases on a routine cycle.

Operational managers evaluate performance data in short-range cycles. A monthly cycle is optimal for reviewing service levels and resources used. This frequency coincides with the monthly reporting cycle of an accounting system, which allows the manager to monitor funding levels at the same time. Significant variances between the budget and expenditures are identified quickly. Remedial actions by operational managers keep

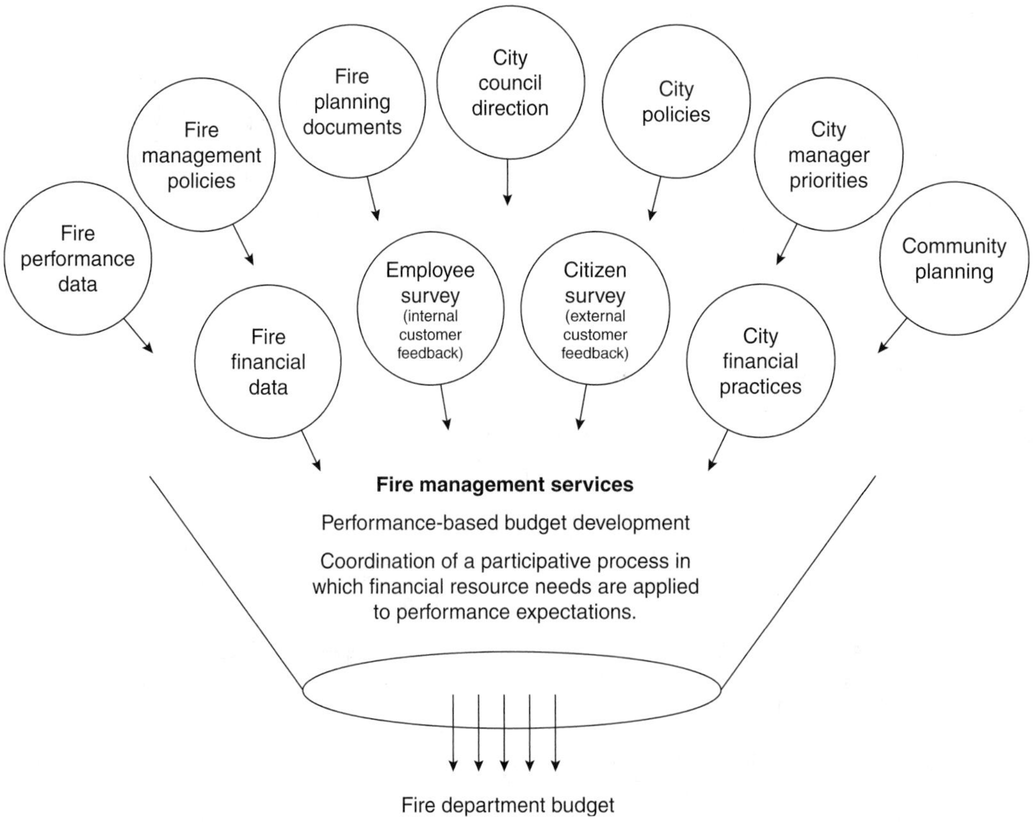

FIGURE 12.2.9 Performance-Based Budget Development

programs on track and funded, over the course of a fiscal year. A monthly cycle identifies service level trends in the early stages, as well. Operational managers are alerted to the possibility that resources may need to be realigned to meet shifts in service level demands. Early detection increases the organization's responsiveness to meet customer needs.

Senior managers evaluate performance data in longer-range cycles. A 6 month cycle is sufficient to support planning activities and budget development. For policy development, related performance data can be produced, as needed.

To integrate a new system, creating a standard report template and establishing the reporting frequencies are key steps. The sophistication of a fully integrated system may not be possible to obtain with initial implementation. In this case, the service levels (outputs), operational goals (targets), strategic goals (outcomes), and resources used (inputs) may have to be provided to operational managers on separate reports. As long as the data is linked, manually or through the use of technology, a thorough evaluation of organizational performance can be conducted.

The key elements of a performance report are summarized in Table 12.2.2 with three "*p*'s": program descriptors, performance information, and planning objectives. Included are proposed characteristics of each and a fictional program example.

MEASUREMENTS AND BENCHMARKS

Measurements and Benchmarks Defined

Measurements and benchmarks provide information. They are the mechanisms to quantify and qualify organizational performance. Using GASB definitions listed earlier in this chapter, measurements come in five major categories: inputs, outputs, outcomes, efficiency and effectiveness. The term *benchmark* has a dual meaning. In one context, it represents the standard to which we measure. In the other, it denotes the search for best practices. The common denominator of measurements and benchmarks is the provision of information about organizational performance.

Measurements linked to benchmarks create a context that increases the value of the information provided. In a numeric format, measurements quantify performance. Measurements linked to a benchmark qualify progress. The measurement is the count and the benchmark is the yardstick to which we measure the count.

The process of measuring organizational performance begins with a count (a number). The number of commercial buildings inspected is a count. The count may be stated as a percentage of a whole. The number of commercial buildings inspected as compared to the total number of commercial buildings in the community is a percentage of a whole. The number may be qualified to represent performance progress. The percent of commercial buildings inspected this year is *X* percent, compared to last year's *Y* percent. In this example, the performance benchmark is the prior year. The value of information increased when the numeric value of the measurement was linked to a benchmark to create a context.

The context of a measurement creates meaning to those who evaluate performance. As an evaluator of performance, we need more than just a number to convert data into information. As an example, a 7 digit number in itself doesn't provide information. If the 7 digit number is the odometer reading in our car, linked to a southern direction, it provides us with information about our driving progress. From our initial reading, we can calculate how far we have traveled and how much further we need to go to reach our destination. From our initial fuel level, we can calculate our miles per gallon and project the amount of fuel we will need to make it to the next gas station. Then we can benchmark our driving progress in many different ways.

Benchmarks vary and are based on the context that provides the most meaningful information to us. They may be based on technical standards, build on historical data, be comparables from like organizations, or be specific to organizational priorities. A benchmark can be the target itself.

Continuing with the example used for measurement context, we drove 600 miles today. To measure our progress, we can compare our measurement to several different benchmarks. We can compare our mileage to a technical standard. For example, our car insurance company has studied safe driving and recommends an average of 500 miles a day. We can compare it to yesterday. We drove 500 miles yesterday and set a goal of driving 500 more miles today. We can compare it to other drivers traveling the same highways. They drive an average of 700 miles per day. We can compare it to our destination. We are halfway to our destination. We can simply plan our trip based on our resources and our priorities at driving 600 miles each day.

An important note about the driving example is that the unit of measure created more opportunities to benchmark. Had we measured our progress in kilometers, it would have been difficult and time consuming to compare with external benchmarks that use miles as the norm. Due to service norms, sometimes the benchmark is selected prior to the units of measure to ensure comparability with external agencies.

Benchmarks as Best Practices

Not all things counted are measurements of performance. Many fire service professionals propose that a count such as fire fighters per capita represents a service norm as opposed to a performance measure. As discussed in *Municipal Benchmarks: Assessing Local Performance and Establishing Community Standards*[6] by David N. Ammons, "national or regional norms . . . can tell officials whether local practices and characteristics lie within or outside normal bounds, but they do not address performance."

Not all things benchmarked are measurements of performance. The term *benchmark* is also used to denote best practices. In *Managing Fire and Rescue Services,*[7] David T. Endicott examines benchmarking as a process of searching for and identifying best practices. The process involves comparing similar services provided by outside agencies in an effort to discover new and innovative practices that lead to improved performance.

Most fire departments benchmark to other fire departments. For those in major metropolitan areas, specific attention is given to neighboring communities with shared borders. This process

TABLE 12.2.2 Key Elements of a Performance Report

Key Element	*Characteristics*	*Example*
Program Descriptors		
Program title	Concise and recognizable	Emergency response
Program scope	Short description of services provided	Rapid response to emergencies dispatched through the 9-1-1 system
Program customers	Group(s) of people to whom services are provided (may be internal or external to the organization)	Residents, businesses, and visitors to the community
Program manager	Primary manager of services provided (operational level)	Deputy chief of fire operations
Strategic goal	Supports mission and directly linked to planning documents	To protect life and preserve property within the community
Operational goal	Supports strategic goal and directly linked to planning documents	Response time of 4 minutes or less, 90 percent of the time
Performance Information		
Reporting period	Date-bound reporting cycle	July 2007–December 2007
Service levels	Measurement of service provided during the reporting period, in the same units of measure as the operational goal	• Average response time: 3 minutes, 52 seconds • Response time within 4 minutes: 69 percent
Service efforts	Measurement of resources used to provide services during the reporting period, stated in format that is meaningful to the organization (may be hours, dollars, percentage of dollars, etc.)	• Regular time staffing budget: 49 percent expended, 50 percent through the fiscal year • Overtime staffing budget: 40 percent expended, 50 percent through the fiscal year
Explanatory factors	Significant factors that affected service delivery during the reporting period	Due to freeway expansion, 20 percent of major traffic corridors in the northeast section of the community have detours, causing emergency response units to use alternate routes
Major objectives	Major activity planned during the reporting period, to support operational goal; may be more than one	• Work with the transportation department to develop an electronic notification system for road construction schedules • Implement by November 30, 2007
Major accomplishments	Result of the major objective planned; may be in progress or completed; may be more than one.	New system implemented on September 18, 2007. Initial results of new system: • 100 percent of emergency response crews were notified, a minimum of 7 days prior to road construction via an e-mail distribution list. • 80 percent of crews reported the process is having a positive effect on their ability to identify the quickest route to an emergency.
Planning Objectives		
Major objectives	Major activity planned during the next reporting period to support operational goal; may be more than one	Research and recommend a digital display monitor for dispatch at multicompany stations by February 8, 2008
Projected outcome	If accomplished, how this activity will support the operational goal	The ability for emergency response crews to see the unit dispatched is projected to have a positive effect on turnout time (a component of overall response time to emergencies).

provides a wealth of useful information. At the same time, great care must be taken when selecting benchmark communities.

Prince William County, Virginia, has performed a process called Service, Efforts, and Accomplishments that selects similar municipal agencies to compare like measurements. They have run into some challenges with truly "like measures." Even though the comparison is made to other combination departments, there are organizational and cultural differences that sometimes equate to comparing apples to oranges or at best to a different type of apple.

Variables in the demographics and service dimensions of every community and region have the potential to skew measurements. An example is found in the measurement of fire fighters per capita. The variable is the scheduled workweek for fire fighters. In some regions of the United States, it is 40 hours per week. In others, it is 56 hours per week. In two communities with different workweeks, the numbers of fire fighters on duty may be the same each day but the number of fire fighters employed to fill the on-duty assignments may be significantly different. In turn, the number of fire fighters employed can skew the measurement of fire fighters per capita. Identifying these types of variables when compiling a profile of benchmark communities will increase the value of comparisons. If a true apples-to-apples comparison cannot be obtained, at least the variables that affect the measurement can be noted and considered in the evaluation process.

The decision about how to use benchmarking goes back to the practice that best matches the philosophy, culture, and mission of the organization. There is an abundance of things to measure and benchmark in a fire department. The key to providing information and not just numbers lies in the selection of what to count and which yardstick to use to create a context that has meaning.

Meaningful Measures

An example of an evaluation process to select meaningful measures is found in Figures 12.2.10 through 12.2.13. Developed by the Ontario Fire Marshal's Office as part of its "Performance Measurement and Benchmarking Project," they provide an evaluation tool to help municipalities measure all the components of community fire protection planning. (The full model is a product of work that is available by contacting the Ontario Fire Marshal's Office.)

In addition to reviewing the Ontario model, the following list of data categories may be useful in the selection of meaningful measures (many were derived from measurements used by Prince William County, Virginia, and Scottsdale, Arizona, and they appear in no particular order of importance):

Emergency Services

- Number of calls for emergency services, total and by type
  - Fire
  - Medical
  - Hazmat
  - Technical rescue
  - Aircraft rescue and fire fighting
  - Other
- Number of units dispatched, total and by type
- Response times to emergency calls, actual and average
  - Percent of responses made in under X minutes
  - Dispatch time
  - Turnout time
  - Travel time
- EMS transports (patients transported)
- EMS quality assurance review results
- AED use, deployment statistics, and usage rates
- Training hours, total and average per member, by type
- Members certified to minimum standards of services provided, by type
  - ALS (paramedic)
  - BLS (EMT)
  - Special operations
- Training participation
  - Promotional processes rates
  - Succession planning rates
  - Recruit retention rates
- Health and wellness participation
  - Exposure rates
  - Fitness rates
  - Health screening participation rates
  - SCBA fit test rates
  - Workers compensation claims, hours lost to injuries

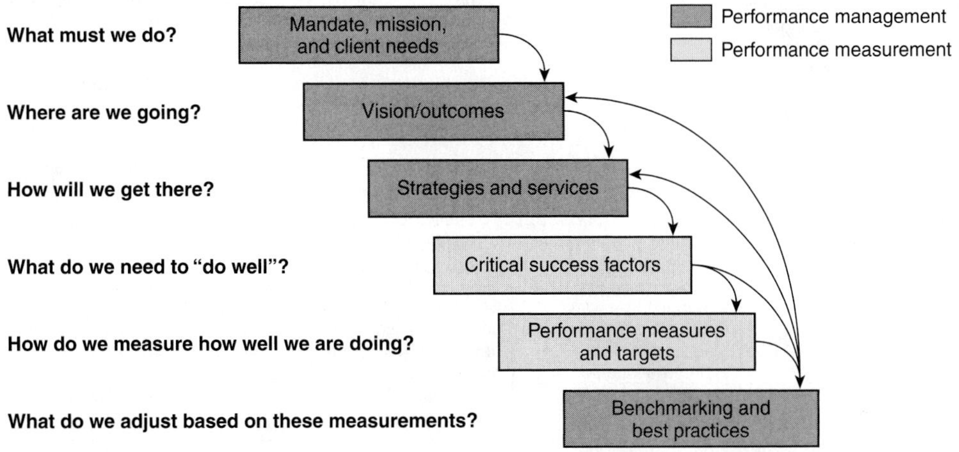

FIGURE 12.2.10 Performance Management Framework (Source: "Ontario Fire Service Performance Measurement and Benchmarking Partnership Project," Office of the Fire Marshal, Province of Ontario, Canada)

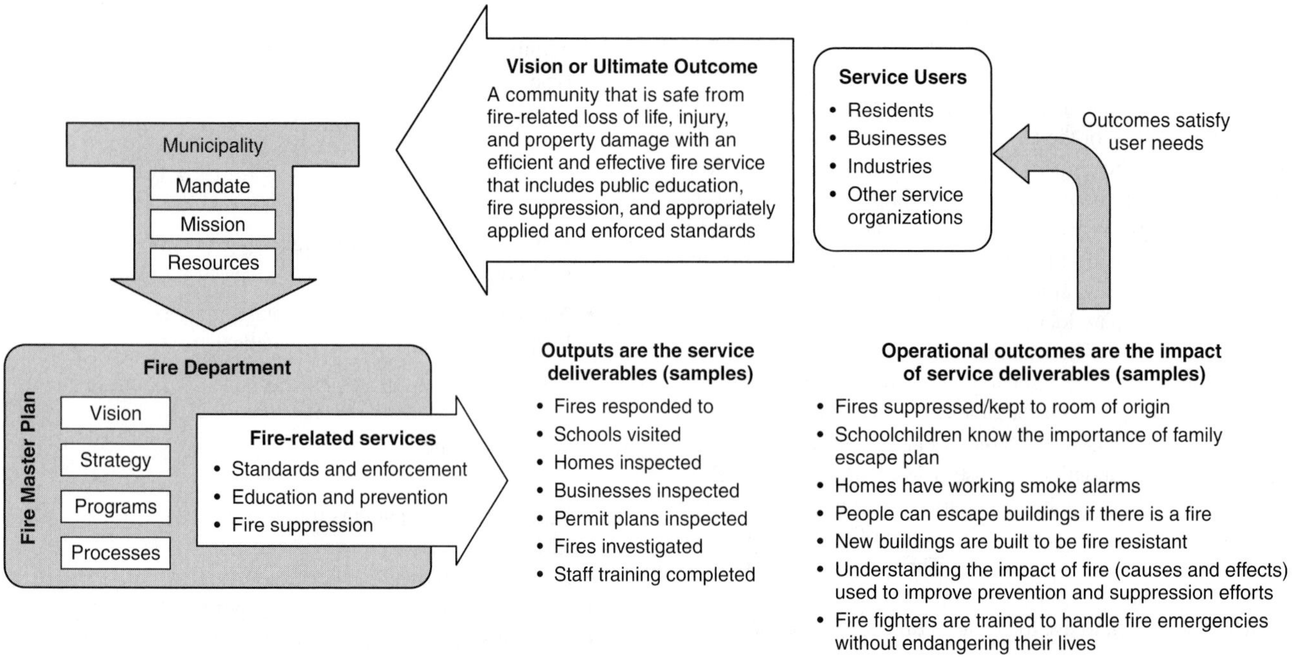

FIGURE 12.2.11 Fire Services Delivery Model (Source: "Ontario Fire Service Performance Measurement and Benchmarking Partnership Project," Office of the Fire Marshal, Province of Ontario, Canada)

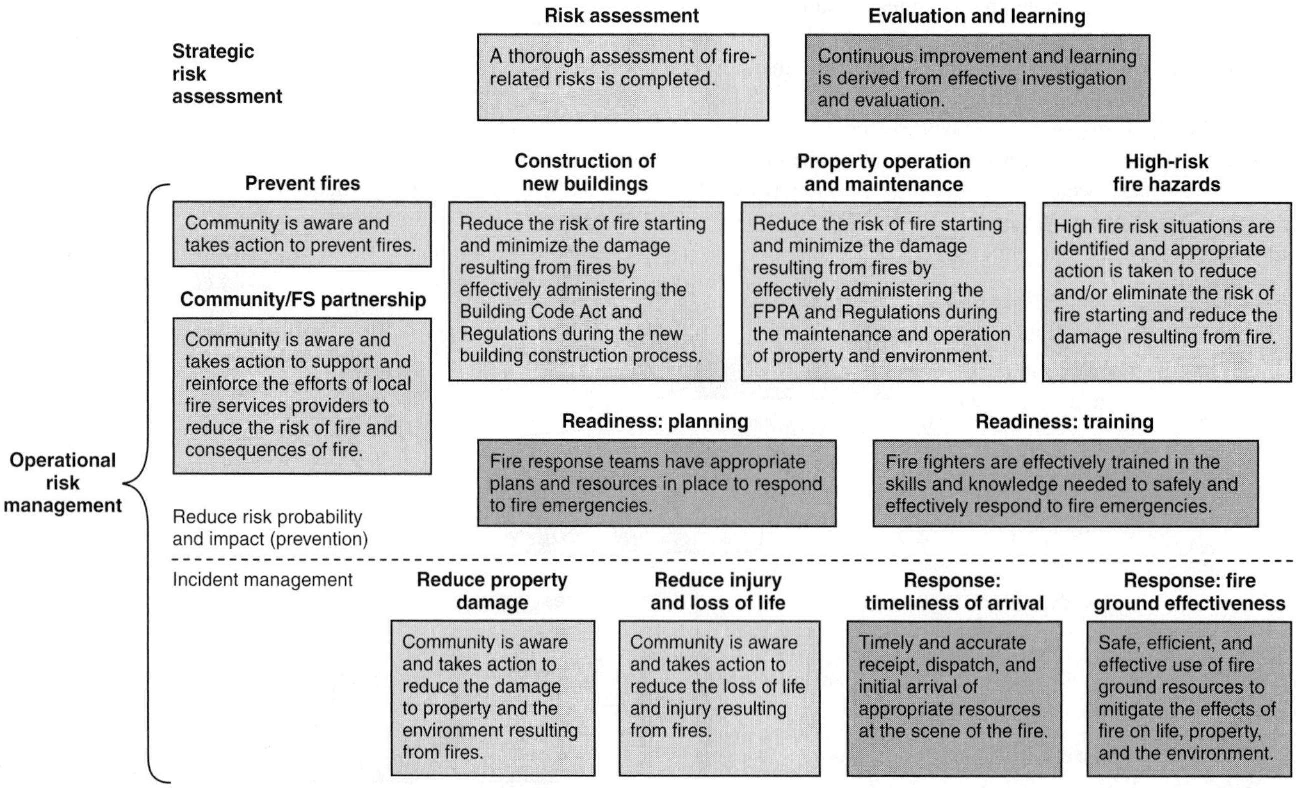

FIGURE 12.2.12 Fire Protection Outcomes (Source: "Ontario Fire Service Performance Measurement and Benchmarking Partnership Project," Office of the Fire Marshal, Province of Ontario, Canada)

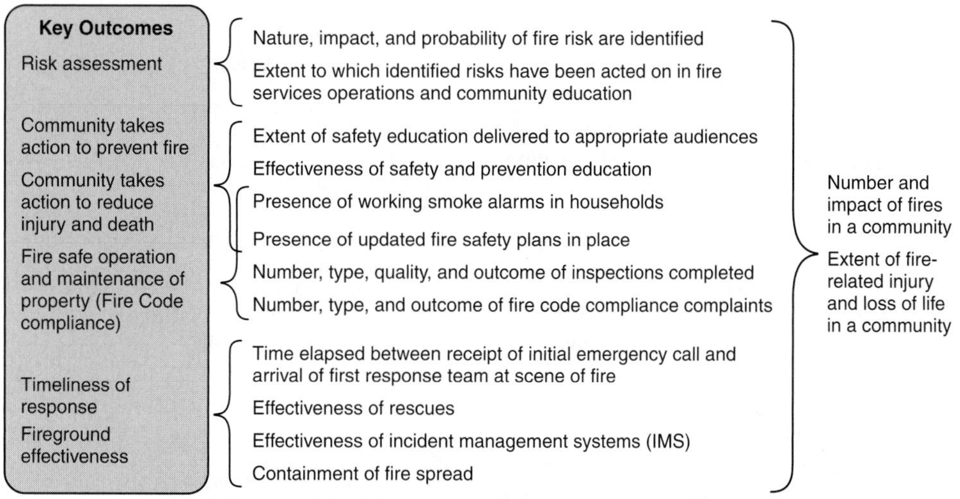

FIGURE 12.2.13 Key Performance Indicators (Source: "Ontario Fire Service Performance Measurement and Benchmarking Partnership Project," Office of the Fire Marshal, Province of Ontario, Canada)

Fire Prevention

- Inspections, numbers conducted, and turnaround time
- Number of occupancies in the community, by type
- Structure fires of the various occupancies
  - Fires contained to room of origin, unit of origin, building of origin
  - Fires contained to the level of involvement on arrival of first fire unit
- Number of false alarms
- Fire loss
- Civilian injury and death rates
- Fire investigations, number conducted
  - Cause and origin determination rates
  - Arson rates, conviction rates
- Plans reviewed, number conducted
  - Customer turnaround time
  - First review approval rates
- Complaints investigated
- Community access rates, use of technology
- Built-in protection
  - Number of residents with smoke detectors
  - Number of residents with fire sprinkler systems

Fire and Life Safety Education

- School programs, by grade level: class hours and students contacted
- Community events, participation rates, by type
  - Car seat inspections
  - Senior events
  - CPR classes
  - Drowning prevention
- Educational literature distributed, by type

Administrative and Support Services

- Citizen satisfaction survey results, by service provided
- Employee satisfaction survey results
- Employee turnover rates
- Emergency operations center (EOC) activations and drills, participation rates
- Community emergency response team (CERT) volunteers, participation rates
- Media releases provided
- Public service announcements produced
- Lawsuits filed
- Vehicle accident rates
- Number of intersections with traffic pre-emption devices
- Mapping update and distribution rates
- Incident records, processing and turnaround times
- Apparatus statistics: in service, by type; out of service, by cause
- Equipment inventory rates: out of service, by cause; lost, by type
- Personal protective equipment statistics
- Supply inventory and usage statistics

Service Dimensions

- Population
- Service area, square miles served
- Total fire department personnel, number of civilians in department, and number of sworn personnel
- Total fire department operating budget by expenditure type, dollars, and labor hours
- Total fire department capital improvement budget, by project
- Number of fire stations
- Number of on-duty personnel, per day
- Per unit staffing, minimum staffing criteria

SUMMARY

A systems approach to organizational benchmarking and performance evaluation captures the key information necessary to communicate performance expectations and success. Effective communication combined with member participation leads to organizational acceptance and accountability for performance results. An environment of universal accountability fosters process improvements and the efficient use of resources. When resources are linked to service delivery, value is added to decision-making processes and customer confidence increases.

An organization with an integrated performance management system has the ability to capture and convert data into information. Data captured on an operational level, when combined with professional judgment and expertise and centralized, provides accurate information. Performance information that is customer focused and has a direct relationship to operational and strategic goals is meaningful. Accurate and meaningful information about an organization's performance leads to excellence in service delivery for customers.

BIBLIOGRAPHY

References Cited

1. Compton, D., *When in Doubt, Lead!,* Oklahoma State University, Fire Protection Publications, Stillwater, OK, Jan. 1999, pp. 9–14.
2. *Reporting Performance Information: Suggested Criteria for Effective Communication,* Governmental Accounting Standards Board, Norwalk, CT, Aug. 2003, pp. 185–189.
3. City of Mesa (Arizona) Fire Department Organizational Charts, Feb. 2006.
4. Rummler, G. A., and Brache, A. P., *Improving Performance: How to Manage the White Space on the Organization Chart,* Jossey-Bass, San Francisco, 1995.
5. *Performance Measurement at the State and Local Levels: A Summary of Survey Results,* Governmental Accounting Standards Board, Norwalk, CT, Nov. 2002.
6. Ammons, D. N., *Municipal Benchmarks: Assessing Local Performance and Establishing Community Standards,* Sage Publications, Thousand Oaks, CA, 2001, pp. 147–149.
7. Endicott, D. T., "Performance Measurement and Organizational Improvement," *Managing Fire and Rescue Services,* International City/County Management Association, Washington, DC, 2002, pp. 310–320.

NFPA Codes, Standards, and Recommended Practices

Reference to the following NFPA codes, standards, and recommended practices will provide further information on organizational benchmarking and performance evaluation discussed in this chapter. (See the latest version of The NFPA Catalog *for availability of current editions of the following documents.)*

NFPA 901, *Standard Classifications for Incident Reporting and Fire Protection Data*

NFPA 1710, *Standard for the Organization and Deployment of Fire Suppression Operations, Emergency Medical Operations, and Special Operations to the Public by Career Fire Departments*

NFPA 1720, *Standard for the Organization and Deployment of Fire Suppression Operations, Emergency Medical Operations, and Special Operations to the Public by Volunteer Fire Departments*

Chapter 3

Needs Assessment and Hazard Analysis

William F. Jenaway

Fire officials, fire departments, and emergency service organizations often do not perform an adequate needs assessment and hazard analysis in their area for use in their planning processes. A needs assessment and hazard analysis is fundamental to determining necessary resources to operate a department and ensure performance of its assigned functions. Knowing what resources a department or organization will need can only be determined by understanding the hazards it faces. However, time, funding, and other priorities continually prevent fire officials from effectively analyzing needs and incorporating appropriate resources into organizational operations.

The purpose of this chapter is to demonstrate the interrelationship of numerous routine or special activities that can be conducted as components of a comprehensive needs assessment and hazard analysis—that is, the identification of the challenges faced and the resources needed to manage these challenges.

For related information see the following chapters in Section 12: Chapter 1, "Planning for Public Fire-Rescue Protection"; Chapter 2, "Organizational Benchmarking and Performance Evaluation"; Chapter 12, "Disaster Planning and Response Services"; Chapter 17, "Pre-Incident Planning for Industrial and Municipal Emergency Response"; Chapter 18, " Pre-Incident Planning for Emergency Response"; and Chapter 19, "Community Risk Reduction."

Chapter Contents

Key Terms

accreditation, community risk assessment, emergency planning, hazard analysis, hazard assessment, Insurance Services Office (ISO), master plan, needs assessment, risk assessment, standard of response cover, strategic plan, water supply

OVERVIEW OF ASSESSMENT COMPONENTS AND RESOURCES

Components of the Assessment Process

Any process to assess needs and analyze hazards must utilize a fundamental decision-making process. There are several such models; however, regardless of the one chosen, the basic components of the process remain the same and include the following:

- Developing the analytical data
- Evaluating the data developed
- Deciding on the data to use or course of action to take
- Implementing the chosen data
- Monitoring and modifying the information implemented

This decision-making process will assist decision makers in understanding what hazards exist, what actions are needed to manage those hazards, and how to fulfill the identified needs. The decision-making activity becomes a path to matching hazards and needs. For reference in this decision-making process, see related chapters in Section 12 for additional information.

William F. Jenaway, Ph.D., CFP, CFPS, SFPE, MIFE, was named Volunteer Fire Chief of the Year by *Fire Chief* magazine and IAFC in 2001. He is employed by VFIS, a division of the Glatfelter Insurance Group, and has spent over 25 years as an insurance field engineer, investigator, and vice-president in fire protection and safety.

Needs Assessment Study

A cooperative study, authorized by U.S. Public Law 106-398, required that the director of the Federal Emergency Management Agency (FEMA) conduct a national study in conjunction with the National Fire Protection Association (NFPA) to accomplish the following:

- Define the current role and activities associated with the fire service
- Determine the adequacy of the current levels of funding
- Provide a needs assessment to identify shortfalls[1]

Evaluation Areas of Study. This initiative focused on six areas. The details of the findings of the report appear throughout this chapter; however, it is important to understand what the study evaluated and its related limitations in overall needs assessment and hazard analysis. The study evaluation areas included the following:

- Services provided
- Personnel and their capabilities
- Fire prevention and code enforcement
- Facilities, apparatus, and equipment
- Communications and communication equipment
- Ability to handle unusually challenging incidents
- New and emerging technology

Although these are all valid considerations, before needs can be defined, the expectations of the public, an understanding of the risks posed within the community, and the expectations of everyone receiving and providing the service must be identified.

Resource Categories. To properly determine how the fire department will do its job, a needs assessment and a hazard analysis are integral to the process. For example, the needs assessment study completed as a result of U.S. Public Law 106-398 identifies several categories of resources, including the following:

- Fire-fighting personnel
- Training for fire-fighting personnel
- Rapid intervention teams
- Certification for fire inspectors
- Wellness and fitness programs for fire-fighting personnel
- Emergency medical service programs provided by fire departments
- Fire-fighting vehicles
- Fire-fighting equipment, including communications and monitoring
- Personal protective equipment for fire-fighting personnel
- Modifications to stations and facilities for reasons of fire fighter health and safety
- Enforcement of fire codes
- Fire prevention programs
- Education of the public about arson prevention and detection
- Recruitment and retention initiatives for volunteer fire fighters in fire departments.[1]

Although these resources were quantified to better understand the magnitude and nature of fire department needs, it must be recognized that specific needs will be driven locally and based significantly on the local hazards faced, without going below the minimum requirements defined in the standards. The study provides insight into key areas of concern at issue nationwide, but its applicability in a specific community is determined by what that community has completed in terms of coordinating hazard analysis with needs assessment.

Study Findings. The FEMA/NFPA study provided findings in the areas of revenues and budget; personnel; fire prevention and code enforcement; facilities, apparatus, and equipment; communications and communications equipment; ability to handle unusually challenging incidents; and new and emerging technology. In the updated needs assessment study of the U.S. fire service created by the U.S. Department of Homeland Security/ U.S. Fire Administration and the National Fire Protection Association four years later,[2] the following were noted:

- Taxes provide at least three-fifths of the revenue for all-volunteer or mostly volunteer fire departments in the United States. Taxes plus other government payments, including per-call reimbursements, raise the total percent of revenue coming from government to at least three-fourths (77%). Fund raising provides at most 19 percent, which is the fund-raising share for rural communities of less than 2500 population.
- Converted vehicles account for 14 percent of apparatus used in communities under 2500 population and 10 percent of apparatus in communities of 2500 to 4999 population.
- Many fire departments fail to deliver a first-arriving complement of at least 4 fire fighters to a structure fire, the minimum complement needed to safely initiate an interior attack.
- An estimated 53 percent of departments are involved in structural fire fighting but have not formally trained all involved fire fighters in those duties. The corresponding percentage is 36 percent for emergency medical services, 36 percent for hazardous material response, 63 percent for wildland fire fighting, and 50 percent for technical rescue. Except for technical rescue, the percentages of departments needing more training are always higher for rural communities (less than 2500 population), in which nearly all departments are all-volunteer.
- One-quarter of the population are protected by fire departments that do not provide plan review and nearly half are protected by fire departments that do not provide permit approval or routine testing of fire protection systems. An estimated 7 percent of the population live in communities where no one conducts fire code inspections, and two-fifths of this unprotected population live in rural communities.
- Similarly, one-third of the population live in communities where there is no fire department program for free distribution of home smoke alarms, and two-fifths of the population are protected by fire departments with no juvenile firesetter program.
- An estimated 36 percent of fire stations are at least 40 years old, 54 percent do not have backup power systems, and 72 percent are not equipped for exhaust emission control.
- Half (49%) of all fire apparatus are at least 15 years old.
- An estimated 65 percent of fire departments do not have enough portable radios to equip all emergency responders on a shift. An estimated 60 percent do not have enough self-contained breathing apparatus (SCBA) and an estimated 48 percent do not

have enough personal alert safety system (PASS) devices to equip all emergency responders on a shift. An estimated 8 percent do not have enough personal protective clothing to equip all fire fighters, most of them being departments in rural communities.

- About three-fourths of departments say they cannot communicate with all their federal, state, and local partners at incident scenes, and one-fourth to one-third say they cannot communicate with any of their partners. Roughly half of all departments have no map coordinate system, and almost none use the U.S. National Grid System, which has been adopted by the Federal Geographic Committee as the system best suited for eventual national standardization.
- Written agreements to direct use of nonlocal resources are lacking for 74 percent of departments with regard to technical rescue and EMS at a defined structural collapse and 70 percent of departments with regard to hazmat and EMS at a defined chemical/biological agent incident. Written agreements are also lacking for major floods and wildland/urban interface fires. On the positive side, the percentage of departments with written agreements increased between the 2001 and 2005 needs assessments.
- Finally, the majority of departments (55%) now have thermal imaging cameras, up from only 24 percent in the 2001 survey.

Each of these situations identified by the needs assessment study pinpoints a fire department need that poses a challenge to be resolved before the hazards identified can be managed.

Terms Defined

In this text the terms *hazard, risk, needs assessment,* and *hazard analysis* are defined as follows:

Hazard: Level of harm associated with exposure to a fire or its effluent.

Risk: Expected loss from a fire of a given severity.

Needs Assessment: An analysis to determine the shortfall between expected performance and current performance.

Hazard Analysis: An analysis to determine the potential impact of a fire scenario when the hazard is involved in fire.

GENERAL PLANS

Over the years a variety of planning processes have been developed and introduced to the fire community. Each process establishes and accomplishes different objectives. The following section defines the processes involved with strategic plans, master plans, community risk assessments, pre-emergency planning, and disaster plans, and discusses what to expect from each of these processes when they are completed.

Strategic Plan

The strategic planning process serves as a single point of collection to coordinate various data points, administrative processes, and planning considerations. This integration of benchmark performance, budgetary commitments, mission statements, emergency service organization activities assessment, and so on serves the management team with a summary report of the efficiency and effectiveness of the organization.

Purpose of Strategic Focus. *Strategic planning* or *strategic focus* has been described as a set of concepts, procedures, and tools designed to assist leaders and managers in exercising control, coping with change, and developing a basis for decision making.[3] The strategic focus process can help answer such questions as these:

- What are the fire department's objectives for the next five years?
- Where will the organization be in seven years?
- What are the fire department's capital purchasing plans for the next ten years?
- What is the fire department's standard of response cover?

In recent years there have been several approaches to performance enhancement in both profit and nonprofit organizations. The terminology may vary; however, as long as managers are driving the organization to future decision and action to ensure organizational success, they are strategically focused and participating in strategic planning.

Strategic Focus Model. Creating and implementing a strategic focus helps the organization understand its resources, capabilities, and needs. In order to develop such a plan successfully, an appropriate planning model is necessary. To enable resources to meet expectations, the strategic focus model (Figure 12.3.1) employs three essential concepts:

- Organization resource assessment
- Defined service expectation
- Priority planning

With these concepts incorporated into the strategic plan, a basic decision and action process is created that helps structure the emergency service organization and spells out what it does and why it does it. In essence the process defines the future of the emergency service organization.

Basic Activities. The following are five basic activities identified in the strategic focus model:

1. Identifying, developing, creating, and analyzing key issues:
    - Mission and vision
    - Standard of response cover
    - Roles and responsibilities
    - Goals and objectives
    - SWOT (strengths, weaknesses opportunities, and threats)
    - Strategic alliances
2. Obtaining direction from key sources of input:
    - Organizational members
    - Community leaders
    - The citizenry
    - The business community
    - Mutual aid agencies

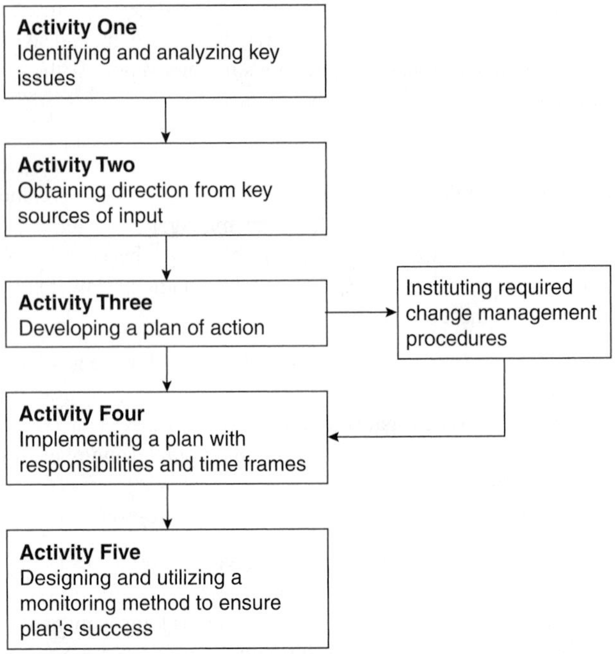

FIGURE 12.3.1 Strategic Focus Model

3. Developing a plan for implementation over a defined time period:
   - Immediate action steps to achieve goals and objectives
   - Long-term plan for implementation
4. Implementing a plan with responsibilities and time frames involving:
   - Finance
   - Personnel
   - Apparatus
   - Equipment
   - Facilities
   - Processes and procedures
5. Designing and utilizing a monitoring method to ensure plan success

Change Management Practices. Identifying and acting on the issues previously described can increase the efficiency of the emergency service organization and can help to plan for future contingencies. The result of any strategic focus initiative is change. Therefore, any such process must be undertaken by an organization that is ready for change. If the organization is not ready for change, then conflict can and will exist. As a result, change management practices must be identified and catalogued for reference as the planning process moves forward.

Identifying and prioritizing the initiatives critical to an organization's performance ensures long-term health and growth of the emergency service organization. The output from this process establishes coordinated goals, objectives, and, in some cases, action steps dealing with the following aspects of the organization:

- Finances
- Personnel
- Facilities
- Apparatus
- Equipment
- Procedures/processes

These are consolidated into planning documents, including identified costs, time frames for completion, and responsibilities for completion. The process then identifies different sets of objectives for organizational action.

In conclusion, although we may want it to be "the same old fire service as the glory years of the 60s," it isn't. Today, emergency service organizations are complex and dynamic and they must identify what they are doing, why they are doing it, and incorporate mechanisms for change if current initiatives are ineffective or problematic. The strategic focus process helps an organization develop the vision of where it wants/needs to be and how to get there.

A strategic plan establishes a "vision" and deals with more than just fire protection. To give an analogy, a strategic plan is a road map, whereas a master plan provides details on the streets, buildings, and related details encountered along the way.

Master Plan

Over the years, the term "master plan" has had several definitions and applications. In fact, some may say it is the same as a need assessment and hazard analysis. A master plan may be best characterized as a plan that helps to zero in on priorities and levels of service provided in specific operational areas. The master plan can assist in addressing adequacy and performance and align specific divisional needs with organizational expectations and the strategic plan.[4] Therefore, its development can serve as a component of comprehensive needs assessment and hazard analysis.

As noted above, a master plan differs from a strategic plan in that a master plan typically determines how much risk a community is willing to assume specifically relating to fire protection.

Community Risk Assessment

Community risk assessment, a fundamental assessment and planning process to assist in defining goals, is used to identify the community's fire protection and other emergency service needs in order to determine potential goals and objectives. Emergency service organizations must expand their use of this planning process to ensure they can meet future demands. All agencies should have a basic source of data and information in order to logically and rationally define the organization's mission. The end result of the process is to establish a long-range general strategy for the operation of the system. Emergency service organizations can achieve this goal by taking the following steps:

1. Documenting area characteristics by collecting historical data and instituting a process by which hazards are de-

fined and potential organizational goals and objectives are established.

2. Assessing the nature and magnitude of the hazards within its jurisdiction by categorizing and listing significant events to allow for future analysis and study in determining standards of coverage and related services.
3. Assessing the nature and magnitude of other hazards and risks within its jurisdiction and identifying appropriate strategies, methods of operation, and resource allocation required to mitigate potential emergencies.
4. Creating a "strategic" or other form of long-term (typically three to five years into the future) planning process that, along with a budget, guides the activities of the organization.
5. Submitting the plan to the appropriate authority having jurisdiction for review and implementation.

The coordination of these actions results in a plan to manage a community's emergency response. This plan, based on facts, will help the community better understand the emergency service organization's goals and help the organization to work toward these goals.

Pre-Emergency Planning

As personnel within the department gain particular information about a risk, they should categorize and develop this information into a database for use when needed and for training—both of which serve the function of hazard analysis and need assessment.

Figure 12.3.2 illustrates how the pre-emergency planning process works, but if data is not documented, communicated (in training and in routine communication), used to access appropriate resources, and formatted to be accessible when needed, the value in its relationship to hazard analysis and needs assessment is lost.

Disaster Plan

One need only look at emergency response information to realize that the emergency service organization responds to more than fires and thus must be prepared for each risk. In fact, in many communities today, the reality is that fires demand fewer responses but larger response capabilities. This can only be defined by a comprehensive threat/risk review and a determination

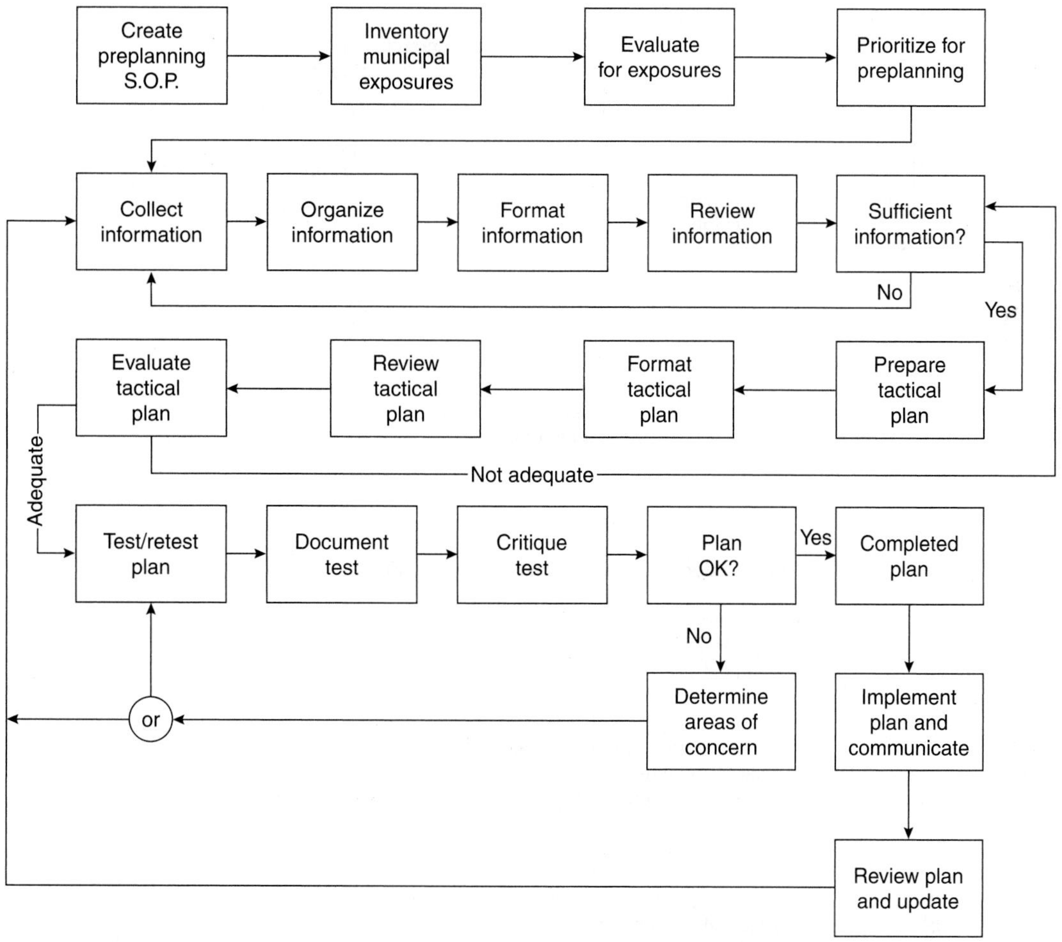

FIGURE 12.3.2 Pre-Emergency Planning Process (Source: W. F. Jenaway, *Pre-Emergency Planning,* ISFSI, Pleasant View, TN, 1996)

of how these risks must be managed. See Section 12, Chapter 12, "Disaster Planning and Response Services," for information on planning for more than fire risk.

ASSESSMENT PROCESSES AND TOOLS

Several assessment processes and tools are available to help in the analysis of hazards and determination of needs. Figure 12.3.3 illustrates related activities that fit into the assessment process, including plans (discussed in the preceding section), processes and tools, and the various stakeholders and assessment information sources.

Accreditation

One such assessment tool is accreditation. The accreditation program managed by the Commission on Fire Accreditation International provides an analytical self-assessment process to evaluate ten categories. Integrated within the ten categories is an expectation for the community to analyze itself by planning zones and for each planning zone to identify the hazards posed, ranking them by potential severity, and, as discussed in a later section, to ensure that the appropriate resources are available to manage the hazards. The accreditation self-assessment process is extremely helpful in determining needs and analyzing risks, even if the emergency service organization does not seek formal accreditation. Once the hazard is evaluated, the resources to manage the hazard can be defined, and an expected service delivery capability—that is, the standard of response cover—can be established.

Standard of Response Cover

The Commission on Fire Accreditation International defines *standard of response cover* as being "those adopted, written policies and procedures that determine the distribution, concentration, and reliability of fixed and mobile response forces for fire fighting, emergency medical service, hazardous materials and other forces of technical response."[5]

The standard of response cover can be considered a tool to accomplish several objectives, including the following:

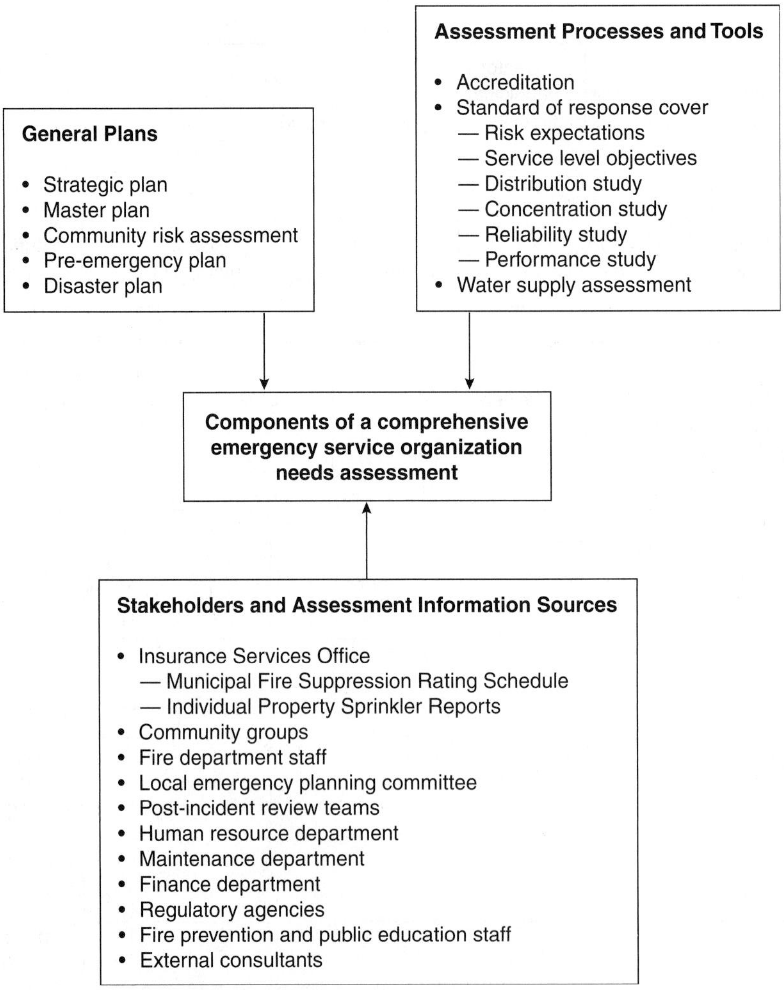

FIGURE 12.3.3 Components of a Comprehensive Emergency Services Organization Needs Assessment

- Evaluating and defining an agency's baseline of operations
- Identifying benchmarks for achieving an agency's goals and objectives
- Determining levels of service for all portions of a community
- Measuring an agency's performance over different budget operational years

Developing a standard of response cover is not quick or easy, but it is valuable to the progressive emergency service organization and should already be in place. The standard of response cover process includes an evaluation of the following eight components, all of which are integrated into a final methodology for standard of response cover (SORC) development:

1. Existing deployment
2. Risk assessment
3. Risk expectations
4. Service level objectives
5. Distribution study
6. Concentration study
7. Reliability study
8. Performance study

Existing Deployment. An evaluation of this component requires the fire department to map, measure, and understand its existing deployment, regardless of how it originated (e.g., insurance services office requirements, community growth, etc.). This will help clarify the department's total reflex and coverage capability.

Risk Assessment. Risk assessment requires the fire department to understand fire flow demand and capability, the probability of an emergency, the consequences to life safety and economic impact, and the estimation and evaluation of risk.

Risk Expectations. Evaluating risk expectations requires the fire department to identify what the community and the emergency service organization want in the form of service, what the outcomes should be, and whether the desired outcomes can be justified. These will assist in establishing critical tasking measures, shown in the following examples:

> *Structure Fire Performance Objective:*
> To stop the development of a moderate fire risk when encountered, conducting search and rescue as required, confining damage to as close to the room of origin as possible, limiting the expansion of heat and smoke damage.
>
> *EMS Risk Objectives:*
> To effectively provide a basic level of medical care at the basic life support level.
> To be on-scene in a timely fashion to:
>
> - Assess and prioritize patient situations
> - Minimize death and disability
> - Stabilize patients to the level of training of responders
> - Intervene successfully in life-threatening situations

Service Level Objectives. Service level objectives require the fire department to assemble and evaluate fire growth and flashover, EMS response needs, special service response needs, reflex and response times of on-scene operations, problem-solving critical tasks, and determining an effective response force. Examples of service level objectives as defined by the Commission on Fire Accreditation International are the following:

> *Service Level Objective:*
> For 90% of all incidents, the first arriving unit shall arrive within five minutes total reflex time (or travel time).
>
> *Service Level Objective:*
> The first arriving unit shall be capable of advancing the first line for fire control or starting rescue or providing basic life support for medical incidents.

Or the service level objective can be even more specific.

Distribution Study. The distribution study component requires the fire department to geographically analyze first-due resources for initial incident intervention to ensure quick deployment in order to minimize and terminate the hazards of average, routine emergencies. The distribution measures are up to the department, but might include percentage of square miles, percentage of equally sized analysis areas, percentage of total road miles in jurisdiction, or some similar measure.

Concentration Study. The concentration study component requires the fire department to look at the arrangement of multiple resource spacing (close enough together) so that an initial "effective response force" can be assembled at the scene within the adopted public policy time frames. The initial effective response force is one that should be able to stop the escalation of the emergency for the risk posed. Concentration measures can be similar to distribution measures.

Reliability Study. The reliability study component requires the fire department to determine the ability to meet performance expectations even if resources are committed on an existing call. This necessitates a historical measure of performance, resource exhaustion, relocation practice, and expectations.

Performance Study. The performance study component requires the fire department to evaluate information and data available, such as the following:

- Existing standards of cover documents
- Risk assessments
- Historical performance
- Cost-benefit evaluations

The information gleaned from evaluating these eight components is then used to develop the standard of response cover.

Water Supply Assessment

The water supply of the community must be known for two basic reasons. For locations subject to fire, knowledge of water supplies is necessary to determine surplus or need. The Insurance

Services Office (ISO) Municipal Fire Suppression Rating Schedule will also provide guidance on the location of hydrants tested during its analysis of water supply needed versus water supply available, indicating if a surplus or need exists for specific locations in the event of fire. (This water supply need can also be determined by the fire department during pre-emergency planning.) If water is needed, the hazard analysis component can be used to then determine where it can be obtained—whether from a static source, from a flowing stream, brought to the scene by a water tender or other means, or obtained from another water supply system—or whether a do-not-fight-the-fire scenario is the reality.

Second, it is important to know the water supply available for individuals providing sprinkler plans for review. It is important to ensure that the available water supply can meet the demand of the sprinkler system being installed, and, if not, how much water is needed and how it will be obtained. The Insurance Services Office (ISO) reports on sprinklered structures, in which the ISO has evaluated individual properties to determine the risk posed and the availability of an adequate water supply, can help provide this information.

In both of the preceding situations, understanding the hazard posed, the amount of water needed, and the amount of water available assists the fire department in hazard analysis and needs assessment.

STAKEHOLDERS AND ASSESSMENT INFORMATION RESOURCES

Insurance Services Office

The Insurance Services Office (ISO) serves the insurance marketplace with statistical, actuarial, underwriting, and claims data; policy language; information about specific locations; fraud-identification tools; consulting services; and information for marketing, loss control, and premium audit. Through its Public Protection Classification (PPC) Program, ISO evaluates municipal fire protection efforts in communities throughout the United States.[6]

ISO provides two primary support roles to the fire department in the area of hazard analysis and needs assessment: the Municipal Fire Suppression Rating Schedule and individual property sprinkler reports (as discussed earlier).

Municipal Fire Suppression Rating Schedule. The municipal fire suppression rating schedule evaluates the following three major areas:

1. The fire department
2. The water supply
3. Receiving and handling of fire alarms

When completed, the process provides an assessment of each area, complete with ratings that are translated into an insurance rate for the community. The process also facilitates the development of "improvement statements," indicating deficiencies and needed improvement in the area of staffing, water supply, equipment, apparatus, pumping capacity, aerial capacity, and so on.

Individual Property Sprinkler Reports. Similarly, ISO will conduct evaluations of structures that contain automatic sprinkler systems (as discussed earlier). These evaluations will determine whether the system is adequate for the hazard it is designed to protect and whether there is sufficient water supply to support the system if it activates. ISO's assessment identifies needs.

Community Groups

One of the most significant sources of input is the community. Not only will individuals in the community communicate their satisfaction, concerns, and expectations, they will be brutally honest. Even if the fire department is providing the best service it believes possible, the "customer" may agree or disagree. For the department to not capitalize on regular communication with the public and build its plan accordingly would be to do without the input of its most important customer. Civic groups, homeowner associations, neighborhood groups, church groups, fraternal organizations, the Rotary Club, the Chamber of Commerce, the Jaycees, and so on can be valuable resources for communication with the community.

Fire Department Staff

Similarly, to not periodically request information on planning from the fire department staff would be a mistake. These individuals know the level of service they are delivering and the hazards they are facing. Seeing the "streets" daily, they have the perspective of knowing what is out there and what is needed to deal with it.

Local Emergency Planning Committee (LEPC)

In many communities, the true hazards are found in the industrial operations of the town. Industrial facilities, often loaded with hazardous materials, pose a significant hazard to the community at large if the hazardous materials are not managed in routine operations, let alone a fire. The local emergency planning committee (LEPC) is charged with obtaining and appropriately distributing information regarding hazardous materials stored and used at various sites. The information the LEPC distributes—be it the chemical name of the hazardous material or the material safety data sheet (MSDS)—provides the critical information needed, including the product name, its hazards, and the control methods during both routine and emergency situations. As it pertains to assessing needs, it may be determined, based on this information, that large quantities of foam concentrate are needed; that extensive spill control or diking equipment should be maintained; or that specialized personal protective equipment is needed. Whatever the need is, it is identified based on the hazard analysis.

Postincident Review Teams

Each incident responded to provides a postincident analysis opportunity to learn about hazards and what is needed to manage incidents involving specific hazards. As each incident recap occurs, the team involved in the response can identify whether it had enough staff to handle the problem, the equipment was adequate, specialized resources were available to meet the need, and so on. In each instance, based on the hazard posed by the incident responded to, the team can determine whether adequate or inadequate resources were at hand to handle the problem.

Human Resource Department

When looking to determine adequate staffing, adequate deployment, and the probability of hazardous situations resulting in accidents or injuries, the fire department needs to look no further than the human resource department. The human resource department can provide input on whether there is sufficient staffing and whether shortfalls exist because department members are unable to respond due to illness, injury, vacation, or some other factor. Because the human resource department probably has some responsibility for the safety function of the fire department, it can provide valuable information regarding the types of injuries incurred by members and the causes of those injuries. The hazard information can be used to redefine job tasks, procure personal protective equipment, or prohibit doing certain tasks to meet organizational needs.

Maintenance Department

Maintenance personnel for the department, whether building maintenance staff or apparatus maintenance personnel, provide valuable input into the condition of apparatus and facilities and thus any hazards posed by working in the stations and with the apparatus. The input of maintenance personnel is critical in determining when repairs, upgrades, rebuilds, or new acquisitions must be made, based on their educated assessment of the hazards at hand in the stations and on the vehicles.

Finance Department

Similar to the human resource department's input, the finance department provides valuable input on the rate at which funds are being spent and the manner in which spending must be managed to meet needs. If budgeted amounts are being encroached on, overtime may need to be better managed and staff may need to be reduced or redeployed, thereby requiring mutual-aid arrangements to meet the need for adequate staffing at an emergency. The same scenario exists for equipment purchasing and helps determine the input for replacement apparatus purchasing.

Regulatory Agencies

A number of regulatory agencies assist the fire department in the identification and analysis processes so needs can be determined. The Occupational Health and Safety Administration (OSHA) has assisted the fire service through the determination of workplace hazards and the actions necessary to manage them. Similarly, the Environmental Protection Agency (EPA) has established guidelines and provided staff to evaluate hazards and determine needs to be addressed. The Resource Conservation and Recovery Act (RCRA) has provided a similar capability, and many others can be found in the workplace today. In each case, the regulations provide a benchmark of safe operation based on the hazard posed, from which the personnel, equipment, materials, and the like to manage the situation at hand can be determined. The procurement or accessing of those items can then be made.

Fire Prevention and Public Education Staff

Staff performing fire prevention and public education functions provide yet another form of input similar to staff performing fire investigations, inspections, code enforcement activities, and so on. Their ability to evaluate risk in the community and create fire prevention and public education programs solves immediate needs in the community. Whether these individuals are addressing the evacuation capability of a high-rise building and educating residents on how to escape, targeting smoking as a fire hazard based on smoking materials causing fires, focusing attention on the lack of smoke detectors in residences, or addressing some other scenario, they are analyzing hazards, solving problems, and meeting the needs of the customer.

External Consultants

The external consultant plays a prominent role in today's fire protection system. Rarely used until the 1990s, consultants now are involved in several aspects of hazard analysis and needs assessment. Not only have consultants designed a number of the risk analysis systems currently in use in the fire service today, they are responsible for the implementation of these same systems in many communities.

External consultants are often called in because local communities are unable to come to a resolution on a situation. These consultants become the solution to determine where a fire station will be placed, to analyze what types of hazards exist in a community, to provide pre-emergency plans, to evaluate workload, to determine what types of apparatus will be purchased and where it will be placed, and so on. The consultants answer the tough questions that local communities cannot answer, most of which involve some type of analysis of hazards and determination of needs. However, caution must be exercised with the use of consultants. A specific "scope of work" must be developed to ensure that the consultant performs work to meet the objectives of the organization and project, with defined timelines, deliverables, and related costs. In addition, consultants should have expertise in performing the tasks defined in the scope of work and utilize staff experienced in the issue and type of community being analyzed.

SUMMARY

The FEMA/NFPA needs assessment study provides a backdrop of identified nationwide needs and serves as an excellent educational and planning tool. However, a fire department's local needs should be driven by the findings from a comprehensive local hazard analysis in which the department's needs are compared with the results of the assessment study to see if there are gaps or unidentified areas, followed by the development of an action plan. Knowing what resources the department will need can only be determined by understanding the hazards it faces.

Once the hazard type is identified, the number of personnel needed to provide the mitigation services can be determined. The number of personnel responding is also defined by the number and types of vehicles carrying these individuals to the incident, with the final variable being the response time established to achieve the response/performance objective to manage the hazard identified. The emergency services community knows that if needed resources (personnel and equipment) do not arrive in time, the nature of the emergency will grow beyond the ability of the resources to manage the problem. The objective of the hazard analysis and needs assessment is, therefore, to develop the knowledge of the hazards being faced, the nature and amount of resources needed to manage the hazard, and the assurance that the resources can be deployed efficiently and effectively. This chapter provided a look at the components of a comprehensive emergency service organization needs analysis, including various planning processes, assessment and planning tools, and the stakeholders and assessment information sources.

BIBLIOGRAPHY

References Cited

1. *A Needs Assessment of the U.S. Fire Service,* FA-240, FEMA/National Fire Protection Association, Emmitsburg, MD, 2002.
2. *Four Years Later – A Second Needs Assessment of the U.S. Fire Service,* FA-303, U.S. Department of Homeland Security/U.S. Fire Administration and National Fire Protection Association, Emmitsburg, MD, Oct. 2006.
3. Bryson, J. M., *Strategic Planning for Public and Nonprofit Organizations,* John Wiley & Sons, San Francisco, 1995.
4. "Strategic Planning: One Plan Type of Many," *Chief Fire Officer's Desk Reference,* Jones and Bartlett Publishers, Sudbury, MA, 2005.
5. *Standard of Response Cover,* Commission on Fire Accreditation International, Chantilly, VA, 2003.
6. *Effective Fire Protection,* ISO Properties, Jersey City, N.J., 2004.

NFPA Codes, Standards, and Recommended Practices

Reference to the following NFPA codes, standards, and recommended practices will provide further information on needs assessment and hazard analysis discussed in this chapter. (See the latest version of The NFPA Catalog *for availability of current editions of the following documents.)*

NFPA 551, *Guide for the Evaluation of Fire Risk Assessments*
NFPA 1201, *Standard for Providing Emergency Services to the Public*
NFPA 1250, *Recommended Practice in Emergency Service Organization Risk Management*
NFPA 1500, *Standard on Fire Department Occupational Safety and Health Program*
NFPA 1620, *Recommended Practice for Pre-Incident Planning*
NFPA 1710, *Standard for the Organization and Deployment of Fire Suppression Operations, Emergency Medical Operations, and Special Operations to the Public by Career Fire Departments*
NFPA 1720, *Standard for the Organization and Deployment of Fire Suppression Operations, Emergency Medical Operations, and Special Operations to the Public by Volunteer Fire Departments*

References

CFAI, *Standard of Response Cover,* Commission on Fire Accreditation International, Chantilly, VA, 2003.
FEMA/NFPA, *A Needs Assessment of the U.S. Fire Service,* FEMA/National Fire Protection Association, Emmitsburg, MD, 2002.
Effective Fire Protection, ISO Properties, Jersey City, NJ, 2004, p. 2.
Jenaway, W. F, *Pre-Emergency Planning,* International Society of Fire Service Instructors (ISFSI), Pleasant View, TN, 1996.
Jenaway, W. F, "Emergency Service Strategic Focus," Communique, VFIS, York, PA, 2004.
"Strategic Planning: One Plan Type of Many," *Chief Fire Officer's Desk Reference,* Jones and Bartlett Publishers, Sudbury, MA, 2005, p. 26.

Chapter 4

Managing Fire-Rescue Departments

Rebecca F. Denlinger

This chapter provides an overview of the elements involved in organizing, administering, and managing agencies that provide fire and rescue response services.

Today's fire protection agencies have their roots in centuries of community efforts that attempted to prevent hostile fire and limit the damage it caused. From the start of night watches and bucket brigades through the first organized fire-fighting forces, those efforts have evolved into the amalgam of fire departments and other fire-fighting agencies that serve the United States and Canada today.

Fire protection in the United States is provided by more than 26,000 fire departments that are organized in different ways to meet their communities' specific needs.[1] Most often, public fire protection is a function of local government, although state, provincial, and federal authorities have also organized fire agencies, primarily to provide wildland fire protection on public lands or structural fire protection for government property. Similarly, large industries often organize or contract with private fire departments at their industrial complexes. The organization and objectives of fire departments vary according to available resources, ranging from simple to complex.

Most fire departments were administered by clearly defined organizational structures and systems before such techniques were widely applied to industry and business with the advent of the industrial age. Fire departments developed systems that broke down responsibilities at a fire into tasks that were assigned to engine and ladder crews. Each person on an apparatus was responsible for performing certain functions in a designated sequence so that each team operated as a coordinated unit, effort was not duplicated, and the common goal—usually to rescue trapped occupants and extinguish the fire—was achieved.

Most public fire departments are structured around the traditional mission of fire suppression. Many now also emphasize fire prevention and public education as more effective ways to protect life and property. Most have taken on other roles in their communities as well, particularly emergency medical and technical rescue services. They may also provide hazardous materials response, building and facility plans review, fire cause determination, and fire code inspection and enforcement.

Fire departments must be organized according to a comprehensive and coordinated plan if they are to operate efficiently and effectively. The organizational plan should clearly outline the roles and responsibilities of all line and staff personnel, their interactions with each other, and their relationship to the total organization.

Emergency response services are usually provided through a decentralized system of fire stations that are strategically located throughout the community and house a range of engine, ladder, rescue, and other companies as local needs demand and resources permit. Fire departments may be staffed by career, part-time, or volunteer personnel, or any combination of these, according to the manner in which the department has developed.

Rebecca F. Denlinger, CFO, is fire chief of the Cobb County (Georgia) Fire and Emergency Services, Marietta, Georgia. She is a member of the International Association of Fire Chiefs; the Board of Directors of the National Fire Protection Association; the Georgia Homeland Security Task Force; Women in the Fire Service, International; Women Chief Fire Officers Association; and Georgia Association of Fire Chiefs. In 2004, President Bush appointed her to serve on the National Infrastructure Advisory Council.

Chapter Contents

Key Terms

call fire fighter, career fire department, city fire department, code enforcement, combination fire department, county fire department, emergency medical services, fire bureau, fire district, fire investigation, fire prevention, fire protection district, fire service, fire suppression, mutual aid, professional qualifications, public fire and life safety education, public fire department, volunteer fire company, volunteer fire department

Neighboring fire departments traditionally help each other when major emergencies or simultaneous events overwhelm one department's response capacity. To be effective, mutual-aid agreements should be carefully drafted and agreed on by all parties involved, and should take into consideration all factors that affect the agencies' ability to function in a joint effort. Mutual aid may extend beyond emergency response into the realms of training facilities, apparatus purchase, and long-range planning.

No fire department can operate well without an effective communications system that receives alarms from the public, dispatches units to the scene and coordinates their activities, and also provides for nonemergency communications for the department. The size and configuration of this system, the personnel staffing it, and the technology used, will vary considerably depending on the size of the agency and the number of emergency responses it makes.

Fire departments may depend on career, call, or volunteer personnel, or any combination of these. The type of personnel a department uses depends on financial resources, the availability of call or volunteer fire fighters, the number of emergency calls received, the range of services the department provides, and any preferences expressed by the community as to the type of fire department it wishes to have. Staffing levels and scheduling must be arranged to comply with budgetary constraints and provide 24-hour coverage with maximum efficiency.

Effective fire department management requires decisions that are suited to meet the needs of the particular community through the efficient practice of organizing, planning, directing, controlling, and analyzing.[2] One key responsibility of management is preparing, submitting, and adhering to the budget for the fire department. Fire department managers must fully understand the budgeting process used by their jurisdiction and be able to develop a budget that is fiscally manageable for the jurisdiction while at the same time allowing the fire department to perform the roles expected of it. The responsibility for personnel management and for achieving cooperation among government agencies and political bodies requires a collaborative management style and a diplomatic temperament.

Fire department equipment and supplies, procured through the jurisdiction's purchasing department, may either be requisitioned from the purchasing agency or, for specialized items, purchased through a bid process. Fire department managers must be knowledgeable about preparing purchasing specifications and interpreting the bids received.

A fire department will be most effective if it develops and maintains good working relationships with other local, state, and federal agencies whose mission overlaps or supports its own. This interaction includes local police and other law enforcement agencies, the building and water departments, and many other agencies of local government. State and federal agencies concerned with transportation, domestic preparedness, and emergency management are also key partners and allies for fire departments of all sizes and types.

For related topics see the following chapters in Section 12: Chapter 1, "Planning for Public Fire-Rescue Protection"; Chapter 2, "Organizational Benchmarking and Performance Evaluation"; Chapter 3, "Needs Assessment and Hazards Analysis"; Chapter 5, "Information Management and Computer Technology"; Chapter 10, "Training Programs for Fire and Emergency Service Personnel"; Chapter 12, "Disaster Planning and Response Services"; Chapter 14, "Fire Rescue Stations and Fire Service Training Centers"; Chapter 15, "Public Emergency Services Alarm, Dispatch, and Communications Systems"; Chapter 16, "Fire Department Apparatus and Equipment"; and Chapter 17, "Pre-Incident Planning for Industrial and Municipal Emergency Response."

EARLY FIRE SUPPRESSION AND FIRE REGULATIONS

Today's public fire departments evolved from groups of citizens who banded together to warn of and limit the spread of a threatening fire. To provide a visual context for this section, Figure 12.4.1 sketches a time line for the history of modern fire protection in the United Kingdom and the United States. The earliest efforts involved the organization of night watches. Next to develop were fire prevention regulations and the appointment of individuals charged with enforcing those regulations. In cities and towns, groups organized to salvage belongings during or after a fire. These groups were followed by volunteer firefighting companies, who banded together to operate pumps to extinguish fires. Eventually, fire fighters and officers were appointed and paid to operate full-time fire departments.

One of the earliest accounts of an organized effort to provide fire protection is from 24 B.C., when a "vigil," or watch service, was created in Rome during the reign of Augustus. Regulations for monitoring and preventing fires were issued, giving the vigils duties similar to today's fire marshal's office or fire prevention bureau. The vigils were also provided with firefighting tools and equipment, such as buckets and axes.

Another early fire protection regulation dates to A.D. 872, in Oxford, England, when a curfew was adopted requiring hearth fires to be extinguished at a specified time. After 1066, William the Conqueror established a general curfew law for England that was apparently aimed not only at fire prevention but also at preventing revolt.

Fire Brigades in the United Kingdom

Prior to 1830, night watches and other services that used fire apparatus operated without any legal authority. *The History of the British Fire Service*[3] mentions an early exception: in 1643, during the English Civil War, a company of 50 women was organized to patrol the town of Nottingham at night and raise the alarm in case of fire.

Following the devastation caused by the Great Fire of London in 1666, several insurance companies created fire insurance brigades. Each brigade fought fires only in properties insured by its company and had no lifesaving responsibilities. The brigades operated without statutory authority or obligation, and it was the insurance offices, not government agencies, who decided where the brigades would be located. In London, the insurance company fire brigades in 1833 were consolidated into the London Fire Engine Establishment, which was taken over by the Metropolitan Fire Brigade in 1865.

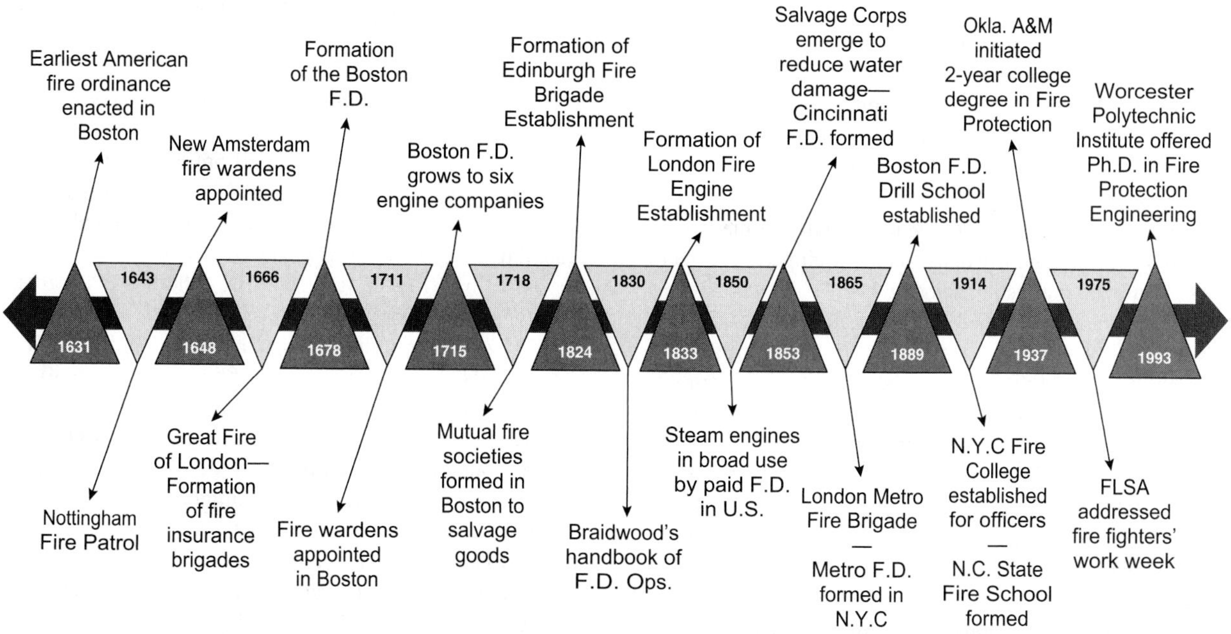

FIGURE 12.4.1 Time Line of the History of Modern Fire Protection in the United Kingdom and the United States (Courtesy of Stuart Shannonhouse, Resource Officer, Cobb County [Georgia] Fire and Emergency Services)

Edinburgh's Fire Brigade Establishment was the first public fire service to develop modern standards of operation. A surveyor named James Braidwood was appointed chief of the brigade. He chose 80 part-time aides between the ages of 17 and 25 and required them to participate in regular drills, including night training. In 1830, he wrote the first comprehensive handbook on fire department operations, which included 396 standards and set forth for the first time the kind of service a good fire department should deliver.

Fire Protection in Early America

The first fire ordinance in the New World was adopted in Boston, Massachusetts, following a disastrous fire in 1631. The ordinance prohibited thatched roofs and wooden chimneys, and was enforced by the colonial city's board of selectmen. In 1648, New Amsterdam (now New York City) appointed five municipal fire wardens with fire prevention responsibilities. This is often considered to be the origin of the first public fire department in North America.

After another conflagration in Boston, which occurred in 1679, destroyed 155 major buildings and a number of ships, laws were adopted requiring stone or brick walls for buildings and slate or tile roofs for houses. That fire also led to the establishment of the first paid municipal fire department in North America, if not the world, in 1678. The town imported a "fire engine" from England—essentially a small wooden box with carrying handles, a pump, and a small hose—and employed 12 fire fighters and a fire chief, Thomas Atkins.[4] From the start, jurisdictions in Massachusetts used paid fire fighters on an on-call basis, as contrasted with the unpaid volunteer fire companies that later were organized in other colonies.

Colonial communities required each household to keep two fire buckets at hand, and when the church bells rang an alarm, to report to the fire to form lines for passing water from wells, springs, or other water sources. As late as 1810, Boston citizens were subject to a $10 fine for failure to respond to alarms with their buckets. When hand-pumped fire engines were first obtained in the 1830s, teams of citizens were organized to operate them, and the bucket brigade supplied the pump's tank. The laws in a number of states and provinces still impose penalties on citizens who refuse to assist in fire-fighting operations upon orders from fire officers. For example, in Toronto, Ontario, the Municipal Fire Code, § 79-15 Refusal to Assist reads:

> If required to do so by the fire department, no person present at a fire shall refuse to assist in:
>
> A. Extinguishing fires;
> B. Pulling down or demolishing buildings or structures to prevent the spread of fires;
> C. Crowd and traffic control; or
> D. Other reasonable ways.
>
> [Amended 2000-10-05 by By-law No. 869-2000]

Fire wardens, who responded with their staff members to fires and supervised bucket brigades, were appointed in Boston in 1711. By 1715, Boston had six fire companies with British-made engines.

Mutual Fire Societies. According to many accounts, these companies were the forerunners of salvage corps. The first mutual fire societies were formed in Boston in 1718 when a group of affluent Bostonians organized to assist each other in salvaging goods from their homes and businesses affected by fire. Each person's equipment included a bag in which to collect valuables, a screwdriver, and a bed key to disassemble and remove beds from burning buildings. (At the time, beds were prized and valuable possessions, not commonly owned.) These societies were active for about a century, until fire insurance became generally affordable.

Salvage Corps. By about 1850, the major cities of the United States had organized paid fire departments equipped with steam engines. Insurance interests in nineteen of these cities formed salvage corps whose job was to reduce water damage at fires. Over time, the increasing cost of operating these corps, combined with improved fire-fighting procedures, made them obsolete, and they were disbanded. Today, public fire departments carry out the function of salvage operations at fires.

Growth of Paid Fire Departments. A lack of discipline within volunteer fire brigades, coupled with their resistance to using fire pumps and steam engines, led to the organization of paid fire departments. Following disorder and occasional violent confrontations between members of competing volunteer fire companies at fire scenes, a paid fire department with horse-drawn steam engines was placed in service in Cincinnati, Ohio, on April 1, 1853. In 1855, two steam pumpers were delivered to New York City, but the volunteer fire fighters refused to use them. Ten years later, the Metropolitan Fire Department, using steamers, replaced New York City's volunteers.

Duty Systems. Until World War I, paid fire fighters worked a continuous-duty system with limited off-duty time. By World War II, most paid fire departments had adopted a two-platoon system, which allowed additional days off and reduced the fire fighter's average number of hours worked per week. Hours worked per week have continued to decline for U.S. fire fighters, although in most jurisdictions they continue to work more hours per week than other public or private workers. Many fire fighters remain on a 24-hour-duty work shift. The 1975 Fair Labor Standards Act reduced to 53 the maximum hours of work per week for a fire fighter: hours worked in excess of the maximum must be paid at a higher wage rate. Additional discussion of many of the numerous duty systems used by fire departments appears later in this chapter.

Training. In 1889, the Boston Fire Department established the first fire fighter drill school, delivering basic training to its members. Uniform company drills were also performed, promoting the task allocation system that remains in use in well-organized fire departments. Most fire departments now provide some form of basic training to their members, and many have sophisticated training divisions that develop individual and company skills in fire suppression, emergency medical services, and technically specialized areas such as hazardous materials response; trench, high angle rope, confined space, and structural collapse. The incident command system, a staple of fire service training for decades, has been adapted to meet the command and control demands of all emergency events and is incorporated into the National Incident Management System (NIMS). NIMS is taught across the United States as part of local, state, and national fire training curricula.

The first fire officer training institution was established in New York City in 1914, when the FDNY Fire College began providing advanced training to its fire officer corps. Today, officer training is a high priority in many career and volunteer fire departments. Quality officer training is available through commercially available computer-based products, consulting companies that deliver training on site, Internet programs provided by the U.S. Fire Administration, and at private, local, state, and federal training institutions around the country.

Also in 1914, the first state fire school was organized in North Carolina. The first state fire schools for volunteer fire fighters were started in Illinois and Iowa in 1925. Today, every state reports offering some level of training service to its fire fighters.[5] Funding for training programs related to weapons of mass destruction and other large-scale events has grown since the first courses that were funded by the Nunn-Lugar-Domenici Act in the 1990s. Such funding is commonly allocated to state or regional initiatives in order to prepare local responders, including fire fighters, to respond to disasters.

College degree programs related to the fire service first appeared in the United States in 1937, when Oklahoma A&M (now Oklahoma State University) initiated its two-year (later four-year) fire protection degree. More than 200 institutions in the United States now offer two-year degrees in fire protection through a variety of methods, including online and other distance learning options as well as resident programs. Several colleges offer four-year programs of study leading to degrees in fire technology or fire service management, and the Worcester Polytechnic Institute and the University of Maryland at College Park offer masters degrees in fire protection engineering. Worcester Polytechnic Institute has also offered a doctoral degree in fire protection engineering since 1993.

TYPES OF FIRE DEPARTMENTS

Career Versus Volunteer Fire-Fighting Personnel

As of 2006, an estimated 313,300 career fire-fighting personnel and frontline supervisors and 823,650 on-call or volunteer fire-fighting personnel served in the United States.[6] The principal distinction between the two is that career personnel are assigned regular periods of duty and are compensated on a regular basis, whereas on-call or volunteer personnel are not normally required to be available except for meetings, training sessions, and emergency responses. They may or may not receive compensation for their services.

Most towns of 25,000 or more employ career personnel and many use auxiliary personnel or volunteers to supplement their regular forces. Other cities and towns use combinations of career, on-call, and volunteer personnel. Some communities have a career fire chief, officers, and/or apparatus operators but rely on on-call or volunteer personnel for the rest of their staffing. Other communities use career personnel only during the daytime and rely on on-call or volunteer personnel at night.

Many fire departments—career, combination, and volunteer—provide an acceptable level of service to their respective communities. The success of their operation does not depend on whether the personnel are paid or unpaid but on their individual and collective ability to perform and to accomplish department objectives. There are no simple guidelines that mandate the type of personnel a fire department should use. The decision must be made at the local level after carefully analyzing all pertinent factors.

Factors Influencing a Fire Department's Personnel

When a community decides to start providing fire protection, several factors influence the type of personnel the new fire department will use. These factors are (1) the financial resources of the community, (2) the availability of on-call or volunteer personnel, (3) the frequency of fire incidents, (4) the range of services expected from the department, and (5) the type of department preferred by the community.

The Community's Financial Resources. The financial resources of smaller communities will often dictate that the department be composed entirely of volunteer personnel. Salaries normally consume a large percentage of a fire department's budget, and the community may have only enough money available to purchase and maintain apparatus and equipment.

On-Call or Volunteer Personnel Availability. Some communities may find they do not have enough people willing and able to serve as volunteer fire fighters, and that the fire department must be staffed fully or partially by career personnel. This situation happens most often in rapidly growing suburbs near major cities. Originally these outlying areas were composed of small communities that provided a climate suitable for volunteer departments. As times changed, however, more and more residents became employed outside the community and were thus unavailable for emergency response in the daytime, or even to participate in the fire department at all. At the same time, rapid suburban growth increased the demand for fire protection and rescue services. As a result, many of these once-volunteer fire departments have added the services of career personnel.

Effect of Incident Frequency. Call volume, or the frequency of emergency response, will often determine the type of personnel chosen to staff a fire department. Densely populated, congested areas, especially those with extensive commercial or industrial development, will usually need fire and rescue services more often than more sparsely settled, largely residential areas. A high level of incident frequency will tend to overwhelm a volunteer operation unless the department has a large membership and the workload can be apportioned to reduce the commitment required of each individual.

In order to track the effects of call volume and the efficiency of volunteer response, the fire department should keep accurate statistics that include the number of volunteers responding per call and the length of time it takes them to respond. Weekends and weekdays should be tracked separately. Monitoring this data will help a community decide when it needs to hire career personnel in order to maintain the level of service desired.

Range of Department Services. The variety and frequency of incidents that occur in the community will determine the range of services the fire department provides. Most departments offer some level of rescue service, as extrication and emergency medical response are universal needs. The extent and type of development in a locality, and the existence of any natural hazards, also influence the scope of services offered by a fire department. In addition, the presence of a target hazard or particular critical infrastructure may also affect the range of services expected of a department.

Type of Department Personnel Preferred by the Community. Communities often have preferences for the type of personnel who staff their fire departments. In some instances, the volunteer fire department serves as a focal point of community activity, and the community is satisfied with the level of service provided by volunteer staff. In others, the career department is a well integrated part of the community. In every case, fire department personnel should be selected, trained, and equipped to provide the best possible service for the community.

ORGANIZING FIRE SERVICE AGENCIES

Most public fire service organizations in North America are established by local governments or by independent local entities created to provide public fire protection. Local government is responsible for organizing fire protection for the vast majority of people in North America. These fire protection services vary widely in character, from volunteer departments with little revenue to full-service agencies that employ career fire fighters and civilian staff. They also differ widely in their source of jurisdictional authority.

One of the most common types of fire protection agencies is the *city fire department,* a department of municipal government. The head of the department is responsible to the chief administrative officer of the municipality, typically the city manager or the mayor, or in some cases to a fire commission. Most large municipalities, as well as many small communities, operate this type of organization.

Less common is a *fire bureau,* which is usually a division of a department of public safety. In this type of organization, the public safety department head manages the administration of several important operations, including fire, police, and 9-1-1 communications center services. Since September 11, 2001, the public safety agency concept is growing in acceptance and use, as communities recognize the value of leveraging expertise of the various public safety disciplines to better effect.

The *county fire department* is gaining acceptance in many areas. In this type of organization, suburban municipalities join together to enjoy the benefits of a large, professionally administered public fire department with staff and service facilities that they could not afford individually. The transition to a county fire department often begins when a county fire prevention office and fire communications system are put in place; fire departments (often staffed by volunteers) initially remain autonomous for fire suppression purposes. Gradually, more functions are assumed by the county organization as the cost effectiveness and organizational expedience win attention and favor.

Another type of public fire protection is the *fire district,* which is organized under provisions of state or provincial law. It is, in effect, a separate, independent unit of government with its own governing body composed of commissioner, trustees, or other officials, and is commonly supported by a tax levied throughout the district. A fire district is usually organized following a vote of residents in the proposed district. The fire district may include portions of one or more political subdivisions, such as townships.

A fifth common type of fire protection authority is the *fire protection district,* which in some states is a legally established, tax-supported unit that contracts for fire protection from a nearby career (or in some instances volunteer) fire department. This arrangement provides timely fire protection for rural or suburban areas that might otherwise find it difficult to maintain effective and experienced fire-fighting forces. Contracts with a fire protection district can be a valuable source of financial support to the small municipal fire departments that participate, as well as providing fire apparatus for use in rural areas.

Another type of public fire service organization is the *volunteer fire company* or *association* that raises a portion of its funds through public activities and sometimes, subscriptions. Tax dollars comprise the majority of the funding available to volunteer fire agencies, and most of the tax dollars come from local tax sources.[1] Donations of equipment may also be received from interested units of government. Many volunteer fire associations maintain excellent equipment and facilities and also provide a location for various community activities. Certain volunteer fire companies prefer to retain independence from government, especially when purchasing equipment. It is common, however, to find independent fire organizations that are coordinated through special governmental advisory boards.

ORGANIZING FIRE-RESCUE DEPARTMENTS

In recent years, the role of the fire service in many communities has expanded far beyond its original mission of fire suppression. The term *fire department* does not begin to cover the many services progressive organizations now provide to their communities: a far broader public safety role has become the "business" of the modern fire department. Twenty-first-century fire services increasingly emphasize such proactive elements as fire prevention, code enforcement, public education, pre-incident planning, and interagency training and coordination. Citizens depend on the fire department to protect them from any emergency: fire, entrapment, explosion, building collapse, and natural disasters and other incidents that can result in mass casualties, such as biological, chemical, and radiological events. Fire departments respond to these demands with a growing range of capabilities, such as hazardous materials, technical rescue, and emergency medical services. In addition, fire-rescue departments typically are now involved in planning and training for response to disasters that exceed the capabilities of public safety agencies in the areas in which they occur.

Each community establishes the array and level of services it expects of its fire-rescue department, and these expectations will change over time. In this dynamic environment, a successful department is one that can effectively and efficiently satisfy these changing community needs. The leadership challenge for the fire service is to determine how the department should deliver needed services and to develop an organization that can manage and administer its operations. Fire chiefs must be prepared to implement changes in their department's service delivery mission that are dictated by governing boards. Fire fighters must be ready to train for and deliver those services.

Some communities have choices in selecting from companies and departments that can deliver the desired services. In such situations, the competitive edge goes to the agency best organized to deliver a range of effective services most efficiently.

Fire Prevention and Code Enforcement

Fire prevention and code enforcement are major areas of responsibility for the fire service. As fire departments have professionalized, they have tended to develop their fire suppression capacities to a much greater extent than their fire prevention abilities. Because emergencies cannot be eliminated or predicted, community protection depends on a reliable and effective response force. As a result, most of a fire department's resources are dedicated to responding to emergencies after the fact; typically, only a small percentage of resources are dedicated to preventing those emergencies. As technologies to improve the prevention, early detection, and automatic suppression of fires develop, more emphasis on proactive prevention, enforcement, and education programs within fire departments will better position communities for a safer future.

Adoption of Building Codes. The local fire department should lead the way in urging the community to adopt a complete nationally recognized fire and building code. Most fire departments have adopted one of the model codes developed by regional and national standard development organizations. These model codes can be amended to adjust for local concerns and needs. Working closely with community building and development officials, fire service leaders can tailor codes and permitting processes to support requirements for delivery of fire and emergency services. Particularly in areas that experience "build out" and consequent in-fill and redevelopment, codes should address the specific issues of street width, turnaround space for apparatus, distance to hydrants, and factors that affect service delivery.

Ideally, fire departments should assign full-time personnel to review plans and inspect buildings and fire protection systems. The widespread adoption of performance-based codes requires professionals, preferably fire protection specialists or engineers, who are trained to evaluate systems plans for adequate performance during the permitting process.

In the past, most fire prevention activities were carried out by a small nucleus of full-time specialists. The size of the fire department and the community determine the need for, and feasibility of, full-time prevention personnel. The prevention responsibilities of the fire department, however, go far beyond what a small cadre of specialists can perform. Many departments now involve fire fighters in inspections and code enforcement. All fire department personnel must recognize that fire safety education and fire prevention are major parts of a fire fighter's responsibilities.

Pre-Incident Planning. Pre-incident planning is a necessary adjunct to tactical operations and should aid in efficiency, reduce fire loss, and help provide an optimum level of emergency service. Pre-incident plans are desirable for all target hazards, for special risks, and for large complexes. (Standard operating procedures are usually sufficient for single-family dwellings and smaller occupancies, as well as routine multidiscipline events.) The planning process must involve all fire suppression personnel on a continuing basis. Pre-incident plans should complement standard operating procedures by familiarizing personnel with unusual buildings and facilities, and with processes and products that pose unusual hazards.

Pre-incident plan information should be presented in a standard format and made available to help the incident commander manage fires or other emergencies at the site. (For an example, see the *Fire Protection Handbook,* Section 12, Chapter 17, "Pre-Incident Planning for Industrial and Municipal Emergency Response" and NFPA 1620, *Recommended Practice for Pre-Incident Planning.*) Plans should be sufficiently flexible to allow for varying conditions and should use the framework of the department's standard operating procedures as a basis. Plans that are too rigid or complex may handicap an operation more than they help it.

Fire chiefs and department staff should encourage and support multidisciplinary planning. Local response partners such as law enforcement, EMS, and public health, should be involved in the process of developing plans for large-scale emergencies. This cooperation will enhance both the quality of the plans and the preparedness of the public safety community. In situations that require unified or area command, incident management will be more effective if the incident commander is familiar with the roles and responsibilities of allied agencies. During the planning process, all relevant response agencies, including utility providers and environmental agencies, should be involved in identifying and targeting critical infrastructure in the community. Planning for response to incidents involving weapons of mass destruction should be done by a group that includes planners from all response agencies. Personnel from all such agencies should become familiar with, and have access to, the resulting plans.

The following steps are part of the pre-incident planning process:

1. *Information gathering.* Pertinent information, such as building construction features, avenues of egress, occupancy, exposures, utility disconnects, fire hydrant locations, and water main sizes, which might significantly affect fire fighting or allied agency operations, must be collected at the selected site.

2. *Information analysis.* The information gathered must be analyzed for what is pertinent and vital to fire suppression operations, so that a plan can be documented in a format that can be used during the incident. A pre-incident plan usually includes a site plan or map; floor plans and diagrams identifying pertinent features, including vertical avenues of fire travel in multistory buildings; hazards and fire control equipment; area maps indicating various staging and rally points; and additional text outlining special problems, specific tactics, hazardous contents, and information on parties responsible for specific areas.

3. *Information dissemination.* Pre-incident plans should be assembled and distributed in a standard format for easy use on the emergency scene. Plans may be maintained on paper and carried in fire apparatus, microfilmed and used with viewers in command vehicles, or stored in computer systems accessed by mobile data terminals or fax machines. Plans should be clearly dated and revised periodically, with revised plans disseminated on a systematic basis.

4. *Class review and drill.* Any fire company that might respond to an incident at a site that has a pre-incident plan should review the plan on a regular schedule. If possible, periodic drills and familiarization tours with all the companies involved should be scheduled on the property. All concerned agencies should periodically review pre-incident plans.

Fire Investigation

Competent fire investigations, performed to determine fire cause as well as to detect criminal activity, can identify factors that can lessen the number and severity of fires in the future. Information gained through investigations is a valuable tool in improving fire prevention by pointing out needed code revisions, updating public education program content, and planning for future fire protection and response needs. In addition, a thorough investigation of all incendiary or suspicious fires is a powerful arson deterrent. Adequately trained and equipped personnel should be available to investigate all fires of unknown or suspicious cause.

Community-Based Safety Education

Fire departments inevitably respond to tragedies. The challenge is to prevent these tragedies from happening in the future, and the most effective place to do this is at the community level. Fire stations have always had a community profile, yet they often have a great deal of unrealized potential. The neighborhood fire station can be a key delivery point for fire and emergency prevention efforts, and fire fighters in the stations can effectively deliver community fire prevention programs. By effectively using demographic and fire experience data, a department can customize prevention education to the needs of individual response territories. The central public education staff can then focus on delivering programs in schools, senior centers, and other facilities where at-risk populations congregate. This staff can also coordinate the prevention initiatives of the fire stations.

Although community fire education has been a part of the fire service for many years, it has only recently emerged as a major component in fire protection. National conferences that champion the public education effort have been introduced in Oklahoma and Texas. The National Fire Protection Association's (NFPA) *Learn Not to Burn®* program is one component that has been successful in reaching and educating schoolchildren on fire safety issues. "Fire safety houses," portable model homes transported on trailers, have proven to be valuable teaching tools in many communities.

To complement the fire service's expansion into emergency medical services, many fire safety education programs are now successfully incorporating NFPA's *Risk Watch*® program. This curriculum goes beyond traditional fire prevention to include accident and injury prevention. In Canada and some areas of the United States, the *community safety village* concept has been developed as a tool for delivering a full menu of public safety education programs to the community. Fire safety programs are integrated into the curriculum of these learning and education centers.

Public Relations and Community Partnerships

Fire departments supported by public funds need public support and interaction to be effective. Only with the public's interest and cooperation can fire protection and prevention programs be fully effective and the fire department operate successfully within its particular political environment. Without community support, it can be difficult for the department to obtain the needed funds to operate at the required level. Accordingly, public information and community service programs, or public relations, are an important fire department management activity.

Good public relations programs keep the public informed of departmental activities. Relations with the news media should be cordial, and the fire department needs to cooperate with representatives of the media, who can be of invaluable assistance in pushing out messages to the public. This is not always easy, because suburban fire departments are often located in communities that depend largely on a metropolitan press, and items that might be of interest to local citizens may not be newsworthy for the entire region. It may be effective to explore options, such as local weekly papers or local-area editions of metropolitan papers that do have local correspondents.

The amount of publicity fire departments get seems to vary greatly among geographic areas. In some areas, citizens are traditionally interested and involved in local governments and their fire departments, whereas in other areas, fire departments are not considered newsworthy. The latter situation obviously requires a greater effort in order to get fire-related information to the public. In general, communities whose citizens regularly participate in town affairs seem to give fire departments better support. Communities with substantial numbers of low-income residents subject to fire dangers are often most concerned with the adequacy of fire department services.

Public education information can be passed through local government publications and regional periodicals, as well as through inserts in utility bills and department newsletters. Fire departments should develop safety and awareness campaigns to target specific communities. Resourceful and energetic public relations officers will find numerous avenues for spreading public information.

News personnel should be given accurate information promptly at incident scenes. Most fire departments specify that only the incident commander or a designated public information officer (PIO) should give out information. This practice should prevent the release of conflicting, inaccurate, or ill-advised statements that might be misleading or could compromise fire investigations. The PIO position is a designated function in an effective incident command system.

Some large fire departments have a designated PIO who also functions as a public relations officer, giving the press all possible cooperation and information regarding the department's activities. In smaller fire departments, the fire chief may perform this function. Staff public relations officers often report directly to the fire chief because of the need for regular communication between the two. The public relations officer may act as a communications or media adviser to the chief, and the chief should keep the public relations officer apprised of all potentially newsworthy department decisions and activities.

Emergency Medical Services Delivery

Emergency medical service (EMS) has become an important function of many fire departments. Although fire departments have operated ambulance services for decades, the major growth in this area has occurred since 1970, stimulated by higher standards for patient care, training, and associated equipment. Increased public, medical community, and local government interest in delivery of emergency medical service has prompted many fire departments to increase their participation in EMS; consequently, the quality of EMS delivery has improved greatly.

In most fire service organizations that provide first-responder or transport EMS services, EMS runs account for 60 to 75 percent of their emergency call volume. This growing service demand has changed the business definition of fire departments throughout the country. Many fire department managers and organized labor groups link the competitiveness of their organizations with emergency medical service delivery.

The addition of the EMS mission to a fire department is a natural extension of responsibilities and can be managed so as to increase organizational productivity without a negative impact on fire protection. Fire service personnel are already oriented toward delivering emergency service and assisting citizens. Fire personnel and apparatus are housed in fire stations that are decentralized to provide rapid response to all areas, served by communications systems that receive emergency requests from the public and dispatch assistance without delay. These two elements provide the foundation of effective EMS delivery.

Increasingly, the emergency medical services delivery system may be solely the responsibility of the fire department, from first responder providing basic life support to advanced life support with paramedic-level care, including transport (Figure 12.4.2).

Nationwide, fire department emergency medical service calls outnumber fire alarms by more than six to one. Even though responding to EMS calls places an increased workload on fire companies, the combination of the two missions has proven very efficient in many jurisdictions. Providing basic EMS equipment on engine and ladder companies with emergency medical technician (EMT)–certified fire fighters enables these units to handle most life-threatening situations. In most communities, the fire department is also the lone provider of extrication and rescue services, provided via the same apparatus and personnel. Paramedics responding on ambulances or rescue

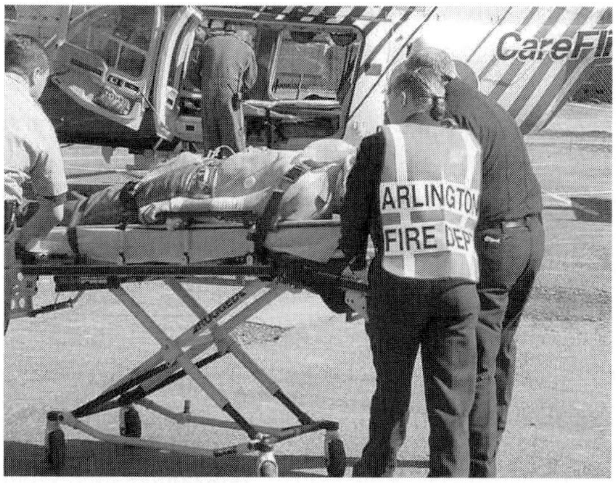

FIGURE 12.4.2 Emergency Personnel Loading a Patient into an Emergency Care Helicopter

vehicles generally back up first responders and EMTs. In some fire departments, all personnel are trained and certified at the EMT or EMT-Intermediate level, and dual-role paramedics are assigned to engine and ladder companies.

Hazardous Materials

Storing, using, transporting, and disposing of hazardous materials and hazardous waste create significant safety risks. Changing federal regulations, along with increased sensitivity to environmental protection, have created a new service demand in many communities. In many cases, the fire department is the lead agency in responding to hazardous materials incidents.

Many fire departments find they have neither the trained personnel nor the funds to support a full hazardous materials emergency response team. Regional hazardous materials response teams have been organized within counties and parishes, and in some cases across greater areas, in order to combine available resources and personnel to best effect.

Fire departments should either lead or participate in the process of gathering and organizing information, identifying risks, and planning for hazardous materials emergencies, as well as in regulating the storage, use, transportation, and disposal of hazardous materials and hazardous wastes. Federal law commonly known as the "Community Right-to-Know" provisions (the Emergency Planning and Community Reporting Act: Title III of the 1986 Superfund Amendments and Reauthorization Act) requires that facilities that hold chemicals above certain quantities report what they have on the premises to the local fire department. Fire departments should receive these reports and use them to inform effective pre-incident plans and to budget for appropriate equipment.

Rescue Services

The level and sophistication of rescue services offered by fire-rescue departments has expanded significantly in recent years. In many communities the local fire-rescue department is the lone provider of extrication services. Heavy rescue and structural collapse services are also increasingly available via the local department. More technically complex forms, such as trench (Figure 12.4.3), confined space, and high angle rope rescue, are also more common. The amount and type of equipment that has been procured through federal Homeland Security funds has made these various rescue services more prevalent than ever before. Fire departments should evaluate the potential for the need for rescue services and pursue the equipment, the training, and, if necessary, the staff to make possible the provision of the appropriate programs to the community.

Management Improvement Systems

A number of systems have been developed to improve management decision making through teamwork and enhanced working relationships. Such systems include organizational development, quality circles, and quality assurance and service improvement programs. Although these have been developed primarily for the private sector, they can also improve how public sector organizations are managed.

Progressive organizations have augmented the traditional, authoritative, fireground chain-of-command management style with private industry processes that focus on quality management. Quality management stresses a total organizational approach that makes the quality of service, as perceived by the customer, the driving force for the organization. The purpose is to improve the quality of service, productivity, and (increase) cost effectiveness through clearly stated, well-developed goals and measurable objectives. These goals and objectives are identified and accomplished by increasing the participation of both managers and workers in the organization's planning and decision making.

Every fire department should have a *mission statement* regarding the scope of services it provides. The mission of fire departments—the menu of services provided to the community—may be very similar from one part of the country to another. Many progressive organizations develop their mission statements by first creating a *vision* that states where they are headed and where they believe the future lies for their

FIGURE 12.4.3 Rescue Effort at Legacy Park, Lawrenceville, Georgia (Source: Courtesy of Cobb County Fire and Emergency Services)

organization. Many fire departments also develop a set of *values*. Values say something very individual about an organization and may reveal what is most important to the department and to the community. In addition, *goals* should be established for the department, along with measurable objectives for each level of the organization.

Information Management Systems

The information generated by a fire department—particularly in the areas of fire protection, EMS delivery, personnel, and fiscal management—should be systematically collected in an information or records management system (RMS). An effective RMS can then be used to analyze the data collected in ways that are useful to department managers. Data analysis is a powerful tool for monitoring the effectiveness of programs and services and for guiding planning. The information can be displayed in a variety of ways, including charts, graphs, maps, and reports.

Information management systems for use by fire departments are available commercially in off-the-shelf and custom formats, or can be developed locally. Sophisticated systems can interface with other computer applications, such as computer-aided dispatch and geographical information systems. Making use of the data captured in such systems requires trained personnel who have sufficient time to analyze, collate, and prepare data for management to interpret.

Some systems collect data regionally and nationally; for example, NFPA analyzes and prepares statistical reports from a national system of data collection. Many standard reports (such as *U.S. Fire Fighter Deaths*) and "customized analysis" are available from the NFPA Fire Analysis and Research Division. This information is available for use by individual departments.

Occupational Safety and Health

Fire fighting has been recognized for many years as one of the most dangerous professions. In each year between 1996 and 2005, an average of 135 fire fighters per year lost their lives[7] and roughly 58,000 were injured.[8] To address this unenviable record, NFPA 1500, *Standard on Fire Department Occupational Safety and Health Program,* was established to guide fire departments in developing fire service health and safety programs. The standard is dedicated to making the fire service less dangerous by reducing the risk of accident, injury, and death during line-of-duty activities and to make fire fighters healthier and more physically fit.

NFPA 1500 addresses the elements of a fire department occupational safety and health program. It was developed by the fire service, for the fire service, and supports the requirements of the federal Occupational Safety and Health Administration (OSHA) fire brigade standard developed for private sector and public fire suppression organizations.

NFPA 1500 addresses health and safety as an overall program to reduce the risks to members of the fire department. The standard applies to all members of the department and specifically identifies management as a provider of the safest possible work environment, given the hazardous nature of the work. Fire service management thus must take the lead in establishing rules and procedures that support an effective health and safety program.

Entering into a comprehensive health and safety program can be difficult, as it involves a number of complex issues as well as inevitable budgetary impact. It may be easiest to implement the program on a phased basis, tailored to the specific needs of the fire department. (See NFPA 1500, Section 1.5, "Adoption Requirements.") Developing a comprehensive implementation plan will require the fire department to assess its strengths and weaknesses, determine what would be required to meet the standard, and then prioritize the steps that will be taken to reach this goal. The implementation plan should address vehicles and equipment, training and education requirements, protective clothing and protective equipment, incident command procedures and safety officer programs, facility safety, health and fitness standards, risk management procedures, and employee assistance programs.

Nearly 80 percent of active fire fighters in the United States are estimated to serve in departments with no fitness and health program.[1] A number of information sources are available on the Internet for departments interested in monitoring fire fighter health and safety issues, including the website sponsored by partnering agencies interested in preventing fire fighter deaths and injuries, http://www.firefighternearmiss.com. The International Association of Fire Chiefs' Safety, Health, and Survival Section and the International Association of Firefighters provide numerous resources for departmental health and safety programs.

DEPARTMENT STRUCTURE

Fire departments, like other organizations, are composed of people working together in a coordinated effort to achieve a common set of objectives. This coordination is achieved through organizational principles that determine how work is divided and coordinated, and through organizational plans that show the relationship of each operating division to the total organization.

Principles of Organization

One basic organizational principle is that work should be divided among individuals and operating units according to a plan. The plan should be based on the functions that must be performed, such as fire prevention, training, and communications.

A second important principle is that, as a department increases in size and complexity, the need for coordination also increases. Small departments allow frequent personal contact among individuals, reducing the need for planned, formal coordination. As departments increase in size and complexity, however, operating units must be coordinated more systematically in order to achieve their objectives. The logical grouping of similar functions and tasks will help to promote interaction that is necessary to successful management.

The most successful organizations operate as a team. Department leaders are organized as a system, in which all divisions and sections are equally important in achieving the desired objective: service to the community. Most fire departments retain a linear organizational structure, but many are recognizing the utility of creating work groups to address many management tasks. For example, the Department Information Systems manager may be responsible for specifying and recommending a new records management system, and may seek the support of a focus group of interested employees in the process. Once the process is completed, the IS manager takes responsibility for the recommendation and moves it up the organization for further action. This team approach to accomplishing organizational goals helps limit the distancing effect that can occur in departments large enough to fund specialized staff positions.

The span of control for each manager and supervisor in an organization should also be considered. Generally, five to seven subordinates per supervisor are considered to be the ideal number for a manageable span of control. However, the complexity, importance, and sheer volume of work involved in the tasks being managed, as well as the manager's level of responsibility, should be taken into account.

Coordinating the systems within a department is an overarching function of the fire chief. This means the chief is responsible for organizing, planning, directing, controlling, and analyzing the work of the department. Activities that monitor, track, review, and revise systems as necessary will help establish and maintain an effective and efficient department that continually meets the needs of the community.

Line Functions

Line functions in fire departments normally refer to activities directly involved with delivering service to the department's customers. Fire suppression officers are considered to be line officers. This does not mean, however, that they do not have other functions. As these officers are promoted within the department they often acquire staff responsibilities as well. At the highest officer levels within the department, line responsibilities diminish and staff responsibilities increase. Line functions may include the following:

Emergency response. Fire suppression, emergency medical services, rescue operations, hazardous materials response, and other emergency services

Fire prevention. Inspection of construction and of existing properties for compliance with codes and ordinances; reviewing plans for new construction, major renovation, or installation of fire protection systems; operation of a public education program; and investigation of fires to determine the reasons fires start and spread

Staff Functions

Staff functions are activities that involve administering to or managing the needs of the department's service units and divisions, rather than dealing with day-to-day emergency incidents. Staff functions may include the following activities:

Training. Training of all personnel in their job skills; administering continuing education programs in special subject areas; administering the fire department safety program; and organizing and administering pre-incident planning

Maintenance. Maintaining apparatus, equipment, and physical facilities; recommending replacement programs for apparatus and equipment; and developing specifications for the purchase of apparatus and equipment

Communications. Providing and maintaining adequate facilities for the receipt of alarms from the public and communication with fire companies both in quarters and by radio in the field; also includes functions of developing and maintaining dispatch policy and response requirements

Research and planning. Creating the new knowledge the fire department needs to provide better service; forecasting long-range department goals; and performing the types of analyses necessary for other department functions to assess program effectiveness

Public information and relations. Maintaining contact with the public and the news media to tell the fire department's story; in larger departments, this function may also be responsible for internal communications

Financial management. Preparing a budget; monitoring expenses against the budget planning for capital expenditures; and supervising the purchase and inventory of needed materials

Personnel management. Supervising the recruitment, selection, and promotion of personnel; administering the retirement system and the benefits program; and supervising the administration of discipline within the department

Fire protection engineering. Developing proposals for code changes; and assisting in the technical aspects of plan review, code enforcement and fire investigations; also used in the research and planning functions

In large fire departments, a staff officer normally supervises each of these functions; these officers are not normally involved in line functions. The number of personnel assigned to a staff officer will vary with the size of the department and the importance of the function. In small departments, line officers may also be assigned staff functions, or a single officer may supervise more than one staff function. In the smallest of departments, the fire chief or assistant chief may directly assume many of the functions.

Organizational Plans

A department that functions effectively will have an organizational plan that shows the relationship between the operating divisions and the total organization, and allows the department to be managed effectively. (Organizational charts with typical structures of small, medium, and large fire departments are shown in Figures 12.4.4, 12.4.5, and 12.4.6, respectively.) A good organizational plan that reflects the current status of the department is essentially a blueprint of the organization.

A list of responsibilities or a job description for each position should accompany the organizational plan. In small departments, a single individual may be responsible for more than one function. For example, a single officer may be responsible for both training and maintenance. This should be detailed in the job description. The organizational chart must show how functions that may demand time and support from other personnel or groups will be coordinated within the department. The organizational plan and chart should reflect, to both fire department personnel and the public, a clear, coordinated effort to provide service to the community.

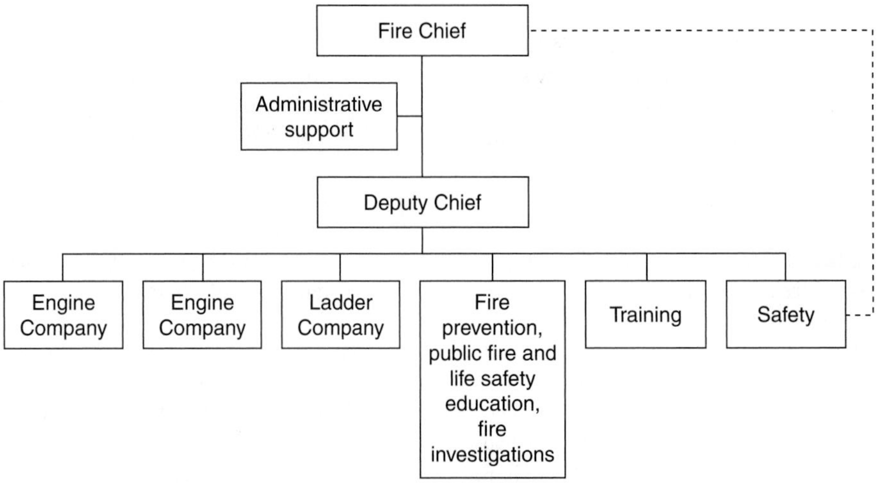

FIGURE 12.4.4 Organizational Chart for a Small Fire Department

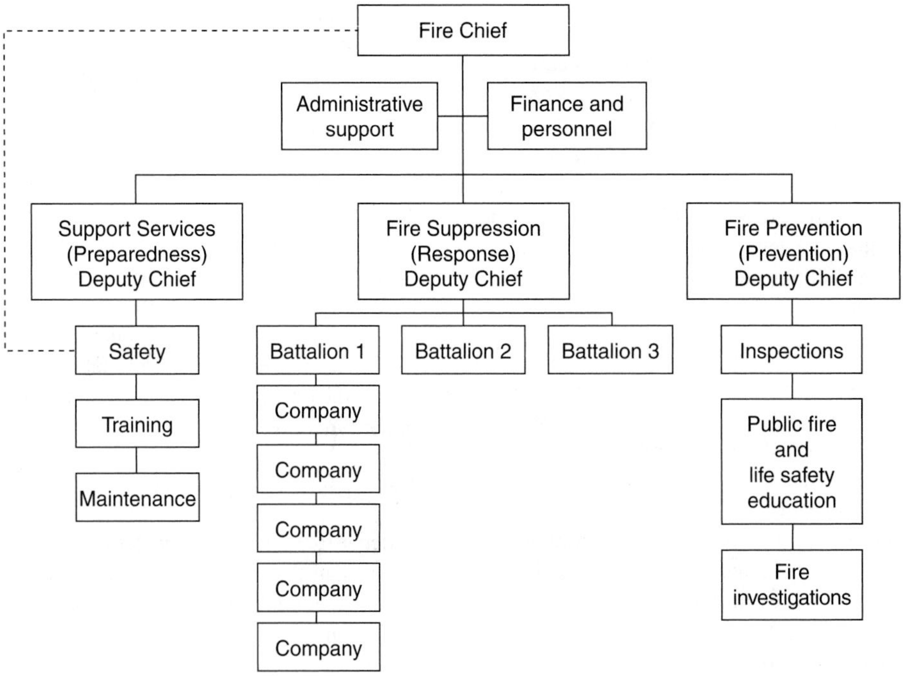

FIGURE 12.4.5 Organizational Chart for a Medium-Sized Fire Department

Rules, Regulations, Procedures, and Guidelines

As with any organization, fire departments need directives to govern operations, set performance standards, and outline expectations of behavior. Every fire department should have a set of rules and regulations, including a code of conduct, and standard operating procedures and guidelines. Operating procedures and guidelines are especially important in the fire service because the hazardous activities that are undertaken require a clear understanding of expected performance to ensure safety.

Chief officers may also issue orders when special circumstances and events require immediate or short-lived directives. Management should also create directives that specify disciplinary procedures for poor performance or for failure to follow regulations.

All directives should be written and distributed in such a manner as to ensure that they are known and accessible to all department members.

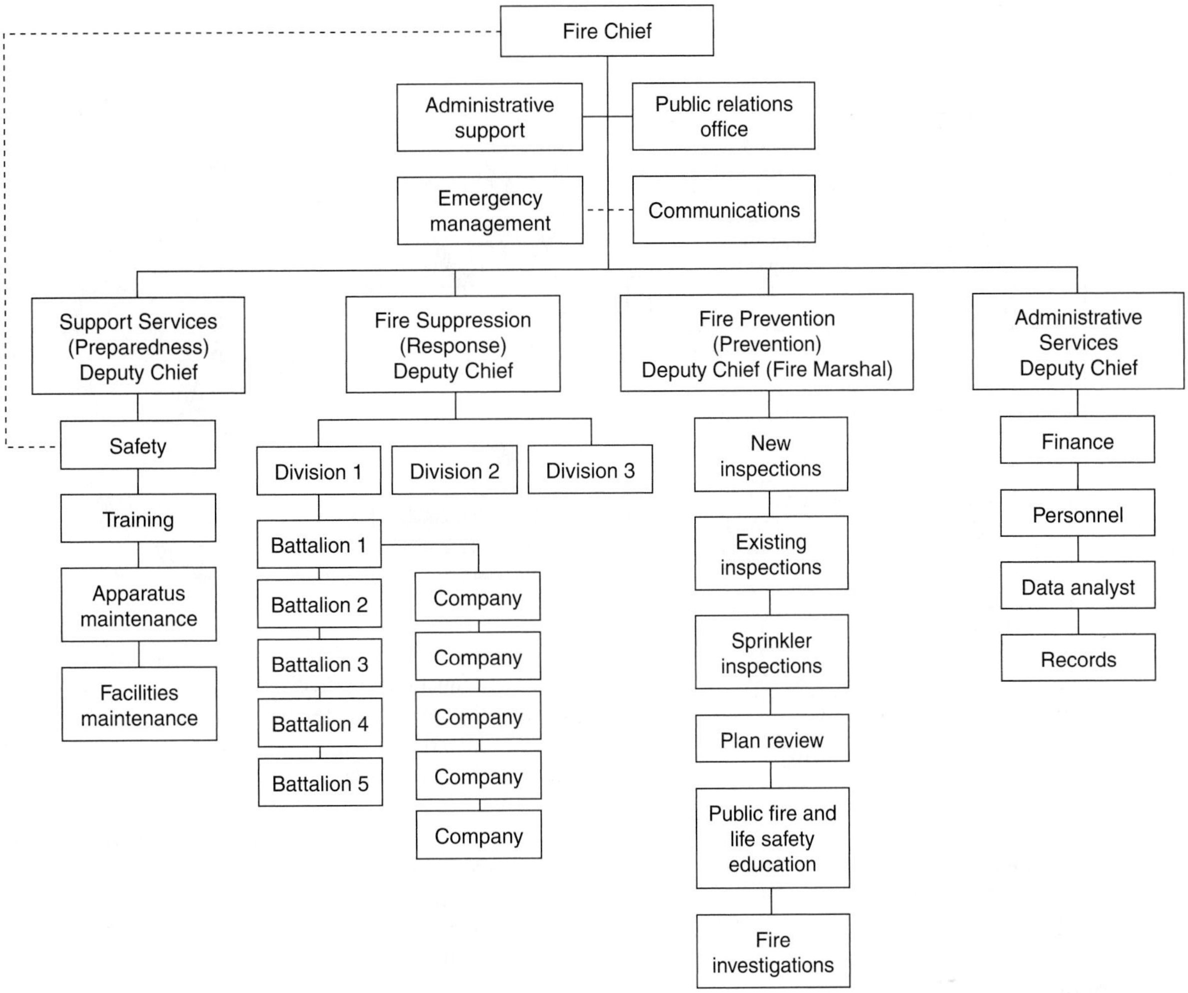

FIGURE 12.4.6 Organizational Chart for a Large Fire Department

ORGANIZING FOR EMERGENCY RESPONSE

Fire Suppression

Fire department structure is usually organized around providing fire suppression. The complexity of the response services section of the department is directly related to the size of the department. In many small fire departments, the fire chief supervises field operations. In larger departments, companies are organized into battalions or districts supervised by intermediate-level command officers (Figure 12.4.7).

The basic tactical unit of the fire department is the company, a group of personnel operating one or more pieces of apparatus under the supervision of a company officer. Several companies may operate from a single fire station. Engine and ladder companies are the most common; others are often provided to perform combined or specialized functions. These companies include rescue squads and companies that operate special tactical or support-function apparatus. In some fire departments, several companies operating from the same station are organized as task forces.

Engine Company. The most common type of company in a fire department is the engine company. The basic unit of apparatus is the engine or pumper, which carries hose, nozzles, a water tank, a pump, ground ladders, and assorted equipment, appliances, and tools. The engine company's basic tactical role in fireground operations is to deliver water through hose lines to control fires. Most engine companies also carry equipment to provide emergency medical services. In most cases, at least one engine company is based at each fire station in order to respond quickly and begin operations at a fire scene.

Ladder Company. The basic ladder company (or "truck company") apparatus is an aerial ladder or elevating platform that provides access above ground level or to rooftops, and can be used to direct elevated master streams onto fires.

Ladder trucks carry a complement of ground ladders and a selection of hand and power tools. On the fireground, ladder

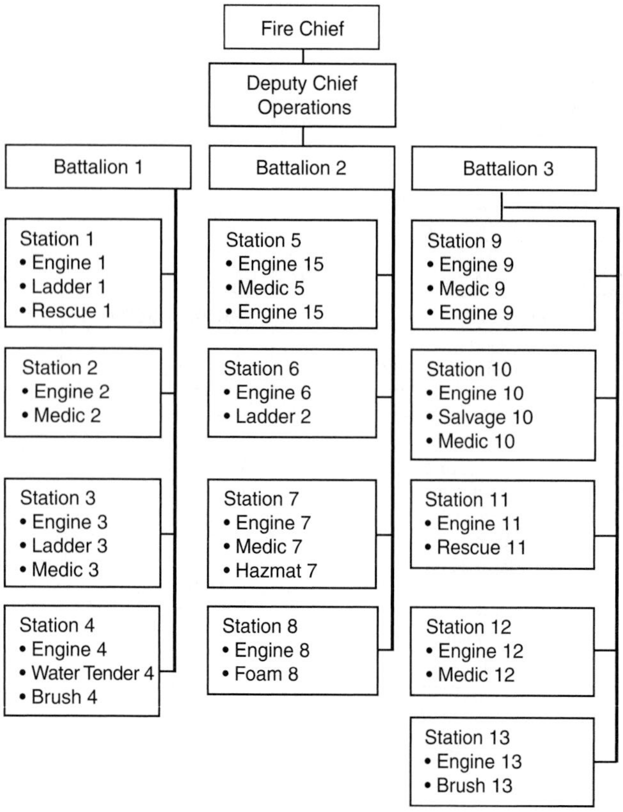

FIGURE 12.4.7 Organizational Chart for Operations Division of a Large-Sized Fire Department

companies perform search and rescue, forcible entry, ventilation, salvage, and overhaul. They also use ladders to gain access to fires and rescue persons trapped above ground level. Many departments operate ladder companies whose apparatus, called a "quint," are also equipped with hose, a water tank, and a pump. This type of ladder company can also apply water to fires through its hose lines.

The need for ladder companies, the design of ladder trucks, and the way ladder trucks are equipped, all depend on the community's needs. In a densely developed city, one ladder company may be provided for every two or three engine companies. In suburban jurisdictions that cover large response areas, the quint concept is particularly prevalent, because engine companies may have farther to travel and a choice of tactical options is desired. In rural and sparsely populated suburban areas, the functions normally performed by ladder companies are often assigned to engine companies carrying additional equipment.

Rescue Company. Many fire departments use separate rescue companies for both fire fighting and non-fire-related incidents. Rescue companies specialize in technical rescue, such as extricating victims from vehicles involved in accidents, removing injured persons from perilous locations, and assisting victims of industrial accidents (Figure 12.4.8).

On the fireground, rescue companies are usually assigned primarily to search and rescue, and to deliver medical treatment

FIGURE 12.4.8 Rescue Personnel Training for High-Angle Rescues

to civilians and responders. They may also take on some ladder company functions, particularly forcible entry, ventilation, and the use of power tools. Rescue companies may also be assigned as rapid intervention teams, with a focus on reducing injury and death to fire fighters operating at fires.

Special Apparatus. Fire departments often use specialized vehicles, such as off-road vehicles for brush fires, water tenders, hose wagons, foam pumpers, hazardous materials units, lighting trucks, breathing-air-supply trucks, and command vehicles. These may be organized as separate companies, or the role may be assigned as a second function to regular companies, with one company of fire fighters responding to an incident on either of two apparatus, depending on the nature of the incident. Some fire departments operate special companies with vehicles designed to carry little equipment other than the protective clothing and breathing apparatus used by the crew. These "flying squads" are intended to provide additional staff in a hurry to task-intensive incidents.

Fire apparatus may be purchased with a variety of options and configurations to suit the needs of the community or fire department. These options include aerial devices, water towers, and foam systems on engine-company apparatus; high-volume pumps and remotely controlled nozzles on ladder trucks; and large electrical generators and air-supply systems. The current trend is to purchase apparatus with multiple capabilities and to equip companies to perform multiple functions.

In many jurisdictions, the fire service has expanded its scope to embrace certain domestic preparedness functions. These departments have acquired specialized apparatus and vehicles for uses such as mobile decontamination trailers, incident communications centers, command and control vehicles, medical operations units, mobile radiological detection and monitoring stations, and multidiscipline response units.

The National Fire Protection Association publishes a series of standards for the design and construction of fire apparatus. Refer to Section 12, Chapter 16, "Fire Department Apparatus and Equipment," for a detailed discussion of fire apparatus.

MUTUAL AID AND MAJOR EMERGENCIES

Fire department managers should always be aware that a fire, natural disaster, disease outbreak, or terrorist attack could overwhelm the local emergency services. For this reason, most fire departments traditionally have rendered assistance to each other in times of need. Mutual-aid plans establish procedures for requesting and dispatching help between fire departments so that each party will know what is expected.

Mutual-aid plans may include immediate joint response of several fire departments to high-risk properties; joint response to alarms near the boundaries between fire department areas; coverage by outside departments when the resources of the local department are engaged; provision of additional units to assist at major fires that are too large for the local department to handle; and provision of specialized types of fire-fighting equipment not available locally in adequate quantity for the particular incident.

Mutual-aid plans also should specify that the National Incident Management System (NIMS) and ICS will be used during all incidents, and include provisions for standard operating procedures, interdepartmental communications, maps, adaptors, and other considerations that directly affect the ability of departments to operate together effectively. Command responsibility, jurisdictional questions, insurance coverage, and legal constraints should be covered in written agreements and supported by enabling legislation to establish effective mutual-aid systems.

Some communities have adopted automatic reciprocal aid agreements under which two or more fire departments are dispatched through one 9-1-1 communications center as though they were a single department. This "total boundary drop" that considers all concerned jurisdictions as one, optimizes emergency response for the citizens in the affected area. It usually results in a savings for the taxpayers as well, because it eliminates the need for multiple communications centers.

Some jurisdictions have extended the automatic-aid concept to the extent that fire department resources are pooled or merged into an integrated system with standardized training procedures. These networks may include shared facilities, joint purchases of specialized apparatus and equipment, and a coordinated approach to long-range planning.

True mutual aid is a relationship in which each member is prepared to assist the other parties to the agreement. In most areas of the country, larger fire departments are willing to assist smaller jurisdictions when requested at major incidents that exceed local capabilities. In many places, communities or individual properties known to be deficient in fire-fighting resources contract in advance to pay another jurisdiction for certain fire-fighting assistance. These programs are known as outside aid programs. In some instances, the contract covers basic first-alarm response; in other cases, additional assistance is provided for fighting major fires.

In all cases of mutual aid and outside aid, carefully worded agreements should be made in advance according to the legal requirements governing fire department operations outside normal jurisdictional areas. Local departments may have different operating methods and types of equipment, and this could hamper effective coordination of resources if a well-constructed agreement is not in place. The parties to the plan may choose to render assistance only to the extent that they feel they can do so without seriously reducing local protection; thus the plan should identify and address any coverage weaknesses.

The ideal plan is an extensive, region-wide agreement that maintains and optimizes coverage for all jurisdictions involved. As experience with natural disasters and other large-scale incidents has shown, effective plans and organizational procedures are crucial in systematically mobilizing fire forces. Most states and provinces have established large-area disaster plans involving all emergency services, coordinated under the NIMS. Such plans must integrate with the normal organizational and command procedures used by fire departments. These large-scale mutual-aid networks form a natural basis for smaller scale, more routine mutual assistance plans.

The amount of work involved in establishing and maintaining the mutual-aid agreements necessary for each jurisdiction can be a significant administrative burden. State legislation that provides mutual-aid agreement between all jurisdictions and emergency service agencies within the state can help to alleviate this burden. Such legislation can be written to allow individual communities or agencies to opt out of the agreement. This approach promotes regional planning and cooperation among all emergency responders and services, which is the cornerstone to successful response to and recovery from disaster. Similarly, interstate mutual aid agreements should be considered. Widespread effects of certain disasters can require the response of resources from states near and far. Interstate mutual-aid agreements should be examined to ensure that they provide for the release of resources for emergency response within hours of requests for assistance.

COMMUNICATIONS

An effective communications system is a key factor in fire department operations. The communications system is responsible for receiving notification of emergencies from the public; alerting and dispatching personnel and equipment; coordinating the activities of the units engaged in emergency incidents; and providing nonemergency communications to coordinate units.

Receiving Alarms

The first fire alarm telegraph system was created in Boston, transmitting the first fire alarm in 1852.[4] Although in many urban areas, municipal alarm systems remain in widespread use, today most alarms are received over landline or cellular telephone systems. Small departments with low activity levels may receive alarms through a variety of systems that provide 24 hour coverage.

In most areas, combined emergency service answering centers called public safety answering points receive calls for police, fire, and emergency medical services through a 9-1-1 emergency number; fire departments in other jurisdictions receive calls at a separate communications office. Enhanced 9-1-1 systems can identify the telephone number and location from which a call made from a landline phone originates. Other sophisticated tracing equipment enables public safety answering points to determine the location of the cell tower closest to the origination of a call made from a cell phone.

As a result of high false alarm rates, many cities have removed municipal alarm systems or converted from telegraph to systems providing voice contact between the dispatcher and the caller. For more information, see NFPA 1221, *Standard for the Installation, Maintenance, and Use of Emergency Services Communication Systems.* Additional information is provided in Section 12, Chapter 15, "Public Emergency Services Alarm, Dispatch, and Communications Systems."

The communications center should provide recording equipment for all telephone lines and radio channels to provide immediate playback capability to verify information and to provide a complete record of all activity. In addition to telephones and municipal alarm systems, many fire departments receive automatic fire alarms from systems installed in buildings in their jurisdiction; these systems are connected directly to the fire department or relayed through a private alarm company.

Dispatching Procedures

Once an alarm has been received, personnel must be alerted and equipment must be dispatched. The complexity of this process varies with the size and population of the area served and the number of units under the alarm center's control.

The dispatcher must identify the units that are to respond to an incident based on the geographic location and type of situation, as well as the current availability of the units. The selection criteria for response units is determined in advance based on distance from, or response time to, the reported location. The type and number of units due to respond to each type of incident, often called the response array, should also be determined in advance based on risk criteria and unit capabilities.

The dispatcher must know the status of each unit in the system and be able to contact immediately all units that are available to respond to an incident. Global positioning systems (GPS) may be installed on response vehicles that enable the dispatcher to consider a unit that is closer than the recommended unit. If regularly assigned units are engaged at another incident or are otherwise unavailable, the system should identify the next units to substitute. This information is also needed if the dispatched units request additional assistance. Many communications centers and public safety answering points have computer-aided dispatch systems (CADS) that automate these functions. Printouts of automated dispatch systems are kept on hand as a backup system. Smaller systems often rely on printed "running cards" or policies to provide the dispatcher with response information for each zone.

The units assigned to respond to an incident may be alerted by radio, microwave, telephone, telegraph, other wired systems, or a combination of these. In some areas, individual pagers, outside sirens, or horns are used to alert volunteer or call personnel. Most departments use a voice message from the dispatcher to the responding unit, carried over the radio or wired circuits to the fire station. The alarm center should have at least two separate means of communication with each fire station, in case of equipment failure. In addition to voice messages, some fire departments use printers or telegraph systems as a backup. Units out of quarters are normally alerted by radio.

Radio Communications

Every fire department vehicle should be equipped with a two-way radio. Units responding to or engaged at incidents should be in radio contact with other units and with the alarm center. For larger departments, this may require several radio channels to provide sufficient communications capacity. The alarm center must be able to contact responding units en route, in order to provide additional information or directions, and units at the scene must be able to request or return additional resources. Mobile data terminals on the responding units provide the responders a view of the best information available to the dispatcher. This equipment saves time that would otherwise be spent gathering this information over the air.

The incident commander should be able to contact the alarm center at all times, providing progress reports, advising on the need for assistance, or releasing units from the scene. A dedicated fireground channel should provide communications between the incident commander and the units operating at the scene. Complex incidents may require multiple for communications within various sectors of the incident management system.

At a minimum, each company officer and sector officer should have a portable two-way radio on a fireground channel. As an essential element of safety, every member operating in a hazardous environment should have a portable radio. Units released from an incident by the incident commander should advise the alarm center when they are available to respond to other incidents.

As fire departments have become more mobile and active, with units spending less time in quarters, radio communications have become more important. The radio system must reach all units and be able to handle the volume of communications a major emergency generates. Regional communications plans are essential to coordinate activities involving units from multiple jurisdictions. Such plans may specify dedicated frequencies, specialized equipment that enables different systems to communicate, or other predetermined methods for providing a communications platform.

Communications Center Staffing

Fire communications centers require trained operators who are familiar with fire department operations and equipment. In very small communities, the fire department telephone number may be arranged to ring in a number of locations where appropriate action can be taken to dispatch fire apparatus. Dispatching may also be handled by the police department, a town office, or other locations that provide 24 hour coverage. Increasingly, small fire departments are being served by regional fire communication centers that are properly equipped and staffed.

Larger communities and regional communication centers require adequate numbers of trained, capable personnel to be on duty at all times. Enough operators must be on duty to handle the volume of communications during busy activity periods and working incidents. Procedures should be in place to call in off-duty personnel or additional trained dispatchers, or otherwise increase capacity when major emergencies and high-activity situations exceed the effective capabilities of on-duty staff.

System maintenance and repair personnel should be on duty or on call at all times. All equipment must be maintained properly and tested for maximum reliability, and backup equipment or systems should be provided in case any key component fails. Every fire department should have a backup facility to which basic communication capability can be transferred if the primary center becomes unusable. In addition, 9-1-1 communications centers should have an agreement with a comparable center to allow for the redirection of 9-1-1 calls and dispatch of units in the event of a local phone system failure.

Information Retrieval and Storage

The communications center should have immediate access to essential information that may be needed in dispatching units to fires and emergencies. The data files must include a complete geofile index of all streets, intersections, and related numbering systems in the area. The geofile should also include all target hazards such as schools, hospitals, critical infrastructure, and large buildings. The system must allow the dispatcher to determine the appropriate response zone and map location for any reported emergency so that the proper units can be dispatched. Maintaining and updating these files is an important ongoing function, whether the information is kept in hard-copy form on cards or index systems or in a computer system. The same approach is necessary to keep pre-incident plan information and maps up to date in the communications center, as well as on fire apparatus.

Communications center data files should also include telephone numbers for responsible parties for target hazards, utility companies, and other agencies to contact during emergencies, as well as other individuals who may have to be notified of, or asked to respond to, certain incidents.

Electronic data processing equipment enhances information storage and speeds its retrieval. Information available on a particular location within a CAD system may include data on building arrangements, construction, hazards, code-inspection access, water supplies, and even prior fire experience. The system may provide for direct transmission of this information to terminals in responding vehicles or for storage in portable computers or microfiche systems carried in command vehicles.

Station/Personnel Alerting Systems

Some fire departments maintain a 24 hour watch at a console or control room in each fire station. The person on watch is responsible for receiving dispatch messages and controlling alerting devices within the station. Instead of maintaining a watch, other departments rely on the communications center to operate audible alerting devices in the stations.

Controls for lights, electrically operated doors, traffic-control devices, and similar equipment are usually located at the watch desk. Other fire departments control some or all of these devices from the communications center via radio signals or hardwired circuits.

In those stations that are staffed entirely by volunteer or on-call personnel, the communications center may alert personnel by activating sirens or horns or by tone activation of radio pagers carried by personnel or kept in their homes.

Communications center managers should carefully evaluate and anticipate the need for additional channels and frequencies and include strategies for funding the addition of these and other needed equipment in their planning. Radio systems, computer equipment, global positioning systems, software interfaces to coordinate these systems, and other communications tools are complex, expensive, and often little understood by the authorities who must agree to fund them.

Communications center managers should plan and train for the coordination of operations among public safety agencies during a disaster. Fire-rescue departments that operate a separate communications center, in particular, should prepare the communications staff for effective interagency operations.

MANAGEMENT AND BUDGETING

The operation of a fire department is normally a function of local government—in the case of a fire district, possibly the only function—that supports the service and is responsible for the level of service rendered. As with any governmental or business operation, this function involves three major areas of responsibility: (1) fiscal management, (2) personnel management, and (3) productivity. Other areas of responsibility include planning, research, and record keeping.

Fiscal Management and Budgeting

In general, fiscal management practices follow those used by the government agency supporting the department. These practices involve budgeting, cost accounting, personnel costs including payroll, and purchasing or procurement costs. The degree to which these factors are a direct responsibility of fire department management varies, depending on the practices of local government.

Fire department budgets are generally prepared and submitted by the fire chief, directly or through management structure, to the elected body that administers the community or district operations. A typical budget consists of operating, personal services, capital replacement, and capital improvement segments. Personnel costs are generally the most significant segment of a fire department's budget, accounting for approximately 85 to 90 percent of the total expenditures of a fully paid fire department.

Fire department managers must thoroughly understand their jurisdiction's budgeting system. Inadequately prepared budgets can lead to serious monetary shortfalls at the end of the fiscal year. Costs must be estimated realistically and expenditures must be monitored on an ongoing basis.

Long-range plans should be created that will project capital replacement costs for items such as staff vehicles, fire apparatus, fire stations, and other major pieces of equipment. Fire apparatus costs normally run from 2 to 3 percent of payroll costs. (Some fire departments include an apparatus replacement allowance in their operating budgets, but this item is regularly reduced or eliminated, with the result that apparatus replacement may be included in a capital expenditures budget. Although this reduces the fire department's annual budget, it may ultimately result in higher taxes due to interest costs. However, such decisions are generally made above the level of the fire department administration.) New fire stations and new service programs are usually included in a capital improvement budget separate from the fire department budget.

Large fire departments may have separate budget accounts for staff divisions, such as fire prevention, maintenance, and training. Expenditures are charged against specific items in the line budget, and the remaining balance is shown after each expense deduction. Usually, the department head or staff division supervisors have the authority to make emergency transfers of funds between line categories, whereas transfers between major categories must be authorized by the municipal manager, finance officer, or other governing body. Purchases and procurement procedures must be executed within the policies of the governing authority.

Budget Submission

Fire department administrators are required to submit their budget estimates by a specified date for the coming fiscal year (or years, in jurisdictions that employ a biennial budget). Budgets are usually submitted to a finance officer or committee, and department heads are then asked to justify specific items. Salary totals may be governed by contract with the employees, but estimates must cover all ranks, overtime costs, and anticipated hiring and retirements. Because salary increases are not always determined before the budget is submitted, it may be necessary to incorporate a projection based on reasonable assumptions.

After a departmental budget has been approved by the governing administration, it must be approved by the city council or other governing body. In some communities, this requires a public hearing. With some municipal charters, the council can reduce but not increase the budget in order to guard against political pressure on the administration. Once approved, the budget takes effect at the beginning of the fiscal year. If not approved in time, it is customary to permit ongoing expenditures at the same rate as the previous year.

The governing authority should clearly define who is responsible for managing each area of the budget. Responsibility for keeping the department within its authorized budget most often rests with the chief of the department.

Personnel Management

A fire department is only as good as the people who work for it. Choosing new fire fighters, and promoting them to officer or other ranks, is to a great extent the job of the fire chief or other upper department management, although human relations departments take over much of this role in many jurisdictions. Hiring and promotional processes are also subject to legal constraints as well as, often, to civil service rules and local government policies. Fire department management is also responsible for assigning employees to positions within the organization (subject in some cases to the work contract agreement) and for supervising them and evaluating their performance.

Recruiting. Fire departments are often very involved in recruiting efforts to fill vacancies in their ranks. A common arrangement is to conduct recruiting efforts jointly with the local government human resources or personnel agency. (Because of their makeup, most fire districts and volunteer departments recruit their own members.) Many large fire departments have recruitment sections. Some departments coordinate recruitment efforts with other allied agencies, such as other fire-rescue departments in the region.

Fire department management has three recruitment responsibilities. The first is to develop and employ appropriate hiring standards. The second is to provide the basic training new recruits need in order to perform their assigned duties properly. The third is to certify that the newly trained fire fighters are ready for appointment as permanent fire fighters or, when individuals prove unable to perform satisfactorily, to recommend that their services be terminated.

Personnel selection must comply with local, state, and federal laws. U.S. courts have ruled that there can be no discrimination in hiring practices based on race, gender, national origin, religion, age, or marital status. State or local law may further define employment practices, expanding the list of nondiscriminatory practices or setting criminal history disqualifiers, for instance. Many communities have identified diversity in the public sector as a value and have established a goal that personnel reflect the diversity of the community they serve. Many departments thus administer comprehensive recruitment, pretraining, and mentoring programs designed to increase the representation of women and people of color within their organizations.

Periodic review of the selection, hiring, and retention practices of the department is a wise practice. Selection practices are a sensitive issue, and knowledgeable counsel should be sought when developing hiring standards in order to ensure a sound legal foundation. For example, some rulings prohibit residence requirements for recruits, although fire department rules of employment may stipulate that, because of the emergency nature of the work, employees must reside within a reasonable distance of the community. One court decision has prohibited entrance examinations that require prior knowledge of fire department practices and equipment.

In most jurisdictions, applications for employment as a fire fighter are obtained from local government personnel offices or the civil service agency. In at least two states, recruitment is handled by a state civil service commission. Age requirements for entry-level appointments vary and have been affected by recent federal regulations.

Qualifications. All fire service personnel must be fully qualified and capable of efficiently performing the wide range of functions necessary to protect life and property. Many states have established commissions on fire fighter standards that require that all personnel employed by fire departments satisfactorily complete basic training before they are given permanent employment. Many states have also adopted, or are in the process of adopting minimum fire fighter qualifications standards.

In 1971, the Joint Council of National Fire Service Organizations (JCNFSO) created the National Professional Qualifications Board for the Fire Service (NPQB) to facilitate the development of nationally applicable performance standards for various levels of responsibility within the uniformed fire service. On December 14, 1972, the board established four technical committees to develop those standards using the NFPA standards-making system. The initial committees addressed the fire fighter, fire officer, fire service instructor, and fire inspector and investigator.

The original concept of the professional qualification standards, as directed by the JCNFSO and NPQB, was to develop an interrelated set of performance standards specifically for the fire service. The various levels of achievement in the standards were to build on each other. In the late 1980s, the standards were changed to recognize that the documents should stand on their own merits in terms of job performance requirements for a given field. Accordingly, the strict career ladder concept was abandoned, except for the progression from fire fighter to fire officer. The later revisions facilitated the use of the documents by other than the uniformed fire services.

In 1990, the NFPA assumed the total responsibility for the appointment of professional qualifications committees and the development of the professional qualifications standards. The NFPA Standards Council appointed the Correlating Committee for Professional Qualifications Standards in 1990, which assumed the responsibility for coordinating the requirements of all of the professional qualifications documents. The chair of each technical committee sits on this committee.

Currently, technical committees are working on the following projects:

- NFPA 1000, *Standard for Fire Service Professional Qualifications Accreditation and Certification Systems*
- NFPA 1001, *Standard for Fire Fighter Professional Qualifications*
- NFPA 1002, *Standard for Fire Apparatus Driver/Operator Professional Qualifications*
- NFPA 1003, *Standard for Airport Fire Fighter Professional Qualifications*
- NFPA 1005, *Standard on Professional Qualifications for Marine Fire Fighting for Land-Based Fire Fighters*
- NFPA 1006, *Standard for Rescue Technician Professional Qualifications*
- NFPA 1021, *Standard for Fire Officer Professional Qualifications*
- NFPA 1031, *Standard for Professional Qualifications for Fire Inspector and Plan Examiner*
- NFPA 1033, *Standard for Professional Qualifications for Fire Investigator*
- NFPA 1035, *Standard for Professional Qualifications for Public Fire and Life Safety Educator*
- NFPA 1037, *Standard for Professional Qualifications for Fire Marshals*
- NFPA 1041, *Standard for Fire Service Instructor Professional Qualifications*
- NFPA 1051, *Standard for Wildland Fire Fighter Professional Qualifications*
- NFPA 1061, *Standard for Professional Qualifications for Public Safety Telecommunicator*

Each of these standards defines the levels of progression within the specified job. The job performance requirements defined for each level of progression are considered the minimum requirements for individuals at that level. The intent of the committees is to develop clear and concise job performance requirements that can be used to determine whether individuals possess the skills and knowledge necessary to perform the related duties and tasks of the job. These job performance requirements can be used by any fire department in any city, town, or private fire service organization.

Under the new leadership of the National Board on Fire Service Professional Qualifications, the NPQB has assumed the role of third-party accreditor of fire service certification programs and developer of a national registry of those certified.

Certification in the fire service is based primarily on the NFPA professional qualifications standards. The Fire Service Accreditation Congress at Oklahoma State University has also been established as an accreditation agency for the fire service. The Center for Public Safety Excellence offers accreditation to qualified fire service agencies and chief fire officers.

The establishment of standards and testing procedures does not in itself ensure that all personnel will achieve the required level of competency; NFPA 1001, *Standard for Fire Fighter Professional Qualifications,* is a professional qualifications standard, not a training standard. Training programs are necessary to prepare members of the fire service to acquire the skills and knowledge necessary to meet the job performance requirements set forth for each grade. However, training should not be random. It must be organized to prepare trainees to meet the specified levels of performance demonstrated by the performance testing described in NFPA 1001.

Courts have ruled that height and other arbitrary requirements are discriminatory and may not be part of hiring criteria. Discrimination against individuals with a disability is also a violation of federal law, but candidates may be required to demonstrate their ability to perform the bona fide duties of a job. Fire departments must evaluate their hiring processes, defining and validating the "essential functions" for fire department positions.

Testing. Fire fighting requires physical endurance and strength, and fire fighters depend on each other in fire suppression and rescue operations. In some jurisdictions, the fire department's training division or other personnel may be used to test candidates for fire fighter positions. Regardless of who provides entry-level testing, recognized standards and all applicable laws and guidelines must be followed carefully. The goal of the testing process should be to select those candidates who, with training, will be capable of carrying out the functions of the job proficiently, without making the results subject to charges of discrimination.

Promotional Practices. In the vast majority of fire departments, officer ranks are filled from the pool of personnel serving in the next lower rank or ranks, although fire departments are increasingly recognizing the potential benefits of allowing qualified personnel from other areas and departments to compete for positions above the entry level. Promotional procedures are designed to take into account technical qualifications for the particular rank, as well as fire department or other relevant experience. Examination procedures in the civil service must be competitive and nondiscriminatory.

Promotional procedures are generally administered by personnel departments or by state or local civil service authorities with the assistance of experienced persons who are knowledgeable about the particular job classification. Such subject matter experts include fire chiefs, fire fighter organizations, department personnel, and technical consultants. Their assistance may include guidance as to the relative weight to be given to experience and to the result of written examinations covering the technical qualifications of the position.

In many systems, however, the testing process is rigidly defined by civil service law or contract. In some systems, performance ratings may be included. Some supervisors tend to be much more demanding than others when rating performance; and their subordinates often have less favorable performance grades than other employees, who may actually be less qualified. Because of the question of their uniform application, subjective performance ratings are now used less frequently in the promotional process.

Some promotional processes include an oral review. Although oral reviews provide an opportunity to evaluate important attributes that are difficult to quantify and test, they can also be very subjective. Few oral interviews are scientifically designed or professionally administered, and they may reflect the interviewer's bias or be subject to a challenge of bias. As a result, more emphasis is given to written examinations that test technical knowledge exclusively.

Where permitted by law, more fire departments are now commonly relying on assessment centers as a means of selecting candidates for promotion. Assessment centers, which have long been used by private industry, require a candidate to demonstrate certain abilities through the use of problem-solving exercises, role playing, prioritization of a list of tasks, incident simulation, and other exercises. Each candidate is observed by a trained assessment team and scored according to performance. Many experts in the field of human resource management agree that the assessment center is the most realistic means of determining a candidate's suitability for a promoted position.

NFPA 1021, *Standard for Fire Officer Professional Qualifications,* specifies the levels of performance for fire officers. Written in performance terms, this standard requires an individual to demonstrate competence by knowledge and performance.

Many fire departments include educational requirements for officers, such as community college fire science certificates or bachelor's degrees for chief officers. It is not uncommon to find fire departments that seek individuals with graduate-level degrees in public administration or management for the position of fire chief. Many jurisdictions specify completion of the National Fire Academy's Executive Fire Officer program in their job qualifications for chief executive officer.

The fire department administration, as an arm of the municipal administration, has an important role to play in the promotional process. First, it must advise the personnel agency of the qualifications required in any job or rank to be filled, for those instances in which such qualifications have not been previously listed. Second, when a list of successful candidates is received from the personnel agency, the administration must normally advise the promoting authority of the promotions to be made. The usual practice is to fill vacancies from the top of the promotional list, except where the head of the fire department specifies in writing valid reasons for rejecting or passing over an individual.

Such reasons might include a record of serious disciplinary problems, including disobedience of written orders; frequent bad judgment when performing assigned duties; or a record of conflicts with other employees. Personnel records should be available to substantiate such rationale. These problems should be relatively current and not relate to behavior that occurred years ago that the individual has corrected.

Personnel Records. The fire department should maintain a careful and complete personnel record for each member. Such records cover all the pertinent facts of the person's fire service career, from probationary appointment through retirement, and include the original application for employment, all assignments, transfers, promotions, commendations, and records of disciplinary action. The record should also contain information on any special skills an individual possesses that may be useful to the department, as well as the individual's educational background.

In addition to the general record of an individual's service, a training file should be maintained, as covered in NFPA 1401, *Recommended Practice for Fire Service Training Reports and Records.* The file will show training periods and subjects in which the individual has received instruction, such as apparatus operation, emergency medical service, and fire inspection.

A medical history must be kept for each member, showing absences due to sickness and service-related injuries. A new addition to the personnel file is a record of exposure to hazardous materials and infectious diseases. This information provides a historical record of the fire fighter's known exposure to toxic materials or to infectious communicable diseases during his or her employment, as well as any appropriate inoculations he or she has received.

Productivity

Effectiveness in the fire service is difficult to measure. The basic objective of the fire service is the protection of life, property, and the environment. Modern fire service practice involves two major activities: controlling hazards to minimize fire losses and to prevent fires, and dealing with actual fires and emergencies to minimize suffering and losses. It is difficult to assess the number of fires and the amount of suffering or loss fire department activities have prevented. Experience demonstrates, however, that a lack of effective fire prevention and control measures invites disaster.

Likewise, the fact that most fires are suppressed with minimal losses and injuries does not indicate conclusively that an adequate level of fire department service has been provided. Experience shows that major fires and emergencies often arise from a combination of circumstances that are beyond the immediate control of fire department management but that must be dealt with effectively by the department to protect the public.

The fact that most fires are suppressed with minimal losses and injuries does not indicate conclusively that an adequate level of fire department service has been provided. Nor does the occurrence of a large-loss fire necessarily mean that the fire department is inadequate. Major fires and emergencies often arise from a combination of circumstances that are beyond the immediate control of the fire department, yet it is left to the department to manage the results.

Because local fire losses do not necessarily reflect fire department performance, fire department management must rely on regional and national fire loss experience to help them develop standards for the department. Frequent training and assessment of company effectiveness can also help provide benchmarks for performance on the fireground.

EMS services provided by fire departments range from first responders assisting ambulance crews to actually providing paramedic engine and ladder companies and an ambulance service. Fire departments involved in this aspect of public safety have seen significant increases in the use of personnel and equipment and in community support.

Increased emphasis on domestic preparedness and large-scale disaster response has caused increasing numbers of fire departments to develop hazardous materials teams. Many metropolitan-area fire service agencies are also active in a federal, state, or regional search-and-rescue team with structural collapse rescue capability. Until a large-scale emergency occurs and the value of their services is realized, the productivity of these specialized programs often is measured in training hours, equipment procured, and exercises completed.

Planning

Planning for the future needs of a fire department is the most important job of fire department managers. Without adequate planning, an administrator will find he or she is handling one crisis after another and can never seem to get ahead. Long-range planning has often been neglected by fire department managers, but with budget constraints, it is absolutely essential. The U.S. Fire Administration (USFA) has developed a master planning process, available to local communities, that outlines the steps a community may take to determine long-range goals for its fire department and explains how these goals can be achieved. The NFA Technical Support Program will assist local governments in developing a master planning process.

All departments, small and large, should develop short- and long-range strategic plans. Short-range plans are generally considered to encompass the next five years; long-range plans cover ten or more years. These plans must be flexible and should be continually updated to reflect changes in the community as well as developments within the fire service. The plans should also be known to department membership and the governing authority. Goals drawn from these plans should guide department budgeting, program development, and decision making. (See Section 12, Chapter 5, "Information Management and Computer Technology," for more information on this topic.)

Research

The term *research* is commonly heard in the fire service, yet few fire departments are staffed or financed to support any significant research activity. Most fire departments are relatively small organizations that do not have sufficient personnel to meet their ongoing fire protection obligations, let alone undertake real research into efficient equipment design.

The development of the Internet and the host of resources available online have made research easier. Websites have emerged that are useful to fire-rescue managers, such as the Lessons Learned Information Sharing site, http://www.llis.gov, maintained by the federal government. The Homeland Security Information Network–Emergency Management site, or HSIN-EM, provides a communication conduit for fire service leaders and managers across the country free of cost. It is intended to facilitate planning and operations activities within the fire community of the emergency services sector, according to the National Infrastructure Protection Plan. Countless other information and research sites are available through the Internet. Fire departments without routine, affordable access to the Internet should seek funding to make this critical connection to the greater fire service community and the world.

Few fire departments have been able to do true research into efficient equipment design. The same is true of most fire equipment suppliers. As competitive, small-volume businesses, they do not often generate a profit margin large enough to fund research and development. Fire apparatus builders have focused much of their engineering effort on meeting the increasingly exacting vehicle safety standards of the U.S. Department of Transportation (DOT). NFPA 1901, *Standard for Automotive Fire Apparatus,* updated every four years, also affects fire apparatus design and development.

One area in which fire department research can readily show returns is in fire record analysis, using programs such as the National Fire Incident Reporting System (NFIRS), which collects data from fire departments around the country. This information yields insights regarding hazards and trends, which allow prevention efforts to be targeted more effectively.

Well-analyzed data can be an informational gold mine, as long as the information is collected in a manner that supports analysis. Commercially produced software is available that will analyze a department's dispatch data. The results can help identify problems in response patterns, such as neighborhoods that receive subpar service delivery. Other applications can model or predict the value a new fire station or company could provide, recommend response arrays, and evaluate effective response times. With the proper tools and training, staff can also analyze data and return useful information.

Fire service managers seeking research expertise and resources can call on a range of fire service allies for help. The NFPA conducts research designed to help fire departments and makes this information available to interested parties around the world. The International Association of Fire Fighters (IAFF) Research Department is available on request to assist its local affiliates with problems. The USFA conducts and sponsors research relating to fire service needs.

Management Records and Reports

The fire chief and other administrative officers should have access to a records system that gives them data indicating how effective the department is at preventing and fighting fires. Complete records of all fires and inspections must be maintained and made available to government officials and the public. All records should be examined in light of their usefulness. A records retention and disposal system should be employed, and a careful review should be made to ensure that the records system meets all legal requirements. (See Section 12, Chapter 5, "Information Management and Computer Technology," for more information on this topic.)

STAFFING PRACTICES

The principal resource of a fire-rescue department is its personnel. In most fire departments, the vast majority of personnel are assigned to the emergency response division. Resource allocation will thus be most effective if all personnel—and particularly those assigned to fire fighting and rescue—are assigned for maximum use. This can be accomplished through careful time-utilization schedules, assigning appropriate portions of work periods to apparatus and equipment maintenance, training, inspections, and other duties expected of the response division. Careful coordination and planning can help create the most effective emergency service delivery program possible.

In some fire departments, a small percentage of personnel are assigned full-time to fire prevention. Typically, these personnel undertake plan review, code enforcement, fire cause determination, public fire education, and similar prevention and enforcement activities. Departments with adequate funding may also assign full-time personnel to perform new and existing code inspections.

Personnel may also be assigned to perform functions that support the operations of the response and prevention divisions. Such functions, which may be grouped together as preparedness activities for the operations of line personnel, include training, equipment and apparatus maintenance, and facilities management. Like fire prevention, the preparedness division also usually comprises a small percentage of a department's personnel.

Factors Affecting Staffing Levels

Staffing levels for fire departments vary considerably and are influenced by such things as the size or risk characteristic of the population protected, population density, fire fighters' work hours per week, response distances, community risk profile, and fire fighter safety. Most fire departments use a three- or four- platoon system that will accommodate a 56 to 42 hour workweek, respectively. A four-platoon system requires about a third more personnel than a three-platoon system. Staffing levels for cities of 250,000 or more population range from 0.5 to 2.9 fire fighters per thousand population, with a median of 1.1 to 1.5 per thousand. Cities in northeastern United States generally have a higher staffing ratio than do cities in the central northern and southern United States, which in turn tend to have higher staffing ratios than cities in the western United States. Communities must assess their needs to determine the level of staffing that meets their requirements. A study conducted with the Dallas, Texas, Fire Department, however, suggests that when staffing falls below four fire fighters per company, fireground effectiveness may be compromised, overtaxing available forces and contributing to higher losses.[9]

Certain fire-rescue service functions place additional requirements on department staffing. Fire departments operating emergency medical service transports need additional personnel, as time spent delivering patients to hospitals could otherwise erode effective fire company strength. In smaller communities, the staffing ratio per population protected may be relatively high because of the need for sufficient on-duty personnel for effective initial attack and rescue operations. This personnel need is especially true in "bedroom communities" where call personnel are not readily available during the workday. Similarly, fire departments in many core metropolitan cities protect more lives and property than population figures reflect. A city of 80,000 may be the business center for an area of 200,000 persons and house a high percentage of low-income groups. The number of high-rise buildings and structures with unusually high square footage to be protected and the frequency of alarms for fires and emergencies should be considered in determining on-duty fire department staffing.

Some very large fire departments may operate with a lower relative strength per thousand population than those in cities of a more moderate size because, with high population densities, these departments have sufficient companies to provide needed coverage while handling working fires. For example, a large city fire department may operate one engine company per 15,000 to 20,000 population and still have a large number of well-distributed fire companies, whereas a city of 30,000 might not be able to muster an effective fire-fighting force with only two engine companies.

Mutual aid plays an important role in providing additional resources. Even the largest jurisdictions rely to some extent on mutual aid from surrounding areas to provide fire-fighting resources on a routine or major emergency basis. Some departments use automatic mutual aid on initial response. Even large cities are making increased use of both regularly assigned and automatic mutual aid. This use is practical especially when companies from neighboring fire departments may be much nearer to an incident than the city's fire companies, and vice versa.

It is frequently impossible for small cities to fully staff all of the fire companies they need to handle working fires throughout the community. In many cases, the population density and the values protected per square mile are relatively low. In such communities, some engine companies may respond with only three persons on duty and ladder trucks with only two. Such low levels of staffing should be reinforced promptly by off-shift or call personnel or by multiple alarm response to ensure adequate operating forces. In some cases, additional apparatus may be assigned to respond, offsetting deficient company strength. In communities with large geographic areas and relatively low concentrations of value, this may be an acceptable arrangement. To promote fire fighter safety, NFPA 1500 recommends that interior fire fighting and rescue operations begin only when four personnel are on the scene. This is a requirement of OSHA as well, with limited exception. In general, each engine company should have a minimum of four fire fighters on duty, including an officer.

Staffing Career Fire Departments

The number and type of fire department emergency response personnel a jurisdiction needs is determined in part by the factors discussed previously in "Types of Fire Departments," such as (1) the financial resources of the community, (2) the availability of on-call or volunteer personnel, (3) the frequency of emergency incidents, (4) the range of services expected from the department, and (5) the type of department preferred by the community.

Other factors, which are elements of a department's Standards of Response Coverage and also influence required staffing, are (1) on-scene operations, which includes fire flow tasks and life safety tasks; (2) critical tasks, which must be conducted in a timely and safe manner to control a fire prior to flashover or to extinguish a fire; (3) the establishment of an adequate effective response force (ERF), which is the minimum staffing and equipment needed to perform the critical tasks; and (4) the ability to reach an emergency scene within a maximum total reflex time, which is the time elapsed from the call receipt to the time the units arrive on-scene.

The primary goal of every fire department should be to arrive at an emergency scene with an adequate number of well-trained and fully-equipped personnel, within the time allotted by a department's response time standard, and in a manner that meets the expectations of the community. This goal is the starting point for determining adequate staffing for a career fire department.

Tours of Duty. Fire departments are traditionally staffed 24 hours a day. The next step in determining adequate staffing is to identify the number of positions that must be covered 24 hours a day throughout the year, plus the number of duty tours, or employee shifts, required for each 24 hour period. If 24-hour shifts are used, there is one duty tour per position per day. With 10 to 14 hour or similar tours of duty, there are 2 per day or 730 per year.

As an example, take a community that has determined that at least 58 officers and fire fighters should be on duty at all times. With a 42-hour-average workweek, including day and night shifts, each shift or group is on duty 182.5 times during a 365 day year. With 58 persons on duty, this requires 42,340 individual tours of duty per year.

This fire department's records show that with vacation, sick and injured leave, and other absences, its fire fighters actually average not 182.5 but 146.5 tours of duty per year. The required 42,340 tours of duty, divided by 146.5 tours worked per person, show that instead of 212 officers and fire fighters, 289 are actually needed to provide a minimum of 58 personnel on duty and cover the anticipated absences. The additional personnel would be distributed among the companies in the district. Even when vacations are carefully scheduled so that only one person from each shift of each company is absent at any given time, off-duty personnel may sometimes have to be used on an overtime basis due to sickness or injury. The budget should allow for contingency overtime as needed to call back members to cover staffing shortfalls as well as major fires and emergencies.

Defining Minimum Staffing. In many fire departments, when an unusually high number of absences occur, stations housing more than one company may be allowed to operate one person below the desired minimum rather than pay overtime, unless the company minimum strength is specified by contract or city ordinance. Other jurisdictions with a defined minimum staffing level may be forced to take units out of service if the funding level cannot support overtime.

Generally, a 42 hour workweek requires not four but five persons per position. Thus, a 20 person company is needed to maintain an average of four on duty. Because this does not allow two members to be away from their shifts at one time, overtime or personnel swaps between companies may occasionally be needed.

With a fire department operating on a three-platoon system with 24-hour duty tours, each platoon covers 122 tours in 366 days (a leap year). It requires 21,208 tours to have 58 officers and fire fighters on duty. The records in this example indicate that the average member works 98 tours per year. Thus, 21,208 divided by 98 requires 216 fire fighters or 72 for each of the three platoons. With a 53-hour maximum workweek permitted under federal labor law (FLSA), however, each member working more than 53 hours in each 28 day work period would exceed the allowable maximum by 3 hours and would be eligible for extra compensation, except possibly when the work cycle is broken by absences.

When minimum company strength of five persons is desired for a 42 hour workweek, most fire companies have 24 persons assigned to the four duty shifts and 28 assigned for approximately every fourth company. In some fire departments where more vacations are scheduled in the summer months, a 4 person minimum may be maintained in the summer and a 5 person minimum maintained in the winter. However, most fire departments prefer to maintain minimum staffing year round rather than attempt to adjust for seasonal trends. If additional personnel are needed during severe winter storms, they are provided on a temporary overtime basis and are paid from the overtime account.

It was customary in the past to allow 10 percent for absences from assigned shifts due to vacations and sickness. Now the figure commonly is 20 percent or more. Vacations have been increased, and employee benefit programs or work contracts often provide for various other compensated absences from duty.

Meeting Minimum Staffing Requirements. The practice of establishing minimum staffing levels for each fire company or duty shift has become widespread in recent decades. It is a policy in many fire departments not to operate engine or ladder companies with fewer than four fire fighters, including an officer, on duty. In rare cases, because of the workload and the population and values protected per company, the minimum is five persons on duty per company. When a company member is sick or injured while another member is on vacation and no on-duty fire fighter is available to cover the absence, the department employs an off-duty fire fighter on an overtime basis to maintain minimum strength.

Labor boards and at least one court have found that minimum staffing agreements or ordinances are reasonable requirements for the protection of the public and personnel. A number of small fire departments that do not attempt to maintain minimum on-duty company strength have established a minimum for the duty shift while employing off-duty personnel to maintain the predetermined minimum effective strength. Such a plan should account for apparatus that must be operated from several fire stations before off-shift or call fire fighters can arrive to assist. In order to meet minimum staffing goals, it is helpful to have a policy that regulates the number of vacancies permitted due to discretionary absences.

As noted above, off-duty personnel may sometimes be used on an overtime basis when unscheduled absences reduce staffing below the minimum level. This use is usually more economical than maintaining a roster that is large enough to prevent these occasions from ever occurring, but if the roster is too small, overtime may cost more than hiring more members. The calculation of staffing levels should thus be made carefully, considering not only scheduled absences but also typical levels of sick, injured, and military leave, temporary reassignment of emergency response personnel to nonemergency functions, and any other factors that can reduce the number of on-duty personnel.

Work Schedules. Most fire fighters who work an average of more than 50 hours per week use a 24 hour tour of duty. Most fire fighters who work 48 or fewer hours per week have day and night shifts; the most common is a 10 hour day shift and 14 hour night shift. When the law states that anyone working more than 40 hours per week will be paid overtime, many fire departments work a 42-hour, four-platoon schedule by paying 2 hours of overtime. Often, this is considerably less expensive than hiring additional personnel, and better teamwork is maintained by keeping crews together on a regular four-shift basis. (The Department of Labor Issues and Collective Bargaining of the International Association of Firefighters has published "The Hours/Schedules Kit," a compendium of various duty shifts and schedules that have been employed by fire departments.)

Occasionally, municipal administrators have suggested that fire fighters be assigned to an 8-hour-day/40-hour-week work schedule similar to police schedules. This schedule has not proven to be practical or desirable. On-duty police staffing properly varies with the time of day and day of the week, as required by demands for traffic control, patrolling, details, and so on. The work involved in fire fighting and rescue requires a team effort, and the team includes platoon chief officers, company officers, apparatus operators, and fire fighters working together on a regular basis. Serious fires and accidents occur at every hour of the day and night and on every day of the week. Thus, the uniform staffing provided by three- and four-platoon systems is essential to effective, timely operations. Work shifts are readily scheduled in seven 24-hour tours of duty per week on a 56-hour average workweek, or fourteen 10- and 14-hour tours of duty per week on a 42-hour average workweek. When the 168-hour calendar week is divided by 8 hour tours, 21 work shifts are required, a number that cannot be used to schedule evenly staffed platoons around the clock.

In most instances where the 8 hour schedule has been proposed, it has been rejected. Very few fire-rescue departments in the entire United States use an 8 hour work shift. The choice between having fire fighters on 24 hour shifts, or reducing staffing or resources by 40 percent to accommodate 8 hour work shifts, means most municipal fire departments can not seriously consider the latter. As the fire service becomes more adept at computerized analysis of emergency incidents and develops a good base of response data, staffing arrangements similar to police staffing may be possible in the future, particularly for EMS personnel. Demand analysis may demonstrate predictable patterns that can be addressed through more flexible staffing levels.

The requirement for overtime has resulted in improved mutual-aid arrangements, as on-duty companies from nearby departments can respond much faster than can off-duty local personnel called back in. Relying on mutual aid in this way also keeps overtime costs down. However, many small fire departments rely heavily on off-duty response on an overtime basis. Usually a minimum of 2- and 4-hour overtime pay is guaranteed for each response. When alarms for structure fires are infrequent, it may be much more economical for a small municipality to contract for overtime response than to provide a fully staffed fire company around the clock. One major drawback to this scheme is increased response times that will adversely affect fire losses.

Staffing Combination and Volunteer Fire Departments

Significant portions of the populations of the United States and Canada live in communities that cannot support career firefighting personnel. According to a 2002 study, whereas 40 percent of the U.S. population is served by career-level fire departments, 26 percent of U.S. citizens live in communities or rural areas whose fire departments are staffed entirely by volunteers.[1]

In most small communities, volunteer fire departments are based on a "neighbor helping neighbor" philosophy in which members receive no compensation other than possibly some reimbursement for personal expenses and uniforms. It is estimated that 84 percent of communities with populations ranging from 2500 to 4999, and 96 percent of those under 2500 are served by all-volunteer fire departments.[1] Various states have recognized the contribution made by their volunteer fire fighters by enacting protective legislation and providing statewide training programs, facilities, retirement systems, tax relief, and similar supportive measures.

Volunteers. When they receive an alarm, members of many volunteer fire departments report to assigned fire stations from which they respond with apparatus; other departments allow members to respond directly to the incident. To guarantee an effective working crew, many departments require the first piece of apparatus to respond with at least three members. NFPA 1720, *Standard for the Organization and Deployment of Fire Suppression Operations, Emergency Medical Operations, and Special Operations to the Public by Volunteer Fire Departments,* states that volunteer fire companies should not conduct interior fire-fighting operations unless at least four trained members are on the scene.

Fire department administrators should periodically review response records to make sure enough members are responding to emergencies at all times and, if this is not the case, should recruit and train new personnel. In an all-volunteer fire department, staff positions are filled by volunteer officers. In other systems, career personnel may be hired to fill fire prevention, training, and/or communications functions.

Career Staff. Employing career fire fighters means a faster response time and greater efficiency. The fire fighters on duty take the apparatus to the fire, and the volunteers go directly to the fire when notified, thus saving an average of about 3 minutes in arrival time. The career apparatus operator normally is in charge of the apparatus and of the fire station, but volunteer officers may direct the fire fighting. One difficulty with this arrangement is that there are few, if any, opportunities for advancement for career personnel.

An arrangement that works successfully is to have the first responding pumper staffed by a career officer, an apparatus operator, and, when staffing permits, an additional fire fighter. This force is supplemented by additional personnel assigned to respond on call. The second-due engine may be staffed by volunteers or paid call personnel, or it may have a career apparatus operator to take the apparatus to the fire, where it is joined by the volunteer or paid call fire fighters. The ladder truck has a career apparatus operator assigned but is staffed at the fire by volunteer or paid call fire fighters. This arrangement permits a reasonably effective initial fire attack that is quickly backed by volunteer or paid call members. In all cases, there should be just one fire department in any jurisdiction, operating under a clearly defined and unified chain of command that is known to all department members.

Teams of Volunteer and Career Staff. In a number of combination fire departments, career fire fighters have complained about being commanded by volunteer officers whom they felt lacked the needed experience and qualifications. All fire officers should meet the appropriate NFPA qualifications for their rank, as many volunteer officers do. When a career apparatus operator is assigned to operate volunteer fire company apparatus, he or she should work under the orders of the volunteer officer of that company on the fireground. It is important that administrators make clear the respective roles and duties of all members, career and volunteer.

As the principal fire protection officer of a community, the chief of the department should be appointed on the basis of qualifications and experience. The increasing legal and technical responsibilities of the job strongly suggest that communities should consider adopting NFPA standards for fire officers and fire fighters as minimum requirements.

Call Fire Fighters

Many fire departments in small communities employ fire fighters who have no regular duty shift in the stations but are paid by the hour or by the incident for response to alarms and drills. Such members are sometimes loosely termed "volunteers," but under federal labor rules they are considered paid employees of the fire department and, as such, are subject to federal wage and hour regulations.

Compensation. In most cases, call fire fighters are local businesspeople and tradespeople who are willing to be part-time fire fighters. The paid on-call members may also be employed by another agency of the jurisdiction, in which case the time they spend on fire department duty may affect their overtime status. Call fire fighters are expected to meet the same standards of performance as career members of the same rank, although they may not be assigned as apparatus operators when there are sufficient career operators on shift duty.

A call fire fighter's service time is based on attendance at fires and training sessions, with a minimum hourly rate specified for response to alarms. Often, on reaching mandatory retirement age, they also receive a prorated pension, based on their years of service and hours of duty. Various methods are used to determine compensation for paid call fire fighters. In many departments, they receive the same hourly wage for their rank as employees who work regular duty shifts.

Another method of compensation is a fixed annual salary based on rank, from which deductions are made for excessive numbers of unexcused failures to respond or train with the assigned companies. Many fire chiefs arrange to excuse members known to be at their regular employment, except in the case of multiple alarm fires. Chiefs should have the authority to dismiss members who frequently fail to respond to fires or to complete required training sessions.

Still another method of compensation is to make an annual appropriation for call fire service, based on past experience, designed to approximate the hourly wage rate for fire fighters. This amount is divided on a regular basis among the call members as determined by individual attendance at fires and training sessions, so that members responding most faithfully receive the largest compensation. Whatever the compensation method used, the fire department should pay for members' insurance, workers' compensation, training, and all protective equipment.

Service Records. Accurate individual service records should be kept in the personnel files of all fire fighters, both career and volunteer. Response and attendance records are also essential, and members who are habitually late in responding should be replaced. Accurate response records can help identify staffing deficiencies and justify hiring additional career personnel. Municipal officials have often believed that because several hundred volunteers' names were on the roster, the fire department had ample strength, when actually most of those listed were no longer active. This type of situation has resulted in serious delays and in the extension of fires that should have been readily controlled.

Senior fire fighters who cannot respond regularly to first alarms may be assigned to operate reserve apparatus or to guide mutual-aid fire companies when serious fires occur. Other senior call members may be assigned to cover the alarm desk when paid apparatus operators are out of quarters.

PROCURING EQUIPMENT AND SUPPLIES

In most municipalities, fire department equipment and supplies are procured through purchasing departments. Items such as office supplies that are common to all departments may be requisitioned from the purchasing agency and charged to the appropriate fire department account. When items are of a specialized nature, such as fire apparatus or fire-fighting tools and equipment, purchasing specifications must be prepared by the fire department, approved by the purchasing department, and advertised for bids. In preparing specifications for such items as fire apparatus and fire hose, current NFPA standards should be followed.

The fire chief, with advice from the apparatus equipment supervisor, should determine whether proposals submitted by bidders meet specifications. In larger jurisdictions, the law requires that a contract be awarded to the lowest responsible bidder. However, bidders frequently take exception to various details in the specifications or offer substitutes. This situation requires that a fire chief determine whether such proposals meet the intentions of the specifications. If they do not, the bids should be rejected. If, however, the proposals conform to the specifications and are within the appropriation, the contract should be awarded. On delivery, new equipment should be tested in accordance with appropriate NFPA standards.

When emergency purchases must be made, it is customary to require bids from several suppliers. If the amount involved is small and funds are available in the appropriate budget item, the fire chief can authorize the expenditure. If funds are not available in the fire department budget, authorization and funds must be obtained from the municipal management or finance officer.

GOVERNMENTAL RELATIONS

Fire departments are but one agency of local government, and much of their success depends on cooperative working relationships with other local, state, and federal agencies. Some of the more important intergovernmental contacts are discussed here.

Building Department

The proper construction and arrangement of buildings is essential to a sound fire protection program. A community's building department is a key component in ensuring quality control in building construction and compliance with the fire protection features of local building codes.

State laws and local ordinances or agreements between fire and building departments increasingly require the head of the fire department to give written approval of specified fire protection features before building and occupancy permits can be issued. Close cooperation is also needed between these departments to control serious fire hazards that commonly are present while buildings are under construction, before the required fire resistance or protection features have been installed. In small communities, the fire chief generally must handle these duties, but in many fire departments, they are some of the responsibilities delegated to the fire prevention bureau.

Law Enforcement Department

Cooperation between the fire department and law enforcement officials is essential. Regular law enforcement response to fire alarms and other emergency scenes is necessary to control traffic and crowds and otherwise support operations. Similarly, fire-rescue departments are frequently called on to respond in support of law enforcement in investigating criminal matters. Such support can include initiating patient care, extricating victims from vehicles, and providing access to roofs. Fire and law enforcement agencies must develop coordinated plans for managing incidents that require the evacuation or closure of areas.

Law enforcement and fire officials must also develop working relationships to deal effectively with criminal investigations of fires. Many areas use fire investigation teams made up of both fire and law enforcement personnel. Many other fire departments employ fire investigators who have received the necessary law enforcement training to obtain "police powers." These personnel undertake the complete investigation to determine fire cause and origin. In these cases, both agencies work together, combining their areas of special expertise in a coordinated effort when arson is suspected.

As partner agencies in public safety, fire and law enforcement agencies must plan and train together. The scope of incidents that require coordination and unified command to be managed successfully is very broad. Heads of public safety agencies should establish mutual goals and plans that can be relied on in any incident, minor or disastrous.

Water Department

Adequate water supplies, including hydrant service, are essential for fire fighting and are the responsibility of the water department. All too often, water authorities have little knowledge of the waterflow requirements of the fire department for various areas and types of property. Thousands of fire hydrants have been set up improperly because water department crews did not understand the proper location and setting of hydrants required for efficient fire fighting. To prevent this, a knowledgeable fire officer should be assigned as liaison with the water authority. In some communities, the fire department is responsible, by ordinance, for determining the location and setting of hydrants.

All hydrants must be serviced regularly and after use, especially in cold weather. After each incident, the fire department should report all hydrants used to the water department promptly. Alert fire departments maintain a list of hydrants in each fire company inspection district with flow data on each hydrant. (In areas where the water distribution system produces fluctuating flows, however, hydrants should not be marked with flow data.) Hydrants should be marked for nighttime visibility. In many communities the development of geographical information systems (GIS) maps has included a layer that shows the location of every hydrant in the jurisdiction. GIS maps available electronically, and those that identify the global positioning system (GPS) location of the hydrants are increasingly common.

Water departments should operate according to nationally recognized standards, such as those published by the Insurance Services Organization (ISO) and the American Water Works Association (AWWA). The fire department liaison officer should be familiar with the standards and guidance used by the water department. The fire department should work closely with the water department to identify areas of responsibility and authority for matters such as private hydrant maintenance (in shopping centers, etc.), records management, and development planning and zoning issues.

Public Health Department

Local public health agencies are key partners in community risk management. Fire-rescue department officials should be familiar with local public health officials and coordinate disaster preparedness, response, and recovery planning. A department liaison officer should identify a point of contact within the local public health agency with which regular contact can be maintained. The local health agency is also a conduit to state and federal public health authorities. Public health planners can share guidance with department members for handling emerging diseases and other biohazards, as well as information that has been prepared to inform the public of these issues.

Transportation Department

The local department of transportation is responsible for building and maintaining local roads and streets, and is in constant contact with regional, state, and federal department of transportation agencies. Fire-rescue departments should establish and maintain a good working relationship with the local department of transportation, including staying abreast of its short- and long-term plans for the area. During transportation emergencies, the department of transportation is an invaluable resource and should be part of the unified command structure.

Many metropolitan areas have a regional transportation authority that acts as the long-term planning body for the region. The plans developed often include light rail, rail, and bus systems. Understanding in advance what new modes of transportation and vehicles of conveyance will be brought into the area can be important to fire-rescue planners. A liaison to the regional transportation authority can assist in setting realistic objectives in long-term planning.

Domestic Preparedness Department

Since the federal Department of Homeland Security was created in 2002, state and local government offices have also been organized to address domestic preparedness concerns. The primary goal of these offices is to prevent acts of terrorism, but they also prepare for, respond to, and lead recovery efforts following such acts. Fire-rescue departments should be aware of and in conversation with any homeland security office with standing in their jurisdiction. If an information sharing and analysis center (ISAC) has been created, the department should ensure that fire-rescue personnel participate in its activities and receive relevant information as it is developed. The resilience of a community and its ability to rebound following a terrorist attack will likely hinge on the degree to which comprehensive planning and networking occurred prior to the attack. Fire-rescue officials should insert themselves into local and regional antiterrorism preparedness efforts, along with their allied planning partners.

Emergency Management Agency

Many fire departments are organized to operate the local emergency management agency (EMA) as well. As EMAs have become larger and taken on a wider range of services, however, independently organized EMAs have sprung up within local government. Fire-rescue departments should position themselves as a main support agency to the local EMA. Planning and preparedness for natural disasters is often the primary focus of the EMA and fire-rescue planners have experience, equipment, and trained, geographically distributed staff to offer the community when disaster strikes.

Public Education Department

In the realm of fire safety education, the local public and private school systems, the parks and recreation department, and the public library system can augment and support the local fire department's educational activities. If public fire safety educational activities are to be successful, the local fire department must be able to serve as a focal point for other community resources and be able to build partnerships across a wide variety of public and private organizations. The *Learn Not to Burn*® program is one of the NFPA's excellent fire safety education programs with proven results.

The community safety village is a successful concept originally developed in Canada and now becoming more common in the United States. These villages offer a delivery point in the community for programs of safety education and can include a wide range of education programs, including fire, bicycle, pool, pedestrian, driver, and gun safety. The typical village incorporates classroom space and a kid-sized town into a campus that is used as a training ground for practical elements of the safety lessons. The safety village thus allows a range of organizations to collaborate in managing risk and improving community safety.

Human Resources Department

Members of career fire departments are public employees, and, as such, their recruitment and promotion may involve cooperation with the human resources agency, which, in some jurisdictions, is responsible for conducting entrance and promotional examinations. Fire department management should work closely with the human resources or personnel office, which usually manages compensation and benefits programs for the employing authority.

Finance Department

Fire departments should work closely with finance officials when developing and administering budgets. Budgeting is generally very complex, and fire budget documents must be well prepared. After budgets have been prepared and adopted, proper records of expenditures must be maintained and spending must be kept within the adopted budget. Although some fire departments may have a finance officer, liaison with the finance department may be handled by designated staff officers.

Purchasing Department

All purchases exceeding stipulated amounts must be made according to specifications, usually with competitive bidding conducted by the purchasing department. Close liaison is necessary to ensure that specifications are drawn properly and meet fire department needs and that, when bids are opened, any proposals that deviate from specifications are rejected.

Data Processing Department

Increasingly, fire departments are using electronic data processing to keep fire records and payroll records for statistical analysis. Each fire department should have persons knowledgeable in data processing. It may be desirable to appoint one officer to coordinate this activity and to be involved in administrative planning for the department.

Planning Department

Fire departments, particularly those in rapidly growing areas, should maintain a close working relationship with local and regional planning groups, such as the local emergency planning council (LEPC) and the regional transportation authority. These agencies can provide valuable information on growth patterns that will affect the resources of the department and demands on those resources. The plans, studies, and reports prepared by the planning agencies can be used to determine whether more personnel, equipment, or station facilities are needed.

A variety of other sources of information are also available to fire department planners. Local academic institutions may provide resources that can aid in strategic planning. Coalitions of government that act to coordinate local government agencies actions in regional emergencies often develop sector-specific committees that can serve as referent information sources to planners. Recently, regional planning bodies that convene to address domestic preparedness issues, such as urban area security initiatives, have also become available as a planning resource. Astute fire-rescue planners will avail themselves of the entire planning and information community.

SUMMARY

Fire departments have evolved into organizations that provide a wide array of services. Although fire prevention and emergency response continue to form the basis of the service, most departments now provide some level of emergency medical service, and others provide specialized rescue and hazardous materials response. The growing threat of terrorism presents a new challenge to the changing fire service.

There are many common denominators that define a successful fire service organization. The most successful ones, however, have developed and have adjusted to meet the changing needs of their local communities. Although regional differences result in a significant diversity in structure and staffing, volunteer, paid, and combination departments all function in an environment in which their effectiveness depends on successful intergovernmental relationships with many agencies that interact to achieve public safety.

BIBLIOGRAPHY

References Cited

1. U.S. Fire Administration and NFPA, "A Needs Assessment of the U.S. Fire Service," FA-240, Federal Emergency Management Agency, Washington, DC, Dec. 2002.
2. Cochran, K. J., "Management and Leadership in the Fire Service," *Chief Fire Officer's Desk Reference,* J. M. Buckman III (Ed.), International Association of Fire Chiefs, Fairfax, VA, 2006.
3. Blackstone, G. V., *A History of the British Fire Service,* Rutledge and Kegan Paul, London, UK, 1957.
4. Ditzel, P. C., *Fire Engines and Firefighters,* Crown, New York, 1976, p. 21.
5. National Fire Academy, "Approximation of State Fire Training Assets (01/01/05)," U.S. Fire Administration, Emmitsburg, MD, 2005.
6. Karter, M. J., *U.S. Fire Department Profile,* National Fire Protection Association, Quincy, MA, Oct. 2006.
7. *Firefighter Fatalities in the United States,* National Fire Protection Association, Quincy, MA, June 2004.
8. *Firefighter Injuries in the United States,* National Fire Protection Association, Quincy, MA, Nov. 2004.
9. Hendrix, M. C., "Manpower Analysis 1969—Dallas, Texas, Fire Department," International Association of Fire Chiefs, Bulletin No. FSTB-401, Washington, DC, 1969.

NFPA Codes, Standards, and Recommended Practices

Reference to the following NFPA codes, standards, and recommended practices will provide further information on the management of fire-rescue departments discussed in this chapter. (See the latest version of The NFPA Catalog *for availability of the current editions of the following documents.)*

NFPA 1001, *Standard for Fire Fighter Professional Qualifications*
NFPA 1021, *Standard for Fire Officer Professional Qualifications*
NFPA 1221, *Standard for the Installation, Maintenance, and Use of Emergency Services Communications Systems*
NFPA 1401, *Recommended Practice for Fire Service Training Reports and Records*
NFPA 1500, *Standard on Fire Department Occupational Safety and Health Program*
NFPA 1620, *Recommended Practice for Pre-Incident Planning*
NFPA 1720, *Standard for the Organization and Deployment of Fire Suppression Operations, Emergency Medical Operations, and Special Operations to the Public by Volunteer Fire Departments*
NFPA 1901, *Standard for Automotive Fire Apparatus*

Chapter 5

Information Management and Computer Technology

Brian P. Duggan

Chapter Contents

Key Terms

computer-aided dispatch, enhanced 9-1-1, geographic information system (GIS), incident reporting system, information management, information technology, interoperable communications, Learning Resource Center (LRC), local area network (LAN), mobile data terminal, office automation, personnel accountability system, thermal imaging, wide area network (WAN)

As the fire service enters a new age of expanded information, technology continues to evolve rapidly. This digital revolution has produced an unprecedented external force that requires fire service organizations to change and adapt in an environment increasingly focused on the instantaneous exchange of information. Information-based technology continues to expand at an exponential rate. Often technology is initially developed for the military, space program, or the business community and then adapted to benefit the fire service. The trend toward expanding information applications, integration, and mobile connectivity should be anticipated, and new fire service applications that extend beyond those mentioned here should be expected. Examples of developing applications include intelligent transportation systems that will provide responding units with incident-related information and voice integration that will allow computers to recognize and respond to an individual's voice.

Information technology can enhance organizational effectiveness and efficiency by providing rapid access to high-quality information and empower fire department personnel to offer a higher level of service. Information technology has become an organizational necessity and provides a means for the fire service to innovate and adapt in an increasingly digital world. Although it is clear that the fire service needs to learn new technologies, its mission must be to harness and drive the technology as opposed to allowing technology to drive the fire service.

For related information, see Section 3, Chapter 3, "Fire Data Collection and Databases"; Section 3, Chapter 4, "Use of Fire Incident Data and Statistics"; and Section 12, Chapter 13, "GIS for Fire Station Locations and Response Protocols."

INFORMATION TECHNOLOGY NETWORKS

The availability of low-cost personal computers, widespread Internet access, and wireless connectivity provides even the smallest fire service organizations with the ability to utilize many of the applications discussed in this chapter. As price points continue to decline, a wider range of technology will become more available. In some cases this technology will become single-use disposable items that are critical to operational success. Technology has become evident in most aspects of our culture and can complement the mission of the fire service. These applications range from the dispatch of apparatus to training personnel and providing public education and information services to target populations. Figure 12.5.1 shows an example of fire service specific handheld technology. This rugged unit provides mobile wireless computing for a wide range of fire service applications including personnel accountability and building inspection.

As with many public sector agencies, the fire service is facing the reality of increased competition and diminished resources. Like all government units, the fire service has been asked to maintain, and even increase, service levels. Information technology can facilitate new levels of communication and can help integrate services that provide a foundation for quality service delivery

Brian P. Duggan is the fire chief in the city of Northampton, Massachusetts, and has served as the director of fire science programs at Anna Maria College in Paxton, Massachusetts. Chief Duggan also chairs the Fire Chief's Association of Massachusetts Technology Committee and co-directs the Massachusetts Fire Mobilization Plan.

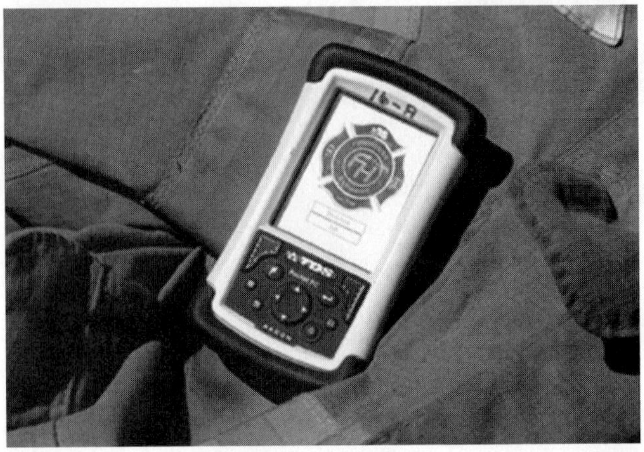

FIGURE 12.5.1 Handheld Technology Specific to Fire Service (Photo provided courtesy of Tripod Data Systems, Inc.)

and innovation. The contradiction of "doing more with less" can be resolved only with improved management practices that result in higher levels of organizational productivity. Information technology can assist the fire service in meeting the increasing challenges of the twenty-first century. Specifically, information technology is being used to support and complement the following fire service functions:

- Administration and office automation
- Emergency management
- Emergency response, operations, and safety
- Enhanced internal and external communication
- Fire prevention public education and community outreach
- Hazard detection
- Research activity reporting
- Resource control and deployment
- Training

Although the extent of automation varies, the development of information technology has become a specialized niche and many larger organizations have hired information managers and Internet specialists to maximize the organization's ability to successfully apply and benefit from information technology. Information technology has produced a focus on enhancing the effectiveness of both internal and external communication. As such, the development of a sound information technology plan that collaborates and coordinates with other agencies is critical to success.

Local Area Networks (LAN) and Wide Area Networks (WAN)

Connectivity and mobile information applications deserve special attention based on the potential of these applications to benefit the fire service. First, internal connectivity provides the ability to rapidly integrate and share information through the use of local area networks (LAN) and intranets by providing a consistent source of enhanced internal organizational communication. Second, connectivity frequently extends beyond a single agency through the use of a wide area network (WAN). For example, every department in a city may be connected and allowed to rapidly share information and communicate through the use of a single WAN. Networks once fed through miles of wire are quickly becoming wireless and as such more versatile.

The Internet

Connectivity can be further extended through the use of the Internet. The Internet—the organized part of which is called the World Wide Web—provides a means of external connection that can facilitate almost instantaneous communication, data transfer, and information exchange across the globe. The Internet is becoming the most frequent portal of organizational contact with the public. At present, most public sector agencies and private companies maintain an easily accessed informational or commerce-based website. NFPA, for example, maintains a home page on the World Wide Web at http://www.nfpa.org. The Internet provides sources of information on any subject. Some of this information can have relevance in supporting programs, establishing contacts with other persons dealing with the same issues, or developing information for research.

As the Internet has expanded it has become a resource that in many ways has replaced text-based reference sources and printed materials. In essence the Internet has become a library of information and as such an indispensable resource. An example of the vast amount of fire service data available through the Internet can be found through the Learning Resource Center (LRC), which is a virtual fire service specific library maintained by the United States Fire Administration. The LRC provides instant access to an extensive quantity of fire service research and publications. This resource can be found on the Internet at http://www.usfa.fema.gov/training/lrc. Those using information from the Internet are cautioned to verify the source and validity of that information because there is no professional oversight as to what is posted other than information posted by technical organizations.

Fire service agencies can use the Internet successfully for an ever-broadening range of communication needs. One example of how the Internet can benefit the fire service is by providing instant access to the current *National Fire Codes*®, which is an option available through a secure portion of the NFPA website. Through this service, the subscriber is ensured access to updated codes. Previously, updates of *National Fire Codes* were mailed out in printed form or on CD-ROM on a regular basis. This use of technology decreases publication costs, enhances the use of current standards, and increases the effectiveness and efficiency of the subscriber.

Other Internet applications include information research, electronic transactions, purchasing, public outreach, voice communication, video transmission, data transmission, and distance learning. The Internet also provides a tremendous potential for the future as technology continues to evolve.

Although the Internet is full of useful information and has become a primary research tool, it also contains hazards. As technology has developed, viruses, unwanted junk e-mail, and unauthorized intrusion into organizational networks have become all too common. Organizations need to be mindful of these threats and provide appropriate protection through the use of firewalls, secure software, and diligent data backup.

Wireless Connectivity and Mobile Data

Wireless connectivity has become commonplace, and this technology can be utilized to further extend fire service capabilities. Mobile data allow responding units and command personnel to have rapid access to critical address-based information (Figure 12.5.2). Mobile data also enhance the effectiveness and efficiency of event reporting, allowing fire, medical, and inspection reports to be completed in the field and uploaded to a secure server. Clearly this provides a more rapid means of data collection and reduces the time personnel previously dedicated to these administrative functions on their return from an incident or fire prevention activity.

The advantages of mobile data and wireless connectivity are evident both at the incident scene and through the application of technology developed for the business world. Fire service agencies can also use wireless technology to dramatically enhance communication and coordination of nonresponse functions. Examples of this include electronic mail, remote retrieval of department records, and scheduling applications.

The information age has also provided additional tools that can be used to enhance both safety and operational effectiveness. Examples include computer-driven infrared imagery, electronic personnel accountability systems, and command management software.

Many fire departments have automated a wide variety of functions. Integration of several applications allows for the sharing and retrieval of information among previously distant platforms. Fire service information can be shared among databases and linked through the common thread of address-, person-, or resource-based information fields. (For related information, see Section 3, Chapter 3, "Fire Data Collection and Databases," and Section 3, Chapter 4, "Use of Fire Incident Data and Statistics.")

FIGURE 12.5.2 Command Officer Using a Mobile Data Terminal (Photo provided courtesy of Livermore-Pleasanton Fire Department)

MANAGEMENT APPLICATIONS

Information Management

The successful functioning of a fire department's *information technology*—a term that is used here to include computers, software, data, applications, connectivity, and personnel—depends on how that technology is organized, managed, and incorporated into the organization. Because every organization is unique and because technology continues to provide expanded application opportunities, there is no single best way to develop information technology. A critical step that is often overlooked, however, is the development and training of personnel. Organizations often fail to invest in training personnel how to use and benefit from technology. Without the appropriate development and training of personnel, their resistance to the new technology that often impedes the effective deployment of applications should be anticipated.

Information management within an organization is critical to an organization's overall success. Consequently, information systems are valuable organizational components that must be well managed. Many fire departments now have senior staff members who are responsible for the management of information systems.

Organizational Needs vis-à-vis Information Systems

A well-developed information system fulfills a variety of organizational needs:

- Strategic planning
- Resource optimization
- Support of daily operations
- Public outreach and communications
- Internal communication and documentation

Strategic Planning. Strategic planning is the process by which fire service leaders decide how future resources will be allocated or deployed in the delivery of services—for example, how and where facilities, emergency equipment, and personnel will be distributed. Some fire departments have developed sophisticated computer-based models for the development of strategic plans; others have contracted outside resource groups to provide such analyses. Although modeling applications are becoming cost-effective and widely available, most fire departments depend on the statistical information from fire incident and emergency medical reporting systems as a basis for decision making.

Resource Optimization. Resource optimization is the process of maximizing the output or service provided by resources. Therefore, by optimizing resources we can ensure a high level of effectiveness and efficiency. Resource optimization begins with implementation of strategic choices identified through strategic planning. It continues with the use of control information to make tactical and operational decisions consistent with the organization's strategy and oversight that all decisions are being implemented as intended. Administrative control and automation are necessary in several areas: (1) finance, (2) personnel, (3) fire prevention, (4) fire investigation, (5) fire suppression, and (6) facility management. Control information is often provided as an additional output of systems designed to support administrative operations. In other words, many applications were initiated for administrative utilization. As an additional benefit, this information can often be used to optimize control of resources such as personnel and equipment. For example, a personnel information system developed to increase the efficiency of collecting and tracking data on individual personnel is likely to permit easy tracking of secondary data useful as controls on the entire workforce (e.g., scheduling of needed training). Applications such as a personnel information-gathering system are often adapted from programs originally developed to meet the needs of the business world.

Support of Daily Operations. The majority of fire service applications and information systems are designed to support day-to-day operations. The most common examples of this type of system are computer-aided dispatch (CAD) and enhanced 9-1-1 (E9-1-1). These systems attempt to optimize response by combining the most accurate data about both the emergency situation and resource availability. Other systems support financial management, fire investigation, equipment inventory and maintenance, inspections, permits, and organizational communications.

Public Outreach and Communications. The ability to provide information to the customer is critical to the future success of the fire service. Websites, e-mail, and distance learning provide an electronic means of enhancing outreach and communication within the community. This form of communication engages the community and provides a previously unheard of level of public contact and customer support. Departments often utilize this conduit to provide information about both the organization and life safety.

Internal Communication and Documentation. The systems applications cited earlier operate as systems of information flow and processing. Each requires certain forms of internal communication and documentation. Strategic planning and resource optimization depend on internal communication of goals, objectives, alternative choices and decisions, and documented field experience, activities, and inventories. Operations support requires internal communications of situation-specific facts and decisions based on the interpretation of principles and procedures in light of these facts. Through integration, systems are often packaged as a function of priorities based on systems planning, organizational needs, and these types of situational factors. There are, however, certain recurring patterns to the way information systems are developed and used within fire service organizations. The following are widely used applications of fire department information systems:

- Word processing
- Electronic mail
- Personnel and facilities scheduling
- Spreadsheet and database programs

Resource Control and Deployment

Program and Organizational Performance Evaluation. Program evaluation is the mechanism by which fire service agencies use facts to make choices about actions that will best achieve their goals. Information technology can be utilized to evaluate an individual program or an entire organization's performance. Points of evaluation must be based on a comparative analysis with other similar service-based agencies. The quality of annual performance and service-level reporting often contributes to resource-level determination. Presenting a compelling case to enhance resource levels is based on the ability to extract and present quality data. This analysis can be used to develop benchmarks that identify both the best practices and the average performance. The benchmarking process can provide a tangible performance analysis of often intangible services. For example, through analysis of trends in fire death and injury statistics, an organization can gauge the overall performance or output of its fire prevention and public education programs. Evaluation can also provide information relating to performance-based criteria, such as the evaluation of response times, or to the need for specialized services, such as advanced life support (ALS), hazardous materials response, or technical rescue.

Fleet Management. Vehicles and equipment represent a significant capital investment, provide safety to fire service personnel, and enable the delivery of high-quality emergency services to the community. Fleet management systems provide the information needed for budgeting and controlling these expenditures, as well as for ensuring that the fleet is maintained in a high state of readiness. The need for information about the fire department fleet exists at all levels: strategic, managerial, and operational. To meet this data-intensive need, fleet management systems involve several components, including fleet inventory, equipment inventory, maintenance records, vehicle replacement schedules, fuel consumption, internal billing for vehicle use (e.g., in the case of citywide carpools), repair cost projection, and performance analysis. Most of these components have become common in the majority of fleet management systems.

At the strategic level, information about the existing fleet is needed to plan and budget for vehicle acquisition and replacement. To make sound replacement decisions, accurate information on maintenance frequency, operating costs, age, and so on for each major piece of equipment is needed. Indeed, those decisions are often so complicated and have such significant political overtones that decision-support software (i.e., operations research models) is needed to help analyze and organize these data.

At the managerial control level, fleet managers need computer support to control preventive maintenance intervals, prioritize work in progress, track fuel consumption, and plan for the appropriate staffing of the maintenance facility. If the maintenance staff members are to be effective, they require immediate access to information, such as vehicle performance, repair records, parts inventory, interchangeable parts data, equipment manuals, and standard repair times. Likewise, administrative services managers need financial data on expenses for budgetary forecasting and control.

Personnel at the operational or task level also need information from a fleet management system. Most important, of course, is the ability to have information on vehicle condition and availability. Although this information is not always provided by the fleet management system per se, dispatchers need to know what equipment is in service and available to respond to a given type of emergency.

Few fire departments develop their own fleet management systems. They either use a commercially available system or a citywide fleet management system. Commercial systems may be difficult to interface directly with other department or city systems. Also, added capabilities, such as vehicle replacement models, may not easily integrate with these systems. Yet, this internal approach can be implemented easily and is cost-effective, especially for fire departments that do not have highly integrated systems.

The citywide approach also suffers from some of the same deficiencies. Since citywide systems are typically designed for standard street vehicles, they may ignore certain features that would be common to fire apparatus and emergency response vehicles. For example, the city system may not have a provision for capturing and maintaining special data on apparatus components, or it may not provide for maintenance records of special equipment unique to the fire service. If these deficiencies are to be eliminated, the fire personnel must actively participate in defining information requirements. When these requirements have been defined, the citywide approach can be worthwhile. As fire service integration advances, fleet management systems that are customized to the specific needs of the fire service are becoming a common part of most fire department records management systems.

Capital Asset and Personnel Planning. The ability to develop and support a capital plan that anticipates service demand has become an extremely technical process that involves several aspects of information technology. This process includes the evaluation of incident type, location history, response time analysis, and the evaluation of resource availability. This information can be used to model station locations, set performance-based goals, determine peak service demand hours, identify service gaps, and forecast personnel, facility, and equipment needs.

EMERGENCY RESPONSE AND OPERATIONAL APPLICATIONS

Computer-Aided Dispatch

Computer-aided dispatch (CAD) is an address- or occupancy-based information application that is oriented toward operations. CAD monitors resource status and optimizes emergency response by rapidly assigning the closest appropriate and available units (Figure 12.5.3). Through integrated CAD systems, resources are tracked, alarms are received, fire stations are alerted, information on hazards can be transmitted, and situations are managed. The system's purpose is to support current activity rather than provide managerial control or strategic planning information. However, the functions of CAD systems often go beyond operational support. In an integrated information systems environment, the CAD system may produce nonoperational information in support of other administrative and planning functions.

FIGURE 12.5.3 Dispatcher Using a Multiscreen CAD System (Photo provided courtesy of Geac Public Safety)

CAD systems support a multitude of fire service dispatch functions:

- Alarm receipt, fire alarm signal decoding, central station communications management, and so on
- Communications and signaling management: alerting unit/station, two-way exchange of data, paging, electronic mail, radio frequency selection, and coordination
- Emergency medical dispatch (EMD) and other situation-based emergency instruction
- Status maintenance: monitor resources, equipment, personnel, and system supervisor
- Response assignment: dynamic assignment based on current availability and relative location of emergency response resources to incident

Although CAD is usually credited with reducing response time, the payoff is not necessarily in this area. Some departments even report an increase in response time after implementing a CAD system. The real benefits of CAD occur in the coordination of emergency response activity. Thus, rapid recall of information, such as apparatus status and occupancy data, is at least as important as response time.

Implementing a CAD System. Choosing a correct approach to implementing a CAD system is a multifaceted problem. The first facet of the problem is related to policy. In some cases, dispatching is a shared public safety responsibility. In others, regional dispatch centers serve multiple jurisdictions. The organizational situation can have an important influence on other aspects of the approach, as well as on the ultimate usefulness of the system.

Determining the System Scope. A major starting point in CAD development is a decision on the scope of the system—that is, whether the system is to be developed only for CAD or whether it will include other applications. Most departments elect to develop a stand-alone CAD system with the necessary interfaces to other applications, for example, the fire incident reporting system. Others may elect to more closely integrate their CAD system with other computerized record management systems (RMS) in the department. Regardless of how many applications may be bundled together, the CAD operation is the top priority and it is designed to continue to operate even if some of the other applications are temporarily unavailable.

Closely related to the issue of scope is the degree of modularity built into the system. A highly modular system permits the system to be expanded to include enhanced CAD functions, such as alarm system interface and alphanumeric paging, as well as other peripheral applications. It also allows new software to be tested in an off-line mode and operators to be trained without interfering with operations. Modularity is important in all applications, but it is especially critical in CAD systems because the systems are subject to almost constant change.

Using Outside Contractors. An outside contractor is often used to develop a department's CAD system, although internal teams have developed effective systems. If an outside contractor is used, both operations and communications personnel must be extensively involved in developing the system requirements and specifications to ensure that the final system meets their needs. Likewise, when the system is installed, all staff members must be involved so they understand the system design and are properly trained to maintain and operate the system. The importance of properly involving and training personnel cannot be overstated.

Interoperable Communications. Communications is another aspect in selecting an approach. Standard telephone service has typically been used for communications between the dispatch center and the fire stations. Increasingly, other ways are being found to transmit data. The 800 MHz radio frequencies have been used successfully, as have microwave links and dedicated data lines. Alphanumeric pagers, computer terminals in fire apparatus with both paper printouts and liquid crystal display (LCD) readouts, fax machines, voice-over Internet, and cellular telephones are also becoming increasingly popular for dispatching apparatus and communicating with company officers and incident commanders.

The ability to operate on multiple frequencies and coordinate operations between agencies has become increasingly complex. Often agencies even with the same jurisdiction operate on different frequencies. The inability to create seamless controlled interoperable communications is an ongoing challenge within public safety agencies. Technology has expanded to provide the ability to bridge frequencies. These efforts, however, must be planned and managed through a communications plan because this technology can quickly create a dysfunctional situation. Interoperability equipment includes both a computer-based patching capability (Figure 12.5.4) and banks of radios (Figure 12.5.5).

Incident Management Support

The effective and efficient management of significant incidents can tax even the largest fire service organizations. The use of technology to coordinate and manage operations during large-scale events has increased, and many jurisdictions have developed mobile technology platforms that are designed to optimize deployment, coordinate activity between multiple agencies, and provide general incident support services. Figure 12.5.6 shows an incident in which a technology platform provided incident support at a large warehouse fire.

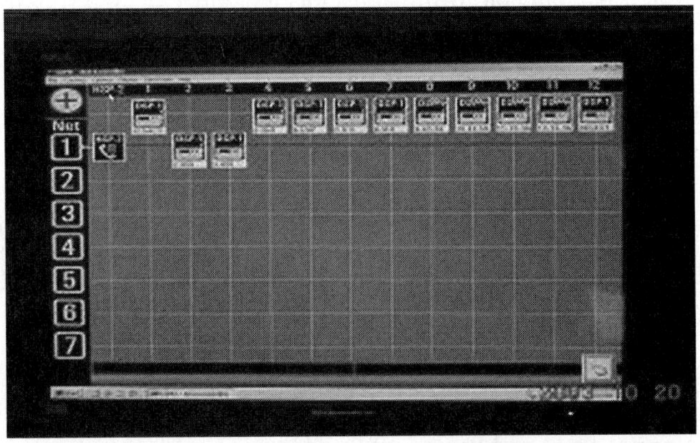

FIGURE 12.5.4 Computer-Based Patching (Photo provided courtesy of the Massachusetts Department of Fire Services)

FIGURE 12.5.5 Banks of Radios (Photo provided courtesy of the Massachusetts Department of Fire Services)

FIGURE 12.5.6 ISU Fire Response (Photo provided courtesy of the Massachusetts Department of Fire Services)

Although some of these platforms, such as the mobile technology platform pictured in Figure 12.5.7, were designed and deployed prior to the tragic events of September 11, 2001, the development of these vehicles, which often serve a large region or multiple agencies, has become commonplace.

The mobile technology platform pictured in Figure 12.5.7 can effectively be utilized to support operations and assist the incident commander. Examples of the technology provided by the mobile platform often include the following:

- Additional communication resources
- Cellular and satellite-based telecommunications
- Coordination of emergency response mobilizations
- Cross-band and multi-agency communications management
- Download of audio and video signals

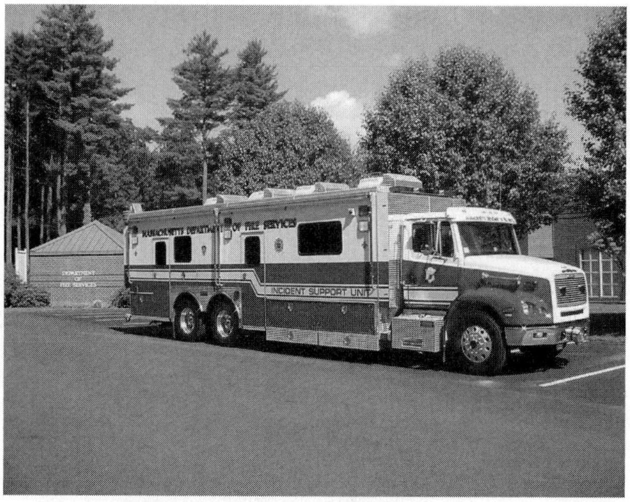

FIGURE 12.5.7 Mobile Technology Platform Used to Support Large-Scale Operations (Photo provided courtesy of the Massachusetts Department of Fire Services)

- Equipment tracking
- Event logging
- Geographic information systems
- Interface with other agencies and units
- Internet and paging access
- Interoperable communications planning and management
- Scheduling and long-term planning
- Thermal video imaging and projection
- Weather monitoring

Many communities replicate some of the foregoing resources within an emergency operations center (EOC), and these mobile technology platforms offer the unique ability to operate at an incident scene. Because this equipment is complex, it is essential to have a trained overhead team that works with this technology on a regular basis.

Emergency Access Systems

Enhanced 9-1-1 System. Enhanced 9-1-1, or E9-1-1, is a highly reliable emergency phone system that displays the caller's telephone number, address, response district, and other important information automatically on the dispatcher's computer screen, along with dispatch information for fire, police, emergency medical service (EMS), or other emergency responders. This system is invaluable, especially in those cases where the caller is unable to give information fully or clearly because of language barriers, incapacitation, confusion, or excitement caused by the incident, age, or even lack of knowledge of the area. E9-1-1 can have a dramatic effect on reducing response times. Because it identifies the actual telephone location from where the call is placed, it also helps reduce false alarms.

This system has been widely installed throughout the United States. Even more sophisticated systems can provide information concerning previous calls to the same address, hazardous materials stored on site, day care or other life-safety–intensive operations at the address, and other information pertaining to a caller's disability or medical condition that is useful to the responding units.

As E9-1-1 continues to develop, cellular triangulation that maps and identifies the relative position of a caller will be implemented. The development of a caller's location can be accomplished through the use of signal triangulation from multiple cellular towers and integration with geographic positioning systems (GPS). This technology is common within the majority of enhanced 9-1-1 systems and has the potential to provide information that will assist in locating an incident, therefore saving both time and lives. As 9-1-1 systems have become accepted by society, they often become overburdened with less than true emergency calls. In an effort to properly channel these informational calls, over two dozen U.S. cities have developed alternative informational numbers such as 3-1-1 to divert call volume and match the callers to the best resource to address their needs.

Although the Internet and other modern technologies are being used globally, the application of these technologies varies widely. Of more specific interest here is whether and what kind of enhanced emergency access systems are found in countries outside the United States. Australia has a system similar to the enhanced 9-1-1 system found in the United States. A call (made to 000, the Australian emergency call number) is received by the national telephone company and passed on to the CAD system covering that area, at which point enhancement kicks in with call line identification and cell phone general area information. The system then captures the information for the incident reports. Utilizing the triangulation of cellular signals in concert with geographic positioning systems, the vast majority of enhanced 9-1-1 systems can rapidly determine the geographic location of a caller.

Across Pacific Asia, enhanced emergency access systems range from very sophisticated systems in Singapore and Hong Kong to very basic systems in other parts of Asia. Of significance to the development of such systems are issues pertaining to the infrastructure currently available, especially within relatively underdeveloped countries.

Geographic Information and Positioning Systems

The integration of digital imagery and mapping technology provides a foundation for the development of location-based applications that combine to form a geographic information system (GIS). This address-based information system serves as a valuable tool to many municipal agencies and can provide a central information link between departments if GIS has been developed, integrated, and networked properly. For example, when a new subdivision is proposed, information relative to the water system would be of interest to the building, fire, planning, and water departments. Information on a structure at a given location is of value both to units responding to an emergency and to the community's tax assessor. Consult Section 12, Chapter 13, "GIS for Fire Station Locations and Response Protocols," for more information on GIS.

GIS represents a mapping application that provides several selectable layers of information. Each layer can be included or excluded depending on the specific need—for example, the zoning information layer would not be of value when configuring GIS to provide a map to be used to search for a missing person. GIS offers a previously unknown ability to consolidate information by address. Specific to the fire service, information pertaining to hazards, permits, structure history, water supply, navigation, and topographical land features are routinely utilized.

GIS can also be used to support fire service planning needs, ranging from response time evaluation to station location analysis. Operationally, GIS can be used to support fire service activity at a variety of emergency situations, including hazardous materials situations, wildfires, and weather-related events. Capitalizing on the ability to integrate multiple applications, officials can now anticipate the track of a severe storm or chemical plume and automatically warn residents within the projected path. Through this technology, evacuations can be expedited and residents can be advised to take appropriate action. Previously, these notifications would take hours and consume vast amounts of resources.

Geographic positioning system (GPS) integrates the mapping of GIS with the ability to determine current location (Figure 12.5.8). This technology, originally developed by the military, can provide accurate location information for aircraft or other responding resources. In addition, GPS can aid navigation by providing directions, inclusive of verbal instructions, to a destination. GPS can be updated to provide optimal routing, given changing traffic conditions. These systems have become popular options in many passenger vehicles, and as they become more affordable, they will continue to gain popularity. In the future, GPS will likely be integrated with intelligent transportation systems and provide an automated reflection of current conditions.

Automatic vehicle location (AVL) further links GPS to GIS. AVL provides the dispatch center with the ability to visually monitor a real-time map that shows resource status, speed, and location. As a result, available units that are closest to a situation can be dispatched. AVL enhances resource control and dramatically reduces response time to emergency situations. This technology truly saves lives, reduces loss, optimizes resource deployment, and complements the fire service mission.

Mobile Data

The ability to provide critical information to responding units can be accomplished through the use of wireless computer technology. Through mobile data systems, responding units can obtain situation updates, directions, prefire plans, digital imaging, structure information, hazard information, water-supply configuration, and hydrant locations (Figure 12.5.9).

In addition, the ability to communicate remotely provides rapid access to reliable data and improves the decision-making process. Mobile data can be transmitted through radio systems or cellular technology; at present, the most popular transmission medium is either the use of secure wireless Internet connection or data bursts sent through cellular digital packet technology (CDPD). As communications networks evolve, mobile data communication will increase in speed and will most likely include the use of both satellites and the Internet.

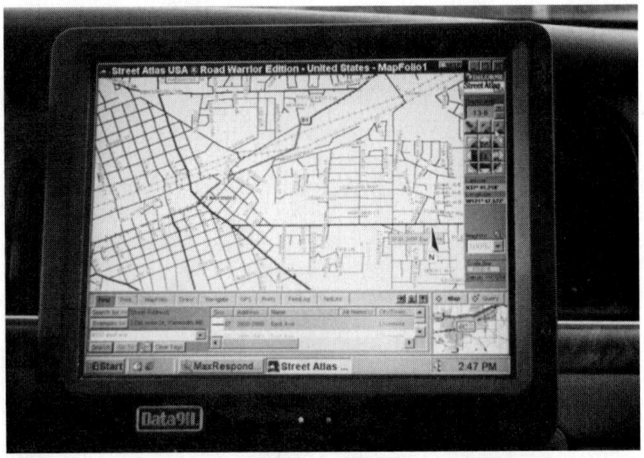

FIGURE 12.5.8 Mobile Geographic Positioning and Mapping Information (Photo provided courtesy of Livermore-Pleasanton Fire Department)

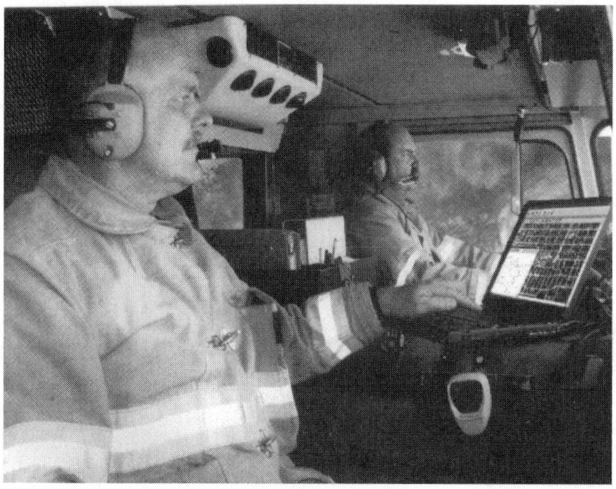

FIGURE 12.5.9 Responding Engine Company Using a Mobile Data Unit (Graphic image provided courtesy of ESRI. Copyright © 1999, 2000 ESRI)

Thermal Imaging

An infrared thermal imagery unit, which detects temperature variations, can penetrate smoke, structural features, and darkness and provide fire fighters with a visual image of reflected temperature (Figure 12.5.10). Light changes indicate temperature variations. This computer-based tool can be harnessed to increase both the ability and safety of fire service personnel. Thermal imagery, the projection of heat images, has several fire service applications, including the following:

- Searching for fire victims
- Searching for hidden fire (in concealed spaces)
- Searching for missing persons
- Identifying malfunctioning equipment
- Identifying fire location
- Providing assistance to other agencies, municipal agencies, and industry

Thermal images can also be transmitted to provide command personnel with improved reconnaissance as they manage a situation from a remote location. The size of thermal imagers continues to decrease and additional technological advances should be expected. Currently thermal imaging has become an affordable technology that continues to evolve. Future enhancements will include the integration of imagers into a fire fighters' turnout gear, color display, levels of warning, and pattern recognition.

Personnel Accountability/Fire Fighter Tracking Systems

The need to track personnel operating at an emergency scene is a basic principle of safe operations. Technology that uses bar code scanning, coded data chips, radio signal transmissions, and personal digital assistant databases assists command and safety personnel with the management of this complex function in less than optimal environments. Currently, automated personnel accountability systems can track personnel assignments, duration of entry, and project air consumption (Figure 12.5.11). These units automatically prompt and record periodic personnel accountability reports. Other systems can be utilized to direct rescue crews toward the location of a lost or injured fire fighter. Although many systems are complex, this emerging technology is becoming easier to use and more cost-effective. The challenge will be to utilize this technology to provide a timely and accurate reflection of operations.

Locating an injured or unresponsive fire fighter has been a difficult task. Automated location systems that provide a directional pointer to the location of a fire fighter in distress can assist a rapid intervention team. Although this technology is currently useful, it should be expected that systems of this type will be enhanced to provide more detailed information.

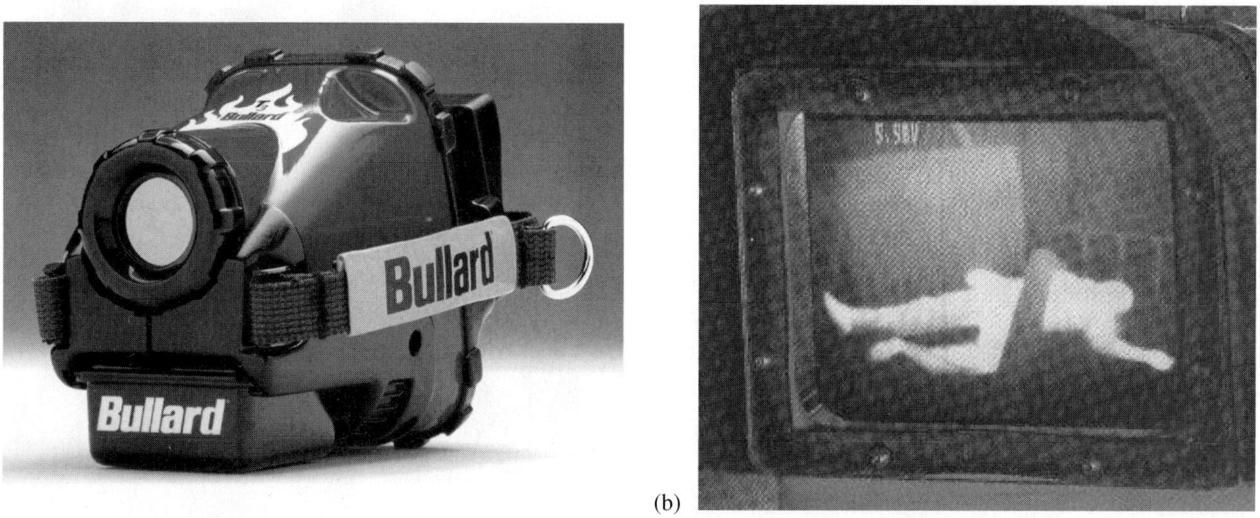

(a) (b)

FIGURE 12.5.10 (a) Thermal Imaging Unit (b) Thermal Image (Photos provided courtesy of Bullard®)

FIGURE 12.5.11 Automated Handheld Personnel Accountability Device (Photo provided courtesy of XTrack.com)

Hazardous Materials Detection

The ability to detect hazardous conditions is firmly based within technology. As the need to handle hazardous materials has increased, the need to detect chemical, biological, radiological, and nuclear threats has developed a wide array of computer-driven metering systems. As this technology matures, these metering devices are becoming increasingly reliable, more compact, and easier to use.

Digital Documentation

In a litigious society the need to document conditions and actions at the incident scene has dramatically increased. Information technology has facilitated this documentation. Most fire service radio traffic and telecommunications are digitally recorded and time/date stamped. This audio recording of voice communication provides a foundation for event documentation.

Digital Imagery

Both still photographs and video expand the ability to provide professional documentation. These images can enhance post-operational review and serve as a training and evaluation tool. Images can also communicate and market the organization's role and mission and can be used as a tool in public education efforts. Documentation is essential to an effective fire investigation program.

Emergency Medical Services

Most fire departments now provide emergency medical service (EMS). Fire equipment and fire fighters are generally dispatched to perform or support EMS activities. The fire department may or may not be involved in the actual patient transport. Ambulances, whether operated by the fire department, another city agency, or the private sector, are often dispatched by the fire department or public safety dispatch center.

Technology has gained an expanding role within emergency medical services over the last 5 years (Figure 12.5.12). Examples of the utilization of technology range from defibrillators that can correct an improper electrical rhythm within the heart to a pulse oximeter that monitors a patient's oxygen level.

In many jurisdictions, the cost of emergency medical service is billed to the patient. Since this practice represents a substantial revenue source for the city or county, the billing process is the most intensive information system within most EMS systems. Other components of an EMS data system include the following:

- Patient care information
- Treatment protocol and reference material
- Response needs and resource allocation
- Training material

The statistics generated from EMS systems are used in both long-range plans and operational planning and control. Response times, locations of incidents, and unit staffing and deployment patterns are required to plan and budget for resources and determine if the units, personnel, and facilities are being configured appropriately.

In some fire departments, separate systems have been designed to handle both the EMS billing system and the EMS incident records. In other departments, data from the billing system are transferred to the fire incident reporting system from which operational statistics are generated. Having all incident data in-

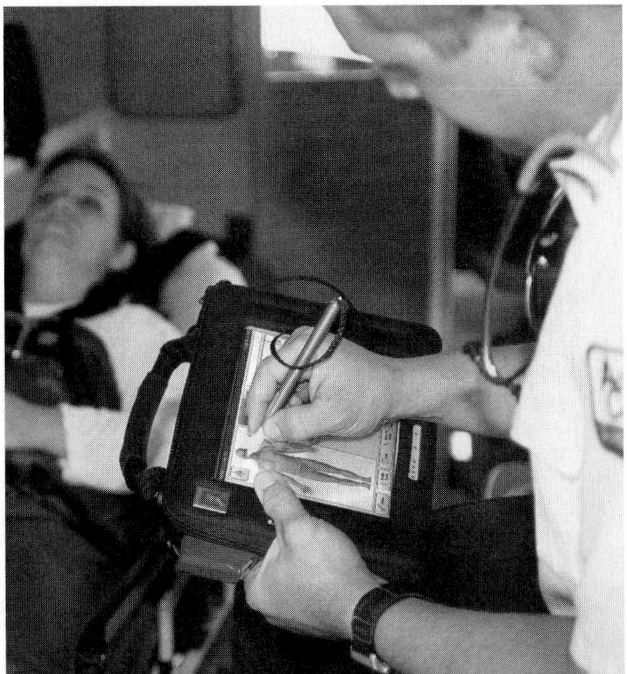

FIGURE 12.5.12 Wireless Reporting System for Patient Care (Photo provided courtesy of Zoll Data Systems, Inc.)

tegrated into the same database is helpful in studying fire department emergency activity.

A basic EMS report form can be used by fire departments to keep track of their EMS activities and can be amended to reflect their specific EMS reporting needs. Mobile EMS reporting has enabled EMS personnel to quickly access and update patient care records while treating a patient. Many of these systems automatically upload and synchronize billing and patient care records.

Technology and information systems facilitate communication between ambulances and hospitals for the transmission of medical directions and telemetry data for physician evaluation. Mobile incident reporting has also become an accurate means of documentation because the report is completed rapidly. In addition, this technology can reduce the time that personnel dedicate to documentation and administrative tasks because reports are completed prior to returning to a fixed facility. As the use of the Internet and mobile data expands, the development of information technology that can transmit medical images and video to a treating physician should be expected. Technology currently in use concentrates on telemetry (sending heart rhythms and other critical patient care information over radio signals) and EMS incident reporting.

INTERNAL AND PUBLIC COMMUNICATION APPLICATIONS

Easy access to computer technology and the widespread acceptance of advancing technology have propelled the use of electronic communication. This shift in communication methodology provides the fire service with a tremendous opportunity to enhance both internal and external communications. Internally, electronic mail allows consistent and rapid communication to all personnel within the organization. Regular communication with shift personnel is increased with e-mail. A LAN, or intranet, which serves as an internal information network, can store reference material and share organizational information, such as policies and standard operating guidelines.

Externally, e-mail and Internet webpages permit the positive projection of an organization. Through increased communication, an organization can strengthen both community outreach and customer service. A webpage often becomes the most accessible public portal, and fire service agencies should recognize the importance of an Internet presence and develop a website that is reflective of the quality of the organization. The Internet, which has become a conduit for public information, allows the rapid dissemination of information. In its attempt to meet the needs of its customers, effective fire services will seize on this communication medium as a tool to educate and become more responsive to the community.

Public presentations often influence both resource allocation and programmatic success. Although a presentation reflects the ability of the speaker, information technology can add professionalism and provide a technological means to make presentations more effective. By using presentation software such as Microsoft PowerPoint and liquid crystal display (LCD) projection, speakers can augment and customize their presentations with audio, digital imagery, and video enhancements. They can then electronically transfer these presentations via the Internet to create a base for distance-learning applications. For example, a fire service agency may post an automated training program specific to fire safety for the elderly on its website and allow the public to download and view this material.

Administration and Office Automation

The term *office automation* refers to a group of applications that support clerical and managerial activities. These applications include word processing, spreadsheets for financial and numeric data, database development for various record-keeping applications, e-mail, "tickler" systems, teleconferencing and videoconferencing, and personal calendar management.

The purpose of these applications is to make the executive and the clerical worker more effective. Although the same may be said about traditional information systems, the focus here is different. Traditional information system applications are process oriented; office automation, in contrast, is more people oriented. The objective is to make office personnel more productive by allowing them to use computers and other technology as a natural extension of their minds and bodies.

Executives and clerical workers need office automation to cope with the complexities and increased demands of today's office environment. Fire agencies must contend with an explosion of information in the form of reports, forms, memoranda, and computer files. The efficient development and effective management of this information resource strain even the most dedicated staff. The computer, through automation applications, extends human intellectual capabilities and allows office staff to do more. Personnel development is essential to harness the abilities of office automation software suites. As office automation is developed, employee input must be considered. Through focus groups and internal training, consistent ways to maximize the potential benefit of this technology can be developed.

Mobile Connectivity

Mobile connectivity extends beyond prefire planning, reporting, and emergency operations. Remote communication through wireless technology, mobile data terminals, personal digital assistants, and cellular technology is growing in popularity (Figure 12.5.13). For example, through wireless integration, a fire inspector can adjust his or her schedule, retrieve technical data, update prefire plans, review facility history, and document activity without devoting administrative time at the office to perform these tasks. Therefore, through this technology the inspector's effectiveness and efficiency have been dramatically increased. Based on technology, the inspector can recall records, spend more time in the field, and be instantly updated.

Networking

To provide the needed integration while retaining the flexibility for stand-alone units, most fire service organizations are developing network-based systems. These are full-fledged computer systems specifically designed (both in terms of hardware and software) to handle office automation and interface with other public safety technology. The individual office computer is connected to a central server that manages data storage and

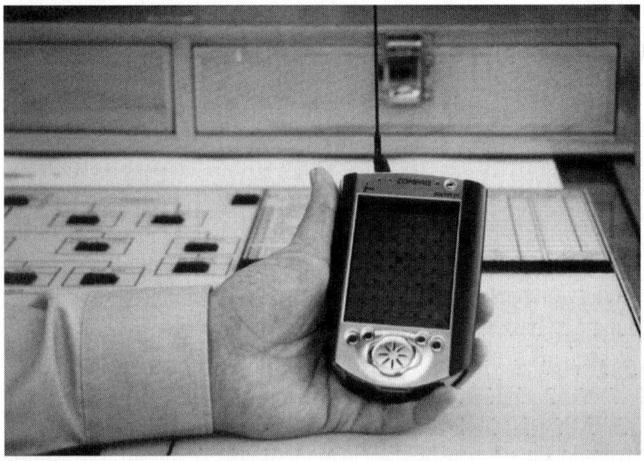

FIGURE 12.5.13 Wireless Personal Digital Assistant (Photo provided courtesy of Livermore-Pleasanton Fire Department)

communication. This setup allows the user to have a stand-alone workstation on a desktop that can perform all the office automation functions and still have access to the databases retained on the central network server (Figure 12.5.14).

There are several variations on network design. Depending on how data are captured and utilized throughout the network, various functions can be performed either by the desktop computers, network servers, or a central microcomputer. For example, a desktop computer might be used for word processing as a stand-alone task but be tied to a network system to transmit electronic mail, link to other computers, and make inquiries into CAD databases on a central computer. The network provides the mechanism to integrate all these activities. Based on the risk posed by mechanical failure, file corruption and virus infection-critical data should be backed up on a frequent basis. At least one full system backup should be stored at a remote location to avoid a potential catastrophic data loss if disaster strikes.

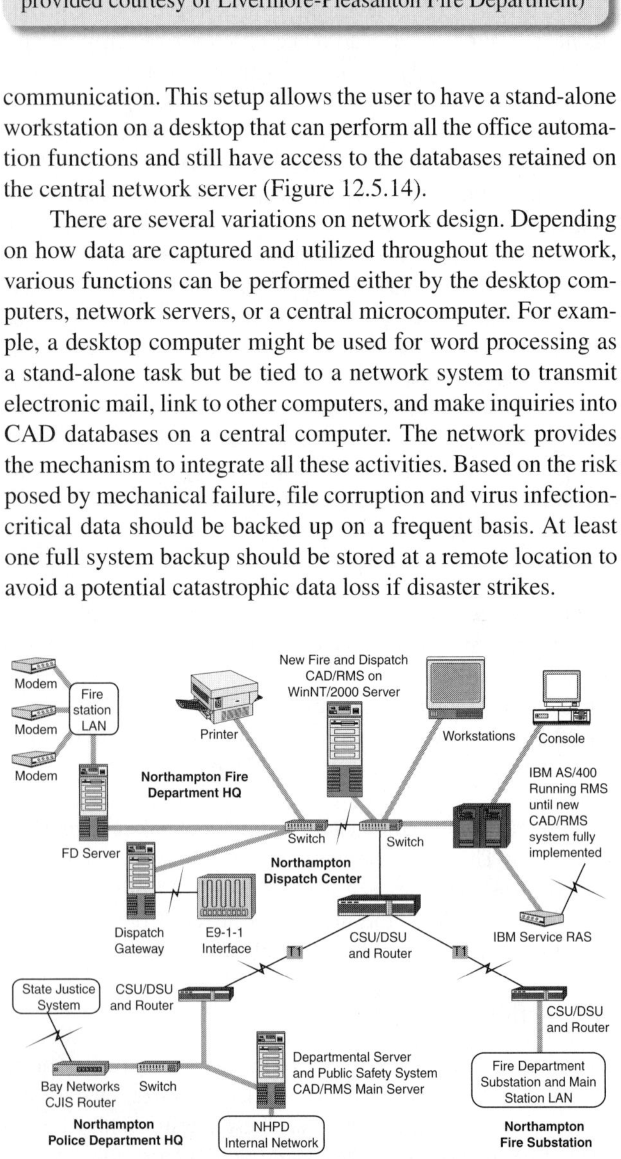

FIGURE 12.5.14 Sample Design for Public Safety Network (Image provided courtesy of Corporation for Public Technology)

Internal Databases

With the advent of desktop and laptop computers, commercial database packages that can develop customized files are becoming the accepted way of gathering information for a fire department. Relational databases not only accomplish one-dimensional tasks but also go much further in their usefulness. The term *relational* means information can be compared in relation to other information; for example, "what if" questions are easily and rapidly answered when data are gathered using a relational database. If a fire chief is asked to cut the budget and the only way to do so is to close a station for some period of time or send fewer engines, he or she can quickly determine the time period when such an action will have the least impact on service to the community. A relational database can analyze incident data to show the best time to close down a station, based on number of alarms, severity of fires, or other criteria the fire chief may want to use to determine the best alternative.

Relational databases, even though created for use on desktop computers, are extremely powerful, highly useful programs. The ease of learning and using these programs has improved dramatically over the past several years, such that most departments, no matter how large or small, would find them valuable tools for all types of information management.

External Databases

Much of the technical and legal information needed by fire departments exists on commercial or governmental databases. These databases are created for general use, and users are charged for access on the basis of either a subscription or a flat hourly rate based on time actually used.

In a very real sense, commercial and governmental databases are a public utility. The source for the information stored in these databases is primarily current technical literature and legal materials. In some databases, abstracts of documents and books are stored; in others, the complete text is stored. For example, *National Fire Codes* is currently available to subscribers through protected electronic access. Numerous firms provide databases. Literally over a million databases, covering various fields, are available today through most technical companies and public communications entities.

The databases of greatest use to the fire service are those dealing with hazardous materials, codes, standards, and legal information. Chemical and hazardous materials databases allow a user to search for a hazardous material by chemical structure, trade name, generic name, CAS registry number, chemical or physical properties, and textual description. These databases can be powerful tools in handling chemical spills, fires involving hazardous materials, and some emergency medical situations.

During the next few years, electronic reference material will become dominant over printed reference material. This growing popularity is based on the increasing ability to rapidly search a large volume of current information.

Fire Service Specific Applications

A variety of programs developed specifically for the fire service exist. Although some perform only one function such as incident reporting, others provide an entire suite of fire service management applications that can assist with fire prevention, training, budgeting, internal communication, and other functions. As software is selected it should be carefully assessed and matched to the needs of an organization.

One advantage to a comprehensive fire service specific software system is that as data are populated in one area, they are shared throughout the other applications, thus reducing the need for redundant data entry. However, these fire service specific systems often fail to have the capability of easily sharing data with other non–fire service municipal applications. Therefore, many communities have selected separate software packages that can be utilized by several municipal departments that need to share data on a frequent basis.

Financial Applications

Financial applications include those systems that support budgeting, fiscal control, general ledger, accounts payable, and billing. Payroll is sometimes included, although more often it is a part of the personnel system. Billing may also be included in specific systems—for example, billing patients for emergency medical services and billing property owners for removal of illegal brush. (Many high-fire-risk states have ordinances requiring clearing of underbrush to reduce fire intensity and the chance of building involvement.)

The implementation of financial systems in fire departments has been slow, partly because the support of staff functions, such as finance, has been secondary to the support of line activities. In addition, municipality-wide financial systems often preempt those in the individual departments.

Perhaps the most critical need for financial information in the fire department occurs during the yearly budget cycle. The arduous and sometimes politically risky process of allocating resources requires considerable analysis. Decisions must be supported and justified by the kinds of facts best stored and manipulated by a fire service information technology system.

Budget control is also a high priority for fire agencies. Management needs to forecast expenditures to determine if the department is staying within budget. Even if central systems are available for this purpose, they may not provide data in sufficient detail or in a form that is useful to the fire department.

The remaining needs addressed by financial systems are primarily operation oriented: general ledger, billing, accounts payable, and payroll. The last three requirements more often than not are a part of associated applications (e.g., payroll in the personnel system, billing in the emergency medical system, and accounts payable in the procurement system). Manual or automated "bridges" are then provided to integrate general ledger and budgeting systems. The most common design approach to financial systems is a strongly centralized one. This is not surprising in view of the fiduciary responsibility of the chief financial officer in the public sector.

Human Resource Functions

Personnel systems are among the most complex and data intensive of all fire department applications. They may be part of a communitywide personnel system or may be specific to the fire department. Consisting of a number of subapplications, these systems are important in large departments to support the multiple functions of personnel administration, such as basic personnel records management, certification tracking, time and attendance reporting, payroll (sometimes part of financial management), duty schedules, physical fitness and medical records, employee evaluation, training records, position control, badge history and control, and disability/injury analysis. Without computer support for the personnel administration functions, large fire departments would find it difficult, if not impossible, to maintain all the necessary information, and little or no analysis of the collected data would be available.

The operational benefits are obvious. In a 1000 person fire department, a large volume of information is needed to carry out standard personnel functions. Fire fighters must be scheduled and personnel assignments must be balanced daily. Detailed training records are required for each department member. Time and attendance records are necessary for payroll. Employee records must be evaluated and considered for promotion. Overtime hours must be monitored and analyzed. These functions require an efficient way of storing, retrieving, sorting, and evaluating information.

The information that is useful for day-to-day operations also has residual value for strategic planning and managerial control. For example, the roster data may be aggregated in such a way that this information becomes useful for position control or personnel resource planning—that is, controlling the number and rank of personnel assigned to ensure that appropriate staffing patterns are employed. Management may use routine, periodic reports to review time and attendance data in an effort to control excessive sick leave or overtime. However, information required for strategic planning and managerial control typically cannot be fully defined prior to the time it is needed. Therefore, it is useful to have the facility for designing ad hoc inquiries using the operational database to provide information properly tailored to the nonroutine strategic or control application.

At the highest level of design, the approach taken will depend on the relationship of fire department personnel functions to city (or county) personnel functions. For example, the payroll may be prepared by the city from prescribed time and attendance records. In such a case, the fire department may have difficulty developing some of the components of a personnel system.

Another aspect of the design approach is the degree to which the components of the personnel system are integrated. In most cases, the personnel system has been built over several years, with one component implemented at a time, with no overall design providing for integration of files and input. A comprehensively planned system provides for integration, even if the components are implemented separately.

Facility Management

As fire facilities become more complex, technology can be employed to monitor critical aspects of operation. Systems that can be controlled through the use of technology include life safety, backup power, communications, access control, and energy management.

The need for security has increased as fire services have evolved. Ranging from basic facility security to controlled access to narcotics and other medications, controlled access is essential to operations. As such, several access technologies have been developed. Commonly, user name and password combinations will protect information system access, and fingerprint or magnetic card readers can provide access and monitor utilization of facilities and critical equipment.

Energy management systems provide information for control of energy costs, including information about the consumption of electric power, natural gas, and heating oil. In some cases, the use of motor vehicle fuel may be monitored, although this function is more properly a function of fleet management systems. The typical approach to the design of energy management systems is to capture energy billing data, update master files, and make various reports available to administrators. This energy conservation strategy can be maximized through the use of either a relational database or a spreadsheet. More sophisticated approaches include real-time monitoring systems and even real-time energy control. Computer-based evaluation models are also used to assess the impact of conservation measures. The cost of implementing a computerized energy management system can be recovered quickly through increased energy resource efficiency. This technology can control multiple systems to ensure comfort and efficiency and can identify problem areas.

Fire Prevention Applications, Inspection, and Permit Tracking

Fire prevention management information systems are address-based tracking systems for storing fire protection–related information on a community's buildings. The heart of a fire prevention system is a flexible file of properties. The application is useful in planning and managing fire prevention activities, controlling hazardous contents, and prefire planning for fire suppression.

Fire prevention records in many communities still consist of long, often handwritten, forms and narratives filed in individual folders, one for each property. This lack of electronic automation makes it virtually impossible to manipulate data and develop any information on patterns of hazards or violations across the community or for particular property classes.

Even within a file on a single property, it can be difficult to ascertain whether the fire department has been providing the kind of frequency of contact called for by the department's policies, community ordinances, and other state and federal laws and regulations. This difficulty exists because such files are often dumping grounds for any and all papers bearing the property's address. Minor, unofficial correspondence and news clippings may share space with inspection reports, violation notices, and detailed construction plans. Files on properties not covered by the fire prevention code (such as single-family dwellings), on fire education contacts, and on contacts by other agencies (such as the building and housing departments) are generally nonexistent or wholly separate and incompatible with the fire inspection files. Fire incident records are rarely tied to files on the violation and hazard histories that may have caused the fires. In fact, it would be difficult to identify any aspect of a fire department's record keeping that is more in need of refinement and automation than fire prevention. Handheld computers serve as tools to make the fire inspection process more effective and efficient. For example, the TDS Ranger pictured in Figure 12.5.15 makes available applications on fire prevention inspection and records management.

As fire prevention activities are address based, utilizing handheld computers that can retrieve, update, and input property-based information can add to an organization's capabilities. Many of these systems can provide an inspector with a complete history of a property and prevent the need to duplicate data entry. In addition, most of these devices synchronize with a network system and create a database that can be shared with other code compliance agencies.

The first requirement for an adequate fire prevention system is a comprehensive address-based inventory of all properties in the jurisdiction. Such a file is difficult to create. Past studies have shown that, despite conscious efforts, fires are reported in properties that should have been subject to fire inspections but did not appear in the inspection records. These were not new businesses or businesses operating illegally out of homes; they were legitimate businesses of some years' standing that simply had been overlooked.

Although file completeness cannot be guaranteed, it can be improved. Address files should be linked to the fire incident records, preferably through a link to the communities' GIS and CAD systems, so that emergency runs or municipal records to corresponding unlisted addresses will lead to the creation of an inspection file.

Sources for both the initial building inventory and periodic updates are the city's tax records, E9-1-1 database, the build-

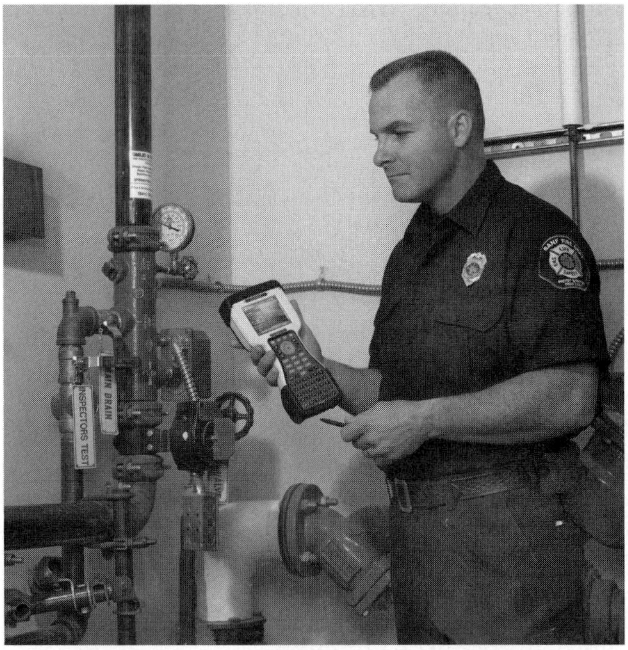

FIGURE 12.5.15 Fire Fighter with a TDS Ranger (Photo provided courtesy of Tripod Data Systems, Inc.)

ing department, any inspection agency, and city-owned utilities, such as the water, sewer, and electric departments. Some lists (e.g., the telephone company's Yellow Pages, cross-indexes, and mail carrier routes) tend to be unwieldy or poor sources for finding missing addresses.

The physical fire inspection procedure itself can be a source of effective property list updates. Inspections conducted on a sequential basis allow inspectors to see properties they might miss if they were to organize their routes with strict attention to those properties identified only by the computer.

Once the file is created, it can be used as a basis for organizing and scheduling inspections. The system can be set to print inspection reports for properties scheduled for inspection in any given time period (weekly, biweekly, or monthly), thereby allowing inspectors to plan their work. Likewise, the need for reinspections to check that hazards are abated or other violations corrected can be easily tracked, and missed inspections can be identified. Inspector workloads can be balanced either by the number of inspections or by the total time spent on inspections if statistics are kept on the typical duration of inspections by type and size of property.

Accuracy is important when automating data on buildings in a community. Although the occupants of a building change from time to time, the building itself usually doesn't change much. Some jurisdictions use the Basic Structure Report, Form 903SR, to gather basic information about structures. This form is an excellent way to capture data about buildings that need to be inspected periodically. Furthermore, the information gathered is extremely valuable for prefire planning efforts at that structure.

For all buildings, especially those that contain more than one occupancy, a basic occupancy report provides a way to gather information (e.g., who is using the building) for both inspection and training functions. The best asset of such an information-gathering system is that the data are classified in a uniform manner, based on NFPA 901, *Standard Classifications for Incident Reporting and Fire Protection Data.* With the data classified, it is easy to analyze the data, assess the severity of hazards being reported, and retrieve records for properties that have similar characteristics. This allows a supervisor to prioritize a fire department's inspection functions, based on the hazards present and the severity of the potential fire problem, especially when that department may not have sufficient resources to inspect every building as often as might be desired.

Incident Reporting and Analysis

Incident reporting systems are used to outline operations, document situations, and maintain statistics on fire, medical emergencies, and other emergencies to which a fire department responds. This application is one of the most common uses of information technology.

The methods of capturing data are rapidly changing. Batch data entry, in which a form or forms are completed after each incident and someone other than the person completing the form inputs the data in batches at a computer, has given way to the fire officer entering the data directly at a computer terminal in the fire station or remotely through wireless and mobile data systems.

Departments with a CAD system usually collect at least some of the incident data as a by-product of a CAD operation. These data can then be displayed on a networked computer or on a terminal where data collected at the incident scene can be added by the company officer or officer in charge. Allowing the officer in charge to enter the data directly has the advantage of ensuring completeness and correctness, because the data can be edited as they are entered and mistakes corrected immediately.

Casualty reporting systems are generally subsets of incident reporting systems. As such, they are linked to the incident record so that cause-and-effect studies can be done. Typically, records on fire fighter casualties and civilian casualties are maintained separately, because the information desired or the level of detail is different for the two.

Data on civilians injured at fires are useful for supporting injury reduction programs. These programs can be educational in nature to correct inappropriate behavior or may be focused at either getting unsafe products off the market or redesigned to make them safer. Code and standards developers can use the data from injury reporting to make prudent decisions based on past history. The criteria outlined in codes and standards can help to reduce injuries.

Fire fighters experience a high number of injuries while doing their jobs. Tracking those injuries is important and may involve more than one part of the fire department's information system. Data about the cause and circumstances of the injury can assist in making decisions for additional training, equipment redesign, or operational changes. For example, data collection has revealed that most fatal fire fighter injuries involve a heart attack or vehicle collision and that fire fighters suffer a higher rate of nonfatal injuries per hundred fires at fires that involve abandoned structures than in other properties.

Medical data about the injury are often important for workers' compensation claims. Data on potential time lost are needed to schedule other fire fighters to fill the shift and could affect the overtime budget.

A basic casualty report provides a method of uniformly gathering casualty data for both civilians and fire fighters. This report provides for the classification of much of the collected data so they can be easily summarized and analyzed to support injury reduction programs. This form is not designed to be a medical form for reporting to workers' compensation, although some of the basic data might be applicable to both needs.

Fire Investigation

The investigation of fire incidents needs to be a well-documented and methodical process. Technology such as digital imaging and prefire planning and fire inspection database systems can be a help in investigations. In addition, through GIS, all municipal information on a fire property, on the owner, and on the structure's history can be easily developed.

A number of computer-based data systems have been developed to profile the properties in the neighborhood and assist in identifying arson-prone buildings. The community group or public officials are then able to implement intervention strategies appropriate for the situation. Much of the early work sponsored by the Federal Emergency Management Agency (FEMA) has led to a developed and tested microcomputer-based arson information management system (AIMS). The system provides both identification of arson-prone buildings and a case management system for fire investigators.

There are many municipal and private databases or record systems that are typically used to support a fire investigation. These sources include data from the fire department incident-reporting system and code-enforcement program, the building department, the assessor's office, the police department crime-reporting system, the prosecutor's office, the tax collector's office, the registry of deeds, mortgage companies, and the insurance industry. Many jurisdictions are choosing to computerize the incident follow-up report in order to increase the information available on significant fires within a jurisdiction. Analysis of this data may reveal patterns showing types of fires that could point to deliberately set fires and other criminal activity.

PLANNING, TRAINING, AND RESEARCH

Emergency Planning

Through GIS and other information technology, emergency personnel can plan for a variety of situations that could affect large portions of a community. Ranging from hazardous materials releases to weather-related events, emergency management systems must be ready to respond to the unforeseen. Most community emergency management plans are currently developed in electronic format and can benefit from integration with other community-based data. Technology allows for hazards to be identified and, through modeling applications and automation, plans can be developed to ensure an appropriate response to a multitude of potential situations (Figures 12.5.16a, b, c). The purpose of such an automated display is for automated notification and evacuation planning.

GIS files can be expanded to include information essential to the emergency management function. Examples of this information include the type, quantity, and location of hazardous materials and the type, frequency, and location of other hazardous activities. The prime difficulty in making a hazard assessment system work is that the situation is dynamic. Types, quantities, and locations of materials may fluctuate widely according to the demands of the business. Annual or even semiannual updating of a central file may be insufficient to give a picture of the community's true hazardous materials profile.

Ownership information on properties can be among the most difficult to obtain. Current ownership is probably not needed until legal proceedings have to be instituted. It is easier and more reliable to check legal ownership in those relatively few cases as they occur than to try to develop and maintain a file on legal ownership for all properties. Knowing who is responsible for the property, however, is important, so that contact can be made in the event of an emergency or to schedule inspections.

Information technology through both the Internet and satellite communication allows the radar monitoring of weather conditions and the projection of the track of events such as tornadoes, flash floods, and blizzards. This technology has saved countless lives by warning the public of a dangerous weather event.

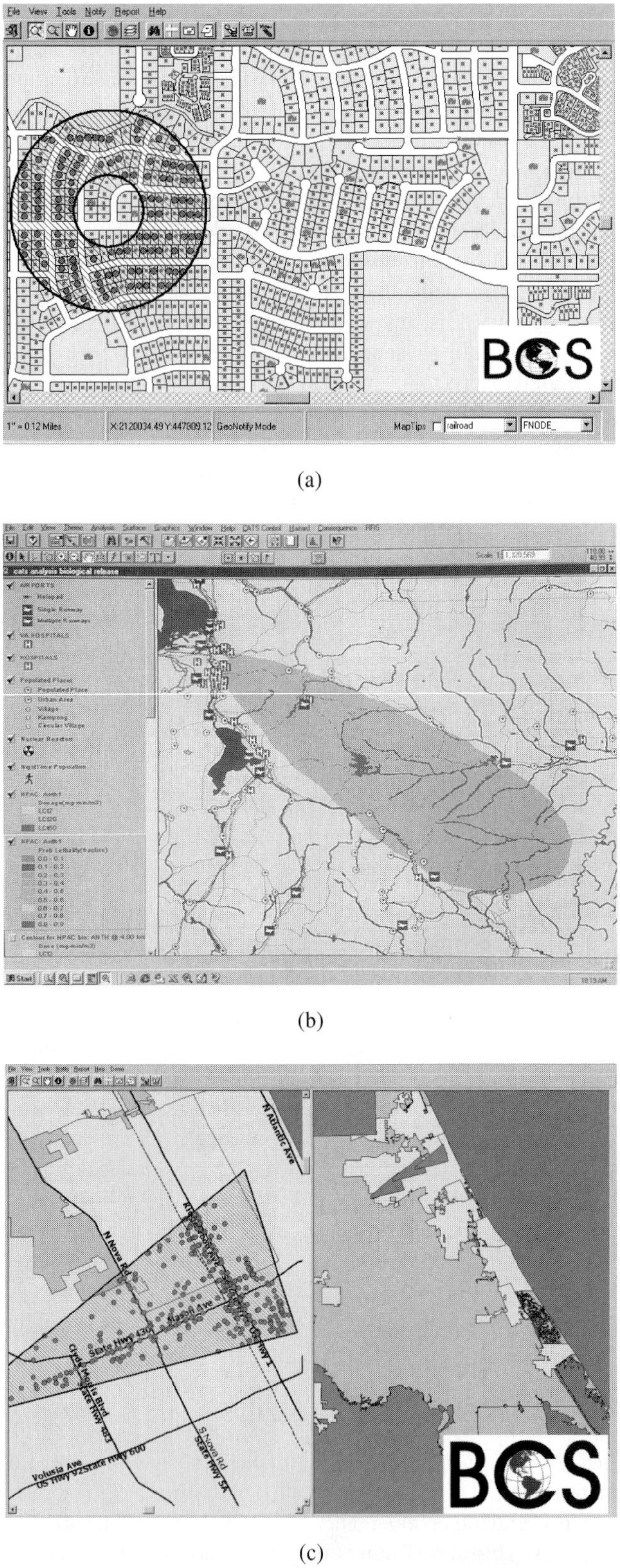

FIGURE 12.5.16 (a) Automated Display of an Evacuation Area Surrounding a Hazardous Materials Incident (b) Automated Modeling and Mapping of a Plume Secondary to a Release of Hazardous Material (c) Automated Path Projection of a Tornado or Other Severe Weather System (Photos provided courtesy of Bradshaw Consulting Services, Inc.)

When weather tracking and other emergency management applications are integrated with automated warning applications, residents can be contacted and given information on the situation. This information may be instructions on whether to seek shelter in place or to evacuate the area.

Through the use of subscription-based Internet calling centers that can quickly distribute thousands of customized voice messages to a targeted population, versatile systems can distribute messages ranging from safety-related messages to instructions on how to shelter in place during an emergency event.

Training and Research

Information technology can provide an exceptional level of support to training, educational, and research activities. Many texts have transitioned to provide CD-ROM study guides, tutorials, and self-paced learning programs. These programs, which focus on the needs of the adult learner, ensure comprehension by requiring students to master lower-level principles before allowing them to proceed to more advanced topics. Therefore, a solid foundation of knowledge is built. The International Fire Service Training Association (IFSTA), for example, offers computer-based and tutorial training for the development of basic fire fighter skills, in accordance with NFPA 1001, *Standard for Fire Fighter Professional Qualifications.* Aircraft orientation and emergency procedures, which crash fire rescue organizations now provide in the form of interactive computer-based training aids, are another example.

These applications are of benefit to fire service personnel because they are a complement to formal training programs. Interactive individual learning can be extended to the evaluation of a student's knowledge, skill, and abilities. Technology has developed realistic incident simulations used to gauge performance or develop a fire officer's confidence and skill (Figure 12.5.17).

Testing and performance during incident simulations and computer-based examinations can be recorded either locally or through secure Internet sites. A fire fighter required to attain a specified performance level can be periodically tested and evaluated through an Internet-based examination. Although this type of testing raises some security issues, these obstacles are being overcome.

FIGURE 12.5.17 Digital Incident Simulation Screen (Image provided courtesy of Digital Combustion, Inc.)

The complexity and specialization of the fire service create the need to use resources outside the organization. Remote locations or entire satellite networks can be reached through distance learning. The Federal Emergency Management Agency (FEMA) and the United States Fire Administration (USFA), for example, have offered online courses of benefit to the fire service.

Through the Internet, new learning opportunities and training materials have become accessible. At present, several fire service websites allow training presentations and materials to be downloaded. The availability of these materials promotes consistency and reduces the program development demands common to local training personnel.

Distance learning is well accepted in the academic environment. Many colleges provide interactive distance learning to enhance the quality of what can be affordably delivered to a remote location, to deliver instruction to smaller audiences, and to increase economy of scale. This interactive instruction is followed by electronic completion of assignments. Several colleges have become paperless institutions with students able to obtain all required materials electronically.

INTEGRATION OF SYSTEMS

Many organizations do not have a systematic approach to the development of information systems. Their approach is piecemeal without an overall plan for the integration of systems. By analogy, an airplane designed in a piecemeal fashion might have three wings, an engine with insufficient power for takeoff, and a fuel tank where there should be cargo or passengers. In short, although each subsystem might fulfill its intended function, the overall system is a failure.

The solution to this problem is information technology planning. As is the case with other organizations, the fire department needs an overall plan for integrating the various component subsystems. All components do not have to be implemented at one time to have a workable system, but a strategic plan for eventual integration and an action plan on how to achieve it are required.

Levels of Integration

Normally, two levels of integration are to be considered. The first is the integration of fire department systems with citywide systems. Considerable benefit can arise from, for example, having a GIS database of occupancy data that can be used by the assessor, tax department, and fire department. In general, however, information resource managers in the fire service should be wary of databases over which they have no control. Nevertheless, the potential benefits are worth the necessary effort in working toward a well-developed multiagency plan. At a minimum, the fire department should think through potential interfaces with city systems and provide the connectivity for future system development. The second level of integration is within the fire department itself where there is significant opportunity for controlling the design of systems, databases, and their interfaces.

Planning Techniques

An organization uses information systems to support strategic planning, managerial control, and operational activities. These activities may be classified into a number of business functions (e.g., scheduling personnel, dispatching, and budgeting). In turn, each function requires a certain subset of the organizational data. Obviously, different functions may require overlapping data subsets. This type of analysis suggests two ways to integrate systems.

Packaging Approach. The first approach to integrating systems is related to the way fire service functions are "packaged" into application systems. For example, a typical entry-level application in a fire department is CAD. In most cases, CAD is implemented on a stand-alone minicomputer. However, the boundary of the system could be expanded to include other records management functions, such as inspections and incident reporting. In the case of inspections, the staff needs information about hazardous materials, occupancy, guard dogs on premises, and so on. In the case of incident data, CAD collects much of the data needed to report fire incident documentation.

Thus, although the focus is still on CAD, the system's boundary would be enlarged to include "subordinate" or supporting functions. The links to supporting functions would be developed as subsystems with their own databases (or files) and have automatic data sharing provided to tie them together.

Data Model Approach. The other approach is based on a data model of the organization. The focus here is on the data and their interrelationships. Whereas the data traditionally have been owned by the application, now the application has become almost insignificant, replaced by transaction sets that update and query the public safety database. In reality, single physical databases are not defined; rather, they are grouped according to some coherent scheme. (Relational databases are appropriate.) Such a scheme should ensure that like entities are grouped together. Although other arrangements are possible, this line of thinking suggests the following groupings:

1. *Personnel database.* Includes data on scheduling of personnel, training, payroll (if not part of the financial system), accidents, assignments
2. *Financial database.* Likely to be citywide in scope; includes data on budgets, flow of funds
3. *Incidents database.* Includes historical data on closed fire and emergency medical incidents
4. *Fire prevention database.* Includes a building inventory and data on occupancy, ownership, hazardous materials; may include arson data
5. *Operational database.* Includes data about incidents in progress; data maintained for relatively short durations; may be moved to incidents database at close of incident or periodically to prevent overloading real-time CAD system with non-real-time data
6. *Supplies and equipment database.* Typically a citywide database; includes supplies inventory and equipment inventory and may include fleet management

SUMMARY

In view of the complexity of information applications, hardware, software, connectivity, and integration, this chapter does not purport to be a complete presentation on fire department information systems and technology. It does, however, attempt to balance technical information with a description of how information technology can be successfully applied to the fire service. Technology continues to evolve at an unprecedented rate; therefore, new applications and innovations beyond those detailed in this chapter should be expected. As new applications develop, they should be evaluated in terms of both reliability and benefit to the fire service.

Technology's increasing interactivity will extend an organization's capabilities. In the fire service, situations are often unforgiving; thus, the reliability of applications is critical. To meet the challenge, organizations should proceed slowly. They should place emphasis on training personnel, evaluating information technology products, and creating a comprehensive technology plan that involves staff members and includes the pilot testing of any new technology. Through this evaluation process, department personnel can ensure that the benefits outweigh the cost and that the best possible applications are selected for the organization.

BIBLIOGRAPHY

NFPA Codes, Standards, and Recommended Practices

Reference to the following NFPA codes, standards, and recommended practices will provide further information on the information management and computer technology discussed in this chapter. (See the latest version of The NFPA Catalog *for availability of current editions of the following documents.)*

NFPA 901, *Standard Classifications for Incident Reporting and Fire Protection Data*

NFPA 1001, *Standard for Fire Fighter Professional Qualifications*

References

Almond, G., "Manchester's New Fire Safety Information System for 2000," *Fire,* Vol. 90, No. 1105, 1997, p. 20.

Aversa, J., "Cellular Phones Add to 911 Routing," *Firehouse.com,* May 1999.

Butters, T., "High Tech on the Highway," *Fire Chief,* Vol. 45, No. 1, 2001, pp. 28–31.

Gary, S., "Data to Go, a Case Study in Wireless Integration," *Fire Chief,* Vol. 44, No. 12, 2000, pp. 32–36.

Gary, S., "Data to Go," *Fire Chief,* Vol. 45, No. 1, 2001, pp. 32–34.

Grier, R., "Voice Over IP: The Next Generation," *Mobile Radio Technology,* Mar. 2001, pp. 40–48.

Griffith, S. J., and Munday, J. W., "Legal Implications of Real Fire Data Collection and Computer Modeling," *Metropolitan Police Forensic Science Laboratory—Proceedings* of the 7th International INTERFLAM Conference, INTERFLAM '96, March 26–28, 1996, Cambridge, UK, Interscience Communications Ltd., London, UK, 1996, pp. 1027–1031.

Holland, P., "Technology Improves Crew Safety on Fireground," *Fire,* Vol. 91, No. 1117, 1998, pp. 21–22.

Kirkwood, S., "Uncharted Technology," *Fire Chief,* Vol. 42, No. 12, 1998, p. 34.

Klein, R. A., "Information Technology (IT) in Strategic and Tactical Planning by the Fire Service. Part 1. Information Integrity and Basic Philosophy Behind the Use of Structured Query Language Databases," *Fire Engineers Journal,* Vol. 57, No. 188, 1997, pp. 36–42.

Klein, R. A., "Information Technology (IT) in Strategic and Tactical Planning by the Fire Service. Part 2. Detailed Requirements for System Hardware and Software, and How to Avoid the More Obvious Problems," *Fire Engineers Journal,* Vol. 57, No. 190, 1997, pp. 32–38.

Klein, R. A., "Information Technology (IT) in Strategic and Tactical Planning by the Fire Service. Part 3. Structured Query Language (SQL) Relational Databases, How They Work, How to Construct a Central Risk Register and How to Write Programmes to Retrieve Stored Information," *Fire Engineers Journal,* Vol. 58, No. 192, 1998, pp. 33–40.

Klein, R. A., "Information Technology (IT) in Strategic and Tactical Planning by the Fire Service. Part 4. Management Issues Involved in the Setting up, Commissioning and Maintenance of a Computer-Based Central Risk Register Database," *Fire Engineers Journal,* Vol. 58, No. 194, 1998, pp. 25–32.

Parker, D., "Cab Computers for West Sussex," *Fire,* Vol. 93, No. 1143, 2000, p. 37.

Pickin, R., "One IT Solution for Two Welsh Brigades," *Fire,* Vol. 91, No. 1117, 1998, p. 29.

Rooney, S., "Computers and the Canadian Fire Service: A Software Solution for Small and Medium-Sized Fire Departments," *Fire Fighting in Canada,* Vol. 41, No. 4, 1997, p. 8.

Ryczkowski, J. J., "Reno Haz Mat Van Surfs the Net and More," *American Fire Journal,* Vol. 51, No. 5, 1999, pp. 12–15.

Werner, C., "Change in the Fire Service Symposium: A Focus on Technology in the Fire Service," *Firehouse.com,* Jan. 2001.

Werner, C., "NFIRS 5.0: An Uncertain Future," *Firehouse,* Vol. 26, No. 5, 2001, pp. 96–97.

Wexler, D., "Seattle Fire Department Is Going Wireless," *Firefighting.com,* Jan. 2001.

Wolfgram, B., "Internet: Another Tool in the Firefighter's Toolbox," *American Fire Journal,* Vol. 51, No. 10, 1999, p. 24.

Woods, P., "Improving Community Safety Through Technology," *Fire Engineers Journal,* Vol. 58, No. 197, 1998, pp. 28–32.

Related Websites

Organization	*Website Address*
Anna Maria College Fire Science Program	http://www.annamaria.edu/Undergraduate/Programs/Fire_Science
Fire Chief Magazine	http://www.firechief.com
Fire Engineering Magazine	http://fe.pennnet.com/home/home.cfm
Firehouse Magazine	http://www.Firehouse.Com/magazine
International Association of Fire Chiefs	http://www.iafc.org
International Association of Firefighters	http://www.iaff.org
International Municipal Signal Association	http://www.IMSAsafety.org
Journal of Emergency Medical Services	http://www.jems.com
Maryland Fire and Rescue Institute	http://www.mfri.org
National Association of State Fire Marshals	http://www.firemarshals.org
National Fire Protection Association	http://www.nfpa.org
National Institute of Standards and Technology	http://fris.nist.gov
National Volunteer Fire Council	http://www.nvfc.org
School of Fire Protection and Safety at Oklahoma State University	http://www.fireprograms.okstate.edu/firet
United States Fire Administration—National Fire Academy	http://www.usfa.fema.gov/nfa/tr. htm
University of Maryland Fire Protection Engineering Program	http://www.enfp.umd.edu
University of Missouri Fire and Rescue Institute	http://www.missouri.edu/~frtiwww
WPI Fire Protection Engineering Program	http://www.wpi.edu/Academics/Depts/Fire

Chapter 6

Liability of Fire Service Organizations for Negligent Fire Fighting

Maureen Brodoff

Chapter Contents

Key Terms

discretionary functions immunity, governmental immunity, liability, limited damages, negligence, public duty rule, punitive damages, tort claims act

In 1955 a large quantity of gasoline was spilled onto a city street in Lawrence, Kansas, during the removal of gasoline storage tanks from a gas station. The local fire department was notified and quickly arrived at the scene. In order to determine the extent of the problem, the fire chief who was supervising the scene instructed a fire fighter to touch a cigarette lighter to the ground. Not surprisingly, a conflagration ensued that destroyed several automobiles. In the lawsuit that followed, the court refused to hold the town liable for the foolhardy tactic of its fire chief.*

This case and many others from the period reflect the traditional view that local governments were not liable for their failure to provide effective fire protection. Indeed, even extreme carelessness in fighting fires would not give rise to liability. Today, however, in the field of fire fighting, as with most modern-day endeavors, the historical limitations on legal liability are eroding, and theories of liability are expanding. Fire service legal liability must now, of necessity, be a concern to the fire service.

This chapter describes the general legal principles that are used in analyzing the legal liability of fire service organizations for negligence in conducting fire-fighting activities.† It should be remembered that the law in this area is not uniform but is governed largely by state and local laws and, therefore, varies from jurisdiction to jurisdiction. The liabilities of individual fire service organizations can only be determined by reference to the specific law in its jurisdiction.‡

For related topics, see Section 1, Chapter 4, "Legal Issues for the Designer and Enforcer."

**Perkins v. Lawrence,* 281 P.2d 1077 (Kan. 1955).

†There are many potential types of legal liabilities encountered in the modern fire service. This chapter treats only one—liability for negligent fire-fighting activities—and is intended only as a general introduction to the subject. It does not deal with other types of liability a fire department could owe to members of the public, such as for negligent inspection or automobile negligence. It also does not deal with employment law issues, such as workers' compensation, wrongful termination of employment, and the expanding field of antidiscrimination law, which has had a widening impact on the fire service in recent years. For the interested reader, there are several works designed for the layperson on these and other legal issues relating to the fire service. See, for example, Callahan, T., *Fire Service and the Law,* 2nd edition (National Fire Protection Association, 1987); Hogan, L. J., *Legal Aspects of the Fire Service,* 3rd edition (Amlex, 2000); Schneid, T. D., *Fire Law: The Liabilities and Rights of the Fire Service* (Wiley, 1995); and Grant, N. K., and Hoover, D., *Fire Service Administration* (National Fire Protection Association, 1993).

‡For convenience, this chapter will generally use the terms "fire service organization" or "municipality" in referring to the entity that may bear liability for negligent fire fighting. The reader, however, should be aware that the actual party that is named in a lawsuit alleging negligent fire fighting will vary depending on how the fire service is organized in a particular locale. Most frequently, fire departments are branches of municipal government and, when a lawsuit is brought, it is the city or town that is named in the suit and that is responsible to pay any judgment. In other cases, it may be an independent fire district or a county that is the responsible party. Sometimes individual fire fighters may be named in such suits. Although such individual liability is beyond the scope of this chapter, protections similar to those described here relating to fire service organizations will frequently protect fire fighters from individual liability for simple negligence. See, e.g., *Love v. Detroit,* 2006 WL 964721 (Mich. Apr. 13, 2006); *Willis v. Beaufort,* 143 N.C. App. 106, 544 S. E.2d 600 (N.C. Ct. App. 2001).

Maureen Brodoff is vice-president and general counsel for the National Fire Protection Association.

NEGLIGENCE IN THE FIRE-FIGHTING CONTEXT

As with any other endeavor, particularly one as fraught with danger and uncertainty as fire fighting, things can go wrong. Fires sometimes cause deaths and injury in spite of the best efforts of the fire service. Property damage may result, not only from the effects of fire but also frequently from the activity of fire fighting itself. A tactical decision made in the midst of impending disaster may, in hindsight, turn out to have been terribly wrong. Bad outcomes alone, however, do not make the fire service liable.

The Elements of a Negligence Case

The principal theory of liability used in lawsuits for personal injury and property damage is what is known in the law as negligence.* The law of negligence does not hold a person liable for *any* damage that results from his or her actions, only damage that results from some act of carelessness in circumstances where the actor had some duty to act with reasonable care. This principle can be understood by way of an illustration drawn from an actual case involving allegations of negligent fire fighting.

In 1978 in the city of Lowell, Massachusetts, a fire occurred in and destroyed five brick buildings.† The fire started on the sixth floor of an unoccupied building. This building had a working sprinkler system and, indeed, the system worked properly in the initial stages of the fire. The fire fighters who responded to the fire, however, chose to use the available water source to operate hoses. This reduced water pressure in the sprinkler system, in effect turning it off. There was evidence that good fire-fighting practice would have been to rely on the building's sprinkler system to fight the fire rather than to have diverted the water from the system to fight the fire with hoses. There was also evidence that the sprinkler system, if allowed to operate, would have put out the fire or contained it until it could have been put out by manual means. Instead, because of the choice of the fire fighters to effectively shut off the sprinkler system, the fire eventually engulfed and destroyed five buildings.

In this case, one can see all of the essential elements of a fire-fighting negligence case. First, under the law, all persons generally have a duty, once they undertake to act, to do so with reasonable care. As explained later in this chapter in the discussion of the "public duty" rule, there is some controversy whether fire fighters owe such a duty of care. In this case, however, it was conceded that once the fire fighters undertook to fight the fire, they had a duty to fight the fire with reasonable care.

*Sometimes other theories of liability are used in suits against the fire service. For example, lawsuits have been brought under a federal law permitting lawsuits for injuries resulting from the deprivation of some civil right. (See 42 U.S.C. § 1983.) These lawsuits require more than allegations of negligence. Typically, they allege some discriminatory action, such as the withholding of adequate fire protection from a minority neighborhood. Lawsuits also sometimes allege deliberate misconduct as opposed to mere negligence. A full discussion of these other theories is beyond the scope of this chapter.

†The fact pattern used for this illustration is drawn from the Massachusetts case of *Harry Stoller & Co. v. Lowell,* 412 Mass. 139 (1992).

Second, the fire fighters breached their duty to act with reasonable care. In lay terms, this simply means that they acted carelessly in fulfilling their duty to fight the fire. Reasonable care, in the context of fire fighting, means that level of care that the reasonably prudent fire fighter would use in similar circumstances. Since the evidence in the case showed that proper fire-fighting practice would have been to leave the sprinklers on, turning them off was viewed in the eyes of the law as negligent.

Third, the fire fighters' breach of their duty to reasonably fight the fire caused the destruction of the buildings. From the evidence, if the sprinklers had been allowed to function, the fire would have been contained. In other words, the fire fighters were the legal cause of the destruction of the buildings, because the destruction of the buildings would not have occurred had the sprinkler system been left on, and the consequences of shutting off the system were reasonably forseeable.

Finally, the fire fighters' negligence resulted in damages. In this case, the damages roughly equaled the value of the destroyed buildings and their contents.

Fire Service Negligence in the Caselaw

This case of the turned-off sprinkler system is a good example of what any case of negligence will have to prove in order to be successful; that is, the existence of a duty of care, the breach of that duty, causation, and damages. It is important to remember, however, that this is but one example of what can be alleged as negligent fire fighting. The types of negligence that can be alleged in the fire-fighting context are infinite. Areas of potential liability include fire suppression activities, tactics and strategies, emergency response system failures, operation of fire service vehicles,* hydrant and water supply maintenance, and maintenance of fire-fighting equipment.

Actual cases that have been brought illustrate the variety of claims that creative lawyers can allege. In an Indiana case, for example, it was alleged that a fire service organization was negligent in failing to maintain a sufficient number of fire fighters for the equipment intended to be used.† In the same case, it was also alleged that there was negligence in the service's failure to supervise and train its fire fighters in controlling and extinguishing fires under the conditions encountered in a particular fire. In an Alabama case, negligence was claimed in the failure of a fire department to respond to a house fire because the apparatus operator had gone home sick.‡ In a Maryland case, negligence was alleged in the failure to properly control and extinguish a brush fire that eventually reignited, causing a second fire in which a

*The laws involving the operation of fire service vehicles present something of a special case, since many states have laws aimed specifically at limiting liability for the operation of emergency and fire service vehicles. These statutes vary from state to state. Indiana, for example, provides immunity for the operation of fire service vehicles only when the operator of the vehicle is an employee of the fire service organization and only in the case of authorized emergency vehicles. [See *Indiana Code* § 9-4-1(d).] Other states have additional requirements, such as that emergency sirens or lights be activated.

†See *Hammond v. Cataldi,* 449 N.2d 1184 (Ind. App. 3d Dist. 1983).

‡See *Williams v. Tuscumbia,* 426 So.2d 824 (Ala. 1983).

warehouse was destroyed.* And in a Massachusetts case, it was alleged that fire fighters were negligent in fighting a fire burning at the rear of a house by spraying water on the front of the house where there was no fire.†

In one particularly dramatic case in Alaska, liability was alleged and found for negligent failure to rescue a person stranded in an upper floor of a burning building during a fire. The rescue failed because the ladder used in the attempt was too short to reach the victim's window. Although the court said this fact alone did not constitute negligence, the fire fighters failed to use other commonsense methods of rescue that were available as an alternative. In particular, the court was deeply disturbed that some spectators who had obtained an extension ladder of sufficient length to reach the victim, and who had raised the ladder and started to extend it, were ordered by a fire official to get away from the building and, when they refused to obey, were driven off by fire hoses.‡

Limits on Fire Service Liability

These illustrations would seem to indicate that liability exists around every corner. Although allegations of negligence are easily made, however, not all negligence claims result in a finding that the fire service was liable. There are two broad reasons tending against findings of fire service liability for negligent fire fighting.

The first reason is that allegations of negligent fire fighting are generally more difficult to prove than in the typical negligence case. In a typical negligence case, a party is accused of creating a dangerous situation that resulted in injury. In the typical fire fighter negligence case, the dangerous situation, that is, the fire, already exists when fire fighters enter the picture. A plaintiff, therefore, is usually in a position of having to prove that the fire fighters either made worse or failed to mitigate a harm that they did not cause. This is a difficult task, especially since the unpredictability and destructive power of fire in general often make it difficult to say with any assurance that some other course of action not taken by the fire fighters would have yielded a better result. Thus, as the Alaska case described previously vividly shows, liability is most often found in the extreme case where the conduct of the fire fighters is viewed as foolhardy or outrageous.

The second reason requires some explaining, but it has even greater impact on fire service liability. As discussed earlier, a case of negligence is built by proving that an individual or group by their careless actions violated a duty to act with reasonable care and, thereby, caused damage. If fire fighting were strictly a private enterprise, carried out by and for the benefit of private parties, such proof would be all that was required to entitle the injured party to hold the fire service organization liable to pay for all damages.

Fire fighting, however, is not a private enterprise. It is generally a governmental function carried out by cities, towns, and other governmental units for the benefit of the public. Because of this, the fire service is the beneficiary of an elaborate body of law that has been developed to shield the government from liability, even when it has acted negligently. This law of "governmental immunity" greatly complicates the question of whether and when a fire service organization can be held liable for damages caused by negligent fire fighting.

THE FIRE SERVICE AND THE DOCTRINE OF GOVERNMENTAL IMMUNITY

Until the last 30 or so years, the doctrine of governmental immunity fully protected governments from lawsuits aimed at governmental functions. Under this doctrine, the government as "sovereign" could do no wrong and could not be sued. In the case of fire-fighting activities, it meant that no matter how negligent a fire department might be or how much damage to life or property that negligence might cause, the municipality whose fire fighting had caused the damage could not be sued.

The doctrine of governmental immunity left no remedy to individuals who had suffered grievous injuries as a result of negligent fire fighting or other governmental negligence. As might be expected, the injustice that the doctrine often seemed to impose led to much criticism of the doctrine and calls for reform.

Beginning in the 1970s, the federal government and the states began, either through court decisions or, more often, through the passage of legislation, to severely limit the absolute governmental immunity that governmental entities had enjoyed. The most common type of legislation, now in existence in some form in most states as well as the federal government, is commonly known as a "tort claims act." Each state act is different but, generally speaking, the acts provide that government entities are liable for injury caused by their negligence in the same manner and to the same extent as a private entity. There are important qualifications, however, that provide the fire service with significant protection against liability.

LEGAL PROTECTIONS FOR THE FIRE SERVICE TODAY

Limits on Amount of Damages

Probably the most important protections for the fire service provided by the various state tort claims acts are the limitations they impose on the amount of damages. Thus, although government entities can now be held liable for their negligence just as can a private individual, the amount they can be required to pay has been limited. In Massachusetts, for example, the amount of liability that a municipality can be required to pay if found negligent is limited to $100,000 per claimant. Frequently, there is an overall cap so that, no matter the number of claimants, the total damages awardable for fire department negligence in any one incident cannot exceed a given amount. Vermont, for example, has a limit of $250,000 per claimant with a maximum aggregate liability of $1,000,000 to all claimants arising out of any given occurrence; Maryland has a limit of $200,000 per claimant with

*See *Utica Mut. v. Gaithersburg-Washington Grove,* 455 A.2d 987 (Md. App. 1983).

†See *Cryan v. Ware,* 413 Mass. 452, 469 (1992).

‡See *Fairbanks v. Schaible,* 375 P.2d 201, 206 (Alaska 1962).

an overall cap of $500,000 per occurrence.* A few states provide lower maximum compensation for property damage than for personal injury.† And in North Carolina municipalities are held to have waived their immunity by purchasing liability insurance and can be held liable up to the amount of the purchased coverage.‡ Finally, punitive damages, that is, damages designed to punish the wrongdoer rather than compensate the injured party, are generally forbidden.§

These various limits on liability are highly significant protections for fire service organizations, since they cap damages at an amount that may frequently represent only a small fraction of the damages actually awarded by a jury. Particularly in the area of fire suppression, where mistakes can result in millions of dollars of personal injury and property damage, the tort claims acts provide a great deal of protection against potentially huge damage awards.

Exceptions Specifically Aimed at Fire-Fighting and Related Activities

Several state tort claims acts have exceptions that specifically retain governmental immunity for fire-fighting and related activities. North Dakota, for example, retains governmental immunity for failure to provide adequate fire prevention personnel or equipment, except if gross negligence can be proved.# Illinois retains governmental immunity for any injury caused by the failure to suppress or contain a fire or while fighting a fire.** Kansas, California, South Carolina, and Texas, by statute, and Indiana, by judicial decision, retain immunity for the failure to provide, or the inadequate provision of, fire protection.††

There are other types of specific exceptions that relate to the fire service, as well. Alaska specifically retains governmental immunity for the performance of duties "in connection with an enhanced 9-1-1 emergency system," and for the performance of duties upon the request of or by agreement with the state "to meet emergency public safety requirements."‡‡ Some states retain immunity for claims relating to the provision of or failure to provide emergency services.§§ Also, many states specifically retain immunity for the failure to make an inspection or the making of an inadequate or negligent inspection.* Finally, some states retain such broad general immunity for governmental functions that fire-fighting activities are more or less categorically immune from liability.†

"Discretionary Functions" Immunity

In addition to the exceptions in some states expressly relating to fire-fighting and related activities, there exists in most state tort claims acts another type of exception that provides significant protection for the fire service. This is known as the "discretionary function" exception, and it requires some explanation.

Although, in passing tort claims acts, the lawmakers of the various states wished to make it possible for citizens to obtain compensation for injuries caused by governmental entities, they were reluctant to abolish immunity for all governmental activities. They were concerned that lawsuits might be used to second guess every governmental policy decision and that the constant fear of lawsuits could severely hamper the ability of municipal officials to govern and to freely exercise the discretion of their office. In order to address these concerns, lawmakers created an exception in the tort claims acts that preserved governmental immunity for "discretionary functions."

The typical discretionary functions exception merely states that the tort claims act, and the governmental immunity that it abolishes, simply does not apply to any claim based on a public employee's performance or failure to perform a "discretionary function."‡ What is a "discretionary function," however, and what does it mean in the context of fire fighting? Many legal battles have been fought over the meaning of this exception.

The main problem has been in determining the breadth of the discretionary function exception that, read literally, could be quite broad indeed. The word "discretion" implies, in its essence, the exercise of judgment, and, therefore, a literal interpretation of the discretionary function exception might lead to the conclusion that all conduct involving the exercise of judgment is immune from negligence liability. In addition, since virtually all fire-fighting activities involve the exercise of judgment, even if only concerning minor details, one might conclude that all fire-fighting activities are immune from suit. This, however, is not the case.

Purpose of Discretionary Function Exemption

Courts have generally rejected a too literal reading of the term "discretionary function." They have felt that granting immunity to all acts that involve some exercise of judgment would, in effect, immunize all governmental activity and, therefore, defeat the whole purpose of the tort claims acts, which was, after all, intended to abolish complete immunity. Courts, therefore, have looked to the purpose of the discretionary function exception. It was only intended to protect conduct involving the kinds of broad public policy and planning judgments that governmental

*See Vt. Stat. Ann. tit. 12, § 5601(b); Md. Cts. & Jud. Proc., § 5-403(a).

†See, e.g., Or. Rev. Stat., § 30.270; N.M. Stat. Ann., § 41-4-19.

‡*Willis v. Beaufort, supra,* 143 N.C. App. at 110; see also N.C. Gen. Stat. §160A-485.

§See, e.g., Mass. Gen. Laws ch. 258, § 2; Minn. Stat. Ann., § 466.04.

#See N.D. Cent. Code, § 32-12.1-03(3).

**See Ill. Rev. Stat. ch. 85, §§ 5-102, 5-103.

††See Kan. Stat. Ann., § 75-6104(n); West's Ann. Cal. Gov. Code § 850.4; S.C. Code Ann. § 15-78-6(6); Tex. Civ. Prac. & Rem. Code Ann., 101.055(3) ; *O'Connell v. Schererville,* 779 N.E.2d 16 (Ind. Ct. Ap. 2002). See also *California v. Superior Court,* 87 Cal. App. 4th 1409, 1412-1415; *Wells v. Lynchburg,* 331 S.C. 296, 501 S.E.2d 746 (1998).

‡‡See Alaska Stat., §§ 09.65.070(d)(6), and (d)(5).

§§See, e.g., Iowa Code, § 613A.4; Tex. Civ. Prac. & Rem. Code Ann., § 101.055(2).

*See, e.g., Kan. Stat. Ann., § 75-6104(k).

†See, e.g., *Davis v. Detroit* 2005 WL 3179537 (Mich App. Nov. 29, 2005).

‡See, e.g., Mass. Gen. Laws ch. 258, § 10(b).

actors need to be able to perform without the constant threat of being sued. In keeping with this purpose, most courts have tended to find immunity, not for all discretionary conduct, but only for conduct that involves "policy making or planning."*

In the context of fire fighting, what does this mean? The legal decisions are far from clear and vary widely in how they treat particular fire service activities. Nevertheless, certain themes emerge.

Administrative Policy Decisions

First, there are aspects of fire service decision making that have an obvious planning or policy basis. These are administrative policy decisions involving the overall structure and makeup of the fire department, the training and equipping of fire fighters, and the allocation of limited fire-fighting resources within the community. They include decisions about the number and location of fire stations, the amount and type of equipment to purchase, the size of the fire-fighting staff, the type and extent of fire fighter training, the number and location of hydrants, or the adequacy of the water supply.†

When lawsuits blame these types of administrative policy decisions for bringing about injury or death, they are frequently dismissed based on the discretionary function exception. For example, a claim that fire fighters were unable to suppress a fire because the nearest fire station was too far away to make timely fire fighting possible would generally fail because decisions about where to locate a fire station are, even if patently unreasonable, protected from liability under the discretionary function exception.

Of course, some courts are more stringent in applying the exception than others. Many courts, for example, will view any broad administrative-level policy decision as categorically immune from liability, without any inquiry into the thought processes of the decision makers. Other courts, however, will require that the fire service organization, in order to claim immunity, present evidence showing that the decision makers actually went through a weighing of policy choices. In a case alleging that fire fighters were not supplied with a particular type of rescue equipment that would have prevented an injury, such a court would, for example, require that the fire service organization show that its failure to provide such equipment was the result of a conscious policy-making decision involving the balancing of competing interests, rather than the result of a simple failure to consider the question whether the equipment was needed.‡

It is clear, therefore, that administrative decisions are generally covered and immune from suit, at least where the decisions involve a conscious weighing of policy considerations. What about operational decisions made in the course of fighting a particular fire? Some have argued, for example, that the initial decision to fight a fire is discretionary, but that all of the subsequent actions in actually fighting the fire are not. Under this view, almost all actual fire suppression activities on the fireground would fall outside the "discretionary function exception" and would, therefore, be subject to potential liability.

This point of view, however, has mostly been rejected. Some courts go so far as to say that all tactical fireground decisions are immune from liability as "discretionary functions."* Most courts, however, have been more selective and have found that, while many decisions taken in the course of fire fighting do not involve policy or planning considerations, some decisions made on the fireground do involve broad public policy choices protected by discretionary function immunity.

Entitlement to Discretionary Function Immunity

How do courts decide whether a fireground decision is entitled to discretionary function immunity? In one recent case, the court looked to whether allegedly negligent fire-fighting decisions were dictated by a statute, regulation, or fire department policy. The case involved a warehouse fire during the course of which the fire department ordered all power to the building turned off. After the fire was extinguished, the fire fighters ordered the power restored, but did so without first either having the electrical system checked or obtaining a permit. The restoration of power resulted in a rekindling of the fire, which then entirely destroyed the building. The municipality argued that the decision to restore the power, even if negligent, was entitled to discretionary function immunity. The court disagreed, however, because there was evidence that the building code as well as fire department policy prohibited restoring power to the building in the way that the fire fighters had done. The court reasoned that, where procedure for the restoration of electrical power was dictated by specific regulations and policies, the decision to restore power was not a matter of discretion and was not, therefore, immune from liability.†

Usually, though, particular fireground decisions are not dictated by a specific rule or regulation. To determine, in these cases, whether a particular operational decision constitutes a discretionary function, courts generally look not at the particular action but at the reasons for fire fighter actions.

To illustrate, consider the case, described earlier in this chapter, of the fire fighters who turned off an operating sprinkler system in an unoccupied building because they wanted to fight the fire with hoses. Their decision to turn off the sprinkler system was clearly negligent, in that good fire-fighting practice would, in the circumstances, have dictated using the sprinkler system to extinguish the fire. The decision to shut off the sprinkler system also did not involve any policy or planning considerations, since the fire fighters simply made a careless decision about how to best fight the fire.

---

*See, e.g., *King v. Seattle,* 84 Wash.2d 239, 525 P.2d 228, 233 (1974); *Keopf v. County of York,* 198 Neb. 67, 251 N.W.2d 866, 870 (1977); *Johnson v. State,* 69 Cal.2d 782, 788, 447 P.2d 352 (1968); and *Harry Stoller & Co. v. Lowell,* 412 Mass. 139 (1992).

†See, e.g., *Adams v. Tenakee Springs,* 963 P.2d 1047 (Ala. 1998).

‡As examples of the differing approaches used by courts, see and compare *Hammond v. Cataldi,* 449 N.E.2d 1184 (Ind. App. 3 Dist. 1993); and *Waldorf v. Shuta,* 896 F.2d 723, 728-730 (3d Cir. 1990).

*See *Jimenez v. LMA Intern, Ltd.,* 2002 WL 31553547 (N.Y. Sup. October 15, 2002).

†See *Commerce and Industry Ins. Co. v. Grinnell Corp.,* 280 F.3d 566 (5th Cir. 2002).

In slightly different circumstances, however, the decision to shut off a sprinkler system could easily involve a significant policy choice. Suppose, for example, that the fire fighters had decided to shut off the sprinkler system in the unoccupied buildings, not merely to deploy hoses, but to divert the water supplying the sprinkler to fight a fire in a neighboring building that was occupied. The decision to sacrifice the unoccupied buildings in order to devote limited fire-fighting resources to saving lives next door clearly involves policy choices about the relative value of property and human life. Thus, even if the decision to shut off the sprinkler system was ultimately shown to be negligent in that the occupied building could have been saved without diverting water from the sprinkler system, the decision was grounded in an important policy choice, and many courts would rule that it was immune from liability under the discretionary function exception.*

In summary, although the court decisions in this area vary widely from jurisdiction to jurisdiction, it can be said that the discretionary function exception provides immunity to the fire service from liability for most broad administrative-level decision making and for many operational-level decisions as well. Though far from comprehensive, and less than certain in any individual case, the discretionary function exception still provides the fire service with substantial protection from liability.

PUBLIC DUTY RULE AS AN ADDED PROTECTION FOR THE FIRE SERVICE

So far, the liability for negligent fire fighting, although complicated, can be summarized quite simply. Initially, the doctrine of governmental immunity completely protected fire-fighting operations from liability, even if a fire was fought negligently. Today, however, fire service organizations can, in some circumstances, be successfully sued for negligence. The extent to which they can be sued is limited in most jurisdictions by the tort claims acts and the court decisions that interpret them. In general, those acts will, through the discretionary functions exception and other exceptions aimed at protecting fire and emergency services, immunize fire service organizations entirely for some activities. Where immunity is abolished, however, the acts will still provide a cap on damages that can be won against a fire service organization.

Immunity Through Public Duty Rule

If the law preferred simplicity, even of a relative kind, the issue might end here. There is, however, one more important twist: "the public duty rule."

Even though state legislatures have abolished governmental immunity and permitted local governments to be sued in many situations, courts have continued to be sympathetic to the problems of cities and towns and their difficulty in paying even the limited awards permitted by the tort claims acts. Particularly in the area of fire and other public protective services, some courts have expressed the fear that imposing even limited liability for negligence could pose a crushing burden on municipalities, particulary in busy urban areas. As one judge pointed out, in extreme circumstances, such as the Los Angeles riots where there were hundreds of fires and severe obstacles to effective fire fighting, the potential costs of liability could be catastrophic.* This fear has led some courts to develop a judge-made rule to shield the fire service and other public protective services, such as police and inspection. The "public duty" rule offers immunity from negligence liability that goes far beyond the limited immunity retained in the tort claims acts.

Under the public duty rule, fire fighting and other public protective services are viewed as an obligation that governments owe, not to any particular individual, but to the general public as a whole. Based on this view, the public duty rule holds, somewhat paradoxically, that, because fire fighting is for the benefit of all, it is, in effect, for the benefit of no one in particular. Under the rule, therefore, no individual can seek damages for injuries caused by negligent fire fighting because, in essence, the fire service owes no duty to any particular individual to act reasonably.

What is the effect of the public duty rule? Its greatest impact is at the operational level of fire fighting. The immunity offered by most state tort claims acts under the discretionary function exception is quite limited, and most decisions made on the fireground can give rise to potential liability, unless they can be said to involve public policy choices. In states that follow the public duty rule, however, such decisions become largely immune, and any fire-fighting activity, even if negligent and even if devoid of public policy implications, cannot give rise to liability.

Limitations to Public Duty Rule

It would seem that fire service organizations in states following the public duty rule have nothing to fear from lawsuits claiming negligent fire fighting. This is largely true. However, in the law every rule has its limitations and exceptions, and so does the public duty rule.

First, courts that follow the public duty rule limit its protection to the suppression of fires not caused by the fire department itself. Thus, if a fire department negligently caused a fire during a fire training exercise or some other non-fire-suppression-related activity, the public duty rule would offer no protection. Also, a few courts would not apply the public duty rule to protect fire fighters in cases where they aggravated an existing fire as opposed to merely failing to suppress it.† These courts, for example, would provide complete immunity where fire fighters negligently failed to put out an existing fire, because they negligently aimed hoses on the wrong part of the building. They would, however, permit liability where fire fighters took some action that actively made matters worse, as, for example, turning off an operating sprinkler system that, left alone, would have contained the fire.

*See, e.g., *Dahlheimer v. Dayton,* 441 N.W.2d 534, 538–539 (Minn. 1989).

*See *Cryan v. Ware,* 413 Mass. 452, 455 (1992).

†See *Cryan v. Ware, supra,* 413 Mass. 452 (1992).

"Special Relationship" Exception

Second, there is an exception to the public duty rule known as the "special relationship" exception. It holds that, even though fire fighting and other protective services are viewed in general as an obligation owed only to the public at large, a fire or other protective service organization can, by words or actions in a particular case, create a special duty to particular private parties.

How does a fire service organization create for itself this "special relationship," where liability may occur? The special relationship exception has been complicated and often inconsistent in application, and, in practice, courts have been reluctant to apply it to hold the fire service liable.* It seems clear that a fire department does not create a special relationship to an individual property owner merely by responding to the owner's call for assistance and fighting the fire on the property.†

Similarly, the fact that a municipality regularly inspected a factory would usually not, by itself, create a special relationship sufficient to expose the municipality to liability for negligent fire-fighting operations later conducted at the site.‡

Generally speaking, in order to demonstrate a special relationship that could expose a municipality to liability, courts have required a showing that the municipality's fire fighters (or other agents) assumed an affirmative duty to provide a service beyond that generally owed to the public, that the fire fighters knew that failure to perform the duty could cause harm, that the duty was established through direct communication or contact between the fire fighters and the injured party, and that the injured party justifiably relied, to his or her detriment, on the fire fighters to perform the duty they had undertaken.§

Examples of "Special Relationship" Exception

The situations that lend themselves to a finding of a special relationship are best understood by looking at some illustrative cases. In one case, for example, involving a factory fire, factory representatives approached fire fighters at the fire scene and warned them that there were metallic chemical elements stored in the building that were not amenable to water suppression methods. The court found that the warning made directly to fire fighters at the scene created a reasonable reliance on the part of the factory owners that the fire fighters would correctly fight the fire. As a result, a "special relationship" was created, and the municipality could be found liable for the damages that resulted when its fire fighters ignored the warnings, as well as the relevant fire codes, and doused the fire with water.#

*Contrast, e.g., the markedly different treatment the court gave police and fire fighters, respectively, in *Cryan v. Ware, supra,* 413 Mass. 452 (1992); and *Irwin v. Ware,* 392 Mass. 745 (1993).

†See, e.g., *Commerce & Indus. Ins. Co. v. Toledo,* 543 N.E.2d 1188 (Ohio 1989).

‡See *State Automobile Mutual Ins. Co. v. Titanium Metals Corp.,* 159 Ohio App. 3d 338, 344, 823 NE2d 934 (Ohio Ct. App. 2004).

§See *State Automobile Mutual Ins. Co., supra,* 159 Ohio App. 3d 343. *See also Babcock v. Mason County Fire Dist. No. 6,* 144 Wash.2d 774, 30 P.2d 1261 (Wash. 2001).

#See *State Automobile Mutual Ins. Co., supra,* 159 Ohio App. 3d 338.

Another case involved an inn fire in which a husband who had managed to awaken and escape from the inn desperately tried to return and save his wife when he realized that she had not likewise escaped. As fire fighters arrived at the scene, he began yelling at them to rescue his wife, who could be heard screaming through a wall that the husband had been trying to break through. The fire fighters, however, allegedly did not respond to his pleas, and when he tried to continue the rescue on his own, fire fighters physically restrained him. It was not until 15 minutes following the restraint of the husband that fire fighters began an attempt to rescue the wife. By then it was too late, and the wife perished. Based on these "extraordinary" facts, the court had little difficulty concluding that, when the fire fighters affirmatively prevented the husband from rescuing his wife, they made an implied promise to rescue her themselves, upon which he was forced to rely. A special relationship was thereby created and the municipality could not claim immunity from liability for any negligence of the fire fighters in failing to rescue the wife.*

As the preceding examples illustrate, the public duty rule does not provide complete immunity for fire service organizations. But even apart from the potential liability opened up by the "special relationship" exception and other limitations on the public duty rule, there is yet another reason why fire service organizations in states that observe the public duty rule should not rest with complete ease. The public duty rule has been widely criticized as fundamentally inconsistent with the tort claims acts, because the rule creates immunity where legislatures have sought to remove it. For a time, therefore, a trend appeared to be taking shape to abolish the rule and many states did so.†

The trend stalled, however, and the majority of states that have considered the issue still recognize the public duty rule.‡

*See *Stata v. Waterford,* 225 A. D.2d 163, 649 N.Y.S.2d 232 (N.Y.A.D. 3 Dept. 1996).

†See *Adams v. State,* 555 P.2d 235 (Alaska 1976); *Leake v. Cain,* 720 P.2d 152, 158-159 (Colo. 1986); *Adam v. State,* 380 N.W.2d 716, 724 (Iowa 1986); *Maple v. Omaha,* 222 Neb. 293, 301 (1986); *Schear v. County Comm'rs,* 101 N.M. 671 (1984); *Coffey v. Milwaukee,* 74 Wis.2d 526 (1976); *DeWald v. State,* 719 P.2d 643, 653 (Wyo. 1986); *Ryan v. State,* 134 Ariz. 308, 310 (1982); *Commercial Carrier Corp. v. Indian River County,* 371 So.2d 1010, 1015-1016 (Fla. 1979); and *Brennen v. Eugene,* 285 Or. 401, 407 (1979). See also *Hollis v. Brighton,* 885 So.2d 135 (Ala. 2004) and *Ziegler v. Millbrook,* 513 So. 2d 1275 (Ala. 1987) (applying public duty rule to volunteer but not to professional fire departments). See also *Dean v. Childs,* 262 Mich. App. 48, 58–59, 684 N.W. 2d 307 (2004) and *Willis v. Beaufort, supra,* 143 N.C. App. at 108–109 (applying public duty rule to police but not to fire protection services).

‡See, e.g., *Yates v. Mansfield Bd. of Edn.,* 102 Ohio St.3d 205, 808 N.E.2d 861 (Ohio 2004); *Babcock v. Mason County Fire Dist. No. 6,* 144 Wash.2d 774, 30 P.2d 1261 (Wash. 2001); *Stata v. Waterford, supra,* 225 A.D.2d 163. *Shore v. Stonington,* 187 Conn. 147 (1982); *Randall v. Fairmont City Police Dep't,* 186 W. Va. 336 (1991). As many as 21 states and the District of Columbia have been cited as following the traditional public duty rule. Excluding Michigan, which, as indicated in the previous note, no longer recognizes the public duty rule for fire-fighting activities, these states include California, Connecticut, Hawaii, Illinois, Indiana, Kansas, Maryland, Minnesota, Missouri, Nevada, New Hampshire, New York, North Carolina, Ohio, Pennsylvania, Rhode Island, South Carolina, Utah, Washington, and West Virginia. See *Jean v. Commonwealth,* 414 Mass. 496, 518 n.1 (1993) (O'Connor, J., concurring).

And at least one state, Massachusetts, has, following court abolition of the rule, revived it by incorporating it into the state tort claims act.* It is safe to say, therefore, that the public duty rule, in many states, still offers fire service organizations a large measure of immunity.

SUMMARY

The degree to which the fire service may be exposed to liability for negligent fire fighting depends, to a large degree, on the law of the state in which the fire service organization is located. Although all states have abolished to one degree or another the total governmental immunity from negligence lawsuits, the amount of protection that remains varies among jurisdictions. In all states, however, it is important to remember that, even in the absence of complete immunity, there are still significant protections offered the fire service. Although the principles defy easy summarization, the following, in general, can be said.

1. In virtually all states, fire service organizations will be protected from suits criticizing broad administrative policy decisions of fire department and municipal administrators. Thus, suits claiming injuries resulting from bad policy decisions about the placement or number of fire stations, the size of fire department staffs, and the adequacy of funding for fire department activities will generally be prohibited under the "discretionary functions" exception or similar legal principles contained in the torts claims acts or caselaw of most states.
2. In the majority of states, fire service organizations will generally be liable for injuries for negligent fire fighting when the claims are based on bad operational decisions made on the fireground about how to fight a particular fire. Even operational decisions, however, will sometimes be protected under the "discretionary functions" exception, particularly where those decisions involve public policy choices.
3. In the minority of the many states that still follow the "public duty" rule, fire service organizations will be protected from negligence suits, even those involving operational decisions, unless the department or its employees have by words or deed created a "special relationship" with an injured party, thus creating a duty beyond that owed to the public as a whole.

The trend of recent years has been to hold fire service organizations liable when fire fighters have acted negligently. This trend, however, is far from complete. As the preceding discussion shows, limited immunity still exists both in the discretionary function exception and in the persistence of the public duty rule, which, despite much criticism, continues to show vitality in many statews. In addition, the caps on damages that exist in all states will continue to serve to soften the impact of negligence cases on the fire service. The explosion of liability that has occurred in all areas of the law in recent years has had only mixed results when it comes to the fire service.

*See Massachusetts General Laws, ch. 258, § 10, as amended by 1993 Stat. Ch. 495, § 57.

Chapter 7

Safety, Medical, and Health Issues and Programs

Revised by
Murrey E. Loflin

Chapter Contents

Key Terms

fire fighter safety, incident command system, industrial fire brigade, infection control, occupational safety and health, rehabilitation, risk management, safety officer

Over the past 35 years, positive changes have emerged in fire service, as fire fighters have increasingly applied occupational safety and health concepts to the practice of our profession. Vast improvements with protective clothing and protective equipment, apparatus and vehicles, command and control of emergency operations, health maintenance, and numerous other components have improved fire fighter safety and health. One method for gauging the effectiveness of a national fire fighter occupational safety and health program is fire fighter fatality and injury statistics, and those numbers are beginning to move downward. This trend indicates that an emphasis on occupational safety and health is becoming a standard part of fire department operations and activities. However, there is still an incredible amount of work ahead for the fire service regarding occupational safety and health. In years past, the fire service had the distinction of being the most hazardous occupation in the country. Slowly, the fire service is losing this pronounced title and taking pride in conducting safe and effective operations. The number of fire fighter fatalities has averaged approximately 100 per year for the past 15 to 20 years. Since 1977 when fire fighter fatality statistics began to be tracked by the National Fire Protection Association (NFPA), the number reached a high of 173 fatalities in 1978 and a low of 75 in 1992 (Table 12.7.1). Progress has been made in the fire fighter safety and health arena, but there is still opportunity for improvement.

The fire service is beginning to understand the necessity and rationale for developing, implementing, and maintaining a proactive, comprehensive occupational safety and health program. However, many fire service personnel still do not subscribe to the safety and health philosophy. Tradition plays a major role in this lack of understanding of fire fighter safety and health. Although the struggle is far from over, the fire service is learning the lesson that safety is good business.

This chapter outlines the history of safety and health legislation as it applies to fire departments and describes relevant NFPA standards and requirements within the context of that history. The chapter concludes with a description of the risk management program that is detailed in NFPA 1500, *Standard on Fire Department Occupational Safety and Health Program.*

For related topics, see Section 12, Chapter 1, "Planning for Public Fire-Rescue Protection"; Section 12, Chapter 8, "Effect of Building Construction and Fire Protection Systems on Fire Fighter Safety"; and Section 12, Chapter 9, "Fire and Emergency Services Protective Clothing and Protective Equipment."

EVOLUTION OF SAFETY AND HEALTH LEGISLATION

On December 29, 1970, the Occupational Safety and Health Act of 1970 (Public Law No. 91-596) was signed into law by President Richard M. Nixon. The Occupational Safety and Health Act had an effective date of April 28, 1971. Coauthored by Senator Harrison A. Williams (D-NJ) and

Murrey E. Loflin is the director of fire training for West Virginia University Fire Service Extension. He has served in the fire service for over 28 years. He is a secretary of the NFPA Fire Service Occupational Safety and Health Technical Committee and a member of the Incident Management Professional Qualifications Technical Committee.

TABLE 12.7.1 Fire Fighter Fatalities and Injuries, 1977–2006

Year	*Total Fatalities*	*Career*	*Volunteer*	*Injuries*
1977	157	70	82	NA
1978	173	64	101	NA
1979	125	58	57	NA
1980	138	61	69	NA
1981	136	58	65	103,340
1982	128	51	67	98,150
1983	113	54	51	103,150
1984	119	43	59	102,300
1985	128	55	66	100,900
1986	119	50	55	96,450
1987	132	49	68	102,600
1988	136	43	81	102,900
1989	118	43	65	100,700
1990	107	26	62	100,300
1991	108	36	66	103,300
1992	75	24	44	97,700
1993	79	21	55	101,500
1994	105	34	38	95,400
1995	98	30	59	94,500
1996	96	27	65	87,150
1997	99	31	59	85,400
1998	91	33	49	87,500
1999	112	37	71	88,500
2000	103	28	58	84,550
2001	103/443	25/365	66	82,250
2002	97	29	50	80,800
2003	106	26	58	78,750
2004	105	29	65	75,840
2005	87	25	54	80,100
2006	89	23	46	83,400

Note: 9/11 fatalities are listed separately for 2001.
Source: NFPA, August 2006.

Congressman William Steiger (R-Wis), the Occupational Safety and Health Act is referred to as the Williams-Steiger Act or the Williams-Steiger Occupational Safety and Health Act. Prior to the passage of the Occupational Safety and Health Act, legislation for general industry was intermittent and grossly inadequate. Most states had little or no safety and health legislation, inadequate safety and health standards, insufficient staffing, and inadequate enforcement procedures. Budgets were poorly funded. In turn, the occupational fatality rate was greater than 14,000 employees killed and 2.2 million suffering work-related injuries annually in the late 1960s. Prior to 1970, the federal legislation for occupational safety and health was erratic. Efforts were directed more toward specific interests than the widespread coverage, as designated in the Occupational Safety and Health Act.

When the Occupational Safety and Health Act of 1970 was enacted, each state was given the opportunity to develop its own safety and health plan. Under the Occupational Safety and Health Act of 1970, the federal Occupational Safety and Health Administration (OSHA) has no direct enforcement to ensure that state and local governments comply with safety and health standards, such as the OSHA Bloodborne Pathogens standard for public employees.

State Plans and Programs

Twenty-four states and two territories have established and maintain an effective and comprehensive occupational safety and health program for public employees. These state plans must meet or exceed the requirements of federal OSHA. OSHA gives each state 6 months from the publication date of any new federal final standard to adopt a similar state standard. All fire departments, whether state, county, or municipal, in any of the 24 states or two territories that have an OSHA plan agreement in effect have the protection of the minimal acceptable safety and health standards mandated by federal OSHA.

The following 24 states and two territories have state OSHA plans that cover public employees:

Alaska	Michigan	South Carolina
Arizona	Minnesota	Tennessee
California	Nevada	Utah
Connecticut	New Jersey	Vermont
Hawaii	New Mexico	Virgin Islands
Indiana	New York	Virginia
Iowa	North Carolina	Washington
Kentucky	Oregon	Wyoming
Maryland	Puerto Rico	

Section 18 of the Occupational Safety and Health Act of 1970 encourages states to develop and operate their own job safety and health programs. OSHA approves and monitors state plans and provides up to 50 percent of an approved plan's operating costs.

There are currently 24 states and jurisdictions operating complete state plans (covering both the private sector and state and local government employees) and 4—Connecticut, New Jersey, New York, and the Virgin Islands—covering public employees only. Eight other states were approved at one time but subsequently withdrew their programs. States must set job safety and health standards that are "at least as effective as" comparable federal standards, though most states adopt standards identical to federal standards. States have the option to promulgate standards covering hazards not addressed by federal standards.

Inspection and Consultation. A state must conduct inspections to enforce its standards, cover public (state and local government) employees, and operate occupational safety and health training and education programs. In addition, most states provide free on-site consultation to help employers identify and correct workplace hazards. Such consultation may be provided either under the plan or through a special agreement under Section 21(d) of the act.

Awareness of Laws and Standards. Regardless of whether a department is mandated to comply with the requirements under the Occupational Safety and Health Act or not, it is a good practice to do so for the protection and welfare of personnel. With more emphasis being placed on health and safety, fire and EMS agencies are now more aware of pertinent laws and standards.

Laws and standards are a critical and significant part of the operations of any emergency services organization. Administrators must remain knowledgeable and compliant with current safety and health regulations. As managers responsible for the delivery of customer services, we must have a thorough understanding of the laws, standards, and regulations that govern the safety and health of members relating to response and actions at the emergency scene.

Regulations for Fire Brigades

With the development of occupational safety and health standards for general industry, there were applicable requirements for the fire service in 29 Code of Federal Regulations (CFR) 1910.156, Industrial Fire Brigades. This standard contains requirements for personal protective equipment, training, respiratory protection, and the use of fire-fighting equipment. Basically, this was the fire service's introduction to safety and health requirements. Attitudes toward safety and health in the fire service have been gradually changing as occupational safety and health requirements have improved over the past 20 years.

Fire Service Processes for Occupational Safety and Health

Federal and/or state laws now regulate components of the fire service occupational safety and health process, which include the following:

- Development of an occupational safety and health program
- Facility safety
- Training and education
- Protective clothing and protective equipment
- Respiratory protection
- Infection control
- Health maintenance

The risk management process must be recognized as a vital component of ensuring the success of the fire department's occupational safety and health program (see the section entitled "Risk Management"). Before dealing with specific risk management programs, it is important to understand the requirements of relevant NFPA codes.

NFPA STANDARDS

NFPA 1500, *Standard on Fire Department Occupational Safety and Health Program,* and Related Standards

This document was intended to function as an umbrella for future standards developed by the Fire Service Occupational Safety and Health Technical Committee. The true advancement of fire fighter safety and health can be tied to the development of NFPA 1500, which was passed at the NFPA Annual Meeting in 1987. The standard was approved at the Standards Council Meeting in July 1987 and was published with an effective date of August 1987. Prior to the comment period of NFPA 1500, no standard had generated this many public comments (1200). NFPA 1403, *Standard on Live Fire Training Evolutions,* generated approximately 1000 comments during the Report on Comments in 1985.

After the initial passage of the standard in May 1987, issues that surfaced focused on incident management, infection control, and health maintenance. Task groups were appointed and work was initiated to begin development of the following standards: NFPA 1561, *Standard on Emergency Services Incident Management System;* NFPA 1581, *Standard on Fire Department Infection Control Program;* and NFPA 1582, *Standard on Comprehensive Occupational Medical Program for Fire Departments.* Also a complete rewrite of NFPA 1501, *Standard for Fire Department Safety Officer* (renumbered to NFPA 1521 during the 1992 revision cycle) was initiated as the requirements of this document had not changed significantly since its inception in 1977. Additionally, the technical committee addressed the continued development of NFPA 1500 to improve on the initial requirements addressed in the 1987 edition of the document. Two additional standards developed were NFPA 1583, *Standard on Health-Related Fitness Programs for Fire Fighters,* and NFPA 1584, *Recommended Practice on the Rehabilitation of Members Operating at Incident Scene Operations and Training Exercises.*

NFPA 1501, *Standard for Fire Department Safety Officer* (now NFPA 1521)

The initial standard that promoted health and safety for fire fighters was NFPA 1501, approved in 1977. The technical committee responsible for the development of NFPA 1501 was dissolved by the NFPA Standards Council and a new technical committee was officially formed in 1983. The scope of the Fire Service Occupational Safety and Health Technical Committee was to address the development of a comprehensive fire service occupational safety and health program.

Evolution of Standards in the 1990s

The issues that surfaced during the public proposal period of NFPA 1500 included the need to identify methods for achieving competencies for fire fighter, driver/operator, fire officer, and safety officer job functions and the need to establish training and education mandates for achieving and maintaining certifications.

Staffing for fire apparatus was also an issue. During the Report on Comment Period, a public comment was submitted to identify the minimum staffing on fire apparatus. The public comment led to a vote at the NFPA Annual Meeting in May 1992 in New Orleans. The issue was taken to the Standards Council for consideration. The staffing requirements remained in the annex under emergency operations.

During the 1997 revision cycle, additions to NFPA 1500 included recommendations on administrative and operational risk management and on conducting fire fighting operations during the incipient stages of an incident (for the initial rapid intervention crew). This crew required sufficient personnel to conduct an "initial operation" in an atmosphere that was either potentially or actually immediately dangerous to life and health (IDLH).

The Occupational Safety and Health Administration defines an IDLH atmosphere as one that poses an immediate hazard to life or produces immediate irreversible debilitating effects on health. This issue, which was discussed and debated during the subsequent revision to NFPA 1500, coincided with OSHA's public review process of 29 CFR 1910.134, Respiratory Protection, which contained the mandates for the "Two in/Two out" requirements. The citing of fire departments caused a great deal of confusion and resistance among the fire service leaders and the governing bodies they reported to. Not until the revised NFPA 1500 was passed in May 1997, and OSHA issued its rules in January 1998, was the inconsistency resolved. The 1997 edition of NFPA 1500 included material that provided a comparison of the requirements 29 CFR 1910.134, Respiratory Protection, and those included in NFPA 1500 including the medical requirements.

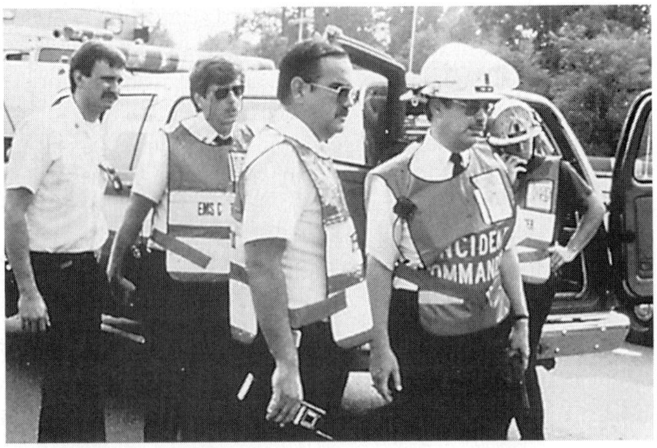

FIGURE 12.7.1 Assessing Risk as Part of the Incident Management System (Photo courtesy of Fairfax County Fire and Rescue Department, Fairfax, Virginia)

Developments in the Twenty-First Century

Evolution of NFPA 1500. The fourth edition of NFPA 1500 was approved at the NFPA 2001 fall meeting and was issued by the Standards Council with an effective date of January 31, 2002. Changes were made based on input from NFPA Data Analysis and Research Division, NFPA fire investigation reports, and the National Institute on Occupational Safety and Health (NIOSH) Fire Fighter Fatality Investigation reports. The changes were made to the standard relating to personal protective clothing and equipment, fire apparatus, training requirements, medical requirements, and several other areas. The Fire Service Occupational Safety and Health Technical Committee working with several other NFPA technical committees developed a complete section that outlines the requirements for a fire department respiratory protection program. The standard provides the user and the enforcer one source in which to develop and implement a comprehensive respiratory protection program.

The 2007 edition of NFPA 1500 was approved at the annual meeting in Orlando, Florida, in June 2006 with an effective date of August 17, 2006. The 2007 edition is a complete revision of the standard, which includes a change in chapter titles, revisions to each chapter based on fire fighter fatality data analysis and reports, and requirements in the chapters addressing the operations of fire apparatus, protective clothing and protective equipment, and emergency operations. Annex material for each chapter was completely reviewed with necessary changes made.

NFPA 1561, *Standard on Emergency Services Incident Management System.* The 2005 edition of NFPA 1561 was prepared by the Technical Committee on Fire Service Occupational Safety and Health, acted on at the NFPA 2004 Fall Meeting, and issued by the Standards Council.

The first edition of this document was issued in 1990 to support requirements in NFPA 1500, *Standard on Fire Department Occupational Safety and Health Program,* requiring fire departments to conduct emergency operations within an effective incident management system (Figure 12.7.1). The committee realized that the safety aspects of an effective and efficient command and control were as important as the operational coordination and effectiveness of the system. In developing this document, the committee examined several incident management systems and variations thereon that were in use in different fire departments and related organizations. The committee determined that, in addition to requiring the use of an incident management system, there should be performance criteria for the components of a system that contribute directly toward safety and health objectives and developed the standard to specifically address those concerns.

The 1995 edition expanded the areas of accountability, use of rapid intervention crews (RIC) for rescue of members, and interagency cooperation and recognized that incident management includes more than fireground operations. The 2000 edition expanded the document to reflect the mainstream utilization of incident management systems. The title of the document was changed to *Standard on Emergency Services Incident Management System* to reflect the fact that all emergency service organizations should use an incident management system. In the 2002 edition, the committee focused on areas of risk management, communications, roles and responsibilities of the Incident safety officer (ISO), rapid intervention crews, and defined command structures. In addition, new annex material was added to assist the users of the standard.

Following the issuance of the 2002 edition, a Tentative Interim Amendment (TIA) was issued to add annex material on position descriptions and roles, responsibilities of command, and general staff positions within an incident management system. This edition expands the TIA and incorporates it into the body of the standard. The response and operational capabilities of the emergency response community are required to be managed through an incident command system. The revisions in the 2005 edition of the standard address specific issues such as incident management teams, unified command, the roles and responsibilities of the incident commander (IC), and command and general staff functions.

DEFINITION OF SAFETY OFFICER ROLES

As previously stated, NFPA 1501, *Standard for Fire Department Safety Officer,* was the association's first fire service safety document. Although other standards dealt with protective clothing, fire apparatus, and other issues related to the fire service, NFPA 1501 was the first to specifically address fire fighter safety and health. The first two editions (1977 and 1982) of this standard addressed areas dealing primarily with the roles and responsibilities of a fire department safety officer. These roles were vague and were interpreted differently from user to user. The committee struggled to make this document a useful tool for the fire department and to make it play a more significant role in fire fighter safety.

Expanding Roles of the Safety Officer

With the appointment of the Fire Service Occupational Safety and Health Technical Committee in 1983, NFPA 1501 was assigned to this new technical committee. During the revision between the 1987 and 1992 editions, a movement began within the fire service to expand the roles and responsibilities of the safety officer. With the revision of the 1992 edition of the standard came a change in the numbering of the standard. This was done to be consistent with other standards developed by the technical committee. The role of the fire department safety officer was divided into two distinct positions—the incident safety officer (ISO) and the health and safety officer (HSO). Note that with the advent of the national incident management system, the term *safety officer* is the correct title for this position on the command staff. NFPA 1521 uses the term *incident safety officer* to distinguish the positions.

Training of Safety Officers

While the technical committee was revising and expanding NFPA 1521, fire service subject matter experts and curriculum developers at the National Fire Academy in Emmitsburg, Maryland, were developing two new courses based on these two distinct roles of the safety officer. These two 16-hour courses, Incident Safety Officer and Health and Safety Officer, outlined the basic requirements and roles and responsibilities of each position. The course included activities that emphasized the decision-making processes each position requires and provided instruction on how to read and utilize NFPA standards, federal laws, and rules and regulations. These two courses were offered to the fire service beginning in early 1996 and were updated in 2003.

These two courses continue to be two of the National Fire Academy's most popular courses. The specific roles for the incident safety officer and health and safety officer within a fire department's occupational safety and health program are a critical component in making the health and safety programs work. In some small or medium-sized departments, one person may be assigned the responsibilities of both positions, which usually leads either to that individual being overworked and frustrated or to the program not being implemented at all.

Roles and Responsibilities of the Health and Safety Officer

Health and safety officers must have a knowledge and understanding of pertinent laws, codes, and standards. Their responsibilities and functions include the following:

- Ensure that training and education programs relating to fire department operations are conducted
- Manage an accident prevention program
- Develop procedures for accident investigation and review
- Maintain records and conduct data analysis pertaining to fire fighter fatalities, injuries, occupational illnesses, health exposures, and accidents
- Review apparatus and equipment specification
- Conduct facility inspections to ensure compliance with applicable codes and standards
- Manage the health maintenance program to ensure compliance with NFPA 1582, *Standard on Comprehensive Occupational Medical Program for Fire Departments*
- Serve as liaison to various internal and external committees that influence the department's occupational safety and health program
- Serve as a member of the department's Occupational Safety and Health Committee
- Serve as the department's infection control officer or maintain a liaison with the infection control officer
- Ensure that the department has a critical incident stress management program
- Ensure that fire fighter safety and health issues are addressed during the post-incident analysis process

Roles and Responsibilities of the Incident Safety Officer

Standard operating procedures define criteria for the response or appointment of an incident safety officer position. The functions of the incident safety officer include the following:

- Serve as the safety officer of the command staff
- Monitor conditions, activities, and operations to determine whether they fall within the criteria as defined in the fire department's risk management plan
- Ensure that the incident commander establishes an incident scene rehabilitation tactical-level management unit during emergency operations
- Monitor the scene and report the status of conditions, hazards, and risks to the incident commander
- Ensure that the fire department's personnel accountability system is being utilized
- After receiving the incident action plan from the incident commander, provide the incident commander with a risk assessment of incident scene operations
- Ensure that established safety zones, collapse zones, hot zone, and other designated hazard areas are communicated to all members present on scene
- Evaluate motor vehicle scene traffic hazards and apparatus placement and take appropriate actions to mitigate hazards

- Communicate to the incident commander the need for assistant incident safety officers due to the need, size, complexity, or duration of the incident
- Ensure that a rapid intervention crew meeting the criteria in Chapter 8 of NFPA 1500, *Standard on Fire Department Occupational Safety and Health Program,* is available and ready for deployment
- Where a fire has involved a building or buildings, advise the incident commander of hazards, collapse potential, and any fire extension in such building(s)
- Evaluate visible smoke and fire conditions and advise the incident commander, tactical-level management units officers, and company officers on the potential for flashover, backdraft, blowup, or other fire events that could pose a threat to operating teams
- Monitor the accessibility of entry and egress of structures and the effect they have on the safety of members conducting interior operations
- Ensure compliance with the department's infection control plan and NFPA 1581, *Standard on Fire Department Infection Control Program,* during emergency medical operations
- Ensure that incident scene rehabilitation and critical incident stress management are established as needed at emergency medical operations, especially mass casualty incidents

Roles and Responsibilities of the Hazardous Materials Incident Safety Officer

The hazardous materials incident safety officer should meet the requirements of NFPA 472, *Standard for Professional Competence of Responders to Hazardous Materials Incidents.* The functions of the hazardous materials incident safety officer include the following:

- Attend strategic and tactical planning sessions and provide input on risk assessment and member safety
- Ensure that a safety briefing, including an incident action plan and an incident safety plan, is developed and made available to all members on the scene
- Ensure that hot, warm, decontamination, and other zone designations are clearly marked and communicated to all members
- Meet with the incident commander to determine rehabilitation, accountability, or rapid intervention needs; for long-term operations, the hazardous materials incident safety officer should ensure that food, hygiene facilities, and any other special needs are provided for members

Roles and Responsibilities of the Incident Safety Officer for Special Operations Incidents

The individual who serves as the incident safety officer for special operations incidents should have the appropriate education, training, and experience in special operations. The functions of the incident safety officer for special operations incidents include the following:

- Upon notification of a member injury, illness, or exposure, immediately communicate this information to the incident commander to ensure that emergency medical care is provided
- In the event of a serious injury, fatality, or other potentially harmful occurrence, request assistance from the health and safety officer
- Prepare a written report for the post-incident analysis that includes pertinent information about the incident relating to safety and health issues; the incident safety officer for special operations incidents participates in the post-incident analysis
- Include information about issues relating to the use of protective clothing and equipment, personnel accountability system, rapid intervention crews, rehabilitation operations, and other issues affecting the safety and welfare of members at the incident scene

RISK MANAGEMENT

Risk Management During Emergency Operations

According to NFPA 1500, the management of risk during emergency operations is a critical factor for ensuring the safety and health of fire fighters. In order to have effective operational risk management, the following components need to be part of the incident command system:

- Routine evaluation of risk in all situations
- Well-defined strategic options
- Standard operating procedures
- Effective training
- Full protective clothing and protective equipment
- Effective incident management and communications
- Safety procedures and the use of an incident safety officer
- Rapid intervention crew(s)
- Adequate resources
- Incident scene rest and rehabilitation
- Regular re-evaluation of conditions
- Pessimistic evaluation of changing conditions
- Experience based on previous incidents and critiques

Using Risk Management Principles

The incident command system starts with the arrival of the first department company. The first company to arrive integrates risk management into the routine functions of incident command. As indicated in NFPA 1500, the concept of risk management should be utilized on the basis of the following principles:

- Activities that present a significant risk to safety of members should be limited to situations in which there is the potential to save endangered lives.
- Activities that are routinely employed to protect property should be recognized as inherent risks to the safety of members, and actions should be taken to reduce or avoid these risks.
- No risk to the safety of members should be acceptable when there is no possibility to save lives or property.

As indicated in the second item just listed, "actions should be taken to reduce or avoid these risks." Identifying potential safety concerns to members and taking actions to reduce risks to fire fighters are without a doubt two of the most important things that can be accomplished.

Reducing Risks. The following are just some of the ways to reduce the overall risks to members operating at the scene of emergency incidents:

- Written guidelines should be established and used that provide for the tracking and inventory of all members operating an emergency incident.
- All members operating in an emergency are responsible to actively participate in the department's personnel accountability system.
- The incident commander should be responsible for the overall responder accountability for the incident. The incident commander should initiate an accountability worksheet at the beginning of the incident and maintain the system throughout the operation.
- The incident commander should maintain an awareness of the location and function of all companies assigned to an incident.
- The incident commander should implement branch directors and division, group, or sector supervisors when needed to reduce the span of control for the incident commander.
- Branch directors and division and group supervisors should directly supervise and account for companies operating under their command.
- Company officers are accountable for all company members, and company members are responsible to remain under the supervision of their assigned company officer. Members should be responsible for following the personnel accountability system procedures, which should be used at all incidents.
- The incident command system should provide for additional accountability responders based on the size, complexity, or needs of an incident. The implementation of division, group, or sector supervisors can assist the incident commander in this area by reducing the span of control.
- The incident commander should provide for control of access to the incident scene.
- A department should adopt and routinely use a standard responder identification system to maintain accountability for each member assigned to an incident. There are several accountability systems used during structural fire fighting.
- The personnel accountability system should provide an accounting of those members actually responding to the scene on each company or apparatus.
- The incident command system should include standard operating guidelines that use emergency traffic communication to evacuate responders from an area where imminent hazard is found to exist and to account for their safety.

Emergency Traffic. The fire department standard operating procedure provides direction in the use of clear text radio messages for emergency incidents. The standard operating procedure should use emergency traffic as the designator to clear the radio traffic. "Emergency traffic" can be declared by the incident commander, division or group supervisor, or member in trouble or subject to emergency conditions. Clear text should be used to describe the emergency conditions present. Examples of emergency conditions that could occur include the following:

1. "Fire fighter down"
2. "Fire fighter missing"
3. "Fire fighter trapped"
4. Serious conditions—"all members evacuate the building"
5. Change in conditions—"wind changed direction from north to south"
6. Hazard identification—"power line has energized a fence to metal roof"
7. Change in tactics—"change from offensive to defensive"

When a member has declared "emergency traffic," that person should use clear text to identify the type of emergency, change in conditions, or tactical operations. The member who has declared the "emergency traffic" should conclude the condition by transmitting "all clear, resume radio traffic" to end the emergency situation or to reopen the radio channels for communication after announcing the emergency message.

Retreat Policy. A fire department should have an operational retreat policy. In addition to an emergency traffic radio message, fire departments could use an additional signal, such as an apparatus air horn, to cause an evacuation of responders. Some departments have incorporated a series of three 10-second short blasts on an air horn with a 10-second silence between each series of blasts of an air horn. For fire departments that adopt this system, it is very important for the incident commander to select apparatus away from the command post to reduce the possibility of missing radio messages while the air horns are sounding.

Personnel Accountability Report. The incident commander should conduct a personnel accountability report (PAR) from each division or group supervisor whenever there has been an announcement of a change in conditions that could create an unsafe operation. When a division or group supervisor is requested to conduct a PAR, this supervisor is responsible for reporting on the accountability of all companies or members working within his or her area of responsibility. (A position description that addresses fire fighter Incident Safety and Accountability Guideline is available from FIRESCOPE and is published in the ICS 910 publication.)

Officer Responsibilities

An incident safety officer should be designated by the incident commander whenever the incident commander cannot perform this vital function due to the size or complexity of the incident. At an emergency incident where activities are determined by the incident safety officer to be unsafe or to involve an imminent hazard, the incident safety officer should have the authority to alter, suspend, or terminate those activities. The incident safety officer should immediately inform the incident commander of any actions taken to correct imminent hazards at the emergency scene. At an emergency incident where an incident safety officer identifies unsafe conditions, operation, or hazards that do not present an imminent danger, the incident safety officer should take appropriate action through the incident commander to mitigate or eliminate the unsafe condition, operation, or hazard at the incident scene.

The incident safety officer should be designated by the incident commander and be integrated with the incident management system as a command staff member. The incident safety officer should survey and monitor the scene and report the status of conditions, hazards, and risks to the incident commander. The incident safety officer can have designated assistant safety officers based on the need, size, complexity, or duration of the incident.

The incident commander should be provided with reports of elapsed time-on-scene at emergency incidents in 15-minute intervals from the emergency service organization communication center until reports are terminated by the incident commander. Members operating in hazardous areas at emergency incidents should operate in crews of two or more.

Deployment

Initial Crew. In the initial stages of an incident where only one crew is operating in the hazardous area at a working structure fire, a minimum of four individuals is required, consisting of two individuals working as a crew in the hazard area and two individuals present outside this hazard area who are available for assistance or rescue at emergency operations where entry into the danger area is required. The standby members should be responsible for maintaining a constant awareness of the number and identity of members operating in the hazardous area, their location and function, and time of entry. The standby members should remain in radio, visual, voice, or signal line communications with the crew. The initial stages of an incident should encompass the tasks undertaken by the first arriving company with only one crew assigned or operating in the hazardous area.

The following examples from NFPA 1500 indicate how a fire department could deploy a team of four members initially at the scene of a structure fire:

- The team leader and one fire fighter could advance a firefighting hoseline into the IDLH atmosphere, and one fire fighter and the pump operator become the standby members.
- The team leader could designate the pump operator to be the incident commander. The team leader and one fire fighter enter the IDLH atmosphere, and one fire fighter and pump operator remain outside as the standby members.
- The two fire fighters could advance the hoseline in the IDLH atmosphere, and the team leader and pump operator remain outside as standby members.

Assignment of Additional Resources. Once a second crew is assigned or operating in the hazardous area, the incident should no longer be considered in the initial stages, and at least one rapid intervention crew/company should comply with the following requirements: (1) on-scene members designated and dedicated as rapid intervention crew/company, and (2) on-scene members performing other functions but ready to redeploy to perform rapid intervention crew/company functions.

The assignment of any responders as members of the rapid intervention crew/company should not be permitted if abandoning their critical task(s) to perform rescue clearly jeopardizes the safety and health of any member operating at the incident. As the incident expands in size or complexity, which includes an incident commander's requests for additional resources beyond the fire department's initial attack assignment, the dedicated rapid intervention crew/company (RIC) should on arrival of these additional resources be either one of the following: (1) on-scene members designated and dedicated as rapid intervention crew/company, and (2) on-scene crew/company or crews/companies located for rapid deployment and dedicated as rapid intervention crews.

During fire fighter rescue operations, each company should remain intact. At least one dedicated rapid intervention company should be in the standby mode with equipment to provide for the rescue of members who are performing special operations or for members who are in positions that present an immediate danger of injury in the event of equipment failure or collapse.

When more than one rapid intervention crew is deployed, consider implementing a rescue group supervisor to manage the multiple rapid intervention companies and to coordinate any rescue attempts when in the deployment mode. Whenever a rapid intervention crew is deployed, the incident commander should designate another rapid intervention crew in the standby mode to provide for fire fighter safety.

Additional areas that are also very important in reducing risks to members include the following: effective training, rest and rehabilitation, continuous evaluation of changing conditions, and past experience.

NFPA 1581, *Standard on Fire Department Infection Control Program*

Emergency Medical Services. As the fire service has expanded its role, the fastest-growing service it provides is that of emergency medical services (EMS). For fire departments that provide a level of emergency medical service, that service constitutes more than 60 to 70 percent of their responses. The fire service provides different models and levels of this service. Included are the basic first responder level, as outlined by the medical regulatory agency; the basic emergency medical technician level (EMT-B); the intermediate level (EMT-I); and the paramedic level (EMT-P). At both the intermediate and paramedic levels, regulatory agencies may allow certain procedures based on need, training, and local medical protocol. The models of service delivery may include treatment and transport at all levels; treatment at all levels with a combination of public, private, or third-party transport; and treatment with only private transport.

In any of these models, the fire service uses largely dual-trained cross-role fire fighters. Many departments now require members to have some level of emergency medical training and certification before they apply for a position within the department.

Exposure to Disease. With these increased roles and services come increased risks. The risks within this context include communicable and infectious disease. The fire service members providing patient care place themselves at risk at an incident scene, but some of these same risks are found in the facilities in which they live and work. NFPA 1581, 1992 edition, was part of the plan of developing standards that could have a significant and immediate impact on fire fighter health and safety. The standard outlined a program that would afford fire fighters a level of protection if they complied with documented practices regarding the following:

- Wearing protective clothing
- Being immunized and vaccinated
- Adhering to an exposure reporting system
- Cleaning and disinfecting clothing and equipment
- Acquiring needed training

Important to note is the fact that when the standard was being issued, there was an outbreak of the AIDS virus, the initial hepatitis B vaccines were being developed, and the fear of fire fighters becoming infected and possibly dying was ongoing. The federal government moved quickly, under the auspices of the Centers of Disease Control and Prevention (CDC), and OSHA developed regulations on protecting emergency response personnel and health care workers (Figure 12.7.2). The Ryan White Act spelled out protection, notification, and confidentiality issues regarding communicable and infectious diseases.

Cleanup. One important aspect of infection control is the cleaning and disinfecting of protective clothing and protective equipment. This cleanup includes the proper cleaning and disinfecting of protective clothing and equipment, a separate room and laundry facilities to accomplish that, a clean work area in the kitchen to wash and prepare meals, and clean and properly spaced living quarters. The 1992 edition of NFPA 1581 provided the initial requirements. The 1995 edition contained those additional requirements and updates on vaccinations and immunizations, facility safety, and worker protection. The 2000 edition has continued along those same avenues and expanded into other areas, including updating the CDC regulations, updating the immunization and vaccination list, expanding the list of infectious and communicable diseases, and developing requirements for cleaning and disinfecting apparatus and vehicles. This standard, along with NFPA 1999, *Standard on Protective Clothing for Emergency Medical Operations,* is an asset to being better educated regarding the hazards of infectious and communicable diseases. The fire service needed an educational venue to explain to fire fighters that the protective clothing they wore at an incident scene contained contaminants that might be harmful. The possibility for such cross-contamination is real and the fire service needs the education component. Even if the station does not have in-house cleaning capabilities, the fire department is required to clean the fire fighters' protective clothing every 6 months at a minimum. The issue is for fire fighters to protect themselves so that they can continue to provide service to the citizens we serve.

NFPA 1582, *Standard on Comprehensive Occupational Medical Program for Fire Departments*

Fire fighter medical requirements were originally included as a component of NFPA 1001, *Standard for Fire Fighter Professional Qualifications.* In 1988 the Occupational Safety and

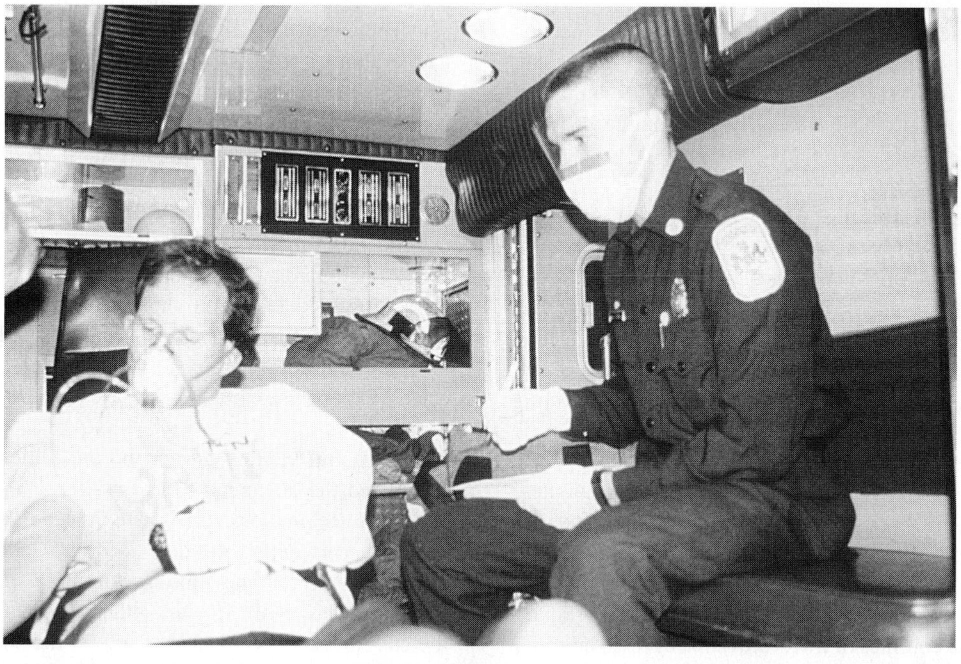

FIGURE 12.7.2 Emergency Response Personnel Protecting Himself While Providing Patient Care (Photo courtesy of Fairfax County Fire and Rescue Department, Fairfax, Virginia)

Health Technical Committee and the Professional Qualifications Technical Committee formed a working subcommittee whose mission was to write a medical requirements standard for both candidate and incumbent fire fighters. This committee, which was composed of occupational medical physicians, fire service personnel at all levels, fire service instructors, and representative fire service organizations, realized early in the process that medical evaluations for fire fighters are an important component of an overall occupational medical program.

Medical Condition of Fire Fighters. The first edition of the standard, issued in 1992, outlined medical requirements that were categorized into A and B conditions. Category A conditions would preclude someone from either becoming a fire fighter or from continuing in a position that included primarily fire suppression. This decision caused difficulty because most fire departments had only one entry portal into the service and that was as a fire suppression fire fighter. An additional complication emerged as fire departments created "light-duty positions" or moved personnel into other positions that had no job description.

Fire department physicians or those hired to perform medical evaluations had no fire fighter job description or task analysis on which to base the medical evaluation and, thus, determine the medical condition necessary to be a fire fighter. Consequently, this raised questions on who was being "accommodated" in order to maintain his or her status as a fire fighter. Although some departments made this practice part of a labor agreement, other departments considered it part of the routine procedure. This issue led to some problems while the 1997 edition of the standard was being written. The technical committee physicians realized that when they examined fire fighters, certain areas within the standard were critical, based on how the 1992 edition was being interpreted.

They identified the following areas as ones that needed greater emphasis and clarification: cardiovascular, neurological, vision, hearing, and metabolic processes. Thus, the committee sought out specialists in those areas to assist them in rewriting the standard.

Americans with Disabilities Act. Concurrently, litigation, citing NFPA 1582, was brought forward regarding the use and interpretation of the Americans with Disabilities Act (ADA). The implementation and interpretation of the ADA law created confusion on how this law impacted employment factors of hiring and promoting within the fire service. The committee worked toward revising the standard and further defining areas by developing a sample job task analysis, a sample job description, an annex that included discussion regarding ADA, and a sample physician's checklist. In the 1997 edition, all these changes were made and the medical requirements were updated. Medical technology changes constantly; the standards-making process, however, cannot keep up with these changes.

The committee members, along with outside physicians, worked within the confines of a short revision cycle to continue to refine the five identified areas in the 1997 edition. Additionally, the committee realized that the work being done by the National Institute for Occupational Safety and Health (NIOSH) in its fire fighter fatality investigations as well as documentation from NFPA Fire Analysis and Research Division would assist it in the future as revisions to NFPA 1582 were being made. The 2000 edition of the standard, therefore, reflects some of those revisions, especially in the areas of diabetes, hearing, and cardiovascular disease.

Common Medical Problems. Statistics tell us that almost 50 percent of fire fighter fatalities are cardiac related and almost 50 percent of those had previous cardiac-related problems. The commonsense approach would be to medically evaluate these personnel annually and try to diagnose these conditions in the early stages and treat them before they occur. Recall that the purpose of an occupational safety and health program is for the fire fighter to leave the profession in the same condition as when he or she entered it. Fire fighting is a hazardous occupation.

In addition to cardiac-related problems, other medical problems are also characteristic of the profession, including a high incidence of cancer, especially of the liver, kidney, colon, prostate, and lung. Screening for these and other occupationally related diseases is a component of an occupational medical program and is included as part of the medical evaluation program.

Role of the Fire Department Physician. The fire department physician plays a significant role in managing the fire department's occupational medical program. Many fire departments that cannot afford their own physicians have grouped together to contract with either a physician or local HMO. Some smaller departments may utilize the physician as a regular member of their fire-fighting force. In any case, the physician oversees the program, reviews medical exams and evaluations, recommends follow-up or specialist exams, and works in conjunction with the health safety officer and the health fitness coordinator.

The 2003 edition addressed the issues of medical care and evaluation of both candidates and incumbents within a fire department; these issues have been discussed in numerous NFPA standards. The initial discussion and mandatory medical requirements were contained in NFPA 1001. Members of both committees have broken significant ground in providing a standard that the user—the fire department physician—can understand. The physicians on the committee have developed a physician guidance text that provides a link between the essential job tasks of a fire fighter doing manual fire suppression and the medical requirements in the standard. This will assist the user in determining, based on medical evaluations, if someone can do the essential job tasks.

Occupational Medical Program. In addition, the standard has delineated the document to address those medical issues of a candidate seeking to become a fire fighter and those incumbents currently performing the tasks of fire fighting. This standard does not differentiate among volunteer, paid-on-call, part-time, and career fire fighters—the tasks are the same. Since the committee has changed the title of the standard to reflect a comprehensive occupational medical program, it has included references to the IAFC-IAFF Joint Wellness Initiative and to NFPA 1583. These two documents outline a health-related fitness program that is medically validated against this edition of NFPA 1582. Although the cost of medical exams continually increases, the organization must weigh the initial costs versus long-term job related illnesses, injuries, and fatality costs. Fire departments spend a lot of money on preventive maintenance of apparatus and equipment; however, that is an inefficient use of resources if they do not have medically qualified personnel to operate them and to respond to emergency incidents.

NFPA 1583, *Standard on Health-Related Fitness Programs for Fire Fighters*

As part of a fire department occupational health and safety program, NFPA 1500 includes text requiring a physical performance program as well as a fitness program. The committee struggled to provide a standard on physical performance requirements that would be required for both candidates and incumbents alike. This standard was doomed from the outset. There was considerable discussion among the technical committee members, as well as litigation within the United States, regarding the validity and content of physical performance testing. Trying to develop a set of physical test skills related by task analysis to the profession of fire fighting and then to validate that test was difficult at best.

The committee skipped a cycle and with a great deal of angst reached consensus on a document that was passed by the NFPA membership and then subsequently appealed to the association's Standards Council. It was returned to the technical committee by the Standards Council and withdrawn from the system after a unanimous vote from the committee members in 1997. The technical committee initiated a new document in the summer of 1997.

Joint Fire Service Wellness Program. As this proposed NFPA standard was withdrawn, a group of 10 cities within North America began work on a joint fire service wellness program. This program, supported and endorsed by the International Association of Fire Fighters (IAFF) and the International Association of Fire Chiefs (IAFC), included Phoenix, Arizona; New York, New York; Los Angeles County, California; Seattle, Washington; Calgary, Alberta, Canada; Austin, Texas; Charlotte, North Carolina; Indianapolis, Indiana; Fairfax County, Virginia; and Metro-Dade County, Florida. IAFF officials from each local, fire chiefs from each city, and fire department physicians worked on this program, which was introduced at both Fire Rescue International and the IAFF Redmond Symposium in 1999. This program has been used successfully by these 10 departments, as well as others across the world. It is a great example of a joint labor-management initiative that benefits all of the fire service.

The Fire Service Occupational Medical and Health Technical Committee began work on a health-related fitness program for the fire service, which initially did not have widespread support from the fire service. Many saw this effort as a revisit of the physical performance test versus what it really was—namely, a standard containing the components of an overall health-related fitness program for the fire service. Managed by both the fire department physician and the health fitness coordinator, this standard has nutrition, wellness, and fitness components that may be accomplished in a number of different ways. The program, as outlined in the standard, is similar to the program developed by the IAFF/IAFC Joint Labor/Management Wellness Initiative.

Fitness Testing. The 10 cities in the initiative then began work on a physical performance component that would be used to test candidates wishing to seek employment in the fire service profession. The testing process was developed with the assistance of the U.S. Department of Justice. The job tasks were validated for the 10 cities, the testing mechanism and props were developed, and then the test was run using incumbents from each department. This test, called the Candidate Performance Agility Test (CPAT), was introduced at both Fire Rescue International and the IAFF Redmond Symposium in 1999. The validity developed within the 10 cities required each to provide a job task analysis and a job description based on that analysis in order to validate the CPAT test for their municipality. The validation process is not a "one size fits all" for those who choose to utilize it. Municipalities must go through the same process as did the 10 cities and validate the CPAT individually. The IAFF has developed a Peer Fitness Training Program that assists those municipalities that wish to use the CPAT.

NFPA 1584, *Recommended Practice on Rehabilitation of Members Operating at Incident Scene Operations and Training Exercises*

The 2003 edition of NFPA 1584 was prepared by the Technical Committee on Fire Service Occupational Medical and Health and acted on by NFPA at its November Association Technical Meeting held November 16–20, 2002, in Atlanta, Georgia. It was issued by the Standards Council on January 17, 2003, with an effective date of February 6, 2003.

The Technical Committee on Fire Service Occupational Medical and Health has responsibility for this document. The members of the committee have developed standards in areas of incident management, occupational medical programs, fitness evaluation, fire department safety officer, and infectious disease control programs. These standards fall under the umbrella of NFPA 1500, *Standard on Fire Department Occupational Safety and Health Program,* 2002 edition. An integral component of both an occupational safety and health program and incident scene management is an organized approach for fire department members' rehabilitation at incident scene operations.

The concept of incident scene rehabilitation has been discussed and utilized throughout the fire service in various sizes and configurations. Many departments have utilized material from the United States Fire Administration, as well as material from emergency medical services. Progressive departments have shared their "lessons learned" in the development of this document. This recommended practice establishes the minimum level of criteria for developing and implementing a rehabilitation process for fire department members at incident scene operations and training exercises. This recommended practice provides for the rehabilitation of members operating within an incident management system rehabilitation component, including but not limited to, the following:

- Medical evaluation and treatment
- Food and fluid replenishment
- Relief from climatic conditions
- Rest and recovery
- Member accountability

RISK MANAGEMENT MODEL

NFPA 1500 requires the development, implementation, and use of a written risk management plan. This plan must consider all fire department activities, operations, and standard operating procedures to ensure that a comprehensive approach is the focus. The health and safety officer is the primary person responsible for this document but must seek assistance as this plan covers all aspects of the fire department.

The risk management model presents a systematic approach for identifying and planning for the control of risks. This methodical process for making decisions can be utilized not only for the nonemergency risks that all organizations must address but also for the risks associated with the response to and mitigation of an emergency incident. The factors at each incident will always vary, but as we have known for years, continual training in all aspects of the approach will yield the best, most consistent results possible.

Five Steps

The model has five primary components, or steps, which serve as a foundation for this process. Each one depends on information generated by the previous step, so it is important to evaluate each one before moving on to the next. The following five steps are discussed in detail in the next sections:

1. Identifying risk
2. Evaluating risk
3. Establishing priorities or prioritization
4. Establishing risk control techniques
5. Monitoring

For each step in the process, it is important to record performance criteria, suggestions, and recommendations. These data will provide the elements that formulate a written risk management plan. The number of pages in the plan has no impact on the plan's effectiveness. Once created, the plan should be periodically updated (at least annually). Consider it a dynamic process, not a static event with a single written record. Keep the plan current based on conditions, circumstances, and experience.

Identifying Risk. The first step of the risk management model involves identifying what could go wrong. To make this identification it is useful to compile a list of all emergency and nonemergency operations in which the department participates. The intent is to plan for the worst but hope for the best. There are many sources to assist with this identification process. The first, and possibly the most effective, is the department's loss prevention data. Seek input and ideas from department personnel, other health and safety officers, jurisdiction risk managers, trade journals, professional associations, and other service providers. When using ideas or information from other fire departments or organizations, simply consider local circumstances when formulating the list.

Evaluating Risk. Once the risks are identified, they can be evaluated from both a frequency and severity standpoint. Frequency addresses the likelihood of occurrence. Typically, if a particular type of incident (e.g., back injuries) has occurred repeatedly, these incidents will continue to occur until effective control measures are implemented.

Severity addresses the degree of seriousness of the incident and can be measured in a variety of ways, such as time away from work, cost of damage, cost of and time for repair or replacement, disruption of service, or legal costs. Using the information gathered in the identification step, the risks can be classified based on severity.

Establishing Priorities. Taken in combination, the results of the frequency and severity determinations will help to establish priorities for determining action. Any risk that has a low probability of occurrence (frequency) but has serious consequences (high risk or severity) deserves immediate action and would be considered a high-priority item (Figure 12.7.3). Nonserious incidents with a low likelihood of occurrence are a lower priority and can be placed near the bottom of the "action required" list.

Establishing Risk Control Techniques. At this point in the process, risks have been identified and evaluated, so it is time to find solutions. There are several approaches to take, including risk avoidance, implementation of control measures, and risk transfer.

In any situation, the best choice is *risk avoidance,* which simply means to avoid the activity that creates the risk. In an emergency services organization, risk avoidance frequently is impractical. Lifting a stretcher presents a serious back injury risk, but you cannot avoid this risk and still provide effective service.

An example of a situation in which avoidance has been very practical is the widespread, hopefully universal, use of sharps containers. The risks associated with recapping needles are well documented; therefore, recapping is no longer an ac-

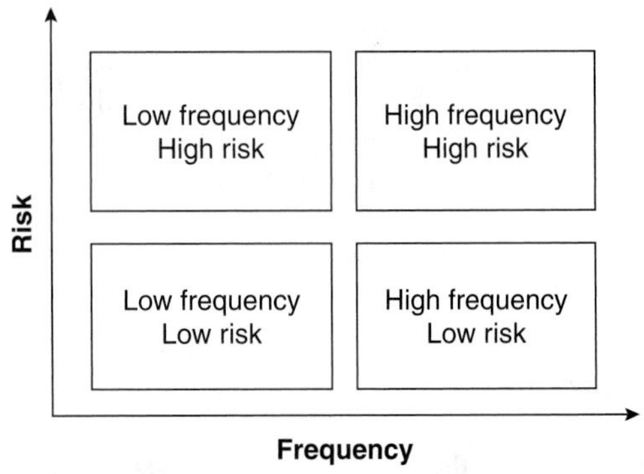

FIGURE 12.7.3 Risk Management Graph

cepted practice. This risky behavior can be avoided through the proper use of a sharps container.

The most common method utilized for the management of risk is the adoption of *effective control measures.* Although control measures will not eliminate the risk, they can reduce the likelihood of occurrence or mitigate the severity. Safety programs, ongoing training and education programs, and well-defined standard operating procedures (SOPs) are all effective control measures.

Some typical control measures instituted to control fireground injuries include accountability, use of full protective clothing, a mandatory respiratory protection program, training and education, and competent standard operating procedures. These control measures coupled together make an effective program that ensures safe fireground operations.

Risk transfer can be accomplished in two primary ways: physically transferring the risk to somebody else or through the purchase of insurance. For a fire or EMS organization, the transfer of risk may be difficult if not impossible. However, an example of risk transfer would be contracting out the operation and maintenance of helicopters for use by responders. The risks associated with those activities have been transferred to a private contractor.

The purchase of insurance transfers financial risk only and does nothing to affect the likelihood of occurrence. Buying fire insurance on a fire station, although highly recommended for protecting the assets of the department, does nothing to prevent the station from burning down. Therefore, insurance is no substitute for effective control measures.

Monitoring. The last step in the process is risk management monitoring. Once control measures have been implemented, they need to be evaluated to measure their effectiveness. Any problems that occur in the process have to be revised or modified. This final step ensures that the system is dynamic and will facilitate periodic reviews of the entire program.

The intent of the risk management plan is to develop a strategy for reducing the inherent risks associated with fire department operations. Regardless of the size or type of fire department, every organization should operate within the parameters of a risk management plan. This is a dynamic and aggressive process that must be monitored and revised annually by the health and safety officer.

Operational Risk Management

In order to address operational risk management and reduce level of risk during emergency operations, several components need to be incorporated into this process. Many components have a positive impact of reducing risk during fireground operations or any other type of emergency including as discussed in the section that follows.

INCIDENT COMMAND SYSTEM (ICS)

In the early 1970s, southern California experienced several devastating wildland fires. The overall cost and loss associated with these fires totaled $18 million per day. This multijurisdictional disaster was the impetus for the development of an improved interagency incident management system known as the incident command system (ICS). The incident command system is one of the beneficial results of a federally funded project called FIRESCOPE that was convened after these fires and whose charter was to examine various aspects of interagency response to incidents.

FIRESCOPE

The Fire Resources of California Organized for Potential Emergencies (FIRESCOPE) incident command system is primarily a command and control system delineating job responsibilities and organizational structure for the purpose of managing day-to-day fire and rescue operations. It also is flexible enough to manage catastrophic incidents involving thousands of emergency response and management personnel.

National Interagency Incident Management System (NIIMS)

This incident command system was developed by the wildland community in order to provide a common system for wildland fire protection agencies at the local, state, and federal levels. The NIIMS organization includes the Bureau of Land Management, the Bureau of Indian Affairs, the U.S. Fish and Wildlife Service, the U.S. Forest Service, representatives of State Foresters, and the National Park Service. NIIMS consists of the following five major subsystems that collectively provide a total systems approach to risk management:

1. The incident command system, which includes operating requirements, eight interactive components, and procedures for organizing and operating an on-scene management structure
2. Training that is standardized and supports the effective operations of the National Interagency Incident Management System
3. A qualification and certification system that provides personnel across the nation with standard training, experience, and physical requirements to fill specific positions in the incident command system
4. Publications management that includes development, publication, and distribution of NIIMS materials
5. Supporting technologies such as orthophoto mapping, infrared photography, and a multiagency coordination system that supports NIIMS operations

FIRESCOPE Model Incident Command System

Since the development of the incident command system, the fire service has experienced several challenges in understanding its application. As a result, inconsistencies in the system began to develop; other hybrid systems came into existence, further distancing a common approach to incident command. A single incident management system is critical for effective command and control of major incidents. At these incidents, a single department may interface with other agencies on the local, state, and federal levels. In order to reduce the inherent confusion that may be associated with larger-scale incidents, a common command system must be used.

Need for a Single Approach

Recognizing the challenges that were occurring in the fire service in applying a common approach to incident command, the National Fire Service Incident Management System Consortium was created. Developed in 1990, its purpose is to evaluate an approach to developing a single command system. The consortium consists of many individual fire service leaders, representatives of most major fire service organizations, and representatives of federal agencies including FIRESCOPE. One of the significant outcomes of the work done by the consortium was the identification of the need to develop operational protocols within the incident command system, so that fire and rescue personnel would be able to apply the incident command system as one common system. In 1993, as a result of this, the IMS consortium completed its first document: *Model Procedures Guide for Structural Firefighting.*

FIRESCOPE adopted this in principle as an application to the Model FIRESCOPE Incident Command System. The basic premise is that the organizational structure found in the FIRESCOPE Incident Command System now is enhanced with operational protocols that allow the nation's fire and rescue personnel to apply the incident command system effectively, regardless of the area in the country to which they are assigned. The National Fire Academy (NFA), having adopted the FIRESCOPE Incident Command System in 1980, has incorporated this material in its training curriculum and will continue to reach the thousands of fire service personnel with one common incident command and control system.

It is important to note that the FIRESCOPE Model Incident Command System has had other applications or modules similar to the structural fire-fighting applications that have been in place for some time. These create a framework for other activities to operate in and further enhance the use of the incident command system. Examples are the multicasualty, hazardous materials, and the urban search and rescue applications.

The Federal Emergency Management Agency (FEMA) formally adopted the FIRESCOPE Incident Command System as the incident management system for any federal response required by the agency. Since then, several other federal agencies have adopted the FIRESCOPE Incident Command System.

Evolution of the Incident Command System

The concept of the incident command system (ICS) was developed more than 30 years ago in the aftermath of a devastating wildfire in California. During 13 days in 1970, 16 lives were lost, 700 structures were destroyed, and over 1.5 million acres burned. The overall cost and loss associated with these fires totaled $18 million per day. Although all of the responding agencies cooperated to the best of their ability, numerous problems with communication and coordination hampered their effectiveness. As a result, Congress mandated that the United States Forest Service design a system that would "make a quantum jump in the capabilities of Southern California wildland fire protection agencies to effectively coordinate interagency action and to allocate suppression resources in dynamic, multiple-fire situations."

The California Department of Forestry and Fire Protection; the Governor's Office of Emergency Services; the Los Angeles, Ventura, and Santa Barbara County Fire Departments; and the Los Angeles City Fire Department joined with the United States Forest Service to develop the system. This system became known as FIRESCOPE .

In 1973, the first FIRESCOPE Technical Team was established to guide the research and development design. Two major components came out of this work, the incident command system (ICS) and the Multi-Agency Coordination System (MACS). The FIRESCOPE ICS is primarily a command-and-control system delineating job responsibilities and organizational structure for the purpose of managing day-to-day operations for all types of emergency incidents. By the mid-seventies, FIRESCOPE agencies had formally agreed on ICS common terminology and procedures and conducted limited ICS field-testing. By 1980, parts of ICS had been used successfully on several major wildland and urban fire incidents. It was formally adopted by the Los Angeles Fire Department, the California Department of Forestry and Fire Protection (CDF), and the Governor's Office of Emergency Services (OES) as well as endorsed by the State Board of Fire Services.

Also during the 1970s, the National Wildfire Coordinating Group (NWCG) was chartered to coordinate fire management programs of the various participating federal and state agencies. By 1980, FIRESCOPE ICS training was under development. Recognizing that FIRESCOPE training could also satisfy the needs of other state and federal agencies in addition to the local users for which it was designed, the NWCG conducted an analysis of FIRESCOPE ICS for possible national application.

Widening the Application of ICS

By 1981, the incident command system was widely used throughout southern California by the major fire agencies. In addition, the use of the incident command system in response to nonfire incidents was increasing. Although FIRESCOPE ICS was originally developed to assist in the response to wildland fires, it was quickly recognized as a system that could help public safety responders provide effective and coordinated incident management for a wide range of situations, including floods, hazardous materials accidents, earthquakes, and aircraft crashes. It was flexible enough to manage catastrophic incidents involving thousands of emergency response and management personnel. By introducing relatively minor terminology, organizational, and procedural modifications to FIRESCOPE ICS, the NIIMS ICS became adaptable to an all-hazards environment.

Although tactically each type of incident may be handled somewhat differently, the overall incident management approach still utilizes the major functions of the incident command system. The FIRESCOPE board of directors and the NWCG recommended national application of ICS. In 1982, all FIRESCOPE ICS documentation was revised and adopted as the National Interagency Incident Management System (NIIMS). In the years since FIRESCOPE and the NIIMS were blended, the

FIRESCOPE agencies and the NWCG have worked together to update and maintain the Incident Command System Operational System Description (ICS 120–1). This document would later serve as the basis for the NIMS ICS.

National Incident Management System (NIMS)

The way this nation prepares for and responds to domestic incidents is changing. It will not be an abrupt change; best practices that have been developed over the years are part of this new comprehensive national approach to incident management known as the National Incident Management System (NIMS). Developed by the Department of Homeland Security and issued in March 2004, the NIMS will enable responders at all jurisdictional levels and across all disciplines to work together more effectively and efficiently.

One of the most important best practices that has been incorporated into the NIMS is the incident command system (ICS), a standard, on-scene, all-hazards incident management system already in use by fire fighters, hazardous materials teams, rescuers, and emergency medical teams. The ICS has been established by the NIMS as the standardized incident organizational structure for the management of all incidents.

In Homeland Security Presidential Directive-5 (HSPD-5), President Bush called on the Secretary of Homeland Security to develop a national incident management system to provide a consistent nationwide approach for federal, state, tribal, and local governments to work together to prepare for, prevent, respond to, and recover from domestic incidents, regardless of cause, size, or complexity.

On March 1, 2004, after close collaboration with state and local government officials and representatives from a wide range of public safety organizations, Homeland Security issued the NIMS. This system incorporates many existing best practices into a comprehensive national approach to domestic incident management, applicable at all jurisdictional levels and across all functional disciplines.

The NIMS represents a core set of doctrine, principles, terminology, and organizational processes to enable effective, efficient, and collaborative incident management at all levels. To provide the framework for interoperability and compatibility, the NIMS is based on a balance between flexibility and standardization. The recommendations of the National Commission on Terrorist Attacks upon the United States (the "9/11 Commission") further highlight the importance of ICS. The commission's report recommends national adoption of the ICS to enhance command, control, and communications capabilities.

BLENDING INCIDENT COMMAND SYSTEMS

There were several efforts to "blend" the various incident command systems. One early effort was in 1987 when NFPA undertook the development of NFPA 1561, then called *Standard on Fire Department Incident Management System.* The NFPA committee quickly recognized that the majority of the incident command systems in existence at the time were similar. The differences among the systems were mainly due to variations in terminology for similar components. That NFPA standard, later revised to its present title, *Standard on Emergency Services Incident Management Systems,* provides for organizations to adopt or modify existing systems to suit local requirements or preferences as long as they meet specific performance measurements.

National Fire Service Incident Management System (IMS) Consortium

Recognizing the continuing challenges occurring in the fire service in applying a common approach to incident command, the National Fire Service Incident Management System (IMS) Consortium was created in 1990. Its purpose was to evaluate an approach to developing a single command system. The consortium consisted of many individual fire service leaders, representatives of most major fire service organizations, and representatives of federal, state, and local agencies, including FIRESCOPE and the Phoenix Fire Department. One of the significant outcomes of the consortium's work was an agreement on the need to develop operational protocols within ICS, so that fire and rescue personnel would be able to apply the ICS as one common system.

In 1993, the IMS consortium completed its first document: *Model Procedures Guide for Structural Firefighting.* As a result, FIRESCOPE incorporated the model procedures, thereby enhancing its organizational structure with operational protocols. These changes enabled the nation's fire and rescue personnel to apply the ICS effectively regardless of what region of the country they were assigned to.

The NIMS provides a consistent, flexible, and adjustable national framework within which government and private entities at all levels can work together to manage domestic incidents, regardless of their cause, size, location, or complexity. This flexibility applies across all phases of incident management: prevention, preparedness, response, recovery, and mitigation. The NIMS provides a set of standardized organizational structures—including the ICS, Multi-Agency Coordination Systems, and public information systems—as well as requirements for processes, procedures, and systems to improve interoperability among jurisdictions and disciplines in various areas.

Department of Homeland Security

The Department of Homeland Security recognizes that the overwhelming majority of emergency incidents are handled on a daily basis by a single jurisdiction at the local level. However, the challenges we face as a nation are far greater than the capabilities of any one community or state but no greater than the sum of all of us working together. There will be instances in which successful domestic incident management operations depend on the involvement of emergency responders from multiple jurisdictions, as well as personnel and equipment from other states and the federal government. These instances require effective and efficient coordination across a broad spectrum of organizations and activities. The success of the operations will depend on the ability to mobilize and effectively utilize multiple outside resources. These resources must come together in an organizational framework that is understood by everyone and must utilize a common plan, as specified through a process of incident action planning. This will be possible only if we unite, plan, exercise, and respond using a common NIMS.

When Homeland Security released the NIMS on March 1, 2004, Secretary Tom Ridge and Under Secretary Brown specifically highlighted compliance with the ICS as being possible fairly quickly. They recognized that in some cities, the fire and police departments have worked together using ICS for years. In other places, only the fire department has used ICS. Although law enforcement, public works, and public health were aware of the concept, they regarded ICS as a fire service system.

The NIMS ends this discrepancy because HSPD-5 requires state and local adoption of NIMS as a condition for receiving federal preparedness funding. Although ICS was first pioneered by the fire service, it is, at its core, a management system designed to integrate resources to effectively attack a common problem. This system is not exclusive to one discipline or one set of circumstances; its hallmark is its flexibility to accommodate all circumstances. Some purists may claim that a particular application of ICS is not consistent with the NIMS. Yet we need not approach ICS with the same mathematical precision used by an engineer. We are changing the culture of organizations and first responders at all levels of government. As long as implementation of ICS is consistent with the basic principles expressed in the NIMS, we will have made significant progress. Further refinements can be achieved over time based on experience with its use.

COMMUNICATION ISSUES

Emergency incidents involving fire fighter fatalities demonstrate that, despite technological advances in two-way radio communications, important information is not always adequately communicated on the fireground or emergency incident scene. Communication is integral to incident scene operations; it is the key to fire fighter safety and survival (Figure 12.7.4).

Fatalities and Injuries

Inadequate fireground communication is repeatedly cited as a contributing factor in many of the incidents through the United States Fire Administration Fire Fighter Fatality and Major Fires Investigation. Communication problems are continually cited as one of the four contributing factors in fires and emergency incidents in which fire fighters are killed or injured. Despite the obvious importance of effective communication on the emergency scene, only a limited amount of published research exists.

There are several United States Fire Administration investigation reports that cite communications-related issues as part of the "lessons learned" component. These investigatation reports include the following:

- *Wood Truss Roof Collapse Claims Two Fire Fighters, Memphis, TN*
  Two fire fighters operating an interior attack line were killed at this fire after a church roof collapsed.
- *Indianapolis Athletic Club Fire, Indianapolis, IN*
  Two fire fighters were killed on the third floor of a nine-story mixed-use building during a fire.

FIGURE 12.7.4 Communication as an Integral Part of Accountability (Photo courtesy of Martin Grube, Virginia Beach Fire Department)

- *Four Fire Fighters Die in Seattle Warehouse Fire, Seattle, WA*
  Four fire fighters were killed in a collapse at an arson fire in a warehouse.
- *Two Fire Fighters Die in Auto Parts Store Fire, Chesapeake, VA*
  Two fire fighters were killed after a roof collapse in a retail auto parts store.

Table 12.7.2 describes several key factors that create problems during emergency operations for fire fighters and continually surface during fire fighter fatality and injury investigation reports.

Standards for Radio Communications

NFPA 1561, *Standard on Emergency Services Incident Management System,* requires the fire department to develop standard operating procedures for radio communications, which address use of protocol and terminology at all types of incidents. There are definitive procedures in NFPA 1561 regarding radio communications, the incident management system, and emergency operations.

These procedures include the following:

- Clear text should be used.
- A radio channel should be provided for dispatch, and a separate tactical channel provided to be used initially during the incident.
- When a division or group is implemented, the fire department should provide a dispatch channel, a command channel, and a tactical channel.
- The fire department should provide the necessary number of radio channels relating to incidents with multiple tactical channels and the complexity of these incidents.
- Standard terminology will be established for transmitting information, strategic modes of operation, situation reports, and emergency notification of imminent hazards.
- The fire department should have procedures for the announcement of emergency conditions, which is termed "emergency traffic," as a designation to clear radio traffic.
- "Emergency traffic" should be declared by the incident commander, tactical level management component, or member who is in trouble or subjected to an emergency condition.
- Standard operating procedures should exist for telecommunicators (dispatchers) to provide support to emergency incident operations.
- Telecommunicators should be trained to function effectively within the incident command system and should

TABLE 12.7.2 Communications Issues

Key Issues	*Comments*
Unsuitable equipment	The chief communication problem reported by fire fighters and company officers is the difficulty with communicating from inside a fire when using full personal protective equipment, including SCBA. The majority of portable radios currently used by fire departments are not suited for the task.
Portable radios needed for all fire fighters	Despite some technical limitations, portable radios are a proven lifesaver during fires and emergency incidents. Portable radios should be considered a critical item of personal protective equipment similar to SCBA. *Ideally, every fire fighter working in an IDLH atmosphere should have a portable radio with an emergency distress feature.*
Little attention paid to human factors	There is available literature pertaining to the impact of human factors on effective fireground communication. Furthermore, while fire departments devote substantial time to manipulative skill training, relatively little training is provided to help fire fighters develop stress-tempered communications skills.
Importance of active listening	All fire fighters on an emergency incident should actively monitor their radios for important information at all times, not just when specifically queried. Communications should be emphasized as an essential part of fire fighters functioning as a tactical team, not just operating as individual entities.
Standard message formats and language	Fire departments can enhance fireground communications by creating standard message formats and using keywords consistently. Plain English is usually preferred over codes, especially when transmitting a complex message.
Tiered message priority	Keywords to prompt immediate action can be tiered based on their priority; for example, "Mayday" signals a life-or-death situation, whereas "Urgent" may be used to signify a potentially serious problem. Such message headers prompt the crew's listening priorities and radio discipline.
Attention to cultural factors	If necessary, fire fighters are not usually reluctant to circumvent the chain of command to report critical safety issues. There may be greater hesitation to communicate problems in completing an assigned task. However, this is usually due to a lack of situational awareness and not a fear of reprisal from other members. Studies on fire fighter communications show that sometimes the culture of bravery in the fire service is reflected in a reluctance to communicate quickly enough when help is needed. Repeated situations of this nature must be investigated by the department.

meet the requirements of NFPA 1061, *Standard for Professional Qualifications for Public Safety Telecommunicator.*

- The incident commander should be provided with elapsed time-on-scene information at emergency incidents in 10-minute intervals from the communications center.

INCIDENT SCENE REHABILITATION

The fire department should develop standard operating procedures that outline a systematic approach for the rehabilitation of members operating at incidents. Provisions addressed in these procedures should include medical evaluation and treatment, food and fluid replenishment, crew rotation, and relief from extreme climatic conditions. This program should outline an ongoing rehabilitation for simple or short-duration incidents as well as a process to transition into the rehabilitation needs of a large or long-duration incident.

Emergency Medical Service

Medical evaluation and treatment in the on-scene rehabilitation area should be conducted according to emergency medical service (EMS) protocols developed by the fire department in consultation with the fire department physician and the EMS medical director. If advanced life support (ALS) personnel are available, this level of EMS care is preferred.

The incident commander should consider the circumstances of each incident and initiate rest and rehabilitation of members in accordance with the fire department's standard operating procedures and with NFPA 1584 and Chapter 8 of NFPA 1500.

The incident scene rehabilitation group or division should include emergency medical care. The minimum level of emergency medical care available should be at least basic life support care. The assignment of an ambulance or other support crew to the rehabilitation function is essential during long-duration or heavy-exertion incident operations. This crew can assist with rehabilitation functions as well as be available to provide immediate basic life support needs for members. However, the advanced life support (paramedic) level of evaluation and treatment must be available quickly to ensure the proper level of care.

Analysis of Weather Conditions

Weather factors during emergency incidents can have a severe impact on the safety and health of the members. When these factors combine with long-duration incidents or situations that require heavy exertion, the risks to members increase rapidly. The fire department should develop procedures, in consultation with the fire department physician, to provide relief from adverse climatic conditions. Typical rehabilitation considerations for operations during hot weather extremes include the following:

- Moving fatigued or unassigned members away from the hazardous area of the incident
- Removing members' personal protective equipment
- Ensuring that personnel are out of direct sunlight
- Ensuring that there is adequate air movement over personnel, either naturally or mechanically
- Providing members with fluid replenishment, especially water
- Providing medical evaluation for personnel showing signs or symptoms of heat exhaustion or heat stroke

Typical rehabilitation considerations for operations during cold weather extremes should include the following:

- Moving fatigued or unassigned members away from the hazardous area of the incident
- Providing shelter from wind and temperature extremes
- Providing members with fluid replenishment, especially water
- Providing medical evaluation for members showing signs or symptoms of frostbite, hypothermia, or other cold-related injury

The incident safety officer should ensure that the incident commander establishes an incident scene rehabilitation tactical-level management unit during emergency operations as required by NFPA 1521, *Standard for Fire Department Safety Officer.*

Rehabilitation Division or Group

This component should be established in a safe environment away from the hazardous area of the incident. The resources needed at the rehabilitation tactical level management unit should include an environment to limit temperature stress, medical equipment, and adequate medical staff. Items that can assist in limiting temperature stress in cold environments include heat, blankets, and protection from the wind. For hot weather, items should include adequate shade, fans, air conditioning, and misting systems. Food and hydration needs include water and oral fluids, food, broth, and fruit. Also, for hydration, a 50/50 mixture of water and an electrolyte replacement drink can be provided. Medical equipment should include blood pressure cuffs, stethoscopes, oxygen, cardiac monitors, thermometers, and intravenous fluid and supplies.

SUMMARY

Fire fighting and the delivery of other emergency services continue to be a hazardous occupation. Significant improvements and advancements have been made in terms of fire fighter safety and health. The process starts with the development of a written risk management program. The risk management plan serves as documentation that risks have been identified, evaluated, and prioritized and that a reasonable control plan has been implemented and monitored. Other critical components that are needed to ensure the safety and health of our members include training and education, protective clothing and equipment, safe vehicle operations, use of an incident management system, an aggressive health maintenance program, and facility safety.

A considerable effort needs to be focused on the issues of fire fighter fatalities, debilitating fire fighter injuries, and occupational illnesses. Moreover, specific emphasis needs to address improvements with incident scene communications, personnel accountability of fire fighters, operation of fire department vehicles responding to an incident, and medical conditions of fire fighters.

BIBLIOGRAPHY

NFPA Codes, Standards, and Recommended Practices

Reference to the following NFPA codes, standards, and recommended practices will provide further information on safety, medical, and health issues and programs discussed in this chapter. (See the latest version of The NFPA Catalog *for availability of current editions of the following documents.)*

NFPA 471, *Recommended Practice for Responding to Hazardous Materials Incidents*

NFPA 472, *Standard for Professional Competence of Responders to Hazardous Materials Incidents*

NFPA 1001, *Standard for Fire Fighter Professional Qualifications*

NFPA 1002, *Standard for Fire Apparatus Driver/Operator Professional Qualifications*

NFPA 1003, *Standard for Airport Fire Fighter Professional Qualifications*

NFPA 1006, *Standard for Rescue Technician Professional Qualifications*

NFPA 1021, *Standard for Fire Officer Professional Qualifications*

NFPA 1041, *Standard for Fire Service Instructor Professional Qualifications*

NFPA 1061, *Standard for Professional Qualifications for Public Safety Telecommunicator*

NFPA 1071, *Standard for Emergency Vehicle Technician Professional Qualifications*

NFPA 1201, *Standard for Providing Emergency Services to the Public*

NFPA 1250, *Recommended Practice in Emergency Service Organization Risk Management*

NFPA 1403, *Standard on Live Fire Training Evolutions*

NFPA 1404, *Standard for Fire Service Respiratory Protection Training*

NFPA 1500, *Standard on Fire Department Occupational Safety and Health Program*

NFPA 1521, *Standard for Fire Department Safety Officer*

NFPA 1561, *Standard on Emergency Services Incident Management System*

NFPA 1581, *Standard on Fire Department Infection Control Program*

NFPA 1582, *Standard on Comprehensive Occupational Medical Program for Fire Departments*

NFPA 1583, *Standard on Health-Related Fitness Programs for Fire Fighters*

NFPA 1600, *Standard on Disaster/Emergency Management and Business Continuity Programs*

NFPA 1851, *Standard on Selection, Care, and Maintenance of Structural Fire Fighting Protective Ensembles*

NFPA 1852, *Standard on Selection, Care, and Maintenance of Open-Circuit Self-Contained Breathing Apparatus (SCBA)*

NFPA 1901, *Standard for Automotive Fire Apparatus*

NFPA 1906, *Standard for Wildland Fire Apparatus*

NFPA 1911, *Standard for Service Tests of Fire Pump Systems on Fire Apparatus*

NFPA 1931, *Standard for Manufacturer's Design of Fire Department Ground Ladders*

NFPA 1932, *Standard on Use, Maintenance, and Service Testing of In-Service Fire Department Ground Ladders*

NFPA 1961, *Standard on Fire Hose*

NFPA 1962, *Standard for the Inspection, Care, and Use of Fire Hose, Couplings, and Nozzles and the Service Testing of Fire Hose*

NFPA 1964, *Standard for Spray Nozzles*

NFPA 1971, *Standard on Protective Ensembles for Structural Fire Fighting and Proximity Fire Fighting*

NFPA 1977, *Standard on Protective Clothing and Equipment for Wildland Fire Fighting*

NFPA 1981, *Standard on Open-Circuit Self-Contained Breathing Apparatus (SCBA) for Fire and Emergency Services*

NFPA 1982, *Standard on Personal Alert Safety Systems (PASS)*

NFPA 1983, *Standard on Life Safety Rope and Equipment for Emergency Services*

NFPA 1991, *Standard on Vapor-Protective Ensembles for Hazardous Materials Emergencies*

NFPA 1992, *Standard on Liquid Splash-Protective Ensembles and Clothing for Hazardous Materials Emergencies*

NFPA 1994, *Standard on Protective Ensembles for First Responders to CBRN Terrorism Incidents*

NFPA 1999, *Standard on Protective Clothing for Emergency Medical Operations*

References

Bartholomew, J. B., Craig, J., Farrar, R. P., and Throne, L. C., "Stress Reactivity in Fire Fighters: An Exercise Intervention," *International Journal of Stress Management,* Vol. 7, No. 4, 2000, pp. 235–246.

Bolstad-Johnson, D. M., Burgess, J. L., Crutchfield, C. D., Storment, S., and Gerkin, R., "Characterization of Firefighter Exposures During Fire Overhaul," *American Industrial Hygiene Association Journal,* Vol. 61, No. 5, 2000, pp. 636–641.

Chapter 8

Effect of Building Construction and Fire Protection Systems on Fire Fighter Safety

Revised by
Glenn P. Corbett

Key Terms

building code, building collapse, building construction (types of), compartmentation, concrete, fire fighter safety, fire resistance, noncombustible construction, ordinary construction, timber

Fire department personnel have a very strong interest in building construction. They must fight fires in buildings, from those under construction to those built hundreds of years ago. Some building methods encountered are long forgotten, but the hazards still exist. For example, a reference to tile arch floors would be difficult to find in modern architectural texts, yet there are thousands of them still in existence and they do present a specific hazard.

This chapter looks at the fire department's involvement in and concerns about various aspects of building construction. For the safety of those they serve as well for their own safety, fire fighters must understand simplified principles of construction, be familiar with the building codes and building construction classification, and be actively involved in pre-incident planning. These activities will make fire fighters aware of issues regarding structural integrity, water supply, and so on when they arrive at the fire scene.

A number of sections and chapters in this handbook deal with aspects of building construction. Relevant chapters include all the other chapters in Section 12 as well as Section 1, Chapter 1, "Challenges to Safety in the Built Environment"; Section 1, Chapter 2, "Fundamentals of Structurally Safe Building Design"; Section 11, Chapter 4, "Fire Hazards of Construction, Alteration, and Demolition of Buildings"; Section 19, Chapter 1, "Types of Building Construction"; Section 19, Chapter 2, "Structural Integrity During Fire"; and Section 19, Chapter 3, "Structural Fire Safety in One- and Two-Family Dwellings."

GENERAL CONCERNS

Fire department functions related to building construction include the following:

- Reviewing and approving plans for fire protection features in new construction in cooperation with the building department. In some cases, the fire department has absorbed the building department.
- Making regular inspections that, among other functions, check on the reliability of code-specified fire protection features—both passive features, such as fire walls and the fire doors that protect openings in the fire walls, and active features, such as fire suppression systems. A most

Glenn P. Corbett, P.E., is an associate professor of fire science at John Jay College of Criminal Justice in New York City; technical editor of *Fire Engineering* magazine; an assistant chief of the Waldwick, New Jersey, fire department; and serves on the Fire Code Advisory Council for the state of New Jersey. He is the coauthor of *Brannigan's Building Construction for the Fire Service,* Fourth Edition. He has served as the administrator of engineering services for the San Antonio, Texas, fire department and as a fire protection consultant for the Austin, Texas, fire department.

important function is ensuring that code-required life safety features, such as exit facilities, are fully usable as intended.

- Making pre-incident planning surveys to assemble and record information vital to the incident commander at a fire scene. It is most important that the information be retrievable instantly at the fire scene. A foremost purpose of pre-incident planning is to identify situations that are or can become hazardous to fire fighters. Some hazards may be sufficiently serious as to call for defensive fire-fighting tactics (i.e., exterior attack with no entry into the building). Examples would include fires involving dilapidated or abandoned buildings, posttensioned concrete in buildings under construction, and unprotected load-bearing steel.
- Acquiring knowledge of building construction. This is important in investigations of the origin, cause, and extent of serious fires.

The geodesic dome of the U.S. exhibit at Expo '67 in Montreal is pictured in Figure 12.8.1. Some architectural writers, unaware of the entire story, still praise this dome. It accommodated a huge number of visitors. After it was turned over to the city of Montreal, a workman accidentally touched a torch to the plastic covering. It totally burned in 10 minutes. The framework stands today as a monument to a tragedy that, by great good fortune, did not happen.

The planked ceiling conference room shown in Figure 12.8.2 is another example of a type of construction that should be avoided. This room is decorated with a virtual lumberyard of planks overhead. It is possible that the planks are treated to be flame resistant. In any case, fire involving the desks and chairs might cause failure of the hangers, usually set in lead anchors, allowing the planks to fall.

SIMPLIFIED PRINCIPLES OF BUILDING CONSTRUCTION

The fire officer should have knowledge of the principles of construction and the proper terms for various building elements.

FIGURE 12.8.1 Geodesic Dome at Expo '67 in Montreal (Source: Photo by D. Lion)

FIGURE 12.8.2 Heavy Fire Load in Conference Room of Fire-Resistive Building

Errors in principles or terminology can adversely affect the credibility of sound fire protection recommendations. Further, court testimony may be fatally discredited on cross-examination.

Some of the more important principles of construction include the following:

- Construction is primarily designed to resist the force of gravity and other stresses such as wind and snow loads under normal conditions.
- The supporting system of a building is composed of many elements designed to transfer the building load to the ground.
- Exposure to fire is not a normal condition and design provisions are made in some types of construction to protect the gravity-resisting (structural) elements from failing when exposed to fire. Unprotected structural elements can result in early and unexpected failure leading to partial or full collapse.
- Contents, not construction elements, typically drive the growth, intensity, and spread of fire; however, combustible construction elements can both contribute to the fire and lead to collapse.

Gravity and Building Collapse

If fire fighters are in, on, or adjacent to a structure when it fails, injury or death can result. Difficult and dangerous rescue efforts might be required. Only seconds may elapse between the time it is recognized that fire fighters should evacuate a structure and the failure of the structure.

In evaluating the hazards of building construction under fire conditions, the entire path of the load to ground must be considered. The parts of the system that can be the quickest to fail, such as connections or unprotected supporting elements, need to be considered. For example, laminated heavy timber beams may have substantial fire resistance but be supported by unprotected steel columns or cables that can result in failure. Lightweight timber trusses that can support the loads of roofs and floors generally have their parts held together with nail plates (sometimes called gusset plates). Exposure of nail plates to fire can char the wood into which they are nailed, releasing the plates and resulting in collapse.

When the incident commander on the scene of a building fire determines that the *structure* is involved in or affected by the fire (e.g., unprotected steel), the announcement should be made that all fire fighters be alert for and report any evidence of potential failure. Fire departments should have an easily recognized signal that means immediate evacuation of a structure. Multiple short air horn blasts and a distinctive Mayday radio signal broadcast on all radio channels should be used. All units should acknowledge the radio announcement.

Evacuation drills should be carried out during routine training activities to overcome any reluctance of fire fighters to abandon their equipment except those tools that might be needed to get out and withdraw. The proudest ships in the navy conduct regular "abandon ship" drills.

Failure on the part of command officers to understand the principles of construction and their repercussions can cause fire fighter injuries and deaths. For example, a cantilever beam can be compared to a seesaw. It is supported in position by connections in the interior of a building. If these connections fail because of fire, the extended portion of the beam, and whatever it supports, will fall. In lieu of a cantilever, a suspended beam may be used. To the building designer, there is little difference in whether the reaction goes downward through a column or upward through a tension member, such as a cable to the wall. However, if the connection fails, the suspended beam becomes an unsupported cantilever and can fall on fire fighters.

In Figure 12.8.3, for example, tendons providing lateral support for the structure will be posttensioned in several increments as the building grows taller. They remain exposed until the building is finished. They will fail at 800°F (427°C) and thus collapse the structure, possibly causing fire fighter deaths. Wooden falsework and other combustibles provide sufficient fuel.

In another example (Figure 12.8.4), the cold drawn steel cable that supports the tram car loses its tensile strength at 800°F (427°C). Many of the stations are made of wood, which could provide sufficient fuel for a destructive fire.

FIGURE 12.8.3 Tendons Providing Lateral Structural Support

FIGURE 12.8.4 Steel Cable at Ski Station

Building Reaction to Fire

All structures have some resistance to fire-caused collapse. This can informally be described as *inherent* fire resistance, as distinguished from *legal* or code-specified resistance. The inherent fire resistance of one structure may be absent in another similar structure. Direct experience with this fire resistance, whether personal or organizational, is not transferable from one structure to another. Simply put, "What you know may not be so."

Through experience the fire service has developed some understanding of and criteria for inherent fire resistance. However, estimates of "safe time" in buildings on fire are invalid because the time elapsed since the start of the fire is rarely known. In particular, fire fighters must understand that a fire resistance rating of 2 hours, for example, does not guarantee 2 hours of safety. A structural element or wall with a fire resistance of 2 hours might not last 2 hours in actual fire conditions. It can fail sooner or last longer. In addition, failure of a single key element may cause a massive collapse. Many times fire fighters risk life and limb without knowing the degree of risk involved. Generally accepted indications of imminent collapse—softening, water flowing between bricks, smoke pushing from mortar joints, strange noises—are grossly inadequate, even for older buildings. If they are relied on solely to protect fire fighters from collapse in today's different, lighter buildings, disasters can certainly result.

Contents

The problems of structure fires cannot be isolated from the structure's contents. Most building fires originate in contents. Fires involving building contents can destroy noncombustible structures and damage fire-resistant structures. The hazard of today's fast-burning, high heat release rate contents is a major problem.

Occupancy classifications found in building codes in some cases provide a general indication of the combustibility of contents (e.g., factory occupancy, moderate hazard storage occupancy, etc.) but must not be relied on for fire-fighting operations. Materials with high rates of heat release and/or rapid flame spread can be found in many occupancy types.

As long ago as 1975, the Society of Fire Protection Engineers (SFPE) warned that "A high rate of fire development can create a condition that may tax or overpower traditional fire defenses. Defenses of the past, both passive and active (evacuation, alarm, ventilation, and manual fire control), have not been designed by engineer or code to anticipate this hazard. This is primarily a furnishings problem. Many occupancies (residences, office buildings, theaters, hospitals) are being affected."[1]

Other Hazards

A building involved in fire presents other serious hazards to fire fighters. Fire can spread in void spaces with little or no external evidence and burst out unexpectedly and increase in intensity when a nearby breach admits oxygen. Buildings of otherwise noncombustible or fire-resistive construction may have combustible interior finish on floors, walls, and ceilings that can contribute to rapid fire spread.

When live fire training is conducted in most typical training school structures, the hazards of collapse, hidden fire, and highly combustible interior finish are absent. There have been serious accidents during live fire training in abandoned buildings when these hazards were present. It is important to have adequate classroom instruction on these issues, followed by pre-incident planning exercises for the hazards of individual major buildings and general building construction.

BUILDING CODES AND BUILDING CONSTRUCTION CLASSIFICATION

Types of Building Construction

Building codes classify buildings according to the type of construction and the fire resistance of the various load-bearing and non-load-bearing elements, such as exterior and interior walls, columns, beams and girders, and floor and roof construction. NFPA 220, *Standard on Types of Building Construction,* describes five types of construction. The fire resistance requirements as determined by NFPA 251, *Standard Methods of Tests of Fire Resistance of Building Construction and Materials,* will vary depending on the building element being considered. The details can be found in Section 19, Chapter 1, "Types of Building Construction." The types of building construction include the following.

Type I. Structural members of approved noncombustible or limited combustible materials with specified fire resistance ratings (exterior bearing walls 4 or 3 hours, etc.).

Type II. Structural members are the same as Type I but with lower or no fire resistance rating.

Type III. Exterior walls and structural members that are part of exterior walls are of approved noncombustible or limited combustible materials; and interior structural members, including walls, columns, and so on, are entirely or partially made of wood; no fire resistance rating greater than 2 hours.

Type IV. Exterior and interior walls and structural members that are portions of such walls are of approved noncombustible or limited combustible materials. Other interior structural members, including walls, columns, floors, and roofs, should be of solid or laminated wood without concealed spaces; no fire resistance rating greater than 2 hours. Note that wood timbers used in Type IV construction are assumed to have "inherent" fire resistance due to their mass and do not have a fire rating.

Type V. Exterior walls, bearing walls, columns, beams, floors, roofs, and so on are entirely or partially made of wood or other approved combustible materials; structural members may have a 1 hour rating or be nonrated.

Bearing in mind that the current classification has varying fire resistance requirements within a given type, the traditional or common terms associated with the NFPA 220 and *NFPA 5000®, Building Construction and Safety Code®*, "construction types" include the following:

Type I: Fire resistive
Type II: Noncombustible
Type III: Ordinary
Type IV: Heavy timber
Type V: Wood frame

These traditional classifications are very general and may not fully describe the fire resistance characteristics of any specific building. In addition, some buildings include several types of construction, particularly when additions have been made to older buildings. Some typical variations include the following:

- The construction of wood frame buildings has changed over the years. Prior to 1940, many multistory buildings were built with vertical framing members that created continuous void channels extending from the foundation to the attic space. This type of construction was referred to as "balloon construction" and allowed fire to spread upward rapidly through the exterior walls, sometimes without being detected by fire fighters. Balloon construction practice was replaced with construction in which each floor comprised a platform extending to the building perimeter. Platform construction cut off the vertical spread of fire. Although wood frame buildings with truss floors may be structurally considered as platform frame construction, the presence of horizontal floor voids interconnected vertically by plumbing voids can result in concealed fire spread similar to balloon frame construction.
- Brick buildings may be partially load-bearing brick or brick/block masonry on some walls and brick veneer over wood bearing walls on others. In some cases, the lower floor(s) are of masonry and the upper floors are brick veneer. Brick veneer may be applied over steel or concrete.
- Heavy timber buildings may have potentially dangerous departures from the ideal "mill construction," which is designed in all aspects to resist collapse from fire.
- Noncombustible buildings may have many combustible features, such as roofs, balconies, overhangs, and combustible materials in metal deck roof systems. Noncombustibility does not necessarily mean resistance to collapse.

• Fire-resistive buildings can have deficiencies that compromise the concept of compartmentation. For instance, large-area concrete floors require expansion joints. In a fire at a U.S. Postal Service Parcel Post Facility in New York City, there were large open areas that were pierced with many unprotected vertical openings; these openings consisted of conveyor belt systems, spiral mail chutes, duct systems, and flush floor openings.[2] In another example, melting aluminum expansion joints in the McCormick Place fire in Chicago dropped to the floor below, igniting combustible materials.[3] Ducts and wiring penetrations can provide paths for the spread of fire and smoke. It is not uncommon for fire barriers to be compromised after buildings are occupied. Inspection of compartmentation in new construction and after modifications and maintenance is important to achieve reliable compartmentation.

Fire-rated elements may vary greatly in materials. The test used, NFPA 251/ASTM E119, *Standard Test Methods for Fire Tests of Building Construction and Materials,* may give equal time rating to a wall of steel studs and plaster and a wall of wood and gypsum. However, S. H. Ingberg, who developed the concept of applying NFPA 251/ASTM E119 to wood structures and is considered the father of the fire resistance testing methods of the National Bureau of Standards (now the National Institute for Standards and Technology), issued the following warning:

> We must particularly distinguish between the fire resistance of a combustible and a noncombustible structure. While they may be equivalent in time, there is a world of difference in the protection afforded as it concerns the individual building, the hazard to nearby structures, and the hazard to life.[4]

Wood Frame Structures

The most prevalent construction material in the United States and Canada is wood. Wood can carry structural loads such as columns and beams. In older buildings, there are huge quantities of nonstructural wood used as lath to support plaster. Wood is also used for decoration and interior trim. A wooden interior in a restaurant in a high-rise building provided such a fierce fire that the fire department was unable to reach three trapped civilians, who finally jumped to their deaths.

For over 150 years, attempts have been made to render wood fireproof or noncombustible with no success. Wood can be surface treated to render it ignition resistant or reduce its surface flame spread. One method is to paint wood with an intumescent coating, which swells up like a marshmallow when heated, retarding ignition and the spread of flame. One problem in using this method to reduce the hazard of installed wood paneling is its untreated reverse side.

Wood can be rendered fire retardant by drawing out the sap and moisture and replacing it with chemicals. Fire-retardant-treated (FRT) wood is just that—fire retardant. It is still combustible.

In recent years, the dimensions of wooden structural members have been reduced and specialized wood structural members have been introduced. The removed wood had provided some inherent fire resistance due to its additional mass. Using sawn or laminated two-by-four lumber or flakeboard in wooden I-beams has reduced the mass of these wooden beams. These lighter beams can be expected to fail earlier in a fire,[5] because as soon as the web starts to burn, the strength of the beam is degraded.

In the construction of wood-frame row-type dwellings, no fire protection provision is resisted more than parapeting fire walls to separate the units. Parapeted fire walls present a special problem to the builder because they require skilled craftsmen to flash the wall properly to prevent leaks. It is much easier to place shingles on a flat, unbroken roof.

Plywood. Some years ago the practice of laying a 4 ft (1.2 m) sheet of ignition-resistant plywood on each side of a fire wall that did not penetrate the roof was adopted in lieu of parapeting. The treated plywood is supported on untreated, lightweight wood trusses, which are subject to early failure. Plywood, laid over the top of masonry fire walls, can delaminate and/or raise up and pass fire over the top of the wall. Furthermore, plywood over a rough-cut, concrete-block fire wall can be difficult to seal against the passage of fire, smoke, and hot gases.

In an attempt to prevent this extension, some codes specified a 4 ft (1.2 m) roof section of fire-retardant-treated plywood to be laid lengthwise along each side of the fire wall. Some of the chemicals used in the treatment reacted to heat and humidity and destroyed the plywood. Thousands of roofs required replacement.[6,7] In at least one jurisdiction, the underside of the replaced roofs is covered with a 4-ft (1.2-m) wide layer of gypsum board along the fire wall line. In the nineteenth century, plastering was used in an attempt to provide fire resistance to wood columns. Rot occurred under the plaster.

Wood Framing with Gypsum Board. Another method of protecting wood from fire is found in floor and ceiling assemblies and wall sections that combine wood framing with gypsum board membranes. A number of such floor and ceiling assemblies have received fire resistance ratings of 1 hour or more after being subjected to the NFPA 251/ASTM E119 test. One problem is that this fire resistance test was developed for floors of homogeneous, noncombustible materials, which were essentially the same from top down and bottom up. The one-way test in which the fire is applied from the bottom of a floor/ceiling assembly may not adequately determine fire resistance in a fully developed fire where the development of flashover can create severe temperatures developed at floor level, sometimes quite early in the fire.

As illustrated in Figure 12.8.5, in the NFPA 251/ASTM E119 test, the floor is exposed to fire only from below. Real fires, however, are different in that a fully developed compartment will involve a floor from the top down. Real fires may also start within the floor assembly itself, and in the case of wood trusses, may easily spread horizontally and vertically throughout a building's void spaces.

Trusses. The difficulty with fire fighters accepting the 1 hour resistance rating as indicating a degree of safety is even more serious in the case of lightweight gusset-plate trusses. When solid wood floor joists are used, each joist can act as a firestop, thus slowing the progress of the fire through the floor construction. In the case of a truss, the entire floor void, along with its

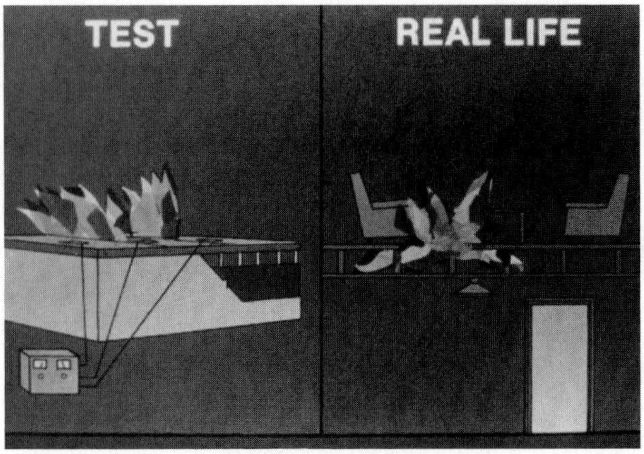

FIGURE 12.8.5 Spread of Test Fire Versus Real Fire

air supply, is available to the fire as soon as fire enters the void. The lightweight members of the truss are of small kindling-like dimensions. The voids can extend over sizable areas.

There are no fire-rated designs for firestopping (preventing vertical fire spread) or draftstopping (preventing horizontal fire spread) in the truss voids of frame buildings. The accepted practice of employing gypsum board is subject to improper installation and inspection, often due to a lack of appreciation of the purpose of draftstopping. Draftstopping is difficult to install and may be ineffective in preventing the extension of fire to adjacent truss voids, particularly when postconstruction penetrations are present. For example, firestopping is at the mercy of any worker with a pipe or cable to run (Figure 12.8.6).

Early collapse of a structure in which fire has penetrated into the truss voids is highly likely. A three-story, trussed-floor apartment house in San Antonio, Texas, collapsed moments after fire fighters evacuated the building. The fire started when a flammable liquid accidentally spilled on a floor, leaked down into the truss void, and ignited.[8]

A dangerous situation can result when trusses are permitted to extend from the floor voids on either side of a stairway to support the platform of a stairway that may serve as the single exit for the occupants and access for fire fighters. Incomplete firestopping can lead to fire spread and subsequent collapse.[9]

FIGURE 12.8.6 Firestopping Affected by Postconstruction Penetration

In another design the extended trusses may support a balcony that can be an area of refuge for occupants or provide entry for the fire department. A piece of gypsum board, plywood, or flakeboard may be used as firestopping to separate the floor void from the balcony void. There are no data indicating that such firestopping is adequate, particularly when it is penetrated for utilities. Casualties could result as fire units attempt to rescue occupants over ground ladders while the fire burns unchecked in inaccessible floor voids.

In one type of truss, the gusset plates and diagonal tension members were stamped from one piece of steel. If a fire causes a floor to collapse, the floor can fall on the floor below, causing it to collapse also because the tension members buckle out of the wood. Another new type of truss uses only finger joints and glue to hold the truss together.

Fire burning down into the floor void can come up on the other side of a rated wall, thus making dubious the concept that compartmentation is provided when a "rated wall" meets a "rated floor."[10] A ceiling light fixture can cause a fire that starts in the truss void. The fire can extend unnoticed from the truss void into the void between the plywood sheathing and the brick veneer and then back into the floor voids above. A collapse can result. In addition to collapse and fire spread, the truss floor provides a void in which carbon monoxide can accumulate.

Heavy Timber

The features of heavy timber construction that contribute to fire fighter safety are heavy masonry and brick walls; heavy dimensional timber used for columns and beams; heavy, thick wooden floors, which collapse only after many hours of fire fighting; and the lack of concealed spaces. However, it is dangerously inaccurate to consider building code–defined heavy timber construction as the equivalent of true mill construction.[11] Heavy timbers are slower to reach sustained burning than lighter wood members. This has lead to the term *slow burning* being applied to buildings of masonry exterior walls and timber interiors. Such a building is expected to retain its structural stability for a long time when subjected to a fire. Unfortunately, the slow-burning characteristic sometimes becomes long burning, so there is no merit to slow burning once the fire department can no longer remain in the building and must operate defensively.

The original concept of heavy timber construction, or mill construction, employed timber columns. Where the column intersected the floor girder, it should have been replaced by a solid cast-iron pintle, which passes through a hole in the girder. (A girder is any beam that supports other beams.) The small cross section of the pintle would cause it to be protected by the mass of wood girder. However, this procedure was ignored in many buildings. Some heavy timber buildings have cast-iron columns that may fail early in a fire. Where these columns pass through the floor girder, there is no reduction in size of the column. As a result, two "half moons" of the timber rest on a shelf protruding from the column. Failure of the shelf, or the loss of a small amount of wood around this column, will cause the floor to fall.

Rehabilitated buildings may be fitted with unprotected steel columns, which can fail early in a fire. Sometimes Lally columns (steel columns filled with concrete) are used. In the nineteenth century, Lally columns were often cast iron and were drilled to release the steam from the concrete. Current columns may not be drilled and could explode when heated because of the steam generated when the concrete core is heated and releases water.

Heavy timber, slow-burning, or mill construction buildings should be carefully examined for these potentially disastrous weaknesses, which make invalid the assumption that the building will retain its stability for any appreciable time. Six Worcester, Massachusetts, fire fighters died in a heavy timber building that had been a cold storage warehouse. A complicated layout and smoke from cork and plastic insulation caused fire fighters to become lost. The building had not been pre-incident planned, and the stability of heavy timber buildings was immaterial to the outcome.

Plank and beam construction is sometimes called *western framing*. The typical 16 in. (406 mm) spacing of floor beams may be considered too boxlike and unattractive. Except in the roughest construction, a ceiling is installed to hide floor or roof beams. A take-off from heavy timber construction provides residences, churches (Figure 12.8.7), and other public buildings with an aesthetically pleasing interior by eliminating the ceiling and exposing the wood structure. Many churches are of plank on laminated wood beam or arch construction, often a fast flame spread potential. Heavy beams, widely spaced, are spanned with heavy tongue-and-groove planks instead of floorboards. The wood surface is planed smooth. Often a clear lacquer is used as a finish. This has the excellent advantage of eliminating void spaces. However, fire may still spread rapidly over these wood surfaces.

Long heavy timbers may be in short supply or are not available. It is common practice to splice timbers to attain the proper length. Laminated arches are commonly shipped in sections to be field spliced. A properly designed spliced timber will carry its load adequately in normal use but may fail disastrously in a fire. The arches of a Florida jai alai fronton were of spliced laminated timbers. Although the timbers were burned only moderately, the arches fell apart because the heated metal of the splice connections simply burned away the wood to which they were attached.[12]

Many old buildings are being adapted to other uses. Dropped ceilings provide huge voids through which hidden fire can travel (Figure 12.8.8). Nailing up "fire-rated" gypsum board does not solve the fire extension problem. As shown in Figure 12.8.9, a peaked truss roof is being erected to change the roofline of a flat-roofed building. The old combustible built-up roof covering was left in place. The exhaust duct was not extended through the new roof. Ventilating the new roof would be hazardous and useless. For additional information on timber construction, see Section 19, Chapter 2, "Structural Integrity During Fire."

Ordinary Construction

Ordinary construction is the term applied to buildings of usually combustible interior with load-bearing masonry exterior walls.

FIGURE 12.8.8 Dropped Ceiling Being Added

FIGURE 12.8.7 Church with Plank on Laminated Wood Beam Construction

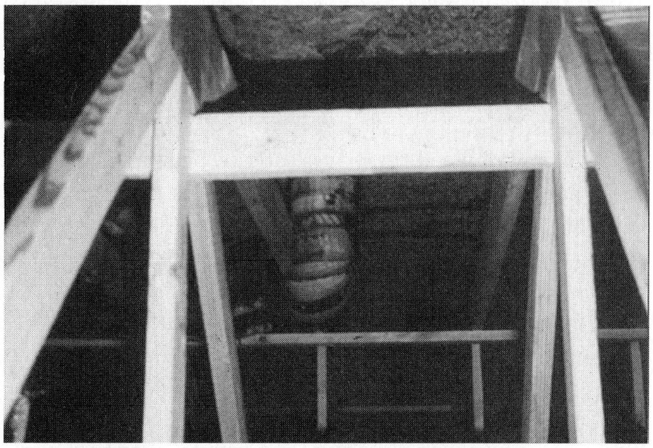

FIGURE 12.8.9 Peaked Truss Roof Being Added (Source: David Harlow)

Originally, such buildings had brick or stone exterior walls and wood floors. The brick or stone walls were often required by law to limit fire spread from building to building in cities. In most building codes, the area of the city required to have construction that limits fire spread is defined by the "fire limits." In more recent times, in addition to brick and stone construction, exterior masonry construction may use brick and clay tile composite, brick and block composite, cast-in-place concrete, concrete block, hollow clay tile, and adobe.

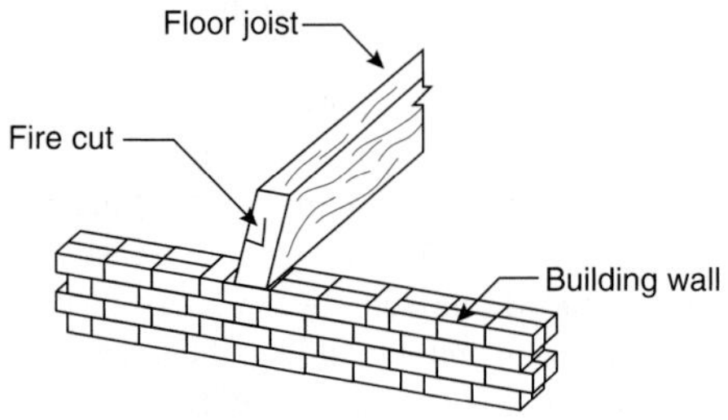

FIGURE 12.8.10 Cutaway Diagram of a Fire Cut on the End of a Wood Floor Joist

Brick. Brick is attractive but expensive. Many buildings that appear to be of brick construction are actually a single layer of brick veneer on the face of a wood building. Brick veneer can be applied to any surface. Brick or stone veneer may be used to rehabilitate an old building. Imitation stone veneer is made of concrete cast in molds.

Brick veneer is totally dependent on the basic structure of the building for stability. If the supporting structure is damaged, the veneer may fall down. A veneer building is not a masonry building. It should be described by its basic construction type, for example, wood frame, steel, or concrete.

In the past it was possible to easily see the difference between brick masonry and veneer, because in solid masonry some brick courses were turned to show the ends (headers), whereas the others were laid lengthwise (stretchers). The development of the masonry wire truss has made it possible to lay all the bricks as stretchers, so the difference between masonry and veneer is no longer obvious.

The following are some causes of masonry wall collapse:

- Many brick walls are not totally brick. It was common practice to insert wood lintels over windows and doors. In many buildings, wood beams were laid in the wall to provide a level surface for floor beams and to tie the wall together lengthwise. When this wood burns out, a collapse is certain. This can be determined only by thorough pre-incident analysis.
- Water-soluble sand-lime mortar was universally used until 1880, was partially used thereafter for many years, and is still used today in the rehabilitation of older brickwork. This type of mortar can be washed out by weather or by hose streams. The loss of mortar to water leaks can cause some collapses when there is no fire.
- Although lightweight steel bar joists can fail early in a fire, first they will elongate. Elongating steel can push down masonry walls.
- Collapse of wood floors was early recognized as a hazard to the masonry in which the floor beams were imbedded. Collapse of floors can precipitate wall collapses. The beams may act as a lever pulling down the brick wall. In some areas builders corbelled out a ledge. The beams were set on the ledge, so that when they fell, the wall was undisturbed. In other cases, a "fire cut" (Figure 12.8.10) was required at the ends of wooden beams. In these beams, a 45 degree cut was made on the end, so that the top was shorter than the bottom. Thus, the beam could fall out of the wall without acting like a lever and disturbing the brickwork. Since wood is removed, the fire-cut beam may collapse earlier than would a beam solidly set into the wall. In some building renovations, fire-cut wooden beams that had sagged over time were simply turned over to provide an upward camber; thus, a minimal amount of wood was bearing on the wall. Another method uses beam boxes, which are cast-iron boxes laid in the brick wall to accommodate a girder. When the girder fails, the box remains in place and the wall is not affected.
- The impact load of debris from a wall collapse can cause the collapse of adjacent buildings with possible loss of fire fighters' lives.
- Unreinforced masonry buildings are liable to collapse in earthquakes, which is a concern to fire fighters who respond to earthquakes.
- Old masonry buildings have been renovated for other uses. Many have included the conversion of old downtown residences into commercial buildings. In many cases, the floor loads from files, safes, and merchandise can be much greater than that which previously existed. These heavier loads can place additional stress on the floor construction as well as the supporting wall construction. Commercial buildings may also represent higher fire loads than did the original residences.
- Some older masonry buildings were built with interior walls of balloon frame construction. Fire in such a wall spreads freely from floor to floor and into the floor voids. The wall is structural, and its damage can precipitate an interior collapse.
- More substantial buildings were built with interior masonry structural walls. Since the practical span of wooden beams was only about 25 ft (7.6 m), there were many small interior rooms. In many cases, walls have been removed to enlarge the interior space. The heavy masonry above was supported on a steel beam that, in turn, was supported by cast-iron columns, usually unconnected to the beam. The connection is vulnerable to any lateral thrust. Such an arrangement provided the larger space needed for a coffee shop in the century-old Vendome Hotel in Boston. Nine fire fighters died in 1972 when the beam-column arrangement failed.[13]

Beliefs About Construction. Beyond these indications, there are other dangers associated with building construction that the fire service needs to be concerned with. Some widely accepted beliefs regarding construction-related issues are open to question. Some of these beliefs may prove fatal to fire fighters or others at the fire scene.

One rule of thumb attempts to specify how far out from the building a wall would fall depending on its height. In other words, to be safe from collapsing walls, fire fighters must be as far away from the wall as the wall is tall. This informal guideline is of doubtful validity: even if true for most of the wall, some bricks and timbers may land much farther out than anticipated.

Collapse of masonry walls is sometimes attributed to contraction caused by cold water hitting hot bricks. This theory is unproved. The greatest amount of water thrown in a defensive attack is directed through windows, not onto a wall. Considering the low heat transmission rate of brickwork, it is likely that the brick is at best only slightly cooled by the water.

Many older buildings have an outer layer of finished brick, which may be a veneer. A hose stream hitting such a wall can get behind the finished brick, tear the bricks off the surface, and endanger persons below.

The interior of ordinary construction buildings is almost completely of combustible construction. Where steel is used it may be left unprotected or enclosed in combustible voids that provide no protection from heat. The fire department may be completely unaware of the hazard of the hidden steel. Another major hazard of the voids that has been noted is the potential for hidden fires.

Alterations of the interior may leave hazardous floor conditions. For example, when a stairway is relocated, the former opening is rarely restored to a strength equal to that of the original floor. This presents a weak floor through which fire fighters can fall. In another example, the roof of the precast tilt slab concrete building shown in Figure 12.8.11 was fire damaged. Because the roof is vital to the stability of the building, the contractor's first move was to replace the tormentors, which braced the walls before the roof was in place. For more detailed discussions, see Dunn.[14]

Noncombustible Construction

Noncombustible construction is a building code term that unfortunately may not be literally true. Fire departments should be aware of what the local code permits under this heading. It is possible that substantial combustible components, such as a wooden balcony or roof or a combustible metal deck roof, are included in a noncombustible building. The fact that a material is noncombustible is not necessarily significant in reducing the fire loss or in reducing hazards to fire fighters. The two common materials of noncombustible construction are steel and concrete.

Steel. Steel is an extremely strong material. Heavy loads can be carried on light structural steel elements. Because of the small mass of the steel, all but very heavy members elongate as they are heated. Steel beams will elongate 9 in. (229 mm) in 100 ft (31 m) at about 1000°F (538°C).[15] This can be sufficient to push out wall panels and cause toppling. Elongating steel has pushed down many walls in this fashion. At slightly higher temperatures, steel reaches its collapse range. Collapse of steel roofs supporting the sprinkler piping can cause sprinkler system failures, resulting in massive destruction in several warehouse fires.

As steel trusses (like those shown in Figure 12.8.12) are heated, connecting ties can transmit undesigned torsional load to other trusses. This may result in failure of trusses away from the fire area. Four fire fighters died in Pennsylvania in the collapse of a "concrete" building in which the floor was supported by unprotected steel columns.[16] These unprotected steel struts could be loaded to twice the limit for permanent structural steel, thus lowering the failure temperature. A fire in combustible materials, often present in excavations, could cause the steel to fail. The adjacent structures could then collapse into the excavation.

Extreme caution should be the rule at any fire where unprotected steel is being heated. The potential consequences are not always evident. Pre-incident planning should be thorough, and limits should be set on fire-fighting procedures to ensure safety of personnel.

Concrete. Concrete is strong in compression but weak in tension. Plain concrete, usually found in the form of concrete

FIGURE 12.8.11 Fire-Damaged Roof

FIGURE 12.8.12 Unprotected Steel Struts

blocks, is used for compressive loads. Reinforced concrete is a composite material. Steel is incorporated into the concrete to provide the tensile strength. By definition, a composite material is one in which both elements must act together to carry the load. A failure of the bond between the steel and concrete destroys the composite nature and strength of the structural element.

Unlike steel, which needs to be protected from fire by an insulating covering, concrete can be inherently fire resistive. The resistance to fire is accomplished by the nature and thickness of the concrete itself. However, it is impossible to distinguish fire-resistive concrete from that which is merely noncombustible by simply looking at the concrete member.

Non-fire-resistive concrete has no specific fire resistance requirement and can fail early in a fire, even when exposed to only modest heat. No valid assumptions can be made as to when fire-exposed, non-fire-resistive concrete will fail. If the building is of monolithic construction, however, the load may be redistributed throughout the building, and a general collapse is unlikely. However, local collapse may cause injuries from falling concrete or from fire fighters falling through holes.

Precast concrete tilt slab buildings are now commonly used for warehouses and factories. Many of them are the equivalent of several stories high to accommodate high-rack storage. The integrity of the roof is vital to the tilt slab building. Failure of the roof can result in collapse of the tilt slab walls.

The roof may be carried on several types of beams. Most common are wood, steel bar joists, and concrete pretensioned tee beams.

Concrete tee beams would not generally be rated fire resistive unless the building was required to be fire resistive. If the concrete below the bottom tendon spalls off, the cold drawn tendon, which typically fails at 800°F (427°C), is exposed to the fire, and the beam is subject to failure.

A Metropolitan Dade County, Florida, fire lieutenant lost his life when prestressed tendons in tee beams in a carpet warehouse roof were heated to failure and the beam(s) collapsed. Massive reinforced concrete, fire-resistive multistory buildings have a good fire record. However, there have been cases of serious destruction, usually during long-duration, high-intensity fires. A recent fire in a concrete building loaded with tires caused heavy damage. A long-burning fire in the top floor of the Military Records Center near St. Louis, Missouri,[17] caused considerable elongation of the roof, which resulted in columns being torn off either the roof or the floor. After the fire, the top floor was removed.

Massive concrete is a substantial heat sink. The heat that is stored in the concrete is not available to extend the fire. However, the retained heat in the concrete may cause serious health hazards to fire fighters during operations and overhauling.

In posttensioned concrete buildings, the load is carried on the tendons (Figure 12.8.13). As a result, a failure of a tendon in a fire can lead to the failure of the building. Finished posttensioned concrete buildings cannot be distinguished by appearance from conventional reinforced concrete buildings. They are very different, however, with respect to fire operations. Spalled concrete can expose the tendons, resulting in failure. It is not safe to drill through a posttensioned floor to attack a stubborn fire on a floor below because the drill might cut a tendon and cause collapse. A hole alongside a tendon might permit the tendon to heat to failure. To cut large holes with jackhammers would be extremely hazardous in a posttensioned building.

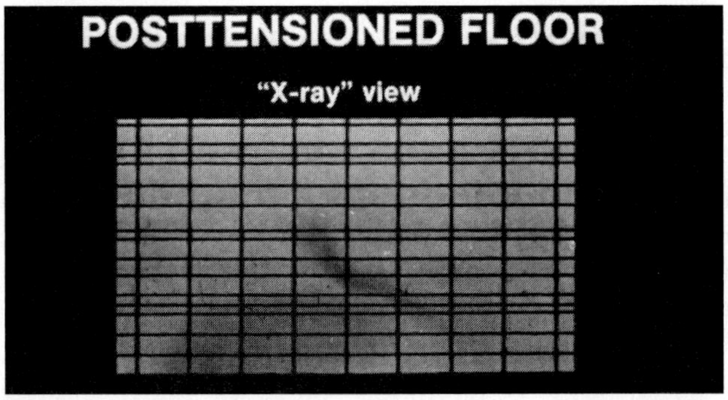

FIGURE 12.8.13 Location of Tendons in Posttensioned Concrete

Concrete Buildings Under Construction. The extraordinary rescue and body recovery operations required at the Oklahoma City, Oklahoma, bombing in 1995[18] could be repeated at a fire in a concrete building under construction if conventional firefighting tactics are followed.

When concrete buildings are under construction, the loads of freshly poured floors and structural elements are supported on temporary forms that are either combustible or, if made of steel or aluminum, subject to fire-caused failure. A massive failure of forms dropping one floor on another is almost certain to cause progressive collapse of several floors, possibly all the way to the ground.

In such cases, the command decision process should be the opposite of the traditional method. Traditionally, fire fighters rush into the structure and withdraw only when it is determined that the structure is unsafe. In the case of fire in concrete forms, which support thousands of pounds (kilograms) of concrete, it may be advisable to stay out until a decision can be made as to whether it is safe to enter the structure or even be near it.

On October 30, 2004, the top five stories of a 10 story parking garage collapsed in Atlantic City, New Jersey. Composed of both precast and sitecast concrete structural members, a column at or underneath the tenth floor (that was being poured) failed, trapping 24 construction workers. Three of them were killed.[19]

The situation in the case of posttensioned concrete construction is even more serious than it is for conventional reinforced concrete. Until the tendons are tensioned and the cables are stretched, the entire weight of the concrete, even hardened and dry to the touch, is supported on the concrete forms. If the forms burn, the entire floor or floors dependent on them will fall, possibly precipitating a total collapse. In 1974 a 14 story, posttensioned concrete structure under construction in Cleveland, Ohio, totally collapsed when fire attacked the forms. The fire chief, aware of the hazard, had kept the fire fighters out of the collapse area.

In 2000, a three-section, posttensioned, residential high rise was under construction in Key Biscayne, Florida.[20] Fire in exterior construction material spread to construction material in the interior. The fire department, cognizant of the posttensioned concrete hazard, adopted a defensive mode; that is, a no-entry mode. Many tendons were exposed to the fire, and three units were so damaged that they were demolished. It took several days for the explosive demolition contractor to prepare a safe plan for placing the explosives.

Fire fighters need to be aware that moisture remains in the concrete used to fill steel columns (Figure 12.8.14). In the nineteenth century, Lally columns were drilled to vent the steel. In a fire, the trapped moisture can heat until it becomes steam under sufficient pressure to cause the columns to explode. The explosion is not only dangerous itself but also can weaken the structure.

Fire-Resistive Construction

The major components of fire-resistive buildings are required to be similar to building components that have been subjected to the NFPA 251/ASTM E119 test. Test results are stated in the time to the last full hour (or half hour) the assembly withstood the assault of the test fire. Thus, a column might be rated as having "1-hour fire resistance" or a floor-ceiling assembly as having "2-hour fire resistance."

There may be no specific relationship between the time given in the rating and the time to failure of the structure in a real fire, however. There are many variables that affect the time a structural element can withstand fire exposure. The limit of confidence that one can have is that a 4-hour fire-resistive building is more fire resistive than a 2-hour fire-resistive building or that a 1-hour fire-resistive building is less fire resistive than a 2-hour fire-resistive building.

Fire-resistive buildings generally fall into the following three classes, corresponding roughly to the time they were built:

1. During the period 1880 to 1920, emphasis was on the building itself. Floors were of tile arch with or without protection of the steel beams. Vertical opening protection was not even considered. Fire resistance consisted of whatever the architect thought proper, because there were few requirements for fire resistance in the building codes. There are many such buildings still in use.

FIGURE 12.8.14 Concrete-Filled Steel Tube Columns

2. From 1920 to 1945, many building components were rated fire resistive in accordance with the ASTM E119 test. Steel frames were fireproofed with concrete. Floors were cast-in-place concrete. Stairways and elevators were generally enclosed. Fire and occupant loads were low because of limited floor areas due to the need for natural light and air. Many exit stairs were designed to provide an atmospheric break between the floor and the stairway, thus providing exit stairs that did not become contaminated with smoke. Sprinklers were generally not provided except for such buildings as the headquarters of the National Board of Fire Underwriters and high-rise factory buildings in New York City as a result of laws passed in the wake of the Triangle Shirtwaist fire. Only a few cities had high-rise buildings of this type. The Empire State Building represents the zenith of this type of fire-resistive construction.

3. From 1945 to present, many changes have occurred in building construction techniques. Air conditioning and fluorescent lighting have made extensive floor areas possible. Compartmentation in the form of full height partitions (found in older high-rise buildings and beneficial for slowing fire spread) have been replaced by short cubicle partitions. The increase in height and floor area has permitted a huge increase in occupants. Timely evacuation is difficult. Air conditioning may require nonoperable windows. Building height can generate strong stack effects, which can become a serious factor in smoke movement.

Combustible Metal Deck Roofs (CMDRs)

The so-called built-up roof of tar and layers of roofing material generally covered in stone is capable of self-sustained combustion when installed on metal decking, irrespective of contents. Such a roof is called a combustible metal deck roof (CMDR). If it is looked at it from below, the tar, which turns to gas when heated, is not visible, and the bar joist and corrugated steel void appear to be noncombustible. Frank Brannigan discovered the problem in 1946 at a fire in the Marine Corps Depot of Supplies in Norfolk, Virginia, and developed a tactical solution whereby heavy caliber streams were directed to the steel decking from a safe location to chill the steel and thus solidify the gas-generating tar. This technique was applied successfully at another fire in 1948. Until the total destruction of the General Motors Transmission Plant in Livonia, Michigan, in 1953, with a loss of $70,000,000, the problem of CMDRs remained largely unapprised.[21] Tests at Factory Mutual showed that 800°F for 5 minutes on the underside of the metal deck produces a self-sustaining fire.[22]

The U.S. Atomic Energy Commission had two roof deck fires in buildings with only minor combustible contents and developed the fixed protection solution, that is, automatic sprinklers to cover the underside of the roof, irrespective of the contents. The U.S. Air Force suffered a $170,000,000 loss at Tinker Field,[23] and the General Services Administration suffered a severe loss in Fort Worth, Texas,[24] both caused by contractors cutting through the CMDR to install skylights. It is unsafe and useless for fire fighters to try to ventilate a combustible metal deck roof manually. Tests at Factory Mutual showed that a 56 ft^2 (5.2 m^2) vent was required to vent a small structure with no contents.[25]

Six Dallas fire fighters, planning to ventilate the roof of a store with a CMDR, fell into the fire when elongating steel bar joists pushed down a concrete block wall. Fortunately, they were near the edge and were recovered.[26] Twenty St. Paul, Minnesota, fire fighters were evacuated from a store with a CMDR 60 seconds before it collapsed. Two Memphis fire fighters were not so lucky when a CMDR in a retail store collapsed on them in 2003. An alternative to CMDRs is to install a Factory Mutual Type I roof or a UL "classified roof," which will not sustain independent combustion.

If there is a significant fire load, the height of the steel above the floor is no guarantee of stability during a fire. After the devastating 1967 McCormick Place Exhibition Hall Fire in Chicago, tests at Underwriters Laboratories Inc. showed that failure temperatures were reached in steel 30 ft (9.2 m) above the floor a few minutes after the fire started.[27]

Hose streams can cool steel being heated by the fire if a safe operating position is available. If the steel is elongating, it will retract to its original length when cooled. If it has started to fail, it will solidify in the shape it had reached. Contrary to a once-prevalent myth, the water does not cause the distortion of the steel. For a full explanation of the origin of the "don't put water on hot steel" myth, see Brannigan.[28]

SPECIFIC CONCERNS

The following areas of concern for the fire service relate, directly or indirectly, to fire fighter and public safety. There are no "minor" deficiencies in buildings being attacked by fire. Any single deficiency may contribute to loss of life or the destruction of the building.

Alarms and Staff Training

Building staff should be properly trained. A potential and, at times, fatal error is for a security guard or maintenance personnel to go to the floor from which the fire alarm has been received—thus walking right into the fire. The lone fatality in the spectacular 1988 First Interstate Bank fire in Los Angeles was the maintenance person who went to the fire floor to investigate.[29] Further, a guard went to the alarm floor of the One Meridian Plaza fire in Philadelphia, Pennsylvania, and barely escaped death.[30]

Sometimes personnel are temporary employees who have not had adequate instruction in their duties and responsibilities. Fire department personnel should inspect buildings during the night shift and question employees as to the actions they would take in the event of a fire alarm or for reported smoke.

Building staff has reset alarms to prevent the alarms from being transmitted to the fire department. This was a factor in a 12 fatality fire in the Westchase Hilton Hotel in Houston, Texas, in 1982.[31]

Delayed alarms can be due to a mistaken management perception that the arrival of the fire department is bad publicity. A policy of charging for false alarms should be carefully monitored to determine if it results in nontransmission of alarms.

Pre-Incident Planning

A thorough study of a target building should be made before the action pre-incident plan is developed. The fire department's pre-incident plan should examine each building as an individual problem. Problems and/or deficiencies in areas noted below may be present in buildings. Most were factors in serious fires.

The World Trade Center had been regarded as a significant advance in reducing weight and cost of high-rise buildings. There are serious questions as to the effectiveness of the "fireproofing" (insulation would be a better word) methods used as well as concerns about lack of compartmentation and "robustness" of shaft enclosures. Fire departments should review the final report of the National Institute of Standards and Technology's National Construction Safety Team investigation of the World Trade Center disaster.[32]

Automatic Sprinklers

Full automatic sprinkler protection, properly maintained, is a proven fire protection measure that can provide reasonable assurance of occupant and building fire safety. However, sprinklers can be inoperable. The fire department should carefully monitor the maintenance and shutdown of sprinkler systems. Special precautions and watch service should be required during periods of sprinkler impairment.

In many cases, building codes permit exceptions from or reductions in code provisions if sprinklers are installed. If the sprinklers are turned off when the building is occupied, it may be in violation of the code provisions.

Water Supply

The water supply system should be carefully checked for possible failures. Examples of water supply problems include water supply pumping system disconnection. At the time of the First Interstate fire, this was the case. Also, falling glass may cut lines supplying standpipes. Improperly marked standpipe connections have also been a major factor at fires.

Compartmentation and Structural Integrity

A fire-resistive building is generally designed to provide for compartmentation and structural integrity in a fire. Unfortunately, the design may be flawed or the construction faulty. Changes after the building was occupied may compromise the value of the compartmentation or structural integrity.

Compartmentation. Early fire-resistive design did not include compartmentation. It was believed to be sufficient that the building was "fireproof." Several disastrous fires in fire-resistive buildings proved the concept of "fireproof" to be faulty, and compartmentation became required. The following are points of failure in compartmentation:

• Many early fire-resistive buildings are still undivided and allow the passage of smoke and toxic gases throughout the structure.

• Floors are penetrated for wiring and other services. The openings are not always properly protected to restrict the passage of heat and smoke. Due to unprotected openings in floors, fire-resistive buildings can resemble a sieve to smoke and gases. The handful of fiberglass stuffed into the opening will not stop smoke and gases. Figure 12.8.15 illustrates penetrations to a floor.

• The reliability of horizontal compartmentation separating floors into fire areas or smoke compartments can be questioned. The wall may remain intact, but there may be utility openings through the walls that are not properly sealed.

• Fire barrier doors into stairways and between fire areas are required to have door closers and latches. These may be removed or doors found blocked open for convenience. This problem occurred at a high-rise apartment house that had both interior stairway doors propped open. A fast-spreading fire erupted, filling the stairs with heat and smoke. Four occupants died. It took almost 200 fire fighters to subdue the fire and to evacuate the tenants.[33]

• Automatic door closers are often made ineffective, generally for the sake of convenience. For example, it can be tempting to remove closers in a high-rise residence for seniors to allow residents to visit neighbors "for a moment." It is possible that the occupant of the apartment in which the fire occurs exits, leaving the door standing open. In such cases the hallway can fill with fire, and fire fighters could find it dangerous and sometimes impossible to advance the hose lines, particularly if the wind is blowing into the apartment. Few people have any concept of the heavy fire load and high rate of fire growth of today's furniture.

The best solution for the conflict between inconvenience and a potential hazard not understood by occupants is to have such doors equipped with magnetic latches. When the door is opened the electromagnet holds it open. Any fire alarm cuts the current to the electromagnet and the door closes. For smoke barrier doors in hallways, a detector is provided on both sides of the door. Some door closers have a smoke detector incorporated in the closer. Closers that incorporate only a fusible link are not effective for life safety since deadly quantities of gases can pass before heat operates the fusible link.

FIGURE 12.8.15 Unprotected Floor Penetrations

Structural Integrity. The structural integrity of a building may depend on how the fire resistance was achieved. The following are issues in structural integrity:

- Buildings with tile arch floors may not provide protection for the steel beams. In later buildings, skewback tiles were provided to protect the steel.
- Steel floor and ceiling assemblies using suspended ceilings are common. Unfortunately, ceiling tiles are easily removed and integrity is hard to maintain. The ceiling voids can allow smoke and fire to pass.
- Permitting steel columns to be unprotected in the plenum space is particularly dangerous. Failure of the ceiling membrane would subject the column to fire temperatures. The heating of only a short length of a column to failure temperature could have costly, or even catastrophic, effects on the building.

Spray-on fireproofing used asbestos fibers for many years. The health hazard of asbestos fibers now requires its removal. A most important question is what, if anything, is done to fire-protect the steel when the asbestos fireproofing is removed.

Flame Spread

Fire departments should be aware of the presence of combustible interior finish, such as plywood and combustible acoustical tile, in buildings. Older acoustical tile was made of compressed wood fibers and will burn furiously. It is usually installed on wood stringers, which enables burning on both sides of the tile. If it is applied with glue, the adhesive can add significantly to the rate of burning. This was discovered in the investigation of the Hartford Hospital Fire in 1961, in which 16 people died.[34] The combustible tile was glued to a suspended gypsum board ceiling that was surface-treated with a flame retardant. When the tile was tested, the adhesive caused a very rapid flame spread. When new tile is installed, it will probably need to meet flame spread requirements. However, there may be no requirement that the old tile be removed (Figure 12.8.16).[35] A very serious potential hazard is created if old combustible tile is left in place when a new "code-approved" suspended ceiling is installed below it.

Similarly, flame spread was a significant factor in the February 2003 Station nightclub fire in West Warwick, Rhode Island, which killed 100 people. Polyurethane foam soundproofing, installed around a platform used by musical performers, was ignited by indoor pyrotechnics. The entire room flashed over in 90 seconds.[36]

Other Areas of Concern

Construction in Occupied Buildings. Buildings can be partially occupied before construction is finished. Many major remodeling projects are carried on in occupied buildings. The fire department should be aware of any such construction. Special permits should be required for any construction after the certificate of occupancy is issued. A typical construction fire in

FIGURE 12.8.16 Old Combustible Tile Retained Above a New Suspended Ceiling

such a building can be a serious threat to the safety of all the occupants.

Lightweight Construction. The almost complete change from sawn lumber to gusset plate wood trusses and wood I-beams has profoundly changed the fire suppression environment. Tactics learned and experience gained on sawn joist and rafter buildings are not transferable to truss buildings. The truss floor introduces a new hazard, which creates a floor void in which carbon monoxide (CO) gas can accumulate.

Vacant Buildings. Large commercial and manufacturing buildings may be vacant due to remodeling for "adaptive use," lack of a tenant, upcoming demolition, or even abandonment by the owner. Sprinklers can have been shut off or removed. Open construction shafts can make vacant buildings one huge fire compartment. As demonstrated by a 1999 fire in a warehouse in Worcester, Massachusetts, which claimed the lives of six fire fighters, searching for homeless people and fighting fires in vacant buildings can be extremely dangerous.[37]

Added Roofs. New roofs can be constructed over the original roof to control leaks (rain roof) or for aesthetic reasons. These present serious problems in fire fighting. Harlow[38] provides detailed information.

Stadiums. Stadium fires in Texas and Georgia focused attention on the severe difficulties faced in fighting fires in the luxury "sky boxes." The potential for flaming plastic windows falling onto occupied combustible seats in the arena below is a serious risk. Fire departments should perform realistic risk assessments and, where indicated, require fire protection improvements.[39]

SUMMARY

This chapter presents the highlights of the problems that the effects of building construction present to fire suppression forces. Further detailed information can be found in *Building Construction for the Fire Service* and in the references cited. Knowledge and experience with building construction methods and materials can help improve fire department safety and efficiency.

BIBLIOGRAPHY

References Cited

1. *Hazard Alert Bulletin,* 75-2, Society of Fire Protection Engineers, Boston, MA, Apr. 1975.
2. *Fire Department City of New York,* Millennium Edition, Turner Publishers, Paducah, KY, 2000, p. 116.
3. *Fire Journal,* Vol. 61, No. 3, 1967, p. 15.
4. *Fire Protection Through Modern Building Codes,* American Iron and Steel Institute, New York, 1961, p. 123.
5. Malanga, R., "Fire Endurance of Lightweight Wood Trusses in Building Construction," *Fire Technology,* Vol. 3, No. 1, 1995.
6. "Razing the Roofs," *Washington Post,* Sept. 16, 1990, p. H1.
7. Parkin, L., "FRT Plywood, Not as Safe as It Sounds," *Fire Engineering,* May 1990, p. 27.
8. Corbett, G., "Lightweight Wood Floor Construction, A Fire Lesson," *Fire Engineering,* July 1988, p. 41.
9. Klem, T., *NFPA Investigative Report: One Meridian Plaza Fire, Philadelphia, PA,* National Fire Protection Association, Quincy, MA, 1991.
10. Brannigan, F. L., "A Field Study of Non Fire Resistive Multiple Dwelling Fires," SFPE Technology Report 74–5, Society of Fire Protection Engineers, Bethesda, MD, p. 7.
11. "Vendome Fire," *Fire Journal,* Vol. 67, No. 1, 1973, pp. 34–41.
12. Brannigan, F. L., *Building Construction for the Fire Service,* 4th ed., Jones and Bartlett Publishers, Sudbury, MA, 2008, p. 144.
13. "Collapse of Vendome Hotel, Nine Fire Fighters Killed," *Fire Journal,* Vol. 67, No. 1, 1973, pp. 84–91. Also see Drawing BCFS3, p. 171.
14. Dunn, V., "Collapse of Burning Buildings," *Fire Engineering,* Saddle Brook, NJ, 1988.
15. Brannigan, F. L., *Building Construction for the Fire Service,* 4th ed., Jones and Bartlett Publishers, Sudbury, 2008, p. 206.
16. Isner, M. S., "Four Fire Fighters Die in Furniture Refinishing Plant Fire," *NFPA Journal,* May/June 1992.
17. Sharry, J. A., "Military Personnel Records Center Fire, Overland, MO," *Fire Journal,* May/June 1974 and "Military Personnel Records Center Fire, Overland, MO, Part 2," *Fire Journal,* July/Aug. 1974.
18. Comeau, E. R., "NFPA Report on the Oklahoma City Bombing," National Fire Protection Association, Quincy, MA, 1996.
19. Foley, J., "Parking Garage Under Construction Collapses," *Fire Engineering,* Feb. 2004.
20. Post, N., and Korman, R., "Implosion Spares Foundations," *Engineering News Record,* June 12, 2000, pp. 12–13.
21. National Fire Protection Association, *NFPA Quarterly,* Vol. XLVII, pp. 105–120.
22. Cotton, P. E., *Monitor Head Vents,* FM Report 13085-S1, Factory Mutual, Norwood, MA, 1957.
23. Goodbread, J., "Fire in Building 3001," *Fire Command,* July/Aug. 1985, p. 34.
24. Harwell, J., "Ft. Worth Collapse," *Fire Engineering,* June 1993.
25. *Insulated Metal Deck Roof Fire Tests,* Factory Mutual, Norwood, MA, May 1955.
26. Brannigan, F. L., "Preplanning Building Fires," *Fire Engineering,* Feb. 1998.
27. Webb, W. E., "Effectiveness of Automatic Sprinkler Systems in Exhibition Halls," *Fire Technology,* Vol. 4, No. 2, 1968, p. 115.
28. Brannigan, F. L., "Fire Fictions II," *Fire Chief,* May 1995.
29. "High-Rise Building Fire, Philadelphia, Pennsylvania, February 23, 1991," NFPA Investigation Report, National Fire Protection Association, Quincy, MA, 2001.
30. Nelson, H., "Fire Growth, First Interstate Fire," *Fire Journal,* July 1989, p. 25.

31. Bell, J., "Twelve Die in Fire at Westchase Hilton Hotel, Houston, Texas," *Fire Journal,* Jan. 1983, p. 11.
32. The entire report may be accessed at http://wtc.nist.gov.
33. Isner, M., "Investigation Report, Apartment High-Rise Fire, Manhattan, New York, January 11, 1988," National Fire Protection Association, Quincy, MA. See also DeVita, A., and Dunn, V., "Fatal Fire on E. 50 St.," *With New York Fire Fighters,* First Issue, New York Fire Department, Fire Academy, Randalls Island, NY, 1988.
34. Juillerat, E., "The Hartford Hospital Fire," *NFPA Quarterly,* Jan. 1962.
35. Isner, M., "Fire Investigation Report: Elderly Housing Fire, Johnson City, TN," National Fire Protection Association, Quincy, MA, Dec. 24, 1989.
36. *Report of the Technical Investigation of the Station Nightclub Fire,* The National Institute of Standards and Technology, Gaithersburg, MD, 2005.
37. "Six Career Fire Fighters Killed in Cold Storage and Warehouse Building Fire—Worchester, Massachusetts," NIOSH Report #99F47, http://www.cdc.gov/niosh/firehome.html, 2000.
38. Harlow, T. D., "New Roofs over Old," *Fire Engineering,* Nov. 1987, pp. 51–56.
39. Isner, M., "Summary Fire Investigation Report, Two Stadium Fires," National Fire Protection Association, Quincy, MA, 1993.

NFPA Codes, Standards, and Recommended Practices

Reference to the following NFPA codes, standards, and recommended practices will provide further information on the effect of building construction and fire protection systems on fire fighter safety discussed in this chapter. (See the latest version of The NFPA Catalog *for availability of current editions of the following documents.)*

NFPA 13, *Standard for the Installation of Sprinkler Systems*
NFPA 220, *Standard on Types of Building Construction*
NFPA 241, *Standard for Safeguarding Construction, Alteration, and Demolition Operations*
NFPA 251, *Standard Methods of Tests of Fire Resistance of Building Construction and Materials*
NFPA 252, *Standard Methods of Fire Tests of Door Assemblies*
NFPA 255, *Standard Method of Test of Surface Burning Characteristics of Building Materials*
NFPA 5000®, Building Construction and Safety Code®

Chapter 9

Fire and Emergency Services Protective Clothing and Protective Equipment

Bruce W. Teele

Chapter Contents

Key Terms

certification, emergency medical services, fire fighter safety, hazardous material, heat stress, industrial fire brigade, life safety rope, occupational safety and health, personal alert safety system (PASS), personal protective equipment (PPE), protective ensemble, safety officer, self-contained breathing apparatus (SCBA), technical rescue

Protecting fire fighters, law enforcement officers, hazardous materials technicians, emergency medical personnel, technical rescue personnel, and other emergency responder personnel from the expected exposures and hostile operating environments that emergency operations pose is a complex issue. The following are key facets in minimizing emergency responder injuries and deaths:

- Thorough training of officers, supervisors, and response personnel
- Considerable medical and physical requirements and health maintenance
- A detailed and well-functioning incident management system
- Adequate staffing
- Closely supervised operating teams or crews
- Company/team/crew cohesiveness
- Clear and concise standard emergency operational procedures
- State-of-the-art personal protective equipment (PPE), including protective ensembles, clothing, and equipment that are consistently and properly used

Much has changed in these areas during the past several decades, and more must be done in the future. Emergency responder organizations should stay well informed of developments in all of these areas and provide the information and training to their personnel to keep them as current and informed as possible. Emergency responder personnel need to realize their human limitations and the dangers they face during operations in hostile environments. They must also understand that the inherent safety of participating as a member of a team in a well-planned operation under a safety-driven incident management system does far more for their safety than just relying on the PPE they use.

For related topics, see "Section 12, Chapter 7, "Safety, Medical, and Health Issues and Programs"; Section 12, Chapter 8, "Effect of Building Construction and Fire Protection Systems on Fire Fighter Safety"; and Section 12, Chapter 16, "Fire Department Apparatus and Equipment."

NFPA INVOLVEMENT

Historical Background

In the early 1970s, the National Fire Protection Association (NFPA) became directly involved with fire service safety issues through its technical committees and new standards. The effort began with the Technical Committee on Fire Department Equipment. This committee established a Sectional

Bruce W. Teele is senior emergency services safety specialist at NFPA. He serves as the staff liaison for the Technical Correlating Committee and the eight technical committees of the Project on Fire and Emergency Services Protective Clothing and Equipment.

Committee on Protective Equipment for Fire Fighters to specifically address these issues. Their documents were directed toward equipment standards.

The sectional committee developed a new document on respiratory protective equipment, and the association membership adopted NFPA 19B, *Standard on Respiratory Protective Equipment for Fire Fighters,* on May 17, 1971. This new standard prohibited the use of filter-type canister masks for protection of fire fighters from the products of combustion and allowed only self-contained breathing apparatus (SCBA) for fire fighter respiratory protection. This action was the direct result of fire fighters dying while wearing filter-type masks during fire-fighting operations. At least one court decision found that filter-type canister masks and other respirators that only filtered the atmosphere and did not provide a source of noncontaminated breathing air were inappropriate for use by fire fighters, as they did not provide protection from the known and expected respiratory hazards that fire fighters encounter during fire-fighting operations.

The second document from the sectional committee, NFPA 19A-T, was a tentative document (a preliminary document that is no longer a part of NFPA's codes and standards development process) that was the first to address protective clothing for structural fire fighting. Although NFPA 19A-T never became a standard, it was the basis for a future document on the same subject, NFPA 1971, *Standard on Protective Ensembles for Structural Fire Fighting and Proximity Fire Fighting.*

In 1974, NFPA restructured the sectional committee as a separate and full technical committee for PPE. This new committee, the Technical Committee on Protective Equipment for Fire Fighters, was no longer under the direction of the Technical Committee on Fire Department Equipment. It assumed the responsibility for NFPA 19B and developed a new document, NFPA 1971, which was adopted on November 18, 1975. This document has been followed by a series of documents on PPE for structural fire fighting, proximity fire fighting, wildland fire fighting, hazardous materials emergencies, emergency medical operations, and special operations. The committee was renamed in 1988 as the Technical Committee on Fire Service Protective Clothing and Equipment.

Because of the continuing increase of the types of PPE being addressed by the committee and the areas other than fire fighting in which the committee was involved, NFPA created a Project on Fire and Emergency Services Protective Clothing and Equipment in late 1994. It is structured with a technical correlating committee managing the project and seven technical committees now responsible for electronic safety equipment; respiratory protection equipment; and for protective ensembles, clothing, and equipment for emergency medical services; hazardous materials; special operations; chemical, biological, radiological, nuclear (CBRN) terrorism incidents; proximity fire fighting; structural fire fighting; and wildland fire fighting; and for the selection, care, and maintenance of the PPE. Within this project, there are currently 15 active documents and more under development or in the planning stages.

In 1973, NFPA established the Technical Committee on Fire Service Occupational Safety and Health. This was the first NFPA committee to focus on the issues of the safety and health of fire fighters instead of just the PPE. In its early years, the committee considered many issues and then wrote a document, NFPA 1501, *Standard for Fire Department Safety Officer,* that was adopted on May 18, 1977.

NFPA 1500, *Standard on Fire Department Occupational Safety and Health Program*

The committee produced NFPA 1500, which became effective on August 7, 1987. NFPA 1500 was developed as an umbrella document, encompassing an entire fire department safety and health program. NFPA 1500 became the first nationally recognized consensus standard to address fire service occupational safety and health. It was the first national document on safety and health to be written by the fire service and fire service interest groups for the fire service. Prior to NFPA 1500, any safety and health measures had to be based on general industry standards and regulations that either did not adequately address fire service problems or were difficult to impose on a nonindustry agency.

The fifth edition of NFPA 1500 became effective in August 2006. NFPA 1500 is the fire services organizations' requirements, as it has the criteria for fire departments and fire fighters, rather than the product requirements that manufacturers must meet. NFPA 1500 is the document that makes it happen, as it requires fire departments to have, and fire fighters to use, protective clothing and equipment.

NFPA 1500 requires the provision and use of protective ensembles, clothing, and equipment that are certified as compliant with the appropriate NFPA PPE standard(s) for the intended application. The basis of the requirements is to provide for the protection of fire fighters who are responsible for various fire-fighting and other emergency operations. The fire department is required to provide the appropriate protective clothing and protective equipment for the task and operation.

The fire department is also required to ensure that the PPE is properly utilized and maintained. Accordingly, each fire fighter is to be provided training in the use and limitations of protective clothing and equipment.

OSHA INVOLVEMENT

In addition to NFPA 1500, in the United States there are federal and state regulations, generally under the federal Occupational Safety and Health Administration (OSHA) or the state equivalent, that include protective clothing and equipment as well as other safety and health issues.

OSHA first addressed fire service occupational safety and health in 1980 when it issued regulation 29 CFR 1910.156, the "fire brigades regulations." Although the federal OSHA regulations did not apply to state and local government employees, states that have federally approved state OSHA plans were, and still are, required to cover state and local government employees.

However, when OSHA issued regulation 29 CFR 1910.120 on hazardous materials emergency response, the U.S. Congress directed the Environmental Protection Agency (EPA) to issue identical regulations that would apply to state and local government employees as well as volunteers in all 50 states. This EPA regulation is 40 CFR 311, which was issued June 23, 1989. Both 29 CFR 1910.120 and 40 CFR 311 include a mandatory reference requiring fire departments to be compliant with 29 CFR 1910.156. Therefore, wherever fire departments also respond to any type of hazardous materials incidents, the OSHA/EPA regulations apply to all operations for all fire departments in the United States whether career, career/volunteer combination, or all volunteer.

NFPA PPE STANDARDS

Two different types of PPE standards produced in the NFPA codes and standards development system are product standards and user standards.

Product Standards

Product standards specify the requirements to which manufacturers produce their PPE, and certification organizations inspect, evaluate, and test the product to determine compliance. All product standards are written to the extent possible in terms of performance requirements with pass/fail criteria and specific testing methods to evaluate each performance. These standards also have a chapter on design requirements covering those items that cannot be defined in performance criteria but must be inspected and evaluated by the certification organization in order to determine product compliance.

All product standards require manufacturers to have their product "certified as compliant" with the applicable NFPA PPE standard in order to claim the product meets the standard. Certification is a very important part of the PPE product standards as it gives a reasonable degree of confidence to end users and purchasers that the product they are purchasing or using has been found to meet the requirements of the standard and has been certified as such. The certification program includes an independent third-party certification organization that is accredited to certify PPE; evaluates and tests the product in accordance with the applicable NFPA PPE standard; applies labeling, listing, and follow-up programs for the product; and administers periodic product recertification and quality assurance programs for the manufacturer. The certification program is addressed in further detail later in this section.

User Standards

User standards specify requirements for the emergency responder organizations and personnel who purchase and use the PPE. These standards are written to assure the correct and safe use of the PPE and the proper selection, care, and maintenance of PPE. NFPA 1500 specifies which types of PPE are to be used for various emergency operations and that the PPE must be certified as compliant with the appropriate product standard. A new type of user standard now specifies the process of selection, care, and maintenance for different types of PPE. The first two standards in this series are NFPA 1851, *Standard on Selection, Care, and Maintenance of Protective Ensembles for Structural and Proximity Fire Fighting,* and NFPA 1852, *Standard on Selection, Care, and Maintenance of Open-Circuit Self-Contained Breathing Apparatus (SCBA).*

These selection, care, and maintenance (SCAM) standards specify requirements for segments of the organization's overall PPE program as required by NFPA 1500 by reference to the SCAM standards. The SCAM standards also specify the procedures for selecting PPE both prior to purchase and, in some cases in which different types of PPE could be used, prior to use, as well as the proper care, cleaning, maintenance, repair, storage, and removal from service or retirement of PPE. These SCAM standards are intended to provide enhanced safety for users by assuring that the PPE remains in optimum condition for user protection.

THIRD-PARTY CERTIFICATION PROGRAM

All NFPA PPE standards for emergency responder personnel require that the PPE be certified in accordance with the certification program specified in each standard. The certification program is an essential means of ensuring the quality of emergency responder PPE.

Certification includes an accredited, independent third-party certification organization that evaluates and tests the product in accordance with the applicable NFPA PPE standard and, on determining that the product does meet the requirements, permits the manufacturer to affix the certification organization's label, symbol, or other identifying mark to the product, indicating compliance. This is called the *labeling* portion of certification. The certification organization must also provide a listing service in which the organization publishes lists of products by specific type or model that have been evaluated, tested, and labeled as compliant products. This is called the *listing* portion of certification. In the *follow-up* portion of certification, the certification organization makes random periodic reviews of the manufacturing process and evaluates and tests the continuing production process to assure that the product remains compliant.

In addition, the certification organization reviews and monitors the manufacturer's quality assurance program. Manufacturers are required to be registered in accordance with the ISO 9001 quality control standard. Some may claim that following the ISO quality control requirements only means the manufacturer documents everything whether good or bad, that it is just a paper project. But when the manufacturer has certified a product as being compliant with an NFPA PPE standard, quality control is evaluated against the PPE standard so that the manufacturer and the certification organization, which monitors the quality assurance program, can always know the status of the product and can quickly identify any problems that could affect product certification. The certification organization also provides annual recertification of the product in which key tests are conducted to assure that the product remains compliant.

All items of emergency responder protective clothing and equipment that are claimed to be compliant with the appropriate NFPA standard *must* carry the label, symbol, or other identifying mark of the certification organization. Any PPE item that does not bear the label or mark of a third-party certification organization is *not* compliant with the appropriate NFPA standard, regardless of the claims or statements that are made by the manufacturer, distributor, advertisement, or the garment or product label.

Requests for bids and purchase specifications should require the manufacturer to submit appropriate evidence of certification of the specific product and model that the manufacturer is bidding on. When releasing purchase specifications to solicit bids, purchasers should obtain copies of listings of certified PPE from certification organizations to assist in their review of bids received. These listings are the certification organizations' documents identifying which products have been tested and found to be in compliance with various standards. In all cases, purchasers should verify directly with the certification organization that the specific product and model certification are still valid *before* the purchase contract is signed or the purchase is made. After purchase, questions regarding the certification of any PPE item should be addressed to the indicated certification organization. Details of the certification and the labeling of PPE can be found in each NFPA product standard on protective ensembles, clothing, and equipment.

CLEANING AND MAINTAINING PPE

In all cases, the manufacturer's instructions for cleaning and maintaining its PPE must be followed. The manufacturer is required to provide specific printed or video cleaning and maintenance instructions with each item of PPE sold in order to be certified as compliant with the NFPA PPE standard. These instructions must be consulted and followed because failure to do so may reduce the protective qualities of the PPE or negate warranties. When the manufacturer's instructions for cleaning and maintenance that were provided with each new PPE item cannot be found, the product manufacturer should be contacted directly to obtain a new set of instructions.

The PPE selection, care, and maintenance (SCAM) standards mentioned earlier further specify the system for the organization's PPE program and how frequently inspections, cleaning, and maintenance must be performed. Recommendations (nonmandatory) for cleaning procedures are given if the manufacturer is no longer available to provide these instructions. Each SCAM standard states that whenever a difference occurs between the manufacturer's instructions and the SCAM standard, the manufacturer's instructions shall be followed.

Clean PPE reduces safety and health risks. It is recommended that PPE be cleaned frequently to reduce the level of, and bodily contact with, contaminants. Cleaning should prolong the life of the protective garments and help maintain the performance. Decontamination may not be possible when protective garments are contaminated with chemical, radiological, or biological agents. When decontamination is not possible, garments should be discarded in accordance with local, state, and federal regulations.

PPE is composed of a combination of materials. Each of these materials has unique characteristics, capabilities, and weaknesses. Even fabrics inherently flame resistant can have this characteristic negated by improper care and use.

Chlorine bleach must *not* be utilized for any PPE cleaning, decontamination, or disinfecting. Some components of PPE lose their physical integrity on exposure to chlorine bleach. Other components will actually lose their flame-resistant properties and thermal insulation capability on exposure to chlorine bleach. In any case, the protection provided by the PPE will be compromised.

Storage of PPE in direct sunlight, even for short periods of time, will substantially reduce protective qualities; the effects of such a reduction might not be visually apparent. Ultraviolet (UV) degradation will destroy or reduce the useful life of the PPE item. Color fading or color change often indicates that the garment has experienced UV degradation.

STANDARDS ON PPE FOR FIRE-FIGHTING OPERATIONS

Protective ensembles, protective clothing, and protective equipment for fire fighting are currently covered by two standards: one for structural fire-fighting protective ensembles and for proximity fire-fighting protective ensembles, and one for wildland fire-fighting protective clothing and protective equipment. These standards provide protection from physical hazards as well as thermal and environmental hazards and are designed to protect fire fighters against exposure to the hazards associated with each type of fire-fighting operation. The performance requirements are not intended to establish the limitations of the fire fighter's working environment but are intended to establish material performance requirements based on empirical field data and laboratory testing.

Proper sizing is an important part of the protection provided by PPE garments. PPE garments that fit properly allow air retention in the composite and the air adds insulation. Garments that are too tightly fitting squeeze air out and reduce the insulative qualities. Garments that are too loose or too tight can prevent the fire fighter from being able to reach, pull, climb, crawl, straddle, or jump and will contribute to fatigue. Improperly fitting garments are safety hazards as they do not permit the wearer to function with as little interference as possible. Sizing must also take into consideration the minimum overlap of two-piece ensembles (coat and trousers instead of a one-piece coverall style) to assure that there is no gap in the protection where the two elements meet. This overlap of protection must be provided in all working positions, including standing straight, crouching, crawling, reaching overhead, and stretching front, back, and side to side.

The preferred method of sizing is to measure persons individually for their PPE garments or ensemble. This assures a proper and safe fit for chest, shoulders, arms, waist, thighs, legs, and garment overlap areas of the fire fighter who will be wearing the garments. Another method used with standard stock garments is numerical sizes that are based on increments of chest and waist measurements, such as 32, 34, 36, 38, and so on. It can give individuals who conform to standard sizing measurements an effective fit in many situations; however, the garment overlap areas must be carefully considered. Yet another sizing method uses general sizing indicators such as S/M/L/XL/XXL. This sizing method is very general and the least accurate, combines a larger increment of chest and waist measurements in each size range, and is not recommended.

Some of the testing that the materials, components, composites, and ensemble elements for fire-fighting PPE are subjected to include the following: flame resistance, thermal stability, thermal insulation, convective heat resistance, radiant heat resistance, total heat loss capability (breathability), durability, dexterity, grip, electrical insulation, corrosion, abrasion, compression, cut, puncture, penetration, impact, energy absorption, retention, water penetration, viral penetration, and common liquids resistance.

Excessive Protection

One point of view about fire-fighting protective clothing is that it allows fire fighters to overextend themselves, thus getting into positions that are more likely to cause injury—positions that they would not be able to get into if they were not wearing such "sophisticated" clothing. Some think that the advanced protective clothing does not allow fire fighters to "feel the heat" and better judge their environment.

Fire fighters who overextend are not operating under close or adequate supervision or in an incident command system that controls the position, function, and safety of all operating teams. The advanced protective clothing can allow fire fighters, who are operating safely within the incident command system, to be able to perform more effectively.

Some advocate different levels of protection for various parts of the same protective ensemble. This is alleged to allow the fire fighters to "feel the heat" in areas of the body that are sensitive to heat but are believed to be not as severely exposed to the fire environment.

All parts of the fire fighter's body are sensitive to heat and equally exposed during most active operations and especially when conditions unexpectedly change. The philosophy of NFPA PPE standards has been to provide protection from the expected environment during proper, supervised operations and, if conditions deteriorate rapidly, to provide a margin of time for fire fighters to escape uninjured or with survivable injuries. The fire fighter must be afforded equal protection throughout the ensemble to reduce the possibility of injury or limit the severity of the injury.

Regardless of the level of protection afforded by any protective clothing, anything *except bare skin* can allow fire fighters to overextend, further enforcing the position that all operations must be managed by the incident command system and that fire fighters operate only under direct supervision within that system. Individual fire fighters who operate alone and not as a member of a company or a team, who operate without direct supervision, or who operate outside of the incident command system (a situation frequently called "freelancing" in the United States) cannot be permitted if safety is to be achieved.

The ability to judge heat buildup can differ depending on what fabrics the fire fighter is wearing. The level or intensity of heat that can be sensed in one garment may feel entirely different in another garment that was manufactured using different fabrics or component layers. There is not a single "measure of heat buildup" that can be applied to all protective garments. Likewise, it is impractical to rely on exposed human body parts to indicate heat exposure, as skin begins to burn at relatively low temperatures (about 135°F [57°C]) after a short exposure. It is actually a cultural issue and a training issue for the fire fighter to become familiar with how a particular ensemble transmits heat.

Heat Stress

Another viewpoint is that the thermal insulation of the protective clothing causes more injuries, due to heat stress, than lighter weight but less protective garments. Some positions state that these injuries are the result of the protective clothing.

Heat stress cannot be addressed by only the garment materials but must be approached from several factors that equally affect it. Simply put, the problem is protecting fire fighters from a very hostile environment in which thermal insulation is required and attempting to reduce heat stress to as low a level as possible.

In mild and moderate environments and at low and moderate work levels, differences in PPE garment materials are likely to have an appreciable effect on heat stress. In the most stressful situations of high-temperature environment or high work rates, PPE garment materials are unlikely to make any significant improvements in tolerance time. In addition to the total heat loss testing and material specifications, heat stress must also be addressed through other means.

Fire fighters spend considerable time in other than high heat environments and at other than high work levels. Relief can be provided from heat buildup inside protective clothing in mild and moderate environments and at low and moderate work levels, and NFPA PPE standards are addressing some of the garment and fabric issues of heat stress with a total heat loss test that measures the breathability of garments. This requirement is currently being met by use of breathable membranes in the PPE garment composite that do not compromise the other required protection.

For garments to be protective from the hostile thermal environment, thermal insulation is needed. Garments alone cannot keep a fire fighter both cool and comfortable and provide adequate thermal insulation necessary for fire-fighting operations in hostile thermal environments. All of the factors affecting stress and heat stress must be evaluated, including fire fighters' age, physical condition, and individual metabolism as well as how fire fighters are managed during incident operations.

Fire fighters who are operating in high-temperature areas or at high work rates must be cared for. These crews must be periodically rotated to allow rest, cooling, rehydration, monitoring of physiological conditions, and other measures as necessary. Simply reducing the insulation or weight of the protective garments will not benefit fire fighters and will not have any meaningful effect on heat stress. The entire spectrum of heat stress and stress-related problems must be fully addressed by the fire department.

Structural Fire-Fighting PPE

Thermal Environment. The PPE for structural fire fighting has been developed over the years after careful consideration of the expected thermal environment. The types of fire involvement and the general range of conditions and maximum exposure durations that might occur are shown in Table 12.9.1.

TABLE 12.9.1 Thermal Classification—Structural Fires

	Occurrence	*Height and Duration of Temperature and Thermal Radiation*
Class I	In a room or enclosed area that has been involved after the fire has been knocked down	Environmental temperatures up to 104°F (40°C) and thermal radiation up to 0.05 W/cm^2 for up to 30 min
Class II	When a small fire is burning in a room or enclosed area	Environmental temperatures from 105 to 203°F (41 to 95°C) and thermal radiation from 0.050 to 0.100 W/cm^2 for up to 15 min
Class III	When a fire in a room or enclosed area more completely involves the contents	Environmental temperatures from 204 to 482°F (96 to 250°C) and thermal radiation from 0.100 to 0.175 W/cm^2 for up to 5 min
Class IV	During ignition of fire gases, a backdraft, or flashover in a room or enclosed area	Environmental temperatures from 483 to 1500°F (251 to 815°C) and thermal radiation from 0.175 to 4.200 W/cm^2 for about 10 sec

Source: Adapted from http://www.cdc.gov/niosh/npptl/pdfs/ProjectHEROES.pdf.

Although achieving these exposure durations could be possible, most situations have other factors that can dramatically affect the durations. Two of many factors are preheating of the PPE at lower-class conditions prior to the higher-class exposure and effects (both positive and negative) on the thermal environment caused by fire-fighting operations. In any case, structural fire fighting is not designed to give full protection for the exposure durations sequentially through each class environment.

Because the thermal environment can change extremely rapidly during structural fire-fighting operations, the wearing of full ensembles is required for all operations when the fire is not under control and for many "under control" operations.

Protective Ensembles Used by the Fire Department of New York. In February 1995, the New York City Fire Department (FDNY), the largest fire department in the United States, required all of its 11,228 fire fighters to be equipped with and to wear both protective coats and protective trousers, rather than just protective coats with boots, for all fire-fighting operations. In 1996, FDNY required protective hoods also be worn with full protective clothing. FDNY's statistics for 1993 through 2005 show a significant reduction in burn injuries (Table 12.9.2) and time lost due to burn injuries (Table 12.9.3).

Over the years, other fire departments have also reported reductions in burn injuries when the change was made to full PPE from only protective coats worn with boots.

TABLE 12.9.2 Reduction in Burn Injuries

	Burn Injuries		
	1993	*2005*	*Change*
Ears	185	43	–76.76%
Face	176	98	–44.32%
Hand	189	64	–66.14%
Head	76	25	–67.11%
Knee	355	43	–87.89%
Arm	283	52	–81.63%
Leg	162	45	–72.22%
Neck	406	72	–82.27%
Torso	64	19	–70.31%
Totals	1832	442	–75.87%

Source: Courtesy of FDNY.

TABLE 12.9.3 Reduction in Time Lost from Burn Injuries

	1993	*2005*	*Change*
Time Lost—Severe	10	0	–100.00%
Time Lost	1144	272	–76.22%
No Time Lost	60	13	–78.33%
Minor	184	27	–85.33%
Totals	1398	312	–77.68%

Source: Courtesy of FDNY.

Protection for Structural and Proximity Fire Fighting Operations. The product standard for structural proximity fire fighting PPE is NFPA 1971, *Standard on Protective Ensembles for Structural Fire Fighting and Proximity Fire Fighting* (formerly NFPA 1971, *Standard on Protective Ensemble for Structural Fire Fighting* and NFPA 1976, *Standard on Protective Ensemble for Proximity Fire Fighting*). This structural fire-fighting protective ensemble consists of the following elements: garments (coat and trousers), hoods, helmets, gloves, and footwear. Figure 12.9.1 from NFPA 1971 shows helmet test areas and landmarks for sample helmets that are conditioned through exposing the area to be impacted/penetrated to a radiant heat source.

The 2007 edition of NFPA 1971, the seventh edition, introduced *optional requirements* for protection from chemical, biological, radiological, and nuclear (CBRN) terrorism agents (chemicals, biological agents, and radiological particulate) that could be released as a result of a terrorism attack. These optional requirements can be selected by fire departments that are concerned about first response of their personnel to terrorism

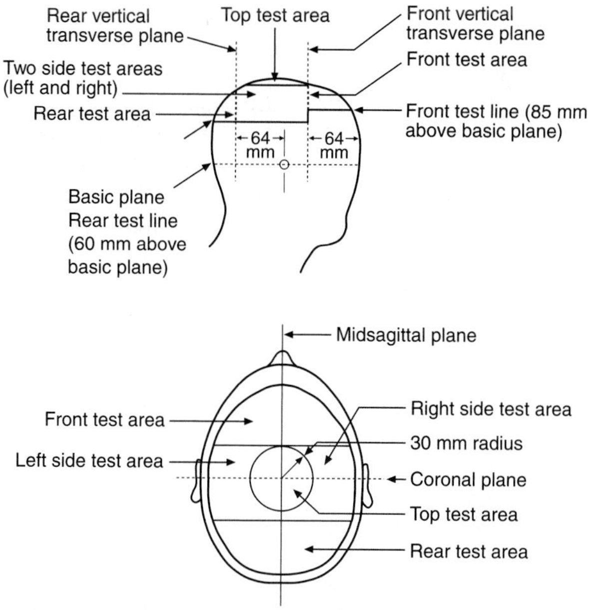

FIGURE 12.9.1 Helmet Test Areas and Landmarks (Source: NFPA 1971, *Standard on Protective Ensembles for Structural Fire Fighting and Proximity Fire Fighting,* Figure 8.1.6.1, 2007, p. 1971-42)

incidents where "normal" fire-fighting protective ensembles offer little or no protection from CBRN terrorism agents. These optional requirements can also be selected where supplementary protective ensembles that are certified as compliant with NFPA 1994, *Standard on Protective Ensembles for First Responders to CBRN Terrorism Incidents,* for protection from CBRN terrorism agents are unlikely to be provided to the vast majority of fire-fighting first responders.

The CBRN optional protection can only be applied to an entire ensemble, including the specified CBRN SCBA for that ensemble, and cannot be applied to individual ensemble elements. The design and performance of the entire ensemble including the CBRN SCBA provide the CBRN protection for the wearer and depend on the proper use of the entire ensemble to accomplish this. No combination of individual ensemble elements short of the entire assembled ensemble will give CBRN protection.

These optional CBRN requirements apply to both structural fire-fighting protective ensembles and proximity fire-fighting protective ensembles and are built into the construction of the "basic" fire-fighting protective ensemble elements, so that nothing has to be added to or subtracted from the basic fire-fighting protective clothing in order to achieve the protection from CBRN terrorism agents. The optional CBRN requirements do not decrease any of the protection for the fire-fighting environments in which these ensembles are used.

Protective Clothing and Equipment (PPE). The use of "full structural fire-fighting protective clothing and equipment" (PPE), certified as compliant with the NFPA 1971, is required by NFPA 1500 for all structural fire-fighting operations. Full PPE includes the previously mentioned ensemble elements, as well as SCBA certified as compliant with NFPA 1981, *Standard on Open-Circuit Self-Contained Breathing Apparatus (SCBA) for Emergency Services,* and PASS (personal alert safety system) certified as compliant with NFPA 1982, *Standard on Personal Alert Safety Systems (PASS).*

The user standard for structural fire-fighting PPE is NFPA 1851. This standard embraces the selection process for purchasing new PPE and the inspection, cleaning, care, repair, and removal from service of "in-service" PPE.

Specialized Fire-Fighting PPE

Approach Fire-Fighting Operations. There are other fire-fighting operations in which personnel can be exposed to very high levels of radiant heat and in which proximity PPE is not suitable. Approach operations are generally limited to incidents at fixed facilities that produce high levels of radiant heat and also produce conductive, convective heat but also include operations conducted at greater distances from the fire so that the principle thermal hazard is the radiant heat. Such operations usually consist of personnel "approaching" the fire area in order to position and set up unstaffed delivery points for exposure protection or application of cooling or extinguishing agents onto the fire area, such as master streams, and then withdrawing from the area affected by the radiant heat.

Radiant heat protection is necessary for personnel involved in such operations, but protection from convective and conducted heat is generally not necessary because personnel are not exposed to significant thermal hazard due to the distance from the fire at which they perform the operations. Lighter weight and more flexible approach protection can permit the personnel to expeditiously complete their functions and withdraw with less stress.

Entry Fire-Fighting Operations. Entry fire-fighting operations are extraordinarily specialized operations at fires that produce extreme levels of conductive, convective, and radiant heat. Entry fire fighting should not be confused with structural fire fighting. In structural fire fighting, fire fighters enter into a structure in which there is a fire in order to search for and rescue victims and to confine and extinguish the fire in the smallest possible area. They do *not,* however, *enter into the flames.*

In entry fire-fighting operations, in contrast, personnel actually *enter into the flames.* These operations are generally limited to incidents at fixed facilities where the need is known beforehand and tasks have been pre-incident planned. Frequently employees of the facility who have been specially trained and equipped perform the operations. Entry is made in order to perform critical tasks. These tasks might include opening or closing valves or operating other controls that will likely result in control of the fire with no other way possible to control the fire without performing these tasks. Because of the scope of these operations, highly specialized thermal protection from exposure to extreme levels of conductive, convective, and radiant heat is necessary for persons involved in such extraordinarily specialized operations. Such entry PPE is specifically designed for the particular situation in which it will be used and for the known and expected hazards. There are no standards for entry PPE due to the unique individuality of each set of PPE.

Proximity Fire-Fighting Operations

Proximity fire-fighting operations are specialized operations that can include the activities of rescue, fire suppression, and property conservation at incidents involving fires producing very high levels of radiant heat, as well as conductive and convective heat. Proximity fire-fighting operations include fires involving bulk flammable liquids, bulk flammable gas, bulk flammable metals, commercial or military aircraft, and similar situations that release high levels of radiant heat.

Specialized thermal protection from exposure to high levels of radiant heat, as well as thermal protection from conductive and convective heat, is necessary for persons involved in such operations. Although fire fighters do not make direct entry into flame, they need such protection because of the scope of these operations and because of their closeness to the fire when conducting these operations. These operations are usually exterior operations but might be combined with interior operations. Proximity fire fighting is not structural fire fighting but might be combined with structural fire-fighting operations. Proximity fire fighting is not entry fire fighting.

The product standard for proximity fire-fighting PPE is NFPA 1971, *Standard on Protective Ensembles for Structural Fire Fighting and Proximity Fire Fighting* (formerly NFPA 1976, *Standard on Protective Ensemble for Proximity Fire Fighting*). This protective ensemble standard consists of the following elements: garments (coat and trousers), helmets, shrouds, gloves, and footwear.

The use of full proximity fire-fighting protective clothing and equipment certified as compliant with NFPA 1971 is required by NFPA 1500 for all proximity fire-fighting operations. Full PPE includes the previously mentioned ensemble elements, as well as SCBA certified as compliant with NFPA 1981, and PASS certified as compliant with NFPA 1982.

Wildland Fire-Fighting PPE

Wildland fire-fighting operations are exterior operations incidents involving fires in natural ground cover, woods, trees, and other such vegetation. Such operations expose fire fighters to radiant heat, to some conductive and convective heat, and to many physical hazards.

Wildland fire-fighting PPE includes garments for upper and lower torso protection, overgarments, helmets, gloves, footwear, and fire shelters. The PPE is not presented as a total ensemble but as individual items that the incident commander can pick from in order to select the best combination for the particular incident conditions. The minimum necessary to meet the requirements of NFPA 1500 includes a fire shelter and protection for head, torso, hands, and feet.

Wildland fire fighting is the one fire-fighting operation in which respiratory protection is not required. At this time, some wildland fire-fighting organizations do use respiratory protection devices, usually of the air purifying respirator (APR) type or the powered air purifying respirator (PAPR) type. (See a more detailed discussion of wildland fire-fighting respiratory protection in the following respiratory protection section.)

The product standard for wildland fire-fighting PPE is NFPA 1977, *Standard on Protective Clothing and Equipment for Wildland Fire Fighting.* The use of PPE certified as compliant with NFPA 1977 is required by NFPA 1500 for all wildland fire-fighting operations. The PPE includes, as a minimum, the protective shirt, pants, helmet, gloves, and footwear (Figure 12.9.2). In addition, PASS certified as compliant with NFPA 1982 is also required.

STANDARDS ON PPE FOR RESPIRATORY PROTECTION

Self-Contained Breathing Apparatus (SCBA)

Self-contained breathing apparatus (SCBA) are required for all fire-fighting operations except wildland fire-fighting operations, as well as for any emergency incident operations where IDLH (immediately dangerous to life and health) atmospheres or oxygen-deficient atmospheres exist or are anticipated, including CBRN terrorism incidents, confined space rescue, hazardous materials emergencies, and certain technical rescue operations.

Both SCBA and supplied-air respirators (SAR, also called "airline respirators") are of the "atmosphere supplying respirator" family in which the respirator supplies the user with breathing air from a source independent of the ambient atmosphere.

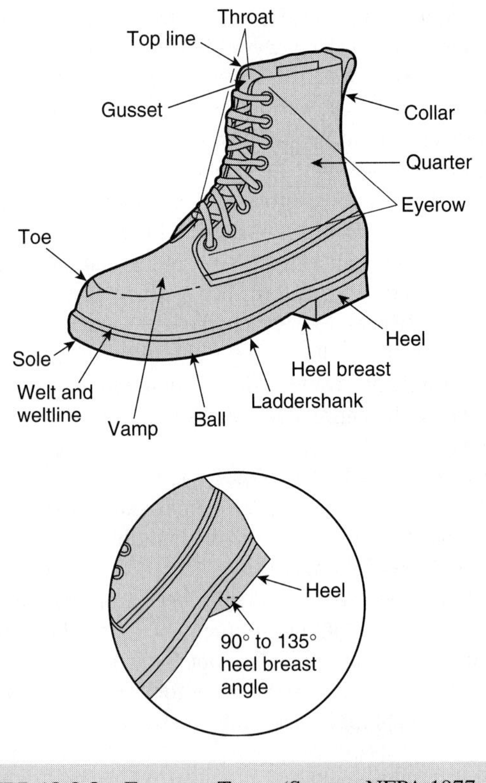

FIGURE 12.9.2 Footwear Terms (Source: NFPA 1977, *Standard on Protective Clothing and Equipment for Wildland Fire Fighting,* Figure 6.4.3, 2005, p. 1977-27)

SARs provide breathing air from a source that is *not* designed to be carried by the respirator user, while SCBA provide breathing air from a source that *is* designed to be carried by the respirator user. Where SARs incorporate a continuous air-line breathing air supply, and the SAR component is an integrated part of an SCBA that has a rated service time of at least 30 minutes, such SCBA/SAR can be used by emergency responders for extended duration operations, or for an increased exit time from the hazardous atmosphere.

There are two types of SCBA: open-circuit and closed-circuit. Open-circuit SCBA are respirators from which exhaled breath is vented to the atmosphere and is not rebreathed; closed-circuit SCBA are respirators in which exhaled air is rebreathed by the wearer.

Positive-Pressure and Demand SCBA

Positive-Pressure SCBA. All SCBA are classified as either positive pressure (also called pressure demand) or demand. OSHA regulations and NFPA standards require use of only positive-pressure SCBA for any IDLH or potentially IDLH atmospheres including structural fire-fighting operations. The use of demand SCBA for such operations is prohibited. The use of only positive-pressure SCBA became mandatory in the United States on July 1, 1983.

During normal use of positive-pressure SCBA, a positive pressure during inhalation and exhalation is maintained inside the facepiece in relation to the ambient atmospheric pressure. This positive pressure reduces the inward leakage of a contaminated atmosphere around the perimeter of the facepiece, but the positive-pressure feature cannot be construed to take the place of proper facepiece fitting and fit testing for each user. The positive-pressure feature cannot and will not compensate for any interference with the facepiece-to-face seal, such as from beards or other facial hair or from facial deformities, from eyeglass temple bows or straps, or from any other condition that passes through the area where the facepiece seals with the face, thereby preventing a proper facepiece-to-face fit.

Demand SCBA. Because demand SCBA operates on the principle of requiring negative pressure (inhalation) to initiate and maintain breathing airflow, OSHA regulations and NFPA standards do not permit use of demand SCBA for fire-fighting or other IDLH operations. The danger of the atmosphere surrounding the facepiece (the contaminated atmosphere) being drawn into the SCBA facepiece is significant.

Open-Circuit SCBA. Of the two types of SCBA, open-circuit is the SCBA where the exhaled breath is vented to the atmosphere and is not rebreathed. Open-circuit SCBA use an expendable source of breathing air that is stored under pressure in a cylinder. The breathing air is made available to the user through a regulator that automatically functions to reduce high air-storage pressures to lower usable pressures and to supply this breathing air to the user.

Open-circuit SCBA use compressed breathing air cylinders and are available in pressure systems from 2216 psi (15,279 kPa), 3500 psi (28,132 kPa), to 4500 psi (31,027 kPa). Regardless of the system pressure, all SCBA should be equipped with carbon filament or composite breathing air cylinders that are rated with a 30-minute or greater service life. The advantage of the carbon or composite breathing air cylinders is a significant lower weight achieved by the cylinder design. High-pressure systems have smaller cylinders that have less bulk and provide a smaller profile than a conventional pressure cylinder. Whereas the 2216 psi (15,279 kPa) cylinders can provide a rated service time of 30 minutes, the 3500 psi (28,132 kPa) cylinders can provide a rated service time of 45 minutes, and the 4500 psi (31,027 kPa) cylinders can provide a rated service time of 60 minutes.

Closed-Circuit SCBA. The second type of SCBA, closed-circuit, is the SCBA in which the exhaled air is rebreathed by the wearer. These SCBA recirculate the user's exhaled gas. The exhaled breath passes through an exhalation hose and through a carbon dioxide absorber, where the carbon dioxide is removed. Then it enters a breathing chamber, where it is mixed with additional oxygen from an oxygen source that is stored under pressure in a cylinder, and it is then available for inhalation. Closed-circuit SCBA can have a rated service life from 30 minutes to 4 hours.

OSHA and National Institute of Occupational Safety and Health (NIOSH) Regulations

Respiratory protection standards in the United States have recognized that unknown types and quantities of toxic elements of the products of combustion encountered during fire fighting do not allow the selection of different respiratory protective equipment for different exposures, as is often the case in the industrial environment. These atmospheres are classified as IDLH and require SCBA for respiratory protection.

OSHA has utilized National Institute of Occupational Safety and Health (NIOSH) and other OSHA regulations to establish minimum requirements for fire fighter respiratory protection. The OSHA *Fire Brigade Regulations,* 29 CFR 1910.156, requires the use of only positive-pressure SCBA that are certified by NIOSH under 42 CFR 84 and have a minimum rated service life of at least 30 minutes. OSHA requires that only positive-pressure SCBA be used during all structural fire-fighting operations; at all hazardous materials incidents; in oxygen-deficient atmospheres; in areas such as sewers, confined spaces, and silos; and wherever a hazardous or oxygen-deficient atmosphere may exist.

Nothing can be allowed to be in or pass through the area where the facepiece-to-face seal is made. Therefore, beards, drooping mustaches, long or wide sideburns, or other facial hair at any point where the face seal with the respirator facepiece is to occur or the wearing of eyeglasses with temple bows or straps are prohibited for persons who are required to use SCBA. OSHA has ruled (February 15, 1990) that ". . . these conditions have been shown to prevent a good facepiece-to-face seal, so that use of an SCBA by a person with any of the noted conditions (i.e., beards, drooping mustaches, long or wide sideburns, and other facial hair, temple bows/straps) is in violation of OSHA regulation 29 CFR 1910.134 (e)(5)(i), *regardless of what fit test measurement can be obtained.*" In addition, persons with conditions such as severe skin pitting, loss of teeth, facial deformities, skull caps or head gear, or any other conditions or devices that prevent a proper facepiece fit are prohibited from using SCBA. SCBA manufacturers offer special prescription lens/frame assemblies that can be affixed inside the facepiece and do not affect the facepiece-to-face seal.

Breathing Air Cylinder U.S. Department of Transportation (DOT) Regulations

Compressed gas cylinders for breathing air are regulated in the United States by the Department of Transportation (DOT). U.S. federal regulations for the construction, testing, and maintenance of compressed gas containers are contained in 49 CFR 178, Subpart C. These DOT specifications apply to steel SCBA and large storage cylinders only. Cylinders constructed of manganese/steel and conforming to the preceding DOT specifications are designated by a DOT3A marking on the cylinder. Steel cylinders constructed of chrome alloy steel and meeting DOT specifications are designated by a DOT3AA marking on the cylinder, followed by the marked cylinder service pressure.

There are no specifications outlined in 49 CFR for composite cylinders. Therefore, the DOT developed special certifications known as "exemptions." DOT authorized composite cylinders to have a maximum service life indicated in the exemption. Most exemptions specify that composite cylinders have a maximum life of 15 years, but newer composite cylinders can have a longer designated service life. Composite cylinders that have a maximum life of 15 years are prohibited from being refilled after 15 years from the original hydrostatic test date. All U.S. retest facilities performing requalifications on composite cylinders are required by DOT to have a current copy of the cylinder's exemption available and must follow its instructions and conditions. DOT, which is the regulatory authority in the United States, specifies the cylinder requalification frequency of every 3 years for composite cylinders and the cylinder requalification frequency of every 5 years for all-metal cylinders. The organization/cylinder owner and retest facility are required by DOT to know how often to have the requalification performed. At this writing, DOT is considering changes to the requalification schedule for all cylinders, so changes to the previously noted cylinder requalification frequencies may be announced.

NFPA 1981, *Standard on Open-Circuit Self-Contained Breathing Apparatus (SCBA) for Emergency Services*

SCBA Design. The product standard for respiratory PPE is NFPA 1981. The basic design and function of the SCBA must be certified by NIOSH in accordance with 42 CFR 84 as being positive pressure, having a rated service life of at least 30 minutes, and weighing no more than 35 lb (16 kg). Labeling of the SCBA must include the NIOSH certification plate and a certification organization's label denoting compliance with NFPA 1981.

SCBA Testing. Airflow performance testing measures the airflow that the SCBA can supply (Figure 12.9.3). Airflow must be provided to the wearer at 100 L/min volume without the facepiece pressure going negative during both inhalation and exhalation. The 100 L/min airflow exceeds the NIOSH certification requirement of 40 L/min volume.

Thermal cycle testing evaluates the proper function of the SCBA when exposed to various temperature extremes and tem-

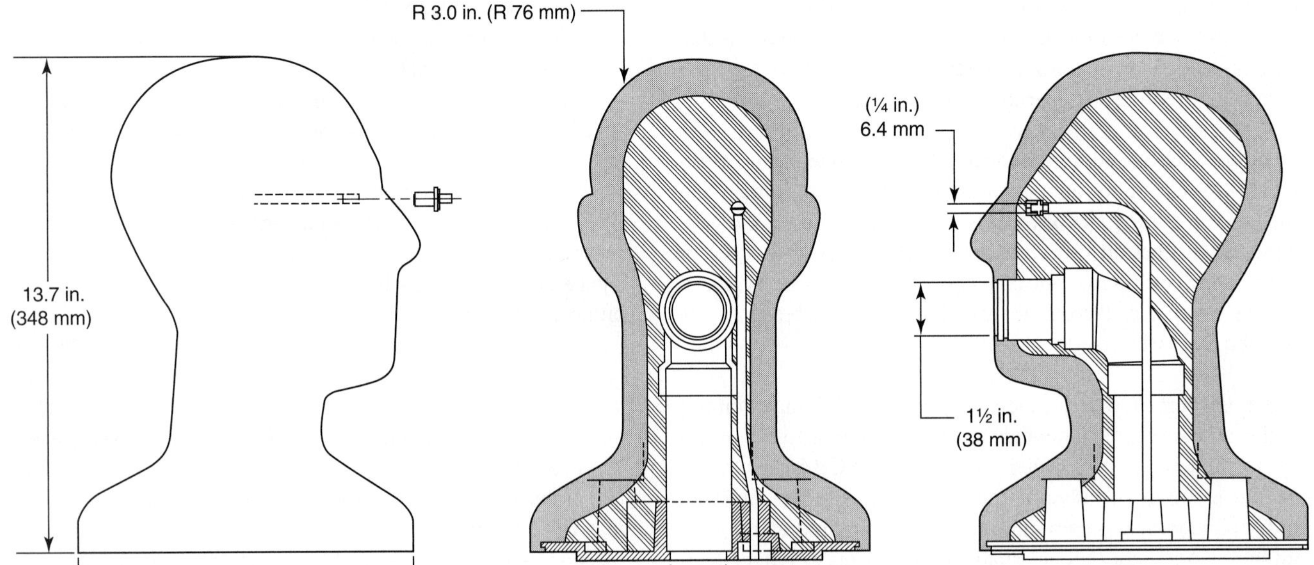

FIGURE 12.9.3 Test Headform (Source: NFPA 1981, *Standard on Open-Circuit Self-Contained Breathing Apparatus (SCBA) for Emergency Services,* Figure 8.1.4.1, 2007, p.1981-23)

perature cycles through a series of four tests (cold-cold, hot-hot, cold-hot, and hot-cold).

Total heat and flame testing is tested for the entire SCBA. The SCBA, while mounted on a mannequin and attached to a breathing machine operating at 40 L/min, is conditioned for 15 minutes in a 203°F (95°C) oven. Immediately following the conditioning, the SCBA breathing rate is increased to 100 L/min and then exposed to a direct-flame contact that engulfs the entire SCBA for 10 seconds at temperatures between 1500°F to 2102°F (816°C to 1150°C), with an average mean of peak temperature at 1742°F (950°C). After this exposure, the SCBA is subjected to a drop test. Through the entire testing, the SCBA must operate as required by the standard, must not show any afterflame of the SCBA and all components beyond 2.2 seconds, must not shift from the proper mounting on the mannequin, and the facepiece lens must not obscure vision greater than 20/100.

SCBA are required to be equipped with a second independent End of Service Time Indicator, a heads-up display (HUD) that provides alerts and warnings on remaining breathing air supply, and a voice communications system in addition to the speaking diaphragm. Other performance requirements test for vibration and shock resistance, corrosion resistance, particulate resistance, fabric flame resistance, fabric heat resistance, and facepiece lens abrasion.

SCBA Certification. The 2007 edition of NFPA 1981, the sixth edition, introduced the major change of requiring all emergency services SCBA to also be NIOSH certified as CBRN SCBA in accordance with the NIOSH *Statement of Standard for NIOSH CBRN SCBA Testing.* This requirement will provide respiratory protection for CBRN terrorism agents (specified chemicals, biological agents, and radiological particulate) that could be released as a result of a terrorism attack.

Although major metropolitan areas may be more likely targets of a terrorist event, emergency responders from smaller communities away from urban areas could be called on to respond to urban areas where the emergency services have become overwhelmed by a terrorist incident and require assistance. Terrorists themselves may reside in small communities while they await their opportunity to strike. They may have the chemical, biological, or nuclear material in their possession, making the possibility of exposure greater for small rural areas. Terrorist attacks aside, CBRN-certified SCBA offers greater protection for the emergency services for a very minimal cost.

Protection from CBRN. CBRN protection offers verification of enhanced protection for emergency responders that is not otherwise available. Without CBRN protection evaluation, no SCBA components are tested for permeation, penetration, corrosion resistance, or other detrimental effects from exposure to toxic industrial chemicals during hazardous materials incidents and hazardous chemical warfare atmospheres. *NIOSH benchmark testing of non-CBRN hardened SCBA against CBRN agents demonstrated that chemical warefare agents (CWA) could cause catastrophic failures within minutes of exposure.*

The selection of the test challenge agents by NIOSH for CBRN protection was based on a comprehensive review of available technical data and consultations with other government agencies (e.g., Departments of Defense, Justice, Energy, etc.). Various chemical data lists were analyzed, including lists from EPA, ATSDR, NFPA 1994, U.S. Army Center for Health Promotion and Preventative Medicine (USACHPPM) Technical Guide 244, and classified sources. This review established a total of 151 toxic industrial chemicals and chemical warfare agents as potential candidates for challenge agents. The candidate agents were evaluated for permeation (molecularly diffusing through material) and penetration (seeping through interfacing components) characteristics as part of a review of their physical properties. This evaluation concluded that sarin (GB) and sulfur mustard (HD) could be selected as the two representative agents for the penetration/permeation test for the complete listing of 151 CWA and toxic industrial chemicals (TICs) due to their physical properties and molecular structure. NIOSH is unaware of any data that indicate the CBRN-certified SCBA provide less protection against TICs than their industrial counterparts.

The evaluation for CBRN protection provides verification and assurance that the component and material combinations in the approved SCBA configurations provide high resistance to permeation and penetration of hazardous atmospheres of toxic industrial chemicals and materials into the breathing air. This assurance is of importance to all responders who are subject to exposures of any hazardous industrial chemicals and materials.

Additional Safety Requirements. In addition to the CBRN requirement, new requirements were added to increase the safety to the users of emergency services SCBA and to better assure the proper functioning of the SCBA including the following:

- New breathing air cylinder retention requirement within the mounted position
- Mechanical voice diaphragm performance requirement increased to 80 percent minimum score at 5 ft (153 cm) distance
- New voice communications system with at least an 85 percent score at 10 ft (305 cm) distance
- New independent pressure gauge that would not be affected by failure of the HUD
- New water immersion requirements for electronic devices that are part of the SCBA that must function properly and remain watertight after exposures to 350°F (177°C) for 15 minutes and water submersion to 5 ft (1.5 m)
- New low power capacity requirements for electronic devices to assure that such devices will continue to function properly for at least 2 hours following activation of the lower power signal

The product standard for breathing air is NFPA 1989, *Standard on Breathing Air Quality for Fire and Emergency Services Respiratory Protection.* This standard provides requirements for breathing air quality of the overall respiratory protection program required by NFPA 1500. It covers testing frequency; qualifications for laboratories performing breathing air quality verification testing; breathing air quality levels for oxygen, carbon monoxide, carbon dioxide, condensed oil, and particulate content; hydrocarbon content; water concentration; and determination of odors.

The user standard for SCBA is NFPA 1852. This standard embraces the organizations' program for respiratory protection, the selection process for purchasing new SCBA, and the inspection, cleaning, care, repair, and removal from service of "in-service" SCBA.

Wildland Fire-Fighting Respiratory Protection Considerations

Wildland fire fighting is the only fire-fighting operation in which respiratory protection is not yet required. Concerns exist regarding the actual dangers of short- and long-term exposure to the products of combustion from wildland fires. Studies of air samples collected on wildland fire fighters and workers indicate potential for hazardous exposure (e.g., respirable particulate, carbon monoxide, formaldehyde, and acrolein). The health implications of short-term exposures and the potential health effects of long-term exposures are being studied.

It is current practice to consider wildfire smoke not IDLH, even though human health hazards have not been quantified. As a prudent practice, wildfire smoke exposure should be reduced. Fire fighters and crew supervisors should consider the level of smoke exposure of the tasks to be performed before committing personnel to action. Mitigation efforts could include short work periods, removal of crews from areas of heavy smoke concentration, rest periods with smoke-free air, or use of respiratory protection. Although SCBA offers the most complete respiratory protection, SCBA is not practical for use by wildland fire fighters who work for extended periods in remote locations. The weight of an SCBA, its limited use time, and breathing air cylinder recharging logistics make it impractical for use by wildland fire fighters.

A high-efficiency particulate air (HEPA) filter-equipped, air-purifying respirator could be considered an option for the filtration of respirable particles from the air to be breathed. The addition of sorbents to remove selected gases and vapors (e.g., P100 high-efficiency particulate filter plus organic vapor [OV] and acid gas [AG]) could also be an option when greater exposure is anticipated, as in a direct attack on a fire. Particulate respirators remove the irritation and make breathing seem easier, but they do nothing to protect from carbon monoxide (CO).

Any respirator being considered for use by wildland fire fighters must be NIOSH certified. Care should be exercised in the use of NIOSH-certified respirators because they have not been tested for heat resistance and flammability of the filter medium and have not been evaluated for their ability to provide protection from the products of combustion of wildfires.

STANDARD ON PPE FOR PERSONAL ALERT SAFETY SYSTEMS (PASS)

Personal alert safety systems (PASS) encompass devices that are known by several names, including personal distress alarm devices, personal distress locators, personal alarm locators, personal alarm monitors, and personal alarm devices. The concept of PASS involves several distinct features. The alarm signal must be able to be activated manually by the user. The PASS must also contain a sensor that senses movement or the lack of movement. The alarm signal must be capable of being activated automatically through interaction with the sensor under a specified series of events. PASS must also have a prealarm signal to prevent false alarms by alerting the user that the sensor has not sensed motion of the user and has activated the automatic alarm signal sequence.

Despite popular belief that PASS are a required part of "fire fighters' SCBA," PASS are not required to be (but can be) integrated with SCBA. PASS can also be a stand-alone device worn on part of the emergency services person's protective clothing. PASS can also be integrated with several items of protective clothing or equipment to enhance the sensing abilities over a wider area of the body, locate the sounders where the users can better differentiate between signals from their PASS and from other PASS, and disperse the weight and power sources over a greater area.

Automatic Notification

Emergency response personnel can become incapacitated during operations and might not be noticed by other members of the crew. These personnel may be aware that they need assistance and may be able to manually activate the alarm. If they are suddenly stricken, however, the automatic alarm must activate and call for assistance. Fire fighters, especially, can become trapped or disoriented in fire-fighting situations and can lose contact with others in their crews. They frequently behave in a disoriented manner as they attempt to escape. This scenario is particularly associated with fire fighter deaths caused by smoke inhalation. Even with the use of SCBA, fire fighters face similar dangers if they operate beyond the time limits of their breathing air supply.

Emergency services personnel need the capability to contact other workers at the emergency scene when they are in need of assistance. Equipping each member assigned to an emergency operation with a portable two-way radio is one approach, but automatic notification that could summon help if the member became incapacitated would still not be provided by today's portable radios.

Applicability of PASS

Although PASS are generally associated with fire fighters for use during emergency operations, PASS protection applies to all emergency services personnel who operate in hazardous environments where they could become entrapped or incapacitated and need assistance. Hazardous materials, emergency medical, technical rescue, skilled trades, and even, for certain operations, law enforcement personnel should use PASS where their safety and well-being can be easily compromised. Confined space, structural collapse, extrication, limited access, complicated area or building layouts and floor plans, and atmospheres that could become IDLH are some of the many emergency operations working environments where PASS should be used.

NFPA 1982, *Standard on Personal Alert Safety Systems (PASS)*

The product standard for PASS is NFPA 1982. PASS performance requirements test for intrinsic safety, corrosion resistance, case integrity, temperature cycling resistance, temperature shock resistance, dust and particulate resistance, immersion and leakage, radiant heat resistance, flame resistance, impact resistance, retention system durability, and water drainage.

National Institute for Occupational Safety and Health (NIOSH)

During the work on the fifth edition of NFPA 1982, the committee addressed reports from the National Institute for Occupational Safety and Health (NIOSH), Division of Safety Research, regarding its investigations of fire fighter fatalities where there was evidence that the PASS alarm signal failed to function or was not heard by other personnel in the area and in some instances that there was water ingress to the electronic components that would diminish or cancel the alarm signal. The National Institute for Standards and Technology (NIST), Building and Fire Research Laboratory, partnered with NIOSH to characterize the performance of PASS devices in the fire-fighting environment. NIST determined that exposure to high-temperature environments caused the loudness of the alarm signal to be reduced. This reduction in loudness may cause the alarm signal to become indistinguishable from background noise of the emergency scene. Initial laboratory testing by NIST highlighted that this sound reduction may begin to occur at temperatures as low as 300°F (150°C). All PASS devices that were evaluated experienced significant alarm signal degradation at temperatures between 300°F and 500°F (150°C to 260°C). As the PASS cooled, the alarm signal on most of the units returned to preexposure sound levels.

NIOSH and others also noted that water ingress did occur or could have occurred in several cases, causing the alarm signal to cease to function with any effectiveness, but that after the PASS electronics dried, the alarm signal might again function.

These issues and others caused significant changes to the requirements, including the following:

1. Water immersion requirements and testing where PASS are exposed to 350°F for 15 minutes and then to water submersion in 4.9 ft (1.5 m) and also for 15 minutes for each of six cycles. It is then tested to determine that all PASS signals and electronic data logging function properly. Following this, PASS are reimmersed in the test water with the power source compartment(s) open for 5 minutes, and the electronics compartment is opened and examined to determine no water ingress.

2. High-temperature resistance and functionality requirements and testing procedures where PASS are exposed to 500°F (260°C) for 5 minutes. The PASS alarm signal must function at or above the required 95 dBA sound level for the required signal duration, electronic data logging must operate properly, and no part of the PASS can show evidence of melting, dripping, or igniting.

3. Tumble-vibration requirements and testing in which PASS are tumbled in a rotating drum for 3 hours and the PASS alarm signal must function at the required 95 dBA sound level and electronic data logging must operate properly

4. Requirements to prevent muffling of the alarm signal where PASS are evaluated in five positions (face down with arms extended, supine left, supine right, fetal right with knees drawn to chest, and fetal left with knees drawn to chest), and the alarm signal must function at or above the required 95 dBA sound level in each of the positions

Limitations of PASS

Users of PASS, whether or not the PASS were certified as compliant to editions of NFPA 1982 prior to the 2007 edition, are cautioned that PASS can fail to sound the alarm signal at the 95 dBA sound level, sound the alarm signal at an insufficient volume to make it audible from background noise on the emergency scene, or not sound the alarm signal at all. PASS could also have alarm signal muffling, water ingress, and vibration issues, all of which can negatively affect the ability of PASS to function properly and signal for help.

Despite PASS, there have been too many fire fighter fatality incidents in which fire fighters became entrapped, lost, or disoriented while performing interior structural fire-fighting activities. In these incidents, many of the fire fighters were wearing PASS devices but had failed to turn them on. The current edition of NFPA 1982 requires automatic activation of PASS, including remote activation, tethering, and integrating PASS with SCBA so that the PASS will be automatically activated when the air supply is turned on.

PASS cannot substitute for an individual's common sense, just as it cannot substitute for an active incident management system, close supervision of operating crews, communications, and a functional and adequate personnel accountability system to ensure that the assignment and location of each fire and emergency services personnel are known at all times. Although the addition of a PASS device does not guarantee safety, it is an important component to the fire fighter's personal protective ensemble.

STANDARDS ON PPE FOR EMERGENCY MEDICAL SERVICES

When emergency services personnel perform emergency medical services (EMS) or otherwise might be exposed to blood or other body fluids, these personnel must be provided with EMS PPE. OSHA regulation 29 CFR 1910.1030, issued March 6, 1992, sets the requirements for all emergency responders, health care workers, and others for appropriate actions to prevent contact with blood-borne pathogens.

Appropriate Clothing and Equipment

The U.S. Centers for Disease Control and Prevention (CDC) *Guidelines for Public Safety Workers* discusses the selection and use of appropriate clothing and equipment during medical emergencies. CDC recommends that disposable gloves be worn by all personnel prior to initiating any emergency patient care tasks involving exposure to blood or body fluids. Extra pairs of gloves should always be available. For multiple victims, gloves should be changed between patient contacts.

Gloves contaminated with blood or other body fluids to which universal precautions apply should be removed as soon as possible, taking care to avoid skin contact with the exterior surface. The use of gloves does not eliminate the need to wash hands after emergency medical incidents. Hand washing is one of the most important elements of infection control.

Masks, eyewear, and gowns should be present on all emergency vehicles that respond or that might respond to medical emergencies or victim rescues. These items should be donned by all personnel prior to any situation in which splashes of blood or other body fluids to which universal precautions apply is likely to occur. Finally, contaminated gloves should be placed and transported in bags that prevent leakage and disposed of properly. In the case of reusable gloves, they should be cleaned, disinfected, and stored properly.

Because of the risk of salivary transmission of other communicable viruses and bacteria (e.g., herpes simplex and Neisseria meningitides, respectively) and the risk of HIV and hepatitis B and C transmission during artificial ventilation of victims, the use of mechanical respiratory-assist devices, such as bag-valve masks and oxygen-demand valve resuscitators, or pocket mouth-to-mouth resuscitation masks (i.e., double lumen systems), designed to isolate emergency response personnel from victims' blood and blood-contaminated saliva, respiratory secretions, and vomitus, is strongly recommended.

NFPA 1999, *Standard on Protective Clothing for Emergency Medical Operations*

The product standard for EMS PPE is NFPA 1999, which is the only standard, both from within and outside the emergency responder community that includes performance tests to ensure that each type of PPE has a barrier against penetration of blood-borne pathogens. The standard requires penetration resistance to body fluids and blood-borne pathogens that personnel can be exposed to during EMS functions. The EMS PPE barrier materials, including seams, are exposed to a bacteriophage suspension of a liquid inoculated with *E. coli* C bacteria for 1 hour. Materials are tested in both directions and cannot allow any penetration of the bacteriophage. EMS PPE items must also meet performance requirements for liquidtight integrity, material strength, physical hazard resistance, seam strength, and closure strength.

NFPA 1999 covers EMS PPE items, including garments, both full and partial, upper and lower torso protection; three types of gloves, examination gloves for patient care, work gloves for situations that pose higher physical hazards such as extrication, and cleaning gloves for handling and cleaning contaminated EMS equipment; footwear; and face protection. EMS PPE must provide the barrier protection to whatever parts of the body they cover. Although no partial protection is allowed for the EMS PPE item, the items might be configured to cover only part of the upper or lower torso, such as arms with sleeve protectors, torso front with apron-styled garments, face with faceshields, and so on.

EMS PPE face protection must meet requirements for liquidtight integrity in those areas of the facewear that are designed to provide biological protection.

For mass casualty incidents where civilian victims could self-present at medical care facilities without having been decontaminated by emergency services personnel at the incident scene, medical first receivers should have PPE protection so they can function and give care without themselves becoming victims. All of the PPE covered by NFPA 1999 will provide blood-borne pathogen protection for these personnel as well.

NFPA 1581, *Standard on Fire Department Infection Control Program*

The existing user document is NFPA 1581. (There is no PPE SCAM document at this time.) This standard is a comprehensive document on infection control and requires that the organization provide EMS PPE for each of its members for use while performing EMS operations. EMS PPE includes single-use gloves, fluid-resistant clothing, pocket masks, splash-resistant eyewear, respiratory-assist devices, approved sharps containers, and leak-proof bags. It also establishes standard operating procedures for the selection and use of the appropriate EMS PPE for the specific hazards of each incident.

STANDARDS ON PPE FOR HAZARDOUS MATERIALS OPERATIONS

Anyone involved in a hazardous materials incident must be protected against potential hazards. The purpose of PPE is to shield or isolate individuals from the chemical and physical hazards that may be encountered during hazardous materials responses. Structural fire-fighting protective clothing and equipment, even when certified to the NFPA standard, provide little or no protection against hazardous materials and should not be used for hazardous materials incidents.

EPA Levels of Protection

The EPA has outlined four levels of hazardous materials protective clothing and respiratory protection: A, B, C, and D. The EPA defined these levels of protection primarily for workers at hazardous waste sites, where emergency conditions do not usually exist. These levels are commonly, and often inappropriately, utilized by emergency responders.

Although EPA levels of protection might be used as the starting point for ensemble selection, each ensemble must be appropriate for the specific situation. Ensemble design or configuration alone is not sufficient to ensure adequate protection. In other words, just having the right components to form an ensemble is not enough. The EPA levels of protection do not define what performance the selected clothing or equipment must offer.

Degree of Coverage

For emergency response, the only acceptable types of protective clothing are fully encapsulating suits, or totally encapsulating suits, and nonencapsulating or "splash" suits combined with accessory clothing items, such as chemically resistant gloves and boots. These descriptions apply to how the clothing is designed and do not apply to performance.

Hazardous materials protective ensembles should completely cover both the wearer and the wearer's respiratory protection. Wearing SCBA or other respiratory equipment outside the ensemble exposes it to the contaminated environment. SCBA used in hazardous materials emergency response is generally the same as that for fire fighting. In general, respiratory protective equipment is not designed to resist chemical contamination and should be protected from these environments.

NFPA Standards

The two product standards for hazardous materials emergencies PPE are NFPA 1991, *Standard on Vapor-Protective Ensembles for Hazardous Materials Emergencies,* and NFPA 1992, *Standard on Liquid Splash-Protective Ensembles and Clothing for Hazardous Materials Emergencies.*

NFPA 1991 requires that SCBA be worn on the inside of vapor-protective suits. NFPA 1992 allows liquid splash-protective suits to be configured either with the SCBA on the inside or the outside. However, it is strongly recommended that respiratory equipment be worn inside the ensemble to prevent its failure and to reduce decontamination problems.

The chemical resistance data provided by the manufacturer of the ensemble should be studied. Technical data packages are required to be provided by the manufacturers of protective ensembles that are certified to NFPA 1991 or NFPA 1992. Manufacturers of vapor-protective ensembles provide permeation-resistance data for their products, and manufacturers of liquid splash-protective garments provide penetration-resistance data for their products. Data should be provided for every primary material in the ensemble, including the suit or garment, hood, visor, gloves, and boots.

Permeation data should include the chemical name, breakthrough time (how soon the chemical permeates), permeation rate (the rate that the chemical comes through), and system sensitivity (comparison of test results from different laboratories).

Ensemble or ensemble element materials that show no breakthrough or no penetration to a large number of chemicals are likely to have a broad range of chemical resistance. If there are specific chemicals within the response jurisdiction that have not been tested, the manufacturer should be asked to supply test data on these chemicals.

The manufacturer's technical data package should document all the features of the ensemble and describe what materials are used in its construction. It should cite specific limitations for the suit and what restrictions apply to its use. Procedures and instructions should be supplied for at least donning and doffing, inspection, maintenance, storage, decontamination, and use.

Vapor-Protective Ensembles

NFPA 1991 covers vapor-protective ensembles that are designed to provide "gastight" and "liquidtight" integrity and are intended for response situations where no chemical contact is permissible or where the exposure is unknown. These ensembles now provide the mandatory requirements for CBRN protection at terrorism incidents where no chemical contact is permissible or where the exposure is unknown. Formerly, this was covered in the 2001 edition of NFPA 1994, *Standard on Protective Ensembles for Chemical/Biological Terrorism Incidents,* Class 1 ensemble requirements.

Performance testing includes permeation resistance to a specific battery of chemicals and gases selected as representative of the classes of chemicals encountered during hazardous materials emergencies. Vapor-protective ensembles must resist permeation by the hazardous materials present during a response. Permeation occurs when chemical molecules diffuse through the material, often without any evidence of chemical attack. Permeation resistance is measured in terms of breakthrough time of at least 1 hour or more. Chemical permeation resistance must be met for each chemical specified in ASTM F1001, *Standard Guide for Selection of Chemicals to Evaluate Protective Clothing Materials.* Any additional chemicals or specific chemical mixtures for which the manufacturer is certifying the ensemble must meet the same permeation performance requirements. Additional performance testing includes gastight integrity, liquidtight integrity, overall suit function and integrity, suit ventilation rate, and physical durability.

Liquid-Splash Protective Ensembles and Protective Clothing

NFPA 1992 covers liquid splash-protective ensembles that are designed to protect emergency responders against liquid chemicals in the form of splashes but not against continuous liquid contact or chemical vapors and gases. Liquid splash-protective ensembles and clothing can be used for protection with liquid chemicals that do not present vapor hazards. Materials that prevent liquid penetration can still allow chemical permeation since this PPE does not offer gastight performance, even if duct tape is used to seal clothing interfaces.

NFPA 1992 specifies a battery of liquid chemicals that are representative of the classes of liquid chemicals likely to be encountered during hazardous materials emergencies. Liquid splash-protective ensembles are for use only for protection from liquids with low vapor pressures and with no known skin absorption toxicity. Liquid splash-protective suits cannot be used for known or suspected carcinogens.

Performance testing includes penetration resistance to a specific battery of liquid chemicals selected as representative of the classes of chemicals that are encountered during hazardous materials emergencies. Penetration resistance is measured in terms of penetration resistance time. A chemical penetration resistance time of at least 1 hour or more must be met for each of the specified chemicals. Any additional chemicals or specific chemical mixtures for which the manufacturer is certifying the ensemble or clothing must meet the same penetration performance requirements. Additional performance testing includes liquidtight integrity, overall suit function and integrity, and physical durability.

Chemical, Biological, Radiological, Nuclear (CBRN) Incident PPE

Called weapons of mass destruction (WMD) by the military community, these or similar CBRN agents are expected to be used in attacks against civilian populations by terrorists. On the civilian side, these agents may take a different form and different concentration than WMD agents in battlefield conditions and are called CBRN terrorism agents.

First Responders. Civilian emergency response personnel will most likely be the first responders to see and be exposed to these terrorism agents. Support from federal government agencies, including the military, will be delayed due to several reasons, the least of which are not assembly and deployment time, transportation time to the incident site, or being committed to similar simultaneous attacks on military installations. Local fire departments, police and other law enforcement agencies, hazardous materials response teams, and emergency medical services providers will be the civilian response.

It is incorrect to view these local government agencies as the "first responders" if that is understood to mean they are involved in only the initial stages. Even though they will be the first to respond, they will remain the responders throughout the duration of the incident. Although, in the United States, state and federal agencies may respond, they will be present to assist and support the local jurisdiction and not to assume command and take over the operation and all the problems.

Because CBRN terrorism agents are intended to injure, incapacitate, or kill large numbers of persons, it is obvious the responders must rapidly identify such situations and protect themselves so that they may help others. PPE does exist for civilian responders to these incidents, and more PPE will be available as the technology progresses. Little of the current military WMD PPE can "transfer" to civilian responders as it is designed for military scenarios where it is used under significantly different environments, operations style, supervision, and deployment conditions.

Limitations to Protection. Civilian emergency response organizations must instruct their personnel that although existing PPE for fire fighting, EMS, or hazardous materials operations might provide some low level of dermal protection for a very short exposure, there is no evaluation or procedure to determine how much protection would be offered by each "in-service" PPE. The fact is that "in-service" (i.e., "used") PPE that is not certified as providing CBRN protection most likely will not provide any protection at all, or might provide only a few seconds of limited protection before the wearer could face severe or lethal exposures. The same problem exists for law enforcement agencies whose normal everyday PPE is not capable of protection from CBRN exposures.

NFPA 1994, *Standard on Protective Ensembles for First Responders to CBRN Terrorism Incidents.* NFPA 1994 is the product standard for CBRN terrorism incident PPE. Although this standard still covers the requirements for three classes of ensembles, the former NFPA 1994 Class 1 ensemble is now covered in the requirements of NFPA 1991.* NFPA 1994 now covers Class 2, Class 3, and Class 4 protective ensembles for CBRN terrorism incidents.

The 2007 edition is the second edition of NFPA 1994. As noted, NFPA 1994 no longer specifies a Class 1 ensemble, but has left the designation "Class 1" vacant. A new Class 4 ensemble was added to provide particulate protection for emergency responders to incidents where no chemical or biological agent is identified but where a particulate threat is present (including "white powder" incidents).

The CBRN protection requirements of NFPA 1994 apply to all emergency first responders at CBRN incidents. Individual agencies (law enforcement, emergency medical, medical first receivers, fire, hazardous materials, and skilled trades) need to define the operations for which their personnel are trained and develop detailed purchase specifications to assure the ensembles are designed to best support their operational needs while providing the CBRN protection.

All Class 2, Class 3, and Class 4 CBRN protective ensembles are required to be certified with a specific respirator certified by NIOSH as a CBRN SCBA, a CBRN APR, or a CBRN PAPR, or multiple CBRN respirators.

NFPA 1994 ensembles are intended to be pristine ensembles maintained in their own package until needed for use. They are intended to be single-exposure PPE and then discarded. These protective ensembles are intended for protection of fire, law enforcement, emergency medical, skilled trades, and other emergency services personnel responding to CBRN terrorism incidents or for emergency services personnel exposed to victims, materials, or the general incident environment during assessment, extrication, rescue, decontamination, triage, and treatment operations.

Ensemble Classes. The three classes of ensembles were developed for use in environments that can be generally described by considering the following:

- Exposure and delivery method
- Potential for skin contact
- Contaminant identification and concentration level
- Persistency (longevity) of the contaminant
- Threat of contamination and cross-contamination

Selection of the appropriate class ensemble must be based on a thorough risk assessment of the incident.

Class 2 and 3 ensembles are designed and tested for permeation resistance to chemical warfare agents and liquid industrial chemicals but at lower exposure rates commensurate with the intended protection level for the respective class. Class 4 ensembles are designed and tested for particulate inward leakage.

All ensembles are tested at exposure rates commensurate with the intended protection level for the respective class, inward leakage of exhaust valves, overall ensemble function and integrity, and for burst strength, puncture propagation, seam strength, closure assembly strength, visual acuity of facepiece or visor, maximum suit airflow, and cold weather performance.

NFPA 1991 (as discussed earlier) also specifies chemical and biological protection requirements for vapor-protective ensembles.

---

*Class 1 ensembles, the highest level of protection from vapor and liquid IDLH hazards, are intended for use at known or suspected CBRN incidents where the identity or concentration of the vapor or liquid is unknown, where most victims appear dead or unconscious and not ambulatory, or where liquid contact is expected, and no direct skin contact or inhalation can be permitted. These ensembles are now covered exclusively by NFPA 1991 vapor-protective ensembles. This high level of protection would be selected at incidents where exposure of personnel at these levels will result in the substantial possibility of immediate death, or immediate serious injury or illness, or the severe impairment of the ability to escape.

STANDARDS ON PPE FOR SPECIAL OPERATIONS

Technical Rescue Operations

PPE for technical rescue operations, including urban search and rescue (USAR), provides protection from physical, environmental, thermal, electrical, chemical flash fire, chemical splash, and blood-borne hazards. Technical rescue operations are commonly performed at incidents involving building/structural collapse, machinery or vehicle accidents, confined space entry, trench/cave-in rescue, and rope rescue. These operations include the functions of victim search, extrication, rescue, body recovery, and site stabilization.

Technical rescue PPE includes garments, helmets, gloves, footwear, and eye and face protection. The clothing portion of these ensembles might also be part of other PPE elements, such as a layer(s) or portion(s) of certain fire-fighting PPE, EMS PPE, and station/work uniforms.

The product standard for USAR and other technical rescue PPE is NFPA 1951, *Standard on Protective Ensembles for Technical Rescue Incidents.* The 2007 edition is the second edition of NFPA 1951. The document's title has been changed to *Standard on Protective Ensembles for Technical Rescue Incidents* to clarify that the standard applies to all emergency services organizations that perform technical rescue incident operations and not just to urban search and rescue (USAR) teams of state or federal governments. It embraces the broader audience of emergency responders for which these types of protective ensembles are developed to provide protection from the expected hazards common to these operations.

This edition specifies requirements for the following three different types of technical rescue ensembles:

1. A *utility* ensemble that provides protection from physical hazards and provides a basic flame resistance for the ensemble and the elements of the ensemble and provides a high level of "breathability" for the ensemble to aid in reducing heat stress for the wearers
2. A *rescue and recovery* ensemble that provides all the physical protection of the *utility* ensemble and in addition a blood-borne pathogen barrier to afford protection from infection from injured or deceased victims
3. A *CBRN* ensemble that, in addition to all the protections of the *utility* and *rescue and recovery* ensembles, also provides limited protection from chemicals, biological agents, and radiological particulates during terrorism incidents where chemical warfare agents or weapons of mass destruction could be used

It remains the choice of emergency services organizations to select the appropriate ensembles for the protection of their emergency responders based on the expected and anticipated technical rescue incidents to which their respective organizations will or could respond.

These ensembles do not apply to PPE for any fire-fighting operations or hazardous materials operations outside of CBRN incidents, due to the severity of those specific exposures. The standard also does not apply to PPE for wilderness search and rescue, water and swiftwater rescue, contaminated water diving, or cave rescue operations.

NFPA 1951 provides performance testing, depending on which ensemble is being evaluated, for total heat loss of garments, tear strength, fabric breaking strength, seam strength, and resistance to abrasion, corrosion, liquid penetration, flame, blood-borne pathogen, limited flash fire, and CBRN agents.

Life Safety Rope Operations

The life safety rope and system components covered by the NFPA PPE standard addresses a type of rope and system that are used to support the weight of emergency responder personnel and civilians during rescue, fire fighting, and other emergency operations, as well as during training for such operations.

Life safety rope is not a utility rope used to secure, raise, lower, or support equipment or machinery. Life safety rope and the system components are not intended for industrial fall situations or for recreational uses and are also not intended for lead climbing, mountain rescue, or cave rescue operations.

Life safety rope is not a dynamic rope; it is a static, low-stretch rope intended for use where the fall factor will not be greater than 0.25. The types of rope covered in the NFPA PPE standard are life safety rope, escape rope, and throwlines. Life safety rope is classified as light use or general use, depending on the minimum breaking strength.

Escape rope is a single-purpose, one-time use, emergency self-rescue (or self-escape) rope and not considered a life safety rope. A throwline is a one-person rope intended to be thrown to a person during water rescue or to tether rescuers entering the water.

The types of system components covered are auxiliary equipment including ascending devices, buckles, carabiners, descent control devices, load-bearing connectors, rapid links, rope grab devices, and snap-links; belts including escape belts and ladder belts; hardware including portable anchors, pulleys, and rings; Classes 1, 2, and 3 life safety harness; and software including anchor straps, pick-off straps, rigging slings, and webbing.

The product standard for life safety rope PPE is NFPA 1983, *Standard on Life Safety Rope and Equipment for Emergency Services.* NFPA 1983 provides performance testing of life safety rope, escape rope, throwlines, life safety harness, belts, auxiliary equipment, hardware, and softwear and includes breaking strength, minimum and maximum elongation, dynamic drop, static load, tensile, corrosion resistance, diameter, melting resistance, and colorfastness.

SUMMARY

Personal protective clothing and equipment play an essential role in the safeguarding of emergency personnel against the hazards of fire fighting. All NFPA product and user standards, including manufacture, cleaning, maintenance, and fit, must be adhered to in order to ensure effectiveness of protection. Fire fighters must be trained in the proper use of PPC and PPE and must also be informed of their limitations. PPC and PPE alone cannot ensure safety from hazardous exposure and must be considered only one factor in a defense system that includes physical fitness, well-planned emergency procedures, and teamwork.

BIBLIOGRAPHY

NFPA Codes, Standards, and Recommended Practices

Reference to the following NFPA codes, standards, and recommended practices will provide further information on fire and emergency service protective clothing and protective equipment discussed in this chapter. (See the latest version of The NFPA Catalog *for availability of current editions of the following documents.)*

NFPA 1500, *Standard on Fire Department Occupational Safety and Health Program*

NFPA 1581, *Standard on Fire Department Infection Control Program*

NFPA 1851, *Standard on Selection, Care, and Maintenance of Protective Ensembles for Structural and Proximity Fire Fighting*

NFPA 1852, *Standard on Selection, Care, and Maintenance of Open-Circuit Self-Contained Breathing Apparatus (SCBA)*

NFPA 1951, *Standard on Protective Ensembles for Technical Rescue Incidents*

NFPA 1971, *Standard on Protective Ensembles for Structural Fire Fighting and Proximity Fire Fighting*

NFPA 1975, *Standard on Station/Work Uniforms for Fire and Emergency Services*

NFPA 1977, *Standard on Protective Clothing and Equipment for Wildland Fire Fighting*

NFPA 1981, *Standard on Open-Circuit Self-Contained Breathing Apparatus (SCBA) for Emergency Services*

NFPA 1982, *Standard on Personal Alert Safety Systems (PASS)*

NFPA 1983, *Standard on Life Safety Rope and Equipment for Emergency Services*

NFPA 1989, *Standard on Breathing Air Quality for Fire and Emergency Services Respiratory Protection*

NFPA 1991, *Standard on Vapor-Protective Ensembles for Hazardous Materials Emergencies*

NFPA 1992, *Standard on Liquid Splash-Protective Ensembles and Clothing for Hazardous Materials Emergencies*

NFPA 1994, *Standard on Protective Ensembles for First Responders to CBRN Terrorism Incidents*

NFPA 1999, *Standard on Protective Clothing for Emergency Medical Operations*

References

Allan, R., Watters, G., and Webster, S., "Re-Assessing Safe Systems for BA Users," *Fire,* Vol. 91, No. 1123, 1999, p. 40.

Austin, C. C., Ecobichon, D. J., Dussault, G., and Tirado, C., "Carbon Monoxide and Water Vapor Contamination of Compressed Breathing Air for Firefighters and Divers," *Journal of Toxicology and Environmental Health,* Vol. 52, No. 5, 1997, pp. 403–423.

Bobetich, K. V., "Chemical and Biological Terrorism: Are You Ready?" *Fire International,* No. 173, Feb. 2000, pp. 22–23.

Crawford, J. K., "Rapid Intervention Teams: Are You Prepared for the Search?" *Firehouse,* Vol. 24, No. 4, 1999, p. 50.

Dahl, R. F., "Nomex Miracle System Uses Trapped Air for Insulation," *Industrial Fire World,* Vol. 14, No. 1, 1999, p. 16.

Donovan, K. J., and McConnell, A. K., "Fire-Fighters' Self-Contained Breathing Apparatus (SCBA): The Effects of SCBA Mass upon Exercise Duration During Treadmill Walks in the Laboratory," *Fire Engineers Journal,* Vol. 59, No. 203, 1999, pp. 28–33.

Hargarten, D. J., "Complying with OSHA's Revised Respiratory Protection Standard," *Fire Engineering,* Vol. 152, No. 1, 1999, p. 101.

Herrick, J., "Breathing Apparatus: A Part of Personal Protection," *Fire Engineers Journal,* Vol. 59, No. 203, 1999, pp. 24–27.

Jirka, G. P., "WMD Protective Clothing for the First Responder," *Advanced Rescue Technology,* Vol. 4, No. 4, 2001, pp. 30–38.

Matthews, D., "Five Decades of Protective Clothing—Protection or a Burden?" *Fire,* Vol. 90, No. 1114, 1998, pp. 51–52.

McCormack, J., "Rapid Intervention: Emergency Air Supply," *Fire Engineering,* Vol. 153, No. 7, 2000, p. 7.

McKenna, M. F., "Eye and Face Safety: Are Your Firefighters Protected?" *Fire Engineering,* Vol. 153, No. 7, 2000, pp. 87–91.

Richardson, M., and Scholer, R., "Thermal Imaging Training: Covering the Basics," *Firehouse,* Vol. 26, No. 4, 2001, pp. 86–88.

Riecher, A., "Are Silvers Coming Back?" OSHA Issues Opinion on Protective Clothing, *Industria Fire World,* Vol. 13, No. 1, 1998, pp. 10–11.

Riecher, A., "Reflecting on Fire P. P. E.," *Industrial Fire World,* Vol. 14, No. 1, 1999, pp. 10–13.

Robinson, B., "Are Firefighters' Lives Being Threatened by Inadequate Equipment? If So, What Can Be Done?" *Fire International,* No. 185, Apr. 2001, pp. 18–19.

Robinson, B., "Firefighter Protection: A Shared Goal for the Whole Fire Service," *Fire,* Vol. 92, No. 1145, 2000, pp. 11–13.

Schnepp, R., "Managing Chemical Exposures: The Engine Company Perspective," *Fire Engineering,* Vol. 152, No. 9, 1999, pp. 53–54.

Smith, S., and Withington, D., " 'White Noise' Can Help Save Stricken Firefighters," *Fire,* Vol. 92, No. 1135, 2000, p. 27.

Veasey, A., "Coping with Loss of Air Supply in Chemical Protective Suits," *Fire Engineering,* Vol. 151, No. 3, 1998, p. 173.

Walker, C., "Fresh Air Fiends Breathing Air Distribution System Links Training Center," *Industrial Fire World,* Vol. 13, No. 1, 1998, pp. 16–17.

Werner, C. L., "Fire Service Technology: Looking Ahead," *Firehouse,* Vol. 25, No. 7, 2000, p. 118.

Winston, R. M., "Basic Wildland Fire Safety for Structural Firefighters," *Firehouse,* Vol. 25, No. 5, 2000, p. 86.

Chapter 10

Training Programs for Fire and Emergency Service Personnel

Jerry W. Laughlin

Chapter Contents

Key Terms

blood-borne pathogen, distance learning, education, fire fighter safety, fire service instructor, Hazardous Waste Operations and Emergency Response (HAZWOPER) Standard, job performance requirement (JPR), learning, live fire training, National Fire Academy training

This chapter is an overview of the broad challenge of providing training for fire and emergency service personnel. The challenge includes a continuous need for training throughout an individual's career. Changes in technology constantly affect the lives of fire fighters in many ways. New hazards evolve and create risks to the public and fire fighters, but technology also provides new ways to deal with the risks. Training helps sort out the differences.

Acquiring and maintaining a high level of training in fire and emergency service personnel is more than a matter of efficiency; it can at any moment become a matter of personal survival. When a fire fighter responds to an emergency incident, a situation is already out of control. With a shortened time to think things through, rapid emergency response makes effective training more important.

In a world of highly specialized medical, legal, and other types of professionals, fire fighters must also remain generalists ready to respond to a bewildering variety of emergency incidents. The next emergency response could be for a residence fire or a high-rise fire, a hazardous materials spill or an explosion, a vehicle rescue or a swiftwater rescue. The response could require checking on a smell of smoke, fighting a raging fire that threatens a structure's stability, or handling a terrorist incident with mass casualties. The call could be for a rescue in an underground confined space or high on the side of a cliff. Training for each response is complex, and the skills needed must already be learned before the current emergency.

For related topics, see Section 4, Chapter 1, "Human Behavior and Fire"; Section 12, Chapter 2, "Organizational Benchmarking and Performance Evaluation"; and Section 12, Chapter 14, "Fire Rescue Stations and Fire Service Training Centers."

NEED FOR TRAINING

Personal Training

Health Education. The difficulty of maintaining a public service for 24 hours every day and the potential need to respond to unlimited types of service requests every day should be ample motivation for fire and emergency service personnel to expect and deliver a high level of training. Even as the number of reported fires has decreased in the last 25 years,[1] the number of medical calls has increased. And even as the number of civilian deaths and injuries has decreased, the number of fire fighters who die or are injured on duty has remained at a level that is too high. Analysis of fire fighter deaths and injuries reveals a long list of training needs that should be addressed, and all of them should be revisited periodically.

Jerry W. Laughlin is assistant executive director at the Alabama Fire College. He is a former fire fighter and previously was editor at *Fire Command* and *Fire Engineering* magazines. He has served as NFPA staff liaison to the technical committees developing the fire service professional qualifications standards. He is currently pursuing a doctorate in higher education administration at the University of Alabama.

Between emergency alarms, there is a need for wellness training to increase the physical fitness of emergency responders. Almost half of all fire fighter deaths on duty are from sudden cardiac incidents.[2] There is ample medical evidence that known risk factors contribute to this high number of deaths.[3] Some risk factors cannot be changed, such as male gender and increasing age. However, most heart attacks suffered by fire service personnel are preventable. Wellness training that addresses modifiable risk factors is not difficult or expensive. Risk factors that can be influenced by training, diet, and exercise between emergency responses include smoking, high blood cholesterol, high blood pressure, physical inactivity, being overweight or obese, and diabetes.

Transportation Safety. Responding to emergency calls has the inherent risks of transporting personnel and equipment in heavy vehicles moving through other traffic. Training is clearly needed to improve awareness of these risks and to improve the skills needed to operate emergency vehicles. NFPA statistics show that "firefighters are more likely to die traveling to or from a fire than fighting one, and motor vehicles pose a greater hazard than flames."[4] Almost all of these vehicle deaths can be prevented by training personnel to operate emergency vehicles safely.

Although the fireground is as dangerous as it ever was, incident by incident, the decreasing total number of fires has been associated with a lower number of fatalities on the fireground over the last 25 years. Now less than a third of fire fighter deaths occur on the fireground.[5] However, it is again clear that the number of fire fighter deaths and injuries on the fireground could be reduced further through training.

Skill Sets. A single "routine" fire emergency incident calls for a complex set of fire fighter skills, and all fireground activities must be completed in rapid succession under stressful and physically demanding conditions. Without retraining, skills deteriorate. Continuing training is necessary to keep these important skills ready for instant use. A fire in the upstairs bedroom of a two-story house provides many examples of the complexity of needed fire fighter skills. Personnel must be trained and equipped to conduct a search for residents who may have been incapacitated by the fire or smoke. If a victim is found, training in emergency medical response is critical. Other personnel must be trained to rapidly provide water to quench the fire, using knowledge of water locations and skills for operating fire department pumps, hose, and nozzles. Other personnel must be trained to assess the buildup of heat and harmful smoke inside the structure and know how to make the right decision about ventilating the heat and smoke through a hole cut in the roof above the fire. All of these complex tasks must be coordinated by an incident commander trained in each of the different tasks, in the responsibilities of command, and in the details of overseeing all of the tasks underway at the same time.

It is clear that the tasks are not only numerous and complex but also highly specialized. Pump operators must have the experience needed to anticipate water needs at the fire. Every fire can have different hydraulic requirements, and the operator must be trained to adjust to every variable. The chemistry of fire and the nature of building construction must be considered by the person intending to ventilate a roof. Individuals must be well trained to use these numerous and specialized skills almost automatically. The success of every task on the fireground can be affected by how quickly the tasks can be completed. The speed of completing the tasks is affected by the level of training.

NFPA Requirements. National standards of competency further specify a personal need for training. NFPA 1500, *Standard on Fire Department Occupational Safety and Health Program,* requires training in many areas. An entire chapter of NFPA 1500 addresses training and education requirements as a department responsibility and as a personal responsibility. Paragraph 5.1.9 states: "As a duty function, members shall be responsible to maintain proficiency in their skills and knowledge, and to avail themselves of the professional development provided to the members through department training and education programs."[6]

Training as an Obligation to the Community

Communities choose to provide emergency response services for protection of the entire community. Communities then have expectations that the services will be available and effective when they are needed. In turn, fire and emergency service personnel have an obligation to develop and maintain appropriate skills. When a citizen's life, family, or property is threatened, fire fighters who perform well under these difficult conditions will earn the highest respect and admiration for the fire department, and community support of the department will be strengthened. But when fire fighters are not trained well enough to perform as expected, community respect and support can disappear. Many times the difference is in the training that the responders have received.

Training is not a one-time event. Knowledge and skill levels must be repeated in order to be maintained. Given the variety of incidents that a fire department may face, many types of fires are not frequently encountered. It is the same with hazardous materials that may be released. Each incident can be significantly different, and considerable time can elapse between similar incidents. Experience alone, therefore, is not enough to keep skills well practiced and ready for instant use. Continuing training is required to prevent degradation of skills.

In addition, new challenges can emerge as manufacturers invent ways to combine chemicals to develop useful new products. During the transportation and storage of chemicals that occur before they are combined, the chemicals can burn, explode, or escape their containers and thereby endanger the populace. If a leak or explosion occurs, fire fighters and hazardous materials response teams must respond. The evolving use of chemicals is yet another situation that forces emergency responders to stay well trained. In addition, fire departments must also be ready to respond to terrorist incidents, which requires even more training.

Federal Requirements

Training increases fire fighter safety, helps fire fighters meet the community's expectation for effective emergency response, and prepares fire fighters for the evolving world around them that presents frequent new challenges. Training is also mandated by federal requirements. These rules are the result of demonstrated problems that have adversely affected the public or the emergency responders. Three important requirements relate to hazardous materials, respiratory protection, and communicable disease.

Hazardous Materials. The Occupational Safety and Health Administration (OSHA) developed hazardous materials regulations to increase safety in hazardous waste operations and related emergency response. Called HAZWOPER and officially designated as 29 CFR 1910.120, this federal regulation details the requirements of employers and responders to plan for and safely respond to emergency incidents. Training is specified for anyone who might respond: "Training for emergency response employees shall be completed before they are called upon to perform in real emergencies. Such training shall include the elements of the emergency response plan, standard operating procedures the employer has established for the job, the personal protective equipment to be worn and procedures for handling emergency incidents."[7] Refresher training is also specified: Employees trained under these requirements "shall receive annual refresher training of sufficient content and duration to maintain their competencies. . . ."[8]

Respiratory Protection. Fire fighter respiratory protection is required in federal regulation 29 CFR 1910.134. The regulation stipulates that employers, including fire departments, must provide breathing protection and training "when such equipment is necessary to protect the health of the employee. The employer shall provide the respirators which are applicable and suitable for the purpose intended."[9] The employer must also create a written respiratory protection program that includes "training of employees in the respiratory hazards to which they are potentially exposed during routine and emergency situations."[10]

Communicable Disease. The blood-borne pathogen federal regulation is intended to protect fire fighters and other employees from infections that could result from contact with another person's blood. This is Code of Federal Regulations number 29 CFR 1910.1030. For anyone who could have occupational exposure to blood-borne pathogens, the employer must provide precautions. Again, training is required: "Employers shall ensure that all employees with occupational exposure participate in a training program which must be provided at no cost to the employee and during working hours."[11] The training must be provided annually. Paragraph (g)(2) lists the training requirements.

State Requirements

Although every state might be expected to offer or encourage training for emergency responders, some states have specific requirements. Washington State, through the Department of Labor and Industries and the Washington Industrial Safety and Health Act, places clear responsibility for training on the employer fire department as follows: "The employer shall provide training and education for all members commensurate with those duties and functions that members are expected to perform. Such training and education shall be provided to members before they perform emergency activities. Fire service leaders and training instructors shall be provided with training and education which is more comprehensive than that provided to the general membership of the fire department."[12]

A further Washington State example addresses training frequency: "The employer shall assure that training and education is conducted frequently enough to assure that each member is able to perform the member's assigned duties and functions satisfactorily and in a safe manner so as not to endanger members or other employees. All members shall be provided with training at least annually. In addition, members who are expected to perform interior structural fire fighting shall be provided with an education session or training at least quarterly."[13] Live fire training in Washington is required to conform to NFPA 1403, *Standard on Live Fire Training Evolutions.*[14]

Other states also mandate that NFPA 1403 requirements for live fire training be followed. For example, Florida enacted such a law after suffering fire fighter fatalities during two live fire training incidents.[15] (See the section in this chapter entitled "Training Safety.") Through its Firefighters Occupational Safety and Health Act, Florida has long required fire fighter employers to "provide training and education for all fire fighters and supervisory personnel commensurate with those duties and functions that such fire fighters and supervisory personnel are expected to perform. Such training and education shall be provided to fire fighters and supervisory personnel before they perform any emergency activities or other activities requiring such training."[16] In other words, before a fire fighter can respond to any emergency, training must already have been provided. The law also states that the fire fighter must be able to perform any activity in a satisfactory and safe manner.

ORGANIZATION OF TRAINING DELIVERY

It might be argued that training for career and volunteer fire departments should be identical because fire behaves in the same way regardless of the kind of fire department that responds. There is merit in this argument, but real-world economics often results in different funding levels for a large-city career department and a rural volunteer department. Different funding levels, when they are present, affect the availability of instructor training, equipment purchases, and time devoted to training. Of course, there can be exceptions in which a volunteer department has greater funding and more commitment for training than a nearby career department. But the complexity of a large city always creates the necessity, if not the funding, for a more varied training program.

Career Departments

A career fire department has the ability to offer and mandate training in ways that a volunteer fire department might not. Larger departments are more likely to have the funding resources to maintain a complete fire training bureau with multiple instructors, ample technical and audiovisual equipment, and realistic training simulators. Smaller departments usually have at least one individual dedicated to training activities for the department.

Career departments in large cities have the added challenge of a more variable fire and emergency risk. Transportation hubs can have a very high exposure from the large volumes of hazardous materials being stored or shipped into, out of, and through them. Most waterfront developments add more specialized risks while at the same time limiting access. In large cities, public assembly events are more likely to occur. Training must be made available to address these and other normal hazards of cities. With the usual higher funding for training in career departments, any failure to provide ample training would invite embarrassing press questions and public resentment concerning the funding that was invested but not used effectively.

Volunteer Departments

Volunteer fire training has its own unique challenges. Volunteer members have the added burden of a full-time job that often interferes with sufficient time for training. Volunteer departments protecting rural communities may have a very low level of response activity, which is fortunate for the community but allows fire-fighting skills to degrade from lack of frequent activity or practice. This in turn makes training extremely important.

Volunteer fire fighters often have fewer average years of experience in fire fighting compared to career fire fighters. The volunteer nature of their service and the demands of other primary jobs and families on limited free time make it harder for volunteers to sustain their service over many years. Training in the basics of fire fighting is a constant need in many volunteer departments, which can interfere with another vital need for specialized training in a variety of hazards that may be present even in a small rural community. Because the needs for training are so great and funding can be low, volunteer fire departments must be innovative to find ways to fund and offer continuous basic training. There is no excuse for any fire department lacking trained members to protect the public.

Comprehensive Training

A fire department's training program can be full service and comprehensive, minimal, or nonexistent, depending on available funds and the training orientation of the fire chief. A minimal or nonexistent training program should not be acceptable. Reports from the National Institute for Occupational Safety and Health (NIOSH),[17] describing the lessons learned from fire fighter fatalities in the United States, repeatedly list prevention warnings that indicate insufficient training. Each warning that follows is from a NIOSH report and describes actions that should have occurred but did not and contributed to a fire fighter fatality. Each of the following represents a training failure:

- "Instruct and train firefighters on initiating emergency traffic (Mayday—Mayday) when they become lost, disoriented, or trapped."
- "Ensure firefighters are trained to recognize the danger of operating above a fire."
- "Train on the SOPs, the incident command system, and lost firefighter procedures with mutual aid departments to establish interagency knowledge of equipment, procedures, and capabilities."
- "Ensure that firefighters from the ventilation crew and the attack crew coordinate their efforts."
- "Develop, implement, and enforce standard operating procedures (SOPs) on the safe operation of emergency vehicles which include the use of seat belts."
- "Ensure that all drivers of fire department vehicles receive driver training at least twice a year."
- "Ensure that the Incident Commander conducts a risk-versus-gain analysis prior to committing firefighters to the interior and continually assesses risk versus gain throughout the operations."
- "Ensure that firefighters train with thermal imaging cameras (TIC) and they are aware of their proper use and limitations."

These lessons from actual incidents demonstrate that any department needs a full-service comprehensive training program to best prepare its members for the dangerous conditions that they face. A fire department that cannot train its members to stay safe also cannot live up to the expectations of the community that depends on an effective response by the fire department.

Many fire departments have some training needs that are similar, such as the basic operation of water delivery, forcible entry, ventilation, use of personal protective equipment, and obvious others. Department needs can also be diverse according to the characteristics of the community protected. An urban department will have different training needs compared to a rural department. A community with heavy industrial risks requires different training than a community with mostly residential structures.

ENSURING QUALITY INSTRUCTION

Instructor Attributes

When a fire department commits to a full-service comprehensive training program to best protect its members and citizens, it will be necessary to consider the qualities of an instructor in order to adequately plan the training program and implement individual training classes. When the NFPA national standard on fire instructor professional qualifications, NFPA 1041, *Standard for Fire Service Instructor Professional Qualifications,* was first developed, it reflected on one message of the influential Wingspread fire service meeting in 1966: "Professionalism begins with education." The NFPA 1041 technical committee concurred and stated that "the quality of any educational program is only as good as its instructional staff."

The professional levels of competence of fire service instructors are the subject of NFPA 1041, which presents the following three levels of progression:

- A Level I instructor "has demonstrated the knowledge and ability to deliver instruction effectively from a prepared lesson plan, including instructional aids and evaluation instruments; adapt lesson plans to the unique requirements of the students and authority having jurisdiction; organize the learning environment so that learning is maximized; and meet the record-keeping requirements of authority having jurisdiction."

- A Level II instructor is someone who, in addition to meeting Instructor I qualifications, "has demonstrated the knowledge and ability to develop individual lesson plans for a specific topic including learning objectives, instructional aids, and evaluation instruments; schedule training sessions based on overall training plan of authority having jurisdiction; and supervise and coordinate the activities of other instructors."
- A Level III instructor is someone who, in addition to meeting Instructor II qualifications, "has demonstrated the knowledge and ability to develop comprehensive training curriculum and programs for use by single or multiple organizations; conduct organization needs analysis; and develop training goals and implementation strategies."

A comprehensive full-service training program should have instructors who meet the requirements of this national standard to at least Level I. That means they have received training on the nature of instruction and have passed the standardized exam to demonstrate competence according to the national standard.

A certified fire service instructor has been exposed to learning opportunities related to communication skills, components of a lesson plan and how to use one, how to prepare and maintain training records, the laws of adult learning, learning styles, methods of instruction, organizing the learning environment, operation and maintenance of instructional equipment, test administration, skills checklists, the need for feedback, and the requirements of educational confidentiality.

It is possible for an experienced fire service instructor to be competent without the formal process of certification, but certification ensures that an individual's competence has been evaluated by more than one person. The best combination is experience and certification of competence to the established national standard of performance.

Nature of Learning

A proper training session is much more than someone standing up and talking about a fire service subject. Even being an expert in a fire service subject does not mean that the expert understands or is automatically good at instruction. Effective training instruction does depend in part on the instructor's subject matter knowledge and skills, but effective instruction also must consider the general principles of learning and the particular needs of adult learners. This statement sums up a body of educational research: "There is increasing evidence that the effectiveness of learning can be determined by the methods used to teach. In other words, the way material is presented has an effect on how well you understand and remember it."[18] Certainly the material must be understood and remembered so that it can be used when it is really needed during an emergency on the fireground.

Individuals in a group of seemingly similar fire fighters from a single department can differ significantly in how they learn best. This does not mean that instruction must be tailored for every variation in individual learning style. However, awareness of these learning style differences can increase the chances that the instruction can be tailored so that is actually useful to the greatest number of individuals who need to learn something new. Therefore, the subject matter expert does need to be aware of learning styles.

So-called laws of learning also can help the instructor to appreciate different impacts on learning. Many laws of learning were studied by Edward Thorndike in the 1920s and 1930s and have been further developed and confirmed through educational research in various other settings. Although they may have differing names,[19] these laws can be applied generally to the fire service.

Law of Exercise. The law of exercise is already frequently applied to the fire service. It states that a person learns best and retains information longer when there is a chance for meaningful practice and repetition during the learning. People learn by doing. Instructors use repetition, but they also make sure that the right skills are being practiced and that the practice is followed by positive feedback.

Law of Effect. When the instructor gives positive feedback following a student's demonstration of correct skills, the law of effect is being used. It states that learning is better when it results in satisfying consequences. This can include praise or any other type of reward that the student values. A positive effect is also present when the adult learner can immediately see the benefits from training. To a lesser extent, this law can have an undesirable result: If the attempt at learning is associated with negative feedback and frustration, learning can be weakened and less likely to persist. This can also be called the law of reinforcement.

Law of Relevance. Other researchers realized that learning is more effective when shown to be highly relevant to the learner's life and work. Fire service training generally follows this approach. Realistic training has higher relevance, which makes it tempting to provide for live fire training, but the overriding safety requirements should not be forgotten.

Law of Response Level. Students may sometimes grumble about their workload, but this law provides that students do only as much as is required of them. It states "learners master skills and knowledge at the level at which they are required to respond during the learning process." This should motivate instructors to maintain high standards and not let any training activity be performed casually, since people will tend to operate at the same level used in training.

Law of Emotional Learning. This law works well in the fire service training environment. It states that when learning events are accompanied by intense emotions, the learning will tend to be longer lasting. This law fits with highly realistic and even stressful training conditions. A variation is the law of intensity, which states that using an intensely vivid or realistic stimulus in learning will more likely result in a change of behavior. There is a limit to the application of this law. When the training scenario becomes too intense, it can become dangerous and interfere with learning.

Law of Expectations. This law states that learner attitudes affect what and how much they actually learn. They are more likely to learn when they expect the learning to be positive. This expectation can be influenced by personal history, course format, attitudes of fellow students, and instructor attitudes. Situations where students and instructors do not want to participate in the training usually result in low levels of learning.

Law of Recency. This law reminds us that recent learning is stronger than earlier learning. Memory deteriorates, which is why frequent retraining is necessary. Information and skills that are not being repeated are being replaced by whatever has been happening more recently.

This sample of the laws of learning makes the point that instructors can be more effective when they understand the fundamental conditions of the learning process. Fire service training may be mandatory, but the good instructor will not make it seem that way. Results are what count. As more schools are being held accountable for the learning of their students, they have started to change their emphasis from just teaching a subject to ensuring that actual learning takes place. This approach is also appropriate for training fire and emergency service personnel. Since the training often involves critical safety messages for fire fighters, it is clear that the instructors should not be satisfied with merely teaching a class; they must use various forms of assessment to ensure that the members are learning.

Evaluation of Learning

A weakness of much in-service fire training is that too often no effort is made to ensure that some learning has occurred and that some behavioral change will take place. In-service training is rarely accompanied by any testing to measure what was learned. The best evidence of learning comes from testing the subject knowledge or skill before starting the instruction and then retesting after the instruction. Comparison of the two results is a measurement of what was actually learned during the class.

Criterion-referenced testing is intended to measure what a person has learned compared to a specific body of knowledge (criteria). The learning can be measured by multiple-choice questions, fill-in-the-blank questions, demonstration, or performance of the skill that has been taught to ensure that it can be accomplished correctly. This kind of testing is included in certification courses for instructors, which again shows the value of formal instruction for instructors. It is unfortunate and potentially fatal for fire fighters to discover during an emergency incident that they did not actually learn some important material in a previous lecture.

Proper evaluation of learning does take extra time, but undiscovered substandard learning can be much more costly. Another aspect of evaluation is that care must be taken to make sure that the evaluation is accurate and valid. The importance of accurate evaluation of learning applies especially to certification courses where there can be serious consequences for failing the criterion-referenced test. State fire training agencies have the means to statistically check the accuracy of the tests they use. Taking the time and effort to properly evaluate learning is an obligation for any instructor or training program.

Education Versus Training

The terms *education* and *training* have different meanings, although they are often used interchangeably. The differences are more important as fire agencies become more complex and need more analytical management skills to build on the technical skills of manual fire fighting.

Fire and emergency training is designed to increase proficiency in a particular skill. Training can also be applied to increasing knowledge in a particular area. It starts with a performance objective that can be described specifically. It ends with the trainee being able to demonstrate an ability to perform according to the stated objective or, if the performance objective is not met, the instructional activity can continue. This can be described as a training loop, in which the instructor provides information input, the student is tested to demonstrate learning, and the instruction is revised as necessary to provide the proper input. A fire fighter certification class is an example of training.

Education is learning that provides the student with a foundation of general knowledge that helps in problem solving and effective thinking. Education involves learning to think and reason. Pursuing a college degree, with core courses in English, math, history, and psychology, is education, even when study in the major subject area results in increasing specific knowledge and skills. The overall process is education when it contributes to efficient analysis techniques.

Although they are different, education and training can be combined. Training by itself, when measured and successful, transfers established facts and skills. Then a behavior, such as ventilating a fire scene, is predictable within a generally defined range. Training by itself can be described as reflexive. The mental functions required to put training techniques into practice could be considered relatively passive when compared to educational analysis. Education provides ways for the student to further analyze and understand why and what kind of ventilation is appropriate for varying conditions. Fire scenes are not always confined to the defined range covered in the ventilation training. There could be, for example, unique reasons why ventilation is not the correct solution in a particular situation. With broader education combined with training, the fire fighter or fire officer can better observe and apply critical thinking and reach informed conclusions.

Education and critical thinking become increasingly important as an individual advances in rank within a fire department. College attendance is not the only way to acquire education, but it is the most efficient way. Improved critical thinking can be the result of long years of experience, but not everyone grows at the same rate from the same experiences.

National Fire Academy Superintendent Dr. Denis Onieal believes that the educational component is most important in considering the fire service as a profession. "Many feel that the distinguishing characteristics of a profession," he writes, "are years of formal education, approval of an accrediting board, and continuing education requirements."[20] Onieal calls for combining our localized systems of training and education into a national one in order to demonstrate a more convincing professionalism. He would integrate the following four existing parts:

1. Training systems now available through local and state agencies and the National Fire Academy (NFA)
2. Standardization of the education systems now available through 2-year and 4-year colleges and universities and through NFA
3. Independent assessment of skills now available through the Pro Board and IFSAC
4. Broader reciprocity among systems of training and education

INTERNAL TRAINING PROGRAMS

Recruit Training

Recruit training is the basic staple of fire service training. Although some fire fighters transfer in from other departments, the typical candidate is completely new to the fire service. Training for this individual must start at the beginning. Although it has been noted that different types of departments in different communities will have different overall training needs, the basic recruit training of any fire fighter should be the same. A fire in one room of a one-story home requires the same response skills whether the department is career or volunteer, suburban or rural.

The recognized standard of fire fighter performance when the duties are primarily related to structural fires is NFPA 1001, *Standard for Fire Fighter Professional Qualifications.* Most state fire training agencies and progressive fire departments use this standard for developing a recruit training course. The standard describes the minimum job performance requirements for fire fighters in the duty areas of communications; fireground operations; rescue operations; and prevention, preparedness, and maintenance. For the recruit fire fighter, there are 19 listed job performance requirements in the duty area of fireground operations, each with related requisite knowledge and skills.

NFPA 1001 also includes an annex with information on how to use the job performance requirements (JPRs) in curriculum development and training design and evaluation. According to Annex B: "The statements contained in this document that refer to job performance were designed and written as JPRs. Although a resemblance to instructional objectives might be present, these statements should not be used in a teaching situation until after they have been modified for instructional use. JPRs state the behaviors required to perform specific skill(s) on the job, as opposed to a learning situation. These statements should be converted into instructional objectives with behaviors, conditions, and standards that can be measured within the teaching/learning environment. A JPR that requires a fire fighter to 'ventilate a pitched roof' should be converted into a measurable instructional objective for use when teaching the skill."

In-Service Training

In-service training sessions are conducted during the normal departmental work shift. Depending on the equipment available as instructional aids, any type of fire service training can be done on an in-service basis. The understanding is that any emergency call or any administrative assignment coming from higher authority will take precedence, and the training will be interrupted until the emergency or the other assignment is completed. When interruptions occur, training effectiveness can be reduced. The in-service instructor is usually from within the department or may be an officer or other member of the crew receiving training. This arrangement has the advantage of being economical, since no additional costs are incurred by instructors who are already on the payroll. A disadvantage is that the training session can suffer from distractions that interfere with learning. Members of the public may enter the station during the training with questions for the officer or some member of the crew. The station phone may ring. After returning from an emergency call, the training may be cut short due to meals or previously scheduled assignments. Some good training can occur in an in-service setting, but it is not the ideal arrangement.

Specialized Courses

The nature of specialized training often involves more detailed planning, special equipment not available at each station, or multiple crews receiving the same training at the same time. Specialized courses are often conducted at a central location such as a training bureau. Rather than a shift supervisor conducting the training, as during in-service training, specialized courses may require specialist instructors. Examples of specialized courses are new training procedures that must be extended to all personnel in a short time frame (such as the adoption of the National Incident Management System), training for new equipment being brought into the department (such as an aerial device or a thermal imaging camera), and highly technical courses (such as surface water rescue or hazardous materials response).

Training for each of these examples should also include a method of assessment to confirm that the intended learning actually occurred and that the training was worthwhile. Also important for specialized courses is to add documentation of this specialized training to the permanent training record of every individual participating in the session (see the section in this chapter entitled "Training Records").

Special Operations Training

Numerous public events remind us of ever-present dangers that call for special operations training for incidents that are outside the realm of routine fire and emergency service duties. Examples can be seen in such diverse incidents as terrorist attacks, major transportation accidents involving hazardous materials spills and explosions, and natural episodes such as hurricanes and multiple tornadoes. Although such incidents occur infrequently, when they break, the demands on fire and emergency services can be the most challenging and expensive situations where the highest level of training is required.

The events of September 11, 2001, provide grim reminders of the threat of overwhelming terrorist incidents using weapons of mass destruction. The Oklahoma City bombing is evidence that the threats can be internal to a country as well as external. In any event the training preparation is the same. Federal funding has provided extended training opportunities, but it remains to be seen if permanent lessons have been learned about training and preparedness. The 9/11 Commission report expresses concern that "We learned that the institutions charged with protecting our borders, civil aviation, and national security did not understand how grave this threat could be, and did not adjust their policies, plans, and practices to deter or defeat it." Will the fire service be better trained and better prepared next time?

Transportation of hazardous materials across the United States is routine but still results periodically in multiple fatalities. In 2004 and 2005, there were train derailments in South Carolina and Texas that resulted in the spillage of the same dangerous chemical, chlorine. Fire departments protecting communities along these railways did not have comprehensive response training complying to the requirements of NFPA 472, *Standard for Professional Competence of Responders to Hazardous Materials Incidents.* Transportation of chemicals may be normal, but emergency service response to spills of any dangerous chemical is not yet normalized. Much work is still to be done to train these responders.

Successive hurricanes force home the importance of special operations training for responding to major natural disasters. At the same time the range of needed training has greatly expanded. From hurricanes like Katrina, responders learned of the importance of backup systems for communications, basic supplies such as batteries, and personnel accountability. A hurricane is an example of the need for multiagency training, since the response will involve multiple overlapping jurisdictions.

Training Classrooms, Buildings, Grounds, and Equipment

It has been mentioned that during training, learning is reduced when there are distractions during the instruction. Distractions can include the occurrence of unrelated physical and noisy activities in the vicinity of the instruction that draw the attention of the student away from the instruction. Ringing phones, fire department radios, and normal fire station activity are examples. For many reasons, classroom training sessions need a proper classroom environment. Trying to conduct classroom-type instruction in an open fire station engine room is difficult. A separate classroom is preferred, with desks or tables for writing, audiovisual equipment, adequate lighting and ventilation, and access to the tools that might be part of the instruction.

NFPA 1402, *Guide to Building Fire Service Training Centers,* provides valuable information for functional and safe training environments. This document addresses facility components and planning considerations, classroom needs, drill tower construction and use, special structures for live fire and smoke training, and space and equipment for outside training activities. Mobile training units are also discussed.

Classrooms and Libraries. For classrooms, NFPA 1402 states that "classroom size is dictated by the number of students and the type of training to be conducted." The guide serves to remind users of some important considerations for training facilities without being overly restrictive. Most hands-on skills training requires more space than instruction that is lecture only. Audiovisual equipment to supplement instruction is important. A good instructional facility will have functional seating and writing surfaces, with a common example being tables and stacking chairs for greater flexibility. Lighting and ventilation need to be adjustable to maintain a comfortable learning environment.

A library of fire-related books and magazines is an essential part of fire service training. The library should include references for departmental regulations, procedures, and history. Copies of national standards should be included. Computers and Internet access are becoming common to all libraries.

Realistic Training Simulations. Drill towers, smoke rooms, and live fire training structures are expensive to build properly, but they are important for training in basic fire fighting. Training towers and smoke and burn rooms allow realistic training simulations that help build confidence in fire fighters. The height of the tower should be typical of the buildings found in the locale, according to NFPA 1402. The value of realistic training simulation also introduces an extra responsibility to consider safety during this training (see the section later in this chapter entitled "Training Safety"). NFPA 1402, paragraph 8.18, recommends that "consideration should be given to the need for an observation/control tower in order to monitor various training functions from one location."

To reduce the frequency of disruption of training due to department emergency response, equipment used for training should be exclusively for training. Otherwise, the training of out-of-service personnel would be interrupted if in-service equipment is taken out of the classroom to respond to an emergency. This is a waste of time that is more costly than the purchase of equipment dedicated for training purposes.

High-Tech Training Center. Most training centers have been in existence for many years. They may be intended to serve a single department's needs, or several departments in a county or region may cooperate to maintain a training center. Most state-level training centers have also been in existence for many years. One of the newest and most comprehensive training centers has been built for the Tarrant County College Fire Service Training Center in Fort Worth, Texas. This 23-acre, $18 million complex with a realistic, all-hazard cityscape provides an impressive number of scenarios for realistic training. This training center calls itself a "high-tech theme park for firefighters."[21] Figure 12.10.1 shows fire fighters engaged in realistic training exercises.

The cityscape at the college is indeed a small city with built-in associated hazards designed to allow challenging training while maintaining safety controls. There are residential, commercial, warehouse, and high-rise structures that add realism to training for size-up, exposure protection, and apparatus placement. A train derailment and 18-wheeler truck fire scenarios can be used, and there are sites for trench and confined space rescue. The center may have the only controlled swiftwater rescue site anywhere available for fire service training.

One of the main motivations for the training center design was to provide a live fire training environment without the safety risks of acquired structures. As a result, the Tarrant County College Fire Service Training Center is one of the largest computer-controlled, gas-fired facilities in the world, according to the school. It features six separate live fire buildings.

FIGURE 12.10.1 Realistic Training Exercises (Courtesy of Tarrant County College)

In addition to the real-world props across the property, there is a 48,000 ft^2 (4460 m^2) classroom and administration building. A high-tech command and control center occupies the third floor, where operators can program, initiate, and monitor all training activities. Control has been emphasized throughout the complex. At the swiftwater site, the "river" flow can change from 80,000 gallons per minute (302,400 L/min) to a trickle with the turn of a switch.

The price tag of the Tarrant County College Fire Service Training Center means that the fire service cannot expect to see these facilities popping up everywhere, but it does represent what is possible in realistic training.

EXTERNAL TRAINING SOURCES

State Fire Training Agencies

Many states have designated an official agency to provide training for fire and emergency personnel throughout the state. In most cases there is a similar legislative authority, but there are significant differences in how state fire training agencies are funded. Fire fighter training is mandated in some states and is voluntary in others. With more funding, state fire agencies typically are able to offer more services.

The earliest state training programs focused almost exclusively on the basic skills of using hose and ladders and operating fire pumpers. Since fire departments in larger cities usually had staff to operate their own training sections, state fire training was often aimed at smaller departments that did not have the resources for a separate training staff. Individual state instructors, many of them retired fire fighters from larger cities, commonly traveled around a state and offered skills training to rural fire departments. The training was informal and the quality varied, depending on the experiences and abilities of the instructor.

Concerns about the adequacy and inconsistency of fire department training activities began to be expressed more forcefully by fire service leaders in the late 1960s. These concerns led to more calls for a set of performance standards to be used for acceptable levels of training and professionalism. Today, the core of most state fire training agencies involves more formal courses based on national standards rather than state or individual preferences.

Starting in the 1980s, state agencies began increasing use of NFPA's national professional qualifications standards to guide training. The use of a national standard was an idea that state political leaders could understand and support and has been accompanied by a rise in the funding for and importance of state certification authority and national accreditation. The organization of state training directors is the North American Fire Training Directors (http://www.nftd.org).

Certification. Certification in state training programs implies valuable benefits for students and for the departments sending the students for training. Certification is a written assurance to the student, the sponsoring fire chief, and the home community that the student conforms to specified requirements. Students should understand the different meanings of certification so that they can assure themselves that they are getting the training that they and their departments need.

The basic meaning of certification may be represented by a certificate of attendance, which usually indicates only an assurance that the student was present when a course of instruction was presented. With a certificate of attendance there is no automatic assurance as to the specific content of the course. There is no measurement of actual learning, such as an exam. One may infer the course content from the title, and there may be a course outline, but there is no accountability for skills learned. A student's experience in class could be passive with limited learning, but the student might still qualify for a certificate of attendance. To be more informative, this certification should specify the length of attendance in the course.

When a course has more requirements than simple attendance and it includes an examination of some kind to measure learning, the result for successful students who demonstrate minimum learning may be a certificate of completion. A person evaluating such a certification would need to know how course completion was defined. A fire training course might include requirements for demonstrating both knowledge and skills, so someone evaluating a certificate of completion needs a way to clarify exactly what was completed. Another factor for evaluating a certificate of completion is the authority of the individual or agency issuing the certification. Someone's mother could physically issue a printed certificate, but her authority and credibility would be evaluated as weak. On the other hand, when an authorized state agency issues a certification of completion, the credibility of the course content can be judged as higher.

Certification to national standards has additional advantages and credibility. Ideally, this certification provides written assurance that a recognized national standard of performance has been met. This assurance should be the result of successful completion of a test based on the national standard. The highest credibility for a certification to national standards is when the certification is accredited.

Accreditation. Accreditation in the fire service is a system of evaluating the certifiers. The award of accreditation to a state fire training agency is a written seal of approval according the definition of accreditation. Creation of an accreditation system in the fire service was an important quality assurance step in making fire service training more valid and reliable. By observing other professions, fire service leaders in the 1960s who wanted to eliminate the unevenness of many training courses based on personal preferences proposed the National Professional Qualifications System, which was created in 1972.[22] Professional qualifications standards for specific fire-fighting job categories were the next step. Under their own authority, states could certify that individuals had been trained and were known to meet the requirements of the national standard.

The best assurance that the state program indeed meets the national standard is demonstrated when the state actions are evaluated by an independent third-party organization to ensure quality and eliminate politics or favoritism. The first national accrediting organization, set up by the Joint Council of National Fire Service Organizations, was the National Board on Fire Service Professional Qualifications (Pro Board, http://www.theproboard.org). A later accrediting organization, the International Fire Service Accreditation Congress (IFSAC, http://www.ifsac.org), grew out of Oklahoma State University. Both evaluate state fire training courses based on the same national standards from NFPA.

As a result, the accredited certification has the highest credibility and provides full disclosure to students about the definition of their certification. For example, a student awarded fire investigator certification from an accredited state fire training agency has assurance that he or she has demonstrated successful completion of tests measuring the knowledge and skills as specified in the national standard, NFPA 1033, *Standard for Professional Qualifications for Fire Investigator,* and that the state certifier has been checked by the independent third-party Pro Board and IFSAC and confirmed as having properly assessed the student's competency.

The Pro Board and IFSAC accrediting organizations use the national professional qualifications standards to accredit certification for the following subjects and levels (new subjects and levels may be added according to demonstrated need):

NFPA 472:	Hazardous Materials Response for Awareness, Operational, Technician, Incident Commander
NFPA 1001:	Fire Fighter I, II
NFPA 1002:	Fire Apparatus Driver/Operator for Pumper, Aerial, Tiller, Wildland, Airport Rescue and Firefighting, and Mobile Water Supply Apparatus
NFPA 1003:	Airport Fire Fighter
NFPA 1006:	Technician Level for Rope Rescue, Surface Water Rescue, Vehicle and Machinery Rescue, Confined Space, Structural Collapse Rescue, Trench Rescue, Subterranean Rescue, Dive Rescue, and Wilderness Rescue
NFPA 1021:	Fire Officer I, II, III, IV
NFPA 1031:	Fire Inspector I, II, III; Plan Examiner I, II
NFPA 1033:	Fire Investigator
NFPA 1035:	Fire and Life Safety Educator I, II, III; Public Information Officer; Juvenile Firesetter Intervention Specialist I, II
NFPA 1041:	Fire Service Instructor I, II, III
NFPA 1051:	Wildland Fire Fighter I, II; Wildland Fire Officer I, II; Wildland/Urban Interface Protection Specialist, Coordinator
NFPA 1061:	Public Safety Telecommunicator I, II
NFPA 1071:	Emergency Vehicle Technician I, II, III
NFPA 1081:	Fire Brigade Member for Incipient Industrial, Advanced Exterior Industrial, Interior Structural Industrial, Industrial Fire Brigade Leader
NFPA 1521:	Health and Safety Officer, Incident Safety Officer

Federal Training Sources

National Fire Academy. The *America Burning*[23] report in 1973 documented the serious nature of the nation's fire problem and concluded that fire prevention and control should remain primarily local responsibilities. However, the commission appointed to study the federal fire problem at that time also recommended a new federal government agency "where the Nation's fire problem is viewed in its entirety, and which encourages attention to aspects of the problem that have been neglected" (p. x). Also recommended was the establishment of a "National Fire Academy for the advanced education of fire service officers and for assistance to state and local training program" (p. xi).

The National Fire Academy (NFA) has completed more than 30 years of operation and has won the respect of the fire service. Its educational courses are offered at the resident facility in Emmitsburg, Maryland, and throughout the nation in cooperation with state and local fire training organizations. Some courses are offered in distance learning formats. Leaving basic training to local fire departments and state fire training agencies, NFA resident courses deliver "specialized training courses and advanced management programs of national impact"[24] in an intensive learning environment.

Emergency Management Institute. Training to minimize the impact of natural and technological disasters on the American public is the emphasis of the Emergency Management Institute (EMI). Its intended audience includes the fire service, but it serves the broader world of emergency management personnel in federal, state, and local governments and also volunteer organizations and other public and private sector representatives. EMI shares the campus of the National Fire Academy in Emmitsburg, Maryland. Courses are taught in residence at EMI and also in the states. Nonresident courses taught in the states are through cooperative agreements with state emergency management agencies.

Office of Domestic Preparedness. The United States Department of Homeland Security Office of Domestic Preparedness (ODP) "provides tailored training to enhance the capacity of states and local jurisdictions to prevent, deter, and respond safely and effectively to incidents of terrorism involving weapons of mass destruction."[25] ODP training is aimed at the full range of first responders, not just fire and emergency medical services.

ODP began in 1998 as a part of the Justice Department, but it was transferred to the Department of Homeland Security in 2002. Other federal training activities were transferred within Homeland Security with the title of Office of State and Local Government Coordination and Preparedness (SLGCP). This office administers the Assistance to Firefighters Grant Program. Grant funds can be used for a variety of fire service needs, including training.

Where the National Fire Academy specifically works with state fire training agencies and local fire departments to extend the outreach of NFA courses, OPD and SLGCP have a narrow coalition of training partners for the development and delivery of its training programs. A recent trend has begun to place more emphasis on partnering with more state and local fire agencies to meet the needs of first responder training.

Colleges and Universities

Individuals in fire and emergency services, as with individuals in any technical and managerial field, are increasingly valuing opportunities for higher education in fire protection and emergency medicine. Colleges and universities have been increasing these opportunities through a wider choice of college-credit courses and through additional degree and certificate programs at all levels.

Associate Degree. Community colleges have long been a source for associate degree programs in fire science technology and fire program administration. An associate degree is becoming more common as a requirement for fire department promotion to higher levels of advancement. When not tied to promotion consideration, some fire departments give value to higher education at the associate degree level by offering salary increases when the degrees are work related. A fire science technology degree also prepares an individual for a career in other areas of fire protection. A fire administration associate degree is especially helpful for someone seeking promotion, or it can be used to qualify for positions in fire safety organizations.

Associate degree fire science programs in community colleges combine study in general education subjects such as English, math, and chemistry with specialty fire protection courses such as fire hydraulics, hazardous waste operations, and building construction as related to fire suppression. Associate degree administration programs include the same general education programs and combine them with more management courses. Some programs may allow limited credit for fire department experiences. More formal programs often allow credit for previous state fire training accredited certifications. Some fire service management programs include teaching such certification courses as Fire Officer III and Fire Officer IV as part of the degree curriculum.

Bachelor's Degree. Universities in all parts of the United States now offer bachelor's degrees related to fire protection. Many are created to allow easy transferability of fire protection associate degrees from community colleges. Bachelor programs may also have several types of specialization, some with application in fire departments and some with application in other areas of fire protection. One state university bachelor's degree in fire protection has options for fire protection administration, fire protection engineering technology, fire and explosion investigation, industrial safety and risk management, and safety and industrial relations. There are also many opportunities for master's and even doctoral degree programs in fire protection that did not exist even 10 years ago.

Distance Learning Opportunities

Distance learning via the Internet has greatly expanded options for fire and emergency training. The fact that virtually every community college and university offers some classes online demonstrates how mainstream this relatively new format has become. The widespread success of online learning suggests that colleges and universities have found it to be successful. This is backed up by educational research showing that measurable student learning and student satisfaction with online courses can be equal to the learning and satisfaction in regular classroom courses.

Online learning can be especially important to adult learners. The typical advantages of online learning often fit closely with adult situations. A training course taught online means that the work of learning can be accomplished at home and on the weekends, so that the adult with a full-time job and family responsibilities does not have to juggle scheduled classes that may require an inconvenient commute. Online learning requires the same effort as classroom learning, but the schedule flexibility may be a critical consideration.

Not all fire and emergency service training can be provided in an online learning format. A fire fighter training course featuring many skill development requirements may not ever be feasible online, but an accredited certification course for Fire Officer I has already been conducted online by a state fire training agency.[26]

Not all online learning courses are created equal. Much variety exists in the educational value of courses labeled as online learning. Some nonrecommended online learning formats allow a single student to work alone without any deadlines for assignments, and the course content may be nothing more than a textbook placed online for student reading. The learning is expected to occur simply from the student flipping the pages and reading the material online. Student satisfaction and completion rates in these courses are not as high as in other formats.

College and university online courses often follow a common format that has many of the successful features of a classroom course. About 80 percent of college and university online courses use similar course management software interfaces, named Blackboard and WebCT, to present online information to students. The course is presented in a normal semester or quarter time frame, and students participate in the class together, although at a distance. Research on this format shows good educational results. One particular benefit comes from student interaction, although again from a distance and in writing. Research shows that important learning, whether in a classroom or online, comes from student interaction during group discussion about the course content.

Training Companies

For-profit training companies have increased their offerings of training opportunities for fire and emergency personnel, even to the level of college courses. For-profit companies competing with colleges to provide technical training are usually big operations with a regional or national reach. In the fire service, the company may be just one or a few instructors with prior fire department experience or specialty experience. For-profit training can be seen with specialty areas in technical rescue, water rescue, and hazardous materials response.

The quality of for-profit training companies depends on the technical and instructional experience of the trainer. When such courses do not usually claim to fully address any national standard and the training company lacks independent third-party accreditation endorsement, anyone contracting for training must make an extra effort to be sure of what training is needed and what quality can be delivered.

Fire Service Organizations

In the United States and other countries, the following not-for-profit associations provide a valuable service to the fire service community in terms of training and other resources:

- The International Association of Fire Chiefs (IAFC, http://www.iafc.org) is an international trade association of fire chiefs. Membership is restricted to upper-level officers in fire departments. IAFC provides a large annual conference and trade show along with an advisory service and publications for its members. This organization also operates the Chief Fire Officer Certification project.
- The International Association of Fire Fighters (IAFF, http://www.iaff.org) is a national labor union representing career fire fighters throughout North America. Extensive advisory and training services are offered to its members with a focus on fire fighter health and safety.
- The International Fire Service Training Association (IFSTA, http://www.ifsta.org) is an advisory group to Fire Protection Publications, a division of Oklahoma State University. Membership is by invitation only. The group reviews and revises the extensive fire service training materials issued by Fire Protection Publications.
- The International Society of Fire Service Instructors (ISFSI, http://www.isfsi.org) is a trade association of individuals engaged in or interested in fire service training. The society provides conferences, seminars, and some training materials for its members and others.
- The National Fire Protection Association (NFPA, http://www.nfpa.org) is a public advocacy association that primarily develops voluntary consensus standards. Many of those standards apply to the fire service and provide valuable technical guidance. In addition, NFPA provides training materials and staff resources in support of fire and emergency service training.
- The National Volunteer Fire Council (NVFC, http://www.nvfc.org) is an organization whose membership is made up of delegates from state volunteer fire service organizations. It also has individual fire departments and fire fighter memberships. The organization is primarily engaged in lobbying for volunteer fire service issues but does provide some valuable training programs and resources.

There are typically several fire service organizations in each state and province that mirror the work of associations at the national level. State and local fire fighters, fire chiefs, fire instructors, and other associations vary in their commitment to training, but nearly all have some resources to offer.

TRAINING SAFETY

Injuries and Fatalities

Fire fighter injuries and fatalities during training in the last 25 years suggest that instructors can forget that a realistic training scenario can have disastrous results when safety is not a paramount consideration. Guidance for realistic but safe training can be found in NFPA 1403, *Standard on Live Fire Training Evolutions.* Development of this document started after numerous training deaths occurred across the United States, especially the tragic deaths of two fire fighters in 1982 during live fire training in Boulder, Colorado, using an abandoned wood-frame building. Rapid fire spread across a combustible low-density fiberboard ceiling, an inadequate water supply, inadequate exits, and a general lack of planning for the potential dangers contributed to these fatalities. The first edition of this standard was in 1986, with revisions following as more experience was gained in subsequent years.

Unfortunately, the availability of this safety guidance sometimes has been overlooked or ignored, with continued disastrous results. Three more fire fighters died in a live fire training exercise in 1987 in Milford, Michigan. Multiple fires had been set in an old frame house in an attempt to create a realistic fire scenario for training. The scenario, with a lack of planning, insufficient paths of escape, inadequate water supply, and large amounts of accelerants, was not in compliance with NFPA 1403. Four area fire departments took part in this exercise, but safety was not a sufficient priority to prevent the unanticipated flashover that occurred with fire fighters still inside.

Failure to follow the requirements of this important standard continues. The following newspaper and magazine headlines remind us of the consequences:

- "Instructor Suspended over Death of Trainee"[27] (Maryland)
- "Apparent Flashover at Controlled Burning Traps, Kills Delaware Asst. Chief"[28]
- "Iowa Firefighter Brothers Burned During Training"[29]
- "Career Lieutenant and Fire Fighter Die in a Flashover During a Live-Fire Training Evolution"[30] (Florida)
- "Volunteer Fire Fighter Dies and Two Others Are Injured During Live-Burn Training"[31] (New York)

The foregoing Florida headline incident from 2002 occurred in a vacant concrete-block dwelling. A fire in the structure was started to accompany search and rescue training. As a result, the two fire fighters in the training exercise did not have a ready water supply. As in the Boulder and Milford fatalities, there were insufficient paths of escape. This incident had designated safety officers and a rapid intervention team, but the fuel load contributed to a flashover only 3 minutes later. Four instructors positioned inside the structure to serve as interior safety officers were able to exit successfully, but the fire lieutenant and fire fighter in the training exercise died from smoke inhalation and thermal injuries. Now state law in Florida requires that training fires be in compliance with NFPA 1403.

The foregoing New York headline incident from 2001 forced a wider fire service audience to become aware of NFPA 1403 when the fire department officer supervising the training exercise was charged with felony counts of manslaughter and assault. The fire fighter trainee who died was 19 years old. The training officer was later convicted of criminally negligent homicide. During sentencing the judge said, "This was not an accident. This was a series of bad decisions, decisions that should never, ever have been made." Now the state offers two programs to prevent a reccurrence of this type of incident: "Live Fire Training Safety" and "Conducting Live Fire Training Evolutions." Both reference NFPA 1403.

Maintaining Controlled Training

NFPA 1403 explains its purpose with this statement: "The ongoing training of fire fighters is the cornerstone of good fire protection in today's world. However, the benefits derived from live fire training can be negated by the injuries and deaths suffered by fire fighters under unsafe and poorly supervised training conditions." Separate chapters address ways to maintain controlled training in acquired structures and in gas-fired and non-gas-fired training center buildings, using exterior props, and using exterior Class B fires.

The chapter on acquired structures for live fire training is especially important because the most preventable injuries and fatalities occur in acquired structures. It calls for students to have prior training to help them understand safety issues and recognize normal and abnormal fire behavior. The structure itself must undergo special preparations to minimize factors that contribute to uncontrolled burning. Fuel loads are limited. Prior to beginning any training fire, participants in a live fire exercise must become familiar with the building, the exit arrangements, and the plan for the training. Adequate water supplies must be available, and training instructors must be available in sufficient numbers to supervise the burn. Flammable or combustible liquids are not allowed to fuel the fire in these exercises.

TRAINING RECORDS

Training activities must be recorded and updated for easy retrieval. They provide a source of information for effective management decisions for planning and budgeting. Records document and guide professional development for all fire and emergency service personnel. Such records show who has had and who needs training for certification and recertification, internally and externally obtained education, and general compliance with personnel performance standards.

Fire training records are also important to meet various legal and statutory requirements, such as those from the Occupational Safety and Health Administration (OSHA). Fire department records are generally public documents, and citizens or members of the press may have the right to access these public records. But some records, such as test questions and employee personal training records, are not freely available to the public. However, these records are subject to disclosure through a court order or, in some cases, through written permission of the employee. The fire department or emergency agency must have clear-cut guidelines to spell out public access and to prevent the unnecessary and illegal disclosure of confidential information. Other NFPA standards also specify accurate and complete training records, including NFPA 1403 and NFPA 1500.

Guidance for record keeping is available in NFPA 1401, *Recommended Practice for Fire Service Training Reports and Records.* Separate chapters address elements and types of training documents, legal aspects of record keeping, and evaluating the effectiveness of the training records system.

Training elements generally include information about the who-what-when-where-why of training for each individual member of the organization. Every type of training that a department offers should be documented by records. Records may be used to identify, investigate, evaluate, or solve various problems. A resulting report should follow five steps as outlined in NFPA 1401 and summarized here as follows:

1. State the purpose and scope of the report.
2. Outline the method or procedure followed.
3. Present the essential facts.
4. Analyze and categorize the facts.
5. State the conclusions and recommendations from the analysis.

Besides the individual records of all training, NFPA 1401 presents five types of training reports that are often compiled. These include an inventory of training apparatus and equipment, plans and costs for needed training improvements, a periodic report on the evaluation of all probationary fire fighters, a monthly summary of all training division activities, and an annual report of activities with projected plans for the upcoming year.

SUMMARY

Training for fire and emergency service personnel should be varied and continuous. It is not only required by numerous federal and state regulations, but it is also the expectation of the people who finance public fire protection. Beyond these considerations, every fire department should make training a moral priority to protect the health and safety of its members. Finally, every fire fighter should demand an ongoing and comprehensive full-service training program to ensure that fire fighters can protect themselves and be ready to provide assistance to anyone else.

There are many sources for necessary training, including federal, state, and local agencies. When the training is provided by the local fire department, its leaders should ensure that the instruction offered concentrates on the right kind of learning and verifies learning through measured assessment. If a fire department, career or volunteer, is not using established national standards as the basis for its training, fire fighters or citizens should demand an explanation.

BIBLIOGRAPHY

References Cited

1. Ahrens, M., *The U.S. Fire Problem Overview Report: Leading Causes and Other Patterns and Trends,* http://www.nfpa.org, National Fire Protection Association Fire Analysis and Research Division, Quincy, MA, 2003.
2. NFPA, *Firefighter Fatalities in the United States, Firefighter Deaths by Cause and Nature of Injury,* http://www.nfpa.org, National Fire Protection Association Research and Reports, Quincy, MA, 2004.
3. American Heart Association, *Risk Factors and Coronary Heart Disease: AHA Scientific Position,* http://www.americanheart.org, American Heart Association, Dallas, TX, 2005.
4. NFPA, *Vehicle Crashes Cause More Firefighter Deaths Than Fires, NFPA Study Finds,* http://www.nfpa.org, NFPA News Releases, National Fire Protection Association, Quincy, MA, 2003.
5. NFPA, *Firefighter Deaths by Type of Duty,* http://www.nfpa.org, Fire Statistics, National Fire Protection Association, Quincy, MA, 2004.
6. NFPA 1500, *Standard on Fire Department Occupational Safety and Health Program,* 2002 ed., paragraph 5.1.9, National Fire Protection Association, Quincy, MA, 2007.
7. *HAZWOPER, 29CFR 1910.120(p)(8)(iii)(A),* Training, http://www.osha.gov/pls/oshaweb/owadisp.show_document?p_table=STANDARDS&p_id=9765, U.S. Department of Labor, Occupational Safety and Health Administration, Washington, DC, 2006.
8. *HAZWOPER, 29 CFR 1910.120(q)(8),* Refresher Training, http://www.osha.gov/pls/oshaweb/owadisp.show_document?p_table=STANDARDS&p_id=9765, U.S. Department of Labor, Occupational Safety and Health Administration, Washington, DC, 2006.
9. *Permissible Practice, 29 CFR 1910.134(a)(2),* http://www.osha.gov/pls/oshaweb/owadisp.show_document?p_id=12716&p_table=STANDARDS, U.S. Department of Labor, Occupational Safety and Health Administration, Washington, DC, 2006.
10. *Respiratory Protection Program, 29 CFR 1910.134(c)(1)(viii),* http://www.osha.gov/pls/oshaweb/owadisp.show_document?p_id=12716&p_table=STANDARDS, U.S. Department of Labor, Occupational Safety and Health Administration, Washington, DC, 2006.
11. *Bloodborne Pathogens Information and Training, 29CFR 1910.1030(g)(2),* http://www.osha.gov/pls/oshaweb/owadisp.show_document?p_table=STANDARDS&p_id=10051, U.S. Department of Labor, Occupational Safety and Health Administration, Washington, DC, 2006.
12. *Safety Standards for Fire Fighters,* Chapter 296-305.05503, http://www.lni.wa.gov/wisha/rules/firefighters/default.htm#WAC296-305-01003, Washington State Department of Labor and Industries, Olympia, WA, 2006.
13. *Safety Standards for Fire Fighters,* Chapter 296-305.05501(1), http://www.lni.wa.gov/wisha/rules/firefighters/default.htm#WAC296-305-01003, Washington State Department of Labor and Industries, Olympia, WA, 2006.
14. *Safety Standards for Fire Fighters,* Chapter 296-305.05501(2), http://www.lni.wa.gov/wisha/rules/firefighters/default.htm#WAC296-305-01003, Washington State Department of Labor and Industries, Olympia, WA, 2006.
15. Florida Statute 633.821, *Florida Firefighters Occupational Safety and Health Act,* Section 633.801 to 633.821, http://www.fldfs.com/SFM/pdf/FS_633_801-821(2005).pdf, Florida Department of Financial Services, Bureau of Fire Standards and Training, Ocala, FL, 2006.
16. Florida Administrative Code, *Firefighter Employment Standards,* Section 62.021(3)(m), http://www.fldfs.com/SFM/pdf/FAC_69A-62_04_1029_Final.pdf, Florida Department of Financial Services, Bureau of Fire Standards and Training, Ocala, FL, 2006.
17. *Firefighter Fatality Investigation and Prevention Program,* http://www.cdc.gov/niosh/fire, National Institute for Occupational Safety and Health, Washington, DC, 2006.
18. Kramer, C., *Success in Online Learning,* Thomson Delmar, Clifton Park, NY, 2002, p. 32.
19. *Laws of Learning,* http://www.tpub.com/content/administration/134t/css/134t_33.htm, Integrated Publishing, Port Richey, FL, 2006.
20. Onieal, D., *Professional Status: The Future of Fire Service Training and Education,* http://www.usfa.fema.gov/training/nfa/higher_ed/pro_dev, National Fire Academy, U.S. Fire Administration, Emmitsburg, MD, 2003.
21. Patterson, D., "One-Stop Training," *Fire Chief,* Mar. 2003, http://firechief.com/training/ar/firefighting_onestop_training.
22. *History and Overview,* http://www.theproboard.org/history_and_overview.htm, National Board on Fire Service Professional Qualifications, Quincy, MA, 2006.
23. National Commission on Fire Prevention and Control, *America Burning: The Report of the National Commission on Fire Prevention and Control,* U.S. Government Printing Office, Washington, DC, 1973.
24. *About the National Fire Academy,* http://www.usfa.fema.gov/training/nfa/about, U.S. Fire Administration, Emmitsburg, MD, 2005.
25. *Overview of the Office of Grants and Training,* http://www.ojp.usdoj.gov/odp/training.htm, U.S. Department of Homeland Security, Washington, DC, 2006.
26. *Alabama Fire College Completes First Accredited Online Certification Course,* http://www.alabamafirecollege.org/NewsArticles/news.htm, Alabama Fire College, Tuscaloosa, AL, 2006.
27. "Instructor Suspended over Death of Trainee," *The Sentinel,* Aug. 9, 2003, http://www.cumberlink.com, Cumberland Publishers, Carlisle, PA, 2003.
28. Iannone, D. J., *Apparent Flashover at Controlled Burn Traps, Kills Delaware Assistant Chief,* April 15, 2000, http://www.firehouse.com/lodd/2000/delaware_apr30.html, Cygnus Business Media, Melville, NY, 2000.
29. Finn, J. T., "Iowa Firefighter Brothers Burned During Training," *JournalStar,* June 29, 2004, http://www.journalstar.com/articles/2004/06/30/local/10051741.txt, Lincoln Journal Star, Lincoln, NE, 2004.
30. *Career Lieutenant and Fire Fighter Die in a Flashover During a Live-Fire Training Evolution,* Fire Fighter Fatality Investigation

and Prevention Program, http://www.cdc.gov/niosh/fire/reports/face200234.html, National Institute for Occupational Safety and Health, Washington, DC, 2003.

31. *Volunteer Fire Fighter Dies and Two Others Are Injured During Live-Burn Training,* Fire Fighter Fatality Investigation and Prevention Program, http://www.cdc.gov/niosh/fire/reports/face200138.html, National Institute for Occupational Safety and Health, Washington, DC, 2003.

NFPA Codes, Standards, and Recommended Practices

Reference to the following NFPA codes, standards, and recommended practices will provide further information on training programs for fire and emergency service personnel discussed in this chapter. (See the latest version of The NFPA Catalog *for availability of current editions of the following documents.)*

NFPA 472, *Standard for Professional Competence of Responders to Hazardous Materials Incidents*

NFPA 1001, *Standard for Fire Fighter Professional Qualifications*

NFPA 1002, *Standard for Fire Apparatus Driver/Operator Professional Qualifications*

NFPA 1003, *Standard for Airport Fire Fighter Professional Qualifications*

NFPA 1006, *Standard for Rescue Technician Professional Qualifications*

NFPA 1021, *Standard for Fire Officer Professional Qualifications*

NFPA 1031, *Standard for Professional Qualifications for Fire Inspector and Plan Examiner*

NFPA 1033, *Standard for Professional Qualifications for Fire Investigator*

NFPA 1035, *Standard for Professional Qualifications for Public Fire and Life Safety Educator*

NFPA 1041, *Standard for Fire Service Instructor Professional Qualifications*

NFPA 1051, *Standard for Wildland Fire Fighter Professional Qualifications*

NFPA 1061, *Standard for Professional Qualifications for Public Safety Telecommunicator*

NFPA 1071, *Standard for Emergency Vehicle Technician Professional Qualifications*

NFPA 1081, *Standard for Industrial Fire Brigade Member Professional Qualifications*

NFPA 1401, *Recommended Practice for Fire Service Training Reports and Records*

NFPA 1402, *Guide to Building Fire Service Training Centers*

NFPA 1403, *Standard on Live Fire Training Evolutions*

NFPA 1451, *Standard for a Fire Service Vehicle Operations Training Program*

NFPA 1500, *Standard on Fire Department Occupational Safety and Health Program*

NFPA 1670, *Standard on Operations and Training for Technical Search and Rescue Incidents*

Chapter 11

Industrial Fire Loss Prevention

Revised by
Michael Snyder

Chapter Contents

Key Terms

emergency management, fire prevention, fire risk management, hazard identification, hot work, industrial fire brigade, industrial loss prevention, insurance, local emergency planning committee (LEPC), pre-incident planning, process safety, risk assessment, risk management

Fire and explosion loss consequences, which can involve property damage, business interruption, life safety hazards, environmental issues, damage to corporate image, and reduced future profitability, present a major threat to corporate goals and survival. Recognition of these consequences has prompted the development of fire and explosion loss prevention programs and emergency response organizations in many commercial and industrial organizations.

For related topics, see Section 3, Chapter 7, "Fire Hazard Analysis Techniques"; Section 7, Chapter 2, "Storage of Flammable and Combustible Liquids"; Section 9, Chapter 6, "Welding, Cutting, and Other Hot Work"; Section 11, Chapter 4, "Fire Hazards of Construction, Alteration, and Demolition of Buildings"; Section 12, Chapter 9, "Fire and Emergency Services Protective Clothing and Protective Equipment"; Section 17, Chapter 8, "Explosion Prevention and Protection"; and Section 20, Chapter 18, "Industrial Occupancies."

FIRE RISK MANAGEMENT

Fire risk management can be defined as the systematic application of management policies, procedures, and practices to the tasks of analyzing, assessing, and controlling fire risk in order to protect employees, the public, the environment, and company assets while avoiding business interruption (Figure 12.11.1). The typical priorities in fire risk management involve the following:

- Identifying and evaluating fire and explosion hazards/risks
- Developing programs and assigning management responsibilities to manage the identified risks
- Establishing emergency organizations to control fire and explosion incidents that do occur

Hazard Identification

A fire or explosion hazard can be defined as a characteristic of a system, plant, or process that represents a potential for an unplanned event leading to undesirable losses. The key words in this definition are "undesirable losses." Hazard identification is the process of recognizing hazards that can pose significant undesirable losses. Hazard identification should be a continuous activity in the evaluation of new materials, plant additions, and production modifications, as well as the continuing inspection and evaluation of existing facilities.

Resources, including various chapters within this handbook, many NFPA standards, and Internet websites such as those maintained by the United States Chemical Safety and Hazard Investigation Board, and the United Kingdom's Health and Safety Executive describe fire hazards in major industries and special process hazards based on current technology and past loss experience.

Michael Snyder, P.E., CFPS, is EHS development manager with Dow Corning Corporation in Midland, Michigan. He serves on the Industrial Fire Protection Section Board.

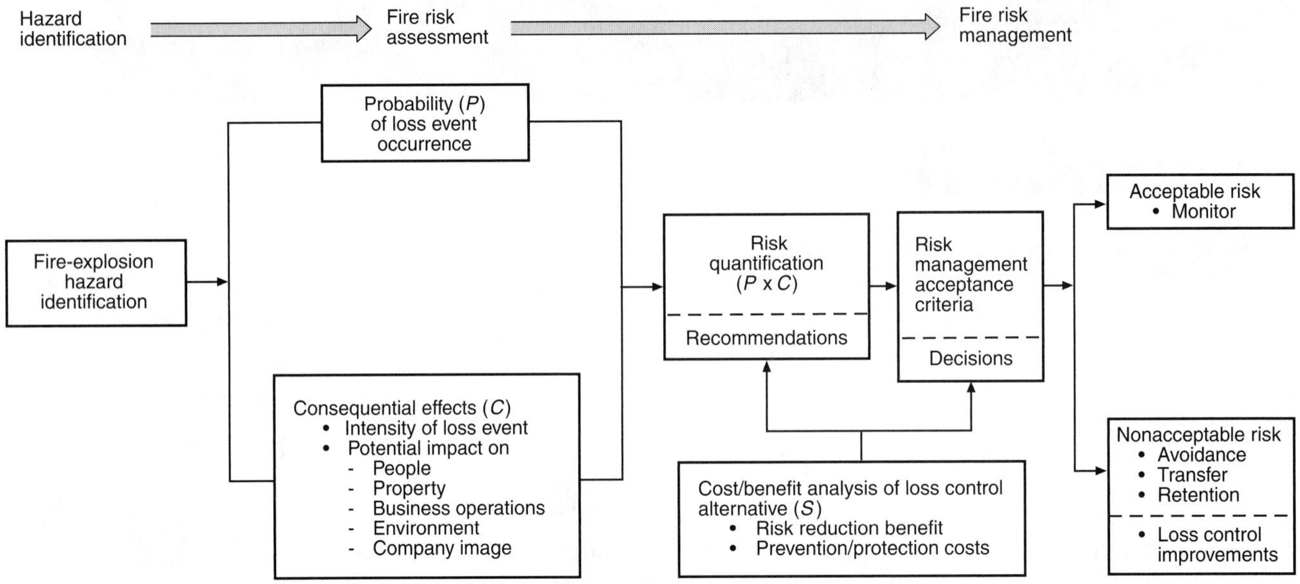

FIGURE 12.11.1 General Framework for Industrial Fire Risk Management

Risk Assessment

The risk assessment process consists of both identifying risks and estimating the probability and magnitude of potential fire and explosion losses. In recent years, there has been an increase in the use of formalized risk assessment methods to support decisions on fire safety issues. Predictive methods that integrate statistical data, deterministic models, and expert opinion increasingly are being used. The primary steps in fire risk assessment include the following:

1. Identification of the fire events that could lead to significant loss
2. Quantification of the fire risk—that is, probability of fire or explosion event occurrences and loss consequences—for the generated fire loss scenarios
3. Development and evaluation of alternative fire prevention and/or fire protection strategies (recommendations) to reduce the fire and explosion risk
4. Measurement of the estimated change in fire and explosion risk (difference in probability and/or consequences) associated with the alternatives

Addressing Probabilities. One of the most difficult tasks in the risk assessment process is addressing probabilities. Fire risk reflects both the probability of fire occurrence and the loss consequences of the fire. In both factors there is an element of uncertainty that must be recognized. Approaches for determining the probabilities of values for fire event occurrences are detailed later. If valid data on fire loss event frequencies are available and applicable, then probabilities can be extracted from this source. Often objective data sources are scarce. To evaluate the application of historical data, it is necessary to look at the following, both for the source of the data and for the situation under consideration:

- Design standards and quality
- Inspection methods and quality
- Maintenance philosophy and quality
- Operational philosophy and quality
- Safety standards and enforcement

If historical data sources are not available for the loss event(s) of interest, probabilities can be evaluated using inferential judgment based on available loss-trending information, such as equipment failures, human error, ignition sources, loss control elements, and damageability factors. Good sources of information include the NFPA Fire Analysis and Research Division and United Kingdom's Health and Safety Executive website.

Subjective estimation processes should be documented and should involve the best judgment a fire protection expert can make based on knowledge of contributing factors from past fire losses, site-specific evidence of loss control deficiencies, and exposed values. A very good reference on equipment failure data sources and application precautions is the AIChE's Center for Chemical Process Safety (CCPS) book entitled *Guidelines for Process Equipment Reliability Data, with Data Tables*[1] as well as the publicly available Process Equipment Reliability Database maintained on the CCPS website.

Quantifying Fire Loss. The physical intensity of fire-explosion consequences can be quantified in terms of the expected energy released (heat exposure, smoke and/or corrosive gas contamination, explosion blast overpressures, etc.), the area involved, and the duration of the fire. Probabilistic engineering assessment—and, in some situations, deterministic fire-explosion modeling tools—are utilized to aid the evaluation process. The *SFPE Handbook of Fire Protection Engineering*[2] provides information on various analytical techniques that can be used in this evaluation.

Once the intensity and duration of the potential fires have been quantified, the impact on both direct and indirect loss potential must be assessed. Direct losses include damage to buildings, equipment, and contents. Indirect losses include business interruption, liability for injury or death, environmental contamination, and damage to company image. For most quantification studies, loss potential is expressed in equivalent monetary terms.

Assessing Risks. The type of risk assessment conducted depends on the significance of the decision, the complexity of the problem, and the time and cost limitations. Routine code-compliance problems can often be handled by simple choices. Complex problems involving new technologies or high-hazard operations require application of more detailed risk assessment and decision analysis methods. Whatever method is used for the risk assessment, it is critical that the assessment is well documented and maintained in an easily accessible format to ensure that complete information is available for routine reviews of the assessment and to be readily available in the event that details of the assessment are questioned by either management or a regulatory authority.

Risk Management

Risk management addresses the value judgments involved in establishing acceptable levels of risk and methods of handling identified risks. The acceptable risk decision-making process is based on specific organizational goals and generally includes (in any order) the following:

- Profit (competitive market position)
- Protection of company assets (major loss exposures)
- Continued company operation (business interruption)
- Continued growth (expansion)
- Humanitarian concerns (employee and public safety)
- Community goodwill (potential embarrassment)
- Legal requirements (liability, building codes, etc.)
- Insurance company requirements
- Environmental concerns

If the risk is acceptable, no immediate action may be necessary, but monitoring for changes that could increase the risk must be done. If the risk is unacceptable, then decisions must be made about how to deal with the risk.

General options available to the risk management decision maker for handling fire and explosion risk exposure include the following:

1. Avoiding the risk by nonparticipation in risky operations
2. Reducing the risk through improved design or use of alternative manufacturing processes
3. Transferring the risk by purchasing insurance to cover potential losses
4. Financing alternative risk transfer arrangements such as captive or corporate funded reserves (self-insurance)
5. Providing loss control improvements
6. Developing a risk management program that includes a combination of the foregoing options

The sixth option generally provides a cost-effective approach for reducing fire loss potential and reducing the risk funding requirements for options 3 and 4. *Risk-Informed, Performance-Based Fire Protection* by T. F. Barry provides a detailed discussion with examples on the subject of risk and industrial fire protection.[3]

An important part of fire risk reduction is the development, implementation, and monitoring of comprehensive loss prevention and control programs. Written documentation should be provided for programs and updated periodically based on the major opportunities for risk reduction.

Recognition of Fire Risk Reduction Opportunities

Figure 12.11.2 illustrates a fire sequence event tree. It depicts primary areas of opportunity for reducing fire risk through implementation of fire loss prevention programs and emergency response organizations.

Initiating Fire. The likelihood of initiating fire events is reduced when fire hazards are adequately identified and evaluated and when quality fire prevention programs are developed, implemented, and audited. Equipment failure rate minimization via good mechanical integrity programs, human error reduction through effective procedures and training practices, and ignition

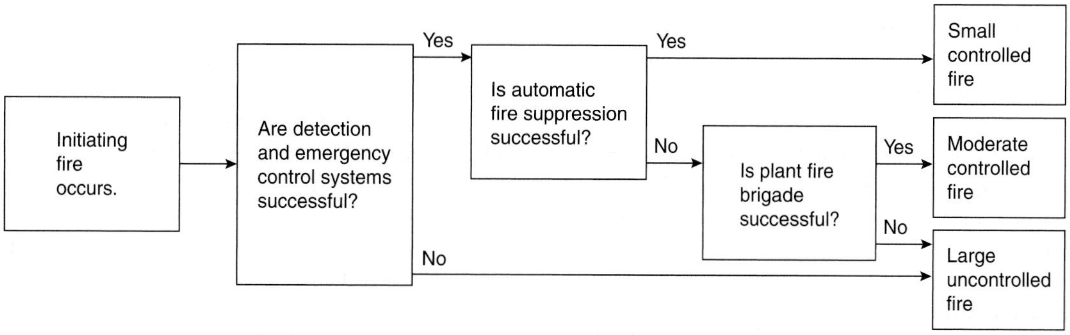

FIGURE 12.11.2 Fire Sequence Event Tree

control procedures such as hot work permits and safe practices all contribute to the overall reduction of initiating fires.

Detection and Emergency Control Success. Rapid detection of fires is the key to reducing the incident magnitude, duration, and the resulting physical damage as well as losses from business recovery time. Prompt detection and intervention through process control systems and successful automatic fire suppression may quickly control incipient fires and prevent them from progressing to large fires that create significant damage.

Process controls can also be used to prevent flammable chemical releases from igniting by quickly isolating flammable releases, thereby stopping the flow of fuel to the atmosphere. Activation of fixed water spray systems can disperse vapors or, with foam water spray, cover and suppress vapors to prevent ignition or control small fires. The prompt response of a well-trained and well-equipped industrial fire brigade can assist the process controls and fixed systems to control the release and limit the size of an emergency fire incident.

Computerized process controls, with extensive emergency shutdown features, are prevalent in large facilities such as refineries, petrochemical plants, and power generation facilities. Process control systems are also prevalent in smaller facilities such as compressed gas cylinder filling, paint spraying, and plywood manufacturing.

Automatic Fire Suppression. Programs related to the inspection, testing, and maintenance of fire protection systems such as sprinkler systems, fire pumps, foam water protection systems, and special extinguishing systems, such as gaseous agents and dry chemicals, improve the reliability of the fire suppression system. Properly designed, effective, and reliable automatic fire suppression systems can quickly control an incipient fire and reduce life safety and property damage exposures.

To ensure that automatic fire suppression systems remain fully functional, it is essential to establish and maintain a fire protection system impairment program that contains the following three aspects:

- Identification and notification of the impaired system
- Minimization of the impairment
- Provision of contingencies (i.e., shutdown of operations, fire watch, use of portable equipment)

The historical collection of large loss fires contains too many examples of situations in which a fire starts in a facility that had an improperly managed fire protection system impairment, which allowed a minor fire to grow, uncontrolled, into a fire resulting in catastrophic loss.

Industrial Fire Brigade Response Success. Industrial fire brigades provide a number of functions at industrial facilities. In addition to providing manual fire suppression support and backup to automatic fire systems, fire brigades assist in the development of prefire planning with responding public fire departments, employee emergency evacuations, and salvage operations following fire incidents. Other duties can include plant fire safety inspections, fire extinguisher training, fire equipment maintenance, and overall emergency coordination. Fire brigade organization and training are discussed later in this chapter.

FIRE PREVENTION AND CONTROL PROGRAM MANAGEMENT

Today few companies, in the face of severe global competition and the high cost of capital, could survive a major loss. Over the years, it has become apparent that people can substantially aid in the minimization of losses. It has been statistically demonstrated by major property insurance companies that the factor with the largest effect on the size of a loss by fire or explosion is what people do or fail to do.

Due to the numerous interfaces between the various engineering disciplines, as well as maintenance and operational programs, it is essential to place the responsibility for the fire protection program with a single individual or small group with direct access to top management. This individual must have sufficient authority to delegate responsibilities affecting plant fire protection across engineering discipline and departmental lines and even across separate divisions, such as engineering, plant services, utilities, safety and loss control, and emergency response. The implementation and enforcement of an effective fire loss control program are dependent on management involvement and support and effective use of property insurance services.

Management Roles

Management can be divided into three echelons, each of which makes important contributions to loss prevention and control: (1) executive management—the board of directors and company officers; (2) middle management—facility managers, department heads, and related staff managers; and (3) line management—the supervisors and team leaders who direct each phase of the operation.

In a relatively small organization, the owner may perform the functions of all three management levels. Although the owner's loss control problems may be fewer, or less complex, than those of the management group in a larger organization, some of the same judgments must be exercised. The owner who tries to be loss control manager may be at a disadvantage, however, because of the lack of specialized training in loss control and the absence of managers with whom to share expertise and creative ideas regarding a sound loss control program. This disadvantage need not pose a major obstacle. Expertise is available from professional loss control consultants, insurance companies, and fire departments.

In today's business environment, facility employees who manage property conservation and or loss prevention may also manage a number of other similar related functions such as safety and health, and security and risk management. To be effective they will need to partner with others within an organization to jointly share goals and objectives while complying with codes and internal programs.

Executive Management. Members of executive management establish company policy, make major financial decisions, determine the product or service to be provided, and establish production levels. Executive management's primary goal is to guide the organization to produce a profit.

Regardless of insurance coverage, losses to plant property by fire, explosion, or other causes can disrupt profitability. On the surface, assets diverted to property protection would appear to be a nonproductive expenditure. However, after a serious loss, the need for an effective loss prevention/control program becomes apparent. For loss control programs to be effective, they must have complete support from executive management. In addition, once a program has been developed and accepted, executive management must insist on regular updates to monitor progress.

Middle Management. Middle management is responsible for the development, implementation, and monitoring of cost-effective loss control programs. The person with primary responsibility for loss control generally has the title of loss control manager. Depending on the organization, titles assigned to individuals vary, and in some cases, the individual may have several other titles when loss control is not a full-time function. To be effective, the assigned individual must have access to decision makers at the executive management level. Direct access would involve reporting to the officer level (e.g., vice presidents of engineering, finance, production, etc.). Indirect access would involve reporting to the director of risk management or other managers with direct access to executive management.

Major responsibilities of the loss control manager include the following:

Overall supervision. Defining loss control program functions, clarifying responsibilities, and ensuring that all procedures are properly carried out

Planning. Anticipating hazards and formulating plans and procedures for fire prevention and overall plant safety

Education and training. Providing employee training in fire prevention; making sure that all production processes and operations are carried out safely, and that contractors follow safe procedures according to company regulations (Figure 12.11.3)

Assignment. Delegating specific maintenance and emergency duties to employees, including guards, caretakers, patrol officers, and night workers

Coordination. Maintaining liaison with the following corporate departments and outside organizations:

- Production and engineering on new processes or materials that can introduce additional fire hazards within the facility
- Plant engineering and maintenance for fire protection installations, impaired protection, maintenance of fire protection equipment, and housekeeping
- The public fire department and insurance company on plant layout, location and type of hazardous processes, coordination of forces, location and type of fire protection equipment, fire doors, fire walls, defense plans, and main defense lines

Review and audit. Periodically checking the efficiency of the entire loss control program; reviewing details of the plan with line management; conducting drills and classes to maintain employee preparedness; auditing

FIGURE 12.11.3 Portable Fire Extinguisher Training—An Important Function for Many Loss Control Departments

and inspecting various facilities for compliance to organization loss prevention policies and plans

In smaller organizations, the facility manager or an appointee must assume these responsibilities.

Line Management. Implementation of a loss control program extends beyond the middle-management level. Unless the members of line management adequately perform their function, the program cannot produce satisfactory results.

Line managers, those with daily personnel contact, should aid in the information collection that middle managers incorporate into loss control programs. Once programs are implemented, line managers are responsible for regular enforcement of company policy.

With regard to employees and work areas under the line manager's supervision, it is the line manager who is responsible for the following:

- Training personnel to carry out individual duties in a loss control program
- Working with the loss control manager and staff in selecting employees for the private fire brigade or other program assignments
- Working with the loss control manager to establish priorities for inspection, testing, and maintenance of fire protection equipment
- Inspiring employees to develop a fire-conscious attitude and respect for the loss control program
- Insisting that access to all protection equipment, as well as all means of egress, be kept open
- Working closely with the loss control manager and staff to ensure that new equipment or processes are adequately protected before startup
- Reporting all occupancy changes that may affect loss control
- Working with the loss control manager and staff to ensure that fire exit drills are held regularly
- Accounting for each employee following facility evacuation
- Supervising emergency action when a fire or other property-related incident occurs in the absence of members of an established emergency organization

Insurance Company Roles

Many property insurance companies focus on recommending management programs that assist facilities to prevent and minimize property damage and business interruption losses. These services are provided to both large industrial sites and small retail operations. When considering the development of a program, management needs to take into consideration the size of the operation, reporting structure within the company, hazards involved, and how the program will be managed and/or directed.

Each insurance program needs to be tailored to address the risk elements that have been identified. Primary management program elements that are typically offered include the following:

- Impairments to fire protection systems
- Smoking regulations
- Maintenance
- Employee training
- New construction
- Preemergency planning
- Hazardous materials evaluation
- Cutting, welding, and other hot work
- Loss prevention inspection
- Handling insurance company recommendations
- Fire protection and security surveillance
- Fire protection equipment inspection
- Hazard identification and evaluation
- Proper housekeeping
- Handling and responding to losses or claims
- Handling inspections from enforcement agencies

Insurance Company Service Options

Today many insurance companies have reduced or eliminated service functions as part of their standard insurance program. In some cases the insurance companies have retained the services but operate with reduced staff and focus on loss prevention activities that support only the insurance underwriting placement. In other cases some property insurance companies have staffed up to sell or offer these services as part of the entire portfolio of insurance products. Some loss prevention services are considered as part of the insurance program but the service has a cost factor attached. The loss control program manager needs to understand what he or she is getting from the insurance companies and clearly understand the scope of the services, cost, and deliverables.

Most insurance policy contracts and loss prevention insurance inspection reports contain a disclaimer that outlines the limitations of the inspection survey or site risk reviews. Before a client spends money on insurance company recommendations compliance, the client needs to determine if the proposed corrective action will impact the insurance program and if the identified recommendation has other more cost-effective options.

Services provided by insurance companies are sometime labeled as "bundled." That is, the insurance policy and loss prevention or risk control services are provided at a fixed cost by one company. Remember that with this approach the loss prevention people work directly for the insurance companies, and the focus of service may be driven from internal insurance company standards or guidelines. In many cases, particularly for small facilities, this approach can serve to fulfill the needs of the risk control client. In other situations, such as a company with many large sites and operations, the client may wish to direct the loss control services to minimize the interruptions to operations in performing the inspections.

With continuing changes in the insurance industry, many more consulting companies now offer high-quality loss prevention and risk control type services, which they call an "unbundled" approach. This approach breaks apart the service elements from the insurance contract. In this method the client purchases the services directly and often separately from insurance coverage.

The following are items that should be included in a service contract with an insurance company:

- Term of agreement
- Duties of both parties—compliance with health, safety, and OSHA standards
- Confidentiality of data security
- Right to work product
- Warranty—limitation of liability
- Indemnity and insurance
- Compensation—upfront payment or schedule
- Termination of contract or agreement
- Miscellaneous rights
- Compliance with jurisdictional codes

These items can also apply to bundled loss prevention service from an insurance company.

Program Monitoring. Based on the approach, unbundled or bundled services, companies need to establish performance requirements in the contracts established for service. It is recommended that the service provider submit a quarterly stewardship report outlining all the activities, cost, and a scorecard measuring the key performance elements of the contract or service agreement.

Facility or company management must routinely audit the insurance services program, thereby providing a means to measure performance of the services delivered. Auditing also provides an effective tool for feedback on the program's strengths and pinpoints deficiencies.

LOSS PREVENTION PROGRAM MOTIVATION AND DEVELOPMENT

Human element factors play a significant role in most fire and explosions. Various statistical studies of loss incidents in a variety of industries have indicated the following general breakdown:

- Human factors (70–85%) (e.g., management program deficiencies, human operator errors)
- Equipment failures (10–20%) (e.g., design or maintenance deficiencies)
- External factors (10–20%) (e.g., earthquake, floods)

It should be noted that some products and equipment are less vulnerable to human error than others, so product or equipment performance can be a factor even though human error is also a factor. It is a mistake to treat the two as mutually exclusive.

To reduce human error leading to fire incidents, many companies are establishing and expanding policies and practices that prioritize the implementation and auditing of loss prevention programs. Integrated into many of these programs are insurance company guidelines, industry recommended practices, regulatory requirements, and NFPA standards.

Insurance Company Guidelines

Traditionally, industrial property insurance companies have focused on recommending management programs that assist in the prevention and minimization of property damage and business interruption losses.

Some of the primary management programs include the following:

- Impairments to fire protection systems
- Smoking regulations
- Maintenance
- Employee training
- New construction
- Pre-emergency planning
- Hazardous materials evaluation
- Cutting, welding, and other hot work
- Loss prevention inspection
- Fire protection and security surveillance
- Fire protection equipment inspection
- Hazard identification and evaluation
- Proper housekeeping

Each major industrial insurance company typically has guidance documents that can be used in conjunction with NFPA standards to implement effective loss management programs.

Modern commercial and industrial programs also include technical reviews of manufacturing equipment and processing hazards and can assist in the risk assessment of many specific manufacturing operations.

U.S. Federal Regulations

The Occupational Safety and Health Administration (OSHA) regulates many aspects of fire prevention and control within commercial and industrial occupancies. Specific regulations include the following:

Part 1910 Subpart E—Exit Routes, Emergency Action Plans, and Fire Prevention Plans

Part 1910 Subpart H—Hazardous Materials

- 1910.106—Flammable and combustible liquids
- 1910.107—Spray finishing using flammable and combustible materials
- 1910.108—Dip tanks containing flammable or combustible liquids
- 1910.110—Storage and handling of liquefied petroleum gases
- 1910.119—Process safety management of highly hazardous chemicals
- 1910.120—Hazardous waste operations and emergency response

Part 1910 Subpart L—Fire Protection

Part 1910 Subpart Q—Welding, Cutting, and Brazing

- 1910.252—General Requirements

Many of the foregoing OSHA regulations are derived from older versions of NFPA standards and have constituted leading industrial loss control practices for many years. Work is underway to update the references to more current versions of the NFPA standards. Several letters of interpretation issued by OSHA accept the use of more modern versions of the NFPA standards with some limitations.

Many states and local jurisdictions have adopted versions of NFPA standards to serve as the basis for regulatory requirements. The most commonly adopted standards include NFPA 30, *Flammable and Combustible Liquids Code,* to regulate the safety of flammable and combustible liquids, and NFPA 58, *Liquefied Petroleum Gas Code,* to regulate the safety of liquefied petroleum gas operations.

OSHA 1910.119, *Process Safety Management of Highly Hazardous Chemicals,* was introduced in 1992 and focuses on the application of performance-based management programs rather than specific engineering guidelines for the prevention of toxic releases, fires, and explosions on plant sites that use or store hazardous materials that exceed specific volume thresholds. Many of the regulatory requirements arising from this standard represented practices used by leading manufacturing companies for many years.

The following are the major program segments in CFR 1910.119:

- Employee participation
- Process safety information
- Process hazard analysis
- Operating procedures
- Training
- Contractors
- Pre-start-up safety reviews
- Mechanical integrity
- Hot work permits
- Management of change
- Incident investigations
- Emergency planning and response
- Compliance safety audits

In the mid-1990s the Environmental Protection Agency (EPA) promulgated 40 CFR Part 68, *Risk Management Program for Chemical Accident Prevention,* which focuses on the exposure of toxic chemical releases and fire and explosions to the public.

EPA's risk management program (RMP) elements include the following:

- Hazard assessments
- Prevention program
- Emergency response program, including procedures for informing the public and response agencies should an accident occur

EPA's RMP regulation requires development and implementation of management programs at facilities that manufacture, process, use, store, or transport regulated hazardous chemicals in quantities that exceed specified threshold limits as listed in the regulation. EPA's regulation rule adopts the OSHA CFR 1910.119 PSM regulation as the RMP's prevention program segment.

MANAGEMENT LOSS PREVENTION AND CONTROL PROGRAM FRAMEWORK

The details and complexity of program elements for loss prevention and control will vary depending on the type of plant facilities, nature of hazardous operations, complexities of processes, and exposures to plant employees and the public.

Primary management program elements can be categorized as follows:

Process Technology

- Process safety information
- Process hazard analysis
- Pre-start-up safety reviews

Mechanical Integrity Programs

- Process equipment
- Emergency safety devices
- Protection systems

Operating Procedures

- Written operating procedures
- Hot work permits
- Fire system impairments
- Flammable liquid handling and ignition control

Management

- Employee training
- Contractors
- Management of change
- New construction

Incident Management and Investigation

- Disaster/emergency management and pre-incident planning
- Incident investigations

Process Safety Information

For process, storage, and transportation operations involving flammable and hazardous materials, it is important to develop, document, and update process safety information, including information pertaining to the following:

- Hazards of the chemicals
- Process technology
- Equipment

Material hazards documentation provides pertinent hazard data for each chemical involved in a process or operation, including physical and chemical properties such as flammability and thermal stability data, reaction data, and any other property relevant to a particular hazard. Toxicity data are an important part of the package. In many cases, material safety data sheets (MSDSs) will satisfy this requirement, provided they contain the necessary details.

Chemical and flammability data can be extracted from numerous sources including the NFPA *Fire Protection Handbook.* Much of the data available in these publications are at atmospheric temperature and pressure. Experimental data appropriate to process conditions will sometimes be needed. Dust explosion data for explosion-venting calculations are presented in NFPA 68, *Standard on Explosion Protection by Deflagration Venting,* which includes additional references. A considerable amount of dust explosion data can be obtained from various U.S. Bureau of Mines and NFPA publications.

Process Hazard Analysis

Hazard evaluation activities can be accomplished by trained plant personnel working with outside specialists when required. It is the hazard evaluation team's responsibility to study the process operation thoroughly, identify all the potential fire and explosion hazards, and recommend changes or further reviews to eliminate or control the identified hazards. A written report of the evaluation must be developed and should include the following:

- List of participants
- Methodology(s) applied
- List of documents, such as part and identification (P&ID) numbers and issue
- Summary of the findings
- Recommendations

All hazard evaluation reports, recommendation status reports, and follow-up documentation should become part of the process documentation file.

An organized approach is essential to conducting effective and efficient hazard evaluations. Hazard evaluation techniques include the following:

- Safety review
- Checklist analysis
- Relative ranking indexes
- Preliminary hazard analysis
- What-if analysis
- What-if/checklist analysis
- Hazard and operability (HAZOP) analysis
- Failure modes and effects analysis (FMEA)
  - Fault-tree analysis
  - Event-tree analysis
  - Cause-consequence analysis
  - Human reliability analysis

Each technique has specific application benefits, limitations, resource needs (staff, time, budget), and documentation requirements. It would be impossible in this chapter to describe each technique. An excellent reference that addresses those techniques in detail and provides illustrative examples is the Center for Chemical Process Safety's (CCPS) *Guidelines for Hazard Evaluation Procedures with Examples.*[4]

Pre-Start-Up Safety Reviews

A pre-start-up safety review should be performed for new facilities and for modified facilities when there may be changes in process safety information. The pre-start-up safety review should confirm the following:

- Construction is in accordance with design specifications.
- Safety, operating, maintenance, and emergency procedures are in place and adequate.
- Recommendations from insurance reviews and any process hazard analysis are adequately resolved.
- Operating procedures are in place and employees are trained.
- Fire prevention and protection systems are in service.

Mechanical Integrity Programs. A primary fire prevention objective is to prevent the release of flammable and hazardous materials from containment. A quality mechanical integrity program (MIP) is a key element in meeting this objective.

The purpose of an MIP is to ensure the safe operation of process and safety equipment through design, inspection, testing, preventive maintenance, and quality assurance monitoring.

The MIP policies and practices at facilities handling flammable and hazardous materials will have a major influence on the level of failures and accidents experienced. Establishing comprehensive programs is a key ingredient in successful loss prevention and control management and should include the following:

- Identification of all critical equipment requiring inspection, testing, and preventive maintenance
- Procedures and schedules for inspecting process vessels, piping, and associated process equipment and safety and protection systems
- Procedures and schedules for testing critical protective devices, such as pressure-relief valves, detection and alarm interlocks, emergency generators, and fire protection systems
- Quality assurance procedures to ensure corrective maintenance functions, employee qualifications, replacement part specifications, and so on

Systems that protect facilities and personnel from hazardous situations (e.g., toxic releases, fire, explosion) must operate effectively and reliably. Emergency safety devices and protection systems generally remain static for long periods of time and, therefore, need scheduled inspection, maintenance, and testing to ensure that these systems function correctly during an emergency. Testing and maintenance of emergency safety and protection devices are very important and must be covered by a formal system with full documentation. Some examples of equipment and systems include the following:

- Pressure-relief systems, vent systems, and devices
- Process monitoring devices and sensors
- Explosion vents
- Electrical grounding and bonding systems
- Dikes and drainage systems
- Gas and flame detectors
- Emergency alarm and communication systems
- Emergency shutdown devices and system interlocks
- Emergency generators
- Sprinkler and water spray systems
- Fire pumps
- Special suppression systems (e.g., dry chemical, foam)

Testing and inspection policies and procedures should follow applicable codes and standards, such as those published by the American Society of Mechanical Engineers (ASME), the American Petroleum Institute (API), the American Institute of Chemical Engineers (AIChE), the American National Standards Institute (ANSI), the American Society for Testing and Materials (ASTM), and the National Fire Protection Association (NFPA), where they exist, or recognized and generally accepted engineering practices.

Fire Protection Systems. An important mechanical integrity program component is the testing and preventive maintenance of fire protection equipment. Facility management must routinely assess the quality of fire protection equipment testing and maintenance programs. Procedures used to conduct this assessment include code compliance reviews, corrective maintenance tracking, maintenance team qualifications, program monitoring and updating, equipment replacement programs, and compliance with appropriate standards. Examples include the following:

- *Code compliance.* Are documented procedures in place that meet current NFPA standards for the maintenance and testing of fire protection systems? Are procedures being properly applied at the required intervals, and are documented/signed-off testing and maintenance logs being maintained and readily available for review?
- *Corrective maintenance tracking.* Are documented corrective maintenance and testing procedures in place, and is a tracking method showing completion-date status with sign-offs to verify completion readily available for review?
- *Maintenance team qualifications.* Are the people doing testing, maintenance checks, and corrective actions properly qualified and continually trained in conducting proper and efficient maintenance and in recognizing and correcting problem areas?
- *Program monitoring and updating.* Do procedures comply with the manufacturer's suggested maintenance for unique and specific equipment functions, and are procedures updated based on the manufacturer's experience, plant-specific experience, and/or equipment modifications?
- *Equipment replacement program.* Are equipment age, operating environment, and availability of spare parts considered in the updating and modification of maintenance and testing efforts, frequencies, and replacement of systems and system components?
- *Compliance with applicable NFPA standards:*

  NFPA 12, *Standard on Carbon Dioxide Extinguishing Systems*

  NFPA 12A, *Standard on Halon 1301 Fire Extinguishing Systems*

  NFPA 17, *Standard for Dry Chemical Extinguishing Systems*

  NFPA 25, *Standard for the Inspection, Testing, and Maintenance of Water-Based Fire Protection Systems*

  NFPA 69, *Standard on Explosion Prevention Systems*

  NFPA 70B, *Recommended Practice for Electrical Equipment Maintenance*

  NFPA 72®, National Fire Alarm Code®

  NFPA 80, *Standard for Fire Doors and Other Opening Protectives*

  NFPA 110, *Standard for Emergency and Standby Power Systems*

  NFPA 780, *Standard for the Installation of Lightning Protection Systems*

NFPA 25 addresses the inspection, testing, and maintenance activities for much of the standard fire protection equipment installed within most facilities, including the following:

- Sprinkler systems
- Standpipe and hose systems
- Private fire service mains
- Fire pumps
- Water storage tanks
- Water-spray fixed systems
- Foam-water systems
- Fire protection valves

Operating Procedures

Written Operating Procedures. It is important to develop and implement written operating procedures that provide clear instructions for safely conducting activities for each process that represents potential hazardous releases, fire, or explosion potential. The written operating procedures should address the following:

Steps for Each Operating Phase

- Initial start-up
- Normal operation
- Temporary operations, as needs arise
- Emergency operations (including shutdown)
- Normal shutdown
- Start-ups following outages

Operating Limits

- Consequences of deviations
- Steps to correct or avoid deviations
- Safety systems and their functions

Safety and Health Considerations

- Properties and hazards of process chemicals
- Exposure precautions, including controls (e.g., engineering, administrative, emergency response)
- Safety procedures for operating equipment
- Control measures in event of exposure
- Any special or unique hazards

Operating procedures should be readily accessible to employees at all times and must be maintained to reflect current requirements.

Flammable Liquid Handling and Ignition Control. The accidental release of flammable liquids or gases from containment and potential ignition present a major loss exposure. An effective management program should address personnel training in the handling of flammable liquids and control of ignition sources. NFPA 30 provides information on this subject. The following highlights some of the management issues, adapted from NFPA's publication, *Understanding Fire Protection for Flammable Liquids:*[5]

- Training of personnel should include the following:
  1. Thorough indoctrination of all employees, including supervisors, in the hazards associated with the storage, transfer, and use of flammable and combustible liquids
  2. Indoctrination of employees in the importance of keeping flammable liquids and vapors confined to closed equipment and containers

3. Indoctrination of employees in the importance of limiting the quantities of liquids in the work area to that amount needed for efficient operations
4. Training of employees in the need for constant attendance during all flammable liquid transfer operations
5. Training of employees in the proper procedure for control and cleanup of leaks and spills

- Control of ignition sources should include the following:
  1. Ensuring electrical equipment and wiring in the area are suitable for the hazard. NFPA 30 and NFPA 70, *National Electrical Code®*, specify the requirements for electrical equipment in hazardous areas.
  2. Not locating any equipment having open flames, hot surfaces, or radiant heat sources in areas where flammable or combustible liquids are used, handled, or stored
  3. Prohibiting the use of friction- and spark-producing equipment in areas where flammable liquids are used
  4. Providing adequate grounding and bonding of all equipment that handles or uses flammable liquids to minimize the accumulation of hazardous static charges. NFPA 77, *Recommended Practice on Static Electricity,* provides the guidelines for grounding and bonding of equipment.
  5. Prohibiting smoking, open-flame torches, and hot work in hazardous areas
  6. Establishing a program to ensure that all vessels, tanks, piping, and process equipment are properly drained and purged of flammable and combustible liquids *prior* to performing maintenance operations

Hot Work Permits. Hot work—that is, work involving burning, welding, or similar operations capable of initiating a fire or explosion—is common in the industrial workplace and is also one of the key element programs covered by OSHA Process Safety standard, 29 CFR 1910.119. Hot work continues to be one of the largest causes of fires in industry.

Hot work is defined in NFPA 51B, *Standard for Fire Prevention During Welding, Cutting, and Other Hot Work,* as any work involving burning, welding, or similar operation that is capable of initiating fires or explosions. Examples of hot work activities include heat treating, grinding, thawing pipe, using powder-driven fasteners, hot riveting, and welding and allied processes (e.g., open-flame soldering, brazing, thermal spraying, oxygen cutting, and arc cutting). Other similar applications, such as grinding, chipping, or abrasive blasting, that produce a spark, a flame, or heat could also be included as hot work. These operations are potentially dangerous, depending on the type of work being performed and the environment in which it is performed. Details regarding the management of a hot work program may be found in Section 9, Chapter 6, "Welding, Cutting, and Other Hot Work."

The centerpiece of an effective hot work program is the hot work permitting process. The three steps to consider for hot work permits are recognition, evaluation, and control. Once the hazard is recognized (in part through the use of the facility-specific checklist on the permit), the extent of the hazard can be evaluated. Based on the severity of the hazard, a control can be developed to minimize or eliminate the hazard, which is then recorded on the permit. The control can include moving the hot work or combustibles, isolating the combustibles, and assigning a fire watch. The hot work permit, which is the start of any good hot work program, is a tool that assists the permit authorizing individual (PAI) to perform all three of these steps in coordination with the person performing the hot work (operator) and the fire watch (see Figure 12.11.4).

FIGURE 12.11.4 Fire Watch Monitoring a Hot Work Area

Precautions for hot work are as follows:

- Hot work should be prohibited in areas where sprinklers are out of service.
- Hot work should not be done in a flammable liquids room unless all liquids are removed.
- Sparks or molten metal should not be permitted to pass through doorways or cracks or holes in walls and floors.
- All exposed combustibles should be moved a minimum of 35 ft (10.7 m) from hot work operations. Noncombustible curtains must be used between the operation and combustible materials when adequate separation cannot be maintained.
- Floors should be swept clean. Wood floors should be wet down or covered with a protective shield, preferably sheet metal.
- Fire extinguishers must always be available at all hot work operations. Any extinguishers that are used should be replaced promptly.
- The immediate area and areas on floors above and below should be inspected for a minimum of 30 minutes after completion of a hot work operation for any sign of smoldering or damage caused by hot slag.
- When oxyacetylene equipment is not in use, the gas should be turned off at the cylinder valve.

Hot work done by an outside contractor should be closely supervised to ensure compliance with the hot work permit system. Approximately one of every three hot work fires reported occurs while outside contractors are engaged in hot work operations.

Fire System Impairment Procedures. Many large fire losses have been directly attributed to impaired fire protection systems or equipment. Major property insurance companies, during routine facility inspections, continue to find fire protection systems of all types out of service. The need for an effective impairment notification program is evident to eliminate the possibility of undetected shutdown of fire protection systems.

A protection system may become impaired for a number of reasons (e.g., maintenance, renovation, construction, equipment failure, or failure to reactivate the system or device). Facility managers and loss control managers should be notified *immediately* of any impairments during normal working hours. During off-hours, depending on the seriousness of the impairment, these same individuals may still want to be notified. This procedure should be addressed in detail in the company policy.

Any impairment program should require the following:

1. Assigning responsibility and authority to control the impairment to one individual. This is normally a plant engineer or fire protection safety supervisor. In an emergency, a shift supervisor or fire brigade chief may have the authority to impair a system, but the overall responsibility for the impairment remains with the loss control manager.
2. Educating plant personnel in basic precautions to be taken when a protection system or equipment is impaired. Precautions include the following:
   - Limiting the number, scope, and duration of impairment
   - Supplementing manual fire protection with extra extinguishers
   - Avoiding hot work operations
   - Shutting down any hazardous processes
   - Completing impairment work in a timely manner
   - Restoring protection system on completion of all work
   - Verifying, by testing, that the protection system is operational

The three forms of impairment are (1) concealed, (2) emergency, and (3) planned.

A concealed impairment is an unknown impairment. It occurs when a fire protection system is left out of service or removed from service by an unauthorized person. Concealed impairments should be discovered during activities conducted as part of a facility's fire protection maintenance and inspection program.

Emergency impairments are caused by unexpected events impairing the normal function of the protection system (e.g., a section of sprinkler piping freezing and bursting). Emergency situations are normally associated with confusion and a sense of urgency. To eliminate much of the confusion, a written procedure should be in a location available to all personnel.

When handling emergency impairments, the following steps need to be performed:

1. Isolate the area where the situation, or condition, is causing the impairment. If possible, the remaining protection system should be kept in service. Doing so may require temporary connections or bypasses.
2. Notify the shift supervisor and fire brigade chief that an impairment has occurred. Institute frequent patrols of the impaired area for fire safety issues.
3. Secure any hazardous production operation in the area where the protection system is impaired.
4. Properly tag out the impaired system or equipment.
5. Start repairs on the impaired system once the area is secured. Work on the impairment should continue until it has been restored to service. Hot work required for the repair should be performed in a protected area.
6. Place additional portable extinguishers and/or charged fire hoses in the impaired area at accessible locations.
7. Notify the public fire department that emergency impairment has occurred and the extent to which the protection system is out of service.
8. Notify the alarm company of the impairment, indicating whether any alarms have been affected.

A planned impairment is a scheduled impairment, typically involving improvement or modification to the present system. Such impairment might involve adding a new section of sprinkler piping or changing old sprinkler heads. When work has been completed, it is important to ensure that fire protection is properly restored. Each of the several steps required should be verified by the individual who authorized the impairment. These steps include the following:

1. Opening all valves that were secured during the impairment and conducting a drain test (Note: If during the test the pressure drops below normal, the system may have a restricted or partially closed valve.)
2. Placing all alarms and/or detection devices back in service

3. Restoring any fire protection equipment to "automatic" that was either secured or placed in "manual"
4. Verifying that portable extinguishers are in place and fully charged and hose lines are returned to racks or reels
5. Notifying plant supervisors (shift supervisors and fire brigade chief) that the fire protection system has been restored
6. Notifying the alarm service or central stations that the fire protection has been restored and that alarms will be verified
7. Notifying the public fire department that the fire protection system has been restored to service and all alarms activated

Self-Inspection. The effectiveness of operating procedures relies heavily on human actions, management oversight, and compliance to established procedures. It is essential that these procedures are audited on a routine basis to evaluate how well they are working and to identify any needs to improvement.

Management must take a positive approach in establishing a program for the periodic auditing of all operating procedures and systems. These audits should be conducted by individuals knowledgeable in the procedures and systems and include a procedure for documenting all findings and reporting them to appropriate levels of management. For those deficiencies that are severe and could be of imminent danger, the facility manager should be notified immediately and should take immediate corrective action. Key areas for self inspections and audits include the following:

Written Operating Procedures

- Check that written procedures are current.
- Ensure that employees are familiar with the content of written procedures.
- Check that the procedures are specific in detailing what should be done during abnormal and emergency situations.

Hot Work Permits

- Decide whether permits are required for all hot work activities.
- Review any facility standards or written procedures governing hot work control.
- View a sample of recently issued work permits for completeness and accuracy.
- Determine whether permit authorized individuals (PAIs) and fire watch personnel are trained.
- Check whether there have been any recent hot work–related fires and whether they were investigated. Determine whether recommendations from the investigation have been implemented.

Fire System Inspections and Impairments

- Review fire equipment inspection records for completeness and timeliness.
- Conduct field inspection of fire systems to ensure conditions match the inspection records.
- Conduct field inspections of fire water control valves and fire water supplies looking for any signs of system impairment.
- Request that facility personnel who are assigned to conduct fire system inspections demonstrate the methods used for their inspections and tests.

Flammable Liquid Handling and Ignition Control

- Check whether employees have a basic knowledge of flammable liquid terminology and hazards.
- Determine if storage of flammable liquid containers is in accordance with NFPA 30.
- Determine whether appropriate safeguards have been taken with open handling of flammable liquids.
- Check that gravity dispensing of flammable liquids uses flame arrestors and self-closing valves.

General Facility Loss Control Conditions

- Check whether poor housekeeping, waste, and combustible materials accumulations exist.
- Determine if careless smoking occurs.
- Check for the presence of oily rag storage in noncombustible containers with lids.
- Determine whether electrical switch gear is blocked and if there is storage of combustible material in electrical rooms.
- Check for improper maintenance of electrical conduits and junction boxes.
- Determine whether there are abnormal amounts of combustible in-process or finished products in areas where fire protection systems have not been adequately designed for this overload.

To simplify facility self-inspections, many property insurance companies and trade associations offer forms with items specific to many different types of occupancies and equipment. Forms should be specific enough to be usable and comprehensive enough so that no element of prevention or protection is overlooked.

Management

Employee Training. Employees should be educated in the hazards involved in the job and in the functions of emergency safety control and fire protection equipment. Employee training should be well documented. This includes initial, refresher, and supplemental training and certification. Initial training requires that all workers involved in a process, as well as newly assigned workers, be trained in the basics of the process, operating procedures, and associated hazards. Refresher and supplemental training should be given at least annually. After training, the employer should certify that workers have received and successfully completed the specified training.

Contractors. Prior to the commencement of work, contractors working at a facility or plant should be informed of the potential hazards of fire, explosion, or toxic releases. Contractors must be trained in the plant's safe work practices, and hot work procedures and be instructed in the provisions of the plant's emergency response plan.

Management of Change. Making design or operational changes that may affect the process hazard level without formal review and authorization can lead to serious fire or explosion incidents. To reduce this potential, a management of change (MOC) program should be implemented. This program should establish written procedures to manage and document any changes to facilities or to process chemicals, technologies, or equipment, including fire protection equipment. Procedures should address the following:

1. Change of elements
   - Technical basis for the change
   - Impact on safety and health
   - Modifications to operating procedures
   - Necessary time period for the change
   - Authorization requirements for the change
2. Employee training prior to implementation
3. Revision of process safety analysis information
4. Revision of operating procedures

New Construction. Loss control managers should be directly involved in new construction project planning. Responsibilities should include the following:

1. *New construction site evaluation.* The loss control manager should determine if the following conditions exist at the site under consideration:
   - Adequate water supply to meet fire protection requirements
   - Exposure to flood
   - Exposure conditions involving adjacent facilities
   - Acceptable support forces, such as public fire departments, disaster relief, and medical teams
   - Impediments to quick response by support forces (e.g., lift bridges, railroad crossings, or heavily traveled highways)
2. *Facility and protection systems planning.* The following are loss control factors to be considered during the planning stage:
   - Using fire-resistant materials
   - Limiting the size of fire areas by the use of fire walls, fire doors, and so on
   - Segregating unusual concentrations of values (e.g., sensitive equipment and highly hazardous operations)
   - Ensuring emergency exits are adequate in number, size, and location
   - Providing physical protection (e.g., automatic sprinklers, hydrants, and standpipes)
   - Providing access for fire protection vehicles
   - Considering design for earthquake, wind, and heavy snow or rain
3. *Production operations involving new equipment or modifications.* Loss control management should participate in process planning, which may require the following:
   - Segregation to limit exposure from other operations
   - Special protection/suppression systems
   - Limited access or improved security
   - Special exit facilities
4. *Fire protection during facility construction.* Loss control management personnel should participate in the following duties:
   - Advising contractor personnel of loss control management policies (facility personnel must have authority to enforce compliance)
   - Acceptance testing of all fire protection equipment
   - Monitoring construction for compliance with specifications

Incident Management and Investigations

Emergency Planning. NFPA 1600, *Standard on Disaster/Emergency Management and Business Continuity Programs,* and NFPA 1620, *Recommended Practice for Pre-Incident Planning,* provide a very good framework for developing, implementing, and maintaining a facility program to mitigate, prepare for, respond to, and recover from disasters and emergencies.

Key elements of an emergency plan include the following:

- Identification of hazards, the likelihood of their occurrence, and the vulnerability of people, property, and the environment to those hazards. Typical hazards considered include fires, explosions, earthquakes, floods, windstorm (tornado and/or hurricane), water/liquid damage, and flammable/combustible liquid spills.
- Preplanned response scenarios for identified hazards posing high risk
- An emergency organization within the facility capable of directing, controlling, and coordinating response and recovery operations
- Defined relationships and operational procedures between the facility emergency organization and municipal emergency service organizations
- Preferred methods of reporting fires and other emergencies
- Emergency escape procedures and emergency escape route assignments
- Procedures for employees who remain to operate critical plant operations before they evacuate
- Procedures to account for all employees after emergency evacuation has been completed
- Rescue and medical duties for those employees who are to perform them
- Procedures to ensure that critical fire protection systems remain operational, if at all possible
- Plans for business continuity in the event of a major emergency, including consideration for salvage, cleanup, and the use of alternative locations for conducting business
- Frequency and scope of training for employees based on their emergency responsibilities
- Plans for routine exercises and evaluations of the emergency plan

Prefire incident plans should be developed for each building and be organized in a format that is useful to the facility fire brigade and municipal fire service organizations. It should contain, at a minimum, the following information:

- A review of the facility layout and best access and evacuation routes for each area
- A discussion of facility construction features and their probable reaction during a fire incident
- An overview of facility operations, equipment, and associated fire hazards

- A review of available water supplies, fire pumps, sprinkler control valves, fire department connections, detection, alarms, and special suppression equipment
- Expected areas for spill and firewater drainage and runoff, and anticipated exposures created by them
- A description of available communications and preestablished plans with the responding public fire department
- The requirements for manual fire-fighting efforts, including the most appropriate tactics, equipment, and approach to be used by the brigade
- Information on ventilation systems that may cause the spread of smoke or may be utilized to prevent smoke spread
- An evaluation of chemical hazards and methods to handle spills
- The location of flammable liquid and gas system isolation valves and electrical power disconnects

FM Global provides several interactive tools, at no cost, to the Public/Volunteer Fire Service that aid in the development of prefire incident plans for sprinklered commercial and industrial properties.[6]

Incident Investigations. It is important to investigate every incident that results in, or could have reasonably resulted in, a major release, fire, or explosion accident. Most current investigation methods focus on determining the root cause of the incident and basing corrective actions on the root cause. Incident investigation program factors include the following:

- Incident investigations should be initiated promptly. Several U.S. government regulations require investigation of large incidents begin within 48 hours.
- Investigation teams should have plant and process knowledge as well as other specialties, such as fire loss investigation and root cause investigation skills.
- Incident reports should include the following:
  - Date of incident and date the investigation begins
  - Appropriate collection of relevant evidence from the investigation
  - Description of incident, root cause, contributing factors, and resulting recommendations
- Reports should be reviewed with appropriate personnel within the facility and retained in loss incident files.
- Recommendations should be addressed and resolved in a timely manner.
- Management should routinely review the status of open investigation reports and recommendations.

QUALITY GRADING OF MANAGEMENT LOSS CONTROL PROGRAMS

Example Grading System

It is beneficial to develop a quality rating system for loss prevention and control programs to provide a framework for budgeting and monitoring program investments versus program quality. Table 12.11.1 provides an example format for grading some primary loss prevention and control programs. This general framework can be expanded and customized as needed.

Many property insurance companies use other rating systems to evaluate the quality of a risk. Although the methods used are proprietary, each company assesses the intrinsic hazards of a facility to fire, natural disaster, and the specific hazards of the occupancy. Additional adjustments are made to the assessment based on the quality of the fire protection systems, capability of the fire water supply, the quality of other loss control programs, and status of previous recommendations at a given facility. It is important to understand the specific methods used by a facility's insurance company for rating risk, and this understanding should be part of an annual discussion with insurance company representatives.

The example quality scoring in Table 12.11.1 is based on the following four fundamental quality elements:

1. Planning (+40 maximum points)
   - Explicit goals and objectives (+5)
   - Well-defined scope (+5)
   - Clear-cut desired outputs (+5)
   - Consideration of alternative achievement mechanisms (+5)
   - Well-defined inputs and resource requirements (+10)
   - Identification of needed tools and training (+10)
2. Accountability (+40 maximum points)
   - Strong sponsorship (+5)
   - Clear lines of authority (+5)
   - Explicit assignments of roles and responsibilities
   - Formal procedures (+10)
   - Internal coordination and communication (+10)
3. Implementation (at the facility level) (+40 maximum points)
   - Detailed work plans (+10)
   - Specific milestones for accomplishments (+10)
   - Initiating mechanisms (+10)
   - Execution (+10)
4. Monitoring (program effectiveness) (+40 maximum points)
   - Performance standards (+5)
   - Performance measurement and reporting (+5)
   - Internal reviews (+10)
   - Audit mechanisms (+10)
   - Corrective action mechanisms (+10)

The following quality grading score ranges indicate the program level:

Example Program Quality Grading

- 140–160 Excellent-quality program score (i.e., exceeds minimum requirements)
- 120–140 Good-quality program score (i.e., meets expected program requirements)
- 100–120 Fair-quality program score (i.e., marginal, minor improvements needed)
- Less than 100 Poor-quality program score (i.e., major improvements needed)

A description and discussion of the following program factors are presented in *Plant Guidelines for Technical Management of Chemical Process Safety.*[7]

TABLE 12.11.1 Example of Management Loss Prevention and Control Program Quality Grading

PMS Program Safety	*Planning (S1)*	*Accountability (S2)*	*Implementation (S3)*	*Monitoring (S4)*	*Program Score S1 + S2 + S3 + S4*
1. Process safety information	20	20	30	35	105
2. Process hazard analysis					
3. Pre-start-up safety					
4. MIP—process equipment					
5. MIP—emergency safety systems					
6. MIP—protection systems					
7. Operating procedures					
8. Hot work permits					
9. Fire system impairments					
10. Facility self-inspection					
11. Flammable liquid handling and ignition control					
12. Employee training					
13. Contractors					
14. Management of change					
15. New construction					
16. Incident investigation					
17. Emergency planning					

MIP = Mechanical integrity programs. Points are allocated for example only.

Program Monitoring

Two important aspects of program monitoring are (1) auditing and (2) recommendation tracking.

Auditing provides a means to measure the performance of loss prevention and control programs. Audits document program progress and success and also demonstrate the interest of plant management in maintaining a high program performance quality. Effective auditing provides valuable feedback on the program's strength and pinpoints deficiencies in program areas that may need improvement.

A system for tracking recommended corrective actions resulting from the audit should be established. The system should assign responsibilities and provide a follow-up reporting mechanism that tracks progress and completion of action items.

EMERGENCY ORGANIZATIONS AND INDUSTRIAL FIRE BRIGADES

Fire-Fighting Capability Options

One of the most important aspects of emergency organizations is the creation, equipping, and training of private fire brigades, usually referred to as industrial fire brigades. The potential benefits versus the costs of a fire brigade program must be evaluated. Typical questions asked during this evaluation include the following:

- How much is a brigade program going to cost?
- How much time will employees need to spend in training?
- Who will conduct the training and where will it take place?
- How will time be scheduled for training all members on all shifts?
- Will personnel become more aware of fire and its causes and contributing factors, making preventing fires more likely?
- Will fires that are fought by trained industrial fire brigade personnel be fought more safely?
- Will property loss likely be minimized through prompt action by a trained brigade?

OSHA Subpart L and NFPA 600, *Standard on Industrial Fire Brigades,* provide many options to facility management when the level of facility fire-fighting capabilities are determined.

Option 1. *No employee will fight a fire.* This means that on notification of a fire, all employees will evacuate the facility. If this option is selected, management must provide the means for protecting its assets and production as well as the integrity of the company. This can be provided through fixed fire protection systems and/or by relying on the local fire department. *Note:* Options 2 through 4 deal with incipient fires. An incipient fire is one that is in the initial or beginning stage and can be controlled or extinguished safely with portable fire extinguishers, Class II standpipes, or small hose systems without the need for protective clothing or breathing apparatus.

Option 2. *All employees will be trained (on an annual basis, at minimum) to use fire extinguishers to fight incipient fires.*

Option 3. *Designated employees will fight incipient fires.* This is the same level of training as required in Option 2. However, only specific employees throughout the plant are trained and are expected to respond to incipient fires.

Option 4. *An organized industrial fire brigade will fight incipient fires.* At this level, the management of the plant has written a specific organizational statement regarding the development of a fire brigade. This statement includes a specific leadership structure, procedures, training, and equipment necessary to perform incipient-level tasks. The organizational statement should be part of the site emergency plan. The brigade leaders must have training exceeding that of the regular brigade member. In addition, special hazards should be addressed in training and procedures for all brigade members. Hands-on training is required on an annual basis.

Option 5. *An organized industrial fire brigade will fight fires beyond the incipient stage.* This option incorporates the more sophisticated organization of Option 4 but adds more requirements. These include assessment of physical fitness, use of protective clothing and positive-pressure self-contained breathing apparatus (SCBA), quarterly training with hands-on training required annually, and higher levels of overall training and education. Fire brigades organized to fight fires beyond the incipient stage must meet the applicable requirements of advanced exterior fire fighting and/or interior structural fire fighting contained in NFPA 600. Option 5 is a significantly larger step than Option 4 in terms of training, organization, and equipment.

Based on the needs assessment of a facility (extent of hazard potential, existing fire prevention and automatic fire protection systems in place, and availability and adequacy of public fire department response), management should evaluate its hazards and select the appropriate option. The considerations for Options 1, 2, and 3 involve appropriate documentation in the facility emergency plan, basic training, and availability of basic fire-fighting equipment including fire extinguishers. Due to the complex considerations involved in Options 4 and 5, the remainder of this chapter will be devoted to them.

Often the type of facility that could benefit from an organized industrial fire brigade does not need a brigade organized to fight fires beyond the incipient stage (Option 5) and would probably find it financially difficult to support one. A team of well-trained individuals equipped to attack incipient fires (Option 4) is relatively easy to develop and maintain. In addition, the incipient fire brigade, due to its proximity to potential fires, its vested interest in the property it is protecting, and its level of training, is an excellent loss control resource. However, many large facilities will need a fire brigade organized to fight fires beyond the incipient stage to meet their loss control objectives.

Fire Brigade Organization

Based on the size and needs of the brigade, it is important that adequate organization and leadership be established. Specific roles and skill competencies for each position within a typical fire brigade are provided in NFPA 1081, *Standard for Industrial Fire Brigade Member Professional Qualifications.* Specific titles such as *chief* and *captain* are not important but are useful for discussing roles and responsibilities.

The *fire brigade chief* has overall responsibility for brigade operations. These include training, equipment, procedures, and maintenance of systems and equipment. The fire brigade chief may report to the *plant emergency coordinator* or may have the dual responsibility of chief and coordinator, depending on the size and needs of the plant. The fire brigade chief should possess qualifications commensurate with the responsibilities of the position.

Assistant chiefs of the fire brigade are the senior fire officers on each shift who report to the fire brigade chief. In this capacity, they are the primary brigade leaders or incident commanders for the typical brigade response on any shift. Personnel in this position generally have other full-time responsibilities. Under the direction of the assistant chief, the *captain* directs a fire brigade crew that is performing tasks such as rescue, fire suppression, salvage, and overhaul. In a small brigade, a *leader* may combine the duties of several leadership positions.

Command and control of fire brigade operations is provided by use of an incident management system compliant with NFPA 1561, *Standard on Emergency Services Incident Management System.* As part of the U.S. Department of Homeland Security's National Response Plan, the incident management system has been expanded to become the National Incident Management System (NIMS). A variety of training courses on the newly introduced National Incident Management System (NIMS) are available through the U.S. Department of Homeland Secuity.

Plant personnel who are selected to participate in the fire brigade must have proper physical, mental, and emotional qualifications, in addition to response availability (which is affected by each person's full-time job assignment). The tasks *brigade members* are expected to perform include regular training, fighting fires, rescue, and any other tasks outlined in the plant's brigade organizational statement.

Based on the occupancy and staffing levels of a particular facility, it may be necessary to include fire brigade support personnel who are not directly involved in fire fighting. For example, an *electrician* is responsible for isolation of electrical circuits in an area or control of specific equipment that the incident commander has directed should be shut down. The electrician should also ensure that the electrical service to fire protection systems is not inadvertently shut down.

A *pipe fitter* is an excellent resource for cycling fire protection system valves or operating process control valves that the incident commander has determined should be closed to isolate specific piping. Maintenance personnel might respond as *fire pump operators* to ensure that the fire pumps have started or to take any manual actions necessary to ensure their operation. In addition, an operator stands by the pumps to monitor their condition or to take actions as directed to shut down the pumps or return them to regular service (standby or automatic start mode).

Staffing

To determine the number of fire brigade members required, it is necessary to define and document what duties the brigade will perform in the brigade's organizational statement. The brigade's primary responsibilities may include controlling and extinguishing the fire, evacuating threatened personnel, minimizing exposures to other areas, and coordinating the efforts of the public fire department.

In order to ensure the safety of brigade members, all fire fighting must be conducted in teams. Since it takes two fire fighters to operate a mobile 1½ in. (38 mm) hose stream of 75 to 100 gpm (300 to 400 L/min), the need for a team concept is further reinforced. A minimum of a five-member brigade fully clothed in their personal protective equipment would be required to provide one 1½ in. (38 mm) hose line: two firefighters to actively fight the fire; two on standby for rescue in the event something happens to the two fighting the fire; and one to act as the incident commander to coordinate the activities and provide communication. Personnel may also be needed to provide additional equipment, operate fire apparatus, set up smoke fans, initiate search and rescue efforts, and so on. In all facilities, minimum staffing levels must also take into consideration vacation schedules, employee absences, and shift schedules. A roster of two to three times the minimum number of responders is usually required to ensure adequate emergency staffing.

Concurrent with the fire-fighting operation, efforts should be made to reduce the damage caused by the fire and the fire-fighting efforts. This is accomplished through salvage and overhaul operations. Obviously, the more responsibilities expected of the brigade through the organizational statement, the greater the number of members that will be required.

Training

No single item is more important to the effectiveness of a fire brigade than a well-organized and well-documented training program. It is too late to develop skills at the time of an emergency. No brigade member should be allowed or expected to perform a duty at an emergency for which he or she has not been fully trained.

NFPA 600 requires that training sessions be held periodically, commensurate with the type of fire fighting expected by the brigade. The actual training frequency for a specific plant will vary depending on the fixed systems provided, the availability and quality of outside fire-fighting help, the frequency of actual fires, the number and experience of brigade personnel involved, the type and level of training provided, and so on. NFPA 1081 specifies a core set of job performance requirements, as well as site-specific requirements for personnel who perform as members of an organized fire brigade.

Training the brigade can be simplified by using contract agencies and groups such as the local fire department, state or county fire academies, colleges with fire programs, and private interests such as training consultants, the National Fire Protection Association, the International Society of Fire Service Instructors, and the International Fire Service Training Association. Public fire department training grounds are often available in the general area of a plant. These are especially helpful since they are usually arranged to emphasize hands-on training with actual fires. To ensure the safety of all training activities involving live fire hands-on training, make sure that the operation is compliant with NFPA 1403, *Standard on Live Fire Training Evolutions.*

As new personnel are added to the brigade, they should receive an orientation that addresses their responsibilities. This orientation should include classroom training that discusses the theory of fire, plant fire hazards, fixed fire detection systems, fixed fire suppression systems, personal protective equipment with special emphasis on self-contained breathing apparatus (for the structural brigade), and manual fire-fighting equipment available to the brigade. Finally, they should receive sufficient practice in actual fire fighting so that some skill is developed. Plant tours are generally needed to show the locations of fire hazards and fire protection equipment.

Fire-fighting training should be made as realistic as possible and should simulate the actual fire conditions expected. Too many brigades rely on stereotyped training that consists only of outside oil-pit fires or scrap-wood fires. This approach seldom prepares the brigade for the typical interior fires that will be encountered. For brigades that will fight fires beyond the incipient stage, practice with SCBA is especially important, since many plant areas have limited capability for ventilation.

An important part of training is conducting fire drills. Unannounced fire drills should be conducted to check the effectiveness of the brigade response and to identify whether the plant prefire plans are viable. It is during these drills that areas that are beyond the reach of hose lines or that are inaccessible because of equipment locations, locked doors, or other obstructions will be identified. The prefire plans should be revised as needed based on the drill critiques. All drill critiques should be documented. Drills should be conducted in a realistic manner using charged hose lines where possible. Brigades responsible for fire fighting beyond the incipient stage should use protective equipment and SCBA during all drills. Appropriate drills will make responses more automatic under the stress of an actual fire emergency.

The use of computer fire models might be considered as an aid in planning drills. These models can be used to predict likely fire-growth and smoke-spread scenarios. With this information, a more realistic assessment of fire conditions can be made and incorporated into drill scenarios. This same information could be adapted for use in prefire plans.

Fire brigade leadership training must be provided to all persons who may direct fire-fighting operations. Their leadership abilities will often determine the success or failure of the fire-fighting effort. This training should emphasize leadership and fire tactics. The brigade leader should possess a working knowledge of the facility layout, fire hazards, existing protection, and plant operations. All brigade members, but especially brigade leaders, should be trained in the use of an incident management system (IMS). NFPA 1561 contains the minimum requirements for an incident management system, and various training courses on the newly introduced National Incident Management System (NIMS) are available through the U.S. Department of Homeland Secuity.

Pre-Incident Plans

NFPA 1620 provides a good framework for evaluating the protection, construction, and operational features of specific occupancies to develop a pre-incident plan that should be used by responding personnel to manage fires and other emergencies in such occupancies using available resources.

Pre-incident plans should be developed for each building and be organized in a format that is useful to the facility fire brigade and municipal fire service organizations. It should contain, at a minimum, the following information:

- A review of the facility layout and best access and evacuation routes for each area
- A discussion of facility construction features and their probable reaction during a fire incident
- An overview of facility operations, equipment, and associated fire hazards
- A review of available water supplies, fire pumps, sprinkler control valves, fire department connections, detection, alarms, and special suppression equipment
- Expected areas for spill and firewater drainage and runoff, and anticipated exposures created by them
- A description of available communications and preestablished plans with the responding public fire department
- The requirements for manual fire-fighting efforts, including the most appropriate tactics, equipment, and approach to be used by the brigade
- Information on ventilation systems that may cause the spread of smoke or may be utilized to prevent smoke spread
- An evaluation of chemical hazards and methods to handle spills
- The location of flammable liquid and gas system isolation valves and electrical power disconnects

FM Global provides several interactive tools, at no cost, to the public/volunteer fire service that aid in the development of pre-fire incident plans for sprinklered commercial and industrial properties.[6]

Fire-Fighting Equipment

The need for fire-fighting equipment varies widely. Equipment should be provided that is commensurate with the duties of the fire brigade and the hazards that it will encounter. When fire-fighting equipment is mentioned, a fire truck is often initially visualized because it is essential to the operation of public fire departments. Many industries, however, have large quantities of water available at a fairly high water pressure for fire-fighting purposes. Since a fire department pumper is used to transport fire fighters and fire equipment and to boost the water pressure, the pumper is seldom needed by the fire brigade. What is needed is a reasonable distribution of yard hydrants and hose houses, even in remote portions of the yard. NFPA 24, *Standard for the Installation of Private Fire Service Mains and Their Appurtenances,* lists equipment required for hose houses.

Inside facility buildings, a well-designed interior standpipe system, installed according to NFPA 14, *Standard for the Installation of Standpipe and Hose Systems,* distributes hose stations throughout large industrial buildings. However, if the fire blocks access to one hose station, others usually will not reach the hazard. In addition, safety dictates that a backup hose line be established for the protection of the primary fire attack team(s). For these reasons, some means of easily transporting fire hose should always be provided within the plant. A vehicle or cart may be useful to carry additional equipment, especially to remote areas of the plant site.

Fire-fighting and supplementary equipment should be distributed throughout the plant with concentrations at convenient brigade access points. Each brigade member who fights fires beyond the incipient stage must be provided with protective equipment, commonly referred to as "turnout" gear, including helmet, coat, boots, trousers, and gloves, as required by NFPA 600.

NFPA 600 also requires the use of protective hoods to protect the head. Fire brigade members' hands receive a high percentage of injuries, indicating the need for gloves specifically designed for use in fire fighting. Foot and eye injuries are also prevalent. Steel-insole fire boots and fire helmets with eye/face shields will reduce these injuries. In addition, goggles and safety glasses have been shown to be effective in reducing eye injuries where SCBA is not needed. NFPA 1971, *Standard on Protective Ensembles for Structural Fire Fighting and Proximity Fire Fighting;* NFPA 1975, *Standard on Station/Work Uniforms for Fire and Emergency Services;* NFPA 1981, *Standard on Open-Circuit Self-Contained Breathing Apparatus for Fire and Emergency Services;* and NFPA 1982, *Standard on Personal Alert Safety Systems (PASS),* cover protective equipment.

Only those familiar with fighting fires inside buildings can appreciate the amount of smoke, heat, and toxic gases generated during a fire. These fire products necessitate the use of positive-pressure SCBA if the fire has developed beyond the incipient stage. The use of protective clothing and SCBA allows fire brigade members to advance safely into a fire area much farther than otherwise would be possible. Because of the limited duration of the air supplied by SCBA during stressful conditions, spare air bottles are necessary.

Specialized equipment may be helpful in conducting fire-fighting operations. Items such as fire-fighting foam concentrate, foam nozzles and eductors, high-expansion foam generators, and handheld infrared heat detectors may be necessary. The need for such special equipment should be identified as a part of the plant fire hazards analysis. Portable communications equipment must be provided if an efficient and safe fire-fighting operation is to be conducted. The brigade leader must have a two-way radio to keep the plant operators and management informed of the situation, to request additional assistance or equipment, and to coordinate the efforts of incoming fire departments. Each fire-fighting team should also be provided with two-way radios to facilitate communications with the brigade leader. Salvage and overhaul equipment will be needed to minimize water, smoke, and fire damage during and after a fire. Salvage equipment should include such items as ventilation fans (fans will require explosion-proof motors in many manufacturing facilities) and flexible ducts for smoke removal, floor squeegees, water vacuums, and tarps.

All fire-fighting, salvage, and personal protective equipment should be inspected regularly to ensure that it is both available and in good condition. Brigade members should conduct these inspections as part of their routine training program.

Municipal Fire Department Assistance

Regardless of the abilities and resources available to the facility fire brigade, it is a good practice to include the public fire department in pre-incident emergency planning. These personnel may be needed only in the case of a failure of the fixed fire suppression systems or in other unique circumstances, but good emergency planning includes providing for such possibilities. The facility emergency organization should realistically evaluate the local fire department to determine the level of assistance available.

If outside fire departments are to be used, it will be necessary to determine the minimum support they can supply and the response times involved. The number of personnel and response time may vary a great deal in many volunteer departments, depending on the time of day. The number and type of equipment available to respond should also be defined so that pre-incident plans can be developed accordingly.

Another reason for involving the local fire department might be the need for special equipment or capabilities that the facility itself cannot economically provide. These may include the ability to draft water from a static source, such as a pond or river. Departments have this basic capability with their pumpers. However, either the plant or the fire department must provide hard suction hose that may not be needed under normal conditions. The pumper must also be provided with adequate access to the water source. Other equipment, such as ladders, foam generators, and fire hose, should be considered. Compatibility of equipment, such as radio frequencies, SCBA cylinders, and hose threads, should be verified.

Management should not assume that the fire fighters from the local fire department have adequate experience and training in industrial fire fighting. In many cases, local fire department personnel may be most familiar with fighting structure fires with very limited water supplies. Such experience would certainly not provide the average fire fighter with an adequate background for attacking a flammable liquid fire inside a structure. It must be determined what the local fire department is familiar with and the levels of training that are provided for its personnel. The plant may even need to supplement the public fire department's training in the fighting of more typical industrial fires, such as those involving flammable liquids.

It is important to identify the legal relationships involved if the plant is located outside the formal fire department jurisdiction and to develop appropriate mutual assistance agreements. It is equally important to ensure that the incident management systems used by the brigade and municipal fire department are able to be effectively integrated, and determination is made on who will have overall command of an emergency incident (see Figure 12.11.5).

All public fire department personnel should be given periodic familiarization tours of the plant and should be involved in

FIGURE 12.11.5 Fire Brigade Leader Meeting with Municipal Fire Department Representative

pre-incident planning. Pre-incident plans made in conjunction with the public fire department should identify personnel assembly points, general fire attack approaches, equipment needs, and personnel requirements. The pre-incident plan should clearly define who will direct the combined fire-fighting efforts of the industrial fire brigade and the public fire department during an emergency. Plans should include a requirement that outside fire department personnel be escorted by facility personnel, whenever possible, for their safety. Regardless of the amount of time expended by the fire department, they cannot be expected to gain sufficient familiarity with the plant so as to operate safely during an emergency that may generate as much confusion as smoke. Combined drills should be conducted regularly so that the brigade and the fire department can learn to function as a team.

Fire Brigade and Hazardous Materials Response

Since the mid-1980s, there has been a substantial amount of legislation in the United States regarding the handling of hazardous materials and the response to emergencies involving hazardous materials. The most prevalent of these new U.S. federal laws are 29 CFR 1910.120, Hazardous Waste Operations and Emergency Response, and the Emergency Planning and Community Right-to- Know Act, which is Title III of the Superfund Amendments and Reauthorization Act of 1986 (commonly known as SARA Title III).

Under SARA Title III, local emergency planning committees (LEPC) were formed to develop pre-emergency plans. The LEPCs are composed of officials from fire departments, emergency medical services (EMS), law enforcement agencies, community groups, and emergency management organizations, as well as facility representatives from every plant that falls under the hazardous materials reporting requirements of the law.

Each community LEPC should have a comprehensive pre-emergency plan completed for each facility covered under the regulation. These plans should indicate what agencies will handle the response to any facility for which the plans were developed. In some cases, fire brigades may have the responsibility for response to hazardous materials incidents. If this is the case, the brigade must meet the requirements for a hazardous materials (hazmat) response team.

The requirements for a hazmat team include mandatory training, medical surveillance, procurement of necessary equipment, development of standard operating procedures, the use of an incident management system, and others, as required by OSHA 1910.120. Also, specific personnel decontamination procedures must be in place to ensure hazmat team members can safely leave a contaminated area.

The complexity of any plant fire brigade's involvement in hazmat activities will vary according to the chemical hazards encountered, the equipment and training necessary to control expected incidents, and the availability of resources from the community. It will also depend on the level of response expected by the response plans developed by the LEPC and the development of a facility emergency plan compliant with NFPA 1600. This may mean that the industrial fire brigade is not involved at all, is involved only as a first responder agency (which is responsible for recognizing that a hazard exists, calling for trained personnel, and securing the area), or is involved as a hazmat team.

Due to the extensive training time and the cost of equipment, a facility may be financially prohibited from having the fire brigade act as a hazmat team. Management must thoroughly understand and consider the costs and organizational commitment required to maintain a competent hazardous materials response team.

If a fire brigade must function as a hazmat team, management may consider developing a full-time emergency response organization because of the disruption that the additional extensive training and drill time would cause to work schedules. One type of facility where management might consider this decision is a high-hazard facility where outside assistance might be delayed.

Beyond the legislation, NFPA has issued two consensus documents regarding response to hazardous materials emergencies and qualifications for the responders. These are NFPA 471, *Recommended Practice for Responding to Hazardous Materials Incidents,* and NFPA 472, *Standard for Professional Competence of Responders to Hazardous Materials Incidents.* These documents provide excellent support in developing hazmat response programs that will aid in complying with OSHA 1910.120 and SARA Title III.

SUMMARY

Industrial fire risk management responsibilities include identifying and evaluating fire and explosion hazards and risks, developing programs and assigning management responsibilities to manage the identified risks, and establishing emergency organizations to control fire and explosion incidents that do occur.

Fire loss prevention programs, which include written operating procedures, hot work permits, fire system impairment procedures, and self-inspections, are a good investment toward minimizing large fire loss potentials. The loss prevention and control program quality grading example provided in this chapter is a good starting point for assessing the quality of existing programs and areas of improvement. Once good programs are established, continuous monitoring and auditing are essential.

A fire brigade can make many contributions to plant risk management and loss control. Assurance that detection and suppression systems are functional and ready for use is a major contribution that is often overlooked. Quick response by a well-trained and well-organized brigade can minimize loss. The time spent developing the fire brigade and the overall emergency organization will raise the consciousness of the general employee toward fire safety. Moreover, it gives employees the message that management is concerned about fire protection and employee safety and, thus, improves employee morale and the efficiency of facility operations.

BIBLIOGRAPHY

References Cited

1. Center for Chemical Process Safety, *Guidelines for Process Equipment Reliability Data, with Data Tables,* American Institute of Chemcial Engineers, New York, 1989.

2. DiNenno, P. J. (Ed.), *SFPE Handbook of Fire Protection Engineering,* 3rd ed., National Fire Protection Association, Quincy, MA, 2002.
3. Barry, T. F., *Risk-Informed, Performance Based Fire Protection,* T. F. Barry Publications, Knoxville, TN, Oct. 2002.
4. Center for Chemical Process Safety, *Guidelines for Hazard Evaluation Procedures with Examples,* 2nd ed., American Institute of Chemical Engineers, New York, 1992.
5. Davenport, J., *Understanding Fire Protection for Flammable Liquids,* 1st ed., National Fire Protection Association, Quincy, MA, 2003.
6. *Prefire Planning for Sprinklered Buildings* [CD-ROM], FM Global, Johnston, RI, 2004.
7. *Plant Guidelines for Technical Management of Chemical Process Safety,* Center for Chemical Process Safety, American Institute of Chemical Engineers, New York, 1992.

NFPA Codes, Standards, and Recommended Practices

Reference to the following NFPA codes, standards, and recommended practices will provide further information on industrial fire loss prevention discussed in this chapter. (See the latest version of The NFPA Catalog *for availability of current editions of the following documents.)*

NFPA 1, *Uniform Fire Code™*
NFPA 10, *Standard for Portable Fire Extinguishers*
NFPA 11, *Standard for Low-, Medium-, and High-Expansion Foam*
NFPA 12, *Standard on Carbon Dioxide Extinguishing Systems*
NFPA 12A, *Standard on Halon 1301 Fire Extinguishing Systems*
NFPA 13, *Standard for the Installation of Sprinkler Systems*
NFPA 13E, *Recommended Practice for Fire Department Operations in Properties Protected by Sprinkler and Standpipe Systems*
NFPA 14, *Standard for the Installation of Standpipe and Hose Systems*
NFPA 15, *Standard for Water Spray Fixed Systems for Fire Protection*
NFPA 16, *Standard for the Installation of Foam-Water Sprinkler and Foam-Water Spray Systems*
NFPA 17, *Standard for Dry Chemical Extinguishing Systems*
NFPA 17A, Standard for Wet Chemical Extinguishing Systems
NFPA 20, *Standard for the Installation of Stationary Pumps for Fire Protection*
NFPA 22, *Standard for Water Tanks for Private Fire Protection*
NFPA 24, *Standard for the Installation of Private Fire Service Mains and Their Appurtenances*
NFPA 25, *Standard for the Inspection, Testing, and Maintenance of Water-Based Fire Protection Systems*
NFPA 30, *Flammable and Combustible Liquids Code*
NFPA 33, *Standard for Spray Application Using Flammable or Combustible Materials*
NFPA 34, *Standard for Dipping and Coating Processes Using Flammable or Combustible Liquids*
NFPA 51B, *Standard for Fire Prevention During Welding, Cutting, and Other Hot Work*
NFPA 58, Liquefied Petroleum Gas Code
NFPA 68, *Standard on Explosion Protection by Deflagration Venting*
NFPA 69, *Standard on Explosion Prevention Systems*
NFPA 70, *National Electrical Code®*
NFPA 70B, *Recommended Practice for Electrical Equipment Maintenance*
NFPA 72®, National Fire Alarm Code®
NFPA 77, *Recommended Practice on Static Electricity*
NFPA 80, *Standard for Fire Doors and Other Opening Protectives*
NFPA *101®, Life Safety Code®*
NFPA 110, *Standard for Emergency and Standby Power Systems*
NFPA 471, *Recommended Practice for Responding to Hazardous Materials Incidents*
NFPA 472, *Standard for Professional Competence of Responders to Hazardous Materials Incidents*
NFPA 600, *Standard on Industrial Fire Brigades*
NFPA 601, *Standard for Security Services in Fire Loss Prevention*
NFPA 654, *Standard for the Prevention of Fire and Dust Explosions from the Manufacturing, Processing, and Handling of Combustible Particulate Solids*
NFPA 780, *Standard for the Installation of Lightning Protection Systems*
NFPA 1081, *Standard for Industrial Fire Brigade Member Professional Qualifications*
NFPA 1403, *Standard on Live Fire Training Evolutions*
NFPA 1500, *Standard on Fire Department Occupational Safety and Health Program*
NFPA 1561, *Standard on Emergency Services Incident Management System*
NFPA 1600, *Standard on Disaster/Emergency Management and Business Continuity Programs*
NFPA 1620, *Recommended Practice for Pre-Incident Planning*
NFPA 1901, *Standard for Automotive Fire Apparatus*
NFPA 1962, *Standard for the Inspection, Care, and Use of Fire Hose, Couplings, and Nozzles and the Service Testing of Fire Hose*
NFPA 1971, *Standard on Protective Ensembles for Structural Fire Fighting and Proximity Fire Fighting*
NFPA 1975, *Standard on Station/Work Uniforms for Fire and Emergency Services*
NFPA 1981, *Standard on Open-Circuit Self-Contained Breathing Apparatus for Fire and Emergency Services*
NFPA 1982, *Standard on Personal Alert Safety Systems (PASS)*
NFPA 2112, *Standard on Flame-Resistant Garments for Protection of Industrial Personnel Against Flash Fire*

Chapter 12

Disaster Planning and Response Services

William Van Helden ❑ Terry Stewart

Chapter Contents

Key Terms

continuity of government (COG), continuity of operations plan (COOP), disaster planning, emergency operations center (EOC), emergency planning, evacuation, hazard vulnerability analysis, incident command system, incident management system, infrastructure, mitigation, mutual aid, preparedness, recovery, response

Disasters are nothing new. They were a fact of human existence long before recorded history. Humans have lived with them and suffered through them. Many disasters have driven changes in how we live and how society has evolved. The 1666 Great Fire of London, for example, essentially resulted in the destruction of the city but also drove the creation of some of the very first building codes aimed at fostering fire safety. Christopher Wren was charged with rebuilding London and his plans required the use of brick and stone and forbade the use of thatched roofs. Improved sanitation was also a by-product that contributed to a healthier populace.

Natural and man-made disasters over the past four to five years have driven home to many the value of the planning required to handle these catastrophic events. Contributing to an awareness perhaps not seen in recent history were events such as the terrorist attacks of September 11, 2001, and the fear and tension that gripped the nation afterwards. Included in this as well were the anthrax contaminations and other scares, such as hurricanes Katrina, Charlie, Ivan, Francis, Wilma, and Jeanne, and the tsunami in Southeast Asia.

One might imagine that such heightened awareness would mean that almost every entity responsible for disaster operations would have well-thought-out, effective, and proven plans for handling these events. Sadly, that is not yet the case. Consider this: With the publication of this twentieth edition of the *Fire Protection Handbook,* this chapter is the very first devoted solely in this reference book to the subject of disaster preparedness.

For related topics, see Section 1, Chapter 7, "Protecting Against Extreme Events"; Section 1, Chapter 8, "Emergency Management and Business Continuity"; Section 4, Chapter 5, "Strategies for Occupant Evacuation During Emergencies"; Section 5, Chapter 3, "Disaster Preparedness Education"; Section 12, Chapter 17, "Pre-Incident Planning for Industrial and Municipal Emergency Response"; Section 12, Chapter 18, "Pre-Incident Planning for Emergency Response"; and Section 12, Chapter 19, "Community Risk Reduction."

NIMS/ICS APPROACH TO EMERGENCY PREPAREDNESS

National Incident Management System (NIMS) Defined

Pursuant to the U.S. Department of Homeland Security and presidential directives, federal, state and local governments have now been instructed to develop guidelines, standards, and protocols to implement a national incident management system (NIMS). In addition, all state and local governments are strongly encouraged to adopt NIMS as their single approach in order to prevent, prepare for, respond to, and recover from terrorist attacks, major disasters, and other emergencies.

William Van Helden has been in the fire service since 1978 and currently serves as the fire chief and emergency management director for the city of Cape Coral, Florida.

Terry Stewart is city manager of Cape Coral, Florida. He is the former fire chief of the city of Lauderdale Lakes, Florida, and also served as assistant fire chief in Pembroke Pines, Florida.

There have been several approaches to managing large incidents and disasters over the past two decades. Many of those had components similar to those of NIMS, but there was never one unified approach designated by the federal government to be the single all-hazards approach to managing disasters and other related incidents. Typically, the use of NIMS or other forms of incident command models began primarily with the fire service and then began to trickle into other branches of government. NIMS is now the single tool that will be used by all branches of federal, state, and local government, including fire, police, public works, and all other aspects in managing critical incidents.

As NIMS relates to planning, it is essential that every government entity identify who will fill the key roles in the system. Information on NIMS and the specific roles that are incorporated into the system can be found on the U.S. Department of Homeland Security website. On this website is a plethora of information to help local governments plan, including grant opportunities, online training, training via the National Fire Academy and Emergency Management Institute, and other key elements for successful implementation of NIMS. The NIMS incident command structure is based on the following three systems:

1. Incident command system (ICS) (Figure 12.12.1)
2. Multiagency coordination system
3. Public information systems

Core Values and Training

Some of the core values in the use of the NIMS have to do with span of control, unity of command, accountability, resource tracking, and operation of incident action plans. In response to the new NIMS compliance standards, most communities that are striving to be NIMS compliant are facing great challenges in the training aspects. One of the most important things to plan for over the next decade is the initial and recurrent training for all entities that will operate in a disaster setting. The level of training is defined in the NIMS documents from the Department of Homeland Security.

PHASES OF EMERGENCY PREPAREDNESS

Emergency Management Cycle

The four phases in the emergency management cycle are mitigation, preparedness, response, and recovery. As described in the following definitions, these four phases of the cycle make a loop and continually build on one another, with some phases perhaps occurring simultaneously:

1. *Mitigation.* Mitigation involves taking actions to reduce or eliminate risk to people and/or property from future hazards and effects.
2. *Preparedness.* Preparedness may be defined as a balance between the public sector, private sector, and the general populace. Plans are developed with all three of these elements in mind to prepare for, respond to, mitigate, and recover from all hazards.
3. *Response.* The organization responds to the actual emergency event with the goals of saving lives and protecting property by responding with the appropriate resources to care for the public and to begin to restore essential services.
4. *Recovery.* The community and organization begin to implement plans and procedures to attempt to bring normalcy back to that community or organization, while taking into consideration ways to mitigate future events.

These four phases are consistent with NFPA 1600, *Standard on Disaster/Emergency Management and Business Continuity Programs,* which was endorsed by the 9/11 Commission for its relevance to the public and private sectors.

Mitigation

Mitigation can be defined as actions that should be taken or accomplished before an event to prevent it from causing disastrous effects or to reduce its impact, including the protection of life and property and ensuring continuity of operations and continuity of government. Considerations in mitigation should be current code compliance, all applicable standards and laws, and the fiscal impact.

Securing funds from the federal government in a post-disaster scenario for mitigation will often be strongly contingent on relationships and agreements between local governments. Therefore, it is essential that all local governments develop a strategic plan to identify those mitigation efforts based on an all-hazards approach. Many communities refer to this concept as a "local mitigation strategy," whereby the strategy helps communities identify areas that continually suffer damage from hazards, identifies means by which to correct the problems, and develops priority rankings for funding these projects.

An all-hazards approach to a mitigation plan must include all threats via a threat assessment and potential impact to a community. All hazards include natural threats, technological threats, and man-made threats. Public officials must be careful not to develop plans that are so rigid that they lack flexibility and diversity because of what might be considered a single major threat, such as a Gulf Coast storm. The public may spend a lot of time planning for hurricanes at the expense of less probable threats such as domestic security–related issues or health-related concerns such as a pandemic flu.

Preparedness

Preparedness may be defined as those plans, procedures, and tasks that are identified by agencies or local governments to allow them to successfully prepare for disasters in both the response and recovery phases. The preparedness phase is the time in which government and businesses have the most flexibility to assign roles and responsibilities to all facets of both the public and private sectors, in addition to educating the public about the critical elements for a successful response and subsequent recovery from a disaster.

Preparedness can consist of almost any action to ensure and improve the safety and effectiveness of a disaster response. Some of the key elements of preparation should be ensuring homeland security, prevention of and response to terrorist events, protecting and restoring critical infrastructure in accordance with the related disaster, preparation for law enforcement activities related

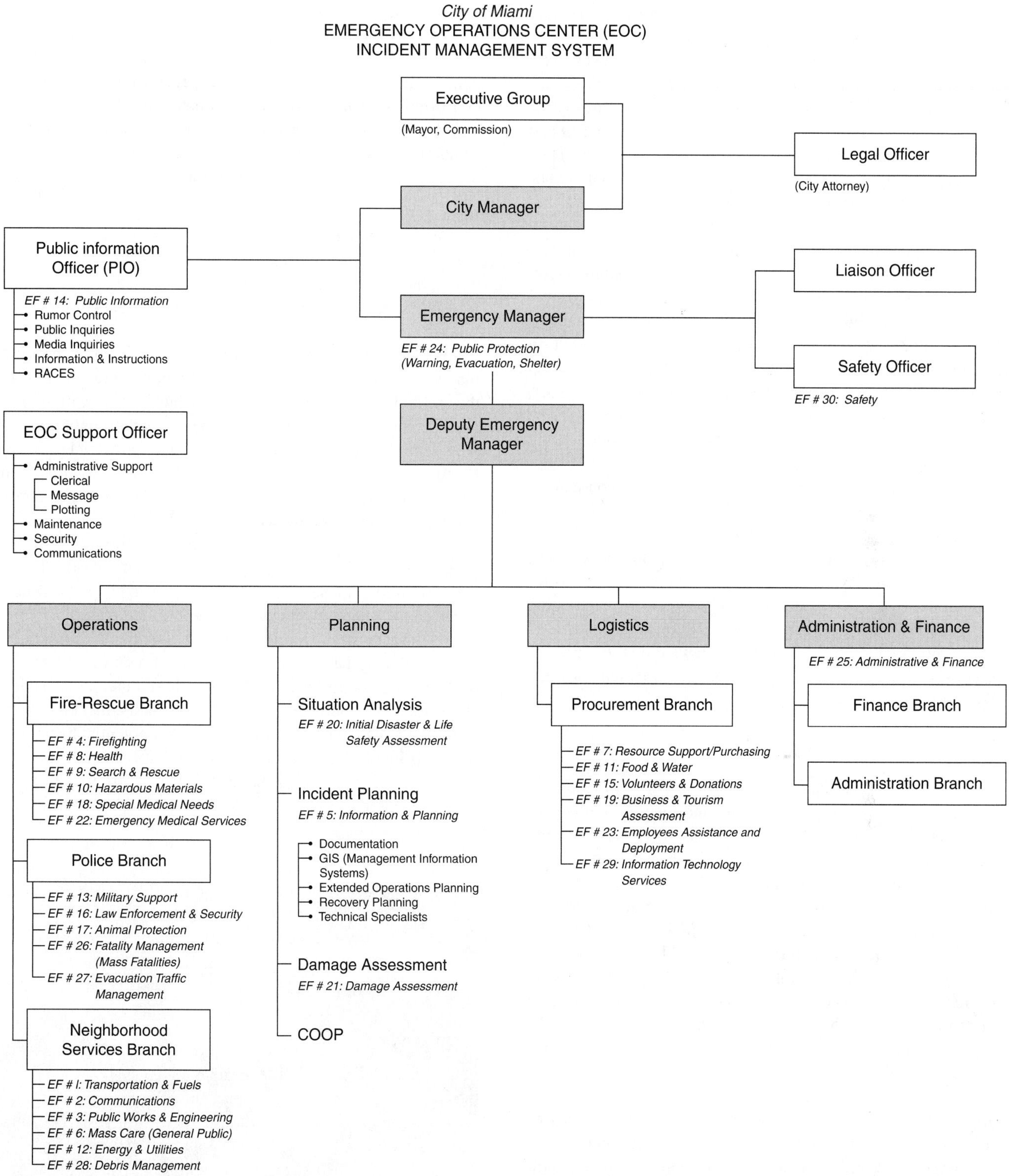

FIGURE 12.12.1 Incident Management System Operations (Courtesy City of Miami Fire Department, Division of Emergency Management)

to an all-hazards approach, and preparedness tasks that will help tie into mitigation efforts and all related recovery issues as noted elsewhere in this chapter. Unfortunately, many preparedness plans designed to be compliant with state and federal guidelines become so comprehensive that they are not practical during a real-time emergency. Therefore, it is strongly recommended that local governments put together a smaller field-operating guide (FOG) or other types of abbreviated versions of their planning efforts when developing comprehensive emergency management plans (CEMPs).

Emergency plans that define actions to be taken in the field or other areas of government might be further enhanced by plans that present well-defined roles in the emergency operations center setting. The individual organization should clearly define and list roles pertinent to the disaster for which it has planned. Then it should identify potential positions or members of that organization to fill those areas of responsibility, as well as any other associated duties, requirements, and equipment that may be required for that role. All these should be tied into the national incident management system. Plans may be divided into several levels, which would include state plans, regional plans, local plans, and those divided into a specific department or agency. It is essential that all the plans work in concert and build on one another, especially as it relates to the request for additional resources via mutual aid and other agreements. See Section 5.7, Planning, and Section 5.10, Operations and Procedures, in the 2004 edition of NFPA 1600 for additional information about emergency management plans and procedures.

This planning effort should ensure a timely response and a maximum benefit-for-cost recovery in the aftermath of a disaster. As with any plan, if it is never exercised, it will be difficult to determine its potential effectiveness. All plans should have prescribed training exercises to draw those strengths or areas for improvement within the different plans. It is critical that training opportunities include all parties potentially involved and could range from a tabletop exercise to a statewide disaster drill for hazards such as hurricanes, earthquakes, or weapons of mass destruction.

Response

Response may be defined as the use of any and all resources to address the immediate, short-term, and long-term effects of a disaster. The goal of emergency response is to minimize and reduce suffering, loss of life, and property damage and to begin the restoration of essential services to that community. The response phase may be diverse in nature, depending on a variety of different factors, including the hazard itself, available resources, available mutual aid resources, public perception, and support from state and federal governments. Support from state and federal entities is not automatic and may often be contingent on that community's ability to fully and accurately portray the impact. During the response phase, communities must perform an impact assessment.

Impact Assessment. The impact assessment should describe the impact to the community, including the location and number of injuries and deaths, type and extent of damage, and immediate victim needs. The impact assessment should also describe the ability of that community to continue to provide essential services, including medical care, law enforcement, fire rescue, and emergency medical services. Impact to local hospitals and impact to local government infrastructure such as public works and utilities must also be detailed.

During the response phase, the request for mutual aid will be contingent on a community's available resources and needs. The importance of doing early reconnaissance of the community's needs during response cannot be stressed enough. Government officials often underestimate the impact to their local community, thereby delaying the response from state and federal officials. It is of critical importance that first responders and local agencies do not become so focused on the immediate situation that they forget to complete a rapid impact assessment of their community. In a nutshell, information to be reported should consist of the following:

- What has happened
- What is being done about it
- What is needed (specifically)
- What the gap analysis is for the needs of that community

All-Hazards Approach. An all-hazards approach to response may have to include a wide variety of initial first responders. In the event of a natural disaster, such as a hurricane or earthquake, management of debris removal on emergency thoroughfares will be essential to clear roadways for emergency vehicle access. Restoration of essential services such as water, ice, food, and power will also be of critical importance during the response and initial recovery phases (Figure 12.12.2).

An example of an all-hazards approach to hurricane preparedness occurred in many communities in Florida during the 2004 hurricane season, where local emergency responders found many people overcome by carbon monoxide poisoning during the aftermath of various hurricanes. Although emergency responders may be responding to the aftermath of a hurricane (natural hazard), all-hazards planning should include considerations such as carbon monoxide from generators, fuel leaks from overturned vessels in waterways, and other potential hazardous materials incidents that resulted from the hurricane.

However, if the disaster itself takes a different turn, as would be the case from the release of a weapon of mass de-

FIGURE 12.12.2 Distribution of Water and Ice at a Cape Coral, Florida, Point of Distribution (POD) Following Hurricane Wilma, October 2005

struction material, such as smallpox or a pandemic flu outbreak, then the response efforts may be drastically different. Local and state health departments will take key leadership roles in these events. Police and fire fighters may find themselves playing more of a supportive role in the response phase. The key to any response plan and successful operation is flexibility. If communities exercise their plans seriously, they will develop the relationships necessary to carry out a successful response to any disaster. However, if local, state, and federal governments fail to plan, train, and exercise accordingly, local governments' ability to respond to a critical event may be severely hampered.

State of Local Emergency. During either the preparedness phase or the response phase, it is common for local governments to declare a state of local emergency. In the interest of public safety, a state of local emergency is essential for city and county officials to enable them to carry out timely decisions. It is critical to have these states of local emergency and other critical ordinances or laws available and drafted by the local attorney's office in order to enact them in a timely manner.

Critical ordinances should include a state of local emergency, provisions for curfew, price gouging, lines of succession (continuity of government), emergency pay procedures that may already be outlined in a human resources manual, and the activation of local mutual aid agreements.

Recovery

Goals. The purpose of recovery planning is to anticipate what will be needed to restore a community to its full functioning capability. Successful recovery from any disaster is contingent on everyone within that community and the local, state, and federal governments understanding their roles and responsibilities. Recovery from a disaster can last anywhere from days to years, as was witnessed in the aftermath of Hurricane Andrew, which struck southern Florida in 1992.

The overall goals are to maintain leadership and continuity of government, maximize the use of local and regional resources, provide for the coordination of state and federal resources to assist a community in recovery, maintain communication to its citizens before, during, and after an event, provide the maximum support for disaster victims, make maximum use of damage assessment tools for the purpose of recovery planning, promote economic recovery, and bring the community back to some sense of normalcy.

Recovery can be broken down into short-term and long-term phases. Goals of short-term recovery would include restoration of essential services such as utilities; delivery of immediate social, medical, and mental health services; restoration of local government operations; reestablishment of transportation routes; debris management and cleanup; and disaster assistance to the local community, including assistance from both private and public sector organizations such as the Red Cross, FEMA, Small Business Administration, and so on.

The goal of long-term recovery is to restore the community to its predisaster state or an improved condition. Some of the major objectives to long-term recovery would include coordinated delivery of long-term health and social services, long-term housing, improved land use planning, restoration of the economy to predisaster levels, recovery of those dollars expended during the disaster through both public and private sector avenues, and the implementation of any mitigation strategies identified before, during, or after the disaster event.

Recovery Functions. The following is a list of recovery functions that may be utilized during a disaster event; the size and scope of the functions listed are completely dependent on the impact to the community from the disaster:

- Impact assessment (disaster assessment)
- Continuity of government
- Public information
- Human services
- Individual assistance
- Volunteers and donations
- Unmet needs
- Debris management
- Reentry and security
- Health
- Safety
- Repair and restoration of public infrastructure and services
- Building inspections and permits
- Rebuilding construction repairs and restoration
- Housing
- Redevelopment (planning and community development)
- Economic restoration and development
- Environmental concerns
- Mitigation
- Recovery administration and finance
- Mutual aid

Some communities have explored the use of a recovery task force. This task force will consist of key personnel from the public and, potentially, the private sectors who would meet before and after a disaster event to help guide and offer options to local government officials and help expedite recovery from a disaster. Although many communities can survive a minor or major disaster, few are prepared for a catastrophic event. Some of the recovery functions will become critical to the survivability of a community and the timeliness by which it is able to recover from an emergency.

Recovery from minor and major disasters is contingent on local and state response with some federal assistance. However, there must be a well-coordinated effort by federal, state, and local entities for a catastrophic event. How a community plans to recover from a catastrophic event is different from its recovery plans from a minor or major disaster. The initial basic considerations are still the same but the long-term reconstruction, rebuilding, and redevelopment issues can be overwhelming. Nothing will take the place of good planning and exercises that reflect those planning efforts. Finally, excellent relationships must exist between all levels of government in order to be successful in meeting a community's needs immediately after a disaster.

EVACUATION

Evacuations for disasters and catastrophic events can be broken down into two basic categories: pre-event and postevent. Unfortunately, many plans only account for evacuations in the predisaster phase and fail to give equal consideration to the repopulation of a community and/or critical facilities, such as nursing homes and hospitals.

Pre-Event Evacuation

Much consideration has been given in some states for people with special needs and transportation issues. They are two distinct categories. Many people with special needs are those who have a medical encumbrance that requires them to have some medical oversight in their home on a regular basis but does not require the definitive care that hospitalization would provide. Planning for the care of special needs people can be broken down into two categories: those that will require hospitalization due to type of equipment and care they need and those whose care can be satisfied at a special needs shelter (if available) where minimal medical care is rendered. Many communities have worked out interlocal agreements between public safety agencies and local health department officials for providing medical care with some additional support from private sector nursing and paramedics when available.

Some of the population of local communities will require special attention in the area of transportation. This can be one of the greatest challenges for communities with large populations of indigent, low income, and elderly. Communities such as Atlantic City, New Jersey, that are used to moving large volumes of people via mass transit and private busing are used to the concept of timely transportation of people to and from a specific area. This is the exception and not the rule. Many communities do not have enough infrastructure in the form of public transportation to facilitate a timely evacuation of the aforementioned populace.

It is important to have developed procedures and secured contracts with local school board resources, private sector bus companies, and even rail and taxi services. The successful use of this multifaceted approach to obtaining resources for evacuation requires extensive planning and written contracts with an associated cost for securing those services from private industry.

On rare occasions, such as the evacuation of New Orleans in 2005 and the evacuation of critical medical facilities in the Florida Keys, the Department of Defense or the National Guard may be used to supplement the local resources. Although in the past federal resources were typically not deployed until a substantial event occurred, there is a growing consensus that federal involvement must occur earlier and with a much stronger presence than in the past. When addressing such a large need for evacuation, the use of a staging officer is essential for coordination and deployment of resources, fleet maintenance, portable restrooms, and fuel, which are essential to the success of the evacuation.

Most communities lack the transportation infrastructure to handle the evacuation of a significant portion of their visitors and residents from a potential threat. Consideration such as contra flow (one-way traffic) must be put in place prior to the time an evacuation order is given in order to prevent gridlock. Unfortunately, studies have shown that many people make their decisions about evacuation based on local media more than direction from public officials. Therefore, the community should make it essential to pay attention to what the local media is stating about the event and should strive to have the best relationship possible with the local television, radio, and print media.

Postevent

The same consideration that is given to the evacuation of the population before the landfall of a hurricane or the arrival of any threat or potential disaster must be given to the repopulation of those evacuated portions of the communities. Critical to those planning efforts would be the coordination of when essential services are restored to the affected areas and the elimination of the threat and subsequent results from the disaster event.

HAZARD VULNERABILITY ANALYSIS

Information Gathering

A hazard vulnerability analysis is one of the initial steps in implementing a preparedness or mitigation program for a local community. Information gathered in a hazard vulnerability analysis will include FEMA documents, state and local government documents, and firsthand information that can be obtained either from local newspaper archives or interviews from people in the community who were present or participated in previous events. Hazards can be categorized typically either into natural, technological, or man-made events. Hazards can be indigenous to a specific community and they may change from location to location based on geography, population, and other specific elements such as critical or high-profile portions of an area or local government.

Probability Versus Impact

Although there are several models for performing a hazard vulnerability analysis, they all boil down to assessing "probability versus impact." Series of matrixes could be designed that would address the hazard and then the probability, whether it be high, moderate, or low, versus the impact, whether it be high, moderate, or low. From those indices communities can then determine the priority for planning and mitigation efforts for those specific hazards.

Hazards

Different elements or hazards to be considered may include agricultural freezes, air transportation accidents, civil disorder, droughts, floods, hazardous materials incidents, hurricanes, earthquakes, nuclear attacks, power failures, radiological incidents, terrorism, tornados, wildfires, tsunamis, cyber-terrorism, landslides, and heavy snow conditions. Criteria for evaluating the potential vulnerability and associated hazards to a community may be somewhat subjective, but all communities will have to perform some sort of benefit/cost ratio. Although the threat of terrorism is widespread throughout many nations and large cities, it may be cost prohibitive to invest a large amount of taxpayer dollars into preparing for terrorism in a small rural community. However, that same rural community, depending on its location and hazards, may need to have substantial planning and investment into plans for tornados, earthquakes, hurricanes, or other threats indigenous to that community.

As each organization performs its own hazard vulnerability analysis, it will become readily apparent what the priorities are and where the critical funding should be allocated. A tiered plan or a master plan that would extend planning for those events for 5 or 10 years may be appropriate in order to prioritize the highest threats and eventually address all that could affect that community. See NFPA 730, *Guide for Premises Security,* for additional information on security planning.

IDENTIFICATION OF CRITICAL FACILITIES AND INFRASTRUCTURE

Purpose

The purpose of identifying critical facilities and infrastructure is to prioritize and identify those critical facilities, lifelines, or resources within the community that are essential to protect and ensure limited interruption in services. Usually it is not feasible to identify and perform an analysis on every critical facility in the community, so planners must identify those that are critical for providing essential services to that community and also those that are essential for response and recovery.

Categorization of Critical Facilities

Critical facilities are typically categorized into, but not limited to, the following areas: fire rescue, police, communications, transportation, utilities, government, hospitals, shelters, nursing homes, pump stations, and evacuation routes. When a critical facilities inventory is taken, certain elements of information to be ascertained are very important, and they may include the following: facility type, population and its nature, facility name, owner/operator, location, contact information, address, function, and importance to the community. It is also advisable when identifying these facilities that, in addition to street addresses, the latitude and longitude of the property are determined and maintained in a safe place.

A good example of a critical facility assessment can be found at the National Oceanic and Atmospheric Administration (NOAA) website at http://www.csc.noaa.gov/rvat/criticalEDD.html. Once the critical facilities assessment is completed, it can be used in many of the planning functions described in this chapter. Some of these functions may be given a higher priority depending on the threat. The vulnerability may also rise depending on the threat assessment to that critical facility through both the public and private sector avenues and the implementation of any mitigation strategies identified before, during, or after the disaster event.

RESOURCE TYPING

Purpose

One of the key elements for any successful disaster response is the successful integration of both public and private sector resources into any type of emergency or disaster. Within the national incident management system (NIMS), resource typing is already defined and broken down into different categories such as law enforcement, public works, fire fighting, and the like. Those resources are further defined into kind and type but the overall approach is to make sure all agencies are using one unified approach to categorizing and classifying those resources available in times of an emergency. Some pitfalls experienced by communities in the past have been requesting something as simple as a generator but not specifying the type, the size, or fuel type or not making sure that the generator had the appropriate electrical hookup. Using the principle of resource typing can assure that when a municipality requests a generator to support a specific mission, both the county and the state will understand what the community is asking and can respond in a timely manner.

Mutual Aid Agreements

It should be noted that resource typing is a work in progress and the federal government will continue to further define resource groups and the respective definitive data sets. However, the core elements for resource typing are in place. The specific terms and definitions are listed in the National Mutual Aid Glossary of Terms and Definitions at http://www.fema.gov/preparedness/mutual_aid.shtm#1.

As stated elsewhere in this chapter, all communities should have the appropriate mutual aid agreements in place in addition to contracts with the private sector for the purpose of acquiring resources that a community may not be able to readily provide through its specific governmental entity. Finally, all government entities are encouraged to participate in the Emergency Management Assistance Compact (EMAC), which will allow the timely redistribution of resources across state lines.

CONTINUITY OF GOVERNMENT (COG)

Government infrastructure and the people that work for governments are not immune from the effects of a disaster. Whether it is a disaster that affects a region, such as a hurricane, or one that is more localized, such as a terrorist bombing, infrastructure, personnel, or both will be affected. Since there is no way to predict the level of impact, plans should be made for the most major circumstance.

Although it is often poorly protected or poorly engineered (witness the levee system around New Orleans during Hurricane Katrina in 2005), infrastructure has received the most attention in disaster preparedness. During hurricanes, for example, most communities manage to get buildings boarded up and to bring in supplies in preparation. What is sorely lacking is the preparation needed to ensure continuity of government.

Continuity of Government Defined

Continuity of government is the survival of a constitutional form of government and the continuity of essential functions. Continuity of government is a legal consideration for continuity of leadership in a government organization, whereas continuity of operations is the administrative support for the continuity of government. (See the next section, "Continuity of Operations Plan (COOP)," for more information about continuity of operations.) In general, those functions are viewed as police, fire, and EMS response and also include provisions for public works functions. The broader and more effective the government services available for dealing with recovery, the less devastating will be the disaster.

Emergency Operation Centers (EOCs)

One of the first areas in which continuity planning began to be used was in the development and construction of emergency operations centers (EOCs). A properly designed and constructed EOC provides adequate room and resources to house the logistics and command elements of emergency services. It also ensures a safe location for these elements leading up to, during, and after the impact phase. EOCs have helped to make a significant difference in emergency services' ability to survive intact and continue operations. If the command and logistics structure of emergency services is crippled or destroyed, emergency personnel and their equipment, even if available and ready to serve, would likely not be very effective.

Fire service incident command systems have been a natural fit for dealing with disasters. They demonstrated the value of bringing together and integrating a variety of resources needed to manage an incident. Likewise, operations in EOCs during disasters now include personnel from utilities, transportation, finance, building departments, and so on. Most elements of the governmental structure are now involved and a part of the team, but something is still missing. Assuming that the EOC survives and functions as intended, preserving the command and logistics elements and enabling effective operations into the recovery phase, we could ask ourselves the following questions to help bring into focus why continuity of operations is so vital:

- How long will personnel be able to continue working if computer and data systems are destroyed or inoperable, meaning, among other things, that employees cannot be paid?
- Local governments often find during the recovery phase that certain important decisions must be made. How is that to be accomplished if the elected officials who should make those decisions are not available due to injury, death, or migration?

Continuity Plan Regarding Elected Officials

To ensure continuity of government, the continuity plan regarding elected officials should include the following actions:

- Prepare a plan for the relocation of some or, if necessary, all of the community's elected officials. Determine beforehand who will stay in the community, who will go, and under what circumstances.
- Be sure to enact enabling legislation, especially if the decision process or number of persons required for decisions is different from what it is normally.
- Craft the logistic mechanisms needed to support the distant interaction of the officials, such as telephone, computer, or videoconferencing.
- If the policy calls for elected officials to temporarily leave the community due to a disaster, be sure to preplan for locations in various geographic sites.
- Select alternative locations for your government's public meetings just in case the normal location is damaged, destroyed, or otherwise unavailable. Choose more than one, as an alternative site may be rendered unavailable as well. Citizens want to see that their government is functioning and want to be able to participate as well.
- Be aware that not every community has clear legislation or policy for the ordered succession of power or authority covering its elected officials. Check local legislation and speak with legal counsel to seek guidance on the matter. Do not rely on everyone to "do the right thing" just because a disaster has struck. Egos, alliances, distrust, dislike, and political maneuvering can quickly derail the government's opportunities for successfully handling a disaster. Being in the middle of a disaster and trying to reach resolution on this subject is not an enviable position. Deal with it well ahead of time. Keep in mind that in many communities this is a subject that may require the approval of the voters.

Continuity Plan Regarding Financial Issues

To ensure continuity of government, the continuity plan regarding financial issues should include the following actions:

- In advance, ensure that emergency purchasing mechanisms are established and authorized or enacted.
- Because disasters often severely tax a community's resources, make sure that the chief financial officer works with the CEO (or city manager, mayor, administrator, etc.) to ensure healthy financial reserves, including those specifically designated for major emergencies. Such reserves may serve to offset the cost of less severe emergencies and help to support the overall costs of major emergencies. Remember that federal and state reimbursing agencies do not compensate 100 percent and may refuse to reimburse for certain costs. Adequate reserves will help to bridge any such gap. In addition, those reserves may provide immediate funding availability until commercial paper loans or other bridge-type financing can be accessed.
- Establish and maintain a line of credit such as commercial paper that can function much like a bridge loan. Cleanup after a disaster can cost millions of dollars, money that a community may not otherwise have readily available. Private providers will not do the work for free, and their willingness to continue working in one community versus another community may hinge on the community's ability to pay. The federal government through FEMA and other agencies may provide reimbursement for a good portion of the costs, but be aware of the fact that reimbursement takes time and is not always guaranteed.

- Ensure that the CFO and his or her department have an excellent working knowledge and familiarity with the record-keeping requirements of FEMA and other federal or state reimbursing agencies. Equally as important is the need to properly train and manage the work of personnel who will be doing the record-keeping work in the field. Failure to properly prepare for and manage this function may well mean failure to receive reimbursement. For most communities, that is not an option that will bode well for its future financial health. Any training that is made available by the agencies is an absolute prerequisite.
- Be aware that in the run-up to and immediately after the impact phase of a disaster, it is possible that certain resources may be acquired only with cash. For this reason, it is wise for the CFO to ensure the creation of policies that will allow an adequate amount of cash to be obtained, safely stored, and legitimately accessed. In this case, "safely stored" means the cash is to be kept safe from the effects of the disaster as well as secure from theft or unauthorized access.

CONTINUITY OF OPERATIONS PLAN (COOP)

Objectives of Continuity of Operations Plan

The objective of a continuity of operations plan (COOP) is to ensure that a viable capability exists to continue essential functions across a wide range of potential emergencies, specifically when the primary operating facility is either threatened or inaccessible. The objectives of COOP planning include the following:

- To ensure the continuous performance of essential functions and operations during an emergency
- To protect essential facilities, equipment, records, and other assets
- To reduce or mitigate disruptions to operations
- To reduce loss of life and minimize damage and losses
- To identify and designate principals and support staff to be relocated
- To facilitate decision making for execution of the plan and the subsequent conduct of operations
- To achieve a timely and orderly recovery from the emergency and resumption of full service to all customers

The following are some other considerations that a COOP plan should include:

- Ability to implement the plan with or without warning
- When activated, ability to implement the plan within a 12 hour period
- Capability of maintaining operations for a period of at least 30 days
- Provision for the establishment of alternative facilities
- Provision for alternative means of operating, including telecommunicating (i.e., allowing employees to conduct business from their home or other remote locations via computer)
- Sharing of facilities with other organizations

All COOPs should be tied to continuity of government plans. Other key elements include payroll, accounts payable, and accounts receivable; in order to foster loyalty, employees who are serving the public in the immediate aftermath of a disaster must be taken care of. COOP planning will provide for specifics as to how those employees will be paid in the event that the normal processes in place to pay staff members are no longer possible.

COOP Steps

Steps in conducting a COOP include the following:

1. Identifying the essential functions to that specific organization
2. Identifying which of those functions must continue regardless of the circumstance
3. Prioritizing those functions
4. Establishing staffing and resource requirements in order to carry out those critical functions. Included in this process are succession planning and delegation of authority at least three levels deep for each individual department.
5. Identifying specific systems and/or facilities that must be provided to carry out those functions
6. Identifying any interdependencies among other related functions from that organization and other organizations within the community to carry out those critical elements

Public Works Considerations

As part of COOP, the community should keep in mind public works considerations such as debris management programs, policies to identify participants, and agreements with suppliers.

Debris Management Program. The community should have contracts in place with private providers to accomplish the pickup and disposal of any debris created by the disaster well in advance of any catastrophe. Be sure that the contract provides for specialized handling of certain hazardous or otherwise dangerous materials if needed. It should also have an element that includes provisions for heavy lifting equipment. Such contracts are essential because few, if any, communities have the resources to handle the volume of work to be done. Many communities have what is called a debris management plan in place, which is an all-encompassing plan outlining the procedures for a community to effectively and efficiently manage debris in the aftermath of a large-scale disaster.

The goal of a debris management plan should be to provide a framework for the rapid removal of debris, thereby protecting public health and safety and the business base of a community; ensure that disaster debris is processed in accordance with environmental regulations; minimize the effect on the existing incinerator and landfills in a given area; and maximize federal reimbursement for response and recovery activities.

Even New York City, one of the largest cities in the world, with far greater resources than most communities can imagine, relied on private providers to assist in the cleanup after the 9/11 terrorist attacks. These contracts may enable a community to quickly clear the roadways and allow emergency response as well as travel routes for other community services. Not the least important of which is that it will also enable a more timely return of the commerce needed to provide resources and support the community's economic health. For a community with rivers, lakes, canals, or ocean access, remember to include those waterways in the cleanup contracts as well, especially where those waterways are navigable.

Establishing Policies That Identify Participants. Establish policies that identify which employees must be available and on what basis. Police, fire, and EMS personnel are accustomed to duty during disasters, but most other employees are not. The changing face of preparedness now recognizes the need for the entire government system to be part of the response. Because these participants are new to this emergency response environment, they may not understand or be comfortable with the demands being placed on them. Inform them ahead of time, adequately train and counsel them, and where possible, provide the support mechanisms to encourage their buy-in. Public works employees are not the only ones who are called on in this response methodology; virtually every government employee will be asked to participate. Personnel involved throughout the process are an indispensable asset for ensuring continuity.

Creating Agreements with Suppliers. Create agreements with fuel suppliers that have resources outside the immediate area. Be sure to include priority clauses in the contracts. Remember to provide for locations and methods to dispense the fuel the community acquires, including power supplies to operate dispensing equipment.

Establish agreements with the local electric utility provider to ensure that the most important facilities receive priority in the return of and maintenance of power. Further explanation of this process can be found in an earlier section, "Identification of Critical Facilities and Infrastructure."

Within purchasing agreements for parts, supplies, materials, and equipment, create clauses to establish how suppliers are expected to interact with other entities during instances of disaster. For example, water and sewer systems often receive significant damage due to uprooted trees, flooding, or other misfortune. The ability to get the systems up and keep them running could hinge on availability of parts and supplies. Do the suppliers normally expect payments within 30 to 90 days? Rather than depending on a supplier's goodwill, it is better to get these matters in writing.

Establish a listing of local heavy equipment resources and persons with the skills to operate them. Various private enterprises may have a variety of such equipment. Knowing who owns the equipment, where it is located, whom to contact, and who can operate it could be most helpful.

Information Technology Systems Considerations

As part of COOP, the community should keep in mind and implement the following information technology systems considerations.

Location of Technology Systems Within EOC. The part of the technology system that directly supports police, fire, and EMS dispatching and record keeping should be located within the EOC. Because an EOC must be designed to withstand and survive extreme natural disasters, it is an ideal location for technology systems. Remember that certain disasters such as radiological incidents or terrorist attacks on the EOC itself will make redundancy essential. A government's technology professionals must plan for redundancy in the system to protect the organization from system failure. Failure of this nature is itself a disaster of sorts. The systems are necessary to keep employee time records and process payroll, to enable accounts payable to process payments for goods and services, and to provide for a myriad of support services and record keeping.

Planning for Redundancy. Establish priorities that determine which systems are to be included in the redundant solution. Decide which elements must remain functional regardless of the circumstances and establish a system hierarchy that will drive the timing of when other elements are to be brought back on line.

Redundancy can be accomplished by contracting with private providers that specialize in this service. It can be done remotely in a different region, or options are available through some providers to bring in systems in completely self-contained semitractor trailers. For small governments with severely limited resources that prevent the acquisition of these services, there is an alternative. It may be possible to identify a similar community in a different region and craft a mutual agreement to provide technology assistance to one another during disasters.

MUTUAL AID AGREEMENTS

Categories of Mutual Aid Agreements

Mutual aid agreements can be divided into three basic categories. The first is the emergency management assistance compact (EMAC). EMAC is an interstate mutual aid agreement that allows states to provide mutual aid to one another through all types of disasters and is managed by the National Emergency Management Association. The next model is the intrastate mutual aid legislation, which is relatively new. This legislation is from the National Emergency Management Association and allows for intrastate mutual aid across different political subdivisions and has been modeled successfully in several states across the country. The third category is a state and county mutual aid agreement. This agreement allows for the deployment of local emergency responders under the auspices of EMAC.

Private Agreements

Private agreements with both the public and private sectors are contracts that can be successfully negotiated prior to a disaster, utilizing the local procurement or purchasing department. Typically, these contracts may have some stipend involved along with a variety of listed performance objectives.

Some communities have taken an all-hazards approach with different private sector models to include debris management, response of emergency generator power, food, comfort stations, rent-a-fence, cell phones, covering structures with tarps, and a wide range of disaster services. Regardless of where a community is located, the most important aspect is to start building and developing those agreements and relationships needed to be successful in a disaster or emergency scenario.

LEVELS OF DISASTER PREPARATION

As stated in Florida Statutes 252.31 to 252.60:

> *Emergency* means any occurrence, or threat thereof, whether natural, technological, or man-made, in war or in peace, which results or may result in substantial injury or harm to the population or substantial damage to or loss of property.
>
> *Disaster* means any natural, technological, or civil emergency that causes damage of sufficient severity and magnitude to result in a declaration of a state of emergency by a county, the Governor, or the President of the United States.

Levels of disaster can be divided into three basic categories. The first is minor disasters. Minor disasters will necessitate the response capabilities of local government with only minimal need for state or federal assistance. Major disasters are those that will require not only the response of local government but also will necessitate state and federal assistance. Finally, catastrophic disasters are those disasters that require substantial state and federal resources and more than likely will include some support from the military.

Minor Disasters

Minor disasters are those that require the extensive use of local and possibly regional resources to respond to and recover from the specific incident. Critical elements to be considered for minor disasters are local mutual aid agreements, partnerships with both private and public sectors on a local level, coordination with state resources if there are multiple events occurring in the state simultaneously, and creating levels of expectation with both the public and elected officials that response and recovery to this disaster should occur within normal time parameters. Examples of a minor disaster might be multiple wildland fires, a flood, a blizzard, or even a minimal category hurricane.

Major Disasters

Major disasters that exceed local and regional capabilities will necessitate the response from both state and federal agencies. Of course, the type of disaster itself will dictate the type of response from both state and federal officials. There are common considerations for an all-hazards approach to major disasters. They are relationships, relationships, relationships. If local governments have not established the appropriate relationships prior to a disaster event, the success of the response to the event is questionable. Examples of major disasters include hurricanes, major fires, earthquakes, and multiple events of similar magnitude that require the response of local, regional, and state assets.

Local governments must forge relationships with their state and federal counterparts through a variety of different mediums such as drills, meetings, and other affiliations in order to make sure that clear lines of responsibility and communications are defined ahead of time. With recent events in the last decade, it has become readily apparent that communities that lack those relationships are not as successful as those that have forged them in advance. Other key elements in responding to and recovering from a major disaster include interlocal/mutual aid agreements, regional agreements to include multiple states, and a clear understanding of the National Response Plan (NRP) and its capabilities and limitations (Figure 12.12.3).

Typically, one of the chief concerns in major disasters is restoration of infrastructure and essential services. Because of the potential for interruption of these services, it is critical that communities have preplanned for these types of events based on a threat analysis and that they have substantial planning components in place for both continuity of government and continuity of operations.

Catastrophic Disasters

Catastrophic disasters are events that will require substantial state and federal assistance with military involvement. More than likely, catastrophic events will affect a community in a way that will overwhelm both local and state resources at least for a short period. Of great concern in catastrophic events is the loss of infrastructure and local government. Catastrophic events may include major hurricanes, earthquakes, weapons of mass destruction, or even a pandemic incident.

Such considerations as succession planning and relocation of critical facilities are essential and accomplished through COG and COOP planning. From a practical standpoint, if there is time to prepare for a catastrophic event, communities may consider relocating a portion of their resources, both human and material, to other locations that might be out of harm's way. Although relocation would not be practical in a disaster such as an earthquake, it could be a consideration for hurricanes and other events that may lend themselves to time for preparation and planning.

Of great concern to any local government would be a catastrophic event such as a widespread pandemic flu. Such an event would necessitate local governments to plan to operate on their own without the help and assistance of entities such as the state and federal governments. This would require substantial planning for a considerable cutback in essential services to any community. The reason for this change in potential support from other agencies could occur if it was an event that affected the whole country.

It is imperative that in advance of a disaster local government officials communicate to the public clearly and responsibly the officials' ability or their lack thereof to respond in the immediate aftermath of a catastrophic event. The public's personal responsibility cannot be overemphasized in planning for a minor, major, or catastrophic event. The responsibility of government is to give the public as much readily available information as possible in order to allow people to make informed decisions about their own safety.

With each disaster there seems to be a continued reliance on government to perform in a manner that it is not prepared for

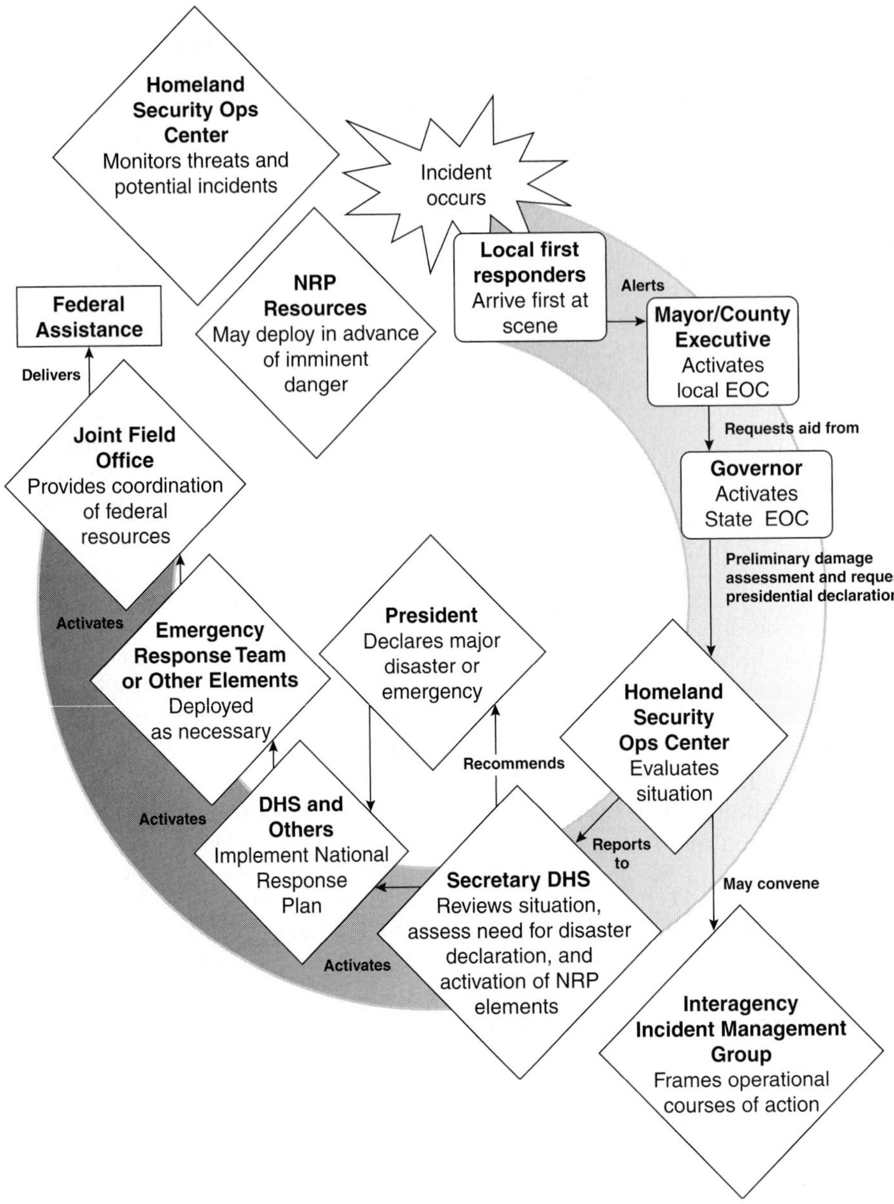

FIGURE 12.12.3 National Response Plan

or may not be equipped to do. In an effort to help mitigate some of these public expectations, it is critical to have a proactive public education program in which local officials are constantly communicating to the public.

GOVERNMENT VERSUS THE PUBLIC'S RESPONSIBILITY

Government organizations in general have become increasingly sophisticated and more efficient and effective in the quality of their responses to disasters. Part of this improvement is a result of constant assessment and refinement of response procedures, some is due to improved training and improved knowledge base of the responders and disaster managers, and another part comes from greater resources to get things done.

Disaster Responsibility in Pre-FEMA Times

In 1964 when the eye of Hurricane Cleo passed over Fort Lauderdale on Florida's east coast, the Federal Emergency Management Agency (FEMA) did not exist. Federal assistance did exist, but it was fractured and divided among many agencies. FEMA was created in 1979 under the administration of President Carter and was brought about by major disasters such as Hurricane Carla in 1962, Hurricane Betsy in 1965, Hurricane Camille in 1969, and Hurricane Agnes in 1972. The Alaskan Earthquake of 1964 and the San Fernando Earthquake in 1971 also tested the foundations of disaster relief. Presidential disaster declarations were eventually established through the enactment of the Disaster Relief Act in 1974.

The individual citizen in pre-FEMA days did not have the level of resources to rely on that exists today. As a result, the average person understood that he or she had a critical responsibility to properly prepare for the disaster and its aftermath. In recent years, with the increased occurrence of natural and man-made disasters, the resources of local, state, and federal governments have been stretched beyond what officials could have ever anticipated. With so many advances in society today, citizens have grown increasingly accustomed to having their needs fulfilled in very short order.

Government's Responsibility in a Disaster

Although government will continue to strive to provide services at the best possible level, citizens must also remain mindful that their responsibility to take care of themselves and their families does not cease in a time of disaster; in fact, that is when it is more critical than ever that citizens have plans in place and ready to be enacted. An additional responsibility for government to aid in this process is the commitment to continually provide public education tools that will provide guidance to citizens in the development of their personal family emergency plans.

Government must continually shoulder a great responsibility in providing resources for disasters, but that does not relieve each person and each family from the responsibility to do their part in preparing for and surviving such events. Although there is no need to go back to the pre-FEMA days when federal assistance was more meager and fractured, there is clearly a need to regain the greater sense of self-reliance that once existed.

EMERGENCY SUPPORT FUNCTIONS, PUBLIC INFORMATION, AND RESOURCES

Emergency Support Functions (ESFs)

Emergency support functions (ESFs) are those functions that are carried out by federal, state, and local governments in response to a disaster. The initial emergency support function concept was developed by the federal government and contains 10 elements. States have taken the emergency support function concept and have expanded it, and local governments have expanded the concept even further.

The following is a list of the emergency support functions that might be found in a comprehensive emergency management plan (CEMP):

Comprehensive Emergency Management Plan Support Functions

Transportation
Communications
Public works and engineering
Fire fighting
Information and planning
Mass care
Resource support
Volunteers and donations
Law enforcement and security
Animal protection
Special medical needs
Business and tourism
Damage assessment
Health
Search and rescue
Hazardous materials
Food and water
Energy and utilities
Military support
Public information
Public protection to include warning and evacuation
Administration and finance
Fatality management
Debris management
Safety
Information technology

To some degree, many of these functions must be accomplished during the preparation, response, and recovery phases. For each function, it is critical that a lead person or organization be designated to carry out the identified tasks. Some functions may be more prominent in the response or recovery phase than others, depending on the threat and the aftermath.

Of significant importance is the ability for incident commanders to ensure that emergency support functions are integrated into a NIMS-compliant plan. There are several models that have successfully integrated these functions. Other communities have NIMS-compliant plans that are less transparent with regard to the emergency support functions. However, all the elements are still incorporated into their response and recovery procedures regardless of nomenclature. The elements described in this section are consistent with successful response and recovery plans.

Public Information

One of the most potentially confusing elements of a disaster occurs in the area of public information. If state and local governments fail to preplan, train, and develop protocol for coordination and communication, they may be creating a recipe for disaster regarding public response and opinion. Under the NIMS plan, a key element for coordination of public information is found in the joint information center (JIC). A JIC, which is an essential point for communication for all local entities involved in disaster response and recovery, is responsible for the overall coordination of public information. This can become essential when disasters cross jurisdictional and geographic boundaries.

Proactive approaches to public information include disaster seminars conducted on potential threats; publications such as an all-hazards brochure that would include all the hazards that may affect a community; and partnerships with local and national media services, which allow for developing and disseminating the multimedia projects a community may develop. Another approach is the use of technology to include interactive websites, DVDs, and other educational tools.

In 2005, for example, the city of Cape Coral, Florida, developed a 30 minute DVD solely dedicated to the process of hurricane planning and preparation as it relates to the unique features and needs of this waterfront community. The DVD has been well received and sought after by residents, businesses, and agencies and is distributed free of charge (Figure 12.12.4). It is also shown on the city's cable access television station regularly throughout hurricane season. Cape Coral's Emergency Management Bureau plans to develop annual updates to the DVD as a continued public education tool for the community.

FIGURE 12.12.4 Cover of the Hurricane Preparedness DVD for the City of Cape Coral, Florida

Emergency Planning Resources

The following is a sample of additional resources to help define the context of this chapter and to provide thought processes for emergency planning:

- NFPA 1600, *Standard on Disaster/Emergency Management and Business Continuity Programs*
- National Institute for Occupational Safety and Health (NIOSH), http://www.cdc.gov/niosh/homepage.html
- USFA Training and Education Learning Resource Center, http://www.usfa.dhs.gov/fireservice/training/lrc/
- State and local emergency agencies and plans
- International City/County Management Association (ICMA), http://www.icma.org/main/sc.asp
- Emergency management practices text (e.g., *Emergency Management: Principles and Practice for Local Government,* published by the International City Management Association [ICMA])
- National Incident Management System (NIMS), http://www.fema.gov/emergency/nims/index.shtm

RELATIONSHIPS BETWEEN LEVELS OF GOVERNMENTS AND PUBLIC AND PRIVATE SECTORS

Relationships Among Levels of Government

Depending on which arm of government the reader may represent, his or her perspective may differ regarding which one is of greatest importance. The reality is that each segment of government has its own vital role toward ensuring a successful response to a disaster.

Local Government. Local governments are most often in the trenches for the entire duration of disaster events, including during the preparation, response, and recovery phases. They are perhaps best positioned for the preparation and immediate response role. Who could possibly better understand the local area, its citizens' expectations, its needs, and the status of resources that are available?

Local governments, however, are ill positioned to handle catastrophic events without some form of assistance, whether that assistance is financial or otherwise. It is best for local governments to acknowledge this reality and work to better understand and facilitate their interactions with county, state, and federal agencies. Most local governments would find great benefit in developing solid relationships with their municipal or county emergency management agencies. These agencies serve as an invaluable source of support and information as well as a link to state and federal resources and training opportunities.

State Government. States serve their best role in bringing together resources and in managing regionally centered communications. They serve well in disseminating and controlling vital information and resources. Through the National Guard, states are also able to provide significant human resources and materials following catastrophic disaster events. Certain states such as Florida have stepped up the preparation element of their responsibilities by identifying strategic locations to prestage resources so they can be delivered with as little delay as possible.

Federal Government. When considering relationships on the federal level, a city that has not accessed opportunities to train and learn all it can about the offerings, rules, and regulations of FEMA is doing itself a disservice. For example, failure to properly complete the FEMA forms required for reimbursement could at the very least mean extended delays in recieving reimbursement for disaster-related expenditures. At worst, it could cause reimbursement to be denied. Understanding and working well with this federal agency is imperative. A wealth of information can be found on FEMA's website at http://www.fema.gov.

Relationships Between the Public and Private Sectors

Federal, state, and local disaster response organizations can bring together and effectively apply tremendous resources in the event of a disaster. All of those resources combined would still fall short without the addition of private sector resources. This is perhaps never truer than in the disaster recovery phase. When an earthquake, tornado, or hurricane strikes, millions of tons of debris must be removed and safely discarded. Few, if any, governmental entities have the resources to handle this work, yet the private sector does. Private providers can bring together resources from across the nation to accomplish this work and leave local resources available to handle the more routine daily functions required of a community.

Private sector organizations often feel a sense of obligation to their communities and are willing to contribute labor and resources toward recovery. It's important for the local government to have a close and cordial relationship with the private sector. Local government officials should not wait until after the event to begin building that much-needed rapport. If the stakeholders and the extent of their available resources are known, gaining access to those resources becomes much easier. Knowing who has heavy or specialized tools and equipment, who has expert skills, and who may have an inventory of materials needed to handle a major incident can make a huge difference in how rapidly or how well a community can respond.

Consider developing a list of what resources might be needed under various disaster scenarios, such as a tornado, hurricane, infectious disease pandemic, or terrorist attack. To do this exercise properly, include all elements of the response/recovery organization in the list, not just police and fire personnel. Then set about determining which persons or companies in the private sector might have those resources. Contact them and let them know what you are doing and that you may need to rely on them at some future date. You may be surprised at how eager they will be to assist.

Homeowners and neighborhood associations, fraternal organizations, and various clubs and professional groups are other types of resources that can help make a difference. Maintain a database, including names and contact information for the leadership of those organizations. Developing these relationships and contacts in advance may be more helpful than just accessing resources. Such contact information may help you in getting information out to the community in difficult times.

INTERNAL RELATIONSHIPS

Defined Leadership Roles

Disasters are a time of intense danger with little room for error. The circumstances are critical, the stakes are high, and the consequences of failure are dire. If the leadership roles have not been clearly defined or if the responsible persons fail to perform properly, things can go dreadfully wrong. Remember that leadership abhors a vacuum. Where leadership does not exist or where it does not appear to exist, it is likely that someone will attempt to fill the vacuum. Just imagine that scenario unfolding in the midst a major event.

"The way you practice is the way you play," according to a saying in the world of sports. In other words, the things that you routinely do are exactly those things that you will do when the pressure is on. It is equally true when dealing with disasters. If organizational leadership is weak or ineffective, it will not suddenly heal itself when a disaster arrives. If the organization is fractured and operates with only marginal departmental cooperation at best, then that is exactly what will exist during disaster operations. No matter how thorough the disaster plans, if the organization is not accustomed to operating as a team, then the chances for substantial error are significant.

There must be a role for every element of the organization. Those roles must be clearly defined, well documented, thoroughly trained, routinely practiced, and refined (Figure 12.12.5). They must also be respected by those assigned to every other area of responsibility. As vital as they are in certain phases of disaster operations, police, fire, and EMS are not the only important elements of the team. The importance level of any of those three will lessen when in the recovery phase of a hurricane; for example, when it becomes necessary to manage the removal and safe disposal of millions of tons of debris.

Role of the CEO and the Incident Commander

In local governments, a city or county manager or perhaps a strong mayor is the chief executive officer (CEO), that is, the top person in charge of the organization's day-to-day activities. Such is not always the case in disaster situations. Following the NIMS organizational structure, the event, if large enough, needs an incident commander. Depending on the nature of the event, the incident commander may be the police chief, the fire chief, the health department director, or someone else. Regardless of who it is, everyone must allow that person to do his or her job. Unfortunately, a CEO's need to control things can lead to conflicts and leadership confusion. The way for a CEO to avoid that and at the same time to reinforce the incident commander's role is to let him or her do the job and to visibly be there in support.

The flip side to this scenario is that the incident commander must be confident in his or her role to exercise strong leadership, perhaps in the physical presence of someone who is his or her superior in day-to-day operations. There is little question that this is a fine balance, which requires the incident commander and the CEO to carefully demonstrate through cooperation and support that they are a team. If the CEO is observed sending the right message, then it is simple for everyone else to accept and support the incident commander. The best way to avoid leadership conflict is through good communication, which starts with a clear understanding of the scope of each person's role, is reinforced with practice, and is further fortified through careful attention to the team concept.

FIGURE 12.12.5 Command Staff, Including the Mayor, City Manager, and Public Information Director at the Activation of the Cape Coral, Florida, EOC During Hurricane Wilma, October, 2005

SUMMARY

In the aftermath of events such as 9/11, tsunamis, earthquakes, floods, tornados, pandemics, and hurricanes that have affected the world in recent years, it is apparent that public and private organizations must plan for events that might impact their community. Such plans must be comprehensive yet easy to read and implement during a crisis. Planning must be pertinent, practical, and precise. Plans must include all the critical elements for response and recovery and do so in a systematic format to assure consistency and continuous improvement. Disaster planning is not an option in today's world. Public and private organizations must make every effort to be prepared for natural and man-made disasters, to move communities into a state of readiness, and to forge relationships with each other to respond to these disasters.

BIBLIOGRAPHY

NFPA Codes, Standards, and Recommended Practices

Reference to the following NFPA codes, standards, and recommended practices will provide further information on disaster planning and response services discussed in this chapter. (See the latest version of The NFPA Catalog *for availability of current editions of the following documents.)*

NFPA 1201, *Standard for Providing Emergency Services to the Public*

NFPA 1561, *Standard on Emergency Services Incident Management System*

NFPA 1600, *Standard on Disaster/Emergency Management and Business Continuity Programs*

References

Comprehensive Emergency Management Plan (CEMP), City of Cape Coral, FL.

Debris Emergency Management Plan, City of Cape Coral, FL.

Comprehensive Emergency Management Plan (CEMP), City of Miami, FL.

Emergency Management: Principles and Practice for Local Government, International City Management Association (ICMA), Washington, DC.

Federal Emergency Management Agency (FEMA), http://www.fema.gov

Florida Statutes Chapter 252, "Emergency Management," the Florida Legislature, Tallahassee, FL.

International City/County Management Association (ICMA), http://www.icma.org/main/sc.asp

National Incident Management System (NIMS), http://www.fema.gov/emergency/nims/index.shtm

National Institute for Occupational Safety and Health (NIOSH), http://www.cdc.gov/niosh/homepage.html

National Oceanic and Atmospheric Administration (NOAA), http://www.noaa.gov

National Response Plan (NRP), http://www.dhs.gov/xprepresp/committees/editorial_0566.shtm

USFA Training and Education Learning Resource Center, http://www.usfa.dhs.gov/fireservice/training/lrc

Chapter 13

GIS for Fire Station Locations and Response Protocols

Russ Johnson ❑ Mike Price

Chapter Contents

Key Terms

deployment, emergency management, emergency medical services, emergency response, fire station, geographic information system (GIS), reflex time, response time

The mission of the fire service is to protect life, property, and natural resources from fire and other emergencies. With increasing demands, the fire service must utilize the best tools, techniques, and training methods to meet public expectations. Risk management, preparedness, and mitigation have taken on new importance in light of the challenges facing fire departments today. One emerging tool that is helping the fire service optimize emergency services delivery is geographic information system (GIS) technology.

GIS supports planning, preparedness, mitigation, response, and incident management. GIS extends the capability of maps—intelligent, interactive maps—with access to all types of information, analysis, and data. When a fire occurs, any delay of responding fire companies can make the difference between the rescue of occupants versus serious injury or death. The critical time between fire containment and flashover can be measured in seconds. From the moment an emergency call is received, through the deployment of tactical resources, GIS helps reduce critical time and increases efficiency. GIS technology brings additional power to fire personnel for hazard evaluation, service demand analysis, and resource deployment. This chapter will examine how GIS technology is helping the fire service meet the needs of the community more efficiently than ever.

For related topics see Section 12, Chapter 14, "Fire Rescue Stations and Fire Service Training Centers"; Section 12, Chapter 15, "Public Emergency Services Alarm, Dispatch, and Communications Systems"; and Section 12, Chapter 16, "Fire Department Apparatus and Equipment."

GIS OVERVIEW

GIS Defined

GIS is a technology that integrates geographic features with tabular data to assess and better understand real-world problems. What is now GIS began around 1960 with the discovery that maps could be programmed using simple code and stored in a computer, allowing for future modification when necessary. This was a tremendous change from the era of cartography when maps had to be painstakingly created by hand; even small changes required the creation of a new map. The earliest version of a GIS was known as computer cartography and involved simple line work to represent land features.

GIS Map Layers

Unlike a flat paper map, a GIS-generated map can present many layers of different information that each provide a unique way of thinking about a geographic space. By linking maps to databases,

Russ Johnson, a public safety industry manager at ESRI, has an AA degree in fire science from San Bernardino Valley Junior College and a BA degree in public administration from the University of Redlands. He has 30 years of service with the federal government in fire management and extensive experience in complex emergency management as national ICS incident management team incident commander.

Mike Price, a public safety GIS analyst at Entrada/San Juan, Inc., has a BS in geology/geophysics from Prescott College (AZ)/Western Washington University. He has over 30 years of experience in municipal fire protection, public safety, and emergency management and an extensive background in GIS mapping, spatial analysis, public safety modeling, and emergency management technology training.

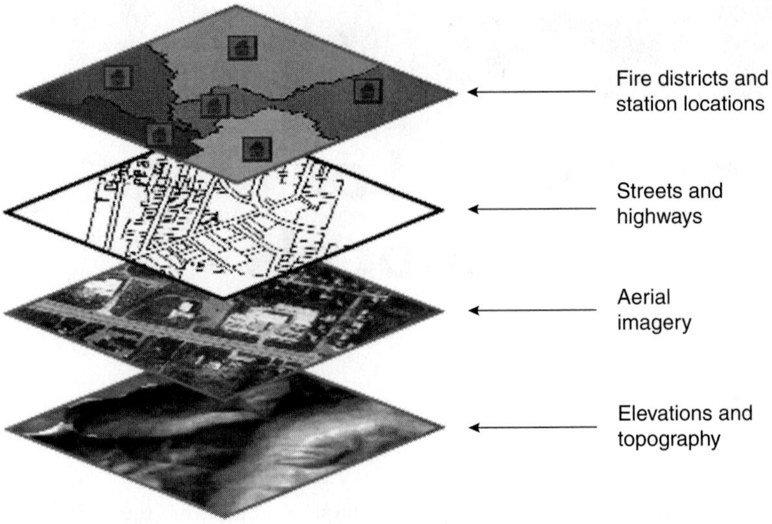

FIGURE 12.13.1 GIS Provision of Data and Information Through Map Layers

GIS enables users to visualize, manipulate, analyze, and display spatial data (Figure 12.13.1). Some GIS map layers that fire departments use include the following:

- Streets
- Parcels
- Fire hydrants
- Utility networks
- Topography
- Lakes and rivers
- Commercial and government buildings
- Fire station locations
- Police station locations
- Hospital locations
- School locations
- Satellite or aerial imagery
- Historical incident or emergency call locations
- Fire districts
- Public occupancies

Map layers can be selected and displayed (overlaid). These layers are linked to data tables that contain detailed information about the geographic features being displayed. The most powerful aspect of GIS is its comprehensive analysis capabilities. GIS analyzes and displays patterns, relationships, and trends through the geographic data layers to help users understand how the world works, make the best choice from among options, or develop plans through what-if scenarios.

GIS ANALYSIS

Incident Analysis

GIS can perform complex incident analysis to display trends, illustrate patterns, and identify areas of high call volume. A GIS display of historical incidents (represented by points or icons on the map where they occurred) includes attribute information for each incident. Attribute information (i.e., descriptive data about a map feature) contained in the underlying database can include the following:

- Incident type
- Incident cause
- Date of incident
- Time of incident report
- Units that responded
- Unit arrival times

Incidents can be queried based on incident type, cause, time, units assigned, or other variables contained in the attribute data (Figure 12.13.2). GIS searches the data tables, gathers data matching the spatial request, and displays the information on the map. Incident trend analysis can be done quickly, displayed

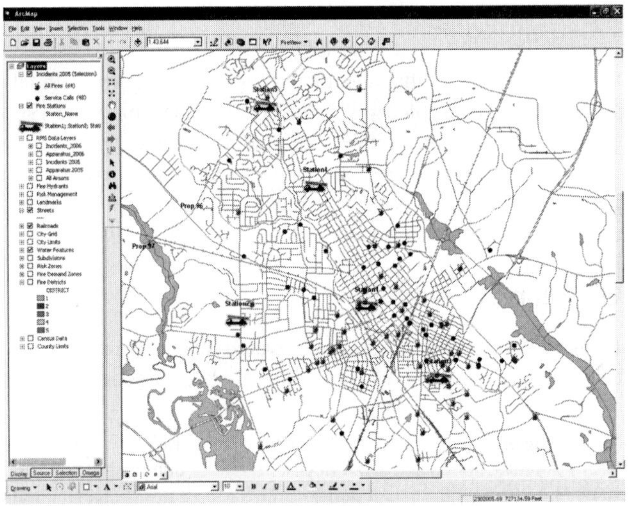

FIGURE 12.13.2 GIS Analysis and Display of Incidents Based on User-Defined Criteria (Time, Location, Cause, Geographic Area, etc.)

logically, and understood easily. For example, a GIS user could request to see arson fires that occurred between the hours of 1:00 a.m. and 5:00 a.m. on Saturdays in Fire Districts 1 and 2. GIS will interrogate the records database and place points on the map that match the request. Such analyses provide decision support for issues related to fire prevention, staffing requirements, and apparatus placement/deployment.

Travel Time Modeling

Using a fire station layer and a street layer, response time analysis can be performed (Figure 12.13.3). A street layer is often represented in GIS as a series of lines that intersect on the map, creating a GIS street network. Each street line segment between intersections contains attribute information such as road type, distance, and travel speeds (miles or kilometers per hour). This allows users to identify a station location, specify a travel time, and run a network analysis. The result will be displayed by an irregular polygon around the station that illustrates where the fire apparatus could travel in any direction for the specified time. This type of analysis can be performed on a single station or simultaneously on all stations to analyze gaps in coverage, establish run orders, and more.

FIRE STATION LOCATION PLANNING

The primary responsibility of a fire department is the delivery of fire and rescue services, normally originating from fire stations located throughout the area to be protected. To provide effective service, crews must respond in the minimum time possible after the incident has been reported and with sufficient resources to initiate fire, rescue, or emergency medical activities. Fire station location planning must take into account a number of variables, including the following:

- Importance of response time
- Flashover
- Fire department total reflex time sequence
- Emergency medical services

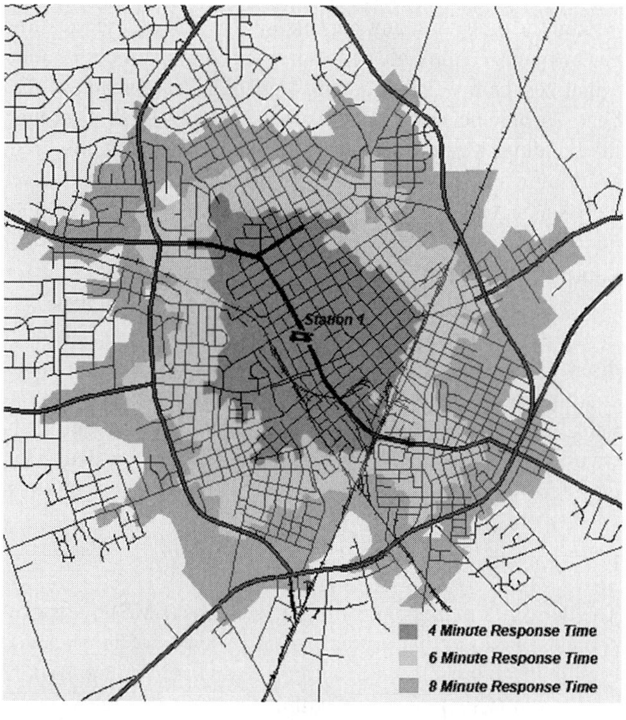

FIGURE 12.13.3 GIS Analysis and Display of Travel Times from a Station, Based on Information Contained in Street Centerline File

Importance of Response Time

Time is the critical element when an emergency is reported. Fire growth can expand at a rate of many times its volume per minute. Time is the critical factor for the rescue of occupants and the application of extinguishing agents to minimize loss.

The time segment between fire ignition and the start of fire suppression has a direct relationship to fire loss. The delivery of emergency medical services is also time critical. Survival rates for some types of medical emergencies depend on rapid intervention by trained emergency medical personnel. In most cases, the sooner trained fire or emergency medical rescue personnel arrive, the greater the chance for survival and conservation of property.

Flashover

Regardless of the speed of growth or length of burn time, all fires go through the same stages of growth. One particular stage, called *flashover,* is significant because it marks a critical change in conditions. Depending on room size, contents of the room, and available oxygen, flashover can occur in less than 2 or more than 10 minutes. Flashover occurs most frequently between 4 and 10 minutes. Measuring the time to flashover is a function of time and temperature. Fire growth occurs exponentially; that is, fire doubles itself for every second of free burn that is allowed. This can be plotted on what is known as the time and temperature curve (Figure 12.13.4).

A number of factors determine when flashover may occur. These include the type and arrangement of the fuels in the room, room size, and so on. Because these factors vary, the exact time to flashover cannot be predicted. Flashover can typically occur from less than 4 to beyond 10 minutes after free burning starts. A postflashover fire burns hotter and moves faster, compounding the search and rescue problems in the remainder of the structure at the same time that more fire fighters are needed for fire attack.

There are a number of critical time frames that the fire department can manage, as well as some it cannot, that affect success. The time from ignition to discovery to reporting of a fire is indirectly manageable. This time period can be managed through requirement of automatic detection and/or suppression systems and automatic reporting to the public safety answering point (PSAP). In a perfect world, all structures would be equipped with automatic detection and/or suppression systems. One factor that has helped to manage this segment of time is the increasing use of automatic smoke detectors in residential

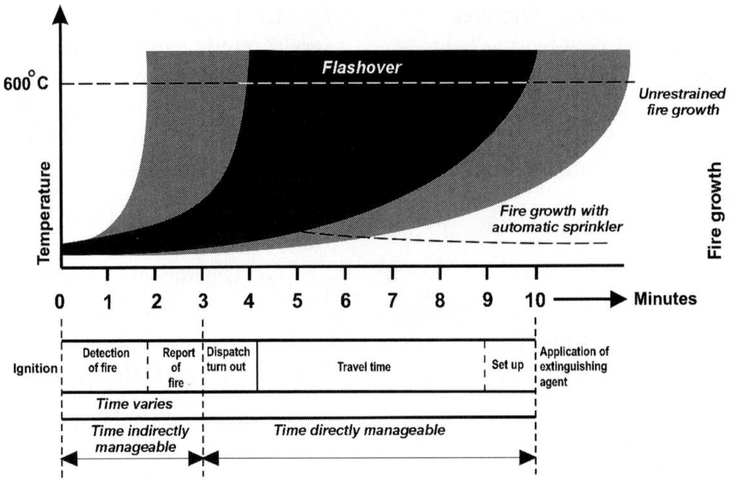

FIGURE 12.13.4 Fire Growth over Time and Sequence of Events That May Occur from Ignition to Suppression

occupancies. What is lacking, however, is automatic reporting to the public safety answering point.

Fire Department Total Reflex Time Sequence

The following are five steps in the fire department total reflex time sequence after receipt of an alarm:

1. Dispatch time
2. Turnout time
3. Response time
4. Access time
5. Setup time

Dispatch Time. Dispatch time is the amount of time that it takes to receive and process an emergency call. This includes the following:

1. Receiving the call
2. Determining the type of emergency
3. Verifying the location of the emergency
4. Determining the resources required to handle the call
5. Notifying the units that are to respond

Dispatch time is manageable by the way that alarms are received and the way that dispatch systems and activities are handled. Enhanced 9-1-1 (E9-1-1) and computer-aided dispatch (CAD) systems can minimize the time required to receive and process alarms.

Turnout Time. Turnout time is the period beginning when units acknowledge notification of the emergency to the initial point of response time. Turnout time may be managed to some degree by improving the method of communications between the dispatch center and the fire station to reduce the time processing the alarm information.

Response Time. Response time is the period beginning when units are en route to the emergency incident and ending when units arrive on the scene (wheel start to wheel stop). Response time is one of the most manageable segments of time in the entire sequence. Travel time can be managed by selecting strategic fire station locations based on the amount of time that it takes to travel from the fire station along the most efficient travel route to the incident scene.

Access Time. Access time is the time required for the crew to move from where the apparatus stops to the emergency. This can include moving to the interior or upper stories of a large building and dealing with any barriers along the way. Access time can be managed through a good prefire planning process that familiarizes the fire fighters with access points, automatic system controls, annunciator panel locations, and travel routes through the building. Key boxes can facilitate getting doors unlocked. Working with security forces at larger facilities to expedite access can also reduce access time.

Setup Time. Setup time is the time required for fire department units to set up, connect hose lines, position ladders, and otherwise prepare to extinguish the fire. Setup time includes disembarking the fire apparatus, pulling and placing hose lines, charging hose lines, donning self-contained breathing apparatus, making entry into the building, and beginning to apply water. The opportunity for saving time during setup is minimal, even for trained personnel.

Emergency Medical Services

The delivery of emergency medical services (EMS) by first responders is also time critical for many types of injuries and events. If a person has a heart attack and cardiopulmonary resuscitation (CPR) is started within four minutes, the victim's chances of leaving the hospital alive are almost four times greater than if the victim does not receive CPR until after four minutes. Figure 12.13.5 shows the survival rate for heart attack victims when CPR is available, and Figure 12.13.6 shows

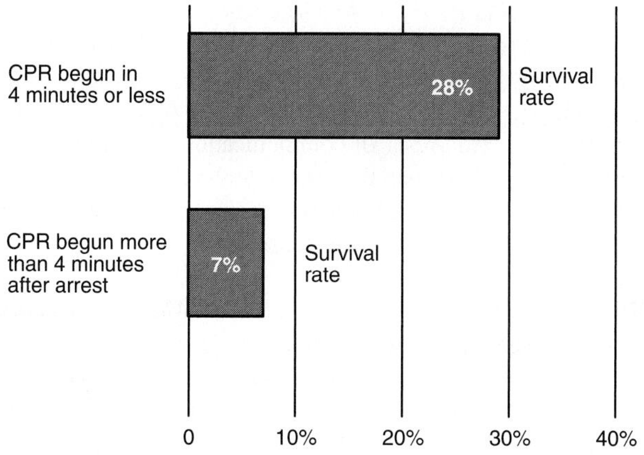

FIGURE 12.13. 5 Survival Rate of Heart Attack Victims When CPR Is Available (Source: Heartsaver Manual, American Heart Association)

the outcome for heart attack victims based on when CPR is provided

For both fire and medical emergencies, the basis for the placement of fire stations should be the amount of time that it takes to deliver adequate emergency resources to the point of demand from each fire station or combination of fire stations.

Reducing Response Times

The most effective way to improve outcomes for both fire and medical emergency response is to reduce response time. By understanding the objectives of each step in the response sequence, a fire department can measure its current performance against these objectives. That information provides the necessary framework for assessing the cost of reducing response time during any of these steps. The rest of this section will describe how GIS can be used to apply a rational decision-making process for reducing overall emergency response time.

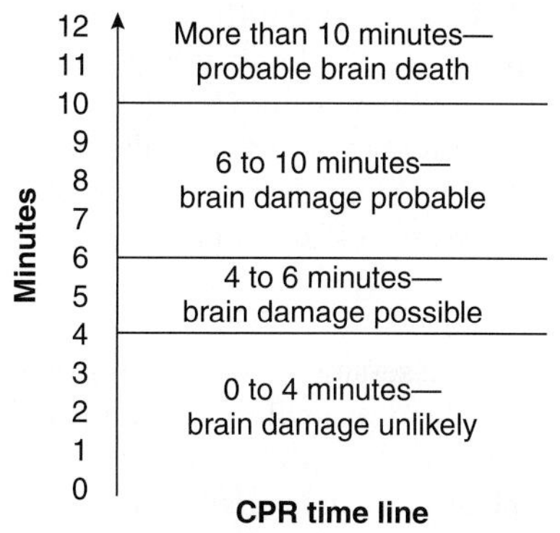

FIGURE 12.13.6 Outcome for Heart Attack Victims Based on When CPR Is Provided (Source: Data from http://www.firstaid.com)

Essentially, each community must decide its desired response and travel times. There are a number of factors that influence the selection of a specific response/travel time. All applicable factors must be considered when making a decision on a specific response/travel time for a community. Factors that should be considered include types of fire department services, reasonable travel time, size of area and type and amount of resources, and acceptable level of risk.

Types of Services. What types of services are delivered by the fire department? Does the department deliver both fire and emergency medical services or fire service only? The delivery of emergency medical services is an important factor in selecting a response/travel time because of the need to provide initial service as rapidly as possible.

Reasonable Travel Time. What is a reasonable travel time for the community? The selection of a response/travel time must be practical. A short response/travel time will enable a department to deliver services within a short period of time but will require more stations. Is there prescription for travel times based on the type of risk, hazard, or demand? Certain hazards or occupancy types may require a faster response time. Response time standards for the community may have to reflect a variation based on these types of considerations. The time or times selected must provide a balance between service expectations and the financial ability of the community to provide the necessary stations and resources.

Area Size and Resources. What is the size of the area being served and the type and amount of available resources? Large rural regions normally have longer response/travel times and fewer resources than urban or suburban areas. For example, a countywide fire response and emergency medical service operated by volunteer personnel will most likely have longer response/travel times than an urban or suburban area staffed by full-time career personnel. The demographics of the area being served and traffic patterns during peak periods, as well as past fire and EMS activity, must be considered.

Acceptable Risk Level. What level of risk is the community willing to accept? When a community selects a longer travel time, it must be willing to accept a larger level of risk. Accepting a larger level of risk may be based on past experience; for example, areas that take longer to reach may be known to have a significantly lower number of incidents.

The selection of a response/travel time for a community should be made after all factors are examined. In many cases, this decision should be made after the analysis has started and decision makers are able to review the results of the analysis.

There are several ways that a community can establish a response/travel time standard. Some of these are (1) the use of historical fire and EMS response data, (2) demand for service, (3) the level of care that the community wants to provide, and (4) the level of care that the community is able to afford. In some cases, the analysis will assist in establishing the standard after a number of scenarios are examined.

RESPONSE/TRAVEL TIME STANDARDS

National Standards

Three National Fire Protection Association (NFPA) standards contain time requirements that influence the delivery of fire and emergency medical services, as follows:

- NFPA 1710, *Standard for the Organization and Deployment of Fire Suppression Operations, Emergency Medical Operations, and Special Operations to the Public by Career Fire Departments*
- NFPA 1720, *Standard for the Organization and Deployment of Fire Suppression Operations, Emergency Medical Operations, and Special Operations to the Public by Volunteer Fire Departments*
- NFPA 1221, *Standard for the Installation, Maintenance, and Use of Emergency Services Communications Systems*

NFPA 1710, *Standard for the Organization and Deployment of Fire Suppression Operations, Emergency Medical Operations, and Special Operations to the Public by Career Fire Departments.* NFPA 1710 contains time objectives that must be established by career fire departments as follows:

- Turnout time: One minute (60 seconds) for turnout time
- Fire response time: Four minutes (240 seconds) or less for the arrival of the first arriving engine company at a fire suppression incident and/or eight minutes (480 seconds) or less for the deployment of a full first alarm assignment at a fire suppression incident
- First responder or higher emergency medical response time: Four minutes (240 seconds) or less for the arrival of a unit with first responder or higher-level capability at an emergency medical incident
- Advanced life support response time: Eight minutes (480 seconds) or less for the arrival of an advanced life support unit at an emergency medical incident, for incidents in which the service is provided by the fire department

The standard states that the fire department must establish a performance objective of not less than 90 percent for the achievement of each response time objective. NFPA 1710 does contain a time objective for dispatch time in the following requirement: "All communications facilities, equipment, staffing, and operating procedures shall comply with NFPA 1221."

For the purposes of NFPA 1710, the following definitions apply:

> *Dispatch Time.* The point of receipt of the emergency alarm at the public safety answering point to the point where sufficient information is known to the dispatcher and applicable units are notified of the emergency
>
> *Turnout Time.* The time that begins when units acknowledge notification of the emergency to the beginning point of response time
>
> *Response Time.* The time that begins when units are en route to the emergency incident and ends when units arrive at the scene

NFPA 1720, *Standard for the Organization and Deployment of Fire Suppression Operations, Emergency Medical Operations, and Special Operations to the Public by Volunteer Fire Departments.* NFPA 1720 contains a time objective for dispatch time that requires "All communications facilities, equipment, staffing, and operating procedures shall comply with NFPA 1221." NFPA 1720 contains requirements for response times related to area population density.

NFPA 1221, *Standard for the Installation, Maintenance, and Use of Emergency Services Communications Systems.* NFPA 1221 requires that 95 percent of alarms must be answered within 15 seconds, 99 percent of alarms must be answered in 40 seconds, and the dispatch of the emergency response agency must be completed within 60 seconds at least 95 percent of the time. The time lines for dispatching shown in Figure 12.13.7 and Figure 12.13.8 are taken from NFPA 1221.

Standards of Response Coverage

Other guidelines for the deployment of emergency resources is the Commission on Fire Accreditation International's standards of response coverage. The standards of response coverage process has the following nine parts:

1. Existing deployment
2. Community outcome expectations
3. Community risk assessment
4. Distribution study
5. Concentration study
6. Historical reliability
7. Historical response effectiveness study
8. Prevention and mitigation
9. Overall evaluation

Existing Deployment. Existing deployment is an assessment of the department's current deployment configuration and capability. Included in the assessment is a review of the historical decision-making process of the agency. Is there a reason stations are in their present locations? What equipment has been purchased and why? Can these past decisions be changed?

Community Outcome Expectations. What are the current community expectations for fire protection and emergency service delivery? Included in this process is a review of response anticipated for the variety of fire risks in the community as well as man-made and natural disasters; it also includes EMS, heavy rescue, hazardous materials, aircraft and airport, and water and shipboard incidents.

Community Risk Assessment. What assets within the community are at risk? For example, structure fire risk might be assessed using fire and life safety factors such as fire flow and code compliance for life safety to determine a risk classification. Risk classes might include low, moderate, and maximum risk. Many communities may identify the majority of areas composed of dwelling units as moderate or typical risks. In addition, different responses may be provided to

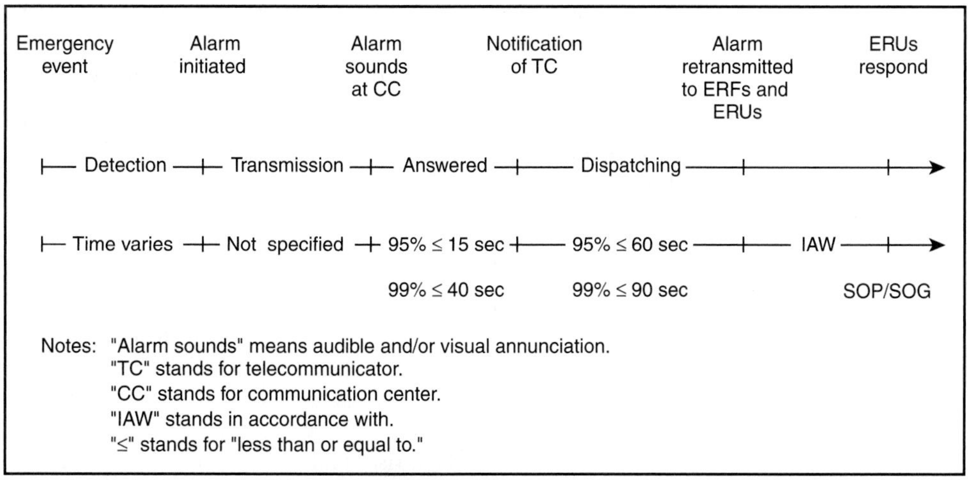

FIGURE 12.13.7 Alarm Time Line Where Primary PSAP Is Communications Center (Source: NFPA 1221, 2007 ed., Figure A.7.4.1[a])

urban, suburban, rural, or remote areas as defined using census terminology.

Distribution Study. Where are the locations of first-due resources?

Concentration Study. Where are incidents concentrated and what is the adequacy of the first alarm assignment or effective response force?

Historical Reliability. Is there a multiple-call frequency issue such as call stacking, or simultaneous calls within a specific area or areas?

Historical Response Effectiveness Studies. What percentage of compliance does the existing system deliver based on current performance goals?

Prevention and Mitigation. Are there tactics that can strategically affect the outcome of events that do occur? The United Kingdom released *The National Plan* in 2004, which replaced earlier standards of coverage documents. The new report found that without prevention and mitigation, the level of safety for responders and the public would reach a plateau. Using analysis of risk and looking at possible strategic actions may not only prevent the incident in some cases, but may also minimize the severity of an incident that does occur.

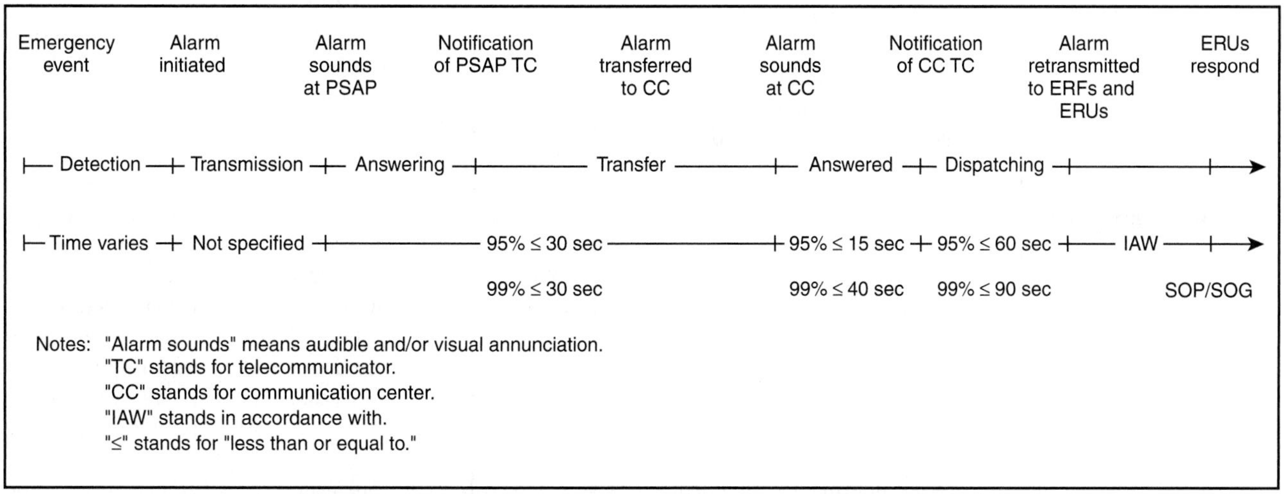

FIGURE 12.13.8 Alarm Time Line Where Primary PSAP Is Not the Communications Center (Source: NFPA 1221, 2007 ed., Figure A.7.4.1[b])

Overall Evaluation. Overall evaluation consists of proposing standards of response coverage statements by risk type, as in the following example:

> In 90 percent of all incidents, the first-due unit shall arrive within 4 minutes' travel or 6 minutes' total reflex time. The first-due unit shall be capable of advancing the first line for fire control or starting rescue or providing basic life support for medical incidents. In a moderate risk area, an initial effective response force shall arrive within 8 minutes' travel or 10 minutes' total reflex time, 90 percent of the time, and be able to provide 1,500 gallons per minute for fire fighting, or be able to handle a five-patient emergency medical incident.[1]

Risks Versus Response Time Standards

Some communities may elect to adopt several response time standards for various levels of risk in the community, or they may adopt one single response time standard for all risks. Here, a *risk* refers to a response location and the potential fire, occupant, and exposure problems that will be encountered. Providing several response/travel times based on the level of risk means that some areas will be reached in a shorter period of time than other areas. A single response time standard for the community or area served will provide approximately the same level of initial response to all areas of the community. Some of the risks that may be considered for various response/travel times follow:

- *Sprinklered versus nonsprinklered.* The fully sprinklered property is theoretically at less risk than the nonsprinklered property. The community may elect to place fire stations closer to the nonsprinklered property because of the ability of sprinklers to automatically put water on a fire.
- *Commercial versus residential.* The community must decide, in this case, where the greater risk is located. Is there a greater risk with the commercial property? At what time of day is the risk greater? Is the risk greater in residential occupancies at night?
- *Multifamily versus single-family residential.* Is the risk greater in multifamily residential areas than in single-family residential areas? Fire station location should be influenced by population factors.

The risk questions should address the following:

- High life hazard (i.e., loss potential) or high dollar value
- High incident rate areas versus low incident rate areas
- High rate of incidents that require a high level of resources versus low rate

The community that chooses to provide various levels of service to different areas, based on the level of risk, will require a much more complex fire station location study.

It should be noted that most of the information provided addresses career fire departments with stations staffed around the clock. For call and volunteer fire departments, turnout time typically will be greater. This is significant and must be considered in overall response time.

DETERMINING FIRE STATION LOCATIONS

Adopting a Response/Travel Time Standard

The first step in determining where a fire station should be located is the adoption of a response time standard or standards for the community based on the items discussed previously. Once the response time standard has been developed, it should be divided into specific time intervals for each of the components that make up total reflex time: dispatch time, turnout time, response time, access time, and setup time.

For most incidents, the dispatch time and turnout time can be established by using historical data. Setup time depends on the type and complexity of the incident. A single-family dwelling fire will generally require less time than a major fire in a high-rise building or an industrial complex. A thorough analysis will examine setup times and incident frequencies for several types of incidents. For larger incidents, the standard may be stated in terms of response time for the last of several units required for the total operation. Relevant times by type of incident can be established through training or historical experience.

Response time minus the cumulative time for dispatch, turnout, access, and setup yields the allotment for travel time. Once the response time standard has been established and a travel time standard selected, the process of determining or planning fire station locations can begin. Even though response time and travel time standards are selected prior to the beginning of the study, this does not mean that other times cannot be examined and used in the analysis. The final response/travel time may be selected after a number of scenarios are examined.

Using GIS for Fire Station Placement

Accuracy of Data. With the advent of modern software and computer technology, the selection of best fire station locations can be determined with a greater degree of accuracy using geography information system (GIS) technology. Unlike previous methods that employed grid and concentric circle analysis, GIS simulates the real road network of the area being analyzed. A high degree of accuracy is ensured by using actual travel distances, vehicle speeds, and time delays for roadway conditions (e.g., congestion, turning radius, weather, hills); accounting for one-way or unusable roadways; and implementing user-defined risk factors.

Additional data that may be used to ensure accuracy are historical response and travel times. This can be data taken from the computer-aided dispatch data or recorded manually. Data may include response/travel time, turnout time, time of day, and day of the week. All of this data can be analyzed to determine if there are specific traffic patterns that affect response times. If so, the base map can be adjusted to reflect alternate response routes or apparatus. In some instances, an alternate fire company may arrive more quickly due to heavy traffic at peak travel hours.

GIS Analysis Results. The results of GIS computer studies are a series of color maps of the street/roadway network that are easy to comprehend. These maps can show a variety of information, such as the street segments that can be reached from all stations for a specified target travel time, the overlap between stations, the response area for each station, and other information, depending on the capability of the software program being used.

GIS analysis can effectively illustrate problem areas as well as proposed solutions. GIS can show various data for simulated responses to specific locations including apparatus and personnel on a time-arrival sequence, multiple alarms, and travel time to each street segment in the system. This will provide accurate information for critical decision making by an incident commander, including the ability to predict the time needed to assign resources for various emergency operations.

The response area for each fire station, based on the travel time specified, can be calculated and displayed. Each station's response area can be shown as different colors on the map. GIS analysis produces color maps that show the overlap between stations for a specified travel time. The color maps show the areas where there are two or more stations whose first-due response areas overlap, with the overlap colors different from the station response area colors. These maps can be used to determine multiple-company response to an area or to show where stations are placed ineffectively. Areas that receive no coverage or deficient coverage are also displayed.

Mutual-Aid Station Analysis. The response from mutual-aid stations can also be analyzed as part of the overall study, to show the arrival of additional resources. This is particularly useful to show the response of special apparatus and teams such as hazardous materials teams, advanced rescue teams, or other special teams. Given limited resources, a whole region can be analyzed using the entire resources of the region.

Examination of Alternative and Future Station Locations. Alternative and future station locations can be examined through the use of what-if scenarios, using various fire station locations and travel times. The information from these programs can be integrated with the data from local and regional planning groups to show where new stations and/or roadways may be needed to best serve existing and growing communities.

Comprehensive GIS Study. A comprehensive GIS-based fire station location study can be the central component of a master plan for fire station locations. This plan can show both the efficiencies and deficiencies of current fire station coverage for a specified travel time and provide a model for future fire station coverage using the specified or other travel time standards. Figures 12.13.9 through 12.13.17 illustrate maps from a GIS analysis that assess existing station locations as well as alternative station locations and additions.

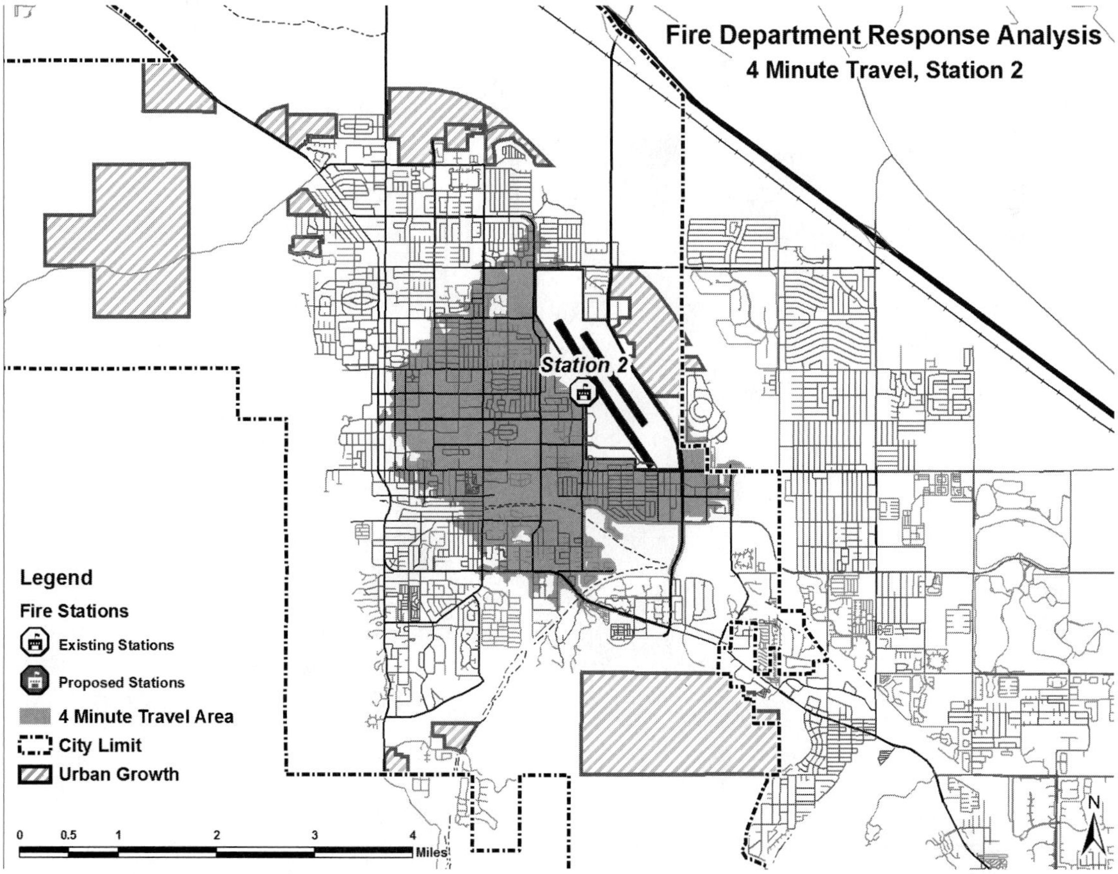

FIGURE 12.13.9 GIS-Generated Map Illustrating a Four-Minute Response Time Analysis from Station 2

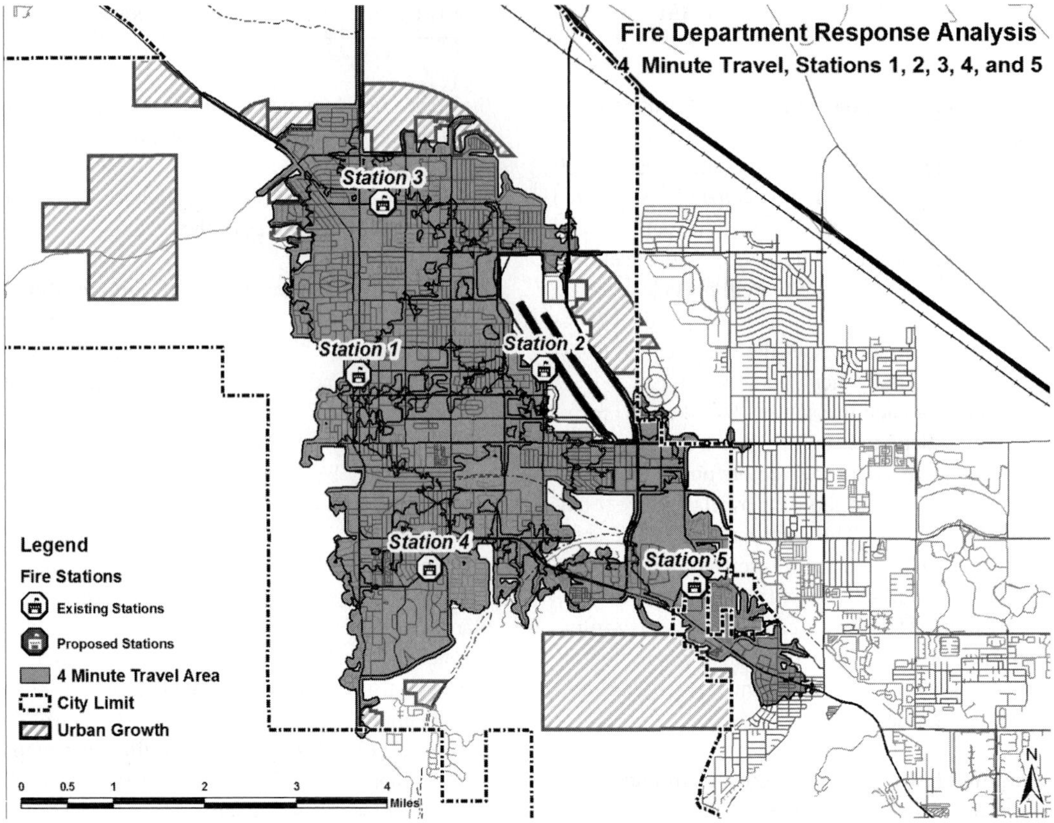

FIGURE 12.13.10 GIS-Generated Map Illustrating a Four-Minute Response Time Analysis from Stations 1, 2, 3, 4, and 5

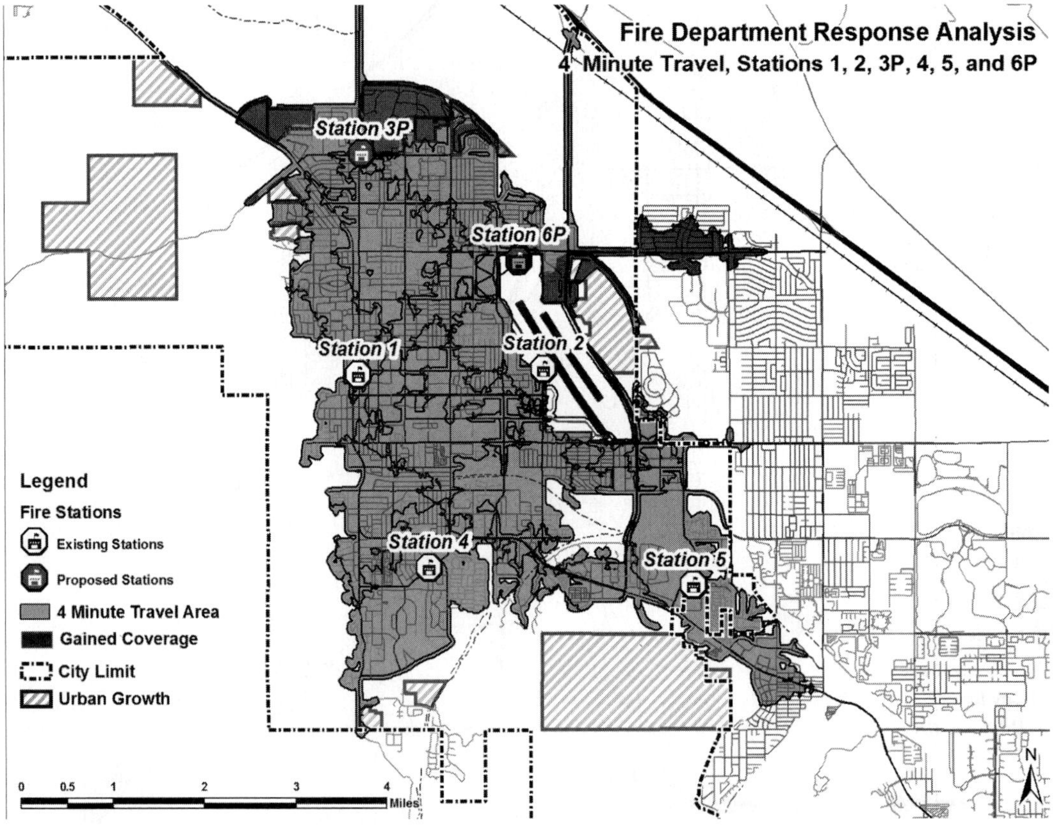

FIGURE 12.13.11 GIS-Generated Map Illustrating a Four-Minute Response Time Analysis from Stations 1, 2, 3P (Proposed Relocation), 4, 5, and 6P (Proposed New Station) and New Coverage Gained with Proposed New Station and Station Relocation

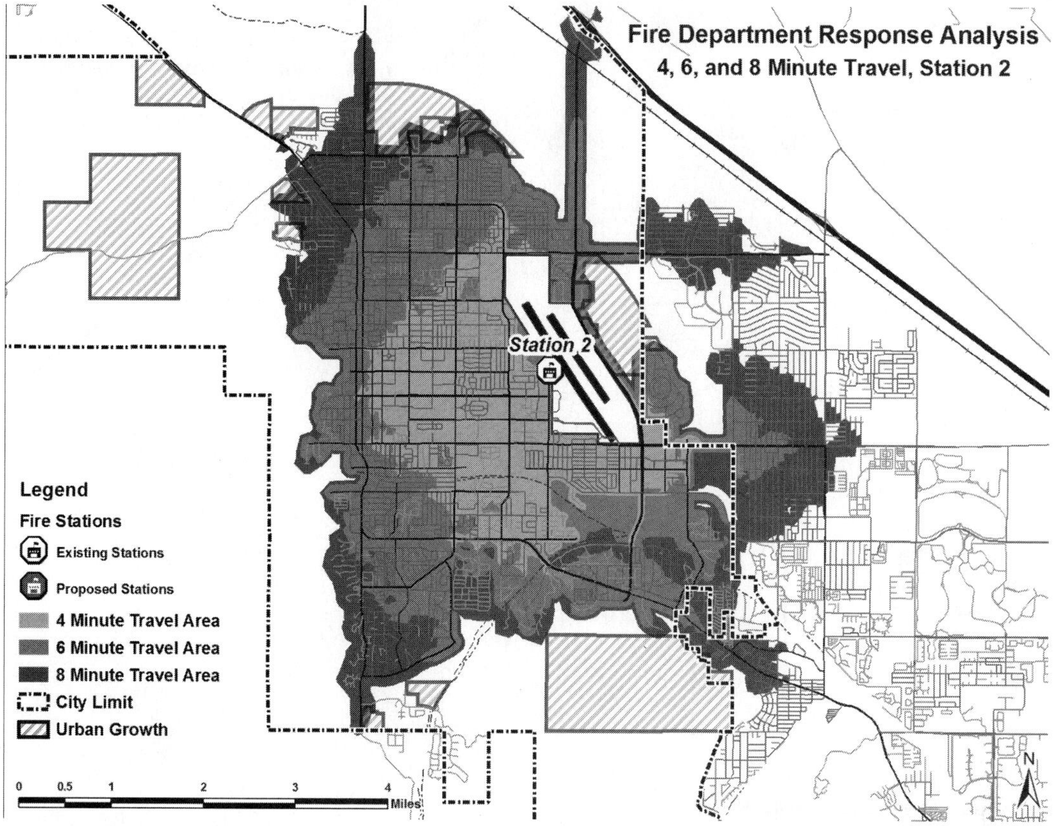

FIGURE 12.13.12 GIS-Generated Map Illustrating a Four-Minute, Six-Minute, and Eight-Minute Response Time Analysis from Station 2

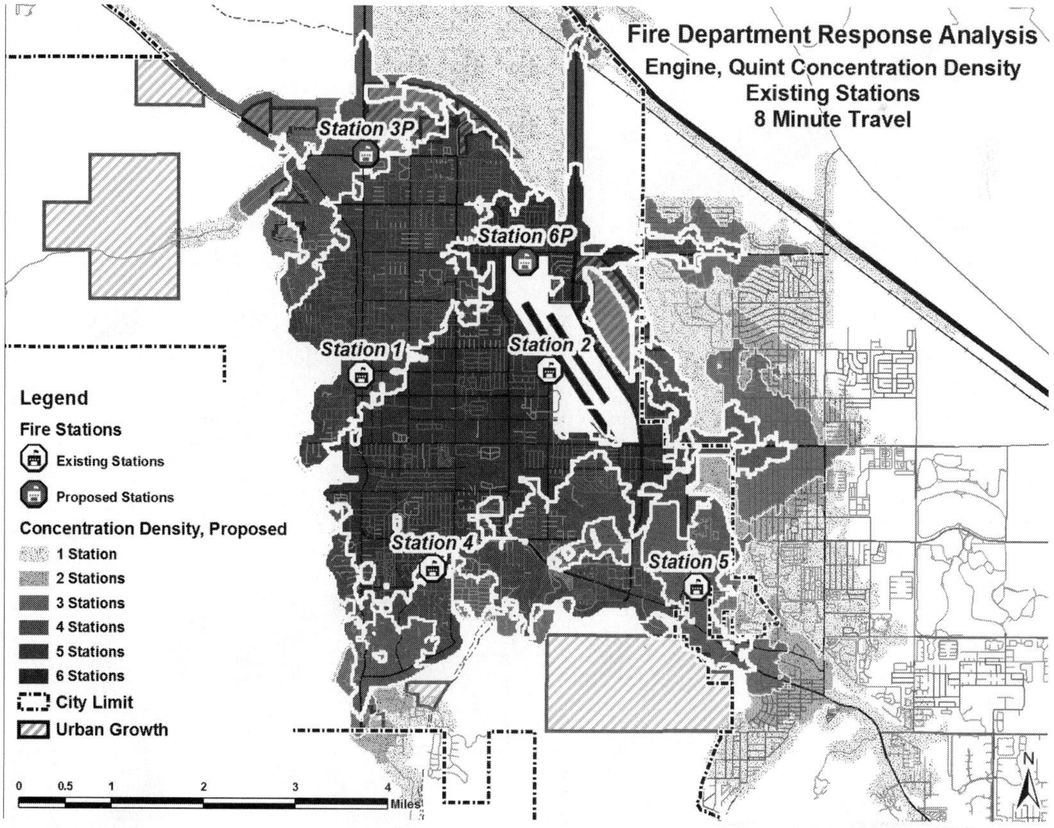

FIGURE 12.13.13 GIS-Generated Map Illustrating an Eight-Minute Response Time Analysis from Stations 1, 2, 3, 4, and 5. Shading indicates the number of apparatus that can be on scene in each area within eight minutes.

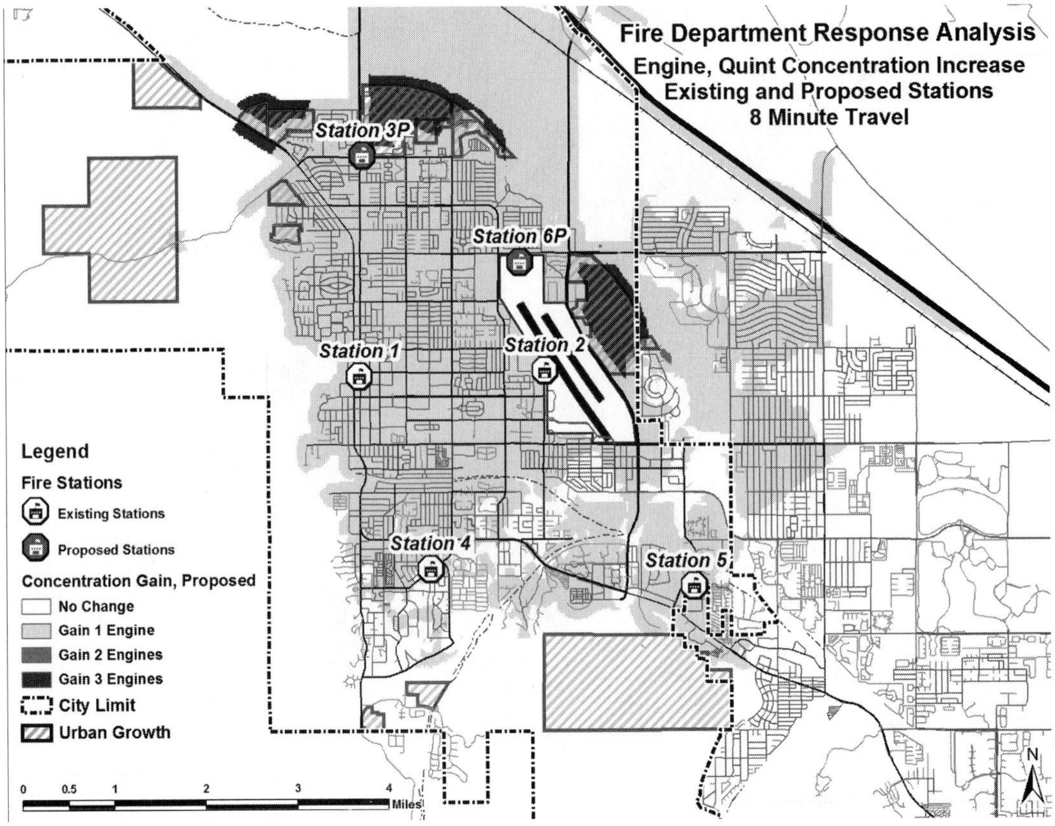

FIGURE 12.13.14 GIS-Generated Map Illustrating an Eight-Minute Response Time Analysis from Stations 1, 2, 3P (Station 3 Relocated), 4, 5, and Proposed New Station 6. Shading illustrates the number of additional apparatus that can be on scene in each area within eight minutes after proposed station changes.

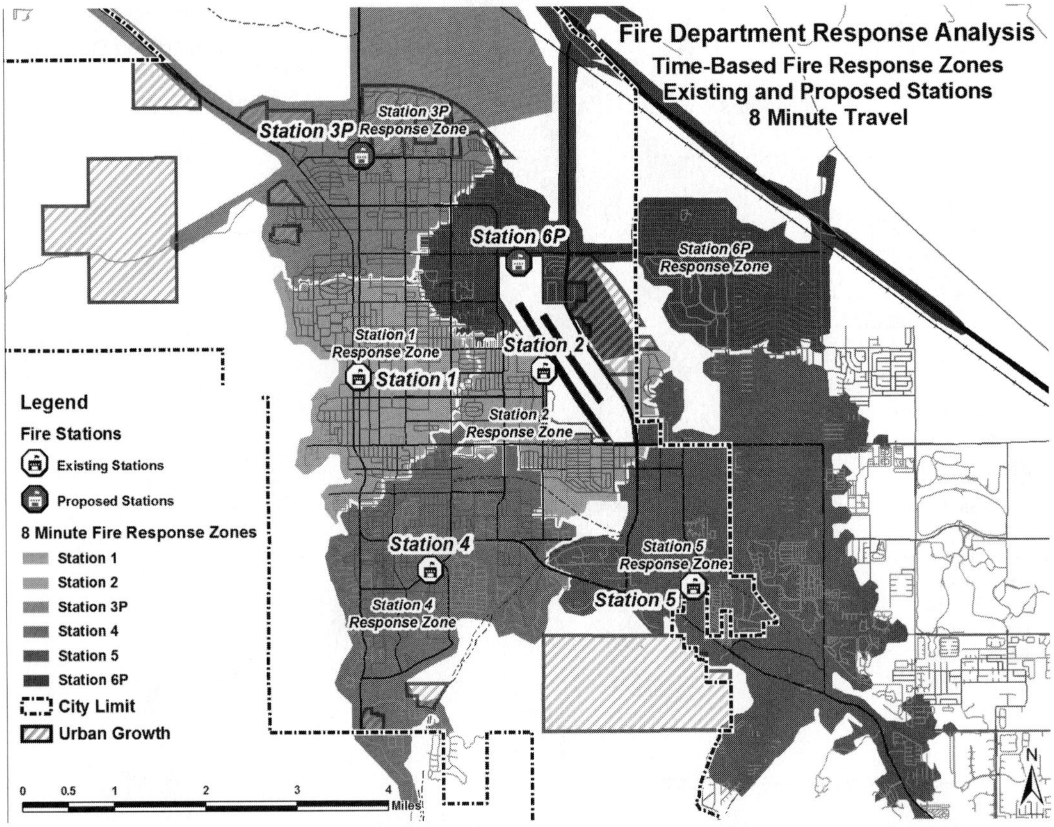

FIGURE 12.13.15 GIS-Generated Map Illustrating Fire Response Zones Based on an Eight-Minute Response Time Analysis from Proposed Stations

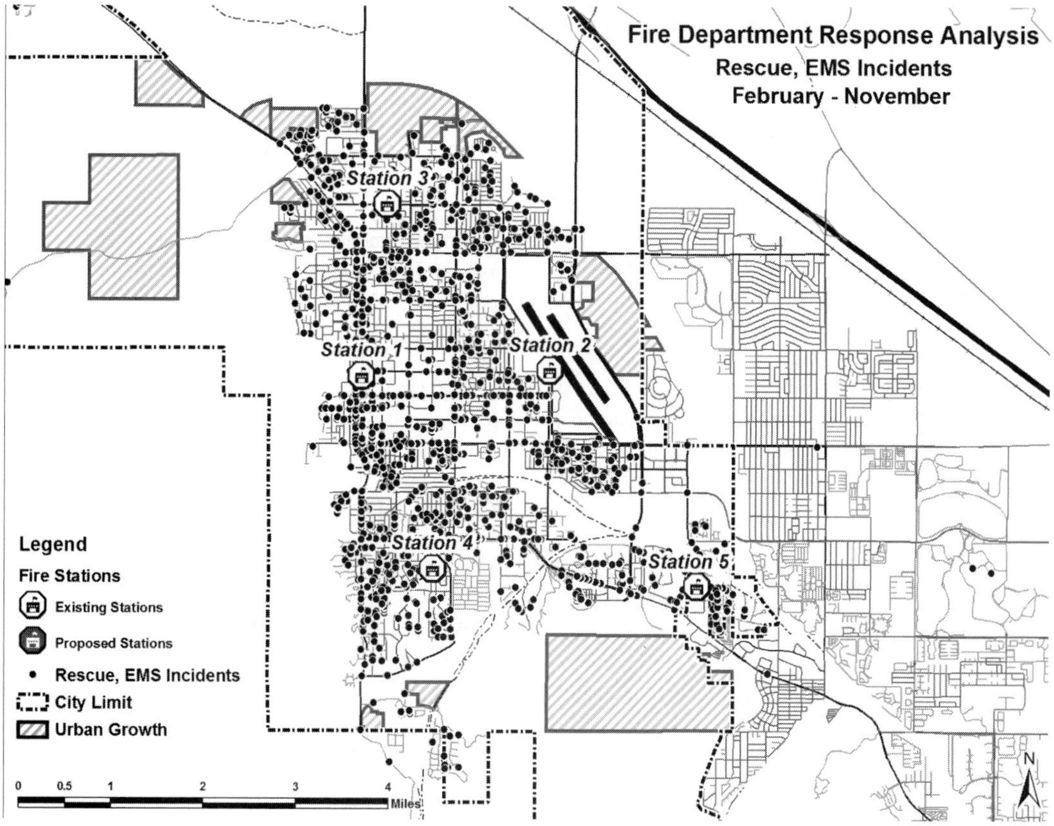

FIGURE 12.13.16 GIS-Generated Map Illustrating Fire, Rescue, and EMS Incidents Between February and November

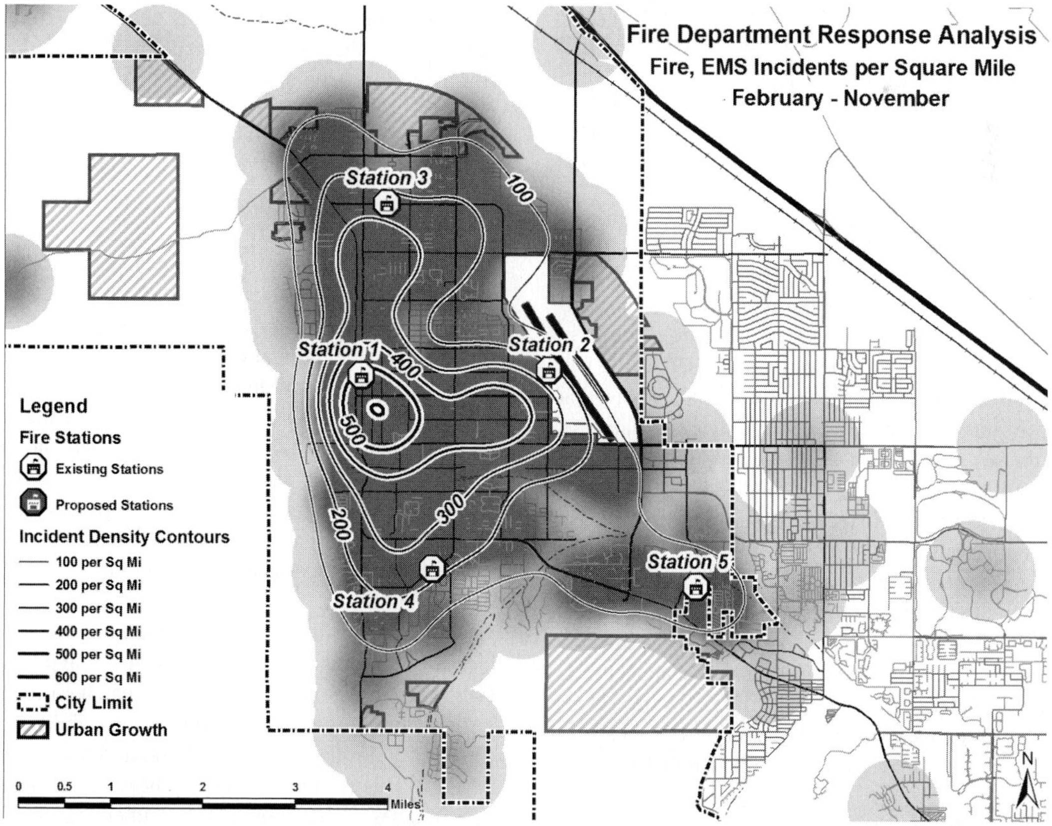

FIGURE 12.13.17 GIS-Generated Map Illustrating a Fire, Rescue, and EMS Incident Density Between February and November

Resource Allocation

Once the locations for fire stations have been selected, the program can be used to allocate resources to most efficiently cover the identified risks. A comprehensive GIS-based fire station location analysis provides the foundation for effective resource allocation that is critical to fire department and community master planning.

The colored maps and data are very useful when making presentations to citizens and elected officials. The computer programs take complex response scenarios, which may include many interrelated factors, and greatly simplifies them by producing color map images. Most of the maps and data are easily understood and provide factual data on the response of emergency equipment to specific locations.

All fire department planning that involves the allocation of resources requires a fire station location study. A proper study will show how the effective deployment of resources through proper station locations can improve emergency service to the community while minimizing both capital and recurring costs.

FIRE STATION SITE SELECTION FACTORS

Terrain

Once a location for a fire station has been determined, there may still be multiple choices for the precise site. One of the general items that should be considered when selecting a site should be the terrain and the susceptibility to flooding or other conditions due to weather. GIS can provide very detailed information regarding terrain features and optimum site location. GIS can analyze and display soil types, earthquake faults, elevations and slope, flood-prone locations, and other features important to station location placement. The size of the structure, the number of personnel assigned, and the provision of a training area will dictate the size of the site that is required.

Traffic Patterns

Another important consideration is the relationship to the adjacent streets and highways. An analysis of traffic patterns in the surrounding area will aid in determining whether the site is suitable for a fire station. The station must be located so that responding apparatus can enter streets and highways as safely as possible and return to the station without disrupting traffic and placing personnel at risk. It may be more desirable to locate a station on a side street rather than on a heavily traveled street.

Traffic pattern requirements for a specific site will differ for volunteer and career personnel. The major reason is that volunteers must respond to the station before responding to an emergency. Therefore, the site must allow easy access for volunteers responding to calls. There may be situations where apparatus is leaving the station and, at the same time, volunteers are still arriving. This is more complex than an all-career station, where all personnel are at the station and respond immediately to a call.

Response Time Standards

A primary responsibility of fire departments is to deliver fire and rescue services. Fire can grow at a rate many times its volume per minute; time, therefore, becomes a critical element when crews respond to an emergency. The timely delivery of services depends to a great extent on the location of the fire stations. Thus, when planning where fire stations should be located, the community needs to develop its response time standards. These standards are based on an analysis of the types of services to be delivered, what a reasonable travel time is, the size of the area to be serviced, the resources available, and the level of acceptable risk. Once the response time standards have been established, GIS can be used to determine fire station placement with a greater degree of accuracy.

GIS RESPONSE PROTOCOLS

GIS technology is being deployed in a number of other emergency response areas to increase efficiency, reduce response time, and provide higher-quality decision support information and data. This includes dispatch, mobile operations, and emergency management.

Computer-Aided Dispatch

Dispatchers have the important responsibility of processing emergency calls and sending the appropriate public safety resources to the emergency location based on the type and urgency of the incident. GIS is an important component of the dispatch system. Dispatch or CAD systems typically contain a file called the Master Street Address Guide (MSAG). This file contains street address information and service areas for the jurisdiction that the dispatch center services. As emergency calls are received, they may be accompanied with address information from the telephone company's emergency phone record database. This address is entered or electronically transferred to the CAD system, which compares it to MSAG. When the address is matched, the specific service area is also identified with the specific units that should be dispatched to the emergency. If the telephone company does not provide a digital address with the call, dispatchers must obtain it from the caller and type it into the system. Many computer-aided dispatch systems have begun to integrate GIS technology. GIS takes the address and automatically geocodes (places a point on the map) the incident and displays it on a map.

There are several benefits of having the incident displayed on a GIS map. New calls reporting the emergency may have different addresses but are reporting the same incident previously recorded. The GIS map display will illustrate that a different address making a call may be in close proximity to the original call location. Other benefits are shown in the following sections.

Global Positioning System (GPS). Many public safety agencies are equipping response units with global positioning system (GPS) devices, which provide the dispatcher (and perhaps other appropriate public safety managers) the ability to locate units through a GIS display and track them to the incident when dispatched. This is important during heavy call volume or for mobile vehicles such as police units and emergency medical units, because it provides dispatchers with a virtual, near real-time view of incident locations and emergency response units to activate an appropriate dispatch based on emergency unit availability.

Routing. GIS can quickly analyze and display a route from a station or GPS location to the emergency call. This route (depending on the sophistication of the street file) may be the shortest path (distance) or the quickest path (depending on time of day and traffic patterns). This information can be displayed to the dispatcher as well as on a mobile computer screen in the response vehicle. Vehicles equipped with mobile computers and GIS can also benefit by providing first responders with access to preplans, hazardous materials locations, photographs, and other location-based documents linked to actual specific locations through the GIS map display.

Move Up and Cover. During periods of high volume and simultaneous calls or a complex emergency, GIS can display areas of high risk that are left substantially uncovered. GIS can provide recommendations for reallocating available resources for better response coverage.

Emergency Wireless Calls. Wireless and cellular telephone technology have added to the necessity of GIS. Wireless phone–reported emergencies are not associated with an address, and the caller may not know his or her address or street location. GPS-enabled cell phones can provide latitude and longitude coordinates during an emergency call. Other technologies are available that triangulate the call location between cell towers or measure strength of signal to provide approximate location information. These coordinates are relatively meaningless to a dispatcher, but GIS can quickly process and display a latitude/longitude or other coordinate location. This enables the dispatcher to see the incident location or general area and the closest or quickest response units on the GIS display.

Records Management System. Dispatch systems often have a database to capture, store, and archive incidents. This database may be called a records management system or a CAD records system. The records stored in this database concerning emergency calls usually contain location information. GIS can link to and geocode (place a point on the map) the location that represents this event. These events can be analyzed and assessed by any field in the records database (time, incident type, etc.). GIS provides a powerful capability to see, understand, and assess a department's volume of business, developing trends, and response performance. The information within a records management system can be leveraged for additional purposes when geospatially enabled.

Mobile Operations

As wireless broadband networks expand, GIS support for tactical operations becomes more powerful. Mobile PCs, computer tablets, and handheld devices with GPS and wireless advances allow first responders to send and receive geographic information and incident updates. As shown in Figure 12.13.18, GIS mobile applications can provide the tactical map interface to information and data important to first responders. Information such as preplans, floor plans, and other documents are linked to building facility addresses and are easily displayed by clicking or touching the map. As fire and emergency medical services expand, the importance of GIS is becoming widely recognized. First responders must get to and size up the emergency and then deploy. The first responder's mission is to save lives and protect property and natural resources. GIS information support to the first responder mission can include the following:

- Incident location
- Quickest route
- Hydrant locations
- Preplans
- Photographs
- Floor plans
- Hazardous materials locations
- Utility control panels

The incident commander requires additional information to perform the command mission. Depending on the complexity and size of the incident, the information and data requirements may include information on the following:

- What exposures or other facilities are threatened by this incident
- Where incoming units should be positioned and assigned
- If a staging area or an incident command post is required, where parking lots, schools, churches, malls, or other suitable facilities are located
- If helicopter evacuation of victims is required, where suitable landing sites are located
- If medical triage or decontamination is required, where it can be implemented
- If hazardous materials are involved or a chemical plume is being generated, in what direction it is traveling, whom does it threaten, and what actions are required to protect and evacuate the public
- If an explosion is possible, who needs to be evacuated and where an immediate evacuation facility is located

All these decisions require maps and a variety of information from different sources. Having access to GIS data, imagery, school locations, parking lots, adjacent exposures, and hydrant locations provides an accurate picture of the event and supports critical command decisions.

Much of the information first responders require has already been collected but resides in a variety of formats and in numerous locations. GIS can integrate the information and provide it graphically to first responders through maps. GIS provides intelligent maps and allows the user to acquire other critical information. GIS can model explosions, plumes, and other potential emergencies. Instead of guessing or estimating evacuation requirements, transportation network problems, and other infrastructure threats, GIS will provide a more accurate prediction of the event and display potential consequences.

Emergency Management

During an emergency or crisis, maps play a critical role in response, search and rescue, mitigating further damage, and understanding the extent of the impacts. GIS is an appropriate platform for organizing the extensive amount of spatial data both generated and utilized during an emergency. A properly designed and implemented GIS will allow managers and

FIGURE 12.13.18 Sample GIS Mobile Application Providing Tactical Map Interface to Information and Data Important to First Responders (Courtesy of Chief Don Oliver, Wilson Fire Department, Wilson, North Carolina)

responders to access critical location data in a timely manner so that lives and property can be protected and restored.

Fire departments are the front line of defense for emergencies of all types. Large-scale emergencies range from natural disasters (e.g., earthquakes, floods, hurricanes, ice storms, etc.) to industrial or technological emergencies (e.g., train car derailments, petroleum fires, hazardous material spills, etc.) to terrorist attacks. Large-scale emergencies often involve multiple casualties, critical infrastructure damage, and evacuations; also, the emergency can last for several days or months.

Managing large-scale emergencies is complex and can involve search and rescue operations; displaced citizens; loss of utility services; and coordination among many departments, agencies, levels of government, and the private sector. One of the most complex challenges of emergency management is determining where damage is most extensive, where lives are most threatened, and where to assign limited emergency response personnel and equipment. During a major search operation for a lost or overdue hiker, GIS can accurately determine which sectors have been searched adequately and which sectors need to be revisited.

GIS provides a primary capability to organize, display, and analyze information for sound decision making. Integrating GIS data layers and imagery of the affected area or areas

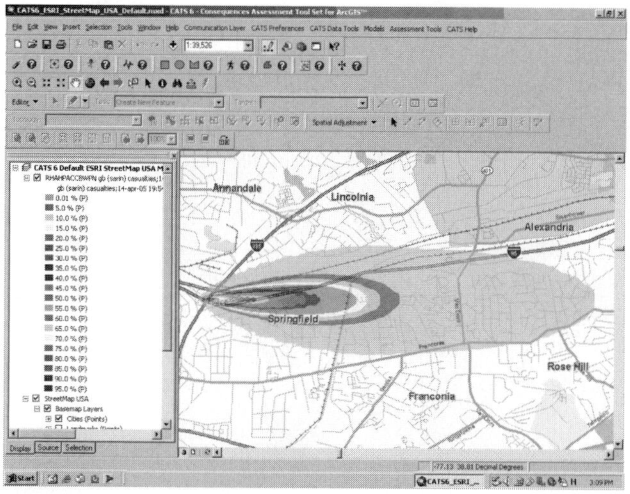

FIGURE 12.13.19 Sample GIS Model Illustrating How an Emergency Event (Plume, Explosion, etc.) May Impact the Area in Which It Occurs (Source: ESRI)

provides incident commanders with a comprehensive view of the emergency. GIS provides a primary capability to create a "common operating picture" for the incident. Emergencies are very dynamic and, as circumstances change, GIS can reflect these changes. GIS can incorporate temporal information (e.g., weather, hazardous materials locations, and emergency personnel locations) and model how an emergency might continue to evolve or what type of damage may be expected. These models could include the following:

- Chemical plume dispersion
- Blast models
- Hurricane tracks and effects
- Flood damage
- Earthquake damage
- Wildfire spread

GIS models illustrate how an emergency event (plume, explosion, etc.) may impact an area (Figure 12.13.19). In addition, GIS will analyze and display population effects, road closure requirements, best evacuation routes, potential shelters, and facilities out of the danger area that may support incident management.

Models provide incident commanders with a relative understanding of where evacuations may be necessary, potential damage to critical infrastructure, transportation network disruption, and so forth. Maps can be printed with the appropriate symbology to illustrate work assignments and incident facilities (e.g., incident command post helispots, staging areas, hot zones, etc.) and quickly dispersed to emergency personnel as part of the incident action plan. Areas with catastrophic damage are often confusing and disorienting to emergency personnel. GIS provides a view of the area before the damage occurred, including underground infrastructure, control points, potential hazardous materials locations, and other information to support emergency response actions.

SUMMARY

The fire service mission is to assist the public in the protection of life and property by minimizing the impact of fire, medical emergencies, and potential disasters or events that affect communities and the environment. Defending communities from natural or man-made emergencies through planning, preparedness, incident response, public education, and code enforcement is best accomplished through accurate information sharing. GIS is one of the most effective tools to analyze, define, clarify, and visualize community issues and problems to deliver emergency services to all.

BIBLIOGRAPHY

Reference Cited

1. The Commission on Fire Accreditation International, *Creating and Evaluating Standards of Response Coverage for Fire Departments,* 4th ed., Chantilly, VA, 2003.

NFPA Codes, Standards, and Recommended Practices

Reference to the following NFPA codes, standards, and recommended practices will provide further information on GIS for fire station locations and response protocols discussed in this chapter. (See the latest version of The NFPA Catalog *for availability of current editions of the following documents.)*

NFPA 1221, *Standard for the Installation, Maintenance, and Use of Emergency Services Communications Systems*

NFPA 1710, *Standard for the Organization and Deployment of Fire Suppression Operations, Emergency Medical Operations, and Special Operations to the Public by Career Fire Departments*

NFPA 1720, *Standard for the Organization and Deployment of Fire Suppression Operations, Emergency Medical Operations, and Special Operations to the Public by Volunteer Fire Departments*

References

American Heart Association, *Heartsaver Manual: A Student Handbook for Cardiopulmonary Resuscitation and First Aid for Choking,* Dallas, TX, 1987.

The Commission on Fire Accreditation International, *Creating and Evaluating Standards of Response Coverage for Fire Departments,* 4th ed., Chantilly, VA, 2003.

National Commission on Fire Prevention and Control, *America Burning, The Report of the National Commission on Fire Prevention and Control,* Government Printing Office, Washington, DC, 1973.

National Fire Prevention and Control Administration, *Urban Guide for Fire Prevention and Control Master Planning,* Government Printing Office, Washington, DC, no date.

Chapter 14

Fire Rescue Stations and Fire Service Training Centers

Revised by
David J. Acomb ❑ Roger M. LeBoeuf

Chapter Contents

Key Terms

fire rescue station, fire service training, live fire training, master plan

Fire stations and fire training centers can range from basic to complex. An adequate fire station could be a single bay with a desk at the back or it could be a multiple-company station that houses engines, ladders, ambulances, and a complete administrative function. Similarly, a training center could consist of just a small training tower or it could be a large campus that offers both classroom and practical education to hundreds of students at one time. Because there is no "one size fits all" solution, it is important to follow a planning and design process that creates the right facility for the community's protection and the department's training needs.

This chapter provides a general overview of the steps necessary to develop fire stations and fire training centers. The steps should be taken with the assistance of knowledgeable architects/engineers (A/Es) and should include the following:

1. Needs assessment
2. Planning
3. Design
4. Construction

This chapter provides ideas and insight for configurations, building options, and training props without providing an exhaustive list of possibilities. For related topics, see Section 12, Chapter 10, "Training Programs for Fire and Emergency Service Personnel"; Section, 12, Chapter 13, "GIS for Fire Station Locations and Response Protocols"; and Section 12, Chapter 16, "Fire Department Apparatus and Equipment."

FIRE RESCUE STATION DESIGN

Fire stations exist in virtually every city and town in the world, and there is a variety of functions that the fire stations have to serve. A fire station may be simply a garage to store a truck; others, in addition to housing trucks, provide housing for a complex hierarchy of offices for managing delivery of safety services. There are, however, many elements of fire stations that need to be present without regard to what is housed in the building. The design professional must be aware of these elements.

One of the most important elements of a fire station is whether or not it represents a safe and efficient place for people to use. A careful analysis of the proposed building and the functions it is

David J. Acomb, AIA, LEED, is the executive vice-president and partner of Rick Swisher Architect, Inc., a Florida- and Ohio-based corporation. With more than 25 years of professional experience, he has developed a nationally recognized expertise in the planning and design of fire rescue and emergency facilities. He has pioneered the concept of incorporating training into fire stations and many of his innovations can be found in stations around the country. His expertise has afforded him the opportunity to speak nationally and author numerous articles on public safety design.

Roger M. LeBoeuf, P.E., specializes in planning and designing fire training centers. He is president of Elliott, LeBoeuf & McElwain in Springfield, Virginia, and has worked on over 140 fire training center projects in 27 states plus Egypt. He serves on the NFPA Technical Committee on Fire Service Training.

expected to serve is required. There are obvious program elements consistent for all stations, such as security, fire protection, weatherproofing, and structural stability. The building where the fire equipment is to be housed must be designed to withstand the forces of man and nature. Other necessary design elements are lighting, heating or cooling, storage facilities, and emergency backup power.

It is very important when designing a fire station that a clear understanding between the design professional and the fire department be established in the conceptual design phase of the project. It is also necessary that the design professional have a clear understanding of the development costs of program elements to keep the total costs within the budget.

The fire station design must address the needs of its users. Even if it is a single-bay station without any other space required, consideration must still be given to the people who are going to use the station. If it is a complex that is planned for housing a mix of civilians and fire rescue personnel, the building must be functional for both the civilian and the fire rescue personnel. If the design professional is not familiar with the necessary elements of a fire station, then the project will be difficult to bring to a successful conclusion. The design professional cannot and should not depend on the fire chief to be aware of all of the elements necessary for a fire station, particularly architectural elements, that need to be considered in the design of the building.

Needs Assessment

Preparedness and planning are inherently important for the success of all public safety providers, particularly those in the fire and emergency services. Similarly in the design of a new station, the preparation and planning begin with a thorough needs assessment. This first step is critical and should be completed prior to any land acquisition. Ideally, determine the required station square footage and operational needs before beginning the assessment of potential sites. It is desirable to formalize this process with a design consultant and key staff. A common approach is to form a building committee to discuss the station issues and make decisions. Do not overlook comments and suggestions made by interested parties and end users, particularly members of the community who may have use of the building. If the future station will have shared or joint use, such as a police substation, be sure to include their representatives.

Another way to think of the needs assessment is comprehensive information gathering. The committee and design team want to know everything that will impact the design and operations of the planned station. This information will be generated from the following three-step assessment:

1. *Existing conditions.* Document existing spaces, room sizes (square footage), staff, equipment, apparatus, and so on.
2. *Current needs.* Determine what program spaces and sizes are currently required for the safe and efficient operation of the station. Consider what services and apparatus are required at this station.
3. *Future needs.* As best as possible, assess the future growth and development of the site's needs at least 20 years into the future. Many guidelines even suggest predicting 50 years out but may not be practical.

Room-by-Room Approach

The best way to approach the gathering of these data is with a room-by-room assessment. Consider who and how many persons will occupy the space and what functions will be supported. Provide the design team with a list of equipment and furniture for each space and note any special requirements such as additional phone/data outlets or storage needs.

Questions to anticipate during the needs assessment process include the following:

- How large will the staff be—current and future?
- What size and type of offices are required—private and shared?
- What type and size of apparatus will be used—current and future?
- Will the public have access to and use of this station?
- Will there be drive-through bays?
- What is the predicted future expansion of this station?
- Is there a current station prototype to follow?
- Where is protective gear cleaned and stored?
- How are hoses cleaned, dried, and stored?
- How will gender issues be addressed?
- What are the present and future storage needs?

Planning

Site Selection. The site for the building must be selected before the structural system can be determined. The site is usually determined by the analysis of many factors, including ISO evaluations and sometimes it is determined by a single factor. In any case, the selection of a building site is a task that requires some knowledge of fire department operations and goals. To properly site a fire station, an analysis of the department's response goals must be undertaken. If it is the goal of the department, for example, to respond to any incident within 4 minutes, the site location will be different than if the goal is a 9 minute response time. The analysis of response time must include a traffic study, addressing potential intersection delays, travel times, and access to travel routes. Response time for volunteers to the station should be part of the analysis, taking into consideration where they will be responding from.

Often a fire station is located in response to past growth; site selection, however, should be preemptive instead of reactive. Future growth projections, including the location and types of land uses, must be considered. The design team must project ahead 50 years to attempt to determine the growth patterns for the area and, thus, develop a site that serves the needs of the fire department.

Often fire stations are located on major travel routes based on the thinking that the response time is the most efficient. This approach has some validity, but it also removes what may be very expensive real estate from the tax base. An alternative approach is to locate the station on a secondary route, just off the major route, and utilize a signalized intersection to allow safe access to the major route. This plan improves emergency egress and access to the station and reduces the risk for vehicular accidents and traffic stacking. With the recently developed technology to allow intersection signal control from fire apparatus, this method of secondary route location is becoming more popular, and the property on the secondary route is often not taxed at the same high rate as the property on the major route.

Once the site has been tentatively selected, it is necessary to consider improvements that must be made to construct the fire station. It is also necessary to consider such areas as parking for both fire fighters and apparatus, keeping in mind that the apparatus must have room to back in and sufficient turning radii, as well as visitor parking; drainage and runoff from storms; and security. A rule of thumb is two parking spaces for each member on a shift to allow for the shift change plus spaces for additional staff and a few spaces for the public.

Site Acquisition/Assessment. (See also sections on site selection and design for training centers.) Some rules of thumb for acquiring a desirable site include the following:

- Avoid congested thoroughfares, which increase the risk for accidents and traffic stacking, particularly during peak hours.
- Locate egress curb cut a minimum of 100 ft (30.4 m) from an intersection.
- Allow for a minimum 60 ft (18.2 m) apparatus apron measured from the street right-of-way to the apparatus bay doors.
- Avoid locating the station at the bottom of a hill.
- Avoid permanent barriers such as railroad tracks, one-way streets, or bridges prone to high-water risk.
- Avoid close proximity to schools or entertainment venues with heavy pedestrian and vehicular traffic.
- Allow 2 percent maximum slope of apparatus apron.
- Ensure minimum road width of 24 ft (7.315 m).
- Ensure good visibility and clear site lines for both approaching and exiting vehicles.

Site Due Diligence. A comprehensive site evaluation requires a thorough due diligence process and failure to do so may result in unexpected project costs or future complications. Potential building sites may have above- and below-ground issues that may create limitations or derail plans for that particular site all together. Some recommended due diligence steps include the following:

- *Environmental investigation.* A minimum Phase I is recommended; however, if the site had previous use for industrial, manufacturing, or filling station purposes, a Phase II investigation is recommended. Contaminated soil mitigation costs can be expensive.
- *Geotechnical investigation.* Many state building codes now define fire stations as essential facilities and require soil investigation as part of the permitting process. Poor soil-bearing capacity will impact the structural design, systems design, and pavement design of the station.
- *Archeological investigation.* For a nominal fee, an archeologist can access records for a Phase I archeological assessment of the site. This initial expense is minimal compared to the generally excessive financial and time constraints incurred when artifacts are discovered during construction.
- *Hazardous material investigation.* Prior to the demolition of any existing structures, certification that the station has been investigated for hazardous materials is required. Asbestos is generally the concern and abatement is normally expensive. The EPA will require certification of hazardous material abatement prior to demolition or construction.
- *Traffic studies.* If traffic is remotely a concern, consider a traffic study for current and future patterns. Peak hour congestion and projected rate increases will negatively impact response time and safety.
- *Future road improvements.* Check agencies with jurisdiction of thoroughfares bordering the potential site. Investigate future road widening or development plans.
- *Utilities.* Investigate existing and proposed utilities for the potential site. Relocation or connection costs and tap fees may be prohibitive. Because some station equipment may require three-phase service, check to see what service is available.
- *Storm water.* The Clean Water Act requires responsibility for the storm water generated from the station site. Consider how the storm water will be removed or detained on the property as it may require additional land or storm water utility upgrades.
- *Community concerns.* Try to gauge the potential negative impact of placing or removing a fire station in an existing neighborhood.

Establishing a Budget. Despite the best planning efforts, at the end of the day most decision makers naturally want to have some idea of the anticipated expenses. In some cases the budget alone will have the greatest impact on the station design and amenities. As such, it is wise to get a handle on the budget at the earliest possible convenience, so that educated decisions can be made before the design team has ventured far into the process. Additionally, the planning process may include determining what funding source or strategy is required and the potential for success. In establishing a budget a total project cost must be estimated. Total project cost is simply the sum of the *construction costs* (hard costs) and project *soft costs.*

Construction costs—often referred to as the bricks and mortar of a project—is the bid submitted by the contractors for material and labor and typically includes contractor overhead and profit, construction contingencies or allowances, and required construction inspections.

Soft costs are often overlooked in the budgeting and design process but are essential to the project. Though all the soft costs may not be known in the early planning phases, it is important to include some estimated amount. Experienced design consultants and vendors can provide valuable assistance. The following are a few of the anticipated soft costs to consider:

- Land acquisition expenses
- Site surveys
- Environmental assessments, studies, and abatement
- Hazardous material assessments and abatement
- Archeological assessment

- Geotechnical testing—soil borings
- Consultant fees
- Infrastructure and utility tap fees
- Permit fees
- FF&E—fixtures, furniture, and equipment
- Moving and storage costs
- Temporary facility costs
- Telephone/data/dispatch/cable
- Demolition expenses
- Audiovisual equipment
- Severe weather siren
- Building signage (beyond that required by code)
- Legal advertising—for consultants and contractors
- Ribbon cutting/grand opening ceremony expenses

Planning for Building Functions. The designer and the fire department personnel must work closely together on the development of the building plan and the relationship of the spaces to each other. The building must function properly for each type of use. If the building contains one or two bays for fire apparatus, it is not difficult to design the building efficiently. If the building will also function as an office, residence, and community center, then careful analysis of the relationship of the different spaces is necessary. One method of evaluating the spaces is to have the fire department personnel fill out a spreadsheet on each proposed room and its relevance to the other rooms in both importance and travel distance.

There are also other items to consider, such as the effect of the apparatus starting, leaving, and returning, on the other operations in the building. The noise and vibration caused by apparatus movement can be a distraction for other building uses. Fortunately, several methods of removing exhaust gases have been perfected and, with the proper installation of one of these systems, the effect of exhaust can be eliminated. However, the method selected for exhaust gas removal must be carefully considered. Some designers have simply opted to totally change the air in the apparatus bay when the apparatus is started or is returning. This method may not be desirable in areas where the air is conditioned either by heating or cooling and where a total change of air will result in the necessity of conditioning entirely new air in a relatively large space. The newer systems either filter the existing air or connect to the exhaust pipe of the vehicle and direct the exhaust completely outside the building.

The proximity of personnel to fire apparatus when a response is required must be considered when laying out a fire station. Because the key time for fire suppression and emergency medical operations is the time spent getting equipment out of the door, the building design should minimize the travel time of the personnel to the vehicles. Several spaces need to be in close proximity to the apparatus floor. They can include staff sleeping area, medical supply rooms, and equipment storage for fire trucks such as hose and spare self-contained breathing apparatus (SCBA) bottles. Locating these spaces next to the apparatus floor limits the travel necessary to replace supplies on the apparatus and increases efficiency.

Single Story Versus Two Story. It is design practice today to attempt to construct a single-story building within the allowable limits of the site. Because of concern over injuries, sliding poles in fire stations are a rapidly diminishing tradition but are still desired by some departments. It is far safer to design and construct a stairway for personnel to use. When a single-story building is not reasonable, care must be taken to properly design the building to limit the amount of travel from the first floor to other levels. One approach is to locate administrative functions on the second level and maintain, as much as possible, response functions, including sleeping accommodations, on the first floor. One-story stations are typically less expensive than two stories, primarily due to the fact that two-story stations will require an elevator and vertical circulation.

When the program for the building has been completed and a conceptual layout for the building has been created, it is necessary to begin to develop designs for structural stability, sewer, water, heating, cooling, ventilation, electrical, and fire protection. Each of these tasks is important to the functionality of the building. The structure of the building must be such that it supports all the operations of the building.

The structure must withstand the forces of nature, including snow, wind, rain, and earthquake. A fire station cannot withstand even the slightest failure of a structural component and, thus, must have a stronger frame than most buildings. The structural engineer must ensure that the building will not fail by using extra bracing and stronger components than normal for a comparable building size. All fire stations, regardless of size, should have a backup power supply in case of emergency. Adequate response time and sufficient power are critical (see FEMA 454 and 543).

Gender Separation. With both men and women in the fire and rescue service, many new issues have developed. Separate shower and bathroom facilities must be provided. Many of the existing fire stations were designed to accommodate only men. Therefore, they had one large "bunk room" where the entire company slept and one shower/bathroom facility. To avoid potential problems, men and women need separate showers and bathrooms. There are three ways to approach gender separation in fire station design, and each will impact the building's layout, construction cost, and departmental policies. The most common areas impacted by gender are sleeping quarters, locker, shower, and restroom facilities. The following are the three approaches:

1. *Separate but equal.* Separate but equally sized spaces and facilities for both male and female fire fighters
2. *Separate but unequal.* Separate but different sized spaces and facilities for both male and female fire fighters; typically larger facilities for male occupants
3. *Gender neutral.* Often referred to as unisex, spaces and facilities that can be equally shared by both. Individual bunk rooms fall into this category. Unisex shower rooms and toilet rooms are also common, and this option tends to be the most flexible and cost-effective.

ADA

The Americans with Disabilities Act (ADA) is a civil rights law that is enforced at the federal level by the United States Department of Justice. A citizen who believes there may be an

ADA violation may file a complaint with this agency. Contrary to some beliefs and actions, local government interpretations and waivers are not recognized in a court of law. As fire stations are public facilities (ADA category Type II), they will need to comply with these accessibility standards. Many states have adopted accessibility standards into their local building codes. Multistory stations are required to have elevators by this federal law. Familiarity and conformance with this law and guidelines in the station design process are required.

Sustainable Design

Sustainable design or green building design is a movement gaining acceptance at all levels of society. These principles stress responsibility for the impact of development and construction on the environment and resources through the promotion of energy conservation and alternative energy sources, sustainable site development, adaptive reuse, recycling, and so on. This entire process has been formalized into a certification process called the LEED (Leadership in Energy and Environmental Design) rating system, which provides standards and requirements for the different levels of certification. Additional information and resources on LEED and sustainable design can be obtained from the U.S. Green Building Council.

Typical Fire Station Space

For a majority of fire stations, the programmed spaces tend to fall into the following four categories:

1. Apparatus and vehicular storage
2. Administration
3. Residential and living areas
4. Operation and support

The following are some of the typical spaces that are programmed into fire stations. Not all of these spaces must be in every building, but this list is a guide to assist in the development of a program for a fire station.

Apparatus and Vehicular Storage. The fire trucks, rescue trucks, ambulances, and other support vehicles are housed in an *apparatus bay* (Figure 12.14.1). Design considerations must address the fact that heavily loaded trucks may sit day after day on the floor and that the trucks are loaded when they enter and leave the building. The trucks will be the full height and width allowed by law, and the station doors (recommended 14 ft × 14 ft [4.26 m × 4.26 m]) should be oversized to reflect this fact. Station bay width (minimum 16 ft [4.8 m] wide) for the trucks should be wider than in a normal garage because the trucks should and do receive some maintenance in place, and there needs to be space to open doors and tilt hoods without forcing the personnel to crawl over or under the trucks. Provide 5 ft (1.5 m) minimum clearance between the station bay doors and the front of the apparatus (see Figure 12.14.1). The bay should also have enough space to store minor repair items, perhaps on some shelves. The bay should be equipped with a system to vent exhaust gases from the trucks and be well lighted and heated. Most floor drains are installed under the trucks with sloping floors to collect drippings from the trucks. If floor drains are

FIGURE 12.14.1 Large, Well-Thought-Out Apparatus Bay

incorporated, then an oil/water separator must be used to limit pollution.

Administration. Several types of *offices* are found in fire stations. Each subset of administration may require a different type of office. The minimum size of each office type does not vary much, but the equipment found in the offices is vastly different and will determine the required size. Shared office space for two or more individuals and open office areas with systems furniture can provide some economy of scale.

A chief's office is similar to that of the CEO of a corporation. The office requires space for the chief to work, as well as a space for meeting with other people. A fire prevention officer's office is essentially an engineering office and requires space for plans review as well as other office functions. The plans review space may be a drafting table or an oversized desk but should accommodate oversized plans sets. A secretarial office must contain space for the secretary to work and for a file cabinet, fax machine, copy machine, and other equipment often found in a modern office. A training office, which is basically a teacher's office, should be located next to a training space or seminar room so that training materials do not need to be carried great distances.

There are other types of tasks that may be required by fire administration such as receivables and payables, and these office types should be structured the same as any other business. In all cases, it is advisable to ascertain early on what personnel require private offices and what furniture and equipment are associated with each.

If the station serves an administrative function, then there should be space in the building for people to wait. This may be a small separate room or it may be a space near the offices, but it should not be a few chairs set up in a corridor. If conference rooms are desired, they are best designed large enough for multiple functions. Consider what activities will take place in each conference room and consider locations for white boards, audiovisual presentations, and storage. This room can serve as a place where administrative personnel can meet with individuals or small groups, for example, the fire prevention officer meeting with a group of prospective developers or builders in a relatively private setting.

If a separate space for *training rooms* is desired, then it should be set up as a classroom (Figure 12.14.2). The room should be spacious, provide desks for the personnel to use, contain blackboards, allow space for slide and overhead projectors, provide adequate space for the display of training materials, and contain equipment for multimedia presentations and interactive training. The training room should also contain a lecture table for the instructor. The training room dimensions and proportions determine what type of audio can be used effectively.

The *watch room,* which has a variety of names (e.g., alarm room, station office), is essentially the office for the apparatus floor. This space can range from a minimum of 120 ft^2 (11 m^2), generally containing a desk, a chair or two, a phone, a map, and usually a radio, to a space for up to six or more people. The typical watch room serves as the place where paperwork for the apparatus, the log-in of calls, and station-to-apparatus communications are handled. The space is generally located adjacent to the apparatus floor to facilitate operations and has visual access to the bays and front apron. Often this is the place where visitors to the fire station first enter without going directly onto the apparatus floor.

A recent addition to fire station design is a small *exam room* near the front entrance of the station. The room can be set up similar to an exam room found at a physician's office. An increase in the number of walk-up emergency cases at fire stations has facilitated the need for this space to accommodate uninsured persons looking to the fire service for emergency care. These rooms serve as a location for blood pressure screening, and in areas prone to natural disasters they can become triage locations.

Residential and Living Areas. In fire stations where personnel are on duty at all times, *sleeping accommodations* commonly called the "bunk room" are provided for sleeping. Traditionally, bunk beds (two beds, one on top of another) were provided to save space. For a more "homelike" feel, many new sleeping areas are now being designed like dormitory rooms, which can vary from very simple (bed and lockers only) to more elaborate accommodations that include desk areas with computer and cable connections.

FIGURE 12.14.2 Training Room with Interactive Whiteboard

A growing trend in the volunteer fire and rescue service is to require or encourage volunteers to perform a "duty night" where they staff the stations at night. In many cases, this can reduce response time to emergencies by 4 minutes or more. To support these efforts, many amenities are being added for such volunteers.

Access from this area to the apparatus bays should be as direct as possible. The best case is to have this room on the same level of the station as the apparatus bays, because injuries have occurred when personnel traveled from the sleeping area to the bays using poles or stairs and because response time is faster. Although stairs are safer than poles, both have caused serious injuries and should be avoided. Some of these sleeping spaces have walls of soundproof materials of partial height, and some are full height.

In a large "bunk room" area, men and women can and do share sleeping facilities with few problems. This type of traditional arrangement helps to ensure that each member feels part of the company. Fire fighting is a team activity and every effort should be made to support the team concept. One problem that needs to be specifically dealt with is the clothing that is acceptable in these situations. Acceptable sleepwear could be an issued item from the fire department.

Some departments have provided separate sleeping facilities for women, which can have some negative consequences. Women may feel alienated by feeling that they are not part of the company. Also, from a practical point of view, it is not known how many men or women will be sleeping at the station on any given night. There may be a whole crew of women (as reported in one large West Coast fire department) or there may be none on duty. Designs that can double the amount of space and furniture needed for sleeping accommodations may result.

Having men and women sleeping in two-person, "dorm-type" rooms should not be allowed. A rule should be enforced that stipulates either all men or all women in each room. Also, using one-half or three-fourths height separation walls will provide privacy without sacrificing the company feeling that is so important to a well-functioning team of fire fighters.

Another trend occurred after fire departments started providing ambulance service. Separate sleeping rooms have been provided so that the EMS crew can be alerted for a call without disturbing other fire crews, which has many of the disadvantages noted in our previous discussion of women in the fire service. If this arrangement is a problem, some other type of alerting should be considered. Designating certain beds for the EMS crew and providing a separate telephone have been successful in some cases.

Adequate clothing storage should be provided for personnel to keep several sets of clean uniforms and other clothing. Many departments provide clothing storage areas for each person assigned to the station (Figure 12.14.3), which can mean up to three or four storage areas for each on-duty person. Volunteer departments that commit to having on-duty companies for immediate response may also need several clothing storage areas

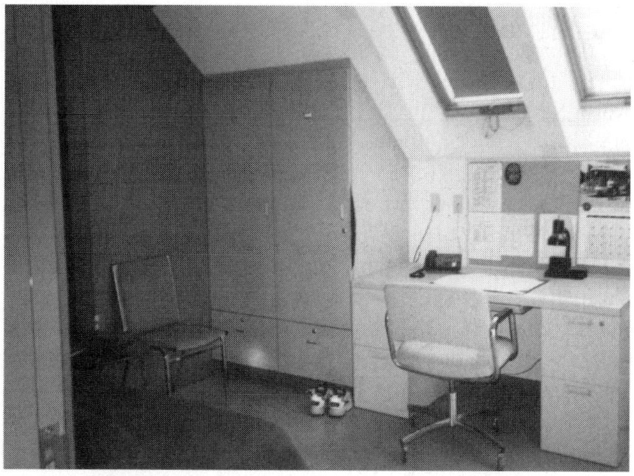

FIGURE 12.14.3 Sleeping Room with Desk and Space for Clothing

for each person on duty. Several designs use a separate room for clothing storage with metal lockers and wooden benches similar to a dressing area of a sports facility.

For a staffed station, the *kitchen* quickly becomes an essential part of the building. The kitchen is where the fire fighters take their meals and their breaks. The eating area of the kitchen can also be used for training. The cooking area should be of commercial quality, due to the almost constant use of the kitchen (Figure 12.14.4). In a station with two or three full companies and a chief, the kitchen can be called on to serve upwards of 60 meals every day. If the kitchen is used in conjunction with a community room or other similar space that is, or may become, accessible to the public, then even more meals can be expected to be served in an emergency situation. Part of the kitchen must be reserved for storage of food, and each shift expected to use the station should have a separate space or pantry for food. The kitchen should also be equipped with at least one dishwasher but two are more desirable to ensure that, even if the station has a busy day, there will be clean, sanitized dishes for meals. The same is true of microwaves, which have an equal amount of heavy use. The kitchen should be designed to be similar in size to a commercial kitchen, and the dining area also should be designed based on the number of expected diners. The dining and kitchen areas need to be separated from the apparatus bay to prevent diesel contamination.

FIGURE 12.14.4 Kitchen Space in a Multiple-Company Station

Lounge or living room areas resemble the typical family room in many homes, except they are larger. A TV and videotape recorder will be found that can be used during training sessions or for relaxation between alarms. Several couches and chairs to accommodate the normal number of personnel in the station will be provided. Many departments prefer reclining chairs, which will require a larger space. The furniture is normally commercial grade to hold up under constant use. The area should provide a homelike environment for the comfort of the fire and rescue personnel.

Most fire departments have recognized the health and safety benefit derived from implementing a fitness or wellness program. If the program is not mandatory, *fitness/wellness rooms* are provided for the voluntary benefit of the staff. In designing this space, it is best to determine the type, sizes, and quantity of desired equipment first. The room size is a function of this information and the required clearances. Allow for a minimum 3 ft (0.914 m) corridor for quick access out of the room. The ceiling height should be established by the highest vertical equipment dimension and clearances. When laying out the room, consider such features as full length mirrors, wall-mounted fans or televisions, drinking fountains, and rubber flooring. Perimeter walls should be stabilized with plywood behind the finished gypsum wallboard and insulation for soundproofing.

Operations and Support. Regardless of whether or not the personnel are medical or hazardous materials responders, it is reasonable to assume that they will at some time encounter a contamination problem, either a biohazard or other type, that will require complete clothing removal. A *decontamination room or space* must be available where personnel can be decontaminated, beginning with the removal of the outer layer of clothes, and cleansing their skin without contaminating the rest of the station or its personnel. A room, or more likely rooms, with equipment to allow contaminated personnel to enter without touching anything, to remove and properly dispose of clothing, to clean themselves, and to don new noncontaminated clothing with some degree of dignity and privacy is required. The equipment involved includes foot-activated hampers, motion- or foot-operated wash basins and soap dispensers, automatic showers, automatic doors, and linen rooms for spare clothes and towels. Locating this room with a direct exterior entrance allows contaminated personnel to avoid spreading the contamination to other areas. Additionally, it is advisable to provide a toilet room adjacent to the decontamination room for similar reasons. As emergency medical services by the fire service become more common, the appropriate supplies for the service become more important. The supplies stored in an *emergency medical supply room* include narcotics, which require a large degree of security. Other medical supplies have shelf lives that require frequent rotation. The diversity of the medical equipment needed to provide effective emergency medical services is increasing at a rapid rate. These items and the need to keep them clean and secure establish the need to have a room dedicated to the storage of medical supplies. This medical supply room should be located near the emergency medical vehicle(s) and must have a lock. It should be of such size that the equipment can be stored in a neat and orderly fashion. The room should be equipped with shelves and small cabinets, as well as a locked cabinet for narcotics and other regulated equipment. A double sink is also handy in this space. A room 10 ft by 12 ft (3.1 m by 3.7 m) generally will serve this purpose.

As with decontamination of personnel, protective clothing also needs to be cleaned. *Laundry rooms* are becoming a popular feature in fire stations. Turnout gear and other personnel clothing worn on the job need to be cleaned. It is not reasonable to expect personnel to take this equipment home to wash, and few commercial laundries will wash turnout gear. A commercial washer and dryer, as well as adequate venting, are necessary for this space. This space may best be incorporated into an area near where the fire personnel hang their protective gear during off-duty time (Figure 12.14.5). Separate and smaller

FIGURE 12.14.5 Lockers Providing Ventilation to Dry Equipment

residential-style laundries can be provided near the dormitory area for washing station laundry and sheets.

A fire station layout must provide space for personnel to wash. Separate or unisex *bathing facilities and toilets* for men and women should include sinks, toilets, showers, and lockers, as well as closets for linen. These spaces should be of tile or some other type of construction to withstand constant use with very little care. The equipment in the space should be of such quality as to give an adequate time of use before renovation. The space allocated for these rooms can be based on the expected number of users. In addition to the space for personnel, space should be allocated in the building design for toilet facilities for other personnel or visitors to the station.

Construction

Construction materials, techniques, and types for fire stations are generally indigenous to the respective regions. Design professionals and engineers are normally well versed in the options and associated costs for construction and will have these discussions early in the planning and design phases. For each material specified and technique used, consider the following:

- Structural capacity
- Durability and degradation—how well the material will hold up to internal and external elements
- Maintenance requirements and costs
- Life cycle and replacement costs
- Energy efficiency

FIRE SERVICE TRAINING CENTER DESIGN

Fire training center design and construction are unique fields that require specialized expertise. Fire training centers can incorporate several types of building functions, such as the following:

- Classrooms
- Offices
- Apparatus bays
- Equipment storage and maintenance areas
- Auditoriums
- Break rooms (or cafeterias)
- Exercise facilities
- Working fire stations
- Emergency operations centers
- 9-1-1 call centers
- Television studios
- Living quarters

As complex as these combinations can be, it is the specialty, hands-on fire training props that make fire training center design especially challenging.

To succeed in designing and constructing a fire training center, the fire department needs to assign personnel who will be highly involved in all stages of the process, from planning through design and construction. This will provide the designers with needed expertise relating to fire training operations and current fire-fighting tactics that need to be taught. It will also ensure that the fire department's needs are heard and implemented.

The fire department should look ahead, beyond design and construction, to make sure that adequate funding and personnel will be in place to operate and maintain the training center once it is built. The basic process for planning, designing, and constructing a fire training center follows, along with types of features, buildings, and props that could be incorporated into the facility.

Needs Assessment

Many fire departments fall into the trap of trying to design the training center as the first step. Although it may be enjoyable to dream about different types of training props and to lay them out on a site plan, it is important to step back to the true starting point—assessing the need for the fire training center. Questions that need to be answered include the following:

- Why do you need a training center?
- Whom do you need to teach?
- What do you need to teach?
- What training resources do you already have?
- Do the existing resources provide effective training for a reasonable cost?
- At what rate is the community growing and will growth affect future training needs?

To answer these and related questions, a valuable resource is a working group representing the entities that might use the training center (see section headed "Identification of Potential Users" that follows). Tools available to the working group include meetings to exchange information plus written surveys to be filled out by potential users, either online or in paper format. It is important to gather data that help evaluate the need, such as the following:

- How many potential students exist?
- What is the geographical distribution of the potential students?
- What are the annual training requirements (curriculum and hours)?
- Where is training currently conducted and at what cost?
- What training requirements are not being met?
- If a new fire training center were built, who would use it?
- What classes and facilities at the new fire training center would be in highest demand?
- Would potential users be willing to pay fees to train at the training center?

These data, if properly gathered and interpreted, should provide enough information for the working group to know if the training center is really needed and, if so, what preliminary resources exist to help build, operate, and maintain it.

Architect/Engineer (A/E) Selection

Selecting an architect/engineer (A/E) should be one of the first steps. The A/E team typically includes an architect, civil engineer, electrical engineer, mechanical engineer, structural engineer, and a fire training center design consultant, if the A/E does not already have this expertise. It might be necessary to add a geotechnical (soils) engineer, environmental engineer, or other specialists to the team.

The role of the A/E is multifaceted. The A/E could participate in the needs assessment or should, at least, validate it. The A/E should perform all of the following:

- Determine training objectives (what skills need to be taught at the training center).
- Determine what buildings and training props are needed to facilitate the training objectives (prepare the program).
- Estimate how much land is required.
- Help find a suitable site.
- Estimate project budget.
- Assist with marketing the project to the city council, grant agencies, potential contributors, or the public at large.
- Prepare the master plan, which includes a site drawing that shows buildings, training props, roads, parking areas, utilities, and other features.
- Design the training center.
- Assist with bidding the project out to contractors who would construct the training center.
- Provide construction administration to help oversee and facilitate the project as it is being built.
- Provide postconstruction assistance with evaluations and maintenance.

While selecting the A/E, the fire department should look for the best combination of qualifications and those qualities that make the department believe it could work well with the A/E for the next several years. Most publicly funded projects require qualifications-based selection (QBS), as opposed to low-price selection, to ensure that the A/E is properly qualified to plan and design this specialized facility. A/Es with no fire training center experience should team with specialty consultants because designing K through 12 schools or fire stations does not provide the necessary expertise to design live fire training structures and other specialty training props (Figure 12.14.6). Vendors that sell training props, equipment, tools, or other items for fire training centers should not be hired as "consultants" for planning and design efforts because of potential conflicts of interest. Fire departments should seek independent advice about all of the options, not just those of one vendor. Be certain that companies that represent themselves as consultants do not also act as sales representatives for vendors.

Identification of Potential Users

Many fire training centers are intended for use only by the local fire department. Others are to be regional facilities used by career and volunteer fire departments from the extended region surrounding the facility.

If many departments and communities are involved, a regional consortium could be formed to pool resources (land, money, and personnel). There are several factors to be evaluated for a consortium. For example, which locality will provide the site? Which will operate and maintain the facility? How will the nonhosting consortium members support construction, operations, maintenance, and other costs? Will there be usage fees for rental and consumables? Will there be an annual contribution from each member of the consortium?

FIGURE 12.14.6 Live Fire Training Structure

Other agencies besides fire departments could be users of the training center. For example, law enforcement, EMS, emergency management, emergency operations center, 9-1-1 call center, and communications center departments are potential partners in a training center. If community resources are limited to the point that having separate facilities for these departments is not feasible, sharing certain facilities at one training center is an option. For example, classrooms, auditorium, physical fitness rooms, conference rooms, driver training course, and a training tower could be shared by the fire department and law enforcement agencies (police and sheriff) to maximize cost-effectiveness. Other critical training functions, however, could be kept separate, so that the fire department live fire training structure (burn building) and drafting pit are separate from the law enforcement shooting range and bomb disposal training area.

Identification of Operation and Maintenance Personnel

Before designing the training center, key personnel and budget decisions should be considered. Will there be full-time administrative staff, full-time instructional staff, and full-time maintenance staff? The answers to these questions will have a significant impact on the operations and maintenance budget once the training center is built.

Even though design has not begun, now is the time to start estimating operations and maintenance budgets. When requesting funding for construction, the department should also request operations and maintenance funds for the years immediately following construction to ensure that the proper budget is in place once the facility is built.

Identification of Funding Sources

Funding a new fire training center can be a tremendous challenge. Municipal capital outlay budgets and bond funds are the most common funding sources, but many departments need to supplement these funds. Other potential funding sources include the following:

- Construction grants
- Federal or state grants
- Local industry
- Donors
- Regional participants
- Other participating municipal or state agencies

Historically, federal grant funds could not be used for building construction, though federal grant rules should be explored for current opportunities before ruling out these funds for construction. Even if federal grants cannot be used for construction, they might be available for funding equipment, mobile training props, and training programs, allowing more of the local resources to be used for the construction of fixed buildings.

It is never too early to start marketing funding sources to gain support for the project. Some departments have needed years to obtain adequate financial support. Some departments have raised funds simultaneously with land acquisition and design phases, shortening the waiting period for construction to begin. Adequate funding ("seed money") for A/E fees for the initial programming, master planning, and perhaps land development submission will be necessary up front. This seed money will result in a well-developed master plan and budget, which could be used to help market funding sources for the full project cost.

Master Plan

Master planning initiates the design process. The key steps in creating the master plan include the following:

- Determine the training objectives.
- Write the program for training facilities needed to support the training objectives, including space requirements (space within buildings and space around training props). This program is the foundation for a successful project and should be established through significant interaction between the A/E and the fire department. Should it be necessary, the program could be adjusted during later stages of planning and design.
- Evaluate current and future needs.
- Create a conceptual site plan (Figure 12.14.7). This task should be coordinated with the "Site Selection and Design"

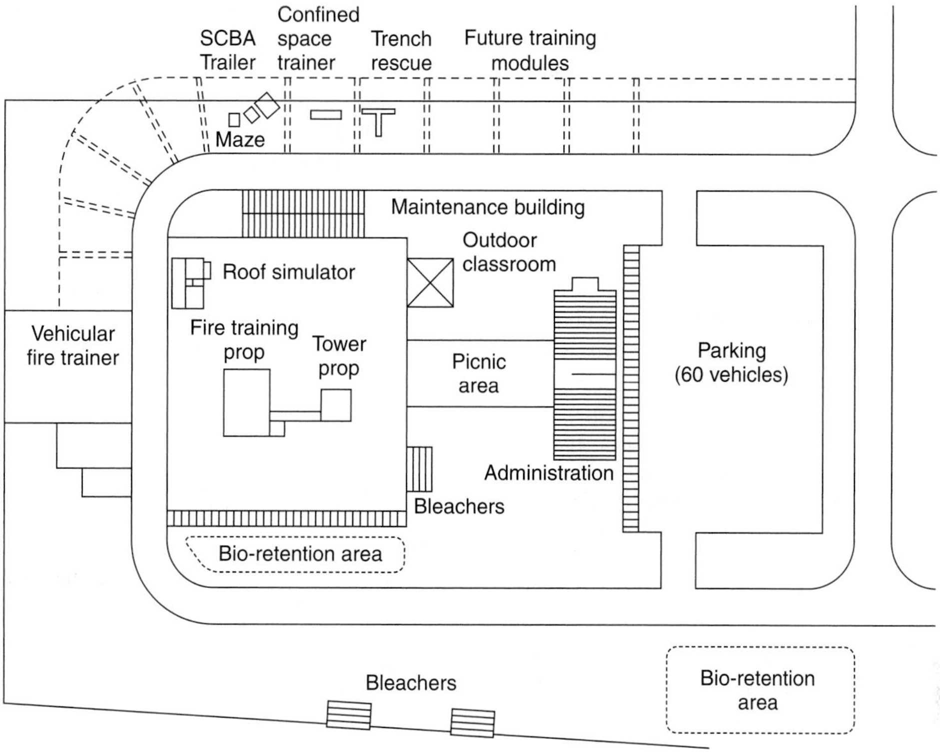

FIGURE 12.14.7 Sample Master Plan

tasks described later. The first draft of the conceptual site plan could be a simple "bubble diagram," showing approximate areas where buildings, props, and site features could be placed on the site. Eventually, the conceptual site plan will be more detailed, showing all features including their approximate shapes and sizes.

- Create conceptual plans of primary buildings and training props (Figure 12.14.8).

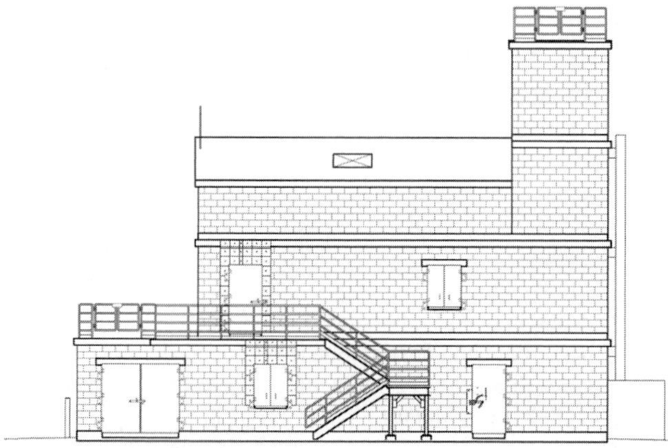

FIGURE 12.14.8 Conceptual Burn Building Elevation to Be Included in Master Plan

- Establish the budget for land acquisition, construction costs, furnishings, equipment, apparatus, and soft costs. Soft costs include fees (design, legal, and permitting), inflation, and contingency.

The site needs to be laid out to allow for future expansion. Training needs should be expected to change in the future, and the training center will need to adapt. Fifty years ago, training centers often did not need classroom spaces, and those classrooms were not designed for the technology demands of modern classrooms. After September 11, 2001, training for mass casualty incidents, building collapses, and multiagency concurrent training have been in higher demand. Many existing training centers do not have enough remaining space to accommodate these new needs. What new training will be needed 10 or 20 years from now? No one can predict, making future expansion capacity a critical component to the master plan. The master plan should consider the site issues listed next under "Site Selection and Design."

Site Selection and Design

Finding a suitable site can be difficult and requires perseverance. The process should coincide with preparation of the master plan because (a) the programming and space requirements of the master planning effort must be known in order to establish the selection criteria needed for the site search; and (b) on the other hand, the site must be selected before the master plan can be finalized.

Evaluating potential sites often involves filling out a criteria matrix that resembles a scorecard. There are many different features to evaluate for each site, as further described later. Scoring each of the needed features on a scale of 1 to 10 helps quantify which potential site is best suited. Some criteria can be weighted more heavily if they are more important. For example, a good score for environmental sensitivity might be more important than a good score for ease of obtaining a permit, especially if the latter could be overcome with a little extra time and effort on the part of the A/E. All potential sites should be scored, even if some appear at first glance to be unworthy of consideration, to validate the process and to confirm that the most suitable site is selected.

Resources for finding potential sites include local knowledge of the municipality and fire department, geographic information systems (GIS), local or state planners, tax maps, real estate companies, U.S. Geological Survey quad sheets, and other regional maps. The list of potential sites, and the evaluation of those potential sites, should look into the following criteria, at a minimum. These criteria will also impact the design.

Zoning. The area master plan, or similar document, should provide information about how potential sites are zoned. Industrial zoning or other suitable classifications are desirable, so that the training center is not located in a residential or commercial area.

Acreage. There seems to be no such thing as too much land at a training center. First, there needs to be adequate setback from neighboring properties, even if the neighbors are industrial in nature. Visible distractions (unsightly appearance of props, lights during night training, visible flames, and fire department activity), noise, and smoke have a negative impact on any neighbor. Creating adequate setback and visual buffering, through use of land berms, vegetation, fences, and buildings, has proven an effective method of minimizing complaints from neighbors.

Second, there needs to be ample space between the training props, so that crews working at the different props do not interfere with each other. If it becomes necessary to overlap working spaces around adjacent props in order to conserve land area, then those two props might not be usable simultaneously, requiring careful scheduling.

Third, there needs to be adequate distance between the training props and the conventional buildings (classrooms, offices, maintenance buildings, etc.). Smoke, noise, and lights interfere with the activities of these buildings and separating the props from the buildings is desirable.

Fourth, room for future expansion of the training center is desirable to be able to accommodate more students in the future plus different types of training that might not be known today but could be critical in the future.

There are many factors that can reduce the land that could be developed at a site. A 15 acre (6.1 hectare) site might have only 7 acres (2.8 hectares) that can be developed, once setbacks, wetlands, easements, or other restrictions are considered. Evaluate the developable acreage in addition to the overall acreage when selecting a site.

Location. On the one hand, it is desirable to have the training center close to the students to reduce travel time to the site. On the other hand, it is desirable to have the training center far from the population base to minimize its impact on the heavily developed portions of the community. A balance must be reached, including thoughts about potential community growth over the next 20 to 50 years. Many training centers that were built in remote, rural parts of a county found themselves surrounded by residential suburbs 10 to 15 years later.

Regardless of the site location, some students inevitably have a significant travel distance to the training center. In some cases, that is not a problem. In other cases, it affects cost (overtime requirements) and community protection (if a company that is training has to remain in service). Possible solutions for these issues include the following:

- Locate the site in a central location to balance the travel time of the students.
- Schedule other companies to backfill a station when that company is training.
- Provide sleeping facilities (dorms) at the training center, so that students attending weekend or longer programs do not have to travel long distances every day. Keep in mind that this solution is less common due to construction and operational costs.
- Provide satellite training centers, so that distant students can accomplish basic training closer to home and travel to the primary training center for specialized training.
- Provide mobile training props to take some of the basic training opportunities to the students rather than the other way around. This solution has been effective for training centers that serve large regions or entire states. Due to their size, it is difficult for mobile props to adequately simulate buildings, but several skills can be taught effectively with mobile props, including fire behavior demonstration, mask confidence (maze), aircraft fire fighting, and confined space skills.

Infrastructure. The site needs to have suitable infrastructure to support buildings, apparatus, and training operations. Site selection and design should consider the following:

- *Water supply.* Is potable water available? It will be required for drinking water, emergency eye washes and showers, restrooms, dining facilities, laundry operations, and similar functions. Potential sources include municipal water and wells. Water for training operations and irrigation could be potable or it could be supplied by tankers, ponds, or drafting pits. Recycling training water should be considered, and the A/E should look into methods for collecting training water and holding it for reuse. The recycling system could have a pumping station to charge hydrants around the site, or the system could include a series of dry hydrants. Water loss due to evaporation and conversion to steam should be considered when designing a recycling system, for the lost water will need to be replaced periodically by the fire department if precipitation is not adequate.
- *Sewer.* Is the site supported by municipal sewers or will a septic tank be required? Runoff from training operations usually does not need to go to sanitary or septic receptacles.

- *Storm water management.* Is a municipal storm sewer available to the site or will storm water be controlled on site through means of ponds, holding tanks, or other devices?
- *Power.* Is power readily available to the site? If not, the construction cost will increase.
- *Soils.* Are the soils suitable for supporting buildings, training structures, and roads used by apparatus? If there are loose fills, expansive clays, or rock on the site, there could be a significant cost impact.
- *Access roads.* Is the road network leading to the site suitable for supporting apparatus loads that will travel to and from the site?
- *Topography.* If the site is too hilly or too flat, the development costs could increase because soil might have to be added or removed. At some point in the site selection or site design process, a topographical survey will be required. This survey should also map the features of the existing site (buildings, areas of major vegetation, utilities, roads, and property lines).

Environmental and Other Restrictions. Due to the industrial nature of a fire training center, finding a site that meets environmental and other developmental restrictions is critical. Here is a sample list of items to evaluate for potential sites:

- Smoke plume and prevailing winds
- Water runoff that could include contaminants (soot, unburned Class A or Class B fuels, fire-fighting chemicals)
- Wetlands
- Endangered species habitats
- Protected vegetation
- Flood plain
- Landfill or hazardous materials
- Historical preservation
- Adjacency to airport or other facility that could impose restrictions on use and airspace above or around site

Public Access. Because there will be times when the public will need to access the site, it is best to design the site so that the public access areas, such as administration building, auditorium, and visitor parking, are near the road and main entrance. In most cases, this also puts the most attractive buildings near the road and main entrance, which is good for public relations.

Security. There are areas where public access should be denied, including training grounds and storage buildings. Fencing should be considered to separate the public access points, such as the visitor parking lot, from the rest of the site. Similarly, receptionists controlling locked doors could separate public areas in the administration building from offices, classrooms, and the rear doors that exit to the training grounds. Other security measures, such as cameras, manned gates at access points into the training grounds, and combination locks into storage rooms that contain harmful chemicals (or weapons if the facility is used by law enforcement), could be considered depending on the security needs.

Caution with Donated Land. Fire departments are sometimes offered land donations for the training center. The donation of an old landfill is a common example. Before accepting such a donation, the land should be evaluated for all of the environmental and other developmental restrictions that could make it expensive to develop, as listed earlier. It should also be evaluated for the infrastructure needs that are listed previously. In some cases, the department might not be able to afford the donation.

Design

Once the site is obtained, the master plan is in place, and the funding is available, it is time to design the facility. If hiring the A/E has been delayed until now, there is a good chance that the budget, land, and expectations could be off target. The A/E would need to validate all the work performed to date before commencing design efforts. Ideally, the A/E would have been retained during needs assessment to avoid potential delays.

The design process for a fire training center is similar to that of a fire station or any other conventional building. First, it is important to follow the applicable codes, standards, and guides. Some documents that relate to fire training center design include the following:

- State and local building codes, interpreted carefully for the training props
- NFPA 54, *National Fuel Gas Code*
- NFPA 58, *Liquefied Petroleum Gas Code*
- NFPA 86, *Standard for Ovens and Furnaces*
- NFPA 1001, *Standard for Fire Fighter Professional Qualifications*
- NFPA 1002, *Standard for Fire Apparatus Driver/Operator Professional Qualifications*
- NFPA 1402, *Guide to Building Fire Service Training Centers*
- NFPA 1403, *Standard on Live Fire Training Evolutions*
- IFSTA, *Essentials of Fire Fighting*
- U.S. Department of Homeland Security, Office for Domestic Preparedness, *WMD Training Program*
- State training guidelines, if any
- OSHA standards

The design process usually follows the standard steps of schematic design (15%), design development (35%), and construction documents (60%, 95%, and final).

The fire department should have constant opportunities to interact with the A/E, including chances to review the drawings at each stage and provide feedback. It is important to be vocal. A/Es require the fire department's input in order to provide a good design, starting with master planning through each step of design. If A/Es do not seem to listen, they should be confronted so that they can provide better service.

Four key design issues include (1) safety, (2) training effectiveness, (3) durability, and (4) ease of maintenance. Be sure the A/E explains at each stage how these issues are being met with the design.

Construction

Once the design is finished, the project will likely be bid to contractors (builders). The bidding process usually follows the state and local procurement laws, especially if public funds are being used. For the most common form of bidding, the project is advertised, contractors give price bids based on information shown on the A/E's drawings and specifications, and the contract is awarded to the lowest responsible bidder.

The fire department should remain heavily involved during construction, including regular visits to the site and attendance at the construction progress meetings. Should anything look unexpected, the fire department should call the A/E. Occasionally, the fire department might want to make a design change during construction, which is feasible but usually requires paying a change order (extra charge) to the contractor, especially if the change alters something that has already been built. In most cases, it is better for design changes to be completed during the design phase.

During construction, the A/E's role includes the following:

- Run routine progress meetings.
- Make periodic site visits to observe construction.
- Review shop drawings.
- Answer questions from the field.
- Answer fire department's questions.
- Design modifications if the fire department requests design revisions or if unforeseen conditions require it.
- Process the payment applications.
- Communicate between the contractor(s) and fire department's representatives.

Postconstruction

When the dedication ceremony is over, there is a need for an operations and maintenance (O&M) budget, starting in the first year. Ideally, this funding would have been placed into the municipal budget during the planning phase. Budget items required for O&M include the following:

- Staff salaries and benefits
- Building maintenance (cleaning, lightbulbs, trash removal, and painting)
- Grounds maintenance (landscaping, roads, parking lots, and snow removal)
- Equipment maintenance (vehicles, gear, mannequins, and SCBAs)
- Utilities (water, electricity, gas, sewer, telephone, and Internet)
- Training fuel costs
- Noise, smoke, and runoff abatement costs, if any
- Training structure and training prop maintenance, including routine structural engineering evaluations of the live fire training structure (burn building), per NFPA 1403

Buildings at Fire Training Centers

The two most common buildings at fire training centers are classroom/administration buildings and support buildings. Other buildings could be included, such as fire stations, dormitories, and vehicle maintenance facilities, but the two primary building types are described next.

Classroom/Administration Building. The classroom/administration building could be a single portable classroom in a trailer or a large, multistory, multifunctional building (Figure 12.14.9).

Classrooms should accommodate the typical anticipated class size but have moveable partitions that could allow for larger or smaller classes within adjoining spaces. The classroom space should be multifunctional. One day it might be used for a classroom lecture, using the latest audiovisual and computer equipment. The next day it might be used to demonstrate SCBA equipment or to teach CPR on mannequins. As a result, it is beneficial to have tables and chairs that could be easily reconfigured or moved out of the way altogether. It is also beneficial to have durable finishes, for even if dirty gear will not be brought into the classrooms, the finishes will see ample wear and tear.

Classrooms could also be equipped to record sessions (video and audio), so that the sessions could be played again later at stations or other regional departments for distance learning opportunities.

Other functions to be considered in a classroom/administration building include the following:

- Dirty classrooms accessible from the outside drill area, so that students could enter in gear for classroom sessions relating to the hands-on training exercises being conducted; this function could also be out on the training grounds, in the form of outdoor classrooms
- Breakout rooms—small meeting rooms that allow for small group activities; a breakout room could also be used as a conference room or room for instructors to create curriculum and prepare for classes
- Offices for permanent staff
- Office for temporary staff and temporary instructors
- Formal conference room; could also serve as a breakout room for classroom sessions
- Work rooms, including printing, copying, and other functions
- Break room/kitchenette; for large fire training centers, there could also be a need for a full kitchen and cafeteria
- Library
- Auditorium for uses including large lectures and graduation ceremonies; tiered seating is problematic for comput-

FIGURE 12.14.9 Classroom/Administration Building

erized testing techniques, so a traditional auditorium might not be functional for examinations
- Audio/video functions, such as recording studio, editing rooms, and storage
- Physical fitness room; could be located in a support building instead
- Locker rooms and showers; not all training centers need these facilities. The training center could support the physical fitness room. If there is no physical fitness room, this function could be located in a support building closer to the training grounds. If this function remains in the classroom/administration building, it should have an exterior entrance from the training grounds, so that students in dirty gear do not pass through the clean portions of the building.
- Restrooms
- Heritage hall
- Storage areas for office supplies, training props, classroom equipment, training records, recordings of classroom sessions, cleaning supplies, break room supplies, and other equipment stored at the facility
- Parking, which should be sufficient to accommodate permanent staff, students, and visitors; if graduation ceremonies or other heavily attended public events are anticipated, the parking areas should be designed accordingly, or overflow parking areas should be identified on the site

Support Building. The support building serves the classroom/administration building as well as the training grounds (Figure 12.14.10). Functions in this building include the following:

- Vehicle storage and minor maintenance
- SCBA storage, refilling, and maintenance
- Locker rooms and showers; this function could be in the classroom/administration building instead
- Physical fitness room; this function could be in the classroom/administration building instead
- Restrooms
- First aid
- Storage for training props, equipment, and gear

FIGURE 12.14.10 Support Building

- CPAT course; a candidate physical ability test course could be set up in the apparatus bays, if the bays are large enough, in order to control the environment during the test

Training Structures and Props

The following is representative of training structures and props commonly found at fire training centers.

Live Fire Training Structure ("Burn Building"). A burn building is usually the first training structure provided at a training center. Its function is vital in teaching skills required by NFPA 1001, especially those requiring live fire training scenarios.

Burn buildings are exposed to harsh conditions and could deteriorate quickly if not designed correctly. There are three primary causes for damage. The first is heat, which could reach as high as 2000°F (1093°C) in areas of direct flame impingement, such as ceilings directly above training fires. The second is thermal shock, which is created when heated surfaces are sprayed with cold water. The third is abuse that is inherent in live fire training, such as impact from direct hose streams and impact from tools and gear carried by personnel.

No building materials are immune to damage from these conditions. Masonry cracks and gradually deteriorates. Steel warps and corrodes. Concrete cracks and spalls, a condition that occurs when pieces of concrete fall out of slabs or walls. Careful design and construction are required to eliminate the potential for damage to structural components.

When designing a burn building, the first step is to determine which type of fuel is required to meet the training objectives. The two primary options are Class A fuels and gas-fired props, which burn either LP or natural gas. The benefits of Class A fuels are the drawbacks of gas props, and vice versa. Some training centers have burn buildings that can accommodate both fuel options to achieve the benefits of both.

The structural elements of the burn building need to be protected with thermal linings. There are several options. For ceilings, the options tend to be proprietary ones. The options currently on the market are not equal products, in that different materials are installed in different ways from one vendor to the next. In choosing a thermal lining, the qualities to be evaluated include initial cost, long-term cost (including maintenance costs), verifiable evidence of durability and insulating capability, and references. Thermal linings for walls and floors could include the proprietary options but could also include more conventional options, such as fire bricks and masonry blocks. Steel is not an insulator, plus it tends to warp when exposed to heat. If steel is used as a thermal lining, it will need to be supplemented with additional insulation or ventilated air spaces, though these might not eliminate warping and the need for periodic steel replacement. Refractory concrete (calcium aluminate concrete) should not be used for structural components in burn buildings, given its track record of severe damage in burn buildings.

Two types of burn buildings are most often constructed. The first is a combination of concrete and masonry (Figures 12.14.11, 12.14.12, and 12.14.13). The second is preengineered steel. Each option has advantages and disadvantages and should

FIGURE 12.14.11 Two-Story Burn Building

FIGURE 12.14.12 Three-Story Burn Building with Attached Four-Story Tower

FIGURE 12.14.13 Five-Story Burn Building with Tower

be considered. Determining factors should include long-term cost, durability, and ability to provide realistic floor plans that simulate occupancies found in the community. The A/E should guide the discussions on options for building types, fuels, and thermal linings, as well as design the burn building and features.

Details should be designed for function as well as safety, durability, and ease of maintenance. For example, various roof pitches, roof ventilation cutout areas, durable doors and shutters that can expand and contract when exposed to heat while still blocking out light and keeping in smoke, and drainage scuppers should all be detailed by the A/E to ensure proper function and durability. Other potential features include forced entry doors, breach wall simulators, standpipes, temperature monitoring systems, rappelling anchors, and mock utility meters.

Around the exterior, it is best for the burn building to be accessible from all sides. Realistic challenges, such as curbs, street signs, and simulated overhead power lines (Figure 12.14.14), could be incorporated at one or more sides at low cost. Paving near the structure needs to be nonslip for ladders and durable for apparatus loads. Consider seasonal conditions as well, for asphalt could soften during hot summer days, making it susceptible to damage from apparatus loads and ladder bases.

In many cases, it is desirable for the burn building to be lockable at all accessible doors and windows, especially if the training grounds are not secured with a fence.

Training Tower. Training towers vary in floor plan and range in height from 3 to 10 stories, though 4 to 6 stories is the most common range (Figures 12.14.15 and 12.14.16). The construction of training towers is typically either wood or concrete, although steel towers have been used. Preengineered steel training towers are also available, usually combined with preengineered burn buildings. Other types of towers can be combined with burn buildings as well.

The following training functions are often performed at training towers and should be considered:

- Ground ladders to windows (could be various size windows), flat roof deck, pitched roof, or balconies
- Aerials; tower height should accommodate tallest aerial that is anticipated to be used in the community in the next 10 to 20 years
- Stair drills, both interior stairwells and exterior fire escapes
- Rappelling from roof, windows, and perhaps other locations unique to the community
- Standpipe connections and charging standpipe at fire department connection
- Search and rescue drills using artificial smoke or smoke from small Class A burns in a barrel, though soot from these fires could damage ropes
- Elevator shaft drills
- SCBA confidence maze (which could alternatively be in a shipping container on the site)
- Forced entry doors
- Technical rescue drills, including tripod over aligned manholes, high angle rescue, and building-to-building rescue

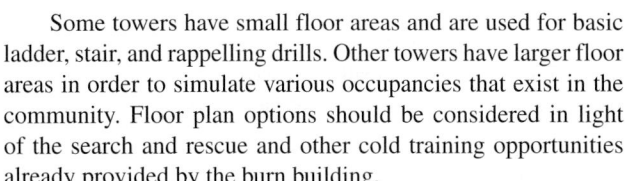

FIGURE 12.14.14 Simulated Power Lines and Other Obstacles Near Training Structure

FIGURE 12.14.15 Small Training Tower

Some towers have small floor areas and are used for basic ladder, stair, and rappelling drills. Other towers have larger floor areas in order to simulate various occupancies that exist in the community. Floor plan options should be considered in light of the search and rescue and other cold training opportunities already provided by the burn building.

In some cases, it is advantageous to combine the burn building and tower together, especially if site space is limited and if mid-rise evolutions need to be combined with live fire training. On the other hand, it could be more advantageous to separate the burn building from the tower, so that live fire training and tower drills could be conducted simultaneously by different classes. Furthermore, separating the two structures allows all four sides of the structures to be used for their intended purpose. If combined into one structure, the D side of the burn building and the B side of the tower, for example, would be eliminated from training possibilities.

Around the exterior, it is best for the training tower to be accessible from all sides, preferably with enough clearance for aerials to be utilized on all sides. Realistic challenges, such as curbs, street signs, and simulated overhead power lines, could be incorporated at one or more sides at low cost. Paving near the structure needs to be nonslip for ladders and durable for apparatus loads. Consider seasonal conditions as well, for asphalt

FIGURE 12.14.16 Large Training Tower

could soften during hot summer days, making it susceptible to damage from apparatus loads and ladder bases.

For hotter environments, consider a canopy roof over the roof, so that rappelling instructors and students can have shade during long training days. Like the burn building, it is often desirable for the training tower to be lockable at all accessible doors and windows.

Exterior Fire Training Props. Exterior fire training props are typically gas fired (LP in most cases because natural gas flames are difficult to see in daylight) and come in many configurations. Vendors offer props configured to simulate car fires, fuel spill fires, tank fires, dumpster fires, railcar fires, aircraft fires, shipboard fires, broken pipe/flange fires, outdoor grill fires, industrial fires, and other simulations. Many fire training centers have utilized the local gas company to design and build these training props as a lower-cost option to vendor-provided props. It is important to follow the gas code and all applicable NFPA documents, including the requirements of NFPA 1402 and 1403, when designing such props. Most A/Es do not have the expertise to design these props.

Mobile gas-fired props are being utilized more frequently, especially for statewide training and regional training. Rather than bringing students to a centralized fire training center, the mobile gas-fired props can be taken to the students. Mobile gas-fired props include trailers to simulate structure fires (though these props cannot provide the proportions of a burn building), car fires, aircraft fires, and tanker truck fires.

Exterior props could utilize Class A fuels instead of LP. For example, Class A materials could be burned in a junked car for training purposes. To conduct such burns, all closed containers, such as tanks, bumpers, pistons, shock absorbers, and some steering columns, must be removed from the car to prevent bursting. Any item that could have hazardous emissions, such as upholstery and plastics, should also be removed. In many cases, the car needs to be stripped to bare metal frame before being used for fire training.

Flammable liquid pits are becoming less common due to concerns about groundwater contamination and black smoke emissions. Should such a pit be utilized at a training center, the proper environmental containment is essential, as is setback from neighbors and other buildings/props at the training center for smoke dissipation.

Vehicle Extrication Training. Although some training centers have utilized gravel areas, most vehicle extrication training areas consist of a concrete pad that can accommodate several vehicles at one time for cutting and extrication exercises. Fluids should be removed from the vehicles before training but the concrete pad should be designed to ensure that any spilled fluids will be contained. Obstacles, such as precast concrete "Jersey barriers," could be added so that vehicles could be placed against the obstacles in order to make the training more challenging.

The vehicle extrication area could also be used for hazmat training by enlarging the pad to hold tanker trucks that could be used to simulate leaks and spills. The paved area provides space to practice containing hazmat spills.

Drafting and Pump Testing Area. When teaching the basics of pumping and drafting, it is necessary to have an area where the pumper can recirculate the water it flows rather than wasting resources and wetting down the training grounds. The two most common options are a pond, which could double as a storm water management device for the site, or a drafting pit, which is an underground concrete tank. For either case, there should be access to the water source for a suction hard sleeve and one or more dry hydrants, depending on the pump sizes. For the drafting pit, there should also be a horn-type steel tube or some other collection device to return the flow into the tank (Figure 12.14.17). The drafting pit should have a minimum capacity of 20,000 gallons (75,700 L). There should be a concrete pad, measuring approximately 50 ft × 25 ft (15.3 m × 7.7 m) adjacent to the pond or drafting pit for the pumper to be parked during operations.

Emergency Vehicle Operations Course (EVOC). An EVOC could include a large driver-training track that consumes more than 50 acres (20.2 hectares) of land, to simulate urban grids and highway interchanges. In most cases, however, a 1.5- to 2-acre (0.6- to 0.8-hectare) paved area is sufficient to teach the basic skills required by NFPA 1002. In many cases, the road network around the training structures and props can be utilized for driver training rather than building a dedicated driver training pad.

Outdoor Classrooms. Outdoor classrooms are typically open pavilion structures, with a wall on one side to hold a white board for use by an instructor. The pavilion offers students a place to sit on benches in the shade in dirty gear, to take in water and be cooled by fans (or warmed by heaters) while listening to instructors brief/debrief training evolutions. These structures also serve as shelters during sudden inclement weather. Outdoor classrooms could be equipped with restrooms, water fountains, emergency showers and eyewashes, first aid equipment, vending areas, and storage. It is good practice to provide several outdoor classrooms strategically located on the training grounds near clusters of training structures and props.

FIGURE 12.14.17 Drafting Pit

Other Training Props. There are numerous other training props that could be utilized, such as the following examples:

- Fire behavior lab, also known as a "flashover simulator," which consists of two shipping containers placed side by side and offset vertically, in order to demonstrate fire behavior
- Confined space prop, which could consist of any combination of connected vertical and horizontal pipes, manholes, tanks, and shipping containers with mazes inside. It is considered safe practice to keep as much of this prop above grade as possible, providing walkout access for all below-grade components.
- Trench rescue prop, which could consist of parallel concrete retaining walls holding back a hillside. Soil is placed between the walls, so that bracing is placed against the concrete walls during excavation. Should mistakes be made, the concrete retaining walls will ensure that a real trench collapse could not occur. The trench could be configured as a straight run, T-shape, or L-shape and should have a walkout condition for safety (Figure 12.14.18).
- Roof ventilation prop, consisting of a sloped, wood-framed structure built on the ground to allow roof ladder cutting exercises with no risk off falling of the roof of an actual building
- Rapid Intervention Team (RIT) prop, also known as FAST prop or RIC prop. This prop is a small, wood-framed structure that simulates conditions where fire fighters could get trapped, requiring rescue.
- Collapse rescue props, which could consist of basic concrete cutting props, basic balancing props, partially collapsed buildings with rubble on the floors, and rubble piles simulating fully collapsed buildings

SUMMARY

When developing a fire station or training center project, many issues must be considered. Because these factors will vary depending on the needs of the community, designers should adapt the application of the information presented in this chapter to suit local conditions and regulations.

The process of needs assessment, A/E selection, master planning, site selection, and design is consistent for both types of facilities, regardless of project scope and budget. Typical fire station spaces include an apparatus bay, sleeping accommodations, a watch room, a kitchen, a lounge or living room area, a decontamination room or space, and other functions. Fire training centers include a classroom/administration building, support building, burn building (live fire training structure), training tower, and various training props, such as drafting pits, exterior fire props, trench rescue props, confined space props, vehicle extrication areas, and others.

In all cases, the primary design issues are safety, functionality, durability, and ease of maintenance.

FIGURE 12.14.18 Trench Rescue Prop

BIBLIOGRAPHY

NFPA Codes, Standards, and Recommended Practices

Reference to the following NFPA codes, standards, and recommended practices will provide further information on fire rescue stations and training centers. (See the latest version of The NFPA Catalog *for availability of current editions of the following documents.)*

NFPA 54, *National Fuel Gas Code*
NFPA 58, *Liquefied Petroleum Gas Code*
NFPA 86, *Standard for Ovens and Furnaces*
NFPA 1001, *Standard for Fire Fighter Professional Qualifications*
NFPA 1002, *Standard for Fire Apparatus Driver/Operator Professional Qualifications*
NFPA 1402, *Guide to Building Fire Service Training Centers*
NFPA 1403, *Standard on Live Fire Training Evolutions*

References

Blackistone, S., "Sexual Harassment Rulings Are Changing Life in the Firehouse," *Firehouse,* Vol. 24, No. 6, 1999, p. 30.
Eisner, H., "Fire Service in the New Millennium," *Firehouse,* Vol. 25,No. 11, 2000, pp. 130–132.
FEMA 454, *Designing for Earthquake: A Manual for Architects*
FEMA 543, *Design Guide for Improving Critical Facilities from Floods and Winds*
Gough, J., "Computerized Tool for Planning Fire Station Locations," *Fire Fighting in Canada,* Vol. 44, No. 293, 2000, pp. 14–15.
Kitchen, M., "Benefits of Shared Use of Facilities at Two Surrey Fire Stations," *Fire Europe,* Vol. 91, No. 1125, 1999, p. 19.
Murphy, B., "Realistic Scenarios at North Wales," *Fire,* Vol. 92, No. 1139, 2000, p. 29.
Namba,Y., and Yasuno, K., "Study of Site Planning of Fire Stations Based on Prediction of Fire Risk," *Bulletin of Japan Association for Fire Science and Engineering,* Vol. 48, No. 2, 1998, pp. 19–27.
Parker, T., "Wilson Fire/Rescue Services' Fire Stations 100% Sprinklered," *Sprinkler Age,* Vol. 19, No. 8, 2000, pp. 20–21.
United States Air Force Fire Station Design Guide, Air Force Civil Engineer Support Agency, Tyndall AFB, FL, 1997.

Chapter 15

Public Emergency Services Alarm, Dispatch, and Communications Systems

Revised by
John M. Merklinger

Chapter Contents

Key Terms

alarm box, communication center, communications system, computer-aided dispatch, dispatch, emergency medical service, enhanced 9-1-1, Federal Communications Commission, fire alarm reporting system, hazardous material, joint powers authority (JPA), public safety telecommunicator, radio communication, radio frequency, repeater, transmitter

The goal of this chapter is to provide the *Fire Protection Handbook* user with an overview of public emergency services communication systems. It addresses issues related to the design, installation, operation, maintenance, and management of such systems and the facilities that house and support them.

In previous editions, this chapter addressed fire department communication systems. However, the widespread adoption of universal emergency number (9-1-1) service, coupled with requirements for formal training and certification of personnel and flexibility in resource allocation, has resulted in many jurisdictions combining central communication functions for all emergency services (fire, police, emergency medical services, etc.) into a single public safety answering point (PSAP) or communication center. Therefore, it has become increasingly difficult to address the emergency communication needs of the fire service without also addressing other emergency services.

NFPA recognized this trend when it changed the title and scope of NFPA 1221, *Standard for the Installation, Maintenance, and Use of Public Fire Service Communication Systems,* to NFPA 1221, *Standard for the Installation, Maintenance, and Use of Emergency Services Communications Systems,* commencing with the 1999 edition.

No two communities are exactly alike. Whether planning a new emergency communication system or evaluating an existing system, it is important to conduct an individualized needs assessment of the service area and then use it to analyze the emergency communication services provided and planned. In all cases, the requirements of NFPA 1221 should be followed.

For related topics, see the following: Section 12, Chapter 4, "Managing Fire-Rescue Departments"; Section 12, Chapter 13, "GIS for Fire Station Locations and Response Protocols"; Section 12, Chapter 16, "Fire Department Apparatus and Equipment"; Section 13, Chapter 9, "Emergency Medical Services and the Fire Department"; Section 14, Chapter 1, "Fire Alarm Systems"; and Section 14, Chapter 4, "Fire Alarm System Interconnections."

COMMUNICATION CENTERS

In creating any communication network, one must first establish a center point (communication center) through which all related process and control functions will be directed (Figure 12.15.1). A communication center may serve a single agency or area, multiple agencies under the control of a single political subdivision, several similar agencies from adjacent political subdivisions, an entire county, or any other large political jurisdiction. Combining fire, police, and emergency medical communications within a specific political jurisdiction (and for several adjacent jurisdictions) has

John M. Merklinger is director of the Monroe County 9-1-1 Communications Center in Rochester, New York. He has been a member of the Gates Fire Department since 1991 and is a past fire chief. He has been a member of Gates Volunteer Ambulance for 27 years.

FIGURE 12.15.1 Communication Center (Photo courtesy of Paul Ramirez, Phoenix Fire Department)

become an increasingly common management concept. If properly planned, such consolidations can provide positive results.

The communication center is where requests for emergency assistance are received and translated into an appropriate response. The communication center should be structured to provide logistical support to the responding units until the situation is under control. Accordingly, as an operating entity, the communication center must ensure that the equipment, personnel, and established procedures are adequate to satisfactorily perform in emergencies.

The communication center is a critical component of the jurisdiction's comprehensive emergency management plan. It is particularly important that communication center and emergency services communication systems be able to survive and continue to function during and after natural disasters such as floods, earthquakes, blizzards, hurricanes, and tornadoes. Such disasters may cause public utilities such as water, gas, and electricity to be unavailable to the communication center for extended periods of time. Lessons learned from past events and the probability of future events must be carefully considered and the communication center designed and equipped accordingly. One example is the resupply of fuel to emergency generators. A large-scale disaster could cut off normal sources of resupply, necessitating greater on-site storage than is required by code. There are resources that specifically address disaster management in the communications center. Resources to address these needs can be found at the National Emergency Number Association (NENA) website at http://www.nena.org or the Association of Public Safety Communication Officials (APCO) at http://www.apco911.org. In addition, the Commission on Accreditation of Law Enforcement Agencies (CALEA) at http://www.calea.org offers a Public Safety Communications Accreditation that specifically addresses disaster as well as all facets of communications. You do not need to be a police agency to use this resource. Finally, many statewide sheriff and chief of police associations offer free information on communication centers and disaster management for the communication center. Much of the free information offered applies to communications for the fire service as well.

Design Considerations

The following are some of the items that should be considered in the development of a communication center:

- Location
- Seismic stability
- Security (building layout and cameras)
- Emergency electrical power
- Wiring access (computer floor)
- Lighting (indirect lighting to prevent screen glare)
- Air conditioning (computers, dispatch, and personal environments)
- Air-conditioning backup
- Workstation layout (per Occupational Safety and Health Administration [OSHA] and Americans with Disabilities Act [ADA] regulations)
- Console arrangement (always consider ergonomics in your design for long-term employee health)
- Acoustics (background noise suppression)
- Restroom facilities
- Kitchen facilities
- Interior design
- Rest areas (lounges)
- Dormitories (sleeping quarters)
- Emergency rations
- Alternate locations
- Building storage areas
- Loading dock access or some type of access for future upgrades and deliveries
- Fire suppression systems

The communication center should be designed and constructed so the probability of interruption to operations due to fire or other causes will be minimized. Security concerns have changed significantly in the last few years. Today most communication centers have sophisticated security systems with features like key card access, security bollards, bullet-resistant or explosion-resistant glass, and much more. Simple things like restricted access to the communication center have become more critical today. When a separate building is not feasible and the communication center must be housed with other operations, such as city hall offices or in a fire station, the communication center should be properly separated from the remainder of the building by vertical and horizontal separations with a fire resistance rating of at least 2 hours and preferably with entrance only from the outside. Protection should be provided against fire exposures and unauthorized entry.

Alternate Communication Facility

An alternate communication facility that, when fully staffed, is capable of performing the emergency functions normally performed at the communication center should be provided. For example, a bomb threat or fire in the center requires both an alternate facility and a plan to evacuate the communication center. This alternate location should be totally removed from the primary location and should have all the necessary requirements for long-term usage. In the event of fire in the center, provisions should be made to continue operations long enough to transfer operations to the alternate facility. In smaller facilities and jurisdictions that cannot afford an off-site backup, the communication center should make arrangements with neighboring jurisdictions for backup services. Many times reciprocal agreements of this nature can benefit both jurisdictions.

Communication Center Protection

Because of the types of activities conducted and the records maintained in any modern communication center, building and systems protection must be provided. Security begins at the entrance to the communication center and can be as simple as a dead-bolt lock or as complex as a computerized entry control system. Only authorized personnel should be allowed access to the center. The center should be protected against damage due to vandalism, sabotage, and civil disturbances. The lowest floor should be above the 100-year flood plain. Entrances into the center directly from the exterior, if provided, should be protected by a security vestibule. Windows, if provided, should be bullet resistant if they face an area accessible to the public. The communication center should be located in a fully sprinklered, fire-resistive, or noncombustible building. Alarms and supervisory signals from the building sprinkler system(s) should be monitored in the operations room. The center and the spaces adjoining the center should be provided with an automatic fire detection system that is monitored in the operations room. Evacuation signals should be designed to avoid interference with communications operations. Portable fire extinguishers should be provided throughout.

Heating, ventilating, and air-conditioning (HVAC) systems serving the center should be independent of the main building HVAC systems to avoid the possibility of smoke contamination from a fire elsewhere in the building. Fresh-air intakes should be located to minimize the possibility of drawing in smoke from a fire inside or outside the building. Consideration should be given to providing operator-controlled smoke-control modes for the center HVAC system. Interior finishes in the center should be noncombustible. Records must be properly safeguarded. Access to records should be limited to authorized personnel only. Off-premises storage of backup records, software, and so on is essential. This backup information should be updated on a regular basis. Cyber-security or computer security is becoming a critical component of communication center operations. It must be part of all plans for protecting the facilities.

Power

The communication center must be able to operate normally in the event of a power failure. Two sources of power need to be provided. Any loss of data can have a severe impact on the communication center, so an uninterruptible power supply (UPS) system is critical. In most cases, the primary source of power will be the commercial electrical distribution network with the secondary source being one or more on-site engine-driven generators. However, in some cases the primary power source may be one or more on-site engine-driven generators with the secondary source being other on-site engine-driven generators. Automatic transfer to standby power on failure of primary power should be provided. During this transfer process, the UPS system should automatically kick in to maintain adequate power while the generators start and come up to full power.

Engine-Driven Generators. Engine-driven generator installations should conform to NFPA 37, *Standard for the Installation and Use of Stationary Combustion Engines and Gas Turbines,* and NFPA 110, *Standard for Emergency and Standby Power Systems.* The generators should be located in secured areas. Fuel should be stored on-site to permit a minimum of 24 hours of operation at full load without resupply, or in some cases a connection to a natural gas supply line should be established. Where the potential exists for longer interruption of primary power caused by natural disasters such as hurricanes and earthquakes, on-site fuel storage should be increased accordingly. Equipment essential to the operation of the generator, such as fuel transfer pumps and cooling systems, must be supplied with backup power from the generator. Generators should not depend on the public water supply (which might fail during a disaster) for engine cooling. Generators should be tested for at least 1 hour each week under load. This can be done by transferring the communication center's load to the generator or by loading the generator through other means such as an electric-resistant grid "load box."

In determining the capacity of the generator, essential loads in addition to those of the communication systems, such as HVAC systems, adequate lighting to permit personnel to perform their duties, fire protection and security systems, water supply and sanitary facilities operation, and so on need to be considered. In many cases your local utility company will provide an energy audit free of charge.

Uninterrupted Power Supplies and Battery Systems. Under worst-case scenarios, engine-driven generators can fail. Therefore, in addition to standby generators, communication centers should be equipped with stored emergency power supply systems (SEPSS) conforming to NFPA 111, *Standard on Stored Electrical Energy Emergency and Standby Power Systems,* to power essential electronic equipment. An SEPSS is defined by NFPA 111 as a system consisting of an uninterrupted power supply (UPS), a central battery system, or a motor-generator set powered by a stored electrical energy source, together with a transfer switch designed to monitor the preferred and alternate power sources and provide desired switching of the load, plus all necessary control equipment to make the system functional.

Electronic equipment, such as a computer-aided dispatch (CAD) system, is sensitive to momentary power interruptions during transfer from primary to standby power, as well as to voltage fluctuations normally associated with commercial power distribution systems. A momentary power outage or surge can cause systems to go off-line or damage sensitive circuits. Where such equipment is present and essential to operation of the communication center or network, it should be powered through a UPS conforming to NFPA 111. A UPS is a system consisting of a battery source, a converter, an inverter, and control equipment designed to provide clean, conditioned power for a finite period of time.

RADIO COMMUNICATIONS SYSTEMS

Radio System Selection

Considerable thought should be given to selecting the proper radio system, and professional personnel should be used to ensure the proper functioning of each system. For new systems, every entity should consider building an APCO Project 25 (P25) compliant radio system. A P25 radio system allows for multiple manufacturers' radios to work on the same system. Some older models are proprietary and can not work on other manufacturers' systems. For more information on P25 radio systems, you can go to the APCO website at http://www.apco911.org. Two other major considerations when upgrading or replacing your radio systems are FCC order 01-092 on narrow banding for UHF and VHF systems and FCC order 04-168 on rebanding for the 800-MHz spectrum. You can find further information on both of these critical subjects at http://www.fcc.gov.

An analysis of the service area and system configuration will help determine the number of base station transmitters, receivers, and repeaters needed and the number of radio channels (frequencies) required to support current usage and allow for future expansion. Small agencies may be able to operate with just a few frequencies. However, if a communication center serves multiple agencies, or if individual agencies consider the need for tactical on-scene frequencies, mutual-aid/interagency frequencies, disaster management, and the like, it is obvious why careful planning is necessary. Coverage overlays will need to be considered along with the topography of your area. Engineering will likely have to be done by the equipment manufacturer or an independent third party. The most important aspect will be the completion of a propagation study of the area. It is also critical that all aspects of the radio system meet recommended grounding standards as set forth by the radio's manufacturer.

Radio Frequency Selection

Several bands of radio frequencies are available to the public emergency services. These bands are VHF low band, VHF high band, UHF 450 MHz, and 700, 800 and 900 MHz. Each band of frequencies has its advantages and disadvantages, and the selection of a particular band will depend on factors such as frequency availability, area to be covered, type of terrain, number of radio units required, frequencies used by bordering fire districts, mutual-aid agreements, type of operation, and use of emergency medical radios.

Due to the finite number of available frequencies, it may be necessary for emergency response agencies to share radio frequencies. For small agencies, sharing radio channels with neighboring agencies having similar missions could be advantageous.

Type of Radio System Operation

The several types of radio systems available are as follows.

Simplex. This system utilizes a single radio frequency for both transmitting and receiving in all radios for each channel. With a simplex system, only one radio can transmit at any time and all others must receive.

Two-Frequency Half Duplex. This system utilizes separate frequencies for transmitting and receiving. As in the simplex system, half duplex allows only one radio to transmit at any one time.

Two-Frequency Full Duplex. The two-frequency, full-duplex system utilizes separate transmitting and receiving frequencies and permits simultaneous conversations in two directions.

Two-Frequency Repeater System. With this system, a high-powered base station repeater is centrally located at a favorable site overlooking the area to be covered, preferably on a mountaintop, a tall building, or a tower. The repeater receives a transmission from any radio in the system on one radio frequency and instantly retransmits or repeats the message on a second frequency that is received by all other radios in the system. A repeater system greatly increases the range of all of the radios in the system. It is especially useful in hilly or mountainous terrain where it might be impossible to talk directly from unit to unit. Repeater systems are two-frequency, half-duplex systems as described earlier.

Trunked Systems. The trunked system uses a group of radio frequencies. The system is controlled by a computer at the communication center or at the base station transmitter site. When a transmitter is keyed, it transmits its unique identity code to the computer. The computer instantaneously selects an available communications frequency and automatically directs the transmitting radio to use that frequency for the transmission. The advantage of this type of system is that it uses a group of available frequencies more efficiently by utilizing the capabilities of the computer to manage the radio traffic on each frequency. Thus, more radio traffic can be handled on the available frequencies without causing congestion and interference. The computer can prioritize traffic from competing transmitters based on their individual identity codes. For example, a request for a clear frequency transmitted by a fire department radio can receive a higher priority than a request from a nonemergency agency's radio. Provisions should be included to keep the system operational in the event of failure of the computer controlling the system.

In the interest of personnel safety, trunked radio system talk groups should not be used to fulfill the requirement for the provision of a simplex radio channel for on-scene tactical communications. A simplex radio channel is required because it enables emergency messages to be transmitted to and from on-scene command without reliance on communication equipment at another location.

Tone-Coded Squelch. In a tone-coded squelch system, each radio transmits a subaudible tone along with the voice signal. This audio tone is used to turn on the receiver so the conversation will be heard. Only the proper tone will activate the receiver, which eliminates the reception of radio interference.

Radio Paging Systems. Contacting emergency response personnel who do not normally monitor voice radio traffic can be easily accomplished with a radio paging system. A paging system includes a paging encoder, which is located in the communication center, and individual pagers. Pagers that receive voice messages, alphanumeric text messages, or both are available. With voice messages, a signal from the communication center activates an alerting device (typically a beeping tone or vibrator) in the pager and turns on the receiver audio. The wearer can then hear the dispatch message. With alphanumeric text pagers, the wearer is alerted in a similar manner and the dispatch message is displayed on a text screen on the pager. In some cases with alphanumeric paging a two-way alphanumeric communication can be established aiding in the dispatch of calls. Systems typically have the capability of alerting an individual pager, a group of pagers, and all pagers associated with the system.

Commercial paging service is available in most areas. Although suitable for administrative paging, its use for emergency dispatching is not permitted by NFPA 1221, since the commercial system is not under the control of the authority having jurisdiction. The volume of traffic in a commercial system may significantly delay transmission of emergency messages. In addition, the authority having jurisdiction cannot ensure that commercial facilities not under its control comply with the requirements of the standard for communication centers and dispatching systems.

Use of Multiple Radio Channels

The size and complexity of each agency will determine the number of radio channels necessary for adequate communications. Very small agencies may require only one radio channel for their exclusive use, whereas agencies in large metropolitan areas will require many. A separate frequency exclusively for on-scene tactical communications is required for each agency (or multiple agencies sharing the same dispatch channel). In addition, all agencies having similar missions adjacent to one another should share a common mutual-aid radio channel. This is provided for by the Federal Communications Commission (FCC) and is usually managed on a statewide basis.

Transmitter and Repeater Locations

Care should be taken in selecting the main transmitter and repeater locations for the radio system. Each radio coverage area is unique and must be dealt with on an individual basis. A high, central location, such as a mountaintop or large hill overlooking the area to be covered, a tall building, or similar structure is generally the ideal site. (This depends on coverage requirements, frequency availability, and requirements for channel sharing.) Again it is critical that proper system engineering and propagation studies are done to provide for adequate coverage. Where none of the foregoing locations is present, a high antenna tower can be utilized. Towers are required, even on mountaintops, to ensure proper antenna system operation.

The availability of commercial power and telephone access is also desirable when locating a transmitter site. Standby power supplied by a generator and backup battery system or UPS must be provided to ensure the site remains "on the air" in the event of a commercial power outage.

In some locations, where commercial power is unavailable, solar power (solar panels), batteries, or generators may be used as the primary source of power for the site. If the base station or repeater location is remote and unattended, provisions should be made to secure the area against unauthorized entry and vandalism. Intrusion alarms should be monitored at the communication center. A chain-link fence should surround the area, and all radio equipment should be located inside a building, out of sight, and protected from the weather. Security, fire protection, standby power, and circuit protection considerations are similar to those of the communication center. Remote camera access from the communication center to monitor the radio sites is an excellent idea.

Alternate Transmitter

An alternate transmitter, preferably at a separate location, should be provided to maintain communications in the event of failure of the primary transmitter. The alternate transmitter should have the same operational capabilities as the primary transmitter. A high central location is also desirable for this site. Primary and backup power, circuit protection, security, and fire protection requirements are the same as those for the primary transmitter site.

The communication center should have the capability of selecting either the main or alternate transmitter. To ensure its readiness, the alternate transmitter should be used at least twice daily.

Radio Site Antenna Configuration

When more than one radio is installed at a single site, an antenna system may be required. It may be impractical for each radio to have its own separate antenna because considerable interference could be generated using separate antennas. When several compatible radios are used, it is customary to provide one or more transmitting antenna systems and a separate receiving antenna system. A base station repeater using a single antenna requires a duplexer in order to transmit and receive simultaneously. Several transmitters can be connected to a single antenna by use of an antenna combiner; several receivers can be connected to a single antenna through the use of a multicoupler. Keep in mind that some output degradation can occur when sharing antennas, so this method may not be the preferred method. Professional assistance should be utilized to design the antenna system for all radio sites.

The antenna design should provide maximum radio frequency (RF) isolation between transmitting and receiving antennas, which is usually accomplished by mounting them one above the other on the antenna structure. Coaxial cables should be used for connections between radios and antennas. These cables should be high quality and low loss, with length as short as practical. Good grounding of the antenna system is required to prevent damage due to lightning.

Access from Communication Center to Radio Site

If base station radio transmitters are located at the communication center, individual wires ("house cables") can be used to connect the operators' consoles to the proper base station. If the base station radios are located remotely from the communication center, they can be connected by dedicated leased telephone lines, a microwave radio system, fiber-optics connectivity, or a point-to-point radio. Redundant links should be provided so that failure of a single link will not prevent operation of the remote transmitter site from the communication center. Adequate circuit protection should be provided at the communication center and at the remote site. Always meet or exceed the manufacturer's recommendations for circuit protection.

Mobile Radios

Mobile radios have high RF power output (typically 20–100 W) and, therefore, have considerable transmitting range. However, because they are vehicle mounted, they cannot provide on-scene communication once personnel leave the vehicle. Each emergency response vehicle should be equipped with a multichannel, two-way mobile radio that is capable of (1) communicating with the communication center over the assigned dispatch channel(s) and (2) communicating with other units on the assigned tactical channel(s). In addition, emergency vehicles that are assigned to respond to airfield emergencies should be equipped with mobile radios capable of operating on the aircraft ground control emergency channel(s). Each mobile radio should be equipped with a visual "transmit" indicator and a carrier control timer that disables the transmitter after a predetermined time as established by the authority having jurisdiction to prevent a malfunctioning radio from tying up a channel indefinitely. Mobile radios equipped with scanning receivers should have an automatic priority feature that causes the radio to revert to its priority channel automatically when that channel is being used. Consider P25 compliant radios. Spare radios should be kept on hand for exchange with malfunctioning radios. The minimum required by NFPA 1221 is one spare radio for each 20 radios or fraction thereof in service and not less than one unit for each (noninterchangeable) radio model in use.

Portable Radios

Each emergency response vehicle should carry at least one multichannel, two-way portable radio capable of operating on the assigned dispatch and tactical channels. Consider P25-compliant radios. Many agencies issue portable radios to each emergency responder on duty for both personnel safety and ease in dispatching. Radio discipline becomes crucial with that many portable units in use. Portable radios have the advantage that they can be carried (worn) by emergency response personnel. However, they have a much lower RF power output than mobile radios and, therefore, have a considerably shorter operating range.

Portable radios should be manufactured for the environment in which they will be used. For example, most portable radios need to withstand exposure to precipitation, rough handling, and ambient temperature fluctuations. Radios used in fire fighting must withstand repeated exposure to very rough handling, water, and high heat and humidity. Radios used where explosive vapors might be present also must be labeled as intrinsically safe. Portable radios should be designed to allow channels to be changed while the user is wearing gloves. Radios that are equipped with keypads should have a means for the user to disable the keypad to prevent inadvertent use. Each portable radio should be equipped with a "transmit" indicator and a carrier control timer that disables the transmitter after a predetermined time. Radios equipped with scanning receivers should have an automatic priority feature that causes the radio to revert to its priority channel automatically when that channel is being used. Battery chargers and stocks of charged spare batteries should be maintained on hand in quantities sufficient to provide for continuous use of portable radios during long-duration incidents. Spare radios (at least one spare for each 10 radios or fraction thereof in service) should be kept on hand for exchange with malfunctioning radios. For personnel who work in very noisy environments, provision of sound-attenuating headsets should be considered.

Diversity Receiver-Voter System. Because portable radios have a very low RF power output, this low power creates problems for communications over large areas. Portables can normally receive the high-power base station, but they do not always have sufficient power to transmit back to the main radio site. This problem can be eliminated by a diversity receiver-voter system in which radio receivers are installed in a uniform manner at various locations throughout the coverage area. This solution provides a receiver for each subarea in the system. In this manner, a portable radio should not be more than a mile or two from one of the receivers in its subarea.

The signal from each of these receivers is fed to the communication center. The voter is capable of switching from receiver to receiver in midsyllable so, as the RF signal rises and fades at each receiver, the dispatcher hears only the best signal received. A diversity receiver-voter system can also be incorporated into a repeater system to greatly exceed portable-to-portable communications. A block diagram of a simple diversity (subarea) receiver-voter system is shown in Figure 12.15.2.

Mobile Data Terminals. Mobile data terminals (MDTs) sometimes also called mobile computer terminals (MCTs) are small computer terminals that may be connected to a radio system, allowing that unit to access another mobile terminal, base station terminal, or computer. These units generally consist of a microcomputer that converts digital information into a signal

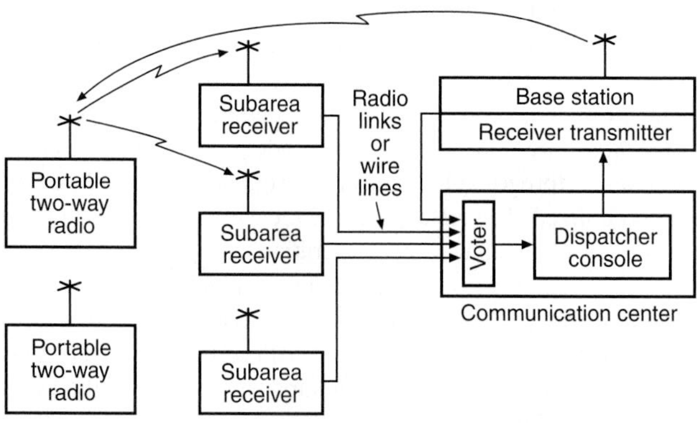

FIGURE 12.15.2 A Simple Diversity (Subarea) Receiver-Voter System

that a radio can transmit or receive. These units may have preprogrammed display capabilities where, by pressing one key, a canned message, such as unit status, condition, operator name, or even the time of day, can be sent. These units can be so reduced in size they can be handheld (including the radio).

Screen formats vary from simple light indicators to complex visual images including text and graphic characters. Some systems even have city maps or building drawings showing specific items relative to access, hydrant location, standpipes, and hazardous materials storage. Some today even have aerial photography for use by the field responders. One major consideration, however, is that these units may require dedicated, conventional radio channels. There are many options for having these computers be able to talk back to the communication center. It can be accomplished via an RF platform that is privately owned by the public safety entity. Some use cellular systems and still others use a hybrid system of RF and wireless hot spots. Consult with the manufacturer on the best system to serve your needs.

Emergency Response Facility Dispatch Notification. There are three items that should be included as part of a dispatch/alerting system: (1) a voice announcement or public address system to alert the company to an emergency response requirement, (2) a remote control for station lights annunciator, and (3) dedicated communication paths to ensure the reliable sending of the dispatch message. For agencies receiving more than 730 alarms per year, at least two means of alerting stations are required. Vehicles may even be included in this alerting process by the use of digital decoders or other suitable audible alarms. You can also consider having remote MDTs in each station connected to the CAD system, thus allowing for the computer event/incident to display in the station prior to response and allowing for a rip-and-tear function, so that the responding units can take the information with them for response. In addition some agencies now provide MDTs in their apparatus as well.

Emergency Medical Service Communications

In many communities, the communication center is involved in dispatching emergency medical services (EMS), both basic and advanced life support, to the citizens they serve (see Section 13, Chapter 9, "Emergency Medical Services and the Fire Department"). Each state has an EMS communications plan on file with the FCC, and these plans identify how the EMS communications system will be implemented in that state. The EMS system differs from the normal fire communications system in the approach the FCC has taken to frequency allocation. The FCC has set aside UHF frequency pairs for communications between field EMS personnel and base hospital personnel. These channels are shared and used in all 50 states. Therefore, to ensure quality, noninterfering communications on these channels during critical life-threatening incidents, it is imperative that local coordination prevail.

Hazardous Materials Team Communications

The development of hazardous materials (hazmat) response teams in the fire service has resulted in new communications requirements for safety. These new requirements are in two major areas: (1) hazardous materials information and (2) hazmat team communications from within encapsulating suits.

A major element in the successful outcome of hazardous materials incidents is the ability to rapidly obtain information about the material(s) involved. This generally involves contacting outside agencies for a variety of information. Mobile radio telephone patch(es) may be considered, but this usually ties up the only available radio channel. Cellular telephones should be carried on the hazardous materials team apparatus to facilitate obtaining needed information. This approach also allows a printer to be installed along with the telephone so that one of the hazardous materials computerized information services can be used for on-scene, rapidly printed information.

Cellular telephones also allow the hazardous materials team member's direct access to hazmat information services, reducing the potential for errors. The medical component of the hazmat team should be equipped with a medical radio for medical control and to obtain toxicological information from base hospitals.

Many hazardous materials team members must work inside encapsulating suits. They require special communications systems designed to meet their requirements for operational safety. Two-way wireless communications, preferably hands free, should be considered. A variety of radio systems that use bone, ear, or throat microphones for voice transmission are available to meet these needs. These radio systems come in simplex, half duplex, or full duplex. They use push-to-talk or voice-actuated circuits to transmit, and mobile repeaters may be integrated into them. An agency should thoroughly examine its needs and the experience of similar agencies in this area prior to purchase.

PERSONNEL

No matter how well designed, installed, and maintained, no system is better than the people who operate it. Communications systems should be supervised by responsible and competent people whose duties include directing, testing, and inspection programs. Public safety telecommunicators should be temperamentally suited to the position and be able to efficiently handle assigned duties. They should have the ability to remain calm, take decisive action during emergencies, remain alert during periods of inactivity and while carrying out normal repetitive operations, and work harmoniously with other people. They should also be familiar with operations.

Work schedules should be structured to provide for maximum efficiency. Stress and high activity lead to operator fatigue. Therefore, operators should be provided with a place to take work breaks in the communication center but outside the operations room.

Training

Communications personnel should not become isolated from the agencies they serve. Their structured training should be directed toward maintaining and improving their call-taking and dispatching skills, but it must also include a full understanding of all agency operations. Standard operating procedures should be provided in writing to ensure standard performance. Continual in-service training is a must to help maintain proficiency, familiarize personnel with new equipment and new technologies, and to prepare employees for the next level.

The authority having jurisdiction should require call takers and dispatchers to be certified as meeting the requirements of NFPA 1061, *Standard for Professional Qualifications for Public Safety Telecommunicator.* Telecommunicators should be familiar with the geographic area they serve, including the locations of streets, landmarks, important and high-hazard structures, and locations of congested areas. Their training should include maintaining their call-taking and dispatching skills and understanding the needs and operating procedures of the agencies for which they take calls and for which they dispatch. It is important to note that many states have now set minimum training standards for telecommunicators. You should check with your state to see what training requirements apply.

Operating Procedures

Standard operating procedures for the telecommunicators should be provided in writing to ensure uniform performance in accordance with the requirements of the authority having jurisdiction in charge of the communication center. The authority having jurisdiction should develop standard operating procedures in conjunction with each emergency response agency served by the communication center to establish when a telecommunicator shall be assigned exclusively to an emergency incident in progress.

Staffing

The authority having jurisdiction should ensure that an adequate number of qualified telecommunicators are on duty at all times to promptly receive and process emergency calls (alarms). With very limited exception, at least one qualified telecommunicator should be on duty in the communication center at all times. Again, many states now require a minimum of two telecommunicators on duty. As the number of alarms increases, the staffing level should increase to ensure prompt receipt and processing of alarms, which may require varying staffing levels at different times based on anticipated call load established from historical data, weather forecasts, large public events, and so on. Where telecommunicators provide emergency medical instructions to callers prior to arrival of emergency response personnel, at least two telecommunicators should be on duty at all times, since giving emergency medical instructions can occupy one telecommunicator full time for several minutes. In addition to the telecommunicators, at least one supervisor should be on duty when more than two telecommunicators are on duty. The supervisor should be assigned to the operations room when more than three telecommunicators are on duty. Also keep in mind that with new federal requirements, the use of the National Incident Management System (NIMS) should be applied in any communications center. Keep in mind that an effective span of control under NIMS is five to seven people per supervisor in the communication center.

In jurisdictions receiving fewer than 730 alarms per year (average of 2 alarms per 24 hour day), a dedicated telecommunicator may not be required to be on duty at all times, where an alternate means approved by the authority having jurisdiction can effect the prompt receipt and processing of alarms as required by NFPA 1221. However, with the trend toward multiple jurisdictions and multiple agencies sharing communication center services, instances where this limited exception to NFPA 1221's requirement for full-time telecommunicators exists are becoming increasingly rare. For additional information on staffing requirements, consult the latest edition of NFPA 1221.

You may also want to consider that some states have now set minimum training and staffing standards for communication center employees. Review those requirements if there are any in your state. The two 9-1-1 organizations, the National Emergency Number Association (NENA) and the Association of Public Safety Communication Officials (APCO), both have recommended staffing standards as set forth by their advisory boards and staff. In some states the regulating authority has recommended adoption of either the NENA or APCO standard as the minimum staffing standard. Further information is available on their websites at http://www.nena.org and http://www.apco911.org.

CONSOLIDATION OF COMMUNICATION CENTERS

Consolidation of Functions

Many small-to-medium-sized jurisdictions have found that by consolidating communications functions with other jurisdictions, they can provide a higher level of service to their citizens at a lower overall cost. One of the major benefits of consolidation for these agencies is the ability to provide highly trained telecommunicators who are on duty 24 hours a day. A larger communication center will also have adequate backup to handle multiple, simultaneous incoming alarms, whereas the smaller center may not have the personnel to cope with them. The major benefit of consolidation is to provide an increased level of service at reduced costs.

Methods of consolidating communication centers vary, but the two most popular are forming (1) a joint powers authority (JPA) to provide this service as an independent agency or (2) one or more jurisdictions contracting with another jurisdiction to provide this service. Either system can work well and provide the same benefits to the participants.

Joint Powers Authority (JPA)

A joint powers authority (JPA) is an independent government entity established to provide specific services. There are several benefits of a JPA arrangement for combined communications versus other arrangements, but the major benefit is shared administration. With a JPA operating with an independent board of directors, no agency or jurisdiction that might set policy unacceptable to another agency or jurisdiction is in control. In this way, each participant has equal representation and equal responsibility to make the operation a success.

REPORTING AN EMERGENCY

Reports of fires and other emergencies originate from three principal sources: (1) the general public, (2) the business community (industrial, institutional, commercial, and mercantile), and (3) other public service/safety agencies. The reporting process may utilize any of the following means, individually or in combination: (1) telephones, (2) public alarm reporting systems, (3) two-way radio communications systems, and (4) intelligent transportation systems.

Telephones

The most common method is the conventional public switched telephone network (PSTN). Increasingly, however, communication agencies are seeing calls placed from wireless cellular customers and most recently from Voice over Internet protocol (VoIP) providers. Currently, almost all interface at some point to the public switched telephone network. However, there are a few VoIP providers that bypass the public switched telephone network and connect directly to the communication center.

Universal emergency number 9-1-1 service, where adopted, provides a universal, easily remembered telephone number for use by the public to summon emergency services. Enhanced 9-1-1 service provides both the calling number and the location of the related telephone instrument directly to the dispatcher. This indication is presented visually on a display screen at the call taker's workstation and can be automatically recorded if the communication center includes computer-aided dispatch (CAD) or computerized logging support systems.

With the relatively new nature of VoIP telephones, 9-1-1 access can be sporadic or nonexistent in some cases. Some VoIP providers are actually answering 9-1-1 type calls in private call centers not staffed by trained 9-1-1 professionals. Any automatic number or automatic location information for VoIP telephones should be considered suspect and possibly not correct. The good news is that many of the VoIP providers realize the critical nature of 9-1-1 and are working with 9-1-1 professionals to resolve these issues. To further complicate matters in many cases, if power goes out, VoIP telephones will have no 9-1-1 access of any kind. The Federal Communications Commission (FCC) has asked all VoIP providers to provide 9-1-1 access.

The increasing use of personal cellular telephones is both a blessing and a challenge to emergency response agencies. On the positive side, many lives have been saved by the ability of a victim or a bystander to dial 9-1-1 from nearly any location and swiftly summon help. However, high-visibility incidents, such as vehicle accidents on a major highway, can generate dozens or hundreds of calls for the same incident, overwhelming call takers and even the 9-1-1 system itself, thereby delaying receipt of calls for other emergencies. Also, use of a cellular phone negates the automatic location information features of the enhanced 9-1-1 system. If the caller is unable to accurately identify his or her location, the telecommunicator cannot determine where to send help. Over the last several years many wireless providers have installed technology to provide the callers cell site location and the latitude and longitude (x, y) coordinates of an actual cellular telephone. Many of the communication centers across the country have installed the technology to receive this information, but some have not. When taking incoming calls, it is necessary to be able to accept this technology and convert the coordinates into a street address. In urban areas, there may be hundreds of buildings and thousands of people within range of that cell site. There are still some issues with the technology, but its accuracy is improving daily. Actually, finding the victim may be much more difficult than if he or she were calling from a conventional, wired telephone.

Where 9-1-1 service is provided, telephone directory listings for emergency response agencies should indicate that 9-1-1 is the number to call for emergencies. Where 9-1-1 service is not provided, a specific telephone number should be assigned for emergency calls and should be publicized as such. Separate business numbers should be assigned for nonemergency use. Emergency telephone numbers should appear on the inside front cover or page facing the front cover of the telephone directory. They should also appear in the body of the directory under the name of the jurisdiction, under the headings "Police," "Fire," and "Ambulance."

Although there are some disadvantages to total dependency on a utility owned, operated, and maintained communications network, specifically with regard to emergency reporting during natural disasters, telephones are often the only means of communication available. Where present, outdoor pay phones increase the availability of telephones for emergency reporting. In general, the public telephone system, widely used for reporting fires and other emergencies, provides a very viable function.

Public Alarm Reporting Systems

From the perspective of the operator receiving an alarm, use of a public alarm reporting station (alarm box) eliminates the difficulty of determining the location from which the alarm is being transmitted. When actuated, an alarm box transmits a distinct code to the communication center, which enables the operator to pinpoint the exact location of the box.

Removal of public alarm reporting systems began to take place in many major metropolitan centers in the mid-1970s. This trend has since spread to smaller communities. System maintenance costs, vandalism, malicious false alarms, and the nearly universal availability of telephones for alarm reporting all contributed to the elimination of public alarm reporting systems in many communities.

Although not an alarm system, the expanding implementation of universal emergency number 9-1-1 service has further reduced the need for public alarm reporting systems. This is especially true where enhanced 9-1-1 service provides the alarm operator with the exact location of the caller.

Recently, however, some jurisdictions have shown an increased interest in the use of public emergency reporting systems. In poverty-stricken areas, many households may not have working telephones, and vandalism and other criminal activity have caused the removal of many public pay phones. Also, public emergency reporting systems have been shown to provide reliable alarm reporting during natural disasters, such as hurricanes, earthquakes, tornadoes, and blizzards, when the public switched telephone network becomes jammed with traffic or is physically damaged.

A typical public alarm reporting system consists of a mix of publicly accessible manual alarm boxes ("street boxes") and "master boxes" that can be actuated both manually and automatically by a connection from a protected premises alarm system. "Auxiliary boxes" that are activated by the protected premises alarm system but lack the ability for manual activation by the public are also sometimes used. In many cases, the operating jurisdictions reduce their legal liability by accepting auxiliarized connections from government buildings only and referring all others to private supervising station alarm companies. Requirements for installation, maintenance, and use of public fire alarm reporting systems are contained in Chapter 6 of *NFPA 72®, National Fire Alarm Code®*.

A public fire alarm reporting system may be used for the transmission of other emergency signals or calls, provided such transmission does not interfere with the proper handling of fire alarms. For example, systems employing voice communications between the street alarm box and communication center can be used to transmit alarms of nonfire emergency nature. Fire alarm boxes in a radio-type system can be provided with push buttons for calling the police department, the emergency medical service, or other emergency services, and signals can be transmitted directly to the service called. With parallel-type telephone systems (each box served by a separate circuit), the telecommunicator can cross connect to the proper emergency service, such as the police department, or systems can be arranged so authorized callers, such as law enforcement personnel, can be connected directly to their own agencies. For additional information on public fire alarm reporting systems, refer to Section 14, Chapter 1, "Fire Alarm Systems."

Another form of the public emergency reporting system is the motorist-aid call box system, installed on some limited-access highways. These systems typically take one of two forms. First, coded radio transmitters may be mounted on pedestals, similar to (or incorporated with) radio fire alarm transmitters, typically with multiple, publicly actuated messages such as requests for fire, police, emergency medical services, and motorist aid (towing) services. These may be battery powered, with solar panels providing battery charging during daylight hours, or user powered. Second, cellular-type telephones (in weatherproof enclosures) may be mounted on pedestals, which are arranged to dial only a preprogrammed telephone number when the handset is lifted or a button is pressed. These are typically battery powered with solar panels providing battery charging during daylight hours. In either case, when actuated, the call box sends a distinct identity code to the receiver so that the location of the actuated box can be readily determined.

Intelligent Transportation Systems

With increasing density in population centers and increased prosperity, vehicular traffic is increasing. This increase funneled into a fixed highway network in turn results in more incidents requiring emergency response. Increasingly, jurisdictions are using technology, including wayside and in-pavement sensors and video cameras, to enable them to monitor traffic on hundreds of miles of highways from a central control center. When an incident occurs, the operators at the central control center can take actions, such as notifying emergency response agencies, redirecting traffic using remote control of traffic signals and/or electronic message boards, and making public announcements via commercial radio and television stations. Mass transit systems and railroads have similar centralized control centers. How these control centers interface and exchange information with traditional emergency communication centers for police, fire, and EMS agencies is not currently addressed in detail in NFPA 1221. The standard may, however, be used voluntarily as a guide for construction and operation of such centers.

Vehicle manufacturers are equipping some of their models with emergency communication devices (based on land-based cellular telephone and/or earth-orbiting satellite systems), which enable the driver to initiate a distress call in an emergency. These messages are answered by telecommunicators at private communication centers, which may be hundreds or thousands of miles away from the incident site. The technology also exists to automatically send a distress message whenever a vehicle is involved in a crash. This message could include information such as the attitude of the vehicle (upright or otherwise), the number of occupants, the negative acceleration forces experienced, whether seat belts were in use, and whether the air bags deployed. These systems are in their commercial infancy, but their use can be expected to grow significantly. They are not currently addressed by an NFPA standard.

Public Alerting Systems

Public alerting systems can be used for the mass alerting of the public to both natural and man-made events (e.g., tornadoes, hurricanes, floods, hazardous materials release) that can be expected to result in the loss of life, health, or property. Public alerting systems utilizing outdoor audible devices such as sirens have been established on a limited basis, usually for specific target hazards (such as nuclear power plants and chemical plants), and their use is likely to grow. A logical control point for such a system is the jurisdiction's emergency communication center. Technology also exists to permit the deployment of personal/in-home alerting devices in conjunction with such systems. Public alerting systems, as such, are not addressed by an NFPA standard as of this writing; however, their inclusion in the 2007 edition of NFPA 1221 has been proposed.

Two-Way Radio Communications Systems

A commonly overlooked alarm/emergency notification source is the two-way radio networks of public safety agencies. Notification of incidents in watershed areas is typically reported by mobile patrols. Similarly, requests for supplemental dispatches to multiple-alarm fires usually originate from units in the field.

Communications between agencies in adjacent jurisdictions, as well as between agencies of a single jurisdiction, may often be expedited by using two-way radios.

PROCESSING COMMUNICATIONS WITHIN THE COMMUNICATION CENTER

Regardless of the method by which an alarm is received, the location of the emergency is the minimum information required to respond to an emergency. The nature of the incident being reported is also obviously essential. However, bear in mind that thousands of responses to nonvoice notifications are made each year.

Data Collection Systems

To efficiently operate a communication center, reliable data must be available. To be useful, these data must be both accurate and readily available. The data may take a wide variety of forms, from card indexes to sophisticated computer files, and may include such categories as the status of vehicles, the availability of resources, geographic information, and personnel information. The following categories outline the various types and uses of data that can be collected and maintained by a communication center.

Incident-Related Data. It is important (and often a legal requirement) to keep accurate records of emergency incidents to which emergency response agencies respond. The types of data worth collecting include the following:

- Time of alarm
- Time of telecommunicator's initial response to alarm
- Time of dispatch
- Address
- Identifications and times of responding units
- Arrival times at the scene
- Departure times from the scene
- Radio traffic voice recordings
- Telephone voice recordings
- Times of significant events at the scene

Operational-Related Data. These data consist of information that must be rapidly available at all times to maintain efficient operation of the communication center. The data include the following:

- Geographic data
- Equipment data
- Response order data
- Occupancy/hazard information
- Additional resource data

Reports. Many types of reports are necessary for overall fire department management. Some of these reports will be required at regular intervals, whereas others will be required on demand to fill a specific departmental information need. A list of probable reports includes the following:

- Response time reports
- Emergency activity reports
- Occupancy activity reports
- Specific incident reports
- Reports for outside agencies
- Fire loss/injury reports
- Equipment-related reports

These reports can be used to project future needs of the agencies, such as location of new stations, hiring of additional personnel, and relocation of existing equipment.

Receipt of Alarms

Most alarms are received by telephone over the public switched telephone network. Automatic recording devices should be interconnected to all types of voice-reporting circuits, including radio systems.

Correct telephone numbers are the only means of positively identifying the location of an informant. Enhanced 9-1-1 service is designed to provide the call taker with an immediate reference to the number of the telephone in use and its specific location. The data are usually displayed on a CRT screen. The data input is formulated for electronic data processing (EDP) usage and can be fed concurrently to a departmental CAD system.

All public emergency reporting systems (e.g., municipal fire alarm systems) provide an individual code for each box installed, and the proper code is transmitted when the box is activated. All incoming coded signals are permanently recorded on printers integral to the specific systems and, in some cases, are also displayed on direct readout (LED, CRT, etc.) devices.

The translation of the numerically coded data into a usable address is performed with the aid of a running-card file or CAD system, which is necessary for processing of alarms.

Voice Recording and Reproducing Systems

The voice recording and reproducing system should consist of a multichannel recording device that provides a permanent, time-referable, unalterable, and court-admissible recording of all emergency-related telephonic/radio communications within the communication center.

The communication center supervisor(s) and at least one of the operators on duty should be totally familiar with the operation and maintenance of the multichannel recording device. Familiarizing other personnel is advisable, but responsibility should lie with no more than two individuals per watch or shift.

A multichannel recording system can provide the following:

- Verification of emergency messages
- A log of all emergency communications within the communication center
- Protection against false or exaggerated complaints
- Substantiation or negation of claims against the agency
- Added protection to the civilian population
- A training tool for telecommunicators
- Validation of response times

The importance of these various benefits will differ from agency to agency.

Running-Card Files

A running-card file contains a dispatch plan for every area of the jurisdiction served. The number of running cards in a given file depends on the size of the jurisdiction and the manner in which it has been indexed for responses. The most common method of indexing is to assign numeric designations to all intersections or to grids superimposed on a map of the jurisdiction. There is a specific running card to each intersection or grid. Public emergency reporting stations (alarm boxes) are normally assigned an identity code corresponding to the intersection or grid closest to their physical location.

When an alarm is received, the telecommunicator utilizes the addresses and/or intersection data obtained from the informant to find the correct running card, which is referenced to determine the appropriate units to be dispatched.

Status-Keeping Systems

The ability to maintain an accurate record of the current status of all emergency units in the system is essential to a successful dispatch system and will aid in (1) minimizing response times, (2) ensuring appropriate response, and (3) collecting nonemergency unit activity information.

Status-keeping systems may involve the tracking of various pieces of information, such as the following:

- Availability of the unit for emergency response
- Service capabilities of the unit (e.g., paramedic service, extrication equipment, all-terrain capability)
- Location of the unit
- Means of contacting the unit (e.g., radio, phone)
- Miscellaneous items based on the particular agency's operating philosophy

The mechanism of a status-keeping system will vary, depending on the number of units on which status must be kept and the actual dispatch process utilized by a communication center. A small agency might utilize a manual system with a small manual status display board; a large agency may require a computer.

Dispatch Circuits and Equipment

A dispatch circuit is the means by which an alarm operator notifies units to respond to an alarm. In general, two separate dispatch circuits must be provided, but only one is required when fewer than 730 alarms per year are received.

The primary dispatch circuit should consist of one or a combination of the following:

- Dedicated wired circuit monitored for integrity
- Voice radio channel with duplicate base station transmitters, repeaters, microphones, encoders, control circuitry, and antennas (system must alert telecommunicator in the event of failure of signal transmission)
- Microwave carrier channel monitored for integrity
- Polling or self-interrogating digital data radio channel (if primary transmitter fails on operation, switchover to the second transmitter should be automatic, accompanied by alerting of the telecommunicator)
- Approved, dedicated telephone circuit that is monitored for integrity
- Fiber-optic connection that is monitored for integrity.

When they detect a circuit fault, systems for monitoring circuit integrity should provide both visual and audible notification to the telecommunicator.

The secondary dispatch circuit need not be monitored for integrity and should consist of one of the following:

- Dedicated wired circuit
- Voice radio channel (duplicate base station transmitters, antennas, etc. are not required for the secondary dispatch circuit)
- Approved dedicated telephone circuit or fiber-optic connection

A telephone connection through a public switched telephone network via regular dial-up mode or nondedicated telephone lines is not considered acceptable as an approved circuit. Where a telephone circuit is used as the primary dispatch circuit, a telephone circuit should *not* also be used as the secondary circuit. When radio channels are used for both the primary and secondary circuits, each circuit should consist of a separate radio system operating on a separate frequency with separate receivers at each emergency response facility.

Radio circuits can be used for voice and/or data transmission and are commonly used for dispatching. They have the advantage of transmitting alarms simultaneously to all units, regardless of whether they are in quarters or out in the field. Also, they are not dependent on wired circuits, unless the transmitter is connected by wired circuit to the communication center.

Wired circuits can be used for data and/or voice transmission. They are limited to transmission to fixed locations. Units in the field must still be contacted by radio.

A telegraph circuit is one example of a wired circuit. Once more commonly used, telegraph circuits are still in use in some jurisdictions. Telegraph systems transmit coded signals to emergency response facilities, where they are received on a variety of instruments, including gongs and punch or printing registers that register the coded signal with holes or marks on a paper tape. The location of the alarm is then decoded manually or electronically in a manner similar to that previously discussed. Other uses of wired circuits include voice, teletype, and computer data transmission.

Computer-Aided Dispatch (CAD)

Computer-aided dispatch (CAD) systems have become increasingly commonplace. NFPA 1221 categorizes CAD systems as Class 1, 2, or 3. The Class 1 system is the most sophisticated, utilizing computers to automatically track the status of all units and to select and recommend the appropriate available units for dispatch. On approval of the dispatch telecommunicator, signals and data are then transmitted by the CAD system to the appropriate emergency response facilities, personnel, or units. A Class 1 CAD system requires complete redundancy and, in the event of a computer failure, must automatically switch over to an online backup computer.

A Class 2 CAD system uses computers to support dispatching operations and transmit and receive data transmissions to and from emergency response facilities, personnel, or units. Redundancy is required; however, manual switchover to the backup computer is permitted.

A Class 3 CAD system uses desktop personal computer (PC) technology to support the dispatching telecommunicator. Typically, data (such as changes in unit status) are manually entered through keyboard operation by the telecommunicator. Class 3 CAD systems may be used to keep track of unit status and to retrieve information regarding appropriate units to dispatch, occupancy hazards, pre-incident plans, and the like. Computer redundancy is not required by NFPA 1221 for Class 3 CAD systems.

Class 3 CAD systems typically utilize off-the-shelf hardware and software. Care must be used to select hardware that fully supports the software. Class 1 and 2 systems are more complex and are typically professionally designed or configured for a specific jurisdiction based on the user's requirements.

In all classes of CAD systems, a manual backup dispatching method must be maintained and available for use in the event of failure of the CAD system. Telecommunicators should periodically practice using the manual backup method so that they are familiar with its use. There should also be a hard-copy file of the information stored in the CAD system readily available on the premises to support manual dispatch should the CAD system fail.

CAD systems should be capable of exchanging data with the 9-1-1 system, other CAD systems, central stations (refer to Section 14 of this handbook), and intelligent transportation systems. CAD system computers should not be used for administrative applications; they should be kept free of time-consuming processes to allow rapid retrieval of dispatch information. It should be understood that CAD is a *method* of dispatching, not a dispatch *circuit.* Therefore, the presence or absence of a CAD system does not negate the requirement for two dispatch circuits.

Other Alerting Facilities

Radio alerting receivers in volunteer residences or places of business and radio pagers (i.e., portable receivers carried on the person) are frequently used for dispatching volunteer and off-duty personnel. Many agencies today also use some form of digital paging for administrative notifications and as a secondary means of notification in addition to voice systems. Many volunteer emergency response agencies have traditionally used outside sirens, air horns, whistles, or bells to alert volunteers when an alarm has been received. Although such devices remain in use in many areas, they do not comply with the requirements of NFPA 1221 as a method of dispatching and are considered supplemental to the required method(s).

Supervision and Testing Facilities

The communication center is where trouble signals from public emergency reporting systems are received and testing facilities are generally provided. In a leased telephone system, some test facilities are located in telephone buildings. In the event of trouble, both an audible and a visual signal should be provided. An audible signal may be silenced, but it should be designed to operate again in the event of trouble in any of the other circuits connected to the same supervisory device.

SUMMARY

Effective and reliable emergency communication systems play an essential part in the delivery of emergency services. In most cases, at least two independent communication paths or circuits should be provided for essential functions. These should be diversely arranged so that an event that damages one circuit is not likely to damage the other. Wire circuits (both metallic and fiber-optic) that are essential to the operation of a communication system should be monitored for integrity. Essential systems must be able to operate during power failures; therefore, backup power sources of adequate duration should be provided both at communication centers and at remote sites.

The communication center is the operational nerve center of the emergency service delivery system. It must be designed to prevent disruption of operations by fire, natural disaster, and criminal activity. An alternate communication center should be provided that, when fully staffed, is capable of performing the essential functions of the primary center. When a public safety answering point (the place where calls for help are first received) is not located within the communication center, it should meet the requirements for a communication center.

Whether serving one political jurisdiction or several, one response agency or many, the communication center needs to be adequately staffed around the clock to process emergency calls. Call takers and dispatchers, collectively called *telecommunicators,* provide human interface between a person calling for help and the emergency service delivery system. They need to be properly trained and familiar with the geographic area and agencies they serve. They need the ability to remain alert during periods of low call activity and calm during periods of high stress.

Two-way radio is an essential part of emergency services communication. Radio systems must be carefully designed to provide complete coverage of the service area. A sufficient number of frequencies should be provided to handle anticipated peak radio traffic. Separate tactical frequencies should be provided for uninterrupted on-scene communication. Where radio is the primary means of dispatching, duplicate radio base station transmitters should be provided. When used as a means of emergency dispatching, wireless paging systems should be under the direct control of the authority having jurisdiction.

Rapid technological and social changes, including proliferation of cellular telephones, increased emergency call volumes, increased demand for separate channels in a finite radio frequency spectrum, and expansion of intelligent transportation systems will continue to challenge the managers of emergency communication systems for many years to come.

BIBLIOGRAPHY

NFPA Codes, Standards, and Recommended Practices

Reference to the following NFPA codes, standards, and recommended practices will provide further information on public emergency services alarm, dispatch, and communications systems discussed in this chapter. (See the latest version of The NFPA Catalog *for availability of current editions of the following documents.)*

NFPA 37, *Standard for the Installation and Use of Stationary Combustion Engines and Gas Turbines*

NFPA 70, *National Electrical Code®*

NFPA 72®, National Fire Alarm Code®

NFPA 110, *Standard for Emergency and Standby Power Systems*

NFPA 1061, *Standard for Professional Qualifications for Public Safety Telecommunicator*
NFPA 1221, *Standard for the Installation, Maintenance, and Use of Emergency Services Communications Systems*

References

Cahill, B., "How Communications Have Changed over the Years," *Fire,* Vol. 90, 1998, p. 49.
Gregerson, J., "9-1-1 Center Responds to Unique Demands," *Building Design and Construction,* Vol. 37, No. 3, 1996, p. 56.
Letts, J., "Staying in Control," *Fire Prevention,* No. 332, 2000, pp. 34–36.
Moore, W. D., "Emergency Alarm Communications Systems," *NFPA Journal,* Vol. 95, No. 3, 2001, p. 50.
Riddet, A., "Replacement Communications Systems: Does This Need to Be a Problem?" *Fire Engineers Journal,* Vol. 58, No. 194, 1998, pp. 20–24.
Tucker, W. R., "Disasters and Emergencies: Managing the Response," *Fire Engineers Journal,* Vol. 60, No. 206, 2000, pp. 33–35.

9-1-1 Trade Organizations

Association of Public Safety Communication Officials (APCO), http://www.apco911.org.
Commission on Accreditation for Law Enforcement Agencies (CALEA), http://www.calea.org.
National Emergency Number Association (NENA), http://www.nena.org.

Chapter 16

Fire Department Apparatus and Equipment

Robert Tutterow

Fire apparatus and the equipment they carry are essential to fire departments for providing fire suppression and emergency services. Without the proper tools and the knowledge of how to use those tools correctly, a fire department cannot do its job effectively. This chapter contains information on the standards used and procurement policies that should be followed in specifying and acquiring apparatus and equipment. In addition, there are many other items described that fire departments should consider in the design of their apparatus.

For related topics, see Section 12, Chapter 9, "Fire and Emergency Services Protective Clothing and Protective Equipment"; Section 15, Chapter 7, "Fire Pump Controllers and Power Supply Arrangements for Motor-Driven Fire Pumps"; and Section 16, Chapter 10, "Standpipe and Hose Systems."

Chapter Contents

Key Terms

acceptance test, aerial ladder, aircraft rescue and fire-fighting vehicle, elevating platform, fire apparatus, fireboat, fire fighter safety, fire-fighting foam, fire hose, ground ladder, mobile water supply apparatus, nozzle (solid-stream), nozzle (spray), pumper, quad, quint, rescue vehicle, service test, squad vehicle, utility vehicle

APPARATUS

The basic fire apparatus in North America is a diesel or gasoline engine-driven vehicle that carries an extensive assortment of tools and equipment for fighting fires. Such equipment may include a pump, hose, water tank, aerial ladder or elevated platform, ground ladders, and various portable tools and appliances. The amount and capacities of the various fire-fighting components carried vary in accordance with the intended service of the particular vehicle.

For pumping operations and fire attack, the size of the pump and the amount of water, hose, and equipment carried will vary with the type of service the fire department provides and the nature of the community it protects, which can be predominantly urban, suburban, rural, or a combination of any of the three. The fire apparatus standards set 250 gpm (950 L/min) as the smallest fire pump, but pumps of 750, 1000, 1250, 1500, and 2000 gpm (2850, 3785, 4732, 5678, and 7570 L/min) capacities are popular for general municipal service. NFPA has promulgated two standards for the design of fire apparatus. They are NFPA 1901, *Standard for Automotive Fire Apparatus,* and NFPA 1906, *Standard for Wildland Fire Apparatus.* It is important to note that the Insurance Services Office (ISO) requires that pumpers meet the general criteria of NFPA 1901, that is, 750 gpm (2850 L/min).

Fire departments can supplement units equipped primarily for pumping and fire attack with other vehicles that provide a large variety of tools and equipment for support functions. These tools include ground ladders, forcible-entry tools, generators, lights, and rescue equipment. Such units are variously termed *rescue, squad,* or *utility vehicles.*

Equipment for Rescue Work

About one-third of the work at an average fire involves the use of tools and equipment in duties classed as rescue or ladder-company work. Apparatus suitably equipped for such service should be

Robert Tutterow is the health and safety officer of the Charlotte Fire Department. He has held this position for over 20 years. He is a member of the NFPA Technical Committee on Fire Department Apparatus and chairs its Safety Task Group. Prior to joining the Charlotte Fire Department, he had over 10 years' experience as a volunteer fire fighter. He was also co-founder and is a board member of F.I.E.R.O. (Fire Industry Equipment Research Organization).

available at all structural fires and at major emergencies, such as significant highway accidents. Although pumping engines may carry considerable equipment, the larger aerial ladder and elevating-platform apparatus commonly transport additional equipment for forcible entry, cutting, and extrication. This type of apparatus provides effective elevated stream service and vehicle-supported, power-operated equipment for access to areas above the normal reach of ground ladders. Some fire departments go a step further and use aerial ladder *tenders* to carry support equipment. The tender does not have an aerial device, nor does it carry water or fire hose. Departmental procedures determine which apparatus respond to an incident.

In rural districts and in the outlying districts of cities where hydrant distribution is not complete, supplemental water-transport apparatus, defined as *mobile water-supply apparatus,* is common. Such apparatus has large water tanks with quick-fill and -dump connections. It may have a permanently installed pump. In most of the United States, they are referred to as "tankers."

A wide combination of fire-fighting equipment is often provided on a single fire apparatus. Besides combinations of water pump, hose, and water tank, commonly termed a *triple combination,* it is not uncommon to provide a booster pump and small-stream equipment on aerial ladder or elevating-platform apparatus or a water tower on a pumping engine. When fire apparatus is equipped with long ground ladders and other usual ladder-company equipment, in addition to the usual pumping engine equipment, the apparatus is referred to as a *quadruple combination,* or *quad.* If a power-operated aerial ladder or elevating platform is added, such apparatus is termed a *quint.*

The trend is toward apparatus designed to improve functional performance. Initial fire-attack capability for pumpers may include not only a variety of preconnected hose lines but also preconnected master stream capability or elevated-stream equipment. Pumpers are built with considerable compartment space for emergency medical service and rescue equipment. Combination fire-fighting rescue/pumpers can now be found in many fire departments.

NFPA 1901 deals with the design, performance, functions, and components of most fire apparatus. The current standard is broken down into chapters that address the requirements for different types of fire apparatus as well as requirements for many of the components installed on those apparatus.

Pumpers. Vehicles designed for sustained pumping operations during structural fire fighting and for supporting associated fire department operations are known as pumpers (Figure 12.16.1). NFPA 1901 requires a pump of at least 750 gpm (2850 L/min) capacity, a water tank of at least 300 gal (1135 L), storage for both supply hose and preconnected attack hose lines, and miscellaneous equipment.

Mini-Pumpers. Initial attack fire apparatus are defined as vehicles designed for making the initial fire suppression attack on structural, vehicular, or vegetation fires and for supporting associated fire department operations. Initial attack apparatus require a pump of at least 250 gpm (950 L/min) capacity, a water tank of at least 200 gal (757 L), and lesser requirements for hose and equipment than a pumper. Another term for initial attack apparatus is *mini-pumper.* This type of vehicle became popular in the early eighties, and then its popularity diminished. Today, mini-pumpers are slowly reemerging in municipal fire departments for use at parking garage fires. The mini-pumper is also now being used by a few departments as a first responder vehicle for emergency medical service.

FIGURE 12.16.1 Modern Pumper (Courtesy of Plano, Texas, Fire Department)

Mobile Water Supply Apparatus. Vehicles designed to transport water to the scene of an emergency where the water is applied by other apparatus or pumping equipment are defined as mobile water supply apparatus. NFPA 1901 requires these vehicles to have a water tank of at least 1000 gal (3785 L) with quick-fill and -dump capability, as well as limited hose and equipment to support the pickup and dumping of the water. Mobile water supply apparatus have a higher rate of rollovers per mile driven than any other type of apparatus. As a result, they also have a higher rate of fire fighter line-of-duty deaths from apparatus accidents than any other type of apparatus. In their design specifications, fire departments should pay particular attention to the center of gravity, braking capabilities, and handling characteristics of these types of vehicles.

Tank baffling is very important to the stability of mobile water supply apparatus. NFPA establishes tank baffling requirements. Fire departments should avoid used trucks with tanks that were used for non–fire service applications such as fuel or milk delivery. Typically, these trucks have little or no baffling.

Elevating-Platform Apparatus. Aerial ladder or elevating-platform fire apparatus are defined as vehicles designed to provide elevated fire-fighting and rescue capability. NFPA 1901 requires that these vehicles have a power-operated, self-supporting aerial device capable of attaining an elevation of at least 50 ft (15.3 m). Aerial ladders are required to support at least 250 lb (113.4 kg) at the tip in any position in which they can be placed. The elevated platform must be able to support at least

750 lb (340 kg) in any position in which it can be placed without water in the water delivery system. NFPA 1901 provides minimum requirements if a pump is installed. From 1997 to 1999, municipal fire departments reported 6300 aerial or ladder apparatus in use.[1]

Quints. Apparatus with a pump, water tank, hose storage area, an aerial or elevating platform with a waterway, ground ladders, and complement of equipment are known as quints. Quints have become popular in many fire departments. However, operating efficiency and capability tend to decrease if too many functions are to be performed by one piece of apparatus. The ability to position a quint on the fire ground for multiple purposes can occasionally be cumbersome. Fire departments must understand the staffing requirements of a multifunctional piece of apparatus. Moreover, if one feature of the apparatus requires repair, the entire apparatus must be taken out of service.

Special Service Vehicles. Apparatus that is multipurpose and that primarily provides support services at emergency scenes is known as a special service vehicle. These services could be rescue, command, hazardous material containment, air supply, electrical generation and floodlighting, or transportation of support equipment and personnel. The systems and components installed on these vehicles will vary with the support they are designed to provide and can range from no fixed systems to elaborate power generation or breathing-air compressor systems.

Mobile Foam Apparatus. Mobile foam fire apparatus is similar to a pumper except it may not carry any water but must have at least a 500 gal (1900 L) foam concentrate tank and foam proportioning capability. This apparatus is generally used in industrial environments for the control and extinguishment of flammable and combustible liquid fires in storage tanks and other flammable liquid spills. For information on foam systems used on other vehicles, see the section on foam and foam proportioning equipment later in this chapter.

Wildland Fire Fighting Apparatus. NFPA 1906 deals with the design, performance, functions, and components of wildland fire-fighting vehicles, defined as vehicles equipped with a pump, water tank, limited hose, and equipment. The vehicle must be capable of supporting pump-and-roll operations. Generally, these are smaller vehicles, frequently equipped with all-wheel drive; a small water tank; forestry hose; a small-volume, high-pressure pump; a number of portable water extinguishers; and various hand tools for fighting wildland fires. Larger vehicles may have up to a 500 gpm (1900 L/min) front-mounted or power takeoff (PTO) pump and a 500 gal (1900 L) or larger water tank to support wildland fire fighting as well as to provide exposure protection when structures or other properties are threatened.

Performance Requirements

NFPA 1906 includes requirements for auxiliary systems that are often installed on wildland fire apparatus. These may include a foam system or compressed air foam system, winches, and vehicle protection systems.

Both NFPA 1901 and NFPA 1906 define performance requirements for the apparatus and define tests to measure this performance. In the annex of each document, there are explanations of the requirements and details, as well as work sheets, to assist in the purchase of the apparatus. A separate annex in the standards provides a form that will guide purchasers through the process of determining and stating their needs in a fire apparatus, a valuable step in the specification process. Also, there is a separate annex outlining the criteria for retiring apparatus.

Persons buying the apparatus must specify the options that make it suitable for local needs. For example, requirements for fighting large brush fires in southern California are quite different from those for fighting fires in below-zero weather in northern Minnesota. Fire departments in the northern regions are well advised to specify snow and ice chain systems for their apparatus. Systems are available that engage the chains with the activation of a switch. NFPA 1901 and NFPA 1906 provide for standardization of many items for which uniform performance, measurable by tests, is desirable, but they allow the necessary flexibility to meet local needs that could not be supplied by one assembly-line production. Such differences include rated pump capacity, water-tank capacity, length of aerial ladders, height of elevating platforms, and many other important design features.

Besides the functional characteristics of a piece of fire apparatus, considerable thought should be given to personnel safety and operations. The design of the vehicle's driving compartment and riding spaces and the location of various components should be studied carefully. Only fully enclosed driving and crew compartments with sufficient seating for all fire fighters who are expected to ride on the apparatus should be specified. Fire fighters should never be allowed to ride standing up or in exposed positions on the rear or sides of the apparatus. The use of seat belts is mandatory in all cases. All of the equipment carried in the crew compartment area should be restrained in mechanical holding devices or placed in compartments. This minimizes the possibility of injury to fire fighters by flying objects in the event of a sudden stop or an accident.

The pump operator's panel may be positioned to the side, to the rear, or in a top amidships position. The position of valve controls and other control equipment will affect the overall efficient and safe operation of the apparatus. The better the operator's view, the more effective he or she can be.

ROADABILITY

Engines, Braking Systems, Weight, and Stability

Engines. Engines may be either diesel or gasoline types, but there are few gasoline engines capable of supplying sufficient power for modern apparatus. Consequently, diesel engines comprise almost all engines in apparatus manufactured. Fire departments must understand that the diesel exhaust is a carcinogen and provisions must be made to remove diesel exhaust from fire stations. This can be accomplished in one of three ways:

1. Source capture (hose connected to the exhaust pipe)

2. Air handling/filtration unit installed in the apparatus bay
3. On-board system contained within the apparatus

The engine size and horsepower must be chosen to correspond with the conditions of service and apparatus design. Apparatus must have enough power to move it over the road network on which it is expected to operate. Road tests are conducted with apparatus fully loaded with hose, water, ground ladders, the applicable personnel weight, and an equipment allowance weight. From a standing start, the vehicle must attain a true speed of 35 mph (56 km/h) within 25 seconds. The vehicle must maintain a minimum top speed of 50 mph (80 kph) on level ground. The vehicle must be able to maintain a speed of at least 20 mph (32 kph) on any grade up to 6 percent. This demonstrates that the vehicle has the necessary power to operate safely and efficiently in traffic. Although these tests demonstrate the power needed to negotiate the grades found in most communities, any special requirements that the apparatus climb very steep grades should be specified, and the finished apparatus should be tested to those requirements.

Braking Systems. A braking performance test is required. The vehicle must come to a complete stop within 35 ft (10.7 m) after attaining a speed of 20 mph (32 km/h). This test is required in NFPA 1901 and NFPA 1906 and Title 49, Code of Federal Regulations, Part 571, Subpart B, "Federal Motor Vehicle Safety Standards." This test is required to be performed only one time, not repeatedly, which is not realistic for emergency vehicles. Many agencies require secondary braking systems to be installed on their apparatus to enhance braking performance. NFPA 1901 requires that secondary braking systems be installed on vehicles weighing over 36,000 lb (16,330 kg) and recommends a system if the vehicle weighs over 31,000 lb (14,062 kg). There are four types of secondary braking systems:

1. Hydraulic retarder
2. Exhaust brake
3. Engine brake
4. Drive line

Agencies should match their driving conditions to the type of secondary brake desired. Secondary braking systems provide an extra margin of safety as well as extend the life of the primary braking system.

The set or parking brake provided is required to hold the vehicle on grades up to 20 percent. This may not be adequate for every fire department, so the agency needs to specify its particular requirements. Some states require parking brakes to hold on any grade.

Weight. Carrying capacity is one of the most important but least understood features of a vehicle. The gross axle weight rating (GAWR) and gross vehicle weight rating (GVWR) of the apparatus must be adequate to carry the weight of the fully equipped and staffed vehicle. This includes 200 lb (76 kg) per person personnel weight, a full water tank, the specified hose load, ground ladders, and a miscellaneous equipment allowance.

Extra care should be taken when determining the miscellaneous equipment allowance. Too many fire departments seriously overload apparatus by adding more equipment than the vehicle was designed to carry. NFPA 1901 specifies minimum equipment allowances of 2000 lb (907 kg) for pumpers and mobile foam fire apparatus, up to 2000 lb (907 kg) for initial attack vehicles depending on their size, 1000 lb (454 kg) for mobile water supply apparatus, and 2500 lb (1136 kg) for aerial ladder fire apparatus, elevating-platform fire apparatus, and quints. The equipment allowance for special service units varies by chassis gross vehicle weight rating from 2000 lb (907 kg) for smaller units to 3000 lb (1360 kg) for the largest units. NFPA 1906 specifies the equipment allowance for wildland fire apparatus, which also varies by chassis gross vehicle weight rating from a low of 300 lb (136 kg) to a high of 2000 lb (907 kg). Probably one of the most important things a fire department can do in developing specification for a fire apparatus is to realistically evaluate the weight of the equipment that the apparatus will carry and be sure the chassis will not be overloaded when that equipment is added to the vehicle.

One of the critical factors is the size of the water tank. Water weighs about 8⅓ lb per U.S. gal (1 kg/L). A value of 10 lb (4.54 kg) per gallon (to include the weight of the tank) is often used when estimating the weight of a full water tank, making a full 500 gal (1893 L) tank 2½ tons (2.27 metric tons). Larger tanks mean heavier vehicles, which may have limited mobility on rural roads and bridges. The efficiency of mobile water supply apparatus when transporting water to a fire depends on the vehicle's over-the-road mobility. Any apparatus that weighs too much for local operating conditions severely limits the capabilities of the fire department.

GAWR is the value specified by the vehicle manufacturer as the loaded weight on a single-axle system, and gross combination weight rating (GCWR) is the value specified by the manufacturer as the loaded weight of a combination vehicle, such as a tractor-trailer unit. GVWR is the value specified by the manufacturer as the loaded weight of a single vehicle, and it is the sum of the weights of the chassis, body, cab, equipment, water, fuel, crew, and all other loads. A number of components affect the GVWR, such as the springs or suspension system, the rated axle capacity, the rated tire loading, and the weight distribution between the front and rear axles. All chassis are designed with a "rated GVWR" or maximum total weight that should not be exceeded, whether by the manufacturer when building the apparatus or by the fire department after the vehicle has been placed in service.

Stability. The improper distribution of weight between the front and rear wheels can make a vehicle difficult to control and may require tires of different sizes to carry the load. Overloading of the vehicle not only affects the handling characteristics but also will result in increased maintenance problems with transmissions, clutches, drive train, and brakes, as well as suspension systems and tires. Many states exempt fire apparatus from meeting weight limitations; however, it is never a good practice to overload the vehicle. In the event the vehicle is involved in an accident, the overloading issue may be used against the department in litigation. Considerable attention is now being given to technology that enables vehicle stability. Most of the technology is electronics based and tied to the braking system. Sensors warn the driver when the vehicle is in a potential rollover situation. Data from these systems can also be part of the information captured in a "black box." These systems are common in Europe and rapidly becoming available in the United States. Fire departments will be wise to learn about these systems and consider them in their design specifications.

Compliance with Government Standards

National governments promulgate motor vehicle safety standards that are applicable to all vehicles, including fire apparatus. In the United States, the Department of Transportation (DOT) enforces this legislation. It is unlawful to sell a vehicle that is not in compliance with the current federal standards. It is unlawful for manufacturers to build fire apparatus that do not conform to these standards. Because fire apparatus are complex and often require considerable lead time between the signing of a contract and delivery, the federal regulations provide that the standards in effect at the time the contract is signed must be those complied with, provided the apparatus is delivered within 2 years.

Additional requirements are placed on the apparatus and engine manufacturers in the United States by the Clean Air Act, which is enforced by the Environmental Protection Agency (EPA). Engines cannot be modified once approved by the EPA. These standards have caused some downgrading in engine performance, often resulting in the need to use larger engines than previously employed to obtain the same performance. Likewise, more frequent maintenance checks may be required due to mandated pollution-control devices.

Safety in Apparatus Design

Fire departments must consider safety as the primary concern when writing specifications and purchasing apparatus. Throughout history, fire fighters have been killed and seriously injured while driving, riding, and operating around fire apparatus (Figure 12.16.2). In a typical year, over one-quarter of all on-duty fire fighter deaths and thousands of on-duty fire fighter injuries have occurred during response or return.[2] In 2003, more fire fighters were killed responding or returning from incidents than killed at incident scenes.

FIGURE 12.16.2 Damaged Fire Apparatus (Courtesy of Charlotte, North Carolina, Fire Department)

The attention to apparatus safety was identified in the February 2004 National Fallen Firefighters Foundation's national summit on fire fighter safety. From this summit, 16 fire fighter life safety initiatives were identified. One of the initiatives was "Safety must be a primary consideration in the design of apparatus and equipment." In addition to apparatus design, there are two other areas of emphasis for safe apparatus that cannot be overlooked. These are driver training and apparatus maintenance. All three areas depend on each other. Failure to adhere to recognized safety standards jeopardizes the safety of fire fighters. Moreover, it puts the community at risk and creates a high risk of potential liability problems.

Fire departments must include an extensive apparatus driver/operator training program as part of their service delivery. Fire apparatus are big, heavy, complicated vehicles, and many drivers have never operated heavy vehicles prior to joining the fire department. It is imperative that no one operates a fire apparatus until he or she has been thoroughly trained. The fire department driver training program should be based on NFPA 1002, *Standard for Fire Apparatus Driver/Operator Professional Qualifications.*

Apparatus maintenance (discussed later in this chapter) has become more critical as apparatus have become more complicated. It is difficult to find qualified technicians to work on today's apparatus.

There are several areas of focus in apparatus design that impact fire fighter safety. These include audible and visible warning devices, steps and surfaces, mounting of equipment, cab ergonomics, and pump-panel layout.

Audible and Visible Warning Devices. The siren and air horn are the predominant audible warning devices for fire apparatus. These devices must be located as low and as forward of the cab as possible so the noise level will not cause hearing loss to fire fighters in the cab. NFPA 1901 states that the maximum noise level in cabs is 90 db while the vehicle is traveling at 45 mph (72 km/h). It must be understood that sirens are not as effective as they used to be, because any external sound is less audible to the occupants of today's road vehicles. Reasons include increased sound insulation in today's vehicles, use of high-volume sound systems, and use of cell phones. Visible warning devices, when specified to NFPA 1901 requirements, are the most effective warning devices.

Visible warning devices should be installed in a manner that portrays an outline of the vehicle. There are requirements for devices installed for the upper portion of the vehicle as well as the lower portion. Each portion must be divided into four warning zone quadrants (front, rear, and the two sides). The upper-portion devices are for warning traffic at a distance; the lower-portion devices are for warning traffic in close proximity to the vehicle. There should be two modes of operation for visible warning devices. One mode is for responding (calling for right-of-way) and the other mode is for blocking the right-of-way. The color of warning lights depends on local laws.

Amber, if permitted, has proven to be very effective at the rear of apparatus.

Fire departments should be careful not to use too many warning lights. Too many brilliant flashing lights can create serious risks, including blinding other motorists, attracting impaired motorists (whether through alcohol, drugs, or drowsiness) directly into the lights, and putting emphasis on the apparatus rather than personnel working at the incident. Purchasers must be aware of the electrical load requirements of audible and visible warning devices. In addition to electrical devices, all apparatus must have at least a 4 in. (100 mm) reflective stripe on at least 50 percent of the cab and body length and the rear and 25 percent on the front. The reflective striping adds an additional margin of safety to the warning lights and provides visibility to motorists in the event of warning light failure.

Steps and Surfaces. Fire departments must remember that many personnel operating on or around apparatus will be wearing personnel protective equipment (PPE), including self-contained breathing apparatus (SCBA), which is considerably more cumbersome than street clothes. In addition, they are often operating in a less than pristine environment, including wet, icy, oily, and nighttime conditions. It is important that all steps, standing surfaces, and walking surfaces be designed and constructed with fire fighter safety in mind. NFPA 1901 has many requirements addressing this issue. All steps must have at least a minimum surface area of 35 in.^{2} (22,580 mm^2) and be able to support a minimum static load of 500 lb (227 kg). The first step leading onto an apparatus cannot be over 24 in. (610 mm) in height, and each succeeding step cannot be over 18 in. (457 mm) in height. All exterior surfaces that are designated by the purchaser as a step, a walking surface, or a standing surface must be slip resistant. NFPA 1901 provides an option of two tests that can be used to determine the coefficient of friction. Handrails must be placed at the entrance of cabs or anywhere else steps are located. The handrails must be slip resistant and between 1 in. (25 mm) and 1⅝ in. (41 mm) in diameter. Ground illumination is required anywhere fire fighters will climb on an apparatus, including beneath the cab.

Mounting of Equipment. Purchasers should review their need to mount equipment in the cab of apparatus and avoid doing so if at all possible. Loose equipment or equipment that can become loose in the case of an accident or sudden deceleration can be lethal. NFPA 1901 requires that, with exception of SCBA, all equipment carried in the cab must be enclosed in a latched compartment capable of withstanding a longitudinal 9-g force and a 3-g force in any other direction. SCBA must be stored in a bracket with a positive mechanical means of holding the SCBA in the event of a 9-g force in any direction.

Cab Ergonomics. Fire departments should consider the ergonomics of the cab from several aspects. The cab should be free of sharp edges and the doors should be free of any handles or latches that can snag clothing. All foot and hand controls should be within convenient reach of the driver. Frequently used controls should be placed so the driver can reach them without diverting attention from the road. Mirrors should be designed and placed so that adjustment is easy from the driver's seat, either through direct contact or remote control. This is also true for de-icing and defogging. The windshield should be large enough so that the driver has excellent visibility to the areas in close proximity to the vehicle. Seats should have a minimum width of 18 in. (457 mm), and headroom should be a minimum of 37 in. (940 mm). More headroom is recommended for apparatus with suspension seats. It is not recommended that helmets be worn inside cabs as they are not crash helmets; wearing them can actually be a contributing factor to an injury. Most importantly, the driver of the fire apparatus should never move the apparatus unless all occupants are seated and belted.

Pump Panel Layout. Fire departments should specify the layout of their pump operator's panel rather than leaving it up to the discretion of the manufacturer. The layout should be as simple and easy to understand as possible. Controls and indicators should be grouped according to their function. All pressure or flow-indicating devices must be located within 6 in. (150 mm) of the control. Ideally, there should be no intakes or discharges at the operator's panel because serious injuries and some deaths have occurred to pump operators as a result of hose rupture near the apparatus. NFPA 1901 prohibits any discharge larger than 2½ in. (65 mm) on the pump operator's panel. Pump and engine controls must be no higher than 72 in. (1829 mm). All controls and gauges must be properly labeled and illuminated.

Roadway Scene Safety. Increasingly, more emergency responders are being struck by motorists while working roadway incidents. In addition to roadway incident standard operating procedures (SOPs), fire departments should design and equip their apparatus to maximize fire fighter safety for such incidents. Consideration should be given to the following:

- Advance warning devices for motorists (such as directional signals and other signage)
- Traffic cones
- Safety vests
- Reflective and fluorescent striping

Chevron pattern reflective striping on the rear of the apparatus is proven to be an effective way to minimize the chances of an apparatus being struck from the rear. Particular attention should be given to the emergency warning lights. Excessive lights can have a detrimental impact, especially during darkness.

Black Boxes. Advances in vehicle electronics have led to the emergence of event date recorders or "black boxes" for fire apparatus. These recorders can capture information such as date, time, hard braking, speed, g-forces, and seat belt usage. They can also be linked to video and audio capturing equipment. Black boxes are very useful in helping with accident investigation. Also, by their nature, they aid in accident prevention as drivers know their actions may be reviewed.

Electrical Power for Apparatus

Electrical power needs for fire apparatus far exceed those of other commercial trucks. Sufficient electrical capacity for the vehicle and its components is a major requirement for fire apparatus. Electricity is essential to start the apparatus reliably under all temperature and weather conditions. Emergency warning lights and sirens impose a heavy electrical demand with vehicle lighting and communication equipment as an added load. Electric rewind hose reels, pump controls, scene lighting, and electrically operated tools can all impose additional loads. Much of the equipment must perform when the apparatus is idling at a fire or other emergency, and the engine is not producing maximum output from the alternator. Electrical system performance tests are required for new apparatus by NFPA 1901.

Batteries, which are an integral part of the electrical system, must be a minimum of 1000 high-cycle, cold-cranking amps (CCA). However, the batteries should not be expected to carry the electrical load when the engine is idling; many of the electronic components on modern apparatus will not function properly if the voltage drops by 10 percent or more. It is also critical to provide a means for keeping the batteries charged while the apparatus is in the station. This can be done with an onboard battery conditioner or charger or with a polarized plug for connection to an external charger.

NFPA 1901 requires a load management system for the electrical components on the vehicle if the total connected electrical load exceeds the alternator output at idle. The load management system will shut off electrical loads if the alternator and batteries cannot keep up with the demand. The fire department should work with the manufacturer to determine which electrical components to shut down. These items should be ones that are less critical to the mission of the apparatus.

Documentation of a vehicle's electrical performance tests is required by NFPA 1901. A written electrical load analysis must include nameplate rating of the alternator, alternator rating at idle, minimum continuous load rating, total connected load, and individual intermittent load.

Fire departments should do considerable research to understand electrical systems before writing specifications and making a purchase. Special attention must be given to the maintenance of the electrical system after the apparatus is placed in service. A vehicle electrical system that needs frequent or major repairs is no asset and no bargain, whatever its purchase price and design capabilities may have been.

A department, when specifying apparatus, should require an electrical audit. The department or manufacturer could perform the audit. The audit determines the amperage required to power all electrical accessories so a determination can be made if the alternator supplied is large enough for the load. With more engine and transmission combinations becoming computer controlled, it is imperative that batteries be maintained properly.

Pumps for Fire Apparatus

A fire pump is defined as a pump of at least 250 gpm (950 L/min) at 150 psi (1035 kPa) net pump pressure. It must be capable of pumping 70 percent of its capacity at 200 psi (1380 kPa) net pump pressure and 50 percent of its capacity at 250 psi (1725 kPa) net pump pressure. The largest rated pump available is 3000 gpm (11,356 L/min). These large pumps are typically used in industrial settings such as refineries. Fire departments most commonly use pumps of 2000 gpm (7570 L/min) or less.

Certification. When new, fire pumps of 750 gpm (2850 L/min) or greater on fire apparatus are certified by tests witnessed by an independent third party. The certification test includes, among other things, a test at draft during which the pump must deliver its rated capacity for 2 hours at 150 psi (1035 kPa) net pump pressure, followed by two half-hour test periods during which 70 percent of rated capacity is delivered at 200 psi (1380 kPa) net pump pressure and 50 percent of rated capacity at 250 psi (1725 kPa) net pump pressure. The apparatus must also perform a 10-minute overload test, discharging rated pump capacity at 165 psi (1138 kPa) net pump pressure to demonstrate reserve engine power.

Pressure. The pump on initial attack fire apparatus is typically a pump of at least 250 gpm (950 L/min) but not more than 700 gpm (2650 L/min) at 150 psi (1035 kPa) net pump pressure. Like fire pumps, they must be capable of pumping 70 percent of their capacity at 200 psi (1380 kPa) net pump pressure, and 50 percent of their capacity is delivered at 250 psi (1725 kPa) net pump pressure. Pumps on initial attack fire apparatus may not be designed for long-duration pumping, although they must meet a 50-minute pump test and can be designed for longer operation.

The design requirements for fire pumps include the ability to develop 22 in. (55.88 cm) of mercury vacuum at 2000 ft (610 m) of elevation and the ability to deliver rated capacity while lifting water up to 10 ft (3.1 m) through 20 ft (6.1 m) of suction hose. Where a pump on a piece of apparatus is expected to perform at an altitude above 2000 ft (610 m), the purchaser must advise the apparatus manufacturer both of the altitude and whether a 10 ft (3.1 m) lift-suction capability is required, so that the proper engine and pump can be provided.

The pump and the attached piping and valves are designed for 500 psi (3448 kPa) hydrostatic pressure. Depending on the size of the pump, one or two large suction intakes and at least one auxiliary gated suction intake are required. This auxiliary intake is normally a 2½ in. (64 mm) intake and is provided so an additional water supply line can be taken into the pump without shutting down. It is also a means of connecting a supply line in mutual-aid operations if hose connections for the large intake are not compatible. As the large suction intake provides the least restriction, normal supply to the pump should be through that intake, whether directly or through a suction siamese.

Discharge Outlets. Discharge piping from the pump feeds a variety of outlets and, in some cases, may feed a master stream device directly. Fire pumps 750 gpm (2850 L/min) or larger are required to have two 2½ in. (64 mm) discharge outlets and enough additional outlets to allow the capacity of the pump to be discharged. If the apparatus is equipped with an aerial device with a prepiped waterway, the pump must be piped directly to the waterway.

To control the development of water hammer in the pump and hose lines, any 3 in. (76 mm) or larger valve should be designed to restrict changing the position of the flow-regulating element from full close to full open, or vice versa, in less than 3 seconds. The pump should be further protected by a permanently installed intake pressure-relief system that is 2½ in. (64 mm) or larger and discharges directly to the atmosphere. The surplus-water-discharge location should be away from the pump operator's position and may terminate in a male fitting so hose can be attached to carry any water away from the apparatus.

The pressure on the discharge side of the pump must also be controlled, either through an automatic relief valve or a pressure control device that controls the excessive discharge pressure. The device is required to limit the pressure rise on activation to a maximum of 30 psi (207 kPa) and be capable of operating over a range of 90- to 300-psi (620- to 2070-kPa) discharge gauge pressure.

Midship Mounting. For the past few decades, the midship-mounted pump has been the standard configuration. It is powered by the vehicle engine through a pump transmission that redirects power from the rear wheels to the pump itself. Power is transferred with the vehicle in a stationary position and only after the parking brake has been set. An interlock should be provided to ensure that the engine speed cannot be advanced until the parking brake is set, the transfer is complete, and the chassis transmission is either in neutral or in the correct gear for pumping. Otherwise, the apparatus may move when the engine speed is advanced. New automatic transmission designs allow the use of a power takeoff (PTO) to transmit power to a large pump. They should be limited to no more than 1250 gpm (4732 L/min), due to horsepower requirements through the PTO. The PTO feature has led to a steady rise (20% per year) in rear-mounted pumps in the U.S. market. (Over 99% of the European market uses rear-mounted pumps.) There are many benefits of a rear-mounted pump, including increased compartment space, a cleaner pump panel, a better pump operator position (270 degree visibility), weight reduction of between 400 lb (181 kg) and 1000 lb (454 kg), and decreased service time. If a fire department chooses a rear-mounted pump, it should also consider a reinforced rear bumper to protect the pump during minor collisions.

On smaller pumps, the power is often transferred to the pump through a PTO device. In some designs, the pump is mounted at the front of the chassis where it is driven through a clutch arrangement from the front of the engine.

Auxiliary Capacity. Some fire apparatus will have auxiliary pumping capability as either a separate pump for small-volume/high-pressure operation or as a third stage in the main pump to develop higher pressures. Typically, auxiliary pumps have a capacity of 100 gpm (379 L/min) or less and may be capable of providing discharge pressures up to 600 psi (4137 kPa) or more. If an auxiliary pump is provided and is interconnected with a fire pump, suitable valving and controls should be provided to preclude the introduction of higher pressures into piping and fire hoses not designed for the pressure. Auxiliary pumps are often used to supply pressurized hose reels of small-diameter hose that can be used in extinguishing rubbish fires, grass fires, and other small fires.

Transfer Pump. Another type of pump, designated as a transfer pump, is used to assist in filling or dumping water tanks on fire apparatus. These pumps have a minimum rated capacity of 250 gpm (946 L/min) at 50 psi (345 kPa) and are typically used with mobile water supply apparatus to draft water from a static source to fill a water tank or to move water from the tank to a folding tank or other tank arrangement on the fire ground.

Wildland Pumps. There is a variety of pump products used on wildland fire apparatus. NFPA 1906 defines four ratings for wildland pumps. Low-pressure pumps are rated at 100 psi (690 kPa), medium-pressure pumps are rated at 150 psi (1035 kPa), high-pressure pumps are rated at 300 psi (2070 kPa), and extra-high-pressure pumps are rated at 400 psi (2760 kPa). All of these pumps are available in a variety of discharge capacities. NFPA 1906 also requires that the pumps be capable of pump-and-roll operation (i.e., pumping while the apparatus is in motion). This is accomplished by either driving the pump through a PTO arrangement or using a separate engine to drive the pump. The use of skid-mounted, self-contained fire-fighting packages, complete with pump and engine, water tank, hose, and equipment, are popular in the wildland fire-fighting arena.

Hose-Carrying Capability

The amount of hose carried should be sufficient to support the function of the apparatus. Operations involving pumpers typically need the most hose. NFPA 1901 requires a minimum of 800 ft (244 m) of 2½ in. (65 mm) or larger hose and 400 ft (122 m) of 1½ in. (38 mm), 1¾ in. (44 mm), or 2 in. (51 mm) hose. However, most fire department pumpers carry a minimum of 1200 ft (366 m) of 2½ in. (65 mm) or larger hose and 400 ft (122 m) of 1½ in. (38 mm), 1¾ in. (44 mm), or 2 in. (51 mm) hose. Some fire departments carry 2000 ft (610 m) or more of 2½ in. (65 mm) or larger hose, and 800 to 1000 ft (244 to 305 m) of 1½ in. (38 mm), 1¾ in. (44 mm), or 2 in. (51 mm) hose on their pumpers to permit more versatile use of the apparatus.

Predominantly, fire departments use hose diameters at least 2½ in. (65 mm) in size for supplying water from a hydrant or in a relay operation. Through comparative analysis, many fire departments have determined that 5 in. (125 mm) is the most efficient and economical size to supply pumpers.

NFPA 1901 requires a minimum of 30 ft^3 (0.85 m^3) of hose storage on a pumper although most pumpers have at least 55 ft^3 (1.56 m^3) of space. A larger hose storage area will likely be needed for large-diameter hose. Even if large-diameter hose is not used, a larger hose bed may be required to carry the hose necessary to flow the capacity of the pump. Often the hose bed space is designed to provide a split hose load. By splitting a hose load into two bed sections, either one long lay or a shorter double hose line can be made quickly, saving considerably on the time and personnel needed to establish flows approaching the capacity of the pumper. A convenient way to relate needed hose capacity to pumper discharge capability is based on the relative water-carrying capacity of various sizes of hose at normal operating pressures, as follows: 250 gpm (946 L/min) for 2½ in. (65 mm) hose; 350 gpm (1325 L/min) for 3 in. (76 mm) hose; 500 gpm (1893 L/min) for 3½ in. (89 mm) hose; 750 gpm

(2839 L/min) for 4 in. (100 mm) hose; and 1300 gpm (4921 L/min) for 5 in. (125 mm) hose. Thus, moving 500 gpm (1893 L/min) 1000 ft (305 m) requires 2000 ft (610 m) of 2½ in. (65 mm) hose or 1000 ft (305 m) of 3½ in. (89 mm) hose. In short lines, some increases in flow may be obtained by higher discharge pressures, but in longer hose lines, increased flow will be minimal.

Fire departments should pay close attention to the accessibility of hose storage areas in developing their specifications. Hose should be stored in a manner that fire fighters can easily deploy without having to climb on the apparatus. The same is also true when repacking hose. There are many places and many ways hose can be stored on an apparatus. It is very common (and advisable) for fire attack lines to be preconnected. Preconnected lines can be deployed from the rear, front, and sides of an apparatus. Some fire departments use slide-out hose trays to facilitate repacking of hose.

In 2005, NFPA issued a requirement that all hose be secured in a manner to prevent accidental deployment. The requirement was prompted by the death of a child who was struck by a hose being dragged by an apparatus. In addition, there were numerous incidents of accidental hose deployment causing property damage. The standard does not specify how hose must be secured. That is left up to the manufacturer and the fire department.

Water Tanks

The majority of fire apparatus equipped with pumps are also equipped with water tanks. The tank supplies water to the pump for initial hose streams before water from hydrants or suction sources is available. NFPA 1901 requires that initial attack vehicles must have a minimum 200 gal (757 L) water tank; pumpers and quints must have a minimum 300 gal (1136 L) water tank; and mobile water supply apparatus must have a minimum 1000 gal (3785 L) water tank. NFPA 1906 requires that wildland apparatus carry a minimum of 125 gal (473 L). Most pumpers in municipal settings have at least a 500 gal (1900 L) water tank; pumpers in rural settings often have 750 gal (2850 L) to 1000 gal (3785 L) water tanks.

All water tanks should be constructed of noncorrosive material or materials that are protected against corrosion and deterioration. Tanks being used today are typically constructed of plastic material. Almost all water tanks, regardless of material, carry a standard lifetime warranty. Water tanks should be equipped with a water-level indicator visible at the pump operator's position. One or more sumps with a 3 in. (76 mm) or larger removable pipe plug should be provided so that debris in the tank can be cleaned out.

All tanks must have baffles to minimize water movement when the vehicle is in motion. The dimension of any spaces in the tank, either transverse or longitudinal, should not exceed 48 in. (1220 mm) or be less than 23 in. (584 mm). The baffle arrangement should allow an adequate flow rate from the tank to the pump, which is typically tested to 80 percent of the tank capacity.

The tank fill opening should be at least 20 in.^{2} (12,900 mm^2) and vents/overflows at least 12 in.^{2} (7742 mm^2). The venting must be matched to the maximum fill and discharge rate so as not to overpressure the tank. The overflow outlet should direct any water behind the rear axle so as not to interfere with rear-tire traction.

NFPA 1901 requires that tanks on mobile water supply apparatus have a single outlet capable of allowing water to be dumped from the tank at an average rate of 1000 gpm (3785 L/min). Likewise, a single external fill connection is required that permits a minimum-filling rate of 1000 gpm (3785 L/min) from sources outside to the unit. Even if the apparatus is not designed specifically to be a mobile water supply apparatus, it is good practice to have this rapid-fill and -dump capability, if the water tank holds more than 1000 gal (3785 L).

Fire departments that use apparatus with water tanks in excess of 1000 gal (3785 L) should pay close attention to the center of gravity and overall stability of the vehicle in order to avoid rollover accidents. Furthermore, these types of apparatus are heavier and require that drivers receive additional training to become familiar with the handling characteristics.

Aerial Ladders

Aerial ladders have been used by fire departments for more than a century to gain access to the upper floors and roofs of buildings (Figure 12.16.3). Aerials can be laborsaving devices if they can be strategically positioned. One fire fighter can set an aerial device, whereas three fire fighters are required to raise a 35 ft (10.668 m) extension ladder. The first aerials were manually operated before spring-assist and air-assist hoists were introduced. Current aerial ladders are steel or aluminum truss construction with hydraulic hoists and ladder controls. All aerial ladders are mounted on a turntable that must be capable of rotating a full 360 degrees in either direction.

Mount and Stabilization. All aerial ladders must have stabilizers and outriggers to keep the units from tipping over during operation. There are many interlocks in an aerial ladder to keep one function from causing problems with another function and causing harm to fire fighters and the apparatus. Fire departments

FIGURE 12.16.3 Aerial Ladders (Courtesy of Charlotte, North Carolina, Fire Department)

must fully understand interlocks and thoroughly train personnel on their function.

Aerial ladders can be mounted on a straight chassis or a tractor-drawn chassis (tillers). The advantage of the tractor-drawn units, which are not as popular as they once were, is improved maneuverability in narrow streets. However, improved designs in straight chassis have provided fire departments the opportunity to purchase highly maneuverable units. In addition, many aerial units built today also have a pump, water tank, and hose bed. These features are not common on tractor-drawn units. Moreover, it takes two fire fighters to drive a tractor-drawn aerial.

Size and Capacity. Common sizes of aerial ladders range from 75 ft (22.8 m) to 135 ft (41.1m). The rated height of an aerial is measured by a plumb line from the top ladder rung to the ground with the ladder fully extended at its maximum elevation. A locking mechanism is required to hold an aerial in its desired extended position. A locking mechanism is also required to hold the aerial in the nested position. The rear-mount aerial ladder has become common. This arrangement places the turntable over the rear wheels, with the ladder extending forward when bedded, which results in shorter overall vehicle lengths. In some cases, a shorter aerial ladder mounted on a pumper chassis provides a useful combination of devices for fire attack. A mid-mount aerial generally provides fire departments a vehicle with lower overall height when the aerial is in the nested position. This is crucial for older fire stations with low door openings and in jurisdictions with low overpasses.

Aerial ladders must have a minimum rated capacity of 250 lb (114 kg). Many departments choose to use a heavier rated capacity. Aerial ladders rated above the minimum are rated in 250 lb (114 kg) increments.

Aerial ladders must have a minimum width of 18 in. (457 mm) at the narrowest point of the ladder. Rungs must be spaced 14 in. (356 mm) on center, and the top rails along the sides must be at least 12 in. (305 mm) high. The ladder must support 250 lb (114 kg) at the tip of the fly section with the ladder fully extended in a horizontal position without water in any permanently piped water system. It must support the same weight at the tip of the fly section with the ladder at 45 degrees with water flowing.

Fixed Waterway. Aerial ladders may be equipped with a fixed waterway to the tip of the fly section or some other section. Where such a waterway is provided, it should be capable of flowing 1000 gpm (3785 L/min) at 100 psi (690 kPa) nozzle pressure through a 45-degree, side-to-side range of motions and through an arc of 135 degrees from a line parallel to the ladder and downward. Often the monitor and nozzle on these systems are controlled remotely by electric wires or radio control. The friction loss in the water system between the base of the swivel and the monitor outlet should not exceed 100 psi (690 kPa) with 1000 gpm (3785 L/min) flowing and the water system at full extension.

When the aerial ladder is not equipped with a prepiped waterway, a detachable ladder pipe provides elevated fire-stream service. When supplied by 3 in. (76 mm) hose up the ladder, 600 gpm (2271 L/min) is the practical maximum that can be supplied in normal fireground operations. The ladder pipe is normally provided with 1¼-, 1⅜-, and 1½-in. (32-, 35-, and 38-mm) smooth bore tips and with a 500 gpm (1893 L/min) spray nozzle.

Stability. The aerial ladder must be stable when a load 1½ times the rated capacity is suspended from its tip while the aerial ladder is in its least stable position and the vehicle on which the ladder is mounted is on a firm, level surface with the stabilizers extended to a firm footing. The aerial ladder must also be stable when a load 1⅓ times the rated capacity is suspended from its tip when the vehicle on which it is mounted is placed on a firm surface that slopes downward at 5 degrees in the direction most likely to cause it to overturn. Again, the stabilizers are extended to a firm footing. The stability of the apparatus is checked during the certification tests, and the vehicle cannot show any signs of instability during these tests. Innovations in aerial devices have led to the development of several nontraditional aerial devices. Elevated piercing nozzles are being installed on airport crash-vehicle apparatus. One manufacturer has teamed with a construction equipment company to develop an elevated device for multiple purposes such as ventilation, breaching concrete walls, removing debris, and an elevated stream.

Elevating Platforms

Elevating platforms are of three principal designs. In the first, the platform is mounted on an articulated boom that travels in the arc desired by the operator. In the second, the platform is mounted on an extendable or telescopic boom, in much the same fashion as an aerial ladder. In the third design, the platform is mounted on booms that are both articulated and telescopic.

Protection Features. For fire fighter safety, an elevating platform is clearly the best choice for aerial devices. By description, the platform provides a more user-friendly work area for fire fighters when in an elevated position. It provides a level of protection not available on straight ladders if fire fighter(s) unexpectedly become enveloped in the products of combustion. It provides a safe working area during rescue operations for both fire fighting and technical rescue incidents. In addition, the platform provides space for tools, hose, and other needed equipment. Finally, the platform is uniquely functional during the rescue of persons with limited physical abilities. This is becoming more important for two emerging reasons: (1) baby boomers are becoming senior citizens and, therefore, the population of persons with limited mobility is rising at a faster rate; and (2) high-rise residential buildings are becoming more numerous in urban areas.

Fire departments are advised to consider the cycle time to raise and lower an elevating platform if there is no ladder from the turntable to the platform. Platforms on extendable ladders provide the best of both worlds when rescuing victims from elevated positions (Figure 12.16.4).

All elevating platforms must have a stabilizer system to keep the units from tipping over during operation. There are many interlocks in an elevating platform to keep one function

FIGURE 12.16.4 Elevating Platform

from causing problems with another function and causing harm to fire fighters and the apparatus. Fire departments must fully understand interlocks and thoroughly train personnel on their function.

Characteristics. Platforms are available with booms designed for elevations from approximately 75 ft to more than 200 ft (23 m to 61 m). The rated height of an elevating platform is measured by a plumb line from the top rail of the platform to the ground, with the platform raised to its maximum elevation. In selecting an elevating platform, it is important to know its reach and elevation capabilities under all operating conditions. The articulated-boom design provides its maximum horizontal reach at approximately half of its maximum elevation. The extendable telescopic boom of the same nominal length generally permits somewhat greater horizontal reach at higher and lower elevations. The telescopic boom often has an extending ladder attached to it, which provides access to and from the platform while it is elevated.

The platform itself must be a minimum of 14 ft^2 (1.3 m^2). There must be a continuous guardrail around the platform. The distance from the top of the guardrail to the floor of the platform must be between 42 in. (1069 mm) and 44 in. (1118 mm). There cannot be an opening below the top of the guardrail that is greater than 24 in. (610 mm) in any direction. A heat reflective shield must be included on the front, sides, and bottom of the platform to protect fire fighters. In addition, a water curtain spray assembly must be installed under the platform for additional protection. The water curtain must flow at least 75 gpm (284 L/min). The surface of the platform must be skid resistant and include holes to drain any water that might accumulate.

All designs provide stable platforms with controls located both on the platform and at ground level. The ground-level controls must be able to override the platform controls so an operator on the ground can move the platform away from danger if the platform operator is in trouble.

An elevating platform should be able to carry a load of at least 750 lb (340 kg) in all operating positions without the water system charged. Units of 110 ft (34 m) or less should be able to reach their maximum elevation and extension and to rotate 90 degrees within 150 seconds. An advantage of an elevating platform in operation is that the platform can be moved quickly from window to window for fire-fighting or rescue purposes.

Platforms are designed to provide elevated fire streams. The platform turret or turrets must be able to rotate through at least 45 degrees up, down, and to each side. The mobility of the platform permits the operator to change the turret location quickly, as desired. The apparatus must be designed so that, regardless of the position of the platform and the direction of the stream, the equipment can be operated safely while it discharges 1000 gpm (3785 L/min) at 100 psi (690 kPa) nozzle pressure. The friction loss in the water system between the base of the swivel and the monitor outlet should not exceed 100 psi (690 kPa) with 1000 gpm (3785 L/min) flowing and the water system at full extension.

The stability requirements described earlier for aerial ladders also apply to elevating platforms. In addition, there are requirements in NFPA 1901 for the hydraulic system, for the structure, and for quality control during manufacture that apply to both aerial ladders and elevating platforms.

Water Towers

The success of elevating platforms on the fireground during the 1960s was a prelude to the use of hydraulically operated water towers designed to apply large flows on a fire from effective heights and positions. Such water towers have proved very useful and have been widely accepted in both large and small communities as an important addition to the attack capabilities of a pumper.

Water towers are designed to discharge 1000 gpm (3785 L/min) or more at 100 psi (690 kPa) nozzle pressure in either a straight stream or a spray pattern and to move the boom and the nozzle both horizontally and vertically under the control of the operator for the best application of water on the fire.

Like elevating platforms, water towers may be of either articulated or telescopic boom design. Heights typically range from 50 to 75 ft (15.2 to 22.9 m). The tower is mounted on a turntable or pedestal to permit it to rotate 360 degrees in either direction and rotate with the nozzle operating at rated capacity. The telescopic type may be equipped with a ladder extending the full length of the boom. In such cases, the ladder should meet the same requirements as those of an aerial ladder.

Water towers are typically installed on pumpers with the controls grouped at the pump operator's position so the operator has full control of the pressure, volume, and stream pattern and position. The stability requirements described for aerial ladders apply for water towers as well. NFPA 1901 also provides requirements for the hydraulic system, the structure, and quality control during manufacture.

Foam-Proportioning Equipment

Where the potential for encountering serious flammable liquid fires is present, fire departments can provide, on the apparatus, various types of foam-making equipment or other agents that are more effective than plain water. NFPA 1901 specifies minimum requirements for foam systems. There are several methods of mixing foam concentrate with water to form the foam that is delivered through a fire stream. Eductors that siphon foam concentrate through a pickup tube that is inserted in a foam concentrate container can be installed in the hose line at the pump discharge. The foam concentrate can also be premixed with water in a tank before it is pumped through a hose line. An around-the-pump proportioning system, consisting of an eductor mounted between the pump's discharge and intake, can be used. Balanced-pressure systems use water pressure between the bladder inside a pressure tank that contains foam concentrate and the walls of the tank to force foam concentrate into a water stream. Another method is to use a concentrate pump to directly inject foam into the pump's discharge. Regardless of the method used, all controls and indicating devices for foam systems must be located at the pump operator's panel.

Foams used for flammable liquid fires (Class B) typically form a film over the surface of the liquid that is on fire, thus removing the oxygen supply. Increasingly, fire departments are using foam for Class A fires such as wildland fires and structure fires. Class A fires typically reduce the surface tension of water, causing it to penetrate burning material and increase the cooling effect of the water. Special foams are also available for certain types of polar solvent/alcohol and unusual liquid fires.

Some departments also use compressed air mixed with water and Class A foam for suppression. This hardware is referred to as compressed air foam systems (CAFS) and was originally developed for wildland fire suppression application, although compressed air foam is now showing strong growth in urban and suburban fire departments for structural fire fighting. The rule of thumb for the ratio of water and air is 1 gallon of water per 1 cfm of air. CAFS systems provide the fire fighter with a lighter weight, charged hose line, and the capability to see exactly where the foam solution has been applied. The use of Class A foam and CAFS is currently gaining widespread acceptance by fire departments.

Portable Pumps

In selecting portable pumps, fire departments should be careful to choose models that will give the needed flow characteristics at a safe, continuous engine speed. Portable pumps for fire department service are usually centrifugal type. They are grouped in categories based on the pressure-volume characteristics that make them suitable for various classes of work. Low-volume streams at high pressure are intended mainly for grass and brush fire operations. Pumps delivering relatively large volumes at low pressures can be used to supply pumps on fire apparatus or to refill water tanks where a static water supply is beyond the reach of suction hose on fire apparatus. These pumps may also be used for dewatering operations. NFPA does not have a standard on portable pumps.

Communications Equipment

Effective communication is essential for any fire department operation. Every fire department vehicle should be equipped with a two-way radio that operates on all frequencies used for dispatch and fireground communication. Providing a radio speaker and microphone at the apparatus operator's position so messages can be heard above the usual noise on the fireground is highly desirable. In addition, each vehicle, including the chief officer's vehicle, should carry portable radios for effective fireground communications.

Vehicles may also be equipped to send and receive hard-copy messages or to receive visual displays of information, including maps and fire hazard data that may be transmitted from the communication center. These can be referred to as mobile data terminals (MDTs) or mobile status terminals (MSTs) depending on the type of data being transmitted. Also, laptop computers, usually in hardened cases, are becoming commonplace in many apparatus. Automatic vehicle locating (AVL) systems are now used in most larger jurisdictions. Cellular phones are also gaining popularity in fire apparatus and chiefs' vehicles. They can be used on the fireground or at hazardous materials incidents. They are especially beneficial in providing added value to the emphasis on customer service in today's fire and EMS service.

Fire departments must consider their communications equipment needs when they purchase the apparatus. The rapid growth of mobile information technology is as applicable to fire apparatus and equipment as to any other sector of society. Typically, communications equipment is installed after the purchaser receives the vehicle from the manufacturer. Considerations include mounting, grounding, visibility, wire chases, antenna, and shielding from outside wave interference.

Specialized Apparatus

There is a wide diversity of fire apparatus designed for special types of service. These units, which should be designed with the rigors of fire duty in mind, should conform to the general requirements outlined in NFPA 1901.

Many fire departments operate a vehicle to support rescue services, carrying equipment that deals with everything from emergency medical service to vehicle extrication to building collapse. The larger of these vehicles are typically equipped with a large 120/240 V electric generator, hydraulic rescue tools, and a wide variety of hand tools, power tools, and devices for jacking, shoring, cutting, and breaching. This emergency equipment typically supplements that carried on pumpers and ladder trucks. Many rescue vehicles have fully enclosed bodies to provide places for personnel to ride, to provide shelter for emergency medical treatment, and to provide an environment for incident scene rehabilitation during inclement weather.

Fire departments are equipping vehicles to support operations dealing with the spill or release of hazardous materials (Figure 12.16.5). The size and amount of equipment on these vehicles will vary with the role that the fire department sees for itself in such operations. Typically, these vehicles carry a library of materials to assist in identifying a hazardous material, tools and equipment for shutting valves or stopping leaks, materials for diking or absorbing spills, and special drums for recovering leaking drums. They also carry specialized clothing to protect the fire fighters while they are working in the contaminated area.

Fire departments can use a dedicated SCBA service unit to field-service SCBA and recharge depleted air cylinders on the fireground. These vehicles may carry numerous spare SCBA

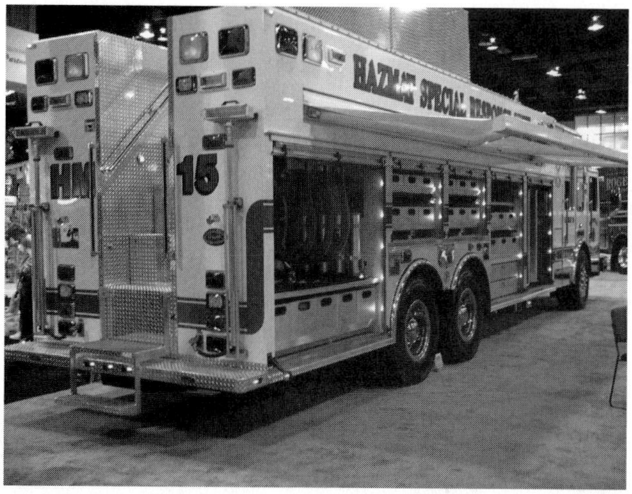

FIGURE 12.16.5 Vehicle That Supports Operations Dealing with Hazardous Materials

cylinders for exchanging depleted cylinders, several large air cylinders arranged to allow for refilling of SCBA cylinders in the field, or both large cylinders and a high-pressure air compressor for filling SCBA cylinders in the field. Small fire departments may not need a separate vehicle, but every fire department should be able to provide full SCBA cylinders in the field.

Some fire departments find it advantageous to have separate vehicles with large generators to provide 120/240 V electricity. These units may have a generator of 15,000 W or larger. The generator may be driven by its own engine or hydraulically, with the hydraulic pump driven by the vehicle engine or directly from a PTO on the vehicle's transmission. These units typically carry floodlights, electrical cord and adapters, and various power tools.

Electrical wiring or equipment on an emergency vehicle must be properly installed and grounded. This equipment is typically used under conditions of extreme wetness, where failure to properly install and maintain the electrical integrity of the wiring and equipment will result in injury or death to persons using the equipment.

Larger departments also have units dedicated as "command" vehicles. These self-contained vehicles typically carry an array of communications equipment as well as provide an environmentally controlled area for command officers to plan and direct emergency operations. Since the September 11, 2001, attacks and several natural disasters, many fire departments have been active in planning and training for possible similar mass destruction events. Considerable federal and state grant monies have been made available to help departments purchase equipment for these types of incidents. Large recreational vehicles (RVs) have been modified into command-type vehicles. Heavy-duty step vans have also been outfitted as command vehicles.

There has been an increase of tractor-drawn units to transport the vast amounts of equipment necessary for large disasters. In addition, there has been a rapid increase in the number of trailers towed by pickup trucks or SUVs. Departments must fully understand the training and state licensing requirements to operate these vehicles.

Chief Officers' Vehicles

Fire departments often provide vehicles for use of staff and command officers. In larger fire departments, sizable fleets of vehicles are maintained. Vehicle transportation is necessary for chief officers, fire prevention officers and inspectors, training officers, communications officers, fire investigators, and others. Some fire departments pay a mileage allowance for the use of private cars. This may not be a good arrangement, especially where response to emergencies may be involved, as private vehicles are generally not properly equipped with warning lights and sirens or otherwise properly marked. They may also not be properly insured for that type of service.

All fire department vehicles that respond to fires and emergencies must be equipped with warning lights, sirens, and radio communication equipment that can operate not only on local emergency networks but also on the mutual-aid frequencies the department shares. The vehicles should be clearly identified as fire department vehicles. They should carry protective clothing and equipment for the officers and their staff aides, as well as portable fire extinguishers, first-aid equipment, and hand lights. If command officers are using the vehicle, it should also carry directories containing prefire plans on properties in the area served, water distribution plans, and reference books on hazardous materials.

Fire departments can provide their command officers with sports utility vehicles (SUVs) or other vehicles with large interiors in which the necessary equipment and materials are mounted or provided for ready access. The SUV has been the vehicle of choice for chief command officers. However, crew cab pickup trucks are proving to be a popular alternative to SUVs. The comfort and space of the cab are similar to that of SUVs, with the improved benefit of isolating stored equipment away from the cab area. This minimizes cab debris, offensive odors from used fire equipment such as personal protective equipment, as well as noise from equipment vibration. With the general public's increasing use of SUVs, vans, minivans, pickup trucks, and crossover vehicles, fire departments should consider the safety and visibility of the chief officer's vehicle. Sedans are usually very low profile and are difficult for other drivers to see. Moreover, chief officers are not able to see other drivers as well if they are in a sedan.

Fireboats

Fireboats are available in various sizes and types, in accordance with local needs, and vary from large tugs to fast, jet-propelled fire and rescue craft. Fire departments or port authorities may operate them. U.S. Navy and Coast Guard vessels are also equipped to provide fire-fighting services. As rescue has evolved into a fire service function, airboats, hover craft, "john" boats, inflatable rafts, and other waterborne craft are now found in many fire departments.

NFPA 1925, *Standard on Marine Fire-Fighting Vessels,* provides the minimum requirements for the construction of new fireboats or the conversion of existing boats to fireboats. The standard designates three classifications based on length, pumping capacity, and other criteria.

Fireboats are principally used to protect vessels in a harbor; protect piers, pier sheds, and cargoes along the waterfront; protect yachts and houseboats in basins and marinas; assist in marine rescue from all types of water accidents; and serve as pumping stations to provide large flows at fires within reach of hose lines supplied by the boats. Fireboats may also provide a valuable emergency source of water for fire protection, should an earthquake or other accident interrupt the normal supply. Some fire departments operate hose trucks, or "fireboat tenders," that carry large-diameter hose to allow fireboat-pumping capacity to be used at shore fires along the waterfront.

The size, type, pumping capacity, and equipment carried by fireboats will depend on the type of service expected of the vessels. Fireboats must carry much of the same equipment as pumpers, ladder trucks, and rescue vehicles on land. They need foam-making equipment and may carry quantities of special extinguishing agents. Fireboats need radar as well as radio communication for safe operation under all weather conditions and, at times, in heavy smoke. SCBA is essential for fireboat crews.

Pumping capacity for individual fireboats varies from 500 gpm (1893 L/min) for very small craft to 10,000 gpm (37,854 L/min) or more for larger vessels. Pumping capacity is rated at 150 psi (1035 kPa) discharge pressure, as with pumpers. Some small jet-powered fireboats rely on their jet pumps to supply water for fire fighting. These pumps may develop substantial volumes at pressures adequate to supply turret nozzles attached to the pump, but it may be difficult to provide the necessary pressure to supply the hose streams to fight ship fires or fires ashore, unless additional pumps are provided to meet standard pressure requirements.

Large pumping capacity boats are not as popular as they used to be because they are slow and cumbersome. Smaller, faster, and more nimble boats capable of working in shallow water are becoming popular. Smaller fireboats are now designed to have a pumping capacity of 2000 gpm (7570 L/min). These boats can also be transported on trailers across land and placed in the water as needed.

Fire departments' decision making on fireboats should be based on the expected responses. If rescue is a function of the boat, then the boat should have a stable platform large enough to accommodate a victim. Sufficient lighting must be available for the work platforms. Another consideration is the ease with which rescue personnel can get a victim out of the water and onto the boat.

For the safety of personnel, fireboats should not be operated by only one person. They should be equipped with enough personal protective equipment for all persons on the boat.

Airport Crash Trucks

Specialized apparatus is required for aircraft rescue and fire-fighting service at airports. In many cities, such equipment is part of the municipal fire department. In others, it is maintained and operated by an airport authority. NFPA 414, *Standard for Aircraft Rescue and Fire-Fighting Vehicles,* covers the design and performance requirements for aircraft rescue and fire-fighting vehicles equipped for rescuing occupants and combating fires in aircraft at or near an airport. The size, number, and type of airport crash trucks needed are determined by Federal Aviation Administration (FAA) regulations. Airports are given an index number based on the number of flights and passengers. The index number determines the number and type of airport crash trucks required.

NFPA 414 covers three types of vehicles: (1) major fire-fighting vehicles, (2) rapid intervention vehicles (RIVs), and (3) combined-agent vehicles. RIVs are intended to reach the emergency site quickly so rescue operations can be started before the major vehicles arrive. Airport crash apparatus should include a small rescue vehicle, which can also serve as a command vehicle, and a "nurse" tanker carrying additional water and extinguishing agents where needed. Crash trucks can be modified to fight fires in hangars and other airport structures, but this use should not detract from the primary function of these vehicles.

Because of off-highway performance needs, the vehicle weight of crash trucks should be distributed equally over all wheels. These vehicles need greater axle and chassis clearances than standard fire apparatus, as well as high-acceleration characteristics. Positive drive to each wheel is required to negotiate soft ground, snow, and ice. The positive drive can be provided by torque proportioning, by no-spin differentials, or by other automatic devices that ensure that each wheel, rather than the axle, is driven independently.

EQUIPMENT CARRIED ON APPARATUS

Apparatus must be equipped with the tools necessary to accomplish fireground operations. The NFPA fire apparatus standards include listings of equipment and appliances needed with various types of fire apparatus. When developing specifications for fire apparatus, the fire department must evaluate its operation and determine how the apparatus will be used and what equipment will be necessary to support its operation.

Most fire apparatus carry hose. Pumpers typically carry the most hose, as the operational purpose of a pumper is to establish a continuous water supply and apply water to the fire. Use of larger-diameter supply hose (4 in. [100 mm] and 5 in. [125 mm]) for supplying water to pumping apparatus is common, with 5 in. (125 mm) providing the most efficiency. The length to be carried will depend on such things as hydrant spacing and distances to water supply points. Attack hose in 1½, 1¾, or 2 in. (38, 44, or 51 mm, respectively) diameters is common for hand-held hose lines for interior attack, and 2½-in. (65-mm) diameter hose lines are common when larger flows are required during exterior attack or to protect exposures. A variety of nozzles that will produce both spray and straight streams are carried for the various sizes of hose.

Besides hose, nozzles, and ground ladders, fire fighters need a wide variety of other equipment to perform their jobs. This includes SCBA, cutting tools for forcing entry and ventilating smoke from a building, positive-pressure fans and/or smoke ejectors for ventilation, salvage covers for protecting unburned contents, and a variety of fittings and adapters for use with hose lines, generators, portable lights, thermal imaging cameras, and electrical cord. The complement of equipment carried will vary from department to department, based on the needs and operations of the companies. Career and combination departments typically must transport their structural personal protective clothing when responding to nonfire events, which historically is stored in the cab. However, consideration should be given to specifying a dedicated compartment for this use. This is particularly true for the driver/operator. In addition, fire departments that perform emergency medical and rescue operations must carry an array of equipment and supplies for delivery of that service.

Fire departments should list all of the equipment that will be carried on the apparatus and determine its weight and storage space requirements. It is critical that sufficient space and carrying weight be allotted for the equipment when the apparatus is designed so the equipment does not cause the apparatus to become overloaded. A well-designed apparatus will maximize the space available for equipment by including pull-out trays, drawers, and other means of organizing the storage. Equipment should be stowed in a manner that is secure and easily identifiable. A missing piece of equipment should leave a conspicuous void space. Heavy pieces of equipment should be stored as low to the ground as possible. In determining space and weight needs, fire departments should anticipate their future needs and understand that they will likely encounter unforeseen needs. The apparatus cab should not be a place to store equipment. Only equipment used during the response should be stored in the cab. The tendency to store equipment in cabs for convenience or quick action upon scene arrival should not override the hazards of having equipment come loose during an apparatus accident. For equipment used during the response that is carried in the cab, it must be positively secured to withstand the g-forces of an impact as described in NFPA 1901.

APPARATUS PROCUREMENT POLICIES

Procurement Process

The responsibility for procurement of fire apparatus and equipment should rest with the agency operating the fire department, whether a municipality, fire district, or private industry. In some cases, procurement is a cooperative measure in which a larger unit of government contributes to the cost of providing fire apparatus for fire departments serving its territory. In a few cases, state governments contribute to local fire apparatus costs. In some areas, several fire departments have banded together to generate standard apparatus specifications to buy apparatus in quantity and realize significant cost savings. Various fire department groups also cooperate in volume purchases of hose and other equipment.

When the fire department is an agency of municipal government, it is the responsibility of the latter to provide for all public fire-fighting equipment. Providing the necessary funds is the responsibility of the appropriate fiscal authorities, but the actual selection of the equipment should be the responsibility of the fire department management. The chief administrative officer of the fire department, aided by a staff of technical specialists, should keep the municipal administrator informed of the age and condition of department equipment and should prepare specifications consistent with applicable national standards for items that need to be replaced. The technical specialists should include at least the following: master mechanic, safety officer, driver/operator, training officer, and fire fighter. In autonomous volunteer fire departments, a purchasing committee may be appointed to procure apparatus. In municipalities, the city purchasing department usually purchases the apparatus. The purchasing department should not try to tell the fire department what type of fire apparatus it should use but should see that required procurement procedures, such as open competitive bidding, are followed.

The annexes of NFPA 1901 and NFPA 1906 contain helpful suggestions covering the purchase of fire apparatus, including developing specifications, reviewing proposals, dealing with manufacturers, and accepting completed apparatus.

In general, the purchase and replacement costs of fire apparatus should be a regular item of the fire department capital budget. In most cases, except for accidents, the requirements can be planned and funded on a long-range basis. Systematic apparatus replacement provides the fire department with reliable apparatus at all times. Improvements in fire apparatus design can be introduced, maintenance costs become more favorable, operating efficiency increases, and equipment remains reliable.

The apparatus procurement process, if performed properly, will take several months. The experience can be rewarding as well as frustrating. The process involves gathering information and learning as much about apparatus as possible. Information can come from several sources. Among the best sources are educational seminars, trade shows, and other fire departments. Once the information is gathered, specifications must be developed. Dividing the specifications into a format consisting of general requirements, construction specifications, and a bid evaluation sheet will facilitate the procurement. An alternative to construction specifications is performance specifications.

Another method of procurement that has gained in popularity in recent years is the request for proposals (RFP). This process allows bidders to be more competitive and it encourages innovation. In some cases, purchasers require bidders to submit their pricing separately. This allows for the evaluation of the technical merits of the bid without the bias of the cost factor. It is always a good idea to have a prebid conference with potential bidders to allow for all questions to be asked and answered in a consistent manner and provide for an equitable base of knowledge about the purchaser's expectations.

Once a bid is awarded, the fire department should have a preconstruction conference with the successful bidder, thus allowing the purchaser and apparatus builder to focus on the construction process. The purchaser should require drawings for approval and should have an understanding of how any change orders will be handled. Throughout the process, it must be clear to both the builder and purchaser how many factory inspection visits are needed and who will pay for them. Many fire departments require three factory visits: a preconstruction visit to understand how the manufacturer builds its apparatus, an intermediate visit to inspect basic components that are not readily visible after final assembly, and the final inspection. Factory visits allow for a quality control inspection by the purchaser as well as an opportunity to identify any unforeseen changes that may be required. The visits assure that the purchaser is getting exactly what is being paid for. They should be conducted thoroughly and professionally.

An often overlooked part of the procurement process is the training and maintenance requirements for the apparatus. The complexity of fire apparatus requires that the user be trained. The purchaser must state up front what the training expectations are from the manufacturer.

Lease or Lease/Purchase

Lease or lease/purchase of fire apparatus can be an alternative to outright purchase. Income tax benefits and depreciation accrue to the actual, commercial owner of the apparatus; and the fire department, which is tax exempt, realizes savings in overall life-cycle cost. In addition, the department does not have to expend a large purchase price at one time but can spread the cost of apparatus over several years. Furthermore, there is no capital tied up in the event the department wishes to trade, exchange, or dispose of the apparatus. Closed and open-ended leases are available, and the finance department of the municipality should evaluate these alternatives carefully. In a smaller or volunteer department, a local banker can advise the purchasers of the advantages of a lease versus a purchase arrangement.

Any lease or lease/purchase contract should clearly spell out who is responsible for maintenance, repairs, and liability. Likewise, the contract should clearly state the conditions under which either party may terminate the arrangement.

As stated earlier in this chapter, there is an annex in both NFPA 1901 and 1906 that provides guidance on the retirement of apparatus. The annex explains how technological and safety advancements should be a primary consideration in the retirement of apparatus. This is especially applicable to apparatus that are not subjected to heavy use. Some departments have determined that rotating its fleet before the apparatus is worn out reduces maintenance costs and provides a much higher return on resale of the apparatus. This method provides for a modern fleet and a more equitable distribution of resources for both fire fighters and the public. A few larger departments have started to implement "total care" arrangements through lease agreements. The apparatus is leased, maintained, tested, and replaced by the supplier in accordance with the contract.

All fire departments should have a fleet replacement plan that averages the costs over several years for ease in budget development and justification. For larger departments, this can be as simple as a certain percentage of apparatus a year. For smaller departments, it could mean allocating and investing appropriate amounts of funds for capital improvements.

Acceptance Tests

Acceptance tests are designed to demonstrate that apparatus will perform as specified in the purchase contract. Tests should be performed within 10 days of delivery and before the apparatus is accepted. The tests should be conducted by the manufacturer's representative and in the presence of persons whom the purchaser may have designated in the delivery requirements. Normally, the fire chief or a designated representative is the acceptance authority. Third-party acceptance is gaining in popularity and should be considered by the agency. Costs for third-party testing are generally associated with the purchase price of the vehicle.

The acceptance-test requirements for fire apparatus and its various components should be detailed in the purchase specifications and should be based on the manufacturer's certification tests and any additional tests the fire department desires to ensure that the apparatus performs to specification. The acceptance tests should always be conducted in the community, so that any problems that developed during the delivery of the apparatus will be detected.

If the apparatus is equipped with a pump, a test plate is required at the pump operator's position that gives the rated discharge and pressures, together with engine speed determined by the manufacturer's certification test for the unit. The no-load governed speed of the engine, as stated on a certified brake horsepower curve, is also given. Tests are conducted to see that the water tank can flow the specified rate to the pump.

Documentation of electrical system performance tests must be supplied with the apparatus. These tests include reserve capacity test, alternator performance test at idle, alternator performance test at full load, and low-voltage alarm test.

Aerial devices are inspected and tested in accordance with the requirements in NFPA 1911, *Standard for Service Tests of Fire Pump Systems on Fire Apparatus,* as part of the certification tests. In addition, the stability of the aerial device is tested with the aerial device on a level surface and then on a firm surface sloping downward at 5 degrees in the direction most likely to cause it to overturn. The vehicle cannot show any signs of instability during these tests. These stability tests should not be conducted other than at the manufacturer's facility.

If the aerial device is equipped with a prepiped waterway, the system is flow tested to determine whether the water system can flow 1000 gpm (3785 L/min) at 100 psi (690 kPa) nozzle pressure with the aerial device fully elevated and extended. If there is a fire pump on the vehicle, the test is conducted using that fire pump, and the intake pressure to the fire pump cannot exceed 20 psi (138 kPa).

Other components and systems on the apparatus such as foam systems, line voltage electrical systems, and air systems should also be tested to be sure they have been installed properly and are working as designed.

INSPECTION, MAINTENANCE, TESTING, AND RETIREMENT OF APPARATUS AND EQUIPMENT

Program Setup

Equally important to the procurement of proper fire apparatus and equipment is their inspection, maintenance, testing, and retirement. Because apparatus are vital to life safety, they must be in top-notch condition. A regular inspection, maintenance, testing, and retirement program should be set up to ensure that all apparatus and equipment are serviced and tested in accordance with the manufacturer's recommendations and NFPA standards. The program should define the roles and responsibilities for the personnel and outside agencies involved. Fire apparatus are becoming increasingly more complex, and attention to such a program cannot be neglected.

Based on concerns expressed by the National Transportation Safety Board (NTSB) in a 1991 report about the quality and type of maintenance on fire apparatus, the NFPA issued a preventive maintenance standard in 2000. In 2007, the NFPA issued a combined standard to include maintenance as well as testing. The new standard is NFPA 1911, *Standard for Service Tests of Fire Pump Systems on Fire Apparatus.* The old pump testing standard and aerial testing standards were merged into this document. NFPA 1911 should be the guiding document for fleet maintenance for all departments. It is a very user-friendly standard with several useful charts and checklists that any department can use. The standard defines the minimum requirements for fire departments to establish a preventive maintenance program. The standard is comprehensive and covers chassis, cab, body, low-voltage pumps, foam systems, aerials, CAFS, line voltage, air systems, winches, and breathing-air systems.

Apparatus safety should be the primary objective of a fire department's fleet management program. In fact, NFPA 1911 states that safety is the primary consideration in the decision to retire apparatus. The program should be in a written format and should include criteria for taking apparatus out of service. A thorough inspection program that covers the various systems of the apparatus should drive the program. Any preventive maintenance program should be conducted in accordance with the manufacturer's requirements.

Only qualified personnel should conduct the fire department's preventive maintenance program. NFPA 1071, *Standard for Emergency Vehicle Technician Professional Qualifications,* defines the minimum job performance requirements for an emergency vehicle technician. The standard prescribes two levels of competency. The EVT Certification Commission (EVTCC) offers a certification program for emergency vehicle technicians. The program recognizes mechanics as having demonstrated a working knowledge and skill required for emergency vehicles. Fire departments should insist that their mechanics become certified. Because of the complex systems associated with fire apparatus, an emergency vehicle technician must have knowledge and training that exceed that of typical automotive mechanics. The emergency vehicle mechanic must be able to inspect, diagnose, maintain, repair, and test the functions of the apparatus. It is the responsibility of the fire department to assure that its vehicles are maintained by qualified mechanics in accordance with their competencies. There are several state and regional fire mechanics associations that offer excellent training and networking opportunities for emergency vehicle technicians.

Retirement of Apparatus

The topic of when to retire a piece of apparatus has been debated for decades. Larger fire departments with high-volume responses typically replace their apparatus based on maintenance costs and general wear and tear. However, most fire departments do not have the call volume to justify maintenance costs or wear and tear as sufficient substantiation to replace apparatus.

NFPA has addressed this situation by calling attention to the technological advances in apparatus, particularly in regards to safety. Annex D of NFPA 1901 references previous editions of the NFPA 1901 as benchmarks for replacement. There are at least two dozen clearly identifiable safety features found on today's apparatus that were not required or available in the seventies or eighties. Safety and technological advances will definitely continue, as will the need to consider apparatus replacement on these criteria.

Service Tests of Pumps. All pumps should undergo service tests at least annually and after any major repairs. These tests demonstrate that the pump/engine combination is capable of meeting the performance requirements of the original certification or acceptance tests. Records of service tests are important evidence of proper apparatus maintenance.

NFPA 1911 outlines the procedures for the service test. The test should cover the following items:

- A test pumping from draft for 20 minutes at 100 percent of rated capacity at 150 psi (1039 kPa) net pump pressure; 10 minutes at 70 percent of rated capacity at 200 psi (1380 kPa) net pump pressure; and 10 minutes at 50 percent of rated capacity at 250 psi (1725 kPa) net pump pressure
- An engine speed test to determine if the engine is capable of reaching its no-load governed speed
- A vacuum test to ensure that the pump and the attached piping are still tight
- A pressure control test to ensure that the pressure control device can control the discharge within the specified limits
- A check of the accuracy of the gauges and flow meters

The purpose of the test is to ensure that the pump is generally in good condition, that the pump casing and various fittings are tight, and that the transfer valve is operating properly, if the pump is a series parallel type. If rated capacity cannot be obtained at 150 psi (1035 kPa) and the pump is not cavitating, or it appears that the pump, engine, pump accessories, or other parts of the power train and pumping equipment are not in good condition, the apparatus manufacturer, an authorized representative, or a competent mechanic should be contacted for advice so the condition can be corrected. Personnel conducting the pump service tests should take safety precautions, including working on a slip-resistant surface and putting guards around pressurized hose lines.

Service Tests of Aerial Devices. Aerial devices also need to be service tested periodically. These devices develop problems not only from use at fires but also from responding to and returning from alarms. NFPA 1911 requires a yearly inspection of the aerial device and of the prepiped water system, if so equipped, and a test of their operation. NFPA 1911 requires additional nondestructive tests, at intervals not exceeding 5 years, that check structural components for hardness, welds for cracks or discontinuities, and bolts and pins for wear or internal flaws. The full testing should be done any time the aerial device has had major repairs or if the department has reason to believe that it has exceeded the manufacturer's design criteria to ensure that it can be returned to service.

A qualified fire department mechanic can normally conduct the annual inspection and testing. The more complex, nondestructive tests require expertise that may be beyond the abilities of fire department personnel. The qualifications of the inspection personnel and the test protocols used are outlined in NFPA 1911. Only personnel meeting those qualifications and having the proper equipment should do nondestructive testing.

Refurbishing Apparatus. Fire departments may wish to consider refurbishing an apparatus rather than purchasing a new one. NFPA 1912, *Standard for Fire Apparatus Refurbishing,* provides the minimum requirements for refurbishing an apparatus. The standard provides for two levels of refurbishment. In a Level I refurbishment, the vehicle receives at least a new chassis frame, cab, front axle, steering, and suspension components. The new items must comply with the latest revision of NFPA 1901. In a Level II refurbishment, the vehicle receives an upgrade of major components or systems but these upgraded components only need to comply with NFPA standards in effect at the time the apparatus was manufactured. The standard provides an excellent specification form in the appendix or annex for purchasers to use. All refurbishments must be performed in accordance with Title 49, Code of Federal Regulations, Part 571, Subpart B, "Federal Motor Vehicle Safety Standards." As with the purchase of new apparatus, a refurbishment process must make safety a primary concern.

The decision to refurbish must be evaluated very carefully. It must be noted that the number of apparatus being refurbished has steadily declined over the past 10 years. Though refurbishments are less expensive than new apparatus, they are still very expensive. A careful cost analysis will aid fire departments in this decision. The analysis should include the age of the vehicle (depreciation), the anticipated remaining life of the vehicle, resale value of the vehicle, proposed cost of refurbishment, and time out of service during refurbishment. The result needs to be related to the cost of a new vehicle. A refurbishment program should not be initiated for the sole purpose of improving the cosmetic appearance of the vehicle.

The refurbishing process is as detailed as purchasing a new apparatus. Detailed specifications should be written as part of an overall procurement process. It is critical that both the purchaser and the manufacturer understand each other's expectations and have them in writing. Refurbishments typically expose unforeseen areas that need to be upgraded or repaired. For this reason, fire departments should establish a contingency fund.

GROUND LADDERS

Ground Ladder Characteristics

Most apparatus carry ground ladders designed for rescuing persons and gaining access to buildings for fire-fighting purposes. Ladders may be constructed of wood, aluminum, fiberglass, or a combination of aluminum and fiberglass. Aluminum is by far the most common material used. All ground ladders used in the fire service should be designed and built to conform to NFPA 1931, *Standard for Manufacturer's Design of Fire Department Ground Ladders.* The NFPA 1901 standard allows fire departments flexibility in determining the appropriate ladder lengths for their needs. There are varying length requirements for pumpers, attack vehicles, quints, and aerial devices.

Loads that fire ladders are designed to support vary according to the type of ladder. Extension ladders, single ladders, and roof ladders built since 1984 are designed for 750 lb (340 kg) maximum load; folding and pompier ladders are designed for 300 lb (136 kg) maximum load. Load limitations are based on the use of the ladder supported at the top end against a building and set at a 75½ degree angle. This angle is measured from the horizontal with the ladder in the raised position. At smaller angles, the ladder may be unable to support the design load.

Although the NFPA apparatus standards list the minimum requirements for ground ladders on each type of vehicle, careful consideration should be given to the ladder needs of the area served. Manually raised extension ladders more than 40 ft (12 m) long are generally not required because aerial ladders and elevating platforms provide adequate emergency access to upper floors and roofs. If congested conditions prohibit the placement of aerial apparatus to provide effective aerial service, however, additional or longer ground ladders should be provided. It must be recognized that additional personnel are required to raise longer ladders and that the space available for ladders on some vehicles is limited.

Ground Ladder Service Testing

NFPA 1932, *Standard on Use, Maintenance, and Service Testing of In-Service Fire Department Ground Ladders,* calls for service testing all ladders at least annually and at any time the ladder is suspected of being unsafe. The tests are designed to show that the ladder is safe for continued use under the conditions for which it was originally designed. The service-test procedures must be carefully observed to ensure that the ladder is not damaged. Ladders also should be inspected visually, as outlined in NFPA 1932, to detect loose rungs, loose bolts and rivets, weld defects, cracks, splintering, breaks, discoloration, and other signs of possible weakness that might warrant testing to determine whether the ladder is safe to use or needs repair.

There is a misconception that the procedures used to test ground ladders are destructive. It is true that the load test may appear to be damaging, but a safe ground ladder will pass the annual load tests for many years.

HOSE, COUPLINGS, AND NOZZLES

Fire hose is the vital link between the water supply and the nozzles used to project streams on a fire. Fire hose failure can put fire fighters at great risk. Hose must be rugged, dependable, and capable of carrying water under substantial pressures, yet flexible and sufficiently easy to handle. Fire department management should be concerned with selecting the proper grades and types of hose and with maintenance to ensure maximum useful life. These two factors are covered in detail in NFPA 1961, *Standard on Fire Hose,* and NFPA 1962, *Standard for the Inspection, Care, and Use of Fire Hose, Couplings, and Nozzles and the Service Testing of Fire Hose.* Aside from unavoidable mechanical injury at fires, a hose's dependability and length of life rest on three factors: (1) the quality and suitability of the hose purchased, (2) the care with which it is handled at fires, and (3) the maintenance and care the hose receives.

Types of Fire Hose

Fire hose is manufactured for at least four uses:

1. *Attack hose.* Fire attack by fire department personnel
2. *Large-diameter supply hose.* Relaying water through large-diameter hose from a source to the fire
3. *Occupant use hose.* Occupant use in buildings from standpipe systems
4. *Forestry hose.* Fire department use at wildland fires

Each of these types has minimum requirements for strength. Attack hose is designed for a minimum service-test pressure of 300 psi (2069 kPa) to meet a normal highest operating pressure of 275 psi (1896 kPa). If a higher working or operating pressure is needed, the purchaser needs to specify a higher service-test pressure. The most common size of interior attack hose is 1¾ in. (44.45 mm). For larger fires, 2½ in. (63.50 mm) is often used.

Large-diameter supply hose has a minimum size of 3½ in. (89 mm) and a minimum design service-test pressure of 200 psi (1380 kPa) to meet a 185-psi (1276-kPa) normal highest operating pressure. Large-diameter hose is typically used as supply hose or hose to supply ground placed master stream appliances. The most common size is 5 in. (127 mm).

Occupant use hose has a minimum size of 1½ in. (38 mm) and a minimum design service-test pressure of 150 psi (1035 kPa) to meet a 135-psi (931-kPa) normal highest operating pressure.

Forestry hose is only available in 1 in. (25 mm) and 1½ in. (38 mm) sizes and has a minimum design service-test pressure of 300 psi (2069 kPa) to meet a 250-psi (1725-kPa) normal highest operating pressure.

All hose must meet a proof-test pressure—formerly an acceptance-test pressure—of twice its service-test pressure, a burst-test pressure of three times its service-test pressure, and a kink-test pressure of one-and-a-half times the service-test pressure.

NFPA 1961 provides requirements for the hose jacket, the lining and the lining adhesion, any covering and its adhesion, the tensile strength of the hose, the ultimate elongation of the hose, and the cold resistance of the hose. Tests are outlined to verify these requirements. Another section in NFPA 1961 defines how the hose must be marked.

Care, Maintenance, and Testing of Fire Hose

Fire hose should be properly maintained to ensure its reliability. Burst hose at a fire may seriously injure fire fighters and other persons and may mean a loss of time in bringing a fire under control. NFPA 1962 and the manufacturer's instructions should form the basis of a hose care and maintenance program.

Hose carried on fire apparatus should be loaded to reduce edge wear and loaded so that air can circulate around it. The hose storage areas should be protected by waterproof covers to keep the hose dry and to protect it from ultraviolet rays and from debris.

Hose installed at yard hydrants at industrial plants should be kept in well-ventilated hose houses in such a way that air can circulate and excessive heat can be avoided.

To prevent damage and permanent set to the rubber tube, hose should be removed from the apparatus or hose house at least quarterly and reloaded so the folds are in a different position. If hose jackets are of cotton or synthetic construction, the hose should be cleaned and dried after use to remove possible abrasive or contaminating material and to protect the hose compartment of the apparatus against rust or water damage.

When used for fighting fires, fire hose is subject to severe strains, pressure surges, burning embers, and abrasion. Care should be taken to lay hose so that damage will not result from contact with sharp or rough objects. Vehicles should not be driven over hose lines. Where it is necessary for fire department vehicles to cross, hose bridges should be used if possible. When it is necessary to hoist hose lines, hose rollers can make the task easier and prevent mechanical injury. A hose extended up a ladder should be supported by a hose-rope tool to minimize the strain on hose couplings.

Pressure surges are a principal cause of damage to fire hose. Shutoff nozzles should be opened and closed slowly because sudden closure of nozzles can cause severe pressure surges, or water hammer, that can be extremely damaging to both hose and pumping apparatus. Pressure-relief devices on pumping engines should always be used to control unexpected, sudden increases in pressure.

In cold climates, care should be taken to prevent water from freezing in the fire hose. Once a hose line has been charged, a small amount of water should be left running through the hose because moving water does not freeze readily. Sharp bends should be avoided in any frozen hose. Care must be used in chopping hose free from ice after a fire so as not to cut the hose. The ice should then be allowed to melt off the hose, and any hose that has been frozen should be service tested before being placed back in service.

Care must also be taken to avoid burning the hose at forest and grass fires. As fire is knocked down and the nozzle is advanced, the hose may come in contact with hot spots or embers. When hose has been returned to the fire station, it should be laid out where it can be inspected, swept, and washed as needed to remove dirt and contaminants.

Good hose record keeping is necessary for accurate data on hose performance. Records for hose on racks, on reels, or in hose houses or similar enclosures may be kept at the hose location or at a central location on the premises where the hose is located. Fire department records should include a complete record of all hose. Upon delivery and acceptance, each length of hose should be given an identification number to be used throughout its service life. The ongoing record of the hose should include all testing and repairs and, ultimately, the reason it was condemned and removed from service.

All fire hose, except occupant use hose, should be tested at least annually and after repairs, or at any time it has had hard usage and its condition is suspect. NFPA 1962 includes required service-test procedures and a typical annual hose-test record form. The standard also specifies service-test pressures for hose manufactured before July 1987. Hose manufactured after that date has the service-test pressure stenciled on it.

Fire departments should avoid using the fire pump of an apparatus to test fire hose if at all possible. Apparatus fire pumps are not intended for hose-testing applications. Using smaller, low-volume, high-pressure pumps will minimize the unnecessary wear on a fire pump. Personnel conducting hose tests should take precautions against being in close proximity to charged hose lines.

Occupant use hose (normally stored on a rack or reel) should be examined carefully at least once a year. This annual physical inspection should consist of a visual examination to see that the hose has not been vandalized, that the couplings and nozzle are attached and free of debris, and that there is no evidence of mildew, rot, chemicals, vermin, or abrasion. Racked hose should be reracked with the folds in a different location. Five years after the date of purchase and every three years thereafter, the hose should be service tested, as it should be any time the condition of the hose is questionable.

Fire Hose Connections

The need for standard fire service connections is most apparent during mutual-aid operations. When hose couplings, nozzles, and other equipment do not conform to standards, it becomes necessary to use adapters, thus complicating fire-fighting operations.

NFPA 1963, *Standard for Fire Hose Connections,* applies to connections on fire-hose couplings, suction-hose couplings, relay supply-hose couplings, fire pump suction, discharge valves, fire hydrants, nozzles, adapters, reducers, caps, plugs, wyes, siamese connections, standpipe connections, sprinkler connections, and all other hose fittings, connections, and appliances that connect to fire pumps, hose, and hydrants.

The standard defines requirements and tests to verify the design and performance of couplings on fire hose. These include issues of minimum waterway size, internal strength, connect and disconnect capability, retention, and performance after rough usage, high-temperature conditions, and low-temperature conditions. There are also requirements for the gasket material used with the couplings.

For threaded connections in the 10 sizes from ¾ to 6 in. (19 to 152 mm) used in fire protection, the standard gives the dimensions for the American National Fire Hose Connection Screw Thread, abbreviated throughout as NH but also known as NST and NS. It also gives the dimensions for gauges, gaskets, and gasket seats associated with threaded connections. These threaded connections are defined by specifying, in sequence, the nominal size of the connection, the number of threads per inch, and the thread symbol. The 10 standard sizes of threaded connections are designated in Table 12.16.1.

To accommodate the increased use of nonthreaded connections on large-diameter hose, the machining dimensions for nonthreaded connections in 4 in. (100 mm) and 5 in. (125 mm) sizes are defined to ensure interchangeability as well as to prevent accidental disengagement of the couplings. Finally, the standard defines when the different thread sizes should be used on hose connections, nozzles and shutoffs, and both the initial connection and subsequent connections on large-stream devices.

TABLE 12.16.1 Standard Sizes of Threaded Connections

0.75–8 NH	3.5–6 NH
1–8 NH	4–4 NH
1.5–9 NH	4.5–4 NH
2.5–7.5 NH	5–4 NH
3–6 NH	6–4 NH

Nozzles

Nozzles used in the fire service are of either the spray or solid-stream design. A spray nozzle can produce a straight stream with similar characteristics as a stream from a solid-bore nozzle. Nozzles for 1, 1½, 1¾, and 2 in. (25, 38, 44, and 51 mm) hose are typically spray nozzles. Nozzles for 2½ in. (65 mm) hand lines and for master stream devices may be of the spray or solid-stream design. All hand line nozzles should be equipped with shutoff valves, either as an integral part of the nozzle or as an attached item.

Fire department nozzles for 1½ in. (38 mm) hose normally are designed to discharge approximately 95 to 125 gpm (360 to 473 L/min). Nozzles for 1¾ and 2 in. (44 and 51 mm) hose normally are designed to discharge approximately 125 to 200 gpm (473 to 757 L/min). Nozzles for 1 in. (25 mm) hose generally discharge in the 20 to 30 gpm (76 to 114 L/min) range. A standard hose stream from a 2½ in. (65 mm) hose with a 1⅛-in. (29-mm) smooth bore tip is 250 gpm (946 L/min) at 50 psi (345 kPa) nozzle pressure.

Solid-bore nozzles have a straight open tip that generally is attached to some type of stream shaper. These nozzles are designed to hold the solid stream together as water is thrown a considerable distance. The design of the nozzles provides a gentle taper from the diameter of the inside of the hose to the diameter of the tip to reduce the turbulence that causes a stream to break up.

Requirements for spray nozzles are covered in NFPA 1964, *Standard for Spray Nozzles.* There are three general types of spray nozzles: (1) the basic spray nozzle, (2) the constant-gallonage spray nozzle, and (3) the constant-pressure (automatic) spray nozzle.

The basic spray nozzle is an adjustable-pattern spray nozzle in which the rated flow is delivered at a designated nozzle pressure and nozzle setting. Due to its basic design, the flow (gpm [L/min]) will vary as the pattern is changed from a straight stream through a wide-spray pattern. This is caused by the orifice size changing to affect pattern adjustment.

The constant-gallonage spray nozzle is an adjustable-pattern spray nozzle in which the flow is delivered at a designated nozzle pressure. At the rated pressure, the nozzle will deliver a constant gallonage from straight-stream through a wide-spray pattern by maintaining a constant orifice size during flow-pattern adjustment. These nozzles are popular because the friction-loss characteristics in the hose and the nozzle pressures remain constant regardless of the selected orifice setting.

A constant-pressure (automatic) spray nozzle is an adjustable-pattern nozzle in which the pressure remains constant through a range of flows. The constant pressure provides the velocity for an effective stream reach at various flow rates, which is accomplished by means of a pressure-activated, self-adjusting orifice baffle. These nozzles can produce streams whose discharge varies considerably but whose visual characteristics and stream reach remain the same. The user should not be misled by a good-looking stream that lacks the adequate flow for proper fire attack. However, these are very effective nozzles if the fire department understands the principles behind the automatic nozzle—namely, that the volume of water, not the pressure alone, extinguishes fire.

There are other nozzles available for special purposes. For decades, fire fighters have argued over the effectiveness of spray nozzles versus smooth bore tips. The argument usually is more emotional than logical. One key difference is that a spray nozzle can be placed in the "straight-stream" mode for basically the same effect as a smooth bore tip. However, a smooth bore tip cannot be converted to a spray pattern. These include nozzles used in the aspiration and delivery of foaming agents, very high-pressure spray nozzles that are designed to deliver small flows at pressures in the 400 to 800 psi (2756 to 5516 kPa) range, and spray nozzles used on standpipe hose for first-aid fire protection.

SUMMARY

The selection and purchase of fire department apparatus and equipment are obviously an important part of any fire department's business. For volunteer fire departments, the largest portion of their budget is dedicated to vehicles and equipment. In career and combination departments, it is usually second to salaries and benefits. Foremost, the selection and purchase process must be based on community needs. Careful research and planning are crucial to meeting these needs. Fire vehicles and equipment are very specialized and technical in their nature. They cannot be purchased at the local car dealership, corner hardware store, or megadiscount store.

Fire departments must be knowledgeable about all applicable standards and laws that impact the design, performance, use, and maintenance of the equipment. The selection and purchase of apparatus and equipment must take into account several factors. The foremost factor is the safety of the fire fighters and the public. As stated earlier in this chapter, one of the 16 Firefighter Life Safety Initiatives of the National Fallen Firefighters Foundation states: "Safety must be a primary consideration in the design of apparatus and equipment." Another factor is how the vehicle or equipment fits in with previous purchases. In addition, the fire department must provide training on the proper use of all the vehicles and equipment and must provide maintenance for the items purchased as described by the manufacturer.

BIBLIOGRAPHY

References Cited

1. Karter, M. J., Jr., *U.S. Fire Department Profile,* NFPA Fire Analysis and Research Division, Quincy, MA, Oct. 2000, Table 19.
2. Analysis by NFPA Fire Analysis and Research Division of data from NFPA Survey and Fire Incident Data Organization.

NFPA Codes, Standards, and Recommended Practices

Reference to the following NFPA codes, standards, and recommended practices will provide further information about fire department apparatus and equipment discussed in this chapter. (See the latest version of The NFPA Catalog *for availability of current editions of the following documents.)*

NFPA 414, *Standard for Aircraft Rescue and Fire-Fighting Vehicles*
NFPA 1002, *Standard for Fire Apparatus Driver/Operator Professional Qualifications*
NFPA 1071, *Standard for Emergency Vehicle Technician Professional Qualifications*
NFPA 1500, *Standard on Fire Department Occupational Safety and Health Program*
NFPA 1901, *Standard for Automotive Fire Apparatus*
NFPA 1906, *Standard for Wildland Fire Apparatus*
NFPA 1911, *Standard for the Inspection, Maintenance, Testing, and Retirement of In-Service Automotive Fire Apparatus*
NFPA 1912, *Standard for Fire Apparatus Refurbishing*
NFPA 1925, *Standard on Marine Fire-Fighting Vessels*
NFPA 1931, *Standard for Manufacturer's Design of Fire Department Ground Ladders*
NFPA 1932, *Standard on Use, Maintenance, and Service Testing of In-Service Fire Department Ground Ladders*
NFPA 1961, *Standard on Fire Hose*
NFPA 1962, *Standard for the Inspection, Care, and Use of Fire Hose, Couplings, and Nozzles and the Service Testing of Fire Hose*
NFPA 1963, *Standard for Fire Hose Connections*
NFPA 1964, *Standard for Spray Nozzles*

References

Emergency Vehicle Safety Initiative, United States Fire Administration/FEMA, Washington, DC, 1994.
Emergency Vehicle Safety Program, International Association of Firefighters, Washington, DC, 2006.
Eckman, W. F., *Fire Department Water Supply Handbook,* PennWell Corporation, Saddle Brook, NJ, 1994.
Wiseman, J. D., and Bertrand, J. E., *The Safe and Effective Use of Fog Nozzles,* PennWell Corporation, Saddle Brook, NJ, 2003.

Chapter 17

Pre-Incident Planning for Industrial and Municipal Emergency Response

Michael J. Serapiglia

Chapter Contents

Key Terms

building construction, industrial fire brigade, occupancy classification, pre-incident planning, public fire department

A pre-incident plan is one of the most valuable tools available for aiding the fire department and the on-site fire brigade if available, in effectively controlling a fire or other emergency incident. The plan can be used by responding personnel to help them effectively manage emergencies with available resources. Planning for fires in industrial and commercial facilities increases the confidence and ability of fire service personnel to deal with most emergency situations. More importantly, it increases the potential for saving lives and property. This chapter will discuss the pre-incident planning process, who needs to be involved in this process, and the type of information industrial and commercial facilities need to gather.

For related topics, see the following chapters in Section 12: Chapter 1, "Planning for Public Fire-Rescue Protection"; Chapter 11, "Industrial Fire Loss Prevention"; and Chapter 18, "Pre-Incident Planning for Emergency Response."

PRE-INCIDENT PLANNING DEFINED

Pre-incident planning can be defined as a written document resulting from the gathering of general and detailed information/data to be used by public emergency response agencies and private industry for determining the response to reasonably anticipated emergency incidents at a specific facility.

In simple terms, pre-incident planning is ensuring that responding emergency personnel know as much as they can about a facility's construction, occupancy, and fire protection systems *before* an incident occurs. With this knowledge, the fire department can compare a potential incident at the facility with its available resources and plan the department's response accordingly. Pre-incident planning is not restricted to building components. It includes other factors and conditions that may be relevant to an emergency at a particular site.

Pre-incident planning is not easy. It takes considerable effort by the fire department to get a pre-incident planning program up and running. As growing demand for an expanding scope of services collides with limited budgets and other resources, fire departments are faced with much competition for staff time and money.

This means that pre-incident planning is more important than ever, not just for the traditional reasons of greater effectiveness and safety, but also for greater efficiency in resource utilization. No matter what effort it takes, fire departments today literally cannot afford *not* to pre-incident plan. The more information available, the better the opportunity for an incident commander to manage the incident successfully. Advance knowledge of the facility could mean the difference in managing the incident properly.

Proper training is also critical to pre-incident planning success. The individuals doing the pre-incident surveys and preparing the resulting documentation (Figure 12.17.1) must have the proper

Michael J. Serapiglia is a health, safety, and environmental coordinator for Saint-Gobain, High Performance Materials, Research and Development Center in Northborough, Massachusetts. Mr. Serapiglia has over 20 years experience in combination and volunteer fire departments. He is a professional member of SFPE, ASSE, and former chairman of the NFPA Technical Committee on Pre-Incident Planning.

FIGURE 12.17.1 Pre-Incident Planning Session

level of training. Conducting the survey requires much more than walking through the building. It requires asking the right questions about construction features, storage arrangements, water supply adequacy, and sprinkler system components and design. This information must then be converted into a usable format for both fire department training and an actual incident.

The burden for successful pre-incident planning does not rest with the fire service alone. Pre-incident planning requires three-way open communication among facility management, the fire service, and the property insurance industry. Other agencies might also be able to provide valuable input during the development of the pre-incident plan. Such agencies include police, security, public utilities, environmental agencies, and contractors.

Facility management must take a coordinating role in pre-incident planning and be willing to host a joint meeting of all three entities. At this meeting, management must be willing to share information that its property insurance carrier has most likely already gathered about the hazards within the facility and the level of protection that is available. Most highly protected risk (HPR) insurance carriers are willing to provide this information, if they have the consent of facility management. The fire department must then take this information and incorporate it into its response plan for the facility.

When pre-incident planning is successful, everyone benefits. The fire department manages its response effectively, which results in a safer response and minimized property loss. A minimized property loss keeps the facility in business, which maintains the tax base for the fire department's budget. And the loss cost is kept low for the property insurance carrier.

Conducting pre-incident planning is not the same as inspecting for code violations. When pre-incident planning, the fire department representative takes the facility "as is" and develops a response strategy around existing conditions. Conducting pre-incident planning is not an attempt to improve fire prevention or identify code violations at the facility. Its sole purpose is to prepare for an incident at the facility under existing conditions. Pre-incident planning assumes an incident will occur. It makes no special effort to prevent a fire or eliminate a hazard, but rather it is preparation for an incident, regardless of the likelihood.

Assume for a moment that a facility in the community is known to have several automatic sprinkler system code deficiencies. Also assume that the facility's management has agreed to correct the situation within 90 days. What happens if a fire occurs the day after tomorrow? Just because the code violations have been documented does not mean a pre-incident plan is not needed. Code inspections and pre-incident planning are two distinct functions with two different purposes.

The fire department that is responsible for both code inspections and pre-incident planning needs to handle these types of situations with tact and diplomacy. When conducting code inspections, it is easy to stand behind the delegated authority of the position. But the fire department will never get the cooperation it needs for effective pre-incident planning if an authoritative approach is taken. The difference between each function must be understood by the fire department and communicated effectively to facility management.

Pre-incident planning is continuous. Many major fire incidents can be traced back to a change—often seemingly minor—that took place at a facility. Perhaps the packaging of the products stored in the warehouse was changed from cardboard to plastic. Or maybe some renovations took place that left concealed spaces unprotected by automatic sprinklers. Maybe the on-site suction tank for the fire pump is going to be drained and repainted over the next several weeks and it is the only adequate water supply for the facility.

If a pre-incident plan is prepared once and never updated, these changes could go unnoticed until it is too late. Keeping up with changes in a facility requires a high level of commitment, communication, and cooperation among the pre-incident partners. For example, depending on total area and intended use, installation of modular office buildings at an existing property may not trigger code requirements for sprinkler protection, but egress issues may be impacted and should be thoroughly evaluated.

Determining the best frequency for updating pre-incident plans depends on the facility. Updating once per year may be fine at some locations but could be woefully inadequate at other locations.

Pre-incident planning requires a willingness by facility management to bring the fire department in and tell them what they need to know (e.g., "The sprinkler system in the warehouse is not currently adequate to protect what we're storing there"). It requires the fire department to know what questions to ask and to react positively when they get the truthful answers to those questions. And it requires the property insurer to act as an information link between the two.

PLANNING PROCESS

From the fire department perspective, once a facility has been selected, the owner/operator should be contacted. The needs and benefits of pre-incident planning might have to be explained in detail. The fire department should explain the nature of the information required, because the facility might have to arrange to have certain specialized employees available when the visit is made.

Situations may arise in which the selected property encompasses building areas in more than one municipality. In such cases, it is important that all fire service agencies involved be included in the planning process. The cooperation of multiple agencies in the planning phase will help assure smooth operations during the emergency incident phase.

When selecting a property, do not limit the choices to the largest facilities. Consider medium and small locations in which on-site emergency response resources and protection features may be limited. Locations such as commercial storage facilities for swimming pool supplies and municipal or private golf courses should not be overlooked. A number of challenging fires involving pool treatment chemicals have been documented over the past 10 years in large bulk retail stores. Although the quantities may be different, similar hazards are presented. When was pre-incident planning last conducted at your local golf course? Large clubhouses, battery charging and storage areas for electric carts, flammable or combustible liquid storage for maintenance vehicles, and significant quantities of pesticides and fertilizer are commonly found at such locations.

The pre-incident planning process can be shown as a flowchart (Figure 12.17.2). Obviously, much time and effort will be needed with the collection of data. This will involve consulting with the facility's staff and other individuals as necessary. The site will need to be visited to get an overview of the layout, construction, occupancy, and fire protection features.

Most major industrial and commercial facilities have developed an emergency operations or crisis plan in which the actions to be taken in the event of an emergency have been specified. A review of the emergency operations plan by the fire department can provide valuable insight into the actions to be coordinated by both facility personnel and the fire department. Incorporating the emergency operations plan into the fire department pre-incident plan is beneficial in case the facility personnel are assigned certain responsibilities but circumstances during the emergency prevent them from performing these duties.

A number of commercially available software programs may be utilized to assist in the recording of data. These programs are also useful in developing building drawings and a general layout of the facility.

Once the data are collected, decisions will need to be made about what data to keep and how the data should be stored, retrieved, and presented. The method of presentation is best left up to the discretion of each fire department, but it should be based on the fire department's incident management system.

Many fire departments keep certain parts of the plan in the dispatch center for reference. The dispatcher may transmit a facsimile of pertinent sections of the plan or the entire plan to a fire station prior to apparatus responding to an incident. This same information may also be sent directly from the dispatcher to the incident commander on scene. Others use computers in apparatus to store and retrieve information. Other departments may keep hard copies of the pre-incident plan in the individual fire stations or the apparatus itself. A sample pre-incident planning data form is shown in Figure 12.17.3.

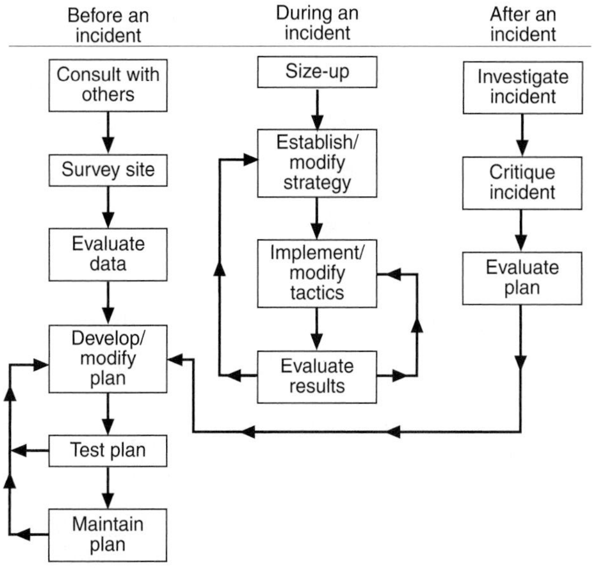

FIGURE 12.17.2 Pre-Incident Planning Process Flowchart

Pre-Incident Planning Data Gathering Form

Date: 7/24/93

Number of employees: 43

Location: 20511 Hicks Rd.

Phone number: 708-634-3035

Sport Fashions

(Name of company and address)

Owner name/operator name: Fashion Apparel USA/Fred Jones Mfg.

Access to site: Streets— 1000-ft private drive with many large potholes to main west of Hicks Rd.

Lockbox: Outside of office door on left side

Annunciator panel—location:

Outside of office door on right side

Fire department connections—location:

1. Front of Guard House at Hicks Rd. entrance; 2. W. corner fenced yard, accessible from Ridge Rd.

Door locations/forcible entry notes:

1. Office-use lockbox key; 2. Dock office, center, E. side, 24-hr occy. ex. weekends;
3. Pump house—lockbox key at main office.

Storage configuration hazards:

Clothing warehouses; stock in cardboard boxes on back-to-back double row racks 23 ft high; 8-ft-wide aisles, ordinary wood pallets; no solid shelves

Construction: Width (side facing fronting street): 345 ft

No. stories: Depth: 200 ft

Height: 1 story = 27 ft

Wall construction: Insulated metal

Roof construction: Support structure — Steel joists on unprotected steel beams and columns

Roof covering — Built-up layers w/tar and gravel

Location of vertical and horizontal cutoffs (space separation—fire walls):

Type of fire doors: 12-in. HCB w/parapet at offices

Utilities:				
	Gas	Unit heaters	Cutoff points	100 ft w/guard house
	Electrical		Cutoff points	1. 200 ft
	Oil pumps	None	Cutoff points	2. Ridge Rd. side
	Propane tank	None	Cutoff points	

Critical exposures: Side 1: Open — Side 2: Automatic sprinkler whse 90 ft

Side 3: Open — Side 4: Open

Protection (on site): Public water: 1650 gpm

Residual pressure: 51 psi — Normal static at site: 65 psi — Test date: 6/14/2007

Sprinkler design: 1380 gpm 57 psi

FIGURE 12.17.3 Pre-Incident Planning Data Form

In-rack sprinklers provided: [x] Yes [ ] No

(#) Booster pump 1500 gpm 40 psi Driver type Elec.

(#) Fire pump 2000 gpm 75 psi Driver type Diesel

Hose stream supply: On site: Pond Public: 16-in. main—Hicks Rd.

Hose length to reach: Hydrant—200 ft; Pond—600 ft

Water demand: for AS: 1610 for hose streams: 500 gpm

Venting: Manual hatches: [ ] Yes [x] No

Automatic: ______ Powered: ______

Power switch locations: ______

______

Special conditions:

Employee head count location: Guard house—Main Hicks Rd. entrance

Contact person: Days—Mgr. Fred Jones; Nights—Shift Foreman

Special units needed: 2nd ladder truck on 1st alarm from Ft. Mudge FD. Shift commander must request dispatch to TX.

Other: ______

Sketch details:

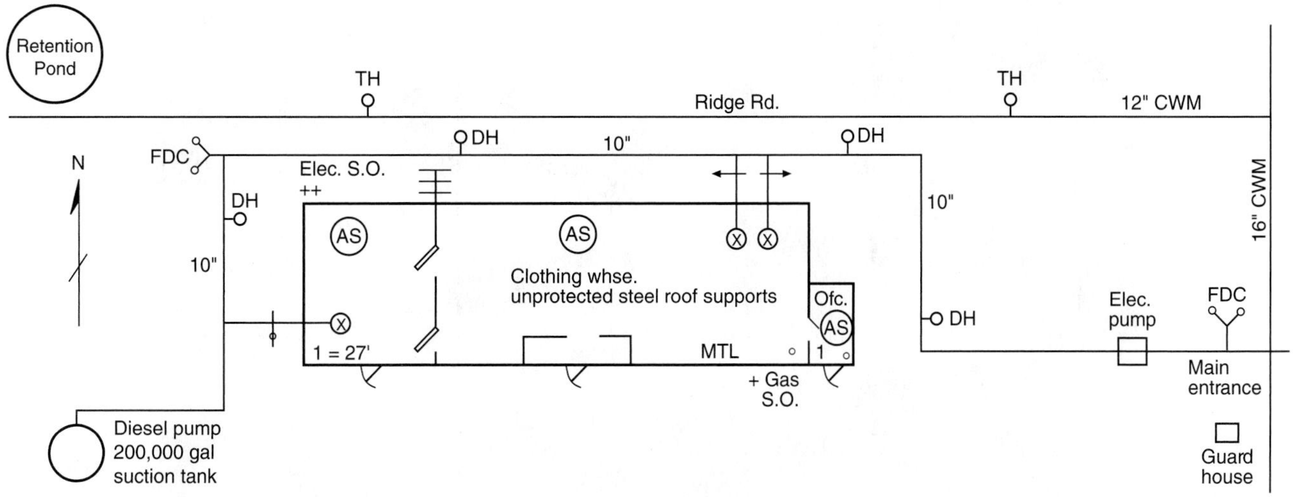

FIGURE 12.17.3 Continued

Testing and practicing the pre-incident plan will provide an opportunity to fine-tune the data and to revise and update the plan.

During the incident, the pre-incident plan should become the foundation for operations. It will provide important data that will assist the incident commander in developing appropriate strategy and tactics for managing the incident. Changes in conditions might dictate a revised strategy, including adjustments to responses and tactics. Throughout the incident, consulting the pre-incident plan will keep the incident commander informed about factors that might affect the success of any given strategic or tactical adjustment.

Each incident provides an opportunity for improvement. Assumptions, predictions, and accuracy of the pre-incident plan should be evaluated in light of the actual results during the incident. Modifications to the pre-incident plan should be made as necessary, and the plan should be retested, especially if the modifications are extensive.

DATA COMPONENTS

Building Construction

Construction features, such as structural framing systems, building materials, and the interior and exterior finishes, can be key factors in the rate and extent of fire spread within a building. The fire conditions in a building of fire resistive construction will be markedly different from those in a building constructed entirely of combustible materials. Fire development, intensity, and spread can be far better controlled in structures of fire-resistive construction. The size of the building, both vertical and horizontal, can also have a drastic effect on the decision process that takes place during an emergency. Awareness of these features by the fire department is important in estimating the potential fire problem and ultimately confining the fire to a limited area. Figure 12.17.4 shows a team reviewing the details of a building's specialized gas detection system.

Wall Construction. The pre-incident plan should include information regarding construction materials for exterior walls, such as metal panel, masonry, or wood frame. This information will be helpful in determining the potential for exposure protection, the potential loss of structural integrity, and the ability to access the building interior.

Roof Construction. Information on roof construction is also needed. This information includes the roof support, such as wood joist, steel joist, or steel beam; the roof deck, such as steel, metal panel, wood plank, or concrete; and the roof covering, such as built-up tar and gravel or insulated membrane system. The type of roof construction can have an impact on ventilation operations, can create exposure problems, and, most importantly, can increase the dangers to fire fighters. The pre-incident plan should also note how venting will be accomplished and the location of any manual or automatic vents. The decision to place fire fighters on a building roof during a fire should be based

FIGURE 12.17.4 Operational Overview of Flammable Gas Detection System

partly on advance knowledge of the particular roof construction. Roofs unprotected by automatic sprinklers, even those of fire-resistive construction, can collapse very early during a fire incident.

While conducting the survey, look for indicators of truss construction and consider marking facilities with an easily identified symbol. One such arrangement exists in the state of New Jersey. The New Jersey Uniform Fire Code requires identifying symbols be permanently affixed to the front of structures with truss construction. "F" signifies a floor with truss construction; "R" signifies a roof with truss construction; "F/R" signifies both a floor and roof with truss construction. Samples of truss identifying symbols are shown in Figures 12.17.5 (a) (b).

Ceilings and Attics. False ceilings and common attics can lead to fire spread within a building and impair the ability of fire fighters to control the fire. These construction features can create safety hazards by permitting fires to burn undetected in areas that are not readily visible. Awareness of these structural features allows fire fighters to prevent or reduce fire spread in these areas.

Floor Construction. Like roofs, similar information should be gathered about the building's floor construction, since the same collapse potential may exist. In addition, information should be obtained regarding the floor's capabilities for drainage, especially where flammable and combustible liquids are used or stored.

Means of Egress. The location of a building's entrances and exits, interior hallways, stairs, or other travel paths can be extremely valuable information in developing strategy or directing rescue, fire control, or other tactical operations. Familiarity with building access is often key to directing fire attack efforts that will confine the fire to the involved area, rather than driving it into uninvolved portions of the structure.

Vertical Openings. Vertical openings can exist in the form of open stairways, conveyor openings, utility shafts, elevator shafts, and so on. These openings can affect the travel of fire, heat, and smoke.

(a) (b)

FIGURE 12.17.5 Truss Symbols (Courtesy of John B. Smith, Fire Sub-code Official and Fire Marshal (Retired), Raritan Township, New Jersey)

Horizontal Openings. Barriers to horizontal smoke and heat movement can exist in the form of fire walls, fire doors, smoke barriers, and so on. Attention should be given to the protection provided for horizontal openings. The types of fire doors provided and their method of closure should be noted.

Occupancy

The type of occupancy is important in establishing incident priorities and tactical operations. An awareness of a facility's operations and contents increases the fire department's ability to fight a fire in that facility effectively and safely.

Life safety considerations should be the first priority for pre-incident planning. Many factors can influence the number and location of people in industrial and commercial facilities: hours of operation, day of the week, time of year, and the physical layout of the facility all have an impact on the type of life safety concerns the fire fighters may be faced with during an incident.

The operations within a facility can be classified into several general categories, such as office, retail, manufacturing, warehouse, and so on. However, each occupancy has its own unique characteristics that should be considered during pre-incident planning. Office buildings may have extensive computer rooms or laboratory areas, retail facilities may have large storage areas, and manufacturing occupancies have many different types of specialized equipment, hazardous materials, and hazardous processes.

Material safety data sheets (MSDS) should be reviewed for information on hazardous materials. Locations of MSDS files and related data, as well as the facility personnel responsible for this information, should be included in the pre-incident plan. Such information may be provided in a lockbox and should be noted on the facility drawing.

Due to extensive chemical inventories at some facilities, consideration should be given to obtaining electronic files. Chemical inventories, material safety data sheets, and related information can be stored on compact discs, portable drives, or on the hard drive of laptop computers. For the latter, some locations may have network connection capabilities and will allow uploading or viewing of site information during emergencies.

Warehouses have a wide range of occupancy considerations: commodity classifications, storage height and configuration, controlled environments, and limited access areas. Special attention should be paid to warehouses storing large quantities of hazardous or toxic materials, flammable or combustible liquids, aerosols, roll paper, rubber tires, and plastics. All of these types of commodities have proved to be substantial fire protection challenges over the years.

The pre-incident plan should detail salvage needs, as well. Often the largest part of a loss within an industrial or commercial occupancy is due to smoke damage outside of the immediate fire area.

With all occupancies, a critical component of pre-incident planning is keeping up with changes. If the occupancy of an area changes, the adequacy of the existing sprinkler system design and available water supply must be reviewed. This is especially important in warehouse occupancies. Changes in product commodity classification and storage height and configuration can be subtle and occur over a period of time. If the sprinkler system design or the water supply are inadequate for the type and arrangement of storage, fire control in the area of ignition is unlikely.

Protection

Knowledge of the fire protection systems in a building, of how these systems operate, and of what actions are necessary to supplement these systems are essential to pre-incident planning.

Automatic Sprinkler Systems. Sprinklers play a vital role in the protection of industrial and commercial facilities. Pre-incident planning must determine not only whether or not the building is sprinklered but also whether or not the sprinkler system (and its available water supply) is adequate for the occupancy of the building. This determination may be beyond the capabilities of the fire department personnel assigned to do pre-incident planning. Resources outside of the fire department must be utilized, if necessary, to make this determination. This is where a team approach to pre-incident planning with the facility's property insurance carrier can be crucial. The facility itself may also have personnel either locally or at the corporate level that have this information. A fire protection engineer might need to be consulted if the information cannot be determined elsewhere. If the sprinkler system is not adequately designed to meet the protection requirements of the occupancy in the building, the building is essentially an "unsprinklered" building.

Pre-incident planning should include obtaining the minimum sprinkler system flow and pressure requirements for each major area of the facility. Most sprinkler systems installed today are hydraulically designed systems, which should have a placard posted on the riser indicating the specific flow and pressure design characteristics of the system. A key point: although the placard indicates what the system was designed for, that design may not be what is needed to protect the current occupancy.

An important part of pre-incident planning for protection features is to anticipate potential sources of sprinkler system failure. These potential problems can be summarized into three major categories:

1. *Design deficiency.* The water supply feeding the sprinkler system or the sprinkler system itself is not properly designed for the occupancy. The original system design might not have been adequate, or a change to a more hazardous commodity or storage array might have resulted in an inadequate system. Even seemingly minor changes in some occupancies, such as warehouses, can compromise existing sprinkler protection.

2. *Impairment to the sprinkler system before a fire.* This generally occurs when a sprinkler system is actually shut off during new construction or building renovations, or when an obstruction, such as a rock, works its way into sprinkler piping and blocks the flow of water.

3. *Impairment to the sprinkler system during a fire.* The system is impaired when any sprinkler control valve is shut prematurely during a fire. This obviously turns off the water to the sprinklers. Well-meaning facility employees or fire fighters may shut the valve in order to reduce smoke or to control water damage; however, this action only prevents sprinklers from gaining control of a fire in its critical development stage. Even if the valve is turned on again later, the fire might have grown beyond the point where sprinklers can control it.

The location of sprinkler control valves, and the building areas they protect, must be determined during pre-incident planning. Facility management should post signs that will help fire fighters locate these valves upon arrival. Knowing where control valves are located is essential because checking to make sure they are open is one of the first actions the fire department should take when it arrives on scene. This action, combined with establishing the water supply, is key to ensuring that the designed sprinkler system is doing the job it was intended to do, that is, protect the building structure and its occupants, including fire fighters entering the building to complete final extinguishment.

The location of the fire department (threaded or quarter-turn) connections should be determined. The connections should be identified as to whether they feed the entire site, individual buildings, individual systems, or standpipes. Threads should be physically checked for compatibility with the fire department thread.

Water Supplies. The most common source of water for the sprinkler system is a public water supply. In some cases, if the volume of the public supply is adequate but the available pressure is too low, a booster pump is connected to the public supply to boost the system's pressure to the necessary level. Current water supply results should be available or tests should be conducted to obtain current information.

A static water source would usually require a fire pump to provide the necessary water volume and pressure to the system. Tanks, wells, reservoirs, and rivers are examples of these suction sources.

Where either booster pumps or fire pumps are provided, it is important to note their size, pressure settings, starting arrangement, and power and fuel supply. Fire fighters responding to an incident should check to make sure that required fire pumps have started, particularly when the fire pumps are the only adequate source of water.

Regardless of the source, a sprinkler system's water supply should be capable of meeting not only the sprinkler demand but also the demand for hose streams. The water source chosen should be carefully selected so that the primary water supply for the sprinkler system will not be reduced. The location and capacity of hydrants, both public and private, should be determined. Where hydrant systems and water mains are not available, alternative resources must be determined to deliver sufficient water to the fire scene.

Special Protection Systems. Some facilities may have other types of protection systems, such as dry chemical, foam, carbon dioxide, or other gaseous extinguishing systems. The presence of these systems should be noted, as well as the areas they protect. In most cases, these systems will be considered supplementary to automatic sprinkler systems.

Standpipes. The pre-incident plan should note if available standpipe systems are of the wet or dry type and the size of the hose discharge outlet. If pressure-reducing or other regulating valves are provided at the outlets, information on adjusting or removing these devices should be understood. Small hose stations may be provided and supplied from the sprinkler system. The pre-incident plan should note if these stations will be impaired if the sprinkler system is shut off in a particular area.

Fire Alarm System. The type of alarm system should be determined as to the type of detection provided (smoke, heat, waterflow) and the method of transmittal to the fire department. The presence of an alarm system does not eliminate the need for a follow-up telephone call from the facility confirming the nature and exact location of the alarm. Figure 12.17.6 shows fire fighters engaged in the pre-incident planning task of studying a building's layout to confirm the location of alarm devices.

Procedures should be established for facility management to notify the fire department when sprinkler systems, fire pumps, special extinguishing systems, or alarm systems are taken out of service, regardless of the duration. If alarms are out of service, a temporary notification procedure should be instituted. When the fire department is notified of an impairment, the pre-incident plan should be referred to and contingency actions considered.

Site Considerations

Access. Familiarity with local streets and roads in the area can provide the best access route to the location. Pre-incident planning can also provide alternative ways to reach the area should normal routes become unusable due to bridges with weight restrictions, narrow streets, road construction, flooding, drifting snow, railroad grade crossings, and so on. Alternative approaches for responding units also allow for the placement of additional apparatus. It is important to determine which units will respond and from what direction they will come. This information can help in the safety of apparatus approaching the same intersection from different directions. Assignments for fire companies based on probable order of arrival, including any neighboring companies that may respond on an automatic mutual aid, can increase the effectiveness of the fireground operation.

Security. Data regarding security service at the site should be obtained. The number of security personnel on duty, where they are normally located, areas of "restricted" access, and the presence of guard dogs are among the items that should be reviewed. The location of any lockboxes and their contents should also be noted. An emergency call list of facility staff for off-hours should be obtained.

Exposures. Exposures to the site can be both structural and nonstructural elements, such as neighboring buildings, fuel storage tanks, standing or tidal waters, vegetation, wooded areas, yard storage, and airport flight paths.

Utilities. All utilities for the site should be reviewed. The type of fuel, storage location, and quantities should be noted, along with the locations of the emergency shutoffs.

FIGURE 12.17.6 Team Checking the Location of Alarm Initiating Devices

The location of the entrance for electric power should be noted. Also the location of the nearest disconnecting means within the facility as well as the nearest one outside the facility should be determined. If an electric-driven fire or booster pump is provided, it is important to determine the reliability of the power supply, noting if power lines run through the facility and if an independent feed has been provided so that the pump will remain running even if the facility has been shut down.

The location of emergency generators should be noted, as well as what equipment is powered when normal power is lost. Special consideration is needed if the emergency generator also supplies power to an electric-driven fire or booster pump.

Heating, ventilation, and air-conditioning (HVAC) systems can contribute to the spread of smoke throughout a facility. The ability to engage or disengage these systems as needed and the location of automatic and manual controls for this equipment should be documented. Facility services, such as domestic water, compressed air, and steam, should also be reviewed.

Environment. Runoff of fire-fighting water contaminated with hazardous waste must be considered. Data should be gathered on the location of water drainage collection points, potable water supply locations, and any other potential exposures. The anticipated exposure should be measured against the expected fire scenario, based on the facility's other construction, occupancy, and protection features.

Outside Assistance

During many incidents, fire service personnel are assisted by other agencies or other industrial facilities capable of providing the support functions necessary to control the fire. Interagency and outside assistance can be vital to the outcome of emergency incidents.

If automatic response agreements result in a mutual-aid fire department arriving first on the scene, this department should be involved in the pre-incident planning process and should receive copies of the finished documentation.

Other assistance may include traffic control by police; the use of specialized resources, such as fire-fighting foam stored at another industrial facility; utility service control for electric, gas, and water systems; and other items, such as sand, barricades, and heavy construction equipment.

Because the amount and type of interagency assistance will vary in different areas, pre-incident plans should identify what is available and how to effectively request a timely response when it is needed.

SUMMARY

Pre-incident planning is a valuable tool for emergency responders to effectively control a fire or other emergency incident. Preparing for emergency incidents by visiting specific target hazards and recording pertinent information is required to successfully manage the incident and minimize the potential for life and property loss.

The pre-incident planning process requires a team effort in collecting information, developing the plan, and implementing the plan. Facility management, the municipal fire service or other emergency response organization, and the property insurance company are all key players. Sharing of information through open and frequent communication is an effective means to address the many facets of developing a pre-incident plan. Very few, if any, fire departments have the resources by themselves to effectively develop pre-incident plans for all types of industrial and commercial facilities within their jurisdiction. The varying nature and complexity of processes found in the industrial sector necessitate a collective approach to plan development.

Pre-incident plans must be viewed as living documents and be periodically updated as conditions warrant. A continuous improvement process should be implemented to assure emergency responders have a tool that is complete and current. Collecting pertinent data must be accomplished by site visits to the targeted facility. However, a pre-incident plan is not a fire safety inspection. Pre-incident planning assumes an emergency incident will occur. Commercially available software programs may be used to record data and develop the plan. Regardless of how the plan is developed, it should be remembered that the plan is intended for use by emergency responders. Therefore, it is necessary for the information to be clearly written, concise, and representative of current conditions.

Although there are many aspects to effectively managing an emergency incident, pre-incident planning is a critical component. Assuming that an incident will occur and preparing for it with a written plan is a proven means to minimize the potential for life and property loss.

BIBLIOGRAPHY

NFPA Codes, Standards, and Recommended Practices

Reference to the following NFPA codes, standards, and recommended practices will provide further information on pre-incident planning for industrial and municipal emergency response discussed in this chapter. (See the latest version of The NFPA Catalog *for availability of current editions of the following documents.)*

NFPA 13, *Standard for the Installation of Sprinkler Systems*
NFPA 13E, *Recommended Practice for Fire Department Operations in Properties Protected by Sprinkler and Standpipe Systems*
NFPA 14, *Standard for the Installation of Standpipe and Hose Systems*
NFPA *101*®, *Life Safety Code*®
NFPA 241, *Standard for Safeguarding Construction, Alteration, and Demolition Operations*
NFPA 600, *Standard on Industrial Fire Brigades*
NFPA 1142, *Standard on Water Supplies for Suburban and Rural Fire Fighting*
NFPA 1201, *Standard for Providing Emergency Services to the Public*
NFPA 1250, *Recommended Practice in Emergency Service Organization Risk Management*
NFPA 1600, *Standard on Disaster/Emergency Management and Business Continuity Programs*
NFPA 1620, *Recommended Practice for Pre-Incident Planning*

References

Harrington, J. L., "Lessons Learned from Warehouse Fires," *Fire Protection Engineering,* No. 29, Winter 2006, Society of Fire Protection Engineers, Penton Media, Cleveland, OH, pp. 22–28.
NFPA Fire Investigations Report, "Bulk Retail Store Fire, Albany, GA, April 16, 1996," National Fire Protection Association, Quincy, MA.

Chapter 18

Pre-Incident Planning for Emergency Response

Revised by
John Norman

Chapter Contents

Key Terms

computer-aided dispatch, exposure hazard, height and area, pre-incident planning, site visit, size-up, standard operating procedure, water supply (fire protection)

Pre-incident planning is a vital tool for all fire departments, municipal or industrial, career or volunteer, large or small. Information gathered during a pre-incident planning visit is a key component of a fire officer's size-up during an actual incident. Size-up can be described as an evaluation of problems and conditions that affect the likely outcome of a fire. Size-up is an information-gathering process, akin to gathering intelligence in a military campaign. Pre-incident planning is done to allow fire-fighting personnel to view conditions within a structure or site, evaluate what these conditions are likely to develop into in the event of an emergency, and then develop strategies for dealing with the potential problems. The great advantage of pre-incident planning is that it is done pre-incident. Three o'clock in the morning, with high winds and heavy rain lashing your face, and fire extending in all directions as you watch, is not the best time for gathering critical information.

NFPA has recognized the necessity for pre-incident planning by issuing a series of consensus standards beginning in 1993. In 1998 the first comprehensive pre-incident standard (NFPA 1620, *Recommended Practice for Pre-Incident Planning*) was adopted and published, with an updated edition following in 2003. This standard and its accompanying appendices present a very detailed examination of the topic and process, including several examples of preplanning forms and documents. NFPA 1620 should be reviewed carefully by any department initiating a pre-incident planning program or updating an existing one. The examples presented in this chapter illustrate one particular approach and the experiences of a fire-rescue department that has engaged in pre-incident planning for many decades.

For topics related directly to this chapter, see the following chapters in Section 12: Chapter 1, "Planning for Public Fire-Rescue Protection"; Chapter 3, "Needs Assessment and Hazard Analysis"; Chapter 8, "Effect of Building Construction and Fire Protection Systems on Fire Fighter Safety"; and Chapter 12, "Disaster Planning and Response Services." For information on calculating water supply requirements, see Section 15, Chapter 3, "Hydraulics for Fire Protection."

OVERVIEW OF THE PRE-INCIDENT PLANNING PROCESS

Prior to implementing a pre-incident planning program, fire department leadership must establish the priorities that it wants to cover in the program. In an ideal world, every structure and site in a department's area of responsibility would be subject to pre-incident planning (PIP). This is a very attainable goal in some organizations, such as suburban towns consisting primarily of large segments of nearly identical tract housing, whereas it may be totally unrealistic in other areas that consist of great numbers of large complex and different buildings. In the case of the former, the PIP may have occurred in the form of past responses that have developed into standard

Deputy Assistant Chief **John Norman** is a veteran of more than 36 years in the fire service, including 27 years with the FDNY, the majority of that time in special operations units. In the days after September 11, 2001, Chief Norman was designated the search and rescue manager for the World Trade Center site. He lectures nationally on a wide variety of fire and rescue topics.

operating procedures or guidelines (SOP/SOG). Departments facing the latter situation have a tendency to preplan only "target hazards" and let SOPs or SOGs take care of the remaining structures. That is fine, as long as the fire understands that and remains cooperative, fitting into the framework of "standard" incidents. Too often though, nonstandard situations develop, and that is where PIP pays dividends. I argue for developing pre-incident plans (Figure 12.18.1) for all locations in your response area.

The Size-Up

To be effective, pre-incident planning should address the information that fire-fighting personnel, particularly the incident commander, will need in order to develop their strategy for dealing with potential incidents. Most pre-incident planning focuses on aspects of the size-up that can be known beforehand and that are likely to remain static until an event occurs, such as building construction or occupancy loads. Pre-incident planning should also be flexible enough to take into consideration temporary situations that pose unusual risks or hazards, such as a disruption to the fire protection water supplies or introduction of a one-time flammable process.

A fire officer's size-up begins at the moment the alarm is received, and it continues until the emergency is under control. Pre-incident planning can give much-needed physical information, such as the size and construction of the building or site. Other parts of a fire officer's size-up however, such as weather conditions, location and extent of the fire, and time of day of the event, cannot be completed until the emergency begins. Pre-incident planning should focus on items that are likely to be difficult to obtain at the time of an incident, such as interconnections between buildings that are not visible from the street.

Pre-Incident Site Visits

Larger departments probably have greater resources than smaller departments, but every department has constraints on the amount of resources that can be devoted to PIP. This is one reason why many departments concentrate their PIP on the target hazards. The collection of data on buildings takes time. The fact is, though, that many buildings have been standing in our communities for 50 or 100 years, just waiting for us to come to preplan them. What valid excuse is there for not having done so if a serious mishap occurs that could have been detected by a pre-incident visit sometime during the previous 100 years?

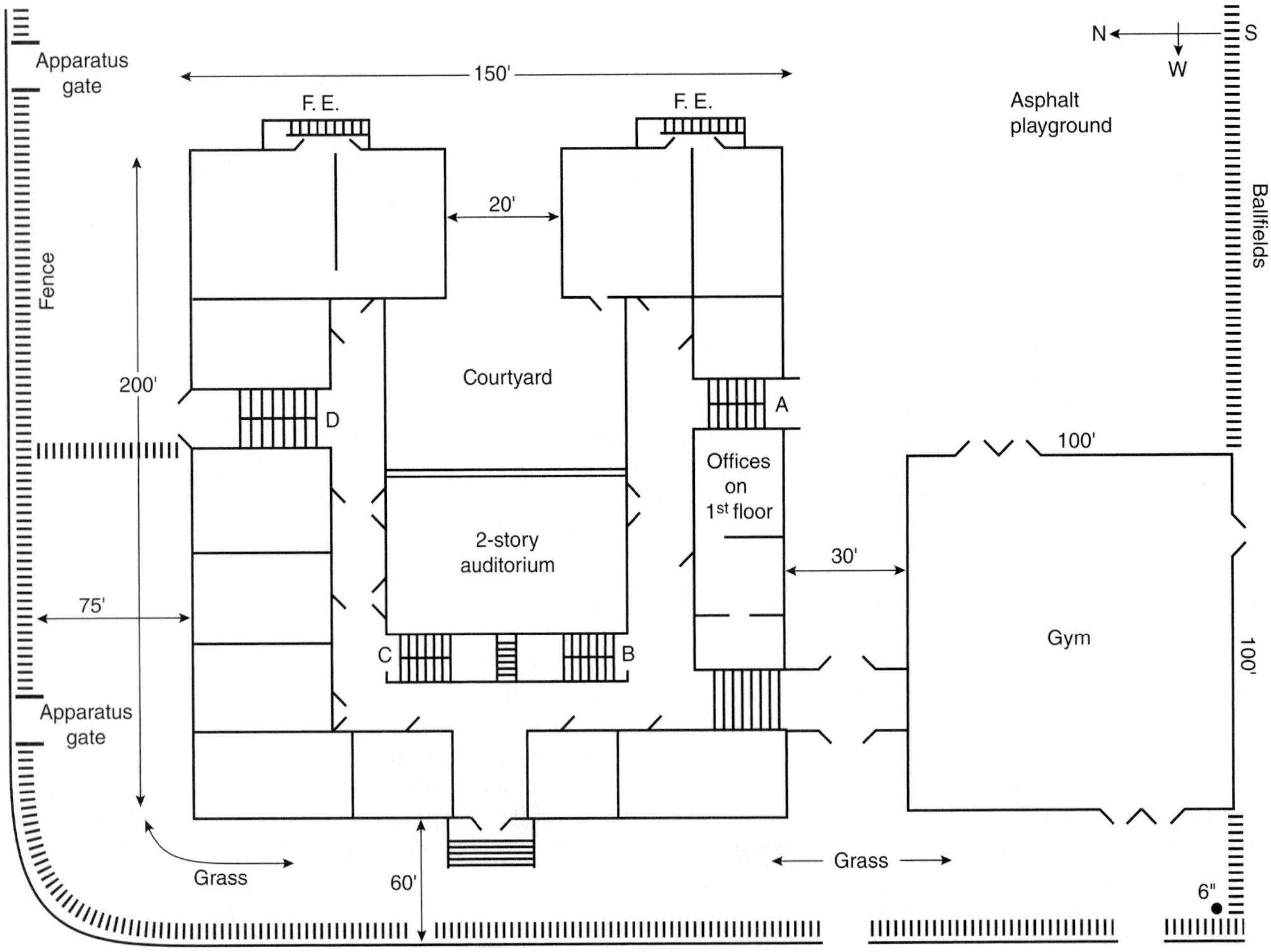

FIGURE 12.18.1 PIP Sketch of a Nonindustrial Facility

When sending fire fighters into a site for a pre-incident planning visit, tell them to approach the site as if they were going to be returning there for a serious fire 15 minutes after they conclude. They will want to examine the location for what could kill them and remember the hazards, so they can avoid them if they were to have a fire. Of course, not all fire fighters remember everything they saw in a building a year or two, or five years prior. That is the point of documenting conditions (Figure 12.18.2) and preparing a written plan or training program that can be reviewed periodically to refresh the memories of fire personnel and can also be used at the time of an actual incident to augment the incident commander's size-up as he develops his strategy and implements tactics.

Identifying Hazards and Obstacles

Pre-incident planning is not just for structural fire fighting. An all-hazards approach is as applicable to PIP as it is to other aspects of emergency services operations. Some nonfire PIP is actually mandated by federal law. For example, OSHA's standard on confined space operations requires that the rescue agency responsible for a premises be permitted access to representative spaces annually to practice rescue procedures. Clearly, this is intended to foster pre-incident familiarization with the space and develop procedures for dealing with potential incidents—that is pre-incident planning.[1]

Outlining and Analyzing Necessary Information

After establishing what types of hazards or occupancies are to be included in the program, the next step in the PIP process is to determine what information will be needed during the data collection phase. This may vary depending on the occupancy of a particular location, but should be geared to gathering the information the incident commander will need to know in order to handle a working structural fire or other emergency. Again, efforts should focus on those aspects that cannot be readily determined from the street upon arrival and create nonstandard situations for which an SOP is not suitable.

Developing a Standard Format. Once the outline of the desired information is determined, a standard format must be developed to capture the information and process it for future use. This can vary from a simple written preplan form to an electronic database that shows details such as floor plans, location of exits and/or hazards, and other details. One tool that has proven to be invaluable is a digital camera. A series of images documenting details about a structure (Figure 12.18.3) can save many miles of travel to and through a site and is extremely valuable for refresher training on a site. It would be helpful if the same person, or a small team of people, collected all the PIP data, since this would produce consistency in what is collected and how it is analyzed, but in larger jurisdictions this may be impractical. (In Phoenix, Arizona, a fire protection engineer attached to the special hazards unit is used in the data collection and formatting phase, leading to a high degree of consistency and expertise.)

Analyzing Information About a Site. Once the site has been visited and the basic data collected, a rational analysis of the site and the hazards present must be conducted, and a plan is created for dealing with the problems that have been detected. The solutions may take many different forms, from taking a

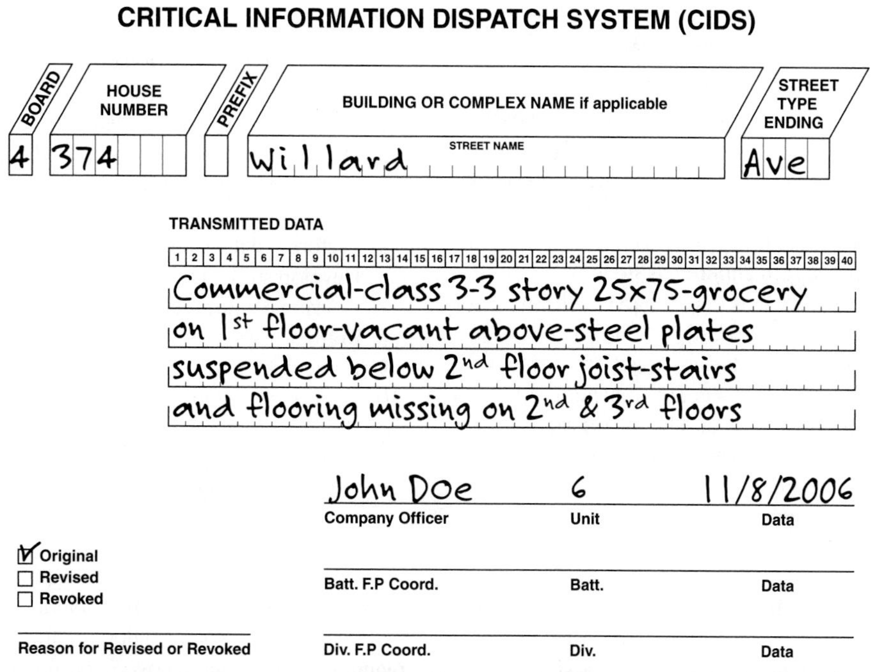
CRITICAL INFORMATION DISPATCH SYSTEM (CIDS)

BOARD: 4 | HOUSE NUMBER: 374 | PREFIX: | BUILDING OR COMPLEX NAME if applicable / STREET NAME: Willard | STREET TYPE ENDING: Ave

TRANSMITTED DATA

1 2 3 4 5 6 7 8 9 10 11 12 13 14 15 16 17 18 19 20 21 22 23 24 25 26 27 28 29 30 31 32 33 34 35 36 37 38 39 40

Commercial-class 3-3 story 25x75-grocery
on 1st floor-vacant above-steel plates
suspended below 2nd floor joist-stairs
and flooring missing on 2nd & 3rd floors

John Doe — Company Officer | 6 — Unit | 11/8/2006 — Data

☑ Original
☐ Revised
☐ Revoked

Batt. F.P Coord. | Batt. | Data

Reason for Revised or Revoked | Div. F.P Coord. | Div. | Data

FIGURE 12.18.2 Critical Information Dispatch System Output for PIP

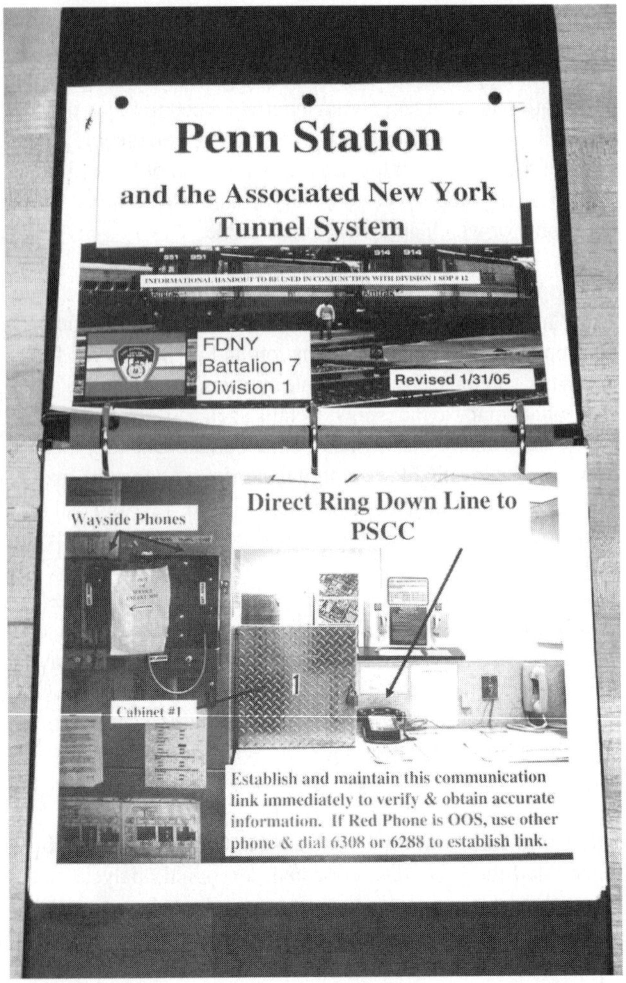

FIGURE 12.18.3 Digital Photos for Use in Pre-Incident Planning Sessions

strictly defensive posture in the event of serious fire exposing lightweight construction elements or some particularly hazardous chemical storage, to arranging for an immediate response of additional resources on the first report of an emergency, such as having an additional ladder company assigned for reports of a fire in a school with handicapped children as students. At some sites, much of the planning, such as determining critical openings in firewalls that will be reinforced with hose streams in the event of a fire, can take place during the site visit. Larger, complex sites may require several visits to complete. It may be necessary to do additional research on chemical hazards, for example. This type of research can better be performed in an office setting with suitable resources at hand. Then the fire fighters can return to the site once a basic plan is established to analyze it in place.

Selecting Personnel to Develop the Plan. The selection of personnel for developing the pre-incident plan is crucial. In many jurisdictions, an experienced chief officer is assigned this task. In some cases, departments have hired private consultants to do much of the basic information gathering. (An excellent example of the work done by one such group is the high-rise building data sheets developed by the Massey Disaster Planning Group. These multipage documents provide a written text-based summary of building features as well as visual illustrations of such elements as floor plans, elevator and stairwell arrangements, HVAC and standpipe riser diagrams, and other critical factors that are essential to the incident commander's size-up.

Avoid the temptation of assigning the task of developing the pre-incident plan to company level officers or members of the Bureau of Fire Prevention (or Special Hazards for that matter). Although they can be extremely helpful in collecting and interpreting the raw site data, the personnel who are actually responsible for fireground command should make all the strategic decisions when formulating the action plan, since they will be deciding what will actually be implemented. It is essential as well that, if a department operates as different shifts, the appropriate commanders of each shift reach a consensus on actions to be taken to avoid conflicting messages or actions.

Using the Plan

After the plan has been developed, it should not be set on the shelf as personnel move on to the next task. The job is not complete until all members who may play a role in the implementation have been thoroughly educated on it and given the opportunity to demonstrate their proficiency. That may require periodic visits to the site for drills or exercises and/or tabletop exercises using the photos and plans developed during prior site visits. These visits should occur at least annually on all affected shifts. Some structures may require more frequent visits due to changing conditions.

The general picture of pre-incident planning that was outlined in the preceding sections can be summarized as follows:

1. Determine priorities to address—that is, life hazards, firefighter traps, and critical infrastructure.
2. Decide what data is needed.
3. Develop a standardized information capture method, preplan form, and so forth.
4. Train collectors to gather information.
5. Perform visits and collect data.
6. Develop strategic and tactical plans.
7. Distribute copies to all potential users.
8. Train users on objectives.
9. Review the plan periodically (annually at minimum).
10. Revise as needed, redistribute, and retrain.

"COAL WAS WEALTH" PROCESS

When deciding what information to include in the plan, it is helpful to consider what will be required in the incident commander's size-up. New York City fire officers use a 13 point outline of factors when conducting their size-up or pre-incident planning. This process covers the majority of fireground considerations and is summarized in the acronym "COAL WAS WEALTH."[2]

The COAL WAS WEALTH process includes the following points:

C Construction
O Occupancy
A Apparatus and staffing
L Life hazard

W Water supply
A Auxiliary appliances
S Street conditions/special matters

W Weather
E Exposures
A Area and height
L Location and extent of fire
T Time
H Hazardous materials

The elements of the COAL WAS WEALTH process are often arranged in order of priority, broken down as shown in the following paragraphs.

Life Hazard

Life hazard is produced by a combination of several other size-up elements: time of day, the occupancy, location, and extent of fire all combine to endanger victims. Pre-incident planning can and should identify the occupancy, especially when there is more to the building than meets the eye. Commercial buildings that are partially occupied with residential areas are prime locations for preplanning, since responding fire units would normally not conduct an aggressive search for life at a late-night fire in what is perceived to be a commercial building. The preplan information gathered here could mean the difference between life and death for sleeping tenants in this situation. Many older cities have seen a renaissance of some of their older commercial neighborhoods as residential occupants moved into vacant manufacturing spaces in loft-type buildings. In New York City, this practice was originally begun by people in the artistic community, who valued the high ceilings and large floor spaces of the former commercial areas for artistic projects such as sculpting and painting. These urban pioneers were known as "artists in residence," and the commercial buildings that had some residential spaces were known as A.I.R. buildings. An extensive campaign was conducted by the fire department to identify these buildings, which then were required to be marked with a prescribed sign to alert responding fire fighters to the A.I.R. Later, when a computer-aided dispatch system came into use, an entry for A.I.R. buildings also served to alert fire fighters to the life hazard in the building they were responding to. Both systems represent pre-incident planning at work.

Occupancy

The occupancy of a structure has many impacts on the fire officers' strategy. One major impact, as just discussed, is the life hazard, which may vary with the time of day. Schools, for example, have a life hazard that varies greatly with the time of day. Hospitals and apartment houses, on the other hand, have a high life hazard around the clock, whereas storage warehouses and similar occupancies have a uniformly low life hazard regardless of time of day. The occupancy should serve to determine the level of risk to fire fighters that will be tolerated when developing the strategy. Where the occupancy poses great threats to fire-fighting personnel, and where the civilian life hazard is minimal, a defensive strategy should be developed.

The occupancy has a great effect on the fire load within the structure, which will dictate water supply requirements, and affect other aspects of the incident commander's strategy. Manufacturing and storage occupancies typically have large, open floor areas that may translate into fires that are beyond the scope of handline control. Large open floor spaces should alert fire fighters to look for truss construction, a collapse danger. Another aspect of occupancy is the presence of hazardous materials that may be a required part of the ongoing business conducted in a facility, such as cyanides in a plating plant. Hazards in other locations are not as obvious however, and fire fighters may have to look deeper for hazards, such as in a freight warehouse where manufacturing and use of dangerous goods does not occur (other than the use of propane for forklifts or similar items) but which can be locations for transshipping nearly any dangerous commodity produced elsewhere. The handling of hazardous materials should be noted on pre-incident planning forms, citing quantities stored, location of storage, and any special concerns such as incompatibility with water or other materials, or the need for special extinguishing agents.

Time

Pre-incident planning may not seem to have a great deal to do with time, since we cannot predict exactly when a fire will strike a given structure, but there are several time-related concerns that directly impact fire-fighting operations, including time of day, time of year, and perhaps most important, the elapsed time from when the fire began. The time of day may prompt the response of an additional ladder truck to a school with handicapped children, but only during school hours. PIP should account for seasonal changes that affect operations, such as winter plans that identify additional resources for snow removal or hydrant thawing or additional brush fire units to be staged during high fire danger periods.

Elapsed burn time is a crucial indicator of the likelihood of structural collapse. Structural collapse is very difficult to predict, due to the many variables that can be involved: the type of construction, fire loading, length of burn before the alarm is transmitted, alterations to the original structural design—either through routine structural alterations or deterioration from exposure to weather or industrial processes. It is important to remember that long before the alarm sounds, the structural engineer who designed the building set a time limit for the effectiveness of fire-fighter actions. A crucial element to understand is that the time frame starts when the fire reaches flashover and begins to attack the structural elements. The elapsed time from flashover is one of the primary indicators of an impending collapse. Knowing the class of construction is an important component of this evaluation, as it is an indicator of how long the building will resist structural failure. Pre-incident plans should make it a high priority to identify structures that will likely face collapse dangers, especially those that are vulnerable to relatively short burn times.

Construction

A critical factor that must be included in any pre-incident plan is the building's construction. The first concern is the ability of a building to resist collapse when attacked by fire. It is not advisable to rely strictly on labels given to building assemblies such as a two-hour rated floor or wall. There are many factors that affect how long it will take a given structural element to fail, including the fire loading of the area that exposes the element, damage that has occurred to it from explosions, prior fires, weather damage, vandalism, and so on. It is good to recall that one of the "three-hour rated" World Trade Center towers collapsed in under one hour of fire exposure.[3]

Construction has other implications, including the amount of compartmentation present, which can either promote or thwart the spread of fire. Large, open floor spaces provide an opportunity for fire to spread readily throughout the exposed area and are indicators of the presence of truss construction.

A third factor is the degree to which the building itself adds to the fire load. With wood construction, the building itself may constitute a heavy fire load. Directly related to a building's combustible construction is the number of hidden voids that fire can travel in. Voids such as cocklofts, pipe chases, and channel-rail voids are responsible for the destruction by fire of more buildings than any other construction-related factor.

A comprehensive listing of all buildings in your area that are built using lightweight techniques is critical to fire-fighter survival, along with a clear department policy stating that a fire that has reached the flashover stage in one of these structures will only be fought from defensive positions until the fire has been knocked down and ventilation and lighting conditions permit a careful examination of the structural elements. This information should be recorded in a computer-aided dispatching system (CADS) message. The idea behind pre-incident planning is to allow rational decisions to be made based on the information that has been gathered during the pre-incident planning visit. Decide what you want your people to do, then write it down for them as policy, and let them know about it!

For a further discussion of the impact of building construction on fire personnel, see Section 12, Chapter 8, "Effect of Building Construction and Fire Protection Systems on Fire Fighter Safety."

Area and Height

The area and height of a given building are two obvious concerns during size-up, since they indicate the maximum potential fire area. Sometimes, however, the size of a structure is deceptive when viewed from the street. This may be because the building is built on a sloping grade, which may cause fire personnel on one side to view the structure as one-storied whereas personnel on another side see it as two-storied. A similar situation contributed to the deaths of four fire fighters at a fire in Seattle in 1995. Pre-incident planning could have established the actual size and facilitated communications during the event, as personnel on different sides of the structure refer to the same area.

The height of the building has obvious effects on the need for aerial devices. PIP can build into a department's protocols the need for calling such aerial devices, especially when they are not normally part of a routine response for that type of structure.

The area of a building is also an important item for PIP. Look for buildings that will require modifications to the standard attack, especially those buildings that exceed the reach of preconnected attack lines. It may be necessary to create a separate hose bed for larger structures, in order to provide a sufficient length attack line to cover all areas. For the most part, the frontage of a building (width and depth) visible from the street indicates the area of the structure, but the obvious is not always correct. The presence of interconnecting openings between what appears to be two separate and distinct buildings effectively combine the structures into one large potential fire area. Such an interconnection should be prominently displayed in the pre-incident plan that is developed for the structure, including a notation of the presence and condition of any opening protective devices, such as fire doors or deluge sprinkler systems.

Location and Extent of Fire

It might be impossible to determine the location and extent of the fire until after a fire starts, but PIP can often identify likely locations for a fire to begin and also give an idea of the likely extent of fire, based on an analysis of the hazards present. Certain process hazards, such as paint spraying, are notorious points of ignition, as are occupancies such as restaurant kitchens, especially those that typically deep-fry foods. Pre-incident planning should indicate the location of such hazardous areas within a facility, and also indicate the proximity to features such as fire barriers and stairwells that may be threatened.

The location of the fire will influence the tactics used to control it. The lower the fire is in a building, the more serious the hazard, since more of the building is exposed to rapid vertical fire spread. Pre-incident plans should focus on identifying any vertical arteries such as pipe and elevator shafts, as well as open stairwells that will require hose-line protection or physical examination.

Some potential fire locations create special fire-fighting problems, and as such, should warrant particular attention during PIP. The top floor of most Type III (ordinary brick and wood-joist) and Type V (frame) structures has some type of void space above the top floor. Known alternately as a cockloft or attic, this void space creates access problems for fire fighting and allows rapid fire spread over the entire top floor in many cases. Pre-incident plans should note the presence of such voids, as well as the location of any access points or fire divisions that may be present.

Exposures

Exposure hazards are another factor that is relatively easy to determine beforehand but which might be difficult to determine at the time of an emergency. The easiest way is often to view the surroundings from the roof of the structure being preplanned. Any structure that is separated from the building in question by less than the height of the building being preplanned can be in immediate danger, due to the potential for collapse of the walls. Other factors to consider are the construction of the walls of both buildings and the number and size of openings (especially windows) in the opposing walls. Frame walls, especially those covered in combustible materials such as asphalt and vinyl siding, should be noted, and plans should be developed as part of the PIP for protecting these exposed walls with hose streams. For buildings that have exposure protection systems in place, such as exposure sprinklers (exterior, often open deluge heads, located at the eave line), those locations and controls should be noted and operating procedures developed. The examination of exposures should include all six sides of the fire area—front and rear, left and right, top and bottom. The risk to taller nearby structures is especially important to preplan for.

Apparatus and Staffing

The items discovered during PIP will assist in determining what resources are required. The pre-incident planning process should have pointed out the need for specific types of apparatus, such as an aerial device to reach areas above grade or to provide an elevated stream for fire attack or exposure protection. Other items that should be part of PIP are the length of supply lines required to reach a source of water supply that is adequate for the hazard. The pre-incident plan should indicate the number of engine companies that will be required to establish a relay if that is required, and many plans indicate items such as the location that each unit should take in order to speed the establishment of such an operation.

Pre-incident plans may have to be created to deal with contingencies that affect the staffing required at an incident. It is common practice in cold weather climates to make provisions for additional staffing during periods of peak snowfall. Similarly, agencies having large wildland areas or urban-wildland interface often place additional staffing on units or place additional units in service during peak wildfire danger periods.

Water Supply

Water supply is a key element of pre-incident planning. Water supply requirements depend on the fire load and the volume or area involved. There are several methods and formulas to determine how much water is required for a given fire area. In the case of larger facilities, in many areas, the insurance services office (ISO) may have already performed a detailed analysis of the needed fire flow. Contact the area ISO office for assistance. For PIP purposes, in most structures it is usually sufficient to utilize some variation of the Iowa State University fire flow formula to determine how much water is required. Briefly stated, the needed fire flow can be estimated by calculating the area of the structure and multiplying this figure by a factor that depends on the fire loading and construction involved. This factor ranges from 14 gpm/100 ft^2 (53.2 Lpm/9 m^2) for lightly loaded areas such as residential rooms and spaces in noncombustible buildings, to 30 gpm/100 ft^2 (114 Lpm/9 m^2) or more for locations with heavy fire loads, such as paint storage. More water is required if the building itself is of frame construction or if exposures may be threatened and require protection. As an example, a one-story, 100 ft by 100 ft (30.3 m by 30.3 m), ordinary construction furniture showroom should have at least 3000 gpm (11,400 Lpm) available to satisfy basic needed fire flow.

After determining the needed fire flow, PIP for water supply involves flow testing the water sources around the hazard, including such alternative supplies as drafting sites, relay operations, and tanker shuttles. Remember to include sources such as nearby private fire pumps taking suction from supplies separate from the municipal system.

The needed fire flow will help to determine apparatus and manpower requirements. Pre-incident planning for providing the needed fire flow involves how the water will be moved to the incident site. Arrange for sufficient numbers of pumpers, with the appropriate size and length of supply lines, to move the water from the source to the incident scene. Also consider the number and type of discharge appliances that will be required to apply the needed fire flow at the most efficient location(s). Often, a combination of handlines, fixed or portable master streams, and aerial streams will be required.

For further information on calculating water supply requirements, see Section 15, Chapter 3, "Hydraulics for Fire Protection."

Auxiliary Appliances

The presence and serviceability of auxiliary fire protection systems is an item that deserves high priority in any pre-incident plan. Sprinkler systems, standpipe systems, foam systems at bulk oil storage plants, halogenated agents, $CO^{2,}$ and dry-chemical systems for special hazards such as restaurant grease ducts and spray paint booths, are all key components of a structure's fire defenses. Auxiliary appliances that are out-of-service require adjustments to the strategic plan and must be prominently displayed in any pre-incident plan. Such a condition, even if only temporary, might require further action, such as temporarily vacating the structure's occupancy, or placing fire guard personnel on duty to provide for prompt detection and suppression in lieu of the out-of-service systems. Such planned activities should be documented in the fire department's plan for the specific facility or in a standard procedure or guideline for such outages.

Pre-incident planning should identify what auxiliary appliances are present, what their operational status is, the location and method of operating controls, and what potential workarounds exist for partial service interruptions. For example, both standpipe systems and sprinkler systems are routinely supplied through a fire department siamese connection. In the event of an obstruction or failure of the siamese, is it possible to supply the system through another connection? Stretching a supply line to a first- or second-floor hose outlet of a standpipe system is one example of such a workaround. With a sprinkler system, a similar arrangement may be possible, with assistance of building engineering personnel. Document all such workarounds in detail in a section of the pre-incident plan dedicated to auxiliary appliances.

Weather

Weather conditions may not seem to be something that can be preplanned, but many specific policies can be pre-planned for common events. Large-scale, high-impact events, such as hurricanes, blizzards, tornadoes, and so on, should each have in-depth plans for continuity of operations in communities that are subject to such events. These plans may require suspension of services during the peak of the storm, relocation of apparatus and personnel out of areas that are subject to dangerous conditions such as flooding, or added staffing prior to the arrival of the most severe conditions. The plan should be available to all personnel beforehand, so they can anticipate what may be asked of them and make arrangements to be available when called on. The fact is that these unexpected events sometimes occur when those who are most familiar with the plan are not available, and it falls on those less familiar with the planning for implementation. It helps to have seen the plan before being called on to deal with it.

Weather can have serious impacts on fire-fighting efforts. High temperature and high humidity rapidly fatigue fire fighters. Freezing temperatures hamper fire-fighting operations by causing ice accumulations and slipping hazards, and fire fighters must use caution to avoid injury. Severe cold can cause mechanical failures, frozen hydrants and freezing of other water supplies. High winds wreak havoc on fire attack, fanning flames into blowtorch-like proportions. All of these events should figure prominently into plans for dealing with their consequences and should be part of a fire department's library of contingency pre-incident plans.

Street Conditions/Special Matters

Street conditions are another item that at first glance appear to have little impact on pre-incident planning, but in fact, many factors that result from difficult street conditions can and should be dealt with in the PIP stage. Construction trenches for water, sewer, or gas mains may separate the apparatus from the fire building, preventing fire fighters from reaching the front of the building. In that situation, the aerial apparatus should enter the block, since it can reach over a trench. Meanwhile the engine company should position at the nearest intersection and hand-stretch a hose line along the sidewalk. This procedure is likely to differ drastically from most departments' normal SOP and might require modifications to apparatus hose loads, but it is a good opportunity to incorporate pre-incident planning into tactical operations.

Similarly, deep snow and ice can bury hydrants and block streets altogether. Pumpers should remain out on the cleared main artery and hand-stretch lines into the snow-clogged side streets. This is very time-consuming and may require additional personnel, an issue that should be addressed in the winter weather contingency preplan.

Another situation that requires pre-incident planning is a work stoppage of mass transit agencies. Bus and subway strikes add tremendous volumes of traffic to urban arteries and can result in emergency vehicles being gridlocked and therefore unable to reach the scene of an emergency. Planning with traffic management and law enforcement personnel should identify emergency routes that will be kept open for emergency vehicles. Again, it may be necessary to hand stretch hose greater distances than routinely envisioned. Be alert for such *temporary* situations and have a plan, and the necessary hosebed arrangements, to deal with them.

Hazardous Materials

The presence of hazardous materials is one of the most important factors to determine in any pre-incident plan. Hazardous materials pose problems for fire fighters, ranging from health hazards to accelerated fire extension. The presence of poisons or explosives could prompt the fire department to take a strictly defensive posture and not conduct any fire-fighting operations. Information about specific hazards should be researched with an emphasis on actions to be taken in the event that fire or other conditions threaten the material. Details of the name(s) and properties of the materials, quantities and locations of the hazardous materials, as well as recommended procedures for dealing with emergencies should be entered prominently into the pre-incident plan. Specialized extinguishing agents can be located and arrangements made for their use in the event of an emergency, including working out financial arrangements for paying for the agent if it is not normally part of the fire departments arsenal.

INFORMATION RETRIEVAL AND DISSEMINATION

Pre-incident planning is a multistep process that involves gathering information, analyzing that information, developing an action plan, and then making that plan available to those who need it during an emergency. This last step, information dissemination, can be as complicated as the other parts, and requires as much forethought to accomplish well.

Three-Ring Binders

The simplest pre-incident plan process involves written documents stored in three-ring binders kept on responding apparatus (Figure 12.18.4). These plans, as others, should be the subject of training sessions to ensure that all responding personnel have at least a basic awareness that such plans exists and knowledge of the more important elements of the specific plans. This training must be ongoing to be effective. One of the biggest drawbacks of the three-ring binder is the "crying wolf" syndrome that develops when it is necessary to manually check every address that you respond to. Another drawback of the three-ring binders is the size of the plans themselves. A typical high-rise building plan, for example, would require a data sheet with building personnel contact information; a site plan; riser diagrams for stairs, elevators, and standpipes; heating, ventilating and air-conditioning (HVAC) zone and riser diagrams; floor plans for typical floors; and a building profile (side view) showing any setbacks where the building changes dimensions. (A setback occurs where a building's floor plan is smaller than the floors below that point, creating a roof area outside the smaller floor. This roof area may be useful to allow fire fighters to work on the outside of the building.) Separate sheets should be provided for each hazardous material used or stored on site. Very quickly, a set of pre-incident plans for an urban response area can take up several large binders, complicating retrieval efforts in moving apparatus. Paper plans should either be laminated or stored in sealed plastic sheet protectors to protect them from the weather

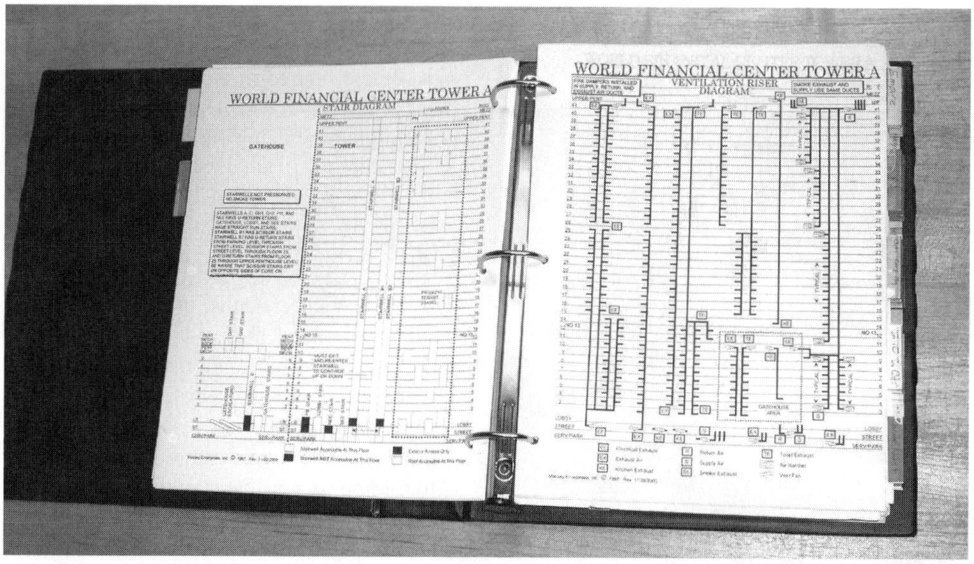

FIGURE 12.18.4 Three-Ring Binders Used to Present Pre-Incident Plan Information

and also allow use of a marker or grease pencil for writing or drawing on them.

In the past, some departments used microfiche cards to provide field commanders with a complete set of pre-incident plans for large numbers of buildings. This system was extremely cumbersome to use due to the need for multiple cards of information that had to be sorted through, as well as the need for a special microfiche reader. An additional drawback was the length of time needed to produce the microfiche cards and the expense of keeping them current.

CADS

When properly used, a computer-aided dispatching system (CADS) is by far the most effective tool for recalling PIP information. CADS surpasses the human memory and the three-ring binder as well in its ability to store and promptly retrieve information. Whereas fire personnel usually know about the most obvious and deadly hazards, other hazards may escape their initial attention. In these situations, a CADS-generated reminder could provide the crucial warning, averting what might otherwise become a fatal encounter.

Data Entry and Retrieval. PIP information should be recalled automatically whenever an alarm is transmitted from a building address that is on file. A CADS systems saves time and effort in its computer searches by only displaying hazard information when there is data on file for the address in question. Of course, any computer-generated information is only as good as the information that was entered. This means that field units must have some quick and simple method of reporting the conditions that they encounter. It also means that the information must be kept up-to-date. For this reason, any occupancy that is subject to CADS hazard display should be inspected at least annually and the information verified.

Responsibilities of Property Owners. Computers have the ability to store large quantities of complex information and display that information in detail. One difficulty is inputting all that information. In many cities, as the CADS systems have been developed or expanded, data entry issues have been resolved by requiring the property owners of certain "target hazards" such as high rise buildings, to provide the information in a standardized electronic format. Often this can be accomplished using a commonly available electronic program that architectural or engineering firms use. This reduces the amount of work required by the municipality and provides a rapid means of updating the system as new structures are erected or as major renovations occur.

Transmission of PIP Messages. Computer-generated PIP messages can be transmitted to field units by any of several means. A dispatcher can read a message to responding units as part of an alert message, highlighting the fact that there is critical information available, or the message can be displayed on a video display terminal, teletyped to each unit, or repeated over radio channels about 1 minute after the initial alarm. The recommended practice is to teletype the alert message (which gives the field unit a hard copy to refer to,) display the information on a mobile data terminal aboard the apparatus, and also broadcast the message over the radio after the units are on the road. These methods serve to present the information to anyone who may have overlooked it, as well as to verify the listing after the fire fighters have had a moment to consider it. The responders can then pull up the detailed plans for each structure and review the individual hazards they have highlighted in advance.

Data Storage. Advances in information storage and retrieval systems have made it feasible to store large amounts of data on laptop or notebook-size computers. In conjunction with wireless communications devices, access to mainframe databases is

FIGURE 12.18.5 Wireless Data Transmission for Field Access to Mainframe Capabilities

possible, placing extremely detailed pre-incident planning information at the incident commander's fingertips (Figure 12.18.5). In the near future, it will be possible for an incident commander to be in touch with multiple sites, providing real-time modeling of events such as a chemical release. Such information, in conjunction with information previously gathered and evaluated during the pre-incident planning stage, will increase the safety of all persons affected by an event. Security of such information must be considered in the age of potential terrorist threats, but this should not stop an emergency response organization from pursuing the gathering and use of as much vital information as is available.

SUMMARY

The pre-incident planning process is a critical component of an incident commander's size-up and decision making process. The failure to gather information about a hazard that could claim the life of a responder and is available beforehand borders on reckless behavior. Emergency responders owe it to themselves, their families, and their communities to avail themselves of as much information as possible about the situations they may face. The specifics of what type of information to gather for each type of structure or occupancy may vary. A military unit would never plan an operation without attempting to gain intelligence about the opposing force. Neither should our emergency responders.

BIBLIOGRAPHY

References Cited

1. OSHA, *Permit-Required Confined Spaces,* 29 CFR 1910.146, U.S. Department of Labor, Occupational Safety and Health Administration, Washington, DC.
2. "Engine Company Operations," *Firefighting Procedures,* Vol. II, Book 1, Chapter 4, New York City Fire Department, Mar. 15, 1997.
3. "Collapse of the World Trade Center Towers," National Institute of Standards and Technology, Gaithersburg, MD, 2005.

NFPA Codes, Standards, and Recommended Practices

Reference to the following NFPA codes, standards, and recommended practices will provide further information on pre-incident planning processes discussed in this chapter. (See the latest version of The NFPA Catalog *for availability of current editions of the following document.)*

NFPA 1620, *Recommended Practice for Pre-Incident Planning*

Chapter 19

Community Risk Reduction

Revised by
Edward Kirtley

Chapter Contents

Key Terms

Learn Not to Burn®, mitigation strategy, NFPA Champion model, public fire and life safety education, risk reduction, *Risk Watch*®, stakeholder

The last decade has seen a significant change in the scope of mission for most fire departments in the United States and Canada, as well as many other nations around the world. It is difficult to find a fire department today that strictly deals with fire suppression. Rather, fire departments have expanded their mission to reflect the changes in society and historical events such as 9/11. Today most fire departments are involved in some level of prehospital medical care varying from first response to advanced life support transport. Some departments, such as the Phoenix Fire Department, are working with local public health providers to assist with preventive health care.

Other programs have grown significantly. Following the Oklahoma City bombing, the first attack on the World Trade Centers, and the 9/11 attacks, many departments have developed technical rescue programs to deal with events involving confined space rescue, whitewater rescue, and high-angle rescue. Also, many fire departments are becoming actively involved in disaster preparedness and response. Hurricane Katrina emphasized the need for the fire department to be an active participant in a community's preparedness for natural disasters.

These changes also extend into the area of prevention. Once a program dedicated to only preventing fires, prevention programs now address such issues as preventing childhood injuries, reducing the impact from disasters, and so on. This expansion of the prevention mission mirrors the growth of other fire department responsibilities. In short, fire departments are now active participants in reducing and mitigating many various risks in the community. This "all-risk" mission is having an impact on how fire departments do business in the new millennium. Specifically, the all-risk mission has resulted in departments utilizing a community-based comprehensive strategy to reduce the highest priority risks faced by the community.

This new all-risk approach to community risk reduction is taken from the approach successfully used by public health agencies for decades. This multifaceted approach builds on the traditional three "E"s of prevention—education, engineering, and enforcement—to include *emergency response* and *economic incentives.* The original three "E"s were first noted in President Harry Truman's 1947 Conference on Fire Prevention. The addition of the two latter "E"s specifically reflects the role of emergency response in risk reduction, something that was previously considered part of prevention. Collectively the five "E"s are known as *mitigation strategies.*

Another significant change in strategy is the active involvement of the community in identifying the risks and participating in the risk reduction process. Again, this strategy is frequently used by public health agencies, especially when working with target groups that are at high risk from illness and injury. With this change fire departments may no longer stay in the shadows and be the silent heroes. The local fire department must become actively engaged in the community, including high-risk groups and neighborhoods that are hard to reach and engage. It is important to look at each of these components of community risk reduction.

See also Section 1, Chapter 1, "Challenges to Safety in the Built Environment"; Section 5, Chapter 3, "Disaster Preparedness Education"; and Section 12, Chapter 12, "Disaster Planning and Response Services."

Edward Kirtley, M.A., is the International Fire Service Training Association/curriculum projects coordinator at Oklahoma State University/Fire Protection Publications. A retired fire chief, he is the former chair of NFPA 1035, Technical Committee for Professional Qualifications for Fire and Life Safety Educator.

COMPONENTS AND FUNDAMENTALS OF A COMMUNITY RISK REDUCTION INITIATIVE

Components

Two major components of a community risk reduction program are use of the five "E"s and engaging the community. The first component, using the five "E"s, is part of a comprehensive approach to reduce the chosen risks. It should be noted that there are numerous risk reduction planning processes that can be employed by a community to determine the leading risk(s) to be addressed. Many are variations of the traditional five-step planning process introduced by the U.S. Fire Administration 30 years ago. For this introduction to community risk reduction the planning process will not be discussed.

The second component of community risk reduction is engaging the community, especially the groups that are mostly likely to be negatively impacted by the risk(s). Engaging the community involves the fire department becoming active in community organizations, participating in community events, and so on. Community engagement taken one step further involves the emergency response crews and companies becoming involved in their specific neighborhoods. The goal of engaging the community is to gain the trust of those living the neighborhoods and community, and from that trust and credibility eventually gaining their support for risk reduction activities.

Both components are discussed in more detail later in this chapter.

Fundamentals

Three fundamentals of community risk reduction help to clarify how and when the five "E"s are applied to risk reduction. These fundamentals are use of a risk reduction planning process, use of the resources of multiple organizations, and use of multiple mitigation strategies.

Risk Reduction Planning. A risk reduction planning process is used to select the highest risk(s), identify the risk factors and contributing factors, and then select the mitigation strategy or strategies—that is, 5 "E"s—which have the highest probability of success with the resources available.

Resources of Multiple Organizations. The community risk reduction process must utilize the resources of multiple organizations to effectively implement the mitigation strategies. A single fire department will seldom—if ever—have adequate resources to implement the five "E"s to the level necessary to reduce risk. Rather, the department seeks out government and community partners who have resources and influence that can be consolidated into one communitywide risk reduction initiative.

Use of Multiple Mitigation Strategies. Any community risk reduction initiative is most effective when all five mitigation strategies are applied to the risk issue. Studies conducted by the United States Centers for Disease Control[1] are clear: the use of only one strategy is unlikely to result in any change in the community risk. Ideally, all five strategies will be applied. However, this is not always possible due to a lack of resources, specific risk factors, and so on. The point is that whenever possible during the planning process as many of the strategies as practical should be applied.

The importance of using several mitigation strategies is clearly demonstrated in the 2000 David and Lucile Packard Foundation report, *The Future of Children: Unintentional Injuries in Childhood.*[2] In its preface, editor Richard E. Behrman, M. D., calls on those in the field to go beyond education alone and to address preventable childhood injury through a multifaceted public health approach:

> . . . the most effective injury prevention efforts are often those that focus on public policy change, reinforced through legislation or regulations. Public policies—such as requirements that young children be restrained in car seats, that prescription medications have child-resistant caps, and that children's sleepwear be flame retardant—save the lives of thousands of children each year. Yet there are many more opportunities to reduce childhood injuries through policy change that have not been seized. Uniform statewide requirements that children and teen bicyclists wear helmets, fences that enclose swimming pools on all sides, and environmental changes that slow the speed and density of traffic in residential areas are just a few strategies that could further reduce childhood injuries if widely implemented.[2]

Dr. Behrman concludes his statement of purpose with an important caveat:

> These public policy strategies have a greater likelihood of being implemented and enforced if they are coupled with community-wide efforts to change social norms about the acceptability of safety behaviors, and adequate financial resources to ensure the availability of safety devices.

THE FIVE "E"S

The five "E"s are the mitigation strategies of education, enforcement, engineering, emergency response, and economic incentives (Figure 12.19.1). Each strategy is summarized below.

Engineering

The objective of engineering is to build safeguards into products and materials that, by their design, eliminate or reduce the risk. These engineering safeguards are built into the environments where we live and into the products we use. For example, the use of fire-resistant sheetrock in residential construction restricts and slows the spread of fire in the home. The resident does not have to take any action for the sheetrock to work. This passive nature of engineering safeguards is a key to their success. Although most fire departments do not specifically design engineering safeguards, fire prevention personnel routinely apply

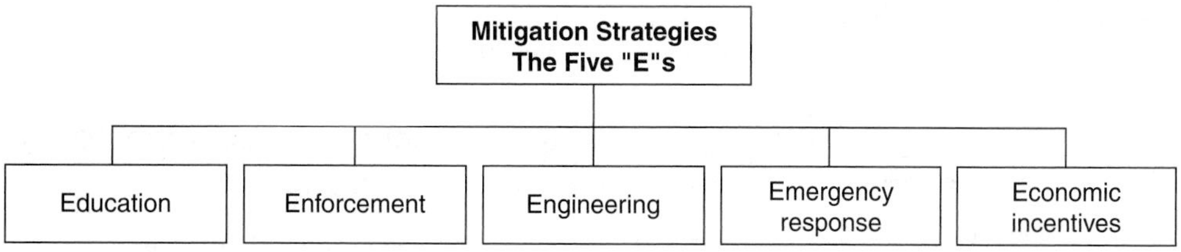

FIGURE 12.19.1 The Five "E"s as Mitigation Strategies for Community Risk Reduction

the safeguards through fire and building codes in both new and existing construction.

Education

Education is a widely used strategy by the fire service. The objective of an education strategy is to raise public awareness and understanding about fire, thereby changing high-risk personal behaviors. This change in behavior results in lowering the incidents of fire as well as reducing the injuries from fire. Public education programs such as the National Fire Protection Association's *Learn Not to Burn*®, *Risk Watch*®, and *Remembering When* have made a significant and measurable impact on reducing the fire problem. As of August 2006, NFPA had documented the following:

- 203 save incidents resulting in 558 lives saved from *Learn Not to Burn*
- 38 save incidents resulting in 71 lives saved from *Risk Watch*[3]

Because public education is so widespread and in some cases easy to implement, this strategy is perceived to be highly effective. Unfortunately, public education when used alone is the least effective of the five strategies.[4] Still, fire safety education remains a vital strategy in community risk reduction. This contribution has resulted, at least in part, in an impressive track record. Fire deaths in the United States and Canada have each fallen by roughly half in the past 25 years and fire deaths relative to population by even more. The role of education in this reduction, although believed to be important, has not been substantiated.

Education is also an important component in changes arising from engineering and enforcement mitigation strategies. North Americans made great strides in both safety technology and the safe use of technology. As of 2004, for example, 96 percent of homes in the United States had at least one smoke alarm, the highest rate of home smoke alarm usage in the world. Changes have been made in the United States and many other countries in the design of products ranging from upholstered furniture to mattresses to lighters to space heaters to manufactured homes. And the well-established systems by which model codes and standards are developed, adopted into law by reference, and enforced by national, state, and local authorities ensure that engineering achievements involving products, structures, vehicles, processes, and systems tend to move fairly rapidly into programmatic achievements at the grass-roots level.

However, much remains to be done. And with most fire departments now also responsible for providing emergency medical services to their communities, a fire department's role in prevention education has expanded to encompass a much broader range of issues.

Enforcement

The goal of the enforcement strategy is to reduce risk through the use of codes and standards. In this regard, enforcement utilizes many engineering innovations. For enforcement to be effective, the local department must have the ability to require compliance with the adopted codes and standards. This is accomplished through the use of code inspectors, building plan reviews, engine company inspections, and so on. As departments move into other risk areas compliance will require cooperation with other agencies that have similar authority.

Economic Incentives

The use of economic incentives is another strategy commonly employed along with other strategies. The goal of economic incentives is to influence personal or corporate behavior through financial incentives or disincentives. For example, when a department provides smoke alarms at no cost to home owners, economic incentive is being used. Similarly, when a developer chooses to install residential fire sprinklers in order to be able to build more houses in the same area under the building code, an economic incentive is being employed.

Emergency Response

Emergency response has always been a fire department function, but the types of emergencies to which fire fighters respond have increased. Consequently, the evolving scope of emergency response makes it the newest addition to the traditional three "E"s of engineering, education, and enforcement. Communities and risk reduction planners have realized that there are many risks that simply cannot be mitigated effectively through the other strategies. In these cases there must be an adequate emergency response capability to mitigate the problem when it occurs. For example, communities in Southern California have adopted codes and standards to minimize the risk of wildland fires. Well-designed public education programs have been delivered. Yet, wildland fires still occur and threaten hundreds of homes each season. Only a well-equipped and well-trained emergency response force can contain and control the fire to protect lives and property. Although the other strategies contribute to mitigating the risk, ultimately fire fighters and fire apparatus are required.

ROLE OF COMMUNITY ENGAGEMENT

The second component of community risk reduction is engaging the community, especially the groups that are mostly likely to be negatively impacted by the risk(s). Engaging the community involves the fire department becoming active in community organizations, participating in community events, and so on. Community engagement taken one step further involves the emergency response crews and companies becoming involved in their specific neighborhoods. The goal of engaging the community is to gain the trust of those living in the neighborhoods and community, and from that trust and credibility eventually gaining their support for risk reduction activities.

For community engagement to have a positive impact on a community risk reduction initiative it must precede the risk reduction initiative. In addition, community engagement should be viewed by the fire department leadership and membership as an everyday approach to doing business in the community. This approach has proven to be very effective for local law enforcement agencies which use the term "community policing" to describe community engagement.

Principles of Community Engagement

The Centers for Disease Control have identified four principles of community engagement.[1] The principles should be built into any fire department effort of engaging the community. The four principles are as follows:

1. The goal of the engagement process must be clearly stated with each neighborhood or community group engaged. In other words, the public must be aware of the goal of the engagement activities. In this case the goal is to build a positive relationship and then get the groups involved in a community risk reduction process.

2. The decision makers and leaders in the fire department must be knowledgeable about the community and the groups living there. Most communities today are diverse and include groups from several ethnic and cultural backgrounds. The leaders must also understand current issues in the community such as the economy, political structures, and so forth.

3. A key foundation of community engagement is establishing a relationship of mutual trust and communication with each stakeholder group in the community. These relationships are built by both senior leaders *and* personnel at the company level who actually provide emergency and nonemergency services to the groups.

4. The senior leaders must understand, and appreciate, that each stakeholder group and neighborhood has the right to self-determination when it comes to the engagement and risk reduction processes. If a group does not want to participate in the risk reduction planning process, the group has that right. The groups also have the right to disagree or even challenge the fire department on risk reduction issues. This principle must be applied during times of conflict if a trusting relationship is to be built and maintained.

Relationships with Stakeholders from Other Cultures

Many of the groups who have a vested interest in the reduction of community risk, called stakeholder groups, will be from cultures that are different from the prevailing community culture. These groups are generally immigrants or members of a minority group. Building relationships with these groups may be the greatest challenge in engaging the community. The University of Kansas's Community Tool Box has developed the following nine recommendations for building relationships with other cultures:[5]

1. Make a conscious decision to establish friendships with people from the other cultures and stakeholder groups. This begins with a commitment by the fire chief to engage the stakeholder groups.
2. Put yourself in situations where you will meet people of other cultures. This is most easily achieved by response companies, code inspectors, and so forth, that is, those who regularly have the opportunity in the course of daily business to meet with the public.
3. Examine your biases about people from other cultures. This should begin when interactions begin.
4. Ask people questions about their cultures, customs, and views.
5. Read about other people's cultures and histories. This information is readily accessible through the Internet.
6. Listen to people tell their stories. This requires spending time with members of another culture.
7. Notice differences in communication style and values; don't assume that the majority's way is the right way.
8. Risk making mistakes. Most members of other cultures will understand and be patient.
9. Learn to be an ally. This is a key to building a trusting relationship.

NFPA Champion Model of School-Based Delivery

Another approach to engaging the community in a prevention or risk reduction initiative was developed by NFPA. Even though the model was designed specifically for a public education application, many of the principles will apply to a community risk reduction initiative. The NFPA Champion Model of School-Based Delivery has been taught as part of the NFPA Champion program since 1995. The NFPA identified several fundamental qualities that appear to correlate with long-term success in implementing public education programs. Together, they comprise the NFPA Champion Model of implementation.

The Champion Model relies on 10 components or "'C's to Success" and these qualities can be used as a checklist to assess a community's readiness to initiate, evaluate, and institutionalize a comprehensive public safety program in the school environment and the community at large. The 10 "C"s provide a framework for success, proven to be effective in establishing and delivering messages and lessons that modify behavior, reduce injuries, and save lives. The 10 "C"s to Success are coalition, champion, careful planning, compelling case, credentials, collaboration, continuity, creativity, camaraderie, and commitment. The information described in each "C" references public education, but the same approach applies to a risk reduction initiative utilizing any or all of the 5 "E"s.

Coalition. For reasons discussed earlier, NFPA has concluded that the most effective way to reduce unintentional injuries is to work through a community coalition. That coalition should include (at a minimum) a representative from each of the following organizations: the fire department; the police department or local law enforcement agency; a health organization (hospital, health department, school nurse, or local SAFE KIDS representative); a school administrator (principal or curriculum director); and a classroom teacher from a school where the program will be implemented.

Champion. Every coalition needs to select a leader (or "Champion") who will be responsible for the coalition's efforts, from planning and implementation to evaluation and expansion of the public education project. Long-term success depends on the Champion's ability to think strategically, to motivate and coach others toward common goals, and to document and communicate program results to key decision makers, coalition members, teachers, other participants, and the public.

Careful Planning. Successful coalitions need to develop a written strategic plan outlining a clear set of written goals, measurements, and timeframes. Although each participating organization will have its own individual priorities, successful coalitions will be able to come to consensus on an achievable number of objectives toward which every member can make a contribution. The strategic plan will assign responsibility for each of the following areas: program development; training and implementation; support, promotion, and communication; strategic alliance building and fundraising; and research and evaluation. Progress needs to be documented. As the coalition develops, the plan must be updated and the leadership structure redefined.

Compelling Case. By analyzing the incidence of unintentional injuries in a community and focusing first on those neighborhoods or areas at highest risk, a Champion coalition can achieve dramatic results early in the program and use that momentum to gain support for further expansion. Start small, document the team's progress, and use concrete examples of the program's effectiveness to justify expansion. The extent to which a coalition can articulate an urgent need and define the tangible benefits of its program will largely determine the level of media attention, funding, and community involvement the program receives. To learn more about how to reach those at highest risk to fire, see Section 5, Chapter 5, "Reaching High-Risk Groups."

Credentials. A program's reputation will be determined by the quality of the materials used and the manner in which they are delivered. A coalition should select an established curriculum that has been thoroughly evaluated by independent researchers. Put professional educators in the lead role of teaching the core subject matter, since they have the necessary training and consistent access to guide student learning. Seek the participation of well-qualified, highly respected experts to serve on the coalition with the common goal of supporting the classroom teachers. Strive to enhance professional development and keep informed of new trends and innovations in the injury control field.

Collaboration. Successful public education initiatives are those that enjoy a high level of commitment from the community: the board of education, teachers, the fire department, the police department, and other agencies that have a specific mission to prevent childhood injuries. After teachers have introduced the core safety lessons to their students, local safety experts can then visit classrooms and reinforce lessons with their "real-world" perspective. NFPA suggests giving experts a copy of key lesson points to ensure consistency and accuracy of messages delivered by outside experts.

Continuity. Because people learn best through repetition and practice, the most effective way to teach injury prevention skills is through repeated, age-appropriate learning opportunities extended over a period of years. A successful program will target each age group in the program with messages they can understand. Injury risks to children change as they grow older; therefore, safety messages should become more comprehensive and complex as students mature. Also, growth brings the ability to understand and absorb more complex information and associated behaviors, and so safety messages should be tailored to a child's development, finding the right time to teach them all they will need to know throughout their lives.

Creativity. Communities are encouraged to supplement public education programs with elements (such as performance experiences) designed to address local needs. The creative use of safety trailers, clowns and puppets, coloring and comic books, and so on helps customize the program and provides an important sense of ownership. Creative reinforcement techniques can also enhance student knowledge gain and retention, so long as the information presented does not replace or conflict with the program's core messages. Educational programs delivered infrequently and with insufficient student preparation and reinforcement have not been shown to yield positive results.

Camaraderie. NFPA always makes time for fun during its public education training workshops. And the same concept can be applied in any community coalition. Sharing meals, attending planning retreats together, even playing an ice-breaker game before meetings can help build strong, trusting relationships and keep everyone on the team coming back for more.

Commitment. Successfully implementing a public education program is a major initiative for any community, regardless of its size or available resources. It requires hard work, the commitment of individuals and community organizations, and, most importantly, persistence. Although your initiative may be filled with challenges, there will also be rewards, including knowing that fewer children are being injured and that your community is a safer place to live, work, and play.

Both engaging the community and building relationships with other cultures requires a strong commitment on the part of the department leadership to community risk reduction. Without this strong commitment from leadership most community risk reduction initiatives are doomed to failure.

ROLE OF LEADERSHIP IN COMMUNITY RISK REDUCTION

Society relies on a basic infrastructure that gives shape to the quality of life in a community. Transportation, utilities, code enforcement, school, and recreational systems are but a few examples of the diverse parts of this infrastructure that allow community residents to make individual choices in an interactive social context. Policy makers understand that weaknesses in these infrastructure systems can result in performance failures at a given point in time and everyone will get less of what they want. Plans that are developed today revolve around design and maintenance of "system" components rather than simply addressing programs and issues separately without considering the impact of decisions on overall system performance. In other words, every problem is considered in a broad systems context, and special care is taken to maintain the infrastructure components that allow systems solutions to work most effectively in a dynamic environment.

Any systems approach begins by laying out the infrastructure of organizations, technologies, incentives, laws, and internal arrangements that seek to give structure to those interactions, so that needless inefficiency and disruption is minimized. Fire departments and other fire service organizations should address community risk reduction more holistically in terms of community infrastructure and systems approaches, rather than as separate programs that may at times appear disconnected from each other.

Systems Management and Leadership Model

A community risk reduction system describes basic components required to protect life and property in a community. The components may be programs or groups or the infrastructure that allows them to work together effectively towards solutions. There is not one single program or intervention strategy that will address the many ways that people can be killed or injured and property destroyed as a result of fire, natural disasters, terrorist attacks, or other causes. Furthermore, every program strategy is affected by many groups, whether it is designed to include them or not.

A system describes the component parts of a whole and their interactions. Each piece depends on the others for overall system effectiveness. Within a fire service organization, its components of this community risk reduction system can be divided into line and staff responsibilities.

Line Services. Line services are mission-driven and include risk reduction involving public education programs, emergency response, and emergency management:

- *Prevention through consensus codes and built-in protection.* These codes for prevention and mitigation govern structures, hazardous facilities and contents, as well as built-in protection, such as automatic fire sprinklers, and so on. Code-related services also include fire investigation, inspection, and enforcement activities.
- *All-risk public education programs designed to teach people how to prevent harmful situations and to survive should a situation occur.*
- *Response to emergency incidents such as fires, medical emergencies, natural disasters, hazardous materials events, or technical rescues.* This would include nonemergency service requests answered by emergency responders and the area of emergency (disaster) management.

Staff Services. Staff services are in place to support the primary mission and are provided to *internal* customers. Too often, risk reduction has been considered a support program to the emergency response system. However, community risk reduction is a line service as its customers are *outside* the fire department. Like any service provided within the mission of the organization, community risk reduction requires adequate staff support to be successful:

- *Prepare members to perform their roles.* This includes training the people in the organization to perform in their assigned roles within all areas.
- *Management of finances and human resources.* Support for the members who actually provide the line and staff services externally and internally. This includes issues such as adequate compensation, policy direction, definitive planning, safety issues, humane treatment, and other areas related directly to making people as effective as possible.
- *Community partnerships, relationships, and politics.* This includes maintaining positive and productive relationships internally and externally, an appreciation for (and understanding of) the importance of developing effective strategic alliances, and functioning effectively in the political arena with policy makers. This is achieved through engaging the community and its stakeholder groups whenever and wherever possible by all members of the department.
- *Management of physical resources and technology.* This means building and maintaining the infrastructure and equipment necessary to be effective. This includes management of facilities, the fleet, dispatch and communications systems, and other nonhuman resources.

These represent the component parts of the community risk reduction infrastructure. The mission is delivered effectively to the extent that these are brought together and managed in a systems approach. Failure of any of the individual parts of the system can result in failure of the mission in a given situation.

Executive Level Commitment

It is almost impossible for any program to be successful without the support and commitment of the chief executive officer of the organization. Programs that function in spite of the chief struggle every day. Be it fire suppression, health and safety, labor relations, fire prevention, media relations, fire and life safety education, EMS, training, or special operations—without the visible, active support of the chief, program results will usually be mediocre at best.

Community risk reduction programs that have full executive level support within the organization are effective, meaningful components of the service delivery system. This executive level support is demonstrated by actions such as the following:

- Representing the importance of community risk reduction inside and outside the organization
- Describing how community risk reduction integrates into the mission
- Identifying community risk reduction as a recognized program within the organizational structure
- Assigning responsibility and accountability for community risk reduction to a specific manager
- Ensuring a community risk reduction voice in decision making and planning processes
- Providing adequate personnel and other resources dedicated to community risk reduction programs
- Supporting the ongoing professional development of those involved in community risk reduction by allocating funds to attend regional and national meetings and trainings or conferences
- Including community risk reduction in strategic and operational plans, as well as budget packages
- "Opening doors" for community risk reduction staff inside the organization and within the community

Community risk reduction, like any other program, is successful in fire departments where the chief and other leaders want it to be successful and consistently act that out. It is treated and represented as a key organizational responsibility and a critical component of the community risk reduction infrastructure of a community.

SUMMARY

NFPA recommends a multifaceted, coordinated risk reduction process at the community level to address local risks. This requires engaging all segments of the community, identifying the highest priority risks, and then developing and implementing strategies designed to mitigate the risks.

Fire departments can serve a vital role in the concerted community risk reduction effort. The public safety needs of communities increasingly place fire department personnel in the role of emergency responders—first on the scene not only in a fire emergency, but in medical emergencies, natural disasters, and acts of terrorism as well. With a proven record in prevention and responding effectively to fire emergencies, fire safety advocates often have the credibility and expertise to organize their communities around broader safety and risk issues. Most fire department leaders are encouraging their members to get more involved in their communities to strengthen organizational credibility and influence. There are a variety of ways this can be accomplished, and community risk reduction is the program that provides perhaps the greatest opportunity.

BIBLIOGRAPHY

References Cited

1. *Principles of Community Engagement,* Centers for Disease Control and Prevention, Public Health Practice Program Office, Atlanta, GA, Apr. 2003.
2. The David and Lucile Packard Foundation, *The Future of Children*, Vol. 10, No. 1, inside cover.
3. Private communication, NFPA Public Education Division, Aug. 30, 2006.
4. *Leading Community Risk Reduction,* U.S. Fire Administration, National Fire Academy, Emmitsburg, MD, 2003.
5. University of Kansas Community Tool Box, *Section 7. Working Together for Healthier Communities: A Framework for Collaboration Among Community Partnerships, Support Organizations, and Funders,* Work Group on Health Promotion and Community Development, University of Kansas, Lawrence, KS, 2003.

NFPA Codes, Standards, and Recommended Practices

Reference to the following NFPA codes, standards, and recommended practices will provide further information on concepts of community risk reduction discussed in this chapter. (See the latest version of The NFPA Catalog *for availability of current editions of the following document.)*

NFPA 1035, *Standard for Professional Qualifications for Public Fire and Life Safety Educator*

References

Ahrens, M., *U.S. Experience with Smoke Alarms,* NFPA Fire Analysis and Research Division, National Fire Protection Association, Quincy, MA, Jan. 2000.

America Burning Recommissioned Commission, *America at Risk: Findings and Recommendations on the Role of the Fire Service in Prevention and Control of Risks in America,* U.S. Fire Administration, Federal Emergency Management Agency, Emmitsburg, MD, 2000.

"Building a Partnership for Community Health Care," *EMS and Public Health Bulletin. Summer 2000,* National Highway Traffic Safety Administration (NHTSA), Washington, DC, 2000.

Burt, C. W., and Fingerhut, L. A., "Injury Visits to Hospital Emergency Departments: United States, 1992–95," *Vital Health Statistics,* Vol. 13, No. 131, 1998.

Conger, J. A., "The Necessary Art of Persuasion," *Harvard Business Review on Management,* 1999, pp. 227–255.

"The Future Role of Emergency Medical Services in Prevention," *Annals of Emergency Medicine,* No. 22, 1992, pp. 1743–1746.

Heifetz, R., and Laurie, D., "The Work of Leadership," *Harvard Business Review on Leadership,* 1998, pp. 171–197.

Institute of Medicine, Committee on Injury Prevention and Control, Division of Health Promotion and Disease Prevention, *Reducing the Burden of Injury: Advancing Prevention and Treatment,* National Academy Press, Washington, DC, 1999, p. 14.

NCHS National Mortality Data, 1997, CDC National Center for Health Statistics, Hyattsville, MD, 1998.

SECTION 13

Organizing for Public Sector Emergency Response

Gary Tokle

For the first time, the *Fire Protection Handbook*® includes one section that concentrates on non-emergency fire department functions (Section 12) and a second section on organizing for public sector emergency response. Section 13 on emergency response is composed of nine chapters, including new chapters on airport rescue fire fighting and on emergency medical services.

Chapter 1, "Fireground Operations," describes the role of standard operating procedures, the incident commander, the national incident management system, pre-incident planning and size-up, and offensive and defensive fire extinguishment, as well as ventilation and overhaul. Fire fighter safety and property conservation are addressed.

Chapter 2, "Organizing Rescue Operations," introduces a highly specialized fire service function. Discussion of community resource planning (CRP), confined space rescue, rescue operations, rope rescue, technical rescue, specialized technical rescue, the technical rescue team, and trench rescue are included.

Fire streams, the topic of Chapter 3, "Fire Streams," are an integral part of fire extinguishment operations. The chapter covers fire department pumpers, solid-stream and spray nozzles, hose line fire stream calculations for flow rate and friction loss, and aerial devices.

Expanded treatment of water shuttle operations is a feature of Chapter 4, "Alternate Water Supplies." The chapter presents information on determining minimum water requirements and estimating available water supply, structure and site surveys, and natural and developed sources of water. Agreements, permits, water supply vehicles, and drivers are also considered.

Chapter 5, "Wildland Fire Management," provides a brief summary of past wildland fires and establishes the characteristics of wildland fire, then discusses the ways to prevent fires in wildlands or the wildland/urban interface and mitigate their effects. "Firewise" communities, prescribed burning, and fire fighter safety are also discussed.

Chapter 6, "Public Fire Protection and Hazmat Management," defines hazardous materials and summarizes the variety of laws, regulations, and consensus standards that govern them.

Chapter 7, "Aircraft Rescue and Fire Fighting (ARFF)," is new to the *Fire Protection Handbook.* The chapter explains the tools, techniques, agents, and objectives of aircraft rescue and fire fighting. Also provided is a review of the regulations and industry standards that influence the levels of training, staffing, and equipment at airports, as well as information about typical aircraft emergencies and ARFF response procedures.

Chapter 8, "Managing the Response to Hazardous Materials Incidents," provides a focus on hazardous materials response by considering hazard classes and divisions, weapons of mass destruction (WMD), bulk packaging, damage assessment, decontamination, and elevated temperature material. Personal protective equipment for hazardous materials response is also covered.

Gary Tokle is assistant vice-president (retired) of NFPA's Public Fire Protection Division.

During the past fifty years, fire service–based delivery of emergency medical services (EMS) has grown to be the principal operational delivery program in the majority of fire departments. In recognition of the significant role of EMS in the fire service, the section closes with another new chapter, Chapter 9, "Emergency Medical Services and the Fire Department." This chapter identifies the various factors, standards, and performance measures that can be utilized by fire departments in their analysis and improvement of the emergency medical services program. A Process Performance Indicator Index is also introduced.

Chapter 1

Fireground Operations

Bernard J. Klaene ❑ Russell Sanders

Chapter Contents

Key Terms

Beverly Hills Supper Club fire, defensive fire extinguishment, emergency action plan, fire fighter safety, incident commander (IC), national incident management system (NIMS), offensive fire extinguishment, overhaul, pre-incident planning, size-up, standard operating procedure, ventilation (fire fighting)

Combating structure fires is the reason fire departments were created, and structure fires remain one of the most formidable challenges facing modern fire departments. Structure fires are often labor-intensive, complex operations requiring a large number of people and equipment resources. Therefore, it is not surprising that the largest share of fire fighter injuries and deaths occurs on the fireground.

When fire prevention and public education efforts fail, or built-in fire protection equipment is unable to completely extinguish the fire, fire suppression by a fire department is the last line of defense for a building and its owner and occupants. In this respect, structural fire fighting today is much the same as it was 100 years ago. The primary tactic then, and now, is applying water directly to the burning fuel. However, over the past century, there have been numerous innovations to aid the modern fire fighter in conducting safe and effective fireground operations. These innovations include the following:

- Application of risk management principles to fireground operations
- Computerized pre-incident planning information
- National incident management system (NIMS)
- Improved fireground communications
- Fire fighter safety standards and regulations
- Improved and standardized personal protective clothing
- Widespread use of lightweight attack fire hose
- Large-diameter water-supply hose
- Thermal imaging devices

Successful fire departments prepare for potential fire operations prior to actual alarms. In pre-incident planning for fires within its jurisdiction, the fire department provides staffing, apparatus, and equipment based on a survey of the fire potential within the department's response area.

Training is also an important part of pre-incident preparation. Therefore, fire fighters receive extensive training on the proper use of apparatus, tools, and equipment, as well as on fireground tactics and strategy.

This chapter follows a logical methodology. It begins with a discussion of preparatory measures, followed by commentary on evaluating a specific fire situation and by the development of an incident action plan based on that evaluation or size-up. The chapter concludes with a review of the deployment and organization of fire department resources needed to safely and effectively limit the loss of life and property.

See also the following chapters in Section 12: Chapter 1, "Planning for Public Fire-Rescue Protection"; Chapter 7, "Safety, Medical, and Health Issues and Programs"; Chapter 8, "Effect of Building Construction and Fire Protection Systems on Fire Fighter Safety"; Chapter 12, "Disaster Planning and Response Services"; Chapter 17, "Pre-Incident Planning for Industrial and Municipal Emergency Response"; and Chapter 18, "Pre-Incident Planning for Emergency Response."

Bernard J. Klaene was the safety/training chief (retired) with the Cincinnati, Ohio, Fire Department.

Russell Sanders is the former chief of the Louisville, Kentucky, Fire Department. He now serves as NFPA's central regional manager, as executive secretary of the Metro Chiefs Section, and as an NFPA representative to Europe.

STANDARD OPERATING PROCEDURES

Some departments prefer very specific procedures; others allow more flexibility. In either case, it is essential that fire fighters be given instructions regarding initial activities at the fire scene. These instructions take the form of standard operating procedures or standard operating guidelines. The term *standard operating procedures* is used here to refer to either standard operating guidelines or standard operating procedures.

Standard operating procedures (SOP) address any operation that can be handled using a standard approach. Some SOPs are the same from one community to the next; others are not. For example, the tactics necessary to extinguish an automobile fire in both a large metropolitan setting and a rural setting are much the same. However, the SOPs for combating a large structure fire in an urban setting with conveniently located fire hydrants versus the same structure fire in a rural setting with a limited water supply would be very different. Furthermore, a high-rise SOP would be useless to a small rural department that does not protect high-rise buildings either within its jurisdiction or within a mutual-aid response area.

As incident situations and resources vary, so should SOPs. However, all departments should have SOPs on some common items, including the following:

- Command
- Company operations
- Water supply
- Staging
- Accountability systems
- Rapid intervention crews
- Use of protective clothing
- Operations in buildings with built-in fire suppression equipment
- Special occupancy operations

When SOPs are being written, regional planning and cooperation are important. Incident management system, accountability system, and rapid intervention crew SOPs are especially important at the scenes of large incidents, because often these incidents require more resources than a single fire department can provide. When mutual-aid operations are likely, it is important for all responding departments to use the same procedures and conduct joint training operations to ensure safe and predictable on-scene operations.

PRE-INCIDENT PLANNING

The pre-incident plan provides information for a specific building or group of buildings. Pre-incident planning is essential to successful operations in large or complex structures and in buildings that are protected with built-in fire protection systems.

The first step in pre-incident planning is to prioritize the buildings that are to be planned. Pre-incident planning is a labor-intensive activity. Few departments have the resources needed to pre-incident plan all buildings within their jurisdiction. Furthermore, rarely would there be the need to develop pre-incident plans for all buildings in a fire department's response district.

Buildings that present an extraordinary hazard to fire fighters and those with a potential for a large loss of life or property top the list of buildings that must be pre-incident planned. In addition, large commercial and industrial facilities usually require a pre-incident plan, as do structures with confusing floor plans and buildings with built-in fire protection systems. (See NFPA 1620, *Recommended Practice for Pre-Incident Planning,* Section 12, Chapter 17, "Pre-Incident Planning for Industrial and Municipal Emergency Response," and Section 12, Chapter 18, "Pre-Incident Planning for Emergency Response.")

Once information is assembled on a specific property, the incident commander (IC) must be able to quickly and easily access the information at the incident scene. Three-ring binders may be an acceptable way to handle a limited number of pre-incident plans, but computerized pre-incident plans are more easily and more quickly searched and can place more information at the IC's fingertips. Pre-incident plan information should be formatted to be user friendly and be limited to information of value to the IC.

When facing a fire at a large or complex property, the IC is placed at a great disadvantage if he or she does not have advance knowledge of the building's contents or layout. Due to the stress and distractions associated with emergency conditions, the IC should be familiar with the pre-incident plan before arriving at the incident scene. Ideally, the IC would take an active role in developing the plan and conducting training sessions using the pre-incident plan.

There are several degrees of pre-incident planning, ranging from formal pre-incident plans to a simple notation regarding hazardous conditions at a specific building. Formal pre-incident plans usually include a narrative in outline form that briefly describes important features of the property. More important, formal pre-incident plans will typically include drawings depicting features important to the IC. Formal pre-incident plan drawings for an industrial complex with several buildings will show the location of various buildings within the complex as shown in Figure 13.1.1. There will also be drawings of each individual

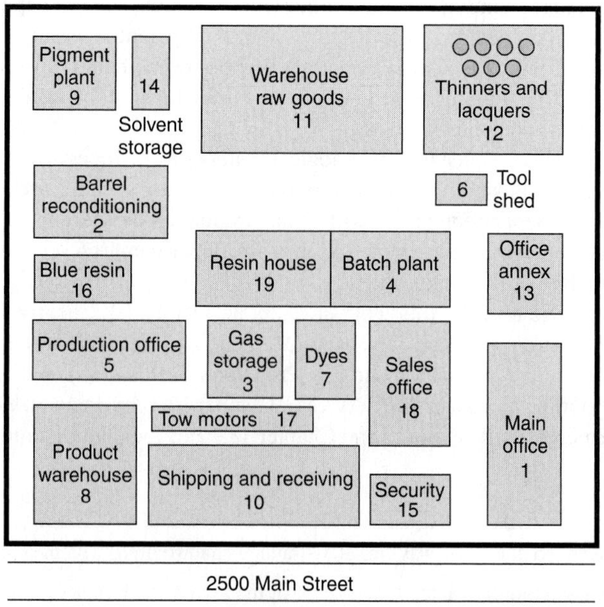

FIGURE 13.1.1 Complex Pre-Incident Plan Drawing

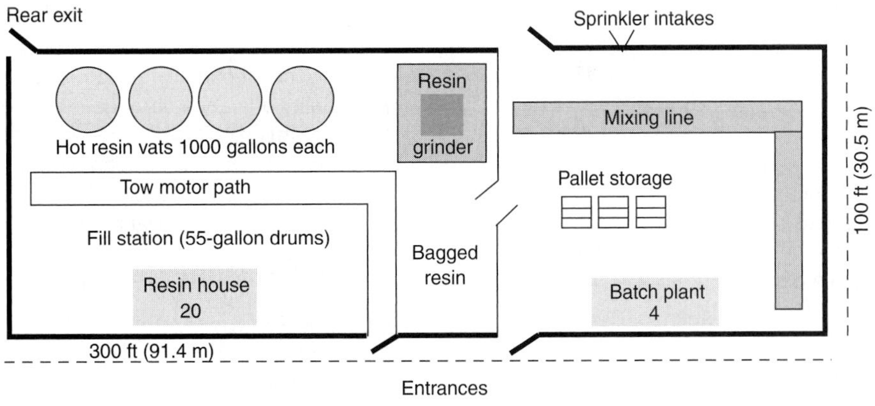

FIGURE 13.1.2 Formal Pre-Incident Plan Drawing

building as shown in Figure 13.1.2. Pre-incident plans for an apartment complex may show only the location of buildings within the property.

Fire officers should survey their response areas on a regular basis, noting hazards, such as deteriorated and vacant buildings, hazardous work locations (overhead cranes, chemicals, heavy machinery, etc.), and anything else that poses a significant safety hazard to responding fire fighters. One of the key reasons for conducting pre-incident planning surveys is to identify potentially dangerous structural conditions and related hazards. These hazardous conditions should immediately be reported and corrected, thereby eliminating hazards that could prove deadly during incident-scene operations. (See Section 12, Chapter 8, "Effect of Building Construction and Fire Protection Systems on Fire Fighter Safety.")

An analysis of the probability of extinguishment should be accomplished during pre-incident planning. Several rate-of-flow formulas are used by fire departments.[1] These formulas are useful in determining the probability of extinguishment, as well as the resources needed to extinguish a fire in large, undivided areas. Most of the rate-of-flow formulas use rudimentary mathematics, but they are very difficult to calculate at the incident scene when interior dimensions may not be known and the IC is busy developing an incident action plan and deploying and organizing fire companies. Therefore, the rate-of-flow formula for large, undivided areas (areas beyond the capability of two standard preconnected hose lines) should be calculated as part of the pre-incident plan.

Both pre-incident plans and standard operating procedures contain information that is critically important to the IC when making his or her incident-specific size-up. Therefore, the IC and all responding fire fighters should have a thorough understanding of these documents and routinely conduct training exercises to reinforce this information.

SIZE-UP

Size-up is the evaluation of factors as they exist at the time of an incident. Many of these factors can be known in advance through pre-incident planning, but some will not be known until the incident occurs.

The relative importance of size-up factors is subject to change. As an example, weather can be categorized as critically important when at the extreme or as unimportant under mild conditions. When occupants are known to be inside a burning building, life safety factors are pre-eminent. Time factors can be closely related to life safety. A high-rise office building may have thousands of occupants during normal business hours but only a few people at other times. Thus, time of day can be a critical size-up factor. Quite often structural conditions are the single most important factor in the size-up. Fire officers must understand the basic structural design elements, their weaknesses, and signs that the building is in danger of collapse. The NFPA publication *Building Construction for the Fire Service*[2] should be considered essential reading for anyone serving as an IC or safety officer at a structure fire.

The significance of size-up factors is directly related to the following operational priority list:

1. Life safety
2. Extinguishment
3. Property conservation

Additional considerations are environmental impact, heritage protection, and business/mission continuity. The size-up list in Figure 13.1.3 includes the major factors affecting size-up.

The size-up process continues throughout the incident as the IC continuously evaluates and reevaluates each critical incident factor. There is a direct correlation between the IC's size-up and the quantity and quality of information available. The more quality information that is available to the IC, the more accurate the size-up. The more accurate the size-up, the better the odds that the incident will be managed in a safe and efficient manner.

INCIDENT ACTION PLAN

The IC uses the information in the SOPs and the pre-incident plan, through the size-up process along with information gathered to develop a safe and effective incident action plan. The result should be a straightforward, easy-to-understand strategy emphasizing the IC's major tactical objectives.

Size-Up Checklist

LIFE SAFETY
- Structural stability
- Collapse zone
- Probability of extinguishment
- Building complexity and layout
- Adherence to SOPs (use of SCBA, etc.)
- Organization and coordination of the operation
- Primary and alternative egress routes
- Accountability and rapid intervention
- Smoke and fire conditions
- Occupancy type
- Evacuation status
- Estimated number of people in the building
- Occupant proximity to fire
- Mobility of occupants
- Awareness of occupants
- Occupants' familiarity with building
- Rescue options (stairs, ladders, others)
- Staffing needed to complete primary search and rescue
- Staffing needed to complete secondary search and rescue
- Medical status of occupants

EXTINGUISHMENT
- Offensive/defensive
- Automatic suppression equipment (sprinkler, deluge, other)
- Manual suppression equipment (standpipe)
- Water supply
- Pump capacity
- Rate of flow
- Fuel load of contents
- Fuel load of the structure (walls, ceilings, support members, etc.)
- Number and size of hose lines needed for extinguishment
- Additional hose lines needed
- Staffing needed for fire lines
- Internal exposures
- External exposures
- Ventilation status

PROPERTY CONSERVATION
- Salvageable property
- Location of salvageable property
- Property susceptability to water damage
- Probability of smoke damage
- Damage resulting from entry and ventilation
- Water pathways to salvageable property
- Salvage methods available
- Alternative water removal methods

STRUCTURE
- Signs of collapse
- Construction type
- Roof construction
- Previous damage
- Live and dead loads
- Water load
- Access/forcible entry
- Extension probability
- Age
- Height and area
- Location of large undivided areas
- Enclosures and fire separations
- Exit facilities

RESOURCES
- Staffing needed versus staffing available
- Additional staffing available (on call, on duty, or mutual aid)
- Staffing available in staging
- Apparatus needed versus apparatus on scene
- Additional apparatus available (department or mutual aid)
- Additional apparatus available in staging
- Water supply needed versus water supply available
- Special resource needs

TIME
- Time of day
- Day of week
- Time of year
- Special (e.g., holiday season)

WEATHER
- Temperature
- Humidity
- Precipitation
- Winds

FIGURE 13.1.3 Size-Up Checklist

Like size-up, the incident action plan is a dynamic process. The IC revises the incident action plan as information gathered through size-up reflects the changing conditions at the incident scene. In developing and revising the incident action plan, the IC compares the fire fighters' risk exposure to potential outcomes (risk-benefit analysis). In structural fire fighting the offensive-defensive decision is often the most critical factor in the risk-benefit analysis and is, therefore, the foundation on which the incident action plan is developed.

The offensive-defensive decision is subject to change based on the IC's ongoing size-up, specifically the risk-benefit analysis. Occupants or fire fighters exposed to extreme risk may warrant placing additional fire fighters at risk. However, once savable occupants and/or fire fighters are evacuated from the building, the benefit side of the risk-benefit analysis is reduced, as is the level of acceptable risk. NFPA 1500, *Standard on Fire Department Occupational Safety and Health Program,* provides the basis of this risk-benefit analysis, stating:

- Activities that present a significant risk to the safety of members shall be limited to situations where there is a potential to save endangered lives.
- Activities that are routinely employed to protect property shall be recognized as inherent risks to the safety of members, and action shall be taken to reduce or avoid these risks.
- No risk to the safety of members shall be acceptable when there is no possibility to save lives or property.
- In situations where the risk to fire department members is excessive, activities shall be limited to defensive operations.

DEPLOYMENT AND ORGANIZATION

With the incident action plan in place, fire-fighting crews and support resources are deployed to accomplish the tactical objectives identified in the incident action plan. As needed, the IC assigns the necessary subordinate sections, branches, divisions, groups, strike teams, and task forces to reduce the span of control and create an effective incident management organization. The IC coordinates, organizes, and manages the overall operation, being careful to avoid dangerous tactics, such as combining offensive and defensive attacks.

Assigning company-level operations should be included in the fire department's SOPs. Fire-fighting task assignments are usually divided into two categories: (1) tasks typically performed by an engine company crew and (2) tasks typically performed by a truck company crew.

Simply put, engine company work involves extinguishing the fire. Members assigned to truck company duties assist engine companies in gaining entry, laddering the building, controlling the spread of fire through ventilation, and evacuating occupants. This assignment of tasks into two basic categories does not mean that an engine company crew could not be assigned to a truck company task, such as search and rescue, or that a truck company crew could not be assigned tasks directly related to extinguishment. However, dividing company-level operations into these two general roles simplifies the deployment of forces and contributes to safe and efficient incident-scene operations. Even departments that do not have an aerial apparatus should divide operating crew assignments into these general types of tasks.

As long as the apparatus carries the right tools and the fire fighters receive proper training, it doesn't matter what type of apparatus delivers the fire fighters and equipment to the scene. What does matter is that both the traditional truck and engine company duties are accomplished in a coordinated manner by properly equipped, well-trained fire fighters.

LIFE SAFETY

The fire fighter's life is valued as being as important as any other human life, and the fire fighter is the most valued resource of any fire department. Measures taken to reduce the risk posed to fire fighters are essential and critical components of the life safety priority. NFPA 1500 identifies many provisions to improve fire fighter safety at the incident scene. (See Section 12, Chapter 7, "Safety, Medical, and Health Issues and Programs.")

NFPA *101*®, *Life Safety Code*®, requires minimum egress facilities for occupants of a building. In many cases, the occupants of a building will use these egress facilities to evacuate on their own, once they realize there is a need to escape. When possible, using the building's normal egress facilities to evacuate is preferred. The design features of the building's egress system, with the exception of elevators, are typically the safest way to exit a burning building and sometimes provide places of safe refuge within the structure. If stairways have not been compromised, they offer the easiest and safest egress routes from the upper floors of a building. Other evacuation methods are available to the fire department, but these tend to be more staff intensive and hazardous.

Rescue and evacuation via interior stairs, fire escapes, aerial apparatus, and ground ladders are common rescue methods used by fire departments. Elevators, scaling ladders, ropes, helicopters, life nets, and air bags are atypical rescue methods and often expose the rescuer and the victim to extraordinary danger.

In terms of search and rescue operations, large, complex buildings present a greater challenge for the IC and increase the risk to fire fighters. Buildings with flexible floor plans or with multiple additions often result in a mazelike configuration that results in confusing paths to egress routes. The tragic fire at the Beverly Hills Supper Club is an example of this problem (Figure 13.1.4).

To protect occupants, the IC must have sufficient staffing to extinguish (or at least contain) the fire, assign adequate personnel to search and rescue operations, and treat and transport the injured while preventing re-entry. The staffing needed to meet the requirements of the life safety priority will depend on several factors, such as the following:

- Number of occupants at risk
- Rescue method(s) used (e.g., stairway, fire escape, aerial apparatus, portable ladder, life line/rope)
- Condition of the occupants at risk
- Fire size and intensity
- Smoke conditions
- Weather conditions
- Accessibility (need to force entry)

EXTINGUISHMENT

Offensive Fire Extinguishment

There are two general types of operations at a structure fire: offensive and defensive. During offensive operations fire fighters enter the burning building and conduct interior life safety, extinguishment, and property conservation duties. Offensive operations are preferred whenever they can be conducted safely and effectively. Even though extinguishment is the second incident priority, offensive extinguishment is often the most important life safety tactic.

Manually extinguishing a fire on the interior of a building is an arduous task. The objective of the offensive fire attack is to apply a sufficient quantity of water directly on the burning

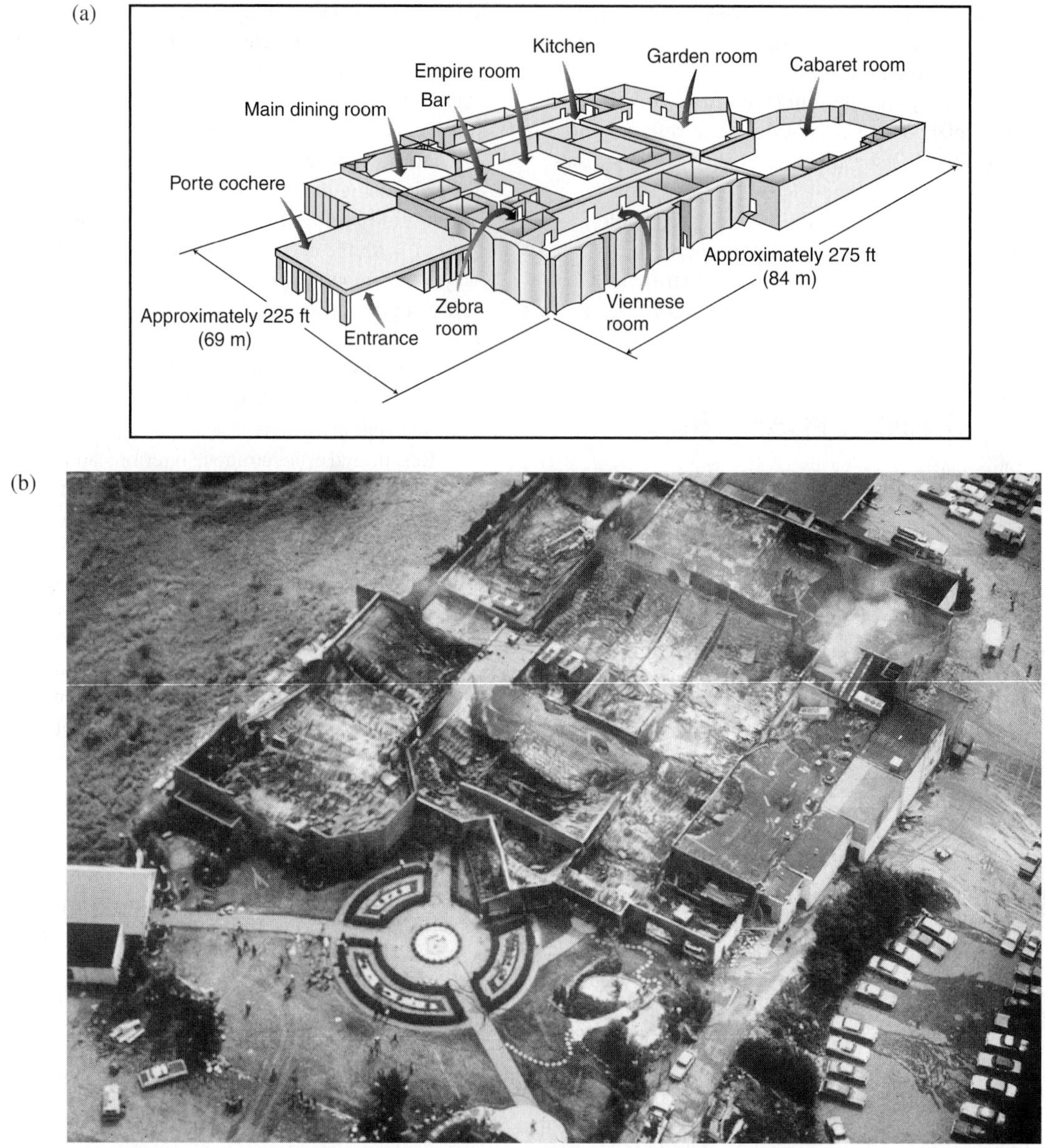

FIGURE 13.1.4 (a) Mazelike Floor Plan of the Beverly Hills Supper Club, Southgate, Kentucky; (b) Beverly Hills Supper Club Fire, 1977

fuel to achieve extinguishment. Once fire fighters determine the location of the fire, the essential question to be answered is how many gallons per minute (gpm) (liters per minute [L/min]) are required to extinguish a given fire with properly placed hose lines. Calculating the rate of flow allows the IC to match the number and size of fire hose lines to the waterflow necessary to extinguish the fire.

Calculating Rate of Flow. Some ICs prefer to use trial-and-error methods in determining the rate of flow. Using a trial-and-error method, the IC continues to add hose lines until the fire is knocked down or extinguished. The problem with trial-and-error methods is that fire fighters generally start with the department's standard preconnected hose line and simply continue adding more hose lines of the same type and size, when larger-diameter hose is actually needed.

There are three basic calculation methods used to determine the rate of flow:

Royer/Nelson: $\frac{\text{Volume in ft}^3}{100} = \text{gpm}$ $\frac{\text{Volume in m}^3}{0.748} = \text{L/min}$

U.S. National Fire Academy: $\frac{\text{Area in ft}^2}{3} = \text{gpm}$ $\frac{\text{Area in m}^2}{0.074} = \text{L/min}$

Sprinkler calculations: Flow based on fire load

Most practitioners agree that there is a minimum flow requirement needed to extinguish a given fire, and that rate-of-flow calculations are useful. However, there is disagreement as to which of the calculations is best. Each of these formulas are useful, but each also has limitations. Some rate-of-flow calculations are entirely empirical in nature; others are based on a considerable body of research and testing. Even the calculations based on research and testing are inaccurate under certain conditions because of the assumptions made and/or research conditions. Thus, rate-of-flow formulas are used to develop a rough approximation of the gpm (L/min) needed to extinguish a fire in a specific compartment.

The rate-of-flow calculations shown on page 13-8 are designed to calculate the required flow for offensive fire attacks within enclosed areas. When using rate-of-flow calculations, the IC's objective is to meet or exceed the calculated flow requirements by assigning the appropriate hose, nozzles, and water supply necessary to deliver, at a minimum, the total flow requirements. To properly calculate the rate of flow, the compartment size or fire area must be determined. Often this is extremely difficult at the incident scene. Therefore, as a practical matter, it is much better to determine the required flow during pre-incident planning and include this information in the pre-incident plan. Likewise, all department members should know the flow rates of the nozzles and hose combinations used by their department.

Protecting Properties with Fire Protection Systems. When fire protection systems protect the structure, the offensive attack takes on an entirely different character. A properly operating and maintained fire suppression system means that manual fire fighting will most likely be limited to supporting the building's suppression system and letting the system do the job it is intended to do. Efforts should be directed toward maintaining the system in a fully operational status and providing backup hose lines to complete extinguishment. Departments protecting properties with fire protection systems should have SOPs addressing operations in these buildings. Pre-incident planning is essential for any building protected by an automatic fire suppression system, as improper tactics could diminish the effectiveness of the building's built-in fire protection systems.

Protecting Properties with Standpipe Systems. Standpipe systems are not automatic fire suppression systems because they require human intervention. However, a standpipe system is an extremely valuable tool when conducting an offensive attack. In fact, in high-rise structures it may be impossible to conduct an effective interior operation on upper stories without a standpipe system. Fire departments should have standpipe SOPs in place and should have prepared pre-incident plans for these buildings. Departments protecting buildings with standpipe systems will normally have standpipe equipment available based on the needs identified within their response area.

An important part of the pre-incident planning process involves determining the flow capacity of fire pumps and the pressures available at various levels throughout the building. If the standpipe is a low-pressure system equipped with pressure-reducing valves or reducing adapters, provisions should be taken to either increase the pressure available at the standpipe outlet or provide hose and nozzles capable of providing an adequate flow at low pressures.

Defensive Fire Extinguishment

A defensive or nonattack strategy is used whenever the risk-benefit analysis reveals that the risk to fire fighters outweighs any possible benefit that might be achieved by conducting an offensive attack. Fighting a fire in a building that is unstable and where there are no lives to be saved is a clear example of the risk to fire fighters outweighing the possible benefits, thus justifying a defensive strategy. However, it is not always that clear-cut, as the IC will often have inadequate information or conflicting reports. The IC's training and experience are key factors in selecting the proper attack (or nonattack) mode.

Defensive attacks are almost always exterior operations and are generally conducted in the following situations:

- A risk-benefit analysis indicates that risk is too great in terms of what can be saved.
- Building's structural integrity or fire conditions prohibit entry.
- Resources needed for an offensive attack are greater than resource capabilities.

When a fire threatens the structural integrity of a building, fire fighters and apparatus should be moved outside the collapse zone. Given the uncertainties associated with how a building will collapse, the collapse zone should be equal to the height of the building plus an allowance for debris to scatter. The inability to apply water from a distance equal to the height of a building may lead to a nonattack decision for tall buildings in danger of collapse.

When evaluating an external exposure, operational priorities remain the same: (1) life safety, (2) extinguishment, and (3) property conservation. With these operational priorities in mind the IC must recognize a total loss when they are confronted with one. During a defensive attack, the building of origin is sometimes written off in favor of saving nearby property.

A question arises during a defensive attack as to whether it is better to apply water directly to the burning building or onto external exposures. Applying hose streams directly into the burning structure is an exposure protection tactic that has merit, but the intensity and depth of the fire may be such that it is impossible to significantly reduce the volume of fire in this manner. If a large volume of fire cannot be contained, and other structures are in close proximity to the fire building, it is best to apply water to the outside of the exposed buildings. Radiant heat will travel through transparent substances such as water. Therefore, directing a stream of water between the buildings is less effective than applying water directly to the exposed buildings. Furthermore, the distance between the exposed structures and the volume and location of the fire have much to do with prioritizing exposure protection. Wind direction and speed also play a role in this decision.

For the majority of defensive fire attack operations, master streams are the streams of choice. The IC should be aware that, if improperly placed, these very powerful streams could push the main body of fire toward areas that are not yet exposed, including into nearby buildings. Once master streams are in position, on-scene personnel must be controlled. Rarely are there too many fire fighters on the scene of an offensive operation.

However, when an unsuccessful offensive operation is discontinued and a defensive operation initiated, it is common to have more fire fighters than needed on the scene. Therefore, it is imperative for the IC to maintain strict control and accountability of on-scene personnel. Personnel inside the fire zone should be kept to a minimum, and offensive attack lines that are no longer needed should be disconnected. These and similar actions will reduce the temptation for fire fighters to freelance and attempt unsafe tactics.

PROPERTY CONSERVATION

Property conservation tactics can substantially reduce property loss. Property conservation is the last priority on the operational priority list; being the last priority should not be misconstrued, however, as being unimportant. Given the fact that fire departments are expected to save both lives and property, property conservation measures are an important part of the incident operation.

Life safety and extinguishment activities are assigned first, with property conservation being delayed until staffing is sufficient to address all life safety and extinguishment tasks. However, personnel should be assigned to specific property conservation duties, such as covering or removing exposed furniture as soon as possible. Also, it is important to remember that when life safety and extinguishment activities are performed properly, property damage is kept to a minimum. For instance, attacking the seat of the fire with the proper size and type of attack line—one that flows at or above the rate of flow—will quickly extinguish the fire and result in less water damage. Likewise, proper ventilation will direct smoke and heat away from the unexposed structure and contents. Once staffing permits, the IC should simultaneously attend to all three operational priorities during offensive fire attacks.

Overhaul

The purpose of overhaul is to ensure that the fire is completely extinguished. When sizing up the building prior to initiating overhaul operations, the IC must determine if the fire has severely damaged the building's structural components. If not, it should be safe to allow fire fighters to enter the building and complete overhaul duties. In some cases, where there is only minor damage to the structure and/or contents, it might be safe to allow the building's occupants to reenter.

To keep property damage to a minimum and to ensure that the fire is completely extinguished, overhaul must be accomplished in a well-planned, systematic manner. Walls, ceilings, and other structural components are checked and, if necessary, opened during overhaul. Opening concealed areas will release smoky, toxic, and smoldering materials into the work area. Ceilings, walls, and floors may contain asbestos or other harmful materials. Therefore, fire fighters and fire investigators operating inside a building during overhaul operations must be in full protective gear, including self-contained breathing apparatus (SCBA), until the building is completely free of smoke and airborne contaminants.

Ventilation

Ventilation is one of the IC's most important tactical considerations. In the past a tactic known as indirect application was popular. The indirect application method involves the application of a finely divided stream of water into an unventilated enclosure to gain maximum heat absorption from the water by converting it to steam. This tactic presents a hazard to occupants who have not escaped the building as it disrupts the heat balance making it much hotter at the floor level, and produces large quantities of steam within the enclosure.

Modern tactics call for a direct fire attack, coordinated with natural or mechanical ventilation. The direct attack involves applying water directly on the burning fuel. While the extinguishment crew applies water on the seat of the fire, a second crew ventilates the building to relieve the structure of heat and toxic products of combustion.

Proper ventilation can have a positive effect on all three operational priorities (life safety, extinguishment, and property conservation). Conversely, improper ventilation can adversely affect all three operational priorities and place both victims and rescuers in grave danger. The effects of proper and improper ventilation on the operational priorities are shown in Figure 13.1.5.

	Proper Ventilation	*Improper Ventilation*
Life Safety	• Pulls fire away from trapped occupants or their means of egress	• Draws fire toward victims or can extend fire through their exit path
Extinguishment	• Limits fire spread by channeling fire toward nearby openings and allows fire fighters to safely attack the fire	• Spreads the fire into previously undamaged areas • Can cause a backdraft or let the fire gain headway while lines are being advanced
Salvage	• Limits smoke, heat, and water damage by allowing an interior attack and removing the products of combustion, which are often the primary cause of damage	• Causes excessive and unnecessary damage • Does not relieve the damaging products of combustion but rather spreads them throughout the building

FIGURE 13.1.5 Effects of Proper and Improper Ventilation

SUMMARY

Pre-incident planning and standard operating procedures (SOPs) are essential elements of successful fireground operations. Pre-incident planning is particularly important in large and complex structures. Advance knowledge of some of the factors leading to strategic decisions before an incident occurs will reduce the information processing needs of the IC in the crucial early moments of an operation. Predesignating initial fireground operations using SOPs allows the IC to process information while a predictable course of action is taking place.

Next the IC develops an incident action plan based on an initial size-up and deploys forces to carry out the strategic objectives. The incident management system then provides the means to organize and manage the on-scene operation. The goal of this process is to fully utilize available resources in a safe, effective, and efficient manner.

This chapter is intended to provide a cursory overview of fireground operations. A complete discussion of this topic is beyond the scope and space limitations of this handbook. For a more detailed study of this and related topics, see the Bibliography.

BIBLIOGRAPHY

References Cited

1. Klaene, B., and Sanders, R., *Structural Fire Fighting,* National Fire Protection Association, Quincy, MA, 2000.
2. Brannigan, F. L., *Building Construction for the Fire Service,* 3rd ed., National Fire Protection Association, Quincy, MA, 1992.

NFPA Codes, Standards and Recommended Practices

Reference to the following NFPA codes, standards and recommended practices will provide further information about fireground operations. (See the latest version of The NFPA Catalog *for availability of current editions of the following documents.)*

NFPA 13, *Standard for the Installation of Sprinkler Systems*

NFPA 13E, *Recommended Practice for Fire Department Operations in Properties Protected by Sprinkler and Standpipe Systems*

NFPA 14, *Standard for the Installation of Standpipe and Hose Systems*

NFPA *101*®, *Life Safety Code*®

NFPA 170, *Standard for Fire Safety and Emergency Symbols*

NFPA 220, *Standard on Types of Building Construction*

NFPA 555, *Guide on Methods for Evaluating Potential for Room Flashover*

NFPA 1142, *Standard on Water Supplies for Suburban and Rural Fire Fighting*

NFPA 1145, *Guide for the Use of Class A Foams in Manual Structural Fire Fighting*

NFPA 1500, *Standard on Fire Department Occupational Safety and Health Program*

NFPA 1521, *Standard for Fire Department Safety Officer*

NFPA 1561, *Standard on Emergency Services Incident Management System*

NFPA 1620, *Recommended Practice for Pre-Incident Planning*

NFPA 1710, *Standard for the Organization and Deployment of Fire Suppression Operations, Emergency Medical Operations, and Special Operations to the Public by Career Fire Departments*

NFPA 1720, *Standard for the Organization and Deployment of Fire Suppression Operations, Emergency Medical Operations, and Special Operations to the Public by Volunteer Fire Departments*

References

Aiken, D. M., "Bands on the Run," *Fire Chief,* Vol. 45, No. 6, 2001, p. 28.

Arbuthnot, K., "Case for a Standard Approach to Incident Command," *Fire,* Vol. 90, No. 1115, 1998, pp. 16–17.

Beirne, M., and Simpson, W., "'Practice Like You Play': Rapid Intervention Teams," *Firehouse,* Vol. 26, No. 3, 2001, p. 76.

Brunacini, A., *Fire Command,* 2nd ed., National Fire Protection Association, Quincy, MA, 2002.

Collins, L., "Buried Alive. Part 1: Size-Up and Initial Operations," *Fire Engineering,* Vol. 152, No. 11, 1999, pp. 53–54.

Elvey, R., "Emergency Traffic Management. Part 1. How the Calgary Fire Department Safeguards Members and the Public," *Firehouse,* Vol. 26, No. 4, 2001, p. 100.

Fire, F. L., "Strategic Planning Progress. Part 1," *Fire Engineering,* Vol. 150, No. 4, 1997, pp. 78–80.

Fire, F. L., "Strategic Planning Progress. Part 2," *Fire Engineering,* Vol. 150, No. 11, 1997, pp. 57–60.

Goldfarb, T., "Putting the Incident Command System in Perspective," *Fire Engineering,* Vol. 150, No. 1, 1997, p. 64.

Kefalas, J., and Weninger, S., "ICS with a Memory," *Fire Chief,* Vol. 45, No. 1, 2001, pp. 37–38.

Klaene, B., and Sanders, R., "Operational Priorities at High-Rise Fires," *NFPA Journal,* Vol. 95, No. 3, 2001, p. 40.

Klein, R. A., "Strategic Planning for Major Incidents: Information Needs and Legislation Relevant to Fire Service Operations," *Fire Engineers Journal,* Vol. 60, No. 206, 2000, pp. 36–43.

Kuehnert, T. T., "Resource Allocation Study Leads to More Efficient Coverage," *Fire Engineering,* Vol. 152, No. 8, 1999, pp. 79–80.

Lasky, R., "Good Communications Vital to Fireground Survival," *Fire Engineering,* Vol. 151, No. 7, 1998, p. 10.

Lynsky, R., and Winder, M. S., "ICS Goes to School," *Fire Chief,* Vol. 44, No. 3, 2000, p. 32.

Morris, G. P., "Rules of Engagement for Incident Management," *Fire Engineering,* Vol. 150, No. 1, 1997, p. 72.

Nicholson, W. C., "Beating the System to Death: A Case Study in Incident Command and Mutual Aid," *Fire Engineering,* Vol. 152, No. 10, 1999, p. 128.

O'Connell, J., "McNichols Arena Collapse Training: 'The Real Thing.' An Unusual Training Opportunity," *Fire Engineering,* Vol. 153, No. 7, 2000, pp. 53–56.

Pascocello, A. J., Jr., "Saving Property: Salvage Operations, Part 1," *Fire Engineering,* Sept. 1996.

Pascocello, A. J., Jr., "Saving Property: Salvage Operations, Part 2," *Fire Engineering,* Oct. 1996.

Reid, B. C., "Managing the Mass-Casualty Incidents: A Quick Reference," *Firehouse,* Vol. 22, No. 8, 1997, pp. 97–98.

Rubin, D. L., "Command Positions and the Transfer of Command," *Firehouse,* Vol. 22, No. 4, 1997, p. 24.

Rubin, D. L., "Incident Command System: Myths, Rumors and Unnatural Acts," *Fire Chief,* Vol. 41, No. 4, 1997, pp. 63–66.

Rubin, D. L., "Roles and Responsibilities of General Staff Officers," *Firehouse,* Vol. 22, No. 6, 1997, p. 30.

Smith, D. L., Petruzzello, S. J., Kramer, J. M., and Misner, J. E., "Effects of Different Thermal Environments on the Physiological and Psychological Response of Firefighters to the Training Drill," *Ergonomics,* Vol. 40, No. 4, 1997, pp. 500–510.

Smith, D. W., "Firefighter's Role in Preserving the Fire Scene," *Fire Engineering,* Vol. 150, No. 1, 1997, pp. 103–108.

Smith, J. S., "Freeway Response: A Second Accident Waiting to Happen?," *American Fire Journal,* Vol. 49, No. 6, 1997, pp. 12–15.

Smith, M. L., "Incident Command at a Building Collapse," *Firehouse,* Vol. 26, No. 3, 2001, p. 62.

Tucker, B., "Planning to Succeed," *Fire Prevention,* No. 327, Dec. 1997, pp. 17–19.

Wagner, M. J., "Tracking Technology Can Save Lives and Improve Forest Firefighting Efficiency," *Fire International,* No. 179, Sept. 2000, pp. 12–13.

Yeager, G., "Art of Incident Command: Initial Incident Command—What Starts Right Ends Right," *Fire Engineering,* Vol. 1550, No. 1, 1997, pp. 59–60.

Chapter 2

Organizing Rescue Operations

Richard Wright

Chapter Contents

Key Terms

community resource planning (CRP), confined space rescue, rescue operations, rope rescue, specialized technical rescue, technical rescue, technical rescue team, trench rescue

The term *rescue* literally means to remove from confinement or danger. Rescue operations constitute a significant part of the functions typically performed by emergency response organizations worldwide. Although some of the more "typical" rescue operations, such as rescuing someone from a burning building, are regarded by some as commonplace, emergency response agencies must be prepared for the more complex situations that require highly specialized training, techniques, and equipment. The complexity of rescue responses can vary greatly with the incident and may prove to be overwhelming to an unprepared response agency. Typically, the training and experience of these responding agencies will be the principal factors in a safe and successful outcome of a rescue operation.

See also Section 12, Chapter 1, "Planning for Public Fire-Rescue Protection"; and Section 13, Chapter 1, "Fireground Operations."

SPECIALIZED TECHNICAL RESCUE

Rescuer Safety

Whatever the circumstances surrounding an incident, perhaps the most important consideration is the preservation and safety of the rescue personnel. An appropriate motto for rescue personnel should be, "Don't become a victim." This advice is especially significant when we consider the number of well-intentioned rescuers who, while attempting to save someone else's life, have lost their own lives due to a total disregard for personal safety. Unfortunately, these heroic individual efforts will often thwart an otherwise effective team effort by adding yet another victim to an already difficult situation. Response organizations should establish a systems safety approach to all rescue operations in order to limit the risk to rescuers while maintaining a viable and effective response and operational capability. *Systems safety approach* may be defined as a definitive system within the scope of technical rescue operations, whereby all rescue equipment, procedures, and operating personnel are continually analyzed in accordance with an established set of safety guidelines to reduce the potential for system or operational failure. The analysis may include both visual and tactile checks of rescue systems and system components as well as confirmations of readiness for those responsible for operating them.

Typical Versus Specialized Technical Rescue

There are several forms of rescue in the world of emergency response. Some of those considered more "typical" may include interior search and rescue within the scope of fireground operations and extrication of entrapped occupants from automobiles involved in motor vehicle crashes. The term *typical* denotes an event that is common. Although each situation is slightly different, this

---

Richard Wright, president of Wright Rescue Solutions, Inc., based in Panama City, Florida, is a nationally recognized specialist in confined space and industrial/urban rope rescue applications. He is actively involved in national standards and training development and serves as principal member on both NFPA 1670 and 1006 committees.

regular occurrence allows the task to become somewhat routine. The emergency response organization generally finds it easier to maintain a desired level of competency with these types of rescue operations because they perform them so frequently.

Contrasted with the everyday rescue situations are those that require rescuers to have specialized training and techniques far above the norm in order to handle the emergency situations appropriately and without additional incident. These rescue operations may be seldom used but are vital when needed. Because of their infrequency of use, they may also pose the greatest risk to response agencies due to the potential for errors in judgment or inefficiencies in the level of skill associated with less familiar territory.

Until a few years ago, very little had been done to identify the most common of these situations and to determine the qualifications necessary for agencies performing these operations. However, the National Fire Protection Association (NFPA) has sought to address these concerns through the establishment and continuing development of two standards: NFPA 1670, *Standard on Operations and Training for Technical Search and Rescue Incidents,* and NFPA 1006, *Standard for Rescue Technician Professional Qualifications.*

NFPA 1670, *Standard on Operations and Training for Technical Search and Rescue Incidents*

NFPA 1670 focuses on *organizations* that wish to achieve a certain level of competency in one of several different technical rescue disciplines. This standard does not address the qualifications for individuals but rather establishes the level of operational capability needed for organizations wishing to perform technical rescue.

Forms of Technical Rescue. Although more disciplines may be added as the document evolves, there are currently seven different forms, or disciplines, of technical rescue identified within this standard, with plans to add additional disciplines in the next revision. The seven forms are as follows:

1. *Structural collapse rescue.* The location and removal of victims from collapsed buildings or other structures
2. *Rope rescue.* The use of rope and associated equipment to raise, lower, access, or otherwise move victims and rescuers in a specific environment; the methods used will vary based on the response area of the authority having jurisdiction
3. *Confined space rescue.* The removal of persons ill or injured within enclosed structures having specific characteristics, including all of the following:
   - Having limited access and egress
   - Able to be bodily entered (a person can get his or her entire body into the space)
   - Not intended for continuous human occupancy
   - Having one or more serious life or safety hazards or, in some cases, merely the potential to contain these hazards
4. *Vehicle and machinery rescue.* The extrication of persons entrapped in various transportation conveyances as well as fixed machinery
5. *Water rescue.* The rescue of persons in one or more of the following four water-related disciplines:
   - Dive
   - Ice
   - Surf
   - Swift water
6. *Wilderness search and rescue.* The location and removal of persons trapped or stranded within a wilderness environment
7. *Trench and excavation rescue.* The location and removal of persons from collapsed trenches or other excavations (Figure 13.2.1)

Note that most of the disciplines classify rescue operations within a specific environment; others (e.g., rope rescue) deal with techniques that are commonly used in almost every environment. Regardless of the discipline, each chapter identifies certain capabilities that must be developed by an organization in order to achieve one of three levels of technical ability: awareness level, operations level, or technician level. Through a hazard analysis and risk assessment, the authority having jurisdiction determines which of the technical rescue disciplines to acquire and the associated level of capability needed.

These requirements, along with those for incident response planning, operational and personal protective equipment, and safety, are all covered within the scope of the chapter on general requirements and are applicable to the responding organization regardless of the technical rescue discipline or disciplines and associated capability they decide to develop.

Levels of Capability. The following is a paraphrased synopsis of the general scope of each of the three levels of capability stated within NFPA 1670.

Awareness: Awareness-level organizations should be capable of recognizing and avoiding the hazard. Intervention is minimal, although allowed in certain circumstances (e.g., external retrieval of a person in a full-body harness that is attached to

FIGURE 13.2.1 Trench Rescue (Photo courtesy of Wright Rescue Solutions, Inc.)

a mechanical winch device). One of the primary responsibilities of an awareness-level organization is to isolate the scene and call for appropriate qualified assistance to handle the situation.

Operations: Operations-level organizations are able to perform certain simpler rescues and are required to have all of the capabilities necessary for the awareness-level agency with additional skills and abilities as listed within that technical rescue discipline. The organization's ability to intervene is greatly enhanced, although the organization must still plan for the deployment and utilization of appropriate specialized assistance.

Technician: Technician-level organizations have determined that they will achieve the highest level of capability afforded by the standard in a particular technical rescue discipline. Although this is the highest level of capability, having this listed capability is not an assurance that the organization is able to handle every situation. There are obviously incidents so complex that even technician-level capabilities may not prepare the organization to mitigate the hazards without specialized assistance.

At each of the levels of capability, a successful technical rescue operation depends on assessing the need for, planning, and acquiring the necessary special equipment and services. Organizations should also note that many of the technical rescue disciplines cited in the standard require certain levels of compliance with other related disciplines. For instance, confined space rescue at the operations level requires both operations-level rope rescue and operations-level trench and excavation rescue, due to the close association of these three technical rescue disciplines.

NFPA 1006, *Standard for Rescue Technician Professional Qualifications*

In contrast to NFPA 1670, NFPA 1006 is directed toward assuring proficiency in *individual* rescue team members. Like NFPA 1670, this standard contains many of the same technical rescue disciplines, but there is currently only one level of capability—the technician level. Rescuers wishing to be compliant with this standard must complete a number of job performance requirements (JPRs) to achieve the status of "rescue technician." The standard utilizes a "core plus one" philosophy—that is, a person who wishes to become a specific type of rescue technician must complete a group of core JPRs that are common to all technical rescue disciplines plus the specific JPRs listed within the chapter for that particular technical rescue discipline. These core requirements are listed in Chapter 3 of the standard and involve four different areas:

1. *Site operations.* The activities to be undertaken at a specific site to manage the rescue incident
2. *Victim management.* The manner of treatment given to those requiring rescue assistance
3. *Maintenance, inspection, cleaning and repair of protective equipment, clothing, and tools*
4. *Ropes/rigging*

Although additional disciplines will be added to future editions, the rescue technician disciplines listed within the current version of NFPA 1006 are as follows:

- Structural collapse rescue
- Rope rescue
- Confined space rescue
- Vehicle and machinery rescue
- Surface water rescue
- Trench rescue

Although the core requirements are common to all of the specific rescue disciplines listed, a person cannot become a generic "rescue technician." Instead, he or she must become a technician specific to one or more rescue disciplines. Most of the technical rescue disciplines correspond to those listed in NFPA 1670. The greatest difference between the two standards is that NFPA 1006 applies to *individuals* and NFPA 1670 applies to *organizations.*

It is interesting to note that, at the time of this writing, the technical committee for NFPA 1006 is proposing significant changes to the structure of the document. In future editions, there may be sections for "Operations" and "Technician" levels for individuals within certain or all disciplines. To a degree, these individual qualifications would correspond with NFPA 1670's organizational requirements. If such changes are implemented, the name of the standard will be modified to a more appropriate title that will address professional qualifications for "technical rescuer" rather than "rescue technicians."

Technical Rescue Operations: The Bigger Picture

NFPA 1006 and 1670 deal with a variety of specific technical rescue disciplines, but many other types of specialized situations occur that require extraordinary expertise not commonly available in most communities. The following is a listing of some, but not all, specialized forms of rescue not addressed within NFPA 1670 and NFPA 1006:

- Urban search and rescue
- Hazardous materials (hazmat) rescue operations
- High-rise rescue
- Helicopter rescue
- Tunnel rescue
- Heavy rescue applicable to air, rail, and maritime
- Large-scale disaster response rescue (of both the natural and human variety)

The need for specialized rescue teams is typically based on a thorough analysis of community risk, which should typically include a review of both present conditions and past situations. Through this analysis, an acceptable level of risk may be determined. What is considered "acceptable" must be identified and balanced with the capabilities of the emergency response organization and the availability of additional specialized assistance. Armed with this information, the response community may take action to become better prepared for those rare but potentially devastating incidents.

The effectiveness of the preparation is based on the degree of awareness, knowledge, training, resources, and planning that has been achieved. Simply identifying the risk and actions necessary to address future incidents is not adequate preparation. Only through structured implementation of the action plan will the response organization be ready and capable of handling the specialized rescue operation.

The development of an effective technical rescue capability requires a thorough understanding of and commitment to every facet of need. The obvious necessities include appropriate training, personnel, and equipment required to safely mitigate the hazards and accomplish the rescue goals. In addition, a high degree of commitment (from all organizational levels, including both motivational and financial support for these programs), good logistical planning, and a thorough investigation into the legal ramifications are necessary to achieve a successful rescue operation. Based on the assessed risk, the cost of the support mechanism may be sizable in terms of money and time. It may very well add up to more than the average response organization can come up with by itself.

The development of specialized technical rescue teams will continue to be a major influencing factor in the national emergency service community. The need for the specialist versus the generalist approach toward operations will drive the development of this unique delivery system. The emergency service community must maintain both proficiency in the delivery of its services and the safety of the personnel who perform those various responsibilities. Identification of and planning for specialized rescue situations enhance incident response capability. The successful outcome of special rescue incidents relies on skills, training, planning, and deployment of adequately prepared and outfitted personnel and resources.

COMMUNITY RESOURCE PLANNING (CRP)

Common technical rescue incidents can often provide significant challenges that border on the overwhelming for smaller organizations. However, even the largest of emergency response agencies can be taxed by the demands of those rescues when associated with large-scale disasters. Despite the effective placement of an incident management system, the planning and logistical demands placed on incident managers, coupled with the requirements for meeting tactical deployment requests, can impede or impair the most efficient of organizations or departments. Because of the potential complexities associated with certain rescue situations and the variety of conditions and parameters that may be present at site-specific or large-scale disaster incidents, outside resources from other agencies and jurisdictions may have to be solicited, and then allocated and deployed when acquired, to enhance and support operational incident requirements.

The need for comprehensive community risk assessment has been well demonstrated and is considered a necessary first step in planning for the complexities of technical rescue. One component of community risk assessment planning focuses on the development of a database of outside resources that could be used to facilitate strategic and tactical objectives.

Through community resource planning (CRP) an agency or jurisdiction can identify internal deficiencies and provide a system for outside resource allocation so the agency's ability to respond to and operate at rescue incidents is augmented and so on-scene incident commanders will have the necessary resources. As with any incident response, the successful intervention, operation, and termination of the incident are directly related to the availability and deployment of resources, coupled with the effectiveness of the tactical assignment of these resources, the incident objectives, and the time management parameters.

A community resource plan delineates the resources needed for various anticipated rescue incidents and, thus, decreases the time required to identify, locate, and request the necessary resources. CRP is not a new concept within the fire and emergency service delivery system. Identifying and using mutual-aid agencies to augment daily fire, rescue, and emergency medical service (EMS) alarm assignments is commonplace in many jurisdictions. Supplementing local personnel and equipment with mutual-aid agency resources allows the receiving agency to deploy adequate resources at a given incident and increases its ability to mitigate the incident conditions.

The size, organizational structure, internal capabilities and resources, operating environment, and technical rescue capabilities of the department, along with the identified community risk hazards, will govern the development of the community resource plan. The magnitude, severity, and frequency of incidents will also dictate the methodology of the planning process.

The method used to identify and formulate the various resources and develop the community resource directory (CRD) is unique to each agency's community resource plan. The CRP and CRD augment the jurisdiction's capabilities during rescue operations and provide the framework and operating structure to build effective, safe, and timely rescue operations. The community resource plan establishes contacts; identifies procedures; and initiates agreements with local, jurisdictional, regional, and/or state and national entities for the procurement of identified resources. Through careful and thorough research and planning, a useful database can be developed that includes procurement procedures and memoranda of agreement.

DEVELOPMENT OF A CRP DATABASE

There are four basic functional areas that can be generally associated with the categories of resource planning for rescue response. These include but are not limited to (1) equipment, (2) supplies, (3) services, and (4) technical support.

Since the CRP and CRD are established and defined by the agency's or department's limitations or deficiencies, they are also directly related to the risk potential to which the community and jurisdiction are susceptible. The agency's current operational capabilities and its existing mutual-aid agreements and assignments are factored in with the community risk profile and analysis in order to determine the agency's limitations and deficiencies.

The resulting information forms the foundation for the research and development of an external resources database. The following lists provide an overview of items that could be included in the database. These lists are not all-inclusive.

Equipment

- Aerial lifts
- Air tools

- Backhoes
- Bulldozers
- Cellular phone companies
- Compressors
- Computer equipment supply and rental companies
- Concrete construction form suppliers
- Concrete cutting, breaking, and sawing firms
- Construction equipment
- Conveyors and material handlers
- Cranes, rigging/erectors
- Excavators
- Fire equipment and supply firms
- Flood lighting and searchlights
- Forklifts
- Generators
- Ham radio operators groups
- Hydraulic, pneumatic, and mechanical equipment
- Hydraulic tool distributors
- Light and heavy equipment firms
- Loaders, trenchers, skid-steer loaders
- Portable pumps
- Public works agencies
- Radio communications and equipment suppliers
- Sawing and cutting equipment
- Scaffolding
- Shoring
- Television and communications companies
- Tent suppliers and distributors
- Welding supply companies

Supplies

- Bag, burlap, and canvas manufacturers
- Battery distributors
- Building materials supply firms
- Chemical supply and distributor companies
- Compressed gases supply distributors
- Fire equipment and supply firms (local/regional)
- Fuel distributors
- Grocers and food suppliers
- Hardware supply firms
- Ice
- Lumberyards
- Medical supply companies
- Portable shelter and tent firms
- Power tool suppliers
- Rental service and supply companies
- Restaurants
- Utility companies

Services

- Aviation/helicopter services
- Awning and canopy manufacturers
- Baking companies
- Banquet and party supply companies
- Beverage suppliers and distributors
- Boat supply companies
- Bottled water distributors
- Buses: public, private, school district
- Catering companies
- Fencing companies
- Glass/windshield repair companies
- Ice distributors
- Motorcycle, all-terrain/ATV firms
- Portable restroom supply companies
- Rubbish/dumpster suppliers and haulers
- Tire distributors/repair firms
- Towing services
- Transportation services
- Tree- and debris-removal firms
- Trucking and leasing companies

Technical Support

- American Concrete Institute
- American Institute of Architects
- American Institute of Steel Construction
- American Public Works Association
- American Society of Consulting Engineers
- American Society of Safety Engineers
- Association of Building Contractors
- Association of Engineering Geologists
- Association of General Contractors
- Concrete Reinforcing Steel Institute
- Construction Specification Institute
- International Association of Bridge, Structural, and Ornamental Iron Workers
- Local and regional professional societies, associations, and trade groups
- National Society of Professional Engineers
- Physicians and surgeons professional associations

Contractors

- Demolition contractors
- Drilling and boring contractors
- Excavation contractors
- General contractors
- Heavy-equipment operators
- Steel erectors and fabricators
- Utility contractors

Consulting Engineers and Architects

- Architects
- Chemical engineers
- Civil engineers
- Construction engineers
- Environmental engineers
- Marine consultants
- Mechanical engineers
- Safety, health, and hygiene engineers
- Sanitary engineers
- Soil engineers
- Structural engineers
- Surveying engineers

Other

- Electric equipment and supply distributors
- Environmental and remedial contractors

- Hazardous waste abatement companies
- Highway and transportation agencies
- Industrial rescue teams
- Land surveyors
- Search-and-rescue dog handlers
- Wilderness search groups/associations

After the appropriate CRP database items are determined, the data collection process must identify local, regional, state, or other appropriate contacts, that is, companies, firms, agencies, or individuals that will ultimately provide the identified resources.

CRP AGREEMENTS

The next phase in the community resource plan requires the initiation, preparation, and adoption of appropriate types of agreements that clearly define the scope and conditions for the provision of services, equipment, and/or supplies established by the CRP. These agreements can take the following forms:

- Memoranda of agreement (MOA)
- Mutual-aid agreements (MAA)
- Service agreements (SA)
- Service retainer or contracts (SR/SC)

These agreements should be reviewed and approved by the legal council having jurisdiction within the department to ensure that the agreement and its parameters are equitable, concise, and that all liability issues have been addressed.

INFORMATION MAINTENANCE

The documents and data contained within the CRD "yellow pages" for complex incident management provide for the timely identification, call-out, and deployment of required resources, based on specific incident parameters. As with any other resource or reference document, the CRD and database should be updated and revalidated on an annual basis, so as to ensure that individual contact names, phone numbers, and conditions are valid and current. In addition, it is important to identify and document any changes in the resource listing that may affect its usefulness within the database. It is not uncommon for products, services, or materials to change or be withdrawn, especially when dealing with equipment, supply, or service companies, thereby compromising the dependability and/or function of the CRP.

Financial constraints, budget curtailments, staffing limitations and reductions, and limited resource acquisitions can prevent the initiation of programs or delay expansion of existing services. All proposals must be thoroughly assessed, properly planned, and adequately developed in order to effectively implement program goals. Technical rescue team development relies heavily on a thorough understanding of the issues surrounding the needs associated with such a team, coupled with an appropriate planning process that will ultimately lead an agency toward its established goal of enhanced rescue capabilities or deployment of specially trained and adequately outfitted personnel for technical rescue responses.

CONCEPTUALIZATION AND PLANNING PROCESS

The conceptualization and planning process is defined by the following 10 parameters. Each of the following must be thoroughly identified and addressed:

1. What type of specialized rescue team(s) is required?
2. What risk factors are present or potential within the jurisdiction?
3. What level of expertise currently exists within the organization?
4. How can system enhancement be best achieved?
    - Short term
    - Intermediate
    - Long term
5. What level or degree of technical capabilities can the plan achieve?
6. How can the services be best achieved?
    - Interdepartmental
    - Local
    - Regional
    - Countywide
    - Intercounty
    - Cooperative agreements with industrial or private teams
    - Outside agencies
7. What is the current projected level of interest of staff and personnel?
    - Interest
    - Motivation
    - Availability for staffing requirements
    - Previous levels of special/specific training
    - Employment/trade experience
    - Fire/rescue/EMS response experience
    - Educational background
    - Time commitment requirements
    - Personal risk factors
    - Dedication
8. What are the projected financial considerations and impacts?
    - Short term
    - Intermediate
    - Long term
9. What influencing regulations/standards must be complied with in the United States?
    - NFPA
    - OSHA
    - ANSI
    - NIOSH
    - DOT
    - DOL
    - API
    - NASAR
    - AAUS
    - Other
10. What is the time commitment for organization, development, and implementation of the program initiative?

Efforts must be made early in the conceptualization and planning process to ensure that the commitments and objectives being developed can be achieved within the organization. Initial interest may be high with any new program but may quickly wane as the demand of increased training and time commitments take their toll.

State/Federal Regulations

Regulatory impact of associated state/federal regulations, along with the influence of recognized national standards (such as those previously discussed of the NFPA), will also influence and help direct the planning, organization, and training process. These regulations and standards may assist the planning group or committee in identifying relevant issues that may impact the development of objectives, goals, and organizational scope for the subsequent team's deployment.

Research and Data Gathering

Efforts should be made by the relevant departments and agencies to research and obtain information from other departments and teams around the country in order to gain the wealth of information that can be analyzed and disseminated, with applicable information applied and augmented in order to meet with local conditions, factors, and team objectives. By eliminating redundancy in program planning and technical rescue team applications, this research and data-gathering network can save a tremendous amount of time and effort. Information gathered from departments that have developed technical response teams in the past added to information about operation methods and equipment and about changes to the methods and equipment as the result of field-proven experience can only help to provide a time-tested and time-proven foundation of data.

TECHNICAL RESCUE TEAMS AND PROGRAM EXAMPLES

Technical Rescue Teams

Departments and agencies that are considering developing specialized technical rescue teams must understand the long-term commitments and the level of dedication required to fulfill the operability and usefulness of team activation. A department or agency must identify the appropriate types and levels of technical service(s) necessary as the needs or risks within the jurisdiction or community change. In the 1980s, many jurisdictions hastily implemented hazardous materials teams as the wave of this concept and the need for a hazmat response swept through the emergency services only to find that the demands of time, financial support, and commitment levels necessitated a reevaluation of their level of commitment and degree of involvement.

Technical Rescue Program Examples

The following examples are typical technical rescue program elements that can facilitate the development of rescue operation capabilities for technical rescue specialties. Although the detailed skills are typical, the time frames for the initial delivery of such programs vary significantly from jurisdiction to jurisdiction. Unless regulated by standards, the time needed to run through the program should be determined by how long it takes to be thoroughly introduced to the necessary skills. This initial session must be followed with ongoing practice sessions and performance evaluations to ensure competency in the skills acquired. Initial training without ongoing practice will allow rescue personnel to forget the specialized techniques vital to the successful completion of a technical rescue operation.

The initial program delivery times represent those commonly seen within today's emergency response community. They should not be misconstrued to be a standard. An appropriate time frame for initial delivery and, more importantly, ongoing refresher training may vary significantly, depending on the learner's experience and level of routine emergency response activity. For instance, a fire fighter assigned to a busy rescue unit may require less formal continuing education time than does a volunteer industrial rescue team member who is normally assigned as an operator on a process unit. The fire fighter is more closely associated with the required skills on a routine basis, which may act as an on-the-job training session. This is not to imply that on-the-job trial and error is the most efficient way to train rescue team members but rather to illustrate that some people may require more formal training than others to achieve the same level of competency. Obviously, the time required to achieve competency will also vary based on the complexity of the subject matter presented.

These examples utilize NFPA 1670 as the basis for their content and outline all three levels of capability. NFPA 1670 provides a basic outline for course content in any one of the seven disciplines currently listed.

Rope Rescue. Rope techniques are a basic underlying skill for most other types of rescue. Most fire fighters will be familiar with basic rope techniques and knot tying as part of the basic fire fighter curriculum. An awareness of rope rescue operations can be taught to most rescuers in only a day (Figure 13.2.2).

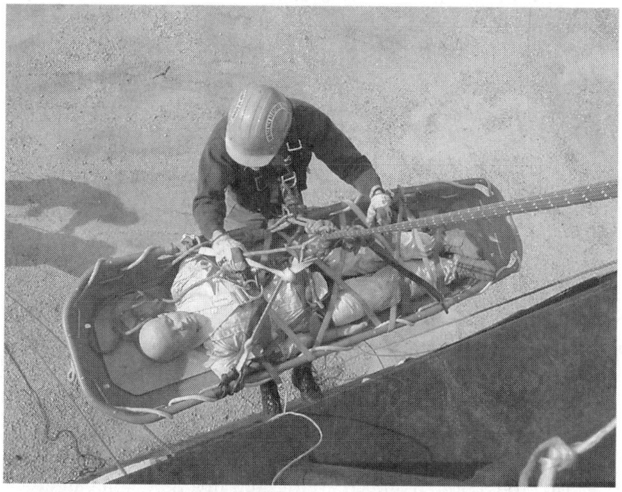

FIGURE 13.2.2 Rope Rescue (Photo courtesy of Wright Rescue Solutions, Inc.)

The initial awareness-level training session should include basic size-up and recognition of the need for rope rescues, information on what resources are necessary for rope rescues and how to procure them, mechanisms and procedures for on-scene site management, recognition of general hazards associated with rope rescue and methods for mitigating them, and development and implementation of procedures for the identification and use of personal protective equipment.

An operations-level training session could cover rope rescue techniques such as knot tying, orientation to rope and rope-related equipment, rigging principles and edge protection, single- and multiple-point anchor systems, belay systems, lowering systems, rope/pulley mechanical advantage for raising, both ascending and descending a fixed rope, and using litter attendants (tenders) in rope rescue systems. With the prerequisite of awareness, it is likely to take three days (24 to 30 hours) to bring an average group to familiarity with operations-level systems and procedures. A combined awareness- and operations-level training session may be commonly presented in a five-day format.

With the awareness- and operations-level programs as prerequisites, the technician-level program can possibly be presented within approximately one week (40 hours). The technician-level program may cover more complex anchoring and rigging techniques, more advanced use of rope/pulley mechanical advantage, high-line rope systems, passing knots through components of the rescue system, and use of other, more specialized rope rescue techniques within the high angle environment. In NFPA 1670, the term *high angle* denotes those environments in which the load is supported predominantly by the rope rescue system. *Low angle* refers to a situation in which the load is supported mostly by itself and not by the rope rescue system.

All sessions, regardless of the time frame, should include a balanced regimen of both classroom and practical application. The rope techniques and systems must also be tailored to the environment in which they will be used. Although conceptually identical, system configurations and application may vary significantly based on the environment and their intended purpose (i.e., mountain rescues versus structural/urban rescues).

Unfortunately, response organizations often dismiss rope rescue technique training because of the absence of high-rise structures or mountainous terrain. A risk assessment may reveal an absence of elevated structures or terrain but it may still reveal the presence of a high degree of risk for incidents associated with removal of victims from depths such as pits, channels, or ravines. These situations may require the same, or greater, level of rope rescue capability as do emergency rescue situations within a community of high-rise structures.

Confined Space Rescue. NFPA 1500, *Standard on Fire Department Occupational Safety and Health Program* and OSHA's 29 CFR 1910.146 define the term *confined space* similarly. Both standards say that a confined space must have all of the following characteristics:

- Be large enough and so configured that a person can enter and perform assigned work
- Have limited or restricted means for entry or exit
- Not be designed for continuous human occupancy
- Have a serious safety or health hazard or, in some cases, the mere potential for such

The hazards within confined spaces are no different from those experienced in other incidents on a regular basis. The real danger of rescue from confined spaces lies in the inability to readily escape those hazards. Because persons are forced to work within these sometimes cramped, poorly ventilated, and congested areas in close proximity to equipment and processes, the potential for incident is significant (Figure 13.2.3).

The OSHA regulation makes provision for those spaces in regulated industry that do not contain actual or potential hazards; the NFPA does not. Because the NFPA standards deal with response for rescue, they assume that any incident to which an emergency rescue team is called may have the potential for some sort of hazard within that space. This is the better-safe-than-sorry approach and constitutes sound reasoning. Another difference is that OSHA deals with worker safety and rescue occurring only within regulated facilities. The NFPA standards are intended for rescue operations regardless of their location, whether within a petrochemical facility or a backyard well. When comparing the two standards, we can see that they are similar in content but different in the scope of application. For this reason, terminology between the two standards may differ slightly even though the goals are similar.

An awareness of confined space rescue may usually be taught within a day. Content should include size-up of existing and potential conditions, initiation and establishment of contact with patients/victims, recognition and identification of hazards

FIGURE 13.2.3 Confined Space Rescue

associated with nonentry rescues, site control and scene management methods, recognition of confined spaces, and procedures for nonentry type rescues.

Organizational training at the operations level is associated with rescues from spaces whose configuration creates minimal potential for difficulty during entry-type rescues. For instance, spaces that have a clear line of sight with the patient/victim, contain no entanglement or other hazards, have an opening large enough to enter with a self-contained breathing apparatus (SCBA) worn in the manner intended by the manufacturer, and can accommodate two or more rescuers should present less difficulty for rescuers than a space that is greatly congested with an 18-in. (0.45-m) round entry portal and a patient/victim who is out of sight, 30 ft (9.1 m) from the entry point.

These training sessions should include certain basic rope systems required for safe entry and egress from less hazardous configurations, protective measures for rescue entrants, methods for assuring that the entrants can physically and psychologically handle working in tight spaces, understanding the duties of the various team functions within the scope of a confined space emergency, atmospheric monitoring procedures, use of appropriate packaging methods for these spaces, procedures for performing an entry-type rescue in these spaces, and some method of transferring patient/victim information to emergency medical services on delivery. Initial training sessions for the operations level are commonly taught within three to five days (24 to 40 hours).

Technician-level organizations should receive training to allow entry-type rescues into more complicated spaces. The initial training for technician-level organizations should include continuing size-up of changing conditions during rescue operations, information on medical surveillance programs for rescue team members, planning response for entry-type rescues into hazardous environments, and implementation of that planned response. Although program duration varies significantly, most technician-level programs are taught within two to five days (16 to 40 hours). Operations-level training should be considered a prerequisite for technician-level training.

SUMMARY

The daily demands imposed on fire and emergency service agencies can, at times, overwhelm the best-prepared and best-trained departments and their personnel. Support for specialized technical rescue operations is often neglected due to already overburdened response demands and budgetary constraints. Although it is true that these highly specialized techniques are not used as frequently as more routine basic rescue and fire suppression techniques, they have a no less vital role in saving human life within the realm of emergency response. Incidents of this type *will* occur. Rescue response organizations *must* have the skills and/or resources necessary for safe and effective deployment and subsequent operations. Departments and agencies should prepare appropriately to meet the challenges and demands associated with the risk potential and hazards present or projected for their jurisdiction and community.

The area of specialized technical rescue operations must be an integrated emergency system. Through proactive planning, community-based risk assessment and evaluation, preparedness training, resource development, and contingency planning, fire and emergency service agencies can effectively prepare and anticipate the manner in which they can handle incident responses, while maintaining the highest degree and consideration for the safety and well-being of their personnel and emergency responders. Technical rescue operations require a fine balance of training, knowledge, skills, risk management, and resources.

BIBLIOGRAPHY

NFPA Codes, Standards, and Recommended Practices

Reference to the following NFPA codes, standards, and recommended practices will provide further information on rescue operations discussed in this chapter. (See the latest version of The NFPA Catalog *for availability of current editions of the following documents.)*

NFPA 220, *Standard on Types of Building Construction*
NFPA 472, *Standard for Professional Competence of Responders to Hazardous Materials Incidents*
NFPA 473, *Standard for Competencies for EMS Personnel Responding to Hazardous Materials Incidents*
NFPA 1001, *Standard for Fire Fighter Professional Qualifications*
NFPA 1006, *Standard for Rescue Technician Professional Qualifications*
NFPA 1201, *Standard for Providing Emergency Services to the Public*
NFPA 1500, *Standard on Fire Department Occupational Safety and Health Program*
NFPA 1521, *Standard for Fire Department Safety Officer*
NFPA 1561, *Standard on Emergency Services Incident Management System*
NFPA 1600, *Standard on Disaster/Emergency Management and Business Continuity Programs*
NFPA 1670, *Standard on Operations and Training for Technical Search and Rescue Incidents*
NFPA 1983, *Standard on Life Safety Rope and Equipment for Emergency Services*

References

Brown, M., and Burrero, A., *Engineering Practical Rope Rescue Systems,* 2nd ed., Thomas Delmar Learning, Albany, NY, 2007.
CMC Rescue, *Confined Space Entry and Rescue,* 2nd ed., CMC Rescue, Santa Barbara, CA, 1997.
Henry, T. V., *Decontamination for Hazardous Materials Emergencies,* Thomas Delmar Learning, Albany, NY, 1998.
Martinette, C. V. B., *Trench Rescue,* Jones & Bartlett Publishers, Sudbury, MA, 2005.
Murnane, L., Fortney, J., and Connell, T., *Technical Rescue for Structural Collapse,* Fire Protection Publications, Stillwater, OK, 2003.
Ray, S., *Swiftwater Rescue: A Manual for the Rescue Professional,* CFS Press, Asheville, NC, 1997.
Roop, M. R., Wright, R., and Vines, T., *Confined Space and Structural Rope Rescue,* Mosby Inc., St. Louis, MO, 1998.
Segerstrom, J., Croslin, M., and Edwards, B., *Swiftwater Rescue Technician 1, Manual,* Rescue 3 International, Elk Grove, CA, 1997.
Smith, B., and Padgett, A., *North American Vertical Rope Techniques,* 2nd ed., National Speleological Society Vertical Section, Huntsville, AL, 1997.
Vines, T., and Hudson, S., *High Angle Rescue Techniques,* 3rd ed., Mosby Inc., St. Louis, MO, 2004.

Chapter 3

Fire Streams

Michael A. Wieder

Chapter Contents

Key Terms

aerial ladder, Bernoulli's equation, continuity equation, Darcy-Weisbach formula, elevating platform, fire department pumper, fire stream, flow rate, friction loss, hose line, hydraulics calculations, nozzle (solid stream), nozzle (spray), pump discharge pressure

Water has always been and remains the primary fire-extinguishing agent. Therefore, the movement of water from its source to the fire is a significant operation in most kinds of fire fighting. A typical fire department delivery system consists of the following:

- A water supply source
- One or more fire department pumpers
- Various types of fire hose to move the water from the source to the fire pump and from the pump onto the fire
- Nozzles for the final delivery

Fire apparatus driver/operators and fire officers must understand the basic principles of water movement through the aforementioned elements in order to establish effective fire suppression operations.

This chapter includes a description of the most important details of producing effective fire streams, including fire department pumpers, nozzles, hose line fire stream calculations, and reaction forces in hose lines and nozzles.

See also Section 13, Chapter 4, "Alternate Water Supplies"; and Section 15, Chapter 3, "Hydraulics for Fire Protection."

FIRE DEPARTMENT PUMPERS

Purpose and Components of Fire Department Pumpers

The primary purpose of fire department pumpers is to move water with adequate pressure from a source to the fire. Water supply sources can be divided into two basic groups: static and pressurized. Static sources include lakes, streams, ponds, rivers, and water shuttle dump tanks. Pressurized sources include fire hydrants, elevated storage tanks, or supply hoses from another fire department pumper. More information on water supply sources can be found in Section 15 of the *Fire Protection Handbook.*

In addition to pumping water for fire streams, fire department pumpers serve other functions, including transporting fire fighters; auxiliary extinguishing agents (foam, dry chemical agents, etc.); and other fire-fighting, emergency medical, and rescue equipment to an incident scene.

Fire pumps may also be installed on other types of fire apparatus, such as mobile water supply apparatus (tenders/tankers), aerial apparatus, aircraft rescue and fire-fighting (ARFF) vehicles, wildland apparatus, rescue vehicles, and fireboats. Design requirements for pumpers, aerial apparatus, water tender/tankers, and rescue vehicles are contained in NFPA 1901, *Standard for Automotive Fire Apparatus.* Design requirements for wildland fire apparatus are contained in NFPA 1906, *Standard for Wildland Fire Apparatus.* Design requirements for ARFF vehicles are contained in NFPA 414, *Standard for Aircraft Rescue and Fire-Fighting Vehicles.*

Michael A. Wieder, assistant director at IFSTA/Fire Protection Publications in Stillwater, Oklahoma, holds undergraduate and graduate degrees in fire protection, safety, and adult education. He has written or edited more than two dozen fire-fighting texts and manuals, including the textbook *Fire Service Hydraulics and Water Supply.*

Modern fire department pumpers, also called engines, wagons, and triples, are generally equipped with a centrifugal-type pump as their main fire pump. The centrifugal pump, a nonpositive displacement pump, consists essentially of one or more rotating discs called impellers. The impellers are mounted on a shaft that may turn from 2000 to 4000 rpm in order to transmit energy in the form of velocity to the water. A casing surrounds each impeller to collect the water and convert the velocity to pressure. A fire pump that has a single impeller on the shaft is called a *single-stage pump.* If the shaft has two impellers mounted on it, the pump is called a *two-stage pump.* Two-stage pumps have transfer valves that allow water to be discharged from one impeller to the next (called series operation; used for maximum discharge pressures) or through both impellers at the same time (called parallel operation; used for maximum discharge volumes). Centrifugal pumps also have the equipment necessary to provide pressure regulation and to prime the pump when using a static water supply source.

Piston, rotary gear, and rotary vane pumps are positive displacement-type pumps that provide a fixed amount of water with each movement of the pump. They are no longer used as the primary pumps on fire apparatus. They are, however, used for special purposes, such as high-pressure booster pumps and as priming pumps for centrifugal pumps.

Characteristics of Fire Pumps

Two important characteristics of fire pumps are (1) the discharge volume and (2) the discharge pressure. They make up the final output of the pump. The discharge volume is the amount of water pumped per unit of time, such as gallons per minute (gpm) or liters per minute (L/min). Apparatus may be equipped with flowmeters to measure the discharge volume being provided by the pump. The discharge pressure is the pressure at which the pump is discharging water. The discharge pressure is measured in pounds per square inch (psi) or kilopascals (kPa). It is also sometimes measured in bar with 1 bar equal to 100 kPa. The discharge pressure (as well as the intake pressure, if any) is measured by pressure gauges attached to the pump piping.

Pumps are rated according to their discharge volume at 150 psi (1035 kPa) when drafting through 20 ft (6 m) of intake hose at a lift of 10 ft (3 m). Apparatus fire pumps are also required to provide 70 percent of their rated capacity at 200 psi (1380 kPa) and 50 percent of their rated capacity at 250 psi (1725 kPa). These ratings are summarized in Table 13.3.1. Common capacities for pumps used on modern fire apparatus range from 500 gpm (2000 L/min) to 2500 gpm (10,000 L/min), although larger-capacity pumps are available.

Pumping operations start with water from either a pressurized source, such as a hydrant, or from a static water source, such as a pond. Drafting operations are required in the latter case. The factors that affect the height (lift) limitations to which water can be drafted and the flow rate are interrelated. These factors are as follows:

- Atmospheric pressure
- Water temperature
- Friction loss in the intake hose and strainer
- Velocity energy

TABLE 13.3.1 Standard Pumps

Rated Flow Rate		70% of Rated Flow Rate		50% of Rated Flow Rate	
gpm @ 150 psi	*L/min @ 1035 kPa*	*gpm @ 200 psi*	*L/min @ 1380 kPa*	*gpm @ 250 psi*	*L/min @ 1725 kPa*
500	2000	350	1400	250	1000
750	3000	525	2100	375	1500
1000	4000	700	2800	500	2000
1250	5000	875	3500	625	2500
1500	6000	1050	4200	750	3000
1750	7000	1225	4900	875	3500
2000	8000	1400	5600	1000	4000
2250	9000	1575	6300	1125	4500
2500	10,000	1750	7000	1250	5000

The lift at a given flow rate can be determined by

Lift = Atmospheric pressure minus water vapor pressure
minus strainer and intake hose friction loss
minus velocity energy

Atmospheric pressure varies from day to day according to the weather conditions and the elevation above sea level. Since drafting is essentially the creation of a partial vacuum in the pump and intake hose, the total energy available for moving the water from the source to the pump is the atmospheric pressure. The nominal atmospheric pressure, 14.696 psi (101.333 kPa) absolute at sea level, usually rounded to 14.7 psi (100 kPa) absolute, can theoretically provide a lift of almost 34 ft (10.5 m). However, remember atmospheric pressure drops about 0.5 psi (3.4 kPa) for each 1000 ft (305 m) above sea level.

As mentioned earlier, fire pumps receive their capacity ratings based on their drafting ability through 20 ft (6 m) of intake hose at a lift of 10 ft (3 m). As the amount of lift is increased, the discharge volume capacity of the pump will be decreased accordingly. Under actual conditions, a pump in excellent condition and able to pump its rated capacity at sea level should be able to draft and pump at least some water at lifts of up to 25 ft (7.6 m).

Often atmospheric pressure is given in inches of mercury. If this is the case, it must be converted to feet of water using:

$$h_w = 1.13h'_{Hg}$$

where

h_w = Feet of water

h'_{Hg} = Inches of mercury

The vapor pressure reduces the amount of vacuum that is possible and, consequently, reduces the total lift. Vapor pressure depends on the water temperature and is measured in terms of feet (meters) of water. Table 13.3.2 lists common values of vapor pressure as a function of water temperature.

Another factor affecting the total lift is the friction loss in the suction hose and the strainer. The friction loss in the suction hose depends on the hose diameter, hose length, and the

TABLE 13.3.2 Vapor Pressure

Water Temperature		Vapor Pressure	
°F	*°C*	*ft of water*	*kPa*
60	16	0.59	1.8
80	27	1.20	3.6
100	38	2.20	6.6
120	49	3.90	11.7

TABLE 13.3.3 Suction Hose Friction Losses per 10 ft (3 m) Length

Suction Hose Diameter		Friction Loss			
in.	*mm*	*psi*	*kPa*	*ft*	*m*
4	100	$0.022q^2$[a]	$0.0109q^2$[b]	$0.0519q^2$	$0.00978q^2$
4½	115	$0.013q^2$	$0.0061q^2$	$0.0291q^2$	$0.00054q^2$
5	125	$0.007q^2$	$0.0034q^2$	$0.0162q^2$	$0.00033q^2$
6	150	$0.003q^2$	$0.0014q^2$	$0.0066q^2$	$0.00014q^2$

[a] q = gpm/100.
[b] q = L/min/100.

flow rate of the water. Equations for the friction loss in various sizes of suction hose are shown in Table 13.3.3. The friction loss through the strainer is a function of the flow rate and the strainer diameter. The friction equations for the various strainer sizes are shown in Table 13.3.4.

TABLE 13.3.4 Suction Strainer Friction Losses (Loss = Cq^2)

Suction Hose Diameter		Friction Loss			
in.	*mm*	*psi*	*bar*	*ft*	*m*
4	100	$0.0418q^2$[a]	$0.0202q^2$[b]	$0.0966q^2$	$0.00229q^2$
4½	115	$0.0367q^2$	$0.0178q^2$	$0.0848q^2$	$0.00142q^2$
5	125	$0.0224q^2$	$0.0108q^2$	$0.0517q^2$	$0.00093q^2$
6	150	$0.009q^2$	$0.0043q^2$	$0.0207q^2$	$0.00054q^2$

[a] q = gpm/100.
[b] q = L/min/100.

The velocity head also affects the total lift of the pump. The velocity head is given by $V^2/2g$, where V is the water velocity in feet per second (meters per second) and g is the acceleration due to gravity and is equal to 32.2 ft/sec^2 (9.81 m/sec^2). The velocity can be found by using the continuity equation, $Q = VA$ where Q is the flow rate in cubic feet per second (cubic meters per second) and A is the cross section of the suction hose in square feet (square meters). However, the flow rate is usually given in gallons (liters) per minute and the suction hose diameter is in inches (millimeters). Consequently, Table 13.3.5 can be used to determine the velocity head in the suction hose without tedious calculations.

To find the friction loss in parallel suction hoses (FL_P), divide the friction loss (FL_T) by the square of the number of lines, that is,

$$FL_P = \frac{FL_T}{\#\ \text{lines}^2}$$

TABLE 13.3.5 Velocity Head (V) for Suction Hose, ft (m) Water

Flow, Q		Suction Hose Diameter (D), in inches and millimeters											
		3.0 in.	76 mm	3.5 in.	88 mm	4.0 in.	100 mm	4.5 in.	114 mm	5.0 in.	125 mm	6.0 in.	150 mm
gpm	*L/min*	*ft*	*m*	*ft*	*m*	*ft*	*m*	*ft*	*m*	*ft*	*m*	*ft*	*m*
100	378	0.32	0.09	0.17	0.05	0.10	0.03	0.06	0.02	0.04	0.01	0.02	0.0
200	757	1.28	0.39	0.69	0.21	0.40	0.12	0.25	0.05	0.17	0.05	0.08	0.0
300	1136	2.88	0.88	1.55	0.47	0.91	0.28	0.57	0.17	0.37	0.11	0.18	0.0
400	1514	5.11	1.56	2.76	0.84	1.62	0.49	1.01	0.31	0.66	0.20	0.32	0.0
500	1892	7.99	2.44	4.31	1.31	2.53	0.78	1.58	0.48	1.04	0.32	0.50	0.1
600	2271	11.51	3.51	6.21	1.90	3.64	1.11	2.57	0.78	1.49	0.45	0.72	0.2
700	2650			8.45	2.58	4.96	1.51	3.09	0.94	2.03	0.62	0.98	0.3
800	3028			11.04	3.36	6.47	1.97	4.04	1.23	2.65	0.81	1.28	0.3
900	3407					8.19	2.50	5.11	1.56	3.36	1.02	1.62	0.4
1000	3785					10.11	3.08	6.31	1.92	4.14	1.26	2.00	0.6
1100	4163					12.24	3.73	7.64	2.33	5.01	1.53	2.42	0.7
1200	4542							9.09	2.78	5.97	1.82	2.88	0.8
1300	4921							10.67	3.25	7.00	2.13	3.38	1.0
1400	5300							12.37	3.78	8.12	2.47	3.92	1.1
1500	5677									9.32	2.84	4.49	1.3

For example, with two parallel suction hose lines of the same size and length, divide the calculated suction hose friction loss by 4.

In solving the lift equation, all units must be compatible, that is, converted to the equivalent feet (meters) of water or kilopascals. Atmospheric pressure is usually given in terms of inches of mercury (or kilopascals). Table 13.3.6 can be used to convert the atmospheric pressure to the equivalent pressure in feet (meters) of water.

For SI units: 1 in. Hg = 3.385 kPa; 1 psi = 6.895 kPa; 1 ft = 0.305 m.

EXAMPLE: Find the lift in feet of water (or kilopascals, which can be converted to meters of water by multiplying by 9.84).

Atmospheric pressure = 27.00 in. of mercury (91 kPa)

Water temperature = 60°F (16°C)

Flow rate = 1100 gpm (4163 L/min)

TABLE 13.3.6 Inches of Mercury Vacuum Compared with Height of Water and Corresponding Pressure

Vacuum	Pressure		
in. Hg	*psig*	*psia*	*ft water*
0.00	0.000	14.696	0.000
1.00	–0.491	14.205	1.132
2.00	–0.982	13.714	2.263
3.00	–1.473	13.223	3.395
4.00	–1.965	12.731	4.527
5.00	–2.456	12.240	5.658
6.00	–2.947	11.749	6.790
7.00	–3.438	11.258	7.922
8.00	–3.929	10.767	9.054
9.00	–4.420	10.276	10.185
10.00	–4.912	9.784	11.317
11.00	–5.403	9.293	12.449
12.00	–5.894	8.802	13.580
13.00	–5.385	8.311	14.712
14.00	–6.876	7.820	15.844
15.00	–7.367	7.329	16.975
16.00	–7.858	6.838	18.107
17.00	–8.350	6.346	19.239
18.00	–8.841	5.855	20.370
19.00	–9.332	5.364	21.502
20.00	–9.823	4.873	22.634
21.00	–10.314	4.382	23.766
22.00	–10.805	3.891	24.897
23.00	–11.297	3.399	26.029
24.00	–11.788	2.908	27.161
25.00	–12.279	2.417	28.292
26.00	–12.770	1.926	29.424
27.00	–13.261	1.435	30.556
28.00	–13.752	0.944	31.687
29.00	–14.244	0.453	32.819
29.92	–14.696	0.000	32.862

Suction hose diameter (strainer diameter) = 5 in. (125 mm)

Suction hose = Two lengths, 10 ft (3 m) each

SOLUTION: U.S. customary units

From Table 13.3.6, atmospheric pressure of 27.00 in. of mercury equals 30.556 ft of water.

From Table 13.3.2, vapor pressure at 60°F equals 0.59 ft of water.

Using Table 13.3.3, the friction loss for 10 ft of 5 in. suction hose is $0.0162q^2$. $Q = 1100$ gpm. However, q is in 100s of gpm and $Q/100 = q$.

Therefore, $q = 11$.

Thus: Friction loss = $(0.0162)(11)^2 = 1.96$ ft for 10 ft
or $(2)(1.96) = 3.92$ ft for 20 ft

From the suction strainer equation listed in Table 13.3.4:

$$\text{Friction loss} = 0.0517q^2$$

Where $q = 11$ as in the suction hose equation

$$\text{Friction loss} = (0.0517)(11)^2 = 6.26 \text{ ft}$$

The velocity head (from Table 13.3.5) is 5 ft.

Therefore, lift = 30.56 – 0.59 – 4 – 6.26 – 5 = 14.71 ft.

SOLUTION: Metric units

Atmospheric pressure = 91 kPa

From Table 13.3.2, vapor pressure at 16°C equals 1.7 kPa.

Using Table 13.3.3, the friction loss for 3 m of 125 mm suction hose is $0.0034q^2$. $Q = 4163$ L/min. However, q is in 100s of L/min, and $Q/100 = q$.

Therefore, $q = 41.63$.

Thus: Friction loss = $(0.0034)(41.63)^2 = 5.89$ kPa for 3 m
or $(2)(5.89) = 11.78$ kPa for 6 m

From the suction strainer equation listed in Table 13.3.4:

$$\text{Friction loss} = 0.0108q^2$$

Where $q = 41.63$ as in the suction hose equation

$$\text{Friction loss} = (0.0108)(41.63)^2 = 18.71 \text{ kPa}$$

The velocity head (from Table 13.3.5) is 14.9 kPa.

Therefore, lift = 91 – 1.7 – 11.78 – 18.71 – 14.9 = 43.91 kPa (converting to meters, 43.91/9.84 = 4.46 m)

NOZZLES

The purpose of a nozzle is to shape the stream and convert pressure energy to velocity (kinetic) energy. In this way, the water can be applied to the fire in the appropriate quantity and from an adequate distance. The two most common basic types of fire service nozzles are solid stream and spray (fog) nozzles (Figure 13.3.1).

The governing hydraulic characteristics of nozzles are flow rate, diameter, and nozzle pressure. Flow rate is the amount of water flowing out of the nozzle per unit time and is measured in gallons per minute or liters per minute. Nozzle pressure is most

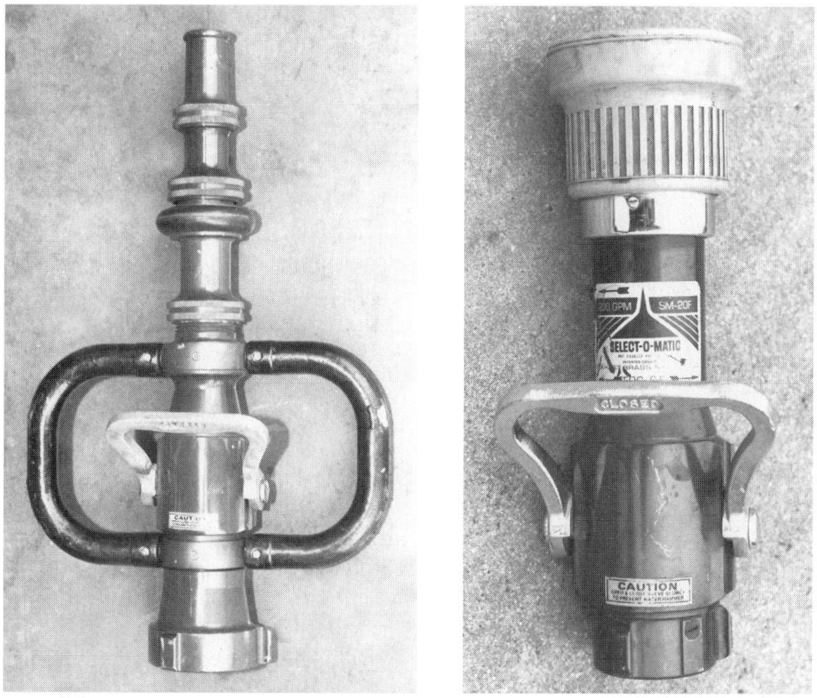

(a) (b)

FIGURE 13.3.1 (a) Solid-Stream Nozzle; (b) Spray Nozzle

commonly measured at the tip of the nozzle in units of pounds per square inch (psi) or kilopascals (kPa).

Solid-Stream Nozzles

Solid-stream nozzles are classified according to the nozzle tip diameter. The diameters range from ¼ to 2½ in. (6 to 65 mm) or larger. The nozzle sizes are generally available in ⅛ in. (3 mm) graduations. Nozzles up to 1⅛ in. (29 mm) or perhaps 1¼ in. (32 mm) are generally considered to be for "handlines," that is, those held manually. As a rule of thumb, handline solid-stream nozzles are usually operated at a nozzle pressure of 50 psi (345 kPa).

Solid-stream nozzles larger than about 1¼ in. (32 mm) have such large reaction forces that they must be mechanically restrained. These are called master stream nozzles. They may be mounted to the apparatus, affixed to a portable base, or attached to an aerial device. As a rule of thumb, master stream solid-stream nozzles are operated at a nozzle pressure of 80 psi (552 kPa).

Solid streams are useful where extreme range is desired, where it is necessary to penetrate soft material, such as peat, or when thermal degradation of spray streams prevents proper penetration to the seat of the fire. Solid streams are also less affected by wind currents than are spray streams. Solid-stream nozzles are also the preferred nozzle for use with compressed air foam streams (CAFS).

Solid-stream nozzles are also useful in measuring waterflows, since both their diameter and discharge pressure can be easily measured. The discharge pressure is measured by holding a Pitot tube and gauge in the fire stream (Figure 13.3.2).

The Pitot tube is inserted in the stream at a point that is equal to one-half the diameter of the nozzle tip away from the tip. From this information, the flow rate can be computed. It is related to the diameter and nozzle pressure by the following equations:

$$Q = 29.7d^2\sqrt{NP}$$

FIGURE 13.3.2 A Typical Pitot Tube and Gauge

where

Q = Flow rate (gpm)

d = Nozzle diameter (inches)

NP = Nozzle pressure (psi)

For SI units, the flow equation is:

$$Q = 0.0666 d_{m}^{2} \sqrt{NP_{m}}$$

where

Q = Flow rate (L/min)

d_m = Nozzle diameter (mm)

NP_m = Nozzle pressure (kPa)

Theoretical flows from various nozzles at different nozzle pressures can be found in Section 15, Chapter 3, "Hydraulics for Fire Protection."

Solid streams, with a lower surface-area-to-volume ratio, do not have as good heat-transfer characteristics as do spray nozzles and, consequently, are not as effective in absorbing heat. Another disadvantage of a solid stream is that it is a better conductor of electricity than a spray stream.

Spray (Fog) Nozzles

Spray nozzles, or fog nozzles as they are sometimes called, produce varying degrees of a water spray pattern. Most modern spray nozzles are adjustable from a straight stream to a very wide-angle spray pattern. The stream pattern angle is customarily measured at the angle between the outer limits of the pattern core and expressed in terms of degrees (e.g., a 30 degree pattern or a 60 degree pattern).

Spray nozzles are generally classified according to the size of their hose coupling and their flow rate in gallons per minute (liters per minute). The flow rate capacity of a spray nozzle will depend on the design of the particular nozzle. There are two basic designs for spray nozzles: (1) fixed gallonage nozzles and (2) automatic nozzles. Fixed gallonage nozzles are designed to flow a set number of gallons of water at a specified nozzle discharge pressure. Most of these nozzles have rated flow volumes when the nozzle pressure is at 100 psi (690 kPa). However, some newer nozzles are designed to operate at lower nozzle pressures. These are particularly useful when operating from a standpipe system in high-rise fire-fighting operations as the pressures may not be available to supply nozzles at 100 psi (690 kPa). Fixed gallonage nozzles may be designed to allow only one specified flow rate, or they may have an adjusting collar that allows the nozzle to be set for one of four or five predetermined flow settings.

Automatic nozzles are the most common type of spray nozzles in use today. Automatic nozzles, also referred to as constant pressure nozzles, are basically variable flow nozzles with pattern-change capabilities and the ability to maintain the same nozzle pressure. If the volume supplied to the nozzle changes, the automatic nozzle maintains approximately the same nozzle pressure and pattern. This feature is made possible by a baffle that moves automatically, varying the spacing between the baffle and the throat.

A stream from an automatic nozzle can "look good" but may not be supplying sufficient water for extinguishment or protection. It should be the goal of the driver/operator to provide an acceptable flow of water at the discharge pressure for which the nozzle is designed. As with fixed gallonage nozzles, most automatic nozzles are designed for a 100 psi (690 kPa) discharge pressure.

The discharge volume available from a spray nozzle will vary depending on the size of the nozzle and hose line and the pressure being supplied from the fire pump. Keep in mind, for example, that a 1½ in. (38 mm) automatic spray nozzle may be used on either a 1½, 1¾, or 2 in. hose line. Table 13.3.7 shows typical flow rates from automatic spray nozzles.

Flow rates are determined experimentally, either by a flowmeter or by flowing water into a tank and measuring the time for a given quantity. Flow rate information is obtained from the manufacturer and, as mentioned previously, is usually reported as the flow rate at 100 psi (690 kPa) nozzle pressure.

Flows for other pressures may be obtained by using the flow equation:

$$Q = 29.7 d^{2} \sqrt{NP}$$

and finding the equivalent nozzle diameter d_e, using

$$d_e = \sqrt{Q/29.7\sqrt{NP}}$$

where

Q = Flow rate (gpm)

29.7 = A constant

d_e = Equivalent nozzle diameter (in.)

NP = Nozzle pressure (psi)

For SI units the flow formula is

$$Q = 0.0666 d_{m}^{2} \sqrt{NP_{m}}$$

and finding the equivalent nozzle diameter d_e, using

$$d_e = \sqrt{Q/0.0666\sqrt{NP_{m}}}$$

where

Q = Flow rate (L/min)

0.0666 = A constant

TABLE 13.3.7 Flows from Typical Automatic Spray Nozzles

	Flow Rate	
Nozzle Type	*gpm*	*L/min*
¾ to 1 in. (19 to 25 mm) automatic nozzle	10–60	38–227
1½ in. (38 mm) automatic nozzle	30–250	114–946
2½ in. (64 mm) automatic nozzle	125–350	473–1,325
Master stream automatic nozzles	350–10,000	1,325–37,854

d_e = Equivalent nozzle diameter (mm)

NP_m = Nozzle pressure (kPa)

HOSE LINE FIRE STREAM CALCULATIONS

The end goal of most fire service hydraulics calculations is for the driver/operator to determine the necessary discharge pressure setting on the fire pump needed to supply the desired amount of water to the nozzle(s) or the next pumper in a relay pumping operation. This pressure setting is most commonly referred to as the *pump discharge pressure (PDP),* although in the past it was also known as the "engine pressure." The methods for mathematically calculating the pump discharge pressure are described here. However, algebraic manipulation of the equations can yield any variable, providing the other quantities are known.

Special techniques, known as "field hydraulics" or "rule of thumb," are used by driver/operators for approximate results. The methods shown here give more precise results, but they are generally too involved for field applications. Details on rule-of-thumb fire stream calculations can be found in the fire-fighting hydraulic texts listed in the bibliography.

The calculation of the pump discharge pressure depends on a number of variables, including the required nozzle pressure, friction loss in the hose layout, and pressure loss or gain due to elevation changes. As previously discussed, the required nozzle pressure will depend on the type of nozzle being used. Handline solid-stream nozzles are operated at 50 psi (345 kPa), master stream solid-stream nozzles are operated at 80 psi (552 kPa), and all standard spray nozzles are generally operated at 100 psi (690 kPa). There are some spray nozzles now available that are designed to operate at 75 psi (518 kPa). The hose friction loss is a function of the hose diameter, hose length, discharge volume, and any appliances, such as wyes or monitors, used in the hose layout.

Elevation pressure (*EP*) is the loss or gain of potential energy due to elevation changes between the pump and the nozzle. This is determined by the equations:

$$EP = 0.434h \text{ (SI units: } EP_m = 9.81h_m\text{)}$$

where

EP = Elevation pressure in psi (kPa)

h = Elevation change or head in ft (m) of water

For ease of calculation, in the fire service these equations are commonly rounded as follows:

$$EP = 0.5h \text{ (SI units: } EP_m = 10h_m\text{)}$$

The basis of these calculations revolves around three fundamental hydraulic principles: Bernoulli's equation, Darcy-Weibach equation, and continuity equation.

Bernoulli's Equation

This equation is a special form of conservation of energy. For a pumper hose line system this becomes:

$$PDP = NP + FL \pm EP$$

where

PDP = Pump discharge pressure in psi (kPa)

NP = Nozzle pressure in psi (kPa)

FL = Friction loss in psi (kPa)

EP = Elevation pressure in psi (kPa)

Darcy-Weisbach Equation

$$FL = (fV^2L)/(2gD)$$

where

g = Acceleration due to gravity, ft/sec^2 (m/sec^2)

f = Friction factor, a dimensionless number

L = Hose length in ft (m)

D = Hose diameter in in. (mm)

V = Velocity in ft/sec

Continuity Equation

This equation is a special form of conservation of mass.

$$Q = VA$$

where

Q = Flow rate, ft^3/sec (m^3/sec)

V = Velocity, ft/sec (m/sec)

A = Area, ft^2 (m^2)

These equations can be manipulated to result in friction loss equations and a modern version of the Underwriters equation.[1]

Friction loss is the loss of energy resulting from the internal friction between the moving particles of water and the friction between the water and the lining of the hose. The friction loss depends on water viscosity, flow rate, hose diameter, hose length, and the roughness characteristics of the hose lining. Although the viscosity is partly a function of the water temperature, the change is insignificant in the ranges of the temperature of water commonly used for fire fighting. The flow volume, hose diameter, and hose length are variables that are determined by the fire-fighting requirements. The roughness of the hose lining cannot be easily measured and is generally determined experimentally and reported as the friction factor. Consequently, all variables, except the flow volume, hose diameter, and hose length, are embodied in the friction factor, *f,* of the Darcy-Weibach equation and in the continuity equation. Putting all constants into one constant factor results in the modern fire service friction loss equation:

$$FL = cq^2l$$

where

FL = Friction loss in the total hose layout in psi or kPa

c = A coefficient based on the size and type of hose

q = Flow of water through the entire layout in hundreds of gallons per minute or hundreds of liters per minute ($q = Q/100$).

l = Length of hose in hundreds of feet or meters ($l = L/100$)

The suggested coefficients for various sizes and types of hose are shown in Table 13.3.8. These coefficients should be considered averages for the size and type of hose to which they are applied. The friction factor for modern fire hose varies from manufacturer to manufacturer. For more specific information on the exact coefficient for any particular brand of hose, contact the manufacturer of the hose.

The preceding equation replaces the old, less accurate, and more complex equation $FL = (2q^2 + q)l$. The old equation required all sizes of hose, other than 2½ in. (65 mm), to first be converted to equivalent lengths of 2½ inch (65 mm) hose before being plugged into the equation. However, the old equation was based on hose technology from the 1930s and 1940s. The results produced by this equation did not reflect the actual friction loss in modern (smoother) fire hose. Those interested in the old equation are referred to the bibliography.

The following are examples of calculating pump discharge pressure using the information described earlier:

EXAMPLE: Calculate the pump discharge pressure necessary to adequately supply 300 ft (90 m) of 2½ in. (65 mm) rubber-lined hose that is equipped with a solid-stream handline nozzle with a 1¼ in. (32 mm) tip. The position of the nozzle is 10 ft (3 m) above the level of the pump.

SOLUTION: U.S. customary units

$$Q = 29.7d^2\sqrt{NP}$$

$$Q = 29.7(1.25)^2\sqrt{50}$$

$$Q = 29.7(1.5625)(7.07)$$

$$Q = 328 \text{ gpm}$$

$$q = 328/100 = 3.28$$

$$FL = cq^2l$$

$$FL = (2)(3.28)^2(300/100)$$

$$FL = (2)(10.7584)(3)$$

$$FL = 64.55 \text{ or } 65 \text{ psi}$$

$$EP = 0.5h$$

$$EP = (0.5)(10) = 5 \text{ psi}$$

$$PDP = NP + FL \pm EP$$

$$PDP = 50 + 65 + 5$$

$$PDP = 120 \text{ psi}$$

TABLE 13.3.8 Recommended Friction Loss Coefficients for Single Hose Lines

Hose Diameter			Friction Loss Coefficient	
in.	*mm*	*Hose Type*	*psi*	*kPa*
¾	19	Booster	1100	1741
1	25	Booster	150	238
1¼	32	Booster	80	127
1¼	32	Linen	127	201
1½	38	Rubber lined	24	38
1½	38	Linen	51.2	81
1¾ with 1½ couplings	45 with 38 couplings	Rubber lined	15.5	24.6
2	50	Rubber lined	8	12.7
2	50	Linen	12.5	19.8
2½	65	Linen	4.26	6.75
2½		Rubber lined	2	3.17
2¾ with 3 couplings	70 with 77 couplings	Rubber lined	1.5	2.36
3 with 2½ couplings	77 with 65 couplings	Rubber lined	0.80	1.27
3 with 3 couplings	77 with 77 couplings	Rubber lined	0.677	1.06
3½	90	Rubber lined	0.34	0.53
4	100	Rubber lined	0.2	0.305
4½	115	Rubber lined	0.1	0.167
5	125	Rubber lined	0.08	0.138
6	150	Rubber lined	0.05	0.083

SOLUTION: Metric units

$$Q = 0.0666d_m^2\sqrt{NP_m}$$

$$Q = 0.0666(32)^2\sqrt{345}$$

$$Q = (0.0666)(1024)(18.5742)$$

$$Q = 1267 \text{ L/min}$$

$$q = 1267/100 = 12.67$$

$$FL = cq^2l$$

$$FL = (3.17)(12.67)^2(90/100)$$

$$FL = (3.17)(160.5289)(0.9)$$

$$FL = 457.99 \text{ or } 458 \text{ psi}$$

$$EP = 10h$$

$$EP = (10)(3) = 30 \text{ kPa}$$

$$PDP = NP + FL \pm EP$$

$$PDP = 345 + 458 + 30$$

$$PDP = 833 \text{ kPa}$$

When using the foregoing formulas to determine the pump discharge pressure for wyed hose lines of the same size and length, keep in mind the following considerations:

1. The friction loss for the total hose lay is the sum of the losses in the supply hose, *one* of the wyed lines, and the wye appliance (if applicable).
2. When determining the flow in the hose line that is supplying the wye, remember to add the flows from *all* of the wyed lines.
3. If the total flow through the wye appliance is less than 350 gpm (1325 L/min), do not consider the friction loss through wye to be important. If the flow exceeds this amount, add 10 psi (70 kPa) to the friction loss in the hose.

EXAMPLE: Calculate the pump discharge pressure necessary to adequately supply 400 ft (120 m) of 4 in. (100 mm) hose that is wyed off into two 150 ft (45 m), 2½ in. (65 mm) rubber-lined attack hose lines. Each attack line is equipped with a spray nozzle that is designed to flow 250 gpm (946 L/min) at 100 psi (690 kPa). There is no elevation change in the hose lay.

SOLUTION: U.S. customary units

$$FL = cq^2l$$

$$FL_{2\frac{1}{2}\text{ inch}} = (2)(250/100)^2(150/100)$$

$$FL_{2\frac{1}{2}\text{ inch}} = (2)(6.25)(1.5)$$

$$FL_{2\frac{1}{2}\text{ inch}} = 18.75 \text{ or } 19 \text{ psi}$$

$$FL_{4\text{ inch}} = (0.2)(500/100)^2(400/100)$$

$$FL_{4\text{ inch}} = (0.2)(25)(4)$$

$$FL_{4\text{ inch}} = 20 \text{ psi}$$

$$FL_{\text{Total}} = FL_{2\frac{1}{2}\text{ inch}} + FL_{4\text{ inch}} + \text{Appliance loss}$$

$$FL_{\text{Total}} = 19 + 20 + 10$$

$$FL_{\text{Total}} = 49 \text{ psi}$$

$$PDP = NP + FL_{\text{Total}} \pm EP$$

$$PDP = 100 + 49 + 0$$

$$PDP = 149 \text{ psi}$$

SOLUTION: Metric units

$$FL = cq^2l$$

$$FL_{65\text{ mm}} = (3.17)(946/100)^2(45/100)$$

$$FL_{65\text{ mm}} = (3.17)(89.49)(0.45)$$

$$FL_{65\text{ mm}} = 127.66 \text{ or } 128 \text{ kPa}$$

$$FL_{100\text{ mm}} = (0.305)(1892/100)^2(120/100)$$

$$FL_{100\text{ mm}} = (0.305)(357.97)(1.2)$$

$$FL_{100\text{ mm}} = 131 \text{ kPa}$$

$$FL_{\text{Total}} = FL_{65\text{ mm}} + FL_{100\text{ mm}} + \text{Appliance loss}$$

$$FL_{\text{Total}} = 149 + 131 + 70$$

$$FL_{\text{Total}} = 350 \text{ kPa}$$

$$PDP = NP + FL_{\text{Total}} \pm EP$$

$$PDP = 690 + 350 + 0$$

$$PDP = 1040 \text{ kPa}$$

If determining the friction loss in wyed lines that have differing flows, hose sizes, or hose lengths, calculate the friction loss in each of the wyed lines and use the highest result added to the supply line and appliance loss (if applicable) in determining the total friction loss for the hose layout and ultimately the required pump discharge pressure.

The friction loss formula described previously may also be used when determining the friction loss in siamesed lines of equal length. However, in this case a different set of coefficients is required. The coefficients for siamesed lines are contained in Table13.3.9. When determining the friction loss in siamesed lines using this formula, q should be determined by using the total flow through both lines.

EXAMPLE: Calculate the pump discharge pressure necessary to adequately supply a portable master stream device equipped with a 500 gpm (1892 L/min) spray nozzle operated at 100 psi (690 kPa) being supplied by two 3 in. (77 mm) with 3 in. (77 mm) couplings, each 600 ft (180 m) long. There is no elevation change in the hose lay, but assume that the master stream appliance creates a 10 psi (70 kPa) pressure loss.

SOLUTION: U.S. customary units

$$FL = cq^2l + \text{Appliance loss}$$

$$FL = (0.17)(500/100)^2(600/100) + 10$$

$$FL = (0.17)(25)(6) + 10$$

$$FL = 25.5 + 10$$

TABLE 13.3.9 Recommended Friction Loss Coefficients for Siamesed Lines of Equal Length

Number of Hose Lines and Their Diameters in in. (mm)	Friction Loss Coefficient *psi*	*kPa*
Two 2½ in. (65 mm)	0.50	0.789
Three 2½ in. (65 mm)	0.22	0.347
Two 3 in. (77 mm) with 2½ in. (65 mm) couplings	0.20	0.316
Two 3 in. (77 mm) with 3 in. (77 mm) couplings	0.17	0.268
One 3 in. (77 mm) with 2½ in. (65 mm) couplings, one 2½ in. (65 mm)	0.30	0.473
One 3 in. (77 mm) with 3 in. (77 mm) couplings, one 2½ in. (65 mm)	0.27	0.426
Two 2½ in. (65 mm), one 3 in. (77 mm) with 2½ in. (65 mm) couplings	0.16	0.253
Two 3 in. (77 mm) with 2½ in. (65 mm) couplings, one 2½ in. (65 mm)	0.12	0.189

$$FL = 35.5 \text{ or } 36 \text{ psi}$$
$$PDP = NP + FL \pm EP$$
$$PDP = 100 + 36 + 0$$
$$PDP = 136 \text{ psi}$$

SOLUTION: Metric units

$$FL = cq^2l + \text{Appliance loss}$$
$$FL = (0.268)(1892/100)^2(180/100) + 70$$
$$FL = (0.268)(357.97)(1.8) + 70$$
$$FL = 172.68 + 70$$
$$FL = 242.68 \text{ or } 243 \text{ kPa}$$
$$PDP = NP + FL \pm EP$$
$$PDP = 690 + 243 + 0$$
$$PDP = 933 \text{ kPa}$$

Attempting to mathematically calculate the pressure loss or pump discharge pressure in siamesed lines of unequal length is an extremely complicated process that involves advanced mathematical techniques. Because these situations are so rare in real-life operations, a detailed description of these operations is omitted here. Consult the references listed in the bibliography of this section for more information on this matter.

REACTION FORCES IN HOSE LINES, NOZZLES, AND AERIAL DEVICES

When water is discharged from a hose line, there are two reaction forces acting on the line: (1) hose line reaction and (2) nozzle reaction. Both contribute in varying degrees to the total reaction that is present in any hose nozzle flow configuration. For purposes of simplicity, each is treated separately in this chapter.

Hose Line Reaction Forces

Reaction forces occur in hose lines when the direction of waterflow is changed by a bend in the hose. Between the hydrant and nozzle, the velocity is constrained in the hose and the acceleration is zero, as shown by the equation

$$Q = AV$$

where

Q = The flow rate

A = The cross-sectional area

V = The average velocity

Figure 13.3.3 illustrates a typical handline situation where enough push must be applied at the bend to resist the reaction force F_3. There is no problem where the hose bends off the ground.

Figures 13.3.4 and 13.3.5 are charts by which values of the reaction F_3, in pounds force, can be directly determined. To obtain reactions in other sizes of hose, Figure 13.3.4 includes a table of conversion factors to use in calculating reaction forces, expressed in pounds force, in hose of other diameters; and Fig-

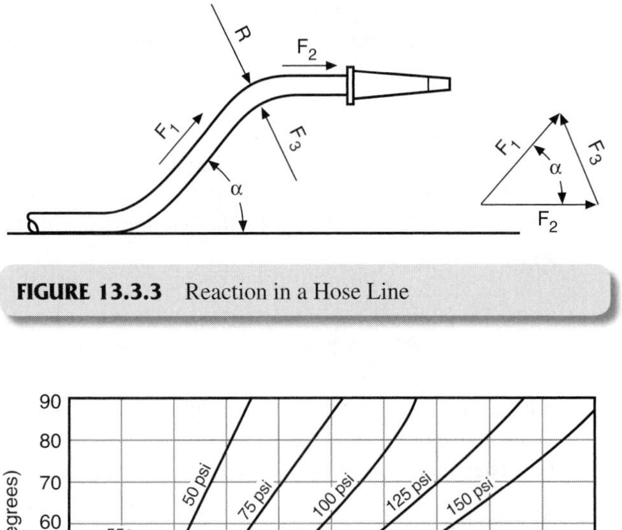

FIGURE 13.3.3 Reaction in a Hose Line

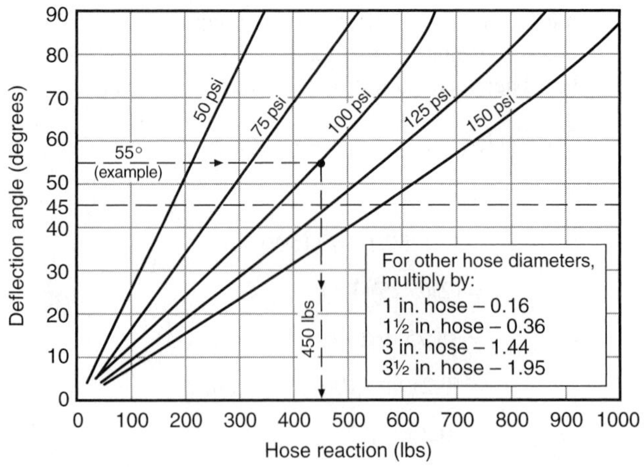

FIGURE 13.3.4 Reaction Forces in 2½ in. Hose

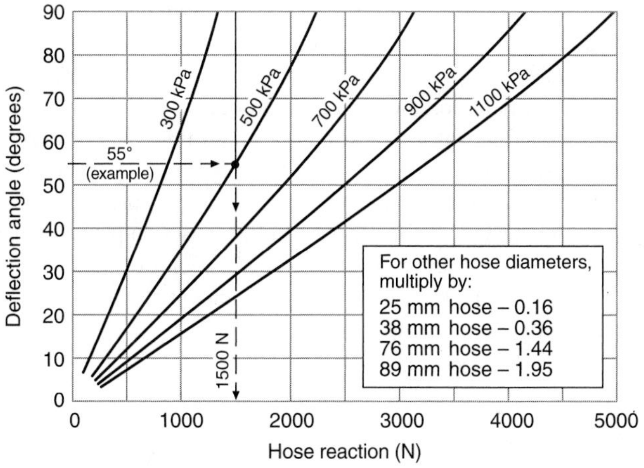

FIGURE 13.3.5 Reaction Forces in 65 mm Hose

ure 13.3.5 includes a table of conversion factors to use in calculating reaction forces, expressed in newtons (N), in hose of other diameters.

EXAMPLE: What is the reaction at a 55 degree bend in 1½ in. (38 mm) hose if the pressure is 100 psi (690 kPa)?

SOLUTION: On the deflection angle side, move horizontally from the 55 degree bend to intersection with the 100 psi (690 kPa) curve. From there go down vertically to the reaction scale and read 450 lb (204 kg). From Figures 13.3.4 and 13.3.5, note that the factor for 1½ in. (38 mm) hose is 0.36. Multiplying 450 (204 kg) by 0.36, the answer is 162 lb (73 kg).

Nozzle Reaction

Water discharging from a nozzle produces a reaction that is opposite the flow of water and known as nozzle reaction. As flow and pressure are increased, the nozzle reaction increases. Nozzle reaction of solid-stream nozzles may be calculated by means of the following formula:

$$NR = 1.5d^2NP$$

where

NR = Nozzle reaction (lb)

1.5 = A constant

d = Nozzle diameter (in.)

NP = Nozzle pressure (psi)

For SI units:

$$NR = 0.0015d_m^2NP_m$$

where

NR = nozzle reaction (N)

0.0015 = A constant

d_m = Nozzle diameter (mm)

NP_m = Nozzle pressure (kPa)

EXAMPLE: Determine the nozzle reaction created when a 1¼ in. (32 mm) solid-stream nozzle is being operated at a discharge pressure of 50 psi (345 kPa).

SOLUTION: U.S. customary units

$$NR = 1.5d^2NP$$

$$NR = (1.5)(1.25)^2(50)$$

$$NR = (1.5)(1.5625)(50)$$

$$NR = 117.19 \text{ lb}$$

SOLUTION: Metric units

$$NR = 0.0015d_m^2NP_m$$

$$NR = (0.0015)(32)^2(345)$$

$$NR = (0.0015)(1024)(345)$$

$$NR = 529.92 \text{ N}$$

Another formula that may be used for both solid-stream and spray nozzles is:

$$NR = 0.0505Q\sqrt{NP}$$

where

NR = Nozzle reaction (lb)

0.0505 = A constant

Q = Nozzle discharge (gpm)

NP = Nozzle pressure (psi)

For SI units:

$$NR = 0.0226Q_m\sqrt{NP_m}$$

where

NR = Nozzle reaction (N)

0.0226 = A constant

Q_m = Nozzle discharge (L/min)

NP_m = Nozzle pressure (kPa)

EXAMPLE: Find the nozzle reaction when a 250 gpm (946 L/min) spray nozzle is operating at 100 psi (690 kPa).

SOLUTION: U.S. customary units

$$NR = 0.0505Q\sqrt{NP}$$

$$NR = (0.0505)(250)(\sqrt{100})$$

$$NR = (0.0505)(250)(10)$$

$$NR = 126.25 \text{ lb}$$

SOLUTION: Metric units

$$NR = 0.0156Q_m\sqrt{NP_m}$$

$$NR = (0.0226)(946)(\sqrt{690})$$

$$NR = (0.0226)(946)(26.27)$$

$$NR = 561.64 \text{ N}$$

Reaction Forces in Aerial Ladder and Elevating Platform Streams

The reaction of master streams, either solid or spray, discharged from aerial ladders or elevating platforms creates a tremendous amount of stress on the aerial device. Some of these stresses, such as leverage effects and displacement of centers of gravity, are magnified as the aerial device is further extended. Thus, the stability of the whole structure could be threatened if the aerial device is extended, or if the elevated master stream is operated, beyond its design limitations. Likewise, a sudden loss of pressure when a hose line bursts or a pump stops may cause a whipping action that can result in damage to the aerial device. Because there are many variable forces acting on aerial ladders, elevating platforms, or water towers in service, it is quite impractical to devise tables of specific reactions.

Fire fighters must be particularly cautious with detachable ladder pipes and hose that are used in conjunction with light-duty aerial ladders. In this circumstance, the detachable ladder pipe should always be operated in line with the main beams or trusses of the aerial ladder. Light-duty aerial ladders have little resistance to torsional effects, so detachable ladder pipes should be incapable of horizontal travel exceeding 15 degrees. Rotation of the ladder turntable is the correct way to rotate the stream from these ladder pipes. When possible, these detachable ladder pipes should be operated from the turntable of the apparatus using sets of ropes to control the up-and-down motion of the nozzle. This eliminates the need to place a fire fighter in the precarious position of directing the stream from the tip of the ladder.

Care should be used also in elevating and lowering the stream, because this changes the direction of the thrust on the ladder mechanism. The fly ladder should not be raised or lowered while a ladder pipe is discharging, and under no circumstances should the vehicle be moved with the ladder pipe discharging. All such streams should be gated to permit movement of the ladder and vehicle without shutting down the pump.

Finally, consult the apparatus manufacturer's recommendation when choosing the size of hose to be used to supply the detachable ladder pipe. Most aerial ladders are designed for a single 3 or 3½ in. supply hose to be run up the ladder to the ladder pipe. Using a larger hose could result in overloading the ladder, thus risking a catastrophic failure of the device.

In general aerial ladders with piped waterways and elevating platforms are equipped with remote-controlled nozzles that are capable of a wider range of motion than are detachable ladder pipes. The remote controls for these devices will typically not allow the nozzle to operate a stream outside of the safe operating area. Driver/operators should be familiar with the recommended operating procedures and safe loading parameters for these devices.

SUMMARY

The effective supply of water through hose lines to nozzles is one of the most basic tenets of fire fighting and municipal fire protection. Fire apparatus driver/operators must be able to effectively calculate the required flows and pressures needed to adequately supply fire fighters operating attack lines. This calculation is important from both an operational and a safety standpoint. The information contained in this chapter allows fire-fighting professionals to realistically calculate waterflow pressure and quantity through hose lines and nozzles. It also allows for the calculation of the resultant reaction pressure that will be created at the nozzle. The application of this information will assist in providing useful pre-incident planning and fire scene tactical operations.

BIBLIOGRAPHY

Reference Cited

1. Purington, R. G., *Fire-Fighting Hydraulics,* McGraw-Hill, New York, 1974.

NFPA Codes, Standards, and Recommended Practices

Reference to the following NFPA codes, standards, and recommended practices will provide further information on fire streams discussed in this chapter. (See the latest version of The NFPA Catalog *for availability of current editions of the following documents.)*

NFPA 414, *Standard for Aircraft Rescue and Fire-Fighting Vehicles*
NFPA 1901, *Standard for Automotive Fire Apparatus*
NFPA 1906, *Standard for Wildland Fire Apparatus*
NFPA 1911, *Standard for Service Tests of Fire Pump Systems on Fire Apparatus*
NFPA 1961, *Standard on Fire Hose*
NFPA 1962, *Standard for the Inspection, Care, and Use of Fire Hose, Couplings, and Nozzles and the Service Testing of Fire Hose*
NFPA 1964, *Standard for Spray Nozzles*

References

Bailey, P., "Water Supply and Transport for Rural Firefighting," *The Voice,* Vol. 27, No. 2, 1998, pp. 7–8.
Baird, D., "Fog or Solid Stream: Deja Vue," *Fire Fighting in Canada,* Vol. 42, No. 9, 1998, p. 16.
Bruyninckx, E., and Andries, M., "Fire Protection Concept for Chemical Plants, Refineries and Terminals," *Journal of Applied Fire Science,* Vol. 5, No. 4, 1995–1996, pp. 285–297.
Chen, E. B., Morales, A. J., Chen, C. C., Donatelli, A. A., Bannister, W. W., and Cummings, B. T., "Fluorescein and Poly(ethylene oxide) Hose Stream Additives for Improved Firefighting Effectiveness," *Fire Technology,* Vol. 34, No. 4, 1998, pp. 291–306.
Coombes, C., "Increasing Influence of Water Supplies on Appliance Design," *Fire,* Vol. 93, No. 1140, 2000, pp. 31–32.
Covey, B., "Static Water Supply Challenges: Australia's Solution," *Fire Engineering,* Vol. 152, No. 8, 1999, pp. 143–144.
Crapo, W., *Hydraulics for Fire Fighting,* Delmar, Albany, NY, 2002.
Davidson, J., and Williams, B., "Metro Hose Pack: Urbanizing a Wildland Success," *Fire Engineering,* Vol. 153, No. 9, 2000, pp. 59–61.
Fornell, D. P., "2-Inch Hose: The Nuts and Bolts," *Firehouse,* Vol. 22, No. 4, 1997, pp. 134–137.
Fredericks, A. A., "Little Drops of Water: 50 Years Later. Part 1," *Fire Engineering,* Vol. 153, No. 2, 2000, pp. 63–64.
Fredericks, A. A., "Little Drops of Water: 50 Years Later. Part 2," *Fire Engineering,* Mar. 2000, pp. 113–114.
Halton, B., and Allen, K., "Water Flow Technology. Part 1. Pumping Water, Fire Flows and Fire Suppression," *Firehouse,* Vol. 26, No. 5, 2001, p. 72.
IFSTA, *Pumping Apparatus Driver/Operator Handbook,* 2nd ed., Fire Protection Publications, Stillwater, OK, 2006.
Kelly, K. J., "Hose Connections: Hose Stations and Hose Systems," *Sprinkler Quarterly,* No. 114, 2001, pp. 39–41.

Kidd, S., "Managing Fire Safety in Heritage Premises," *Fire Protection,* Vol. 23, No. 2, 1997, pp. 12–17.

Kobayashi, S., "Tokyo Prepares Water Sources for Future Earthquakes," *Fire International,* No. 166, 1999, pp. 15–16.

Leihbacher, D., "Overcoming Common Water Supply Problems," *Fire Engineering,* Vol. 151, No. 4, 1998, pp. 119–124.

Loeb, D. L., "Don't Stop Fire Training," *Fire Chief,* Vol. 41, No. 4, 1997, p. 56.

O'Sullivan, K., "Compressed Air Foam: A Developing Technology," *Fire,* Vol. 91, No. 1119, 1998, p. 76.

Pucci, W. E., "Not Software for the Fire Protection Community," *NFPA Journal,* Vol. 91, No. 1, 1997, pp. 51–56.

Regan, J., and Fredericks, A. A., "Improving the Quality of Your Solid Streams," *Fire Engineering,* Vol. 153, No. 4, 2000, pp. 59–60.

Rielage, R. R., "Molehill Out of a Mountain," *Fire Chief,* Vol. 41, No. 3, 1997, p. 50.

Singh, S., Jain, J. P., Jain, N., Tyagi, N. S., Singh, N., and Singh, I., "Fire Stop Technology for Protection in Cable Installations," *Chemical Engineering World,* Vol. 31, No. 9, 1996, p. 127.

Smith, W. P., "Motorway Emergency Water Scheme," *Fire Engineers Journal,* Vol. 57, No. 190, 1997, pp. 25–27.

St. Louis, E., and Wilder, S., "Train Disasters Test the Fire Service: Tragedy on the City of New Orleans," *Fire Engineering,* Vol. 152, No. 6, 1999, pp. 61–62.

Sturtevant, T., *Introduction to Pump Operations,* Delmar, Albany, NY, 2005.

Toth, W. J., "Water Delivery Basics: From Pea Shooters to Cannons," *American Fire Journal,* Vol. 48, No. 10, 1996, pp. 11–14.

Tracy, G. A., "High-Rise Standpipe Flow Test," *Fire Engineering,* Vol. 152, No. 4, 1999, pp. 107–109.

Tracy, J., "Firefighting Operations in High-Rises Under Construction," *Fire Engineering,* Vol. 150, No. 12, 1997, pp. 47–52.

Wieder, M. A., *Fire Service Hydraulics and Water Supply,* Fire Protection Publications, Stillwater, OK, 2005.

Williams, A. S., and Halford, S. D., "Improving Water Supply in Nonhydrant Areas: One Department's Approach," *Fire Engineering,* Vol. 151, No. 4, 1998, pp. 109–118.

Zenofsky, S., "Fire on the Horizon: Preventing the Loss from Bush, Forest, Brush, Grass and Wildland Fires," *Fire Engineers Journal,* Vol. 59, No. 201, 1999, pp. 6–9.

Chapter 4

Alternate Water Supplies

Laurence J. Stewart

This chapter provides information for the planning and utilization of a water supply or supplies that the fire department creates and uses for fire suppression. Fire suppression cannot be accomplished without water sources and the ability to move the water by some selected method. The water in the "supply" created by all types of alternative water supply methods should always be considered nonpotable water.

The development of alternative water supplies is a four-step planning process centering on answers to the following questions:

- How much water is required?
- Where is the water?
- How can dry hydrants help?
- How can water be moved to the fire?

This chapter does not cover (1) the providing of water to any government-operated or government-subsidized water system that is either out of water or has its supply drastically curtailed or (2) the providing of water to forest fire suppression units.

See also Section 15, Chapter 1, "Fixed Water Storage Supplies for Fire Protection"; and Section 15, Chapter 6, "Water Distribution."

Chapter Contents

Key Terms

alternate water supply, cistern, construction (type of), dry hydrant, minimum water requirement, occupancy hazard classification, water shuttle operations, water source (developed), water source (natural), water supply (mobile)

SOURCES OF ALTERNATE WATER SUPPLIES

A fire department operating without a water system with hydrants or one with a very limited number of hydrants has two means of getting water: (1) from supplies on the fireground, which can be constructed or natural, or (2) from supplies transported to the scene. Alternative water supplies for fire department operations come from water obtained directly from either static water, flowing water, or water contained within some type of storage tank. Water from these sources is not part of a pressurized water system. Alternative water supply operations can also encompass the use of water from fire hydrants that are part of a pressurized water system. In such a case, the water from the hydrants is "loaded" into mobile water supply apparatus and shuttled to a distant fire scene, or it may be moved both within and beyond the "boundaries" of the pressurized water system through the use of hose. The distinctive feature of this type of water use is that the fire department provides the water by means of hose, varying types of pumping apparatus, and/or mobile water supply apparatus. (The latter will be referred to in this chapter as MWS apparatus.)

Proper planning in developing water supplies for fire fighting requires that built-up areas and water supply needs be identified within the response area. The fire service has always experienced fire control difficulties in isolated areas. One of the main problems is the lack of an adequate water supply. The availability of an adequate amount of water for control and extinguishment is an important consideration for fire chiefs and a factor that influences the majority of their fire-fighting decisions. A portion of the training of suburban and rural fire departments emphasizes the need for the conservation of the meager water supply available in many areas. A limited amount of water at a working fire challenges all phases of fire fighting. Once the areas with waterflow needs have been identified, a building/site survey should be conducted to determine the water supply needed for fire protection.

Laurence J. Stewart is a fire service specialist for the NFPA Public Fire Protection Division. He has 23 years of experience within the fire and emergency services.

Minimum water supplies are determined by the following criteria:

- Classification of occupancy hazard
- Classification of construction
- Structure dimensions
- Exposures, if any

In order to establish the necessary quantity of water available for fire suppression, various criteria must be converted into numerical equivalencies. Tables 13.4.1 and 13.4.2 provide the data for establishing the variables used in the water supply formula. The following occupancy hazard classes number and Table 13.4.2 classification number will be used in the formulas calculating minimum water requirements.

OCCUPANCY HAZARD CLASSIFICATION

Occupancies are divided into categories based on the risk and the development of fire spread. The occupancy hazard classification number is a mathematical factor to be used in calculating minimum water supplies. The lowest occupancy hazard classification number is 3; it is assigned to the highest hazard group. The highest occupancy hazard classification number is 7; it is assigned to the lowest hazard group. NFPA 1142, *Standard on Water Supplies for Suburban and Rural Fire Fighting,* provides the minimum water supply requirements, based on occupancy classification, construction classification, and total volume of the structure.

Occupancy Hazard Class 3

Occupancies in Class 3 are considered severe hazard occupancies, in which quantity and combustibility of contents are high. A fire in a Class 3 occupancy would tend to develop very rapidly and have high rates of heat release. Examples of this classification include occupancies having conditions similar to the following:

- Cereal or flour mills
- Combustible hydraulics facilities
- Cotton picker and opening operations (cotton gins)
- Die casting facilities
- Explosives and pyrotechnics manufacturing and storage facilities
- Feed and gristmills
- Flammable liquid spraying facilities
- Flow coating/dipping facilities
- Linseed oil mills
- Manufactured homes/modular building assembly facilities
- Metal extruding facilities
- Plastic processing facilities
- Plywood and particle board manufacturing facilities
- Printing plants using flammable inks
- Rubber reclaiming facilities
- Sawmills
- Solvent extracting facilities
- Facilities with straw or hay in bales
- Textile picking facilities
- Facilities upholstering with plastic foams

Occupancy Hazard Class 4

Occupancies in Class 4 are high hazard occupancies, in which quantity and combustibility of contents are high. Examples of this classification include occupancies having conditions similar to the following:

- Barns and stables (commercial)
- Building materials supply storage facilities
- Department stores
- Exhibition halls, auditoriums, and theaters
- Feed stores (without processing)
- Freight terminals
- Mercantile facilities
- Paper and pulp mills
- Paper processing plants
- Piers and wharves
- Repair garages
- Rubber products manufacturing and storage facilities
- Warehouses (e.g., those used for furniture, general storage, paint, paper, and woodworking industries)

Occupancy Hazard Class 5

Occupancies in Class 5 are considered moderate hazard occupancies, in which the quantity or combustibility of contents is

TABLE 13.4.1 SI Metric Unit Conversion Factors for Occupancy Classifications

Occupancy Classification Number	*SI Metric Unit Conversion Factor*
3	0.0224
4	0.0299
5	0.0373
6	0.0448
7	0.0523

TABLE 13.4.2 Construction Classification Numbers

0.5	*0.75*	*1.0*	*0.75*	*1.50*
Type I construction (fire resistive)	Type II construction (noncombustible)	Type III construction (ordinary)	Type IV construction (heavy timber)	Type V construction (wood frame)

expected to develop moderate rates of spread and heat release. Examples of this classification include occupancies having conditions similar to the following:

- Amusement centers
- Clothing manufacturing plants
- Cold storage warehouses
- Confectionery product warehouses
- Farm storage buildings (e.g., corn cribs, dairy barns, equipment sheds, hatcheries)
- Laundries
- Leather goods manufacturing plants
- Libraries (with large stockroom areas)
- Lithography shops
- Machine shops
- Metalworking shops
- Nurseries (plant)
- Pharmaceutical manufacturing plants
- Printing and publishing plants
- Restaurants
- Rope and twine manufacturing plants
- Sugar refineries
- Tanneries
- Textile manufacturing plants
- Tobacco barns
- Unoccupied buildings

Occupancy Hazard Class 6

Occupancies in Class 6 are considered low hazard occupancies, in which the quantity or combustibility of contents is expected to develop relatively low rates of spread and heat release. Examples of this classification include occupancies having conditions similar to the following:

- Armories
- Automobile parking garages
- Bakeries
- Barber or beauty shops
- Beverage manufacturing plants/breweries
- Boiler houses
- Brick, tile, and clay product manufacturing plants
- Canneries
- Cement plants
- Churches and similar religious structures
- Dairy products manufacturing and processing plants
- Doctors' offices
- Electronics plants
- Foundries
- Fur processing plants
- Gasoline service stations
- Glass and glass products manufacturing plants
- Horse stables
- Mortuaries
- Municipal buildings
- Post offices
- Slaughterhouses
- Telephone exchanges
- Tobacco manufacturing plants
- Watch and jewelry manufacturing plants
- Wineries

Occupancy Hazard Class 7

Occupancies in Class 7 are considered light hazard occupancies, in which the quantity or combustibility of contents is expected to develop a relatively light rate of spread and heat release. Examples of this classification include occupancies having conditions similar to the following:

- Apartments
- Colleges and universities
- Clubs
- Dormitories
- Dwellings
- Fire stations
- Fraternity or sorority houses
- Hospitals
- Hotels and motels
- Libraries (except large stockroom areas)
- Museums
- Nursing and convalescent homes
- Offices (including data processing)
- Police stations
- Prisons
- Schools
- Theaters without stages

STRUCTURE AND SITE SURVEY

Information needed to compute the minimum water supplies that should be collected during the structure/site survey (Figure 13.4.1) includes the following:

- Area of all floors, including attics, basements, and crawl spaces
- Height between floors or crawl spaces and in attics from floor to ridgepole
- Construction materials used in each structure, including walls, floors, roofs, ceilings, interior partitions, stairs, and so forth

FIGURE 13.4.1 On-Site Survey of Structure

- Occupancy (occupancies) of structures
- Occupancy (occupancies) of yard areas
- Exposures to structures and yard storage and distances between them
- Fire protection systems, such as automatic and manual protection systems, hydrants, yard mains, and other protection facilities
- On-site water supplies, including natural and constructed sources of water

Classification of Construction

There are five recognized types of construction, with the type of materials used in each type of construction listed and the type of construction assigned a numerical number. The assigned number becomes another mathematical factor to be used in the formula for calculating minimum water supplies. The slowest burning or lowest hazard type of construction (i.e., fire resistive) is construction classification number 0.5. The fastest burning or highest hazard type of construction (i.e., wood frame) is construction classification number 1.5. Where there is more than one type of construction in a structure, the higher classification number should be used for the entire structure.

Construction classifications listed in Table 13.4.2 have been simplified for quick use. If more complete definitions are needed, refer to NFPA 220, *Standard on Types of Building Construction.*

Calculating Minimum Water Requirements

Before determining such things as the type of pumpers and MWS apparatus to use and how to pump water from a source, the fire department should focus on the water requirements of the response area. This means determining how much water is required to extinguish a fire at each structure in the response area. To calculate this amount, three pieces of information are needed: the materials stored in the building, the building's construction, and the size (total volume) of the structure. This information can be gathered during the on-site surveys of the buildings in the response area outside of the pressurized water system. (The formulas were developed by an NFPA 1142 committee.)

Structures without Exposure Hazards: Minimum water supply

$$= \frac{\text{Total volume of structure}}{\text{Occupancy hazard classification number}} \times \text{Construction classification number}$$

Structures with Exposure Hazards: Minimum water supply

$$= \frac{\text{Total volume of structure}}{\text{Occupancy hazard classification number}} \times \text{Construction classification number} \times 1.5$$

NATURAL WATER SOURCES

Using natural water sources, such as streams, springs, lakes, ponds, and wells, provides a relatively inexpensive quantity of water. Reliability must also be considered when planning water supply distribution. Research may be necessary to determine that a source can supply the minimum water requirements in all seasons and during all variations in weather. Inspection of water sources is an ongoing process. Records should be updated with any seasonal fluctuations, flood or drought conditions, and freezing problems noted.

Streams

Streams, including rivers, bays, creeks, and irrigation canals, can represent a continuously flowing source of substantial capacity. When considering water from flowing streams as potential water sources, the fire department should take into account the following factors:

- *Flowing capacity.* The stream should deliver water in capacities compatible with the water requirements determined necessary for the hazard.
- *Climatic characteristics.* Streams that deliver water throughout the year and are not susceptible to drought are desirable for fire protection. However, if such streams are not available, a combination of supplies might be necessary. In many sections of the country, streams cannot be relied on during drought seasons. If the stream is subject to flooding or freezing, special measures might be necessary to make the stream usable under such conditions (Figure 13.4.2). Similar circumstances might exist during wet periods or when the ground is covered with snow.
- *Accessibility.* A water site should provide the necessary access to ensure availability to the site in all normally expected weather conditions encountered in the area 24 hours per day, 365 days per year. Distance and terrain from the all-weather road to the source should be such as to make the water readily available. In some cases, special equipment should be used to obtain the water, especially in areas where the water surface may become frozen. Where roadways to the water supply are provided, they should be constructed with a suitable approach for fire department access.

Ponds

Ponds tend to offer lower quantities of water but may be numerous in the area. Reliability issues are similar to those of streams. Ponds can include lakes or farm ponds used for watering livestock, irrigation, fish culture, recreation, or other purposes while serving a secondary function for fire protection. Valuable information concerning the design of ponds can be obtained from county agricultural agents, cooperative extension offices, county engineers, and so forth. Most of the factors listed relative to streams are pertinent to ponds, with the following items to be considered:

- The minimum annual level should be adequate to meet the water supply needs of the fire problem the pond serves.
- Silt and debris can accumulate in a pond or lake, reducing its actual capacity, while its surface area and level remain con-

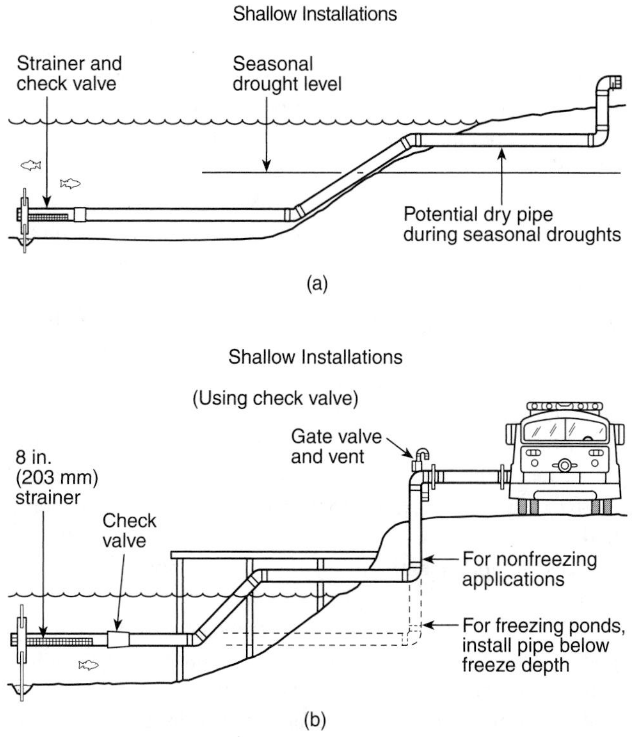

FIGURE 13.4.2 Dry Hydrant Installation (a) Shallow Stream Installation Based on Seasonal Drought (b) Shallow Stream Installation Based on Seasonal Drought and Freezing Conditions (Courtesy of Stan Merrett, ETT, L.L.C.)

stant. This can provide a deceptive impression of capacity and calls for at least seasonal inspections.

- Accessibility should always be considered. Many recreational lakes are provided with access by roads, driveways, and boat-launching ramps and are available for fire department use. Some large lakes, formed by a dam on a river, might have been constructed for purposes such as generating power, controlling floods, or regulating the flow of a river. During certain periods of the year, droughts, drawdowns, and so forth can cause such lakes to have very low water levels. The water under such conditions might not be accessible to the fire department for drafting by the fire department pumping unit, even where a paved road for boat launching has been provided and extended into the water at normal water levels for several feet or meters. Under such conditions, other provisions should be made to make the water supply fully accessible to the fire department.

Other Natural Water Sources

Other natural water sources might include springs and artesian wells. Individual springs and occasional artesian water supplies exist in some areas. These other natural water sources are generally of more limited capacity, but they can be useful for water supply, subject to reasonable application of the recommendations listed for ponds and streams. In many cases, it might be necessary to form a temporary natural pool or form a pond with a salvage cover, for example, to collect water for the use of the fire department when using a spring or an artesian well.

DEVELOPED SOURCES OF WATER

The developed sources of water supplies adapted for fire fighting are limited only by the innovation of the fire department. Developed sources include cisterns, swimming pools, quarries, mines, automatic sprinkler system supplies, stationary tanks, driven wells, and dry hydrants.

Cisterns

Cisterns, one of the oldest sources of emergency water supply, are important sources of water for fire fighting, domestic consumption, and drought storage in many rural and beach areas. Cisterns should have a minimum usable volume as determined by the authority having jurisdiction, using the methods described in NFPA 1142. There is no real limit to the maximum capacity. A cistern should be accessible to the fire apparatus or other pumping device, but it should also be located far enough from the hazard so that personnel and equipment are not endangered. The water level of a cistern can be maintained by rainfall, by water pumped from a well, by water hauled by a MWS apparatus, or by the seasonal high water of a stream or river. Because its surface is often relatively inaccessible and the water is stagnant, the cistern can present a freezing problem. One method for minimizing freezing is to use a dry hydrant protruding into the water at a point below the local frost line. Cisterns should be capped for safety, but they should have openings to allow inspections and use of suction hose where needed. There should also be some type of protective boundary for the area in which the cistern is located to prevent unauthorized entrance to the area.

If a dry hydrant is not installed in a cistern, then (depending on local conditions) a heavy pipe or a pike pole can be adequate to break an ice formation. In fact, the weight of the suction hose itself can be sufficient to break the ice, provided there is no danger of damaging the strainer, the hose, or the hose threads. Floating a log, a bale of hay, or a bale of straw or placing a partly filled, floating barrel on the surface of the water are some methods for providing an ice-free surface area in a cistern or other water source.

The construction of cisterns is governed by local conditions of soil and material availability. Practical information can be obtained from local governmental departments or agricultural agencies.

Some engineering considerations to be taken into account in designing cisterns include the following:

- The base, walls, and roof should be designed for the prevailing soil conditions and for the loads encountered where heavy vehicles are parked adjacent to each other.
- If groundwater conditions are high, the cistern should not float when empty.
- Suction piping should be designed to minimize whirlpooling.
- Vent piping should be of sufficient size (as shown in NFPA 1142).

Maintenance factors to be considered by the fire department include the problem of the evaporation of water or other low water conditions and the freezing problems previously discussed.

Swimming Pools

Swimming pools are an increasingly common source of water for fire protection. Even in some areas with normally adequate hydrant water supplies, swimming pools have been a factor in providing protection, such as in cases in which water demands have exceeded availability. Swimming pools provide an advantage in that they are sources of clean water, but they have major drawbacks due to the weight of fire department vehicles and poor accessibility for large apparatus.

Swimming pool distribution is better than hydrant distribution in some areas of the country. If the fire department intends to use a swimming pool as a water supply, it should develop these water sources by working with property owners through pre-incident planning.

If fire department accessibility is considered when designing the pool, a usable water supply should be available to the fire department for supplying direct hose lines or a source of water for MWS apparatus filling. Most swimming pools are built in areas requiring security fencing or walls, and these can complicate accessibility. Fences and walls can be designed for fire department use. However, should there be an incident in which fire department use of the pool has been permitted and there has been no other method provided for access through the protective area created by a fence, the fence can be lifted to allow the suction hose to be used (Figure 13.4.3).

A swimming pool located virtually under the eaves of a burning house can be a very poor location from which to pump if there are problems of fire exposure to the work area. Pumping from a neighboring pool, if it is close enough, or setting the water-hauling program in motion is frequently preferable to pumping from the pool of the burning house.

In most cases, a solution to the problems of accessibility can be achieved through pre-incident planning and might call for long lengths of suction hose, portable pumps, dry hydrants, siphon ejectors, or properly spaced gates. Portable (or floating) pumps, which are designed for large-volume delivery at limited pressures to deliver water to portable folding tanks or fire department pumpers, are frequently ideal for use where accessibility problems exist.

FIGURE 13.4.3 Fire Fighters Entering a Fenced-Off Swimming Pool Area

Fire fighters must take care to ensure that structural damage will not occur to a pool and the surrounding area if the water is used for fire fighting. Lightly built cement or poured concrete pools can be subject to structural damage, cracking, or collapse when drained. In addition, a pool in extremely wet soil will tend to float upward when drained; therefore, it might be necessary to refill the pool as soon as the fire is under control and MWS apparatus can be released from fire duties.

Some pools are holes of compacted earth covered by a plastic surfacing or light-gauge metal panels placed against such earth or a special fill. Such pools can collapse internally if emptied. It might be possible to use a limited portion of such water sources but not the entire available water supply. Therefore, not using these pools at all might be prudent.

Another consideration is whether the ground surrounding a pool will support the weight of a fire department vehicle without collapsing. The fire department should study and know the various pool limitations within the area served by consulting with the builders and installers of these pools.

Livestock Watering Ponds and Tanks

The local fire department representative responsible for planning water supplies should contact the owner of a farm, ranch, or similar type of area where livestock are kept and make him or her aware of the need for, and amount of, water required for that fire department to supply fire suppression to any/all buildings. Such tanks and ponds should be sized to be adequate in volume for both farm and fire department use and should be located to be readily available to the fire department. Tanks should be placed on the edge of the barnyard and on a side accessible to the fire department, with the pumper or pump taking suction through a connection on the tank or by suction hose. These watering tanks and ponds are often filled and maintained by a pump operated by a windmill or by an electric pump (Figure 13.4.4).

Wells and Well Systems

Wells and well systems are becoming increasingly popular as water supplies for fire-fighting purposes at industrial properties, shopping centers, subdivisions, and farmhouses located in rural areas beyond the reach of a municipal water distribution system.

In areas with suitable soil conditions—for instance, areas that have soils of a very sandy nature—driven wells or water-jetted wells might be used to obtain water for fire fighting. These wells are pipes that have been driven into the ground and that usually have perforations about the base to allow the entry of water. From the threaded pipe head (or a fitting attached to the body of the pipe), a pump connection can be made to draft water, much as from a well hydrant. A high water table is a prerequisite to using this method of obtaining water. Fire-fighting units in areas conducive to this technique should have the necessary equipment

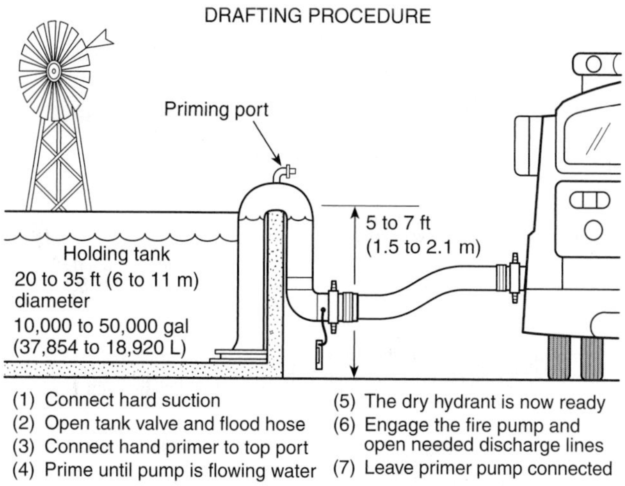

FIGURE 13.4.4 Drafting Procedure for Farm Holding Tanks (Courtesy of Stan Merrett, ETT, L.L.C.)

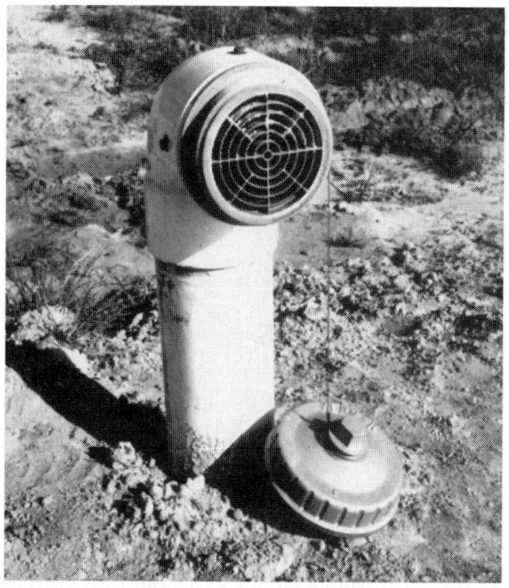

FIGURE 13.4.5 Dry Hydrant

for such installations. Some state and local governments have regulations or licensing requirements that govern well construction. Such restrictions will probably increase in the future.

Where water is supplied by one or more electricity-driven or engine-driven pumps used for irrigation or industrial use and where fuses and/or batteries are removed during periods when the water is not needed, the fire department should make provisions with the pump owner to ensure that power can be made available when needed for water supply.

Dry Hydrants

Per NFPA 1142, a dry hydrant is defined as "an arrangement of pipe permanently connected to a water source other than a piped, pressurized water supply system that provides a ready means of water supply for fire-fighting purposes and that utilizes the drafting (suction) capability of fire department pumpers" (Figure 13.4.5). Dry hydrants have the following features:

- Consist of a nonpressurized pipe system
- Use relatively inexpensive piping materials and other supplies
- Are permanently installed in existing lakes, ponds, streams, and cisterns
- Provide a means of access whenever needed, regardless of weather
- Allow years of simple operation with a minimum of maintenance

Dry hydrants should be installed at reliable water sources. The placement of dry hydrants at water sites should follow a process of planning, design criteria based on the site and water location, permit (i.e., land owner permission), and the construction and installation of the hydrant on site. A strategically placed dry hydrant system, with all-weather road access, significantly reduces water point setup and turnaround time to the fireground, improves the life safety of the fire fighter, and may reduce insurance costs.

Design Characteristics. Local topography, climatic conditions, and access to materials, among other factors, will determine the design characteristics of each installation (Figures 13.4.6 and 13.4.7). Distance to the water combined with the difference in elevation between the hydrant head and the water source and the desired gallon-per-minute (liter-per-minute) flow will affect the pipe size that needs to be used. All installations should use, as a minimum, 6 in. (152 mm) pipe. With longer lateral runs and higher volume flow, 8 in. (203 mm) or 10 in. (254 mm) pipe sizes can become necessary for the horizontal lengths.

Local preferences and experience, along with access to materials, will determine the type of pipe and fittings best suited for the job. In some parts of the country, brass and bronze caps and steamer connections, along with iron, steel, and bituminous cement pipe and fittings, are being used for hydrant materials.

In many parts of the country, however, Schedule 40—and in areas where there are freezing conditions expected as normal

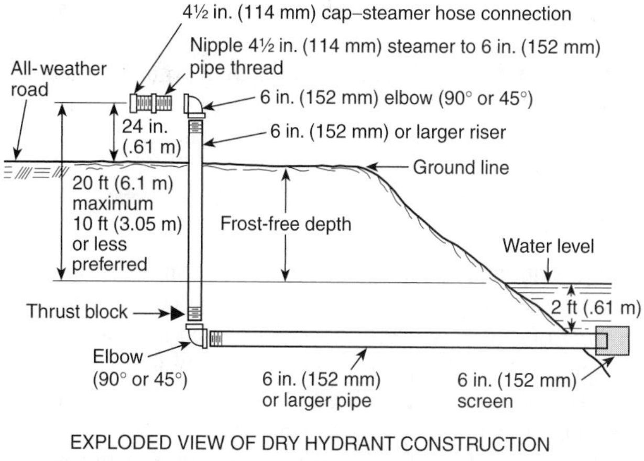

FIGURE 13.4.6 Dry Hydrant Construction Using Iron, Steel, or PVC Pipe

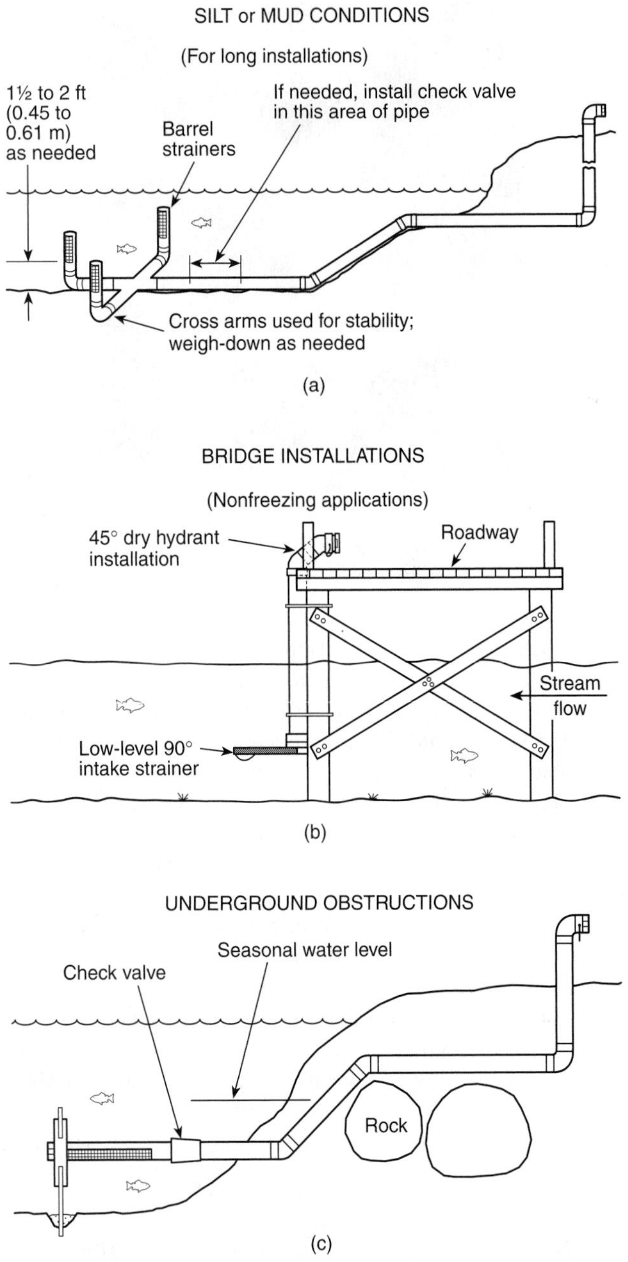

FIGURE 13.4.7 Dry Hydrant Installation (a) for Silt and Mud Conditions, (b) from a Bridge, and (c) Overcoming Underground Obstructions (Courtesy of Stan Merrett, ETT, L.L.C.)

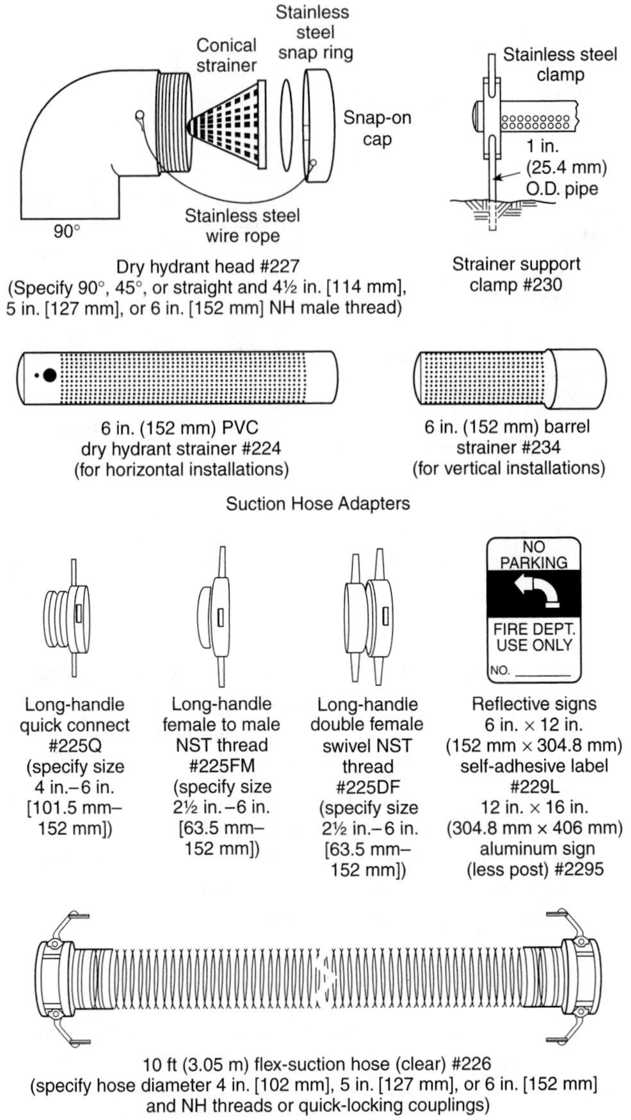

FIGURE 13.4.8 Commercially Available Dry Hydrant Components (Source: Wisconsin Department of Natural Resources)

weather criteria, Schedule 80—PVC pipe, fittings, and connections are used (Figure 13.4.8). Many fire service manufacturers are now offering premade and preassembled suction screens, hydrant heads, and supports that come ready to attach to the pipe. Steamer fittings should be compatible with the fire department's hard suction hose size and thread type.

The dry hydrant design has features that make its use accessible to many rural fire departments and property owners in terms of personnel and financial resources. The type and class of pipe for a particular dry hydrant installation should be determined through the consideration of the following conditions: soil, corrosion susceptibility, climate, and susceptibility of pipe to other external loads, including earth loads and traffic or vehicle loads. All exposed surfaces should be primed and painted to protect the pipe and prevent deterioration of the material.

Preferably no more than two 90 degree elbows should be used in the total dry hydrant system. Also desirable is the installation of long-sweep elbows at the bottom of the riser where the lateral run connects. Long-sweep elbows can be constructed with two 45 degree elbows and a 2 ft (0.6 m) length of pipe. If any portion of the dry hydrant above ground level becomes damaged in any manner that would make the hydrant unusable when connection is made to pump suction hose, the use of a long-sweep elbow could allow drafting to continue, although at a much reduced rate of flow.

NFPA 1142 contains numerous design criteria, such as a recommendation for a 6 in. (150 mm) minimum inside diameter of the pipe and limit of 10 to 12 ft (3 to 3.7 m) for static lift. See Figure 13.4.9 for a checklist of dry hydrant design features.

Dry Hydrant Design Features Checklist

Design factors are affected by:

- ☐ Desired flow from the hydrant in gpm
- ☐ Suitability of pipe materials
- ☐ Size and type of available fire aparatus pumper

The following design features are suggested for dry hydrants using PVC pipes:

- ☐ Use 6-in. (150-mm) diameter pipe as a minimum.
- ☐ Use Schedule 40 pipe as a minimum.
- ☐ Prime and paint all exposed pipe.
- ☐ Use a minimum number of elbows.
- ☐ Joint and cement all connections properly.
- ☐ Purchase or construct a suction screen with adequate hole openings.
- ☐ Ensure that total area of strainer holes exceeds four times the area of the diameter of the pipe.
- ☐ Ensure that installation depth is below the frost-free depth for the area. (Consult local university extension service or state Department of Natural Resources.)
- ☐ Ensure that installation depth is sufficiently below the average 50 year drought or appropriate state criteria for drought. (Consult engineer, soil conservationist, or hydrologist.)
- ☐ Place horizontal pipe level on minus grade of 1 to 2 in. (25.4 to 50.8 mm) per 100 ft (30.5 m), unless depth of cut is too great.
- ☐ Note that for streambed installation (with low flow depth less than 2 ft [0.6 m]) the strainer section may be buried below bed of stream and covered with gravel.
- ☐ Install dry hydrant as close as practical to the water source.
- ☐ Note that a flow of 600 to 1000 gpm (2271 to 3785 L/min) from the hydrant is desirable.
- ☐ Avoid designs with lifts in excess of 17 ft. (Above this height vapor pressure will begin to exceed atmospheric pressure and cavitation will occur, making pumping virtually impossible.)
- ☐ Consider friction loss at high lifts. (Calculate losses using Mannings formula or Hazen-Williams equations.)
- ☐ Position the pump intake at a higher elevation than the hydrant connection. (Doing so will eliminate air bubbles, which will limit flow and also prevent the operator from getting wet.)
- ☐ When rock is encountered, adjust installation to fit the rock profile. (Additional bends may be necessary.)

FIGURE 13.4.9 Dry Hydrant Design Features Checklist

Advantages of Dry Hydrants. Knowing the quantity of available water in area streams, ponds, and cisterns gives the fire department an advantage only if the water is readily accessible. Where a water site is located so that MWS apparatus will be the water transportation method, the amount of available water will be less than it would be if pumped directly onto a fire from the same water site. Whenever MWS apparatuses are used, critical factors become the supply of an uninterrupted flow, the supply of a predictable amount of water being transported, and the maintenance of the supply for the duration of the fire or until a lesser flow is required.

Improved Access. Installation of as many dry hydrants as possible where permits can be obtained and the sites made all-weather accessible will ease both the complexities and the lesser availability of water that will be incurred when comparing shuttle operations to water transported directly to the fire scene by hose from a water site. Additionally in those areas without water mains and domestic fire hydrants, dry hydrants can provide a simple, cost-effective solution to water sources without delay.

Time Saving. The time saving is considerable. Multiple lengths of hard suction hose extending to the water are not needed; usually one section to the dry hydrant is enough. The strainer is also permanently attached, saving more time. Fewer people are needed to make a hookup compared to the number needed to make a conventional direct drafting hookup. Planned placement of dry hydrants with the proper accessibility will allow fire departments to supply water for fire protection to all areas where coverage can effectively be provided.

Cost Saving. The saving can be financial, as well. Fire departments can save money by reducing fuel and equipment costs through shorter transportation distances and lower operational demands. Because dry hydrants use untreated water, communities can preserve more of their treated water supplies. Homeowners may also save on their insurance rates.

Planning Considerations. Planning for dry hydrants involves several considerations and should involve all affected agencies and private concerns so a coordinated effort can take place. Some factors to consider are:

- Current and future population and building trends
- Protection of property values
- Potential for loss
- Fire history of the area protected
- Current water supply systems
- Other potential water sources
- Cost of project
- Equipment and personnel of the local fire department
- Training needs of the fire department
- Other specific factors of local concern

Location of Dry Hydrants. The location of individual dry hydrants is also influenced by several factors. After conducting a water source survey of the area, the fire department should use a county road map to mark potentially good sites. These sites should be marked in a priority order, since most fire departments will not have sufficient funding for all the dry hydrants that may be desired. The following features should be considered when considering dry hydrant sites.

Maximum Travel Distance Between Dry Hydrants. The travel distance between dry hydrants can vary for several reasons. For use in shuttle operations, it has been found that the amount of water transported by MWS apparatus to the fire scene, regardless of the size of the water tank on the MWS apparatus, will not be appreciably increased when water fill sites are further than 3 mi (4.8 k) from the fire site. This distance would produce a travel time of about 6 minutes between the water and the fire, assuming an average safe constant speed for a loaded truck of 35 mph (56 kph).

Water Depth at the Source. Careful note should be made about the useful depth of a lake or pond, which is from the minimum foreseeable low-water surface level to the top of the suction strainer (not the bottom of the lake). The low-water mark considers tides, drought, freezing, and other considerations, such as when the water level is lowered to generate power. The absolute lowest level must be not less than 2 ft (0.6 m) to prevent a vortex or whirlpool, which could allow air to enter the pump and cause loss of pump prime. Consideration for the height of the "low" water level above the strainer should be made for conditions such as ice and for floating leaves during the fall of the year. Plans for these or for any other conditions, even if seasonal, that could cause clogging of the strainer or cavitation of the pump should be made.

Composition of Bottom Material. For long-term useful hydrant operation, the best composition for the bottom of a lake, stream, or pond is sand, gravel, rock, or a combination of these. Decaying vegetative matter could clog the suction screen.

Ease of Digging. Surface area and condition in the vicinity of the dry hydrant site is a factor in the installation of a dry hydrant. A backhoe or whatever machinery is to be used to "trench the dry hydrant" will need to get close enough to the water's edge so as to be able to dig out below the surface of the water to the needed depth for the dry hydrant.

Protection of the Connection. A location that is conveniently accessible to fire apparatus may also be exposed to accidents from passing vehicles. An impact barrier constructed of partially buried posts may be needed to prevent a vehicle from damaging a dry hydrant in a heavily traveled area. Special markings, as deemed appropriate by the authority having jurisdiction, should be used to avoid damage from snowplows.

Cost. The cost of a dry hydrant installation depends on local practices and the length of pipe needed. This cost must be factored in when deciding where to locate dry hydrants.

Presence of Other Utilities. The presence of other utilities in the digging area must be considered. A careful check should be made for the presence of buried lines and pipes; utility companies should be notified before digging is started. The numbers to call in each state can often be found in the local telephone company phone book and are found with a title similar to "Call Before You Dig."

Ownership of the Land. The water supply officer or other authority should contact the legal property owner to secure written permission in conjunction with the attorney representing the government entity in whose legal area the land lies. If a possible dry hydrant site is along a road right-of-way, then town, county, or state approval may be required. In some cases Corps of Engineers or power company approval may also be needed. Obtaining written permission is an important requirement that may take some time.

AGREEMENTS/PERMITS

Regardless of the type of water source used and the water site from which it is obtained, a document granting permission by the owner for the use of the area as well as documents listing any other locally applicable considerations should be on file. A written explanation of what is needed and what the fire department will do to install the dry hydrant can be mailed or delivered personally. Conditions for the best use of the particular site should be set forth. This explanation will usually provide the prospective property owners with information that will make them more comfortable with the conversations and legal technicalities that will follow.

The attorney representing the local government whose fire department will be utilizing the site should formalize all legal issues. The local government attorney should consider all actions that can reasonably be assumed to be involved and to arise out of the use of water source site and should enumerate them in the legal paperwork. The agreement should be signed by the property owner, the head of the government entity (or his or her designated representative), the chief of the fire department, all other departments of the entity (or contractors if they are to be used) that will have a part in the development/improvement of the site, and the entity's attorney. At a minimum these people should be listed on the agreement since they will deal with the greatest number of actions involved in the completion of each site for fire department use and continued operations.

ESTIMATING AVAILABLE WATER SUPPLY CAPACITY

A simple method for estimating the flow of water in a creek is to measure the width and depth of the creek, drop a cork or any light, floating object into the water, and then determine the time it takes the cork to travel 10 ft (3.1 m). To obtain complete accuracy, the sides of the creek should be perpendicular, the bottom should be flat, and the floating object should not be affected by the wind. Where the sides and bottom of the stream are not uniform, the width and depth can be averaged. For example, consider a creek with a width of 4 ft (1.2 m) and a depth of 6 in. (15.2 cm) and where the flow of water is such that it takes 45 seconds for a cork to travel 10 ft (3.1 m). The following equation applies:

$$\text{Volume of water} = W \times D \times TD = \text{ft}^3\ (\text{m}^3) \text{ of water}$$

$$\text{Flow rate} = (\text{Volume of water})/T$$

where

W = Width (ft [m])

D = Depth (ft [m])

TD = Travel distance (ft [m])

T = Time (sec)

$$4 \text{ ft} \times 0.5 \text{ ft} \times 10 \text{ ft} \times 20 \text{ ft}^3 \text{ of water}$$

or

$$1.2 \text{ m} \times 0.15 \text{ m} \times 3.1 \text{ m} \times 0.56 \text{ m}^3 \text{ of water}$$

Since the cork takes 45 seconds to travel a 10 ft (3.1 m) distance:

$$\text{Flow rate} = 20 \text{ ft}^3/45 \text{ sec} = 0.444 \text{ ft}^3 \text{ of water/sec}$$

or

$$\text{Flow rate} = 0.558 \text{ m}^3/45 \text{ sec} = 0.0124 \text{ m}^3 \text{ water/sec}$$

and

$$1 \text{ ft}^3 = 7.5 \text{ gal and } 60 \text{ sec} = 1 \text{ min}$$

Therefore,

$$(0.444 \text{ ft}^3/\text{sec}) = (0.444 \text{ ft}^3/\text{sec})(60 \text{ sec/min})(7.5 \text{ gal/ft}^3)$$
$$= (0.444/0.00223) \text{ gpm} = 199 \text{ gpm}$$

Also

$$1 \text{ m}^3 = 1000 \text{ L and } 60 \text{ sec} = 1 \text{ min}$$

Therefore,

$$(0.014 \text{ m}^3/\text{sec}) = (0.0124 \text{ m}^3/\text{sec})(60 \text{ sec/min})(1000 \text{ L/m}^3)$$
$$= (0.0124/0.0000167) \text{ L/min} = 744 \text{ L/min}$$

A short-form method of estimating pool capacity is as follows:

$$L \times W \times D \times 7.5 \text{ gal } (1000 \text{ L})$$
$$= \text{Estimated capacity in gallons (liters)}$$

where

L = Length (ft [m])

W = Width (ft [m])

D = Estimated average depth (ft [m]) from water line (ft [m])

These dimensions should be estimated or rounded off if the pool is of stylized construction.

$$1 \text{ ft}^3 = 7.5 \text{ gal } (1 \text{ m}^3 = 1000 \text{ L})$$

For a noncircular pond of irregular shape, sketch the pond outline to scale on grid paper. Circumscribe straight lines to average the irregular outline as much as possible around the shape. Calculate the area of a rectangle covering the entire pond. Subtract the scaled grid squares that fall outside the pond area. Use the final figure as $L \times W$ in the foregoing formula.

To make a rough estimate of the water volume in a pond when exact dimensions are not known, visualize the relative size of a football field, if you can, and use that area as a starting point. A football field is roughly an acre. Every foot (0.30 m) of average usable depth would provide about 325,000 gallons (1,230,000 L).

WATER SUPPLY VEHICLES, WATER SHUTTLE OPERATIONS, AND DRIVERS

Mobile Water Supply (MWS) Apparatus

The term *mobile water supply (MWS)* will be used here as referenced in NFPA 1901, *Standard for Automotive Fire Apparatus*. Incident management system (IMS) terminology and designation of what has always been termed a *tanker* is a "vehicle" (aircraft or helicopter) that delivers water from above. For ease of use throughout, we will refer to a wheeled ground apparatus (vehicle) as an MWS apparatus. We will consider the MWS apparatus as being mounted on a single- or tandem-axle chassis. Issues dealing with tractor-trailer water supply vehicles are not addressed in this chapter.

Rural fire departments are often fortunate to have usable water supplies in their jurisdictions, but that water is rarely in the immediate area of a fire where it is needed. MWS apparatus are necessary for any fire department that wants a method to provide a water supply to areas where there is no existing water supply system. MWS apparatus can also be used to supplement areas where the existing water supply system may not provide the desired flow of water. MWS apparatus are necessary for most rural fire departments and can be useful to suburban departments with weak municipal systems.

MWS apparatus may be found in a variety of configurations, with or without pumps on board. Fire apparatus may be generally classified as pumpers or MWS apparatus, or they may be manufactured to provide both functions. Some vehicles used previously for transporting other liquids have been used by fire departments, but safety considerations should be more important than economic ones. The fire department should ensure that any vehicle used to transport water passes a safety inspection; that it has reliable brakes, chassis, and transmission; and that it is designed to carry the weight of the water that it will transport. Above all, the weight of water should never allow the total vehicle weight to be greater than the rated maximum weight rating of the vehicle.

Over the years, departments utilizing hauled water have tended to use any means to carry water and have exercised a great deal of ingenuity in doing so. Recently, there has been a trend in fire departments in rural areas to use standard pumpers and MWS apparatus with tanks in the 1000 to 1500 gal (3785 to 5678 L) range. Significant progress has been made in such MWS apparatus techniques as loading and unloading and in maintaining a continuous fire stream, based on the fire flow study, during the entire fire-fighting operation.

Specially built and designed MWS apparatus are ideal, but many fire departments are forced to fight fires without adequate standard equipment. Since the job of putting out fires will require, on occasion, water-carrying capacity greater than a fire department's capability, a sound mutual-aid or automatic-aid program is necessary and is far superior to makeshift, unsafe equipment that is not designed for emergency service.

In building and buying nonstandard apparatus, serious consideration should be given to the safety and serviceability of the equipment as well as the safety of the members of the department. A department that depends on an assortment of MWS apparatus designed primarily for other use might need expert assistance in checking the equipment for safety before putting it in service.

If satisfactory service is to be obtained from MWS apparatus, the size of chassis necessary to safely carry the load, the horsepower of the engine necessary to perform on the road and at the fire site, the completed vehicle's weight distribution, and the gear train combination best suited for the operation in that specific locale are factors that should be carefully considered in the purchase or construction of the apparatus. The apparatus components, such as the baffling of the tank and the center of gravity, are just as important as the engine, axles, and other driveline components and should not be overlooked. Some fire departments that have pumpers equipped with large booster tanks have retrofitted these pumps with a dump system.

Water Shuttle Operations

Obviously, sufficient water supply for fire suppression services is a very critical component to the overall fire suppression capabilities of a fire department. Typically, rural areas do not have the necessary infrastructure to support "urban type" water delivery systems. Where fire hydrants exist, they are typically on smaller water lines with relatively low flow capacity and are generally spaced quite some distance apart. As a result, fire departments with large rural areas within their protection areas must rely on alternate means of providing adequate fire flow during fire suppression activities.

It is important for companies to be able to obtain water from sources other than hydrants at the fireground and operate a MWS apparatus shuttle to provide adequate water supply for fire-fighting operations. This is not limited to rural applications and may be necessary to supplement hydranted areas where there is inadequate water supply.

Key components in MWS apparatus shuttle operations in rural water supply include the following:

- Selecting water sources
- Selecting MWS apparatus travel routes
- Developing MWS apparatus fill and dump station operations
- Calculating and meeting waterflow requirements

A critical part of establishing a water supply on a continuous basis is the capability to deliver water to the scene within 5 minutes of the initial arriving fire apparatus. Calculating the rate of water delivery to the scene is based on the total water supply required. The rate of water delivery is a separate calculation from the water application rate.

The following are two primary factors to be considered in the development of MWS apparatus operations:

1. The amount of water carried on initial responding units
2. The amount of water that can be continuously delivered after initial response

A number of fire departments have developed water-hauling operations to the point where they have a maximum continuous flow capability (a sustained fire flow) of 1000 to 2000 gpm (3785 to 7570 L/min) at the fire scene. Such continuous flow requires several MWS apparatus to haul such large quantities of water with a developed water source near the fire site. To improve the safety factor by reducing congestion on the highways, the departments often send the MWS apparatus to the water source by one road and use another route for the MWS apparatus to return to the fire scene. Therefore, the time for the department to travel from the fire to the water source (T_1) might be a different time than the travel time back to the fire (T_2). The reduction of congestion on the highway provides for a safer operation and can increase the actual amount of water hauled.

The maximum continuous flow capability at the fire scene is calculated as follows:

$$Q = [V/(A + T_1 + T_2 + B)] \times k$$

where

Q = Maximum continuous flow capability (gpm [L/min])

V = Mobile water supply capacity (gal [L])

A = Time (in minutes) for the MWS apparatus to drive 200 ft (61 m), dump water into a drop tank, and return 200 ft (61 m) to starting point

T_1 = Time (in minutes) for the MWS apparatus to travel from fire to water source

T_2 = Time (in minutes) for the same MWS apparatus to travel from water source back to fire

B = Time in minutes for the MWS apparatus to drive 200 ft (61 m), fill MWS apparatus at water source, and return 200 ft (61 m) to starting point

k = 1.0 for vacuum/pressure MWS apparatus; 0.9 for all other MWS apparatus due to spillage, underfilling, and incomplete unloading

The dumping time (A) and filling time (B) for the formula should be determined by drill and by close study of water sources. Equipment does not have to be operated under emergency conditions to obtain travel time (T), which is calculated using the following equation:

$$T = 0.65 + XD$$

where

T = Time (in minutes) of average one-way trip travel

X = Average safe constant speed factor

D = One-way distance (miles [kilometers])

The factor 0.65 represents an acceleration/deceleration constant based on miles per hour developed by the Rand Corporation.

Where an apparatus is equipped with an adequate engine, chassis, baffling, and brakes, a safe constant speed of 35 mph (56.3 km/hr) can generally be maintained on level terrain, in light traffic, and on an adequate roadway. Where conditions will not permit this speed, the average safe constant speed should be reduced.

Using an average safe constant speed of 35 mph (56.3 km/hr), the X factor is calculated as follows:

$$X = 60/\text{average safe speed} = 60/35 \text{ mph} = 1.7$$

The formulas make it possible to determine water availability at any point in an area. As an example of how to calculate the water available from a supply where the water has to be trucked to the fire scene, consider the following applications of the formula.

EXAMPLE: If tank capacity (V) is 1500 gal (5678 L), the time (B) to fill the MWS apparatus with water is 3.0 minutes, and the time (A) to dump the water into a portable tank is 4.0 minutes.

The distance (D_1) from the fire to the water source is 2.1 mi (3.38 km). As the MWS apparatus returns by a different road, the distance (D_2) from the water source is 1.8 mi (2.9 km).

SOLUTION: First, solve for T_1, the time for the MWS apparatus to travel from the fire to the water source, and then solve for T_2, the time for the MWS apparatus to travel from the water source back to the fire.

Due to good weather and road conditions, the constant MWS apparatus speed traveling from the fire to the water source is 35 mph (56.3 km/hr).

Use the travel time formula as follows:

$$T_1 = 0.65 + XD_1$$

where

$X = 1.7$

$D_1 = 2.1$

and where at a constant speed of 35 mph (56.3 km/hr)

$$T_1 = 0.65 + 1.7D_1$$

$$T_1 = 0.65 + 1.7 \times 2.1$$

$$T_1 = 0.65 + 3.57$$

$$T_1 = 4.22$$

At a constant speed of 35 mph (56.3 km/hr), a MWS apparatus traveling 2.1 mi (3.8 km) will take 4.22 minutes. Due to traffic lights, the average MWS apparatus speed between the fire and the water source is 30 mph (48.3 km/hr).

Use the time travel formula as follows:

$$T_2 = 0.65 + XD_2$$

where

$X = 2.0$

$D_2 = 1.8$

and where at a constant speed of 30 mph (48.3 km/hr)

$$T_2 = 0.65 + 2.0D_2$$

$$T_2 = 0.65 + 2.0 \times 1.8$$

$$T_2 = 0.65 + 3.6$$

$$T_2 = 4.25$$

Use the following formula for calculating the maximum continuous flow capability:

$$Q = [V/(A + T_1 + T_2 + B)] \times k$$

where

Q = Maximum continuous flow capability (gpm)

$V = 1500$

$A = 4.0$

$T_1 = 4.22$

$T_2 = 4.25$

$B = 3.0$

Therefore,

$$Q = [1500/(3.0 + 4.22 + 4.25 + 4.0)] \times 0.9$$

$$Q = (1500/15.47) \times 0.9$$

$$Q = 97 \times 0.9 = 87 \text{ gpm } (329.3 \text{ L/min})$$

The maximum continuous flow capacity available from this 1500 gal (5678 L) MWS apparatus is 87 gpm (329.3 L/min).

To increase the maximum continuous flow capability of the MWS apparatus, any of the following changes can be made:

- Increase the capacity of the MWS apparatus
- Reduce the fill time
- Develop and provide additional fill points, thus reducing travel time
- Reduce the dump time

With rural fire response distances normally being very long, the number and size of MWS apparatus available to the department are of paramount importance. This information will assist the department in calculating the probable mobile water supply volume that will be available at various fire locations. Equally important in increasing the maximum continuous flow capability of a mobile water supply is the reduction of the distance between the source and the building or fire. The distance can be reduced by increasing the number of water supplies, drafting points, or both.

The minimum water delivery rate to the fire scene is based on the total water supply needed. Table 13.4.3 provides the rate at which water should be available at the fire scene to meet the demands of the fireground operations.

Driver Training

Drivers of emergency vehicles, especially those carrying large quantities of water, face circumstances that make driver training especially important. Fire departments often overlook this reality. Included in this oversight are some of the following factors:

- Few fire department members have been previously trained, drive vehicles of this type in their professional life, or are

TABLE 13.4.3 Minimum Water Delivery Rate to Meet Water Supply Needs

Total Water Supply Required	*Rate Water Is Available at Incident*
Up to 2,499 gal (9,459 L)	250 gpm (950 L/min)
2,500 to 9,999 gal (9,460 to 37,849 L)	500 gpm (1,900 L/min)
10,000 to 19,999 gal (37,850 to 75,699 L)	750 gpm (2,850 L/min)
20,000 gal (75,700 L) or more	1,000 gpm (3,800 L/min)

aware of the action of liquids during transport. Only effective training can prepare them to handle this type of vehicle. Continuous testing should be planned to ensure personnel continue to meet qualifications.

- Because of the effect of the load on the vehicle's center of gravity, even a two- or three-axle vehicle used as an MWS apparatus will have driving characteristics unlike those of other vehicles or fire apparatus.
- The weight of the water can reduce handling characteristics and increase braking distances. Water weighs 8.3 pounds per gallon (1 kg/L); in a 1000 or 2000 gallon (3785 or 7570 L) tank, the extra weight can be a dangerous factor if it is not considered at all times.
- The occurrence of fires is usually infrequent, allowing specialized driving skills to deteriorate unless training is regular.
- Roadways in rural areas may not always be repaired as frequently as they are in urban areas. Potholes and washed-out areas can be extremely hazardous for a heavily loaded truck.
- Emergency situations produce dangerous distractions to apparatus drivers (and anyone else). There is a natural tendency that makes everyone want to perform each task faster so the fire can be stopped as quickly as possible. However, too much haste results in poor decisions, and numerous safety factors can be overlooked.

Vehicle Weight and Safety

The weight of any large fire apparatus, and especially the weight of water in an MWS apparatus, produces extra stress on the vehicle's chassis, transmission, and brakes. Drivers must be trained regularly on the special risks of driving emergency apparatus.

The fire department should check every bridge and culvert location in its response districts, both primary response and mutual aid, to ensure that all bridges and culvert locations are rated to safely carry the weight of every responding fire department vehicle/apparatus. The ability of fire department personnel to determine bridge ratings should not be the overwhelming task that it might initially appear to be. In view of the current use of computers by state highway departments to inventory their bridges, load limits should be readily available.

If there is any bridge or culvert that will not support the weight of a particular department unit, the driver of that unit should be made aware of this fact. The fire department should have other specific routes planned to ensure response to fires within the area involved or should take specific action to ensure that adequate water supply can be delivered by other means. Examples include using a pumper taking suction from the river to pump water across the bridge through large hose lines or servicing the area from another water supply site that has a safe bridge to the area or, ideally, that does not require the use of a bridge to respond.

Access to Water Supplies

The location of any water site and the water available from that source will be usable for fire department operations only if the site is accessible. Training at the site for fire department operations, including making personnel aware of any limitations of the site and/or of the waterflow, should be part of planned fire department operations.

Access Roadways. Often a suitable approach, which might call for a roadway, must be provided to allow the fire department to reach within 10 ft (3.1 m) of the water supply. However, at some sites and in some areas of the country, constructing a roadway may not be necessary due to soil conditions. Other sites might already have roadways provided or pavement installed with the construction of an entranceway or a gate to provide access to the water supply. Other sites may be reached on foot only and may require a path to be constructed and maintained so that portable pumps can be carried to the site. Each site should be evaluated by the fire department to determine the best way, within the fire department's means, for using the water supply.

Most artificial lakes are constructed with heavy earth-moving equipment. In order for the property owner to construct a roadway for fire department use, the fire department should make the property owner aware of the needs of the fire department while the heavy equipment is still on the job.

While the roadway to the water supply is being developed, consideration should be given to providing a 90-ft (27.4-m) diameter turnaround for the mobile water supply apparatus. Where conditions at the supply site do not make a turnaround feasible, adequate hose lengths from the pumping unit at the supply site will be needed to provide water for MWS apparatus to fill up at the location or locations where they will be stopped. Regardless of this fill-up location, adequate room must be provided for the MWS apparatus to maneuver during arrival at and departure from the parking/standing area. However, a turnaround or looped facility will still need to be provided at the fill point on the right-of-way.

In some states, a fire department cannot use a bridge to park a mobile water supply while it is being filled because it would block traffic on the road. However, the fire department might be able to use the water source by moving the fill point off the bridge and to the right-of-way. The fire department needs to check with the state department of transportation and abide by the appropriate laws governing the situation.

In some cases, such as in marsh or swamp areas, installing a dry hydrant with a suction line in lieu of an access road is desirable. The fire department will have access to the hydrant from the shoulder of the main road. So as not to block the road during pumper operations, a suitable parking area on the shoulder of the road should be provided. The basic recommendations in Table 13.4.4 can be useful in the design of such an area so that pumpers can be employed efficiently and safely.

Bridges. Bridges that were built years ago may have been built for farm-to-market use and were designed for much lighter vehicles than are in use today. Those bridges now carry not only greatly increased traffic loads but heavier vehicles as well. As a result of this situation, which exists in many suburban and rural areas and probably even in some urban areas in the United States, some bridge collapses have occurred. In addition, many states did not provide complete bridge inspection and maintenance programs. Because of these major factors, most states now subject bridges to certain types of inspections and mandate those inspections within specific time frames.

As a result of bridge failures, the U.S. Federal Highway Act of 1968 required, among other things, that all states, counties, and cities receiving federal highway funding implement a program to inspect each bridge in the federally funded system every two years. Additional bridge collapses prompted amendment of this law in 1976 to include all bridges on the public roads system.

During the last few years, a number of states have set up bridge inspection programs, and the current safe tonnage is now being posted. Throughout the entire country, a large number of bridges have been restricted to below the legal weight limit for which the road and bridge were originally designed. One state with over 15,000 bridges reported that 50 percent of all its bridges are now posted below the original maximum load limits, and 25 percent of these bridges are unsafe for use by a fully loaded school bus or fire department apparatus.

In some states, the state highway department has consulted fire officials, explained the situation, and required that the fire department list the unsafe bridges in order of their importance to the fire service. The highway departments then attempt to upgrade these bridges on the basis of fire department priority.

The long-range nature of the bridge problem makes it a matter for serious consideration when planning purchases of apparatus. MWS apparatus size must be restricted to volumes that will not cause overloading. State law determines whether a fire service is held financially responsible for damage to a bridge; however, a good policy for every fire department is to check the bridge load restrictions before purchasing a new piece of apparatus. The lighter the equipment, the more bridges the department can use. Although this may necessitate the purchase and use of smaller tank size MWS apparatus, prior planning will enable these units to be used just as effectively as MWS apparatus with larger tanks and should not be considered a limitation to fire service operations.

TABLE 13.4.4 Recommendations for Roads to Water Supplies

Road Feature	*Recommendation*
Width	Roadbed—12 ft (3.7 m) Tread—8 ft (2.4 m) Shoulders—2 ft (0.6 m)
Alignment	Radium centerline curvature—50 ft (15.2 m)
Gradient	Maximum sustained grade—8 percent
Side slopes	All cut-and-fill slopes to be stable for the soil involved
Drainage	Bridges, culverts, or grade dips at all drainageway crossings
	Roadside ditches deep enough to provide drainage
	Special drainage facilities (e.g., tile) at all seep areas and high water table areas
Surface	Treatment as required for year-round travel
Erosion control	Measures as needed to protect road ditches, cross drains, and cut-and-fill slopes
Turnaround	Designed to handle the equipment of the responding fire department with a minimum diameter of 90 ft (27.4 m)
Load-carrying load capacity	Adequate to carry maximum vehicle expected
Condition	Suitable for all-weather use

Source: NFPA 1142, *Standard on Water Supplies for Suburban and Rural Fire Fighting,* Table B-6.2, National Fire Protection Association, Quincy, MA, 1999.

SUMMARY

Providing water for fire suppression purposes by using alternate water supplies enables fire departments to have a continuing water supply where none existed previously or may provide additional water for emergency or backup use. The alternate water supply sources include natural water sources, such as streams, springs, lakes, and ponds, and developed sources of water, such as cisterns, swimming pools, stationary tanks, driven wells, and dry hydrants.

Once the community's water needs have been determined, the water sources pinpointed, and agreements made with property owners, a plan should be worked out for moving the water to where it is needed. The chapter discusses the location, use, and preparation of water sites and the use of mobile water supply apparatus. The use of alternate water supply sources helps a community meet its water supply needs in time of emergency.

BIBLIOGRAPHY

NFPA Codes, Standards, and Recommended Practices

Reference to the following NFPA codes, standards, and recommended practices will provide further information on alternate water sources

Chapter 5

Wildland Fire Management

Revised by
James C. Smalley

Wildland fires occur in every state of the United States at some time during the year. Information from the U.S. Department of Agriculture (USDA) and the U.S. Department of the Interior shows the yearly pattern of wildfires during "normal peak fire seasons" in the 1990s. But following a decade of increasingly severe wildfires, it is now becoming difficult to define "normal peak fire seasons." Eight to ten years ago, a wildland fire exceeding 100,000 acres (40,470 ha) was the sign of an unusually severe fire season. Today, these large-scale fires are no longer the exception; they are starting to define what a normal peak fire season may be for years to come.

As debate over "prescribed fire"—that is, how much, where, when, and at what cost to use—continued, the price of suppression systems for tackling wildfires climbed and more unprotected homes and structures were lost, even though federal and state land management agencies treated millions of acres to reduce the fire risk using prescribed fire and mechanical means (such as cutting and clearing). Fires in largely untreated areas were the problem.

This chapter provides a brief summary of past wildland fires and their significance. The historic review will set the stage for the current challenges that accumulating forest fuels, increased public recreation in state and national lands, and the threat of unwanted fires present to federal, state, and local fire agencies and residents in and near forested and grassy plains areas. After establishing both the usual and unusual characteristics of wildland fire, the chapter explores the many ways (e.g., prevention, education, research, legislation, and suppression) that we seek to prevent disasters, save lives, protect the environment, share the responsibilities of protecting our natural environment, and continue to enjoy safely the beauty of national and state forests, parks, rivers, and wildlife.

See also Section 1, Chapter 7, "Protecting Against Extreme Events"; Section 2, Chapter 1, "Physics and Chemistry of Fire"; and Section 13, Chapter 1, "Fireground Operations."

Chapter Contents

Key Terms

aerial fuel, fire fighter safety, fire triangle, Firewise, forest fire, ground fuel, heat transfer, Miramichi and Maine fire, Peshtigo fire, prescribed fire, Smokey Bear, spot fire, topography, wildland, wildland/urban interface

BRIEF HISTORY OF U.S. WILDLAND FIRES

General Trends

Multiple large forest fires, such as the one shown in Figure 13.5.1, involving hundreds of thousands of acres, are starting to define what a normal peak fire season may be for years to come. Fire seasons have been worsening for several years. In 2003, however, the numbers were down from the 10-year average. In 2003, the numbers of fires (62,000) and acres burned (3.8 million acres [1.5 million ha]) were below the average of 64,000 fires and 4.6 million acres (1.9 million ha) (see Figures 13.5.2 and 13.5.3). In the same year, less acreage burned than in recent years, but what did burn was acreage in populated areas.

Although the numbers may vary from year to year, the longer-term trends are important, and a definite and troubling trend is becoming evident. Although the number of fires appears to be dropping, the affected acreage is growing. This trend may mean fewer fires in the future but the fires may involve increasingly larger acreage. Larger fires may also have a significant future impact on the environment, fire suppression resources, fire fighter safety, and structural loss.

James C. Smalley is the manager of NFPA Wildland Fire Protection and the Firewise Communities Program (National Wildland/Urban Interface Fire Program). He is a member of the Society of American Foresters, the Institute of Fire Engineers, and the Society of Fire Protection Engineers.

FIGURE 13.5.1 Large Forest Fire (Photo: James C. Smalley)

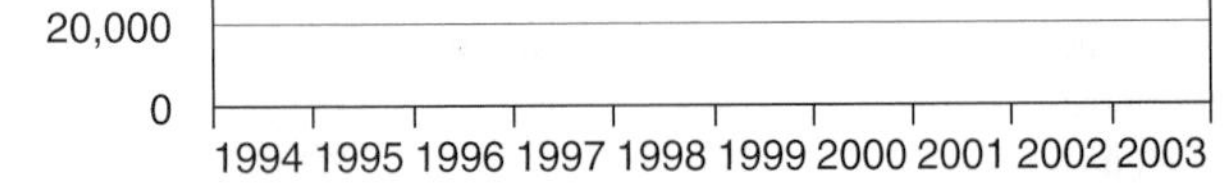

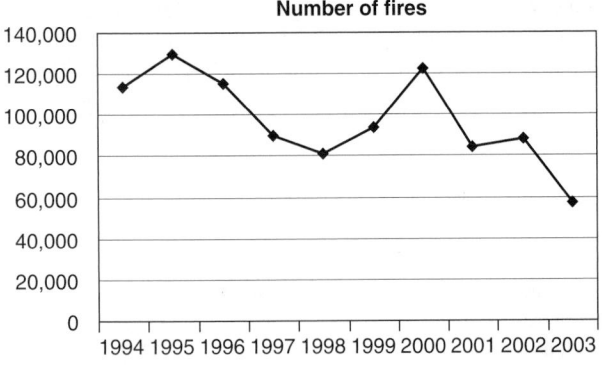

FIGURE 13.5.2 Number of Wildland Fires in the United States, 1994 to 2004

Considered the worst fire season in 80 years, 2000 was a landmark year, perhaps most remembered by the "escaped prescribed" fire in Bandelier National Monument near Los Alamos, New Mexico, that burned 47,650 acres (19,284 ha) and destroyed 235 homes. A moratorium on prescribed fire was put into effect

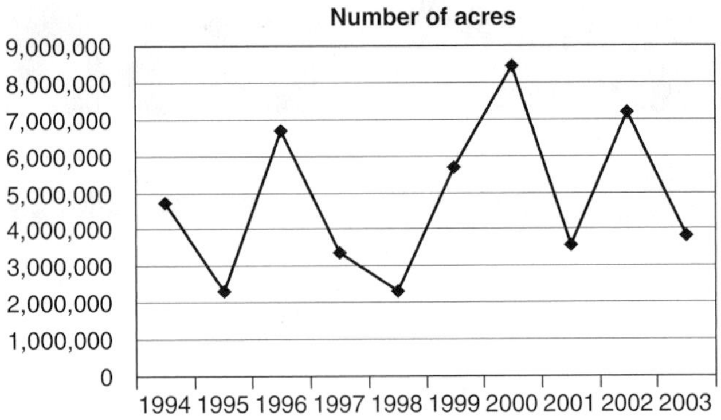

FIGURE 13.5.3 Number of Acres Burned in the United States, 1994 to 2003

following the blaze. The Cerro Grande fire was a harbinger of one of the most difficult seasons in the last half century. In 2002, the National Interagency Fire Center's annual summary included an average "worst" summary, noting that, based on previous years' activities, fire seasons of 85,000 fires and 6 million acre (2,428,200 ha) damage could be expected in the future.[1]

Significant Historical Fires

Possibly the largest wildfires (known as the Miramichi and Maine fires) occurred in October 1825, burning from Maine through New Brunswick, Canada. A group of loggers ignited a fire in a drought area that soon burned out of their control and eventually destroyed 3 million acres (1.2 million ha) of forest and killed more than 160 people. The most devastating fire in U.S. history in terms of human lives and property lost was in Peshtigo, Wisconsin, in 1871. The fire killed over 1500 people in a single night and burned more than 1 million acres (404,700 ha). Other significant historical fires are summarized in Table 13.5.1.

CHALLENGES TO MANAGING U.S. WILDLANDS

There are 747 million acres (302,300,175 ha) of forestland in the United States, about 71 percent as much as there was in 1630. Today, the United States has about the same amount of land (or slightly less) covered by trees as in 1907. Over half (54%) of America's forests are owned by private individuals, 37 percent are under the management of public agencies, and 9 percent are owned by private industries.[2] With mixed ownership and changing expectations for public use and future of those lands, national policies regarding the management of those forests have changed dramatically over the last 100 years.

Four Threats to U.S. Forests

With progress in understanding better how fire shapes ecosystems, including watersheds, technology has made remarkable advances in assisting land managers and fire professionals in fire management through geographic information systems

TABLE 13.5.1 Significant Historical Fires

Year/Month	*Name*	*Location*	*Acres (ha)*	*Significance*
1871/October	Peshtigo	Wisconsin and Michigan	3,780,000 (1,529,760)	1500 dead in Wisconsin
1881/September	Michigan	Michigan	1,000,000 (404,700)	169 dead
1894/September	Hinckley	Minnesota	Undetermined	418 dead
1894/September	Wisconsin	Wisconsin	Several million	Undetermined, some dead
1902/September	Yacoult	Washington and Oregon	1,000,000 + (404,700)	38 dead
1903/April	Adirondack	New York	637,000 (257,790)	Large amount of acreage burned
1910/August	Great Idaho	Idaho and Montana	3,000,000 (1,214,100)	85 dead
1918/October	Cloquet-Moose Lake	Minnesota	250,000 (101,175)	450 dead
1933/August	Tillamook	Oregon	311,000 (125,861)	1 dead; same area burned again in 1939
1947/October	Maine	Maine	205,678 (83,238)	16 dead, 9 towns leveled, 3500 displaced, 2500 homeless, 851 homes and 397 summer homes destroyed, 20,000 fire fighters engaged in fire suppression
1949	Mann Gulch	Montana	4,339 (1,756)	13 smoke jumpers killed
1967	Sundance	Idaho	56,000 (22,663)	50,000 acres burned in just 9 hours
1961/November	Bel Air	California		505 homes destroyed
1970/September	Laguna	California	175,425 (70,995)	382 structures destroyed
1977/July	Sycamore	California	805 (326)	234 structures destroyed
1980/November	Panorama	California	23,600 (9,551)	325 structures destroyed
1985/May	Black Friday Fires	Florida	110,000 (44,517)	1 dead, at least one fire in nearly every county of the state, 600 homes lost (400 of those lost in 1 day)
1987	Siege of '87	California	640,000 (259,000)	Valuable timber lost on the Klamath and Stanislaus National Forests
1988	Yellowstone	Montana and Idaho	1,585,000 (641,450)	Large amount of acreage burned
1988	Canyon Creek	Montana	250,000 (101,175)	Large amount of acreage burned
1990/June	Painted Cave	California	4,900 (1,983)	641 structures destroyed
1990/June	Dude Fire	Arizona	24,174 (9,783)	6 dead, 63 homes destroyed
1991/October	Oakland Hills	California	1,500 (607)	25 dead and 2,900 structures destroyed
1992/August	Foothills Fire	Idaho	257,000 (104,000)	1 dead
1994/July	South Canyon Fire	Colorado	1,856 (751)	14 dead
1994/July	Idaho City Complex	Idaho	154,000 (62,324)	1 dead
1996/August	Cox Wells	Idaho	219,000 (88,629)	Largest fire of the year
1996/June	Millers Reach	Alaska	37,336 (15,110)	344 structures destroyed
1997/July	Inowak	Alaska	610,000 (246,867)	Threatened 3 villages
1998	Volusia Complex	Florida	111,130 (44,570)	Thousands of people evacuated from several counties
1998	Flagler/St. John	Florida	94,656 (38,307)	Forced the evacuation of thousands of residents
1999/August	Dunn Glen Complex	Nevada	288,220 (116,643)	Largest fire of the year
1999/August–November	Big Bar Complex	California	140,947 (57,041)	Series of fires caused several evacuations during a 3½-month period
1999/September–November	Kirk Complex	California	86,700 (35,087)	Hundreds of people evacuated by this complex of fires that burned for almost 3 months
2000/May	Cerro Grande	New Mexico	47,650 (19,284)	Originally a prescribed fire, 235 structures destroyed and Los Alamos National Laboratory damaged
2003/October	19 fires throughout the state	California	730,000 + (295,431)	More than 3,600 homes destroyed, 22 people dead, more than 200 injured, more than 500 farms and commercial properties damaged

Source: National Interagency Fire Center, Boise, Idaho, and the Insurance Services Offices, Jersey City, New Jersey.

(GIS), globally positioned satellites (GPS), remote sensing of weather and fire conditions, fire and related land management simulation models, and the Internet. A major consideration in the twenty-first century is what Americans want and expect from their national forests and grasslands.

In a presentation to the Idaho Environmental Forum in 2004, USDA Forest Service Chief Dale Bosworth pointed out four major threats to the forestlands in the United States: fires, invasive species, loss of open space, and unmanaged outdoor recreation.[3]

Fires. Since 2000, the United States has had some of the worst fire seasons in 50 years. In 2002, record-breaking fires burned in four different states, and a fifth came close to breaking past records. In 2003, the fire season in southern California resulted in the deaths of at least 20 people and more from the debris flows that followed when rains fell on slopes where fires had burned away the vegetation.

Because many of the nation's fire-dependent ecosystems have become overgrown and unhealthy, the proper response is to reduce fuels *before* the big fires break out. The use of thinning techniques and the effective and safe reintroduction of fire into the ecosystem will help reduce the damage that fire makes each year in nearly every state.

Invasive Species. Plant species that evolve in one place and show up in another, where the ecological controls they evolved with are missing, take advantage of their new surroundings to crowd out or kill off native species, destroying habitat for native wildlife. Where cheatgrass takes over, for example, the range loses forage value for deer and elk, affecting the nation's heritage at a cost of billions of dollars.

Loss of Open Space. Every day, America loses about 4000 acres (1619 ha) of open space to development, about 3 acres (1.2 ha) per minute, and the rate of conversion is accelerating. In some places, the loss is to large, relatively undisturbed forests that provide needed habitat for animals like marten, bear, and cougar. In other places, the loss is to rangeland needed by many other animals and plants. Where private open space is lost, recreational pressures on public lands tend to grow.

Unmanaged Outdoor Recreation. Ninety-nine percent of recreational users are careful to protect the land. However, with millions of users, even a tiny percentage of problem use becomes relatively huge. Each year, the national forests and grasslands get hundreds of miles of unauthorized roads and trails due to repeated cross-country use. Every season, more erosion, water degradation, and habitat destruction occur. Conflicts between users and among land managers are rising. The challenge is to improve land management in order to get the most desirable and responsible recreational use based on sound outdoor ethics.

Causes of Wildland Fires

Leading Causes. Causes of forest fires differ from region to region but nationally they maintain a consistent ranking within percentage ranges (Table 13.5.2).[4] The leading cause of wildfires in the United States is intentional burning, or arson, which accounts for one-quarter to one-third of the fires and burned-over area. Debris burning accounts for an additional one-fourth of the fires, whereas lightning accounts for another one-tenth to one-seventh of the fires but affects a larger share of the burned area. Other prominent causes of fires include equipment use, careless smoking, children playing with matches, campfires, and railroad use.[5]

Nearly all of these fires are controlled at a size of 100 acres (40 ha) or less. However, roughly 2 percent of fires result in two-thirds of the total burned-over area. Altogether, hundreds of thousands of wildfires occur each year in the United States, burning millions of acres of forest, brush, and grass-covered lands.

The relative importance of the fire causes just mentioned varies considerably among the different geographical regions of the country. In terms of the number of fires and burned areas, lightning is the leading cause in the northwestern part of the country, as well as in Arizona and New Mexico. For the entire eastern half of the United States, intentional burning, or arson, and debris burning are the chief causes. In California, equipment use and arson rank highest, and debris burning and lightning are the main problems in the central Rockies. Alaska's wildfires can be blamed chiefly on debris burning and lightning.

In Canada, thousands of wildfires occur each year, burning millions of acres of wildlands. About one-third of these fires are caused by lightning, although fires started by lightning account for most of the burned-over area.

Role of Lightning. On a global scale, lightning is common; 8 million cloud-to-ground discharges occur per day around the world. One percent of these strikes results in wildland fires. In fact, dry lightning is responsible for 80 percent of all fires in wildland areas. Dry lightning occurs during thunderstorms when the humidity is so low (the air is so dry) that rain evaporates before it reaches the ground. Even though the rain does not reach the ground, the lightning does. Although the energy per lightning bolt varies greatly, 250 kilowatt-hours is a good estimate of the average energy discharged in each stroke. Almost 75 percent of a lightning bolt's energy is converted to heat during discharge. This is more than sufficient to ignite most fuels.

There are two types of discharge: cold and hot stroke. Cold strokes exhibit high voltage of short duration, generally with

TABLE 13.5.2 Causes of Wildland Fires

Cause	*Percentage Range*
Arson	25–39
Trash burning	18–23
Careless smoking	17–19
Miscellaneous/unknown	10–14
Lightning	9
Machine use	7–8
Railroads	5
Campers	3–6

mechanical or explosive effects. Hot strokes discharge a lesser current for a longer duration, thus starting more fires. Approximately 21 percent of all lightning moves from cloud to ground. Of this amount, 20 percent is hot stroke, according to studies in the northern Rockies. Therefore, in the northern Rockies, one stroke in 25 has the electrical characteristics to start a fire, depending on where or what it strikes and on the local weather conditions.

PRINCIPLES OF COMBUSTION

Fire is a chemical reaction in which energy is produced. When forest material burns, the oxygen in the air combines chemically with wood, pitch, and/or other burnable elements in the fuel. In the forest, several stages in the fire process are normally encountered: first, the igniting spark; then a period of smoldering; and, finally, the more rapid combustion of fuels. This process may continue to involve leaping flames, dense smoke, intense heat, loud noises, and occasional explosions. Throughout its life, the action of a fire is governed by certain natural laws or principles of combustion. An understanding of these principles is basic in judging the effect of various environmental factors on fire behavior.

The Fire Triangle

Three elements—heat, oxygen, and fuel—are required in proper combination for ignition and combustion to occur.* If any one of the three is absent or if they are not in proper balance, ignition or combustion will not occur. Variations in balance among heat, oxygen, and fuel govern the violence of a fire and determine whether the fire will smolder and spread slowly or flame brightly and travel rapidly.

Heat. Because of the variation in the nature of forest fuels, specifying the amount of heat required to ignite the fuels is difficult. Vegetative material is high in carbon content and ignites at relatively low temperatures, provided the moisture content is low and the substance is freely exposed to the air. During the forest fire season, a large part of the vegetative matter in a forest—duff, dead limbs, pine needles, tree branches, rotted logs, and so on—is dry enough to be ignited easily. The temperature requirement for ignition of forest fuels varies from approximately 500 to 750°F (260 to 399°C). Many common ignition sources can provide the required heat, including a burning match, a glowing cigarette, or a lightning bolt.

Ignition often depends on the length of time the fuel is exposed to heat. Dry pine needles may be ignited in a few seconds by the heat from a flaming match. Moist pine needles also may be ignited by a match if subjected to the heat for several minutes. When wood fuels are exposed to heat for a long time, the normal ignition temperature may be lowered. Studies have shown that wood exposed to a temperature of 400°F (204°C) for approximately 30 minutes may ignite.

The ease of ignition of forest fuels exposed to heat for a considerable time has an important influence on fire behavior. In a coniferous forest, a hot fire burning in a tangle of downed logs and dry limbs may generate enough heat to make the green tree crowns above the fire easily ignitable. All that is needed to cause the tree crowns to ignite is a flying ember and a gust of wind. Similarly, a fire smoldering in a pile of leaves may generate enough heat to lower the normal ignition temperature of the entire pile. When the leaves are stirred up, the whole pile breaks into flame. The stirring of the pile lets in enough oxygen for the preheated leaves to be ignited easily.

Oxygen. The atmosphere is about 21 percent oxygen and since most wildland fires burn in a free-burning state in an uncontained environment (unlike structure fires), removing the oxygen side of the triangle (smothering the fire) is usually impractical to extinguish a wildland fire. In the forest, there is usually enough oxygen to permit ignition and combustion. However, some of the forest fuels may be arranged so that oxygen is not available in sufficient amount to support a fire. In deep, tightly compacted duff, only the top particles can get enough air to permit a fire to burn. In this situation, a fire will burn from the top down as each layer is exposed to the air. By contrast, in a very loose layer of pine needles, the entire mass is fairly well exposed to air and, consequently, combustion will take place rapidly.

The air mass near a fire, as represented by weather elements that can be measured, is perhaps the most variable component of the fire environment.[2] When wind blows on a fire, it usually speeds up the combustion process. Wind forces oxygen around fuel particles where the flow of air normally may be restricted. In addition, wind has a physical reaction on the flames, often bending them into positions that create more favorable situations for the spread of the fire.

Fuel. Under forest conditions, fuel is a major variable in the fire triangle. The fire fighter must become acquainted with the general nature of forest fuels to understand their burning characteristics.

The ease of ignition and rate of combustion of forest fuels depend mainly on the type of fuel—is it logging slash or dense duff in a green forest? On fuel continuity—is the fuel distributed more or less evenly over the area, or is it only present in patches? On moisture content—does it feel damp when touched, or does it crackle and appear very brittle? On fuel temperature—is the fuel exposed to the heat of the sun, or does it lie in cool shade?

Combustion Process. When fuels are heated to their ignition temperature, they produce gases that will ignite if combined with oxygen. When a log burns, the flames may appear to be coming directly from the fuel. Actually, the flames come from the ignited fuel gases emerging from the heated log.

In forest fires, the two common stages of combustion are smoldering and flaming. In the smoldering stage, heat is

*Although it is recognized that there is a fourth component involved in the combustion process (a chemical chain reaction), for the purposes of this chapter only, the components that make up the commonly referred to "fire triangle"—heat, fuel, and oxygen—will be addressed. The process of breaking the chemical chain reaction is not normally addressed in relation to wildland fire suppression methods. For a discussion relating to the fire tetrahedron and the chemical chain reaction process, see Section 2, Chapter 1, "Physics and Chemistry of Fire."

liberated, and a rise in fuel temperature occurs, whereas flames are absent or appear only intermittently. The absence of flames is caused by insufficient oxygen or by moisture in the fuels, which slows the oxidation process.

When a fire is in the flaming stage, all the elements of the fire triangle—that is, heat, oxygen, and fuel—are in proper combination for rapid oxidation to occur. The flames of very hot fires may be observed intermittently in the smoke at a considerable distance above the fire. This occurs when oxygen is consumed so rapidly near the base of the fire that combustion of the gases is incomplete. As these superheated gases rise, they reach a fresh oxygen supply and break into flames, giving the appearance that the smoke itself is flaming.

Reignition of apparently dead fires is an important factor in forest fuels. Although neither flames nor smoke may be observed, a fire can break out again if sufficient heat remains. Reignition occurs easily where fuels have been subjected to heat for a considerable length of time. To prevent reignition, an experienced fire fighter feels out fuels by hand before leaving the area. If heat continues to be present, the danger of reignition exists, and the control job remains incomplete.

Breaking the Fire Triangle

In fire control operations, the objective is to prevent combustion by breaking the fire triangle. If a sufficient volume of water is applied, the fuel temperature can be lowered below the ignition point. Smothering fires with dirt deprives them of oxygen. Building a line in which all flammable material is removed from the path of the fire prevents further spread by robbing the fire of fuel.

In forest fire fighting, the actual method of suppression is often dictated by the equipment and fire fighters available. The most effective methods for each stage of a suppression operation can be determined by keen observation of the combustion process.

Reducing Heat. Water being used to reduce fuel temperatures should be applied directly on the fuels being consumed. It is a mistake to apply water on the flames rather than the fuels. If the liberation of these gases is to be stopped, the fuels themselves must be cooled by the water. Although some of the water played on the flames may reach the fuels, a large part will either miss its mark or be lost through vaporization. If water is being used for cooling purposes, the ultimate target is always the fuel.

In a very hot fire accompanied by leaping flames, the nozzle user may not be able to get close enough to the fuels to apply water directly on the trouble spot. In such cases, a fog nozzle should be used to knock down the flames. The water particles help cool the heated gases being liberated by the fuels. Once the flames have been knocked down, the water should be used to thoroughly cool the heated fuels that are generating flammable gases.

Reducing Oxygen. Fires burning in forest fuels are difficult to smother completely. Soil thrown on burning forest materials may retard combustion by shielding portions of the fuel surface from the air, but the porous nature of most soils makes it difficult to completely shut off the supply of oxygen in this manner. Throwing dirt on a fire is nevertheless an important means of reducing the rate of combustion, after which the control operation may be continued by attacking one of the other legs of the fire triangle.

In very fine fuels such as dry grass, the oxygen supply may be reduced easily. Fuels of this nature do not retain heat for long periods and, therefore, combustion normally may be checked by temporarily shielding the fuel surface from the air. Gunnysacks, fire swatters, and a shovelful of dirt correctly applied are effective implements in smothering grass fires. When larger accumulations of flammable materials, such as dead stems and leaves, lie beneath a stand of grass, the danger of reignition exists. The understory material may hold enough heat to cause the fire to reignite once an adequate supply of oxygen becomes available. This danger can be determined by the careful observation and "feeling out" of the fuel.

Removing Fuel. In wildland fire suppression, the removal of fuel from the path of the fire is a common method of attacking the fire triangle. The fire continues to burn until its fuel is consumed, but it is prevented from spreading any further. A slowly advancing fire burning in sparse ground fuels may be checked simply by constructing a fireline down to mineral soil (soil with little humus or organic matter). A hot or fast-running fire may require several fuel removal operations. Snags of trees or tall brush that could cause spot fires may have to be felled. Thickets of reproduction or dry brush may need to be weeded out. Low-hanging limbs may have to be removed to prevent the build-up of a crown fire. Concentrations of limbs and logs may have to be broken up. The objective of these operations is to remove or reduce the flammable substances that could allow the fire to either build in intensity or continue to spread.

Heat Transfer

The rate and amount of heat transferred influence the rate of spread and the intensity of a fire. Combustion cannot be sustained unless heat continues to be transferred. Heat transfer occurs by three means: radiation, convection, and conduction.

Radiation. In forest fires, radiation is the most significant means of transferring heat from burning fuels to exposed fuels. The location and width of firelines must be governed, in part, by the rate of radiant heat transfer. Potentially hot fires and spots where dangerous flare-ups might occur can often be prevented by the breaking up of the fuels to reduce the radiant heat transfer between them.

The degree of slope influences the amount of radiant heat transmitted to fuels upslope and downslope of the fire. Most forest fires will burn in the direction of the wind, partly due to the effects of radiant heat. Wind influences radiant heat transfer in two ways: (1) it increases the rate of combustion, thus creating a hotter fire; and (2) it bends the flames, thus decreasing the distance between the heat source and the fuels lying in the path of the fire. The dual effect of the hotter fire and the bent-over flames dries and heats the fuels laying ahead to such an extent that rate or spread may be greatly accelerated.

Often a fire will burn into the wind because the wind increases combustion to such a degree that a large amount of radiant heat may be transmitted to the fuels lying on the upwind side. On the upslope side of a fire, the fuels receive more radiant heat, which is one reason fires often spread more rapidly up steep slopes than on level ground.

Convection. In a forest fire, the fuels lying in the path of convection currents are heated and, thus, transformed into a more ignitable condition. The hot air mass rising from a surface fire transfers a large amount of heat to the tree crowns, thus bringing them nearer to the ignition temperature.

When fires break out in tree crowns and in other aerial fuels, heat transfer by convection is usually increased. Sparks and burning embers (firebrands) from burning tree crowns and snags will also drop and start new fires in fuels on the ground. As these ground fires gain in intensity, more hot air masses rise through the aerial fuels, and a type of chain reaction may be created. Fire fighters must always be alert to the danger of hot surface fires burning underneath a forest canopy. These surface fires must be cooled promptly, and fuel masses must be broken up to reduce convective heat transfer.

Heat transfer through convection is also increased by wind, which moves hot masses of air ahead of the fire. Wind both increases the rate of combustion and accelerates the transport of hot air masses. When driven by wind, the hot convection currents may move closer to the ground fuels and, thus, create more flammable conditions in the understory vegetation of the forest.

Fuels located above the fire on steep slopes also receive heat by the movement of convection currents up the slope and are, thus, subjected to an accelerated rate of heating and drying. This fact is one more reason why fires often burn very rapidly up the sides of steep slopes.

Conduction. Wood is a poor conductor of heat, and the conduction method of heat transfer is relatively minor in evaluating forest fire behavior.

TOPOGRAPHY

Topography provides a useful and easily recognized indicator of fire behavior. Fires often have distinctive behavior characteristics according to aspect, elevation, position on slope, steepness of slope, and shape of the surrounding countryside. These topographic features are usually easy to identify in the field and, thus, are important factors in the evaluation of fire behavior.

Differences in topography may cause local variations in climate and day-to-day weather conditions. These variations, in turn, influence the character of forest growth and the flammability of fuels. In rough terrain, such as the northern Rocky Mountains, topography has a great influence on fire behavior.

Aspect

Aspect, sometimes referred to as exposure, describes the direction a slope faces. Fire conditions vary greatly according to aspect because different aspects receive varying amounts of sunshine and wind.

In general, southern and southwestern slopes provide favorable conditions for the ignition and spread of fires. Because these slopes receive direct sunshine, the air and fuel temperatures are somewhat higher and cause snow to melt earlier on southern slopes. For these reasons, vegetation on south-facing slopes is not only sparser but also drier and more flammable than vegetation on north-facing slopes.

There are also variations in temperature and relative humidity on northern and southern slopes. On south-facing slopes, the average July through August temperature is higher, and the relative humidity is lower. The time of day is also critical. South- and west-facing slopes are most dangerous in the afternoon and early evening. When the combined effects of aspect and elevation are considered, some striking indicators of fire behavior become evident.

Elevation

In the Rocky Mountains, there is a vertical difference of more than 10,000 ft (3048 m) between the lowest valleys and the highest mountains. At Lewiston, Idaho, the elevation is only 757 ft (231 m) above sea level. Along the Continental Divide, there are many peaks over 10,000 ft (3048 m), and in northwestern Wyoming, some peaks are over 13,000 ft (3962 m) above sea level. Between these extremes of elevation is a variety of weather and fuel conditions that creates distinctive fire control problems.

Position of Fire on Slope

Fire behavior at various positions on a slope may be influenced not only by aspect and elevation but also by the magnitude of the fuel body and by topographic barriers. When a fire starts at the bottom of a slope, an entire mountainside of fuels may lie in its path. Once a fire starting at the base of a slope gains headway, the availability of a continuous fuel body makes a large burn possible.

Steepness of Slope

Other conditions being equal, fires burn more rapidly on steep slopes. In general, as the steepness of the slope increases, the rate of fire spread increases. As explained previously, combustion is accelerated on steep slopes primarily due to increased heat transfer through radiation and convection. A fire will double in rate of spread on a 30 percent slope. On a 55 percent slope it will double again.

Shape of Country

In rugged, mountainous areas, the shape of the country is of great importance to the fire fighter who must evaluate fire behavior. Narrow canyons, side drainages, sharp ridges, and massive, irregular slopes all have a bearing on the direction of travel, rate of spread, and general behavior of fires.

Experience has shown the following topographic features to be of special importance:

- *Narrow canyons.* Wind direction normally will follow the direction of the canyon. Wind eddies and strong upslope air movement may be expected at sharp bends in a canyon. Radiant heat transfer from one slope to another is great and, as a result, fires may spot across the canyon easily. Near the bottom of the canyon, there is little difference between conditions on various aspects.

• *Wide canyons.* Prevailing wind direction will not be altered to any great extent by the direction of the canyon. Cross-canyon spotting of fires is not common except in high winds. Strong differences will occur between general fire conditions on northern and southern aspects.

• *Box canyons.* Fires starting near the base of box canyons will react similarly to a fire in a stove. Air will be drawn in from the canyon bottom, thus creating very strong upslope drafts. These same conditions may occur at the heads of narrow canyons and at the heads of high mountain valleys.

• *Ridges.* Fires burning along lateral ridges may change direction when they reach a point where the ridge drops off into a canyon. This change of direction is caused by the flow of air in the canyon. In some cases, a whirling motion by the fire may result from a strong flow of air around the point of a ridge.

FUELS

Keen observation of variations in forest fuels is essential in reliably estimating fire behavior. Fuel is the material of primary concern to fire control agencies. A good fire fighter must be able to evaluate flammability and difficulty of control in the various fuel situations encountered in a forest area.

Flammability Analysis

In a forest, great differences exist in the character of flammable materials. Deep duff, newly fallen dead leaves, clumps of grass, litters of dry twigs and branches, downed logs, low shrubs, green tree branches, hanging moss, snags, and many other types of material are present. Each of these materials has distinctive burning characteristics. The flammability of a particular fuel body is governed by the burning characteristics of individual materials and by the combined effects of the various types of materials present.

Before flammability can be analyzed, the physical characteristics of combustible forest materials must be classified. Such a classification permits the identification of the fuel factors that influence flammability. After the fuel has been classified properly, topographic and weather factors must be considered before the rate of spread and the general behavior of fires in that fuel can be determined.

Because forest fuels are so varied and complex, developing a systematic approach to flammability analysis is necessary. First, the fuel body is subdivided into two broad classes: ground fuels and aerial fuels. Then each of these classes is evaluated according to the arrangement, compactness, continuity, volume, and moisture content of the principal materials involved. Aspect also affects the flammability of fuels. Southwest-facing slopes heat up to a greater extent. With practice, this procedure can be performed quickly and easily.

Ground Fuels

Ground fuels include all flammable materials lying on or immediately above the ground or in the ground. The principal materials are duff, tree roots, dead leaves, grass, fine deadwood, downed logs, stumps, large limbs, low brush, and reproduction or young stands of timbers.

Duff. Duff is composed of partially decayed vegetative matter found on the forest floor. Duff seldom has a major influence on the spread rate of fire as it is typically moist and tightly compressed so that little of its surface is freely exposed to air and its rate of combustion is slow. In forest fires, most of the duff is consumed down to mineral soil. Occasionally, duff contributes to the rate of spread by furnishing a path for the fire to creep along between patches of more flammable material.

The smoldering characteristics of duff fires make them somewhat difficult to control. Firelines must be dug down to mineral soil in duff areas unless the lower layers of duff are too wet or too tightly compressed to burn. Duff fires inside a fireline are best mopped up by turning over the duff with a shovel, loosening the material for better exposure to air, and allowing it to burn out. Water may be used effectively, but great care must be taken to stir the fuel to ensure that all particles are thoroughly soaked. Extinguishing duff fires by smothering them with dirt is very difficult to accomplish.

Tree Roots. Tree roots are not an important factor in rate of fire spread, as the greatly restricted air supply prevents rapid combustion. However, fires can creep slowly in roots—in fact, some fires have escaped control because a root provided an avenue for the fire to cross the control line. The most flammable roots are the large laterals stemming from dead snags. Root fires are controlled simply by cutting the root where it crosses the fireline. Mop-up of persistent fires may require complete excavation of roots.

Dead Leaves. As leaves decay on the ground, they gradually become part of the duff layer. Before this decay takes place, however, leaves are a highly flammable material and should be considered separately in evaluating ground fuels. In northern Rocky Mountain forests, the cover of dead leaves on the ground is composed primarily of needles dropped from coniferous trees. Ponderosa pine needles are the most flammable because their large size and shape lead to a loose arrangement allowing free circulation of air. Smaller needles, such as those from Douglas fir, are generally less flammable as they are more tightly compacted on the ground.

Needles that are still attached to dead branches are especially flammable because they are exposed freely to air and are not typically in direct contact with the more moist material on the ground. Needles remaining on fallen limbs form highly combustible kindling for larger material. For this reason, logging slash containing dry needles is dangerous fuel.

Many techniques are necessary to control fires for which leaves or needles are the primary fuel. The advance of a fast-running fire may be checked temporarily by smothering it with dirt or by cooling it with water. Only a light cover of dirt thrown with the sweeping motion of a shovel is necessary to slow down a needle fire.

When water is used to check the advance, a spray or fog-type stream is most effective, with the water being aimed at the base and directly in front of the flames. A penetrating straight stream of water is most effective for mopping up a needle fire. Careful stirring of all flammable material is required. A fireline is essential around all fires burning in a continuous cover of needles.

Grass. Grass, weeds, and other small plants are important ground fuels that influence the rate of fire spread. The key factor in these fuels is the degree of curing. Succulent green grass acts as a fire barrier. During the course of a normal fire season, however, grass gradually becomes drier and more flammable until the stems and leaves die due to lack of moisture. At this time, the major part of the grass cover becomes highly flammable. Cured grass, if present in large and uniform volume, provides the most flammable ground fuel in the region.

Grass and other small plants occur on the floor of almost all forests. Fire fighters need to observe the volume and continuity of the grass cover. In dense forests where little sunlight reaches the ground, very little grass is found. In more open forests, such as in mature stands of ponderosa pine, there may be a large amount. If there is a more or less continuous cover of dry grass on the forest floor, the spread rate of a fire will be governed largely by that cover rather than by the heavier fuels normally associated with a forest.

The ease with which fires in dry grass can be controlled depends mainly on the volume of grass. When the volume is low, the fire is often cool enough to permit fire fighters to work near the edge of the flame front. When the volume of grass is great, however, the resulting hot fire may prevent work close to the fire front.

In grass fires, smothering with dirt or swatters and cooling with a spray or fog stream of water are effective control methods. Both methods require follow-up to ensure that no hangover fires remain. Wherever forest material, such as a mat of dead pine needles, twigs, or small limbs, is intermixed with the stand of grass, a fireline dug down to mineral soil is usually required.

Fires in dry grass often have high rates of spread. For this reason, special safety measures need to be observed.

Fine Deadwood. Fine deadwood consists of twigs, small limbs, bark, and rotting material. Normally, the fine deadwood classification is confined to material with a diameter of less than 2 in. (50.8 mm). These fine dead ground fuels are among the most important of all materials influencing the rate of fire spread and general fire behavior in forest areas. Fine deadwood ignites easily and often provides the main avenue for carrying fire from one area to another. It is the kindling material for larger, heavier fuels.

In areas where a great volume of fine deadwood exists, a fire can rapidly develop tremendous heat. The greatest volume of fine deadwood is usually found in areas containing logging slash. Under dry conditions, fires in such areas burn violently, and the strong convection currents created by the intense heat pick up burning embers and throw them out ahead, causing spot fires beyond the main fire front. In some areas, the occurrence of fine deadwood may be spotty. Troublesome situations may be avoided by breaking up the worst bunches of fine deadwood before a fire reaches them.

Granulated dry rotten wood, although not an especially important factor in the rate of fire spread, is a highly ignitable fuel. Flying embers from the main fire often cause spot fires in rotten wood lying on the ground or in hollow places on old logs or stumps. Fire fighters searching for spot fires should seek out and carefully check these areas.

In most forest fires, the control job must be aimed largely at checking the spread of fires in fine deadwood and in the associated material—that is, duff and leaves—lying underneath. Unless a large volume of dry grass is present, the fine deadwood is the most important fuel and should receive the first and most concentrated attention. If the fire is very hot, the first action may be to smother it with dirt or cool it with water. Final control requires a fireline dug down to mineral soil in nearly all cases.

Downed Logs, Stumps, and Large Limbs. Heavy fuels, such as downed logs, stumps, and large limbs, require long periods of hot, dry weather before they become highly flammable. When such material reaches a dry state, however, very hot fires may develop. The most dangerous heavy fuels are those containing stringers of dry wood, shaggy bark, or many large checks and cracks. Smooth-surfaced material is less flammable as it dries out more slowly, has little surface exposed to air, and contains less attached kindling fuel. Extremely hot fires may develop in piles of downed logs and large limbs or in crisscrossed windfalls as the various fuel components radiate heat to each other. Individual limbs and logs will not burn very hot unless the fire is supported by large accumulations of fine deadwood.

The control of an advancing fire seldom rests on the fire fighters' ability to suppress the fire in heavy fuels. Usually, fires will not advance from log to log unless finer fuels are present or the area is covered with logs that radiate heat to each other.

Once a fire becomes well established in heavy fuels, complete suppression becomes difficult. A control line around the area is essential. Smothering with dirt or cooling with water is effective, but both these methods require very large volumes of suppression agent. In some cases, it is necessary to allow the fire to burn out until the heat has subsided sufficiently to permit final mop-up operations to take place. When a fire is allowed to burn out in logs containing stringers of bark, a careful lookout must be kept for spot fires caused by embers carried in the strong convection currents. If at all possible, hot fires in such areas should be cooled promptly by any available means.

Low Brush and Reproduction. Low brush, tree seedlings, and small saplings are classified as ground fuels because they are so closely intermixed with the flammable material on the forest floor. This understory vegetation may either accelerate or slow down the spread rate of a fire. During the early part of a fire season, the shade normally provided by understory vegetation prevents other ground fuels from drying out rapidly. As the season progresses, however, continued high air temperature and low relative humidity dry out both the fuel lying on the ground and the understory vegetation. When this happens, most of the low vegetation, particularly small coniferous trees, becomes fire carriers.

The understory vegetation in a forest often provides a link between ground fuels and aerial fuels. The crowns of small trees may catch fire and, in turn, spread the fire to aerial fuels in the forest canopy. Either thickets of reproduction or dead brush may provide the first means for a surface fire to flare up and spread into the crowns of the overstory trees. In anticipation of this possibility, alert fire fighters break up reproduction thickets and dead brush along the fireline or, wherever possible, locate control lines to prevent fire from spreading into these danger areas. It is not uncommon for fire to creep through ground fuels under low brush or reproduction during periods when there is a low burning index, such as during the night. Heat from the creeping fires dries out the leaves and stems of the low brush and reproduction. Then, on the following day, as the burning index increases, a reburn occurs. Often on the reburn, the dried, low vegetation burns hotly and carries the fire to the aerial fuels, causing a crown fire.

Aerial Fuels

Aerial fuels include all green and dead materials located in the upper forest canopy. The main aerial fuel components are tree branches, crowns, snags, tree moss, and high brush.

Tree Branches and Crowns. The live needles of coniferous trees are a highly flammable fuel. Their arrangements on the tree branches allow free circulation of air. In addition, the upper branches of trees are more freely exposed to wind and sun than most ground fuels. These factors, plus the volatile oils and resins in coniferous needles, make tree branches and crowns important components in aerial fuels.

Tree branches and crowns are fuels that can flash quickly with changes in relative humidity. Crown fires seldom occur when relative humidity is high. However, coniferous needles dry out quickly when exposed to hot, dry air. The dryness of needles is influenced by the transpiration process in a tree. When the ground is moist, trees pump a large amount of moisture into the air through the leaves. As the ground becomes drier, the transpiration process slows and, as a result, leaves and branches become drier and more flammable.

Dead branches on trees are an important aerial fuel. Concentrations of dead branches, such as those found in insect- or disease-killed stands, may cause fire to spread from tree to tree. Concentrations of dead branches on the lower trunks of trees may provide an additional avenue for fires to spread from ground fuels into tree crowns. The most flammable dead branches are those still containing needles.

Fires in the upper crowns of trees are extremely difficult to control. The main control method must be aimed at suppressing the fire in ground fuels and preventing the fire from entering the tree crowns. Removal of limbs on the lower trunks of trees is one method of preventing crown fires. Limbs should be removed wherever a concentration of ground fuels makes a crown fire likely.

Snags. Snags, or tree stumps, are one of the most important aerial fuels that influence fire behavior. Although green trees greatly outnumber snags in most forests, more fires start in snags because they are drier and are arranged for easier ignition.

Snags vary widely in character and, consequently, in their effect on fire behavior. Smooth, solid snags that contain very little bark and few checks or cracks are not highly flammable. On the other hand, broken-topped, shaggy-barked, or partially decayed snags ignite easily and have a major influence on the spread of fires. Burning embers blown from shaggy-barked snags are prolific starters of spot fires. In areas containing large numbers of snags, fire may spread from one trunk to another because of the intense radiation of heat.

Fires in burning snags must be controlled promptly. Wherever possible, the main control effort on the fire must be designed to prevent the blaze from getting into snags. When fires become established in snags, the control method usually requires that the snags be felled. Snag felling is especially important if shaggy bark might be carried from the burning trunk by wind or strong convection currents.

Tree Moss. Moss hanging on trees is the lightest and flashiest of all aerial fuels. Moss is important principally because it provides a means of spreading fires from ground fuels to other aerial fuels or from one aerial component to another. Like other light fuels, moss reacts quickly to changes in relative humidity. During dry weather, crown fires may develop easily in heavily moss-covered stands. Methods of controlling moss fires are aimed primarily at breaking up ground fuels to prevent fire from entering the tree crowns through hanging moss. In addition, lower limbs containing tree moss should be removed at all danger spots.

High Brush. Crowns of high brush are classified as aerial fuels because they are separated distinctly by distance from ground fuels. In the northern Rocky Mountain region, heavy stands of brush may develop in old burns, and they often form the principal vegetative cover in such areas. Crown fires in brush fuels ordinarily do not occur unless heavy ground fuels are present to develop the required heat. In some brush stands, however, a high proportion of dead stems may create a sufficient volume of fine dead aerial fuels to permit very hot and fast-spreading crown fires. Key factors in evaluating the behavior of fires in high brush are volume, arrangement, the general condition of ground fuels, and the presence of fine dead aerial fuels.

Fuel Conditions

Fuel Continuity. Fuel continuity describes the distribution of fuels in a given area. Fuel continuity is an important factor in fire behavior because the distribution of fuels influences the potential area where a fire may spread, as well as the rate of spread. If a dangerous fuel is uniformly distributed over an entire area, a high potential exists for a complete burn to occur at a rapid rate of spread. If the fuel body is broken up by patches of bare ground or much less flammable material, both the potential area of the burn and the rate of fire spread are reduced.

A wide range of fuel continuity conditions is found in most forest areas. For the sake of simplicity in making fire behavior estimates, the following two broad fuel continuity classes are recognized:

- *Uniform fuels.* Uniform fuels include all fuels distributed continuously over the area being evaluated. Areas containing a network of stringers, or blocks, which connect with each other to provide a continuous path for the spread of fire, are included in this classification.

- *Patchy fuels.* Patchy fuels include all fuels distributed unevenly over the area being evaluated. Definite breaks should be present, such as patches of rocky outcropping or plots where the dominant vegetation is of much lower flammability than the main fuel body.

Volume. As the amount of flammable materials in a given area increases, the amount of heat a fire produces also increases. The hottest fires, as well as those most difficult to control, occur in areas containing the greatest quantity of fuel.

In evaluating fuel volume, fire fighters should observe the quantity of both small- and large-sized fuel components. A great volume of small materials, such as fine deadwood, indicates ample kindling for the ignition of other fuels. A great volume of either small- or large-sized material indicates a high potential for a hot fire. Where fires develop in areas containing a great volume of large-sized material, there is intense radiation of heat to fuels lying in the path of the fire.

Fuel Compactness. Fuel compactness—that is, the number of individual fuel particles per unit of volume—varies greatly in all kinds of fuel, but it is significant principally in duff and dead leaves lying on the ground. Fires burn rapidly in loosely compacted fuels because more of the individual fuel particles are freely exposed to air.

Live Fuel Moisture. Two conditions of fuel moisture have major influence on the rating of fuel types. One concerns the greenness, or curing stage, of vegetation. The other relates to the shade and protection furnished by green timber.

In grass fuels, moisture content is a critical factor in determining flammability. Fires spread only at a low rate, or not at all, in grasses that are green, but when the same grasses become cured and dry, fires will race through them at an extremely rapid rate. The degree of curing of grass is difficult to evaluate and requires keen observation of the grass stand. For purposes of considering fire behavior, the moisture content of grass can be judged according to the state of curing, as follows:

- *Green.* The condition can be recognized by the green color and the cool, moist feel when crushed in the hand.
- *Curing.* As hot, dry weather prevails, grasses ordinarily progress through a period of gradual curing. This stage is detected by close observation of the individual grass clumps or stems. For cheatgrass, the curing stage is typified by a lavender tinge commonly referred to as "the purple stage." For most other grasses, the curing stage begins when the tips of grass blades become tan or brown, or when individual grass blades take on a cured appearance.
- *Cured.* In the cured stage, grasses are dried completely to a tan or brownish hue, and the stems feel dry or crackly when crushed or rubbed in the hand.

Soils influence curing primarily because of soil moisture relationships. In the deep, moist soils bordering creeks, curing is much slower than in the thin soils on slopes. Some grasses seldom reach a dangerous cured condition. The shade and protection afforded by timber stands influence fuel type ratings due to the favorable fuel moisture conditions that are created. In a dense forest, ground fuels are protected from the sun and wind. Temperatures and wind velocities are lower so that moisture does not evaporate as rapidly from the dead fuels on the ground. Lower ratings are assigned to fuels situated beneath dense timber canopies.

The moisture content of fuels is influenced also by aspect, altitude, time of year, time of day, and other factors. For the purpose of fuel type classification, these factors are disregarded, and fuel types are classified on the basis of the physical characteristics of the fuels themselves.

Dead Fuel Moisture. Dead fuel moisture is changed by the moisture content of the air. Time lag is the time it takes for the moisture content of the dead fuels and the surrounding air to equalize. Time lag is expressed as a rate (usually in hours) (Table 13.5.3).

SPECIAL FIRE BEHAVIOR FACTORS

Spot Fires

The development of spot fires depends not only on topographic and weather factors but also on the character of the fuels in the main fire and fuels beyond the main fire. In the main fire, rotten, shaggy-barked snags, such as broken-topped hemlock snags, and large quantities of ground fuels, such as heavy logging slash, are the fuels most likely to cause spot fires. Spot fires frequently are started by crown fires. Widespread crown fires, with their intense heat and strong convection currents, can throw burning embers far out ahead of the main fire. In many wildland/urban interface fires, significant structure loss occurs primarily from ember (firebrand) exposure.

Fuels that are ignited most readily by embers thrown out ahead of the main fire, listed in order of susceptibility, include the following:

1. Rotten wood on the ground, on logs, and in snags
2. Moss and lichens in treetops
3. Slash, particularly when compacted in tight piles
4. Duff
5. Cured grass

Spot fires become more frequent and severe with lower fuel moisture and increased wind. On an average dry, late summer afternoon, the smallest sparks quickly ignite rotten wood or tree moss. In compacted slash, in duff, and in cured grass, larger

TABLE 13.5.3 Dead Fuel Moisture: Time Lag Relationship to Fuel Size

Size Time Lag	*Diameter of Fuel*	*Examples*
1 hr	Less than ¼ in.	Annual grass
10 hr	¼ to 1 in.	Coastal sage, juniper, and chaparral
100 hr	1 to 3 in.	Logging slash
1000 hr	3 to 8 in.	Logs and mature standing timber

Note: For SI units: 1 in. = 25.4 mm.

burning embers are required to start spot fires unless sufficient wind exists to fan smoldering material into flames.

Crown Fires

Many forests contain a combination of aerial and ground fuels that favors the development of crown fires. Fuel conditions that influence the probability and character of crown fires include the following:

- Volume and arrangement of the timber canopy
- Volume and arrangement of fine dry aerial fuels, such as moss and dead twigs
- Position of aerial fuels above ground fuels
- Character of ground fuels

In open forests where single trees or small clumps of trees are well isolated from each other, crown fires are usually confined to single trees or to small groups of trees. Crowning, in such cases, increases rate of spread by intensifying heat and causing spot fires, but it will not result in racing crown fires like those that sometimes occur in dense forests.

When the timber canopy is sufficiently dense and continuous to carry broadcast crown fires, the severity of the crown fire is influenced by the quantity, character, and arrangement of dry fuels in the air and on the ground.

An important consideration in evaluating fuel conditions is the likelihood of reburns in tree crowns over previously burned ground fuels. A combination of fuel, weather, and topographic conditions may confine a fire to ground fuels for a considerable period of time. While the fire is burning on the ground, the aerial fuels may be scorched and singed and may become critically dry. If conditions change, a crown fire may develop and sweep back over the area. This type of crown fire may develop rapidly and burn more explosively because the aerial fuels have been dried by surface fire.

WILDLAND/URBAN INTERFACE (WUI)

Wildland/Urban Interface (WUI) Defined

The potential dangers of the wildland/urban interface (WUI) depend on a specific set of physical conditions that vary according to season (time of year), weather (humidity, winds), vegetation, and the structures in proximity of vegetation (construction, density). Attempts to define the interface as a geographic location or locations fail to account for the other factors that contribute to the potential for significant fire losses and unusual fire behavior. As defined in NFPA 1144, *Standard for Reducing Structure Ignition Hazards from Wildland Fire,* the wildland/urban interface is the "presence of structures in locations in which the AHJ [authority having jurisdiction] determines that topographical features, vegetation fuel types, local weather conditions, and prevailing winds result in the potential for ignition of the structures within the area from flames and firebrands of a wildland fire."

WUI as a National Concern

The destruction of an average of more than 900 homes per year over the last three decades is the result of the wildland/urban fire interface. Although of growing concern and attention, the problem is not new. Significant home destruction and numerous human fatalities had occurred for over a century before 1984. Historical records indicate that for the years between 1921 and 1984, over 5000 homes were destroyed by wildfires. During the 50 years prior to that (1870–1920), thousands of lives were lost and numerous communities were destroyed.[6]

In 1985, more than 1400 homes were lost to wildfires burning primarily in two states, California and Florida. Of the 1400 homes destroyed, 600 were in Florida, and 400 of the 600 were destroyed in 1 day. Never in the twentieth century had a loss of this magnitude occurred in a southeastern state.

As tragic as wildfires seem, today's wildland/urban fire losses are not as economically significant as other natural events, such as hurricanes and earthquakes, and the life and property losses from individual residential fire events. Severe hurricanes that impact urban areas do more damage in a matter of hours than severe wildfires do in a matter of days or weeks. Property damages and loss of life from even the most severe wildland/urban fire seasons do not come close to the magnitude of America's annual structural and life losses from even residential fires.* But there is more to the modern issue of wildfire disaster than just the economic impact of homes burning, because communities are more than homes and subdivisions. These communities include the surrounding natural environment, which allows and supports the economic, ecological, and social mechanics of a functioning community.

After these significant structural losses and resulting environmental damages from wildfires in California and Florida, wildland/urban fire received national attention from federal and state lands and forestry agencies, researchers, planners, insurance companies, and other key fire and safety organizations.[7] Since that time, the momentum has evolved into a national program, highlighted by Firewise Communities™, supported by numerous agencies from wildland/forestry and structural fire services, to emergency management and national security. Other regional/state programs like FireSafe Councils (California and Nevada) and FireFree (central Oregon) have been organized and funded to educate and implement programs to reduce community losses and damages from wildfire.

The term "wildland/urban interface" can distort the perception of the primary issue, directing attention to *where* homes are located (e.g., at the edge of communities near wildlands) rather than *if they are ignitable.* And that distraction may often result in a concentration on factors that won't make a big difference in reducing home loss (i.e., how fire fighters and equipment get there, what type of fire equipment is needed, road signs). In other words, knowing the width of roads and the location of hydrants is of little value if more homes are at risk than equipment is available to protect them or if it's too dangerous for fire fighters to be safely there in the first place. The wildland/urban interface is a set of conditions that may exist in many communities. The community illustrated in Figure 13.5.4, which is located in the Pine Barrens area of central New Jersey, escaped an 1800 acre fire through a quick response

*Comparison of data available from Insurance Service Offices, NFPA, and the Institute for Business & Home Safety.

FIGURE 13.5.4 Community in New Jersey That Escaped 1800 Acre Fire Through Quick Fire Fighter Response and Adequate Separation Between Vegetation and Structures (Photo: James C. Smalley)

FIGURE 13.5.5 Increasing Residential Density Resulting from Development into Formerly Wild or Rural Areas That Creates Volatile Interface Conditions (Photo: James C. Smalley)

by fire fighters and adequate separation between the vegetation and structures.

The essence of the wildland/urban interface issue is not where homes and domestic landscapes adjoin wildlands but rather the location, density, and availability of ignitable homes. A meaningful question, then, is: which homes are at greatest risk? Ignition-resistant homes closely bordering the wildlands are at less risk than a dense subdivision with wood shingle roofs several miles away from wildland fuels.

WUI Conditions

The wildland/urban interface fire problem is a volatile set of conditions leading to loss of life, property, and resources in the United States every year. These conditions include the following:

- Residential density is increasing. This condition is resulting from the rapid movement of development into formerly wild or rural areas, without consideration of how the potential of wildfire will impact this development (Figure 13.5.5). When a wildfire occurs, public perception tends to be that the fire came from federal or state agency-managed lands that have fire-fighting resources and that the losses are someone else's responsibility and outside a resident's authority and control.
- Community infrastructure, supporting rapid and expanding growth, is aging. This condition is placing pressures on basic protective aspects, such as roads for evacuation, water supplies for fire suppression, and storm water drainage.
- Inadequate planning and construction techniques plague existing homes and communities in the wildland/urban interface.
- Property owners and residents in the wildland/urban interface practice poor landscaping and landscape maintenance.
- Wildland conditions, including drought, insect infestation, invasive species, and overgrowth, contribute to more frequent and intense wildfires. A perception that needs our continued scrutiny is that all trees and forests are "natural" and should not be cut, thinned, or altered in any way. This thinking leads to overcrowded forest stands of native and nonnative tree species that bring with them a variety of undesirable consequences, including reduced water tables and stressed trees prone to insect and disease infestations and vulnerable to dangerous and devastating wildfires.
- Extreme weather events are being brought about by global climate changes over time. Long-term ecosystem changes have altered natural fuel beds and now severe wildfires burn outside natural fire regimes and can damage soils and the natural cycles of plant succession. For instance, when excessive wildland vegetation is allowed to grow unchecked for long periods of time, a fire that would normally burn surface fuels under the canopies of trees may ignite ladder fuels and reach the tree canopies, becoming a crown fire that causes devastating tree and forest mortality.

Sequence of Events in WUI Fire Disasters

The term "disaster" is a defining event in which resources have become overwhelmed and economic loss, property damage, or loss of life occurs. When lightning starts a severe wildland fire in a remote area, well away from communities (i.e., human presence), it is seen as a natural event rather than a disaster. The definition of today's wildland/urban interface fire disaster seems to depend on fire fighters being unable to prevent homes from burning.

A sequence of events typifies most WUI fire disasters. Although some variation exists in each severe occurrence, the following sequential elements are generally always present and the impacts are consistent time after time:

1. *Severe fire conditions exist.* Certainly, home loss from wildfires can occur without severe fire conditions and behavior, but the large-loss disasters most always occur under severe conditions—that is, the worst-case combination of fuels, weather, and/or topography.

2. *Wildland fire occurs.* Once a fire ignites under the worst-case conditions, it can spread rapidly through vegetation with growing intensity.

3. *Wildland fire becomes an urban fire.* The change from wildland to urban fire is the point in the combustion process that fuel types move from vegetation to constructed materials (i.e., homes). It is the point at which a "wildland fire" becomes a "wildland/urban interface fire." Preventing the ignition of those constructed materials is the best opportunity to prevent the inevitable disaster. If the homes don't burn, there is no interface disaster.

4. *Fire suppression resources are overwhelmed.* During extreme fire conditions with dry wildland fuels and high winds, fire fighters, equipment, and water supplies can become depleted as numerous homes ignite and burn. Fire-fighting forces struggle to position themselves to stop large flames pushed by strong winds. Suppression effectiveness is dramatically reduced in these conditions as tactics shift and fire-fighting forces initiate life/safety procedures by evacuating the public.

5. *Fire protection effectiveness is reduced.* Fire engines and crews cannot simultaneously evacuate residents and effectively take suppression action in a subdivision of homes igniting within a few minutes of each other. With multiple ignitions, the effectiveness of fire protection forces in these situations becomes compromised.

6. *Disaster!* In these disaster scenarios, when fire protection forces are overwhelmed and standard operating procedures fall short, fire protection forces cannot stop the large flames from these intense wildland fires from entering a residential area and cannot prevent numerous homes from becoming ignited. Valiant efforts may save a few homes but, most often, hundreds of homes are threatened or destroyed in a matter of hours and numerous lives may be lost.

Preventing the Disaster

When individual homes ignite or a single wildland ignition occurs, local fire agencies' standard operating procedures (SOPs) are very effective. The success rate in containing these ignitions is routinely in the 98 to 99 percent range. When ignitions occur in dense fuels (whether structural or vegetative) during periods of severe fire conditions, numerous homes may become involved. Rapidly spreading fire cannot be stopped and suppression efforts are dramatically reduced. The world sees the resulting "wildland/urban fire disaster."

Disaster Prevention Factors. Future wildfires will continue to enter communities, but homes and adjacent vegetative fuel beds do not have to ignite. A community made up of ignition-resistant homes, healthy surrounding forests, and noncontinuous fuels (i.e., breaks in the fuels from vegetation to single homes to multiple homes) becomes less vulnerable to encroaching wildfire. Vegetation doesn't combust near homes, houses don't ignite from firebrands, and severe structural property losses and human fatalities are dramatically reduced or potentially eliminated.

Fire Fighter Safety and Suppression Effectiveness in the WUI. Standard fire suppression operations are largely ineffective against severe wildland fire behavior, driven by high winds and producing huge flames, along with intense heat and showering firebrands. Often, during these situations, fire fighters must "fall back" to implement their own necessary life safety procedures. Because fire suppression strategies and tactics in interface fires may differ from those employed during structure fires or forest fires individually, fire departments join with forestry agencies to provide basic wildland fire training and to hold joint training sessions.

WUI Fire "Watch-Out Situations." Because of the ways that vegetation and structures interact in a fire in the wildland/urban interface, the following additional cautions for "watch-out situations"[8] were developed for both wildland and structural fire crews and officers:[9]

- Poor access and narrow one-way roads
- Bridge load limits
- Wooden construction and wood shake roofs
- Power lines, propane tanks, and HazMat threats
- Inadequate water supply
- Natural fuels 30 feet or closer to structures
- Structures in chimneys, box canyons, narrow canyons, or on steep slopes (30% or greater)
- Extreme fire behavior
- Strong winds
- Evacuation of public (panic)

Reducing Home Ignitions in WUI Fires. Case studies and experimentation by the USDA Forest Service and other organizations point to some general aspects of house construction and landscaping that can minimize risk of ignition. One of the most critical aspects is roofing. Findings from California studies have indicated that houses with flammable roofing have an 81 percent chance of being destroyed in wildfires, whereas the ratio of houses with nonflammable roofing is much lower at 30 percent. Moreover, 62 percent of houses without a maintained vegetation clearance of at least 30 ft (9 m) were destroyed as opposed to those (22%) whose vegetation clearance is maintained to at least 30 ft (9 m). In all, the effect of these two elements together provides the minimum guidance for homeowners, developers, and builders.[9,10] The combined effects are displayed in Table 13.5.4.

FIREWISE AND FIREWISE COMMUNITIES/USA

Development of the Firewise Programs

After the extreme fire season of 1985, representatives of NFPA and the USDA Forest Service met to discuss the increasing trend of wind-driven fire in populated areas and formed what is now the National Wildland/Urban Interface Fire Program. In 1992, the advisory group for the program adopted the term "Firewise" to describe the state of being knowledgeable and prepared for wildfire in residential or urban settings. In 1999 the advisory group became the Wildland/Urban Interface (WUI) Working Team of the National Wildfire Coordinating Group, which oversees the National Wildland/Urban Interface Fire Program and its Firewise Communities program. The Firewise website was launched in 1996, and the national workshop series began

TABLE 13.5.4 Effects of Roofing and Vegetation on Destruction of Structure in Wildfire

Factor	*Percent of Houses Destroyed*
Flammable roof and vegetation clearance not maintained	96
Nonflammable roof and maintained vegetation clearance	14

in 1999. Today, the Firewise Communities team continues its mission of wildland/urban interface fire education through its website, workshop series, community recognition program, and information resources.

Firewise Approach

The best approach to wildfire preparedness involves utilizing the wide range of Firewise practices that individuals and communities can take to reduce their vulnerability to wildfire. The National Firewise Communities Program offers a series of practical steps and/or supporting documents in the following areas:

- Land use and community development planning
- Improved planning for fire protection infrastructure
- Cooperative approaches to forest management adjacent to wildland/urban interface communities
- Regulation, codes, deed restrictions
- Improved education of interface residents (including landscaping and home construction and design)
- Response to and evacuation of interface areas
- Firewise Communities and Firewise Communities/USA Recognition Program

By implementing at least one recommended mitigation measure or planning element, individuals and communities can begin to protect against the risk of fire in the wildland/urban interface. Examples of Firewise techniques for property owners include the following:

- Creating a defensible space around residential structures by thinning trees and brush
- Choosing fire-resistant plants
- Selecting ignition-resistant building materials
- Positioning structures away from slopes
- Working with fire fighters to develop emergency plans

Firewise Communities Workshops

From 1999 through 2003, the National Firewise Communities Program offered national workshops and continues to support regional and local organizations interested in hosting Firewise workshops using materials supplied by the national program. Firewise Communities workshops prepare community leaders and fire service professionals to recognize WUI fire hazards, make homes and landscapes Firewise, deliver fire education to residents, and incorporate Firewise planning into existing and developing areas of communities. These dynamic workshops can feature interactive discussions, mapping, and wildfire simulations. Firewise workshops are most successful when they are attended by a variety of community representatives, such as planners, business leaders, homeowner association members, and emergency service professionals.

Firewise Communities/USA Recognition Program

To facilitate local solutions to wildfire preparedness goals, the Firewise Communities/USA program recognizes communities for working together to protect residents and property from fire in the wildland/urban interface. To be recognized as a Firewise Communities/USA site, local communities must create and implement a local plan with cooperative assistance from state forestry agencies and local fire staff. In addition, communities are required to continue regular maintenance and education to retain recognition status.

Community Definition. Homeowner associations and towns of 500 residents or fewer are the most appropriate venue for the Firewise Communities/USA Recognition Program. Individual homeowner commitment is the cornerstone of a successful Firewise Communities/USA program. Residents of a smaller geographic unit can more easily create and execute a plan that reflects the needs of its specific locale. The program is intended to engage residents in playing an active role in shaping and implementing the neighborhood plan and supporting the larger Community Wildfire Protection Plan (CWPP).*

Recognition Criteria. Working with local wildland fire staff, communities can earn an annually renewable Firewise Communities/USA status by meeting the following criteria:†

- Enlist a wildland/urban interface (WUI) specialist to complete a community assessment and work together to create a plan that identifies agreed-upon achievable solutions to be implemented by the community. Development of a local WUI plan may take up to 6 months.

*The Healthy Forest Restoration Act of 2003 (HFRA) (P.L. 108-148) recommended that interface communities develop, in cooperation with local, state, and federal fire agencies, a Community Wildfire Protection Plan (CWPP). The HFRA provides communities with an opportunity to influence where and how federal agencies implement fuel reduction projects on federal lands. A CWPP is the most effective way to take advantage of this opportunity. Communities with CWPPs in place will be given priority for funding of hazardous fuels reduction projects carried out under the auspices of the HFRA. The "communities" involved in a CWPP are political jurisdictions ranging in size from small incorporated towns to largely urbanized counties. A handbook on developing CWPPs is available from the Society of American Foresters (http://www.safnet.org). The handbook outlines how to convene other interested parties, what elements to consider in assessing community risks and priorities, and how to develop a mitigation or protection plan to address those risks.

†Becoming a Firewise Communities/USA recognition site begins with the community itself. A community representative completes an online request form on the Firewise Communities/USA website or contacts the state forestry agency. Applications and renewal forms are downloadable in PDF format at http://www.firewise.org/usa.

- Organize a multidisciplined Firewise board/committee. The team should include homeowners and fire professionals. Participation by planners, land managers, urban foresters, and/or members of other interest groups is also encouraged.
- Observe a Firewise Communities/USA Day each year that is dedicated to a local Firewise project.
- Invest a minimum of $2.00 per capita annually in local Firewise projects. The investment may be met through financial donations, state grants, or an equivalent amount of volunteer labor. Work by municipal employees or volunteers using municipal and other equipment can be included, as can state/federal grants dedicated to that purpose. A specialist can work with the community to identify and seek project implementation funds, should they be necessary.
- Submit an annual report to Firewise Communities/USA that documents continuing compliance with the program.

WILDLAND FIRE ORGANIZATIONS

Public Land Agencies

In the United States, wildland fire protection is handled by federal, state, county, and in some cases, city agencies, as well as by private corporations and career/volunteer fire departments. The U.S. Forest Service protects about 200 million acres (81 million ha) of national forest and other lands. Approximately 587 million acres (236 million ha) of other federal lands, mostly in the public domain, are protected by the Department of the Interior agencies: Bureau of Land Management (BLM), the National Park Service (NPS), the U.S. Fish and Wildlife Service, and the Bureau of Indian Affairs.

States, local governments, corporations, and career/volunteer fire departments protect about 840 million acres (340 million ha) of the country's essentially undeveloped lands. About 158 million acres (64 million ha), or roughly 9.5 percent, of the wildlands in the United States are not protected.[11]

In Canada, wildland fire protection is handled by 10 provinces, 2 territories, and Parks Canada, as well as by private corporations and career/volunteer fire departments.

U.S. and Canadian Coordinating Organizations

Wildland Fire Leadership Council (WFLC). The Wildland Fire Leadership Council (WFLC) was established in April 2002 by a Memorandum of Understanding between the Secretaries of Agriculture and the Interior. The purpose of the council is to support the implementation and coordination of the National Fire Plan and the Federal Wildland Fire Management Policy.

WFLC is a cooperative interagency organization dedicated to achieving consistent implementation of the goals, actions, and policies in the National Fire Plan and the Federal Wildland Fire Management Policy. WFLC provides leadership and oversight to ensure policy coordination, accountability, and effective implementation of the National Fire Plan and the Federal Wildland Fire Management Policy. Since its inception in 2002, the council has been successful through its collaborative work at reducing the interdepartmental differences for a seamless delivery of a coordinated fire protection program.

National Wildfire Coordinating Group (NWCG). The National Wildfire Coordinating Group (http://www.nwcg.gov) is made up of the USDA Forest Service; four agencies of the Department of the Interior: Bureau of Land Management (BLM), National Park Service (NPS), Bureau of Indian Affairs (BIA), and the U.S. Fish and Wildlife Service (FWS); and state forestry agencies through the National Association of State Foresters. The purpose of NWCG is to coordinate programs of the participating wildfire management agencies so as to avoid wasteful duplication and to provide a means of constructively working together. Its goal is to provide more effective execution of each agency's fire management program. The group provides a formalized system to agree on standards of training, equipment, qualifications, and other operational functions. Policies, standards, and procedures are implemented directly through regular agency channels.

The NWCG operates through subject- or task-focused "working teams," a concept that provides a means for the exchange of knowledge about all dimensions of fire management. Each working team is small (8 to 10 persons), interagency in nature, and geographically balanced. The current teams work in key areas, such as training, incident operations, fire use, fire equipment, wildland fire education, safety and health, incident business practices, information resource management, fire danger, fire weather, social science (task group), and the wildland/urban interface.

There are several avenues in which individuals or agencies can interface with the NWCG to retrieve information, make recommendations, or raise issues. Contact with NWCG can be made through agency representatives of the parent group and/or the working teams, working team chairpersons, or the executive secretary.

National Interagency Coordination Center (NICC). The National Interagency Coordination Center (NICC) is the focal point for coordinating the mobilization of resources for wildland fire and other incidents throughout the United States. Located in Boise, Idaho, the NICC also provides products designed to be used by the internal wildland fire community for wildland fire and incident management decision making.

Wildfire suppression is built on a three-tiered system of support—the local area, one of the 11 geographic areas, and the national level. When a fire is reported, the local agency and its fire-fighting partners respond. If the fire continues to grow, the agency can ask for help from its geographic area. When a geographic area has exhausted all its resources, it can turn to NICC at the National Interagency Fire Center (NIFC) for help in locating what is needed, from air tankers to radios to firefighting crews to incident management teams.

The center coordinates activities through 11 geographic-area coordinating centers: Southern Eastern, Northern Rockies, Rocky Mountain, Southwest, East Basin, West Basin, Northwest, Alaska, Northern California, and Southern California.

National Multi-Agency Coordination Group (NMAC). The NMAC comprises representatives from the Bureau of Land Management, Bureau of Indian Affairs, National Park Service, Forest Service, U.S. Fish and Wildlife Service, Federal Emergency

Management Administration, and the State Foresters. The NMAC group at NIFC prioritizes and allocates resources when there are critical shortages of national resources such as smoke jumpers, air tankers, or Type 1 incident management teams (IMTs).

Canadian Interagency Forest Fire Centre (CIFFC). CIFFC was opened on June 2, 1982, with a mandate to provide operational forest fire management services to member agencies that would, by agreement, gather, analyze, and disseminate fire management information to ensure a cost-effective sharing of resources. It would also actively promote, develop, refine, standardize, and provide services to member agencies in order to improve forest fire management in Canada.

CIFFC operates as a private, nonprofit corporation with two levels of management that direct the operation. The board of corporate trustees is made up of deputy-ministers responsible for forestry representing each of the provinces, territories, and the federal government. This group sets policy, gives direction, and approves annual budgets for CIFFC. The board of directors is made up of the directors responsible for forest fire management for each of the provinces, territories, and a representative of the federal government. This group prepares budgets and policies and controls the operation and expenditures of CIFFC. CIFFC staff operate and implement programs approved by the board of directors and the board of corporate trustees. In addition, CIFFC coordinates and directs working groups assembled to address specific tasks.

LEGISLATION AND POLICY

National Fire Plan (NFP)

Following a landmark wildland fire season in 2000, the National Fire Plan was developed with the intent of actively responding to severe wildland fires and their impacts to communities while ensuring sufficient fire-fighting capacity for the future. The NFP addresses five key points: fire fighting, rehabilitation, hazardous fuels reduction, community assistance, and accountability.

The National Fire Plan provides invaluable technical, financial, and resource guidance and support for wildland fire management across the United States. Together, the USDA Forest Service and the Department of the Interior work to successfully implement the key points outlined in the National Fire Plan by taking the following steps:

1. Assuring that necessary fire-fighting resources and personnel are available to respond to wildland fires that threaten lives and property
2. Conducting emergency stabilization and rehabilitation activities on landscapes and communities affected by wildland fire
3. Reducing hazardous fuels (dry brush and trees that have accumulated and that increase the likelihood of unusually large fires) in the country's forests and rangelands
4. Providing assistance to communities that have been or may be threatened by wildland fire[12]
5. Committing to the Wildland Fire Leadership Council, an interagency team created to set and maintain high standards for wildland fire management on public lands

Healthy Forests Restoration Act of 2003

The Healthy Forests Restoration Act of 2003 (P.L. 108-148) (HFRA) became law in December 2003. HFRA includes provisions to speed up hazardous-fuel reduction and forest-restoration projects on specific types of federal lands at risk of wildland fire and/or of insect and disease epidemics. The HFRA was designed to help states, tribes, rural communities, and landowners restore healthy forest and rangeland conditions on their respective lands. The provisions of HFRA can be applied to as many as 20,000,000 acres (8.1 million ha) of land managed by the Forest Service and the Bureau of Land Management.

With direct respect to hazardous fuels reduction and wildfire protection, HFRA provisions include the authority for expedited vegetation treatments on certain types of Forest Service and Bureau of Land Management lands that (1) are at risk of wildland fire, (2) have experienced windthrow, blowdown, or ice-storm damage, (3) are currently experiencing disease or insect epidemics, or (4) are at imminent risk of such epidemics because of conditions on adjacent land. The act also requires the Forest Service and Bureau of Land Management to maximize retention of larger trees in areas other than old-growth stands and to ensure that the agencies' actions are consistent with the objective of restoring fire-resilient stands and protecting "at-risk" communities and federal lands through collaboration among federal agencies and local communities, particularly when Community Wildfire Protection Plans (CWPPs) are prepared. At least 50 percent of the funding allocated to HFRA projects is to protect areas adjacent to communities at risk of wildland fire, with performance of these actions to be monitored when agencies conduct hazardous-fuel reduction projects. Multiparty monitoring is encouraged especially in projects that include communities and other diverse stakeholders (i.e., interested citizens and tribes).

In addition, HFRA encourages biomass removal from public and private lands following fuel reduction projects and provides technical, educational, and financial assistance to improve water quality and address watershed issues on nonfederal lands.

FEDERAL AGENCIES THAT AFFECT PUBLIC FIRE SAFETY

U.S. Department of Agriculture (USDA)

The fire protection programs of the U.S. Department of Agriculture (http://www.usda.gov) are aimed at fire prevention and education in rural areas; they are carried out by the USDA Forest Service and the Rural Housing Service.

USDA Forest Service. Known to millions through its familiar symbol Smokey Bear, the USDA Forest Service (http://www.fs.fed.us) provides fire protection to more than 200 million acres of forests, grasslands, and nearby private lands (National Forest System), conducts research and develops improved methods in forest fire management, provides technical and financial assistance to state forestry organizations to improve fire protection efficiency on nonfederal wildlands, and provides international assistance in formulating policy and coordinating U.S. support for the protection and sound management of the world's forest resources.

Rural Housing Service (RHS). The Rural Housing Service (http://www.rurdev.usda.gov/rhs) operates a range of programs formerly administered by the Farmers Home Administration to support affordable housing and community development in rural areas. An agency in the U.S. Department of Agriculture, the RHS distributes loans and grants to improve housing and community facilities, including police stations and fire stations.

U.S. Department of the Interior (DOI)

The U.S. Department of the Interior (http://www.doi.gov) is composed of the Bureau of Land Management, the Bureau of Indian Affairs, the U.S. Fish and Wildlife Service, and the National Park Service (NPS).

Bureau of Land Management (BLM). The Bureau of Land Management (http://www.blm.gov) provides protection against wildfires on over 630 million acres (255 million ha) of public land, natural resources, and other values. It services and supports the National Interagency Fire Center in Boise, Idaho.

Bureau of Indian Affairs (BIA). The responsibility of the Bureau of Indian Affairs (http://www.doi.gov/bureau-indian-affairs.html) is the administration and management of 55.7 million acres (22.5 million ha) of land held in trust by the United States for American Indians, Indian tribes, and Alaska Natives. There are 562 federally recognized tribal governments in the United States. Developing forestlands, leasing assets on these lands, directing agricultural programs, protecting water and land rights, and developing and maintaining infrastructure and economic development are all part of the agency's responsibility.

U.S. Fish and Wildlife Service (FWS). The mission of the U.S. Fish and Wildlife Service (http://www.fws.gov) is to conserve, protect, and enhance fish, wildlife, and plants and their habitats. The service manages the 93-million-acre National Wildlife Refuge System of more than 520 National Wildlife Refuges and thousands of small wetlands and other special management areas; operates 66 National Fish Hatcheries, 64 fishery resource offices, and 78 ecological services field stations; and enforces federal wildlife laws.

National Park Service (NPS). The National Park Service (http://www.nps.gov) provides presuppression and suppression services and administers law enforcement, structural and wildland fire protection, and emergency medical services to protect visitors, national park employees, resources, and facilities.

National Interagency Fire Center

The National Interagency Fire Center (http://www.nifc.gov), located in Boise, Idaho, provides logistical support for the USDA Forest Service, the Department of Commerce's National Oceanic and Atmospheric Administration (NOAA), and the BLM, BIA, NPA, and FWS services of the Department of the Interior.

FIRE DETECTION, SUPPRESSION, AND RESOURCES

Fire Detection

In many wildland areas, lookouts in fire towers and aircraft patrols are the ones who discover, locate, and report fires. Additionally, travelers, campers, woodcutters, hunters, and others annually report thousands of fires. In the western United States and parts of Canada, lightning strikes are routinely detected electronically and their locations plotted by computer. Computer programs have been developed to assess the likelihood of ignition at various locations, as well as the characteristics of the strikes themselves. Automated fixed-point infrared detection systems have been developed but they have yet to be used extensively in North America, although they are used in some European countries. Although fire detection from satellites is technically feasible, the complication of discriminating between legitimate heat sources and incipient fires has not yet allowed the practical use of this technology.

Fire Suppression

Fire suppression includes all work to extinguish or confine a fire, beginning with its discovery. Suppressing or fighting a fire is usually difficult work that is inherently dangerous. However, knowing and applying safety principles and fire-fighting tactics serve to increase the safety and effectiveness of operations.

How agencies respond to a reported incident is well organized and planned in advance. As the incident requires, additional resources are dispatched from the local agency. Once the incident goes beyond the local agency's ability to continue supplying resources, requests for additional resources are forwarded to the nearest geographical area coordination center (GACC).

Suppression of Small Fires. Wildland fire management strategies are aimed at prompt, safe, aggressive suppression action of all wildfires. Small fires pose the same kind of suppression problems and require the same kind of practices as larger fires. Effective suppression of small fires involves the following steps: first attack, line location, line construction, burning out, mop-up, patrol, and declaring the fire out. Suppression strategies range from prompt control at the smallest acreage possible to containment using a combination of fireline and natural or constructed features, to merely ensuring that the fire remains confined to a defined geographical area.

Principles of Attack. The following principles of initial attack include sizing up a fire, selecting a point of attack and making an attack, mopping up, patrolling, and declaring the fire out:

- *Sizing up a fire.* Going around the fire as quickly and safely as possible or inspecting it from a vantage point. Fire fighters should not, however, go around the head of the fire if it is moving rapidly because entrapment is likely. Sizing up a fire should be performed from a vantage point or from the flanks of the fire.
- *Selecting a point of attack and making an attack.* The universal rules are to take prompt action on an attack point, to stay

with the fire, to take the most effective action possible with the available forces and equipment, to inform the dispatcher of the situation by radio, and to continue to work day or night, if night work can be done safely.

• *Mopping up.* After primary line construction work is completed and a fire is called "controlled," many things remain to be done to make the fireline "safe" and put the fire out. This work is called mop-up (Figure 13.5.6). The objective of mop-up is to put out all embers or sparks to prevent them from crossing the fireline. A certain amount of mop-up work is done while building the control line. Mop-up becomes an independent part of fire fighting as soon as the spread of the fire has been stopped and all lines have been completed. Ordinarily, mop-up is composed of two actions: putting the fire out and disposing of fuel, either by burning it to eliminate it or by removing it so it cannot burn.

• *Patrolling.* Patrolling is that portion of the mop-up job that consists of moving back and forth over the control line and the edges of burn areas to check for and put out any fire that may burn or blow across the line and, at the same time, to check for and put out spot fires outside the line.

• *Declaring the fire out.* Before abandoning a fire, and as a follow-up, the incident commander should take steps to ensure that the fire has been extinguished and that any fireline that has been constructed is adequate should a flare-up occur within the fireline.

Wildland Fire-Fighting Resources

Most agencies have full-time fire fighters but also hire a fair number of employees on a seasonal basis (generally from May to September). Almost without exception, regardless of the type of work seasonal employees are hired to do, everyone receives basic fire fighter training. During seasons when there are a lot of fires, people who have had basic fire training are called on to help organize fire crews.

FIGURE 13.5.6 Mop-Up, or Extinguishment of All Embers, Subsurface Fires, and Sparks, Being Performed by Fire Fighters to Ensure Safety of Fireline (Photo: James C. Smalley)

Hotshot Fire Crews. Hotshot fire crews are highly trained, skilled, and experienced crews made up of fire fighters who have had at least one season of experience as a wildland fire fighter. There are 68 hotshot crews nationwide—a total of 1360 fire fighters. These fire fighters are generally given assignments on the toughest part of a fire and use a variety of specialized hand tools, including chainsaws and fireline explosives. The crew members serve in all phases of wildland fire fighting—building firelines, burning out, setting backfires, and mopping up. Hotshot crew members are employed for a minimum of 130 days.

Smoke Jumpers. Smoke jumpers are airborne fire fighters who parachute from planes to attack wildland fires in remote and inaccessible areas. Generally, smoke jumpers are the initial attack force on remote, inaccessible fires. Competition for smoke jumper jobs in recent years is resulting in applicants with four to five seasons of wildland fire-fighting experience competing for the very limited number of jobs that become available each year.

Engine Crews. Engine crews are made up of three to five wildland fire fighters. A typical wildland fire engine is a heavy-duty off-road vehicle able to carry up to 800 gallons (3028 liters) of water. Engines also carry foam to use on wildland fuels. The foam can also be used to protect the exterior walls of a structure.

Hand Crews. Hand crews consist of about 20 individuals who have been organized and trained and are supervised principally for operational assignments on an incident (Figure 13.5.7). Generally, these crews are made up of people who have been trained to fire fight, but whose everyday job is something other than fire fighting, that is, timber, wilderness rangers, recreation, range management. There are approximately 500 hand crews in the United States.

Helitack Crew. Helitack crews are specially trained in the tactical and logistical use of helicopters for fire suppression. These crews can be rapidly deployed and are often the first to respond

FIGURE 13.5.7 Hand Crew Members Clearing Vegetation to Create a Fireline (Photo: James C. Smalley)

to a wildland fire. Helitack crews are also trained to rappel from a hovering helicopter in areas where the terrain or vegetation does not allow the helicopter to land. A primary job for the crew is to load and unload slings of equipment and supplies needed for fire fighting.

Aircraft Used in Wildland Fire Suppression

Helicopters. In a typical year, there are 15 to 20 heavy and medium helicopters under contract in the United States for wildland fire-fighting purposes. Also, there are 175 additional helicopters under contract on a call-when-needed basis. Helicopters support fire fighters on the ground by dropping water, foam, or retardant on flaming trees, brush, and even structures to cool hot spots and prevent a fire from spreading (Figure 13.5.8).

SEAT. The single engine air tanker (SEAT) is one of the newer tools in aerial fire fighting. The SEAT is a small agricultural "crop duster" airplane that has been modified to drop 500 to 800 gallons (1893 to 3028 liters) of fire retardant on wildfires (ideal for use on smaller, incipient fires). These aircraft are designed to fly low and slow, which is ideal for dropping retardants to slow or retard the spread of the fire.

Air Tankers. Air tankers are large planes fitted with tanks for transporting and dropping fire retardant or water. Their capability ranges from 2000 gallons (7,571 liters) to the larger aircraft that are capable of delivering 3000 gallons (11,356 liters). Air tankers drop their load in a long string, creating a line of retardant. The purpose of the retardant is to slow the fire down in order to give ground support forces the opportunity to build firelines. A pink dye is added to give the pilot an idea of where the drop landed. In a typical year, 40 to 50 air tankers are under contract to state and federal agencies for wildland fire-fighting purposes.

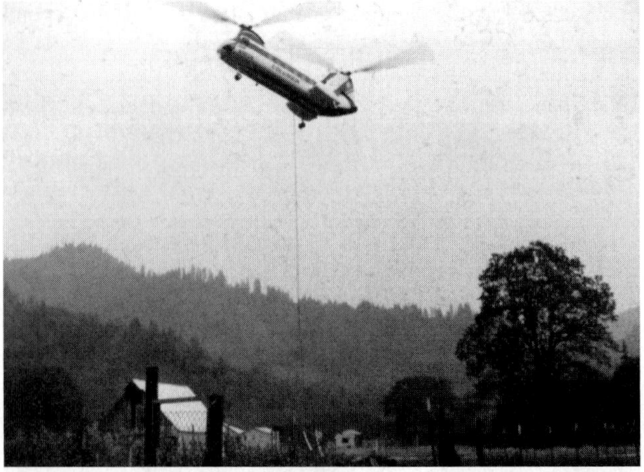

FIGURE 13.5.8 Helicopter Supporting Fire Fighters on the Ground by Dropping Water, Foam, or Retardant on Trees, Brush, and Structures to Cool Hot Spots and Prevent Fire from Spreading (Photo: James C. Smalley)

Modular Airborne Fire-Fighting System (MAFFS). A MAFFS unit is a pressurized 3000 gal (11,356 L) tank system containing either water or a water-based retardant designed to fit into a C-130 aircraft. Air tankers equipped with pressurized discharge systems are used to drop retardant or water on fires, under the direction of incident managers and guided by small aircraft known as lead planes. MAFFS units can only be utilized when there is imminent danger to life and property and other aerial resources are exhausted or committed (Figure 13.5.9).

Lead Planes. Lead planes, also called bird dogs, are used to lead the air tankers to and through their retardant drops and are also used for aerial reconnaissance of fire areas.

Infrared Aircraft. Infrared aircraft are equipped with highly specialized infrared mapping systems (Figure 13.5.10). The infrared scanners locate hot spots inside and outside a fire's perimeter. Infrared scanners can pinpoint a 6 in. (15 cm) hot spot from an altitude of 8000 feet (1.5 miles or 2.4 km) above ground

FIGURE 13.5.9 Air Tanker Equipped with Pressurized Discharge System Dropping Retardant on Fire (Photo: James C. Smalley)

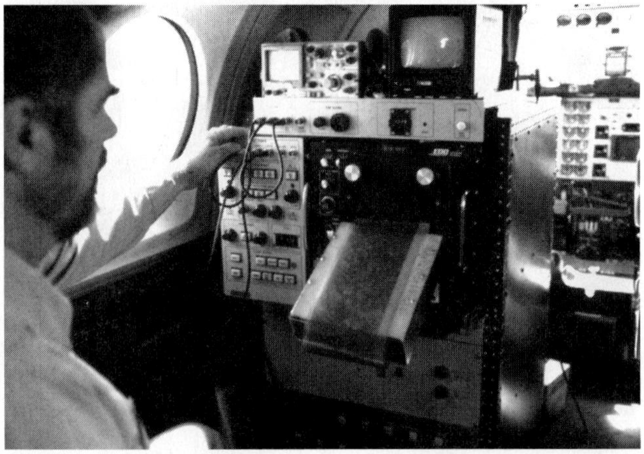

FIGURE 13.5.10 Infrared Mapping System in Light Aircraft Used to Locate Hot Spots (Photo: James C. Smalley)

level and can cover almost 1 million acres (404,700 ha) in 1 hour. Flights are generally flown after sunset and before sunrise when temperatures between the terrain and the fire differ the most, making it easier to pinpoint heat sources.

Other Wildland Fire-Fighting Resources

Other wildland fire-fighting resources include incident management teams and remote automated weather stations (RAWSs).

Incident Management Teams. An incident management team is a team of highly trained, experienced individuals who are organized to manage large and/or complex incidents.

Remote Automated Weather Stations (RAWSs). Remote automated weather station (RAWS) units collect, store, and forward six critical weather elements hourly, via a geostationary operational satellite (GOES) 22,300 miles (35,887 km) above the equator, to a computer system located at the National Interagency Fire Center in Boise, Idaho. There are approximately 1150 RAWSs strategically positioned throughout the United States. The types of weather information involved include wind speed and direction, wind gusts, precipitation, air temperature, relative humidity, and fuel moisture. Resource managers also use RAWSs to monitor environmental conditions and air quality. Some RAWS units are used as early-alert warning systems for floods, mud slides, or hazardous material levels.

Fire Fighter Hand Tools. Most of the hand tools used by fire fighters are combination tools; that is, they have more than one purpose or use. Hand tools used by fire fighters must be effective, efficient, versatile, portable, simple, easy to maintain and repair, and standardized, so they can be pooled, traded, and transported quickly. The following are among the handtools that are repaired, sharpened, and stockpiled at the base camp for crews to use on the fireline:

- *Pulaski.* A Pulaski is a combination tool, ax, and mattock invented by Ed Pulaski in 1910. This tool enables fire fighters to cut trees and limbs with the ax side and to dig and scrape with the mattock side. Figure 13.5.11 shows cutting tools like Pulaski tools and shovels being sharpened.
- *McLeod.* The McLeod, a heavy-duty combination rake-and-hoe tool, is named after Ranter Malcolm McLeod. Fire fighters use this tool to cut through matted litter and duff and clear loose surface materials.
- *Ax.* Axes, the most common ones being the double-bitted, are used for cutting trees and limbs. The single-bitted or poleax is common in the East and is used for cutting trees and limbs and for driving wedges.
- *Shovel.* The shovel is a combination tool. The edges are sharpened so that the user can chop down small trees and cut limbs and roots. Fire fighters also use shovels to scrape away needles and other duff as they construct firelines down to mineral soil. They are specifically designed for fire use.
- *Drip torch.* Fire fighters use drip torches for igniting backfires or burnouts.
- *Backpack pump.* Fire fighters carry backpack pumps (Figure 13.5.12), usually made from collapsible neoprene, during mop-up operations. They are effective for cooling down hot spots.

FIGURE 13.5.11 Cutting Tools Like Pulaski Tools and Shovels Being Sharpened (Photo: James C. Smalley)

FIGURE 13.5.12 Fire Fighter Using a Backpack Pump to Cool Down a Hot Spot (Photo: James C. Smalley)

Wildland Fire Fighter Training and Safety

Two reports, eight years apart, to the U.S. Congress about the roles of volunteers in protecting lives, property, and resources illustrate that the need for training is essential.[2] *Rural Fire Protection in America: A Challenge for the Future,* published by the National Association of State Foresters in 1994, listed training as the third most pressing problem and the second priority for any federal funding received by small rural fire departments. The report found that many communities have no funds to pay for the training and that most volunteers do not have the money to afford such training.

A more recent report by NFPA and the U.S. Fire Administration, *A Needs Assessment of the U.S. Fire Service: A Co-operative Fire Department Study,* confirmed that training remains a problem. It showed that 30 to 50 percent of uncertified and untrained structural fire fighters are serving communities of 2500 or less. Consistently, both reports found over 40 percent of the rural fire fighters had no wildland fire training. Although some instances may have improved, a wide gap remains in attaining a trained fire-fighting force for small communities across America.

To help meet the need for wildland fire training in these small fire departments, the National Wildland/Urban Interface Fire Program[3] produced a three-part training program targeted at small community and volunteer fire departments, designed to raise the fire fighter's awareness of his or her surroundings in an interface fire. The program, complete with videotapes or DVDs, computer presentations, and handouts, was distributed free of charge to fire departments in over 10,000 small communities in the United States. It will eventually be offered as a Web-based, self-study course on the Firewise website (http://www.firewise.org).

Ten Standard Fire Orders. The 10 Standard Fire Orders* were developed in 1957 by a task force studying ways to prevent fire fighter injuries and fatalities. The standards discuss fire behavior, fireline safety, and organizational control and are delineated as follows:[9]

Fire Behavior

1. Keep informed on fire weather conditions and forecasts.
2. Know what your fire is doing at all times.
3. Base all actions on current and expected behavior of the fire.

Fireline Safety

4. Identify escape routes and make them known.
5. Post lookouts when there is possible danger.
6. Be alert. Keep calm. Think clearly. Act decisively.

Organizational Control

7. Maintain prompt communications with your forces, your supervisor, and adjoining forces.
8. Give clear instructions and ensure they are understood.
9. Maintain control of your forces at all times.

If 1–9 are considered, then . . .

10. Fight fire aggressively, having provided for safety first.

Eighteen Watch-Out Situations

Shortly after the 10 Standard Fire Orders were incorporated into fire fighter training, the 18 Situations That Shout Watch Out were developed. These following 18 situations are more specific and cautionary than the 10 Standard Fire Orders and describe situations that expand the 10 points of the fire orders:[9]

1. Fire not scouted and sized up
2. In country not seen in daylight
3. Safety zones and escape routes not identified
4. Unfamiliar with weather and local factors influencing fire behavior
5. Uninformed on strategy, tactics, and hazards
6. Instructions and assignments not clear
7. No communication link between crew members and supervisors
8. Constructing line without safe anchor point
9. Building line downhill with fire below
10. Attempting frontal assault on fire
11. Unburned fuel between you and the fire
12. Cannot see main fire, not in contact with anyone who can
13. On a hillside where rolling material can ignite fuel below
14. Weather gets hotter and drier
15. Wind increases and/or changes direction
16. Getting frequent spot fires across line
17. Terrain or fuels make escape to safety zones difficult
18. Feel like taking a nap near fireline

If fire fighters follow the 10 Standard Fire Orders and are alerted to the 18 Watch-Out Situations, much of the risk of fire fighting can be reduced.

Fire Fighter Fatalities

A very serious concern will continue to be the risk to fire fighters. Of the 999 fire fighters who died on duty between 1996 and 2005, 159 (or 15.9%) died as a result of wildland fires or control burns. As shown in Figure 13.5.13, the number of deaths in any one year was as low as 8 and as high as 26. Over the period, 25.5 percent of all fireground deaths occurred at wildfires and control burns. This examination of wildfire deaths was prompted by the large number of wildfire-related fire fighter fatalities in 2003 (26 of the 106 fire fighter deaths).[8]

The unusually high number of deaths among fire-fighting aircraft personnel, particularly in 2003, and the subsequent grounding of aircraft due to safety reasons in early 2004, may place more pressure on initial attack crews. In many cases, initial attack responders are from small community and volunteer fire departments. In addition, without traditional air support, ground crews may be expected to work harder, covering more acreage in shorter times at each fire. The concerns for fire fighter safety are extremely grave but, at the same time, may result in new methods of training in the future.

Wildland fire fighters carry special tent shelters, meeting the requirements of NFPA 1977, *Standard on Protective Clothing and Equipment for Wildland Fire Fighting.* In Figure 13.5.14, a fire fighter has deployed the shelter, stepped into the bottom, and is falling to the ground as a wildfire approaches. The deployment of shelters is a last resort and each deployment is recorded and investigated for the purpose of improving safety on the fireline.

Common Denominators of Fire Behavior

Four major common denominators of fire behavior have been noted in fires where a fire fighter has been killed or from which

*During the years since their inception, the Ten Standard Fire Orders were rearranged to provide fire fighters a mneumonic learning aid, so that the first letter of the first word of each order spelled out F-I-R-E-O-R-D-E-R-S. In May 2002, the NWCG approved the revision of the Ten Standard Fire Orders in accordance with their original arrangement. The original arrangement of the orders are logically organized to be implemented systematically and applied to all fires.

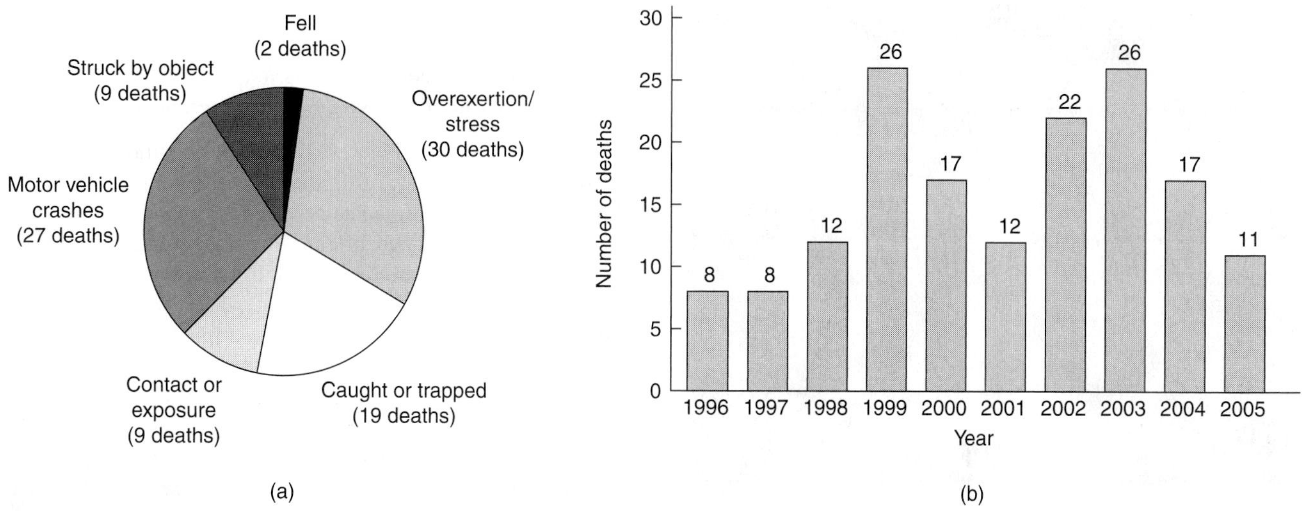

FIGURE 13.5.13 Fire Fighter Fatalities in Wildland Fires, 1996–2005: (a) On the Fireground, by Cause of Death; (b) by Year

FIGURE 13.5.14 Wildland Fire Fighter Deploying Special Tent Shelter (Photo: James C. Smalley)

fire fighters narrowly escaped. Such situations often occur in the following conditions:

1. On relatively small or deceptively quiet areas of large fires
2. In areas with relatively light fuels, such as grass, herbs, and light brush
3. When there is an unexpected shift in wind direction or wind speed
4. When the fire responds to topographic conditions and runs uphill

These factors should not be considered all-inclusive. For example, a sudden change of wind may change the direction of fire spread, regardless of topography. Each set of circumstances has the potential for creating a tragedy or near-miss fire. Often human behavior is the determining factor. Sociologists Jon Driessen, Lisa Outka-Perkins, and Leslie Anderson in their report, "Two Entrapment Avoidance Projects: Studying Crew Cohesion as a Social Human Factor," studied crew cohesion and how a breakdown in the crew affects the level of fatalities and injuries to wildland fire fighters.[13] Fire fighters who remain calm when the wind direction changes and move back into a burned area should survive. Those who try to outrun a fire under similar conditions may die. The difference between a tragic fire and a near-miss fire may be due to luck, skill, and/or advance planning. In all cases, it is important to be alert and aware of conditions that may signal a sudden change in fire behavior. In a few words, be alert and watch out for light fuels, wind shifts, steep slopes, and "chimneys." Those who remain alert and on the lookout for possible trouble have the best chance of survival.

FIRE PREVENTION

Challenge of Prevention

In the United States, about 2.5 million acres (1 million ha) of developed lands and wildlands burn every year. Often the carelessness of people leads to fires in wildlands. Some wildland fires are caused by campers who neglect to properly extinguish campfires. Other wildland fires result from lit cigarettes tossed onto the dry ground. Unwanted fires threaten valuable resources and, for this reason, fire prevention is an ongoing job. Fire prevention is one of the most important parts of a fire protection agency's responsibilities.

Smokey Bear Program

One of the most effective educational programs in the United States since 1944 has been Smokey Bear (Figure 13.5.15). This program has been a major factor in the prevention of thousands of unwanted human-caused fires, saving millions of dollars in damages and fire suppression costs. Nine out of every 10 wildfires is human caused. The program is managed by the partnership of the USDA Forest Service, the Ad Council, and National Association of State Foresters.

FIGURE 13.5.15 Smokey Bear (Source: U.S. Forest Service)

Following a series of changes in fire management policies and practices over the past decade, Smokey's message subtly changed from preventing forest fires to preventing wildfires, recognizing that unwanted fires on forests and grasslands (particularly those that destroy homes) are now the targets of prevention.

Over time, the Smokey program developed partnerships to reach new groups. Such partnerships include the American cowboy, pro-sports figures, and amateur athletes, all of whom have joined with Smokey to get the fire prevention message to the public. In 2005, Smokey Bear partnered with the Disney Corporation to deliver a fire prevention message with the DVD release of the Disney movie *Bambi.*

Specific prevention programs have been developed by different agencies and areas of the country. The Keep Washington Green Program, California Fire-Safe Councils, and central Oregon's Free Program are examples of programs developed to meet regional needs. Other individual states have very active wildfire prevention programs.

RESEARCH

Both Canada and the United States maintain fire research programs whose ultimate goals are to reduce the loss of life, property, and forest resources from wildfires and to introduce prescribed fire to achieve forest and range management objectives at reduced costs.

Joint Fire Science Program

The Joint Fire Science Program (JFSP), a partnership of six federal wildland and fire and research organizations, was established in 1998 to provide scientific information and support for fuel and fire management programs. All JFSP projects require scientist-manager partnerships along with strong emphasis on transferring research findings to the field. Guidance for the program includes the following four original principal purposes, all related to wildland fuels:

- Fuels inventory and mapping
- Evaluation of fuels treatments
- Scheduling of fuels treatments
- Development of protocols for monitoring and evaluation

Digital mapping (Figure 13.5.16) helps build inventories of forest health issues, fire-fighting resources, fuels, wildland/urban interface developments at risk from wildfire, and other forest and land management concerns. Mapping also provides the opportunity for spatial relationships to be examined, for example, the relationships between watersheds, wildlife habitat, and either a wildfire or the impact of a prescribed fire in the area.

In 2001, Congress further directed JFSP to expand its research efforts in postfire rehabilitation and stabilization, local assistance, and aircraft-based remote sensing. JFSP research also examines air quality, smoke management and social aspects of fire, and fuels management. In setting priorities for funding, the program responds to congressional direction, recommendations from advisory committees and member agencies, along with collective input from key agency personnel, workshops, and informational meetings. The program focus is on short-term, applied research that provides information and tools to specialists and managers, helping them make the best possible decisions and develop sound, scientifically valid plans.

Fire Behavior Research

Current U.S. Research. Current U.S. fire research is being conducted at six forest and range experiment stations. Much of the work is done at forest fire laboratories located in Macon, Georgia; Missoula, Montana; and Riverside, California. Major research projects include the following:

- *Fire behavior.* Fundamental studies in fuel chemistry, combustion and ignition processes, fire spread mechanisms, time-temperature heat flux interrelationships, and effects of fuel moisture, wind, and slope; development of systems to aid fire and land managers in dealing with the growth of large fires,

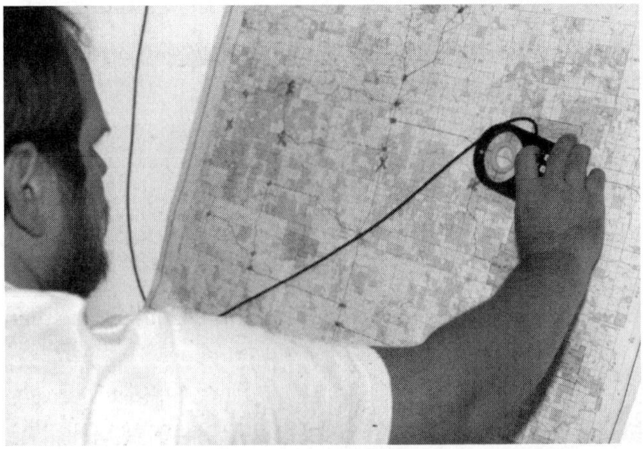

FIGURE 13.5.16 Digital Mapping Used to Provide Information on Forest and Land Management Concerns (Photo: James C. Smalley)

fuel consumption and energy release, probability of ignition by lightning, and fire spread in nonuniform fuels

- *Fire suppression.* Development of real-time and planning guidelines for individual suppression activities related to primary fuel and fire variables; integration of production rate knowledge into real-time and planning guidelines for fire suppression strategies and tactics; and development of design criteria for chemical formulations and for aerial and ground delivery systems for primary strategies and tactics
- *Fire effects, use, and ecology.* Research to determine how, when, and where prescribed fire may be used to improve tree growth, provide better wildlife habitat, reduce fire hazard, and accomplish other forestry goals; includes studies on soil to ascertain biological responses, impacts on soil, stand structure, and so on
- *Fire management planning.* Studies to relate wildland fires and social benefits desired from wildlands; to determine the effectiveness of fire prevention activities; to determine the influence of weather and climate on fire occurrence, control, and effects; and to determine the productivity and effectiveness of air tanker systems
- *Other.* Additional research projects involving smoke management for prescribed fires, reducing residues from forestry activities, evaluating the economics of fire protection systems, and aiding managers with systems for applying knowledge gained through research projects

Canadian Research. The Canadian Forestry Services (CFS) of Canada's Department of the Environment is the principal research organization in Canada. Its forest fire research program is centered at the Petawawa National Forestry Institute in Chalk River, Ontario. Fire research work is also carried out at regional forest research centers in Victoria, British Columbia; Edmonton, Alberta; and Sault Ste. Marie, Ontario. These research programs address the following six major areas:

1. *Fire behavior.* Fuel moisture physics, fire spread physics, prediction of fire danger by forest type, fire/weather interactions, fire danger rating system, and spatial weather models
2. *Fire ecology.* Postfire forest regeneration mechanisms, cyclic forest development from fire to fire, predictors of postfire forest development, and age-class distribution in fire-cycled forests
3. *Fire suppression.* Performance testing of fire management equipment, air tankers, fire retardant and water additives, aerial ignition devices, backfiring methods, and new suppression methods
4. *Prescribed fire.* Tree damage and mortality, use of fire for slash removal, seedbed preparation and vegetation control, design of prescriptions for proper burning conditions, and operational techniques
5. *Economics.* Estimation of values at risk, effect of fire on timber supply, relation between fire management costs and burned area, allowable cut effect, and ultimate impact on the forest economy
6. *Fire management systems.* Remote sensing applications; computerized systems for integrating weather, fuel type, and terrain into fire spread and growth models; prediction of lightning and human-caused fires; air patrol routing; resource deployment; and fire management strategies

Social Science Research. As national policies and practices changed over the past decade, a renewed interest developed in learning how the public would react to changes in fire policy, accepting the concept of good fire on the landscape and smoke in the air. To better understand and explain the interrelationships between people and natural environments, social research has been a focus of the U.S. Forest Service and other agencies in examining how people relate to, value, and impact the environment, that is, how the severity of forest and rangeland fires can be reduced through human interaction. Analogous to physical research that examines how fuel moisture in various types of vegetation affects flame lengths, social research examines the dynamics of changing values, public policies, and forest use, productivity, and management practices.

For more information on the overall research agenda, consult *Burning Questions: A Social Science Research Plan for Federal Wildland Fire Management.* In July 2000, the National Wildfire Coordinating Group commissioned an interagency research plan for understanding the human dimensions of federal wildland fire management. The resulting report describes the applicability of social science to wildland fire management problems, articulates high-priority needs for social science research, and organizes a research agenda that the NWCG advocates. This report is the foundation for NWCG's participation in the further development of a strong social science base to federal wildland fire management.

Programs such as Firewise Communities are based on steps that communities can take to reduce their risk from wildfire. Even in areas not traditionally considered at high fire risk, storm events, changing climate, and pest/disease outbreaks have focused attention on the potential for catastrophic fire. In addition, in areas where fire is viewed as a natural part of the ecosystem, the fact that more and more people choose these places to live means that there is a greater potential for significant fire impacts.

In research funded by the National Fire Plan, the North Central Research Station of the USDA Forest Service has found that actions to increase wildfire preparedness are affected by decisions made by individuals and the community. Individuals have resources that influence and are used to implement decisions regarding the siting of structures, building materials, landscaping, access, and other factors that impact wildfire preparedness. Communities also have resources that influence and are used to implement their decisions relating to zoning, planning, education, and other activities that impact wildfire preparedness. Agencies within these communities have resources that influence and are used to implement their decisions relating to the purchase and availability of equipment and gear, scheduling and conduct of training, and implementation of protocols. Decisions made at both the individual and community levels come together in a set of actions aimed at increasing wildfire preparedness. Figure 13.5.17 indicates that, as a result of these actions, communities can minimize losses from wildfire, and recovery or restoration following a fire will be quicker and more effective.

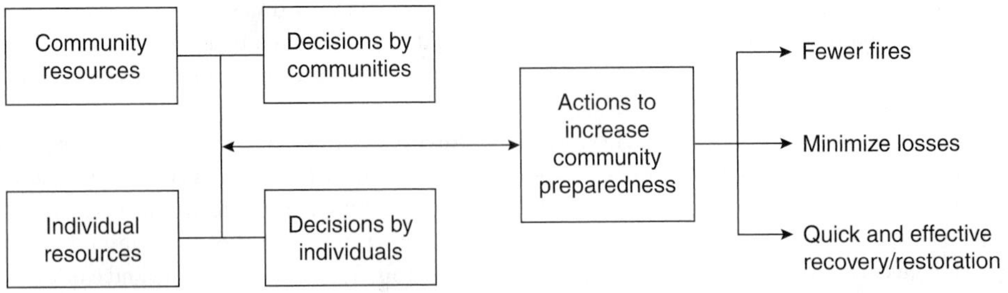

FIGURE 13.5.17 Model for Understanding Community Preparedness for Wildfire

Based on pilot studies in northern Minnesota on the Gunflint Trail; Bend, Oregon; and Waldo, Florida, to test the model, the focus turned to the following five community resources or characteristics that are critical to wildfire preparedness:

- *Social capital.* The community characteristics that contribute to collective social action; communities that are described as having social capital would have strong leadership within the community, networks to encourage coordination and cooperation, and the ability to mobilize resources
- *Human capital.* Knowledge and skills an individual obtains through education and training
- *Cultural capital.* Knowledge and skills possessed by individuals because of their heritage, experience, and attachment to place
- *Agency involvement.* Agency involvement (one agency working alone, a couple of agencies working separately but toward a common goal, or multiple agencies truly integrating their activities) was important in affording the local community access to the myriad of public programs providing funding and materials for wildfire preparedness; agencies also provide expertise and skills to the community to aid in wildfire preparedness
- *Landscape.* Vegetation and topography that have a huge influence on fire frequency and risk; there are also social aspects to landscape, for example, land ownership as a social characteristic of landscape that affects wildfire preparedness

The product of this and related research will be a more detailed understanding of the relationship of humans to the environment and recommendations for actions to increase wildfire preparedness based on the ecological characteristics of the landscape and the social characteristics of the community. The outcome of this research will be communities that, if they experience a wildfire, will minimize their losses and recover and restore their communities more quickly because they have taken steps to increase wildfire preparedness and have identified the necessary resources to implement these steps.[14]

SUMMARY

The historic and potential loss of human life, the financial impact on the national economy, and the increased value of natural resources make it undesirable to lose thousands of acres of valuable timber, rangeland, and watersheds. Continuing efforts to mitigate accumulating forest fuels, to guide growth of residences near forests, to prepare fire managers and fire fighters to use the beneficial aspects of prescribed fire, and the control of unwanted fires are growing in importance.

Because mitigating strategic fuels around communities requires action largely on private property, most fire agencies support and complement the national Firewise Communities program. The overarching objective of Firewise is, in a sense, to transfer the responsibility for mitigation and preparation for wildfires from the public sector to the private sector—that is, the homeowners and residents in hillside and grassy plains communities everywhere. Firewise Communities is a highly successful program emphasizing individual responsibility for fire hazard mitigation on community and private property through land use planning, building methods and materials, creative landscaping, intelligent zoning, and innovative community fire protection planning. The Firewise program educates and supports community leaders, fire professionals, planners, and individuals on wildland/urban interface fire issues; maintains an educational website; and provides varied assistance to organizations and individuals for wildland fire mitigation.

BIBLIOGRAPHY

References Cited

1. *Statistics for the United States and Canada Wildland Fires, 1980–2001,* http://www.nife.gov, National Interagency Fire Center, Boise, ID, 2002.
2. Wenger, K. F. (Ed.), *Forestry Handbook,* Wiley & Sons, New York, 1984.
3. Bosworth, D., USDA Forest Service Chief, speech, Boise, ID, 2004.
4. Pyne, S., Andrews, P., and Laven, R., *Introduction to Wildland Fire,* Wiley & Sons, New York, 1996; *Forest Protection,* Unit 10, National Educational Corporation, Scranton, PA, 1994.
5. National Fire Plan Narrative, http://www.fireplan.gov; Canada Wildland Fire Facts 1990–2001, http://www.nofc.forestry.ca/fire/frn/English/frames.htm.
6. *Assessing Wildfire Hazards in the Home Ignition Zone,* www.firewise.org, NWCG Wildland/Urban Interface Working Team, 2006.
7. *Wildland Fires Strike Home,* National Wildland/Urban Interface Fire Program, National Fire Protection Association, Quincy, MA, 1987.
8. Fahy, R., *Wildland Firefighter Fatalities, 1994–2003,* National Fire Protection Association, Quincy, MA, 2004.
9. *NWCG Fireline Handbook,* PMS 410-1 (NFES 0065), National Interagency Fire Center, Boise, ID, March 2004.

10. Babrauskas, V. (Ed.), *Ignition Handbook,* Fire Science Publishers, Issaquah, WA, 2003, p. 631.
11. National Fire Plan, "Report to the President of the United States," http://www.fireplan.gov, Sept. 2000.
12. The Firewise Communities Program is a key method to deliver this assistance to encourage collaboration and cooperation among the public and fire management agencies. See http://www.fireplan.gov and http://www.firewise.org.
13. Driessen, J., Outka-Perkins, L., and Anderson, L., "Two Entrapment Avoidance Projects: Studying Crew Cohesion as a Social Human Factor," Eighth International Wildland Fire Fighter Safety Summit: Human Factors—10 Years Later, April 26–28, 2005, Missoula, MT, sponsored by the International Association of Wildland Fire, Hot Springs, SD.
14. For more information, refer to the North Central Research Station website http://www.ncrs.fs.fed.us.

NFPA Codes, Standards, and Recommended Practices

Reference to the following NFPA codes, standards, and recommended practices will provide further information on wildland fire management discussed in this chapter. (See the latest version of The NFPA Catalog *for availability of current editions of the following documents.)*

NFPA 1051, *Standard for Wildland Fire Fighter Professional Qualifications*

NFPA 1143, *Standard for Wildland Fire Management*

NFPA 1144, *Standard for Reducing Structure Ignition Hazards from Wildland Fire*

NFPA 1906, *Standard for Wildland Fire Apparatus*

References

Babrauskas, V. (Ed.), *Ignition Handbook,* Fire Science Publishers, Issaquah, WA, 2003.

Blake, C. (Ed.), *American Perspectives on the Wildland/Urban Interface,* National Wildland/Urban Interface Fire Program, http://www.firewise.org, National Fire Protection Association, Quincy, MA, 2004.

Brunson, M., and Evans, J., "Badly Burned? Effects of an Escaped Prescribed Burn on Social Acceptability of Wildland Fuels Treatments," *Journal of Forestry,* Apr./May, 2005, pp. 134–138.

Butler, B., and Cohen, J., "Firefighter Safety Zones: How Big Is Big Enough?" *Fire Management Notes,* Vol. 58, No. 1, 1998, pp. 13–16.

Butler, B., "Fundamental Fire Behavior Research: Some of Its Applications to Firefighter Safety," *Proceedings* of the Canada/U.S. Wildland Fire Safety Summit, Rossland, BC, International Assoc. of Wildland Fire, Fairfield, WA, 1998.

Cohen, J., *An Examination of the Summerhaven, Arizona, Home Destruction Related to the Local Wildland Fire Behavior during the June 2003 Aspen Fire,* unpublished U.S. Forest Service Report to the Assistant Secretary of Agriculture, July 2003.

Comeau, E., "Preventing Wildfire Meltdown," *NFPA Journal,* Vol. 95, No. 5, 2001, pp. 64–68.

Driessen, J., *Crew Cohesion, Wildland Fire Transitions, and Fatalities,* Tech. Rep. 0251-2809-MTDC, United States Department of Agriculture Forest Service, Missoula Technology Development Center, Missoula, MT, 2002.

Fire Fighter Safety in the Wildland/Urban Interface [video series], National Wildland/Urban Interface Fire Program, http://www.firewise.org, National Fire Protection Association, Quincy, MA, 2004.

Gardner, K., "Principled Approach," *Wildfire Magazine,* http://www.wildfiremag.com, May/June 2005.

Jakes, P. M., Kruger, L., Monroe, M., Nelson K., and Sturtevant, V., A Model for Improving Community Preparedness for Wildfire, http://www.ncrs.fs.fed.us/4803/highlights/Intro%20to%20website.pdf, 2002.

Johnson, M. A., "Los Alamos Cerro Grande Fire: An Abject, Object Lesson," *Natural Hazards Observer,* Vol. 25, No. 1, 2000, pp. 1–2.

Kim, Y.-S., and Wells, A., "The Impact of Forest Density on Property Values," *Journal of Forestry,* Apr./May 2005, pp. 146–151.

Meck, S., and Schwab, J., *Planning for Wildfires,* PAS 529/530, American Planning Association, Chicago, IL, 2005.

National Wildland/Urban Interface Fire Program, *Wildland/Urban Interface Fire Hazard Assessment Methodology,* http://www.firewise.org, National Fire Protection Association, Quincy, MA, 1997.

National Wildland/Urban Interface Fire Program, *Using Water Effectively in the Wildland/Urban Interface* [Video], http://www.firewise.org, National Fire Protection Association, Quincy, MA, 2004.

National Wildland/Urban Interface Fire Program, *Home Improvement: A Firewise Approach* [Video], http://www.firewise.org, National Fire Protection Association, Quincy, MA, 2003.

National Wildland/Urban Interface Fire Program, *Operation Water: Planning for Water Supply & Distribution,* http://www.firewise.org, National Fire Protection Association, Quincy, MA, 1992.

Pyne, S. J., *Fire in America—A Cultural History of Wildland and Rural Fire,* Princeton University Press, Princeton, NJ, 1989.

Pyne, S. J., Andrews, P., and Laven, R., *Introduction to Wildland Fire,* 2nd ed., Wiley & Sons, New York, 1997.

Pyne, S. J., *Year of the Fires: The Story of the Great Fires of 1910,* Viking, New York, 2001.

Smalley, J., "Running Wild: A Look at Wildland Fires in the U.S.," *Fire Prevention & Fire Engineers Journal,* Institute of Fire Engineers, Apr. 2005.

Smalley, J. (Ed.), *Protecting Life and Property from Wildfire,* National Fire Protection Association, Quincy, MA, 2005.

Wenger, K. F. (Ed.), *Forestry Handbook,* Wiley and Sons, New York, 1984.

Chapter 6

Public Fire Protection and Hazmat Management

Michael S. Hildebrand ❑ Gregory G. Noll

Public interest in the environment and major catastrophes involving hazardous materials (hazmats) have resulted in promulgation of a wide range of laws, regulations, and standards that mandate fire department involvement. Many laws created at the federal level assign overlapping responsibility for public safety to federal, state, and local agencies. Organizing an effective hazardous materials prevention and enforcement program within a fire department can be a difficult task. Consider the fact that the U.S. Congress has passed six major pieces of legislation concerning hazardous materials and public safety. These laws have produced seven different major federal agency regulations that contain no fewer than six different legal definitions for a hazardous material. Add the fact that there are also 50 individual state codes and over 70 different voluntary consensus standards, and it is easy to see why the code enforcement issue can be confusing.

This chapter has been written for the fire department prevention and enforcement specialist who wants to learn the fundamentals of hazardous materials laws, regulations, and standards. It begins by defining what a hazardous material is and provides an overview of the major elements of a hazardous materials prevention and enforcement program. The chapter provides an in-depth overview of the key elements of each of the major federal laws and regulations, as well as a general summary of the primary hazardous materials codes and standards.

See also Section 7, Chapter 5, "Hazardous Waste Control"; and Section 13, Chapter 8, "Managing the Response to Hazardous Material Incidents."

Chapter Contents

Key Terms

Clean Air Act, hazardous material, Hazardous Waste Operations and Emergency Response (HAZWOPER) Standard, Resource Conservation and Recovery Act, Superfund, Superfund Amendments and Reauthorization Act (SARA)

DEFINITION OF A HAZARDOUS MATERIAL

The first step in understanding hazardous materials from a prevention and enforcement perspective is to define what a hazardous material actually is. Many of the commonly used hazardous materials terms are sometimes used interchangeably, but they have distinctively different meanings. Various state and federal regulations govern the manufacture, transportation, storage, use, and cleanup of chemicals in the United States and Canada, and use numerous terms, definitions, and lists to convey information.

Hazardous materials: Any substance or material in any form or quantity that poses an unreasonable risk to safety and health and property when transported in commerce (U.S. Department of Transportation, 49 CFR 171).

Hazardous substances: Any substance designated under the Clean Water Act and the Comprehensive Environmental Response, Compensation, and Liability Act (CERCLA) as posing a threat to waterways and the environment when released (U.S. Environmental Protection Agency [EPA], 40 CFR 302). It should be noted that the term "hazardous substances," as used within Occupational and Safety Health Administration (OSHA) 1910.120, refers to any substance defined by EPA within Section 101 of CERCLA; any biological agent or other disease-causing agent as defined by EPA within Section 101 of CERCLA; any substance listed by Department of Transportation (DOT) as

Michael S. Hildebrand, CSP, and **Gregory G. Noll,** CSP, are consultants specializing in hazardous materials emergency response issues. They are the authors of the textbook *Hazardous Materials: Managing the Incident* and serve on the technical committee for NFPA 472, *Standard for Professional Competence of Responders to Hazardous Materials Incidents.*

a hazardous material; and any hazardous waste, as defined by EPA in 40 CFR 261.3 or by DOT in 49 CFR 171.8.

Extremely hazardous substances (EHS): Chemicals determined by the EPA to be extremely hazardous to a community during an emergency spill or release as a result of their toxicities and physical/chemical properties (U.S. EPA, 40 CFR 355).

Hazardous chemicals: Any chemical that would be a risk to employees if exposed in the workplace (U.S. OSHA, 29 CFR 1910). Examples of a "physical hazard" are combustible liquids, compressed gases, explosives, flammables, organic peroxides, oxidizers, pyrophorics, unstables (reactives), or water-reactives. "Health hazard" means a mixture of chemicals or a pathogen for which there is statistically significant evidence, based on at least one study conducted in accordance with established scientific principles, that acute or chronic health effects may occur in exposed employees. The term "health hazard" includes chemicals that are carcinogens, toxic or highly toxic agents, reproductive toxins, irritants, corrosives, sensitizers, hepatoxins, nephrotoxins, neurotoxins, agents that act on the hematopoietic system, and agents that damage the lungs, skin, eyes, or mucous membranes.

Hazardous wastes: Discarded materials regulated by the EPA because of public health and safety concerns. Regulatory authority is granted under the Resource Conservation and Recovery Act (RCRA) (U.S. EPA, 40 CFR 260–281).

Marine pollutant: Materials that have an adverse impact on the marine environment.

Dangerous goods: An internationally used term under the International Maritime Dangerous Good Code (IMDG). In Canadian transportation, the U.S. term "hazardous materials" has basically the same meaning as "dangerous goods."

HAZARDOUS MATERIALS PREVENTION AND ENFORCEMENT PROGRAMS

A comprehensive and integrated public safety hazardous materials program should consist of four major program elements: (1) prevention, (2) preparedness, (3) response, and (4) recovery. The prevention program element usually consists of four subelements: (1) construction and design standards; (2) an inspection and enforcement program; (3) a public education program; and (4) handling, notification, and reporting requirements.

Process, Container Design, and Construction Standards

Almost all hazardous materials facilities, containers, and processes are designed and constructed to some engineering standard. This standard may be based on voluntary consensus standards, such as those developed by the National Fire Protection Association (NFPA) and the American Society for Testing and Materials (ASTM) or on government regulations. Many major petrochemical companies, hazardous materials companies, and industry trade associations have also developed their own respective engineering standards and guidelines.

All containers used for the transportation of hazmats are designed and constructed to both specification and performance regulations established by the U.S. DOT. These regulations are referenced in Title 49 of the Code of Federal Regulations (CFR). In certain situations, hazmats may be shipped in non-DOT-specification containers that have received a DOT exemption.

Inspection and Enforcement

Fixed facilities, transportation vehicles, and transportation containers are subject to some form of hazardous materials inspection. Fixed facilities will commonly be inspected by state and federal OSHA and EPA inspectors in addition to state fire marshals and local fire departments. It should be recognized that many of these inspections will focus on fire safety and life safety issues and may not adequately address either environmental or process safety issues.

Transportation vehicle inspection is generally based on criteria established within Title 49 CFR. The enforcing agency is usually the state police; however, some local fire departments and state fire marshal's offices are also involved in inspecting hazardous materials cargo tank trucks. This will vary according to the individual state, the hazardous materials being transported, and the mode of transportation.

Among the U.S. DOT agencies with primary hazardous materials regulatory responsibilities are the following.

U.S. Department of Transportation (DOT) Pipeline and Hazardous Materials Safety Administration (PHMSA): Responsible for safe and secure movement of hazardous materials to industry and consumers by all transportation modes, including the nation's pipelines.

Federal Motor Carrier Safety Administration (FMCSA): The mission of FMCSA is to improve truck and bus safety on the nation's highways and to reduce hazardous materials security risks that could potentially harm the public and the environment.

Federal Railroad Administration (FRA): Responsible for enforcement of regulations relating to hazardous materials carried by rail or held in depots and freight yards.

Federal Aviation Administration (FAA): Responsible for the enforcement of regulations relating to hazardous materials shipments on domestic and foreign carriers operating at U.S. airports and in cargo-handling areas.

U.S. Coast Guard (USCG): Responsible for the inspection and enforcement of regulations relating to hazmats in port areas and on domestic and foreign ships and barges operating in the navigable waters of the United States.

Public Education

Hazardous materials are a concern not only for industry but also for the community. The average homeowner contributes to this problem by improperly disposing of substances such as used motor oil, paints, solvents, batteries, and other chemicals used in and around the home. As a result, many communities have initiated full-time household chemical waste awareness, education, and disposal programs. In other instances, communities have established used motor oil collection stations and chemical cleanup days in an effort to reclaim and recycle these materials.

Handling, Notification, and Reporting Requirements

These guidelines actually act as a bridge between planning and prevention functions. There are many federal, state, and local regulations that require those who manufacture, store, or transport hazmats and hazardous wastes to comply with certain handling, notification, and reporting rules. Key federal regulations include the facility reporting requirements of Superfund Amendments and Reauthorization Act (SARA), Title III, and the release notification requirements of CERCLA (Superfund). There are also many state regulations that are similar in scope and that often exceed the federal requirements.

FEDERAL HAZARDOUS MATERIALS LAWS

Laws are primarily created through an act of Congress or by individual state legislatures. Laws typically provide broad goals and objectives, mandatory dates for compliance, and established penalties for noncompliance. Federal and state laws enacted by legislative bodies usually delegate the details for implementation to a specific federal or state agency. For example, the U.S. Occupational Safety and Health Act enacted by Congress delegates rule making and enforcement authority on worker health and safety issues to the Occupational Safety and Health Administration.

History shows that hazardous materials laws have been enacted by Congress in response to specific catastrophes, such as Love Canal, New York; Bhopal, India; and the terrorist attacks of 9/11. Laws now regulate everything from finished products to hazardous waste.

Because of their lengthy official titles, many simply use abbreviations or acronyms when referring to these laws. The following summaries outline some of the more important laws impacting hazardous materials emergency planning and response.

Comprehensive Environmental Response, Compensation, and Liability Act (CERCLA)

Known as "Superfund," this law addresses hazardous substance releases into the environment and cleanup of inactive hazardous waste disposal sites. It also requires those individuals responsible for the release of the hazardous materials (commonly referred to as the responsible party) above a specified "reportable quantity" to notify the National Response Center.

In 1980, Congress passed the Comprehensive Environmental Response, Compensation, and Liability Act (CERCLA) and established a fund of $1.6 billion called the "Superfund" (PL 96-510) to be administered by the EPA. Under this legislation, the EPA is authorized to inventory all uncontrolled hazardous waste sites in the nation. If the substances at these sites pose an immediate danger to public health and/or the environment, and those responsible for the contamination cannot be identified or cannot pay for the cleanup, the EPA can use the Superfund to clean up chemical spills or toxic wastes.

Resource Conservation and Recovery Act (RCRA)

In 1976, Congress passed major legislation establishing a uniform national policy for hazardous and solid waste disposal. This act is called the Resource Conservation and Recovery Act (RCRA). Congress intended that states assume responsibility for implementing RCRA, with oversight from the federal government. The rationale was that states are more familiar with the regulated community and are in a better position to administer the programs and respond to specific state and local needs most effectively. The state program must be fully equivalent to the federal program. However, states may impose requirements that are "more stringent" or "broader in scope" than the federal requirements.

There are four major programs established under RCRA: (1) solid waste, (2) underground storage tanks, (3) medical waste, and (4) hazardous waste.

Solid Waste. Subtitle D of the act encourages states to develop and implement solid waste management plans. These plans, among other purposes, are intended to promote recycling of solid wastes and require closing or upgrading of all environmentally unsound dumps.

Underground Storage Tanks. Subtitle I of the act regulates petroleum products and hazardous substances (as defined under Superfund) stored in underground tanks. The objective of this section is to prevent leakage to groundwater from tanks and to clean up past releases. There are also performance standards for new tanks and regulations for leak detection, prevention, closure, financial responsibility, and corrective action at all underground tank sites.

Medical Waste. Subtitle J addresses the problem of medical waste mismanagement. Included are requirements pertaining to medical waste generation, treatment, destruction, and disposal.

Hazardous Waste. Subtitle C establishes a program to manage hazardous wastes from "cradle to grave." The objective of the program is to ensure that hazardous waste is handled in a manner that protects human health and the environment. These regulations cover the generation, transportation, and treatment, storage, or disposal of hazardous wastes. Any facility generating more than a minimum amount of hazardous waste must follow the RCRA requirements for storage, transportation, and disposal.

Regulations of both the DOT and the EPA govern the transportation of hazardous wastes. A hazardous waste manifest system, among other purposes, ensures that the material is properly identified; states the place of origin and destination for treatment, storage, or disposal; classifies the waste; provides the quantity and flashpoint of the substance; and gives special handling instructions. Each shipper handling a hazardous waste cargo must sign the manifest certifying acceptance.

Comprehensive guidelines have been established by the EPA for tracking the movement, treatment, storage, and disposal of these waste products. Among the provisions of the guidelines are the following:

1. Identification and listing of materials classified as hazardous waste
2. A system of record keeping and labeling
3. Procedures for providing correct information regarding hazardous waste contents to and by persons transporting, storing, or disposing of this waste
4. A manifest and permit system regulating the transport of wastes to authorized sites
5. Requirements that transporters of hazardous wastes properly label hazardous waste shipments and carry them only to treatment, storage, or disposal sites licensed under RCRA
6. Requirements that operators of toxic storage disposal (TSD) facilities maintain records and comply with the manifest system. Only EPA-approved methods of treatment, storage, and disposal can be used as indicated in the permit issued by the EPA.
7. A mandate for producers and site operators to develop contingency plans in the event of a hazardous waste emergency. The plans must be the result of consultations with local fire, police, and hospital officials. These organizations must be included as part of the local response team. Contingency plans provide detailed information, such as the industrial site plan, the on-scene coordinator's phone number, and types of hazards present.
8. Encouragement for states to develop and manage their own hazardous waste programs consistent with RCRA guidelines. In the absence of a state plan, RCRA authorizes EPA to impose a federal plan for the state.

RCRA also requires hazardous waste generators to do the following:

1. Consult the list of hazardous and toxic organic and inorganic compounds published by the EPA to determine if a chemical waste is hazardous.
2. Subject all unlisted wastes to chemical analysis to determine if they possess any of the hazardous waste characteristics established in the regulations.
3. Declare a waste hazardous (based on knowledge of the material or processes used in its production).
4. Obtain an EPA identification number by filing with the EPA's regional administrator. Fire officials and local emergency-planning committees can obtain a list of hazardous waste generators in their area by contacting their EPA regional office. This list is updated on a regular basis and will provide the name and address of the facility, its EPA identification number, and its hazardous waste generator classification. Hazardous waste generators are classified in one of three categories, as follows:
   a. *Large-quantity generator (LQG).* Generates more than 2200 lb (1000 kg) of hazardous waste or more than 2.2 lb (1 kg) of acutely hazardous waste in a month. Once the first 2200 lb (1000 kg) has been accumulated, the waste must be shipped within 90 days. There is no limit to the amount that can be accumulated.
   b. *Small-quantity generator (SQG).* Generates less than 2200 lb (1000 kg) of hazardous waste in a month and/or less than 2.2 lb (1 kg) of acutely hazardous waste as listed by the EPA.
   c. *Conditionally exempt small-quantity generator (CESQG).* Generates less than 220 lb (100 kg) of hazardous waste or less than 2.2 lb (1 kg) of acutely hazardous waste in a month.
5. Apply for a facility permit if waste is accumulated on the generator's site for more than 90 days. The waste is considered to be stored at the site when it remains on the generator's property for more than 90 days. If this condition continues, the generator must secure a facility permit for storage of hazardous wastes, under RCRA Section 3005.
6. Treat, store, or dispose of hazardous wastes on site subject to requirements under RCRA Sections 3004 and 3005.
7. Transport hazardous wastes to other locations for use, storage, treatment, or disposal in properly labeled and approved containers, and prepare a hazardous waste manifest.

On November 8, 1984, Congress passed the Hazardous and Solid Waste Amendments Act of 1984, which modified waste-management practices and strengthened RCRA by:

1. Establishing tighter requirements for hazardous waste land disposal
2. Regulating underground storage tanks for new or waste products under RCRA
3. Bringing small-quantity generators (i.e., those generating between 220 and 2200 lb [100 and 1000 kg] of hazardous waste per month) under RCRA's authority
4. Giving the authority to order corrective action at RCRA-regulated facilities to the EPA
5. Setting forth "minimum technological standards," such as double liners, two-leachate collection systems, and groundwater monitoring, for new land-disposal facilities, as well as requiring interim-status facilities to either be retrofitted or stop receiving, storing, or treating hazardous waste
6. Establishing new requirements for delisting hazardous wastes

Clean Air Act (CAA)

This act establishes requirements for airborne emissions and the protection of the environment. The Clean Air Act Amendments of 1990 addressed emergency response and planning issues at certain facilities with processes using highly hazardous chemicals. This included the establishment of a national Chemical Safety and Hazard Investigation Board; EPA's promulgation of 40 CFR, Part 68, "Risk Management Programs for Chemical Accidental Release Prevention"; and OSHA's promulgation of 29 CFR 1910.119, "Process Safety Management of Highly Hazardous Chemicals, Explosives, and Blasting Agents." In addition, certain facilities are required to make information available to the general public regarding the manner in which chemical risks are handled within a facility.

Superfund Amendments and Reauthorization Act of 1986 (SARA)

SARA has had the greatest impact on hazardous materials emergency planning and response operations. As the name implies, SARA amended and reauthorized the Comprehensive Environmental Response, Compensation, and Liability Act of 1980 (CERCLA or Superfund). Although many of the amendments pertained to hazardous waste site cleanup, SARA's requirements also established a national baseline with regard to hazardous materials planning, preparedness, training, and response.

Title I of this act required OSHA to develop health and safety standards covering numerous worker groups who handle or respond to chemical emergencies and led to the development of OSHA 1910.120, "Hazardous Waste Operations and Emergency Response (HAZWOPER)."

Most familiar to the emergency response community is SARA, Title III. Also known as the Emergency Planning and Community Right-to-Know Act (EPCRA), SARA, Title III, led to the establishment of the State Emergency Response Commissions (SERC) and the Local Emergency Planning Committees (LEPC).

The Right-to-Know Act of 1986 includes four major sections affecting public safety. These include (1) Sections 301 through 303: emergency planning; (2) Section 304: emergency release notification; (3) Sections 311 and 312: community right-to-know reporting requirements; and (4) Section 313: toxic chemical release inventory.

Emergency Planning (Sections 301 through 303). Sections 301 through 303 of the act required the governor of each state to appoint a state emergency response commission (SERC) that, in turn, was required to designate local emergency planning districts and appoint a local emergency planning committee (LEPC) for each district. Membership in the LEPC is required to include elected state and local officials; members of fire, police, civil defense, and public health organizations; environmental, hospital, and transportation officials; and representatives of industry, business, the community, and the media.

The primary responsibility of the LEPC is to develop a comprehensive emergency response plan and submit it to the SERC. After being reviewed by the SERC, the plan is returned to the LEPC with approval or recommendations for revision. This emergency response plan is required to be revised and updated annually. The plan must include the following:

1. The identification of specific sites and transportation corridors in which extremely hazardous materials are stored, used, or transported
2. Emergency response procedures
3. Designation of a community coordinator and facility coordinator to implement the emergency plan
4. Emergency notification procedures
5. Procedures for determining the occurrence of a chemical release and the probable area and population that will be affected
6. Description of community and industrial emergency response equipment and resources and the identity of personnel responsible for them
7. Evacuation plans
8. Description and schedule of a chemical emergency response training program
9. Method and schedule for conducting emergency response plan exercises

Emergency Release Notification (Section 304). Section 304 requires facility owners or operators to give immediate notification to the community emergency coordinator of the LEPC, and to the SERC, of any release of a listed hazardous substance or its vapor that will extend beyond the facility's property and possibly endanger the general public. In most communities, the initial notification point will be to the emergency 9-1-1 telephone number or the local equivalent.

Under Section 304, the term "facility" means any building, structure, installation, equipment, pipe or pipeline (including any pipe into a sewer or publicly owned treatment works), well, pit, pond, lagoon, impoundment, ditch, storage container, motor vehicle, rolling stock, or aircraft, or any site or area where a hazardous substance has been deposited, stored, disposed of, or placed, or otherwise come to be located; this, however, does not include any consumer product use or any waterborne vessel.

Releases that result only in exposure to persons solely within the site on which the facility is located are not required to be reported to the LEPC or SERC but may require the owner or operator to notify the National Response Center, under Section 103(a) of CERCLA. Hazardous substances that are subjected to these reporting requirements can be found on a list of approximately 360 extremely hazardous substances that was published by the EPA in the Federal Register (40 CFR 355) or on a list of approximately 725 substances subject to emergency notification requirements, under CERCLA, Section 103(a), 40 CFR 302.4. There are additions and deletions to these lists on a periodic basis, and some of the substances can be found on both lists.

Initial emergency notification of a release by the owner or operator can be made by telephone, radio, or in person. To the extent it is known at the time of the notice, and as long as it does not result in a delay in responding to the emergency, the notification must include the following information:

1. The name or identity of the involved substance or substances
2. An indication of whether the substance or substances are on the extremely hazardous list
3. An estimate of the quantity of the substance or substances released into the environment
4. The time and duration of the release
5. The medium or media (air, land, water) into which the release occurred
6. Any known or anticipated acute or chronic health risks associated with the emergency, and, if necessary, advice regarding medical attention for exposed individuals
7. Proper precautions to take as a result of the release, such as evacuation
8. The name and telephone numbers of the person or persons to be contacted for further information

As soon as possible after a release that requires notice, the owner or operator must provide a written follow-up emergency notice. As more information becomes available, the owner or operator must update the information originally required and include additional information with respect to the following:

1. Actions taken in responding to and containing the release
2. Any known or anticipated acute or chronic health risks associated with the release
3. When appropriate, advice regarding medical attention necessary for exposed individuals

Notification of releases of hazardous substances during transportation or during storage relating to the transportation of such substances must be reported by dialing emergency 9-1-1 or, in the absence of a 9-1-1 emergency telephone number, by calling the operator.

Community Right-to-Know Reporting Requirements (Sections 311 and 312). Section 311 requires that the owner or operator of a facility prepare or have available a material safety data sheet (MSDS) for each hazardous chemical covered under the Occupational Safety and Health Act of 1970 (and any regulations promulgated under that act) and submit an MSDS to each of the following:

1. The local emergency planning committee
2. The state emergency-response commission
3. The fire department with jurisdiction over the facility

If the hazardous chemical is a mixture, the owner or operator of the facility can fulfill the requirements of Section 311 by submitting an MSDS for, or identifying on a list, each element or compound in the mixture that is a hazardous chemical. The owner or operator may also submit an MSDS for, or identify on a list, the mixture itself.

In lieu of an MSDS, the owner or operator may submit a list of the hazardous chemicals grouped in categories of health and physical hazards according to OSHA or in terms of groups of hazardous chemicals that present similar hazards in an emergency, as designated by the EPA administrator. The list of hazardous chemicals must include (1) the chemical name or common name of each substance, as provided on the MSDS and (2) any hazardous component of each substance, as provided on the MSDS.

An MSDS or revised list must be provided when new hazardous chemicals become present at a facility in quantities at or above established threshold levels. Upon request by the local emergency planning committee, an owner or operator who submits a list of chemicals must provide the appropriate MSDS for any chemical on that list. If requested by any member of the general public, the LEPC must make available to that person an MSDS for any hazardous chemicals required to be submitted to them. This information may be given at a location designated by the LEPC during normal working hours.

Within three months following the discovery by an owner or operator of significant new information concerning an aspect of a hazardous chemical for which an MSDS was previously submitted to the LEPC, a revised MSDS must be provided to the LEPC.

Section 312 stipulates that owners or operators of a facility who are required to prepare or have available an MSDS for each hazardous chemical covered under the Occupational Safety and Health Act of 1970 (and any regulations promulgated under that act) prepare and submit an emergency and hazardous chemical inventory form to the local emergency planning committee, the state emergency response commission, and the fire department with jurisdiction over the facility.

The inventory form must include all hazardous chemicals above specified thresholds that were present at the facility at any time during the previous calendar year. The EPA has established threshold quantities for hazardous chemicals covered by Section 312. If the quantities of hazardous chemicals are below that set forth by EPA, a report is not required. Current threshold quantities are as follows:

1. For extremely hazardous substances: 500 lb (227 kg) or the threshold planning quantity, whichever is lower
2. For all other hazardous chemicals that meet or exceed 10,000 lb (4450 kg) for which OSHA requires an MSDS; it should be noted that there are over 500,000 chemicals and mixtures for which OSHA requires an MSDS be maintained

Facilities may file either a Tier I or Tier II inventory form. Tier I reporting requires owners or operators to submit the following information for each of the hazard categories set forth under OSHA regulations:

1. Fire, sudden release of pressure, reactivity, acute health hazard, chronic health hazard
2. An estimate (in ranges) of the maximum amount of hazardous chemicals in each category present at the facility at any time during the preceding calendar year
3. An estimate (in ranges) of the average daily amount of hazardous chemicals in each category present at the facility at any time during the preceding calendar year
4. The general location of hazardous chemicals in each category

The EPA administrator may modify the OSHA categories of health and physical hazards by requiring information to be reported in terms of groups of hazardous chemicals that present similar hazards in an emergency or require reporting on individual hazardous chemicals of special concern to emergency response personnel. Tier I inventory forms are required to be submitted on or before March 1 of each year and contain data with respect to the preceding calendar year.

Tier II inventory reporting forms are required if requested by a state emergency response commission, an LEPC, or a fire department with jurisdiction over the facility. If an owner or operator of a facility files a Tier II inventory form, a Tier I form is not required, as long as the same deadlines are followed. The public may also request Tier II information from the LEPC or SERC. Tier II information must include the following:

1. The chemical name or common name of each chemical, as provided on the MSDS
2. An estimate (in ranges) of the maximum amount of hazardous chemicals present at the facility at any time during the preceding calendar year
3. An estimate (in ranges) of the average daily amount of hazardous chemicals present at the facility at any time during the preceding calendar year

4. A brief description of the manner of storage of the hazardous chemical
5. The location at the facility of the hazardous chemical
6. An indication of whether the owner elects to withhold location information of a specific hazardous chemical from disclosure to the public

Upon request by a fire department with jurisdiction over any facility that files an inventory form under Section 312, the owner or operator must allow the fire department to conduct an on-site inspection of the facility and must provide to the fire department specific location information on hazardous chemicals at the facility.

Toxic Chemical Release Inventory (Section 313). Section 313 requires owners or operators of certain facilities to file an annual Toxic Chemical Release Inventory Form (Form R) with the EPA and to those officials designated by the governor of the state on or before July 1 of each year. A release is defined as any spilling, leaking, pumping, pouring, emitting, emptying, discharging, injecting, escaping, leaching, dumping, or disposing into the environment (including the abandonment or discarding of barrels, containers, and other closed receptacles) of any toxic chemical. Section 313 applies to facilities that have 10 or more full-time employees, fall under the Standard Industrial Classification (SIC) Codes 20 through 39, and that manufactured, processed, or otherwise used a listed toxic chemical in excess of specified threshold quantities during the previous calendar year. The threshold quantity is 25,000 lb (11,350 kg) per year for toxic chemical manufacturing or processing. The threshold quantity with respect to use at a facility is 10,000 lb (4450 kg) of toxic chemical per year. The initial List of Toxic Chemicals subject to the provisions of Section 313 was published in August 1986 for the Senate Committee on Environment and Public Works. Through rule making, the EPA has modified this list to date by adding nine chemicals and delisting six. Chemicals may be added to the list if there is sufficient evidence to establish any one of the following:

1. The chemical is known to cause, or can reasonably be anticipated to cause, significant adverse acute human health effects at concentration levels that are reasonably likely to exist beyond facility site boundaries as a result of continuous, or frequently recurring, releases.
2. The chemical is known to cause, or can reasonably be anticipated to cause, cancer or teratogenic effects, or serious or irreversible reproductive dysfunction, neurological disorders, heritable genetic mutations, or other chronic health effects in humans.
3. The chemical is known to cause, or can reasonably be anticipated to cause, because of its toxicity, its toxicity and persistence in the environment, or its toxicity to bioaccumulate in the environment, a significant adverse effect on the environment of sufficient seriousness, in the opinion of the EPA, to warrant reporting under Section 313.

The EPA has established and maintains a national toxic-chemical inventory database (TRI database) on the information submitted. The computer database is accessible by the public and government officials via computer telecommunications and is intended to help answer questions about toxic chemical releases in a community. The EPA is using the data to target problem pollution areas and as a screening tool for the development of regulations, guidelines, and standards. Researchers from the government or universities conducting environmental analysis can also access the data.

Toxic Substances Control Act (TSCA)

The Toxic Substances Control Act (TSCA—pronounced Tosca), passed by Congress in 1976, establishes regulations with respect to the inventory and testing of all chemical substances manufactured or processed in the United States. This act makes the EPA the central implementation arm of the federal government. TSCA authorizes the EPA to do the following:

1. Develop a uniform listing of all chemical substances.
2. Establish a testing procedure for chemicals already in use and any one of approximately 1000 new chemicals developed each year.
3. Determine if these chemicals present an unreasonable risk to the public's health or the environment.
4. Prohibit or limit the manufacture, processing, use, application, and concentration of such chemicals.
5. Recall or seize by civil action hazardous substances that are determined to be imminently harmful to the public's health or the environment.

Federal Water Pollution Control Act (FWPCA)

In 1970, the Federal Water Pollution Control Act (PL 92-500) was amended in Section 311 to include oil and hazardous spills. Through this legislation, both the EPA and the U.S. Coast Guard are mandated to regulate spills of oil and/or other hazardous substances that threaten coastal waters and inland waterways.

Spill Prevention, Control, and Countermeasure Plan (SPCC)

This regulation was issued by the EPA in 40 CFR 112 and applies to facilities engaged in drilling, producing, gathering, storing, processing, refining, transferring, distributing, or consuming oil and oil products, which due to location could reasonably be expected to discharge oil in quantities that may be harmful into or upon navigable waterways or adjoining shorelines, or upon the waters on the contiguous zone.

Owners or operators of these facilities must prepare a Spill Prevention, Control, and Countermeasure (SPCC) plan that includes appropriate containment and/or drainage control structures or equipment to prevent discharged oil from reaching navigable water before cleanup occurs.

Facilities that are excluded from being required to have a SPCC plan are facilities that do not have an aboveground storage capacity of at least 1320 gal (4996 L) of oil. No single container at these facilities can hold more than 660 gal (2498 L) of oil.

Oil Pollution Act of 1990 (OPA)

Commonly referred to as OPA, this act amended the Federal Water Pollution Control Act. Its scope covers both facilities and carriers of oil and related liquid products, including deepwater marine terminals, marine vessels, pipelines, and railcars. Requirements include the development of emergency response plans, regular training and exercise sessions, and verification of spill resources and contractor capabilities. The act also requires the establishment of Area Committees (AC) and the development of Area Contingency Plans (ACP) to address oil and hazardous substance spill response in coastal zone areas.

HAZARDOUS MATERIALS REGULATIONS

Regulations, sometimes called "rules," are created by federal or state agencies as a method of providing guidelines for complying with a law that was enacted through legislation. A regulation permits individual governmental agencies to enforce the law through inspections, which may be conducted by federal and state officials.

Laws delegate certain details of implementation and enforcement to federal or state agencies that are then responsible for writing the actual regulations that enforce the legislative intent of the law. Regulations will either (1) define the broad performance required to meet the letter of the law (i.e., performance-oriented standards) or (2) provide very specific and detailed guidance on satisfying the regulation (i.e., specification standards).

Federal Regulations

The following summary includes several of the more significant federal regulations that affect hazardous materials emergency planning and response.

Hazardous Waste Operations and Emergency Response (29 CFR 1910.120). Also known as HAZWOPER, this federal regulation was issued under the authority of SARA, Title I. The regulation was written and is enforced by OSHA in those 23 states and two territories with their own OSHA-approved occupational safety and health plans. In the remaining 27 "non-OSHA" states, public sector personnel will be covered by a similar regulation enacted by the EPA (40 CFR Part 311).

The regulation establishes important requirements for both industry and public safety organizations that respond to hazardous materials or hazardous waste emergencies. This includes fire fighters, law enforcement, emergency medical personnel (EMS), hazardous materials responders, and industrial emergency response team (ERT) members. Requirements cover the following areas:

1. Hazardous materials emergency response plan
2. Emergency response procedures, including the establishment of an incident management system, the use of a buddy system with backup personnel, and the establishment of a safety officer
3. Specific training requirements covering instructors and both initial and refresher training
4. Medical surveillance programs
5. Postemergency termination procedures

Of particular interest to hazardous materials managers and responders are the specific levels of competency and associated training requirements identified within OSHA 1910.120(q)(6).

First Responder at the Awareness Level. These are individuals who are likely to witness or discover a hazardous substance release and who have been trained to initiate an emergency response notification process. The primary focus of their hazardous materials responsibilities is to secure the incident site, recognize and identify the materials involved, and make the appropriate notifications. These individuals would take no further action to control or mitigate the release. First responder–awareness personnel must have sufficient training or experience to objectively demonstrate the following competencies:

1. An understanding of what hazardous materials are and the risks associated with them in an incident
2. An understanding of the potential outcomes associated with a hazardous materials emergency
3. The ability to recognize the presence of hazardous materials in an emergency and, if possible, identify the materials involved
4. An understanding of the role of the first responder–awareness individual within the local emergency operations plan; this would include site safety, security and control, and the use of the *Emergency Response Guidebook* (ERG)
5. The ability to realize the need for additional resources and to make the appropriate notifications to the communications center

The most common examples of first responder–awareness personnel include law enforcement and plant security personnel, as well as some public works employees. There is no minimum hourly training requirement for this level; the employee would have to have sufficient training to objectively demonstrate the required competencies.

First Responder at the Operations Level. Most fire department suppression personnel fall into this category. These are individuals who respond to releases or potential releases of hazardous substances as part of the initial response for the purpose of protecting nearby persons, property, or the environment from the effects of the release. They are trained to respond in a defensive fashion without actually trying to stop the release. Their primary function is to contain the release from a safe distance, keep it from spreading, and protect exposures.

First responder–operations personnel must have sufficient training or experience to objectively demonstrate the following competencies:

1. Knowledge of basic hazard and risk assessment techniques
2. Knowledge of how to select and use proper personal protective clothing and equipment available to the operations-level responder
3. An understanding of basic hazardous materials terms
4. Knowledge of how to perform basic control, containment, and/or confinement operations within the capabilities of the resources and personal protective equipment available

5. Knowledge of how to implement basic decontamination measures
6. An understanding of the relevant standard operating procedures and termination procedures

First responders at the operations level must have received at least 8 hours of training or have had sufficient experience to objectively demonstrate competency in the previously mentioned areas, as well as the established skill and knowledge levels for the first responder–awareness level.

Hazardous Materials Technicians. These are individuals who respond to releases or potential releases for the purposes of stopping the release (Figure 13.6.1). Unlike the operations level, they generally assume a more aggressive role, in that they are often able to approach the point of a release in order to plug, patch, or otherwise stop the release of a hazardous substance.

Hazardous materials technicians are required to have received at least 24 hours of training equal to the first responder–operations level and have competency in the following established skill and knowledge levels:

1. Capable of implementing the local employers' emergency operations plan
2. Able to classify, identify, and verify known and unknown materials by using field survey instruments and equipment (direct reading instruments)
3. Able to function within an assigned role in the incident management system
4. Able to select and use the proper specialized chemical personal protective clothing and equipment provided to the hazardous materials technician
5. Understand hazard and risk assessment techniques
6. Able to perform advanced control, containment, and/or confinement operations within the capabilities of the resources and equipment available to the hazardous materials technician
7. Understand and implement decontamination procedures
8. Understand basic chemical and toxicological terminology and behavior
9. Understand termination procedures
10. Understand basic chemical and toxicological terminology and behavior

Many communities and facilities have personnel trained as emergency medical technicians (EMT) who nevertheless do not have the primary responsibility for providing basic or advanced life support medical care. Similarly, hazardous materials technicians may not necessarily be part of a hazardous materials response team. However, if they are part of a designated team as defined by OSHA, they must also meet the medical surveillance requirements within OSHA 29 CFR 1910.120.

Hazardous Materials Specialists. These are individuals who respond with, and provide support to, hazardous materials technicians. Their duties parallel those of the technician, but they require a more detailed or specific knowledge of the various substances they may be called on to contain. This individual

FIGURE 13.6.1 Hazardous Materials Technicians Donning EPA Level A Personal Protection Clothing

would also act as the site liaison with federal, state, local, and other governmental authorities, with regard to site activities.

Similar to the technician level, hazardous materials specialists must have received at least 24 hours of training equal to the technician level and have competency in the following established skill and knowledge levels:

1. Capable of implementing the local emergency operations plan
2. Able to classify, identify, and verify known and unknown materials by using advanced field survey instruments and equipment (direct reading instruments)
3. Have knowledge of the state emergency response plan
4. Able to select and use the proper specialized chemical personal protective clothing and equipment provided to the hazardous materials specialist
5. Understand in-depth hazard and risk assessment techniques
6. Able to perform specialized control, containment, and/or confinement operations within the capabilities of the resources and equipment available to the hazardous materials specialist
7. Able to determine and implement decontamination procedures
8. Able to develop a site safety and control plan
9. Understand basic chemical, radiological, and toxicological terminology and behavior

Whereas the hazardous materials technician possesses an intermediate level of expertise and is often viewed as a "utility person" within the hazardous materials response community, the hazardous materials specialist possesses an advanced level of expertise. Within the fire service, the specialist will often assume the role of the safety officer or hazardous materials branch. Furthermore, the specialist must meet the medical surveillance requirements outlined within OSHA 129 CFR 1910.120. The reader should note that a hazardous materials specialist, as defined by OSHA, is different from "specialist employee," as defined by NFPA 472, *Standard for Professional Competence of Responders to Hazardous Materials Incidents.* The differences in these terms is often a source of confusion among industrial emergency responders. They are two different titles and have different levels of competency.

On-Scene Incident Commander. Incident commanders, who will assume control of the incident scene, must receive at least 24 hours of training equal to the first responder operations level. In addition, the employer must certify that the incident commander has competency in the following areas:

1. Know and be able to implement the employer's incident management system
2. Know how to implement the employer's emergency operations plan
3. Understand the hazards and risks associated with working in chemical protective clothing
4. Know of the state emergency response plan and of the federal regional response team
5. Know and understand the importance of decontamination procedures

Skilled Support Personnel. These are personnel who are skilled in the operation of certain equipment, such as cranes and hoisting equipment, and who are needed temporarily to perform immediate emergency support work that cannot reasonably be performed in a timely fashion by emergency response personnel. It is assumed that these individuals will be exposed to the hazards of the emergency response scene.

Although these individuals are not subject to the HAZWOPER training requirements, they must be given an initial briefing at the site prior to their participation in any emergency response effort. This briefing must include elements such as instructions in using personal protective clothing and equipment, the chemical hazards involved, and the tasks to be performed. All other health and safety precautions provided to emergency responders and on-scene workers must be used to ensure the health and safety of these support personnel.

Specialist Employees. These are employees who, in the course of their regular job duties, work with and are trained in the hazards of specific hazardous substances and who will be called on to provide technical advice or assistance to the incident commander at a hazardous materials incident (Figure 13.6.2). This would include industry responders, chemists, and related professional or operations employees. These individuals must receive training or demonstrate competency in the area of their specialization annually. Appendix E in 29 CFR 1910.120, *Hazardous Waste Operations and Emergency Response,* provides nonmandatory guidelines for an effective training curriculum.

Hazard Communication Standard (29 CFR 1910.1200). The Hazard Communication Standard (HCS) was originally issued by OSHA in November 1983. OSHA's most recent revision of the HCS was issued on March 11, 1994, and covers manufacturers, importers, distributors, and users of hazardous chemicals. The Hazard Communication Standard is commonly called the right-to-know law or HAZCOM.

HAZCOM is a federal regulation that requires hazardous materials manufacturers and handlers to develop written material safety data sheets (MSDSs) on specific types of hazardous chemicals. These MSDSs must be made available to employees who request information about a chemical in the workplace. Examples of information on an MSDS include known health hazards, the physical and chemical properties of the material, first aid, fire-fighting and spill control recommendations, protective clothing and equipment requirements, and emergency telephone contact numbers. Under HAZCOM, hazmat health exposure information should be provided to emergency responders during the termination phase of an emergency, and all exposures should be documented. The basic responsibilities are outlined in Table 13.6.1.

Hazard Determination. Chemical manufacturers and importers are required to review the scientific information on the chemicals they produce or import and to report the information they find to their employees and to employers who distribute or use their products. Downstream employers can rely on the evaluations performed by the chemical manufacturers or importers to establish the hazards of the chemicals they use.

FIGURE 13.6.2 Specialist Employees Working with Specific Hazardous Substances

TABLE 13.6.1 Responsibilities Outlined by Hazardous Communications Standard

Chemical Manufacturers/ Importers	*Determine the Hazards of Each Product*
Chemical manufacturers/ importers/ distributors	Communicate the hazard information and associated protective measures downstream to customers through labels and MSDSs
Employers	Identify and list all hazardous chemicals in their workplace Obtain MSDSs and labels for each hazardous chemical Develop and implement a written hazard communication program, including labels, MSDSs, and employee training Communicate hazard information to employees through labels, MSDSs, and formal training programs

The chemical manufacturers, importers, and any employers that choose to evaluate hazards are responsible for the quality of the hazard determinations they perform. Each chemical must be evaluated for its potential to cause adverse health effects and its potential to pose physical hazards, such as flammability. In addition, chemicals that have been evaluated and found to be suspected or confirmed carcinogens must be reported as such.

Written Hazard Communication Program. Employers that fall under the requirements of HAZCOM must develop, implement, and maintain a written hazard communication program that includes provisions for container labeling, collection, and availability of MSDSs and employee training. It also must contain a list of the hazardous chemicals in the workplace, the means the employer will use to inform employees of the hazards of nonroutine tasks, and the hazards associated with chemicals in unlabeled pipes. If the workplace has multiple employers onsite (e.g., a construction site), HAZCOM requires these employers to ensure that information regarding hazards and protective measures be made available to the other employers on-site, where appropriate.

Labels and Other Forms of Warning. Chemical manufacturers, importers, and distributors must be sure that containers of hazardous chemicals leaving their facilities are labeled, tagged, or marked with the identity, appropriate hazard warning, and the name and address of the manufacturer or other responsible party.

In the workplace, each container must be labeled, tagged, or marked with the identity of the hazardous chemicals contained within and must show hazard warnings appropriate for employee protection. The hazard warning can be any type of message, words, pictures, or symbols that convey the hazards of the chemical(s) in the container. Labels must be legible, in English (plus other languages, if desired), and prominently displayed.

Material Safety Data Sheets. Chemical manufacturers and importers must develop a material safety data sheet (MSDS) for each hazardous chemical they produce or import and must provide the MSDS automatically at the time of the initial shipment of a hazardous chemical to a downstream distributor or user. Distributors must also ensure that downstream employers are similarly provided an MSDS.

Each MSDS must be in English and include information regarding the specific identity of the hazardous chemical(s) involved and the common names. In addition, information must be provided on the physical and chemical characteristics of the hazardous chemical, known acute and chronic health effects and related health information, exposure limits, whether the chemical is considered to be a carcinogen, precautionary measures, emergency and first-aid procedures, and the identification of the organization responsible for preparing the MSDS.

Copies of the MSDS for hazardous chemicals in a given work site are to be readily accessible to employees in that area. Although OSHA has developed a model MSDS format (OSHA form 174), there is currently no specific MSDS form required by the regulation. OSHA's model MSDS is divided into nine separate sections: (1) chemical identity, (2) hazardous ingredients, (3) physical and chemical characteristics, (4) fire and explosion hazard data, (5) reactivity details, (6) health-hazard information, (7) precautions for safe handling, (8) use of the material, and (9) any control measures to be taken.

The American National Standards Institute (ANSI) has developed a standard on the preparation of MSDSs. ANSI Z400.1, *Hazardous Industrial Chemicals, Material Safety Data Sheet—Preparation,* is used by many chemical manufacturers as a standardized format for MSDS preparation.

Employee MSDS training must include methods and observations that may be used to detect the presence or release of a hazardous chemical in the work area (e.g., monitoring conducted by the employer, continuous monitoring devices, visual appearance, or odor of hazardous chemicals when released). Physical and health hazards of the chemicals used and measures that the employees can take to protect themselves from these hazards must be covered, as well as specific procedures the employer has implemented to protect employees from exposure to hazard.

Trade Secrets. A "trade secret" is something that gives an employer an opportunity to obtain an advantage over competitors who do not know about the trade secret or who do not use it. For example, a trade secret may be a confidential device, pattern, information, or chemical makeup. Chemical industry trade secrets are generally formulas, process data, or a "specific chemical identity." The last is the type of trade secret information referred to in the Hazard Communication Standard. The term includes the chemical name, the chemical abstract services (CAS) registry number, or any other specific information that reveals the precise designation. It does not include common names.

The HCS standard strikes a balance between the need to protect exposed employees and the employer's need to maintain confidentially of a bona fide trade secret. This is achieved by providing limited disclosure to health professionals who are furnishing medical or other occupational services to exposed employees, or employees and their designated representatives, under specified conditions of need and confidentiality.

Medical Emergency. The chemical manufacturer, importer, or employer must immediately disclose the specific chemical identity of a hazardous chemical to a treating physician or nurse when the information is needed for proper emergency or first-aid treatment. As soon as circumstances permit, the chemical manufacturer, importer, or employer may obtain a written statement of need and a confidentiality agreement.

Hazardous Materials Transportation Regulations (49 CFR 100 through 199). This series of regulations is issued and enforced by DOT. The regulations govern container design, chemical compatibility, packaging and labeling requirements, shipping papers, transportation routes and restrictions, and so on. The regulations are comprehensive and strictly govern how all hazardous materials are transported by highway, railroad, pipeline, aircraft, and water. There are some local fire departments that routinely perform inspections of hazardous materials cargo tank trucks using DOT regulations.

Retention of DOT Markings, Placards, and Labels (29 CFR 1910.1201). In 1994, OSHA issued requirements that those facilities that receive containers of hazardous materials, which are required to be marked, labeled, or placarded in accordance with DOT regulations, retain those markings, labels, or placards on the container until the container is sufficiently cleaned of residue and purged of vapors to remove any potential hazards.

National Contingency Plan (NCP) (40 CFR 300, Subchapters A through J). The National Contingency Plan (NCP) outlines the policies and procedures of the federal agency members of the National Oil and Hazardous Materials Response Team, also known as the National Response Team (NRT). The regulation provides guidance for emergency responses, remedial actions, enforcement, and funding mechanisms for federal government response to hazardous materials incidents. The NRT is chaired by the EPA, whereas the vice-chairperson represents the U.S. Coast Guard (USCG).

Each of the 10 federal regions also has a Regional Response Team (RRT) that mirrors the makeup of the NRT. RRTs may also include representatives from state and local government and Indian tribal governments.

When the NRT or RRT is activated for a federal response to an oil spill or hazardous materials incident, a federal on-scene coordinator (OSC) will be designated to coordinate the overall response. The OSC will represent either the EPA or the USCG, based on the location of the incident. If the release or threatened release occurs in coastal areas or near major navigable waterways, the USCG will usually assume primary OSC responsibility. If the situation occurs inland and away from navigable or major waterways, the EPA will serve as the OSC. Local emergency responders should contact EPA and USCG personnel within their region to determine which agency has primary responsibility and will act as the federal OSC for their respective area.

If the incident is a terrorism-related event, the Federal Bureau of Investigation (FBI) will assume the role as Federal On Scene Coordinator during the emergency response phase; the Department of Homeland Security/Federal Emergency Management Agency (FEMA) would assume the role for the postemergency response.

Process Safety Management of Highly Hazardous Chemicals (29 CFR 1910.119). Issued by OSHA in 1992, this regulation applies mainly to hazardous materials manufacturing facilities, such as refineries and chemical plants. Other affected sectors include natural gas liquids, farm product warehousing, electric, gas, and sanitary services.

The requirements apply to companies that deal with any of more than 130 specific toxic and reactive chemicals in EPA-listed quantities. It also applies to flammable liquids and gases in quantities greater than 10,000 lb (4540 kg).

The regulation includes the following major requirements:

1. *Process safety information* must include information on the hazards of the highly hazardous chemicals used or produced by the process, information on the technology of the process, and information on the equipment in the process.
2. *Process hazards analysis* must include an initial process analysis (hazard evaluation) appropriate for the complexity of the process and must identify, evaluate, and control the hazards involved.
3. *Written operating procedures* must be developed and implemented that provide clear instructions for safely conducting activities involved in each process. Procedures must address initial startup and shutdown, operating limits, and safety and health considerations.
4. *Employee participation* must be solicited on the conduct and development of process management.
5. *Training programs* must include initial employee training on health and safety hazards, refresher training provided at least every three years on current operating procedures, and a training documentation program. The regulation also applies to contractors performing maintenance, repair, renovation, or specialty work on a process.
6. *Prestartup safety review* must be provided for new facilities and for modified facilities when the modification is significant enough to require a change in process safety.
7. *Mechanical integrity* must be provided for pressure vessels and storage tanks, piping systems, relief and vent systems and devices, emergency shutdown systems, controls and alarms, and pumps.
8. *Management of change* must be provided for written procedures to manage changes to process chemicals, technology, equipment, and so on.
9. *Incident investigation* must include a thorough investigation of incidents to identify the chain of events and causes, so that corrective measures can be developed and implemented.
10. *Emergency planning and response procedures* must be provided for handling spills and releases at the facility.
11. *Compliance audit* must be provided that includes mandatory process safety management reviews every three years to verify that procedures are adequate and being followed.

Risk Management Programs for Chemical Accidental Release Prevention (40 CFR Part 68). Promulgated under amendments to the Clean Air Act, this regulation requires that facilities that manufacture, process, use, store, or otherwise handle certain regulated substances above established threshold values develop and implement Risk Management Programs (RMPs). The regulation is similar in scope to the OSHA Process Safety Management (PSM) standard, with the primary focus being community safety as opposed to employee safety.

Risk Management Programs consists of the following three elements:

1. *Hazard assessment* of the facility, including the worst-case accidental release and an analysis of potential off-site consequences
2. *Prevention program,* which addresses safety precautions, maintenance, monitoring, and employee training; EPA believes that the prevention program should adopt and build upon the OSHA Process Safety Management standard
3. *Emergency response considerations,* including facility emergency response plans, informing public and local agencies, emergency medical care, and employee training

State Regulations

Each of the 50 states and the two U.S. territories maintain an enforcement agency that has responsibility for hazardous materials. The three key players in each state usually consist of the (1) state fire marshal, (2) state Occupational Safety and Health Administration, and (3) State Department of the Environment (sometimes known as Natural Resources or Environmental Quality). Although there are many variations, the state fire marshal is typically responsible for the regulation of flammable liquids and gases, due to the close relationship between the flammability hazard and the fire prevention code; the state environmental agency would be responsible for the development and enforcement of environmental safety regulations.

Most states have the equivalent of the federal OSHA. Approximately 23 states and two U.S. territories have adopted the federal OSHA regulations as state law. State governments also maintain an environmental enforcement agency that usually enforces the federal RCRA, CERCLA, and CAA laws at the local level. Increased state involvement in hazardous materials waste regulatory enforcement has significantly increased the number of hazardous materials incidents reported. This increase is expected to continue in the future and will generate more fire service activity at the local level in both enforcement and response.

VOLUNTARY CONSENSUS STANDARDS

Voluntary consensus standards are normally developed through professional organizations or trade associations as a method of improving the individual quality of a product or system. Within the emergency response community, NFPA is recognized for its role in developing consensus standards and recommended practices that impact fire safety and hazardous materials operations. In the United States, standards are developed primarily through a democratic process, whereby a committee of subject specialists representing varied interests writes the first draft of the standard. The document is then submitted to either a larger body of specialists or the general public, who then may amend, vote on, and approve the standard for publication. This procedure is known as the consensus standards process.

When a consensus standard is completed, it may be voluntarily adopted by government agencies, individual corporations, or organizations. Many hazardous materials consensus standards are also adopted as a reference in a regulation. In effect, when a federal, state, or municipal government adopts a consensus standard by reference, the document becomes a regulation.

Standards developed through the voluntary consensus process play an important role in increasing both workplace and public safety. Historically, a voluntary standard improves over time, as each revision reflects recent field experience and adds more detailed requirements. As users of the standard adopt it as a way of doing business, the level of safety gradually improves over time.

Voluntary consensus standards provide a way for individual organizations and corporations to self-regulate their business or profession. All of the national fire codes in the United States are developed through the voluntary consensus standards process; the two most active associations are (1) NFPA and (2) Western Fire Chiefs Association. Standards developed by these two associations address many hazardous materials issues, including hazardous materials storage and handling, personal protective clothing and equipment, and hazardous materials professional competencies.

NFPA Standards

NFPA has over 60 individual hazardous materials–related voluntary consensus standards. These standards are developed through the committee process, according to NFPA rules and procedures.

NFPA's hazardous materials standards are widely used by both industry and public safety organizations as recommended practices for inspection, safe handling, and installation, and so on. They do not have the force of law unless they are adopted by a government agency. For example, state governments that have approved state OSHA plans under Section 18b of the Occupational Safety and Health Act of 1970 must adopt standards to enforce requirements that are at least as effective as federal requirements.

The current OSHA regulations on flammable and combustible liquids adopt NFPA 30, *Flammable and Combustible Liquids Code,* by reference. Consequently, although NFPA does not specifically write regulations, NFPA standards often result as law through a similar adoption process.

Unfortunately, the pace of revising and updating federal and state regulations lags behind the development and approval of revised NFPA standards. Many state regulations that have adopted NFPA standards, such as NFPA 30 and NFPA 58, *Liquefied Petroleum Gas Code,* have adopted editions that are 5 to 10 years behind current editions. Most consensus standards reflect current and accepted practices, as opposed to "cutting-edge" technology, practices, and procedures. This means that an organization that adopts a 2003 edition of a standard, as a local or state regulation, is actually adopting a standard that may not be based on the most recent technology.

The following list summarizes current NFPA hazardous materials–related standards. They have been categorized by the authors for easier reference by the standards users and are not necessarily grouped by committee responsibility.

Flammable Liquids Related Standards

NFPA 30, *Flammable and Combustible Liquids Code*
NFPA 33, *Standard for Spray Application Using Flammable or Combustible Materials*
NFPA 34, *Standard for Dipping and Coating Processes Using Flammable or Combustible Liquids*
NFPA 326, *Standard for the Safeguarding of Tanks and Containers for Entry, Cleaning, or Repair*
NFPA 329, *Recommended Practice for Handling Releases of Flammable and Combustible Liquids and Gases*
NFPA 385, *Standard for Tank Vehicles for Flammable and Combustible Liquids*

Flammable Gases Related Standards

NFPA 51A, *Standard for Acetylene Cylinder Charging Plants*
NFPA 54, *National Fuel Gas Code*
NFPA 58, *Liquefied Petroleum Gas Code*
NFPA 59, *Utility LP-Gas Plant Code*
NFPA 59A, *Standard for the Production, Storage, and Handling of Liquefied Natural Gas (LNG)*
NFPA 306, *Standard for the Control of Gas Hazards on Vessels*

Dusts and Powders Related Standards

NFPA 91, *Standard for Exhaust Systems for Air Conveying of Vapors, Gases, Mists, and Noncombustible Particulate Solids*
NFPA 654, *Standard for the Prevention of Fire and Dust Explosions from the Manufacturing, Processing, and Handling of Combustible Particulate Solids*

Explosives and Reactive Chemicals Standards

NFPA 35, *Standard for the Manufacture of Organic Coatings*
NFPA 51, *Standard for the Design and Installation of Oxygen–Fuel Gas Systems for Welding, Cutting, and Allied Processes*
NFPA 53, *Recommended Practice on Materials, Equipment, and Systems Used in Oxygen-Enriched Atmospheres*
NFPA 55, *Standard for the Storage, Use, and Handling of Compressed Gases and Cryogenic Fluids in Portable and Stationary Containers, Cylinders, and Tanks*
NFPA 68, *Standard on Explosion Protection by Deflagration Venting*
NFPA 69, *Standard on Explosion Prevention Systems*
NFPA 430, *Code for the Storage of Liquid and Solid Oxidizers*
NFPA 432, *Code for the Storage of Organic Peroxide Formulations*
NFPA 490, *Code for the Storage of Ammonium Nitrate*
NFPA 495, *Explosive Materials Code*
NFPA 498, *Standard for Safe Havens and Interchange Lots for Vehicles Transporting Explosives*
NFPA 655, *Standard for Prevention of Sulfur Fires and Explosions*
NFPA 1124, *Code for the Manufacture, Transportation, Storage, and Retail Sales of Fireworks and Pyrotechnic Articles*

Nuclear Standards

NFPA 801, *Standard for Fire Protection for Facilities Handling Radioactive Materials*

NFPA 805, *Performance-Based Standard for Fire Protection for Light Water Reactor Electric Generating Plants*

Facilities and Related Manufacturing Standards

NFPA 30B, *Code for the Manufacture and Storage of Aerosol Products*
NFPA 32, *Standard for Drycleaning Plants*
NFPA 36, *Standard for Solvent Extraction Plants*
NFPA 45, *Standard on Fire Protection for Laboratories Using Chemicals*
NFPA 86, *Standard for Ovens and Furnaces*
NFPA 820, *Standard for Fire Protection in Wastewater Treatment and Collection Facilities*

Electrical Standards

NFPA 70, *National Electrical Code®*
NFPA 77, *Recommended Practice on Static Electricity*
NFPA 79, *Electrical Standard for Industrial Machinery*
NFPA 110, *Standard for Emergency and Standby Power Systems*
NFPA 496, *Standard for Purged and Pressurized Enclosures for Electrical Equipment*
NFPA 497, *Recommended Practice for the Classification of Flammable Liquids, Gases, or Vapors and of Hazardous (Classified) Locations for Electrical Installations in Chemical Process Areas*
NFPA 499, *Recommended Practice for the Classification of Combustible Dusts and of Hazardous (Classified) Locations for Electrical Installations in Chemical Process Areas*
NFPA 780, *Standard for the Installation of Lightning Protection Systems*

Emergency Response Standards

NFPA 471, *Recommended Practice for Responding to Hazardous Materials Incidents*
NFPA 472, *Standard for Professional Competence of Responders to Hazardous Materials Incidents*
NFPA 473, *Standard for Competencies for EMS Personnel Responding to Hazardous Materials Incidents*
NFPA 704, *Standard System for the Identification of the Hazards of Materials for Emergency Response*
NFPA 1991, *Standard on Vapor-Protective Ensembles for Hazardous Materials Emergencies*
NFPA 1992, *Standard on Liquid Splash-Protective Ensembles and Clothing for Hazardous Materials Emergencies*

Relevant Standards

NFPA 72®, National Fire Alarm Code®
NFPA *101®*, *Life Safety Code®*
NFPA 434, *Code for the Storage of Pesticides*

Hazardous Materials Emergency Response Standards. Within the hazardous materials community there are three major consensus standards that have been widely accepted as the baseline standard for hazardous materials response teams, as follows:

1. NFPA 471, *Recommended Practice for Responding to Hazardous Materials Incidents*
2. NFPA 472, *Standard for Professional Competence of Responders to Hazardous Materials Incidents*
3. NFPA 473, *Standard for Competencies for EMS Personnel Responding to Hazardous Materials Incidents*

As the titles imply, these standards primarily address the emergency response and field operational aspects of hazardous materials. Nevertheless, they provide an excellent basis for developing hazardous materials inspection and enforcement personnel.

NFPA 471, Recommended Practice for Responding to Hazardous Materials Incidents. The document covers planning procedures, policies, and application of procedures for incident levels, personal protective clothing and equipment, decontamination, safety, and communications. The purpose of NFPA 471 is to outline the minimum requirements that should be considered when dealing with responses to hazardous materials incidents and to specify operating guidelines.

NFPA 472, Standard for Professional Competence of Responders to Hazardous Materials Incidents. The purpose of NFPA 472 is to specify minimum competencies for those who will respond to hazardous materials incidents. The overall objective is to reduce the number of accidents, injuries, and illnesses during response to hazardous materials incidents and to prevent exposure to hazardous materials to reduce the possibility of fatalities, illnesses, and disabilities affecting emergency responders.

It is important to recognize that NFPA 472 covers all hazardous materials emergency responders from both the public and private sector.

NFPA 472 provides competencies for the following levels of hazardous materials responders. These levels parallel those listed within OSHA 1910.120, with the exception that the hazardous materials specialist has been deleted and the specialist employee has been expanded on and clarified, as follows:

1. *First responders at the awareness level.* These are individuals who, in the course of their normal duties, may be the first on scene of an emergency involving hazardous materials. They are expected to recognize the presence of hazardous materials, protect themselves, call for trained personnel, and secure the area.

2. *First responders at the operations level.* These are individuals who respond to releases or potential releases of hazardous materials as part of the initial response to the incident for the purpose of protecting nearby persons, the environment, or property from the effects of the release. They must be trained to respond in a defensive fashion to control the release from a safe distance and keep it from spreading.

3. *Hazardous materials technicians.* These are individuals who respond to releases or potential releases of hazardous materials for the purpose of controlling the release. Hazardous materials technicians are expected to use specialized chemical protective clothing and specialized control equipment (Figure 13.6.3).

4. *Incident commander.* This is the person who is responsible for directing and coordinating all aspects of a hazardous materials incident.

FIGURE 13.6.3 Hazardous Materials Technicians Cleaning Up a Spill in EPA Personal Protective Clothing

5. *Private sector specialist employee.* These are individuals who, in the course of their regular job duties, work with or are trained in the hazards of specific materials and/or containers. In response to incidents involving chemicals, they may be called on to provide technical advice or assistance to the incident commander relative to their area of specialization. The following are three levels of private sector specialist employees:

   a. Level C are those persons who may respond to incidents involving chemicals and/or containers within their organization's area of specialization. They may be called on to gather and record information, provide technical advice, and/or arrange for technical assistance consistent with the organization's emergency response plan and standard operating procedures. The individual is not expected to enter the hot/warm zone at an incident.
   b. Level B are those persons who, in the course of their regular job duties, work with or are trained in the hazards of specific chemicals or containers within their organization's area of specialization. Because of their education, training, or work experience, they may be called on to respond to incidents involving chemicals. The Level B employee may be used to gather and record information, provide technical advice, and provide technical assistance (including working within the hot/warm zone) at the incident consistent with the organization's emergency response plan and standard operating procedures and the local emergency operations plan.
   c. Level A are those persons who are specifically trained to handle incidents involving chemicals and/or containers for chemicals used in their organization's area of specialization. Consistent with the organization's emergency response plan and standard operating procedures, the Level A employee must be able to analyze an incident involving chemicals within the organization's area of specialization, plan a response to that incident, implement the planned response within the capabilities of the resources available, and evaluate the progress of the planned response (Figure 13.6.4).

NFPA 473, Standard for Competencies for EMS Personnel Responding to Hazardous Materials Incidents. The purpose of NFPA 473 is to specify minimum requirements of competence and to enhance the safety and protection of response personnel and all components of the emergency medical services system. The overall objective is to reduce the number of EMS personnel accidents, exposures, injuries, and illnesses resulting from hazardous materials (HM) incidents. The following are the two levels of EMS/HM responders:

1. *EMS/HM Level I.* Persons who, in the course of their normal duties, may be called on to perform patient care activities in the cold zone at a hazardous materials incident. EMS/HM Level I responders provide care to only those individuals who no longer pose a significant risk of secondary contamination. Level I includes different competency requirements for basic (BLS) and advanced life support (ALS) personnel.

2. *EMS/HM Level II.* Persons who, in the course of their normal duties, may be called on to perform patient care activities in the warm zone at a hazardous materials incident. EMS/HM Level II responders may provide care to those individuals who still pose a significant risk of secondary contamination. In addition, personnel at this level must be able to coordinate EMS activities at a hazardous materials incident and provide medical support for hazardous materials response personnel. Level II includes different competency requirements for basic (BLS) and advanced life support (ALS) personnel.

NFPA Technical Committee on Hazardous Materials Protective Clothing and Equipment (NFPA 1991, NFPA 1992, NFPA 1994). This technical committee is responsible for the development of standards and documents pertaining to the use of personal protective clothing and equipment (excluding respiratory protection) by emergency responders at hazardous materials incidents. The committee scope includes personal protective equipment (PPE) selection, care, and maintenance.

The following three hazmat protective clothing standards have been developed:

FIGURE 13.6.4 NFPA 472 Level A Private Sector Specialist Employees Handling a Hazardous Materials Incident

1. NFPA 1991, *Standard on Vapor-Protective Ensembles for Hazardous Materials Emergencies*
2. NFPA 1992, *Standard on Liquid Splash-Protective Ensembles and Clothing for Hazardous Materials Emergencies*
3. NFPA 1994, *Standard on Protective Ensembles for First Responders to CBRN Terrorism Incidents*

Other Standards Organizations

There are many other important standards-writing bodies that develop hazardous materials safety and emergency response–related standards. The more significant organizations include the American Society of Mechanical Engineers (ASME), the American Society for Testing and Materials (ASTM), the American Petroleum Institute (API), the Compressed Gas Association (CGA), and the Safety Equipment Institute (SEI). Each of these organizations approves or creates standards, ranging from hazardous materials container design to personal protective clothing and equipment. Standards produced by these groups usually follow the standards development guidelines of the American National Standards Institute (ANSI). ANSI is an approval body and is recognized by the International Organization for Standardization (ISO).

SUMMARY

This chapter is aimed at the fire department prevention and enforcement specialist who needs to understand the fundamentals of hazardous materials laws, regulations, and standards. The chapter began by defining the term *hazardous materials* and continued with a discussion of the key elements of a hazardous materials prevention and enforcement program. The rest of the chapter was devoted to an overview of the major federal laws and regulations governing hazardous materials and the main hazardous materials codes and standards

BIBLIOGRAPHY

References

Burke, R., "Highway Bulk Containers," *Firehouse,* Vol. 25, No. 2, 2000, p. 28.

Elliott, C., "Inside Track on Safety," *Fire Prevention,* No. 333, June 2000, pp. 26–27.

Federal Emergency Management Agency, et al., *Liability Issues in Emergency Management,* National Emergency Training Center, Emmitsburg, MD, 1992.

Hough, E., "Moving towards Integrated Disaster Protection," *Fire International,* No. 178, 2000, pp. 12–13.

Hutton, J., "Nuclear Gamble," *Fire Engineering,* Vol. 154, No. 3, 2001, pp. 156–157.

Ignatowski, A. J., and Rosenthal, I., "Chemical Accident Risk Assessment Thesaurus: A Tool for Analyzing and Comparing Diverse Risk Assessment Processes and Definitions," *Risk Analysis,* Vol. 21, No. 3, 2001, pp. 513–532.

National Fire Protection Association, *Hazardous Materials Response Handbook,* 4th ed., National Fire Protection Association, Quincy, MA, 2002.

National Response Team, "Hazmat Emergency Planning Guide," NRT-1, National Response Team, Washington, DC, 2000.

Nighswonger, T., "Where Do You Set the Standard," *Occupational Hazards,* Vol. 62, No. 5, 2000, pp. 59–60.

Noll, G., Hildebrand, G., Michael, S., and Yvorra, J. G., *Hazardous Materials: Managing the Incident,* 3rd ed., Oklahoma State University, Stillwater, OK, 2005.

Pegliuca, G., "Hazardous Materials: Changes in European Regulations," *Fire International,* No. 183, Feb. 2001, p. 18.

Peterson, D. F., "Are All Chemical Spills or Releases 'Emergencies'?" *Fire Engineering,* Vol. 153, No. 5, 2000, pp. 79–83.

Ross, D., "Safety at the Hazmat Incident," *Health & Safety,* Vol. 9, No. 3, 1998, p. 1.

Stringfield, W. H., *A Fire Department's Guide to Implementing SARA, Title III, and the OSHA Hazardous Materials Standards,* International Society of Fire Service Instructors, Ashland, MA, 1987.

Thomas, P., "Safe Transport of HazMats: Complying with DOT Title 49," *Professional Safety,* Vol. 46, No. 3, 2001, pp. 31–32.

U.S. Environmental Protection Agency, *Hazmat Team Planning Guidance,* U.S. Environmental Protection Agency, Washington, DC, 1990.

U.S. Environmental Protection Agency, et al., *Handbook of Chemical Hazard Analysis Procedures,* U.S. Environmental Protection Agency, FEMA, DOT, Washington, DC, 1989.

U.S. Environmental Protection Agency, et al., *Technical Guidance for Hazards Analysis—Emergency Planning for Extremely Hazardous Substances,* U.S. Environmental Protection Agency, FEMA, DOT, Washington, DC, 1987.

U.S. EPA Title III, *List of Lists,* "Consolidated List of Chemicals Subject to Reporting Under the Emergency Planning and Community Right-to-Know Act," EPA 560/4-90-011, U.S. Environmental Protection Agency, Washington, DC, Jan. 1990.

U.S. Occupational Safety and Health Administration, *HAZWOPER Interpretive Quips,* OSHA Office of Health Compliance Assistance, Washington, DC, Mar. 1993.

Waight, D., "Legal Elements," *Fire Prevention,* No. 331, Apr. 2000, pp. 26–27.

Chapter 7

Aircraft Rescue and Fire Fighting (ARFF)

Jack Kreckie

Modern aircraft have evolved from the early days when gliders were crafted of wood and stretched fabric. This evolution has occurred rather swiftly since the Wright Brothers' first successful flight from Kitty Hawk in 1903. In a century, aviation has evolved from wind-powered aircraft (gliders), to man-powered aircraft (using pedals or cranks), to piston engine-driven propellers, to turbo props and jets. The days of supersonic transport (SST) have given way to the era of new large aircraft (NLA). These mammoth aircraft can be configured to carry over 800 passengers in double-deck cabins. Statistically, aviation is very safe. There are, however, certain risks associated with air travel. Mechanical failure, human error, and weather add an undeniable risk that a small percentage of commercial aircraft will be involved in aircraft incidents and accidents. The primary responsibility of aircraft rescue and fire-fighting (ARFF) personnel is to provide for the safety of all aircraft passengers at aircraft incidents that occur at an airport. This specialized career continues to become increasingly more complex.

This chapter discusses the mission of aircraft rescue fire fighters and provides an explanation of the tools, techniques, agents, and objectives that are used to satisfy that mission. Also provided is a review of the regulations and industry standards that influence the levels of training, staffing, and equipment at airports as well as information to help the reader gain an understanding of typical aircraft emergencies and ARFF response procedures.

See also Section 6, Chapter 2, "Combustion Products and Their Effects on Life Safety"; and Section 13, Chapter 2, "Organizing Rescue Operations."

Chapter Contents

Key Terms

aircraft accident, aircraft fire fighting, aircraft rescue, aircraft rescue and fire-fighting (ARFF), aircraft rescue and fire-fighting vehicle, airport fire fighter, Federal Aviation Administration (FAA), International Civil Aviation Organization (ICAO), National Transportation Safety Board (NTSB), personal protective equipment (PPE), practical critical fire area (PCA), rapid response area, response time, theoretical critical fire area (TCA)

OVERVIEW

Aircraft Rescue and Fire-Fighting (ARFF) Mission

Federal regulations and industry standards determine the minimum requirements for aircraft rescue and fire fighting (ARFF) at airports. ARFF fire fighters put these regulations and standards to practical use. The primary ARFF mission is to protect the lives of the flying public. However, airport fire fighters work under a variety of structures. Some are members of municipal or state-run fire departments that serve the community in which the airport is located. The airport assignment might be a bid position or one attained through seniority. Other airport fire departments are staffed by employees of the Airport Authority or Port Authority that holds the operating certificate for the airport. Private-contract fire departments are also used by a small number of airports, whereas military or federal fire fighters staff bases and mixed military-civil airfields.

In terms of total mission, there are several variables as well. Small airports might support the ARFF requirements using employees who serve dual roles. Maintenance, security, or airport operations personnel are often cross-trained to satisfy the requirements of the regulations governing

Jack Kreckie, a 31 year veteran of the fire service, served the last 28 years with Massport Fire Rescue at Boston Logan International Airport. He retired in 2007 at the rank of Deputy Fire Chief/Chief of Operations at Boston Logan International Airport and L.G. Hanscom Field in Bedford, Massachusetts. Deputy Chief Kreckie has served over 10 years on the management team of the ARFF Working Group, is a member of the FAA-Aviation Rulemaking Advisory Committee (ARAC), and co-chaired the ARAC ARFF Requirements Working Group tasked with developing recommendations for revisions to 14 CFR Part 139. He has served on a number of committees for the FAA and NTSB.

ARFF. Some airport departments are responsible for "all hazards," including structural, EMS, hazmat, confined space, technical rescue, and water rescue. Other departments handle only the ARFF response and depend on off-airport response for other types of emergencies. Dual-role departments, typically called public safety officers, provide both law enforcement and fire department functions. The argument as to which approach is better will never be satisfied. Regardless of how the service is provided, all ARFF fire fighters and the apparatus they depend on must meet the qualifications and requirements of the regulatory authority having jurisdiction.

The underlying mission of aircraft rescue fire fighters has not changed. Fire fighters, by their very nature, will exhaust every resource and their last ounce of energy to rescue the people they are sworn to protect. What has evolved over time, however, are the methods, agents, expertise, and equipment they use to satisfy that mission.

Aircraft Construction Design and Materials

The "jet age" arrived in 1958. Pan American Airways led the way with the introduction of the Boeing 707 as the first U.S. passenger jet. The B-707 burned kerosene fuel, which was half the cost of the high-octane gasoline used in more traditional planes of the era. The jet engines proved more reliable than the piston-driven engines and could carry up to 180 passengers traveling at speeds of up to 550 miles per hour.

The evolution of this new era continued with the introduction of wide-body (two aisles) jets. The Boeing 747 arrived in 1969, followed by the MacDonnell Douglas DC-10 and the Lockheed L-1011 in 1970. With the introduction of jet aircraft, injury and fatality rates relative to survivable accidents have increased. This increase was found to be largely attributable to seats, overhead bins, cabin partitions, and other cabin interior furnishings breaking loose at relatively low-impact loads. An example of a low-impact load incident could be a controlled descent terminating in a landing without landing gear deployed or a landing in a field or on other nonpaved irregular terrain. The resulting conditions injured or trapped occupants, thereby impeding or preventing their escape.

Since the arrival of the jet age, a great deal of attention has been paid to increasing survivability through aircraft construction design and materials. Composite materials have been developed that provide increased strength at lower weight; interior fabrics and finishes must meet more stringent flammability testing; and a layer of fire-resistive fabric has been added in seat construction to further reduce the risk to passengers in the event of a cabin fire.

Modern aircraft are now built with a number of redundant systems. Designs that incorporate redundant systems provide a margin of safety for incidents or accidents caused by mechanical failure. In such cases when a mechanical failure occurs, a backup system takes over, and the flight terminates safely.

Hazards and Risk

The hazards associated with aircraft vary with the size and type of loading of the particular flight. As is the case in structures, the risk is increased or decreased depending on the aircraft's contents and occupancy. Each offers its own set of unique challenges and risks for its occupants and for ARFF responders. Large aircraft carrying hundreds of passengers, small military aircraft carrying ordinance, cargo aircraft loaded with freight that may include manifested or unmanifested hazardous materials, general aviation, helicopters, and ultralights are all in the air, and all experience in-flight emergencies on a regular basis (Figure 13.7.1).

The one element that exists in every powered aircraft is fuel. The fire service prepares for the worst-case scenario based on greatest risk. This risk for occupants of a survivable crash is exposure to fire and the products of combustion from a fuel fire.

Escape Time and Survival Time

For passengers on board an aircraft involved in fire, time is the enemy. From the time of the crash or the outbreak of fire, the survival clock begins ticking. Human tolerance is a measurable effect. In 1965, Don W. Conley prepared a report for the Federal Aviation Administration (FAA) titled, " Post Crash Fire Fighting

(a)

(b)

FIGURE 13.7.1 (a) American Airlines, Boeing 757 Beginning Its Takeoff Roll at Boston Logan International Airport; (b) Aircraft Lining Up on Taxiway Awaiting Their Turn for the Departure Runway (Source: Courtesy of Rudy Chiarello)

Studies on Transport Category Aircraft."[1] Among the research items presented is a study on the parameters of human tolerance. ARFF fire fighters know it is crucial to remove victims from a toxic or dangerous environment or to remove the dangers and toxins from the victim's environment before the limits of human tolerance are reached. Understanding what those limits are is helpful for a better understanding of the urgency and complexity of the ARFF mission.

Escape Time. In a number of documented survivable crashes involving fire, occupants have escaped the hostile environment by their own means. Those surviving the impact have a certain period of time during which they can escape before being overcome by one of the life-threatening hazards of a postcrash fire. The amount of time available, which has been termed *escape time*, varies depending on the type of aircraft, the crash severity, and a variety of other conditions. Escape time is defined in the Conley study as "the elapsed time from the instant fire began to the instant when a human tolerance limit (based on heat or carbon monoxide) was reached that could cause an inability to escape on the part of the would-be occupant." The study calculates escape time and survival time in a number of categories. Each illustrates how little time an ARFF fire fighter has to effectively rescue an occupant who was unable to escape on his or her own.

Survival Time. The most dramatic of the findings relative to human tolerance levels or unbearable pain were data taken from a crash test program conducted by the National Advisory Committee on Aeronautics (NACA) in the early 1950s and referenced in the Conley study. During a fire test on a C-97, the temperature inside the aircraft cabin remained at 70°F (21.1°C) while the spill fire burned for 2 minutes. This occurred as a result of cabin insulation and closed major hatches. At 130 seconds, burn-through occurred and the temperatures soared. At 138 seconds, the temperature reached unsurvivable temperatures.

Many efforts have been made since the days of the Conley study to improve aircraft construction, insulation, and fire block material. In modern transport aircraft, the sidewall panels, partitions, overhead bins, and ceiling panels are typically composite assemblies with a Nomex core, phenolic-impregnated fabric facesheets, and colored thermoplastics. Seat fire-blocking is often polybenzimiazole or a blend of Nomex and Kevlar. All of these efforts are dedicated to improving cabin safety and increasing survival time. Ultimately, once the fire enters the cabin as a result of impingement and burn-through, an open door, or a hull fracture from the impact, the survival clock ticks faster than one can act.

With this in mind, it is understandable why the mission of an ARFF fire fighter is so critical and why lifesaving actions are measured in seconds. Seconds saved through training, technology, methods, and skills translate into lives saved at an aircraft accident.

ARFF REGULATORY AND STANDARD-DEVELOPING ORGANIZATIONS

As aircraft evolve, obviously so must the regulations that identify the minimum standard for ARFF equipment, personnel, and fire-fighting agents at airports around the world.

Federal Aviation Administration (FAA)

In 1970, the FAA administrator was given the statutory authority to issue airport operating certificates. This authority, found in Title 49, United States Code (U.S.C.) Section 44706, Airport Operating Certificates, was used to establish minimum safety standard requirements for the operation and certification of certain U.S. airports. Title 14, Code of Federal Regulation (CFR) Part 139 (14 CFR 139), *Certification and Operations: Land Airports Serving Certain Air Carriers*, spells out these requirements.

This statutory authority, which was limited to land airports serving passenger operations of an air carrier conducted with aircraft having a seating capacity of more than 30 passengers, was broadened by the FAA Reauthorization Act of 1996. The act allowed the FAA to certificate airports that serve any scheduled passenger air carrier operations operating aircraft designed for more than nine passenger seats. Alaska, however, is exempt from this authority.

International Civil Aviation Organization (ICAO)

In addition to the FAA for U.S-certificated airports, the International Civil Aviation Organization (ICAO), a specialized agency of the United Nations, was created on December 7, 1944, at the convention on International Civil Aviation in Chicago, to set international aviation standards. One of ICAO's principal goals is the establishment of international standards, recommended practices, and procedures covering the technical fields of aviation including aircraft rescue and fire fighting (ARFF), search and rescue, and aircraft accident investigation. These standards (related to ARFF) are under constant review and amended, as necessary, by the ICAO Rescue and Fire Fighting Study Group (RFFSG).

National Fire Protection Association (NFPA)

The NFPA develops standards relative to ARFF but the NFPA standards are not always in total agreement with the minimum standards set forth by the FAA. At every meeting of the groups that review federal aviation regulations, NFPA standards, and ICAO standards, there is a desire to harmonize the documents. Given the differences in the documents, it is difficult to have standardized equipment or training for all airports. Manufacturers of ARFF equipment struggle with different requirements for FAA-funded equipment and international customers.

REGULATORY REQUIREMENTS AND STANDARDS

Title 14 Code of Federal Regulations Part 139[2] lists the current U.S. requirements for ARFF personnel, agent quantities, response times, and related topics. "The Rule" is issued by the FAA and compliance is measured by the FAA's regional office, which dispatches a certification inspector to evaluate ARFF equipment, personnel, and training records. Failure to meet the minimum standards of 14 CFR Part 139 could threaten an airport's operating certificate.

Some of the key sections of Part 139 that are specifically related to ARFF are the airport certification manual, personnel requirements, and airport index determination. Comparisons of key differences between FAA, ICAO, and NFPA requirements and guidance are shown in Table 13.7.1.

Airport Certification Manual (ACM)

As set forth in Section 139.205, maintaining an ACM is one of the requirements for an airport certificate holder. The ACM must contain a description of how each requirement of Part 139 is satisfied. Included in that list of requirements are:

- A grid map or other means for identifying airport locations and terrain features that are significant for emergency operations
- A description of facilities, equipment, personnel, and procedures for meeting the rescue and fire-fighting requirements in Sections 139.317 and 139.319
- Procedures for complying with the requirements of Part 139.321, relating to hazardous materials and substances
- An emergency plan, as required by Section 139.325

Personnel

"The Rule" does not prescribe specific minimum staffing numbers. Section 139.303 does, however, require

That sufficient rescue and fire fighting personnel be available during all air carrier operations to operate the vehicles, meet the response times, and meet the minimum fire fighting agent discharge rates specified within the regulation.

Airport Index

As set forth in Section 139.315, an airport index is currently determined with a formula based on the overall length of the aircraft servicing the airport and the number of daily departures of that aircraft. If there are five or more average daily departures of air carrier aircraft in a single group serving that airport, the longest index group with an average of five or more daily departures is the index required for the airport.

If there are less than five average daily departures of air carrier aircraft in a single index group serving that airport, the next lower index from the longest index group with air carrier aircraft in it is the index required for the airport. The minimum designated index is Index A. The airport index (A through E) is determined through this formula; the minimum number of ARFF vehicles and quantities of agent carried are based on the index. A provision in 14 CFR Part 139.319 (ARFF Operational Requirements) allows for a reduction in rescue and fire-fighting capabilities.

TABLE 13.7.1 Comparison of ARFF Index Requirements of FAA, ICAO, and NFPA

FAA Index	*Aircraft Length*	*ICAO Cat.*	*Aircraft Length up to But Not Including*	*Aircraft Width up to But Not Including*	*NFPA Cat.*	*Aircraft Length up to But Not Including*	*Aircraft Width up to But Not Including*	*Sample Aircraft*
GA-1	NA	1	29 ft (9 m)	6.6 ft (2.00 m)	1	30 ft (9.0 m)	6.6 ft (2.00 m)	Cessna 182
GA-1	NA	2	39 ft (12 m)	6.6 ft (2.00 m)	2	39 ft (12.0 m)	6.6 ft (2.00 m)	Cessna Caravan
GA-2	NA	3	59 ft (18 m)	9.8 ft (3.00 m)	3	59 ft (18.0 m)	9.8 ft (3.00 m)	Cessna 404
A	<90 ft (28.0 m)	4	78 ft (24 m)	13.1 ft (4.00 m)	4	78 ft (24.0 m)	13.0 ft (4.00 m)	EMB120
A	<90 ft (28.0 m)	5	91 ft (28 m)	13.1 ft (4.00 m)	5	90 ft (28.0 m)	13.0 ft (4.00 m)	CRJ-200, Saab 340
B	90–126 ft (28–39 m)	6	127 ft (39 m)	16.4 ft (5.00 m)	6	126 ft (39.0 m)	16.4 ft (5.00 m)	DC-9, A320
C	126–159 ft (39–49 m)	7	160 ft (49 m)	16.4 ft (5.00 m)	7	160 ft (49.0 m)	16.4 ft (5.00 m)	B757-200; B767-200ER
D	159–200 ft (49–61 m)	8	200 ft (61 m)	22.9 ft (7.00 m)	8	200 ft (61.0 m)	23.0 ft (7.00 m)	A300, B757-300
E	>200 ft (61 m)	9	249 ft (76 m)	22.9 ft (7.00 m)	9	250 ft (76.0 m)	23.0 ft (7.00 m)	A340-600, B777
		10	295 ft (90 m)	26.2 ft (8.00 m)	10	295 ft (90.0 m)	25.0 ft (8.00 m)	AN-225, A380

Source: *Final Recommendation to ARAC, Airport Certification Issues Group Relative to 14 CFR Part 139, Subpart D, March 2004 (6),* Table 2; Paper produced for the U.S. Department of Transportation, Federal Aviation Administration, by the Aviation Rulemaking Advisory Committee, Airport Certification Issues Group, ARFF Requirements Working Group.

(c) During air-carrier operations with only aircraft shorter than the Index aircraft group required by paragraph (a) of this section, the certificate holder may reduce the rescue and fire fighting to a lower level corresponding to the Index group of the longest air carrier aircraft being operated.

This reduction in requirements is known as the remission factor. The remission factor was incorporated into regulatory language to reduce the financial burden for airports that have a low frequency of flight operations for the longest aircraft conducting scheduled operations at that airport. In January 2005, ICAO eliminated the remission factor from its standard. NFPA 403, *Standard for Aircraft Rescue and Fire-Fighting Services at Airports,* has no provision for remission. Table 13.7.1 provides comparisons among the requirements of the FAA, ICAO, and NFPA.

ARFF AGENTS

Original Quantity-Determining Formula

Determining the quantities of agent required to control or extinguish an aircraft fire must be approached using science, logic, historical data, and repeatable tests. Formulas derived from this process must be adaptable to different-sized aircraft. The theoretical critical area (TCA)/practical critical area (PCA) methodology has survived the test of time and remains the standard over three decades after its introduction. This is not to say that these formulas are adopted by every regulation or standard.

Current debate may require some expansion or modifications to these formulas. Some form of change needs to be brought about to sufficiently provide agent quantities for new large aircraft (NLA). Full-length, double-deck aircraft, like the Airbus Industries A-380, have drawn attention to the fact that the formula assumes a standard height when the number of gallons required for ARFF is determined. This assumption is not reasonable.

The Boeing 747 was the first aircraft with a double deck cabin. However, the original double deck was seen as a "bump" on the front of the fuselage, with a spiral staircase leading to a lounge or small seating area. It was seen as a novelty and never raised a flag as to whether tactical ARFF challenges or minimum agent requirements needed to be reconsidered. Typically, these aircraft flew into only larger airports, which usually maintain more than the minimum required quantities of agent.

Over the years, Boeing introduced new models of the 747, and the second deck grew to greater lengths. Finally, with the introduction of the A-380, the ARFF industry realized it could no longer treat variations in height as rare exceptions of no practical significance.

The number of ARFF vehicles and the minimum quantities of agent required at each index or category of airports are directly related to the ARFF departments' ability to control and/or extinguish an aircraft fire. FAA requirements and requirements mandated in standards established by the NFPA and ICAO differ significantly. To understand the rationale used to determine the actual quantities needed, a review of the historical and technical basis of TCA/PCA methodology employed by the NFPA since the early 1970s is helpful.

Theoretical Critical Area/Practical Critical Area (TCA/PCA) Methodology

Critical Fire Area. The critical area concept was used as a method for determining a level of protection for aircraft of every size. This was the minimum area that was to be protected post-crash to permit safe evacuation of the occupants of an aircraft. The critical fire area is a rectangle with its size determined by using a formula based on the length and width of the aircraft. This method of determining minimum agent quantities does not consider tactical fire attack challenges or conditions. It is simply a repeatable formula that could be applied to any category of aircraft. It is not intended to represent the minimum, average, or maximum fire area based on spill size. NFPA 403 defines *theoretical critical area (TCA)* as

> The fire area adjacent to the aircraft that must be controlled to ensure temporary fuselage integrity and to provide an occupant escape area.

The theoretical critical area served only to categorize aircraft by size and the area of the potential fire hazard that could become involved.

The data on hand indicated that the practical critical area (PCA) was approximately two-thirds of the TCA. NFPA 403 defines *practical critical area (PCA)* as

> The area used to calculate minimum agent quantities and flow rates. The PCA is defined as 2/3 of the size of the TCA, as determined by the ICAO RFFP-II committee.

Discharge and Application Rates. Once the area to be protected was determined, the ICAO RFFP-1 (Rescue and Fire Fighting Panel) began to focus on discharge rates and extinguishing agents during its first meeting in March 1970.[3] In order to determine quantities of agent needed, it was necessary to calculate the rate of discharge and the time required to control and/or extinguish the fire. The RFFP-1 determined that control and extinguishment needed to be considered separately. *Control time* is defined as the time required from the arrival of the first fire-fighting vehicle to the time the intensity of the fire is reduced by 90 percent. *Extinguishment time* is the time required from the arrival of the first fire-fighting vehicle to the time the fire is completely extinguished.

At the time of these studies, protein fire-fighting foam was typically carried. The committee based its recommendations on protein foam but acknowledged that when dual-agent attacks were utilized (foam and dry chemical, CO_2, or a halocarbon), a reduced application rate could be used.

In June 1972, the ICAO Rescue and Fire Fighting Panel met for a second time (RFFP-2). During these deliberations, an application rate of 0.13 U.S. gpm/ft^2 for aqueous film-forming foam (AFFF) was found to be suitable.[4] This application rate is still used for AFFF. The RFFP-2 also confirmed the application rate of 0.15 U.S. gpm/ft^2 for protein foam that was recommended by RFFP-1.

Additional Quantity-Determining Formulas

In determining the quantities of agent(s) required, additional formulas were agreed upon. The quantities required for each milestone in a tactical event are identified and calculated separately. These quantities are expressed as *Q1* and *Q2*.

Quantity *Q1*. Quantity *Q1* is the quantity required to obtain a 1-minute control time in the PCA. The formula for the water required for control (*Q1*) in the PCA is expressed as

$$Q1 = PCA \times R \times T$$

where

PCA = Practical critical area

R = Rate of application for specific foam

T = Time of application

Quantity *Q2*. Quantity *Q2* is the quantity required for maintaining control of the fire after the first minute, or as required for total extinguishment, or both. The RFFP-2 recognized that the exact quantity for *Q2* could not be accurately determined without considering a number of variables. These variables, expressed as *f* in calculating formulas, were assigned values for each category airport based on maximum gross weight, maximum passenger loads, maximum fuel loads, and analysis of previous aircraft rescue and fire-fighting operations.

$$Q2 = f \times Q1$$

The RFFP-2 used these factors (*f*) to determine *Q2* values for each airport category. The range of values for *f* ranged from 3 percent to 170 percent for Category 1 through Category 8 airports, respectively.

Quantity Q3. This general process is still in use today with revisions made over the years. The most significant revision was the introduction of Q3 quantities needed for interior fire-fighting operations.

The values of Q3 are based on accepted waterflow requirements for the type of fire-fighting operations to be experienced when combating an interior aircraft fire. They are determined as follows:

Airport Category	*Q3 Equals (U.S. gal)*
1	0
2	0
3	60 gpm 5 min = 300 gal
4	60 gpm 10 min = 600 gal
5	125 gpm 10 min = 1250 gal
6	125 gpm 10 min = 1250 gal
7	125 gpm 10 min = 1250 gal
8	250 gpm 10 min = 2500 gal
9	250 gpm 10 min = 2500 gal
10	500 gpm 10 min = 5000 gal

Agent Quantity Totals (*Q*). NFPA standards define the total quantity of water (*Q*) as

$$Q = Q1 + Q2 + \text{Q3}$$

Beyond this basic introduction of calculating agent quantities, additional factors are introduced to calculate area based on actual aircraft size and category. NFPA 403 provides a comprehensive description of the process. Table 13.7.2 compares the agent quantities as required (or recommended) by the FAA, ICAO, and NFPA. The quantities listed under NFPA are the only quantities that include gallons required for Q3. It should be noted that, although ICAO used the PCA/TCA formulas to calculate agent quantities required, it reduced its quantities in Category 5 through Category 10 by 1000 gallons. This reduction was made to lessen the financial impact on airports.

TABLE 13.7.2 Agent/Quantity Comparison

		Water (U.S. Gallons)			
Category	*Index*	*ICAO Q1 + Q2*	*FAA Q1 + Q2*	*NFPA Q1+ Q2 + Q3*	*Example Aircraft*
1	GA-1	61	—	120	Cessna 206
2	GA-1	177	—	200	Cessna 414
3	GA-2	317	—	670	Beech 1900
4	A	634	100	1340	DHC-8-100
5	A	1427	100	2760	ATR-72
6	B	2087	1500	3740	B737-300; Emb-145
7	C	3197	3000	4880	B757
8	D	4808	4000	7780	A300; B767-300
9	E	6419	6000	9570	B747-200; A340-400
10		8533	—	14,260	AN-225; A380

Note: NFPA Agent Quantities include gallons required for Q3.

Source: *Final Recommendation to ARAC, Airport Certification Issues Group Relative to 14 CFR Part 139, Subpart D, March 2004 (6),* Table 4; Paper produced for the U.S. Department of Transportation, Federal Aviation Administration, by the Aviation Rulemaking Advisory Committee, Airport Certification Issues Group, ARFF Requirements Working Group.

Complementary Agent Requirements

In addition to the requirements for water and foam, complementary agent must also be carried. Every index airport is required to carry a minimum of 500 lb of dry chemical powder or 500 lb of clean (halogenated) streaming agent, Halon 1211, or Halotron.

Dry Chemical Agents. Dry chemical fire-extinguishing agents are available in a variety of chemical compounds. Potassium bicarbonate and potassium bicarbomate–based powders have proven effective in quickly extinguishing flammable liquid fires when applied at the proper rate and with the proper technique.

Halogenated/Halon Alternative Agents. Halogenated agents are hydrocarbons that have had one or more hydrogen atoms replaced by atoms from the halogen series, usually fluorine (F), bromine (Br), or chlorine (Cl). The extinguishing mechanism of halogenated agents seems to interfere with the combustion process. Halogenated agents are discharged as a liquefied gas, which allows excellent penetration of difficult-to-access areas. Because it leaves no residue, it is an excellent choice for fighting fires in avionics compartments, electronic or electrical components, and engine fires.

ARFF VEHICLES AND EQUIPMENT

Apparatus Features

Fire apparatus is designed to satisfy the needs of the particular mission it primarily serves. Aircraft rescue and fire-fighting apparatus is specifically designed to satisfy its primary mission, namely, response to aircraft incidents and accidents. ARFF vehicles must be designed and built to be compliant with the standards required by the customer. If the apparatus is being funded by the FAA, it must be in compliance with the FAA Advisory Circular 150/5220-10D, "Guide Specification for Aircraft Rescue and Fire Fighting Vehicles." Most U.S. manufacturers will not build a truck that is not compliant with the relevant NFPA standard, in this case, NFPA 414. ARFF vehicles have a number of specialized features that are not typically on structural fire apparatus.

Large Water Tanks. Large water tanks are a functional requirement of the ARFF mission. Because of the critical relationship between time and survival factors, establishing water supply prior to initiating fire attack is not practical. Fire hydrants are not readily available on most runway systems. A hydrant is considered an obstruction near a runway and, for safety purposes, must be located a distance away from the runway. Underground hydrants are available on some airfields but are not practical during initial fire attack because of their inaccessibility and time delays in opening manholes, as well as groundwater and drainage issues. ARFF crews "bring their water with them"; apparatus manufactured today are available with tank sizes ranging from 1000 to 4500 gal. Each truck also has foam quantities commensurate with the water tank size. The standards call for a double shot of foam, so that ARFF vehicles can discharge two tanks of water without having to reservice the foam tanks (Figure 13.7.2).

Aqueous film-forming foam (AFFF) is the standard foam used at airports. The FAA now requires the foam used at certificated airports to meet mil specification MIL-F-24385. The primary reason for this is to guarantee compatibility of foam concentrates. Ensuring compatibility is important for both bulk foam storage tanks and apparatus-mounted foam tanks.

Many ARFF departments have bulk foam storage tanks tied into rapid reservice facilities. In order to maintain sufficient reserve quantities of foam concentrate, the tanks are never emptied. When the reorder level is reached, the tank is topped off. If the foam concentrates are not compatible, all the foam in the tank could become contaminated through a reaction of the two products.

This same logic is used in the refill of apparatus-mounted foam tanks. Many training, testing, or fire-fighting evolutions will consume foam concentrate but not empty the foam tank. As the vehicle is reserviced, the foam tank is topped off. If the foam being added is not guaranteed to be compatible (as mil spec foam is), it is possible to contaminate all of the foam in the tank.

AFFF foam is mixed with water, using foam-proportioning systems installed on the apparatus. These systems automatically proportion the foam to the selected percentage based on the discharge or discharges opened. Foam discharges on an ARFF vehicle can include primary turret (Figure 13.7.3), secondary turret, high-reach extendible turret (HRET), piercing nozzles, hand lines, hose reels, and undertruck nozzles. The nozzles used are both aerated and nonaerated, per airport choice.

With regard to the debate on the environmental concerns of the use of this foam, all AFFF on the market is currently in compliance with EPA requirements. However, the FAA is looking for a "greener" alternative to AFFF, but so far nothing else is as effective.

FIGURE 13.7.2 Massport Fire Rescue Engine 7, Oshkosh T-B 3000 ARFF Vehicle with 3000-Gallon Water Tank and 420-Gallon Foam Tank Carrying 3 Percent AFFF Foam Concentrate (Source: Jack Kreckie)

FIGURE 13.7.3 Oshkosh T-1500 ARFF Vehicle Discharging Through Its Primary Roof Turret at a Training Fire (Source: Jack Kreckie)

TABLE 13.7.3 ARFF Vehicle Requirement Comparison

		Vehicles			
Category	*Index*	*ICAO*	*FAA*	*NFPA*	*Example Aircraft*
1	GA-1	1	NA	1	Cessna 206
2	GA-1	1	NA	1	Cessna 414
3	GA-2	1	NA	1	Beech 1900
4	A	1	1	1	DHC-8-100
5	A	1	1	2	ATR-72
6	B	2	1–2	2	B737-300; Emb-145
7	C	2	2–3	3	B757
8	D	3	3	3	A300; B-767-300
9	E	3	3	4	B747-200; A340-400
10		3		4	AN-225; A380

Source: *Final Recommendation to ARAC, Airport Certification Issues Group Relative to 14 CFR Part 139, Subpart D, March 2004 (6),* Table 7; Paper produced for the U.S. Department of Transportation, Federal Aviation Administration, by the Aviation Rulemaking Advisory Committee, Airport Certification Issues Group, ARFF Requirements Working Group.

"Pump and Roll" Capability. ARFF vehicles have "pump and roll" capability. This feature allows ARFF fire fighters to begin agent application prior to stopping the apparatus. The vehicle can be driven around the fire while agent is being discharged through turrets or undertruck nozzles. It also allows the truck to continue to pump for protection if a flowing fuel fire threatens the apparatus and its occupants and an escape becomes necessary.

Turrets. Traditionally, the primary turret on ARFF vehicles was located on the roof of the apparatus facing forward. Over the years, testing has been completed to evaluate the effectiveness of a low-attack, high-volume turret. These low-attack turrets, which are mounted below the windshield, have proven to be more effective than roof-mounted turrets. Fire fighters operating the newer turrets benefit by seeing the origin of their stream as well as the target. It also reduces the amount of agent falling on the windshield and obscuring the view.

Piercing Nozzles. Piercing nozzles are used to introduce agent into a fuselage without introducing oxygen to the fire through opening a door. Piercing nozzles are available as handheld tools attached to attack lines or mounted on high-reach extendible turrets (HRETs) operated by means of a joystick from the ARFF vehicle cab.

Vehicle Requirements

The number of vehicles required at an airport is driven by several factors. The minimum requirement of the regulatory authority provides a number based on the airport index or category, as illustrated in Table 13.7.3. If only the minimum number of vehicles is maintained at the airport, however, no provision exists for taking a piece of apparatus out of service for maintenance, repairs, or training. The size of the airport is a major factor. Some airports with large airfields maintain the minimum requirement of vehicles at each station in order to satisfy the timed response requirements for each runway.

RESPONSE TIME REQUIREMENTS

The successful mitigation of the effects of an aircraft accident depends on the successful completion of a number of actions. Swift notification with accurate location and conditions is critical. Time is the single most important factor to increase survivability of the occupants of an aircraft involved in a major accident. Requirements for response times to the scene of an accident are difficult to define or measure. Requirements for response are measured using known distances and conditions to demonstrate ability. The FAA, ICAO, and the NFPA all use different standards to establish response time requirements.

ICAO Standards and Recommendations

ICAO's International Standards and Recommended Practices (SARPs) for Annex 14 to the Convention on International Civil Aviation, Aerodromes[5] states:

> The operational objective of the rescue and fire fighting service *shall* be to achieve a response time not exceeding three minutes to any point of each operational runway, in optimum visibility and surface conditions.

In addition to these standards, ICAO also publishes recommendations. The following recommendation follows the preceding standards in the SARP.*

> The operational objective of the rescue and fire fighting service *should* be to achieve a response time not exceeding two minutes to any point of each operational

*The key words *shall* and *should* point out the difference between standards and recommendations.

runway, in optimum visibility and surface conditions. The operational objective of the rescue and fire fighting service *should* be to achieve a response time not exceeding three minutes to any other part of the movement area in optimum visibility and surface conditions. . . . Any other vehicles required to deliver the amounts of extinguishing agents specified *should* arrive no more than one minute after the first responding vehicle(s) so as to provide continuous agent application.

NFPA 403, *Standard for Aircraft Rescue and Fire-Fighting Services at Airports*

Of the three sources, NFPA 403 is certainly the most stringent, as well as the clearest:*

> The demonstrated response time of the first responding vehicle to reach any point on the operational runway shall be 2 minutes or less and to any point remaining within the on-airport portion of the rapid response area shall be no more than 2½ minutes, both in optimum conditions of visibility and surface conditions. Other ARFF vehicles necessary to achieve the required discharge rate shall arrive at intervals not exceeding 30 seconds.

FAA's 14 CFR Part 139

The U.S. government has chosen not to adopt NFPA 403 and has filed differences to ICAO Annex 14 with respect to response time. The current response requirements from 14 CFR Part 139.319(h)(2) state

> (i) Within three minutes from the time of the alarm, at least one required airport rescue and firefighting vehicle shall reach the midpoint of the farthest runway serving air carrier aircraft from its assigned post, or reach any other specified point of comparable difference on the movement area which is available to air carriers, and begin application of agent;
>
> (ii) Within four minutes from the time of the alarm, all other required vehicles shall reach the point specified (above) from their assigned post and begin application of agent.

ARFF TRAINING REQUIREMENTS

Each airport must develop its own ARFF fire fighter training program that is designed to prepare the fire fighter for the specific mission of the airport. The program should be carefully developed to meet the qualifications and requirements of NFPA 1003, *Standard for Airport Fire Fighter Professional Qualifications,* and NFPA 405, *Standard for the Recurring Proficiency of Airport Fire Fighters.*

**Rapid response area* is defined by the NFPA as a rectangle 500 ft to either side of a runway centerline and extending 1650 ft beyond each runway end, remaining within the airport property line.

Fire Fighter Training

In 14 CFR Part 139.319(i)(2), the FAA requires that

> all rescue and firefighting personnel are properly trained to perform their duties in a manner authorized by the administrator. Such personnel must be trained prior to initial performance of rescue and firefighting duties and receive recurrent instruction every 12 consecutive calendar months. The curriculum for initial and recurrent training must include at least the following areas: airport familiarization; aircraft familiarization; rescue and firefighting personnel safety; emergency communications; use of fire hoses, nozzles and appliances; application of extinguishing agents; emergency aircraft evacuation assistance; firefighting operations; adapting structural firefighting equipment for ARFF; aircraft cargo hazards including haz mat; and ARFF responsibilities within airport emergency plan.

Each ARFF fire fighter must participate in at least one live-fire drill that simulates an aircraft fire of the size typical to the airport index certificate (Figure 13.7.4).

Training Records

Training records must be maintained by the airport fire department training officer for each member. During the annual airport certification inspection, the FAA inspector inspects the records for compliance. Inspectors can evaluate or test any member for proficiency in any or all of the training requirements. They will also conduct a surprise test run to see a demonstration of the department's ability to satisfy the response test requirements of 14 CFR Part 139.319.

Airport Emergency Exercise

14 CFR Part 139.325 requires all Class 1 airports to hold a full-scale airport emergency exercise at least every 36 months. This

FIGURE 13.7.4 Live-Fire Training Exercises (Source: Jack Kreckie)

FIGURE 13.7.5 Tri-Annual Emergency Response Exercise Being Conducted at Allentown Bethlehem International Airport (Source: Jack Kreckie)

exercise is required to test the airport emergency plan and to demonstrate the ability of those with responsibilities under the emergency plan to fulfill their obligations (Figure 13.7.5).

ARFF PERSONAL PROTECTIVE EQUIPMENT (PPE)

For years there has been debate in the industry relative to the proper personal protective equipment (PPE) for ARFF fire fighters. This issue is primarily raised by departments that serve dual roles of ARFF and structural. Many fire fighters felt that traditional ARFF PPE "silvers," or proximity fire-fighting ensembles (Figure 13.7.6), were too stiff and cumbersome and that they were safer in gear that allowed more freedom of movement. The opposition was typically from departments that were primarily dedicated to ARFF and spoke of the value of reflecting the heat away from the fire fighter.

Many research sources are available to understand the debate but, more importantly, to understand the laws that govern ARFF. The single most important factor is fire fighter safety. If the level of protection is lower than that which is required, fire fighter safety and level of effectiveness will not be maximized.

OSHA Requirements

In the United States, the Department of Labor's Occupational Safety & Health Administration (OSHA) oversees the safety of workers. OSHA standards are federal laws. On July 15, 1997, an Interpretation Record[6] was issued to interpret OSHA's position on proximity gear for ARFF fire fighters in Standard Number 1910.120; 1910.156:

- If a firefighter's primary job is crash and rescue, he or she must be adequately protected for that job (NFPA 1971, proximity protective ensemble). This is true even for those large combined fire departments with multiple tasks where personnel are rotated from station to station and expected to perform crash and rescue duties.
- If a firefighter's primary job is structural, then he or she must be adequately protected for that job (NFPA 1971, structural protective ensemble). This does not preclude being trained for incidental response to aircraft crashes as crashes do occur in unexpected locations.

FIGURE 13.7.6 ARFF Fire Fighter in Silvers (Source: Jack Kreckie)

An example given in the memo referred to the San Diego combined fire department. It stated that all 300 members can be tasked to do any type of fire fighting at any time (usually on a rotational basis). OSHA determined that in this case, all 300 members would have to be equipped to fight any type of fire. In another example where aircraft crash and rescue was less than 5 percent of the tasking, proximity fire fighting was incidental and not the primary job.

FAA Recommendations

FAA Advisory Circular 150/5210-14B, Airport Rescue and Fire Fighting Personnel Protective Ensemble for Proximity Fire Fighting,[7] identifies the standards for design, performance, testing, and safety of personal protective ensembles for proximity fire fighting. This document serves as a recommendation by the FAA for all airports. It is mandatory for PPE purchased under federally funded projects and serves as an acceptable means of compliance with 14 CFR Part 139 as it pertains to PPE for airport fire and rescue personnel. It states:

> If ARFF personnel engage in any fire and rescue activity where there is any hazard or potential hazard of high radiant heat fuel fire, then the operational consideration and risk assessment mandates the use of proximity protective clothing.
>
> *Recommendations from Advisory Circular:*
>
> a. Proximity Protective Ensemble
>   1) Design, Performance, Testing and Certification Standards. Proximity Protective Ensembles as a minimum shall meet the most recent edition of NFPA 1971, *Standard on Protective Ensembles for Structural Fire Fighting and Proximity Fire Fighting.*
>   2) For Safety and Health Standards, Proximity Ensemble, as a minimum, shall meet the requirements of NFPA 1500, *Standard on Fire Department Occupational Safety and Health Program.*

AIRCRAFT EMERGENCIES

The vast majority of responses by ARFF departments for aircraft emergencies are precautionary. Aircraft are designed and built with a number of redundant critical systems and can fly safely with certain systems shut down. Although the aircraft are capable of these things, it is still not considered normal, and failure of a system will cause an aircraft to return and land (if it occurs shortly after takeoff) and notify the tower of the problem. In order to provide appropriate levels of protection for the landing aircraft, the authority having jurisdiction (AHJ) at each airport must have established procedures to provide the necessary level of response to all types of aircraft emergencies.

Aircraft Emergencies with Prior Warning

The majority of aircraft emergency responses for ARFF departments are announced prior to the landing of the aircraft. There is often several minutes' warning that the aircraft is inbound and a description of the problem is provided. The calls are typically received from the air traffic control tower (ATCT) or flight service center (FSS).

Problem Information Provided. In most cases, the following information is provided:

- Make, model, and flight number of the aircraft
- Problem reported by the pilot
- Landing runway
- Number of "souls" on board (SOBs)
- Quantity of fuel on board
- Whether or not the pilot is "declaring an emergency" or "requesting the equipment" (requesting ARFF vehicles at the runway)
- Estimated time of arrival (ETA)

Response Objectives. Response to calls with advance warning results in apparatus response to designated runway standby positions. Runway hold-off positions should be designed to accommodate a number of objectives. These objectives are satisfied more easily at airports with multiple pieces of apparatus responding:

- Minimize delays in reaching burning aircraft in the event the aircraft crashes or has a fire on board.
- Provide observation points from different angles and sequences of landing to observe unsafe or reportable conditions.
- Minimize risk to ARFF personnel and vehicles by not locating several assets together. (An aircraft skidding off the runway could wipe out several vehicles if co-located.)
- Provide strategic locations planning for prestaging to include tactical consideration for rapid access to all sides of the aircraft as well as factoring in wind and terrain.

Aircraft Emergencies with No Prior Warning

Some ARFF responses to aircraft emergencies occur with little or no warning. Crashes due to catastrophic failures during landing and takeoff are examples. Another scenario would be an aircraft that experiences an emergency on takeoff roll or on short final (i.e., immediately prior to becoming airborne or immediately upon touchdown). A call from the tower might say, "He just aborted takeoff due to a bird strike! He's at the departure end of Runway 9. He's requesting equipment!" or "Aircraft is on Final for 4R, he has a Fire Warning Light for Number 1 engine. Pilot's declaring an emergency! He's over the numbers now!" (indicating the aircraft is still airborne but about to touch down). In these scenarios, the ARFF vehicles would respond directly to the aircraft rather than to runway standby positions.

ARFF ACTIONS

Size-Up/Set-Up

Initial Observations Reported. Every vehicle approaching an aircraft incident or accident should immediately perform a quick size-up. Initial observations reported to other responding units as well as the aircraft cockpit are among the most critical initial actions. Visible smoke, fire, physical damage, and fuel spills should all be reported immediately. These are items that will factor into decision making in the cockpit as to whether the aircraft should be evacuated or not.

Incident Action Plan. This information is also taken into consideration by the incident commander (IC). At a small airport, there may only be one truck and one person responding. In any case, the IC needs to make a decision based on the initial size-up. He or she must gather the assessment information and develop an incident action plan based on the resources available. The operational priorities for an aircraft accident are no different from any other emergency response:

1. Rescue
2. Fire control

3. Loss control
4. Environmental consideration

Set-Up Factors. The positioning of arriving ARFF vehicles is critical to the success of the mission. In many cases, the positioning of the first arriving piece dictates the position of the remaining apparatus. There are a number of factors to be considered in the set-up phase. Wind, grade, terrain, exposures, spilled fuel, passenger evacuation, and limitations of the apparatus all need to be considered. In addition, each piece of apparatus or specialized equipment needs to have access to the area it was designed to service. If a high-mounted engine is on fire, the best area for tactical deployment of a high-reach extendible turret or aerial device should be left accessible. If the department has a mobile stair truck, the rescue side of the aircraft must be determined and the safest door for deplaning must be left accessible for the stairs.

The decision as to where to position must be made within seconds. Once in position, it is difficult to move vehicles around due to their size and other vehicles at the scene. Although the decisions are made very quickly, the video from media helicopters and long-range lenses will be on display forever with subject matter experts and attorneys questioning every step and criticizing every decision. Decisions made relative to the positioning of apparatus need to be deliberate and for good reason. Training evolutions and critiques of incidents will help ARFF fire fighters develop good instincts and make rapid decisions at the next incident.

Aircraft Cabin Fires Requiring Aircraft Evacuations

Time Requirement. Interior fires on aircraft, whether postcrash or in-flight fires, pose obvious life-threatening hazards to occupants. In either case, the immediate objective of the aircraft crew is to evacuate the occupants of the aircraft. The certification of the aircraft includes a requirement that the aircraft design is such that a full evacuation of the aircraft using half of the exits is accomplished in 90 seconds or less. This ability must be demonstrated prior to certification for revenue service.

Escape Slide. According to an FAA study relating to aircraft cabin fire safety:[8]

> Accident data studies indicate that, in most survivable air transport crashes to date, occupant survival has been largely determined by the ability of uninjured passengers to leave their seats and find an exit before being overcome by fire or smoke.

Air carrier aircraft that make use of escape slides depend on them to satisfy the evacuation requirement. These inflatable devices are not fail-safe. They are subject to failure for mechanical reason or to damage due to the landing or crash. They are designed to be effective for an aircraft sitting on a runway, up on all of its gear. If the attitude of the aircraft is affected, or the gear collapsed upon landing, the value of the slides is reduced or negated. The slides are also affected by heat and wind.

During an emergency evacuation, fire fighters should be positioned at the base of the slides to secure them, help passengers to their feet, and direct them to a safe area of refuge. Fire fighters anchoring the slides from the effects of wind, providing a fire-free escape area, and assisting passengers to areas of safety will help to minimize injuries.

On June 27, 2000, the National Transportation Safety Board (NTSB) adopted a safety study entitled "Emergency Evacuation of Commercial Airplanes." This study collected data from accident investigations and from crew and passenger interviews from 46 emergency evacuations involving 2846 occupants that occurred between September 24, 1997, and January 24, 1999. During this period, an evacuation occurred on average, every 11 days. In the 46 study cases, 92 percent (2614) of the 2846 occupants were uninjured, 6 percent (170) sustained minor injuries, and 2 percent (62) sustained serious injuries.[9]

Removal from Hazardous Atmosphere. Postcrash aircraft accident fatalities are typically due to exposure to products of combustion. For the effects of such exposure, see Section 6, Chapter 2, "Combustion Products and Their Effects on Life Safety." In addition to the effects of the toxic atmosphere, the survival of the occupants depends on the level of air temperature in the aircraft cabin. In postcrash fires, the cabin air temperatures can increase as a result of the ignition of interior cabin components or as a result of fire gases entering the fuselage from outside fires.

To increase the chance for survival, occupants need to be removed from the hazardous atmosphere before they suffer effects of exposure to toxins in the atmosphere and prior to the air temperatures reaching the limits of human tolerance. The other option is to make the atmosphere in the cabin safe for occupants. This may be the only alternative if extrication is required for trapped victims.

Interior Fire Attack and Ventilation

According to the International Fire Service Training Association (IFSTA),[10] ARFF fire fighters should try to determine the location and extent of the fire prior to attempting entry. Ventilation should be immediately initiated to allow the smoke and steam created by interior fire attack to escape. Applying water to the fire will quickly cause the limited space in the cabin to fill with smoke and steam. This condition compounds the difficulty for rescuers making entry and puts occupants and rescuers at risk for steam burns. Making entry and initiating fire attack should be simultaneous to ventilation efforts. Entry, search and rescue, and interior fire attack should be initiated from the unburned side of the aircraft (Figure 13.7.7).

In order to affect interior fire attack in time periods that will increase survivability, efforts must be initiated immediately. The ability to immediately launch exterior fire-fighting efforts to protect escape paths, begin ventilation, and perform interior rescue and fire-fighting actions requires that properly trained and equipped teams be on hand very quickly. It also means that water supply to satisfy *Q1, Q2,* and Q3 quantities must also be available. The personnel and equipment required for these operations need to be on airport or prestaged to arrive in the first few critical minutes if they are to be effective.

FIGURE 13.7.7 Fire Fighters at Orlando International Airport Being Trained on Making Entry Through Emergency Over-Wing Exit (Source: Jack Kreckie)

ARFF personnel at certificated airports should be equipped, trained, and capable of interior aircraft fire fighting. Such operations should be performed in accordance with OSHA, as detailed in 29 CFR Part 1910.134(g)(4). The standard details certain procedures for interior structural fire fighting to ensure respiratory protection and safe practices when entering atmospheres that are immediately dangerous to life and health (IDLH):

> At least 2 employees enter the IDLH atmosphere and remain in visual or voice contact with one another at all times; At least two employees are located outside the IDLH atmosphere; and all employees engaged in interior structural firefighting use Self-Contained Breathing Apparatus (SCBAs)[11]

An interior fire on an aircraft is certainly IDLH. This OSHA regulation is known in the industry as the "two-in/two-out" rule. Federal Aviation Regulation FAR Part 139 certificate holders should develop and implement policies addressing aircraft firefighting operations.

CARGO AIRCRAFT

ARFF Requirements

Currently the FAA authority and, therefore, the applicability of Part 139 extend only to passenger-carrying aircraft under 49 USC 44706. This means that the U.S. requirements for index determination, agent/vehicle quantities, and aircraft training do not include cargo aircraft. To illustrate the point, an airport could conduct flight operations all day long with Boeing 747 cargo aircraft, but the FAA would not require any ARFF coverage.

Although there may not be any legal responsibility on the part of the certificate holder to provide ARFF coverage for these flight operations, most airports realize that they have a moral obligation to protect the aircraft occupants, the airport, and the surrounding communities. In some cases, the costs associated with providing this protection are carried by the cargo operators.

Cargo Aircraft Hazard

Cargo aircraft contain the same fuel loads as passenger aircraft of the same size or class; therefore, the potential for fire and associated damage on the ground is the same, regardless of whether the aircraft is configured for cargo operations or passenger service. Cargo aircraft may actually provide a greater risk for those on the ground since cargo aircraft frequently carry hazardous materials not permitted in passenger operations. Morally to suggest that the lives of the occupants of a cargo aircraft are not eligible for the protection or benefit provided by ARFF services is reprehensible. Human life must always remain the highest priority, regardless of the primary mission of the aircraft these individuals occupy.

Occupant Evacuation

Fires on cargo aircraft offer different challenges from those on passenger aircraft. The life hazard for occupants is obviously less due to the fewer number of people on board. Crew members will attempt to escape through normal exit doors or through the emergency exits in the cockpit. After determining that all occupants have escaped from the aircraft, all efforts can be placed on protecting exposures and attacking the aircraft fire.

Interior Fire Attack

In an intact fuselage, access through normal doors may not provide access to the area of the fire. "Space" on a cargo aircraft is the commodity from which cargo carriers generate their revenue. The intention of the cargo carrier is to fill every space with freight. An open aisle down the center of the fuselage is like flying a passenger aircraft with mostly empty seats. Profits depend on full aircraft. This factor complicates interior fire attack because of the access problem. Opening a cargo bay loading door on an aircraft with an interior fire may intensify the fire due to the introduction of oxygen and not provide any access to extinguish the fire due to the cargo load itself. On most fully loaded cargo aircraft, there are only a few inches between the cargo containers and the fuselage.

Incident Action Plan. Before initiating interior fire attack, crews should attempt to determine the quantities and types of hazardous materials on board. The airway bills and manifests are stored on board the aircraft, usually in the cockpit or adjacent to the main loading door. Aircraft that carry quantities or types of dangerous goods that are not allowed on passenger aircraft are usually stored in designated areas in the forward portion of the cargo bay. If the dangerous goods are in smaller quantities and of a class that would be allowed on passenger aircraft, they may be mixed throughout the aircraft. In all incidents involving a fire on a cargo aircraft, a hazardous materials team should be on site and involved in developing the incident action plan.

Aircraft Skin-Piercing Nozzles. The use of aircraft skin-piercing nozzles may be the best tactic to attack an interior fire on a cargo aircraft. The use of forward-looking infrared (FLIR) cameras is helpful in determining the location and severity of the interior fire. Penetrations in the skin, using handheld piercing nozzles or those installed on ARFF vehicles equipped with high-reach extendible turrets, are an efficient way of introducing agent to an area that is not accessible due to cargo loading (Figure 13.7.8). It also minimizes the amount of air introduced to small holes punched in the fuselage by the piercing tip. The effectiveness of the fire attack can be monitored through the FLIR camera, which is focused on the "bloom," or heat signature, from the onboard fire. In most cargo aircraft fires, venting occurs when the fire burns through the roof of the fuselage. If the fire is attacked prior to burn-through, ventilation will have to be factored into the incident action plan.

ACCIDENT INVESTIGATION AND SCENE PRESERVATION

Fire Department and Law Enforcement Responsibilities

An aircraft accident is considered a crime scene until proven otherwise. Following ICS/NIMS protocol, the fire department is in charge until all rescue has been completed, the fire is extinguished, and the scene is made safe. At that time, command of the incident is handed over to law enforcement. Local, state, and federal law enforcement agencies are responsible for securing the scene, debris field, personal effects, cargo, and mail. They will collect documentation, gather intelligence, record the scene, and begin analysis of the accident site. Law enforcement looks specifically for anything that might have been a criminal or intentional act or an act of war or terrorism.

Fire fighters need to remain aware that when the scene is declared safe, every inch will be studied and scrutinized by trained investigators. Every bit of damage will be evaluated to determine the specific cause. Damage caused by rescuers during fire fighting, forcible entry, or extrication efforts should be documented for the investigation that will follow. The location of every piece of debris may be an important clue in determining the cause of the accident. The location of personal effects, survivors, bodies, or body parts may be the key to identifying a victim. Care should be taken to touch only things that must be touched to accomplish the critical tasks of the fire fighters' mission.

FIGURE 13.7.8 Oshkosh TI-3000 ARFF Vehicle with High Reach Extendible Turret (HRET) with Piercing Tip (or Snozzle®) (Source: Jack Kreckie)

National Transportation Safety Board (NTSB)

The National Transportation Safety Board (NTSB) investigates every civil aviation accident in the United States. In compliance with international treaties, it also provides investigators to serve as U.S.-accredited representatives for aviation accidents overseas involving U.S.-registered aircraft or involving aircraft or major components of U.S. manufacture. The NTSB launches teams from its headquarters in Washington, DC, or from one of the ten regional offices in the United States. The NTSB maintains the U.S. government's database on civil aviation accidents. The NTSB Accident Incident Database is available to the public at http://www.ntsb.gov/avdata.

AIRCRAFT TECHNOLOGY ADVANCES

Aircraft technology advances, such as aircraft cabin-zoned waterspray systems and emergency locator transmitters (ELT), would increase survivability and are, therefore, justified from a safety or survival standpoint. The associated costs of some of these advances, however, are prohibitive and thus not likely to be implemented at this time.

Aircraft Cabin-Zoned Waterspray Systems and Aircraft Cabin Sprinklers

In the United States, building a structure designed for public assembly, which would accommodate up to 800 people, without fire sprinklers would be unthinkable. Yet in the twenty-first century, new aircraft carry these numbers of people. The area of assembly (the fuselage) is nestled between two wings that are loaded with jet fuel. This area of assembly is then lifted off the ground by powerful jet engines and travels at 30,000 to 40,000 ft above the ground at 500 mph. Based on a study performed by the FAA, "Fire Management/Suppression Systems/Concepts Relating to Aircraft Cabin Fire Safety" (Oct. 1983),[8] the cost of an aircraft cabin-zoned waterspray system for a wide-body jet was estimated to add $86,000 (approximately $140,000 in 2006 dollars) to the cost of the aircraft. The study indicated that, historically, major losses have occurred in postcrash or emergency landing fires.

Unfortunately, this initial cost is the least significant expense to be considered. The weight of a zoned waterspray system for a wide-body jet is 1190 gross lb. This weight is multiplied by the total number of miles flown throughout the anticipated life of the aircraft. The fuel cost and space allowance, combined with annual maintenance, inspection, and repair, reveal the actual cost to the airline. Although the concept of aircraft suppression systems has great merit in the areas of survivability and loss reduction, it is difficult to calculate a favorable cost/benefit analysis due to the limited number of incidents on which to base benefits. Weight is money in aviation, and automatic suppression systems are not mandated by the FAA, so it is not likely such systems will be installed unless concerns for the number of people at risk in the new large aircraft (NLA) bring back the debate on this issue.

Smart ELT Technology

The key to survival for the occupant of an aircraft involved in a survivable crash is time. The occupant needs to be removed from the fuselage, which is rapidly filling with smoke and fumes (products of combustion), or the atmosphere of that space must be made safe. The elements of response for rescue crews include notification, activation, response, and control time. Notification of emergency crews is usually handled by the air traffic control tower (ATCT) that was handling the flight. Depending on location, visibility, weather, and other factors, this report might have very specific accident location, last known location, or perhaps best estimate location. In cases of survivable crashes, where delays in response and arrival are caused by the inability of the ATCT to provide specific accident location, survival risks are increased. American Airlines Flight 1420, Little Rock, Arkansas, is a perfect example. The following conclusion was published in the NTSB Abstract of the accident report:[12]

> A crash detection and location technology would help expedite the arrival of emergency responders at an accident scene, thus maximizing the possibility for saving lives and reducing the severity of injuries.

Most light aircraft are equipped with emergency locator transmitters (ELT). These ELTs transmit an emergency radio signal that can be tracked to help locate a downed aircraft. Commercial vessels are required by the U.S. Department of Transportation to be equipped with a Category I emergency position indicating reporting beacon (EPIRB). If a ship sinks, the EPIRB will separate itself from the vessel and float to the surface, as it sends out a signal to search and rescue assets.[13]

Technology exists today that combines ELT technology with differential global positioning systems. This smart ELT could be activated manually by the pilot or automatically by deceleration forces and could send out aircraft identification and location information.

Fire Fighter Preparedness

Post–9/11 thinking further complicates everything done in the fire service. On September 11, 2001, aircraft became weapons of mass destruction and airports became their launching pads. It is speculated that these terrorists, who have forever changed life in the United States, spent years watching U.S. airports, studying the system, and flying on airplanes. Much like ARFF fire fighters walking through parking garages and airport terminals on building familiarization, these terrorists walked the same routes. They found every weakness in the system and used it to cause thousands of deaths. Fire fighters everywhere need to reassess every incident they approach; complacency is the enemy. For every routine incident response, there are additional concerns that must be factored into the assessment:

- Could this be a diversion?
- Could there be a secondary device?
- Could this fire be a dispersal method for radiation or other weapons of mass destruction (WMD)?

Incident action plans and SOPs must always hold contingencies for the "what ifs." Transportation centers are critical infrastructure; therefore, airports are high-risk targets for terrorist acts. ARFF fire fighters are the front-line level of protection to minimize threats and mitigate effects of these acts.

There are no federal regulations or industry standards that prepare ARFF fire fighters for what could occur at airports, but they will be the first on the scene. In a multiple-hit scenario, additional events may occur in the cities outside the airport. These are the same cities that provide mutual aid to airports. In these cases, there may be no help coming. It has been said that the only difference between a WMD release and a hazmat incident is intent. The same could be said of a gas explosion in a terminal complex or airport hotel and improvised explosive devices (IEDs) detonated by suicide bombers in the middle of security checkpoints. The bottom line is simply that preparedness is key.

SUMMARY

The challenges presented in a survivable aircraft accident are great. ARFF fire fighters, through training and experience, will exhaust all available resources in an attempt to rescue every occupant. The enemy in this event is time. Most ARFF departments are not staffed with sufficient numbers of personnel to accomplish all the tasks critical to the survival of the occupants in the time allowed. Continued training and development of faster, more capable fire-fighting technology will contribute to their success, but advances in aircraft safety technology might provide the additional edge needed. This chapter discussed a number of pieces of technology, such as aircraft cabin-zoned waterspray systems or emergency locator transmitters, that would further increase survivability but have not been introduced to the fleet mix. Although it is clear that these items can be justified from a safety or survival standpoint, the associated cost will probably prevent their introduction.

This chapter discussed the mission of the aircraft rescue fire fighter and followed it by a review of the evolution of the aircraft itself. As the aircraft evolved, so did the regulations and consensus standards that ARFF protection at airports is modeled around. Basic ARFF response procedures as well as specific hazards to fire fighters and aircraft occupants alike were reviewed. For the ARFF fire fighter, all of the information provided and referenced here is nothing more than "ARFF 101." The basic requirements of the regulations that govern ARFF departments are a foundation for the knowledge base each ARFF fire fighter must develop to be proficient in his or her mission.

Responsibilities change daily with changes in fleet mix, passenger load factors, unknown cargo loads, and the new age threat of the day.

A simple review of the scenario that every ARFF fire fighter trains and prepares for shows how important proficiency in every required skill set is to the survival of the occupants of an aircraft involved in a survivable crash. Consider this:

- According to a study released in 1996,[14] which examined NTSB reports from 60 survivable aviation accidents, 78 percent of all fatalities occurred after impact, and 95.4 percent of them resulted from smoke inhalation or burns.
- In postcrash fires, cabin air temperatures can rise from both the ignition of the cabin interior and from fire gases entering the fuselage through open doors or fractured fuselage. In an FAA study,[8] the cabin air temperature at the ceiling reached 1300°F (704.4°C) in 50 seconds with open doors. Closing all but one door retarded the flow of heat, which still reached 400°F (204°C) in the same time.

Statistically, therefore, the fatalities that occur in a survivable crash will occur postcrash. The fire that is likely to occur will rapidly create an environment that cannot support life for those unable to escape by themselves. The lives of surviving occupants are totally dependent on the swift actions of highly trained and properly equipped ARFF fire fighters. Every action, every second spent or saved, from the moment of the impact until all survivors are safe will have an effect on who lives and who does not. For ARFF fire fighters, the minimum standard is never enough. Commitment to mission, training, coordination, and cooperation is the key to successful incident accident plans.

BIBLIOGRAPHY

References Cited

1. Conley, D. W., "Post Crash Fire Fighting Studies on Transport Category Aircraft," Data Supplement to SDRS Report No. RD-65-50, Appendix 1, May 1965, 1-1–1-4.
2. *Federal Aviation Regulation, Certification of Airports,* Title 14 CFR Part 139, U.S. Department of Transportation, Federal Aviation Administration, revised Feb. 10, 2004 (as amended May 3, 2004, and June 4, 2004).
3. Hewes, B. V., (Chairman), "Report of the First Meeting of the ICAO Rescue and Fire Fighting Panel (RFFP-I)" (meeting minutes), International Civil Aviation Organization (ICAO), Montreal, Quebec, Canada, March 10–20, 1970.
4. Harley, R. A., (Chairman), "Report of the Second Meeting of the ICAO Rescue and Fire Fighting Panel (RFFP-II)," International Civil Aviation Organization (ICAO), Montreal, Quebec, Canada, June 5–16, 1972.
5. ICAO, "International Standards and Recommended Practices (SARPs) for Annex 14 to the Convention on International Civil Aviation, Aerodromes," amendment 4, paragraph 9.2.21, International Civil Aviation Organization (ICAO), Montreal, Quebec, Canada, Jan. 11, 2001.
6. OSHA, "Proper PPE for Firefighters," Standards Interpretation and Compliance Letters, http://www.osha-slc.gov/OshDoc/Interp_data/I19970715B.html, July 15, 1997.
7. FAA, "Airport Rescue and Fire Fighting Personnel Protective Ensemble for Proximity Fire Fighting," *Advisory Circular 150/5210-14A,* U.S. Department of Transportation, Federal Aviation Administration, Washington, DC, 1995.
8. *Fire Management/Suppression Systems/Concepts Relating to Aircraft Cabin Fire Safety,* document reference no. DOT/FAA/CT-82/134, U.S. Department of Transportation, Federal Aviation Administration, Atlantic City, NJ, Oct. 1983.
9. National Transportation Safety Board (NTSB), "Emergency Evacuation of Commercial Airplanes," Safety Study, PB2000-917002, NTSB/SS-00/01, Notation 7266, National Transportation Safety Board, Washington, DC, June 27, 2001.
10. *International Fire Service Training Association (IFSTA)—Aircraft Rescue and Firefighting,* 4th ed., Fire Protection Publications, Oklahoma State University, Stillwater, OK, 2001, p. 179.
11. OSHA Regulations and Standards, 29 CFR, Part 1910, Subpart I PPE, Standard 1910.134, "Respiratory Protection," U.S. Department of Labor, Occupation Safety and Health Administration, Washington, DC, http://www.OSHA.gov.
12. NTSB, "Abstract of Final Aviation Accident Report, Runway Overrun During Landing Involving American Airlines Flight 1420, McDonnell Douglas MD-82, N215AA," NTSB-AAR-01/02(5), National Transportation Safety Board, Little Rock, AR, June 1, 1999.
13. *The ALPA Guide to Accident Survival Factors,* Airline Pilots Association International, Herndon, Virginia, 1998.
14. "Surviving the Crash," *The Need to Improve Lifesaving Measures at Our Airport,* Coalition for Airport and Airplane Passenger Safety (CAAPS)/International Association of Fire Fighters (IAFF), Washington, DC, 1999.

NFPA Codes, Standards, and Recommended Practices

Reference to the following NFPA codes, standards, and recommended practices will provide further information on aircraft rescue and fire fighting discussed in this chapter. (See the latest version of The NFPA Catalog *for availability of current editions of the following documents.)*

NFPA 402, *Guide for Aircraft Rescue and Fire Fighting Operations*

NFPA 403, *Standard for Aircraft Rescue and Fire-Fighting Services at Airports*

NFPA 405, *Standard for the Recurring Proficiency of Airport Fire Fighters*

NFPA 412, *Standard for Evaluating Aircraft Rescue and Fire-Fighting Foam Equipment*

NFPA 414, *Standard for Aircraft Rescue and Fire-Fighting Vehicles*

NFPA 1003, *Standard for Airport Fire Fighter Professional Qualifications*

NFPA 1500, *Standard on Fire Department Occupational Safety and Health Program*

NFPA 1971, *Standard on Protective Ensembles for Structural Fire Fighting and Proximity Fire Fighting*

References

Airline Pilots Association, *Large Frame Aircraft (LFA) Fire Fighting Validation—TCA/PCA Methodology Evaluation,* Airline Pilots Association International, Herndon, VA, Jan. 1995.

"Analysis of Test Criteria for Specifying Foam Firefighting Agents for Aircraft Rescue and Firefighting," Final Report, DOT/FAA/CT-94/04, U.S. Department of Transportation, Federal Aviation Administration, Atlantic City International Airport, NJ, Aug. 1994.

"Final Recommendation to ARAC, Airport Certification Issues Group relative to 14 CFR Part 139, Subpart D, (6)," Aviation Rulemaking Advisory Committee, Airport Certification Issues Group, ARFF Requirements Working Group, U.S. Department of Transportation, Federal Aviation Administration, Washington, DC, Mar. 2004.

"Guide Specification for Aircraft Rescue and Fire Fighting Vehicles," FAA-AC 150/5220-10D, U.S. Department of Transportation, Federal Aviation Administration, Washington, DC, Sept. 2007.

Websites

Aircraft Rescue & Fire Fighting Working Group (ARFFWG)
http://www.arffwg.org

International Aviation Fire Protection Association (IAFPA)
http://www.iafpa.org.uk

Federal Aviation Administration/Airport Technology R&D Branch
http://www.airtech.tc.faa.gov/safety/resfire.asp

National Transportation Safety Board (NTSB)
http://www.ntsb.gov

Canadian Transportation Safety Board (TSB)
http://www.tsb.gc.ca

Chapter 8

Managing the Response to Hazardous Material Incidents

Charles J. Wright

Chapter Contents

Key Terms

bulk packaging, damage assessment, decontamination, elevated temperature material, emergency, *Emergency Response Guidebook,* hazard class, hazardous material, hazardous material data sheet, incident management system (IMS), personal protective equipment, shipping paper, weapons of mass destruction (WMD)

Hazardous materials may be an important part of our high standard of living, but when a release occurs, it can harm people, including response personnel, property, and the environment. It can disrupt critical systems, damage reputations, and create a residual fear of hazardous materials. The effective management of hazardous materials and other chemicals in the community requires (1) prevention, (2) preparedness, (3) response, and (4) recovery activities. This chapter focuses on a risk-based response process, but the underlying concepts apply to the other hazardous material management activities as well.

The purpose of the response effort is "to change the sequence of events constituting the emergency before it has run its course naturally and to minimize harm that would otherwise occur."[1] To accomplish this purpose, the following four duties are undertaken (Figure 13.8.1):

1. Analyze the problem.
2. Plan the response.
3. Implement the planned response.
4. Evaluate progress and adjust accordingly.

Each duty involves a series of tasks and steps that must be considered and resolved by decisions and actions. These duties, when supported by the response community, are the framework for an appropriate, survival-oriented response to hazardous material incidents. Reasoned decisions based on this approach will minimize the harm resulting from a hazardous material incident and reduce the risk to responders.

See also Section 7, Chapter 5, "Hazardous Waste Control"; and Section 13, Chapter 6, "Public Fire Protection and Hazmat Management."

DEFINITIONS

The following terms are used in this chapter.

Bulk packaging is any containment system, including transport vehicles and freight containers, having a capacity meeting one of the following criteria: liquid—internal volume of more than 119 gal (450 L); solid—capacity of more than 882 lb (400 kg); or compressed gas—water capacity of more than 1000 lb (454 kg).

Containment systems (or containers) are a combination of a container and its closures used to isolate the contents from the surrounding environment. A closure is a device for closing the openings in a container.

Elevated temperature material (DOT) means a material that, when offered for transportation or transported in a bulk packaging, is (1) in a liquid phase and at a temperature at or above 212°F

Charles J. Wright is manager of hazardous materials training at the Union Pacific Railroad in Omaha, Nebraska.

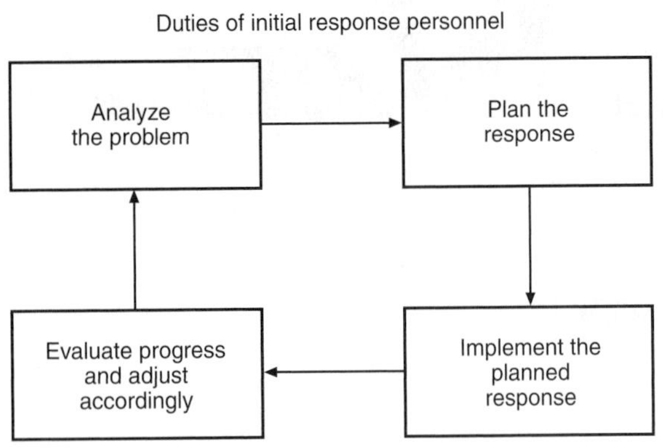

FIGURE 13.8.1 Response Duties Associated with Emergencies Involving Hazardous Materials

(100°C), (2) in a liquid phase with a flashpoint at or above 100°F (37.8°C) that is intentionally heated and offered for transportation or transported at or above its flashpoint, or (3) in a solid phase and at a temperature at or above 464°F (240°C).

Emergency is the term used for a sudden, generally unexpected disruption in a normal sequence of events requiring immediate action.

Hazardous material, for the purpose of this chapter, is a substance that on release has the potential of causing harm to people, property, or the environment, including weapons of mass destruction (WMD).

Hazardous material (DOT) means a substance or material that has been determined by the Secretary of Transportation to be capable of posing an unreasonable risk to health, safety, and property when transported in commerce, and that has been so designated. Table 13.8.1 lists the internationally accepted hazard classes and divisions associated with hazardous materials in transportation. This definition includes hazardous materials, hazardous substances, hazardous wastes, elevated temperature materials, marine pollutants, and dangerous goods internationally.

Hazardous substance (DOT) means a material, including its mixtures and solutions, in a quantity, in one package, that equals or exceeds the reportable quantity (RQ) listed in DOT's Hazardous Materials Regulations (49 CFR, Parts 171–172).

Hazardous waste (DOT) means any material that is subject to the Hazardous Waste Manifest Requirements of the U.S. Environmental Protection Agency (EPA) specified in 40 CFR, Part 262.

Hazardous material incident is an emergency involving the release or potential release of hazardous materials/weapons of mass destruction (WMD) with or without fire.

Marine pollutant (DOT) means a material that is harmful to aquatic life (listed in 49 CFR 172.101, Appendix B).

Nonbulk packaging is any containment system having a capacity meeting one of the following criteria: liquid—internal volume of 119 gal (450 L) or less; solid—capacity of 882 lb (400 kg) or less; or compressed gas—water capacity of 101 lb (454 kg) or less.

Outcomes are the direct and indirect results or consequences associated with an emergency. Direct outcomes include death, injury, property damage, and environmental damage. Indirect outcomes include system disruption, damaged reputations, and residual fear of hazardous materials.

Response community is composed of those individuals, agencies, or companies who have resources and can become involved in handling a hazardous material incident. These may include fire service personnel, law enforcement personnel, rescue and emergency medical personnel, private sector response personnel (carriers, manufacturers, and contractors), and local, state and federal government response personnel.

Weapons of mass destructions (WMD) are defined in NFPA 472, *Standard for Competence of Responders to Hazardous Materials/Weapons of Mass Destruction Incidents*, as (a) any destructive device, such as any explosive, incendiary, or poison gas, bomb, grenade, rocket having a propellant charge of more than four ounces (112 grams), missile having an explosive or incendiary charge of more than one quarter ounce (7 grams), or device similar to the above; (b) any weapon involving toxic or poisonous chemicals; (c) any weapon involving a disease organism; (d) any weapon that is designed to release radiation or radioactivity at a level dangerous to human life.

HAZARD CLASSES AND DIVISIONS

The following list presents the internationally accepted definitions of the nine numbered hazard classes and divisions. These definitions should not be used to determine compliance with the regulations, because they do not indicate the exceptions and specificity found in the regulations in all cases.[2]

Class 1 *(Explosives and Blasting Agents)*

Explosive means any substance or article, including a device, that is designed to function by explosion (i.e., an extremely rapid release of gas and heat) or that, by chemical reaction within itself, is able to function in a similar manner even if not designed to function by explosion. Explosives in Class 1 are divided into six divisions. Each division will have a letter designation (compatibility group letter.)

Division 1.1. Consists of explosives that have a mass explosion hazard. A mass explosion is one that affects almost the entire load instantaneously.

Division 1.2. Consists of explosives that have a projection hazard but not a mass explosion hazard.

Division 1.3. Consists of explosives that have a fire hazard and either a minor blast hazard or a minor projection hazard or both, but not a mass explosion hazard.

Division 1.4. Consists of explosive devices that present a minor explosion hazard. No device may contain more than 0.9 oz (25 g) of a detonating material.

Division 1.5. Consists of very insensitive explosives. These substances have a mass explosion hazard but are so insensitive that there is very little probability of initiation or of transition from burning to detonation under normal conditions of transport.

TABLE 13.8.1 International Hazard Classes and Divisions

Classes and Divisions	*Examples of Materials (by Hazard Class or Division)*	*General Hazard Properties (Not All-Inclusive)*
Class 1—Explosives and blasting agents		Explosive; exposure to heat, shock, or contamination could result in thermal and mechanical hazards
Division 1.1—explosives with mass explosion hazard	Dynamite, TNT, black powder	
Division 1.2—explosives with projection hazard	Projectiles with bursting charges	
Division 1.3—explosives with fire, minor blast, or minor projection hazard	Propellant explosives, rocket motors, special fireworks	
Division 1.4—explosive devices with minor explosion hazard	Common fireworks	
Division 1.5—very insensitive explosives	Ammonium nitrate–fuel oil mix, blasting agent	
Division 1.6—extremely insensitive explosives		
Class 2—Gases		Under pressure; container may rupture violently (fire and nonfire); may be flammable, poisonous, corrosive, asphyxiant, and/or thermally unstable
Division 2.1—flammable gases	Propane, butadiene, acetylene, methyl chloride	
Division 2.2—nonflammable, nonpoisonous (nontoxic) gas	Carbon dioxide, anhydrous ammonia	
Division 2.3—poisonous (toxic) gas by inhalation	Arsine, phosgene, chlorine, methyl bromide	
Class 3—Flammable liquids *(flashpoint less than 141°F [60°C])*	Acetone, amyl acetate, gasoline, methyl alcohol	Flammable; container may rupture violently from heat/fire; may be corrosive, toxic, and/or thermally unstable
Class 4—Flammable solids and reactive liquids and solids		Flammable, some spontaneously; may be water reactive, toxic, and/or corrosive; may be extremely difficult to extinguish
Division 4.1—flammable solids	Nitrocellulose, matches	
Division 4.2—spontaneously combustible materials	Phosphorus, aluminum alkyls, charcoal	
Division 4.3—dangerous when wet materials	Calcium carbide, potassium	
Class 5—Oxidizers and organic peroxides		Supplies oxygen to support combustion; sensitive to heat, shock, friction, and/or contamination
Division 5.1—oxidizers	Ammonium nitrate fertilizer	
Division 5.2—organic peroxides	Dibenzoyl peroxide	
Class 6—Toxic (poisonous) materials		Toxic by inhalation, ingestion, and skin/eye contact; may be flammable
Division 6.1—poisonous (toxic) material	Aniline, arsenic, tear gas, carbon tetrachloride	
Division 6.2—infectious substances	Anthrax, botulism, tetanus	
Class 7—Radioactive materials	Cobalt, uranium hexafluoride	May cause burns and biologic effects; may be in form of energy or matter
Class 8—Corrosive materials	Hydrochloric acid, sulfuric acid, sodium hydroxide	Disintegration of contacted tissues; may be fuming and/or water reactive
Class 9—Miscellaneous hazardous materials	Adipic acid, molten sulfur, dry ice, PCBs	

Division 1.6. Consists of extremely insensitive articles that do not have a mass explosion hazard. These articles contain only extremely insensitive detonating substances and demonstrate a negligible probability of accidental initiation or propagation.

Class 2 *(Gases)*

Division 2.1. *Flammable gas* means any material that is a gas at 68°F (20°C) or less and 14.7 psi (101.3 kPa) of pressure, or a material that has a boiling point of 68°F (20°C) or less at 14.7 psi (101.3 kPa) that meets either of the following criteria:

1. Is ignitible at 14.7 psi (101.3 kPa) when in a mixture of 13 percent or less by volume with air
2. Has a flammable range of at least 12 percent in air at 14.7 psi (101.3 kPa) regardless of the lower limit

Division 2.2. Nonflammable, nontoxic (nonpoisonous) compressed gas, including compressed gas, liquefied gas, pressurized cryogenic gas, and compressed gas in solution means any material (or mixture) that exerts in the packaging an absolute pressure of 41 psi (280 kPa) at 68°F (20°C).

A *cryogenic liquid* means a refrigerated liquefied gas having a boiling point colder than –130°F (–90°C) at 14.7 psi (101.3 kPa) absolute.

Division 2.3. *Toxic (poisonous) gas* means a material that is a gas at 68°F (20°C) or less and a pressure of 14.7 psi or 1 atm (101.3 kPa), that has a boiling point of 68°F (20°C) or less at 14.7 psi (101.3 kPa), and that has either of the following characteristics:

1. Is known to be so toxic to humans as to pose a hazard to health during transportation
2. In the absence of adequate data on human toxicity, is presumed to be toxic to humans because, when tested on laboratory animals, it has an LC_{50} value not more than 5000 ppm

Class 3 *(Flammable Liquids)*

Flammable liquids are any liquids having a flashpoint of not more than 140°F (60°C).

In the United States and Canada, an additional worded hazard class, *combustible liquids,* has been added to designate liquids with flashpoints above 140°F (60°C) and below 200°F (93°C). Actually, the U.S. regulations allow shippers to reclassify liquids with flashpoints above 100°F (38°C) as *combustible liquids.*

Class 4 *(Flammable Solids and Reactive Liquids and Solids)*

Division 4.1. *Flammable solid* means any of the following three types of materials:

1. *Wetted explosives.* Explosives wetted with sufficient water, alcohol, or plasticizers to suppress explosive properties
2. *Self-reactive materials.* Materials that are liable to undergo, at normal or elevated temperatures, a strongly exothermal decomposition caused by excessively high transport temperatures or by contamination
3. *Readily combustible solids.* Solids that may cause a fire through friction and any metal powders that can be ignited

Division 4.2. *Spontaneously combustible solid* means either of the following materials:

1. *Pyrophoric material.* A liquid or solid that, even in small quantities and without an external ignition source, can ignite within 5 minutes after coming in contact with air
2. *Self-heating material.* A material that, when in contact with air and without an energy supply, is liable to self-heat

Division 4.3. *Dangerous-when-wet material* means a material that, by contact with water, is liable to become spontaneously flammable or to give off flammable or toxic gas at a rate greater than 1 L/kg of the material, per hour.

Class 5 *(Oxidizers and Organic Peroxides)*

Division 5.1. *Oxidizer* means a material that may, generally by yielding oxygen, cause or enhance the combustion of other materials.

Division 5.2. *Organic peroxide* means any organic compound containing oxygen (O) in the bivalent -O-O- structure and that may be considered a derivative of hydrogen peroxide, whereby one or more of the hydrogen atoms have been replaced by organic radicals.

Class 6 *(Toxic or Poisonous Materials and Infectious Substances)*

Division 6.1. *Toxic (poisonous) material* means a material, other than a gas, that is either known to be so toxic to humans as to afford a hazard to health during transportation, or in the absence of adequate data on human toxicity, is presumed to be toxic to humans.

Division 6.2. *Infectious substance* means a viable microorganism, or its toxin, that causes or may cause disease in humans or animals. Infectious substance and etiologic agent are synonymous.

Class 7 *(Radioactive Materials)*

Radioactive material is any material containing radionuclides where both the activity concentration and the total activity of the shipment exceed specific values.

Class 8 *(Corrosive Materials)*

Corrosive material means either a liquid or solid that causes visible destruction or irreversible alterations in human skin tissue at the site of contact, or a liquid that has a severe corrosion rate on steel or aluminum.

Class 9 *(Miscellaneous Hazardous Materials)*

Miscellaneous hazardous material means a material that presents a hazard during transport, but that is not included in another hazard class, including the following:

1. Any material that has an anesthetic, noxious, or other similar property that could cause extreme annoyance or discomfort to a flight-crew member so as to prevent the correct performance of assigned duties
2. Any material that is not included in any other hazard class (a hazardous substance or a hazardous waste)

ORM-D Materials

In the United States, the hazard class ORM-D material (Other Regulated Materials-D) is used to designate materials, such as consumer commodities and some small arms ammunition, that present a limited hazard during transportation, due to their form, quantity, and packaging.

Other Definitions

The following are *hazard zones* associated with gases (Class 2) and listed as poison-inhalation hazards:

- *Hazard zone A.* LC_{50} less than or equal to 200 ppm
- *Hazard zone B.* LC_{50} greater than 200 ppm and less than or equal to 1000 ppm
- *Hazard zone C.* LC_{50} greater than 1000 ppm and less than or equal to 3000 ppm
- *Hazard zone D.* LC_{50} greater than 3000 ppm and less than or equal to 5000 ppm

The following are *hazard zones* associated with liquid and listed as poison-inhalation hazards in Classes 3, 4, 5, 6, and 8:

- *Hazard zone A.* LC_{50} less than or equal to 200 ppm
- *Hazard zone B.* LC_{50} greater than 200 ppm and less than or equal to 1000 ppm

Forbidden means prohibited from being offered or accepted for transportation. Prohibition does not apply if these materials are diluted, stabilized, or incorporated in devices.

ANALYZING THE HAZARDOUS MATERIAL PROBLEM

Background

Responding to emergencies involving hazardous materials is not easy. Just the sheer numbers of these materials present an intimidating list for those who respond to the emergencies they create. Consider the following examples:

1. A review of the Chemical Abstract Service's (CAS) list indicates that out of 1.5 million chemicals or chemical formulations found outside of the laboratory, more than 63,000 are considered hazardous.
2. The U.S. Department of Transportation (DOT) regulates the transportation of some 4000 hazardous materials.
3. The Occupational Safety and Health Administration (OSHA) of the U.S. Department of Labor regulates about 600 hazardous substances on the basis of occupational exposure.

A national study by Industrial Economics, Inc., sponsored by the U.S. Environmental Protection Agency (EPA),[3] and subsequent regional studies indicate that the most commonly released chemical is vehicle fuel. The following are two other findings that are of interest:

- 49.5 percent of the rest of the releases involved only 10 chemicals in addition to vehicle fuels. (Table 13.8.2 lists these chemicals.) These additional 10 chemicals are typically produced in the largest volume.
- 74.8 percent of the releases occurred in facilities (production, storage, and use) whereas the remaining 25.2 percent occurred in transportation.

Regional differences from this national study may change the makeup of the list locally.

Overview

The process of analyzing the hazardous material problem (sizeup) provides a way of determining the specific hazards and the potential magnitude of the problem in terms of outcomes. An understanding of the magnitude of the problem is the basis for subsequent decisions on the handling of an incident. Failure to consider all the hazards increases the responder's risk.

The analysis process begins when a responder receives notification of a problem and continues throughout the incident, typically at the scene threatened by any hazardous materials involved. Pre-emergency planning, following the same tasks and steps, lessens the time expended to achieve a safe and cost-effective response at a hazardous material incident, and also increases the available response options for that response.

An analysis of the hazardous material problem involves completing the following tasks (Figure 13.8.2):

1. Detect presence of hazardous material.
2. Initiate command and control activities.
3. Survey hazardous material incident.
4. Collect and interpret hazard and response information.
5. Assess extent of damage to containment system.
6. Predict likely behavior of containment system or contents.
7. Estimate potential outcomes within engulfed area.

Detecting the Presence of Hazardous Materials

The first task in analyzing, and ultimately understanding and solving, hazardous material problems is that of recognizing

TABLE 13.8.2 Most Commonly Released Hazardous Materials with Percentage of Releases and Percentage of Deaths and Injuries Associated with the Material[3]

Chemical Name	*Percentage of Releases*	*Percentage of Deaths and Injuries*
PCB (polychlorinated biphenyls)	23.0	2.8
Sulfuric acid	6.5	4.7
Anhydrous ammonia	3.7	6.8
Chlorine	3.5	9.6
Hydrochloric acid	3.1	5.6
Sodium hydroxide	2.6	1.9
Methyl alcohol	1.7	0.4
Nitric acid	1.7	1.5
Toluene	1.4	2.4
Methyl chloride	1.4	0.0

Source: Based on Industrial Economics, Inc., database.

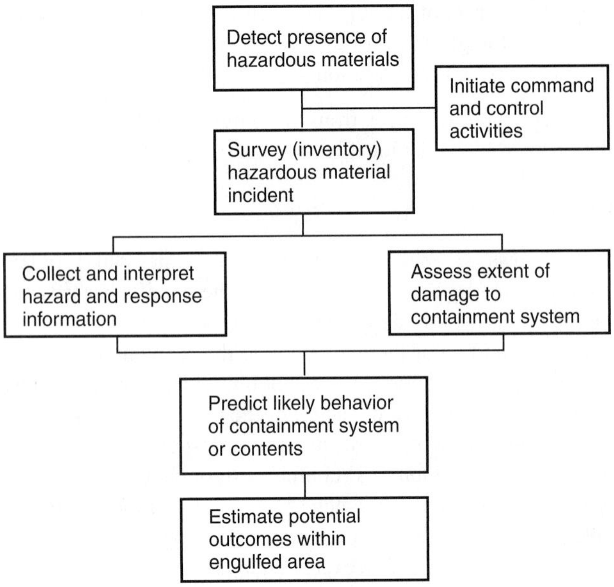

FIGURE 13.8.2 Tasks Associated with Analyzing a Hazardous Materials Problem

those situations where hazardous materials are present. This recognition task begins with the receipt of the initial notification of an emergency and continues throughout the handling of an emergency. Any emergency should be approached from a direction that will provide protection if hazardous materials are present. As with all tasks in the analysis process, detection should be performed from a safe location—upwind, uphill, and upstream, if possible.

The following steps should be taken when responding to any emergency:

1. *Review the initial information received for indications of hazardous materials.* Clues to the presence of hazardous materials may be provided by the caller or dispatcher.

2. *Review the occupancy, location, or local planning documents for indications of hazardous materials.* Planning documents, such as local emergency response plans, industry site-specific plans, and fire service pre-emergency response plans, may indicate the presence of hazardous materials. During pre-emergency planning activities, typical occupancies and locations where hazardous materials are manufactured, transported, stored, used, or disposed of in the community are identified.

3. *Look for containment system characteristics that indicate hazardous materials.* The hemispherical ends on the container or the protective housing around the fittings on top of a pressure tank car are indications of hazardous materials. An awareness of the various types of hazardous material containment systems is useful.

4. *Look for facility and transportation markings and color that indicate hazardous materials.* The use of color is not consistent nationwide; however, color markings may be consistent in local areas. Various markings indicate the presence of hazardous materials. Some examples are as follows.

Identification numbers are four-digit numbers assigned to a specific hazardous material or group of hazardous materials. They are used to cross-reference the name of a material in order to access hazard and response information for that material. In transportation, identification numbers must be displayed on the following:

- Nonbulk packages of hazardous materials (except limited quantities) printed adjacent to the required labels on the package
- Bulk packages of hazardous materials, such as cargo tanks, portable tanks, tank cars, and other bulk shipments; on bulk packages, identification numbers can be displayed on an orange panel, in the center of the appropriate placard, or in the center of a placard-sized, square-on-point white display (Figure 13.8.3)

On shipping papers, identification numbers are preceded by the prefix "UN" (United Nations) for domestic and international shipments or "NA" (North American) for shipments considered hazardous only within North America.

NFPA 704 *markings* are diamond-shaped symbols used within facilities to alert people to the type and degree of

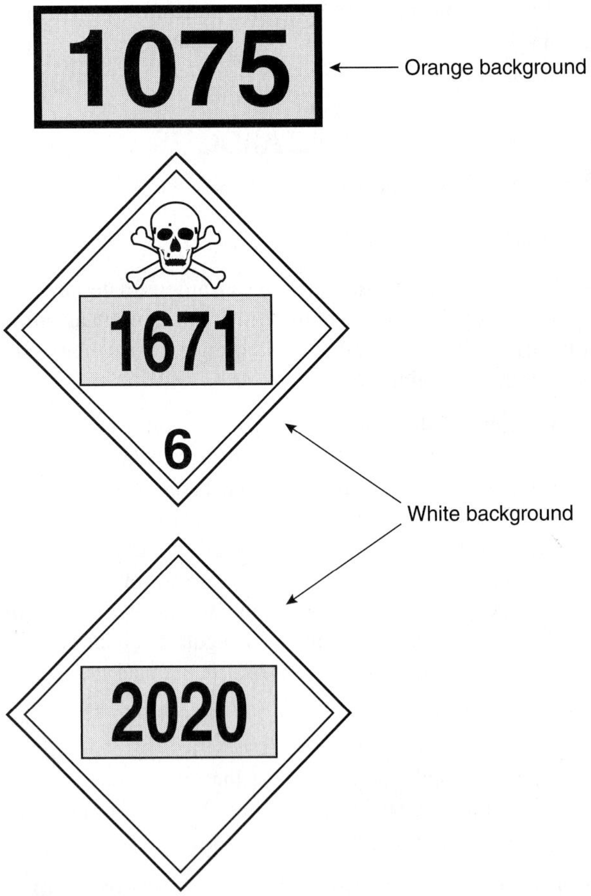

FIGURE 13.8.3 Identification Numbers. The rectangular box has an orange background. The diamonds have white backgrounds.

hazard. (See NFPA 704, *Standard System for the Identification of the Hazards of Materials for Emergency Response.*) They may be found on nonbulk packages; however, they are not used on transport vehicles. The diamond-shaped symbol is divided into four color-coded quadrants (Figure 13.8.4). The blue in the left quadrant refers to the health hazard; the red in the top quadrant indicates the flammability hazard; the yellow in the right quadrant refers to the reactivity hazard; and the bottom quadrant carries special information, such as "OX" for oxidizers or "~~W~~" for water-reactive materials. Each quadrant contains a number from 0 to 4 that represents the relative degree of hazard (0 is low; 4 is high) (Figure 13.8.5).

FIGURE 13.8.4 Sample NFPA Marking (Source: 2007 edition of NFPA 704, *Standard System for the Identification of the Hazards of Materials for Emergency Response*)

NFPA 704 Marking System

Scale	Health Hazard	Flammability Hazard	Instability Hazard
4	Materials that, under emergency conditions, can be lethal	Materials that will rapidly or completely vaporize at atmospheric pressure and normal ambient temperature or that are readily dispersed in air and that burn readily	Materials that in themselves are readily capable of detonation, explosive decomposition, or explosive reaction at normal temperatures and pressures. This includes materials that are sensitive to localized thermal or mechanical shock at normal temperatures and pressures.
3	Materials that, under emergency conditions, can cause serious or permanent injury	Liquids and solids that can be ignited under almost all atmosphere and temperature conditions. Materials in this degree produce hazardous atmospheres with air under almost all ambient temperatures or, though unaffected by ambient temperatures, are readily ignited under almost all conditions	Materials that in themselves are capable of detonation, explosive decomposition, or explosive reaction but that require a strong initiating source or that must be heated under confinement before initiation
2	Materials that, under emergency conditions, can cause temporary incapacitation or residual injury	Materials that must be moderately heated or exposed to relatively high ambient temperatures before ignition can occur. Materials in this degree would not under normal conditions form hazardous atmospheres with air but under high ambient temperatures or under moderate heating might release vapor in sufficient quantities to produce hazardous atmospheres with air.	Materials that in themselves undergo violent chemical change at elevated temperatures and pressures
1	Materials that, under emergency conditions, can cause severe irritation	Materials that must be preheated before ignition can occur. Materials in this degree require considerable preheating, under all ambient temperature conditions before ignition and combustion can occur.	Materials that in themselves are normally stable but that can become unstable at elevated temperatures and pressures
0	Materials that, under emergency conditions, would offer no hazard beyond that of ordinary combustible materials	Materials that will not burn. This includes any material that will not burn in air when exposed to a temperature of 1500°F (816°C) for a period of 5 minutes.	Materials that in themselves are normally stable even under fire conditions

FIGURE 13.8.5 Significance of Numbers on NFPA 704 Marking System (Source: 2001 edition of NFPA 704, *Standard System for the Identification of the Hazards of Materials for Emergency Response*)

Military markings are used to indicate hazardous materials for military shipments.

Special hazard communication markings are used in facility situations to indicate hazardous materials.

Warning labels indicate the presence of hazardous materials using words such as *warning, danger, caution,* and *poison.*

Pipeline markers mark the location of pipelines, especially where the pipeline crosses a street.

Container markings, such as the stenciled name of the contents, also may indicate the presence of hazardous materials.

5. *Look for placards and labels.* Placards and labels are diamond-shaped symbols that are used internationally to communicate the presence of hazardous materials in transportation. Placards 10.8 in. by 10.8 in. (273 mm by 273 mm) are required on some bulk packages, such as transport vehicles (e.g., cargo tanks, portable tanks, tank cars, and hopper cars). Labels, 4 in. by 4 in. (102 mm by 102 mm) or smaller for cylinders, are found on some nonbulk packages. Placards and labels convey information by their color, symbol, hazard class and division number, and either the hazard class wording or four-digit identification number. DOT Chart 12 provides examples of U.S. and Canadian placards and labels (Figure 13.8.6).

Transport vehicles and freight containers could contain up to 1000 lb (454 kg) of certain hazardous materials without a placard being applied. Limited-quantity, Division 6.2 (infectious substance/etiologic agents), and ORM-D shipments do not require placards. To determine load/empty status, use the shipping papers. Square white backgrounds are used behind Division 1.1, Division 1.2, Division 2.3, Division 6.1 Packing Group I Zone A, and Class 7 placards to indicate special handling. The dangerous placard indicates a mixed load of several classes of hazardous materials.

6. *Obtain and review facility documents or shipping papers.* Shipping papers accompany each shipment during transportation and provide detailed information about the contents of the shipment. These shipping papers are used in the various modes of

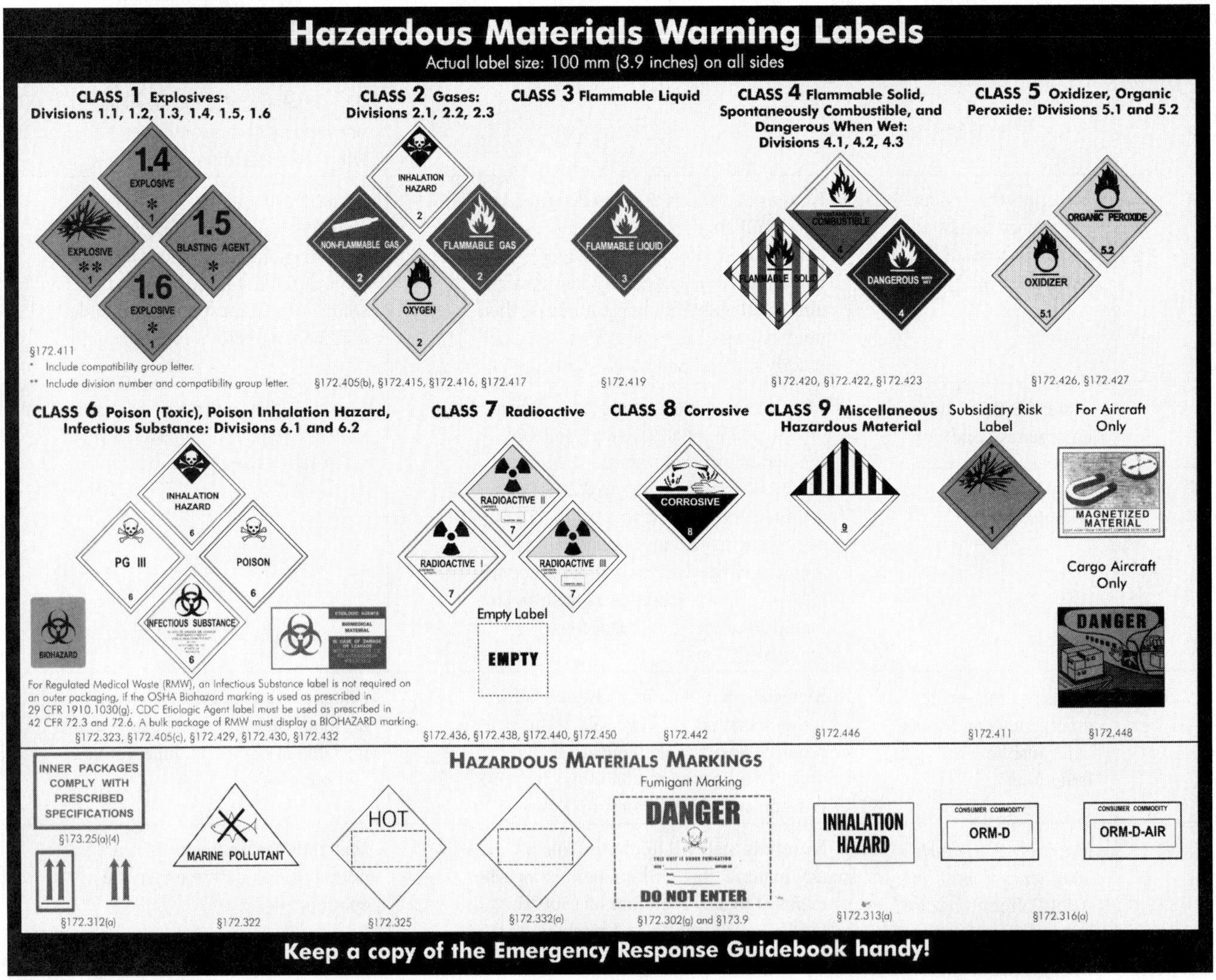

FIGURE 13.8.6 DOT Chart 12 Depicting Hazardous Materials Marking, Labeling, and Placarding

TABLE 13.8.3 Shipping Papers by Mode of Transportation, Title of Shipping Paper, Location, and Responsible Person

Mode of Transportation	*Title of Shipping Paper*	*Location of Shipping Papers*	*Responsible Person*
Highway	Bill of lading or freight bill	Cab of vehicle	Driver
Rail	Train list or train consist and/or waybill	With member of train crew (conductor or engineer)	Conductor
Water	Dangerous cargo manifest	Wheelhouse or pipelike container or barge	Captain or master
Air	Air bill with shipper's certification for restricted articles	Cockpit (may also be found attached to the outside of packages)	Pilot

transportation (highway, rail, water, and air) and are listed in Table 13.8.3 by mode of transportation, title of shipping paper, location of shipping papers, and the person responsible. Shipping papers may indicate the presence of hazardous materials through a variety of required entries (all of which are not always present). The most common entries include the proper shipping name, hazard class or division, identification number, packing group, and the total quantity (by weight, volume, or as otherwise appropriate).

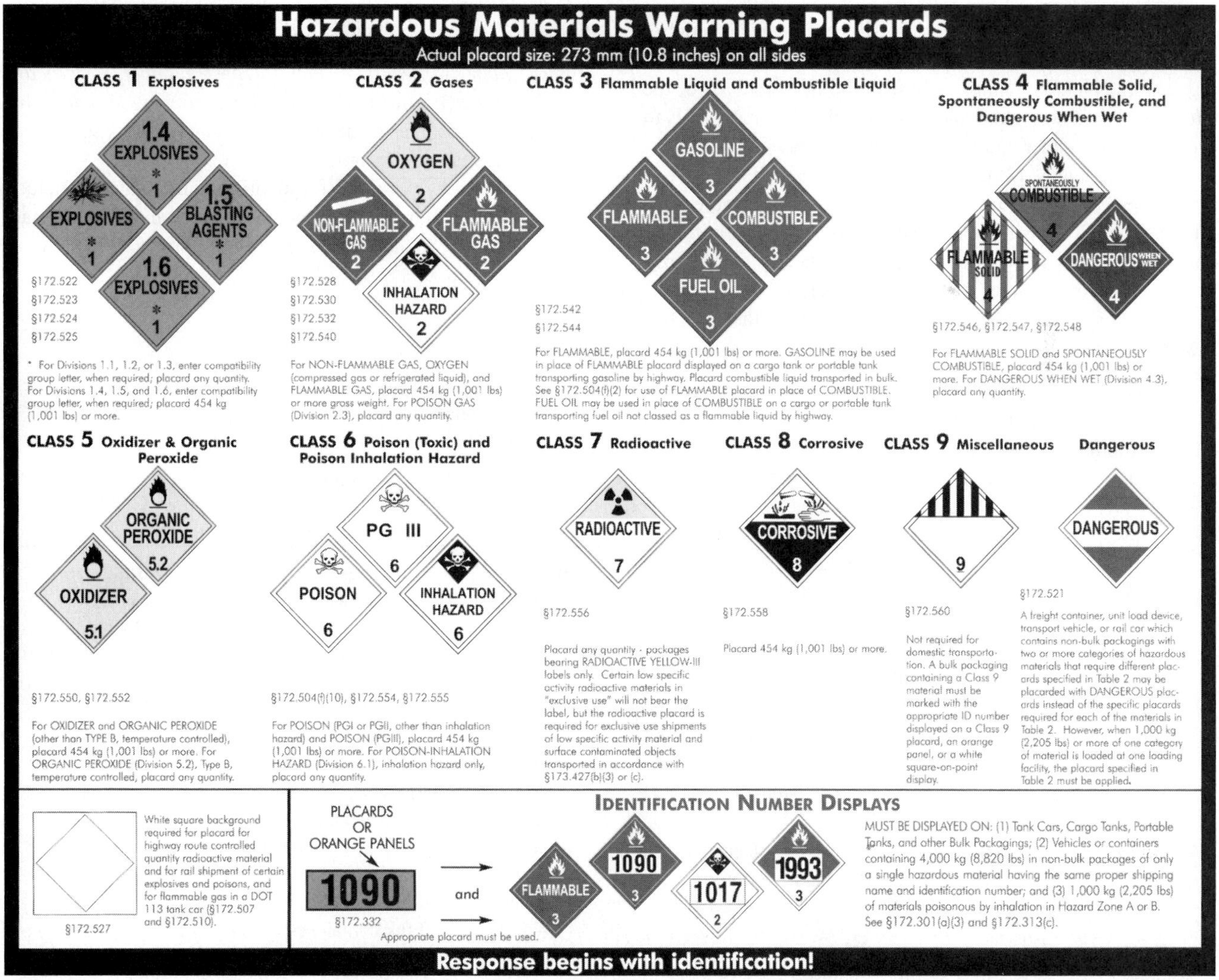

FIGURE 13.8.6 Continued

Additional entries may include technical and chemical group names, the letters RQ (reportable quantity notation) POISON—INHALATION HAZARD, LIMITED QUANTITY notation, DANGEROUS WHEN WET notation, and shipper contact information. Shipping papers also include telephone number and emergency-response information for the specific commodity.

Facility documents include the material safety data sheet (MSDS). The MSDS is a document that provides information about the composition, physical and chemical properties, health and safety hazards, emergency response, and waste disposal of materials required by OSHA in 29 CFR 1910.1200.

7. *Identify clues (other than occupancy/locations, container shape, markings/color, and placards/labels) that use sight, sound, and odor to indicate hazardous materials.* Sensual indications include chemical odors, dead animals and fish, vapor clouds, flames or smoke, irritation of the skin or eyes, the hiss of escaping gas, or the sound of an explosion.

As soon as the presence of hazardous materials is detected, move to the next task in the analysis process.

Initiating Command and Control Activities

Although not part of the analysis process, command and control activities should be initiated on detecting the presence of hazardous materials and simultaneously with the initial survey of the situation. These command and control actions are taken: (1) to protect the responder and others during completion of analysis and planning duties, (2) to provide for a command structure at the incident, and (3) to provide for notification of resources required to handle the situation. Specific procedures for initiating command and control activities are found in the local emergency response plan or organization's standard operating procedures.

To initiate command and control activities, take the following steps:

1. *Implement an incident command system.* This step provides organization of the incident scene and may begin prior to arrival on the scene.
2. *Locate personnel at a safe distance from the problem.* With consideration of the terrain and weather conditions, response personnel should stop at a safe location from the incident—uphill, upwind, and upstream. Suggested minimum "safe" distances should be specified in the local emergency response plan or the organization's standard operating procedures. At this point, the analysis process is not complete, and sufficient information is not available to determine safe distances.
3. *Initiate the notification process.* Specific procedures and contacts for notification of required resources should be developed prior to an emergency and listed in the local planning documents.
4. *Control access to the site.* Prevent unauthorized persons from entering the area to reduce the negative outcomes in the incident.

The command and control actions taken depend on both the responder's level of training and the resources available. They should be attempted without risk to the responder.

Surveying the Hazardous Materials Incident

After detecting the presence of hazardous materials in an emergency, and while initiating command and control activities, the next task is to survey or inventory the hazardous material incident. Completion of this task provides an inventory of the containment systems and materials involved, materials released, and surrounding conditions. This incident survey should be conducted from a safe distance, using aided vision, without exposure to the released materials.

The following steps should be completed during the survey of a hazardous material incident:

1. *Identify each containment system by type, identifier, and size.* Containment systems fit into one of three types: (1) nonbulk, (2) bulk, or (3) facility containment systems (Table 13.8.4). The containment system identifier (e.g., facility or carrier name and number) is used to differentiate one containment system from another and to allow tracking of that container throughout the incident. The quantity within, or capacity of, the containment system can be obtained from markings on the container or entries on the shipping papers or facility documents. The quantity information will help indicate the magnitude of the problem.

2. *Identify the name, identification number, or placard applied to each hazardous material containment system.* This information provides a means of accessing various sources of hazard and response information.

For facilities. Sources for identifying the material include pre-emergency planning document, markings and color, contact with the facility manager, and review of appropriate MSDS.

TABLE 13.8.4 Types of Nonbulk, Bulk, and Facility Containment Systems[4]

Transportation		*Facility Containment Systems*
Nonbulk	*Bulk*	
Bags	Bulk bags	Buildings
Bottles	Bulk boxes	Machinery
Boxes	Cargo tanks	Open piles (outdoors and indoors)
Carboys	Covered hopper cars	Piping
Cylinders	Freight containers	Reactors (chemical and nuclear)
Drums	Gondolas	Storage bins, cabinets, or shelves
Jerricans	Intermediate bulk containers (IBCs)	
Multicell	Pneumatic hopper trailers	
Tanks and storage vessels packages	Portable tanks and bins	
Wooden barrels	Protective overpacks for radioactive materials	
	Tank cars	
	Tank containers	
	Ton containers	
	Van trailers	

In transportation. The identity of the hazardous material can be determined from the identification number, commodity stencil, type of placard or label applied, shipping paper entries, and manufacturer, shipper, or consignee contacts using the 24-hour emergency telephone number on the shipping papers. Pipeline markers provide the name of the commodity or at least the name and telephone number of the pipeline company.

3. *Identify leaking containment systems.* Clues indicating leakage include material on the outside of the containment system, taste or smell, the presence of vapor clouds, or the operation of a pressure relief valve. If possible during the survey, note the form of the released material (solid, liquid, or gas) and the location of the release.

4. *Identify the surrounding conditions.* Surrounding conditions should be noted when surveying hazardous material incidents. These conditions include topography, land use (including utilities and fiber optic cables), accessibility, weather conditions, bodies of water (including recharging ponds), public exposure potential, and the nature and extent of injuries. If a facility is involved, look for information about floor drains, ventilation ducts, air returns, and so on, as appropriate.

For ease of collection, recording, and interpretation of information obtained during the survey of an incident, a hazardous material incident survey form or similar form may prove helpful (Figure 13.8.7).

Finally, the information collected in the incident survey should be reviewed to verify its accuracy. For example, if the shipping paper identifies the material as a gas and a solid is being released, some of the information obtained may not be correct. An understanding of the characteristics of various containment systems will help to verify information on the contents.

Collecting and Interpreting Hazard and Response Information

Once a hazardous material is identified, information about the material's hazards, behavior characteristics, and suggested response options is collected. This information, which may be collected simultaneously with determining the extent of containment system damage, is used to predict the behavior of that material. The information to be collected is divided into six basic groups: (1) material identification information, (2) physical properties, (3) chemical properties, (4) physical hazards, (5) health hazards, and (6) response information. The task of obtaining, recording, and interpreting hazardous material information can be lengthy and rigorous. Various forms are being used to record hazard and response information (Figure 13.8.8).

A number of resources are available for this task, including the following.

Printed Materials. Printed materials include various response guides and MSDSs.

Various *response guides* are available for use in obtaining hazard, behavior, and response information. A listing of the sources of the most common response guides is found in Table 13.8.5. As one will note from the X's in Table 13.8.6, no one printed material source provides all the information. Therefore, more than one resource may have to be consulted to obtain the needed information. An understanding of the type of information available from each resource is important. These references augment personal knowledge and experience.

Material safety data sheets (MSDSs) are available at facilities from the manager or other facility personnel and may be found in transportation. CHEMTREC, the Chemical Transportation Emergency Center, has more than 500,000 MSDSs on file if one is not available locally. MSDSs typically provide the following types of information:

1. Physical and chemical characteristics
2. Physical hazards of the material
3. Health hazards of the material
4. Signs and symptoms of exposure
5. Routes of entry
6. Permissible exposure limits
7. Responsible party contact
8. Precautions for safe handling (including hygiene practices, protective measures, and procedures for cleanup of spills or leaks)
9. Applicable control measures including personal protective equipment
10. Emergency and first aid procedures

Technical Resources. A number of technical resources are available, including the following:

1. CHEMTREC is part of the American Chemical Council (ACC). CHEMTREC operates around the clock to receive toll-free calls from the United States and Canada through a wide-area telephone service number (800) 424-9300. If in Washington, DC, or Alaska, call (202) 483-7617. CHEMTREC can usually provide immediate hazard information from the CHEMTREC files. CHEMTREC will also contact the shipper; therefore, be prepared to provide CHEMTREC with the following information when available:

- Caller's name and phone number where caller can be reached
- Name of the carrier, shipper, manufacturer, or facility operator
- Nature, location, and time of the incident
- Name of the material (or other identifying information)
- Container type, railcar or truck number, vessel name, or other identifying information such as a railcar's reporting marks (initials) and number

CHEMTREC can also provide a teleconferencing bridge, connecting technical specialists with those needing technical information.

2. *National Response Center* (NRC), operated by the U.S. Coast Guard, receives reports required from spillers of hazardous substances. The NRC also acts as the notification, communications, technical assistance, and coordination center for the National Response Team. After receiving a report, the NRC will immediately relay the information to the responsible, predesignated, federal on-scene coordinator and other resources of

Hazardous Material Incident Survey Form

Location ____

Date ___ - ___ - ___ Time: ___ : ___ ___ Weather Conditions ______________________

Terrain ____

Closest Populated Buildings ______________________________

Closest Bodies of Water ______________________________

Closest Other Buildings ______________________________

No. Deaths ______ No. Injuries ______ Remedial Actions Taken ______________________

Containment System			Material Identification			Release		
Container Type	Container ID No.	Qty	DOT ID No.	Placard	Name of Material	Yes	Form	Location
						☒	☐ Solid ☐ Liquid ☐ Gas	
						☒	☐ Solid ☐ Liquid ☐ Gas	
						☒	☐ Solid ☐ Liquid ☐ Gas	
						☒	☐ Solid ☐ Liquid ☐ Gas	
						☒	☐ Solid ☐ Liquid ☐ Gas	
						☒	☐ Solid ☐ Liquid ☐ Gas	

Sketch of scene

N

FIGURE 13.8.7 Hazardous Material Incident Survey Form. This worksheet is used for recording information collected during the task of surveying a hazardous material incident.[5]

Hazardous Material Data Sheet	Containment System ID.

Material Name ______________________ DOT ID № _______ STCC № __________

Synonyms ______________________

Hazard Class ______________________

NFPA 704 Marking: Health _______ Flammability _______ Reactivity _______ Other __________

Physical Properties

Form	Color	Odor	Chemical Formula	Molecular Wt.
☐ Solid ☐ Liquid ☐ Gas				

Chemical Properties

Actual Temp.	Boiling Point	Melting Point	Vapor Pressure	Expansion Ratio	Specific Gravity	Vapor Density	Soluble?	Degree of Solubility
							☐ Yes	

Physical Hazards

	Actual Temperature	Flashpoint	Ignition Temperature
Flammable (heat/fire) ☐ Yes Cryogenic (cold) ☐ Yes Oxidizer (supports combustion) ☐ Yes Explosive ☐ Yes Reactive ☐ Yes To What? _______			
	Actual Concentration	**Flammable Range**	**Toxic Products of Combustion**

Health Hazards

	Actual Concentration	Non–Life Threatening Exposure Limits		
		TLV-TWA(PEL)	TLV-C	TLV-STEL
Acute Health Hazards: Poisonous ☐ Yes Corrosive ☐ Yes To What? _______ Asphyxiation ☐ Yes Etiologic ☐ Yes Radiation ☐ Yes Type: alpha beta gamma				
	Odor Threshold	**Life Threatening Exposure Limits**		
		IDLH	LC_{50}	LD_{50}

Chronic Health Hazards:	Route of Entry ☒ = YES		Toxicity Rating	Notes
Carcinogen ☐ Yes	Inhalation	☐	1 2 3 4 5 6	
Mutagen ☐ Yes	Dermal	☐	1 2 3 4 5 6	
Teratogen ☐ Yes Aquatic Hazard ☐ Yes	Ingestion	☐	1 2 3 4 5 6	

Response Information

Evacuation Distances ______________________

First Aid ______________________

____

Personal Protective Equipment ______________________

Decontamination ______________________

Extinguishing Agents ______________________

Neutralizing Agents ______________________

FIGURE 13.8.8 Hazardous Material Data Sheet. This worksheet is used for recording information obtained during the task of collecting and interpreting hazard and response information.[5]

TABLE 13.8.5 Common Reference Guides for Collecting Hazardous Response Information and Their Sources

Printed Information	*Source*
Emergency Response Guidebook	U.S. Department of Transportation Research and Special Programs Administration Washington, DC 20590
Fire Protection Guide to Hazardous Materials, National Fire Protection Association (NFPA 325, NFPA 49, and NFPA 491M)	National Fire Protection Association 1 Batterymarch Park Quincy, MA 02269
Emergency Handling of Hazardous Materials in Surface Transportation (EH) *Emergency Actions Guides* (EAG)	Association of American Railroads 50 F Street, NW Washington, DC 20001
U.S. Coast Guard CHRIS Manual Series (CHRIS) *Hazardous Chemical Data* CG-446-2	Superintendent of Documents U.S. Government Printing Office Washington, DC 20402
Farm Chemicals Handbook (FCH)	Meister Publishing Company 37841 Euclid Avenue Willoughby, OH 44094
NIOSH/OSHA References (NIOSH) *Pocket Guide to Chemical Hazards*	Superintendent of Documents U.S. Government Printing Office Washington, DC 20402
Threshold Limit Values for Chemical Substances and Physical Agents and Biological Exposure Indices	American Conference of Governmental Industrial Hygienists Kemper Woods Center 1330 Kemper Meadow Drive Cincinnati, OH 45240

Abbreviations Used for References

Primary Resources		*Secondary Resources*	
ERG	*Emergency Response Guidebook*	**EAG**	Association of American Railroads' *Emergency Action Guides*
NIOSH	*Pocket Guide to Chemical Hazards*	**EH**	Association of American Railroads' *Emergency Handling of Hazardous Materials in Surface Transportation*
		NFPA	National Fire Protection Association's *Fire Protection Guide to Hazardous Materials*
		CHRIS	U.S. Coast Guard's *Hazardous Chemical Data*
		ACGIH	American Conference of Governmental Industrial Hygienists' *Threshold Limit Values and Biological Exposure Indices*
		FCH	*Farm Chemicals Handbook*
		MSDS	Material safety data sheet

Source: Ericksen, Keffer, and Wright.[5]

the federal government. The NRC can be contacted by calling (800) 424-8802.

3. *Local poison control center.* For consumer products, comprehensive hazard information is available through regional poison control centers. The local planning documents should contain the telephone number.

4. *Manufacturer's technical medical staff.* For bulk industrial chemicals, assistance may be available from the technical medical staff of the manufacturer. CHEMTREC will make the contact.

5. *Agency for Toxic Substances and Disease Registry (ATSDR).* For chemical mixtures or wastes, when a second opinion is required or when the chemical is unknown, a preferred source of information is the ATSDR, a part of the Centers for Disease Control and Prevention of the U.S. Department of Health and Human Services. ATSDR can be reached by calling (404) 498-0120.

6. *Department of Energy.* For radioactive materials, contact the Department of Energy by calling (202) 586-8100.

TABLE 13.8.6 A Cross-Reference of Information Available in Common Reference Guides[5]

	Primary Resources		Secondary Resources						
Required Information	*ERG*	*NIOSH*	*EAG*	*EH*	*NFPA*	*CHRIS*	*ACGIH*	*FCH*	*MSDS*
DOT ID No.	X	X	X	X		X			X
STCC No.			X	X					
Synonyms		X	X		X	X		X	X
Hazard class			X	X	X	X		X	X
NFPA 704 marking			X		X	X			
Form		X	X	X	X	X		X	X
Color		X	X	X	X	X		X	X
Odor		X	X	X	X	X		X	X
Chemical formula		X	X		X	X		X	X
Molecular weight		X	X			X			X
Boiling point		X	X		X	X		X	X
Melting point		X	X			X		X	X
Vapor pressure		X	X			X			X
Expansion ratio									
Specific gravity			X	X	X	X			X
Vapor density			X	X	X	X			X
Soluble		X	X	X	X	X		X	X
Degree of solubility		X	X	X	X	X		X	X
Flashpoint		X	X	X	X	X		X	X
Ignition temperature			X		X	X			X
Flammable range		X	X		X	X			X
Toxic products of combustion			X			X		X	X
Reactive to what	X	X	X	X		X			X
Odor threshold			X			X			X
IDLH		X				X			X
LD_{50}						X		X	X
LC_{50}								X	X
TLV-C		X				X	X		X
TLV-STEL			X			X	X		X
TLV-TWA		X	X				X		X
PEL		X							X
Route of entry	X	X	X	X	X	X		X	X
Toxicity rating					X	X			
Evacuation distances	X		X	X		X			X
First aid	X	X	X	X		X		X	X
Personal protective equipment	X	X	X	X	X	X		X	X
Decontamination	X	X	X					X	X
Extinguishing agents	X		X	X	X	X		X	X
Neutralizing agents			X	X		X			X

Note: An "X" in the intersection of the resource and the required information indicates that the information is typically found in that publication.

Source: Ericksen, Keffer, and Wright.[5]

7. *Hazardous material emergency response teams.* Assistance from these sources ranges from immediate telephone advice to the dispatching of emergency teams to actual assistance in field operations. Some common examples include the following:

- Pesticide Safety Team Network
- CHLOREP Teams
- U.S. Coast Guard Strike Teams
- Carrier Response Teams

- U.S. Environmental Protection Agency Regional Response and Technical Assistance Teams
- Association of American Railroads, Bureau of Explosives

On contact with these resources, provide as much information as possible; especially the full name, form, use, and concentration of the chemical, when available. An occupational-health physician may be required to obtain or interpret information from any of these sources. Assistance in contacting many of these technical resources may be obtained from CHEMTREC or the NRC, if not listed in the local planning documents.

Assessing the Extent of Containment System Damage

Information on the types and extent of damage to a containment system is used in predicting the likely behavior of the containment system and its contents. This task can be initiated simultaneously with collecting information about the materials involved. Provide appropriate personal protective equipment for the response personnel if they could be exposed to released materials. Contact technical personnel with knowledge of the type of containment systems involved for assistance.

The following steps will help determine the extent of damage to a containment system:

1. *Identify containment systems that are damaged.* Indications of damage include abnormal orientation or position of the containment system, damage to other containment systems in the area, or a change in shape of the containment system.

2. *Determine the construction of the damaged containment system.* Before inspecting the damaged containment system, review the containment system's basic design, construction, and secondary containment features.

3. *Determine the type and location of closures on the containment system.* Review the closures on the containment system by name and purpose. Use of standard terminology will help describe the problem to the technical resources.

4. *Determine the type and location of any damage to the container or its closures.* Dents, cracks, gouges, scores, corrosion, and punctures should be noted. Using appropriate personal protective equipment when necessary, the containment system must be evaluated for signs of failure or potential failure. If the containment system has not already failed, it may have been weakened and result in failure.

5. *Determine the extent of the damage to the container or its closures.* Information on the extent of damage (e.g., the radius of curvature for dents or the depth of scores and gouges on pressure tank cars) should be determined. It may be necessary to determine the pressure in a bulk packaging or facility containment system using either a pressure gauge or the temperature of the contents.

6. *Estimate the release rate.*

Figure 13.8.9 provides an example of a form used for determining the extent of damage to tank cars.

Predicting Likely Behavior

After information on the characteristics of the material and the extent of damage to the containment system has been collected, the next task is to predict their likely behavior. This prediction, or "mental movie," is used throughout the response activity as a reference point. A mental movie is made for each containment system and hazardous material involved and is based on the worst possible case. As additional information is obtained, the mental movie is modified. The steps for predicting the behavior of the containment system and its contents include the following:

1. *Identify the types of stress or potential stress on a containment system and/or its contents.* Stress is the applied force or system of forces that tend to strain or deform a body (either the containment system or the contents). The types of stress include thermal, mechanical, chemical, irradiation, and etiologic. Thermal, mechanical, and chemical stresses can typically be identified visually, whereas irradiation and etiologic are more difficult to identify. Considerations include type and characteristics of the containment system, type of stress, amount of stress applied, intensity of stress, and duration of stress.

2. *Predict the way in which the containment system will breach.* A breach is an opening (failure) caused by damage to the containment system through which matter and/or energy can or does escape. The types of breach include disintegration, runaway linear cracking, closures that open up, punctures, and splits or tears. Considerations include type and duration of the stress being applied, behavior of the containment system under the stresses applied, behavior of the contents, location of the applied stresses, force of opening of the containment system, size of breach, and speed of the breach event. Even if the containment system has already breached, this prediction step must be considered in light of a further breach.

3. *Predict the way in which the contents will be released.* Release is the escape of the contents through a breach in a containment system. The types of release include *detonation*—the disintegration of the containment system and/or detonation of the contents; *violent rupture*—the runaway cracking of the containment system or the rapid expansion of the contents that burst the containment system abruptly; *rapid relief*—pressurized flow of the contents through closures, splits or tears, and punctures; and *spill or leak*—gradual flow through closures, splits or tears, and punctures. Considerations include type of breach, location of breach, quantity of contents, flow characteristics of contents, release rate, length of release, and weather conditions.

4. *Predict the dispersion pattern that will create the engulfed area.* Dispersion is the scattering of the matter and/or energy (from the point of release) to form an engulfed area. The engulfed area is the actual or potential area of exposure from a hazardous material or its containment system. The types of dispersion patterns include hemisphere, cloud, plume, cone, stream, pool, and irregular. Considerations include type of release, form of the released contents, weather conditions, topography, release rate, solubility of material, secondary reactions,

Tank Car Damage Assessment

Car Initials & Number

Material

Tank Car Characteristics/Features

Type of Car: ☐ Non-pressure ☐ Pressure ☐ Cryogenic ☐ Other ____________________

Specification No:	**Tank Test Pressure:**	**Tank Capacity:**

Build Date: | **Underframe:** ☐ Continuous ☐ Stub Sill

Jacketed: [Y] [N] | **Thermal Protection:** [J] Jacketed [T] Sprayed on | **Insulated:** [Y] [N]

Construction Material: *Type/Grade* ____________ *Thickness* _______ | **Stress:** [T] [M] [C] [O] [N]

Fitting Damage

Type Fitting	Damage	Description Damage/Leak
☐ Liquid Valve	[Y] [N] ☐ Leaking	
☐ Vapor/Air Valve	[Y] [N] ☐ Leaking	
☐ Bottom Outlet Type: ____________	[Y] [N] ☐ Leaking	
☐ Pressure Relief Device Type: ____________	[Y] [N] ☐ Leaking	
☐ Vacuum Relief Valve	[Y] [N] ☐ Leaking	
☐ Gauging Device Type: ____________	[Y] [N] ☐ Leaking	
☐ Manway Cover Plate	[Y] [N] ☐ Leaking	
☐ Fill Hole	[Y] [N] ☐ Leaking	
☐ Sample Line	[Y] [N] ☐ Leaking	
☐ Thermometer Well	[Y] [N] ☐ Leaking	
☐ Washout	[Y] [N] ☐ Leaking	
☐ Sump	[Y] [N] ☐ Leaking	
☐ Other Type: ____________	[Y] [N] ☐ Leaking	

Jacket, Tank, and Head Damage

Indicate location and severity of damage (punctures, cracks, scores, gouges, wheel burns, dents, rail burns, underframe, and leaks) on the appropriate diagram(s).

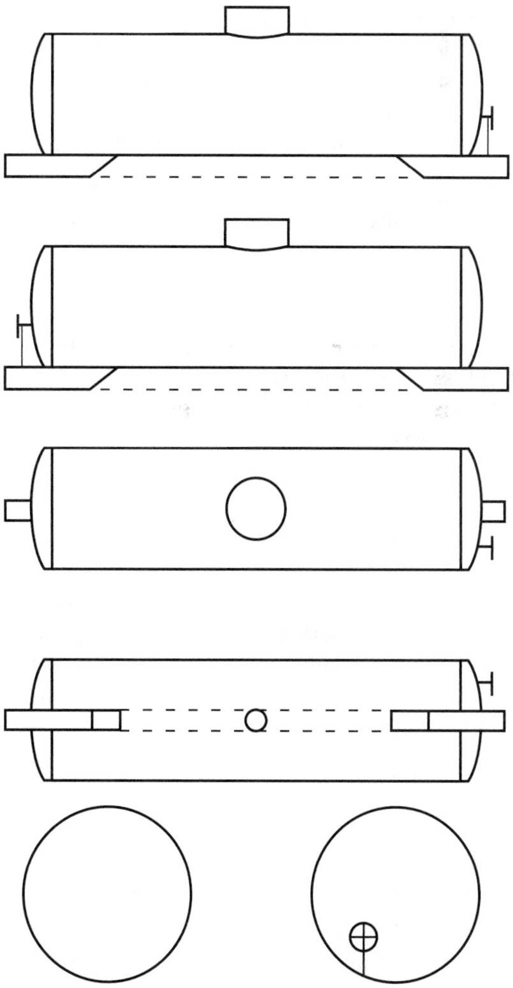

FIGURE 13.8.9 Tank Car Damage Assessment. This worksheet is used for recording results of damage assessment for rail tank cars.

melting point, freezing point, boiling point, vapor density, specific gravity, secondary containment, vapor pressure, and expansion ratio. For fixed facilities, consider tank spacing, impoundment and diking, tank venting and flaring systems, transfer operations, monitoring and detection systems, and fire protection systems.

5. *Predict the length of contact that exposures will have with the released contents. Contact* means to be exposed to something undesirable or injurious. Type of contact is considered in relation to time: short term refers to minutes and hours; medium term is associated with days, weeks, and months; and long term is in terms of years and generations. Considerations include form of the material on release, dispersion pattern, weather conditions, topography, distance to exposure, barriers or shielding, speed of dispersing materials, and quantity released.

6. *Predict the hazards that will cause harm.* Harm is the injury or damage caused by being exposed to the hazards of the released contents. Types of hazards include physical hazards, including thermal and mechanical effects; and health hazards, including chemical (poisonous, corrosive, and asphyxiation), radiation, and etiologic effects. Considerations include hazards associated with the released contents, concentrations of released materials, duration of contact, and how often the exposures will come into contact with the released materials.

To assist in predicting the behavior of the containment system and its contents, a behavior model form is suggested (Figure 13.8.10).

If unable to make all the predictions necessary to analyze the incident, seek help from the following resources: manufacturer, shipper and consignee, carrier, and federal, state, and local agencies involved with hazardous materials. A number of response guides also indicate the effects of mixing various chemicals.

Estimating Outcomes

This final task in the analysis process results in an indication of the magnitude of the problem in terms of outcomes within the engulfed area. The engulfed area is the actual or potential area of exposure from a hazardous material. The following steps should be taken to estimate outcomes in the engulfed area:

1. *Determine the dimensions of an engulfed area.* Using the Table of Initial Isolation and Protective Action Distances in the *Emergency Response Guidebook,* planning documents, or dispersion modeling programs, identify the potential size of the dispersion pattern (Table 13.8.7). Considerations include wind speed and direction and topography.

2. *Estimate the number of exposures within the engulfed area.* Exposures include people, property, the environment, and critical systems. Considerations include direction of wind, time of day, day of the week, setting (rural or urban), occupancies in area (schools, businesses, industry, transportation), bodies of water, sewer systems, and essential services.

3. *Determine the concentrations of a released hazardous material within the engulfed area.* Resources, such as monitoring equipment, computer dispersion modeling systems, toxic chemical release reporting forms, and a programmable calculator with equations, are available for this step. Information about odor may provide an insight on the level of concentration, but not without risk.

In some cases, monitoring equipment may be used to identify or classify unknown materials, verify the identity of hazardous materials, or determine the concentration of the hazardous materials. Monitoring equipment includes, but is not limited to, the following:

- Colorimetric tubes
- CO meter
- Combustible-gas meter
- Organic-vapor analyzer
- Oxygen meter
- Passive dosimeter
- Personal air-monitoring equipment
- Photoionization detectors
- pH papers and strips
- Radiation-detection instruments

Where monitoring equipment is available, personnel should be able to select the appropriate monitoring equipment considering its limitations, perform field testing procedures, operate the equipment to collect data, and record and interpret the results. If monitoring equipment is not provided, the potential sources of monitoring equipment and personnel to operate the equipment should be identified as part of the pre-emergency planning activities.

4. *Predict the extent of physical, health, and safety hazards within the engulfed area under the current conditions.* Predicting health hazards requires an understanding of the various exposure limits, including (1) immediately dangerous to life and health value (IDLH), (2) lethal concentrations (LC_{50}), (3) lethal dose (LD_{50}), (4) permissible exposure limit (PEL), (5) threshold limit value-ceiling (TLV-C), (6) threshold limit value-short-term exposure limit (TLV-STEL), and (7) threshold limit value-time weighted average (TLV-TWA).

5. *Predict the areas of potential harm within the engulfed area.* Considerations address likely concentrations, lethal concentrations, length of contact, frequency, and intensity of harm.

6. *Estimate the outcomes within an engulfed area* (Figure 13.8.11). Considerations include number of exposures in the engulfed area, age and condition of the exposures, anticipated reaction of exposures on contact with material, and weather conditions.

The purpose of analyzing the hazardous material problem is to determine the likely magnitude of the problem in terms of outcomes. Although time consuming, this process is an essential part of managing a hazardous material incident. As the incident conditions change, analysis information must be reviewed and updated. When decisions regarding protective actions and control measures are made before completing the analysis process, the risk to the responder is greater.

Behavior Model	Containment System ID.

Material: ______________________ Quantity: ______________

Form of Released Material: ☐ Gas ☐ Liquid ☐ Solid

Containment System Type: ______________________

Weather Conditions: Ambient Temperature: ________° Wind Speed: ________ m.p.h. Rain ☐ Snow ☐

Terrain: ______________________

Event Sequence

Stress	Breach	Release	Engulf	Contact	Harm

Prediction Steps

Identify the Type of Stress	Predict the Type of Breach	Predict the Type of Release	Predict the Dispersion Pattern	Predict the Length of Exposure	Predict the Hazard Causing the Harm

Behavior Options

Thermal Mechanical Chemical	Disintegration Runaway linear cracking Closures open up Punctures Splits or tears	Detonation Violent rupture Rapid relief Spill or leak	Hemisphere Cloud Plume Cone Stream Pool Irregular	Short term Medium term Long term	Physical *Thermal* *Mechanical* Health *Poisonous* *Corrosive* *Asphyxiation* *Radiation* *Etiologic*

FIGURE 13.8.10 Behavior Model. This worksheet is used for predicting the behavior of a containment system and its contents in a hazardous material incident (Source: Adapted from Ludwig Benner's *Hazardous Materials Emergencies,* 1978[6])

TABLE 13.8.7 Sample of Table of Initial Isolation and Protective Action Distances

		Small Spills (from a small package or small leak from a large package)						Large Spills (from a large package or from many small packages)					
		First **ISOLATE** in All Directions		Then **PROTECT** Persons Downwind during—				First **ISOLATE** in All Directions		Then **PROTECT** Persons Downwind during—			
				Day		Night				Day		Night	
ID No.	*Name of Material*	*Feet*	*(Meters)*	*Miles*	*(Kilometers)*	*Miles*	*(Kilometers)*	*Feet*	*(Meters)*	*Miles*	*(Kilometers)*	*Miles*	*(Kilometers)*
1005	Ammonia, anhydrous	100 ft	(30 m)	0.1 mi	(0.2 km)	0.1 mi	(0.2 km)	200 ft	(60 m)	0.3 mi	(0.5 km)	0.7 mi	(1.1 km)
1005	Ammonia, anhydrous, liquefied												
1005	Ammonia, solution, with more than 50% ammonia												
1005	Anhydrous ammonia												
1005	Anhydrous ammonia, liquefied												
1008	Boron trifluoride	100 ft	(30 m)	0.1 mi	(0.2 km)	0.4 mi	(0.6 km)	700 ft	(215 m)	1.0 mi	(1.6 km)	3.2 mi	(5.1 km)
1008	Boron trifluoride, compressed												
1016	Carbon monoxide	100 ft	(30 m)	0.1 mi	(0.2 km)	0.1 mi	(0.2 km)	400 ft	(125 m)	0.4 mi	(0.6 km)	1.1 mi	(1.8 km)
1016	Carbon monoxide, compressed												
1017	Chlorine	100 ft	(30 m)	0.2 mi	(0.3 km)	0.7 mi	(1.1 km)	900 ft	(275 m)	1.7 mi	(2.7 km)	4.2 mi	(6.8 km)
1023	Coal gas	100 ft	(30 m)	0.1 mi	(0.2 km)	0.1 mi	(0.2 km)	200 ft	(60 m)	0.2 mi	(0.3 km)	0.3 mi	(0.5 km)
1023	Coal gas, compressed												
1026	Cyanogen	100 ft	(30 m)	0.2 mi	(0.3 km)	0.7 mi	(1.1 km)	1000 ft	(305 m)	1.9 mi	(3.1 km)	4.8 mi	(7.7 km)
1026	Cyanogen, liquefied												
1026	Cyanogen gas												
1040	Ethylene oxide	100 ft	(30 m)	0.1 mi	(0.2 km)	0.1 mi	(0.2 km)	200 ft	(60 m)	0.3 mi	(0.5 km)	1.1 mi	(1.8 km)
1040	Ethylene oxide with nitrogen												
1045	Fluorine	100 ft	(30 m)	0.1 mi	(0.2 km)	0.3 mi	(0.5 km)	600 ft	(185 m)	0.9 mi	(1.4 km)	2.5 mi	(4.0 km)
1045	Fluorine, compressed												
1048	Hydrogen bromide, anhydrous	100 ft	(30 m)	0.1 mi	(0.2 km)	0.3 mi	(0.5 km)	400 ft	(125 m)	0.7 mi	(1.1 km)	2.1 mi	(3.4 km)
1050	Hydrogen chloride, anhydrous	100 ft	(30 m)	0.1 mi	(0.2 km)	0.4 mi	(0.6 km)	600 ft	(185 m)	1.0 mi	(1.6 km)	2.7 mi	(4.3 km)
1051	AC **(when used as a weapon)**	200 ft	(60 m)	0.1 mi	(0.2 km)	0.3 mi	(0.5 km)	1500 ft	(460 m)	1.0 mi	(1.6 km)	2.4 mi	(3.9 km)

Source: *2004 Emergency Response Guidebook.*[7]

Estimating Loss and Salvageable Amount Worksheet

Exposures	Estimated Exposed	Estimated Type of Harm	Estimated Outcomes	Amount Already Lost	Amount That Could Be Saved
People	#	Deaths	#		
		Injuries	#		
Property	$	Damage	$		
Environment	$	Damage	$		

FIGURE 13.8.11 Worksheet for Estimating Loss and Salvageable Amount. A worksheet is used for estimating both the outcomes in an emergency and the amount that could be saved.

PLANNING THE RESPONSE

Overview

Based on the magnitude of the problem, appropriate preventive measures and control actions are identified. Control actions include containment, confinement, and extinguishment. The potential impact (benefits and losses) to people, property, equipment, and the environment of each decision is considered.

The result of the planning process is the direction that the response effort will take to influence the sequence of events in the emergency and favorably change the outcome. Response planning is a process for identifying and evaluating response objectives (strategy) and response options (tactics). This process considers the available resources (e.g., personnel, personal protective equipment, and other tools and equipment). The planned response should be consistent with the local emergency response plan and the organization's standard operating procedures.

The planning process begins as part of the pre-emergency response planning efforts prior to the incident and continues on the scene of the incident, again from a safe location. Federal, state, and local agencies, industry, and carrier personnel may be called on to help.

The process of response planning is based on the following tasks:

1. Determine the response objectives.
2. Determine the available response options that could favorably change the outcomes.
3. Identify the personal protective equipment for the response options.
4. Identify an appropriate decontamination process for each response option.
5. Select the response options within the response community's capabilities that will most favorably change the outcomes.
6. Develop a plan of action including safety considerations.

Determining the Response Objectives (Strategy)

The first task in planning the response is to determine the response objectives (strategy) based on the estimated outcomes. The response objectives, based on the stage of the incident, are the strategic goals for stopping the event now occurring or keeping future events from occurring. The following two basic principles apply to these decisions:

1. One cannot influence events that have already happened or change the outcomes of those events.
2. The earlier that the event sequence can be interrupted, the more acceptable the loss.

The following steps should be taken when determining response objectives:

1. *Estimate the exposures that could be saved.* The level of response and the acceptable risk associated with a response is based on the exposures that can be saved. The number of exposures that could be saved is based on the estimated outcomes minus the exposures already lost (Figure 13.8.11).

2. *Determine the response objectives.* The response objectives, based on the stage of the incident, are the strategic goals for stopping the event now occurring or keeping future such events from occurring. Decisions should focus on changing the actions of the stressors, the containment system, and the hazardous material.

Determining Response Option (Tactics)

Two types of response options are available. Corrective actions are taken to resolve the immediate problem, whereas preventive actions are taken to prevent the immediate problem from escalating. The following actions are intended to keep losses to a minimum:

1. *Determine the potential response options available by response objective.* Response options are the tactical activities for stopping the event now occurring or keeping a predicted event from occurring. Response options are associated with the specific events in the emergency (Figure 13.8.12). An understanding of the procedures, equipment, and safety precautions for each technique is critical to this decision. Response options include one of the following types: defensive, offensive, and nonintervention. Control options involve either containment or confinement options. The responder must determine which type is appropriate for the incident based on the analysis of the problem.

Response Objective Analysis Form	Containment
	Material

Event Sequence

Stress	Breach	Release	Engulf	Contact	Harm

Response Objectives

Change Applied Stresses	Change Breach Size	Change Quantity Release	Change Size of Danger Zone	Change Exposures Contacted	Change Severity of Harm

Sample Response Options

Move stressor Move stressed system Shield stressed system	Chill contents Limit stress levels Activate venting devices Mechanical repair	Change container position Minimize pressure differential Cap off breach Remove contents	Barriers Dikes and dams Adsorbents Absorbents Diluents Reactants Overpack	Provide sheltering Begin evacuation Personal protective equipment	Rinse off contaminant Increase distance from source Provide shielding Provide prompt medical attention

FIGURE 13.8.12 Response Objective Analysis Worksheet. This worksheet is used for identifying response options in a hazardous material incident by response objective (Source: Adapted from Ludwig Benner's *Hazardous Materials Emergencies,* 1978[6])

2. *Estimate how each response option will affect the outcomes.* Before a response option is selected, the effect of that response option or combination of response options on the sequence of events and ultimately the outcomes should be reviewed (Figure 13.8.13).

The response options must be based on their expected effect on the outcomes.

Identifying Appropriate Personal Protective Equipment (PPE)

The purpose of identifying appropriate personal protective equipment for each response option is to determine the equipment required to implement the various response options identified. Again, pre-emergency planning cannot be overemphasized in the selection of personal protective equipment.

Estimating Effect of Each Response Option Worksheet

Exposures/Harm	Amount that could be saved	Amount that could be saved with option 1	Amount that could be saved with option 2	Amount that could be saved with option 3	Amount that could be saved with option 4	Amount that could be saved with option 5	Amount that could be saved with option 6
People death	#	#	#	#	#	#	#
People injuries	#	#	#	#	#	#	#
Property damage	$	$	$	$	$	$	$
Environ. damage	$	$	$	$	$	$	$

FIGURE 13.8.13 Worksheet for Estimating Effect of Each Response Option. This worksheet is used for estimating the effect of each response option on the outcomes of the incident.

The following PPE-related definitions are used for the purpose of this chapter.

Personal protective equipment is protective clothing and respiratory protection used to shield or isolate a person from the chemical and biological, physical, or thermal hazards that may be encountered at a hazardous material incident. No single combination of personal protective equipment is capable of protecting against all hazards. Personal protective equipment should be used in conjunction with other protective methods, such as medical monitoring and environmental surveillance. For any given situation, personal protective equipment should be selected to provide an adequate level of protection. Both overprotection and underprotection can be hazardous and should be avoided.

Protective clothing includes those pieces of apparel that are designed to protect the wearer from dermal (skin and eye) contact with the hazardous material. Protective clothing is divided into the following types:

Chemical-protective clothing

- Liquid splash-protective clothing
- Vapor-protective clothing

High temperature-protective clothing

- Proximity suit
- Entry suit

Structural fire-fighting protective clothing

Respiratory protection is the equipment designed to protect the wearer from inhaling the hazardous material. Respiratory protection is divided into the following six types:

1. Positive pressure self-contained breathing apparatus (SCBA)
2. Positive pressure air-line respirators with required escape unit
3. Closed circuit SCBA
4. Powered air-purifying respirators (PAPR)
5. Air-purifying respirator (APR)
6. Particulate respirator

Breakthrough time is the time it takes for the hazardous material to move through the protective material.

Penetration is the movement of a chemical through zippers, stitched seams, or imperfections, such as pinholes, in a protective equipment material.

Permeation is the process by which the chemical dissolves in and moves through a protective clothing material on a molecular level.

Degradation is the physical decomposition of the material due to exposure to chemicals, use, or ambient conditions, such as sunlight.

The identification of appropriate personal protective equipment requires completion of the following steps:

1. *Determine the name, concentration, and hazards of each of the materials involved.* This information should have been developed during the process of analyzing the hazardous material problem.

2. *Predict the types of exposure associated with each response option.* The types of exposure include the following:

- Immersion (e.g., standing in or handling the chemical)
- Splash (e.g., splash of a liquid from a drum or decontaminating people or equipment coming in direct contact)
- Airborne (e.g., exposure to airborne chemicals as a result of sampling)

3. *Determine the level of personal protective equipment required.* This step provides a list of the required pieces of personal protective equipment, including suits, gloves, and boots. If the chief threat is through liquid contact, the protective clothing should resist chemical degradation and penetration. For a threat from vapor contact, the protective clothing may have to be airtight and impermeable. The minimum requirement for respiratory protection, set by OSHA in 29 CFR 1910.120, for emergency conditions at hazardous material incidents (until concentrations have been determined) is positive-pressure self-contained breathing apparatus.

The U.S. Environmental Protection Agency identifies the following four levels of protection:

- *Level A* is the highest level of protection and should be worn when respiratory, skin, eye, and mucous membrane protection is needed.

- *Level B* is the second highest level of protection and should be worn when a lesser level of skin and eye protection is needed. It is the minimum level recommended for initial site entries until the hazards have been determined by monitoring, sampling, or other reliable methods of analysis.
- *Level C* is the third highest level of protection and may be worn only when the type of airborne substance is known, concentration measured, criteria for using air-purifying respirators met, and skin and eye exposure is unlikely. Periodic monitoring of the air must be performed while working in level C.
- *Level D* is the lowest level of protection and is primarily a work uniform. It should not be worn on any site where respiratory or skin hazards exist.

Responders must understand the advantages, limitations, and use of each of the levels of protection at hazardous material incidents. If the appropriate level of protection is not available, arrange to obtain it from other resources.

4. *Identify chemically compatible materials for the chemicals involved.* Look for breakthrough times of at least 2 hours. A breakthrough time of 2 hours represents the normal physical limits of a responder's capacity for effective work in protective equipment. Resources for identifying chemically compatible materials include *Guidelines for the Selection of Chemical Protective Clothing*[8] or the *Quick Selection Guide to Chemical Protective Clothing,*[9] various emergency response guides, and chemical compatability charts provided by the manufacturers of chemical protective clothing.

Figure 13.8.14 provides a worksheet for recording chemically compatible materials identified.

5. *Match the material requirements with personal protective equipment provided or available.* Using chemical-compatibility charts provided with the protective equipment available, identify the available equipment that provides the required protection. Multiple materials can be layered to provide the appropriate level of protection.

6. *Identify the appropriate personal protective equipment needed for each response option.* Keep in mind the requirement for the buddy system and backup personnel. Considerations include availability of sufficient equipment in the appropriate sizes and the potential of multiple layers providing required protection. The use of personal protective equipment itself can create significant responder hazards, such as heat stress, physical and psychological stress, as well as impaired vision, mobility, and communication.

Identifying Appropriate Decontamination Procedures

With the potential that personnel, personal protective equipment, apparatus, and tools and equipment may become contaminated in a hazardous material incident, a decontamination (contamination reduction) process is established.

Decontamination (Contamination Reduction). This is the act of removing or neutralizing contaminants from equipment or personnel to preclude the occurrence of foreseeable adverse health effects outside the engulfed area. Possible decontamination options include absorption, adsorption, chemical degradation, dilution, neutralization, or solidification.

Decontamination procedures should be tailored to the specific hazards of the incident. They may vary in complexity and number of steps, depending on the level of hazard and the level of exposure to the hazard. The steps to be taken to select an appropriate decontamination (contamination reduction) process include the following:

1. *Identify what needs to be decontaminated.* This includes injured persons, response personnel, personal protective equipment, other equipment, and emergency-care facilities.

Chemically Compatible Materials Identification Worksheet

Chemical	Chemical concentration	Chemically compatible clothing material required		
		> 8 hr	> 2 hr	Less than ½ hr

FIGURE 13.8.14 Chemically Compatible Materials Identification Worksheet. This worksheet is for recording the chemically compatible protective clothing materials by hazardous material.

2. *Determine the contaminant and the type and amount of contamination.* Considerations include whether the material is organic or inorganic, in the solid, liquid, or gas form, a dermal or inhalation hazard, a local or systemic material, and whether the contaminant is life threatening, injurious, or irritating. Another consideration is whether physical trauma is involved.

3. *Seek appropriate advice.* Immediate decontamination guidelines are found in the *Emergency Response Guidebook*[7] (under first aid on the numbered guide pages), the NIOSH *Pocket Guide to Chemical Hazards,*[10] or local planning documents. Follow-up guidance can be obtained from local poison control centers, the shipper or manufacturer through CHEMTREC, or the Agency for Toxic Substances and Disease Registry.

4. *Identify methods for isolating and securing and then disposing of clothing and equipment that cannot be decontaminated.* The local emergency response plan or the organization's standard operating procedures provide guidelines on decontamination (contamination reduction) procedures. Other resources should be identified in pre-emergency planning activities. Follow-up resources include the Agency for Toxic Substances and Disease Registry, poison control centers, and the shipper or manufacturer through CHEMTREC.

Selecting Response Options

The selection of response options to change the outcomes favorably must be consistent with the local emergency response plan and the organization's standard operating procedures and also within the capability of available personnel, personal protective equipment, and control equipment. The steps to be taken in selecting the response options include the following:

1. *Determine the required resources to implement each response option.* Required resources include the time to implement the option, availability of sufficient personnel with the appropriate training, and appropriate personal protective equipment, materials for decontamination (contamination reduction) activities, and control equipment.
2. *Inventory the resources available and identify those resources available.* These resources should be readily accessible.
3. *Determine how to obtain the needed resources.* A review of the planning documents should provide these answers.
4. *Select the response option(s) consistent with the available resources.* Evaluate the potential reaction of the hazardous material to the control action and the ability to contain the side effects of the response option. Surrounding conditions, including topography and weather conditions, and response times can also affect the decision to select the response options.

Developing a Plan of Action

After selecting the response option for a hazardous material incident, a plan of action including safety and health considerations should be developed. This plan of action describes the response objectives and options and the personnel and equipment required to accomplish the objectives. The plan provides a permanent record of the decisions made at the incident. An organization's standard operating procedures provide the basis of this plan of action. Input from all segments of the response community is considered in developing the plan. Based on the specific incident conditions, the standard operating procedures are modified without having to write an entire plan for each incident.

A plan of action also outlines the safety and health procedures to protect responders and the public from the potential hazards at an incident. These procedures should address incident management, communications protocol (both internal and external), control zones for incident security, personal protective equipment use, decontamination procedures, and documentation. They also include designation of a safety sector and a safety officer, emergency medical care procedures, environmental monitoring, emergency procedures, and personnel monitoring.

Components for a typical plan of action include the following:

1. Site description
2. Entry objectives
3. On-scene organization and coordination
4. On-scene control
5. Hazard evaluation
6. Personal protective equipment
7. On-scene work assignments
8. Communication procedures
9. Decontamination procedures
10. On-scene safety and health considerations including designation of the safety officer, emergency medical care procedures, environmental monitoring, emergency procedures, and personnel monitoring

Response personnel at a hazardous material incident must recognize and understand the potential hazards associated with the incident. They must also be familiar with the procedures contained in the plan of action. Therefore, prior to working on-scene, all personnel must be provided a safety briefing. The safety briefing will describe the assigned tasks and their potential hazards, coordinate activities, identify methods and precautions to prevent injuries, and plan for emergencies. The plan of action can serve as a guide to this safety briefing.

The result of planning a response to a hazardous material incident is a plan of action consistent with the local emergency response plan and the organization's standard operating procedures and within the capability of the resources available. Development of a written plan ensures that all safety aspects of the response are thoroughly examined. Plans should be modified as necessitated by changing conditions on the scene.

IMPLEMENTING THE PLANNED RESPONSE

Overview

Once the plan of action is determined, response personnel must implement the response options in that plan. The following tasks are associated with implementing the planned response to a hazardous material incident:

1. Implement the incident management system (IMS).

2. Implement the selected protective actions.
3. Establish and enforce scene-control procedures.
4. Implement planned control actions.

Initiating the Incident Management System

The incident management system (IMS) is an organized approach to control and manage operations effectively at an emergency through a system of roles, responsibilities, and standard operating procedures. The incident management system should be developed as part of pre-emergency planning efforts, including the local emergency response plan and an organization's standard operating procedures.

One individual is in charge of managing the incident. This individual may delegate responsibility for performing various tasks to others on the scene. All communications are routed through the command post. Delegation of tasks may be by location or by function. Some of the functions include: medical services, evacuation, water supply, resources, media relations, safety, and site control. The incident management system reduces confusion, improves safety, organizes and coordinates actions, and facilitates effective management of the incident.

The National Incident Management System (NIMS) provides an example that includes the following elements of an incident management system used to coordinate response activities:

1. Common terminology
2. Modular organizations
3. Integrated communications
4. Unified command structure
5. Consolidated action plans
6. Manageable span of control
7. Predesignated incident facilities
8. Comprehensive resource management

Responders should understand the roles and responsibilities of the various positions in the local incident management system as defined in the local emergency response plan or the organization's standard operating procedures.

The incident management system includes the procedures for notification and use of other than local resources, including private, state, and federal government personnel. The incident commander should be familiar with and comply with the requirements of the following plans:

1. Organization's emergency response plan
2. Organization's standard operating procedures
3. Local emergency response plan
4. State emergency response plan
5. Regional emergency response plan, including the resources available from the regional response team
6. Federal emergency response plans

Response personnel should be aware of the primary local, state, regional, and federal government agencies and understand the scope of their regulatory authority (including the regulations) pertaining to the production, transportation, storage, and use of hazardous materials and the disposal of hazardous wastes. They should also be aware of private sector resources offering assistance during a hazardous material incident and identify their role and the type of assistance or resources available.

The incident management system should provide a focal point for information transfer to the media and local elected officials. A public information officer should be designated to provide appropriate information to the media and local, state, and federal officials.

Implementing Selected Protective Actions

Protective measures are those taken to preserve the health and safety of emergency responders and the public during an incident involving the release of hazardous materials. Protective actions include the following:

1. *Isolate the hazard area and deny entry.* Keep all persons away from the area if they are not directly involved in emergency response operations. Unprotected emergency responders should not be allowed within the isolation area. Planning documents should include techniques to isolate the hazard area and deny entry to unauthorized persons at hazardous material incidents.

2. *Evacuate persons in the threatened area.* Evacuation is defined as a process to "move all people from the threatened area to a safer place."[7] To perform an evacuation, there must be enough time for people to be warned, to get ready, and to leave the area. Even after people are evacuated, they should not be allowed to congregate on the perimeter of the control zones. Evacuees should be sent upwind to a definite place, by a specific route, far enough away so that they will not have to be moved again if the conditions change.

3. *Protect persons who cannot be evacuated in place.* In-place protection is defined as a "means to direct people to quickly go inside a building and remain inside until the danger passes."[7] Certain protective actions must be taken inside the building. In-place protection is used when evacuating the public would cause greater risk than directing them to stay where they are or when an evacuation cannot be performed.

Establishing and Enforcing Scene-Control Procedures

Scene-control procedures must be implemented quickly. Control zones (Figure 13.8.15), decontamination (contamination reduction) activities, and communication must be established and maintained throughout the incident. Personnel should move between control zones through access control points.

Scene control is established through the use of control zones based on safety and the degree of hazard. The hot zone is the area surrounding a hazardous material incident. It extends far enough to prevent adverse effects from hazardous material releases to personnel outside the zone. The warm zone is the area where personnel and equipment decontamination (contamination reduction) takes place. The cold zone is the area containing the command post and other support functions. Access to various zones is determined by need and level of personal protection provided as specified in the plan of action.

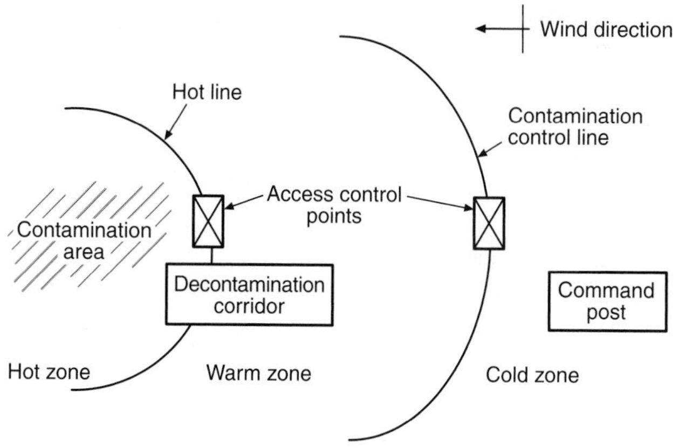

FIGURE 13.8.15 Control Zones

Extreme caution is necessary when providing emergency medical care to victims of hazardous material incidents.

Performing Control Functions

Responders are expected to perform control functions identified in the plan of action. They will have to select the tools, equipment, and materials for the tasks assigned. They should also understand the precautions for controlling releases from the containment systems involved.

In conjunction with their ability to use personal protective equipment, response personnel should be able to identify the symptoms of heat and cold stress. Response personnel should be aware of the physical and psychological stresses that can affect users of personal protective equipment. Personnel should be able to identify the signs and symptoms of exposure to any hazardous material involved. Response personnel should be able to record the use, repair, and testing of chemical protective clothing.

EVALUATING PROGRESS AND ADJUSTING ACCORDINGLY

The fourth and final duty in responding to hazardous material incidents is to evaluate the progress of the planned response—whether it stabilizes, intensifies, or otherwise changes. This duty evaluates the effectiveness of the following:

1. Personnel being used
2. Personal protective equipment
3. Established control zones
4. Decontamination process
5. Selected action options

A comparison of the actual behavior to that predicted indicates the effectiveness of the operations. Negative feedback initiates a re-evaluation of the situation, including another analysis of the problem, response objectives and options, and a modified plan of action. Positive feedback indicates successful operations; however, modification of the plan may still be necessary.

Termination

Termination of a hazardous material incident is that portion of incident management in which personnel are involved in documenting safety procedures, site operations, hazards faced, and lessons from the incident. Termination is divided into three phases: (1) debriefing the responders, (2) postincident analysis, and (3) critiquing the incident.[11]

Debriefing the responders is the process of reviewing a hazardous material incident focusing on the following factors:

1. Informing responders of any potential exposure to hazardous materials and the signs and symptoms associated with that exposure
2. Identifying equipment damage and unsafe conditions
3. Assigning information-gathering responsibilities for a critique
4. Summarizing the activities performed

Postincident analysis is the reconstruction of the incident to establish a clear picture of the events that took place during the incident. The postincident analysis focuses on four key topics: (1) command and control, (2) tactical operations, (3) resources, and (4) support services.

Critiquing the incident—emphasizing successful and unsuccessful operations—should be conducted with all response community members. The procedures for conducting a critique of a hazardous material incident should be in the local emergency response plan or the organization's standard operating procedures including written reports to management that suggest ways to improve future operations.

At the termination of the emergency phase, authority may be transferred to those responsible for the recovery activity in the incident. The local emergency response plan or the organization's standard operating procedures outline the steps for terminating the emergency phase of the incident.

Providing Reports and Subsequent Documentation

Responders to hazardous material incidents must comply with the reporting requirements of federal, state, and local agencies. All reports and other incident documents should be consistent with the local, state, and federal requirements.

Training records, exposure records, incident reports, and critique reports should become part of the file for the incident. An activity log and detailed exposure records should be maintained on each hazardous material incident. Typically, requirements for filing documents and maintaining records are found in the local emergency response plan and the organization's standard operating procedures.

SUMMARY

As with any emergency, favorably changing the outcomes requires a logical sequential process involving four duties: (1) analysis, (2) planning, (3) implementation, and (4) evaluation. Each of these duties is made up of tasks that need to be accomplished to complete that duty. Each task requires that certain steps be performed to complete the task. The topics in this chapter describe the duties, tasks, and steps associated with managing the response to hazardous material incidents.

BIBLIOGRAPHY

References Cited

1. Benner, L., Jr., "D.E.C.I.D.E. in Hazardous Materials Emergencies," *Fire Journal,* Vol. 69, No. 4, 1975, p. 13.
2. DOT Regulations
3. *Acute Hazardous Events,* Database, Industrial Economics Inc., Cambridge, MA, Dec. 1985.
4. Chemical Manufacturers Association and Association of American Railroads, *Technical Bulletin on Packaging for Hazardous and Non-Hazardous Materials,* Chemical Manufacturers Association, Washington, DC, 1989.
5. Ericksen, N. A., Keffer, W. J., and Wright, C. J., *Introduction to Hazardous Materials Incident Response,* U.S. Environmental Protection Agency and Union Pacific Railroad, Omaha, NE, 1989.
6. Benner, L., Jr., *Hazardous Materials Emergencies,* 2nd ed., Lufred Industries, Inc., Oakton, VA, 1978.
7. *2004 Emergency Response Guidebook,* U.S. Department of Transportation, Research and Special Programs Administration, Washington, DC, 2004.
8. *Guidelines for the Selection of Chemical Protective Clothing,* prepared by A. D. Little, Inc., Cambridge, MA, 1987.
9. Forsberg, K., and Mansdorf, S. Z., *Quick Selection Guide to Chemical Protective Clothing,* 2nd ed., Van Nostrand Reinhold, New York, 1995.
10. NIOSH, *Pocket Guide to Chemical Hazards,* U.S. Department of Health and Human Services, Government Printing Office, Washington, DC, 2005.
11. Noll, G. G., Hildebrand, M. S., and Yvorra, J. G., "Terminating the Incident," *Hazardous Materials: Managing the Incident,* 3rd ed., Oklahoma State University, Stillwater, OK, 2005.

NFPA Codes, Standards, and Recommended Practices

Reference to the following NFPA codes, standards, and recommended practices will provide further information on managing response to hazardous material incidents discussed in this chapter. (See the latest version of The NFPA Catalog *for availability of current editions of the following documents.)*

NFPA 471, *Recommended Practice for Responding to Hazardous Materials Incidents*
NFPA 472, *Standard for Professional Competence of Responders to Hazardous Materials/Weapons of Mass Destruction Incidents*
NFPA 704, *Standard System for the Identification of the Hazards of Materials for Emergency Response*
NFPA 1971, *Standard on Protective Ensembles for Structural Fire Fighting and Proximity Fire Fighting*
NFPA 1981, *Standard on Open-Circuit Self-Contained Breathing Apparatus (SCBA) for Emergency Services*
NFPA 1991, *Standard on Vapor-Protective Ensembles for Hazardous Materials Emergencies*
NFPA 1992, *Standard on Liquid Splash-Protective Ensembles and Clothing for Hazardous Materials Emergencies*
NFPA 1994, *Standard on Protective Ensembles for First Responders to CBRN Terrorism Incidents*

U.S. Government Publications, U.S. Government Printing Office, Superintendent of Documents, Washington, DC 20402

Handbook of Chemical Hazard Analysis Procedures (FEMA, DOT, EPA).
Hazardous Materials Emergency Planning Guide (NRT-1), National Response Team, 1987.
National Incident Management System, Homeland Security, 2004.
National Response Plan, Homeland Security, 2004.
Occupational Safety and Health Guidance Manual for Hazardous Waste Site Activities, NIOSH/OSHA/USCG/EPA, U.S. Department of Health and Human Services, NIOSH, 1985.
Occupational Safety and Health Standards, Title 29, Code of Federal Regulations, Part 1910.120, "Hazardous Waste Operations and Emergency Response Final Rule," 1989.
Occupational Safety and Health Standards, Title 29, Code of Federal Regulations, Part 1910.1200, "Hazard Communication Standard," 1987.
Standard Operating Safety Guides, Environmental Response Branch, Office of Emergency and Remedial Response, U.S. Environmental Protection Agency, 1988.
Technical Guidance for Hazard Analysis (EPA, FEMA, DOT).
Title 40 CFR Part 261.33 (EPA).
Title 40 CFR Part 302 (EPA).
Title 40 CFR Part 355 (EPA).
Title 49 CFR Parts 170–179 (DOT).

Chapter 9

Emergency Medical Services and the Fire Department

Jack J. Krakeel

Chapter Contents

Key Terms

advanced life support (ALS), ambulance service, basic life support (BLS), benchmarking, emergency medical responder, emergency medical services, emergency medical technician (advanced), emergency medical technician (basic), EMS coordinator, enhanced 9-1-1, medical control, medical director, medical first responder, paramedic, patient transport, process performance indicator index (PPII), response time performance

The fire service plays a significant role in the delivery of emergency medical services (EMS). During the past 50 years, fire service–based emergency medical services (EMS) has grown to be the principal operational delivery program in the majority of fire departments. In 2004, the 14.1 million EMS calls by local fire departments constituted 62 percent of total emergency responses, and the EMS share grows every year. In 2005, 67 percent of fire departments reported that they provide EMS response, up slightly from 65 percent in 2001. These departments protected 86 percent of the population, as most departments not providing EMS coverage were all-volunteer departments protecting rural communities. The term *cross-trained dual-role fire fighter* is generally being replaced by the recognition that fire fighters are the personnel who respond to the needs of their communities irrespective of the nature of the emergency.

As is the case with other fire department programs and responsibilities, the manner and degree of EMS system involvement is predicated to a great extent on the community being served. The recognition that "all EMS is local" is offset by the fact that common elements are applicable to all EMS systems. The core components of EMS systems were defined in legislation passed by Congress over 40 years ago. Since that time efforts by individual groups, including the American Ambulance Association (AAA), the International Association of Fire Chiefs (IAFC), the International Association of Fire Fighters (IAFF), the National Association of State EMS Directors (NAEMSD), the National Association of EMS Physicians (NAEMSP), the National Fire Protection Association (NFPA), and others, have expanded the understanding of EMS systems and the factors that define and influence the effectiveness and efficiency in the delivery of emergency medical services.

EMS is not a fast ride to an emergency room by ambulance nor is it singularly delivered by the fire department. It is a complex set of coordinated activities and responsibilities working in unison to deliver optimum service to a citizen in need of emergency medical care. NFPA 450, *Guide for Emergency Medical Services and Systems,* defines an EMS system as

> A comprehensive, coordinated arrangement of resources and functions which are organized to respond in a timely, staged manner to medical emergencies regardless of their cause.

Irrespective of the role of a fire department, from functioning as a first responder providing basic life support to one providing advanced life support critical care transport services, the adherence to accepted standards and measures of performance is essential to ensuring optimum patient care.

This chapter intends to provide the reader with an understanding of the role of emergency medical services delivery by fire departments. In addition, it identifies the various factors, standards, and performance measures that can be utilized by fire departments in their analysis and improvement of the emergency medical services program.

For related topics see also Section 12, Chapter 4, "Managing Fire-Rescue Departments"; Section 13, Chapter 2, "Organizing Rescue Operations"; and Section 13, Chapter 7, "Aircraft Rescue and Fire Fighting (ARFF)."

Jack J. Krakeel, MBA, is the chief of the Fayette County Department of Fire and Emergency Services, Georgia. During his 32 year career, he has been an advocate for fire-based EMS at the local, state, and national levels.

FIRE DEPARTMENT'S ROLE IN EMS

Historical Background

The delivery of emergency medical services by fire departments must be viewed within the historical and modern context of the fire service. Although the current nomenclature of prehospital or, if preferred, out-of-hospital emergency medical services was not defined until the genesis of modern EMS systems over 40 years ago, fire agencies across the country have routinely responded to rescues of all types since their founding with the delivery of first-aid services to those in need. The fire service's history in EMS is well documented within the history of departments such as Phoenix, Arizona, Chicago, Illinois, Columbus, Ohio, Miami, Florida, and others.

During the past 40 years, the evolution of the fire service to include EMS as an element of its core mission, "saving lives and property," has been the result of multiple factors, not singularly and simply the decline of fires. As early as 1976, communities across the country witnessed the lifesaving heroic actions of Squad 51 as the television series *Emergency* showcased the capabilities of trained Los Angeles County fire fighters delivering emergency medical care. The publication *EMS Agenda for the Future,* considered by many to be the second white paper in EMS, credits the show with being one of the influential factors of modern EMS system design.[1] The term *white paper* denotes the importance attached to the document in serving as a catalyst for change. The first white paper, published in 1967 and titled *Accidental Death and Disability: The Neglected Disease of Modern Society,*[2] functioned as the principal document from which modern EMS system improvements were generated.

Federal Funding. Whereas the period from the 1960s to the 1970s was known for the vast amount of federal funding committed to the development of EMS systems, the decade of the 1980s reversed that trend and placed the responsibility of supporting emergency medical services squarely on the shoulders of local government. Demand for service coupled with declining federal grant revenues resulted in many local governments turning to their fire departments for the delivery of EMS programs and services. Table 13.9.1 provides a summary of funding for the development of EMS systems.

Patient Transport. The consolidation of the patient transport industry during the decade of the 1990s resulted in further development of fire service–based systems as large corporate organizations shed nonprofitable transport service markets to focus attention on those environments conducive to corporate growth and consolidated market share.

The first few years of the new millennium have seen further strengthening of the fire department's role in EMS, specifi-

TABLE 13.9.1 Summary of Funding for EMS Systems

Legislation	*Time Period*	*Source*	*Amount*	*Explanation*
National Highway Safety Act of 1966 (Public Law 89-564, 23 U.S.C. 401)	1966–1973	Department of Transportation	Approx. $48 million	
National Highway Safety Act of 1966 (Public Law 89-564, 23 U.S.C. 401)	1966–1973	Department of Health, Education and Welfare (HEW)	Approx. $73 million	
Emergency Medical Services (EMS) Systems Act of 1973 (42 U.S.C. 300d)	1973–1976	Department of Health, Education and Welfare (HEW)	Approx. $50 million	
Emergency Medical Services (EMS) Systems Act of 1973 (42 U.S.C. 300d)	1973–1976	Health Resources Administration	Approx. $15 million	
	1974–1978	Robert Woods Johnson Foundation (private philanthropic foundation)	Approx. $14 million	Grants for the improvement of EMS systems
Omnibus Budget Reconciliation Act of 1981 (Public Law 97-35)	1981			Transferred federal funding of EMS to states through preventative health and health services block grants

cally through the absorption of third service municipal transport systems. Beginning during the mid-1990s, local governments' efforts to achieve cost savings through various economies of scale merged these agencies into their fire departments. Highly publicized mergers included those in New York, San Francisco, and St. Louis.

Development of 9-1-1 and E-9-1-1. Contributing to the multiple factors that influenced the widespread inclusion of emergency medical services within fire departments is the recognition of the development of 9-1-1 and enhanced 9-1-1 (E-9-1-1) systems throughout the country. As of late 2005, 98.5 percent of U.S. local fire departments, protecting 99.4 percent of the U.S. population, had some type of 9-1-1 service. What is more, 70.6 percent of U.S. local fire departments, protecting 86.7 percent of the U.S. population, had E-9-1-1 service. The growth of both 9-1-1 and E-9-1-1 since 1967 has resulted in this service being recognized as a fundamental and essential local government service. Responsibility for direct access to the EMS system through 9-1-1 has local governments and their elected leadership intrinsically involved in the EMS system design decision-making process.

The fire service has grown to be the largest provider of emergency medical care throughout the continuum of the EMS system from education and prevention, to system entry, through first response, and ultimately patient transport to a definitive care facility during the last 50 years. In light of the major demographic shifts (aging of the population) and new risks (terrorism, pandemics), there do not appear to be any major influences that will significantly alter the role of the fire service in responding to the emergency medical needs of their constituents.

Factors Influencing EMS Development

The emergence of modern prehospital emergency medical services and the widespread inclusion of fire departments in EMS can be traced to the middle of the twentieth century as a result of various factors that coalesced to define EMS as it is known today. These factors included (1) innovations and technological developments, (2) battlefield medical experience, (3) fire service attributes, (4) cardiac research, and (5) federal legislation and grant funding.

Innovations and Technological Developments. During the 1950s, Dr. Peter Safer, a noted physician trained in surgery and pathology, introduced the concept of airway control and artificial ventilation combined with external chest compressions that resulted in the lifesaving skill of cardiopulmonary resuscitation. In his groundbreaking work, Dr. Safer demonstrated that by training first responders and citizens in CPR, the opportunity for someone to survive cardiac arrest outside of traditional medical institutions could be improved. Dr. Safar authored the text *ABC of Resuscitation* in 1957.

Following the development of CPR and mass instruction to first responders and the lay community, researchers led by cardiologist Dr. Frank Pantridge from the Royal Victoria Hospital in Belfast, Ireland (1966), expanded on the work of researchers at Johns Hopkins Hospital in the development of portable cardiac defibrillators. Their innovation led to the institution of mobile coronary care units in Belfast. His efforts are generally considered to have led to the first mobile-based advanced life support (ALS) units to serve the general public.[3]

Battlefield Medical Experience. Concurrent with these innovations and technological developments were the experiences of military emergency physicians who served on the battlefields of Korea and Vietnam. They questioned why many of the lessons learned from the successes they witnessed in the combat theater, where early care was provided at the point of injury and forward medical bases (MASH) were used, could not be transferred to the civilian community. Drawing on their experiences, these physicians defined the country's failures for prompt and effective emergency care through a study conducted by the National Academy of Sciences, National Research Council's Committees on Trauma, Shock, and Anesthesia. Their publication was entitled *Accidental Death and Disability: The Neglected Disease of Modern Society.*[2] The first paragraph of the publication summed up the gravity of their findings:

> In 1965, 52 million accidental injuries killed 107,000, temporarily disabled over 10 million and permanently impaired 400,000 American citizens at a cost of $18 billion. This neglected epidemic of modern society is the nation's most important environmental health problem. It is the leading cause of death in the first half of life's span.[2]

Demonstrating the paucity of adequate ambulance services, the study stated:

> Adequate ambulance services are as much a municipal responsibility as firefighting and police services. . . . Very few communities provide sufficient financial support for adequate ambulance services. Where they are provided, they are usually maintained by the fire or police department. . . . First class ambulance service exists in few cities. Some such as the City of Baltimore employ highly trained full-time ambulance attendants with up-to-date vehicles and equipment as a separate mission of the fire department.[2]

Although many of the recommendations for improving care to the injured centered on hospital-based initiatives, some were specific to the out-of-hospital environment and applicable to the fire service community including the following:

- Extension of basic and advanced first aid training to greater numbers of lay population
- Preparation of nationally accepted texts, training aids, and courses of instruction for rescue squad personnel, police, fire fighters, and ambulance attendants
- Implementation of traffic safety legislation to ensure completely adequate standards for ambulance design and construction, for ambulance equipment and supplies, and for the qualifications and supervision of ambulance personnel
- Adoption at the state level of general policies and regulations pertaining to ambulance services

- Adoption at district, county, and municipal levels of ways and means of providing ambulance services applicable to local conditions, control and surveillance of ambulance services, and coordination of ambulance services with health departments, hospitals, traffic authorities, and communication services
- Delineation of radio frequency channels and of equipment suitable to provide voice communication between ambulances, emergency departments, and other health-related agencies at community, regional, and national levels
- Day-to-day use of voice communication facilities by the agencies serving emergency medical needs[2]

Fire Service Attributes. Individual fire agencies understood that they were uniquely positioned to embody many of the recommendations made by this pivotal study, recognizing that their organizations offered the following attributes in support of delivering emergency medical services:

- Dedicated and trained workforce
- Defined and practiced command/control functions
- Established communication systems
- Ability to function under emergency conditions
- Geographic deployment of assets and resources to respond in a time-sensitive manner
- Day-to-day involvement of responding to medical emergencies
- Public trust and confidence
- History of EMS service

Cardiac Research. Cardiac researchers in the United States, eager to expand the work of Pantridge, et al., engaged fire departments in their communities for the implementation of advanced mobile coronary care units. Cities and fire departments such as Seattle, Jacksonville, Los Angeles, Dayton, and others pioneered the concept of delivering advanced cardiac life support during this era. In 1966, the Columbus, Ohio, Fire Department introduced the concept of the "Heartmobile," considered to be one of the first advanced cardiac life support units (Figure 13.9.1). In their article on the evolution of prehospital care in the United States, the authors state: "Most of the early paramedic programs were based in fire departments."[4] In 1969, under the direction of Dr. Eugene Nagel, the Miami, Florida, Fire Department started the nation's first paramedic program.

Federal Legislation and Grant Funding. The publication of *Accidental Death and Disability: The Neglected Disease of Modern Society* served as the stimulus for the emergence of the federal government's role in EMS. Concurrently with the inclusion of payment for ambulance transport services in the Social Security Act of 1967, the focus on improving emergency medical care in the United States gained momentum, culminating with the passage of legislation designed to provide funding and guidance for the development of EMS systems across the country.

The first of the federal efforts to improve emergency care came about as a result of the passage of the National Highway Safety Act of 1966 (Public Law 89-564, 23 U.S.C. 401). Confronted with the reality that many of the injuries and deaths were directly attributable to automobile accidents, federal responsibility for EMS was placed within the Department of Transportation (DOT). Although there have been changes during the last 50 years, the principal federal agency charged with EMS responsibilities continues to reside within the agency responsible for roadway safety, the National Highway Transportation and Safety Administration (NHTSA). The National Highway Safety Act charged the DOT with the development of training texts and curriculum for basic emergency medical technicians (EMTs).

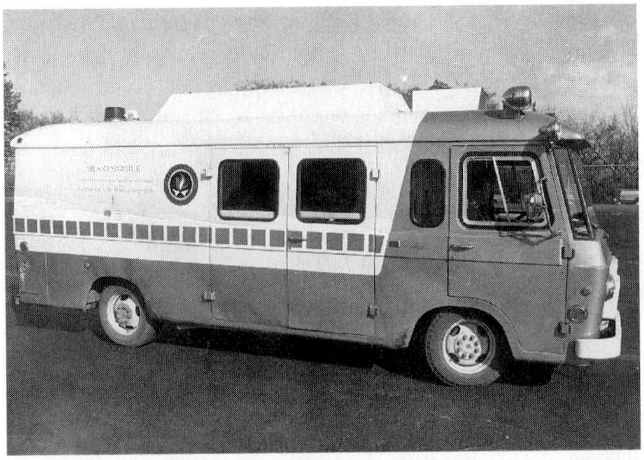

FIGURE 13.9.1 Heartmobile (Source: Courtesy of Columbus, Ohio, Fire Department)

Generally regarded as the most comprehensive EMS legislation passed was the Emergency Medical Services Act (EMS) Systems Act of 1973 (42 U.S.C. 300d). This landmark legislation promoted the development of regional EMS councils with specific responsibility for the coordination of EMS within their regions including ensuring adequate staffing, training, emergency facilities, communication, and transportation capabilities for persons in need of EMS services in their area. The 15 core elements or components of an EMS system were defined in the act. To receive federal block grant funding, the regional councils were required to meet the requirements of these 15 elements. The core components of EMS defined in 1973 continue to this day to serve as the basic building blocks of an effective and efficient EMS system design.

During the decade from 1966 to 1976, it is estimated that the federal government provided approximately $200 million for the improvement of EMS. The majority of this funding, administered by multiple federal agencies, was in the form of grants to states and local communities. Access to grant funds paved the way for the emergence of local government involvement in emergency medical services. Many local governments took advantage of the historic 75 percent federal and 25 percent local match grant program. This funding allowed for the acquisition of ambulances and equipment leading to a greater role of the fire service in delivering EMS within their communities. By 1976, morticians who prior to 1966 provided more than 50 percent of ambulance service in the country, had essentially been replaced by an array of public, private, and volunteer ambulance services.[4]

In addition to making grant funding available, the federal government developed the first series of ambulance design specifications. Currently known as KKK-1822E and administered through the Government Services Administration, the specifications and standards that continue to be used by the industry include vehicle style, design, and construction; performance characteristics; specifications for individual components such as the electrical system, oxygen delivery system, communication system; and optional and required medical equipment. The earliest units constructed in compliance with the first set of standards were marked with the distinctive "Omaha" orange stripe (Figure 13.9.2).

EMS-INVOLVED ORGANIZATIONS

During the 1980s, as the federal government's role in and funding for EMS systems waned, national organizations emerged to provide leadership for EMS systems and issues. Through collaboration and consensus-based processes, these and other organizations have essentially provided many of the standards and performance measures currently utilized by the industry.

International Association of Fire Chiefs (IAFC) and International Association of Fire Fighters (IAFF)

The International Association of Fire Chiefs (IAFC) was established in 1873 and has approximately 13,000 members. The organization provides leadership to chief officers and consists of both national and international membership. The association formed its first EMS committee in 1985; by 1991 the EMS committee had evolved as one of the largest sections within the organization. The International Association of Fire Fighters (IAFF) represents fire fighters in more than 3500 communities in the United States and Canada. Its membership of more than 274,000 members includes full-time professional fire fighters and paramedics who protect the lives and property of 85 percent of the nation's population. In 1991, the IAFC and the IAFF signed a joint memorandum of understanding (MOU) that defined the role of the fire service in the delivery of EMS.[5] The MOU initiated a series of collaborative efforts by both labor and management on emergency medical services issues of common concern to the fire service (Figure 13.9.3).

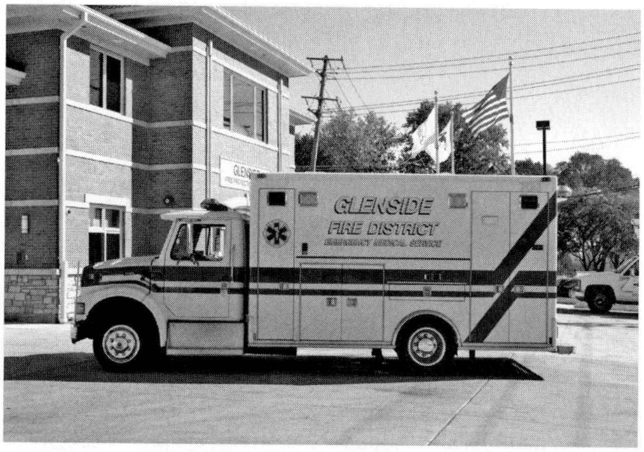

FIGURE 13.9.2 1970s Era Ambulance with Required Horizontal Orange Stripe (Source: Courtesy of Glenside Fire Protection District)

Commission on Fire Accreditation International

In 1995, the Commission on Fire Accreditation International was formed and included EMS as a core program that identified criteria and core competencies and performance indicators relative to EMS. Collaborative organizational fire service efforts with respect to EMS included transforming federal legislation that had the potential for inhibiting the role of fire departments in the delivery of emergency medical services. Of specific concern to the industry was the application of the 7K overtime exemption to medical services performed by fire departments. The Fair Labor Standards Act was amended in 1999 after joint efforts by the IAFC and the IAFF to reflect the role of fire fighters in the delivery of EMS. Historically, fire fighters were exempt from overtime compensation only in the performance of actual fire-fighting duties. Congress amended the act as a result of a redefinition of a fire fighter's duties by the Department of Labor that included emergency medical care. Known as Section 203(y), it states:

> "Employee in fire protection activities" means an employee, including a firefighter, paramedic, emergency medical technician, rescue worker, ambulance personnel, or hazardous material worker, who—
>
> (1) is trained in fire suppression, has the legal authority and responsibility to engage in fire suppression, and is employed by a fire department of a municipality, county, fire district, or State; and,
>
> (2) is engaged in the prevention, control and extinguishment of fires or response to emergency situations where life, property or the environment is at risk.[6]

In 2000, in a survey of its membership, the IAFC found that over 90 percent of fire departments participated in the delivery of emergency medical services.[7] This participation extended throughout the continuum of EMS care, including basic and advanced life support first responder services as well as over 50 percent of responding departments providing advanced life support transport services. These statistics are confirmed in the *Journal of Emergency Medical Services* (*JEMS*) publication in which its annual survey reflects that over 50 percent of the 200 most populated cities have fire department transport services and nearly all have either basic or advanced life support first responder services.[8]

National Association of State EMS Directors

In 2006, the National Association of State EMS Directors officially became the National Association of State EMS Officials, representing various state EMS agencies and their officials,

THE INTERNATIONAL ASSOCIATION OF FIRE CHIEFS
and
THE INTERNATIONAL ASSOCIATION OF FIRE FIGHTERS
JOINT RESOLUTION ON EMERGENCY MEDICAL SERVICES

WHEREAS, Pre-hospital emergency medical service is a major service provided by America's fire service, and;

WHEREAS, As first responders to most emergency situations, it is imperative that the fire service continue to provide pre-hospital medical care, and;

WHEREAS, The fire service has been hampered by lack of public recognition and support for its vital role in providing emergency medical care;

THEREFORE BE IT RESOLVED, That the leadership of the International Association of Fire Fighters and the International Association of Fire Chiefs agrees that America's fire service must continue to provide pre-hospital emergency medical care, and;

BE IT FURTHER RESOLVED, That the International Association of Fire Fighters and the International Association of Fire Chiefs urge all elected officials, professional associations and health care providers to recognize and support the provision of emergency medical care by the fire service.

Adopted by

Chief David W. Hilton, President
International Association of Fire Chiefs

Alfred K. Whitehead, President
International Association of Fire Fighters

FIGURE 13.9.3 IAFC/IAFF Joint Resolution on Emergency Medical Services

including state directors, medical directors, and training coordinators. It is considered a leading national organization for EMS, serving as an advocate for the development of effective, integrated, community-based, universal, and consistent EMS systems. In 2003, the National Association of State EMS Directors conducted a national EMS survey. The survey, completed by state EMS directors, reflected that with respect to EMS systems, approximately 48.6 percent are nonfire, non–hospital based, 44.9 percent are fire based, and 6.5 percent are hospital based.[9] Nonfire, non–hospital based services include private providers, volunteer agencies, and governmental services not affiliated with a fire department. State EMS agencies have fundamental responsibilities for the certification and recertification of EMS providers and the licensure of ambulance services.

EMS Standard-Developing Organizations

Between 1984 and 2005, the National Fire Protection Association (NFPA) developed and published various standards and guides for fire agencies specific to EMS. During this time period, other organizations made significant contributions to EMS. The American Ambulance Association developed the Commission on Accreditation of Ambulance Services. Its standards are utilized primarily by patient transport providers in an effort to be officially accredited by the agency. The National Association of EMS Physicians serves as the principal platform for the involvement of physicians certified in emergency medicine. Its initial efforts focused on the role, training, and certification of the medical director. The National Association of State EMS Directors and others took on a more visible role addressing the issues facing its constituencies, as examined earlier.

EMS ORGANIZATIONAL MODELS

Fire departments have generally been organized along functional lines of program and service delivery. The complexity of the organizational matrix depends on various factors, including agency size, community size, services being provided, and fiscal capability. Depending on these factors, an EMS organization within the fire department generally follows one of two matrices, which are delineated by the level of EMS being provided. A shared common element that exists between both transport and nontransport systems is that of medical direction. Service levels typically define the role of the agency within the system and represent either first response, transport, or both. Service levels are further defined based on level of care being provided, which generally parallels individual provider certification.

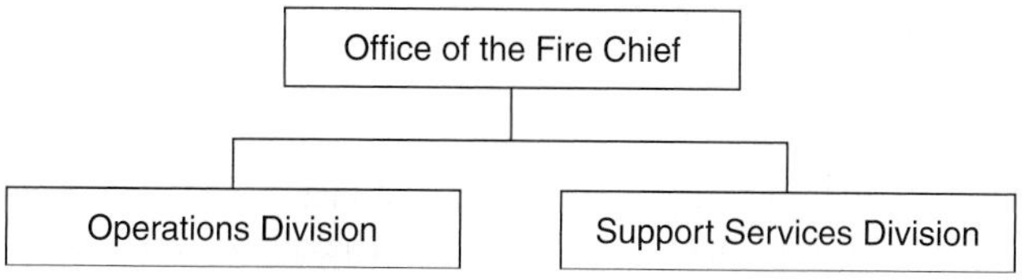

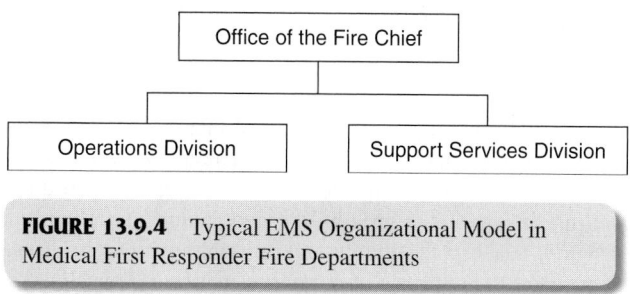

FIGURE 13.9.4 Typical EMS Organizational Model in Medical First Responder Fire Departments

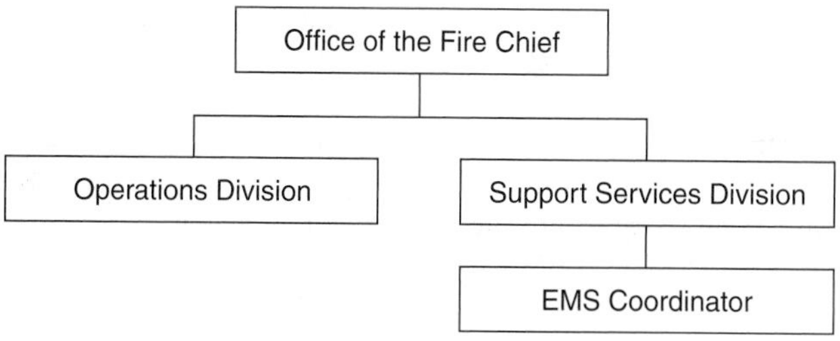

FIGURE 13.9.5 Typical EMS Organizational Model in Smaller Patient Transport–Based Fire Departments

Medical First Responder Fire Departments

In simple, less complex, and typically smaller organizations, such as those often found in rural and small municipal environments, duties and responsibilities for EMS administration and management are generally shared by existing personnel, both administratively and operationally (Figure 13.9.4).

Consistent with other operational programs, in this organizational model responsibility for EMS administration resides within the office of the fire chief. The fire chief has agency-wide responsibility for administrative functions, including planning, directing, controlling, and organizing the various aspects of EMS. In this model, the fire chief usually has a direct relationship with the medical director.

The operations division is generally responsible for the delivery of field programs such as fire suppression, hazmat, rescue services, and emergency medical services. Consistent with these duties are the day-to-day management of individual stations and companies.

The support services division includes all of the responsibilities to ensure that field programs have the essential resources and capabilities to fulfill their primary mission, including such functions as training, facility and fleet management, and supply and equipment management.

Patient Transport–Based Fire Department

The scope of responsibilities for EMS management and administration changes dramatically when the agency has responsibility for EMS transport services, irrespective of agency size. The complexities of patient transport require additional staff for the coordination of associated responsibilities, including medical direction and coordination, quality assurance, training and certification, billing, inventory control, equipment maintenance, and procurement. In smaller organizations that provide patient transport services, the position of an EMS coordinator is generally found within the support services division (Figure 13.9.5).

Depending on agency size, the position of the EMS coordinator generally consists of a dedicated full-time position. In smaller organizations, it may be a shared position that includes EMS training in addition to coordinating the various aspects associated with patient transport activities. Organizations following this model are typically found in smaller communities and less densely populated environments.

In more complex organizations serving larger populations the organization typically reflects a divisional structure. These organizations are prevalent in urban and suburban environments (Figure 13.9.6).

The responsibilities for EMS administration and management are predicated on the recognition that certain functions must be carried in order for the system to be able to meet the demands of the population.

EMS Service Levels

The terms *service levels* and *level of care provided* are often used synonymously. Although there are parallels, service levels generally reflect the level of service being provided to a patient, which can consists of basic life support, advanced life support, or critical services. Service levels can be applied to both first responder as well as transport providing agencies.

Level of care can be defined as the provision of patient care services as determined by provider certification and licensure. Certification and licensure of personnel to perform within their specific scope of practice levels lie within the domain of

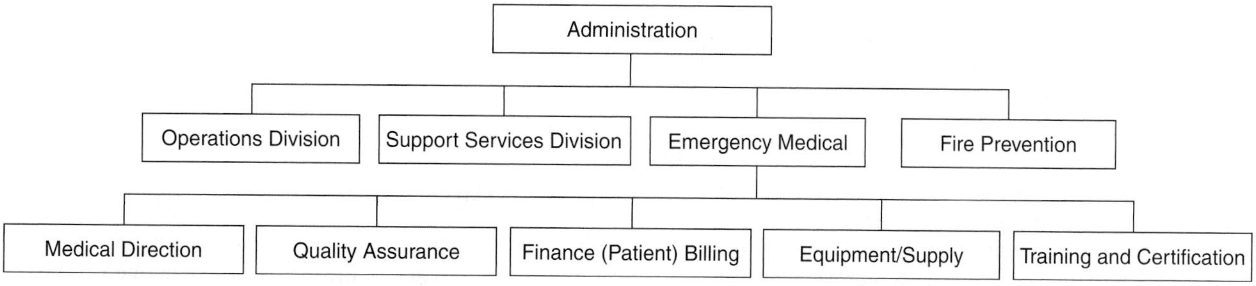

FIGURE 13.9.6 Typical EMS Organizational Model in Larger Patient Transport–Based Fire Departments

state and territory regulatory agencies. In addition, certification state and territorial agencies also govern the ability of agencies to provide services at a specified level and, depending on location, may include the authority to provide first response or patient transport services. These regulations and licensure requirements vary from state to state and are one of the reasons for the variation in EMS service delivery through the country. Although there are differences between the states and territories, certification levels include the following:

First responder
Basic emergency medical technician
Intermediate emergency medical technician
Paramedic

In addition to state and territorial rules and regulations, the Centers for Medicare Services also describe service levels for the purpose of patient transport reimbursement.[10] The establishment of the National Fee Schedule for Ambulances in 2002 defined CMS service levels as follows:

- *Basic Life Support Non-Emergency.* Scheduled transfer of patients from one facility to another requiring only basic life support services
- *Basic Life Support Emergency.* 9-1-1 call or equivalent response to a request for assistance requiring only basic life support services
- *Advanced Life Support Non-Emergency.* Scheduled transfer of patients from one facility to another requiring advanced life support services
- *Advanced Life Support Level 1.* 9-1-1 call or equivalent response to a request for assistance requiring advanced life support assessment services
- *Advanced Life Support Level 2.* Response to a request for assistance requiring advanced life support services that includes provision of at least one invasive procedure or administration of at least three separate medications
- *Critical Care Transport.* Provision of patient care services that exceed capabilities of a paramedic without additional training and certification

Within the fire service, there may be a single role such as that of a first responder or additional roles to include ambulance transportation. The level of care that certified fire fighters are capable of providing may encompass the entire spectrum from first responder certification to paramedic certification.

As of late 2005, 98 percent of U.S. local fire departments providing EMS service had all of their involved personnel certified to at least the first responder level. Also, 26 percent had all of their involved personnel certified to at least basic life support, and 87 percent had at least some involved personnel certified to that level. In addition, 3 percent had all their involved personnel certified to at least advanced life support, and 50 percent had at least some involved personnel certified to that level. Finally, no departments had all involved personnel certified to the level of paramedic, but 18 percent had at least some personnel certified to that level. For additional discussion and information on fire departments and organizational structures, refer to Section 12, Chapter 4, "Managing Fire-Rescue Departments."

SYSTEM PERFORMANCE EVALUATION

Performance Measures and Standards

The goal of any fire department should include a commitment to quality in its delivery of services. The quality process encompasses a number of activities, including the institution and use of various criteria by the department to measure its progress in achieving quality or modifying its program. These criteria may encompass performance measures, benchmarks, or standards.

Performance Measurement. According to the Joint Commission on Accreditation of Health Care Organizations (JCAHO):

> Performance measurement is used internally by health care organizations to support performance improvement and externally, to demonstrate accountability to the public and other interested stakeholders. Performance measurement benefits the health care organization by providing statistically valid, data-driven mechanisms that generate a continuous stream of performance information. This enables a health care organization to understand how well their organization is doing over time and have continuous access to objective data to support claims of quality. The organization can verify the effectiveness of corrective actions; identify areas of excellence within the organization; and compare their performance with that of peer organizations using the same measures. Similarly, performance data can be used by external stakeholders to make value-based decisions on where to seek quality health care.[11]

Benchmarking. Benchmarking is the process of emulating another agency's level of performance or excellence. Benchmarking can be valuable to an agency when comparative analysis reflects similar organizational attributes or service levels. Using benchmarking techniques reduces the time needed to implement best practices and reduces the potential for error in program implementation or modification.

Standard. A standard is generally defined as an accepted industry practice based on a consensus process that employs affected stakeholders in the development of the standard. Requirements may or may not be based on scientific research.

Efforts at developing performance measurements and standards within EMS that are designed to measure performance or serve as a basis for system improvement have been undertaken by various regulatory and nonregulatory agencies and organizations. The vast majority of these efforts have focused on consensus-based processes involving regulators, educators, practitioners, providers, and physicians.

System Performance Criteria

Efforts at developing system performance criteria have focused on how the system and the elements that define a system are functioning. EMS system evaluation can be conducted at the national, state, regional, and local levels.

EMS Performance Audit. The National Highway Transportation Safety Administration (NHTSA) routinely provides state EMS regulatory agencies with a process for evaluating their EMS system from a state perspective utilizing the core components of system design. Known as an EMS performance audit, the agency contracts with emergency medical service experts to conduct the audit of the state EMS administrative agency and through its efforts provide a blueprint for state EMS system improvement.

NFPA Standards and Guides. The National Fire Protection Association between 1984 and 2005 developed and published various standards and guides for fire agencies specific to EMS. These standards and documents include the following:

- NFPA 450, *Guide for Emergency Medical Services and Systems*
- NFPA 473, *Standard for Competencies for EMS Personnel Responding to Hazardous Materials Incidents*
- NFPA 1581, *Standard on Fire Department Infection Control Program*
- NFPA 1710, *Standard for the Organization and Deployment of Fire Suppression Operations, Emergency Medical Operations, and Special Operations to the Public by Career Fire Departments*
- NFPA 1999, *Standard on Protective Clothing for Emergency Medical Operations*

In 2001 the National Fire Protection Association established an EMS technical committee. As stated in NFPA 450, the committee's scope recognizes that it

> shall have primary responsibility for documents on the training and education requirements for personnel, personal protective equipment, health and safety programs, and quality assurance programs which incorporate physicians and the community in the planning process. It shall also be responsible for documents relating to emergency medical services, except those covered by other NFPA committees that have primary responsibility.

The committee's first effort resulted in the development of a comprehensive guide designed to assist individuals and agencies with a process for evaluating their EMS system. The application of NFPA 450 from a system's perspective can encompass local and regional systems. Although any analysis of an EMS system must recognize the core elements that have historically been defined to constitute an EMS system, other factors must be taken into consideration, including system design, finance, and medical direction.

NFPA 450 recognizes the following components as essential elements of an EMS system that are intrinsically linked and should therefore be coordinated:

- System regulation and policy
- Analysis and planning
- Finance
- Medical direction
- Quality management, clinical quality
- Public information, education, and relations
- Communications
- Equipment and facilities
- Human resources
- Operations

System Relationships

EMS organizations do not exist in a vacuum. Their success and ability to provide effective and efficient services are dependent on the various relationships the fire department has within the system's local domain. This system consists of multiple entities that impact the organization's ability to deliver quality services. Some of these relationships are reflected in Figure 13.9.7. As one can discern, these relationships are dependent on each other and any change in one can have an effect on the rest of the system. In order to quantify changes and their impacts, system analysis from both an historical as well as a prospective basis should be undertaken by the agency on a regular basis.

Response Time Performance. To illustrate the impact of the relationships that exist in a system when there is a lack of coordination, one can view the performance element of response time. Response time performance standards have existed for many years in the EMS industry, yet in many systems the ability to differentiate the contributions to response time from the various participants that make up a system's overall response time

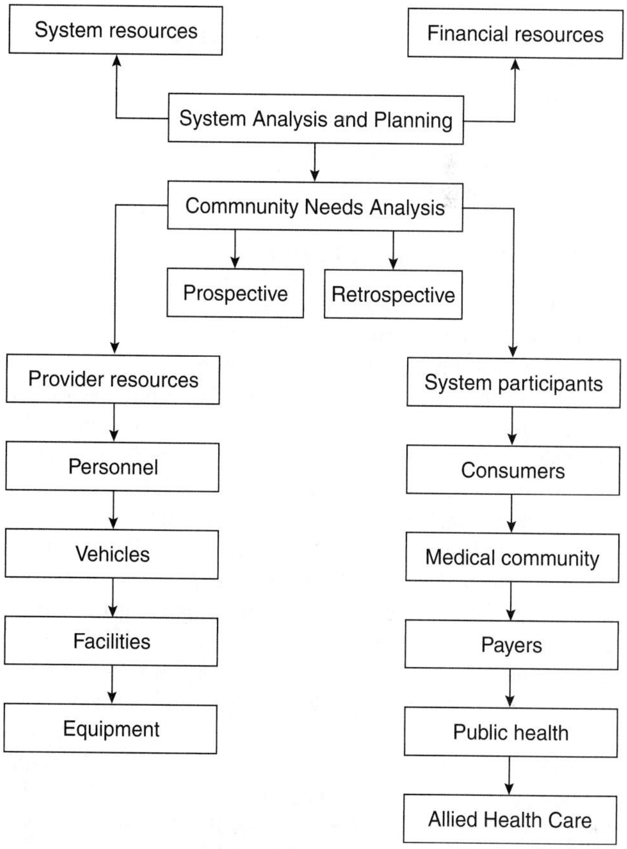

FIGURE 13.9.7 EMS System Relationships

do not exist or are not analyzed in the context of the contributing agencies. Without system coordination, analysis, and review, the time it takes a dispatch center to process a call, the turnout time of a first responder, the travel time to the scene of a transport unit, or the time it takes to turn a patient over to definitive care has little value in determining whether the system is performing consistent with expectations. Failure of any element of the agencies that contribute to response time performance can have a detrimental effect with respect to system performance.

Process Performance Indicator Index (PPII). Other efforts at developing a comprehensive identification of performance measures are ongoing. The Open Source EMS Initiative, an organization devoted to the collection of best practices and resource information for EMS agencies, has developed a draft of a comprehensive collection of areas for which EMS performance indicators should be established, including the following:[12]

- Administration/leadership
- Field operations
- Clinical care
- Medical direction
- Human resources
- Fleet management
- Supply management
- Dispatch and communications
- Information services
- Support services
- Prevention, community education, and access
- Special events and services
- Financial services
- Safety and risk management
- Research
- System measures

EMS Agenda for the Future

The *EMS Agenda for the Future,* a published federal document, consisted of a joint effort by the National Association of EMS Physicians and the National Association of EMS Directors to produce a vision for the future of EMS. The effort was funded through grants provided by NHTSA and the U.S. Department of Health and Human Services' Maternal Health Services Division. Utilizing experts from the industry, the *EMS Agenda for the Future* established a visionary blueprint for the progression and improvement of EMS in the United States. The document has been widely used by the federal government as its road map for providing a federal focus and improving EMS from a national perspective. Building on the efforts of the agenda, a companion document entitled *Emergency Medical Services Agenda for the Future Implementation Guide*[13] provides specific strategies, objectives, and responsibilities for implementing the vision. Other documents emanating from the agenda include the *Emergency Medical Services Education Agenda for the Future: A Systems Approach*[14] and the *National EMS Research Agenda.*[15] Both of these publications provide a blueprint for activities to improve EMS within their respective domains from a national perspective.

PERFORMANCE EVALUATION ORGANIZATIONS

During the last 20 years several accrediting bodies have been developed that wholly or partly have EMS-specific elements. Their efforts focus primarily on the individual agency. Generally included within their documents are requirements with respect to external relationships. The agency is required to demonstrate how they interact with organizations that impact their service delivery. Departments can voluntarily undertake accreditation as demonstration of compliance with accepted industry standards and performance and recognition of excellence.

Commission on Fire Accreditation International (CFAI)

Initiated by the International Association of Fire Chiefs and the International City-County Management Association, the Commission on Fire Accreditation International (CFAI) accredits fire departments internationally when they complete a self-assessment and peer review process of compliance with its criteria and performance standards. The accrediting body currently resides within the Center for Public Safety Excellence, Inc., an organization that also administers the Commission on Professional Credentialing. Provision of EMS as a core program of a fire department is included within the document. The Tempe, Arizona, Fire Department was the first agency to achieve CFAI accreditation. An essential component of the accreditation process is the development of a "Standard of Cover" document, which defines the agency's performance measurements for the various service delivery programs provided by the department.

Compliance with recognized performance measures can occur only when true system coordination exists and the individual participants in the system, from dispatch through definitive care, recognize their contribution and the critical role each plays to ensure the overall welfare of the patient needing emergency medical care. It should follow that the discussion of performance measures or standards for the various elements that constitute EMS should correlate to the progression of the medical event, the resources utilized to manage the critical care needs of the patient, and the contributors that provide resources and personnel in ensuring that the system is effective. Without ensuring that coordination exists in the various elements that make up an EMS system, ensuring quality or making improvements to the system would be difficult to achieve.

Commission on Accreditation of Ambulance Services (CAAS)

The first effort to accredit ambulance services was initiated by the American Ambulance Association. In May 1984, the AAA Board of Directors formed a committee on accreditation and standards. The standards developed by the committee represented a consensus-based process involving EMS officials from throughout the country. The efforts of the committee resulted in the formation of an independent Commission on Accreditation of Ambulance Services (CAAS) in 1990.

CAAS accreditation is based on the agency's seeking accreditation to demonstrate compliance with various standards and performance measures specific to the individual agency. The accreditation is focused on patient transport providers. In 1999, the Lubbock, Texas, Fire Department became the first fire-based transport provider to be accredited by CAAS. One of the most widely utilized performance measurements by the EMS industry identified in the document is 90 percent compliance with a response time performance of 8 minutes, 59 seconds (8:59) to life-threatening calls for service. This performance measurement is frequently used as a core requirement in contracts for patient transport services.

International Association of Fire Fighters (IAFF)

The International Association of Fire Fighters (IAFF) has developed a collection of performance measures specific to fire department–based EMS programs. Included are measures for call processing, turnout time, travel time, staffing, deployment, geographic coverage, protocol compliance, patient outcomes, availability of defibrillation, extrication capability, frequency of employee illness or injury, employee turnover rate, quality programs, and multicasualty response plans.

American Heart Association

According to its mission statement, the American Heart Association "is a national voluntary health agency whose mission is to reduce disability and death from cardiovascular diseases and stroke." Founded in 1924, the association has developed various programs specifically addressing cardiac care in the prehospital environment. The association, although not a standards-setting body, does publish peer-reviewed scientific journals and recommends changes to cardiac care based on scientific research. Within the prehospital environment, the American Heart Association offers specialty certification courses such as advanced cardiac life support, pediatric cardiac life support, as well as basic life support.

American Ambulance Association

The American Ambulance Association, founded in 1979, represents ambulance services across the United States. It is estimated that the association's membership serves over 75 percent of the U.S. population with emergency and nonemergency care and medical transportation services. The organization provides leadership services to its members and services as a voice and clearinghouse for ambulance services across the nation. The American Ambulance Association developed the "Contracting Guide for Ambulance Services," a document that contains various performance criteria for agencies involved in providing patient transport services. In addition, the document is designed to provide information on alternative system design and efficiencies.

American Society for Testing and Materials (ASTM) International

American Society for Testing and Materials (ASTM) International, one of the largest voluntary standards development organizations in the world, is a trusted source for technical standards for materials, products, systems, and services. The committee responsible for the development of these standards is known as the F30 Committee. ASTM has been developing EMS standards for the last 20 years, including the following:

- F1086-94(2002), *Standard Guide for Structures and Responsibilities of Emergency Medical Services Systems Organizations*
- F1149-93(2003), *Standard Practice for Qualifications, Responsibilities, and Authority of Individuals and Institutions Providing Medical Direction of Emergency Medical Services*
- F1224-89(2004)e1, *Standard Guide for Providing System Evaluation for Emergency Medical Services*
- F1268-90(2003), *Standard Guide for Establishing and Operating a Public Information, Education, and Relations Program for Emergency Medical Service Systems*
- F1286-90(2002), *Standard Guide for Development and Operation of Level 1 Pediatric Trauma Facilities*
- F1288-90(2003), *Standard Guide for Planning for and Response to a Multiple Casualty Incident*
- F1339-92(2003), *Standard Guide for Organization and Operation of Emergency Medical Services Systems*
- F1493-93(2003), *Standard Guide for Financing and Financial Accountability of Medical Transportation Systems*
- F1629-95(2007), *Standard Guide for Establishing Operating Emergency Medical Services and Management Information Systems, or Both*
- F1652-95(2007), *Standard Guide for Providing Essential Data Needed in Advance for Prehospital Emergency Medical Services*

SYSTEM DESIGN ELEMENTS AND PERFORMANCE

The Emergency Medical Services Systems Act of 1973 defined the essential elements of EMS system design. Although the core components have been modified, they stand largely intact as the fundamental elements of an EMS system. Performance measures and standards generally correlate to these elements. They include the following elements, some of which will be discussed here: public information and education, communications, human resources training, public safety, transportation, access to care, facilities, critical care, patient transfers, financial control, medical direction, quality management, resource deployment, record keeping, evaluation, disaster preparedness, mutual aid, and consumer participation.

Recognizing that there are multiple contributors to any EMS system, development of performance measures and standards has been predicated to a great extent on the contribution that each participant provides to the system and by the organizations that generally represent a specific professional constituency.

Public Information and Education

In the United States, the fire service has largely been successful in educating the general public and modifying the public's behavior to reduce illness or injuries. Fire prevention efforts have been highly successful in reducing fire deaths and injuries. Similarly, efforts toward reducing injuries and death from non-fire-related causes have also been proven successful.

The role of the fire service in illness and injury prevention has progressed significantly in recent years. Although fire prevention continues to be a fundamental effort, programs such as NFPA's *Risk Watch*® that focus on injury prevention and reduction have been instituted in many communities, with the fire department often taking a leadership role.

Advances in technology, especially in the area of automatic external defibrillators, provide opportunities for departments to serve as the focal point for the institution of community automatic external defibrillator (AED) programs.

Benchmarking these and other similar programs provides the fire service with an excellent opportunity to expand its role in community education and prevention measures that focus on illnesses and injuries.

During the past five years, professional organizations such as the IAFC have expanded their role in providing leadership to fire departments by means of publications addressing preparedness for organizational and community health concerns. The impetus for the development of these documents varies, but the overall goal is to expand organizational awareness of the issues that departments and communities may face within the health care arena.

The first of these documents, published in 2001, is the *Fire Department Guide to Smallpox.*[16] The second document, published in 2005, is the *Fire Department Guide to Pandemics.*[17] Both of these documents provide organizational leaders with information and education to assist organizations in preparing for and managing health care crises in their communities.

Communications

The success of 9-1-1 to access public safety services and emergency medical care since the first system went into service in Haleyville, Alabama, in 1967[18] has been unparalleled from a public education perspective. The communication and dispatch centers serve as the primary access point for emergency medical care in most communities. Given this enormous responsibility, these centers and the personnel in their employ are recognized as being critical to ensuring that the appropriate resources and medical assistance are provided to constituents in need of EMS.

The *EMS Agenda for the Future,* a visionary document on how the future of emergency medical services may be constructed, utilizes the communication process diagram shown in Figure 13.9.8 to describe potential alternative decisions that could be made available in the future for EMS dispatch centers in order to optimize scarce response resources while simultaneously ensuring that callers' medical needs are appropriately met.

Dispatcher Certification. Various standards and performance criteria have been developed specific to the communication and dispatch function. In 1987, the NHTSA developed the curriculum for emergency medical dispatcher certification. The

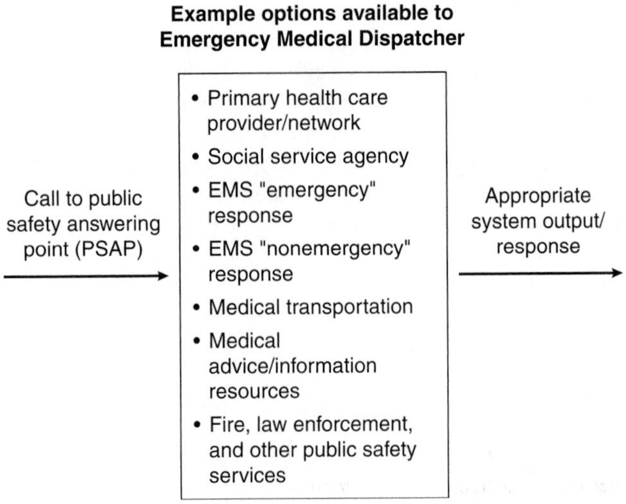

FIGURE 13.9.8 Sample Emergency Medical Dispatcher Options

certification available through state training agencies provides the essential skills and knowledge base for individuals charged with the responsibilities of providing emergency medical care instructions prior to the arrival of response units.

Dispatching Protocols. Subsequent to the creation of the dispatcher curriculum, independent efforts have resulted in the development of standardized dispatching protocols designed to provide a hierarchical process for determining patient criticality and correlating prehospital care instructions. In 1987, Dr. Jeffrey Claussen developed a proprietary card system process that the dispatcher uses to ask specific questions. Based on the answers to the questions, the dispatcher is able to determine whether to dispatch basic or advanced life support units. The system also provides instructions in patient care for the dispatcher to relay to the patient or bystanders.

Using a process that allows for the identification of appropriate resource allocation is critical not only from a cost-containment perspective but also to ensure that the provider of transport services can recover revenues consistent with the dispatch of resources. The Centers for Medicare Services, through its modification of payment policies for Medicare patient transports in 2001, allows for the payment of advanced life support if the initial information provided to the dispatch agency indicated a need for an advanced life support response even though the patient may have needed only basic life support services.

Communication Standards and Performance Measures Resources. The principal organizations providing communication standards and performance measures include the following:

- *Association of Public-Safety Communications Officials (APCO).* The APCO Institute provides an Emergency Medical Dispatch program that is based on the *NHTSA National*

Standard Curriculum for EMD as well as ASTM International guidelines in a comprehensive EMD package. Emergency Medical Dispatch is a structured and sequential program that enables communication personnel to properly determine the nature and priority of an emergency medical call, dispatch the appropriate response, and provide the caller with specific medical self-help instructions to assist the patient until EMS personnel arrive.

- *National Fire Protection Association (NFPA).* NFPA 1221, *Standard for the Installation, Maintenance, and Use of Emergency Services Communications Systems,* is a standard for communication systems and facilities.
- *Commission on Accreditation of Law Enforcement Agencies (CALEA).* In 1996, CALEA and APCO collectively developed an accreditation program for public safety communications agencies. The CALEA *Accreditation Standards Manual* contains 216 standards designed to include the following categories: organization, direction and authority; human resources; recruitment and selection; training; and operations.
- *Commission on Fire Accreditation International (CFAI).* The CFAI, established in 1996, provides a voluntary accreditation program to fire departments encompassing 10 program categories that include performance indicators.

Response Time Performance Measurements

The ability to reach a victim of an accident or illness within time-sensitive parameters has long been a hallmark of the fire service. Strategically deployed resources throughout a community allow for rapid response to any emergency event. The single performance measurement most frequently utilized to measure an EMS system's performance is that of response time. The American Heart Association considers critical components of EMS systems to include appropriate access by citizens as well as timely dispatch of responders. According to the American Heart Association:

> Passage of time drives all aspects of emergency cardiac care and determines patient outcomes.[19]

Development of Response Time Standards. Initial efforts to establish response time standards were developed during the late 1970s by Dr. Michael Eisenberg. In his studies he found that patients who received CPR during the first 4 to 6 minutes followed by advanced emergency medical care in 8 minutes had a statistically higher probability of survival.[20] Since that time, the 8 minute standard for advanced life support has been universally adopted and reflected in community EMS system requirements and accreditation programs. In 1995, the Commission on Accreditation of Ambulance Services (CAAS) clarified its 8:00 minute standard to represent 8 minutes, 59 seconds.

NFPA 450 provides a comprehensive listing and definitions for response times including discrete time stamps, process intervals, and functional intervals. The identification of these measurements was established in an effort to create uniformity in how agencies define response time as well as the elements that constitute response time. In addition, acceptance and utilization of these values will facilitate system-to-system comparison and analysis.

Discrete Time Stamps. Discrete time stamps are identified as fixed points in time that can be captured electronically throughout the continuum of an EMS call. The value of these fixed points lies in the recognition that multiple system participants contribute to the overall lapse of time from the initial call to definitive care. These baseline points can then be aggregated and analyzed to determine system response time performance improvements as shown in Table 13.9.2.

Functional Intervals. Functional intervals represent the span of time during which specific functions are performed by system participants. The analysis of functional time intervals allows agencies and system administrators to determine whether any particular modification is necessary and designates the agency and personnel responsible for making improvements.

Process Intervals. Process intervals are designed to capture the time for the completion of specific elements within the system in accomplishing their objectives. The compilation and analysis of process intervals provide additional insight into overall system performance and whether there are unique circumstances or environments that have an impact on system performance.

Response Time Standards and Performance Measures Resources. The principal organizations providing response time standards and performance measures include the following:

- *Commission on Fire Accreditation International (CFAI).* CFAI's accreditation standard requires performance compliance of 60 seconds for turnout of personnel in urban and suburban communities to an emergency event.
- *National Fire Protection Association (NFPA).* NFPA 1710, *Standard for the Organization and Deployment of Fire Suppression Operations, Emergency Medical Operations, and Special Operations to the Public by Career Fire Departments,* establishes a 4 minute response time for the arrival of a unit with first-responder or higher capability to EMS calls and 8 minutes or less for an arrival of an advanced life support unit when such service is provided by the fire department. The standard further allows a 1 minute turnout time. Call processing time is covered by NFPA 1221, *Standard for the Installation, Maintenance, and Use of Emergency Services Communications Systems,* and requires that calls be handled in 60 seconds or less 95 percent of the time.
- *Commission on Accreditation of Ambulance Services (CAAS).* CAAS's accreditation standard allows 8 minutes, 59 seconds for arrival of advanced life support ambulance in urban and suburban communities from point of response unit notification of the event to life-threatening emergencies.
- *Centers for Medicare Services (CMS).* CMS provides a definition of an emergency response as one in which resources are mobilized and responding within the first 5 minutes from notification of the event. Definition is utilized to qualify for the payment of an emergency response versus a nonemergency request for Medicare-eligible patient transports.

TABLE 13.9.2 EMS Time Template

Column A *Discrete Time Stamps*	*Column B* *Function Intervals*	*Column C* *Process Intervals*
1. Event occurs	Recognition interval (1 to 2)	Call processing (4 to 11)
2. Discovery of event	System access interval (2 to 3)	System response (4 to 13)
3. Call for help	Switching interval (3 to 4)	Agency response (6 to 13)
4. Phone rings in 1st PSAP	Answer interval (4 to 5)	Unit response (11 to 13)
5. Phone "off hook" answered in 1st PSAP	Routing interval (5 to 6)	Patient contact (14 to 17)
6. Secondary dispatch phone rings (if appropriate)	Answer Interval (6 to 7)	Event to treatment (1 to 14)
7. Secondary dispatch phone "off hook" answered (if appropriate)	Interrogation interval (7 to 8)	On-scene management (13 to 15)
a. Interview begins	Resource selection interval (8 to 9)	Citizen reaction (1 to 3)
b. Pre-arrival instructions begin	Alert interval (9 to 10)	Unit cycle (11 to 18)
c. Pre-arrival instructions end	Acknowledgment interval (10 to 11)	Event elapsed (1 to 18)
8. Interview ends	Turn-out interval (11 to 12)	
9. Response resources identified	Travel interval (12 to 13)	
10. Dispatch time	Patient access interval (13 to 14)	
11. Unit acknowledgment	Scene management interval (14 to 15)	
12. Wheels turning (en route to scene)	Transport interval (15 to 16)	
13. Wheels stopped (arrived at scene)	Care transfer interval (16 to 17)	
14. Patient contact	Unit-ready interval (17 to 18)	
15. Wheels turning (en route to hospital)		
16. Wheels stopped (arrived at hospital)		
17. Transfer of care		
18. Available for service		

Source: NFPA 450, 2004 edition, p. 450-22.

Human Resources

The role of establishing educational criteria has largely been within the domain of the federal government through the National Highway Traffic Safety Administration (NHTSA). This statutory responsibility can be found in the Emergency Medical Services Systems Act of 1973.

Provider Level Skills and Knowledge. Since its initial development of the basic EMT curriculum, the NHTSA has undertaken various efforts to expand on the essential training and education for EMS personnel. In 1992, NHTSA developed the National Practice Blueprint designed to identify the essential skills and knowledge for each provider level:

- *First Responder.* Provision of care consistent with the guidelines prescribed in the *National Practice Blueprint for First Responder.* This certification level generally is limited to provision of basic first aid and CPR.
- *Basic EMT.* Provision of care consistent with the guidelines prescribed in the *National EMS Education and Practice Blueprint* for basic EMTs. This certification level is considered to be the minimum level of certification requirement to function on an ambulance. Many fire departments utilize this certification level as a requirement for their personnel in the same manner as NPQ FFI is required.
- *Intermediate EMT.* Provision of care consistent with the guidelines prescribed in the *National EMS Education and Practice Blueprint* for intermediate EMTs. This certification level serves to bridge the practice skills and capabilities of Basic EMTs and those of paramedics. Use of Intermediate EMTs is especially prevalent in areas where there is a lack of paramedics.
- *Paramedic.* Provision of care consistent with the guidelines prescribed in the *National EMS Education and Practice Blueprint.* The care and skills capability of this certification allows for the administration of various medications and invasive procedures such as intubation, pleural decompression, manual cardiac defibrillation, and other procedures as permitted under medical direction.

National Scope of Practice Model. In 2000, The National Highway Traffic Safety Administration convened a stakeholders' meeting to review EMS education comprehensively. Patterned after the highly successful *EMS Agenda for the Future,* the task force developed the *EMS Education Agenda for the Future.* Included in its findings and recommendations was the development of a *National EMS Scope of Practice Model.*[21] The work toward developing a National Scope of Practice Model was concluded in 2005. The model has recommended a new continuum of EMS providers that includes the following:

Emergency Medical Responder
Emergency Medical Technician
Paramedic
Advanced Practice Paramedic

The development of these new provider levels was based on a consensus process; thus the federal government does not have any regulatory authority to require their adoption. Whether there will be widespread acceptance and adoption of the recommendations from the Scope of Practice task force will be determined by individual state regulatory agencies that generally have statutory authority over provider training, certification, and licensure.

Many states utilize testing and certification conducted by the National Registry of EMTs. The organization established in 1980 conducts comprehensive task analysis of provider skills. Through this analysis, the registry established testing materials and provides initial certification. Approximately 47 states and territories currently use the National Registry testing and certification process for personnel within their respective geographic areas.

Human Resource Standards and Performance Measurement Resources. The principal organizations providing human resource standards and performance measures include the following:

- International Association of Fire Fighters
  EMS Performance Measures
- State EMS Regulatory Agencies
- National Registry of Emergency Medical Technicians
- National Fire Protection Association
  NFPA 473, *Standard for Competencies for EMS Personnel Responding to Hazardous Materials Incidents*

Financial Control

Without appropriate financial controls and adherence to sound financial practices, EMS systems are subject to undue risk and potentially their demise. According to NFPA 450, EMS systems should have a comprehensive method for determining the cost of the EMS system. At a minimum the document recommends the establishment of an EMS financial plan that includes a cost analysis, short-term and long-term financial plans, and a financial reporting system.

Cost Analysis. A cost analysis should be conducted to study start-up costs, ongoing costs, and indirect costs:

Start-up costs. Generally include equipment, vehicles, supplies and materials, and personnel—including primary and support staff and training costs

Ongoing costs. Include equipment, vehicles, fuel, supplies and materials, communication systems, and personnel—including the cost of benefits, education/training, and certification costs

Indirect costs. Include insurance, legal services, medical oversight, contract services, regulatory compliance, billing services, and information management costs

Short-Term and Long-Term Financial Plans. Consistent with proper fiscal planning, the document identifies the development of a short-term financial plan, which consists of both an operating budget and a capital budget. A long-term financial plan should also be developed to insulate the agency from changes that can affect the organization fiscally. This plan should reflect new programs or services that are anticipated in the future, potential reimbursement changes, revenues, and cash flow projections. A contingency plan should be constructed if any of the analysis determines that the organization is at risk.

Financial Reporting System. Agencies that provide patient transport services should have a financial reporting system that provides the agency with information on the efficacy of revenue generation. Agencies should be able to identify and calculate gross billings, collection rate, payer mix, billing mix for advanced life support (ALS) and basic life support (BLS), scheduled and unscheduled transports, and miles per transport. The agency should be capable of determining bad debt expense, contractual allowances, write-offs, net revenue, revenues per transport, and accounts receivable turnover rate.

Finance Standards and Performance Measures Resources. The principal organizations providing finance standards and performance measures include the following:

- National Fire Protection Association
  NFPA 450, *Guide for Emergency Medical Services and Systems*
- American Ambulance Association
  Contracting Guide for Ambulance Services
  Medicare Compliance Manual
- Governmental Accounting Standards Board

Medical Direction

Medical direction is central to an agency's ability to provide patient services. Although there are exceptions, EMS personnel providing patient care are usually considered to be an extension of the physician and therefore require physician authority for the services they provide. Historically, physicians have provided their medical oversight services on a voluntary basis in the interest of patient care. However, with increasing demands on their time for the multitude of services being required of medical directors, the trend throughout the industry is to contract for and subsequently provide payment for medical director services.

The National Association of EMS Physicians (NAEMSP) and the American College of Emergency Physicians (ACEP) have been the principal agencies providing leadership and guidance for medical direction. In 2000, NHTSA in conjunction with NAEMSP and ACEP developed the National Standard Curriculum for Medical Direction.

Medical Oversight. Medical oversight provided by physicians encompasses the entire range of patient care activities provided by the EMS organization. The two principal functions of these services are online services and off-line services. Online services generally refer to medical control decisions affecting patient care at the time those services are provided. Off-line services refer to the additional services that the medical director is engaged in, including protocol development, education and evaluation of personnel, administrative services, patient advocacy, medical community liaison, and participation in quality review and management processes.

Medical Direction Standards and Performance Measures Resources. The principal organizations providing medical direction standards and performance measures include the following:

- National Highway Transportation Safety Administration (NHTSA)
- National Association of EMS Physicians
- American College of Emergency Physicians
- National Fire Protection Association (see NFPA 450, *Guide for Emergency Medical Services and Systems*)

Quality Management

The process for ensuring that patient care services are delivered consistent with community expectations and organizational standards is known as quality management. The core component that drives the quality management program is the ability to generate meaningful data that can be analyzed, measured, and compared to established organizational expectations.

EMS Quality Management Elements. Elements of an effective EMS quality management program include conducting or measuring patient outcomes, effective review of clinical care, analysis and evaluation of system participant integration, human resource activities, data collection validation, and performance standard compliance. The process of quality management is ongoing, recognizing that changes based on the evaluation and analysis process require that change itself is monitored and evaluated to determine whether the desired results have been achieved.

Quality Management Standards and Performance Measures. The principal organizations providing quality management standards and performance measures include the following:

- National Fire Protection Association

  NFPA 450, *Guide for Emergency Medical Services and Systems*
- National Highway Transportation Safety Administration (NHTSA)

  National EMS Information System
  A Leadership Guide to Quality Improvement for EMS Systems
  Uniform Pre-Hospital Data Elements and Definitions
- National Institute of Standards and Technology

  Malcolm Baldrige National Quality Award

Resource Deployment

The management of assets and resources in an EMS system is critical in ensuring effective and efficient delivery of services. In fire-based systems, resources are, with few exceptions, deployed from a fixed location. These locations are generally fire stations whose locations are routinely predicated on time and distance studies to meet specific response time objectives.

Deployment Models. In addition to fixed deployment models, variable deployment models are also used by the industry. These models are predicated on moving ambulance transport resources to various locations based on volume and location analysis. Time-of-day and computer-generated predictability patterns for call locations are also used to shift resources to predetermined points in the service area. This model of resource deployment, referred to as system status management, is routinely used by the private sector and by third-party service providers responsible for high-volume systems.

Tiered Response. The use of multiple agencies for the delivery of EMS is commonly referred to a tiered response. In a single-tier system, one organization has responsibility for response and care at a single level of care. Fire-based EMS transport systems fall into the single-tier category because they provide both the initial response as well as the patient transport at usually the advanced life support level of care. Multiple-tiered response systems are those in which an agency provides first response and initial care but delegates patient transport responsibilities to another entity. There are various types of multitiered systems; the most common is a fire-based first response system supported by a separate patient transport system provider, either public or private.

Resource Deployment Standards and Performance Measures. The principal organizations providing resource deployment standards and performance measures include the following:

- National Fire Protection Association

  NFPA 450, *Guide for Emergency Medical Services and Systems*
  NFPA 1500, *Standard on Fire Department Occupational Safety and Health Program*
  NFPA 1710, *Standard for the Organization ad Deployment of Fire Suppression Operations, Emergency Medical Operations, and Special Operations to the Public by Career Fire Departments*
- American Ambulance Association

  Contracting Guide for Ambulance Services
- International Association of Fire Fighters

  Effectiveness of Fire Based EMS
  IAFF Performance Measures
- American Society for Testing and Materials

  ASTM F1224-89(2004)e1, *Standard Guide for Providing System Evaluation for Emergency Medical Services*
  ASTM 1339-92(2003), *Standard Guide for Organization and Operation of Emergency Medical Services Systems*
  ASTM F1517-94(2007), *Standard Guide for Scope of Performance of Emergency Medical Services Ambulance Operations*

SUMMARY

The evolution of EMS during the last 50 years has resulted in fire departments being the dominant provider of emergency medical care in their communities. The fire department's integration of EMS is not based singularly on a reduction in fire suppression activity but as a result of multiple factors. The factors responsible for the evolution of EMS and the fire service have been varied but are representative of local, state, and national issues. Fire departments have changed in concert with the environment in which they operate.

Successful delivery of EMS services by the fire department in the local community is dependent on the successful integration of multiple partners and a committed adherence to established standards and performance measures. As such, fire departments occupy a central role in responding to the emergency medical care needs of their constituents. Although changes are certain to occur in the industry, the delivery of EMS by fire departments is established and will continue to reflect a major operational program of the local fire department.

ACKNOWLEDGMENT

The late James O. Page is regarded as the "Father of Fire-Based EMS." His devotion and commitment to and advocacy of emergency medical services, particularly as a core service element of the fire department, are well known to those in the industry. He was a friend and mentor and his untimely passing will no doubt leave a great void in our profession.

BIBLIOGRAPHY

References Cited

1. National Highway Transportation Safety Administration, *EMS Agenda for the Future,* Washington, DC, 1996.
2. National Research Council, *Accidental Death and Disability: The Nweglected Disease of Modern Society,* National Academy of Sciences, Washington, DC, 1966.
3. Pantridge, J. F., and Geddes, J. S., "A Mobile Intensive-Care Unit in the Management of Myocardial Infarction," *Lancet,* Vol. 2, 1967, pp. 271–273, [Cardiac Dept., Royal Victoria Hosp., Belfast, Northern Ireland].
4. Eisenberg, M. S., et al., "The Revolution and Evolution of Pre-Hospital Cardiac Care," *Archives of Internal Medicine,* Vol. 156, No. 15, 1996.
5. International Association of Fire Chiefs, International Association of Fire Fighters, "Memorandum of Understanding," International Association of Fire Chiefs and International Association of Fire Fighters, Washington, DC, 1991.
6. Fair Labor Standards Act Amendment, P. L. 106-151, 113 Stat. 1731 (1999).
7. International Association of Fire Chiefs, "EMS Data Survey," International Association of Fire Chiefs, Washington, DC, 2000.
8. "Annual Survey: 200 Most Populated Cities," *Journal of Emergency Medical Services,* 2004.
9. *2003 National Emergency Medical Services (EMS) Survey,* U.S. Department of Health and Human Services, Health Resources Services Administration, University of North Carolina, Chapel Hill, Department of Emergency Medicine, Washington, DC, 2003.
10. Centers for Medicare Services, Negotiated Rulemaking Committee, *Federal Register,* Washington, DC, 2001.
11. Joint Commission on Accreditation of Health Care Organizations, http://www.jointcommission.org.
12. Open Source EMS Initiative, http://www.mhf.net/opensource.
13. *Emergency Medical Services Agenda for the Future Implementation Guide,* National Highway Traffic Safety Administration, http://www.nhtsa.dot.gov/people/injury/ems/agenda.
14. *Emergency Medical Services Education Agenda for the Future: A Systems Approach,* National Highway Traffic Safety Administration, http://www.nhtsa.dot.gov/people/injury/ems/EdAgenda/final.
15. *National EMS Research Agenda,* National Highway Traffic Safety Administration, http://www.nhtsa.dot.gov/people/injury/ems/ems-agenda/EMSResearchAgenda.pdf, Dec. 31, 2001.
16. International Association of Fire Chiefs, *Fire Department Guide to Smallpox,* International Association of Fire Chiefs, Washington, DC, 2001.
17. International Association of Fire Chiefs, *Fire Department Guide to Pandemics,* Washington, DC, 2005.
18. "History of 911," *Dispatch Monthly Magazine,* http://www.911dispatch.com/911/history, 1995.
19. Cummins, R. O. (Ed.), *Advanced Cardiac Life Support,* American Heart Association, Dallas, TX, 1997.
20. Eisenberg, M. S., Bergner, L., and Hallstrom, A., "Cardiac Resuscitation in the Community: The Importance of Rapid Delivery of Care and Implications for Program Planning," *JAMA,* Vol. 241, 1979, pp. 1905–1907.
21. *National EMS Scope of Practice Model,* National Highway Traffic Safety Administration, 2005.

NFPA Codes, Standards, and Recommended Practices

Reference to the following NFPA codes, standards, and recommended practices will provide further information on medical services and the fire department discussed in this chapter. (See the latest version of The NFPA Catalog *for availability of current editions of the following documents.)*

NFPA 450, *Guide for Emergency Medical Services and Systems*
NFPA 473, *Standard for Competencies for EMS Personnel Responding to Hazardous Materials Incidents*
NFPA 1581, *Standard on Fire Department Infection Control Program*
NFPA 1710, *Standard for the Organization and Deployment of Fire Suppression Operations, Emergency Medical Operations, and Special Operations to the Public by Career Fire Departments*
NFPA 1999, *Standard on Protective Clothing for Emergency Medical Operations*

Detection and Alarm

SECTION 14

Shane M. Clary

Historically, detection and alarm have been fire protection's first line of defense after an ignition has occurred. As technology has improved, fires and their by-products have been detected earlier and earlier. More recently, various forms of detection and alarm have become interconnected. At the same time, the fields of fire protection and security have grown closer together.

Section 14 of the *Fire Protection Handbook*® reflects the evolution of detection and alarm technologies. The 19th edition included the first chapter on carbon monoxide detection in residential occupancies. In this 20th edition, the section has been expanded to include a new chapter entitled "Security and Intrusion Detection Systems."

Chapter 1, "Fire Alarm Systems," describes types of signals and basic system components before explaining the basic types of systems: protected premises, central station, proprietary, remote station, and auxiliary. The chapter also discusses emergency voice/alarm communication systems and a new concept for the alerting of individuals, mass notification systems.

Chapter 2, "Automatic Fire Detectors," has been expanded to include video-based smoke and flame detection. After describing several types of detectors (heat, smoke, gas, radiant energy, and multisensor), the chapter discusses detector selection, installation, maintenance, and testing.

Chapter 3, "Notification Appliances," concentrates on notification devices that *NFPA 72*®, *National Fire Alarm Code*®, defines as fire alarm system components, such as bells, horns, speakers, and light or text displays that provide audible, tactile, or visible outputs (or any combination of those outputs). Mass notification systems and intelligibility are discussed.

Chapter 4, "Fire Alarm System Interconnections," presents the interface of process monitoring and building management systems (such as elevator control, door control, and heating, ventilating, and air-conditioning control) and fire protection systems.

Chapter 5, "Inspection, Testing, and Maintenance of Fire Alarm Systems," explains reliability analysis and prediction, as well as topics such as acceptance and reacceptance testing, a design lifetime, and sensitivity measurement. Schedules for system and component inspection, testing, and maintenance are presented.

Chapter 6, "Household Fire Warning Equipment," discusses why household fire warning systems are needed, the history of residential fire warning systems, research into system effectiveness, the importance of having a system in the home and how to make the best use of it, and the importance of an effective escape plan. Types of systems and detectors are covered, along with installation and testing guidelines.

The section considers the human element of detection and alarm in Chapter 7, "Fire Protection Surveillance and Security Services." This chapter discusses topics such as the management of security services, communications equipment, security service functions and supervision, security officers, and patrol routes and rounds.

Shane M. Clary, Ph.D., is vice-president of codes and standards compliance at Bay Alarm Company in Pacheco, California. He is the chair of the Technical Committee for the Fundamentals of Fire Alarm Systems, a member of the NFPA Standards Council, serves on a number of other NFPA technical committees, and is the author of the *NFPA Pocket Guide to Electronic Security System Installation.*

Chapter 8, "Gas and Vapor Detection Systems and Monitors," addresses the detection of flammable, combustible, or toxic gases and vapors that represent a hazard to the occupants or the facility.

The physical properties, sources, and hazards of CO are described in Chapter 9, "Carbon Monoxide Detection in Residential Occupancies." The chapter then outlines carbon monoxide standards and detection technologies and provides a discussion of fire service response to carbon monoxide alarms.

The section closes with a new subject in Chapter 10, "Security and Intrusion Detection Systems." This chapter provides a brief overview of premises security systems that are covered by two NFPA documents first approved in 2005: NFPA 730, *Guide for Premises Security,* and NFPA 731, *Standard for the Installation of Electronic Premises Security Systems.*

Chapter 1

Fire Alarm Systems

Wayne D. Moore

Chapter Contents

Key Terms

auxiliary fire alarm system, central station fire alarm system, emergency voice/alarm communications, fire alarm control unit, fire alarm signal, fire alarm system, fire barrier, fire detection system, mass notification system, McCulloh system, proprietary supervising station fire alarm system, protected premises, remote supervising station fire alarm system, supervisory signal, trouble signal

A fire detection and alarm system is a key element among the fire protection features of any building. Because most fire deaths in the United States result from building fires, the use of fire detection and alarm systems in buildings can help to significantly reduce the loss of life from fire. Also, if properly specified, designed, manufactured, installed, maintained, tested, and used, a fire alarm system can help limit property fire losses in buildings, regardless of occupancy.

Strictly adhering to the requirements of *NFPA 72®*, *National Fire Alarm Code®*, is fundamental to maintaining an appropriate level of quality control through the steps that lead to the successful provision of a fire detection and alarm system. This document, working in concert with NFPA 70, *National Electrical Code®*, particularly Article 760 on wiring for fire alarm systems, forms the basis for requirements that have been created through the consensus standards-making process. These requirements represent the combined experience and professional judgment of the members of the eight technical committees that write the various chapters of *NFPA 72.*

This chapter discusses the philosophical basis for fire alarm system design, as well as the major operational characteristics of the various types of fire alarm systems currently in use.

For related topics see Section 14, Chapter 2, "Automatic Fire Detectors"; Section 14, Chapter 3, "Notification Appliances"; Section 14, Chapter 4, "Fire Alarm System Interconnections"; Section 14, Chapter 5, "Inspection, Testing, and Maintenance of Fire Alarm Systems."

SELECTING THE SYSTEM

In making the basic decision regarding what type of fire alarm system is needed for a particular building, certain questions must be answered. In answering these questions, one must bear in mind that the most successful approach to the overall protection of life and property is a holistic approach—an approach that relies on the fact that the protection provided by the sum of the individual components of the fire protection system will always be much greater than if one was to rely on each individual component alone. Thus, effective protection is a combination of interlocking, interrelated fire protection systems, designed to function in concert with each other to provide the desired level of protection.

It is not a matter of whether or not automatic sprinklers or a fire alarm system should be provided. Rather, automatic sprinklers, a fire alarm system, and proper building construction features such as fire barriers along with a host of other valuable prevention and protection features, all built on a foundation of management commitment to fire prevention and control, can assure a building owner or occupant that a facility is safe.

With this foundational truth in mind, fire alarm system selection must be based on answering the question: "What are the protection goals?" Is the building owner attempting to provide a level of life safety that will meet the needs of the people occupying the building and satisfy the requirements of the local building code and local authority having jurisdiction (AHJ)? Or is the building owner intent on providing a needed level of property protection? Or is the building owner trying to ensure that the mission of the facility is not interrupted by fire? Other protection goals include cultural/heritage preservation, environmental protection, and first responder safety. In most cases the development of the owner's fire protection goals will require a risk analysis of the property. A

Wayne D. Moore, P.E., is a principal and director of operations for the New England offices of Hughes Associates, Inc. He is chair of the Technical Correlating Committee on the *National Fire Alarm Code®* and is coeditor of the fire alarm newsletter *The Moore-Wilson Signaling Report.*

risk analysis involves identifying the most probable fire threats to the owner's property and then analyzing the impact of those fire threats on the building and operation.

The final answer may be "yes" to one or more of these questions. And, with each "yes" answer, the building owner will be guided to select the fire alarm system that will meet the needs of the facility.

MAKING THE SYSTEM WORK

Just as building fire protection is most effective when it consists of a series of interlocking, interrelated fire protection systems, ensuring the mission effectiveness or operational reliability of a fire alarm system is the result of specific attention given to a series of interlocking, interrelated steps:

- Specify
- Design
- Manufacture
- Install
- Maintain
- Test
- Use

Determining Goals

The user of the fire alarm system must define the reason why the system is being provided. This definition step will identify the protection goals of the user and also the external factors that may influence the fire alarm system installation. The user may determine that the protection goal is the preservation of the lives of the persons occupying the building. Such a *life safety goal* and the protection features it dictates will help determine the type of fire alarm system. Or the user may determine that the protection goal is the preservation of the physical building and its contents. Such a *property safety goal* and the protection features unique to this goal will also help determine the type of fire alarm system that can most effectively provide protection.

In analyzing the particular needs of a facility, the user may determine that the protection goal is the preservation of the ability to produce a product or provide a service. Such a *mission protection goal* will help determine the type of fire alarm system needed at the facility.

It may even be that the user determines that the protection goal actually embraces a combination of all three primary goals: (1) life safety, (2) property protection, and (3) mission protection. An analysis of how fire will affect the mission (business impact) involves identifying the critical business functions within the organization and determining the impact of a fire incident on that business function and whether or not the business can recover from the expected fire incident. Once the protection goals are clearly defined, the features of the fire alarm system can be determined. If the user simply wants to build his or her building to be compliant with the minimum requirements of the codes in force in the jurisdiction, the designer must still understand how the codes may combine to be able to properly design the fire alarm system to meet the user's needs.

Additionally the user may be a representative of the federal government and want a mass notification system (MNS) to be integrated with the fire alarm system. Care must be taken to ensure that the MNS and the fire alarm system operate as required. The MNS is the only system allowed to interrupt a fire alarm system to allow additional safety information to be announced to the occupants.

Generally speaking the user will not develop this information without consulting a fire protection engineer. The engineer will review the features selected to develop a clear and concise written set of specifications. These specifications will include the needed features and will include statements as to how the quality of the installation is to be ensured, including the initiating device, notification appliance, and signaling line circuit performance. This document will guide the system supplier in making recommendations regarding particular equipment, as well as guide the supplier by providing the required quality control measures.

Based on the specifications, a fire protection engineer working either as a consultant to the user or as an employee of, or consultant to, the system supplier can develop a detailed system design. *NFPA 72,* recognizes the need for trained designers and installers and provides guidance for both the owner and authority having jurisdiction to assist in determining if these individuals are qualified. Certification by a national organization is one of the recommendations of the code. By exercising care to ensure that the design meets both the specifications and the requirements of *NFPA 72,* the designer will greatly enhance the overall quality of the fire alarm system.

Meanwhile, the manufacturer of fire alarm system components has been studying the needs of fire alarm users and has developed products with a wide variety of features. The manufacturer will provide products of high quality that can meet the requirements of *NFPA 72* and pass the tests of the nationally recognized testing laboratories, such as Underwriters Laboratories Inc. (UL) and FM Global Research.

A qualified fire alarm system installer can now take the manufacturer's equipment that satisfies the user's specifications and the fire protection engineer's design and install a fire alarm system. The process of installation must also meet the requirements of *NFPA 72.* Quality assurance during installation is critical to the long-term usefulness and stability of the fire alarm system. There are several ways of ensuring installation quality and meeting the mission effectiveness goals.

Ensuring Installation Quality

To help ensure installation quality, UL has developed two fire alarm certificate programs. One certificate is for central station fire alarm systems. The other is for local, auxiliary, remote station, proprietary, and emergency voice alarm/communication systems. UL-listed contractors may apply to UL for a certificate covering the installation of a fire alarm system at a specific protected premises. The certificate describes the system, and states that the contractor has met the requirements of *NFPA 72* and the relevant UL standards. It further states that the contractor has a contract with the user for periodic testing and routine maintenance of the fire alarm system to ensure quality continuity. Periodically, UL representatives inspect a statistical sampling of certificated installations of each contractor to check on the accuracy of the information supplied on the certificate and to verify compliance with *NFPA 72* and relevant UL standards.

FM Global Research has developed a placard that the contractor may post at the fire alarm installation, stating that the system has been installed to comply with the requirements of *NFPA 72* and the relevant FM requirements. When FM representatives visit facilities insured within the FM system, they look for this placard as an indication that standard fire alarm service has been provided.

Some AHJs require that installers demonstrate competency to install systems. Competency may be demonstrated by achieving certification through the National Institute for Certification in Engineering Technologies in fire protection, subfield fire alarms. The International Municipal Signaling Association also has an interior fire alarm certification program that has minimum competency requirements. Alternately, some AHJs may have developed an examination of their own that installers must pass. Many states, although not all, require that installers of fire alarm systems be licensed in that specialty in order to install these systems.

To ensure continuity of quality, a fire alarm system must be tested and maintained. *NFPA 72* sets forth the requirements for maintenance and testing in Chapter 10. Once again, the competency of the persons performing the testing and maintenance is critical to achieving an appropriate level of quality. (See Section 14, Chapter 5, "Inspection, Testing, and Maintenance of Fire Alarm Systems.")

Finally, just as the components of the fire alarm system must be listed by a nationally recognized testing laboratory for the specific use, the way the fire alarm system is used must conform to the requirements of *NFPA 72*. By carefully working through the steps (i.e., specify, design, manufacture, install, maintain, test, and use), the user of the fire alarm system will have a system that will serve the facility well for many years to come.

TYPES OF SIGNALS

Fire alarm systems may provide three types of signals: (1) alarm, (2) supervisory, and (3) trouble.

An *alarm signal* is a warning of fire danger that requires immediate action.

A *supervisory signal* indicates that action is needed in connection with the operation of other fire protection systems that are being monitored by the fire alarm system. Such systems may include extinguishing or suppression systems, such as automatic sprinkler systems, carbon dioxide systems, dry chemical systems, foam systems, and gaseous agent systems. They may also include the supervision of guards who make fire patrol tours throughout the protected premises. A supervisory signal may be either an "off-normal" signal, indicating a condition requiring attention; or a "restoration-to-normal" signal, indicating the condition that initiated the original off-normal signal has been resolved.

A *trouble signal* indicates a fault in a monitored circuit or component of the fire alarm system or the disarrangement of the primary or secondary power supply.

FIRE ALARM SYSTEM BASICS

Fire alarm systems are classified according to the functions they are expected to perform. Their installation, maintenance, and use are specified in *NFPA 72*.

The basic components of each system are:

1. A system control unit (Figure 14.1.1)
2. A primary, or main, power supply
3. A secondary, or standby, power supply
4. One or more initiating device circuits or signaling line circuits to which manual fire alarm boxes, sprinkler waterflow alarm initiating devices, automatic fire detectors, and other fire alarm initiating devices are connected
5. One or more fire alarm notification appliance circuits to which audible and visible fire alarm notification appliances, such as bells, horns, stroboscopic lamps, and speakers, are connected
6. Many systems also have an off-premises connection to a central station, proprietary supervising station, remote supervising station, or public fire service communication center by means of an auxiliary fire alarm system

FIGURE 14.1.1 Fire Alarm System Control Unit (Source: Mircom Ltd., Toronto, CN; Mammoth Fire Alarms, Lowell, MA)

Primary and Secondary Power Supplies

The primary and secondary power supplies at both the protected premises and at a subsidiary or supervising station must meet the requirements of *NFPA 72*. The primary power is usually supplied by a connection to utility-generated electric power. The connection must be from a branch circuit dedicated to the fire alarm system. The circuit and connections must be mechanically protected. The circuit disconnecting means must have a red marking, be accessible only to authorized personnel, and be identified as "Fire Alarm Circuit Control." Inside the fire alarm system control unit, a permanent legend must identify the location of the electrical panel board that contains the circuit disconnecting means.

Very remote areas may not have utility-generated power available. In these cases, electricity is usually supplied by generators on the site of the facility. Most often more than one generator is provided, each operated for a number of hours at a time to help ensure the reliability of the electric power. Primary power for fire alarm systems at geographically remote facilities is, therefore, supplied by generators.

Secondary power supply for a fire alarm system is required to automatically supply the energy to the system within 30 seconds whenever the primary power supply is not capable of providing the minimum voltage required for proper system operation.

The size of the secondary supply usually is measured in the amount of time that the secondary supply will operate the system, followed by a prescribed time period for the system to operate in an alarm condition. Local (protected premises), central station, remote station, proprietary, and auxiliary systems must have 24 hours of standby power, followed by 5 minutes of alarm. Emergency voice/alarm communication systems must have 24 hours of standby power, followed by 2 hours of emergency operation. To allow calculation of the power required for 2-hour emergency operation, *NFPA 72* specifies that the 2 hours of emergency operation are the equivalent of 15 minutes of operation under full load (i.e., with all input devices and output appliances operating).

The required capacity of the secondary power can be supplied by storage batteries; storage batteries with 4 hours of capacity in conjunction with an engine-driven generator; or multiple engine-driven generators, each of which must be capable of supplying the entire standby power load. This generator is considered "dedicated" to the fire alarm system. This means that the reason the generator was installed was to supply secondary power to the fire alarm system. Of course, if the generator has a greater capacity than is needed by the fire alarm system, it may also be used to supply loads related to the fire alarm system, such as lighting or air-conditioning equipment serving the room where the fire alarm system is located.

Engine-driven generators used to provide secondary power for a protected premises fire alarm system must comply with NFPA 110, *Standard for Emergency and Standby Power Systems,* Section 2.2, requirements for a Type 10, Class 24, Level 1 System. Installation must be in accordance with the *NEC,* Article 700. In addition, where survivability of circuits is required by Chapter 6, equal protection must be provided for power supply circuits.

Circuits

Fire alarm systems have three basic types of circuits: (1) initiating device circuits (IDC), (2) notification appliance circuits (NAC), and (3) signaling line circuits (SLC).

All fire alarm system cable and the wiring installation must conform to Article 760 of the *NEC* and the additional requirements of *NFPA 72.*

Initiating device circuits connect conventional (nonaddressable) fire alarm and supervising initiating devices to the system control unit. Notification appliance circuits connect notification appliances (audible and visible) to the system control unit. The term *signaling line circuits* is used to define circuits over which two-way data communications take place. This communication can take place between an addressable device and system control unit or the system control unit and the off-premises connection, such as a central station, a public fire service communications center, a remote station, or a proprietary supervising station.

There is at least one manufacturer that has the capability of using an SLC for the notification appliance circuit. The feature is software driven and permits selective area evacuation using the same SLC. When a Class B circuit is allowed, the notification appliances can be "T-Tapped" off the SLC and still meet the code requirements for monitoring of wiring and appliance integrity. The addressable controller for the appliances constantly polls the appliances to verify communications. Using short circuit fault isolators also helps to ensure survivability of the circuit.

NFPA 72 provides the fire alarm system designer with various circuit configurations that provide different levels of operation and integrity. The circuit configuration can only be defined when both the fire alarm control unit operation and the wiring configuration are known.

A typical circuit used in many fire alarm systems consists of a two-wire circuit with an end-of-line resistor. Initiating devices, with normally open contacts, are connected in parallel. A small amount of electrical current flows through the wire to monitor the wiring integrity. A break in the wire causes a trouble condition at the system control unit. Everything electrically beyond the break in the wiring is out of service until repairs are made to the circuit. Operation of an initiating device shunts the resistor, thus increasing the current, which causes the system control panel to respond in an alarm condition.

A two-wire circuit configuration that operates up to the single fault (open-circuit or ground-fault condition) is labeled a Class B circuit. A circuit configuration that requires the wiring to be returned to the system control unit, where the system control unit is configured to allow a device or appliance to operate on either side of a single open-circuit or ground-fault condition, is labeled a Class A circuit. Both of these designations can be applied to initiating device circuits, notification appliance circuits, and signaling line circuits.

Many fire alarm system control units have more than one initiating device circuit, so that the fire location can be indicated on an annunciator panel by floor, wing, subsection, or room. The annunciator can be built into the control unit or located in a lobby, maintenance area, telephone switchboard room, or some other location where it is accessible to building and fire service personnel.

Depending on the size of the building and the fire alarm system, addressable and addressable analog systems will have one or two signaling line circuits. The code does not require more signaling line circuits than the number of connected devices dictates. However, it is prudent to "not put all of your eggs in one basket" and to use a minimum of two signaling line circuits for all except the smallest of systems.

Annunciation is principally designed to serve the fire department. Therefore, coordination with the fire department is important if the annunciation of alarms is to be effective. With the new liquid crystal display (LCD) annunciators and addressable technology, it is tempting to annunciate each point at a remote annunciator. This tactic results in too much information that will tend to confuse rather than help first responders.

NFPA 72 has Annex A material that details the guidelines for a standard fire service interface. Annunciators, information display systems, and controls for portions of the fire alarm system provided for use by the fire service should be designed, arranged, and located in accordance with the needs of the organizations intended to use the equipment.

Where annunciators, information display systems, and controls for portions of the fire alarm system are provided for use by the fire service, these should have a common design and operation to avoid confusion for users. The standard fire service interface uses an icon-based design that can be implemented in various manners on a range of system sizes and still maintain sufficient familiarity so that fire service personnel, with training, should be able to use effectively any variation that follows the guidelines presented in the Annex material.

NFPA 72®, National Fire Alarm Code®, Format

NFPA 72 comprises 11 chapters presented in the following format:

- Chapter 1 Administration
- Chapter 2 Referenced Publications
- Chapter 3 Definitions
- Chapter 4 Fundamentals of Fire Alarm Systems
- Chapter 5 Initiating Devices
- Chapter 6 Protected Premises Fire Alarm Systems
- Chapter 7 Notification Appliances for Fire Alarm Systems
- Chapter 8 Supervising Station Fire Alarm Systems
- Chapter 9 Public Fire Alarm Reporting Systems
- Chapter 10 Inspection, Testing, and Maintenance
- Chapter 11 Single- and Multiple-Station Alarms and Household Fire Alarm Systems

In *NFPA 72* the requirements for fire alarm systems that provide household fire warning have their own chapter (Chapter 11), and the requirements for fire alarm systems for all other occupancies are contained in Chapters 1 through 10.

In *NFPA 72* a fire alarm system that meets the requirements of Chapters 4 and 6 forms the basic fire alarm system "building block." A protected premises fire alarm system, whether it is used to notify the occupants so they may safely evacuate, used to actuate a fire suppression or extinguishing system, or used to oversee conditions at a facility and report status changes to a supervising station, must meet the requirements of these two chapters. The initiating devices and notification appliances connected to the protected premises fire alarm system must meet the requirements contained in Chapters 5 and 7, respectively. A supervising station fire alarm system must meet the requirements contained in Chapter 8. And a protected premises fire alarm system, its initiating devices and notification appliances, along with a supervising station fire alarm system, must all meet the testing and maintenance requirements contained in Chapter 10.

Because of the familiarity and wide usage of industry terms that have evolved over the years, *NFPA 72* has retained such terminology. One example of this terminology is the system designations: protected premises system, emergency voice/alarm communication system, central station system, proprietary system, remote station system, public fire reporting system, and auxiliary system.

PROTECTED PREMISES SYSTEM

The main purpose of a protected premises fire alarm system is to activate local audible and visible alarm notification appliances to notify the occupants that they must evacuate the protected building (Figure 14.1.2). Such a system could be limited to the basic features described earlier. The system could also interface with other protective systems that would help make the building safer in case of fire. Such features might include, for example, the operation of a fire-extinguishing or suppression system; the recall of elevators; the unlocking of doors; the closing of smoke barrier doors; the control of heating, ventilation, and air-conditioning (HVAC) equipment; or the operation of smoke control systems.

In a protected premises system, the alarm is not relayed automatically to a fire department. Instead, when the alarm sounds, someone must use some other means to notify the fire department. If the building is unoccupied at the time of the alarm, fire department response would depend on a neighbor or passerby hearing or seeing the audible and/or visible fire alarm notification appliances and telephoning the fire department.

Additionally a fire alarm system may be interfaced with a smoke control system. When such an interface occurs, the fire protection engineer and mechanical engineer must coordinate their efforts to ensure that the design and operation of the combined systems will work as expected by the authority having jurisdiction. Many jurisdictions now have a policy that the system design must be submitted with a narrative describing the system interface and operation of the systems, both individually and as combined systems.

EMERGENCY VOICE/ALARM COMMUNICATION SYSTEM

This system is used in occupancies, such as high-rise buildings and large assembly occupancies, where it is necessary to relocate occupants to areas of refuge rather than evacuate them (Figure 14.1.3). The voice/alarm system consists of a series of high-reliability speakers located throughout the building. They are connected to, and controlled from, the fire alarm communication console located in an area designated as a building fire command station. From the building fire command station, individual speaker zones or the entire building can be selected to receive an alert tone followed by a voice message that gives specific instructions to the occupants. Some systems have fire

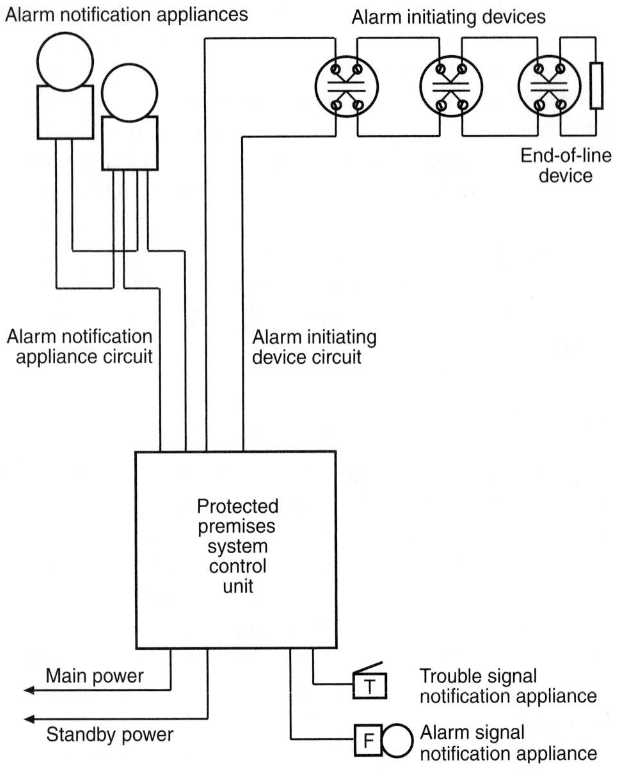

(a)

(b)

FIGURE 14.1.2 (a) Typical Arrangement of a Local Fire Alarm System; (b) Local System Control Unit (Source: Mircom Ltd., Toronto, CN; Mammoth Fire Alarms, Lowell, MA)

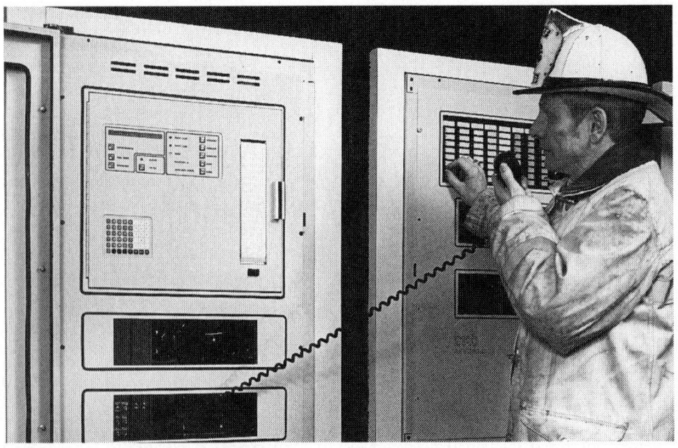

FIGURE 14.1.3 Emergency Voice/Alarm Communication System. A fire officer gives building occupants specific instructions during a fire. (Source: SimplexGrinnell Company)

warden telephone stations on each floor, or within each fire zone, to which a fire warden would report to assume local command and pass on specific evacuation instructions.

A trained building employee usually operates the fire command station until the fire department arrives, at which time the officer in charge takes over. The fire warden telephone stations may also be used during fire-fighting operations for communication with the fire fighters whose hand-portable two-way radios may not function properly in the high-rise building. *NFPA 72* recognizes that the installation of two-way, in-building radio communications enhancement systems will ensure that fire department radios will work in all areas of a high-rise building. A bidirectional amplifier is an example of such a system. The two-way, in-building radio communications enhancement system is permitted to be monitored by the building fire alarm system.

One important aspect of a voice/alarm communication system is that, since complete building evacuation is not always feasible, it can instruct occupants to relocate to areas of refuge where they can safely wait for the fire to be brought under control. In such cases, communication with these relocated occupants must be maintained to keep occupants informed and, therefore, more comfortable with the soundness and safety of decisions that leave them still inside a burning building.

The most recent edition of the *National Fire Alarm Code* allows mass notification systems (MNS) to be integrated with emergency voice/alarm communication systems. The MNS can be a stand-alone system that interfaces with the fire alarm system to allow the MNS system to stop all alarm notification in the building while more specific instructions can be given. A typical example would be a terrorist event when occupants may be instructed to stay inside the building. The MNS can also be integrated with the fire alarm system using the same speakers as the fire alarm system. Annex material is provided in the *National Fire Alarm Code* to assist the designers, installers, and authorities having jurisdiction in understanding mass notification systems.

CENTRAL STATION FIRE ALARM SYSTEM

A central station fire alarm system is designed to receive signals from a protected premises at a constantly attended location operated by a company whose purpose is providing central station service. This operating company must be listed by either UL or FM Global Research. Central station installations must have either the UL certificate or FM Global Research placard; whichever means of verifying the character of the installation is required by the AHJ. It may be expected that central station service will be provided for only industrial and commercial facilities of relatively high value. In such cases, the central station fire alarm system is intended to enhance the property protection aspects of a facility in order to satisfy the recommendations submitted by a highly protected risk property insurance company acting in its role of AHJ for matters relating to property insurance.

In some cases, a central station operating company may collect signals from a specific geographic area at a subsidiary station and then transmit the signals to a central station for handling. Although the subsidiary station is not normally staffed, *NFPA 72* requires that it be capable of being staffed in an emergency. Such an emergency might include the failure of the communication channels between the subsidiary station and the central station.

There are eight elements of central station service: four at the protected premises and four at the central station. The four at the protected premises are installation, testing, maintenance, and runner service. The four at the central station are management or oversight of the system, monitoring of signals from the protected premises, retransmission of fire alarm signals to the public fire service communication center, and record keeping. Of course, a listed central station is allowed to contract for other services that do not include the eight points described previously. A central station may simply provide monitoring for alarm, supervisory, and trouble signals such as provided by a remote station.

Central station service may be provided entirely by a listed central station operating company, by a listed central station operating company that contracts one or more elements of central station service at the protected premises to a subcontractor, or by a listed local fire alarm installation company that will provide the four elements at the protected premises and subcontract the four elements at the central station to a listed central station operating company.

Signals may be transmitted from a protected premises using a variety of transmission technologies stated in *NFPA 72,* Chapter 8. Such technologies include active multiplex system encompassing leased line, optical fiber cable, private microwave radio system, and telephone-company-provided derived local channel system; digital alarm communicator system; digital alarm radio system; McCulloh system (the code now states that unless accepted by the authority having jurisdiction, McCulloh systems are not permitted to be installed after June 2003); two-way RF multiplex system; one-way private radio alarm system; or a directly connected noncoded system.

When they receive fire alarm, supervisory, or trouble signals, operators at the central station take actions prescribed by *NFPA 72.* In addition to notifying the public fire service communication center in the case of a fire alarm signal, the central station operators must notify designated persons either at the protected premises or at their homes. The operators must also dispatch a runner or service technician when equipment at the protected premises must be reset by someone from the central station. This runner must reach the premises within 1 hour.

Similarly, supervisory signals and trouble signals also require a runner response. Unresolved guard tour signals require a runner response within one-half hour of the expiration of a 15-minute grace period. Other unresolved supervisory signals require a runner to reach the protected premises within 1 hour. In the case of a trouble signal, the service technician must arrive at the protected premises within 4 hours and begin making repairs to the fire alarm system.

PROPRIETARY SYSTEM

The proprietary fire alarm system is widely used in large commercial or industrial occupancies (Figure 14.1.4).

Signals transmitted over a proprietary system are received and automatically and permanently recorded at a constantly attended proprietary supervising station located either at the protected premises or at another location of the property owner. In very simplistic terms, a proprietary system is similar to a central station system but with the supervising station owned and operated by the property owner and located at the protected premises or another location of the property owner.

Many existing proprietary systems have separate initiating device circuits for each building zone or subsection, similar to local, auxiliary, and remote station systems. However, due to the increasing use of electronics, newer proprietary systems for larger buildings often have signal multiplexing and built-in minicomputer systems. These systems receive all signals from the protected building over one or more communication paths and determine the exact location of the fire by use of digitally coded information. Figure 14.1.5 shows the complexity and interrelationships among the many facets of a modern

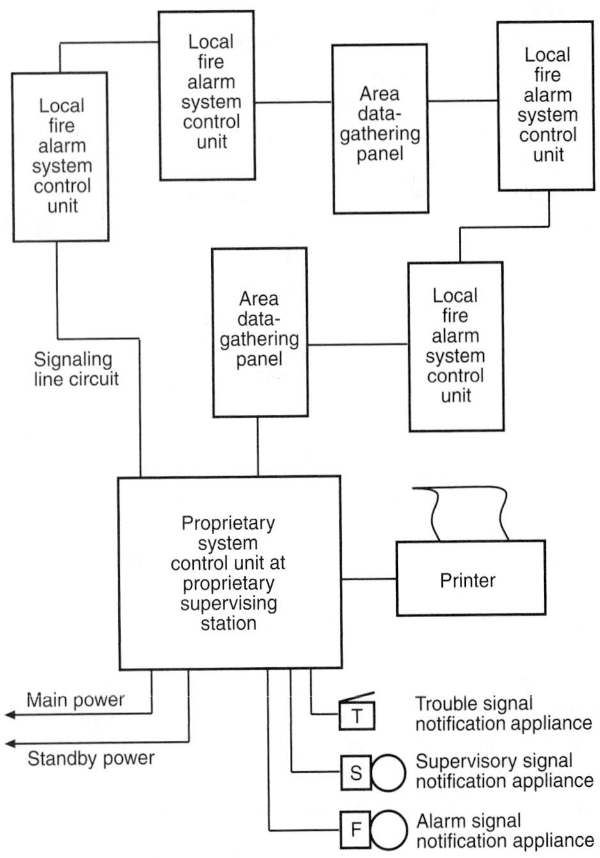

(a)

(b)

FIGURE 14.1.4 (a) Typical Arrangement of a Proprietary Protective Signaling System; (b) Central Supervisory Station. An attendant constantly monitors the proprietary protective signaling system. The printer on the desk provides a permanent record of signaling traffic. (Source: SimplexGrinnell Company)

computer-controlled proprietary fire alarm system serving one large building. Proprietary systems can be used in one building as shown in Figure 14.1.5 or serve multiple campus-style such as shown in Figure 14.1.4(a).

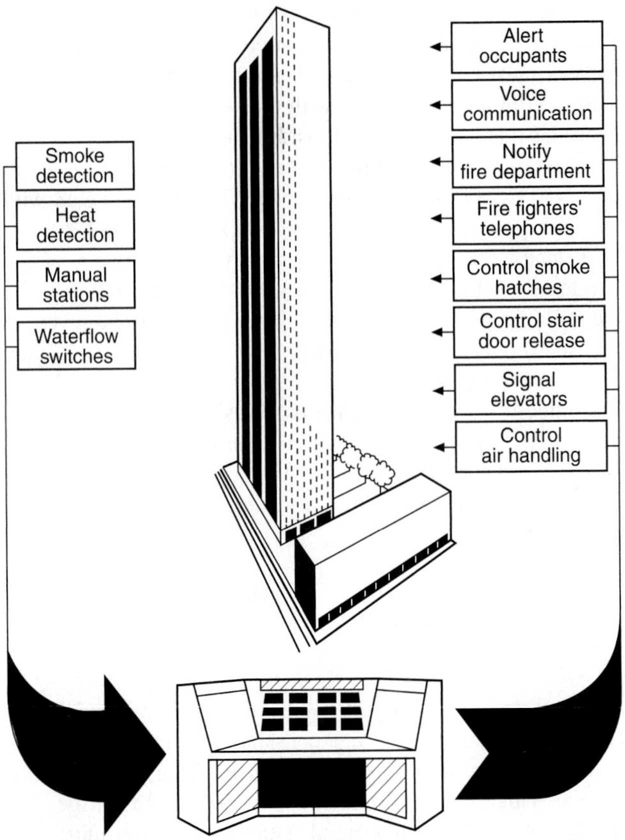

FIGURE 14.1.5 Modern Computer-Controlled Proprietary Fire Alarm System

Proprietary control units are required to transmit alarm, supervisory, and trouble signals to the supervising station. Signals may be transmitted from a protected premises using a variety of transmission technologies as stated in *NFPA 72,* Chapter 8. Such technologies include active multiplex system encompassing leased line, optical fiber cable, private microwave radio system, and telephone-company-provided derived local channel system; digital alarm communicator system; digital alarm radio system; McCulloh system (the code now states that unless accepted by the authority having jurisdiction, McCulloh systems are not permitted to be installed after June 2003); two-way RF multiplex system; one-way private radio alarm system; or a directly connected noncoded system.

Upon receipt of fire alarm signals, supervisory signals, or trouble signals, a runner must be dispatched to investigate. Fire alarm signals must also be retransmitted to the public fire service communication center.

REMOTE STATION SYSTEM

A remote station fire alarm system connects the outputs from a building fire alarm control unit and transmits them to a remote location (Figure 14.1.6). *NFPA 72* specifies that fire alarm signals must be received at the public fire service communication center, at a fire station, or at the location of the public

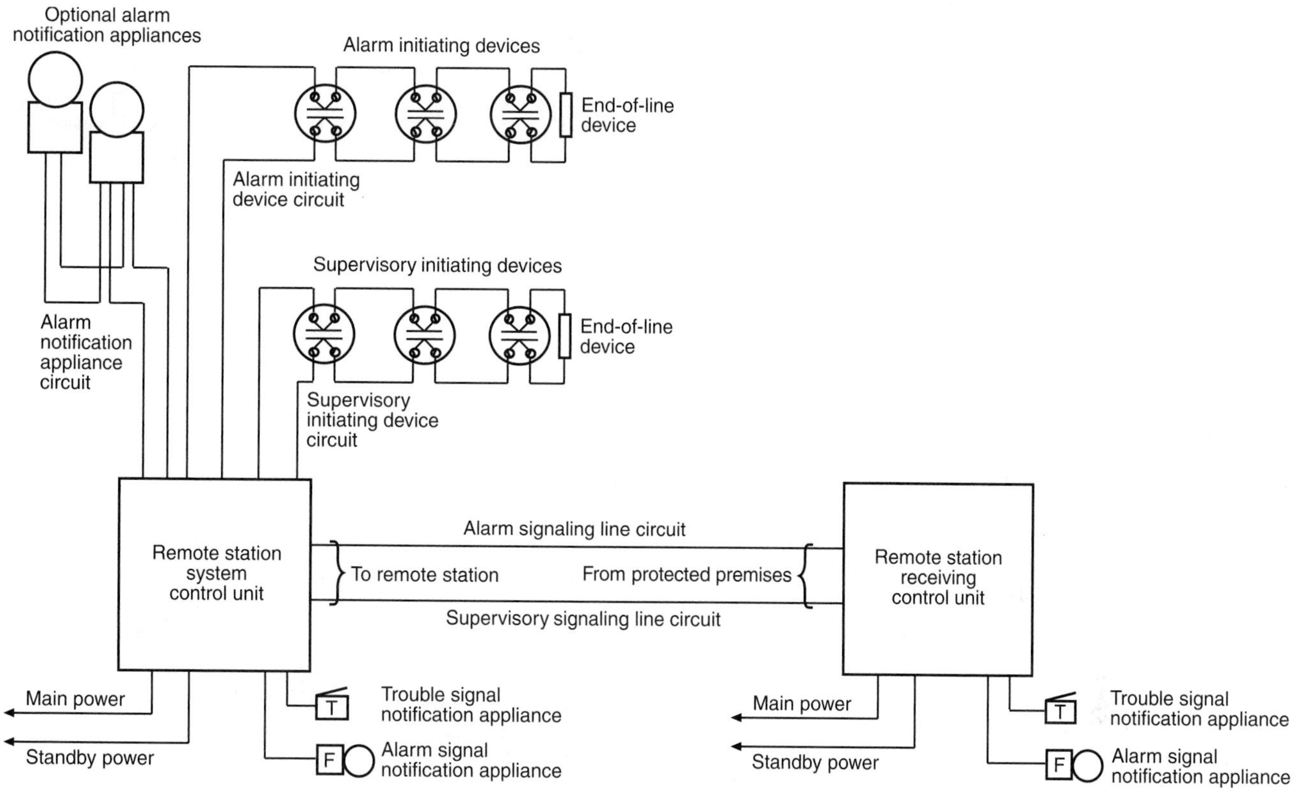

(a)

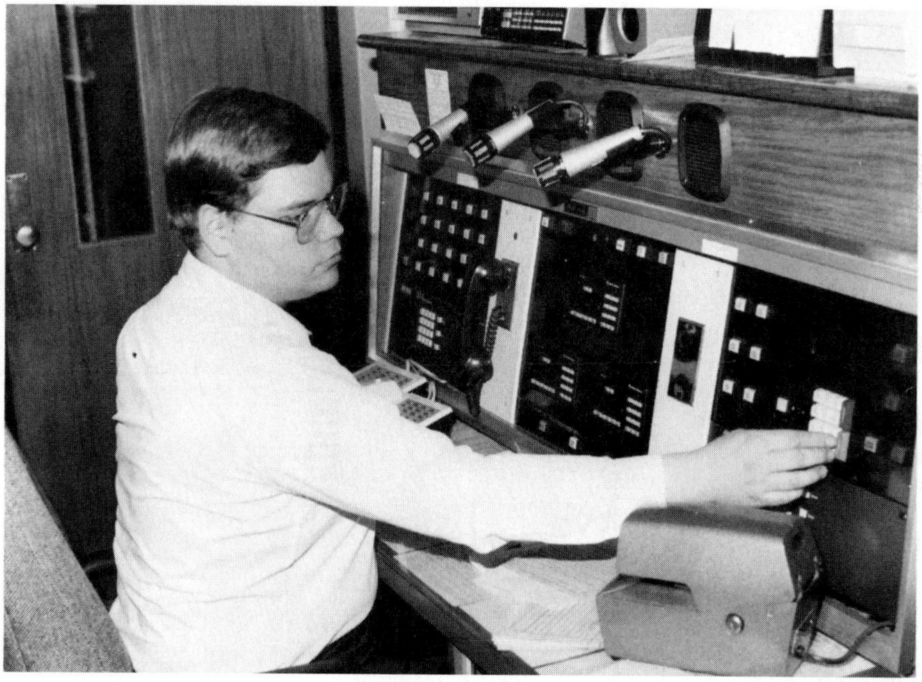

(b)

FIGURE 14.1.6 (a) Typical Arrangement of a Remote Station Fire Alarm System. Note that, if a direct circuit connection is used, fire alarm and supervisory signals must be transmitted over separate signaling line circuits. (b) Remote Station Receiving Control Unit. Upon receipt of a remote station sprinkler waterflow alarm, the fire dispatcher prepares to retransmit the alarm to the fire companies that will respond.

agency that has the responsibility to receive fire alarms from the public.

If the public agency is unwilling to receive the remote station fire alarm signals, or if that agency is willing to allow another organization to receive those signals, then the signals may be received at a location acceptable to the AHJ that is attended by trained personnel 24 hours a day, such as a central station or monitoring company that will contract to provide the services required of a remote station. Upon receipt of fire alarm signals, the personnel retransmit the signals to the public fire service communication center.

In some cases, the public agency receiving fire alarm signals may also be willing to receive supervisory signals and trouble signals. In most cases, supervisory signals and trouble signals are transmitted to a constantly attended location acceptable to the AHJ, such as a monitoring company or a central station.

Signals may be transmitted from a protected premises using a variety of transmission technologies stated in *NFPA 72*, Chapter 8. Such technologies include active multiplex system encompassing leased line, optical fiber cable, private microwave radio system, and telephone-company-provided derived local channel system; digital alarm communicator system; digital alarm radio system; McCulloh system (the code now states that unless accepted by the authority having jurisdiction, McCulloh systems are not permitted to be installed after June 2003); two-way RF multiplex system; one-way private radio alarm system; or a directly connected noncoded system.

AUXILIARY SYSTEM

An auxiliary fire alarm system provides the interface between a protected premises fire alarm system and a public fire reporting system (Figure 14.1.7). *NFPA 72* states requirements for public fire reporting systems in Chapter 9. *NFPA 72* also states requirements for auxiliary fire alarm systems in Chapter 9. If a community does not have a public fire reporting system, then a protected premises within that community cannot have an auxiliary fire alarm system.

The transmission technology employed between the protected premises and the public fire service communication center is determined by the type of public fire reporting system (i.e., coded wired, coded radio, series telephone, or parallel telephone). The auxiliary fire alarm system interface may be a shunt-type or local energy-type connection to a coded wired, coded radio, or series telephone master fire alarm box (Figure 14.1.8). Or the auxiliary fire alarm system may be directly connected to a parallel telephone system circuit.

NFPA 72 states that only fire alarm signals may be transmitted by an auxiliary fire alarm system. In cases where the protected premises fire alarm system must also cover supervisory signals, these are usually transmitted by a remote station system or a central station contracted to receive supervisory signals as a remote station. Trouble signals are either received only at the protected premises, or they are transmitted by a remote station system or a central station contracted to receive trouble signals as a remote station.

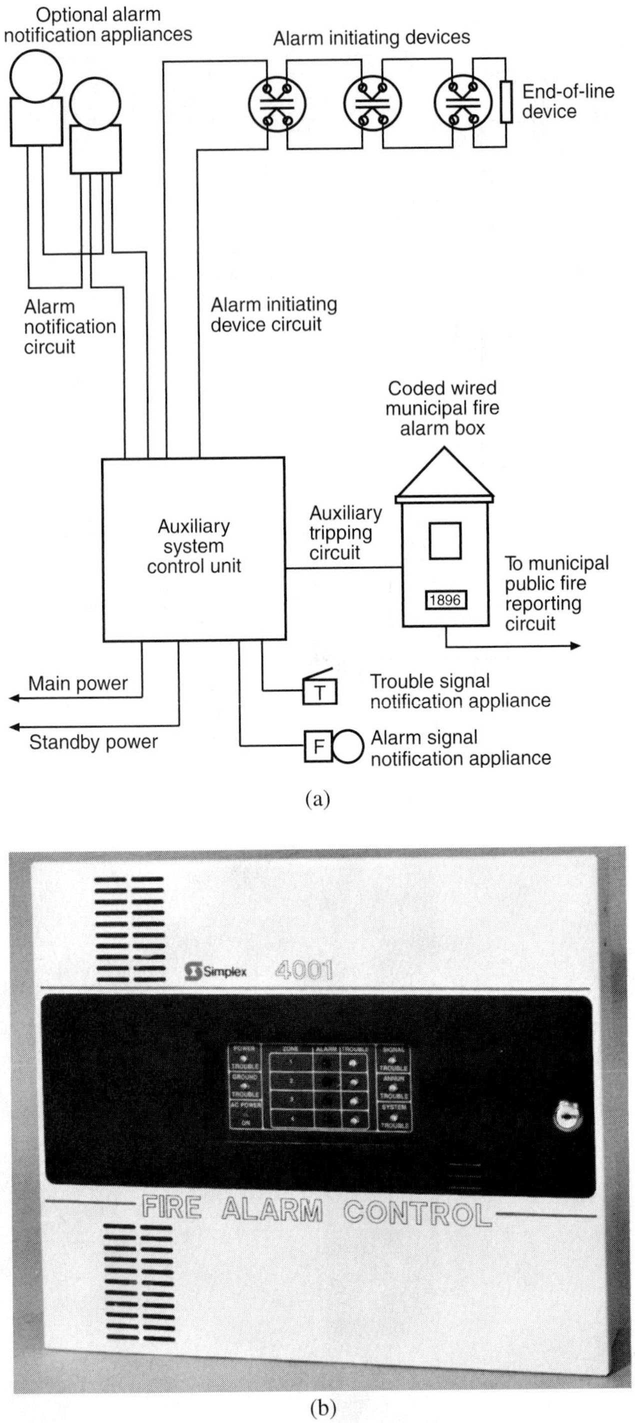

FIGURE 14.1.7 (a) Typical Arrangement of an Auxiliary Fire System; (b) Auxiliary System Control Unit (Source: SimplexGrinnell Company)

SUMMARY

Fire alarm systems play an essential role in protecting property and lives from fire. An effective system is a combination of individual components designed to work together to provide the

FIGURE 14.1.8 Local Energy-Type Masterbox That Connects the Protected Premises Fire Alarm System to the Public Fire Reporting System (Source: Gamewell-FCI, Div. Honeywell Inc.)

desired level of protection. The user of the fire alarm system must define the goal of the system, for example, whether the priority is life safety or property safety, in order to select the appropriate system. Once installed, the fire alarm system needs to be properly maintained and tested in order to ensure it will function as intended during an emergency.

BIBLIOGRAPHY

NFPA Codes, Standards, and Recommended Practices

Reference to the following NFPA codes, standards, and recommended practices will provide further information on fire alarm systems discussed in this chapter. (See the latest version of The NFPA Catalog *for availability of current editions of the following documents.)*

NFPA 13, *Standard for the Installation of Sprinkler Systems*
NFPA 20, *Standard for the Installation of Stationary Pumps for Fire Protection*
NFPA 70, *National Electrical Code®*
NFPA 72®, National Fire Alarm Code®
NFPA *101®*, *Life Safety Code®*
NFPA 5000®, Building Construction and Safety Code®

References

Aridsson, T., and Gale, M., "Homing in on Smoke Alarms," *Fire Prevention,* No. 338, Nov. 2000, pp. 53–55.
Birch, D., "Smoke Alarm Policy: Is It Working?" *Fire Engineers Journal,* Vol. 61, No. 211, 2001, pp. 9–11.
Brennan, P., "Modelling Cue Recognition and Pre-Evacuation Response," *Proceedings* of 6th International Symposium, Fire Safety Science, July 5–9, 1999, Poitiers, France, International Association for Fire Safety Science (IAFSS), Boston, MA, 2000, pp. 1029–1040.
Bruck, D., "Who, What, Where and Why of Waking to Fire Alarms: A Review," *Fire Safety Journal,* Vol. 36, No. 7, 2001, pp. 623–639.
Bukowski, R. W., "Development of a Standardized Fire Service Interface for Fire Alarm Systems," *Fire Protection Engineering,* Spring 2000, p. 4.
Bunker, M., "Improved *NFPA 72,*" *NFPA Journal,* Vol. 94, No. 1, 2000, pp. 24–25.
Bushby, S. T., "Integrating Fire Alarm Systems with Other Building Automation and Controls Systems," *Fire Protection Engineering,* No. 11, Summer 2001, pp. 5–11.
Coleman, R. J., "Elements of Notification, or How to Embrace a Battler," *Fire Chief,* Vol. 45, No. 3, 2001, pp. 32–34.
Comeau, E., "Capitol Challenge," *NFPA Journal,* Vol. 94, No. 6, 2000, pp. 57–61.
Coppola, L., and Gecchele, G., "Fire Safety for Historical Buildings and Performance Criteria for Their Use," *Proceedings* of 2nd International Symposium, Human Behavior in Fire: Understanding Human Behavior for Better Fire Safety Design, March 26–28, 2001, Boston, MA, Interscience Communications Ltd., London, UK, 2001, pp. 451–458.
Davis, W. D., and Forney, G. P., "Sensor-Driven Fire Model Version 1.1," National Institute of Standards and Technology, Gaithersburg, MD, NISTIR 6705, Jan. 2001.
Faulkner, A., "Expanding the Capabilities of Analogue Addressable Fire Control," *Fire Safety Engineering,* Vol. 7, No. 3, 2000, pp. 28–29.
Freestone, A., "Standardizing Fire Alarm Panels," *NFPA Journal,* Vol. 94, No. 5, 2000, pp. 66–69.
Grace, T., Woodger, N., and Olsson, P., "On the Use of Voice Alarm Systems," *Proceedings* of 2nd International Symposium, Human Behavior in Fire: Understanding Human Behavior for Better Fire Safety Design, March 26–28, 2001, Boston, MA, Interscience Communications Ltd., London, UK, 2001, pp. 185–196.
Grosshandler, W. L., "Multi-Function Sensing for Cybernetic Building Systems," *Proceedings* of the 15th Joint Panel Meeting, U.S./Japan Government Cooperative Program on Natural Resources (UJNR), Fire Research and Safety, March 1–7, 2000, San Antonio, TX, 2000, Vol. 2, pp. 357–364.
Hasofer, A. M., "Stochastic Model for the Time to Awaken in Response to a Fire Alarm," *Journal of Fire Protection Engineering,* Vol. 11, Aug. 2001, pp. 151–163.
Jones, W. W., and Reneke, P. A., "High Reliability Safety Systems for Emergency Response in the Built Environment," *Proceedings* of the Fire Suppression and Detection Research Application Symposium, Research and Practice: Bridging the Gap, February 7–9, 2001, Orlando, FL, National Fire Protection Research Foundation, Quincy, MA, 2001, pp. 282–296.
Kidd, S., "Upgrading Fire Safety in an Austrian Royal Palace," *Fire International,* No. 175, Apr. 2000, pp. 14–15.
Lathrop, J. K., "Consider the Firefighter in Building and Fire Protection System Design," *Fire Protection Engineering,* No. 6, Spring 2000, pp. 10–12.
LeBlanc, D. J., and Toossi, V., "Retrofitting Fire Protection Systems," *Fire Protection Engineering,* No. 2, Spring 1999, p. 17.
Leighton, G., "Fire Safety Awareness for Disabled People," *Fire,* Vol. 93, No. 1150, 2001, pp. 14–15.
Letts, J., "Design, Installation, Commissioning and Maintenance of Systems," *Fire Safety Engineering,* Vol. 7, No. 4, 2000, p. 30.
Li, Z., Liu, W., Wang, A., and Su, J., "Open Distributed Fire Detection System," *Proceedings* of the 12th International Conference on Automatic Fire Detection, AUBE '01, March 25–28, 2001, Gaithersburg, MD, National Institute of Standards and Technology, Gaithersburg, MD, NIST SP 965, Feb. 2001, pp. 592–601.
Liu, Z., Makar, J., and Kim, A. K., "Development of Fire Detection Systems in the Intelligent Building," *Proceedings* of the 12th International Conference on Automatic Fire Detection, AUBE '01, March 25–28, 2001, Gaithersburg, MD, National Institute of Standards and Technology, Gaithersburg, MD, NIST SP 965, Feb. 2001, pp. 561–573.
Martin, T., and Buchanan, S., "Fire Protection: Life Safety Assessment Performance Based Design Concept," *Proceedings* of the Fire Suppression and Detection Research Application Symposium, Research and Practice: Bridging the Gap, February 7–9,

2001, Orlando, FL, National Fire Protection Research Foundation, Quincy, MA, 2001, pp. 537–575.
Meacham, B. J., "The Use of Artificial Intelligence Techniques for Signal Discrimination in Fire Detection Systems," *Journal of Fire Protection Engineering,* Vol. 6, No. 3, 1994, pp. 125–136.
Moore, W. D., "System Integration: It's Here!" *NFPA Journal,* Vol. 94, No. 1, 2000, p. 30.
Moore, W. D., "Why Is Testing So Important?" *NFPA Journal,* Vol. 94, No. 3, 2000, p. 55.
Moore, W. D., "Why Is Testing So Important?" *NFPA Journal,* Vol. 94, No. 4, 2000, p. 34.
Moore, W. D., "Industrial Facilities: Unique Alarm Challenges," *NFPA Journal,* Vol. 95, No. 5, 2001, pp. 40–41.
Moore, W. D., and Wilson, D. K., *The Moore-Wilson Signaling Report,* Hughes Associates, Inc., Baltimore, MD, 1980–2007.
Page, I., "How Economic Are Smoke Alarms and Fire Sprinklers?" *Build,* Sept./Oct. 2001, pp. 16–17.
Parsons, P., "World First SCADA Standard for Fire Alarm Monitoring," *Fire Engineers Journal,* Vol. 57, No. 188, 1997, pp. 33–35.
Peeples, L. C., "Automatic Alarm Mindset," *Fire Engineeering,* Vol. 153, No. 12, 2000, p. 14.
Proulx, G., "Why Building Occupants Ignore Fire Alarms," *Construction Technology Update,* No. 42, Dec. 2000, pp. 1–4.
Rattlidge, J., "Audible Fire Warning Devices," *Fire Safety Engineering,* Vol. 7, No. 2, 2000, pp. 31–33.
Rogers, D., "Wireless Detection," *Fire Prevention,* No. 330, Mar. 2000, pp. 36–37.
Schmitz, G., and Witschital, P., "Internet Technology: New Perspectives for Alarm Systems," *Proceedings* of the 12th International Conference on Automatic Fire Detection, AUBE '01, March 25–28, 2001, Gaithersburg, MD, National Institute of Standards and Technology, Gaithersburg, MD, NIST SP 965, Feb. 2001, pp. 243–251.
Wilson, D. K., "Wiring Fire Alarms for Reliability," *NFPA Journal,* Vol. 94, No. 5, 2000, pp. 71–74.

Automatic Fire Detectors

Revised by
Kenneth W. Dungan

Chapter Contents

Key Terms

air sampling–type detector, combination fixed-temperature/rate-of-rise detector, electronic spot-type heat detector, fire signature, fixed temperature heat detector, flame detector, heat detector, infrared absorption detector, ionization smoke detector, multisensor detector, optical density, photoelectric smoke detector, rate compensation heat detector, rate-of-rise heat detector, smoke detector, spark/ember detector, thermal lag, video-based detection

Fire produces a variety of environmental changes called "fire signatures," which help make its presence known. Human beings are excellent fire detectors when able to effectively use the senses of smell, sight, and so on. However, human senses can be impaired by sleep, disability, illness, or distractions, so that timely, effective warning may not result. Beginning in the mid-nineteenth century, a number of mechanical, electrical, and electronic devices have been developed to substitute for human senses in detecting the environmental changes created by fire.

The fire signatures most often used as the basis for detection are heat, smoke (aerosol particulates), and radiant energy (IR, visible, UV). Several factors complicate the ability of any detector to sense fire reliably. (1) Different types of fires can have widely divergent fire signatures. For example, some materials burn intensely with little or no smoke, whereas smoldering fires have no visible flame and generally very low heat output. (2) The environmental change(s) being monitored must reach the fire detector and must exceed a threshold amplitude and/or rate of change before alarm can occur. (3) Nonfire conditions can produce ambient changes that mimic fire signatures and that may cause false (nuisance) alarms.

Most building codes require what amounts to partial coverage by detection systems, meaning some rooms or spaces do not have detectors in them. Designers must be aware that this can substantially delay detection and alarm because fire signatures become weaker as the distance from the fire to a detector increases, especially if there are any physical barriers between them. A minimum code design may not meet expectations.

The proper selection and location of automatic fire detectors are essential for achieving protection objectives. For example, the use of spot-type smoke detectors on a very high ceiling will delay detection of a fire until it grows very intense. In addition, detector access for testing, cleaning, or replacement may also be very difficult. In this particular application, the use of projected beam-type smoke detectors may be much more suitable.

Every application of detectors needs to be properly evaluated. This begins with a clear understanding of the protection objectives, likely fire scenarios, and the expected environment in each protected space. With that knowledge, the fire protection engineer can (1) evaluate the fire signatures expected from potential hostile fires at various times in their growth, (2) determine the effect of ambient conditions on various detector options, and (3) select the detector type(s) that will offer the best balance of fire response and discrimination (avoidance of nuisance alarms from nonfire ambient conditions). This chapter will help designers understand how the various types of automatic fire detectors operate, their performance capabilities, and how they are applied.

See also Section 2, Chapter 6, "Fundamentals of Fire Detection"; Section 14, Chapter 4, "Fire Alarm System Interconnections"; and Section 14, Chapter 5, "Inspection, Testing, and Maintenance of Fire Alarm Systems."

HEAT DETECTORS

Heat detectors are the oldest type of automatic fire detection device. They began with the development of automatic sprinklers in the 1860s and have continued to the present with a

Kenneth W. Dungan, P.E., is a principal of Risk Technologies in Knoxville, Tennessee. He is a fellow of the Society of Fire Protection Engineers.

proliferation of various types of devices. A sprinkler can be considered a combined heat-activated fire detector and extinguishing device when the sprinkler system is provided with waterflow indicators connected to the fire alarm control system. Waterflow indicators detect either the flow of water through the pipes or the subsequent pressure change upon actuation of the system.

Heat detectors are very reliable and have the lowest false alarm rate of all automatic fire detectors. They are best suited for fire detection in small confined spaces where rapidly building high-heat-output fires are expected, in areas where ambient conditions would not allow the use of other fire detection devices, or where very early warning of fire is not required.

Heat detectors are generally located on or near the ceiling and respond primarily to the convected thermal energy of a fire. They operate either when the detecting element reaches a predetermined fixed temperature or when a specified rate of temperature change occurs.

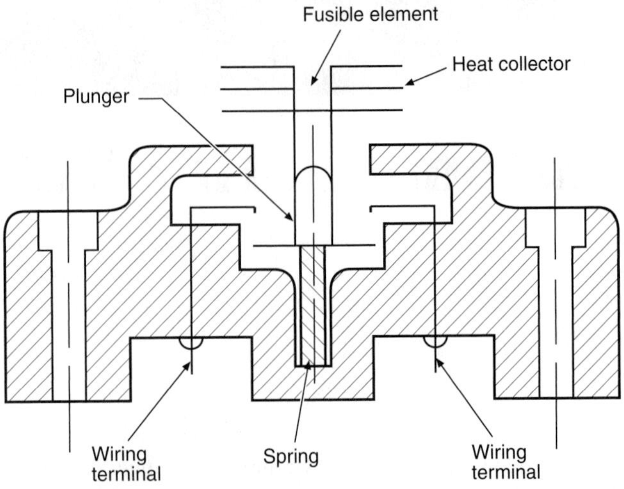

FIGURE 14.2.1 Fixed-Temperature Heat Detector, Spot-Type, Fusible Element

Operating Principles of Fixed-Temperature Heat Detectors

Fixed-temperature heat detectors are designed to alarm when the temperature of the operating element reaches a specified point. The air temperature at the time of alarm can be considerably higher than the rated temperature (depending on the fire growth rate), because it takes time for the air to raise the temperature of the operating element to its set point. This condition is called *thermal lag*. Fixed-temperature heat detectors are available to cover a wide range of operating temperatures—from about 135°F (58°C) on up. Higher temperature detectors are necessary so that detection can be provided in areas normally subjected to high ambient temperatures (i.e., boiler rooms, attics, etc.) or in special applications requiring detectors that operate only if close to the fire.

Fusible-Element Type. Eutectic metals—alloys of bismuth, lead, tin, and cadmium that melt rapidly at a predetermined temperature—can be used as operating elements for heat detection. The most common use is the fusible element in an automatic sprinkler. Fusing of the element allows the cover on the orifice to fall away, water to flow in the system, and the alarm to be initiated.

Eutectic metals may also be used to actuate electrical heat detectors. Often they are used as a solder to secure a spring under tension. When the element fuses, the spring action closes contacts and initiates an alarm (Figure 14.2.1). Devices using eutectic metals cannot be restored; either the device or its operating element must be replaced following operation.

Continuous Line Type. As alternatives to spot-type fixed-temperature detection, various methods of line-type detection have been developed. The detector shown in Figure 14.2.2 uses a pair of steel wires in a normally open circuit. The conductors are held apart by a heat-sensitive insulation. The wires, under tension, are enclosed in a braided sheath to form a single cable assembly. When the design temperature is reached, the insulation melts, the two wires contact, and an alarm is initiated. Following an alarm, the fused section of the cable must be replaced to restore the system.

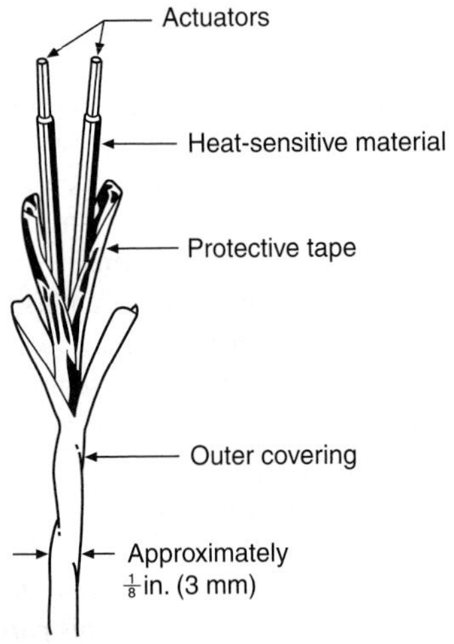

FIGURE 14.2.2 Line-Type Heat Detector

A similar alarm device utilizing a semiconductor material and a stainless steel capillary tube has been used where mechanical stability is also a factor (Figure 14.2.3). The capillary tube contains a coaxial center conductor separated from the tube wall by a temperature-sensitive glass semiconductor material. Under normal conditions, a small current (i.e., below alarm threshold) flows in the circuit. As the temperature rises, the resistance of the semiconductor decreases, allows more current flow, and initiates the alarm.

Bimetallic Type. When two metals with different coefficients of thermal expansion are bonded together and then heated, differential expansion causes bending or flexing toward the metal having the lower expansion rate. This action closes a normally

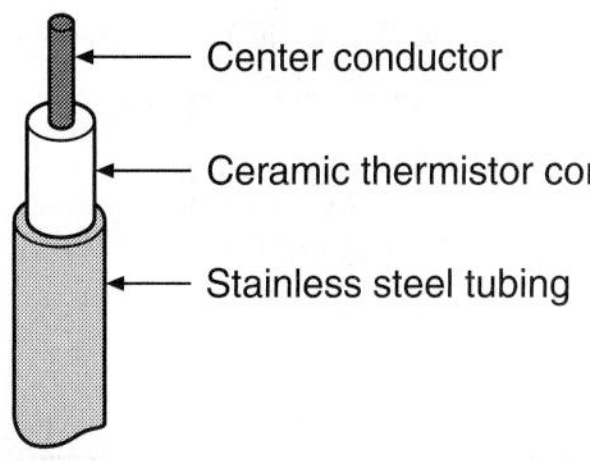

FIGURE 14.2.3 Construction of the Continuous Thermal Sensor Showing Outer Tubing, Ceramic Thermistor Core, and Center Wire

open circuit. The low-expansion metal commonly used is Invar™, an alloy of 36 percent nickel and 64 percent iron. Several alloys of manganese-copper-nickel, nickel-chromium-iron, or stainless steel may also be used for the high-expansion component of a bimetal assembly. Bimetals are used for the operating elements of a variety of fixed-temperature detectors. These detectors are generally of two types: (1) the bimetal strip and (2) the bimetal snap disc.

As it is heated, a bimetal strip deforms in the direction of the contact point. With a given bimetal, the width of the gap between the contacts determines the operating temperature: the wider the gap, the higher the operating point. The operating element of a snap disc device is a bimetal disc formed into a concave shape in its unstressed condition (Figure 14.2.4). Generally, a heat collector is attached to the detector frame to speed the transfer of heat from the room air to the bimetal. As the disc is heated, the stresses developed cause it to suddenly reverse curvature and become convex. This provides a rapid positive action that closes the alarm contacts. The disc itself usually is not part of the electrical circuit. All heat detectors using bimetal elements are automatically self-restoring after operation, when the ambient temperature drops sufficiently below the operating point.

Rate Compensation Detectors

A rate compensation detector is a device that responds when the temperature of the surrounding air reaches a predetermined level, with the rate of temperature rise having minimal effect on response (low thermal lag). This makes them rather sensitive fixed-temperature detectors (Figure 14.2.5).

A typical example is a spot-type detector with a tubular casing of metal that tends to expand lengthwise as it is heated, and an associated contact mechanism that will close at a certain point in the elongation. A second metallic element inside the tube exerts an opposing force on the contacts, tending to hold them open. The forces are balanced so that, with a slow rate of temperature rise, there is more time for heat to penetrate to the inner element. This inhibits contact closure until the total device has been heated to its rated temperature level. However, with a fast rate of temperature rise, there is less time for heat to penetrate to the inner element. The element, therefore, exerts less of an inhibiting effect, so contact closure is obtained when the total device has been heated to a lower level. This, in effect, compensates for thermal lag.

Thermal detectors using expanding metal elements are also automatically self-restoring after operation, when the ambient temperature drops to some point below the operating point.

Rate-of-Rise Detectors

One effect that a flaming fire has on the surrounding area is to rapidly increase air temperature in the space above the fire. Fixed-temperature heat detectors will not initiate an alarm until the air temperature near the ceiling exceeds the design operating point. The rate-of-rise detector, however, will function when the rate of temperature increase exceeds a predetermined value, typically around 12 to 15°F (7 to 8°C) per minute. Rate-of-rise detectors are designed to compensate for the normal changes in ambient temperature (less than 12°F [6.7°C] per minute) that are expected under nonfire conditions.

When applying rate-of-rise heat detectors, use care to avoid locating them in areas where temperatures might normally be expected to rise as much as 12 to 15°F (7 to 8°C) in 1 minute (or less) in order to avoid unwanted alarms. These include commercial kitchens, laundries, or dishwashing areas, truck or construction equipment repair facilities, in front of ceiling-mounted space heaters or air diffusers, near the outside doors of air-conditioned facilities, and in attics. Remember that these detectors will respond for the prescribed rate-of-rise in temperature, even if the current ambient temperature is frigid.

Rate-of-rise detectors that operate by pneumatic action have been manufactured for decades. In a pneumatic fire

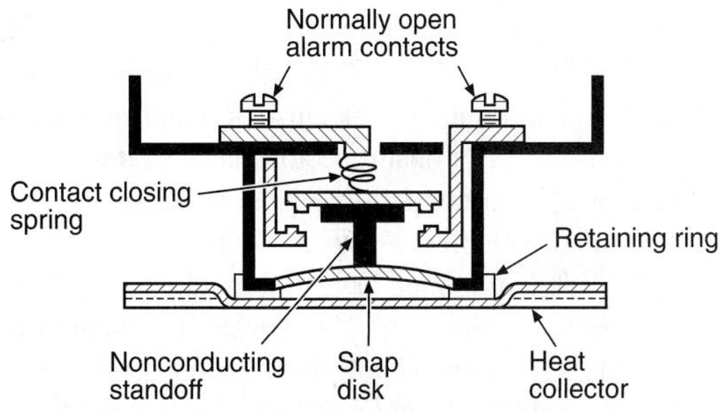

FIGURE 14.2.4 Spot-Type Fixed-Temperature Snap Disc Detector

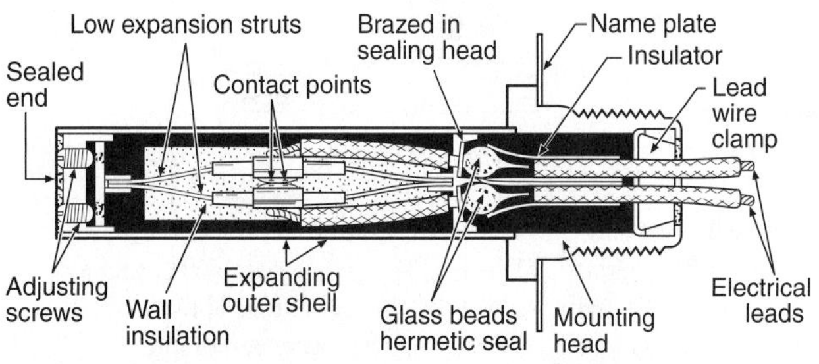

FIGURE 14.2.5 Section of Spot-Type Rate Compensation Detector

detector, air heated in a tube or chamber expands, increasing the pressure in the tube or chamber. This exerts a mechanical force on a diaphragm that closes the alarm contacts. If the tube or chamber were hermetically sealed, slow increases in ambient temperature, a drop in the barometric pressure, or both, would cause the detector to initiate an alarm regardless of the rate of temperature change. To overcome this, pneumatic detectors have a small orifice to vent the higher pressure that builds up during slow increases in temperature or during a drop in barometric pressure. The vents are sized so that when the temperature changes rapidly, as in a fire, the rate of expansion exceeds the venting rate and the pressure rises. When the temperature rise exceeds 12 to 15°F (7 to 8°C) per minute, the pressure is converted to mechanical action by a flexible diaphragm. Pneumatic heat detectors are available for both line- and spot-type detectors. A schematic of a spot-type pneumatic heat detector is shown in Figure 14.2.6, and a line type is shown in Figure 14.2.7.

Line Type. The line type consists of metal tubing, in a loop configuration, attached to the ceiling or side wall near the ceiling of the area to be protected (see Figure 14.2.7). Lines of tubing are normally spaced not more than 30 ft (9.1 m) apart, not more than 15 ft (4.5 m) from a wall, and with no more than 1000 ft (305 m) of tubing on each circuit. Also, a minimum of at least 5 percent of each tube circuit or 25 ft (7.6 m) of tube, whichever is greater, must be in each protected area. Without this minimum amount of tubing exposed to a fire condition, insufficient pressure would build up to achieve proper response.

In small areas where the line-type tube detectors might have insufficient tubing exposed to generate sufficient pressures to close the alarm contacts, air chambers or rosettes of tubing are often used. These units act like a spot-type detector by providing the volume of air required to meet the 5 percent or 25 ft (7.6 m) requirement. Since a line-type rate-of-rise detector is an integrating detector, it will actuate either when a rapid heat rise occurs in one area of exposed tubing or when a slightly less rapid heat rise takes place in several areas where tubing on the same loop is exposed.

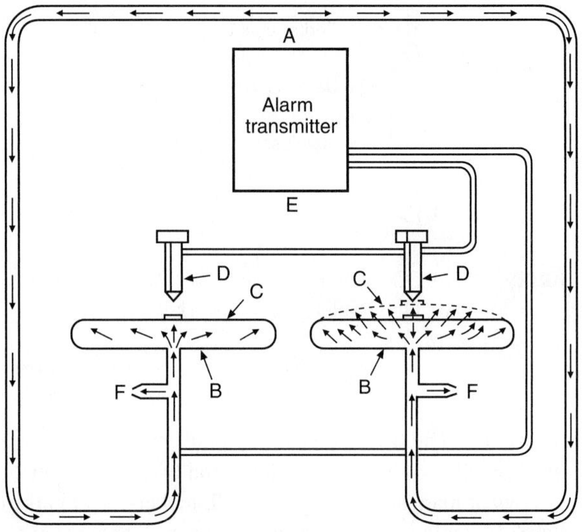

FIGURE 14.2.7 Line-Type Rate-of-Rise Heat Detector. The copper tubing A is fastened in a continuous loop to ceilings or walls and terminates at both ends in chambers B having flexible diaphragms C, which control electrical contacts D. When air in the tubing expands under the influence of heat, pressure builds within the chambers, causing the diaphragms to move and close a circuit to alarm transmitter E. Vents F compensate for small pressure changes in the tubing brought about by small changes in temperature in the protected spaces.

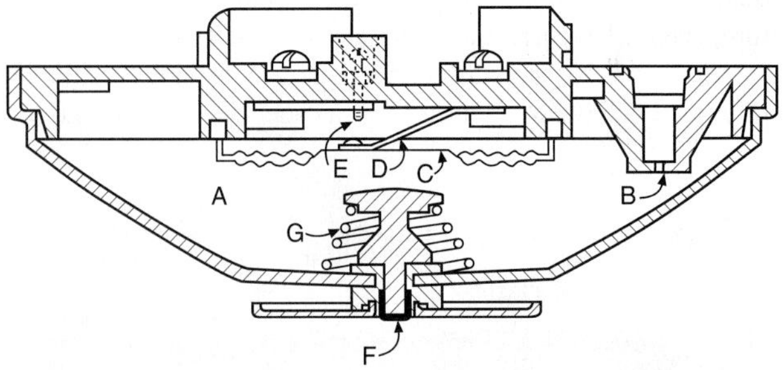

FIGURE 14.2.6 A Spot-Type Combination Rate-of-Rise, Fixed-Temperature Detector. The air in chamber A expands more rapidly than it can escape from vent B. This causes pressure to close electrical contact D between diaphragm C and contact screw E. Fixed-temperature operation occurs when fusible alloy F melts, releasing spring G, which depresses the diaphragm closing contact points.

Spot Type. The pneumatic principle is also used to close contacts within spot detectors (see Figure 14.2.6). The difference between the line- and spot-type detectors is that the spot type contains all of the air in a single container rather than in a tube that extends from the detector assembly to the protected area(s).

Combination Fixed-Temperature/ Rate-of-Rise Detectors

Combination fixed-temperature/rate-of-rise detectors contain more than one element that responds to a fire. These detectors may be designed to respond from either element or from the combined partial or complete response of both elements. An example of the former is a heat detector that operates on both the rate-of-rise and fixed-temperature principles. Its advantage is that the rate-of-rise element will respond quickly to a rapidly developing fire, while the fixed-temperature element will respond to a slowly developing fire when the detecting element reaches its set point temperature. The most common combination heat detector uses a vented air chamber and a flexible diaphragm for the rate-of-rise function, while the fixed-temperature element is usually leaf-spring restrained by a eutectic metal (see Figure 14.2.6). When the fixed-temperature element reaches its design operating temperature, the eutectic metal fuses and releases the spring, which closes the contacts.

Electronic Spot-Type Heat Detectors

A thermoelectric effect detector is a device that utilizes a sensing element consisting of one or more thermistors, which produce a change in electrical resistance in response to an increase in temperature (Figure 14.2.8). This resistance change is monitored by associated electronic circuitry, and the detector responds when the resistance changes at an abnormal rate (rate-of-rise type) or when the resistance reaches a specific value (fixed-temperature type).

The very low mass of the sensing elements used in electronic spot-type heat detectors gives them low thermal lag (for faster response), and their analog outputs can be analyzed by complex signal processing algorithms to further improve performance. This makes them the technology of choice for use in multisensor smoke detectors, discussed later in this chapter.

Rate-of-rise detectors of this type use two thermistors. One is exposed to changes in atmospheric temperature. When the temperature rapidly changes as in a fire situation, the temperature of the exposed thermistor increases faster than the temperature of the unexposed reference thermistor, generating a net change in resistance causing the detector to go into alarm condition. Most rate-of-rise detectors are designed with a fixed-temperature backup feature so that, should the temperature rise be slower than 15°F (8°C) per minute, the detector will operate when the exposed thermistor has reached a predetermined fixed temperature.

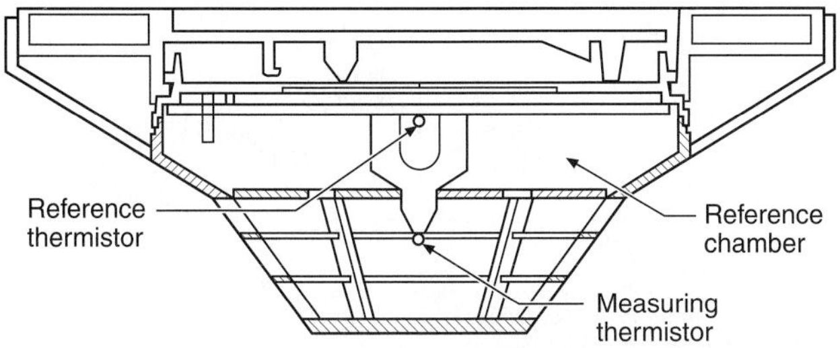

(a)

(b)

FIGURE 14.2.8 Solid-State Electronic Heat Detector with Dual Thermistor Sensing Circuit (Source: System Sensor®)

SMOKE DETECTORS

A smoke detector detects most fires much more rapidly than a heat detector. Smoke detectors are identified by their operating principle as being either (1) ionization, (2) photoelectric, or (3) video. As a class, ionization smoke detectors are spot-type detectors, which provide somewhat faster response to high-energy (flaming) fires, since they respond to the number density of smoke particles, and such fires produce large numbers of relatively small particles. Photoelectric smoke detectors, as a class, provide superior response to low-energy (smoldering) fires, since they respond to the optical density of smoke, and such fires produce a preponderance of visible size range smoke particles. Their performance advantage for detecting smoldering fires is substantial; this can result in much earlier warning when the fire growth rate is slow. They may equal or even surpass ionization detector response to flaming fires when the fire is not in close proximity, such as in duct smoke detector applications. For these reasons, photoelectric smoke detectors have captured an increasing share of the market in recent years. Photoelectric smoke detectors can be spot type, beam type, or air sampling type. Video-based smoke detection uses video cameras and computer software to analyze changes in the recorded images. Since this method of detection does not require transport of the smoke to a detector or a sampling port, it offers advantages in large open and high-ceiling spaces.

For decades, virtually all smoke detectors were nonanalog,* meaning they had only two operating states: normal and alarm. Typically they were not addressable devices, meaning they did not provide their specific identification or location information to the control unit, except as part of a zone (protected area) consisting of multiple detectors on a common fire alarm initiating circuit. Their ability to avoid false (nuisance) alarms was hampered by their fixed sensitivity and limited on-board signal processing ability. Some jurisdictions even required these smoke detectors to have a specified minimum sensitivity level in order to avoid excessive alarms from transient nonfire conditions such as smoking.

The advent of low-cost microprocessors and surface-mount electronics technology enabled detector manufacturers to utilize new smoke detector concepts, including the use of analog technology to monitor conditions in the protected space. Another advance was to make them addressable, meaning they individually communicate with the fire alarm control unit (FACU), so the specific device reporting is displayed. The data produced by these new technology smoke detectors are analyzed using complex signal-processing algorithms that are either on board the detectors or in the FACU. Some detectors offer a choice

*Nonanalog detectors have commonly been called "conventional" smoke detectors. However, because most new system installations now utilize analog-addressable smoke detectors, "nonaddressable" is the preferred term for those older technology devices.

of several field-selectable algorithms for specific applications (ambient conditions).

Microprocessors also make comprehensive self-diagnostics possible. The sensitivity of most analog-addressable smoke detectors can automatically be monitored by the control unit and adjusted over time as needed to hold a constant sensitivity, despite the effects of dust buildup, component drift, or gradual changes in ambient conditions. The FACU can also arrange individual detectors to have different sensitivity settings for day and night or weekend to take advantage of different ambient conditions when the business is closed. Some detector models use distributed intelligence so that several capabilities like this reside within the detector itself to reduce communication traffic on the signaling line circuit. This may permit less stringent wiring methods to be used.

Addressable devices are constantly polled by the control unit, typically every few seconds, and immediate notice is given if a detector fails to report or needs servicing. Some multisensor smoke detectors are able to report as many as 20 to 30 specific trouble conditions to the FACU. The substantial performance advantages and unique features offered by analog-addressable smoke detectors make them the sensor of choice for most smoke detection applications. Nonaddressable smoke detectors are now primarily used for replacement purposes in existing or very small systems.

Ionization Smoke Detectors

As stated, smoke detectors utilizing the ionization principle are usually of the spot type. An ionization smoke detector has a very small amount of radioactive material (an alpha emitter) that ionizes the air in the sensing chamber, rendering the air conductive and permitting a minute current flow through the air between two charged electrodes. This gives the sensing chamber an effective electrical conductance. When smoke particles enter the ionization area, they decrease the conductance of the air by attaching themselves to the ions, causing a reduction in ion mobility. The current flow is monitored and when conductance is below a predetermined level, the detector is in alarm (Figure 14.2.9). With analog-addressable detectors, this alarm threshold can be varied to compensate for ambient conditions.

Photoelectric Smoke Detectors

The presence of suspended smoke particles generated during the combustion process affects the propagation of a light beam

AUTOMATIC FIRE DETECTORS

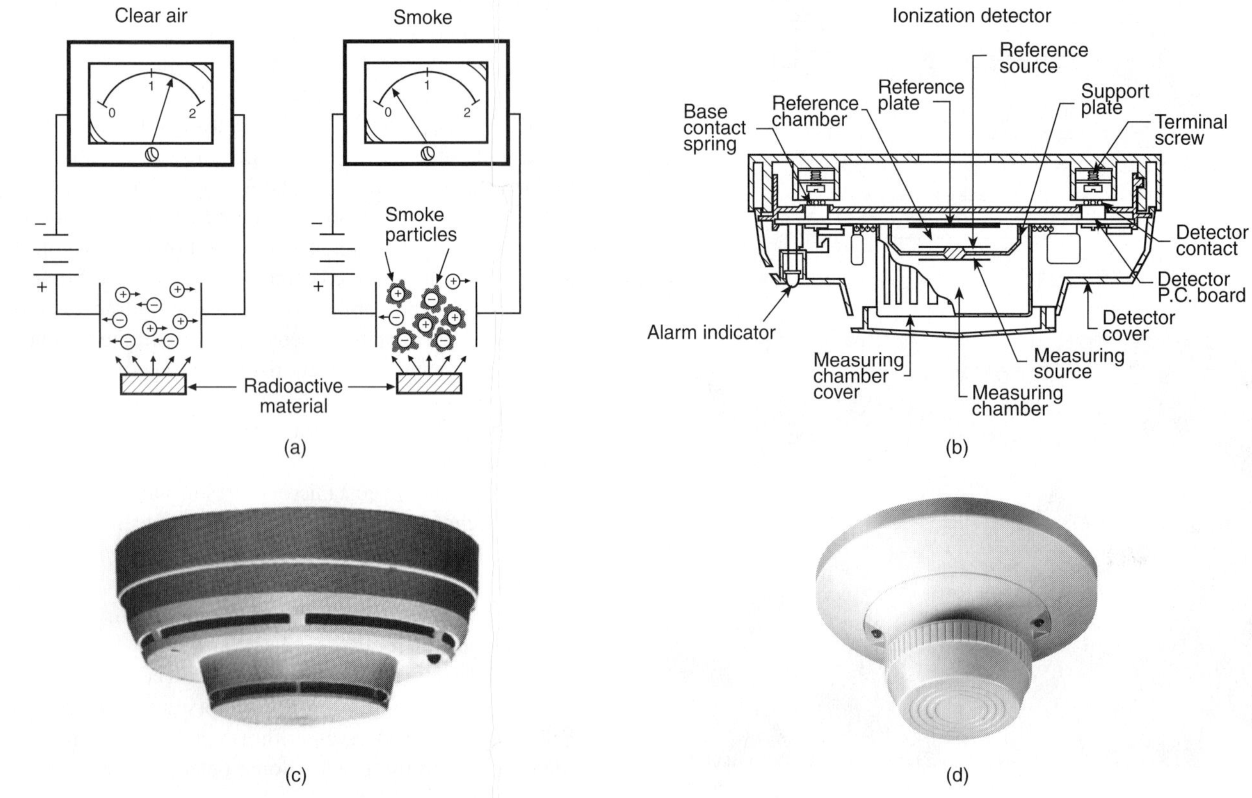

FIGURE 14.2.9 (a) Principle of Operation for Ionization Smoke Detector; (b) Cross-Sectional View of an Ionization Smoke Detector; (c) Ionization Smoke Detector (Source: Siemens Building Technologies, Fire Safety Division); (d) Ionization Smoke Detector (Courtesy of Gamewell-FCI)

passing through the air. The effect can be utilized to detect the presence of a fire in two ways: (1) obscuration of light intensity over the beam path or (2) scattering of the light beam.

Light Obscuration Principle. Smoke detectors that operate on the principle of light obscuration consist of a light source, a light beam collimating system, and a photosensitive device. When dense smoke obscures part of the light beam, or less dense smoke obscures more of the beam, the light reaching the photosensitive device is reduced, and this initiates the alarm (Figure 14.2.10).

Most light obscuration smoke detectors are the beam type and are used to protect rather large spaces such as atriums, auditoriums, manufacturing areas, and so on. Each projected beam smoke detector is equivalent to a row of spot-type smoke detectors along the beam path. They are installed with the transmitter (pulsed IR light source) at one end of the area to be protected and the receiver (photosensitive device) at the opposite end.

The transmitter and receiver must have a completely unobstructed view of each other that cannot normally be blocked. In the event of any sudden accidental blockage, the detector generates a trouble signal rather than an alarm, since smoke buildup from a fire would not cause a sudden, complete blockage of the beam. If multiple parallel sets of these smoke detectors are installed, it may be prudent to alternate the transmitter and receiver locations to avoid possible cross-talk between adjacent units. Some models may also be sensitive to intense flashing lights, such as on large machinery or vehicles, if the source is close to their optical axis.

Projected beam smoke detectors have a permitted operating range, for example, 33 to 330 ft (10 to 100 m). This range varies from model to model, as does the permitted minimum mounting distance below the ceiling, and so on. They require very stable mounting surfaces, so that alignment of the IR light beam can be maintained. This becomes more important at longer ranges and less so when the beam's throw distance is shorter. In all cases the manufacturer's detailed instructions for installation and beam alignment must be followed.

Light-Scattering Principle. When smoke particles enter a light path, scattering results. Smoke detectors utilizing the photoelectric light-scattering principle are usually of the spot type. They contain a light source and a photosensitive device arranged so the light rays normally do not fall onto the device. When smoke particles enter the light path, light strikes the particles and is scattered onto the photosensitive device, causing the detector to respond (Figure 14.2.11).

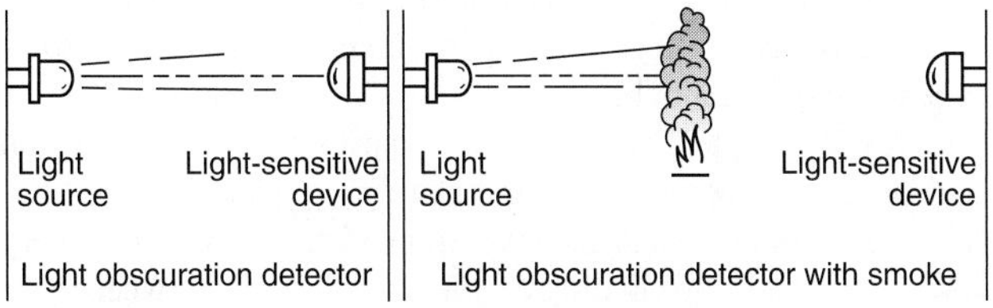

(a)

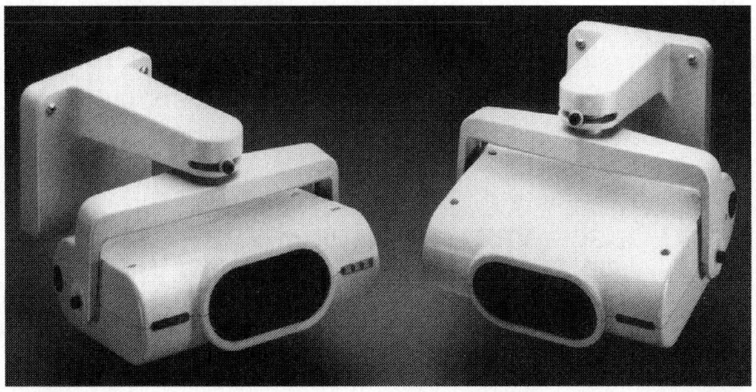

(b)

FIGURE 14.2.10 (a) Principle of Operation for Photoelectric Obscuration Smoke Detector; (b) Typical Photoelectric Obscuration–Type Smoke Detector (Source: System Sensor®)

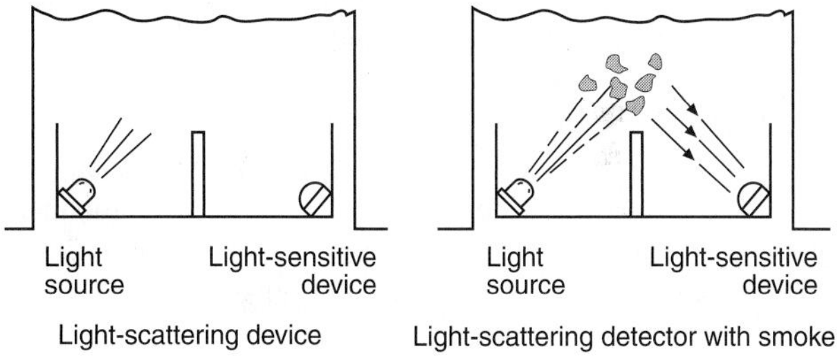

(a)

(b)

(c)

FIGURE 14.2.11 (a) Cross-Sectional View of a Photoelectric Scattering Smoke Detector; (b) Photoelectric Smoke Detector (Source: System Sensor®); (c) Photoelectronic Smoke Detector (Courtesy of GE Security)

The photosensitive device used in scattering detectors usually is a photodiode or a phototransistor. The light source is typically an infrared light-emitting diode (LED), pulsed to reduce power drain. However, several manufacturers recently introduced a photoelectric spot-type smoke detector utilizing a very sharp laser beam. Because the laser beam is so intense, more light is reflected into the sensing chamber than with a standard LED. A signal-processing algorithm is used to discriminate between airborne dust particles and smoke particles entering the sensing chamber. These attributes enable it to have up to 100 times the sensitivity of LED units and still be very stable. It's intended for special applications, like cleanrooms, telecommunications hubs, archives, and computer rooms, where very early warning of incipient fires is essential.

Air Sampling–Type Smoke Detectors

As the name implies, air sampling–type smoke detectors draw in air from the protected space and analyze it for smoke particles. The fact that air is mechanically transported to the sensor permits the use of filters to remove most dust particles, a common source of false alarms for ordinary nonaspirating smoke detectors. Almost all air sampling–type smoke detectors utilize the photoelectric light-scattering principle, enhanced by various means to give it the capability for very high sensitivity. However, there are at least three rather different design approaches.

Continuous Air-Sampling Smoke Detection. These devices use a network of tubing or piping (with spaced intake ports) and an aspirating fan to draw a sample of air from the protected area. Their photoelectric detector has an intense light source, either a pulsed laser or a xenon strobe, to increase the amount of light that any smoke particles will forward scatter toward a photosensitive element. This makes these units capable of very high sensitivity, surpassing all spot-type smoke detectors, except the laser source design previously discussed.

The use of a tubular network to draw air back to the detector permits the sensor to be located out of harm's way, for applications such as prisons and mental hospital isolation rooms. Typically, these devices also have several user-definable alert and alarm levels to take advantage of their capability for high sensitivity and, for special applications like computer room fire suppression system control, to initiate various actions, including gaseous agent release.

There are limitations imposed on the application of these devices as a result of the method of sampling air and transporting it back for analysis. (1) Transport time limits the length of the sampling network and, therefore, the size of the area covered by the detector. (2) Smoke dilution reduces their inherent high sensitivity, proportional to the number of sampling ports in the network, and this fact must be considered in design. (3) The piping network is supervised for breakage or blockage but the airflow condition of an individual sampling port usually cannot be sensed. (4) The ability to zone these systems is limited, but some models can monitor several different piping networks, on a rotating basis (using air valves), as long as each network is within the permitted length.

Cloud Chamber Principle Air-Sampling Smoke Detection. These devices also use a network of tubing or piping (with spaced intake ports) and an aspirating fan to draw individual samples of air from the protected area. After being filtered to remove dust particles, it enters a humidifier where distilled water is used to raise the relative humidity to approximately 100 percent. Then the sample of air is subject to some reduction in air pressure, using a vacuum pump, so that it becomes supersaturated. If any smoke particles are present, they act as condensation nuclei for water droplets, triggering formation of a cloud in the sensing chamber. The density of the cloud is measured by a photoelectric light-scattering detector, which will respond if a threshold alert or alarm value is exceeded.

This phenomenon is effective for detecting the submicron particles that are produced in abundance by thermal decomposition during the pyrolysis or precombustion phase of incipient fires. For example, an electric motor that is "cooking out" releases large numbers of decomposing molecules from insulation on the winding, long before there is any visible smoke or flame. This gives cloud chamber principle smoke detectors unsurpassed ability to provide very early warning of incipient fire.

The need to transport the sampled air back to the unit through a piping network imposes the same limitations on these devices as previously discussed. In addition, they require more frequent servicing than other types of smoke detectors, including replenishment of the distilled water supply. They are most often used where the protected space has very high value or mission-critical contents that demand very early warning of incipient fires and justify the expense.

Spot-Type Aspirating Smoke Detection. This design combines the technology of spot-type photoelectric smoke detection with filtered, periodic aspiration. The objective is to detect smoke reliably in very dusty environments where regular spot-type detectors cannot be used.

Air is sampled by a small on-board fan, which cycles on and off to reduce power drain. The time between samples is less than a minute, and airflow (filter status) is verified every few hours. The filter is replaceable and the time between filter clogs can vary from a few months up to several years, depending on ambient conditions. Typical applications are heated stables, paper plants, cotton and textile mills, commercial laundries, food processing areas, and so on. A separate power supply is required for fan power. They are not intended for outdoor use, nor for locations with potential explosion hazard.

Video-Based Smoke Detectors

Video-based smoke detectors operate on the principle of identifying changes in the digitized video image from a camera or series of cameras. Closed-circuit TV (CCTV) cameras view an area and the images that are within the field of view of the cameras are transmitted to a computer. The computer looks for areas of change as it digitizes the images. Only those pixels that show a change are further processed to discriminate the particular characteristics of smoke. These cameras work in the visible light range and therefore need an illuminated space. The use of video cameras also provides a visual image to an operator monitoring the system, which can provide very useful input to emergency management decisions. The software allows masking of portions of the field of view to minimize unwanted alarms from ambient sources of smoke or dust. As previously stated, these devices can offer significant advantages in large open facilities, where transport of smoke to other means of smoke detection can cause delays in identifying and locating a fire condition. Examples of such applications include the turbine hall of electrical generating facilities, large assembly plants, or aircraft hangars.

GAS-SENSING FIRE DETECTORS

Many changes occur in the gas content of the environment during a fire. It has been observed that detectable levels of gases are reached after detectable smoke levels and before detectable heat levels. One of three operating principles, that is, semiconductor, catalytic element, or infrared absorption, may be used in a gas-sensing fire detector or in a combination (multisensor) detector.

Semiconductor Principle

Fire-gas detectors of the semiconductor type respond to either oxidizing or reducing gases by creating electrical changes in the semiconductor. The subsequent conductivity change of the semiconductor causes actuation of the detector.

Catalytic Element Principle

Fire-gas detectors of the catalytic element type contain a material that, in itself, remains unchanged, but that accelerates the oxidation of combustible gases. The resulting temperature rise of the element causes detector actuation.

Infrared Absorption Principle

Carbon dioxide, carbon monoxide, water vapor, and hydrocarbons absorb different frequencies of infrared light. This principle can be used to measure the presence of and concentration of one or more of these gases from a fire.

MULTISENSOR AND MULTICRITERIA DETECTORS

The combination of sensors placed in a single spot-type detector has been a common practice for decades. The early devices were combinations of a heat detector with a smoke detector. *NFPA 72®*, *National Fire Alarm Code®*, required that any heat detector combined with a smoke detector should have a listed spacing of 50 ft (15.25 m). For these devices both sensors act independently, carry independent listings, and require independent testing of each element.

With the development of analog-addressable or "intelligent" detectors, the use of multicriteria detectors was introduced. These devices are typically smoke detectors that integrate the response of two or more sensors to achieve greater sensitivity (early response) without sacrificing stability (increasing unwanted alarms). These devices can incorporate a thermal sensor with a smoke sensor or multiple smoke sensors (e.g., ion and photo). The signal from each sensor is analyzed and combined using proprietary algorithms to establish alarm thresholds. Development is under way by some manufacturers to incorporate gas sensors such as CO or CO_2 to improve the performance of smoke detectors.

RADIANT ENERGY–SENSING FIRE DETECTORS

Radiant energy–sensing devices sense the radiant energy (electromagnetic radiation) emitted as a by-product of the combustion reaction, which obeys the laws of optics. This includes radiation in the ultraviolet, visible, and infrared portions of the spectrum, emitted by flames or glowing embers. They are categorized as flame detectors and spark/ember detectors.

The selection of the radiant energy–sensing detector requires that the device's spectral response be matched to the spectral emissions of the potential fire to be detected. The fire protection engineer must also evaluate any nonfire radiant energy sources in the area to be protected to determine if they could cause nuisance alarms in the detector being considered.

All flame and spark/ember detectors respond in accordance with the inverse square law, which defines the fire size versus distance curve for the detector. Therefore, if the distance from the detector to the fire is doubled, the signal received drops to $(½)^2 = ¼$ of what it previously was. Sensitivity also drops off as the source of radiant energy being detected is displaced from the optical axis of the detector. Each detector model will have manufacturer's data on its effective (normalized) sensitivity versus angular displacement (Figure 14.2.12)

Because these detectors are line-of-sight devices, they must be positioned so that no point requiring detection in the hazard

100% represents the maximum detection distance for a given fire. The sensitivity inreases as the angle of incidence decreases.

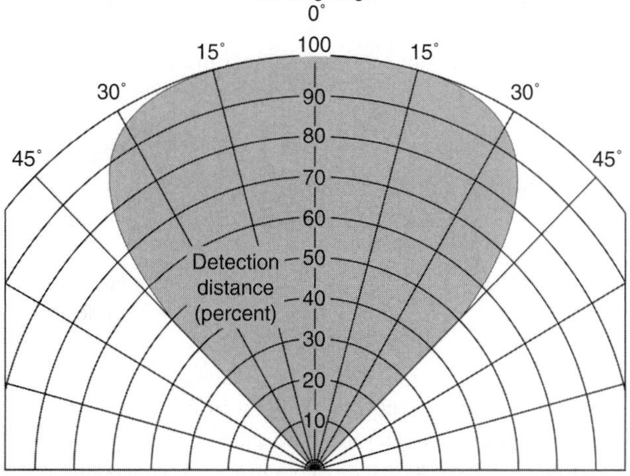

FIGURE 14.2.12 UV Fire Detector Cone of Vision (Courtesy of Detector Electronics Corporation)

area is obstructed or outside the field of view of at least one detector. Spacing will depend on the overall protection objectives of the system, including the minimum size of flaming fire or spark/ember that must be detected and the response time required.

An additional consideration for all applications of radiant energy–sensing fire detectors is the effect of the medium between the anticipated fire and the sensor. Different wavelengths of radiant energy are absorbed with varying degrees of efficiency by materials suspended in the air or that may accumulate on the optical surfaces of the detector. Some examples include atmospheric humidity, smoke, dust, aerosol film, fog, rain, and snow. Detector lens clarity must be assured between maintenance intervals by electronic monitoring or inspection, possibly augmented by a lens air purge device. Protective housings (behind glass, plastic, etc.) should not be used unless listed for the purpose, because some optical materials are absorptive at the wavelength(s) used by these detectors.

FIGURE 14.2.13 Typical UV Detector Assembly (Courtesy of Detector Electronics Corporation)

Flame Detectors

Other than video-based flame detectors, discussed later in the chapter, flame detectors operate in the UV and/or IR portion of the spectrum. Most such flame detectors exhibit some kind of fuel specificity and are qualified based on a defined fire under specific conditions. When employing these detectors for fuels other than the defined fire, the designer should make appropriate adjustments to the maximum distance between the detector and the fire. The various types of UV/IR flame detectors and their principles of operation follow.

Ultraviolet Flame Detectors. The ultraviolet spectrum comprises wavelengths ranging from approximately 0.1 μm to 0.35 μm. UV detectors typically use a vacuum photodiode Geiger-Muller tube to detect the ultraviolet radiation that is produced by a flame. The photodiode allows a burst of current to flow for each UV photon that hits the active area of the tube. When the number of current bursts per unit time reaches a set level, the detector initiates an alarm. A special control unit is required to monitor the count rates from UV detectors and initiate alarm (Figure 14.2.13).

UV detectors are sensitive to most fires, including hydrocarbons (liquids, gases, and solids), ammonia, sulfur, hydrogen, hydrazine, and metals such as magnesium. However, the smoke produced by combustion of middle and heavy fraction petroleum distillates is highly absorptive in the UV end of the spectrum, and this must be compensated for in system design if UV detectors are used.

Potential sources of UV detector nuisance alarms include lightning, arc welding, X rays (used in industrial nondestructive testing of metals), and radioactive materials.

Infrared Flame Detectors. The total infrared spectrum comprises wavelengths ranging from approximately 0.76μm to 220 μm. IR detectors basically comprises a filter and lens system used to screen out unwanted wavelengths and focus those remaining on a photovoltaic or photoresistive cell sensitive to IR energy. They can respond just to the resulting net IR component of the flame or in combination with a flame flicker sensor (typically looking for a flicker rate of 5 to 30 Hz).

Although almost all materials that participate in flaming combustion emit UV radiation to some degree during such combustion, only carbon-containing fuels emit significant radiation in the 4.35 μm (carbon dioxide) band used by many IR detectors to sense flame (Figure 14.2.14). This means that IR flame detectors are not responsive to carbon-free fuels, such as hydrogen and sulfur.

Potential sources of nuisance alarms from infrared flame detectors include gas (oxy-acetylene) welding in their field of view and solar radiation from sunlight (a strong IR source). Several measures are available to prevent sunlight from being a problem, including the use of multiple wavelength technology. This design (commonly referred to as an IR/IR detector) employs filters to pass radiation from different portions of the infrared spectrum to separate IR sensors. The two outputs are

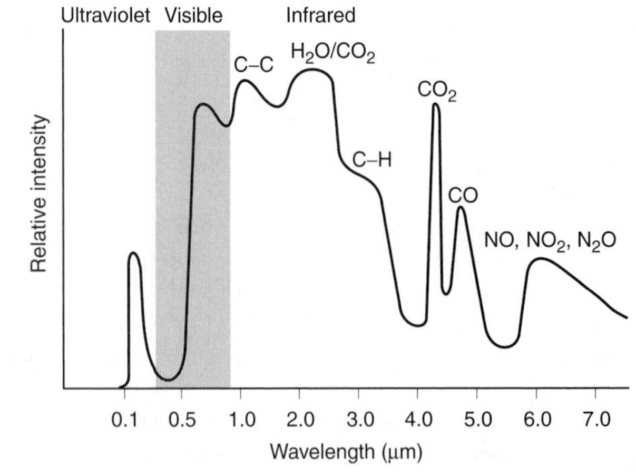

FIGURE 14.2.14 Spectrum of a Typical Flame (free-burning gasoline)

continuously compared and an alarm is initiated when the relationship between them indicates a fire.

Ultraviolet/Infrared Flame Detectors. Combination UV/IR devices sense radiation from portions of both spectrums and use the resulting signal to indicate a fire. They typically require both UV and IR sensor response to cause an alarm, resulting in better false alarm rejection than either UV or IR detectors alone. (In circuit design this is called an "AND" circuit because it requires condition A and condition B to exist before declaring that an alarm should sound. If either the UV or the IR sensor could trigger an alarm, that would invoke an "OR" circuit.) An AND circuit makes the system subject to the combined limitations of both technologies.

Spark/Ember Detectors

Spark/ember detectors are primarily installed to detect sparks and embers that could, if allowed to continue to burn, precipitate a much larger fire or even an explosion. They are typically mounted on a duct or conveyor to monitor the fuel as it passes by. Usually it is necessary to enclose the portion of a conveyor where the spark/ember detectors are located, because they normally require a dark environment to operate properly.

Radiant energy from an ember is primarily of infrared and, to a lesser degree, visible wavelengths. In general, embers do not emit significant ultraviolet energy until their temperature reaches approximately 3240°F (1727°C).

Spark/ember detectors are often used to control in-duct fire-extinguishing systems for woodworking plant dust collectors or textile plant ventilation. For example, sawdust or textile fiber embers may be traveling past the unit at 328 ft/sec (100 m/sec), and their detection triggers a very brief burst from a downstream water spray nozzle. Typically, a subsequent detector further downstream verifies extinguishment and, if necessary, repeats the spray burst at another point in the duct. For applications such as this, spark/ember detectors are required to have a very fast response time.

Common sources of nuisance alarms include incident light, electrostatic discharge in the fuel stream, and electromagnetic interference (EMI/RFI).

VIDEO-BASED FLAME DETECTION

Operating Principles and Applications

Video-based flame detection operates in the visible light range and as with video-based smoke detection previously described uses video cameras. The images from one or more cameras are processed by computer software to look for and identify the characteristics of a flame. The cameras also provide a video image of the area to assist the operators in managing the emergency. The detectors/cameras are enclosed in explosionproof electrical enclosures. Since they view visible light, they are not affected by UV or IR sources and can be enclosed behind a glass or plastic view port. As with video-based smoke detectors, portions of the camera field of view can be masked to eliminate ambient sources of unwanted alarms. Commercially available models are capable of detecting a 10 kW flaming fire (one ft^2 [0.093 m^2] gasoline pan fire) at a distance of 65 ft (20 m) and can operate in temperatures ranging from –40°F (–40°C) to 158°F (70°C). Examples of applications of video-based flame detection include offshore petroleum facilities (e.g., platforms and vessels) and land-based petrochemical facilities (Figure 14.2.15).

Combination Video Technologies

The combination of smoke and flame video technologies is also being applied. As the software matures and field experience grows, the advantages of video camera technology will broaden their application.

SELECTION OF DETECTORS

When a fire detection system is being planned, the choice of detectors is critical for ensuring proper performance. Numerous factors must be considered in order to make the right choice. This is true whether the design is prescriptive (per a regulatory formula), is performance based (the usual case for flame or spark/ember detection systems), or uses some elements of both. Regardless of the design method, the following basic steps should normally be included in the selection of automatic fire detectors:

1. Determine the specific fire protection goals for the system, such as life safety, property protection, continuity of operations, and compliance with building codes, statutes, and criteria of the authority having jurisdiction (AHJ).

FIGURE 14.2.15 Video-Based Flame Detector (Source: Micropack Detection (Americas) Inc.)

2. Obtain stakeholder input to quantify these goals as explicitly as possible.
3. Develop general design objectives that outline how the preceding goals will be met.*
4. Evaluate the fire threat, including possible ignition sources, the type and quantity of fuels available, their expected growth rate, whether a fire suppression system is present, and so on. For example, very different threats would be posed by a petrochemical processing area, a hotel, and a woodworking shop.
5. Determine what fire signature(s) would be presented by potential fires at various points in their growth and what the area's normal ambient conditions would be (without fire present).
6. Weighing the foregoing factors, select fire detectors on the basis of their sensitivity to the fire signatures, response time (signal processing time), and relative immunity to false alarms in the anticipated ambient conditions (or their discrimination ability).

There is normally an inverse relationship between the sensitivity/speed of detection and the detector's ability to discriminate between fire and nonfire conditions. In general, heat detectors have the lowest false alarm rate but the slowest response time. Because the heat generated by small fires tends to dissipate fairly rapidly, heat detectors are best used to protect confined spaces or installed directly over hazards where flaming fires could be expected. They are typically installed in a grid pattern at their listed spacing or at reduced spacing for faster response. The operating temperature of a fixed temperature heat detector should be at least 25°F (14°C) above the maximum expected ambient temperature in the area protected. (For application information on rate-of-rise–type heat detectors, see previous comments in the corresponding portion of this chapter.)

Smoke detectors normally have much faster response times than heat detectors. The fire plume (buoyancy effects), air currents from HVAC, and diffusion may all be involved in transporting smoke. The response time advantage of smoke detectors becomes larger as the size of the space increases. Although frequently installed in a grid pattern, at a uniform recommended spacing, they are more properly located by considering the sources of potential fires and how the smoke would be transported. (For application information on the various types of smoke detectors, see previous comments in the corresponding portion of this chapter.)

Radiant energy–sensing detectors generally offer extremely fast response to any source of radiation within the spectrum they monitor. However, this can result in high false alarm rates if they are applied improperly. Since most are listed for NFPA 70, *National Electrical Code*®, Class I or II locations, they are well suited to protecting areas where potentially explosive or flammable vapors or dusts may be present. (For application information on the various types of radiant energy–sensing detectors, see previous comments in the corresponding portion of this chapter.)

*For performance-based design these design objectives are explicitly stated and quantified and then are used to develop specific performance criteria for the system, stated in fire protection engineering terms. See *NFPA 72*®, *National Fire Alarm Code*®, Annex B, for a more thorough description of the performance-based design process.

DETECTOR INSTALLATION

After selection of the most suitable detectors to use, the next step is to determine where to locate them within the space to be protected. Video-based smoke and flame detection offer distinct advantages in large open spaces. The potential to detect fires before the transport of smoke to a high ceiling and the ability to view and record the visual images of the area can provide additional benefits over spot-type or beam-type smoke detectors. Likewise the visual image provided with the video flame detectors provides an additional emergency management tool.

Detector Placement

Spot-type detectors are usually installed on the ceiling, not less than 4 in. (0.1 m) from the wall. If their listing permits, they are also permitted to be installed on the wall, with their highest edge no less than 4 in. (0.1 m) and no more than 12 in. (0.3 m) from the ceiling (Figure 14.2.16).

Where subject to mechanical damage, detectors must be protected. Any mechanical guard used with a smoke or heat detector must be listed for use with the detector. Otherwise, sensor performance may be degraded. Smoke detectors are often required to be set at higher sensitivity when used with plastic or perforated metal guards due to their effect on smoke entry. One manufacturer has a unique metal guard that looks like the series of smoke detectors it protects and that is engineered not to affect detector sensitivity.

Smoke detectors should not be installed in an air stream from an HVAC supply grill, because that will inhibit smoke from a fire in the protected space from reaching the detector. (The smoke detector would be bathed in a clean air stream when the HVAC supply fan is running.) This can also affect heat detector performance, usually to a lesser degree. Locations adjacent to a return air grill should also be avoided, because returns can affect air circulation patterns in the room so as to inhibit the detection of smoke from low-energy fires.

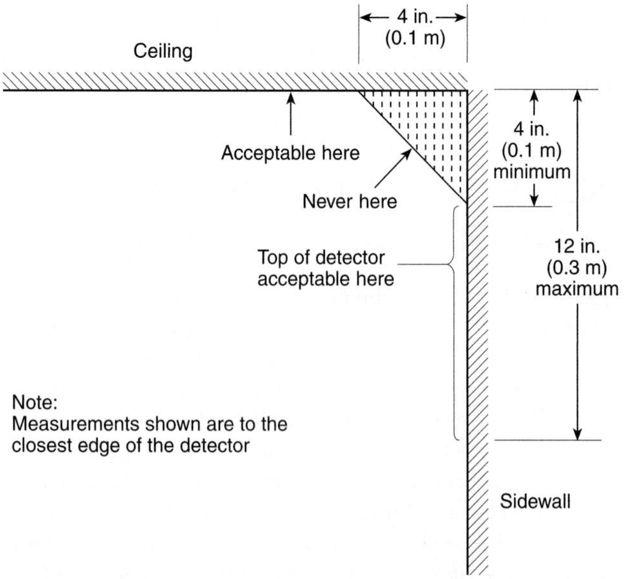

FIGURE 14.2.16 Mounting of Spot-Type Detectors

Where ceilings are high or ceiling construction is not smooth, the spacing of smoke or heat detectors should be reduced appropriately. Specific information on the treatment of joisted, beamed, and sloped ceilings can be found in *NFPA 72*.

When heat detectors are installed at their listed spacing, detection times will approximately equal the operating times of standard 165°F (74°C) sprinklers. If a faster response is desired, detector spacing should be reduced.

Spacing of Heat Detectors on High Ceilings

The hot air in a fire plume is diluted by entrainment with cooler air as it rises. Therefore, it had generally been assumed that heat detectors should be spaced more closely together on a high ceiling to achieve the same response time that they would provide on a standard 8 ft to 10 ft (2.5 to 3.0 m) high ceiling. To determine how much closer the detectors should be, a series of full-scale fire tests was funded by the Fire Detection Institute. These tests explored different ceiling heights in addition to several other design parameters. The data clearly showed that heat detectors must be spaced more closely together on a high ceiling to achieve the same response time that they would have on a 10 ft (3 m) ceiling (Table 14.2.1).[1]

Annex B of *NFPA 72* was developed from these tests and presents a performance-based design approach that can be used to determine the effect of changes in various design parameters on heat detectors in a flaming fire scenario only (plume-dependent response). The formulas it contains take into account the detector's listed spacing and temperature rating, the ceiling height, the design fire size, the fire growth rate, the normal ambient temperature, and the response time index (RTI) of the device. The thermal response characteristics of a heat detector describe how fast heat is transferred to the sensor. The plunge test used characterizes this as a response time index. The RTI allows the calculation of the time it takes for the heat-sensing element to reach its alarm threshold, based on the temperature and velocity of the fire plume or ceiling jet passing by the device.[2]

TABLE 14.2.1 Heat Detector Spacing Reduction Based on Ceiling Height

Ceiling Height Above		Up to and Including		*Multiply Listed Spacing By*
ft	*m*	*ft*	*m*	
0	0.00	10	3.05	1.00
10	3.05	12	3.66	0.91
12	3.66	14	4.27	0.84
14	4.27	16	4.88	0.77
16	4.88	18	5.49	0.71
18	5.49	20	6.10	0.64
20	6.10	22	6.71	0.58
22	6.71	24	7.32	0.52
24	7.32	26	7.93	0.46
26	7.93	28	8.54	0.40
28	8.54	30	9.14	0.34

The formulas can be used by entering a set of known values and design objectives and then calculating for one unknown, such as the required detector spacing in a given situation.

Spacing of Smoke Detectors

Nationally recognized testing laboratory approval (listing) tests for smoke detectors do not yield a listed spacing as they do for heat detectors. However, because the largest spacing evaluated in the fire test room used for these tests is 30 ft (9.1 m), manufacturers use that figure as the normal recommended spacing when smoke detectors are installed on a flat, smooth ceiling. Reductions in spacing may be required to address factors that can affect response, including ceiling height, beamed or joisted ceilings, and high rates of air movement (such as in a computer room). Room size, corridor width, and beam pocket size must also be considered. Calculations have demonstrated that in corridors and in small rooms, reduced spacing for nonsmooth ceilings may not be required.[3]

In design applications where predicting the response of smoke detectors is not critical, the prescriptive criteria in the body of *NFPA 72* should provide sufficient information to design a basic smoke detection system. The performance-based design methodology of Annex B can also be used for smoke detector design calculations. Again, this applies only to the flaming fire scenario, where fire plume and ceiling jet flows are major factors in smoke transport to the sensor. Thus, it cannot be used for low-energy (smoldering) fires. There are other limitations resulting from the fact that smoke detector response varies for different burning materials, and the properties of smoke itself change as it ages. These limitations will continue to affect the ability of fire protection engineers to more accurately predict smoke detector response until such time that testing laboratories are able to determine (and publish) meaningful performance metrics for all smoke detectors.

Special Applications

Duct smoke detectors are installed in the return and/or supply ducts of HVAC systems in buildings to prevent smoke from a fire being spread throughout the building by its recirculating HVAC system. Return duct smoke detectors, where required, are permitted to be replaced by total coverage smoke detection in the area served by the HVAC system or by spot-type smoke detectors located in each return air opening. Upon the detection of smoke, the HVAC system either shuts down or transitions to a smoke control mode such as 100 percent exhaust and/or 100 percent outside fresh air. The detection of duct smoke is made difficult by its dilution with return air from other spaces (away from the fire) and possibly with outside fresh air. Also, when the HVAC system fan is not running, smoke may not reach the duct detector. For these reasons, air duct smoke detectors must never be considered as a substitute for open area protection.

Smoke detectors are also used to initiate the closure of smoke doors in buildings to limit the spread of combustion products in the event of fire. This can be accomplished with detectors located near each controlled door or by door frame mounted hold-open devices with integral smoke detectors.

Smoke and/or heat detectors are often used for control of fire suppression systems such as gaseous (clean agent) and preaction or deluge sprinkler installations. The design of these special systems should be undertaken only by fire protection engineers or other qualified individuals.

DETECTOR MAINTENANCE AND TESTING

A systematic program of preventive maintenance and regular testing is essential to ensure the continuous, proper performance of detectors. Analog-addressable detectors have an inherent advantage in this regard due to their on-board diagnostics and constant reporting for each roll call. Whereas a nonaddressable detector could be dead for months and not found until the next scheduled test, failure of an analog-addressable detector would be known in seconds. However, it is still necessary to periodically inspect smoke detectors and test them with smoke or equivalent aerosol to ensure that their smoke entry remains unaffected by such possibilities as conduit stack effect, HVAC air streams (supply diffuser changes), or even the detector being painted, taped up, or bagged. (See Section 14, Chapter 5, "Inspection, Testing, and Maintenance of Fire Alarm Systems" and *NFPA 72* chapter on inspection, testing, and maintenance.)

SUMMARY

Automatic fire detectors are activated by environmental changes known as fire signatures, principally heat, smoke, and radiation. Various types of systems have been developed to detect these divergent fire signatures, including heat detectors, smoke detectors, gas-sensing fire detectors, and radiant energy–sensing fire detectors. The type of fire detection system installed depends on several factors, including reliability, sensitivity, and environmental characteristics. The detectors must be properly installed, positioned, maintained, and tested to ensure dependable fire protection.

BIBLIOGRAPHY

References Cited

1. Heskestad, B., and Delichatsios, M. A., "Environments of Fire-Detectors—Phase 1: Effect of Fire Size, Ceiling Height, and Material," *Measurements,* Vol. 1, (NBS-GCR-77-86), *Analysis,* Vol. II (NBS-GCR-77-95), National Technical Information Service, Springfield, VA, 1977.
2. Nam, S., "Predicting Response Time of Fixed-Temperature, Rate-of-Rise, and Rate-Compensated Heat Detectors by Utilizing Thermal Response Time Index," *Proceedings* of the Fire Suppression and Detection Research Application Symposium, February 1–3, 2006, Fire Protection Research Foundation, National Fire Protection Association, Quincy, MA, 2006, pp. 3–24.
3. O'Connor, D. J., "Smoke Detector Performance for Level Ceilings with Deep Beams and Deep Beam Pocket Configurations," *Proceedings* of the Fire Suppression and Detection Research Application Symposium, February 1–3, 2006, Fire Protection Research Foundation, National Fire Protection Association, Quincy, MA, 2006, pp. 25–30.

NFPA Codes, Standards, and Recommended Practices

Reference to the following NFPA codes, standards, and recommended practices will provide further information on automatic fire detectors discussed in this chapter. (See the latest version of The NFPA Catalog *for availability of current editions of the following document.)*

NFPA 72®, National Fire Alarm Code®

References

Anderson, D. D., "Fire Signatures Provided by Laser Technology Spot Smoke Detectors," NISTIR 5904, Annual Conference on Fire Research: Book of Abstracts, October 28–31, 1996, National Institute of Standards and Technology, Gaithersburg, MD, 1996, pp. 113–114.

Anderson, D. D., "Laser Spot Detector Technology for Early Warning of Smoke," *Proceedings* of the 11th International Conference on Automatic Fire Detection "AUBE '99," (Internationale Konferenz uber Automatischen Brandentdeckung), H. Luck (Ed.), March 16–18, 1999, Duisburg, Germany, 1999, pp. 447–457.

Cleary, T. G., Chernovsky, A., Grosshandler, W. L., and Anderson, M., "Particulate Entry Lag in Spot-Type Smoke Detectors," *Proceedings* of the 6th International Symposium, International Association for Fire Safety Science (IAFSS), M. Curtat (Ed.), July 5–9, 1999, Poitiers, France, Intl. Assoc. for Fire Safety Science, Boston, 2000, pp. 779–790.

Conforti, F., "Smoke Detection in Dusty, Dirty and Wet Environments," *Proceedings* of the Fire Suppression and Detection Research Application Symposium, Research and Practice: Bridging the Gap, February 24–26, 1999, National Fire Protection Research Foundation, Orlando, FL, 1999, pp. 165–170.

Davies, R., "Use of Multi-Sensor Detectors in Modern Fire Protection," *Fire Safety Engineering,* Vol. 7, No. 6, 2000, pp. 28–30.

Gagnon, R. M., and Mosman, T., "Smoke-Detection Evaluation in Enclosures with High-Velocity Airflow." *Fire Protection Engineering,* No. 8, Fall 2000, pp. 25, 28–30.

Gottuk, D., Rose-Pehrsson, S., Shaffer, R., and Williams, F., "Early Warning Fire Detection via Probabilistic Neural Networks and Multi-Sensor Arrays," *Proceedings* of the Fire Suppression and Detection Research Application Symposium Research and Practice: Bridging the Gap, February 23–25, 2000, Fire Protection Research Foundation, Orlando, FL, 2000, pp. 365–369.

Gottuk, D. T., and Williams, F. W., "Development of Multi-Signature Fire Detection Systems," NISTIR 6242, Annual Conference on Fire Research, *Book of Abstracts,* K. A. Beall (Ed.), November 2–5, 1998, National Institute of Standards and Technology, Gaithersburg, MD, Oct. 1998, pp. 7–00.

Hagen, B., and Milke, J. A., "Use of Gaseous Fire Signatures as a Mean to Detect Fires," *Fire Safety Journal,* Vol. 34, No. 1, 2000, pp. 55–67.

Peberdy, B., "Fire Detection in Cold Stores," *Fire Safety Engineering,* Vol. 7, No. 3, 2000, pp. 14–15.

Schifiliti, R. P., Meacham, B. J., and Custer, R. L. P., "Design of Detection Systems," *SFPE Handbook of Fire Protection Engineering,* National Fire Protection Association, Quincy, MA, 2001.

Shaffer, R. E., Rose-Pehrsson, S. L., Williams, F. W., Barry, C., and Gottuk, D. T., "Development of an Early Warning Multi-Criteria Fire Detection System: Analysis of Transient Fire Signatures Using a Probabilistic Neural Network," NRL/MR/6110-00-8429, Naval Research Laboratory, Washington, DC, Feb. 16, 2000.

Snegirev, A. Y., Makhviladze, G. M., and Roberts, J. P., "Effect of Particle Coagulation and Fractal Structure on the Optical Properties and Detection of Smoke," *Fire Safety Journal,* Vol. 36, No. 1, 2001, pp. 73–95.

Wong, J. T., Gottuk, D. T., Rose-Pehrsson, S. L., Shaffer, R. E., Hart, S., Tatem, P. A., and Williams, F. W., "Results of Multi-Criteria Fire Detection System Tests," NRL/MR/6180-00-8452, Naval Research Laboratory, Washington, DC, May 22, 2000.

Wright, M. T., Gottuk, D. T., Wong, J. T., Pham, H., Rose-Pehrsson, S. L., Hart, S. J., Hammond, M., Williams, F. W., Tatem, P. A., and Street, T. T., "Prototype Early Warning Fire Detection System: Test Series 2 Results, April 25–May 5, 2000," NRL/MR/6180-00-8506, Naval Research Laboratory, Washington, DC, Oct. 23, 2000.

Chapter 3

Notification Appliances

Robert P. Schifiliti

Key Terms

audible appliance, fire alarm system, household fire-warning equipment, notification appliance, temporal code-three signal, visible signal

Fire alarm systems and household fire-warning equipment protect life by automatically indicating the need for the occupants to evacuate or relocate to a safe area. They may also notify emergency forces or other responsible persons who may then assist the occupants or assist in controlling and extinguishing the fire. Emergency communication systems (ECS) and mass notification systems (MNS) are used to provide information to occupants of a building or area for a variety of threats and emergencies. Audible and visible notification appliances alert the occupants, and, in some cases, emergency forces, and convey information to them.

A fire alarm system that simply sounds an audible signal and flashes strobe lights in a space is conveying a single bit of information—fire alarm. Systems that send voice announcements or that use text or graphic annunciators typically convey multiple bits of information. They may signal a fire alarm or other threat and give a specific location and information on how and where to evacuate or relocate. As the cost of emergency voice/alarm systems (EVAC) comes down closer to conventional systems, they are being used more and more by designers. They are almost always required by codes in high-rise buildings but can also be effectively used in smaller buildings. When provided with detailed information about a fire or other emergency, people tend to evacuate or respond to the information more quickly and effectively than to alarms that merely produce an audible signal or flash. The audibility requirements for voice systems are the same as for conventional systems except that it is only an alert tone, not the actual voice that is measured for proper audibility. In addition to audibility, the intelligibility of the signal content becomes important.

Audible and visible appliances may also be used to indicate a trouble condition in the fire alarm system or they may be used as supervisory signals to indicate the condition or status of other protection systems, for example, automatic sprinklers.

For related topics see Section 12, Chapter 15, "Public Emergency Services Alarm, Dispatch, and Communications Systems"; Section 14, Chapter 1, "Fire Alarm Systems"; and Section 14, Chapter 5, "Inspection, Testing, and Maintenance of Fire Alarm Systems."

OPERATING MODES FOR NOTIFICATION APPLIANCES

There are two operating modes for alarm notification appliances: (1) public operating mode and (2) private operating mode. In the public operating mode, audible and visible signaling is intended for the occupants or inhabitants of the area protected by the fire alarm system, emergency voice/alarm systems (EVAC), emergency communication systems (ECS), or mass notification systems (MNS). In the private operating mode, audible and visible signaling is intended only for persons directly concerned with implementation and direction of emergency actions in the area protected by the system. For example, in a bank or shopping mall, the fire alarm is intended to alert all occupants and convey the need for them to evacuate. This scenario describes a public mode system. If an EVAC or ECS system is used, it may be used to convey information to all occupants or to some subset of the occupants, but would still be considered to be in the public mode. In a prison or

Robert P. Schifiliti, P.E., is president of R. P. Schifiliti Associates, Inc., a fire protection engineering and consulting firm located in Reading, Massachusetts. He chairs NFPA's Technical Correlating Committee on *Signaling Systems for the Protection of Life and Property* and is a member and past chair of the *NFPA 72*® Notification Appliances for Fire Alarm Systems Technical Committee. Mr. Schifiliti is the vice-chair of the NFPA Fire Protection Research Foundation's Detection and Alarm Research Council and chair of the Council's Research Planning Committee.

hospital, the system may be designed to notify only the trained staff. They will then initiate emergency procedures, including assisting occupants who might not otherwise be able to evacuate or relocate. This scenario describes a private mode system. Similarly, a supervisory signal at a guard's station indicating an off-normal status of a fire pump is considered to be private mode signaling.

The operating mode of the system affects the selection and placement of notification appliances. In general, the requirements for private mode signaling are less stringent, because they are intended for a professional staff that has been trained to look and listen for that signal and to immediately take certain actions when it is seen or heard.

AUDIBLE SIGNALING

Audible notification appliances are the most common method for signaling a fire alarm or other emergency condition in a building or area. There are two factors that affect the performance of audible notification systems. Here performance is defined as the ability to alert and convey information. The first is the rating of the audible appliance. Typically, audible appliances are rated by measuring the sound pressure level (SPL) at a fixed distance in a special room.

Rating of Audible Appliances

Without giving the exact mathematical definition, sound pressure level is a measurement of how loud something is. The measurement is expressed in decibels (dB). For almost all emergency alarm applications, the sound pressure level is expressed in dBA (i.e., decibels, A-weighted). A sound pressure level expressed in dBA has been adjusted to account for the way the human ear perceives different frequencies. Typically, high-pitched sounds (high frequency) are heard better than low frequency, bass, sounds. The A-weighting adjustment corrects for this so that the loudness of sounds that are composed of different frequencies can be compared.

Audible appliance ratings are usually stated as a certain sound pressure level (SPL) at a distance of 10 ft (3.05 m). This is a starting point for the design or analysis of audible signaling systems. Because the rating is measured in a room with certain reverberation characteristics, the actual performance will vary depending on the field conditions. In a room or hallway with concrete block walls, a sheetrock ceiling, and a tile floor, the actual SPL at 10 ft (3.05 m) will probably be greater than the rating of the audible appliance. However, in an acoustically soft situation, such as a room with wood walls, carpet on the floors, and an acoustical tile ceiling, the SPL may be less than the appliance's rating.

The second factor affecting the performance of audible notification systems is the net sound pressure level produced throughout all of the building or area served by the system. As one moves away from an audible appliance, the SPL decreases. As one gets closer, the SPL increases. In a wide-open space where the sound does not reflect off any surfaces (no reverberation), the SPL decreases by roughly 6 dB every time the distance from the source is doubled. This condition is called the free-field condition. An anechoic chamber, designed to absorb all sound waves, simulates a free-field condition. In almost all other situations there is some reverberation. Nevertheless, the 6 dB rule can be used when designing a system or analyzing the expected performance of a system. Note that dBA is used when expressing an absolute SPL that has been adjusted using the A-weighting scale. However differences are always expressed as dB.

For example, if an appliance has a rating of 90 dBA at 10 ft (3.05 m) and the distance is doubled to 20 ft (6.1 m), one would expect to measure an SPL of approximately 84 dBA (Figure 14.3.1). At a distance of 40 ft (12.2 m), one would expect an SPL of 78 dBA. At 80 ft (24.4 m), the SPL would be approximately 72 dBA.

When there are multiple audible appliances in a space, their combined SPL is greater than any one, but the individual SPLs are not simply added together to get the result. For example, consider two appliances rated 90 dBA at 10 ft (3.05 m) that are spaced 40 ft (12.2 m) apart. Alone, each unit would produce about 84 dBA (90 – 6) in the center (20 ft [6.1 m] from each). With both units operating, a measurement taken between the two at 20 ft (6.1 m) from each would be about 87 dBA (3 dB greater than a single unit). Fire alarm designers usually ignore this effect so that their designs are conservative.

This type of analysis works well in open spaces. However, sound loss through walls and doors requires more complex calculation methods. Of course, in an existing building a temporary audible appliance can be used to study sound transmission and attenuation throughout the space and through the walls and doors. By measuring sound loss from one side of a door/wall assembly, designers can obtain representative values for a structure to be used in later design and analysis of the fire alerting system. The *SFPE Handbook of Fire Protection Engineering*[1] contains calculation methods that can be used in design and analysis of audible alerting systems.

Fire Alarm Audibility Design Goals

How loud should an alerting system be? Obviously, the audible signals must be louder than the ambient noise in a space. So, the first step is to measure the ambient noise. When designing new systems, tables of ambient noise levels may be used as an estimate. Annex A of *NFPA 72®, National Fire Alarm Code®*, contains such a table. Two different ambient noise levels are required to complete a system design: (1) the average SPL dur-

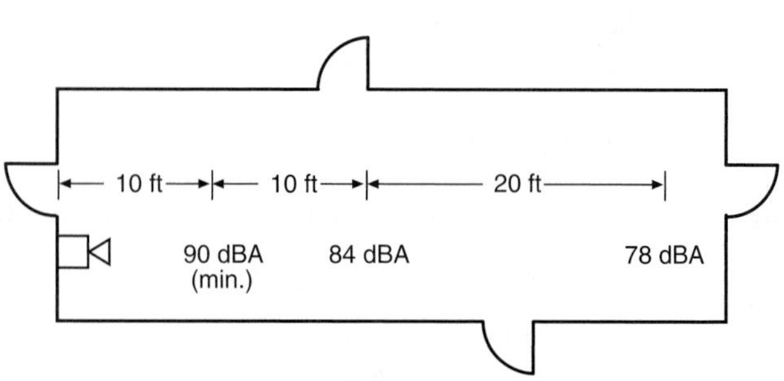

FIGURE 14.3.1 Example of 6 dBA Rule (1 ft = 0.305 m)

ing the time the area is occupied, and (2) the maximum SPL that lasts 60 seconds or more.

Fire alarm audibility goals are dependent on the mode of operation. In the public operating mode, the fire alarm system must produce a sound pressure level that is 5 dB above any ambient noise that lasts 60 seconds or more, or 15 dB above the 24 hour average, whichever is greater. In the private operating mode, the fire alarm system must produce a sound pressure level that is 5 dB above any ambient noise that lasts 60 seconds or more, or 10 dB above the average, whichever is greater. In either case, if the area will be used for sleeping, the minimum SPL required of the fire alarm system is 75 dBA. When designing an EVAC or MNS system, the same goals should be used for the audibility of the system's alert tone.

A fire alarm or other emergency tone signal may have the same SPL or less, measured in dBA, than the ambient noise and still be clearly heard. This occurs when the two signals (ambient and alarm) operate at different frequencies. In high noise occupancies such as manufacturing plants, it might be more effective to conduct a frequency analysis of the ambient noise and then design a fire alarm signal at frequency bands not occupied by noise. See Figure 14.3.2 for an example. The figure shows a one-third octave band analysis of noise and an alarm signal in a compressor room. The loudness of each frequency band is measured in dB (*Y* axis). The *X* axis shows the center frequency for each band measured in Hertz (Hz = cycles per second). The frequency bands range from low, bass-level frequencies on the left through midrange tones and up through very high-frequency tones. (Middle C on a piano is approximately 262 Hz.) On the far right, L_P represents the logarithmic sum of all the frequency bands while L_A is the logarithmic sum adjusted using the A-weighting scale to correct for how the human ear hears different frequencies. The noise can be thought of as a picket fence. To hear a fire alarm signal above the background noise, it does not have to be louder than all the component frequencies added together; it just has to be louder than one. As long as one of the alarm signal's frequency bands (pickets) is taller than the corresponding noise picket, you will hear the signal, even if the total broadband sound pressure level of the noise is greater than the total broadband sound pressure level of the signal. Consult *NFPA 72,* ISO, or an audio design text for more information.

Because building codes require residential and other sleeping-type occupancies to have a minimum degree of soundproofing, they represent the most challenging scenarios for fire alarm system design. Given the high SPL that must be achieved to alert a sleeping person, it has been shown that audible appliances are almost always needed in each sleeping room.[1] In other occupancies, such as offices and schools, it may be sufficient to place audible appliances in the corridors only. In any case, careful design is needed to ensure that audibility requirements are met.

Audibility Requirements. Once the system is installed, a complete test, including SPL measurements, must be done to prove that the system meets the signaling requirements. Various types of sound level meters are available for use in testing system audibility. Some are very expensive and have many features for special system analysis, and others are very inexpensive, yet serve the purpose. It is important that the meter have an A-weighting scale for measurement of the ambient and fire alarm SPLs.

In addition to the minimum sound pressure levels that a fire alarm must produce, there is a maximum allowable SPL of 100 dBA. This is below the threshold of pain, which occurs at about 130 dBA, and is intended to reduce the chances of damaging someone's hearing. It is possible to achieve fire alarm audibility requirements by using a few very loud appliances or a larger

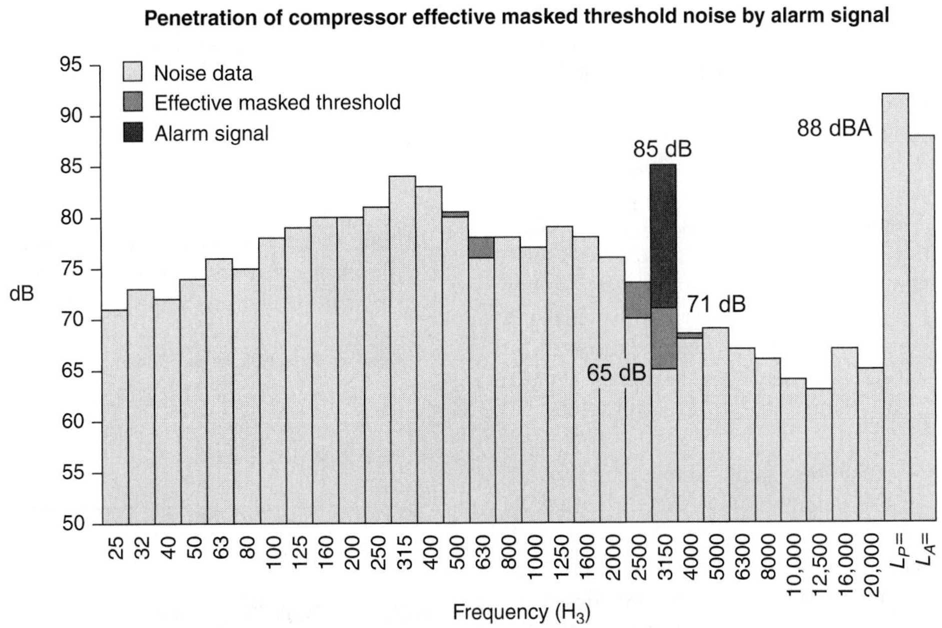

FIGURE 14.3.2 One-Third Octave Band Analysis

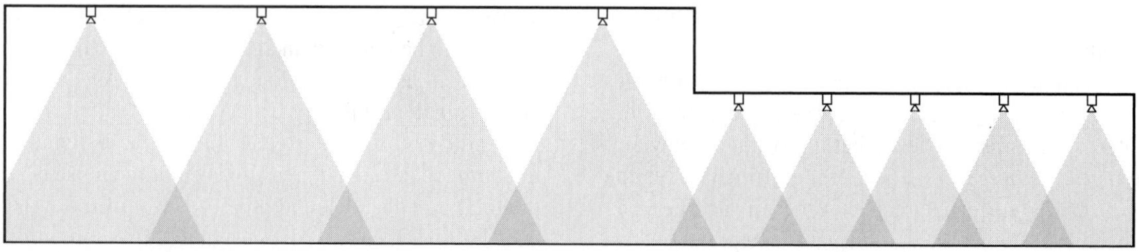

FIGURE 14.3.3 Spacing Between Textual Audible Appliances for Direct Field Coverage

number of units at a lower SPL rating. In general, system reliability is better with a larger number of lower SPL units. Also, the cost may be lower using a larger number of lower SPL units.

Intelligibility Requirements. If the system is being designed to transmit voice messages, the design should use a larger number of low-power units so that the voice message is intelligible. If only a few high-power speakers are used, reverberation or echoes of the sound may make it difficult to understand the message.

For voice communication, a sufficient audible level does not guarantee that the message will be intelligible. There are many factors affecting speech intelligibility in addition to the audible level. Some of the factors are a part of the audio system design and installation; others are a part of the architectural/acoustical environment. In addition, the talker and the listener are also a part of intelligibility, although they are generally taken to be "average" or slightly below "average."

For systems used to reproduce voice, specifying a louder system may result in degradation of the intelligibility of the message. One of the basic concepts in the design of intelligible voice systems is to have all listeners in the direct field of a single speaker, and to avoid having the system so loud that sound reverberates from other locations to the listener. If a person is in the direct field of two speakers, the sound from the farther one arrives some time after the sound from the closer speaker. The same effect occurs when the sound bounces off a wall and comes back to the listener (reverberation). The degree of impact on intelligibility depends on the time difference between the first arrival of the word or sound and the arrival from the second source. Distributing the speakers to reduce or eliminate the overlap of the direct field sound is the best design practice. Though at first counterintuitive to many fire alarm system designers, the lower ceiling height requires a smaller spacing between the speakers (see Figure 14.3.3). For additional information about the factors affecting speech intelligibility and their effects on system design, consult *NFPA 72* and "Understanding Speech Intelligibility and the Fire Alarm Code," by Kenneth Jacob.[2]

Audible Emergency Evacuation Signal. *NFPA 72* requires all audible evacuation signals to comply with ANSI S3.41, *Audible Emergency Evacuation Signal.*[3] (Note: *NFPA 72* does not itself require existing systems to comply with current requirements.) That signal is commonly referred to as a temporal code-three signal. The pattern consists of an "on" phase (a) lasting 0.5 seconds ± 10 percent, followed by an "off" phase (b) lasting 0.5 seconds ± 10 percent, for three successive "on" periods, which is then followed by an "off" phase (c) lasting 1.5 seconds ± 10 percent. The signal should be repeated for a period appropriate for the building, but not less than 180 seconds. A single-stroke bell or chime sounded at "on" intervals lasting 1 second ± 10 percent, with a 2 seconds ± 10 percent "off" interval after each third "on" stroke, is acceptable (Figures 14.3.4, 14.3.5, and 14.3.6.). The

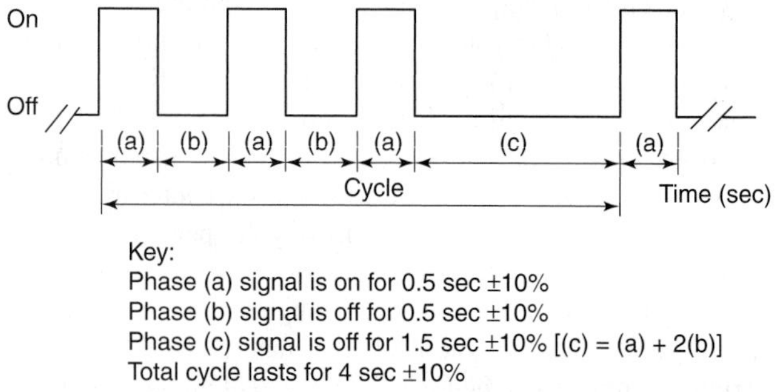

FIGURE 14.3.4 Temporal Pattern Parameters (Source: *NFPA 72®, National Fire Alarm Code®*, Figure A.6.8.6.5.1(a), 2007, p. 72-150)

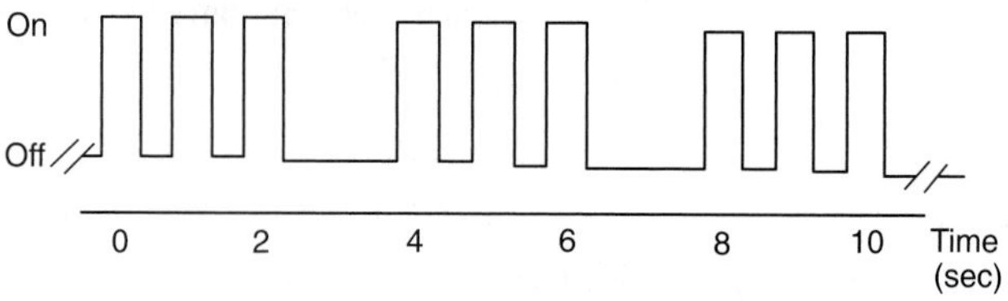

FIGURE 14.3.5 Temporal Pattern Imposed on Audible Notification Appliances That Otherwise Emit a Continuous Signal While Energized (Source: *NFPA 72®, National Fire Alarm Code®*, Figure A.6.8.6.5.1(b), 2007, p. 72-150)

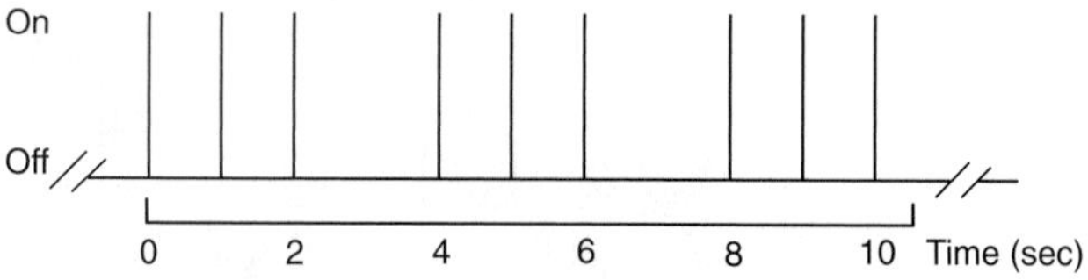

FIGURE 14.3.6 Temporal Pattern Imposed on a Single-Stroke Bell or Chime (Source: *NFPA 72®, National Fire Alarm Code®*, Figure A.6.8.6.5.1(c), 2007, p. 72-150)

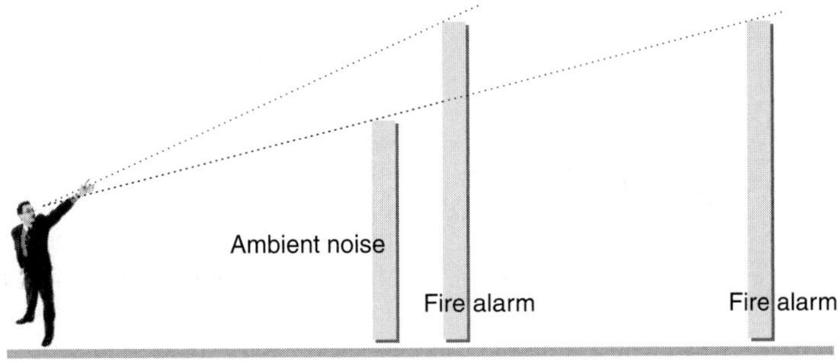

FIGURE 14.3.7 Effect of Ambient Noise on Ability to Perceive an Alarm

type of signal is not important; it may be a bell, horn, chime, whoop, or any other sound, provided it is not used for any purpose other than fire alarm. The intent is that the pattern of the sound will be standard from system to system. Systems intended to relocate people or to simply alert them of a nonfire emergency must not use the standard evacuation signal.

Importance of Location

The farther your ear or sound meter is from a sound source, the less loud it will be. Basic design practice is to analyze or estimate the ambient noise and then select and place alarm appliances to overcome that background noise. The picket fence analogy is useful here again (Figures 14.3.7 and 14.3.8). It is possible to hide a larger object that is farther away with a smaller object close by. Similarly, when you are at a certain location and the noise is at a certain level, there is a distance at which an alarm signal will be clearly heard, and there is a distance at which it will not be heard. Also, for set levels of noise and alarm and for set distance between their sources, there is a point where you can be so close to the noise that it will mask the alarm, as shown in Figure 14.3.8.

VISIBLE SIGNALING

Visible fire alarm notification appliances are often intended only to augment audible appliances. However, when it is expected that hearing-impaired persons may be in the protected area or when ambient noise levels are high, visible appliances may be the primary means of occupant notification that a fire emergency exists. Increasingly, visible appliances are being used as an integral part of occupant notification systems. For MNS or EVAC systems, simple visible appliances, such as strobes, are used to signal the need to "get additional information." Other types of visible appliances, such as scrolling signs, annunciators, and displays may be used to convey visible information during an emergency.

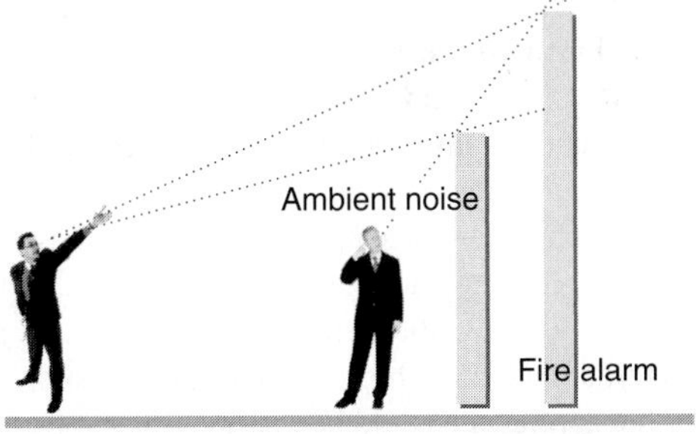

FIGURE 14.3.8 Effect of Proximity on Ability to Perceive an Alarm

Building codes, NFPA *101*®, *Life Safety Code*®, and *NFPA 72,* as well as state and federal laws, all contain requirements for the use of visible notification appliances under certain circumstances. At present, only the use of strobe lights is addressed by *NFPA 72.* Other appliances and systems, such as revolving beacons or the flashing of building lights, have also been shown to be effective under certain circumstances. However, requirements necessary to ensure their availability and effectiveness are not addressed by the code at this time.

Factors Affecting Performance of Visible Appliances

Visual signaling and notification using strobe lights involve a large number of complex variables. For this reason, *NFPA 72* uses prescriptive code language to provide simple, preengineered solutions. As with audible appliances, *NFPA 72* addresses two factors affecting the performance of visible notification appliances: (1) source intensity and (2) illumination at some distance from the source.

Source intensity is a measure of the light output of the appliance. The unit of measure is the candela (cd). (This unit was formerly called "candlepower." There is a one-to-one relationship between candela and candlepower.) As one moves away from any light source, the illumination it provides decreases. Illumination is measured in units of lumens (lm) per ft^2, or lumens per m^2 (also called "lux"). Formerly, the unit used to describe illumination was the "footcandle." One footcandle equals one lumen per ft^2. One lumen per m^2 equals 0.926 footcandles. Figure 14.3.9 shows the relationship between source intensity and illumination.

The inverse square law is used to determine the illumination, *E,* at some distance, *d,* from a source of intensity, *I* (i.e., $E = I/d^2$).

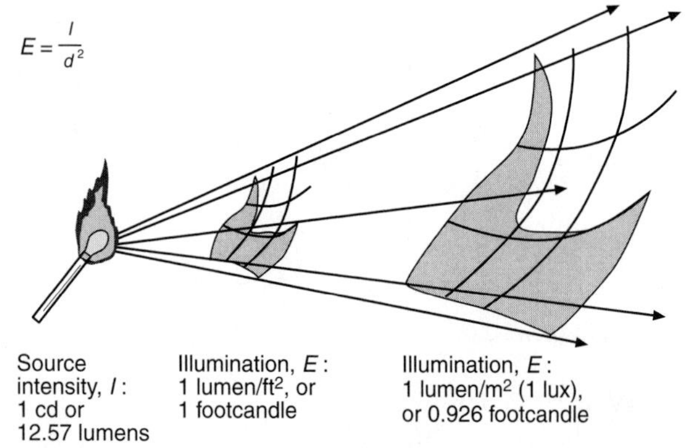

FIGURE 14.3.9 Visible Intensity Versus Illumination

Because strobe lights flash for a very brief period of time, the perceived brightness can vary depending on the actual peak source strength and duration of the flash (Figure 14.3.10). One appliance might reach a peak intensity of 1000 candelas in 0.1 second, while another might reach 750 candelas in 0.2 second. Nevertheless, the human eye might perceive both as being equally bright. A complex mathematical relationship is used to relate the perceived brightness of a strobe light to that of a constantly burning light. The result is called the "effective intensity" (candela effective [cd eff]).

The design of visible notification systems involves many additional factors beyond those discussed herein. Many other factors, such as how much light is absorbed versus how much is reflected by a surface, the angle that the light strikes a surface, and the color of the surface, affect the performance of the notification system. For instance, as light strikes a surface at some angle, only a portion of that light is reflected back to the human eye. The term used to describe the reflected light is "luminance." Thus, a certain intensity appliance produces a certain illumination at some distance on a surface, but a person looking at that surface sees a certain luminance.

To simplify the process of designing and evaluating visible notification systems, *NFPA 72* contains prescriptive requirements for the intensity and spacing of visible appliances that are sufficient in almost all applications to alert persons. In essence, *NFPA 72* provides preset designs that can be used for a variety of actual field conditions.

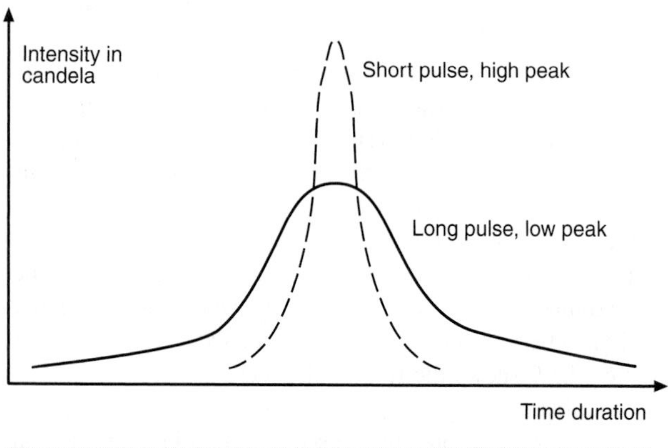

FIGURE 14.3.10 Visible Peak Versus Effective Intensity

The prescriptive requirements contained in *NFPA 72* are based, in part, on tests performed by Underwriters Laboratories Inc. (UL).[4] The tests were conducted in real classrooms and test facilities with similar size characteristics. Use of *NFPA 72* methods for larger spaces may not be valid. For example, in large stores or warehouses, it is not known if these methods will be conservative or ineffective.

Fire Alarm Visibility Design Goals

NFPA 72 contains tables listing the minimum intensity strobe required in certain size rooms to alert the occupants. For instance, a single 15 cd eff strobe can be used when centered on one wall of a 20 ft × 20 ft (6.1 m × 6.1 m) room. There are also listings for use of multiple units in a single room. Using the 20 ft × 20 ft (6.1 m × 6.1 m) room as an example, the illumination on the opposite wall would be $15/20^2 = 0.0375$ lumens per ft^2. *NFPA 72* permits a performance-based design approach using this level of illumination as the requirement. See *NFPA 72* and the *SFPE Handbook of Fire Protection Engineering* for examples.

Occupancies where hearing-impaired persons may sleep must have higher strobe intensities than for nonsleeping areas to ensure that the hearing-impaired person can be awakened. A 110 cd eff strobe no more than 16 ft (4.9 m) from the pillow was sufficient to awaken hearing-impaired persons. Other methods, such as bed shakers or fans, may be used to supplement visible signaling. In practice, a bedroom strobe light is often combined with a smoke detector. In that case, the strobe light must have an even higher intensity (177 cd eff) to overcome potential obscuration by a smoke layer at the ceiling.

Some spaces, such as corridors, can be treated differently from those rooms where a person may have his or her face turned away from a strobe light. In corridors, a person's view path is more concentrated, and the person is usually moving. Recognizing this, *NFPA 72* allows the use of 15 cd eff strobes at longer distances than what would be required for rooms. The luminous intensity required is actually less, given that a person is likely to directly see the appliance or to see more surfaces illuminated by the strobe.

When designing the audible part of an occupant-notification system, it is best to use a greater number of lower-power SPL units. The opposite is true for visible appliances. The use of a lower number of higher-intensity units will usually be more cost-effective. Furthermore, with fewer appliances, the distance between them is greater, and the chances of a person directly viewing more than two units at a time is reduced or eliminated. That, in turn, reduces the likelihood of triggering a seizure in a person who has photosensitive epilepsy.

When choosing and placing visible appliances, every effort should be made to place the unit in the concentrated viewing path of the target audience. For example, in a meeting room or classroom, the appliance should be on the wall that the majority of people face. This, however, is not a requirement of the code, since the entire methodology for signaling in rooms is based on having sufficient illumination for indirect alerting. Furthermore, a mounting height of 6.5 to 8 ft (2.03 to 2.44 m) ensures that the visible appliance is unlikely to be blocked by common furnishings.

In spaces such as large auditoriums the use of high-intensity indirect signaling may be warranted. This method of indirect signaling uses much higher-intensity strobes that must be located so that they cannot be directly viewed by the human eye (they could temporarily or permanently impair vision). The light from the strobes is used to illuminate large areas of walls and ceilings. The UL research used indirect illumination. However, the illumination was on a wall in front of the test subjects, and the maximum intensity was low enough to allow direct viewing of the appliance's element. Another possible method of visible signaling in such high-challenge spaces is to flash some or all of the building lights. Although these methods may prove effective, at this time there are few test data to support specific performance requirements for these notification methods. It should be noted that the authority having jurisdiction (AHJ) must approve any type of alternate arrangement that is not directly covered by code requirements.

In the past, guidelines for meeting the visible signaling requirements of the Americans with Disabilities Act (ADA)[5] have cited strobe intensities and distances different from those specified in *NFPA 72.* However, through a process called "equivalent facilitation," the requirements of *NFPA 72* have been shown to meet or exceed the original ADA "Accessibility Guidelines" (ADAAG). The ADAAG have been revised to follow *NFPA 72* requirements.

Visible Signaling in Warehouse Stores

In large warehouse spaces and large distribution spaces such as superstores, it is possible to provide visible signaling using strobe appliances. However, mounting strobe lights at a height of 2.0 to 2.4 m (80 to 96 in.) along aisles with rack storage subjects the lights to frequent mechanical damage by forklift trucks and stock.

Tests of systems in large warehouse/superstores designed using ceiling-mounted strobes, and the prescriptive approach of *NFPA 72*, showed that the systems worked because of both indirect and direct signaling effects.[6] The signal-to-noise ratio produced by the operating strobes was low in many locations due to high ambient light. However, with strobes located over the aisles or unobstructed by stock, indirect and some direct notification was sometimes achieved. Direct notification can occur even when occupants do not look up toward the ceiling-mounted strobes due to the extended cone of vision shown in Figure 14.3.11.

Tests showed that the strobe intensity and spacing resulting from the prescriptive design were generally sufficient for occupant notification by a combination of direct and indirect signaling. The best performance was achieved where strobes were directly over aisles or where strobes in adjacent aisles were not obstructed by stock. The performance-based design method will almost always result in aisles not having a line of strobes in them, since the spacing of strobes can be greater than the spacing of aisles. Also, it is recognized that aisles may be relocated after installation of the system. Good design practice is to place strobes over aisles, especially those that are likely to remain unchanged such as main aisles and over checkout areas. Where reorganization of aisles results in strobes not in or over an aisle, or where that is the base design, it is important to have a clear view from that aisle to a nearby strobe (Figure 14.3.12). Some spaces may have marginal strobe effect (direct or indirect). However, occupants in these large stores and storage occupancies move frequently and place themselves in a position where they receive notification via the strobes.

COMBINATION AUDIBLE/VISIBLE UNITS

To meet the requirements of ANSI S3.41, *Audible Emergency Evacuation Signal,*[3] some systems will require separate circuits for audible and visible appliances. Some combination audible/visible appliances may be available that can be installed on a common circuit. In any case, it will be important to size the circuit to handle the expected load. Greatest flexibility is obtained by putting fewer than the maximum number of units on a circuit when the system is first designed or installed. In this way, if the acceptance test shows deficiencies in some areas, additional units can be added without overloading the circuits or the system.

Most codes do not require audible and visible appliances to be on separately controlled circuits. However, if they are, the audible circuits can be silenced after a building has been completely evacuated, and the visible appliances can be left

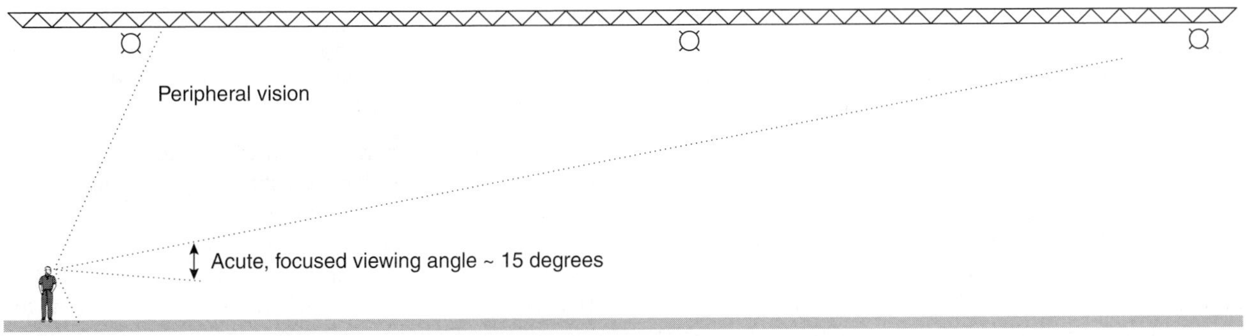

FIGURE 14.3.11 Occupant Perception of Notification Through Extended Cone of Vision

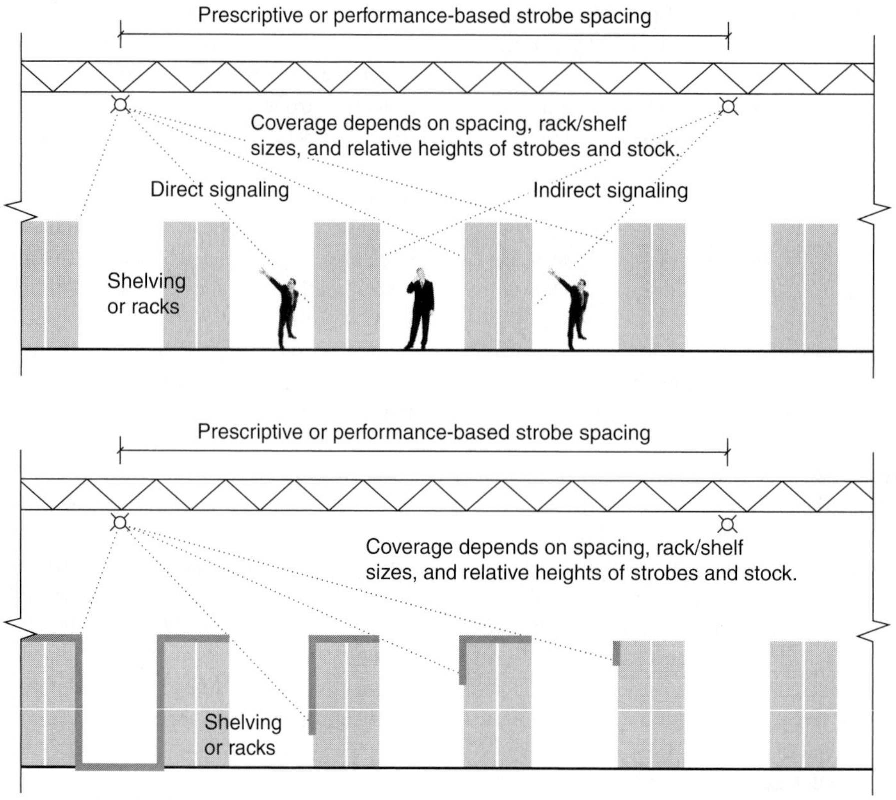

FIGURE 14.3.12 View of Strobe from Aisle

in operation. This is a way of telling people not to reenter the building or space. Similarly, good design practice is to include an audible and a visible appliance on the outside of the building to assist arriving fire fighters in locating the building or building entrance. Placing appliances on each side of a building or at each entrance also helps inform persons that they should not enter the building or space.

When designing or installing occupant notification systems utilizing both audible and visible appliances, it is best to determine the locations of the visible units first. This is because their location is more dependent on viewing angles, intersections of corridors, and blockage by furnishings. Once the visible appliances have been placed, audible appliances can be located so that some or all of the units can be combination audible and visible appliances. The use of combination units may reduce installation costs slightly. Figure 14.3.13 shows examples of both visible and combination audible/visible notification appliances.

FIGURE 14.3.13 Typical Visible and Combination Audible/Visible Notification Appliances (Source: Gentex Corp.)

SUMMARY

Audible and visible notification appliances are used to alert occupants of a building that they need to evacuate or relocate to a safe area. In addition, they may alert emergency personnel or indicate a problem in the fire alarm system or other protection system, such as automatic sprinklers. When used in the public operating mode, the notification appliance will alert the occupants of an area, such as a shopping mall, that they need to evacuate. In the private operating mode, the notification appliance is intended for trained staff responsible for undertaking emergency actions in locations such as hospitals or prisons.

Audible notification appliances are the type most commonly implemented, and their placement, decibel setting, frequency, and length of signal are calculated according to numerous factors, including the physical parameters of the area being protected. Visible notification appliances are usually used to supplement the audible alarm system, but in certain cases (such as loud ambient noise) they may be the primary alarm system. As with audible systems, the design of visual notification appliances must use many calculations based on a variety of factors, including the physical properties of light.

BIBLIOGRAPHY

References Cited

1. Schifiliti, R. P., Meacham, B. J., and Custer, R. L. P., "Design of Detection Systems," *SFPE Handbook of Fire Protection Engineeringw,* 3rd ed., P. J. DiNenno et al. (Eds.), National Fire Protection Association, Quincy, MA, 2002.
2. Jacob, K., "Understanding Speech Intelligibility and the Fire Alarm Code," Bose Professional Systems, May 2001, http://www.rpsa-fire.com.
3. ANSI S3.41, *Audible Emergency Evacuation Signal,* American National Standards Institute, New York, 1990.
4. "Report of Research on Emergency Signaling Devices for Use by the Hearing Impaired," Underwriters Laboratories Inc., Northbrook, IL, Mar. 1991.
5. Americans with Disabilities Act, Public Law 101–336, Title III, Rule 36, Appendix A, "Accessibility Guidelines," 1990.
6. Schifiliti, R. P., *Direct Visual Signaling as a Means for Occupant Notification in Large Spaces,* Fire Protection Research Foundation, National Fire Protection Association, Quincy, MA, Mar./Apr. 2006.

NFPA Codes, Standards, and Recommended Practices

Reference to the following NFPA codes, standards, and recommended practices will provide further information on notification appliances discussed in this chapter. (See the latest version of The NFPA Catalog *for availability of current editions of the following documents.)*

NFPA 72®, National Fire Alarm Code®
NFPA *101®*, *Life Safety Code®*

Chapter 4

Fire Alarm System Interconnections

Fred Leber

Chapter Contents

Key Terms

automatic sprinkler system, building automation system, fire alarm control unit, fire alarm system, interconnection, protected premises, waterflow alarm

Many fire protection systems, fire safety control functions, process monitoring systems, and building operation and control systems can contribute to life safety in a building. A significant benefit can be obtained if these systems are interfaced with the building fire alarm system. *NFPA 72®*, *National Fire Alarm Code®*, requires that all fire protection systems in a protected property be connected to the protected premises (local) fire alarm system. Many interface strategies are now also required by building codes and (other) relevant standards.

The integration of commercial fire and nonfire protection systems has existed for many years. In addition to the benefits to life safety, the combination of systems was an attempt to conserve valuable construction dollars through systems integration. In other cases, systems integration was seen as a necessity for ease of building management—for example, combination security/access control and fire alarm systems or building automation and fire alarm systems.

There are some commercially available combination systems that are tested, listed, and manufactured to serve as combination systems. However, many systems provide some form of protection or management of a building, such as elevator control, door control, and heating, ventilating, and air-conditioning (HVAC) control, which can benefit by being integrated or interfaced with the fire alarm system. These systems are not necessarily manufactured, tested, or listed as a single integrated system. Their interface with fire protection systems will be presented in this chapter.

See also Section 2, Chapter 6, "Fundamentals of Fire Detection"; Section 14, Chapter 1, "Fire Alarm Systems"; Section 14, Chapter 10, "Security and Intrusion Detection Systems"; and Section 16, Chapter 3, "Automatic Sprinkler Systems."

AUTOMATIC SPRINKLER SYSTEMS

The fire protection system that will provide the most obvious benefit by interfacing to a fire alarm system is the automatic sprinkler system, which can be monitored both for waterflow alarms and for disablement of system components or water supply. Fire and building codes as well as other relevant standards identify the specific system functions that must initiate alarm and supervisory signals. In addition, "good engineering practice" may conclude that certain functions or devices should be supervised.

The value of installing an automatic sprinkler system for life safety and property protection has been well documented over many years of service in a variety of specific applications. It is obviously necessary to ensure that the automatic sprinkler system is maintained in such a condition that it is always ready to discharge water on a hostile fire, holding the fire to its area of origin, and helping to control smoke development.

One way of making certain that an automatic sprinkler system remains fully in service is to supervise its operational features as well as the availability of water supplies. At the same time, it is necessary to initiate an alarm signal whenever the sprinkler system does operate so that personnel

A. M. (Fred) Leber is CEO of Leber/Rubes, Inc., a fire protection and building code consulting engineering firm in Toronto. A member of the NFPA Standards Council and a fellow of the Society of Fire Protection Engineers, he is chair of Subcommittee 2 of Underwriters Laboratories of Canada. Mr. Leber also chairs two ISO committees.

may respond promptly and take whatever action is needed. Thus, these two functions—waterflow alarm and automatic sprinkler system supervision—are vital elements of an overall fire protection program.

AUTOMATIC SPRINKLER SYSTEM WATERFLOW ALARMS

Notification Functions

Notification of a waterflow alarm may be as simple as a hydraulically operated water motor gong serving a single sprinkler riser (see Section 16) or as complex as a multiplex proprietary fire alarm system monitoring several hundred sprinkler risers at a very large industrial facility. In either case, there are certain basic functions that must be provided by whatever waterflow alarm equipment is installed, including the following:

1. The prompt detection of the discharge of a certain number of gallons per minute (L/min) at nominal pressure that would be equivalent to the amount of water discharged from a single operating sprinkler having the smallest orifice of those sprinklers installed in that particular system
2. The reliable operation of a suitable audible alarm notification appliance; the exact nature of the particular appliance will depend on the purpose of the specific waterflow alarm system
3. The provision of suitable facilities to test the operation of the waterflow alarm device, preferably by an actual flow of water equivalent to the discharge from a single automatic sprinkler having the smallest orifice of those sprinklers installed in the system

Notification of waterflow alarms can be categorized according to their purpose and according to their method of operation. For example, the notification of a waterflow may be an alarm signal to alert someone either outside the building or in the immediate area protected by the sprinkler system riser. Such a signal would normally be produced by the operation of either a hydraulically operated or electrically operated bell. The waterflow alarm system also may be installed to provide an alarm signal that will sound throughout the protected building. This will normally be achieved by connecting the waterflow alarm initiating device to a protected premises (local) fire alarm system.

The waterflow alarm signal may transmit the signal off-premises to a constantly attended location by means of a signaling system for central station service, an auxiliary fire alarm system, or a remote station fire alarm system. The waterflow alarm signal may provide a signal that will be transmitted to a constantly attended location on the protected premises or to another location of the same owner. This will normally be accomplished by connecting the waterflow alarm initiating device to a proprietary fire alarm system.

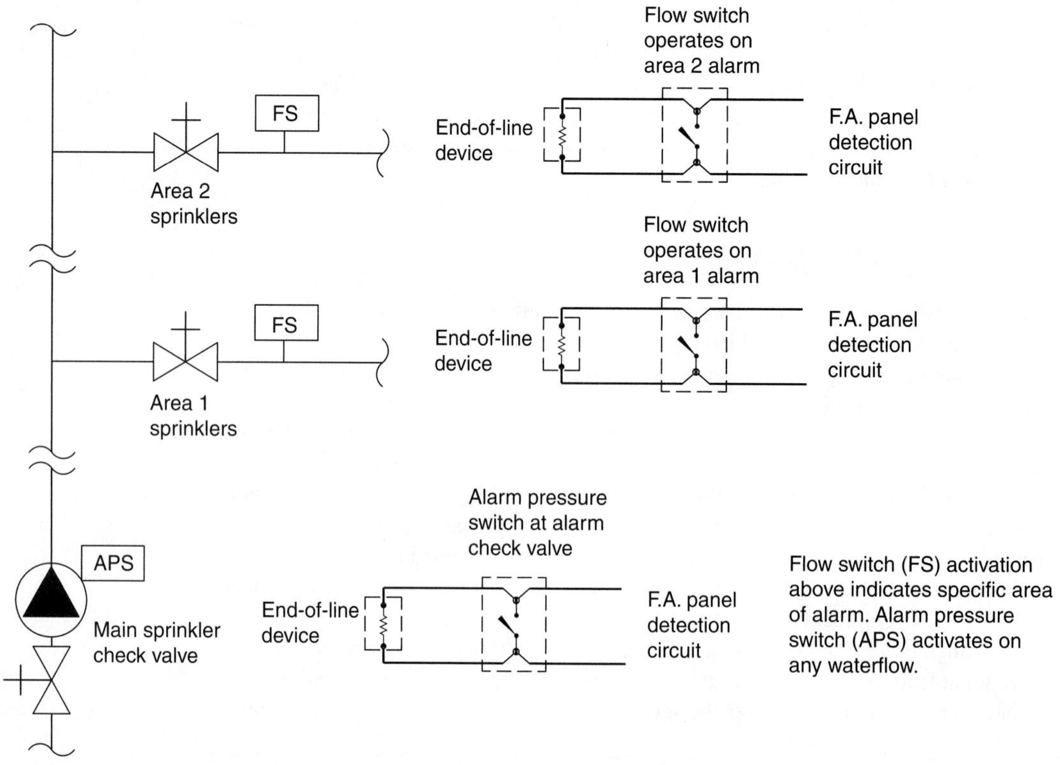

FIGURE 14.4.1 Alarm Pressure Switch Connection

Electrically Operated Waterflow Alarms

Waterflow alarms may be signaled using electrically operated fire alarm notification appliances, such as vibrating bells, horns, sirens, chimes, and several varieties of flashing lights. Such signals usually are initiated by electrical switches incorporated into some type of pressure- or flow-operated device.

Waterflow Alarms for Wet Pipe Automatic Sprinkler Systems

For wet pipe automatic sprinkler systems, the flow of water is generally detected hydraulically by an alarm check valve or by a vane-type waterflow alarm initiating device. The alarm check valve and waterflow alarm initiating device cause an electrical contact closure when waterflow is detected. This contact is connected to the fire alarm system. Either of these would be installed at the point the water supply piping enters the building from the underground. Supplementary vane-type devices could also be installed at various points in the piping system, for example, on each floor of a high-rise building. This allows a more precise determination of the location where water is flowing and subsequently aids in obtaining a timely response to the emergency.

Alarm Check Valves

Depending on the specific design, alarm check valves are generally referred to as being either "plain type" or "differential type." (See Section 16, Chapter 3, "Automatic Sprinkler Systems," for more information on alarm check valves.) The basic design of most alarm check valves incorporates a clapper that lifts from its seat when water is discharged from sprinkler system piping above the valve. The movement of the clapper is used to allow waterflow into an "alarm port." This port can be connected to electrical or mechanical devices that initiate an alarm at the fire alarm system. Since the clapper may be subject to movement as a result of sudden changes in water pressure, a retard mechanism is installed that takes up the water surge and prevents clapper movement and subsequent false alarms.

Pressure-Operated Switch Waterflow Alarm Initiating Devices

A pressure-operated switch could be mounted on a fitting connected to the alarm port of the alarm check valve, as long as there is no shutoff valve in the connection. In such a case, it would normally be necessary to provide an electronic or electropneumatic retard mechanism, either built into the pressure-operated switch or installed at the fire alarm system control unit, if one exists. A pressure-operated switch so located could be used to initiate a fire alarm signal on a central station, local, auxiliary, remote station, or proprietary fire alarm system (Figure 14.4.1).

Vane-Type Waterflow Alarm Initiating Devices

Far and away the most common electrically operated waterflow alarm initiating device is the vane-type waterflow switch

FIGURE 14.4.2 Vane-Type Waterflow Alarm Switch

(Figure 14.4.2), which is designed to be inserted into the riser just above the point at which the water supply piping enters the building from underground. Even if the wet pipe system has been equipped with an alarm check valve, a vane-type waterflow alarm initiating device may still be used. In this case, it normally would be installed just above the alarm check valve.

A small hole approximately 1 in. (25 mm) in diameter is drilled into the riser. The drill bit has a special piece of spring steel wire that captures the metal center of the hole, which is called the "coupon." Once the coupon is removed from the drill bit, it is usually attached to one of the mounting bolts of the waterflow alarm initiating device to show future inspectors that it was not left inside the pipe where it might possibly move upward into the sprinkler system and become an obstruction to the proper operation of the sprinkler system. The plastic or thin metal vane is rolled up and inserted into the riser. Once it resumes its original shape, it forms a thin barrier that covers almost all of the interior of the riser. When a sprinkler fuses, water flowing past the vane will push the vane upward, actuating a switch. When the switch contacts close, they initiate an alarm by activating the fire alarm system.

Two problems that may occur occasionally with vane-type waterflow alarm initiating devices are leaks around the point of entrance into the riser and detached vanes. The laboratories that test and list such devices require that each vane have a supplementary means of attaching the vane to the device so that, even if the vane breaks off, it will be retained near its original point of connection.

Waterflow Alarms for Dry Pipe, Preaction, and Deluge Automatic Sprinkler Systems

Automatic sprinkler systems equipped with dry pipe valves, preaction valves, or deluge valves also must have appropriate waterflow alarms. Each of these types of valves has a passageway that is uncovered when the clapper of the valve trips into the open position. Since these three types of valves are not affected generally by surges in the water system, no retard chamber is necessary. Piping connected to the outlet from the alarm passageway of these valves may be attached to a water motor gong or to a pressure-operated switch.

Vane-type waterflow alarm initiating devices are not permitted to be used for dry pipe valve, preaction, or deluge sprinkler systems. This prohibition comes from concern that the hydraulic shock occurring when these valves trip would increase the possibility that the vane might become detached.

Drop-in-Pressure Waterflow Alarms

An alternative arrangement designed to initiate a waterflow alarm, even if the main automatic sprinkler system control valve is shut, is the drop-in-pressure waterflow alarm. The supervision of all fire protective system control valves 2½ in. (63.5 mm) nominal size or larger is considered very important, especially when a fire alarm system is used to supplement or supplant standard guard service. Occasionally, it is simply not possible to obtain this valuable supervision. In such cases, it is essential that some method of detecting sprinkler system waterflow be used that will initiate an alarm even if the sprinkler control valve is shut. One method of accomplishing this is to use a waterflow alarm initiating device that detects a drop in sprinkler system pressure as a means of detecting the discharge of water from the system.

Such devices may use an ancillary storage chamber connected to the sprinkler system through a restricted orifice. Under normal conditions, the pressure in the ancillary chamber is the same as that in the sprinkler system. When system pressure drops, the pressure stored in the chamber acts on a diaphragm to activate an alarm initiating switch. Other such devices may employ a pressure-sensing transducer and associated electronic circuitry to detect the rate of pressure change in the system. A slow rate of change is reported as a trouble signal, whereas a rapid rate of change is reported as an alarm.

The most common drop-in-pressure waterflow alarm initiating device uses a pressure switch to sense the pressure in the system and, for wet pipe systems, employs a small riser-mounted excess pressure pump (Figure 14.4.3). (An excess pressure pump is not needed for dry pipe systems.) When the water pressure in a wet pipe system or the air pressure in a dry pipe system drops to a predetermined pressure setting, the pressure switch initiates an alarm signal. The automatic excess pressure pump maintains a pressure of 29 to 47 psi (200 to 325 kPa) in excess of the water supply pressure above an alarm check valve. A continuous white pilot light, controlled by a differential switch, indicates when the pressure in the sprinkler system is more than 29 psi (200 kPa) above the supply pressure. Should the water supply fail, a low-pressure switch shuts off the current

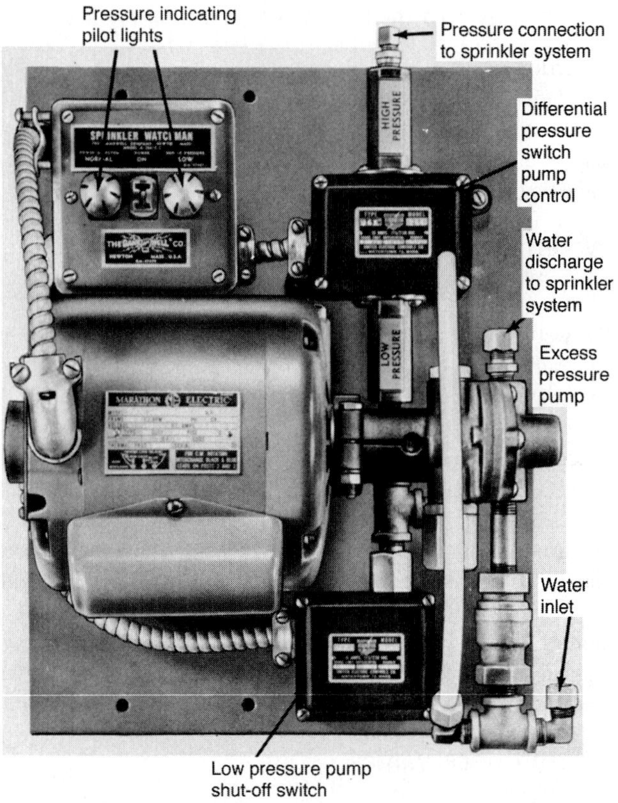

FIGURE 14.4.3 Excess Pressure Pump for Installation on a Wet Pipe Sprinkler System (Source: The Gamewell Co.)

to the pump so that it will not run without water. This switch also controls a red pilot light to show when the supply pressure drops below 29 psi (200 kPa). A second pressure switch on the sprinkler system (not a part of the pump unit) is connected into the sprinkler system alarm circuit and gives an alarm if system pressure fails completely (e.g., a closed water control valve) when a sprinkler operates. A third pressure switch gives a warning by a local bell or other means in the event the pressure pump fails to maintain system pressure within the established excess pressure range.

Drop-in-pressure-type waterflow alarm initiating devices should be connected to the sprinkler system through an automatic stop-and-waste valve. Such a valve automatically "wastes" the pressure trapped between the valve and the device to the atmosphere. Thus, a signal is initiated whenever the valve is closed. This eliminates the possibility of tampering with the device without producing a signal.

Testing Waterflow Alarm Initiating Devices

The piping connected to the alarm outlet from alarm check valves, dry pipe valves, preaction valves, or deluge valves usually is connected also through a normally closed valve to a point of water supply below the alarm check valve, dry pipe valve, preaction valve, or deluge valve. Opening this test bypass valve will allow water to flow into the alarm piping, actuating the water motor gong or pressure-operated switch. Unless the dry pipe valve, preaction valve, or deluge valve is going to be performance tested with a full actuation of the system, opening the alarm test bypass valve is the only way to test the alarms.

In the case of a dry pipe valve, care must be taken to be certain that the automatic velocity drain from the intermediate chamber of the dry pipe valve is not stuck in the closed position and that the check valve at the alarm outlet from the dry pipe valve intermediate chamber is not stuck in the open position. The combination of these two faults will most likely cause the dry pipe valve to trip when the alarm test bypass valve is opened. This tripping occurs when water from the test bypass valve flows back into the intermediate chamber of the dry pipe valve, destroying the differential between the air seat and the water seat inside the valve.

For wet pipe automatic sprinkler systems, the only proper way to test the operation of a vane-type waterflow alarm initiating device, and the preferable way to test all other types of waterflow alarm initiating devices, is to open the valve at the inspector's test connection. This valve, installed on a 1 in. (25 mm) piece of pipe—for older installations, it is often located at the most remote point of the sprinkler system, and, for more modern installations, it is often located at the top of the riser—terminates outside the building in an orifice that can simulate the discharge from a single sprinkler having the smallest orifice used by those sprinklers installed on the system. Thus, opening the inspector's test connection will simulate the fusing of a single sprinkler.

Last but not least, it is important to consider the consequences of a test when systems are interfaced. The testing of a sprinkler system could, for example, cause an unnecessary building evacuation. This could lead to injury as well as disruption of building operations. In addition, other interfaced systems such as heating and cooling equipment and elevators may be actuated or de-energized inadvertently, again creating potential risk to building occupants. Where testing is conducted and interfaced systems are disconnected temporarily, it is absolutely necessary to reconnect any bypassed functions on completion of the test. Interfaced system functions must also be tested but this should be done deliberately, with full knowledge of consequences, and not by negligence.

AUTOMATIC SPRINKLER SYSTEM SUPERVISION

Supervisory Initiating Devices

To ensure that an automatic sprinkler system is ready to discharge water on a hostile fire and hold the fire to its area of origin, a central station, local, remote station, or proprietary fire alarm system may be connected to supervisory initiating devices that will supervise critical operating features of the sprinkler system. Fire and building codes as well as other relevant standards identify the specific equipment required to be supervised and must be considered when assessing an existing system or designing a new one. As well, good engineering practice may conclude that certain functions or devices should be supervised.

Functions or Devices to Be Supervised

Supervision may include the following devices or functions:

1. *The position of sprinkler water shutoff valves.* Normally, only those valves that are 2½ in. (63.5 mm) or larger are supervised. This supervision is provided by mounting a supervisory initiating device on the valve that will initiate an off-normal signal whenever the valve is operated into a closed position and that will initiate a restoration-to-normal signal whenever the valve is returned to a fully open position.

When mounting an initiating device where it will come in contact with the threaded shaft of the valve, care must be taken that the device is adjusted so that it will not falsely initiate a restoration signal if the shaft stops turning with the sensing portion of the device between two of the threads. This is a particularly troubling problem with larger sizes of control valves (Figures 14.4.4 and 14.4.5).

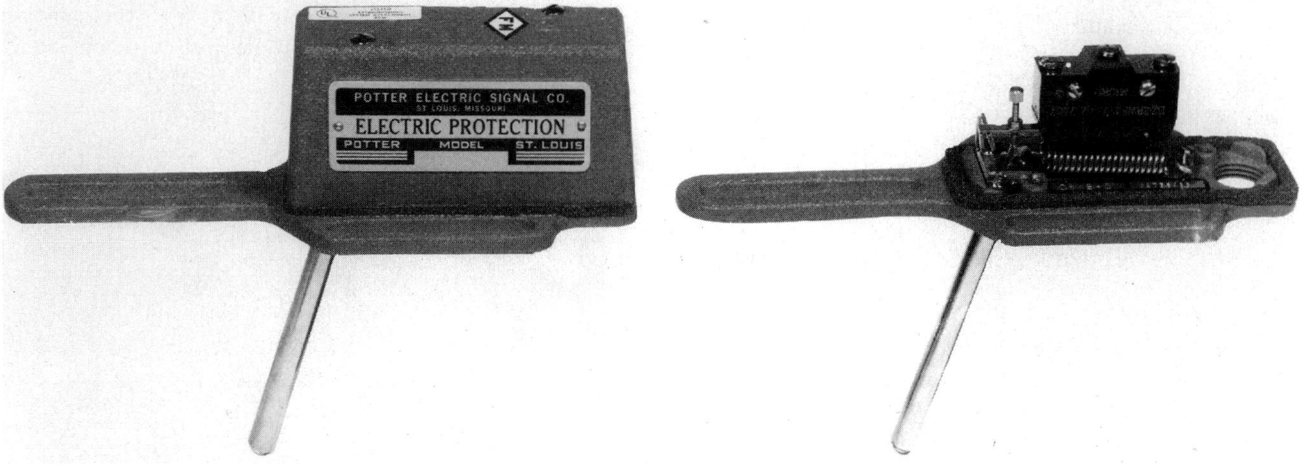

FIGURE 14.4.4 Valve Supervisory Switch for an Outside Screw and Yoke (OS&Y) Valve

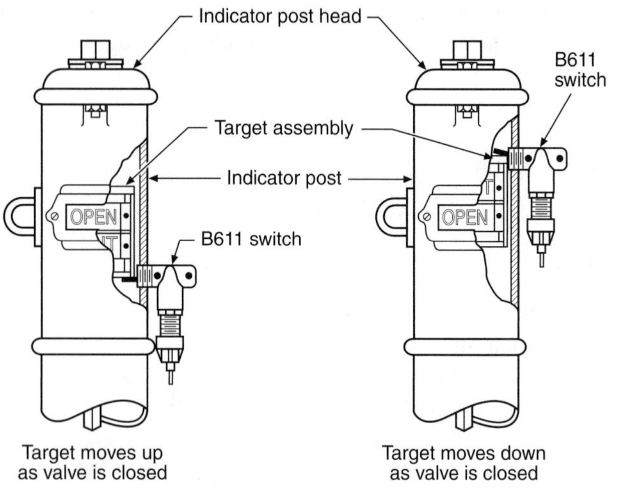

FIGURE 14.4.5 Valve Supervisory Switch for a Postindicator Valve (PIV)

FIGURE 14.4.6 Low-Temperature Switches for a Water Storage Tank

Some systems employ a metal or other loop attached to the water shutoff valve. One end of the loop plugs into an electrical switch mechanism such that a turn of the valve requires removal of the loop from the switch mechanism. These are not generally allowed in new systems because they can be plugged into the switch once the valve is closed, thereby allowing the fire alarm system supervisory circuit to return to normal unless latching circuitry is used in the monitor circuit.

2. *The air pressure in a dry pipe sprinkler system or water pressure tank and the supervisory air pressure in a preaction sprinkler system.* Connecting an air pressure supervisory initiating device to the system being supervised allows it to be monitored. Such a device is designed to initiate a supervisory off-normal signal whenever the air pressure climbs above or drops below a designated set point. Conversely, the device will initiate a restoration-to-normal signal whenever the air pressure is restored to the valve at which the device is set.

During installation, it is important that provision be made to allow testing of the device by simulating its operation during abnormal conditions. One method of accomplishing this is to connect the device to the sprinkler system through a stop-and-waste valve. When operated, such a valve automatically "wastes" the pressure trapped between the valve and the device to the atmosphere. Thus, whenever the valve is closed, a signal is initiated. This eliminates the possibility of tampering with the device without producing a signal.

3. *Low temperature in a building equipped with a wet pipe automatic sprinkler system, in a closet protecting a dry pipe valve, preaction valve, or deluge valve from freezing, or of the water inside a storage tank.* Mounting a temperature supervisory initiating device at the location to be supervised allows it to be monitored. Such a device is designed to initiate a supervisory off-normal signal whenever the temperature drops below a designated set point. Conversely, the device will initiate a restoration-to-normal signal whenever the temperature is restored to the value at which the device is set (Figure 14.4.6).

4. *The level of the water in a storage tank.* Mounting a water-level supervisory initiating device in a storage tank allows the water level to be supervised. Such a device is designed to initiate a supervisory off-normal signal whenever the water level rises above or drops below a designated set point. Conversely, the device will initiate a restoration-to-normal signal whenever the water level is restored to the value at which the device is set. During installation, it is important that provision be made to allow testing of the device by simulating its operation during abnormal conditions (Figure 14.4.7).

5. *The operation and integrity of a fire pump.* Connecting supervisory initiating device circuits to the "remote signal" contacts inside the fire pump controller allows it to be monitored. When an electric motor–driven fire pump operates into a running condition or when the power to the motor is interrupted, distinct supervisory signals are initiated. Similarly, when an engine-driven fire pump operates into a running condition—that is, its main switch is placed in a position other than "automatic start"—the battery charger fails, the engine experiences an abnormal condition or fails to start, or the controller fails, distinct supervisory signals are initiated. Conversely, a restoration-to-

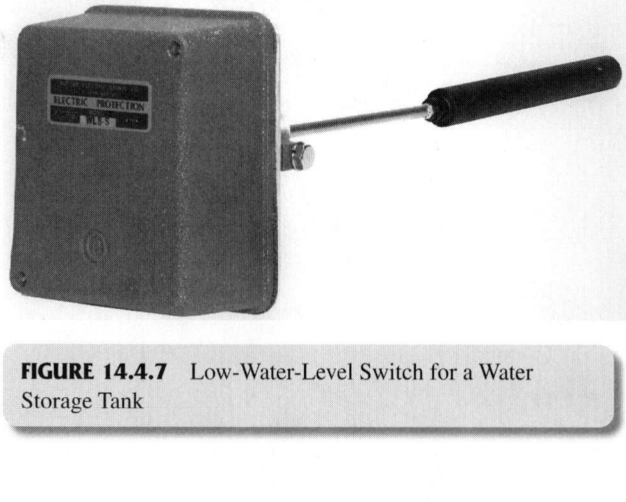

FIGURE 14.4.7 Low-Water-Level Switch for a Water Storage Tank

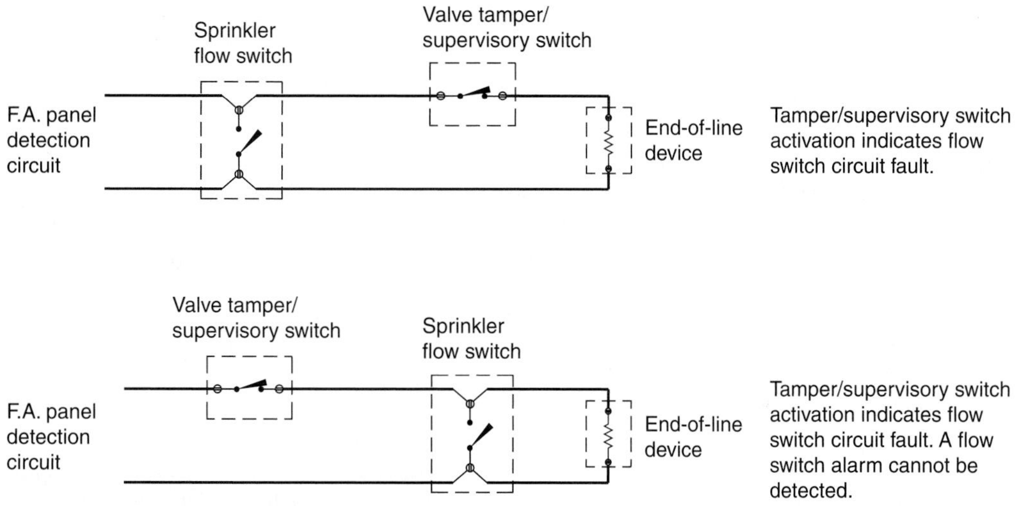

FIGURE 14.4.8 Incorrect Wiring of a Flow Tamper Switch

normal signal will be initiated whenever the particular feature of the fire pump that is off-normal is restored to normal.

6. *Tampering with a waterflow switch cover.* The switch cover may be monitored for removal (tampering that could affect the switch's ability to activate an alarm) by a supervisory switch connected to activate when the cover is removed.

NFPA 72 requires that three signals be identified at the fire alarm control unit: (1) alarm, (2) supervisory, and (3) trouble. In order to comply with that requirement, supervisory initiating devices must not be on the same initiating device circuit as alarm initiating devices. A common wiring configuration has been to install the waterflow alarm initiating device on the same circuit with the supervisory initiating device, for example, an OS&Y supervisory switch (as shown in Figure 14.4.4).

Although electrically this configuration may work, the wiring configuration with both devices on the same circuit will not provide the differentiation between a broken connection (trouble condition) and a closed valve (supervisory condition). If the wiring configuration and panel operation (such as with addressable devices) can provide the signal differentiation required by *NFPA 72,* then the devices can be wired on the same electrical circuit. Refer to Figures 14.4.8 and 14.4.9 for descriptions of incorrect and correct means of connecting these devices to a fire alarm system.

OTHER AUTOMATIC FIRE SUPPRESSION SYSTEMS

There are many other types of fire suppression systems found at protected premises, such as a kitchen hood/duct suppression system or a carbon dioxide or other gaseous suppression system. Each of these fire suppression systems must be connected to the protected premises fire alarm system to initiate an alarm. Each of these systems must also be supervised for proper operation. In most cases, there is an NFPA or other relevant standard describing the respective fire suppression system, and that standard provides information as to interfacing requirements with the fire alarm system. The supervisory devices must be listed for the intended application and installed in accordance with *NFPA 72.*

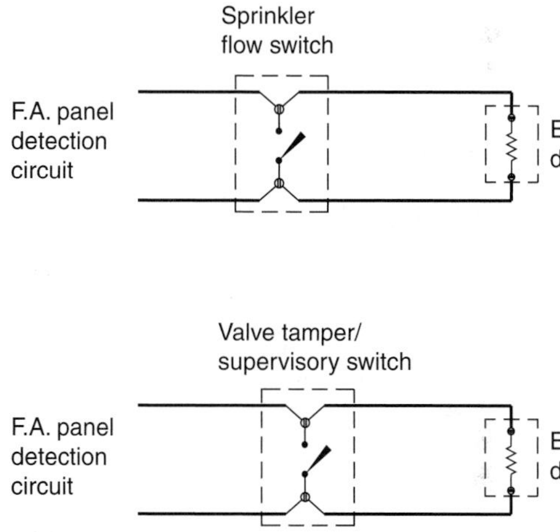

FIGURE 14.4.9 Correct Wiring of a Flow and Tamper Switch

Automatic fire pumps and special service pumps must be supervised in accordance with the requirements of NFPA 20, *Standard for the Installation of Stationary Pumps for Fire Protection,* and the authority having jurisdiction (AHJ). Examples of other standards include NFPA 14, *Standard for the Installation of Standpipe and Hose Systems,* NFPA 22, *Standard for Water Tanks for Private Fire Protection,* and NFPA 24, *Standard for the Installation of Private Fire Service Mains and Their Appurtenances.*

FIRE SAFETY FUNCTION INTERFACES

NFPA 72 also provides guidance for installation requirements of fire safety control functions that will be interfaced with fire alarm systems. These fire safety control functions can include elevator control, door control, building automation system control, and process monitoring and control systems.

General

Fire safety control functions are those functions that contribute in some way to life safety in a building. In many cases these functions are required to be implemented by law. As such and in recognition that they contribute to life safety, it is reasonable to connect these functions to their respective devices with circuits that are monitored for integrity per *NFPA 72* to ensure that someone is notified if they are disabled. Supervised circuits may be provided in a number of ways as illustrated below (Figures 14.4.10 and 14.4.11).

Elevator Control

Fire alarm systems are interfaced to elevator control systems to initiate an elevator recall sequence or to initiate a power shutdown. The interface is generally accomplished by connection from the fire alarm system to a relay that is in turn connected to the elevator controller.

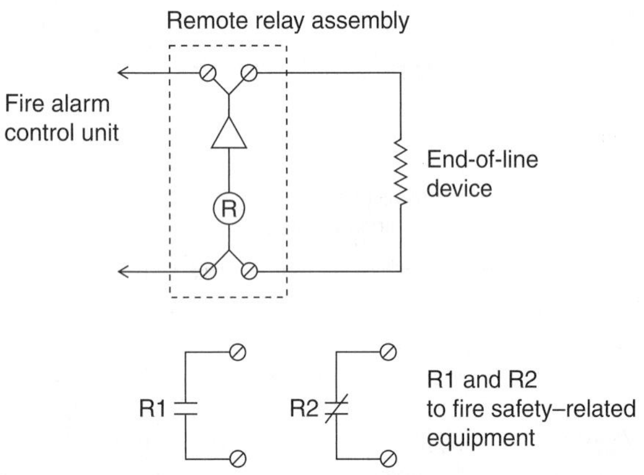

FIGURE 14.4.10 Polarity Reversing Circuit. Note: The remote relay assembly will be mounted within 3 ft (0.9 m) of the controlled fire safety–related equipment.

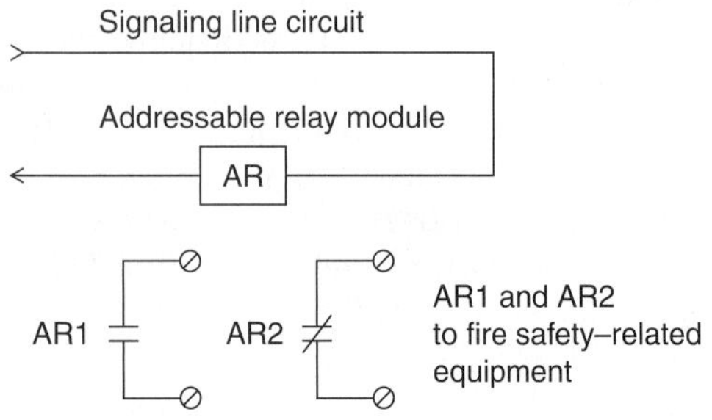

FIGURE 14.4.11 Addressable Circuit. Note: The addressable relay module will be mounted within 3 ft (0.9 m) of the controlled fire safety–related equipment.

Elevator Recall. Fire alarm systems are interfaced to elevator control systems to actuate the elevator recall sequence. The recall sequence and initiation requirements are found in Chapter 3 of *NFPA 72.* In most jurisdictions, only the elevator lobby and machine room smoke detectors are required to initiate recall of the elevators. The standard that originally provided the smoke detector placement requirements and requires the elevators to be recalled is ANSI/ASME A17.1, *Safety Code for Elevators and Escalators.* The ANSI/ASME A17.1 committee has now developed a liaison relationship with the *NFPA 72,* Chapter 3 committee, and all detection and interface requirements are contained in *NFPA 72,* Chapter 3. Additional requirements may be found in local building and fire codes or other elevator codes and standards.

Elevator Shutdown. When the elevator machine room or hoistway is protected with automatic sprinklers, ANSI/ASME A17.1 requires that the power to the elevators be shut down prior to or on discharge of water from the sprinklers. The power shutdown or shunt trip can be accomplished in either of two ways. When heat detectors are used, they must be installed within 2 ft (0.6 m) of each sprinkler, have both a lower temperature rating and a higher sensitivity than the sprinkler head, and be installed in accordance with *NFPA 72,* Chapter 6. When pressure or waterflow switches are used to shut down the elevator power, they must not have a time delay associated with their operation. In either case, it is assumed that elevator recall will have already taken place through the operation of the smoke detectors required for the elevator recall function.

Door Control

Doors may be connected to a fire alarm system for either of two reasons: to release a door normally held open such that it closes automatically or to unlock a door that is normally locked to allow unrestricted egress from a building. The interface is generally accomplished by connection from the fire alarm system to a relay that is in turn connected to either the hold open or locking device mechanism or to a security system that provides door control functions. In each case, the circuit should be arranged to provide a fail-safe operation. In other words, the circuit design must allow release of the door in case of circuit failure, security system failure, or power failure.

Door Release Service. When smoke and fire doors are held in the open position to allow free movement in corridors of buildings, it is required that the doors be released when a fire alarm system is activated. These hold-open devices are commonly magnetic units that are normally powered from a 24- or 120-V ac supply that is interconnected through a relay in a smoke detector or in the fire alarm control unit. *NFPA 72* does not require the door hold-open devices to be connected to the standby power because the units operate in a fail-safe fashion. When power is lost, the hold-open units deactivate and the doors close.

Alternatively, an unnecessary release of the doors (even during a nonemergency power failure) may not be desirable, and in this case the door hold-open devices should be powered from a separate "no-break," battery-supported power supply. The standby time should be equivalent to fire alarm system standby duration if practical.

If it is necessary to use the fire alarm system power supply (which is not encouraged and may not be allowed by the AHJ), then the fire alarm system power supply must not be disabled by any fault in the door hold-open device or related circuit, and the standby battery calculations for the fire alarm system must include the full load power required by the door hold-open devices during the required fire alarm supervisory and alarm periods (Figure 14.4.12).

Door Unlocking Devices. The life safety objectives of NFPA *101, Life Safety Code*®, and local building codes are achieved, in part, by establishing prescriptive requirements intended to ensure that building occupants can freely and promptly evacuate buildings during an emergency. The objective and scope of a security system may differ from the primary occupant life safety objective of the codes. Subjects of security protection may include persons, building assets, or contents. Threats may originate from within the building or from outside. It may therefore be desirable to control movement of persons into, through, and out of buildings. Conflict arises when security systems attempt to control occupant movement in buildings in contravention of the principle of the codes to permit freedom of movement for self-preservation during an emergency. The security system cannot override the code requirements established to provide life safety.

NFPA *101*®, *Life Safety Code*®, requires all stairway exit locked doors be unlocked when an alarm occurs in the building. This is based on the danger of fire deaths occurring in smoke-filled stairways where occupants are trapped after discovering that they have entered an unsafe area and cannot return to the corridor. The proper way to interconnect these unlocking devices (including electromagnetic locks and electric strikes) is so that when power is lost, they unlock. This is a fail-safe operation, and when the unlocking devices are wired in this fashion, the interconnecting wiring does not require monitoring for integrity. This is generally achieved by connecting locking devices through a normally closed contact that opens on fire detection. This contact may be part of a relay controlled by the fire alarm system or a contact within a manual pull box near the locking device.

Sometimes a locking device is connected to a security system that monitors, powers, locks, and unlocks the doors. Even in this case it is prudent to connect the fire-alarm-controlled, normally closed relay contact directly to the locking device by a method allowing fail-safe operation. The security system may fail to respond as required or the connection between the security system and fire alarm system may be lost. In all cases the locking device must release on loss of power to the device (Figure 14.4.13).

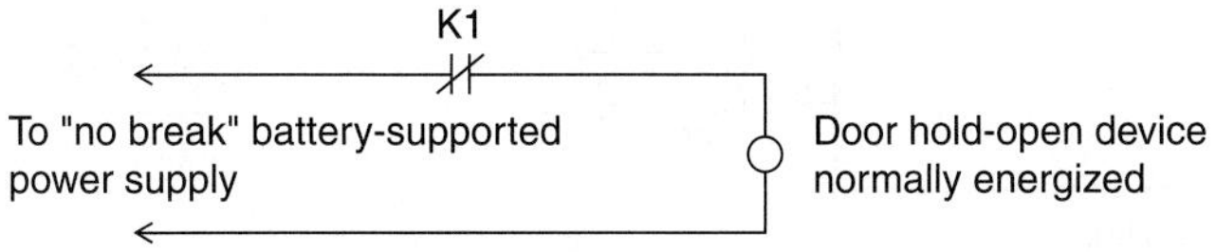

FIGURE 14.4.12 Door Release Control Circuit. Note: K1 is typically operated by fire alarm system activation. This may be supervised conventional relay or addressable relay module.

Building Automation Systems

It has become necessary in many cases to connect building control systems, such as heating and ventilation systems, to the fire alarm system. This has come from recognition that smoke spread can be controlled by use of the building environmental systems and by use of dedicated fans and dampers designed for the purpose. The control of smoke movement and the ability to exhaust smoke aid in providing the time necessary for occupants to leave a building.

Practically speaking, there are many pitfalls in implementing a smoke control strategy. The fire alarm system is generally implemented by a separate contractor with a different skill set than that needed for the mechanical systems employed in smoke control. Also, the systems are generally completed at different times and are commissioned by different people at different times. The fact that there are numerous ways to interface the fire alarm system with building automation and control systems equipment just confirms that this is one of the most difficult systems interface challenges.

The fire alarm system and heating, ventilation, and air-conditioning (HVAC) system may be interfaced by appropriate electrical contacts, digital data interfaces, and other methods listed for the purpose. Appropriate testing of the final interconnected equipment is critical to achieving the building design objectives.

Non-Computer-Controlled Building Systems. Many building HVAC systems are controlled during an emergency by direct connection from the building fire alarm system to the respective fan and/or damper that is to be controlled. Power is generally switched on or off via a relay contact in the fire alarm system or located near the controlled equipment or controlling motor control center (MCC). The wiring for these controls must be monitored for integrity in accordance with *NFPA 72*. In addition, it may be required or desirable to monitor the controlled device to confirm activation or initiate interlocks to prevent undesirable events. Please refer to NFPA 96, *Standard for Ventilation Control and Fire Protection of Commercial Cooking Operations*, for examples. See Figures 14.4.14 and 14.4.15 for examples of appropriate connections.

Computer-Controlled Building Systems. The computerization of building control systems has led to the integration of these systems with the fire alarm system control unit. Because the fire

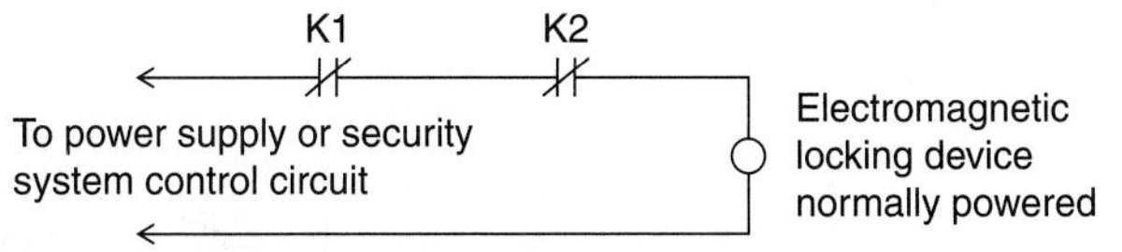

FIGURE 14.4.13 Electromagnetic Lock Control Circuit. Note: K1 is typically operated by fire alarm system activation. This may be by supervised by conventional relay or addressable relay module. K2 is contact operated when manual station at the controlled door is activated.

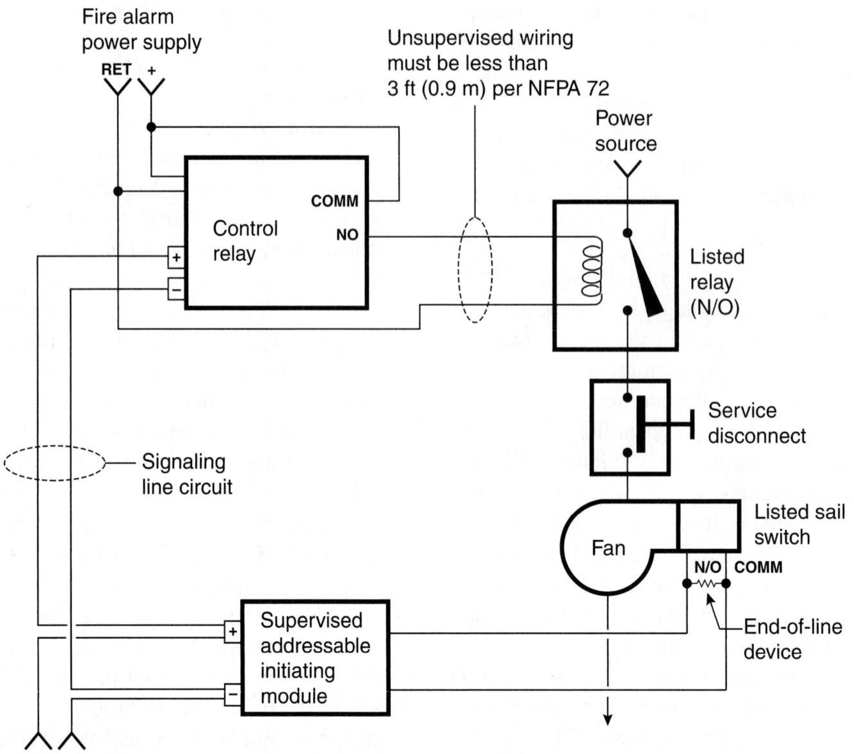

FIGURE 14.4.14 Direct Fan Control with Feedback (Courtesy of SimplexGrinnell, Westminster, MA)

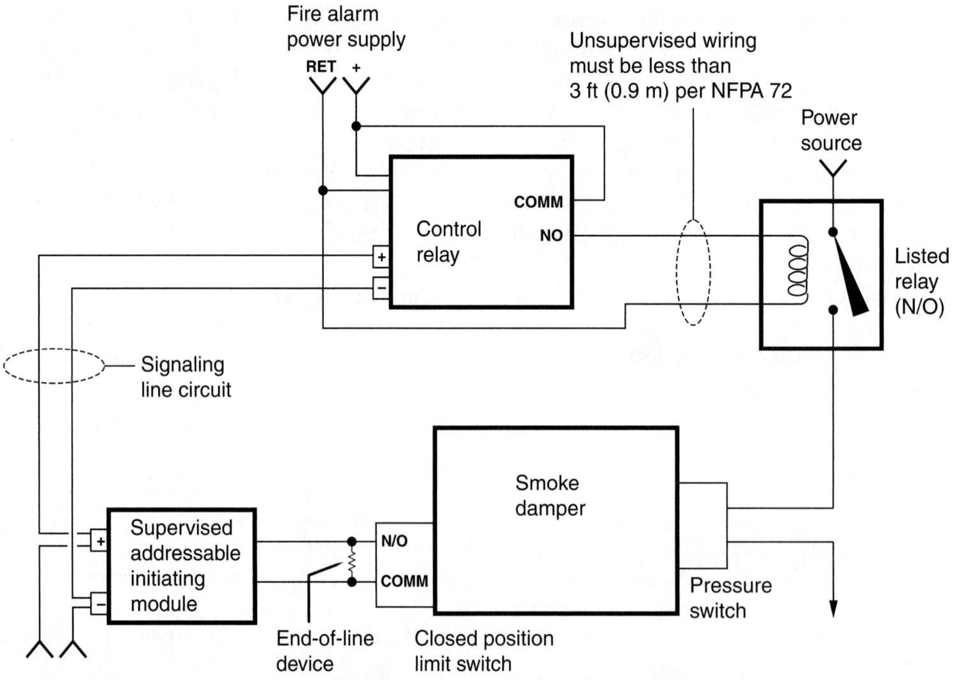

FIGURE 14.4.15 Direct Damper Control with Feedback (Courtesy of SimplexGrinnell, Westminster, MA)

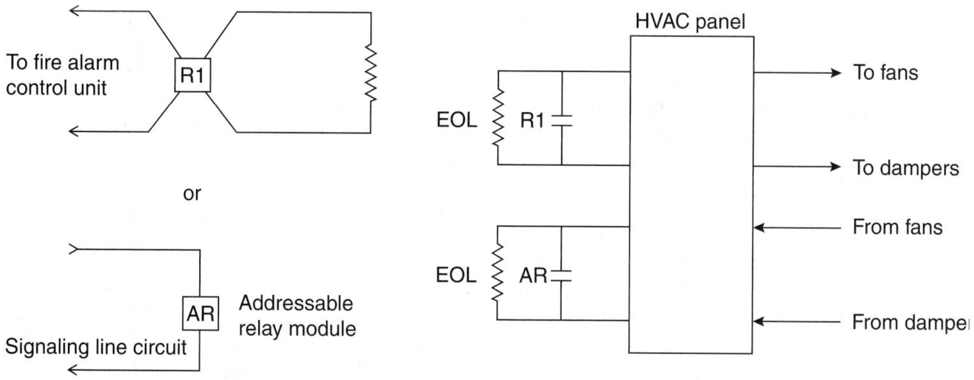

FIGURE 14.4.16 Computer-Controlled Building Systems Relay Interface

safety control function devices must be listed for compatibility with the fire alarm system control unit, so as not to interfere with the fire alarm system's operation, the system designer and the installer must be careful not to interconnect computerized devices together that have not been listed for compatibility. One of the areas that presents this problem is the interconnection of the fire alarm system to the HVAC system direct digital control (DDC) devices used to control fire/smoke dampers. In many cases, the fire alarm system is connected directly to the fire/smoke damper and not to the HVAC system DDC device. This is done instead of connecting the fire alarm system directly to the damper control. This is due to the compatibility requirement and also due to technician/programmers who lack expertise in fire alarm systems working on the interface, the DDC type of interconnections should be approached very carefully.

A computer-controlled HVAC or other building system may be interconnected to the fire alarm system via electrical contacts. These are actuated by the fire alarm system to advise the HVAC system of the fire location such that appropriate HVAC equipment functions can take place. In this case, the relay contact may either activate the fans and dampers directly as described earlier, or the contact may activate an HVAC system–monitored input circuit at an HVAC system control unit.

A computer-controlled HVAC or other building system may be interconnected to the fire alarm system via a digital data interface or via a network connection. Where a fire alarm system is connected to other equipment via a network to share data, this communication must be implemented by means listed for the purpose by a recognized laboratory. The network interconnection must be monitored for integrity and may not interfere in any way with the required operation of the fire alarm system. Data received by the fire alarm system from other equipment may not alter or affect the fire alarm system operation in any way other than to display information for operator use (Figures 14.4.16 and 14.4.17).

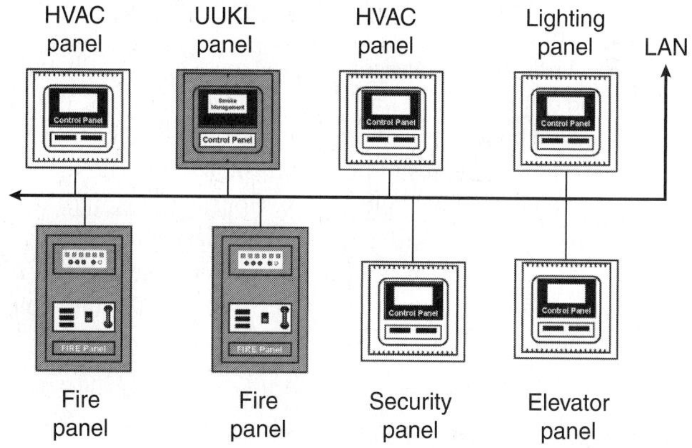

FIGURE 14.4.17 Computer-Controlled Building Systems Interface via LAN (Courtesy of SimplexGrinnell, Westminster, MA)

INTERCONNECTED FIRE ALARM CONTROL UNITS

There are numerous occasions where it is necessary or required by design to interconnect fire alarm control units. This function may occur during an addition to a building, such as a new wing to a hospital, or during a renovation to an existing building. In the past, there was no guidance as to the proper way to interconnect different manufacturers' control equipment. This created the potential for makeshift interconnections that were improper, unreliable, and unmonitored. *NFPA 72* requires that the interconnected fire alarm control units be connected by listed methods and the interconnection must be monitored for integrity. In addition to monitoring the interconnected system for alarm conditions, the interconnected control must be monitored for conditions that are essential for the proper operation of the interconnected system.

When an owner or designer suggests that two different manufacturers' control units be interconnected, the AHJ would be wise to ask each manufacturer for a letter indicating the approved interconnection method or drawing showing the approved interconnection method. If the interconnection is being made using relay configurations, the relays used must be listed and compatible with the control units being interconnected.

The objective of the interconnection and its consequences must be carefully considered. Many times it is desirable for one system to actuate the other. One example is where the systems provide protection and audible signaling for adjacent spaces. When the first system actuates it may cause an alarm condition in the second system. The second system may then actuate the first system in return. Special measures must be taken to allow a reset condition since both control panels must be reset simultaneously or they will continue to actuate each other.

Another example of room for error is the possibility of shared control of fire safety systems by two interconnected fire alarm systems. It may be that the first fire alarm system or one of its components is in close proximity to an exhaust fan for a smoke shaft whereas the second fire alarm system is in close proximity to dampers in the exhaust shaft. If the fan and dampers are connected to different fire alarm systems and the interface between them is compromised, then it is possible for the exhaust fan to start based on an alarm initiation on the first system. Since the second system may not be aware of the alarm, there may not be an open damper in the shaft, which could lead to collapse of the shaft.

Fire alarm system interconnections must be carefully considered and designed to ensure only desirable operations. Where the connection between two fire alarm systems is deemed necessary, the design of the resulting system should emulate the operation and control of a single system. Consideration must also be given to the final commissioning and annual testing protocols that will be used. System failure can almost be guaranteed if, over time, different service companies work on the interconnected systems.

INTERFACED EQUIPMENT

Nonfire Alarm Interfaced Equipment

There are times when an owner may wish to interconnect a process monitoring system or some other type of nonfire alarm system to the fire alarm system. Caution should be exercised, and the AHJ should be consulted. If the system being interfaced is monitoring conditions affecting the life safety of occupants or protection of the property, then it may be required to have that system initiate an alarm condition on the fire alarm system. Otherwise, these nonfire signals must be considered supervisory in nature.

Interface Areas of Concern

The most important areas of concern when interfacing the fire alarm control unit with a fire safety function control device are that (1) the relay used to initiate control must be located within 3 ft (0.9 m) of the controlled circuit or device; (2) the relay, digital data interface, or other interface method must be listed for the intended purpose; (3) the relay, digital data interface, or other interface method must be compatible with the fire alarm control unit; (4) the wiring between the fire alarm control unit and the relay, digital data interface, or other interface method must be monitored for integrity, unless the control device is connected in a fail-safe manner; and (5) the relays, digital data interfaces, or other listed means of providing fire safety functions must not interfere with other operations of the fire alarm system.

TESTING INTERFACED SYSTEMS

Whether the interfaced system is a security system or a special hazard suppression system, care must be taken when performing acceptance and periodic testing of the fire alarm system. The technicians performing the tests must be totally familiar with all of the systems interfaced to the fire alarm system or must have other technicians present for the test who are familiar with the interfaced systems.

Interfaced systems equipment connections must be tested by operating or simulating the operation of the equipment being supervised. Signals required to be transmitted must be verified at the control panel. The test frequency for the interfaced equipment is governed by the applicable NFPA standard(s) for the equipment being supervised by the fire alarm system.

The system's test protocol, required sequence of operation, and test results must be documented to assure appropriate ongoing testing and system reliability. The testing protocol must recognize that the interconnected systems are designed and installed by different disciplines. Action must be taken to ensure that results are consistent with performance requirements and that connections present during testing remain in place following final commissioning or annual testing.

SUMMARY

The purpose of this section is to make the reader aware of the need to address interface requirements early in the design stage to ensure the reliable operation of both the fire alarm system and the systems being interfaced to the fire alarm system. Ensuring compatibility and correct operation during the acceptance tests is required to achieve reliable operation.

BIBLIOGRAPHY

NFPA Codes, Standards, and Recommended Practices

Reference to the following NFPA codes, standards, and recommended practices will provide further information on fire alarm system interconnections discussed in this chapter. (See the latest version of The NFPA Catalog *for availability of current editions of the following documents.)*

NFPA 13, *Standard for the Installation of Sprinkler Systems*
NFPA 20, *Standard for the Installation of Stationary Pumps for Fire Protection*
NFPA 70, *National Electrical Code®*
NFPA 72®, National Fire Alarm Code®
NFPA *101®*, *Life Safety Code®*

References

ANSI/ASME A17.1, *Safety Code for Elevators and Escalators,* Rules 211.3 through 211.8, American National Standards Institute, New York, 1993.

Davis, W. D., and Forney, G. P., "Sensor-Driven Fire Model Version 1.1," NISTIR 6705, National Institute of Standards and Technology, Gaithersburg, MD, Jan. 2001.

Evans, D. H., Weber, R. D., and Quiter, J. R., "Luxor Hotel and Casino: An Application of Performance-Based Fire Safety Design Methods," *Proceedings* of Pacific Rim Conference and 2nd International Conference on Performance-Based Codes and Fire Safety Design Methods, May 3–9, 1998, Maui, HI, International Code Council, Birmingham, AL, 1998, pp. 393–401.

Factory Mutual Approval Guide, Factory Mutual Research Corporation, Norwood, MA. (Published annually.)
Fire Protection Equipment List, Underwriters Laboratories Inc., Northbrook, IL. (Published annually, with bimonthly supplements.)
Lathrop, J. K., "Consider the Firefighter in Building and Fire Protection System Design," *Fire Protection Engineering,* No. 6, 2000, pp. 10–12.
LeBlanc, D. J., and Toossi, V., "Retrofitting Fire Protection Systems," *Fire Protection Engineering,* No. 2, 1999, p. 17.
Martin, T., and Buchanan, S., "Fire Protection: Life Safety Assessment Performance Based Design Concept," *Proceedings* of Fire Suppression and Detection Research Application Symposium, Research and Practice: Bridging the Gap, February 7–9, 2001, Orlando, FL, National Fire Protection Research Foundation, Quincy, MA, 2001, pp. 537–575.
Mongeau, E., "Building a Fire-Safe Dorm," *NFPA Journal,* Vol. 93, No. 1, 1999, pp. 60–64.
Mowrer, F. W., "Fire Safe Student Housing: A Guide for Campus Housing Administrators," Maryland University, College Park, Feb. 1, 1999.
Page, I., "How Economic Are Smoke Alarms and Fire Sprinklers?" *Build,* Sept./Oct. 2001, pp. 16–17.
Proulx, G., Laroche, C., Jaspers-Fayer, F., and Lavallee, R., "Fire Alarm Signal Recognition," IRC-I-828, National Research Council of Canada, Ottawa, Ontario, June 2001.
Respondek, J., "Performance-Based Fire Safety Design Approach: Current Developments in Switzerland," *Proceedings* of Fire Suppression and Detection Research Application Symposium, Research and Practice: Bridging the Gap, February 7–9, 2001, Orlando, FL, National Fire Protection Research Foundation, Quincy, MA, 2001, pp. 576–595.
Schmid, R., "Telecommunications and e-Commerce," *Fire Protection Engineering,* No. 12, 2001, pp. 9–11.
Wu, S., "Fire Safety Design of Apartment Buildings," Fire Engineering Research Report 01/10, University of Canterbury, Christchurch, New Zealand, Mar. 2001.
Yung, D., and Benichou, N., "Consideration of Reliability and Performance of Fire Protection Systems in FIRECAM," *Proceedings* of inFIRE (International Network for Fire Information and Reference Exchange) Conference, Fire Information in the New Millennium: Challenges and Opportunities, May 9–12, Ottawa, Ontario, Canada, 2000, pp. 1–12.
Yung, D., and Hadjisophocleous, G. V., "Assessment of the Impact of Reliability of Fire Alarms and Automatic Sprinklers on Life Safety in Buildings," *Proceedings* of Fire Suppression and Detection Research Application Symposium, Research and Practice: Bridging the Gap, June 25–27, 1997, San Francisco, CA, National Fire Protection Research Foundation, Quincy, MA, 1997, pp. 132–141.
Zhao, L. D., "Using Risk-Based Time Method to Determine the Maximum Travel Distance for Building Design," *International Journal on Engineering Performance-Based Fire Codes,* Vol. 2, No. 3, 2000, pp. 81–89.

Chapter 5

Inspection, Testing, and Maintenance of Fire Alarm Systems

John M. Cholin

Chapter Contents

Key Terms

acceptance test, design lifetime, failure, fire alarm control unit, fire alarm system, household fire-warning equipment, inspection, maintenance, notification appliance, protected premises, reacceptance test, reliability, reliability prediction, semiconductor, sensitivity measurement, supervising station

With each passing year, improvement in the understanding of fire and its behavior enables designers to better design fire alarm systems to achieve specific objectives and levels of performance rather than compliance with a minimum prescriptive standard. Yet, when designers employ performance-based design, the whole fire protection strategy becomes far more dependent on the fire detection portion of the protection system. This increased reliance on the fire detection and alarm system places a greater importance on maintaining the predictability of the fire detection system response, necessitating an effective inspection testing and maintenance program. Furthermore, no performance-based or objective-oriented design is complete without an explicit quantitative assessment of the level of confidence one can have that the fire alarm system will perform as intended. All computational methods that have been developed to assess this parameter are predicated upon an inspection, testing, and maintenance program at specified regular and predictable times throughout the life of the system. Consequently, without a thorough understanding of the impact the inspection, testing, and maintenance program has on the mission effectiveness of the fire alarm system, one cannot use a performance-based, objective-oriented design approach.

This chapter first develops the concepts of reliability analysis and prediction that form the foundation on which all inspection, testing, and maintenance programs should be based. It then reviews the types of electronic components from which fire alarm systems are constructed. These two background areas form the basis for inspection, testing, and maintenance requirements for fire alarm systems, components, and scheduling. Further, design concepts are applied to the household fire alarm system. Finally, this chapter addresses criticality of inspection, testing, and maintenance on the mission-effectiveness of the system.

This chapter is specifically limited to inspection, testing, and maintenance of fire alarm systems. These are the electronic and electrical systems that are designed (1) to sense a fire, transmit that information to a control unit of some type, and activate personnel warnings, whether for persons occupying the site or at a remote location; and (2) for remedial response, such as the discharge of extinguishing systems and activation of devices designed to enhance the compartmentation of the fire.

This chapter does not cover maintenance of specific remedial response systems. Inspection, testing, and maintenance of these systems are addressed in NFPA 11, *Standard for Low-, Medium-, and High-Expansion Foam;* NFPA 12, *Standard on Carbon Dioxide Extinguishing Systems;* NFPA 12A, *Standard on Halon 1301 Fire Extinguishing Systems;* NFPA 13, *Standard for the Installation of Sprinkler Systems;* NFPA 15, *Standard for Water Spray Fixed Systems for Fire Protection;* NFPA 16, *Standard for the Installation of Foam-Water Sprinkler and Foam-Water Spray Systems;* NFPA 17, *Standard for Dry Chemical Extinguishing Systems;* NFPA 20, *Standard for the Installation of Stationary Pumps for Fire Protection;* NFPA 25, *Standard for the Inspection, Testing, and*

John M. Cholin, P.E., FSFPE, is an independent fire protection consultant and engineer with J. M. Cholin Consultants, Inc., in Oakland, New Jersey.

Maintenance of Water-Based Fire Protection Systems; and NFPA 2001, *Standard on Clean Agent Fire Extinguishing Systems.*

For related topics, see the following chapters in Section 14: Chapter 1, "Fire Alarm Systems"; Chapter 2, "Automatic Fire Detectors"; Chapter 3, "Notification Appliances"; Chapter 4, "Fire Alarm Interconnections"; and Chapter 6, "Household Fire Warning Equipment."

RELIABILITY

Murphy's law is familiar. Anything that can go wrong will go wrong. From this truism we can then conclude that any "system" will suffer a failure of one of its constituent components at some moment during its design lifetime. A fire alarm system is a "system" as used in this context. It is also a system on which people rely for life safety, property preservation, and mission continuity. Yet we are assured by Murphy's law that every fire alarm system will experience a failure of some component over the lifetime of the system. This establishes a compelling justification for a regimen of inspection, testing, and maintenance to be employed with every fire alarm system.

Reliability Defined

The reliability of a system includes both the ability to (1) detect and correctly respond to every occurrence of fire and (2) not render a fire alarm indication except when the legitimate fire alarm stimulus actually occurs. For a system to be deemed reliable, alarm signals will occur if, and only if, there is a fire. For the purposes of this chapter, reliability is defined as the measure of the certainty that the system will provide the appropriate response to the conditions that occur, as they occur, during the defined lifetime of the system.

Fire Alarm System Objectives

The driving force behind every inspection, testing, and maintenance program is the need to make system reliability as high as possible. Reliability is essential for fire alarm systems, simply due to mission objectives for these systems. Fire alarm systems are intended to fulfill three essential objectives: (1) ensure life safety, (2) conserve property, and (3) ensure continuity of the mission of the site. The life safety objective is achieved through timely warning of occupants. This is usually the highest priority. Mitigation of property damage is achieved through the timely actuation of automatic fire-extinguishing systems and transmission of fire alarm signals to the fire service. This is generally the second priority. After the first two objectives are met, the third objective, that is, continuity of the mission of the site, becomes attainable. In many cases, the mission objective places greater demands on the fire alarm system. The objectives cannot be attained if the system is unstable, nor can they be attained if the system allows too large a fire to develop prior to the actuation of fire-extinguishing systems. The three objectives can only be achieved when the fire alarm system operates reliably.

System Elements

Experience has shown that reliability of a system is the result of contributions from four system elements: (1) design, (2) installation, (3) equipment, and (4) maintenance. Each of these elements contributes to the overall reliability of the system. Often some "problems" are designed into the system. For example, a smoke detector located above a normally occurring source of aerosols that are not indicative of a fire is a problem that is designed into the system. This represents a reduction of the system reliability that was present during the design process. Other examples of design problems are rate-of-rise heat detectors in an area where rapid and wide fluctuations in temperature are expected, control panels mounted on surfaces that are vibrating, or smoke and heat detectors improperly mounted relative to the ceiling plane. Initial inspection and testing of the system should identify any problems that are designed into the system, so they can be corrected before the system is accepted.

Other problems are introduced during installation. These also deduct from the attainable system reliability. For example, installation problems include substandard wiring, general-purpose conduit and boxes where weathertight materials are needed, insufficient torque on screw terminals, abraded wire insulation, and so on. The initial inspection and test of the system should uncover these types of problems. If they are not corrected prior to acceptance, they will create problems over the operational lifetime of the installation. Furthermore, design and installation problems may not always be apparent during initial inspection. These errors are most likely discovered as a result of a system failure or in the context of the regularly scheduled maintenance program. These examples illustrate the necessity of an initial inspection and test program to uncover problems that are literally designed or installed into the system.

Another source of failures is the equipment itself. Most of today's electronic fire alarm system devices are extremely reliable. They are mature technologies, produced under stringent quality assurance programs that are audited by nationally recognized testing laboratories, such as Underwriters Laboratories Inc. (UL) and FM Global. However, all electronic components manifest a statistical failure rate that results in failures of these devices over time. These failures occur after the system has been accepted and consequently can only be uncovered through a program of regular maintenance and testing.

A program of inspection, testing, and maintenance of fire alarm systems is critical to achieving the design objectives of the system. This is the final element affecting the reliability of every system. It is through the inspection, testing, and maintenance program that errors in product manufacture, system design, and system installation are discovered and corrected. A fire alarm system without an inspection, testing, and maintenance program is every bit as incomplete as a car with only three wheels.

Although inspection, testing, and maintenance schedules have traditionally been developed based on the qualitative judgment of technical committee members, the emergence of performance-based and objective-oriented designs demands a more rigorous method of assessing the reliability of a system. Performance-based design requires that the inspection, testing, and maintenance schedules provide the reliability necessary to achieve the performance objectives of the design. If reliable performance is to be achieved from a fire alarm system, a rigorous inspection, testing, and maintenance program on a schedule that is derived from the computed reliability of the system and its components is crucial.

Reliability Prediction Techniques for Fire Alarm Systems

The reliability of a fire alarm system, like any electronic system, can be computed using a method developed during World War II by a German rocket scientist named Lusser, who discovered that the reliability of a system was the product of the reliabilities of the individual components. According to the Lusser product law, as the number of components increases, the reliability of each individual component has to be improved commensurately to maintain the reliability of the overall system. The Lusser product law is expressed mathematically by

$$P_T = P_1 \times P_2 \times P_3 \times \cdots \times P_n$$

where

P_T = Probability of successful operation for the system, or reliability

P_n = Probability of successful operation of the nth component

n = The number of constituent components

This equation applies to systems in which the failure of any one component will mean the failure of the system. The probability of successful operation of a system is not directly computable. It is computed from failure rate data for each of the constituent components of that system. Failure rate, that is, the probability of failure, is related to the probability of successful operation by

$$\Lambda_T = 1 - P_T$$

where

Λ_T = Failure rate of the total system

P_T = Probability of successful operation for the system, or reliability

The failure rate, Λ, of a system assembled from components having exponential failure rates, is computed from the sum of the failure rates of each of the components, Λ_n, from

$$\Lambda = q_1\lambda_1 + q_2\lambda_2 + q_3\lambda_3 + \cdots + q_n\lambda_n$$

where

Λ = Failure rate of the total system

q_n = Quantity of the nth component in the system

λ_n = Failure rate of the nth component in the system

The component failure rates are usually expressed as failures per million device operating hours (f/mdoh), and the system failure rate is expressed as failures per million operating hours (f/moh). The previous equation enables one to calculate the reliability of a system based on the failure rates of the constituent components. Each fire alarm system component, that is, a control panel, detector, or notification appliance, has a calculable failure rate and, hence, the system failure rate can be computed. The failure rate of each of these major components is computed from the failure rates of the individual electronic components from which it is made.

Bathtub Curve. Research into the reliability of systems and components has shown that, for most physical systems, when the failure rate is plotted versus time, a curve of familiar shape results from the empirical data.[1,2] This curve is termed the *bathtub curve.* The bathtub curve can be modeled as the sum of two bell-shaped, Gaussian curves, one centered at the time the product is made and called the *turn-on curve,* and the other centered at the design lifetime and termed the *lifetime curve.*[3]

The first, the turn-on curve, shown in Figure 14.5.1(a), describes the rate at which failures can be expected to occur from the date of manufacture, forward over time, due to inherent defects in both constituent components and manufacturing technique. It illustrates the phenomenon known as "infant mortality" in the components and finished product. The second curve, shown in Figure 14.5.1(b), is also a Gaussian distribution, but it is centered at the design lifetime. It describes the distribution of failure rates due to long-term aging.

When the failure rates from the initial turn-on and the lifetime curves are added together (having adjusted the standard

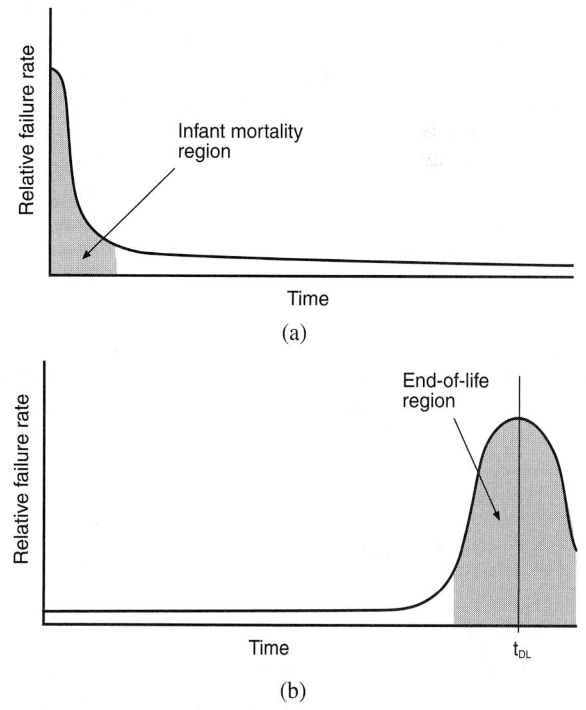

FIGURE 14.5.1 (a) Initial Turn-On Curve Showing Failure Rate of a Component or System at Turn-On; (b) Lifetime Curve Plotting the Failure Rate due to Long-Term Aging of Components and Establishing the Design Lifetime, t_{DL}

deviations for each of the distributions to match the experimentally measured failure rates for each failure mechanism), their sum yields a bathtub curve as shown in Figure 14.5.2.

The bathtub curve is divided into three regions. The leftmost is the "infant mortality" region. This is the initial turn-on phase where failures due to inherent defects in constituent components and manufacturing techniques usually appear. In order to ensure that these failures occur before the product is shipped to a customer, most manufacturers "burn-in" their products for time periods sufficient to allow inherently defective products to fail prior to shipment.

The right-hand portion of the bathtub curve is the "end of useful life" portion. This portion of the curve is used to establish the *design lifetime* of the assembly. The design lifetime of a product is that age at which the probability of operability at the end of the recommended service interval is less than 0.5, due to the acceleration in the frequency of failures resulting from long-term deterioration of constituent components. As the failure rate of the constituent components continues to escalate, it becomes increasingly difficult to maintain the operability of the assembly.

The region of the bathtub curve between the infant mortality region and the design lifetime region is the statistical region, where failures are entirely random. The statistical failure rate region of the curve is very long compared to the infant mortality region and end-of-life region. Over the statistical failure rate region, failures are randomly unpredictable. This region is essentially flat, indicating a fairly uniform failure rate per unit time over this region. Although the actual failure rate may be low, it is always a finite, positive number. Regardless of the time (distance along the x axis) between and the failure rate in the statistical failure region will, to the limits of precision available from the actual data, approach a horizontal line indicating a constant, evenly distributed failure rate. Because this region is flat, one can use the concept of the mean time between failures (MTBF), a quantification of failure rate, to predict the length of time the system can be expected to remain operational. It is a statistical average that is valid over a population of systems, but does not provide any guidance on what will happen with any specific system at any specific time.

Failure Rates. Since the failure rate is essentially constant over the statistical failure rate region of the bathtub curve, the failure rate of any electronic component and, hence, any electronic system assembled from electronic components can be derived from the failure rate data established in *Military Handbook: Reliability Prediction of Electronic Equipment.*[2] This handbook, known as *MIL Handbook 217,* provides experimentally derived failure rate data on electronic components commonly found in electronic assemblies, including fire alarm system components. *MIL Handbook 217* allows the engineer to compute the failure rates of the detectors, notification appliances, control panels, relay panels, interfaces, and other system components. From these failure rates the engineer can then compute the inherent failure rate (IFR) for the system. It is derived from the failure rates of the components from which the system has been assembled. It is important to keep in mind that this inherent failure rate does not include failures due to improper design or installation. Failures caused by design errors or installation errors must be added to the inherent failure rate computed from *MIL Handbook 217* before one can calculate the failure rate of a device or system.

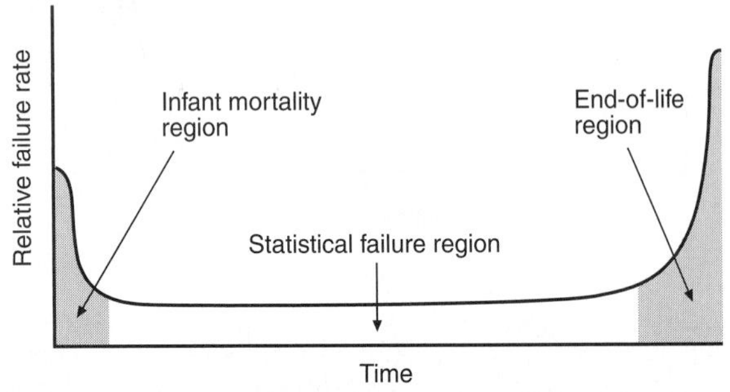

FIGURE 14.5.2 Bathtub Curve, the Sum of the Turn-On and Lifetime Curves

Once the inherent failure rate has been computed, the reliability of the system can be calculated:

$$R = e^{-\Lambda t}$$

where

R = Reliability of the system

e = Napierian logarithm base, 2.71828

Λ = Inherent failure rate of the system

t = Time period for which reliability has been computed[4,5]

This relation allows one to determine the maintenance interval based on the inherent failure rate of the system and the reliability level sought. The factor t is the interval of time between each execution of the inspection, testing, and maintenance procedures for the system. Assuming maintenance restores the entire system to complete operability, the required maintenance interval is computed from

$$t_R = \ln R_R/(-\Lambda)$$

where

$\ln R_R$ = Napierian log of the required reliability, R_R

Λ = Inherent failure rate of the system

t_R = Required maintenance interval to achieve the required reliability

The mathematical relations shown give the engineer the ability to calculate a recommended maintenance interval on a totally new product. It allows the engineer to calculate a maintenance interval that is specifically intended to produce a system with a predetermined reliability. Indeed, most high-technology systems and products have maintenance regimens developed from these relations rather than the consensus committee method used for fire alarms.

An Example Analysis

To illustrate the usefulness of the above computational method, consider the fire alarm system shown in Figure 14.5.3. It consists of 10 smoke detectors, a horn/strobe notification appliance, and a control panel. Its design objective is to alert the occupants of a fire, enabling them to make safe egress from the facility, with a reliability of 90 percent (0.9). For the purposes of this example only, and with the understanding that these failure rates are not derived from any specific device but are intended to be of the same order of magnitude as commercially available products, use the failure rates in Table 14.5.1.

The inherent failure rate of the system as described is 43.65 f/moh:

$$43.65 \text{ f/moh} = 0.00004365 \text{ failures per hour (f/h)}$$

$$\Lambda = 0.3824 \text{ failures per year}$$

Using the required interval equation

$$t_R = \ln R_R/(-\Lambda)$$

where

$$\ln R_R = \ln 0.90 = -0.11$$

$$\Lambda = 0.3824$$

$$t_R = -0.11/-0.3824$$

$$t_R = 0.288 \text{ yr}$$

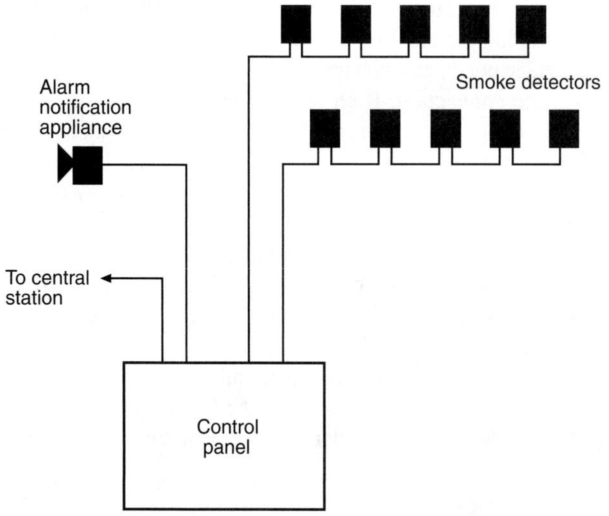

FIGURE 14.5.3 Simplified Example Fire Alarm System

TABLE 14.5.1 Compilation of Computed Failure Rates Providing the Basis for the Reliability Calculation

System Component	*Quantity (q)*	*Failure Rate (λ) (f/mdoh)*	*$(q_x\lambda_x)$ (f/moh)*
Smoke detectors	10	1.00	10.00
Horn/strobe	1	2.50	2.50
Control panel	1	25.00	25.00
Screw terminals	49	0.10	4.90
Wire segments	25	0.05	1.25
Inherent failure rate, Λ			43.65

This indicates that this system, with the component failure rates used, will require a complete inspection, test, and maintenance routine every 0.288 years in order to maintain at least a 90 percent reliability in achieving its design objectives. As performance-based, objective-oriented designs become more prevalent, reliability predictions for those systems similar to this example will be required to determine the maintenance frequency necessary to achieve the performance criteria. A reliability of 0.9 is a very high reliability, well above that of most systems. It means that there is only a 10 percent chance that there will be any form of failure during the time periods between inspection, testing, and maintenance routines.

The concept of failure is very broad here. Failures include trouble conditions resulting from supervised conditions; spurious alarms; failure to alarm within the design sensitivity or time frame for the design fire; and failures of electronic components, even if the component failure does not cause a system performance malfunction. A reliability of 0.9 (90 percent) is much higher than most owners need. This same system (see Figure 14.5.3 and Table 14.5.1) could achieve a 50 percent reliability with a maintenance schedule of 1.8 years. A maintenance program predicated on an inspection and testing regimen performed every 1.8 years will surely be less expensive than one based on a time interval of every 0.288 years. So how would one determine what target reliability one should use? Clearly, a balance must be achieved between the cost of the service/maintenance program and the inherent reliability of the system. Ideally, the reliability to be achieved should reflect analysis of the cost of failure, which will in turn need to distinguish among different types of failures, as listed above.

The inspection, testing, and maintenance schedules required by *NFPA 72*®, *National Fire Alarm Code*®, are prescriptive in nature and are based on a consensus opinion of what an average system requires. They are not the result of actual reliability calculations. The facility owner/operator must keep in mind that the prescriptive requirements represent the minimum acceptance criteria. There are often circumstances that demand that these minimum criteria be exceeded. It is obvious from the preceding that the larger or more complex the system is, the more frequently it must be inspected and tested if the design performance is to be achieved.

The implications of reliability cannot be overstated. The failure to maintain a system virtually assures the owner/operator of the protected site that the fire alarm system will *not* achieve the design objective.

ELECTRONIC COMPONENTS

The anticipated reliability of an electronic system such as a fire alarm system can be computed because the reliability of the individual electronic components has been thoroughly studied and documented, primarily under the auspices of the U.S. Department of Defense. This prior research has shown that each general type of electronic component exhibits particular and predictable failure modes. Understanding these failure modes leads to understanding the impact such a failure may have on a fire alarm system component (detector, notification appliance, control unit, or other such system component). It is important for the owner/operator or responsible party to be aware of these failure modes, as the test methods prescribed by *NFPA 72* are intended to uncover those system components that have suffered a component failure.

Semiconductors

Semiconductor devices fail either to a short or open circuit. The semiconductors in use in modern fire alarm systems often include integrated circuits (IC) consisting of hundreds of thousands of simple semiconductor diodes and transistors. This is especially true of the microcomputers at the operational core of the control unit. Regardless of the complexity of the component, most semiconductor failures are catastrophic in nature, meaning that they fail completely and precipitously, often with a little puff of white smoke curling up from the circuit board.

Semiconductor failures are the result of one of three causes: (1) internal flaw, (2) overcurrent, or (3) overvoltage. Internal flaws are becoming less common as semiconductor manufacturing science continues to advance. Nevertheless, occasionally thermal ion migration or die-bond failure, typical internal flaws, cause a semiconductor to fail.

Since microcomputer memory consists of large integrated circuit arrays of transistor memory cells, there is the possibility of a memory failure. Usually, memory failures are catastrophic in nature and the entire device fails. It is rare that a single memory cell (location) or group of cells fails to retain data. Often, control units have diagnostic programs that are executed during the regularly scheduled maintenance to detect memory location failures. Additionally, regular thorough functional tests provide a measure of assurance that there are no memory location failures where the executable programs are stored.

The probability of this type of event is addressed in the reliability calculations presented earlier. Given enough time, a failure of this type is likely to occur, even with the highest-quality electronic equipment. The testing frequency and methods stipulated by the manufacturer and *NFPA 72* are intended to identify these types of failures with a minimum elapsed time period between the occurrence of the failure and its discovery. In other words, the time between failure and its discovery is as short as possible.

Overcurrent and overvoltage failures are usually associated with some other event that places an unintended stress on the system. Occasionally the event is the failure of some other electronic component subjecting adjacent components to the overvoltage or overcurrent. More frequently, overvoltages and overcurrents are the result of wiring and interconnection errors. Regardless, both overvoltages and overcurrents cause severe overheating of the semiconductor die, and the current-carrying portion of the die melts and/or vaporizes. Obviously, this type of damage is irreversible. Usually, these types of failures result in trouble signals and unwarranted activations of parts of the system and generally do not go unnoticed. It is important to correctly identify the source of the failure quickly. Otherwise, it is likely to occur again. Electrical transients caused by lightning, power supply spikes and surges, operation of highly inductive or capacitive equipment in close proximity to the fire alarm system, and even radio frequency interference have been known to cause these types of failures. Generally, the reliability computations presented earlier do not explicitly address the contribution of these external events to the failure rate of the system.

Resistors, Capacitors, and Inductors

These components are classified as "passive" components. They are less likely to fail than semiconductor devices because their structure is much simpler. Usually, these components fail to an open circuit. This generally causes some type of inexplicable action by the system, such as a trouble signal or the unwarranted actuation of some control system function. Rarely do these failures occur, and on those occasions when they do, they are immediately noticed. These failures are included in the reliability computations presented earlier.

Circuit Board Solder Bonds

A major source of electronic system failures occurs in the solder bonds between the electronic components and the circuit board. Solder bonds are occasionally broken during shipping and installation, rendering the unit "dead on arrival." Unfortunately, broken solder bonds do not always show up immediately. Broken solder bonds can behave as either an intermittent or high-resistance connection. Both of these cause spurious operation of portions of the system or intermittent trouble signals. There is no guarantee that these failures will be noticed when they occur. Broken solder bonds are just as likely to allow the unit to "fail silent."

As a system ages, the lead and tin atoms in the solder begin to migrate, allowing the solder to crystallize and become brittle. Variations in temperature, vibrations, and excessive moisture also contribute to the premature failure of solder bonds. A significant percentage of the computed failure rate for a fire alarm system component is derived from the failure rate assigned to each of the hundreds of solder bonds in that component.[2]

Transformers

Transformers are generally very reliable. Furthermore, since most transformers are used in the power supply section of a control unit, their failure will cause obvious indications, making timely repair likely.

Relays

Those switching functions that cannot be accomplished with solid-state (transistor) switches are accomplished with relays. Relays are electromechanical switches that are activated by causing current to flow through an electromagnetic coil situated such that the magnetic attraction developed by the coil pulls a switch from one pole to another. Often several switches are connected together so that the energization of the coil causes all of the switches (poles) to transfer at the same time.

As in any other mechanical component with moving parts, there is a possibility of a mechanical impediment to operation from dust, corrosion, or wear. There is also the possibility that, even though the electromagnet has mechanically closed the contacts, electrical current fails to flow due to contact contamination by oxide, dirt, or some other material. The continuity of the electromagnetic coil can be lost, rendering the relay inoperative.

With all of these potential failure modes, relays do not provide the level of reliability of solid-state components. Nevertheless, most fire alarm system control units are equipped with relays, because they are very useful for providing a general-purpose switching function, especially for circuits that operate at higher voltages, such as 115 V ac. Although some relays are available in sealed versions, most relays are constructed with simple dust covers. This is usually adequate for normal indoor installations, but extra care must be exercised when testing a unit that is installed where it is exposed to a wide variation in ambient temperature, dust, excessive humidity, or corrosive aerosols. All of these environmental factors have been implicated in relay failures.

When "operation-critical" functions are performed by a fire alarm system with relays, the failure rate of the relay must be included in the reliability computation for the fire alarm control unit. The testing regimen for a fire alarm control unit must test the operability of all of the relays to verify that they are still operable.

Switches

Switches enable an operator to introduce electronic signals into the fire alarm system. The least reliable part of any switching system is the human operator. Nevertheless, once the operator is taken out of the picture, there are two general failure modes for switches: (1) failing to operate when they should and (2) operating when they should not. Since switches are usually mechanical components with moving parts, they suffer relatively high failure rates. The exception to this rule are some of the newer capacitive and membrane switch technologies where the parts do not actually move.

The first failure mode is of lesser concern, because an operator is present and the failure is immediately apparent. It is extremely rare that a fire alarm system is designed requiring that an operator activate a switch in order to secure the life safety and property conservation objectives of the system. Usually, system switches are used to interrupt the automatic functions of the control unit. In this scenario, failure of the switch should result in a safe condition.

The second failure mode usually takes the form of intermittence and generally causes trouble signals. The listing criteria for the nationally recognized testing laboratories require that the off-normal position of any switch result in a trouble signal. This requirement came from years of experience with failures of switches.

Screw Terminals

The least reliable part of a screw terminal is the person with the wire stripper and screwdriver. However, screw terminals do occasionally vibrate loose. *NFPA 72* requires that the wiring to initiating devices and notification appliances be monitored for integrity. However, wiring within the control unit enclosure is not required to be, and is often not, monitored for integrity. Consequently, the failure rate of the screw terminals must be factored into the reliability calculations.

Fuses

Fuses demonstrate one principal failure mode: they fail to an open circuit. This failure mode led nationally recognized testing laboratories to establish a listing criterion requiring that all fuses be monitored for integrity. The failure of any fuse should result in a trouble signal. It is required that monitoring fuses for integrity be done during testing.

Indicator Lamps

The invention of light-emitting diodes (LEDs) ended the reliability problems with indicator lamps. Although it is possible for an LED to fail, it is not a common occurrence. When LEDs fail, they cease making light. LED indicators are generally deemed inherently reliable and are not always monitored for integrity. Their failure rate is included in the reliability prediction for the control unit.

Batteries

Batteries are the most commonly used source of secondary power for fire alarm systems. It is important to understand how batteries fail in order to understand the importance of proper testing. Batteries are designed to provide a specified current for a specified time at a specified voltage. The specified current for a specified time is called capacity. Batteries undergo failure modes where they lose their capacity. Batteries can also lose their output voltage. These two failure modes are separate and distinct, occurring independently of each other.

The loss of capacity cannot be discovered by simply measuring open terminal potential, nor does the loss of terminal potential necessarily imply a loss of capacity. When a totally "dead" battery, that is, one that cannot provide any current at any voltage, is measured with a voltmeter under "open terminal conditions," the meter will usually show very close to nominal potential (voltage). That is because the mechanism of failure which results in the loss of capacity does not necessarily change the open terminal potential of the battery. When a battery is measured with a voltmeter and shows less than nominal open terminal potential, it may still have the ability to provide very large currents in spite of its lower terminal voltage. Consequently, the testing regimen for battery systems must test the ability of the battery to perform its intended function: to store and supply, as needed, electrical energy. A measurement of terminal potential and whether the battery "holds charge" does not provide an adequate assessment of the battery set.

Wires

Wiring is subject to two general classes of failure: (1) breakage of the conductor and (2) loss of insulation. The continuity of wiring conductors used in signaling line circuits, initiating device circuits, and notification appliance circuits is required to be monitored for integrity per *NFPA 72*. When fire alarm control units are used to actuate extinguishing systems, the wiring to the actuating mechanism and other critical functions should be monitored for integrity also. However, the monitoring circuitry in most fire alarm system control units does not have the ability to distinguish between a normal conductor and one that is damaged. Close visual inspection is necessary on initial acceptance and whenever revisions are made.

The insulation on wiring conductors represents a different problem. Thermoplastic wire insulation behaves much like a supercooled liquid, in that it can flow over time away from a point of compression. This is particularly common when conductors are pulled taut against the edge of a metal enclosure or when pinched between an electrical box and its cover (both indicative of substandard installation practice). Under these conditions, the insulation will slowly flow away from the stress point, eventually allowing the conductor to make electrical contact with the enclosure. This creates a "ground fault."

The nationally recognized testing laboratories require that fire alarm system control units operate completely isolated from earth ground and provide ground-fault detection. These requirements ensure that a single ground fault will be detected, yet will not impair the operation of the system. It is imperative that the first ground fault be corrected before a second one occurs, as the second ground fault introduces a circuit via ground between two separate circuits in the system.

We can see that there is a direct mathematical connection between the reliability of a system and the failure rates of the constituent components. We have also reviewed the types of failures that occur with the types of electronic components that are used in the detectors, notification appliances, and control units in a fire alarm system. If an engineer were given a target reliability level to be achieved, the quantities of each fire alarm system component in the system, complete parts lists for each and every system component, and the failure rate data of each of those electronic components, she/he could, conceptually, calculate a maintenance interval for the system. In actual practice, this is rarely done. Instead, minimum-compliance prescriptive maintenance intervals are used.

INSPECTION, TESTING, AND MAINTENANCE REQUIREMENTS FOR SIGNALING SYSTEMS AND COMPONENTS

The reliability analysis presented earlier establishes the demand that fire alarm systems be maintained. *NFPA 72* establishes this requirement and places the responsibility for the regular inspection, testing, and maintenance on the owner/operator of the site. *NFPA 72* references the manufacturer's instructions, effectively making the manufacturer's instructions part of *NFPA 72* by reference and thus enforceable by the local authorities having jurisdiction (AHJ).

Definitions

To discuss the inspection, testing, and maintenance of fire alarm systems, one must define several terms that are not explicitly defined in *NFPA 72*, but are important in establishing the expected course of conduct.

Inspection. An *inspection* is a close visual observation of the item being inspected without causing the item to perform its intended function. There is said to be a facility manager who insists that the inspector's nose be less than 12 in. (305 mm) from the object to qualify as an inspection. This rule differentiates between a casual glance at a device and an inspection. It works for the manager. An inspection does not require the operation of the device being inspected, but it does require that a written record be made of the observed status of the device. Is it clean? Dirty? Bent? Covered with paint? In "as installed" condition?

Test. A *test* is a process where the device under test is provided a stimulus to determine if it is functional, and a written record of the response of the device under test is made. The term *test* does not necessarily imply that the stimulus is of a similar magnitude to that expected from the fire the unit is intended to detect. However, it does imply that the device has also been inspected while the test was conducted. Many tests require that the system be intentionally impaired to determine if the system properly responds to the impairment. *It is critical that all conditions created in the context of a test be returned to the normal state before the test is deemed completed.* The written record should include both the observed status of the unit and whether it was found to be functional.

Sensitivity Measurement. *Sensitivity measurement* is the quantitative measurement and recording of the stimulus necessary to achieve an alarm signal from an initiating device. This is very different from a test. A test does not imply that the stimulus is of a similar magnitude to that obtained from the design fire. A sensitivity measurement determines how large a stimulus is necessary to cause an alarm response. This measurement is to be compared to the value for the unit as shipped to quantify any change in the performance one can anticipate from the unit. Thus, the sensitivity measurement is intended to assess the ability of the detector to perform its intended function when the design fire occurs. It is understood that initiating devices are also inspected and tested when the sensitivity is measured. The written record should contain the observed status, the sensitivity measurement, and the verification of the functionality of the unit.

Bear in mind that many "intelligent/analog" detectors are actually addressable sensors where the alarm set point is stored in a memory location at the control panel. These systems continuously measure the sensor output and compare it to the value stored in memory for that particular device. These systems often can provide a printout of the current measured values for the initiating devices and their alarm points, thus satisfying the requirements of *NFPA 72.* Observations of physical status and verification of operability are normally associated with measurement of sensitivity, and these must be separately performed when "intelligent/analog" detection is encountered.

Acceptance Test. An *acceptance test* of a system is the process wherein every initiating device is provided an appropriate stimulus that simulates the existence of the design fire, and the design sequence of operations of each system component in the entire system is verified and recorded in written form. This is usually achieved with a sensitivity measurement, including the functional test to initiate an alarm. Once the alarm is initiated, the technician verifies that all system functions, including interconnections to other building systems, operate as designed. It is preferable to repetitively operate all interconnections for each initiating device rather than verify their operation once and assume that all other initiating device alarms will cause the same operations. Often, problems show up after several operational cycles that would otherwise be missed. Programming errors in some software architectures can lead to problems that can only be uncovered with complete function verifications.

Reacceptance Test. A *reacceptance test* is an acceptance test performed after modifications have been made to the system. Modifications include any change, repair, adjustment to hardware or wiring, or any change in system software. The scope of a reacceptance test can be limited. All components, circuits, system operations, or software functions that are known to be affected by the change in the system must be tested, in addition to 10 percent of the initiating devices (up to a maximum of 50) known to not be directly affected by the change. A reacceptance test does not necessarily imply a complete acceptance test in all cases. However, there are times when a reacceptance test is equivalent to an acceptance test because of the nature of the modifications or repairs performed.

Documentation

Every form of evaluation of a fire alarm system must be completely documented. This includes inspections, tests, sensitivity measurements, acceptance tests, and reacceptance tests. This documentation should be retained in a secure location for future reference. The lack of complete documentation is often viewed by the courts and regulatory authorities as presumptive evidence that the required testing and inspection have not been done. A minimum compliance form for documenting the inspection and testing of a fire alarm system is provided in *NFPA 72*. However, many AHJs require a more complete form as part of a test plan.

Personnel

NFPA 72 establishes qualifications criteria for individuals inspecting and testing fire alarm systems. The facility owner is responsible for making certain that the people performing these functions are qualified. Many fire alarm systems are connected to supervising stations and automatic extinguishing systems. The personnel testing a fire alarm system must be sufficiently familiar with these interconnections to take the appropriate steps to prevent accidental discharge of an extinguishing system or reporting of a fire alarm to the municipal fire service during testing of the system.

Preparation and Coordination of Inspection, Testing, and Maintenance Activities

Many fire alarm systems are connected to off-premises monitoring services, fire pump controllers, special agent extinguishing systems, and building management systems. There are times when the functional testing of a fire alarm system will cause serious interruptions in site operations due to these interconnections. By the same token, it is critical to verify that the interconnections are operative and that the fire management plan for the entire site is achieved when a fire alarm signal occurs.

This presents a dilemma to the facility manager. Should a shutdown be endured, a major problem if the facility is the hub of an online computer network, or should the shutdowns be bypassed, thereby failing to verify complete system operability? Usually the question is not an all or nothing situation, and reasoned decisions must be made regarding which automatic interconnections to bypass and which to allow to operate. The facility manager must recognize that some interconnections actuate extinguishing systems that represent a significant cleanup and/or recharge expense if they are actuated. Understandably, these types of systems must be disabled for routine inspection, testing, and maintenance. However, the portion of the system that is disabled should be as small as possible. For example, many extinguishing system actuators are removable from the extinguishing agent containers, allowing all of the electrical components to be tested. This is a very desirable feature. However, since the electrical supervision cannot recognize this type of impairment, there is the danger that the system will be left with the actuators removed from the agent storage containers. Extra care must be taken to ensure that all of the actuators are properly reinstalled at the conclusion of the inspection, testing, and maintenance program.

Some interconnections, such as smoke management systems, automated process controls, and data processing systems, will interrupt site productivity to the point that the cost of an unwarranted actuation is too high to allow during routine inspection, testing, and maintenance. Systems with these types of interconnections can be designed with built-in disconnect switches that are supervised when in the off-normal state. However, remember that when these functions are disabled, their operability is not verified. It may be reasonable to permit the inspection, testing, and maintenance program to be performed with these types of functions disabled during normal operations time in a site that has experienced no modifications since the initial acceptance tests; however, it is not appropriate if revisions or modifications have been made. If it is critical for a function to occur in order to achieve the design objectives of a fire protection system, then it is equally critical that those functions be inspected and tested.

Finally, off-site reporting and resulting responses must be addressed. These can be effectively managed with prior notification. All impairments must be monitored. Usually, at the beginning of a service visit, the technician places a telephone call to the monitoring entity to advise them that the system is being tested and to disregard alarm and trouble signals. The monitoring entity should be under strict instructions that, when such a call is received, the following are addressed:

1. Call back the facility manager to verify that testing is about to commence.

2. Verify that an alternative procedure to report a fire is in place.
3. Require verification when testing will be completed and deem any signal occurring after that time as a real signal, unless a second call is received rescheduling the estimated completion time.
4. Require a follow-up call on completion of the maintenance visit that confirms the system has been restored to fully automatic status.

System impairments that facilitate inspection, testing, and maintenance should not be granted casually. A system impairment can permit an inconsequential fire to become a large-loss fire. It is also possible for fires to grow to serious proportions because the monitoring entity failed to report the fire. Fire alarm systems should be designed and serviced with these considerations in mind. Every system must be serviced, and often the service activities necessitate disabling portions of the fire alarm system or interconnections. However, the disabling should be limited to the smallest possible portion of the building fire protection assets. Furthermore, if at all possible, those portions that are directly affected by the testing should be disabled individually, thereby keeping operative as many building fire protection assets as possible.

The Test Plan

The inspection, testing, and maintenance regimen for a fire alarm system must stipulate the following:

1. What procedure is to be performed?
2. How it is to be performed?
3. What data are to be recorded in the documentation?
4. How frequently is the specific procedure to be performed?

These four criteria are usually organized into a test plan. A formal test plan is often a very good investment. It establishes a formal procedure to ensure the complete inspection and testing of the system and a record of the results for future reference. Once a test plan has been developed, it is used each time the inspection and test program are performed. Consistency of the presentation of results facilitates identifying problem areas.

NFPA 72, Chapter 10, "Inspection, Testing, and Maintenance," is organized to facilitate the development of a formal test plan. It establishes test methods and then stipulates an inspection and testing frequency. The test methods outline what procedures are to be performed. They are intended to be used in conjunction with the manufacturer's instructions for the specific make and model of equipment involved. Thus the manufacturer's instructions provide the specific "how to" information. The issue of documentation is addressed by *NFPA 72,* Chapter 10, in the section on records.

The frequency of each procedure varies, depending on the general class of device. For example, batteries are inspected more frequently than initiating devices. The frequency of visual inspections is different (i.e., more frequent) than testing. The frequencies provided by *NFPA 72* have been based primarily on experience developed over the recent past rather than reliability data for the fire alarm system components.

Supervising Station Systems

Supervising station systems monitor a number of protected premises fire alarm systems via one or more types of communication paths. The principal concerns during the inspection and testing of these systems is that each communication path is intact and operable and that the supervising station fire alarm control unit is fully operational.

The inspection, testing, and maintenance procedures for specific models of a control unit for a supervising station fire alarm control system are established by the manufacturer. Since supervising station fire alarm systems include many of the same components that make up a protected premises system but organized in a manner that fulfills the design requirements for a supervising station system, the inspection and testing requirements for these components are the same, regardless of the type of system in which they are used.

Protected Premises Systems

There are two general objectives in the testing and inspection of a protected premises fire alarm system. The first is to verify the operability of the system and identify any failures in system components that have failed to a "silent" state. Any failures identified during the course of the inspection and testing must be repaired to restore the system to a fully operational state. The second is to identify changes in the occupancy that render a formerly appropriate system inappropriate, based on the hazard area to be protected. Both objectives affect proper response to a fire.

Fire Alarm Control Unit

The manufacturer for each make and model of fire alarm control unit (FACU) provides a recommended service procedure for the control unit. These procedures are included in *NFPA 72* by reference. However, the fire alarm control unit is one building block in a much larger system, and the manufacturer rarely knows how the overall system is designed. Consequently, there are at least two layers of functions that must be tested. The first layer comprises those functions that are an integral part of the FACU, irrespective of the particular system in which it is used. These functions include supervision of relays, fuses, main power supply, batteries, wiring integrity, alarm indications, trouble indications, supervisory indications, and isolation from ground. The second layer is specific to the facility or system. These are usually in a "sequence of operations" format, establishing the response functions that occur as a result of each input (initiating or supervisory device) signal.

Functions. All functions of the system should be tested. The supervision of all signaling line circuits, initiating device circuits, notification appliance circuits, and signal transmission circuits must be tested. Furthermore, when the FACU is used for the actuation of extinguishing systems, all circuits activating equipment whose operation is critical to successful extinguishment must also be supervised. The testing of these functions consists of creating breaks and ground faults on each circuit and verifying that the appropriate trouble signal is rendered by the FACU.

The sequence of operations must then be tested to verify the operability of all those functions the control unit is intended to implement specifically for the hazard area it protects. These functions are application specific and vary from one site to another.

Annex C of *NFPA 72* provides specific tests for each type (style) of circuit. Trouble signals can be introduced on signaling line circuits and initiating device circuits by temporarily removing detectors (from their mounting bases) or wiring conductors from detectors. Similar techniques are used for notification appliance circuits. Signaling line circuits are usually interrupted at the FACU screw terminals, with a verification that the trouble signal is received. Alarm signals must be generated on each initiating device circuit or zone by causing a detector to alarm with heat, smoke, or radiant energy, as appropriate, to verify that the design alarm response occurs. The alarm response will include actuation of the notification appliances, alarm indication at the control unit, actuation of interconnected equipment, and signal transmission to the off-premises receiving station.

Conductors on each initiating device, notification appliance, and signaling line circuit must be temporarily grounded to verify that the ground detection circuitry and associated trouble indications are operative. The applications manual for most FACUs stipulates the amount of resistance between conductors and ground that should be detected. A fixed resistor reflecting that criterion should be used to test ground-fault detection.

Special hazards extinguishing systems employ specialized equipment to address the unique needs of the various extinguishing system equipment designs and agent limitations. Each manufacturer is required to provide an engineering manual that addresses the inspection, testing, and maintenance needs of the control unit and ancillary equipment necessary to operate the special hazards extinguishing system. These functions include cross-zone detection, matrix detection, verified detection, sequential detection, detector counting detection, abort switches, solenoid activation (release), and squib actuation (release). When these functions are implemented by the FACU, the specific inspection and testing requirements established by the manufacturer must be observed.

The functional test serves to verify that all of the system interconnects are energized when appropriate and that the system achieves the basic functions it was designed to achieve. However, this type of general "macroscopic" test does not fully evaluate all the system components. There are specific tests to evaluate these components.

Fuses. The listing standards of the nationally recognized testing laboratories require that all fuses be supervised. However, it is possible that the supervisory circuitry could fail and not provide an indication that such a critical component was inoperative. Furthermore, it is conceivable that the fuse may have been replaced with another of the wrong value. Consequently, all fuses must be checked for supervision and correct value. Keep in mind that a fuse cannot be properly checked visually. The only way to check a fuse for continuity is with a volt-ohm meter (VOM) or multimeter.

Indicating Lamps. All indicating lamps must be operated to verify that they are still functional. Modern fire alarm control panels use LEDs for indicator lamps. LEDs are much more reliable than the old incandescent lamps but can still fail. Most fire alarm control units are equipped with a lamp-test switch specifically for this purpose, while others have a key-pad code that performs the lamp-test function.

Main Power Supply. There are electronic component failures that could render the main power supply incapable of supporting the design current load on the system during fires yet not appear under normal, quiescent conditions. The main power supply test entails temporarily disconnecting the secondary supply and applying the maximum design current load to the system while monitoring the output voltage of the system power supply. If the power supply voltage drops below that stipulated in the manufacturer's applications manual, remedial action must be taken.

Engine-Driven Generators. In those instances where an engine-driven generator is used as a required power source, either as a primary or a secondary supply, it must be tested according to the procedures outlined in NFPA 110, *Standard for Emergency and Standby Power Systems.*

Uninterruptable Power Supply (UPS). In those cases where a UPS system is dedicated to the fire alarm system, it must be tested per NFPA 111, *Standard on Stored Electrical Energy Emergency and Standby Power Systems.* Note that a UPS is used for a number of purposes, one of which is the fire alarm system. UPS is treated by *NFPA 72* as being no different than public utility power, and the requirement for a secondary power supply for the fire alarm system is still enforceable.

Secondary Power Supply. The secondary power supply must be able to support the full current load of the fire alarm system when the primary supply is lost. Primary power is often lost during a fire. Testing of the secondary power supply entails temporarily disconnecting the primary power supply and applying the maximum design current load to the system while monitoring the output voltage of the secondary system power supply. If the secondary power supply voltage drops below that stipulated in the manufacturer's applications manual, remedial action must be taken. Additional and more specific testing is required when the secondary power supply consists of a battery set.

Batteries. The lead/acid battery chemistry is the most commonly used type in fire alarm system service. These batteries are typically found as unsealed lead/acid batteries, unsealed calcium grid (lead-calcium) batteries, sealed lead/acid batteries, and gelled electrolyte lead/acid batteries. All of these batteries use a solution of sulfuric acid in water as the electrolyte. These various types require slightly different charging potentials and maintenance. It is imperative that the battery charger be properly matched to the battery, consistent with the listing.

Battery Testing. The testing of a battery set consists of general tests that are performed regardless of battery chemistry and specific tests for specific types of batteries. A visual inspection is required for all types to discover any terminal corrosion, looseness in terminal connections, or electrolyte leakage. All of these are serious conditions that can cause an increase in the series resistance of the battery set, thus depriving the fire alarm system of the necessary operating potential under large current load conditions.

Batteries exhibit a number of failure modes that result in either a loss of operating potential or a loss of capacity. The exact mechanism of each class of failure mode is dependent on the battery chemistry; nickel/cadmium batteries behave somewhat differently than lead/lead peroxide batteries.

Battery Test Regimens. In general, the test regimen for all batteries includes the following:

1. Battery charger test
2. Discharge test, in which the batteries must support a design current load
3. Load voltage test, in which the voltage is measured while the batteries support a design current load
4. Open circuit test, in which the open-circuit potential of the battery is measured

Battery Discharge Rates. There is a relationship between the output potential of a battery, measured in volts, and the output capacity of the battery, measured in ampere hours (Ah). This relationship is illustrated with a "family" of potential versus discharge time curves for a number of discharge currents, as shown in Figure 14.5.4. When the terminal potential reaches 85 percent of original value, the battery is generally considered effectively depleted. The discharge current multiplied by the length of time it takes to deplete the battery is its capacity (C), measured in Ah (ampere hours). Typically, batteries exhibit smaller capacities when the discharge rates are higher. The battery industry usually uses a 20 hour discharge rate for their specifications. A 10 Ah battery will support a 0.5 A load for 20 hours and be at 85 percent of its fully charged potential after having been discharged at that rate for that time period.

The capacity of the battery is a function of the number of charge carriers stored in the unit. Unfortunately, there are chemical reactions that occur within a battery that "lock up" charge carriers into precipitates, thus removing them from the electrochemical reservoir of available charge carriers. This results in the battery becoming depleted far sooner than expected.

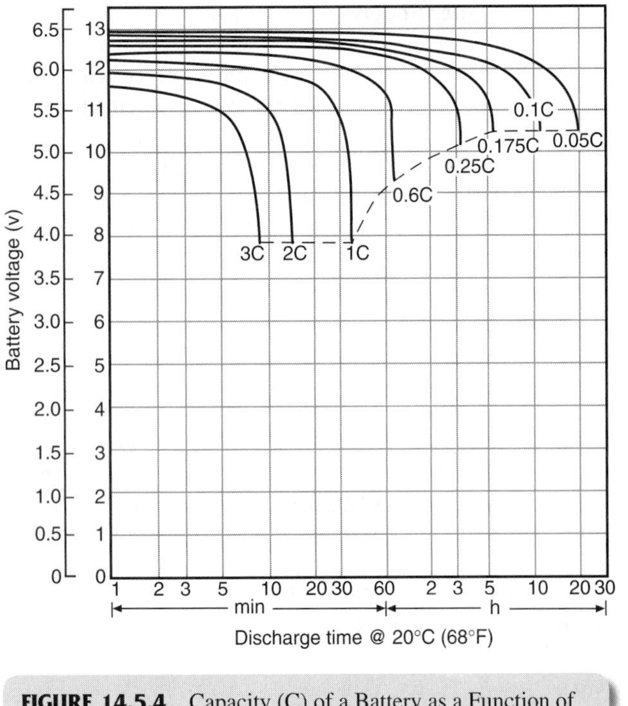

FIGURE 14.5.4 Capacity (C) of a Battery as a Function of Discharge Rate, Time, and Voltage

Battery Deterioration. Two symptoms indicate a deterioration of the battery: (1) loss of capacity (Ah) and (2) loss of potential (voltage). These symptoms can usually be traced to the stresses inherent in recharging and maintaining charge. When the battery is being charged, lead sulfate is converted to lead and lead dioxide. As charging continues, hydrogen and oxygen gas are formed from the electrolysis of the water in the electrolyte solution. In the sealed and gelled electrolyte batteries, the hydrogen and oxygen are contained within the battery until sufficient pressure is achieved to cause the battery to vent. In the unsealed type, these gases are allowed to escape. The loss of hydrogen and oxygen represents a loss of water from the electrolyte. This increases the concentration of the acid in the electrolyte. As a result, a lead sulfate and lead sulfite precipitate begins to form, "locking up" the lead in an insoluble and unusable form. This process is called sulfation. Since the capacity of the battery is directly proportional to the quantity of lead available, a sulfated battery cannot support the current load it could before the sulfation occurred.

With unsealed lead/acid batteries the acid concentration is determined by measuring the specific gravity of the electrolyte. As water is lost, the specific gravity of the electrolyte increases. When the specific gravity reaches the upper allowable limit, reagent-grade distilled water is added, restoring the acid con-

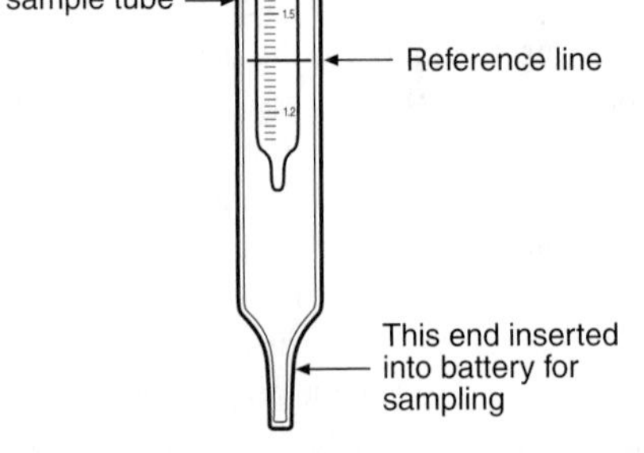

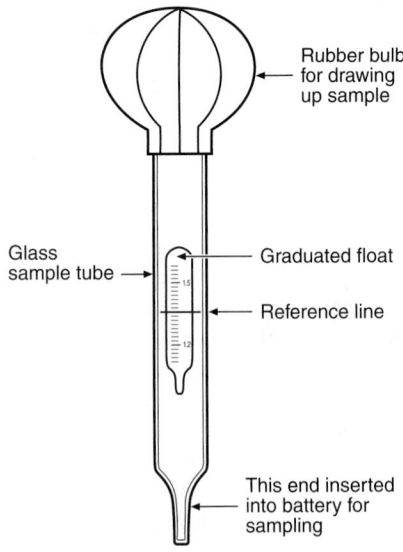

FIGURE 14.5.5 Hydrometer

centration to the design value. The measurement of electrolyte specific gravity is done with a hydrometer, similar to that shown in Figure 14.5.5. Always use one that has a float and a graduated scale.

The sealed lead/acid and gelled electrolyte lead/acid batteries have no provision for returning the electrolyte to the design specific gravity range. These batteries are designed to minimize the loss of hydrogen and oxygen and include design features to offset the effect of the slow leakage that often accompanies continuous float charge. Eventually, the loss of water allows sulfation to occur, with the resultant loss of capacity. If the recharging current is properly matched to the batteries, these types of batteries usually provide reliable service over a time period generally between 3 and 5 years, after which they must be replaced. Figure 14.5.6 shows a typical capacity versus time curve for a sealed or gelled electrolyte lead/acid battery.

Loss of potential failure in batteries comes from either the shorting of a cell or internal deterioration that causes an increase in the internal resistance of the battery. Both of these failure mechanisms result in a battery set that cannot provide sufficient potential for the fire alarm system to operate as intended.

Shorted Battery Cells. Shorted cells usually result from the recharging and maintenance of charge over a period of time. During the recharging of the battery, lead ions move between the lead-dioxide plate and the lead plate. Occasionally a needlelike crystal forms. As it continues to grow, it eventually extends from one plate to an adjacent plate, making an electrically conductive contact between the two. This shorts out the cell, resulting in a battery with a terminal potential 2.2 V lower than originally designed.

When a cell becomes shorted, two serious problems arise. The first is that the battery charger, sensing an inordinately low battery potential, forces a greater charging current into the battery. The increased current overcharges the remaining cells, dehydrating the electrolyte, ultimately causing catastrophic failure. Second, if the fire alarm system loses primary power supply while connected to a battery with a shorted cell, it will not receive an adequate operating potential and will very likely not be able to support the design output load.

Increase of Resistance Within Batteries. Batteries can also lose the ability to maintain output potential due to increases in internal resistance within the battery. During the discharge and recharge of the battery, lead ions migrate through the electrolyte

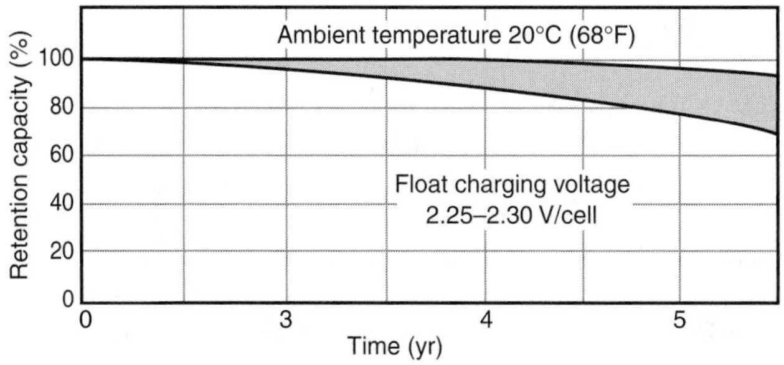

FIGURE 14.5.6 Capacity Versus Time Curve of a Sealed or Gelled Electrolyte Lead/Acid Battery

between the plates within the battery. Eventually, electrical resistance within portions of the plate, interconnecting conductor bars, and electrolyte begins increasing. This causes the internal resistance of the battery to increase. This condition only shows up when the battery is required to supply current to a load (the fire alarm system). The larger the current load placed on the battery, the larger the drop in voltage due to internal resistance, and, hence, the easier it is to detect.

The likelihood of a shorted cell failure and increased resistance failures increases as the length of time under recharging conditions increases. This fact underscores the importance of using the battery that has been listed for use with the battery charger and of performing the maintenance as prescribed by *NFPA 72.*

Nickel/Cadmium Batteries. Nickel/cadmium battery secondary power supplies are rarely encountered in connection with fire alarm systems, but when they are, it is only as sealed batteries. Sealed nickel/cadmium batteries manifest similar failure modes to the lead/acid units. However, there is an additional failure mechanism called the "memory effect" associated with some nickel/cadmium batteries that is unique to that chemistry. Fire alarm systems are "float-charge" applications. These are applications where the battery is maintained at full charge by a battery charger over long periods of time and, occasionally, are partially discharged, only to be restored to full charge when the primary power is restored. Some nickel/cadmium batteries exhibit a "memory effect," where the usable capacity of the battery declines to that quantity that has been recurrently used.[6] Thus, a 20 Ah battery discharged several times by 2 or 3 Ah will lose the ability to supply more than the 2 or 3 Ah. Nickel/cadmium batteries are much better adapted to cycle charge applications where the unit is completely discharged prior to recharging. This is an additional loss of capacity failure mode that must be addressed in the test program.

Battery Charger and Load Tests. Because the failure modes of batteries are so complex, battery secondary power supplies represent a challenge for any testing program. NFPA 72 provides specific tests for each type of battery. Each type requires a charger test, where the recharge potential of the battery charger is measured with a multimeter to verify that the recharge potential is within acceptable limits. Since most battery failure mechanisms are related to recharging and overcharging, the charger test is essential.

For each type of battery there is a load test. A current load is placed on the batteries and the battery potential is measured. This test is intended to identify batteries that have excessive internal resistances. Consequently, the larger the load, the better. The ideal load is one that is equivalent to the fire alarm system in full alarm with all notification appliances operating, the emergency voice evacuation system operating, and extinguishing system solenoid valves energized. A bank of power resistors can be used to simulate the system load for the battery load test (Figure 14.5.7). One 24 ohm (Ω), 100 W resistor allows 1.0 A to flow at 24 V. Current increases for parallel-connected resistors.

Where the battery is being used for a public fire alarm reporting system, the load tests must be modified and the potential between each side of the battery and earth-ground must be

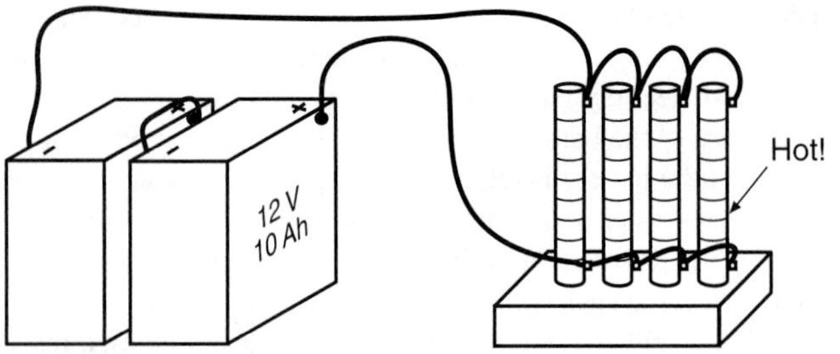

FIGURE 14.5.7 Bank of Power Resistors

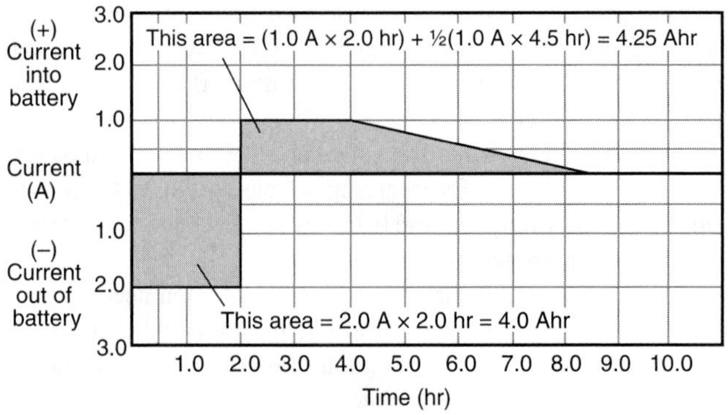

FIGURE 14.5.9 Partial Discharge/Recharge Integration Used to Infer Battery Capacity

included. The standard multimeter cannot be used for testing public fire alarm reporting system power supplies due to the possible erroneous readings caused by voltage differentials in the ground potential. A standard 10-M input impedance meter can be converted to read battery potentials for a public reporting system power supply, with the addition of a properly sized ballast resistor (Figure 14.5.8).

$$R = 100\ \Omega/\text{V} \times \text{Battery voltage}$$

For a 12-V battery

$$100\ \Omega/\text{V} \times 12\ \text{V} = 1200\ \Omega$$

It is important to note that none of these tests actually tests for battery capacity. The load test is used to infer that no serious loss of capacity has occurred. This inference is supported by the observation that loss of capacity is almost always accompanied by an increase in internal resistance. A better inference can be drawn from a timed discharge/recharge test. In this test, a fraction of the battery capacity is discharged and then the battery is returned to the battery charger, while the current is monitored over time. A curve similar to Figure 14.5.9 results. If the capacity returned to the battery, measured in Ah, is no more than 110 percent of the capacity removed, then the battery has retained its design efficiency and one can be more certain that no loss of capacity has occurred. The only sure way to completely verify design battery capacity is a full, measured discharge of the battery set at the design discharge rates with subsequent monitored recharge.[6]

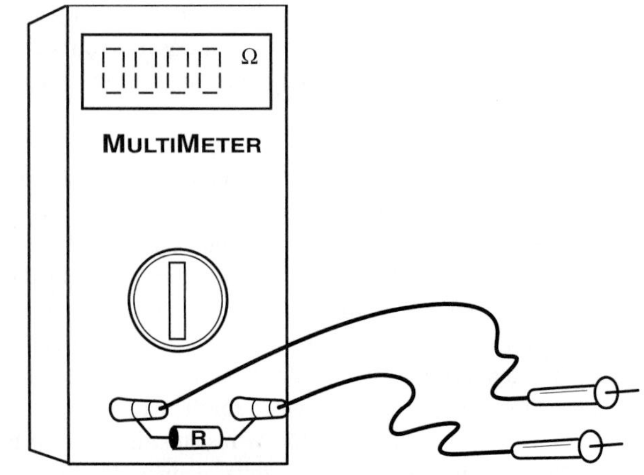

FIGURE 14.5.8 Multimeter

Recently, meters have become available that purport to measure battery capacity by measuring the dynamic impedance of the battery. While some of the manufacturers of these meters proffer "research reports" supporting the ability of the meter to distinguish batteries with compromised capacity from those with full rated capacity, none of these meters has been listed by UL or FM for this purpose, as of the time this chapter was written.

Transient Suppressors. Since fire alarm systems must maintain isolation from ground and monitor that isolation, they are vulnerable to damage from the electromagnetic pulse (EMP) that occurs during a lightning strike. Transient suppressors are designed to absorb a finite quantity of energy before they overheat and fail, melting to a short circuit or vaporizing to an open circuit. These devices must be tested with a multimeter to verify that they are still intact.

Remote Annunciators. Many fire alarm systems include a remote annunciator to provide information regarding the status of the control unit and the identity of alarm signals at a remote location. Representative signals must be generated at the fire alarm control unit, and correct annunciation verified. Remember that most remote annunciators serve to provide the first responding fire service members with critical information relating to the nature and location of the fire alarm. The presentation of this information must be clear and understandable.

Interface Equipment. Commonly, fire alarm control units are interconnected with other control systems in the protected site. These interfaces must be inspected and tested in a manner consistent with the requirements established by the manufacturer and the expected operation of the interfaced systems.

Off-Premises Signal Transmitters. Fire alarm systems often transmit signals to monitoring stations that are off the immediate premises. The transmitter and the signaling line circuit from the protected premises to the supervising station must be inspected and tested as part of the inspection and testing program for the protected premises fire alarm system.

The oldest type of off-premises signaling is the McCulloh system. Where this type of signaling is used, the fire alarm control unit terminals must be regularly inspected for corrosion, and the function must be tested for successful signal transmission, in spite of each of the following four fault conditions:

1. Open circuit in one conductor
2. Ground fault on one conductor
3. Short circuit between the two signal conductors
4. A concurrent open circuit and ground fault

Currently, digital alarm communicator systems are the most commonly provided method for communication to a remote supervising station. Since it is impossible to supervise the entire signal path from protected premises to supervising station, two "numbers" (lines) are used: (1) primary and (2) secondary.

Digital alarm communicator transmitters are tested by verifying that they transmit the appropriate signal to the remote supervising station receiver. When an alarm signal is created in the fire alarm system, it must be verified that the DACT seizes the line and transmits the alarm signal to the supervising station. Similarly, the line seizure and trouble signal transmission must result from a trouble signal on the fire alarm control unit. When either of the signaling lines (numbers) is disconnected, the DACT must transmit a trouble signal on the alternative line within 4 minutes.

Systems similar to the digital alarm communicator are now available using radio communication. These are referred to as digital alarm radio transmitters and receivers (DART and DARR, respectively). These systems must also have provisions for secondary communications paths and must be tested in a similar manner as the DACT/DACR system.

Emergency Voice Communication Equipment. The inspection of the emergency voice communication equipment includes the remote phone jacks, handsets, phone hooks, control panel interface, and amplifiers. These components must be inspected for damage or deterioration due to ambient conditions. The testing includes a verification of the operability of both the primary and backup amplifiers, as well as the switching between them. A verification that the call-in silence, off-hook indication, and the operability of the communication from remote jacks to the base station must be achieved in the testing. Each phone set must be tested and determined to be operable. Finally, system operability with a simulated fire condition communications load, involving the concurrent operation of at least five phone sets, should be conducted to assess the voice quality and clarity of the system.

Guard Tour Monitoring Equipment. When guard tour monitoring equipment is integrated into the fire alarm control unit, it must be added to the inspection and testing schedule for the system. The inspection and testing procedures for this equipment prescribed by the manufacturer should be followed.

Metallic Conductors. Metallic conductors installed in a building are subject to damage and gradual deterioration. The inspection and testing of a fire alarm system must include an evaluation of the wiring. Stray potentials can be introduced into the fire alarm system from a number of sources. These are most often related to leakage currents and electromagnetic interference from high-voltage ac conductors that have been installed in close proximity to the fire alarm system conductors. However, sources of dc leakage currents have also been encountered. The multimeter is used to measure the conductor-to-conductor and conductor-to-ground potentials, both ac and dc, for each fire alarm system circuit. Where the potential differs from that stipulated in the manufacturer's installation manual by more than 1.0 V (ac or dc), the source of the potential must be identified and the problem corrected.

Fire alarm system conductors can also become shorted. There are many circumstances where a shorted circuit will not result in a "trouble" signal at the control panel, because the control unit circuitry does not monitor for short-circuit conditions. Consequently, fire alarm circuits should also be tested with the multimeter to verify the proper impedance on circuits that are not connected to normally closed contacts of other intentionally closed circuits.

Finally, damage to conductors can cause an increase in conductor resistance that will prevent successful operation of the devices served by the circuit. One method to test for this condition is to short the circuit at the end and measure the loop resistance to verify it is within the limits established by the equipment manufacturer. If this method is elected, particular care must be exercised to ensure that no shorting devices can accidentally be allowed to remain in place at the conclusion of the testing. An alternative method requires that detailed records be kept of the loop resistance as installed, including (1) the end-of-line supervisory component and (2) comparing subsequent tests to the as-installed values to identify circuits where the resistance has changed. This method may not be available when testing addressable detector fire alarm systems.

Initiating Devices

Initiating devices sense a fire or a change in the state of some other monitored condition that has an effect on the fire safety of the protected site. These initiating devices, listed in the same order as in *NFPA 72,* include the following:

1. Heat detectors
2. Smoke detectors
3. Radiant energy sensing detectors
4. Sprinkler system waterflow alarms
5. Extinguishing system operation initiating devices
6. Manually activated alarm initiating devices (manual fire alarm boxes)
7. Supervisory signal initiating devices

Each of these devices must be tested to verify that its ability to sense the condition for which it was designed has not deteriorated. The specific test is dependent on the type of device and how it senses the condition it is intended to monitor.

Heat Detectors. A source of failure for heat detection devices is a layer of insulating material between the detector and the fire which retards or prevents response. This can be found in the form of paint or some other coating. Physical damage can also be found to be a source of problems, causing both spurious alarms as well as failure to alarm.

There is a wide variety of heat sensor designs in common use. *NFPA 72* categorizes heat detectors into various classes based on their general operating characteristics and physical form. Each type has unique features and, hence, specific requirements regarding the inspection, testing, and maintenance of detectors of that type. The method of testing is established by the manufacturer of the detector, and it is reviewed by nationally recognized testing laboratories as part of the listing evaluation. Consequently, it must be followed meticulously for the results to be credible.

Most methods involve the use of a heat source to simulate the flow of heated air and smoke beneath the ceiling across the detector surface. *NFPA 72* requires that restorable, spot-type, and line-type heat detectors be tested by heating them in the manner required by the manufacturer and verifying an alarm within 1 minute. Nonrestorable, spot-type, and line-type detectors, such as those that use a eutectic alloy of specific melting point, are not tested until they are 15 years old, at which time they are either all replaced or a sample is removed and tested by a nationally recognized testing laboratory to substantiate their continued operability. The actuation of nonrestorable heat detectors is simulated by shorting the circuit conductors for verification of the circuit operability.

Smoke Detectors. As with heat detectors, there is a wide variety of smoke detectors using a number of different design concepts. Since smoke detectors exist as spot-type, line-type, and air-sampling-type devices, specific methods must be employed that are appropriate to the detector type. However, all inspection, testing, and maintenance methods relating to smoke detectors are designed to ensure three general criteria:

1. Smoke can enter the sensing "chamber" of the detector.
2. The detector attains the alarm state at the smoke concentration for which the detector was listed.
3. The detector alarm signal is received and processed by the fire alarm system control panel.

Spot-type smoke detectors are available using the ionization technology and the photoelectric technology. In ionization detectors, the accumulation of dust within the sensing chamber over time can interfere with the flow of electrical current through the sensing chamber in a manner similar to the effect of smoke. This tends to render the affected detector more sensitive and, hence, more prone to spurious alarms. The same effect is seen in the photoelectric detectors. The accumulation of dust increases the internal reflectance within the sensing chamber, making it more sensitive and prone to render a spurious alarm. A sensitivity measurement is critical in order to identify units that have suffered a change in sensitivity due to dirt accumulation that is not apparent from an external inspection.

Spot-type detectors are also subject to clogging from airborne dust or, worse yet, paint. The application of paint to the exterior of a spot-type smoke detector permanently changes the smoke entry characteristics of a detector and is prohibited by *NFPA 72*. Detectors must be carefully inspected to ensure that smoke entry is uninhibited. Room air-handling equipment can create airflows of such magnitude that it is impossible for the smoke from the design fire to reach the detectors. Consequently, an "in place" test is required to ensure the continued ability for smoke to reach the detector. Usually, an aerosol can of surrogate smoke or some other method outlined in the manufacturer's instructions is used to simulate the flow of the ceiling jet and access to the detector to verify this criterion.

Line-type smoke detectors are usually of the projected beam, light-obscuration type, which use the protected room as a sampling chamber. These detectors respond when the optical transmission of light across the room is reduced due to the presence of smoke. The accumulation of dust and dirt on the optical surfaces of these units can cause an increase in detector sensitivity. Consequently, they must also be inspected. Since the alarm threshold of the projected beam-type detectors must be adjustable to accommodate different room dimensions, the manufacturers of this type of detector provide a test method that was evaluated during the listing evaluation. The sensitivity of the unit must be measurable. Often, neutral density filters or test screens are placed between the emitter and receiver units of the projected beam detector to simulate the optical effect of a smoke accumulation in the protected space.

Air-sampling smoke detectors use a set of sampling tubes and a fan to convey air from the protected space to the detector unit. Detailed inspection and testing methods for these units are stipulated by the manufacturers. The test methods must verify that all of the air-sampling ports and tubes are operative at their design flow rates and that the detector unit, including the sampling fan, is operating within the parameters established by the listing. This implies a sensitivity measurement similar to that required of all of the other detector types.

Smoke detectors are also often used to monitor the air in heating, ventilating, and air-conditioning (HVAC) ducts. Generally, spot-type detectors are used for this type of service, installed in specially listed housings equipped with sampling tubes that allow air to be sampled from the duct. The inspection, testing, and maintenance for these units include the inspection and testing of the spot-type detector within the housing and the testing of the airflow through the sampling tubes, similar to that required for air-sampling-type units.

Traditionally, smoke detectors were designed with fixed alarm thresholds. However, recently "analog/addressable" detectors have been introduced where the alarm threshold for each detector is a numerical value stored in the fire alarm control panel memory. The control panel sequentially addresses each detector, and the unit responds with a voltage or current that is the analog of stimulus its sensing element is sensing at that moment. The analog voltage or current is compared to the value in memory, and the "alarm" decision is made in the control panel. The sensitivity of this type of detector is determined by the difference between the sensed analog value and the stored threshold value. This type of detector and control panel design minimizes the need for individual detector sensitivity measurements, but does not change the need for regular inspections and maintenance.

Radiant Energy–Sensing Detectors. This category includes flame detectors and spark/ember detectors. These detectors depend on the optical clarity of their lenses and windows, as well as a clear, unobstructed line of sight to the fire. The inspection of these detectors must verify these two critical parameters. The inspection must include a review of the location of the detector and any opaque objects that may have been introduced into the hazard area since the last inspection to verify that the ability of the detector to respond to the design fire has not been impaired.

A close inspection of the detector window/lens must be made to determine if any opaque materials have adhered to the optical surfaces, reducing the sensitivity of the unit. Keep in mind that many materials are transparent in the visible portion of the spectrum but opaque in either the ultraviolet or infrared portions of the spectrum, where the detectors may operate. Many radiant energy–sensing detectors are available with a lens clarity monitoring feature. This feature is often associated with flame detectors using ultraviolet sensing as all or part of the detection method, since very small levels of contamination can have a very significant effect on the effective sensitivity of the unit.

Window clarity monitoring is not a sensitivity measurement. Sensitivity measurement for radiant energy–sensing detectors requires a means by which a radiant emitter, listed for the purpose, is used to provide emissions of the specific wavelengths and intensities representative of the fire the unit is designed to detect. The response of the detector is measured to determine whether a variation in the calibration has occurred.

The measurement of the sensitivity of a radiant energy–sensing detector, whether a flame detector or a spark/ember detector, is a required part of the inspection and testing regimen required by *NFPA 72*. A flame detector equipped with a built-in sensitivity checking and test lamp that performs both functions is shown in Figure 14.5.10. Sensitivity measurements are used to identify which detectors have suffered a loss of sensitivity due to aging of internal electronic components or deterioration of the optical clarity of the detector window or lens. In the author's experience, a common source of performance deterioration in radiant energy–sensing detectors is a loss of clarity in the detector's optical surfaces. Particular attention must be paid to this fact when maintaining these detectors.

FIGURE 14.5.10 Flame Detector (Source: J. M. Cholin Consultants)

Sprinkler System Waterflow Alarms. Sprinkler system waterflow alarm initiation devices are often the only form of automatic fire detection in the protected site which can render a fire alarm signal during those periods when the building is unoccupied. The flow of water through the sprinkler system is an indication that a serious condition exists. Consequently, failure to render a signal when waterflow occurs is a doubly serious concern. This establishes the background for the aggressive inspection, testing, and maintenance schedules for these devices.

Sprinkler system waterflow alarm initiating devices are tested by operating the valve controlling flow through the inspector's test connection on the sprinkler system. If the waterflow initiating device is monitoring dry-pipe, preaction, or deluge systems, the alarm bypass connection, specifically installed for this purpose, is used for testing of waterflow initiating devices. Operation of the appropriate test connection causes a flow equivalent to the smallest orifice sprinkler head installed in the system. The waterflow alarm initiating device must transmit a signal to the fire alarm control panel within 90 seconds of the start of the waterflow. The delay between the time that flow begins and the time the alarm is transmitted to the fire alarm control panel is necessary to accommodate the oscillatory flows that often occur in large sprinkler systems and, as a result, surges in the public water supply pressure.

Extinguishing System Operation Initiating Devices. These initiating devices usually take the form of discharge switches specifically designed for the particular model of extinguishing system involved. Some of these discharge switches have a means to simulate the pressure of the extinguishing agent and, thus, test the operability of the initiating device. Others do not, and the testing can only be performed by shorting the contacts at their wiring terminations. In either case, each extinguishing system discharge initiating device must be tested as specified by the manufacturer and appropriate system functions verified.

Manually Activated Alarm Initiating Devices. Manually activated alarm initiating devices, commonly called manual fire alarm boxes, have traditionally consisted of a mechanical means to cause an electrical switch to transfer from open to closed, thereby shorting the conductors of the fire alarm initiating device circuit. Two aspects of these devices should be inspected and tested. First, the mechanical portion of the unit should be inspected and the operability should be verified. Recent legislation establishes maximum allowable forces for the operation of manual fire alarm boxes. Any unit that appears to have suffered corrosion, damage, or some other potentially adverse effect should be tested to verify that the operation force is within the limits for the make and model device in question. This is especially important in hazard areas where the walls have been painted subsequent to the installation of the manual station. Second, the manually actuated alarm initiating devices should be actuated to verify that the internal switch contact is electrically operative. Furthermore, many fire alarm systems actuate different responses due to the operation of manual stations in different areas of the building or facility. The proper sequence of operation must be verified for each area.

Publicly accessible fire alarm boxes, commonly known as street boxes, are addressed in *NFPA 72*. These devices exist in a wide variety of types, connected to a variety of municipal signaling systems. The maintenance of these units is a municipal function, and the appropriate means of inspection and testing is established by the municipality.

Supervisory Signal Initiating Devices. Supervisory signal initiating devices monitor the status of critical fire protection assets. These include sprinkler system control valve status, water pressure status, water level, air pressure, and temperature. It is imperative to recognize that the failure mode and probability of the electrical supervisory initiating device is not related to the probability of failure of the monitored condition. Any coincidence in the frequency and scheduling of the inspection and testing of a supervisory signal initiating device with the supervised device is just that, a coincidence. Control valves do not fail on the same timetable as valve status supervisory signal initiating devices. The failures of valves are due to the compression welding of bronze components, tuberculation of the piping, galvanic corrosion, and the polymerization of seat grease. Failure of status switches is related to the corrosion of electronic contacts and the fatigue of copper wiring conductors and mounting brackets. The inspection and testing of the supervisory signal initiating devices are necessary to ensure that these devices are providing an accurate indication of the status of the supervised equipment and a reliable indication of the change in status of the equipment if and when it occurs.

Inspection and testing of the supervisory signal initiating devices usually involve a close inspection of each device to verify that the ambient conditions have not caused any deterioration in the device, followed by a temporary simulation of a change in status to verify that the supervisory signal initiating device transmits the indication of the change in status to the fire alarm control unit. Once the receipt of the change-in-status signal at the fire alarm system control unit has been verified, the simulated change in status is restored to normal and the receipt of the return-to-normal signal at the control unit is verified. Transmission of a change in status to the fire alarm system control unit should occur without any undue delay. If delays are encountered, the cause should be identified and corrected.

Notification Appliances

The principal objective of every fire alarm system is to ensure timely notification to all building occupants, enabling them to make safe egress from the fire location; therefore, the inspection and testing of the alarm notification appliances are crucial.

The three general types of notification appliances referenced in *NFPA 72* are (1) audible notification appliances, (2) visible notification appliances, and (3) speakers for emergency voice communication. Each type of notification appliance has a test method that verifies that the unit is providing the notification signal at a level consistent with the design objective.

Audible Notification Appliances. These include bells, horns, sirens, chimes, speakers, buzzers, and any other device designed to make a sound other than human speech. They all have a means of converting electrical energy into sound, often involving the making and breaking of an electrical switch contact connected to a bell clapper or a diaphragm and an electromagnet, thus producing a mechanical oscillation and sound. Corrosion, metal fatigue, paint clogging, mechanical damage, electrical contact erosion, and electrical conductor fatigue all can cause a deterioration in the quantity of sound a device produces. Each audible notification appliance must be inspected for signs of deterioration.

The audibility must also be tested to verify that the audibility criteria for the hazard area are still being achieved by the system. Audibility is verified through the measurement of the sound pressure produced by the audible notification appliance. Sound pressure is measured in units of decibels, dBA (the A signifies the A-scale which is designed to weigh sound pressure versus frequency in a manner that approximates human hearing). The sound pressure measurement is made with a sound meter. Only sound meters that comply with ANSI S1.42, *Design Response of Weighting Networks for Acoustical Measurements,*[7] should be used for the assessment of fire alarm systems. Care must also be taken that the sound pressure meter is used as directed by the operating manual to minimize measurement errors (Figure 14.5.11).

Two criteria must be met by the audible notification appliances. First, the system is required to produce a sound pressure level of 15 dBA above the average ambient and 5 dBA above the maximum sound pressure level having a duration of at least 60 seconds, measured 5.0 ft (1.5 m) above the floor in the occupiable area. Because sound intensity usually varies inversely with the distance from the audible appliance, the sound pressure readings are taken at a location furthest from the audible appliance. Generally, if the minimum compliance sound level is achieved at that location, it can be safely assumed that closer locations will also be above the minimum compliance sound level. However, "usually" does not mean always. Occasionally, buildings have unexpected acoustics that affect the sound intensities at various locations within the building. This should be noted when assessing audibility and additional measurements should be taken wherever the audibility seems lower than "normal."

The second criterion is the maximum allowed sound pressure level at the closest occupiable location to the audible

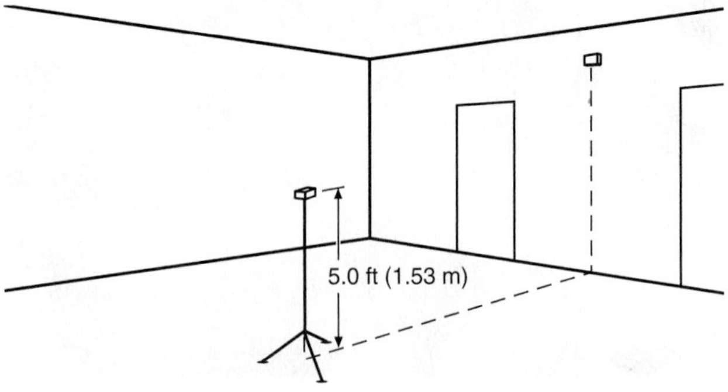

FIGURE 14.5.11 Sound Pressure Meter Mounted on a Tripod for an Audibility Measurement

appliance. This sound level cannot exceed 110 dBA without subjecting the occupant to potential hearing injury, according to the U.S. Occupational Safety and Health Administration (OSHA). System component failures rarely result in higher sound output from audible notification appliances. However, changes in the occupancy, such as installation of catwalks, stairs, mezzanines, and so on, can render a formerly unoccupiable location occupiable. This is consistent with the inspection of all other system components, in that the role of the inspection includes identifying changes in the protected space that may have an impact on the fire alarm system.

Speakers. Emergency voice communication speakers are also audible notification appliances, and they are required to achieve sound levels equivalent to audible notification appliances. The inspection should identify any form of damage, for example, mechanical deformation, corrosion, metal fatiguing, and paint clogging. The testing is similar to that for audible notification appliances. The sound level is measured with an ANSI S1.42–compliant sound level meter.[7] The minimum compliance sound level must be verified throughout the hazard area, and the test must verify that the maximum allowable sound level is not exceeded at any occupiable location.

An additional test criterion, one that is not relevant to other audible notification appliances, is included when emergency voice communication speakers are evaluated. This criterion is the intelligibility or clarity of the voice communication. In the testing of emergency voice communication speakers, the intelligibility of the speech message must be assessed. For existing systems, installed prior to 1999, the intelligibility assessment is essentially qualitative—can the speech message be understood by the intended recipients? Generally, intelligibility is maximized by using more audible notification appliances, so that each dissipates less power rather than using fewer higher-power audible notification appliances.

More recently, the trend has been toward using more quantitative intelligibility assessment methods, especially in acoustically challenging spaces where highly reflective wall, floor, and ceiling surfaces dominate or where very large power levels are needed to attain the requisite sound pressure levels. These challenging spaces include arenas, museums, atria, airport concourses, rail stations, and similar "special-purpose" spaces. An assessment method has been referenced in Annex A of *NFPA 72* and is outlined in Annex A of IEC 60849, *Sound Systems for Emergency Purposes.*[8] The method relies on the measurement of the common intelligibility scale (CIS) for the system. The objective means of determining intelligibility, and hence calculating the CIS, are found in IEC 60268, *The Objective Rating of Speech Intelligibility by Speech Transmission Index.*[9] Subjective techniques are also available, as found in ANSI S3.2-1999, *Method for Measuring the Intelligibility of Speech over Communications Systems.*[10] These methods are generally employed by sound engineers in the design of commercial sound systems and can be applied equally well to fire alarm emergency voice systems.

Visible Notification Appliances. Visible notification appliances are inspected and tested to verify that they are still capable of achieving the design objectives of the fire alarm system. A light meter analogous to the sound-level meter is not in common usage as of this writing. This limits the inspection and testing to those procedures recommended by the manufacturer of the specific visible notification appliance used.

During the inspection and operational testing of the visible notification appliances, particular attention must be paid to any furnishings such as shelves, ornamental plants, lamps, banners, sculptures, and so on, or added construction features, for example, stairs, catwalks, ladders, lighting fixtures, and partitions, that interfere with a clear line of sight to the visible notification appliances. Furthermore, many systems rely on synchronization to ensure that the combined effective light pulse rate does not exceed 4 Hz, a frequency at which there is concern over the effect on those persons prone to seizures. Synchronization is achieved by different means from manufacturer to manufacturer; most manufacturers produce both synchronized and unsynchronized product. Consequently, where the design relies on synchronized visible notification, the inspection must verify that all of the visible notification appliances visible from any single viewing location are still synchronized or are separated by at least 55 ft (16.8 m).

INSPECTION, TESTING, AND MAINTENANCE SCHEDULING FOR SYSTEMS AND COMPONENTS

The requirements regarding the inspection, testing, and maintenance of fire alarm signaling systems must also be scheduled. Since different components have different failure rates, those with the higher failure rates require more frequent inspections and testing if the overall system reliability is to be kept at an acceptable level. Inspection, testing, and maintenance interval recommendations come from both the predicted reliability derived from failure rate analyses and from experience data derived over time. Manufacturers provide specific schedules for the service requirements for their products, and these must be observed where they establish a more frequent regimen of inspection, testing, and maintenance.

The objectives of an inspection program are to identify cases where the hazard area has changed, rendering the existing fire alarm system inappropriate for the hazard area, or some episode of physical abuse has occurred that has damaged the component, rendering it incapable of performing in a manner consistent with the system design. The frequency of these types of conditions is a function of the hazard area, not the inherent reliability of the system components. Consequently, some sites will require more frequent inspections due to the unique nature of the particular site. *NFPA 72* provides the required visual inspection frequencies, reproduced here as Table 14.5.2.

Testing of fire alarm system components occurs on a schedule that is less frequent than the inspections. The testing uncovers failures that are not apparent from a visual inspection and are generally attributable to the combined effect of the ambient conditions and the inherent failure rates of the components. There are applications where the testing frequency established in *NFPA 72* as a minimum compliance criterion is not adequate to achieve the required level of reliability. The effective reliability

TABLE 14.5.2 Visual Inspection Frequencies

Component	*Initial/ Reacceptance*	*Monthly*	*Quarterly*	*Semiannually*	*Annually*
1. Control equipment: fire alarm systems monitored for alarm, supervisory, and trouble signals					
(a) Fuses	X	—	—	—	X
(b) Interfaced equipment	X	—	—	—	X
(c) Lamps and LEDs	X	—	—	—	X
(d) Primary (main) power supply	X	—	—	—	X
2. Control equipment: fire alarm systems unmonitored for alarm, supervisory, and trouble signals					
(a) Fuses	X (weekly)	—	—	—	—
(b) Interfaced equipment	X (weekly)	—	—	—	—
(c) Lamps and LEDs	X (weekly)	—	—	—	—
(d) Primary (main) power supply	X (weekly)	—	—	—	—
3. Batteries					
(a) Lead/acid	X	X	—	—	—
(b) Nickel/cadmium	X	—	—	X	—
(c) Primary (dry cell)	X	X	—	—	—
(d) Sealed lead/acid	X	—	—	X	—
4. Transient suppressors	X	—	—	X	—
5. Fire alarm control unit trouble signals	X (weekly)	—	—	X	—
6. Fiber-optic cable connections	X	—	—	—	X
7. Emergency voice/alarm communications equipment	X	—	—	X	—
8. Remote annunciators	X	—	—	X	—
9. Initiating devices					
(a) Air sampling	X	—	—	X	—
(b) Duct detectors	X	—	—	X	—
(c) Electromechanical releasing devices	X	—	—	X	—
(d) Fire extinguishing system(s) or suppression system(s) switches	X	—	—	X	—
(e) Fire alarm boxes	X	—	—	X	—
(f) Heat detectors	X	—	—	X	—
(g) Radiant energy fire detectors	X	—	X	—	—
(h) Smoke detectors (excluding one- and two-family dwellings)	X	—	—	X	—
(i) Supervisory signal devices	X	—	X	—	—
(j) Waterflow devices	X	—	X	—	—
10. Guard's tour equipment	X	—	—	X	—
11. Combination systems					
(a) Fire extinguisher monitoring device/systems	X	—	—	X	—
(b) Carbon monoxide detectors/systems	X	—	—	X	—
12. Interface equipment	X	—	—	X	—
13. Alarm notification appliances—supervised	X	—	—	X	—
14. Exit marking audible notification appliances	X	—	—	X	—

TABLE 14.5.2 Continued

Component	*Initial/ Reacceptance*	*Monthly*	*Quarterly*	*Semiannually*	*Annually*
15. Supervising station fire alarm systems—transmitters					
(a) DACT	X	—	—	X	—
(b) DART	X	—	—	X	—
(c) McCulloh	X	—	—	X	—
(d) RAT	X	—	—	X	—
16. Special procedures	X	—	—	X	—
17. Supervising station fire alarm systems—receivers					
(a) DACR*	X	X	—	—	—
(b) DARR*	X	—	—	X	—
(c) McCulloh systems*	X	—	—	X	—
(d) Two-way RF multiplex*	X	—	—	X	—
(e) RASSR*	X	—	—	X	—
(f) RARS*	X	—	—	X	—
(g) Private microwave*	X	—	—	X	—
18. Public fire alarm reporting system transmission equipment					
(a) Publicly accessible fire alarm box	X	—	—	X	—
(b) Auxiliary box	X	—	—	—	X
(c) Master box					
(1) Manual operation	X	—	—	X	—
(2) Auxiliary operation	X	—	—	—	X

*Reports of automatic signal receipt shall be verified daily.

Source: *NFPA 72®, National Fire Alarm Code®*, 2007 ed., Table 10.3.1, pp. 72-93–72-94.

of such a fire alarm system can be improved by implementing a more frequent testing program. *NFPA 72* provides the required testing frequencies, reproduced here as Table 14.5.3.

HOUSEHOLD FIRE WARNING EQUIPMENT

Household fire alarm systems have been implemented in a number of different ways. More recent design concepts correct the performance shortcomings of older design philosophies and reflect the improved performance of modern equipment.

NFPA 72 requires the monthly inspection and testing, per the manufacturer's instructions, of all smoke detectors in a household fire alarm application, regardless of whether those detectors are single-station units, interconnected multiple-station units, or detectors integrated into a complete household fire alarm system. This monthly testing should include a verification that all audible and visible notification appliances are operative. Furthermore, *NFPA 72* requires that household fire alarm systems, that is, systems consisting of detectors, notification appliances, and a control panel, be inspected and tested at least every three years by a qualified alarm technician with a procedure in compliance with the manufacturer's instructions.

UL 217, *Standard for Safety Single and Multiple Station Smoke Detectors,* allows a maximum failure rate of 4.0 f/mdoh for the detector circuitry.[11] This failure rate can be expressed as 1.0 failure per 250,000 device operating hours, or 1.0 failure per 8760 hr/yr × 28.5 yr, or 0.035 failures per year. The battery for the smoke detector can only operate the unit for one and a half years before it is depleted. The depletion of the battery is not included in the failure rate assigned to the battery. The failure rate for the household fire alarm is the failure rate per detector and the depletion rate for the battery multiplied by the number of units in the household. Assuming six detectors in the average house and a failure rate of 1 – (1 – 0.667)(1 – 0.035) = 0.679, one obtains 6 × 0.679 = 4.074 failures per year for Λ. Using the equation developed earlier, that is,

$$R = e^{-\Lambda t}$$

where

R = Reliability of the system

e = Napierian logarithm base, 2.71828

Λ = Inherent failure rate of the system

t = Time period between performing recommended inspection and testing, 1/12 of a year or 0.0833 yr

$$R = e^{-4.074 \times 0.0833}$$

$$= 0.712 \text{ or } 71.2 \text{ percent}$$

TABLE 14.5.3 Testing Frequencies

Component	*Initial/ Reacceptance*	*Monthly*	*Quarterly*	*Semi-annually*	*Annually*	*Table 10.4.2.2 (NFPA 72) Reference*
1. Control equipment—building systems connected to supervising station						1, 7, 16, 17
(a) Functions	X	—	—	—	X	—
(b) Fuses	X	—	—	—	X	—
(c) Interfaced equipment	X	—	—	—	X	—
(d) Lamps and LEDs	X	—	—	—	X	—
(e) Primary (main) power supply	X	—	—	—	X	—
(f) Transponders	X	—	—	—	X	—
2. Control equipment—building systems not connected to a supervising station	—	—	—	—	—	1
(a) Functions	X	—	X	—	—	—
(b) Fuses	X	—	X	—	—	—
(c) Interfaced equipment	X	—	X	—	—	—
(d) Lamps and LEDs	X	—	X	—	—	—
(e) Primary (main) power supply	X	—	X	—	—	—
(f) Transponders	X	—	X	—	—	—
3. Engine-driven generator—central station facilities and fire alarm systems	X	X	—	—	—	—
4. Engine-driven generator—public fire alarm reporting systems	X (weekly)	—	—	—	—	—
5. Batteries—central station facilities						
(a) Lead/acid type	—	—	—	—	—	6b
(1) Charger test (Replace battery as needed.)	X	—	—	—	X	—
(2) Discharge test (30 minutes)	X	X	—	—	—	—
(3) Load voltage test	X	X	—	—	—	—
(4) Specific gravity	X	—	—	X	—	—
(b) Nickel/cadmium type	—	—	—	—	—	6c
(1) Charger test (Replace battery as needed.)	X	—	X	—	—	—
(2) Discharge test (30 minutes)	X	—	—	—	X	—
(3) Load voltage test	X	—	—	—	X	—
(c) Sealed lead/acid type	X	X	—	—	—	6d
(1) Charger test (Replace battery within 5 years after manufacture or more frequently as needed.)	—	X	X	—	—	—
(2) Discharge test (30 minutes)	X	X	—	—	—	—
(3) Load voltage test	X	X	—	—	—	—
6. Batteries—fire alarm systems						
(a) Lead-acid type	—	—	—	—	—	6b
(1) Charger test (Replace battery as needed.)	X	—	—	—	X	—
(2) Discharge test (30 minutes)	X	—	—	X	—	—
(3) Load voltage test	X	—	—	X	—	—
(4) Specific gravity	X	—	—	X	—	—
(b) Nickel/cadmium type	—	—	—	—	—	6c
(1) Charger test (Replace battery as needed.)	X	—	—	—	X	—
(2) Discharge test (30 minutes)	X	—	—	—	X	—
(3) Load voltage test	X	—	—	X	—	—
(c) Primary type (dry cell)	—	—	—	—	—	6a
(1) Age test	X	X	—	—	—	—

TABLE 14.5.3 Continued

Component	*Initial/ Reacceptance*	*Monthly*	*Quarterly*	*Semi-annually*	*Annually*	*Table 10.4.2.2 (NFPA 72) Reference*
(d) Sealed lead/acid type	—	—	—	—	—	6d
(1) Charger test (Replace battery within 5 years after manufacture or more frequently as needed.)	X	—	—	—	X	—
(2) Discharge test (30 minutes)	X	—	—	—	X	—
(3) Load voltage test	X	—	—	X	—	—
7. Power supply—public fire alarm reporting systems	—	—	—	—	—	—
(a) Lead/acid type batteries	—	—	—	—	—	6b
(1) Charger test (Replace battery as needed.)	X	—	—	—	X	—
(2) Discharge test (2 hours)	X	—	X	—	—	—
(3) Load voltage test	X	—	X	—	—	—
(4) Specific gravity	X	—	—	X	—	—
(b) Nickel/cadmium type batteries	—	—	—	—	—	6c
(1) Charger test (Replace battery as needed.)	X	—	—	—	X	—
(2) Discharge test (2 hours)	X	—	—	—	X	—
(3) Load voltage test	X	—	X	—	—	—
(c) Sealed lead/acid type batteries	—	—	—	—	—	6d
(1) Charger test (Replace battery within 5 years after manufacture or more frequently if needed.)	X	—	—	—	X	—
(2) Discharge test (2 hours)	X	—	—	—	X	—
(3) Load voltage test	X	—	X	—	—	—
(d) Wired system—voltage tests	X (daily)	—	—	—	—	7d
8. Fiber-optic cable power	X	—	—	—	X	13b
9. Control unit trouble signals	X	—	—	—	X	10
10. Conductors—metallic	X	—	—	—	—	12
11. Conductors—nonmetallic	X	—	—	—	—	13
12. Emergency voice/alarm communications equipment	X	—	—	—	X	21
13. Retransmission equipment (The requirements of 10.4.9 of *NFPA 72* shall apply.)	X	—	—	—	—	—
14. Remote annunciators	X	—	—	—	X	11
15. Initiating devices	—	—	—	—	—	14
(a) Duct detectors	X	—	—	—	X	—
(b) Electromechanical releasing device	X	—	—	—	X	—
(c) Fire extinguishing system(s) or suppression system(s) switches	X	—	—	—	X	—
(d) Fire-gas and other detectors	X	—	—	—	X	—
(e) Heat detectors (The requirements of 10.4.4.4 of *NFPA 72* shall apply.)	X	—	—	—	X	—
(f) Fire alarm boxes	X	—	—	—	X	—
(g) Radiant energy fire detectors	X	—	—	X	—	—
(h) System smoke detectors—functional test	X	—	—	—	X	—
(i) Smoke detectors—sensitivity testing in other than one- and two-family dwellings (The requirements of 10.4.4.2 of *NFPA 72* shall apply.)	—	—	—	—	—	—

(continued)

TABLE 14.5.3 Continued

Component	*Initial/ Reacceptance*	*Monthly*	*Quarterly*	*Semi-annually*	*Annually*	*Table 10.4.2.2 (NFPA 72) Reference*
15. Initiating devices *(continued)*						
(j) Single- and multiple-station smoke alarms (The requirements for monthly testing in accordance with 10.4.5 of *NFPA 72* shall also apply.)	X	—	—	—	X	—
(k) Single- and multiple-station heat alarms	X	—	—	—	X	—
(l) Supervisory signal devices (except valve tamper switches)	X	—	X	—	—	—
(m) Waterflow devices	X	—	—	X	—	—
(n) Valve supervisory switches	X	—	—	X	—	—
16. Guard's tour equipment	X	—	—	—	X	24
17. Combination systems						
(a) Fire extinguisher monitoring device/systems	X	—	—	—	X	21a
(b) Carbon monoxide detectors/systems	X	—	—	—	X	21b
18. Interface equipment and fire safety functions	X	—	—	—	X	22, 23
19. Special hazard equipment	X	—	—	—	X	17
20. Alarm notification appliances	—	—	—	—	—	15
(a) Audible devices	X	—	—	—	X	—
(b) Audible textual notification appliances	X	—	—	—	X	—
(c) Visible devices	X	—	—	—	X	—
21. Exit marking notification appliances	X	—	—	—	X	16
22. Off-premises transmission equipment	X	—	X	—	—	—
23. Supervising station fire alarm systems—transmitters	—	—	—	—	—	18
(a) DACT	X	—	—	—	X	—
(b) DART	X	—	—	—	X	—
(c) McCulloh	X	—	—	—	X	—
(d) RAT	X	—	—	—	X	—
24. Special procedures	X	—	—	—	X	25
25. Supervising station fire alarm systems—receivers	—	—	—	—	—	19
(a) DACR	X	X	—	—	—	—
(b) DARR	X	X	—	—	—	—
(c) McCulloh systems	X	X	—	—	—	—
(d) Two-way RF multiplex	X	X	—	—	—	—
(e) RASSR	X	X	—	—	—	—
(f) RARSR	X	X	—	—	—	—
(g) Private microwave	X	X	—	—	—	—
26. Public fire alarm reporting system transmission equipment	—	—	—	—	—	—
(a) Publicly accessible fire alarm box	X	—	—	X	—	8a
(b) Auxiliary box	X	—	—	—	X	8b
(c) Master box						8c
(1) Manual operation	X	—	—	X	—	
(2) Auxiliary operation	X	—	—	—	X	

Source: *NFPA 72®*, *National Fire Alarm Code®*, 2007 ed., Table 10.3.1, pp. 72-106–72-108.

Thus, generally available residential smoke detectors when installed, inspected, and tested monthly per the manufacturer's instructions and *NFPA 72* can be expected to provide a functional reliability of a nominal 71.2 percent.

CRITICALITY OF INSPECTION, TESTING, AND MAINTENANCE ON THE EFFECTIVENESS OF THE SYSTEM

Electronic systems are, at this time, the only systems on which solid reliability data exist in the quantity and quality that allow one to develop a predictive computational method to assess various design alternatives. All physical systems have failure modes, and each system component demonstrates failure at a finite rate over the majority of its operational lifetime. Nonelectrical fire alarm systems are not necessarily more reliable than electronic systems. It is possible to compute the reliability of electrical systems only because good failure rate data exist.

The one concept to be gained from reliability analysis and prediction computations is that all systems are destined to fail, given enough time. It is a probability so high as to approach a *certainty*. A performance-based design cannot be deemed complete until it includes a quantitative assessment of the likelihood that the system will perform as designed. This assessment is dependent on the service and maintenance interval for the system. With long time intervals between inspection and testing procedures, the probability increases that the system will be operating with some type of unnoticed impairment during the intervening time periods. Obviously, the time during which the system is partially and perhaps even completely impaired increases with the increase in the time interval between each exercise of the required inspection and testing. Consequently, no performance- or objective-oriented design is complete without a preventive maintenance program that includes inspection and testing on an interval that is predicated upon the size and complexity of the system itself.

Consider the example fire alarm system presented earlier. A system consisting of 10 smoke detectors, a notification appliance, and a control panel produced a predicted failure rate of 0.3824 failures per year. Table 14.5.4 shows the effect of varying inspection and testing intervals on the reliability of this system. The reliability of the system and, hence, the needed maintenance interval are dependent on the size and complexity of the system. Table 14.5.5 demonstrates the impact that increasing system size has on the needed inspection and testing interval in order to maintain a uniform design reliability of 71.2 percent (0.712). Clearly, as the size or complexity of the system increases, the frequency of the inspection and testing program must be increased to retain a constant reliability. If the inspection and testing frequency is held constant, then the reliability of the system decreases each time the size and complexity of the system are increased.

TABLE 14.5.4 System Reliability Dependent on the Inspection and Testing Interval System (actual values based on the reliability data used in the example)

Inspection and Testing Interval	*Reliability*
Quarterly	0.904
Semiannually	0.826
Annually	0.682
Biannually	0.465

TABLE 14.5.5 Inspection and Testing Interval Necessary to Maintain a 71.2 Percent Reliability as System Size Is Increased (values based on the reliability data used in the example)

System Size	Λ	*Inspection and Testing Interval (yr)*
10 detectors, 1 notification appliance	0.3824	0.93
20 detectors, 2 notification appliances	0.5278	0.68
40 detectors, 4 notification appliances	0.8554	0.42
80 detectors, 8 notification appliances	1.4860	0.24

Tables 14.5.3, 14.5.4, and 14.5.5 demonstrate the importance of the inspection, testing, and maintenance program. A system cannot be expected to achieve the design objectives if the inspection, testing, and maintenance program does not reflect the reliability objectives of the design. The failure to maintain a system in a manner consistent with the design assures the owner/operator of the protected site that the fire alarm system will *not* achieve the design objective.

SUMMARY

The essential objectives of a fire alarm system—life safety, property protection, and continuity of the site's mission—will be achievable in the event of a fire only if the alarm system functions properly. An inspection, testing, and maintenance regimen employed at regular intervals is essential for ensuring the reliable performance of the fire alarm system. Because at some point in its lifetime any system will suffer a failure, a schedule of inspection, testing, and maintenance must be developed based on the size and complexity of the system. The four main system elements—design, equipment, installation, and maintenance—are critical to the reliability of the system and should be the focus of the regimen.

BIBLIOGRAPHY

References Cited

1. Institute of Electrical and Electronics Engineers, Inc., *Reliability: An IEEE Spectrum Compendium,* IEEE, Piscataway, NJ, 1981.

2. U.S. Department of Defense, *Military Handbook: Reliability Prediction of Electronic Equipment,* MIL-HDBK-217F, U.S. Government Printing Office, Washington, DC, 1990.
3. Moore, W. D., and Cholin, J. M., "Reliability Analysis and Prediction Techniques for Fire Protective Signaling Systems," 1995 NFPA Annual Meeting, published by the authors, 1995.
4. Klote, J. H., and Milke, J. A., *Design of Smoke Management Systems,* American Society of Heating, Refrigerating, and Air-Conditioning Engineers, Atlanta, GA, 1992.
5. Schifiliti, R. P., et al., "Design of Detection Systems," *SFPE Handbook of Fire Protection Engineering,* 3rd ed., P. J. DiNenno et al. (Eds.), National Fire Protection Association, Quincy, MA, 2002.
6. General Electric, *Nickel-Cadmium Battery Application Engineering Handbook,* GET-3148A, General Electric Company Battery Business Dept., Gainesville, FL, 1975.
7. ANSI S1.42, *Design Response of Weighting Networks for Acoustical Measurements,* American National Standards Institute, New York, 1986.
8. IEC 60849, *Sound Systems for Emergency Purposes,* 2nd ed., International Electrotechnical Commission, Geneva, Switzerland, 1998.
9. IEC 60268, Part 16, *The Objective Rating of Speech Intelligibility by Speech Transmission Index,* 2nd ed., International Electrotechnical Commission, Geneva, Switzerland, 1998.
10. ANSI S3.2-1999, *Method for Measuring the Intelligibility of Speech over Communications Systems,* American National Standards Institute, New York, 1999.
11. UL 217, *Standard for Safety Single and Multiple Station Smoke Detectors,* Underwriters Laboratories Inc., Northbrook, IL, 1993.

NFPA Codes, Standards, and Recommended Practices

Reference to the following NFPA codes, standards, and recommended practices will provide further information on inspection, testing, and maintenance of fire alarm systems discussed in this chapter. (See the latest version of The NFPA Catalog *for availability of current editions of the following documents.)*

NFPA 11, *Standard for Low-, Medium-, and High-Expansion Foam*
NFPA 12, *Standard on Carbon Dioxide Extinguishing Systems*
NFPA 12A, *Standard on Halon 1301 Fire Extinguishing Systems*
NFPA 13, *Standard for the Installation of Sprinkler Systems*
NFPA 15, *Standard for Water Spray Fixed Systems for Fire Protection*
NFPA 16, *Standard for the Installation of Foam-Water Sprinkler and Foam-Water Spray Systems*
NFPA 17, *Standard for Dry Chemical Extinguishing Systems*
NFPA 20, *Standard for the Installation of Stationary Pumps for Fire Protection*
NFPA 25, *Standard for the Inspection, Testing, and Maintenance of Water-Based Fire Protection Systems*
NFPA 72®, National Fire Alarm Code®
NFPA 110, *Standard for Emergency and Standby Power Systems*
NFPA 111, *Standard on Stored Electrical Energy Emergency and Standby Power Systems*
NFPA 2001, *Standard on Clean Agent Fire Extinguishing Systems*

Chapter 6

Household Fire-Warning Equipment

Revised by

Daniel T. Gottuk

America's fire death rate is dominated by fires in U.S. homes. Household warning systems, specifically smoke alarms, provide a rare combination of effectiveness and affordability in reducing the risk of death in home fires. The dominance of U.S. homes in fire deaths is demonstrated each year. In recent years, four of every five deaths have occurred in U.S. homes, as have over 90 percent of fire deaths in structures. Analyses by the National Fire Protection Association (NFPA) indicate that when a fire occurs, having detectors present cuts the chances of dying nearly in half. If every home had an operable smoke alarm, home fire deaths would be reduced by an estimated 36 percent, approximately 1100 lives saved per year.[1]

Although heat detectors for residential use have been available since 1921, field tests have shown that they are not as effective as smoke alarms in detecting fires in the home. Fire tests in residential occupancies have shown that measurable amounts of smoke have preceded measurable amounts of heat in almost all cases. In the other cases, the smoke and heat appeared almost simultaneously. Consequently, codes and standards have mandated the use of smoke alarms because they provide a greater level of protection.

Residential smoke alarms were relatively expensive when they began to appear in the marketplace in the late 1960s. In 1970, however, the introduction of a battery-operated smoke alarm, along with line-powered (AC-powered) smoke alarms, initiated a period of public acceptance of single-station residential smoke alarms. In 2004, 96 percent of U.S. homes had at least one smoke alarm.[2]

This chapter discusses the reasons household fire-warning systems are needed, the history of residential fire-warning systems, research into system effectiveness, the importance of having a system in the home and how to make the best use of it, and the importance of an effective escape plan. The types of systems and detectors will also be covered, along with guidelines for installing and testing household fire warning equipment.

For related topics see the following chapters in Section 14: Chapter 1, "Fire Alarm Systems"; Chapter 2, "Automatic Fire Detectors"; Chapter 3, "Notification Appliances"; and Chapter 9, "Carbon Monoxide Detection in Residential Occupancies."

Chapter Contents

Key Terms

heat detector, household fire alarm, Indiana Dunes Report, interconnected smoke alarm, intrusion detection, multiple-station alarm, notification appliance, Operation School Burning, single-station alarm, smoke alarm

RESIDENTIAL FIRE DETECTOR RESEARCH

Early Test Programs

Current performance requirements and installation practices for residential fire detectors are the result of knowledge and experience gained from several test programs. The first major test programs using heat and smoke detectors were Operation School Burning and Operation School Burning No. 2, conducted by the Los Angeles (California) City Fire Department in 1959 and 1961, respectively. These tests had a major impact on fire protection and proved two significant points:

Daniel T. Gottuk, Ph.D., is a senior engineer at Hughes Associates, Inc., and is a project manager for a variety of fire-related forensic, research, testing, and development programs. He is chair of the NFPA Technical Committee on Single- and Multiple-Station Alarms and Household Fire Warning Systems.

(1) smoke alarms could provide a high level of life safety due to their fast response to a fire, and (2) detectable quantities of smoke usually precede detectable levels of heat.

The next significant test series was conducted by the Bloomington (Minnesota) Fire Department in May 1969. Although all detectors employed in the Bloomington tests were system-connected units, the results of these tests—such as time of detector response, order of response as a function of detector and fire type, and conditions at time of response—correlated well with subsequent tests.

Four Levels of Protection Concept

In 1974 NFPA members adopted a major change to NFPA 74, *Household Fire Warning Equipment.* Prior to this, NFPA 74 required that, in addition to a smoke alarm, a home be protected with a heat detector in every major room of the dwelling. The 1974 edition recognized two facts: (1) the mandatory total system approach was impractical for the majority of the population, and (2) heat detectors were not the most effective detectors for the home. Therefore, an NFPA committee developed a matrix of four "levels of protection" from which the homeowner could choose. The four levels of protection concept was finally adopted by the NFPA membership, but not without a fight. The opposition (principally some fire chiefs and fire marshals) felt that they could not recommend anything less than complete protection, and that effectiveness of Level 4, which provided for one or two smoke alarms in the home, had not been proved by test data.

Indiana Dunes Report and Minneapolis Fire Department Study

Based on this latter argument, the National Bureau of Standards (NBS) (now the National Institute of Standards and Technology [NIST]) contracted with IIT Research Institute and Underwriters Laboratories Inc. (UL) to provide just such test data. The results of the first phase of this test program were published in August 1975 under the title "Detector Sensitivity and Siting Requirements for Dwellings." The study, more commonly known as the Indiana Dunes Report, showed, in fact, that Level 4 coverage was inadequate under certain conditions. The report recommended that at least one smoke alarm on each story of the residence be used as a minimum requirement. This system was referred to as the "every level" smoke detection system. Based primarily on the results of this report, NFPA 74 was revised again in 1978 by dropping the four levels of protection and adopting a minimum required system of one smoke alarm on each story (floor level) of a home. Also, because of the slow response of heat detectors when compared to smoke alarms, NFPA 74 no longer permitted the use of heat detectors as the prime method of fire detection.

Shortly after publication of the first phase of the Indiana Dunes Report, the Minneapolis Fire Department conducted a similar independent study on smoke alarm performance. The Minneapolis and Dunes tests were very similar in that each was conducted in a two-story house with basement, with detectors installed on each floor. Likewise, the conclusions of the Minneapolis and Dunes tests were essentially identical; thus, the Minneapolis tests provided an independent verification of many of the conclusions of the Dunes tests. Over the next quarter century, a number of additional studies would be conducted on the performance of home smoke alarms and all confirmed the earlier studies.[2–4]

CODES AND STANDARDS

It is well known that compliance with strong smoke detection laws offers the potential of significant reduction in loss of life and property from fire. For uniformity, laws adopted statewide are preferable to local ordinances. Most states and communities now require residential occupancies from single-family dwellings to hotels and motels to be equipped with smoke alarms. Although most model building codes and life safety codes include specific requirements for smoke alarms in residential occupancies, the development of these requirements has generally originated from what is now known as *NFPA 72®*, *National Fire Alarm Code®*.

In 1993, NFPA 74 was combined with the other fire alarm system standards and now appears as Chapter 11 of *NFPA 72.* In the latest editions of the code, Chapter 11 was changed to address equipment requirements rather than occupancy-specific requirements; this is reflected in the current technical committee and chapter name, Single- and Multiple-Station Alarms and Household Fire Alarm Systems. Chapter 3 of *NFPA 72* provides definitions for these different types of fire alarm equipment. A single-station alarm is a device that includes a sensor and notification appliance in one unit and a power source that is typically a self-contained battery and/or connection to an AC circuit in the dwelling. A multiple-station alarm is a single-station alarm that has the means to be interconnected to other alarms (that is, when one sounds an alarm signal, all connected devices will sound). A household fire alarm system is different in that it incorporates a fire alarm control panel to power and monitor smoke detectors and often to provide alarm notification through separate appliances. Smoke detectors are different from smoke alarms in that they require a panel to operate, whereas a smoke alarm is a stand-alone device.

In 1989, NFPA 74 added requirements for interconnected smoke alarms in new construction, and in the 1993 conversion of NFPA 74, the requirement for a smoke alarm in each sleeping room in new construction was introduced in *NFPA 72.* This change specifically addressed the protection of the occupant of the sleeping room. Detection of smoke from a fire within the sleeping room by an alarm outside the sleeping room, especially with the door closed, has been a problem. The interconnection of devices located in bedrooms also provided better distribution of the alarm signal, particularly for fires detected by alarms remote from the sleeping area. In 2007, *NFPA 72* was changed to require a uniform set of installation requirements regardless of occupancy age (i.e., new or existing). These changes are partly enabled by several new wireless technologies that permit smoke alarms to be interconnected.

ELEMENTS OF RESIDENTIAL FIRE PROTECTION

The many elements of fire safety and fire protection can be grouped into six elements that need to work together in an integrated system for best results:

1. Fire prevention
2. Prevention of unusually rapid early growth or spread
3. Automatic detection
4. Automatic suppression
5. Compartmentation or containment
6. Evacuation or escape

Each is important individually, and all are interdependent in any successful residential fire protection scheme. From the perspective of household early warning systems, these six elements need to be examined in terms of the essential steps that make the automatic detection element successful and the other fire elements that can render detector protection unsuccessful. Taking them in order, one may focus on prevention of ignition and of rapid early growth or spread under a generic title of minimizing fire hazards.

Although automatic residential sprinkler systems are gaining acceptance for new home construction and are mandated in several jurisdictions, the general consensus among fire safety professionals is also to recommend automatic smoke detection in accordance with *NFPA 72,* Chapter 11, "Single- and Multiple-Station Alarms and Household Fire Alarm Systems," providing a minimum level of life safety protection.

Minimization of Fire Hazards

Preventing a fire before it occurs is always easier than detecting it once it has occurred; therefore, minimizing fire hazards in and around the home is the first key element to minimizing hazards. This prevention includes care in the selection and use of all potential heat sources (e.g., tobacco products, heating and cooking equipment, the electrical system, appliances, lighting appliances) and fuel sources (e.g., furnishings and contents, interior finishes). Preventing rapid early growth or spread implies special attention to removing all unessential flammable liquids and other highly combustible items from the home. Further, it should also mean strict adherence to and enforcement of building and fire codes in the construction of residential occupancies, use of only low-flame-spread materials for interior finish, and use of low-flammability or fire-retardant-treated materials in residential furnishings. Proper compartmentation is also essential to slow the fire as it moves from zone to zone, extending the time to hazardous exposure for most occupants.

It must be realized that, if a fire develops rapidly enough, residential smoke alarms may not provide enough time for the occupants of a dwelling to escape before their exit routes are cut off. Therefore, it is highly dangerous for people to be careless, thinking smoke alarms will protect them from their carelessness.

Installation of Smoke Alarms

Full effectiveness for household warning systems means the right number of smoke alarms, located in the right places and operating properly. As required by *NFPA 72,* Chapter 11, "Single- and Multiple-Station Alarms and Household Fire Alarm Systems," the acceptable minimum consists of one smoke alarm in each bedroom, outside each sleeping area and one on each habitable story, including the basement of the home. It is also recommended that the minimum package be supplemented by additional smoke alarms in other areas as needed. For example, a smoke alarm could be located in living and family rooms, and smoke or heat alarms could be located in the kitchen, attached garage, attic, and furnace room. Each additional alarm could provide more time for the family to escape. When more than one smoke alarm is installed, the alarms should be arranged so all of the devices sound when any one device detects smoke. This chain of alarms can be done by installing either multiple-station smoke alarms or a complete household fire alarm system with smoke detectors, panel, and notification appliances.

Equally as important as the installation are proper care and maintenance of the equipment. Each residential smoke alarm comes with an owner's booklet describing the necessary maintenance procedures. A smoke alarm with a dead or missing battery will be useless in a fire. In fact, NFPA analysis of reported fires has shown roughly one-third of U.S. home smoke alarms are not working when fires occur, typically because of dead or missing batteries. This is a major obstacle to achieving full success with home smoke alarms. Because of the battery problem, *NFPA 72* and many local building codes mandate use of both primary AC and secondary battery power, with an exception in some cases that allows an alarm with a nonrechargeable, nonreplaceable 10 year life battery.

Development of Escape Plan

The last key element in residential fire protection is the development and practice of a family escape plan. Remember, residential smoke alarms can do no more than warn occupants of a fire in the home; they will not extinguish the fire. Also, depending on the speed at which the fire is developing, the amount of time available for escape may be limited. It is critical that all occupants leave the home immediately and *call the fire department once outside the home.* Delay can be fatal if people take extra time, for example, to get dressed, gather valuables, or look for pets. Also, it is important that everyone have an alternative way out of each room in case the primary exit is blocked by fire. There must be a prearranged outside meeting place so everyone will know that the entire family has escaped the fire. Any delay can be fatal, including reluctance to climb out of windows. Any actions that increase the risk of death can be fatal, such as re-entering a burning home to look for people who may very well have already escaped.

Information on how to formulate a family escape plan is contained in the homeowner's booklet provided with each residential smoke alarm and by NFPA in its EDITH (Exit Drills in the Home) materials.

TYPES OF SYSTEMS

Residential fire detection may range in size from one single-station smoke alarm in an apartment, manufactured home, or recreational vehicle to a centrally wired system containing numerous detectors and separate alarm notification appliances. The fire detection system may be combined with a burglar alarm system and an emergency medical alert system. It may be connected to an alarm monitoring company by leased telephone lines or by a digital alarm communication transmitter. The number of devices and the complexity of the system are determined, on the low end, by the minimum acceptable for a given dwelling, and, on the high end, by the extent of the occupant's needs and finances. *NFPA 72* states that the minimum requirements for detection can be met either by the installation of smoke alarms or with a fire alarm system using smoke detectors.

Single- and Multiple-Station Smoke Alarms

A single-station alarm (Figures 14.6.1, 14.6.2, 14.6.3, and 14.6.4) is a self-contained device that consists of a detecting element, electrical control components, an alarm-sounding appliance, and a provision for connection to a separate power supply source (such as the direct AC wiring of a home) or an integral power source or both.

A direct-wired type, when provided with one or more additional wires for interconnection with other similar smoke alarms, is referred to as a multiple-station smoke alarm (Figure 14.6.5). When interconnected according to the instructions provided, an alarm from any one of the interconnected smoke alarms activates the alarm in all the devices. This is important because the smoke alarm near the bedrooms should sound when a smoke alarm located in another area senses smoke. New technologies now allow for wireless interconnected battery-powered smoke alarms, as well as AC-powered ones (Figure 14.6.6). These wire-

FIGURE 14.6.1 Single-Station Photoelectric Smoke Alarm (Source: Gentex Corporation)

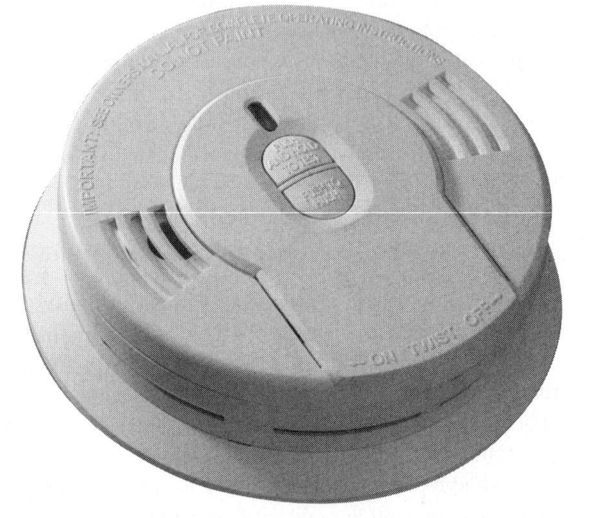

FIGURE 14.6.3 Ion Ten-Year Battery Smoke Alarm (Source: Kidde: A UTC Fire and Security Company)

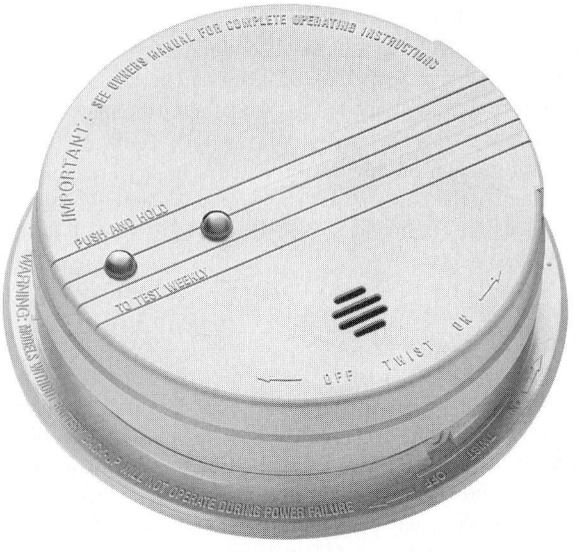

FIGURE 14.6.2 AC Battery Backup Smoke Alarm (Source: Kidde: A UTC Fire and Security Company)

FIGURE 14.6.4 Ion with Backup Battery Smoke Alarm (Source: Kidde: A UTC Fire and Security Company)

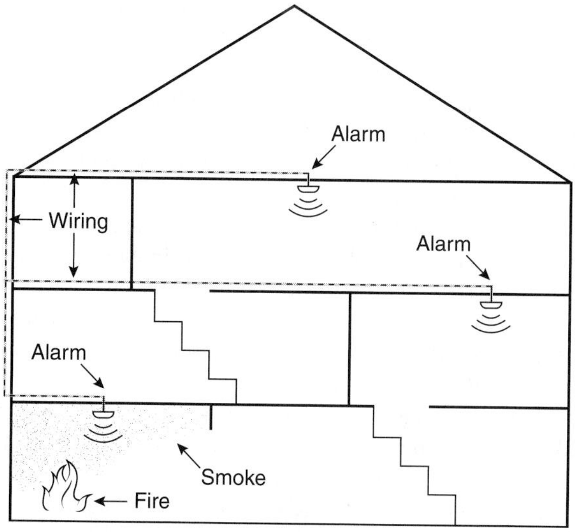

FIGURE 14.6.5 Multiple-Station Smoke Alarms with Hardwired Interconnection (Source: Hughes Associates, Inc.)

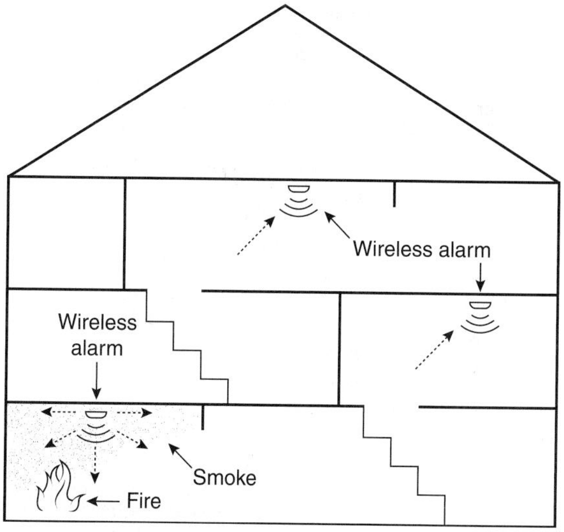

FIGURE 14.6.7 Wireless Interconnected Smoke Alarms (Source: Hughes Associates, Inc.)

FIGURE 14.6.6 Wireless Interconnected Battery-Powered Smoke Alarm (Source: Kidde: A UTC Fire and Security Company)

less interconnected alarms can be easily used in existing homes (Figure 14.6.7), whereas previously to convert to interconnected alarms generally required expensive rewiring of the house. The number of smoke alarms that are permitted to be interconnected is limited to 12 by *NFPA 72,* Chapter 11. Additional multiple-station alarms, other than smoke alarms, are permitted with limitations as specified in Chapter 11 of *NFPA 72.*

NFPA 72, Chapter 11, "Single- and Multiple-Station Alarms and Household Fire Alarm Systems," requires that low-power wireless systems comply with all of the requirements given in *NFPA 72,* Chapter 6, "Protected Premises Fire Alarm Systems."

Wireless systems are composed of smoke alarms with built-in low-power radio transmitters. System operability, including battery condition, is verified by periodic transmission via repeaters, when necessary, to a central receiver. Both repeaters and the central receiver operate from AC power with standby battery, thus providing a reliable system.

Household Fire-Warning System

In addition to single- and multiple-station alarms, there are household fire-warning systems similar in makeup and operation to the local fire alarm systems described in *NFPA 72,* Chapter 6, "Protected Premises Fire Alarm Systems." Such a system typically consists of a fire alarm control unit (panel) that derives main power from the AC house wiring and contains a rechargeable standby battery capable of operating the system for at least 24 hours (Figure 14.6.8). In addition, this system uses smoke detectors and heat detectors of the system-connected type. Some detectors include a self-contained sounder for alarm.

The fire alarm system can also have separate alarm notification appliances, such as bells, horns, or electronic sirens. The control unit also might have provision for connection to an automatic digital dialer, central station, or television cable to transmit the alarm to a point beyond the household. Where the system is connected to a supervising station, *NFPA 72,* Chapter 11, permits the station to verify alarm signals prior to reporting them to the fire service provided that the verification process does not delay the reporting by more than 90 seconds.

The most popular method for such a connection is digital communication. *NFPA 72* permits (1) operation with only one telephone line and (2) programming to call only one digital alarm control receiver (DACR) number.

Combination Systems

Both wired and wireless household fire alarm systems often include intrusion detection in addition to fire alarm functions.

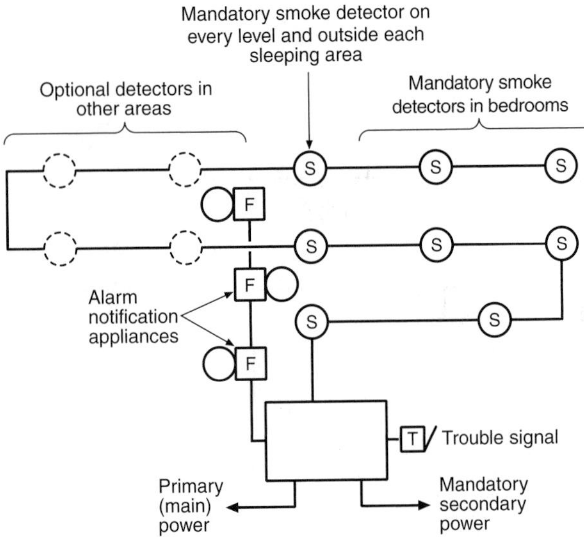

FIGURE 14.6.8 Typical Household Fire Alarm System, with Separate Control Panel

This could make the system more cost effective. In combined systems, the fire alarm signal must take precedence over the intrusion detection alarm signal. The audible alarms are required to be distinctive so the homeowner can immediately discern the difference between a fire and an intrusion. In addition, a system that provides for transmission of alarms to a point beyond the household by means of a digital dialer will sometimes have a medical alert feature that can be used to summon medical help.

DETECTION SYSTEM COMPONENTS

Smoke Alarms

Single- and multiple-station alarms may be of either the ionization or photoelectric type. Tests have shown that listed smoke alarms of either the ionization or photoelectric type should provide adequate warning to the occupants for most residential fires. It might be noted that, as a class, ionization alarms generally respond faster to open flaming fires than photoelectric alarms. Conversely, the photoelectric alarms generally respond faster to smoldering fires. Because residential occupancies experience both flaming and smoldering fires, an extra margin of occupant safety might be achieved if the home were equipped with one alarm of each type. However, the number of potential nuisance alarms may increase. Both types of smoke alarms are subjected to, and must pass, the same test fires for listing by a testing laboratory. Typical test fires are described in UL 217, *Standard for Safety Single- and Multiple-Station Smoke Detectors,* and ANSI/UL 268, *Standard for Safety Smoke Detectors for Fire Protective Signaling Systems.*

Alarm Notification Appliances

A smoke alarm sounds an audible alarm at the device itself. *NFPA 72* requires that a device should provide at least 15 dBA above the maximum ambient sound level at the ear of the sleeping person or at least 75 dBA, whichever is greater. Per the design and listing requirements, the sound level output of an alarm must be at least 85 dBA at a distance of 10 ft (3.05 m). This should be sufficient to meet the *NFPA 72* requirements and to alert most sleeping people as long as the alarms are located per the current code requirements.[5,6]

If alarms are not installed per the current codes (i.e., interconnected and located on every floor and in every bedroom), occupants should be aware of the factors that may impact the effectiveness of alarms to wake people. Long distances between the alarm and the bedroom, closed bedroom doors, a noisy appliance in the bedroom such as an air conditioner or humidifier, or impaired hearing could prevent an occupant from being awakened by the alarm. This possibility is why it is important for alarms to be interconnected and to sound in the bedroom.

A wired or wireless household fire alarm system normally has an alarm-notification appliance circuit for connection of various appliances, such as fire alarm bells, horns, or electronic sirens. These devices can produce higher sound levels and can be located independently of the detectors. They can be clearly audible throughout the house or even outside, where neighbors might hear the alarm. Regardless of the type of devices installed in the home, alarm signals should be measured in each bedroom.

Several studies have examined the response of adult occupants to the smoke alarm signals; Bruck[7] provides a summary of these. In general, an unimpaired sleeping adult will awake quickly to a smoke alarm signal that reaches the occupants at a sound level of 55 to 60 dBA. Recent studies have also shown that most older adults, who as a population group generally experience hearing loss compared to the general population, will wake to smoke alarms installed per the current codes.[6,8] Other studies[9,10] have specifically investigated the waking effectiveness of smoke alarms with children. These studies have shown that a 55 to 60 dBA signal will not reliably wake children between the ages of 6 and 15 years. Even at a sound level of 89 dBA at the pillow, 71 percent of 6- to 10-year-olds and 29 percent of 11- to 15-year-olds slept through alarms. Children under 6 years old would be even less likely to awaken than the 6-year-olds.[11] Due to the deep sleep behavior of children, many simply will not awaken to smoke alarms, even at extremely loud levels of 123 dBA[12] that can be painful to individuals. The key point to understand: children will likely sleep through an alarm and will need assistance to escape from a fire. Though parents typically realize that they have difficulty in waking their children at times, many parents seem quite surprised when presented with these findings. Occupants must plan to help both young children and people with disabilities that will impede waking or escape.

INSTALLATION PRACTICES

Smoke Alarm Location Guidelines

Alarms should be located on the ceiling, at least 4 in. (102 mm) from the wall, or on the side wall, 4 to 12 in. (102 to 305 mm) from the ceiling to the top of the device (Figure 14.6.9). On floors containing bedrooms, the ceiling of the hallway serving

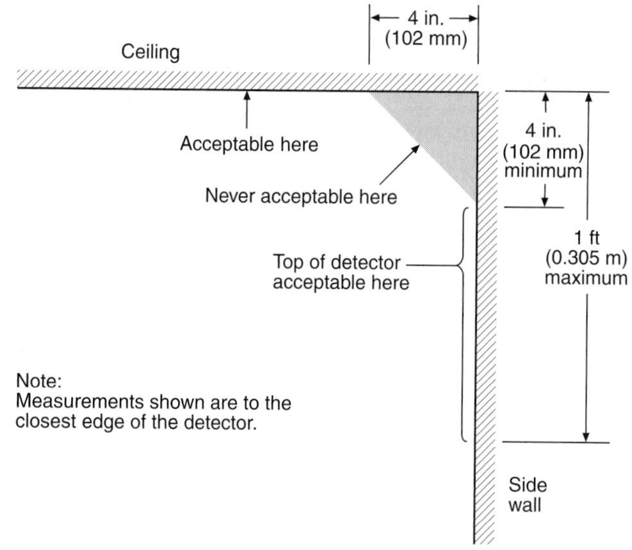

FIGURE 14.6.9 Proper Mounting of Smoke Alarms

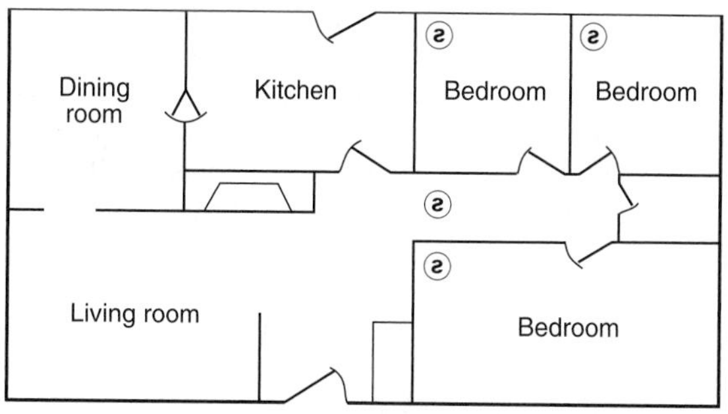

FIGURE 14.6.11 Smoke Alarm to Be Located in Each Bedroom and Between Sleeping Area and Rest of Family Living Unit (Source: *NFPA 72®*, *National Fire Alarm Code®*, 2007 ed., Figure A11.5.1[b])

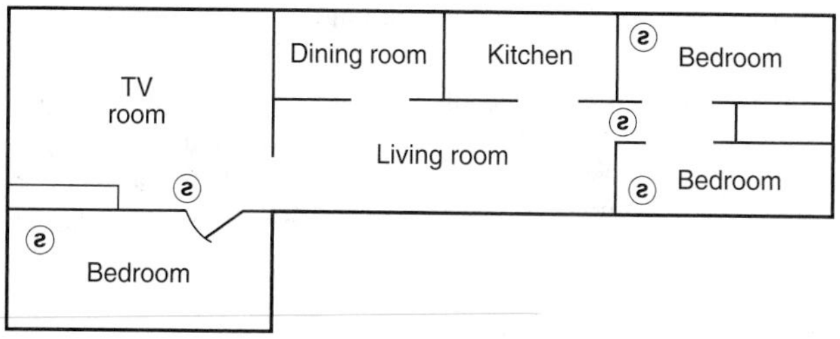

FIGURE 14.6.12 Smoke Alarm to Be Located in Each Sleeping Area as Well as in Each Bedroom (Source: *NFPA 72®*, *National Fire Alarm Code®*, 2007 ed., Figure A11.5.1[c])

the bedrooms is the usual alarm location. On other floors, alarms should be located near the stairways to intercept smoke rising from lower floors. Smoke alarms (indicated by a backward "S" in the figures) must be located on each story (Figure 14.6.10) as well as between the sleeping area and the rest of the family living unit (Figure 14.6.11). A smoke alarm should be provided to protect each sleeping area in addition to smoke alarms required in bedrooms (Figure 14.6.12).

Alarms should be located no closer than 3 ft (0.9 m) from heating vents so that air issuing from the vent will not blow the smoke away from the alarm. Some smoke alarms are not suitable for location within kitchens, because of false alarms from cooking vapors. Chapter 11 of *NFPA 72* requires that smoke alarms located within 20 ft (6.1 m) (horizontally) of cooking appliances incorporate temporary silencing (hush) features or be of the photoelectric type. Also, some smoke alarms are not permitted in garages, where automobile exhaust might cause alarms, or in attics or other unheated spaces where extremes of temperature or humidity might affect their operation. Before a smoke alarm is installed in any of these locations, its specifications should be checked to ensure it is appropriate for the intended area.

Another consideration is the temperature of the mounting surface. If a smoke alarm is installed on a surface that can be even a few degrees warmer or cooler than the room temperature, its response may be delayed by the cold or warm air layer at the mounting surface. Smoke alarms should not be installed on uninsulated exterior walls, ceilings below uninsulated attics, or ceilings containing radiant heating coils. If the alarm is colder than the air temperature and if the relative humidity is high, condensation of water vapor may occur in the alarm and either produce a false alarm or disable the alarm. Condensation, dust, and insects are three of the most common things that lead to alarm malfunction.

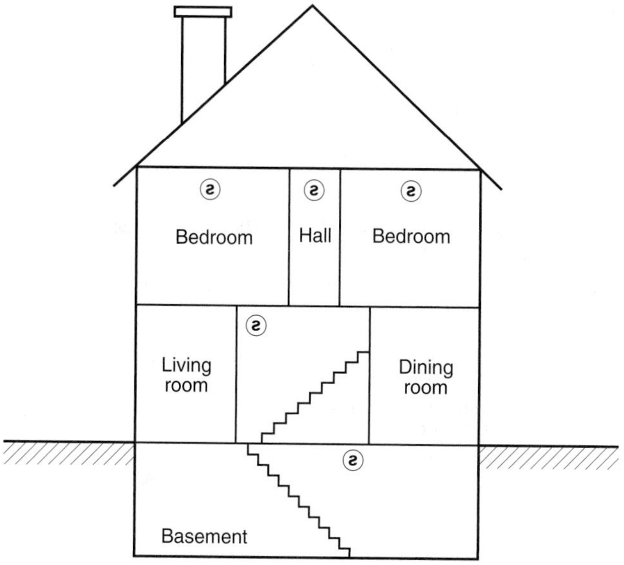

FIGURE 14.6.10 Smoke Alarm to Be Located on Each Story (Source: *NFPA 72®*, *National Fire Alarm Code®*, 2007 ed., Figure A11.5.1[d])

Special Considerations for the Disabled

In general, households with disabled or elderly occupants need a higher level of protection to provide additional escape time. If the disabled person could not escape without assistance, provisions should be made for someone to provide help. Alarms that signal to remote receivers could be used, for instance, to sound the alarm in a neighbor's home. For hearing-impaired occupants, some alarms can be connected to bed vibrators, flashing strobes (see *NFPA 72,* Chapter 4, "Notification Appliances for Fire Alarm Systems"), or fans to provide tactile or visual as well as aural stimulation (Figure 14.6.13).

MAINTENANCE AND TESTING

Maintenance

Household fire-warning equipment should be maintained in accordance with the recommendations of the equipment manufacturer. In general, this means little more than keeping the equipment clean and free of dust and replacing the batteries when needed. Alarms should never be disconnected due to nuisance alarms. If a smoke alarm sounds a nuisance alarm caused by cooking, the problem can typically be corrected either by moving the alarm to another location, farther from the cooking source, or by replacing it with a smoke alarm that is not as sensitive to cooking smoke.

Testing

The importance of testing smoke alarms cannot be emphasized too strongly. Smoke alarms are basically electronic devices, and, because all devices will fail at some time, the failure rate projection of a smoke alarm can be estimated. From these projections, the life expectancy or the average failure rate of the smoke alarm can be determined. *NFPA 72* requires that smoke alarms in one- and two-family dwellings be replaced when they fail to respond to the operability test (i.e., pushing the test button) or after 10 years from the date of manufacture. This recommendation was developed in part on the estimate that after 10 years there will be a 30 percent chance that a unit will fail.

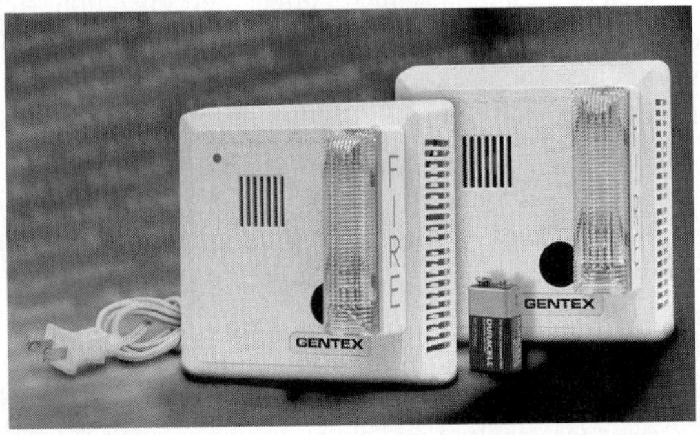

FIGURE 14.6.13 Combination Photoelectric Smoke Alarm/ Strobe Light (Source: Gentex Corporation)

To reduce the period of time that a smoke alarm could be out of service because of failure, the alarm that has failed can best be identified by periodic testing and then replaced. The following example is merely illustrative and is not indicative of currently available units, but it demonstrates the importance of periodic testing of smoke alarms. Assuming a 10-year life of a smoke alarm and a predicted failure rate of 4 failures per million hours of operation (which is the minimum listed design requirement for alarms), if the alarm is never tested, the residents could be unprotected for 276 weeks, or over 5 years. On the other hand, with an alarm that is tested monthly, residents will be unprotected only for at most 5 weeks. This example has a built-in factor of 2 weeks, so a defective alarm can be removed and a replacement can be obtained and installed. However, a defective alarm should be replaced immediately. This example dramatically shows how important it is to test a smoke alarm frequently.

Guidelines for testing smoke alarms can be found in *NFPA 72,* Chapter 10, "Inspection, Testing, and Maintenance," and in the manufacturers' instructions.

SUMMARY

In the United States, fire deaths occur predominantly in the home, and thus household fire-warning equipment is essential for life safety. The types of systems and smoke alarms vary according to minimum standards and the occupants' specific needs. Installation of an adequate fire-warning system and ongoing maintenance and testing ensure that the system will work effectively. Fire protection in the home also involves formulating an escape plan and minimizing fire hazards.

BIBLIOGRAPHY

References Cited

1. Ahrens, M., *U.S. Experience with Smoke Alarms and Other Fire Detection/Alarm Equipment ,* Fire Analysis and Research Division, National Fire Protection Association, Quincy, MA, Nov. 2004.
2. Bukowski, R. W., "Studies Address Performance of Residential Detectors," *NFPA Journal,* Vol. 87, No. 1, 1993.
3. Su, J. Z., Crampton, G. P., Carpenter, D. W., McCartney, C., and Leroux, P., "KEMANO Fire Studies, Part 1: Response of Residential Smoke Alarms," Research Report 108, Institute for Research in Construction, National Research Council Canada, Ottawa, Canada, Apr. 2003.
4. Bukowski, R., Peacock, R., Averill, J., Cleary, T., Bryner, N., Walton, W., Reneke, P., and Kulogowski, E., *Performance of Home Smoke Alarms, Analysis of the Response of Several Available Technologies in Residential Fire Settings,* NIST Technical Note 1455, National Institute for Standards and Technology, Gaithersburg MD, 2004.
5. Lee, A., "The Audibility of Smoke Alarms in Residential Homes," CPSC-ES-0503, U.S. Consumer Product Safety Commission, Washington, DC, 2005, http://www.cpsc.gov/library/foia/foia05/os/audibility.pdf.
6. Geiman, J., and Gottuk, D., "Reducing Fire Deaths in Older Adults: Optimizing the Smoke Alarm Signal," Fire Protection Research Foundation, National Fire Protection Association, Quincy, MA, May 2006.

7. Bruck, D., and Brennan, P., "Recognition of Fire Cues During Sleep," *Human Behavior in Fire—Proceedings* of the Second International Symposium, March 26–28, 2001, Boston, MA, Interscience Communications Ltd., London, England, 2001.
8. Bruck, D., Thomas, I., and Kritikos, A., "Investigation of Auditory Arousal with Different Alarm Signals in Sleeping Older Adults," Fire Protection Research Foundation, National Fire Protection Association, Quincy, MA, May 2006.
9. Bruck, D., "Non-awakening in Children in Response to a Smoke Detector Alarm," *Fire Safety Journal*, Vol. 32, 1999, pp. 369–376.
10. Bruck, D., and Bliss, R. A., "Sleeping Children and Smoke Alarms," *Proceedings* of the 4th Asia-Oceania Symposium on Fire Science and Technology, 2000, pp. 603–611.
11. Bruck, D., "Waking to Smoke Alarms," National Fire Protection Association World Fire Safety Congress and Exposition, Dallas, TX, May 2003.
12. Busby, K., and Pivik, R. T., "Auditory Arousal Thresholds During Sleep in Hyperkinetic Children," *Sleep*, Vol. 8, No. 4, 1985, pp. 332–341.

NFPA Codes, Standards, and Recommended Practices

Reference to the following NFPA codes, standards, and recommended practices will provide further information on household fire warning equipment discussed in this chapter. (See the latest version of The NFPA Catalog *for availability of current editions of the following documents.)*

NFPA 13, *Standard for the Installation of Sprinkler Systems*
NFPA 70, *National Electrical Code®*
NFPA 72®, National Fire Alarm Code®
NFPA *101®*, *Life Safety Code®*

Chapter 7

Fire Protection Surveillance and Security Services

Lawrence J. Wenzel

Chapter Contents

Key Terms

fire alarm system, patrol, security, security officer, security tour, surveillance, watchclock

Effective fire protection at a commercial or industrial facility depends on the degree to which the management of the facility is committed to providing an appropriate level of fire loss prevention and fire control. Once the hazards of the facility have been identified and evaluated, and built-in fire protection systems have been provided to offset the impact of those hazards, the protection features must be consistently managed.

A fire alarm system is a management tool that oversees fire protection surveillance. The fire alarm system can monitor the availability of other fire suppression systems. It may also monitor the activities of guards making fire patrol tours.

The fire alarm system should monitor all fire alarm initiating devices. Examples are manual fire alarm boxes; heat, smoke, radiant energy, fire-gas, or other fire detection devices; and the discharge and supervisory device connections for automatic sprinkler systems and other fire suppression or extinguishing systems, such as dry chemical, foam, foam-water, water mist, carbon dioxide, and other gaseous agents.

The fire alarm system should also monitor pertinent supervisory initiating devices for both "off-normal" and "restoration to normal" conditions. These include the following:

- Any automatic sprinkler control valve 2½ in. (63.5 mm) or larger
- Dry pipe or preaction valve high and low air pressure
- Fire protection water tank or reservoir level
- Fire protection water-pressure tank high and low air pressure
- Electric-driven fire pump operation, power failure, loss of phase, and phase reversal
- Diesel-engine-driven fire pump operation, controller switch in a position other than "automatic," engine or controller problems, and failure of the battery charger
- Steam-driven fire pump operation and steam availability
- Low public water system pressure when fire protection systems are fed from a dead-end public water main, or when the public water system is deemed unreliable

In addition, for those geographic areas subject to freezing winter temperatures, the fire alarm system should monitor low temperature for the following:

- Buildings protected by wet pipe automatic sprinklers
- Dry pipe, deluge, or preaction valve closets
- Fire pump rooms
- Fire protection water tanks

Section 14, Chapter 4, "Fire Alarm System Interconnections," discusses these interfaces into the fire alarm system in detail. In order to ensure immediate attention to signals generated by the protected premises fire alarm system, to ensure that management is promptly notified of the nature of these signals, and to keep proper records of signals received, it may be wise to connect the fire alarm system to a central station, proprietary, remote station, or combination auxiliary and remote station fire alarm system. This will ensure that signals receive attention at all times.

Lawrence J. Wenzel, P.E., is a senior fire protection engineer with Hughes Associates, Inc., Oakdale, Connecticut.

For those facilities where some type of security service is included, and intended to be part of the overall fire protection surveillance, the protected premises fire alarm system can also monitor the patrol tours made by security officers.

For related topics, see the following chapters in Section 14: Chapter 1, "Fire Alarm Systems"; Chapter 4, "Fire Alarm System Interconnections"; Chapter 5, "Inspection, Testing, and Maintenance of Fire Alarm Systems"; and Chapter 10, "Security and Intrusion Detection Systems."

FIRE AND SECURITY SERVICES

Containment of fire to its area of origin involves several factors, one of the most important of which is early detection. During normal business hours, most occupiable areas (i.e., areas other than concealed spaces, exterior surfaces) are continuously or routinely occupied or observed by the people in the areas. (Intermittent occupation might apply to areas such as lavatories, hallways, or closets.) By their presence, the occupants provide fire protection surveillance because they are able to detect a fire when it occurs. A carelessly discarded cigarette, for example, may ignite the contents of a wastebasket; that fire may spread until the entire building is involved. However, someone who discovers the fire while it is still in its incipient stage may be able to extinguish it with a portable fire extinguisher. In some cases, the occupants can also detect conditions, such as a malfunctioning machine, that might lead to a fire. Similarly, increased security surveillance is vital in guarding against fires of incendiary origin.

Security officers generally serve three purposes in helping to protect a property against fire loss: (1) watch the property at times when the management is not present; (2) facilitate and control the movement of persons into, out of, and within the property; and (3) carry out procedures for the orderly conduct of some operations on the property, such as the shipping and receiving functions. Security officers may be facility employees or employees of outside firms that provide these services on a contract basis, or a combination of both. The duties of these individuals may be supplemented or, in some cases, replaced in part by various approved fire and security protective signaling systems.

MANAGEMENT OF SECURITY SERVICES

In conjunction with fire and explosion suppression systems and various other management programs for loss prevention and control, a comprehensive program of fire protection and security surveillance provides a means of (1) continually monitoring the facility for conditions that might lead to a fire or explosion, (2) promptly notifying the public fire department or private fire brigade that a fire or explosion has occurred, and (3) effectively inhibiting unauthorized access to the facility. Management must determine how this surveillance can be best achieved.

In concept, security officers should patrol thoroughly all unoccupied areas of a facility often enough to be able to detect conditions likely to result in a fire or other emergency. These patrols should be supervised in some way so management can verify that the security officer is indeed making the patrol tours.

The highly protected risk (HPR) property insurance carriers generally recommend that the first patrol tour begin within 30 minutes of vacancy and that subsequent patrol tours be made every hour at night and every other hour (bihourly) during the day. Each tour should not exceed 45 minutes in actual length, allowing the security officer at least 15 minutes of rest.

Management Roles

Management should develop a written surveillance plan for both fire protection and security in the facility. To do this, the property manager should determine which areas of the facility are unoccupied during both working and nonworking hours. The property manager should also designate a management representative who will be responsible for overseeing the surveillance program. It is very important that management retain supervisory control of surveillance to maintain program integrity. This representative should review surveillance reports daily and evaluate changes in the facility that might require modification of the surveillance plan.

The facility's fire loss prevention and control manager should be consulted during the establishment of procedures to be followed by security officers. Procedures and instructions to security officers should be geared to the specific actions required. General instructions or superficial training are of little value. Meaningful, specific instructions cannot be prepared, however, without an investment of both time and thought by those who manage the property. Management should also establish a clear line of succession in the event of absences. Even when there are only two security officers employed, one should be designated as the leader.

Supervision of security officers provided under contract with outside firms should be through the designated representatives of the company providing the security service. In the contract for services or supplementary documents, the company should be given details as specific and complete as possible regarding the services expected.

Security Officer Equipment

Management is responsible for providing security officers assigned to patrol a property with adequate equipment and information with which to safeguard their own health and safety. Potential situations that must be considered include the following:

- Sudden illness or injury while the security officer is alone at the property
- Possibility of a security officer being overpowered by an intruder
- Development of a situation requiring management decisions

The first situation can be addressed by equipping security officers with devices for prompt, efficient communication, such as portable two-way radios, which would allow them to summon aid.

In the second situation, an intruder may prevent the security officer from using any communications equipment. It then becomes necessary to have a system or procedure whereby the security officer's failure to transmit a signal or meet a predetermined schedule will be investigated promptly.

Third, situations that require management decisions may arise at times when the property is attended by security officers only. Such decisions may involve conditions ranging from the unscheduled arrival of merchandise or supplies to anonymous bomb threats. Security officers must have instructions and the means for contacting management personnel.

COMMUNICATIONS EQUIPMENT

Security officers should be provided with facilities for communication within and outside the property. A control center should provide a point with which officers may communicate, and the center should have communications facilities to points outside the property. Such a center is needed even when there is very limited security service. For example, in a facility with only one or two officers, this control center might simply be a room with a telephone. Even with a complete fire alarm and security system covering all areas of the property, a control center on the property is necessary.

If an emergency voice/alarm communication fire alarm system is provided, security officers may communicate with the building fire command station by using the fire warden telephones.

Where the equipment for security officer communications, including officers on watch patrol, requires that signals from officers be monitored, the control center should be provided with an operator. Additional operators needed to staff a 24 hour operator service should be provided at the control center, according to the character of security service provided. For some services, runners, or security officers who can be dispatched to investigate signals, should also be provided.

A directory of names and telephone numbers (including any other information to assist in making emergency calls to the outside) should be kept at the control center in a visible index or other quickly accessible form. This directory should give information about the public fire and police departments, key management personnel, and other outside agencies that may have to be contacted in an emergency.

SECURITY PATROL TOUR SUPERVISION

Off-premises security officer supervisory service designed to report the performance of a security officer may be provided by central station, proprietary, or remote station fire alarm systems. Portable watchclocks may also be used to supervise the security officer if centralized, immediate supervision is not required.

Tour supervisory systems generally consist of security officer patrol tour supervisory initiating devices of some type and a means of recording signals initiated from these devices. Many companies refer to this equipment as "guard tour supervisory" devices. Two types of supervisory service systems are (1) compulsory and (2) noncompulsory, based on whether the guard follows a compulsory preset pattern or not.

Compulsory Tour Supervisory Systems

This system involves one or more "active" security patrol tour supervisory initiating devices that are installed in conjunction with several "passive" security patrol tour supervisory initiating devices. These devices are arranged so that the security officer must progress in a fixed route from one station to another. Ordinarily, the officer carries some type of device called a "key," which can be a "wand" that serves as a handheld computer with a memory function. The initiating devices can be arranged so that the passive devices condition the key so that it may operate the next device, whether that device is active or passive. In addition to conditioning the key for the next device, active initiating devices also either transmit a signal to an on- or off-premises central recording location or cause a signal to be recorded inside the key, which indicates the date and time that the active initiating device was operated. This system is particularly useful when, because of the nature of the facility, it is essential that the security officer follow a carefully prescribed route. One disadvantage to this system from a security standpoint is that the tour may not be varied. This is sometimes felt undesirable because a potential intruder who is observing the movement of the security officer might be able to readily discern a pattern to the officer's movement.

In many compulsory tour systems, the security officer initiates a starting signal at the beginning of a round and initiates a finishing or completion signal at the end of the round. All of the other stations in between would be passive initiating devices. A fixed schedule of starting and finishing times is arranged in advance when a compulsory tour is monitored by an off-premises facility. If the security officer fails to either begin or end a round within the prescribed times, on the expiration of a "grace" period of usually no more than 10 or 15 minutes in length, the off-premises monitoring facility will initiate action. Normally, an attempt will be made to contact the security officer by telephone. On failure to reach the officer, the off-premises monitoring facility will normally dispatch the police department and notify the management of the facility that the security officer has failed to respond.

When a compulsory tour system is used in conjunction with a proprietary fire alarm system, the process works much the same, except that, since the receiving location is normally located on the protected premises, the operator at the receiving location will be more readily able to determine why the guard has not begun or ended a round.

Noncompulsory Tour Supervisory Systems

In this system, all of the initiating devices are active. The security officer progresses from station to station, with each initiating device indicating the date and time of the officer operating the station. By following the progression of signals, the off-premises or on-premises monitoring station can follow the progress of the security officer during the course of the round. In some cases, combination manual fire alarm boxes/officer patrol tour supervisory initiating stations are grouped in the same physical housing. These stations are arranged so that they may be actuated by any person to indicate a fire, but may also be operated by a security officer to indicate the progress of a tour.

Delinquency Reporting Systems

Some compulsory or noncompulsory tour supervisory systems are arranged so that, rather than reporting every time the security officer operates an active initiating device, the system only transmits a signal when the officer has failed to operate the device within a prescribed time period. Such delinquency reporting systems are utilized when it is desired to reduce the amount of signal traffic associated with the officer patrol tour supervisory system. Many remote station fire alarm systems that supervise security officer patrol tours are arranged in this fashion.

Telephone, Radio, and Other Voice Reporting Systems

Occasionally, a security officer patrol tour is supervised by means of the guard reporting from a specific location by means of a voice reporting system. Probably the most common system uses a telephone system equipped with calling subset identification. When the security officer initiates voice communication over such a system, the system indicates and records the specific location from which the officer is calling. Other systems employing means of voice communication, including radio systems, can also be used. In some radio systems, a tour supervisory initiating device must be inserted into the radio before the security officer establishes patrol tour contact. This device transmits a digital code that gives a specific location, thus indicating that the officer is at the prescribed tour station.

Portable Watchclocks

In many cases, management determines that it is not necessary to provide immediate supervision of the security officer patrol tours, and elects to provide retrospective security officer patrol tour supervision by means of a stationary or portable watchclock. Figure 14.7.1 shows a portable watchclock. This clock provides an embossed record tape, made directly from type on the recording key. The tape has 24 ruled segments and is synchronized with the clock mechanism. If a security officer fails to punch in, the omission is indicated by a prominent white space on the tape. This clock indicates when it was opened. The records from these devices must be reviewed the following day to determine that the officer has indeed made the prescribed tours and operated all of the tour supervisory initiating devices. Although this method lacks the immediacy of the other tour supervisory methods, it is sufficiently cost-effective to be the most common tour supervisory method employed. Traditionally, a spring-wound clock mechanism—either at a single location in the case of a stationary watchclock or in a portable case that the guard can carry from location to location—is used to drive some type of recording medium. The most common recording medium is a paper disk or a paper tape. In this case, the tour supervisory initiating devices are embossing keys that must be inserted into the portable watchclock and turned, making their impression on the paper tape. The tour supervisory initiating devices for the stationary clock are usually some type of electric switch or, in at least one design, a magneto that must be operated by the officer, causing the stationary clock to record the specific location.

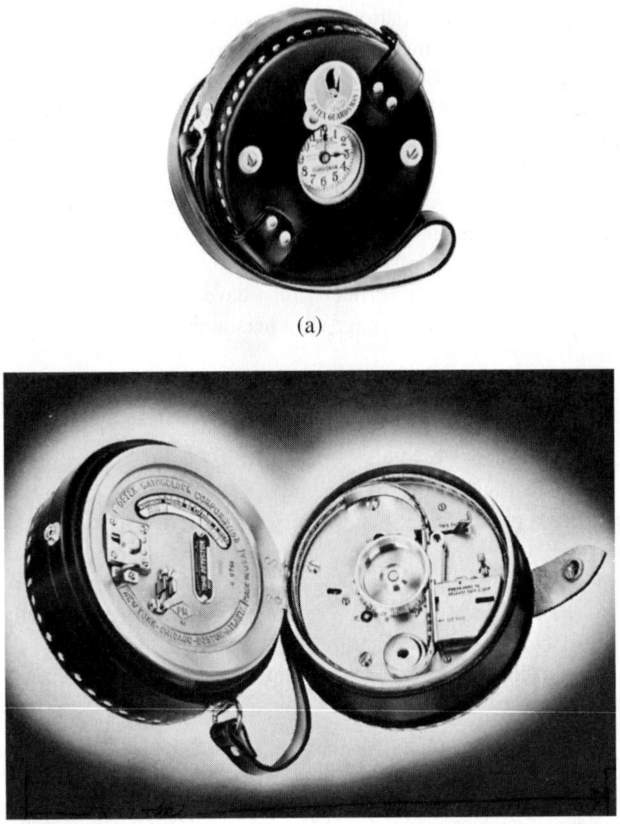

(a)

(b)

FIGURE 14.7.1 Portable Watchclock: (a) Front view; (b) Interior view (Source: Detex Corp.)

The portable watchclock can be an effective supervisory tool if access to the clock is carefully controlled so that the security officer cannot have access to the internal mechanism of the watchclock. This means that someone in management should actually open the clock and retrieve the record each day. To safeguard against premature opening of the clock, a telltale device places a mark on the paper disk or tape whenever the clock is opened. Even when a security service company provides the security officer patrol tour service, it is advisable to have management supervise the retrieval of records from the watchclock to prevent any collusion between upper-level officers, such as sergeants or lieutenants, and the guards themselves.

Another type of portable watchclock uses computer-based equipment to supervise the route and timing, if desired, of the security officer. As shown in Figure 14.7.2, manufacturers have developed scanners that read the station and store the station's information in the handheld unit carried by the officer. The equipment shown in Figure 14.7.2 is typical of the hardware available for use by security officers, who carries the handheld "wand" unit or a similar device and passes it over data strips or

FIGURE 14.7.2 Computer-Based Equipment for Route Supervision (Source: ProxiGuard)

similar points installed throughout the premises (Figure 14.7.3 and 14.7.4). The use of handheld wands or similar readers is very much the norm for security officers to register their rounds. The handheld unit is then attached to some type of download device for computer storage of the report (Figure 14.7.5).

The security officer can then download the information from the handheld unit to a data-gathering unit designed specifically for this equipment, or in some cases to a computer outfitted with the corresponding program information. Other designs allow the handheld unit to be placed on a base unit that will produce a printed report. Components may be as simple as a bar code strip fixed to a piece of equipment to more sophisticated electronic stations. This type of equipment gives management a number of options to help detail the activities of the security officer.

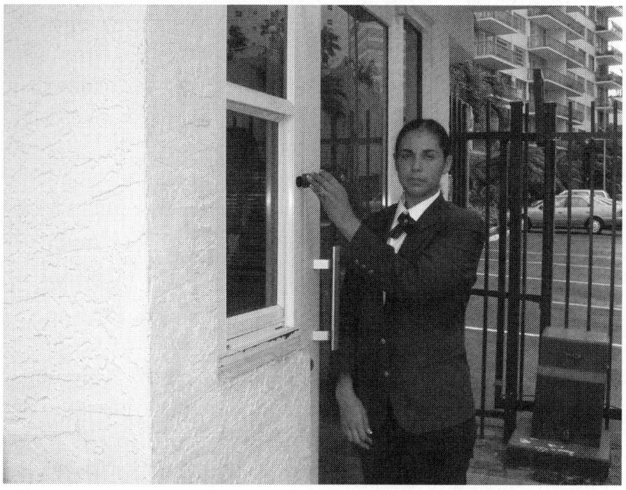

FIGURE 14.7.3 Security Officer Registering Rounds (Source: ProxiGuard)

FIGURE 14.7.4 Handheld Wand (Source: ProxiGuard)

SECURITY SERVICE FUNCTIONS

A sufficient number of security officers should be provided to accomplish the needed services. If officers are assigned to other part-time duties in addition to their regular security officer services, these duties should be arranged so they will not interfere with regular officer duties.

Control of Pedestrians and Vehicles

Fireguard service can facilitate and control the movement of persons within a property when the property requires such service. Duties in this category include the following:

- Preventing the entry of unauthorized persons who might set a fire or do damage to the facility
- Controlling the activities of people authorized to be on the property, but who may not be aware of procedures established for the prevention of fire
- Controlling pedestrian and vehicular traffic during exit drills, and evacuating the property or parts of it during emergencies
- Controlling gates and vehicular traffic to facilitate access to the property by the public fire department, members of a private fire brigade, and off-duty management personnel in case of fire or emergency

Control of Operations

Security service should be established to carry out certain procedures for the orderly conduct of operations on the property, including procedures for fire loss prevention and control, both by personnel associated with the property and outside contractors. Duties in this category include the following:

- Promptly discovering a fire and calling the public fire department (also the fire brigade of the property, where there is such a brigade)
- Operating equipment provided for fire control and extinguishment *after* giving the alarm and before the response of other persons to the alarm
- Monitoring signals of fire alarm systems
- Patrolling routes chosen by management to ensure surveillance of all the property at appropriate intervals

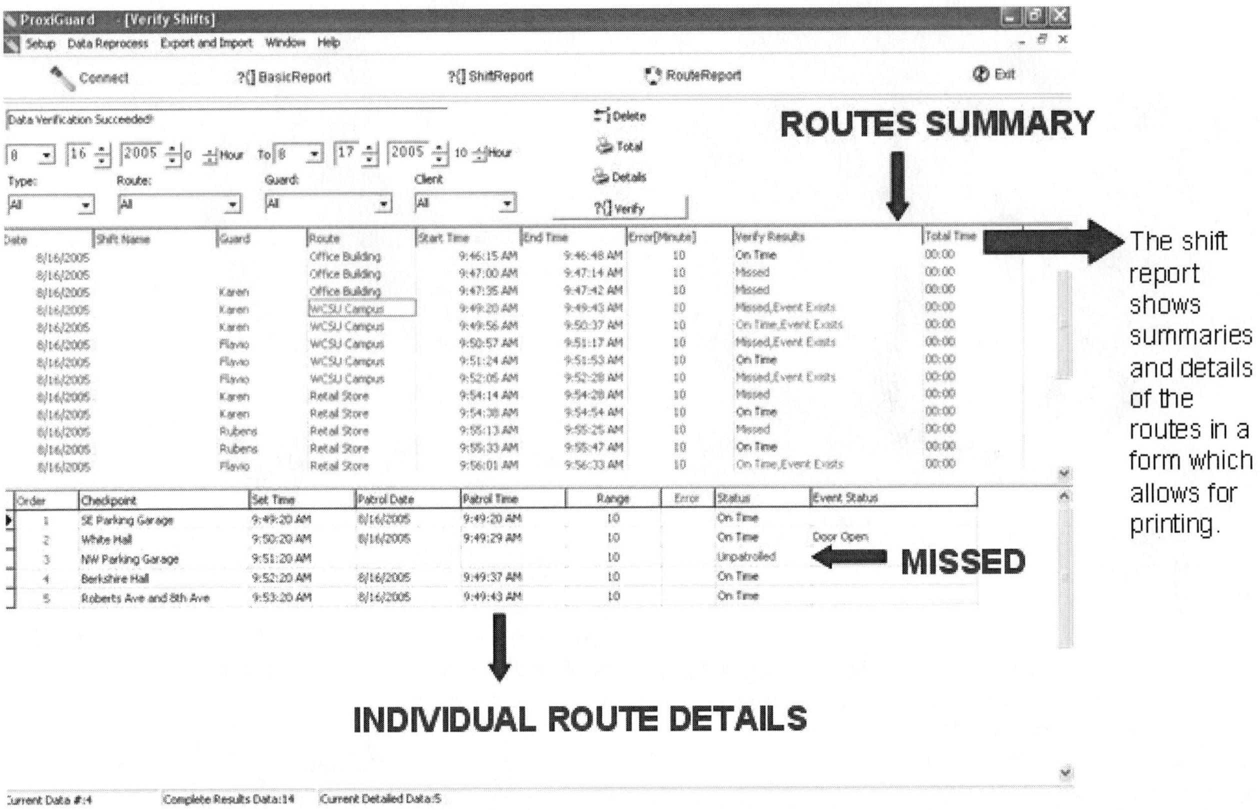

FIGURE 14.7.5 Report Generated from Information Downloaded from Handheld Wand

- Starting up and shutting down certain equipment when no other personnel are provided for this purpose
- Checking permits for "hotwork," including cutting and welding, and standing by to operate fire-extinguishing equipment when necessary
- Detecting conditions likely to cause a fire, such as leaks, spills, and faulty equipment
- Detecting conditions likely to reduce the effectiveness with which a fire may be controlled, such as portable fire extinguishers not in place, sprinkler valves not open, and water supplies impaired
- Performing operations to ensure that fire equipment will function effectively including, for example, testing automatic sprinkler and other fixed fire protection systems, including fire pumps, and other equipment related to these systems and assisting in the maintenance of this equipment; checking portable fire extinguishers and fire hose and assisting in pressure tests and maintenance service on these items; testing fire alarm systems; and checking equipment provided on any fire apparatus and carrying out the periodic tests and maintenance operations required for the apparatus

PATROL ROUTES AND ROUNDS

Each route to be patrolled should be laid out by the responsible manager. The security officer responsible for each route should be given instructions on all details of the route, and what is expected in covering it (Figure 14.7.6). The route should be laid out to prevent shortcuts so that the security officer is required to pass through the entire patrol area. A reasonable rest period between rounds must be provided.

Security officers should make rounds at intervals determined for the particular situation by management. When operations in the property are normally suspended, rounds should be made hourly, unless management is willing to accept rounds at less frequent intervals. When there are special conditions, such as the presence of exceptional hazards or when protection is impaired, management should institute as many additional rounds as necessary to meet the fire safety requirements of such conditions.

The first round of a patrol should begin as soon as possible after the end of activities of the preceding work shift. The officers should be instructed to make a thorough inspection of all buildings or spaces on the route during their first round. Their instructions should cover the following:

- Outside doors and gates should be closed and locked. Windows, skylights, fire doors, and fire shutters should be closed.
- All oily waste, rags, paint residue, rubbish, and similar items should be removed from buildings or placed in approved containers.
- All fire apparatus should be in place and not obstructed.
- Aisles should be clear.
- Motors or machines carelessly left running should be shut off and reported.

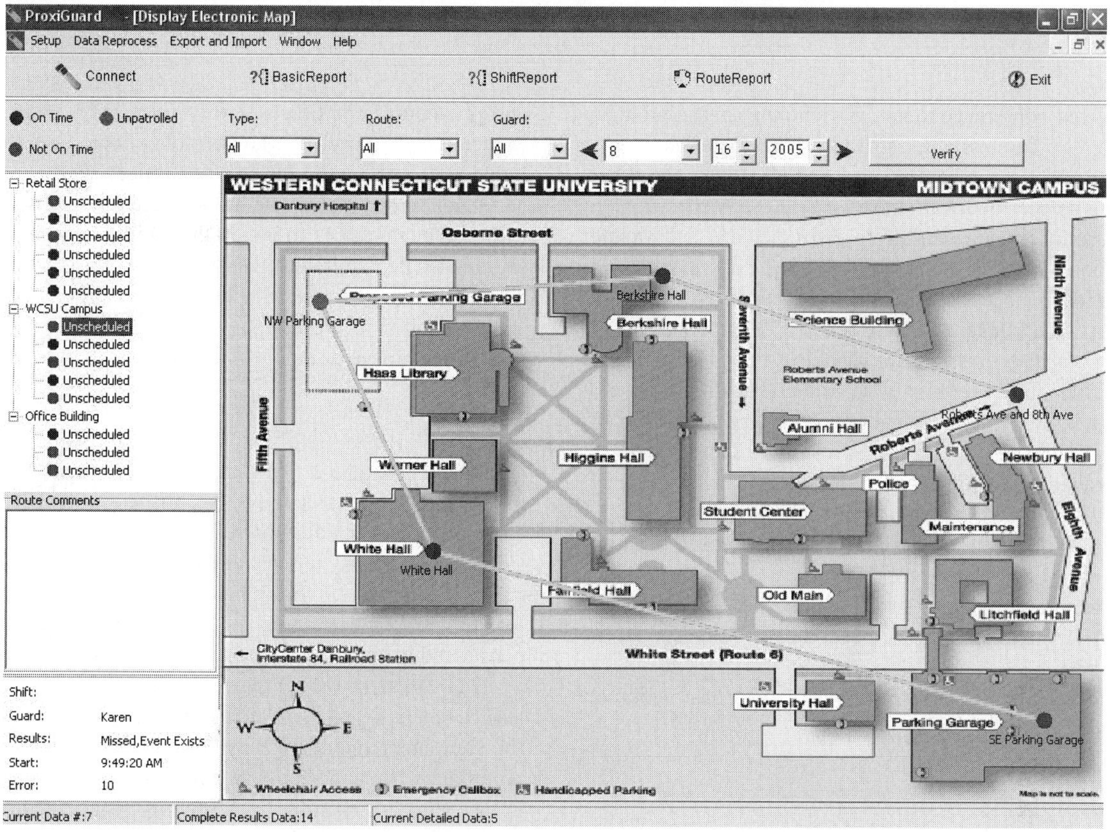

(a)

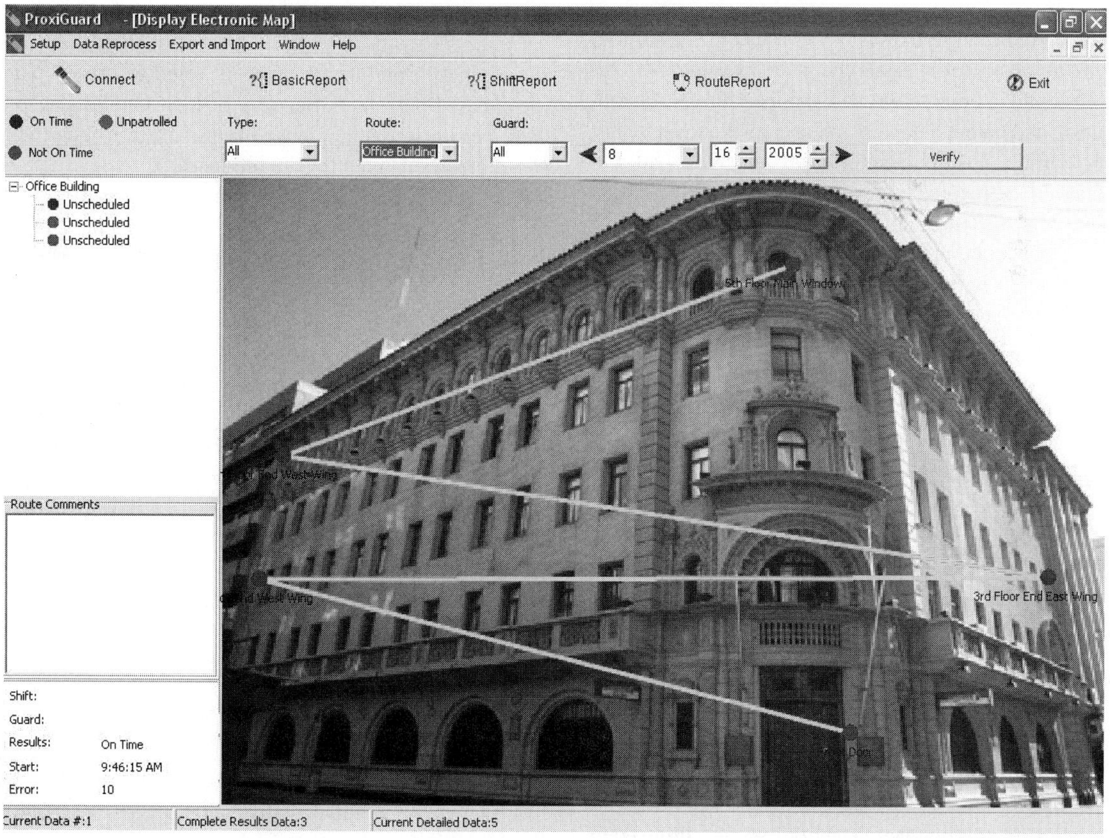

(b)

FIGURE 14.7.6 (a) Route Map of Security Officer Path; (b) Route Map Superimposed on a Building (Source: ProxiGuard)

- All offices, conference rooms, and smoking areas should be checked for carelessly discarded smoking materials.
- All gas and electric heaters, coal and oil stoves, and other heating devices on the premises should be checked.
- All hazardous manufacturing processes should be left in a safe condition. The temperature of dryers, annealing furnaces, and similar equipment that continue to operate during the night, holidays, and weekends should be noted on all rounds.
- Hazardous materials, such as gasoline, rubber cement, and other flammable and highly volatile combustibles, should be kept in proper containers or removed from buildings.
- All normally open sprinkler control valves should be open, with gauges indicating proper pressures. Gauges not open should be reported immediately.
- During cold weather, all rooms should be checked to determine if they are heated properly.
- All water faucets and air valves found leaking should be closed. If leaks cannot be stopped, the condition should be reported.
- Particular attention should be given to new construction or alterations that may be in progress.

SECURITY OFFICERS

Selection and Contracts

Management should require individuals considered for security officer service to satisfactorily pass a character investigation. This investigation should attempt to evaluate the individual's reliability, self-control, and potential loyalty to the employer. Applicants for a security officer position should be fingerprinted and particulars of any police records obtained. The local police should be furnished with this information, should corroborate it, and should ask for checks by other police agencies. The fingerprint data should be cleared with state, national, or appropriate international agencies that maintain clearing facilities for police records. All applicants for a position as a fire or security officer or patrol person should be required to state any military service record and to submit evidence of such service that may assist in an evaluation of the individual's suitability for security officer service.

Contracts for security officer service should include a provision that the company furnishing security officer service will replace any employee who, in the judgment of the company purchasing the service, is not qualified.

Qualifications and Examinations

Management should be satisfied that individuals considered for security officer service are mentally alert and have good powers of observation, intelligence, and judgment. Investigation should attempt to evaluate the individual's personality and temperament. Such an evaluation is more realistic than arbitrarily testing education or intelligence or setting an age limit. Very young people may not qualify because they have not acquired a sense of responsibility or judgment. Very old people may have impaired alertness. Individuals should be sought who are known to be "clear-headed" in an emergency.

Officers should be required to pass an annual written examination dealing with information about the property protected and procedures for fire loss prevention with which they are expected to be familiar. Management should also require that individuals considered for security officer service pass an examination to determine whether they are physically able to perform the guard duties to which they will be assigned. Officers should also be required to pass an annual physical examination. The officers do not need to be athletes, but they should not have a heart condition or other physical ailment that might work to their disadvantage in moments of stress.

Training

Management should establish a continuing training program for its officers. Its scope should be established by the manager or by a fire loss prevention and control manager acting for the manager. Courses for security officers and fire fighters, available through training programs of vocational training agencies, schools, universities, and other training and educational agencies, should be considered in any training program for security officer.

Management should require officers to have completed at least elementary courses of instruction in the use of portable fire equipment and emergency first aid. The time spent in such preliminary training should be a minimum of two working days in each subject. During service, security officers should be given not less than the equivalent of two full working days per year of training to increase their knowledge and experience in the use of portable fire extinguishers, first aid, and other useful training. Officers should be required as part of their training to participate in appropriate meetings devoted to prefire planning with operating personnel. Security officers can help accomplish this by working together with the public fire department when it establishes its plan for the premises.

Management should require security officers to know the location of portable fire extinguishers, hand hoses, standpipes and hydrants, valves controlling sprinkler systems, inside riser valves, post-indicator valves, and sectional valves in the property's own water system. They also should know how to start fire pumps. Officers also need to know the location and purpose of valves controlling water for purposes other than fire protection, and valves controlling steam, gas, and other services. Management should require security officers to know the locations of dangerous machinery or materials and inform them of hazardous manufacturing processes, especially those continuing during the night, holidays, or weekends.

EVALUATING FIRE SECURITY SERVICE

There are several items to be considered when evaluating fire security service.

Tour Records

Management's representative should ensure the following:

- All unoccupied areas of the facility are included in each tour.
- All key stations or tour supervisory transmitters in each tour have been recorded clearly in a regular hourly pattern at night and in a bihourly pattern during the day.
- Tours last no longer than 45 minutes, allowing for a rest period of at least 15 minutes each hour.

- Tours begin within one half-hour of the time the area becomes unoccupied and continue to within one half-hour of the resumption of occupancy.
- The "telltale" of a portable or stationary watchclock is recording each time the clock is opened. Look for indications that the clock has been opened more than once a day or at unusual times. This might indicate that unauthorized persons have access to a clock key.

Basic reports on security officer tours can take many forms. Figure 14.7.7 shows a report generated in spreadsheet format.

Inspecting Tour Supervisory System Initiating Devices

Key stations, tour supervisory transmitters, or intermediate stations should be inspected once a month to ensure they are firmly attached and, if required, sealed with a "tamper" seal, and have not been relocated or removed. The key should be checked for damage. If there is evidence of tampering, the key stations, tour supervisory transmitters, or intermediate stations should be checked more often and suitable action taken.

Evaluating Security Officers

Management should expect, and is entitled to receive, security officer service of the highest quality. Officers must be conscientious in the performance of their duties, note and report all infractions of company regulations, and closely follow the orders given to them. When evaluating security officers, management should consider the following:

1. Security officers hold positions of trust, which require individuals who are physically able, mentally alert, and morally responsible. Therefore, their physical and emotional stability should be evaluated by appropriate management personnel.
2. Security officers must be sufficiently intelligent, calm in the face of an emergency, mature with sound judgment, and possess the physical stamina required for the job.
3. A sufficient number of security officers should be provided to maintain proper surveillance in the facility. It is undesirable for officers to be assigned part-time duties unrelated to surveillance. If they are so assigned, however, these duties must not interfere with surveillance responsibilities.
4. Security officers should receive full support of management in the performance of their duties.
5. When the officers are facility employees, management should establish the scope of the service and provide necessary training and supervision for the guards.
6. If a contract security service is used, management should not assume that it will be adequate. Rather, management should prepare detailed specifications and investigate the ability of prospective contractors to meet these specifications. When

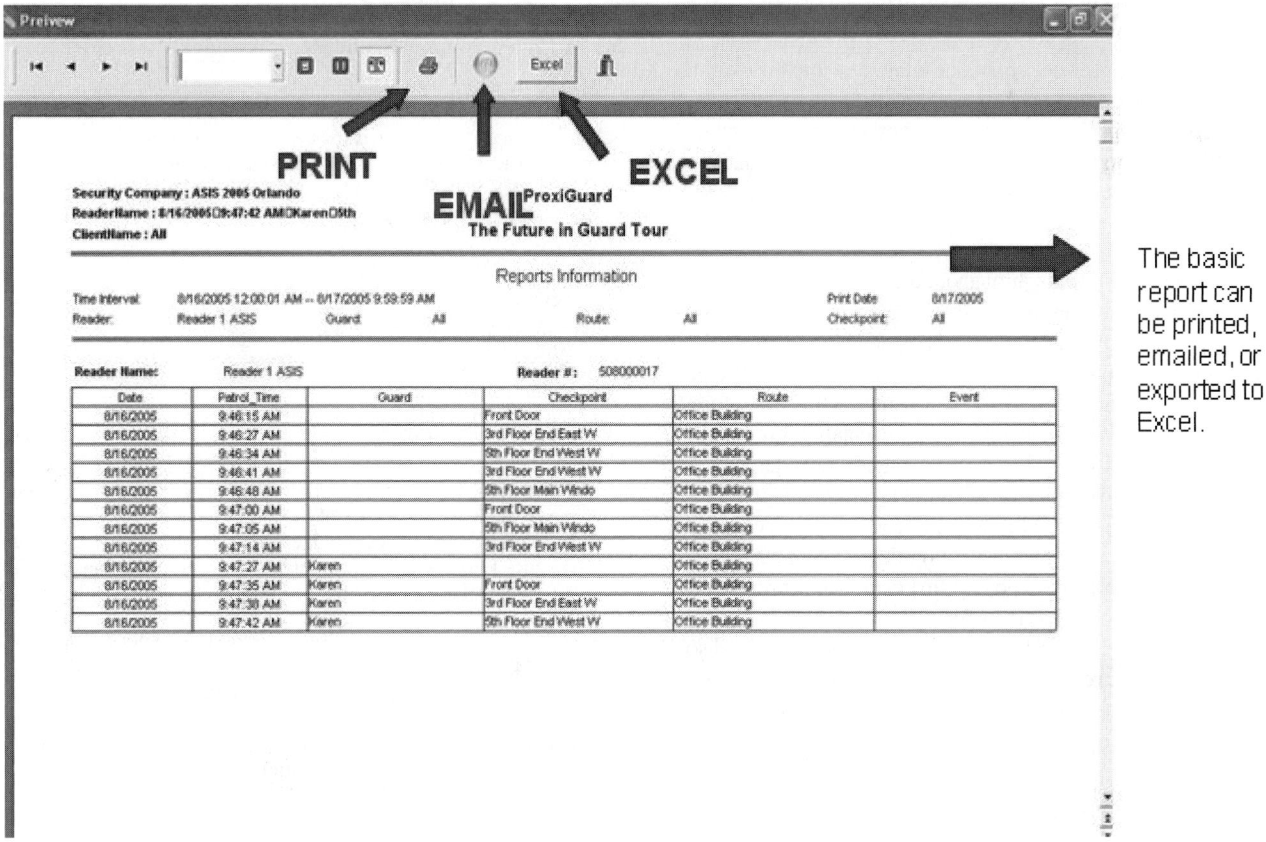

Date	Patrol_Time	Guard	Checkpoint	Route	Event
8/16/2005	9:46:15 AM		Front Door	Office Building	
8/16/2005	9:46:27 AM		3rd Floor End East W	Office Building	
8/16/2005	9:46:34 AM		5th Floor End West W	Office Building	
8/16/2005	9:46:41 AM		3rd Floor End West W	Office Building	
8/16/2005	9:46:48 AM		5th Floor Main Windo	Office Building	
8/16/2005	9:47:00 AM		Front Door	Office Building	
8/16/2005	9:47:05 AM		5th Floor Main Windo	Office Building	
8/16/2005	9:47:14 AM		3rd Floor End West W	Office Building	
8/16/2005	9:47:27 AM	Karen		Office Building	
8/16/2005	9:47:35 AM	Karen	Front Door	Office Building	
8/16/2005	9:47:38 AM	Karen	3rd Floor End East W	Office Building	
8/16/2005	9:47:42 AM	Karen	5th Floor End West W	Office Building	

FIGURE 14.7.7 Security Officer Tour Report (Source: ProxiGuard)

the contract has been met, management should make sure that its intent is being carried out.

7. Initial and continued training of officers should be by a formal, comprehensive, written program covering all applicable protection procedures. The following must be met by each guard:
   - Be acquainted with the general nature of the facility's operations and possess specific knowledge of any hazardous operations
   - Be familiar with all of the facility's manual and automatic fire protection equipment. Security officers should be especially aware of the location of all sprinkler valves and know which area each controls. Officers should periodically accompany the person making fire protection equipment inspections, in order to gain a working knowledge of facility protection features and hazards.
   - Be familiar with the location and operation of manual fire alarm boxes and other means of transmitting fire alarms. Such means should be provided throughout the facility so guards can easily report a fire.
   - Be taught to notify the fire department *before* taking any other action
   - Be taught how to admit public fire apparatus to the property and how to direct fire department officers to the location of the fire
   - Be taught to properly notify company officials when an emergency occurs or when potential trouble is observed
   - Be taught to maintain a shift log and to prepare reports to management of observations made and actions taken during tours
8. Security officer service should be integrated into the overall emergency planning program.
9. General and special instructions and other data required by the officers should be written down and kept up-to-date.

Detecting and Reporting Fires

While making regular tours throughout the facility, officers must be alert for all emergencies, paying special attention to known hazardous areas. Security officers are in a position not only to detect and correct unsafe conditions that might develop into or contribute to a serious fire, but also to discover an incipient fire. Therefore, the officers should be familiar with the fundamentals of fire control and with the proper use of all available extinguishing equipment.

The importance of notifying the fire department *before* taking any other action should be stressed in security officer training. Officers should report any situation that may endanger the facility—for example, an exposing fire in adjacent properties. Any unusual condition that the officers cannot correct without assistance must be reported immediately to the proper official so the situation can be remedied without undue delay. Such situations include the interruption of sprinkler service or the failure of heating equipment.

Encountering Natural Hazards

In addition to carefully following written emergency plans, security officers must be resourceful and capable of applying common sense to any unusual conditions, such as "natural" hazard threats, they may encounter. If the facility is being subjected to freezing weather, for example, the guard should be alert to those areas of the facility where fire protection systems or process equipment might be vulnerable to freezing. Such areas should be checked frequently to ensure the heating system is properly maintaining the temperature necessary to avoid damage. If a thermometer is unavailable, a resourceful guard might set out a small container of very cold water to observe whether the area is approaching a dangerously low temperature. See NFPA 601, *Standard for Security Services in Fire Loss Prevention.*

SUMMARY

A fire alarm system in a commercial or industrial facility can monitor a variety of conditions and instruments related to fire protection, including alarm initiating devices, supervisory initiating devices, and environmental conditions such as low temperatures. The fire alarm system can also monitor the patrol tours of the security service. The fire alarm system should be connected to a location that ensures the signals receive immediate attention. The extent of the fire alarm system and security service must be determined by management based on the level of fire protection deemed necessary for the particular facility. The security officers must be supplied with a comprehensive surveillance plan and proper communication equipment in order to perform their duties effectively.

BIBLIOGRAPHY

NFPA Codes, Standards, and Recommended Practices

Reference to the following NFPA codes, standards, and recommended practices will provide further information on fire protection surveillance and security services discussed in this chapter. (See the latest version of The NFPA Catalog *for availability of current editions of the following documents.)*

NFPA 72®, National Fire Alarm Code®

NFPA 601, *Standard for Security Services in Fire Loss Prevention*

References

Bushby, S. T., "Integrating Fire Alarm Systems with Building Automation and Control Systems," *Fire Protection Engineering,* No. 11, Summer 2001, pp. 5–7.

Carter, R. A., "Fire Safety and Security in Schools," Fire Engineering Research Report 99/1, University of Canterbury, Christchurch, New Zealand, Mar. 1999.

Grosshandler, W. L., "Multi-Function Sensing for Cybernetic Building Systems," *Proceedings* of the 15th Joint Panel Meeting, U.S./Japan Government Cooperative Program on Natural Resources (UJNR), Fire Research and Safety, March 1–7, 2000, San Antonio, TX, National Institute of Standards and Technology, Gaithersburg, MD, NISTIR 6588, Vol. 2, Nov. 2000, pp. 357–364.

Moore, W. D., "Systems Integration—It's Here," *NFPA Journal,* Vol. 94, No. 1, 2000, p. 30.

Seaton, M., "Who Takes It from Here?" *NFPA Journal,* Vol. 91, No. 3, 1997, pp. 60–63.

Solomon, R. S. (Ed.), *Fire and Life Safety Inspection Manual,* 8th ed., National Fire Protection Association, Quincy, MA, 2002.

Winter, J., "Smoke Signals," *Fire Prevention,* No. 350, Nov. 2001, pp. 20–21.

Woodward, N., "Safe and Secure," *Fire Prevention,* No. 320, May 1999, pp. 31–32.

Chapter 8

Gas and Vapor Detection Systems and Monitors

John M. Cholin

Chapter Contents

Key Terms

carbon monoxide detector, fire alarm system, flammable gas, flammable vapor, gas detection, hazardous (classified) location, resistive-thermal device, sensor

Two concerns drive the use of gas and vapor detection systems and monitors. First, the existence of flammable gases or vapors represents (1) an elevation in the potential for a fire, either in and of itself as the concentration reaches the critical value sufficient to support a flame; or (2) an indication of a leak, implying an immediate potential of loss of containment of a large quantity of fuel. Second, there is a life safety concern whenever breathing air is contaminated with gases or vapors that are not normal constituents of air. Although one could argue the theoretical position that this second concern is not strictly within the purview of the fire protection engineer, in the context of actual applications it is very rare that these two concerns can be rationally separated from each other. Consequently, the fire protection specialist must have a working knowledge of gas and vapor detection systems and monitors both for flammable and toxic materials.

For many years there was no NFPA standard explicitly establishing requirements for the design, installation, and maintenance of gas and vapor detection systems. Currently, one recommended practice, NFPA 720, *Standard for the Installation of Carbon Monoxide (CO) Warning Equipment in Dwelling Units,* has been adopted. Other than this one document, there are no NFPA standards relating to the design of systems to detect combustible or toxic gases or vapors employed in commercial or industrial occupancies, nor is there a standard for gas monitors. Nevertheless, there are a number of NFPA standards that make reference to gas and vapor detection systems in their requirements. For example, NFPA 86, *Standard for Ovens and Furnaces,* governs the fire protective features of drying ovens such as those where painted parts are cured. NFPA 86 allows reduced airflow rates conditioned on a system for monitoring the concentration of combustible vapor in the ventilation air. Since the fire safety of the curing oven is predicated on the vapor monitoring system, that system becomes a critical part of the fire protection for the site. Failure of the flammable vapor detection system to perform its intended function, whether due to flawed system design, installation error, inadequate maintenance, or component failure, could result in a catastrophic fire loss. This dependence on flammable gas and vapor detection systems to maintain the required level of fire safety argues for the application of sound fire protection engineering in the selection, design, installation, and maintenance of gas and vapor detection systems.

This chapter addresses the detection of flammable, combustible, or toxic gases and vapors that represent a hazard to the occupants or the facility. This hazard can be the risk of fire or deflagration due to ignition of an ignitible concentration of the flammable or combustible gases or vapors. It can also be the physiological threat to the health of the occupants resulting from inhalation or exposure to the vapors or gases. This chapter does not address flammable, combustible, or toxic gases that are the *result* of a fire. The term *fire-gas* was used previously in some fire protection standards and references as part of an effort to distinguish the gaseous components of smoke from the particulate components. Subsequent research and standards derived therefrom found that such a distinction was not particularly helpful and the term has fallen into disuse over the past two decades.

For related topics, see Section 6, Chapter 10, "Gases"; Section 6, Chapter 12, "Flammable and Combustible Liquids"; and Section 14, Chapter 4, "Fire Alarm System Interconnections."

John M. Cholin, P.E., FSFPE, is an independent fire protection consultant and engineer with J. M. Cholin Consultants, Inc., Oakland, New Jersey.

TERMINOLOGY

The terminology used in the gas and vapor detection community may not be familiar to many fire protection specialists.

Gas. A gas is matter in which the average thermal kinetic energy of the constituent molecules at standard temperature and pressure (STP) exceeds the cohesive forces between them, and consequently the matter expands to occupy the entire containment volume. STP is 77°F (25°C) and 760 mm(Hg) absolute pressure or 1 atm. It is necessary to stipulate temperature and pressure in this definition, because any normally gaseous compound can be compressed and cooled to the point where it will exist in a liquid state.

The gases that are routinely addressed in the context of gas detection, whether flammable gas or toxic gas, include carbon monoxide, carbon dioxide, sulfur dioxide, hydrogen sulfide, hydrogen, methane, ethane, propane, butane, acetylene, ethylene, propylene, silane, germane, diborane, phosphine, arsine, allane, fluorine, and chlorine.

Vapor. Vapor is matter in the gas phase that normally exists at STP as a liquid. This term is not essential. However, it is used too frequently not to be addressed in the context of this chapter. The term is commonly used because of the inference it provides regarding the source of the gaseous matter. Vapors are the result of the evaporation of a liquid and, consequently, are normally associated with a liquid source. There is an equilibrium state at the interface above a pool of liquid and the gas above it. As liquid molecules attain excess thermal energy, they escape the cohesive forces of adjacent molecules and leave the liquid as a gas. When gas molecules lose thermal energy, they condense back into the liquid phase. When vapors are dispersed in air, they behave as gases until a temperature is reached where they begin to condense. The principal distinction between the compounds normally thought of as gases and those as vapors is the temperature and pressure at which they condense.

Combustible/Flammable Gases and Vapors. Combustible/flammable gases and vapors are those gases and vapors that burn in air when the concentration of the gas or vapor is within the range of concentration where combustion can occur. The distinction between combustible and flammable is established in NFPA 30, *Flammable and Combustible Liquids Code.* This distinction is predicated on the flashpoint of the liquid. The flashpoint is the temperature at which the vapor pressure of the liquid is sufficiently high to produce a concentration of gaseous fuel in the air above the liquid in excess of the lower flammable limit (LFL) and, hence, sufficient to support a flame. This distinction has little relevance in the context of detection of molecular species dispersed in the ambient air, except to imply possible origin. Unfortunately, the community of manufacturers and users of gas detection systems and instruments come from an instrumentation background where the term *combustible* has been adopted. In an effort to provide consistency with the terminology and concepts presented in this handbook, this chapter will use the term *flammable gas* to include all chemical species dispersed in the gas phase in ambient air, regardless of source or chemical composition, that will burn in air.

Concentration of flammable gas is typically measured in percent of the lower flammable limit (percent LFL). If the lower flammable limit of a given gas is 4.0 percent, a measurement of 25 percent LFL means that there is 1 percent of that gas by volume in the measured sample of air.

Lower Flammable Limit (LFL). The lower flammable limit is the lowest concentration of a flammable gas in air that will support a flame. Below the LFL there is insufficient fuel per unit of air volume to sustain a flame through the volume. Therefore, when a source of ignition is introduced, the resulting flame will remain at the source of ignition. Once the concentration exceeds the LFL, a flame front will propagate through the air volume. (Note that the term *lower explosive limit (LEL)* was formerly used for this concentration of flammable gas and is occasionally still encountered in older literature.)

Upper Flammable Limit (UFL). The upper flammable limit is the highest concentration of a flammable gas in air that will sustain a flame. As the concentration of flammable gas increases, the oxygen-containing air is displaced. Eventually, the concentration of flammable gas is so high that there is insufficient oxygen remaining to sustain a flame when an ignition source is introduced. (Note that the term *upper explosive limit (UEL)* was formerly used and is occasionally still encountered.)

Toxic Gases and Vapors. Toxic gases and vapors are molecular species dispersed in air in the gas phase that have an adverse effect on living organisms, as defined by the Occupational Safety and Health Administration (OSHA). The concentration of toxic gas is usually measured and displayed as parts per million (ppm) concentration. To convert from percent to parts per million, multiply by the conversion factor of 10,000 ppm/percent. The commonly monitored toxic gases include carbon monoxide, carbon dioxide, hydrogen sulfide, sulfur dioxide, methane, silane, arsine, phosphine, chlorine, and fluorine. Most flammable gases are also toxic at some concentration, but not all toxic gases are flammable.

Oxygen Concentration. Oxygen concentration is the measure of the portion of the air within a space that is oxygen. This is an important life safety and fire protection parameter. The depletion of the oxygen in a gas volume reduces the ability of life to survive in that volume and also reduces the ability of that gas volume to support combustion. The nominal oxygen concentration of air is 23.2 percent oxygen by weight and 21.0 percent oxygen by volume. The difference in the numerical value of the oxygen concentration by weight versus volume comes from the different densities of the constituent gases in the mixture called "air."

Fixed Gas/Vapor Detection System. A fixed gas/vapor detection system is a permanently installed system usually consisting of at least one sensor, transmitter, and display unit (Figure 14.8.1). The sensor is located in the area where the gas or vapor may occur. It produces a minute current or voltage that is pro-

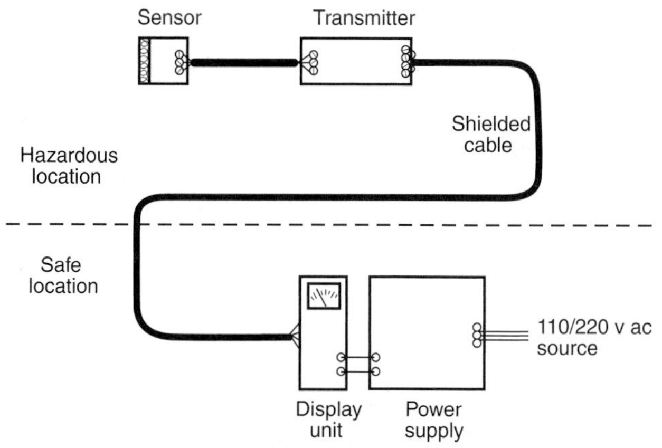

FIGURE 14.8.1 A Fixed Gas Detection System

portional to the concentration of the gas. The sensor is connected via wiring to a transmitter. Generally the distance between the sensor and transmitter is quite limited. The transmitter linearizes the signal from the sensor, corrects it for zero and span (due to variations in sensor output), and converts it into an electrical format that can be transmitted a long distance without interference. The most popular format is the "4–20 milliampere" format. The transmitter is connected to the display unit via a second set of wires. The maximum wiring distance between the transmitter and the display unit can often be as far as several thousand feet. The display unit expresses the output of the transmitter in a format that is understandable to the operator (Figures 14.8.2 and 14.8.3). Some displays utilize analog meters, whereas others provide bar-graph and numeric displays. Most display units are equipped with output relays that transfer when the measured concentration of gas exceeds pre-established threshold concentrations. This provides for different types of responses as the measured gas concentration increases. For example, a warning response might be activated when the concentration reaches 20 percent LFL, and inerting or shutdown activated when the concentration reaches 50 percent LFL.

Portable Gas/Vapor Monitoring Instrument. Portable gas/vapor monitoring instruments are hand-carried portable instruments, utilizing no external source of power, designed to warn the person carrying it of the presence of dangerous levels of gas or vapor, or dangerously low concentrations of oxygen in the ambient breathing air. Some monitors are simple single gas-warning devices, whereas others are multiple-gas devices. All are designed to measure the gas concentration and warn the user if the concentration begins approaching the threshold limit value (TLV), as established by OSHA, for that particular gas.

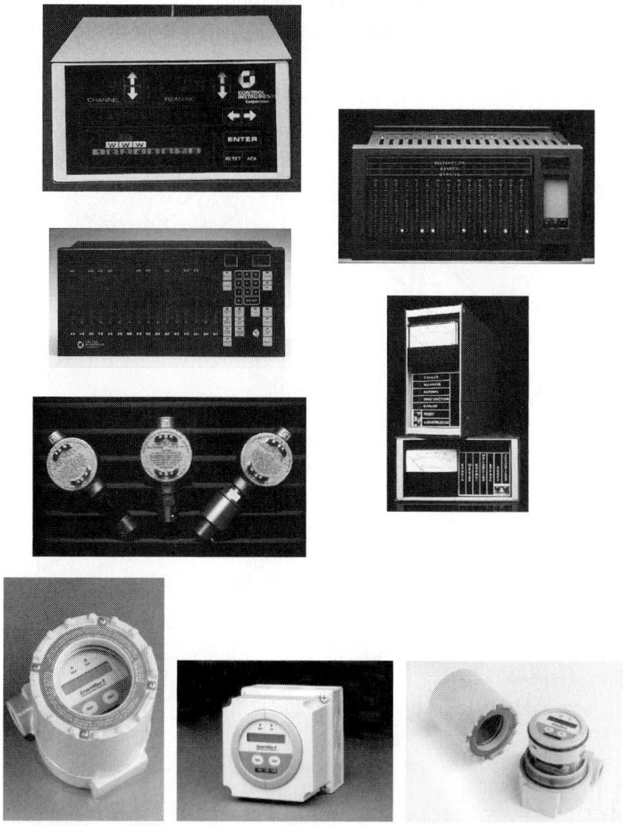

FIGURE 14.8.2 Examples of Modern Fixed Gas Detection Systems and Control Units (Source: Control Instruments® Corp.)

FIGURE 14.8.3 Fixed Gas Detection System Using a Sensor and Display Integrated into a Common Unit, Shown Here with the Enclosure Cover Removed (Source: Control Instruments® Corp.)

Hazardous Location. Places where a flammable gas or vapor is able to escape into the surrounding air are considered *hazardous locations.* In the United States hazardous locations are defined in Article 500 of the *NEC* (NFPA 70, *National Electrical Code*®). The *NEC* divides hazardous locations into Class 1, Class 2, and Class 3.

Section 500.5(B) of the *NEC* states that Class 1 hazardous locations are those "in which flammable gases or vapors are or may be present in air in quantities sufficient to produce explosive or ignitible mixtures." Class 2 hazardous locations are those that are hazardous because of the presence of combustible dusts. Class 3 hazardous locations are those that contain ignitible fibers and combustible flyings.

Both flammable gases and vapors and combustible dusts represent an explosion hazard when either is present in the air in sufficient concentration. The NEC further classifies hazardous locations based on the probability that a combustible material will be present at any particular time by assigning a "division" classification to the location. Class 1, Division 1 is assigned to occupancies that (1) contain flammable gases or vapors as part of the normal operating environment, (2) contain flammable gases or vapors frequently due to routine repair, maintenance, or leakage, or (3) contain equipment or processes where breakdown or production upsets could result in both a flammable atmosphere *and* an ignition source.

Class 1, Division 2 is assigned to occupancies where (1) flammable gases or liquids that produce flammable vapors are handled or processed in closed containers or systems and are only subject to release under conditions of equipment malfunction, breakdown, or process upset, (2) the development of a flammable atmosphere is normally prevented by positive mechanical ventilation, the failure of which could lead to a hazardous atmosphere, or (3) areas adjacent to a Class 1, Division 1 location subject to occasional ingress of flammable gas or vapor. Analogous divisions for Class 2 hazardous locations are also established in Article 500 of the NEC for combustible dusts, but these are not relevant to the discussion of gas and vapor detection.

In the European Union a similar hazard classification system has recently been adopted, known as the ATEX Directive. Under the ATEX Directive all process environments that can represent an explosive atmosphere must be so designated by the owner/operator of the facility. Once designated, all equipment used in that environment as well as products and equipment used to manage the hazard must be tested under a set of uniform EU testing standards and found suitable for that environment, as signified by the CE (Communité European) mark on the product labeling. A product that has not been certified by a nationally recognized testing laboratory as being suitable, as evidenced by the CE mark, is prohibited from use within the EU. The hazard classifications under the ATEX Directive are *not* the same as those established by the NEC. Consequently, products must go through two sets of testing if they are to be marketed in both the U.S. and EU markets.

SENSORS

The sensor is the single most critical part of any fixed gas detection system or portable monitoring instrument. The sensor is the portion of either the fixed system or portable instrument that actually does the sensing of the presence of gas in the air. The sensor generates an electrical signal, either current or voltage, proportional to the concentration of gas in the air. The gas detection system can be no better than the sensors used and, consequently, the development of sensors has accounted for much of the research and development effort. As with fire detection, there are a limited number of sensor technologies in common use and then some specialized technologies tailored to the needs of special applications. In general, the design focus has been to develop sensors that are specific to a given gas and that maintain their response characteristics in spite of the presence of other gases.

Most flammable-gas sensors designed to detect the hydrocarbon gases and vapors from hydrocarbon liquids are based on the detection of the heat of combustion of the flammable gas, using resistive-thermal devices (RTDs) and the Wheatstone bridge circuit. An RTD is an electronic component whose resistance varies with temperature. RTDs include metal oxide resistors, resistance wires, and thermistors. These devices can all be wired into a circuit called the Wheatstone bridge, shown in Figure 14.8.4.

The resistors shown as the sample and reference legs of the bridge circuit can be any type of RTD. The sample RTD is coated with a material that acts as a catalyst of the combustion of hydrocarbons. Alloys of both palladium and platinum are often used for this purpose. The reference RTD is enclosed in a manner that prevents contact with the ambient, gas-containing

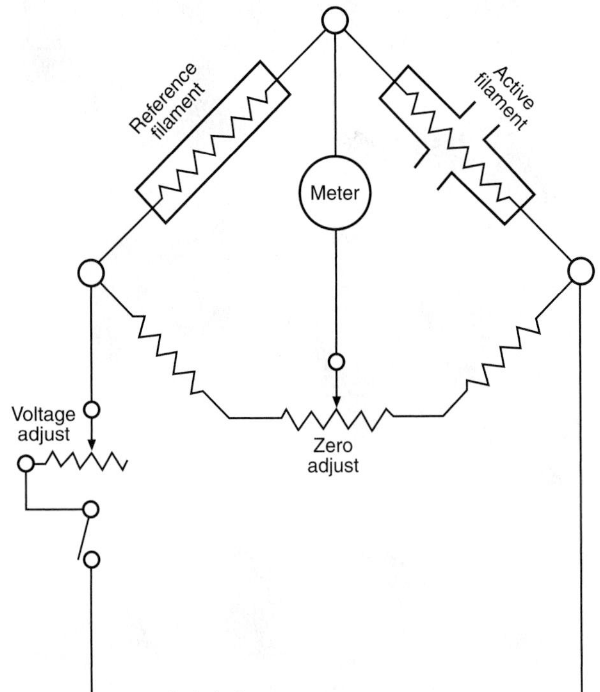

FIGURE 14.8.4 Basic Wheatstone Bridge Circuit as Used in Many Gas Detection Systems

air. Electric current is passed through the bridge circuit, causing all of the legs of the bridge to become warm. When flammable gas impinges upon the sample RTD, the gas oxidizes, releasing heat from the combustion process occurring on the surface of the RTD. This raises the temperature of the sample RTD, and causes the electrical resistance of the sample RTD to change compared to the reference RTD, which remains at normal operating temperature. The change in the sample RTD resistance causes a potential (voltage) difference across the "voltmeter," which is proportional to the concentration of flammable gas.

Theoretically, the heat derived from the combustion of a gas on the surface of a catalyst-coated RTD is dependent on both the concentration and the heat of combustion of the flammable gas. However, the heats of combustion of most chemical compounds encountered in the context of gas detection are very close in value. This allows the heat of combustion term to be considered nominally constant, especially when the gas concentrations are at or below the LFL. This approximation is not perfect. Carbon disulfide vapor yields readings that are lower than the actual concentration under these conditions, while natural gas yields readings that tend to be higher than the actual concentrations. These discrepancies increase as the concentrations increase. However, this is easily addressed with specific calibrations where these gases are present. For most purposes, where the sought-after condition is a hazardous gas–free atmosphere, the differences between various gases disappear as the actual concentration approaches zero.

One of the more popular types of RTD is the catalyst-coated thermistor, called the *catalytic bead.* A *thermistor* is an electrical resistor, fabricated from one of a number of rare-earth ceramics, that exhibits a large change in electrical resistance as a function of temperature, usually referred to as a *temperature coefficient.* Many have a temperature coefficient that is negative, meaning that the electrical resistance goes down as the temperature increases. A *catalyst* is a material, usually a chemical or mixture of chemicals, that facilitates a particular chemical reaction. Certain metals and metal salts catalyze the combustion reaction involving hydrocarbon chemical species. The catalytic effects of such metals and metal salts are often specific for certain hydrocarbon species, meaning that a catalyst that facilitates the combustion of methane would not be particularly effective at facilitating the combustion of butane or gasoline. Coating the thermister of a gas detection sensor with a particular catalyst can make the sensor somewhat selective for particular gases or groups of gases.

Air mixtures containing concentrations of flammable gas much lower than the LFL, approaching zero, will "burn" on the surface of a heated catalytic material, yielding heat in direct proportion to the concentration of the flammable gas. This is called *surface* or *catalytic* combustion. Some RTD designs depend on the flow of electric current through the thermistor bead to generate the requisite operating temperature of the catalyst. Others use a separate resistance heater integrated into the bead. Obviously, the combustion of the flammable gas on the surface of the catalyst could conceivably cause ignition once the concentration exceeded the LFL. Consequently, sensors are contained within a flame arrester of either wire mesh or sintered metal, as shown in Figure 14.8.5, that prevents the propagation of combustion

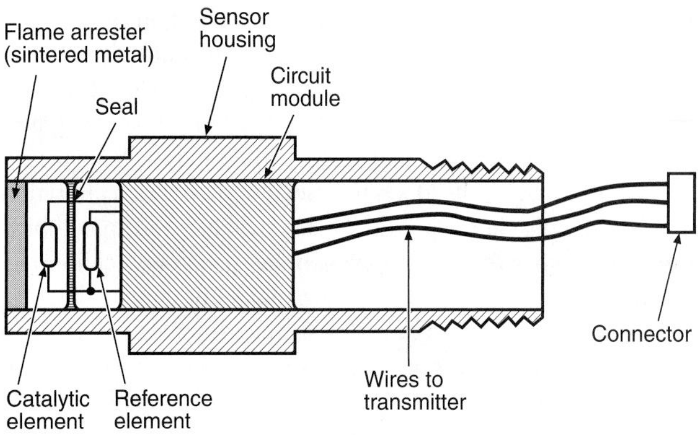

FIGURE 14.8.5 Flammable-Gas Sensor Using Catalytic Bead Technology

outside the sensor. These flame arresters are generally suitable for conventional gas-air mixtures. However, if the atmosphere is oxygen enriched to concentrations greater than 21 percent oxygen by volume, or if the partial pressure of oxygen exceeds 21.27 kPa or 160 mm(Hg), special arresters may be necessary.

Most sensors use a catalyst that is derived from the catalytic properties of platinum, palladium, and nickel. Careful control over the alloying of the catalysts and the operating temperature enables the manufacturer to make sensors that are specific for a particular group of gases. Catalytic beads have a very small mass; therefore, they respond rapidly to the heating produced by the combustion of flammable gas on their surfaces. Response often begins within a few seconds of the introduction of the gas. However, when the influx of flammable gas is large, it may take as long as a minute to attain full-scale response of the sensor. The speed of response of a sensor is an important factor when choosing the best sensor for a given hazard.

Catalytic bead flammable-gas monitoring instruments are designed specifically for measuring combustibles in air. The oxygen in the air is necessary for the combustion of the flammable gas and the generation of heat that the unit senses to infer the presence of flammable gas. These instruments give a reasonably accurate indication of the presence of combustible gas, even when the oxygen concentration has been substantially reduced by oxidation, biological action, or displacement. Generally, one should expect the accuracy of a catalytic-bead sensor to suffer as the ambient oxygen concentration decreases to less than 10 percent. Also note that inerting agents, such as Halon 1301 or the replacement clean agents, interfere with either the combustion reaction on the catalyst surface or increase the heat capacity of air and, hence, reduce the temperature resulting from the combustion of the flammable gas, rendering measurements unreliable when inerting agents are present.

Catalytic bead sensors do suffer from "poisoning" to varying degrees. Poisoning occurs when a noncombustible material impinges upon the bead and only partially burns, leaving a residue on the surface of the bead. The coated surface no longer oxidizes the flammable gas in the air, and the sensor ceases responding to the presence of flammable gas in the air. Although considerable progress has been made in reducing the tendency for beads to become poisoned, this is a limitation of catalytic sensors that necessitates regular calibration to adjust for the progressive loss of sensing ability over time. Regular field calibration is necessary to adjust the zero and span of the display unit as compensation for drift and aging of the catalytic bead.

Many catalytic bead sensors are supplied with calibration curves showing the response of the particular unit to combustible gases other than that on which the device was calibrated. Calibration curves for one particular model of combustible gas indicator are shown in Figure 14.8.6. Since all manufacturers do not use the same gas for base factory calibrations, the curves for one instrument cannot be used with curves of another type.

Semiconductor (MOS) Devices

Metal oxide semiconductor (MOS) sensors can be used to detect a number of "reducing gases" such as hydrogen, methane, ethane, ammonia, and carbon monoxide. Metal oxide semiconductors can be fabricated with precisely controlled band-gap energies by manipulating the concentrations of the various oxides in the crystal. (This is called "doping.") When a MOS sensor has a voltage across it and a gas with the right chemical structure impinges on it, the current through the sensor changes, indicating the presence of the gas. The semiconductor can be modified to maximize response for a specific gas or group of gases by adjusting the relative concentrations of the constituent oxides (doping) or with the application of specific surface coatings. However, MOS sensors generally cannot be made specific for a single gas and care must be used to ascertain whether an unanticipated gas is causing the response of the sensor. Often, MOS sensors are operated at an elevated temperature to improve the response specificity of the sensor.

Calibration curves for field reference					
Gas or vapor	LEL % by volume	Curve no.	Gas or vapor	LEL % by volume	Curve no.
Acetone	2.5	5	Hydrogen	4.0	1
Acetylene	2.3	3	Methyl alcohol	6.7	2
Benzene	1.4	5	Methyl ethyl ketone	1.8	6
Carbon disulfide	1.0	10	Natural gas	4.8	3
Carbon monoxide	12.5	1	Octane	1.0	9
Ethyl acetate	2.2	7	Pentane	1.4	5
Ethyl ether	1.7	7	Propane	2.2	4
Gasoline	1.3	8	Toluene	1.3	4
Hexane	1.2	7	Xylene	1.0	7

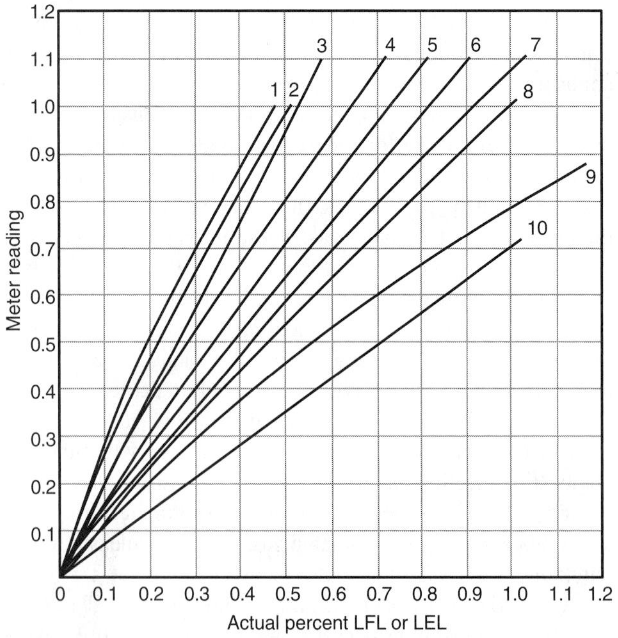

FIGURE 14.8.6 Calibration Curves for a Catalytic Bead Sensor. Note that, despite wide variations at higher concentrations, the error becomes negligible as the zero concentration is approached.

Electrochemical Devices

Electrochemical cells are primarily used for the detection of the toxic gases. The electrochemical cell is designed somewhat like a battery in which air can diffuse into the electrolyte of the cell. If the air contains the toxic gas for which the cell has been designed, an electrochemical reaction takes place, producing a minute voltage within the cell. This voltage causes a current to flow through the sensor electronics. The current is proportional to the concentration of the gas in the air. This enables the concentration to be measured by measuring the current from the cell. The diffusion path and the electrolyte can be varied to limit the response of the sensor to a particular gas.

Electrochemical cells are the predominant method for sensing carbon monoxide, chlorine, nitrogen oxide, sulfur dioxide, and hydrogen sulfide. Electrochemical cells are also used for oxygen-level monitoring by the same means as used for toxic gases. Semiconductor and catalytic bead sensors depend on a level of oxygen in the air in order to provide accurate results, whereas electrochemical cells do not. Furthermore, electrochemical cells usually provide high levels of specificity relative to other technologies.

Flame Cell Devices

When measurement capability for a wide range of hydrocarbon gases and vapors is needed, flame cell technology is often considered. Flame cell sensors are very often employed when LFL monitoring is needed for the atmosphere within an oven where flammable solvent vehicles (vapors) are driven off as part of a curing or finishing operation. This system uses a flame cell that contains a flame fueled by a flammable gas provided by the unit, and ventilated by air sampled from the hazard area. A temperature sensor measures the heat output of the flame. When flammable hydrocarbons are introduced into the hazard area atmosphere, the contaminated air flows from the hazard area to the sensor via sample conveyance tubing to the flame cell. As the hydrocarbon-containing air enters the flame cell, the hydrocarbons burn, adding to the heat available to the temperature sensor. The sensor temperature rises proportional to the concentration of the hydrocarbon gas (vapor) in the air (Figure 14.8.7).

Flame cell sensors are more complex than the other types discussed thus far. However, there are numerous applications where they represent the best cost/benefit solution. They are not affected by poisoning the way catalytic bead sensors are and

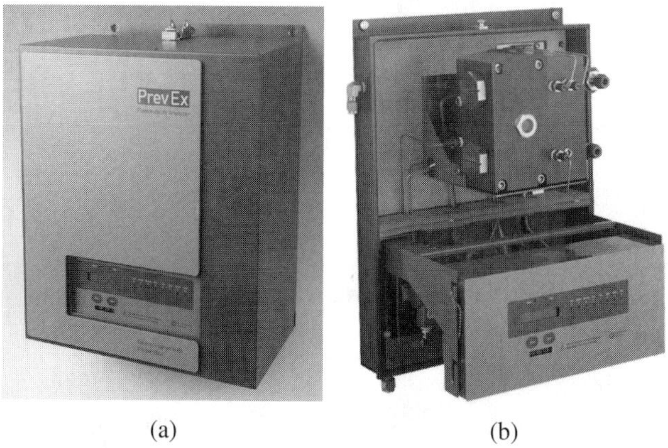

(a) (b)

FIGURE 14.8.7 (a) Flame Cell Sensor; (b) Flame Cell Sensor with the Enclosure Open, Showing the Internals (Source: Control Instruments® Corp.)

require far less frequent calibration. However, since sampling tubes convey the sample atmosphere to the detection unit, provisions must be made to ensure that there is no condensation of flammable or combustible vapors on the interior surfaces of the sample conveyance tubing, as this would create serious errors in the flammable gas concentration measurements. The flame cell sensor as a sampling-type device, connected to the hazardous area via a sampling tube, is shown in Figure 14.8.8.

Flame Ionization Devices

In some applications, where a means for detecting very low concentrations of flammable gas is needed, flame ionization detectors are often the sensor of choice. Flame ionization detectors consist of an enclosed flame cell equipped with a high-voltage field. It is fueled from a source of hydrogen, with combustion air coming through the sampling system. When the combustion air includes hydrocarbon molecules, these molecules are pulled apart by the high-voltage electric field, producing ions. These ions flow through the flame to the positive (+) and negative (–) electrodes, creating a current that is directly proportional to the concentration of hydrocarbon gas in the air sample.

Flame ionization sensors, like the flame cell sensors, are more complex than the other spot-type sensors. However, there are numerous applications where they represent the best cost/benefit solution. They are able to measure much smaller concentrations than the other types of gas sensors. They are not affected by poisoning the way catalytic bead sensors are and require far less frequent calibration. Flame ionization sensors (Figure 14.8.9) are installed like the flame cell devices, with a sampling tube that conveys a sample of the hazardous atmosphere to the sensor. Consequently, provisions must be made to ensure that there is no condensation of flammable or combustible vapors on the interior surfaces of the sample conveyance tubing, as this would create serious errors in the flammable gas concentration measurements.

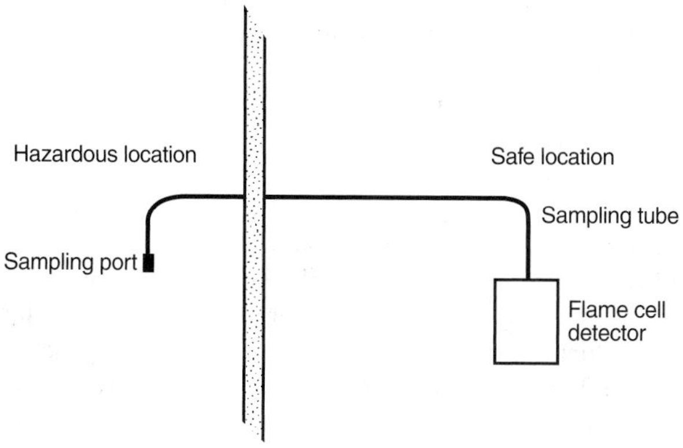

FIGURE 14.8.8 Flame Cell Sensor

Nondispersive Infrared (NDIR) Sensors

Gaseous molecules absorb infrared radiation at specific and characteristic wavelengths. This is analogous to the infrared emission detection that is the basis for many of the advanced technology flame detectors in use today. Infrared gas detectors, using the correlation between specific molecular species and specific wavelengths in the infrared spectrum, have recently been made available. Like smoke detectors, infrared gas detectors are either spot devices or open-path devices analogous to the projected beam smoke detector.

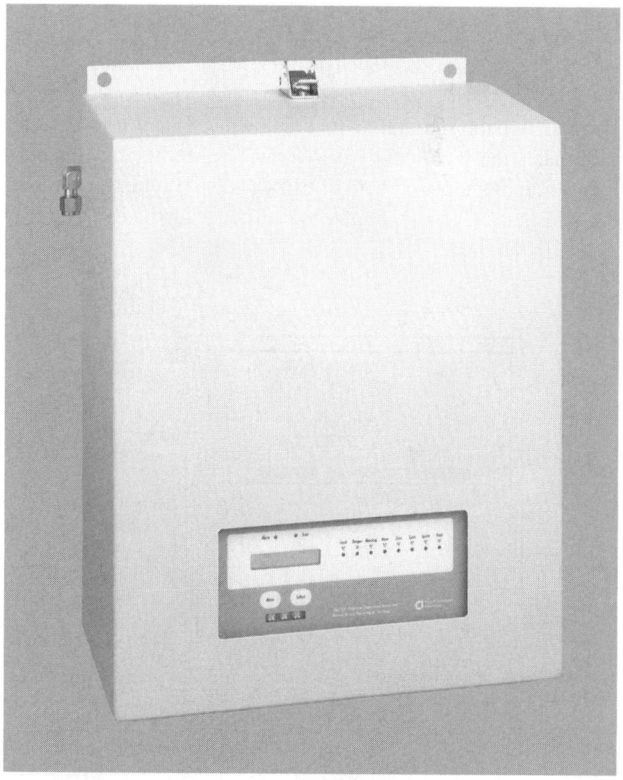

FIGURE 14.8.9 Flame Ionization Sensor (Source: Control Instruments® Corp.)

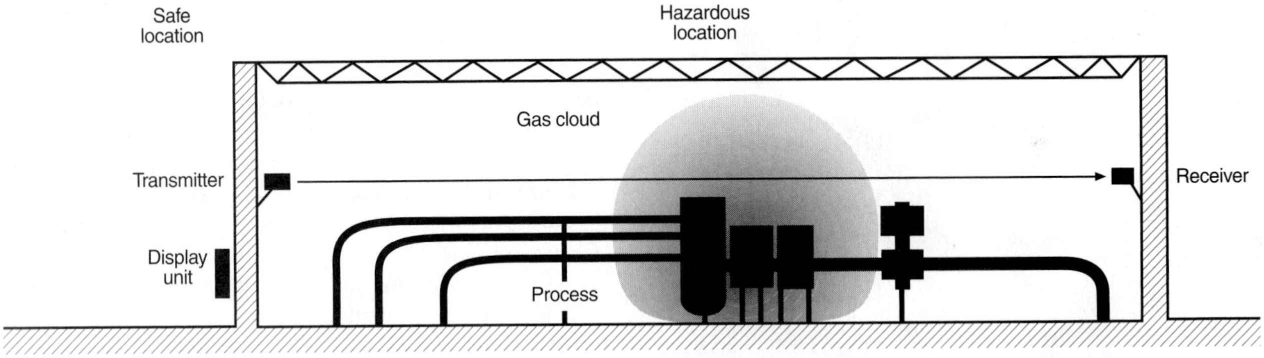

FIGURE 14.8.10 Open-Path Infrared Gas Detector

Open-path gas detectors operate with one or more infrared emitters and one or more receivers. These units compare the optical absorbance of the air in the optical path at two wavelengths, one at which the gas absorbs and a reference wavelength at which the gas does not absorb. The detection system electronics compare the intensities at the two wavelengths. If gas exists along the beam path, it will absorb the sample wavelength while allowing the reference wavelength to pass unattenuated. The difference in received intensities is proportional to the concentration of the gas and the percentage of the path length that contains that concentration. This value is transmitted via the common 4–20 mA analog signal to the display unit. It is displayed as LFL-meters, the product of the percent LFL and the distance. As shown in Figure 14.8.10, the open-path NDIR gas detector covers a large area; however, the reading is the product of the distance and the concentration over that distance.

Spot-type IR gas sensors operate on a similar principle, but the optical path is contained within the detector enclosure. This eliminates the path length as a variable, and they display concentration in simple percent of LFL. The spot-type sensor often contains an integral 4–20 mA transmitter that sends the analog signal to the display unit (Figure 14.8.11).

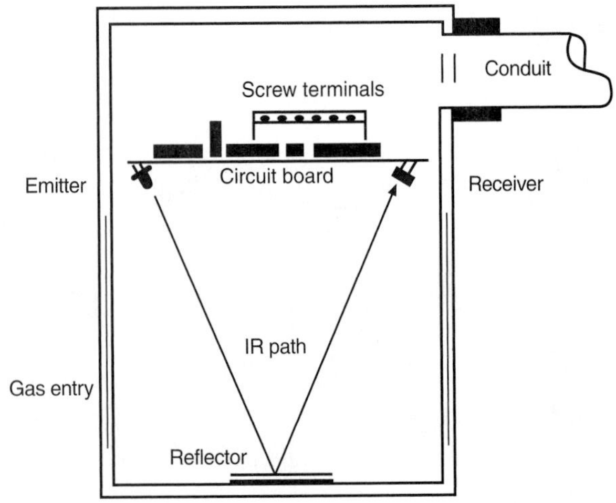

FIGURE 14.8.11 Spot-Type IR Gas Sensor

Infrared gas detectors are reputed to require far less maintenance and calibration than catalytic bead, electrochemical, and semiconductor devices.

FIXED GAS DETECTION SYSTEMS

Throughout modern industry there exist enclosed areas where gaseous contaminants can accumulate. Whether these gases are flammable, toxic, or both flammable and toxic, they represent a serious threat to personnel, the facility, and the operations housed within the facility. Reliable monitoring of known gas hazards is critical if losses are to be prevented.

Where known permanent gas hazards exist, a fixed gas detection system is necessary. These hazards are commonly encountered in public utility electric generating stations; publicly owned water treatment works; petroleum exploration, production, refining, and distribution facilities; pharmaceutical, chemical, and petrochemical production, storage, and distribution facilities; metallurgical facilities; semiconductor fabrication facilities; distilleries; paint and varnish manufacturing facilities; and mines.

Concurrent with the detection of the presence and concentration of both flammable and toxic gases, there is the need to measure the oxygen concentration in the atmosphere in many applications. Measurement of the oxygen concentration is important as a means of evaluating the effectiveness of inerting processes, of protecting personnel from the effects of oxygen deficiency, and of determining that sufficient oxygen is present in the atmosphere to ensure reliable concentration readings from combustible gas detectors.

It is important to note that one cannot use the spacing criteria for smoke detectors in *NFPA 72®*, *National Fire Alarm Code®* as a guide for the location and spacing of gas detectors. The spacing and location criteria in *NFPA 72* for smoke detectors are based on fire plume dynamics in which the heat released by the combustion of the fuel serves as the driving force behind the development of a fire plume and a ceiling jet. No such energy source exists in the context of a gas leak. When a contaminant gas leaks into the surrounding atmosphere, it mixes with the air, changing its density. In a mixture of gases, the density of the mixture is a function of the constituent gases and the portion of the mixture that they represent. Under still air conditions where there is no ambient air movement, higher concentrations are usually observed at higher locations within the enclosing space when lighter-than-air gases are involved. Conversely, higher concentrations are usually observed at lower locations within the enclosing space when heavier-than-air gases are involved. One can use the specific density of the gas in question to aid in predicting whether the gas in question will tend to rise or sink when a leak occurs (Table 14.8.1).

The data in Table 14.8.1 must be used carefully. It is often necessary to take into account the refrigeration effect that occurs when a gas at high pressure leaks into a region of much lower pressure. The volumetric expansion of the leaking gas causes it to cool the air into which it is flowing. The cooled air is no longer at STP conditions of 77°F (25°C) and 760 mm(Hg) absolute pressure or 1 atm. This cooling causes the air/gas mixture to contract, increasing in density. As the mixture moves from the locus of the leak, it continues to absorb heat from the ambient, and slowly reaches thermal equilibrium with the ambient. These thermodynamics must be observed when using data, such as that in Table 14.8.1, to develop a sensor placement strategy.

Flammable Gas Detection

Most of the fixed gas detection systems in service are designed to measure the concentration of one or more flammable gases.

TABLE 14.8.1 Specific Densities of Commonly Encountered Gases and Vapors*

Standard Conditions of Temperature and Pressure

Gas/Vapor	*Molecular Formula*	*Specific Density, Air = 1.0000*
Air	—	1.0000
Hydrogen	H_2	0.7000
Carbon monoxide	CO	0.9670
Carbon dioxide	CO_2	1.5280
Methane	CH_4	0.5540
Acetylene	C_2H_2	0.9110
Ethane	C_2H_6	1.0490
Hydrogen sulfide	H_2S	0.9109
Phosphine	PH_3	1.1840
Propane	C_3H_8	1.5500
Silane	SiH_4	1.1140
Sulfur dioxide	SO_2	2.2640
Acetone	$(CH_3)_2CO$	2.0
Benzene	C_6H_6	2.8
Carbon disulfide	CS_2	2.6
Cyclohexane	C_6H_{12}	2.9
Ethanol (ethyl alcohol)	CH_3CH_2OH	1.6
Ethyl ether	$CH_3Ch_2OCH_2CH_3$	2.6
Gasoline	mixture	3.4
Mineral spirits	mixture	3.9
Naphtha (VM&P)	mixture	<1.0
Toluene	$C_6H_5CH_3$	3.1

*See NFPA 86, *Standard for Ovens and Furnaces.*

These systems are generally found in petroleum exploration, production, refining, and distribution facilities; power generation plants; water treatment plants; landfills; chemical and pharmaceutical facilities; and numerous industrial processes where flammable solvent (vehicle) vapors are driven off in ovens. Generally, these systems are designed to respond to a broad range of hydrocarbon gases and vapors, such as methane, ethane, propane, butane, ethylene, propylene, acetylene, and similar gases, as well as the vapors from the evaporation of hydrocarbon liquids, such as gasoline, acetone, ethyl ether, methylethyl ketone, methylisobutyl ketone, carbon disulfide, turpentine, and lacquer thinner, to list a few.

The predominant sensor for flammable gas detection in general, normally occupied spaces is the catalytic bead sensor, which is designed to comply with the performance criteria outlined in ANSI/ISA S12.13, *Performance Requirements, Combustible Gas Detectors.*[1] Sensors are situated where there is the probability that gas will accumulate when a leak occurs. When the gas to be detected is methane, natural gas, or other lighter-than-air gases, sensors are generally located above the gas-containing equipment. When propane, butane, and most vapors are involved, the sensors are located low in the air space of the hazard area. Flammable gas sensors must be placed to take advantage of normally occurring air currents and the differences in the density of air and the flammable gas(es) in question. The installation, operation, and maintenance of flammable gas detectors are addressed in ISA RP12.13, Part II-87, *Recommended Practice: Installation, Operation, and Maintenance of Combustible Gas Detection Instruments.*[2]

The gas sensors are connected via multiconductor cable to the appropriate transmitter, which is then connected to the display unit, as shown in Figure 14.8.12. Generally, the distance between the sensor and transmitter is quite limited. The transmitter linearizes the signal from the sensor, corrects it for

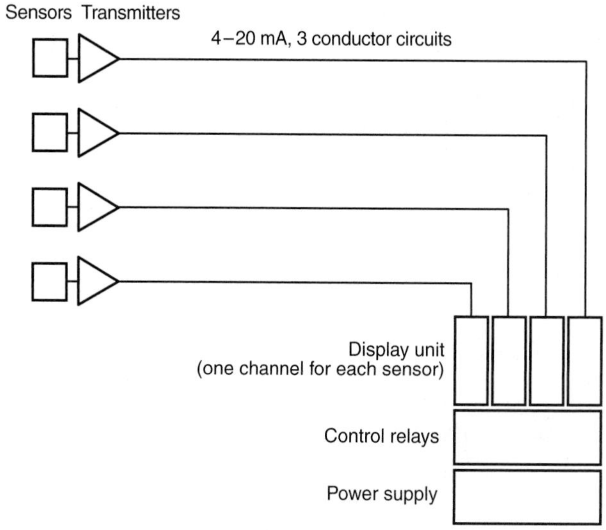

FIGURE 14.8.12 Wiring Architecture for the Traditional and Currently Most Likely Encountered Flammable Gas Detection System

zero and span, and converts it into an electrical format that can be transmitted a long distance without interference. The most popular format is the "4–20 mA" format. A second set of wires connects the transmitter to the display unit. The maximum wiring distance between the transmitter and the display usually can be as far as several thousand feet.

Large numbers of "points" are generally wired to a centrally located display unit where the status of the facility can be monitored by facility staff. The unit displays the output of the transmitter. Some display units utilize analog meters, whereas others provide bar-graph and numeric displays.

Addressable gas detection systems have been introduced that enable the system to be wired in a manner similar to a traditional smoke detector circuit. The transmitter converts the analog data from the sensor into a binary format and transmits it serially along with its identity to the display unit. The display unit presents the analog data in the customary fashion (Figure 14.8.13).

Most display units are equipped with output relays that transfer when the measured concentration of gas exceeds preestablished threshold concentrations. This provides for different types of responses as the measured gas concentration increases. For example, a warning response might be activated when the concentration reaches 20 percent LFL, and inerting or shutdown actuated when the concentration reaches 50 percent LFL.

ANSI/ISA S12.13[1] requires that the flammable (combustible) gas detection system supervise for the following:

1. The failure of the unit power supply
2. The loss of continuity of the sensor element (catalytic bead)
3. The continuity of all conductors to the detector head (the sensor and transmitter)
4. Down-scale reading, below zero, equivalent to a concentration of more than 5 ppm

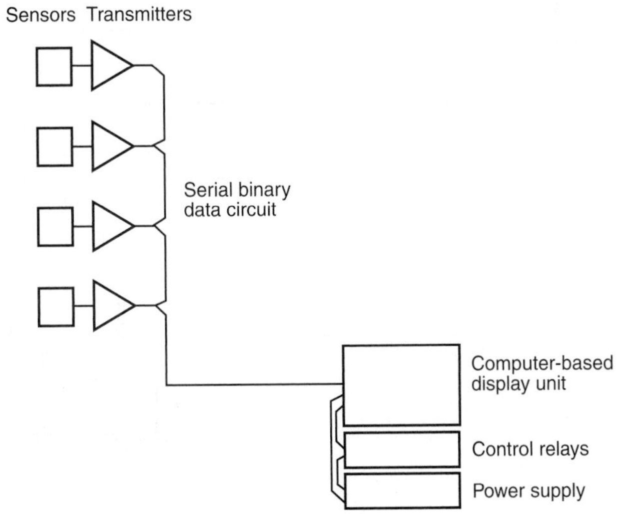

FIGURE 14.8.13 Wiring Architecture of the Addressable Flammable Gas Detection System

This is not entirely consistent with the supervisory requirements of *NFPA 72*. Furthermore, ANSI/ISA RP12.13 does not address supervision of any of the connections that are intended to initiate any type of automatic response to a gas concentration above threshold levels. This inconsistency is one of several system design issues that come into play when integrating or interconnecting flammable gas detection systems with fire protective systems. *NFPA 72* includes specific requirements for the power supplies, electrical supervision, isolation from ground, programming security, and supervision of output circuits that might not have been observed by the manufacturer of the gas detection system. The actuation of inerting, warning, and ventilation systems in response to high-level gas indication are all fire-protective actions that should be achieved with inherently reliable, supervised designs, as described in *NFPA 72*. Some authorities having jurisdiction (AHJ) might apply the requirements of *NFPA 72* to flammable gas detection systems when the flammable gas detection is integrated into the facility fire protection systems.

Toxic Gas Detection

The detection of many toxic gases is necessary in the same environments where flammable gases must be monitored. Most frequently, hydrogen sulfide gas is commonly encountered in petroleum exploration and production involving sour crude and/or sour gas. Consequently, many gas detection systems in place in the petroleum industries include both flammable gas and toxic gas detection for hydrogen sulfide, sulfur dioxide, and fluorine in the same system.

The architecture of most fixed gas detection systems lends itself to this reality. The systems are designed with transmitters and display units that can accommodate a number of interchangeable sensors, specifically designed for a particular gas. Combined flammable and toxic gas detection systems are commonly encountered.

The semiconductor and electrochemical sensors are most commonly used for the detection of toxic gases. The measurements are expressed in ppm and generally the threshold limit value (TLV) established by OSHA for the gas in question is placed in the upper half of the display range.

ANSI/ISA S12.15, PT I-90, *Performance Requirements for Hydrogen Sulfide Detection Instruments (10–100 ppm)*,[3] requires that the toxic gas detection system supervise for the following:

1. The continuity of all conductors to the detector head (the sensor and transmitter)
2. The failure of the unit power supply
3. The loss of continuity of a circuit protection device
4. A down-scale reading, below zero, equivalent to a concentration of more than 5 ppm

This is not entirely consistent with the supervisory requirements of *NFPA 72*, which establishes requirements on the equipment design that are not normally assumed to be relevant when a manufacturer outside the fire protection community undertakes the design of a product. This becomes an important issue when integration of gas detection and fire alarm systems is contemplated.

Calibration and Maintenance

Both flammable and toxic gas detection systems require regular calibration and maintenance if reliable measurements are expected.[2,4] Each system has a specific set of calibration and maintenance criteria that is incorporated as part of the listing investigation by the nationally recognized testing laboratory. These procedures must be carefully and meticulously followed. In general, most systems using catalytic bead, semiconductor, and electrochemical sensors require calibration on a monthly schedule. The flame cell and flame ionization detectors usually require less frequent calibration.

The calibration of a gas detector, whether flammable or toxic, involves adjusting the electrical output of the transmitter to accurately reflect the atmosphere at the sensor. The first step is the zero adjustment. While the sensor is under normal ambient conditions with no gas present, the output of the transmitter is adjusted to 4.0 mA output to the display unit. The sensor is exposed to *test gas*. Test gas is a mixture of air and the gas to be detected, stored at elevated pressure in a specially designed cylinder with a sensor test fitting attached. The mixture is certified by the manufacturer as being accurate to within 1.0 percent LFL or 1.0 ppm, whichever is appropriate. Since there is an obvious hazard if the test gas concentration is at 100 percent LFL or 100 percent TLV, the test gas concentration is usually at 50 percent LFL or TLV, again whichever is appropriate. Exposure to the test gas is used to adjust the span output of the transmitter to the appropriate value for the test gas and sensor in question. In this way the electronics of the transmitter are used to correct for any nonlinearities and drift in the sensor. The display unit merely reads the current passing through the 4–20 mA circuit to the transmitter and displays it. Consequently, there is usually no calibration necessary at the display unit.

Eventually, the zero and span adjustments on the transmitter are insufficient to achieve both a zero and a correct span adjustment. This indicates that the sensor has aged to the point where it must be replaced. The rate of aging is very application specific and can occur without any apparent warning. Consequently, regular calibration is the only means to be confident that the gas detection system is operative and displaying an accurate measurement of the actual gas concentrations in the hazard areas.

Integration with Fire Alarm Systems

There are inconsistencies between the *NFPA 72* requirements for fire alarm signaling systems and the ISA standards for gas detection instruments. These inconsistencies become relevant when the conditions in the hazard area demand an integrated approach. Obviously, the presence of a flammable gas in an area sufficiently hazardous to warrant a fire alarm system represents an aspect of that hazard area that warrants immediate remedial action. Whether that remedial action consists of merely the activation of a notification appliance or whether it requires the activation of purge fans, process shutdown, deployment of an inerting agent, or some other response, these actions must be designed into the system in a manner that provides a high degree of intrinsic reliability and supervision if they are to represent a meaningful response. Typically, these responses are executed by a fire alarm system control unit that has been listed for releasing device service, and the flammable gas detection system serves as an initiating device in that system.

Since many gas detection systems use earth-ground as a circuit common, a practice that is forbidden in the context of fire alarm systems, there is often a fundamental power supply incompatibility between the gas detection control unit and the fire alarm system control unit. Consequently, the interface between the gas detection and the fire alarm system is often achieved through dry relay contacts. This is not the ideal means of signal transmission due to the relatively low reliability of dry relay contacts compared to solid-state devices. However, it is often what is found in the field. This circuit is shown in Figure 14.8.14.

It is important to understand that when flammable gas leaks occur it is not unusual for the cause of the leak to also lead to a heat source of ignition, making flammable gas detection an important fire prevention strategy. The commonly encountered flammable gases, such as natural gas, methane, ethane, and propane, are all dielectric materials. Being dielectrics they accumulate static electric charges when the velocity of the flow varies widely across the flow stream. Such velocity differentials regularly exist in the context of a leak of flammable gas from a high-pressure source. Consequently, the flow through the leak may generate large electrostatic potentials that are discharged as the gas escapes, creating electric sparks, which may be of sufficient energy and power to ignite the flammable gas/air mixture. This reality underscores the importance of detecting and expeditiously correcting flammable gas leaks.

PORTABLE GAS MONITORING INSTRUMENTS

Wherever there is the reasonable possibility of an accidental release of either flammable or toxic gas, there is the need to equip personnel with a portable instrument to warn them of such a hazard on entering. Both flammable and toxic gases are encountered in diverse locations throughout industry, for example, as a result of some form of accidental or opportunistic event, such as leakage from piping systems (both above and below ground) into the surrounding soil; from spillage or the decomposition of natural organic material in the soil; or sanitary landfills. Regardless of the source, the possibility and probability that a dangerous concentration of a flammable or toxic gas might exist in an area within a facility establish the need for portable gas monitors (Figure 14.8.15).

There are portable gas monitors designed for a wide range of performance objectives. It is important that the performance objectives for the gas monitoring instrument be fully understood before a unit is selected. Some applications require oxygen monitoring to ensure that there is sufficient oxygen for safe occupation of the space. Many applications require a monitor for only one specific gas, whereas other applications represent a number of concerns justifying the use of a multifunction monitor. Areas that contain concentrations of flammable gas above the LFL will necessitate an explosionproof or intrinsically safe

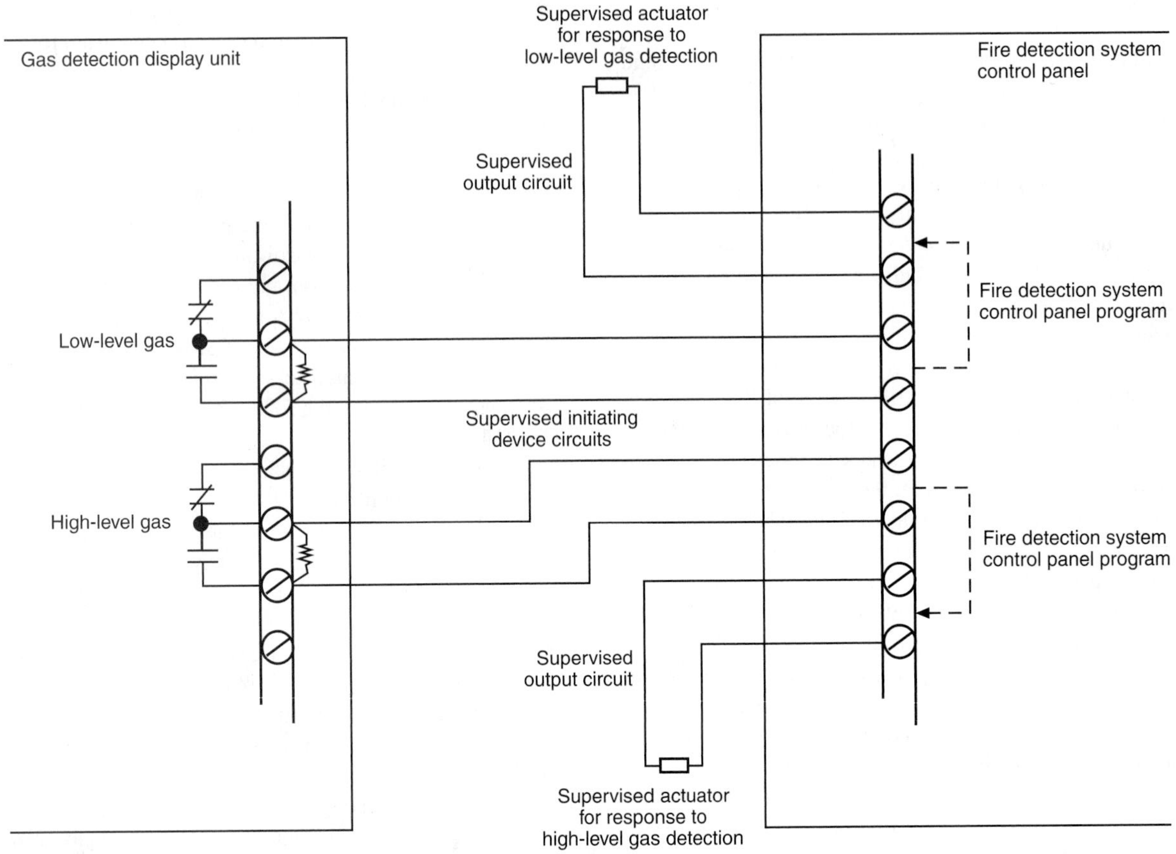

FIGURE 14.8.14 Commonly Encountered Interface Between the Gas Detection and the Fire Alarm System Used to Activate Automatic Responses to the Gas Detection Level Alarms

FIGURE 14.8.15 Portable Gas Monitor

instrument. Finally, some applications require that the unit operate continuously while the user is in the hazardous space, whereas others are intended to be used as a portable survey instrument operated on an intermittent basis. All of these intended use considerations have an important bearing on the selection of an instrument.

Portable gas monitoring instruments are available in a wide variety of forms. Some units depend on the diffusion of the air-gas mixture into the sensor. Others have provisions for a forced sampling means. Samples are drawn through a hose or tube, which is frequently equipped with a rigid extension or probe for ease in reaching inaccessible points. Suction is provided by a hand-operated rubber aspirator bulb or a battery-powered built-in motor-driven pump.

When using portable gas monitoring instruments the operator must keep in mind that all such instruments have a finite range of ambient conditions under which they can operate. Extremes in temperature, humidity, and barometric pressure (altitude) are likely to affect the accuracy and precision of the measurements they provide. Sampling steamy atmospheres is not recommended, since condensation of water within the instrument is likely to cause errors. Sampling from ovens or dryers operating at temperatures much higher than instrument ambient should also be avoided. Unless the solvents in question have flashpoints below instrument ambient temperature, vapors might condense within the sampling tubing or measuring instrument, again causing errors.

Finally, if the portable gas monitoring instrument is to be used in areas where ignitible concentrations of flammable gas might exist, it should be designed and listed for use in hazardous locations as defined in Article 500 of NFPA 70. The manufacturer's label and instructions indicate the type of approval granted for the particular instrument.

Flammable (Combustible) Gas Monitoring Instruments

Flammable gas monitoring instruments generally use a catalytic bead or semiconductor sensor. The output from the sensor is directly displayed with a number of different techniques, ranging from an analog meter to digital readout. Most also include some form of audible alarm set at a level considered immediately hazardous. As a rule, flammable gas instruments must be set to read "zero" in uncontaminated air each time they are used. Like the fixed systems, the gas concentration is displayed in percent LFL. Generally, flammable gas monitoring instruments respond to all flammable gases or mixtures of flammable gases, irrespective of their chemical composition (Figure 14.8.16). This is usually desirable in a portable monitor, as it is unnecessary to know the exact identity of the flammable gas or gases prior to being able to assess the fire risk of the area being surveyed. Where it is necessary to selectively measure the concentration of some specific flammable gas, especially while in the presence of other combustibles, infrared absorption and gas chromatographic techniques on samples transported to a laboratory must be used.

Toxic Gas Monitoring Instruments

Similar to the flammable gas monitoring instruments, toxic gas monitoring instruments are often necessary in order to ensure personnel safety. Hydrogen sulfide monitors usually employ electrochemical sensors as do the sulfur dioxide, chlorine, and fluorine monitors. Carbon monoxide monitors are available using either the semiconductor sensor or the electrochemical sensor technologies (Figure 14.8.17). Other techniques that involve electrical detection of gas-specific chemical reactions are also employed. These include chemical stain, electro-conductance, and membrane permeability methods. These units generally display the concentration in ppm and include an audible signal when the concentration reaches a threshold value above which the threat to life and health is unacceptable.

Oxygen Concentration Monitoring Instruments

Oxygen concentration monitoring instruments are often critical life safety tools. Generally they utilize an electrochemical sensor. The partial pressure of the oxygen in the atmosphere controls the rate at which it diffuses through a porous membrane and into the electrochemical cell. Once in the cell, the oxygen enters into an electrochemical reaction, generating an electric current that is electronically scaled to display the oxygen concentration. The oxygen concentration is usually displayed as a simple "percent oxygen," usually on a scale graduated from 0 to 25 percent. Portable oxygen monitoring instruments usually include an audible alarm set for a level around 18 percent (Figure 14.8.18).

Except for setting the meter to read 20.8 percent while aspirating fresh air at the elevation (atmospheric pressure) where tests are to be made, no other calibration is necessary

FIGURE 14.8.16 Portable Multiple-Range Gas Monitoring Instrument (Source: Heath Consultants, Inc.)

FIGURE 14.8.17 Electrochemical Carbon Monoxide Monitoring Instrument That Includes an Indicator and Alarm (Source: MSA [Mine Safety Appliances Co.])

FIGURE 14.8.18 Individual Oxygen Indicator for Remote Sampling (Source: MSA [Mine Safety Appliances Co.])

for accurate reading in the range of oxygen concentrations in which it is permissible for people to work. (Current regulations require a minimum of 19.5 percent oxygen; otherwise, air must be supplied or self-contained breathing equipment must be used.) Enclosed spaces should also be tested to ensure sufficient oxygen is present to permit reliable gas measurements. Where readings are intended to be significant in the low range, that is, with inerting systems, the zero setting can be confirmed by sampling an oxygen-free gas, such as propane or nitrogen.

Calibration of Portable Gas Monitoring Instruments

Portable gas monitoring instruments require calibration on a regular basis if their measurements are to be relied on. The procedures for calibration vary from instrument to instrument. However, as with the fixed detection systems, most employ the use of a test gas. The "zero" of the unit is adjusted. Then it is subjected to test gas containing a known, certified concentration of the gas it is designed to measure. The span adjustment is then employed to achieve a measurement reading consistent with the known gas concentration.

The frequency at which units should be calibrated is determined by the authorities responsible for the life safety of the facility staff. Some authorities recommend calibration be verified daily, before use. Such a calibration check is accomplished by passing test gas through the instrument.

SUMMARY

This chapter is by no means a complete, authoritative presentation on gas detection. It is an introduction to this topic. The reader must be cautioned that the gas detection industry has developed over the years as part of the instrumentation industry, serving the needs of the chemical process and petroleum industries. Generally, the language is different from that used in the fire protection industry. Furthermore, the standards that have evolved over the years relating to gas detection do not address the concerns of the fire protection community in the customary manner. For example, consider that the 4–20 mA data transmission circuit is not recognized by *NFPA 72*.

As fire alarm systems become increasingly interactive with the facilities and production processes they protect, conflicts are expected to emerge in the requirements of various standards. These conflicts can only be resolved when fire protection professionals understand the basics of this technology and the objectives the standards were written to ensure. As fire alarm systems are more thoroughly interfaced with process control systems, questions of reliability, operability during impairment, and maintainability must be addressed in a manner that satisfies the needs of both fire protection and rigorous process control.

BIBLIOGRAPHY

References Cited

1. ANSI/ISA S12.13, *Performance Requirements, Combustible Gas Detectors,* Instrument Society of America, Research Triangle Park, NC, 1986.
2. ISA RP12.13, PT II-87, *Recommended Practice: Installation, Operation, and Maintenance of Combustible Gas Detection Instruments,* Instrument Society of America, Research Triangle Park, NC, 1987.
3. ANSI/ISA S12.15, PT I-90, *Performance Requirements for Hydrogen Sulfide Detection Instruments (10–100 ppm),* Instrument Society of America, Research Triangle Park, NC, 1990.
4. ISA RP12.15, PT II-90, *Recommended Practice: Installation, Operation, and Maintenance of Hydrogen Sulfide Detection Instruments,* Instrument Society of America, Research Triangle Park, NC, 1990.

NFPA Codes, Standards, and Recommended Practices

Reference to the following NFPA codes, standards, and recommended practices will provide further information on gas and vapor detection systems and monitors discussed in this chapter. (See the latest version of The NFPA Catalog *for availability of current editions of the following documents.)*

NFPA 30, *Flammable and Combustible Liquids Code*
NFPA 70, *National Electrical Code®*
NFPA 72®, National Fire Alarm Code®
NFPA 86, *Standard for Ovens and Furnaces*
NFPA 720, *Standard for the Installation of Carbon Monoxide (CO) Warning Equipment in Dwelling Units*

Chapter 9

Carbon Monoxide Detection in Residential Occupancies

Art Black

Chapter Contents

Key Terms

biometric carbon monoxide detector, carbon monoxide, carbon monoxide detector, carboxyhemoglobin, electrochemical carbon monoxide detector, metal-oxide semiconductor carbon monoxide detector, temporal 3 signal, temporal 4 signal

Although the popularity of carbon monoxide (CO) detectors and requirements for CO detection installation have been growing in recent years, it cannot be assumed that everyone is familiar with the hazards of carbon monoxide, the symptoms of CO poisoning, the requirements for alarms and detectors, or the installation and mounting details for alarms and detectors. The fire service may value further guidance on best ways to respond to CO alarm and detector actuations.

For related topics, see Section 2, Chapter 6, "Fundamentals of Fire Detection"; Section 6, Chapter 2, "Combustion Products and Their Effects on Life Safety"; and Section 14, Chapter 3, "Notification Appliances."

PHYSICAL PROPERTIES AND SOURCES OF CARBON MONOXIDE

Physical Properties

Carbon monoxide is a colorless, odorless gas produced by incomplete combustion. Carbon monoxide is minimally denser than air under ordinary conditions. It burns in air with a characteristic blue flame. As a reducing agent, it removes oxygen from many compounds and is used in the reduction of metals from ores. When air containing carbon monoxide in any amount is inhaled, the oxygen in hemoglobin is replaced by carbon monoxide, resulting in oxygen starvation throughout the body.

Sources

Hazardous concentrations of CO can accumulate in any occupancy, whether a single-family dwelling unit, a hotel guest room, or a nonresidential occupancy. The vast majority of deaths due to CO poisoning, however, occur in one- and two-family dwellings.[1] Generally, the accumulation of CO is the result of improperly operating heating appliances; insufficient make-up air in the space; blocked, poorly designed, or poorly installed chimneys or vents; or a complete absence of needed vents. Other potential sources of CO, however, exist, including idling automobiles in attached garages and portable equipment, such as generators and barbecue grills.

In multiresidential occupancies such as hotels, apartment buildings, or condominium buildings, malfunctioning furnaces, boilers, or swimming pool heaters, or problems with the venting of such appliances, can cause potentially fatal build-ups of CO.

CARBON MONOXIDE HAZARDS

Solid, liquid, or gaseous fuels can produce CO gas in lethal concentrations. According to U.S. death certificate data, 200 to 300 unintentional-injury deaths a year are due to CO. With detection and early warning, the majority of these deaths could be readily prevented. It is also possible that a considerable number of additional CO deaths are not recognized as such, because the symptoms

---

Art Black is chair of the NFPA Technical Committee on Supervising Stations for Fire Alarm Systems and the past chair of the Technical Committee on Carbon Dioxide Warning Equipment. A 30-year veteran of the fire service, he is the principal of Carmel Fire Protection Associates in Carmel, California, a fire protection consulting company providing fire prevention services to the public sector.

are not sufficiently unique as to prompt a routine postmortem examination. Every year, there are nearly a hundred additional deaths due to gas or vapor—principally CO—for which it is never determined whether the injury was intentional (e.g., suicide) or unintentional.

Exposure

The dangers of CO exposure depend largely on a number of variables, including the subject's health and activity level. Infants, pregnant women, and people with physical conditions that limit their body's ability to use oxygen (including people with emphysema, asthma, and heart disease) can be more severely affected by lower concentrations of CO than healthy adults. The subject's length of exposure and the initial carboxyhemoglobin (COHb) level, which could be elevated by smoking or exposure to operating motor vehicles in a confined space, are additional important variables. A person exposed to CO can be poisoned by a small amount of CO over a longer period of time or by a large amount of CO over a shorter period of time.

Symptoms of Carbon Monoxide Poisoning

The reactions to CO poisoning vary depending on several factors, including the age, general health, fitness, and general activity level of the victim immediately prior to the poisoning. The following equation can be used to determine the estimated percent of carboxyhemoglobin in the blood:[2]

$$\%COHb_t = \%COHb_0[e^{-(t/2398B)}] + 218[1 - e^{-(t/2398B)}] \times [0.0003 + (ppmCO/1316)]$$

where

$\%COHb_t$ = Percentage of COHb at time t

$\%COHb_0$ = Percentage of COHb in the blood at time 0

t = Time (min)

B = 0.0404 (work effort)

The concentration of CO, measured in parts per million (ppm), is a determining factor in the symptoms for an average healthy adult, as shown in Table 14.9.1.

TABLE 14.9.1 Carbon Monoxide Concentrations and Symptoms

Concentration (ppm CO)	*Symptoms*
50	No adverse effects with 8 hours of exposure
200	Mild headache after 2–3 hours of exposure
400	Headache and nausea after 1–2 hours of exposure
800	Headache, nausea, and dizziness after 45 minutes of exposure; collapse and unconsciousness after 2 hours of exposure
1000	Loss of consciousness after 1 hour of exposure
1600	Headache, nausea, and dizziness after 20 minutes of exposure
3200	Headache, nausea, and dizziness after 5–10 minutes of exposure; collapse and unconsciousness after 30 minutes of exposure
6400	Headache and dizziness after 1–2 minutes of exposure; unconsciousness and danger of death after 10–15 minutes of exposure
12,800 (1.28% by volume)	Immediate physiological effects; unconsciousness and danger of death after 1–3 minutes of exposure

CAUTION: The values in Table 14.9.1 are approximate values for healthy adults. Children, the elderly, and persons with pre-existing physical conditions might be more susceptible to the effects of carbon monoxide exposure. Continued exposure after unconsciousness can cause death.

Source: NFPA 720, *Standard for the Installation of Carbon Monoxide (CO) Warning Equipment in Dwelling Units,* Table B.1, 2005, p. 720-10.

DEVELOPMENT OF CARBON MONOXIDE DETECTION STANDARDS

After several well-publicized incidents in the early 1990s, the U.S. Consumer Product Safety Commission petitioned the National Fire Protection Association to create a standard for CO detection. The NFPA Standards Council acted on this request in 1993 by assigning development of a new document to the Technical Committee on Household Fire Warning Equipment. This committee was chosen because it had the necessary expertise in residential detection principles in its development of *NFPA 72®, National Fire Alarm Code®*.

In 1995 the Technical Committee on Household Fire Warning Equipment presented a "Recommended Practice on the Installation of CO Warning Equipment" to the NFPA membership at the annual meeting, where it was returned to the committee. In early 1996 the Standards Council reassigned the project to a new Technical Committee on CO and Fuel Gas Detection, which was given the task of developing two documents—one on detection of CO and the other on detection of fuel gas vapors.

The first NFPA document on CO detection, NFPA 720, *Recommended Practice for the Installation of Household Carbon Monoxide Warning Equipment,* was approved by the NFPA membership in 1997. NFPA 720 was a recommended practice, not a standard, so the installation details in the document were advisory only. Further, since the scope of the document was for family living units only, the document specifically excluded hotels, motels, and similar occupancies. NFPA 720 made recommendations for the selection, installation, operation, and maintenance of equipment that detects concentrations of CO that could pose a health hazard to occupants of a single-family living unit. Because of the multiple alarm thresholds involved, it was not intended to regulate CO detectors designed to detect hostile fire signatures.

The technical committee attempted a revision of NFPA 720 in 2000, which would have extended the recommendations to all occupancies; however, that revision was returned to the committee at the NFPA fall meeting. The technical committee made some minor revisions to the 2003 edition of NFPA 720, including revisions pursuant to the changes in NFPA's Manual of Style. With the growing number of jurisdictions adopting requirements for installation of carbon monoxide warning equipment and the difficulty of a jurisdictional authority to reference a recommended practice, the Technical Committee converted the document into a standard in 2005. The Technical Committee is currently working on a modification to NFPA 720 to answer the growing need of jurisdictional authorities who are requiring carbon monoxide detection in other than single-family residences.

INSTALLATION OF CARBON MONOXIDE DETECTION EQUIPMENT

NFPA 720, now titled *Standard for the Installation of Carbon Monoxide (CO) Warning Equipmnt in Dwelling Units,* is the standard that provides guidelines for operation, installation, testing, and maintenance of carbon monoxide detectors in household occupancies (Figure 14.9.1). Currently there are no standards for carbon monoxide detection equipment in commercial occupancies (hotels, congregate residential buildings, and other commercial nonresidential buildings).

Household Dwelling Units

It is important to note that NFPA 720 is an installation standard and does not require the installation of carbon monoxide warning equipment. When required to be installed, or where protection is desired, CO detectors or alarms are to be located in any residential occupancy containing a fuel-burning appliance or fireplace or having an attached garage. A CO detector or alarm needs to be installed outside each separate sleeping area in the immediate vicinity of the bedrooms. Audibility of the warning signal is a determining factor when deciding how many detectors or alarms to install. Where bedrooms are separated and audibility could be impaired, more than one unit may be required.

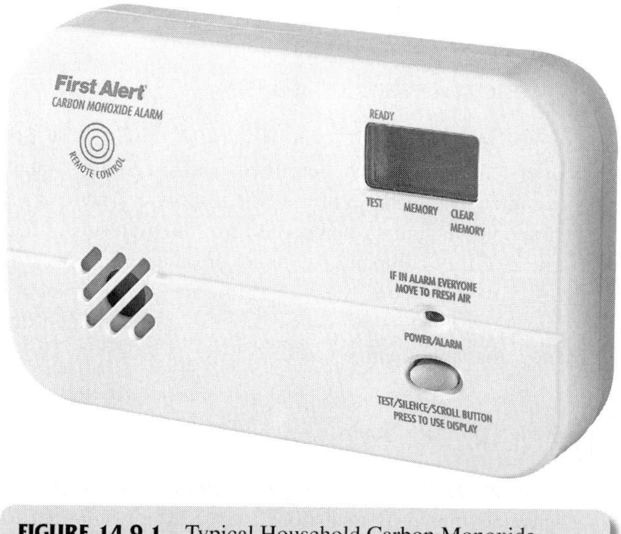

FIGURE 14.9.1 Typical Household Carbon Monoxide Detector (Source: BRK Brands, Inc.)

CO is minimally denser than air, and concerns have been voiced about "plug-in" detector models that are mounted at the level of convenience receptacles located near the floor. Since the vapor density of CO is very close to that of air, however, it will readily mix with air given any air movement in the room, and detectors can thus be mounted either on the ceiling or on the wall. Underwriters Laboratories Standard 2034, *Standard for Single and Multiple Station CO Alarms,*[3] is the manufacturing standard for CO warning equipment. This standard requires that mounting specifications be part of the documentation required to be included with a CO detector or alarm. These manufacturer's directions need to be followed.

CO detection equipment is recommended in any family living unit containing a fuel-burning appliance or fireplace or any family-living unit having an attached garage. NFPA 720 parallels UL 2034 in the requirements for CO warning equipment as it relates to power supplies, equipment performance, and alarm signals.

NFPA 720 also contains provisions which require carbon monoxide warning equipment be interconnected to a household fire alarm control unit or a household combination fire/burglary alarm unit as a supervisory device. This information is of primary importance to the fire service, because on a fire alarm or combination fire/burglary alarm panel, an alarm signal would mean "fire." It is important to ensure that an incorrect alarm condition is not transmitted to a public fire service communications center.

Hotel and Congregate Residences

Because the scope of NFPA 720 is limited to single-family dwellings, there are no requirements in the document regarding CO detection equipment in hotels and congregate residences. However, where CO detection is required or desired in such occupancies, it is recommended that the CO warning equipment or detectors be installed in close proximity to fuel-burning equipment, such as furnace rooms and pool heater rooms. In addition, these devices should be connected to the premises fire alarm system as supervisory devices. This will allow for the on-site staff to be immediately notified of a CO problem.

Other Commercial Occupancies

As stated above, NFPA 720 applies solely to single-family dwellings. Where carbon monoxide detection is required or desired in commercial occupancies, sound engineering judgment is to be used in determining placement of carbon monoxide detection equipment and the necessary interconnection to building alarm systems.

CARBON MONOXIDE WARNING EQUIPMENT ALERT SIGNALS

The standard signal for a CO alarm is a single-tone "temporal 4" pattern, consisting of four cycles of 100 milliseconds "on" and 100 milliseconds "off," followed by 5 seconds "off." The signal should continue until the alarm resets or the detector is manually reset. To conserve battery power, an exception allows the manufacturer to extend the 5 seconds "off" period to 60 seconds "off" after the first 4 minutes of alarm. The signal was selected as a unique alternative to existing smoke alarm signals or the temporal 3 pattern required for newer smoke alarms (Figure 14.9.2). Because many CO detectors and alarms resemble smoke detectors and alarms in appearance, developers saw the need to make the audible signal for CO detectors and alarms distinctively different. Another factor in the development of this signal was the need for the CO alarm to have enough power to continue operation for 12 hours, based on the premise that if the CO emissions began after the resident left for the day, the signal would need to last long enough for the resident to hear the signal on his or her return at the end of the day. Some CO detectors have a button to display the highest reading ever taken, so occupants can check for problems even after prolonged absences from the home.

CARBON MONOXIDE DETECTOR TECHNOLOGIES

Most commercially available carbon monoxide alarms use one of three detection technologies: biometric, metal-oxide semiconductor, or electrochemical.

Biometric

Biometric detectors are also called biomimetric, colorimetric, chem-optical technology, or gel-cell detectors. This sensor technology utilizes a material that mimics the response of human hemoglobin to carbon monoxide. In the presence of carbon monoxide, the amount of infrared light that will pass through the sensing material declines. The rate of change of the transmittance is used to calculate CO gas concentrations. Biometric sensors have demonstrated immunity to other gases that may be present and are not prone to false alarms.

Metal-Oxide Semiconductor

These detectors use tin dioxide (SnO_2) as a sensing element. The sensing material is heated by a heating element and CO gas is catalytically broken down at the surface. Electrons are released and reabsorbed by the tin dioxide. Electronics are utilized to measure the sensor resistance and from this to calculate the concentration of CO. These sensors have demonstrated excellent resistance to sensing other gases that may be present.

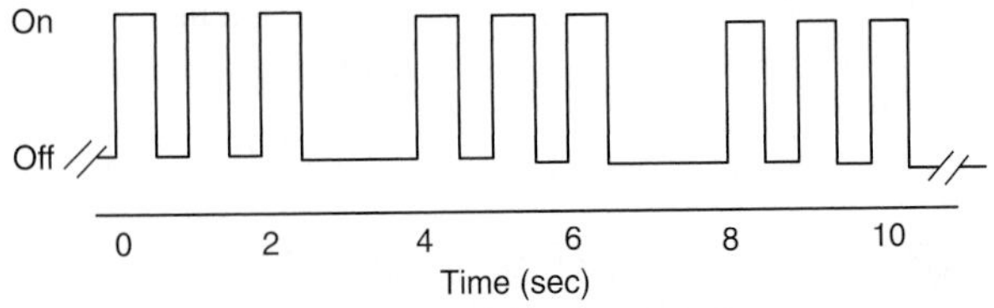

FIGURE 14.9.2 Temporal 3 Pattern Fire Alarm Evacuation Signal

Electrochemical

Electrochemical technology involves an acid electrolyte solution and platinum electrodes. The presence of carbon monoxide causes a chemical reaction that instigates a current flow through the circuit. This technology utilizes external circuitry to monitor the changes in potential and uses this information to calculate the concentration of CO. Electrochemical sensors are mechanically more complex than sensors using other technologies, but can provide much more accurate measurements of CO concentrations. These sensors have demonstrated good immunity to interfering gases.

RESPONSE TO CARBON MONOXIDE ALERTS

Occupant Response

The initial response by the occupant is to take "appropriate action" based on the knowledge that the CO detector has detected CO in the atmosphere. The recommended response includes the following:

- Opening windows to ventilate the area
- Assessing the medical condition of the occupants
- If necessary, calling the public fire service communications center (fire department)

In most cases, because of the low alarm threshold required by UL 2034, there is no need to call the fire department if the residence is immediately ventilated and appropriate service personnel are called to investigate the source of the CO. By the time service personnel (or the fire department responders) arrive, CO may no longer be present because the occupant took appropriate action by opening windows and doors. If any occupants are suffering from symptoms of CO poisoning and require medical attention, the emergency medical services system should be activated.

Emergency Service Response

Emergency response to CO alarms may be provided by first responders, primarily fire department and emergency medical personnel. The purpose of the first responders' action is to protect people, including themselves, from toxic levels of CO. In addition, utility company personnel or other "secondary responders" should respond to a CO alarm. The primary function of secondary responders is to service combustion equipment and appliances that are potential sources of CO.

SUMMARY

Hazardous concentrations of CO, a colorless, odorless gas produced by incomplete combustion, cause several hundred unintentional-injury deaths a year. The majority of these deaths occur in one- and two-family dwellings as the result of improperly operating heating appliances, insufficient make-up air in the space; blocked, poorly designed, or poorly installed chimneys or vents; or a lack of vents. Additional sources of CO include idling vehicles in attached garages and portable equipment such as generators. For protection from toxic levels of CO, CO detection equipment is recommended in any family-living unit containing a fuel-burning appliance or fireplace or having an attached garage.

BIBLIOGRAPHY

References Cited

1. National Safety Council, *Injury Facts,* Ithaca, IL, annual.
2. NFPA 720, *Standard for Installation of Carbon Monoxide (CO) Warning Equipment in Dwelling Units,* Annex B.
3. UL 2034, *Standard for Single and Multiple Station Carbon Monoxide Alarms,* 2nd ed., Underwriters Laboratories Inc., Northbrook, IL, 1996.

NFPA Codes, Standards, and Recommended Practices

Reference to the following NFPA codes, standards, and recommended practices will provide further information on carbon monoxide detection in residential occupancies discussed in this chapter. (See the latest version of The NFPA Catalog *for availability of current editions of the following documents.)*

NFPA 72®, National Fire Alarm Code®

NFPA 720, *Standard for the Installation of Carbon Monoxide (CO) Warning Equipment in Dwelling Units*

References

"IAFC Refutes Claims of CO False Alarm Burden," *Fire Fighting in Canada,* Vol. 40, No. 6, 1996, p. 30.

Laluvein, B., "Effective Detectors for Fire Protection," *Fire Safety Engineering,* Vol. 7, No. 5, 2000, pp. 23–26.

Montagna, F. C., "Responding to CO Detector Activations," *Fire Engineering,* Vol. 149, No. 1, 1996, pp. 99–102.

Ross, D., "Carbon Monoxide Detectors," *Good Building Guide 30,* Apr. 1999.

Chapter 10

Security and Intrusion Detection Systems

Shane M. Clary

Chapter Contents

Key Terms

central station, electronic premises security system, enhanced call verification, intrusion detection, security, security vulnerability analysis (SVA), site survey

Fire protection and security are interrelated. The installation of an electronic security system within the premises is part of the built environment. How it operates with other systems within the same building is integral to the complete protection platform that may be installed. Such platforms protect occupants, contents, structures, business operations and first responders.

Security has been on the minds of many people since September 11, 2001. Security has many facets, from the protection of our borders, background checks of future employees, physical security, private security force deployment, cybersecurity, electronic security countermeasures, and intrusion detection systems, to name just a few. This chapter will provide a brief overview of premises security systems that are covered by two documents that were approved by the NFPA membership and subsequently by the NFPA Standards Council in 2005:

- NFPA 730, *Guide for Premises Security*
- NFPA 731, *Standard for the Installation of Electronic Premises Security Systems*

This chapter contains very limited text from NFPA 730; the practitioner needs to obtain a copy for a full understanding of the document.

The designer of a premises security system should be familiar with both NFPA 730 and NFPA 731, as well as many other publications available through the literature. Practitioners need to be as familiar with the concepts and principles of security as fire protection engineers are with their skill set. The consequences of a poor design can be just as devastating to the property or building owner, or the victim of a crime that occurs at or within a protected facility, as lack of adequate fire protection.

Also see Section 1, Chapter 6, "Premises Security"; and Section 14, Chapter 7, "Fire Protection Surveillance and Security Services."

A BRIEF HISTORY OF SECURITY

Security in one form or another has been around since at least ancient Egypt, in which the first documented use of locks is recorded.[1] The use of locks is mentioned in both the New and Old Testaments of the Bible.[2,3] One of the first—if not the first—security alarm systems was developed and used by the Romans.[4] Geese were used as both the detector and notification appliance.

Early Technology

Security up to around the 1800s primarily involved the use of private and public security forces. Security was one aspect of their duties; watching for and sounding the alarm for a fire was another. This early linkage of fire and security marked the beginnings of electronic security as we know it today.

Shane M. Clary, Ph.D., is vice-president for codes and standards compliance at Bay Alarm Company in Pacheco, California. He is chair of the Fundamentals of Fire Alarm Systems Technical Committee, is a member of the NFPA Standards Council, serves on several NFPA technical committees, and is the author of the *NFPA Pocket Guide to Electronic Security System Installation.*

The first telegraph was patented in 1837 by Samuel Morse. It occurred to William F. Channing[5] of Boston, Massachusetts, that one should be able to use the technology of the telegraph to transmit the signal of a fire alarm. Up until this time, the transmission of the signal was done manually, generally by ringing bells to alert the fire companies. The use of electricity was new, however, and it was not until 1851 that the first system was approved for installation in Boston. By this time, Channing had teamed up with Moses G. Farmer, an electrical engineer who improved on the original design of the telegraph. This system was the first auxiliary municipal telegraph system, which used a series of 40 signal boxes, consisting of over 40 miles of wire installed throughout Boston and connected to a central station that would receive the signals. The system went operational on April 29, 1852.[6]

As word of this system spread, John N. Gamewell saw the potential of these systems in other cities. By 1859 he has secured most of the U.S. patents for this new technology. Unfortunately, the Civil War got in the way. Gamewell, being a native of South Carolina, was viewed by the United States government as being a supporter of the Confederacy. His patents were seized and sold. Gamewell was not able to return to his concepts and designs until after the end of the war.

While Gamewell continued to expand the fire alarm industry, Edwin Holmes was one of the first to see a need for electric burglar alarm protection. Holmes foresaw an industry that would be resistant to the financial swings of the time. He purchased the patent of Augustus R. Pope, who is thought to have patented the first burglar alarm system. Holmes set up his first shop in Boston, but the level of crime at that time was not sufficient to support an emerging industry. He therefore relocated to New York City. Even in the 1860s, intrusion detection systems were marketed as a deterrent to crime.[7]

The development of fire and burglar alarms continued on a parallel track. One of the most important innovations was the formation of the central station. A key contributor to this new technology was E. A. Calahan, who was also the inventor of the stock market ticker. In 1871, Calahan sold his central station patents to a syndicate of investors in New York City, who formed the American District Telegraph Company. By 1874, they had opened sixteen central stations in the New York City area, twelve being in Manhattan. A number of these central stations shared facilities with Western Union. Over time, American District Telegraph began to offer fire alarm systems in addition to burglar alarm systems. This did not go unnoticed by Gamewell, who in Boston, began to offer security systems.

A key development during this time was the invention of the McCulloh circuit. Up until this time, any break in the circuit would prevent signals from being received until the fault was cleared. Chauncey F. McCulloh designed a circuit that restores or reroutes a circuit around a single fault. This greatly improved the reliability of the signal transmission from the premises to the central station.

As this work was being done, Holmes was developing sensor technology that could be used to automatically detect an intrusion. Systems up until this time were still manual, in that the building occupants had to trip the system to transmit a signal to the central station. This was before the use of telephones and was, at that time, the fastest way to summon assistance. Holmes used a system of protective wiring, metallic foil, and brass contacts. He also developed a use for the galvanometer with directly connected systems so that each premises system could have a unique identifier.

Shift in Technology

Some of the technology that was developed during the 1800s was still in use in the 1990s. Although McCulloh circuits have been replaced, directly connected circuits are still in use. The brass contact has been replaced by the reed contact switch and foil has been replaced by audio discriminators or glass break detectors. Advances in this technology have transitioned from McCulloh and direct connect circuits to digital dialers, long-range radio, and, within the past several years, broadband. Detection technology, as described later in this chapter, has moved from protective wiring, foil, and contacts to space protection, sound and vibration detection, and contacts. The security practitioner needs to know the strengths and weaknesses of both the transmission methods and detection technologies.

SECURITY VULNERABILITY ASSESSMENT

The practitioner must take into consideration the entire property to be protected and the level of the threat against which one is trying to provide protection. Before any design work can be performed, a security vulnerability assessment (SVA) must be performed. According to NFPA 730, an SVA is "a systematic and methodical process for the following: (1) Examining ways an adversary might exploit an organization's security vulnerabilities to produce an undesired outcome [and] (2) developing countermeasures to address adversarial events." NFPA 730 further describes an SVA as "a technique for assessing the current status of an organization's threat exposures, security features and preparedness and can be used in developing and strengthening both security and safety layers of protection."[8]

Steps of an SVA

NFPA 730 outlines seven steps that should be taken as part of the SVA.

Formation of a Team. The team may be made up of both outside experts and key members of the facility to be protected. The goal is to receive as much relevant input as possible to design a system or program that will meet the needs of the end users.

Organization/Facility Characterization. This step involves the identification of assets; physical features and operations; laws, regulations and corporate polices; social and political environment; and internal activities.

Threat Assessment. Threat assessment includes the classification of critical assets, identification of potential targets, consequence analysis, and definition of potential threats.

Threat/Vulnerability Analysis. The threat/vulnerability analysis includes the identification of actual and potential threat scenarios and estimation of a relative security risk level.

Define the Specific Security Countermeasures. All the information obtained in the first four steps are analyzed to develop effective countermeasures to mitigate the defined threats and reduce the security risk.

Assess Risk Reduction. Take into account the countermeasures defined in Step 5 and reassess the relative security risk levels that were developed in Step 4 and consider additional security risk reduction measures that may be appropriate.

Document Findings and Track Implementation. Produce a written document of the findings and recommendations. The report would also track the implementation of the accepted recommendations.

With respect to Step 5 (Define the Specific Security Countermeasures), the practitioner should consider how to increase existing security layers for the premises. There should be a focus on the concentric circles of protection design methodology, as shown in Figure 14.10.1.

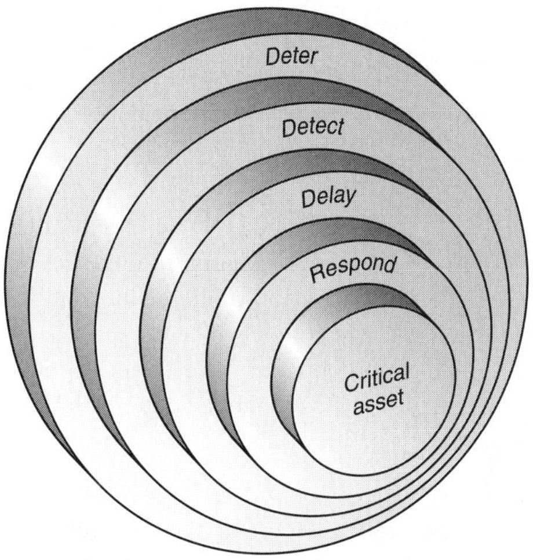

FIGURE 14.10.1 Concentric Circles of Protection (Source: NFPA 730, *Guide for Premises Security,* 2006, Figure A.5.2.5)

Primary Protection Elements

The SVA methodology considers four primary protection elements: deter, detect, delay, and respond.

- *Deter:* discouraging an adversary from attempting an assault by reducing the likelihood of a successful attack
- *Detect:* determining that an undesirable event has occurred or is occurring; includes sensing the event, communicating the alarm to an attended location, and assessing the alarm
- *Delay:* impeding adversary penetration into a protected area
- *Respond:* counteracting adversary activity and interrupting the undesirable event

The threat level may be placed into three categories as shown in Table 14.10.1.

OVERVIEW OF PHYSICAL SECURITY

Security for the protection of a premises can be divided into two broad categories: physical security (environmental design) and electronic security.

TABLE 14.10.1 Threat Analysis Guidelines

Threat Level	*Nature of Threat*	*Required Capabilities*
Low	Stand off surveillance/espionage Minimum/occasional penetration Limited pilferage Minor demonstrations	Denial of surveillance and penetration Detection and deterrence of intruders Selective surveillance of critical areas Apprehension of pilferers
Medium	All of low threat intensified Sabotage Harassment Minor destruction and disablement Dissident demonstrations	Intensify response to low threat Earlier detection Immediate response (small groups) Increased mobility of response forces Identification and location of sabotage Capture of intruders
High	All of medium threat intensified Organized attack/armed conflict Major destruction Combat intelligence	Intensify response to medium threat Complete penetration denial Immediate response (large and small groups) Armed resistance, capture, destroy Sabotage detection and prevention Remote controlled and/or automated response capability Interface with allied forces

Crime Prevention Through Environmental Design (CPTED)

Generally, when one thinks of physical security, an image of fences, gates, and exterior lighting may come to mind. Although these are all forms of physical security, the practitioner must take into consideration the entire site, and if practicable the local environment as well. Crime prevention through environmental design (CPTED) is a holistic approach in which individual citizens and law enforcement come together to apply security concepts to entire neighborhoods or major urban districts, as well as urban subsystems such as a public venue.[9] CPTED is made up of four general principles:

- *Natural surveillance:* provides features that allow for intruders to be readily seen; this would include windows and doors that face streets and well-lit parking lots and sidewalks
- *Territorial reinforcement:* creates a sphere of influence; sets and defines the private property and spaces from public property and spaces
- *Natural access control:* creates a perception of risk; provides gateways that are clearly public and discourages access to private areas
- *Target hardening:* uses window locks, door locks, fencing

Although CPTED should be considered for new large-scale projects or in areas that over time have demonstrated a history of security-related issues, it may not be warranted or possible for a single site.

Role of the Site Survey

Before beginning any security-related project, the practitioner needs to conduct a site survey. Even if the project has yet to be constructed, the designer needs to review the local environment in which the facility will be located. This would include a review of crime statistics for the geographic area. If the facility already exists, the practitioner needs to perform an extensive review of the security features that are in place as well as the general construction of the facility.

CONSIDERATIONS FOR A SITE SURVEY

A site survey deals with the exterior of a premises. Several key components should be taken into consideration when performing an examination or specifying physical security:

- Physical barriers
- Lighting
- Locks
- Glazing
- Passive barriers

Physical Barriers

Physical barriers can be both natural and structural. Natural barriers include mountains, cliffs, canyons, rivers, or other terrain that is difficult to traverse. Structural barriers include fences, walls, bollards, floors, and roofs.

One of the most common types of fence used today is the chain-link. Chain-link fencing can be used almost anywhere there is a need to define the physical boundaries of a facility. To be most effective, a chain-link fence should be designed and installed to a nationally recognized standard. For chain-link fencing this standard is ASTM F567, *Standard Practice for the Installation of Chain-Link Fence*.

When possible, the fence line should be located no closer than 50 ft (15.2 m) to the buildings or outside storage areas, and 20 ft (6.1 m) to other areas. Chain-link fencing comes in a variety of heights; the most common for commercial and industrial use is 8 ft (2.4 m). Depending on the risk to the premises, greater heights can be specified. When an 8 ft (2.4 m) fence is specified, 7 ft (2.1 m) is for the fabric and the top foot is for a top guard. Posts are used to secure the fabric. For a fence with 7 ft (2.1 m) of fabric height, the posts should be set in concrete at a minimum depth of 36 in. (0.9 m). The line posts should be spaced equidistant at intervals not exceeding 10 ft (3 m). End posts, if used, should be set within 2 in. (50 mm) of building walls. A top tension wire should be provided as a support for the fence fabric. A top rail can also be used if appearance is critical but should be avoided as it provides a handhold for one that is attempting to climb over the fence. The fabric of a fence should be steel wire, No. 9 gauge or heavier. The fabric needs to be stretched taught and securely fastened to the posts. The bottom of the fabric should extend to within 2 in. (50 mm) of the hard ground or paving. For soft ground, the fabric should extend below the ground. The top of the fence should be provided with a top guard to deter attempts at climbing the fence. A top guard should be made up of three strands of No. 12 gauge barbed wire, at an angle of approximately 45°. For those facilities that require a higher level of protection, razor ribbon should be considered.

Lighting

The purpose of lighting is to provide and enhance visibility and deter intrusion. The use of protective lighting should be considered both along the fence line and the outside of the premises. Table 14.10.2 provides the recommended minimum illumination levels for fencing. Table 14.10.3 gives recommended minimum intensities for outdoor protective lighting for pedestrian and vehicle use areas among others. The practitioner should also

TABLE 14.10.2 Recommended Minimum Illumination Levels for Fencing

Location	*Footcandles (on horizontal plane at ground level)*
Perimeter of outer area	0.15
Perimeter of restricted area	0.4
Vehicular entrances	1.0
Pedestrian entrances	2.0
Entrances (inactive)	0.1

Source: NFPA 730, *Guide for Premises Security,* 2006, Table 6.4.6.1. Originally in U.S. Army Field Manual 19-30, 1979.

TABLE 14.10.3 Recommended Minimum Intensities for Outdoor Protective Lighting

Location	*Footcandles (on horizontal plane at ground level)*
Perimeter of outer area	0.15
Perimeter of restricted area	0.4
Vehicular entrances	1.0
Pedestrian entrances	2.0
Sensitive inner areas	0.15
Sensitive inner structures	1.0
Entrances (inactive)	0.1
Open yards	0.2
Docks/piers	1.0

Source: NFPA 730, *Guide for Premises Security,* 2006, Table 6.5.2.1. Originally in U.S. Army Field Manual 19-30, 1979.

consult the *Lighting Handbook*, 9th edition, published by the Illuminating Engineering Society of North America (IESNA).

There are a number of light sources that may be considered, based upon the application, including incandescent, fluorescent, and high-intensity discharge (HID). Types of HID lamps include mercury vapor, metal halide, and high-pressure sodium. In addition to the light source, the luminaire must also be considered. The luminaire is a complete lighting unit consisting of a lamp or lamps together with the parts designed to distribute the light, to position and protect the lamps, and to connect the lamps to a power source. The four general types of luminaires used for protective lighting are floodlights, streetlights, Fresnel lens units, and searchlights.

Locks

As mentioned above, locks in one form or another have been around since around 3000 B.C. Table 14.10.4 shows the categories and subcategories of locking systems that are in use today. The practitioner must take into account the level of protection required, the type of door or access portal in which the locking system is to be installed, and the type of key control system that is to be used. If tracking of personnel entering or leaving a secured area is required, the use of an access control system should be considered.

TABLE 14.10.4 Lock Types

Category	*Type*
Mechanical locks	Mortice Rim
Electrical locks	Electric solenoid bolts Electric strikes (fail secure, fail safe) Monitor strikes Motor lock
Electromagnetic locks	Direct hold Shearlock

Source: *NFPA Pocket Guide to Electronic Security System Installation,* 2005, Exhibit IV.33.

Locks are designed to provide various levels of deterrence or delay to entrance. Prior to laying out any locking and access control system, NFPA *101*®, *Life Safety Code*®, *NFPA 5000*®, *Building Construction and Safety Code*®, or the locally adopted building and fire codes should be consulted. It is vital that individuals within a premises are not trapped inside during an emergency event.

Although locking mechanisms that act to prevent access to buildings, floors, or specific rooms are permissible, these locks can in no way impede free egress from the space.

Glazing

Glazing or windows provide a means for natural light from the outside of a premises to be transmitted to the inside. Glazing can also be one of the weakest points of protection for a building. A common method of gaining unauthorized entry into a building is by the method of "smash-and-grab." Glazing can be decorative as well as resistant to attack and bullets. The types of glazing material that can be designed to be burglary-resistant include laminated glass, acrylic, and polycarbonate. When selecting the type of burglary-resistant glazing material to use, the practitioner should use UL 972, *Standard for Burglary Resistant Glazing Material*, 2002, and UL's *Burglary Protection Equipment Directory* as a guide. The directory may also be accessed via the Internet at http://database.ul.com/cgi-bin/XYV/template/LISEXT/1FRAME/index.htm.

In addition to the types of glazing material shown, these materials with the addition of composites may be used for bullet-resisting glazing material. Underwriters Laboratories (UL) has established eight ratings for bullet-resisting glazing material, Levels 1 through 8, based on penetration resistance from medium-, high-, and superpower small arms; high-powered hunting and sporting rifles; submachine guns; assault rifles; and shotguns.

Passive Barriers

Passive barriers, designed to blend into the background of a building or site as a design feature, are in place to deter or delay an attack—not only the smash-and-grab attack but also the crash-and-grab, in which a truck or other vehicle is driven into a building. This method of attack can be used not only for burglary but also by a hostile force attempting to place an explosive device in or near a building. The basic types of passive barriers are concrete planters, bollards, and Jersey barriers. See Figures 14.10.2 through 14.10.4 for examples of each.

VAULTS AND SAFES

Depending on the facility and its use, the practitioner may also have to consider using vaults and safes.

Vaults

The practitioner should be familiar with UL 608, *Burglary Resistant Vault Doors and Modular Panels.* There are four

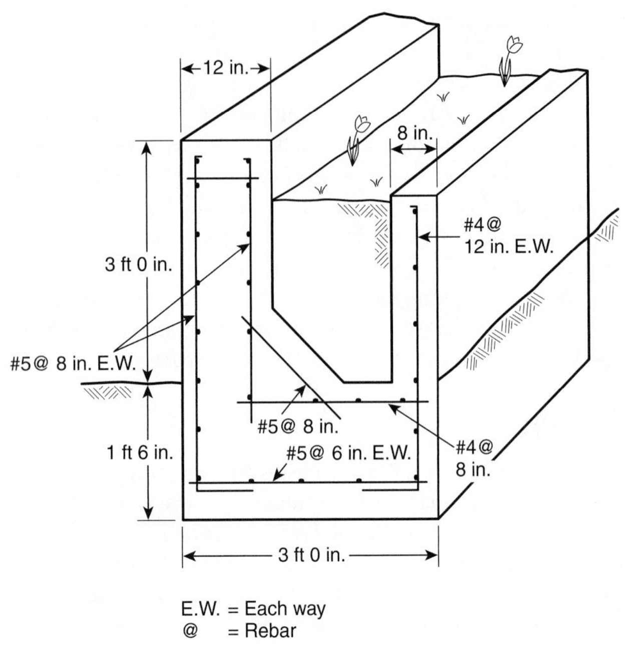

FIGURE 14.10.2 Concrete Planter (Source: NFPA 730, *Guide for Premises Security,* 2006, Figure 6.9.1.1)

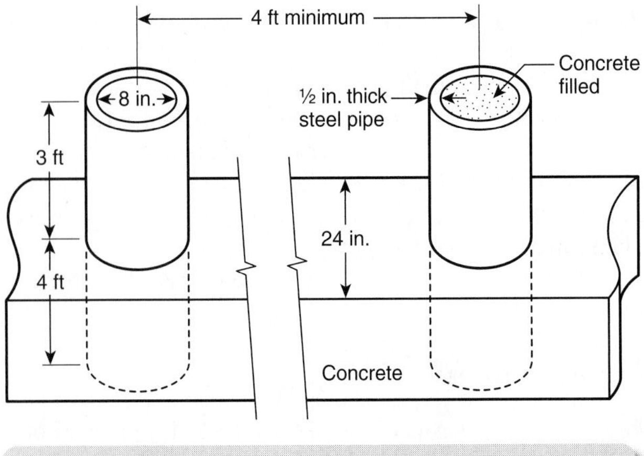

FIGURE 14.10.3 Concrete-Filled Bollard (Source: NFPA 730, *Guide for Premises Security,* 2006, Figure 6.9.2.1)

classifications for vault doors and walls, based on the time that the vault will resist the efforts of an attack:

- Class M ¼ hour
- Class 1 ½ hour
- Class 2 1 hour
- Class 3 2 hours

Alternate means of vault construction allows the use of reinforced concrete, steel lining, reinforced concrete blocks, or a combination of these materials. Table 14.10.5 shows the reinforced concrete equivalencies for the four types of UL-listed vault doors and modular panels.

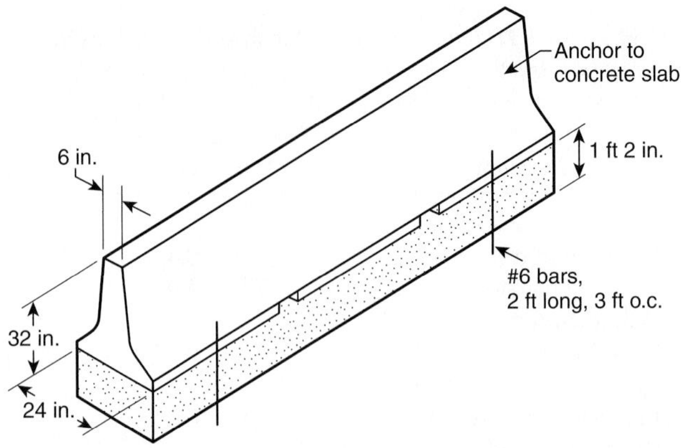

FIGURE 14.10.4 Jersey Barrier (Source: NFPA 730, *Guide for Premises Security,* 2006, Figure 6.9.3)

Safes

If the use of a safe is being considered, the practitioner should refer to UL 687, *Burglary Resistant Safes*. UL rates burglary-resistant safes according to the length of time a safe will resist attack. A UL label affixed to the door of the safe will identify that the safe has been listed by UL. UL-listed safes must also have a combination lock rated as Group 1 or 1R in accordance with UL 768, *Standard for Combination Locks*, and have a relocking device. The group rating signifies the ability of a mechanical lock to withstand expert manipulation. A Group 1 lock must be able to withstand 20 man-hours of expert manipulation. The Group 1R lock has this same specification, as well as being X-ray resistant. The UL-listed safe must also weigh a minimum of 750 lbs (340.2 kg) or be provided with a means of anchoring the safe to the premises. Table 14.10.6 shows UL-listed safe ratings.

COMPONENTS AND ISSUES IN ELECTRONIC SECURITY

Components of electronic security include central station monitoring, exterior and interior intrusion detection systems, access controls, and video surveillance. As mentioned previously, electric and now electronic security protection has been in place since the 1850s. Although the basic principles remain the same, the methods and technology have changed. The first advances from the technology of the 1800s occurred with the development of the ultrasonic detector by Sam Bagno[10] in 1948. This was the first form of volumetric protection using the Doppler effect to trigger the system.

Central Station Monitoring

The second great advance was the use of multiplex and the digital dialer. Prior to this innovation, signals were transmitted to the central station by either the McCulloh circuit or by means of a direct wire connection. These two means of signal transmission limited the distance that the central station could be from the protected premises. Central stations were generally located

TABLE 14.10.5 Reinforced Concrete Equivalencies to UL-Listed Vault Doors and Modular Panels

UL Classification	Thickness of Reinforced Concrete *in.*	Thickness of Reinforced Concrete *cm*	*Reinforcement Number of Rows of #5 Rebars*	*Reinforcement Number of Grids of Expanded Metal*
Class M	9	22.9	2	2
Class 1	12	30.5	3	2
Class 2	18	45.7	4	3
Class 3	27	68.6	5	4

Source: NFPA 730, *Guide for Premises Security,* 2006, Table 7.5.3.1.2.

near a telephone company's central office. During the 1960s the telephone companies began to notify the industry that copper or metallic circuits would in time no longer be available for use. These circuits were classified by the telephone industry as being Series 1000, which only carried direct current. The telephone industry now had Series 3000 circuits, which were of voice grade and carried alternating current. These circuits provided faster transmission rates and more data to be sent and received. Although there were attempts to digitize the McCulloh signal, by 1974 AT&T abandoned its efforts.

By the mid 1970s, a number of firms provided multiplex transmitters and receivers. Despite being more expensive than

TABLE 14.10.6 Safe Ratings

Rating	*Attack Tools*	*Body Construction*	*Area(s) of Attack*	*Entry Requirements*	*Attack Times*
TL-15	Common hand tools, picking tools, mechanical or portable electric tools, grinding points, carbide drills, and pressure applying devices and mechanisms	One-in. (25.4 mm) open hearth steel, or its equivalent, having a tensile strength of 50,000 psi (3,515,347 g/cm^2) or equivalent material	Door and front face	Opening the door or making a 6 in.^{2} (38.71 cm^2) opening	15 minutes
Record Safe	Same as TL-15 and including fishing and trapping devices and mechanisms			Same as TL-15 and including fishing and trapping	
TL-30	Same as TL-15 and including abrasive cutting wheels and power saws			Same as TL-15	30 minutes
TRTL-30	Same as TL-30 and including the oxyacetylene torch	Same as TL-15, with body encased in 3 in. (36.2 mm) of reinforced concrete or constructed of equivalent material	Door and front face	Opening the door or making a 2 in.^{2} (12.9 cm^2) opening	30 minutes
TL-15×6	Same as TL-30	Composite materials	Door and body	Same as TL-15	15 minutes
TL-30×6					30 minutes
TRTL-15×6	Same as TL-30 plus impact tools	Composite materials	Door and body	Same as TRTL-30	15 minutes
TRTL-30×6					30 minutes
TRTL-60×6					60 minutes
TXTL-60×6	Same as TRTL-15×6 plus explosives				

Notes: TL = Tool resistant.
TRTL = Torch and tool resistant.

Source: *NFPA Pocket Guide to Electronic Security System Installation,* 2005. Originally in UL 687, *Standard for Burglary Resistant Safes,* Underwriters Laboratories, Northbrook, IL, 2000.

McCulloh and direct wire, they did provide more information from the protected premises than the former technologies. The central station could now begin to receive zone annunciation from a single transmitter, allowing the central station to have a clearer picture of where the signal was coming from within the protected facility. As the multiplex system was constantly poling between the receiver and the transmitters, the central station could always be aware of the status of the phone line and the transmitter. With further advances in cryptographic transmission methods, multiplex transmissions are still used today for high-security assets.

But multiplex did not solve the larger problem of freeing the central station industry from its dependence on the Bell Operating Companies. Developed during the late 1970s and early 1980s, the digital dialer allowed the transmission of signals via Plain Old Telephone Service (POTS) lines. With the release and use of this technology, the central station was no longer required to be near the central office. A new industry of third-party central stations came into being, and the local alarm company no longer had to maintain their own central station. Today, although there are a number of firms that operate their own central stations, the majority of firms use a third-party central station. Although either type of firm can provide a high level of service, the practitioner should inquire into the location of the central station and whether it is operated by the security provider. In some cases, the central station may be located thousands of miles from the protected premises. The practitioner should always review the signal handling protocols of the central station and be aware of any restrictions that the local law enforcement provider might have placed on the response to alarms.

Issues in Electronic Security

Enhanced Call Verification. At the present time, a number of law enforcement agencies are requiring the use of Enhanced Call Verification, in which the protected premise and then a subscriber are contacted prior to making a service call. Although this has been successful in reducing the number of false alarms, it does insert a delay in the actual response. A number of agencies have promulgated ordinances that there is to be no response until the alarm is physically verified to ensure that an intrusion has occurred. This is a new concept. In bygone days, the police would respond prior to a third party verifying that an actual break-in had occurred.

Line Security. Digital dialers or communicators have one weakness that other transmission methods do not have, which is line security. When the phone line is cut from a premises that has a digital dialer, the central station will not be made aware of the loss. Other forms of signal transmission, including McCulloh, direct wire, multiplex, derived channel and long-range radio, provide the central station with an indication that a break has occurred. The practitioner needs to determine during the risk assessment phase if a backup communications path is required. The most common methods today are via cellular phone transmission or long-range radio. These methods may also be used as the primary path. If POTS is to serve as the primary means, the phone line should be supervised, either locally or by a second path. The supervision detects the voltage on the phone line. When the voltage is decreased or cannot be detected, the alarm control unit at the premises will activate a local trouble alarm or will transmit a supervisory signal over the second path to the central station. The practitioner should either review or specify the procedure that will be followed by the central station and the responsible party of the premises in the event of a lost phone line.

Broadband Communications. At the time that this chapter was written, broadband communications or the Internet was starting to be used for signal transmission. As with any new technology, there may be bends in the road before the final results are known. The practitioner should verify the operation of this method of signal transport if it is to be considered.

ELECTRONIC SECURITY AND INTRUSION DETECTION SYSTEMS

Intrusion detection systems can protect both the exterior and interior of a premises. The security practitioner should be familiar with NFPA 731, *Standard for the Installation of Electronic Premises Security Systems*, when laying out an intrusion detection system, closed-circuit television (CCTV) system, or access control system. One of the objectives of the risk assessment and site survey is to determine the level of protection to be provided. In addition to physical security as discussed previously, various forms of electronic security may also be seen as being appropriate.

UL Certification

Depending on the value of the property being protected, the practitioner may specify that the installed intrusion detection system be certificated by Underwriters Laboratories Inc. UL provides third party oversight and review of security systems that are installed in accordance with UL 681, *Standard for Installation and Classification of Burglar and Holdup Alarm Systems*. UL 681 provides a number of levels of protection or extents that the designer can specify. As the extent of protection increases, the level of detection within the premises increases. Table 14.10.7 provides an overview of the UL protection extents.

Exterior Detection

Exterior sensors must have a high probability of detection for all types of intrusions and a low unwanted-alarm rate for all expected environmental and site conditions.

The designer, in addition to the threat and risk assessment, needs to take into consideration the cost of the protection, both the equipment and its installation, as well as the cost of maintaining the equipment after the installation. For example, methods and equipment used for a power plant may not be required for a lumber storage yard.

Exterior devices include the following, several of which will be discussed in more detail:

- Audio
- Contacts
- Motion detection

TABLE 14.10.7 Extents of Intrusion Detection Protection for Premises and Stockrooms

		External Openings				External Surfaces	
	Extent of Protection	*Accessible*	*Inaccessible*	*Movable Accessible*	*Movable Inaccessible*	*Walls, Floors, and Ceilings*	*Special Considerations*
4		Partial (2)					Contacts on at least two interior doors; or motion or sound detection on one or more selected areas; or one or more channels of radiation to limit movement within the premises.
3	Perimeter	Complete					
	Motion (4)			Partial (2,5)			Four-step (6) movement in each enclosed area with external openings.
	Sound			Partial (5)			Sound detectors in each enclosed area with external openings. Limited to buildings with good acoustical qualities.
	Channels			Partial (5)			Minimum length of beams equal to longest dimension of each enclosed area with external openings. Motion detectors can be used for channel protection.
2	Perimeter	Complete (3)			Partial (5)	Complete (7)	Exterior surfaces of monolithic concrete do not require protection.
	Motion			Partial (5)			Four-step (6) movement in each enclosed area with external openings.
	Sound			Partial (5)			Sound detectors in each enclosed area with external openings. Limited to buildings with good acoustical qualities.
	Channels	Complete (3)					Beams arranged to divide each enclosed area with external surfaces into at least three subdivisions. Maximum 1000 ft^2 for each subdivision.
1	Perimeter	Complete (3)	Complete (3)			Complete (7)	Protective wiring installed on all external surfaces.
	Sound or Vibration			Partial (5)	Partial (5)		Detectors adjusted to initiate an alarm if a manhole size opening is created in an opening, ceiling, floor, or wall.

Notes

1. Accessible means less than 18 ft (5.5 m) for grade or adjacent roofs; less than 14 ft (4.3 m) from horizontal openings; or less than 3 ft (0.91 m) from openings on same wall.
2. Doors only.
3. Complete protection of an opening means wiring or other recognized means applied to protect the opening (fixed or movable) plus contacts on movable openings.
4. Motion detection is provided by equipment such as ultrasonic, microwave, and passive infrared motion detectors. It is installed throughout each area.
5. Partial protection means a contact installed on a movable opening.
6. Four-step movement is a means of confirming volumetric radiation coverage by performing a series of walk tests through the enclosed area.
7. Complete protection of a surface means wiring or other recognized means to protect a wall, floor, or ceiling.

Source: *NFPA Pocket Guide to Security System Installation,* 2005, Exhibit III.42. Originally in Richard L. Sampson (Chairman), *A Practical Guide to Central Station Burglar Alarm Systems*, Central Station Alarm Association, Bethesda, MD, 1997, Table 4.

- Fence strain system
- Protective cabling
- Electric-field system
- Proximity
- Shock sensors
- Stress sensors
- Photo-electric cell
- Leaky coaxial

Motion Detection. The principal type of motion detection used for exterior protection is the microwave. Microwave detection sensors are categorized as bistatic or monostatic. Bistatic sensors use transmitting and receiving antennas located at opposite ends of the microwave link. Monostatic use the same antenna. Care should be taken when selecting a microwave detection system so that the field of detection does not extend beyond the area to be protected. Microwave energy can extend beyond the intended target area and cause false alarms from movement outside of the protected field.

When it has been determined that a fence is to be protected by a detection system, a paramount consideration in selecting the detection system is that the false or unwanted alarm rate is low. The fence itself must be in good condition and meet the minimum requirements of the detector's manufacture.

Fence-Strain System. The fence-strain system uses cables as transducers that are uniformly sensitive along their entire length. They generate an analog voltage when subject to mechanical distortions or stress resulting from fence motion.

Electric-Field System. An electric-field system consists of an alternating-current field generator, one or more field wires and one or more sensing wires, and a signal processor. The generator excites the field wires around which an electrostatic field pattern is created. The electrostatic field induces electrical signals in the sense wires, which are monitored by the signal processor.

Capacitance-Sensor System. A capacitance-sensor or proximity sensor measures the electrical capacitance between the ground and an array of sense wires. Any change in capacitance caused by an intruder approaching or touching one or more of the sense wires initiates an alarm.

Leaky Coaxial Cable System. Leaky coaxial cable (LCX) has been used for a number of years for perimeter protection. This method is also referred to as a ported cable system. The system involves lining the perimeter with two parallel LCX cables buried just below the surface of the ground. The depth is determined by the manufacture and coverage the designer wishes to obtain. These cables are generally buried in soil, but they can also be placed underneath asphalt and concrete. The LCX cable is slotted or ported so as to allow RF energy to be released. Two LCX cables are run parallel, one for transmission and the second for receiving. This generates a constant volume of EM field above the ground. Movement of objects with high capacitive properties above the cables will disturb the field, leading to detection when the coupled signal deviates from the stable reference signal.[11]

Interior Detection

Interior detection includes both perimeter and space detection. Perimeter protection is installed along the perimeter of the premises—doors, windows, walls, and roofs. Space protection provides detection within the interior of the premises.

Interior devices include the following, several of which are discussed further:

- Protective wiring
- Foil
- Traps
- Shock sensors
- Glass break sensors
- Sound detectors
- Motion detectors

Protective Wiring. Protective wiring is primarily found in older systems. The designer may find these methods useful for the protection of vents, skylights, and high windows. Protective wiring within mesh screens are still in common use for residential applications.

Shock Sensors. Shock sensors detect any vibration caused by attempted forced entry. The practitioner should take care in their application and avoid locations subject to high vibrations.

Glass Break Sensors. Glass break sensors are both audio (sound discriminators) and shock. They are activated by the frequency of breaking glass, or a combination of the frequency of breaking glass and the shock or vibration to the structure of the glass being broken. The use of glass break detectors has replaced the used of foil as the principal method of protecting glass. The practitioner should be aware that the placement of various films on the glazing material may dampen the effectiveness of the detector.

Sound Detectors. Sound or audio detectors can be used effectively to protect enclosed areas, vaults, warehouses, and similar enclosures. Microphone speaker sensors are installed on walls and ceilings of the protected area. The sensitivity of the system can be adjusted.

Motion Detectors. Motion detectors include microwave, passive infrared (PIR), two or more technologies (hybrid), and video motion. As discussed previously, the first form of motion detection was ultrasonic. Due to a high probability of false alarms, this method of space detection is rarely used today. The designer must use care in selecting and placing these detectors. Improper placement of these otherwise effective devices causes false and unwanted alarms.

Microwave. Microwave detectors used for interior detection are typically monostatic. The shape of the transmitted beam is a function of the antenna configuration. A variety of detection patterns can be generated. Movement in the area will produce a Doppler frequency shift in the reflected signal and will produce an alarm if the signal satisfies the sensor's alarm criteria. Microwave detectors are best at detecting movement toward and away from the source. The practitioner should use care in selecting and placing this detection technology. Microwave energy can pass through glass doors and windows as well as lightweight walls or partitions constructed of plywood, plastic, or fiberboard. Microwave motion detectors are also susceptible to fluorescent lighting.

Passive Infrared. Passive infrared motion sensors detect a change in the thermal energy pattern caused by a moving intruder and initiate an alarm when the change in energy satisfies the detector's alarm criteria. The sensor's detection pattern is determined by the arrangement of lenses or reflectors. The pattern is not continuous but consists of a number of fingers, one for each mirror or lens segment. Numerous detection patterns are available, and the designer should select the one which meets the requirements of the protected space. PIR motion sensors are best at detecting movement across the field of view. PIR detectors should not be pointed toward a heat source or outside window that may catch the lights of traffic during the evening hours. Under no circumstances is a PIR motion detector that is listed for security to be used as part of an automatic fire detection system.

Video Motion. Video motion detection (VMD) combines space protection and closed-circuit TV (CCTV). A camera is mounted to cover the field of view. The active component for the VMD is not within the camera, but is a part of the processing equipment that is located at the receiving and viewing end of the system. During the programming of the system, active cells are selected within the field of view that is displayed by a camera to the monitor. When an object passes through an active field, the VMD will detect the movement and trigger an alarm. Detection is caused by the stable static view being disturbed by the motion through the active cells within the field of view.

ELECTRONIC SECURITY AND ACCESS CONTROL

Another form of electronic security is the access control system. Access control systems can control, restrict, and track the flow of personnel and visitors through a protected premises. The components of an access control system are controllers, readers, and tokens and credentials.

Controller

The controller is the front end of most access control systems. The controller may be a stand-alone unit or integrated with a computer. The controller contains information related to time schedules, access groups, and enrolled personnel. Before laying out any access control system, the practitioner should be familiar with the operating protocols of the premises. For larger systems the use of groups and access areas may come into play.

Readers and Credentials

Readers and credentials are closely related. The type of reader selected will dictate the type of credential to be used, and vice versa. Card readers may be of the following types:

- Hollerith
- Magnetic stripe
- Barium ferrite (BaFe)
- Radio frequency identification (RFID) (Proximity)
- Bar code
- Wiegand

Table 14.10.8 compares these systems according to various factors.

For enhanced security the practitioner may use biometric readers, which require a unique data set from the holder of a credential. Biometric credentials may be one of the following:

- Hand/finger geometry

TABLE 14.10.8 Comparison of Reader/Card Technologies

Card Type	*Technology*	*Durability*	*Resistance to Compromise*	*Reprogramming*	*Cost*
Magnetic Stripe	Magnetic media stripe	M	M	Y	L
BaFe	Magnetic pattern	H	M	Y	L
Wiegand	Magnetic pattern	H	H	N	M
Bar Code	Light/dark patterns	L	L	N	L
Hollerith	Hole patterns	L	L	N	L
Proximity	Electromagnetic	H	H	N	M

Notes:
L = Low
M = Medium
H = High
Y = Yes
N = No

Source: *NFPA Pocket Guide to Electronic Security System Installation,* 2005. Originally in Gerard Honey, *Electronic Access Control,* Newnes, Oxford, UK, 2000, Table 3.2.

- Fingerprints
- Handwriting
- Eye scan
- Voice recognition
- Face recognition

VIDEO SURVEILLANCE

Video surveillance systems, or CCTV, allow one to view and capture images from a protected location. The basic CCTV system is made up of a camera and monitor. If the image is to be captured for future viewing, then a recording device is required. CCTV systems can vary from a single camera with no recording device, perhaps located in a small mercantile shop for the manager to view the sales floor from the office, to systems that have over 1000 cameras with multiple monitors and recording devices, such as in a gaming establishment. Systems can monitor conditions both inside and outside the building.

The most important question that the practitioner must consider is "What is to be viewed?" Is the target to be the transactions that occur at a point-of-sale or activity along an exterior fence line? Does the system need to make out a car's license plate number or just the type of vehicle? The entire image recorded is the *field of view*; the focus of attention, such as a license plate, is the *critical viewing area.* For cameras placed to record images at a point of customer transactions, such as a teller window, the critical viewing area (face) should cover 15 percent of the camera's field of view under normal resolution. Action within the scene should cover at least 20 percent or more of the overall width of the field of view. The designer should always consider the appearance of the final image when making camera and lens selections.

CCTV cameras that are produced today for the majority of systems are charge-coupled device (CCD) units. Table 14.10.9 provides an overview of the various types of CCD cameras that are available at the time this chapter was written.

CCD cameras come in a variety of imager formats, the most common being the following:

- ¼ in.
- ⅓ in.
- ½ in.
- ⅔ in.
- 1 in.

The imager format is the usable part of the imager that is to be used. It is measured diagonally across the chip. The format of the camera will affect the view provided by the lens selected. The practitioner must look at both the camera format and the lens in order to make certain that the view selected is the view achieved.

Field of View

One can calculate the field of view by scene width as shown in Equation 1 or by scene height as shown in Equation 2.

TABLE 14.10.9 CCD (Charge-Coupled Device Cameras)

Camera Type	*Light Type*	*IR Sensitivity*	*Resolution*	*Lag Time*	*Retain Image*	*Auto-Iris Lens*	*Expected Life*
C-MOS/CCD	Full/fairly consistent 20–50 lx	Extreme high 1050–1300 nm average	Good/fair—Inside Fair/poor—Outside 300–400 TVL	None	None	Dependent on application	3–5 years dependent on conditions
Interline Transfer CCD	Low/full variable 3–5 lx	Extreme high 1050–1300 nm average	Very good to good 350 TVL & up average	None	None	Dependent on application	3–5 years dependent on conditions
Frame Transfer CCD	Low/full variable 0.1–5 lx	Excellent 800–850 nm	Excellent to very good 400 TVL & up	None	None	Dependent on application	3–5 years dependent on conditions
Hyper HAD CCD	Note 1 1–50 lx	None	Very good to good 375 TVL & up	None	None	Dependent on application	3–5 years dependent on conditions
Intensified CCD	Low/full variable .003 lx	None Visible light only	Good to fair 275 to 400 TVL	Note 2	Chip-None Note 3	Always	1–2 years dependent on conditions

Editor's Note: The CCD camera is the most popular CCTV camera in use at this time. They are entirely solid state.

Notes:

1. Due to design of chip, telephoto lenses will produce a sharper image.
2. The method of light amplification that is used will determine the amount of lag time in lower light conditions.
3. It is possible to burn an image into the 2nd generation intensifier that may be used in these cameras.

nm = nanometers
TVL = TV lines

Source: Exhibit V.9, *NFPA Pocket Guide to Electronic Security System Installation,* 2005. Originally in Charlie Pierce, *Application & Design of CCTV,* LeapFrog Training & Consulting, Davenport, IA, 2002, p. 28.

$$f = c\left(\frac{d}{w}\right) \tag{1}$$

where

c = Width of the charge-coupled device (CCD) chip

d = Distance from camera

w = Width of field of view

f = Focal length of camera lens

$$f = v\left(\frac{d}{h}\right) \tag{2}$$

where

v = Height of CCD chip

d = Distance from camera

h = Height of field of view

f = Focal length of camer lens

Another method takes into account the total critical viewing area as a percentage of the monitor. If the critical object takes up only a quarter of the total field of view within the monitor, then it would be 25 percent of the view. If the critical object took a third of the total field of view it would be 33.3 percent of the view and so forth (Table 14.10.10). Calculate the viewing area of the scene and also of the critical viewing area by multiplying the horizontal and vertical dimensions. Divide the critical viewing area by the total viewing area to obtain the critical viewing area in the monitor.

If the proportion of the critical viewing area is as expected, use the calculated focal length. If not, then change the focal length until the correct proportion is found, or change the distance of the camera until the correct proportion is found. In some cases, the solution will be in a new lens being selected.

Lenses

Lenses come in a number of formats. Table 14.10.11 lists common lens formats used with CCD cameras. The designer should use a field of view calculator to make the final determination. These calculators are available from most lens manufacturers. To select the proper lens for the format of the camera and the field of view, the designer should make an object distance calculation (Figure 14.10.5). When calculating the target view of the camera, the object distance must be considered. In addition to the actual distance of the camera from the target, the height of the camera must also be taken into consideration. The Pythagorean theorem is used in part to calculate the actual view distance. The square root of the number calculated is the object distance. Once the actual object distance is known, the designer can calculate the target size for a given, as seen in Table 14.10.12. CCTV cameras use a 4:3 aspect ratio. As such, the vertical view will always be 75 percent of the size of the horizontal view.

TABLE 14.10.10 Viewing Area as a Percentage of the Monitor

Camera Formats (in.)	*Horizontal (mm)*	*Vertical (mm)*
1/4	3.2	2.4
1/3	4.4	3.3
1/2	6.4	4.8
2/3	8.8	6.6

Source: NFPA 731, *Standard for the Installation of Electronic Premises Security Systems,* 2005, Table B.1(c).

TABLE 14.10.11 Lens Formats

Focal Length	*Lens*	*Range*
4 mm	Very wide angle	4–6 ft (1.2–1.8 m)
8 mm	Wide angle	12 ft (3.6 m)
16 mm	Standard	25 ft (7.6 m)
25 mm	Telephoto	45 ft (13.7 m)
50 mm	Long telephoto	50–60 ft (5.2–18.3 m)

Source: *NFPA Pocket Guide to Security System Installation,* 2005, Exhibit V.20.

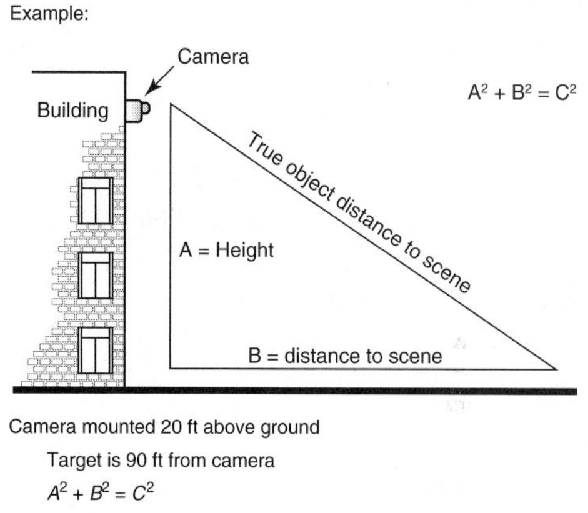

FIGURE 14.10.5 Object Distance Calculations (Source: *NFPA Pocket Guide to Security System Installation,* 2005, Exhibit V.21)

TABLE 14.10.12 Camera Formats

Camera format size	1/4 in.	1/3 in.	1/2 in.	2/3 in.	1 in.
Diagonal format	4 mm	5.5 mm	8 mm	11 mm	16 mm
Horizontal format	3.6 mm	4.8 mm	6.4 mm	8.8 mm	12.8 mm
Vertical format	2.7 mm	3.6 mm	4.8 mm	6.6 mm	9.6 mm

Source: *NFPA Pocket Guide to Security System Installation,* 2005, Exhibit V.22.

Depth of Field

Finally, when setting up an image to be viewed, lighting and depth of field must be considered. Depth of field is the region within the picture that will appear sharp in focus (Table 14.10.13). The format of the lens will affect the depth of field. The amount of available light will also affect the depth of field for a camera. In order to calculate the depth of field for an object that is not close to the camera, Equation 3 should be used.

Far Focus Limit

$$FF = (H \times D)/[H - (D - L)] \quad (3)$$

where

FF = Far focus limit (in mm)

H = Hyperfocal distance (in mm)

D = Lens focus distance (in mm)

L = Lens focal length

Example: 16 mm focal length, f-8 f-stop, ⅓ in. format, 150 ft focus distance (45.72 mm or 45,720 mm)

FF = (246,153 mm × 45,720 mm)/[246,153 mm – (45,720 mm – 16 mm)]

FF = 11,254,115,160 mm/246,153 mm – 45,704 mm

FF = 11,254,115,160 mm/200,449 mm

FF = 56,144 mm (56.144 m or 184 ft)

Editor's Note: In the example given, the object or target would be in focus. The hyperfocal distance is the plane on which everything within the view is at optimal focus.

To calculate the depth of field for an object that is close to the camera, Equation 4 should be used.

Near Focus Limit

$$NF = (H \times D)/[H + (D - L)] \quad (4)$$

where

NF = Near focus limit (in mm)

H = Hyperfocal distance (in mm)

D = Lens focus distance (in mm)

L = Lens focal length

Example: 16 mm focal length, f-8 f-stop, ⅓ in. format, 150 ft focus distance (45.72 mm or 45,720 mm)

NF = (246,153 mm × 45,720 mm)/[246,153 mm + (45,720 mm – 16 mm)]

NF = 11,254,115,160 mm/246,153 mm + 45,704 mm

NF = 11,254,115,160 mm/291,857 mm

NF = 38,560 mm (38.56 m or 126.5 ft)

To obtain the optimal image, in which the entire view would be in focus, Equation 5 would be used.

Hyperfocal Distance

$$H = (L \times L)/(f \times d) \quad (5)$$

where

H = Hyperfocal distance (in mm)

L = Lens focal length

f = Lens aperture f-stop

d = Diameter of circle of least confusion (in mm)

Example: 16 mm focal length, f-8 f-stop, ⅓ in. format

H = (16 mm × 16 mm)/(8 × 0.00013)

H = 256/0.00104

H = 246,153 mm

The circle of least confusion is the area that is out of focus before and after the hyperfocal distance. The circle is the area of greatest light concentration behind the lens but in front of the imager of the camera. See Table 14.10.14.

Recording

At the time that this chapter was written, the primary method of image storage was the digital video recorder (DVR). The number of images that can be stored on a single DVR is dependent on the size of the storage disk within the DVR, the image size, number of images per second, and quality.

SUMMARY

This chapter is only a snapshot of the knowledge base that the practitioner should understand prior to designing and specifying the security for a premises. The practitioner should also consult a number of the text references that are listed in the Bibliography.

TABLE 14.10.13 Depth of Field

Broad Depth of Field	*Narrow Depth of Field*
Wider angle of lens	More telephoto
More light	Less light

Source: *NFPA Pocket Guide to Security System Installation,* 2005, Exhibit V.29.

TABLE 14.10.14 Circle of Least Confusion

Format	*Circle of Least Confusion*
¼ in.	0.00019 mm
⅓ in.	0.00013 mm
½ in.	0.00009 mm
⅔ in.	0.00007 mm
1 in.	0.00005 mm

Source: *NFPA Pocket Guide to Security System Installation,* 2005, Exhibit V.31.

This chapter did not cover such topics as private security, data and information services security, pre-employment background checks, and a host of other subjects. Security can be both for the exterior and interior of the site. A site survey is an important step to be taken prior to any design or installation work being performed. A risk and vulnerability assessment should also be conducted. Present technology provides a vast variety of options that may be used in providing effective layers of protection and detection at a site. The objective of any security program is to deter, delay, detect and respond.

BIBLIOGRAPHY

References Cited

1. Greer, W., *A History of Alarm Security,* National Burglar and Fire Alarm Association, Bethesda, MD, 1991, p 1.
2. Greer, W., *A History of Alarm Security,* National Burglar and Fire Alarm Association, Bethesda, MD, 1991, p 1.
3. Judges 4.23: "Then Ehud went into the vestibule and locked them"; and Matthew 16.19: "the keys to the kingdom of heaven."
4. Greer, W., *A History of Alarm Security,* National Burglar and Fire Alarm Association, Bethesda, MD, 1991, p. 4.
5. Greer, W., *A History of Alarm Security,* National Burglar and Fire Alarm Association, Bethesda, MD, 1991, p. 19.
6. Greer, W., *A History of Alarm Security,* National Burglar and Fire Alarm Association, Bethesda, MD, 1991, p. 23.
7. Greer, W., *A History of Alarm Security,* National Burglar and Fire Alarm Association, Bethesda, MD, 1991, p. 39.
8. NFPA 730, *Guide for Premises Security,* Section 5.1.1, National Fire Protection Association, Quincy, MA, 2006.
9. Fennelly, L. J., *Effective Physical Security,* Elsevier Butterworth-Heinemann, Burlington, MA, 2004, p. 49.
10. Greer, W., *A History of Alarm Security,* National Burglar and Fire Alarm Association, Bethesda, MD, 1991, p. 120.
11. Wong, S. C., *Perimeter Security Using RF Coupled Leaky Coax System,* Duke University, Durham, NC, 2003, p. 3.

NFPA Codes, Standards, and Recommended Practices

Reference to the following NFPA codes, standards, and recommended practices will provide further information on security and intrusion systems discussed in this chapter. (See the latest version of The NFPA Catalog *for availability of current editions of the following documents.)*

NFPA *101®*, *Life Safety Code®*
NFPA 730, *Guide for Premises Security*
NFPA 731, *Standard for the Installation of Electronic Premises Security Systems*
NFPA 5000®, *Building Construction and Safety Code®*

SECTION

15

Water Supplies for Fixed Fire Protection

David R. Hague

Section 15 of the *Fire Protection Handbook*® is the first of three sections concentrating on the myriad forms of fire suppression. Because water is the most prevalent fire suppression agent and water supply can determine the success or failure of fire suppression efforts, it is appropriate that the first of this handbook's suppression sections addresses water supplies for fixed fire suppression.

Chapter 1, "Fixed Water Storage Supplies for Fire Protection," contains information on the design, installation, and maintenance of constructed water storage supplies and the ways in which naturally occurring surface and groundwater supplies can be used for fire protection. Of particular interest are the provisions described for preventing water stored for fire protection supplies from freezing during cold weather and maintaining stability and functionality following a seismic event.

Chapter 2, "Water Supply Requirements for Public Supply Systems," gives information on planning for public water supply systems and outlines the methods used to evaluate public supplies for their adequacy and reliability. Hydraulic calculations and the Insurance Services Office (ISO) grading schedule are introduced.

Chapter 3, "Hydraulics for Fire Protection," provides a more in-depth review of material introduced in Chapter 2. Topics covered include relevant formulae, coefficient of flow, flow measurement, elastic wave theory, friction loss, K-factor, and use of a Moody diagram.

The next two chapters explore water and automatic sprinkler systems. Chapter 4, "Water Supplies for Sprinkler Systems," identifies the types of water supplies that are acceptable for fire sprinkler systems and the variables that must be considered in the system design. Chapter 5, "Microbiologically Influenced Corrosion in Fire Sprinkler Systems," addresses MIC and biological growth control, which have been extensively researched in allied engineering fields, but whose treatment in fire sprinkler systems is relatively new.

Chapters 6 and 7 turn to the important topic of fire pumps used in fixed fire protection. Chapter 6, "Water Distribution," covers types of pumps, their principles of operation, curves, head, horsepower, drives, and tests. Chapter 7, "Fire Pump Controllers and Power Supply Arrangements for Motor-Driven Fire Pumps," focuses on the electrical and control aspects of electric motor-driven fire pump installations and is specific to fire pump controllers, motors, and electrical power supply arrangements. Chapter 7 was expanded for this edition of the handbook to introduce variable speed motor-driven fire pumps, their applications, and field experience.

David R. Hague, P.E., is principal fire protection engineer in NFPA's Systems and Applications Engineering Division.

SECTION 15

Chapter 1

Fixed Water Storage Supplies for Fire Protection

Revised by
Bruce A. Edwards

Chapter Contents

Key Terms

air lock, alternative water supply, fire pump, freezing prevention, static water supply, storage tank (elevated), storage tank (embankment-supported), storage tank (gravity), storage tank (ground-level), storage tank (suction), water supply

In a broad sense, fire protection water storage supplies include all bodies of water available as sources of supply, whether they are contained by constructed or natural barriers. Elevated, ground-level, or underground storage tanks of metal, wood, plastic, or rubberized fabric are examples of constructed storage facilities; rivers, ponds, and lakes, or other surface water sources are examples of natural storage facilities.

Open bodies of water, such as human-made reservoirs and freshwater pools created by the damming of streams, are sometimes used in private fire protection to supplement public water supplies or furnish the primary source of water for fire protection if public supplies are unavailable, insufficient in volume or pressure, or both or if they lack dependability. A common method of providing a fire protection water supply is to use elevated gravity tanks or ground-level suction tanks with fire pumps. Pressure tanks, with their limited capacity, may be used where storage requirements are relatively small or other means of storing water for fire protection are impractical.

This chapter contains information on the design, installation, and maintenance of constructed water storage supplies and the ways in which naturally occurring surface and groundwater supplies can be used for fire protection. Of particular interest are the provisions described for preventing water stored for fire protection supplies from freezing during cold weather and in seismic areas maintaining stability and functionality following a seismic event.

For related topics, see Section 13, Chapter 4, "Alternate Water Supplies"; Section 15, Chapter 4, "Water Supplies for Sprinkler Systems"; Section 15, Chapter 6, "Water Distribution"; and chapters in Section 16, "Water-Based Fire Suppression Equipment."

STORAGE TANKS (GRAVITY AND SUCTION)

The prevalence of the installation of hydraulically designed automatic fire sprinkler systems in new construction and renovations has reduced the reliance and use of elevated tanks for fire protection water supplies. The use of ground-level suction tanks, combined with fire pumps, has increased (Figure 15.1.1). Nevertheless, there are many elevated gravity tanks still in service used solely for fire protection water supplies, and they require high standards of maintenance to continue their reliability and functionality as sources for systems.

Tanks used for fire protection water supplies should not be used for any other purpose. In addition to negatively affecting the quantity of water and duration of flow available, tanks used for other purposes must usually be refilled frequently, and they become settling basins that collect large accumulations of sediment. When water is drawn from the tank, the sediment also is drawn into the yard or extinguishing system and may block the system.

If the tank is wood and is refilled frequently, the alternate drying and wetting of the lumber may appreciably shorten the life of the tank; with a steel tank, more frequent painting may be

Bruce A. Edwards is a senior underwriting specialist at Liberty Mutual Property in Weston, Massachusetts. He is chair of NFPA's Technical Committee on Water Tanks.

FIGURE 15.1.1 Suction Tank with Attached Pump House (Source: Columbian TecTank)

necessary, which means not only greater expense but also more time out of service.

Dual-purpose tanks will seldom be full, because domestic and industrial consumption constantly draws them down. In addition, the normal water level may continue to drop if the industry grows. If a fire occurs several years after the tank is installed, sufficient water at sufficient pressure might not be available. Should a dual-purpose tank be necessary, the outlet for the domestic and industrial supply should be set at a water level above the water dedicated for fire protection service.

Location

A gravity tank supported on an independent steel tower with foundations placed in the ground rather than on a building is the best arrangement. The tank should be built so that it will not be exposed to fire or physical damage. If lack of yard room makes this impossible, the exposed steelwork should be suitably protected by fire-resistant construction or coverings. The steel protection, when necessary, should include steelwork within 20 ft (6 m) of combustible buildings or openings from which fire might issue.

If the tank and supporting trestle are to be placed on the rooftop of a building, the building must be designed and constructed to carry the maximum load.

Suction tanks should be located so as to minimize yard piping. The pump house is generally placed close to the tanks to minimize suction piping. The tanks should not be located where they will be exposed to physical damage or fires from adjacent combustible construction or yard storage (Figure 15.1.2).

Design for Earthquake Resistance

Fire protection water storage tanks need to be designed to resist earth movement including earthquakes. In an earthquake, ground shaking sets up a rocking action and sloshing of water in the tank. These forces may produce stresses beyond those provided for in a design that allows only for ordinary dead, live, and wind loads. In areas where earthquakes are likely or possible, or where earthquake protection is required by local codes or authorities, fire protection water storage tanks should be designed to resist earthquakes. The primary goals are first to improve the reliability and likelihood that the fire protection system will remain in service after an earthquake and then to minimize potential water damage from a fire protection system

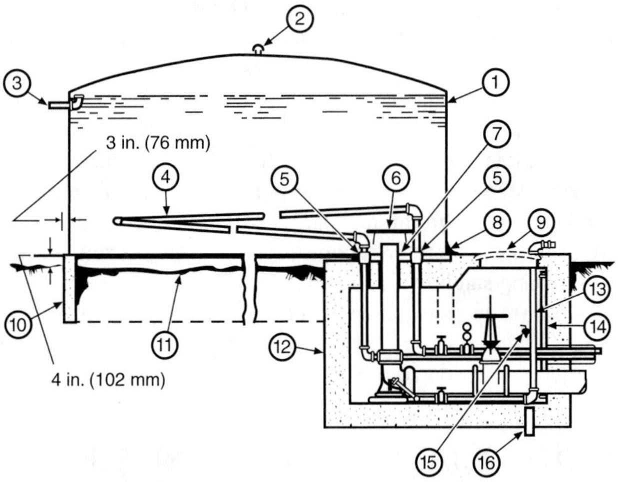

1. Pump suction tank
2. Screened vent
3. Stub overflow pipe
4. Steam coil for heating
5. Extra-heavy couplings welded to tank bottom
6. Vortex plate
7. Watertight lead slip joint
8. Flashing around tank
9. Manhole with cover
10. Concrete ring wall
11. Sand or concrete pad (depending on soil condition)
12. Valve pit
13. Drain pipe
14. Ladder
15. Drain cock
16. Valve pit drain

FIGURE 15.1.2 Ground-Level Suction Tank Showing the Discharge Pipe Connected to the Bottom of the Tank in a Valve Pit (Source: FM Global Property Loss Prevention Data Sheet 3-2, "Water Tanks for Fire Protection." © 2006 FM Global. Reprinted with permission. All rights reserved.)

leakage, with an understanding of the unpredictable nature of the size and severity of seismic events.

Water tanks and reservoirs fall into three categories—ground-level tanks, elevated tanks, and embankment-supported tanks.

Ground-Level Tanks. Ground-level tanks that either provide a suction supply for an adjacent fire pump or act as gravity tanks to provide sufficient water pressure for the fire protection system are the most common type in areas where seismic protection is required. For ground-level tanks, the four main seismic considerations are as follows:

1. Flexibility of pipe connections to tank. When the tank discharge pipe runs horizontally to a pump, two flexible couplings on the pipe should be provided between the tank and the pump. One should be as close to the tank wall as possible and the other within 24 in. (0.6 m) of the pump. When the tank discharge pipe feeds into an underground main, two flexible couplings must be provided between the tank and the ground entrance. One should be as close to the tank wall as possible; the other should be within 24 in. (0.6 m) of the ground entrance.
2. Anchorage of the tank and foundation to prevent horizontal and vertical displacement. Ground-level tanks should be anchored for seismic protection for the appropriate seismic ground motion. Additionally, the foundation design, which is often done separately from the tank design, should be coordinated with the tank design to ensure that the foundation is of sufficient size and mass to prevent rocking of the tank. Anchorage and foundation design details are best provided and/or reviewed by a qualified structural engineer. American Water Works Association standards D100, *Welded Steel Tanks for Water Storage,* and D103, *Factory-Coated Bolted Steel Tanks for Water Storage,* provide seismic design criteria for anchorage of tanks.
3. Clearance around pipe penetrations through pump house or other structural walls. At least 2 in. (50 mm) clearance should be provided on all sides of piping that passes through structural walls or other fixed structures.
4. Proper steel thickness near base of tank to avoid elephant footing. In areas with a high probability of strong ground motion, unanchored tanks may have significant vertical and horizontal displacements. Depending on the diameter of the tank and the height-to-diameter ratio, these expected displacements may vary. However, the main point is that unanchored tanks may create displacements that may not only damage the tank but also rupture the attached piping.

Elevated Tanks. Elevated tanks, where the tank body is mounted on legs or a pedestal, are less common in areas where seismic protection is required. Because of the complexity of any seismic analysis for this type of tank, a qualified structural engineer can best handle seismic analysis and design.

Embankment-Supported Tanks. Embankment-supported fabric tanks have an earthen embankment that supports a lined reservoir. Because of the complexity of any seismic analysis for this type of tank, seismic analysis and design are best handled by a qualified structural engineer.

Tank Capacities

Today it is usually uneconomical to install a gravity tank big enough and tall enough to be connected directly into the fire protection system and furnish an adequate supply for both hose streams from hydrants and water-based fire protection systems.

Years ago, because of limited capacity and pressure requirements, a gravity tank holding at least 30,000 gal (114 m^3) with its bottom at least 75 ft (22.9 m) above the ground could adequately supply both hose lines from hydrants and the extinguishing systems. Storage tank selection is still determined by the capacity and pressure required for both hose streams and areas' fire sprinklers for the possible duration of a fire; but because of the increased design density requirements of today, the suction tank and pump are often more economical than a gravity tank or gravity tank and booster pump.

Gravity and suction tanks are generally erected in standard sizes (Tables 15.1.1 and 15.1.2). The capacity required is determined by the intended use of the tank and is specified in the number of gallons (cubic meters) available from the tank (1 gal = 0.00379 m^3).

Steel gravity tanks are constructed on single pedestals or with suspended bottoms erected on towers with four columns for capacities from 50,000 to 200,000 gal (190 to 750 m^3) inclusive, six columns for capacities from 200,000 to 300,000 gal (750 to 1100 m^3) inclusive, and eight columns for tanks over 300,000 gal (over 1100 m^3).

Construction of Tanks

Existing gravity tanks are built of wood or steel and are supported by steel towers. Most new gravity tanks are built of steel

TABLE 15.1.1 Standard Sizes of Gravity Tanks

Steel Tanks		Wood Tanks		Standard Height	
gal	*m³**	*gal*	*m³**	*ft*	*m**
30,000	115	30,000	114	75	22.9
40,000	150	40,000	150	100	30.5
50,000	190	50,000	190	125	38.1
60,000	230	60,000	230	150	45.7
75,000	290	75,000	290	—	—
100,000	380	100,000	380	—	—
150,000	570	—	—	—	—
200,000	760	—	—	—	—
300,000	1100	—	—	—	—
400,000	1480	—	—	—	—
500,000	2000	—	—	—	—

*Figures rounded off as approximations from nominal customary American tank sizes.

TABLE 15.1.2 Common Sizes of Steel Pump Suction Tanks

gal	*m*^{3}*	*gal*	*m*^{3}*
50,000	190	250,000	950
75,000	290	300,000	1100
100,000	380	400,000	1500
125,000	475	500,000	2000
150,000	575	750,000	3000
200,000	750	1,000,000	4000

*Figures rounded off as approximations from nominal customary American tank sizes.

with some wood on pedestals. Reinforced concrete towers are sometimes used, and tanks can also be placed directly on top of the structures they supply. In a few cases, concrete has also been used for the tank shells themselves. Typical gravity tanks are shown in Figures 15.1.3 and 15.1.4. In Figure 15.1.4, note that the higher the tank, the greater the water pressure at the base of the tank.

Tanks should be designed and installed according to NFPA 22, *Standard for Water Tanks for Private Fire Protection,* which gives full requirements for construction materials, loads, unit stresses, details of design, foundations, accessories, and workmanship. Welding of towers should conform to code requirements for welding in building construction.[1]

Steel for tanks and towers should conform to the specifications in NFPA 22. Chief among these specifications are the American Water Works Association standards for steel tanks,[2,3] which give the thickness of steel plates and the welding and bolting practices that should be followed. Other standards referenced in NFPA 22 cover steel shapes, plate materials, bolts, anchor bolts and rods, forgings, castings, reinforcing steel, and filler material for welding.

Steel tanks and towers should be riveted, welded, or bolted (if factory coated). Unfinished bolts and nuts should be used only where not exposed to weather, water, or corrosive environments and in (1) field connections of nonadjustable tension

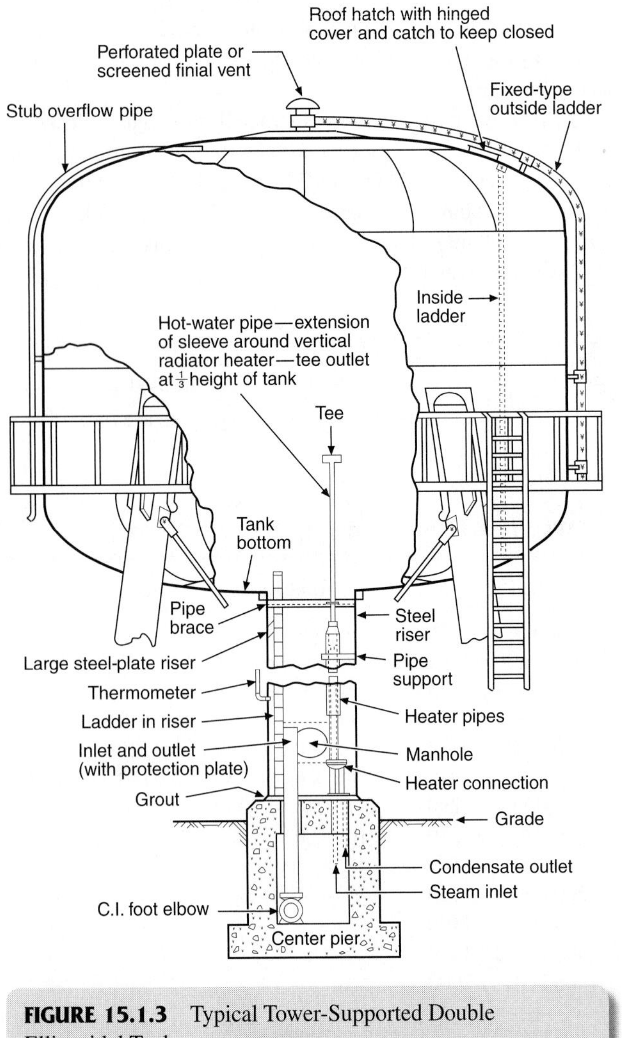

FIGURE 15.1.3 Typical Tower-Supported Double Ellipsoidal Tank

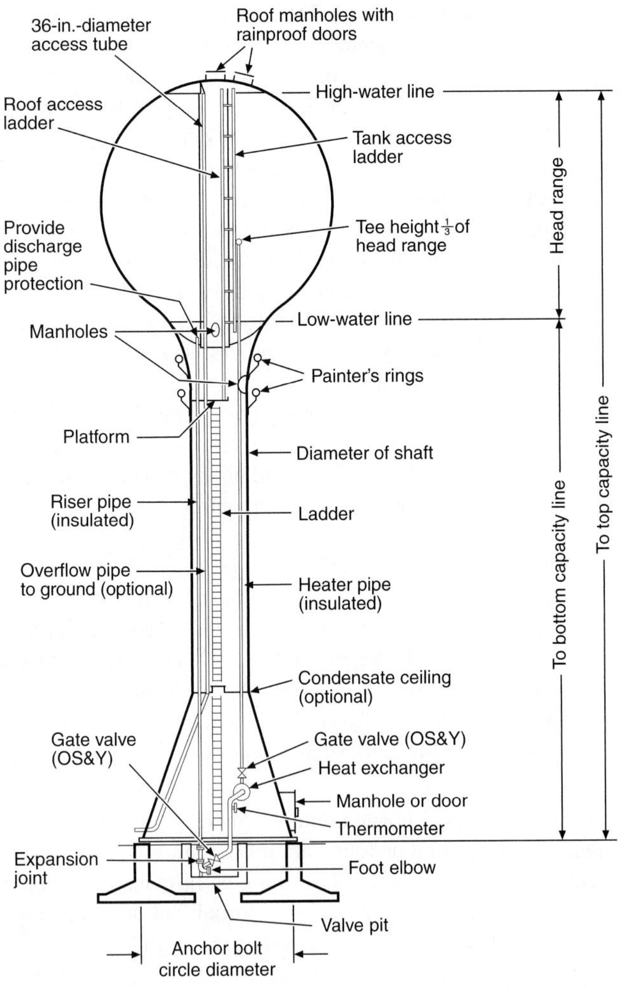

FIGURE 15.1.4 Typical Pedestal Tank

members carrying wind stress and (2) field connections of compression members and grillages in towers supporting tanks of 30,000 gal (114 m^3) or less capacity. Wood tanks and towers should conform to the specifications in NFPA 22, including types and dimensions of wood suitable for use, processes that should be used, and proper hoop materials and design, as well as unit loads and unit stresses for steel tanks and towers, and working stresses for timber for wood tanks.

During assembly and erection, plates should be bolted firmly together before riveting. Drift pins should not be used to bring parts together or to enlarge unfair holes.

No waste material, such as boards, roofing, paint cans, and so on, should be left in the tank or in the space at the top of the tank after its completion, because it may obstruct the piping.

Tanks should be put in service promptly after completion. Wood tanks may be damaged by shrinkage if left empty.

TANK AND TOWER FOUNDATIONS

The following are principles of good foundations for suction tanks and gravity tank towers.

Foundations in the Ground

Foundations should be designed to carry the maximum loads without excessive settlement. If wood piles are used above permanent low-groundwater level, they should be protected as specified by the American Wood Preservers Association.[4] Foundations should not be constructed over buried pipes or immediately adjacent to existing or former deep excavations unless the foundation bases go below the excavation.

Material. Foundations and footings should be built of concrete with a specified compressive strength not less than 3000 psi (20.69 MPa). The cement and aggregates, and the mixing and placing of the concrete, should conform to American Concrete Institute requirements for reinforced concrete.[5] Concrete work should conform to all requirements of ACI 301.[6]

Steel or wood pump suction tanks should be set on compacted crushed stone or granular base, or on concrete foundations. At least 3 in. (76.2 mm) of clean, dry sand, laid on compacted grade should be provided at the finished tank grade and should slope up toward the center of the tank at the rate of 1 in. in 10 ft (25.4 mm in 3 m). If the soil is good, at least 4 in. (100 mm) of crushed stone or sand is suggested. The material should then be laid on moistened and compacted gravel after removing unsuitable soil. Special consideration (outlined later) must be given if soil is poor.

A reinforced concrete ring wall at least 2½ ft (760 mm) deep below finished grade and 10 in. (250 mm) thick should surround the tank foundation. This ring normally projects 6 in. (152 mm) above the surrounding grade and should be reinforced against temperature and shrinkage and reinforced to resist the lateral pressure of the confined fill with its surcharge. If the ring wall is outside of the tank shell, asphalt flashing should be installed between the tank and the ring wall at ground level.

Where the soil does not provide direct support for the tank without excessive settlement, shallow foundation construction is not adequate, and a proper foundation needs to be designed by a structural engineer.

Form. The tops of foundations should be level and at least 6 in. (150 mm) above ground. The bottoms of foundation piers for towers should be located at a level that is below the frost line and, in the case of piers, at least 4 ft (1.2 m) below grade, resting on thoroughly tamped soil or rock.

Grouting and Flashing. Bearing or base plates should have complete bearing on the foundation or be laid on minimum 1 in. (25.4 mm) thickness cement grout to secure a complete bearing. The stressed portion of anchor bolts should not be exposed. If the stressed portions of anchor bolts must be exposed, they should be encased in cement mortar to protect against corrosion unless they are accessible for complete cleaning and painting. If structural shapes, plates, and bolts enter or are supported by masonry or concrete, the joint between the metal and masonry or concrete should be flashed with asphalt. (This does not refer to base plates under columns.)

Soil-Bearing Pressure. In order to find the proper depth of the foundation, the soil-bearing pressure must be determined by analyzing the subsurface and checking the foundations of other structures in the area. Test borings should be made by or under the supervision of an experienced soils engineer or soils testing laboratory. The borings should be made deep enough to determine the adequacy of the support (usually a minimum of 20 to 30 ft [6 to 9 m]). Evaluate the potential for subsidence, collapse, soil liquefaction, and settlement where the presence of limestone or other soluble rock types are present or suspected and include cavity investigation and competency of bedrock with the subsurface investigation.

Avoid constructing foundations over buried pipes or adjacent to existing or former deep excavations.

Piers

Pier foundations may be of any suitable shape and may be either plain or reinforced concrete. If they support a tower, their center of gravity should lie in the continued center of the gravity line of the tower column or else be designed for eccentricity. The height of piers should not be less than the mean width. The top surface should extend at least 3 in. (756 mm) beyond the bearing plates on all sides and be generally chamfered at the edges.

The tops of foundation piers should be level and at least 6 in. (152 mm) above grade, located at the correct elevations. The bottom of foundations should be located at a level that is the greater of either below the frost line or at least 4 ft (1.2 m) below grade.

Anchorage. The weight of piers should be sufficient to resist the maximum net uplift that occurs when the wind blows from any direction on the empty tank. The weight of dirt directly above the base of the pier may be included in the calculations.

Anchor bolts should be arranged to engage a weight at least equal to the net uplift with the tank empty and the wind blowing from any direction. Their lower ends should be hooked or fitted with anchor plates.

Anchor bolts should be accurately located with sufficient free length of thread to fully engage their nuts. Expansion bolts are not acceptable. The minimum size of anchor bolts should be 1½ in. (38 mm).

Center Pier. In addition to the weight of the water in a large plate riser, the weight of the column of water directly above the riser in the tank, and the weight of the steel plate, the center pier should be considered as supporting a hollow cylinder of water in the tank. If the hemispherical or ellipsoidal bottom is rigidly attached to the top of the large riser by a flat horizontal diaphragm plate, the radius of the hollow cylinder of water should be determined as specified under large risers discussed later in this chapter.

TANK TOWERS

Steel is generally used for the construction of tank towers (Figure 15.1.5). Details on the specific types of steel used in tanks can be found in NFPA 22.

Both dead loads and live loads should be considered when designing towers. The dead load is an estimate of the weight of all permanent construction and fittings. The live load is considered as the weight of the water when it overflows the top of the tank. Consideration should also be given to temporary loading, such as ice and snow.

The weight of the water located directly above any riser need not be considered when figuring loads unless the riser is suspended from the tank bottom. If the riser is used to support the tank bottom, the entire weight supported by the riser should be considered, including the weight of the water.

Additional factors to consider are wind, balcony, and earthquake loads. Wind loads are based on 30 lb/ft^2 (147 kg/m^3) for vertical plain surfaces and 18 lb/ft^2 (88 kg/m^3) over the total area of the vertical projection on cylindrical surfaces. These loads are applied to the center of gravity of the projected areas. A vertical load of 1000 lb (454 kg) should be applied to any 10 ft^2 (0.93 m^2) of area on a balcony floor and on each platform; 500 lb (227 kg) applied to any 10 ft^2 (0.93 m^2) of area on the tank roof; and 350 lb (159 kg) applied to each vertical section of the ladder. Snow loading is additional and considered in these loadings. Earthquake loading must be designed specifically for local conditions.

FIGURE 15.1.5 Elevated Wood Gravity Tank on Steel Tower (Source: Isseks Brothers)

Ladders and Balconies

All tanks should have ladders on both the outside and inside, with convenient passage from one ladder to the other and through the roof hatch, arranged not to interfere with the opening of the hatch cover. Ladders are for inspection and maintenance of the tank's interior and exterior surfaces; they should be constructed of materials compatible to those of the tank and tower, and they should be easily accessible. Equipment exceeding 20 ft (6.1 m) should be equipped with a cage, a rigid notched rail, or another listed ladder safety device.

Balconies and walkways constructed of wood or steel are recommended for towers over 25 ft (7.6 m) high. Balconies on tanks having a diameter in excess of 15.5 ft (4.7 m) should have a minimum width of 24 in. (607 mm) and, for smaller diameter tanks, a width of not less than 18 in. (457 mm). Railings should be at least 42 in. (1067 mm) high. Balconies and walkways should also be made of materials compatible with the tank and tower materials.

Tower Construction

During field erection, the columns of towers should be built on thin metal wedges driven to equal resistance so that all columns will be loaded equally after the structure is completed. The spaces beneath the base plates and the anchor holes should be completely filled with cement mortar.

Sections of structural members for towers should be symmetrical and built of standard structural shapes or tubular sections. Structural shapes should be designed with open sections so that all surfaces exposed to air or moisture and subject to corrosion can be painted. Tubular sections of columns and struts should be airtight.

TANK HEATING EQUIPMENT

Fire protection water supplies in tanks subject to freezing must be heated. An ice plug in a riser pipe may make the tank water unavailable in case of fire and may break the pipe. Ice in or on tank structures has been the direct cause of collapse in several cases. The heating system must, therefore, be reliable and allow convenient and economical operation to 50°F (10°C). However, overheating can seriously damage wood tanks and the paint on steel tanks and, thus, it should be avoided.

Determination of Heater Capacity

To prevent freezing in any part of a tank during the coldest weather, the heating system must be of such capacity that the temperature of the coldest water in the tank or riser, or both, will be maintained at or above 42°F (5.6°C). The coldest weather temperature used to determine the need of heating should be based on the lowest mean temperature for one day, as shown on the isothermal map (Figure 15.1.6).

Tables 15.1.3 and 15.1.4 show the heat losses from tanks of common sizes exposed to various atmospheric temperatures. To determine, for example, what heater capacity would be needed for a 75,000 gal (284 m^3) steel tank in Duluth, Minnesota, one could interpolate from Figure 15.1.6 that the lowest mean temperature for one day in Duluth is –28°F (–33°C). According

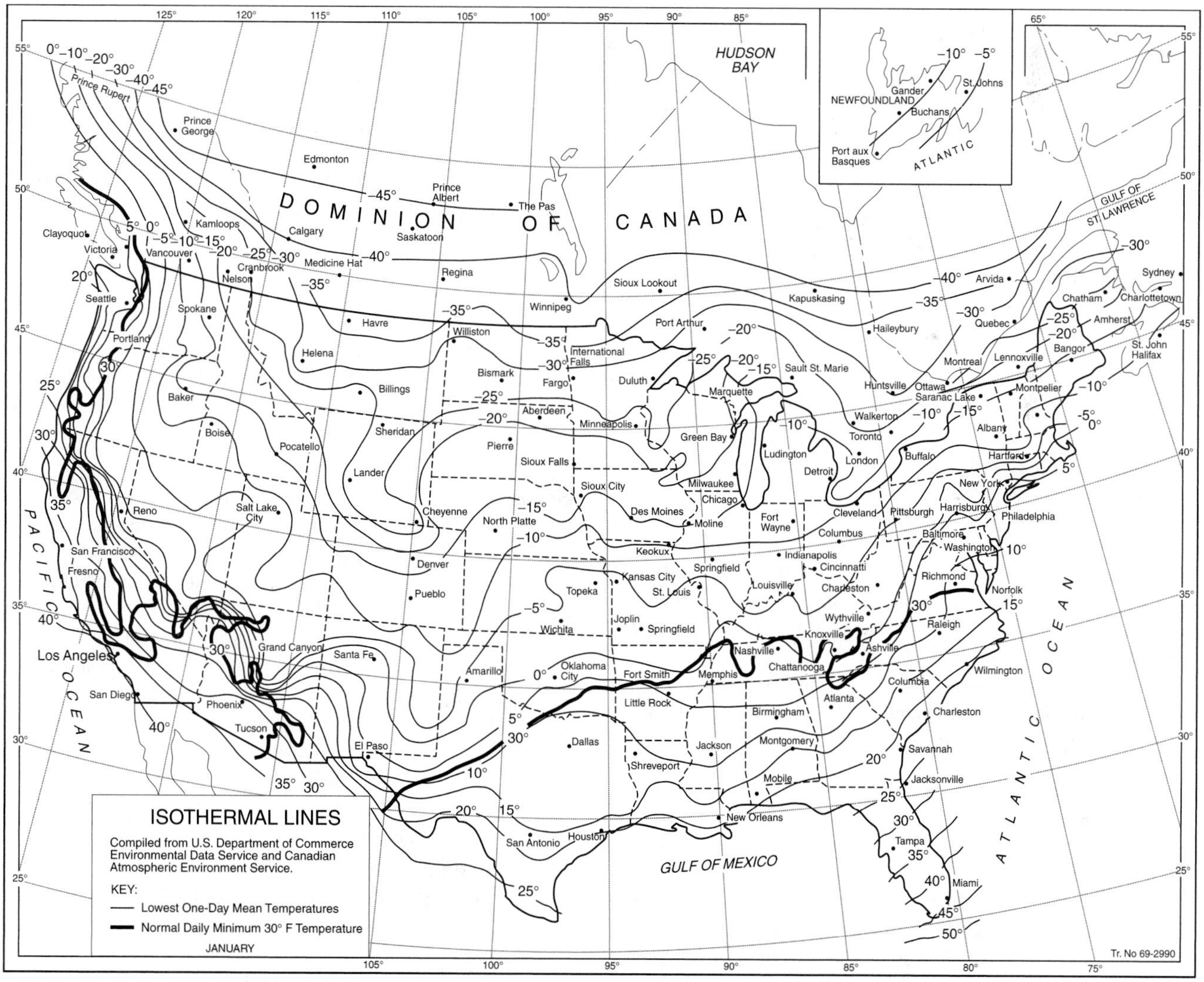

FIGURE 15.1.6 Isothermal Lines—Lowest One-Day Mean Temperature (for SI units, °C = (°F – 32) × 5/9)

TABLE 15.1.3 Heat Loss from Standpipes and Steel Suction Tanks

Thousands of British thermal units lost per hour when the temperature of the coldest water is 42°F (5.6°C). To determine capacity of heater needed, find the minimum mean atmospheric temperature for one day from the isothermal map, Figure 15.1.6, and note the following corresponding heat loss.

Temperature		Tank Capacities (thousands of gallons)															
		100,000 gal ($378\ m^3$)		150,000 gal ($567\ m^3$)		200,000 gal ($757\ m^3$)		300,000 gal ($1135\ m^3$)		400,000 gal ($1514\ m^3$)		500,000 gal ($1892\ m^3$)		750,000 gal ($2838\ m^3$)		1,000,000 gal ($3785\ m^3$)	
°F	*°C*	*Btu/hr*	*W*	*Btu/hr*	*W*	*Btu/hr*	*W*	*Btu/hr*	*W*	*Btu/hr*	*W*	*Btu/hr*	*W*	*Btu/hr*	*W*	*Btu/hr*	*W*
35	2	85	25	114	33	135	40	175	51	206	60	238	70	312	91	380	111
30	−1	121	35	162	47	193	57	248	73	294	86	340	100	445	130	542	159
25	−4	161	47	216	63	257	75	330	97	393	115	453	133	594	174	722	211
20	−7	202	59	271	79	323	95	414	121	493	144	568	166	745	218	907	266
15	−9	245	72	329	96	391	115	502	147	597	175	689	202	904	265	1099	322
10	−12	290	85	389	114	463	136	595	174	707	207	816	239	1071	314	1232	361
5	−15	337	99	452	132	539	158	691	202	822	241	949	278	1244	364	1514	443
0	−18	388	114	521	153	620	182	796	233	947	277	1093	320	1434	420	1744	511
−5	−21	441	129	592	173	705	207	905	265	1076	315	1241	364	1628	477	1987	582
−10	−23	498	146	669	196	797	234	1023	300	1216	356	1403	411	1841	539	2239	656
−15	−36	557	163	748	219	891	261	1143	335	1360	398	1569	460	2058	603	2503	733
−20	−29	619	181	830	243	989	290	1270	372	1510	442	1742	510	2286	670	2787	816
−25	−32	685	201	920	270	1096	321	1406	412	1673	490	1930	565	2532	742	3080	902
−30	−34	752	220	1010	296	1203	352	1545	453	1837	538	2119	621	2781	815	3383	991
−35	−37	825	242	1108	325	1320	387	1694	496	2015	590	2325	681	3050	894	3710	1087
−40	−40	898	263	1206	353	1437	421	1844	540	2193	643	2531	742	3320	973	4039	1183
−50	−46	1059	310	1422	417	1694	496	2175	637	2586	758	2984	874	3915	1147	4762	1395
−60	−51	1229	360	1651	484	1966	576	2524	740	3002	880	3463	1015	4544	1331	5528	1619

to Table 15.1.4, the heat loss at −28°F (−33°C) for a 75,000 gal ($284\ m^3$) steel tank is approximately 659,000 Btu per hour (19,300 W). For a wood tank with these same specifications, Table 15.1.4 indicates a maximum heat loss of approximately 254,000 Btu per hour (74.4 kW).

Selection of Heating Method

The selection of a heating method depends primarily on the type of tank (height, construction, material, size, and shape) and its geographical location. The recommended methods of heating are covered in detail in NFPA 22.

There are three basic methods of heating tank water: (1) gravity circulation of hot water, (2) steam coils inside tanks, and (3) direct discharge of steam.

Gravity Circulation of Hot Water

Heating by gravity circulation is dependable and economical if correctly planned. Cold water received through a connection from the discharge pipe or from near the bottom of a suction tank or standpipe is heated and rises through a separate hot water pipe into the tank. Steam, coal burning, or oil heaters are ordinarily used; gas heaters or electric heaters are also satisfactory.

A steam heater ordinarily consists of a cast-iron or steel shell through which water circulates by gravity around steam tubes or coils of brass or copper. It should be located in a valve pit, in a heater house, or in a nearby building at or near the base of the tank. When the tank is over a building, the steam heater should be located in the top story.

Heater Thermometer. The convenience of a gravity system is that it permits discovery of the temperature of the coldest water in the system. A recording thermometer should be placed in the cold-water return pipe near the heater; it should be checked frequently to make sure that the temperature does not fall below 42°F (5.6°C). The temperature reading should be observed daily during subfreezing temperature conditions. (Water has its maximum density at 39.2°F [4°C]. When the temperature of the water falls below 39.2°F [4°C], there is an inversion, and the warmer water settles to the bottom of the tank while the colder water rises. Therefore, if the circulation heater is to be effective, sufficient heat must be provided so that the temperature of the coldest water will be above 42°F [5.6°C].)

Water Circulating Pipes. The size of pipe used for the circulation of heating water is given in Table 15.1.5. Pipe should be either copper water tubing or brass (85 percent copper) throughout. The hot water discharges into the tank through a tee fitting at the end of the hot-water pipe at a height about one-third up from the bottom of the tank. The return pipe connects into the discharge pipe at a point that guarantees circulation throughout

TABLE 15.1.4 Heat Loss from Elevated Tanks

Thousands of British thermal units lost per hour when the temperature of the coldest water is 42°F (5.6°C). To determine capacity of heater needed, find the minimum mean atmospheric temperature for one day from the isothermal map, Figure 15.1.6, and note the following corresponding heat loss.

Wood Tanks

Atmospheric Temperature		10,000 gal ($38 m^3$)		15,000 gal ($57 m^3$)		20,000 gal ($76 m^3$)		25,000 gal ($95 m^3$)		30,000 gal ($114 m^3$)		40,000 gal ($151 m^3$)		50,000 gal ($189 m^3$)		75,000 gal ($284 m^3$)		100,000 gal ($378 m^3$)	
°F	°C	Btu/hr	W	Btu/hr	W	Btu/hr	W	Btu/hr	W	Btu/hr	W	Btu/hr	W	Btu/hr	W	Btu/hr	W	Btu/hr	W
35	−2	8	2	10	3	11	3	13	4	14	4	19	6	21	6	28	8	33	10
30	−1	11	3	14	4	16	5	19	6	21	6	27	8	31	9	40	12	49	14
25	−4	15	4	20	6	21	6	25	7	28	8	36	11	42	12	54	16	65	19
20	−7	19	6	25	7	27	8	32	9	35	10	46	13	54	16	69	20	83	24
15	−9	24	7	31	9	34	10	39	11	44	13	57	17	66	19	85	25	102	30
10	−12	28	8	36	11	40	12	46	13	51	15	68	20	78	23	100	29	121	35
5	−15	33	10	43	13	47	14	54	16	60	18	78	23	92	27	117	34	142	42
0	−18	38	11	49	14	53	16	62	18	69	20	90	26	106	31	135	40	164	48
−5	−21	43	13	56	16	61	18	71	21	79	23	103	30	120	35	154	45	187	55
−10	−23	49	14	63	18	69	20	80	23	89	26	116	34	136	40	174	51	211	62
−15	−26	54	16	71	21	77	23	89	26	100	29	130	36	153	45	195	57	236	69
−20	−29	61	18	79	23	86	25	99	29	111	33	145	42	169	50	217	64	262	77
−25	−32	68	20	87	25	95	28	110	32	123	36	160	47	188	55	240	70	291	85
−30	−34	74	22	96	28	104	30	121	35	135	40	176	52	206	60	264	77	319	93
−35	−37	81	24	105	31	115	34	133	39	148	43	193	57	226	66	289	85	350	103
−40	−40	88	26	114	33	125	37	144	42	162	47	210	62	246	72	317	93	382	112
−50	−46	104	30	135	40	147	43	170	50	190	56	246	72	290	85	372	109	450	132
−60	−51	122	36	157	46	171	50	197	58	222	65	266	78	307	90	407	119	490	144

Steel Tanks

Atmospheric Temperature		30,000 gal ($114 m^3$)		40,000 gal ($151 m^3$)		50,000 gal ($189 m^3$)		75,000 gal ($284 m^3$)		100,000 gal ($378 m^3$)		150,000 gal ($568 m^3$)		200,000 gal ($757 m^3$)		250,000 gal ($946 m^3$)		300,000 gal ($1136 m^3$)	
°F	°C	Btu/hr	W	Btu/hr	W	Btu/hr	W	Btu/hr	W	Btu/hr	W	Btu/hr	W	Btu/hr	W	Btu/hr	W	Btu/hr	W
35	17	43	13	51	15	59	17	77	23	92	27	120	35	145	42	168	49	69	20
30	12	62	18	72	21	83	24	110	32	132	39	171	50	207	61	242	71	192	56
25	7	82	24	96	28	111	33	146	43	175	51	228	67	275	81	323	96	340	100
20	2	103	30	120	35	139	41	183	54	220	64	287	84	346	101	405	119	506	148
15	−3	125	37	146	43	169	50	222	65	267	78	347	102	419	123	491	144	692	203
10	−8	147	43	172	50	200	59	263	77	316	93	411	120	496	145	582	171	893	262
5	−13	171	51	200	59	233	68	306	90	367	108	478	140	577	169	676	198	1092	320
0	−18	197	58	231	68	268	79	352	103	423	124	551	161	664	195	779	228	1309	384
−5	−23	224	66	262	77	304	89	400	117	480	141	626	183	755	221	884	259	1536	450
−10	−28	253	74	296	87	344	101	452	132	543	159	707	207	853	250	1000	293	1771	519
−15	−33	283	83	331	97	384	113	506	148	607	178	790	231	954	280	1118	328	2020	592
−20	−38	314	92	368	108	427	125	562	165	674	197	878	257	1059	310	1241	364	2291	671
−25	−43	348	102	407	119	473	139	622	182	747	219	972	285	1173	344	1375	403	2568	752
−30	−48	382	112	447	131	519	152	683	200	820	240	1068	313	1288	377	1510	442	2860	838
−35	−53	419	123	490	144	569	167	749	219	900	264	1171	343	1413	414	1656	485	3174	930
−40	−58	456	134	534	156	620	182	816	239	979	287	1275	374	1538	451	1803	528	3494	102
−50	−68	538	158	629	184	731	214	962	282	1154	338	1503	440	1814	532	2126	623	4186	122
−60	−78	624	183	730	214	848	248	1116	327	1340	393	1745	511	2105	617	2467	723	4936	144

Note: For each lineal foot of uninsulated riser 4 ft (1.2 m) in diameter, add the number of Btus or W in this column to the total heat loss at the different temperatures of the various tank capacities.

TABLE 15.1.5 Sizes of Circulating Pipes Required for Elevated Steel Tanks

Minimum One-Day Mean Temp.		Tank Capacity																			
		15,000 gal (57 m^3)		20,000 gal (76 m^3)		25,000 gal (95 m^3)		30,000 gal (114 m^3)		40,000 gal (151 m^3)		50,000 gal (189 m^3)		60,000 gal (227 m^3)		75,000 gal (284 m^3)		100,000 gal (378 m^3)		150,000 gal (568 m^3)	
°F	°C	in.	mm	in.	mm	in.	mm	in.	mm	in.	mm	in.	mm	in.	mm	in.	mm	in.	mm	in.	mm
10	−12	2	50	2	50	2	50	2	50	2	50	2	50	2	50	2	50	2	50	2½	65
5	−15	2	50	2	50	2	50	2	50	2	50	2	50	2	50	2	50	2	50	2½	65
0	−18	2	50	2	50	2	50	2	50	2	50	2	50	2	50	2	50	2½	65	2½	65
−5	−21	2	50	2	50	2	50	2	50	2	50	2	50	2	50	2	50	2½	65	2½	65
−10	−23	2	50	2	50	2	50	2	50	2	50	2	50	2	50	2½	65	2½	65	2½	65
−15	−26	2	50	2	50	2	50	2	50	2	50	2½	65	2½	65	2½	65	2½	65	3	80
−20	−29	2	50	2	50	2	50	2	50	2	50	2½	65	2½	65	2½	65	2½	65	3	80
−25	−32	2	50	2	50	2	50	2	50	2½	65	2½	65	2½	65	2½	65	3	80	3	80
−30	−34	2	50	2	50	2	50	2	50	2½	65	2½	65	2½	65	2½	65	3	80	3	80
−35	−37	2	50	2	50	2	50	2½	65	2½	65	2½	65	2½	65	3	80	3	80	3	80
−40	−40	2	50	2	50	2	50	2½	65	2½	65	2½	65	2½	65	3	80	3	80	3	80

the portion of the discharge pipe subject to freezing. A typical arrangement of a circulating heater and piping in a valve pit is shown in Figure 15.1.7.

Steam Coils Inside Tanks

Steam coils inside the tank do not permit convenient observation of water temperatures and have other faults that make them unsuited for heating elevated tanks except in areas of the South where only intermittent heating is necessary. This method may, however, be used for heating suction tanks and standpipes with flat bottoms supported near the ground level if coils are submerged continuously. The coil consists of at least 1¼ in. (32 mm) brass or copper pipe or 2 in. (50 mm) steel pipe, pitched to drain, supplied with steam at not less than 10 psi (0.7 bar) pressure through a pipe of sufficient size to furnish the needed quantity of steam from a reliable source. The coil should contain an area of heating surface to maintain the temperature of the coldest water at not less than 42°F (5.6°C). The surface water temperatures for elevated tanks, standpipes, and suction tanks should be determined by means of a listed temperature-detecting device.

Direct Discharge of Steam

Steam from a reliable supply is blown directly into the tank water through a pipe not less than 1 in. (25 mm) in diameter extending inside the frost-proof casing and through the bottom to a point above the maximum water level, then extending horizontally for a short distance and then downward to a point 3 or 4 ft (0.9 or 1.2 m) below the normal fire service water level. An air vent and check valve in the pipe above the surface of the water keeps the water from siphoning back down the steam line. This method is employed where the lowest mean temperature for one day is 5°F (−15°C) or above.

Solar Heating of Elevated Steel Tanks

With the increase in fossil fuel prices, work was done in Canada on the feasibility of solar heating of elevated steel tanks.[7] The basic technique is to insulate the entire tank, leaving a window on the south side through the insulation. The tank shell in the

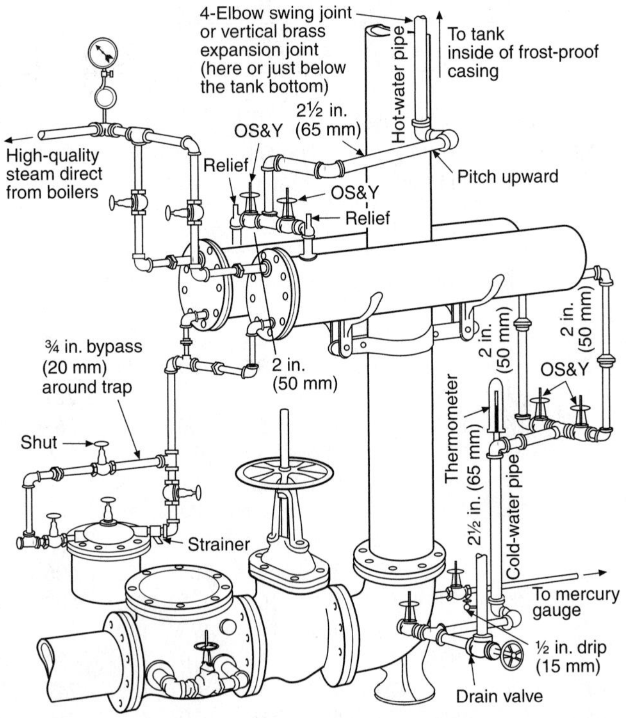

FIGURE 15.1.7 Piping Arrangement for a Multi-Unit, Steam-Heated Water Heater for a Gravity Circulation System

opening is painted flat black to absorb heat from the sun and the opening is double glazed.

Retrofit installations of solar heating systems on existing tanks involve special precautions in the attachment of components to the tank, such as the use of adhesives. The costs would be relatively high and the payback period long.

For new tanks, low-cost welding techniques can be used for attachment of collector components to the tank. With substantially all energy being supplied by the sun, a backup heating system can be a low-cost electrical system. Compared to a conventional tank with a fossil fuel–fired boiler heating system, a solar-heated tank with an electrical backup heating system is likely to have a lower capital cost. A solar-heated tank should have a backup heating system.

TANK EQUIPMENT AND ACCESSORIES

A complete installation of a gravity or suction tank includes the necessary pipe connections, valve enclosures, and, where appropriate for the particular tank, such features as a frost-proof casing for the riser.

Valve Pits

A valve pit should be of sufficient size to provide at least 12 in. (305 mm) to 18 in. (457 mm) around all necessary and contained equipment. Details of the construction of the pit and its arrangement, including clearance around equipment, waterproofing, manhole and ladder, and drainage, should conform to the recommendations given for valve pits (Figure 15.1.8).

Valve Enclosures

The tank heater and other fittings are sometimes installed in an enclosure above grade. In such a case, the indicating valve and the check valve are generally placed in the horizontal pipe below the frost line in a small pit heated sufficiently to maintain a temperature of at least 40°F (4.4°C) during the most severe weather. Ground fault interruption should be provided on all electrical circuits.

The enclosure may be of concrete, brick, cement plaster on metal lath, or any other noncombustible material with suitable heat-insulating properties. The roof should be strong enough to support the frost-proof casing and other loads without excessive deflection.

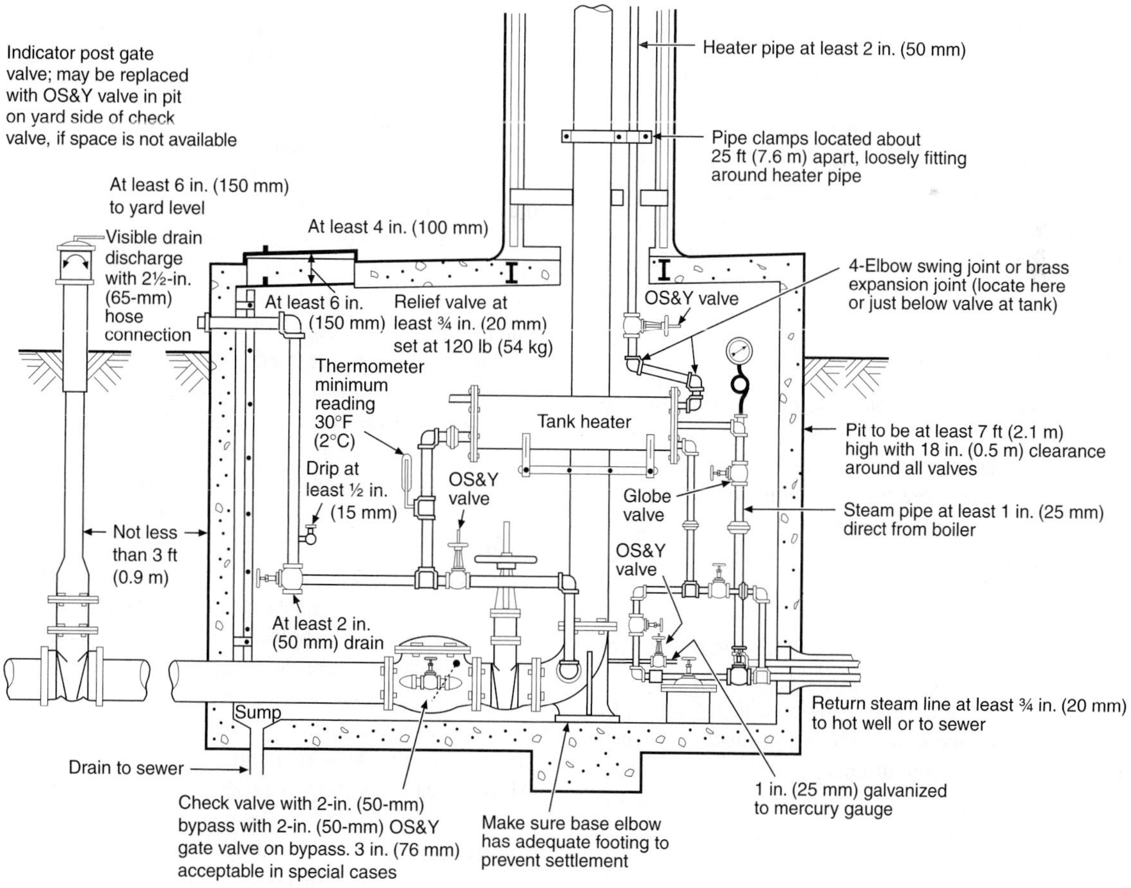

FIGURE 15.1.8 Valve Pit and Tank Connections at Base of Riser

Frost-Proof Casings

Except in the case of a large steel riser, a frost-proof casing around all exposed tank piping is necessary in localities where the lowest mean atmospheric temperature for one day as shown by the isothermal map (see Figure 15.1.6) is 20°F (–6.7°C) or lower. Tank piping subjected to temperatures below freezing within unheated buildings or dry risers of elevated tanks must also be adequately protected. Noncombustible frost-proof casings should be used where there is danger of serious fire exposure.

Large Risers

Large steel-plate riser pipes 3 ft (0.9 m) or more in diameter, without frost-proof casings, are often desirable and acceptable where properly heated. The fire hazard and upkeep of the frost casing are thereby avoided, the expansion joint in the discharge pipe is eliminated, and it is not necessary to have a walkway to reach the valves. When the tank is on an independent tower, a concrete valve pit at the base of the discharge pipe and the pier are usually built as a single unit to support the riser (see Figure 15.1.3). On the other hand, the larger valve pit at the base of the riser makes the initial cost higher than it is for equipment with small risers.

Water-Level Indicators

A water-level gauge of suitable design must be provided and located to prevent it from freezing. Careful installation, adjustment, and proper maintenance of the gauge are necessary. Where an altitude gauge is used, it should be a minimum 6 in. (152 mm) in diameter and of noncorrosive construction.

Mercury gauges are no longer permitted for new installations. Where existing mercury gauges are used/installed, they should be maintained in accordance with NFPA 22.

Overflow Pipes

The inlet of the overflow pipe should be located at the top capacity or high-water line of the tank. The pipe below the roof support structure and below any unwelded seams should be of adequate capacity for the operating conditions, but should not be less than 3 in. (80 mm) in diameter. Overflow pipes should be brought to grade. However, if dripping water or a small accumulation of ice is not objectionable, the overflow may pass through the side of the tank near the top and extend not more than 4 ft (1.2 m), with a slight downward pitch to discharge beyond the balcony and away from the ladders.

When a stub pipe is undesirable, the overflow pipe can be extended down through the tank bottom and inside the frost-proof casing or steel-plate riser, discharging through the casing near the ground or roof level. The section of the pipe inside the tank should be brass, flanged cast iron, or steel.

Painting Tanks, Seams, and Margins

All interior surfaces of steel tanks exposed to water immersion of the vapor phase zone above the high water level, inside dry surfaces, and exterior surfaces shall be cleaned, primed, and painted. After construction, all weld seams, unprimed margins, and any areas where the primer has been damaged shall be cleaned, primed, and painted. Only lead-free paints and primers should be used. Wax coating systems are no longer permitted.

EMBANKMENT-SUPPORTED COATED FABRIC SUCTION TANKS

Embankment-supported coated fabric (ESCF) tanks can be used as suction tanks for fire protection. NFPA 22 contains details on construction, installation, and maintenance of ESCF tanks.

The tank is usually composed of a reservoir liner with an integral flexible roof and is designed to be supported by earth underneath and on all four sides. The material of some ESCF tanks is a nylon fabric coated with an elastomer compounded to provide resistance to abrasion and weather. Support is provided by a specifically prepared excavation and earthen berm.

Preparation of the installation site is critical to the reliability of an ESCF tank. The embankment should be designed for stability and drainage. Usually, a shallow excavation the size of the bottom of the tank is made where local soil and groundwater conditions permit. The excavated earth is then graded to form a stable embankment for the upper sides of the tank. The exterior of the berm should be graded to allow for rain and snow drainage and pipe connections, and the interior graded to match the contour of the tank, including rounded corners. ESCF tanks may be placed underground with the top of the tank at grade level, or they may be placed above ground where the earthen berm provides the entire support.

When the excavation meets the shape requirements of the tank and all sharp rocks and debris have been carefully removed from the floor of the tank excavation, a 6 in. (150 mm) layer of fine sand or clean soil is spread over a 3 in. (75 mm) underlayment of selected pea gravel, which provides a firm smooth bed with good drainage. The tank is then placed in the foundation, and all connections are made. Installation of the tank in the prepared embankment shall be accomplished with the assistance of the tank manufacturer's field technician. The tank should be shipped to the site packaged in a material that is designed for ease of handling by a crane and winch and that facilitates efficient placement in the enclosure. The fittings shall be installed on site. At the time of installation, the tank should be filled and final adjustments on the tank made to ensure that it rests uniformly against the embankment on all four sides. The tank must be tested for leakage after installation. After the tank is filled, a coating is applied to the exposed surface to protect it from the atmosphere. See Figure 15.1.9 for a typical ESCF installation.

As with other types of storage tanks, water temperature in ESCF tanks should be maintained at not less than 42°F (5.6°C). An acceptable method of providing heat is a water recirculation system with a heat exchanger (Figure 15.1.10). When the ambient water temperature drops below 42°F (5.6°C), a thermostat activates a pump that draws water from the tank through an inlet-outlet fitting and pumps the heated water back into the tank through a recirculation fitting located in the bottom of the tank diagonally opposite the inlet-outlet fitting. Heat losses in ESCF tanks are given in Table 15.1.6.

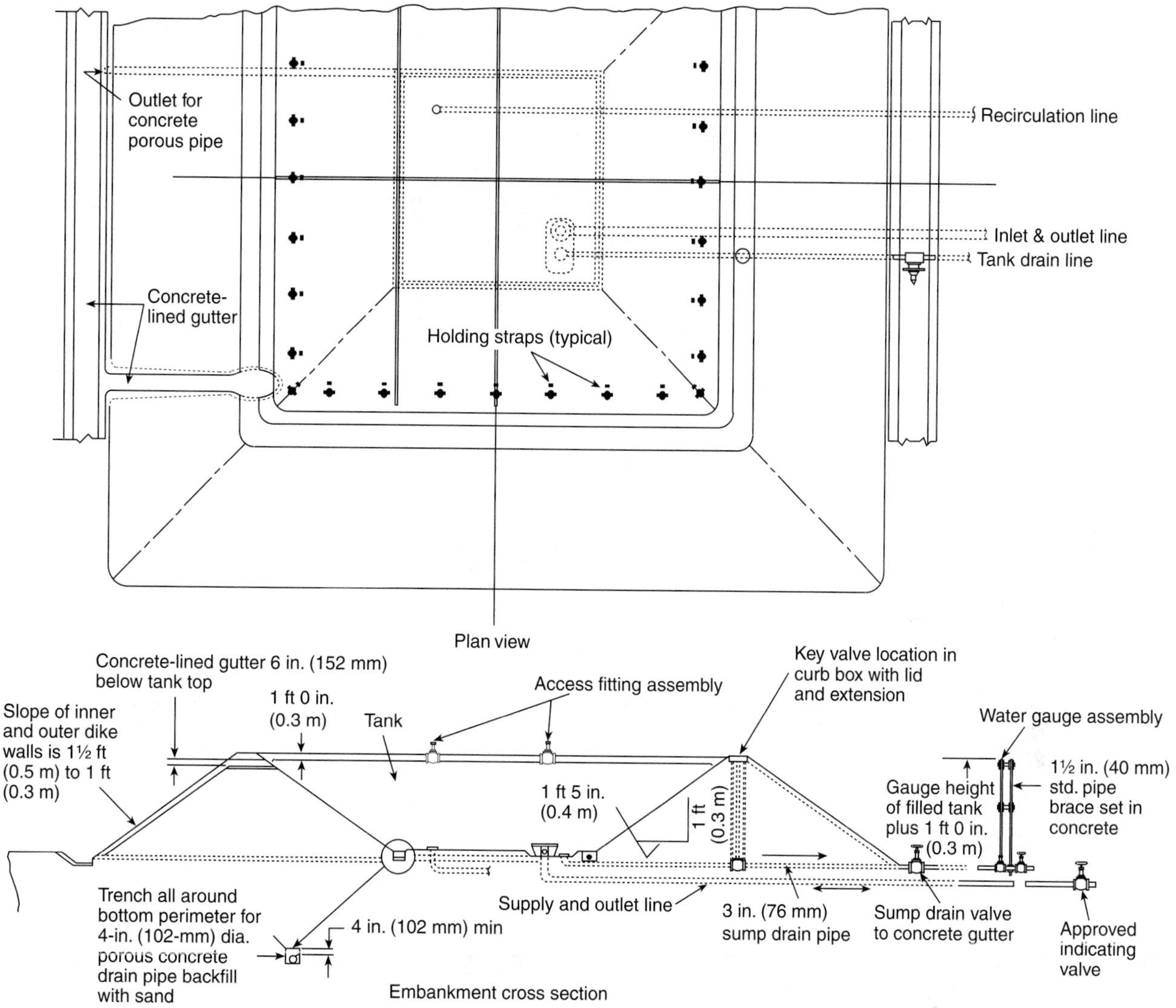

FIGURE 15.1.9 Installation Details of a Typical Embankment-Supported Fabric (ESF) Tank, Including Fittings

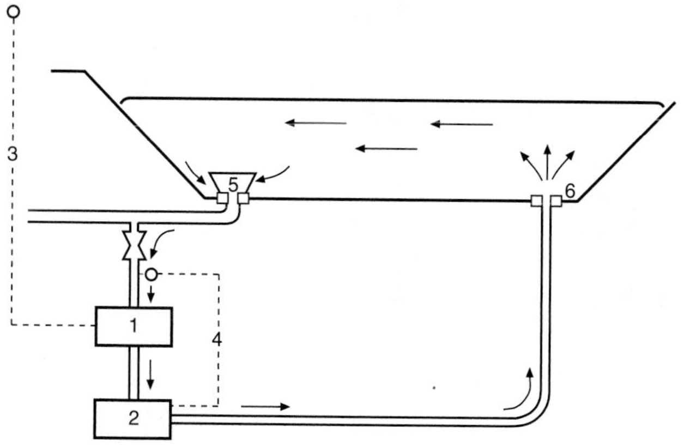

1. Recirculation pump
2. Heat exchanger
3. Unit sensing atmosphere temperature starts pump and water recirculation enabling heat stored in ground to transfer into water at higher rate.
4. Unit sensing water temperature starts heat exchanger when required.
5. Inlet-outlet fitting
6. Recirculation fitting

FIGURE 15.1.10 Recirculation and Heating System for an ESF Tank

PRESSURE TANKS

Pressure tanks are used for limited private fire protection services, such as sprinkler systems, standpipe and hose systems, and water spray fixed systems. A typical pressure tank installation is shown in Figure 15.1.11.

Tank capacity should be approved by the authority having jurisdiction (AHJ) and is considered to be the total contents, both air and water in the cylinder. Pressure tanks are sized by the supply of water needed to meet the demand of the fire protection system as calculated in Chapter 14 of NFPA 13, *Standard for the Installation of Sprinkler Systems*. The pressure shall be sufficient to push all of the water out of the tank while maintaining the necessary residual pressure required by NFPA 13 at the top of the sprinkler system.

Most pressure tanks are located above the top level of the sprinklers. Tanks exposed to combustible contents within the room or enclosure, or within rooms or enclosures of combustible construction, should be protected by automatic sprinklers.

Subject to the approval of the AHJ, tanks may be located in the basement or elsewhere. When the AHJ permits the tank to be buried, the requirements of NFPA 22 must be followed. Tanks for this service generally are not over 15,000 gal (34 m^3)

TABLE 15.1.6 Heat Loss from Embankment-Supported, Rubberized Fabric Suction Tanks

Thousands of British thermal units lost per hour when the temperature of the coldest water is 42°F (5.6°C). To determine capacity of heater needed, find the minimum mean atmospheric temperature for one day from the isothermal map, Figure 15.1.6, and note the following corresponding heat loss.

Exposed Tank Surface				Tank Capacities															
Atmospheric Temperature		Heat Loss Tank Radiating Surface		100,000 gal (378 m^3) 2,746 ft^2 (255 m^2)		200,000 gal (757 m^3) 4,409 ft^2 (410 m^2)		300,000 gal (1,136 m^3) 6,037 ft^2 (561 m^2)		400,000 gal (1,514 m^3) 7,604 ft^2 (706 m^2)		500,000 gal (1,893 m^3) 9,139 ft^2 (849 m^2)		600,000 gal (2,274 m^3) 10,630 ft^2 (988 m^2)		800,000 gal (3,407 m^3) 13,572 ft^2 (1,261 m^2)		1,000,000 gal (3,785 m^3) 16,435 ft^2 (1,527 m^2)	
°F	*°C*	*Btu*	*k/m²*	*Btu*	*W*	*Btu*	*W*	*Btu*	*W*	*Btu*	*W*	*Btu*	*W*	*Btu*	*W*	*Btu*	*W*	*Btu*	*W*
35	–2	22	252	61	693	98	1113	134	1522	168	1,908	202	2,294	235	2,669	300	3,407	363	4,122
30	–1	29	324	78	886	126	1431	173	1965	217	2,464	261	2,964	304	3,452	389	4,417	470	5,337
25	–4	35	399	96	1090	155	1760	212	2407	266	3,021	320	3,634	372	4,224	476	5,405	576	6,541
20	–7	42	472	114	1295	183	2078	251	2850	315	3,577	379	4,304	441	5,008	564	6,405	682	7,745
15	–9	48	545	132	1499	212	2407	290	3293	364	4,134	438	4,974	510	5,792	652	7,404	789	8,960
10	–12	55	619	149	1692	241	2737	329	3736	413	4,690	497	5,644	579	6,675	740	8,403	896	10,175
5	–15	61	693	167	1896	269	3055	369	4190	463	5,258	557	6,325	648	7,359	828	9,403	1003	11,390
0	–18	68	767	185	2101	298	3384	408	4633	512	5,814	616	6,995	717	8,142	916	10,402	1109	12,594
–5	–21	74	839	203	2305	326	3702	447	5076	561	6,371	675	7,665	786	8,926	1004	11,401	1216	13,809
–10	–23	80	913	220	2498	355	4031	486	5519	610	6,927	734	8,335	855	9,709	1092	12,401	1322	15,013
–15	–26	87	986	238	2703	384	4361	525	5962	659	7,484	793	9,005	924	10,493	1180	13,400	1429	16,228
–20	–29	93	1060	256	2907	412	4679	564	6405	708	8,040	852	9,675	992	11,265	1268	14,399	1536	17,443
–25	–32	100	1134	273	3100	441	5008	604	6859	758	8,508	912	10,357	1061	12,049	1356	15,399	1642	18,647
–30	–34	106	1206	291	3205	469	5326	643	7302	807	9,164	971	11,027	1130	12,832	1444	16,398	1749	19,862
–40	–40	119	1355	327	3713	526	5973	721	8188	905	10,277	1089	12,367	1268	14,399	1620	18,397	1962	22,809
–50	–46	132	1498	362	4111	584	6632	799	9073	1003	11,390	1207	13,707	1406	15,967	1796	20,395	2175	24,699
–60	–51	145	1648	397	4508	641	7279	878	9971	1102	12,514	1326	15,058	1544	17,534	1972	22,394	2389	27,129

Note: Heat loss for a given capacity with a different radiating surface than shown above is obtained by multiplying the radiating surface by the tabulated heat loss per ft^2 (m^2) for the atmospheric temperature involved. The minimum radiation surface area is the wetted surface exposed to atmosphere. No heat loss is figured for tank bottoms resting on grade.

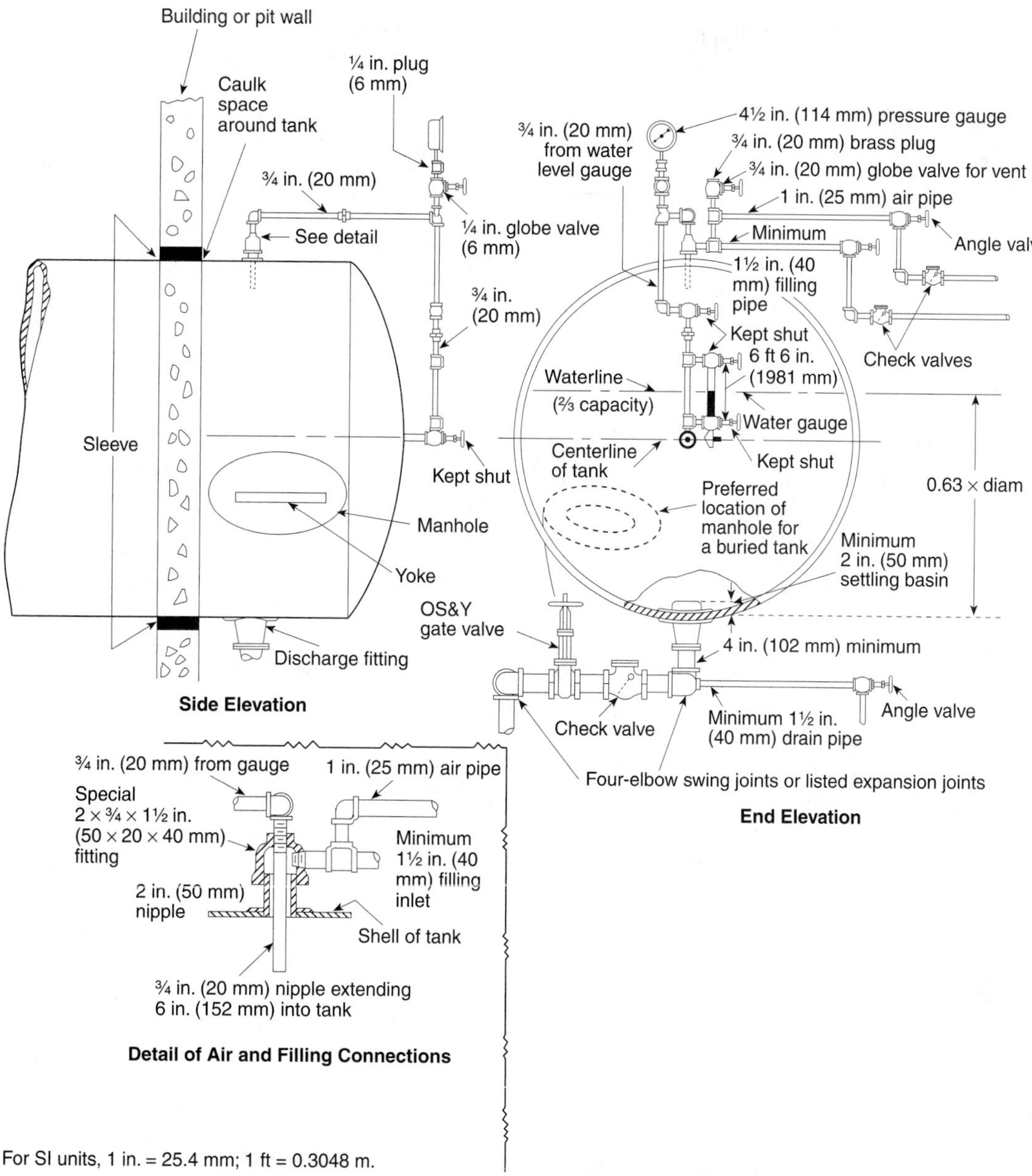

FIGURE 15.1.11 Typical Pressure Tank Installation (Source: Adapted from NFPA 22, *Standard for Water Tanks for Private Fire Protection*, Figure B.1(a), 2003, pp. 22–65)

capacity. For larger supplies, more than one tank would be employed (Table 15.1.7).

The tank is normally kept two-thirds full of water (a water-level gauge provided and the tank plate marked "2/3 capacity line") and a gauge pressure of at least 75 psig (517 kPa) is maintained. A listed air pressure gauge with a maximum range equivalent to twice the normal working pressure should be installed. As the last of the water leaves the pressure tank, the residual pressure shown on the gauge should not be less than zero and should give at least 15 psi (103 kPa) pressure at the highest automatic discharge device under the main roof of the building.

Air for pressure tanks should be supplied by compressors capable of delivering not less than 16 ft^3/min (0.045 m^3/min) of free air for tanks of 7500 gal (28.4 m^3) total capacity and not less than 20 ft^3/min (0.057 m^3/min) for larger sizes.

Relationship of Air Pressure and Volume in Tanks

The volume of air in the tank at any time varies inversely with the pressure:

$$\frac{P_1}{P_2} = \frac{V_2}{V_1}$$

Pressures are absolute pressures, not gauge pressures, as used in the preceding general formula. Let us apply this

TABLE 15.1.7 Typical Dimensions of Horizontal Pressure Tanks of Standard Sizes

Approx. Gross Capacity		Approx. Net Cap. 2/3 Full		Inside Diam.		Inside Length		Approx. Wt. of Water 2/3 Full	
gal	*L*	*gal*	*L*	*in.*	*m*	*ft*	*m*	*lbs*	*kg*
3000	11,355	2000	7,570	60	1.5	20.2	6.2	16,670	7,568
3000	11,355	2000	7,570	66	1.7	17.0	5.2	16,670	7,568
3000	11,355	2000	7,570	72	1.8	14.2	4.3	16,670	7,568
4500	17,033	3000	11,355	66	1.7	25.4	7.7	25,000	11,350
4500	17,033	3000	11,355	72	1.8	21.3	6.5	25,000	11,350
4500	17,033	3000	11,355	78	2.0	18.2	5.5	25,000	11,350
6000	22,710	4000	15,140	72	1.8	28.2	8.6	33,340	15,136
6000	22,710	4000	15,140	78	2.0	24.2	7.4	33,340	15,136
6000	22,710	4000	15,140	84	2.1	21.0	6.4	33,340	15,136
7500	28,388	5000	18,925	78	2.0	30.3	9.2	41,670	18,918
7500	28,388	5000	18,925	84	2.1	26.2	8.0	41,670	18,918
7500	28,388	5000	18,925	90	2.3	22.7	6.9	41,670	18,918
9000	34,065	6000	22,710	84	2.1	31.4	9.6	50,000	22,700
9000	34,065	6000	22,710	90	2.3	27.3	8.3	50,000	22,700
9000	34,065	6000	22,710	96	2.4	24.0	7.3	50,000	22,700

Note: 4500 gal (17 m^3) gross capacity is the minimum ordinarily accepted for pressure tanks for automatic sprinkler systems.

formula to the special condition that exists in a tank used to supply water for sprinklers. Except where there is danger of air lock, it is desirable to have a gauge pressure of 15 psi (103 kPa) remaining in the tank when the last water leaves. Thus,

$$P_2 = \text{Residual pressure required} + \text{atmospheric pressure}$$

$$= 15 \text{ psi} + 15 \text{ psi}$$

$$= 30 \text{ psi}$$

Since at this condition the tank is full of air,

$$V_2 = 1$$

If the tank is at or above the top line of sprinklers, the tank will be normally kept two-thirds full of water, so,

$$V_1 = \frac{1}{3}$$

Therefore,

$$P_1 = P_2 \times \frac{V_2}{V_1} = 30 \times \frac{1}{1/3} = 30 \times 3 = 90 \text{ psi}$$

The corresponding gauge pressure would be 90 psi (710 kPa), minus the atmospheric pressure, 15 psi (103 kPa), or 75 psi (517 kPa).

If the tank is below the top line of sprinklers, the required residual pressure would be increased 0.434 psi for every foot (0.912 kPa/m) of elevation represented in the distance between the base of the tank and the highest sprinkler. If we call this value *H*, we have

$$P_1 = P_2 \times \frac{V_2}{V_1} = (30 + 0.434H)\frac{V_2}{V_1}$$

Gauge pressure to be carried in the tank would be $P_1 - 15$, or

$$(30 + 0.434H)\frac{V_2}{V_1} - 15$$

For a tank ⅓ full of air $\frac{V_2}{V_1} = 3$, and gauge pressure would be

$$3(30 + 0.434H) - 15 = 75 + 1.30H$$

For a tank ½ full of air $\frac{V_2}{V_1} = 2$, and gauge pressure would be

$$2(30 + 0.434H) - 15 = 45 + 0.87H$$

Air Lock

A condition known as air lock can occur when a pressure tank and a gravity tank are connected into the sprinkler system through a common riser. Air lock occurs when the gravity water pressure at the gravity tank check valve is less than the air pressure trapped in the pressure tank and the common riser by a column of water in the sprinkler system, after water has been drained from the pressure tank. For example, if the pressure tank is kept two-thirds full of water with an air pressure of 75 psi (5.2 bar), and a sprinkler opens 35 ft (10.7 m) or more above the point the common tank riser connects to the sprinkler system, the pressure tank drains, leaving an air pressure of 15 psi (1.0 bar) balanced by a column of water of equal pressure (35 ft [10.7 m] of head) in the sprinkler system. The gravity tank check valve is held closed unless the water pressure from the gravity tank is more than 15 psi (1 bar) (35 ft [10.5 m] head).

Air lock can be prevented by increasing the volume of water and decreasing the air pressure in the pressure tank so that little or no air pressure remains after water has been exhausted. For example, if the pressure tank is kept four-fifths full of water, with an air pressure of 60 psi (4.1 bar), the air pressure remaining in the tank after water has been drained is zero, and the gravity tank check valve opens as soon as the pressure at that point from the pressure tank drops below the static head from the gravity tank.

Under normal conditions, air lock can be conveniently avoided in new equipment by connecting the gravity tank and pressure tank discharge pipes together 45 ft (13.7 m) or more below the bottom of the gravity tank (Figure 15.1.12) and by placing the gravity tank check valve at the level of the connection.

Construction of Pressure Tanks

Pressure tanks are constructed in accordance with *ASME Boiler and Pressure Vessel Code,*[8] with modifications given in NFPA 22. Important modifications are a minimum hydrostatic test at 150 psi (10 bar) and a test for tightness.

Where subject to freezing, tanks should be located in substantial noncombustible housings. Tank rooms should be large enough to provide free access to all connections, fittings, and manholes, at least 18 in. (457 mm) around the rest of the tank. The distance between the floor and any part of a tank should be at least 3 ft (0.9 m).

The interiors of pressure tanks are inspected at three-year intervals to determine whether corrosion is taking place and whether repainting or repairing is needed. When necessary, tanks should be scraped, wire brushed, and repainted with an approved metal-protective paint. Relief valves should be tested at least once each month.

Provisions should be made to drain each tank independently of all other tanks and the sprinkler system by means of a pipe not less than 1½ in. (40 mm) in diameter.

The filling supply or pump should be reliable and capable of replenishing the water to be maintained in the tank against the normal tank pressure in not more than 4 hours.

Plastic Tanks

Plastic tanks are increasingly being used for fire protection water supplies, however, not without limitations mainly related to capacity. Polyethylene tanks used in aboveground applications as gravity tanks have maximum capacities of 12,000 to 15,000 gallons. Fiber reinforced plastic (FRP) tanks used in underground applications as suction tanks have a maximum capacity of 50,000 gallons. Advantages of plastic tanks are that they do not rust or corrode, are lighter in weight, and do not require assembly. Disadvantages of plastic tanks include their limited capacity and combustibility (requiring sprinkler protection where installed in buildings).

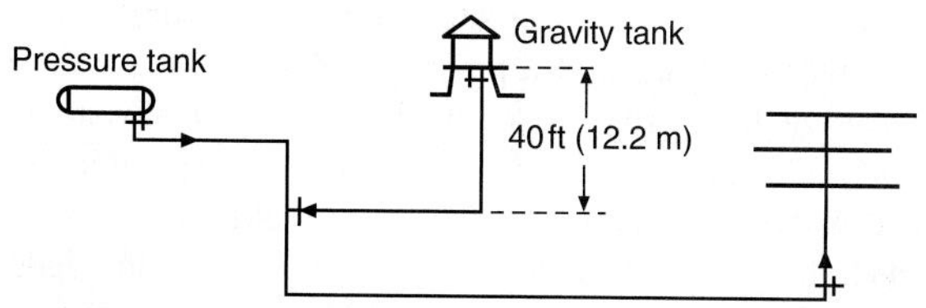

FIGURE 15.1.12 Gravity Tank and Pressure Tank Showing How Risers Are Connected to Avoid Air Lock

NATURAL AND CONSTRUCTED SUCTION FACILITIES

The advantages of piped systems make them the first choice for a water supply for fire protection, but sometimes other water may be more convenient or less expensive. Examples are rural areas and resorts without a piped water system for fire protection. In many of these, however, water is available for fire protection in the ocean, lakes, ponds, rivers, and streams. Cisterns or tanks can be used at locations distant from natural water sources. Small ponds in parks and swimming pools are not particularly good sources of emergency water because this competes with their regular purposes.

For water sources such as those mentioned, the general term *suction supplies* is used to distinguish these supplies from the conventional public water systems for fire protection. Static suction supplies must, in general, be used where they are found and require drafting to lift the water and pumping to move the water to the point of use by fire protection systems. Although there have been instances where water in suburbs, farms, and forests was used to provide effective fire streams at very long distances, laying hose lines more than 750 to 1000 ft (225 to 300 m) seldom makes it possible to provide good protection because of the time required to lay the long lines and the greater difficulty in operating them. Before using naturally occurring water supply sources such as rivers, streams, ponds, lakes, and wells, their reliability, accessibility, and ability to meet required fire protection system demands must be verified. Seasonal fluctuations due to other usage, drought, and freezing must be considered and evaluated. Water supplies from rivers, streams, ponds, lakes, and wells need to be managed to avoid the introduction of mud, sediment, and vegetation. In addition, these water supplies should pass through removable screens and strainers that are installed and maintained to ensure an unobstructed water supply.

Ground Tanks and Cisterns

If no hydrant on a water system is available, one way to ensure the amount of water required for fire fighting is to store it in underground tanks or cisterns at locations where hydrants would normally be installed. The fire department pumper can then get water from a connection on the tank or by dropping a suction hose into the tank. Such tanks and cisterns are filled from domestic water sources too small for fire fighting. The water does not have to be changed so frequently that it presents difficulties.

Static water supplies are of obvious value in rural, farm, and remote areas, but they are equally important for emergency conditions in more urban areas. Before the present public water systems were developed, some cities provided underground reservoirs or cisterns for fire protection. When water was needed for fire fighting, a pumper suction hose was simply dropped through a manhole. Some of these cisterns are still used in San Francisco and Chicago. Even though San Francisco has a regular water system and a separate system of high-pressure mains, it has been considered prudent, because of the threat of earthquake, to keep over 100 cisterns in service, most of which hold 75,000 gal (284 m^3). Some of the oldest cisterns have brick walls. Newer ones are reinforced concrete.

Rivers and Ponds

Rivers and ponds are important auxiliary water sources, but merely because the water can be seen does not mean that it can be used for fire fighting. These sources of water must have suitable approaches so that fire apparatus can get near the water without becoming mired. A cleared space and some fill in many cases will provide access. These sources must be studied to determine that the water is available all year round and to select the best possible approach. They should also be recorded and mapped and given periodic attention in much the same manner that hydrants are maintained.

At such locations, it is usually necessary to provide a wet pit, basin, or cistern into which water can flow and the pumper suction strainer can be placed. There should be a screen or weir so that large objects will not interfere with the suction strainer. In some places, a permanent suction pipe and strainer can be installed. The details of such an arrangement are the same as those for a fire pump operating under a lift. NFPA 20, *Standard for the Installation of Stationary Pumps for Fire Protection,* contains guidelines for proper arrangement of wet pits for supplying vertical shaft fire pumps taking suction under a lift. The suction pipe should be laid with enough cover so that it will not freeze. It can be connected at the top to a hydrant with one or more pumper suction connections.

Small Streams and Brooks

Where water supply comes from a brook or stream, it is usually best to drain the water into a sump rather than attempt to use it straight from the flowing stream. If there is a marshy bank or shore, it may be best to go out into the pond or stream to a point where water can be collected in a sump. From the sump in the pond or stream, a pipe should be laid for draining to another sump, the latter located near where the fire apparatus will stand.

In some sumps, and particularly in open water that freezes over in winter, covers may not be feasible at the point where the sump is provided for pumper suction. At such locations, an anchored plug of wood can be floated where the pumper suction should be taken. Such a plug should have a minimum diameter larger than the pumper suction hose and be tapered so that, when frozen in ice, it can be driven down and out of position with a sledgehammer.

In some parts of the country, streams do not flow continuously. A covered cistern of generous capacity may be filled when water flows. Thus, the water may be stored for a longer period than it would keep in an open reservoir.

Water from streams and ponds is more important in areas without public water systems. There are areas where even a brook, if dammed and with a proper pumper approach and a suction basin, can provide good protection at little cost.

For projects in which a stream will be dammed to form static water, experienced civil engineers should be consulted. Details of the dam construction and decisions about the amount of water to be impounded depend on many factors and may require a comprehensive engineering survey. The dam's effect on users of the stream and flood conditions also has to be considered.

Harbors and Rivers

The principal problem with using harbors and rivers as suction supplies is that their water levels change. In harbors, ocean tide levels vary continuously throughout any given 24 hour period. River water levels are seasonal, but the problem is generally the same.

Where there is little fluctuation in the level of a natural water source, a simple pier or platform may be all that is needed to make the water available. If a pumper can be driven onto a sturdy pier, it can go to work when its suction line is dropped over the side. But where the water level varies, special arrangements are needed. If the water is always deep enough for drafting, a hinged ramp leading down to a large float is feasible. But more common is a sloping beach down which the water recedes too far to be accessible at all times. Reservoirs that can be filled at high tide are one solution to this problem.

Where a bridge passes over tidewater, water can be obtained by permanently installing a deep-well pump with a discharge pipe to a point convenient for fire department pumper use. The most practical way to use tidewater supplies is to provide pumps on boats, supplementary to any fireboats in service. Relatively large quantities of water for fire fighting can be obtained from river and harbor sources because large-capacity pumps are normally provided on fireboats, and where there are no fireboats, large pumps can be installed on a boat or barge and pressed into use to supply water for fire protection. To use the water on land, it is necessary to provide a place at which a fireboat or a barge with pumps can tie up and discharge into tanks or a special pipe system with hydrants from which land-based pumping equipment can take the water.

Wells

Wells have become increasingly popular for both domestic use and fire supply for industrial sites, and in more rural areas, located beyond the reach of a piped water supply. Before a well is constructed, a thorough examination of the groundwater must be made. This examination generally includes an aquifer performance analysis and a review of the history of nearby wells. The water in the ground must be of sufficient capacity and dependability and of reasonably good quality. A vertical-shaft turbine pump is used to draw the water from wells into the fire system or into a storage tank.

SUMMARY

Water storage facilities and pump suction supplies are a crucial element for fire protection systems. To ensure an adequate and usable water supply for fire protection, it is necessary to properly design and engineer these supplies to (1) ensure an adequate capacity and duration for the fire protection system being supplied; (2) make sure that the structural design includes all necessary features for resistance to earthquakes and other external exposures (including fire); and (3) ensure that an adequate heating system is provided to prevent freezing of the stored water supply. The discussion within this chapter is intended to make that process easier. For best results, it would be prudent to employ the services of experienced designers and suppliers to meet those goals.

BIBLIOGRAPHY

References Cited

1. AWS D1.1-2006, *Structural Welding Code, Steel,* American Welding Society, Inc., Miami, FL, 2006.
2. AWWA D100-05 (AWS D5.2-84), *Welded Steel Tanks for Water Storage,* American Water Works Association, Denver, CO, 2005.
3. AWWA D103-97, *Factory-Coated Bolted Steel Tanks for Water Storage,* American Water Works Association, Denver, CO, 1997.
4. *Standard Specifications of the American Wood Preservers Association,* American Wood Preservers Association, Washington, DC, 2003.
5. ACI 318M-2005, *Building Code Requirements for Reinforced Concrete,* American Concrete Institute, Detroit, MI, 2005.
6. ACI 301-2005, *Specifications for Structural Concrete for Buildings,* American Concrete Institute, Detroit, MI, 2005.
7. *Testing and Monitoring Program for Solar-Heated Water Storage Tanks,* prepared for the National Research Council of Canada, Ottawa, Ontario, 1984.
8. *Boiler and Pressure Vessel Code,* American Society of Mechanical Engineers, New York, 2004.

NFPA Codes, Standards, and Recommended Practices

Reference to the following NFPA codes, standards, and recommended practices will provide further information on fixed water storage facilities discussed in this chapter. (See the latest version of The NFPA Catalog *for availability of current editions of the following documents.)*

NFPA 13, *Standard for the Installation of Sprinkler Systems*

NFPA 20, *Standard for the Installation of Stationary Pumps for Fire Protection*

NFPA 22, *Standard for Water Tanks for Private Fire Protection*

NFPA 25, *Standard for the Inspection, Testing, and Maintenance of Water-Based Fire Protection Systems*

Chapter 2

Water Supply Requirements for Public Supply Systems

Lawrence J. Wenzel

The amount of water needed and the economics of supplying it are basic questions underlying the planning of water supply systems for fire suppression.

This chapter gives information on planning for public water supply systems and outlines the methods used to evaluate public supplies for their adequacy and reliability. The chapter does not cover the specifics of water supply requirements for automatic suppression systems within individual properties.

Specifics are covered in the following chapters of Section 16: Chapter 3, "Automatic Sprinkler Systems"; Chapter 6, "Residential Sprinkler Systems"; Chapter 8, "Water Mist Fire Suppression Systems"; Chapter 9, "Water Spray Protection"; and Chapter 10, "Standpipe and Hose Systems."

FACTORS AFFECTING PUBLIC WATER SUPPLY DESIGN

Most public water supply systems serving a substantial number of customers are, and should be, designed for a dual purpose: (1) to supply water for normal domestic demands, such as drinking and sanitary purposes, as well as for processing and industrial uses, and (2) to provide water for emergency purposes. The latter purpose would include the supply for fire department use, such as through hydrants, and for fixed automatic suppression systems, such as automatic sprinklers and standpipe systems.

The variety of hazards encountered in most communities and the need to plan for future growth must be considered when evaluating these objectives. In some cities, there may be a heavy industrial demand. At the same time, demands for industrial use and lawn sprinkling may affect the required capacity of the system. The adequacy of a public water system for fire protection cannot be taken for granted, and the other demands must be determined to estimate their effects on the capacity of the system.

Public water systems must also be reliable. Because the occurrence of a fire should not affect domestic demands, the water system must be designed to meet the simultaneous demand rates for both purposes. In addition, portions of the pumping or distribution system may be out of service due to breakdown or scheduled maintenance, so the consequences of these interruptions must be examined for acceptability when evaluating system reliability.

When assessing reliability, another factor to take into account is the system's ability to supply increased amounts of water in peak periods that may last only a relatively short time. For example, oceanfront communities in northern climates, such as areas on Cape Cod, Massachusetts, will have a much higher seasonal demand that will begin Memorial Day and end around Labor Day each year. The increase in demand due to the influx of people has a definite effect on the system's ability to supply water at the time of an emergency. The system's ability to provide fire flow during peak usage seasons must be considered in any evaluation. Thus, testing to evaluate a system's reliability must consider the time that the system will be subjected to its highest flows.

Lawrence J. Wenzel, P.E., is a senior engineer with Hughes Associates, Inc., in Baltimore, Maryland.

Chapter Contents

Key Terms

American Water Works Association (AWWA), hydraulic calculations, Insurance Services Office (ISO) grading schedule, needed fire flow (NFF), water pressure, water supply (domestic service), water supply (fire protection), water supply (public)

WATER REQUIREMENTS

Demands for Domestic Purposes

To determine the domestic demands on a public water supply, it is necessary to focus on variations in water consumption with respect to the time of year, the day of the week, and even the hour of the day. Obviously, as more water is used in a given system for normal consumption, less remains for fire protection. Normal consumption demands are usually expressed in the following terms:

- Average daily demand, or the average of the total amount of water used each day during a 1 year period.
- Maximum daily demand, or the maximum total amount of water used during any 24 hour period in a 3 year period. Unusual situations that might have caused an excessive use of water, such as refilling a reservoir after cleaning, should not be considered when determining this figure.
- Peak hourly demand, or the maximum amount of water used in any given hour of a day.

A joint report of committees from the American Society of Civil Engineers, the American Water Works Association (AWWA), and others suggested that the maximum general service demand on a waterworks system be taken as the peak hourly demand during a test year.[1] The report noted that this figure was the only figure that could be fairly compared with the maximum fire flow requirement.

The maximum daily demand can be estimated as 1.5 times the average daily consumption if the actual maximum is not known. The peak hourly rate usually varies from two to four times the normal hourly rate. The effect these varying consumption rates have on the ability of the system to deliver required fire flows varies with the system design. Both maximum daily consumption and peak hourly consumption should be considered to ensure that water supplies and pressures do not reach dangerously low levels during these periods and that adequate water will be available if there is a fire. But keep in mind that these are only estimates and there may be other issues to consider. For example, a water supply for an area that has a high concentration of carpet or textile mills as its primary industrial base may have periods that can severely skew these estimates. If all of the carpet mills open their "dye beks" at the same time on a given day, and conduct a heavy amount of dyeing operations for an extended period of time, there can be a severe spike in the daily consumption. For the period that their operations are being conducted, the water supply in the area may be dangerously low. These types of industrial periods must be considered.

Water Requirements for Fire Fighting

The water requirements for fire fighting include the rate of flow, the residual pressure required at that flow, and the total quantity required. The American Water Works Association defines the required fire flow as "the rate of water flow, at a residual pressure of 20 psi and for a specified duration that is necessary to control a major fire in a specific structure."[2] The fire protection community has informally adopted the figure of 20 psi as the lowest pressure to which fire protection systems will be designed. These include sprinkler systems and fire pumps using the municipal supply as a suction or supply source.

CALCULATING FIRE FLOW RATES

The required flow rate for properties protected by automatic sprinklers is based either on the sprinkler system design as required by NFPA 13, *Standard for the Installation of Sprinkler Systems* (hereinafter referred to as NFPA 13), or on the exact details of the hydraulic sprinkler system design for the systems installed in the structure. (Also see NFPA 13R, *Standard for the Installation of Sprinkler Systems in Residential Occupancies up to and Including Four Stories in Height,* and NFPA 13D, *Standard for the Installation of Sprinkler Systems in One- and Two-Family Dwellings and Manufactured Homes.*) The flow required is that of the sprinkler system plus the anticipated hose stream or manual fire-fighting requirements. It also may be necessary to consider additional water supply needs for buildings with neighboring structures that present an exposure to the structure being considered.

Several methods are currently used to calculate required waterflow rates for *nonsprinklered* properties. These include the following:

- The Insurance Services Office (ISO) method
- The Iowa State University (ISU) method
- The Illinois Institute of Technology Research Institute method

Insurance Services Office (ISO) Method

Probably the most comprehensive and widely recommended methods for estimating fire flow requirements are found in the Insurance Services Office's *Fire Suppression Rating Schedule.*[3] It provides guidance for estimating fire flow requirements for specific structures and was designed for insurance rating purposes. The flows determined by this method are generally considered a good estimate, and, as a result, the ISO method has received widespread use. The ISO method considers building construction, occupancy, adjacent exposed buildings, and fire communication paths between buildings.

The basic formula in the schedule is

$$NFF_i = (C_i)(O_i)(X + P)_i$$

where

NFF_i = Needed fire flow (*NFF*) in gal per min (L/min)

C_i = A construction factor that depends on the construction of the structure under consideration

O_i = An occupancy factor that depends on the combustibility of the occupancy

$(X + P)_i$ = An exposure factor that depends on the extent of exposure from and to adjacent structures

The subscripts in the formula indicate that, where portions of a building have differing characteristics, a factor can be calculated for each section and multiplied by the percentage it represents of the effective area to obtain a weighted factor. The weighted C_i factor should not be less than the individual factor required for any individual section.

Construction Factor. The construction factor, C_i, is calculated from the following formula:

$$C_i = 18f\sqrt{A_i}$$

where

F = Coefficient related to the class of construction

= 1.5 for construction class 1 (frame)

= 1.0 for construction class 2 (joisted masonry)

= 0.8 for construction class 3 (noncombustible) or construction class 4 (masonry, noncombustible)

= 0.6 for construction class 5 (modified fire resistant) or construction class 6 (fire resistive)

A_i = Effective building area

The effective building area is the total square foot (m^2) area of the largest floor plus one of the following:

- For construction classes 1 through 4, 50 percent of all other floors
- For construction classes 5 and 6, 25 percent of the area not exceeding the two other largest floors when all of the vertical openings have at least 1½-hour-rated protection, or 50 percent of the area not exceeding eight other floors when vertical openings are unprotected or have less than 1½ hour protection

The value of C_i should never be less than 500 gpm (1893 L/min) for any construction class, nor greater than 8000 gpm (30,280 L/min) for construction classes 1 and 2, and 6000 gpm (22,710 L/min) for construction classes 3, 4, 5, and 6, or any single, one-story building, regardless of construction.

Occupancy Factor. The occupancy factor, O_i, reflects the combustibility of the occupancy on the needed fire flow and is determined from the occupancy combustibility class. Occupancy factors can be found in Table 15.2.1. Typical occupancies and their classification can be found in Table 15.2.2. For more detailed occupancy classification information, see NFPA *101*®, *Life Safety Code*®.

Exposure and Communication [$(X = P)_i$] Factors. The exposure and communication factors are determined as

$$(X + P)_i = 1 + \sum_{i=g}^{n} X_i + P_i$$

where

n = Number of sides of subject building

$(X + P)_i$ = A maximum value of 1.75

The exposure factor, X_i, reflects the need for additional water to reduce the exposure to adjacent buildings. It depends on the separation distance, the construction of the exposed building wall, and a length-height value—that is, the length of the exposed wall in feet (m) multiplied by the height in stories. Values can be obtained from Table 15.2.3.

TABLE 15.2.1 Occupancy Factors

Occupancy Combustibility Class	*Occupancy Factor (O_i)*
C-1 (Noncombustible)	0.75
C-2 (Limited combustible)	0.85
C-3 (Combustible)	1.00
C-4 (Free burning)	1.15
C-5 (Rapid burning)	1.25

The fire communication factor, P_i, reflects the potential fire spread through open or enclosed communicating passageways between buildings and is taken from Table 15.2.4. Where there is more than one connection, only the one with the largest factor is used. Where there are no openings, $P_i = 0$.

Needed Fire Flow. The needed fire flow (*NFF*) is calculated from the formula given previously and from the foregoing factors. The *NFF* calculated from the formula should be rounded to the nearest 250 gpm (946 L/min) for flows under 2500 gpm (9463 L/min) and to the nearest 500 gpm (1893 L/min) for larger flows and then adjusted by the following:

- For buildings with a wood roof, add 500 gpm (1893 L/min).
- The needed flow should not exceed 12,000 gpm (45,420 L/min) nor be less than 500 gpm (1893 L/min). The practical reason for these figures is that manual fire-fighting methods using hose streams and heavy stream appliances are not likely to need a larger supply, considering the general arrangement of buildings and the availability of hydrants.
- For habitational buildings, use the calculated *NFF* up to 3500 gpm (13,248 L/min) maximum.
- For groupings of one-family and small two-family dwellings not more than two stories high, the required fire flow given in Table 15.2.5 may be used.

Iowa State University (ISU) Method

The Iowa State University method[4] is another common method used to determine waterflow rates for fire fighting. It uses a more theoretical approach and is based on the amount of water needed to deplete the oxygen in a confined area when the water is vaporized into steam by the heat of the fire. Tests conducted by the university indicate that a fire is best controlled if the amount of water necessary to deplete the oxygen is applied within 30 seconds.

The required flow in gpm is given as

$$\text{Required flow} = \frac{V}{100}$$

where V is the enclosed volume (length of the structure multiplied by its width and height) in cubic feet. (For SI units: 1 gpm = 3.785 L/min; 1 ft^3 = 0.0283 m^3.)

This method is unique in that it does not consider the occupancy hazard, only the volume of the building to be filled with steam. It is essentially a formula that is used in determining the

TABLE 15.2.2 Occupancy Classification

C-1 (Noncombustible)	C-4 (Fire burning)
Steel or concrete products storage, unpackaged	Aircraft hangers, with or without servicing/repair
C-2 (Limited combustible)	Apparel manufacturing
Apartments	Auditoriums
Ceramics manufacturing	Breweries
Churches	Building material sales and storage
Concrete products manufacturing	Cotton gins
Courthouses	Food processing
Dormitories	Freight depots, terminals
Hospitals	Furniture—new or secondhand
Hotels	Metal coating or finishing
Metal products fabrication	Paper and paper product sales and storage
Metals industries (primary)	Paper products manufacturing
Motels	Printing shops and allied industries
Offices	Rubber products manufacturing
Parking garages	Theaters, other than motion picture
Schools	Warehouses
	Wood product sales and storage
	Woodworking industries
C-3 (Combustible)	**C-5 (Rapid burning)**
Amusement park buildings, including arcades and game rooms	Cereal or flour mills
Automobile sales and services	Chemical manufacturing
Baking and confectionery	Chemical sales and storage
Dairy processing	Cleaning and dyeing material sales and storage
Department stores	Distilleries
Discount stores	Meat or poultry processing
Food and beverage—sales, service, or storage	Paint sales and storage
General merchandise—sales or storage	Plastic or plastic product sales and storage
Hardware, including electrical fixtures and supplies	Plastic products manufacturing
Leather processing	Rag sales and storage
Motion picture theaters	Textile manufacturing
Pharmaceutical retail sales and storage	Textile products fabrication, except clothes
Repair or service shops	Upholstering shops
Soft drink bottling	Waste and reclaimed materials sales and storage
Supermarkets	
Tobacco processing	
Vacant buildings	

amount of water required to begin to reduce the size of a compartment fire.

Due to inefficiencies in applying water, some experts feel that the rate should be 2 to 4 gal per 100 ft^3 (7.6 to 15.0 L/2.8 m^3) of building volume rather than the 1 gal per 100 ft^3 (3.785 L/2.8 m^3) in the formula. Other variations include changing the value in the denominator based on the occupancy hazard. Obviously, high-hazard occupancies require more water to absorb the heat release of the burning occupancy.

This formula has been used for approximately 50 years and is extremely simple to apply. For most buildings, the entire volume of the structure should be used, including the volume of basements, attics, crawl spaces, and other concealed spaces. For groups of buildings, the largest calculated flow rate should be used.

Illinois Institute of Technology Research Institute Method

The Illinois Institute of Technology method was based on a survey of 134 fires in the Chicago area. The results of the survey were used with regression analysis to develop fire flow formulas based on building area. The fire flow rate is based on one of the following formulas:

$$\text{Flow for residential occupancies} = 9 \times 10^{-2}A^2 + 50 \times 10^{-2}A$$

$$\text{Flow for other occupancies} = -1.3 \times 10^{-5}A^2 + 42 \times 10^{-2}A$$

where A is the area of the fire in square feet. (For SI units: 1 ft^2 = 0.0929 m^2.)

TABLE 15.2.3 Factors for Exposure, X_i

			Construction of Facing Wall of Exposed Building Classes			
				2, 4, 5, and 6		
Construction of Facing Wall of Subject Building	*Distance (ft) to the Exposed Building*	*Length-Height of Facing Wall of Exposed Building*	*1, 3*	*Unprotected Openings*	*Semiprotected Openings (Wired Glass or Outside Open Sprinklers)*	*Blank Wall*
Frame, metal, or masonry with openings	0–10	1–100	0.22	0.21	0.16	0
		101–200	0.23	0.22	0.17	0
		201–300	0.24	0.23	0.18	0
		301–400	0.25	0.24	0.19	0
		Over 400	0.25	0.25	0.20	0
	11–30	1–100	0.17	0.15	0.11	0
		101–200	0.18	0.16	0.12	0
		201–300	0.19	0.18	0.14	0
		301–400	0.20	0.19	0.15	0
		Over 400	0.20	0.19	0.15	0
	31–60	1–100	0.12	0.10	0.07	0
		101–200	0.13	0.11	0.08	0
		201–300	0.14	0.13	0.10	0
		301–400	0.15	0.14	0.11	0
		Over 400	0.15	0.15	0.12	0
	61–100	1–100	0.08	0.06	0.04	0
		101–200	0.08	0.07	0.05	0
		201–300	0.09	0.08	0.06	0
		301–400	0.10	0.09	0.07	0
		Over 400	0.10	0.10	0.08	0
Blank masonry wall	Facing wall of the exposed building is higher than subject building. Use the above table, except use only the length-height of facing wall of the exposed building above the height of the facing wall of the subject building. Buildings five stories or over in height consider as five stories. When the height of the facing wall of the exposed building is the same or lower than the height of the facing wall of the subject building, $X_i = 0$.					

For SI units: 1 ft = 0.305 m.
Source: Insurance Services Office © 1980.

OTHER FLOW CONSIDERATIONS

Regardless of the method used to determine the flow rate, the required fire flow should be available simultaneously with consumption at the maximum daily rate.

When evaluating the flow required for general public protection, both the AWWA and the ISO suggest that 3500 gpm (13,248 L/min) is the upper limit to be provided and that large facilities or those with severe hazards that need flow rates up to 12,000 gpm (45,420 L/min) be individually analyzed to determine the required flow rate.

There are fires in which quantities of water in excess of the required fire flow are used. Water supplies of 50,000 gpm (189,250 L/min) or greater have been used in fire suppression, but designing systems capable of delivering flows of that magnitude is not cost-effective nor practical. Expecting the municipal system to deliver these large flow rates is not reasonable; thus, private supplies are often developed to become the primary supply for large-flow industrial sites, or to augment the municipal supply. This development is a site-by-site determination, based on the available municipal flow rates and supplies.

Fire Flow Duration

The number of hours during which the required fire flow should be available varies from 2 to 10 hours, as indicated in Table 15.2.6. It should be noted that many water authorities place an upper limit of 2 to 4 hours on fire water supply duration due to economics.

Evaluating System Capacity

The capacity of a water system is determined by the total amount of water it must furnish. This amount is the sum of water required for domestic or industrial uses and water required for the fire service. In small towns the requirements for fire protection almost always exceed other requirements.

The AWWA recommends that the rate used be either the peak hourly rate or the maximum daily rate plus fire flow,

TABLE 15.2.4 Factors for Communications, P_i

	Fire-Resistive, Noncombustible, or Slow-Burning Communications				Communications with Combustible Construction					
	Open	Enclosed			Open			Enclosed		
Description of Protection of Passageway Openings	*Any Length*	*10 ft or Less*	*11 ft to 20 ft*	*21 ft to 50 ft*[a]	*10 ft or Less*	*11 ft to 20 ft*	*21 ft to 50 ft*[a]	*10 ft or Less*	*11 ft to 20 ft*	*21 ft to 50 ft*[a]
Unprotected	0	[b]	0.30	0.20	0.30	0.20	0.10	[b]	[b]	0.30
Single Class A fire door at one end of passageway	0	0.20	0.10	0.00	0.20	0.15	0.00	0.30	0.20	0.10
Single Class B fire door at one end of passageway	0	0.30	0.20	0.10	0.25	0.20	0.10	0.35	0.25	0.15
Single Class A fire door at each end or double Class A fire doors at one end of passageway	0	0.00	0	0.00	0.00	0.00	0.00	0.00	0.00	0.00
Single Class B fire door at each end or double Class B fire doors at one end of passageway	0	0.10	0.05	0.00	0.00	0.00	0.00	0.15	0.10	0.00

For SI units: 1 ft = 0.305 m.
Note: When a party wall has communicating openings protected by a single automatic or self-closing Class B fire door, it qualifies as a division wall (defined in greater detail in the ISO *Commercial Fire Rating Schedule*) for reduction of area.
Note: Where communications are protected by a recognized water curtain, the value of P_i is 0.
[a]For over 50 ft, $P_i = 0$.
[b]For unprotected passageways of this length, consider the two buildings as a single fire division.

TABLE 15.2.5 Fire Flows for Groups of Dwellings

Exposure Distances		Suggested Required Fire Flow	
ft	*m*	*gpm*	*L/min*
Over 100	30.5	500	1893
31–100	9.5–30.5	750–1000	2839–3785
11–30	3.4–9.2	1000	3785
10 or less	3.1 or less	1500	5678

whichever is larger. In most large cities, the peak hourly rate exceeds the maximum daily consumption rate plus fire flow and is, therefore, the controlling factor in the supply system design. In smaller communities, however, the reverse is true and the maximum daily consumption rate plus fire flow is the controlling factor. For many years, water consumption has been increasing in most municipalities, resulting in increased peak hourly rates. Consequently, there has been an increase in the number of municipalities in which the peak hourly rate controls designs of the supply system. However, there is no guarantee that a fire will not occur at the peak hour, and some recommend that the capacity of the system be sufficient to meet the peak hourly rate plus the fire flow rate.

Fire flows are a very important consideration in all areas served by the distribution system and, in many instances, they govern the size of pipe used in these locations. In all systems, the supply should be sufficient to provide for automatic sprinklers and other automatic water-based fire suppression systems, in addition to the other demand rates imposed on the system. For example, many smaller cities and large towns restrict lawn watering in summer months to specified periods, depending on local conditions. The demand rates imposed by lawn watering are excessive in many water supply systems, possibly depleting storage facilities and reducing pressure throughout the system for many hours. In such situations, there would be little or no water available for fire suppression systems, particularly at higher elevations.

PRESSURE CHARACTERISTICS OF SYSTEMS

The pressures for which systems are normally designed are the result of practical attempts to provide adequate pressures both for domestic consumption and for fire protection. If either demands special ranges of pressure, materials and design methods are available that will allow almost any desired range.

For example, San Francisco has a separate system, designated the "high-pressure system," that is under the control of the fire department. All system pipe is heavy cast iron, tar coated, and lined, and it is tested on installation and repair to 450 psi (3103 kPa). Two steam-operated pump stations can pump water from San Francisco Bay into the system, and 20,000 gpm (75,700 L/min) at 250 psi (1724 kPa) can be delivered to most of the principal mercantile district. San Francisco provided this

TABLE 15.2.6 Duration of Required Fire Flow

Required Fire Flow					Required Fire Flow				
gpm	*L/min*	*Million Gallons per Day*	*Million Liters per Day*	*Duration Hours*	*gpm*	*L/min*	*Million Gallons per Day*	*Million Liters per Day*	*Duration Hours*
1000	3,785	1.44	5.45	2	4,500	17,033	6.48	24.53	4
1250	4,731	1.80	6.81	2	5,000	18,925	7.20	27.25	5
1500	5,678	2.16	8.18	2	5,500	20,818	7.92	29.99	5
1750	6,624	2.52	9.54	2	6,000	22,710	8.64	32.71	6
2000	7,570	2.88	10.90	2	7,000	26,495	10.08	38.16	7
2250	8,516	3.24	12.26	2	8,000	30,280	11.52	43.61	8
2500	9,463	3.60	13.63	2	9,000	34,065	12.96	49.06	9
3000	11,355	4.32	16.35	3	10,000	37,850	14.40	54.51	10
3500	13,248	5.04	19.08	3	11,000	41,635	15.84	59.96	10
4000	15,140	5.76	21.80	4	12,000	45,420	17.28	65.41	10

system primarily because an earthquake might put the regular public water system out of service. A few other cities have similar high-pressure systems.

Modern fire department pumpers make heavy streams and high pressures available from ordinary water systems where adequate volume is provided. Cities that formerly had separate fire main systems operating at so-called high pressures now generally keep them at normal public water pressures. The second system still provides an advantage, though, even if it is not at high pressure, because it is still available and becomes a valuable source of "volume."

Public water systems reflect a compromise on the question of pressures. Pressures in the range of 65 to 80 psi (448 to 552 kPa) are common. This range, which is adequate for ordinary consumption in buildings up to about 10 stories, will provide a good supply of water for automatic sprinkler systems in buildings of about four stories, in which occupancies are classified as "ordinary" or "light." Where pressures of this order are provided, it is reasonably easy to compensate for local fluctuations.

Because of the increased cost of energy, closer scrutiny is being given to the water pressure that systems should provide. A reduction in water pressure will substantially reduce pumping costs. Before a general reduction is made, however, a study should be conducted as to the effects it could have on sprinklers and other fixed fire suppression systems. If a reduction in pressure is planned, it is imperative that the system remain capable of meeting anticipated demand rates, or steps must be taken to lower the demand rates to a point where they will be within the capability of the system. In many cases, the reduction of pressure will have an adverse effect on private industrial and commercial-building fire protection systems using pumps, as the municipal supply is the suction source for many private systems.

A minimum residual pressure of at least 20 psi (138 kPa) should be maintained at hydrants delivering the required fire flow. Pumpers will operate where hydrant pressures are less. Where hydrants are well distributed and of the proper size and type so that friction losses in the municipal system will not be excessive, it may be possible to set 10 psi (69 kPa) as the minimum operating pressure. Sufficient hydrant pressure should be maintained to prevent a negative pressure from developing in the street mains, which might cause damage to the municipal system. In some older systems, back siphonage of polluted water from some interconnected source may still be a problem. But, in most areas and municipal systems, better backflow prevention has eliminated this problem. Many state health departments prohibit the use of residential pressures of less than 20 psi (138 kPa). However, in a severe fire situation in many locations, a pressure lower than 20 psi (138 kPa) may have to be used to develop necessary fire flows and the movement of water volume from one area to another. Proper emergency planning on the part of the public fire officials can generally eliminate this situation.

Pressures in a public water system may be considered excessive as they approach 150 psi (1034 kPa). As pressures increase, they tend to cause leaks in domestic plumbing, and special attention is required to restrain pipelines in the ground. Pipe and fittings used in ordinary public water systems are designed for maximum working pressures of 150 psi (1034 kPa), but it is not good practice to operate with pressures that high. Pressure-reducing valves can be used in sections of a system where variations in topography result in excessive pressures. Individual water services to buildings may require pressure-reducing valves to keep the pressure on domestic piping at safe levels.

SYSTEMS FOR HIGHER ELEVATIONS

When water must be supplied to high elevations, a separate water distribution system is usually provided for the elevated section so that reasonable pressures are maintained. In such cases, the elevated area should be provided with its own water storage facility, and pumps may be provided to boost the water from other parts of the system.

Likewise, the upper stories of a high-rise building are sometimes provided with dedicated risers (express risers) to deliver water to these upper floors. High-rise structures are normally divided into a number of pressure zones, and zones of more than 12 stories can be outside the normal pressure ranges. In any case, each pressure zone must be provided with water in the amounts needed for sprinkler system and hose stream use, and each system is usually supplied by a series of pumps and, sometimes, tanks arranged so that each zone is fed from the zone below. Care should be taken to ensure that pumps would be able to operate even during power failures.

For information and guidance concerning water supplies for high-rise structures, see NFPA 13; NFPA 14, *Standard for the Installation of Standpipe and Hose Systems;* and NFPA 20, *Standard for the Installation of Stationary Pumps for Fire Protection.*

ADEQUACY AND RELIABILITY OF SUPPLY

The adequacy of any given water supply system can be determined by engineering estimates. The source (e.g., storage facilities and distribution system) must be sufficient to furnish all the water that combined fire and domestic needs may call for at any one time. The arrangement of the supply and pumping facilities may render the supply inadequate or affect its reliability.

Pumping systems commonly are arranged so that one set of pumps takes suction from wells or from a river, lake, or other body of water. If the water does not have to be filtered, the pumps may discharge directly into the distribution system. Where filtration or other treatment is necessary, pumps take suction from the primary or raw water source and discharge to sedimentation basins or other facilities and then to filter beds. After the water is processed, it flows to clear-water reservoirs from which a second set of pumps takes suction and discharges the water directly into the supply system. Unfortunately, failure of any part of the equipment may affect the entire system.

There are still communities that use direct-pumping methods and have no stored water capacity. These types of systems rely on pumps operating in stages, based on the demand. These "pump-only" systems require constant attention to the mechanics of the equipment, as each piece of pumping equipment is that much more important. Without storage capacity, which can buy maintenance time for repairs and parts replacement, additional thought has to be put into keeping critical equipment maintained and backed up.

When assessing the reliability of the supply works, one should evaluate the following:

- Minimum yield
- Frequency and duration of droughts
- Condition of intakes
- Possibility of earthquakes, floods, and forest fires
- Ice formations
- Silting up or shifting of river channels
- Security of installations to prevent physical damage
- Availability of replacement equipment and parts
- Ability to divert flow within the system to avoid local outages and reduced pressure

Reservoirs out of service for cleaning and the interdependence of parts of waterworks also affect reliability. The condition, arrangement, and dependability of individual units of plant equipment, such as pumps, engines, generators, electric motors, fuel supply, electric transmission facilities, and similar items, are also factors. Pumping stations of combustible construction may be destroyed by fire unless they are protected by automatic sprinkler systems.

Duplication of pumping units and storage facilities, and arrangement of mains and other distribution piping so that water may be supplied to any area from more than one direction, are measures that can ensure continuous operation. The importance of duplicate facilities is shown by the frequency of their use. Many utilities design their systems so that the peak hourly rate and required fire flow rate can be supplied when any pump or section of the distribution system is out of service.

The amount of water needed to control and extinguish a fire in a given property currently cannot be established in precise terms. Better fire experience databases should make it possible to tailor fire flows more specifically to conditions that might be expected at the time of a fire. Better analysis may indicate a need to increase fire flow beyond what is presently required, or it may result in a water system design based on a balance between the risk involved and the economics of maintaining the water system.

A detailed discussion of all the factors to be considered in designing a water supply system is beyond the scope of this handbook. An overview of the subject can be found in AWWA M24, *Dual Water Systems,* and AWWA M31, *Distribution System Requirements for Fire Protection.*

FACTORS AFFECTING WATER REQUIREMENTS

Codes and Ordinances

Fire prevention codes can effectively limit hazards and ignition sources within buildings, which, in turn, may limit the number and size of fires by controlling combustibles in a fire area. A good building code further reduces the chance for a serious fire by requiring construction materials and building assemblies that will contain a developing fire to a given area. Codes alone can reduce considerably the amount of water needed for fire fighting. Zoning ordinances that establish distances between properties can be effective in controlling exposure situations.

Fire Detection and Extinguishing Systems

The increased use of automatic suppression systems, whether they use water or some other agent, will affect the quantities of water required. As more widespread use is made of early warning systems and automatic suppression systems, it will be possible to equate the effect of these systems with required fire flow, and there may well be a reduction to the amount of water needed to suppress a fire. Water supply requirements are just one factor in a system that determines what the potential for a fire is, how extensive that fire will be, and what measures will be needed to suppress it. Research continues to measure all these factors, and experience adds valuable information, allowing the establishment of fire flows on the basis of thoroughly researched and documented principles.

HISTORY OF WATER SUPPLY SYSTEMS

Historically, water supply systems for cities and towns were developed primarily to provide drinking water and water for sanitary purposes rather than for fire protection. However, it was found that large cities that required substantial amounts of water for domestic purposes usually had enough water to provide a useful supply for fire-fighting purposes.

This supply issue led to inquiries in the late nineteenth century into the additional cost of waterworks that could provide water for fire fighting, as well as other uses. A number of distinguished engineers associated with individual waterworks examined the problem and presented their findings in technical papers at engineering society meetings. Papers by J. Herbert Shedd,[5] J. T. Fanning,[6] and Emil Kuichling[7] give the details of discussions in which standards for American and Canadian waterworks were first developed (Table 15.2.7). Keep in mind that at the turn of the century, when these engineers practiced, the advent of automatic sprinkler protection was just arriving. Thus, most of their research and findings dealt with the effectiveness of hose streams. It continues to be a cornerstone in determining the validity of hose stream use by today's fire service, in a very general nature.

NUMBER OF HOSE STREAMS

In these discussions, the starting point for computing the cost of water for fire protection was to estimate the number of hose streams that a fire department might need for fire fighting. This was usually estimated using as a basis the central portion of a city where the largest buildings were located and where there was the greatest building congestion. The number of streams was found to be related, in a very rough way, to the population. Shedd's proposal,[5] which was the first, used hose streams discharging 200 gpm (757 L/min). He suggested that a community of 5000 would need about 5 such streams and that the needs of other cities could be graduated up to 30 streams in a city of 180,000. Fanning[6] proposed streams requiring about 54 psi (372 kPa) pressure. His figures were similar to Shedd's,[5] beginning at 7 streams for a community of 4000 and going up to 25 streams for a city of 150,000.

Kuichling[7] suggested a formula in which the number of streams required would be the square root of the population in thousands multiplied by 2.8. There were arithmetical differences as to how these estimates worked out for individual cities, but they were all of the same general order (see Table 15.2.7). Most important, they provided a basis from which waterworks designers could estimate costs.

The most important paper produced during this time was John R. Freeman's "The Arrangement of Hydrants and Water Pipes for the Protection of a City Against Fire," published in 1892.[8] Freeman had done the fundamental work on waterflow through hose and nozzles, so he was able to pin down the definition of a standard fire stream to one with a discharge of 250 gpm (946 L/min) at 40 to 50 psi (276 to 345 kPa) pressure. He said that the relationships suggested by Shedd[5] and Fanning[6] between population and the number of streams required were of the right order, but he did not think the needs of individual cities could be quite so definitely ascertained. He suggested two to three streams as a minimum for a population of 1000, graduated up to 30 to 50 streams at 200,000 (see Table 15.2.7). Most significantly, he warned, "Ten streams, or as large a proportion thereof as the financial consideration will permit, may be recommended for a compact group of large, valuable buildings, irrespective of a small population."[8]

ENGINEERING: DISTRIBUTION NETWORK, HYDRANT SPACING, STORAGE

Freeman[8] noted a fundamental difference between systems designed to supply ordinary water needs and those for fire

TABLE 15.2.7 Estimates of Fire Flow

	Number of Fire Streams Required Simultaneously				
Population in Thousands	*Shedd 1889*	*Fanning 1892*	*Freeman 1892*	*Kuichling 1897*	*NBFU 1911*
1	—	—	2–3	3	4
4	—	7	—	6	8
5	5	—	4–8	6	9
10	7	10	6–12	9	12
20	10	—	8–15	12	17
40	14	—	12–18	18	24
50	—	14	—	20	26
60	17	—	15–22	22	28
100	22	18	20–30	28	36
150	—	25	—	34	44
180	30	—	—	38	48
200	—	—	30–50	40	48

Sources: Shedd,[5] Fanning,[6] Kuichling,[7] Freeman,[8] and Metcalf, Kuichling, and Hawley.[9]

protection: fire draft required concentration of the water, whereas domestic draft was a matter of distribution.

Freeman[8] asserted that, if a water system were to supply fire protection needs, the distribution system should be designed to concentrate the needed amounts of water. Small pipes were sufficient for distribution, but larger ones were needed to concentrate supply to fire streams. He suggested 6-in. (152-mm) diameter pipe as the minimum for residential districts and noted that 8 in. (203 mm) pipe was adequate only if it formed part of a network of distribution pipes whose intersections were not far apart.

Another important point Freeman[8] made was that hydrants should be placed where they could concentrate streams at specific blocks or groups of buildings rather than be placed arbitrarily a certain number of feet (m) apart on the street mains. His work on hose streams showed how long hose lines reduced the water that can be delivered promptly to a fire. Therefore, he suggested a working rule for hydrant spacing of 250 ft (76 m) between hydrants in compact mercantile and manufacturing districts and 400 ft (122 m) to 500 ft (153 m) in residential districts. These working rules are still used as guides for good design.

Freeman[8] further insisted that fire supply should be in addition to maximum domestic consumption, and he laid the foundation for the eventual recognition of this principle. He also calculated how much water should be stored in standpipes, elevated tanks, or elevated reservoirs. He figured that flow for all of the hose streams required should be supplied from a reliable source, such as an elevated storage reservoir, for at least 6 hours when the system was also furnishing maximum demands for domestic and other uses. He also calculated that to supply the combined fire and domestic needs in a system provided with reliable pump capacity a 1 hour supply in a standpipe, elevated tank, or elevated reservoir would be acceptable.

THE INSURANCE GRADING SCHEDULE

As early as 1889, the National Board of Fire Underwriters (NBFU) began to make fire protection surveys of municipalities. This work was intensified in 1904 after a conflagration in Baltimore, Maryland. Today the ISO surveys communities in all but a few states. The ISO survey, called the *Fire Suppression Rating Schedule,*[3] was discussed in detail earlier in this chapter.

The current ISO procedure for establishing fire flows is different from the original NBFU formula, which was commonly used for many years as a guide to determine the fire flow required in downtown business districts of municipalities (see Table 15.2.7). The formula gave the fire flow, G, in gpm as a function of the population, P, in thousands. (For SI units: 1 gpm = 3.785 L/min.)

$$G = 1020\sqrt{P}(1 - 0.01\sqrt{P})$$

In making fire protection surveys, engineers from NBFU and insurance bureaus estimated the fire flow requirements in sections of municipalities outside the downtown business district. As cities became more decentralized, the formula based on population became less reliable as a guide for the fire flow needed downtown. In addition, it became apparent that a guide to engineering judgment was needed for the other sections of the cities. In 1948, a paper by A. C. Hutson,[10] assistant chief engineer at NBFU, provided some specific suggestions for estimating fire flow requirements in these sections, based on the type of construction and the area of a building. This eventually led to the current ISO rating system.

SUMMARY

The time to worry about the requirements of a fire protection water supply is not when the fire has broken out but rather long before the incident occurs. Fire protection water is almost always a shared entity with the domestic users, and fire protection supplies are needed only when there is an emergency. However, the total supply available to an area has to consider both normal and emergency uses.

The fire service has a number of methods available to help determine the adequacy and reliability of the water supply in the event of a fire. The amount of water needed will always be a function of the occupancy and the construction of the building in question, and in many cases, the outside exposures to the structure. There are quick ways to develop fire flow needs that encompass all of these parameters, and the fire service uses these routinely.

Adequacy and reliability of the water supply system when needed are not to be taken for granted. Careful planning as to what is needed and then careful analysis of availability are key to planning before an incident occurs.

BIBLIOGRAPHY

References Cited

1. ASCE, "Fundamental Considerations in Rates and Rate Structures for Water and Sewage Works: A Joint Report of Committees of the American Society of Civil Engineers and the Section of Municipal Law of the American Bar Association and of Representatives of the American Water Works Association, National Association of Railroad and Utilities Commissioners, Municipal Finance Officers Association, Federation of Sewage Works Association, American Public Works Association, and Investment Bankers Association of America," *ASCE Bulletin No. 2,* American Society of Civil Engineers, New York, 1951.
2. AWWA M31, *Distribution System Requirements for Fire Protection,* American Water Works Association, Denver, CO, 1989.
3. *Fire Suppression Rating Schedule,* Insurance Services Office, New York, 1980. Also see http://www.isomitigation.com/fire73.html.
4. Iowa State University, Engineering Extension Service, Bulletin No. 18, "Water for Fire Fighting, Rate-of-Flow Formula," Iowa State University, 1959.
5. Shedd, J. H., Discussion on a paper by William B. Sherman, "Ratio of Pumping Capacity to Maximum Consumption," *Journal of New England Water Works Association,* Vol. 3, 1889, p. 113.
6. Fanning, J. T., *Distribution Mains and the Fire Service—Proceedings* of the American Water Works Association, Vol. 12, 1892, p. 61.
7. Kuichling, E., *The Financial Management of Water Works—Transactions* of the American Society of Civil Engineers, Vol. 38, 1897, p. 16.

8. Freeman, J. R., "The Arrangement of Hydrants and Water Pipes for the Protection of a City Against Fire," *Journal of the New England Water Works Association,* Vol. 7, 1892, p. 49.
9. Metcalf, L., Kuichling, E., and Hawley, W. C., *Some Fundamental Considerations in the Determination of a Reasonable Return for Public Fire Hydrant Service—Proceedings* of the American Water Works Association, Vol. 31, 1911, p. 55.
10. Hutson, A. C., "Water Works Requirements for Fire Protection," *Journal of the American Water Works Association,* Vol. 40, No. 9, 1948, p. 936. (Also reprinted in Special Interest Bulletin No. 266, National Board of Fire Underwriters [now American Insurance Service Group], New York.)

NFPA Codes, Standards, and Recommended Practices

Reference to the following NFPA codes, standards, and recommended practices will provide further information on water supply requirements for public supply systems discussed in this chapter. (See the latest version of The NFPA Catalog *for availability of current editions of the following documents.)*

NFPA 13, *Standard for the Installation of Sprinkler Systems*
NFPA 13D, *Standard for the Installation of Sprinkler Systems in One- and Two-Family Dwellings and Manufactured Homes*
NFPA 13R, *Standard for the Installation of Sprinkler Systems in Residential Occupancies up to and Including Four Stories in Height*
NFPA 14, *Standard for the Installation of Standpipe and Hose Systems*
NFPA 20, *Standard for the Installation of Stationary Pumps for Fire Protection*

Reference

Davis, L. W., *Rural Firefighting Operations,* International Society of Fire Service Instructors, Ashland, MA, 1986.

Chapter 3

SECTION 15

Hydraulics for Fire Protection

Kenneth W. Linder

Hydraulics is a subset of fluid mechanics that deals with the flow of water. As applied to fire protection, it involves the flow of water through pipes, valves, fittings, and orifices such as hydrant outlets, nozzles, and sprinklers. This chapter describes the physical properties of water that are pertinent to hydraulic calculations and the basic formulas used to calculate flow and pressure loss in fire protection systems. It does not include details on the specific rules required to design hydraulically calculated sprinkler systems in accordance with NFPA 13, *Standard for the Installation of Sprinkler Systems,* or the algorithms used to determine how the flow splits in looped systems or more complex gridded piping systems.

For related topics see Section 17, Chapter 3, "Characteristics and Hazards of Water and Water Additives for Fire Suppression."

Chapter Contents

Key Terms

Chezy formula, coefficient of flow, Darcy-Weisbach formula, elastic wave theory, friction loss, Hazen-Williams formula, hydraulic calculations, hydraulically designed system, K-factor, Moody diagram, velocity head, velocity pressure, water hammer

HYDRAULIC PROPERTIES OF WATER

As used in this handbook, water refers to fresh water unless otherwise specified. All calculations are made in U.S. gallons (gal), unless otherwise indicated. One U.S. gal equals 3.78 L. An Imperial gal equals 1.20 U.S. gal (4.54 L).

Material Properties

Density. Density, ρ, is defined as mass per unit volume:

$$\rho = \left(\frac{\text{mass}}{\text{volume}}\right)$$

The density of water, as with many other liquids, varies with temperature. The maximum density of water occurs at 39.2°F (4.0°C) and is 62.43 lbm (pound mass) per ft^3 (1000 kg/m^3 [kilograms per m^3]) in vacuum or 62.35 lbm per ft^3 (998.7 kg/m^3) in air. For most hydraulic calculations, an approximate value of 62.4 lbm per ft^3 (1000 kg/m^3) is usually used. Average seawater has a density of 64.1 lbm per ft^3 (1030 kg/m^3) at 39.2°F (4.0°C).

Specific Weight. The specific weight of a material, *w,* is defined as $w = \rho g$ where g is the acceleration due to gravity. The specific weight is usually measured in lbf (pound force) per ft^3 in U.S. customary units and kgf (kilogram force)/m^3 in SI units and is

$$w = \rho g = 62.4\,\frac{\text{lbm}}{\text{ft}^3} \times 32.2\,\frac{\text{ft}}{\text{sec}^2} \times 1\,\frac{\text{lbf} \cdot \text{sec}^2}{32.2\ \text{lbm} \cdot \text{ft}} = 62.4\,\frac{\text{lbf}}{\text{ft}^3} = 1000\ \text{kgf per m}^3$$

A common, though incorrect, practice is to use the terms *pound mass* (lbm) and *pound force* (lbf) interchangeably, since one lbm has a weight of one lbf under standard gravity. (A similar situation exists in SI units with kg (kilogram) and kgf [kilogram force].) In this chapter, pound (lb)

Kenneth W. Linder is NAT CAT manager for Swiss Re, Industrial Risk Insurers, and also serves as a senior research consultant to Global Asset Protection Services.

means pound force (lbf) and kilogram (kg) means kilogram force (kgf), as is common in engineering practice.

One ft^3 (0.028 m^3) equals 7.48 U.S. gal. Assuming the specific weight of water is 62.4 lb per ft^3 (1000 kg/m^3), 1 gal of water, therefore, weighs 62.4 lb per ft^3 ÷ 7.48 gal per ft^3, or 8.34 lb (3.78 kg).

Viscosity. Viscosity is a measurement of a fluid's resistance to flow and is usually measured in pound sec per foot^2 (lb sec/ft^2) in U.S. customary units or newton sec per meter^2 (N·sec/m^2) in SI units. Viscosity, like density, varies with temperature. At 32°F (0.0°C), water has an absolute viscosity, μ of 3.746 × 10^{-5} lb sec/ft^2 (1.793 × 10^{-5} N·sec/m^2). In hydraulic problems, viscosity is often divided by density. This relative viscosity, called kinematic viscosity, υ, is defined as

$$\upsilon = \frac{\mu}{\rho}$$

Although viscosity is an important factor in fluid flows, most fire protection hydraulics applications assume water at ambient conditions, and the empirical formulas normally used to calculate losses do not take into account changes in viscosity.

An exception are hydraulic calculations involving foam concentrate solutions in foam-water sprinkler systems or large antifreeze solutions in blast freezers or other very cold areas where the solution is significantly more viscous than water at ambient conditions.

Pressure

Pressure, p, is the unit that measures the force, caused by compression, per unit area in a fluid. In fire protection hydraulics, pressure is normally measured in pounds per square inch (psi) or in kilopascals (kPa), as indicated by a pressure gauge, or as head, h, in feet (ft) or meters (m) of water. Pressure is also commonly measured as a head of mercury, atmosphere, bar, or newtons per square meter (N/m^2).

For waterflow in pipes, the total pressure, p_t, is the sum of normal pressure, p_n and velocity pressure, p_υ:

$$p_t = p_n + p_\upsilon$$

Normal Pressure. Net or normal pressure is the pressure exerted against the side of a pipe or container by the liquid in the pipe or container with or without flow. Without flow, this pressure is called "static pressure" or "static head." With flow, this pressure is called "residual" pressure.

The pressure exerted by a column of water is related to its specific weight. Expressed slightly differently, the specific weight is

$$\frac{62.4 \text{ lb}}{\text{ft}^3} = \frac{62.4 \text{ lb}}{\text{ft}^2 \text{ ft}} \times \frac{1 \text{ ft}^2}{144 \text{ in}^2} = 0.433 \text{ psi per ft}$$

It follows that pressure and static head are related by the following formulas:

$$p = wh = 0.433h$$

$$h = \frac{p}{w} = \frac{p}{0.433} = 2.31p$$

For SI units, the weight of a 1 m column of water equals a force of 9.81 kPa or

$$p = 9.81h$$

$$h = \frac{p}{9.81} = 0.102p$$

A 1 in. (25.4 mm) head of mercury generates a pressure of 0.491 psi (3.39 kPa) and is equivalent to a 1.135 ft (0.3456 m) head of water.

Normal atmospheric pressure is taken as 14.7 psi (101.4 kPa), equivalent to a head of water of 33.95 ft (10.35 m) and a head of mercury of 29.9 in. (760 mm).

Velocity Head or Velocity Pressure. The velocity, υ, produced in a mass of water by pressure acting upon it is the same as if the mass were to fall freely, starting from rest, through a distance equivalent to the pressure head in feet. This relationship is represented by Torricelli's equation:

$$\upsilon = 2\sqrt{gh}$$

where υ = the velocity produced in ft/sec (m/sec), g = the acceleration due to gravity or 32.2 ft/sec^2 (9.81 m/sec^2), and h = the head in ft (m) producing the velocity.

Just as a static head can be converted into a velocity head, velocity head can be converted to an equivalent static pressure head. This relation is

$$h_\upsilon \text{ (velocity head)} = \frac{\upsilon^2}{2g} \text{ (ft)}$$

Because

$$p_\upsilon = 0.433h_\upsilon$$

the velocity pressure can be expressed as

$$p_\upsilon = 0.433\frac{\upsilon^2}{2g} \text{ (psi)}$$

In SI units

$$p_{\upsilon m} \text{ (kPa)} = 9.81\frac{\upsilon^2}{2g}$$

for υ in m/s.

Values of velocity pressure for different rates of flow in various pipe sizes are shown in Figure 15.3.1. (For SI units see Figure 15.3.2.) Velocity head or velocity pressure may be calculated by formulas involving velocity and pipe diameter:

$$h_\upsilon = \frac{\upsilon^2}{64.4} \text{ or } p_\upsilon = \frac{0.433\upsilon^2}{64.4} = \frac{\upsilon^2}{149}$$

In SI units

$$h_{\upsilon m} = 0.0151\upsilon^2 \text{ and } p_{\upsilon m} = 0.5\upsilon^2$$

A convenient equation for calculating velocity in feet per second (fps) from the rate of flow can be developed from the principle of conservation of mass. For a steady-state one-dimensional flow with average velocity υ, this principle can be stated as

$$Q = a\upsilon$$

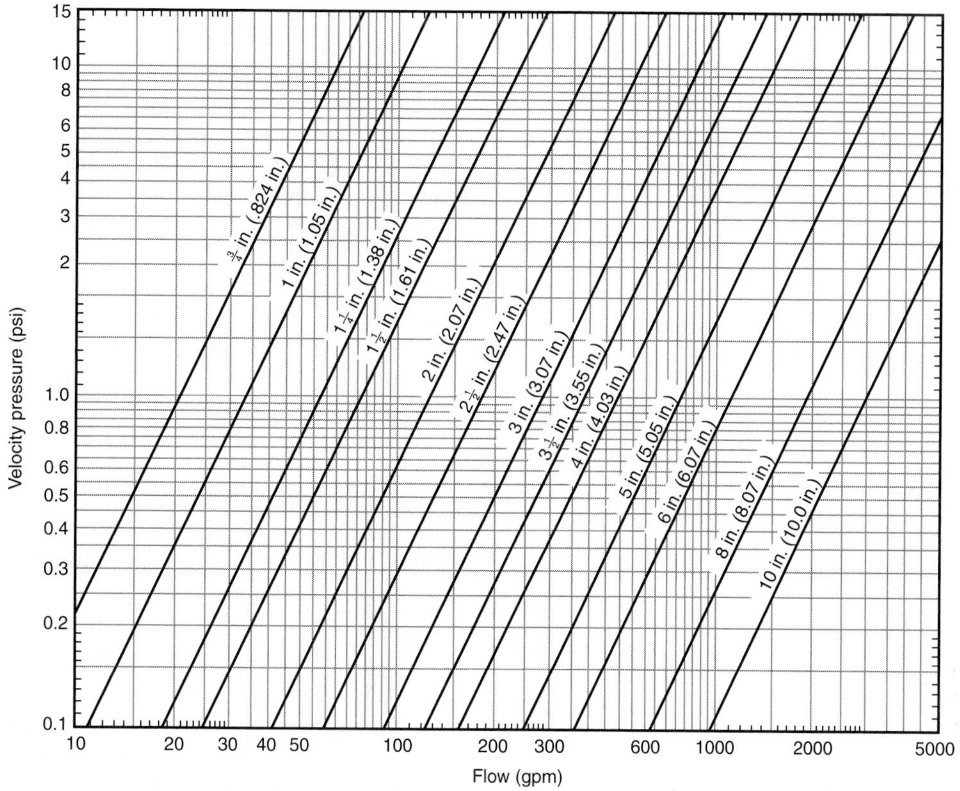

FIGURE 15.3.1 Graph for the Determination of Velocity Pressure (English Units)

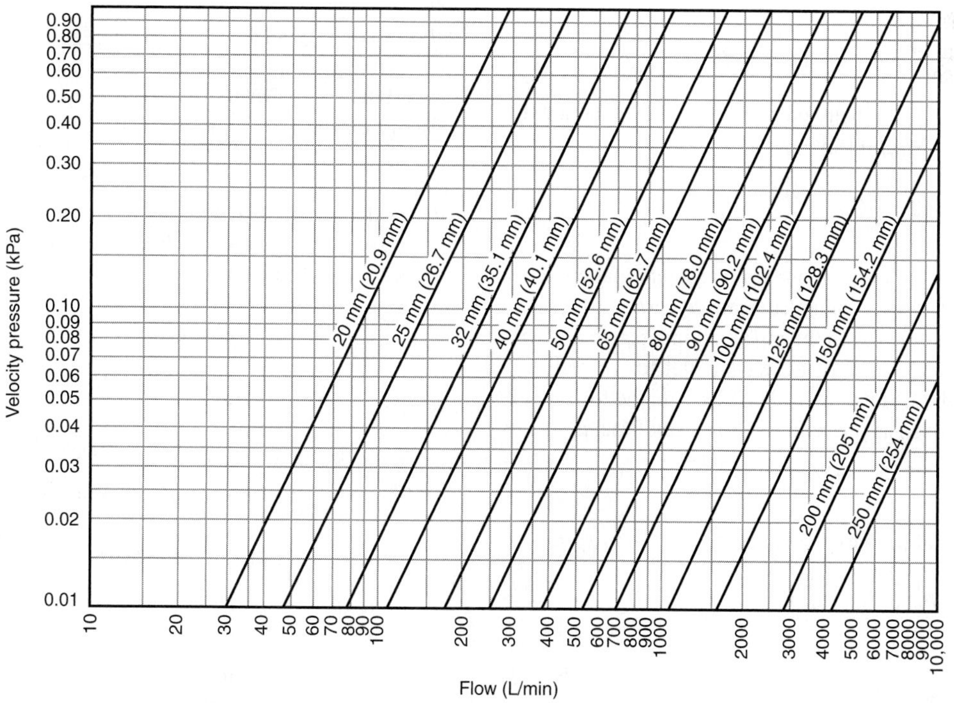

FIGURE 15.3.2 Graph for the Determination of Velocity Pressure (SI Units)

It follows that

$$\upsilon = \frac{Q}{a}$$

where υ = the average velocity in ft/sec, Q = the flow in ft^3/sec, and a = the cross-sectional area of the pipe in ft^2.

For a pipe with flow in gpm and diameter in in., the velocity is

$$\upsilon(\text{fps}) = \frac{Q(\text{gal/min})}{60\ \text{sec/min} \times 7.48\ \text{gal/ft}^3} + \frac{\pi d^2\ (\text{in.})^2}{4 \times 144\ \text{in.}^2/\text{ft}^2}$$

$$= \frac{Q \times 4 \times 144}{60 \times 7.48 \times \pi d^2} = \frac{0.4085 \times Q}{d^2}$$

It follows that h_υ and p_υ are

$$h_\upsilon = \frac{\upsilon^2}{2g} = \frac{(0.4085Q)^2}{(d^2)^2} \div 64.4 = \frac{Q^2}{d^4}\frac{(0.4085)^2}{64.4} = \frac{Q^2}{386d^4}$$

$$p_\upsilon = \frac{Q^2}{d^4} \times \frac{0.433}{386} = \frac{Q^2}{891(d)^4}$$

In SI units, the formula for velocity pressure is expressed as

$$p_{\upsilon m} = 225\frac{Q_m^2}{d_m^4}$$

where

$p_{\upsilon m}$ = Velocity pressure (kPa)
Q_m = Flow (L/min)
d_m = Inside diameter (mm)

EXAMPLE 1: Find the velocity pressure in 1-in. Schedule 40 pipe with 36 gpm flowing. The actual diameter of the pipe is 1.049 in.

SOLUTION: $p_\upsilon = \dfrac{Q^2}{891(d)^4} = \dfrac{36^2}{891(1.049)^4} = 1.20$ psi

EXAMPLE 2: Find the velocity pressure in a 25-mm (actual diameter) pipe with 100 L/m flowing.

SOLUTION: $P_{\upsilon m} = 225\dfrac{Q_m^2}{(d_m)^4} = \dfrac{225 \times (100)^2}{(25)^4} = 5.8$ kPa

Total Head. At any point within a piping system that contains water in motion, there is a pressure head, h_p (normal pressure head), acting perpendicular to the pipe wall independent of velocity, and a velocity head, h_υ acting parallel to the wall but exerting no pressure against the wall. Therefore, the total head, $H = h_p + h_\upsilon$, expressed as pressure (psi) instead of feet is

$$p_t = 0.433h_p + 0.433\frac{\upsilon^2}{2g}$$

In SI units, total head expressed in kPa is

$$p_{tm} = 9.81h_{pm} + 9.81\frac{\upsilon_m^2}{2g}$$

where

p_{tm} = Total pressure (kPa)
h_{pm} = Head (m)
υ_M = Velocity (m/sec)

Pressure Sources

The sources of pressure head commonly found in fire protection hydraulic systems include the following.

Gravity (Elevated Tanks, Reservoirs, Standpipes). Head is the elevation of the water supply surface above the point under consideration, measured directly in ft (m) or converted from a pressure gauge reading.

Pumping. Head is the combination of pump discharge pressure and any difference in elevation between the pump discharge gauge and the point under consideration.

Pneumatic (Pressure Tanks). Head is the tank air pressure combined with any difference in elevation in tank water surface and the point under consideration.

Combination. Any combination of the above pressure sources.

BERNOULLI'S THEOREM

Bernoulli's theorem expresses the physical law of conservation of energy applied to problems of incompressible fluid flow. The theorem can be defined as follows: "In steady flow without friction, the sum of the velocity head, pressure head, and elevation head is constant for any incompressible fluid particle throughout its course." In other words, the total pressure (head) is the same at all locations within the system.

(Note that, in Bernoulli's theorem, all of the individual head terms, i.e., velocity head, pressure head, and elevation head are expressed in ft [m]. When using velocities in fps [m/sec] and gauge pressure in psi [kPa], they must be converted to ft [m], or all of the terms expressed as pressures.)

Bernoulli's Theorem Expressed Mathematically

Real systems are not frictionless, however, and in practice, losses due to pipe friction and other factors are accounted for. Expressed mathematically, Bernoulli's theorem, when applied to locations A and B, is

$$\frac{\upsilon_A^2}{2g} + \frac{p_A}{w} + z_A = \frac{\upsilon_B^2}{2g} + \frac{p_B}{w} + z_B + h_{AB}$$

where

υ (υ_m) = Velocity in fps (m/sec)
g (g_m) = Acceleration of gravity (32.2 fps [9.81 m/sec^2])
p (p_m) = Pressure (lb/ft^2 [kPa])
z (z_m) = Elevation head (distance above assumed datum, in ft [m])
w (w_m) = Specific weight of the fluid in lb/ft^3 (64.4 pcf or 9.81 kN/m^3 for water)
$\dfrac{\upsilon^2}{2g}\left(\dfrac{\upsilon_m^2}{2g}\right)$ = Velocity head in ft (m)

$\frac{p}{\omega}\left(\frac{p_m}{\omega_m}\right)$ = Pressure head in ft (m)

$h_{ab}(h_{abm})$ = Lost head between location A and location B in ft (m)

Application of Bernoulli's Theorem

Consider a reservoir and a pipeline discharging water to atmosphere at B (Figure 15.3.3). Assuming datum through B, Bernoulli's theorem applied from the water surface at A to the outlet at B is

$$\frac{\upsilon_A^2}{2g} + \frac{p_A}{w} + z_A = \frac{\upsilon_B^2}{2g} + \frac{p_B}{w} + z_B + h_{AB}$$

The velocity at A is practically zero because the tank is very large, and the gauge pressure is zero because only atmospheric pressure works on the water surface. At A, the elevation is z_A measured in ft (m) above the datum.

At B, the elevation above the datum is zero; the gauge pressure is zero, since the water is discharging to atmosphere; and only velocity pressure is available as the water leaves the outlet. (A gauge at a right angle to the emerging stream would register zero pressure.)

Therefore,

$$0 + 0 + z_A = \frac{\upsilon_B^2}{2g} + 0 + 0 + h_{AB}$$

or

$$\frac{\upsilon_B^2}{2g} = z_A - h_{AB}$$

Lost head, h_{AB}, is the sum of (1) hydraulic losses at the reservoir where water enters the pipeline, at the valve, and at the discharge outlet, plus (2) the friction loss in the pipeline. The values of the components producing lost head can be estimated, as discussed later in the chapter.

As another example, calculate the head loss across 1000 ft of 8 in. pipe with 750 gpm flowing from a 2½ in. hydrant outlet at B and a residual pressure at hydrant A of 40 psi. With no flow, hydrant A has a 60 psi static pressure, and hydrant B has an 80 psi static pressure. Assume a datum through hydrant B. Again, Bernoulli's theorem applied from point A to point B applies:

$$\frac{\upsilon_A^2}{2g} + \frac{p_A}{w} + z_A = \frac{\upsilon_B^2}{2g} + \frac{p_B}{w} + z_B + h_{AB}$$

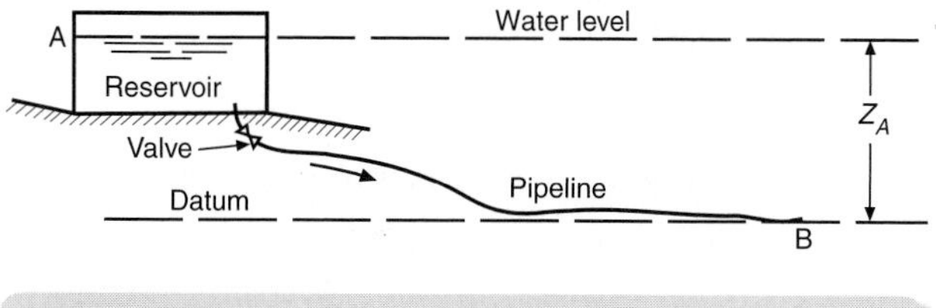

FIGURE 15.3.3 Graphic Representation of the Application of Bernoulli's Theorem to a Reservoir and Pipelines

Because we are interested in finding the head loss from A to B (h_{AB}), we rearrange Bernoulli's equation to solve for this term:

$$h_{AB} = \frac{\upsilon_A^2}{2g} + \frac{p_A}{w} + z_A - \frac{\upsilon_B^2}{2g} - \frac{p_B}{w} - z_B$$

The next step is to use the information provided to calculate each of the terms on the right side of the equation, starting with the velocity head at A:

$$\upsilon_A = \frac{Q}{a} = \frac{Q}{\frac{\pi d^2}{4 \times 144}}$$

$$= \frac{\frac{750 \text{ gpm}}{7.48 \text{ gal/ft}^3 \times 60 \text{ sec/min}}}{\frac{3.1416 \times (8 \text{ in.})^2}{4 \times 144 \text{ in.}^2/\text{ft}^2}} = 4.79 \text{ fps}$$

$$\frac{\upsilon_A^2}{2g} = \frac{(4.79 \text{ fps})^2}{64.4 \text{ fps/sec}} = 0.36 \text{ ft} \approx 0.4 \text{ ft}$$

Next we calculate the pressure head at A:

$$\frac{p_A}{w} = \frac{40 \text{ psi} \times \frac{144 \text{ in.}^2}{\text{ft}^2}}{62.4 \text{ pcf}} = 93.2 \text{ ft}$$

$$z_A = (80 \text{ psi} - 60 \text{ psi}) \times 2.31 \text{ ft/psi} = 46.2 \text{ ft}$$

Because we are using point B as our datum or zero-elevation reference, z_A is the elevation difference between points A and B. We can use Bernoulli's equation with no flow to determine this difference. Because there is no flow, the velocity head terms are zero. Also, because there is no flow, there is no friction or head loss. We know that because the static pressure at B is greater than the static pressure at A, the elevation of A is positive. Solving for the elevation difference we get

$$z_A - z_B = \frac{p_B}{w} - \frac{p_A}{w}$$

We know the pressure head at B is 80 psi and that head at A is 60 psi. Because the elevation at B is zero, substituting and converting the units we get

$$z_A = (80 \text{ psi} - 60 \text{ psi}) \times 2.31 \text{ ft/psi} = 46.2 \text{ ft}$$

The velocity at B is calculated in the same manner as at A:

$$\upsilon_B = \frac{Q}{a} = \frac{\frac{750 \text{ gpm}}{7.48 \text{ gal/ft}^3 \times 60 \text{ sec/min}}}{\frac{3.1416 \times (2.5 \text{ in.})^2}{4 \times 144 \text{ in.}^2/\text{ft}^2}} = 49.02 \text{ fps}$$

$$\frac{\upsilon_B^2}{2g} = \frac{(49.02 \text{ fps})^2}{64.4 \text{ fps}} = 37.3 \text{ ft}$$

There is no normal pressure, as the flow discharges to atmosphere.

$$\frac{p_B}{w} = 0$$

$z_B = 0$ since the datum goes through hydrant B. Thus

$$h_{AB} = 0.4 + 92.3 + 46.2 - 37.3 - 0 - 0 = 101.6 \text{ ft}$$

One further problem is expressed in SI units. Water is pumped via a pipeline, up a 5.0 m incline from A to B. The pipeline at A has an inside diameter of 80 mm and a static pressure of 300 kPa. If the pipeline has changed in diameter to 70 mm at B and there is frictional head loss over the length of the pipe (h_{AB}) of 12 m, determine the residual pressure at B for a flow rate of 4200 L/min.

The solution is expressed as

$$\frac{\upsilon_A^2}{2g} + \frac{p_A}{w} + z_A = \frac{\upsilon_B^2}{2g} + \frac{p_B}{w} + z_B + h_{AB}$$

Rearranging for the pressure head at B,

$$\frac{p_B}{w} = \frac{\upsilon_A^2}{2g} + \frac{p_A}{w} + z_A - \frac{\upsilon_B^2}{2g} - z_B - h_{AB}$$

Substituting,

$$\upsilon_a = \frac{Q}{a_a} = \frac{\dfrac{4200 \text{ L/min}}{60 \text{ sec/min} \times 1000 \text{ L/m}^3}}{\dfrac{\pi\,(80 \text{ mm})^2}{4 \times 10^6 \text{ mm}^2/\text{m}^2}}$$

$$\frac{\upsilon_A^2}{2g} = \frac{(13.9 \text{ m/sec})^2}{2 \times 9.81 \text{ m/sec}^2} = 9.8 \text{ m}$$

$$\frac{p_A}{w} = \frac{300 \text{ kPa}}{9.81 \text{ kPa/m}} = 30.6 \text{ m}$$

$$z_A = 0 \text{ (datum through A)}$$

$$\upsilon_B = \frac{Q}{a_B} = \frac{\dfrac{4200 \text{ L/min}}{60 \text{ sec/min} \times 1000 \text{ L/m}^3}}{\dfrac{\pi\,(70 \text{ mm})^2}{4 \times 10^6 \text{ mm}^2/\text{m}^2}} = 18.2 \text{ m/sec}$$

$$\frac{\upsilon_B^2}{2g} = \frac{(18.2 \text{ m/sec})^2}{2 \times 9.81 \text{ m/sec}^2} = 16.9 \text{ m}$$

$$z_B = 5.0 \text{ m}$$

$$h_{AB} = 12 \text{ m (friction loss)}$$

Then

$$\frac{p_B}{w} = 9.81 + 30.6 + 0 - 16.9 - 5 - 12 = 6.5 \text{ m}$$

In pressure terms

$$6.5 \text{ m} \times 9.81 \frac{\text{kPa}}{\text{m}} = 64 \text{ kPa}$$

that is, the residual pressure at B is 64 kPa.

FLOW OF WATER THROUGH ORIFICES

As a liquid leaves a pipe, conduit, or container through an orifice and discharges to atmosphere, the normal pressure is converted to velocity pressure. The rate of flow though an orifice can be expressed in terms of velocity and cross-sectional area of the stream, the basic relations being $Q = a\upsilon$, where Q = rate of flow in ft³/sec (m³/sec); a = area of cross section in ft² (m²); and υ = velocity at the cross section in ft/sec (m/sec) (Table 15.3.1). From the previous discussion in this chapter on velocity head, it is known that

$$Q = a\sqrt{2gh}$$

and h (ft) = 2.307p (psi). It follows that, with the orifice diameter in inches, Q in gal/min, and h in psi,

$$Q = 60 \times 7.4805 \times \frac{\pi d^2}{4 \times 144} \times \sqrt{64.4 \times 2.3077 p_\upsilon}$$

$$Q = 29.84 d^2 \sqrt{p_\upsilon}$$

In SI units, the flow formula is expressed as

$$Q_m = 0.0666 d_m^2 \sqrt{p_{\upsilon m}}$$

where

Q_m = Flow rate (L/m)

d_m = Inside diameter (mm)

$p_{\upsilon m}$ = Velocity pressure (kPa)

The above equations (and tables derived therefrom) assume that (1) the jet is a solid stream the full size of the discharge orifice, and (2) 100 percent of the available total head is converted to velocity head, which is uniform over the cross section. This is a theoretical situation only, however, as these two conditions are not totally attainable, as the following discussion will show.

COEFFICIENTS OF FLOW

In actual flow from nozzles or orifices, the velocity, considered to be average velocity across the entire cross section of the stream, is somewhat less than the velocity calculated from the head. The reduction is due to friction of the water against the nozzle or orifice and turbulence within the nozzle and is accounted for by a coefficient of velocity, designated c_υ. Values of c_υ are determined by laboratory tests. With well-designed nozzles, the coefficient of velocity is nearly constant and is approximately equal to 0.98.

Some nozzles are designed so that the actual cross-sectional area of the stream is somewhat less than the cross-sectional area of the orifice. This difference is accounted for by the coefficient of contraction, designated c_c. Coefficients of contraction vary greatly with the design and quality of the orifice or nozzle. For a sharp-edged orifice, the value of c_c is about 0.62.

The coefficients of velocity and contraction are usually combined as a single coefficient of discharge, designated c_d:

$$c_d = c_\upsilon \times c_c$$

The basic flow equation can now be written as

$$Q = 29.84 c_d^4 d^2 \sqrt{p_\upsilon}$$

In SI units the formula is

$$Q = 0.0666 c_d d_m^2 \sqrt{p_{\upsilon m}}$$

TABLE 15.3.1 Theoretical Flow Through Circular Orifices—gpm (L/min)

This table may be computed from the formula $Q = 29.84cd^2\sqrt{p}$ ($Q = 0.0666cd_m^2\sqrt{p_m}$) with $c = 1.00$. The theoretical discharge from seawater, as from fireboat nozzles, may be found by subtracting 1 percent from the figures in the following table or from the value computed using the formulas.

When pressures are read with a Pitot gage at a nozzle, the nozzle discharge in most cases will correspond to the values in the table within a range of 1 to 3 percent for nozzles up to 1⅜ in. (35 mm) in diameter. For larger diameter nozzles, the principles discussed in "Nozzle Method of Measuring Flow" in this chapter of the handbook apply. Appropriate coefficients should be applied where it is read from a hydrant outlet. Where more accurate results are required, a coefficient appropriate to the particular nozzle must be selected and applied to the figures of the table.

The discharge from circular openings of sizes other than those in the table may readily be computed by applying the principles that quantity discharged under a given head varies as the square of the diameter of the opening.

		Orifice Diameter in. (mm)																					
Pressure psi (kPa)	*Velocity ft/sec (m/sec)*	*0.375 (9.53)*	*0.5 (12.7)*	*0.625 (15.9)*	*0.75 (19.1)*	*0.875 (22.2)*	*1 (25.4)*	*1.125 (28.6)*	*1.25 (31.8)*	*1.5 (38.1)*	*1.75 (44.5)*	*2 (50.8)*	*2.25 (57.2)*	*2.375 (60.3)*	*2.5 (63.5)*	*2.625 (66.7)*	*2.75 (69.9)*	*3 (76.2)*	*3.25 (82.6)*	*3.5 (88.9)*	*3.75 (95.25)*	*4 (102)*	*4.5 (114)*
1	12.2	4.20	7.46	11.7	16.8	22.8	29.8	37.8	46.6	67.1	91.4	119	151	168	187	206	226	269	315	366	420	477	604
(6.89)	(3.71)	(15.9)	(28.2)	(44.1)	(63.4)	(86.4)	(113)	(143)	(176)	(254)	(345)	(451)	(571)	(636)	(705)	(777)	(853)	(1020)	(1190)	(1380)	(1590)	(1800)	(2280)
2	17.2	5.93	10.6	16	23.7	32.3	42.2	53.4	65.9	95.0	129	169	214	238	264	291	319	380	446	517	593	675	855
(13.8)	(5.25)	(22.4)	(39.9)	(62.4)	(89.8)	(122)	(160)	(202)	(249)	(359)	(489)	(638)	(808)	(900)	(998)	(1100)	(1210)	(1440)	(1690)	(1960)	(2240)	(2550)	(3230)
3	21.1	7.27	12.9	20.2	29.1	39.6	51.7	65.4	80.8	116	158	207	262	292	323	356	391	465	546	633	727	827	1050
(20.7)	(6.43)	(27.5)	(48.9)	(76.4)	(110)	(150)	(195)	(247)	(305)	(440)	(599)	(782)	(990)	(1100)	(1220)	(1350)	(1480)	(1760)	(2060)	(2390)	(2750)	(3130)	(3960)
4	24.4	8.39	14.9	23.3	33.6	45.7	59.7	75.5	93.3	134	183	239	302	337	373	411	451	537	630	731	839	955	1210
(27.6)	(7.43)	(31.7)	(56.4)	(88.2)	(127)	(173)	(226)	(286)	(353)	(508)	(691)	(903)	(1140)	(1270)	(1410)	(1560)	(1710)	(2030)	(2380)	(2770)	(3170)	(3610)	(4570)
5	27.3	9.38	16.7	26.1	37.5	51.1	66.7	84.4	104	150	204	267	338	376	417	460	505	601	705	817	938	1070	1350
(34.5)	(8.31)	(35.5)	(63.1)	(98.6)	(142)	(193)	(252)	(319)	(394)	(568)	(773)	(1010)	(1280)	(1420)	(1580)	(1740)	(1910)	(2270)	(2670)	(3090)	(3550)	(4040)	(5110)
6	29.9	10.3	18.3	28.6	41.1	56.0	73.1	92.5	114	164	224	292	370	412	457	504	553	658	772	895	1030	1170	1480
(41.4)	(9.10)	(38.9)	(69.1)	(108)	(156)	(212)	(276)	(350)	(432)	(622)	(847)	(1110)	(1400)	(1560)	(1730)	(1910)	(2090)	(2490)	(2920)	(3390)	(3890)	(4420)	(5600)
7	32.3	11.1	19.7	30.8	44.4	60.4	78.9	100	123	178	242	316	400	445	493	544	597	711	834	967	1110	1260	1600
(48.3)	(9.83)	(42.0)	(74.7)	(117)	(168)	(229)	(299)	(378)	(467)	(672)	(915)	(1190)	(1510)	(1680)	(1870)	(2060)	(2260)	(2690)	(3150)	(3660)	(4200)	(4780)	(6050)
8	34.5	11.9	21.1	33.0	47.5	64.6	84.4	107	132	190	258	338	427	476	528	582	638	760	891	1030	1190	1350	1710
(55.2)	(10.5)	(44.9)	(79.8)	(125)	(180)	(244)	(319)	(404)	(499)	(718)	(978)	(1280)	(1620)	(1800)	(2000)	(2200)	(2410)	(2870)	(3370)	(3910)	(4490)	(5110)	(6460)
9	36.6	12.6	22.4	35.0	50.4	68.5	89.5	113	140	201	274	358	453	505	560	617	677	806	946	1100	1260	1430	1810
(62.0)	(11.1)	(47.6)	(84.6)	(132)	(190)	(259)	(338)	(428)	(529)	(761)	(1040)	(1350)	(1710)	(1910)	(2110)	(2330)	(2560)	(3040)	(3570)	(4140)	(4760)	(5410)	(6850)
10	38.6	13.3	23.6	36.9	53.1	72.2	94.4	119	147	212	289	377	478	532	590	650	714	849	997	1160	1330	1510	1910
(68.9)	(11.7)	(50.2)	(89.2)	(139)	(201)	(273)	(357)	(451)	(557)	(802)	(1090)	(1430)	(1810)	(2010)	(2230)	(2460)	(2700)	(3210)	(3770)	(4370)	(5020)	(5710)	(7220)
11	40.4	13.9	24.7	38.7	55.7	75.8	99.0	125	155	223	303	396	501	558	619	682	748	891	1050	1210	1390	1580	2000
(75.8)	(12.3)	(52.6)	(93.5)	(146)	(210)	(286)	(374)	(473)	(585)	(842)	(1150)	(1500)	(1809)	(2110)	(2340)	(2580)	(2830)	(3370)	(3950)	(4580)	(5260)	(5990)	(7580)
12	42.2	14.5	25.8	40.4	58.1	79.1	103	131	162	233	317	413	523	583	646	712	782	930	1090	1270	1450	1650	2090
(82.7)	(12.9)	(54.9)	(97.7)	(153)	(220)	(299)	(391)	(495)	(611)	(879)	(1200)	(1560)	(1980)	(2200)	(2440)	(2690)	(2960)	(3520)	(4130)	(4790)	(5490)	(6250)	(7910)
13	44.0	15.1	26.9	42.0	60.5	82.4	108	136	168	242	329	430	545	607	672	741	814	968	1140	1320	1510	1720	2180
(89.6)	(13.4)	(57.2)	(102)	(159)	(229)	(311)	(407)	(515)	(636)	(915)	(1250)	(1630)	(2060)	(2290)	(2540)	(2800)	(3080)	(3660)	(4300)	(4980)	(5720)	(6510)	(8240)
14	45.6	15.7	27.9	43.6	62.8	85.5	112	141	174	251	342	447	565	630	698	769	844	1000	1180	1370	1570	1790	2260
(96.5)	(13.9)	(59.4)	(106)	(165)	(237)	(323)	(422)	(534)	(660)	(950)	(1290)	(1690)	(2140)	(2380)	(2640)	(2910)	(3190)	(3800)	(4460)	(5170)	(5940)	(6750)	(8550)
15	47.2	16.3	28.9	45.1	65.0	88.5	116	146	181	260	354	462	585	652	722	796	874	1040	1220	1420	1630	1850	2340
(103)	(14.4)	(61.3)	(109)	(170)	(245)	(334)	(436)	(552)	(681)	(981)	(1340)	(1740)	(2210)	(2460)	(2730)	(3000)	(3300)	(3920)	(4610)	(5340)	(6130)	(6980)	(8830)
16	48.8	16.8	29.8	46.6	67.1	91.4	119	151	187	269	366	477	604	673	746	822	903	1070	1260	1460	1680	1910	2420
(110)	(14.8)	(63.4)	(113)	(176)	(253)	(345)	(451)	(570)	(704)	(1010)	(1380)	(1800)	(2280)	(2540)	(2820)	(3110)	(3410)	(4060)	(4760)	(5520)	(6340)	(7210)	(9130)
17	50.3	17.3	30.8	48.1	69.2	94.2	123	156	192	277	377	492	623	694	769	848	930	1110	1300	1510	1730	1970	2490
(117)	(15.3)	(65.4)	(116)	(182)	(261)	(356)	(465)	(588)	(726)	(1050)	(1420)	(1860)	(2350)	(2620)	(2900)	(3200)	(3510)	(4180)	(4910)	(5690)	(6540)	(7440)	(9410)

(continued)

TABLE 15.3.1 Continued

Pressure psi (kPa)	Velocity ft/sec (m/sec)	0.375 (9.53)	0.5 (12.7)	0.625 (15.9)	0.75 (19.1)	0.875 (22.2)	1 (25.4)	1.125 (28.6)	1.25 (31.8)	1.5 (38.1)	1.75 (44.5)	2 (50.8)	2.25 (57.2)	2.375 (60.3)	2.5 (63.5)	2.625 (66.7)	2.75 (69.9)	3 (76.2)	3.25 (82.6)	3.5 (88.9)	3.75 (95.25)	4 (102)	4.5 (114)
18	51.7	17.8	31.7	49.5	71.2	96.9	127	160	198	285	388	506	641	714	791	872	957	1140	1340	1550	1780	2,030	2,560
(124)	(15.7)	(67.3)	(120)	(187)	(269)	(366)	(478)	(606)	(748)	(1080)	(1470)	(1910)	(2420)	(2700)	(2990)	(3300)	(3620)	(4310)	(5050)	(5860)	(6730)	(7,660)	(9,690)
19	53.1	18.3	32.5	50.8	73.2	100	130	165	203	293	398	520	658	734	813	896	984	1170	1370	1590	1830	2,080	2,630
(131)	(16.2)	(69.2)	(123)	(192)	(277)	(377)	(492)	(622)	(768)	(1110)	(1510)	(1970)	(2490)	(2770)	(3070)	(3390)	(3720)	(4430)	(5190)	(6020)	(6920)	(7,870)	(9,960)
20	54.5	18.8	33.4	52.1	75.1	102	133	169	209	300	409	534	676	753	834	920	1010	1200	1410	1630	1880	2,140	2,700
(138)	(16.6)	(71.0)	(126)	(197)	(284)	(386)	(505)	(639)	(789)	(1140)	(1550)	(2020)	(2560)	(2850)	(3150)	(3480)	(3820)	(4540)	(5330)	(6180)	(7100)	(8,080)	(10,200)
21	55.9	19.2	34.2	53.4	76.9	105	137	173	214	308	419	547	692	771	855	942	1030	1230	1440	1680	1920	2,190	2,770
(145)	(17.0)	(72.8)	(129)	(202)	(291)	(396)	(517)	(655)	(808)	(1160)	(1580)	(2070)	(2620)	(2920)	(3230)	(3570)	(3910)	(4660)	(5470)	(6340)	(7280)	(8,280)	(10,500)
22	57.2	19.7	35.0	54.7	78.7	107	140	177	219	315	429	560	709	789	875	964	1060	1260	1480	1710	1970	2,240	2,830
(152)	(17.4)	(74.5)	(132)	(207)	(298)	(406)	(530)	(670)	(828)	(1190)	(1620)	(2120)	(2680)	(2990)	(3310)	(3650)	(4010)	(4770)	(5600)	(6490)	(7450)	(8,480)	(10,700)
23	58.5	20.1	35.8	55.9	80.5	110	143	181	224	322	438	572	724	807	894	986	1080	1290	1510	1750	2010	2,290	2,900
(159)	(17.8)	(76.2)	(135)	(212)	(305)	(415)	(542)	(686)	(847)	(1220)	(1660)	(2170)	(2740)	(3060)	(3390)	(3730)	(4100)	(4880)	(5720)	(6640)	(7620)	(8,670)	(11,000)
24	59.7	20.6	36.5	57.1	82.2	112	146	185	228	329	448	585	740	825	914	1010	1110	1320	1540	1790	2060	2,340	2,960
(165)	(18.2)	(77.6)	(138)	(216)	(310)	(423)	(552)	(699)	(862)	(1240)	(1690)	(2210)	(2790)	(3110)	(3450)	(3800)	(4170)	(4970)	(5830)	(6760)	(7760)	(8,830)	(11,200)
25	61.0	21.0	37.3	58.3	83.9	114	149	189	233	336	457	597	755	842	933	1030	1130	1340	1580	1830	2100	2,390	3,020
(172)	(18.5)	(79.2)	(141)	(220)	(317)	(431)	(564)	(713)	(880)	(1270)	(1730)	(2250)	(2850)	(3180)	(3520)	(3880)	(4260)	(5070)	(5950)	(6900)	(7920)	(9,020)	(11,400)
26	62.2	21.4	38.0	59.4	85.6	116	152	193	238	342	466	609	770	858	951	1050	1150	1370	1610	1860	2140	2,430	3,080
(179)	(18.9)	(80.8)	(144)	(225)	(323)	(440)	(575)	(728)	(898)	(1290)	(1761)	(2299)	(2910)	(3240)	(3590)	(3960)	(4350)	(5170)	(6070)	(7040)	(8080)	(9,200)	(11,600)
27	63.3	21.8	38.8	60.6	87.2	119	155	196	242	349	475	620	785	875	969	1070	1170	1400	1640	1900	2180	2,480	3,140
(186)	(19.3)	(82.4)	(147)	(229)	(330)	(449)	(586)	(742)	(916)	(1320)	(1795)	(2344)	(2970)	(3310)	(3660)	(4040)	(4430)	(5270)	(6190)	(7180)	(8240)	(9,380)	(11,900)
28	64.5	22.2	39.5	61.7	88.8	121	158	200	247	355	484	632	799	891	987	1090	1190	1420	1670	1930	2220	2,530	3,200
(193)	(19.6)	(83.9)	(149)	(233)	(336)	(457)	(597)	(755)	(933)	(1340)	(1830)	(2390)	(3020)	(3370)	(3730)	(4110)	(4510)	(5370)	(6310)	(7310)	(8390)	(9,550)	(12,100)
29	65.7	22.6	40.2	62.8	90.4	123	161	203	251	362	492	643	814	906	1004	1110	1220	1450	1700	1970	2260	2,570	3,250
(200)	(20.0)	(85.5)	(152)	(237)	(342)	(465)	(608)	(769)	(949)	(1370)	(1860)	(2430)	(3080)	(3430)	(3800)	(4190)	(4600)	(5470)	(6420)	(7440)	(8550)	(9,720)	(12,300)
30	66.8	23.0	40.9	63.8	91.9	125	163	207	255	368	501	654	827	922	1020	1130	1240	1470	1730	2000	2300	2,620	3,310
(207)	(20.3)	(86.9)	(155)	(241)	(348)	(473)	(618)	(782)	(966)	(1390)	(1890)	(2470)	(3130)	(3490)	(3860)	(4260)	(4680)	(5560)	(6530)	(7570)	(8690)	(9,890)	(12,500)
31	67.9	23.4	41.5	64.9	93.5	127	166	210	260	374	509	665	841	937	1040	1140	1260	1500	1750	2040	2340	2,660	3,360
(214)	(20.7)	(88.4)	(157)	(246)	(354)	(481)	(629)	(796)	(982)	(1410)	(1920)	(2510)	(3180)	(3550)	(3930)	(4330)	(4750)	(5660)	(6640)	(7700)	(8840)	(10,100)	(12,700)
32	69.0	23.7	42.2	65.9	95.0	129	169	214	264	380	517	675	855	952	1060	1160	1280	1520	1780	2070	2370	2,700	3,420
(221)	(21.0)	(89.8)	(160)	(250)	(359)	(489)	(639)	(808)	(998)	(1440)	(1960)	(2560)	(3230)	(3600)	(3990)	(4400)	(4830)	(5750)	(6750)	(7820)	(8980)	(10,200)	(12,900)
33	70.0	24.1	42.9	67.0	96.4	131	171	217	268	386	525	686	868	967	1070	1180	1300	1540	1810	2100	2410	2,740	3,470
(228)	(21.4)	(91.2)	(162)	(253)	(365)	(497)	(649)	(821)	(1014)	(1460)	(1990)	(2600)	(3280)	(3660)	(4050)	(4470)	(4910)	(5840)	(6850)	(7950)	(9120)	(10,400)	(13,100)
34	71.1	24.5	43.5	68.0	97.9	133	174	220	272	391	533	696	881	981	1090	1200	1320	1570	1840	2130	2450	2,780	3,520
(234)	(21.6)	(92.4)	(164)	(257)	(370)	(503)	(657)	(832)	(1030)	(1480)	(2010)	(2630)	(3330)	(3710)	(4110)	(4530)	(4970)	(5920)	(6940)	(8050)	(9240)	(10,500)	(13,300)
35	72.1	24.8	44.1	69.0	99.3	135	177	223	276	397	541	706	894	996	1100	1220	1340	1590	1860	2160	2480	2,820	3,570
(241)	(22.0)	(93.8)	(167)	(261)	(375)	(511)	(667)	(844)	(1040)	(1500)	(2040)	(2670)	(3380)	(3760)	(4170)	(4600)	(5040)	(6000)	(7050)	(8170)	(9380)	(10,700)	(13,500)
36	73.1	25.2	44.8	69.9	101	137	179	227	280	403	548	716	906	1010	1120	1230	1350	1610	1890	2190	2520	2,860	3,630
(248)	(22.3)	(95.2)	(169)	(264)	(381)	(518)	(677)	(856)	(1060)	(1520)	(2070)	(2710)	(3430)	(3820)	(4230)	(4660)	(5120)	(6090)	(7150)	(8290)	(9520)	(10,800)	(13,700)
37	74.2	25.5	45.4	70.9	102	139	182	230	284	408	556	726	919	1020	1130	1250	1370	1630	1920	2220	2550	2,900	3,680
(255)	(22.6)	(96.5)	(172)	(268)	(386)	(525)	(686)	(868)	(1070)	(1540)	(2100)	(2740)	(3470)	(3870)	(4290)	(4730)	(5190)	(6180)	(7250)	(8410)	(9650)	(11,000)	(13,900)
38	75.2	25.9	46.0	71.9	103	141	184	233	287	414	563	736	931	1040	1150	1270	1390	1660	1940	2250	2590	2,940	3,720
(262)	(22.9)	(97.8)	(174)	(272)	(391)	(532)	(695)	(880)	(1090)	(1560)	(2130)	(2780)	(3520)	(3920)	(4350)	(4790)	(5260)	(6260)	(7350)	(8520)	(9780)	(11,100)	(14,100)
39	76.1	26.2	46.6	72.8	105	143	186	236	291	419	571	745	943	1050	1160	1280	1410	1680	1970	2280	2620	2,980	3,770
(269)	(23.2)	(99.1)	(176)	(275)	(396)	(540)	(705)	(892)	(1100)	(1590)	(2160)	(2820)	(3570)	(3980)	(4400)	(4860)	(5330)	(6340)	(7440)	(8630)	(9910)	(11,300)	(14,300)

40	77.1	26.5	47.2	73.7	106	144	189	239	295	425	578	755	955	1060	1180	1300	1430	1700	1,990	2,310	2,650	3,020	3,820
(276)	(23.5)	(100)	(178)	(279)	(402)	(547)	(714)	(903)	(1120)	(1610)	(2190)	(2860)	(3610)	(4030)	(4460)	(4920)	(5400)	(6420)	(7,540)	(8,740)	(10,000)	(11,400)	(14,500)
41	78.1	26.9	47.8	74.6	107	146	191	242	299	430	585	764	967	1080	1190	1320	1440	1720	2,020	2,340	2,690	3,060	3,870
(283)	(23.8)	(102)	(181)	(282)	(407)	(553)	(723)	(915)	(1130)	(1630)	(2210)	(2890)	(3660)	(4080)	(4520)	(4980)	(5470)	(6510)	(7,630)	(8,850)	(10,200)	(11,600)	(14,600)
42	79.0	27.2	48.3	75.5	109	148	193	245	302	435	592	774	979	1090	1210	1330	1460	1740	2,040	2,370	2,720	3,090	3,920
(290)	(24.1)	(103)	(183)	(286)	(412)	(560)	(732)	(926)	(1140)	(1650)	(2240)	(2930)	(3700)	(4130)	(4570)	(5040)	(5530)	(6590)	(7,730)	(8,960)	(10,300)	(11,700)	(14,800)
43	79.9	27.5	48.9	76.4	110	150	196	248	306	440	599	783	991	1100	1220	1350	1480	1760	2,070	2,400	2,750	3,130	3,960
(297)	(24.4)	(104)	(185)	(289)	(417)	(567)	(740)	(937)	(1160)	(1670)	(2270)	(2960)	(3750)	(4180)	(4630)	(5100)	(5600)	(6660)	(7,820)	(9,070)	(10,400)	(11,800)	(15,000)
44	80.9	27.8	49.5	77.3	111	152	198	251	309	445	606	792	1000	1120	1240	1360	1500	1780	2,090	2,420	2,780	3,170	4,010
(303)	(24.6)	(105)	(187)	(292)	(421)	(573)	(748)	(947)	(1170)	(1680)	(2290)	(2990)	(3790)	(4220)	(4670)	(5150)	(5660)	(6730)	(7,900)	(9,160)	(10,500)	(12,000)	(15,100)
45	81.8	28.1	50.0	78.2	113	153	200	253	313	450	613	801	1010	1130	1250	1380	1510	1800	2,110	2,450	2,810	3,200	4,050
(310)	(24.9)	(106)	(189)	(296)	(426)	(579)	(757)	(957)	(1180)	(1700)	(2320)	(3030)	(3830)	(4270)	(4730)	(5210)	(5720)	(6810)	(7,990)	(9,270)	(10,600)	(12,100)	(15,300)
46	82.7	28.5	50.6	79.1	114	155	202	256	316	455	620	810	1020	1140	1260	1390	1530	1820	2,140	2,480	2,850	3,240	4,100
(317)	(25.2)	(108)	(191)	(299)	(430)	(586)	(765)	(968)	(1200)	(1720)	(2340)	(3060)	(3870)	(4320)	(4780)	(5270)	(5790)	(6890)	(8,080)	(9,370)	(10,800)	(12,200)	(15,500)
47	83.6	28.8	51.1	79.9	115	157	205	259	320	460	627	818	1040	1150	1280	1410	1550	1840	2,160	2,510	2,880	3,270	4,140
(324)	(25.5)	(109)	(193)	(302)	(435)	(592)	(773)	(979)	(1210)	(1740)	(2370)	(3090)	(3920)	(4360)	(4830)	(5330)	(5850)	(6960)	(8,170)	(9,470)	(10,900)	(12,400)	(15,700)
48	84.5	29.1	51.7	80.8	116	158	207	262	323	465	633	827	1050	1170	1290	1420	1560	1860	2,180	2,530	2,910	3,310	4,190
(331)	(25.7)	(110)	(195)	(305)	(440)	(599)	(782)	(989)	(1220)	(1760)	(2390)	(3130)	(3960)	(4410)	(4890)	(5390)	(5910)	(7040)	(8,260)	(9,580)	(11,000)	(12,500)	(15,800)
49	85.3	29.4	52.2	81.6	117	160	209	264	326	470	640	836	1060	1180	1310	1440	1580	1880	2,210	2,560	2,940	3,340	4,230
(338)	(26.0)	(111)	(197)	(309)	(444)	(605)	(790)	(1000)	(1230)	(1780)	(2420)	(3160)	(4000)	(4460)	(4940)	(5440)	(5970)	(7110)	(8,340)	(9,680)	(11,100)	(12,600)	(16,000)
50	86.2	29.7	52.8	82.4	119	162	211	267	330	475	646	844	1070	1190	1320	1450	1600	1900	2,230	2,580	2,970	3,380	4,270
(345)	(26.3)	(112)	(200)	(312)	(449)	(611)	(798)	(1010)	(1250)	(1800)	(2440)	(3190)	(4040)	(4500)	(4990)	(5500)	(6040)	(7180)	(8,430)	(9,780)	(11,200)	(12,800)	(16,200)
52	87.9	30.3	53.8	84.1	121	165	215	272	336	484	659	861	1090	1210	1340	1480	1630	1940	2,270	2,640	3,030	3,440	4,360
(358)	(26.8)	(114)	(203)	(318)	(457)	(622)	(813)	(1030)	(1270)	(1830)	(2490)	(3250)	(4120)	(4590)	(5080)	(5600)	(6150)	(7320)	(8,590)	(9,960)	(11,400)	(13,000)	(16,500)
54	89.6	30.8	54.8	85.7	123	168	219	278	343	493	672	877	1110	1240	1370	1510	1660	1970	2,320	2,690	3,080	3,510	4,440
(372)	(27.3)	(117)	(207)	(324)	(466)	(634)	(829)	(1050)	(1290)	(1860)	(2540)	(3310)	(4200)	(4670)	(5180)	(5710)	(6270)	(7460)	(8,750)	(10,200)	(11,700)	(13,300)	(16,800)
56	91.2	31.4	55.8	87.2	126	171	223	283	349	502	684	893	1130	1260	1400	1540	1690	2010	2,360	2,740	3,140	3,570	4,520
(386)	(27.8)	(119)	(211)	(330)	(475)	(646)	(844)	(1070)	(1320)	(1900)	(2590)	(3380)	(4270)	(4760)	(5280)	(5820)	(6380)	(7600)	(8,920)	(10,300)	(11,900)	(13,500)	(17,100)
58	92.8	32.0	56.8	88.8	128	174	227	288	355	511	696	909	1150	1280	1420	1570	1720	2050	2,400	2,780	3,200	3,640	4,600
(400)	(28.3)	(121)	(215)	(336)	(483)	(658)	(859)	(1090)	(1340)	(1930)	(2630)	(3440)	(4350)	(4850)	(5370)	(5920)	(6500)	(7730)	(9,080)	(10,500)	(12,100)	(13,700)	(17,400)
60	94.4	32.5	57.8	90.3	130	177	231	293	361	520	708	925	1170	1300	1440	1590	1750	2080	2,440	2,830	3,250	3,700	4,680
(414)	(28.8)	(123)	(219)	(342)	(492)	(669)	(874)	(1110)	(1370)	(1970)	(2680)	(3500)	(4430)	(4930)	(5460)	(6020)	(6610)	(7870)	(9,230)	(10,700)	(12,300)	(14,000)	(17,700)
62	96.0	33.0	58.7	91.8	132	180	235	297	367	528	719	940	1190	1330	1470	1620	1780	2110	2,480	2,880	3,300	3,760	4,760
(427)	(29.2)	(125)	(222)	(347)	(499)	(680)	(888)	(1120)	(1390)	(2000)	(2720)	(3550)	(4490)	(5010)	(5550)	(6120)	(6710)	(7990)	(9,380)	(10,900)	(12,500)	(14,200)	(18,000)
64	97.5	33.6	59.7	93.3	134	183	239	302	373	537	731	955	1210	1350	1490	1640	1810	2150	2,520	2,920	3,360	3,820	4,830
(441)	(29.7)	(127)	(226)	(352)	(508)	(691)	(902)	(1140)	(1410)	(2030)	(2760)	(3610)	(4570)	(5090)	(5640)	(6220)	(6820)	(8120)	(9,530)	(11,100)	(12,700)	(14,400)	(18,300)
66	99.0	34.1	60.6	94.7	136	186	242	307	379	545	742	970	1230	1370	1520	1670	1830	2180	2,560	2,970	3,410	3,880	4,910
(455)	(30.2)	(129)	(229)	(358)	(516)	(702)	(917)	(1160)	(1430)	(2060)	(2810)	(3670)	(4640)	(5170)	(5730)	(6320)	(6930)	(8250)	(9,680)	(11,200)	(12,900)	(14,700)	(18,600)
68	101	34.6	61.5	96.1	138	188	246	311	384	554	754	984	1250	1390	1540	1700	1860	2210	2,600	3,010	3,460	3,940	4,980
(469)	(30.6)	(131)	(233)	(363)	(523)	(712)	(931)	(1180)	(1450)	(2090)	(2850)	(3720)	(4710)	(5250)	(5820)	(6410)	(7040)	(8370)	(9,830)	(11,400)	(13,100)	(14,900)	(18,800)
70	102	35.1	62.4	97.5	140	191	250	316	390	562	765	999	1260	1410	1560	1720	1890	2250	2,640	3,060	3,510	3,990	5,060
(483)	(31.1)	(133)	(236)	(369)	(531)	(723)	(944)	(1200)	(1480)	(2120)	(2890)	(3780)	(4780)	(5330)	(5900)	(6510)	(7140)	(8500)	(9,970)	(11,600)	(13,300)	(15,100)	(19,100)
72	103	35.6	63.3	98.9	142	194	253	320	396	570	775	1010	1280	1430	1580	1740	1910	2280	2,670	3,100	3,560	4,050	5,130
(496)	(31.5)	(135)	(239)	(374)	(538)	(733)	(957)	(1210)	(1500)	(2150)	(2930)	(3830)	(4840)	(5400)	(5980)	(6590)	(7240)	(8610)	(10,100)	(11,700)	(13,500)	(15,300)	(19,400)
74	105	36.1	64.2	100	144	197	257	325	401	578	786	1030	1300	1450	1600	1770	1940	2310	2,710	3,140	3,610	4,110	5,200
(510)	(31.9)	(136)	(243)	(379)	(546)	(743)	(970)	(1230)	(1520)	(2180)	(2970)	(3880)	(4910)	(4570)	(6060)	(6690)	(7340)	(8730)	(10,200)	(11,900)	(13,600)	(15,500)	(19,600)
76	106	36.6	65.0	102	146	199	260	329	406	585	797	1040	1320	1470	1630	1790	1970	2340	2,750	3,190	3,660	4,160	5,270
(524)	(32.4)	(138)	(246)	(384)	(553)	(753)	(984)	(1240)	(1540)	(2210)	(3010)	(3930)	(4980)	(5550)	(6150)	(6780)	(7440)	(8850)	(10,400)	(12,000)	(13,800)	(15,700)	(19,900)
78	108	37.1	65.9	103	148	202	264	334	412	593	807	1050	1330	1490	1650	1820	1990	2370	2,780	3,230	3,710	4,220	5,340
(538)	(32.8)	(140)	(249)	(389)	(561)	(763)	(997)	(1260)	(1560)	(2240)	(3050)	(3990)	(5050)	(5620)	(6230)	(6870)	(7540)	(8970)	(10,500)	(12,200)	(14,000)	(15,900)	(20,200)

(continued)

TABLE 15.3.1 Continued

Pressure psi (kPa)	*Velocity ft/sec (m/sec)*	*0.375 (9.53)*	*0.5 (12.7)*	*0.625 (15.9)*	*0.75 (19.1)*	*0.875 (22.2)*	*1 (25.4)*	*1.125 (28.6)*	*1.25 (31.8)*	*1.5 (38.1)*	*1.75 (44.5)*	*2 (50.8)*	*2.25 (57.2)*	*2.375 (60.3)*	*2.5 (63.5)*	*2.625 (66.7)*	*2.75 (69.9)*	*3 (76.2)*	*3.25 (82.6)*	*3.5 (88.9)*	*3.75 (95.25)*	*4 (102)*	*4.5 (114)*
80	109	37.5	66.7	104	150	204	267	338	417	601	817	1070	1350	1510	1670	1840	2,020	2,400	2,820	3,270	3,750	4,270	5,400
(552)	(33.2)	(142)	(252)	(394)	(568)	(773)	(1010)	(1280)	(1580)	(2270)	(3090)	(4040)	(5110)	(5690)	(6310)	(6960)	(7,630)	(9,090)	(10,700)	(12,400)	(14,200)	(16,200)	(20,400)
82	110	38.0	67.6	106	152	207	270	342	422	608	828	1080	1370	1520	1690	1860	2,040	2,430	2,850	3,310	3,800	4,320	5,470
(565)	(33.6)	(144)	(255)	(399)	(574)	(782)	(1020)	(1290)	(1600)	(2300)	(3130)	(4090)	(5170)	(5760)	(6380)	(7040)	(7,720)	(9,190)	(10,800)	(12,500)	(14,400)	(16,300)	(20,700)
84	112	38.5	68.4	107	154	209	273	346	427	615	838	1090	1380	1540	1710	1880	2,070	2,460	2,890	3,350	3,850	4,380	5,540
(579)	(34.0)	(145)	(258)	(404)	(582)	(792)	(1030)	(1310)	(1620)	(2330)	(3170)	(4140)	(5230)	(5830)	(6460)	(7120)	(7,820)	(9,310)	(10,900)	(12,700)	(14,500)	(16,500)	(20,900)
86	113	38.9	69.2	108	156	212	277	350	432	623	847	1110	1400	1560	1730	1910	2,090	2,490	2,920	3,390	3,890	4,430	5,600
(593)	(34.4)	(147)	(262)	(409)	(589)	(801)	(1050)	(1320)	(1630)	(2350)	(3200)	(4190)	(5300)	(5900)	(6540)	(7210)	(7,910)	(9,420)	(11,100)	(12,800)	(14,700)	(16,700)	(21,200)
88	114	39.4	70.0	109	157	214	280	354	437	630	857	1120	1420	1580	1750	1930	2,120	2,520	2,960	3,430	3,940	4,480	5,670
(607)	(34.8)	(149)	(265)	(414)	(595)	(810)	(1060)	(1340)	(1650)	(2380)	(3240)	(4230)	(5360)	(5970)	(6620)	(7290)	(8,010)	(9,530)	(11,200)	(13,000)	(14,900)	(16,900)	(21,400)
90	116	39.8	70.8	111	159	217	283	358	442	637	867	1130	1430	1600	1770	1950	2,140	2,550	2,990	3,470	3,980	4,530	5,730
(620)	(35.2)	(150)	(267)	(418)	(602)	(819)	(1070)	(1350)	(1670)	(2410)	(3280)	(4280)	(5420)	(6030)	(6690)	(7370)	(8,090)	(9,630)	(11,300)	(13,100)	(15,000)	(17,100)	(21,700)
92	117	40.2	71.6	112	161	219	286	362	447	644	877	1140	1450	1610	1790	1970	2,160	2,580	3,020	3,510	4,020	4,580	5,800
(634)	(35.6)	(152)	(270)	(423)	(609)	(828)	(1080)	(1370)	(1690)	(2430)	(3310)	(4330)	(5480)	(6100)	(6760)	(7450)	(8,180)	(9,740)	(11,400)	(13,300)	(15,200)	(17,300)	(21,900)
94	118	40.7	72.3	113	163	222	289	366	452	651	886	1160	1460	1630	1810	1990	2,190	2,600	3,060	3,540	4,070	4,630	5,860
(648)	(36.0)	(154)	(273)	(427)	(615)	(837)	(1090)	(1380)	(1710)	(2460)	(3350)	(4380)	(5540)	(6170)	(6840)	(7540)	(8,270)	(9,840)	(11,600)	(13,400)	(15,400)	(17,500)	(22,100)
96	119	41.1	73.1	114	164	224	292	370	457	658	895	1170	1480	1650	1830	2010	2,210	2,630	3,090	3,580	4,110	4,680	5,920
(662)	(36.4)	(155)	(276)	(432)	(622)	(846)	(1110)	(1400)	(1730)	(2490)	(3390)	(4420)	(5600)	(6240)	(6910)	(7620)	(8,360)	(9,950)	(11,700)	(13,500)	(15,500)	(17,700)	(22,400)
98	121	41.5	73.9	115	166	226	295	374	462	665	905	1180	1500	1670	1850	2040	2,230	2,660	3,120	3,620	4,150	4,730	5,980
(676)	(36.8)	(157)	(279)	(436)	(628)	(855)	(1120)	(1410)	(1750)	(2510)	(3420)	(4470)	(5660)	(6300)	(6980)	(7700)	(8,450)	(10,100)	(11,800)	(13,700)	(15,700)	(17,900)	(22,600)
100	122	42.0	74.6	117	168	228	298	378	466	671	914	1190	1510	1680	1870	2060	2,260	2,690	3,150	3,660	4,200	4,770	6,040
(689)	(37.1)	(159)	(282)	(441)	(634)	(864)	(1130)	(1430)	(1760)	(2540)	(3450)	(4510)	(5710)	(6360)	(7050)	(7770)	(8,530)	(10,200)	(11,900)	(13,800)	(15,900)	(18,000)	(22,800)
105	125	43.0	76.4	119	172	234	306	387	478	688	936	1220	1550	1720	1910	2110	2,310	2,750	3,230	3,750	4,300	3,890	6,190
(724)	(38.1)	(163)	(289)	(452)	(650)	(885)	(1160)	(1460)	(1810)	(2600)	(3540)	(4620)	(5850)	(6520)	(7230)	(7970)	(8,740)	(10,400)	(12,200)	(14,200)	(16,300)	(18,500)	(23,400)
110	128	44.0	78.2	122	176	240	313	396	489	704	958	1250	1580	1770	1960	2160	2,370	2,820	3,310	3,830	4,400	5,010	6,340
(758)	(38.9)	(166)	(296)	(462)	(666)	(906)	(1180)	(1500)	(1850)	(2660)	(3620)	(4730)	(5990)	(6670)	(7400)	(8150)	(8,950)	(10,600)	(12,500)	(14,500)	(16,600)	(18,900)	(24,000)
115	131	45.0	80.0	125	180	245	320	405	500	720	980	1280	1620	1800	2000	2200	2,420	2,880	3,380	3,920	4,500	5,120	6,480
(793)	(39.8)	(170)	(302)	(473)	(681)	(926)	(1210)	(1530)	(1890)	(2720)	(3710)	(4840)	(6130)	(6820)	(7560)	(8340)	(9,150)	(10,900)	(12,800)	(14,800)	(17,000)	(19,400)	(24,500)
120	134	46.0	81.7	128	184	250	327	414	511	735	1000	1310	1650	1840	2040	2250	2,470	2,940	3,450	4,000	4,600	5,230	6,620
(827)	(40.7)	(174)	(309)	(483)	(695)	(946)	(1240)	(1560)	(1930)	(2780)	(3790)	(4940)	(6260)	(6970)	(7720)	(8520)	(9,350)	(11,100)	(13,100)	(15,100)	(17,400)	(19,800)	(25,000)
125	136	46.9	83.4	130	188	255	334	422	521	751	1020	1330	1690	1880	2090	2300	2,520	3,000	3,520	4,090	4,690	5,340	6,760
(862)	(41.5)	(177)	(315)	(493)	(710)	(966)	(1260)	(1600)	(1970)	(2840)	(3860)	(5050)	(6390)	(7120)	(7880)	(8690)	(9,540)	(11,400)	(13,300)	(15,500)	(17,700)	(20,200)	(25,500)
130	139	47.8	85.1	133	191	260	340	431	532	766	1040	1360	1720	1920	2130	2340	2,570	3,060	3,590	4,170	4,780	5,440	6,890
(896)	(42.3)	(181)	(322)	(502)	(724)	(985)	(1290)	(1630)	(2010)	(2890)	(3940)	(5150)	(6510)	(7260)	(8040)	(8860)	(9,730)	(11,600)	(13,600)	(15,800)	(18,100)	(20,600)	(26,000)
135	142	48.8	86.7	135	195	265	347	439	542	780	1060	1390	1760	1960	2170	2390	2,620	3,120	3,660	4,250	4,880	5,550	7,020
(931)	(43.1)	(184)	(328)	(512)	(737)	(1000)	(1310)	(1660)	(2050)	(2950)	(4010)	(5240)	(6640)	(7390)	(8190)	(9030)	(9,910)	(11,800)	(13,800)	(16,100)	(18,400)	(21,000)	(26,500)
140	144	49.7	88.3	138	199	270	353	447	552	794	1080	1410	1790	1990	2210	2430	2,670	3,180	3,730	4,330	4,970	5,650	7,150
(965)	(43.9)	(188)	(334)	(521)	(751)	(1020)	(1330)	(1690)	(2090)	(3000)	(4090)	(5340)	(6760)	(7530)	(8340)	(9200)	(10,100)	(12,000)	(14,100)	(16,400)	(18,800)	(21,400)	(27,000)
145	147	50.5	89.8	140	202	275	359	455	561	808	1100	1440	1820	2030	2250	2480	2,720	3,230	3,800	4,400	5,050	5,750	7,280
(1000)	(44.7)	(191)	(340)	(531)	(764)	(1040)	(1360)	(1720)	(2120)	(3060)	(4160)	(5430)	(6880)	(7660)	(8490)	(9360)	(10,300)	(12,200)	(14,300)	(16,600)	(19,100)	(21,700)	(27,500)
150	149	51.4	91.4	143	206	280	365	463	571	822	1120	1460	1850	2060	2280	2520	2,760	3,290	3,860	4,480	5,140	5,850	7,400
(1030)	(45.4)	(194)	(345)	(539)	(776)	(1060)	(1380)	(1750)	(2150)	(3100)	(4220)	(5520)	(6980)	(7780)	(8620)	(9500)	(10,400)	(12,400)	(14,600)	(16,900)	(19,400)	(22,100)	(27,900)

The coefficient of discharge, c_d, is defined as the ratio of the actual discharge to the theoretical discharge. For any specific orifice or nozzle, values of c_d are determined by standard test procedures using this definition. The actual rate of flow is measured by calibrated meters, or "weigh tanks." The theoretical flow is calculated using $c_d = 1.0$, the carefully measured orifice or nozzle diameter, and the measured velocity pressure in the flow equation.

Standard Orifice

An orifice with a sharp entrance edge, shown as form (1) in Figure 15.3.4, is known as a standard orifice and is commonly used to measure waterflow. If the shape of the orifice is changed so as to decrease the contraction, its capacity will be increased. Form 1 in the illustration is a standard orifice having a sharp edge on the approach side. Form 2, when in a thin plate, gives the same stream characteristics as Form 1. Form 3 is the reverse of 1. In Form 4, the edge is rounded to conform to the shape of the stream. The coefficients of discharge of 3 and 4 are greater than those of the standard orifices, approaching a value of 1.0 in the case of 4. As water leaves the orifice, it contracts to form a jet whose cross-sectional area is less than that of the orifice. The contraction is complete at the plane a', which is located a distance from the plane of the orifice equal to approximately half the diameter of the jet (Figure 15.3.5).

The quantity flowing is obviously the same at the orifice a as at the contracted section a', so the quantity flowing could be obtained by measuring the velocity and area at either of these planes. Expressed in a formula, where Q is ft³/sec (m³/sec), υ is velocity in ft/sec (m/sec), and a is the area in ft² (m²),

$$Q = \upsilon a = \upsilon' a'$$

The coefficient of discharge for a standard orifice is the product of the coefficient of velocity and the coefficient of contraction, or $c = 0.98 \times 0.62 = 0.61$.

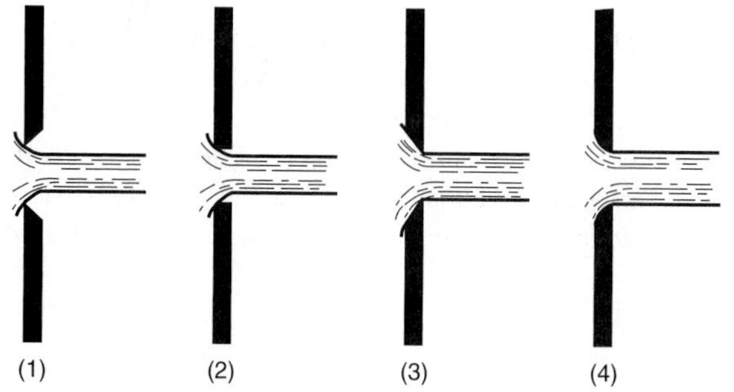

FIGURE 15.3.4 Orifices of Various Shapes

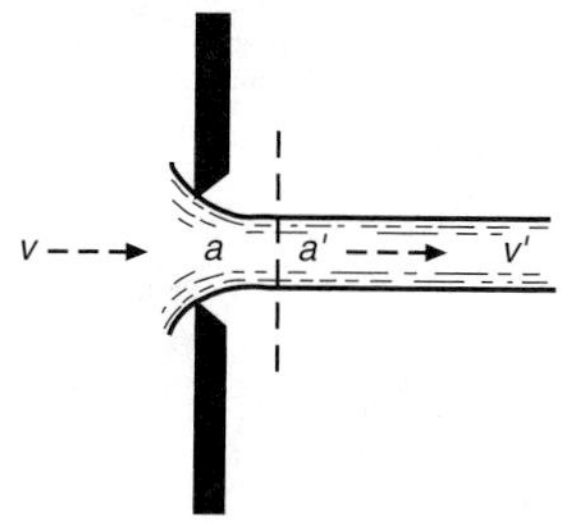

FIGURE 15.3.5 Flow Through a Standard Orifice

Other Orifices

The hydraulic characteristics of good solid-stream nozzles are consistent within a wide range of flow conditions. The velocity at the surface of the stream of most such nozzles is reduced slightly by friction against the orifice or nozzle. A coefficient of velocity of 0.97 is usually applied to nozzles of fire stream sizes to account for this friction.

Coefficients of discharge are available for the flow through hydrants, hose nozzles, automatic sprinklers, and other common fire protection discharge outlets. Representative values for the coefficients of discharge are given in Table 15.3.2. Again, these coefficients only apply when there is flow through the full orifice or nozzle opening with a reasonably uniform velocity profile. Three general types of hydrant outlets and their coefficients of discharge are shown in Figure 15.3.6.

TABLE 15.3.2 Typical Discharge Coefficients of Solid-Stream Nozzle

Spray sprinkler, average (nominal ½-in. dia.)	0.75
Spray sprinkler, average (nominal 17⁄32-in. dia.)	0.95
Large-drop sprinkler (0.64 in. dia.)	0.90
Standard orifice (sharp edge)	0.62
Smooth-bore nozzles, general	0.96–0.98
Underwriter playpipes or equal	0.97
Deluge or monitor nozzles	0.997
Open pipe, burred opening	0.80
Open pipe, smooth, well rounded	0.90
Hydrant butt, smooth and well-rounded outlet, flowing full*	0.90
Hydrant butt, square and sharp at hydrant barrel*	0.82
Hydrant butt, outlet square, projecting into barrel*	0.70

*See Figure 15.3.6.

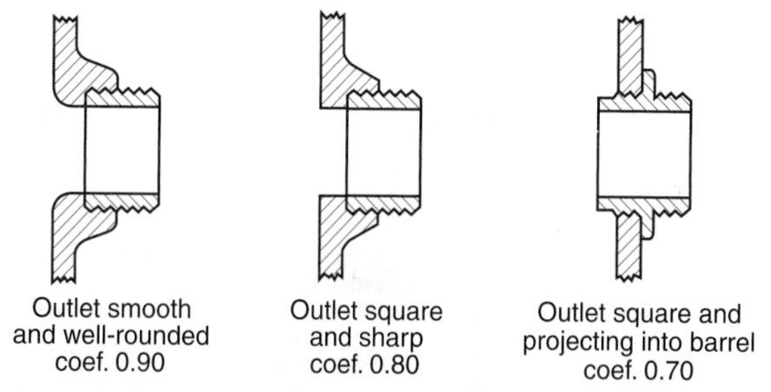

FIGURE 15.3.6 Three Types of Hydrant Outlets and Coefficients of Discharge

Flow in Short Tubes

A tube attached to an orifice is known as a standard short tube if it is 2½ to 3 times longer than the diameter of the orifice, and its diameter is the same as the orifice. A shorter tube will not flow full, and friction losses in a longer tube will affect results when used as a measuring device, hence the specified length limit.

The characteristics of a standard short tube and a short conical converging tube are shown in Figures 15.3.7 and 15.3.8, respectively. The principles of flow in orifices apply, but with different coefficients. With the conical tube, the coefficients c_υ and c_c vary with the angle β. When β is 0 degrees, the converging tube becomes a cylindrical tube, with $c_c = 1$ and $c_\upsilon = 0.82$; c_d is then 0.82. As the angle β increases, the coefficient of contraction (c_c), develops, and the coefficient of velocity (c_υ) increases, approaching the 0.98 value for a sharp-edge orifice. Relations are such that the coefficient of discharge attains a maximum value of 0.94, with a β angle of about 13 degrees.

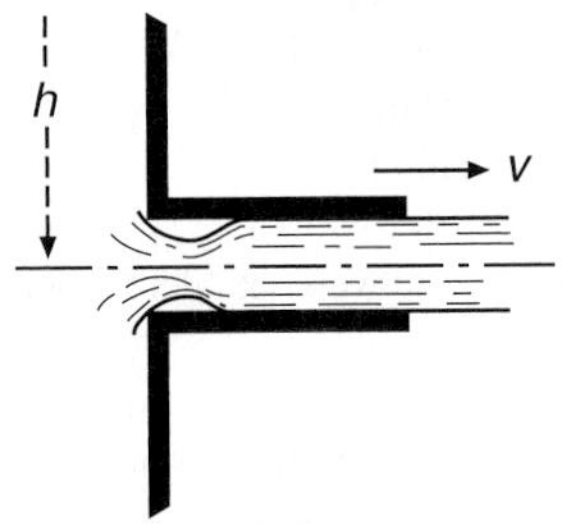

FIGURE 15.3.7 Flow in Cylindrical Short Tube

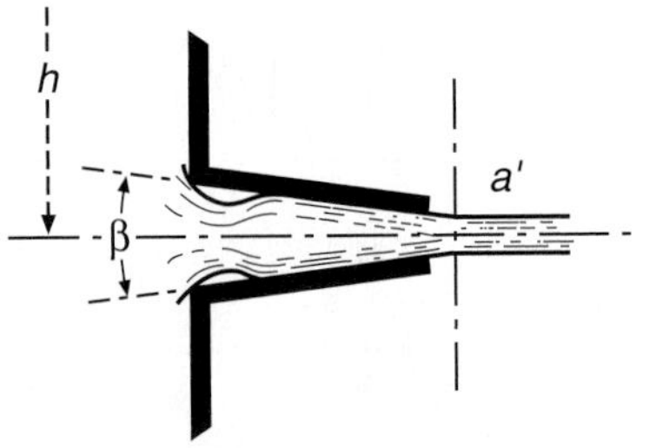

FIGURE 15.3.8 Flow in Short Conical Converging Tube

FLOW MEASUREMENT

Pitot Tube Method of Measuring Flow

The most commonly used method of measuring flow in an open stream discharging from an orifice, nozzle, or open pipe is by direct measurement of the velocity head that produces the flow. This measurement process makes use of the well-known Pitot tube and pressure gauge combination.

When the small opening (usually not over 1⁄16 in. [1.6 mm] in diameter) is inserted into the center of a stream at the point of maximum contraction, with the opening directly in the line of flow, the gauge will indicate the total head at that location. With the stream open to the atmosphere, there will be no pressure head, so the indicated reading will be velocity head alone, and thus the velocity of the stream can be calculated directly. As a result, velocity pressure is sometimes referred to as Pitot pressure.

If the area of the cross section of the stream at the location of the velocity measurement location is known, the quantity flowing can be determined from the relation, $Q = a\upsilon = 29.84c_d d^2\sqrt{p}$ or in SI units, $Q_m = 0.0666c_d d_m^2\sqrt{p_{\upsilon m}}$, previously derived. In practice, discharge tables are usually used to determine the flow from hydrants and nozzles (see Table 15.3.1).

A typical Pitot tube as used in the measuring of the flow from a fire stream nozzle is shown in Figure 15.3.9. For the usual forms of orifices and nozzles, the coefficient of discharge (c_d) is accurately known, so that $a = c_d \times$ actual discharge opening. For example, with a sharp-edge orifice the area of the stream may be determined from the actual diameter of the orifice opening and the use of the 0.62 coefficient of discharge, as outlined in the previous section on flow-through orifices.

When measuring flow from a straight-stream fire nozzle, the use of the Pitot tube method only holds with reasonable accuracy for tip sizes up to 1⅜ in. (35 mm) supplied from 2½-in. (64-mm) hose. Above that, the error rate increases beyond acceptable limits, as the assumptions of uniform velocity and full flow become less valid. An exception is the Underwriters playpipe that maintains a uniform coefficient over a wide range of flows and pressures for tip sizes of 1⅛ or 1¾ in. (29 or 45 mm).

The Pitot tube method is also commonly used to measure the flow discharging from the outlets of fire hydrants to determine the water supply available for fire protection. Unlike the flow entering a nozzle on the end of a pipe or hose line, the flow through large hydrant outlets, or through smaller hydrant outlets at high velocities, has neither a uniform velocity profile nor full flow, since the additional turbulence generated by the flow passing through the hydrant has not dissipated.

In cases such as these, the flow conditions must be changed so that the assumptions needed for the Pitot tube method are valid, or an alternative method, such as the one described next under "Nozzle Method of Measuring Flow," should be used. If

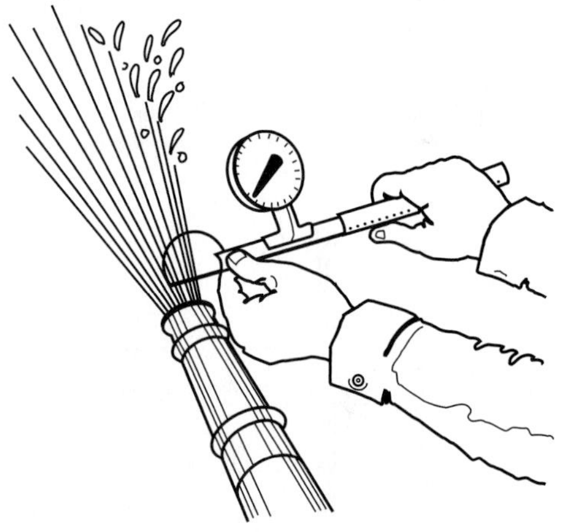

FIGURE 15.3.9 Taking Nozzle Pressure with a Pitot Tube

flow is from an open hydrant outlet, hoses and nozzles, a reducer, or a short tube can often be connected to the outlet to improve the flow characteristics.

Nozzle Method of Measuring Flow

The rate of discharge can also be calculated from the gauge pressure at the base of the nozzle. The flow formula for using base pressure is

$$Q = \frac{29.84cd^2\sqrt{p_1}}{\sqrt{1 - c^2\left(\frac{d}{D}\right)^4}}$$

where

Q = Flow in gallons per minute

c = Coefficient of discharge

d = Diameter of outlet (in.)

p_1 = Gauge pressure at base of nozzle (psi)

D = Inside diameter of fitting to which gauge is attached (in.)

For SI units, the formula is expressed as

$$Q = \frac{0.0666cd_m^2\sqrt{p_{1m}}}{\sqrt{1 - c^2\left(\frac{d_m}{D_m}\right)^4}}$$

where

Q_m = Flow (L/min)

c = Coefficient of discharge

d_m = Diameter of outlet (mm)

p_{1_m} = Gauge pressure at base of nozzle (kPa)

D_m = Inside diameter of fitting to which gauge is attached (mm)

This is the same formula that is used for discharge from an orifice, except that (1) gauge pressure at the base of the nozzle is substituted for Pitot pressure, and (2) a factor is added that represents the ratio between gauge pressure (normal) and total pressure at the nozzle base. (Total pressure is gauge plus velocity pressure.)

When base pressure is to be used, the gauge is attached to a fitting close to the nozzle with a straight piece of approach pipe or hose to eliminate turbulence or unstable flow conditions. To obtain greater accuracy than provided by a simple fitting, a piezometer fitting may be used. With this device, the gauge is connected to an annular tube or channel having a number of small holes drilled into the waterway around the circumference. The mean or resultant static pressure indicated by the gauge is p_1 in the formula above.

Although accurate and convenient for fixed test arrangements, the measurement of pressure at the base of a nozzle is not practical for usual hose stream operations. However, because a Pitot gauge is useless with spray-type nozzles, or other devices producing special types of discharge, the base pressure method is necessary.

Discharge Calculations

The most common method of estimating nozzle or orifice discharge is to use Table 15.3.1. The flow from the table, corresponding to the measured Pitot pressure and orifice diameter, is multiplied by the discharge coefficient (see Table 15.3.2).

EXAMPLE 1: A Pitot reading of 20 psi was measured on an open 2½-in. smooth and well-rounded hydrant butt. From Table 15.3.2, the discharge coefficient is 0.90. From Table 15.3.1, theoretical flow for a 20-psi velocity head is 834 gpm. The discharge is $Q = 834 \times 0.90 = 751$ gpm. (Or subtract 10 percent from 834 and get 751 gpm.)

EXAMPLE 2: A Pitot reading was 200 kPa at a 38.1-mm pipe with a square sharp opening (discharge coefficient = 0.80). From Table 15.3.1, 200 kPa gives a theoretical flow of 1370 L/min. The actual flow would be 0.8 × 1370 = 1100 L/min

Discharge curves, such as those shown in Figure 15.3.10, are available for many nozzles and are sufficiently accurate for most fire flow calculations. These usually incorporate the specific discharge coefficients for the nozzle involved, but occasionally plot theoretical flow. Nozzle discharge can also be determined by the standard formulas previously discussed. (See "Flow of Water Through Orifices" and "Nozzle Method of Measuring Flow" in this chapter).

EXAMPLE 3: Calculate the rate of discharge from a 2 in. (51 mm) nozzle with a pressure measured by a 2½ in. (64 mm)

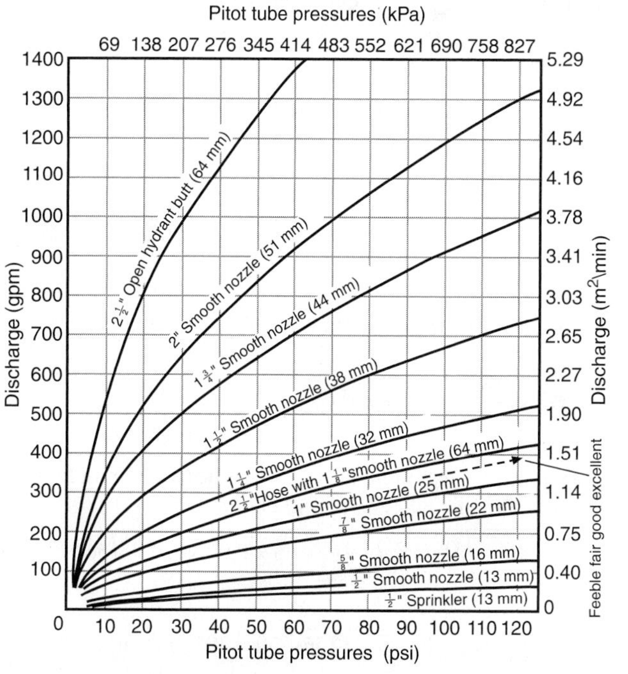

FIGURE 15.3.10 Relative Discharge Curves

piezometer ring and gauge of 80 psi (552 kPa) at the base of the nozzle. The nozzle has a coefficient of discharge of 0.99.

Using the formula for the nozzle method of measuring flow,

$$Q = \frac{29.84cd^2\sqrt{p_1}}{\sqrt{1 - c^2\left(\frac{d}{D}\right)^4}}$$

$$Q = \frac{29.84 \times 0.99 \times (2)^2\sqrt{80}}{\sqrt{1 - (0.99)^2\left(\frac{2}{2.5}\right)^4}}$$

$$Q = 1366 \text{ gpm } (5171 \text{ L/min})$$

To simplify calculations for a specific orifice or nozzle, the constants in the flow formula can be combined, reducing the formula to

$$Q = \text{K}\sqrt{p}$$

where K combines the constants 29.84 (0.0666 in SI units), c_d, and d^2. Table 15.3.3 lists K-factors of some common discharge orifices used for fire protection. For SI units, use the K_m values.

Because

$$\text{K} = \frac{Q}{\sqrt{p}}$$

the K values of spray nozzles can be calculated from data in testing laboratory listings of nozzles. For some nozzles, the flow rate at 25 and 125 psi (170 and 162 kPa) pressure is given, from which the K-factor can be calculated.

EXAMPLE 4: A certain fire service spray nozzle is rated for 83 gpm at 50 psi. What is the discharge at a pressure of 25 psi? Since we know the flow at a known pressure, we can calculate the K-factor. The K-factor is

$$\text{K} = \frac{83}{\sqrt{50}} = \frac{83}{7.07} = 11.7$$

At 25 psi pressure, the discharge would be

$$11.7\sqrt{25} = 11.7 \times 5 = 58.5 \text{ gpm}$$

Because the K-factor is constant, we can also calculate the new flow directly. Since $Q = \text{K}\sqrt{p}$, it follows that $\text{K} = \frac{Q}{\sqrt{p}}$ and that $\frac{Q_1}{\sqrt{p_1}} = \frac{Q_2}{\sqrt{p_2}}$.

Therefore, $\frac{83}{\sqrt{50}} = \frac{Q_2}{\sqrt{25}}$ and $Q_2 = \frac{83 \times \sqrt{25}}{\sqrt{50}} = 58.5.$

EXAMPLE 5: Determine the discharge from a 51 mm hydrant butt ($c_d = 90$) at a pressure of 350 kPa.

$$\text{K}_\text{m} = 0.0666cd_\text{m}^2 = 0.0666 \times 0.90 \times 51^2 = 156$$

Thus,

$$Q_\text{m} = \text{K}_\text{m}\sqrt{p_\text{m}} = 156\sqrt{350} = 2918 \text{ L/min}$$

Alternatively, from Table 15.3.3, $\text{K}_\text{m} = 154.7$. Thus,

$$Q_\text{m} = \text{K}_\text{m}\sqrt{p_\text{m}} = 154.7\sqrt{350} = 2894 \text{ L/min}$$

TABLE 15.3.3 Values of K for Various Discharge Orifices

Type of Orifice	Nominal Diameter *(in.)*	Nominal Diameter *(mm)*	K-Factor *gpm/p*$^{1/2}$	K-Factor *lpm and* P_m^2
Sprinkler	1/4	7	1.3–1.5	1.9–2.2
Sprinkler	5/16	8	1.8–2.0	2.6–2.9
Sprinkler	3/8	10	2.6–2.9	3.7–4.2
Sprinkler	7/16	11	4.0–4.4	5.8–6.3
Sprinkler	1/2	13	5.3–5.8	7.6–8.4
Sprinkler	17/32	14	7.4–8.2	10.6–11.8
Sprinkler	5/8	16	11.0–11.5	15.9–16.6
Sprinkler	3/4	19	13.5–14.5	19.5–20.1
Sprinkler	25/32	19.8	16.0–17.6	23.1–25.4
Sprinkler	15/16	23.6	23.9–26.5	38.9–43.0
Nozzle	1/2	13	7.2	10.3
Nozzle	7/8	22	22.2	32.0
Nozzle	1	25	29.1	41.9
Nozzle	1 1/16	27	32.8	47.2
Nozzle	1 1/8	29	36.8	53.0
Nozzle	1 3/16	30	41.0	59.0
Nozzle	1 1/4	32	45.4	65.4
Nozzle	1 5/16	33	50.1	72.1
Nozzle	1 3/8	35	54.9	79.1
Nozzle (c = 0.97 for all nozzles)	1 7/16	37	60.0	86.4
Nozzle	1 1/2	38	65.4	94.2
Nozzle	1 9/16	40	70.9	102.0
Nozzle	1 5/8	41	76.8	110.6
Nozzle	1 11/16	43	82.8	119.2
Nozzle	1 3/4	44	89.0	128.2
Nozzle	1 13/16	46	95.5	137.5
Nozzle	1 7/8	48	102.0	146.9
Nozzle	1 15/16	49	109.0	157.0
Nozzle	2	51	116.0	167.0
Hydrant butt (c = 0.90)	2	51	107.4	154.7
Hydrant butt (c = 0.90)	2 1/4	57	135.9	195.7
Hydrant butt (c = 0.90)	2 1/2	64	167.8	241.6

Note that in this example the answers from the two methods are close but do not exactly match. Care needs to be taken that the results do not imply a higher degree of accuracy than actually exists. Given the nature of the flow from a hydrant butt, assuming a flow of about 2900 L/min would be appropriate in this case.

Flow Meters

When it is not convenient to discharge water to the atmosphere, meters are used to determine flow.

Venturi Tube. The Venturi principle has a number of applications in fire protection. The Venturi tube is essentially a tapered constriction in a pipe. In the constricted part, the velocity must be greater than in the straight tube, and the pressure is correspondingly less, in accordance with Bernoulli's theorem. If the increase in velocity through the restricted portion is sufficient, the pressure at that point will be less than atmospheric, and a suction will be created at any opening into the side of the tube. The Venturi tube is illustrated in Figure 15.3.11. The diverging portion of a Venturi tube serves only to restore the system pressure with a minimum of friction loss.

Venturi Meter. The Venturi principle as applied in the Venturi meter for the measurement of flow in closed pipelines under pressure is as follows.

With no elevation difference along the line of flow, Bernoulli's theorem becomes

$$\frac{v_1^2}{2g} + \frac{p_1}{w} + 0 = \frac{v_2^2}{2g} + \frac{p_2}{w} + 0$$

In Figure 15.3.11,

$$\frac{p_1}{w}$$

is represented by h_1, and

$$\frac{p_2}{w}$$

by h_2, which are used in the following equations.

The quantity of liquid passing through all portions of the Venturi meter must be the same. Therefore,

$$Q = a_1 v_1 = a_2 v_2 \text{ or } v_1 = \frac{Q}{a_1} \text{ or } v_2 = \frac{Q}{a_2}$$

Substituting in Bernoulli's theorem,

$$\frac{\left(\frac{Q}{a_1}\right)^2}{2g} + h_1 = \frac{\left(\frac{Q}{a_2}\right)^2}{2g} + h_2$$

$$\frac{\left(\frac{Q}{a_2}\right)^2}{2g} - \frac{\left(\frac{Q}{a_1}\right)^2}{2g} = h_1 - h_2$$

$$Q^2\left(\frac{1}{a_2^2} - \frac{1}{a_1^2}\right) = 2g(h_1 - h_2)$$

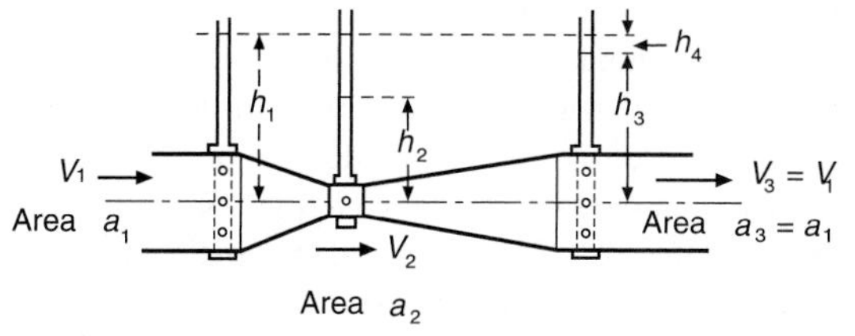

FIGURE 15.3.11 The Venturi Tube

$$Q^2\left(\frac{a_1^2 - a_2^2}{a_1^2 a_2^2}\right) = 2g(h_1 - h_2)$$

$$Q = \frac{a_1 a_2}{\sqrt{a_1^2 - a_2^2}}\sqrt{2g(h_1 - h_2)}$$

For any specific Venturi meter, a_1 and a_2 are known constant values. There is also a friction loss coefficient, which is usually determined by test and which does not remain constant with very low velocities. Combining the known constant values, the Venturi meter formula is generally expressed as

$$Q = \text{K}\sqrt{(h_1 - h_2)}, \text{ or } Q = \text{K}\sqrt{\frac{p_1}{w} - \frac{p_2}{w}}$$

By test, a value of k for any specific meter can be established with reasonable accuracy, thus allowing the measurement of flow to be calculated from the pressure differential across the meter.

When used as a device for inducing gas or liquid into the stream, as is made possible by the reduced pressure, in the throat section, the hydraulic performance will not be in strict accordance with the above theoretical calculations because energy is expended on the induced substance.

Orifice Meters. When water flows through a thin sharp-edged orifice (such as the standard orifice discussed earlier) within a pipe, the flow diameter contracts the same way it does when the flow discharges to atmosphere and then increases back to the full pipeline diameter. The pressure at the pipe wall is reduced due to this change in flow and is related to the flow rate (Figure 15.3.12).

Bernoulli's equation can be applied to an orifice meter in the same way as it is applied to the Venturi meter. The resultant K-factor or discharge coefficient depends on several factors, including the ratio of orifice/pipe diameter and the location of the pressure taps upstream and downstream of the orifice.

ASME Flow Nozzle. Flow can also be measured by an ASME flow nozzle, as shown in Figure 15.3.13. The pressure taps for this device are normally one pipe diameter upstream of the nozzle and one-half pipe diameter downstream from the nozzle inlet. Combining known constant values, the Venturi meter formula is generally expressed as

$$Q = \text{K}\sqrt{(h_1 - h_2)}, \text{ or } Q = \text{K}\sqrt{\frac{p_1}{w} - \frac{p_2}{w}}$$

FLOW OF WATER IN PIPES

The theory of liquid flow in pipes involves the same continuity principles used in the previous discussions. These include continuity of energy (Bernoulli's theorem with friction) and continuity of flow.

When water flows through a pipe, there is always a drop in pressure. Theoretically, the lost head between two points is caused by (1) friction between the moving water and the pipe wall and (2) friction between water particles, including that produced by turbulence when flow changes direction or when

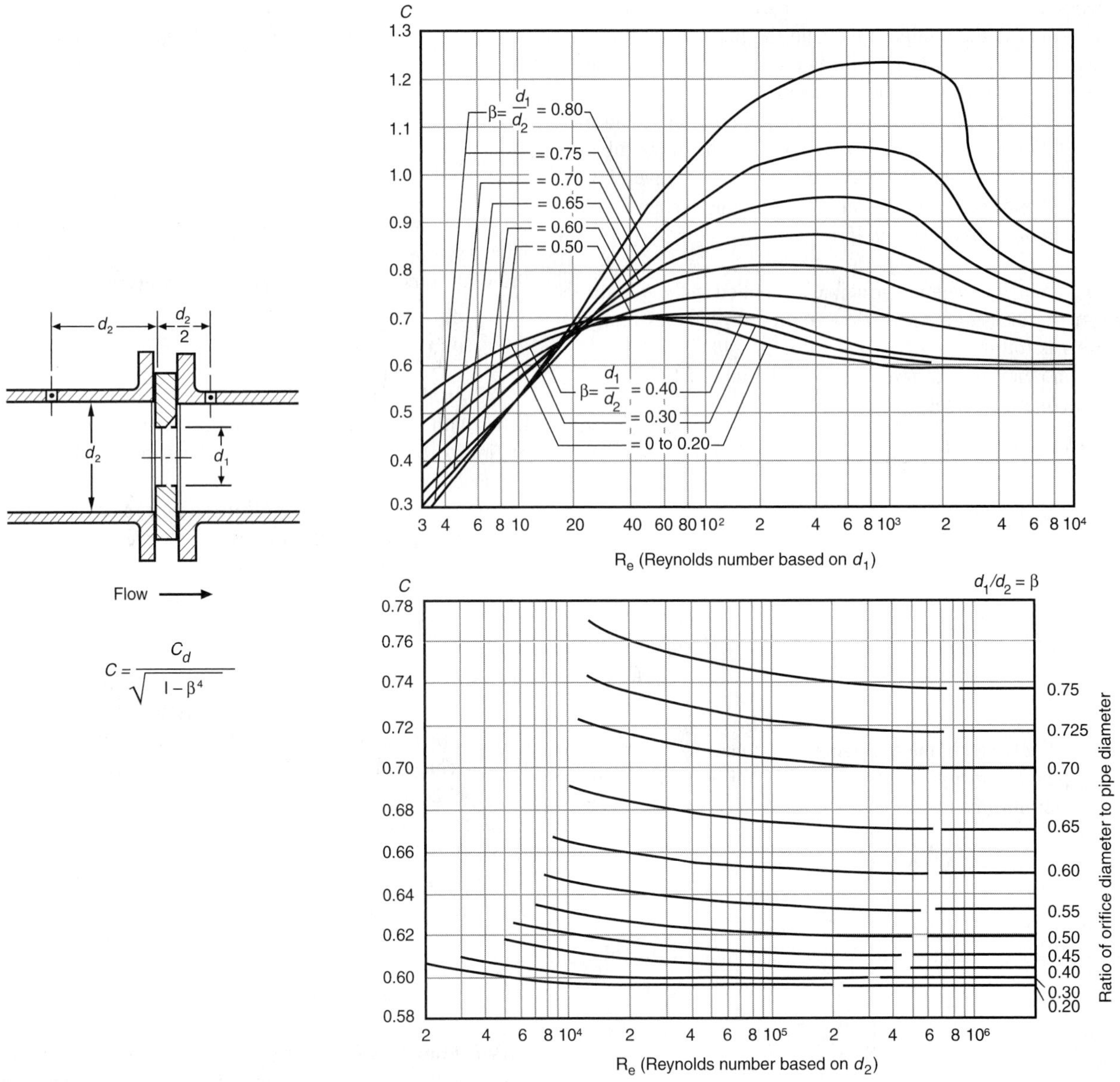

FIGURE 15.3.12 Flow Coefficient *C* for Square-Edged Orifice Meters

a rapid increase or decrease in velocity takes place, such as at abrupt changes in pipe diameter. A change in velocity results in some conversion of velocity head to pressure head, or vice versa.

At low velocity in a smooth pipe, very little turbulence is produced, and the flow is called "laminar" or "streamline" flow. With this condition, all particles of water move along the pipe in definite paths, which are essentially straight lines in concentric layers. Friction loss occurs due to shear stress, mainly in a thin boundary layer at the pipe wall, and also between adjacent stream layers. The friction loss is small compared to that of turbulent flow.

The flow within either a smooth or a rough pipe remains laminar until the velocity reaches what is called critical velocity. At this point, there is a range of unstable flow that is neither laminar nor completely turbulent, which is called the transition zone.

As the flow continues to increase, it becomes turbulent. In turbulent flow the fluid moves in an eddying mass, and, at any point, the individual water particles move rapidly in a random manner rather than in a straight line.

Reynolds demonstrated that for any fluid the critical point at which the flow changes from laminar to turbulent could be predicted. In circular pipes, the critical point occurs when the dimensionless parameter $dv\rho/\mu$ (called the Reynolds number) is approximately 2000. The transition to complete turbulence is complete for Reynolds numbers exceeding 4000.

Most fire protection systems and water distribution mains function under turbulent flow conditions, and friction losses within the pipe itself account for most of the lost head. Other

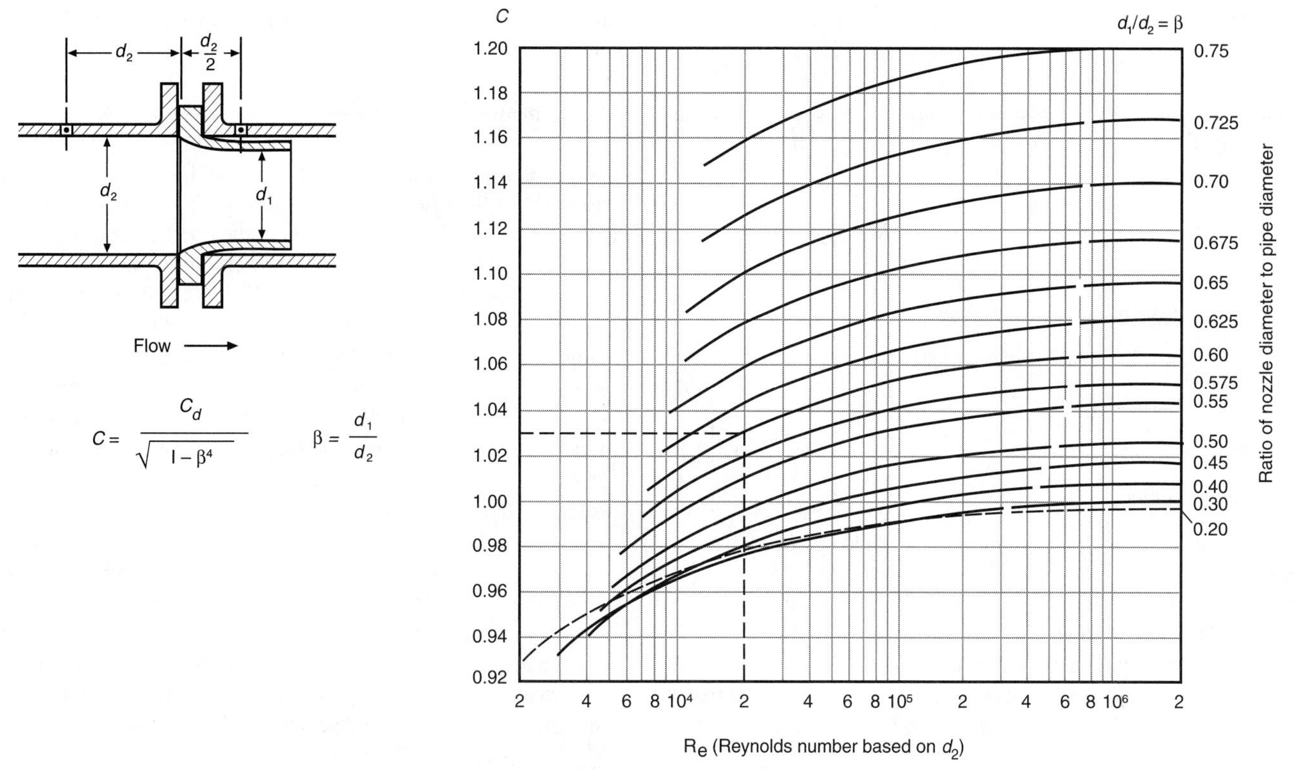

FIGURE 15.3.13 Flow Coefficient *C* for ASME Flow Nozzles

losses are usually considered together and are called "minor losses" or "losses in fittings."

Friction (Head) Loss Flow Formulas

Experimental data have established that frictional resistance in a pipe shall be as follows:

1. Independent of pressure in the pipe
2. Proportional to the amount and character of the flow
3. Variable with the velocity of the flow (nearly proportional to the second power of the velocity for velocities above the critical; if velocity is below critical, resistance varies with the first power)

The Chezy Formula. One of the best-known and oldest expressions relating velocity to friction loss in piping is known as the Chezy formula:

$$v = c\sqrt{rs}$$

where

c = A factor that is dependent on the kind and roughness of the pipe

r (the hydraulic radius) = Area/circumference = $d/4$ where d = diameter of the pipe in ft (m)

s = The hydraulic slope = h/l = slope of hydraulic gradient in which h is the head loss in length of pipe l in ft (m). (See Section 15, Chapter 1, "Fixed Water Storage Supplies for Fire Protection," for a discussion of hydraulic gradients.)

Therefore,

$$v = c\sqrt{d/4 \times h/l} \text{ or } h = \frac{4lv^2}{c^2 d}$$

The Darcy-Weisbach Formula. Another classic formula for friction loss, applicable to long, straight pipes of uniform diameter and roughness, is ascribed to Darcy, Manning, Fanning, and others. In modern textbooks, the formula is derived by analysis of forces acting on a flowing particle of water in a pipe. Often called the Darcy-Weisbach formula, it is a variation of Chezy's formula, with a friction factor f replacing c, and expressed as follows:

$$h = f\frac{l}{d}\frac{v^2}{2g}$$

where

h = Friction head

f = Friction factor

l = Length of pipe

d = Diameter of pipe

v = Velocity

g = Acceleration of gravity

The Darcy-Weisbach formula is suitable for all Newtonian fluids. (A Newtonian fluid is one where the viscosity is constant at a specific temperature, regardless of pressure and the rate of shear.) The friction factor f is dimensionless and variable and depends on the pipe roughness and the Reynolds number.

The value of f can be computed by the Colebrook-White equation, which is neither a completely empirical nor rigidly theoretical formula. This equation is usually written as

$$\frac{1}{\sqrt{f}} = -2\log_{10}\left[\frac{\varepsilon}{3.7D} + \frac{2.51}{R\sqrt{f}}\right]$$

where

ε = Linear measure of roughness

f = Darcy-Weisbach friction factor

D = Pipe diameter (ft)

R = Reynolds number

(For SI units: 1 ft = 0.305 m.)

Computing f by the formula can be avoided by using tables and charts known as "Moody" diagrams.

Figure 15.3.14 is a Moody diagram (© Hydraulic Institute, 1954) from which f can be read directly off the chart. Values for friction factor are on the vertical scale, at left. The dimensionless parameter, ε/D is sometimes difficult to obtain, and it may be necessary to assume a value for ε/D based on experience and judgment. The roughness factor of new pipe usually can be provided by the manufacturer.

The Hazen-Williams Formula. The friction-flow formulas commonly used in fire protection hydraulics have been developed by experiment and experience. These formulas (which are variations of the Chezy formula) are usually exponential in the form $v = Cr^x s^y$, where v is velocity, c the coefficient of friction, r the hydraulic radius (area divided by circumference), and s the hydraulic slope (loss of head divided by length). The most popular exponential formula is the Hazen-Williams, its basic form being $v = 1.31Cr^{0.63}s^{0.54}$. The friction coefficients in formulas of this type are constant for a specific roughness of pipe and are independent of velocity, and thus the accuracy of these formulas is variable. However, the fixed values generally assumed for viscosity and density are considered adequate for most fire protection hydraulic work.

The basic form of the Hazen-Williams formula ($v = 1.31cr^{0.63}s^{0.54}$ is not practical for ordinary fire protection flow calculations. The form normally used is expressed in terms of pressure loss in psi rather than velocity, in terms of actual diameter rather than the hydraulic radius, and in terms of flow in gpm.

Because the hydraulic radius is the area divided by the circumference, it can be expressed as

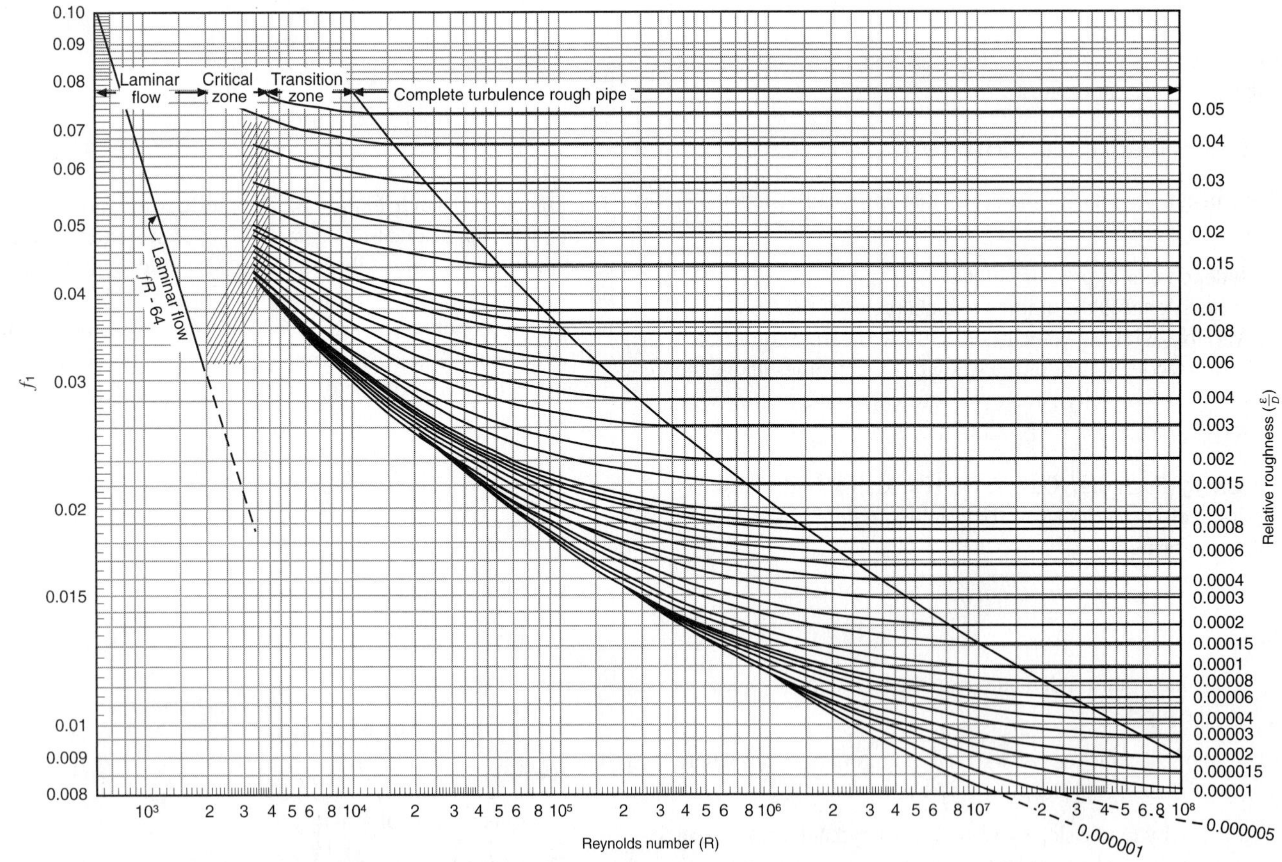

FIGURE 15.3.14 Moody Diagram for Friction in Pipe

$$r = \frac{\text{Area}}{\text{Circumference}} = \frac{\pi d^2/4}{\pi d} = \frac{d}{4}$$

where the diameter is in terms of feet or

$$r = \frac{d}{4} \times \frac{1 \text{ ft}}{12 \text{ in.}} = \frac{d}{48}$$

where the diameter is expressed in inches.

The hydraulic slope (s) is simply the pressure loss divided by the length. The Hazen-Williams formula is usually used to determine the pressure loss per ft of pipe, so the length is 1 and can be replaced by the pressure loss (p), again in ft.

Because we want to use flow rather than velocity, we know from the discussion on velocity pressure that

$$v = \frac{Q}{a} = \frac{0.4085Q}{d^2}$$

where Q is expressed in gallons per minute and d is expressed in inches. Substituting,

$$\frac{0.4085Q}{d^2} = 1.31C\left(\frac{d}{48}\right)^{0.63}(2.31p)^{.54}$$

Solving for p we get

$$(2.31p)^{.54} = \frac{0.4085Q/d^2}{1.31C(d/48)^{0.63}} = \frac{0.3118Q}{Cd^2(d/48)^{0.63}}$$

$$2.31p = \frac{0.3118^{1/0.54}Q^{1/0.54}}{C^{1/0.54}d^{2/0.54}(d/48)^{0.63/0.54}}$$

$$= \frac{0.3118^{1.85}Q^{1.85}}{C^{1.85}d^{3.7}(d/48)^{1.17}} = \frac{0.11579Q^{1.85}}{C^{1.85}d^{4.87}48)^{1.17}}$$

$$p = \frac{4.64Q^{1.85}}{C^{1.85}d^{4.87}} \cong \frac{4.52Q^{1.85}}{C^{1.85}d^{4.87}}$$

which is the formula normally used for fire protection purposes. The derived constant 4.64 is slightly different than the normally accepted constant of 4.52 due to rounding errors in the derivation and the constants in the original formula. The remainder of this discussion will use the generally accepted formula with a constant of 4.52.

In SI units the formula is

$$p_m = 6.06 \times \frac{Q_m^{1.85}}{C^{1.85}d_m^{4.87}} \times 10^2$$

where

p_m = Pressure loss (kPa) per m of pipe

Q_m = Rate of flow (L/min)

d_m = Inside diameter (mm)

Friction Loss Calculations. The solutions of many fire protection problems involving pipe flow and friction do not require direct calculation using formulas, since tables and charts are readily available. However, in using the simplifying charts and tables, great care must be taken to identify the C value (coefficient of friction) on which the chart or table is based. Where the type or condition of a pipe necessitates the use of a different C value, the friction loss from the table must be multiplied by a conversion factor to obtain the correct results for the desired C value.

By way of illustration, Table 15.3.4 gives values of p when C = 100 for standard pipe sizes from ½ in. to 30 in. in diameter. For values of C other than 100, the tabular value losses are multiplied by the corresponding factor in Table 15.3.5. Where a different type of pipe is used, the friction loss from the table can be corrected using the formula

$$\Delta p_a = \Delta p_{40}\left(\frac{d_{40}}{d_a}\right)^{4.87}$$

where

Δp_a = Actual friction loss

Δp_{40} = Friction loss in Schedule 40 pipe

d_{40} = Internal diameter of Schedule 40 pipe

d_a = Internal diameter of actual pipe

EXAMPLE: Determine the friction loss with 700 gpm, flowing in 700 ft of 8-in. cast-iron pipe having a C value of 80.

SOLUTION: From Table 15.3.4, the loss for 700 gpm per 100 ft of 8 in. pipe with C = 100 is 0.662 psi. From Table 15.3.5, the conversion factor for C = 80 is 1.51. Because friction loss is directly proportional to the length of pipe, multiply 0.662 × 7 × 1.51 = 6.95 psi (answer). Since other than Schedule 40 steel pipe is used, this value must be adjusted using the previously discussed formula:

$$\Delta p_a = \Delta p_{40}\left(\frac{d_{40}}{d_a}\right)^{4.87}$$

$$= 6.95\left(\frac{8.071}{8.23}\right)^{4.87}$$

$$= 6.32 \text{ psi}$$

The Hazen-Williams Diagram. Figure 15.3.15 is a graphical representation of Table 15.3.4, except that it is based on a Hazen-Williams coefficient of C = 120 rather than C = 100, as used in the table. For other C values use: Value of C: 80 100 120 130 140 150; multiplying factor: 2.12 1.40 1.00 0.86 0.75 0.66. It is limited in scope to pipes not over 10 in. in diameter, and due to the reduced scale is less accurate than the table.

Figure 15.3.16 gives data in SI units for pipes up to 10 in. (254 mm) in diameter, again based on C = 120. For other C values use: Value of C: 80 100 120 130 140 150; multiplying factor: 2.12 1.40 1.00 0.86 0.75 0.66.

EXAMPLE 1: What is the friction loss in 300 ft (90 m) of 8-in. cement-lined cast-iron pipe, flowing 1500 gpm (5678 L/min)?

SOLUTION: From the intersection of the 1500 gpm vertical line with the sloping 8 in. pipe diameter line in Figure 15.3.15, read

TABLE 15.3.4 Friction Loss[a] in Pipe

Flow	Pipe Size[b]										Flow
Gpm	*½*	*¾*	*1*	*1¼*	*1½*	*2*	*2½*	*3*	*3½*	*4*	*Gpm*
5	17.9	4.55	1.40	0.369	0.174	0.052	—	—	—	—	5
10	64.5	16.4	5.06	1.33	0.629	0.186	0.078	0.030	—	—	10
15	*5*	34.7	10.7	2.82	1.33	0.394	0.166	0.064	0.028	—	15
20	—	59.1	18.2	4.89	2.27	0.671	0.282	0.109	0.048	0.027	20
30	0.019	*6*	38.6	10.2	4.80	1.42	0.598	0.231	0.102	0.057	30
40	0.033	—	65.8	17.3	8.17	2.42	1.02	0.393	0.174	0.097	40
50	0.050	.020	*8*	26.2	12.3	3.66	1.54	0.593	0.263	0.147	50
60	0.069	.029	—	36.6	17.3	5.12	2.16	0.831	0.369	0.206	60
70	0.092	.038	—	48.7	23.0	6.81	2.87	1.11	0.490	0.274	70
80	0.118	.049	—	62.4	29.4	8.72	3.67	1.41	0.628	0.350	80
90	0.147	.060	—	77.6	36.6	10.8	4.56	1.76	0.781	0.435	90
100	0.178	.074	—	*10*	44.5	13.1	5.55	2.14	0.949	0.529	100
120	0.250	.103	—	—	62.3	18.5	7.77	3.00	1.33	0.741	120
140	0.333	.137	0.034	—	82.9	24.6	10.3	3.98	1.77	0.986	140
160	0.426	.175	0.043	—	106.0	31.4	13.2	5.10	2.26	1.26	160
180	0.529	.218	0.054	0.018	*12*	39.1	16.5	6.34	2.81	1.57	180
200	0.643	.265	0.065	0.022	—	47.5	20.0	7.71	3.42	1.91	200
220	0.768	.316	0.078	0.026	—	56.7	23.9	9.19	4.08	2.28	220
240	0.902	.371	0.091	0.031	0.013	*14*	28.0	10.8	4.79	2.67	240
260	1.05	.430	0.106	0.036	0.015	—	32.5	12.5	5.56	3.10	260
280	1.20	.493	0.122	0.041	0.017	—	37.3	14.4	6.37	3.55	280
300	1.36	.562	0.138	0.047	0.019	—	42.3	16.3	7.24	4.04	300
350	1.81	.746	0.184	0.062	0.026	0.012	*16*	21.7	9.63	5.37	350
400	2.32	.955	0.235	0.079	0.033	0.015	—	27.8	12.3	6.88	400
450	2.88	1.19	0.292	0.099	0.041	0.019	—	34.6	15.3	8.55	450
500	3.51	1.44	0.353	0.120	0.049	0.023	0.012	42.0	18.6	10.4	500
550	4.18	1.72	0.424	0.143	0.059	0.028	0.015	50.1	22.2	12.4	550
600	4.91	2.02	0.498	0.168	0.069	0.033	0.017	58.8	26.1	14.6	600
650	5.70	2.34	0.577	0.195	0.080	0.038	0.020	68.2	30.3	16.9	650
700	6.53	2.69	0.662	0.223	0.092	0.043	0.023	*18*	34.7	19.4	700
750	7.42	3.05	0.752	0.254	0.104	0.049	0.026	—	39.4	22.0	750
800	8.36	3.44	0.848	0.286	0.118	0.056	0.029	—	44.5	24.8	800
850	9.35	3.85	0.948	0.320	0.132	0.062	0.032	—	49.7	27.7	850
900	10.4	4.28	1.05	0.356	0.146	0.069	0.036	—	*20*	30.8	900
950	11.5	4.73	1.17	0.393	0.162	0.076	0.040	—	—	34.1	950
1000	12.6	5.20	1.28	0.432	0.178	0.084	0.044	—	—	37.5	1000
1250	19.1	7.85	1.94	0.653	0.269	0.127	0.066	—	—	*24*	1250
1500	*30*	11.0	2.71 (18.7)	0.914	0.376	0.178	0.093	—	—	—	1500
1750	—	—	3.61	1.22	0.501	0.236	0.123	—	—	—	1750
2000	.007	—	4.62	1.56	0.641	0.303	0.158	0.089	0.053	0.022	2000
2250	.009	—	—	1.94	0.797	0.376	0.196	0.111	0.066	0.027	2250
2500	.011	—	—	2.35	0.969	0.457	0.239	0.134	0.081	0.033	2500
2750	.013	—	—	2.81	1.16	0.545	0.285	0.160	0.096	0.040	2750
3000	.016	—	—	3.30	1.36	0.641	0.334	0.188	0.113	0.046	3000
4000	.027	—	—	—	2.31	1.09	0.569	0.321	0.192	0.079	4000
5000	.040	—	—	—	3.49	1.65	0.860	0.485	0.290	0.119	5000

For SI units: 1 psi = 6.895 kPa; 1 gpm = 0.378 L/min; 1 in. = 25.4 mm.

Note: Actual inside diameter for sizes ½ in. through 3½ in. is given for greater accuracy as these sizes include sprinkler branch lines and the smaller sizes of cross mains. For sizes 4 in. and greater, the nominal diameters were used as a fairly safe average for the diameters of various types of underground pipes as follows: cast-iron unlined and Enameline, greater than nominal; cast iron cement lines and Class 200 asbestos cement, less than nominal; Class 150 asbestos-cement sizes 6 and 8 in. less than nominal, and other sizes even nominal. (A 0.10 variation is true for Class 150 cement lined only—see ASHD FT-9 through 45 for actual IDs.)

This table will be useful in approximating friction loss in flow through existing underground piping where the type, inside diameter, and condition are frequently unknown. However, in such cases, a flow test is recommended.

When the type, inside diameter, and condition are known, and in designing new systems for all sizes and types of pipes, the friction loss tables should be used. Friction tables based on Hazen-Williams formula are published in *Automatic Sprinkler Hydraulic Data* by "Automatic" Sprinkler Corporation of America, and tables based on the Darcy-Weisbach formula are published in *Standards of the Hydraulic Institute.*

[a]Friction loss in lb/in.^{2} per 100 ft of pipe and are based on a Hazen-Williams C of 100. To convert friction loss to other values of C, see Table 15.3.5.

[b]Calculations are based on the internal pipe diameter of Schedule 40 steel pipe for pipe sizes ½ to 3½ in. and the nominal pipe diameter for pipe sizes 4 to 30 in.

TABLE 15.3.5 Conversion Factors for Friction Loss in Pipe for Values of Coefficient Other Than 100

C	*Factor*	*C*	*Factor*	*C*	*Factor*
150	0.472	110	0.838	70	1.93
145	0.503	105	0.914	65	2.22
140	0.537	100	1.00	60	2.57
135	0.574	95	1.10	55	3.02
130	0.615	90	1.22	50	3.61
125	0.662	85	1.35	45	4.38
120	0.714	80	1.51	40	5.48
115	0.772	75	1.70	35	6.97

left horizontally for a loss of head value, which is found to be 0.019 psi per foot. For 300 ft, the loss would be 300 × 0.019 psi or 5.7 psi. The probable *C* value of cement-lined pipe is 140 (Table 15.3.6), and the conversion factor is 0.75 (Figure 15.3.15). Therefore, the friction loss is 5.7 × 0.75 = 4.3 psi. Since other than Schedule 40 steel pipe is used, this value must be adjusted using the previously discussed formula.

$$\Delta p_a = \Delta p_{40}\left(\frac{d_{40}}{d_a}\right)^{4.87}$$

$$= 4.3\left(\frac{8.071}{7.98}\right)^{4.87}$$

$$= 4.54 \text{ psi}$$

EXAMPLE 2: What is the friction loss in 400 m of 150 mm 30-year-old unlined cast-iron pipe ($C = 80$) for a flow of 10,000 L/min?

SOLUTION: From the intersection of the 10,000 L/min vertical line with the sloping 150 mm pipe diameter line in Figure 15.3.16, read left horizontally for a loss of head value, which is 480 kPa per 100 m. For 400 m, the loss would be 4 × 480 kPa or 1920 kPa, based on $C = 120$. For cast-iron pipe, $C = 80$ and the conversion factor is 2.12 (see Figure 15.3.16). Therefore, the friction loss is 1920 × 2.12 = 4070 kPa.

Equivalent Pipes. Problems involving piped water supplies and fire protection systems occasionally require substitution of one pipe for another. The term "equivalent pipe" usually means a pipe having the same friction loss as the pipe for which it is

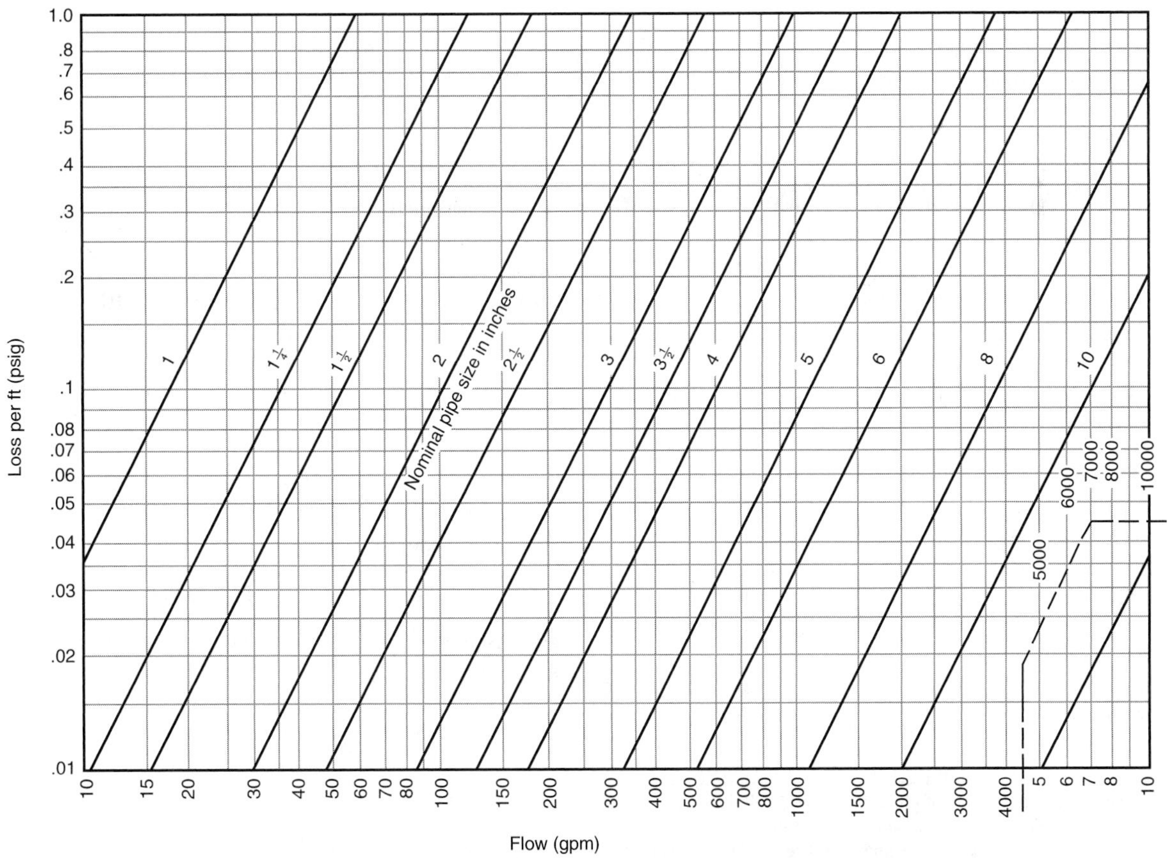

FIGURE 15.3.15 Friction Loss in Schedule 40 Steel Pipe, Hazen-Williams $C = 120$

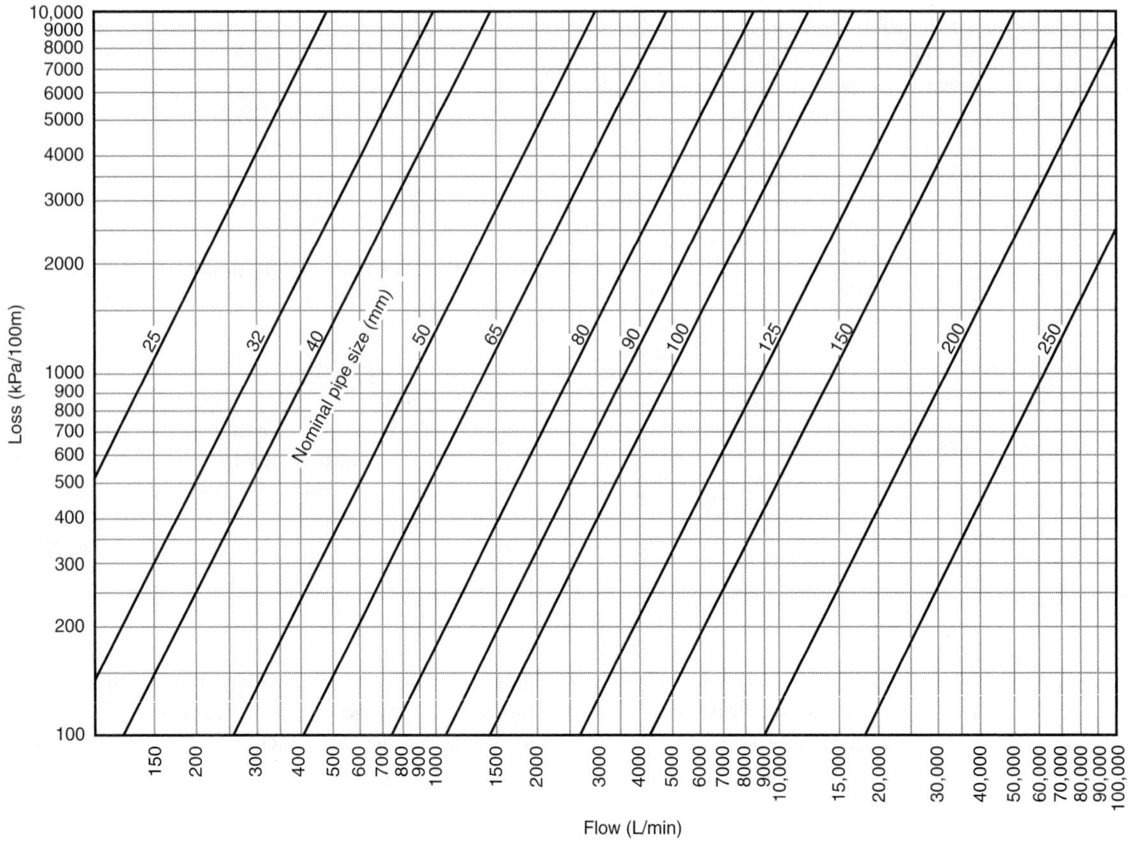

FIGURE 15.3.16 Friction Loss (SI units) in Schedule 40 Steel Pipe, Hazen-Williams $C = 120$

TABLE 15.3.6 Guide for Estimating Hazen-Williams *C*

	Value of *C*		
Kind of Pipe	*1*[a]	2[b]	*3*[c]
Cast iron, unlined			
10 years old	110	90	75
15 years old	100	75	65
20 years old	90	65	55
30 years old	80	55	45
50 years old	70	50	40
Cast iron, unlined, new		120	
Cast iron, cement-lined		140	
Cast iron, bitumastic enamel-lined		140	
Average steel, new		140	
Riveted steel, new		110	
Asbestos-cement		140	
Reinforced concrete		140	
Plastic		150	

Note: *C* values chosen for design of piping systems should be based on applicable NFPA standard or the authority having jurisdiction.
[a]Water mildly corrosive. Use same values for fire-protection mains having no mill-use or domestic draft.
[b]Water moderately corrosive.
[c]Water severly corrosive.

being substituted. The formula for using the friction loss table is applicable here.

EXAMPLE: What length of 8 in. pipe ($C = 110$) is equivalent to 700 ft of 6 in. pipe ($C = 85$)?

SOLUTION: $N_1 \times \frac{L_1}{100} \times T_1 = N_2 \times \frac{L_2}{100} \times T_2$

where

$N = C$ factor conversion for each pipe

$L =$ Length of each pipe

$T =$ Friction loss from Table 15.3.4

Assume a rate of flow (say, 1000 gpm) and substitute known values:

$$1.35 \times \frac{700}{100} \times 5.20 = 0.838 \times \frac{L_2}{100} \times 1.28$$

Solving for L_2,

$$\frac{1.35 \times 700 \times 5.20}{0.838 \times 1.28} = 4581 \text{ ft}$$

which can be rounded off to 4600 ft.

Minor Losses

Although the friction loss within the pipe normally accounts for most of the lost head, head losses also occur when the flow in a pipe changes direction, the pipe size changes, or a valve or other fitting is encountered. These losses are typically referred to as minor losses even though they can be significant for some fittings, such as swing check valves or backflow preventers, that are commonly found in fire protection systems.

The amount of minor losses from fittings can be found in many references and is often expressed in various forms. The most common are as an equivalent length (l/d), a resistance coefficient (k), or a flow coefficient (C_v).

Equivalent Length. For most fire protection calculations, friction loss is obtained by using the equivalent length method from a table such as Table 15.3.7, which expresses the friction loss of the fitting as an "equivalent pipe length" having the same friction loss as the fitting. This length is then added to the length of the pipe to which the fittings are connected to obtain the total friction loss of pipe and fittings.

EXAMPLE: Calculate total friction loss for 600 L/min flow through 200 m of nominal 2 in. (50 mm) pipe (C = 120) that incorporates three 90 degree elbows, one tee junction (90-degree turn), and two butterfly valves.

SOLUTION: Using Table 15.3.7 for equivalent lengths of fittings (C = 120),

Fittings or Pipe	*Number*	*Equivalent Length per Fittings (m)*	*Total Equivalent Length (m)*
Std. elbow	3	1.5	4.5
T-junction	1	3.1	3.1
Butterfly	2	1.8	3.6
Pipe	1	200.0	200.0
		Total equivalent pipe length =	211.2

From Figure 15.3.15, the total friction loss of 600 L/min flow in 50 mm (2 in. nominal) pipe is 500 kPa per 100 m of

TABLE 15.3.7 Equivalent Pipe Length Chart

	Fittings and Valves Expressed in Equivalent ft (m) of Pipe						
	¾ in. (20 mm)	*1 in. (25 mm)*	*1¼ in. (32 mm)*	*1½ in. (40 mm)*	*2 in. (50 mm)*	*2½ in. (50 mm)*	*3 in. (80 mm)*
45° Elbow	1 (0.3)	1 (0.3)	1 (0.3)	2 (0.6)	2 (0.6)	3 (0.9)	3 (0.9)
90° Standard elbow	2 (0.6)	2 (0.6)	3 (0.9)	4 (1.2)	5 (1.5)	6 (1.8)	7 (2.1)
90° Long-turn elbow	1 (0.3)	2 (0.6)	2 (0.6)	2 (0.6)	3 (0.9)	4 (1.2)	5 (1.5)
Tee or cross (flow turned 90°)	4 (1.2)	5 (1.5)	6 (1.8)	8 (2.4)	10 (3.1)	12 (3.7)	15 (4.6)
Gate valve	—	—	—	—	1 (0.3)	1 (0.3)	1 (0.3)
Butterfly valve	—	—	—	—	6 (1.8)	7 (2.1)	10 (3.1)
Swing check*	4 (1.2)	5 (1.5)	7 (2.1)	9 (2.7)	11 (3.4)	14 (4.3)	16 (4.9)

	Fittings and Valves Expressed in Equivalent ft (m) of Pipe						
	3½ in. (90 mm)	*4 in. (100 mm)*	*5 in. (125 mm)*	*6 in. (150 mm)*	*8 in. (200 mm)*	*10 in. (250 mm)*	*12 in. (300 mm)*
45° Elbow	3 (0.9)	4 (1.2)	5 (1.5)	7 (2.1)	9 (2.7)	11 (3.4)	13 (4.0)
90° Standard elbow	8 (2.4)	10 (3.1)	12 (3.7)	14 (4.3)	18 (5.5)	22 (6.7)	27 (8.2)
90° Long-turn elbow	5 (1.5)	6 (1.8)	8 (2.4)	9 (2.7)	13 (4.0)	16 (4.9)	18 (5.5)
Tee or cross (flow turned 90°)	17 (5.2)	20 (6.1)	25 (7.6)	30 (9.2)	35 (10.7)	50 (15.3)	60 (18.3)
Gate valve	1 (0.3)	2 (0.6)	2 (0.6)	3 (0.9)	4 (1.2)	5 (1.5)	6 (1.8)
Butterfly valve	—	12 (3.7)	9 (2.7)	10 (3.1)	12 (3.7)	19 (5.8)	21 (6.4)
Swing check*	19 (5.8)	22 (6.7)	27 (8.2)	32 (9.8)	45 (13.7)	55 (16.8)	65 (19.8)

Use with Hazen-Williams C = 120 only. For other values of C, the figures in this table should be multiplied by the factors below.

Value of C	80	100	120	130	140	150
Multiplying factor	0.472	0.713	1.00	1.16	1.32	1.51

(This is based on the friction loss through the fitting being independent of the C factor applicable to the piping.)

Specific friction loss values or equivalent pipe lengths for alarm valves, dry pipe valves, deluge valves, strainers, and other devices or fittings should be made available to the authority having jurisdiction.

Note: Use the equivalent ft (m) value for the "standard elbow" on any abrupt 90 degree turn, such as the screw-type pattern. Use the equivalent ft (m) value for the "long-turn elbow" on any sweeping 90 degree turn, such as a flanged, welded, or mechanical joint elbow type.

*Due to the variations in design of swing check valves, the pipe equivalents shown in this table should be considered average.

pipe. Because friction loss is directly proportional to length of pipe, total loss is given by

$$\frac{211.2}{100} \times 500 = 1056 \text{ kPa}$$

The loss due to fittings is given by

$$\frac{11.2}{100} \times 500 = 56 \text{ kPa}$$

or 5.3 percent of the total friction loss.

Resistance Coefficients. Resistance coefficients are sometimes used to express the head loss in a fitting as a function of velocity according to the relationship:

$$h_f = k\frac{v^2}{2g}$$

The equivalent length and the resistance coefficient methods are related. Using the basic Darcy-Weisbach formula,

$$h = f\frac{l}{d}\frac{v^2}{2g} = k\frac{v^2}{2g}$$

or

$$k = f\frac{l}{d}$$

Most entrance losses are calculated using resistance coefficients. Figure 15.3.17 provides resistance coefficients for some common entrance conditions and fittings.

Flow Coefficients. Where the loss in a fitting is defined by a flow coefficient C_v, the coefficient is defined as the flow of water that will produce a known friction loss (usually 1 psi) through the fitting. The relationship is usually shown as

$$Q = C_v\sqrt{h}$$

We know from our discussion on pressure that pressure (expressed in terms of psi) and head (expressed in terms of ft) are related by the formula

$$h = \frac{p}{w} = \frac{p}{.433}$$

Substituting, we get

$$Q = C_v\sqrt{\frac{p}{4.33}} \quad \text{or} \quad \sqrt{\frac{p}{4.33}} = \frac{Q}{C_v}$$

Squaring both sides and solving for p we get

$$p = 0.433\frac{Q^2}{C_v^2}$$

The flow coefficient can be shown to be related to the resistance coefficient. Because

$$h = k\frac{v^2}{2g} \quad \text{and} \quad h = \frac{Q^2}{C_v^2} \quad \text{then} \quad k\frac{v^2}{2g} = \frac{Q^2}{C_v^2}$$

Rearranging we get

$$C_v^2 = \frac{2gQ^2}{kv^2}$$

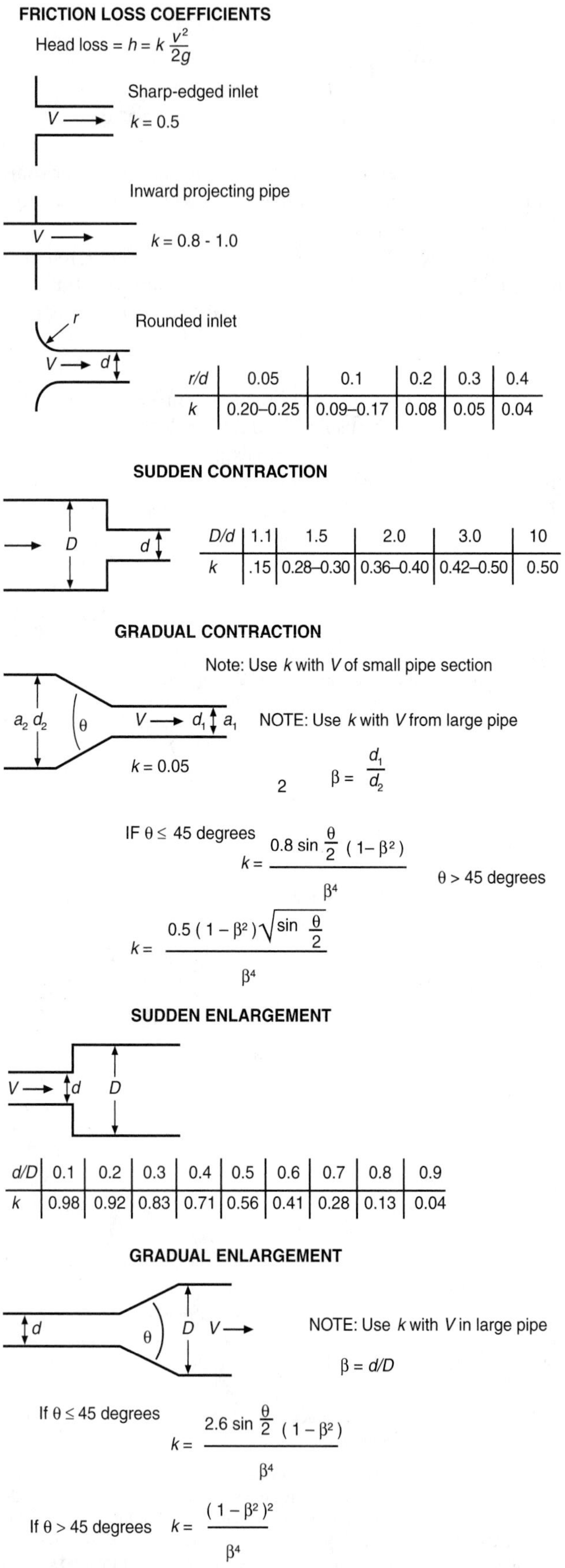

FIGURE 15.3.17 Friction Loss Coefficients

Because $Q = av$ and $a = \pi d^2/4$ we get

$$C_v^2 = \frac{2g(\pi d^2 v/4)^2}{kv} = \frac{2gd^4\pi^2 v^2}{16kv^2} = \frac{gd^4\pi^2}{8k}$$

Solving for C_v we get

$$C_v = \frac{\sqrt{g}d^2\pi}{\sqrt{8k}} = \pi d^2\sqrt{\frac{g}{8k}}$$

For d in inches, and C_v in gpm/$\sqrt{\text{psi}}$, the formula is normally expressed as

$$C_v = \frac{29.9d^2}{\sqrt{k}}$$

EXAMPLE 1: Water at a flow rate of 1500 gpm is flowing into an 8 in. pipe with a sharp entrance where it attaches to the side of a tank. What is the friction loss in psi due to the losses caused by the sharp entrance?

SOLUTION: From Figure 15.3.17, a sharp entrance has a resistance coefficient (k) of 0.5. We know that $h = k\frac{v^2}{2g}$, and from the earlier discussion on velocity that $v = \frac{0.4085 \times Q}{d^2} = \frac{0.4085 \times 1500}{8^2} = 9.37$ ft/sec. We want the pressure loss in terms of psi, and not feet, so

$$p = 0.433h = 0.433 \times 0.5 \times \frac{9.37^2}{2g} = 0.30 \text{ psi}$$

EXAMPLE 2: Given the same tank and pipe, what flow would result in an entrance loss of 1 psi?

SOLUTION: We could use the same equations as in the first example and solve for the velocity that creates a loss of 1 psi. An alternative solution is to calculate the flow coefficient, which is defined as the flow that generates a 1 psi loss. We know that for d in inches and C_v in gpm/$\sqrt{\text{psi}}$ that

$$C_v = \frac{29.9d^2}{\sqrt{k}}$$

In this case $d = 8$ and the resistance coefficient k is 0.5, so

$$C_v = \frac{29.9 \times 8^2}{\sqrt{0.5}} = 2706 \text{ gpm}$$

WATER HAMMER

Water hammer is an effect of the pressure rise (surge) that accompanies a sudden change in the velocity of water flowing in a pipe. When deceleration of velocity is rapid or completely stopped, the kinetic energy of the moving water column is absorbed temporarily by elastic deformation of the pipe and by the compressibility of water. A pressure wave is then formed that is reflected back and forth within the pipe.

Pressure surges may be initiated by the closing of a valve, stopping of a pump, or by the sudden development of abnormal water demand when a water main breaks. Occasionally, the operation of automatic control valves in sprinkler systems may result in the reversal of flow and a buildup of high pressure in the fire protection system.

Consideration of water hammer and transient pressure surges is traditionally based on the elastic wave theories of Joukowski and Allievi. Chapter 4-2 of the *SFPE Handbook of Fire Protection Engineering* provides an alternative discussion based on the elastic wave theories of Zhukovsky.

The force of water hammer is sometimes sufficient to rupture pipes, fittings, or hose lines. Theoretically, the resultant forces could be infinite if the system were totally inelastic.

The elasticity of hose tends to reduce the danger from water hammer, but the sudden closing of shutoff nozzles on long hose lines may cause a pressure rise sufficient to rupture the hose. Tests on water hammer were conducted by Robert Fitzgerald of the New York City Fire Department and published in that department's *WNYF Magazine* in July 1949. Tests with low-pressure hydrants indicated that pressure surges from the closing of nozzles became acute in long hose lines and that shock waves developed that traveled from the nozzle to the hydrant and back toward the nozzle, developing pressure surges approximately twice the hydrant pressure. These tests point to the advantage of operating nozzle valves slowly.

Discharge lines from pumps are subject to water hammer caused by water column separation. This may occur when a pump suddenly stops (due to power failure, manual shutdown, etc.) or if the discharge valve is closed too quickly with the pump operating. Separation takes place somewhere downstream, especially at a summit, or where the downward slope of the pipe increases sharply. When forward movement becomes exhausted, the flow reverses direction and closes the gap.

When a pump is located at an elevation above the system outlet, a vacuum breaker in the line may provide effective control. When there is static head on a pump at discharge, it is practically impossible to completely eliminate a water column reversal. Surge suppressors or special-type vacuum breakers designed to bypass a portion of the reverse flow water column around the check valve or control valve may be effective.

The restarting of a fire pump too quickly after a tripout may cause excessive surging, and installations subject to intermittent operation should be protected by time-delay relays. Simple relief valves are considered useless, because their operation is too slow to counteract the speed of the pressure rise. In fire protection systems, a jockey pump is used to maintain a high pressure on the system and reduce the water hammer causing surge when the fire pump starts. If the jockey pump pressures are set too low, the starting of a fire pump can cause a significant surge of water into the fire protection system and result in water hammer. To avoid this surge the jockey pump should be set to maintain a pressure just above the churn pressure of the pump, so that when the pump starts, there is minimal waterflow and pressure increase on the piping system.

The principal factors contributing to water column separation are (1) rate of flow stoppage, either by rapid closing of a valve, or the fast deceleration of a pump; (2) length of pipe system (this factor determines the time that pressure continues to fall before positive-pressure waves returning from the far end of the line counteract the initial pressure drop); (3) the normal operating pressure at critical points, such as the crests of hills;

and (4) the velocity of the water just before pump stoppage or valve closure occurs; the greater the velocity, the larger the size of the void, reverse flow velocity, and the final pressure rise.

ELASTIC WAVE THEORY

The basic concepts of elastic wave theory (EWT) are as follows:

1. The magnitude of the pressure rise is proportional to the fluid velocity destroyed and to the velocity of the pressure wave.
2. The pressure rise is independent of the length and profile of the pipe.
3. The velocity of the pressure wave is the same as the velocity of sound through water.

The theoretical pressure rise when flow is stopped instantly may be calculated by the formula

$$\Delta p = \frac{0.433av}{g}$$

where

Δ_p = Pressure rise (psi)

a = Velocity of the pressure wave (ft/sec)

v = Waterflow velocity (fps)

g = Acceleration of gravity (ft/sec^2)

In SI units, the formula is

$$\Delta p_m = \frac{9.81 a_m v_m}{g_m}$$

where

Δp_m = Pressure rise (kPa)

a_m = Velocity of the pressure wave (m/sec)

v_m = Waterflow velocity (m/sec)

g_m = Acceleration of gravity (m/sec^2)

In practice, the calculated Δp may be reduced, allowing for valve closure characteristics and friction loss in the pipe. Usually, this is a matter of judgment and experience. For the pipe sizes used in fire protection systems, an allowance of 100 to 125 psi (690 to 860 kPa) is suggested.

The pressure rise, Δp, is at maximum when the flow is stopped in a time equal to or less than the critical time of the pipe, which is the time required for the pressure wave to travel from the point of closure to the end of the pipe and return. The formula for critical time is

$$T = \frac{2L}{a}$$

where L = length of pipe.

The wave velocity, a, is

$$a = \frac{12}{\sqrt{\frac{w}{g} \times \left(\frac{1}{k} + \frac{d}{E \times e}\right)}}$$

where

w = Weight of water (lb/ft^3)

g = Acceleration of (ft/sec^2)

k = Bulk modulus of compressibility of water (psi)

E = Young's modulus of elasticity of pipe wall material (psi)

e = Thickness of the pipe wall (in.)

d = Inside diameter of the pipe (in.)

To avoid calculating a, use the chart in Figure 15.3.18. The figures on the curves represent values of E in millions of pounds per inch^2 (bulk modulus of elasticity).

The calculated pressure rise in a 6-in. cast-iron pipe is about 60 psi per foot (1357 kPa/m) of arrested velocity.

The water hammer potential of distribution systems, especially those with automatic pumps, should be examined and practical steps taken to reduce the probability of destructive pressure surges. It should be noted, however, that because of the conditions under which dedicated fire protection distribution systems are designed (automatic operation of pumps with check valves in their discharge lines), the potential for water hammer cannot be completely eliminated.

To prevent water hammer, valves and hydrants should be maintained in good condition and operated carefully to prevent an abrupt reduction in flow; remote-controlled power-operated valves should be carefully timed to prevent them from closing too fast (never less than 5 sec).

SUMMARY

Water is the most universally used agent for fire protection. It can be applied manually using hydrants, standpipes, and hose lines or automatically via sprinkler, water spray, or other water-based

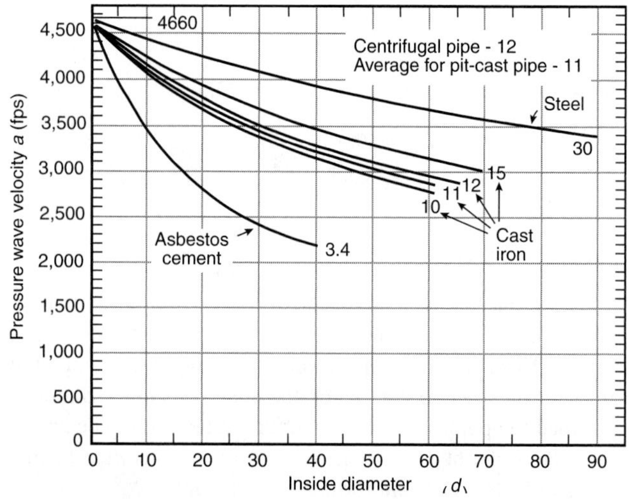

FIGURE 15.3.18 Surge Wave Velocity Chart for Water

systems. It is commonly available through public or private piping systems and storage tanks on the protected property.

The fundamentals of hydraulics presented in this chapter are applied in the design of these systems. The chapter covered the basic properties of water; the concepts of pressure, velocity, and velocity head were combined with Bernoulli's theorem on the conservation of energy for noncompressible fluids to derive the basic equations for the flow of water through orifices and ways to measure that flow. Energy losses occur in real systems, and several methods can be used to calculate those losses. The empirical relationship developed by Hazen and Williams is the most widely used and accepted of these methods to determine the friction loss of water in pipes of fire protection systems. Finally, methods were provided to deal with losses to fittings that are found in piping systems and a glimpse into the problem of water hammer in closed piping systems. The methods provided can be used to make most of the common fire protection water calculations and are the basis for calculating more complex piping arrangements, including those involving looped or gridded piping systems and those with multiple sources of water supply.

BIBLIOGRAPHY

References

AWWA M11, *Steel Pipe—A Guide for Design and Installation,* American Water Works Association, Denver, CO, 1989.

Baumeister, T., Avallone, E. A., Baumeister, T., III (Eds.), *Marks' Standard Handbook for Mechanical Engineers,* 8th ed., McGraw-Hill, New York, 1978.

Casey, James F. (Ed.), *Fire Service Hydraulics,* 2nd ed., Dun-Donnelley, New York, 1970.

Crocker, S., and King, R. C. (Eds.), *Piping Handbook,* McGraw-Hill, New York, 1967.

DeNevers, N., *Fluid Mechanics,* Addison-Wesley, Reading, MA, 1970.

DiNenno, P. J. (Ed.), *SFPE Handbook of Fire Protection Engineering,* 3rd ed., National Fire Protection Association, Quincy, MA, 2002.

"Flow of Fluids Through Valves, Fittings, and Pipe," *Crane Technical Paper No. 410,* Crane Co., Chicago, IL, 1976.

Hydraulic Institute, *Engineering Data Book,* Hydraulic Institute, Cleveland, OH, 1970.

Idelchik, I. E. (Ed.), *Handbook of Hydraulic Resistance,* 2nd ed., Hemisphere, Washington, DC, 1986.

Jeppson, R. W., *Analysis of Flow in Pipe Networks,* Butterworth, Boston, MA, 1976.

Parmakian, J., *Water Hammer Analysis,* Dover, New York, 1963.

Perry, R. H., and Chilton, C. H., *Chemical Engineers Handbook,* 5th ed., McGraw-Hill, New York, 1973.

Wass, H. S., *Sprinkler Hydraulics,* 2nd ed., Society of Fire Protection Engineering, Bethesda, MD, 2000.

Chapter 4

Water Supplies for Sprinkler Systems

Wayne M. Martin

Every automatic sprinkler system must have at least one automatic water supply of adequate pressure, capacity, and reliability. An "automatic" supply is one that is not dependent on any human intervention to manually operate valves, start pumps, or make connections to supply water at the time of a fire. Both the rate of flow and the duration of that flow must be considered.

This chapter identifies the types of water supplies that are acceptable for fire sprinkler systems and the variables that must be considered in the system design. The following factors are to be considered: occupancy hazard classification, supplementary hose stream demand, adequate pressure demands, the fundamentals of a hydraulically designed sprinkler system, and sprinkler system piping sizes matched with the available water supply.

Chapters in Section 15 of this handbook covering water supplies for fixed fire suppression focus on understanding the complexities of providing adequate water supplies for sprinkler systems. Of particular interest are the following chapters in Section 15: Chapter 1, "Fixed Water Storage Supplies for Fire Protection"; Chapter 2, "Water Supply Requirements for Public Supply Systems"; Chapter 6, "Water Distribution"; and Chapter 3, "Hydraulics for Fire Protection," which discusses the fundamentals of waterflow through pipes and orifices. Also relevant is Section 16, Chapter 9, "Water Spray Protection," which is of value because there is no definitive line between sprinkler systems and water spray systems, and many of the water supply requirements that pertain to sprinkler systems apply equally to water spray systems.

Chapter Contents

Key Terms

automatic sprinkler system, fire department connection, fire pump, hydraulically designed system, hydraulic calculations, K-factor, microbiologically influenced corrosion (MIC), pipe schedule method, private water supply, public water supply, reduced pressure zone, velocity pressure

TYPES OF SUPPLIES

Automatic fire sprinkler systems can be supplied from a single source or a combination of sources such as a municipal water supply, elevated gravity tanks, at-grade tanks or reservoirs, pressure tanks, rivers, lakes, and ground well water.

In theory, a single water supply would seem to be all that is necessary for satisfactory protection. However, a single supply may be temporarily out of service, it may be disabled at the time of a fire or before a fire is completely extinguished, or its pressure or capacity may be below normal during an emergency. Therefore, a secondary supply is recommended depending on the strength and reliability of the primary supply; the value and importance of the property; the area, height, and construction of the building; the use or occupancy; and the outside exposures.

Connections to Public Waterworks Systems

A connection from a reliable public waterworks system of adequate capacity and pressure is the preferred single or primary supply for automatic sprinkler systems. In determining its adequacy, one must consider not only the normal capacity and pressure of the system but also the minimum

Wayne M. Martin, P.E., is retired from the Los Angeles City Fire Department. He is a licensed civil engineer and fire protection engineer, and is principal of Wayne Martin & Associates, Inc., a fire protection and code consulting firm. He is a member of the NFPA 13 Technical Committee on the Installation of Sprinkler Systems.

pressures and flows available at unfavorable times, such as the summer months; periods of heavy demand on the system, such as those created by large industrial areas; or periods of impairment caused by flood or by ice conditions in winter. These conditions are typically referred to as seasonal lows.

Daily demands will fluctuate as well. Consider the early morning hours when the population is preparing for work or school. Demands created by domestic plumbing system use will be greater than at other times of the day.

The size and arrangement of street mains and feeders from public water supplies are also important. Connections from large mains fed two ways or from two mains on a grid system may provide an excellent supply. Street mains less than 6 in. (152 mm) in diameter are usually considered inadequate and unreliable. Feeds from dead-end mains are also undesirable. Water meters, if required, should be of types listed for the fire service. Flow and pressure tests under varying conditions of demand are generally necessary to determine the amount of public water available for fire protection.

Cross Connections Between Public and Private Supplies

Where a secondary supply is needed to supplement the public water supply, public and private fire service mains can be connected to feed into a single fire protection system. When the private fire service main is from a nonpotable source and it is connected to the public main, the systems are said to be cross connected. In some localities, cross connections may be prohibited or closely regulated by health authorities.

Federal regulations approved in 1986 require states to provide quality water when it is intended for public consumption. States and municipal governments have taken various steps beyond the federal mandate to protect the potable water supply. Double check valves and reduced pressure zone (RPZ) backflow prevention devices may be required when the sprinkler system will be supplied by a potable water source.

These devices, which are intended to protect the public water supply from potential contamination, are oftentimes costly and have a negative impact on the available water supply and pressures to the sprinkler system. Although no documentation exists of any actual problems with respect to sprinkler systems and potable water, many state health and environmental agencies have been successful in mandating such devices to protect the public from some perceived or potential threat.

Gravity Tanks

Gravity tanks of adequate capacity and elevation make a good primary supply and may be acceptable as a single supply. Details of the construction, heating, and maintenance of gravity tanks are given in NFPA 22, *Standard for Water Tanks for Private Fire Protection.* In determining tank size and elevation, the following information should be considered: sprinkler system design area; density or rate of water application; duration of operation; water allowances for inside hose, outside hydrants, water curtain, and exposure sprinklers; and arrangement of the underground supply piping and fire department connections.

Suction Tanks

With the advent of hydraulically designed sprinkler systems, suction tanks have become an acceptable means of design. Suction tanks are typically constructed of steel, concrete, or embankment-supported coated fabric. NFPA 22 should be consulted for details.

Fire Pumps

A fire pump with a reliable source of power and a reliable suction water supply is a desirable piece of equipment. Fire pumps are used to a great extent because of the hydraulic advantages of having a water supply available at high pressure. With ample water, a fire pump can maintain a high pressure over a long period of time and may be a necessary part of some installations requiring greater water pressure than would be available otherwise. For details of power sources, pump construction, installation, and methods of control and operation, consult NFPA 20, *Standard for the Installation of Stationary Pumps for Fire Protection.*

Most fire pumps today are started automatically. Automatic control of fire pumps is needed where an immediate water demand is necessary, as with a sprinkler or standpipe system. Automatic fire pumps must have their suction under a positive pressure to avoid the delays and uncertainties of priming.

Most fire pumps are powered by electric motors or diesel engines. Where a reliable source of power is available at all times, an electrically driven installation may be the most desirable. Where the power supply is questionable, a diesel-driven fire pump would be preferred. In some critical installations, such as hospitals and high-rise buildings, a diesel-driven emergency power generator may be used to supply secondary power to the electric motor. The use of a diesel-driven fire pump in a critical installation would eliminate the need for much of the capacity of the emergency generator.

The automatic control of electrically driven centrifugal pumps must be arranged to prevent frequent, repeated starting of the motor, either by initiating continuous running until stopped manually or by using a timing device that stops the motor automatically only after a predetermined period of operation. The frequent repeated starting and stopping of a fire pump can be alleviated by the installation of a pressure maintenance pump or jockey pump.

Pressure Tanks

Pressure tanks have several possible uses in automatic sprinkler protection. An important limitation is the small volume of water that can be stored in such tanks.

In situations where an adequate volume of water can be supplied by a public or private source but where the pressure is not sufficient to serve a sprinkler system directly, the pressure tank gives a good starting pressure for the first sprinklers that operate. In tall buildings where the public water pressure is too low for effective water distribution to the highest sprinklers, pressure tanks may be used to supply such sprinklers during the time required for an automatically operated fire pump to begin supplying water.

Each proposed use of pressure tanks calls for special consideration and analysis of water capacity, location, and arrangement of the connection to the sprinkler system. Each installation must usually have specific approval. Details on the construction and installation of pressure tanks are given in NFPA 22.

Fire Department Connections

Under fire conditions that cause a considerable number of sprinklers to operate, public water or tank supplies may not provide water at sufficient pressure for effective sprinkler discharge and distribution. In addition, the pressure in many public water supplies to sprinkler systems may be reduced materially by hose streams from hydrants. In such cases, a connection through which the fire department can pump water into the sprinkler system provides an important secondary supply. A fire department connection is a standard part of a fire sprinkler system installation and would be omitted only if the building were inaccessible to the fire department or the sprinkler system exceeded the pumping capacity of the fire department, such as a deluge system. A fire department connection may also be omitted from a single-story building that does not exceed 2000 ft^2 (186 m^2) in size.

Fire department connections must be located and arranged so that hose lines can be readily and conveniently attached without interference from nearby objects. Each fire department connection must be properly identified with a sign, for example, autosprinkler or standpipe. Each connection must be fitted with a check valve, but not with a gate valve, so that the connection will not be shut off inadvertently. There should be a proper drain, as well as a drip device between the check valve and the outside hose coupling. Figures 15.4.1 and 15.4.2 show the main features of a fire department connection. In Figure 15.4.1, a check valve allows the use of a single hose line. Other details of installation and pipe size are given in NFPA 13, *Standard for the Installation of Sprinkler Systems.*

Where a wet pipe sprinkler system has a single riser, the fire department connection should be attached to the system side of the controlling valve, as shown in Figure 15.4.3. For a dry pipe system, the fire department connection should be between the

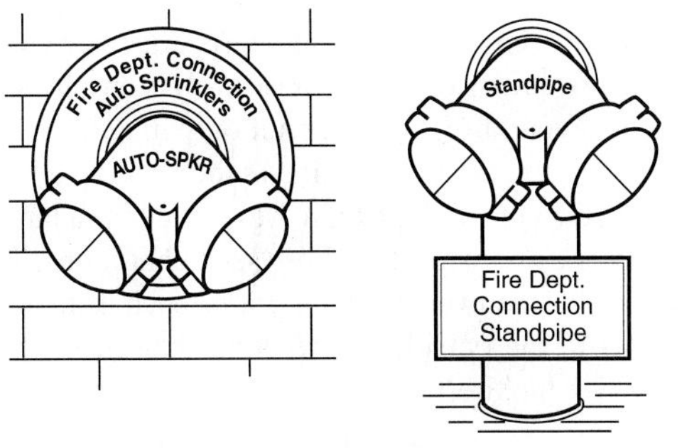

FIGURE 15.4.1 Typical Siamese Connections for Sprinkler Systems and Standpipes

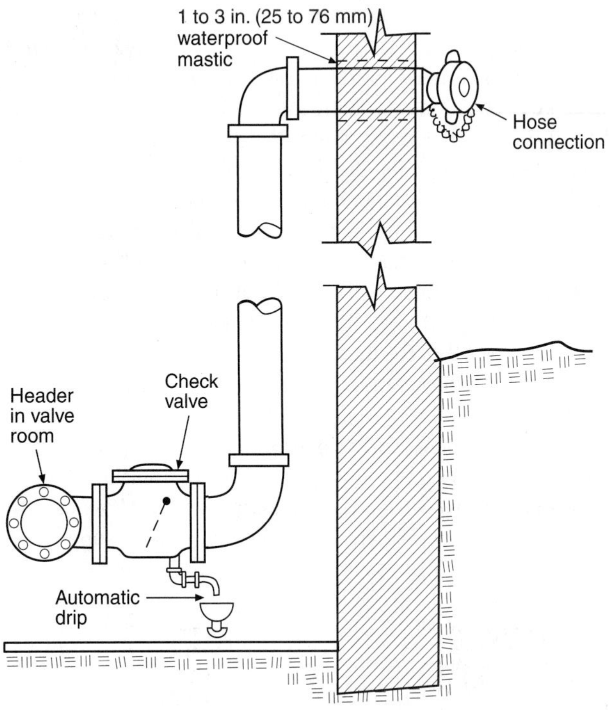

FIGURE 15.4.2 Typical Fire Department Connection

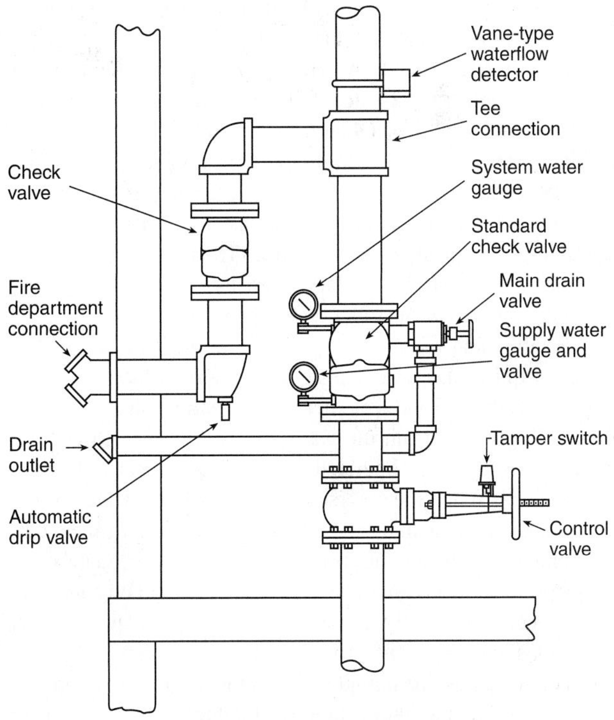

FIGURE 15.4.3 Straight Pipe Riser (Source: *Automatic Sprinkler Systems Handbook,* 1999, Exhibit 5.26)

system control valve and the dry pipe valve. This makes it possible to pump water into the system even if the valve is closed. If there are two or more sprinkler system risers, each with its own separate connection to a public main, each system must have its own fire department connection. If more than one riser is connected to a yard system, the fire department connection should feed into the yard system on the supply side of all riser shutoff valves, and there must be a check valve in all other water supply connections into the yard system to prevent backflow and loss of water supplied through the fire department connection. If one riser is shut off, the fire department connection can still supply all other risers. If two or more sprinkler system risers are fed by one sprinkler connection, one fire department connection can supply both risers.

In an emergency, a fire department can pump water from public hydrants or other sources of water into a sprinkler system through hose connected to a yard hydrant or other hose connection using a double female hose coupling, if other supply connections have a check valve or a gate valve that can be closed.

INFLUENCE OF VARIOUS FACTORS ON WATER SUPPLY NEED

Determining the water supply requirement for most sprinkler systems is not always easy because of the many variables involved. If a water source that can supply all the sprinklers is available, there is no problem, but such a water supply is seldom practical except in the case of small systems. The water supply requirement for any sprinkler system is directly related to the number of sprinklers expected to operate, which is determined by the hazard classification and the anticipated use of outside and inside hose stream demands.

Records kept by NFPA before 1970 show that 20 or fewer sprinklers opened in 93 percent of all anecdotally reported fires in sprinklered buildings. Older data are almost certainly skewed to bigger fires and more severe outcomes. Given this history, it is not surprising that water supply adequacy is not usually difficult to assure and inadequacy is rarely the cited reason for unsatisfactory sprinkler performance. Thus, water supply is a significant concern, particularly with large sprinkler systems and with systems protecting greater-than-ordinary hazards.

Establishing the water supply requirement for a sprinkler system requires the system designer to consider factors relating to sprinkler control and sprinkler system extinguishment. Where the cooling effect from the water discharged by sprinklers is greater than the heat liberated by the fire, the sprinklers can gain control. When the reverse occurs, as when a water supply is overtaxed or system design is inadequate, the sprinklers cannot control the fire and the sprinkler system may ultimately fail. Where all conditions are favorable, the fire should be controlled by the operation of only a small number of sprinklers. Because conditions vary with different classes of occupancy, areas, and types of buildings, the number of sprinklers expected to operate to control a fire may range up to the total number in the design area, and the water supply should be provided accordingly.

The following factors affect the number of sprinklers that might open in a fire and must therefore be considered in determining the water supply requirement.

Hazard of Occupancy (Including Flash Fire Hazard and Potential Rate of Heat Release)

This is the most important factor and one requiring experienced judgment to evaluate. Where a flash fire hazard is present, it is usually necessary to provide enough water to operate all of the sprinklers in any individual fire area.

Initial Water Pressure

When fire sprinklers are submitted to testing laboratories for listing, they are subjected to water distribution and fire tests. These tests are conducted at a minimum flow of 15 gpm (57 L/min) per sprinkler. The pressure required to produce this flow through a standard ½ in. orifice (12.7 mm) sprinkler with a nominal K-factor of 5.6 is approximately 7 psi (0.5 bar). The minimum operating pressure of any sprinkler is 7 psi (0.5 bar) according to NFPA 13. The designer must verify the listing for a specific sprinkler. The listing may require minimum operating pressure greater than 7 psi (0.5 bar).

At higher initial water pressures, the discharge is correspondingly greater. For example, at a pressure of 15 psi (1.03 bar), a sprinkler (K = 5.6) will discharge 22 gpm (83 L/min) or an average of approximately 0.17 gal/ft^2/min (6.8 L/min/m^2) for one sprinkler with an area of coverage of 130 ft^2 (12 m^2). At 30 psi (2.07 bar), the discharge is 31 gpm (117 L/min), and at 50 psi (3.45 bar), it is 40 gpm (151 L/min). With a greater discharge, there is a better chance of fire control from a small number of sprinklers and less need for large volumes of water to supply a large number of sprinklers.

Obstructions to Distribution of Water from Sprinklers

Nonstructural building elements such as high piled stocks, pallets, racks, and shelving must be considered, especially in extra hazard and various types of storage occupancies. Obstructions create a greater chance that a larger number of sprinklers needing larger water supplies will open and a lesser likelihood that the fire will be controlled in its initial stages.

High Ceilings and Air Current Conditions

With ceilings of unusual height, there is a greater chance that natural air movement will carry heat away from the sprinklers immediately over a fire, resulting not only in a delay in the application of water, but also resulting in the opening of sprinklers remote from the area of fire origin. More water or a larger sprinkler density is usually needed under such conditions. The same situation exists wherever there are drafts, such as in areas open on the sides to the outside where winds can divert heat from sprinklers over the fire.

Unprotected Vertical Openings

Sprinkler systems in multistory buildings are usually designed on the assumption that fire will be controlled on the floor of origin. Where there are unprotected openings up through which heat and fire may spread, it may be expected that more sprinklers will open, particularly in the case of a fire originating near the vertical opening. In the case of high combustibility, the interconnected floors may need to be considered as one fire area. This means more water and larger pipe sizes in risers and supply lines.

Wet Pipe versus Dry Pipe Systems

Because of the delay due to exhausting air from dry pipe systems, more sprinklers are expected to open on dry pipe systems than on wet pipe systems. This may call for greater water supplies. Design areas are increased by 30 percent to account for this delay.

Obstructions to Sprinkler Discharge

Sprinkler discharge patterns may be significantly affected by an obstruction. Historically building structural members and other building elements such as ducts were considered. Recently other types of smaller building elements such as piping and light fixtures were considered as obstructions to water distribution. Columns, beams, girders, bar joists, light fixtures, soffits, and HVAC ductwork can obstruct water distribution to the point where additional sprinklers may be necessary to account for the obstruction, the result being more sprinklers in the design area. Floor-mounted obstructions, such as privacy curtains, freestanding interior partitions, and room dividers, require similar special treatment. NFPA 13 addresses the areas of concern with regard to obstructions. Each type of sprinkler—that is, standard spray, sidewall, large drop, extended coverage, and early suppression fast response (ESFR)—is treated separately with its own obstruction requirements.

Extent of Coverage and Exposures

Any fire in an unsprinklered space extending to an area with automatic sprinklers places an abnormal demand on the sprinkler system and requires increased water supplies so that the system may function effectively.

Regardless of the size of the building, NFPA 13 requires a specific design area that relates to the occupancy fire hazard rather than the size of the building. The idea behind this concept is to provide a water supply that is adequate to cover this design area for a given period. The sprinklers in the most remote portion (hydraulically remote areas) of this area are used as the basis of design. The capability of supplying sprinklers in this area automatically means that sprinklers that are physically closer to the water supply source can be supplied as well.

WATER SUPPLY REQUIREMENTS FOR SPRINKLER SYSTEMS

Notwithstanding the general problems involved in arriving at water supply requirements, the fire hazard represented by different building occupancies has made it possible to establish requirements for water supplies for sprinkler systems. The occupancy classification is the primary consideration, with latitude allowed for other contributing factors.

Selection of the appropriate water supply guide table in NFPA 13 is based on the design approach for sprinkler piping. The pipe schedule approach is the oldest version and first appeared in the standard in 1896. The concept of hydraulically designed systems was advanced in 1969 and is the predominate design approach method used today. Minimum water supply requirements for the pipe schedule design method, as shown in Table 15.4.1, are based on occupancy classification (light or ordinary hazard).

The total water supply required is determined from Table 15.4.1, and the water for hose streams is included. If stored water is used, the total waterflow required would have to be multiplied by the duration of flow to determine whether the capacity of the stored supply is adequate, a factor that would not be pertinent for a reliable municipal water source.

The pipe schedule method that is the basis of Table 15.4.1 has certain limitations and should be used only with experienced judgment. The pipe schedule method is permitted only for new installations of 5000 ft^2 (465 m^2) or less at a minimum residual of 15 psi (1.03 bar) at the base of the riser, or if the area exceeds 5000 ft^2 (465 m^2) the minimum residual must be 50 psi (3.4 bar) at the elevation of the sprinkler. The pipe schedule design method is also permitted for modifications to existing pipe schedule systems. The effectiveness of a pipe schedule system is limited to the use of ½ in (12.7 mm) orifice sprinklers. Extra hazard occupancies and storage occupancies involve complex factors requiring special consideration and the use of the hydraulic calculation design method.

Where fire pumps contribute to the sprinkler system water supply, pumps of standard size used with adequate rates of discharge are required. The water supply for a pump must be adequate and reliable to provide for continuous pump operation.

Where pressure tanks furnish the water supply, the tank installation should comply with the appropriate provisions of NFPA 22. Where a combination of different water supplies is provided in the interest of reliability, it is good practice to have the rate of supply from each source at least equal to the minimum requirement for the system.

OCCUPANCY CLASSIFICATIONS

Light-Hazard Occupancies

The quantity or combustibility of contents is low and fires with relatively low rates of heat release are expected. Examples of

TABLE 15.4.1 Water Supply Requirements for Pipe Schedule Sprinkler Systems

Occupancy Classification	*Minimum Residual Pressure Required (psi)*	*Acceptable Flow at Base of Riser (Including Hose Stream Allowance) (gpm)*	*Duration (min)*
Light hazard	15	500–750	30–60
Ordinary hazard	20	850–1500	60–90

For SI units: 1 gpm = 3.785 L/min; 1 psi = 0.0689 bar.

light-hazard occupancies are residential buildings, dormitories, office buildings, the seating areas of restaurants, and hospitals. In these occupancies, the potential rate of heat release is low, areas are usually subdivided, and a small number of sprinklers normally should control any fire. For hydraulically designed systems, 150 gpm (568 L/min) for sprinkler operation and an additional 100 gpm (378 L/min) for hose stream demand (Table 15.4.2) will generally make a good starting point for system demand. A total of 500 to 750 gpm (1893 to 2839 L/min) for pipe schedule systems may be necessary for the same hazard, thereby making this a less desirable design approach.

Ordinary-Hazard Occupancies

Ordinary-hazard occupancies are divided into two groups: Group 1 and Group 2.

Group 1. This ordinary-hazard classification includes occupancies, such as parking garages, bakeries, laundries, and canneries, in which the combustibility of contents is moderate, stockpiles of combustibles do not exceed 8 ft (2.4 m), and the rate of heat release for a fire is greater than that for the light-hazard classification. Ordinary-hazard Group 1 occupancies will require a minimum of 225 gpm (851 L/min) for sprinkler operation and an additional 250 gpm (946 L/min) to support inside and outside hose streams. If a pipe schedule approach is selected, a minimum flow of 850 gpm (3217 L/min) is necessary.

Group 2. This ordinary-hazard classification includes occupancies such as clothing factories, mercantile, pharmaceutical manufacturing, certain woodworking occupancies, and repair garages. With this group, the combustibility of contents, storage heights, and obstruction features are moderate to high, stockpiles do not exceed 12 ft (3.7 m), and the rate of heat release is greater than Group 1. Ordinary-hazard Group 2 occupancies will require a minimum flow of 300 gpm (1125 L/min) for sprinkler operation, plus an additional 250 gpm (946 L/min) to operate the inside and outside hose streams. If design is based on the pipe schedule method, a minimum total flow of 850 gpm (3217 L/min) is necessary.

Extra Hazard Occupancies

Extra hazard occupancies consist of properties where quantity and combustibility of contents is very high. Flammable and combustible liquids, dust, lint, or other materials may be present, introducing the probability of rapidly developing fires with high rates of heat release. Closely spaced sprinklers and larger pipe sizes are expected. Extra hazard occupancies are divided into two groups: Group 1 and Group 2.

Group 1. Extra hazard occupancies (Group 1) include those that may produce severe fires where little or no flammable or combustible liquids are present. These include such occupancies as die casting, plywood and particleboard manufacturing, printing (using inks with below 100°F [37.8°C] flashpoints), rubber manufacturing operations, sawmills, textile operations, and upholstering with plastic foam operations.

Group 2. Extra hazard occupancies (Group 2) include those that may produce severe fires where moderate to substantial amounts of flammable or combustible liquids are present, or where shielding of combustibles is extensive. These include such occupancy hazards as asphalt saturating, flammable liquids spraying, flow coating, open oil quenching, solvent cleaning, and varnish and paint dipping.

In any treatment of hazards by general groups of occupancy, it must be noted that individual properties differ markedly and that buildings of the same nominal occupancy classification may show widely different individual hazards that should be considered in any determination of water supply.

WATER SUPPLY REQUIREMENTS FOR HOSE STREAM PROTECTION

The values given in Table 15.4.1 include hose stream requirements. In considering water requirements for hose streams, one should realize that if sprinklers perform effectively, little hose stream assistance is required. Although this is generally the case, a realistic view must be taken of possible contingencies and of the amount of water that might be needed for hose stream protection under adverse conditions. Hose streams may also be necessary to accomplish final extinguishment of the fire. However, it should be noted that current sprinkler system technology is intended to control a fire, not necessarily to extinguish it.

In evaluating hose stream requirements, one should consider several possibilities, such as the amount of water necessary for final extinguishment and cleanup operations, or the steps that may have to be taken in the event that sprinklers are retarding fire spread but are not fully effective in gaining control of the fire and extinguishing it.

HYDRAULICALLY DESIGNED SPRINKLER SYSTEMS

Planning new water supplies or evaluating existing supplies for sprinkler systems requires information about the hydraulic behavior of sprinkler piping systems.

A hydraulically designed sprinkler system is one in which pipe sizes are selected on a pressure loss basis to provide a prescribed density in gallons per minute per square foot ([L/min]/m^2), or a prescribed minimum discharge pressure or flow per sprinkler, distributed with a reasonable degree of uniformity over a specified area. This system permits the selection of pipe sizes in accordance with the characteristics of the water supply available. The stipulated design density and area of application will vary with occupancy hazard. This language is the verbatim definition of a hydraulically designed system, taken from NFPA 13. This definition sets the basic premise for the preferred method of sprinkler system design.

Table 15.4.2 and Figure 15.4.4 are used to determine density, area of sprinkler operation, and water supply requirements for hydraulically designed sprinkler systems. Systems must be calculated to satisfy a single point on the appropriate design curve, and interior piping must be based on this design point. It

TABLE 15.4.2 Hose Stream Demand and Water Supply Duration Requirements for Hydraulically Calculated Systems

Hazard Classification	*Inside Hose (gpm)*	*Total Combined Inside and Outside Hose (gpm)*	*Duration (min)*
Light	0, 50, or 100	100	30
Ordinary	0, 50, or 100	250	60–90
Extra hazard	0, 50, or 100	500	90–120

For SI units: 1 gpm = 3.785 L/min.

is not necessary to meet all points on the selected curve. In some cases where a large water supply is available, it might be advantageous, because of the elimination of a fire pump, to design the system using the top portion of the curve. In other cases, it might be better to design with smaller areas of application and higher densities, because these tend to limit fire size, even though a fire pump is required.

When selecting a point on the curve in Figure 15.4.4, it should be noted that more total water is necessary in terms of flow and capacity as one moves up the curve. As an example, for a light-hazard system, a 1500-ft^2 (139-m^2) area requires a density of 0.10 gpm/ft^2 (4.1 [L/min]/m^2), or a flow of 150 gpm (568 L/min). If a 2500-ft^2 (232-m^2) area is selected, the density is only 0.08 gpm/ft^2 (3.2 [L/min]/m^2), but the total flow is increased to 200 gpm (757 L/min).

The same hazard occupancy classifications that apply to pipe schedule sprinkler systems apply to hydraulically designed sprinkler systems. However, the recommended water supply figures are somewhat lower due to the greater efficiency of a calculated system.

The water allowances for inside and outside hose streams may be combined and added to the system requirement at the system connection to the underground main. The total water requirement must be calculated through the underground main to the point of supply.

For deluge and water spray systems with open orifices, calculations are essential. Automatic sprinkler systems protecting high-piled storage require a specific water density for fire control. Because the hydraulic design approach results in superior design, it always should be selected as the preferred method.

Hydraulic Calculation Programs

Since NFPA 13 first permitted the use of hydraulic calculations, several computer programs have been developed that can assist the designer with this particular task. These programs are not required to be listed nor are they governed by NFPA 13. They must, as a minimum, be capable of providing the information required for any hydraulic calculation procedure. This information includes, but is not limited to, the hydraulic reference points, the flow and pressure at specific points, the pipe diameter, and, for a grid system, a printout showing the flow direction and quantities.

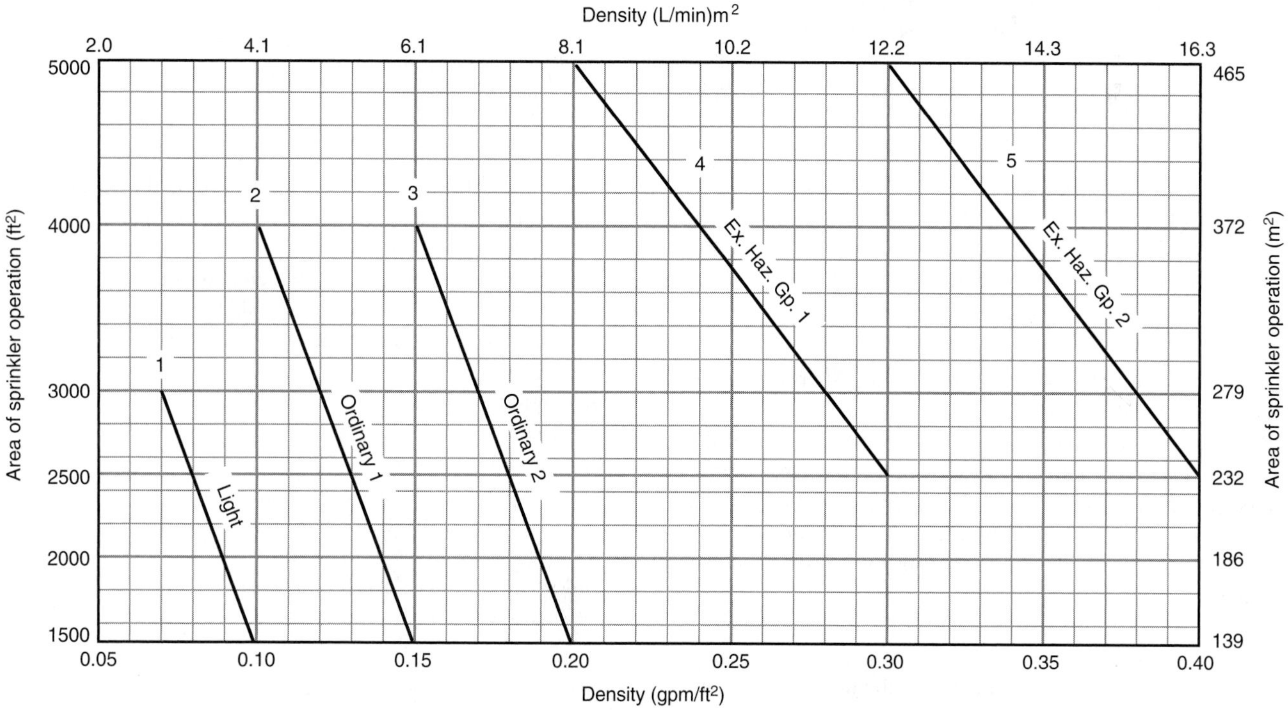

FIGURE 15.4.4 Design Curves for Hydraulically Calculated Sprinkler System

The capabilities and limitations of computer programs are as wide ranging as the cost differences among them. Before buying one of these programs, the user should investigate and compare the various hydraulic software programs, including the support the programs offer.

Flow Calculation Method

A method of making flow calculations for sprinkler systems is given in NFPA 13.

The design area for flow calculations should be chosen as the most hydraulically demanding area for the sprinkler system. The area should have a dimension parallel to the branch line of 1.2 times the square root of the area of anticipated sprinkler operation. The 1.2 times the square root of the area is added to ensure that the long side of the rectangle is along the branch line. In grid systems, the hydraulically most demanding area must be verified using at least two additional sets of calculations. This technique is referred to as "peaking," and it is merely a check to prove that the most demanding area has been calculated.

Each sprinkler in the design area must discharge at a flow rate at least equal to the stipulated minimum water application rate or density. Begin calculations at the sprinkler hydraulically farthest from the supply connection. In common system configurations, this will be the end sprinkler on the end branch line. The minimum operating pressure for any sprinkler must not be less than 7 psi (48 kPa) or the pressure necessary to deliver the design density at the hydraulically most remote sprinkler or a higher minimum pressure as specified in the laboratory listing. Special sprinklers, such as extended-coverage, ESFR, in-rack, and large drop, will require operating pressures well in excess of this 7 psi (48 kPa) minimum.

Most Remote Sprinkler

Assuming a minimum pressure of 10 psi (69 kPa) at the most remote sprinkler and a discharge coefficient of 0.75 for a standard ½ in. (12.7 mm) orifice sprinkler, there is a discharge of 17.7 gpm (67 L/min) calculated from the formula

$$Q = 29.83cd^2\sqrt{p}$$

used in calculating flows through orifices and short tubes. For a given sprinkler, the product of these numbers in the equation—$29.83cd^2$—becomes a constant and is denoted as the sprinkler K-factor. In the case of a ½ in. (12.7 mm) orifice sprinkler, the constant is 5.6 and is derived by multiplying the following numbers: $29.83 \times 0.75 \times (½)^2 = 5.6$. A simplified equation may now be used to describe flow through the sprinkler orifice. The new equation is

$$Q = K\sqrt{p}$$

Velocity pressure is not a factor at the most remote sprinkler, but it may be considered at all the other sprinklers in the example that follows. Some organizations ignore velocity pressure in their calculations. The omission of velocity pressure is conservative and on the safe side.

Example for Second Sprinkler from the End

The following example considers the effects of velocity pressure. Some computer programs consider velocity pressure and others do not. The hydraulic calculation example presented in the Annex of NFPA 13, Figure A.14.3.2(a) through Figure A.14.3.2(d), does not consider velocity pressure and is an example of hydraulic calculations by the old-fashioned method, by hand, not computer generated.

Assuming sprinklers 10 ft (3.05 m) apart on branch lines, with the end section of pipe 1 in. (25.4 mm) nominal diameter, the friction loss at 17.7 gpm (67 L/min) flow with a Hazen-Williams formula coefficient of 120 (value for black steel pipe) will be 1.0 psi (7 kPa).

The total pressure at the second sprinkler will be 10.0 + 1.0 psi (69 +7 kPa) = 11.0 psi (76 kPa). Velocity pressure, if used in the procedure, is calculated from the formula

$$P_v = 0.001123\frac{Q^2}{D^2}$$

where

P_v = Velocity pressure (psi)

Q = Flow (gpm)

D = Inside pipe diameter (in.)

The velocity pressure relates to the system design by

$$P_n = P_t - P_v$$

where

P_n = Normal pressure

P_t = Total pressure

P_v = Velocity pressure

Of this, velocity pressure based on a flow of 17.7 gpm (67 L/min) will be 0.3 psi (2 kPa). The normal pressure (pressure acting perpendicular to the pipe wall) acting on the second sprinkler is the total pressure of 11.0 psi (76 kPa), less the velocity pressure of 0.3 psi (2 kPa), which equals 10.7 psi (74 kPa). On all sprinklers except the end sprinkler, only normal pressure is considered as acting on the sprinklers. The discharge from the second sprinkler, at a pressure of 10.7 psi (74 kPa), will be 18.3 gpm (69 L/min).

The pipe between the second and third sprinkler, also 1 in. (25.4 mm) in diameter, 10 ft (3.05 m) long, and with a flow of 17.7 gpm (67 L/min) + 18.3 gpm (69 L/min) = 36.0 gpm (136 L/min), will have a friction loss of 3.8 psi (26 kPa) and a velocity pressure of 1.2 psi (8 kPa). Normal pressure at the third sprinkler is 10.7 psi (74 kPa) + 3.8 psi (26 kPa) – 1.2 psi (8 kPa), or 13.3 psi (92 kPa).

Other Sprinklers on a Branch Line

Figure 15.4.5 can be used to establish the velocity pressure correction needed for various pipe sizes and flows. This figure may be used for any pipe type, but it is based on the use of Schedule

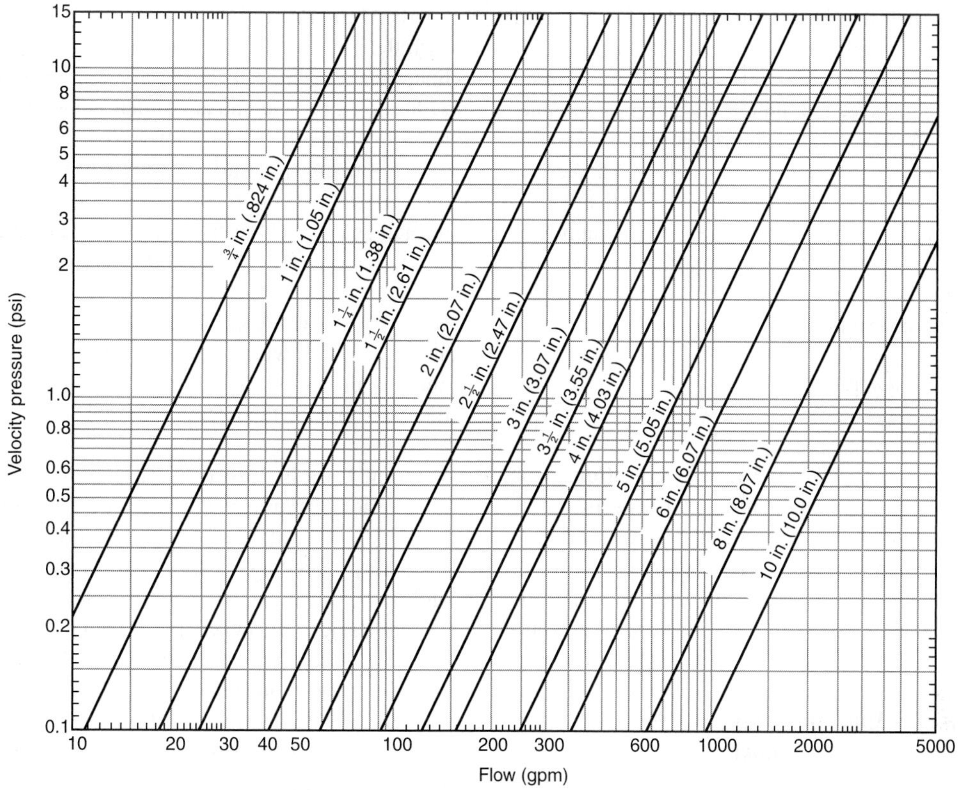

FIGURE 15.4.5 Graph for the Determination of Velocity Pressure

40 pipe. The difference in velocity pressure is minuscule as it relates to schedule of pipe.

Figure 15.4.6 is an example of the velocity pressure component, determined as follows: The flow between the last sprinkler and the next to last sprinkler on the branch line was determined to be 17.7 gpm (67 L/min) and the pipe size is 1 in. (25.4 mm). The graph in Figure 15.4.5 is now used to locate a flow of 17.7 gpm (67 L/min) on the *x*-axis, going vertically from this point until the 1 in. (25.4 mm) line is intercepted. The corresponding pressure is taken from the *y*-axis and is determined to be 0.3 psi (2.1 kPa). This procedure can now be repeated for each combination of pipe sizes and flows.

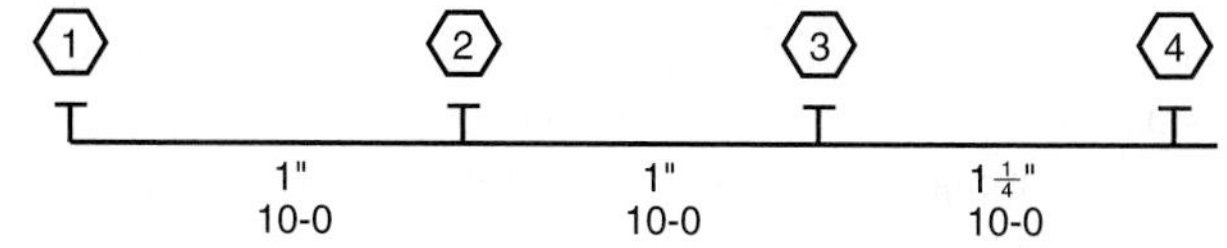

Summary

	Flow (gpm)	Friction loss (psi)	Velocity pressure (psi)	Normal pressure (psi)
1–2	17.7	1	0.3	11
2–3	36	3.8	1.2	13.3
3–4	57.5	3.9	1.0	15.0

FIGURE 15.4.6 Example of Velocity Pressure

Up to this point, velocity pressure has been based on flow downstream from the sprinkler being considered; this has been confirmed by tests. It has also been shown by those tests that beyond the second sprinkler, velocity pressure should be figured from the flow on the upstream side of the sprinkler being considered. This figuring is done by trial and error, assuming a flow from the sprinkler, calculating the velocity pressure from the total flow, determining a normal pressure, and calculating a flow from the normal pressure. If the calculated flow is not reasonably close to the assumed flow, assume a different flow and repeat the procedure until the two are close.

For example, assume a flow from the third sprinkler of 19.0 gpm (72 L/min) and assume that the pipe between the third and fourth sprinkler is 1¼ in. (32 mm). Total flow is 36.0 gpm (136 L/min) + 19.0 gpm (72 L/min) = 55.0 gpm (208 L/min). Velocity pressure is 0.9 psi (6 kPa), and normal pressure at the third sprinkler is therefore 15.7 psi (108 kPa) – 0.9 psi (6 kPa), or 14.8 psi (102 kPa). Corrected flow then becomes 21.6 gpm (82 L/min), which is not close enough to the 19.0 gpm (72 L/min) assumed. Try an assumed flow of 21.4 gpm (81 L/min). Velocity pressure at 57.4 gpm (217 L/min) is 1.0 psi (7 kPa); normal pressure is 14.7 psi (101 kPa), and the new corrected flow is 21.5 gpm (81 L/min). Total flow at the third sprinkler then becomes 36.0 gpm (136 L/min) + 21.5 gpm (81.4 L/min) = 7.5 gpm (217.6 L/min). The calculating procedure for the other sprinklers on the branch line is the same as it is for the third sprinkler. If this set of conditions is compared to pipe schedule design, it will be seen that the 15 psi (103 kPa) minimum riser pressure has been exceeded, unless, as is quite probable, the pressure with 57.5 gpm (217.6 L/min) flow is substantially higher than that with a 500 gpm (1893 L/min) flow. Whether the pressure with 57.5 gpm (217.6 L/min) flow is higher than 15 psi (103 kPa) depends on the characteristics of the water supply. In any case, it appears that with not many more sprinklers open, the pressure at the most remote sprinkler will be less than the 10 psi (69 kPa) selected in this example.

Branch Lines, Cross Mains, Risers, and Fittings

Cross-Main Pressure at the Branch Line Connection. This pressure is the normal pressure at the nearest open sprinkler increased by the friction loss and the velocity pressure in the intervening pipe. If the branch line is fed through a tee and nipple, additional friction loss allowances must be made, although the friction loss in nipples less than 6 in. (152 mm) long is customarily neglected.

Two Branches in One Line of Sprinklers. These may have the same or different numbers of sprinklers. The pressure at the entrance to the two branches will always be the same. The computations starting at the end sprinklers will be duplicated for the number of open sprinklers. After the discharge from any number of sprinklers on a branch line has been computed and the pressure needed to produce the flow has been determined, the entire branch line can be considered to have the discharge characteristics of a single orifice, and the discharge constant K in the formula $Q = K\sqrt{p}$ can be determined, P being the net pressure where flows are taken from tees in the cross main.

Branches on Opposite Sides of a Cross Main. These branches may have different numbers of sprinklers open, in which case the cross-main pressure must be the higher of the two computed values. This situation increases the discharge from the branch giving the lower computed pressure, and the actual discharge must be calculated for the higher pressure using the equation

$$\frac{Q_1}{Q_2} = \sqrt{\frac{P_1}{P_2}}$$

where P_2 is taken as the higher pressure, Q_2 the corresponding increased discharge to be determined, and P_1 and Q_1 the pressure and corresponding discharge from the branch requiring only the lower pressure. This proportion and its associated concept is important in that only one pressure can be present at a particular junction point.

After the appropriate increased discharge has been determined, the two rates of flow can be combined and K calculated for the combined branches.

When sprinklers on the second branch line are assumed to have opened, starting at the cross-main sprinkler, the opened sprinkler most remote from the cross main is considered as the end sprinkler in the branch line computation, the next opened is the second, and so on, regardless of nonoperating sprinklers on the outer end of the branch.

Cross-Main Pressures. Cross-main pressures are calculated with the same procedure used for sprinklers on a single branch line, except that it is not necessary to use the trial-and-error procedure for the third and additional branch lines because the effect of change in velocity pressure with flows passing through tees in the cross main is usually negligible. The net pressure producing the flow in successive branch lines is taken as the normal pressure at the end branch line, increased by the friction loss in the pipe between the branches.

Riser Pressure. Riser pressure is taken as the normal pressure at the nearest flowing branch, increased by the total friction loss between this branch and the riser and by the velocity pressure in the cross main at the riser connection.

Friction Loss in Fittings. This friction loss is generally included in calculations only when the fitting involves a change in the direction of flow. An exception to this is the fitting immediately preceding the sprinkler. Friction loss in control, gate, and check valves and in strainers, meters, backflow devices, and similar devices is always included. The friction loss in piping between the source of supply and the opened sprinklers obviously must be included in all calculations.

Differences in elevation must be allowed for on the basis that each foot (meter) of height represents 0.433 psi (9.82 kPa/m). In multistory buildings, this may be a substantial factor. Feed mains, cross mains, and branch lines within the same system may be looped or gridded to divide the total water flowing to the design area.

Grid Systems. Many grid systems are currently being installed. The use of grid systems means that every sprinkler is fed from several directions, with a resulting reduction in pipe sizing. The hydraulic calculations required for a grid system are complex and almost impossible without the use of computers.

Water Supply Treatment

Microbiologically influenced corrosion (MIC) is now addressed in NFPA 13. In areas with water supplies known to have contributed to MIC, water supplies shall be tested and appropriately treated prior to filling or testing the metallic piping systems.

MIC is corrosion occurring on the interior of copper tubing and all types of steel piping that is accelerated by microorganisms. The overall effect is the formation of deposits or colonies and the pitting of metallic system piping in relatively short periods of time. Aside from the pinhole leaks that MIC creates, obstructions caused by tubercles can change the friction factor and the cross sectional area of the pipe.

Corrosion experts have known about MIC for decades, but the presence of MIC in fire protection systems is a relatively new phenomenon.

SUMMARY

Perhaps the most important item of an automatic fire sprinkler system is the water supply. The sprinkler system discharge criteria must be satisfied by the water supply in terms of adequacy and reliability. Adequacy refers to the pressure, rate of flow, duration, and in general the amount of water present. Reliability is more subjective and dependent on the availability of the water from the source or combination of sources.

Many variables are involved in determining the water supply requirements for most sprinkler systems. System design, occupancy classifications, obstructions to discharge, and hose stream allowances are a few of the variables to be considered.

An adequate water supply is the crucial factor when a fire occurs in a fire sprinkler protected property. Sufficient water must be available to control or suppress the fire when sprinklers actuate.

BIBLIOGRAPHY

NFPA Codes, Standards, and Recommended Practices

Reference to the following NFPA codes, standards, and recommended practices will provide further information on water supplies for sprinkler systems discussed in this chapter. (See the latest version of The NFPA Catalog *for availability of current editions of the following documents.)*

NFPA 1, *Uniform Fire Code™*
NFPA 13, *Standard for the Installation of Sprinkler Systems*
NFPA 13D, *Standard for the Installation of Sprinkler Systems in One- and Two-Family Dwellings and Manufactured Homes*
NFPA 13R, *Standard for the Installation of Sprinkler Systems in Residential Occupancies up to and Including Four Stories in Height*
NFPA 15, *Standard for Water Spray Fixed Systems for Fire Protection*
NFPA 20, *Standard for the Installation of Stationary Pumps for Fire Protection*
NFPA 22, *Standard for Water Tanks for Private Fire Protection*
NFPA 291, *Recommended Practice for Fire Flow Testing and Marking of Hydrants*

References

Allinson, T., "Fire Protection: Things to Know for the Design Build Market," *Plumbing Engineer,* Vol. 29, No. 5, 2001, pp. 39–40.
Averill, J. D., "Performance-Based Codes: Economics, Documentation, and Design," National Institute of Standards and Technology, Gaithersburg, MD, NIST GCR 98-752, July 1998.
Bennett, J. A., "Highrise Firefighting from Top to Bottom. Part 2," *American Fire Journal,* Vol. 53, No. 3, 2000, pp. 12–15.
Bromann, M., *Design and Layout of Fire Sprinkler Systems,* Technomic Publishing Co., Inc., Lancaster, PA, 1997.
Bromann, M., *Design and Layout of Fire Sprinkler Systems* (2nd ed.), Technomic Publishing Co., Inc., Lancaster, PA, 2001.
Bryan, J. L., *Automatic Sprinkler and Standpipe Systems,* 2nd ed., National Fire Protection Association, Quincy, MA, 1997.
Bsharat, T. K., "Detection, Treatment, and Prevention of Microbiologically Influenced Corrosion in Water-Based Fire Protection Systems," National Fire Sprinkler Association, Patterson, NY, June 1998.
Budnick, E. K., "USFA Residential Water Mist Test Program (Initial Feasibility)," *Proceedings* of Demonstration of Limited Water Supply Fire Suppression Technologies, Mar. 12, 1996, Gaithersburg, MD, National Institute of Standards and Technology, Gaithersburg, MD, 1996, pp. 1–48.
Bychowski, J. A., and Balingit, C., "Back-Flow Prevention for Today's Sprinkler Systems," *Consulting-Specifying Engineer,* Vol. 20, No. 4, 1996, pp. 54–56.
Cain, B., "Will Your Sprinkler System Function Correctly?" *Fire Safety Engineering,* Vol. 7, No. 5, 2000, pp. 9–10.
Carey, B., "Reduction in the Quantity of Stored Water for MHSS Systems," *Proceedings* of Demonstration of Limited Water Supply Fire Suppression Technologies, Mar. 12, 1996, Gaithersburg, MD, National Institute of Standards and Technology, Gaithersburg, MD, 1996, pp. 1–24.
Comeau, E., and Duval, R. F., "School Fire, Pangnirtung, Northwest Territories, Canada, March 9, 1997," National Fire Protection Association, Quincy, MA, NFPA Fire Investigation Report, 1998.
Coughlin, P., "Your Next Sprinkler System?" *Fire Chief,* Vol. 45, No. 6, 2001, pp. 44–47.
Dubay, C., "Fire Protection and Life Safety for Road Tunnels," *Fire Protection Engineering,* No. 5, Winter 2000, pp. 19–22.
Dubay, C., "Pressure's Building," *NFPA Journal,* Vol. 91, No. 4, 1997, pp. 68–72.
Feeney, M., "Significance of Sprinkler Effectiveness in Performance Based Design of Steel Buildings for Fire," *Proceedings* of the International Conference, Engineered Fire Protection Design . . . Applying Fire Science to Fire Protection Problems, June 11–15, 2001, San Francisco, Society of Fire Protection Engineers, Bethesda, MD, 2001, pp. 437–448.
"Group Accommodation Guidelines," Country Fire Authority, Victoria, Australia, February 1997.
Huggins, R., and Brown, P., "Fire Pumps, Overhead Doors, Corrosive Conditions?" *Sprinkler Age,* Vol. 15, No. 7, 1996, p. 44.
"Hydraulics of Fire Protection Systems," Loss Prevention Data Sheet 3-0, Factory Mutual Research Corp., Norwood, MA.
Isman, K. E., "Large Drop Sprinklers for General Storage Protection," *Sprinkler Quarterly,* No. 96, Fall 1996, p. 12.
Kerr, K. J., "Backflow Prevention for Fire Protection Systems," *Plumbing Engineer,* Vol. 27, No. 6, 1999, pp. 35–36.
Lewis, D. P., Piontkowski, J. M., Straney, R. W., Knowlton, J. J., and Neuhauser, E. F., "Method for Assessing the Risk of Zebra Mussel Dressena Polymorpha Infestation in Industrial Fire Protection Systems," *Fire Technology,* Vol. 33, No. 3, 1997, pp. 214–229.
"Limited Water Supply Fire Suppression Technologies Demonstrated at NIST," *U.S. Fire Sprinkler Reporter,* Vol. 10, No. 10, 1996, p. 1.
NFPA, *Automatic Sprinkler Systems Handbook*, 8th ed., National Fire Protection Association, Quincy, MA, 1999.
NFPA Fire Pump Handbook, 1st ed., National Fire Protection Association, Quincy, MA 1998.
NFPA Pocket Guide to Sprinkler System Installation, National Fire Protection Association, Quincy, MA, 2001.
Pisciotta, T., "Preplanning Construction Site Hazards," *Fire Engineering,* Vol. 153, No. 11, 2000, pp. 79–82.
"Quakeproofing Your Fire Protection: A System Approach," *Sprinkler Age,* Vol. 16, No. 8, 1997, pp. 16–19.
"Recreational Accommodation Guidelines," Country Fire Authority, Victoria, Australia, Feb. 1997.
Schulte, R. C., "Engineers and Sprinkler System Design," *Plumbing Engineer,* Vol. 28, No. 10, 2000, p. 10.
Schulte, R. C., "Engineers and Sprinkler System Design. Part 2," *Plumbing Engineer,* Vol. 28, No. 12, 2000, p. 12.
Smith, D., "Residential Sprinkler Code Brings Water to the Tucson Desert," *American Fire Journal,* Vol. 49, No. 10, 1997, pp. 11–14.
Smith, J. P., "High-Rise Firefighting. Part 2," *Firehouse,* Vol. 23, No. 12, 1998, p. 14.
Wass, H. E., *Sprinkler Hydraulics and What It's All About,* Society of Fire Protection Engineers, Washington, DC, 1999.
Yates, S., "Traditional Recipe for Disasters," *Fire Prevention,* No. 314, 1998, pp. 36–37.

Microbiologically Influenced Corrosion in Fire Sprinkler Systems

Bruce H. Clarke ❑ Anthony M. Aguilera

Chapter Contents

Key Terms

automatic sprinkler system, corrosion (general), C-factor, Hazen-Williams formula, microbiologically influenced corrosion (MIC)

Beginning in the early 1990s, concerns began to increase about microbiologically influenced corrosion (MIC) affecting fire sprinkler systems due to multiple cases involving the abnormally rapid development of pinhole-sized leaks and highly obstructive interior biological pipe growths. Most of these occurred in systems well before the end of the system's life expectancy, after 5 to 20 years of service. However, some systems began to show signs of critical obstruction and began developing leaks in less than one year. Research into the cause of these leaks, which have greatly increased in the last two decades, has led to a growing awareness of the problem. In the past 20 years MIC has grown from a relatively unknown topic of regional discussions to one now generating widespread concern throughout several countries. MIC in fire protection systems also has become the subject of a wide array of speculation, debate, and, in some cases, gross inaccuracies.

At the time this chapter is being written, there are still few well documented time-proven solutions that are also universally accepted "best practices" throughout the fire protection industry. Although MIC and biological growth control have been extensively researched in many allied engineering fields for decades, treatment in fire sprinkler systems is relatively new. And although there are several detection and treatment systems that appear to be effective, long-term data to support overall effectiveness claims are still limited. This chapter will provide an overview of the issues related to microbiologically influenced corrosion in the fire protection industry.

For related topics, see the following chapters in Section 16: Chapter 1, "Principles of Automatic Sprinkler System Performance"; Chapter 2, "Automatic Sprinklers"; Chapter 3, "Automatic Sprinkler Systems"; and Chapter 11, "Care and Maintenance of Water-Based Extinguishing Systems."

DEFINING CORROSION

General Corrosion

Generating a universal "working definition" for MIC in fire protection is complex. And to understand the relationship of MIC and sprinkler components, general corrosion and its various causes must first be understood. One edition of *Webster's* defines corrosion as "the wearing away of materials by chemical action(s)." Another edition simply defines it as "the wearing away of material gradually." The online encyclopedia Encarta describes corrosion as "specifically being related to the gradual action of natural agents such as air or salt water on metals." All these definitions are generally true but are also very confusing to those in the fire protection industry who are looking for answers. Even definitions presented by the corrosion engineering communities, though more detailed, can at times appear somewhat contradictory and very confusing.

Bruce H. Clarke is eastern regional manager of field services and a fire protection/loss prevention trainer with Swiss Re Global Asset Protection Services.

Anthony M. Aguilera is director of loss prevention and risk management for Honeywell Aerospace.

Corrosion can occur from many biophysical reactions and be described from a multitude of scientific viewpoints. *General corrosion* typically refers to uniform corrosion that occurs on most unprotected metallic systems. This corrosion can be associated with the uniform rust layer seen on many steel structures. Besides rust from oxidation, several other types of general corrosion include stray current, uniform biological, galvanic, molten salt, dealloying, chemical, high temperature, and general carburization. And some specific nonbiological corrosion processes having adverse effects on fire protection sprinkler systems that must always be considered with MIC include oxygen, acid, and oxygen-acid corrosion.[1]

Microbiologically Influenced Corrosion

In contrast to general, or uniform, corrosion, MIC is a form of localized corrosion. Material is lost at discrete points instead of universally across an entire surface. There are several types of localized corrosion, including pitting, crevice, cratering, and filiform (Figure 15.5.1).

As with the various other types of corrosion, MIC can take many forms and affect different systems in unique ways. But, for the fire protection profession, an industry-specific definition can be developed. This definition captures both the causes and effects of this problem with several continuous generalities to avoid some of the current inaccuracies. Thus, microbiologically influenced corrosion in fire protection systems can be described as "an electrochemical corrosion process that is concentrated and accelerated by the activity of specific bacteria within a fire sprinkler system resulting in the premature failure of metallic system components."[2]

THE CORROSION PROBLEM

Concentrated and Accelerated Corrosion

All metallic systems normally begin to corrode to various degrees from the instant moisture contacts metal, which typically appears as general corrosion. By definition, in comparison, the MIC process is both concentrated and accelerated. With general corrosion, when moisture is introduced into a system, a thin layer of oxidation occurs relatively evenly throughout the pipe wall surface. This type of corrosion is typically not a significant concern in fire sprinkler systems and does not require treatment because it does not change a pipe's interior surface roughness (i.e., C-factor) unevenly. The rate of decay is also typically slow. A typical corrosion rate in sprinkler pipe is highly dependent on water quality, but with MIC, this relatively slow corrosion rate is abnormally accelerated and not evenly dispersed. The result changes a relatively smooth pipe to one with pits and valleys.

$$p = 4.52Q^{1.85}/(c^{1.85}d^{4.87})$$

where

p = Frictional resistance in psi/ft

Q = Flow in gpm

c = Frictional loss coefficient

d = Internal diameter of pipe

Although there has not been a detailed study on exactly what amount of pipe change (or changes in pipe wall roughness) are

FIGURE 15.5.1 Interior Pinhole Leak

unacceptable, the Hazen-Williams formula makes several points clear:

1. Pipe surface texture is critical in sprinkler system effectiveness. With *c* based on pipe wall smoothness, any increase in roughness decreases the value of *c* and thereby increases the pressure loss in each linear foot of sprinkler pipe. Even a small amount of internal corrosion, especially in smaller main feed areas, could potentially make a system less effective in fire control.
2. Pipe diameter is a significant contributor to friction loss. Thus the smaller the pipe, the more dramatically corrosion affects friction loss and overall performance.

Although this formula is not intended to be used for nonuniform pipe surfaces, it is clear that random pockets of biological growth have the potential to affect performance. This result is especially likely if a sprinkler system has a minimum design buffer, which is regularly the case (Figure 15.5.2 and Figure 15.5.3).

MIC is the result of specific bacteria (see section on defining MIC). A multitude of bacteria is always omnipresent in all ecosystems, including the interior of sprinkler systems. Just as only a small number of bacteria on earth have the potential to cause human sickness, only a relatively small number of bacteria have the potential to cause the rapid system destruction currently linked to MIC. Thus, as defined, only a few specific bacteria concentrate and accelerate the general or uniform corrosion process.

Premature Failure

The ultimate effect of MIC in fire protection systems is the premature failure of metallic components.

Premature Failure Defined. It is clear that MIC and other related forms of corrosion cause sprinkler systems to fail prematurely. What constitutes "premature" with regard to the integrity

FIGURE 15.5.2 Exterior View of Pipe with No Signs of Internal Corrosion

FIGURE 15.5.3 Interior View of Pipe Shown in Figure 15.5.2 with Approximately 65% Obstruction to 6 in. Tee Connection

of specific system components has not officially been defined in the industry. Long-term warranties are not typical with system components; however, with proper maintenance a sprinkler system is typically expected by the industry to last over 50 years before major repairs are required. In most cases of MIC, it has appeared that after treatment of the affected areas healthy systems can be expected to exceed this normal life expectancy.

However, as discussed, failure is a function of both integrity and function. And a system without leaks is never considered acceptable if it fails functionally (i.e., in fire control). Any time a system is in service and fails to operate as designed, it has experienced an unacceptable premature failure.

Forms of Premature Failure. Premature failure can take two forms, both requiring individual consideration. First is the failure of a system to hold water, in other words, pinhole leaks that require component replacement (Figure 15.5.4). Leaks can cause significant damage and require immediate action. Leaks can also lead to excessive direct and indirect costs, as well as inherent risks from repeated system impairments.

In one known case, MIC-related leaks resulted in the shutdown of an aerospace manufacturer's global computing center.[3] A pinhole leak developed in a wet pipe sprinkler branch line located over the mainframe equipment of the computing center. Water from the leak not only damaged computing equipment but also resulted in over 5000 hours of lost operations time. Property damage from similar leaks at other sites has also been documented in the millions of dollars.[3,4]

The second and more concerning effect is the failure of a system to operate as designed to achieve fire control. This failure not only affects property loss but also could threaten lives. Several systems with MIC have been found with obstructed sprinkler drops, the result of debris generated as a by-product of microbial activity (called biofilm or biosludge). Many in the industry have found systems with feed mains over 60 percent obstructed from biological growth.[4,5] An analysis of corrosion

FIGURE 15.5.4 Exterior Pinhole

buildup indicates that thousands of pounds of debris can accumulate in medium-sized piping.[6] This buildup of debris presents an obvious hydraulic concern as many affected sprinkler systems today will not provide fire control as the required discharge criteria, in terms of flow and pressure, are not available due to obstruction and associated frictional pressure loss.

Extent of MIC in the Sprinkler Industry

Currently only a limited number of credible national studies on the extent of the MIC problem in the fire protection industry exist. Most data are primarily anecdotal. No detailed comparative engineering-based study on effectiveness of the various treatment options currently being marketed has been completed. Complicating this lack of data, reported MIC cases rarely have secondary analysis to differentiate MIC as a primary contributing cause over other types of corrosion involving similar symptoms. Equally important, follow-up engineering data on treatment are rarely published.

The results of MIC in other industries are well documented. The Energy and Power Research Institute has estimated that corrosion in the U.S. electric power industry costs $5 billion to $10 billion each year. Corrosion is said to be the culprit in half the forced outages each year in steam generating plants.[7] And data collected from before the 2001 U.S. power shortage showed corrosion to be the primary factor in more than 10 percent of U.S. power generation costs.[7] In the gas and nuclear industries, MIC is specifically said to account for 15 to 30 percent of corrosion-related failures.[8] And reports indicate that to prevent such problems, North American companies spend in excess of $1.5 billion per year (over $7 billion globally) on treatment chemicals to prevent microbial corrosion and fouling. Similar information, as mentioned, is not available for the fire protection industry. Although several industry groups have been attempting to compile data on this problem for several years, only two national studies have been published for the fire protection industry.[9,10] Thus, the true extent and cost of the problem are still not fully known.

In 1996, the National Fire Sprinkler Association sent out a questionnaire in its quarterly membership magazine requesting member information on sprinkler system failures that have been experienced. Results yielded approximately 40 responses from across the United States and Canada, which appeared to indicate that MIC was a "widespread problem." However, due to the reasons previously stated, the quality of analytical techniques used by respondents to confirm MIC as a cause and the lack of investigation after detection and treatment bring the results of this study into question.

The only other related studies and data compilations completed have been conducted by FM Global. In its studies, in losses involving sprinkler systems, corrosion is the fifth leading cause of system failures. This conclusion is based on a review of data from 1988 to 1997. In another study by the FM Metallurgical Laboratory between 1994 and 2000 reviewing 155 cases of sprinkler system leaks, MIC was found to be present in approximately 40 percent of cases. Details on whether the presence of MIC directly caused leaks were not indicated in all these cases.[10] In another FM study of piping field samples between 1991 and 2002, over 60 percent of these failures are attributed to MIC.[11]

Pinning the Blame

Part of the problem in obtaining detailed conclusive evidence is the complexity and cost of such investigations. This problem is also a major point of frustration with owners experiencing these types of problems. Due to the nature of electrochemical corrosion, most corrosion engineers agree that the degree to which

MIC specifically increases or contributes to general corrosion can never be conclusively determined. In fact, the complex biological interactions between bacteria and host materials are still not fully understood in many cases. There are simply too many variables and uncertainties that affect all corrosion reactions, especially those involving bacterial interactions. Thus, a percentage of blame or rate of corrosion from MIC likely cannot be numerically defined in any study. Any database generated at this point will likely list only reported cases, not confirmed cases. Thus, the best that can be achieved in the future is a regularly updated database indicating where reported cases are occurring, method of failure detection, interior condition of pipe, methods of testing, and treatment with future corrosion monitoring.

Materials Affected by MIC

Although steel sprinkler pipe is the typically observed first point of failure, sprinkler orifice caps, control valves, fittings, and supply tanks may also be subject to damage from MIC. Numerous cases of obstructive growth and pinhole leaks associated with MIC have been found within 20 feet of the discharge side of site fire pumps—an interesting phenomenon due to the velocity of waterflow at this point in the system piping. Although evidence suggests that only metallic components are susceptible to MIC, it is clear that some grades and alloys of steel are definitely more susceptible than others. As an example, certain grades of stainless steel are more susceptible than regular steel pipe, whereas others appear to show signs of resistivity. And although plastic components, such as underground water mains, are not subject to direct MIC, they are subject to the effects of biofouling or bacterial debris blockage from upstream corrosion activity.

DEFINING MIC

Oxygen Tolerance

MIC-related bacteria are classified primarily by oxygen tolerance; that is, they are aerobic or anaerobic. Aerobic bacteria require oxygen to flourish and reproduce. Anaerobic bacteria do not require oxygen to flourish and reproduce.[9] The most damaging MIC appears to take place within a highly complex community with multiple species of bacteria. This community includes not only aerobic and anaerobic bacteria but also facultative bacteria, those MIC bacteria that function in both aerobic and anaerobic environments. All three types of bacteria can play a role in the somewhat random interactions that can occur in microbiologically influenced corrosion.[12]

Metabolism

In defining MIC bacteria further, classification is not absolute and can become confusing. The most commonly used method of categorizing bacteria associated with MIC is by metabolism. These categories are basically definitions of what each bacteria type eats (or metabolizes) and excretes as a by-product. As these terms imply, where plants use photosynthesis (i.e., light) to develop energy, bacteria use chemosynthesis (i.e., eating/breathing various chemicals or minerals) to sustain life. Metabolic classifications are not universally replicated among scientists and can be somewhat confusing. A single bacteria type may fall under more than one metabolic definition. Some of the commonly referenced categories include sulfur-reducing bacteria, metal-reducing bacteria, acid-producing bacteria, iron-depositing bacteria, low-nutrient bacteria, iron-related bacteria, iron-reducing bacteria, iron-oxidizing bacteria, sulfate-oxidizing bacteria, slime-forming bacteria, and iron bacteria.[9,12–14]

Scientific Nomenclature

Finally, all bacteria (i.e., all plants and animals) can be classified by their scientific name under phylum, class, order, family, genus, and species. For example, one type of sulfate-reducing bacteria is anaerobic and metabolizes sulfate to sulfide. The sulfate-reducing bacteria group includes the genera *Desulfovibrio, Desulfobacter,* and *Desulformaculum.*[2] All are of the phylum Thiopneutes, which interestingly translates from Greek to "sulfur-breathers."

SOURCES OF MIC INFECTION

Although there are no conclusive relational studies in the fire protection industry, as noted there are growing beliefs that a sprinkler system's water supply is not the only (and possibly primary) source of bacterial infection. Bacteria capable of causing MIC are potentially present in soil, air, and cutting oils as well as water. Thus, the manufacture, shipping, storage, and flushing of system materials should be addressed in all MIC investigations. MIC does not occur only in water-filled systems. Dry pipe systems are also susceptible. Dry systems may even be more susceptible to damage than are wet systems, due to the humidified atmosphere that is created after trip testing. A trip test and subsequent drain can create the right atmospheric moisture content for some bacterial colonies to thrive. Complete drainage and the subsequent use of truly dried air or nitrogen gas appear to mitigate this problem. With regard to tubercle growth alone, dissolved oxygen content, not bacteria, may be the only considerable factor in prevention.

MIC CORROSION PROCESS

As with other forms of corrosion, MIC removes material through a series of electrochemical interactions. As such, both an electrical component and a chemical component occur with MIC. The electrical component occurs through electron transfer. Electron transfer removes pipe wall material one electron at a time. With MIC, this exact interaction is highly dependent on the specific bacteria involved. Within a sprinkler system, metallic parts become anodic in relation to the cathodic corrosion cell and surrounding water. Basic cathodic depolarization occurs as electrons are stripped away through various forms of oxidation and are pulled to an atom with another electrical potential. Although many of the complex cellular interactions of bacteria are still unclear and can vary by system, there appear to be several somewhat universal steps in the MIC process. They are as follows:[2]

1. Bacteria enter the system, attach to metallic components, and begin to rapidly colonize and reproduce.
2. Aerobic colonies metabolize nutrients from the water and/or the metal surfaces they are attached to and, subsequently, excrete a polymer film by-product that bonds together to form crustaceous nodules called tubercles.
3. Tubercles and associated biofilms create microenvironments on the metallic material surface (under the tubercles). Tubercles are hard protective shells formed by biological activity. Tubercles typically have an open interior fluid cavity over the corrosion floor area with an approximate 3–4 pH (Figure 15.5.5).
4. The underdeposit area (i.e., under the tubercles) becomes oxygen depleted (i.e., anaerobic and anodic) in relation to the surrounding system's water or air, which remains aerobic and cathodic. Thus, electrons in the anodic metal flow to the cathode through a reduction reaction.
5. Underdeposit anaerobic bacteria metabolize pipe wall materials and excrete acids (such as acetic acid) as by-products, which are very aggressive to the carbon steels used in sprinkler piping. Relative acidity and alkalinity levels within the tubercle shells are reduced to an approximate pH of 2–4, which chemically attack the metallic component surface. On painted sprinkler piping, it is common to observe blisters where through-wall penetration has occurred. Testing of the fluid within these blisters has shown a pH of less than 3.

The described corrosion process can continue indefinitely until the aerobic and anaerobic bacteria in the system are killed. The tubercles created from bacterial colonization must also be broken down to destroy the underdeposit microenvironment. Even without bacteria in the underdeposit of a corrosion cell, the process can continue indefinitely, as the corrosion chain in its final phases is no longer reliant on their activity.

PREVENTION AND TREATMENT

References from Allied Fields

Currently, the fire protection industry has a very limited number of directly usable references supported by scientific data. However, there is excellent information on data from other industries. The National Association of Corrosion Engineers (NACE) has published multiple studies about MIC detection and treatment for many years. The American Society for Testing and Materials (ASTM) offers several publications on proper bacterial testing practices. Also the American Water Works Association (AWWA) offers standards describing the proper management of the somewhat hazardous chemicals typically used in injection devices attached to sprinkler systems for microbial control.

Fire Protection Codes and Standards

The National Fire Protection Association (NFPA) also addresses MIC. NFPA 25, *Standard for the Inspection, Testing, and Maintenance of Water-Based Fire Protection Systems,* discusses MIC treatment, inspection, and detection in some detail. NFPA 13,

FIGURE 15.5.5 Interior Tubercle

Standard for the Installation of Sprinkler Systems, contains a requirement that provides more guidance. In covering water supply treatment, NFPA 13 states:

> Water supplies and environmental conditions shall be evaluated for the existence of microbes and conditions that contribute to microbiologically influenced corrosion (MIC). Where conditions are found that contribute to MIC, the owner(s) shall notify the sprinkler system installer and a plan shall be developed to treat the system. . . .

Although this requirement has generated curiosity, the resulting questions about effective treatment remain. NPFA 13 indicates that water supplies "shall be evaluated for the existence of microbes and conditions that contribute to microbiologically influenced corrosion (MIC)" . . . and if present or suspected . . . "a plan shall be developed to treat the system." The who, how, and when are still in debate by those addressing this issue. Who is best qualified to make the determination of when a failure is the result of MIC and if a biocidal treatment program will prevent all future failures? And how is a system best tested (i.e., with the most technical accuracy and cost-effectiveness) to confirm MIC? Almost anything requiring laboratory work can be overtested. And undertesting can lead to a false sense of security. Answers to these questions are still evolving.

Operational Considerations

As the industry continues to develop methods to treat and prevent MIC, building owners are faced with the challenge of managing associated risks to their assets and business operations. At-risk businesses should review the interdependence of various operations to identify critical locations.

Proper Diagnosis

The analysis required to properly select a course of action to address MIC is typically outside the scope of most sprinkler contractors and engineers. Thus, until treatment methods become universally proven and standardized, the most critical step in proper mitigation begins with the selection of a qualified corrosion control consultant.

With the wrong choice, a large amount of money can be spent on a problem that may not be correctable. A poor treatment choice could actually accelerate the corrosion rate and increase the affected area beyond that experienced before treatment. The company chosen to determine treatment must have detailed knowledge not only of microbial corrosion control but also of metallurgy and sprinkler system dynamics. Fire sprinkler systems have flow characteristics and concerns that are much different from other industrial processes and systems where MIC is typically addressed.

Specific Considerations for Fire Sprinkler Systems

Other industries deal with MIC in systems containing fluids that are either always static or always flowing, such as in cooling towers. Unlike sprinkler systems, dynamic systems have flow rates that are relatively constant, requiring that prescribed chemical dose rates be constant. A constant flow rate does not occur in sprinkler systems. Variable differences are seen with system drains and refills, inspector testing, and main drain tests. The dose rate for each of these flows must be considered to ensure that the chemical injection rate is always effective. Other industrial systems also have multiple points where biocidal chemicals can be injected. In contrast, sprinkler system water can realistically only be treated at system risers, backflow apparatus, or suction tanks.

Finally, it must again be stated that it is critical to understand that premature system failure can be a function of both bacterial infection and water quality that is incompatible with components. In the majority of premature system failure cases, water chemistry or poor design may be the only likely factors requiring consideration. A high bacterial count does not always indicate that MIC will occur, and conversely, a low bacterial count does not discount that MIC has occurred in the past, in a given system, and will not occur again in the near future.

Detection in Existing Systems

In existing systems suspected of being infected, the first step is to have all possible water supply sources (tank, city mains, ponds, rivers, etc.) and the interior of each system tested for bacterial levels and activity. Although current technology makes this detection easy, analysis of the results is somewhat complex. And, as previously stated, in determining treatment, bacterial detection is worthless without factoring in water quality. The laboratory used for analysis should be capable of giving conclusive details of water supply mineral and chemical levels, pipe wall deposit compositions, and type-specific bacterial counts. Multiple tests are used in these analyses from simple bacterial incubation with visual inspection to sulfur print or DNA testing. Obviously, not all tests are required or are necessarily needed. Current preferred analysis methods run the spectrum, depending on the consultant chosen. Costs for such testing can also vary widely.

Mitigation in Affected Systems

When MIC is confirmed in operational systems, the building owner is first faced with a fundamental question. Can the system be salvaged (i.e., cleaned) or does it have to be replaced? Currently, this cost/benefit decision requires further study and is not supported one way or the other by documented best practices in the fire protection industry.

Pipe cleaning is typically an option when corrosion (i.e., pitting) is not excessive. However, *excessive* is a relative term. The after-cleaning quality of the pipe must be considered, both for future longevity and system hydraulics. The resulting frictional loss from numerous pits after cleaning could affect system performance. This result, of course, is typically outside the scope of work of most corrosion control consultants. When replacement materials are chosen that are different than those of the original system, they must also be accounted for in hydraulic analysis of the posttreated system. Case studies suggest that pipe cleaning may remove corrosion by-products that are, in effect, stopping the flow of water through existing pipe penetrations, subsequently resulting in leaks.[12] Prudence dictates that complete mitigation must include some form of treatment once pipes are cleaned.

Prevention in New Systems

In new systems, it is critical that susceptibility be determined before any systems are filled or tested with any water. If water tests are positive for MIC-related bacteria, a chemical injection system must be installed and used from the first fill. This includes hydrostatic testing and preliminary fills. The treatment methodology must also consider that water delivery of treatment chemicals might not effectively treat high spots, remote areas, or areas that trap air within the system.

If MIC is anticipated, one form of risk reduction may be to specify thicker piping in the design. Although this option only tends to buy time, it may serve as a prudent measure until universally accepted treatment methods are developed. Thicker walls buy time, not because they are less susceptible to MIC—a point on which evidence to date is inconclusive—but simply because a thicker wall has more material to corrode before a through-wall leak develops.

Another possibility in design is to remove the risk of leaks before MIC treatment is even evaluated. Areas such as those occupied by critical energized equipment can often be addressed by removing overhead sprinkler piping and limiting leak exposure through use of sidewall sprinkler coverage. Where it is not feasible to relocate large feed mains, piping can be sleeved so as not to permit potential leaks to contact energized equipment. Although these efforts provide some measure of immediate relief, they do not address the root cause or present a long-term solution to the problem.

Finally, the frequency of sprinkler and waterflow device testing must be addressed. Most agree that repeated draining and refilling of sprinkler systems can increase both biological and nonbiological forms of corrosion. Draining and refilling provide nutrients and oxygen to bacterial colonies and oxygen for general tuberculation. Some facilities have noted substantial reductions in the frequency of leaks by reducing the frequency of drain and alarm testing.

It is critical to note that once a system is filled with infected water, treatment can become exponentially more complex because any future treatment from a chemical injection system must now be effective in remote and stagnant system legs. In bacteria-positive areas, several additional water quality tests should be completed throughout the first year of service to ensure that contamination has not occurred from any other sources.

Chemical Injection

Once system components have been cleaned and sterilized or replaced, a chemical injection system must be installed to prevent recurrence. Once installed, this system will be required to be operational continuously. As with any other mechanical system, this system will require continuous preventive maintenance.

Several commercially available chemical injection systems have been specifically designed for installation on fire protection systems. Some simply use existing hardware and chemicals modified from MIC treatment in other utilities, such as cooling towers. At the time of this writing, none of the systems currently available were believed to be specifically listed or approved for use as a sprinkler system component. Although most systems appear to be effective when properly installed and maintained, reliability and effectiveness have not been time-proven when compared with other industrial system benchmarks. Past references should always be investigated with any choice.

Most injection systems currently available are designed to work with specific chemicals. These selected chemicals and dose rates are critical. Some bacteria can develop chemical resistance over time if doses are not strong enough and bacteria are not quickly killed. A small number of bacteria believed to be related to MIC (such as the genera *Bacillus* and *Clostridium*) are known to have the ability to convert to a spore state when they encounter adverse conditions that are not lethal.[2,15] Spores are impervious to penetration by most chemicals and can thus survive biocide treatments indefinitely. Although subsequent treatments may slow or stop their activity, spores will reappear if and when treatments are stopped and resume colonization. With a weak chemical attack, bacteria may also become resistant to the chemicals chosen.

As with other factors involved in treatment, the choice of chemical depends on the consultant. These chemicals generally include penetrants and biodispersants to break up the tubercles that protect underdeposit colonies, a biocide to kill the bacteria in the colonies, and a corrosion inhibitor to protect the interior surfaces of the system.

When such a system is chosen, the applicable authority having jurisdiction (AHJ) should be consulted. In addition to frictional loss concerns mentioned from changes in pipe surface roughness, increased backflow prevention hardware may be required. This could mean a pressure drop of 10 psi (0.7 bar) or more to sprinkler systems in addition to that created by pitting if cleaning is chosen. In new system designs, added alarm system contacts should also be planned to monitor injection system chemical levels, operational status, and trouble conditions such as loss of power. Many pre-engineered systems provide contact points for these signals. As with fire detection, the perceived "best choice" is at the discretion of the person choosing, and opinions on this subject are highly variable.

Unlike other industrial systems treated for MIC, several unique interactions must be considered. First, sprinkler systems are typically located directly over people. The chemicals used must therefore be nontoxic in contemplation of accidental discharge or exposure to fire fighters under fire conditions. The effect of chosen chemicals on fire fighting (i.e., heat absorption) and chemical reaction with fire (i.e., heat) also needs consideration. Second, system designs typically place water discharge (such as from an inspector's test ports) into foliage or biologically sensitive drains and dry wells. Most municipal wastewater treatment plants (to which typical drains ultimately flow) require bacterial activity to decompose waste. Too large a quantity of biocides in municipal drains could be a problem.

In conclusion, a complete toxicity review with the highest possible biocidal chemical concentration must be completed. As much as possible, these chemicals should be noncombustible, colorless, odorless, and nontoxic. These chemicals must also be nondeteriorating to rubbers and polymers such as those used on pipe couplings, sprinkler O-rings, and valves. Chemical storage should also be reviewed, as several chemicals currently in use degrade rapidly with heat and may create relatively toxic vapors.

Opinions of which chemicals are believed to be "most effective" in control vary. Choices are available from those currently used for treatment in cooling towers and boilers to specifically patented compounds for fire protection systems. Some of the more common chemicals currently in use specifically for microbial control in sprinkler systems include quaternary ammonium compounds, organosulfur compounds, bromines, carbamates, isothiazalone, phosphates, and chlorines. Sodium silicate is effectively used in bulk quantities by several municipalities as an inhibitor, but this use should be avoided for individual systems due to the potential for sprinkler plugging that overdosing can cause. At the writing of this article, no chemical can conclusively be said to be proven as the most effective. The chemical choice may greatly depend on the bacteria present and system water quality.

SUMMARY

Current testing and treatment options can be confusing. Treatment is slowly evolving and research is continuing. Several industry groups, allied groups, and insurance companies are looking at the problem and applicable solutions. Many universities, governments, and private industry groups also continue to research microbial control in general industry, as they have for the past several decades. These efforts will continue to provide improved treatment options in our industry.

As the need to address this problem draws on the industry's creativity for resolution, prudent thinking requires us to evaluate each solution's impact on overall sprinkler system integrity and performance. In light of this problem, the overwhelming value of sprinkler systems should not be regarded as tarnished or tainted. Although some with repeated MIC problems may view sprinklers as a risk to property, the reduction of risk to life and property from fire these systems provide should never be overshadowed.

BIBLIOGRAPHY

References Cited

1. Christ, B. W., "Corrosion Process Inside Steel Fire Sprinkler Piping," *Fire Protection Engineering,* Summer 2005.
2. Clarke, B., "Microbiologically Influenced Corrosion in Fire Protection Systems," *Fire Protection Engineering,* Society of Fire Protection Engineers, No. 9, Winter 2001, pp. 14–16.
3. Cappers, M. A., "Investigation of Microbiological Influenced Corrosion in Sprinkler Systems," *Proceedings* of Fire Suppression and Detection Research Application Symposium, Research and Practice: Bridging the Gap, February 12–14, 1997, Orlando, FL, National Fire Protection Research Foundation, Quincy, MA, 1997, pp. 69–81.
4. Kammen, J., "Bacteria Spell Doom for Fire Sprinklers," *The Arizona Republic,* October 24, 1999.
5. Shenkiryk, M., "Pipe-Klean Project—McCarran Airport," *HERC Products,* July 25, 1996.
6. Duncan, B., "Pipe Corrosion and Its Growing Threat to Office Building and Plant Operations," *Corrosioneering Journal,* July 2002.
7. Hoffman, S., *Bugging Water Systems for Corrosion Control,* Hoffman Publications, Morgan Hill, CA, 1999.
8. "The Mitigation and Detection of Microbial Corrosion," Argonne National Laboratory, *Programs and Capabilities Database No. 526-002,* 1999.
9. Bsharat, T. K., "Detection, Treatment, and Prevention of Microbiologically Influenced Corrosion in Water Based Fire Protection Systems," National Fire Sprinkler Association, Patterson, NY, June 1998.
10. FM Global Property Loss Prevention Data Sheet 2-1, *Internal Corrosion in Automatic Sprinkler Systems,* Factory Mutual Insurance Company, Johnston, RI, 2001.
11. Yee, G. G., "Detection and Diagnostic Studies of MIC in Fire Protection Systems," 2005 NFPA World Safety Conference and Exposition, June 9, 2005.
12. Little, B. J., Ray, R. I., and Wagner, P. A., "Tame Microbiologically Influenced Corrosion," *Chemical Engineering Progress,* September 1998.
13. Borenstein, S. W., *Microbiologically Influenced Corrosion Handbook,* Woodhead Publications Ltd., Cambridge, UK, 1994.
14. Pope, D. H., Duquette, D. J., Johannes, A. H., and Wayner, P. C., "Microbiologically Influenced Corrosion of Industrial Alloys," *Materials Performance,* Vol. 23, No. 4, July 1984.
15. Hero, H. M., *The Nalco Guide to Cooling Water System Failure Analysis,* McGraw-Hill, New York, 1993.

NFPA Codes, Standards, and Recommended Practices

Reference to the following NFPA codes, standards, and recommended practices will provide further information on microbiologically induced corrosion in fire sprinkler systems discussed in this chapter. (See the latest version of The NFPA Catalog *for availability of current editions of the following documents.)*

NFPA 13, *Standard for the Installation of Sprinkler Systems*
NFPA 25, *Standard for the Inspection, Testing, and Maintenance of Water-Based Fire Protection Systems*

Chapter 6

Water Distribution

John D. Jensen

This chapter covers the operating principles of stationary pumps used for fire protection, the methods of driving them, and the testing and maintenance procedures that should be followed to keep them in top operating condition.

Fire pumps are used to increase the water supply pressure available from public mains, gravity tanks, reservoirs, or other sources. The first modern fire pumps were the wheel-and-crank reciprocating-type, belt-driven pumps from mill machinery. If plant operations were stopped during a fire, the pump could not operate. At best, these pumps were inadequate.

Better water supplies became necessary as automatic sprinkler systems became more common, and mill pumps were replaced by rotary, or displacement, pumps driven by friction drive from horizontal waterwheels supplying power to the plant. As steam supplanted waterpower, the reciprocating steam pump was adopted for fire protection. For many years the Underwriter duplex, double-acting, direct-steam-driven unit was universally accepted as the "standard" fire pump.

Today, the stationary centrifugal and positive displacement fire pump is standard (Figures 15.6.1 and 15.6.2). Its compactness, reliability, easy maintenance and hydraulic characteristics, and the variety of available drivers—electric motors, steam turbines, and diesel engines—have made the Underwriter pump obsolete, although not entirely extinct.

Although the centrifugal fire pump is most widely used and is the basis for this chapter, the positive displacement fire pump is briefly defined and described.

The NFPA standard on fire pumps is NFPA 20, *Standard for the Installation of Stationary Pumps for Fire Protection* (hereinafter referred to NFPA 20). Other NFPA documents that contain information on fire pumps include NFPA 11, *Standard for Low-, Medium-, and High-Expansion Foam;* NFPA 13, *Standard for the Installation of Sprinkler Systems;* NFPA 14, *Standard for the Installation of Standpipe and Hose Systems;* NFPA 15, *Standard for Water Spray Fixed Systems for Fire Protection;* NFPA 16, *Standard for the Installation of Foam-Water Sprinkler and Foam-Water Spray Systems;* NFPA 22, *Standard for Water Tanks for Private Fire Protection;* NFPA 25, *Standard for the Inspection, Testing, and Maintenance of Water-Based Fire Protection Systems* (hereinafter referred to as NFPA 25); and NFPA 750, *Standard on Water Mist Fire Protection Systems.*

For related topics, see Section 15, Chapter 7, "Fire Pump Controllers and Power Supply Arrangments for Motor-Driven Fire Pumps."

Chapter Contents

Key Terms

affinity law, cavitation, discharge specific speed (N_d), fire pump (centrifugal), fire pump controller, fire pump (positive displacement), impeller, net positive suction head (available), net positive suction head (pump), total head (*H*), water hammer

CENTRIFUGAL FIRE PUMP

An outstanding feature of a horizontal or vertical centrifugal pump is the relation of discharge to pressure at constant speed; that is, when the pressure head is increased, the discharge is reduced. With positive displacement pumps, the rated capacity can be maintained against any head if the power is adequate to operate the pump at the rated speed and if the pump, fittings, and piping can withstand the pressure.

Listed horizontal and vertical fire pumps are available with rated capacities from 25 to 5000 gpm (95 to 18 925 L/min). Pressure ratings range from 40 to 394 psi (276 to 2758 kPa) for horizontal pumps and 26 to 510 psi (517 to 3448 kPa) for vertical turbine pumps. Listed centrifugal fire pump designs include horizontal-end-suction, vertical in-line, split-case (horizontal and vertical shaft),

John D. Jensen, P.E., is president of JFP Engineering PC in Centerville, Utah. He is chair of NFPA's Technical Committee on the Installation of Stationary Pumps for Fire Protection.

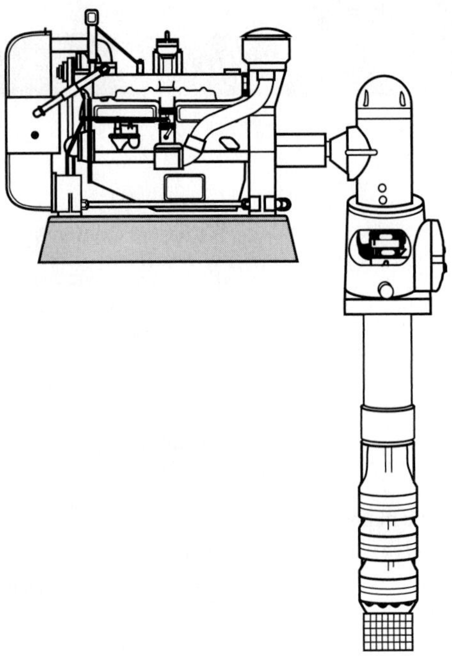

FIGURE 15.6.1 Vertical Turbine Fire Pump with a Right-Angle Gear and Engine Drive

and vertical-turbine types. Vertical turbine pumps are centrifugal pumps with one or more impellers discharging into one or more bowls and a vertical educator or column pipe that connects the bowls to the discharge head on which the pump driver may be mounted. It is anticipated that larger-capacity fire pumps will be listed in the future (Table 15.6.1).

The "size" of a horizontal centrifugal pump is generally the diameter of the discharge outlet. However, it is sometimes indicated by both suction and discharge pipe flange diameters. The size of a vertical turbine pump is the diameter of the pump bowl (see Figure 15.6.1).

POSITIVE DISPLACEMENT FIRE PUMP

Positive displacement fire pumps have been used in fire protection for many years. In fact, they were the first pump type to be used for mobile fire truck applications. Positive displacement pumps by nature are capable of high discharge pressures, something the fire service requires for many types of fire fighting.

Positive displacement, as defined by the Hydraulic Institute, essentially means that the same volume of liquid is displaced per revolution of the pumping element or rotor. Many different styles of positive displacement pumps exist; however, this short synopsis is not meant to define the wide variety of positive displacement pumps. Rather, it is intended to advise the fire protection professional that positive displacement pumps are vastly different from the more familiar centrifugal pumps.

Positive displacement pumps in general operate at lower revolutions per minute than centrifugal pumps do, can generate very high discharge pressures, and are capable of pumping a wide variety of fluids, both thin and thick.

Starting in the 1960s, gear pumps have been used to pump foam concentrate agents both on fire truck and fixed foam systems for stationary uses such as aircraft hangars, flammable liquid storage tank fire protection, and refinery process units.

Centrifugal pumps are not well suited to pumping foam concentrates because centrifugal pumps do not offer the necessary slower operating speeds, low foam agitation and shear, self-priming vapor locking, and other critical features that positive displacement pumps offer.

NFPA 20 recognizes that positive displacement pumps are suited for foam concentrate and the low-flow/high-pressure requirements of water mist systems. The 1999 edition of NFPA 20 was expanded to include an entire chapter on positive displacement pumps. Adding that chapter was necessary because of the increasing application of these types of pumps in the fire protection industry and their suitability for foam and water mist systems. The chapter has specific language that guides users and design engineers on selecting and applying a positive displacement pump for both foam and water service.

A key part of this chapter in NFPA 20 is the requirement for the positive displacement pump to be listed or approved for the intended service, meaning that the positive displacement pump must have a third-party listing and verification of performance standards whether the pump is used for foam or water service.

PRINCIPLES OF OPERATION

The two major components of a centrifugal pump are a disc, called the impeller, and the casing in which it rotates (Figure 15.6.3). It operates by converting kinetic energy to velocity and pressure energy. Power from the driver, which is an electric motor, a diesel engine, or a steam turbine, is transmitted to the pump through the shaft, rotating the impeller at high speed. The way that energy is converted varies with the type of pump. The major classes are known as radial flow and mixed flow. These pumps are identified by the direction of flow through the impeller, with reference to the axis of rotation (Figure 15.6.4).

The horizontal-shaft, single-stage, double-suction volute pump is the type most commonly applied to fire protection service and to commercial use (Figure 15.6.5). In these pumps, waterflow from the suction inlet in the casing divides and enters the impeller from each side through an opening called the "eye." Rotation of the impeller drives the water by centrifugal force from the eye to the rim and through the casing volute to the pump discharge outlet. The kinetic energy acquired by the water in its passage through the impeller is converted to pressure energy by gradual reduction of velocity in the volute.

Multistage Pumps

In order to give high pressure, two or more impellers and casings can be assembled on one shaft as a single unit, forming a multistage pump (see Figure 15.6.2). The discharge from the first stage enters the suction of the second stage, discharge from the second stage enters the suction of the third, and so on. The pump capacity is the rating in gal per min (L/min) of one stage; the pressure rating is the sum of the pressure ratings of the individual stages, minus a small head loss.

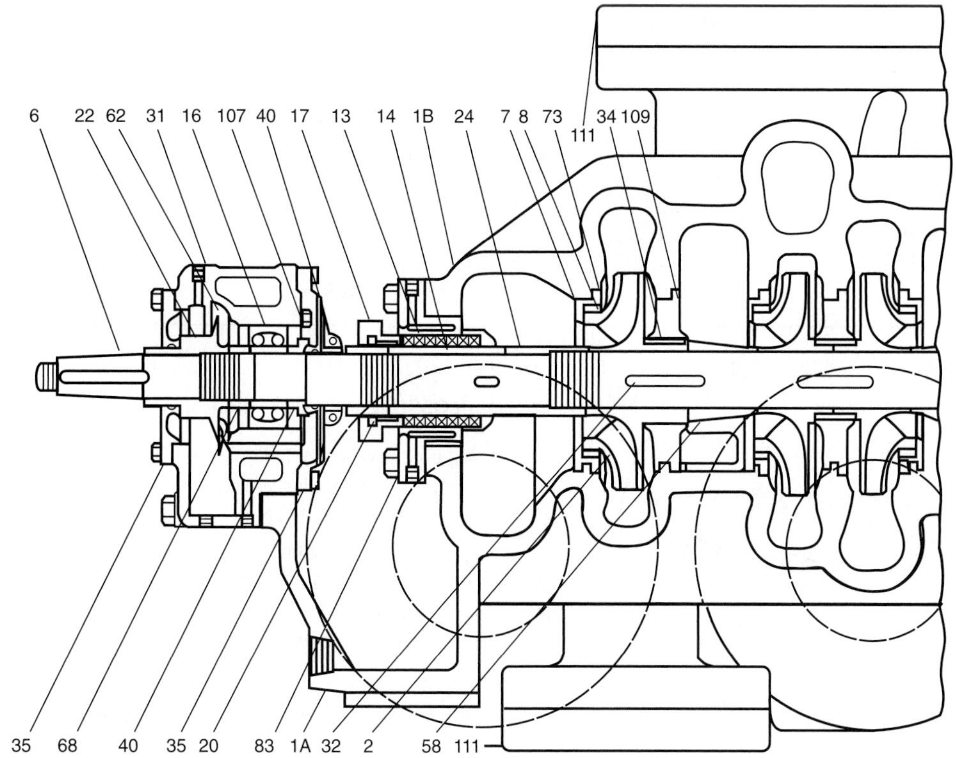

1A Casing, lower half
1B Casing, upper half
2 Impeller
5 Diffuser
6 Shaft, pump
7 Ring, casing
8 Ring, impeller
13 Packing
14 Sleeve, shaft
16 Bearing, inboard
17 Gland
18 Bearing, outboard
20 Nut, shaft sleeve
22 Locknut, bearing
24 Nut, impeller
31 Housing, bearing, inboard
32 Key, impeller
33 Housing, bearing, outboard
34 Sleeve, impeller hub
35 Cover, bearing, inboard
37 Cover, bearing, outboard
40 Deflector
45 Cover, oil, bearing cap
56 Disc or drum, balancing
58 Sleeve, Interstage
62 Thrower (oil or grease)
63 Bushing, stuffing box
68 Collar, shaft
72 Collar, thrust
73 Gasket
83 Stuffing box
107 Shield, oil retaining
109 Diaphragm, interstage
111 Crossover, interstage
113 Bushing, interstage diaphragm
115 Ring, balancing
117 Bushing, pressure reducing
119 Coupling, oil pump
121 Pump, oil

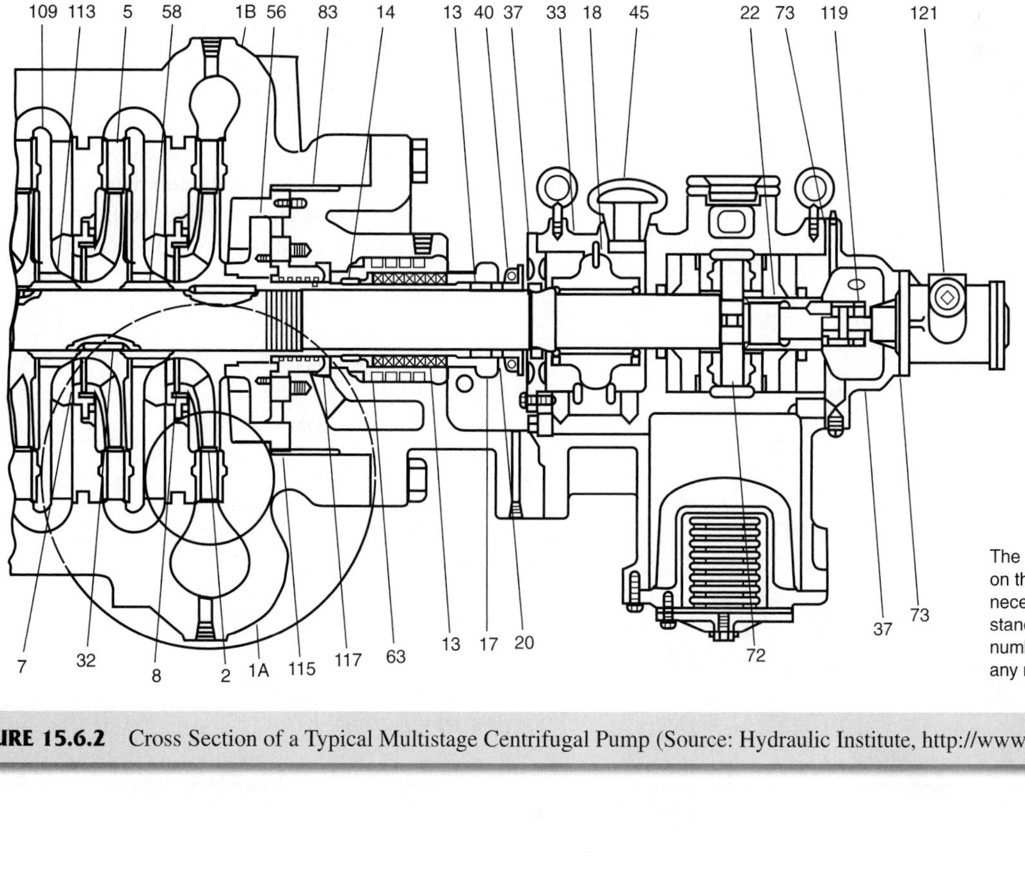

The numbers shown on this drawing do not necessarily represent standard part numbers in use by any manufacturer.

FIGURE 15.6.2 Cross Section of a Typical Multistage Centrifugal Pump (Source: Hydraulic Institute, http://www.pumps.org)

TABLE 15.6.1 Pump Types and Their Pressure and Capacity Ranges

	Pressure Range		Capacity Range	
Pump Type	*psi*	*kPa*	*gpm*	*L/sec*
Horizontal-end-suction	40–186	276–1282	25–750	1.6–31.5
Suction in-line	40–186	276–1282	25–750	1.6–31.5
Split case (horizontal and vertical)	40–294	276–2027	150–5000	9.5–315.4
Vertical turbine	25–510	179–3516	250–5000	15.8–315.4

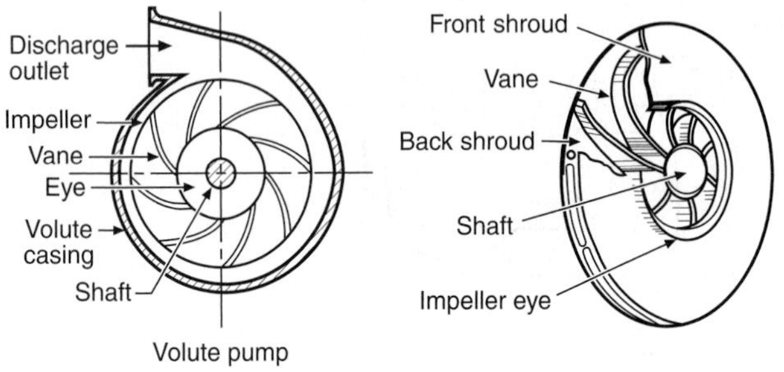

FIGURE 15.6.3 Volute Casing and Impeller

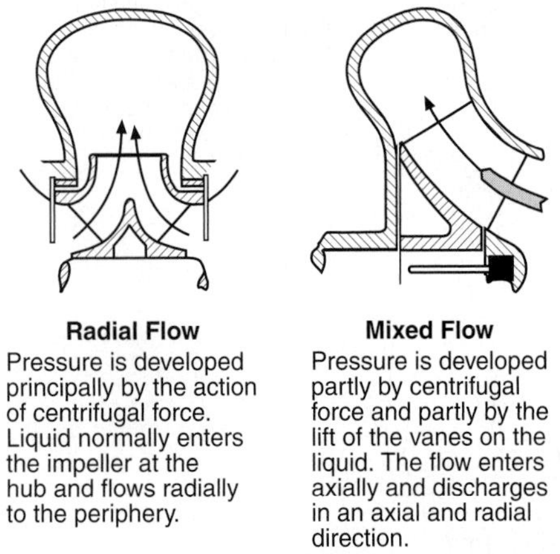
Radial Flow
Pressure is developed principally by the action of centrifugal force. Liquid normally enters the impeller at the hub and flows radially to the periphery.
Mixed Flow
Pressure is developed partly by centrifugal force and partly by the lift of the vanes on the liquid. The flow enters axially and discharges in an axial and radial direction.

FIGURE 15.6.4 Two Major Types of Fire Pumps

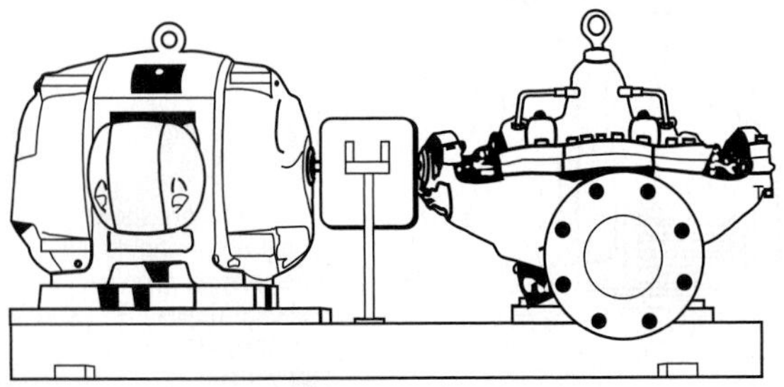

FIGURE 15.6.5 Horizontal Shaft, Single-Stage Centrifugal Pump, with Cutaway View of the Pump

High-Pressure Service Pumps

Single-stage pumps can be designed for high-pressure service by increasing the impeller diameter or the rated speed. In addition, single-stage pumps can also be installed in series to achieve the necessary pressure. In some high-rise buildings, vertical turbine pumps are installed in a subbasement and take suction from a sump pit. As shown in Table 15.6.1, these pumps are capable of developing pressures in excess of 500 psi (3448 kPa).

CHARACTERISTIC PUMP CURVES

The characteristic curves (Figure 15.6.6) of a horizontal-, centrifugal-, or vertical-turbine-type pump are as follows:

1. Total head versus discharge (ft of head or psi of pressure versus gpm)
2. Brake horsepower versus discharge
3. Efficiency versus discharge (water hp/input hp versus gpm)

Illustrated curves in Figure 15.6.6 are for a 500-gpm, 100-psi, 2000-rpm, diesel-engine-drive pump with a 14 in. impeller. Note that the shutoff point (churn pressure) is 110 psi; the maximum brake horsepower is 55; and the maximum efficiency is 75 percent at the overload point (150 percent of rated capacity). Head is 90 psi at the 65 percent minimum required at overload.

These curves assume that the pump is operated at a constant speed equal to its rated rpm (revolutions per minute). In

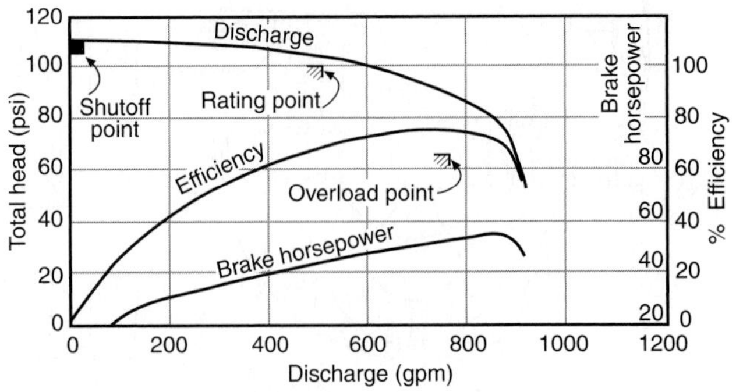

FIGURE 15.6.6 Typical Centrifugal Fire Pump Characteristic Curves

actual service, the speed of the driver varies with changes in the flow capacity.

Curves for positive displacement–type pumps are shown in Figure 15.6.7.

The flow and pressure ratings of commercial pumps are usually established on the basis of maximum efficiency and desired speed. Impellers can be designed for flat, medium, or steep head-discharge characteristics, as required for various uses. Figure 15.6.8 illustrates how the head-discharge curve is affected by the diameter of the eye, the width of the impeller, the number of vanes, and the shape or angle of the vanes.

TOTAL HEAD

The total head of a pump is the energy imparted to the liquid as it passes through the pump. It may be expressed in various units of pressure, but for fire protection it is generally given in pounds per square inch (psi) or kilopascals (kPa), or in feet (ft) or meters (m) of liquid measured vertically. The total head is calculated by subtracting the energy in the incoming liquid from the energy in the discharging liquid. The total head (H) of a pump is calculated by the formula

$$H = h_d + h_{Vd} - h_s - h_{Vs}$$

where

H = Total head (ft [m])

h_d = Discharge head (ft [m])

$h_{Vd} = \frac{Vd^2}{2g}$ = discharge velocity head (ft [m])

h_s = Total suction head (ft [m])

$h_{Vs} = \frac{Vv^2}{2g}$ = suction velocity head (ft [m])

V = Average velocity (ft/sec [m/sec])

g = Acceleration due to gravity (32.2 ft/sec^2 [9.81 m/sec^2])

For a horizontal split-case pump, the individual heads (h_V) are measured at the pump discharge nozzle flange and at the suction flange (Figure 15.6.9). The heads are read from pressure gauges attached to the pump flanges. The velocity head must be calculated for the volume of liquid passing through the flanges. One expression of this relationship is

$$h_v = \frac{V^2}{2g}$$

If the flanges have the same diameters, there will be no difference between the incoming and outgoing velocity, and the calculation can be omitted.

For a vertical turbine pump, the discharge head is theoretically read at the discharge flange of the pump. Since this flange usually is inaccessible for gauge readings, a gauge is used at the discharge fitting at the top of the pump column pipe (Figure 15.6.10). The discharge pressure at the pump discharge flange therefore equals the pressure at the gauge above, plus the pressure effect of the vertical distance between

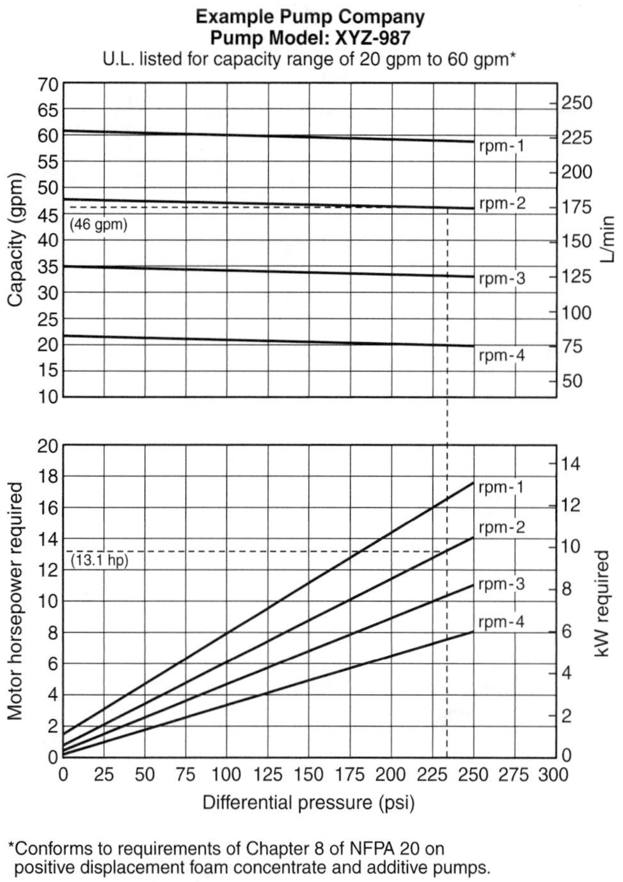

FIGURE 15.6.7 Typical Positive Displacement Pump Characteristics Curve

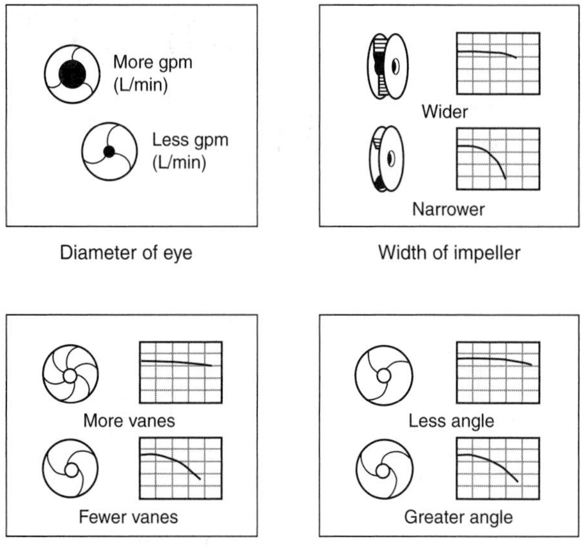

FIGURE 15.6.8 Effect of Impeller Design on Head-Discharge Curves for Fire Pumps

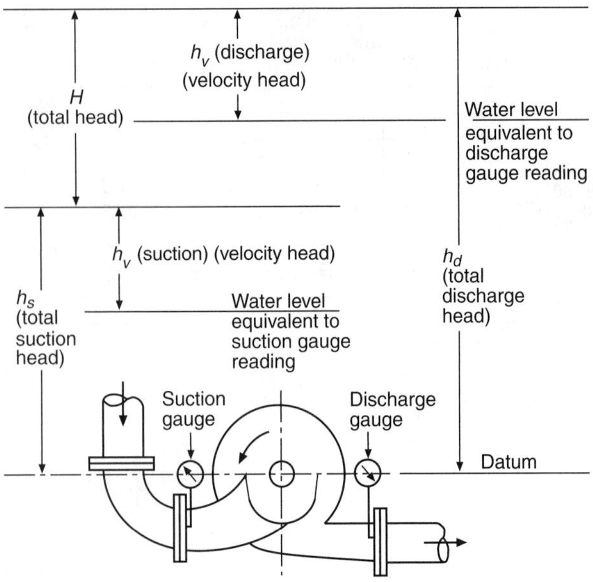

Installation with suction head above atmospheric pressure shown.

FIGURE 15.6.9 Typical Head of Horizontal Shaft Centrifugal Fire Pumps

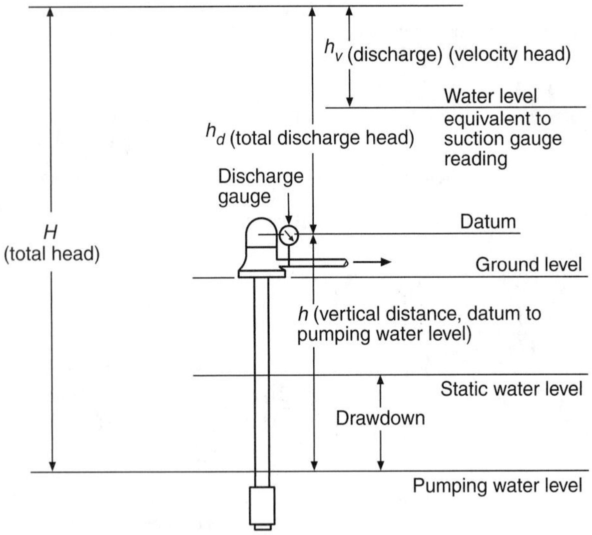

FIGURE 15.6.10 Total Head of Vertical-Turbine-Type Fire Pumps

the two points, plus the friction loss between the two points. In most cases, the friction loss is so small that it may be disregarded.

The suction head is the vertical distance from water level to the pump discharge flange. The velocity head of the incoming liquid is assumed to be zero. Hence, the formula would now take the following form:

$$H = h_d + h_{Vd} - h_s = (h_{gd} + L) + h_{Vd} - h_s$$

where

h_{gd} = Discharge gauge reading (ft [m])

L = Gauge pump flange (ft [m])

h_s = Water level when pumping to pump flange [ft (m)]

However, $L - h_s = h$, the vertical distance between the discharge gauge and water level. Therefore the formula becomes

$$H = h_{gd} + h_{Vd} + h$$

Hydraulic and power losses within the pump due to turbulence, disc friction, and shock are represented by the efficiency rating.

Total head at rated capacity is used to establish the rated head of a pump. Actually, the rated head is the amount of energy given to the water.

The total head of a vertical-turbine-type pump may also be defined as the vertical water-to-water dimension of the system in which the pump operates. However, there is a difference in the method of measuring total head. As shown in Figure 15.6.10, it is the sum of the vertical distance between water level in the well or pit, the discharge head indicated by the gauge on the pump outlet, and the velocity head at the gauge connection.

DISCHARGE SPECIFIC SPEED (N_d)

Discharge specific speed is a number relating the head, capacity, and speed of a centrifugal pump for design purposes. Actually, discharge specific speed is the revolutions per minute (rpm) of a geometrically similar impeller that will discharge 1 gpm (3.8 L/min) at 1 ft (0.3 m) total head. The formula for calculating discharge specific speed of a centrifugal pump is

$$N_d = \frac{\text{rpm} \times \text{gpm}^{1/2}}{H^{3/4}}$$

where

N_d = Specific speed number

H = Head (ft [m])

When values of head, speed, and capacity in the formula correspond to pump performance at optimum efficiency, the specific speed may be used as one measure of pump performance. Impellers designed for high heads usually have low specific speeds, and impellers designed for low heads have high specific speeds.

A pump of low specific speed will operate satisfactorily with greater suction lift than a pump of the same head and capacity with a higher specific speed. Experience shows that specific speed is a useful guide for determining maximum suction lift or minimum suction head.

Fire pumps are not allowed to take suction under lift. However, some existing installations may be encountered when a centrifugal pump is subject to lift conditions exceeding 15 ft (4.5 m), and it may be necessary to provide a larger pump at less speed. With low lift or positive head on the suction, a smaller pump operating at greater speed may be used. Abnormally high suction lifts may seriously reduce pump capacity and efficiency or cause excessive vibration and cavitation.

NET POSITIVE SUCTION HEAD

Net positive suction head (NPSH) is the pressure head that causes liquid to flow through the suction pipe and fittings into the eye of a pump impeller. The pump itself has no ability to "lift," and the suction pressure depends on the nature of the supply.

Although not permitted, a horizontal pump being supplied from a pond, stream, open well, or uncovered reservoir, where the water level is below the pump, would have a suction head equal to atmospheric pressure minus the lift. If the water level is above the pump, as from a water main or aboveground tank, the suction head is atmospheric pressure plus static pressure.

Pressure readings at the inlet flange of a pump operating under lift are negative with respect to the gauge but positive when referred to absolute pressure—hence, the expression "net positive suction head." Absolute pressure is gauge pressure plus barometric pressure.

There are two kinds of NPSH to consider. Pump NPSH is a function of the pump design and varies with the capacity and speed of any one pump and with the designs of different pumps. Available NPSH is a function of the system in which the pump operates and can be calculated readily. Curves of NPSH versus gallons per minute usually can be obtained from pump manufacturers.

Figure 15.6.11 shows an NPSH curve for a typical fire pump. Note that the required NPSH is 10 ft at 2000 gpm and 18 ft at 3000 gpm. The shutoff point equals the churn pressure at zero flow; the overload point equals 150 percent of rated flow at 65 percent of the rated pressure.

When the water source is above the pump, available NPSH = atmospheric pressure (ft or m) + static head on suction (ft or m) – friction and fitting losses in suction piping (ft or m) – vapor pressure of liquid (ft or m). Note that the vapor pressure of water at 90°F (32°C) is 1.6 ft (0.48 m).

For any pump installation, the available system NPSH must be equal to or greater than the pump NPSH at the desired operating conditions.

CAVITATION

Cavitation is a complex phenomenon that can take place in pumps or other hydraulic equipment. As water flows through the suction pipe of a centrifugal pump and enters the eye of the impeller, the velocity increases and pressure decreases. If the pressure falls below the vapor pressure corresponding to the temperature of the water, pockets of vapor will form. When the vapor pockets in the flowing water reach a region of higher pressure, they collapse with a hammer effect, causing noise and vibration. Tests have shown that the extremely high instantaneous pressures that may be developed in this manner may pit various parts of the pump casing and impeller. Conditions may be mild or severe, and mild cavitation may occur without much noise. Severe cavitation can cause reduced efficiency and, ultimately, failure of the pump if it is not corrected.

PUMP AFFINITY LAWS

The mathematical relationships among head, capacity, brake horsepower, and impeller diameter are called the pump affinity laws. Law 1 assumes constant impeller diameter with change of speed. Law 2 assumes constant speed with change in diameter of the impeller. These laws are expressed by proportion, as follows:

Law 1

$$\frac{Q_1}{Q_2} = \frac{N_1}{N_2}, \quad \frac{H_1}{H_2} = \frac{N_1^2}{N_2^2}, \quad \frac{\text{bhp}_1}{\text{bhp}_2} = \frac{N_1^3}{N_2^3}$$

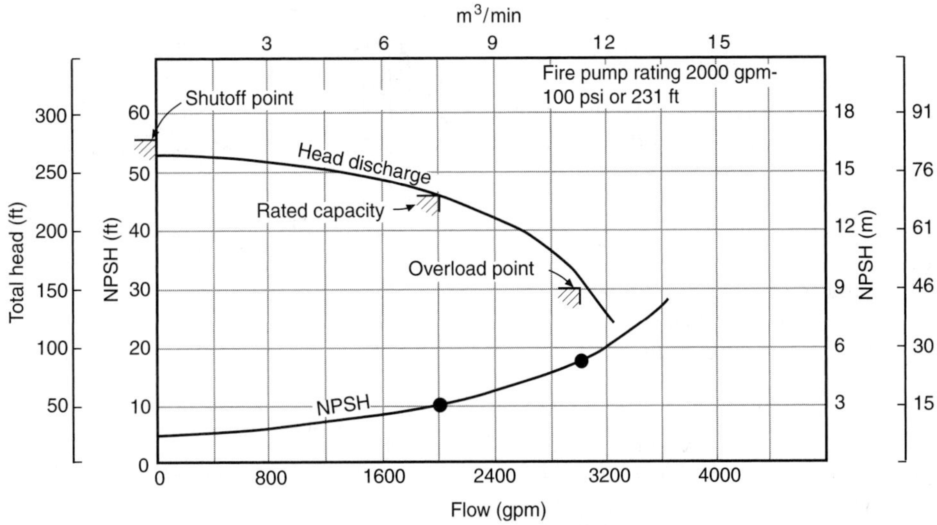

FIGURE 15.6.11 NPSH Curve of a Typical Fire Pump

Law 2

$$\frac{Q_1}{Q_2} = \frac{D_1}{D_2}, \frac{H_1}{H_2} = \frac{D_1^2}{D_2^2}, \frac{\text{bhp}_1}{\text{bhp}_2} = \frac{D_1^3}{D_2^3}$$

The nomenclature for the relationship is

Q = Capacity

H = Head, N = Speed

D = Impeller diameter

bhp = Brake horsepower

Thus,

Q_1 = gpm (L/min) at N_1 or D_1 Q_2 = gpm (L/min) at N_2 or D_2

H_1 = Head in ft (m) at N_1 or D_1 H_2 = Head in ft (m) at N_2 or D_2

bhp_1 = Brake horsepower (kW) at N_1 or D_1 bhp_2 = Brake horsepower (kW) at N_2 or D_2

Law 1 applies to common types of pumps, including horizontal centrifugal pumps and vertical turbine pumps. Law 2 applies to centrifugal pumps with reasonably close agreement between calculated and tested performance. Generally, pumps with low specific speeds show closer agreement than do pumps with high specific speeds.

The pump affinity laws should be applied when proposed changes in a fire pump installation would increase the speed or significantly raise the pressure of the suction supply. Greater speed would increase the power demand, and high discharge pressure might be undesirable. In some instances, it is possible to trim the impeller. This should not be done without the approval of the pump manufacturer. Likewise, when a variable pump driver is used, the pump affinity laws will apply when the rotational speed of the pump is changed to control the output head in feet (m) available.

STANDARD HEAD DISCHARGE CURVES

The shape of the standard head discharge curve of a fire pump is determined by three limiting points: the shutoff, the rating, and the overload.

Shutoff

With the pump operating at rated speed and no flow, the total head of a horizontal centrifugal pump, vertical turbine pump, or an end-suction pump at shutoff must be between 100 and 140 percent of the rated head pressure at the 100 percent flow capacity.

The shutoff point represents the maximum allowable total head pressure. Otherwise, the pump would have a rising or convex characteristic curve. Such pumps are not listed. With a convex curve, there could be two flow points for one pressure.

Rating

The curve should pass through or above the point of rated capacity and head (Figure 15.6.12).

Overload

At 150 percent of rated flow capacity, the total head pressure should not be less than 65 percent of the rated total head. The curve should pass through or above the overload point. Most fire pumps have curves with a small margin above the theoretical overload, and some models have a cavitation or "break" point in the curve just beyond overload.

HORIZONTAL-SHAFT CENTRIFUGAL FIRE PUMPS

Horizontal-shaft centrifugal fire pumps are required to be installed to operate under positive suction head. If the water supply is such that suction lift cannot be avoided, vertical turbine fire pumps should be installed. NFPA 20 does not allow the use of horizontal-centrifugal fire pumps taking suction under lift for new installations.

Types of Pump

Horizontal centrifugal fire pumps are of the split-case, vertical in-line, or end-suction type (Figures 15.6.5 and 15.6.13). The end-suction type is manufactured to ANSI specifications[1] for centrifugal pumps. In general, there are no limits on the capacities of split-case fire pumps, but the maximum rated capacity of any listed fire pump is currently 5000 gpm (18 925 L/min).

Suction Supplies from Public Mains

When streams, ponds, and other open bodies of water are used, properly screened intakes should be provided to prevent fish,

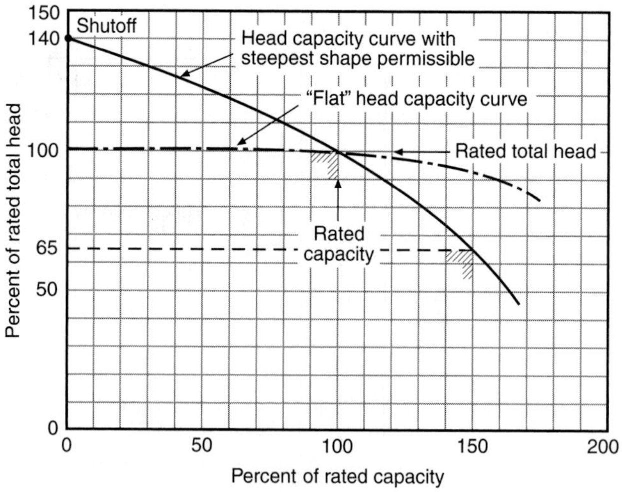

FIGURE 15.6.12 Pump Characteristic Curves

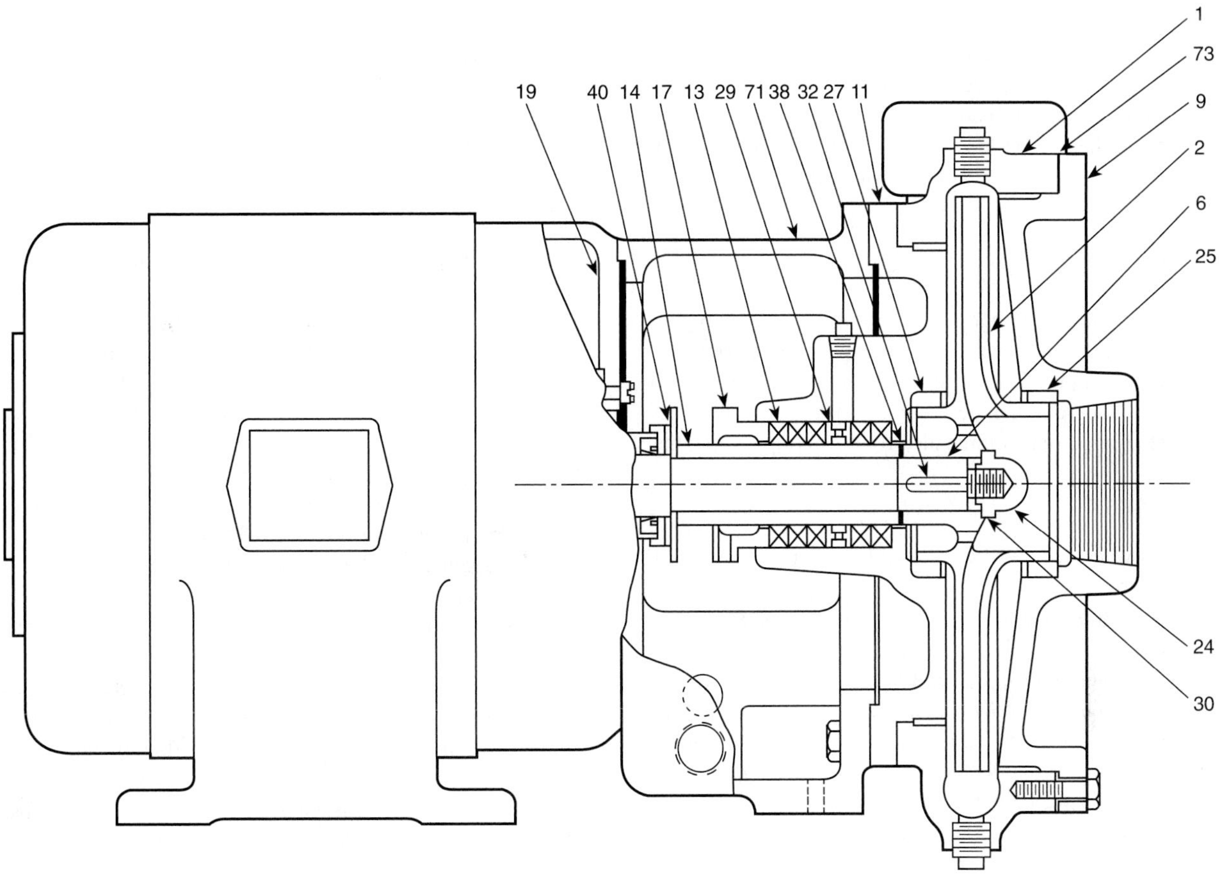

1 Casing
2 Impeller
6 Shaft
9 Cover, suction
11 Cover, stuffing box
13 Packing
14 Sleeve, shaft
17 Gland
19 Frame
24 Nut, impeller
25 Ring, suction cover
27 Ring, stuffing box cover
29 Ring, lantern
30 Gasket, impeller nut
32 Key, impeller
38 Gasket, shaft sleeve
40 Deflector
71 Adapter
73 Gasket

NOTE: The numbers used in this figure do not necessarily represent standard part numbers used by any manufacturer.

FIGURE 15.6.13 An Overhung Impeller, Close-Coupled, Single-Stage, In-Line, Vertical Fire Pump (Source: Hydraulic Institute, http://www.pumps.org)

eels, and foreign material from entering the pump and the fire protection system. Some older pumps may have a foot valve such as the one shown in Figure 15.6.14. However, pumps taking suction under lift are not allowed for new installations as per NFPA 20.

Use of nonpotable water should be avoided when fire pumps discharge into a system that is also connected to public mains or to other potable supplies. Otherwise, there will be cross connections, which are restricted in some locations by federal clean water act regulations or health or water utility authorities. In those cases where cross connections cannot be avoided, listed or approved backflow prevention devices acceptable to health and water authorities are required to prevent contamination of potable water supplies. Such devices should be installed on the discharge side of the pump. Where a backflow preventer is required to be installed in the suction piping, it must be at least

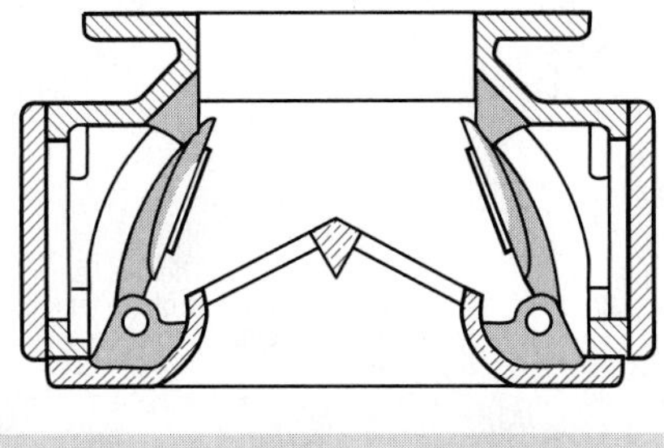

FIGURE 15.6.14 A Typical Foot Valve of Good Design Shown in the Open Position

10 pipe diameters from the suction flange of the fire pump. It is preferred, however, to locate the backflow preventer at least 50 ft (16 m) from the pump suction flange. When a diesel engine pump driver is used and the source of cooling water is connected to the pump discharge, a reduced pressure backflow preventor is required to be installed in the cooling water piping as shown in the annex to NFPA 20.

Suction Water Storage Tanks

The volume of suction storage should be sufficient to supply the pump or pumps at 150 percent of the pump's rated capacity for the required duration of the water demand. This is normally 1 to 4 hours. Aboveground, underground, or fire well tanks filled with potable water are recommended for supplying fire pumps.

Break Tanks

At locations where a direct connection between a public water supply and a private fire protection system is prohibited, either for public health or hydraulic reasons, a break tank installation may be desirable. A break tank is an automatically filled tank that provides a suction supply for a fire pump without a direct connection to a public supply (Figure 15.6.15). This is done by an actual physical break or gap between the public supply and a private protection system. Water from the public supply enters the break tank from a height above the tank's overflow outlet and falls freely to the surface of the water in the tank. A fire pump is needed to take suction from the tank, as the water is no longer under pressure from the public supply. The fire pump may be a vertical turbine, horizontal, or positive displacement type.

A separate tank may be provided for each fire pump in an installation. The flow into the tank from the public supply is controlled by an automatic fill mechanism, and since the water in the tank is considered potable, the top of the tank should be closed.

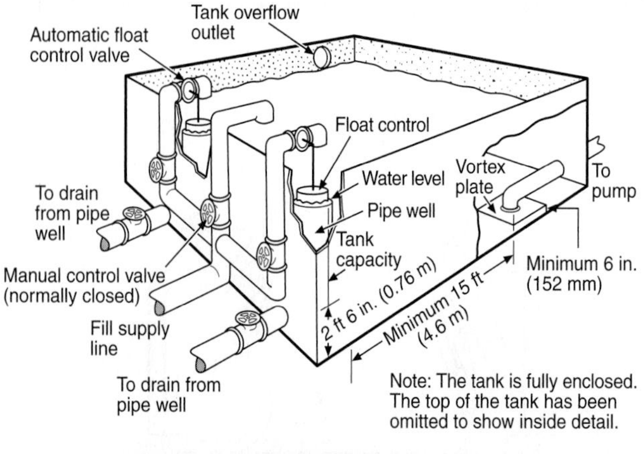

FIGURE 15.6.15 A Break Tank Used in Connection with a Fire Pump When a Direct Connection Between a Public Water Supply and a Private Fire Protection System Is Prohibited

Break tanks are less reliable than good, full-sized suction tanks, as the automatic fill mechanisms could fail. There is no NFPA standard for the design and installation of break tanks, but to the extent possible, the requirements of NFPA 22 and NFPA 20 should be used.

Booster Pumps

These are fire pumps taking suction from public water mains or industrial water systems. (In a mechanical sense, all pumps are booster pumps.) As a prelude to purchasing and installation, the available fire waterflow is obtained by conducting flow tests. The pump is sized by first conducting a flow test of the water supply and plotting the test on a water-supply graph having pressure versus volume (gpm), semi-log $N^{1.85}$ paper (SI units: 1 gpm = 3.785 L/min). The required water demand is then plotted to determine what pressure is required. The manufacturer's characteristic curves are researched to find one that adds the required pressure at a volume range of 90 percent of rated capacity to 130 percent of the rated pump capacity. The pump should be sized so that, when pumping is at 150 percent of rated (overload) capacity, the pump does not lower the water supply pressure to a gauge pressure less than 10 psi (69 kPa), or a safe point that may be determined by the local health authorities. Full overload capacity of the pump, plus the probable flow drawn from area hydrants by the fire department, are calculated, and they should not drop the gauge pressure in the water mains below 10 psi (69 kPa) or that allowed by the public health authorities. Head rating of the pump should be sufficient to meet all pipe friction in the connection plus pressure demand.

Pump Accessories

Auxiliary devices have an important bearing on the complete functioning of a pump as a fire protection water supply, and their provision or omission should never be decided solely on the basis of cost. NFPA 20 gives detailed information concerning their installation. The following items are worthy of special consideration.

Relief Valves. These are required on the pump discharge line when the operation of the pump can result in excess pressure that would exceed the pressure rating of the fire protection system. The design of this device is very critical to the proper operation of the fire protection water supply. If the pump is oversized for flow and pressure, the main relief valve should not be used to limit the pressure and discharge excess quantities of water during the normal weekly run test and annual flow test. This is of particular importance in climates where there is freezing weather for a portion of the year. In these situations the designer should look further at other pump choices and optional drivers for the pump that will limit the discharge head. A good example is a variable-speed diesel engine or electric motor listed system.

Hose Valves. Approved 2½-in. (64-mm) hose valves can be used in testing pumps and for hose stream(s) fire protection. The valves are attached to a header or manifold outside the pump room, or otherwise located to avoid water damage to the pump, driver, and controller. The number of valves needed depends on the pump capacity. The number of 2½ in. (64 mm) outlets provided is based on a 250 gpm (946 L/min) flow per outlet. Design consideration should be made to use a fixed, listed flowmeter with water discharging back to the water source to conserve water and improve the accuracy of flow test results. When the water supply is tested, the hose valves, fire hose, and nozzles should be used for the test.

Automatic Air Release Valves. These are installed on the top of the pump casing(s) and arranged for automatic or remote-control operation. The purpose is to release trapped air in the casing and to minimize pump cavitation. An automatic air release is desirable on any pump with a casing that is normally full of water.

Circulation Relief Valves. These are installed on pumps that start automatically or by remote control. Their function is to open at slightly above rated pressure, when there is little or no discharge, so that sufficient water is discharged to prevent the water in the pump from overheating. These valves are not required on diesel-engine-driven pumps where cooling water is taken from the pump discharge.

Vertical Turbine Fire Pumps

Vertical turbine pumps were originally designed to pump water from wells. As fire pumps, they are recommended in instances where a fire well is used as the water source or the horizontal pumps would operate with suction lift. An outstanding feature of vertical pumps is their ability to operate without priming. Vertical pumps may be used to pump from streams, ponds, wet pits, wells, underground water storage tanks, cisterns, and break tanks.

Suction from wells is acceptable if the adequacy and reliability of the well has been established and the entire installation is built in conformance with NFPA 20. There is no maximum pump depth. The water level in the well is required to cover the pumping bowls to a depth required by the pump manufacturer's recommendations. If the yield from a well is too small to supply a fire pump, low-capacity, commercial well pumps can be used to fill conventional ground-level tanks or reservoirs for the fire pump supply.

A vertical fire pump assembly consists of a discharge head or right-angle gear drive, a pump column pipe and discharge fitting, an open or enclosed drive shaft, a bowl assembly containing the impellers, and a suction strainer (Figures 15.6.16 and 15.6.17). The principle of operation is comparable to that of a multistage horizontal centrifugal pump. Except for shutoff pressure, the characteristic curve is the same as it is for horizontal pumps (see Figure 15.6.12).

Vertical Turbine Barrel or Can Pump

Sometimes vertical-type multistage pumps are installed in a casing called a "barrel" or "can" for high-pressure installations (Figure 15.6.18).

Vertical pumps have the same standard capacity ratings that horizontal fire pumps have. Pressure ratings are standardized and vary by the number of bowls and diameter of the bowls.

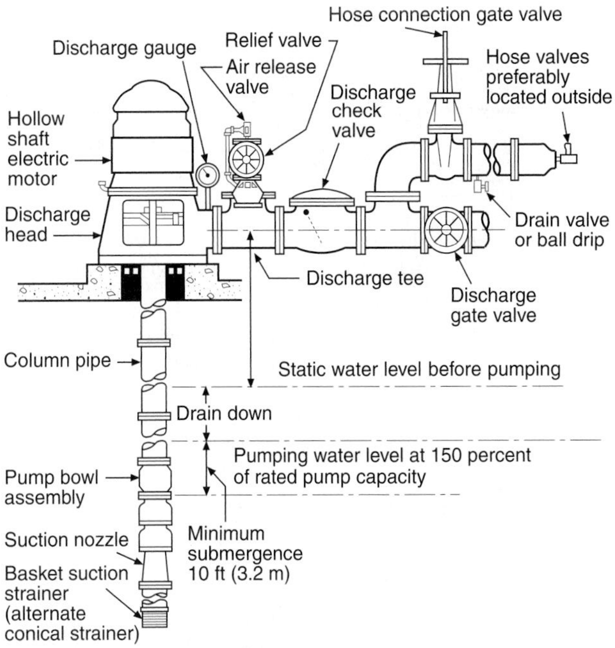

FIGURE 15.6.16 Vertical-Shaft-Turbine-Type Pump Installation in a Pit. Note: The distance between the bottom of the strainer and the bottom of the wet pit should be one-half of the pump bowl diameter but less than 12 in. (305 mm).

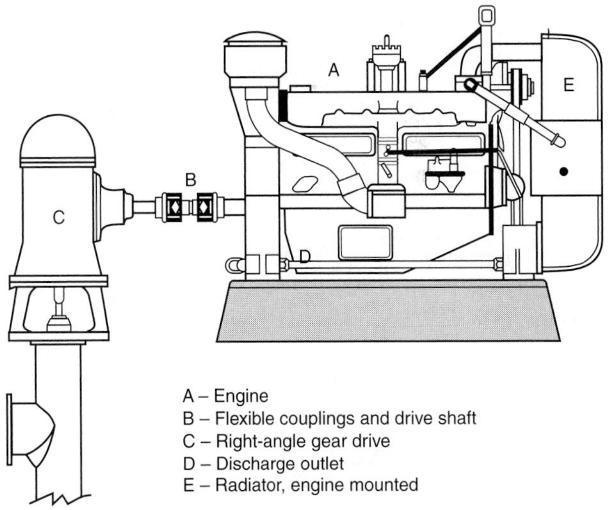

FIGURE 15.6.17 Engine-Driven Vertical Fire Pump

By changing the number of stages, or the impeller diameters, or both, the pump manufacturer can provide a specific total head at rated speed. Pressures are available up to 520 psi (3585 kPa). Vertical or horizontal mounted electric motors can be used, as well as hollow shaft motors. Diesel engines (mounted vertically or horizontally) or steam turbines can be used by means of right-angle gear heads.

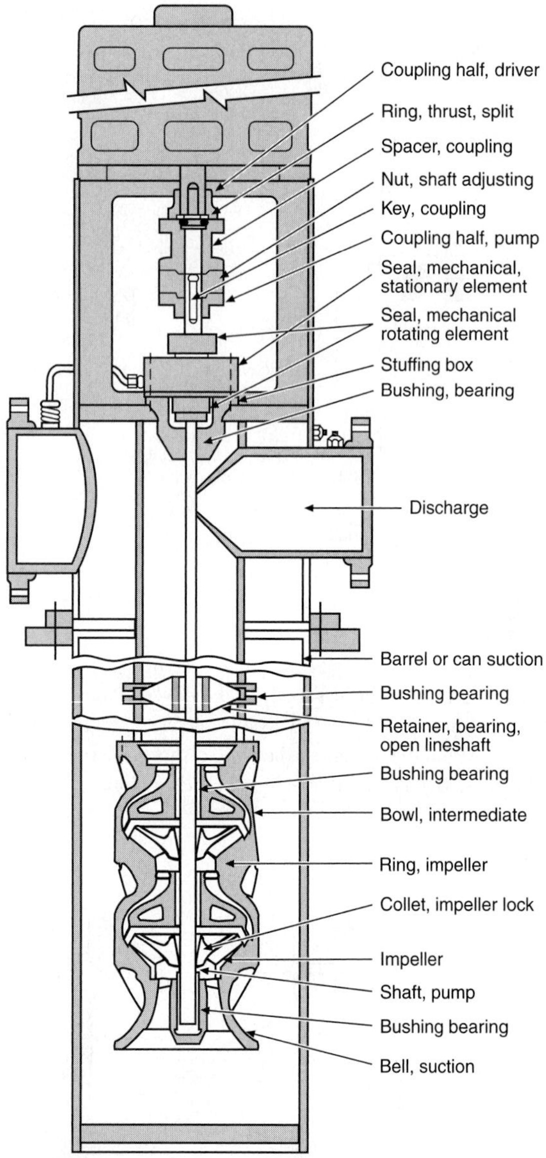

FIGURE 15.6.18 A Turbine-Type, Vertical, Multistage, Barrel or Can Pump

FIRE PUMP CAPACITY AND HEAD RATING

The capacity and pressure ratings of fire pumps must be adequate to meet flow and pressure demands consistent with water supply requirements for the property in question. Fire pumps are designed to provide their rated capacity with a safety factor built in (150 percent of rated capacity at 65 percent of rated pressure) to provide some protection in case of greater-than-expected demand at the time of a fire. The following examples show one method of how rated capacity and pressure can be determined by using the standard fire pump curve for a typical manufacturer's pump characteristic curve (see Figure 15.6.12).

EXAMPLE 1: HORIZONTAL CENTRIFUGAL PUMP The estimated water demand for sprinklers and hose streams is 1400 gpm at 90 psi. The suction supply is a ground-level storage tank, and the minimum inlet gauge pressure is 0 psi at maximum flow.

PROBLEM: Determine the required rated capacity and pressure of the pump.

SOLUTION: Solution is determined by the following steps:

1. Meet the demand of 1400 gpm with the capacity of the pump, which is 150 percent of rated capacity.
2. Thus, 1400 ÷ 150 percent = 933 gpm. The nearest standard pump rating is approximately 1000 gpm.
3. Therefore, 1400 gpm demand would be 140 percent of capacity.
4. From the manufacturer's pump characteristic curve, it is determined that, at 140 percent capacity, the total pressure is 72 percent of rated pressure.
5. Under conditions of operation, the total pressure equals the discharge pressure (90 psi) plus suction pressure (0 psi).
6. Therefore, net pressure at 1400 gpm equals 90 + 0 = 90 psi, and rated pressure at 1000 gpm = 90 ÷ 72 percent = 125 psi.

ANSWER: Pump rating should be not less than 1000 gpm at 125 psi.

EXAMPLE 2: HORIZONTAL CENTRIFUGAL PUMP (SI UNITS) The estimated water demand for a sprinkler system is 2000 L/min at a pump discharge pressure of 400 kPa. The suction supply is a well with a lift of 5 m from water surface to the pump.

PROBLEM: Determine the required rated capacity and pressure of the pump.

SOLUTION: Solution is determined by the following steps:

1. Meet the demand of 2000 L/min with the overload capacity of the pump which is 150 percent of rated capacity.
2. Thus, 2000 ÷ 150 percent = 1330 L/min. The nearest standard pump rating is approximately 1500 L/min.
3. Therefore, 2000 L/min demand would be 2000/1500 × 100 percent = 133 percent of rated capacity.
4. From the manufacturer's pump characteristic curve, it is determined that, at 133 percent capacity, the total pressure is 78 percent of rated pressure.
5. Under conditions of operation, the net pressure equals the discharge pressure (400 kPa) minus suction pressure (5 m head = 5 ÷ 9.81 kPa = 50 kPa).
6. Therefore, net pressure at 2000 L/min equals 400 + 50 = 450 kPa, and rated pressure at 1500 L/min = 450 ÷ 78 percent = 580 kPa.

ANSWER: Pump rating should be not less than 1500 L/min at 580 kPa.

EXAMPLE 3: VERTICAL TURBINE PUMP IN A WELL The estimated water demand at ground level is 1100 gpm at 100 psi.

Tests and weather records show that the aquifer, or underground water source, is reliable and adequate at all seasons. The static level is 45 ft below the surface. The draw down, or vertical distance, between the static and pumping water levels is 40 ft at 1100 gpm pumping rate.

PROBLEM: Determine the rated capacity and pressure of the pump.

SOLUTION: Solution is determined by the following steps:

1. Meet the demand of 1100 gpm with the rated capacity of the pump, which is 100 percent of rated capacity.
2. Thus, 1100 ÷ 100 percent = 1100 gpm. The nearest standard pump rating is approximately 1100 gpm.
3. Therefore, the 1100 gpm demand would be 110 percent capacity.
4. From the manufacturer's pump characteristic curve, it is determined that, at 110 percent capacity, the total pressure is 70 percent of the rated pressure.
5. At 1100 gpm, pressure demand at the surface = 100 psi.
6. Static level (ft) + drawdown level (ft) = Pumping level (ft). In the example 45 ft static water level + 40 ft drawdown level = 85 ft pumping level. Now converting ft of water to psi, 85 ft × 0.434 psi/ft = 37 psi. Determine the pumping pressure required for the example: 100 psi + 37 psi = 137 psi, and 100 psi/137 psi = 0.73 (%), and finally, 137 psi/0.73 = 188 psi.

ANSWER: The pump rating should be not less than 1000 gpm at 188 psi.

EXAMPLE4:BOOSTERPUMPONPUBLICWATERCONNECTION A sprinklered building in a city has an estimated sprinkler demand of 750 gpm at 60 psi. Based on fire flow tests from nearby street hydrants, 750 gpm at 27 psi is available for sprinklers at the inlet flange of the pump. Allowance has already been made for hose streams.

PROBLEM: Determine the rated capacity and pressure of the pump.

SOLUTION: Solution is determined by the following steps:

1. Meet the demand of 750 gpm with the rated capacity of the pump, which is 100 percent of rated capacity.
2. Thus, 750 ÷ 100 percent = 750 gpm, a standard pump rating.
3. The total pressure at 100 percent capacity is 100 percent rated net pressure.
4. With positive head suction supply, the net pressure equals discharge pressure minus suction pressure; thus, at 750 gpm flow, net pressure equals 60 – 27 = 33 psi.
5. Therefore, 33 ÷100 percent = 33 psi.

ANSWER: The pump rating should be 750 gpm at 33 psi.

NFPA 20 recommends that the pump not be used at over 140 percent capacity. This leaves a small reserve as pump curves drop off sharply after 150 percent. Generally, a one size larger pump is recommended than the calculations indicate. When the pump is used above its rated capacity, the available pressure is reduced.

HORSEPOWER OF FIRE PUMPS

Before matching a driver to a pump, it is necessary to know the maximum brake horsepower demand of the pump at rated speed. This demand can be determined directly from the horsepower curve provided by the pump manufacturer. Typical fire pumps reach maximum brake horsepower between 140 and 170 percent of rated capacity.

Engine Horsepower

Engines specifically designed for use with fire pumps are rated by measuring the horsepower developed with all accessories in operation and then making some allowance for wear and tear. When equipped for fire pump driver service, an allowance of not less than 10 percent greater than the maximum brake horsepower is required by the pump under any conditions of pump load. Typical bare engines and usable horsepower curves are shown in Figure 15.6.19.

The engine manufacturer's test curves are based on barometric pressure of 29.61 in. (752 mm) Hg, which approximates 300 ft (90 m) above sea level and 77°F (25°C). The usable horsepower of a fire pump engine should be reduced for each 1000 ft (300 m) rise in altitude above 300 ft (90 m) by 3 percent for a diesel engine and 1 percent for each 10°F (5.6°C) rise above 77°F (25°C).

If the curves are not available, horsepower can be calculated by the formula (in U.S. customary units)

$$\text{bhp} = \frac{5.83QP}{10{,}000 \times E} \quad \text{or} \quad \text{bhp} = \frac{QP}{1710 \times E}$$

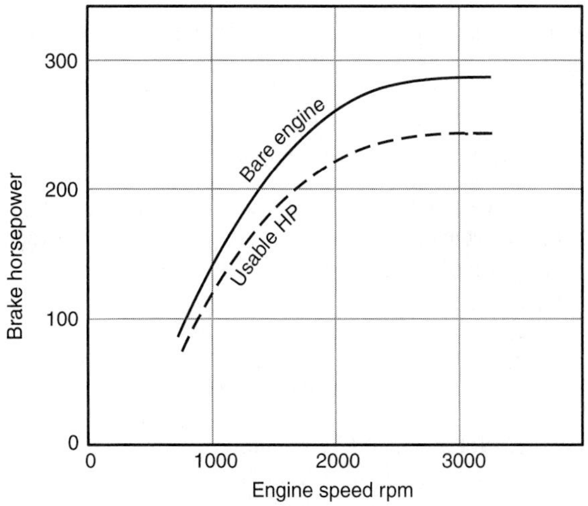

FIGURE 15.6.19 Typical Engine Horsepower Curves

where

bhp = Brake horsepower

Q = Gallons per minute

P = Total head (psi)

$$E = \text{Efficiency} = \frac{\text{Water horsepower}}{\text{Input horsepower}}$$

The efficiency at maximum brake horsepower is usually 60 to 75 percent.

PROBLEM: Find by formula the minimum horsepower needed to drive a 1000 gpm, 100 psi, 1760 rpm horizontal centrifugal fire pump.

SOLUTION: Solution is determined by the following steps:

1. Assume 65 percent efficiency at 160 percent capacity.
2. From a standard pump curve, the pressure is 55 percent at 160 percent capacity or 55 psi at 1600 gpm.
3. By formula,

$$\text{bhp} = \frac{5.83 \times 1600 \times 55}{10{,}000 \times 0.65} = 79$$

ANSWER: Not less than 79 usable brake horsepower.

IN SI UNITS.

$$\text{Output power} = \frac{0.167 Q_m P_m}{10{,}000E}$$

where

kw = Power output (kilowatts)

Q_m = Liters per minute

P_m = Total head (kPa) or net pressure

$$E = \text{Efficiency} = \frac{\text{Water power output}}{\text{Input power}}$$

PROBLEM: Find by formula the minimum power output needed to drive a 4000 L/min, 700 kPa, 1760 rpm horizontal centrifugal fire pump.

SOLUTION: Solution is determined by the following steps:

1. Assume 65 percent efficiency at 160 percent capacity.
2. From a standard pump curve, the pressure is 55 percent at 160 percent capacity or 385 kPa at 6400 L/min.
3. By formula,

$$\text{Power output} = \frac{0.167 \times 6400 \times 385}{10{,}000 \times 0.65} = 63 \text{ kW}$$

ANSWER: Not less than 63 kW output.

FIRE PUMP DRIVERS

Power for driving fire pumps is selected on the basis of reliability, adequacy, safety, and economy. The reliability of utility electric power may be judged by the record of outages and by review of the power sources and distribution layout of the system in question.

Some public utilities in metropolitan areas operate steam distribution systems. When high-pressure steam is available, it is practical to use steam turbine-driven fire pumps. Some remote industrial plants generate their own electricity using steam or hydro power, or both. Utility electric power is also used.

Diesel engines have the advantage of not being dependent on outside sources of power.

Electric Motors

Electric motors for driving fire pumps must be listed for fire pump service. These motors are designed in accordance with specifications of National Electrical Manufacturers Association (NEMA) or Electrical Manufacturers Association of Canada (EMAC). All electrical equipment and wiring in a fire pump installation is required to comply with NFPA 70, *National Electrical Code®*, Article 675.

Section 15, Chapter 7, "Fire Pump Controllers and Power Supply Arrangements for Motor-Driven Fire Pumps," provides a detailed discussion on electric motor design considerations.

Electric Motor Controllers

The fire pump controller used for an electric-driven pump is a critical component to ensure the successful operation of the pump. Such controllers are equipped with a variety of internal components to achieve this level of reliability. These components may include elements such as circuit breakers, disconnecting means, timers, and similar devices. Recently, an electric motor controller that uses a variable-speed system has been listed for use in fire pump applications. This controller is an additional tool that can be used by the designer to control the discharge head developed by a fire pump. This type of system is of particular value where the pump takes suction from a variable pressure source such as a city water supply that has a higher pressure in some seasons of the year and a very low pressure in other times of the year. It is also of value for some of the new sprinklers that require a high operating pressure to maintain a water application rate to control a fire in warehouses and high-hazard occupancies.

Section 15, Chapter 7, "Fire Pump Controllers and Power Supply Arrangements for Motor-Driven Fire Pumps," describes details for the design and selection of electric motor controllers.

Engine Controllers

Controllers are used for automatic operation of engine-driven fire pumps. The specifications for construction, location, and methods of actuation of engine controllers are the same as for electric motor controllers. Automatic controllers are equipped with manual starting and stopping switches. Diesel engine controllers are available as electric or air starting types. Unlike electric motor controllers that are available in a limited service type for less than 30 hp, all diesel engines, large or small, require the same operational features. Details on the design of the electric operated diesel engine controller are found in Section 15,

Chapter 7, "Fire Pump Controllers and Power Supply Arrangements for Motor-Driven Fire Pumps." Air-operated diesel engine controllers are required to have the same operational features as the electric controller.

Audible supervisory devices are provided to indicate low oil pressure in the lubrication systems, high engine-jacket water temperature, failure of the engine to start automatically, and shutdown from overspeed.

Steam Turbine

When adequate and reliable steam supplies are available, turbine-driven fire pumps are acceptable. Only well-built machines of good design with industrial records of proven reliability are used. Special arrangements are needed for automatic operation. Speed rating should not exceed 3600 rpm, because this is the maximum speed of listed fire pumps. Detailed requirements for steam supply, speed governors, and controls are contained in NFPA 20.

Diesel Engines

Engines that are powered by diesel fuel are used for fire pump service. Engines powered by gasoline, natural gas, or LP-gas are not recognized by NFPA 20.

In addition to NFPA 20, reference should be made to NFPA 31, *Standard for the Installation of Oil-Burning Equipment,* and NFPA 37, *Standard for the Installation and Use of Stationary Combustion Engines and Gas Turbines.* Installations should be made in conformance to local codes.

The development of unsatisfactory conditions, such as pump running, failure to start, high cooling water temperature, and low oil pressure, should be indicated by supervisory signals, not by shutting down the engine. The intent is to keep the pump operating just as long as possible. The importance of constant supervision for automatic pumps is obvious. Recently, a new operating system has been developed to control the discharge head (or pressure) from a diesel engine driven fire pump. This system operates as part of the diesel engine and not the controller like the electric motor driven fire pump. Both have the same advantage of being able to accurately control the pump discharge pressure when the suction pressure is variable or the pressure needs of a fire sprinkler system in a warehouse or high-hazard occupancy need to be maintained at a constant pressure to control a fire in the occupancy.

Cooling Systems. An adequate cooling system is vital to the reliable operation of a diesel engine. A closed pipe system with a heat exchanger and a thermally insulated manifold is the preferred cooling arrangement for a diesel engine recognized in NFPA 20. Only clean or potable water should be circulated through the engine block. Raw water is piped from the fire pump and discharged through the heat exchanger tubes to free discharge in a visible location, such as the cone of the building drain or building exterior. On some engines, the manifolds, oil coolers, and other parts are equipped with water jackets, as recommended by the engine manufacturer. Most engines require a raw waterflow of 15 to 30 gpm (57 to 114 L/min).

In cooling water systems connected to potable water systems and where an antifreeze with inhibitors is used inside of the engine block, federal clean water act regulations and local water suppliers are requiring that reduced-pressure backflow preventors be installed in the cooling water piping upstream of the heat exchanger in both the main cooling waterline and the bypass line. Details of the acceptable arrangement are found in the annex to NFPA 20.

Figure 15.6.20 shows the raw water from the fire pump entering the system through the strainer (1), which prevents sediment from entering the system, and the pressure regulator (2), which protects the heat exchanger from excessive pressure. The solenoid valve (3) is required with automatic control of the engine. The valve (4), normally closed, may be used to bypass the regulator and solenoid valve. The exhaust manifold (5) may be cooled by the clean water circulating system.

Another method of providing cooling to the diesel engine is a closed loop radiator. The radiator can be remotely installed outside of the pump room or on the engine platform. When the radiator is mounted on the engine skid, it should be arranged to pull the air across the engine and out through the radiator. The radiator is sized, according to engine manufacturer's recommendations, to remove the engine-radiated heat and to provide the internal engine cooling requirements.

Fuel Tanks. The storage tank for the diesel engine fuel is sized to contain at least an 8 hour supply. A larger capacity can be provided if facilities for prompt refilling are not available. Tank capacity is estimated by allowing 1 gal/hp. (For SI units: 1 pt = 0.473 L, and 1 gal = 3.785 L.) (See diagrams of typical fuel systems in NFPA 20.)

The fuel storage tank is required to be installed inside the fire pump room, because all listed diesel engines require fuel to be available by gravity, thereby eliminating the fuel pump on the engine. The bottom of the tank is at or above the level of the fuel injectors. This location also allows for easy inspection and maintenance of the tank.

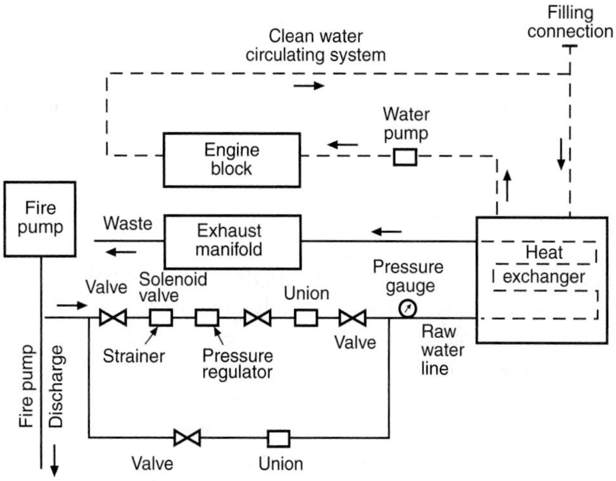

FIGURE 15.6.20 A Typical Heat-Exchanger Cooling System for an Automatically Controlled Engine-Driven Fire Pump That Does Not Require Backflow Protection

Battery Chargers. The energy source needed for automatic starting of a diesel-driven fire pump depends on a sufficient capacity from the battery system. The charges used to satisfy this requirement are specifically listed for fire pump service, and consist of rectifiers, transformers, and relays.

Batteries are provided in two banks with alternate starting cycles to increase the system reliability.

Automatic Pump Control

Most fire pump installations are arranged for automatic operation, preferably with automatic start and manual shutdown. The choice between manual and automatic shutdown depends on the specific conditions involved in a pump's installation and use. Horizontal centrifugal pumps under automatic control must always operate under a head to avoid the need for priming.

Each engine controller is equipped with a separate pressure switch and sensing line that actuate the pump unit when pressure in the water system piping drops to a preset level. Unless the normal water supply static pressure is higher than the pump starting pressure, an automatic jockey (pressure maintenance) pump must be provided to maintain pressure in the system at the higher level.

Actuation of a pump by waterflow instead of by pressure drop is desirable for certain installations, such as those in which: the opening of a moderate number of sprinklers would not drop the system pressure enough to move the pressure switch; high-hazard occupancies in which a fire would demand fire pump service without delay; combined fire protection and plant service systems where a pressure maintenance pump would be impractical; and occupancies in which pressure fluctuates so much that a stable cut-in pressure could not be obtained.

The wiring system of a pump controller includes terminals for connection of a relay to an external supervisory circuit from a sprinkler, deluge, or special fire protection system. To secure reliable pump actuation, external circuits should be installed in conformance with the following NFPA standards, depending on the nature of the signaling system:

NFPA 70, *National Electrical Code®*, Article 695
NFPA 72®, *National Fire Alarm Code®*

Circuits for remote automatic starting of fire pumps should be powered from the controller power.

FIELD ACCEPTANCE TESTS

After a new fire pump has been installed, it is required to make a performance test. Defects and faults are discovered and steps are taken to remedy them. These tests enable the purchaser to determine that the contract has been properly concluded. They also demonstrate the need for future maintenance tests.

Details of the acceptance tests are given in NFPA 20. The test demonstrates the adequacy of the pump and the ability of the pump to deliver water in accordance with its head-capacity curve. The prime mover is operated under various conditions and its performance recorded. There are provisions for electric motors, steam turbines, and diesel engines. Repeated operation of the controlling equipment is required to ensure that full operation of the unit will result from either manual or automatic operation of the controller.

Flow tests are conducted to develop the pressure-discharge characteristic curve of the pump. The procedure followed is to run the pump at three to four different flows, including shutoff (no water flowing). The rate in gallons per minute (L/min) is determined with a Pitot tube and gauge at the nozzles (preferably standard 30-in. [762-mm] long Underwriter playpipes) attached to hose lines from an outside hose-valve header. The discharge is varied by changing the number of lines, the size of nozzle tips, or both; or by using an installed waterflow meter with flow to an open source. Flow is varied by opening or closing the valve on the meter line.

The nozzles may be attached directly to outdoor headers, without hose lines, if water damage can be avoided. Disposal of test water is often a problem, and the length of hose lines depends on the drainage facilities available and the exposure to property and people.

For every flow, pressure readings are taken at the suction gauge and the discharge gauge. The revolutions per minute are also measured using a revolution counter or a tachometer, if available.

The net pressures are calculated from the pump gauge readings, and the flows in gallons per minute corresponding to the Pitot readings are obtained from discharge tables. The flow required for coolant purposes for diesel engine-driven pumps can be added to the measured flow. However, it is usually difficult to accurately measure this flow, so an estimate based on the manufacturer's recommendations may have to be used. In many cases, this flow is small enough to be considered negligible.

With the growing problems of waste water disposal, many pump installations are equipped with waterflow meters for the acceptance test and the periodic service tests. The meters should be installed in conformance with NFPA 20, in order to function properly and not interfere with the operation of the pump.

Vertical turbine fire pumps are tested in the same manner as horizontal pumps, except that there is no suction gauge. The pumping water level should be recorded at each test point.

Figure 15.6.21 presents data obtained by a typical field acceptance test of a horizontal 1500 gpm, 100 psi, 1760 rpm (5678 L/min, 689 kPa, 1760 rpm) diesel-engine-driven centrifugal pump. The net pressure and total flows are calculated from the observed data and plotted (Figure 15.6.22). The curve best

Acceptance Test for a 1500-gpm, 100-psi, 1760-rpm Fire Pump

			Hose	Streams				Corrected to 1760 rpm		
rpm	Discharge (psi)	Suction (psi)	Net (psi)*	No.	Size (in.)	Pitot Pressure (psi)	gpm*	Total*	gpm*	Net (psi)*
1700	125	+16	109	0	–	–	–	0	0	118
1695	120	+18	102	1	1¾	70	742	742	772	110
1690	110	+16	94	2	1¾	60, 60	687, 687	1374	1420	101
1686	95	+17	79	3	1¾	55, 55, 55	657, 657 657	1971	2060	85
1675	85	+16	69	4	1¾	35, 37, 48, 48	525, 540 614, 614	2293	2410	76

* Calculated from observed data.

FIGURE 15.6.21 Example of a Log for a Fire Pump Acceptance Test

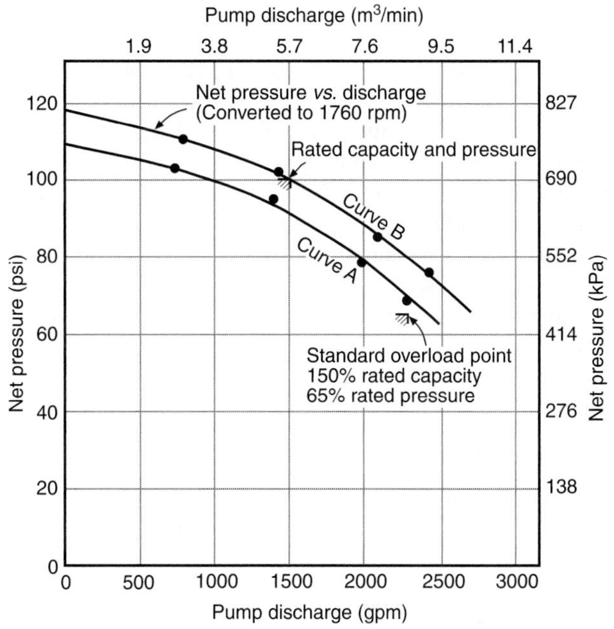

FIGURE 15.6.22 Head Capacity Curves Plotted from Data Compiled in a Fire Pump Acceptance Test

fitting the plotted points is then drawn (Curve A). In this installation, the engine governor appeared to be out of adjustment, restricting the average speed to 1689 rpm, whereas the rated speed was 1760 rpm.

Since the pump was tested at less than rated speed, the observed net pressures and flows were converted to what they would have been at the rated speed of 1760 rpm. Curve B is the characteristic curve at rated conditions. Although the rating point was barely reached, the overload point exceeded the minimum by a good margin. With the engine adjusted to operate at full speed, the pump performance would be acceptable. The following is the conversion calculation procedure that was followed.

Flow is directly proportional to rpm; net pressure is proportional to rpm.[2] For example, test flow, 1971 gpm at 1686 rpm:

$$\text{Flow at 1760 rpm} = 1971\left(\frac{1760}{1686}\right) = 2060 \text{ gpm}$$

Net pressure for 1971 gpm at 1686 rpm is 78 psi. Net pressure for 2060 gpm at 1760 rpm is

$$78\left(\frac{1760}{1686}\right)^2 = 85 \text{ psi}$$

Similar calculations can be carried out in SI units using the affinity laws mentioned previously in this chapter.

LOCATION AND HOUSING OF CENTRIFUGAL PUMPS

Fire pumps are preferably housed in buildings of fire-resistant or noncombustible construction. Even when the climate is so mild that there is no danger of freezing, sufficient enclosure is needed to protect against dirt, corrosion, and tampering. Structural separation of the pump room from other parts of a property is a requirement.

Pump rooms and power facilities should be as free as possible from exposure to fire, explosion, flood, earthquake, and windstorm damage.

Light, heat, ventilation, and floor drainage should be provided for pump rooms. A dry location above-grade is preferred. Pump rooms should be large enough to facilitate easy access to all equipment and devices for inspection, testing, and maintenance.

Fire pumps are located as close as possible to those areas where protection is most important. In some large properties, it may be necessary to have water supplies at more than one point to obtain the most favorable distribution system.

PUMP TESTS

A fire pump must be flow tested annually to ensure that the pump, driver, suction, and power supply function properly and to correct faults that may be found. The hydraulic performance of the pump is measured by a flow test, using a flow meter or hose and nozzles connected to the pump header or yard hydrants. Three points on the standard curve are checked: (1) shutoff, (2) overload (150 percent of rated capacity), and (3) at capacity rating.

Automatic operation is tested by lowering the system pressure, giving due consideration to the layout of the fire protection system, that is, pressure drop or waterflow actuation, jockey pump, and so on.

The water level of wells, ponds, and reservoirs and the condition of suction screens and intakes, above- and below-ground tanks, and so on should be carefully inspected. The history of power outages, low water, and failure of any kind that involves pump, driver, or associated equipment also should be investigated and gauge records from engine controllers recorded for future evaluation.

PUMP OPERATION AND MAINTENANCE

A fire pump can be depended on to work in an emergency only if it is properly operated and maintained. (See NFPA 25 for requirements for inspection, testing, and maintenance of these systems.) It is required that an inspection and testing program that includes written instructions and recordkeeping be implemented. It is further required to have someone at the property at all times who is designated and instructed to operate the pump and its driver. A short (30-min diesel engine; 10-min electric motor) test is required to be made each week by discharging water from some convenient outlet or recirculating through a flow meter.

Fire Alarm Interface

When a supervisory signal indicates an automatic fire pump is operating, the person responsible for the fire pump should proceed to its location immediately. The pump should be allowed to run until the emergency is over, when it may be shut down manually. During this and every other operating period, the equipment should be checked carefully to see that it is performing properly.

To minimize too-frequent starting and stopping, an electric motor controller has a timer that keeps the motor running for at least 1 minute for each 10-hp motor rating; not less than 10 minutes is required. With electric motors, it is necessary to allow the electrical windings to cool down after starting, to minimize damage to the windings.

It is preferable with all pump drivers to permit the unit to run until it is shut down manually.

When there is more than one automatic fire pump, the controllers are arranged to operate the pumps in a predetermined sequence. The diesel engine is usually first, followed by the electric motor or second diesel engine. Control of the pump from one or more remote pushbuttons, which will start but not stop the pump, may be provided, if desired. If there is deluge valve control of an open discharge device system, the pump may be started by a drop-out relay in a closed circuit. The cooling and lubrication of a centrifugal fire pump is so dependent on water that the pump must never be run unless the pump casing is full of water. Close attention should be given to the bearings and stuffing boxes during the first few minutes of running to see that they do not heat up and need no adjustment. When water reaches the water seal, a small leak at the stuffing box glands is desirable. The suction inlet and discharge outlet pressure gauges should be read weekly to see that the inlet is not obstructed by a choked screen or partially closed valve.

With a vertical-shaft-turbine-type fire pump, the water level can be observed if suction is from a visible supply. If the pump takes suction from a well, water level testing equipment must be used. The groundwater level at the pump should be checked at the weekly test interval during the year and the drawdown should be determined during the annual 150 percent capacity test. These tests should indicate any important change in the groundwater supply.

The direction of rotation of the pump and the speed of operation should be checked each week.

Power Supply Maintenance

The source of electric power for the pump should be checked weekly. With an electric motor drive this means current supply for the motor and its auxiliary equipment. For steam turbine drive, it means the steam supply up to the control valve and the absence of condensate from supply, turbine, and exhaust. If the pump is driven by a diesel engine, there must be adequate fuel for 8 hours of operation. The batteries must be fully charged.

The starting equipment must be test-operated and its functioning carefully checked. Any evidence of a drop in voltage greater than –15 percent (nominal voltage less 15 percent) to an electric motor or a drop in steam pressure to a turbine must be investigated.

With a diesel engine drive, the crankcase oil must be replenished or renewed as needed, the oil filter and air cleaner given the necessary attention, the automatic battery charging equipment checked, and the specific gravity of battery electrolyte determined at least once a month.

RECIPROCATING STEAM FIRE PUMPS

Although no new reciprocating steam fire pumps have been installed in recent years, a few may still be in service. These fire pumps are commonly referred to as Underwriter steam fire pumps. The general features of a direct-acting duplex steam pump are shown in Figure 15.6.23. The size of the steam and exhaust ports of this type of pump is larger than it is in the general-purpose steam pump, thus permitting higher speeds. The steam supply pipe should be an independent line run from boiler to pump in such a way that it will not be damaged by fire or other hazards.

Automatic control can be provided by a pressure governor to regulate steam supply to the pump in accordance with the water pressure on the pump discharge. For successful operation, it is nearly always necessary to provide a small, automatically controlled jockey pump to maintain system pressure, control supply leakage, and avoid continuous operation of the large pump.

FIRE PUMP APPROVAL AND LISTING

NFPA standards for design and installation of various fire protection systems require the use of approved equipment, or listed equipment, or both, including fire pumps, for installations requiring them. Under the testing and listing approval system, the manufacturer is responsible for providing a listed or approved pump that will perform satisfactorily when installed in conformance with NFPA 20. Contractors or others are responsible for installing the driver-pump combination in accordance with the provisions of NFPA 20, whereas it is the customer's obligation to provide adequate data about the pump driver, power supply, water supply, location, and so on.

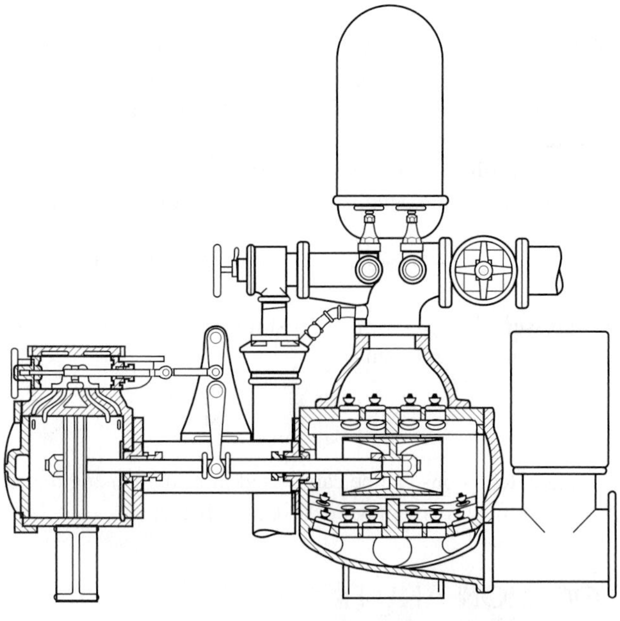

FIGURE 15.6.23 Sectional View of an Approved Duplex Steam Pump

Fire pumps are designed to provide maximum reliability and specific net head-discharge characteristics. Except for periodic inspections and tests, fire pumps are idle most of the time. Pumps for commercial use, on the other hand, are chosen for maximum efficiency and economy.

To obtain a listing of a new pump, the manufacturer submits plans and specifications to a testing agency for review and comment. After any revisions or corrections have been agreed to, arrangements are made for representatives of the testing agency involved to witness the required approval tests at the manufacturer's plant.

If the results are satisfactory, the new pumps are listed in the usual manner or with any restrictions considered desirable. It is the duty of the manufacturer to shop-test every unit sold and to furnish certified curves of head, efficiency, and brake horsepower versus discharge. The NPSH curve of the pump should be provided on request.

Many of the listed fire pumps used today are top-quality commercial units. These pumps are upgraded when necessary, trimmed, and fitted to meet all the approval requirements for fire protection.

SUMMARY

Fire pumps provide the water supply pressure, or they enhance the existing water supply pressure, for powering fire protection systems such as automatic sprinklers. This chapter described different types of fire pumps, that is, centrifugal pumps and positive displacement pumps. The chapter further discussed the principles of fire protection operation, including a discussion of the power sources that drive fire pump systems. The chapter concluded with a description of field acceptance tests and pump operation and maintenance procedures.

BIBLIOGRAPHY

References Cited

1. ANSI B73.1, *Specification for Horizontal End-Suction Centrifugal Pumps for Chemical Process,* American National Standards Institute, New York, 2001.
2. *Hydraulic Institute Standards,* 16th ed., 2005.

NFPA Codes, Standards, and Recommended Practices

Reference to the following NFPA codes, standards, and recommended practices will provide further information on water distribution discussed in this chapter. (See the latest version of The NFPA Catalog *for availability of current editions of the following documents.)*

NFPA 11, *Standard for Low-, Medium-, and High-Expansion Foam*
NFPA 13, *Standard for the Installation of Sprinkler Systems*
NFPA 13D, *Standard for the Installation of Sprinkler Systems in One- and Two-Family Dwellings and Manufactured Homes*
NFPA 13E, *Recommended Practice for Fire Department Operations in Properties Protected by Sprinkler and Standpipe Systems*
NFPA 13R, *Standard for the Installation of Sprinkler Systems in Residential Occupancies up to and Including Four Stories in Height*
NFPA 14, *Standard for the Installation of Standpipe and Hose Systems*
NFPA 15, *Standard for Water Spray Fixed Systems for Fire Protection*
NFPA 16, *Standard for the Installation of Foam-Water Sprinkler and Foam-Water Spray Systems*
NFPA 20, *Standard for the Installation of Stationary Pumps for Fire Protection*
NFPA 22, *Standard for Water Tanks for Private Fire Protection*
NFPA 24, *Standard for the Installation of Private Fire Service Mains and Their Appurtenances*
NFPA 25, *Standard for the Inspection, Testing, and Maintenance of Water-Based Fire Protection Systems*
NFPA 31, *Standard for the Installation of Oil-Burning Equipment*
NFPA 37, *Standard for the Installation and Use of Stationary Combustion Engines and Gas Turbines*
NFPA 54, *National Fuel Gas Code*
NFPA 70, *National Electrical Code®*
NFPA 72®, National Fire Alarm Code®
NFPA 110, *Standard for Emergency and Standby Power Systems.*

Chapter 7

Fire Pump Controllers and Power Supply Arrangements for Motor-Driven Fire Pumps

Revised by

James S. Nasby ❑ John R. Kovacik

Chapter Contents

Key Terms

combination controller, fire pump controller, fire pump (diesel-engine driven), fire pump (electric-motor driven), fire pump (steam-turbine driven), fire pump (variable speed), power transfer switch

Where determined to be necessary through hydraulic analysis, a fire pump is a critical component of the overall water-based fire protection system. A successful outcome to a fire incident depends on the proper operation of the fire pump or pumps because the pump generates the necessary waterflow and pressure for fire control or extinguishment. In this regard, it is not just the fire pump that is of concern. All components that enable the pump to operate must be considered and be properly designed, installed, and maintained. This chapter focuses on the electrical and control aspects of electric motor–driven fire pump installations and is specific to fire pump controllers, motors, and electrical power supply arrangements.

Specific requirements concerning the design, construction, and performance of fire pump components are covered in NFPA 20, *Standard for the Installation of Stationary Pumps for Fire Protection.* NFPA 70, *National Electrical Code®*, addresses how the electrical equipment—including the wiring of the power supply, fire pump controller, fire pump motor, and ancillary circuits—are to be installed. NFPA 20 covers the commissioning (acceptance testing) of fire pump equipment, whereas NFPA 25, *Standard for the Inspection, Testing, and Maintenance of Water-Based Fire Protection Systems,* addresses the routine servicing of fire pump equipment after it has been commissioned.

This chapter is intended to assist those involved with fire pump installations with making better decisions that will lead to more reliable and successful fire protection. This chapter provides added detail and establishes a perspective for the requirements spelled out in NFPA 20, NFPA 25, and NFPA 70 as they pertain to the electrical and control aspects of fire pump installations. In the end, the fire pump installation needs to be reliable and adequate for the life of the building. If determined not to be, corrective actions need to be immediately identified and executed in order to maintain the reliability of the fire protection of the building and maintain the expected degree of property and life-safety protection.

This chapter first appeared as new Section 10, Chapter 8, in the 19th edition of the *Fire Protection Handbook.* The revision in this edition primarily incorporates the extensive changes to the power supply text and requirements of the 2007 edition of NFPA 20. This revision also recognizes the introduction of variable speed motor-driven fire pumps, their applications, and field experience.

For related topics see, Section 15, Chapter 4, "Water Supplies for Sprinkler Systems"; and Section 15, Chapter 6, "Water Distribution."

James S. Nasby is director of engineering at Master Control Systems, Inc., in Lake Bluff, Illinois.

John R. Kovacik is a principal engineer at Underwriters Laboratories Inc., in Northbrook, Illinois.

WORLDWIDE STANDARDS FOR FIRE PUMP CONTROLLERS

Fire pumps and fire pump controllers are widely used throughout the world wherever the need for water exceeds the ability of water supply systems to provide it. The style or type of fire pumps, drivers, and controllers used in North America are the type governed by NFPA 20, *Standard for the Installation of Stationary Pumps for Fire Protection.* In much of the rest of the world, this type of equipment is known as either the NFPA type of fire pump installation or the North American style of fire pump installation. Although many countries have adopted other NFPA standards, such as NFPA 70, *National Electrical Code®*, only a few countries outside of the United States and Canada (e.g., Brazil, Panama, Malaysia, Korea, Indonesia, and Australia) have also adopted NFPA 20 for fire pumps. In other countries, "NFPA-style" equipment is used when North American insurance, financing, or ownership is involved. The other U.S.-based fire pump controller standards are UL 218, *Approval Standard for Fire Pump Controllers,* by Underwriters Laboratories Inc. and FM 1321/1323, *Approval Standard for Fire Pump Controllers for Electric Motor Driven and Diesel Engine Driven Fire Pumps,* by Factory Mutual (FM Global).

Outside of the United States, fire pump controllers and drivers are very different from the NFPA-style equipment. Specifically, most of Europe uses LPC-style equipment. LPC stands for the Loss Prevention Council, which is headquartered in England. The LPC's Loss Prevention Certification Board publishes a list of approved LPC equipment. The Loss Prevention Certification Board is in the process of establishing standards for diesel engines and electric motor–driven fire pump controllers, namely, LPS1236 and LPS1237, respectively. In addition, the British Standards Institute (BSI) offers standard BS 5306: Part 2, a fire pump standard in which the equipment described is similar to that in LPC-type installations. Further, a new European norm, EN 12845, on automatic sprinkler systems is now being used in certain countries. Table 15.7.1 summarizes the key salient features of these two types of fire pump equipment.

ELECTRIC POWER SUPPLY ARRANGEMENTS FOR MOTOR-DRIVEN FIRE PUMPS

The major components of a motor-driven fire pump installation include the pump, the electric motor, and the controller. Another less obvious but equally important component is the electric power supply. Because electric motors require an electric power supply to operate, the arrangement and type of electric power supply used is critical. Loss of electrical power during a fire incident would totally disable the fire protection system, which could then result in potential loss of the building. Therefore, the electric power supply is as critical as any other component of the fire pump installation.

When a fire pump operates, it must do so as intended for the length of time necessary for fire protection operations. Therefore, the electrical power supply must also remain available for this time period. Sufficient electrical capacity to start the fire pump motor and to maintain proper operating speeds once started must also be available. Additionally, the electrical supply must be of sufficient capacity for the locked rotor condition.

A locked rotor condition occurs when a rock or other object gets lodged in the fire pump between the fire pump casing and the impeller or if the pump shaft is seized (frozen) due to long periods of neglect. If the pump shaft cannot rotate freely, it will cause the motor to draw high currents, usually during the starting sequence, as the motor attempts to turn the pump shaft. This prolonged high current can cause significant damage to the electrical equipment and the motor, impairing the entire fire protection system. A prolonged locked rotor condition is not considered a normal condition.

The intent of NFPA 20 is to set higher limits on the overcurrent protection devices than what is normally allowed or required by NFPA 70 to increase the likelihood that the fire pump motor can dislodge an obstruction or free a frozen pump and allow pumping to commence or continue. For some motor starting methods, especially for emergency mechanical starting, the current required for starting the motor can reach a locked rotor condition. Various methods are employed so that the short-term high-inrush starting currents do not open the disconnecting means in the fire pump controller during pump starting.

Overall, electrical safety and preservation of electrical equipment are considered secondary objectives in NFPA 20. This philosophy is contrary to the general requirements of NFPA 70, in which requirements are written to minimize electrical hazard to buildings and occupants, reduce the likelihood of damage to electrical equipment, and decrease the possibility of ignition from overloaded electrical circuits. In this regard, NFPA 70 specifies certain safety devices to protect people and equipment from hazardous voltages and electrical currents. NFPA 20, however, which essentially pertains to the effective and continued operation of the fire pump once a fire has occurred, overrides the general safety provisions of NFPA 70. NFPA 20 considers the fire pump equipment to be sacrificial so as to provide continued water delivery for fire-fighting operations for as long as possible. The potential for damaging the motor or other equipment because of high electrical currents is not considered an appropriate reason for shutting down the fire pump and the water-based fire protection system.

The 2007 edition of NFPA 20 included significant revisions to the power supply requirements in Chapter 9. Sections 9.1, 9.2, and 9.3 were rewritten to clear up the following concerns with the existing text:

1. The portion of the power supply that must be dedicated to the fire pump installation
2. Questions on whether the normal supply arrangement is allowed to change based on provisions for backup power
3. Clarification of the requirements for using the "campus-style" arrangement
4. Questions on whether more than one backup source of power is permitted
5. Increased guidance for services over 600 volts (privately owned transformers)

In the 2007 edition, NFPA 20, Section 9.1, "General," is essentially the same as in the 2003 edition, except that a new Sec-

TABLE 15.7.1 Comparison of Fire Pump Controller Characteristics

Parameter or Attribute	*LPC*	*NFPA*
All Controllers (Both Diesel and Electric Motor Driven)		
Manual stop required (no automatic stop)	All fire pumps	All sole-source pumps
Enclosure type (protection)	IP65 (dust tight, spray resistant)	NEMA 2 (drip proof)
Usual location of pressure switch	Separate from controller	Within controller
Pressure recorder required	No	Yes
Electric Motor Drive Controllers (Low-Voltage Full-Service Controllers)		
Power for electric motor driver	Separate building circuit	Separate service or feeder
Maximum load on electric motor driver	90.9%[a]	115%
Separate isolating switch required	No	Yes
Overcurrent protection	Fuses	Circuit breaker
Overcurrent protection	200%, for 5 hr minimum	300% or less, no trip
Motor locked rotor protection timing	75% of motor burn-out time	8 to 20 sec
Emergency run manual operator required	No	Yes
Overload relays allowed	No	No
Diesel Engine Drive Controllers		
Maximum load on diesel engine driver	90.9%[a]	90.9%[a]
Overspeed shutdown	Prohibited	Mandatory
Low oil and high-temperature shutdown	Prohibited	During test only
Cranking batteries	Two	Two
Battery capacity	6 cranks each	12 cranks each
Cranking cycle times (sec)	15 sec cranking, 10 sec resting	15 sec cranking and resting
Cranking cycles	Six on one battery	Six, alternating
Emergency manual cranking	Both batteries in parallel	Either or both[b]
Test start light after a pump demand run	Required	Not required
Automatic weekly test circuit	Not required	Required
Battery charger size (for lead acid batteries)	3.5 to 7% of 10-hr capacity	Total capacity recharge of both batteries in 24 hr or less
Typical charger size for 100 amp-hour batteries	3.5 to 7 amperes	10 amperes[c]
Typical charger size for 200 amp-hour batteries	7 to 14 amperes	10 amperes[c]
Location of tachometer and speed switch	In controller	On engine

[a]Driver must be 110% of maximum pump load.
[b]Varies with the controller design (manufacturer); some have one start button, others two.
[c]Either two 10 ampere chargers or a single divided 20 ampere charger is typical.

tion 9.1.4 was added as a relocation of an existing requirement that all power supplies are to be located and arranged to protect against damage by fire from within the premises and exposing hazards. This requirement previously applied where power was supplied by a service. It now applies to all power sources. Section 9.2 was retitled "Normal Power," and Section 9.2.2 was rewritten to identify the types of power supplies that may serve as the normal source of power to the electric motor–driven fire pump. The requirements for the one allowable disconnecting means and associated overcurrent protection installed in the power supply to the fire pump controller are now covered in Section 9.2.3. Section 9.3 was retitled "Alternate Power," and Section 9.3.1 was rewritten to relocate an existing requirement that at least one alternate source of power is to be provided when the height of the structure is beyond the pumping capacity of the fire department apparatus. Since it applies to the need for alternate power, its new location is more appropriate. The types of power supplies that may serve as the alternate source of power to the electric motor–driven fire pump where reliable power cannot be obtained from a service connection or on-site power production facility are identified in Section 9.3.2.

Sources of Electric Power Supplies

The following electrical power supplies are acceptable for fire pump installations under specific conditions. As will be described, only a reliable utility service or private power station can be used as a stand-alone individual power supply.

Utility Service. *Service* is the conductors and equipment for delivering energy from the electricity supply system to the wiring system of the premises served. Generally stated, the service is the equipment provided by the public utility used to deliver electrical power to the facility for all normal operations. Specifically, the service begins where the utility wiring stops (service point), and the service ends at the customer side of the service disconnecting means (usually the main switch or main circuit breaker). Ideally for fire pump installations, electrical power should be provided through a direct dedicated circuit to the fire pump controller from the service point as indicated in Figure 15.7.1. The connection is made from either a dedicated service or as a tap ahead of the service disconnect supplying the premises' electrical equipment. For either of these arrangements, the fire pump controller serves as the service disconnecting means. If this direct connection is not possible, other options exist and are discussed in the following section on dedicated connection of supply conductors. In general, the service equipment needs to be located and arranged to minimize the possibility of damage by fire and other hazards from both within the premises and external exposures.

On-Site Electrical Power Production Facility. On-site generation encompasses one or more prime movers and generators located on the premises that serve as the normal electric power source for the premises. In other words, the on-site generation supplies all electrical loads on the facility. This power supply is also referred to as a private power station. A prime mover is described as a mechanical device such as a turbine used to drive a generator. As with the utility service described previously, electrical power should ideally be provided via a direct dedicated circuit to the fire pump controller from the private power station, and the power generation facility needs to be located and protected to minimize the possibility of damage by fire and other hazards from within the premises and from external exposures. This equipment must be located in a separate building or in a structure cut off from the remainder of the premises. An on-site

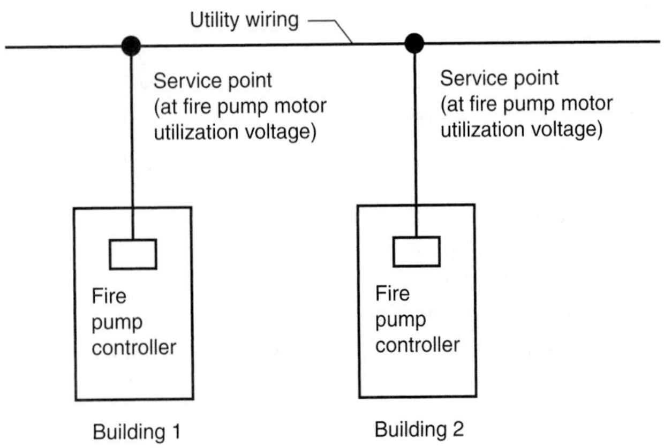

FIGURE 15.7.1 Direct Connection to Utility Service

standby or emergency generator as described next cannot be considered on-site generation because its purpose is to supply emergency electrical loads only.

On-Site Standby (or Emergency) Generator. Generators are considered an emergency or backup electrical power supply. Generators are not intended to serve as the normal source of power for the facility and are, therefore, not considered a private power production facility. Generators do not need to be dedicated solely to fire pump operations but must be of sufficient capacity to allow normal starting and running of the fire pump motors while supplying all other simultaneously operated loads such as elevators and emergency lighting. NFPA 110, *Standard for Emergency and Standby Power Systems,* addresses the installation of these generators.

Feeder Sources. Feeders constitute a power supply arrangement in which power is delivered from a single service point to fire pump equipment in more than one building through a non-dedicated circuit. Unlike the arrangement for a utility service or private power station that requires a dedicated circuit from the service point to the fire pump equipment, feeders employ conductors from the service point to deliver power to multiple buildings. Figure 15.7.2 illustrates two feeder arrangements, one supplied from a utility service and the other supplied from a private power station.

Feeder sources are limited to multibuilding campus-style arrangements with fire pumps located at one or more buildings, where the utility service or private power station arrangement is not practicable and where the feeder arrangement is acceptable to the authority having jurisdiction (AHJ). A campus-style facility generally encompasses a considerable contiguous area. Under these circumstances, two feeder sources or a single feeder source in combination with another power supply can be considered a reliable source of electrical power. (See the section on individual sources of power supplies for additional information.)

Other Sources. Diesel engines and steam turbines can also serve as power supplies for fire pumps, although not for the electric motors. Diesel engines and steam turbines are stand-alone power supplies not requiring a backup or emergency source of power. Where diesel engines or steam turbines are used in combination with electric motor drives, they serve as an entirely redundant fire pump arrangement to the electric motor–driven fire pump. Although NFPA 20 does not require this type of arrangement, insurance companies may do so depending on the risk in question. The installation of diesel engines and steam turbines is addressed in Section 15, Chapter 6, "Water Distribution."

Individual Sources of Electric Power Supplies

The basic rule for power supply is that electrical power is to be supplied to the motor-driven fire pump by an individual stand-alone reliable source or by two or more (multiple) independent sources. Therefore, if the utility service or private power station is considered reliable, only one source is needed. If a single power supply is unreliable, then additional sources of electrical power must be provided. Additionally, regardless of the reliability of a proposed single power supply, where the height of the

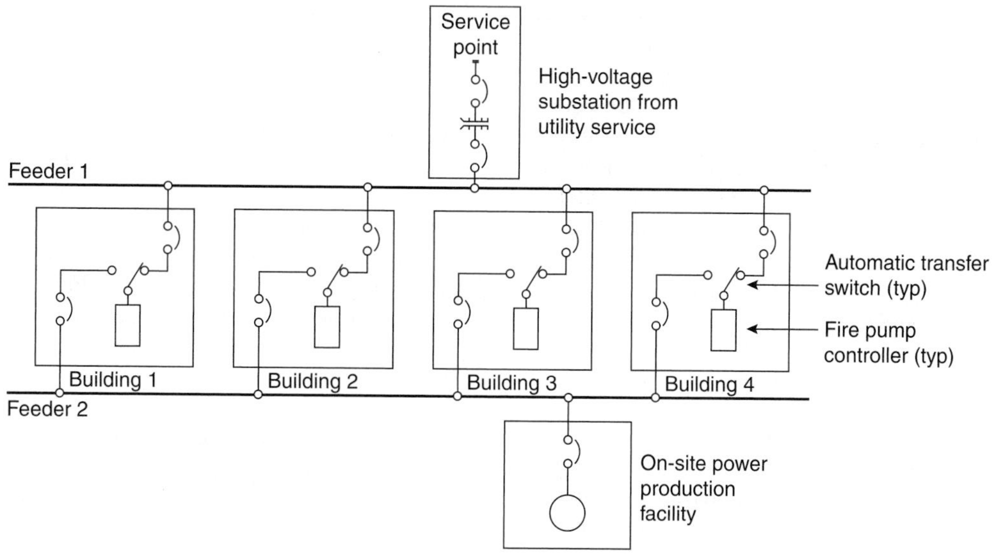

FIGURE 15.7.2 Feeder Arrangement from Two Independent Sources

building is beyond the pumping capacity of the fire department, a second source of power needs to be provided. This provision addresses the situation of the electrical power supply being inadvertently lost or intentionally disconnected during a fire, and the fire department not being able to deliver the necessary water pressure and flow to fight the fire.

Local regulations often override the requirements of NFPA 20 and usually specify additional conditions under which more than one power supply is required even if a single source is considered reliable. For example, the building code in one state requires that all fire pumps serving high-rise buildings, assembly and educational facilities with more than 300 occupants, buildings classified as hazardous occupancies, and institutional facilities in which surgical or treatment operations are conducted be provided with emergency power.

Reliability of Electrical Power Supply

Reliability of the power supply generally pertains to the availability of the power supply and how it is arranged and connected to the fire pump controller. NFPA 20 suggests that a reliable electrical power supply is one that experiences only infrequent power disruptions from environmental conditions or human interaction. This statement implies that a reliable power source can tolerate some limited interruptions and supports the notion that zero risk is unattainable. Responsibility for determining reliability of the power source in terms of its availability and whether it meets the intent of NFPA 20 rests with the AHJ.

The service owned by the public utility and a private on-site electrical power production facility are the only two electric power sources that NFPA 20 would consider to be reliable. However, local regulations and other conditions usually specify additional restrictions in this regard. In some instances, the AHJ might not consider the public utility or private power station as a reliable electrical power source for the fire pump(s) due to frequent power interruptions. For example, under the rolling power blackout conditions in California during 2000 and 2001, the single power source, the public utility, was not considered reliable and corrective action was needed for emergency power. As described previously, it is important to recognize that a private on-site power generation facility or private power station is not the same as an on-site generator.

There have always been questions as to what defines a reliable power supply. The 2003 edition of NFPA 20 first introduced annex material that provided guidance on the selection of such a power supply. The 2007 edition revised that annex material to provide more specific criteria. The Fire Pump Committee included the following guidance for determining the reliability of the power supply:

1. The source power plant has not experienced any shutdowns of longer than 4 continuous hours in the year prior to plan submittal.
2. No power outages have been experienced in the area of the protected facility that were caused by failures in the power grid that were not due to natural disasters or electric grid management failure.
3. The normal source of power is not supplied by overhead conductors outside the protected facility.
4. Only the disconnect switches and overcurrent protection devices permitted by Section 9.2.3 are installed in the normal source of power. The committee did add two requirements to the body of the standard to specify certain levels of performance that, to a certain degree, define the capability (and reliability) of the power supply. The standard now states that all power supplies shall (a) have the capacity to run the fire pump on a continuous basis and (b) comply with the voltage drop requirements of Section 9.4. These are key elements of pump performance.

The use of phase converters as part of the power supply to the fire pump motor has raised concerns regarding the reliability of such a supply. The 2007 edition of NFPA 20 added annex material stating that "Phase converters that take single-phase power and convert it to three-phase power for the use of fire pump motors are not recommended because of the imbalance in the voltage between the phases when there is no load on the equipment. If the power utility installs phase converters in their own power transmission lines, such phase converters are outside the scope of this standard and need to be evaluated by the AHJ to determine the reliability of the electric supply." Although there are no requirements prohibiting their use, phase converters are not considered a reliable source of power and are not recommended for fire pump service.

Multiple Sources of Power

Where multiple electric power sources are provided, NFPA 20 requires that they be arranged and located so that a fire, structural failure, or operational accident that interrupts one source will not cause an interruption of the other source. Additionally, on-site standby generators must be protected to minimize the possibility of damage by fire and other hazards from within and external to the premises.

When reliable electrical power cannot be obtained from either the utility service or a private power station, a redundant or backup source of power by one of the following arrangements is required:

- Combination of two or more sources of either utility service or private power station
- Combination of on-site standby generator and either utility service or private power station
- Combination of feeders from two separate sources
- Combination of feeder source and on-site standby generator
- Diesel engine–driven or steam turbine–driven fire pump

Combination of Two or More Sources of Either Utility Service or Private Power Station. Under this arrangement, a combination of two independent utility sources, two separate private power stations, or a utility source and private power station would suffice. It is important to recognize that where two utility sources are considered, they must be independent of one another. An arrangement consisting of two separate service points from the same utility equipment would not be considered an acceptable combination of power sources.

Combination of On-Site Standby Generator and Either Utility Service or Private Power Station. In this case either the utility service or the private power station would provide power for normal operations and the standby generator would provide backup power. In the event that normal power is lost and a fire occurs, the standby generator would be available to start and operate the fire pump motor. This arrangement should not be interpreted to mean that only the standby generator should be arranged to start and operate the pump. The normal electrical power supply also needs to be sized and arranged to execute this function.

Combination of Feeders from Two Separate Sources. This arrangement is depicted in Figure 15.7.2. Feeder 1 delivers power from the utility service, and feeder 2 delivers power from the private power station. Under this arrangement, both feeder conductors constitute an independent power source because they are delivering power from two separate sources. The intent is that failure of one source will not or should not affect or cause the failure of the other source. If feeder sources were arranged such that two separate feeder conductors supplied power to a building from two separate service points from the same utility service, the feeder source would only be considered as a single unreliable power source. As previously indicated, the feeder source can only be used for multibuilding campus-style complexes where a direct connection to the utility service or a private power station is not practicable and where such an arrangement is acceptable to the AHJ.

Combination of Feeder Source and On-Site Standby Generator. This arrangement is depicted in Figure 15.7.3. The feeder connects the utility service power source to multiple buildings and each building contains a standby generator. As indicated in the previous section, the feeder source can only be used for multibuilding campus-style complexes where a direct connection to the utility service or a private power station is not practicable and where such an arrangement is acceptable to the AHJ.

Diesel Engine–Driven or Steam Turbine–Driven Fire Pump. The diesel engine or steam turbine would be redundant to the electric motor–driven pump, which in turn is supplied by the utility service or a private power station. The diesel engine or steam turbine cannot be redundant to an electric motor fire pump powered exclusively by a feeder source or an on-site generator. However, as previously discussed, where a diesel engine or steam turbine fire pump arrangement is provided, NFPA 20 permits the diesel engine or steam turbine to serve as a standalone driver not requiring any backup power supplies.

Dedicated Connection of Supply Conductors

To minimize the possibility of accidentally disconnecting the power supply to the fire pump, the power supply to the fire pump must not be disconnected when the power for the facility is disconnected. For this reason, a reliable power supply is one that contains a separate dedicated connection to the service point or a connection to the supply side of the service disconnecting means. The only exception to this general rule pertains to feeder sources in which the disconnection of power to the fire pumps is permitted under circumstances that automatically ensure the continued availability of the alternate power supply. Because feeders use a single circuit to supply several buildings, disconnecting power to the feeder at any one of a number of points would potentially cut off power to all buildings served by the feeder and, thus, their fire pumps as well. It is also strongly advised that the power circuit for any fire pump not be routed through any other building to minimize the chance of a fire in one building knocking out the fire protection in any other building(s).

The most preferred power supply arrangement is a direct connection, as illustrated in Figure 15.7.4. In this arrangement, the power supply conductors directly connect the service point

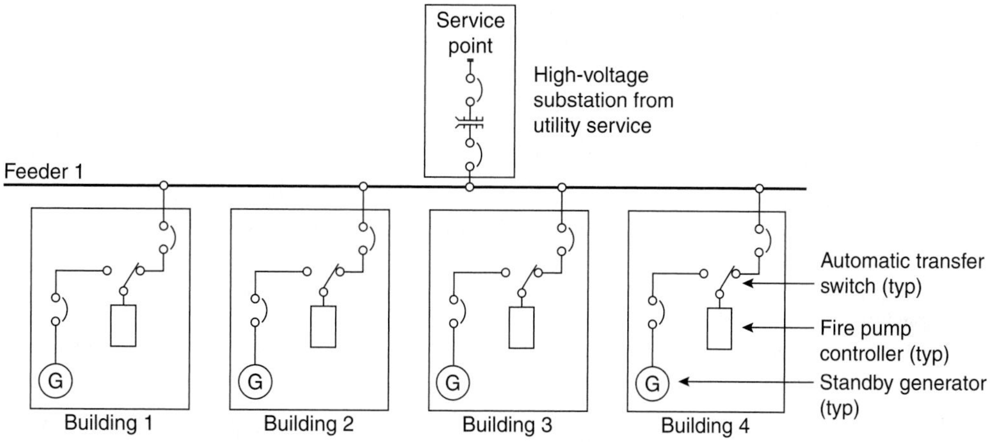

FIGURE 15.7.3 Feeder Source in Combination with an On-Site Standby Generator

or private power station to the fire pump controller or a combination fire pump controller power transfer switch, where more than one power supply is used. Under this arrangement, there is no disconnecting means or overcurrent protection device(s) other than that provided by the fire pump controller. In essence, the fire pump controller becomes the service disconnecting means and overcurrent protection device and is listed as such. Arranging the power supply in this manner minimizes the possibility that the fire department will inadvertently cut off power to the fire pump when the facility's power supply is disconnected.

NFPA 20 recommends that where anticipated risks are large and interruption for fire pump service would seriously affect protection, at least two separate circuits from the power supply to the pump room be provided. The circuits should be run by separate routes or in such a manner that failure of more than one at the same time would be only a remote possibility.

Supervised Connection of Supply Conductors

Where a utility service or private power station serves as the power supply but a direct connection from these sources is not practicable, NFPA 20 allows for two other power supply arrangements. These include a supervised connection and a connection incorporating a transformer. Note that connections for feeder sources are addressed separately later. For both arrangements, the circuits that supply electric motor–driven fire pumps must be supervised against inadvertent disconnection. The first arrangement, referred to as a supervised connection, allows for a single disconnecting means and overcurrent protective device(s) to be installed ahead of the fire pump controller, as illustrated in Figure 15.7.5. A supervised connection is allowed under specific conditions only, pertaining to selection of the overcurrent protective device, means of disconnecting power, marking of the disconnecting means and the controller, and supervision of the disconnecting means as described in the following sections.

Overcurrent Protective Device Selection. Overcurrent is any current in excess of the rated current of equipment such as the fire pump motor, or the ampacity of a conductor, and can result from overload, short circuit, or ground fault. An overload condition for an electric motor includes locked rotor in which the motor is loaded so heavily that the motor shaft cannot turn. Locked rotor can be caused when a stone or other obstruction prevents the fire pump impeller from freely rotating. The overcurrent protective device, normally a circuit breaker for fire pump applications, serves to protect the motor from destroying itself under specific overload conditions. It senses when the amount of current flowing through the supply conductors exceeds a certain value and opens the circuit.

For a supervised connection, the overcurrent protective device on the supply conductors serving the fire pump equipment must be selected or set to carry indefinitely the sum of

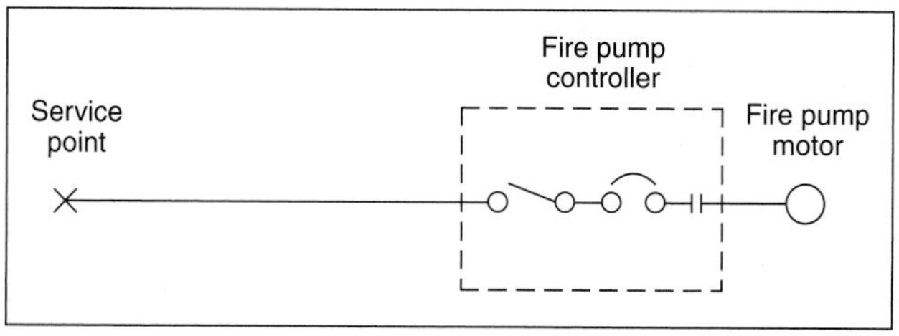

FIGURE 15.7.4 Direct Connection Between Service Point and Fire Pump Motor

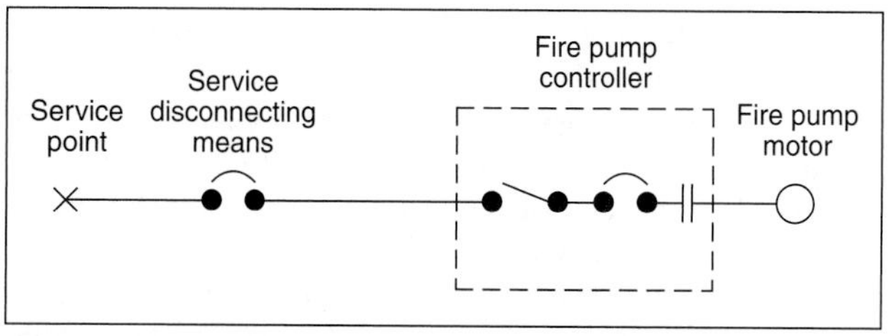

FIGURE 15.7.5 Installation of a Disconnecting Means

the locked rotor current of the fire pump motor(s), the pressure maintenance pump motor(s), and the full-load current of the associated fire pump accessory equipment when connected to this power supply. This value of overcurrent protection is set higher than that typically required for NFPA 70 for nonfire pump equipment. In other words, more current is allowed to pass through the conductors and motor, increasing the potential for equipment failure and the possibility of an additional ignition source. The reason for allowing more current to pass is to permit operation of the fire pump equipment for as long as possible during a fire. As previously indicated, the fire pump equipment is considered sacrificial and preservation of fire pump equipment is not an acceptable reason for disconnecting power to the pump equipment during a fire.

Although the overcurrent protective device is required to carry the locked rotor current indefinitely, in actuality this time period is normally limited by the disconnecting means located in the controller. When a motor is started, a large inrush current occurs and, in many cases, especially for manual (emergency mechanical) starting, is as high as that experienced during a locked rotor condition. For this reason, the overcurrent protective device must have a sufficiently high ampere rating to avoid opening the circuit on the occurrence of large but temporary inrush currents required for motor starting. In this regard, the locked rotor protection in the fire pump controller will allow for the motor to be started without disrupting the circuit. The upstream overcurrent protective device is required to hold the motor locked rotor current indefinitely to allow the fire pump controller to govern when or if the circuit is to be interrupted.

Disconnecting Means. The disconnecting means is a manually or automatically operated device that removes electrical circuits from their power supply. The disconnecting means can consist of circuit breakers for most controllers or fused switches in medium-voltage controllers. The supplemental disconnecting means permitted through a supervised connection is supplemental to the manual and automatic disconnecting means located in the fire pump controller and is intended for only periodic use. The supplemental disconnecting means must possess the following characteristics:

- Identified as suitable for use as service equipment
- Lockable in the closed position
- Located at a sufficiently remote location from other building or other fire pump source disconnecting means that inadvertent operation at the same time would be unlikely

Service equipment is the necessary equipment that connects the lead end of service conductors to the electrical circuits of a building or other structure. Service equipment usually consists of a circuit breaker(s) or fused switch(es) and their accessories and is intended to constitute the main control and cutoff of the electrical supply. Service equipment is intended to disconnect all ungrounded conductors in a building from the service-entrance conductors. The disconnecting means at any one location should not consist of more than six circuit breakers or six switches and is required to be readily accessible either outside the building or inside nearest the point of entrance of the service-entrance conductors.

Disconnect Marking. The disconnecting means must be permanently marked "Fire Pump Disconnecting Means" to make clear the purpose of the disconnecting means. The letters are to be marked at least 1 in. (25.4 mm) in height and they are to be visible without opening enclosure doors or covers.

Controller Marking. A placard must be placed adjacent to the fire pump controller stating the location of the additional disconnecting means and the location of the key if the disconnecting means is locked.

Supervision. The disconnecting means must be supervised in the closed position by one of the following methods:

- Central station, proprietary, or remote station signal device
- Local signaling service that will cause the sounding of an audible signal at a constantly attended location
- Locking of the disconnecting means in the closed position
- Sealing of the disconnecting means and approved weekly recorded inspections where the disconnecting means are located within fenced enclosures or in buildings under the control of the owner. The intent of monitoring is to ensure that if the power supply is inadvertently disconnected, corrective action can be immediately taken.

Power Supply Connection Incorporating a Transformer

Where the supply voltage differs from the utilization voltage of the fire pump motor, that is, the loaded voltage and the rated motor voltage, a transformer meeting the requirements of NFPA 70 along with a disconnecting means and overcurrent protection can be installed between the fire pump controller and the service point, as illustrated in Figure 15.7.6. Where this arrangement is employed, specific conditions pertaining to the selection of the overcurrent protective device, the means of disconnecting power, the marking of the disconnecting means and the controller, and supervision of the disconnecting means as described for a supervised connection apply. It is important to note that secondary side overcurrent protection on the transformer is not permitted.

The transformer must be dedicated to fire pump equipment unless it supplies a feeder source as described in the section on feeder arrangement. The transformer must be rated at mini-

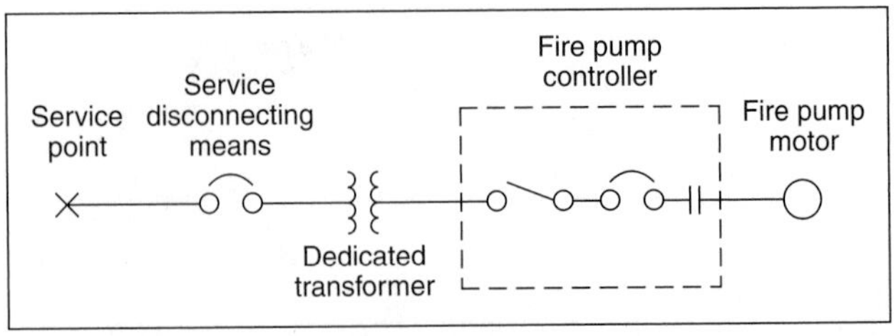

FIGURE 15.7.6 Installation of a Disconnecting Means and a Transformer

mum of 125 percent of the sum of the fire pump motor(s) and pressure maintenance pump motor loads and 100 percent of the associated fire pump accessory equipment supplied by the transformer. Note, however, that this rating is a thermal rating and that 125 percent will almost never be large enough to meet the voltage drop requirements.

The most critical limiting conditions for both the supervised connection and the transformer connection are the location of the disconnecting means that are to be remote from the other service disconnecting means and the overcurrent protection setting that is to be set to carry indefinitely the sum of the locked rotor current of the fire pump motors and the pressure maintenance pump motors, plus the full-load current of the connected fire pump accessory equipment.

Feeder Arrangement

Where feeder sources are used, the 2007 edition of NFPA 20 indicates that the overcurrent protection and the disconnecting means are to be arranged as indicated in NFPA 70 rather than that specified for a supervised connection as indicated previously. However, the 2008 edition of NFPA 70 provides no latitude in this regard and requires that the overcurrent protection and disconnecting means be arranged like that for a supervised connection. In other words, the circuit breaker on the feeder conductor needs to be set to carry indefinitely the sum of the locked rotor current of the fire pump, jockey pump, and other accessory equipment; and the disconnecting means must be suitable as service equipment, lockable in the closed position, and located at a sufficiently remote location from other building or fire pump source disconnecting means. Additionally, where more than one disconnecting means is supplied by a single feeder, the overcurrent protective device in each disconnecting means must be coordinated with all other supply side overcurrent protective devices. This requirement is to ensure that only the breaker nearest the fault or short circuit trips open.

The transformer on the feeder conductor may serve loads other than those dedicated to the fire pump. The transformer must be rated at a minimum of 125 percent of the sum of the fire pump motor(s) and pressure maintenance pump(s) motor loads and 100 percent of the remaining load supplied by the transformer, that is, all other loads served by the feeder. As described in the section on connection incorporating a transformer, the transformer will normally need to be larger to meet the voltage drop criteria.

Connection to a Power Transfer Switch

Perhaps the most complex arrangement is that of multiple power sources serving a fire pump motor. Transfer of power to the fire pump controller between the normal supply and the alternate supply, including an on-site generator, is to take place within the pump room. Figure 15.7.7 illustrates two acceptable arrangements for two power sources feeding a single fire pump motor. The combination fire pump controller/power transfer switch shown in arrangement I of Figure 15.7.7 must be listed for such fire pump service. Arrangement II of Figure 15.7.7 shows where a separately mounted power transfer switch is used. As in the case of the combination fire pump controller/power transfer switch, the separately mounted power transfer switch must be listed for fire pump service. Unless the emergency power source is an on-site generator, the disconnecting means and overcurrent protective devices shown must meet the requirements for a supervised connection as specified previously.

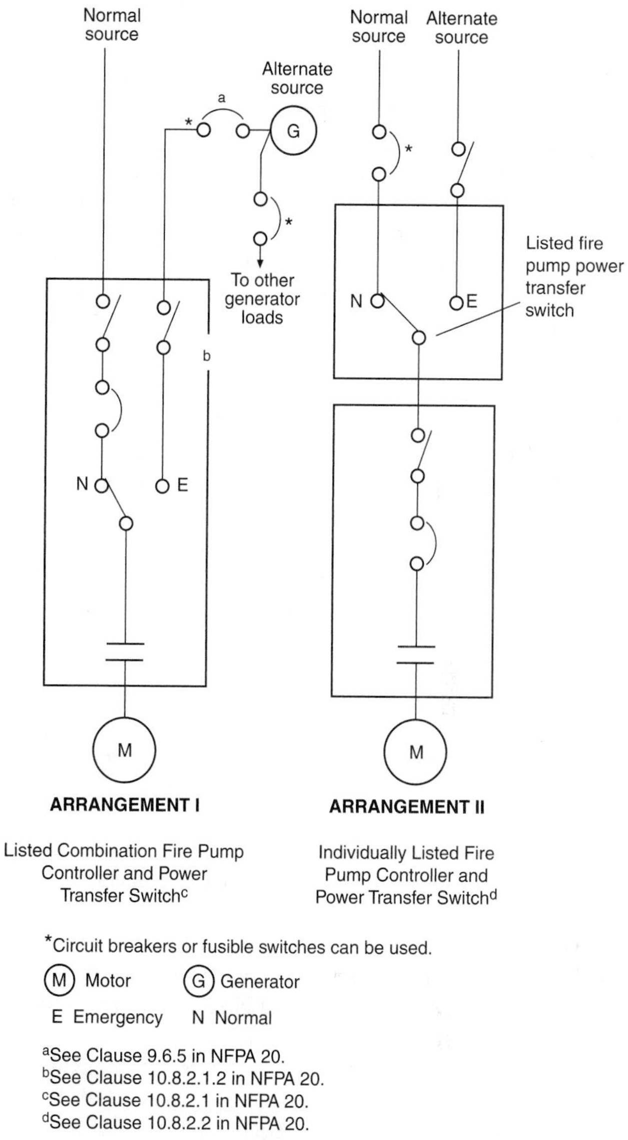

FIGURE 15.7.7 Two Acceptable Arrangements for Two Power Sources Feeding a Single Fire Pump Motor (Source: NFPA 20, *Standard for the Installation of Stationary Pumps for Fire Protection,* Figure A.10.8, 2007, p. 20-75)

Physical Protection of Supply Conductors

In general, conductors feeding fire pumps and their accessories must be protected to resist possible damage by fire, structural failure, or operational accident.

Supply Conductors. These are physically routed outside buildings and installed as service-entrance conductors in accordance with NFPA 70. If supply conductors cannot be physically routed outside buildings, they can be routed through buildings if installed under not less than 2 in. (50 mm) of concrete beneath the building, or if installed within a building in a raceway that is encased in concrete or brick not less than 2 in. (50 mm) thick. For a feeder arrangement, the requirement for protecting service conductors applies to all supply conductors on the load side of the service disconnecting means that constitute the normal source of supply to that fire pump. However, where there are multiple sources of supply with means for automatic connection from one source to the other, the requirement only applies to those conductors on the load side of the point of automatic connection between sources.

Circuit Conductors. These are on the load side of the final disconnecting means and overcurrent protective devices permitted for a supervised connection and must be kept entirely independent of all other wiring. The conductors are to supply only loads that are directly associated with the fire pump system, and they are to be protected to resist potential damage by fire, structural failure, or operational accident. They are permitted to be routed through buildings if encased in 2 in. (50 mm) of concrete, or within enclosed construction dedicated to the fire pump circuit(s) and having a minimum 2 hour fire resistance rating, or be listed electrical circuit protective systems with a minimum of 2 hour fire resistance. The 2008 *NEC* increased the fire resistance ratings from 1 to 2 hours to be consistent with *NFPA 72®, National Fire Alarm Code®*, which requires 2 hour survivability of the notification circuits and the interconnecting wiring of the fire command center.

Wiring. The installation must comply with any restriction provided in the listing of the electrical circuit protective systems used. The supply conductors located in the electrical equipment room where they originate and in the fire pump room are not required to have the minimum 2 hour fire separation or fire resistance rating, unless otherwise required by NFPA 70.

All wiring from the controllers to the pump motors needs to be rigid metal conduit, intermediate metal conduit, liquid-tight flexible metal conduit, or liquid-tight flexible nonmetallic conduit Type LFNC-B or Type MI cable. Where wire connectors are used in the fire pump circuit, the connectors must also be listed. All wiring from engine controllers and batteries must be protected against mechanical injury and must be installed in accordance with the controller and engine manufacturer's instructions. See the section on motor wiring in *Pumps for Fire Protection* for more information in this regard.

The 2007 edition of NFPA 20 added a requirement addressing the use of single conductors entering the fire pump controller enclosure. The requirements addressed two concerns. Single conductors entering the fire pump controller enclosure separately could produce significant heating of the metallic enclosure due to magnetic forces. Also, certain electrical circuit protective systems could produce flammable gases that must be prevented from entering the fire pump controller enclosure. The new requirement states: "Where single conductors are used, they shall be terminated in a separate junction box" (not the fire pump controller). This permits splicing to a different wiring method that allows for all phase conductors to enter the controller through the same raceway. It also allows for the sealing of cables outside of the fire pump controller enclosure to keep flammable gases at a safe distance from the controller enclosure.

Fire Pump and Fire Pump Controller Power Transfer Switch. Although not directly pertaining to the protection of conductors, the fire pump controller and fire pump power transfer switch are not to be used as a junction box to supply other electrical equipment, including the pressure maintenance pump. Additionally, the fire pump controller and fire pump power transfer switch cannot serve any loads other than the fire pump for which it is intended. In this regard, a fire pump controller cannot serve more than one fire pump.

Buried Installation. A completely underground circuit from the service point or the private power station to the pump room is strongly recommended and should be arranged where practicable. This guideline also pertains to feeder conductors. Where such buried installation is not possible, that portion of the overhead circuit adjacent to the property served by the fire pump or to exposing properties or structures should be installed with consideration to potential damage in case of fire or other hazard. Where the pump room is part of, or in close proximity to, the property or structures that the pump is intended to protect, the conductors should be underground for some distance from the pump room.

The physical protection of the supply conductors provides a means of minimizing the impact from external exposures as well as minimizing the spread of fire as a result of overcurrent within the conductors themselves. During fire conditions, conductors from the service point or private power station are susceptible to direct impact and failure from collapsing buildings and other structural members on the facility as well as failure from direct impact by the fire. Where ignition is a result of overcurrent in the fire pump power supply conductors, the general construction arrangement described previously also serves to minimize the spread of fire.

Junction Boxes. The 2007 edition of NFPA 20 added requirements addressing the use of junction boxes for routing conductors to or from a fire pump controller. As previously mentioned, where single conductors are used to provide power to a fire pump controller, they must be terminated in a separate junction box. In addition, junction boxes are often used to terminate cables and change to some other form of wiring to the fire pump controller. The new requirements state that:

1. The mounting and installing of a junction box shall not violate the enclosure Type (NEMA) rating of the fire pump controller(s).
2. The mounting and installing of a junction box shall not violate the integrity of the fire pump controller(s) and shall not affect the Short Circuit Rating of the controller(s).
3. At a minimum, a (NEMA) Type 2, dripproof enclosure (junction box) shall be used and the enclosure shall be listed to match the fire pump controller enclosure Type rating.
4. Terminals, junction blocks, splices, and the like, when used, shall be listed.

Voltage Drop and Conductor Sizing

The voltage at the controller line terminal must not drop more than 15 percent below normal (controller-rated voltage) under motor-starting conditions. The voltage at the motor terminal must not drop more than 5 percent below the voltage rating of the motor when the motor is operating at 115 percent of the full-load current rating of the motor. (See the section on controllers for discussion of starting of motors.) This limitation does not apply for emergency-run mechanical starting, which may experience larger inrush currents.

Conductors supplying a fire pump motor(s), pressure maintenance pumps, and associated fire pump accessory equipment will have a minimum rating of 125 percent of the sum of the fire pump motor(s) and pressure maintenance motor(s) full-load currents and 100 percent of the associated fire pump accessory equipment. Conductors supplying only a fire pump motor(s) will have a minimum rating of 125 percent of the fire pump motor(s) full-load current(s).

Arrangements for an On-Site Standby Generator

An on-site generator used to supply backup power to fire pump motors needs to be of sufficient capacity to allow normal starting and running of the motor(s) driving the fire pump(s) while supplying all other simultaneously operated load(s). Generally, the generator does not need to be sized for locked rotor current if locked rotor current is not required for normal starting, such as for part winding and autotransformer starting. Where protective devices are installed in the on-site power source circuits at the generator, such devices need to be set to allow instantaneous pickup of the full pump room load. Additionally, a tap ahead of the on-site generator disconnecting means is not required as is for the connection of other power sources.

On-site standby generators are to comply with the voltage drop requirements previously discussed and are to meet the requirements of Level 1, Type 10, Class X systems of NFPA 110. The fuel capacity is to be sufficient to provide 8 hours of fire pump operation at 100 percent of the rated pump capacity in addition to the supply required for other demands. Where the generator is installed to supply power to loads in addition to one or more fire pump drivers, the fuel supply should be sized to provide adequate fuel for all connected loads for the desired duration. These connected loads can include such loads as emergency lighting, exit signage, and elevators.

Where more than one fire pump and motor are used, such as for high-rise buildings, automatic sequencing of the starting of the fire pumps is both permitted and required, as described in the following section on controllers. Starting all pumps simultaneously is not desirable from a pump performance standpoint. Additionally, this would create tremendous inrush currents and a higher voltage drop as more than one motor attempts to start.

ELECTRIC DRIVE CONTROLLERS

Controllers are devices that govern, in some predetermined manner, the starting and stopping of the fire pump driver as well as the monitoring and signaling of the starters and the condition of the fire pump unit (Figure 15.7.8). This section describes attributes of the different types of electric drive controllers and provides a broad perspective on the use of various types of controllers.

Fire Pump Controller Characteristics

Because of their intended function, fire pump controllers possess unique characteristics when compared to controllers for other types of applications. The most obvious is the limited protection of the fire pump motor and the motor circuit and components. The power path components of the controller, like the fire pump motor and power wiring circuits, are considered sacrificial. (Note that fire pump equipment is considered sacrificial because safeguards associated with other building equipment to preserve equipment do not apply. Fire-fighting operations must continue until the fire is extinguished even if the fire-fighting equipment is eventually damaged.) Controllers do not include motor overload relays and the only overload, overcurrent, or short circuit protection for the controller, motor, and wiring is provided by the fire pump controller circuit breaker. Note that the requirements differ for limited-service fire pump controllers, which use a different type of circuit breaker, and for medium-voltage controllers, which use special fuses and overcurrent sensing. Nonetheless, these controllers also sacrifice the fire pump motor and wiring similar to all other fire pump controllers.

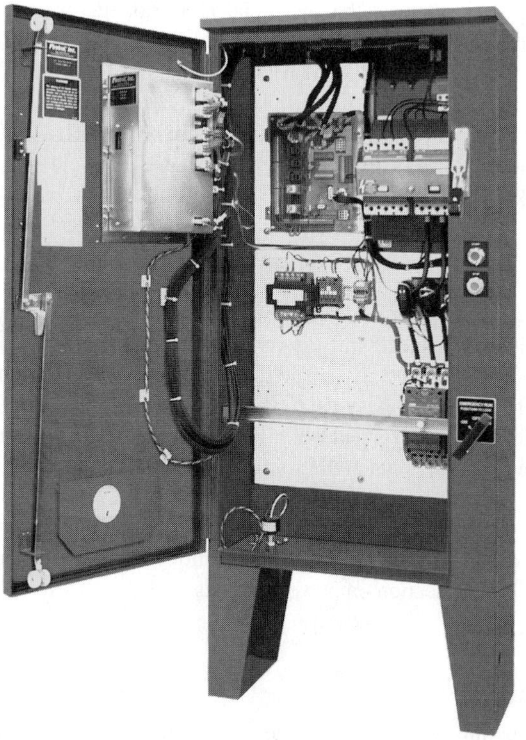

FIGURE 15.7.8 Electric Fire Pump Controller (Source: ASCO Power Technologies, Firetrol Brand Products)

Motor Overheating. The fire pump circuit breaker is not allowed to trip on currents less than 300 percent of FLA (full-load amperes), which is seven times the motor-rated heating compared with that at rated FLA. Running the motor at these high currents will overheat the motor's windings, which will damage or destroy the motor, the controller, and/or the power wiring in a fairly short time. Although not a desirable condition, operating the motor at these high currents is permissible so that fire-fighting operations can continue. This is the reason the motor, controller, and wiring are considered to be sacrificial. Nonetheless, this equipment must be protected from needless damage, stress, or destruction. It is, therefore, recommended that the motor current be monitored for overload (overcurrent) conditions. All listed controllers are available with an optional motor overcurrent alarm circuit.

Ground Fault Monitoring. Another unique characteristic is that ground fault protection is prohibited. However, ground fault monitoring is allowed. The same applies for low voltage, phase loss, phase reversal, underfrequency, and so on. Monitoring is allowed or mandated for some of these conditions, but the controller must keep the fire pump motor running under any of these conditions. The only exception is allowing the controller to protect the motor from attempting to start under a single-phase condition that would destroy the motor. In this condition it is better to protect the motor, as there is no opportunity to start a three-phase motor at rest when supplied with a single-phase power source.

Critical Path Control Circuitry. Another peculiarity of fire pump controllers is the sacrificial nature of the critical path control circuitry. The critical path or critical starting path encompasses every component and connection needed for successful starting of a fire pump. NFPA 20 mandates that the control circuitry within the controller not be protected by fuses or circuit breakers other than the controller's main motor circuit breaker.

Critical Electrical Parameters

Among other things, three electrical parameters are absolutely crucial to the successful starting and running of any fire pump motor: (1) the starting (locked rotor) voltage drop at the controller (15% maximum drop allowed), (2) the service factor (115% maximum) load current voltage drop at the motor (5% maximum allowed), and (3) the ability to start the motor without any false tripping of the fire pump breaker (in the fire pump controller) or any upstream overcurrent protection (fuses or circuit breaker). The voltage drop considerations are covered in more detail in the section on power supplies.

LIMITED-SERVICE CONTROLLERS

Fire pumps and their associated fire pump controllers come in two service types: full service and limited service. Limited-service fire pumps and controllers were introduced in the late 1940s in response to a major insurance organization request for simpler, less expensive controllers for use on smaller risks. One way of helping to assure that these units would be restricted to use on smaller risks was to impose the 30 horsepower (22 kW) maximum size limitation. The controllers are allowed to use the common "inverse time" nonadjustable circuit breaker rather than the special characteristic fire pump circuit breaker as required in full-service controllers. Typical listed limited-service controllers use thermal-magnetic-type circuit breakers. A further cost savings is accomplished by not requiring the separate isolating switch as is required in full-service controllers. In accordance with NFPA 20, these controllers are allowed only where such use is acceptable to the AHJ. Each such installation must be so approved.

Limited-service controllers must meet all of the requirements of full-service controllers with the two exceptions noted previously. By not requiring a full-service fire pump controller, the following characteristics of overcurrent protection are *not* required and are not normally found in these units: (1) they need not hold 300 percent continuously, (2) they need not meet the trip time requirements of 8 to 20 seconds at locked rotor current, and (3) they need not be adjustable. Moreover, the inverse time circuit breaker is required to be between 150 percent and 250 percent of the motor full-load current. This provides a wide range of motor locked rotor trip times. Based on commercially available and commonly used circuit breakers, the trip times can be far less than the minimum 8 second trip time and well over the 20 second maximum time required of full-service controllers. This is due to the difference in circuit breaker trip curves among different ratings, types, and manufactures of thermal-type circuit breakers and due to the motor rated full load current versus the breaker rated current.

Single-Phase Limited-Service Controllers

NFPA 20 states that limited-service controllers can be used for across-the-line starting of squirrel-cage motors of 30 horsepower or less. In some cases the motor horsepower is small enough to allow the use of single-phase motors and controllers when the use of same is approved by the AHJ. Listed controllers are available for those cases where a single-phase pump motor is adequate and where the source of supply will tolerate the starting and running currents while still meeting the voltage drop requirements of 15 percent maximum while starting and 5 percent maximum while running at 115 percent of motor full-load amperes (FLA).

Three-Phase Limited-Service Controllers

Most limited-service controllers and motors are three-phase types. The advantage of three-phase units is lower line currents for any given horsepower at a given voltage. More importantly, three-phase squirrel-cage motors are inherently more reliable than single-phase versions. This is because a single-phase motor contains a start winding in addition to the run winding and also contains a start winding cutout switch or relay to accelerate the motor. These extra components serve to reduce reliability over the simpler three-phase motors that contain none of these extra items.

Means of Starting Limited-Service Controllers

All limited-service controllers are required to be across-the-line, full-voltage, starting types only. This requirement further limits their complexity and, thus, costs. The maximum allowed horsepower limitation of 30 hp (22 kW) also limits the size of the power path components. The circuit breaker is either of the so-called E frame or F frame size. The contactors are similarly limited in size.

FULL-SERVICE CONTROLLERS

All fire pump controllers, with the exception of limited-service controllers, are known as full-service controllers solely to differentiate them from the limited-service types. All full-service controllers must be three phase since regular fire pump motors must be three-phase motors. There are no listed single-phase full-service fire pump controllers.

Low Voltage (600 Vac Maximum)

The majority of fire pump motors and controllers are of the so-called low-voltage type, in electrical power utility terminology, meaning that they are used on power sources of 600 Vac or less. Typical low-voltage power source voltages range from 120 Vac at 60 Hz or 220 Vac at 50 Hz, single phase, and up to 600 Vac, three phase.

Medium Voltage (Up to 7200 Vac)

Some installations use medium-voltage motors and controllers for convenience because the facility already has this voltage available, for example, in large mills and process plants. Another example is multibuilding campus-style sites where the power distribution is at medium voltage. Medium-voltage controllers are also used to avoid the step-down transformer, which would otherwise be needed to reduce the voltage to the range of low-voltage (600 Vac or less) controllers and motors. This transformer also requires upstream disconnect and overcurrent protection. Lastly, medium-voltage controllers are being used more often because the "service" from the power utility is increasingly at medium voltage rather than at low voltage, as was nearly universal not too many years ago.

Medium-voltage fire pump controllers differ from low-voltage controllers by one significant item: the customary fire pump circuit breaker is replaced by three special "R"-rated, medium-voltage, current-limiting motor circuit fuses and a contactor tripping circuit. The tripping circuit has the same characteristics as the circuit breaker in low-voltage controllers, namely, the 300 percent no-trip and the 8- to 20-second trip time at locked rotor (600%). The motor contactor is used to break overload currents whereas the fuses break the higher short circuit currents. Matching the controller and motor horsepower or FLA is vital to prevent false tripping of the fuses, which take considerable time to replace. Note that the NFPA 20 standard does not require the controller to be equipped with spare fuses. It only requires that the controller have a "compartment or rack" within it for the fuses and that a "spare set of fuses be kept readily available" therein by someone.

Low-Voltage, Full-Service Controller Starting

The fire pump is generally required to be connected directly to the incoming service to minimize the chance of unintentional disconnection of the fire pump power supply during a fire. However, this often results in one of two opposite conditions. The first is that the service is of very high capacity and across-the-line starting can safely be used, particularly if emergency power or alternate standby power will not be needed for the pump. In these cases, the short circuit ratings are of utmost importance. The second case is where a dedicated step-down transformer is used for the fire pump. In this case, the size of the dedicated transformer can be reduced somewhat (but not all the way down to the thermal rating) by the use of reduced inrush starting.

Where emergency power is needed and supplied by an on-site generator, the fire pump(s) is often the largest load on the genset. In these cases, the extra cost of the reduced inrush starting fire pump controller, and sometimes of the special motor, is often justified by the savings in the size and cost of the genset. Nonetheless, all fire pumps, whether or not reduced inrush starting, must be capable of starting by the use of the emergency mechanical operator. This mechanical operator is the reason that the genset must be large enough to start the pump or pumps in the ATL (across-the-line) full-voltage starting mode while supplying all other simultaneously operated load(s). This can result in an increase in the size of the genset even though the 15 percent maximum starting current voltage drop under motor-starting conditions is waived for this method of starting. Table 15.7.2 summarizes the various types of starting methods.

Across-the-Line (ATL or Direct-on-Line) Starting

Across-the-line starting mode is the simplest and most common form of fire pump motor starting. ATL starting is also the least expensive, making it the logical choice where the electrical supply or supplies are adequate for the high- inrush (600%) currents that are incurred by this method. This method also produces the highest starting torque, namely, the motor's full-rated starting torque, ignoring any voltage drop. Both NFPA 20 and the *NEC* require that the voltage drop during starting must not exceed 15 percent of the controller's rated voltage at the controller inlet (line) terminals. It is important to note that this requirement applies to any and all sources feeding the controller. With combination transfer switch fire pump controller units, this requirement applies to both of the two input source line terminals and requires a fairly "stiff" power source. Long power wiring runs will cause additional voltage drop, requiring less voltage drop from the source, and must be taken into account to ensure that the voltage drop during pump starting does not exceed the 15 percent limit. This also applies to a genset or to a transformer used to supply a fire pump.

The reason for the maximum drop of 15 percent during starting is based on the fire pump controller contactor and control circuit operating voltages. These components typically have a specified operating voltage of 85 percent of rated nominal voltage. An unloaded power line will usually be at or above the rated voltage. However, as soon as the motor contactor closes, the

TABLE 15.7.2 Fire Pump Starting Type Characteristics for Electric Fire Pump Motors and Controllers

Starting Type	*Motor Type Note*	*Starting Steps Note*[a]	*Closed Transition*	*Starting Amps and KVA % LRA*	*Starting Amps and KVA % FLA*	*Starting Power Factor*	*Starting Power % ATL*	*Starting Torque % ATL*	*Accelerate Full Load to Full Speed*
Across-the-line[b]	Any	1	N/A	100	600	40	240	100	Yes
Part winding[c]	Special[d]	2	Yes	65	390	40	156	48	Usually
Primary resistor[e]	Any	2	Yes	65	390	80	314	42	Yes
Primary reactor[e]	Any	2	Yes	65	390	30	111	42	Yes
Neutral reactor[e]	6/12 Lead	2	Yes	65	390	30	111	42	Yes
Wye-delta open[f]	6/12 Lead	3	No	33/100	200/600	40	80/240	33	No
Wye-delta closed[f,g]	6/12 Lead	4	Yes	33/100	200/600	40	80/240	33	No
Soft start/stop[h]	Any	2	Yes	40/67	240/400	Varies	Ramps	16/44	Yes
Autotransformer[e,i]	Any	3	Yes	46	276	40	110	42	Yes

Note: Refer to section on reduced voltage starting for details.

[a]The three- and four-step methods are basically two steps (accelerate and run) with the third and fourth steps being transition steps.

[b]Also called ATL or *direct-on-line*. Motor power factor taken as 40%. Other values shown are due to the effects of the controller.

[c]Part-winding parameters vary with the motor. Starting amps and KVA vary from around 60% to 70%; starting torque from around 45% to 50%. The motor can start a fully loaded pump if it has no large torque dip or cusp. See the text discussion on part-winding starting for details.

[d]Part-winding motors must be wound specifically for this service. Some motors may not accelerate to full speed in the starting mode. See Note (c).

[e]Figures are for tap set at 65%, which yields a motor voltage of 65% of line (main) voltage.

[f]The dual figures are for starting and transition. The transition values are to finish accelerating a fully loaded pump. Examples include deluge or open systems, restarting a fully loaded pump after a power failure or interruption, and failure of another pump feeding the same system.

[g]Ignores the momentary transition resistor loads.

[h]Varies with pump load and particular soft starter used. Values shown are for a fully loaded pump and are typical only.

[i]The 46% starting amps and KVA figures include the autotransformer exciting current.

motor locked rotor impedance is applied to the power source, which will always cause some amount of voltage drop. If this voltage drop exceeds the maximum allowed 15 percent value, the motor contactor or other control components may not have enough voltage to remain closed and may cause disconnection of the motor, which will cause highly destructive rapid cycling (chattering) of the motor contactor and will cause the controller breaker to trip and/or damage or destroy the contactor(s) and/or the motor or pump coupling.

Given adequate voltage, the ATL motor torque will be more than adequate to start a fully loaded fire pump under any conditions of ultimate pressure and flow that comply with NFPA 20. NFPA 20 requires that the motor current in any phase not exceed 115 percent of FLA under *any* condition of pump load or voltage imbalance. This requirement determines the minimum size motor (horsepower) needed for a given pump. When this motor size requirement is met and given that the line voltage is 85 percent or more of rated voltage during starting (no more than a 15% drop), the motor torque will easily be able to accelerate the pump to full rated speed, regardless of the pump hydraulic load. Figure 15.7.9 illustrates the voltage curve for ATL starting versus the pump curve.

The first torque shown on the curve in Figure 15.7.9 is the locked rotor torque, also known as the motor's stall torque. This is the amount of torque that the motor will deliver to "break away" a frozen, stiff, or stuck pump. The second torque shown is the so-called pull-up torque. This is the minimum motor torque in the acceleration (starting) region. The torque curve from this point increases, as does the pump torque requirements. The motor torque, however, is always greater than the required pump torque by a wide margin, about twice what is needed. The third torque shown is the so-called breakdown torque, which is the border between the motor's starting torque region and its running torque region. The final torque shown is the full-flow pump torque, which must be less than the motor's rated full-load (plus service factor) torque. When this condition is not met, the motor current will likely exceed the maximum allowed 115 percent FLA current and the motor will likely overheat. Finally, it is important to note that the motor's starting torque (i.e., all three previously named torques) is proportional to the square of the voltage applied to the motor during starting.

Reduced Voltage Starting

All reduced inrush starting types are of the reduced voltage type, the reduced current type, or both. However, the reduced voltage types also reduce the motor's starting current, since in the starting region, the motor's current draw is proportional to the voltage applied to it. This relationship is the opposite of the case

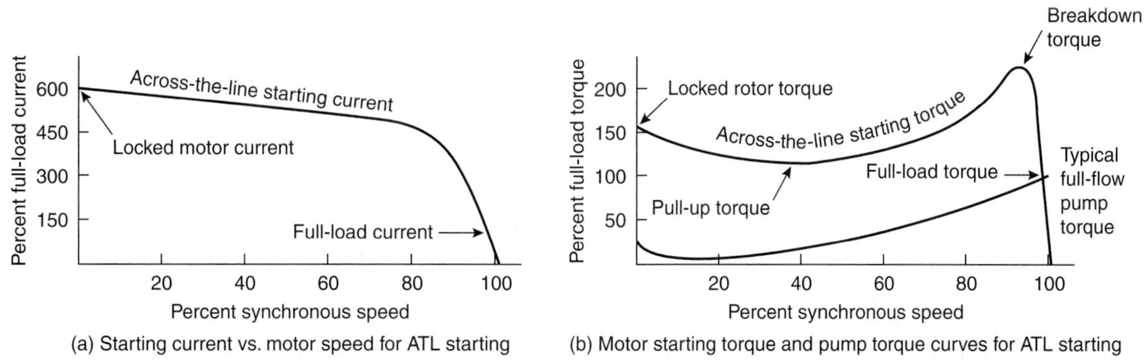

FIGURE 15.7.9 ATL Motor Starting Characteristics for a Typical 75 hp, 4 pole, Nema B, Code G Motor: (a) Starting Current vs. Motor Speed for ATL Starting, and (b) Motor Starting Torque and Pump Torque Curves

in the motor's running region, where the motor draws more current when given less voltage in order to draw enough electrical power to produce the required mechanical power.

The comments regarding voltage drop are just as important for reduced controllers as they are for across-the-line controllers, if not more so. All reduced voltage controllers have more contactors and control components than do ATL controllers, so they are more prone to the relay dropout and contactor chattering problems. An additional, and more likely, mode of failure exists, whereby the accelerate timer may not time out or operate, which then leaves the controller and motor in the accelerate mode indefinitely. This will cause motor overheating, depending on the motor (pump) load, which will ultimately lead to motor burnout followed by tripping of the controller circuit breaker, usually after the motor has been damaged or destroyed. The controller will likely also suffer varying degrees of damage, depending on its type and other factors.

The usual purpose of reduced inrush type of controllers is to reduce the starting current, which makes it easier to meet the 15 percent maximum allowed starting current voltage drop. Another reason that they are often used is to reduce the required size of an alternate (backup) source genset needed to meet the voltage drop requirements. Reduced inrush controllers are sometimes also used, especially soft start type controllers, to reduce the hydraulic surge on pump starting and/or to reduce the water hammer that can occur on pump shutdown when the pump check valve closes. Even so, these systems must still be able to start the motor in the full-voltage ATL mode, using the emergency mechanical operator, which is required of *every* fire pump controller type, without causing any blown fuses (where used) or any tripped circuit breakers, either upstream of the controller (if used) or the controller's circuit breaker. In either case, the sizing requirement for upstream circuit protection, where used, remains the same, namely, that any upstream protection must meet the NFPA 20 (and *NEC*) requirements for holding (carrying), indefinitely, the sum of the fire pump(s) locked rotor current(s) plus all other connected loads, except for the alternate (emergency) source side, if used.

Part Winding Starting. This method of starting requires motors to have two windings operating in parallel for running *and* to be manufactured and labeled as suitable for part winding. As a result, the applications for this starting type are somewhat limited, especially at the higher voltages, which often need the motor windings connected in series rather than in parallel for running.

Part winding starting is a reduced current type of starting because only half of the motor's windings are energized during starting, which nearly doubles the motor load impedance and nearly halves the motor current. Due to magnetic effects, the actual starting current is about 65 percent of the rated locked rotor current, which yields a starting current of around 390 percent of FLA. The stall torque is close to 50 percent of nominal because full voltage is delivered to one-half of the motor's windings. However, there does exist a "cusp," or torque dip, during acceleration, usually at one-half of the rated speed of the motor.

At the end of the acceleration period, which is limited to 10 seconds, the second motor contactor closes to energize the second set of motor windings, which then supplies the motor with its full running power, making this starting type a "two-step" starting means. It is also of the closed transition type because power is never interrupted or disconnected from the motor starting windings. This starting method has the same power factor as the motor itself during acceleration of around 40 percent (0.40 power factor) as it does not add to or change the motor's impedance other than using only half of the motor windings. Thus, this method is usable for starting from a genset for dual-source installations, but it is not the best method. Other methods have lower starting power (kilowatt) demands.

Primary Resistor Starting. Primary resistor starting has long been used to reduce the starting (inrush) current of fire pump controllers. It is a reduced voltage starting method because three resistors, or sets of resistors, are inserted in series with the motor during the starting (accelerating) period. The usual value used is 65 percent, which is the voltage supplied to the motor (at stall). The other 35 percent of the voltage is dropped vectorially across the three resistors, which are in each of the incoming lines. The motor torque follows the square of the voltage law, yielding a stall torque around 42 percent of rated stall torque. Meanwhile, the starting current is reduced to 65 percent of locked rotor amperes (LRA) or around 390 percent of FLA. At the end of the acceleration period, the main motor contactor bypasses the resistors to apply full-line voltage to the motor, which makes this starting type a two-step starting means. It is also of the closed transition type because power is never interrupted or disconnected from the motor. This starting method can be used with any fire pump motor, including three-lead motors. This starting method changes the starting power factor to a higher value than the motor's own power factor because the resistors represent a unity (100%) power factor load. All other starting methods have a lower starting power (kilowatt) demand.

For economic reasons, the resistors need to provide only a 5 second acceleration period. As a result, this is the only reduced starting type limited to less than the otherwise maximum allowed 10 second acceleration period. Normal controller construction includes venting the cabinet that houses the resistors due to the large amount of heat generated during starting (around 130 kW for a 100 horsepower motor).

Primary Reactor Starting. Primary reactor starting has also long been used to reduce the starting (inrush) current of fire pump controllers. It is a reduced voltage starting method because a saturable reactor is inserted in series with the motor during the starting (accelerating) period. The reactors have multiple voltage taps, but the usual value used is 65 percent, which is the voltage supplied to the motor (at stall) with the other 35 percent of the voltage being vectorially dropped across the reactor coils. The result is a stall torque around 42 percent of rated stall torque. Meanwhile, the starting current is reduced to 65 percent of LRA or around 390 percent of FLA. On the 65 percent tap with 42 percent of the motor torque available for starting, the motor will normally accelerate a pump even if it is fully loaded. This is particularly true because the accelerate timer can be set for the full allowed maximum time of 10 seconds, as the reactors must be capable of 15 seconds of accelerate time, which also makes this method a very robust reduced inrush starting method.

At the end of the acceleration period, the main motor contactor bypasses the starting reactor coils to apply full-line voltage to the motor making this starting type a two-step starting means. It is also of the closed transition type because power is never interrupted or disconnected from the motor. This starting method can be used with any motor, including three-lead motors.

The reactor has a very low power factor (less than 5%) and, therefore, has very little heat dissipation. As a result, no venting is required for these controllers, and so any cabinet construction type can be had. This low power factor leads to a combined value lower than the motor's own power factor. As a result, the size (horsepower and kilowatts) of the genset can be basically the same for either reactor or autotransformer starting.

Wye-Delta (Star-Delta)—Open Transition Starting. Like part winding starting, wye-delta (also known as star-delta) starting changes the motor windings to affect the reduced inrush starting. A detailed description of the characteristics of these motors appears in the book *Pumps for Fire Protection Systems.* These motors must be of the so-called delta run type, meaning that the windings are meant to be connected in delta (end to end) while running. Both ends of each winding coil must be brought out to the motor junction box for external connection to allow the windings to be connected in the wye (star) configuration for starting.

Although wye-delta starting gives the largest current reduction, it also produces the least starting torque. The starting torque follows the square law for the coils, which have only 58 percent of their rated current, and so the motor delivers only 33 percent of rated starting torque. Although useful for unloaded motors, such as unloaded chiller compressors, or loads that are small compared to the motor horsepower, this starting method will *not* accelerate a loaded centrifugal pump up to speed if the pump horsepower demand is anywhere close to the motor's rated horsepower. It often will not have enough torque to accelerate a pump at shutoff (churn), especially with high-speed pumps, which typically have a higher churn horsepower load. If the motor is not up to speed during the acceleration period, the motor will have to finish accelerating the load (pump) after the acceleration period when it is in the full-voltage (delta) configuration. Unfortunately, this situation will also result in normal starting currents of near locked rotor (LRA) until the pump (motor) is up to speed. The resulting characteristic is sometimes called delayed across-the-line starting.

As the voltage applied to the windings is less than normal rated voltage, the wye-delta method of starting is of the reduced voltage type, although the voltage reduction takes place entirely within the motor. In operation, the controller uses three motor contactors, typically designated as M1, M2, and Y. Initially contactors M1 and Y close to connect the motor coils in the wye configuration for acceleration. At the end of the acceleration period the controller opens the wye contactor. As one end of each winding is now open, the motor is deenergized at this point and loses some of its speed. After some delay, the second main motor contactor (M2) connects these open ends of the motor windings to the respective incoming lines. This is the full-voltage, delta-configuration running mode. This delay is anywhere from a few milliseconds up to a full second, depending on the controller design. Any delay longer than the minimum of a few milliseconds will result in motor deceleration and high starting (accelerating) currents when the motor is reenergized at full voltage in the delta running configuration.

This method, therefore, is a three-step starting method. Because the motor windings are deenergized for at least some period of time, this is also known as an open transition starting means, referring to the conditions of the windings (open circuited) prior to the instant of reconnection to full-line voltage.

In addition to possibly incurring full ATL starting currents, there may also be a brief, but very high, current spike at the instant of transition to full voltage due to the open transition method of switching the motor windings. This spike occurs when the motor magnetic vector phase angle differs from that of the line (mains) voltage when the M2 contactor closes. The greater the phase angle difference, the greater will be the current spike, which can be up to 18 times FLA (1800%). The magnitude of the transient will be higher on larger or stiffer power sources. This spike can cause undesired tripping of the circuit breaker when it occurs. This current spike is worse if the motor does reach full speed during the acceleration period, because the back electromotive force (EMF) (generated voltage) is a function of the motor speed—hence, the conundrum. If the motor does not reach full speed, it will draw ATL starting currents, after the transition, for as long as it takes the motor to reach full speed. In the opposite case where the motor does reach full speed, the motor's back EMF can cause large transition spikes and cause unintended circuit breaker tripping sooner or later.

Three methods have been used to mitigate this current spike condition. The first is to turn down the accelerate timer to a short interval (a few seconds or less) so that the motor does not have time to come up to full speed. The second method is to add a delay to the transition period to allow the motor magnetic field and, hence, its back EMF to decay. Although these measures will reduce the spike, they will also allow the motor to lose much of its speed. The results are full ATL starting currents and no benefit from reduced inrush starting. Either of these methods amounts to a delayed ATL starting of the motor.

The third method is to make the transition rapidly and also control the direction of the winding vector angle change. The idea is to have the vector angle fall back rather than jump ahead and, thus, serve to cancel the effect of the motor slowdown phase angle shift. This requires the use of a controller with a built-in leading phase monitor and means for changing the closing (transition) phase angle from lagging to leading.

Like ATL and part winding starting, this method has the same power factor as does the motor during acceleration, that is, around 40 percent (0.40 power factor) because it only changes the voltage applied to the motor windings. This method is of only limited use for starting from a genset for dual-source installations because the motor will not likely be up to speed during the acceleration period. As a result, the genset will necessarily have to attempt to produce across-the-line starting currents for at least some amount of time.

Wye-Delta (Star-Delta)—Closed Transition Starting. Closed transition wye-delta (star-delta) starting has the same starting characteristics as the open transition wye-delta starting method. The main difference between closed transition and open transition wye-delta starting is the reduction of the transition transient (spike) current. The starting current is the same, and the starting torque is the same (33%) for either open or closed transition wye-delta starting. This, again, is not enough torque to fully accelerate most loaded pumps.

During acceleration, this method is the same as the open transition starting method and is, therefore, also of the reduced voltage type. In operation, the controller uses four rather than three motor contactors. Initially, the motor windings are connected together in wye as with the open transition starting. At the end of the acceleration period, a transition (S) contactor closes to connect one end of each of three transition resistors to the line power, which briefly puts the three resistors in wye in parallel with the motor windings. A short time later, the Y contactor opens, which places the motor windings in series with the resistors. The resistors allow the line voltage to pull the motor magnetic vector to that of the line voltage phase angle or close to it. At the end of this time, the second main motor contactor (M2) short circuits the resistors and, thus, connects the ends of the motor windings to the respective incoming lines, which is the full-voltage, delta running mode.

As a result, this method is four-step starting. The motor windings are never deenergized at any time, making a closed transition starting means. As with the open transition starting, if the motor has not reached full speed during the acceleration period, the motor will finish accelerating in the across-the-line (full-voltage) mode with resulting ATL starting currents for the duration of the acceleration period. It also has the same starting power factor as the open transition starting; that is, around 40 percent (0.40 power factor) or the same as the motor itself.

This method also has the same limitations as open delta when used with a genset for dual source installations. As the motor may not be up to speed, the genset will have to attempt to produce ATL starting currents for some period of time. If the genset is not sized to produce these starting currents, the resulting voltage drop may cause contactor chattering and ultimately controller and/or motor damage or destruction.

Soft Start (SCR) Starting. Soft start starting is a newer method of motor starting. Basically, it varies the voltage fed to the motor over the acceleration period and, thus, affects the starting current and, therefore, the starting torque. The usual case is to start with a lower voltage and increase (ramp up) the voltage to the full-line voltage during the acceleration period. Because the acceleration period is limited by code to a maximum of 10 seconds, this period is usually selected for the voltage ramp-up time and, thus, the motor acceleration period. In addition to soft start starting, all listed fire pump controllers using this scheme also offer the so-called soft stop deceleration when the pump is no longer needed. Because the voltage to the motor is being controlled, this method of starting is the reduced voltage type.

Soft start starters are specified and used for one of two reasons, if not both: (1) for reduced inrush starting and (2) for hydraulic reasons, mainly to reduce pressure and/or flow surges during start-up, and/or to reduce the water hammer or hydraulic shock that can occur during pump shutdown when the pump check valve closes (slams shut).

The soft starter operates in a manner similar to a large variable transformer. The motor is usually started with around 30 to 40 percent of the rated voltage (the so-called ramp start voltage) and yields an initial starting torque of 9 to 16 percent, which assures no sudden acceleration. The voltage then ramps up, usually in a linear fashion. The motor torque still follows the square of the voltage law and, therefore, the motor torque builds up as the square of the applied voltage. After the voltage has reached 100 percent (or within 10 seconds), the main motor contactor closes to bypass the soft starter. This operation reduces the heat buildup in the controller that would occur if the soft starter continued to supply the motor running current. This starting method is a two-step starting type; however, the distinction is minor because the motor should already be at full voltage by the time the main motor contactor closes. Since the motor is at no time deenergized during or after the starting (accelerate) cycle, this starting method is of the closed transition starting type. This main motor contactor also provides for the required emergency mechanical starting of the fire pump motor. Some designs also employ an isolating (start) contactor to shield the soft start starter from line voltage transients while in the standby mode. Some also employ a mode switch to allow the unit to work in an across-the-line mode for start-up (commissioning) or emergency automatic fire protection.

Because the voltage varies over time in a continuous fashion, both the motor torque and starting current draw also vary over time. One estimate gives an accelerate time of around 7 seconds for a fully loaded (full-flow) pump with a peak starting current of around 400 percent and an estimate of around 3 seconds and peak current of around 300 percent for an unloaded (no-flow) pump.

The soft stop shutdown cycle is basically the reverse of the starting cycle. To stop the pump, the controller first opens (deenergizes) the main motor contactor (M) with the soft starter SCRs set to 100 percent (full voltage). The soft starter then ramps the voltage down. Some designs incorporate a delay or pedestal dwell time as part of the stopping sequence. Designs employing an isolating (start) contactor open (deenergize) same at the end of the ramp-down time to isolate the soft starter from line transients.

Because the motor voltage is both nonlinear and time variant, the circuit power factor is not constant. It remains inductive because the motor itself is inductive. The power factor is the same as that of the motor when the SCRs are fully on (full voltage to the motor), around 40 percent (0.40 power factor). The motor will "appear" more inductive at lower voltages due to the delayed conduction angle. When these starters are used with gensets, the gensets must be sized conservatively as the starting current cannot be easily determined without analyzing the motor, starter, and pump dynamics during starting under full pump load. In any case, the worst case size needed would be that needed for across-the-line starting.

Autotransformer Starting. Autotransformer starting has also long been used for reduced (inrush) starting of fire pump controllers. It too is a reduced voltage starting method. The transformer is of the autotransformer type, which is about half the size of a normal isolated winding-type transformer. The autotransformer has multiple voltage taps, but the usual value used is the 65 percent tap, which is the voltage supplied to the motor (at stall) and gives a stall torque of around 42 percent of the rated stall torque. Meanwhile, the starting current is reduced to around 46 percent of LRA or around 270 percent of FLA when the autotransformer exciting (saturation) current is accounted for.

During acceleration, a Y contactor connects the autotransformer low side terminals together, and a start contactor(s) connects the top of the autotransformer windings to line power. The motor connects directly to the autotransformer's voltage reduction taps. At the end of the acceleration period, the controller disconnects (opens) the autotransformer wye connection, which is the second step. During this brief step, the autotransformer acts as a saturable reactor (series impedance) similar to the primary reactor starting method. Finally, after a fraction of a second, the main motor contactor (M) short circuits the top of the transformer windings to apply full voltage to the motor, which makes this method a three-step starting means. This method is also of the closed transition type since power is never interrupted or disconnected from the motor. This starting method can be used with any motor including three-lead motors.

Like the saturable reactor, the autotransformer is actually overdesigned because it too must be designed for 15 second acceleration periods to meet NFPA 20 requirements. As the maximum allowed acceleration period is only 10 seconds, this method is also a very robust reduced starting method and results in very low stress and temperature rise of components.

The autotransformer preserves the motor's 40 percent starting power factor during acceleration as it does not add to or change the motor's impedance but merely increases its magnitude to reduce the starting current. This characteristic makes it advantageous for starting from a genset for dual-source installations as it is least demanding of genset power and, therefore, size. Therefore, it is on a par with primary reactor starting on a power (kilowatt) size basis; however, it reduces the current further. This current reduction is an advantage when long power lines separate the genset from the fire pump or in remote areas or other areas where current reduction is as important or more important than starting power reduction. Like primary reactor starting, this method also has very little heat dissipation during starting. As a result, no venting is required for these controllers. Thus, one can have any cabinet construction type. Also, like the reactor case, multiple starting rarely causes the autotransformer to be more than slightly warm.

Medium- (High-) Voltage Full-Service Controller Starting

Across-the-Line (ATL or Direct-on-Line) Starting. This starting method is electrically the same as the low-voltage ATL starting method. The difference in controller construction relates to the fact that all currently listed medium-voltage fire pump controllers use vacuum contactors for the main motor contactor. Also, Class R motor circuit fuses are used in place of the fire pump circuit breaker used in low-voltage controllers. The motor locked rotor protection is provided by deenergizing the motor contactor instead of tripping the circuit breaker in low-voltage units. Further, additional safety interlocking is used due to the dangerous amount of electrical energy available. Some controllers use triple safety interlocking. First, the isolating switch is interlocked with the main contactor (M) in a two-way fashion so that the isolating switch may neither be opened nor closed while the contactor is closed. Second, the high-voltage door is interlocked with the isolating switch so that it cannot be opened if the isolating switch is closed. Third, the isolating switch cannot be closed if the high-voltage door is open. Some designs also interlock access to the incoming wiring (bus bar) compartment to the high-voltage door and also electrically interlock the control transformer(s) to allow for low-voltage testing of control circuitry. Another difference with medium-voltage controllers is that the interrupting and short circuit ratings are given in MVA (megavolt-amperes) rather than in symmetrical amperes.

Primary Reactor Starting. The primary reactor starting method has the same motor starting characteristics as the low-voltage counterpart. The controller construction differs slightly in the way the two motor contactors are connected. The run contactor and the reactor are connected to the output of the main contactor to allow the full safety interlocking of the main contactor to provide full safety for the second (run) contactor, the reactor, and all other medium-voltage components and wiring. Because there are two contactors used to run the motor at full voltage, there are also two emergency mechanical manual operator handles, providing the added benefit of reduced inrush starting even when the manual operators are used. The main contactor operator is actuated first, and when the motor is up to speed or within 10 seconds, the second run contactor operator is actuated.

Neutral Reactor Starting. This method is a variation of the primary reactor starting method, except that the reactor is moved from the line (primary) side of the motor to the wye point (neutral) of the motor, which must be of the six-lead wye-wound type. The operation and characteristics are otherwise identical to those in the primary reactor starting method. The advantage of this method is that the reactor is not subjected to full-line voltage. This method is used for controllers rated above 5000 V.

Autotransformer. This starting method is also electrically comparable with its low-voltage counterpart. All electrical characteristics and type descriptions are the same as for the low-voltage equivalent with the previously stated differences for medium-voltage controllers.

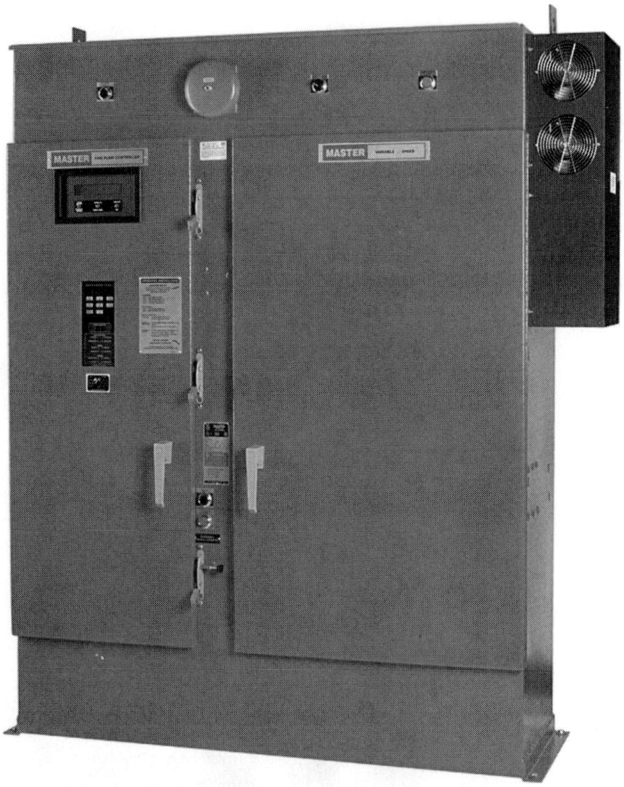

FIGURE 15.7.10 Closed Door View of Model ECV-250-46, 250 hp, Single-Source, Variable Speed Source Fire Pump Controller in NEMA 12 Enclosure with Air-to-Air Heat Exchanger (Source: Master Control Systems, Inc.)

VARIABLE SPEED ELECTRIC MOTOR–DRIVEN FIRE PUMPS

This section summarizes a significant change occurring in fire pump technology by outlining the availability, application, and installation of variable speed fire pumps (Figures 15.7.10 and 15.7.11) and controllers. More specifically, this section covers (1) the relevant changes to the fire pump standard, (2) the state of the art, including a brief history, (3) example installations, (4) the equipment involved including controller features and functions, (5) application needs, and (6) hydraulic considerations, particularly system time constants. This type of fire pump operation is new and requires both additional and innovative design and application considerations. As a result, certain sections are both detailed and exhaustive where needed to avoid incomplete information.

The section also describes how the 2007 edition of NFPA 20 affects variable speed fire pumps.

Update on NFPA 20

Although variable speed pumps have been used for a number of years in pumping applications such as process pumps and domestic booster pumps, the 2003 edition of NFPA 20 contains the first mention of variable speed fire pumps. That edition added both diesel engine–driven and electric motor–driven variable speed fire pumps. With the exception of wound rotor manually controlled fire pumps in New York City, variable speed fire pumps have not heretofore been used in stationary fire pump applications.

Prior to the 2003 edition of NFPA 20, fire pumps were considered to be constant speed units. Although designed to run at a fixed speed under normal conditions, traditional diesel-driven fire pumps have always been considered variable speed drivers since the engine speed can exceed normal rated running speed should certain failures occur. The only pressure control allowed was the required pressure relief valves to prevent an overspeed occurrence from damaging the sprinkler system due to excessive pressure. As such, from a sprinkler design standpoint, diesel-driven pumps are considered to be constant speed systems.

The initial considerations of variable speed systems to *actively* control system pressures were incorporated into the 2003 edition of NFPA 20 and constituted the first recognition of variable speed fire pump systems, both diesel engine–driven and electric motor–driven fire pump systems. Another significant change in the 2003 edition of NFPA 20 in this regard is the prohibition of the use of main relief valves for "normal" system pressure control. They are only allowed for the purpose of preventing system damage during *abnormal* conditions. Both variable speed diesel drivers and electric motor drive variable speed controllers use active feedback control to regulate the pump discharge pressure. Active feedback control makes use of mechanical or electrical (electronic) means to compare the pump output pressure against a preset desired (set point) pressure and adjust the speed of the driver up or down as needed in order to

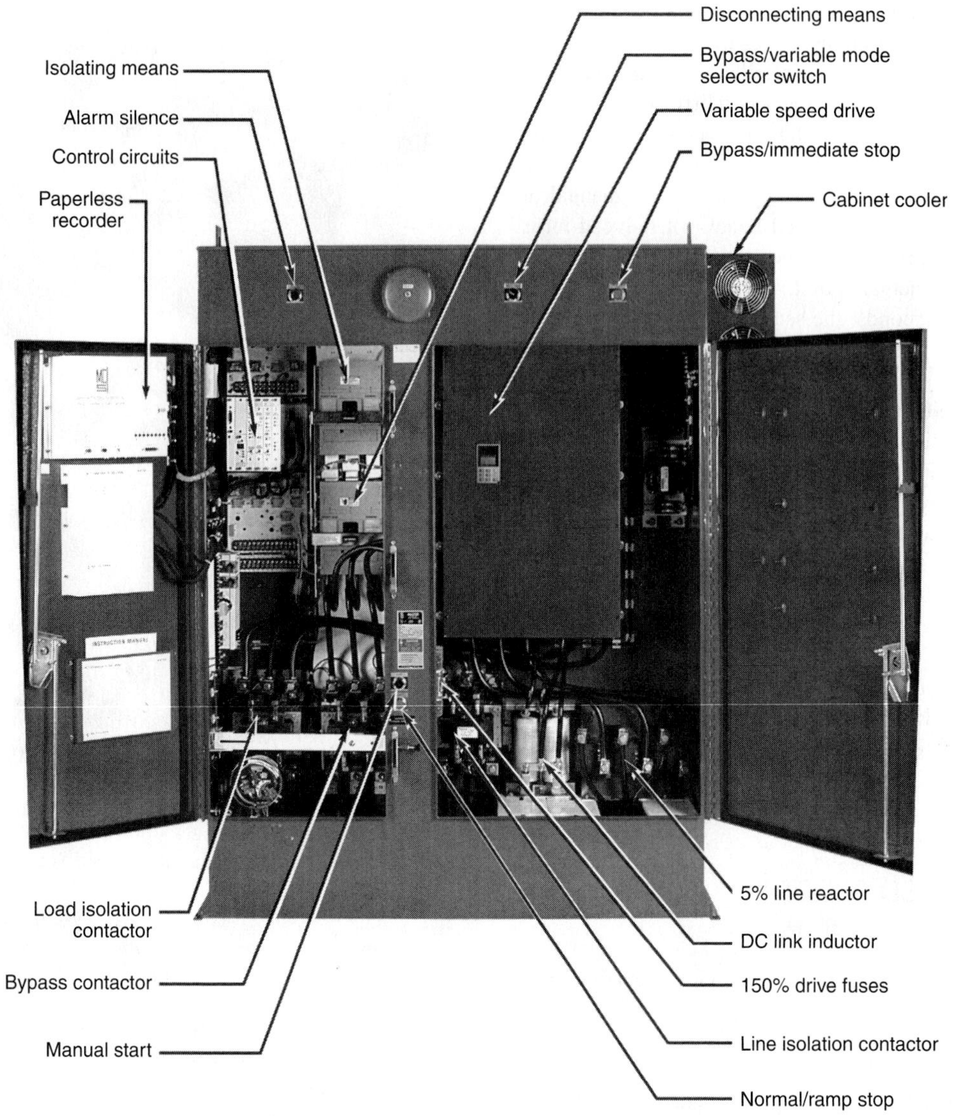

FIGURE 15.7.11 Open Door Flagged View of Model ECV-250-46, 250 hp Single-Source, Variable Speed Source Fire Pump Controller (Source: Master Control Systems, Inc.)

match the pump output pressure to the desired set point value. In operation, a difference value between the actual output pressure and the set point pressure is created and amplified and used to control the speed of the driver to minimize the magnitude of said error signal. Accordingly, they are able to limit system pressures to safe values or provide a source of closely regulated pressure or both. The feedback control scheme tends to maintain the pump output pressure close to the desired set point value and, thus, compensate for suction pressure variations, suction side friction losses, and pump curve variations over the full range of output flow (gpm) rates.

Finally, the 2007 edition of NFPA 20 established a significant body of requirements for variable speed motor drive fire pump controllers that is delineated next. Much of this work was done by two task groups, namely, an NFPA 20 Variable Speed task group and a NEMA Variable Speed Controller task group. The 2007 edition also establishes requirements for break tanks, which are another means of dealing with pressure variations in the suction supply.

State of the Art, Variable Speed Electric Motor–Driven Fire Pump Controllers

The first UL-listed variable speed electric drive fire pump controller was available in 2003. The balance of this section presents an overview description of the unit, a brief history of its application, and application examples.

Controller Overview. All compliant variable speed controllers consist of both a full-service fire pump controller and a separate variable speed controller section. There are two main operating modes for these controllers, namely, the variable speed mode and the bypass mode. In the bypass mode, the unit operates as a fixed full-speed, full-service fire pump controller. These controllers may be either the single power source type or the dual power source combination transfer switch and fire pump controller type. The normal operating mode for these units is the variable speed mode. In this mode, the controller compares the system pressure to a previously set desired value, that is, the pressure set point, and adjusts the speed of the pump to produce the desired system pressure. Typical pressure regulation accuracy is better than one-tenth of 1 psi. For example, with a system set to 140 psi (9.6 bar), the variable speed controller will produce a pump output pressure within 0.1 psi of the desired 140 psi (9.6 bar) set point pressure over the full range of rated pump flow. The same is true whether the set point is 70 psi (4.8 bar), 175 psi (12 bar), or any pressure within the capability of the pump involved.

The bypass path is used for full-speed pump testing, commissioning, and servicing. It is also used on failure of the variable speed portion of the controller. The bypass mode can be manually selected by a manual mode switch, although the controller will automatically revert to the full-speed bypass mode should the variable speed portion either fail to operate or fail to meet system pressure requirements. The starting means in the bypass mode may be either full voltage or reduced voltage starting types. These are used to reduce the size of the genset required where emergency power is utilized. Reduced inrush starting controllers installed to date are either of the primary reactor or the soft start types. Since the bypass path constitutes a complete full-service fire pump controller, it includes an emergency mechanical operator. Since this feature connects the pump motor directly to the power source, its use always causes the pump to run at full speed.

In the variable speed mode, the controller makes use of a variable frequency drive (VFD) to control the voltage and frequency fed to the fire pump motor. In this way, the unit controls both the speed and torque of the motor. All units currently in service also incorporate both soft starting (ramp-up) and soft stopping (ramp-down) operation. In this mode of operation, the controller ramps up the motor (pump) speed to a preset idle speed, typically two-thirds of rated speed. At this speed, the pump pressure produced is around 44 percent of rated pressure boost since the pump pressure gain is related to the square of the pump rpm (revolutions per minute). At this low-boost pressure the pump normally does not produce any flow if the system is pressurized. If the system pressure is below the controller set point pressure, the controller will continue to accelerate the pump to the speed required to meet the set point pressure. If need be, the controller will accelerate the pump all the way up to full speed in order to cause the pump to produce the desired pressure. If and when the pump does achieve the desired set point pressure, the controller maintains the pump at that speed. If necessary, the controller will adjust the motor speed up or down in order to maintain the pressure at the desired set point value.

A main relief valve is required if the fire pump can exceed the system rated pressure when operating at full speed, at churn (shut off), and with the maximum anticipated suction pressure. This requirement is important since the pump will operate at full speed in the bypass mode, including the emergency mechanical operator mode of operation.

Application History. Designing fire sprinkler systems has become a challenge for a number of reasons, including the following:

1. Higher pressure demand at the top of high-rise buildings, typically 100 psi (6.9 bar) at the roof hydrants
2. Varying suction pressures, especially when dual water supplies are required (municipal and tank)
3. Need to limit maximum pressures to 175 psi (12 bar) component ratings to avoid the cost of higher pressure components
4. Need to limit pressure at certain types of sprinklers, such as large drop sprinklers, to avoid exceeding their operating ratings or degrading their performance
5. Requirement for backflow preventers in most systems
6. Various pressure drops that occur with large orifice sprinklers and increasing waterflow, including pump curve, suction piping friction loss, and discharge piping friction loss
7. Dual water supply requirements (tank and municipal) that are required in some jurisdictions

In the past, because of these design constraints, some designers and installers have made use of active pressure control means by the use of a so-called "main relief valve." However, these were prohibited with the 2003 edition of NFPA 20. The other hydraulic means sometimes used to control pressure are main or riser pressure regulating or pressure reducing valves (PRVs). The latter are different from those used to control the pressure of fire water on a given floor of a high-rise building, where allowed by local code. However, variable speed fire pumps or break tanks are now being used for the purpose of pressure control.

The first variable speed fire pumps were motor-driven units commissioned in spring 2004. They have since been used in numerous fire sprinkler systems and also in dual-use systems. Some examples of dedicated fire sprinkler system applications include (1) airport parking garages, (2) college housing midrise buildings that have been retrofitted with full sprinkler coverage, (3) a 1.8 million ft^2 (167,200 m^2) distribution center, (4) a municipal courthouse, (5) high-rise condominium buildings, and (6) a three-zone, high-rise commercial office building, among others. These particular units are all booster pumps taking suction from city water mains.

Dual-purpose applications in service include (1) combination domestic (potable) water and fire water pumps (four booster pumps) for a very large shopping center, (2) dual-purpose process water and fire water for a multibuilding commercial and residential complex where the process water is used for heat pumps for both cooling and heating, and (3) triple-purpose domestic water, fire water, and water tower fill pump with three distinct operating modes for a multibuilding medical housing complex.

Most of these units are combination transfer switch units, which are also reduced voltage starting in the bypass mode (Figure 15.7.12) since emergency power is from an on-site genset. A few units are single-source type but receive emergency power as part of the site power distribution. Units in service vary in size

FIGURE 15.7.12 Open Door View of Model ECVRT-125-46, 125 hp, Dual-Source, Variable Speed Fire Pump Controller with Reduced Inrush (Primary Reactor) Starting in Bypass Mode (Source: Master Control Systems, Inc.)

from 30 hp to 300 hp. As to pump types currently in operation, one unit is a vertical pump taking suction from a below-the-floor reservoir. Several are vertical in-line pumps; two are vertical deep well pumps; and the remainder are horizontal split-case pumps. One of the deep well pumps is of the water-lubricated type since the water is potable. Water-lubricated vertical pumps require special considerations to assure adequate lubrication water is supplied in time and also maintained under worst-case conditions.

Application Example—The Triple-Purpose Pump. The previously mentioned triple-purpose pump is a vertical deep well pump that uses the water tower for backup domestic and fire water. For filling the tower, the controller is started remotely by the site building management system, which also controls the speed of this pump in this mode. The speed is controlled to less than full-pump output flow to provide for optimum water treatment (chlorination, etc.). The pump can also be started remotely by the complex fire alarm system, in which case the controller accelerates the pump to full speed. If the controller pressure switch trips, which is the third operating mode, the controller accelerates the pump to full speed unless it detects that the tower is full. In this system the pressure cannot exceed 80 psi (5.5 bar) on a continual basis since that is the pressure that will overflow the tower.

Application Example—The Dual-Purpose Pump. The dual-purpose process water and fire water system is also a vertical deep well pump. In this system, a second well pump provides a backup source of water. It also shares the duty of providing the water since this system operates on a 24 hour, seven day basis. The two pumps alternate duty on a weekly basis and also operate in a so-called duplex mode of operation. In this mode, if the running pump controller (lead pump) ramps its pump to near full speed (97% of full speed), it will call for the reserve pump (lag pump) to start and ramp up to its idle speed. If the reserve pump needs to accelerate above its preset idle speed to meet the pressure demand, it signals the lead pump to lock to full speed so that the lag pump can take over the job of regulating system pressure. In this way only one controller is regulating the system pressure rather than having two competing for the job. If and when the reserve pump drops back down to idle speed, it unlocks the primary (lead) pump controller so that it can resume the job of regulating system pressure. If the reserve (lag) pump remains at idle for a predetermined length of time, it ramps the pump down to around one-third rated speed and then stops it.

Since the controllers operate independently, either will accelerate to full speed if the system pressure cannot be satisfied in the normal manner. This way, failure of one controller does not inhibit the operation of the other. No central pressure control is involved since both pumps and controllers operate independently other than causing the other pump to start or to lock the other pump to full speed. This system operates at around 140 psi (9.6 bar). Since both wells are within 20 ft (6.1 m) of a major river, there is no chance of depleting either. The two wells are separated from one another by some distance in order to keep them independent of one another.

Application Example—A Four-Pump System. The four pumps at the major shopping center mentioned earlier operate in a triplex mode where one, two, or three pumps operate as system flow demands. In this system, two 30 hp (22 kW) pumps serve as the lead and second pump to supply domestic water demands and also fire water if the demand is not too great. The third pump is a 60 hp (45 kW) unit and is capable of supplying needed fire water. The fourth pump is also 60 hp (45 kW) and serves as a backup for the third pump. It takes over the duty of the third pump if that pump or its motor or controller fails. The triplex operation is similar to the duplex operation described previously. The lead pump starts upon pressure drop sufficient to trip its pressure switch or via a remote start input signal from the site fire alarm system. It regulates the system pressure needs (around 95 psi [6.6 bar]) unless the system demand causes it to ramp up to near full speed. In that event, it signals the second 30 hp (22 kW) pump to start and accelerate to its idle speed. If pump 2 needs to accelerate above its idle speed, it locks the lead pump to full speed and takes over regulating the system. If the second pump accelerates to near full speed, it signals the third pump (60 hp [45 kW]) to start and accelerate to its idle speed. Similarly, if pump 3 accelerates above idle speed, it locks pump 2 to full speed and takes over the job of pressure regulation. If pump 3 fails, pump 4 takes over and shuts down pump 3 to keep from overloading the genset if the system is running under emergency power.

If and when the system flow demand diminishes sufficiently, the pump controllers reverse the described operation as follows. If the lag pump (pump 3) decelerates down to idle speed, it unlocks pump 2 so that pump 2 can take over pressure regulation. If pump 3 remains at idle for the automatic stop interval, or if the minimum run time has elapsed and if the idle stop delay has also elapsed, controller 3 shuts down pump 3. If the system demand drops down enough for pump 2 to reduce to its idle speed, it unlocks pump 1 (lead pump) to take over the system pressure regulation. If and when all timers are satisfied, controller 2 will shut down pump 2. Since there is no central control, failure of one controller will not affect the operation of the others. Like the duplex system, these units are equipped with sequential starting as required by NFPA 20 to prevent all three pumps from starting simultaneously. Although this situation will not normally occur when the controllers are in the variable speed mode, it would happen if they are in the bypass mode if not equipped with the required sequential starting feature. This system also has a commercial domestic pumping system, but in the event of a power failure, the variable speed fire pumps will take over the job of providing the shopping center with domestic water as well as fire water if needed. These multipurpose units already have tens of thousands of hours of accumulated variable speed operating (running) time.

Equipment Description

The equipment and functions described hereinafter are those required by the 2007 edition of NFPA 20. The primary emphasis in NFPA 20 is that the variable speed path and the bypass path are both reliable and robust and also are as independent of one another as possible. This philosophy is to protect the integrity and independence of the bypass path to the fullest extent practical. In this way, variable speed controllers can be more reliable than a traditional fire pump controller if, as required, two conditions are met: (1) the design and construction of the bypass path is not diminished in any way from that of any other full-service fire pump controller, and (2) the variable speed path does nothing to diminish or potentially damage the controller bypass path. These two conditions being met yields a full-service fire pump controller with a redundant variable speed path. It is also desirable for said variable speed path (Figure 15.7.13) to also be reliable and robust as is expected from any fire pump controller to provide a reliable source of fire water at the expected controlled pressure.

Controller Equipment Features

In order for active pressure control to be achieved in a reliable and robust manner, certain unique functions are also required of the controller. The major functions are delineated next.

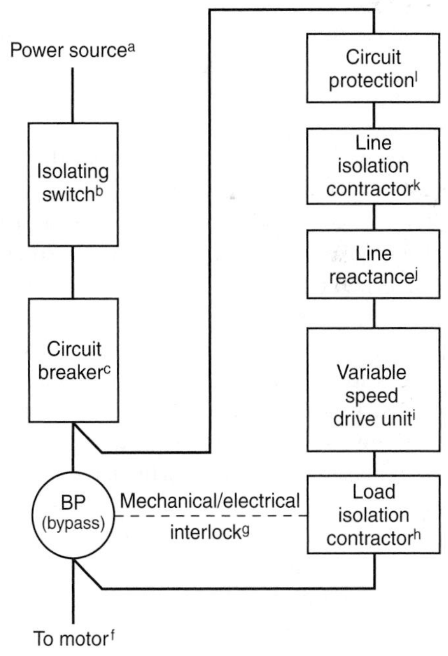

[a]See Section 9.2 in NFPA 20.
[b]See Clause 10.4.2 in NFPA 20.
[c]See Clauses 10.4.3 and 10.4.4 in NFPA 20.
[d]See Clause 10.4.5 in NFPA 20.
[e]See Clause 10.5.3.2 in NFPA 20.
[f]See Clause 9.5.1.3 in NFPA 20.
[g]See Clause10.10.3.3 in NFPA 20.
[h]See Clause 10.10.4 in NFPA 20.
[i]See Clause 10.10.1.1 in NFPA 20.
[j]See Clauses 10.10.6.1 and 10.10.6.2 in NFPA 20.
[k]See Clause 10.10.4 in NFPA 20.
[l]See Clause 10.10.5 in NFPA 20.

FIGURE 15.7.13 Variable Speed, Pressure-Limiting Control (Source: NFPA 20, *Standard for the Installation of Stationary Pumps for Fire Protection,* Figure A.10.10, 2007, p. 20-75)

Control and Alarm Elements. The major control and alarm elements of controller equipment include the following:

- Separate pressure switch for controller start and stop control and for use by the pressure bypass timer
- A low-pressure timer to automatically switch the controller into the bypass mode if the controller pressure switch remains tripped too long
- Separate and independent pressure sensing for the VFD (also known as a VSD, variable speed drive) or ASD (adjustable speed drive) speed control
- A manual mode control switch to allow operation in the full-speed bypass mode or the normal variable speed mode
- Alarm light and remote contacts to indicate drive (VFD) failure detected
- Drive failure timer to automatically switch the controller into the bypass mode on detection of a failure of the VFD
- Alarm light and remote contacts to indicate controller in bypass mode

Power, Isolation, and Circuit Protection. The major power, isolation, and circuit protection elements of controller equipment include the following:

- Full horsepower rated isolating contactor to keep the VFD powered down until needed. The purpose of this contactor is to prolong the life of the VFD and also to avoid VFD capacitor overvoltage shutdown due to power line surges, spikes, or overvoltage when the controller and pump are on standby (not running).
- Full horsepower rated VFD output motor (load) contactor to isolate the VFD from the bypass path.
- Full horsepower rated bypass contactor as part of the controller bypass path. This contactor is also operated by the emergency mechanical operator (see Figures 15.7.11 and 15.7.13). These last two contactors are both electrically and mechanically interlocked to prevent backfeeding line power to the VFD when the controller is operating in the bypass mode. Backfeeding would damage the VFD and probably cause the fire pump circuit breaker to trip and would disable the bypass path, leaving the fire pump inoperable.
- Circuit protection (fuses or circuit breaker) to isolate the VFD power path on circuit or component failure. This protection is set to trip at a value and time that will avoid tripping the controller fire pump circuit breaker, and thus leave the controller bypass path intact.
- A 5 percent or better line reactor to reduce harmonic currents within and upstream of the controller. This reactor also reduces harmonic currents within the VFD and protects the VFD rectifiers and capacitors from line voltage spikes and transients. Most importantly, it reduces the likelihood of VFD overvoltage shutdown due to these same spikes and transients.

System-Related Elements. The major system-related elements of controller equipment include the following:

- Alarm light and remote contacts to indicate that the system pressure is exceeding the VFD set point. This can be caused by a failure within the controller or by other pumps pressurizing the system.
- The means to control the system pressure in view of the multiple hydraulic, electrical, and mechanical time constants involved. This control is needed for successful and stable controller operations and requires the use of a full 3 term PID (proportional-integral-derivative) process controller or, at least a 2 term PI controller with suitable means to adjust and adapt to the conditions and requirements of the installation. This degree of control is needed to yield both stable operation and timely adjustment of the pump speed to give prompt response to changes in the system demand (flow) or suction pressure variations or both. Time constants are discussed later in this section.
  - The settings required for all of the preceding elements must both be lockable and also be marked and visible for service personnel.
  - For multiple variable speed pump installations, no common pressure control is allowed. Each controller must sense and control pressure independently to avoid a single point of failure in multiple-pump installations.

Additional Considerations. The controller equipment must be designed with the following requirements in mind:

- The controller must be able to deal with the heat given off by the VFD unit, which is typically 2 to 3 percent of the motor horsepower rating and is similar to the amount of heat given off by the motor itself. Better controllers do this without pulling air through the controller. This method requires an isolated means of cooling and keeps the inside of both the controller and the sensitive control portions of the VFD unit free from dirt, dust, and moisture that would otherwise occur in vented units.
- The VFD must be rated for the type of pump involved. Positive displacement pumps require a VFD unit with a higher current rating than that needed for centrifugal pumps for a given horsepower. Centrifugal pumps present a variable torque load to the pump motor, which reduces the power needed from the VFD as compared to positive displacement pumps because these present a load whose torque is relatively constant over speed.
- The controller must be designed to take care to avoid causing excessive currents when switching modes, particularly from variable speed mode to the bypass mode. This can be done with a motor restart delay of a few seconds to allow any motor magnetic flux and resultant back EMF (voltage) to decay to safe values before connecting said motor to the power source, especially if the bypass mode incorporated full-voltage (across-the-line) starting.
- There are a number of additional design considerations (Figure 15.7.14 and 15.7.15) that, if properly accounted for and manufactured, can further enhance the ability of these units to deal with various field conditions in a forgiving and robust manner.

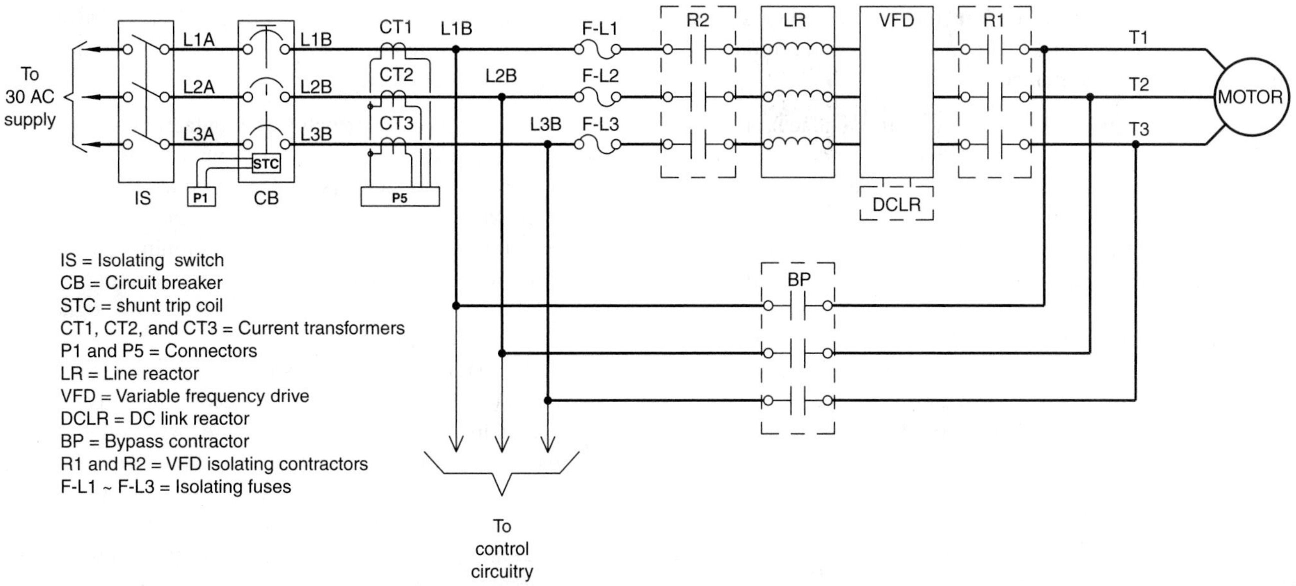

FIGURE 15.7.14 Single-Source, Variable Speed Fire Pump Controller with Full-Voltage (ATL) Starting in Bypass Mode (Source: Master Control Systems, Inc.)

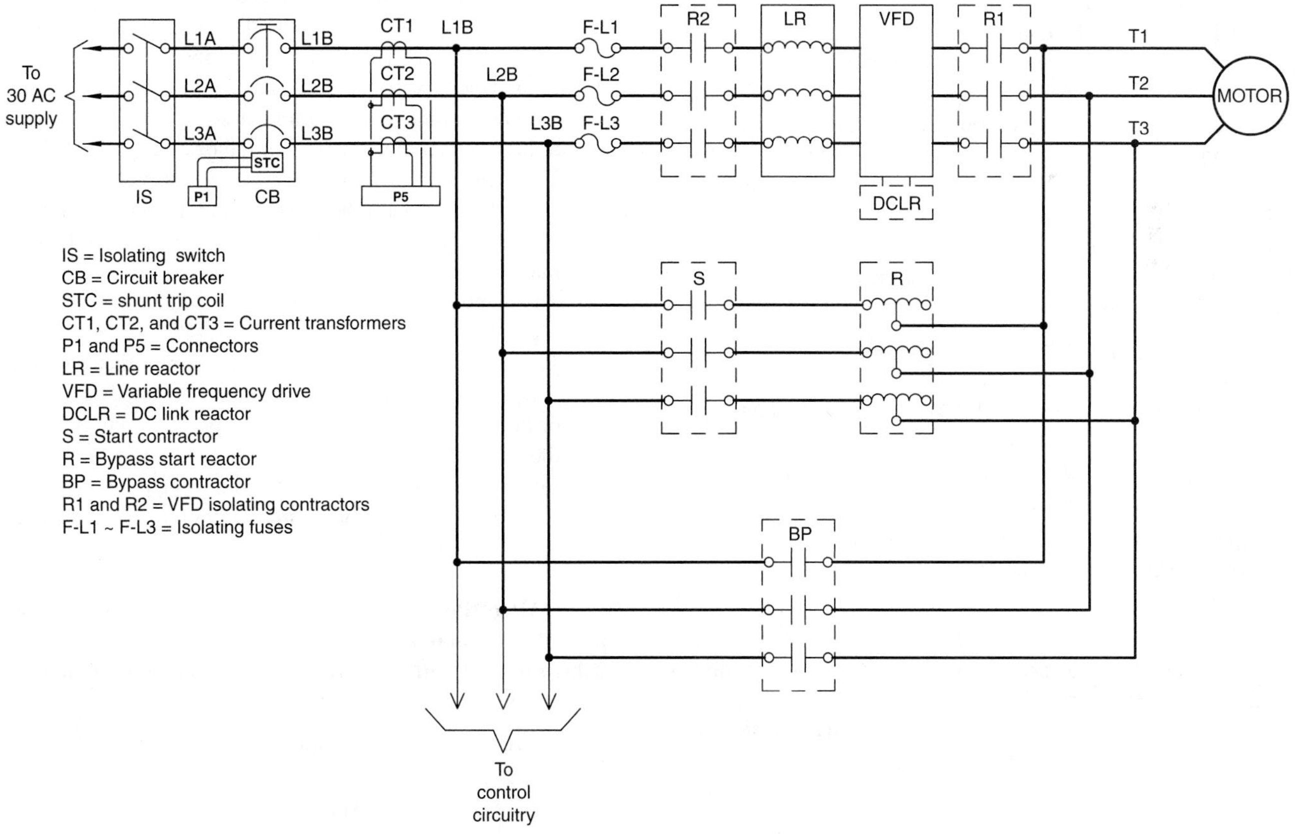

FIGURE 15.7.15 Variable Speed Fire Pump Controller with Reduced Inrush Starting in Bypass Mode (Source: Master Control Systems, Inc.)

Special Application-Related Controller Requirements. The controller equipment must be designed to meet the following application-related requirements:

- Where motor wiring distance exceeds manufacturer's ratings, a motor dV/dT (spike) filter or a load reactor must be incorporated into the controller to reduce motor voltage spikes to a safe and tolerable level.
- Skip frequencies may be required to be programmed into the VFD for vertical pumps. Application requirements are discussed later.
- Special enclosures such as NEMA 12 (UL Type 12) or better. Special enclosures will likely require upgrading the VFD cooling means or equipment.
- Additional door interlocking is needed where multiple bay controllers are involved for safety.

Functions

Certain new functions are required of these controllers, either by code (NFPA 20) or otherwise for successful operation. These include:

1. *Bypass mode lock-on.* When either the drive failure or the low-pressure timers time out to switch the controller automatically to the bypass mode of operation, the controller must lock onto that mode until manually shut down. Although the controller may be equipped with an automatic stop feature, that feature is not allowed to stop a pump running in the bypass mode. This lock-on also prevents the controller from switching modes back and forth between variable and full-speed bypass operation. Once in bypass, the controller must both stay in that mode and also not cause the pump to stop. The requirement is necessary as the bypass mode of operation represents a fallback either due to a failure or due to the manual mode switch being manually set to bypass. The controller must not interfere with this mode of operation since it is presumed that the variable speed mode has experienced a failure.

2. *Two stop push buttons.* These provide both normal ramp-down stopping and emergency instant pump stopping. The emergency stop push button is also the method of stopping the pump if it is running in the bypass mode.

3. *Coordination of start and stop pressures of the controller pressure switch with the VFD set point pressure for proper operation of the controller.* This coordination is needed whether the controller is set for manual stop or for automatic stop operation.

4. *Automatic stop based on VFD operating frequency.* The controller must not stop itself automatically if there is a requirement for water (fire water still being delivered). This means that the system pressure must both be at or above the pressure set point and that the pump running is no longer needed.

Operating Sequence

The description that follows briefly outlines normal controller and pump operation for a single fire pump. For proper operation, the VFD pressure set point is set to a value above the controller pressure switch reset (stop) set point.

Normal Operation—Variable Speed Mode—Automatic Pressure Loss Start. The following steps outline normal controller and pump operation:

1. Controller pressure switch trips (contacts close) to signal a pressure loss (pressure drop) pump demand.
2. The two VFD contactors (line side and load side) close to energize the VFD and to connect it to the motor.
3. The drive failure timer (DFT) begins timing.
4. The low-pressure timer (LPT) also begins timing.
5. If the VFD is healthy, it sends a "Drive Ready" signal that stops the DFT timer.
6. The VFD accelerates the motor to its set idle speed and continues to ramp up the motor speed sufficiently to cause the pump to raise the system pressure high enough to reset the controller pressure switch, which stops the LPT timer.
7. The VFD controls the motor in a closed loop mode (feedback) using the PID or PI process controller to maintain and regulate the system pressure at the programmed VFD pressure set point.
8. The VFD promptly responds to changes in water demand to adjust the motor and pump speed without excessive pressure overshoot or excessive delay to prevent excessive pressure drop.
9. Likewise, the VFD responds suitably to changes in pump supply (suction) pressure changes.
10. The VFD adjusts the pump speed to bring the pressure to within 1 psi (0.07 bar) of the desired pressure set point under stable demand (flow) conditions.
11. If and when the system demand drops to either low or no-flow conditions, the VFD throttles back the pump speed to that needed to just maintain the desired pressure. This is typically around two-thirds of pump rated speed resulting in a pressure boost of around 44 percent of rated boost, which will be too low to flow any water under normal conditions.

12a. The pump remains at this speed if the controller is set for manual stop, or

12b. The VFD signals the automatic stop timer that no water is being delivered. If the minimum run time has already occurred, the controller stops the pump. If not, it keeps the pump at idle speed until the minimum run timer is satisfied (times out), and then it stops the pump.

13. This leaves the controller and pump in the normal standby mode.

Normal Operation—Variable Speed Mode—Remote Deluge Valve Start Demand or Remote Momentary (Remote Start Push-Button) Demand. The following steps outline normal controller and pump operation:

1. The controller starts the motor as previously.
2. If there is no demand for water, the pump remains at the pressure maintenance speed.
   a. If started from a remote momentary (push-button) demand, the controller continues to run the pump at the low pressure maintenance speed until manually shut down.
   b. If started from a remote deluge (static) demand and depending on the controller type, the unit will remain run-

ning at low speed or stop after the minimum run timer times out if arranged for automatic stop.

3. If a demand for water occurs during the time that the pump is running, the VFD will accelerate the pump as needed. The controller will not shut the pump down even if or when the automatic stop time occurs in units set for automatic stop.

Normal Operation—Variable Speed Mode (Local Start Push-Button Demand). The following steps outline normal controller and pump operation:

1. The controller starts the motor as previously.
2. If there is no demand for water, the pump remains at the pressure maintenance speed.
3. The unit will remain running at low speed, or if a demand for water occurs, the VFD will accelerate the pump as needed. The controller will not stop the pump since it was started locally (manually).

Manually Set Bypass Mode (Mode Switch Set to Bypass). In this mode, the fire pump controller acts as a nonvariable speed (full-speed) full-service fire pump controller except as follows:

1. On a pressure loss demand (controller pressure switch trip), the controller starts the pump motor and runs it at full-line voltage and frequency to cause the motor to run at full rated speed. The controller continues to run until manually stopped regardless of whether it is equipped for automatic stop and regardless of whether the controller pressure switch is reset.
2. On a remote deluge start pump demand signal, the controller starts and runs the pump until manually stopped as in the preceding exception.
3. On a remote momentary demand (remote push button), the controller starts and runs the pump until manually stopped as in the first exception.

Abnormal Operation. The following steps outline abnormal controller and pump operation:

1. If the drive fault timer (DFT) times out, the controller begins its switch to bypass sequence. It will:
   a. Deenergize both VFD contactors to isolate both the VFD and the pump motor.
   b. Pause for the motor restart time (a few seconds) to allow motor flux to decay to reduce the motor back EMF (voltage) to a safe level.
   c. Restart the pump motor in the bypass full-speed mode.
   d. Continue running the pump at full speed until stopped manually.
2. If the low-pressure timer (LPT) timer times out, the controller will begin the switch to bypass sequence as above.
3. If the controller pressure switch recloses any time during variable speed running operation:
   a. The controller ramps the pump motor up to full speed, if not already there.
   b. The low-pressure timer (LPT) begins timing.
   c. If the pressure climbs high enough to reset the pressure switch, the LPT timer resets and the drive continues normal variable speed operation.
   d. If the LPT times out, the controller begins the switch to bypass sequence as above.
4. Should a fault in the motor occur during variable speed running, the VFD will normally shut down the motor since the output current from the VFD is limited to safe values.
5. If a fault occurs in the VFD input circuitry or if the VFD otherwise begins to draw excessive current, one of the following events occurs:
   a. The VFD branch (path) circuit protection (fuses or circuit breaker) trips to prevent the main fire pump circuit breaker from tripping.
   b. The drive fault timer begins timing and causes the controller to initiate the switch to bypass sequence.
   c. Since the motor is stopped, the pressure will likely drop enough to trip the controller pressure switch, which will start the low-pressure timer and subsequently cause the controller to initiate the switch to bypass sequence.
6. If the line voltage has spikes, transients, or voltage surges of sufficient magnitude, it will cause the VFD, if running, to go into its "overvoltage" shutdown mode. Better-quality VFD units, including all variable speed fire pump controllers installed as of this writing, will tolerate up to 800 Vdc on the capacitors before shutting down the VFD. This is 18 percent higher than the nominal 680 Vdc (480 × 1.414) on a 480 Vac system. In the event that the VFD goes into its overvoltage shutdown mode:
   a. The VFD will stop the motor and clear the drive ready signal.
   b. When the drive fault timer (DFT) times out, the controller begins its switch to bypass sequence as above.
   c. In the process, the VFD is disconnected from the power source and will reset the overvoltage shutdown mode. If not damaged by the overvoltage condition, it will be available for service on the next pump demand.
   d. The unit switches to bypass until manually shut down.

Application Considerations

For a variable speed fire pump installation to be successful (reliable and robust), certain unique requirements of the installation are needed. At a minimum, they include the following:

1. Adequate ventilation is required. The controller mounting must be per the manufacturer's instructions so as to not block controller ventilation requirements.
2. The pump room or pump house must be adequately cooled or ventilated to prevent heat from both the controller and the motor from exceeding the maximum allowed controller-rated ambient temperature.
3. The motor wiring length must not exceed the manufacturer's rating to avoid excessive motor voltage spikes that can damage the motor insulation.
4. As with other fire pumps, the motor must be a NEMA Design B, Starting Code G.

5. The motor must be suitable for and labeled for use with a variable speed drive (e.g., it must be marked as an inverter duty motor).
6. The motor-rated horsepower may not be exceeded. It is not allowed to use the motor into its service factor. The maximum allowed motor running current is 1.0 times the motor nameplate full-load current (FLA), not 1.15 times.
7. The pump and motor must be rigidly coupled to prevent motor torque oscillations.
8. For horizontal pumps, the pump and motor must be properly grouted for the same reason.
9. A relief valve is required for emergency and manual full-speed operation if the pump can exceed the system pressure rating when running at full speed and at churn.
10. For vertical turbine pumps, all resonant frequencies (or speeds) up to full speed must be known and programmed into the controller. These are skip frequency(s).
11. For water-lubricated pumps specify minimum speed and maximum allowed acceleration time to said speed, if applicable. Also specify the minimum idle speed needed to keep the top bearing wet at the lowest anticipated well-water level.

Basic Hydraulic System Considerations

Feedback Control Theory. With the availability of variable speed fire pumps, the system designer can now design for the worst-case low suction pressure and maximum pump demand factors and not have to worry about how high the pressure rises during low-flow or no-flow conditions, such as occur during pump testing. Note that actively controlling pressure implies the use of a feedback control system, which is the case with either diesel engine or electric motor–driven systems. This operation is always the case whether these systems are referred to as pressure limiting or not. The control of pump discharge pressure occurs by way of sensing the pressure at the pump discharge, comparing it to a set reference value, the "set point pressure," and using the difference, either positive or negative, to increase or decrease the speed of the pump driver in order to bring the pump pressure up to or down to the desired set point value as other system parameters vary, such as system flow and suction pressure.

Feedback System Control Gain. The gain of the system determines how close the controlled variable comes to the desired set point value. In the case of variable speed electric motor–driven controllers, the gain should always be high enough to allow controlling pump discharge pressure to within 0.1 psi (6.9 mbar) of the desired set point value. However, if the gain is too high, the system may not converge on the desired final value (set point value) in a smooth manner. Too much gain can lead to either overshoot or oscillation and unstable operation. These problems will not occur with properly set and operating PID or PI feedback controller.

System Time Constants. Every feedback control system has one or more time constants—the time that it takes for such a system to settle to within 37 percent of its ultimate value. A hydraulic system, such as a fire sprinkler system, may be either an open system or a closed system.

Open Systems. An open system is one that is open to the atmosphere somewhere. Typical are sprinkler systems fed from elevated tanks or towers. System pressure is determined by gravity and the height of the water in the tower or tank. These can have long time constants. Several seconds is not unusual. The longest time constants on one multibuilding medical housing campus measured 20 to 24 seconds along with several shorter ones.

Closed Systems. Most building fire sprinkler systems are closed, meaning that system pressure is maintained by means other than gravity. In hydraulic systems, the system time constant is dependent on a number of variables, but the two primary variables are the size of the system and the amount of air in the system. Pressure in these systems is maintained by a pressure maintenance pump, also called "Jockey Pump" or "make-up pump," whose start and stop pressures are coordinated with the churn pressure of the fire pump. The size of the system determines how many tons of water are entrained within the system. The amount of air trapped in the system determines both the amount of stored energy in the system and the overall system time constant. Specifically, with very little trapped air, the system time constant can be very short, even less than 1 second. This case can occur in high-rise buildings when the air has been bled out of the branch piping. On the other hand, large factory or warehouse buildings often have a large amount of trapped air in the system and, therefore, have long time constants.

Multiple Time Constants. Sprinkler systems may have numerous branches, each of which will have varying amounts of trapped air. These several branches will, therefore, have varying time constants. Most important is the time constant of the system as viewed from the variable speed fire pump. In systems with multiple buildings and multiple underground loops, there can be several time constants due to varying sizes of subsystems (buildings) and varying amounts of trapped air (Figure 15.7.16).

Hydraulic Versus Electrical Time Constants. A second source of multiple time constants is the variable speed pump itself. When the pump is off, the system will have a main (fundamental) time constant or resonant point. When the pump is turned on or is accelerating, it can cause a different, usually shorter, time constant, since it is acting as a forcing function in feedback theory terms. Also, the motor and controller times are under the control of both the VFD set parameters as well as the PID set parameters. These time constants are important only while the system check valve is open, meaning when the pump is delivering water.

Other Applications. Time constant considerations will be different for other systems but must still be considered for stable and responsive system operation. Examples of these other systems are agent pumps (foam agent, etc.) and water mist systems. Some of these employ positive displacement pumps that also require the use of unloader valves during motor starting.

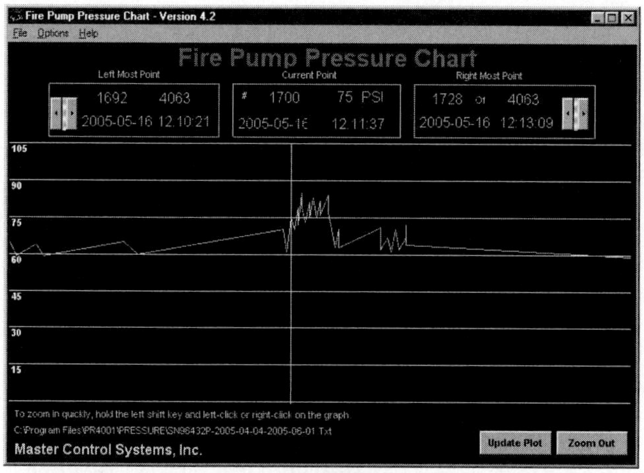

FIGURE 15.7.16 Screen Shot of Pressure Plot Showing Several Different System Time Constants (Source: Master Control Systems, Inc.)

CONTROLLER PARAMETERS

It is paramount that the fire pump installation and the fire pump package (pump, motor, and controller) be coordinated. Any mismatch can result in a nonfunctional package that will have to be corrected or replaced. Worse yet, the mismatch can result in an installation that appears to work but is unreliable. This situation may not be discovered until the pump is needed for fire suppression. Finally, since substantial fault currents and voltages exist, miscoordination can and does result in unsafe installations.

Nameplate Parameters

Voltage. The controller's parameters must match the incoming power and the motor that it will be controlling. The line voltage must be the same as the controller-rated voltage and the motor-rated voltage. Special care must be taken for part winding and wye-delta (star-delta) starting controllers to determine that the intended motor is rated for the respective type of starting at the intended voltage. This is especially true of dual-voltage (series/parallel) motors.

Frequency. The controller-rated frequency must match that of the incoming power (mains). To be specific, 60 Hz controllers will not be reliable when used at 50 Hz and vice versa, unless the controller is designed, rated, marked, and listed for such dual-frequency service. Most controller components that operate at the line frequency are affected by the applied frequency in one of two ways. First, 60 Hz components used at 50 Hz at the same voltage will draw more current due to the reduced inductive impedance (reactance) at the lower frequency and will thus run hotter and possibly overheat. The second, and often the more important, effect occurs with AC-powered relays, contactors, timers, and so forth. When used at a higher frequency than intended, such as with a 50 Hz coil used at 60 Hz, the coil will have a lower inrush (pickup or pull-in) current. Such use will result in lower pull-in force, which may not be adequate under normal or low-line voltage conditions. Note that some devices are rated, and labeled, for such dual-frequency use because they have been designed, tested, and listed under both frequencies.

Horsepower or Motor Kilowatt Rating. The controller components are sized for a specific maximum motor FLA and service factor. Applying a larger-than-rated motor voids the controller listings, invalidates the design, and usually voids the controller warranty. It is also dangerous and unreliable, especially when the unit is needed to deliver water at full flow for any length of time. The use of a smaller-than-rated motor must be approved by the controller manufacturer to assure proper coordination because the sizing of the circuit breaker shunt trip unit (for the motor locked rotor protection) covers only limited ranges of motor FLA.

Short Circuit Rating

Every fire pump controller has a labeled short circuit current rating in accordance with NFPA 20. The current is given in either symmetrical amperes (A) or in symmetrical kiloamperes (kA) where 1 kA is 1000 A. As detailed in NFPA 20, these ratings are established by the listing agencies Underwriter's Laboratories (UL) and Factory Mutual (FM) by way of testing, which is often destructive. The testing affirms that the equipment can both withstand the rated short circuit current and that the equipment can safely interrupt said short circuit currents. In order to pass the test, the equipment may not become a shock hazard or a fire hazard. NFPA 20 also makes it clear that to determine the suitability of the controller, the short circuit current availability of the power source supplying the controller must be determined. This determination requires a short circuit study. A controller rated at 30,000 A is an entirely unknown variable if connected to a power source capable of delivering more than 30,000 A. If the controller short circuit rating is exceeded, the equipment may become a fire or shock hazard during or after a short circuit event. It is important to note that the interrupting capacity rating of the circuit breaker (and/or isolating switch) inside of the controller is not the rating of the controller. These two different ratings should never be confused or used interchangeably.

With dual-power sources, two short circuit ratings are involved and must be coordinated with the alternate (emergency) power source (genset, other utility, etc.), namely, the interrupt capacity rating and maximum allowed ampere size upstream circuit breaker. See the section on power transfer switches for details.

STANDARD CONTROLLER COMPONENTS

Certain elements are common to all or most fire pump controllers.

Nameplate

A listed electric motor–driven fire pump controller must bear a ratings nameplate that gives the important electrical parameters, including operating voltage, motor horsepower or ampere rating, or both, the minimum operating temperature, and the enclosure type, among other parameters. The ratings also include the required short circuit rating. UL listing and FM approval marks are also required.

Isolating Switch

An isolating switch is required and is present on all controllers except on limited-service controllers. These are sized to have an ampere rating at least 115 percent of the full-load current rating of the motor and/or be horsepower rated at not less than the motor horsepower. An isolating switch is not necessarily a load break rated switch. If the isolating switch is not mechanically interlocked with the controller circuit breaker, a warning label must also be present to warn of operating (opening or closing) the isolating switch if the circuit breaker is closed. This is because the isolating switch is not required to be rated or tested for closing on to or interrupting faults.

Circuit Breaker (Disconnecting Means)

The fire pump circuit breaker serves several purposes. It is an important and integral part of the controller short circuit design and rating. It must safely interrupt fault currents up to the rated short circuit rating of the controller. In many, if not most, modern designs, both the isolating switch and the circuit breaker are of the molded case construction and share the task of clearing high fault (heavy short circuit) currents between the two devices. The circuit breaker is required to be rated at 115 percent or more of the motor FLA. The circuit breaker will have an interrupt capacity rating. However, this rating is not the same as the controller short circuit rating. It may be either higher or lower than the circuit breaker's interrupt capacity rating. Note that medium-voltage fire pump controllers use current-limiting, R-rated motor circuit fuses instead of a circuit breaker for this fault-clearing function.

Motor Locked Rotor Overcurrent Protection

Modern controllers use a separate current sensing trip unit in conjunction with a shunt trip solenoid, which is part of the circuit breaker. The circuit breaker itself is usually a molded case switch with a shunt trip solenoid. The trip unit senses the motor current flowing and compares it with the desired tripping curve characteristics. The two points that define the breaker trip characteristic curve are the 300 percent no-trip value and the 8 to 20 second trip time at 600 percent of the motor FLA. These trip units have setting switches to select a range of motor FLA values for the motor being used. Using a trip setting higher than the motor FLA value is more likely to result in a motor that will burn out before the trip unit can open the circuit breaker. If the trip unit setting is lower than the motor FLA, the circuit breaker is more likely to trip prematurely. Trip units with smaller ranges (more settings) are able to provide more precise motor protection.

Limited-service controllers are allowed to have a wider range of motor protection by allowing the use of thermal circuit breakers. Medium-voltage controllers use the trip unit to deenergize the motor contactor to take the motor off-line under overload conditions up to and including locked rotor. The contactors are tested for this duty to UL 347 on high-voltage industrial control equipment.

Motor Contactor(s)

The main motor contactor(s) takes the place of a motor starter in conventional combination motor controllers. There is no motor overload relay. Motor tripping is accomplished by opening the circuit breaker. The number and purpose of contactors vary with the controller starting type, as illustrated in Table 15.7.3.

Pressure Switch

An automatic controller of the pressure-actuated type will be equipped with a pressure-actuated switch. The pressure switch is required to have independent high and low set point adjustable settings. This pressure switch has traditionally been a Bourdon tube type pressure switch, although pressure transducers, along with amplifier circuitry, are used in some designs instead, especially in those jurisdictions where products incorporating mercury are prohibited. This switch has been a hermetically sealed mercury "tilt bottle" type of pressure switch, which protects the contacts from atmospheric and environmental conditions.

The pressure switch settings are normally determined by the hydraulic design of the installation and by the AHJ over the installation. The setting of the start and stop pressure of every fire and jockey pump in a system is of vital importance. The settings need to be correct for the fire protection system (the fire sprinkler system) to function correctly and deliver the required amount of water or agent. Moreover, incorrect settings can damage the system by either overpressure or excessive water surging, either of which can damage an underground piping system (loop).

Start and Stop Push Buttons

Every controller has a manual "Start" push button known as the manual electric control at controller. Operation of the "Start" push button locks the controller into a running condition. If the controller is of the reduced inrush starting type, the starting will be in the reduced inrush starting mode. In most controller de-

TABLE 15.7.3 Summary of Number of Motor Contactors Versus Starting Type for Fixed and Variable Speed

Starting Type	*Number of Contactors*
ATL	1
Part winding	2
Primary resistance	2
Primary reactor	2
Wye-delta open transition	3
Wye-delta closed transition	4
Soft start	2[a]
Auto transformer	3
Variable speed	At least 3[b]

[a]Three for soft start if an isolating (start) contactor is provided.
[b]Depending on which bypass starting method is used.

signs, the "Stop" push button will stop the pump regardless of whether or not a demand still exists. If there is still a demand, the pump will restart when the "Stop" button is released.

Emergency-Run Mechanical Control at Controller

The emergency mechanical operator will start the pump motor by physically closing the main motor contactor M or both of the two main motor contactors (typically M1 and M2). As a result, the motor is started at full voltage. Most low-voltage controllers have an electrical assist mechanism to avoid undue contact erosion due to arcing or welding of the contacts because of slow opening or slow closing of the contactor.

Emergency Stopping

With low-voltage, single-source (nontransfer switch) controllers, emergency stopping of the pump can always be accomplished by opening the controller circuit breaker. This operation allows stopping of the motor in case there are one or more welded contacts in the motor contactor(s). This method of stopping will still work if a dual-source (transfer switch) controller is running on the normal source. Some dual-source controllers (the so-called dual-utility controllers) have two circuit breakers, allowing emergency stopping of the motor regardless of which source it is connected to.

In medium-voltage controllers, it is the motor contactor that must always break the motor circuit. The only exception is when a controller is equipped with a suitably rated disconnect switch in lieu of the usual isolating switch. As noted earlier, the motor circuit fuses interrupt the motor current only during a high-current short circuit. These fuses are coordinated with the motor size and the other power path components. Therefore, the "Stop" push button serves as both the normal and the emergency stopping means.

Surge Arrester

The surge arrester offers mixed benefits. The purpose of the surge arrester is to protect the fire pump controller from line surges, mainly lightning surges, although no secondary equipment (nonutility equipment) will survive a direct lightning hit on its incoming lines. The surges in question are induced surges caused by capacitive or inductive coupling from a nearby lightning strike rather than a direct strike. When a surge does occur, it will find the path of least resistance. This will be equipment or wiring devices having the weakest dielectric strength (voltage withstand). The purpose of surge arresters is to absorb this surge energy before it can cause damage to equipment or wiring devices. Equipment having the highest voltage withstand will not conduct the surge energy since other equipment and/or equipment having arresters will do that job instead. Equipment having a high enough voltage withstand will thus be unaffected by such surges.

For lightning arresters to be effective, they need to be sized in accordance with the energy available versus their ability to absorb said energy. Basically, they should be sized in accordance with the upstream impedance, which limits the energy. Arresters are rated on how large of a current surge they can absorb and how often they can absorb the same. When an arrester absorbs more than this rated energy, its leakage current (follow-on current) can be high enough to destroy it, even if a first surge or a repeated surge does not. This can be immediate or may be delayed due to a condition known as thermal runaway. This condition occurs when the self-heating caused by leakage current leads to internal heating faster than the heat can be dissipated. Suitably rated and well-designed arrester equipment is available. However, the cost and size prevent their widespread use inside fire pump controllers as standard equipment. They are sometimes installed in parallel with fire pump controllers. Because of this hazard, some designs mount the arresters "out of sight" for personnel safety. Some designs also provide fuses to protect the equipment from damage due to blown arresters.

STANDARD CONTROLLER FEATURES

The description of certain standard features of electric drive fire pump controllers follows. The list is not exhaustive. For a complete list, see NFPA 20.

Devices and Controls

Locks. Most or all listed controllers have, or should have, a lockable cabinet. The means may be by way of padlock hasps, a lockable door handle(s), key-lockable handle(s), or separate key lock(s). If the pressure switch is a Mercoid Bourdon tube type, its setting knobs are lockable or can be sealed with a seal wire. Most or all controllers have isolating switch or circuit breaker operator handles that can be locked on or off. The "On" position is used to lock the unit in the standby fire protection mode, whereas the "Off" position is used as a lockout for servicing.

Interlocks. Most listed controllers have an interlock between the cabinet door(s) and the isolating switch operator mechanism or handle. This interlock prevents opening of the door while the isolating switch is in the "On" position (unit energized). The interlock also prevents closing of the isolating switch while the door is still open. These interlocks are important because the controllers operate at lethal voltages. They are also very important for controllers that are connected to high-fault power supplies. These controllers are very unforgiving of accidental short circuits. It is also most important to be sure that the door is closed before energizing the unit, especially when closing the circuit breaker. Should a pump demand exist and a short circuit exist, there will be venting of ionized gases in one or more of the power devices. This can cause explosive pressures within the controller. If the controller door(s) is not closed and latched, serious injury can occur. This is also the reason for greater emphasis on short circuit availability and controller short circuit rating coordination. Medium-voltage controllers have additional interlocking between the motor contactor and the isolating switch and the high-voltage door.

External Operators. All listed electric fire pump controllers have an emergency mechanical operator. Low-voltage controllers also have a circuit breaker operator. Medium-voltage controllers have an isolating switch operator in lieu of the circuit breaker operator. Full-service low-voltage controllers have either two operators or one combined operator for the isolating switch and the circuit breaker. The required external operators are shown in Table 15.7.4.

Manual Electrical Control. All listed controllers have, as a minimum, the required "Start" and "Stop" push buttons. Controllers have circuitry that keeps the pump running if started from the local "Start" push button independent of an automatic stop (minimum run timer) circuit. The same applies for a remote lockout or remote shutdown circuit. Because the pump was started manually and locally, it should not be stopped automatically or remotely.

Pressure Loss Starting. Controllers used for pressurized systems also have the pressure switch described previously.

Remote Starting. When controllers are used for an unpressurized system, a deluge system, or a monitor nozzle system, the controller must be equipped with a remote start option circuit. The controller might not be equipped with a pressure switch. These units are actuated by the opening of a remote (external) contact, such as from a deluge valve contact, a fire or smoke alarm relay contact, or a remote or central station push-button contact, among others, to signal the controller to start. Some systems are a combination of both pressurized and deluge type sprinklers. For these systems, the controller has both a pressure switch and a remote start option circuit.

Accelerate Time. Reduced inrush (reduced current) type of controllers have one or more means to set the accelerate time. Most, but not all, are adjustable. In addition, primary resistor, primary reactor, and autotransformer controllers have two or more taps for setting the motor starting voltage. Similarly, soft start controllers have various adjustments for setting the voltage and time parameters.

Input Signals

All electric fire pump controllers have power inlet terminals for the motor power circuit. Dual-source controllers have two such inputs. A second (or third) power source is sometimes also supplied to a controller equipped with certain options. This additional source is the so-called supervisory power supply, usually a 115 Vac (at 60 Hz) or 220 Vac (at 50 Hz) branch circuit. It is used for a supervisory power loss start circuit option for a so-called built-in alarm set circuit option.

All automatic controllers have at least one pump demand input to signal the controller to start the fire pump. The most common is a pressure sense line fitting that connects to the controller's internal pressure switch. Other inputs include the aforementioned remote start circuit. Some controllers have separate remote start inputs, either as standard equipment or as optional equipment, one specifically for deluge or fire alarm contacts and the other specifically for remote start push-button contacts. Some designs use circuitry to keep the automatic stop circuitry from canceling the latter demand as it is initiated manually.

A controller may also have an input for a remote stop or lockout signal, either as standard equipment or as optional equipment. This input signal is sometimes used to keep a second pump from starting unless a first pump has failed to start.

Controllers can also have other inputs, usually for alarm, monitoring, or supervising purposes. Some of these are described in the section on alarms and indications.

TABLE 15.7.4 External Operators

Controller Type	Controller Voltage: *Low Voltage*	Controller Voltage: *Medium Voltage*
Limited service	Circuit breaker operator only	(not applicable)
Full service	Circuit breaker operator and isolating switch operator	Isolating switch operator only

Output Signals

The main output from an electric fire pump controller is the motor power, which comes from the main motor contactor(s) as described previously. Controllers may also be equipped (as standard or optional equipment) with auxiliary control power output at the same voltage levels as those described for supervisory power input. This power is often used as one of the power inputs to a remote alarm set (alarm panel). In jurisdictions that allow or mandate low-suction shutdown, this auxiliary power may be used as one source of power for a low-suction shutdown panel. This source of power is usually limited to a current of 1 A or less and is normally protected by a fuse or circuit breaker to prevent damage to the controller's control power transformer because this is often in the critical starting path of the controller.

Controllers used in multiple-zone installations (the so-called high-zone and low-zone installations) have an output signal from the high-zone controller(s) to signal the lower-zone pumps to start in order to supply water to the higher-zone pump suction inlets. The low-zone controller(s) have inputs, such as remote start, to accept the start signals from the high-zone controller(s). See the section on high-zone delay for pumps in series.

All controllers must be equipped with a minimum of three output alarm contacts, for motor (or pump) running, power available (or power failure or phase loss), and phase sequence reversed (or phase reversal). Dual-source (transfer switch) controllers must also supply two additional output alarm contacts: one to indicate when the transfer switch is in the emergency (alternate) source position and the other to indicate when the emergency isolating switch is opened. Various controller options supply additional contacts for alarm, monitoring, or supervisory purposes. Some of these are described next.

Alarms and Indications

All electric fire pump controllers must have at least two indicator pilot lights (visible indicators). One is used to indicate that power is available in all phases at the line terminals of the contactor(s). The other is used to indicate a phase reversal of the power source to which the line terminals of the motor contactor are connected. Controllers may also have an optional motor (pump) running signal light, among others.

When the pump room is not constantly attended, alarms must be provided "at a point of constant attendance." In the absence of such an attendant, the mandatory three (or five for dual-source controllers) alarm contacts should be connected to either an on-site alarm set installed at a point of constant attendance (switchboard, security post, etc.) or an off-site monitoring location such as a central watch or alarm service. Not monitoring the alarm contacts results in degraded fire protection because pump failure conditions go unheeded and uncorrected for some period of time. Similarly, a pump running condition should always cause someone to be in attendance at the pump to watch for problems. More importantly, a pump running alarm might be due to the pump responding to an actual fire condition. Such a condition should always initiate a course of action that includes immediate attendance at the fire pump to monitor its operation and possibly allow for intervention in the event of trouble with the pump, motor, or controller.

All electric controllers must also signal an alarm condition if a single-phase condition occurs, whether or not the motor is running. This condition may be either annunciated as separate light and alarm contacts or it may be combined with the power available/phase loss alarm light and contacts.

Strictly speaking, only the loss of phase open or closed contact is required. However, all listed controllers provide both open and closed contacts. Since these contacts operate in opposition, they can signal power failure (phase loss) and power available conditions.

Dual-source controllers (combination transfer switch fire pump controllers) require additional alarms related to the transfer switch itself. These are a pilot light and contacts to indicate when the transfer switch is in the normal source position and when it is in the emergency (alternate) source position. The same is required to indicate when the emergency source side isolating switch is open as well as a local audible alarm for this indication. These units also require contacts to initiate genset starting when the alternate source is a standby generator set. The required alarms for electric fire pump controllers are given in Table 15.7.5.

TABLE 15.7.5 Required Alarms for Single- and Dual-Source (Transfer Switch) Controllers

Alarm	*Contacts*	*Visible*	*Audible*
All Fire Pump Controllers			
Power available	Yes	Yes	Optional
Motor (pump) running	Yes	Optional	Optional
Phase sequence reversed	Yes	Yes	Optional
All Variable Speed Controllers			
Drive failure (variable speed drive failed)	Optional	Yes	Optional
Bypass mode (full speed running)	Optional	Yes	Optional
Overpressure (115% of set pressure)	Optional	Yes	Optional
Dual-Source Controllers or Power Transfer Switches			
Transfer switch in normal position	Optional	Yes	Optional
Transfer switch in emergency position	Yes	Yes	Optional*
Emergency isolating switch open	Yes	Yes	Yes

*Some controllers provide this audible alarm as standard in addition to the emergency isolating switch open audible alarm.

High-Zone Delay for Pumps in Series

In high-rise buildings, a lower-zone pump is often used to supply suction pressure to the next or higher-zone pump. This arrangement is usually done when more than one pump is needed to supply the required head (psi pressure). When the suction of one pump is supplied directly from the discharge of another pump, the pumps are considered to be in series.

Each pump supplying pressure to another pump must be arranged to start before the pump it supplies. The starting requirement prevents the higher-zone pump from running dry or cavitating. When only two zones are involved, a demand for the high-zone pump causes the high-zone controller to send a demand signal to the lower-zone pump before energizing the high-zone pump motor. The delay is required to be between 5 and 10 seconds, which allows the lower-zone pump to come up to speed and supply water to the high-zone pump. In practice, the high-zone controller merely delays the actuation of the motor contactor(s) for a fixed delay time (5 to 10 seconds), while sending the demand (start) signal to the low-zone controller. The high-zone controller should impose this start delay for every demand source to avoid cavitation or dry running. This delay interval is usually known as the high-zone delay.

In case of more than two zones, all the higher-zone pumps must delay starting their motors while sending a start signal to the lower-zone pump controller. In the case of three zones, when the highest-zone controller receives a demand signal, it sends the demand signal to the middle-zone pump remote start input while delaying the start of the high-zone motor by 10 to 20 seconds. The middle-zone controller likewise sends a demand signal to the low-zone pump controller. The low-zone controller starts its pump motor immediately and supplies suction pressure to the middle-zone pump. In 5 to 10 seconds, the middle-zone controller starts its pump motor and supplies suction pressure to the high-zone pump. In 10 to 20 seconds the third- (highest-) zone pump starts to provide discharge (system) pressure.

Failure of a leading motor to start must not prevent subsequent pumps from starting. This requirement is accomplished with the aforementioned delay scheme because the high- or higher-zone pumps will start unconditionally after their set time delay, regardless of the state of other pumps. This scheme is followed with the intent that the high(er)-zone pumps will still have enough suction pressure to provide at least some pressure and flow.

Sequence Starting for Pumps in Parallel

When pumps feed a common system or manifold, they are considered to be pumps in parallel. This scheme is usually implemented when more than one pump is needed to supply the required flow or when the added reliability of having more than one pump is desired. Although electric motor–driven pumps are used in parallel, many applications for parallel pumps for increased flow capacity (gal/min) use diesel drives.

Controllers for each unit of multiple-pump units must incorporate a sequential timing device to prevent any one motor from starting simultaneously with any other motor. There are two main reasons for this requirement. One is to prevent excessive load on the electrical systems from simultaneous starting of pumps. The other is to reduce the stress on the associated piping system. In these installations, the controllers are equipped with a sequence start timer, which inhibits pump starting during the delay period. The delays are set in the required 5 to 10 second intervals, although the first unit need not have any delay in most applications. At the end of the time interval, the controller in question will start the pump regardless of whether previous pumps have started or not. The only exception is controllers that reset if the demand signal ceases during the timing interval.

Control of Pumps in Series and Parallel

Some installations use two fire pumps in each zone in order to provide a backup pump in case the primary pump fails. In a three-zone installation, there is a total of six pumps. Where emergency (alternate) power is required, the controllers are sometimes interlocked to prevent both motors in any zone from starting to avoid overloading the alternate power source genset. One scheme uses a combination of failure to start, motor overload, or power failure signals from the primary pump to lock it out and pass the demand signal to the low-zone pump. When motor current exceeds a fixed percentage (e.g., 15%) a motor running signal is sent to the backup pump to lock it out. The backup pump is equipped with sequence start delay in order to allow the primary pump to start.

High-Pressure Wet Parts (Plumbing, Pressure Switch, and Recorder)

Most listed controllers are rated at 275 to 300 psi (19 to 21 bar) working pressure and use 300 psi (21 bar) full-scale pressure-sensing elements (pressure switches or pressure transducers and pressure recorders, where used). Pressure switches suitable for higher-pressure applications are available for use with these systems. The pressure switch and pressure recorder are the most delicate devices with regard to overpressure.

Stainless Steel Wet Parts (Plumbing, Pressure Switch, and Pressure Recorder)

Although more common with diesel drive fire pump controllers, this feature is needed when the pump takes suction from seawater or other brackish or corrosive water sources. The book *Pumps for Fire Protection Systems* provides additional detail in this regard.

NONMANDATORY CONTROLLER FEATURES

Listed electric fire pump controllers are available with a great number of options, features, and modifications. Some of these affect controller or pump operation and/or functionality. Some provide additional information (indications or readings) or additional protection for the equipment or the installation. Others modify the construction of the controller itself. The following paragraphs describe some of the options that affect pump operation and/or reliability of operation.

Motor Burnout Protection

Motor Overload Alarm. A motor overload alarm is one of the best ways to provide increased fire pump reliability, if properly used and monitored. This feature is available as an option with most listed controllers. Because the code prohibits the usual overload relay in the interest of keeping the flow of water running during a fire, the motor is subject to damage or destruction by any number of overload or overcurrent conditions. Although no overload relay or protection is allowed by code, other than that provided by the controller circuit breaker, an overload alarm feature is allowed. This alarm will warn of an overloaded motor due to pump problems, a low line voltage condition, a controller stuck in the accelerate mode for any reason, a single-phase condition, or a damaged or degraded motor.

Single-Phase Start Protection. All electric fire pump motors and controllers are three phase except for a small number of limited-service controllers and pumps. Attempting to start a three-phase pump with only single-phase power will cause the motor to draw starting currents until it is destroyed, until the fire pump circuit breaker trips, or often both. Fortunately, all electric fire pump controllers inherently protect the motor from starting during a single-phase condition on two of the incoming lines, namely, the lines that are used to supply control power to the motor contactor(s). Some designs also complete the protection by providing single-phase motor start protection on the third phase as well. This difference is seen during wide-area single-phase events. Note that the fire pumps will attempt to start after the jockey pump or pumps trip off-line due to the same single-phase condition.

Motor Restart Delay. If a running motor is briefly taken off-line and then reconnected (restarted), a very high transient can occur, depending on the phase angle difference between the motor's back EMF voltage and the line voltage to which it is reconnected. This phenomenon is the same as that described in the preceding section on wye-delta controllers, but it can be worse as the motor will have full-line voltage rather than the smaller 57 percent wye-mode voltage. This can cause a false trip of the circuit breaker, which takes the pump off-line until someone manually resets the fire pump circuit breaker or possibly the upstream (service) breaker or replaces the fuses. To prevent this situation, some controllers are equipped with a restart delay as standard equipment, which operates by sensing when the motor contactors drop out (deenergize). The circuit then inhibits the contactors from reenergizing for a few seconds, which is enough time to allow the motor magnetic flux, and the resultant motor back EMF voltage, to decay to a safe value. After the delay period, the restart delay circuit allows the controller to restart the motor and also resets itself to be ready for the next motor interruption.

Exterior Measurement Means. The exterior measurement means facilitates reading controller (motor) voltages and currents from outside the controller. This means addresses personnel safety since both lethal voltages are always present and very high and dangerous short circuit fault currents are available. The best personnel protection against this danger is for the controller door to be securely closed and latched. This measurement means also provides an easy way to monitor the health of the installation and its power source if adequate records are kept of the motor running voltage and current readings during the weekly test running.

Alarms and Other Signals

As previously mentioned, additional alarm inputs and/or outputs are available as optional equipment in these controllers. Some of the more commonly used additional signals and alarms follow. The terms *pump room* and *pump house* are used interchangeably.

Sensor (Input) Signals. Some of the commonly used sensor (input) signals include the following:

- Low pump room temperature (freeze alert)
- Low reservoir temperature (freeze alert)
- Low suction pressure
- Low reservoir level
- Reservoir empty
- Relief valve open
- Flow meter on

Output Signals. Some of the commonly used output signals include the following:

- Motor overload (amperes exceed 115% of FLA) alarm
- Failure to start (within time limit) alarm
- AC volts low alarm (precise detector)
- Load shed signal (transfer switch units)
- Communications options, including telephone dialer to a remote location or pocket pager or cell phone, network reporting, Internet access, or wide area access

Other Selected Options

Automatic Weekly Test Start. Although required in all diesel fire pump controllers, this option is seldom specified in electric drive controllers. NFPA 25 now requires weekly rather than monthly test starting of these pumps. This feature can aid in meeting this requirement, although NFPA 25 does require the weekly test to be attended by qualified operating personnel. Note that electric drive pumps must be equipped with circulation relief valves in order to provide enough waterflow to keep the pump from overheating due to running at churn (shutoff).

Failure to Start. This alarm is a complement to the pump running alarm as it indicates that the pump should be running but is not. This alarm is of utmost importance during a fire.

Built-In Alarm Set. This option provides an audible alarm (bell, horn, etc.) for the standard alarms listed in the section on alarms. It uses a separate source of power—supervisory power—for this function. This option also includes a means of silencing the audible alarm.

Control Power Loss Start. In some high-risk applications, this option starts the pump in the event of internal control power loss. This feature overcomes the inaction that would ensue when a pump demand occurs.

Supervisory Power Loss Start. Supervisory power loss start is an older method of annunciating loss of supervisory power by way of the motor running alarm. Better methods provide two sources of power or battery backup or dial-up communications to monitor and alarm a loss of supervisory power.

Built-In Recording and/or Telemetry. Most controllers are available with built-in pressure recorders of the paper chart, strip chart, or paperless variety. Some units also record alarms and/or other parameters. Some units allow local or remote data access because they can transmit said data on command or on occurrence via various network communications media.

Environmental, Construction, and Other Treatment Options and Modifications

Controller Enclosure (Cabinet) Space Heaters (Strip Heaters). High moisture, especially condensation, is ruinous to electrical and electronic equipment. This condition occurs when the equipment is subjected to either damp atmospheres or varying temperatures (hot in daytime and cool at night). Cabinet heaters help avoid this condensation or excessive moisture. Some designs use heaters that are operated at one-half of their rated voltage, which reduces the temperature of the heater and increases its life. Also, some designs control the heater by use of a humidistat rather than a thermostat, which is more efficient because the purpose of the heaters is to control humidity. Designs that leave the heaters on continuously are outmoded and wasteful of energy.

Motor Heaters. Controllers may be equipped with pilot contacts to enable the motor heater or, depending on the wattage, the slave contactor for the motor heater. This contact will be closed except during motor running.

Controller Enclosure (Cabinet) Construction. NFPA 20 requires a minimum enclosure construction of NEMA Type 2 (UL Type 2), which is rated as and suitable for indoor use only and is dripproof only. Note that this is the minimum requirement. NFPA 20 also requires that the "fire pump, driver, and controller" be protected against possible interruption of service through damage caused by "any adverse conditions." A NEMA 2 enclosure rating only "provides a degree of protection against limited amounts of falling water and dirt." They are tested for water dripping from the downward vertical direction only. They do not necessarily provide any degree of splash, spray, or water impingement from any of the numerous possible sources of pressurized water within the pump room, especially when the pump room is equipped with fire sprinklers. Also, NEMA 2 enclosures are not necessarily dustproof. The enclosure types described in Table 15.7.6 provide better protection than the standard NEMA 2 rating.

Another enclosure that is also available is the so-called NEMA 3R rated enclosure. It is rated for outdoor use for rain protection. This construction is typically the kind used for outdoor disconnect switches, such as on air conditioning units and outdoor advertising signs. It is basically a variation of NEMA 1 construction and it specifically allows water to enter the enclosure and accumulate within it, although the water is not allowed to wet electrical parts or accumulate to the level of the lowest electrical live part. This construction offers only limited protection of the controller since moisture can enter and accumulate therein. In some cases, the manufacturer builds a NEMA 3R enclosure similar to a NEMA 4 enclosure instead.

TABLE 15.7.6 Enclosure Types

Enclosure Type[a]	*Location*	*Protection*
NEMA 12	Indoor	Dripping water and dust (was splash and oil resistant)
NEMA 13	Indoor	Spraying water (and oil) and dust
NEMA 3	Outdoor	Rain, dust, and ice
NEMA 4	Outdoor	Rain, dust, ice, splashing, and hose-directed water (hose-tight)
NEMA 4XA	Outdoor	Same as NEMA 4, but corrosion resistant (special paint finish)
NEMA 4XB	Outdoor	Same as NEMA 4, but also corrosion resistant of type 304 stainless steel[b]
NEMA 4XC	Outdoor	Same as NEMA 4, but also corrosion resistant of type 316 stainless steel
NEMA 4XCL	Outdoor	Same as NEMA 4XC, but type 316 low-carbon stainless steel

[a]Differences exist between exact definitions and testing methods. The NEMA 4XA, 4XB, 4XC, and 4XCL designations are unofficial and are for reference only. These enclosures are considered as 4X.

[b]The 400 series of stainless steels (such as type 403) is magnetic and does not offer nearly the level of corrosion protection that the nonmagnetic 300 series of stainless steels offers.

The current requirements for raceway terminations for fire pump controllers address the problem of the fire pump controller Type rating being compromised by (1) the use of improperly rated conduit hubs and fittings and (2) field modifications made to the controller enclosure not endorsed by the controller manufacturer.

Current requirements for raceway terminations state the following:

1. Listed conduit hubs shall be used to terminate raceway (conduit) to the fire pump controller.
2. The (NEMA) Type rating of the conduit hub(s) shall be at least equal to that of the fire pump controller.
3. The installation instructions of the manufacturer of the fire pump controller shall be followed.
4. No alterations to the fire pump controller other than conduit entry per the *NEC* shall be allowed.

Other Approvals. To comply with NFPA 20, these controllers are all listed for fire service. Although other possibilities exist, they are all UL listed and almost all are also FM Global approved. Some equipment is available with "CE" (compliance with European norms) compliance certification. Note that these European norms (compliance requirements standards) are widely adopted equipment safety standards within and throughout the European Economic Community.

Electromagnetic Compatibility (EMC). Microprocessor-controlled equipment can and does radiate a certain amount of high-frequency noise. It is also susceptible to disruption by nearby portable radio equipment. Another approval available from some manufacturers is UL EMC certification of compliance (conformance) to standards covering electromagnetic radiation and other electrical disturbances such as transients, surges, and dropouts. The EMC standard used to access conformance (conformity) requires a two-way evaluation, meaning that the equipment is both tested for immunity (susceptibility) from these influences as well as tested and evaluated for emissions (radiation) of deleterious energy. Both radiated and line (power mains) conducted energy are evaluated.

TRANSFER SWITCHES

Where more than one source of electric power supply is needed, a power transfer switch is required to connect the power supplies to the controller. Some combinations use more than one such switch. The following section discusses other considerations and requirements regarding these switches.

There are two different methods of incorporating a power transfer switch. The first includes a listed combination fire pump controller and power transfer switch. The second includes an individually listed fire pump controller and power transfer switch. It is specifically required that both types of transfer switches be listed for electric motor–driven fire pump service. An ordinary listed transfer switch is neither adequate nor permitted. Fire pump transfer switches are also examined and tested to the requirements of UL 1008.

Combination Transfer Switch Fire Pump Controllers

Combination controller-transfer switch units are more common and provide for control of the pump motor and for the switching of the electric power supplies. These units are commonly called dual-source controllers (Figure 15.7.7).

Limited-Service Combination Units. As with single-source controllers (nontransfer switch controllers), these units are also available as listed and approved complete units. Most listed units can be used as service-entrance equipment. These units feature the same controller functions described in the section on limited-service controllers. They also provide all the required features of the power transfer switch as are required of full-service units. These units are subject to the same 30 hp (22 kW) limitation as their single-source counterparts.

Full-Service Combination Units. Full-service dual-source units are available as listed equipment in roughly the same variety as listed single-source controllers. They are available in the same starting types (ATL and reduced inrush starting) and in the same low-voltage ranges and horsepower ranges. Note that listed medium-voltage combination units are not available as of this writing. The listing criteria for these units examines their coordination, identification, location, interwiring, and interlocking requirements. Specifically, these units are examined against UL standards UL 1008 (transfer switches), UL 508 (industrial control equipment), UL 218 (fire pump controllers), and FM Standard FM-1321/1323 (fire pump controllers). The following discussion centers on those items that are not found in single-source controllers or that were not previously covered.

Short Circuit Ratings. The nameplate parameters of voltage, frequency, horsepower (or motor kilowatt) rating, and service factor are covered in the section on controllers. Short circuit ratings require additional concern with these transfer switch units as two sources of power are involved, which require two separate short circuit ratings. Also note that the controller normal side short circuit rating is the same as was discussed in the section on controllers. The emergency (alternate) source side will normally have both a short circuit rating and a maximum allowed size rating for the upstream circuit breaker.

When the alternate source of power is provided by a second utility power source, NFPA 20 requires an emergency side circuit breaker meeting the same requirements as the normal side (or single-source) fire pump circuit breaker. The emergency side nameplate short circuit ratings will give the required maximum short circuit rating of this (alternate utility side) power source in the same manner as the required normal side rating.

The more common case of a second power source is a standby generator. An emergency side circuit breaker is not required for smaller gensets. In the absence of this emergency side circuit breaker, the controller must show both the emergency side short circuit rating and maximum size (ampere) rating or rating of the upstream circuit breaker. This maximum upstream fuse or breaker size rating (restriction) is based on the tested and listed short circuit ratings of the transfer switch, which are based on the upstream device that limits and finally interrupts the fault current. Like the controller itself, the transfer switch short circuit ratings are also established by testing. This testing uses a maximum size breaker (or fuses) to limit the fault current that the transfer switch will be subject to and is capable of handling. Larger-frame-size circuit breakers (or fuses) will allow more fault current to pass compared to a comparable but smaller-frame-size breaker or fuse. This is why the use of a larger than rated breaker violates the transfer switch short circuit ratings. On the other hand, if the circuit breaker or fuses are too small, they may trip or blow prematurely, disabling emergency power to the fire pump. The result of either condition is an installation that is unreliable and unsafe to both personnel and property. Note that although upstream fuses are allowed and used, circuit breakers eliminate the need to search for replacement fuses, and also they avoid the problem of incorrect replacement fuses being used.

In general, standard controllers have emergency side short circuit ratings that are lower than the normal side ratings on any particular unit. They also vary with horsepower because the size of the internal transfer switch varies with horsepower. Larger switches have higher short circuit ratings and abilities. Some units use so-called self-protecting switches for the emergency side isolating switch, and, as a result, rate both sides with the same short circuit ratings. This is possible as they have been examined and/or tested to meet the short circuit and interrupting requirements in order to be so rated. For the same reason, the upstream breaker size restriction may no longer apply.

Additional Parameters. The following issues should be considered:

- *Normal side voltage sensors.* The transfer switch is required to transfer to the alternate source if the voltage in any phase falls below 85 percent of the motor's rated voltage. All listed controllers have a means to adjust the transfer voltage(s).
- *Phase reversal.* When a phase reversal of the normal source occurs, the transfer switch must initiate a transfer to emergency (by simulating a normal source power failure). Some designs use the controller's usual phase reversal circuitry on the load side of the transfer switch, whereas others use two separate sensors for the purpose.
- *Emergency side voltage and frequency.* The transfer switch is inhibited from transferring unless and until the genset output voltage has reached suitable voltage and frequency levels. This is usually monitored in only one phase of the emergency source to reduce costs.
- *Second utility (emergency side) three-phase voltage sensors.* If the unit is designed for dual utility application, the single-phase voltage/frequency sensor is replaced by three-phase sensing like that used on the normal source side.
- *Genset start signal (transfer) delay.* An adjustable delay is usually set for a few seconds to prevent nuisance starting of the genset on short duration power glitches (dropouts).
- *Retransfer delay.* Another adjustable delay is used to delay retransfer from the alternate power source to the normal source

until the normal source is stabilized (see NFPA 20). This is typically set to 30 minutes or so to avoid transferring back to the normal source while it is still experiencing outages, dropouts, or single-phase events, as is typical during a lightning storm. Retransfer delay also prevents problems caused when the genset runs for a short period of time.

Standard Components. The following issues should be considered:

- *Barriered or separate compartment.* It is important that faults occurring in the normal source compartment not be allowed to propagate into the emergency compartment and vice versa. This consideration is more critical at voltages above 240 Vac because the resulting arcs are more difficult to extinguish and more ionized gases are created. Besides being highly destructive, these ionized gases are highly conductive and are a means of fault propagation.
- *Emergency source isolating switch.* In these controllers, the other isolating switch is known as the normal source isolating switch. This emergency side isolating switch must be equipped with means to prevent starting of the emergency source generator from this controller if this isolating switch is open. This means, however, does not prevent starting of the genset from other means. This isolating switch must also be supervised both locally and remotely, which is usually done with multiple pilot switch or limit switch contacts actuated by the isolating switch or its mechanism.
- *Manual (mechanical) transfer.* A means for safe manual (nonelectrical) operation of the power transfer switch must be provided. This manual means need not be externally operable. At present, no listed units are externally operable. Thus, the controller door(s) must be opened to manually transfer the switch. As most standard transfer switches are not rated for manual switching under load, it is important that they be deenergized by opening both isolating switches before attempting a manual transfer. Both the normal and the emergency isolating switches must be opened to completely deenergize the power sources before attempting a manual mechanical transfer. Not following the prescribed procedure is a distinct safety hazard, especially if a short circuit is involved.
- *Push buttons.* Transfer switch controllers have a test push button to simulate a loss of normal source power. Although not specifically required, most or all listed controllers also have a bypass push button to retransfer the transfer switch back to the normal position. Note, however, that this retransfer is predicated on having suitable normal source power present. This bypass push button bypasses the retransfer delay timer, which is often set for around 30 minutes.
- *Other items.* The required controls (push buttons), lights, alarms, and remote alarm contacts are covered in the section on controllers.

Standard Features. The primary standard features have been discussed in the sections on standard equipment or important and other parameters. These include voltage and frequency sensors, phase reversal sensing, transfer and retransfer delays, and the genset start signal. Also required is a means to prevent higher-than-normal inrush currents when transferring the fire pump motor from one source to the other. These are the same high transient (spike) currents that can occur if a spinning motor is transferred to a source whose phase angle differs significantly from that of the motor's back EMF voltage. This is the same phenomenon described in the section on controllers (under restart delay and wye-delta open transition starting). The usual method to prevent such transient currents is for the transfer switch to signal the controller to shut down the motor for a few seconds while inhibiting transfer of the transfer switch. This is to allow enough time for the motor magnetic flux to decay to a safe level.

Another means that can be used is the so-called program neutral type of transfer switch. Rather than switching immediately from one source to another, the transfer switch has an in-between (neutral) open position in which the load is not connected to either source. In operation, the switch first moves to this in-between (neutral) position and dwells there for a few seconds. At the end of this delay, the switch completes its travel to the other power source.

A third method is sometimes specified for these controllers for this same purpose. It is the so-called in-phase monitor circuit available from transfer switch suppliers. This scheme is highly variable in fire pump installations. It should not be used without one of the other schemes for controlling transient currents. The variables are due to several factors. The first one is the low-inertia nature of centrifugal pumps, which causes very rapid spin down when power is interrupted. The second variable is the fact that there can be a permanent difference of phase angle between the two sources such as with a dual utility, even though the phase sequence (rotational sense) can still be correct. For example, one source can be described as having phases A-B-C whereas the other might be B-C-A or C-A-B. These last two phases are 120° apart from the first and from each other. The third factor is that the transfer may be due to a phase reversal.

Other Features of Combination Controllers. Another standard feature can include an emergency source circuit breaker. As stated earlier, where the alternate (emergency) source is another utility source (i.e., a second utility), the controller must have a second circuit breaker and locked rotor overcurrent protection the same as the normal source side of the controller. Its emergency isolating switch must meet all the requirements of the normal source isolating switch. In certain installations, the alternate source is on-site generation from large gensets such as those used with "emergency bus" type installations. Moreover, the emergency bus may be normally fed by more than one source through one or more transfer switches, is usually normally "hot" (energized), and usually fed by a utility source in the normal or standby condition. This is another reason for having an emergency side (second) circuit breaker in the controller in these installations, because this utility source may be capable of high-fault currents. In any case, the controller emergency side short circuit rating must be suitable for the sources to which it is or to which it can be connected, particularly when a combination of upstream transfer switches may ultimately connect to a utility source of power.

Nonmandatory Features. Some transfer switch controller combinations have a mechanical interlock between the normal source isolating switch and the emergency source isolating switch. This interlocking prevents the emergency source side switch from closing if the normal source side switch is still open. This prevents false or inadvertent starting of the genset due to lack of power on the normal source side circuitry. Similarly, the normal side switch cannot be opened until the emergency switch is also opened. The transfer switch and genset can still be tested in these designs by opening the normal side circuit breaker.

The following issues should be considered:

- *Engine "overrun" (cooldown) timer.* All listed controllers have either an optional or a standard engine overrun timer. This timer keeps the start signal to the genset asserted after the transfer switch has retransferred back to the normal source. The purpose is to allow the engine to cool down with no load applied to its generator, which, therefore, allows the engine to run unloaded. This timer is typically set for 10 to 30 minutes.
- *Load shed contacts.* Load shed contacts are used to signal another load to disconnect from the genset in order to provide enough power and current to start the fire pump. These contacts are usually maintained for the entire time that the fire pump runs. In other cases, the contacts are momentary to unload the genset enough to start the fire pump but then allow some loads to reconnect to the genset. This scheme may also include delaying the start of the fire pump for up to 10 seconds to allow time for the shed loads to disconnect.
- *Higher short circuit ratings.* All listed controllers are available in higher short circuit ratings on the emergency source side as well as on the normal source side.
- *Emergency side circuit breaker.* Even when not mandatory, this option provides better protection for the fire pump motor. It may also be used in conjunction with higher short circuit ratings on the emergency source side, particularly when used with higher-capacity gensets or on high-capacity emergency bus systems.
- *Other options and modifications.* Other optional equipment or features are available from the various listed controller manufacturers. Oversized transfer switches are sometimes requested for higher reliability and/or higher short circuit ratings. Sometimes transfer switches from a specific manufacturer are specified and supplied to coordinate with other transfer switches used in a facility or building. Also, some transfer switches are supplied with communication ports to allow communication of status information with so-called building automation systems, telemetry systems, or remote monitoring and alarm recording systems. Additional or other nonstandard alarm and signal contacts and/or alarm lights are also available.

Individual Power Transfer Switch and Fire Pump Controllers

Individual power transfer switch and fire pump controller units consist of a listed single-source (nontransfer switch) fire pump controller and a listed fire pump power transfer switch (see Figure 15.7.7). As previously stated, both the transfer switch and fire pump controller must be listed for fire protection service. It should be noted that not all UL-listed transfer switches are listed for fire service.

Much of the section on combination controllers also applies to these separate transfer switches. This section will detail different and/or additional requirements for installations using separate transfer switches. These are also known as upstream transfer switch installations.

Location. The transfer of power to the fire pump controller between the normal supply and the alternate supply must take place within the pump room. Hence, the fire pump transfer switch must be installed in the same pump room or pump house as the fire pump controller to which it is connected.

Number of Switches Required. If alternate power is required for one or more fire pumps, each fire pump controller requires its own dedicated transfer switch. More than one fire pump (controller) cannot be fed from a single transfer switch.

Coordination of Short Circuit Current Ratings. The same considerations regarding short circuit ratings for the combination controller transfer switch also apply to the separate transfer switch. Here, however, neither the manufacturers of the controller nor the transfer switch provide the coordination.

NFPA 20 requires an isolating switch, or service disconnect, where required, ahead of the normal input terminals of the transfer switch. This requirement will be the case for any transfer switch unless the service device, usually a circuit breaker, is supplied as part of the transfer switch and the transfer switch is rated, listed, and labeled as service entrance equipment. If this circuit breaker is not provided, an upstream device must be supplied. It must meet, among other things, the 600 percent rule that requires that any such overcurrent protective device be selected or set to carry indefinitely the sum of the locked rotor current of the fire pump motor plus any additional connected loads. This requirement is a very important limitation to the transfer switch short circuit rating since its size must not exceed the maximum upstream device size qualification of the transfer switch short circuit rating.

With separate transfer switches, this rating will apply to both incoming sides, normal and emergency, unless circuit breakers are supplied as part of the transfer switch. As a result, the coordination may be missing or incorrect. A dangerous and unreliable situation then ensues. For specifics, see NFPA 20 and NFPA 70.

The transfer switch must be sized at 115 percent of the motor FLA current. However, the transfer switch will most likely have to be larger in order to meet the maximum size rating of the upstream circuit breaker (or fuse).

The matter is further complicated by the listed transfer switch manufacturers typically having two or three different short circuit device rating charts. Typical is (1) the any breaker or the any molded case breaker rating, (2) the specific breaker or coordinated breaker ratings, and (3) the fuse category, which is usually of a particular type (class) of fuse.

Coordination of Phase Reversal Switching. The transfer switch is required to switch to emergency power on reversal of the normal source power. This phase reversal sensing circuitry should be included as part of the transfer switch. Either two such circuits are needed, or else one such circuit should be on the load side of the transfer switch.

Coordination of Alternate Source Isolating Switch. When the alternate power source is a second utility, another upstream service and overcurrent device like the one described previously is required and must also meet the 600 percent sizing rules. Otherwise, for the more typical genset alternate power source installations, an emergency side isolating switch is required. Again, due to cost, such a switch is not standard equipment on all listed fire pump transfer switches. It must either be ordered as an option with the switch or purchased and installed separately. In any case, the switch must meet the following requirements:

- It must be lockable in the "On" position. Note, incidentally, that all listed enclosed isolating or safety switches can be locked in the "Off" position, but not all of them are capable of being locked in the "On" position.
- A placard with large (1.0 in. [25.4 mm]) lettering must be affixed to the outside of this switch reading "Fire Pump Isolating Switch."
- Another placard must be mounted in the pump room "adjacent to the fire pump controller," stating the location of this switch and the location of the key for unlocking it.
- The isolating switch must be supervised to indicate when it is not closed. Four methods are allowed and listed in the standard.
- The supervision must operate an audible and visual (alarm light) on the transfer switch and also at a remote point where required.
- Contacts to interlock with the transfer switch engine start contacts are required to prevent signaling the genset to start if this isolating switch is open.

Alarm Circuits. The transfer switch will usually have at least one set of position-indicating remote alarm contacts as standard. It may or may not have the position-indicating lights as standard. It will not likely have the isolating switch alarm light and contacts unless it is ordered with an isolating switch as part of the transfer switch.

Generator Start Circuit Override. The transfer switch will normally have the engine start contacts as standard equipment. However, it will not normally have the engine start override (lockout) means, unless it is ordered with an isolating switch option. These contacts are needed to prevent undesired and/or unexpected starting of the genset by this transfer switch when the isolating switch (wherever it is located) is opened. Note, however, that other transfer switches can and will start the genset.

Higher-Than-Normal Inrush Currents. A means must be provided to prevent higher-than-normal inrush currents when transferring the fire pump motor from one source to the other. As discussed in the section on combination units, there are currently three methods used for this purpose. The momentary motor shutdown method requires signaling circuitry (contacts) wired from the transfer switch to the fire pump controller, properly equipped, to momentarily shut down the fire pump motor.

Checklist. All the following should be verified for each installation. The following is usually supplied:

- NEMA 2 enclosure as a minimum
- The manual (mechanical) transfer means
- The three normal side voltage sensors
- The alternate side single-phase voltage and frequency sensor (for genset applications)
- The manual (mechanical) transfer means
- The two position indicator lights
- The engine start delay timer and the retransfer delay timer
- The engine start contacts
- The test (transfer) switch (push button)

The following may not be supplied as standard equipment:

- Three-phase voltage sensing on the alternate source side for dual (second) utility jobs
- The normal side service disconnect and overcurrent protection fuses or breaker
- A second service-entrance device for dual-utility jobs
- The emergency side isolating switch
- The ability to lock the emergency side, isolating switch in the "on" position
- An external fire pump isolating switch placard
- A placard next to the controller giving the location of this isolating switch
- Supervision of the isolating switch by one of the four means given
- Contacts to interlock with the engine start contacts
- Audible and visible alarm to indicate isolating switch open
- Isolating switch contacts for remote alarm
- Means to prevent higher-than-normal motor inrush currents
- Phase reversal sensing and transfer circuitry

Finally, the coordination of both the normal source side and the alternate source side short circuit ratings must be performed by someone. This coordination must include (1) any upstream protective device(s), (2) the transfer switch, (3) the fire pump controller, and (4) the available short circuit current. Unfortunately, miscoordination may not be discovered until it is uncovered during an inspection; worse yet, miscoordination may not be discovered even then. Installations that are not coordinated for proper short circuit protection are more likely to be unreliable and unsafe from a personnel and fire hazard standpoint.

SUMMARY

Fire pumps are critical to fire protection systems because they generate the necessary waterflow and pressure needed for fire control and extinguishment. It is especially true where more than one pump must be relied on for proper system operation. Therefore, the components that go into fire pumps are equally important and must be properly designed, installed, and maintained. This chapter presented information on fire pump components, specifically on the electric power supply and control aspects of motor-driven fire pump installations.

BIBLIOGRAPHY

NFPA Codes, Standards, and Recommended Practices

Reference to the following NFPA codes, standards, and recommended practices will provide further information on the fire pump controllers and power supply arrangements for motor-driven fire pumps discussed in this chapter. (See the latest version of The NFPA Catalog *for availability of current editions of the following documents.)*

NFPA 13, *Standard for the Installation of Sprinkler Systems*
NFPA 13D, *Standard for the Installation of Sprinkler Systems in One- and Two-Family Dwellings and Manufactured Homes*
NFPA 13E, *Recommended Practice for Fire Department Operations in Properties Protected by Sprinkler and Standpipe Systems*
NFPA 13R, *Standard for the Installation of Sprinkler Systems in Residential Occupancies up to and Including Four Stories in Height*
NFPA 14, *Standard for the Installation of Standpipe and Hose Systems*
NFPA 15, *Standard for Water Spray Fixed Systems for Fire Protection*
NFPA 20, *Standard for the Installation of Stationary Pumps for Fire Protection*
NFPA 22, *Standard for Water Tanks for Private Fire Protection*
NFPA 24, *Standard for the Installation of Private Fire Service Mains and Their Appurtenances*
NFPA 25, *Standard for the Inspection, Testing, and Maintenance of Water-Based Fire Protection Systems*
NFPA 31, *Standard for the Installation of Oil-Burning Equipment*
NFPA 37, *Standard for the Installation and Use of Stationary Combustion Engines and Gas Turbines*
NFPA 70, *National Electrical Code®*
NFPA 72®, National Fire Alarm Code®
NFPA 110, *Standard for Emergency and Standby Power Systems*

References

Earley, M. W., Sheehan, J. V., and Caloggero, J. M. (Eds.), *National Electrical Code Handbook,* 10th ed., National Fire Protection Association, Quincy, MA, 2005.
FM 1321/1323, *Approval Standard for Fire Pump Controllers for Electric Motor Driven and Diesel Engine Driven Fire Pumps,* Factory Mutual Research, Norwood, MA, 2002.
FM 1333, *Approval Standard for Diesel Engine Fire Pump Drivers,* Factory Mutual Research, Norwood, MA, 2004.
Harvey, B. M., "Fire Pumps: Problems and Solutions, Part 1 through Part 5," *Sprinkler Age,* May 1999–Feb. 2000.
NEMA ICS 14, *Application Guide for Electric Fire Pump Controllers,* National Electrical Manufacturers Association, Rosslyn, VA, 2004.
NEMA ICS 15, *Instructions for the Handling, Installation, Operation and Maintenance of Electric Fire Pump Controllers Rated Not More Than 600V,* National Electrical Manufacturers Association, Rosslyn, VA, 2004.
Puchovsky, M. T., and Isman, K. E. (Eds.), *Fire Pump Handbook,* National Fire Protection Association, Quincy, MA, 1998.
Puchovsky, M. T., and Isman, K. E. (Eds.), *Pumps for Fire Protection Systems,* National Fire Protection Association, Quincy, MA, 2002.
UL 50, *Enclosures for Electrical Equipment,* Underwriters Laboratories, Northbrook, IL, 2003.
UL 218, *Fire Pump Controllers,* Underwriters Laboratories, Northbrook, IL, 2006.
UL 347, *High Voltage Industrial Control Equipment,* Underwriters Laboratories, Northbrook, IL, 2000.
UL 508, *Industrial Control Equipment,* Underwriters Laboratories, Northbrook, IL, 2005.
UL 1004A, *Fire Pump Motors,* Underwriters Laboratories, Northbrook, IL, 2006.
UL 1008, *Transfer Switch Equipment,* Underwriters Laboratories, Northbrook, IL, 2004.
UL 1247, *Diesel Engines for Driving Centrifugal Fire Pumps,* Underwriters Laboratories, Northbrook, IL, 2004.

SECTION 16

Water-Based Fire Suppression Equipment

Christian Dubay

The eleven chapters in Section 16 of the *Fire Protection Handbook®* review water-based fire suppression equipment. Water-based fire suppression was perhaps the first fire protection technology and has evolved to become a widely used mainstay of fire protection.

Chapter 1, "Principles of Automatic Sprinkler System Performance," describes the thermal response, water distribution, and spray cooling characteristics of sprinklers and distinguishes between fire control and fire suppression by sprinklers.

Chapter 2, "Automatic Sprinklers," presents the operating principles, temperature ratings, and water discharge characteristics of automatic sprinklers and describes types of sprinklers. In a similar vein, Chapter 3, "Automatic Sprinkler Systems," covers topics such as system components and materials, installation requirements, and design considerations, as well as plans, calculations, and system acceptance.

Chapter 4, "Hanging and Bracing of Water-Based Systems," considers hangers, hanger installation, earthquake bracing, and joint restraint of underground piping.

Chapter 5, "Sprinkler Systems for Storage Facilities," begins with a discussion of commodity classification and storage arrangement, height, and clearance. It then discusses sprinkler systems and associated design factors unique to storage operations.

Automatic sprinkler systems were first developed for and are still predominantly used in nonresidential occupancies. By contrast, Chapter 6, "Residential Sprinkler Systems," describes specialized technology for residential sprinkler systems, residential sprinkler standards, residential sprinkler experience, and incentives for more widespread use of residential sprinklers.

The section next turns to two highly specialized types of systems. Chapter 7, "Ultra-High-Speed Water Spray Systems," introduces types of systems that are available for explosion protection, including squib-actuated systems, pilot-actuated systems, and portable systems. The use of water mist fire suppression, discussed in Chapter 8, "Water Mist Fire Suppression Systems," came about as a result of requirements for sprinklers on passenger ships and the search for alternatives to ozone-depleting halocarbons. The chapter provides details on the components, types of systems, calculation methods for single and twin fluid systems, pump selection and application of positive displacement pumps, and maintenance issues.

Chapter 9, "Water Spray Protection," covers the uses and applications of water spray systems for fire suppression, control, and extinguishment and describes the components of spray systems and the specialized uses of the systems. The primary distinction between a water spray and a sprinkler system is that of specific coverage versus general area coverage. Water spray systems have typically been provided to protect a specific piece of equipment with surface coverage.

Chapter 10, "Standpipe and Hose Systems," describes design and installation considerations, commissioning, and fire department operations using standpipe systems. Outside hose systems are also reviewed.

Christian Dubay, P.E., is NFPA's vice-president, codes and standards, and chief engineer.

The section concludes with treatment of system inspection and maintenance. Chapter 11, "Care and Maintenance of Water-Based Extinguishing Systems," covers the activities that are central to system reliability. Among other topics, the chapter covers sources of obstruction in sprinkler system pipes and methods for flushing and cleaning them, as well as sprinkler leakage and water damage.

Chapter 1

Principles of Automatic Sprinkler System Performance

Russell P. Fleming

Chapter Contents

Key Terms

actual delivered density (ADD), automatic sprinkler system, convective heat flow, density/area curve, heat release rate, required delivered density (RDD), spray pattern, sprinkler sensitivity, thermal response, water distribution

Most fire sprinkler systems are designed so that each individual sprinkler can react to heat from a fire, operating to distribute water over the source of that heat. The complex nature of the interaction of fire and sprinklers historically has prevented an analytical approach to sprinkler system design, but today there is a growing appreciation for measuring the performance characteristics of sprinklers and for using those characteristics in new combinations to achieve specific fire protection goals. The characteristics include thermal response, water distribution, and fire suppression and control capability.

This chapter discusses the response, distribution, and fire-extinguishing characteristics of automatic sprinkler systems and the mechanisms by which it is believed that those characteristics work together for successful sprinkler system performance.

See also Section 2, Chapter 7, "Theory of Fire Extinguishment," and other chapters in Section 16, particularly Chapter 2, "Automatic Sprinklers"; and Chapter 6, "Residential Sprinkler Systems."

THERMAL RESPONSE OF SPRINKLERS

Although it is possible to equip sprinkler systems with elaborate detection systems intended to recognize other fire products or signatures, it is heat detection that serves as the basis of sprinkler system response. Therefore, a basic understanding of heat production and movement in a fire is an important first step in an analysis of the way fire sprinkler systems work.

Convective Heat Flow in Fires

Since combustion is an exothermic process, burning fuels produce heat. Even smoldering fires produce heat, although the level of heat can be so low as to be ineffective in actuating thermal detectors. However, smoldering fires generally develop to a flaming stage before producing untenable room conditions. Once the fire reaches the flaming stage, the heat release rate of the fire will grow in a manner related to the nature of the fuel and its arrangement, the ventilation conditions, and other factors.

Heat is released from a fire in several forms: radiation, conduction, and convection. It has been determined that convective heat transfer is most important in activating sprinklers.[1] Convective heat transfer involves heat transfer through a circulating medium, which, in the case of fire sprinklers, is the room air. The air heated by the fire rises in a plume, entraining other room air as it rises. When the plume hits the ceiling, it generally splits to produce a ceiling gas jet (Figure 16.1.1). The thickness of this ceiling jet flow is approximately 5 to 12 percent of the height of the ceiling above the fire source, with the maximum temperature and velocity occurring 1 percent of the distance from

Russell P. Fleming, P.E., is executive vice-president for the National Fire Sprinkler Association, Inc., in Patterson, New York. He has served on more than a dozen different NFPA technical committees, including the Technical Correlating Committee on Automatic Sprinklers.

FIGURE 16.1.1 Plume-Ceiling Interaction

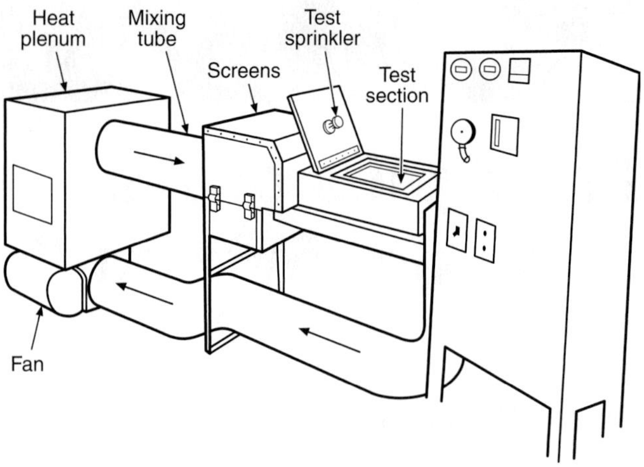

FIGURE 16.1.2 Sprinkler Plunge Test Apparatus

the ceiling to the fire source.[2] The heat-sensing elements of sprinklers within this ceiling jet are then heated by conduction of the heat from the air.

Quantifying Sprinkler Sensitivity

Tremendous effort has been made in recent years to quantify the thermal sensitivity of sprinklers and other heat-actuated detectors. This effort is aimed at making it possible to use analytical methods to predict the time of sprinkler response.

Several terms have come into use as part of this process. One is the time constant τ (tau), which is a measure of the thermal sensitivity of a body and is defined as:

$$\tau = \frac{mc}{h_c a}$$

where

m = Mass of the body

c = Specific heat of the body

h_c = Convective heat transfer coefficient

a = Area of the body exposed to gas flow

The time constant has units of seconds but cannot be determined readily for any specific body due to difficulties in estimating the convective heat transfer coefficient. This term varies with the velocity of the gases that pass by the body. As a result, the time constant is measured using a plunge test apparatus, first developed for use with sprinklers in 1976.[3] This apparatus generally consists of a circulating air oven with a known air temperature and velocity (Figure 16.1.2). The air temperature is set well above the nominal operating temperature of the sprinkler. At time $t = 0$, a sprinkler is "plunged" into the heated air. The amount of time it takes for the sprinkler to operate is recorded and is presumed to be the time necessary for the sprinkler operating mechanism to move from room temperature to the nominal operating temperature.

The use of the plunge test permits determination of the time constant, because it provides two data points with regard to the sensitivity of a sprinkler. It is known that the sprinkler was at ambient room temperature, T_a, at $t = 0$, and it is known that the sprinkler reached its nominal operating temperature, T_L, at time $t = t_{act}$, the time of sprinkler activation. Based on the known shape of the curve by which a body takes on or loses heat to its environment, the time constant can be determined. Under plunge test conditions, involving a constant environmental temperature, the time constant is effectively the amount of time that would be needed for the body to move 62.8 percent of the way to the temperature of its heated environment (Figure 16.1.3). In an environment in which the temperature is constantly increasing, the time constant is the amount of time by which the body lags behind its environment after some initial period of time equal to approximately four times the time constant (Figure 16.1.4).

Due to the fact that the time constant varies with the velocity at which it is measured, it is not a particularly useful term. Researchers at Factory Mutual Research Coporation (now FM Global) therefore developed a new term, "response time index" (RTI), as a measure of sprinkler sensitivity independent of velocity.[4] The researchers observed that the convective heat transfer coefficient of blunt bodies in cross-flows was roughly

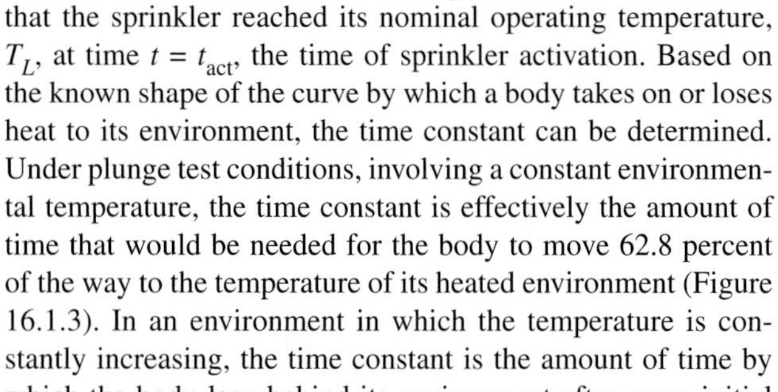

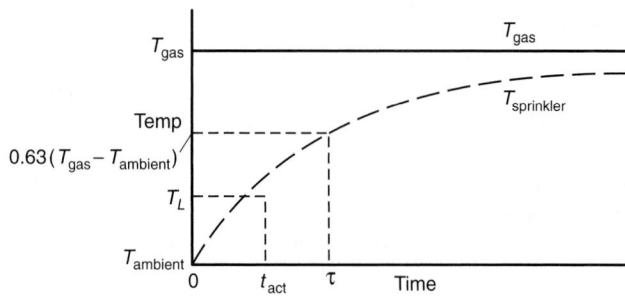

FIGURE 16.1.3 Representation of Time Constant τ for Constant Temperature Condition

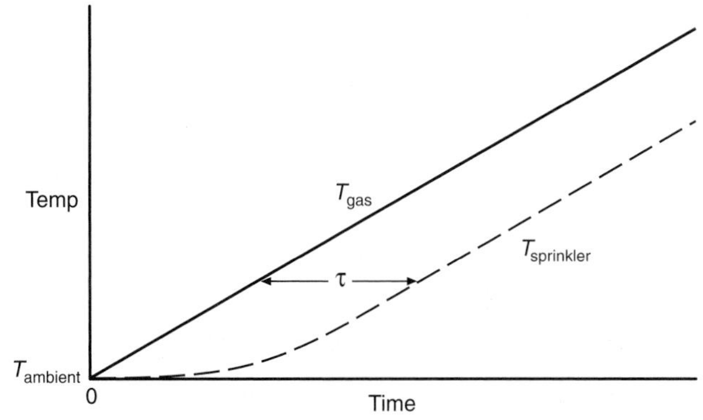

FIGURE 16.1.4 Representation of Time Constant τ for Constantly Increasing Temperature Condition

proportional to the square root of the velocity of those flows. This meant that the time constant is roughly proportional to the inverse of the square root of flow velocity. By multiplying the time constant by the square root of its corresponding velocity, they could eliminate the effects of the convective heat transfer coefficient's dependence on flow velocity:

$$\text{RTI} = \tau u^{1/2} = \text{A constant}$$

It should be noted that, depending on the units of velocity used, the actual units of RTI are either $m^{1/2}sec^{1/2}$ or $ft^{1/2}sec^{1/2}$. U.S. customary RTI values are 1.81 times the equivalent metric RTI values.

Laboratory determination of the RTIs of various devices has permitted the development of computer programs that predict the operating time of heat detectors and sprinklers based on the heat release history of a fire in conjunction with the ceiling height and radial distance of the detector or sprinkler from the fire.[5] These programs must be used with caution, since they represent only a rough correlation to actual conditions. It should also be noted that they are not appropriate for use with sprinklers following the start of water discharge.

The models of sprinkler sensitivity have recently been modified to account for conduction losses from the sprinkler operating mechanism to the sprinkler frame, fittings, and water in the adjacent piping. These new complexities are not taken into account by the original computer models.

The importance of conduction losses was established in 1986 sprinkler industry test work comparing various sprinklers.[6] These tests showed that the apparent RTI of some sprinklers increased at low velocities, particularly for sprinklers with high conductivity between the sprinkler operating mechanism and the sprinkler body. For example, Figure 16.1.5 shows response time indexes as a function of velocity.[6] In Figure 16.1.5, sprinklers D-P and D-S represent specific models of standard pendent and sidewall sprinklers, A and MA represent quick-response, flush-type pendent and sidewall sprinklers, and FR represents a specific quick-response sprinkler model with conventional frame arms.

Although it might seem beneficial to seek to control the conduction effect to maintain a constant RTI, the tests also demonstrated that the phenomenon could be helpful in preventing

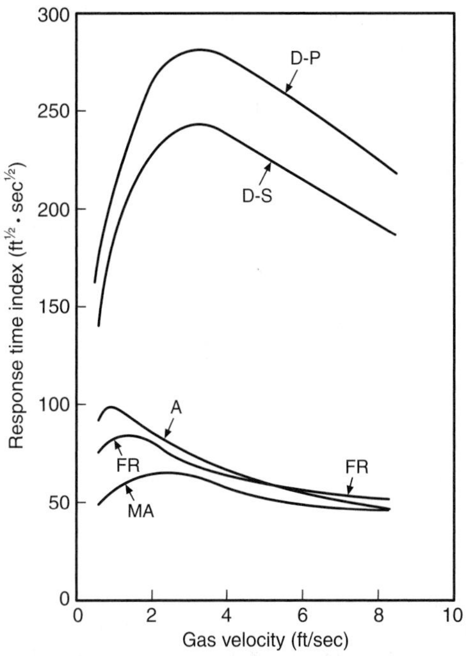

FIGURE 16.1.5 Response Time Indexes as a Function of Velocity (Courtesy of Tyco Fire & Building Products)

excessive sprinkler operations, since velocities tend to decrease with distance from the fire.

Following those tests, the FMRC researchers reviewed the original thermal response model and RTI concept and the plunge test devised for measuring RTI. They then introduced a modified model that incorporated a conductive heat loss factor.[7]

Additional testing using the plunge test apparatus yields a value for *C*, the conductivity factor. For purposes of using computer models to estimate the time of sprinkler activation, a value of "virtual RTI" can be calculated as:

$$\text{RTI}_v = \frac{\text{RTI}}{1 + C/u^{1/2}}$$

The virtual RTI can be used successfully whenever the gas velocity is fairly constant or does not change rapidly with time. With the exception of small turbulent fluctuations, this is usually the case with actual fires.

The revised model assumes that the sprinkler fitting is essentially at ambient temperature and that the conductive heat loss rate is proportional to the temperature rise of the sprinkler operating element. Experimental programs have demonstrated the accuracy of the revised model.

WATER DISTRIBUTION AND SPRAY COOLING CHARACTERISTICS OF SPRINKLERS

Relatively little can be accomplished from a design engineering standpoint with regard to the specific spray patterns produced by sprinklers. The distribution pattern of most types of sprinklers is tested only for overall coverage under specific geometric conditions. At present, there is no method of predicting the actual amount of water that will be delivered to a specific unit of floor area under actual fire conditions, especially since spray patterns vary with water discharge pressures.

Figure 16.1.6 demonstrates the variability of the spray pattern of a typical pendent spray sprinkler with a nominal orifice coefficient of K = 5.6 (K_m = 80) when discharged under nonfire conditions at selected pressures. A 7 psi (0.5 bar) operating pressure is considered minimum by NFPA 13, *Standard for the Installation of Sprinkler Systems*. At that minimum pressure, the extent of the spray pattern roughly approximates that of the maximum light-hazard spacing permitted by NFPA 13, when the sprinkler is located 8 ft (2.4 m) above the floor. The spray pattern enlarges as the operating pressure is increased to about 70 psi (4.8 bar), then begins to contract at higher pressures, becoming more elliptical in shape at the upper end of the allowable pressure range. Within the wetting area, the water application rates vary considerably, such that the concept of an average density over the coverage area of a sprinkler provides only the roughest approximation of the amount of water that might actually be reaching a particular unit of floor area.

Some studies have been made of individual droplet size and motion. For geometrically similar sprinklers, the median droplet diameter in the sprinkler spray has been found to be inversely proportional to the one-third power of water pressure and directly proportional to the two-thirds power of sprinkler orifice diameter,[8] such that:

$$d_m \propto \frac{D^{2/3}}{\rho^{1/3}} \propto \frac{D^2}{Q^{2/3}}$$

where

d_m = Median droplet diameter

D = Orifice diameter

ρ = Pressure

Q = Rate of waterflow

Total droplet surface area is proportional to the total water discharge rate, divided by the median droplet diameter

$$A_s \propto Q / d_m$$

where A_s is the total droplet surface area.

Combining these relationships, it can be seen that:

$$A_s \propto (Q^3 \rho D^{-2})^{1/3}$$

The heat absorption rate of a sprinkler spray can be expected to depend on the total surface area of the water droplets, A_s, and the temperature of the ceiling gas layer in excess of the droplet temperature. The total cooling ability of a sprinkler also depends on the depth of the ceiling jet or smoke layer through which the droplets pass.

INTERACTION OF SPRINKLER DISTRIBUTION AND BURNING FUEL

Sprinklers can be effective against fires in a number of ways. One of the most efficient, in terms of use of water, is simply through the cooling effects of the water spray. The production of a mist of fine water droplets can cause significant cooling, which reduces the radiative feedback to the fire below that which is needed to sustain combustion. In addition, the evaporation of water droplets can produce steam with a volume more than 1700 times that of the water and can deprive the fire of needed oxygen. This combination of "spray cooling" and "smothering," although efficient, has its limitations. It generally works well only if the fire is contained within an unventilated enclosure.[9]

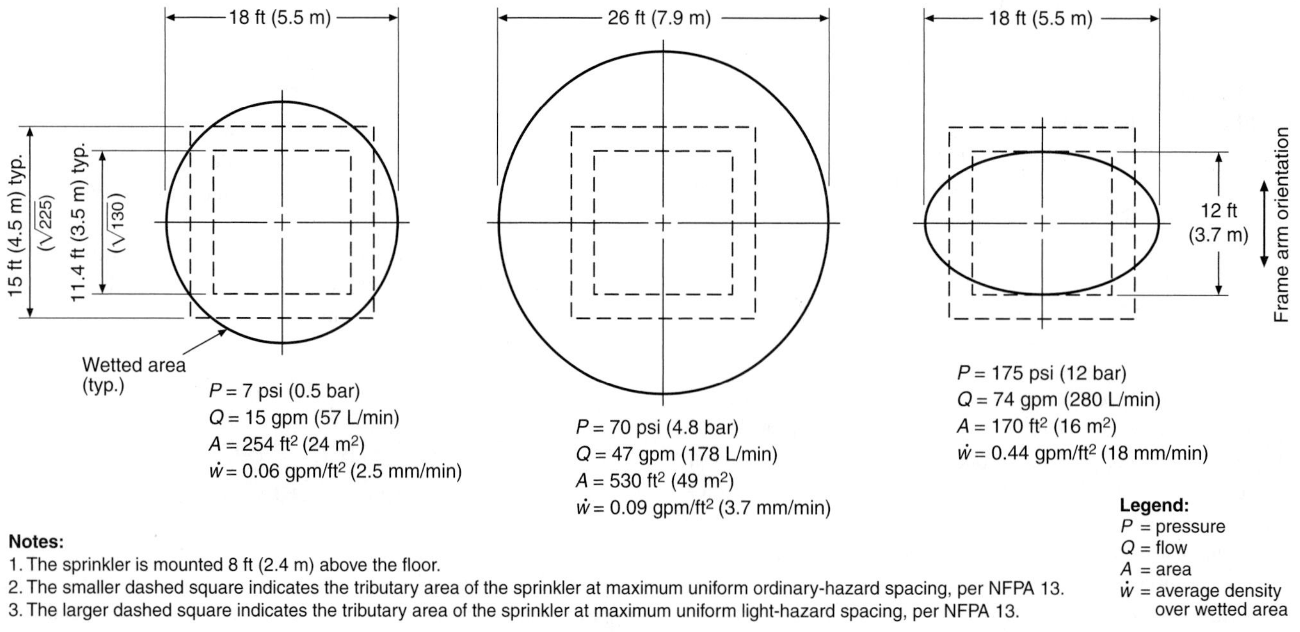

FIGURE 16.1.6 Spray Pattern (Floor Level) Versus Discharge Pressure

The greatest efficiency is in the smallest enclosures, since almost all water droplets can be evaporated by contact with enclosing surfaces, and smothering is enhanced.[10]

In 1955, Nash and Rasbash[10] reviewed extensive tests of manual water extinguishment of fully developed room fires and suggested that there is a minimum "critical rate" of water application below which the fire cannot be extinguished. With increased rate of water application above the critical rate, the time needed to control or extinguish the fire falls rapidly. With further increases in the rate of water application, the time to extinguish diminishes more slowly (Figure 16.1.7).[10] Under the best of conditions, fires in model rooms could be extinguished with scanned jets or sprays with about 1 (imperial) gal per 1000 ft^3 (4.5 L/28.4 m^3) of room volume. It was found that a fixed spray with a medium degree of ventilation could extinguish the fire with about 2 (imperial) gal per 1000 ft^3 (9 L/28 m^3) of room volume.

Automatic sprinklers, of course, are expected to operate before total room involvement. To some extent, this makes their job more difficult, since the sprinkler spray is not readily evaporated to steam.

In a large, open, or well-ventilated area, a strong fire can create updrafts that sweep away the small droplets, making them ineffective. For this reason, traditional sprinkler system design is based on the idea of distributing a variety of droplet sizes over the burning fuel area to maintain relatively low ceiling temperatures while controlling or extinguishing the fire.

FIRE CONTROL BY SPRINKLERS

The traditional method by which sprinkler systems control fires currently is being termed the "fire control" approach. This method anticipates that a certain number of sprinklers will be opened surrounding the fire area. Although the sprinklers immediately over the fire may not be able to actually extinguish the fire, they will work with other open sprinklers to cool the atmosphere and to prevent sprinklers outside the general vicinity of the fire from operating. In the meantime, the open sprinklers outside the immediate fire area also can be expected to prewet adjacent combustibles, helping to prevent the spread of fire.

Figure 16.1.8 represents the fire control condition that can be achieved by sprinklers. In this steady-state condition, two separate energy balances must take place. At the level of the fuel, the water reaching the fire must be capable of reducing the burning rate to the point at which, in combination with the prewetting of adjacent combustibles that has taken place, the fire will not spread to additional fuel. Simultaneously, at the ceiling level, the cooling effect of the water spray from open sprinklers must be sufficient to absorb the heat of the fire plume so as to prevent additional sprinklers from operating and to maintain temperatures below those that would result in structural damage to the building.

In the fire control condition, the area over which sprinklers open generally exceeds the maximum area of the fire. The appendix of NFPA 13 provides typical examples of relative sizes of damaged areas of the test array and sprinkler operating areas (Table 16.1.1).

With sprinklers operating in the fire control mode, the central fuel package is eventually depleted and the fire is extinguished. For fire control by sprinklers, the heat release rate of the fire over time can be characterized, as shown in Figure 16.1.9.

Various studies have been made of the water application rate needed to extinguish or control fires in fully ventilated

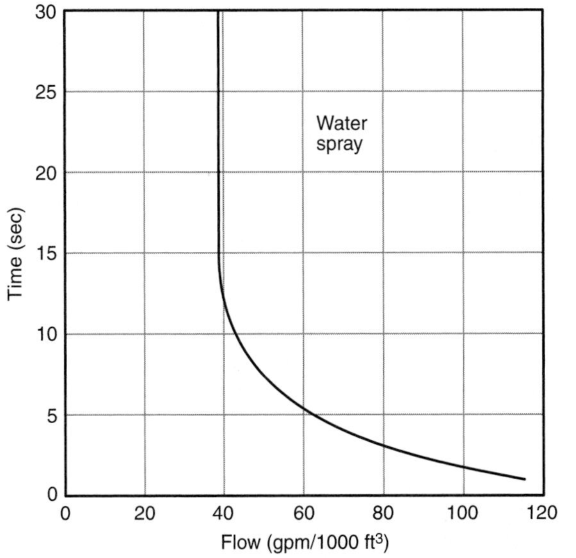

FIGURE 16.1.7 Time to Extinguish Fire in Model Room at Various Flows. For S.I. units: 1 gpm = 3.785 L/min; 1 ft^3 = 0.0283 m^3.

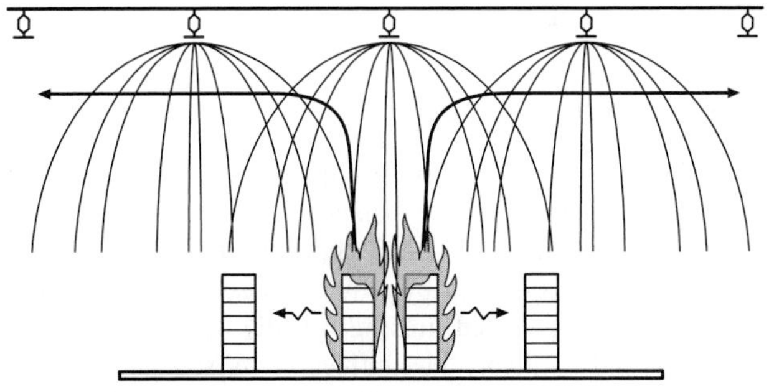

FIGURE 16.1.8 Fire Control by Sprinklers (Conceptual)

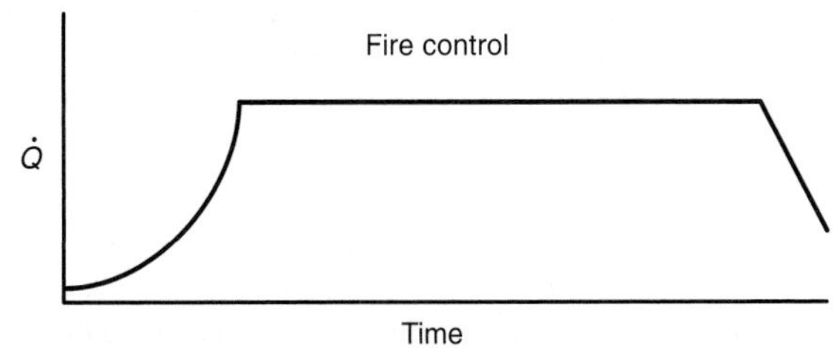

FIGURE 16.1.9 Representation of Fire Control by Sprinklers; Heat Release Rate ($\dot{Q}$) Versus Time

TABLE 16.1.1 Sprinkler Operation in Test Array

Density			Fire Damage in Test Array			Sprinkler Operation Area (165°F) (74°C)	
gpm/ft²	*mm/min*		*Percentage*	*ft²*	*m²*	*ft²*	*m²*
0.30	12.3	(Ceiling only)	22	395	37	4500–4800	420–450
0.375	15.4	(Ceiling only)	17	306	28	1800	167
0.45	18.4	(Ceiling only)	9	162	15	700	65
0.20	8.1	(Ceiling only)	28–36	504–648	47–60	13,100–14,000	1220–1300
0.20	8.1	(Sprinklers at ceiling and in racks)	8	144	13	4100	380
0.30	12.3	(Sprinklers at ceiling and in racks)	7	126	12	700	65

areas, both on simple surfaces and in complex fuel arrangements. The critical rate for wood appears to be between 0.0022 and 0.0044 gpm/ft² (0.09 and 0.18 mm/min), increasing to a degree with preburn.[11] For some plastic surfaces, the critical rate appears to be in the range of 0.02 to 0.065 gpm/ft² (0.82 and 2.67 mm/min), higher with external radiation.[12] These values are per unit of burning surface area, not floor area, and are determined under laboratory conditions.

For realistic fuel arrangements, the unit surface area of burning combustibles can be many multiples of the unit floor area protected by sprinklers. British fire tests have indicated that, for midsize wood cribs, water applied through impinging jet nozzles at rates less than 0.275 gpm/ft² (11.2 mm/min) of unit surface area had little effect on the actual burning zone.[13] The tests also indicated that application rates as low as 0.0625 gpm/ft² (2.56 mm/min) of unit surface area were found to be sufficient to limit flame spread within the crib.

Density/Area Curves

The density/area curves that form the basis of standard sprinkler system design can be considered to reflect historical experience with the fire control concept. Although most fires are extinguished or contained by only a few sprinklers, the more troublesome deep-seated fires historically have opened more sprinklers and justifiably have influenced the standards writers. System design criteria must address a reasonably worst-case situation.

The first edition of NFPA 13, published in 1896, contained simple pipe schedules that limited the maximum number of sprinklers that could be fed through each size of pipe. Combined with a minimum supply pressure of 25 psi (1.7 bar) at the highest line of sprinklers, the pipe schedule was expected to adequately provide water to at least 15 sprinklers.

The pipe schedule for sprinkler systems was altered many times, and the concept of different pipe schedules for various "hazards" was instituted with the development of "Class B" (later to become light-hazard) criteria in 1930 and the development of an extra-hazard pipe schedule in 1940.

The use of hydraulic calculation methods for fire sprinkler systems actually started in 1929, with the first formal compilation of Hazen-Williams friction loss tables and other hydraulic data in 1931.[14] NFPA 13 first addressed hydraulic calculations in its 1955 edition, but the use of such calculations was limited essentially to deluge system and water spray applications until the inclusion of density/area criteria in the 1972 edition of the standard. NFPA 231C, *Rack Storage of Materials,* the first standard developed based on fire test data, was adopted in 1971, and 1972 saw the insertion of density/area curves into NFPA 231, *Standard for General Storage,* although basic criteria had appeared as early as 1965. Density/area curves from NFPA 231 and 231C were merged into NFPA 13 beginning with the 1999 edition. The density/area curves in NFPA 13 were modified significantly in 1974 and again in 1991 as part of an overall reorganization and simplification of the standard. As developed in 1974, the curves reflect the hydraulic capability of pipe schedule designs that had proved satisfactory in nearly a century of experience.

The merging of ordinary-hazard groups 2 and 3 in the 1991 edition of NFPA 13 created a system design point of 0.2 gpm/ft² (8.1 mm/min) over 1500 ft² (135 m²) for a hazard that could essentially be considered the processing and display of ordinary combustibles. This relates well to the historical development and use of the standard sprinkler system. The 1991 density/area curves are shown in Figure 16.1.10.

The density/area curves have traditionally provided some flexibility in system pipe sizing. Under provisions of NFPA 13, meeting any point on the appropriate curve is acceptable. This permits the use of higher densities over smaller areas or lower densities over larger areas. Higher densities with smaller areas will generally result in larger branch-line piping but lower main sizes and lower overall water supply requirements. For this reason, a high-density, small-area point is often selected as the most economical.

Modifications to the density/area curves have traditionally been made to reflect special conditions. The use of high-temperature sprinklers, where permitted for fast-developing fires, is expected to help limit the area over which sprinklers operate. The delay in water delivery resulting from the use of a dry-pipe system is expected to open additional sprinklers prior to the onset of fire control, necessitating a larger sprinkler design area.

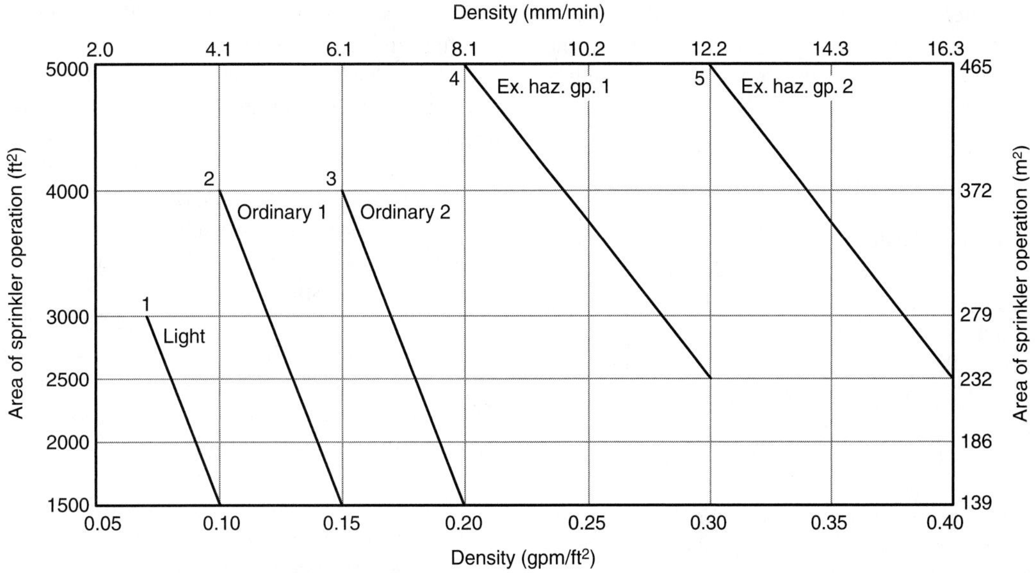

FIGURE 16.1.10 Density/Area Curves

Beginning with the 1996 edition of NFPA 13, a decrease in design area was permitted based on ceiling height with the use of quick-response sprinklers in wet-pipe systems in light and ordinary hazard occupancies. Although the faster actuation of quick-response sprinklers is expected to more quickly establish the conditions for fire control, the real basis for the area reduction is the recognition that ceiling height plays a major role in the fire control performance of sprinklers. Higher ceilings permit fires to grow larger prior to actuation of sprinklers. As far back as 1967, it was found that the size of the fire at the time of sprinkler operation increased with the square of ceiling height when the fire was located directly beneath a sprinkler and linearly with ceiling height when the fire was offset 5 ft (1.5 m) horizontally from the sprinkler.[13] The 1996 edition of NFPA 13 also introduced a corresponding design area increase for ceilings with slopes exceeding 2 in 12, based on modeling studies that showed operating patterns of sprinklers could be irregular under such conditions, causing larger numbers of sprinklers to operate.[15]

Tests conducted in 1998 suggested that fire control of high-challenge storage fires is better achieved through the use of larger orifice sprinklers. When standard orifice sprinklers were used to provide high-application densities, it was theorized that misting of the sprinkler discharge due to the high operating pressures reduced the effectiveness of the water spray in controlling the fire, allowing substantial fire damage despite the operation of few sprinklers.[16] For this reason, beginning with the 1999 edition of NFPA 13, minimum orifice sizes were specified for spray sprinklers protecting general storage, rack storage, rubber tire storage, roll paper storage, and baled cotton storage. For design densities of 0.34 gpm/ft^2 (13.9 mm/min) or less, standard-response sprinklers with a nominal orifice coefficient of $K = 8.0$ ($K_m = 115$) or larger must be used. For design densities exceeding 0.34 gpm/ft^2 (13.9 mm/min), standard-response sprinklers with a nominal orifice coefficient of $K = 11.2$ ($K_m = 160$) or larger and that are specifically listed for storage applications must be used.

Compartmentation and Fire Control

It has been observed in a number of test programs that walls tend to assist the sprinkler system in the control mode by limiting the number of sprinklers that can operate. If a fire takes place near a wall, the total number of sprinklers that operate will tend to be reduced by the fact that presumed "outer ring" sprinklers are not available on at least one side.

This will tend to conserve water for the operating sprinklers, resulting in higher application rates and earlier achievement of the fire control energy balances. Carried to an extreme, it is the benefit of walls that is recognized in the "room design method" permitted by NFPA 13 as an alternate to the area/density method.

However, one might ask how the same amount of heat can be absorbed by fewer operating sprinklers. In other words, if those fringe sprinklers are not available to operate and absorb some of the heat from the fire plume, doesn't that same heat flow back across the room in the other direction and simply open more sprinklers on the opposite side?

Two factors argue against this. One is that, unless the fire is almost exactly along the wall, it will entrain the same amount of air as a centered fire, producing the same amount of ceiling jet gases. However, the wall will prevent it from breaking into an axisymmetric ceiling jet, and the resulting ceiling jet or smoke layer will be thicker. The thicker smoke layer actually will permit more cooling to take place from the discharge of each sprinkler, since the path of each droplet through the layer is longer.

The other factor is that the spray cooling ability of each sprinkler is enhanced at higher pressures. Cooling depends on droplet surface area, which is increased with flow and with the production of smaller-diameter droplets, both of which result from higher pressures. With fewer sprinklers operating in the vicinity of the fire, higher water supply pressures are available and more cooling takes place.

FIRE SUPPRESSION BY SPRINKLERS

Recent years have seen the development of new types of sprinklers that purport not only to control a fire but also to actively suppress the fire. To achieve fire suppression, water must be delivered by sprinklers to the burning fuel surface in sufficient quantity to disrupt the combustion process, knocking down the rate of heat release and preventing fire regrowth (Figure 16.1.11). If suppression is achieved at an early stage of the fire, only the sprinklers immediately over the fire area are expected to operate.

For this reason, the term "early suppression" has been developed. Today the term is being used both as the name for a concept and for a particular type of sprinkler. The concept is that fast response of sprinklers can produce an advantage in a fire if the response is accompanied by an effective discharge density—that is, a sprinkler spray capable of fighting its way down through the fire plume in sufficient quantities to suppress the burning fuel package.

The first sprinkler to include the term in its name, the early suppression fast-response (ESFR) sprinkler, was developed to apply the concept to a particular class of fire: protection of high-rack storage of FMRC's standardized plastic commodity, using ceiling sprinklers only. As part of the ESFR development program, FMRC researchers created new terms to investigate and to define the early suppression phenomenon: RDD and ADD.

Required Delivered Density

Required delivered density (RDD) is the minimum rate of water application that, if delivered to the top of the fuel package, is capable of providing early suppression. For the purposes of FMRC's ESFR program, early suppression was, in turn, defined as a sustained knockdown of the fire sufficient to prevent the operation of sprinklers beyond the initial ring.

Specialized test apparatus was developed by FMRC researchers to measure RDD. The apparatus consists of a series of perforated pipes suspended over the burning fuel package that are capable of spreading a fairly uniform water distribution directly over the top of the fuel, such that the water does not have to fight its way down through the fire plume (Figure 16.1.12). The pipes and fuel are all positioned below the fire products collector, a large calorimeter that collects all fire gases and determines the total rate of heat release of the fire as a function of time. The water application is initiated at a time simulating the operation of sprinklers, based on an assumed sprinkler location, sensitivity, and temperature rating. The heat release history generated while the water fights the fire can then be used to predict the operation of sprinklers beyond the first ring, based on their presumed location with respect to the fire.

Figure 16.1.13 shows the results of several RDD tests for a particular fuel package. Suppression can be considered to occur when the heat release rate of the fire is quickly knocked down and is prevented from resurging.

With regard to the standard plastic commodity stored in racks, FMRC confirmed that a relationship existed between RDD and height of storage (Table 16.1.2).

Under the sponsorship of the National Fire Protection Research Foundation, there has been an attempt to extend the early suppression concept to sprinkler protection of ordinary hazards.

Prior freeburn testing had been performed to determine the heat release histories of selected fuel packages. Among the fuel

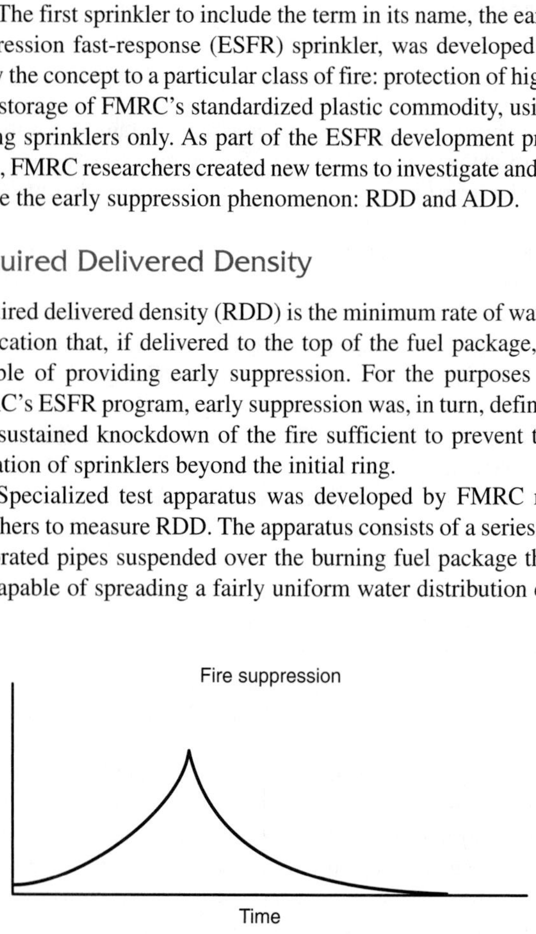

FIGURE 16.1.11 Representation of Fire Suppression by Sprinklers, Heat Release Rate ($\dot{Q}$) Versus Time

FIGURE 16.1.12 RDD Test Apparatus (© 2008 FM Global. Reprinted with permission. All rights reserved.)

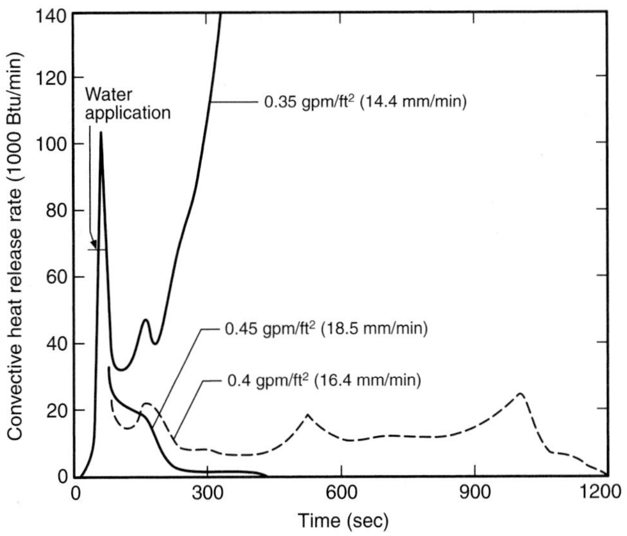

FIGURE 16.1.13 RDD Test Results Using Three Different Water Application Rates (© 2008 FM Global. Reprinted with permission. All rights reserved.)

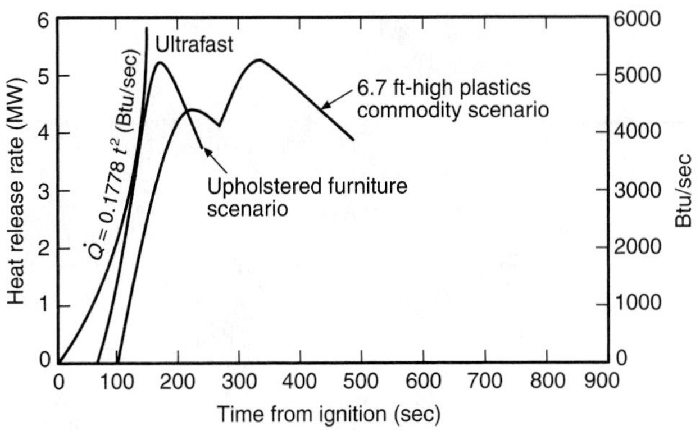

FIGURE 16.1.14 Comparison of Fire Growth Rates for Selected Fuel Packages and the "Ultrafast" t^2 Fire. For SI units: 1 ft = 0.305 m; 1 Btu = 0.055 kJ.

TABLE 16.1.2 Standard Plastic Commodity—RDD Determination

Fast Response Sprinklers—30 ft (9.1 m) Racks	Storage Height in Racks		RDD Determination	
	ft	*m*	*gpm/ft²*	*mm/min*
3 tiers	15	4.6	0.35	14.4
4 tiers	20	6.1	0.45	18.5
5 tiers	25	7.6	0.65	26.7

packages tested were the upholstered furniture corner scenario used during the development of the residential sprinkler and a 6.7-ft (2.0-m) high storage configuration of the standardized plastic commodity in corrugated cardboard cartons that was used in the ESFR sprinkler program. Nineteen RDD tests were conducted by Underwriters Laboratories Inc. under the foundation's sponsorship to compare the relative suppressibilities of the two different fuel packages.[17,18]

In the freeburn testing, both these fuel packages were found to produce a total heat release history that could be approximated by an "ultrafast *t*-squared" fire, with a maximum heat release rate of about 5 MW. This refers to a standardized curve in which heat release grows proportionally to the square of time (Figure 16.1.14).

The specific water application rates needed to provide early suppression are still under study. However, it was observed clearly that the densities required for suppression of the plastic commodity were considerably higher than those required for the upholstered furniture for the same size fires. The tests conclusively demonstrated that some fuel packages are more easily suppressed than others, even if their heat release rate histories appear to be similar.

Actual Delivered Density

Actual delivered density (ADD) is the actual rate of water application that a particular configuration of flowing sprinklers is capable of delivering to the top of a fuel package, depending on the strength of the upward fire plume.

The ADD measuring apparatus consists of a series of collection pans situated over a gas burner (Figure 16.1.15). The 0.5 m^2 pans simulate the top of a storage array and measure the rate at which each such area receives water from any particular configuration of flowing sprinklers. The gas burner is used to produce upward fire plume forces through the simulated flue spaces between the pans. In this manner, the ability of the flowing sprinkler(s) to deliver water to the fuel package can be checked against a wide range of fire strength conditions, simulating different points in the fire history. Typically, ADD decreases as the fire gets larger.

Since the water spray distribution of a sprinkler is not uniform, the collection pans collect different quantities of water during an ADD test. The development of ADD values from test results is accomplished using a probability distribution identified by, and named for, W. Weibull of Sweden. It was first applied to the distribution of liquid droplet sizes in 1951.[19] Using the Weibull distribution, the pan collections of each sprinkler spray acting through a fire plume of a given strength are fitted to a probability curve with a characteristic or average ADD θ and a uniformity value (b). The higher the uniformity value, the more likely it is that a characteristic ADD θ higher than the RDD will suppress the fire, since the needed water is being distributed in usable fashion.

The uniformity factor affects the basic shape of the probability distribution curve. Figures 16.1.16 and 16.1.17 indicate the relative effects of changing the scale parameter θ and the uniformity parameter b on the frequency distribution of the statistical model. These computer-generated figures demonstrate the superior ability of larger water droplets to penetrate the fire plume when a large fire is located directly below a sprinkler.

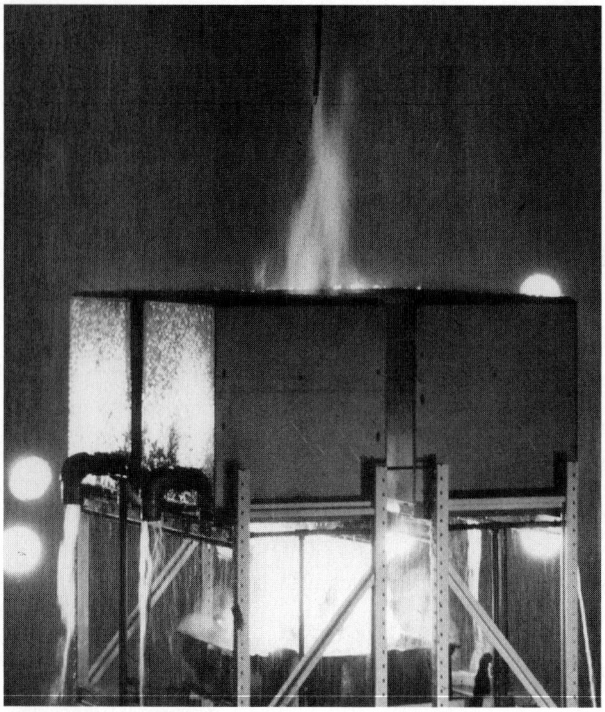

FIGURE 16.1.15 ADD Measuring Apparatus for Rack Storage (© 2008 FM Global. Reprinted with permission. All rights reserved.)

The variable x represents any given measurement. Typically, the ADD uniformity values range from about 1 to 7. A uniformity value of infinity would represent a perfectly uniform distribution.

The probability concept can also be applied to RDD data. A uniformity value b can be determined despite the fact that the RDD is measured in a test using the special water applicator intended to provide fairly uniform distribution. A "characteristic" RDD can be calculated as:

$$\theta_{\text{RDD}} = \frac{\text{RDD (proposed)}}{(1/b)!}$$

The probability distribution concept can also be used to rank the relative suppression capability of sprinklers. If ADD measurements are taken for three prototype sprinklers under the same fire, spacing, and flow conditions, and values of characteristic ADD and uniformity are found for each, the probability that each sprinkler will meet or exceed the characteristic RDD at any selected point on the fuel surface can be calculated from the relationship:

$$P(\text{ADD} \geq \theta_{\text{RDD}}) = \exp\left[-\left(\frac{\theta_{\text{RDD}}}{\theta_{\text{ADD}}}\right)b^{\text{ADD}}\right]$$

RECENT DEVELOPMENTS

The preceding discussion shows that the present understanding of the theory of fire sprinkler performance is incomplete. For some aspects of sprinkler system performance, such as thermal response and the hydraulics of water delivery, research has led to a good understanding of the mechanisms at work. On the other hand, the science of understanding how the water is dis-

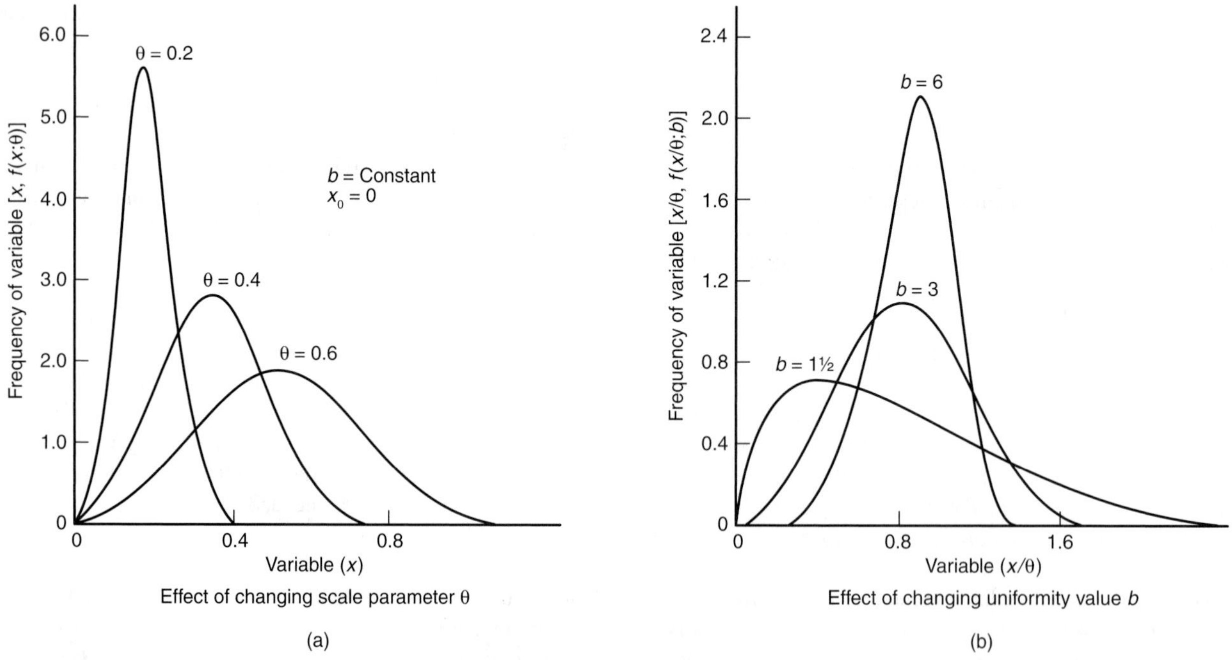

FIGURE 16.1.16 Effect of Changing (a) Scale Parameter θ; (b) Uniformity Value b

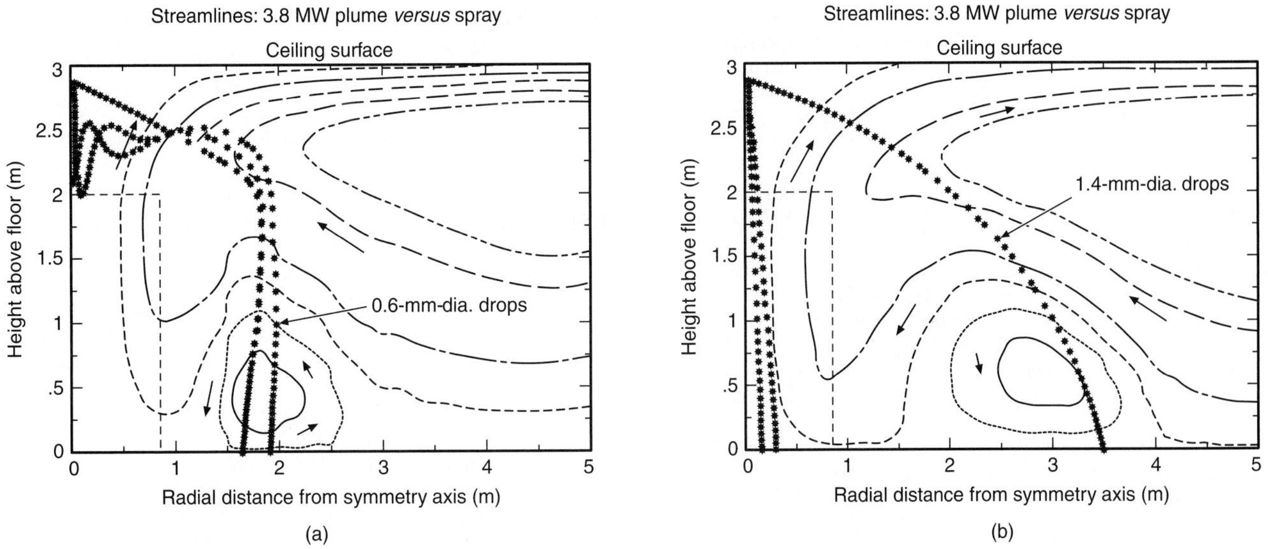

FIGURE 16.1.17 (a) Drops (0.6-mm diameter) Swept Away by the Upward Plume Velocities; (b) 1.4-mm Diameter Drops Following Their Trajectories.[19] For U.S. units: 1 in. = 25.4 mm; 1 ft = 0.305 m.

tributed remains very weak. Almost all the advances made in mathematical modeling of sprinkler performance in the past 25 years deal only with the time up to which the sprinkler starts to put water on the fire.

Research in the 1980s at FMRC, funded partly through the National Institute of Standards and Technology (NIST), began the effort of using computers to analyze the complex interactions between water droplet sprays and the gas flows induced by a building fire.[20] The work was based on very simplified assumptions, with the presumed fire located directly under a single sprinkler producing droplets of uniform size in a few specific directions (see Figure 16.1.17).

Continuing advances in computational fluid dynamics led to NIST efforts to model sprinkler response and suppression as part of a study of the interaction of sprinklers, vents, and draft curtains.[21] The NIST sprinkler/spray interaction model, now part of the Fire Dynamics Simulator, is currently accessible to practitioners through the NIST website at http://www.bfrl.nist.gov. However, potential users should be cautioned that there is still no accepted mechanism for measuring and characterizing sprinkler droplet size and distribution. Until such a mechanism is developed and validated, results of sprinkler system suppression modeling will be considered suspect. Recent work suggests that the suppression modeling problem is made even more difficult by the fact that the presence of water droplets tends to widen the fire plume and slow the upward velocity of the plume.[22]

SUMMARY

Automatic sprinkler systems are an effective means to control fires in enclosed areas, and in recent years models have been developed to perform early fire suppression. Continued improvements in design will require a greater understanding of the scientific principles involved in sprinkler performance. Whereas the thermal response and hydraulic mechanisms of sprinklers are well understood, the properties of water distribution are more complex and difficult to measure. Future advances in the fire suppression and control capability of automatic sprinkler systems will be the result of additional research based on computer analysis.

BIBLIOGRAPHY

References Cited

1. Heskestad, G., and Smith, H. F., “Investigation of a New Sprinkler Sensitivity Approval Test: The Plunge Test,” FMRC No. 22485, Factory Mutual Research Corp., Norwood, MA, Dec. 1976.
2. Alpert, R. L., “Calculation of Response Time of Ceiling-Mounted Fire Detectors,” *Fire Technology,* Vol. 8, No. 3, 1972.
3. Heskestad, G., and Smith, H. F., “Plunge Test for Determination of Sprinkler Sensitivity,” J.I.3A1E2.RR, Dec. 1980, Factory Mutual Research Corp., Norwood, MA, 1980.
4. Heskestad, G., “The Sprinkler Response Time Index (RTI),” *Paper (RC81-TP-3)* presented at the Technical Conference on Residential Sprinkler Systems, Factory Mutual Research Corp., April 28–29, 1981.
5. Evans, D. D., and Stroup, D. W., “Methods to Calculate the Response Time of Heat and Smoke Detectors Installed Below Large Unobstructed Ceilings,” NBSIR 85-3167, National Bureau of Standards, Gaithersburg, MD, 1985.
6. Pepi, J. S., “Design Characteristics of Quick-Response Sprinklers,” Grinnell Fire Protection Systems Co., Providence, RI, May 1986.
7. Heskestad, G., and Bill, R. G., “Conduction Heat-Loss Effects on Thermal Response of Automatic Sprinklers,” FMRC J.I. ONOJ5.RU, Factory Mutual Research Corp., Norwood, MA, Sept. 1987.
8. Dundas, P. H., “Optimization of Sprinkler Fire Protection, Progress Report No. 10—The Scaling of Sprinkler Discharge: Prediction of Drop Size,” FMRC No. 18792, Factory Mutual Research Corp., Norwood, MA, June 1974.

9. Braidech, M. M., and Neale, J. A., "The Mechanism of Extinguishment of Fire by Finely Divided Water," NBFU Research Report No. 10, Underwriters Laboratories Inc., Chicago, IL, 1955.
10. Nash, P., and Rasbash, D. J., "The Use of Water in Fire Fighting," F.R. Note No. 202/1955, Fire Research Station, Borehamwood, UK, 1955.
11. Heskestad, G., "The Role of Water in Suppression of Fire: A Review," CIB/W14/80-35, Factory Mutual Research Corp., Norwood, MA, 1980.
12. Magee, R. S., and Reitz, R. D., "Extinguishment of Radiation-Augmented Plastic Fires by Water Sprays," Fifteenth Symposium (International) on Combustion, Combustion Institute, 1975.
13. O'Dogherty, M. J., Nash, P., and Young, R. A., "A Study of the Performance of Automatic Sprinkler Systems," *Fire Research Technical Paper No. 17,* Joint Fire Research Organization, London, UK, 1967.
14. Wood, C. M., *Hydraulic Data for Fire Protection Systems,* Automatic Sprinkler Corp. of America, Youngstown, OH, 1961.
15. Heskestad, G., "Model Study of ESFR Sprinkler Response under Sloped Ceilings," FMRC J.I. 0N0E3.RU(2), Factory Mutual Research Corp., Norwood, MA, Nov. 1988.
16. Pabich, M. L., "Technical Report of Palletized Paper Products Fire Tests Conducted for the Procter & Gamble Company," Underwriters Laboratories Inc., Northbrook, IL, Aug. 1998.
17. Carey, W., *Group 2 RDD Test Program,* National Fire Protection Research Foundation, Quincy, MA, 1989.
18. Budnick, E., and Fleming, R., "How Quick-Response Sprinklers Perform," *Fire Journal,* Vol. 83, No. 5, 1989.
19. Goodfellow, D. G., "A Statistical Model for Analysis of Sprinkler Water-Spray Distributions," Factory Mutual Research Corp., Norwood, MA, Aug. 1985.
20. Alpert, R. L., and Delichatsios, M. M., "Calculated Interaction of Water Droplet Sprays with Fire Plumes in Compartments," NBS-GCR 86-520, National Bureau of Standards, Gaithersburg, MD, Dec. 1986.
21. McGratton, K. B., Hamins, A., and Evans, D. D., "Sprinklers, Vent, and Draft Curtain Interaction—Modeling and Experiment," *Proceedings*—Fire Suppression and Detection Research Application Symposium, National Fire Protection Research Foundation, February 1998.
22. Schwille, J., and Lueptow, R., "A Simplified Model of the Effect of a Fire Sprinkler Spray on a Buoyant Fire Plume," *Journal of Fire Protection Engineering,* Vol. 16, No. 2, 2006.

NFPA Codes, Standards, and Recommended Practices

Reference to the following NFPA codes, standards, and recommended practices will provide further information on the principles of automatic sprinkler performance discussed in this chapter. (See the latest version of The NFPA Catalog *for availability of current editions of the following documents.)*

NFPA 1, *Uniform Fire Code™,* 2006 edition
NFPA 13, *Standard for the Installation of Sprinkler Systems*

References

Arvidson, M., "An Initial Evaluation of Different Residential Sprinklers Using Heat Release Rate Measurements," SP Swedish National Testing and Research Institute, Boras, Sweden, 2000.
Croce, P., Hill, J., and Chow, W. K., "An Investigation of the Causative Mechanism of Sprinkler Skipping," *Journal of Fire Protection Engineering,* Vol. 15, No. 2, 2005.
Fleming, R., "Solid Shelves in Racks vs. Shelf Storage," *NFPA Journal,* Jan./Feb. 2006.
Gavelli, F., Ruffino, P., Anderson, G., and diMarzo, M., "The Effect of Minute Water Droplets on a Simulated Sprinkler Link Thermal Response," GCR 99-776, National Institute of Standards and Technology, Gaithersburg, MD, June 1999.
Golinveaux, J., "Dry Pipe Sprinkler Software," *NFPA Journal,* Mar./Apr. 2004.
Isman, K. E., "Which Sprinkler to Choose?" *Fire Protection Engineering,* Issue No. 9, Winter 2001.
Troup, J., "Protection of Warehouse Retail Occupancies with Extra Large Orifice (ELO) Sprinklers," *Journal of Fire Protection Engineering,* Vol. 8, No. 1, 1996.
Troup, J., "Extra Large Orifice Sprinklers: An Overview of Full-Scale Fire Test Performance," *Journal of Fire Protection Engineering,* Vol. 9, No. 3, 1998.
Vincent, B. G., Kung, H. C., LeBlanc, L., and Troup, J., "ESFR Sprinkler Protection for Warehouse Storage of Flammable Liquids in Small Metal Containers," *Journal of Fire Protection Engineering,* Vol. 9, No. 2, 1998.
Yu, H. Z., Pounder, D., and Fischer, M., "Fire Performance Evaluation of a K-16.8 Suppression-Mode Upright Sprinkler," *Journal of Fire Protection Engineering,* Vol. 14, No. 2, 2004.

Chapter 2

Automatic Sprinklers

Kenneth E. Isman

Chapter Contents

Key Terms

automatic sprinkler system, deflector, early suppression fast response (ESFR) sprinkler, flush-type sprinkler, K-factor, large drop sprinkler, pendent sprinkler, recessed sprinkler, sidewall sprinkler, standard spray sprinkler, upright sprinkler

Automatic sprinklers are thermosensitive devices designed to react at predetermined temperatures by automatically releasing a stream of water and distributing it in specified patterns and quantities over designated areas. The automatic distribution of water is intended to extinguish a fire or to prevent its spread in the event that the initial fire is out of reach of the sprinkler's discharge or is of a type that cannot be extinguished by water discharged from sprinklers. The water is fed to the sprinklers through a system of piping, ordinarily overhead, with the sprinklers placed at intervals along the pipes.

This chapter covers the operating principles, including operating temperatures, of the various types of automatic sprinklers currently available and describes their construction in some detail. Sprinklers for special service conditions are also covered.

The National Fire Protection Association (NFPA) does not have standards that cover the manufacture of sprinklers. However, NFPA does maintain many fire protection standards (most important of which is NFPA 13, *Standard for the Installation of Sprinkler Systems,* hereinafter referred to as NFPA 13) that only allow sprinklers listed by reputable product evaluation organizations to be used in sprinkler systems. Listing of sprinklers in a national organization's listing service is an indication that the sprinklers have been scrutinized for their reliability and compliance with the organization's test criteria for sprinklers.

For related topics, see Section 16, Chapter 1, "Principles of Automatic Sprinkler System Performance"; and Section 16, Chapter 3, "Automatic Sprinkler Systems."

SPRINKLER HISTORY

Since they were introduced in the latter part of the nineteenth century, the performance and reliability of automatic sprinklers have been improved continually through experience and the efforts of manufacturers and testing organizations.

In 1952 and 1953, a new sprinkler was developed with a more efficient umbrella-shaped spray pattern. This "spray sprinkler" became the standard sprinkler in 1958 for use in conformance with NFPA 13; sprinklers of the older design became known as "old-style" or "conventional" sprinklers. Redesign of the deflector was the principal feature of the new standard sprinklers.

Due to the development of many new types of sprinklers during the 1980s, it became questionable whether any single type of sprinkler could be considered standard in the future. As such, the term *spray sprinkler* was brought back into use with the 1991 edition of NFPA 13. This also conforms better to internationally accepted terminology.

OPERATING PRINCIPLES OF AUTOMATIC SPRINKLERS

In order to appreciate the ruggedness, mechanical simplicity, reliability in operation, and freedom from premature operation of an automatic sprinkler, a familiarity with the basic principles of its design, construction, and operation is necessary.

Kenneth E. Isman, P.E., is vice-president of engineering for the National Fire Sprinkler Association, Patterson, New York. He currently serves on relevant NFPA technical committees, including the Committee on Sprinkler System Installation Criteria.

Operating Elements

Under normal conditions, the discharge of water from an automatic sprinkler is restrained by a cap or valve held tightly against the orifice by a system of levers and links or other releasing devices pressing down on the cap and anchored firmly by struts on the sprinkler.

Fusible Sprinklers. A common fusible-style automatic sprinkler operates when a metal alloy of predetermined melting point fuses. Various combinations of levers, struts, and links or other soldered members are used to reduce the force acting on the solder so that the sprinkler will be held closed with the smallest practical amount of metal and solder. This construction minimizes the time of operation by reducing the mass of fusible metal to be heated.

The solders used with automatic sprinklers are alloys of optimum fusibility composed principally of tin, lead, cadmium, and bismuth; all have sharply defined melting points. Alloys of two or more metals may have a melting point that is lower than that of the individual metal with the lower melting point. The mixture of two or more metals that gives the lowest melting point possible is called a "eutectic" alloy.

Bulb Sprinklers. A second style of operating element uses a frangible bulb (Figure 16.2.1). The small bulb, usually of glass, contains a liquid that does not completely fill the bulb, leaving a small air bubble trapped in it. As heat expands the liquid, the bubble is compressed and finally absorbed by the liquid. Once the bubble disappears, the pressure rises substantially, and the bulb shatters, releasing the valve cap. The exact operating temperature is regulated by adjusting the amount of liquid and the size of the bubble when the bulb is sealed.

Sprinkler Dynamics. Figure 16.2.2 shows how the mechanical force exists in a solder-type link-and-lever-style automatic sprinkler. The construction shown is diagrammatic and does not represent any particular sprinkler.

The mechanical force normally exerted on the top of the cap or valve is many times that developed by the water pressure below, so that the possibility of leakage, even from water hammer or exceptionally high water pressure, is practically eliminated. The mechanical force in a link-and-lever sprinkler is produced by tension in the sprinkler frame, usually created by tightening the screw that holds the deflector down against the toggle joint formed by the levers. This pressure is applied against the valve or cap, but the line of force is not direct. The eccentricity of the loading permits a leveraged reduction of the force, first by the toggle effect of the two levers, and second by the mechanism of the link parts. The force resisted by the solder is made relatively low because solder of the composition needed to give the desired operating temperatures is subject to cold flow under high stress. The sprinkler frame or other parts usually possess a degree of elasticity to provide the energy that produces a positive, sharp release of the operating parts.

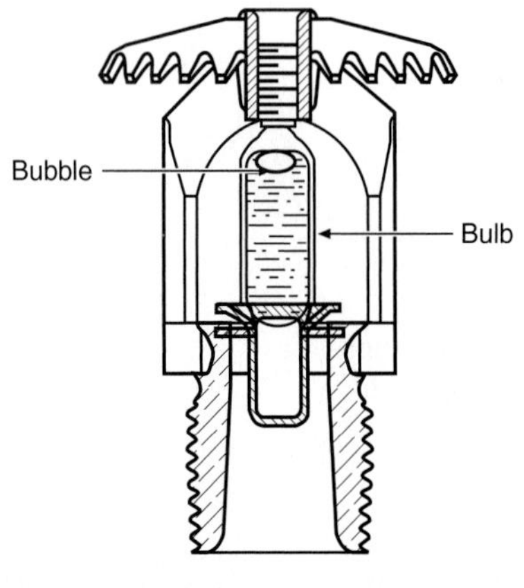

FIGURE 16.2.1 Grinnell Quartzoid, Issue D

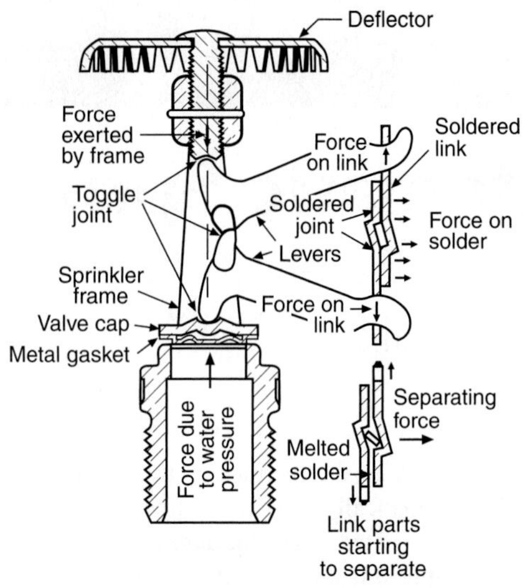

FIGURE 16.2.2 Representative Arrangement of a Solder-Type Link-and-Lever Automatic Sprinkler

Sprinklers illustrated in Figure 16.2.3 use modifications of the common link-and-lever construction, some of which employ solder under compression, tension, and shear.

To ensure that cold flow will not be a problem, the laboratories that test and list sprinklers use statistical methods to simulate long-term loading of heat-responsive elements. Statistical methods are also employed to ensure that the crush strength of glass bulbs is sufficiently higher than the frame loads that will be applied to the bulbs.

Deflector Design

Attached to the frame of the sprinkler is a deflector or distributor against which the stream of water is directed and converted into a spray designed to cover or protect a certain area. The amount of water discharged depends on the flowing water pressure and the size of the sprinkler orifice. A flowing pressure of 7 psi (48 kPa) is generally considered a minimum for development of a reasonable spray pattern. At this pressure, a sprinkler having a nominal ½ in. (12.7 mm) orifice ($K = 5.6$, or, in metric units, $K_m = 80$) will discharge approximately 15 gpm (58 L/min). (See Spray Sprinklers with Different Orifice Sizes in this chapter for the definition of K-factor.) At the same 7 psi

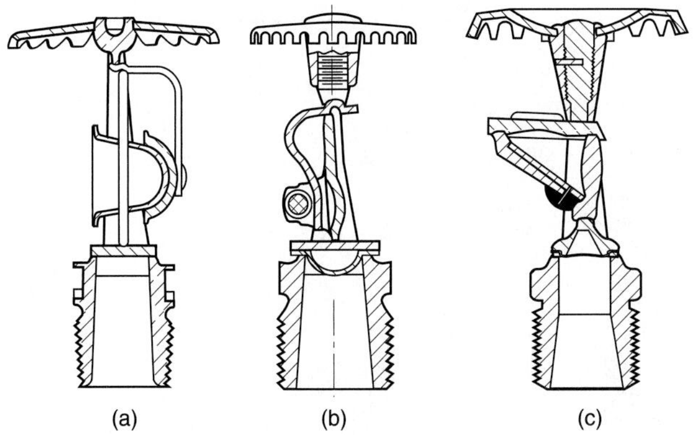

FIGURE 16.2.3 Some Modifications of the Common Link-and-Lever Construction: (a) Grinnell F950 Duraspeed, (b) Reliable Model G, and (c) Firematic Type S

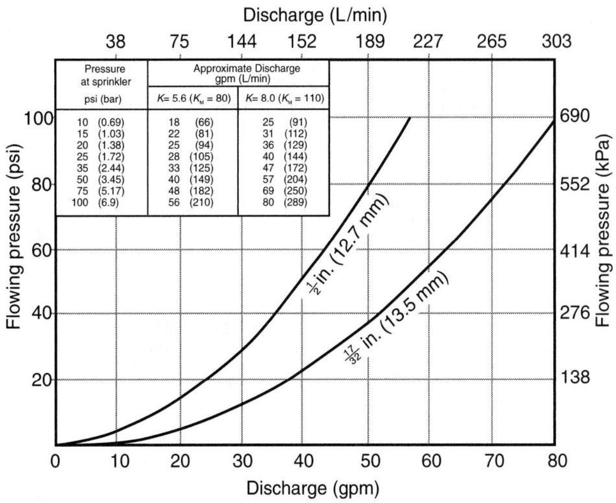

FIGURE 16.2.4 Water Discharge Rates of Typical Nominal K = 5.6 (K_m = 80) and K = 8.0 (K_m = 110) Automatic Sprinklers

(48 kPa) pressure, a nominal 17⁄32 in. (13.5 mm) orifice (K = 8.0, or, in metric units, K_m = 110) sprinkler will discharge approximately 21 gpm (79 L/min). (See Figure 16.2.4 for the quantity of water discharged at various water pressures.)

In order to have even the minimum flowing pressure at sprinklers that are remote from the point of water supply, especially when a number of sprinklers are operating simultaneously, water supply pressures in the range of 30 to 100 psi (316 to 690 kPa) are customarily provided. Hydraulically calculated systems are designed around the normally available water supply volume and pressure.

The distribution of water from a sprinkler is not expected to be axisymmetric, particularly because sprinkler frame arms obstruct the spray pattern and the serrated edges of the deflector create a "fingering" effect. A contour plot of the flow pattern of a pendent spray sprinkler is shown in Figure 16.2.5.[1]

Because the distribution of water from sprinklers is a complex phenomenon, the testing laboratories have fairly broad requirements in this area. For upright and pendent spray sprinklers, for example, Underwriters Laboratories Inc. (UL) requires a turntable test to "fingerprint" the spray pattern. For a sprinkler with an orifice of K = 5.6 (K_m = 80) or K = 8 (K_m = 110), water distribution is not permitted outside a 16-ft (4.9-m) diameter circle in a horizontal plane 4 ft (1.2 m) below the sprinkler when operating at minimum pressure. A separate "16 pan" distribution test checks the ability of four flowing sprinklers to cover the area between them with their overlapping spray patterns. Factory Mutual Research Corporation (FMRC) applies an additional six-sprinkler flow test, which looks at the area covered between two adjacent sprinklers.

TEMPERATURE RATINGS OF AUTOMATIC SPRINKLERS

Automatic sprinklers have various temperature ratings that are based on the need to make sure that sprinklers do not operate when exposed to natural heat sources that are not a fire (Table 16.2.1). In order to make sure that sprinklers will open at the proper temperature, a sample sprinkler is immersed in a liquid

TABLE 16.2.1 Temperature Ratings, Classifications, and Color Codings

Maximum Ceiling Temperature		Temperature Rating				
°F	*°C*	*°F*	*°C*	*Temperature Classification*	*Color Code*	*Glass Bulb Colors*
100	38	135–170	57–77	Ordinary	Uncolored or black	Orange or red
150	66	175–225	79–107	Intermediate	White	Yellow or green
225	107	250–300	121–149	High	Blue	Blue
300	149	325–375	163–191	Extra high	Red	Purple
375	191	400–475	204–246	Very extra high	Green	Black
475	246	500–575	260–302	Ultra high	Orange	Black
625	329	650	343	Ultra high	Orange	Black

Source: NFPA 13, *Standard for the Installation of Sprinkler Systems.*

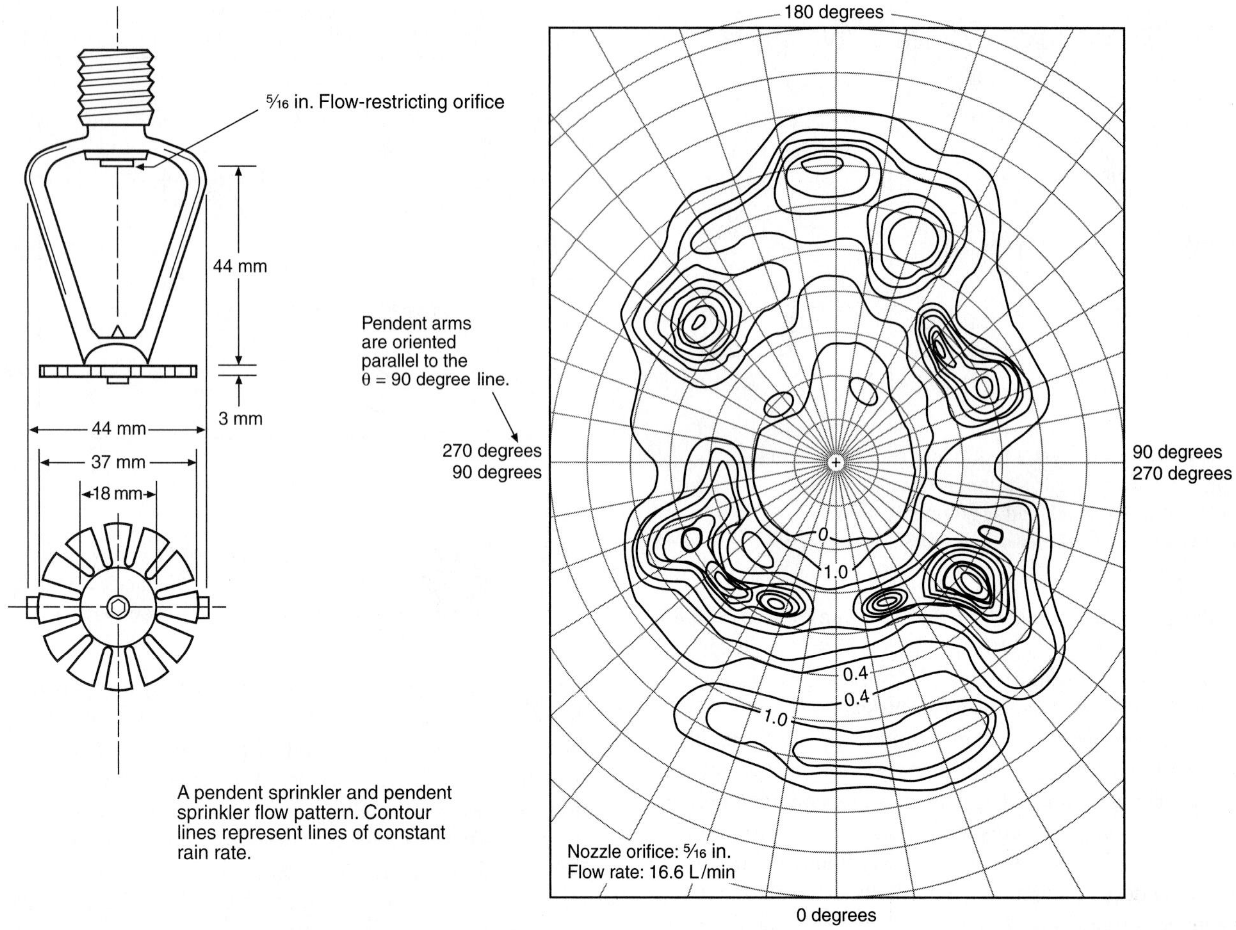

FIGURE 16.2.5 Pendent Spray Sprinkler and Flow Contours

and the temperature of the liquid is raised very slowly until the sprinkler operates.

The temperature rating of all fusible-element-style automatic sprinklers is stamped on the soldered link. For bulb sprinklers, the temperature rating must be stamped or cast on some visible part. Color codes are also used for glass bulbs and for frame arms of fusible-element sprinklers.

The recommended maximum room temperature is restricted for both bulbs and fusible-element sprinklers. This restriction is because solder begins to lose its strength somewhat below its actual melting point. Premature operation of a solder sprinkler usually depends on the extent to which the normal room temperature is exceeded, the duration of the excessive temperature, and the load on the operating parts of the sprinkler. Although glass bulb sprinklers do not lose strength at temperatures close to their operating temperatures, using them at such temperatures can result in continuous loss and reforming of the air bubble, which creates stresses on the bulb.

The general rule of not using sprinklers of ordinary (135 to 170°F [57 to 77°C]) temperature rating where temperatures exceed 100°F (38°C) is necessary to provide a margin of safety. General practices regarding the use of automatic sprinklers of higher than the ordinary rating are given in Tables 16.2.2 and 16.2.3. Sprinklers of ordinary temperature rating can be used inside buildings and other places where they are not subject to direct sun rays, except in monitors and in blind attics without ventilation, under metal or tile roofs, near or above heat sources, or in confined spaces where normal temperatures may be exceeded.

When there is doubt as to maximum temperatures at sprinkler locations, maximum reading thermometers should be used and the temperature determined under conditions that would show the highest readings to be expected.

Sprinklers with high temperature ratings are often used in place of ordinary-rated sprinklers in situations where a high rate of heat release can be anticipated. The sprinklers rated for higher temperatures may have the advantage of reducing the number of sprinklers that would otherwise operate outside the fire area.

Automatic sprinklers may require a longer time period to operate when exposed to a slowly developing fire as opposed to the high heat release of a rapidly developing fire. They are designed to operate quickly enough to control a fire and prevent its spread.

The speed of operation depends on the physical properties of the sprinkler's mechanism. The time involved to operate depends, among other factors, on the shape, size, and mass

TABLE 16.2.2 Temperature Ratings of Sprinklers Based on Distance from Heat Sources

Type of Heat Condition	*Ordinary Degree Rating*	*Intermediate Degree Rating*	*High Degree Rating*
(a) Heating ducts			
1. Above	More than 2 ft 6 in.	2 ft 6 in. or less	
2. Side and below	More than 1 ft 0 in.	1 ft 0 in. or less	
3. Diffuser	Any distance except as shown under Intermediate Degree Rating column	*Downward discharge:* Cylinder with 1 ft 0 in. radius from edge extending 1 ft 0 in. below and 2 ft 6 in. above *Horizontal discharge:* Semicylinder with 2 ft 6 in. radius in direction of flow extending 1 ft 0 in. below and 2 ft 6 in. above	
(b) Unit heater			
1. Horizontal discharge		*Discharge side:* 7 ft 0 in. to 20 ft 0 in. radius pie-shaped cylinder extending 7 ft 0 in. above and 2 ft 0 in. below heater; also 7 ft 0 in. radius cylinder more than 7 ft 0 in. above unit heater	7 ft 0 in. radius cylinder extending 7 ft 0 in. above and 2 ft 0 in. below unit heater
2. Vertical downward discharge		7 ft 0 in. radius cylinder extending upward from an elevation 7 ft 0 in. above unit heater	7 ft 0 in. radius cylinder extending from the top of the unit heater to an elevation 7 ft 0 in. above unit heater
(c) Steam mains (uncovered)			
1. Above	More than 2 ft 6 in.	2 ft 6 in. or less	
2. Side and below	More than 1 ft 0 in.	1 ft 0 in. or less	
3. Blowoff valve	More than 7 ft 0 in.		7 ft 0 in. or less

For SI units: 1 in. = 25.4 mm; 1 ft = 0.305 m.
Source: NFPA 13, *Standard for the Installation of Sprinkler Systems.*

TABLE 16.2.3 Ratings of Sprinklers in Specified Locations

Location	*Ordinary Degree Rating*	*Intermediate Degree Rating*	*High Degree Rating*
Skylights		Glass or plastic	
Attics	Ventilated	Unventilated	
Peaked roof: metal or thin boards, concealed or not concealed, insulated or uninsulated	Ventilated	Unventilated	
Flat roof: metal, not concealed	Ventilated or unventilated	Note: For uninsulated roof, climate and insulated or uninsulated occupancy can necessitate intermediate sprinklers. Check on job.	
Flat roof: metal, concealed, insulated or uninsulated	Ventilated	Unventilated	
Show windows	Ventilated	Unventilated	

Note: A check of job condition by means of thermometers may be necessary.
Source: NFPA 13, *Standard for the Installation of Sprinkler Systems.*

of the thermosensitive mechanism; the temperature differential between the surrounding atmosphere and the operating temperature of the sprinkler; and the velocity of the heated fire gases past the sprinkler operating element.

In cases where extreme speed of operation is necessary owing to the likelihood of a rapidly developing and spreading fire as, for example, in explosives manufacturing, the practice is to use deluge systems incorporating open sprinklers. These systems can be activated by heat detectors, special detection systems using infrared or ultraviolet light detection, smoke detection, or other means to open a valve and quickly allow water to enter the system and discharge through the open sprinklers. In cases where extremely fast response is required, the sprinkler piping is prefilled with water up to the open sprinklers, which are equipped with blow-off plugs or caps. This system is sometimes referred to as a "hot" deluge system.

STANDARD SPRAY SPRINKLERS

Standard spray sprinklers are generally similar in appearance to old-style sprinklers and use the same style frame and linkage or other release mechanism. The essential difference is in the deflector; seemingly minor differences in deflector design make major differences in discharge characteristics. Several representative standard spray sprinklers are illustrated in Figure 16.2.6. Clockwise from upper left is a fusible link-and-lever style (Reliable Issue C); a perforated heat-collector style, which is a variation of the link-and-lever style (Grinnell F950 Duraspeed); a center-strut style with solder under compression (Chemetron Stargard Model H); and a frangible-bulb style (Viking Model M).

FIGURE 16.2.6 Standard Spray Sprinklers Showing the Various Arrangements of Releasing Mechanisms

On the assumption that discharging water against the ceiling was essential to fire extinguishment, early research on automatic sprinklers was largely concerned with securing reasonably uniform distribution of water over the area protected by one sprinkler and with wetting the ceiling. Later research showed that more effective extinguishment and a larger area of coverage could be secured by directing all the water downward and horizontally. Research further showed that, with this pattern, discharge is effective even in controlling fires on the ceiling above the sprinklers because of the improved cooling effect of the spray, better high-level water distribution, and decreased exposure to the ceiling because of more effective direct discharge of water on burning materials below.[2]

The design of the deflector causes the solid stream of water issuing from the orifice of a standard sprinkler to break up to form an umbrella-shaped spray. The pattern is roughly that of a half-sphere filled with spray.

Standard spray sprinklers are made for installation in an upright or pendent position and must be installed in the position for which they are designed. (Note the difference in design of the deflectors shown in Figure 16.2.7.) It is customary to replace old-style sprinklers with spray sprinklers in existing installations, although NFPA 13 permits replacing old-style sprinklers with similar devices. Some manufacturers, however, have discontinued producing old-style sprinklers.

Several manufacturers developed a double deflector as their first design for use as standard spray upright sprinklers. A typical double deflector is shown in Figure 16.2.8. Such sprinklers are no longer manufactured but, if previously listed, are as acceptable as the currently approved upright spray sprinklers with a one-piece deflector.

WATER DISCHARGE

The general patterns of water discharge from the old-style and from the standard spray sprinklers are shown in Figures 16.2.9 and 16.2.10, respectively.

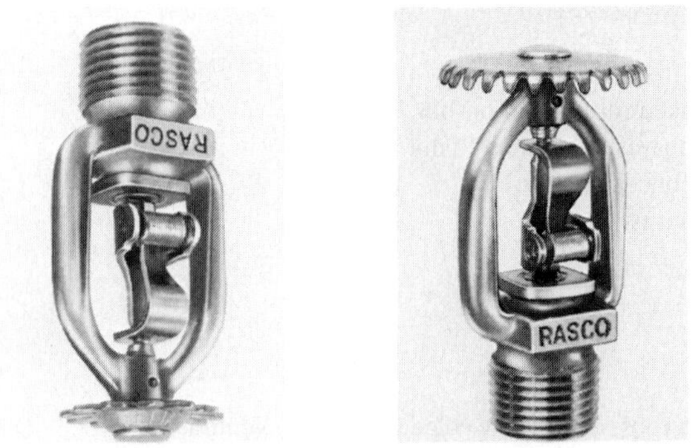

FIGURE 16.2.7 Listed Sprinkler Showing Upright (Right) and Pendent (Left) Models of the Same Issue (Reliable Model G)

FIGURE 16.2.8 Standard Upright Spray Sprinkler with Double Deflector

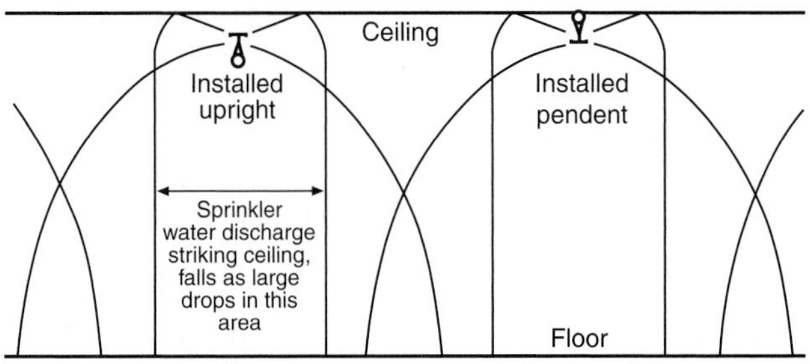

FIGURE 16.2.9 Principal Distribution Pattern of Water from Old-Style/Conventional Sprinklers

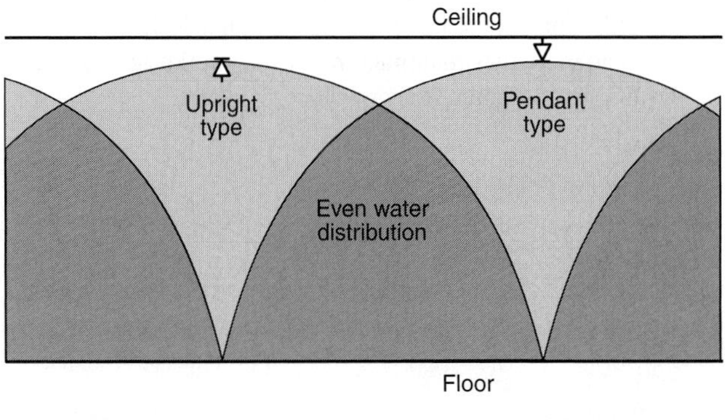

FIGURE 16.2.10 Principal Distribution Pattern of Water from Standard Spray Sprinklers

The water distribution characteristics of sidewall automatic sprinklers, picker trunk sprinklers, window sprinklers, and cornice sprinklers are described later in this chapter. The rate of water discharge from a sprinkler follows hydraulic laws and depends on the size of the orifice or nozzle and on the water pressure. Approximate rates of discharge at different pressures may be obtained from the plotted curve or from the table given in Figure 16.2.4.

Sprinklers discharging water through smaller or larger orifices are discussed later in this chapter. With similar forms of sprinkler nozzles and at the same water pressure, the discharge from these styles of sprinklers is approximately proportional to the nominal size of the orifice.

To obtain acceptance or approval of their sprinklers, manufacturers submit them to fire-testing organizations. After extensive tests and verification of the manufacturer's ability to manufacture the product properly, sprinklers found satisfactory are listed. Acceptance of a sprinkler by inspection departments or other regulatory agencies is based on such a listing.

Standard spray sprinklers are designed to be installed and operated in their proper position—that is, upright or pendent, as sometimes indicated by a stamping on the deflector bearing the appropriate word or the letters SSU (spray sprinkler upright) or SSP (spray sprinkler pendent).

Recessed Sprinklers

A recessed sprinkler is a type of ceiling sprinkler in which part or most of the body of the sprinkler, other than the part that connects to the piping, is mounted in a recessed housing. Its operation is similar to that of a standard pendent sprinkler (Figure 16.2.11).

Flush-Type Sprinklers

A typical flush-style sprinkler is shown in Figure 16.2.12. This style of sprinkler is used where appearance is considered to be

FIGURE 16.2.11 Central Model H Recessed Sprinkler

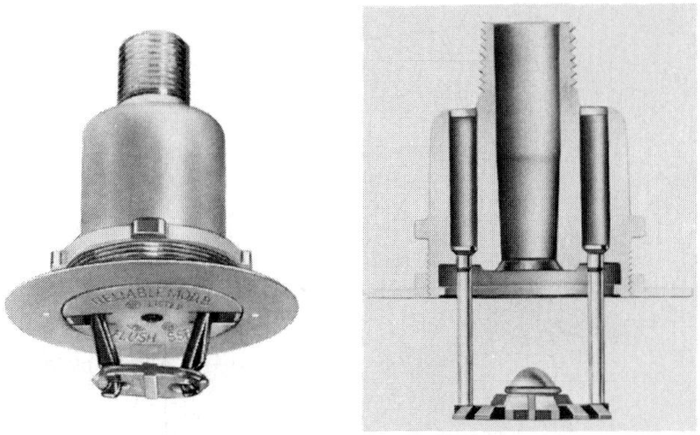

FIGURE 16.2.12 Flush-Style Ceiling Sprinkler (Reliable Model B)

of prime importance. (The diagram at the right shows the sprinkler after operation.) The special design of this type of ceiling sprinkler allows a minimum projection of the working parts of the sprinkler below the ceiling in which it is installed without adversely affecting the heat sensitivity or the pattern of water distribution.

In an effort to provide sprinkler protection in low-risk occupancies where aesthetics are important, sprinklers have been designed that attractively blend with the ceiling. Only the ceiling plate and thermosensitive assembly are visible from the floor when these sprinklers are installed. When a fire occurs and the thermosensitive element operates, the deflector drops to a position below the ceiling and water discharge commences.

Concealed Sprinklers

A concealed sprinkler is a type of ceiling sprinkler whose entire body, including the operating mechanism, is above its concealing cover plate. When a fire occurs, the cover plate drops, exposing the thermosensitive assembly. The subsequent operation of the thermosensitive assembly initiates discharge (Figure 16.2.13).

Ornamental Sprinklers

Ornamental sprinklers are automatic sprinklers that have been decorated by plating or enameling to give desired surface finishes. Ornamentation or special decorative design must not affect the operation or the water distribution unfavorably. Listed styles of ornamental sprinklers are for pendent installation in accordance with NFPA 13 (Figure 16.2.14). Such decorative coatings can be applied only by the manufacturer of the device.

Dry Pendent and Dry Upright Sprinklers

Dry pendent, dry upright, and dry-horizontal-sidewall sprinklers are used to provide sprinkler protection in unheated areas, such as freezers, where individual sprinklers are supplied from a wet-

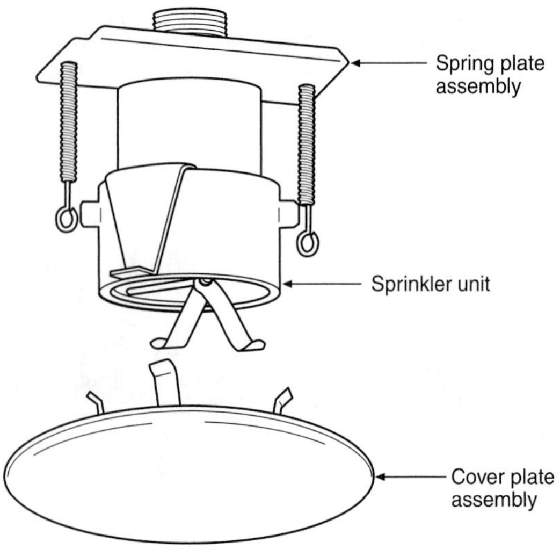

FIGURE 16.2.13 Concealed Ceiling Sprinkler (Stargard Model G)

FIGURE 16.2.14 Prussag SFH Glass-Bulb-Style Decorative Sprinkler

pipe system outside the unheated area. Dry pendent sprinklers must also be used on all dry-pipe systems where it is desirable to install pendent sprinklers.

A seal is provided at the entrance of the dry sprinkler to prevent water from entering until the sprinkler operates. The heat-sensitive operating mechanisms are adaptations of those used with automatic standard sprinklers.

See Figure 16.2.15 for an example of a dry pendent automatic sprinkler. When the ambient temperature rises beyond the operating temperature of the soldered link, the solder melts and the link plates separate on roller key. Levers held in place by a deflector screw are released, and the fixed tension of the frame, acting as a spring, ejects the levers and link parts clear of the sprinkler. Because the inner tube, which also serves as a discharge orifice, is no longer held in place by the levers, it moves to a predetermined position. With the support of the inner tube eliminated, the elements forming the watertight seal at the piping inlet pass through the inner tube and away from the sprinkler, allowing water to flow through the unobstructed waterway and strike the deflector, which distributes it in a spray pattern comparable to that of a ½ in. (12.7 mm) standard sprinkler. Shown is Reliable's Model C Dry Pendent. Other manufacturers have similar arrangements of proprietary equipment for dry-type sprinklers.

SPRINKLERS FOR SPECIAL SERVICE CONDITIONS

The sprinkler system using listed upright or pendent spray sprinklers is adaptable to a wide variety of conditions. However, there

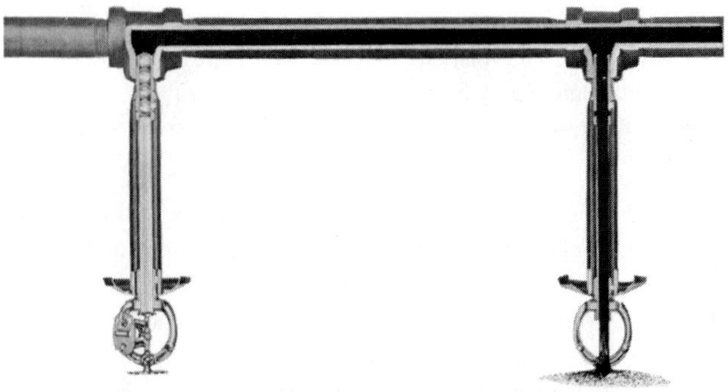

FIGURE 16.2.15 Representative Dry Pendent Automatic Sprinkler

are situations for which special styles of sprinklers and special sprinkler arrangements are suited. In some cases, such as with sidewall sprinklers, special patterns of water distribution are necessary; in others, unusual ambient temperatures or corrosive atmospheres call for special design or construction features.

Residential Sprinklers

Residential sprinklers are sprinklers that have been specifically listed for use in residential occupancies. These fast-response sprinklers have special low-mass fusible links or bulbs that make the time of temperature actuation much less than that of a sprinkler with a conventional operating element.

Residential sprinklers also have different discharge characteristics than spray sprinklers. They are required to throw water within 18 in. (457 mm) of the ceiling. This high-wall wetting pattern, along with the faster response, helps the residential sprinkler control or suppress typical residential fires with flows much lower than standard spray sprinklers.

Because of the life safety aspects of fast response, these sprinklers can be used in a variety of residential occupancies. Where a conventional system installed according to the provisions of NFPA 13 might not be as practical, such as in a single-family dwelling or a low-rise residential property, NFPA 13D, *Standard for the Installation of Sprinkler Systems in One- and Two-Family Dwellings and Manufactured Homes,* and NFPA 13R, *Standard for the Installation of Sprinkler Systems in Residential Occupancies up to and Including Four Stories in Height,* may be used. These standards have been developed specifically around the life safety capabilities of the residential sprinkler. A representative residential sprinkler is shown in Figure 16.2.16. (Residential sprinkler installations are discussed in detail in Section 16, Chapter 6, "Residential Sprinkler Systems.")

Large Drop Sprinklers

Large drop sprinklers are special sprinklers with a nominal K-factor of 11.2 ($K_m = 160$). (Nominal K-factors for standard ½ in. [12.7 mm] sprinklers are 5.6 [$K_m = 80$].) The deflector of a large drop sprinkler is specially designed and, combined with the greater discharge, produces large drops of such size and velocity as to enable the spray to penetrate strong updrafts generated by high-challenge fires. The special requirements for large drop sprinklers are found throughout NFPA 13 and are organized by subject category. These special requirements supersede the density/area requirements used for standard spray sprinklers. A representative large drop sprinkler is shown in Figure 16.2.17.

On/Off Sprinklers

On/off sprinklers have two separate operating mechanisms. The first is very similar to a standard sprinkler link. The second is a heat-operated valve or snap disk. When a fire occurs, both operating mechanisms sense the rise in temperature and open up. After the environment around the sprinkler cools, the secondary valve or snap disk senses the drop in pressure and automatically closes, stopping the flow of water. If the fire has not been suppressed and grows again, the secondary valve or snap disk reopens allowing water to flow.

Once an on/off sprinkler has activated, it does need to be replaced. The secondary valve or snap disk will not completely seal the valve and may leak. After activation, the sprinkler may also not be able to handle the surge pressures that might occur in the system.

Currently, no manufacturer makes an on/off sprinkler, but they have been described here because they have been manufactured in the past.

Sprinklers for Corrosive Conditions

Measures have been developed to protect automatic sprinklers from corrosive conditions, and testing organizations have studied the value of each method. A complete covering of wax that has a melting point slightly below the temperature at which the sprinkler operates is the protective coating most commonly used. A lead coating for the body of the sprinkler and the levers in combination with wax for protecting fusible elements is also common. Traditional coatings include wax only (Figure 16.2.18), asphalt only, lead only, wax over lead, and asphalt over lead. In recent years, sprinklers have been listed with enamel, polyester, and Teflon® coatings. Stainless steel sprinklers are available from some manufacturers. Other coatings are also available and should be selected on the basis of the expected environment.

Whatever the protective measures taken, they must not delay the operation of the sprinkler, nor interfere with the

FIGURE 16.2.16 Representative Residential Sprinkler

FIGURE 16.2.17 Representative Large Drop Sprinkler

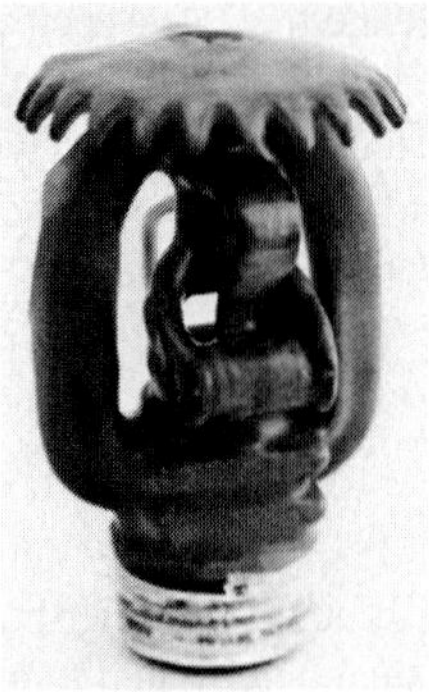

FIGURE 16.2.18 Wax-Coated Upright Sprinkler for Corrosive Atmospheres (Source: Automatic Sprinkler Corporation of America)

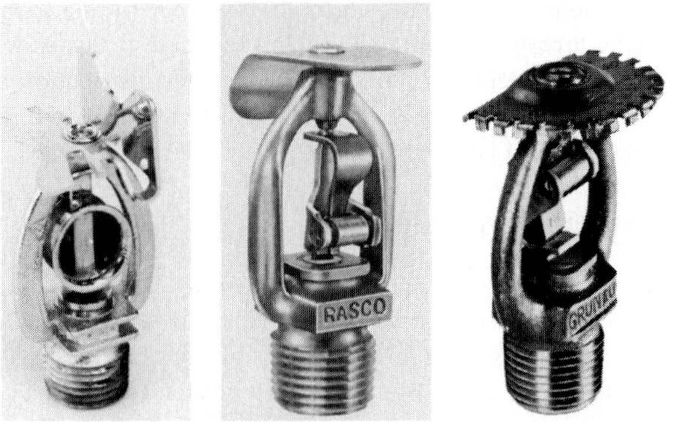

FIGURE 16.2.19 Representative Selection of Listed Sidewall Sprinklers Showing Various Shapes of Deflectors

release of operating parts, nor significantly alter the pattern of water distribution. As with decorative sprinklers, these coatings may also be applied only by the manufacturer.

Sidewall Sprinklers

Sidewall sprinklers have the components of standard sprinklers except for a special deflector, which discharges most of the water toward one side in a pattern somewhat resembling one-quarter of a sphere. A small proportion of the discharge wets the wall behind the sprinkler. Located and mounted either vertically or horizontally along the junction between a ceiling and wall, sidewall sprinklers provide protection adequate for light-hazard occupancies, such as hotel lobbies, dining rooms, and executive offices. Some sidewall sprinklers have been tested and listed for use in ordinary-hazard occupancies.

Sidewall sprinklers are generally used where pipe would be difficult to install in a ceiling. This concern might be the case with certain types of ceiling construction or in retrofit situations in which the building owner does not want to disturb asbestos above an existing ceiling. Sidewall sprinklers are also sometimes used where the space above a ceiling is subjected to cold temperatures in order to keep the sprinkler pipe in a heated space in the wall, rather than in the ceiling space where freezing conditions could be encountered.

The directional character of the discharge from sidewall sprinklers makes them applicable to occasional special protection problems. They may be installed to give discharge in any desired direction.

Figure 16.2.19 shows typical sidewall sprinklers. Selection has been made to show the different shapes of a variety of deflectors. Many vertically mounted sidewall sprinklers may be installed in either the pendent or upright position.

Extended Coverage Sidewall Sprinklers

Extended coverage sidewall sprinklers are used in the horizontal position. They have larger areas of coverage than the areas of coverage allowed for standard sidewall sprinklers. They may be used in light-hazard occupancies, particularly in hotels and similar occupancies where a sprinkler system can be installed in an existing building without having piping exposed in living areas, which could be objectionable aesthetically.

The water pressure required to obtain the greater coverage is specified in the listings for the sprinklers and is greater than that required for standard sidewall sprinklers. Installation requirements are also a part of the listing.

An extended coverage sidewall sprinkler with a conventional link release is shown in Figure 16.2.20.

Open Sprinklers

Automatic sprinklers from which the valve cap and heat-responsive elements have been omitted are used in deluge sprinkler systems where the water supply is controlled by an automatic water control valve actuated independently of the automatic sprinklers (Figure 16.2.21). The water distribution pattern and the density of the discharge are designed to be appropriate for the hazard to be protected.

Small- and Large-Orifice Sprinklers

The terms *small orifice* and *large orifice* are used to describe sprinklers with orifice sizes other than ½ in. ($K = 5.6$). Automatic sprinklers having a water discharge rate greater or less than that of a standard $K = 5.6$ ($K_m = 80$) orifice sprinkler operating at the same pressure have characteristics desirable in protecting certain occupancies. High-discharge, large-orifice sprinklers operating at discharge densities of 0.45 gpm/ft^2 (18 [L/min]/m^2) and greater provide a quantity discharge not available from nominal

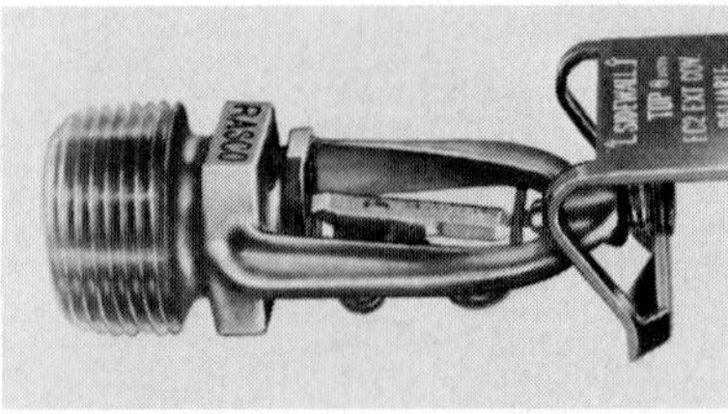

FIGURE 16.2.20 Representative Extended Coverage Sidewall Sprinkler

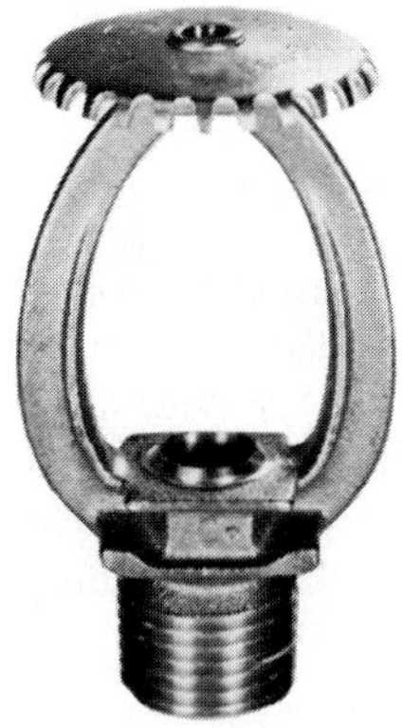

FIGURE 16.2.21 Standard Upright Sprinkler with Its Operating Elements Removed

FIGURE 16.2.22 Representative K = 4.2 (K_m = 60) Sprinkler in the Pendent Position

K = 5.6 (K_m = 80) orifice sprinklers. The pattern of the water discharge from small- and large-orifice sprinklers is similar to that of the standard K = 5.6 (K_m = 80) sprinkler.

Whenever sprinklers are replaced, care must be taken to replace them with the proper styles. Replacement of sprinklers with others of the correct orifice size is critical in hydraulically calculated systems.

Spray Sprinklers with Different Orifice Sizes

For many years, sprinklers have been manufactured with different orifice sizes to achieve different flows at available pressures. The smaller the orifice size, the lower the flow that will discharge from the sprinkler when it opens. The characteristic used for measuring the size of the orifice is called the K-factor, and it represents the mathematical constant relating the flow from the sprinkler at the available pressure as indicated in the following formula:

$$Q = K\sqrt{P}$$

where

Q = Flow in gpm (L/min)

K = Flow constant

P = Pressure in psi (bar)

The K-factor is constant for any given sprinkler, only changing with the diameter and shape of the orifice and waterway leading to the point where water gets discharged from the sprinkler. The standard spray sprinkler developed in the late 1950s had a K-factor in English units of 5.6. In metric units, this sprinkler has a K-factor of 80. Sprinklers with K-factors of 5.6 are still very commonly used.

Sprinklers with orifice sizes smaller than the standard K-factor of 5.6 are available when the designer wishes to restrict the flow into a space (Figure 16.2.22). Typically, this happens where a sprinkler protects a relatively small room, where the density can be achieved at a relatively small pressure. NFPA 13 allows the smaller orifice sprinklers to be used in light-hazard occupancies. The K-factors range from K = 1.4 (K_m = 20) to K = 4.2 (K_m = 60). Where the K-factor is less than 2.8 (K_m = 40), a strainer needs to be installed near the water supply to catch the sediment that might plug a sprinkler with a very small orifice.

Table 16.2.4 shows the various orifice sizes for the sprinklers smaller than the standard K = 5.6 (K_m = 80) sprinkler.

Sprinklers with orifice sizes larger than the standard K = 5.6 (K_m = 80) are available when the designer wishes to get larger flows from the sprinkler at the same pressure (Figure 16.2.23). Another way of looking at the advantages of these sprinklers is that the designer can get the required flow from the sprinkler at a lower pressure.

Sprinklers with larger orifice sizes tend to produce better size water droplets with better droplet momentum than K = 5.6 (K_m = 80) orifice size sprinklers. These larger orifice sprinklers are better at fighting high-challenge fires such as those in storage occupancies, where the water droplets from the sprinklers need to overcome the momentum of the fire plume in order to achieve fire control or suppression. For this reason, starting with the 1999 edition of NFPA 13, restrictions on the use of K = 5.6 (K_m = 80) and K = 8.0 (K_m = 110) sprinklers have been put in place. For storage occupancies, the K = 5.6 (K_m = 80) and K = 8.0 (K_m = 110) sprinklers can be used only where the design density necessary for fire control is relatively small. Table 16.2.5 summarizes the various orifice sizes for the sprinklers larger than the standard K = 5.6 (K_m = 80) sprinkler.

TABLE 16.2.4 Orifice Sizes for Sprinklers Smaller Than K = 5.6

Nominal K-Factor gpm/(psi)$^{1/2}$	*Nominal K-Factor L/min/(bar)$^{1/2}$*	*Percentage of Discharge at Same Pressure Compared to K = 5.6 (K_m = 80) Sprinkler*
1.4	20	25.0
1.9	30	33.3
2.8	40	50.0
4.2	60	75.0
5.6	80	100.0

FIGURE 16.2.23 K = 14 (K_m = 200) Spray Sprinkler (Source: Viking Corporation)

TABLE 16.2.5 Orifice Sizes for Sprinklers Larger Than K = 5.6

Nominal K-Factor gpm/(psi)$^{1/2}$	*Nominal K-Factor L/min/(bar)$^{1/2}$*	*Percentage of Discharge at Same Pressure Compared to K = 5.6 (K_m = 80) Sprinkler*
5.6	80	100
8.0	110	140
11.2	160	200
14.0	200	250
16.8	240	300
19.6	280	350
22.4	320	400
25.2	360	450
28.0	400	500

Discharge characteristics of various large- and small-orifice sprinklers are given in Table 16.2.6.

Picker Trunk Sprinklers

Picker trunk automatic sprinklers have a small, smooth deflector that aids in reducing collections of lint and fiber on the sprinklers when they are placed inside ducts or enclosures where moving air carries such foreign materials in suspension. Freedom from obstruction and a general breakup of the water stream are of more importance than any specific pattern of distribution (Figure 16.2.24).

Intermediate-Level Sprinklers

Intermediate-level sprinklers, also referred to as in-rack sprinklers, have large discs (shields) designed to protect the thermosensitive assembly from the spray of sprinklers suspended at higher levels. Without the protective shields, the impinging

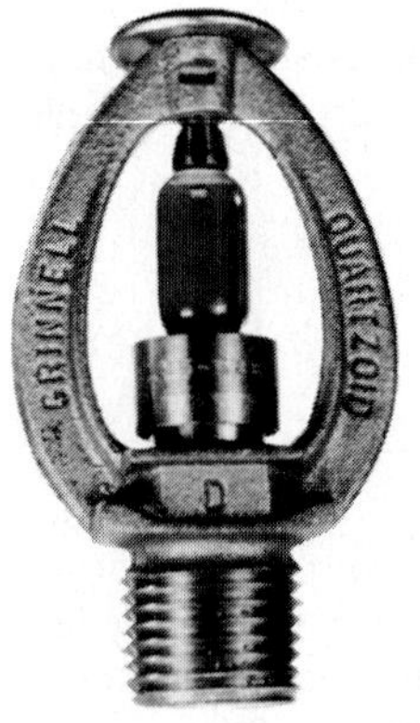

FIGURE 16.2.24 Picker Trunk Sprinkler (Source: Tyco Fire & Building Products)

TABLE 16.2.6 Sprinkler Discharge Characteristics Identification

Nominal K-Factor gpm/(psi)$^{1/2}$	*K-Factor Range gpm/ (psi)$^{1/2}$*	*K-Factor Range dm^3/min/ (kPa)$^{1/2}$*	*Percentage of Nominal K = 5.6 Discharge*	*Thread Type*
1.4	1.3–1.5	1.9–2.2	25.0	½ in. NPT
1.9	1.8–2.0	2.6–2.9	33.3	½ in. NPT
2.8	2.6–2.9	3.8–4.2	50.0	½ in. NPT
4.2	4.0–4.4	5.9–6.4	75.0	½ in. NPT
5.6	5.3–5.8	7.6–8.4	100.0	½ in. NPT
8.0	7.4–8.2	10.7–11.8	140.0	¾ in. NPT or ½ in. NPT
11.2	11.0–11.5	15.9–16.6	200.0	½ in. NPT or ¾ in. NPT
14.0	13.5–14.5	19.5–20.9	250.0	¾ in. NPT
16.8	16.0–17.6	23.1–25.4	300.0	¾ in. NPT
19.6	18.6–20.6	27.2–30.1	350.0	1 in. NPT
22.4	21.3–23.5	31.1–34.3	400.0	1 in. NPT
25.2	23.9–26.5	34.9–38.7	450.0	1 in. NPT
28.0	26.6–29.4	38.9–43.0	500.0	1 in. NPT

Source: NFPA 13, *Standard for the Installation of Sprinkler Systems.*

water could cool the thermosensitive element and retard sprinkler operation. Both upright and pendent intermediate-level sprinklers are listed by testing organizations (Figure 16.2.25).

ESFR Sprinklers

The early suppression fast response (ESFR) sprinkler was developed in the late 1980s and came into widespread use starting in the 1990s for storage occupancies. The ESFR sprinkler was developed to provide fire suppression for high-challenge storage occupancies, usually without the use of in-rack sprinklers. Whereas most sprinklers are designed to provide fire control (and achieve fire suppression as a by-product of good design and extra safety factors), the ESFR sprinkler is designed specifically to provide fire suppression. Although the ESFR sprinkler has many advantages, it does not work for all types of buildings and ceiling construction, so architects and building owners need to make sure that the building and potential obstructions at the ceiling are closely coordinated with the sprinkler installation. Figure 16.2.26 compares an ESFR sprinkler to a standard $K = 5.6$ ($K_m = 80$) spray sprinkler.

Specific Application Control Mode Sprinklers

The specific application control mode sprinkler was developed in the beginning of the twenty-first century to provide more effective fire control of high-challenge storage occupancies, usually without in-rack sprinklers. The specific application control mode sprinkler produces good-quality water droplets with high mass and velocity. The combination of mass and velocity creates water droplets with sufficient momentum to penetrate the fire plumes developed by many storage commodities. Although this sprinkler provides improved protection over standard spray sprinklers, it still is considered a control mode sprinkler, meaning it is designed to control the fire, but may achieve suppression in some circumstances. It is not designed to promise suppression in all cases. Being the newest of the sprinklers developed for storage protection, the types of occupancies that can be protected with this sprinkler are constantly changing. Check with the manufacturer to see whether additional approvals have been developed. Figure 16.2.27 shows an example of a specific application control mode sprinkler.

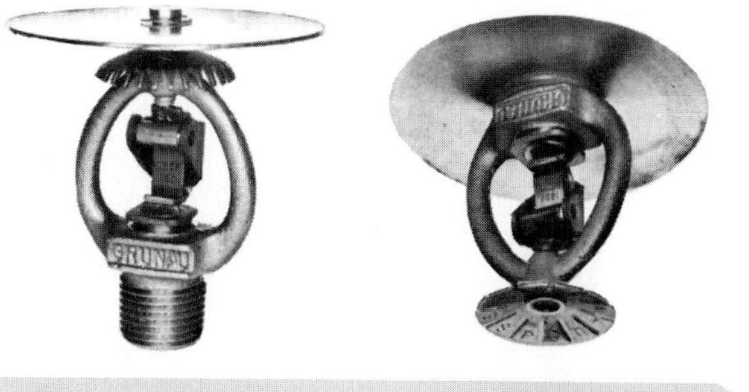

FIGURE 16.2.25 Intermediate-Level (Rack Storage) Sprinklers Showing Integral Shields That Protect Operating Elements from the Discharge of Sprinklers Installed at Higher Levels (Star Model LD)

SUMMARY

The purpose of an automatic sprinkler system is to extinguish a fire or prevent its spread by automatically releasing a stream of water and distributing it over the protected area. The sprinklers

FIGURE 16.2.26 $K = 14$ ($K_m = 200$) ESFR Sprinkler (Left) Compared to $K = 5.6$ ($K_m = 80$) Standard Spray Sprinkler (Right) (Source: Victaulic® is a registered trademark of Victaulic Company)

FIGURE 16.2.27 Specific Application Control Mode Sprinkler (Source: Tyco International)

are fed water through a system of piping and are triggered by predetermined temperatures. Several different types of sprinkler systems have evolved over the years since their introduction in the latter half of the nineteenth century. The type of automatic sprinkler system installed and the settings used depend on many factors, including the purpose of the building (whether residential or commercial) and aesthetic considerations. As fire protection devices, automatic sprinklers have been found to be rugged, mechanically simple, reliable in operation, and generally free from premature operation.

BIBLIOGRAPHY

References Cited

1. Wendt, B., and Prahl, J. M., "Discharge Distribution Performance for an Axisymmetric Model of a Fire Sprinkler Head," NBS-GCR-86-517, Oct. 1986, Case Western Reserve University, sponsored by National Bureau of Standards, Gaithersburg, MD.
2. Thompson, N. J., *Fire Behavior and Sprinklers,* National Fire Protection Association, Quincy, MA, 1964.

NFPA Codes, Standards, and Recommended Practices

Reference to the following NFPA codes, standards, and recommended practices will provide further information on automatic sprinklers discussed in this chapter. (See the latest version of The NFPA Catalog *for availability of current editions of the following documents.)*

NFPA 13, *Standard for the Installation of Sprinkler Systems*

NFPA 13D, *Standard for the Installation of Sprinkler Systems in One- and Two-Family Dwellings and Manufactured Homes*

NFPA 13R, *Standard for the Installation of Sprinkler Systems in Residential Occupancies up to and Including Four Stories in Height*

NFPA 25, *Standard for the Inspection, Testing, and Maintenance of Water-Based Fire Protection Systems*

Chapter 3

Automatic Sprinkler Systems

Revised by
Roland Huggins

Chapter Contents

Key Terms

automatic sprinkler system, ceiling construction, control valve, deluge system, density/area curve, dry pipe system, K-factor, occupancy hazard classification, preaction system, sprinkler spacing, sprinkler system, wet pipe system

The first document published by NFPA, in 1896, provided the initial set of standardized rules for automatic sprinkler systems. The document was awkwardly titled *Rules and Regulations of the National Board of Fire Underwriters for Sprinkler Equipments, Automatic and Open Systems as Recommended by the National Fire Protection Association.* This NFPA document evolved to be NFPA 13, *Standard for the Installation of Sprinkler Systems.*

NFPA 13 provides standardized rules for the design, installation, and acceptance testing of sprinkler systems. Various options are presented for achieving effective sprinkler system performance, including among other considerations the selection of system components such as sprinklers, valves, and piping materials, as well as the determination of the fire hazard to be protected against and the calculation of system discharge rates.

The fundamental principles and assumptions about sprinkler systems have remained fairly consistent over the past century. However, the past 30 years have witnessed significant developments regarding the performance and effectiveness of sprinkler systems in providing life safety and property protection. Although the modern-day version of NFPA 13 is an expansion of the early principles of sprinkler system protection, it includes a much broader scope and addresses the application of many new technologies.

This chapter provides an introduction and overview to the fundamentals of automatic sprinkler systems and describes how the current edition of NFPA 13 has evolved to address a number of situations. The benefits of sprinklers are discussed followed by a review of current rules and practices that are associated with these systems.

Properly designed, installed, and maintained systems are a key element of many fire protection plans integral to modern building design and construction. Suppression, detection, and compartmentation are key safety features that allow buildings of a certain height or area to be constructed. A proper understanding of what sprinkler systems can and cannot do by those designing, installing, and approving such systems is critical to the overall effectiveness of the system.

See also Section 2, Chapter 7, "Theory of Fire Extinguishment"; Section 15, Chapter 1, "Fixed Water Storage Supplies for Fire Protection"; Section 15, Chapter 3, "Hydraulics for Fire Protection"; Section 15, Chapter 6, "Water Distribution"; Section 15, Chapter 7, "Fire Pump Controllers and Power Supply Arrangements for Motor-Driven Fire Pumps"; Section 16, Chapter 1, "Principles of Automatic Sprinkler Performance"; Section 16, Chapter 2, "Automatic Sprinklers"; Section 16, Chapter 5, "Sprinkler Systems for Storage Facilities"; and Section 16, Chapter 6, "Residential Sprinkler Systems."

DEVELOPMENT OF AUTOMATIC SPRINKLERS

A sprinkler is a thermosensitive device that is designed to discharge a certain amount of water in a certain pattern, is only activated when a fire generates a sufficient quantity of heat, and will control or suppress the fire once it has activated. NFPA 13 identifies and defines various types of sprinklers.

Roland Huggins, P.E., is vice-president of engineering and technical services at the American Fire Sprinkler Association and a member of the NFPA Standards Council.

Water is distributed to each sprinkler in the system through a series of specially sized pipes or tubes. Control valves are installed on the system to manually shut off waterflow to all or a portion of the system piping and the sprinklers.

The earliest sprinkler systems consisted of steel pipe networks with drilled holes or perforations provided along the length of pipe. This type of system often involved the use of a manually operated water supply. If the fire occurred when the building was not occupied, the system would be of little or no benefit. Additionally, the piping for these systems was often corroded, the holes were often plugged, and the water discharge from the pipe could generously be described as poor.

A derivative of the perforated pipe involved attachment of an open sprinkler device to the pipe. This improved the water distribution pattern of the system, but concerns with human intervention and corrosion remained.

The concept of employing a heat-actuated device dates back to approximately 1860. However, it was not until 1875 that Henry Parmelee incorporated this concept into a fire sprinkler device. The Parmelee sprinkler is credited as the first "automatic" sprinkler. Although the device was crude when compared to modern sprinklers, it established a specific water distribution pattern that was effective and efficient in controlling a fire. Figure 16.3.1 illustrates the discharge pattern from a Parmelee Number 3 sprinkler. The sprinkler consisted of a brass cap soldered over a perforated distributor and was designed to screw onto a nipple. Figure 16.3.2 shows a cross-sectional view of the Parmelee No. 3 sprinkler.

Other variations of the Parmelee sprinkler soon followed, and each one had a unique shape or form. Some of the sprinklers available when the 1896 edition of NFPA 13 was published include Neracher (Figure 16.3.3), National Manufacturing Company (Figure 16.3.4), New Grinnell (Figure 16.3.5), and Kane (Figure 16.3.6).

The introduction of these new automatic sprinkler devices that did not require human intervention to initiate waterflow prompted greater acceptance and use of sprinkler systems for factories and storage facilities.

VALUE OF AUTOMATIC SPRINKLER PROTECTION

The insurance industry in combination with the Industrial Revolution in the United States can be credited for promulgating and

FIGURE 16.3.1 Discharge of an Early Automatic Sprinkler

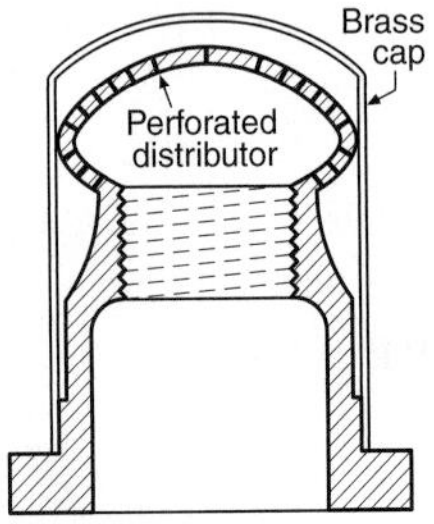

FIGURE 16.3.2 Cross-Sectional View of the Parmelee No. 3 Sprinkler

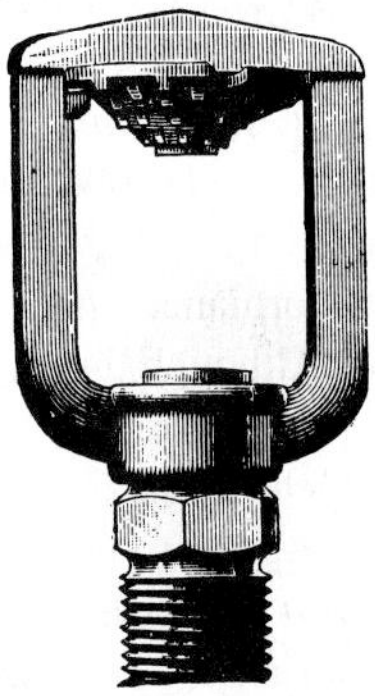

FIGURE 16.3.3 Neracher Sprinkler

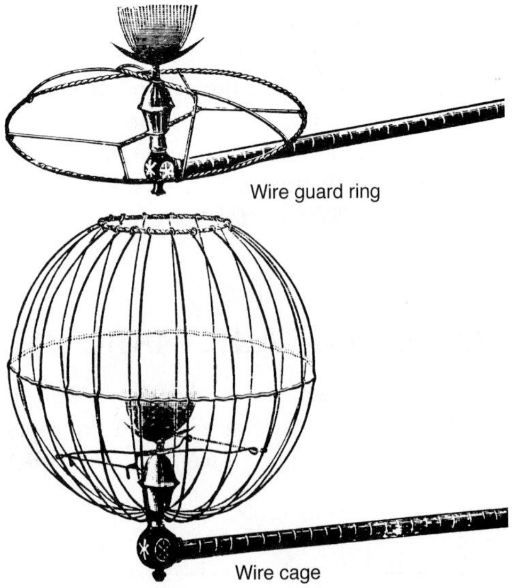

FIGURE 16.3.4 National Manufacturing Company Sprinkler

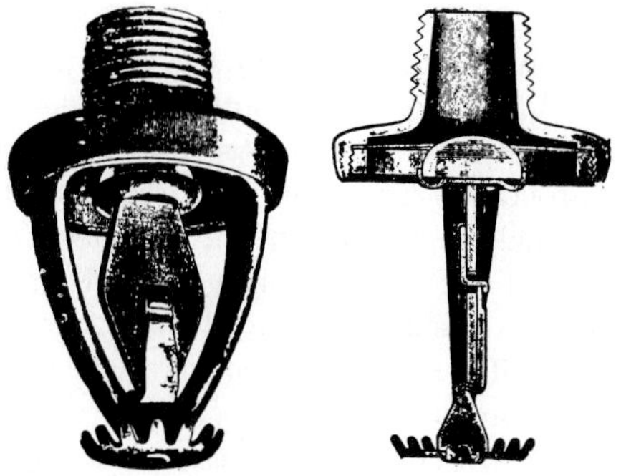

FIGURE 16.3.5 New Grinnell Sprinkler

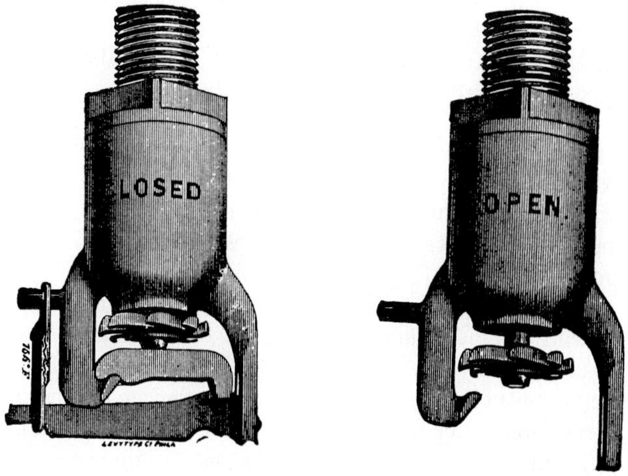

FIGURE 16.3.6 Kane Sprinkler

expanding the use of sprinkler systems. Initial system use was justified by the acute reduction in property loss that was evident in fires involving sprinkler systems when compared to those fire events in which no sprinkler systems were installed.

Because of their immediate recognition as greatly improving property protection risks, high-value facilities such as warehouses and industrial manufacturing facilities were particularly high-priority settings for protection by automatic sprinkler systems. This distinction could even mean the difference between a company staying in business versus not being able to recover from a fire and going out of business.

Although sprinklers were not immediately recognized for their life safety benefits, a trend indicating reductions in fire-related deaths in which sprinkler systems were present became apparent. Large-area, high-rise, high-value, and dense population structures soon became primary facilities where sprinkler systems would be of benefit.

Life Safety Benefits

The life safety benefit of sprinklers is intuitive since sprinkler discharge suppresses or controls a fire, thereby diminishing the threat to the occupants. Additionally, the operation of the sprinkler system sounds an alarm, warning building occupants of a fire condition. Although early sprinkler system designs focused primarily on property protection, the systems did improve the overall life safety features of the building. Current technology provides for numerous types of systems, some of which specifically focus on life safety with property protection as a secondary objective. The residential sprinkler system falls into this category. Section 16, Chapter 6, "Residential Sprinkler Systems," provides information on the development of the residential sprinkler. Although limited to residential occupancies, since its introduction to the marketplace in 1980, the application of the residential sprinkler has been expanded from use in single-family homes to high-rise occupancies such as hotels and apartments. NFPA *101*®, *Life Safety Code*®, and other building codes recognize the life safety benefits of sprinkler systems. Extended travel distances, reductions in rated wall assemblies, and interior finish materials with higher flame-spread ratings are permitted when sprinklers are present. NFPA *101* also mandates sprinkler systems in buildings that fit the high-rise category, as well as those buildings where evacuation of the occupants is impractical, such as health care facilities and some types of nursing homes.

Up until 1970, NFPA maintained a database on the performance and effectiveness of sprinkler systems. Unfortunately, collection of this type of information was discontinued when the data became skewed toward those instances in which large numbers of sprinklers tended to operate or in which the dollar losses were quite large. Such data appeared to indicate that sprinklers were only of marginal value and were not as effective as they actually were. Although substantial dollar losses can occur because of fires in sprinklered buildings, these large losses in sprinklered buildings represent a small percentage of overall fire losses. Furthermore, the majority of devastating fires in sprinklered buildings can usually be attributed to some type of human error, such as failure to maintain the system, rather than a mechanical failure of the system itself.

Even the skewed data, however, showed that a substantial number of fires in sprinklered buildings are controlled or even extinguished with the operation of only one or two sprinklers. Many more of these sprinkler successes control fires with such minimal damage that they are not reported to a fire department or insurance company. It is hoped another data collection program can be instituted in the future with the widespread use of central station alarm systems and the fact that most of today's sprinkler systems are equipped with some type of automatic alarm feature. However, at the time of this writing no formal efforts have been initiated.

Data Sources

Other data sources exist that provide some perspective on the number of sprinklers that operate in certain types of fires. The fewer the number of sprinklers that operate, the more likely that the fire is controlled by the sprinkler system. As previously indicated, the data suggest that a small number of sprinklers tend to control most fires.

NFPA's Fire Analysis and Research Division produces an annual report entitled *U.S. Experience with Sprinklers and Other Fire Extinguishing Equipment.* Table 16.3.1, based on Table 6 of that report, provides information on the number of

TABLE 16.3.1 Number of Sprinklers Operating in Structure Fires Where Sprinklers Were Present and Operated, 1999–2002 Structure Fires (Excluding Confined Fires) Reported in NFIRS Version 5.0 to U.S. Fire Departments

A. By Type of Sprinkler System

Number of Sprinklers Operating	*Wet Pipe (%)*	*Dry Pipe (%)*	*Other Type Sprinkler (%)*
1	65	41	55
2 or fewer	81	56	72
3 or fewer	88	65	83
4 or fewer	91	73	92
5 or fewer	93	77	92
6 or fewer	94	80	96
7 or fewer	95	80	100
8 or fewer	95	82	100
9 or fewer	96	83	100
10 or fewer	97	86	100

Note: These are fires reported to U.S. municipal fire departments and so exclude fires reported only to federal or state agencies or industrial fire brigades. Wet pipe systems outnumbered dry pipe systems 7 to 1. Wet pipe systems outnumbered "other type sprinkler" systems by nearly 30 to 1. However, 38 percent of the incidents had type of sprinkler system unreported. Percentages are based on fires where sprinklers were reported present and operating and there was reported information on number of sprinklers operating.

Source: Rohr, K., *U.S. Experience with Sprinklers and Other Fire Extinguishing Equipment,* Table 6, National Fire Protection Association, Quincy, MA, Aug. 2005.

sprinklers operating in structure fires. The report discusses the benefits of automatic sprinklers and provides comparisons of fires in sprinklered and nonsprinklered buildings.

One of the most compelling points made in the NFPA report is the life safety benefits of sprinkler systems. The following statements are taken directly from the 2005 report:

> NFPA has no record of a fire killing more than two people in a completely sprinklered building where the system was properly operating, except in an explosion or flash fire or where industrial fire brigade members or employees were killed during fire suppression operations.

Another statement that is directed at specific occupancies indicates that:

> NFPA has no record of a fire killing more than two people in a completely sprinklered public assembly, educational, institutional, or residential building where the system was properly operating.

The Fire Analysis and Research report indicates that when fatalities do occur in sprinklered buildings, the victims tend to be in close proximity to the fire or intimate with ignition. In other cases, the victim was incapacitated or otherwise incapable of self-preservation.

The "Fire Watch" column in the *NFPA Journal* usually summarizes one or two stories about sprinkler system performance during a fire. In addition, the information collection process through the National Fire Incident Reporting System (NFIRS), NFPA's data collection survey, and insurance summaries all indicate that sprinklers are a very effective means to reduce fire fatalities and damage. The Fire Analysis and Research report summarizes these data as indicating that sprinklers reduce the chances of dying if fire occurs and the average property damage per fire by one-third to two-thirds.

Because of their effectiveness, various building codes, insurance regulations, and local laws require sprinkler systems in numerous types of buildings. If properly designed, installed, and maintained, sprinkler systems remain among the best options for providing cost-effective life safety and property protection.

FINANCIAL IMPLICATIONS OF SPRINKLER SYSTEM INSTALLATIONS

A number of devastating fires have been investigated by NFPA over the years. In nearly every one of these incidents, findings indicate that the lack of a properly functioning automatic sprinkler system was a key factor in the accelerated rate of fire growth and spread.

When a fire occurs, a certain degree of damage to building contents and the building are expected. These property losses are tangible and can be measured in direct financial terms. However, a somewhat less tangible impact of a fire can be business interruption, which not only affects the business owner and the long-term viability of the enterprise but also the employees and local community. Catastrophic losses to large employers deteriorate the local tax base affecting community services.

Another undesirable outcome of a fire in financial terms can be impending lawsuits in which litigation expenses and judgments can be severe and, when they occur, can exceed other combined direct and indirect losses. This is especially true when a loss of life has occurred. Financial aspects of lawsuits, although typically not a key consideration to most building owners or business owners, can devastate a company, its employees, and ultimately the local community.

Automatic sprinkler systems are designed to operate during the early stages of fire development and minimize the fire's overall impact. In addition, most systems are provided with an electrically supervised waterflow alarm that can automatically notify the fire department when the sprinkler system operates. Although many systems will suppress or even extinguish a fire, it is anticipated that in most cases the fire department or fire brigade will completely extinguish a fire.

Contrary to some Hollywood portrayals and public perceptions of sprinkler system activation in which all sprinklers in a building appear to operate at once, only those sprinklers that are in close proximity to the fire will operate. As previously shown in Table 16.3.1, a relatively small number of sprinklers tend to operate in most fires. Because only those sprinklers near a fire operate, considerably less water damage occurs during a fire when a sprinkler system is present. Where sprinkler systems are not present, fire damage and the magnitude of damage from master streams and other fire-fighting operations are typically more extensive, often considerably.

Nonetheless, water damage and inadvertent system discharge often concern building owners. Reports that cite collateral water damage as larger than the fire damage encourage a misleading comparison. For instance, some news accounts have been selectively prepared, indicating that the fire damage was limited to $1000 whereas the collateral water damage from sprinklers was perhaps $1500. No mention is made about the total value of the contents and the building; no mention is made about no one being injured; and no mention is made of the fatalities that did not occur.

Although inadvertent discharge of water from system piping, valves, or a sprinkler is rare, it can occur. To minimize this possibility, NFPA 13 controls system components to ensure integrity of the system. In addition, NFPA 13 governs a number of methods and techniques that help to protect against such problems. Quality control of installation practices and procedures is also an important consideration. Special materials and methods are specified for use in corrosive atmospheres, areas subject to freezing, and for systems installed in areas requiring seismic protection.

Some Incentives for Sprinklers

The major incentive for installing sprinkler systems can be directed toward the system's inherent highly effective and cost-efficient life safety and property protection features. However, direct financial benefits can also be realized by property owners. Many insurance carriers offer reduced premiums for fully sprinklered facilities. In addition, the cost of sprinkler system design and installation can often be amortized over the life of the building.

Although sprinkler systems are mandatory in many types of buildings, most building codes permit certain construction modifications when systems are installed. These modifications include increases to building heights and areas, reductions to fire-resistance ratings for partitions, and reductions in physical separations between adjacent structures. These changes often offset the cost of the sprinkler system.

Installing sprinkler systems in existing buildings also greatly improves overall fire and life safety and offsets previous fire protection concerns. Although installing sprinklers after building construction has been completed is more costly, laws mandating sprinkler systems on a retroactive basis usually allow for the installation to be phased over time. This permits building owners to coordinate the installation with other building upgrades and renovations.

STANDARDS FOR INSTALLING SPRINKLERS

NFPA 13, *Standard for the Installation of Sprinkler Systems,* is the principal document that addresses the design and installation of sprinkler systems. Although considered by some to be a variation of a plumbing system, they are not. Sprinkler systems are unique systems requiring specialized knowledge for their proper design, installation, and maintenance.

NFPA 13 is categorized as a standard and, therefore, specifies the rules and other information necessary for the proper design, layout, and installation of sprinkler systems. NFPA 13 does not specify the types of facilities or buildings in which sprinkler systems are required. This requirement is addressed by building codes, NFPA *101,* and other regulations.

In 1999, NFPA 13 underwent a major expansion and restructuring. Although still containing requirements concerning water supply, allowable materials and components, sprinkler placement and location, discharge criteria, working plans and calculation procedures, the document's scope has been greatly expanded to include sprinkler system information from over 40 other NFPA codes and standards. This extracted information, though, is still controlled by the original technical committee and is simply copied in NFPA 13.

Effective with the 1999 edition, all requirements pertaining to the design and installation of automatic sprinkler systems were, to the extent possible, centralized in NFPA 13. The scope of NFPA 13 was expanded to include sprinkler system design and installation requirements for storage facilities, formerly located in the NFPA 231 series of documents (NFPA 231 was titled *Standard for General Storage*). The design and installation requirements for underground piping and private fire service mains from NFPA 24, *Standard for the Installation of Private Fire Service Mains and Their Appurtenances,* were also included.

The 1999 edition incorporated sprinkler system information copied from other NFPA standards to assist NFPA 13 users with the design and installation of automatic sprinkler systems for hazards and facilities not previously addressed by NFPA 13. Sprinkler system information from over 40 NFPA codes, standards, and recommended practices is cited in NFPA 13. For example, sprinkler system information specific to solvent extraction plans, laboratories using chemicals, and fixed guideway transit systems, among others, are included. The 2002 edition improved the ability to find this extracted information by incorporating it into one chapter. NFPA 13 continues to expand and refine criteria. Another change made in the 2002 edition was a restructuring of the hanging and bracing chapter. Restructuring continued into the 2007 edition where the presentation of the storage criteria was divided into nine chapters.

A number of assumptions have been employed in the writing of NFPA 13 to achieve an acceptable level of life safety and property protection while maintaining costs. For instance, the standard anticipates a single fire source, that is, no multiple ignitions in the building while the sprinkler system is operating. Nor does NFPA 13 address the likelihood of a fire occurring in one space area as opposed to another area. NFPA 13 treats the likelihood of a fire occurring in any given space on an equal footing regardless of the actual probabilities of ignition. For these reasons, the fundamental design principal that only a certain number of operating sprinklers are needed to control a given fire exists. In other words, it is only those sprinklers in the general vicinity of the fire that are expected to operate and discharge water.

A fundamental premise about buildings also serves as a basis for NFPA 13 criteria. Effective system design is a direct function of the building contents and the fire hazard associated with the contents. Building construction materials do not impact the assigned discharge density. For example, a building of concrete construction does not receive any special preference when compared to a building of wood construction. The use and associated hazard of the contents of the building need to receive primary consideration when initiating a sprinkler system design. The structure does play a significant role in defining the type of allowed sprinklers, the minimum area of coverage, minimum starting pressure, and other installation criteria. For instance, an attic is a light-hazard occupancy but the area of coverage can be as low as 120 ft^2 (11.1 m^2) instead of the possible 400 ft^2 (37.2 m^2), as well as having a minimum starting pressure of 20 psi (1.4 bar) instead of the usual 7 psi (0.5 bar).

Although NFPA 13 serves as the primary resource for sprinkler system design and installation around the world, other documents also address sprinkler systems. Many of these documents fall within NFPA's fire codes set and address sprinkler system protection for specific hazards, building uses, and safety objectives. For example, NFPA 30, *Flammable and Combustible Liquids Code,* addresses the storage of flammable and combustible liquids; NFPA 851, *Recommended Practice for Fire Protection for Hydroelectric Generating Plants,* addresses hydroelectric generating plants; and NFPA *101* addresses the use of a sprinkler system solely for life safety purposes. Starting with the 1999 edition of NFPA 13, other NFPA documents that deal with sprinkler system design and installation are specifically referenced. In addition to NFPA's documents, local and national building codes may also address sprinkler system design and installation to some degree. Other nations and some insurance companies also maintain their own sprinkler system rules.

Terminology

Because of the complexity associated with the various aspects of sprinkler system design and installation, NFPA 13 defines various terms to establish a degree of consistency and uniformity. Some of the more prevalent terms are paraphrased here.

The most fundamental term, *sprinkler system,* is described as a combination of underground and overhead piping that is connected to an automatic water supply. The piping is specially sized or hydraulically designed with that portion of the piping within the building generally located overhead. Sprinklers are attached to the overhead piping in a systematic pattern and a valve controlling each riser is located either directly on the system riser or in the supply piping. The system is usually activated by heat from a fire and discharges water over the fire area. A device actuating an alarm when the system operates is located on the system riser. Figure 16.3.7 illustrates various aboveground and buried components that can comprise a fire sprinkler system. Note that the rules addressing fire pumps and water storage tanks can be found in NFPA 20, *Standard for the Installation of Stationary Pumps for Fire Protection,* and NFPA 22, *Standard for Water Tanks for Private Fire Protection,* respectively. The criteria from NFPA 24 is repeated in NFPA 13.

System Types

Most sprinkler systems fall within one of four categories. These include (1) wet pipe, (2) dry pipe, (3) preaction, and (4) deluge with the wet pipe being the most common. The need to use one type of system rather than another depends on the environmental conditions in which the system will be used and the nature of the space being protected.

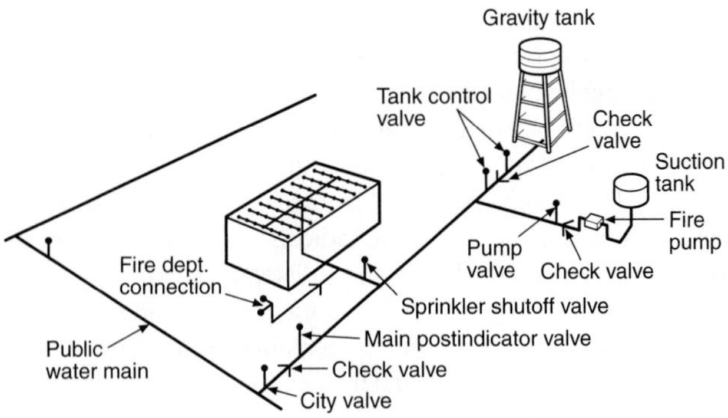

FIGURE 16.3.7 Hypothetical Sprinkler System Installation Illustrating Various Water Supply Sources and System Attachments

Wet Pipe System. This type of system is the preferred, most reliable option. It is also the easiest to design and install and the simplest to maintain. Wet pipe systems contain water under pressure at all times and utilize a series of closed sprinklers. When a fire occurs and produces a sufficient amount of heat to activate one or more sprinklers, because an automatic water supply is mandated, water immediately discharges from the open sprinklers. Wet pipe systems should be the first choice of designers and installers because they are more inherently reliable and less costly to maintain. However, wet pipe systems should not be considered when temperatures to which the system could be exposed fall below 40°F (4°C). Figure 16.3.8 illustrates a basic wet pipe system.

Dry Pipe System. These systems should only be used when system components will be exposed to temperatures below 40°F (4°C). System piping contains no water prior to system activation but rather is charged with air or nitrogen under pressure. These systems experience more internal corrosion than a wet pipe system due to moisture in the air and constant replenishment of oxygen. A dry pipe valve holds back the water supply and serves as the water/air interface. Most listed dry pipe valves act on a pressure differential principle, in which the surface area of the valve face on the air side is greater than the surface area on the water side. Figure 16.3.9 shows a typical dry pipe valve. There are also many dry pipe valves that use a latching mechanism and a pressure differential.

If a fire occurs and a sufficient amount of heat is generated, one or more sprinklers operate, causing system air pressure to drop. Once the air pressure falls below a predetermined level, the dry pipe valve opens, allowing water to flow through the system to the open sprinklers. Dry pipe systems are more complex than wet pipe systems. They require a reliable air supply source and, because of the delay associated with water delivery from

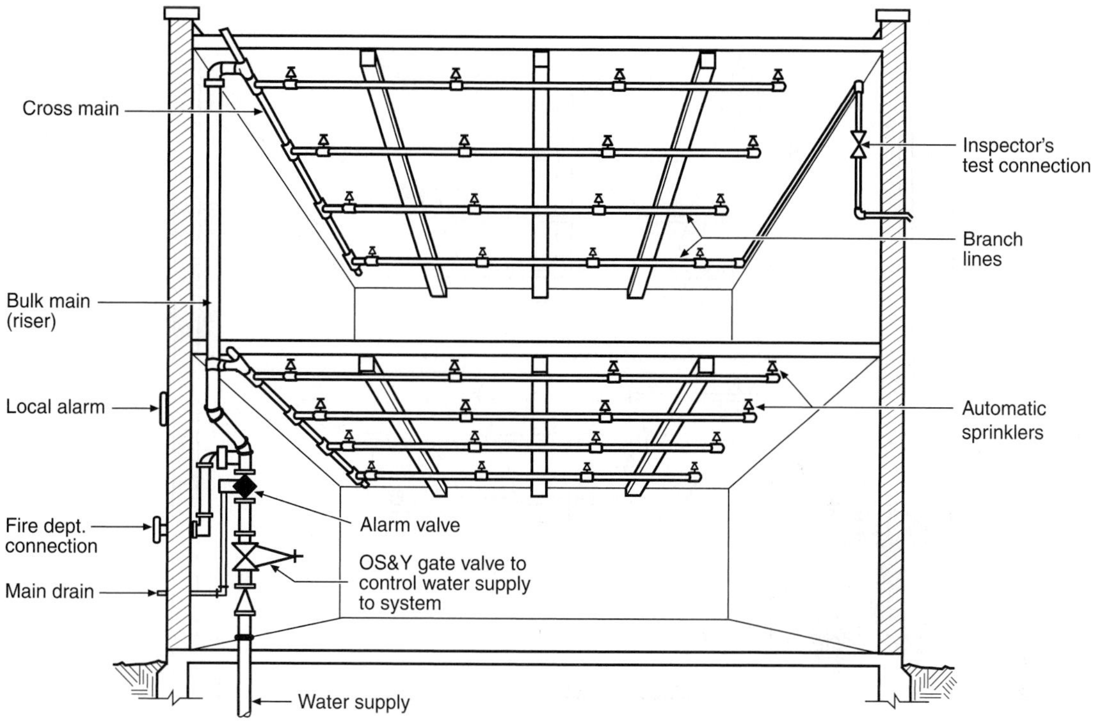

FIGURE 16.3.8 Basic Components of a Wet Pipe Sprinkler System

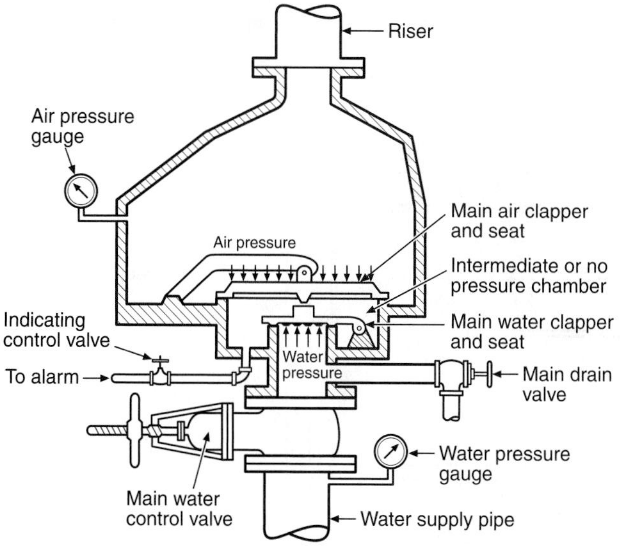

FIGURE 16.3.9 Typical Dry Pipe Valve

the dry pipe valve to the open sprinklers, are subject to certain design limitations. These limitations can include restriction of system size, the need for additional components such as accelerators, and the need for a larger design area due to an increase in the number of anticipated operating sprinklers.

In addition to serving as stand-alone systems, dry pipe systems can comprise a subsystem of a larger wet pipe system in which small coolers and loading docks need to be protected. Figure 16.3.10 illustrates a hypothetical dry pipe system.

Preaction System. Similar to a dry pipe system, a standard or single-interlock preaction system piping is charged with air under pressure rather than water. However, the air pressure associated with preaction systems is generally less than that for dry pipe systems. It also experiences a greater amount of internal corrosion. The water supply is held back by means of a preaction valve. The system is equipped with a supplemental detection system. Operation of the detection system allows the preaction valve to automatically open and admit water into the pipe network. Water will not discharge from the system until a fire has generated a sufficient quantity of heat to cause operation of one or more sprinklers. In essence, the system appears as a wet pipe system once the preaction valve operates. Figure 16.3.11 shows a typical preaction system.

Air pressure maintained in the piping is used to monitor the integrity of the pipe. If the pipe develops a leak, the air pressure will drop and an alarm will sound, indicating a low air-pressure condition. Because water is held back with a preaction valve rather than a dry pipe valve, water will not flow into the system until the supplemental fire detection system operates, signaling the preaction valve to open. The preaction valve stays in its normal position until the detection system is activated.

A variation of the single-interlock preaction system is the double-interlock preaction system. The double-interlock system has characteristics of both the single-interlock system and the dry pipe system. For water to enter the system piping both the

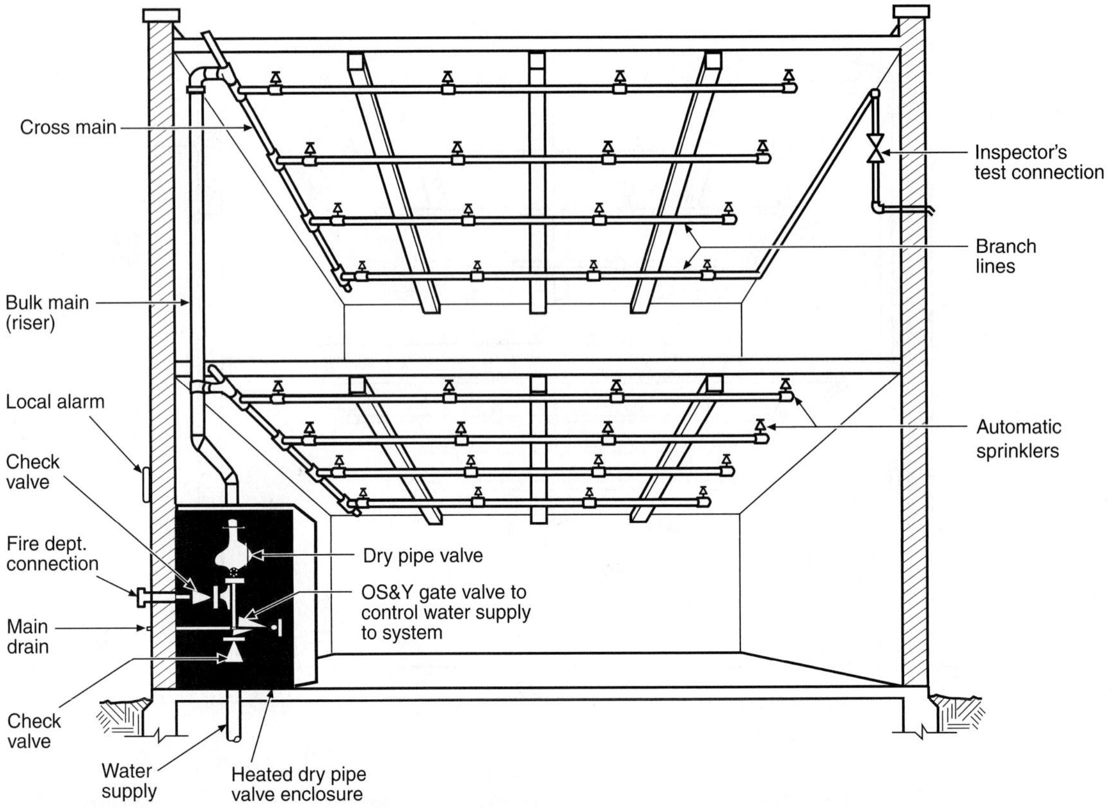

FIGURE 16.3.10 Hypothetical Dry Pipe System

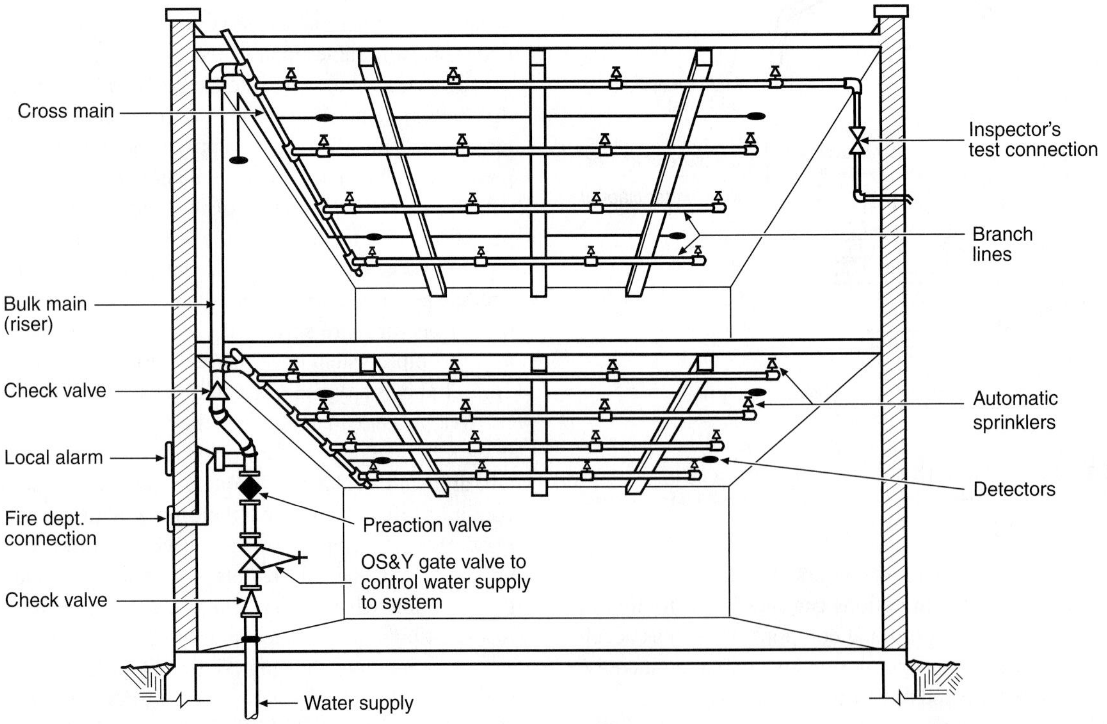

FIGURE 16.3.11 Typical Preaction Sprinkler System

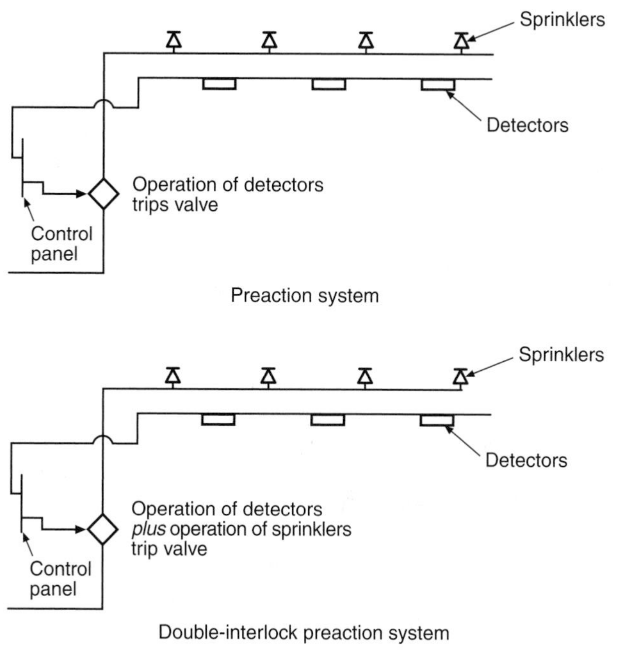

FIGURE 16.3.12 Comparison of Operating Features for the Types of Preaction Systems

supplemental detection system and the sprinklers on the system must operate. Figure 16.3.12 illustrates the double-interlock arrangement. Another variation of a preaction system is the noninterlock system in which either activation of the supplemental detection system or a sprinkler initiates waterflow through the system. Preaction systems are typically found in spaces containing computer or communications equipment, museums, and other facilities where inadvertent water leakage from system piping is of major concern. The double-interlock system is most common in deep-freeze facilities where accidental valve operation can result in the almost immediate freezing and damage of system piping.

Deluge Systems. Deluge systems, as the name implies, deliver large quantities of water over specified areas in a relatively short period of time. These systems are used to protect against rapidly growing and spreading fires. Sprinklers used in a deluge system do not contain thermally sensitive operating elements and are referred to as open sprinklers. A deluge valve controls the system water supply and is activated by a supplemental fire detection system. Because open sprinklers are employed, system piping is at atmospheric pressure. As water reaches each sprinkler in the system, it is immediately discharged from the system.

The nature of this system makes it appropriate for facilities in which significant amounts of highly combustible materials are present. The system is also used for situations in which thermal damage is likely to occur in a relatively short period of time. Aircraft hangars are one area of application of deluge systems. Figure 16.3.13 shows a typical deluge system.

Other Systems. Several variations to each one of these four basic systems exist. One such system is the antifreeze system that is essentially a wet pipe system with a certain amount of antifreeze concentrate added to provide a degree of protection

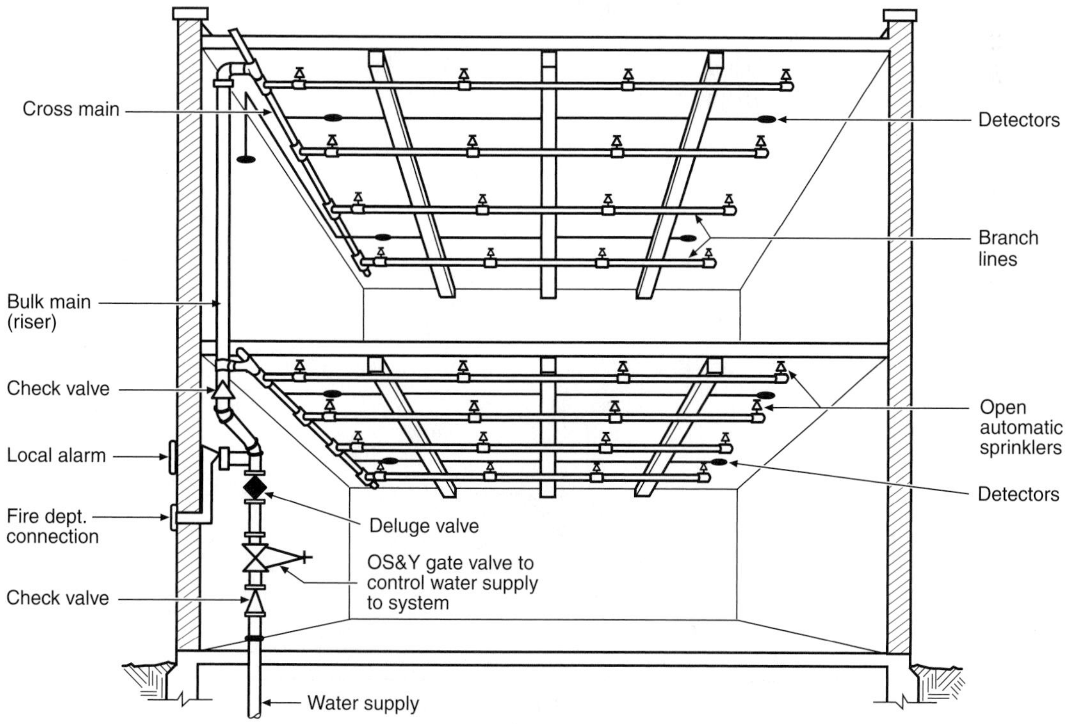

FIGURE 16.3.13 Deluge System

against freezing. Because of the cost associated with these systems, antifreeze systems are usually used to protect smaller spaces exposed to cold temperatures such as outside loading docks or exterior canopies. There has been an increased use of antifreeze for large systems protecting freezers with early suppression fast-response (ESFR) sprinklers. NFPA 13 specifies which types of antifreeze can be used and the percentage of concentrate needed.

Design Objectives

In general terms of property protection, sprinkler systems are typically designed to achieve fire control, although certain types of sprinklers allow for fire suppression to be attained in certain storage arrangements. Fire control can be described as limiting the fire size by decreasing the rate of heat release and prewetting adjacent combustibles, while maintaining ceiling gas temperatures so as to avoid structural damage. Fire suppression can be described as a sharp reduction in the heat release rate to a point at which regrowth is not possible as a result of the application of large quantities of water through the fire plume to the surface of the burning fuel. Figure 16.3.14 provides a graphical representation of these phenomena in terms of the rate of heat release as a function of time.

Where property protection is a secondary objective, options for designing systems targeted principally at life safety within the room of fire origin exist for certain types of facilities. Because property protection is typically more difficult to achieve than is life safety, more cost-effective systems can be considered, but it must be recognized that these systems might not provide the same degree of property protection in all circumstances. Systems targeted for life safety employ residential sprinklers that are intended to maintain a tenable environment in the room of fire origin. The use of residential sprinklers is limited to residential-type facilities. Since their development in the mid-1980s, building codes and NFPA *101* have mandated the use of residential sprinklers or quick-response sprinklers in apartments, hotels, and patient care rooms in health care environments. Both property protection and a higher level of life safety can be provided where facilities are protected throughout in accordance with NFPA 13 and quick-response sprinklers are used.

Occupancy Hazard Classification

To a large degree, the occupancy hazard classifications form the basis of the design and installation criteria of NFPA 13. The occupancy hazards provide a convenient means of categorizing the fuel loads and fire severity associated with certain building operations. The classifications also present a relationship between the burning characteristics of these fuels and the ability of a sprinkler system to control the associated types of fires. The likelihood of ignition is not considered in the occupancy classifications.

NFPA 13 defines three fundamental hazard levels: (1) light hazard, (2) ordinary hazard, and (3) extra hazard. These are defined in a subjective manner and generally focus on the heat release rate and the quantity of combustible fuel. The ordinary-hazard and extra-hazard categories are both subdivided into Group 1 and Group 2 categories. Larger quantities of fuel are typically present in the respective Group 2 categories. As previously stated, the properties of the contents in the building rather than the materials of construction of the building determine the classification. An extensive list of examples of various buildings is placed in the annex of NFPA 13. Defining the hazard is, thus, the first step in selecting and designing the system.

Some examples of occupancies in each of these classifications are as follows:

Light Hazard

- Office buildings
- Schools

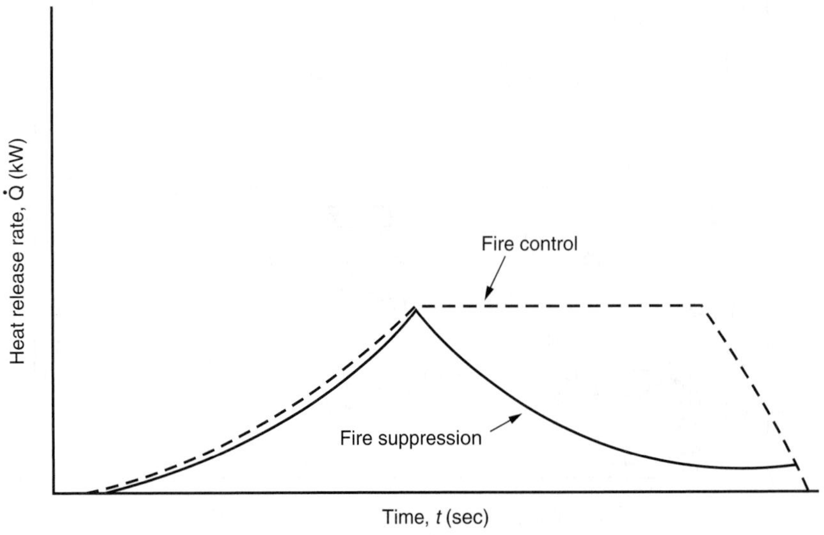

FIGURE 16.3.14 Simplified Fire Control/Fire Suppression Analogy

- Residential occupancies
- Public assembly

Ordinary Hazard

- Canneries (Group 1)
- Electronics plants (Group 1)
- Restaurant service areas (Group 1)
- Dry cleaners (Group 2)
- Library—large stack rooms (Group 2)
- Repair garages (Group 2)
- Wood product assembly (Group 2)

Extra Hazard

- Combustible fluid use area (Group 1)
- Printing that uses inks with flashpoints below 100°F (38°C) (Group 1)
- Upholstering with plastic foams (Group 1)
- Flammable liquids spraying (Group 2)
- Manufactured home assembly (Group 2)
- Plastics processing (Group 2)

Although the occupancy hazard classifications in NFPA 13 address a large majority of building operations, they are not all-encompassing. Certain building operations fall outside the scope of the occupancy hazard classifications and must be treated differently. One such instance includes storage facilities. Where large amounts of materials are stored in a building, the associated fire hazard of the contents in terms of determining appropriate sprinkler system protection is described through commodity classifications. Section 16, Chapter 5, "Sprinkler Systems for Storage Facilities," provides more information in this regard. A similar situation also holds true where flammable and combustible liquids are stored. NFPA 30 provides more information in this regard. Additionally, NFPA 13 further identifies those building operations that require special consideration in terms of either sprinkler system design or installation.

Ceiling Construction

Ceiling construction in terms of the depth, spacing, and openness of the structural and other members affects a sprinkler's activation time and discharge pattern and, therefore, must be considered when placing and positioning sprinklers throughout the building. A sprinkler's allowable area of coverage and the distance below the ceiling will be affected by the ceiling construction classification.

NFPA 13 considers two types of ceiling construction: (1) obstructed and (2) unobstructed. Obstructed construction includes ceiling members that can substantially impede heat flow or water distribution in such a manner that the ability of the sprinkler to suppress or control the fire can be more easily compromised. Under unobstructed construction, ceiling members have less of an impact on sprinkler activation and discharge pattern. NFPA 13 defines unobstructed construction as follows:

- Openings in the member must be at least 70 percent of the cross-sectional area.
- Depth of the member does not exceed the smallest dimension of the openings.
- The members are spaced more than 7 ft 6 in. (2.3 m) on center.

Figure 16.3.15 illustrates an example of obstructed and unobstructed general construction. Within the unobstructed ceiling types, there is a subcategory called smooth ceilings. Some sprinklers, such as the sidewall type, are restricted to just smooth ceilings.

SYSTEM COMPONENTS AND MATERIALS

Maintaining integrity and reliability of a sprinkler system is accomplished in a number of ways. This includes restricting the types and quality of materials and components that comprise the system. As a general rule, NFPA 13 requires that almost all system components, such as sprinklers, valves, and pipe hangers, be listed. While specifically defined by NFPA 13, being listed implies that the equipment and materials to be used on the system have been evaluated by a third party for their intended purpose and marked as such.

Sprinklers

Sprinklers must be listed, and only new sprinklers are permitted for use. Various types of sprinklers are available on the worldwide market. Table 16.3.2 identifies certain sprinkler characteristics. One of these characteristics is the K-factor, which describes the size and angle for the inlet of the sprinkler's orifice (Table 16.3.3). Although sprinklers can be used to protect against various types of fire hazards as classified by NFPA 13, it must be recognized that there might be limitations on the use of a given sprinkler. For example, sprinklers with a K-factor smaller than 5.6 are limited to light-hazard occupancies. Additionally,

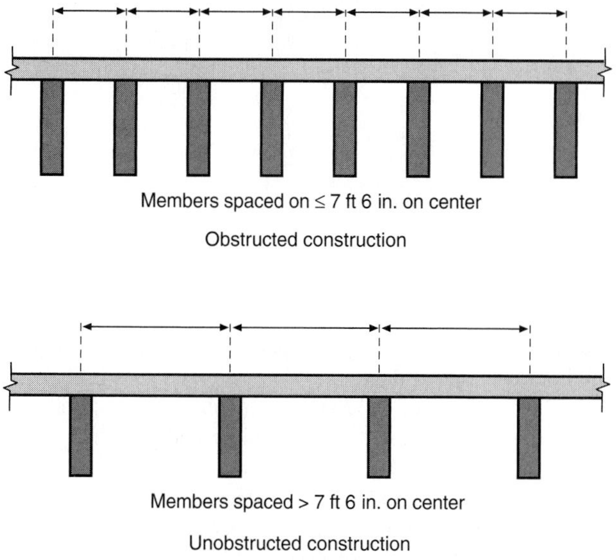

FIGURE 16.3.15 (Top) Obstructed Construction, (Bottom) Unobstructed Construction

TABLE 16.3.2 Sprinkler Discharge Characteristics Identification

Nominal K-Factor gpm/(psi)$^{1/2}$	*K-Factor Range gpm/(psi)$^{1/2}$*	*K-Factor Range dm^3/min/(kPa)$^{1/2}$*	*Percentage of Nominal K = 5.6 Discharge*	*Thread Type*
1.4	1.3–1.5	1.9–2.2	25.0	½ in. NPT
1.9	1.8–2.0	2.6–2.9	33.3	½ in. NPT
2.8	2.6–2.9	3.8–4.2	50.0	½ in. NPT
4.2	4.0–4.4	5.9–6.4	75.0	½ in. NPT
5.6	5.3–5.8	7.6–8.4	100.0	½ in. NPT
8.0	7.4–8.2	10.7–11.8	140.0	¾ in. NPT ½ in. NPT
11.2	11.0–11.5	15.9–16.6	200.0	½ in. NPT ¾ in. NPT
14.0	13.5–14.5	19.5–20.9	250.0	¾ in. NPT
16.8	16.0–17.6	23.1–25.4	300.0	¾ in. NPT
19.6	18.6–20.6	27.2–30.1	350.0	1 in. NPT
22.4	21.3–23.5	31.1–34.3	400.0	1 in. NPT
25.2	23.9–26.5	34.9–38.7	450.0	1 in. NPT
28.0	26.6–29.4	38.9–43.0	500.0	1 in. NPT

Source: NFPA 13, *Standard for the Installation of Sprinkler Systems.*

TABLE 16.3.3 Nominal Sprinkler Orifice Sizes

Nominal K-Factor	Nominal Orifice Size *in.*	*mm*
1.4	1/4	6.4
1.9	5/16	8.0
2.8	3/8	9.5
4.2	7/16	11.0
5.6	1/2	12.7
8.0	17/3	13.5
11.2	5/8	15.9
14.0	3/4	19.0
16.8	—	—
19.6	—	—
22.4	—	—
25.2	—	—
28.0	—	—

Source: NFPA 13, *Standard for the Installation of Sprinkler Systems.*

the type of system, such as dry pipe, can require the use of a minimum K-factor value.

The 5.6 K-factor or ½-inch (12.7-mm) orifice sprinkler is considered the standard orifice sprinkler and generally serves as a benchmark against which to compare the discharge of other sprinklers. Sprinklers with K-factors less than 5.6 have traditionally been considered small orifice sprinklers. Sprinklers with K-factors larger than 5.6 traditionally have been referred to as large, extra large, and very extra large orifice sprinklers. However, the current trend is to develop sprinklers with larger and larger K-factors, the largest currently at 25. Thus, the terms *large orifice* and *extra large orifice* have lost their meaning and are no longer used.

Sprinklers must also satisfy other criteria concerning thread type and marking. Sprinkler manufacturers and listing laboratories are bound to some degree to the limits of NFPA 13. For example, a sprinkler with a K-factor of 14 cannot have a ½ in. (12.7 mm) NPT thread. Restrictions on thread type and orifice diameter are imposed on larger sprinklers because of the poor hydraulic features associated with flowing large quantities of water through a relatively small opening.

Another feature of the sprinkler that is governed by NFPA 13 is the temperature rating, as indicated in Table 16.3.4. The first column indicates the maximum ambient temperature to which the sprinkler is expected to be exposed. As the expected ambient temperature increases, sprinklers with higher temperature ratings need to be used. For example, where the ambient temperature during any given day can be expected to exceed 100°F, such as a non-air-conditioned warehouse in one of the southern states, ordinary temperature rated sprinklers cannot be used. For the most part, sprinklers with higher temperature ratings, such as ultrahigh, are intended for use around process equipment that generates substantial amounts of heat.

Although the general provisions outlined in Table 16.3.4 apply in most situations, there are additional situations in which higher temperature ratings are necessary. The installation rules in NFPA 13 govern these situations and identify conditions in which higher temperature rated sprinklers are needed, such as under skylights.

As noted in Table 16.3.4, sprinklers are color coded to facilitate the identification of the temperature rating. Eutectic metal or solder-type sprinklers use the color scheme in the next to last column, whereas glass-bulb sprinklers use the color scheme in the last column. The liquid in a glass-bulb sprinkler is basically a low-boiling-point alcohol. An air bubble within the glass bulb

TABLE 16.3.4 Temperature Ratings, Classifications, and Color Codings

Maximum Ceiling Temperature		Temperature Rating				
°F	°C	°F	°C	*Temperature Classification*	*Color Code*	*Glass Bulb Colors*
100	38	135–170	57–77	Ordinary	Uncolored or black	Orange or red
150	66	175–225	79–107	Intermediate	White	Yellow or green
225	107	250–300	121–149	High	Blue	Blue
300	149	325–375	163–191	Extra high	Red	Purple
375	191	400–475	204–246	Very extra high	Green	Black
475	246	500–575	260–302	Ultrahigh	Orange	Black
625	329	650	343	Ultrahigh	Orange	Black

Source: NFPA 13, *Standard for the Installation of Sprinkler Systems.*

is volume controlled to achieve a certain temperature rating. The larger the bubble, the higher the operating temperature. The liquid is dyed the appropriate color to correspond to the color code system in the table. Selection of the correct temperature rating for the environment is critical to ensure that sprinklers will not operate during nonfire conditions.

Sprinklers can be manufactured with special coatings to improve their corrosion resistance or aesthetic qualities. Sprinklers installed in corrosive atmospheres can be lead- or wax-coated or made of stainless steel to provide protection against premature corrosion. Sprinklers with special finish coatings are also available and can enhance the architectural features of a space. The choice of coating can be restricted by the type of sprinkler. For instance, quick-response sprinklers cannot be wax-coated.

In both the case of listed corrosion-resistant sprinklers and sprinklers with special decorative finishes, such finishes may only be applied by the manufacturer. Under no circumstance can sprinklers be "field coated" with any type of material. Sprinklers that have been coated or painted must be replaced. Such coatings may impair the spray pattern of the sprinkler or they may react with some functional part of the sprinkler assembly, such as the operating element or the Teflon® seal, which is used to seat the orifice cap on the orifice.

Pipe and Tube

A number of piping materials are acceptable for use in sprinkler systems. Steel, copper, and nonmetallic pipe materials are currently addressed by NFPA 13. These pipe materials must meet certain pipe manufacturing standards, certain listing requirements, or both. Limiting the types of pipe that are acceptable for use will increase reliability of not only the system installation, but it will also ensure the integrity of the system piping during a fire. In addition to identifying the type of pipe materials that can be used, NFPA 13 also specifies how the pipe is to be joined.

Steel Pipe. Steel pipe has been a viable option for use in sprinkler systems since the first edition of NFPA 13, published in 1896. Steel pipe of at least schedule 10 wall thickness manufactured in compliance with certain ASTM (American Society for Testing and Materials) standards as specified by NFPA 13 and summarized in Table 16.3.5 is not required to be listed. However, this does not preclude a manufacturer from having steel pipe specifically listed for fire protection service.

Copper Tube. Copper tube was first discussed as an optional material for sprinkler systems in 1954. Concern over the failure of solder materials or the brazing materials used to join the copper tube was expressed as being a potential failure point of the system during a fire. Joint research by the listing laboratories and the Copper Development Association addressed those concerns, and recommendations were made to restrict the types of brazing material and solder materials. Table 16.3.6 indicates the relevant standards for both copper tube and the joining materials. Copper tube systems have been installed in a large number of buildings. Some notable buildings with copper systems are the Trans-America building in San Francisco, the Monterey Aquarium, and the Library of Congress.

Nonmetallic Pipe. NFPA 13 previously identified two types of plastic pipe for use in sprinkler systems. Polybutylene (PB)

TABLE 16.3.5 Pipe or Tube Materials and Dimensions

Materials and Dimensions	*Standard*
Ferrous Piping (Welded and Seamless)	
Specification for Black and Hot-Dipped Zinc Coated (Galvanized) Welded and Seamless Steel Pipe for Fire Protection Use	ASTM A795
Specification for Welded and Seamless Steel Pipe	ANSI/ASTM A53
Wrought Steel Pipe	ANSI B36.10M
Specification for Elec.-Resistance Welded Steel Pipe	ASTM A135

Source: NFPA 13, *Standard for the Installation of Sprinkler Systems.*

TABLE 16.3.6 Pipe or Tube Materials and Dimensions

Materials and Dimensions	*Standard*
Copper Tube (Drawn, Seamless)	
Specification for Seamless Copper Tube	ASTM B75
Specification for Seamless Copper Water Tube	ASTM B88
Specification for General Requirements for Wrought Seamless Copper and Copper-Alloy Tube	ASTM B251
Fluxes for Soldering Applications of Copper and Copper Alloy Tube	ASTM B813
Brazing Filler Metal (Classification BCuP-3 or BCuP-4)	AWS A5.8
Solder Metal, 95-5 (Tin-Antimony-Grade 95TA)	ASTM B32
Alloy Materials	ASTM B446

Source: NFPA 13, *Standard for the Installation of Sprinkler Systems.*

pipe was first listed for use in systems in NFPA 13D, *Standard for the Installation of Sprinkler Systems in One- and Two-Family Dwellings and Manufactured Homes,* in 1984. An obvious concern with plastic pipe is failure when exposed to fire and even its possible contribution to fire growth. This concern was addressed by requiring the pipe to be installed behind a protective membrane. Such a protective barrier would shield the pipe from direct heat exposure. The exposing temperature would be expected to be substantially decreased, since the operating sprinkler would be controlling the fire. Although PB pipe can still be used for sprinkler systems, since April 1996, the resin used to manufacture the pipe is no longer available. All reference to polybutylene pipe was removed from the 2007 edition of NFPA 13.

A second type of nonmetallic pipe, chlorinated polyvinyl chloride (CPVC), was introduced in 1986. CPVC pipe was listed for use in systems complying with NFPA 13D and for systems complying with NFPA 13 for light-hazard occupancies.

CPVC piping materials must be manufactured in accordance with the piping standard in ASTM F442 *and* must be specifically listed for use in automatic sprinkler systems. The listing criteria include a number of conditions and restrictions. Some of these conditions are as follows:

- Limited for use in systems that comply with NFPA 13D; NFPA 13R, *Standard for the Installation of Sprinkler Systems in Residential Occupancies up to and Including Four Stories in Height;* and NFPA 13 (light-hazard occupancies only)
- Can be used in all wet pipe systems but limited for dry pipe and preaction systems
- Must be installed behind a thermal barrier. Note that CPVC pipe may be installed exposed if used with listed residential sprinklers that are installed in accordance with their listing or if used with listed quick-response (QR) sprinklers, where the QR sprinklers are installed within 8 in. (203 mm) of the ceiling
- Must be joined with listed fittings or materials
- Not permitted to be installed in concealed combustible spaces that require sprinkler protection by NFPA 13

NFPA 13 requires that all of the manufacturer's installation instructions be followed in addition to the design and installation rules of NFPA 13.

Specially Listed Steel Pipe. In the same manner that NFPA 13 previously allowed manufacturers to produce pipe with materials other than steel and copper, a similar provision also permits the use of other types of steel pipe that have a thickness of less than schedule 10. These materials are typically referred to as thin-wall steel pipe and may have a wall thickness similar to that for schedule 5. They must be specifically listed for use in automatic sprinkler systems.

The listing process evaluates a number of pipe properties such as hydraulic characteristics, corrosion resistance, beam strength (for determining hanger spacing for piping support), and joining methods of joining the pipe, among others.

System Valves

Automatic sprinkler systems are required to have at least one listed valve installed to allow for the system to be shut down. As a matter of course, sprinkler systems should never be shut down except when system modifications are being accomplished or during the time following a fire to allow for replacement of any sprinklers that operated. The types of valves used in a sprinkler system vary with the location of the valve in the water supply system or portion thereof.

Valves may be of the isolation type to shut the system off, they may be a one-way or check valve to prevent flow of water in one direction, or they may be a pressure-regulating valve to permit the pressure entering part of the system to be maintained at a certain level. In all cases, the valves must be listed for use in fire protection systems, they must be supervised in their normally open position, and they must be identified as to the area or segment of the system that they control.

Listed control valves are evaluated for such characteristics as the maximum working pressure to which they can be exposed, the hydraulic profile or equivalent pipe lengths that result, and the means of supervising equipment that they may use.

Indicating Features. The purpose of an indicating feature on a valve is to allow a method to quickly determine if the valve is in the open or closed position. One of the more common methods for accomplishing this is the use of a listed outside screw and yoke (OS&Y) valve. The rising stem feature of this valve is the indicator if the valve is open or closed. The stem rises as the valve is set to the open position. The opposite end of the stem is equipped with a gate valve that raises out of the pipe network as the valve wheel is operated. OS&Y valves are often installed at, or near, the system riser.

A postindicator valve (PIV) is frequently installed outside of the structure. The indicating feature on this device is a viewing window with a sliding metal plate. As the valve is operated with the special wrench, the stem, which is connected to the gate device on the end of the stem (the stem is internal to the post on a PIV), also repositions the sign. When the valve is in the open position, the sign labeled "OPEN" will be evident in the small viewing window on the side of the PIV housing. Likewise, when the valve is operated to the closed position, the sign labeled "CLOSED" will be evident in the viewing window. Figure 16.3.16 illustrates two types of control valves.

Listed indicating butterfly valves (IBV) do not have the same type of physical features of either the OS&Y valve or the PIV valve; thus, it must use an indicating feature that is substantially different from either of the first two valves. The indicating feature with an IBV is usually a directional arrow, mounted on the housing of the valve. This feature points in the "position" of the valve. For example, when the valve is open, the arrow is aligned with the flow direction of the water. When the valve is in the closed position, the arrow points in a direction perpendicular to the pipe, indicating that water cannot travel beyond the valve.

Supervisory Features. Another requirement of NFPA 13 is to provide some means to ensure that the valve remains in its normal position. Supervision of system valves dates back to the 1896 edition of NFPA 13, in which Rule 60 stated "All gate valves in supply pipes to sprinklers to be of indicator pattern, and to be strapped open with riveted leather straps passing around the riser and spoke of the wheel, or secured open with a seal." The methods for supervising valves include the following:

- Electrically supervised in a manner to allow a signal to be heard at a central station facility
- Electrically supervised in a manner to allow a signal to be heard at a constantly attended point at the protected facility
- Locking valves in the open position
- Sealing valves in the open position, with a weekly surveillance program

It is important to remember that, although NFPA 13 allows any of these options, for sprinkler systems required by other building codes, the code typically dictates that the valve be electrically supervised at a central station.

In addition to those valves used to control the system supplies or a portion of the system supply, other types of valves are used to test the system or drain the system pipe. Although such valves are not required to meet the same level of reliability as control valves, they must still be installed to facilitate testing of the system, as well as to allow for the system to be drained during a period of maintenance. The main drain or test valve is located at the system riser. Its purpose is twofold. First, it may be used as a central point to drain water from the entire system. Its second purpose is to conduct the main drain test. This test is done when the system is commissioned, in order to allow for a set of baseline values to be established. The points of interest are (1) the static pressure and (2) the residual pressure when the valve is fully open. Figure 16.3.17 shows the common arrangement of the main drain valve.

Another type of valve used is the inspector's test valve, or the alarm test connection. The location of the valve depends on the type of system. When installed on a wet pipe system, the main purpose of this device is to test the operation of the waterflow device. Although it can be located anywhere after the waterflow device, the preferred location is as close to the system riser as possible. This limits the extent of corrosion within the system. When installed on a dry pipe system, its purpose is twofold. First, it is used to establish the trip time of the dry pipe valve and the transit time of the water to the connection. Second, it establishes the time for the waterflow device to operate and the actual operation of the alarm device. For these reasons, it must be located at the end of the most remote branch line.

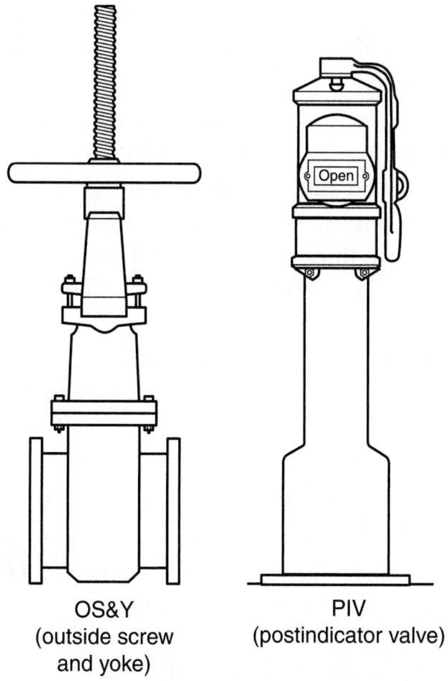

FIGURE 16.3.16 Two Sprinkler System Indicating Control Valves

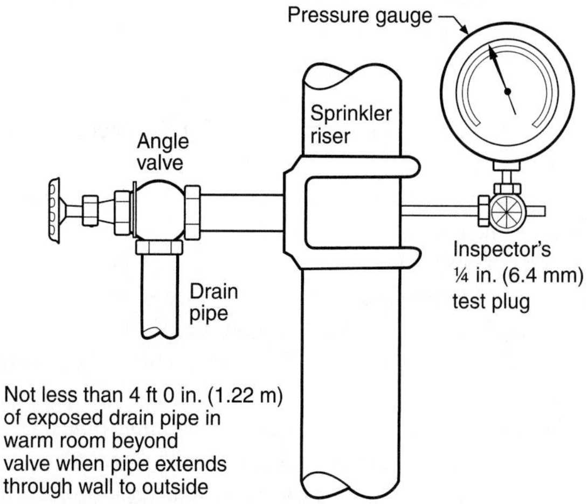

FIGURE 16.3.17 Main Drain Connection for System Riser

INSTALLATION RULES FOR AUTOMATIC SPRINKLER SYSTEMS

The basic principles of NFPA 13 concerning sprinkler system installation are as follows:

1. Sprinklers are to be installed throughout the premises.
2. The maximum allowed protection area per sprinkler is not to be exceeded.
3. Sprinklers are to be positioned to allow for timely operation and distribution.

Installing Sprinklers Throughout the Premises

Installing sprinklers throughout the premises is necessary in order to achieve the desired level of life safety and property protection. Since there are no standardized methods to predict where a fire is likely to start in a structure, the basic rules of NFPA 13 require sprinklers to be installed in most areas of the building. In general, a fire that originates in an unsprinklered area is expected to overpower the capabilities of a system that may be installed in a nearby or adjacent space. In general, this correlation holds true. There have been instances in which sprinklers did actually contain or extinguish a fire that originated in an unsprinklered space. The most notable of these fires was the One Meridian Plaza fire in Philadelphia in 1991. In this incident, an uncontrolled fire had spread between eight stories in a high-rise office building. On reaching the thirtieth floor, which had been equipped with sprinklers, a total of nine sprinklers operated to completely stop the further spread of the fire.

Some codes that focus exclusively on life safety might not require sprinklers in all areas of the building. This is in recognition of the assumption that the threat to life or injury as a result of fire in these spaces is considered minimal. Because NFPA 13 focuses on both property protection and life safety, very few exceptions for omitting sprinkler coverage exist.

Some areas that do not require sprinkler coverage include bathrooms in residential-type occupancies that are not over 55 ft^2 (5.1 m^2) in area and are composed of noncombustible or limited-combustible materials. Small closets in hotel occupancies are also not required to be protected with sprinklers. In both instances, there is recognition that the fuel loading in such spaces is minimal and that fires that originate in such spaces do not normally become threatening to either the occupants or the structure.

Two other exceptions to sprinkler protection center on electrical equipment rooms and elevator shafts. Electrical equipment rooms that (1) use dry-type equipment, (2) are used for no other purpose, and (3) are separated by 2-hour fire-rated construction are not required to be protected with automatic sprinklers. In this instance, strict controls are imposed on the use of the room and the materials of construction.

Passenger elevator shafts that use noncombustible construction and utilize elevator cabs constructed in accordance with ASME 17.1, *Safety Code for Elevators and Escalators,* are not required to be provided with a sprinkler at the top of the shaft. Sprinklers are not required at the bottom of similar shafts, unless the elevator lift mechanism uses hydraulic fluid. It is important to note that such exceptions do not extend to the elevator equipment or machine rooms.

Concealed spaces, such as those found above a ceiling within the building, do not require sprinklers, provided the space is constructed of noncombustible materials. Conversely, concealed spaces of combustible construction or materials require sprinkler protection. There are a number of exceptions to this general rule, however. Exceptions to sprinkler protection center on two basic ideas: (1) that physical limitations within a space may prevent a meaningful arrangement of sprinklers to be installed, and (2) that the nature and arrangement of the combustible materials may have some inherent fire resistance. The 2007 edition of NFPA 13 contains 14 exceptions that address the specific instances in which sprinklers can be omitted from concealed combustible spaces. Buildings are still considered to be sprinklered throughout when these exceptions are applied.

Areas of Coverage

A number of limits are imposed on the size of the area that a particular type of sprinkler can protect. In arriving at the area of coverage for a particular type of sprinkler, a number of variables are considered. These include the type of sprinkler in question, the nature of the hazard being protected, the type of construction contemplated, and the spacing of the construction members. Tables 16.3.7 through 16.3.10 summarize the maximum areas of coverage permitted for standard upright and standard pendent spray sprinklers. Protection areas for other types of sprinklers are provided in NFPA 13. Exceeding the area of coverage limits specified by NFPA 13 can result in failure of the sprinkler to control the fire.

The area of coverage of a sprinkler is established through a set of principles based on an evaluation of the relationship between the distance between sprinklers located on the branch line and the distance between sprinklers on adjacent branch lines. The first value is defined as "S" (along the branch line), whereas the second value is defined as "L" (between adjacent branch lines). In the same manner that maximum limits are imposed on the overall area of coverage, limits are also placed on these distances. Once again, the type of sprinkler, the hazard to be protected, and the characteristics of the construction are factored into these limits. Tables 16.3.7 through 16.3.10 show the permitted values for "S" and "L" identified as the maximum spacing.

The area of coverage is then determined by multiplying the "L" and "S" values together. It should be noted that sprinklers installed on the ends of a branch line near a wall and those sprinklers installed on the branch line that runs closest to a wall receive special treatment and may alter the selected values for "S" and "L." (See NFPA 13 for a further discussion on this issue.) Even a slight deviation in these limits may result in the sprinkler system not being able to adequately control the fire.

Extended coverage (EC) sprinklers use a slightly different method of determining their area of coverage. In essence, the area of coverage is identical to whatever the sprinkler is listed to. Pendant-mounted extended coverage sprinklers are listed with equal-sided, even-numbered dimensions. An EC sprinkler

TABLE 16.3.7 Protection Areas and Maximum Spacing (Standard Spray Upright/Standard Spray Pendent) for Light Hazard

Construction Type	*System Type*	Protection Area *ft²*	Protection Area *m²*	Spacing (Maximum) *ft*	Spacing (Maximum) *m*
Noncombustible obstructed and unobstructed and combustible unobstructed with members less than 3 ft (0.9 m) on center	Pipe schedule	200	18.6	15	4.60
	Hydraulically calculated	225	20.9	15	4.60
Combustible obstructed with members less than 3 ft (0.9 m) on center	All	168	15.6	15	4.60
Combustible with members less than 3 ft (0.9 m) on center	All	130	12.1	15	4.60
Combustible concealed space under a pitched roof having combustible wood joist or wood truss construction with members less than 3 ft (0.9 m) on center with slopes having a pitch of 4 in 12 or greater	All	120	11.1	15 parallel to the slope 10 perpendicular to the slope	4.60 parallel to the slope 3.05 perpendicular to the slope

Source: NFPA 13, *Standard for the Installation of Sprinkler Systems.*

TABLE 16.3.8 Protection Areas and Maximum Spacing (Standard Spray Upright/Standard Spray Pendent) for Ordinary Hazard

Construction Type	*System Type*	Protection Area *ft²*	Protection Area *m²*	Spacing (Maximum) *ft*	Spacing (Maximum) *m*
All	All	130	12.1	15	4.6

Source: NFPA 13, *Standard for the Installation of Sprinkler Systems.*

that is listed for 16 ft × 16 ft (4.9 m × 4.9 m) has an area of coverage of 256 ft^2 (23.8 m^2). These values become fixed with respect to system design. For example, even if this type of sprinkler is used in an area or room with dimensions of 15 ft × 15 ft (4.6 m × 4.6 m), it must still be designed for the listed spacing of 16 ft × 16 ft (4.9 m × 4.9 m), or 256 ft^2 (23.8 m^2). Sidewall sprinklers are treated in a similar manner but the area can be a rectangle with changes in either dimension limited to 2 ft increments. There is an exception to the area of coverage rule. Extended coverage pendent sprinklers listed for an extra-hazard occupancy and storage shall apply the S × L rule.

TABLE 16.3.9 Protection Areas and Maximum Spacing (Standard Spray Upright/Standard Spray Pendent) for Extra Hazard

Construction Type	*System Type*	Protection Area *ft²*	Protection Area *m²*	Spacing (Maximum) *ft*	Spacing (Maximum) *m*
All	Pipe schedule	90	8.4	12	3.7
				(In buildings with storage bays 25 ft [7.6 m] wide, 12 ft 6 in. [3.8 m] shall be permitted)	
All	Hydraulically calculated with density ≥0.25	100	9.3	12	3.7
				(In buildings with storage bays 25 ft [7.6 m] wide, 12 ft 6 in. [3.8 m] shall be permitted)	
All	Hydraulically calculated with density <0.25	130	12.1	15	4.6

Source: NFPA 13, *Standard for the Installation of Sprinkler Systems.*

TABLE 16.3.10 Protection Areas and Maximum Spacing (Standard Spray Upright/Standard Spray Pendent) for High-Piled Storage

Construction Type	*System Type*	Protection Area *ft²*	Protection Area *m²*	Spacing (Maximum) *ft*	Spacing (Maximum) *m*
All	Hydraulically calculated with density ≥0.25	100	9.3	12 (In buildings with storage bays 25 ft [7.6 m] wide, 12 ft 6 in. [3.8 m] shall be permitted)	3.7
All	Hydraulically calculated with density <0.25	130	12.1	15	4.6

Source: NFPA 13, *Standard for the Installation of Sprinkler Systems.*

Sprinkler Activation and Discharge Characteristics

The position of the sprinkler with respect to the ceiling and any nearby construction features, such as lighting fixtures, construction elements, and the like, can impact the performance of the sprinkler in two distinct ways. First, if the sprinkler is located in a manner so that it is not directly exposed to the heat from the fire, the subsequent delay in sprinkler operation may result in the fire becoming too large for proper control by the sprinkler. To minimize this possibility, NFPA 13 controls the positioning of the sprinkler with respect to walls and ceilings.

The second area of concern lies within the distribution pattern of the sprinkler. In other words, once the sprinkler operates, is it likely that the water that discharges from the sprinkler will be able to reach the fire and surrounding objects. NFPA 13 deals with this by specifying obstruction rules for each type of sprinkler. The requirements of NFPA 13 that address sprinkler activation are specific to the type of sprinkler involved. Although specific requirements for a given type of sprinkler vary, the fundamental principles remain the same: (1) control the distance between the sprinkler deflector and the ceiling/roof, and (2) determine if the ceiling construction features will impede heat flow from the fire to the sprinkler. Ceiling construction features were previously discussed. The position of the sprinkler beneath the ceiling is predicated on the principle that a dynamic heat layer consisting of hot gases from the fire develops below the ceiling and ultimately contains a sufficient amount of energy in terms of heat to activate the sprinkler. In essence, heat from the fire rises to the ceiling surface where, if unobstructed, it spreads out across the ceiling. As the layer builds because of the developing fire, the thermally sensitive components of the sprinklers eventually activate, allowing for the discharge of water. For this reason, NFPA 13 limits the distance that the sprinkler can be positioned below the ceiling.

Dealing with obstructions to sprinkler discharge can be a rather complex issue. A building with a completely smooth, flat, horizontal ceiling that utilizes recessed lighting fixtures, or flush-mounted heating, ventilating, and air-conditioning (HVAC) exhaust grilles, and that otherwise has no projections from the ceiling is the most desirable in terms of sprinkler discharge. However, this situation is rare.

The many combinations of architectural features, lighting components, structural members, and related building systems can create detrimental obstructions to sprinkler discharge. Since the first edition of NFPA 13 in 1896, many rules and requirements have been added to address the issue. The fundamental philosophy concerning obstructions has not changed in over 100 years, but details concerning type, size, and shape of obstruction are important as well as how close that obstruction has to be before it becomes a concern.

NFPA 13 addresses three general areas of concern with regard to obstructions. However, rules are specific for each category of sprinkler identified by NFPA 13. The first concern is the overall objective, which is to ensure that a sufficient amount of water from the sprinkler reaches the fire. The concern was previously referred to as a horizontal obstruction and dealt primarily with continuous obstructions such as beams, top chord members, and ducts that are tight or very near the ceiling and in close proximity to the sprinkler.

The second concern deals with the obstruction to sprinkler discharge pattern development. This concern addresses continuous and noncontinuous obstructions such as piping, light fixtures, truss webs, or building columns located within the first 18 in. (457 mm) below the sprinkler deflector. Obstructions located in this zone prevent the proper sprinkler discharge pattern from developing. As a result sprinklers are required to be positioned so that they are located a certain radial distance away from the obstruction. NFPA 13 addresses the correct position for each type of sprinkler.

The 18 in. (457 mm) distance was established in 1952 as the clearance below the newly developed spray sprinkler. It was determined that this volume of clear space was necessary for proper spray pattern development. Starting with the 1996 edition of NFPA 13, the rules for obstructions went through a significant change. Within the 18 in. zone, spray sprinklers are to be separated a radial distance equal to three times the larger dimension of the obstruction. For some types of sprinklers such as extended coverage sprinklers, the separation is increased to four times the dimension. The sensitivity to obstructions is not only affected by the type of sprinkler but also by the occupancy hazard classification. As added in the 1999 edition of NFPA 13, when using standard pendent or upright sprinklers in light- and ordinary-hazard occupancies, only structural members in this zone need be accounted for as obstructions. In general, the obstruction rules in NFPA 13 allow for a portion of the sprinkler's spray pattern to be impacted.

The third area of concern deals with obstructions that prevent the sprinkler discharge from reaching the hazard. These obstructions typically consist of continuous and noncontinuous obstructions that interrupt the water spray pattern once it is below the 18 in. (457 mm) discharge pattern development zone. These types of obstructions can include overhead doors, ducts, or decks. When the width of these obstructions exceeds 4 ft, additional sprinklers are required to be installed beneath them. As indicated by such a large dimension being acceptable, once the pattern has developed, obstructions present much less of a threat to acceptable sprinkler performance.

Another category of obstruction applicable to certain types of sprinklers includes obstructions that are suspended from the ceiling, such as privacy curtains in a hospital or floor-mounted partitions that do not reach the ceiling, such as those found in offices. In both cases, sprinklers must be positioned so that a sufficient portion of the sprinkler discharge sprays over the obstruction.

It is important to note that certain types of sprinklers are more "obstruction sensitive," in that they have little or no tolerance for objects that disrupt the spray pattern. Large-drop and ESFR sprinklers both fit into this category, and their performance can be severely affected by relatively small obstructions.

DESIGN CONSIDERATIONS FOR AUTOMATIC SPRINKLER SYSTEMS

The basic design consideration for sprinkler systems is to verify that the sprinkler system can discharge a sufficient amount of water for the period of time necessary to either control or suppress the types of fires anticipated. Determination of the appropriate occupancy hazard classification is critical in this regard. However, certain installation criteria also play a role. For example, ceiling construction, whether obstructed or unobstructed, influences the area of coverage for a particular sprinkler and this bears on the overall water demand requirements of the system. Another instance focuses on the presence of concealed combustible spaces, which can increase the overall system design area. In protecting a single building or within a single floor area, multiple designs options can be applied. Each option is treated independently.

Two general design methods exist in NFPA 13: (1) the pipe schedule method and (2) the hydraulic design method. The pipe schedule method dates back to the late 1800s. It basically uses a prescribed schedule that specifies the number of sprinklers that can be supplied by a given size pipe. NFPA 13 contains schedules for both copper tube and steel pipe. The use of this particular design method is severely restricted by NFPA 13, almost to the point where it is impractical in most instances.

In addition to the schedule or table that is provided for a light-hazard or ordinary-hazard occupancy (pipe schedule design is no longer permitted for extra hazard), a second table is used to specify the minimum flow and pressure at the base of the system riser (Table 16.3.11). This table is limited to installations no larger than 5000 ft^2 (464.7 m^2). The flow is a minimum, and in the case of a light-hazard occupancy, that flow must be made available at the base of the system riser at a pressure of 15 psi (103.4 kPa) plus the pressure that is necessary to reach the highest sprinkler. In the case of a light-hazard occupancy that has its highest sprinkler positioned 38 ft (11.2 m) above the base of the riser, the minimum flow would have to be available at a pressure of 31.5 psi (217.2 kPa). Table 16.3.11 indicates that not less than 500 gpm (1892.5 L/min) must be provided at this point. If the installation was greater than 5000 ft^2 (464.7 m^2), the minimum residual pressure is increased to 50 psi (344.8 kPa). The above example would require 66.5 psi (458.5 kPa). Such flows are not typical of most municipal water supplies.

The more accurate method of determining the demand for a sprinkler system is through hydraulic calculation. Additionally, this method provides the designer and the building owner with a more cost-effective system. This method offers a number of other advantages in that it is not limited to use with a particular type of pipe, a particular type of sprinkler, or a particular type of occupancy hazard. These are all limitations associated with the pipe schedule approach.

The process by which the calculations are completed is based on an evaluation of the sprinkler system from the hydraulically most remote point. This is that portion of the system that is expected to produce the greatest demand on and tax the system to its greatest extent. It sometimes, but not always, coincides with the physically most remote point in the system (i.e., the point farthest away from the base of the system riser). The concept here is that, if one can satisfy the most demanding point hydraulically, then one can also satisfy any point that is hydraulically closer to the system water supply.

TABLE 16.3.11 Water Supply Requirements for Pipe Schedule Sprinkler Systems

Occupancy Classification	Minimum Residual Pressure Required *psi*	*bar*	Acceptable Flow at Base of Riser *gpm*	*L/min*	*Duration in Minutes*
Light hazard	15	1.03	500–750	1892–2839	30–60
Ordinary hazard	20	1.38	850–1500	3217–5677	60–90

Source: NFPA 13, *Standard for the Installation of Sprinkler Systems.*

In determining this most remote point, a design area or system area of operation must be established based on the criteria of NFPA 13. This area should take the shape of a rectangle with a minimum area of 1500 ft^2 (139.4 m^2) for light- and ordinary-hazard occupancies and 2500 ft^2 (232.3 m^2) for extra-hazard occupancies. The selected area is then matched to a corresponding discharge density in accordance with Figure 16.3.18, which is taken from NFPA 13. The designer needs only to satisfy a single point on this curve in order to produce an acceptable design.

A designer is free to select a matching area of sprinkler operation and density along the representative curves. However, it is more advantageous to select the smallest corresponding area of operation (vertical axis) and highest density (horizontal axis). Other points higher on the curve are acceptable but only result in the system requiring more water overall. Interestingly, less water is made available to any given area on the floor when such points are selected.

Up until this point in the design process, the only fixed parameter is the occupancy hazard to be protected. Once the demand point has been selected from the curve, other influencing factors come into play. One of these factors involves the protection (or lack thereof) of concealed combustible spaces. In some instances, the design area must be increased from 1500 to 3000 ft^2 (139.4 to 278.7 m^2). Another factor is the area of coverage for each sprinkler and the spacing that is provided between sprinklers on each branch line (dimension "S," which was previously described).

This type of information becomes critical since the area of system operation is to be converted to a number of sprinklers expected to operate. The number of sprinklers expected to operate is the result of the system area of operation (in units of ft^2) divided by the area of coverage for a sprinkler (in units of ft^2 per sprinkler) (1 ft^2 = 0.0929 m^2). A sprinkler that covers a 200 ft^2 (18.6 m^2) area in a light-hazard occupancy, and in which a system area of operation was selected to be 1500 ft^2 (139.4 m^2), could also be said to have a system area of operation of 1500 ft^2 (139.4 m^2) divided by 200 ft^2 (18.6 m^2) per sprinkler or 7.5 sprinklers. In this process, any fractional amount is always rounded up to the next whole number. In this case, the 1500 ft^2 (139.4 m^2) hydraulically most remote area may also be described as being an eight-sprinkler hydraulically most remote area. This translates to the need to provide a sufficient amount of water to these eight sprinklers in order to control a fire.

The longer dimension of the rectangular area should be parallel to the system branch lines and its length, represented by the number of sprinklers along the branch line in the design area, is determined by the following formula:

$$\frac{1.2\sqrt{A}}{S}$$

where A represents the system design area and S represents the distance between sprinklers along the branch lines. Considering the example in which the design area is 1500 ft^2 and sprinklers are spaced 10 ft (3.1 m) apart along the branch line, the longer side of the design area will contain five sprinklers as follows:

$$\frac{1.2\sqrt{1500}}{10} = 4.6 \text{ sprinklers}$$

(1 ft = 0.305 m)

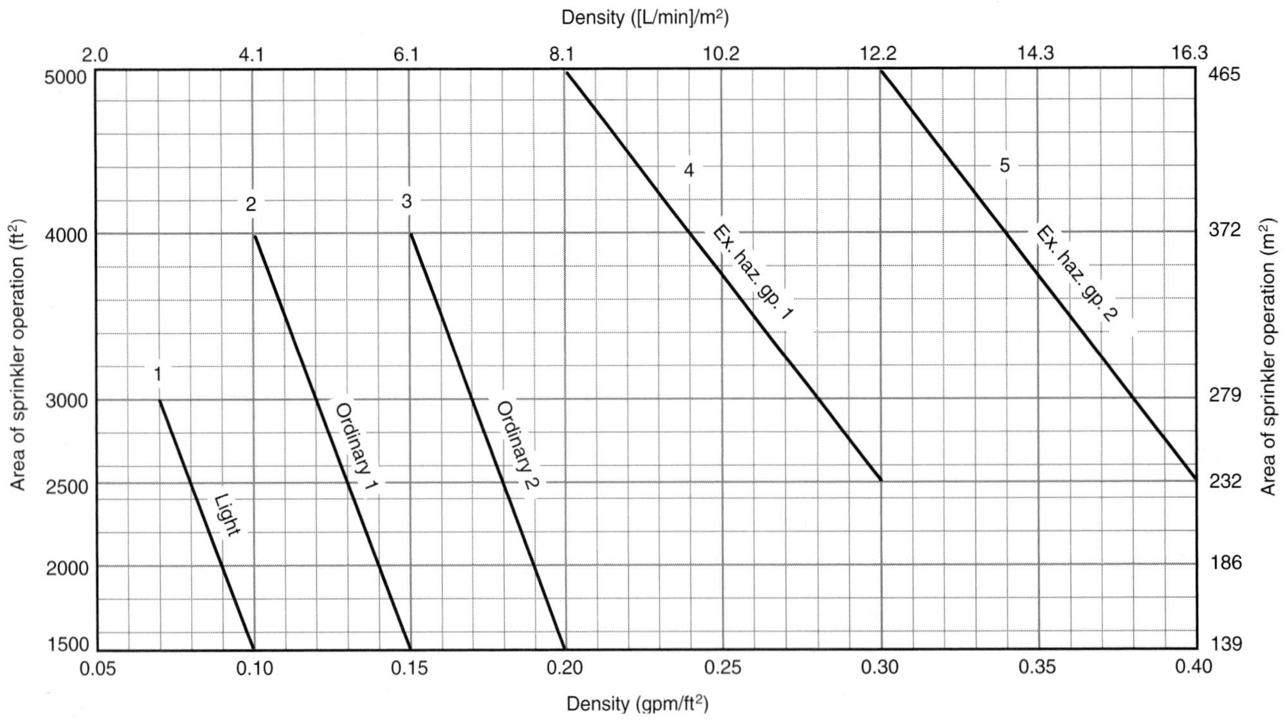

FIGURE 16.3.18 Density/Area Curve (Source: NFPA 13, *Standard for the Installation of Sprinkler Systems*)

As noted before, it is necessary to always round the calculated value up to the nearest whole number of sprinklers—in this case, five. In this example, the remote area consists of a total of eight sprinklers, five on the first branch line in the remote area and three on the second branch line in the remote area.

Using the number of sprinklers is a good means to estimate the size of the remote area. The actual floor area covered must still be verified. This becomes an issue when the distance to the adjacent wall(s) is not symmetrical with the distance to the opposite branch line or sprinklers. When this happens, the assigned area of sprinkler coverage is greater than the actual floor area covered, resulting in a remote area that is too small.

Once the shape and size of the remote area are established, the hydraulic calculation procedures can be initiated. The flow from the most remote sprinkler in the design area can be determined by multiplying the area of coverage of the sprinkler by the selected density. For example, if a density of 0.01 gpm/ft^2 was selected from the design curves and the sprinkler spacing is 200 ft^2 (18.6 m^2) per sprinkler, the flow from the sprinkler is:

$$Q = A \times \text{Density} = 200 \times 0.01 = 20 \text{ gpm}$$

This gives the flow from the most remote sprinkler. The pressure for that first sprinkler is then determined by the following formula, which describes the relationship between the sprinkler orifice (K-factor), the flow (Q), and the pressure (P):

$$Q = \text{K}\sqrt{P}$$

rearranged to $P = (Q/\text{K})^2$.

The flow from the hydraulically most remote sprinkler is then carried upstream to the next sprinkler. The pressure at this sprinkler can then be determined. This pressure is the pressure for the hydraulically most remote sprinkler plus the pressure needed to overcome the losses due to friction for the flow through the pipe connecting the second remote sprinkler on the branch line. Additionally, pressure losses for any fittings and elevation changes are also considered. Once again, the relationship between flow (Q), sprinkler characteristic (K), and pressure (P) is used. The K-factor for the sprinklers used is known as is the pressure; thus, the flow from that sprinkler can be determined.

The total system flow at this point is the additive discharge from these two sprinklers. The flow for these two sprinklers is used to calculate up to the next sprinkler, and the process is repeated as previously described.

This method of conducting hydraulic calculation uses the Hazen-Williams equation. It was developed in the 1920s and provides sufficiently accurate results for sprinkler systems. The hydraulic design can be completed through the application of formulas, hydraulic tables as indicated in Table 16.3.12, or computer programs. Refer to related chapters of this handbook, the *NFPA Sprinkler Systems Handbook,* or a hydraulics text for more detailed information.

Special Design Features

Where sprinkler systems are used to protect hazards that are not classified by the occupancy hazard classifications specified in NFPA 13, other approaches should be used. Additionally, the approach just described applies to spray sprinklers only. Where other types of sprinklers such as ESFR, large-drop, or residential sprinklers are used, other methods need to be used. See the chapters on sprinklers, residential sprinkler systems, and sprinkler systems for storage applications in this handbook for additional information in this regard.

Under certain circumstances, adjustments to the area/density curve might be necessary. For example, where extended coverage sprinklers are used, NFPA 13 mandates that no fewer than five sprinklers be included in the design of a system. Without this rule, a system that used an extended-coverage sprinkler listed for 400 ft^2 (37.1 m^2) could be designed with only four sprinklers (1500 ft^2 ÷ 400 ft^2 = 3.75 or 4 sprinklers) (1 ft^2 = 0.0929 m^2). Other adjustments require a 30 percent increase to the design area where excessive roof slopes exist or when dry pipe systems are being considered.

A reduction in the system area of operation is permitted where quick-response (QR) sprinklers are used. This provision is limited to those situations in which the occupancy is either a light or ordinary hazard and in which certain ceiling configurations are present. Figure 16.3.19 shows the allowable reduction. The application of this reduction is further limited to spaces containing smooth, flat ceilings that are no higher than 20 ft (6.1 m). Where the ceiling is sloped, the maximum roof height needs to be used. When the size of the remote area is reduced, the density for whatever size was initially selected from Figure 16.3.18 is applied. This special rule was developed as the result

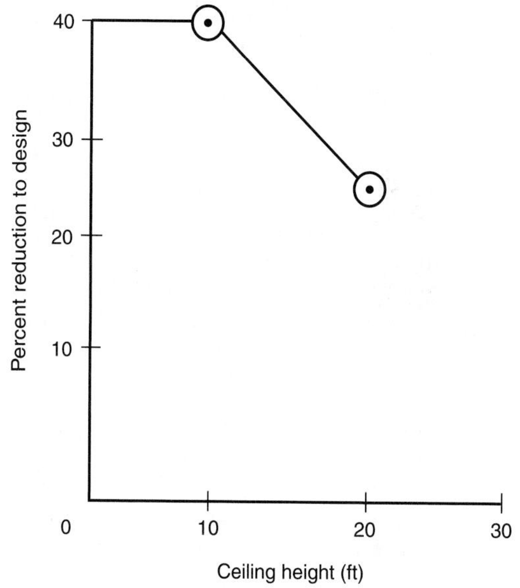

Note: $y = \frac{-3x}{2} + 55$

For ceiling height ≥ 10 ft and ≤ 20 ft, $y = \frac{-3x}{2} + 55$;

For ceiling height < 10 ft, $y = 40$;

For ceiling height > 20 ft, $y = 0$.

For SI units: 1 ft = 0.31 m.

FIGURE 16.3.19 Allowable Reduction in System Area When Quick-Response Sprinklers Are Used (Source: NFPA 13, *Standard for the Installation of Sprinkler Systems*)

TABLE 16.3.12 Friction Loss—PSI per Lineal Foot of Pipe, American Standard Weight, Black Steel Pipe

gpm	*1 in. (1.049 mm)*	*1¼ in. (1.380 mm)*	*1½ in. (1.610 mm)*	*2 in. (2.067 mm)*	*2½ in. (2.469 mm)*	*3 in. (3.068 mm)*	*3½ in. (3.548 mm)*
1	0.0005	0.0001	0.0001	—	—	—	—
2	0.0018	0.0005	0.0002	0.0001	—	—	—
3	0.0039	0.0010	0.0005	0.0001	0.0001	—	—
4	0.0066	0.0017	0.0008	0.0002	0.0001	—	—
5	0.0100	0.0026	0.0012	0.0004	0.0002	0.0001	—
6	0.0140	0.0037	0.0017	0.0005	0.0002	0.0001	—
7	0.0187	0.0049	0.0023	0.0007	0.0003	0.0001	—
8	0.0239	0.0063	0.0030	0.0009	0.0004	0.0001	0.0001
9	0.0297	0.0078	0.0037	0.0011	0.0005	0.0002	0.0001
10	0.0361	0.0095	0.0045	0.0013	0.0006	0.0002	0.0001
11	0.0431	0.0113	0.0053	0.0016	0.0007	0.0002	0.0001
12	0.0506	0.0133	0.0063	0.0019	0.0008	0.0003	0.0001
13	0.0587	0.0154	0.0073	0.0022	0.0009	0.0003	0.0002
14	0.0673	0.0177	0.0084	0.0025	0.0010	0.0004	0.0002
15	0.0764	0.0201	0.0095	0.0028	0.0012	0.0004	0.0002
16	0.0861	0.0226	0.0107	0.0032	0.0013	0.0005	0.0002
17	0.0963	0.0253	0.0120	0.0035	0.0015	0.0005	0.0003
18	0.1070	0.0282	0.0133	0.0039	0.0017	0.0006	0.0003
19	0.1180	0.0311	0.0147	0.0044	0.0018	0.0006	0.0003
20	0.1300	0.0342	0.0162	0.0048	0.0020	0.0007	0.0003
21	0.1420	0.0375	0.0177	0.0052	0.0022	0.0008	0.0004
22	0.1550	0.0408	0.0193	0.0057	0.0024	0.0008	0.0004
23	0.1690	0.0443	0.0209	0.0062	0.0026	0.0009	0.0004
24	0.1820	0.0480	0.0226	0.0067	0.0028	0.0010	0.0005
25	0.1970	0.0517	0.0244	0.0072	0.0030	0.0011	0.0005
26	0.2110	0.0556	0.0262	0.0078	0.0033	0.0011	0.0006
27	0.2270	0.0596	0.0281	0.0083	0.0035	0.0012	0.0006
28	0.2430	0.0638	0.0301	0.0089	0.0038	0.0013	0.0006
29	0.2590	0.0681	0.0321	0.0095	0.0040	0.0014	0.0007
30	0.2760	0.0725	0.0342	0.0101	0.0043	0.0015	0.0007
31	0.2930	0.0770	0.0363	0.0108	0.0045	0.0016	0.0008
32	0.3100	0.0817	0.0385	0.0114	0.0048	0.0017	0.0008
33	0.3290	0.0864	0.0408	0.0121	0.0051	0.0018	0.0009
34	0.3470	0.0913	0.0431	0.0128	0.0054	0.0019	0.0009
35	0.3660	0.0964	0.0455	0.0135	0.0057	0.0020	0.0010
36	0.3860	0.1020	0.0479	0.0142	0.0060	0.0021	0.0010
37	0.4060	0.1070	0.0504	0.0149	0.0063	0.0022	0.0011
38	0.4270	0.1120	0.0530	0.0157	0.0066	0.0023	0.0011
39	0.4480	0.1180	0.0556	0.0165	0.0069	0.0024	0.0012
40	0.4690	0.1230	0.0582	0.0172	0.0073	0.0025	0.0012
41	0.4910	0.1290	0.0610	0.0181	0.0076	0.0026	0.0013
42	0.5130	0.1350	0.0637	0.0189	0.0079	0.0028	0.0014
43	0.5360	0.1410	0.0666	0.0197	0.0083	0.0029	0.0014
44	0.5600	0.1470	0.0695	0.0206	0.0087	0.0030	0.0015
45	0.5830	0.1530	0.0724	0.0214	0.0090	0.0031	0.0015
46	0.6080	0.1600	—	0.0223	0.0094	0.0033	0.0016
47	0.6320	0.1660	0.0785	0.0232	0.0098	0.0034	0.0017
48	0.1730	—	0.0816	0.0242	0.0102	0.0035	0.0017
49	0.6830	0.1800	0.0848	0.0251	0.0106	0.0037	0.0018
50	0.7090	0.1860	0.0880	0.0261	0.0110	0.0038	0.0019

of a series of tests done in 1988, which compared the number of QR sprinklers operating to the number of standard-response sprinklers operating under similar fire scenarios.

One final point on system design involves fire department operations. This chapter has addressed considerations for correct operation of the system, which entail control or suppression of a fire. Final extinguishment of the fire, which can be accomplished by the sprinkler system in many cases, is normally contemplated as a function of the fire department. To ensure that water is available for fire department use while the sprinkler system is operating, NFPA 13 requires an allowance for hose streams. NFPA 13E, *Recommended Practice for Fire Department Operations in Properties Protected by Sprinkler and Standpipe Systems,* provides guidance on the fire department interaction with the sprinkler system.

PLANS, CALCULATIONS, AND SYSTEM ACCEPTANCE

Plans

Factors impacting system design and installation must be documented. Knowledgeable designers need to present the design plans and specifications to the authority having jurisdiction (AHJ) for review and/or approval prior to the commencement of any installation work. The purpose of such documents is to ascertain that the appropriate system elements have been considered and incorporated. Detailed plans should include items such as the layout of the pipe, the location of the sprinklers, the location or spacing of supports, the location of the system riser, the location of any water supply control valves, and the location of the system water supply source, among other items, as required by NFPA 13.

Hydraulic Calculations

Where hydraulic calculations were conducted, they should be detailed and comprehensive. A summary sheet showing the design area of operation, the design density, the occupancy hazard, the hose stream allowance, the water supply information, and the total system demand should also be included. Detailed calculation sheets that document the proper sequence of sprinkler demand points must also be provided. These calculations must originate in the hydraulically most demanding portion of the system and reflect the hydraulic characteristics between that point and the water supply source.

Acceptance Test

The system acceptance or checkout test is used to verify that items previously submitted on the contract plans and reviewed by the AHJ were indeed provided, installed, incorporated, and located as indicated. Test provisions can include items such as a hydrostatic test of the system piping. This test is used to verify the quality of the pipe and fitting installation. In addition to being hydrostatically tested, dry pipe systems must also be pneumatically tested for 24 hours to make sure that air is not being lost to faulty installation of fittings or pipe.

On completion of the acceptance test described in NFPA 13, the contractor's material and test certificate is signed by the installing contractor, the AHJ, and the building owner (or the designated representative). This certificate becomes the basis for final acceptance and commissioning of the system and often becomes a determining factor in allowing the certificate of occupancy to be issued for the building.

Once system acceptance has occurred, it is now incumbent on the building owner to follow up with periodic inspection, testing, and maintenance of the system as specified in NFPA 25, *Standard for the Inspection, Testing, and Maintenance of Water-Based Fire Protection Systems.* Future changes to the building or the contents are likely to impact the sprinkler system and need to be accounted for. Ignoring changes to the system and the associated fire hazard can lead to inadequate system performance during a fire. For example, relatively minor architectural changes can create severe obstructions to a sprinkler's discharge pattern and prevent water from reaching the fire area.

MARINE APPLICATIONS

Marine applications of sprinkler systems were formally introduced for the 1996 edition of NFPA 13.

Since 1991, the U.S. Coast Guard has provided a circular on merchant vessel sprinkler systems. This circular basically requires the use of a NFPA 13–type sprinkler system on certain categories of vessels. The prevalence of gaming-type excursion vessels on both inland and coastal routes has been a motivating factor in this aspect of sprinkler protection.

Sprinkler systems are not exclusively limited to these vessel types. The span of marine vessels that will require systems in the near future includes not only excursion boats for both gaming and pleasure but also cruise ships and merchant vessels used to haul various commodities. The Safety of Life at Sea (SOLAS) regulations, promulgated by the International Maritime Organization (IMO), also require sprinkler systems.

The marine chapter in NFPA 13 deals with the unique aspects of a ship's operating environment. In general, all of the current rules of NFPA 13 will still be applicable, except those that are amended or modified by this particular chapter. Many design considerations are similar between a ship and building, but differences exist. These include references to decks instead of floors, shore connections instead of fire department connections, and sprinkler pumps instead of fire pumps. The terms and connotations are similar but the arrangement and importance of each will differ.

One aspect of the design of a sprinkler system on a merchant vessel that is underway, as compared to a building, is that the ship must be entirely self-reliant. That is, occupants cannot be readily evacuated; the fire department cannot be summoned to assist with manual fire suppression; and a maintenance contractor cannot be called in at a moment's notice to repair a system fault. Because of these factors, additional redundant features will be found on the ship that otherwise would not be considered in the design of a land-based structure.

Other conditions that must be considered include the potential for the heaving and rolling that a ship may experience and the resulting impact it would have on sprinkler system piping.

This problem can be dealt with by incorporating some of the seismic design features that are discussed in NFPA 13.

The exposure of certain pipe materials and sprinklers to corrosive atmospheres is also a concern. The use of nonmetallic pipe and the special corrosion-protection measures that are discussed in NFPA 13 are applicable to this situation.

Perhaps the most crucial design consideration is the arrangement and reliability of the water supply. In most circumstances, a nearly infinite supply is readily available to a merchant vessel, but how it is arranged and supplied to the ship's sprinkler system is of paramount importance. A number of water supplies (never less than two) are deemed acceptable, and each must be arranged to ensure that a high level of reliability is obtained. A pressure tank is considered an acceptable method to satisfy part of the water supply requirements. This source must be charged with a quantity of fresh water that will supply the system for a period of at least 1 minute, in the case of a wet pipe system. The supply for a dry pipe system should be adequate to allow for complete filling of the pipe volume plus a quantity of water to permit 1 minute of system discharge.

A sprinkler pump is one of the supply sources that must always be provided. The sprinkler pump has characteristics that are similar to a fire pump, and it must be specifically listed for marine application. The power supply for a sprinkler pump must be arranged to minimize the chances of a fire affecting the starting or operation of the pump. This is done by obtaining the power supply for the pump from the main switchboard on the ship. A backup source of power from a generator must also be provided.

In addition to these arrangements, the water supply for the onboard sprinkler system must also be interconnected with the ship's fire main system. The fire main system is the equivalent of an underground distribution system that is also used to supply strategically located hose outlets on the ship. Figure 16.3.20 shows one basic configuration of a pressure tank, a fire pump, and the ship's fire main.

The fire department connection depicted in Figure 16.3.20 should typically be of the same style and size of those used on fixed structures. Such connections may be supplied by land-based fire department pumpers. In other cases, the source of supply for this connection may be from a fireboat when the vessel is in or near a port area. The companion international shore connection (ISC) is a universal water supply hookup for vessels operating outside of their home port at the time of a fire. As shown in Figure 16.3.20, both types of connections may be used to supplement the other automatic sources of supply for the sprinkler system.

Another feature associated with this unique operating environment is the need to carry additional spare parts to facilitate basic repairs while the vessel is underway. Certain merchant vessels and cruise ships may be as much as four days away from the nearest port capable of repairing system impairments.

SUMMARY

Automatic sprinkler systems serve as one of the most effective methods for providing fire protection and life safety. Sprinkler systems can be installed in various types of buildings and facilities such as manufactured homes, high-rise buildings, warehouse facilities, manufacturing facilities, and, more recently, merchant vessels. Technological advances continue with piping materials, sprinklers, fittings, and hangers both in terms of the products offered and the manner in which they are installed. Advances in technology will continue to produce more effective and cost-efficient sprinkler systems for an increasing number of applications. The greatest obstacle to even broader

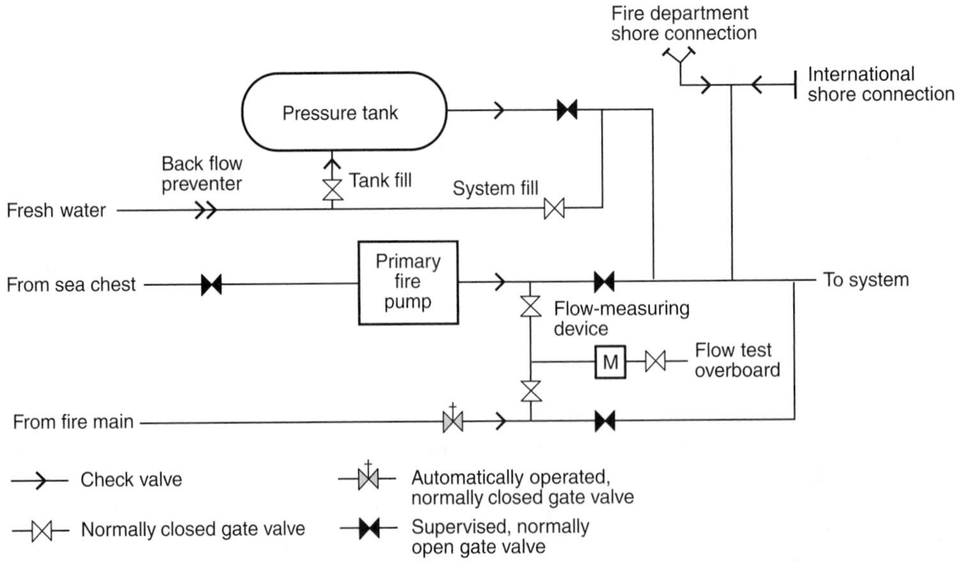

FIGURE 16.3.20 Abbreviated Example of a Water Supply with Fire Pump Backup for Marine Applications

use of sprinkler systems is public perception rather than limitations with available technology.

BIBLIOGRAPHY

NFPA Codes, Standards, and Recommended Practices

Reference to the following NFPA codes, standards, and recommended practices will provide further information on automatic sprinkler systems discussed in this chapter. (See the latest version of The NFPA Catalog *for availability of current editions of the following documents.)*

NFPA 13, *Standard for the Installation of Sprinkler Systems*
NFPA 13D, *Standard for the Installation of Sprinkler Systems in One- and Two-Family Dwellings and Manufactured Homes*
NFPA 13E, *Recommended Practice for Fire Department Operations in Properties Protected by Sprinkler and Standpipe Systems*
NFPA 13R, *Standard for the Installation of Sprinkler Systems in Residential Occupancies up to and Including Four Stories in Height*
NFPA 20, *Standard for the Installation of Stationary Pumps for Fire Protection*
NFPA 22, *Standard for Water Tanks for Fire Protection*
NFPA 24, *Standard for the Installation of Private Fire Service Mains and Their Appurtenances*
NFPA 30, *Flammable and Combustible Liquids Code*
NFPA *101®*, *Life Safety Code®*

References

"2006 Legislative Review: An Overview of Codes, Standards and Regulations in the U.S. and Canada," *Sprinkler Age,* Vol. 25, No. 11, 2006, pp. 32–39.
Back, G. G., Parker, A. J., Scheffey, J. L., Williams, F. W., Gott, J. E., and Tabet, R. J., "Effects of Water Sprinklers on the Performance of Low Level AFFF Aircraft Hangar Fire Suppression Systems," NRL/MR/6180-000-8456, Naval Research Laboratory, Washington, DC, May 20, 2000.
Bryan, J. L., *Automatic Sprinkler and Standpipe Systems,* 4th ed., National Fire Protection Association, Quincy, MA, 2006.
Dubay, C., *Automatic Sprinkler Systems Handbook,* National Fire Protection Association, Quincy, MA, 2007.
Fleming, R. P., "Automatic Sprinkler System Calculations," *SFPE Handbook of Fire Protection Engineering,* 2nd edition, National Fire Protection Association, Quincy, MA, 2002.
Gagnon, R., *Designer's Guide to Automatic Sprinkler Systems,* National Fire Protection Association, Quincy, MA, 2005.
Hague, D. R., *Commissioning Fire Protection Systems,* National Fire Protection Association, Quincy, MA, 2005.

Chapter 4

Hanging and Bracing of Water-Based Systems

Russell P. Fleming

Chapter Contents

Key Terms

automatic sprinkler system, bracing, earthquake, floor-mounted support, hanger, piping (underground), restrained joint system, thrust block, water-based fire protection

Physical support of a water-based fire suppression system is considered essential to the system's proper operation, and specific requirements addressing hanging of automatic sprinkler systems have been included in NFPA 13, *Standard for the Installation of Sprinkler Systems,* since the first edition of the standard was published in 1896. This chapter identifies the various aspects of hanging and bracing that apply to water-based systems, and provides an understanding of some of the assumptions and conventions that underlie the specific rules contained in the NFPA system installation standards.

The earliest sprinkler system hanger rules called for either U-type hangers made of round wrought iron or malleable cast iron, ring clips, or approved adjustable hangers. Flat U-type hangers were permitted if they were at least 3/16 in. (5 mm) thick. Hangers were required to be at least 12 in. (300 mm) from sprinklers to avoid interference with water distribution, except that round hangers were permitted as close as 3 in. (75 mm). For concrete construction, cast iron inserts were recommended, although expansion bolts could be used in existing buildings, preferably in a horizontal position. Those familiar with current hanger rules will recognize that some of these rules are still in place.

Guidance for protecting automatic sprinkler systems against earthquakes was first included in the 1947 edition of NFPA 13. The insurance rating bureaus on the West Coast of the United States had urged that special features be included in systems installed in earthquake-prone areas. Yet there were no major earthquakes in the continental United States between 1940 and 1970, and it was not until the San Fernando earthquake in California in 1971 that the NFPA 13 guidance was tested. Following that earthquake it was observed that the performance of the sprinkler system obviously depended on how well the building itself survived the ground movement—if the sprinklered building fared well, so did the sprinkler system. Studies of the performance of sprinkler systems in the Loma Prieta earthquake in the San Francisco area in 1989 and the Northridge earthquake in the Los Angeles area in 1994 were the basis of additional refinements to sprinkler system rules, which are also often applied to other water-based fire protection systems.

The hanger rules of NFPA 13 are also directly referenced or at least serve as the basis for rules within NFPA standards for other water-based fire suppression systems. For this reason, the committee responsible for the hanging and bracing criteria is designated the Committee on Hanging and Bracing of Water-Based Fire Protection Systems. Today, the rules within NFPA 13 that address structural support can be considered in four parts: rules for hangers, rules for hanger installation, rules for bracing systems against earthquake movement, and rules for joint restraint of underground piping systems.

For related topics, see the following chapters in Section 16: Chapter 1, "Principles of Automatic Sprinkler System Performance"; Chapter 2, "Automatic Sprinklers"; and Chapter 3, "Automatic Sprinkler Systems."

Russell P. Fleming, P.E., is executive vice-president for the National Fire Sprinkler Association, Inc., in Patterson, New York. He has served on more than a dozen different NFPA technical committees, including the Technical Correlating Committee on Automatic Sprinklers.

TABLE 16.4.1 Maximum Pipe Stand Heights

		Pipe Stand Diameter									
Diameter of Pipe		*1½ in.*		*2 in.*		*2½ in.*		*3 in.*		*4 in.*	
1½ in.	(40 mm)	10 ft	(3.0 m)	14 ft	(4.3 m)	18 ft	(5.5 m)	28 ft	(8.5 m)	30 ft	(9.1 m)
2 in.	(50 mm)	8 ft	(2.4 m)	12 ft	(3.7 m)	16 ft	(4.9 m)	26 ft	(7.9 m)	30 ft	(9.1 m)
2½ in.	(65 mm)	6 ft	(1.8 m)	10 ft	(3.0 m)	14 ft	(4.3 m)	24 ft	(7.3 m)	30 ft	(9.1 m)
3 in.	(75 mm)	—	—	8 ft	(2.4 m)	12 ft	(3.7 m)	22 ft	(6.7 m)	30 ft	(9.1 m)
>3 in.	(>75 mm)	—	—	—	—	—	—	—	—	10 ft	(3.0 m)

Source: NFPA 15, *Standard for Water Spray Fixed Systems for Fire Protection.*

HANGERS

Hanger Types

Various types of hangers (Figure 16.4.1) are used to support fire protection piping, with a variety of components used to attach to the building structure or to attach to the piping. Some types of hangers combine the building attachment component and the pipe attachment component. This would include U-type hangers and short straps, sometimes referred to as clips. Adjustable swivel ring hangers (also commonly known as adjustable steel band hangers), clevis hangers, and split ring hangers are the pipe attachment components used most commonly for suspending horizontal fire protection piping. C-type clamps are the most common structure attachment components for steel structures, and attach rigidly to one edge of the top or bottom flange of a structural member. All-thread mild steel rods are commonly used between the structural attachment and the piping attachment.

Listing of Hangers

Hanger components that attach directly to the building structure or to the piping are required by NFPA standards to be listed for use in fire protection systems. An exception is made within NFPA 13 for components that are made of ferrous metal, are certified by a professional engineer to meet the load requirements stated previously, and are supported adequately and in conformance with the maximum spacing rules.

Hangers made from mild steel rod, such as U-hooks and eye rods, are not required to be listed. Mild steel rods are considered to have demonstrated through practice their ability to support the required loads with adequate safety factors. Pipe straps are not included in the exception and therefore must be listed. Typical fasteners such as screws and bolts are also exempt from the listing requirement.

Special listed pipe can be required to use special hangers or hanger spacing as part of its listing limitations and restrictions. Manufacturers are obligated to make such product data available.

Floor-Mounted Supports

NFPA system installation standards have not traditionally discussed floor supports. Because most fire protection piping systems are located within buildings and because it is desirable to maximize usable floor space, piping is usually supported on hangers from overhead structural members. Nevertheless, floor-mounted supports have often been used for risers other than those protruding straight upward through the floor. A floor support usually includes some type of saddle to help avoid slippage of the pipe.

NFPA 15, *Standard for Water Spray Fixed Systems for Fire Protection,* provides rules governing sizing of pipe stands used to support fire protection piping in the absence of a building structure (Tables 16.4.1 and 16.4.2). The criteria include allowance to increase spacing between vertical supports by up to half of the length of braces extending from the vertical supports to the horizontal piping (Figure 16.4.2).

Hanger Loads

There is a difference between the safety factors applied to the hanger versus those for the building structure. In general, the hanger components are expected to support five times the weight of the water-filled piping plus a load of 250 lb (114 kg) at any point of piping support. The intent is not to simultaneously require loading of all hangers, but to represent the possibility of an individual using the piping to support the weight of a human body. This has often been the case in industrial occupancies, where sprinkler system piping may be temporarily loaded during maintenance operations such as ceiling cleaning or painting. The 250 lb (114 kg) load is specified at the point of

TABLE 16.4.2 Pipe Stand Distance

Loop Size		Distance Between Pipe Stands	
in.	*mm*	*ft*	*m*
1	25	10	3.0
1½	40	12	3.7
2	50	14	4.3
2½–8	65–200	15	4.6

Source: NFPA 15, *Standard for Water Spray Fixed Systems for Fire Protection.*

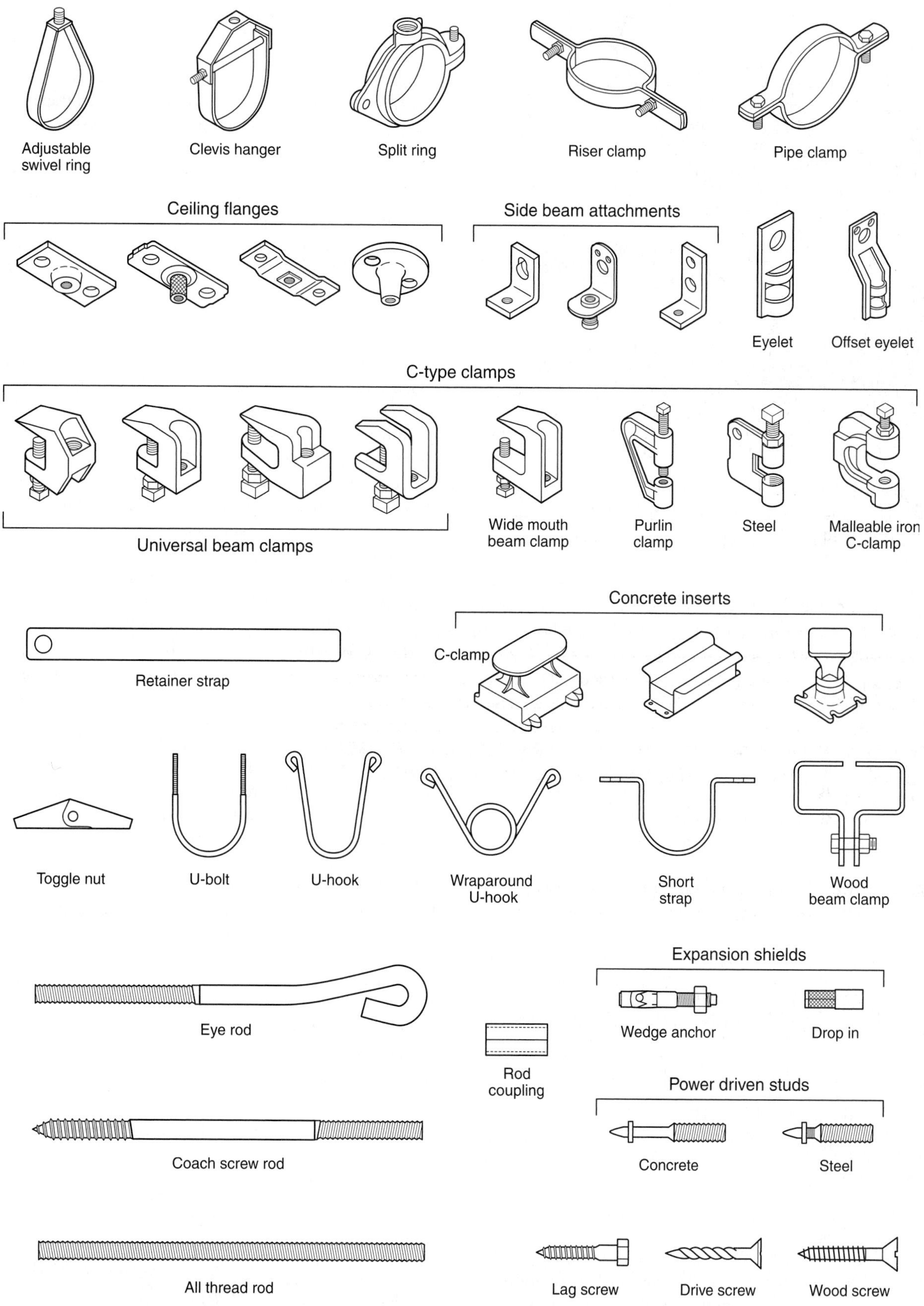

FIGURE 16.4.1 Common Types of Acceptable Hangers

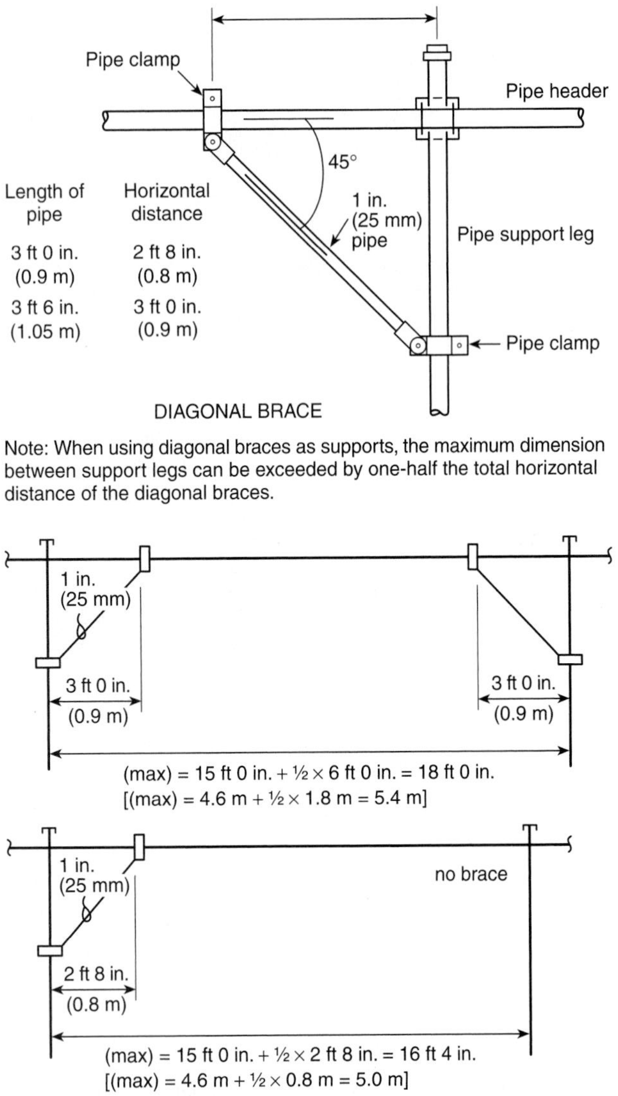

FIGURE 16.4.2 Sway/Support Brace

hanging because it is recognized that some types of piping will not support the additional load at midspan.

The structure itself must be capable of supporting the weight of the water-filled pipe plus a load of 250 lb (114 kg) at each point of support. The safety factor of five is not applied so as to permit the installation of systems in a wider number of existing buildings. There are two exceptions to the structural support requirements stated within the standard. One permits toggle hangers for piping 1½ in. (40 mm) or smaller under ceilings of hollow tile or metal lath and plaster. The other permits drilling or punching vertical members of metal deck for support of pipe 1 in. (25 mm) and smaller and using through bolts. Neither of these special options would be expected to carry the 250 lb (114 kg) load in addition to the weight of the water-filled pipe. The use of a suspended ceiling to support a listed flexible sprinkler drop is another exception, although not specifically addressed as such within NFPA 13.

Trapeze Hangers

Trapeze hangers are used where there is a need to provide a support for hangers between the structural members of the building. Like the trapeze that supports an acrobat, a trapeze hanger provides a span for the support of a sprinkler system or other fire protection piping (Figure 16.4.3).

In a fire sprinkler system, trapeze hangers usually support the larger piping, or mains. This is because it is most efficient to run the branch lines perpendicular to the closely spaced joists or purlins. In this manner, the joists or purlins provide ready points of attachment for hangers for most of the system piping. This means that the mains must generally be supported from the primary structural members that are supporting the joists, or purlins. Where there is a need for points of support between the primary structural members, trapeze hangers can be provided, attached on both ends to adjacent joists or purlins.

NFPA 13 treats trapeze hangers as an extension of the building structure, based on the fact that a trapeze hanger is always an alternative to a modification of the structure that would permit an acceptable point of hanging. This is especially true with wood frame structures. Joists are sometimes added where needed to attach system hangers. Some manufacturers of composite wood joists publish details showing how wood trapeze members are to be affixed between adjacent joists to provide attachment points for sprinkler piping. Because trapeze hangers are considered an extension of the building structure, their requirements are not based on the "five times" safety factor used for hangers, but rather on the requirement used for the building structure, that is, the weight of the water-filled piping plus 250 lb (114 kg).

NFPA 13 contains two tables that simplify the selection of trapeze hangers. Both tables are based on the concept of the trapeze hanger as a simple center-loaded span. Based on the use of steel with a tensile strength of 15 ksi supporting a maximum 15 ft (5 m) of pipe, Table 16.4.3 provides the minimum section modulus needed based on the span of the trapeze and the diameter of the pipe to be supported. Values are separately provided for Schedule 10 pipe and for Schedule 40 pipe, or Schedule 30 for sizes 8 in. (200 mm) and larger. A formula in Appendix A of

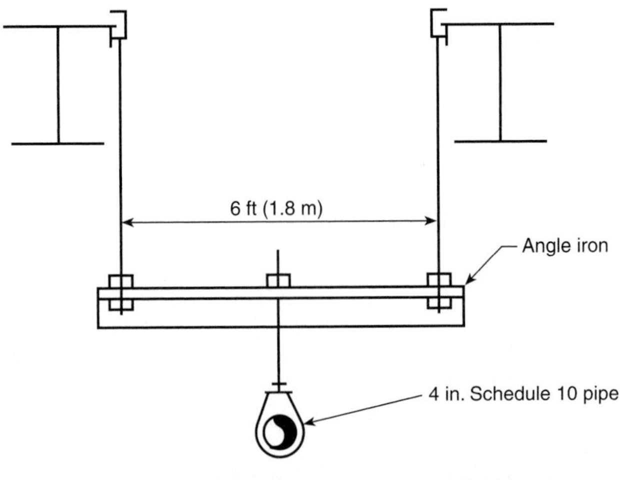

FIGURE 16.4.3 Trapeze Hanger

TABLE 16.4.3 Section Modulus Required for Trapeze Members (in.^{3})

Span of Trapeze	*1 in.*	*1¼ in.*	*1½ in.*	*2 in.*	*2½ in.*	*3 in.*	*3½ in.*	*4 in.*	*5 in.*	*6 in.*	*8 in.*	*10 in.*
1 ft 6 in.	0.08	0.09	0.09	0.09	0.10	0.11	0.12	0.13	0.15	0.18	0.24	0.32
	0.08	0.09	0.09	0.10	0.11	0.12	0.13	0.15	0.18	0.22	0.30	0.41
2 ft 0 in.	0.11	0.12	0.12	0.13	0.13	0.15	0.16	0.17	0.20	0.24	0.32	0.43
	0.11	0.12	0.12	0.13	0.15	0.16	0.18	0.20	0.24	0.29	0.40	0.55
2 ft 6 in.	0.14	0.14	0.15	0.16	0.17	0.18	0.20	0.21	0.25	0.30	0.40	0.54
	0.14	0.15	0.15	0.16	0.18	0.21	0.22	0.25	0.30	0.36	0.50	0.68
3 ft 0 in.	0.17	0.17	0.18	0.19	0.20	0.22	0.24	0.26	0.31	0.36	0.48	0.65
	0.17	0.18	0.18	0.20	0.22	0.25	0.27	0.30	0.36	0.43	0.60	0.82
4 ft 0 in.	0.22	0.23	0.24	0.25	0.27	0.29	0.32	0.34	0.41	0.48	0.64	0.87
	0.22	0.24	0.24	0.26	0.29	0.33	0.36	0.40	0.48	0.58	0.80	1.09
5 ft 0 in.	0.28	0.29	0.30	0.31	0.34	0.37	0.40	0.43	0.51	0.59	0.80	1.08
	0.29	0.29	0.30	0.33	0.37	0.41	0.45	0.49	0.60	0.72	1.00	1.37
6 ft 0 in.	0.33	0.35	0.36	0.38	0.41	0.44	0.48	0.51	0.61	0.71	0.97	1.30
	0.34	0.35	0.36	0.39	0.44	0.49	0.54	0.59	0.72	0.87	1.20	1.64
7 ft 0 in.	0.39	0.40	0.41	0.44	0.47	0.52	0.55	0.60	0.71	0.83	1.13	1.52
	0.39	0.41	0.43	0.46	0.51	0.58	0.63	0.69	0.84	1.01	1.40	1.92
8 ft 0 in.	0.44	0.46	0.47	0.50	0.54	0.59	0.63	0.68	0.81	0.95	1.29	1.73
	0.45	0.47	0.49	0.52	0.59	0.66	0.74	0.79	0.96	1.16	1.61	2.19
9 ft 0 in.	0.50	0.52	0.53	0.56	0.61	0.66	0.71	0.77	0.92	1.07	1.45	1.95
	0.50	0.53	0.55	0.59	0.66	0.74	0.81	0.89	1.08	1.30	1.81	2.46
10 ft 0 in.	0.56	0.58	0.59	0.63	0.68	0.74	0.79	0.85	1.02	1.19	1.61	2.17
	0.56	0.59	0.61	0.65	0.74	0.82	0.90	0.99	1.20	1.44	2.01	2.74

Notes:
1. Top values are for Schedule 10 pipe; bottom values are for Schedule 40 pipe.
2. The table is based on a maximum allowable bending stress of 15 ksi and a midspan concentrated load from 15 ft (4.6 m) of water-filled pipe, plus 250 lb (114 kg).

For SI units, 1 in. = 25.4 mm; 1 in.^{3} = 16,387 mm^3; 1 ft = 0.3048 m.

Source: NFPA 13, *Standard for the Installation of Sprinkler Systems.*

NFPA 13 can be used to compute a shorter equivalent length of span where it can be established that the load will be to one side as opposed to the center of the trapeze span.

Table 16.4.4 provides the section modulus available using Schedule 10 pipe, Schedule 40 pipe, or selected steel angles as the trapeze member. It is only necessary to ensure that the trapeze selected from Table 16.4.4 has a section modulus greater than or equal to that needed from Table 16.4.3.

NFPA 13 requires that the trapeze member be secured to prevent slippage. Because pipe is readily available to sprinkler contractors, it is the most common type of trapeze member, and it is typically a smaller pipe size than the pipe being supported. To ensure adequate strength of hanger components, NFPA 13 requires that all ring, strap, or clevis hangers supporting the larger pipe be sized for the larger pipe. The ring or strap must be shaped to accommodate the smaller pipe size. Otherwise the potential exists for the ring or strap to elongate over time with the load, which could result in a change of pitch of the piping.

Aside from steel pipe and angles, other types of structural members are used as trapeze members, provided the section modulus is acceptable. This allows the use of such things as steel channels, where the manufacturers or specifiers would be expected to ensure the minimum tensile strength and to provide information on the available section modulus. Because the section modulus of a nonsymmetrical member changes with orientation, it is important that orientation be considered.

The NFPA 13 language does not specifically allow the use of wood trapeze members, and the language in the standard calling for ferrous hangers and banning the use of nails as fasteners might appear to prohibit their use. This is when it must be recognized that the building designer always has the option of allowing a modification of the building structure to provide a built-in trapeze. The manner in which extensions are made to the building structure must be acceptable to the responsible design professional.

HANGER INSTALLATION

Spacing of hangers is based essentially on the expected beam strength of the piping. For this reason, NFPA 13 and related standards reduce allowable spans for piping with less beam strength than traditional standard weight (Schedule 40) steel pipe. Table 16.4.5 shows the maximum distance between hangers based on type of piping. Other rules, such as the general requirement that hangers be provided on crossmains between every two branch lines, can supersede these maximum spacings.

Special rules relate to hanger installation. For example, nails are not permitted to fasten hangers. Holes must be predrilled for

TABLE 16.4.4 Available Section Moduli of Common Trapeze Hangers (in.^{3})

Pipe (in.)	*Modulus*	*Angles*	*Modulus*	*Pipe (in.)*	*Modulus*	*Angles*	*Modulus*
Schedule 10				Schedule 40			
1	0.12	1 1/2 × 1 1/2 × 3/16	0.10	1	0.13	3 × 2 1/2 × 3/16	0.43
1 1/4	0.19	2 × 2 × 1/8	0.13	1 1/4	0.23	3 × 3 × 3/16	0.44
1 1/2	0.26	2 × 1 1/2 × 3/16	0.18	1 1/2	0.33	2 1/2 × 2 1/2 × 5/16	0.48
2	0.42	2 × 2 × 3/16	0.19	2	0.56	3 × 2 × 1/4	0.54
2 1/2	0.69	2 × 2 × 1/4	0.25	2 1/2	1.06	2 1/2 × 2 × 3/8	0.55
3	1.04	2 1/2 × 1 1/2 × 3/16	0.28	3	1.72	2 1/2 × 2 1/2 × 3/8	0.57
3 1/2	1.38	2 1/2 × 2 × 3/16	0.29	3 1/2	2.39	3 × 3 × 1/4	0.58
4	1.76	2 × 2 × 5/16	0.30	4	3.21	3 × 3 × 5/16	0.71
5	3.03	2 1/2 × 2 1/2 × 3/16	0.30	5	5.45	2 1/2 × 2 1/2 × 1/2	0.72
6	4.35	2 × 2 × 3/8	0.35	6	8.50	3 1/2 × 2 1/2 × 1/4	0.75
		2 1/2 × 2 1/2 × 1/4	0.39			3 × 2 1/2 × 3/8	0.81
		3 × 2 × 3/16	0.41			3 × 3 × 3/8	0.83
						3 1/2 × 2 1/2 × 5/16	0.93
						3 × 3 × 7/16	0.95
						4 × 4 × 1/4	1.05
						3 × 3 × 1/2	1.07
						4 × 3 × 5/16	1.23
						4 × 4 × 5/16	1.29
						4 × 3 × 3/8	1.46
						4 × 4 × 3/8	1.52
						5 × 3 1/2 × 5/16	1.94
						4 × 4 × 1/2	1.97
						4 × 4 × 5/8	2.40
						4 × 4 × 3/4	2.81
						6 × 4 × 3/8	3.32
						6 × 4 × 1/2	4.33
						6 × 4 × 3/4	6.25
						6 × 6 × 1	8.57

For SI units, 1 in. = 25.4 mm; 1 in.^{3} = 16,387 mm^3; 1 ft = 0.3048 m.
Source: NFPA 13, *Standard for the Installation of Sprinkler Systems.*

TABLE 16.4.5 Maximum Distance Between Hangers (ft-in.)

	Nominal Pipe Size (in.)											
	3/4	*1*	*1 1/4*	*1 1/2*	*2*	*2 1/2*	*3*	*3 1/2*	*4*	*5*	*6*	*8*
Steel pipe except threaded lightwall	NA	12-0	12-0	15-0	15-0	15-0	15-0	15-0	15-0	15-0	15-0	15-0
Threaded lightwall steel pipe	NA	12-0	12-0	12-0	12-0	12-0	12-0	NA	NA	NA	NA	NA
Copper tube	8-0	8-0	10-0	10-0	12-0	12-0	12-0	15-0	15-0	15-0	15-0	15-0
CPVC	5-6	6-0	6-6	7-0	8-0	9-0	10-0	NA	NA	NA	NA	NA
Polybutylene (IPS)	NA	3-9	4-7	5-0	5-11	NA	NA	NA	NA	NA	NA	NA
Polybutylene (CTS)	2-11	3-4	3-11	4-5	5-5	NA	NA	NA	NA	NA	NA	NA
Ductile Iron Pipe	NA	NA	NA	NA	NA	NA	15-0	NA	15-0	NA	15-0	15-0

For SI units, 1 in. = 25.4 mm; 1 ft = 0.3048 m.
Note: IPS = iron pipe size; CTS = copper tube size.
Source: NFPA 13, *Standard for the Installation of Sprinkler Systems.*

proper installation of lag screws and coach screw rods. Wood screws must be installed with a screwdriver. Drive screws are permitted only in the horizontal position and only for pipe 2 in. (50 mm) and smaller.

Hangers in Earthquake Areas

Special limitations apply to hangers in areas considered subject to earthquakes. Retaining straps must be provided for all C-type clamps. The retaining strap either must be listed as part of the hanger listing or must meet specified minimum dimensions. In the absence of an adequate lip on the structural member to hold the retaining strap, the strap can be secured with a bolt or screw.

Unless they are specially listed for use in high-risk earthquake areas, powder-driven fasteners are not permitted to attach hangers where the assigned earthquake accelerations exceed half of gravity, or, in other words, where the lateral forces to be resisted exceed half the weight of the water-filled pipe.

Momentum Restraint

Relatively little attention has been given to the subject of restraint or bracing against momentum of waterflow within water-based fire suppression systems. Because linear momentum of fluid flow is conserved, unbalanced momentum forces can occur at changes in piping direction when water surges into a deluge, dry, or preaction system, and to a lesser extent can take place within a wet pipe system as well. However, it is generally believed that the safety factors inherent in the system to resist hydrostatic forces adequately handle such momentum forces, especially with regard to threaded and mechanical joints. To resist permanent shifting of the piping the system relies on the structural attachment components, in combination with the rigidity of the system piping. Where flexible couplings allow angular displacement and the pipe is therefore not capable of resisting loads internally, the hanger attachments must provide sufficient resistance through their method of attachment to avoid being pulled off the building structural component.

Beginning in 1987, NFPA 13 was modified to recognize the impulse force that is the reaction to flow of water through individual sprinklers. Concern was expressed that a single pendent sprinkler extending through a ceiling and operated under high pressure could be lifted above the ceiling from the thrust forces. Subsequent tests showed that a standard $K = 5.6$ ($K_m = 8.0$) orifice spray pendent sprinkler operating at 150 psi (10.3 bar) would experience a thrust force of 70–90 lb (10–13 N). Figure 16.4.4 shows the upward deflection of 1 in. (25.4 mm) Schedule 40 pipe under steady state flow of sprinklers with nominal orifice coefficients $K = 5.6$ ($K_m = 80$) and $K = 8.0$ ($K_m = 115$) at various pressures in the absence of any special restraint.

A pendent sprinkler at the end of a branch line should be given special restraint where the maximum pressure at the sprinkler exceeds 100 psi (6.9 bar) and the sprinkler extends downward through a ceiling. The special restraint involves use of a hanger assembly that prevents upward movement of the sprinkler, located no more than 12 in. (300 mm) from the end of steel pipe branch line, or no more than 6 in. (150 mm) from the end of a copper tube branch line. If these limits are exceeded, the branch line can be extended beyond the last sprinkler on the

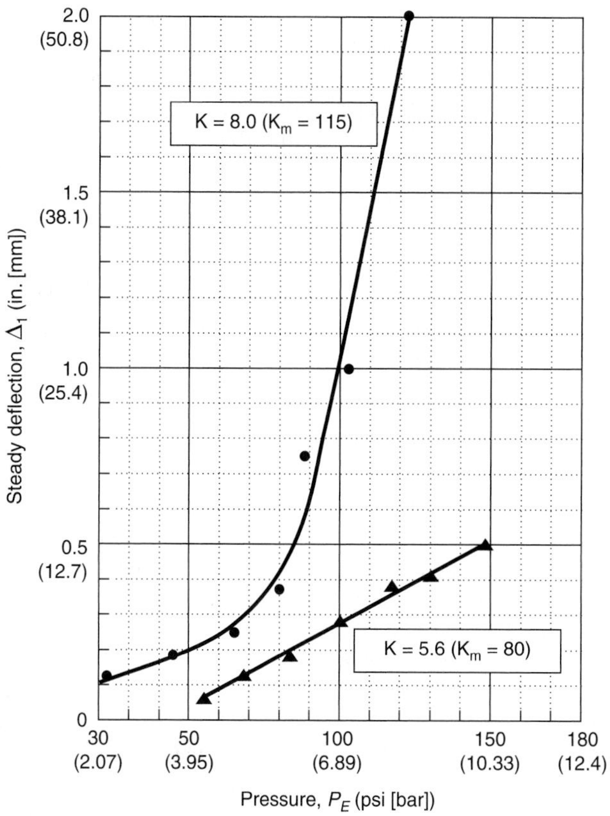

FIGURE 16.4.4 Pipe Deflection

branch line. A parallel provision applies to pendent sprinklers through ceilings located on armovers.

The uplift phenomenon occurs only with the end sprinkler operating. The uplift is considerably reduced with a second sprinkler flowing, and is negligible for the next-to-end sprinkler flowing alone. A formal interpretation was issued by the Committee on Automatic Sprinklers to clarify that the 100 psi (6.9 bar) trigger does not include potential pressure supplied through the fire department connection.

EARTHQUAKE BRACING

Bracing is only one aspect of protecting fire sprinkler systems against earthquakes, but it is probably the most visible aspect. The others are providing necessary flexibility through the use of flexible couplings and clearances and providing restraint. Like bracing, restraint helps to hold piping in place, but to a lesser degree.

Successful bracing of fire protection systems involves determination of appropriate force factors, tentative placement of sway bracing, determination of loads to braces, and verification that the loads can be carried by the sway brace components.

Determination of Force Factors

The determination of seismic force levels is of primary significance in providing bracing, because bracing must be sized and spaced to resist the anticipated forces. NFPA 13 has never dealt with the issue of where earthquake protection is to be required, but only provided a means of protecting the system. The decision to require protection of sprinkler systems or other mechanical systems against earthquake forces, as well as the magnitude of those forces, is generally stated within building codes, or determined by other authorities having jurisdiction. The decision is based on the past seismic activity of an area and its potential for future earthquakes.

Changes in Protection Criteria. Since past building codes were not always specific with regard to anticipated earthquake forces, NFPA 13 protection criteria traditionally were based on an assumed horizontal acceleration of half of gravity or 0.5 g. This acceleration resulted in a horizontal force factor of $F_p = 0.5W_p$ or a horizontal force equivalent to half the weight of the water-filled piping. This acceleration was judged to be suitably conservative for even highly active earthquake areas, and it was not considered economically justified to fine-tune system bracing loads to accommodate lower expected earthquake forces in some localities. The 0.5 g value continues to serve as the default value for bracing criteria. However, since the 1994 edition, NFPA 13 has permitted the use of other force factors to accommodate code requirements that specify the use of higher or lower horizontal acceleration values. Use of alternative force factors is becoming common for the following two reasons:

1. Both the 1989 Loma Prieta and 1994 Northridge earthquakes in California demonstrated horizontal accelerations in excess of 0.5 g.
2. Earthquake protection of sprinkler systems is now mandated in many areas where expected maximum accelerations are less than 0.5 g.

Essentially, the force equation became $F_p = C_pW_p$, where the value of C_p was determined by the code or other authority, and could be higher or lower than 0.5.

Coordination of Earthquake Protection Provisions. In a tentative interim amendment (TIA) to the 2002 edition, which became effective August 6, 2003, and to an even greater extent in the changes to the 2007 edition, additional changes were made to better coordinate the earthquake protection provisions of NFPA 13 with those of the National Earthquake Hazards Reduction Program's *Recommended Provisions for Seismic Regulations for New Buildings and Other Structures.*[1] These provisions, which have themselves gone through several iterations, were developed through the Building Seismic Safety Council of the National Institute of Building Sciences, with funding from the U.S. Federal Emergency Management Agency. The provisions have served as the basis of successive changes to model building codes in the United States and are now incorporated in ASCE 7, *Minimum Design Loads for Buildings and Other Structures.*[2] ASCE 7 is in turn adopted by reference in current model building codes, with the 2005 edition (ASCE 7-05) adopted by the 2006 editions of both the International Building Code®[3] and *NFPA 5000®, Building Construction and Safety Code®*.

Seismic Design Force Formula. The 2003 TIA to NFPA 13 reduced the allowable fastener loads to match current industry standards, limited the maximum spacing of lateral braces to 40 ft (12.2 m) on center, and provided clarification of how NFPA 13 could be used in conjunction with the seismic design force formula contained in ASCE 7 for use with nonstructural components:

$$F_p = 0.4a_pS_{DS}W_p\frac{1+2(z/h)}{R_p/I_p}$$

where

F_p = Seismic design force

S_{DS} = Design spectral acceleration, short period, found as $S_{DS} = \frac{2}{3}S_{MS}$, where S_{MS} is the maximum considered earthquake (MCE) acceleration, and is in turn found as $S_{MS} = F_aS_S$, where F_a is an acceleration-based site coefficient and S_S is the short period mapped acceleration (Figure 16.4.5)

W_p = Component weight, in this case the sprinkler piping contributing to the load on a brace

a_p = Component amplification factor affected by the type of seismic attachment

z = Height in the structure of the point of attachment of the component

h = Average roof height of the structure

R_p = Component response modification factor

I_p = Component importance factor

Applying the Force Formula. In using this equation, certain values are assigned for fire sprinkler systems in ASCE 7-05. The importance factor I_p is 1.5. The component response modification factor R_p for a steel piping system is 4.5, and the component amplification factor a_p is 2.5. It is worth noting that these values changed between the 2002 and 2005 editions of ASCE 7. The TIA issued on the 2002 edition of NFPA 13 in 2003 suggested the use of $R_p = 3.5$, correlating with the 2002 edition of ASCE 7. ASCE 7-02 also specified a value of 1.0 for a_p compared to the value of 2.5 specified in the 2005 edition.

As noted above, ASCE 7–05 is the standard referenced by the 2006 editions of the International Building Code and *NFPA 5000,* whereas ASCE 7-02 is referenced for use by the 2003 editions of the International Building Code and *NFPA 5000.* The 2000 edition of the International Building Code also included text parallel to the 2002 edition of ASCE 7. As such, compliance with the 2000 or 2003 editions of these codes would produce an a_p/R_p ratio of 1.0/3.5 = 0.29, whereas compliance with the 2006 editions of these codes produces a ratio of 2.5/4.5 = 0.55, resulting in significantly higher forces with the use of the equation. To some extent this has been offset by the clarification that the calculated design force can be reduced by a factor of 1.4 in recognition of the fact that ASCE 7 is based on strength design, whereas NFPA 13 uses allowable stress design. Prior to the 2007 edition, all loads in NFPA 13 were at allowable stress levels with the exception of the buckling loads for brace members. In the 2007 edition, tables that contained the allowable loads on braces were reduced to add a factor of safety appropriate to the use of allowable stress design.

The 1+2(z/h) factor in the design force equation leads to force levels that are three times as high at the top of the building than at the base, regardless of building height. Because it is presumed that sprinkler systems are installed through the building, the simplifying assumption generally used is that $1+2(z/h) = 3$, with forces determined on the basis of the worst case, or, in other words, the highest level.

The Soil Factor. In the determination of $S_{DS} = \frac{2}{3} S_{MS} = \frac{2}{3} F_a S_S$, F_a is a site-specific soil factor. This factor can range from 0.8 for hard rock up to 2.5 in areas with softer soil and low seismic accelerations. S_S is the short period (0.2 second or 5 cycles per second) seismic acceleration representing a 2 percent probability of being exceeded in 50 years. The 0.2 second period is considered reasonably representative of the shortest effective period of buildings and structures, and the 2 percent probability of being exceeded in 50 years means that it relates to the 2500 year earthquake. Values of S_S are available on maps developed by the U.S. Geological Survey (USGS) and can be accessed at the USGS website. Figures 16.4.5 (a)

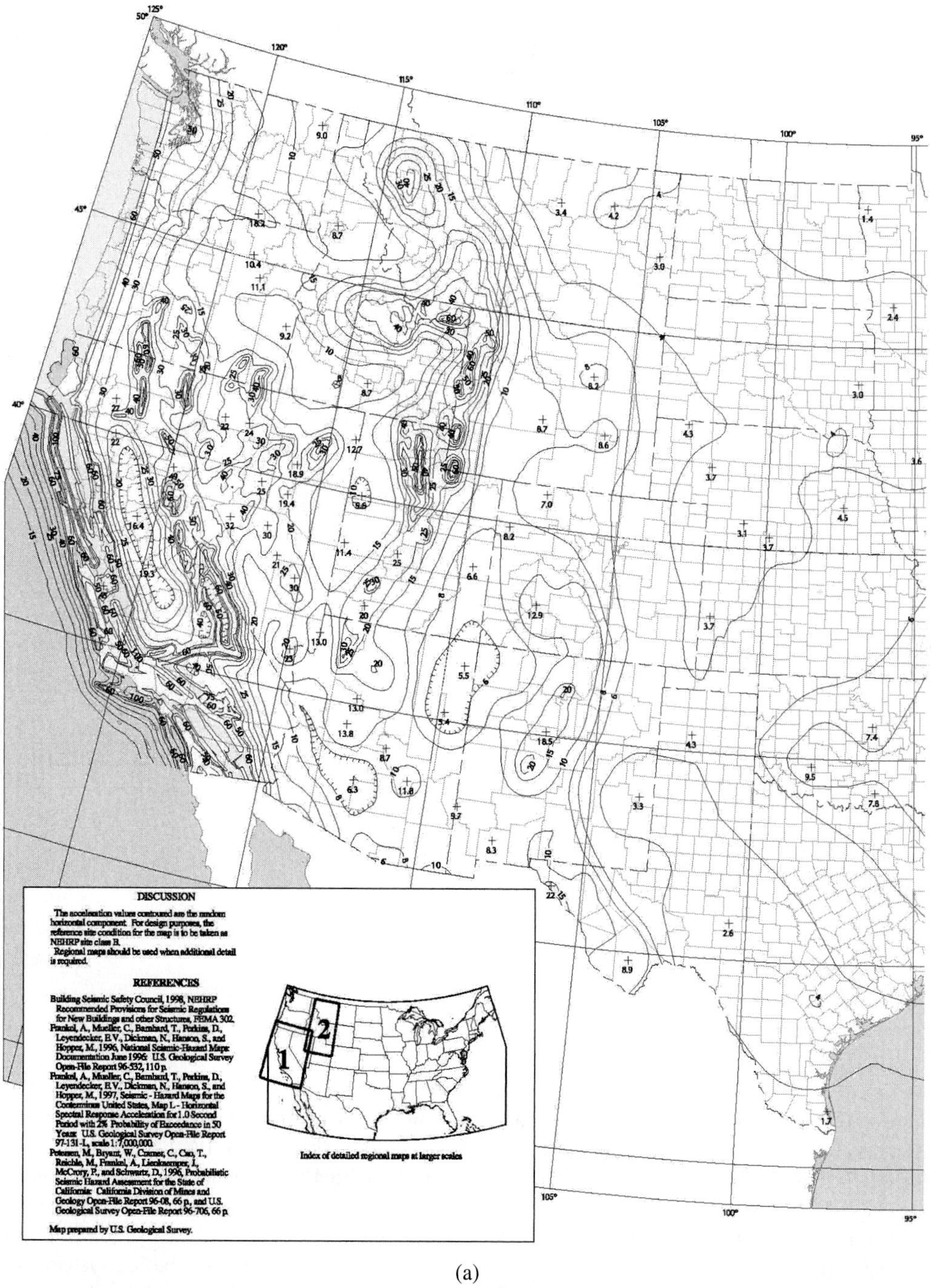

(a)

FIGURE 16.4.5 Values of S_S for (a and b) the Continental United States and (c and d) Region 1 of the United States (Courtesy U.S. Geological Survey)

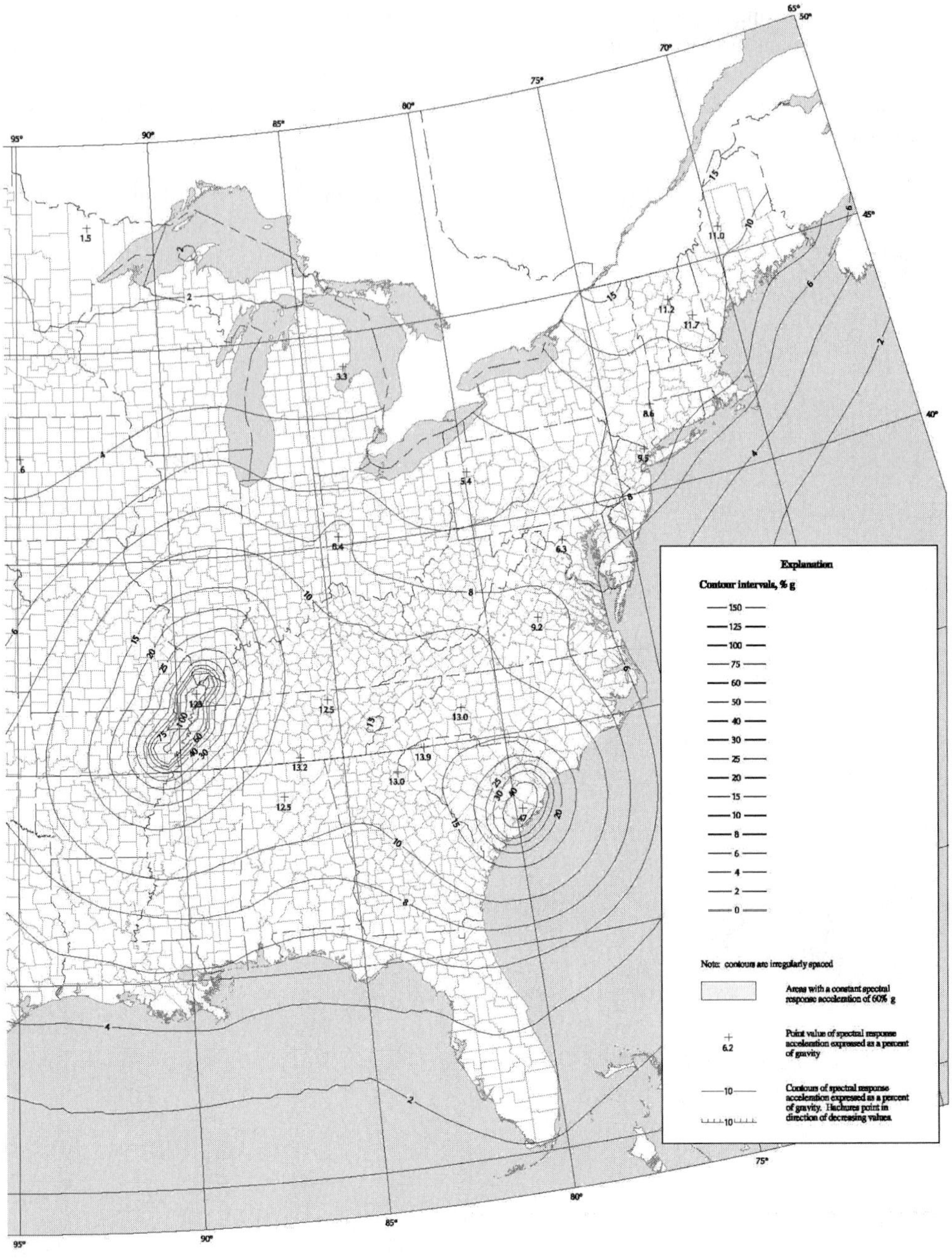

(b)

FIGURE 16.4.5 Continued

through (d) show the values of S_S for the continental United States and in more specific detail for the seismically active state of California. Figures 16.4.5 (a) and (b) show the maximum considered earthquake ground motion for the coterminous United States of 1.0 second spectral response acceleration (5 percent of critical damping), Site Class B. Figures 16.4.5 (c) and (d) show the maximum considered earthquake ground motion of 1.0 second spectral response acceleration (5 percent of critical damping), Site Class B for Region 1 of the United States.

Using a Seismic Coefficient. A simplified approach to determining seismic forces on sprinkler systems was developed for the 2007 edition of NFPA 13 and involves the factors shown in Table 16.4.6. The table assigns the "seismic coefficient " or acceleration factor C_p based directly on the mapped value of S_S from Figures 16.4.5(a), (b), (c), or (d). Multiplying the acceleration factor C_p by the contributing system weight W_p gives the force that must be resisted by an earthquake brace.

A number of conservative assumptions were used in the development of the NFPA 13 simplified approach. In addition

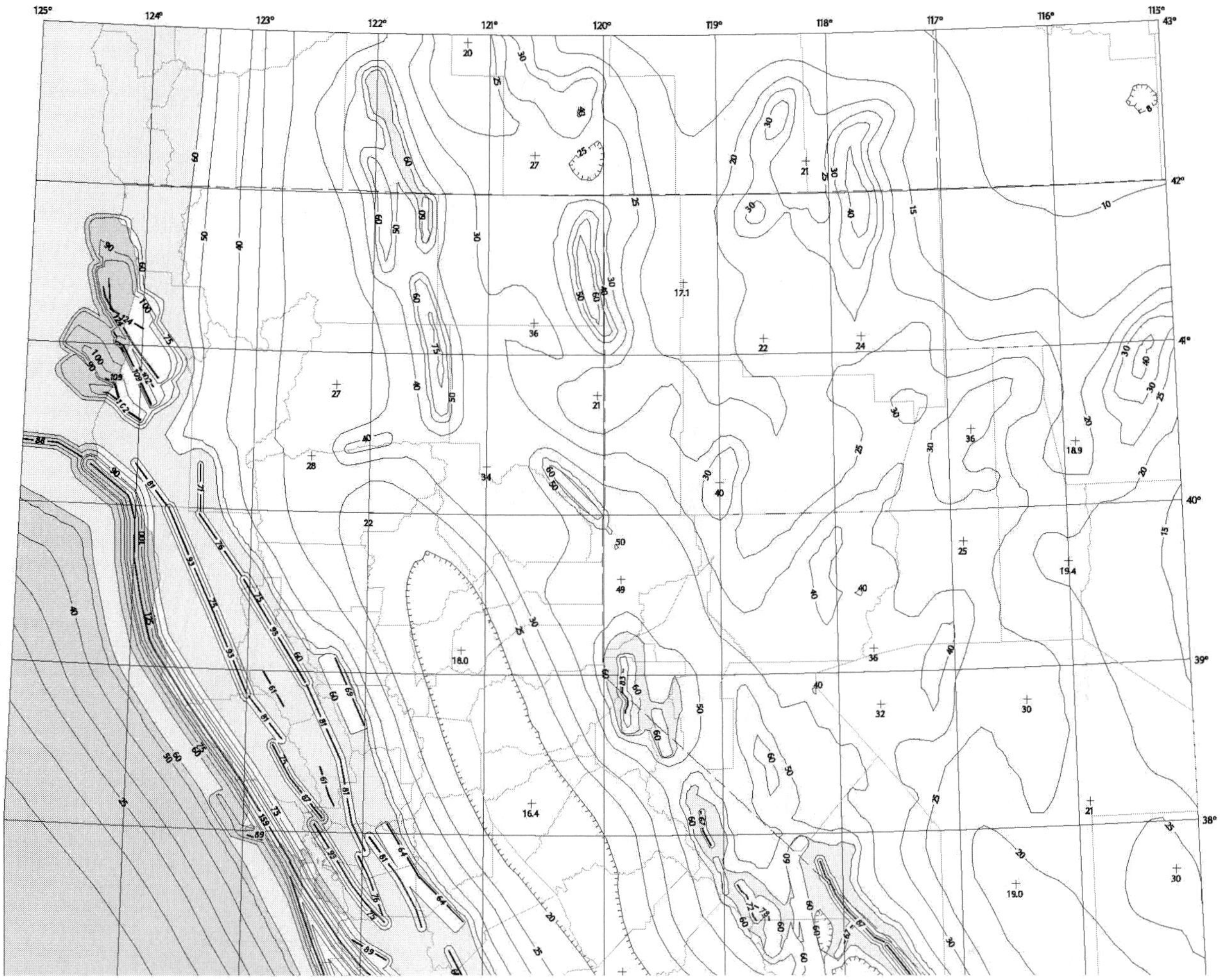

(c)

FIGURE 16.4.5 Continued

TABLE 16.4.6 Seismic Coefficient Table

S_s	C_p
0.33 or less	0.31
0.50	0.40
0.75	0.43
0.95	0.50
1.00	0.52
1.25	0.60
1.50	0.71
2.00	0.95
2.40	1.14
3.00	1.43

Source: NFPA 13, *Standard for the Installation of Sprinkler Systems*, Table 9.3.5.6.2, 2007, p. 13-101.

to the top-story assumption discussed above, the table is based on the maximum value of F_a for a given range of S_S, or in other words, poor soil conditions. The user of the standard always has the option to determine lateral forces in accordance with the actual equation of ASCE 7-05, as part of a more detailed analysis allowed by NFPA 13. For mapped acceleration values of S_S less than or equal to 0.33, the table provides a minimum lateral design acceleration of $C_P = 0.31$, which is less than the traditional default value of 0.5, but higher than would be obtained through the use of the ASCE 7 equation in many low-risk seismic areas.

Sway Bracing Placement

Sprinkler systems are provided with sway bracing to resist both lateral and longitudinal horizontal seismic loads as well as to prevent vertical motion resulting from strong seismic loads. The structural components to which bracing is attached must be capable of carrying the added applied loads.

Earthquake bracing can be either lateral (preventing motion perpendicular to the run of the pipe) or longitudinal (parallel to

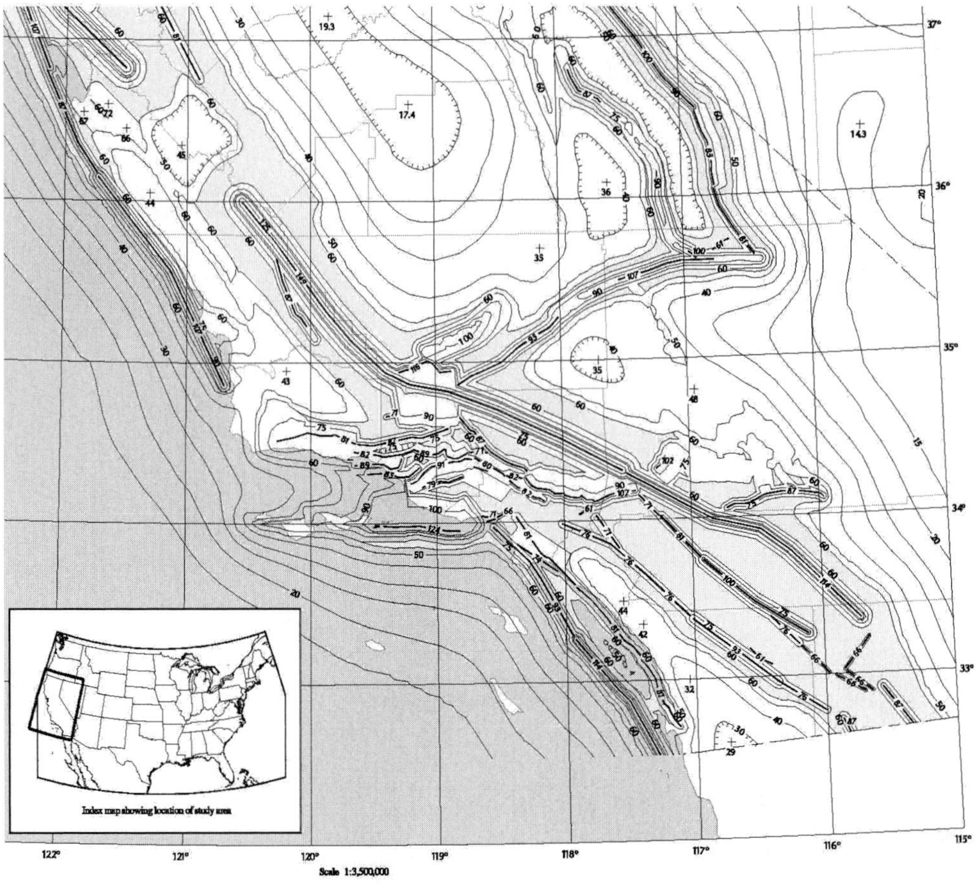

(d)

FIGURE 16.4.5 Continued

the run of the pipe). A four-way brace is one that prevents both lateral and longitudinal movement.

Both lateral and longitudinal (four-way) bracing is required at the top of the riser. This keeps the top of the riser lined up with the floor/ceiling assembly.

Longitudinal bracing must be provided for all feed and cross mains at maximum 80 ft (24.4 m) intervals. The last brace must be within 40 ft (12.2 m) of the end of the main.

Lateral bracing must be provided for all feed and cross mains, and for branch lines with diameters 2½ in. (65 mm) and larger, although 2½ in. (65 mm) branch line starter pieces are not required to be braced if they do not exceed 12 ft (6.1 m) in length. A major change to the 2007 edition was the limitation of maximum lateral sway brace spacing based on the size of the pipe being braced and the contributory load. The traditional maximum brace spacing of 40 ft (12.2 m) still applies, but in situations involving high lateral forces or heavy branch lines, the maximum spacing may need to be reduced. This reduction is in recognition of the fact that maximum lateral brace spacing is related to the beam strength of the piping and in an attempt to limit pipe deflection as well as pipe stresses.

An exception allows the elimination of lateral bracing where piping is supported by hanger rods less than 6 in. (150 mm) in length. This length is measured between the top of the pipe and the point of attachment to the building structure.

For both longitudinal and lateral bracing, pipe runs less than 12 ft (3.6 m) are allowed to be included with adjacent runs and do not require their own braces provided the maximum distance between braces is observed. Braces within 2 ft (0.6 m) of a turn in the piping run can serve as both a lateral brace for one run and a longitudinal brace for the perpendicular run.

Determination of Loads

Prior to 1999, NFPA 13 permitted two methods of determining the loads to be carried by braces: the assigned load table and the zone of influence method. These two methods somewhat paralleled the pipe schedule method and hydraulic calculation method used to size pipe in sprinkler systems. Just as the role of pipe schedule systems has diminished in favor of consideration of actual water pressures, the assigned load table was deleted in favor of consideration of actual loads.

Using the zone of influence method involves evaluating the load that contributes to each brace. A longitudinal brace is expected to carry the load of the main to which it is connected in a length halfway to the adjacent braces in each direction. A lateral brace is similarly expected to carry the loads from the piping halfway to the next brace in both directions. However, for the lateral brace this includes the contributions of branch lines as well as mains. During an earthquake, the branch lines are not expected to move uniformly, preventing the contribution of their loads to the longitudinal braces on mains.

The weights of the piping contributing to each brace are accumulated and the total horizontal force calculated as $F_p = C_p W_p$ as explained above. A brace acting as both a lateral brace for one main and a longitudinal brace for another would be expected to carry the combined load simultaneously. Beginning with the 2002 edition of NFPA 13, the value of W_p was specified to be 1.15 times the nominal weight of the water-filled piping to account for the additional weight that might be imposed by fittings or sectional valves. Table 16.4.7 includes piping weights with the 1.15 multiplier.

Where multiple braces are to be installed with the same configuration along a main, it is standard practice to select the worst-case brace for purposes of determining the load to be carried. This would be the brace with the zone of influence that includes the heaviest total piping.

Loads on Sway Brace Components

The sway braces themselves are generally constructed of pipe, but can be of angles, rods, flats, channels, or other structural members with slenderness ratio limited to a maximum of 300. The slenderness ratio is found as l/r where l is the length and r is the least radius of gyration. Traditional bracing resists movement in both tension and compression, but tension-only cable bracing is now also available. Such tension-only bracing systems must be specially listed for use with sprinkler systems. Because the cables can only provide resistance to movement in tension, they must be provided on both sides of the piping at each point of support.

The sway braces are used as part of a sway brace assembly, which in addition to the brace typically consists of the sway brace fitting (the attachment to the pipe being braced) and the structure attachment fitting. These fittings must be listed and have been assigned maximum allowable loads. The allowable loads must be reduced where braces are installed, other than at the full horizontal (90 degree) position. Similar reductions in allowable loads for braces and fasteners are built into the tables contained in NFPA 13. The allowable load for a sway brace assembly is based on the weakest link of the brace, the sway brace fitting, the structure attachment fitting, and the fastener. The allowable load for a brace assembly must meet or exceed the load determined using the assigned load table or zone of influence method.

Sway braces are to be fastened tight and concentric, with eccentric loadings avoided. Welded tab attachments are acceptable for use in connecting longitudinal braces. Pipe must not be braced to building sections that will move differentially. Fastener load tables within the standard are based on various orientation/angle conditions of lag screws in wood, through bolts in wood, expansion shields in concrete and through bolts in steel.

NFPA 13 contains special rules for the fastening of sway braces. C-type clamps (with or without retaining straps) are prohibited from use in attaching sway braces to the building structure. Power-driven fasteners are also prohibited from use in attaching braces unless specifically listed for this service.

An appendix section cautions that although most current concrete fasteners in the marketplace are expansion anchors, the table within the standard is based on the use of "shield-type" or "lead cinch" concrete anchors. Professional engineers may specify alternative fastening arrangements.

Although NFPA 13 states its intent to prevent vertical motion resulting from seismic loads, it is generally expected that the downward force of gravity will sufficiently offset any

TABLE 16.4.7 Piping Weights

Nominal Dimensions		Weight of Water-Filled Pipe		1.15 Weight of Water-Filled Pipe		Nominal Dimensions		Weight of Water-Filled Pipe		1.15 Weight of Water-Filled Pipe	
in.	*mm*	*lb/ft*	*kg/m*	*lb/ft*	*kg/m*	*in.*	*mm*	*lb/ft*	*kg/m*	*lb/ft*	*kg/m*
Schedule 40 Pipe (in.)						Schedule 10 Pipe (in.)					
1	25	2.05	3.05	2.36	3.51	1	25	1.81	2.69	2.08	3.09
1¼	32	2.93	4.36	3.37	5.01	1¼	32	2.52	3.75	2.90	4.31
1½	40	3.61	5.37	4.15	6.18	1½	40	3.04	4.52	3.50	5.20
2	50	5.13	7.63	5.90	8.77	2	50	4.22	6.28	4.85	7.22
2½	65	7.89	11.74	9.07	13.50	2½	65	5.89	8.77	6.77	10.09
3	80	10.82	16.10	12.44	18.52	3	80	7.94	11.82	9.13	13.59
3½	90	13.48	20.06	15.50	23.07	3½	90	9.78	14.55	11.25	16.73
4	100	16.40	24.41	18.86	28.07	4	100	11.78	17.53	13.55	20.16
5	125	23.47	34.93	26.99	40.17	5	125	17.30	25.75	19.90	29.61
6	150	31.69	47.16	36.44	54.23	6	150	23.03	34.27	26.48	39.41
8*	200	47.70	70.99	54.86	81.64	8	200	40.08	59.65	46.09	68.60

*Schedule 30.

upward vertical earthquake loads, and that system hangers have sufficient safety factors to handle any downward vertical earthquake loads. As a result, the standard only addresses the net vertical reaction that would result from strong horizontal loads where the brace angle from vertical is relatively low. Where the horizontal force factor exceeds $0.5W_p$ and the brace angle is less than 45 degrees from vertical, or where the horizontal force factor exceeds $1.0W_p$ and the brace angle is less than 60 degrees from vertical, the braces are to be arranged to resist the net vertical reaction. For traditional rigid braces, this can be accomplished by providing an additional brace on the opposite side of the main. For special listed cable type braces, this can be accomplished by reinforcing the hanger rods to prevent buckling as well as upward movement.

JOINT RESTRAINT OF UNDERGROUND PIPING

Traditional bell and spigot underground piping using push-on joints relies on the resistance provided by the surrounding soil to hold it in place. This is sufficient for straight runs, but the forces at changes in direction must be resisted. For this reason, NFPA standards require all tees, plugs, caps, bends, and hydrant branches to be restrained against movement. NFPA 13 and NFPA 24, *Standard for the Installation of Private Fire Service Mains and Their Appurtenances,* share the criteria for underground piping, including joint restraint.

Like most overhead piping, underground piping with fused joint systems, including welded, soldered, brazed, and threaded pipe, requires no additional joint restraint. Otherwise, joint restraint must be provided through the use of thrust or restrained joint systems.

Thrust Blocks

Thrust blocks are large concrete blocks used to transfer horizontal loads to undisturbed soil or to resist upward vertical loads by means of their mass. Thrust blocks must be made of a concrete mix that is not leaner than one part cement, two and a half parts sand, and five parts stone aggregate. If possible, thrust blocks must be placed so that the joints are accessible for repair. (See Annex A in NFPA 13 for additional guidance, including formulas that can be used to size horizontal [bearing] and vertical [gravity] thrust blocks based on the bearing strength of the undisturbed soil, size and orientation of pipe, and maximum expected water pressures [Figures 16.4.6 and 16.4.7].) Care should be taken when obtaining soil bearing strength values because they are often not the same in the horizontal and vertical planes.

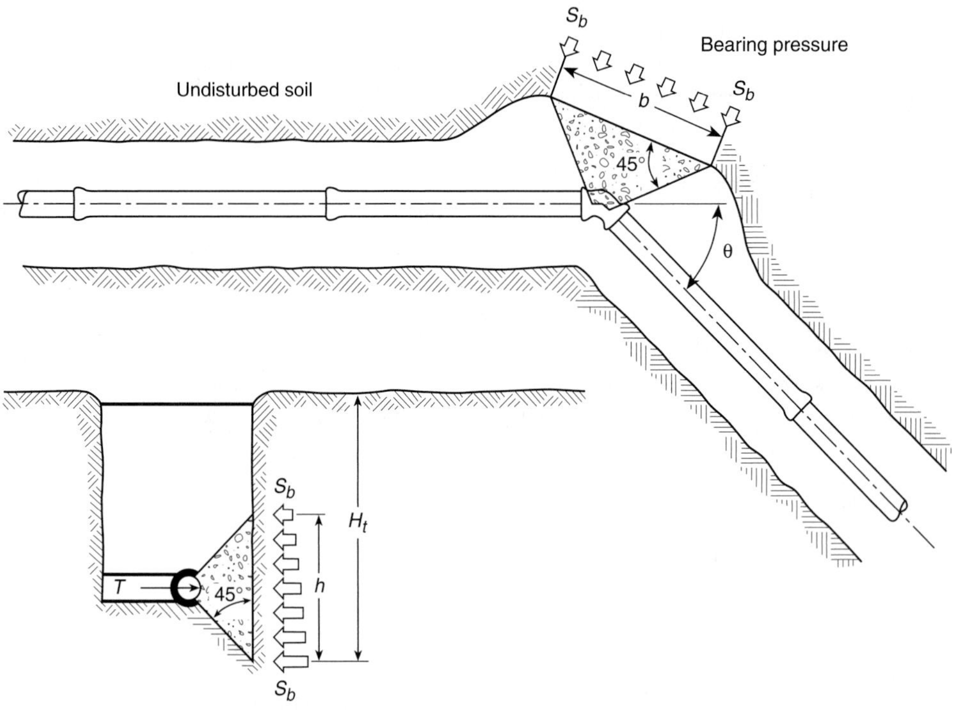

T = Thrust force resulting from the change in direction of flow
S_b = Horizontal bearing strength of the soil
h = Block height
H_t = Total depth to bottom of block

FIGURE 16.4.6 Bearing Thrust Block

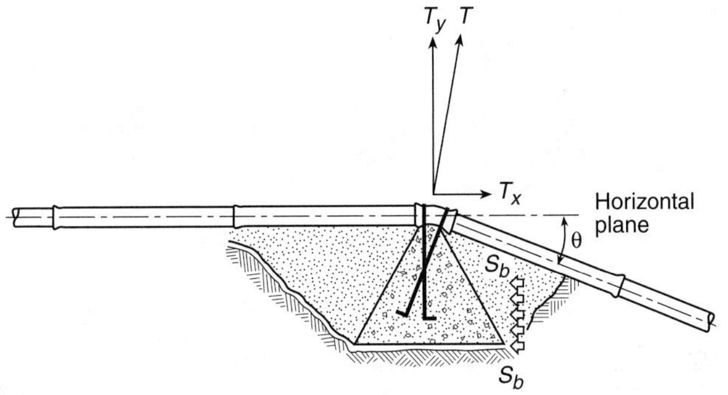

FIGURE 16.4.7 Gravity Thrust Block

Restrained Joint Systems

Fused joint systems and threaded joints are considered acceptable as restrained joint systems, as are locking mechanical joints, joints using setscrew retainer glands, bolted flange joints, pipe clamps and tie rods, and other methods and devices approved by the authority having jurisdiction. NFPA standards provide specific guidance for sizing the clamps, rods, bolts, and washers associated with restrained joint systems. After installation, all rods, clamps, bolts, nuts, and washers must be cleaned and coated with a bituminous or other material to help prevent corrosion.

Some confusion has been caused in the past by the figure within NFPA 13 showing the "typical connection to a fire protection system riser" (Figure 16.4.8). In this depiction of an underground stub-up, rods are shown as necessary to hold the base of the flange and spigot piece within the bell opening of the last length of bell and spigot piping at the base of the riser. However,

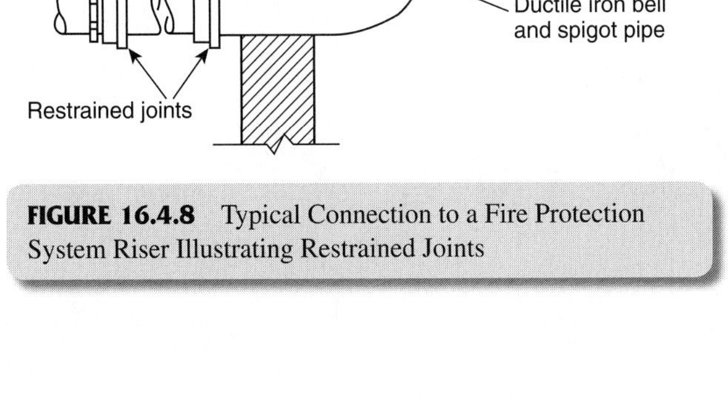

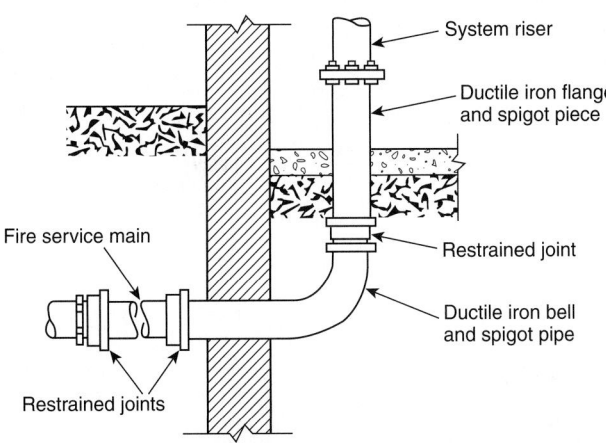

FIGURE 16.4.8 Typical Connection to a Fire Protection System Riser Illustrating Restrained Joints

such rods and clamps are not necessary if other measures are taken to ensure that sufficient restraint is provided.

Adequacy of joint restraint is verified by means of a 2 hour hydrostatic test, at not less than 200 psi (13.8 bar), but at least 50 psi (3.4 bar) above the maximum expected static pressure. The piping between an exterior fire department connection and the check valve in the connection's inlet pipe must also be hydrostatically tested. All thrust blocks should be hardened before testing, and the trench must be backfilled between joints to prevent movement of the pipe. Where necessary to hold the pipe in place, joints can also be backfilled as long as the contractor remains responsible for locating and correcting leaks.

Appendix sections of NFPA 13 and 24 recommend that the underground piping be filled with water for a 24 hour period prior to the hydrostatic test to stabilize the system. These appendix sections also recommend that the test pressure be held for 1 hour, that the pressure then be decreased to zero to look for signs of leakage, and that it then be repressurized for the second hour.

SUMMARY

In the development and application of rules for structural support of fire protection system piping, fire sprinkler systems have received great attention. This is expected given their widespread use. But the features related to hanging and bracing can also readily be applied to other types of fire protection systems and components, including pumps and tanks. The weight of any components required to be braced could be substituted for the weight of system piping in the application of the rules for braces and fasteners. The NFPA 13 hanging and bracing criteria, continually improved over decades based on practical experience, represents the best available guidance on supporting fire systems and protecting them from earthquake damage.

BIBLIOGRAPHY

References Cited

1. FEMA 450-1/2003, *NEHRP Recommended Provisions for Seismic Regulations for New Buildings and Other Structures,* Building Seismic Safety Council, National Institute of Building Sciences, Washington, DC, 2003 edition.
2. ASCE 7-05, *Minimum Design Loads for Buildings and Other Structures,* American Society of Civil Engineers, Reston, VA, 2002 and 2005 editions.
3. *International Building Code,* International Code Council, Country Club Hills, IL, 2000, 2003, and 2006 editions.

NFPA Codes, Standards, and Recommended Practices

Reference to the following NFPA codes, standards, and recommended practices will provide further information on hanging and bracing of water-based systems discussed in this chapter. (See the latest version of The NFPA Catalog *for availability of current editions of the following documents.)*

NFPA 13, *Standard for the Installation of Sprinkler Systems*
NFPA 14, *Standard for the Installation of Standpipe and Hose Systems*
NFPA 15, *Standard for Water Spray Fixed Systems for Fire Protection*
NFPA 5000®, Building Construction and Safety Code®

References

Fleming, R., "The Flexibility Factors in Earthquake Design," *Sprinkler Quarterly,* National Fire Sprinkler Association, No. 48, Winter 1983.

Fleming, R., "Bracing for Earthquakes," *Sprinkler Quarterly,* National Fire Sprinkler Association, No. 49, Spring 1984.

Fleming, R., "The Shift in Earthquake Protection Requirements," *Sprinkler Quarterly,* National Fire Sprinkler Association, No. 83, Summer 1993.

Fleming, R., "Analysis of Fire Sprinkler System Performance in the Northridge Earthquake," NIST GCR 98-736, National Institute of Standards and Technology, Building and Fire Research Laboratory, 1998.

Greenberg-Ribley, C., "Revised Earthquake Protection Standards for Water-Based Fire Suppression Systems," *NFPA Journal,* July/Aug. 2000.

Huggins, R., "Sprinkler Shake-Up," *NFPA Journal,* Jan./Feb. 2005.

ISO/FDIS 6182-11, *Requirements and Test Methods for Pipe Hangers,* International Organization for Standardization, Geneva, Switzerland, 2003.

Lingireddy, S., Wood, D., and Zloczower, N., "Pressure Surges in Pipeline Systems Resulting from Air Releases," *Journal AWWA,* American Water Works Association, Vol. 96, No. 7, July 2004.

MacDonald, N., "New Seismic Fire Sprinkler Regulations," *PM Engineer,* Oct. 2004.

Mitchell, S., "Trapeze Hanger Design," *Sprinkler Age,* American Fire Sprinkler Association, May 2005.

Mitchell, S., "Earthquake Protection for Fire Sprinkler Systems," *Sprinkler Age,* American Fire Sprinkler Association, Sept. 2005.

Valentine, V., "Trapeze Sprinklers," *Sprinkler Quarterly,* National Fire Sprinkler Association, No. 127, Summer 2004.

Valentine, V., "Seismic Bracing—When Clearance Is Needed," *Sprinkler Quarterly,* National Fire Sprinkler Association, No. 129, Winter 2004.

Chapter 5

Sprinkler Systems for Storage Facilities

James E. Golinveaux

Chapter Contents

Key Terms

automatic sprinkler system, bulk storage, commodity classification, pallet, pile storage, plastic, rack storage, storage, warehouse, water supply

This chapter addresses sprinkler system protection for storage operations. It is an unfortunate fact that many of the factors that enhance the efficiency of a storage facility also increase the fire risk presented by that storage. The more efficiently storage volume is used, the more combustible materials there are in that volume, and the more material there is to burn.

Access to the stored materials requires space between storage units. Efficient use of storage space requires that these spaces (flues) be as small as possible. The result is an array that could hardly be any more conducive to maximum burning rate and fire spread than if it had been designed with that purpose in mind. Therefore, well-designed, properly installed, and carefully maintained fire protection is critical if a catastrophic fire is to be avoided.

This chapter reviews basic fire protection principles primarily in the context of NFPA sprinkler system and storage standards. It begins with a discussion of commodity classification and storage arrangement, height, and clearance and then discusses sprinkler systems and associated design factors unique to storage operations. Then it presents an overview of special commodities and special storage facilities. The remaining sections highlight other fire protection features that a comprehensive fire protection program needs and fire safety problems of construction.

This chapter covers fire protection for a broad range of materials and storage arrangements, but it does not discuss the protection of special hazards such as flammable liquids and gases, explosives, and so on. For protection of special hazards, see Section 6, Chapter 10, "Gases"; Section 6, Chapter 12, "Flammable and Combustible Liquids"; Section 16, Chapter 3, "Automatic Sprinkler Systems"; and Section 17, Chapter 8, "Explosion Prevention and Protection."

NFPA STORAGE STANDARDS

NFPA standards outline methods for providing effective fire protection for various types of storage occupancies. These standards include NFPA 13, *Standard for the Installation of Sprinkler Systems.* For the most part, sprinkler systems are the backbone of an effective fire protection strategy for storage facilities. The changing footprint and potential pile collapse in storage facilities make manual fire fighting difficult. A well-designed and properly maintained automatic sprinkler system is the best means of fire control in storage facilities.

NFPA storage standards are based on full-scale fire tests and past loss experience. The standards address storage situations in which test data are available or in which conclusions could be drawn from the extrapolation of available data, judgment, or experience. Not all recognized protection technologies are equal. The NFPA standards identify the minimum acceptable level of protection for storage facilities. Operational planning or type of construction may limit the use of some recognized technologies. For this reason it is very important to understand certain protection scheme limitations before selecting a design method. For storage situations beyond the scope of a specific NFPA document, engineering judgment and other sources may be used but only with care and by professionals with an in-depth knowledge of fire protection science and practice. NFPA

James E. Golinveaux is the senior vice-president of research and development for Tyco Fire Products in Cranston, Rhode Island. He is a member of NFPA's Technical Committees on Automatic Sprinkler Systems, Parking Structures, and the Industrial Storage and Miscellaneous Occupancies.

storage documents and this chapter outline basic fire protection concepts for storage operations and can provide guidance where specific standards are not available.

To effectively prepare a fire protection plan for a storage occupancy, the following steps should be followed:

- Determine the commodity classification.
- Identify the storage arrangement.
- Establish the storage height and clearance from the top of storage to sprinklers.
- Develop a protection scheme (automatic sprinkler system).

In addition to the basic steps just outlined consideration also is needed for the following:

- Water supply
- Special commodities
- Special storage facilities
- Supplemental means of fire protection
- Construction

Changes to any one of the above, whether daily, weekly, seasonally, or over the life of the building can seriously impact the adequacy of protection. For this reason, it is very important to consider all of the storage variables that are known to exist or are expected to exist due to normal operations.

COMMODITY CLASSIFICATION

Proper design of sprinkler systems requires that the commodities to be stored are identified and categorized according to their burning characteristics. Categorizing commodities is a difficult task because a wide variety of products can be found within stored commodities. Some storage facilities are designed to support seasonal changes in commodity types and packaging. This has to be taken into consideration in selecting the worst case commodity classification. Additionally and probably the most difficult is to consider possible planned commodity changes, such as replacing steel parts with plastic. Although these changes can be handled through system upgrades in the future, it is much more cost-effective to address the known variables during the initial system design.

The classification of a commodity is based on a unit of storage of the commodity. For the most typical commodities, the unit of storage is the pallet load and includes the pallet, the packaging of the commodity, and the commodity itself. Commodity classification does not take into account mixed storage of commodities. For example, a storage area containing pallet loads of paper products, which are Class III commodities, mixed with pallet loads of Group A plastic commodities cannot be classified as Class IV storage based on the relative number of pallet loads of each commodity. The most challenging commodity (highest class number) determines protection for everything in an undivided, unseparated area. The paper products must be protected as a plastic commodity, unless the commodities are separated and each is properly protected.

The reason for this is quite simple. The fire tests on which NFPA 13 is based involve no more than a 200 ft^2 (18.6 m^2) fire area. Fires that were not confined to that size by sprinklers were typically not controlled. So the severity of a fire in mixed commodity storage is dictated by where the fire starts, not the overall mix of commodities. And, since any point of origin is possible, the most challenging point—near the most challenging commodities—sets the need for protection of the entire space.

Classifications reflect the burning rate and heat release rate of a commodity, as well as the effect of water (from sprinklers) on the commodity. For this reason, small-scale tests, which measure heat of combustion or relative horizontal burning rates, are of little use in determining commodity classification.

Full-scale fire tests can be used to determine commodity classification, but full-scale tests can be quite expensive. Intermediate-scale test methods (such as the fire products collector commodity classification method developed by Factory Mutual Research and used by FM Global and Underwriters Laboratories) provide a more economical means to accurately determine commodity classification.

NFPA Categories

NFPA 13 provides an approach that categorizes materials into one of seven major categories—Classes I through IV and Groups A, B, and C plastics. (NFPA 13 contains a comprehensive list of commodities and their classifications.) The definitions of the various commodity classifications are as follows:

- *Class I.* Class I commodities are noncombustible products in corrugated containers with or without single-thickness cardboard dividers, stored on wood pallets. The standard Class I test commodity is glass jars in compartmented cardboard cartons on wood pallets.
- *Class II.* Class II commodities are Class I products with slightly increased amounts of combustible packaging (such as multiple-layer cartons) or trim (such as plastic knobs). The standard Class II test commodity is a metal-lined double triwall corrugated carton on a wood pallet (Figure 16.5.1).
- *Class III.* Class III commodities include ordinary combustibles (wood, paper, natural fiber cloth) in cardboard cartons on wood pallets. The standard Class III test commodity is paper cups in compartmented cardboard cartons on wood pallets.
- *Class IV.* Class IV commodities are Class I, II, or III products containing limited amounts of Group A plastics in corrugated cartons and Class I, II, and III products in ordinary corrugated cartons, with limited amounts of expanded Group A plastic packaging on wood pallets. Limited amounts of Group A plastics are considered to be 5 to 15 percent by weight and 5 to 25 percent by volume. The standard Class IV test commodity is a mixture of paper and plastic cups (15 percent plastic by weight) on wood pallets.

Classification of Class I through IV commodities is based on the assumption that they are stored on wood pallets. When *unreinforced* polypropylene or high-density polyethylene plastic pallets are used, the classification of the commodity unit is increased one class (e.g., Class III will become Class IV, and Class IV will become cartoned unexpanded Group A plastics). When *reinforced* polypropylene or high-density polyethylene plastic pallets are used, the classification of the commodity unit is increased two classes, except for Class IV commodity, which will be increased to a cartoned unexpanded Group A plastic

FIGURE 16.5.1 Standard Class II Test Commodity (Source: Underwriters Laboratories)

FIGURE 16.5.2 Nonexpanded Group A Test Commodity—16 oz (473 mL) Polystyrene Plastic Jars Individually Separated by Cardboard (Source: Underwriters Laboratories)

commodity (e.g., Class II will become Class IV and Class III and IV will become a cartoned unexpanded Group A plastic commodity). Plastic pallets are assumed to be reinforced if no permanent marking or manufacturer's certification of nonreinforcement is provided. This can complicate the decision to convert from wood pallets to plastic pallets in storage areas, as the existing sprinkler protection probably will no longer be adequate and will require modification. However, there now exist listed plastic pallets that can be treated as standard wood pallets for determining the commodity type.

Plastics

Plastics present a greater fire protection challenge because their combustion can produce about 1½ to 3 times as much heat per unit of weight as wood or paper. In addition, plastics can burn at a much faster rate, resulting in a very challenging, high heat release rate fire.

Plastic materials are categorized in NFPA standards into one of three groups: A, B, or C. Group A plastics present the most severe hazard (Figure 16.5.2), whereas Group C plastics present the least severe. Group B plastics behave similarly to Class IV commodities, and Group C plastics behave similarly to Class III commodities.

The following list identifies a number of plastics according to their potential fire severity. The list contains unmodified plastic materials. Although fire-retardant modifiers and other additives can inhibit ignition, once ignited, heat release is usually the same as for unmodified plastic. Intermediate or full-scale testing is the best means to determine a modified material's classification. The plastics are categorized as follows:

Group A

- ABS (acrylonitrile-butadiene-styrene copolymer)
- Acrylic (polymethyl methacrylate)
- Acetal (polyformaldehyde)
- Butyl rubber
- EPDM (ethylene-propylene rubber)
- FRP (fiberglass-reinforced polyester)
- Natural rubber (if expanded)
- Nitrile rubber (acrylonitrile-butadiene rubber)
- Polybutadiene
- Polycarbonate
- Polyester elastomer
- Polyethylene
- Polypropylene
- Polystyrene
- Polyurethane
- PVC (polyvinyl chloride—highly plasticized—e.g., coated fabric, unsupported film)
- SAN (styrene acrylonitrile)
- SBR (styrene-butadiene rubber)

Group B

- Cellulosics (cellulose acetate, cellulose acetate butyrate, ethyl cellulose)
- Chloroprene rubber
- Fluoroplastics (ECTFE—ethylene-chlorotrifluorethylene copolymer, ETFE—ethylene-tetrafluoroethylene copolymer, FEP—fluorinated ethylene-propylene copolymer)
- Natural rubber (not expanded)
- Nylon (nylon 6, nylon 6/6)
- PET (thermoplastic polyester)
- Silicone rubber

Group C

- Fluoroplastics (PCTFE—polychlorotrifluoroethylene, PTFE—polytetrafluoroethylene)

- Melamine (melamine formaldehyde)
- Phenolic
- PVC (polyvinyl chloride—rigid or lightly plasticized—e.g., pipe, pipe fittings)
- PVDC (polyvinylidene chloride)
- PVF (polyvinyl fluoride)
- PVDF (polyvinylidene fluoride)
- Urea (urea formaldehyde)

In determining the classification of a commodity that is a mixture of different materials, the amount of the most hazardous material and its effect on a fire must be considered. If the most hazardous material dominates the behavior of the burning commodity, then the product must be classified the same as the most hazardous material. For instance, thick, expanded Group A plastic packing material surrounding a Class IV commodity in a corrugated carton will completely dominate fire behavior in the early stages of the fire, when the protection battle is won or lost. So the commodity must be classified as an expanded Group A plastic.

STORAGE ARRANGEMENT

Storage configuration has a major impact on how a fire burns. Therefore, a commodity's storage arrangement must be considered when preparing the fire protection plan. Materials are most commonly arranged as bulk storage, solid pile, palletized pile, or rack storage. Bins and narrow shelves also are used, more commonly in smaller stockrooms holding moderate quantities of product. Most warehouses combine these various storage arrangements.

The most critical factor among the various storage arrangements that affect fire behavior and the difficulty of controlling a fire is the presence of flue spaces. Storage configurations create these horizontal and vertical air spaces. Air passes through flue spaces, oxidizing the fire. Although flue spaces are not desirable, they should not be obstructed when present. Obstructed flue spaces can prevent heat and combustion products from reaching a fire detector or sprinkler and also can prevent water or other fire protection media from reaching the fire.

Bulk Storage

Bulk storage consists of piles of loose, free-flowing materials, including powder, granules, pellets, or flakes, and agricultural items, such as peanuts. The materials are typically stored in silos, bins, tanks, or in large piles on the floor. Flue spaces are typically not present. Fires in large piles tend to burrow down into the pile, making them difficult to extinguish. This type of fire requires prolonged soaking to reach the seat of the fire. Bulk storage arrangements are also subject to spontaneous ignition. Fires starting inside the piles are difficult to locate, unless heat sensors immersed in the pile continually monitor internal heating.

Material handling equipment, such as belt conveyors, air-fluidizing ducts, and bucket conveyors ("legs") are often employed to transfer the material to and from its storage location. This moving process agitates and disturbs material. Airborne combustible material presents an explosion hazard. This concern is significant, especially in grain storage facilities. In addition, conveyor belts and other components can be combustible and can burn together with the commodity in inaccessible places high above the floor, in tunnels, and in housings around conveying equipment.

Solid Pile Storage

Solid piling consists of cartons, boxes, bales, bags, and so on in direct contact with each other. Air spaces, or flues, exist only where contact is imperfect, or where a pile is close to, but not touching, another pile. Because pallets are not typically used, stacking is done by hand or by lift trucks using side clamps or prongs, which are pried between packages or bales without damaging the product.

Figure 16.5.3 illustrates a type of solid piling in which spaces left between cartons accommodate lift-truck prongs. Wide aisles give the lift truck plenty of room to maneuver. The dark pipes at the ceiling are sprinkler lines.

Relative to palletized and rack storage arrangements, solid piling gives fire the least opportunity to develop and spread due to restricted air access for burning, resulting in a fire challenge less than that for palletized or rack storage. Still, high piling presents a significant fire hazard, especially where the pile's surface consists of a material susceptible to rapid flame spread properties. Also, the higher the pile, the more difficult it is to break up and separate during a fire.

Palletized Pile Storage

Palletized storage consists of unit loads placed on pallets that are then stacked on top of one another. A pallet load usually takes the form of a cube, with sides of about 4 to 5 ft (1.22 to 1.52 m), consisting of a single package or multiple packages. The top surface of the pallet load must adequately support other pallet loads so that the commodity is not crushed or so that the pile does not become unstable. Due to these considerations, the maximum height of palletized storage usually does not exceed 30 ft (9.1 m).

FIGURE 16.5.3 Example of Solid Pile Storage

Pallets contain open horizontal spaces for forklift trucks. These horizontal spaces make this storage arrangement functional, but they increase the fire hazard. Air spaces usually continue in one direction along the entire width of a pile. Like vertical flue spaces, horizontal spaces let air easily pass to the fire. In addition, their configuration lets a fire burn in the space while shielding it from the water from an overhead sprinkler system.

Early fire collapse can be a positive factor in protection of solid pile and palletized storage, but the key word is early. In order for early pile collapse to be a positive factor for fire protection, it must occur within 2 to 3 minutes of the time the first sprinkler operates. Almost any commodity in solid pile storage will ultimately collapse, but credit can be given only if it can be assured that early pile collapse will occur. In general, the great majority of stored commodities will not qualify for credit for pile collapse.

Rack Storage

A storage rack is a structural framework in which a commodity is placed, usually as a pallet load. The design of rack storage systems maximizes vertical storage capability. The ceiling height or the vertical reach of materials-handling equipment limits storage heights. Some rack storage arrangements are over 100 ft (9.3 m) high.

The most common racking configurations are single-row and double-row racks. Single-row racks include racks up to 6 ft (1.83 m) wide, separated from other storage by at least 3.5 ft (1.07 m) aisles. Double-row racks consist of two single-row racks placed back-to-back, with a combined width up to 12 ft (3.66 m) and aisles at least 3.5 ft (1.05 m) wide on each side (Figures 16.5.4 and 16.5.5). Multiple-row racks, which can use a flow-through or drive-in configuration, are also becoming more widely used. They consist of racks greater than 12 ft (3.66 m) wide, or single- or double-row racks separated by aisles less than 3.5 ft (1.07 m) wide whose overall width exceeds 12 ft (3.66 m) (Figures 16.5.6 and 16.5.7). Note that with the multiple-row, drive-in storage racks pictured in Figure 16.5.7, forklift trucks drive into the rack to deposit and withdraw loads in the depth of the rack.

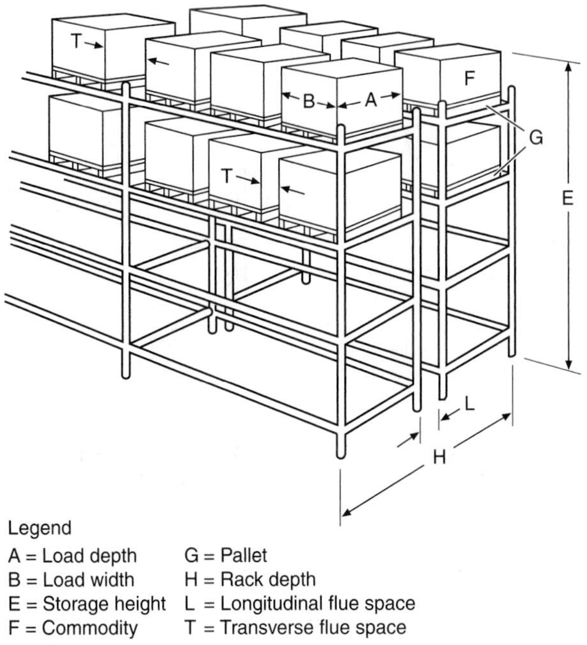

FIGURE 16.5.5 Double-Row Rack Holding Pallet Loads

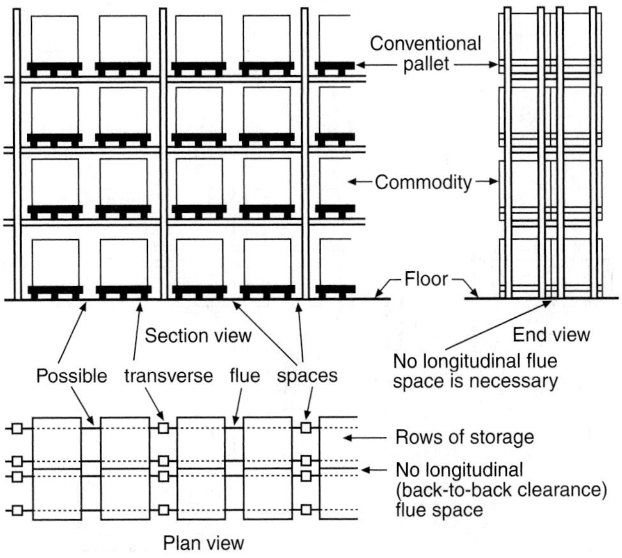

FIGURE 16.5.4 Typical Double-Row Rack with Back-to-Back Loads

Bin Box Storage. Bin box storage is a variation of rack storage in which substantial (wood or metal) vertical dividers create five-sided storage bins where the only open side faces an aisle. There are no gaps between the top, bottom, sides, and the back of the bin. Bins are usually no more than 3 ft (0.91 m) wide, 3 ft (0.91 m) high, and 3 ft (0.91 m) deep, and the stored commodity does not extend into the aisle beyond the face of the bin. Storage height is usually less than 20 ft (6.1 m). This storage arrangement creates the equivalent of solid five-sided storage

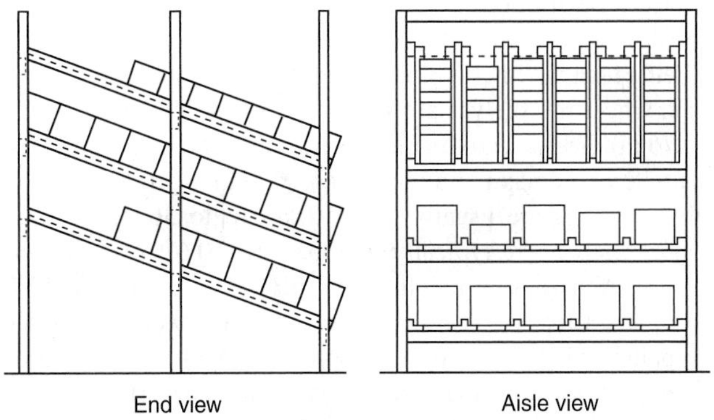

FIGURE 16.5.6 Multiple-Row Flow-Through Rack

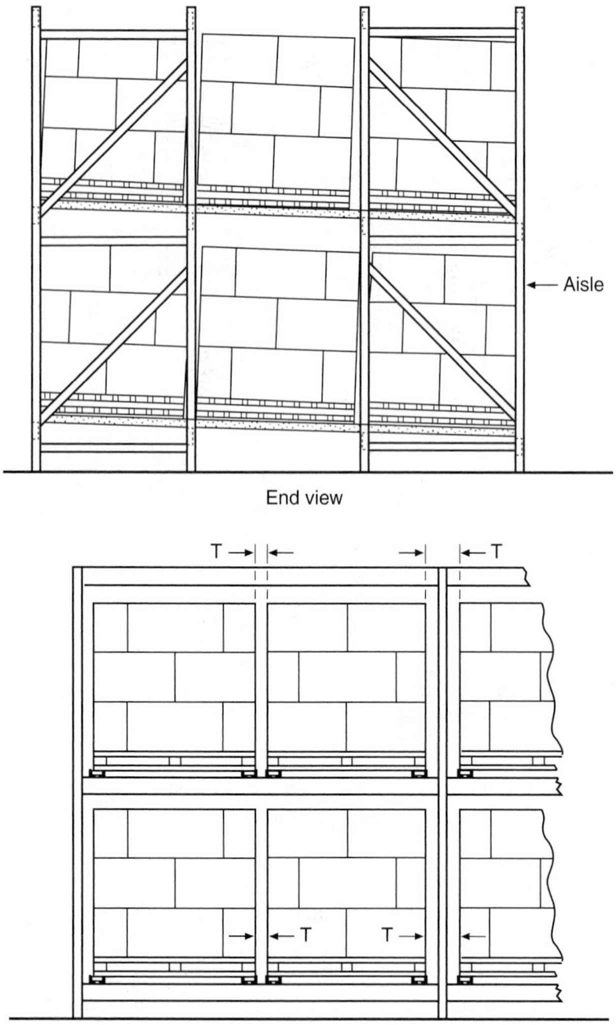

FIGURE 16.5.7 Multiple-Row, Drive-In Storage Rack, Two or More Pallets Deep

containers that limit vertical and horizontal fire spread. As a result, although the storage resembles rack storage, it can be protected as if it were solid-piled or palletized storage.

Shelf Storage. Shelf storage is another variation of rack storage, where the shelves are solid but narrow, measuring 30 in. (0.76 m) or less, and the racks are arranged in single rows, so that there is a maximum dimension of 30 in. (0.76 m) between aisles. Aisles are usually 24 in. (0.61 m) to 36 in. (0.91 m) wide. Shelves are typically less than 2 ft (0.61 m) apart vertically. And storage height is usually not greater than 15 ft (4.57 m). This storage can be protected as if it were solid-piled or palletized storage, so long as the shelf width (as measured from aisle to aisle) does not exceed 30 in. (0.76 m).

Other Types of Storage Racks. Other types of storage racks are also used. These include cantilever racks in which arms that extend horizontally from columns support the load. The load can rest on the arms or on shelves the arms support (Figure 16.5.8). Movable racks are connected to fixed rails or guides. They can be moved back and forth only on a horizontal, two-dimensional plane. A moving aisle is created as abutting racks are loaded or unloaded and then moved across the aisle to abut other racks (Figure 16.5.9). Portable racks are also used. They are not fixed in place and can be arranged in a number of configurations, as shown in Figure 16.5.10. A combination of rack and palletized storage can also be used (Figure 16.5.11).

Depending on the height and type of the rack structure, various types of materials-handling equipment can be used. These include manual and automated devices, as shown in Figures 16.5.12 through 16.5.14. Note that with the high storage racks pictured in Figure 16.5.13, stacker machines ride on floor rail, guided from the top.

Rack structures inherently create flue spaces within the storage arrangement allowing air to reach the fire. Racks also provide stability during a fire so that the burning commodity cannot collapse upon itself. As a result, fires in rack storage configurations can be the most difficult to control and extinguish.

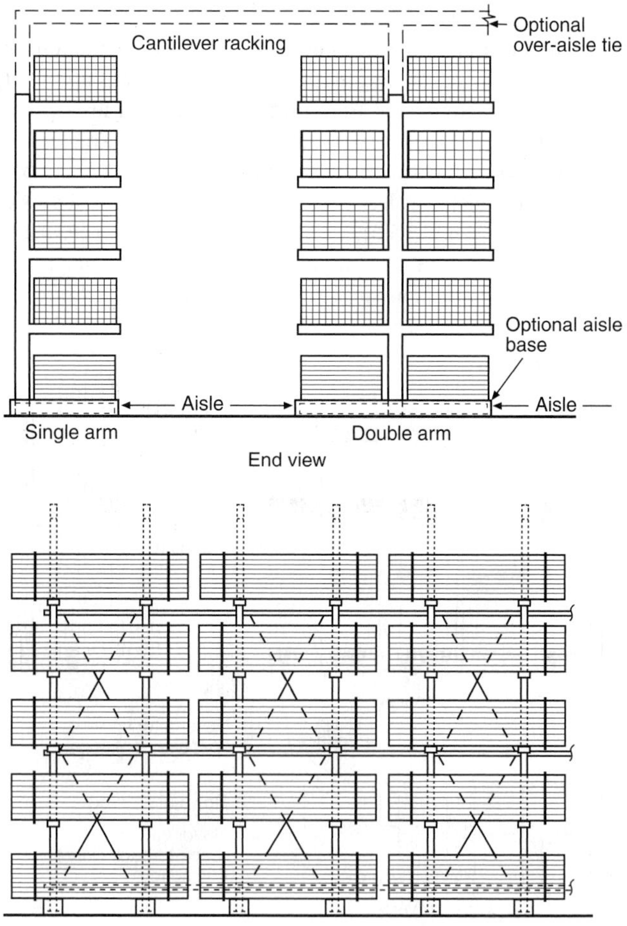

FIGURE 16.5.8 Cantilever Storage Rack

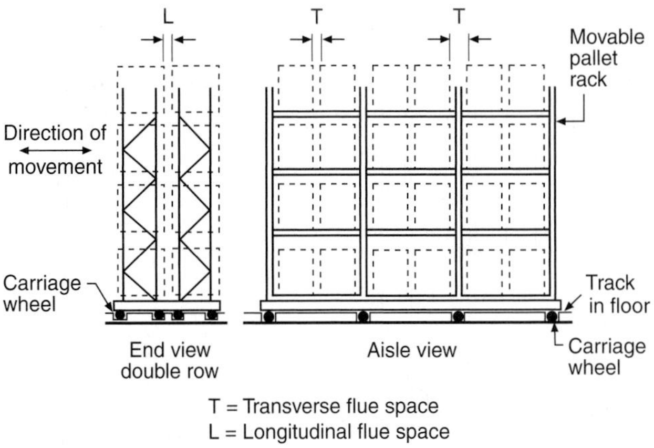

FIGURE 16.5.9 Movable Racks

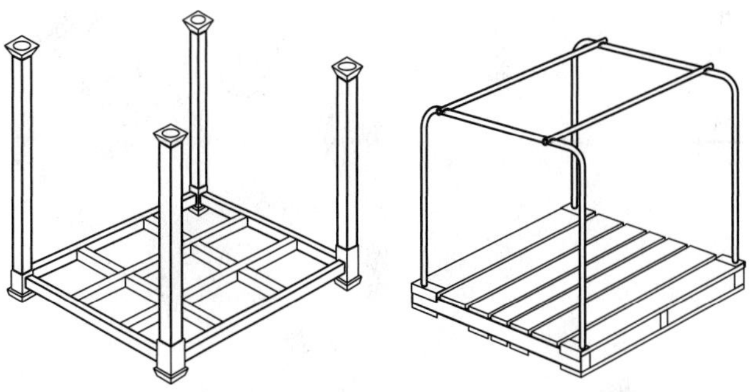

FIGURE 16.5.10 Portable Racks

Fires in racks typically burn up through flue spaces while consuming products on the racks. However, flue spaces should be kept unobstructed because they let heat from the fire reach and activate sprinklers. Flue spaces also provide a means for sprinkler discharge to penetrate the rack structure, prewet uninvolved material, and reach the fire.

Even if content damage is not severe in high-rack storage fires, heat from the fire can make the rack structure vulnerable to distortion and warping. This adversely affects materials-handling equipment because it must be accurately aligned to function properly. Such damage can impair the entire warehouse operation. Fortunately, storage racks are usually permanent structures that can support in-rack sprinklers. In-rack sprinklers are designed to contain fire to a small, localized area by reducing the horizontal and vertical spread of fire. Without in-rack sprinklers, fires in high-rack configurations can pose an impossible situation for a conventional sprinkler system installed at the ceiling. (Refer to the discussion of in-rack sprinklers later in this chapter.)

Aisle Width. Aisle spaces between stored materials let water from the ceiling sprinklers reach the fire and mitigate its spread from one storage pile or rack to another. The wider the aisle, the more advantageous it is to fire protection. In addition, aisles provide access for fire-fighting and salvage operations. Aisle widths are also a key factor in determining whether the rack arrangement is single, double, or multiple row.

For rack storage up to 25 ft (7.6 m) high, aisle widths significantly impact sprinkler system requirements. NFPA 13 provides sprinkler criteria for single- and double-row racks with 4 ft (1.22 m) and 8 ft (2.44 m) aisles as indicated in Figure 16.5.15. Interpolation is required for aisle widths between 4 ft (1.22 m) and 8 ft (2.44 m).

Racks incorporating 4 ft (1.22 m) aisles require greater sprinkler protection than those using 8 ft (2.44 m) aisles. Aisles wider than 8 ft (2.44 m) provide no more benefit than an 8-ft (2.44-m) wide aisle and, therefore, no reduction in sprinkler criteria is provided. If aisles are narrower than 3.5 ft (1.07 m), then

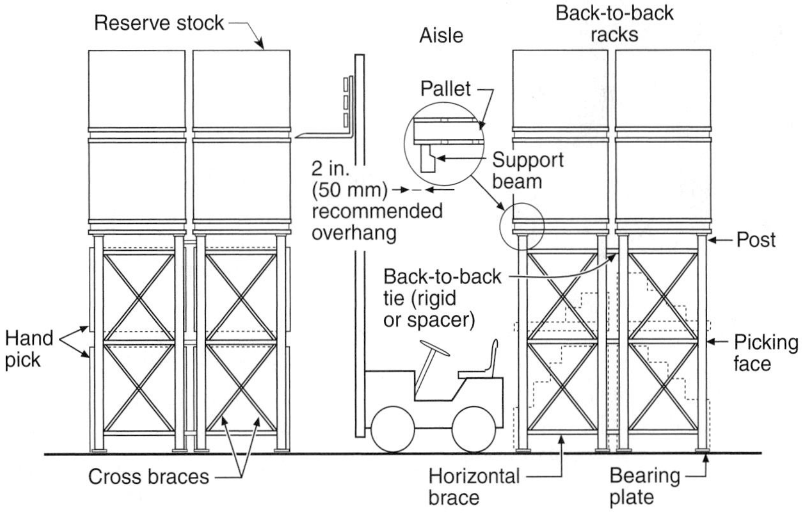

FIGURE 16.5.11 Common Arrangement of Double-Row Storage Racks with Palletized Storage Atop (Source: Unarco Material Handling, Inc.)

FIGURE 16.5.12 Unusual Storage Racks with Three Pallets Between Uprights—Three Transverse Flues (Source: Clark Material Handling Company)

FIGURE 16.5.13 High Storage Racks (53 ft [16 m]) with Narrow Aisle (Source: Unarco Material Handling, Inc.)

the rack arrangement is considered multiple row. Multiple-row racks demand a more powerful sprinkler system than double-row racks: the narrower aisles increase the likelihood of a fire spreading from rack to rack.

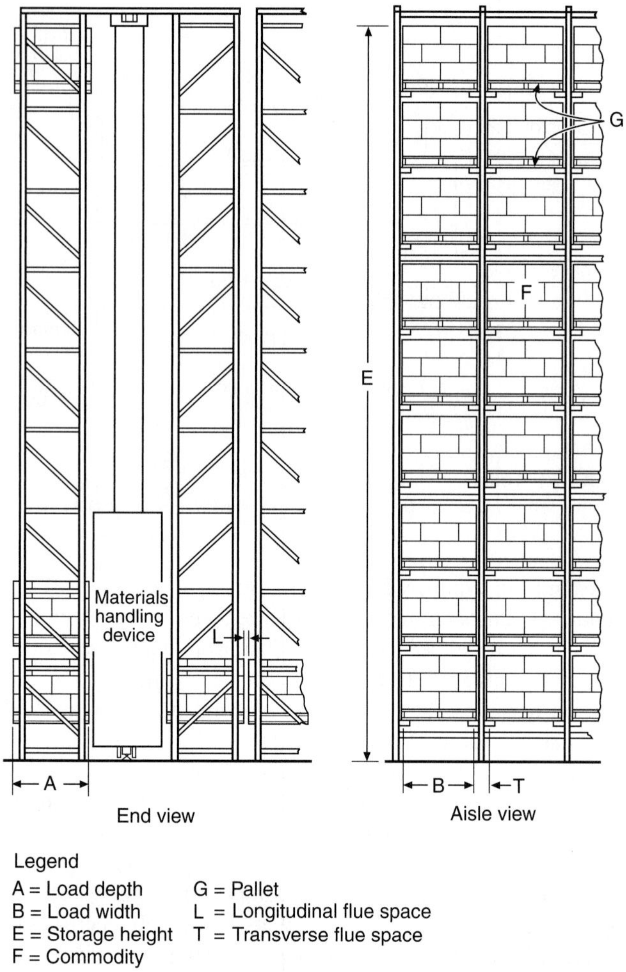

FIGURE 16.5.14 Automatic Storage-Type Rack

Aisles between palletized storage piles should not be more than 50 ft (15.2 m) wide. This lets streams from small hose lines penetrate 25 ft (7.6 m) into the center of the pile. Although NFPA 13 does not specially consider wide or frequent aisles, it assumes the presence of aisles. The aisles should be at least 8 ft (2.4 m) wide. This requirement is not unreasonable, considering that aisles are necessary for materials-handling operations and 8 ft (2.4 m) are typically needed to maneuver a lift truck. When judging the adequacy of existing sprinkler protection, aisle spacing and frequency need consideration.

STORAGE HEIGHT AND CLEARANCE

After commodity classification and storage arrangement, probably no other factor more profoundly influences a fire and its controllability than does storage height and clearance from the top of storage to sprinklers. As expected, the higher the storage arrangement, the more challenging the fire is. This is because an increase in storage height results in a larger fire size (heat release rate) at the time sprinklers operate, which in turn requires increased sprinkler performance to control.

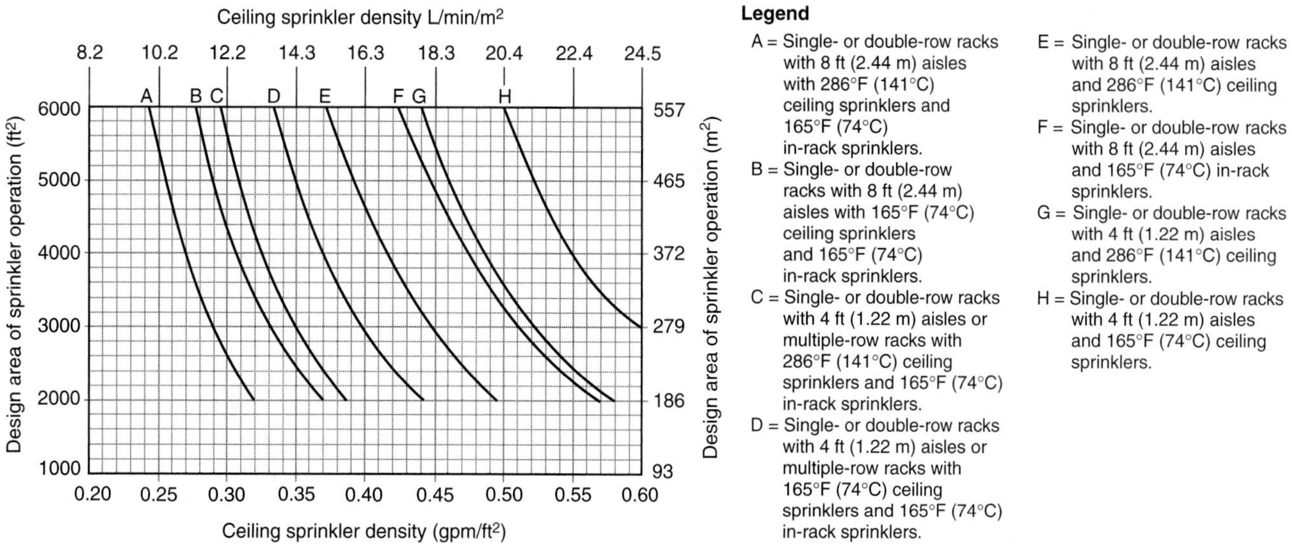

FIGURE 16.5.15 Sprinkler System Design Curves for 20-ft (6.1-m) High Rack Storage of Class IV Unencapsulated Commodities Using Conventional Pallets

Clearance also produces a significant effect on fire challenge. Increasing clearance from the top of storage to sprinklers increases the time required for sprinklers to operate in a fire of a given commodity and storage height, resulting in a larger fire size at the time sprinklers operate. Increased clearance also results in a larger fire plume above the top of storage, which reduces the ability of water from sprinklers to reach the seat of a fire.

In designing protection for a storage facility, the protection scheme must properly account for both storage height and clearance. The storage height used for design should be the maximum height expected. What may not be as obvious is that the clearance used for design should also be the maximum anticipated clearance.

NFPA 13 requires that, when ceiling heights exceed 30 ft (9.14 m) and the distance between the ceiling height and top of storage exceeds 20 ft (6.1 m), protection be provided for the storage height that would result in a 20 ft (6.1 m) distance between the ceiling height and top of storage. The clearance between the storage and the roof/ceiling is an important factor for control-mode density/area protection. Implicit in storage protection requirements is that protection for a given storage height in a building of a given height must also be adequate to protect any lesser storage height in that building. This requirement becomes necessary because warehouses are never completely full, and storage heights can fluctuate widely over both the short and long term. Clearances greater than 20 ft (6.1 m) are beyond the scope of testing used to develop the protection requirements for control-mode density/area sprinklers. Therefore, protection adequate for a storage height that results in a clearance of less than 20 ft (6.1 m) will be adequate for lesser storage heights, despite the fact that clearance exceeds 20 ft (6.1 m).

Warehouses are highly transient facilities, with the amounts of products varying widely from morning to night, week to week, and season to season. A sprinkler design cannot take advantage of low clearance (i.e., design area reductions for clearance from ceiling to top of storage less than 4½ ft [1.37 m]) unless the clearance will never be greater than that used in determining the sprinkler system design.

The minimum clearance of 18 in. (0.46 m) required below ceiling sprinkler deflectors is the minimum that will allow the proper spray pattern to develop. When early-suppression fast-response (ESFR) or specific-application control-mode sprinklers are used, the minimum clearance required is 36 in. (0.91 m).

AUTOMATIC SPRINKLER PROTECTION

Automatic sprinkler protection supplemented by manual firefighting operations and sound storage and housekeeping practices is the most effective and practical means of fire protection. Properly designed, installed, and maintained systems will perform their intended tasks. However, a fire protection plan incorporating an inadequate, impaired, or partial sprinkler system cannot be expected to produce good results.

Recent advances in sprinkler technology provide three basic approaches for sprinkler protection of storage operations. These include the use of (1) control-mode density-area sprinklers, (2) control-mode specific-application sprinklers, and (3) suppression-mode (ESFR) sprinklers. Each of the three approaches is associated with varying sprinkler types, sizes, and installation arrangements, thus providing a number of possible alternatives for sprinkler system design for most storage situations. There is no single "best" method for protecting a given storage arrangement, as each design must take into consideration the overall effectiveness, flexibility, and cost in relation to the design goals. Any of the protection alternatives specified in NFPA 13 for storage facilities will meet the basic goals of fire control. However, certain alternatives more effectively minimize property damage, maximize flexibility in relation to future changes in storage arrangement, or minimize cost.

The most common design approach is to determine the design that satisfies the minimum requirements of NFPA 13 at the least initial cost. Implicit in this approach is the assumption that any design that satisfies the requirements of NFPA 13 is equivalent to any other, and that the initial cost of installation is the only factor of consequence. In actual fact, minimizing the original cost of installation often doesn't even minimize the true cost of the sprinkler system over its useful life, much less maximize its overall cost effectiveness. The best approach, therefore, is to establish a comprehensive design that takes into consideration in a rational way clearly identified long-term operational and fire protection goals. This requires, in addition to an understanding of the requirements of NFPA 13 and sprinkler systems, in-depth knowledge of the strengths and limitations of the wide variety of sprinkler hardware and designs currently available and an understanding of the associated fire hazards.

Miscellaneous Storage

Most every occupancy outside of storage occupancies have some type/amount of storage. It is not the intent of the NFPA standards to trigger stringent storage rules every time incidental storage occurs in occupancy hazards. Storage protection per NFPA 13 can occur in occupancy hazards such as ordinary and extra hazards without changing the occupancy classification if the storage is incidental to the occupancy and meets the following definition:

> Storage that does not exceed 12 ft (3.66 m) in height and is incidental to another occupancy use group. Such storage will not constitute more than 10 percent of the building area or 4000 ft^2 (372 m^2) of the sprinklered area, whichever is greater. Such storage will not exceed 1000 ft^2 (93 m^2) in one pile or area, and each such pile or area will be separated from other storage areas by at least 25 ft (7.62 m).

Meeting this definition will result in an occupancy (ordinary or extra hazard) method of protection rather than a storage method of protection.

Control-Mode Density-Area Sprinklers

Control-mode density-area sprinklers are the oldest technology used to protect current storage methods. One key indicator of a control-mode density-area sprinkler is the description of the design area by a density, such as 0.3 gpm (12.2 mm/min), over an area of 2000 ft^2 (186 m^2). Control-mode density-area sprinklers are the only sprinklers that can change their minimum operating pressure by changing the spacing. The area of protection for each sprinkler dictates the minimum operating pressure, unlike control-mode specific-application and ESFR sprinklers that have a minimum operating pressure regardless of sprinkler spacing. The control-mode density-area category includes sprinklers with K-factors ranging from 5.6 (80.6) to 25.2 (362.9) in which discharge densities operating over a certain size area are selected from NFPA 13. The performance of these sprinklers in the protection of storage is characterized by the fact that the first sprinklers that operate work to contain or rather control the fire. Through a combination of prewetting of combustibles surrounding the initial fire area and cooling at roof/ceiling level, the fire is confined to a relatively small area until it is manually extinguished or burns itself out. Recent full-scale fire tests have shown that larger K-factor sprinklers have a distinct performance advantage.[1] That fact, coupled with the fact that the larger K-factor sprinklers require less pressure to achieve a specified discharge density, means that the minimum K-factor for sprinklers used to protect storage should be no less than 8.0 (115.2) and preferably 11.2 (161.4) or greater for certain applications.

NFPA 13 specifies both ceiling-only and ceiling-plus-in-rack sprinkler designs for protection of certain rack storage configurations using control-mode density-area sprinklers. Although there are a number of negative aspects associated with in-rack sprinkler protection (chief among which are installation cost and the potential for leakage due to mechanical damage), it remains the most effective and reliable method for protecting rack storage.

Control-Mode Specific-Application Sprinklers

Control-mode specific-application sprinklers are control-mode sprinklers whose performance characteristics have been enhanced through the use of orifice/deflector designs that produce larger water droplets that better penetrate a fire plume. This enhanced performance provides certain advantages over traditional control-mode density-area sprinklers. The discharge criterion for this type of sprinkler is specified as a number of sprinklers operating at a minimum pressure rather than a minimum density and design area.

The first control-mode specific-application sprinkler was the large-drop sprinkler. More recently, control-mode specific-application sprinklers with larger K-factors have been developed. The design requirements and applications of various types of control-mode specific-application sprinklers can differ and are based on fire testing. It cannot be assumed that, because one type of control-mode specific-application sprinkler is permitted by standards for protection of a type of storage, other types of control-mode specific-application sprinklers may be used.

Suppression-Mode Sprinklers

Suppression-mode, or ESFR, sprinklers are a radical departure from control-mode sprinkler technology and come with their own unique set of strengths and limitations. The fundamental premise of suppression-mode sprinkler protection is that a sensitive sprinkler capable of producing an optimized high-volume, high-momentum discharge can actually suppress (rather than simply control) a fire in storage. The primary advantage of suppression-mode sprinklers is their ability to protect many rack storage arrangements without the need for in-rack sprinklers. Although they are much more effective in protecting such storage than ceiling-only control-mode sprinklers, they are no more effective than a ceiling/in-rack sprinkler design using control-mode sprinklers. They also have their own quite complex and sensitive installation rules.

Comparison of Types of Sprinkler Protection

Looking at the design requirements for 20-ft (6.1-m) high storage of Class I to IV storage protection provided by the previously referenced technologies will help to develop an understanding of the different protection options available. Tables 16.5.1 through 16.5.7 show the design requirements for the protection of 20-ft (6.1-m) high storage of Class I to IV storage using the three types of sprinkler protection. Notice the effect of storage arrangements and encapsulation on control-mode density-area sprinklers, whereas there is little effect on control-mode specific-application sprinklers and no effect on suppression-mode sprinklers. Although there are many other commodities and storage heights, these simple comparisons will give the user a better understanding of the different protection methods available for a single commodity class.

TABLE 16.5.1 Sprinkler System Design Density for Palletized, Solid-Piled, in Bin Boxes, or in Shelf Storage of Class IV Commodity Storage 20 ft (6.1 m) High

		Sprinkler Temp.			
		High Temp.		Ordinary Temp.	
Storage Height	*Commodity Class*	*gpm/ft²*	*mm/min*	*gpm/ft²*	*mm/min*
20 ft (6.1 m)	IV	0.30	12.2	0.39	15.9

Control-Mode Density-Area Sprinklers. The effect of the storage arrangement is shown for control-mode density-area sprinklers by interpreting the design density curves in NFPA 13 for 20-ft (6.1-m) high Class IV storage. Tables 16.5.1, 16.5.2, and 16.5.3 show the design densities required at a 2000 ft² (186 m²) hydraulically remote area (unless noted otherwise) for palletized/solid-piled, single-/double-row rack, and multiple-row rack, respectively. Minimum operating pressure changes with spacing. Density is applied based on the actual floor coverage area. Although clearance or ceiling height limitation are not in the protection table for control-mode density-area sprinklers, the clearance is limited to a 20 ft (6.1 m) maximum (see the previous discussion in Storage Height and Clearance).

Control-Mode Specific-Application Sprinklers. Spacing of control-mode specific-application sprinklers (from their

TABLE 16.5.2 Sprinkler System Design Density for Single- or Double-Row Racks—Class IV Commodities—Storage Height 20 ft (6.1 m) Without Solid Shelves

					20 ft (6.1 m)							
					With In-Rack				Without In-Rack			
					High Temp.		Ordinary Temp.		High Temp.		Ordinary Temp.	
		Sprinklers Mandatory	Aisles									
Commodity Class	*Encapsulated*	*in Racks*	*ft*	*m*	*gpm/ft²*	*mm/min*	*gpm/ft²*	*mm/min*	*gpm/ft²*	*mm/min*	*gpm/ft²*	*mm/min*
IV	No	No	4	1.2	0.39	15.9	0.44	17.9	0.58	23.6	0.60*	24.5
			8	2.4	0.32	13.0	0.37	15.1	0.50	20.4	0.57	23.2
	Yes	1 level	4	1.2	0.48	19.6	0.55	22.4	NA	NA	NA	NA
			8	2.4	0.39	15.9	0.45	18.3	NA	NA	NA	NA

*Design area = 3000 ft² (278.7 m²).
NA = Not available.

TABLE 16.5.3 Sprinkler System Design Density for Multiple-Row Racks (Class IV Commodities)—Rack Depth up to and Including 16 ft (4.9 m), Aisles 8 ft (2.4 m) or Wider, Storage Height 20 ft (6.1 m)

			20 ft (6.1 m)					
			With In-Rack				Without In-Rack	
			High Temp.		Ordinary Temp.			
Commodity Class	*Encapsulated*	*Sprinklers Mandatory in Racks*	*gpm/ft²*	*mm/min*	*gpm/ft²*	*mm/min*	*High Temp.*	*Ordinary Temp.*
IV	No	1 level	0.39	15.9	0.44	17.9	NA	NA
	Yes	1 level	0.48	19.6	0.56	22.8	NA	NA

NA = Not available.

minimum to maximum allowable spacing) does not affect the minimum operating pressure required in the tables. Notice the addition of ceiling/roof height to Tables 16.5.4 and 16.5.5, which is important to the system design.

Suppression-Mode Early-Suppression Fast-Response (ESFR) Sprinklers. Notice that the ceiling/roof height is now the primary factor in determining the appropriate design criteria (see Tables 16.5.6 and 16.5.7). Unlike control-mode technology, the ESFR is not affected by clearance between the top of the storage and the sprinkler at the ceiling. It is one of the first technologies providing protection for the full height of the building and will not be affected by changes in storage heights. Spacing of ESFR sprinklers (from their minimum to maximum allowable spacing) does not affect the minimum operating pressure required in the tables.

In-Rack Sprinklers

Rack structures inherently create obstructions to rising heat and combustion products from a fire and to water discharge from a ceiling sprinkler system. As a result, a fire in racks can become very challenging, quickly overpowering most ceiling sprinkler systems. This phenomenon becomes more pronounced when storage heights increase and when both horizontal and structural flue spaces become obstructed. Sprinklers installed in racks alleviate this concern.

In-rack sprinklers work to contain a fire in a small, localized area. Once activated, they discharge water on or near the fire's source, without the delay associated with conventional ceiling sprinklers. In-rack sprinklers also prewet the area directly near the fire, thus reducing horizontal and vertical fire spread. In-rack sprinklers also minimize the potential water damage to stock because water is only applied to the localized area of the fire, usually eliminating the activation of the ceiling sprinkler system. Using in-rack sprinkler systems also reduces the demand on the ceiling sprinkler system and uses water supply more efficiently.

In-rack sprinklers are installed in the longitudinal flue spaces of the rack structure. As rack height increases, additional in-rack sprinklers may also be needed in the transverse flue spaces within 18 in. (0.49 m) of the aisle. Such in-rack sprinklers, referred to as "face sprinklers," protect against fire spread over the rack's vertical face and help prevent a fire from jump-

TABLE 16.5.4 Specific-Application Control-Mode Sprinkler Design Criteria for Palletized and Solid-Piled Storage of Class I Through IV Commodities Stored 20 ft (6.1 m) in Height

Storage Arrangement	*Commodity Class*	*Nominal K-Factor*	Maximum Storage Height *ft*	Maximum Storage Height *m*	Maximum Ceiling/Roof Height *ft*	Maximum Ceiling/Roof Height *m*	*Type of System*	Number of Design Sprinklers/Minimum Pressure *psi*	Number of Design Sprinklers/Minimum Pressure *bar*
Palletized	IV	11.2	20	6.1	30	9.1	Wet Dry	20/25 NA	20/1.7 NA
Solid pile	IV	11.2	20	6.1	30	9.1	Wet Dry	15/50 NA	15/3.4 NA
		11.2	20	6.1	30	9.1	Wet Dry	15/50 NA	15/3.4 NA

NA = Not available.

TABLE 16.5.5 Specific-Application Control-Mode Sprinkler Design Criteria for Single-, Double-, and Multiple-Row Racks Without Solid Shelves of Class IV Commodities Stored 20 ft (6.1 m) in Height

Commodity Class	*Nominal K-Factor*	Maximum Storage Height *ft*	Maximum Storage Height *m*	Maximum Ceiling/Roof Height *ft*	Maximum Ceiling/Roof Height *m*	*Type of System*	Number of Design Sprinklers/Minimum Pressure *psi*	Number of Design Sprinklers/Minimum Pressure *bar*
IV	11.2	20	6.1	25	7.6	Wet Dry	15/50 NA	15/3.4 NA
IV	11.2	20	6.1	30	9.1	Wet Dry	20/25 NA	20/3.4 NA
IV	11.2	20	6.1	30	9.1	Wet Dry	15/75 NA	15/5.2 NA

NA = Not available.

TABLE 16.5.6 ESFR Protection of Palletized and Solid-Pile Storage of Class IV Commodities

Commodity	Maximum Storage Height *ft*	*m*	Maximum Ceiling/Roof Height *ft*	*m*	*Nominal K-Factor*	Minimum Operating Pressure *psi*	*bar*
Class IV, encapsulated or unencapsulated (no open-top containers or solid shelves)	20	6.1	25	7.6	11 14 25.2	50 50 20	3.4 3.4 1.4
	25	7.6	30	9.1	14 25.2	50 20	3.4 1.4
	30	9.1	35	10.7	14 25.2	75 30	5.2 2.1
	35	10.7	40	12.2	14 25.2	75 40	5.2 2.8
	40	12.2	45	13.7	25.2	50	3.4

TABLE 16.5.7 ESFR Protection of Rack Storage Without Solid Shelves of Class IV Commodities Stored up to and Including 25 ft (7.6 m) in Height

Storage Arrangement	*Commodity*	Maximum Storage Height *ft*	*m*	Maximum Ceiling/Roof Height *ft*	*m*	*Nominal K-Factor*	Minimum Operating Pressure *psi*	*bar*
Single-row, double-row, and multiple-row rack (no open-top containers)	Class IV, encapsulated or unencapsulated	20	6.1	25	7.6	11 14 25.2	50 50 20	3.4 3.4 1.4
		25	7.6	30	9.1	14 25.2 25.2	50 20 50	3.4 1.4 3.4
		30	9.1	35	10.7	14 25.2	75 30	5.2 2.1
		35	10.7	40	12.2	14 25.2	75 40	5.2 2.8
		40	12.2	45	13.7	25.2	50	3.4

ing across the aisle to an adjacent rack. In some cases solid horizontal barriers covering the rack's entire length and width are also used with in-rack sprinklers. These barriers help activate the in-rack sprinklers and reduce the number of in-rack sprinklers needed. Figure 16.5.16 illustrates these concepts. Note in Figure 16.5.16 how horizontal barriers within the racks (right) reduce the number of in-rack sprinklers required (left). The symbols O, Δ, and X indicate sprinklers installed in a vertical or horizontal alternating or staggered arrangement on the sprinkler piping.

Sprinklers installed in racks can be standard or fast-response type with standard or large orifices. Ordinary-temperature-rated sprinklers should be used. However, intermediate-temperature- and high-temperature-rated sprinklers are required near heat sources. Water shields are required to guard against cooling or cold soldering of unactivated sprinklers by the water spray from in-rack sprinklers located higher in the rack. Figure 16.5.17 illustrates typical in-rack sprinklers. The upright standard-response sprinkler is shown on the left and the upright fast-response sprinkler is shown on the right. Pendent sprinklers can be field-equipped with water shields. The fast-response type is appropriate for protection under open-girded catwalks between racks, shelves, or bins.

The need for in-rack sprinklers depends on a number of factors, including the condition and type of ceiling sprinkler system, commodity type, and storage height. Generally, when spray sprinklers are used, in-rack sprinklers are required for rack storage over 25 ft (7.6 m), regardless of the commodity. For storage up to 25 ft (7.6 m), the need for in-rack sprinklers varies. When ESFR sprinklers are used, in-rack sprinklers are

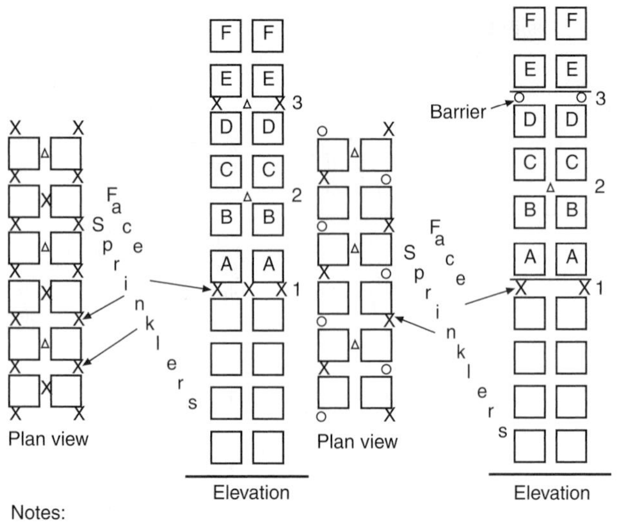

Notes:

1. Sprinklers labeled 1 required where loads labeled A or B represent top of storage.
2. Sprinklers labeled 1 and 2 required where loads labeled C or D represent top of storage.
3. Sprinklers labeled 1 and 3 required where loads labeled E or F represent top of storage.
4. For storage higher than represented by loads labeled F, the cycle defined by Notes 2 and 3 is repeated.
5. Symbols O, Δ, and X indicate sprinklers on vertical or horizontal stagger.
6. Each square in the figure represents a storage cube measuring 4 to 5 ft (1.25 to 1.56 m) on a side.

FIGURE 16.5.16 In-Rack Sprinkler Arrangement for Class I, II, or III Commodities, with Storage Heights over 25 ft (7.6 m)

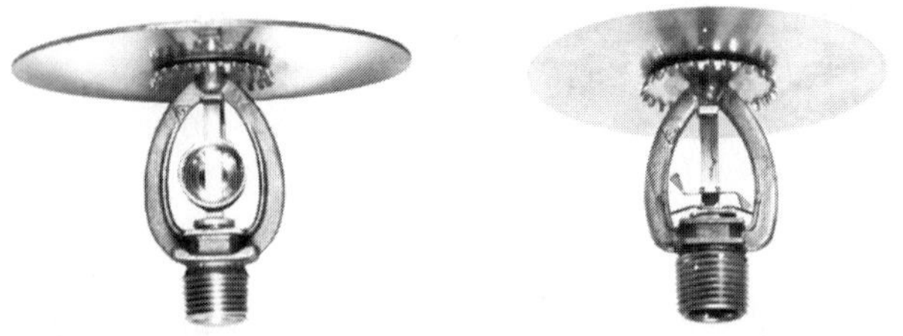

FIGURE 16.5.17 Typical In-Rack Sprinklers (Source: Grinnell Fire Protection Systems Co., Inc.)

not required in most cases. (See the discussion of sprinkler response time later in this chapter.)

NFPA 13 provides criteria to determine if in-rack sprinklers are necessary, their number, and arrangement. Various combinations of in-rack sprinkler installations have been found effective, so several design options are available.

Sprinkler Spacing

NFPA 13 provides the minimum and maximum spacing for the different types of sprinklers. It is just as important to recognize the minimum spacing requirements as the maximum spacing requirements to prevent the cold solder and skipping of adjacent rings of sprinklers in the event of a fire. The maximum spacing for most sprinklers is 100 ft^2 (9.3 m^2), whereas extended coverage sprinklers may be spaced at 196 ft^2 (59.7 m^2) for storage applications.

Temperature Rating of Ceiling Sprinklers

In control-mode sprinkler protection, the temperature rating of a sprinkler can exert a significant effect on the number of sprinklers that operate. Due to the comparatively weak performance of smaller-orifice sprinklers, ceiling gas temperatures can be high, even though control is achieved. This means that sprinklers further away from a fire can operate, and that fact must be taken into consideration in design. For larger-orifice control-mode and ESFR sprinklers, this effect is minimized and lower-temperature-rated sprinklers do not pose as great a concern.

Sprinkler Response Time

With the exception of ESFR sprinklers, testing has shown[2] that quick-response sprinklers offer neither significant advantages nor disadvantages in the protection of storage. However, NFPA 13 specifies the use of standard-response sprinklers unless quick-response sprinklers listed for storage applications are to be used. The same design requirements apply equally to both types.

Protection System Types

Dry Pipe Versus Wet Pipe Sprinkler Systems. In a wet pipe sprinkler system, the piping attached to the automatic sprinklers contains water under pressure at all times. In a dry pipe system, the piping contains air or nitrogen under pressure. When a sprinkler operates in a dry pipe system, air pressure is reduced, a dry pipe valve opens, water enters the piping, and after a short delay flows out the open sprinklers. Dry pipe systems should only be used in areas subject to freezing temperatures. Refer to Section 16, Chapter 3, "Automatic Sprinkler Systems," for discussions of various types of sprinkler systems.

Where dry pipe systems are used, the time delay associated with water delivery lets a fire grow and spread heat that in turn can activate more sprinklers beyond the immediate fire area. To compensate, the required design area of sprinkler operation usually increases by 30 percent for dry pipe systems. Density should be selected so that, after the 30 percent increase, the design area does not exceed the maximum allowable design area of sprinkler operation.

High-Expansion Foam. Although automatic high-expansion foam extinguishing systems can independently suppress a fire, some are reluctant to use them as the sole means of automatic fire control in certain cases. They are usually more expensive and more complicated than sprinkler systems, do not protect the roof structure until foam reaches it, involve the entire contents of a protected area regardless of the fire's size, and leave foam residue on unburned materials. However, they can be desirable when used with automatic sprinklers for certain high-challenge storage occupancies. A high-expansion foam system uses a series of foam-makers at ceiling level. When activated by the fire detection system throughout the area, the foam system sprays water mixed with special foam concentrate in each foam-maker and strikes a screen while a fan blows through it. The system produces many uniformly sized bubbles, which cascade down into and gradually fill the warehouse area. The foam's expansion ratio is up to 1000:1. It flashes to steam on contact with burning material and engulfs other material, keeping it from burning. Building doors should automatically close when the system activates.

When high-expansion foam systems combine with ceiling sprinkler systems, the ceiling sprinkler discharge density may be reduced to one-half the density otherwise required. However, the density cannot be less than the following:

- 0.15 gpm/ft^2 (6.1 L/min/m^2) for Class I through IV solid-piled or palletized commodities, including idle pallets or plastics
- 0.24 gpm/ft^2 (9.8 L/min/m^2) for rubber tire storage
- 0.25 gpm/ft^2 (10.2 L/min/m^2) for roll paper storage

In-rack sprinklers are not required for rack storage when high-expansion foam is installed. In addition, ceiling density can be reduced to 0.2 gpm/ft^2 (8.1 L/min/m^2) for Class I, II, and III commodities, and to 0.25 gpm/ft^2 (10.2 L/min/m^2) for Class IV commodities.

WATER SUPPLY

The water supply must adequately supply the demands of the ceiling sprinklers, in-rack sprinklers if used, and hose streams. NFPA 13 outlines hydraulic calculations for determining the demand of the sprinkler system, including in-rack sprinklers. Sprinkler demand is expressed as a flow rate, such as gal/min (L/min), at a corresponding minimum residual pressure. Typically 500 gpm (1894 L/min) is added to the sprinkler demand for large and small hose streams. Hose streams are intended to operate concurrently with the sprinkler system, so the residual pressure demand for the sprinklers is typically used.

The sprinkler system piping design (i.e., pipe size, fittings, and material), affects the residual pressure. In general, at least 30 to 50 psi (207 to 345 kPa) pressure is needed at the ceiling-level distribution point or top of the riser. When greater pressure is available, more economic system design is possible. However, exposing the most remote conventional sprinkler to pressures over 60 psi (414 kPa) is undesirable. High pressures may create very fine, but not very effective, spray patterns.

The water supply needs to be available long enough for the sprinklers to control the fire, manual fire fighting, and mop-up operations. Two hours are typically required. However, if a central station monitors the fire alarms, this period can be reduced to 90 minutes.

The reliability of available water supplies also needs consideration, especially for high-value locations. A multiple-supply arrangement (e.g., a fire pump connected to a suction tank in conjunction with an adequate public supply) might be advantageous. Such redundancy is based on engineering judgment. For example, a $100 million warehouse may be connected to a single city water main. Although the supply may be adequate, it is possible that supply could be out of service for some time or deteriorate.

The layout of yard mains, tanks, pump houses, power supply to pumps, hydrants, and valves warrants qualified fire protection engineering attention in the planning stage. To correct a water supply deficiency, alternate methods can be considered. The factors discussed earlier offer such alternatives. Adding a booster fire pump may be an economical alternative for a sprinkler system requiring high pressure. On the other hand, it may be more economical to do one of the following:

- Upgrade the piping layout only in that system
- Replace ceiling sprinklers for that system with ones of a different temperature rating
- Install in-rack sprinklers in that area
- Lower pile heights in that area (not a good long-range solution)
- Combine methods

SPECIAL COMMODITIES

Many commodities have been studied separately because of the fire properties associated with their physical form, method of storage, and difficulty of fire control. The following describes some of the unique characteristics of special commodities.

Idle Pallets

Pallets used as storage aids are considered part of the commodity classification. Pallets are approximately 4 in. (102 mm) high and usually composed of wood or plastic, although some are metal or cardboard. A pallet's main purpose is to aid storage practices by allowing products to be moved easily by forklift trucks and to provide stability. The commodity classification does not include idle pallets because of their unique combustion characteristics. When stored outdoors, all types of pallets should be located away from a building at the distances indicated in Table 16.5.8.

Wood Pallets. Stockpiling idle pallets indoors or outdoors presents a very severe fire hazard. Wooden pallets tend to dry out so their edges become frayed and splintered. In this condition, a relatively small ignition source can ignite them. Their dried-out condition, high rate of heat release, and overall arrangement result in a quickly developing fire. The undersides of the slats or planks, shielded from the discharge of automatic sprinklers, make controlling or extinguishing a fire difficult. Figure 16.5.18 shows a conventional wooden pallet.

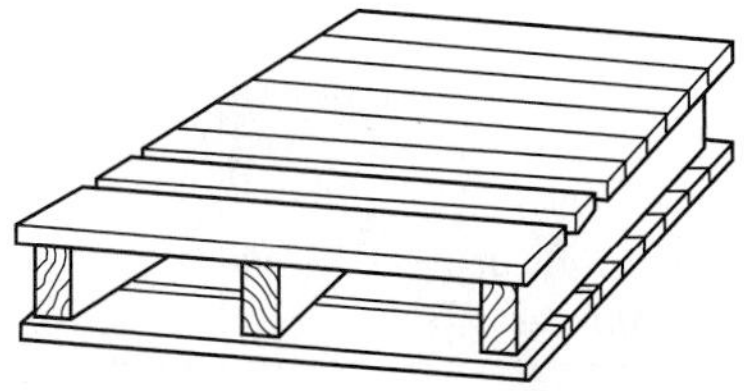

FIGURE 16.5.18 Conventional Wooden Pallet

TABLE 16.5.8 Recommended Clearances Between Outside Idle Pallet Storage and Building

Wall Construction: *Wall Type*	Wall Construction: *Openings*	Minimum Distance (ft [m]) of Wall from Storage Of: *Under 50 Pallets*	*50 to 200 Pallets*	*Over 200 Pallets*
Masonry	None	0	0	0
	Wired glass with outside sprinklers 1 hour doors	0	10 (3.0)	20 (6.1)
	Wired or plain glass with outside sprinklers ¾ hour doors	10 (3.0)	20 (6.1)	30 (9.1)
Wood or metal with outside sprinklers		10 (3.0)	20 (6.1)	30 (9.1)
Wood, metal, or other		20 (6.1)	30 (9.1)	50 (15.2)

The fire hazard idle pallets present can be mitigated by strictly limiting storage arrangements and employing an appropriate sprinkler system or by moving idle pallets outside and away from the building. Tables 16.5.9, 16.5.10, and 16.5.11 list protection criteria found to be effective for pallets stored indoors. However, the provisions of these tables need not be applied if the idle pallets meet any of the following conditions:

- Stacked no higher than 6 ft (1.8 m)
- Stored in piles not exceeding four stacks
- Stored in piles separated by a distance of 8 ft (2.4 m) from one another or by 25 ft (7.62 m) of commodity

Plastic Pallets. Plastic pallets other than nonexpanded polyethylene solid-deck pallets present an even greater fire hazard. Additional precautions must be taken. Refer to NFPA 13 for details.

Rubber Tires

Fires in rubber tires are very hot, smoky, and difficult to control and extinguish. High sprinkler densities are needed to control the fire and protect the building. (See NFPA 13.)

Tires are stored in piled form, in compact portable racks referred to as pallets, and in racks. They may be arranged on tread,

TABLE 16.5.9 Control-Mode Area-Density Protection of Indoor Storage of Idle Wood Pallets

Type of Sprinkler	*Location of Storage*	Maximum Storage Height: *ft*	*m*	Sprinkler Density: *gpm/ft²*	*mm/min*	Areas of Operation, High Temperature: *ft²*	*m²*	Areas of Operation, Ordinary Temperature: *ft²*	*m²*
Control mode area-density	On floor	Up to 6	Up to 1.8	0.2	8.2	2000	186	3000	279
		6 to 8	1.8 to 2.4	0.3	12.2	2500	232	4000	372
		8 to 12	2.4 to 3.7	0.6	24.5	3500	325	6000	557
		12 to 20	3.7 to 6.1	0.6	24.5	4500	418	—	—

TABLE 16.5.10 Control-Mode Specific-Application Protection of Indoor Storage of Idle Wood Pallets

Type of Sprinkler	*Location of Storage*	*Nominal K-Factor*	Maximum Storage Height: *ft*	*m*	Maximum Ceiling/Roof Height: *ft*	*m*	*Type of System*	Number of Design Sprinklers by Minimum Pressure: *25 psi (1.7 bar)*	*50 psi (3.4 bar)*	*75 psi (5.2 bar)*
Large drop	On floor	11.2	20	6.1	30	9.1	Wet	15	15	15
							Dry	25	25	25

TABLE 16.5.11 ESFR Protection of Indoor Storage of Idle Wood Pallets

Type of Sprinkler	*Location of Storage*	*Nominal K-Factor*	Maximum Storage Height		Maximum Ceiling/Roof Height		Minimum Operating Pressure	
			ft	*m*	*ft*	*m*	*psi*	*bar*
ESFR	On floor or rack without solid shelves	14.0	25	7.6	30	9.1	50	3.4
			35	10.7	40	12.2	75	5.2

on side, or in a laced configuration (Figure 16.5.19). Because tires are not packaged, they contribute their own circular air space to the storage, forming considerable horizontal or vertical flues. Interiors of tire carcasses can flame vigorously, mostly beyond the reach of water from sprinklers. Final extinguishment involves laboriously applying water to individual tires, usually after removing them from the building.

Combined with sprinklers, high-expansion foam is very effective on rubber tires and causes minimal water damage or contamination. To fully penetrate the inner reaches of the tires, an additional hour of foam soaking is advised after the sprinklers are shut off to maintain the foam level.

Roll Paper

Roll paper is stored on its side or, more commonly, on end. One might assume that the latter arrangement permits easier paths for sprinkler water to penetrate the vertical air spaces and slow the fire, but experience with roll paper shows otherwise. In storage on end, peeling or exfoliation during a fire is a major concern. This phenomenon can be abated somewhat by metal banding, tightly applying steel baling wire by hand, covering ends as well as sides with fire-retardant-treated tight paper wrappers or closely spacing the columns of rolls. In effective close spacing, stacks or columns are less than 4 in. (101 mm) apart.

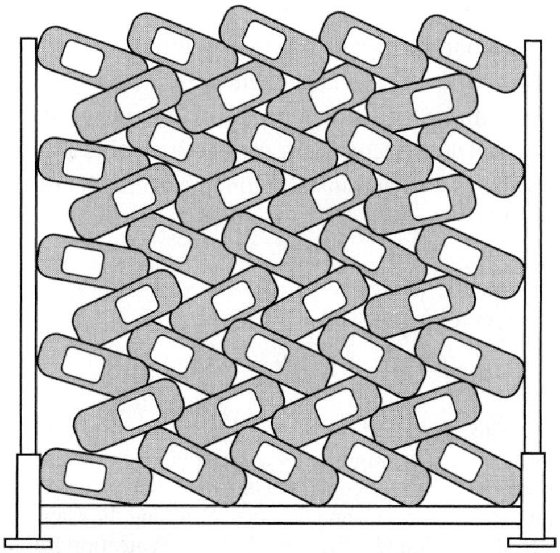

FIGURE 16.5.19 Laced Tire Configuration

NFPA 13 prescribes sprinkler density-area requirements according to the rolls' arrangement, whether they are banded or unbanded, the piles' height, and the paper's weight (i.e., heavy, medium, light, or tissue). Because rolled paper tends to absorb water from a discharging sprinkler and swells in size, it should be stored with sufficient clearance from walls.

Carpet Storage

Rugs or carpeting in rolls are generally stored in racks that accommodate 12- to 15-ft (3.7- to 4.6-m) long rolls. Therefore, racks are at least that deep and sometimes placed back-to-back, forming a total width of 24 to 30 ft (7.3 to 9.1 m) between aisles. Of course, small carpet pieces and rolls may be placed in cartons and stored in regular solid or palletized piles or conventional racks.

Long carpet rolls will deflect if their length is not supported, so solid or slatted shelves are used in wide racks, or in some cases, rolls of carpet are stored in paperboard tubes. A strict application of NFPA 13 requirements for solid-shelf rack storage would require in-rack sprinklers under each solid or slatted shelf in racks, unless transverse flue spaces at least 6 in. (152 mm) wide are provided no more than 4 ft (1.22 m) apart. With carpet racks having only one tier for each roll of carpet, installation of in-rack sprinklers becomes problematic. A reasonable compromise is to provide minimum 3-in. (51-mm) wide transverse flue at all vertical supports, which are normally 10 to 12 ft (3 to 3.7 m) apart, and providing in-rack sprinklers (including face sprinklers) at approximately every third tier, with a maximum vertical dimension of 10 ft (3.05 m) between levels of in-rack sprinklers.

Figure 16.5.20 illustrates racks for storing carpeting on slatted shelves. The tiers' closeness to each other, plus their depth, complicates problems of providing in-rack sprinkler protection.

Carpet Padding

Padding or backing for carpet is typically expanded plastic. When stored in carpet warehouses, it should be protected as an expanded plastic, which will typically require in-rack sprinklers at every level of storage.

Baled Fibers

The main hazard of baled cotton and other fibers of vegetable origin comes from the multitude of exposed minute fibers on

FIGURE 16.5.20 Racks for Storing Carpeting on Slatted Shelves (Source: Clark Material Handling Company)

the surfaces of the bales. Fire can flash quickly over these vertical surfaces, loose particles on the floor, and lint on overhead piping and structure. Fire on one side of an automatic-closing fire door can progress through the open doorway on loose floor scraps before the door can close automatically. Housekeeping, therefore, is especially important.

Fire also can easily penetrate between and into bales, requiring their removal from the building for extinguishment. Considerable smoke emission can complicate fire fighting. Certain fibers, such as jute, swell when wet, so they should be piled with regard to stability in a fire and with proper clearance from walls.

NFPA 13 limits the height of tiered or rack storage to 15 ft (4.6 m) and pile sizes to 700 bales, with a 12 ft (3.7 m) main aisle and 4 ft (1.2 m) cross aisles, in maximum fire divisions of 10,000 bales. The standard calls for large operating areas for sprinklers. (Factory Mutual Research Corporation's Loss Prevention Data Sheet 8-7 covers baled combustible fibers generally, including wool, which burns much more slowly than most fibers.)

Ordinary dry chemical (BC-type) fire extinguishers very effectively knock down surface fires on bales. However, they should be backed up by water spray from small hose or garden hose or by water-type extinguishers with spray nozzle attachments to extinguish smaller fires that may have penetrated the bales. Preferably, "wet water," which is water with a chemical additive that increases its penetrating and spreading ability, should be used.

Baled Waste Paper

Like baled fibers, baled wastepaper is typically stored in solid piles in which fire can easily burrow. Fire can flash over the surface of finely shredded paper bales, as it does over baled fiber. Wastepaper becomes mushy and difficult to handle when wet; in fact, the bales' integrity slowly disappears as the hose stream application progresses, making removal of burning bales difficult. Smoke can also be troublesome. Baled paper sometimes is stored at great heights because of its low unit value, but fire protection standards utilizing conventional sprinklers do not apply to storage over 30 ft (9.1 m) high, except in racks. Baled wastepaper is often stored in sheds with only partial walls, if any. Anecdotal loss experience suggests that even relatively light winds can significantly increase the intensity of baled wastepaper fires. It is best that, wherever possible, baled waste storage be well separated by distance or substantial walls from valuable equipment or finished goods.

Pesticides

Poisonous to insects and small animals, pesticides can harm and even kill humans when ingested or breathed as combustion products. They are stored as solutions in flammable or combustible liquids, as powders or granules in combustible packages, or as compressed gases for fumigation. Special attention must be given to the personnel hazard in addition to the commodity's combustibility. Pesticide fires can endanger persons fighting the fire or standing nearby, and poisonous runoff from fire fighting can pollute water or soil in the area.

Automatic sprinkler protection is advisable with provision for safe accumulation and disposal of water runoff. Fire-fighting strategy should include plans to use protective clothing and respiratory equipment, spray nozzles rather than straight streams to reduce water runoff, and specialized medical backup services. Container breakup and pesticide dispersal must be avoided. NFPA 434, *Code for the Storage of Pesticides,* gives general requirements for both inside and outside storage of pesticides.

SUMMARY

Protecting storage facilities from fire presents a particular challenge. An efficient use of space, such as small flues between stored materials, is also conducive to maximum burning rate and fire spread. An effective fire protection strategy needs to take into account various factors, including the commodity classification, the storage arrangement, the storage height and clearance from top of storage to sprinklers, water supply, and construction. These factors and others determine the sprinkler types, designs, sizes, and installation arrangements of the automatic sprinkler system.

BIBLIOGRAPHY

References Cited

1. Golinveaux, J., "Under Pressure: How the K-17 and K-25 Sprinklers Performed in Rigorous Warehouse Conditions," *Proceedings* of Fire Suppression and Detection Research Application Symposium, Research and Practice: Bridging the Gap, February 24–26, 1999, Orlando, FL, National Fire Protection Research Foundation, Quincy, MA, 1999, pp. 292–317.
2. Vincent, B. G., Stavrianidis, P., and Kung, H. C., "Large-Scale Fire Testing of Fast-Response Sprinklers and Conventional-

Response Sprinklers in a Fire-Control-Mode Scenario," JI0Q0E1.RA, FM Global Research, Norwood, MA, 1989.

NFPA Codes, Standards, and Recommended Practices

Reference to the following NFPA codes, standards, and recommended practices will provide further information on sprinkler systems for storage facilities discussed in this chapter. (See the latest version of The NFPA Catalog *for availability of current editions of the following documents.)*

NFPA 10, *Standard for Portable Fire Extinguishers*
NFPA 13, *Standard for the Installation of Sprinkler Systems*
NFPA 14, *Standard for the Installation of Standpipe and Hose Systems*
NFPA 24, *Standard for the Installation of Private Fire Service Mains and Their Appurtenances*
NFPA 25, *Standard for Inspection, Testing, and Maintenance of Water-Based Fire Protection Systems*
NFPA 30, *Flammable and Combustible Liquids Code*
NFPA 30B, *Code for the Manufacture and Storage of Aerosol Products*
NFPA 51B, *Standard for Fire Prevention During Welding, Cutting, and Other Hot Work*
NFPA 72®, National Fire Alarm Code®
NFPA 88A, *Standard for Parking Structures*
NFPA 102, *Standard for Grandstands, Folding and Telescopic Seating, Tents, and Membrane Structures*
NFPA 204, *Standard for Smoke and Heat Venting*
NFPA 307, *Standard for the Construction and Fire Protection of Marine Terminals, Piers, and Wharves*
NFPA 434, *Code for the Storage of Pesticides*
NFPA 505, *Fire Safety Standard for Powered Industrial Trucks Including Type Designations, Areas of Use, Conversions, Maintenance, and Operations*
NFPA 600, *Standard on Industrial Fire Brigades*
NFPA 601, *Standard for Security Services in Fire Loss Prevention*

Chapter 6

Residential Sprinkler Systems

Daniel Madrzykowski ❑ Russell P. Fleming

Chapter Contents

Key Terms

automatic sprinkler system, Home Fire Sprinkler Coalition, quick-response (QR) sprinkler, residential sprinkler system, response time index (RTI)

Automatic sprinkler systems have been successfully used to protect industrial and commercial buildings and their occupants for more than 100 years. Historically, the place that has offered the least amount of fire protection to occupants was and still is their own home. This situation was brought to light in 1973 by the Report of the National Commission on Fire Prevention and Control, *America Burning.*[1] At the time of the report, approximately 8000 people died in fires every year in the United States. Eight out of ten of those victims died in their homes.

In the more than 30 years since *America Burning* was published, the number of lives lost in fires in the United States has decreased to less than 4000 per year. Unfortunately, 8 out of 10 victims still die in home structure fires.[2] Although residential sprinkler installations are increasing, it is estimated that less than 3 percent of all residential dwellings in the United States have them installed.[3]

In response to the information from the *America Burning* report, the National Fire Protection Association's Technical Committee on Automatic Sprinklers assigned a subcommittee to develop a standard for residential sprinkler systems in 1973. NFPA 13D, *Standard for the Installation of Sprinkler Systems in One- and Two-Family Dwellings and Manufactured Homes,* was adopted in May 1975, based on expert judgment and the best information available at that time.

Significant testing and development of residential sprinkler systems has continued since then, resulting in the evolution of NFPA 13D and the development of NFPA 13R, *Standard for the Installation of Sprinkler Systems in Residential Occupancies up to and Including Four Stories in Height.*

The purpose of a residential sprinkler system built to the standard is to "provide a sprinkler system that aids in detection and control of residential fires, and thus provides improved protection against injury, life loss, and property damage."[4] From a performance perspective, if the room of fire origin is sprinklered, a sprinkler system designed and installed in accordance with the residential sprinkler standards is expected to prevent flashover and improve the occupant's opportunity to escape or to be rescued.[4]

Residential sprinkler systems designed and installed in accordance with NFPA 13D or NFPA 13R have significantly different requirements than those for residential occupancies designed in accordance with NFPA 13, *Standard for the Installation of Sprinkler Systems.* NFPA 13D and NFPA 13R systems have been optimized for certain types of residential occupancy buildings in an effort to minimize the cost of the system while improving the degree of fire safety.

New developments in residential sprinkler system technology continue to be made in an effort to increase the ease of installation and reduce the cost of installation while maintaining the effectiveness and reliability of the system. Residential sprinkler systems have been required in dwellings in several communities for more than a decade. Information from these communities is providing compelling data concerning the effectiveness of residential sprinkler systems. These data, in addition to code requirements and other incentives, are increasing the numbers of sprinkler installations around the country.

Daniel Madrzykowski, P.E., is a fire protection engineer with the Building and Fire Research Laboratory of the National Institute of Standards and Technology in Gaithersburg, Maryland. He has served on many different NFPA technical committees, including the Technical Committee on Residential Sprinkler Systems.

Russell P. Fleming, P.E., is executive vice-president of engineering for the National Fire Sprinkler Association, Inc., in Patterson, New York. He has served on more than a dozen different NFPA technical committees, including the Technical Correlating Committee on Automatic Sprinklers.

For related topics, see Section 3, Chapter 1, "An Overview of the Fire Problem and Fire Protection"; and Section 16, Chapter 8, "Water Mist Fire Suppression Systems."

DEVELOPING A SPRINKLER SYSTEM IN RESPONSE TO THE HOME FIRE PROBLEM

The development of a residential sprinkler standard with the main focus on life safety required a multifaceted approach. Fire incident data had to be collected and analyzed to obtain an understanding of the nature of the residential fire safety problem. In addition, technical challenges had to be overcome to develop an effective, practical, and economically acceptable residential sprinkler system design.

The more common home fire hazards had to be characterized in terms of leading areas of origin. The rankings and percentages have changed little since then, and more recent data are shown in Table 16.6.1, which demonstrates the number of fire fatalities and injuries based on the area of origin. Over 50 percent of home fires, over 70 percent of home fire fatalities, and over 70 percent of home fire injuries are the result of

TABLE 16.6.1 Structure Fires in Homes by Area of Origin, 1999–2002 Annual Averages

Area of Origin	*Fires*		*Civilian Deaths*		*Civilian Injuries*		*Direct Property Damage (in Millions of Dollars)*	
Kitchen or cooking area	95,200	(26%)	460	(16%)	4620	(30%)	761	(14%)
Bedroom	44,800	(12%)	760	(26%)	3820	(25%)	928	(17%)
Confined cooking fire	29,800	(8%)	0	(0%)	470	(3%)	10	(0%)
Common room, living room, family room, lounge, or den	23,600	(6%)	870	(29%)	1900	(12%)	596	(11%)
Laundry room or area	15,800	(4%)	30	(1%)	390	(3%)	170	(3%)
Exterior wall surface	13,300	(4%)	10	(0%)	140	(1%)	168	(3%)
Attic or ceiling/roof assembly or concealed space	10,600	(3%)	10	(0%)	110	(1%)	290	(5%)
Confined chimney fire	10,600	(3%)	0	(0%)	10	(0%)	7	(0%)
Garage or vehicle storage area	9,900	(3%)	40	(1%)	340	(2%)	314	(6%)
Heating equipment room	9,600	(3%)	30	(1%)	270	(2%)	128	(2%)
Chimney	9,600	(3%)	10	(0%)	30	(0%)	57	(1%)
Lavatory or bathroom	9,400	(3%)	40	(1%)	350	(2%)	107	(2%)
Crawl space or substructure space	8,600	(2%)	50	(2%)	300	(2%)	202	(4%)
Wall assembly or concealed space	7,600	(2%)	30	(1%)	120	(1%)	146	(3%)
Exterior balcony or open porch	7,100	(2%)	30	(1%)	210	(1%)	180	(3%)
Unclassified structural area	5,100	(1%)	70	(2%)	150	(1%)	162	(3%)
Unclassified	4,800	(1%)	50	(2%)	140	(1%)	141	(3%)
Closet	4,400	(1%)	20	(1%)	180	(1%)	71	(1%)
Unclassified function area	4,200	(1%)	110	(4%)	300	(2%)	102	(2%)
Ceiling/floor assembly or concealed space	4,000	(1%)	30	(1%)	90	(1%)	107	(2%)
Hallway, corridor, or mall	3,100	(1%)	40	(1%)	160	(1%)	39	(1%)
Confined fuel burner or boiler fire or malfunction	2,900	(1%)	0	(0%)	10	(0%)	2	(0%)
Exterior roof surface	2,600	(1%)	0	(0%)	20	(0%)	61	(1%)
Dining room, bar, or beverage area	2,600	(1%)	40	(1%)	160	(1%)	59	(1%)
Unclassified storage area	2,600	(1%)	10	(0%)	80	(1%)	44	(1%)
Storage of supplies or tools or dead storage	2,500	(1%)	20	(1%)	100	(1%)	50	(1%)
Multiple areas of origin	2,100	(1%)	30	(1%)	60	(0%)	68	(1%)
Trash or rubbish chute, area, or container	2,000	(1%)	0	(0%)	30	(0%)	15	(0%)
Other known means of egress	5,700	(2%)	50	(2%)	220	(1%)	96	(2%)
Other known outside area	4,200	(1%)	10	(0%)	70	(0%)	64	(1%)
Other known service or equipment area	3,400	(1%)	0	(0%)	50	(0%)	64	(1%)
Other known area	6,600	(2%)	100	(3%)	350	(2%)	171	(3%)
Contained trash or rubbish fire	4,600	(1%)	0	(0%)	20	(0%)	1	(0%)
Other confined or contained area	200	(0%)	0	(0%)	0	(0%)	1	(0%)
Total	372,900	(100%)	2,960	(100%)	15,300	(100%)	5,383	(100%)

Source: Marty Ahrens, *U.S. Fires in Selected Occupancies: Homes,* National Fire Protection Association, Quincy, MA, Mar. 2006, Table 8.

fires starting in a living room, bedroom, or kitchen. The impact sprinklers would have in these locations was clear. Analysis of this data was used to determine those rooms of a residence in which sprinkler protection would have the most positive impact on life safety. Table 16.6.2 shows the first items ignited in home fires.[4] It shows that over one-fourth of all home fire deaths involved the initial ignition of furniture or bedding. Other data showed that these ignitions were most often caused by a smoldering heat source (e.g., cigarette) or a small open flame source (e.g., match or lighter). This information provided a sense of the types of fire hazards that residential sprinklers would have to mitigate.

Another aspect of the residential fire problem concerns those who typically die in residential fires. Figure 16.6.1 presents the number of fire deaths per million people of a given age range, and Figure 16.6.2 presents the relative risk of dying in a fire by age.[3] Both figures show the trends that children 4 years of age and under and adults 65 years of age and older are more likely to die in a residential fire than are other segments of the population. For adults 65 and older, the risk increases significantly with age. Because these high-risk groups may depend on assistance to exit the dwelling, anything less than automatic suppression may not be enough to save them.[5]

TABLE 16.6.2 Structure Fires in Homes by Item First Ignited, 1999–2002 Annual Averages

Item First Ignited	*Fires*		*Civilian Deaths*		*Civilian Injuries*		*Direct Property Damage (in Millions of Dollars)*	
Cooking materials, including food	59,600	(16%)	140	(5%)	3110	(20%)	296	(6%)
Confined cooking fire	29,800	(8%)	0	(0%)	470	(3%)	10	(0%)
Structural member or framing	29,300	(8%)	210	(7%)	610	(4%)	917	(17%)
Electrical wire or cable insulation	23,500	(6%)	90	(3%)	480	(3%)	297	(6%)
Mattress or bedding	18,000	(5%)	410	(14%)	2000	(13%)	358	(7%)
Rubbish, trash, or waste	17,400	(5%)	50	(2%)	360	(2%)	135	(3%)
Unclassified	16,700	(4%)	120	(4%)	550	(4%)	171	(3%)
Exterior wall covering or finish	14,900	(4%)	30	(1%)	190	(1%)	281	(5%)
Interior wall covering, excluding drapes	13,100	(4%)	140	(5%)	510	(3%)	321	(6%)
Clothing	13,000	(3%)	200	(7%)	780	(5%)	160	(3%)
Confined chimney fire	10,600	(3%)	0	(0%)	10	(0%)	7	(0%)
Flammable or combustible liquid or gas, filter, or piping	10,500	(3%)	170	(6%)	980	(6%)	244	(5%)
Multiple items first ignited	10,500	(3%)	190	(6%)	480	(3%)	350	(6%)
Upholstered furniture or vehicle seat	10,200	(3%)	560	(19%)	1130	(7%)	283	(5%)
Floor covering, rug, carpet, or mat	8,100	(2%)	110	(4%)	350	(2%)	159	(3%)
Unclassified structural component or finish	7,500	(2%)	60	(2%)	200	(1%)	245	(5%)
Cabinetry, including built-in	6,900	(2%)	40	(1%)	400	(3%)	136	(3%)
Unclassified furniture or utensils	6,000	(2%)	130	(5%)	530	(3%)	136	(3%)
Insulation within structural area	5,200	(1%)	10	(0%)	90	(1%)	71	(1%)
Appliance housing or casing	4,900	(1%)	20	(1%)	180	(1%)	50	(1%)
Magazine, newspaper, or writing paper	4,600	(1%)	60	(2%)	230	(2%)	71	(1%)
Contained trash or rubbish fire	4,600	(1%)	0	(0%)	20	(0%)	1	(0%)
Box, carton, bag, basket, or barrel	4,300	(1%)	30	(1%)	190	(1%)	64	(1%)
Dust, fiber, lint, sawdust, or excelsior	4,300	(1%)	0	(0%)	70	(0%)	26	(0%)
Unclassified soft goods or wearing apparel	3,900	(1%)	60	(2%)	200	(1%)	66	(1%)
Exterior roof covering or finish	3,700	(1%)	0	(0%)	40	(0%)	118	(2%)
Curtains, blinds, drapes, or tapestry	3,600	(1%)	20	(1%)	280	(2%)	57	(1%)
Exterior trim, including doors	3,400	(1%)	10	(0%)	40	(0%)	51	(1%)
Linen other than bedding	3,400	(1%)	20	(1%)	140	(1%)	33	(1%)
Confined fuel burner or boiler fire or malfunction	2,900	(1%)	0	(0%)	10	(0%)	2	(0%)
Interior ceiling cover or finish	2,500	(1%)	10	(0%)	60	(0%)	56	(1%)
Light vegetation, including grass	2,000	(1%)	0	(0%)	20	(0%)	25	(0%)
Other known item	13,800	(4%)	60	(2%)	570	(4%)	186	(3%)
Other confined fire	200	(0%)	0	(0%)	0	(0%)	1	(0%)
Total	372,900	(100%)	2,960	(100%)	15,300	(100%)	5,383	(100%)

Source: Marty Ahrens, *U.S. Fires in Selected Occupancies: Homes,* National Fire Protection Association, Quincy, MA, Mar. 2006, Table 9.

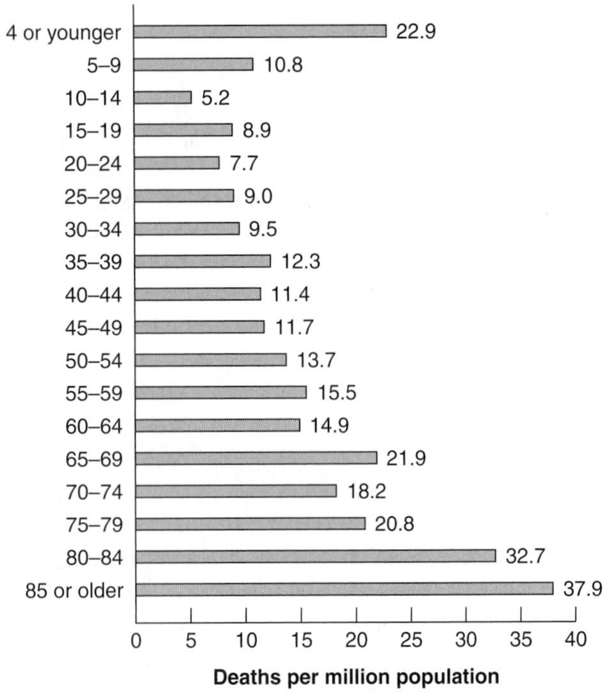

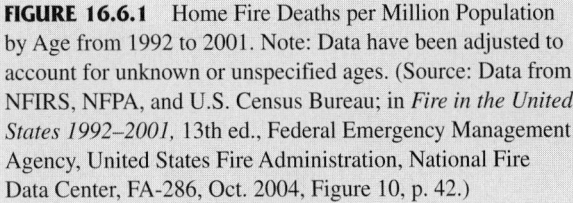

FIGURE 16.6.1 Home Fire Deaths per Million Population by Age from 1992 to 2001. Note: Data have been adjusted to account for unknown or unspecified ages. (Source: Data from NFIRS, NFPA, and U.S. Census Bureau; in *Fire in the United States 1992–2001,* 13th ed., Federal Emergency Management Agency, United States Fire Administration, National Fire Data Center, FA-286, Oct. 2004, Figure 10, p. 42.)

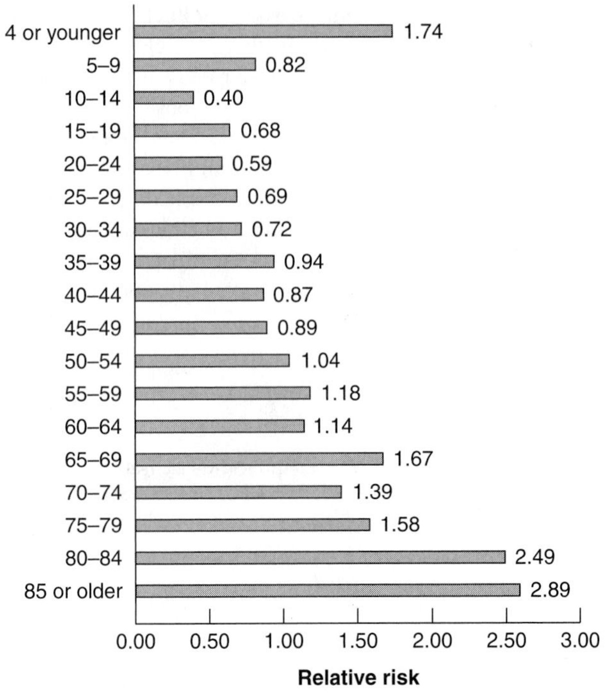

FIGURE 16.6.2 Relative Risk of Home Fire Deaths by Age from 1992 to 2001. Notes: 1. *Relative risk* compares the per capita rate (Figure 16.6.1) for a particular group (here, an age group) to the overall per capita rate (i.e., the general population). For the general population, the relative risk is set at 7. 2. Data have been adjusted to account for unknown or unspecified ages. (Source: Data from NFIRS, NFPA, and U.S. Census Bureau; in *Fire in the United States 1992–2001,* 13th ed., Federal Emergency Management Agency, United States Fire Administration, National Fire Data Center, FA-286, Oct. 2004, Figure 11, p. 43.)

Once it was determined where sprinklers in a home would be most effective in reducing life loss, the technical challenge of developing an effective and economically viable sprinkler system was pursued. The sprinkler system would have to activate automatically while a fire was small and the smoke and heat conditions in the home were survivable. Once the system was activated, it needed to control the fire with a smaller amount of water relative to a commercial sprinkler system, because the water supply to a home is typically less than the water supply to a commercial or industrial occupancy.

NFPA 13D, First Edition, 1975

Based on the review of then-available fire incident data, NFPA's Technical Committee on Sprinkler Systems developed a residential sprinkler installation standard that covered the principally occupied areas of a dwelling and that met the goals of (1) preventing flashover, (2) providing sufficient time for safe egress or rescue, and (3) economic viability.

As specified in the initial version of NFPA 13D, a residential sprinkler system would use a ½ in. (12.7 mm) orifice, standard response sprinkler, with a maximum of 256 ft^2 (23.8 m^2) coverage, and a spray density of 0.10 gpm/ft^2 (4.1 L/m^2), yielding a flow rate of 25 gpm (94.6 L/m^2). If the system was not supplied by an adequate public water source, a 250 gal (946.3 L) stored water supply was required to provide a 10-minute water supply.

To keep costs down, it was proposed that sprinklers be located only in principally occupied rooms. For this reason, sprinklers were not required in bathrooms 40 ft^2 (3.7 m^2) or less, small closets 24 ft^2 (2.2 m^2) or less, attics not used as a living space, porches, carports, garages, and foyers. Table 16.6.1 shows how much of the home fire problem begins in these excluded spaces, as well as in or on concealed spaces and exterior surfaces, which were also excluded. The system was to have a local waterflow alarm. NFPA 13D permitted sprinklers to be omitted from certain areas where the incidence of life loss from fires was statistically shown to be low. NFPA 13 had always required complete sprinkler protection in order to safeguard property adequately. In departing from the concept of complete coverage, the 1975 edition of NFPA 13D became the first "life safety" sprinkler standard. In spite of these concessions, actual installations based on this standard were rare, primarily due to cost.

The initial residential sprinkler system was crafted from existing technology and improvements were needed. Jensen noted that "much of this first edition was based on the collective experience of the committee members; little was based on real-world fire testing."[6]

Residential Sprinkler Research

Beginning in 1976, the National Fire Prevention and Control Administration, renamed the United States Fire Administration (USFA) in 1979, supported a significant number of research programs on a wide variety of topics relating to residential sprinkler systems. The objective of the USFA research program was to assess the impact sprinklers would have on reducing deaths and injuries in residential fires.[7] The USFA—working in conjunction with the National Fire Protection Association, Factory Mutual Research Corporation, Underwriters Laboratories, and many other groups and individuals—evaluated the design, installation, practical usage, and water acceptance factors that would have an impact on achieving reliable and acceptable systems,[8] the minimum water discharge rates and automatic sprinkler flow required; and response sensitivity and design criteria.[9–11] Full-scale fire experiments were conducted to develop residential sprinkler designs and validate their effectiveness.[12–16] In addition, standards for testing and evaluating residential sprinklers were developed. These included tenability criteria for occupants that the sprinklers were required to maintain in the room of fire origin.

Residential Sprinkler Sensitivity and Response

Although researchers at the Factory Mutual Fire Insurance Companies recognized the need for "faster" or more "sensitive" sprinklers in 1884, it was not until the late 1960s that a "quick-response sprinkler" subcommittee was formed within the NFPA 13 technical committee.

Research showed that a more sensitive sprinkler was needed to respond faster to both smoldering and fast-developing home fires for two reasons. First, fires had to be controlled quickly in order to prevent the development of lethal conditions in typically small home compartments. In addition, fires had to be attacked while still small if they were to be controlled with the water supplies typically available in single-family dwellings, that is, 20 to 30 gpm (76 to 114 L/min).

Measuring Sprinkler Sensitivity

Much of the original work in the area of measuring sprinkler sensitivity was done at FM Global Research under the sponsorship of the United States Fire Administration (USFA) during the development of the residential sprinkler.[17,18] Important contributing research was also performed at the British Fire Research Station and the National Institute of Standards and Technology (NIST).[19–22]

The progress in this area climaxed late in 1990, when an agreement was reached within the working group on sprinkler and water spray equipment of the International Standards Organization (ISO) for a standardized approach to sprinkler sensitivity requirements and testing. The agreement, included in ISO 6182/1, "Requirements and Methods of Test for Sprinklers," uses a combination of sprinkler test procedures developed by laboratories in the United States and Europe and establishes the three ranges of sprinkler sensitivity characteristics, shown in Figure 16.6.3.

These ranges of sensitivity are based both on the response time index (RTI) of the device and on its conductivity (C). RTI is a measure of pure thermal sensitivity, which indicates how fast the sprinkler can absorb heat from its surroundings sufficient to cause activation. The conductivity factor is important in measuring how much of the heat picked up from the surrounding air will be lost to the sprinkler fittings and waterway.[23] Figure 16.6.3 shows three broad ranges of sprinkler sensitivity: standard, special, and fast response. Traditional sprinkler hardware falls into the standard-response category. The fast-response category is used for new types of sprinklers for which fast response is considered important. The special-response category is used in some countries for special types of sprinklers that may be installed in conformance with appropriate national installation standards. In the United States, this category includes some of the extended coverage sprinklers.

Sprinkler response time as a function of the temperature rating of the operating element is well understood; that is, a 165°F (74°C) rated sprinkler will operate when its temperature reaches 165°F (74°C), plus or minus a few degrees. Because of the "thermal lag" of the link or bulb mass, however, the air temperature may be significantly higher before the element operates. The

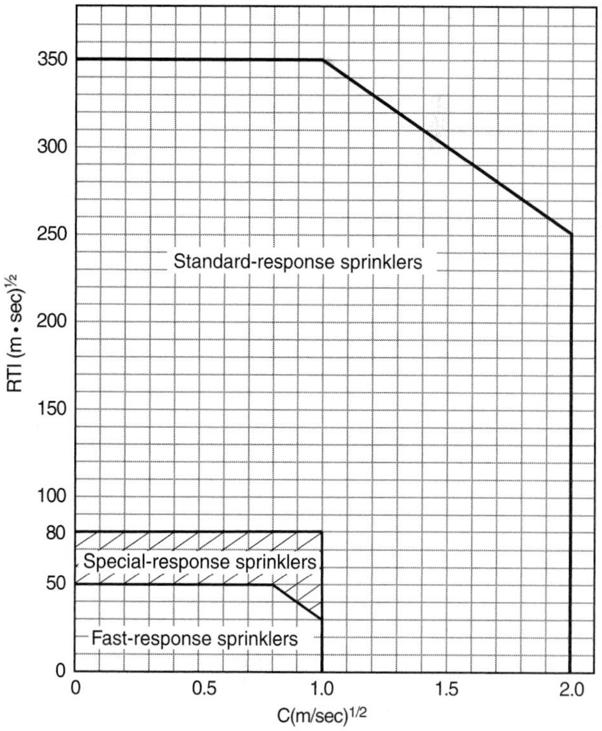

FIGURE 16.6.3 International Sprinkler Sensitivity Ranges, Response Time Index (RTI) versus Conductivity (C). For SI units: 1 ft = 0.305 m.

smaller mass of the operating element of a fast-response sprinkler permits it to follow a temperature rise in the surrounding air more rapidly, resulting in faster operation. The actual sensitivity requirements of the first fast-response sprinklers, intended as residential sprinklers, were arrived at somewhat by trial and error during developmental test work. To measure sensitivity, FM Global Research researchers first applied the concept of the "tau" (τ) factor and later developed the RTI.

Sensitivity Testing

Both the τ factor and RTI refer to the performance of a sprinkler or its operating element in a standardized air oven tunnel or thermal sensitivity test. The test is known as a "plunge" test because a sprinkler at room temperature is plunged into a heated airstream of known constant temperature and velocity.[17,18] In the plunge test, the τ factor is the time at which the temperature of the sensing element of the sprinkler is approximately 63 percent of the difference between the hot gas temperature and the original temperature of the sensing element. In other words, the τ factor is the time at which the temperature of the sprinkler thermal element has risen 63 percent of the way to the higher temperature of the heated air. The smaller the τ factor, the faster the sprinkler sensing element heats up and operates. Figure 16.6.4 shows a time-temperature graph for several τ values ranging from 25 to 200.[24]

The τ factor is independent of the air temperature used in the plunge test, but is inversely proportional to the square root of the air velocity. During the early development of the residential sprinkler, a τ factor of 21 seconds was considered to indicate the needed level of sensitivity, but this was associated with the specific velocity of 5 ft/sec (1.52 m/sec) used in the FM Global Research plunge test. Since the τ factor changes with the velocity of heated air moving past the sprinkler, it is a fairly inconvenient measure of sprinkler sensitivity.

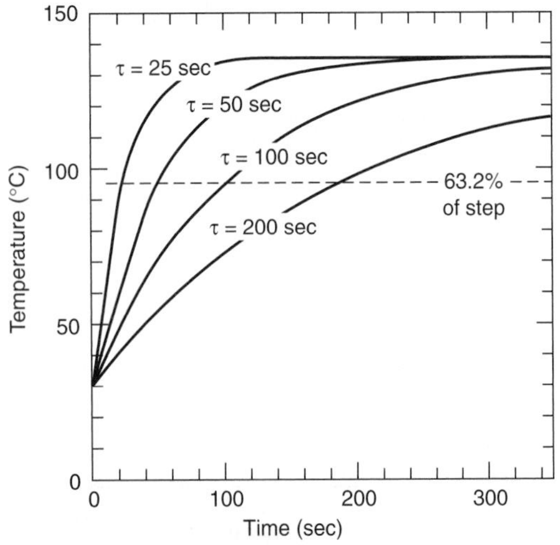

FIGURE 16.6.4 Calculated Sprinkler τ Values Responding to a Step Change Temperature Increase of 105°C with a Gas Velocity of 8.33 ft/sec (2.54 m/sec)

The RTI has replaced the τ factor as the measure of sensitivity and is determined simply by multiplying the τ factor by the square root of the air velocity at which it is found. The RTI is therefore practically independent of both air temperature and air velocity. Comparisons of RTI give a good indication of relative sprinkler sensitivity. The smaller the RTI, the faster the sprinkler operation. Standard-response sprinklers have RTIs in the range of 180 to 650 $sec^{1/2}ft^{1/2}$ (100 to 350 $sec^{1/2}m^{1/2}$), whereas the RTI range for residential sprinklers is about 50 to 90 $sec^{1/2}ft^{1/2}$ (28 to 50 $sec^{1/2}m^{1/2}$).

The need to add a conductivity term to the model of sprinkler response was recognized in 1986.[23,25] The conductivity term accounts for the loss of heat from the sprinkler operating element to the sprinkler frame, its mounting, and even the water in the pipe. These losses can become significant under low-velocity conditions, particularly for some of the flush-type sprinkler designs with little insulation between the operating element and the sprinkler body.

Fast-Response Sprinkler

Full-scale tests conducted by FM Global Research resulted in the development of a prototype fast-response sprinkler that could control or suppress typical residential fires with the operation of not more than two sprinklers. It could also operate fast enough to maintain survivable conditions within the room of fire origin.[12] Survivable conditions were established as follows:

- Maximum gas temperature at eye level of 200°F (93°C)
- Maximum ceiling surface temperature of 500°F (260°C)
- Maximum carbon monoxide concentration of 1500 ppm

Thus, the sprinkler concept expanded from the traditional role of property protection to include life safety. Full-scale field tests were then conducted in Los Angeles to establish system design parameters using the new prototype fast-response residential sprinkler.[13–16] Data from these tests were studied by the National Fire Protection Association Technical Committee on Automatic Sprinklers and used to establish the criteria for the 1980 edition of NFPA 13D.

RESIDENTIAL SPRINKLER STANDARDS

It is important to recognize that, in addition to their fast-response characteristics, residential sprinklers have a special water distribution pattern. Because the effective control of residential fires often depends on a single sprinkler in the room of fire origin, the distribution of residential sprinklers must be more uniform than that of standard spray sprinklers, which in large areas can rely on the overlapping patterns of several sprinklers to make up for voids. Additionally, residential sprinklers must protect sofas, drapes, and similar furnishings at the periphery of the room. In their discharge patterns, therefore, sprinklers must not only be capable of delivering water to the walls of their assigned areas but also be high enough up on the walls to prevent the fire from getting "above" the sprinklers. The water delivered close to the ceiling not only protects the portion of the wall close to the ceiling but also enhances the capacity of the spray to cool gases at the ceiling level, thus reducing the likelihood of excessive sprinkler openings.

Residential Sprinkler Testing

Because of their differences, residential sprinklers are not listed by product evaluation organizations under the same product standards as standard sprinklers. Underwriters Laboratories Inc., for example, has developed UL 1626, *Standard for Safety for Residential Sprinklers for Fire-Protection Service,* for residential sprinklers, and FM Global Research has published Approval Standard FM 2030, *Research Approval Standard for Residential Automatic Sprinklers,* for residential sprinklers. Both of these standards include a plunge test with specific sensitivity requirements and a distribution test that checks the spray pattern in the vertical plane as well as the horizontal plane. Product standards for standard spray sprinklers contain neither test. Both UL 1626 and FM 2030 also include a fire test that is intended to simulate a residential fire in the corner of a room containing combustible materials representative of a living room environment.

UL 1626 Test Procedures. The UL 1626 fuel package and test procedure was recently revised to (1) enhance the reproducibility of the tests and (2) increase the similarity between the fire performance of the fuel package used in the standard tests and that of the fuel packages used as part of the principal residential sprinkler research effort.[13,15,16] Details of the UL 1626 simulated furniture are shown in Figure 16.6.5. The arrangement of the fuel package within the test room is shown at the upper left of the figure.

The three fire test configurations are shown in Figures 16.6.6, 16.6.7, and 16.6.8. Figure 16.6.6 shows the configuration used to test pendent, upright, flush, recessed pendent, and concealed sprinklers. Figures 16.6.7 and 16.6.8 present the configurations used to test sidewall sprinklers; in the first case the sprinklers are located opposite the fuel package, and in the second case the sprinklers are located on the same wall as the fuel package.

The floor plan dimensions of the test room depend on the rated sprinkler coverage. As shown in Figure 16.6.5, the width of the test room, *w*, equals the rated sprinkler coverage width, and the length of the test room equals twice the rated coverage length, *L*. For the sidewall sprinkler configurations, the dimensions of the test room should be the rated sprinkler coverage length, *L*, by 1½ times the sprinkler coverage width, *w*, plus 9 ft (2.7 m). The ceiling height in all cases is a nominal 8 ft (2.4 m). The fuel package is composed of several different components: a wood crib, two simulated sofa ends covered with foam, two sheets of ¼ in. (6.3 mm) Douglas fir plywood, a pan with heptane, and two heptane-soaked cotton wicks. The wood crib is composed of 16 pieces of nominal 1½ in. by 1½ in. (38 mm by 38 mm) kiln-dried spruce or fir lumber 12 in. (300 mm) in length and 5.5 to 7.0 lb (2.5 to 3.2 kg) in weight. The pieces of lumber are to be arranged in four layers, with four pieces of wood per layer. The pieces of lumber should be evenly spaced along the length of the previous layer of wood members and stapled in place. The layers of lumber are to be placed at right angles to the layer below. The finished size of the wood crib is approximately 12 in. (305 mm) on a side and 6 in. (152 mm) high.

The simulated sofa ends are composed of a wood frame support and a ½-in. (12.7-mm) thick piece of plywood, 33 in. by 31 in. (840 mm by 790 mm) high in a vertical position. The plywood has 3-in. (76-mm) thick uncovered urethane foam cushions 30 in. (760 mm) high by 32 in. (810 mm) wide attached to the side facing the crib. The foam has a density of 1.70 to 1.90 lb/ft^3 (27.2 to 30.4 kg/m^3). The walls of the test room are covered with 4 ft by 8 ft by ¼ in. (1.2 m by 2.4 m by 6.4 mm) Douglas fir plywood paneling (flame spread rating 130 ± 30) attached to wood furring strips. The ceiling of the test room is 8 ft (2.4 m) high and covered with 2-ft by 4-ft by ½-in. (0.61-m by 1.20-m by 12.7-mm) thick acoustical panels (flame spread rating 25 or less) with a density of 13.5 ± 1.5 lb/ft^3 (216 ± 24 kg/m^3) attached to wood furring strips.

A 12-in. by 12-in. by 4-in. (305-mm by 305-mm by 104-mm) high steel pan containing 16 oz. (0.5 L) of water and 8 oz. (0.24 L) of heptane is positioned under the wood crib and ignited to start the test.

Fire Control Requirements. To meet the UL 1626 test criteria, residential sprinklers, installed in a fire test enclosure with an 8-ft (2.4-m) ceiling, are required to control a fire for 10 minutes with the following limits:

1. The maximum gas or air temperature adjacent to the sprinkler—3 in. (76.2 mm) below the ceiling and 8 in. (203 mm) horizontally away from the sprinkler—must not exceed 600°F (316°C).
2. The maximum temperature—5 ft 3 in. (1.6 m) above the floor and half the room length away from each wall—must be less than 200°F (93°C) during the entire test. This temperature must not exceed 130°F (54°C) for more than a 2 minute period.
3. The maximum temperature—¼ in. (6.3 mm) behind the finished surface of the ceiling material directly above the test fire—must not exceed 500°F (260°C).
4. No more than two residential sprinklers in the test enclosure can operate.

The enclosure is kept at an initial ambient temperature of 80°F (27°C) ± 5°F (3°C) and it is ventilated through two door openings on opposite walls. The fire test is conducted for 10 minutes after the ignition of the wood crib. The waterflow to the first sprinkler that operates and the total waterflow when the second sprinkler operates are specified as part of the listing limitations for the sprinklers in the test. The total waterflow for two sprinklers must be a minimum of 1.2 times the minimum flow for a single sprinkler.

Water Distribution Requirements. The water distribution test requirements are based on the distribution pattern of the prototype residential sprinkler used in the Los Angeles test fires.[16] The distribution requirements involve collections in both the horizontal and vertical planes. All residential sprinklers in the test must discharge water at the flow rate specified by the manufacturer for a 10 minute period simulating one sprinkler operating and two sprinklers operating. The quantity of water collected on both the horizontal and vertical surfaces is measured and recorded.

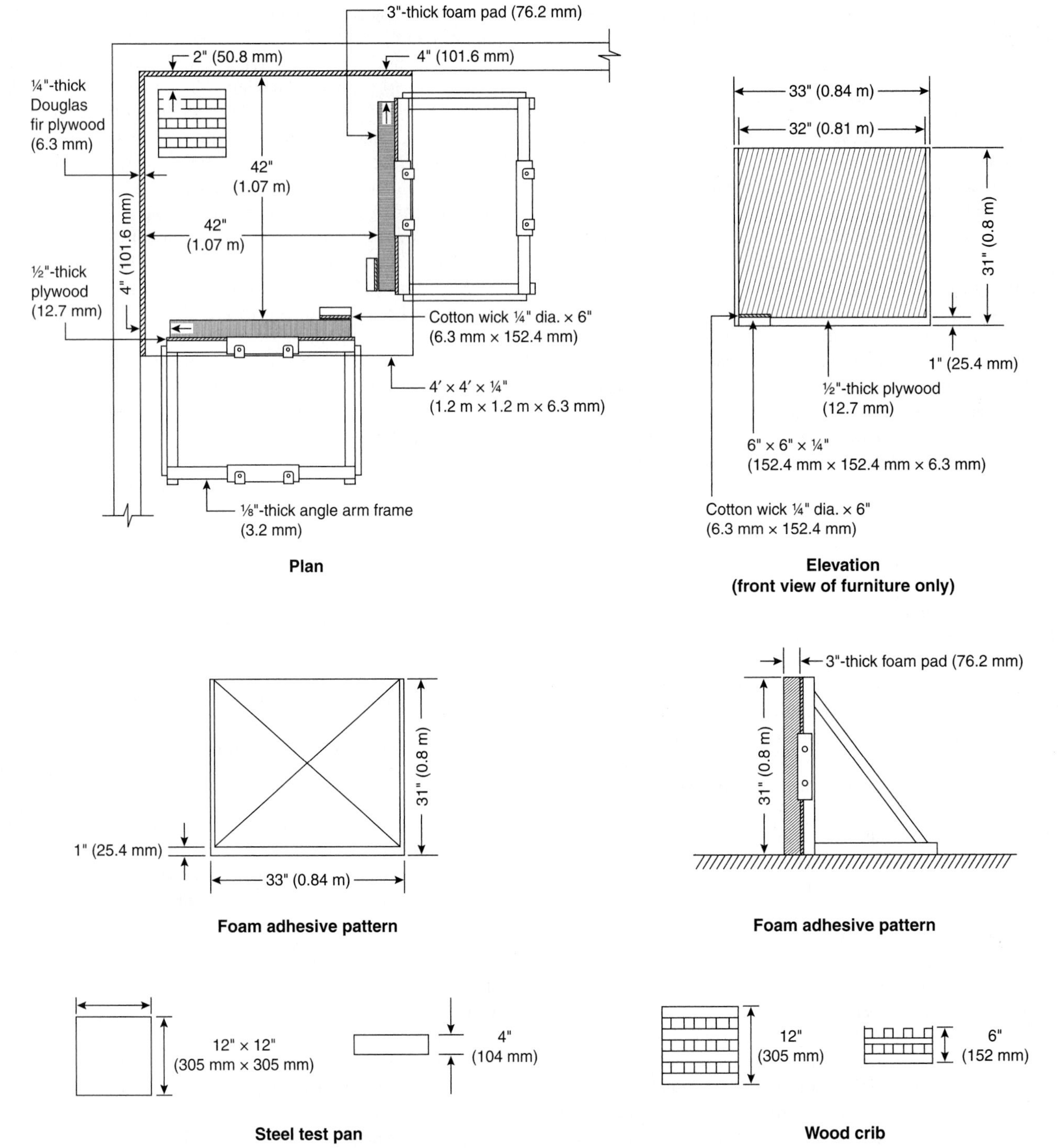

FIGURE 16.6.5 Simulated Fuel Package from UL 1626

Sprinklers being tested are required to discharge a minimum of 0.02 gpm/ft^2 [(0.8[L/min]/m^2) over the entire horizontal design area, with the exception that no more than four 1-ft^2 (0.09-m^2) areas shall be allowed to be at least 0.015 gpm/ft^2 (0.6[L/min]/m^2). They must also wet the walls of the test enclosure to a height not less than 28 in. (711 mm) below the ceiling with one sprinkler operating. Each wall surrounding the coverage area is required to be wetted with a minimum of 5 percent of the sprinkler flow.

Changes to the 2002 editions of NFPA 13D and NFPA 13R were coordinated with revised listings for residential sprinklers, calling for a minimum water spray density of 0.05 gpm/ft^2 (2.05 mm/min). Although the number of sprinklers to be included in the design area did not change for the 13D and 13R standards, the concept of the reduced multiple-sprinkler flow rate was abandoned. Residential sprinklers are now listed with a single minimum flow rate for a given area of coverage.

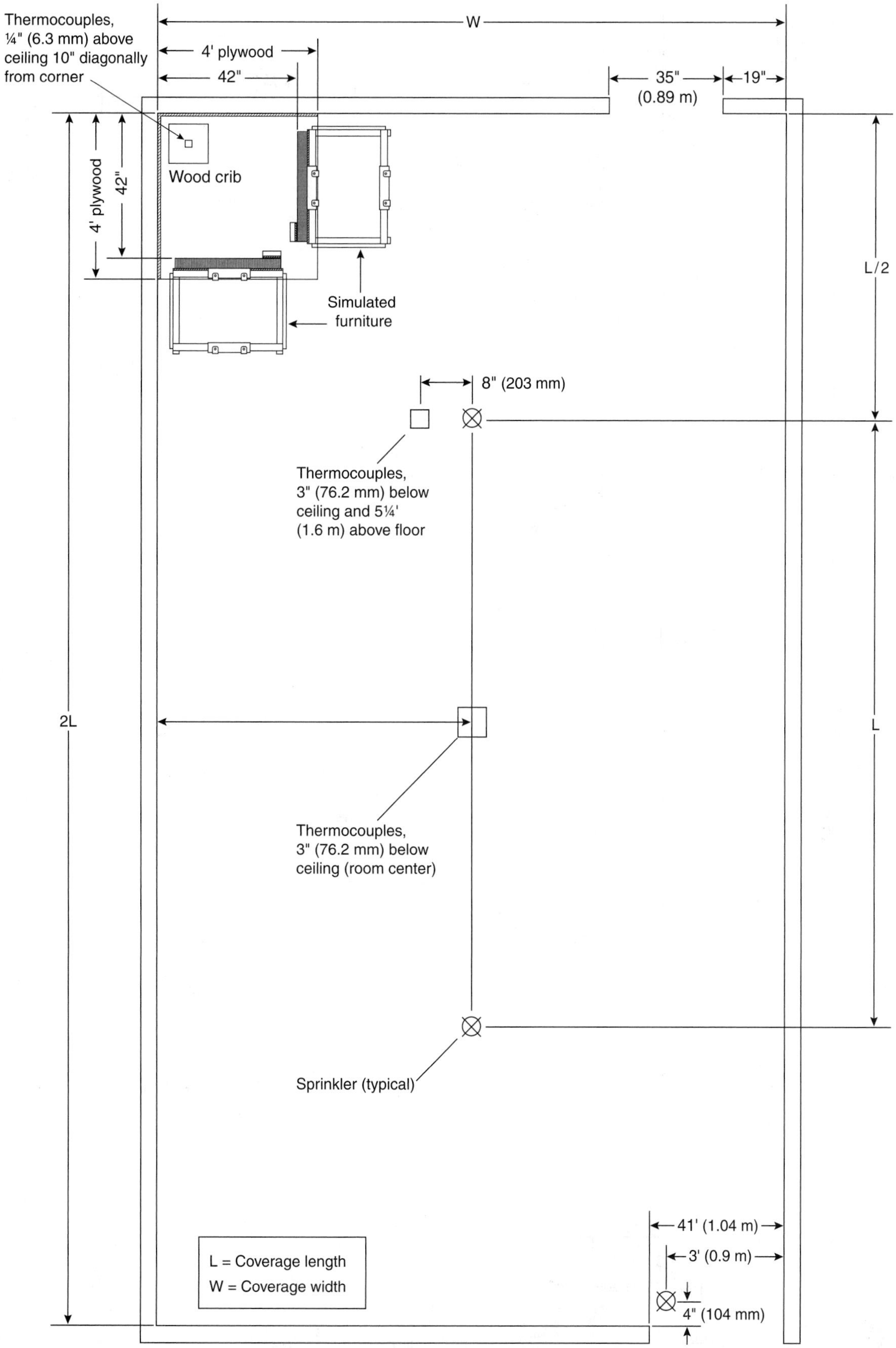

FIGURE 16.6.6 Fire Test Arrangement from UL 1626 for Pendent, Upright, Flush, Recessed Pendent, and Concealed Sprinklers

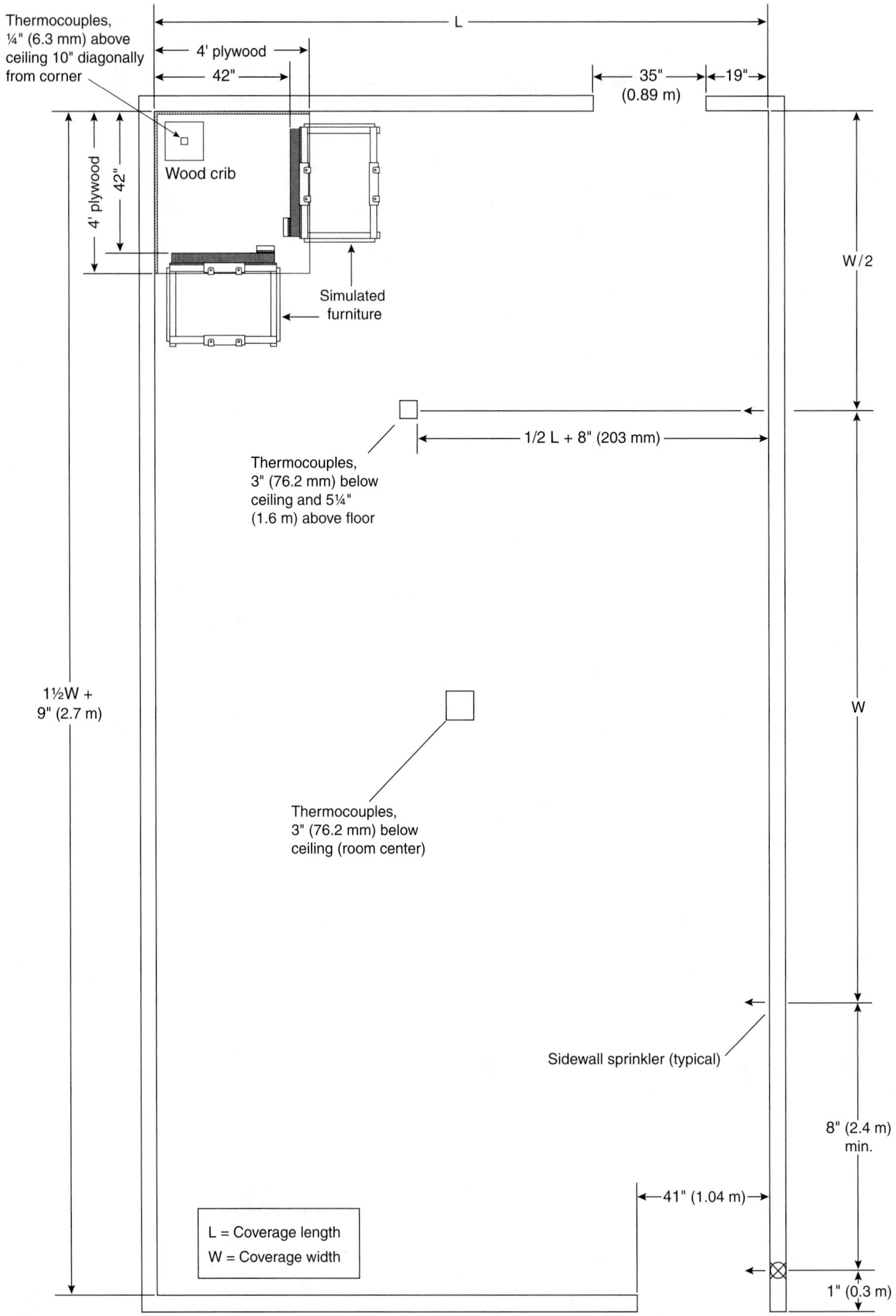

FIGURE 16.6.7 Fire Test Arrangement from UL 1626 for Sidewall Sprinklers, Test Arrangement 1

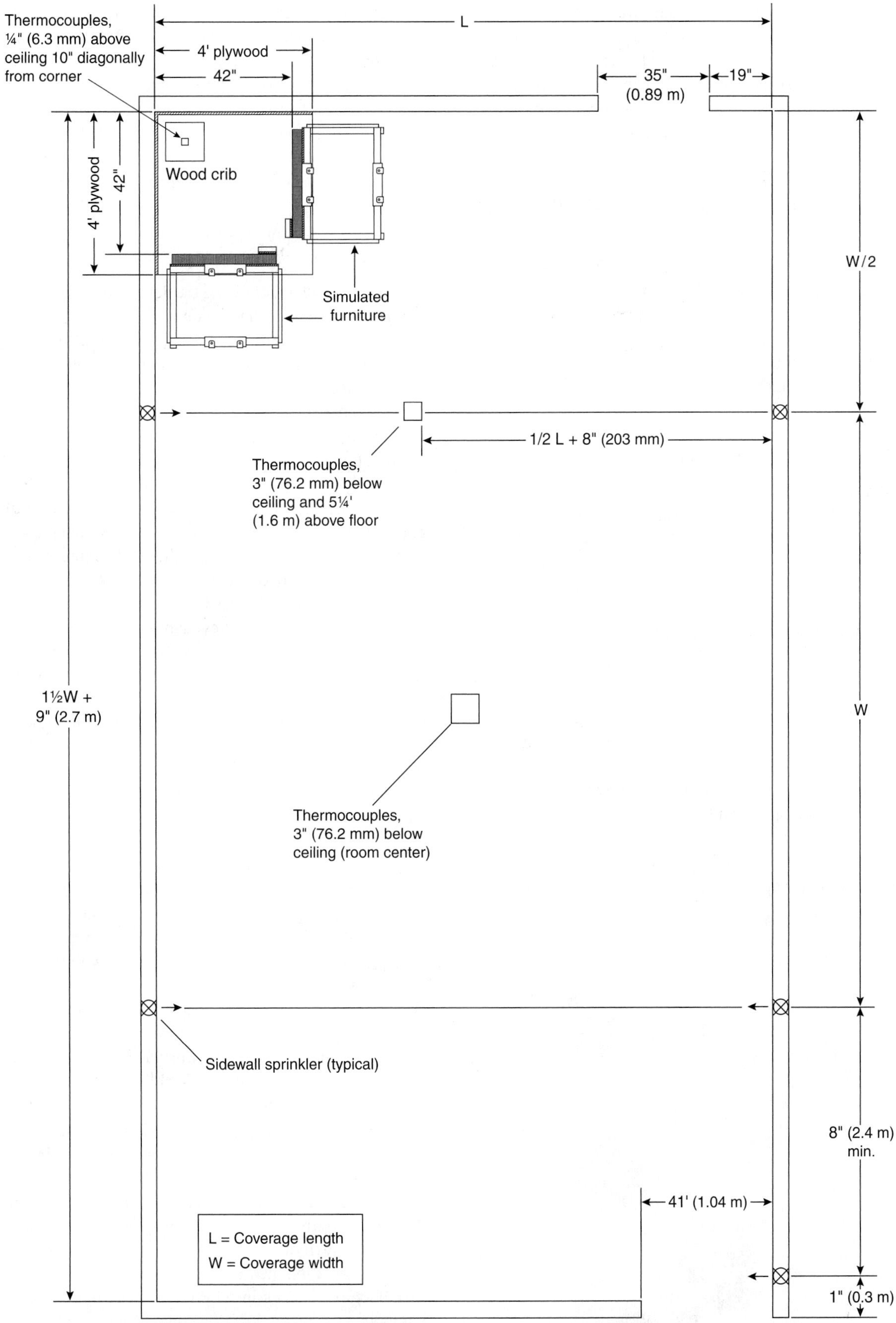

FIGURE 16.6.8 Fire Test Arrangement from UL 1626 for Sidewall Sprinklers, Test Arrangement 2

Research on residential and domestic sprinklers outside the United States supports the trend toward a single minimum flow rate for residential sprinklers. Swedish research published in 2001 indicated that the minimum water application rate of 0.05 gpm/ft^2 (2.05 mm/min) was sufficient to achieve reasonably good protection when the fire test scenario involved upholstered furniture.[26]

Revised NFPA 13D Design Requirements

The design criteria in the 1980 edition of NFPA 13D included for the first time the requirement that all sprinklers be "listed residential sprinklers" (Figure 16.6.9). Other initial basic design requirements in the revamped NFPA 13D were as follows.

Performance Criteria. To prevent flashover in the room of fire origin, when sprinklered, and to improve the chance for occupants to escape or be evacuated.

Design Criteria. Design criteria include the following:

- Only listed residential sprinklers to be used
- Minimum 18 gpm (68 L/min) to any single operating sprinkler and 13 gpm (49 L/min) to all operating sprinklers in the design area up to a maximum of two sprinklers
- Maximum area protected by a single sprinkler of 144 ft^2 (13.4 m^2)
- Maximum distance between sprinklers of 12 ft (3.7 m)
- Minimum distance between sprinklers of 8 ft (2.4 m)
- Maximum distance from a sprinkler to a wall or partition of 6 ft (1.8 m)

Application rates, design areas, areas of coverage, and minimum design pressures other than those specified above were permitted to be used with special sprinklers listed for such special residential installation conditions.

Sprinkler Coverage. Sprinklers to be installed in all areas, with the following exceptions:

- Sprinklers allowed to be omitted from bathrooms no larger than 55 ft^2 (5.1 m^2)

FIGURE 16.6.9 Listed Residential Sprinkler

- Sprinklers allowed to be omitted from closets where the least dimension does not exceed 3 ft (0.9 m), the area does not exceed 24 ft^2 (2.2 m^2), and the walls and ceiling are surfaced with noncombustible materials
- Sprinklers allowed to be omitted from open-attached porches, garages, carports, and similar structures
- Sprinklers allowed to be omitted from attics and crawl spaces that are not used or intended for living purposes or storage
- Sprinklers allowed to be omitted from entrance foyers that are not the only means of egress

In the 30 years following the development of the residential sprinkler, special listings involving expanded protection areas and reduced flows proliferated to the point that the original flow and spacing criteria have become all but obsolete. Residential sprinklers are now listed for coverage areas up to 400 ft^2 (37.2 m^2) per sprinkler.

Since 1985, the use of residential sprinklers has also been permitted under some conditions in accordance with NFPA 13. Essentially, NFPA 13 allows residential sprinklers in dwelling units located in any occupancy, provided they are installed in conformance with the requirements of their listing and the positioning requirements of NFPA 13D. A dwelling unit is defined as one or more rooms arranged for the use of one or more individuals living together, as in a single housekeeping unit, normally having cooking, living, sanitary, and sleeping facilities. Dwelling units include hotel rooms, dormitory rooms, sleeping rooms in nursing homes, and similar living units. Occupancies encompassing dwelling units include apartment buildings, board and care facilities, dormitories, condominiums, lodging and rooming houses, and other multiple-family dwellings. For NFPA 13 applications involving residential sprinklers in dwelling units, the design area must consist of the four most hydraulically demanding sprinklers (Figure 16.6.10).

Other areas, such as attics, basements, or other types of occupancies outside of dwelling units but within the same structure, must be protected in accordance with regular provisions of NFPA 13, including the appropriate water supply requirements. The decision as to which areas are to be protected with sprinklers is also regulated in accordance with the normal provisions of NFPA 13. This protection means, for example, that combustible concealed spaces generally require sprinklers. For NFPA 13 applications, although the four-sprinkler design area can be used in the dwelling units when protected with residential sprinklers, any sprinklers installed within such concealed spaces would have to use a different design approach.

Residential sprinklers installed in systems designed to NFPA 13 requirements are spaced and positioned in accordance with their residential listings, not with the spacing requirements of NFPA 13. The water demands for the residential sprinklers are the same as in NFPA 13 applications, except that the multiple-sprinkler flow requirement is extended to four sprinklers rather than the two stipulated for one- and two-family dwellings and manufactured homes in NFPA 13D. The more liberal piping, component, hanger, location, and water supply duration allowances of NFPA 13D are not permitted in these systems. Beginning in 1996, NFPA 13 requires residential sprinklers or quick-response sprinklers in residential areas.

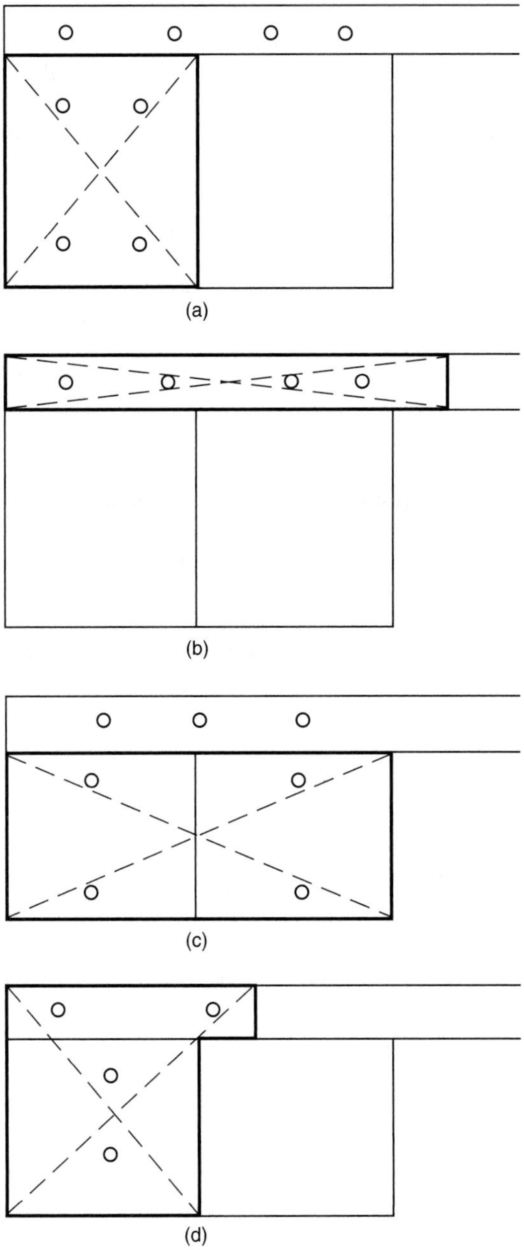

FIGURE 16.6.10 Design Areas for Dwelling Units

Ceiling Fan Criteria. Technical improvements to NFPA 13D are made with each new edition. One of the major areas of improvement to the 2007 edition was the development of criteria for the obstructions created by ceiling fans. Figure 16.6.11 shows a sprinkler obstructed by a ceiling fan. Research conducted in 2005 by the National Fire Sprinkler Association at the facilities of the Viking Corporation involved distribution and fire testing using three different styles of ceiling fans, one with the housing tight against the ceiling, one with a suspended housing, and one with large blades obstructing half of the plan view of the area swept by the blades.[27] Based on the results of the tests, the Committee on Residential Sprinkler Systems agreed that the minimum distance from a sprinkler to the center of a ceiling fan should be 3 ft (0.9 m) for pendent sprinklers and 5 ft (1.5 m) for sidewall sprinklers.

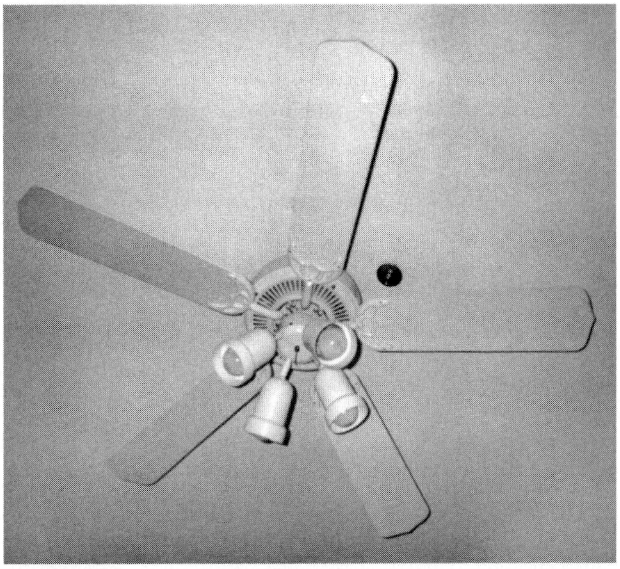

FIGURE 16.6.11 Residential Sprinkler Obstructed by Ceiling Fan

Development of NFPA 13R

Like NFPA 13D, NFPA 13R, *Standard for the Installation of Sprinkler Systems in Residential Occupancies up to and Including Four Stories in Height,* is oriented toward economical life safety protection from fire. Sprinklers can be omitted from building areas that have been found to have a low incidence of fatal fires, including combustible concealed spaces, small bathrooms and closets, and attached porches. As with NFPA 13D, residential sprinklers are required throughout dwelling units, with some minor exceptions. A four-sprinkler design area is required unless the largest compartment contains fewer sprinklers.

In recognition of the greater risk associated with multifamily occupancies, NFPA 13R is more conservative than NFPA 13D in some areas. Requirements for plans, hydraulic calculations, and system acceptance certificates parallel those of NFPA 13. Unlike NFPA 13D, NFPA 13R requires a consideration of the likelihood that simultaneous domestic flows might occur through combined service piping. In addition, pumps and other key equipment are required to be listed. In NFPA 13R systems, areas outside dwelling units can be protected with standard spray sprinklers, using NFPA 13 design criteria.

NEW TECHNOLOGY IN RESIDENTIAL SPRINKLER SYSTEMS

Multipurpose Piping Systems

Although NFPA 13D has had the option for a combined or multipurpose piping system for many years, in 1999 the committee further encouraged the use of this option by allowing nonlisted pipe to be connected to the sprinkler system for the purpose of supplying plumbing fixtures and by specifying a working pressure requirement of not less than 130 psi (8.9 bar) at not less than 120°F (49°C). The combined system may be a means to integrate the sprinkler system into new homes as a standard feature instead of as an option.

The multipurpose system uses the cold water piping to serve as a supply for both the domestic fixtures, such as sinks and showers, and the fire sprinklers. Given the potential for a reduced amount of pipe and fittings, there is a potential for reduced system cost. Supplying the sprinklers from the domestic water system can provide increased system reliability because any impairment to the water supply would be more quickly recognized. In addition, a combined system eliminates the need for backflow prevention devices. This setup also helps to reduce the cost of the system and eliminates any water pressure losses that would be incurred by a backflow prevention device.

New piping materials composed of cross-linked polyethylene have recently been listed by UL for use in residential sprinkler systems.[28] This piping is similar to piping already used in domestic plumbing systems and is therefore easily used in combined systems.

Residential Water Mist System

Residential fire suppression/control systems are also being developed under NFPA 750, *Standard on Water Mist Fire Protection Systems.* A water mist system uses very fine water sprays to control or extinguish fires by cooling of the flame and fire plume, oxygen displacement by water vapor, and radiant heat attenuation.[29]

Water mist systems typically use smaller amounts of water at significantly higher pressures when compared to a NFPA 13D residential sprinkler system. The spacing of water mist nozzles tends to be smaller than the spacing of residential sprinklers; hence more nozzles are needed to provide fire protection for a given area. Studies sponsored by the U.S. Fire Administration showed that in some cases water mist systems could provide equivalent levels of fire safety relative to a residential sprinkler system, however, at a significantly higher cost.[30,31] (For further information, see Section 16, Chapter 8, "Water Mist Fire Suppression Systems.")

RESIDENTIAL SPRINKLER EXPERIENCE

Scottsdale, Arizona

Due to the proven effectiveness of residential fire sprinklers, communities in 25 states require sprinklers in one- and two-family homes.[32] One of these communities, Scottsdale, Arizona, has conducted a detailed 10 year study on the impact of residential fire sprinklers on its community. In June 1985, the city of Scottsdale passed a comprehensive fire sprinkler ordinance that required all new multifamily and commercial structures to be protected by sprinklers, beginning in July 1985, and all new single-family homes, beginning in January 1986.[33]

The results of the study held some surprises. The average installation cost of a residential sprinkler system decreased significantly over the 10 year period. In 1986, the average installation cost was $\$1.14/ft^2$. By January 1996, the average cost was $\$0.59/ft^2$, a decrease of approximately 45 percent.[33]

Surveys of the home insurance companies in the Scottsdale area yielded an average discount of 10 percent for homes with residential sprinkler systems installed.[33] The Scottsdale study also examined the issue of water usage during a fire incident. The first 38 sprinklered fire incidents, a combination of fires in commercial, multifamily, and single-family units, were investigated. Based on the incident time lines, the waterflow times for the sprinkler systems were determined and the total waterflow was calculated. The average amount of water used per fire was 357 gal. Assuming that manual suppression could be accomplished in the same amount of time as the sprinkler flow time, the average amount of water used per fire incident by the fire department would amount to more than 4800 gal.[33]

In 1996, a review of the 109 fires that had occurred in sprinklered buildings in Scottsdale included 44 residential fires. In over 90 percent of the incidents, the fire was controlled with one or two sprinklers activated. The average amount of water flowed by the sprinklers was 299 gal per fire versus an estimated manual suppression usage of approximately 6000 gal per fire.

In 2001, the Scottsdale data were updated to include 15 years of experience with the Scottsdale sprinkler ordinance.[34] The updated data show the trends continuing, with the average fire loss in a sprinklered home to be \$2166, as compared to \$45,019 in a home without sprinklers. Efforts are under way to update the study to include 20 years of experience.

Prince Georges County. Maryland

Prince Georges County, Maryland, enacted an ordinance in 1990 by which all new residential structures were required to be sprinklered beginning in January 1, 1992. A report of the first 8 years' experience was compiled in January 2001.[35] The total fire loss in 117 fire incidents in which sprinklers were involved was reported as \$401,220, as compared to an estimated \$38,230,000 had sprinklers not been present. Although 7 minor injuries were reported in these fires, 154 lives were reported as having been saved by the sprinkler systems.

Among the 121 reported fire incidents, more than one residential sprinkler operated in only 11. In 7 of those, more than two sprinklers operated. An investigation revealed that those 7 involved some extenuating circumstance, such as the use of an accelerant or human intervention, which contributed to the operation of the additional sprinklers. During this same time period, there were only 4 incidents of sprinkler discharge for reasons other than a fire.

Residential Fire Sprinkler Activation Project

Starting in July 2003, the National Association of State Fire Marshals established a residential fire sprinkler activation reporting system on its website (http://www.firemarshals.org). The objective of the project is to collect current and detailed data pertaining to residential sprinkler activations.[36] There are 18 data fields, which include the type of occupancy, number of stories, story of origin, room of origin, area of the room of fire origin, number of sprinklers installed in room of origin, number of sprinklers activated, type of sprinkler activated, and reason for activation. Other inputs regard smoke detectors, and estimates for lives saved, dollar loss due to fire, and dollars saved by sprinkler activation.

During the first two years of the project, 448 incidents were submitted by 167 different fire departments. Over 60 percent of the sprinkler activations documented occurred in apartment buildings. The sprinkler activations in kitchens accounted for 40 percent of the recorded incidents. Of the incidents where the number of sprinklers was reported, approximately 83 percent of the activations involved only a single sprinkler. This project is supported by a grant from the U.S. Fire Administration.

INCENTIVES FOR MORE WIDESPREAD USE OF RESIDENTIAL SPRINKLERS

Certain incentives can stimulate interest in residential sprinklers. These incentives are discussed in the following paragraphs.

Reduction in Government Spending

Reduction in all forms of government spending, resulting from public pressure to reduce property taxes, is a prime factor in the future growth of the residential sprinkler concept. Many fire departments are forced to protect larger areas and more subdivisions with the same number of or even fewer people because financial restrictions hamper a fire department's ability to grow with the community. As a result, alternatives to traditional fire-fighting techniques must be found. One of them is the use of residential sprinklers. San Clemente, California, was the first community in the United States to pass a residential sprinkler ordinance in 1980 as part of the fire department's master plan. This ordinance requires automatic sprinkler systems to be installed in all new residential construction. The prime motivation for the passage of this ordinance was San Clemente's cutbacks in government spending brought about by Proposition 13, the state's tax-capping measure. Many communities across the country face similar situations. Automatic sprinklers in residences may be the answer to fewer fire fighters and longer response times from the fire department.

Insurance Savings

Although the greatest benefit from widespread installation of residential sprinklers will be the lives saved and injuries prevented, lower property losses will be a secondary and substantial benefit. An ad hoc committee from the insurance industry sponsored a number of test fires in Los Angeles during the early 1980s and concluded that residential sprinklers have the potential for reducing homeowners' claim payment expenses.[37] As a result, the Insurance Services Office (ISO) Personal Lines Committee recommended that a 15 percent reduction in the homeowner's policy premium be given for installation of an NFPA 13D residential sprinkler system. Although this would not pay for the system over a short period of time, as is the case in many commercial installations, the continuing increases in the cost of insuring a single-family home make this a significant incentive nonetheless. NFPA analysis indicates that home sprinklers, like other sprinkler installations, reduce average fire loss per home fire by a much larger one-half to two-thirds.[38]

Real Estate Tax Reductions

In 1981, the state of Alaska enacted into law a significant piece of legislation that has a dramatic impact on the installation of sprinkler systems throughout that state. The law provides that 2 percent of the assessed value of any structure is exempt from taxation if the structure is protected with a fire protection system. The word *structure* is significant in the law, because it also applies to homes. In effect, if a home were assessed at $100,000 for purposes of taxation, the assessed value would be computed at $98,000, provided that it contained a fire protection system.

It actually may be considered an incentive simply to add the value of a fire sprinkler system to the assessed value of a property. In a national poll commissioned by the Home Fire Sprinkler Coalition in December 2000, it was found that 69 percent of homeowners believe having a fire sprinkler system increases the value of a home, and 38 percent said they would be more likely to purchase a new home with sprinklers than one without.[39]

Zoning

Greater land use may be possible with zoning changes that would permit fully sprinklered residences to be built on smaller parcels of land. The assumption is that the space between houses will not be as important from a fire protection standpoint if an entire street or neighborhood is fully sprinklered. One could argue, however, that if the sprinkler system fails, the resultant fire involving a number of residences could be much greater. The more complex analysis required to assess the net effects of full sprinklering of a neighborhood with smaller lot sizes has yet to be conducted.

Sprinkler Legislation

In addition to the San Clemente ordinance, a number of other California communities have passed residential sprinkler legislation, including Orange County and Los Angeles County. In 1993, more than 4 million Californians lived in communities in which residential sprinklers were mandated in all new homes.[40] Since 1982, Greenburgh, New York, and several surrounding communities have enacted sprinkler ordinances that require the installation of automatic sprinklers in virtually all new construction, including all new multiple-, one-, and two-family dwellings. A similar law went into effect in Prince George's County, Maryland, in 1992.

The state of Florida in 1983 passed a law requiring that all public lodging and time-share units three or more stories high in the state be sprinklered. It also required that all existing units be sprinklered by 1988.

In 1983, the city of Honolulu, Hawaii, adopted legislation that required all new and existing high-rise hotels, which are those more than 75 ft (23 m) above grade, to be sprinklered.

In the late 1980s, additional jurisdictions, including Atlanta, Georgia, the state of Connecticut, and the commonwealth of Massachusetts, acted to require retroactively the installation of sprinkler systems in high-rise residential buildings. In 1990, the federal government enacted the Hotel and Motel Fire Safety Act, which contains strong incentives for complete sprinkler protection of hotels, because only hotels with satisfactory levels of fire protection are eligible for federal employee travel.

The Federal Fire Safety Act of 1992 requires automatic sprinkler systems or an equivalent level of safety in all federally assisted housing four or more stories in height, as well as in office buildings owned or leased for more than 25 federal employees. Perhaps the most significant legislation promoting the use of sprinkler systems, however, is the 1990 Americans with Disabilities Act. In 1991, the U.S. Department of Justice published criteria that became mandatory for places of public accommodation and commercial facilities designed for first occupation after January 26, 1993. Alterations to existing buildings must also comply. A key feature of the criteria is the need for areas of refuge. Floors of buildings that do not have direct access to the exterior at grade must provide areas of rescue assistance, except those buildings that have a supervised automatic sprinkler system.

Adoption of fire sprinkler ordinances continues in various areas. One of the most active areas in the early twenty-first century are the suburbs of Chicago. Between 2000 and 2005 the number of communities that had adopted an NFPA 13D ordinance grew from 3 to 35, with 14 of those adopted in 2005.[41] Lessons learned from the experience of communities that have adopted ordinances is being used to provide guidance to others that might wish to pursue their own ordinances.[42]

Construction

Many authorities having jurisdiction have used building code modifications as an incentive to install sprinklers. Cobb County, Georgia, was one of the first communities to amend its Buildings and Construction Code to include such an approach for multifamily structures equipped with residential sprinkler systems. Although these construction alterations can be a major incentive to install residential sprinklers, the disaster potential must always be considered if a fire, for whatever reason, should overpower the sprinkler system. This possibility of disaster is especially true if the system is designed with the minimal water supplies required by NFPA 13D.

The city of Dallas, Texas, adopted a building code that requires all new buildings or those undergoing major renovation, having an area greater than 7500 ft^2 (697 m^2), to have automatic sprinklers. At the same time, this building code encourages the installation of sprinkler systems by allowing design options that may allow different levels of "passive" fire protection features in exchange for "active" automatic sprinkler alternatives.

Code Requirements

Beginning with the 1991 edition, NFPA *101®*, *Life Safety Code®*, required the use of quick-response or residential sprinklers in new health care occupancies in smoke compartments that contain patient sleeping rooms. This generally means all patient rooms and their adjacent corridors. Beginning with the 1994 edition, quick-response or residential sprinklers were also required in all new hotel and dormitory guest rooms and guest room suites. Beginning in 1996, NFPA 13 requires quick-response or residential sprinklers in all new light hazard construction.

Because of these and other incentives, the use of new technology, such as residential and quick-response sprinklers, increased by a factor of 15 in the United States between 1990 and 2000, while the total number of sprinklers installed nearly doubled.[43] There is growing recognition of the enhanced ability of residential and other types of fast-response sprinklers to protect life and property from fires.

A major milestone for residential sprinkler came in August 2005 with the issuance of the 2006 editions of NFPA *101®* and *NFPA 5000®*, *Building Construction and Safety Code®*, both of which require fire sprinkler systems in all new one- and two-family dwellings.

SUMMARY

Residential sprinkler systems are an effective means of controlling fire in the home, allowing occupants the time to escape or be rescued. Several different systems exist, and research is ongoing to develop systems that are more efficient and cost-effective. The design and installation must take into account where sprinklers in a home are most effective in reducing the risk to life and property. The sprinkler system needs to activate automatically while a fire is small and the smoke and heat conditions in the home are survivable. Once the system is activated, it needs to control the fire with a smaller amount of water relative to a commercial sprinkler system.

Although most fire-related deaths in the United States occur in the home, it is estimated that less than 3 percent of one- and two-family dwellings have sprinkler systems installed. This percentage will rise as more legislation is passed requiring new homes to have sprinkler systems and as technology and costs continue to improve.

BIBLIOGRAPHY

References Cited

1. *America Burning,* the Report of the National Commission on Fire Prevention and Control, U.S. Government Printing Office: 1973-0-495-792, May 1973.
2. Karter, M. J., "Fire Loss in the United States during 2004, Full Report," National Fire Protection Association, Quincy, MA, Sept. 2005.
3. *Fire in the United States 1992–2001,* 13th ed., Federal Emergency Management Agency, United States Fire Administration, National Fire Data Center, FA-286, Oct. 2004.
4. NFPA 13D, *Standard for the Installation of Sprinkler Systems in One- and Two-Family Dwellings and Manufactured Homes,* 2007 ed., National Fire Protection Association, Quincy, MA.
5. Bryan, J. L. *Automatic Sprinkler and Standpipe Systems,* 2nd ed., National Fire Protection Association, Quincy, MA, 1990.
6. Jensen, R., "A Brief History of Sprinklers, Sprinkler Systems and the NFPA Sprinkler Standards," *Automatic Sprinkler System Handbook,* 8th ed., Supplement, National Fire Protection Association, Quincy, MA, 1999.
7. Halpin, B. M., Dinan, J. J., and Deters, O. J., "Assessment of the Potential Impact of Fire Protection Systems on Actual Fire Incidents," Johns Hopkins University—Applied Physics Laboratory (JHU/APL), Laurel, MD, Oct. 1978.
8. Yurkonis, P., "Study to Establish the Existing Automatic Fire Suppression Technology for Use in Residential Occupancies," Rolf Jensen & Associates, Inc., Deerfield, IL, 1980.

9. Kung, H. C., Haines, D., and Green, R., Jr., "Development of Low-Cost Residential Sprinkler Protection," Factory Mutual Research Corporation, Norwood, MA, 1978.
10. Henderson, N. C., Riegel, P. S., Patton, R. M., and Larcomb, D. B., "Investigation of Low-Cost Residential Sprinkler Systems," Battelle Columbus Laboratories, Columbus, OH, 1978.
11. Clark, G., "Performance Specifications for Low-Cost Residential Sprinkler System," Factory Mutual Research Corporation, Norwood, MA, 1978.
12. Kung, H. C., Spaulding, R. D., and Hill, E. E., Jr., "Sprinkler Performance in Residential Fire Tests," Factory Mutual Research Corporation, Norwood, MA, Dec. 1980.
13. Cote, A. E., and Moore, D., "Field Test and Evaluation of Residential Sprinkler Systems," Los Angeles Test Series (A Report for the NFPA 13D Subcommittee), National Fire Protection Association, Quincy, MA, Apr. 1980.
14. Moore, D., "Data Summary of the North Carolina Test Series of USFA Grant 79027 Field Test and Evaluation of Residential Sprinkler Systems" (A Report for the NFPA 13D Subcommittee), National Fire Protection Association, Quincy, MA, Sept. 1980.
15. Kung, H. C., Spaulding, R. D., Hill, E. E., Jr., and Symonds, A. P., "Technical Report, Field Evaluation of Residential Prototype Sprinkler Los Angeles Fire Test Program," Factory Mutual Research Corporation, Norwood, MA, 1982.
16. Cote, A. E., "Final Report on Field Test and Evaluation of Residential Sprinkler Systems," National Fire Protection Association, Quincy, MA, July 1982.
17. Heskestad, G., and Smith, H., "Investigation of a New Sprinkler Sensitivity Approval Test: The Plunge Test," FMRC No. 22485, Factory Mutual Research Corporation, Norwood, MA, 1976.
18. Heskestad, G., and Smith, H., "Plunge Test for Determination of Sprinkler Sensitivity," J.I. 3A1E2.RR, Factory Mutual Research Corporation, Norwood, MA, 1980.
19. Pickard, R. W., Hird, D., and Nash, P., "The Thermal Testing of Heat-Sensitive Fire Detectors," F.R. Note No. 247, Fire Research Station, Borehamwood, Herts, UK, 1957.
20. Evans, D. D., and Madrzykowski, D., "Characterizing the Thermal Response of Fusible-Link Sprinklers," NBSIR 81-2329, National Bureau of Standards, Washington, DC, 1981.
21. Theobald, C. R., "FRS Ramp Test for Thermal Sensitivity of Sprinklers," *Journal of Fire Protection Engineering,* Vol. 1, No. 1, 1989, p. 23.
22. Beever, P. F., "Estimating the Response of Thermal Detectors," *Journal of Fire Protection Engineering,* Vol. 2, No. 1, 1990, p. 11.
23. Heskestad, G., and Bill, R. G., "Conduction Heat-Loss Effects on Thermal Response of Automatic Sprinklers," J.I. OMOJ5.RU, Factory Mutual Research Corporation, Norwood, MA, 1987.
24. Madrzykowski, D., "The Effect of Recessed Sprinkler Installation on Sprinkler Activation Time and Prediction," Master's Thesis, University of Maryland, College Park, MD, Nov. 1993.
25. Pepi, J. S., "Design Characteristics of Quick-Response Sprinklers," Grinnell Fire Protection Systems Company, Providence, RI, 1986.
26. Arvidson, M., and Larsson, I., "Residential Sprinkler and High-Pressure Water Mist Systems," Fire Technology Report 2001:16, SP Swedish National Testing and Research Institute, Boros, Sweden, 2001.
27. Valentine, V., "Ceiling Fan Obstruction Testing," *SQ*, National Fire Sprinkler Association, Mar./Apr. 2006.
28. UL Online Certification Directory, http://www.ul.com/database, category: cross-linked polyethlyne (PEX) sprinkler pipe and fittings VIXR.
29. NFPA 750, *Standard on Water Mist Fire Protection Systems,* 2006 ed., National Fire Protection Association, Quincy, MA.
30. Feasibility Study of Water Mist Applications for Residential Fires, Contract No. EMW-93-4247, Hughes Associates, Inc., Baltimore, MD, Feb. 9, 1995.
31. Bill, R. G., Stavrianidis, P., Hill, E. E., and Brown, W. R., "Water Mist Fire Protection in Residential Occupancies," J.I. OY1N9.RA OZOJ1.RA, Factory Mutual Research Corporation, Norwood, MA, Nov. 1995.
32. Residential Fire Safety Institute, http://www.firesafehome.org/sprinklers/jurisdictions.asp, June 2006.
33. "Automatic Sprinklers, A 10-Year Study, A Detailed History of the Effects of the Automatic Sprinkler Code in Scottsdale, Arizona," Rural/Metro Fire Department, Scottsdale, AZ, 1997.
34. Ford, J., "A Fifteen Year Update on the Impact and Effectiveness of the Scottsdale Sprinkler Ordinance," http://www.oregon.gov/OOHS/SFM.
35. Siarnicki, R. J., "Residential Sprinklers: One Community's Experience Twelve Years After Mandatory Implementation," Paper submitted to the National Fire Academy's Executive Fire Officer Program, Jan. 2001.
36. "Residential Fire Sprinkler Activation Report," National Association of State Fire Marshals, Washington, DC, 2006.
37. Jackson, R. J., "Report of 1980 Property Loss Comparison Fires," Federal Emergency Management Agency/United States Fire Administration, Washington, DC, 1980.
38. Rohr, K. D., *U.S. Experience with Sprinklers,* NFPA Fire Analysis and Research Division, Quincy, MA, Sept. 2001.
39. Paul, P., "New National Survey Shows a Majority of Homeowners Believe that Fire Sprinklers Increase a Home's Value," Press Release of the Home Fire Sprinkler Coalition, Quincy, MA, Jan. 12, 2006.
40. Hart, S., "Executive Summary Report on the 1993 Fire Sprinkler Ordinance Survey," Fire Sprinkler Advisory Board of Southern California, Cerritos, CA, May 31, 1993.
41. Lia, T., "Number of NFPA 13D Ordinances Passed Each Year," http://www.firesprinklerassoc.org, Northern Illinois Chapter of National Fire Sprinkler Association, May 2006.
42. Dalton, J., and Hart, S., "Residential Fire Sprinklers . . . A Step-by-Step Approach for Communities," http://www.nfsa.org, National Fire Sprinkler Association, June 2003.
43. Vinicello, J. A., private communication, Oct. 2001.

NFPA Codes, Standards, and Recommended Practices

Reference to the following NFPA codes, standards, and recommended practices will provide further information on residential sprinkler technology discussed in this chapter. (See the latest version of The NFPA Catalog *for availability of current editions of the following documents.)*

NFPA 13, *Standard for the Installation of Sprinkler Systems*
NFPA 13D, *Standard for the Installation of Sprinkler Systems in One- and Two-Family Dwellings and Manufactured Homes*
NFPA 13R, *Standard for the Installation of Sprinkler Systems in Residential Occupancies up to and Including Four Stories in Height*
NFPA *101*®, *Life Safety Code*®
NFPA 750, *Standard on Water Mist Fire Protection Systems*
NFPA 5000®, *Building Construction and Safety Code*®

Chapter 7

Ultra-High-Speed Water Spray Systems

Robert M. Gagnon

Ultra-high-speed suppression systems for explosive hazards have come to symbolize many things to different people. To fire protection engineers, they are the cutting edge of today's fire protection technology. To some contractors, they may be too difficult to install. To the general public, they may connote an air of mystery and foreboding. Clients may consider them to be temperamental or hard to maintain. It is this diversity of impressions that has necessitated further developments in ultra-high-speed fire suppression system technology.

Two fundamental types of suppression systems are available to fire protection professionals for the control or extinguishment of explosive hazards: (1) ultra-high-speed water spray systems, which are discussed in significant detail in this chapter, and (2) explosion suppression systems, covered briefly in this chapter and well detailed in Section 17, Chapter 8, "Explosion Prevention and Protection."

Since the ultra-high-speed water spray system is essentially a highly sophisticated water spray system, a review of the fundamentals of water spray system design may be of considerable assistance. See Section 16, Chapter 9, "Water Spray Protection."

Further information is available in Section 2, Chapter 8, "Explosions"; Section 6, Chapter 15, "Explosives and Blasting Agents"; Section 14, Chapter 2, "Automatic Fire Detectors"; Section 16, Chapter 9, "Water Spray Protection"; Section 17, Chapter 8, "Explosion Prevention and Protection"; and Section 18, Chapter 4, "Venting Practices."

Chapter Contents

Key Terms

area protection, deluge system, detection system, explosion suppression, explosion venting, flame detection, point protection, reaction time, ultra-high-speed water spray systems, water spray system

SYSTEM DEFINITION AND APPLICATION

Definition

An ultra-high-speed water spray system is defined by NFPA 15, *Standard for Water Spray Fixed Systems for Fire Protection,* as one that can commence the initiation of discharge of water to a volatile commodity within 100 milliseconds of detection, measured from presentation of an energy source to the detector to flow of water from the nozzle being tested. This level of response is required where materials of very high flame spread and heat release, such as propellants and pyrotechnic materials, are involved. With recent advancements in detection and electronic technology, ultra-high-speed water spray system response times in the 10 millisecond range are achievable, with 10 milliseconds being a mandatory response time for very rapidly spreading fires.

The NFPA Technical Committee on Water Spray Fixed Systems has determined that a line of demarcation must exist between ultra-high-speed water spray systems, covered in NFPA 15,

Robert M. Gagnon, P.E., SET, FSFPE, is president of Gagnon Engineering, a fire protection consulting firm in Woodbine, Maryland. He is chair of NFPA's Committee on Foam-Water Sprinkler Systems and secretary of NFPA's Committee on Water Spray Fixed Systems and Committee on Water Tanks. He is a member of NFPA's Committee on Automatic Sprinkler Systems, Committee on Private Water Supply Piping Systems, and Committee on Water Cooling Towers. He also serves on the Technical Correlating Committee on Automatic Sprinkler Systems. Mr. Gagnon has served as a lecturer at the University of Maryland Department of Fire Protection Engineering since 1993, and formerly served as a lecturer at Montgomery College. He is the author of four books on detection and suppression design.

and explosion suppression systems, covered in NFPA 69, *Standard on Explosion Prevention Systems.* Explosion suppression systems are required to be designed in accordance with NFPA 69 for enclosed vessels or other devices or conveyances where overpressurization or rupture is the primary concern. Ultra-high-speed water spray systems are predominantly designed in accordance with NFPA 15 for rooms or open, unconfined areas where rupture resulting from overpressurization is not the primary concern. Tightly sealed rooms and enclosed, or partially enclosed, process equipment are examples of applications that may be appropriate for the design of either ultra-high-speed water spray systems or explosion suppression systems, depending on the configuration of the commodity and its associated manufacturing process. Explosion suppression systems are not normally used in ordinance operations, because their response time is slower than ultra-high-speed water spray systems for the volume of the space requiring protection.

When personnel are present in a room with the potential for a rapidly spreading fire, room overpressurization and rupture are not the primary concerns because personnel are in jeopardy well in advance of an impending room rupture. An ultra-high-speed water spray system is needed to halt the expanding flame front before room overpressurization becomes a concern.

Both ultra-high-speed water spray systems and explosion suppression systems can be satisfactorily designed for the suppression of deflagrations or fires where the expanding flame front travels at a velocity less than the speed of sound. Neither system has been found to be effective for applications where a detonation, or a fire where the expanding flame front travels at a velocity greater than the speed of sound, could occur. Laboratory test data or empirical field testing of the commodity with respect to flame spread and heat release may be necessary before selecting a suppression system for a particular explosive hazard.

Application

Examples of facilities where ultra-high-speed water spray systems are advantageous include rocket fuel manufacturing or processing; solid propellant manufacturing or handling; paint spray can filling; ammunition manufacturing; pyrotechnics manufacturing; maintenance/renovation/demilitarization of ordinance items containing pyrotechnic materials; and the manufacture or handling of other volatile solids, chemicals, dusts, and gases. An example of a situation where an ultra-high-speed suppression system is not likely to be effective would be the protection of stored munitions whose manufacture has been completed.

Certain types of munitions, such as C-4 explosives, may promote a fire scenario that transitions from a deflagration to a detonation. An ultra-high-speed water spray system has been found to be effective for the suppression of such fires when the expansion of the flame front has been halted in its incipient stages.[1]

For military applications, it has become customary to use a nine-hazard classification system developed by the United Nations Organization (UNO) to promote the safe manufacture, storage, and transport of explosives. Class 1 contains the majority of energetic materials that are ordinarily protected by ultra-high-speed water spray systems. Class 1 is subdivided into six divisions, with Divisions 3 and 4 providing the most opportunity for high-speed suppression (Table 16.7.1).

REACTION TO FIRE EVENTS

Reaction Time

Reaction time is defined as the total time required from initiation of combustion and detection to the presence of water at the nozzle. It can be broken down into 11 segments for clarity as to what is included in reaction time and what is currently not being considered during the testing of ultra-high-speed water spray systems (Table 16.7.2).[2]

The 100 millisecond maximum response time required by NFPA 15 considers the period from detector reaction to flow at nozzles, or the time elapsed from segments 4 through 9. Since different detectors have differing reaction times, it is imperative that a detector be chosen with the shortest reaction time available, that the detectors be placed as close as possible to the target, and that no retards or delays be present.

Of great concern to fire protection engineers is the time required for the water to travel from the nozzle to the target, segment 10. To minimize water travel time, nozzles must be placed as close as physically or practically possible to the target. Increased nozzle pressure can increase water velocity and decrease travel time. It is highly recommended that the water travel time be considered in the total response time where feasible. High-speed photographic equipment or other sophisticated

TABLE 16.7.1 Classification of Explosives

Class 1, Division 1	Mass detonation. Includes explosives, ammunition, and liquid propellants that are too energetic to be protected by an ultra-high-speed water spray system.
Class 1, Division 2	Explosion with fragments. Includes ammunition and explosives that may be too energetic to be protected by an ultra-high-speed water spray system.
Class 1, Division 3	Mass fire. Includes ammunition and explosives that may be extinguished during manufacture if suppressed at an early stage. The majority of ultra-high-speed water spray systems protect commodities within this division.
Class 1, Division 4	Moderate fire. Includes ammunition and explosives that can be extinguished by an ultra-high-speed water spray system.
Class 1, Division 5	Very insensitive explosives
Class 1, Division 6	Extremely insensitive ammunition

TABLE 16.7.2 Reaction Time

1	The energetic material is subject to excessive energy input.
2	Deflagration begins.
3	The deflagration develops to a point that puts it in the detector's field of vision.
4	The detector begins to react to the fire.
5	The detector determines that there is sufficient light energy to be considered a fire.
6	The detector sends out a fire signal.
7	A high-speed module on the control panel receives the signal from the detector and activates the squib or solenoid-actuated valve.
8	Mechanical components associated with the ultra-high-speed water spray system go into motion.
9	Water leaves the nozzle and travels toward the target.
10	Water spray impinges on the target.
11	Waterflow is maintained to achieve cooling, dispersion, or extinguishment.

time measurement tools are needed to measure water travel time as a component of the total response time.

When no explicit guidance is given for specific situations, 36 in. (914.4 mm) is frequently used as a default distance between a point hazard and ultra-high-speed water spray system nozzles and detectors. Although increased nozzle pressure can reduce water travel time, pressurization of a nozzle beyond its effective range can result in distorted and inefficient nozzle spray patterns.

General Detection Concerns

To achieve the aforementioned rapid response time, optical flame detection for open areas or pressure detection for areas subject to overpressurization is necessary. Examples of optical flame detection devices include ultraviolet (UV) or infrared (IR) detectors placed in close proximity to the hazard. Such detectors instantaneously detect flashes of light associated with the wavelengths normally found in combustion. Pressure detectors sense a buildup of explosive pressure in an enclosure; they are very effective but generally provide slower actuation times than optical flame detectors.

Multiple-band optical detectors are now being specified for use with ultra-high-speed water spray systems. The U.S. Army's Advanced Fire Protection Deluge System Project (AFPDS) investigated multiband IR/IR and UV/IR multiple-band optical detectors as possible replacements for UV detectors and found that they can be as fast as the UV detectors and less likely to falsely actuate. False actuations of ultra-high-speed water spray systems are a major concern for defense and industrial applications. Furthermore, environmental concerns relative to containment and disposal of potential pollutants mixed with water from ultra-high-speed water spray systems may also be a major concern and a rationale for selection of multiple-band optical detectors.

The signal emitted by a detector is received by a high-speed module on the fire alarm control unit. To enhance actuation response times, it is necessary that the control unit be specifically designed for ultra-high-speed systems. It is the fire alarm control unit and its associated detection system that makes an ultra-high-speed suppression system unique from other types of water-delivery fire protection systems. The proper choice and design of supervisory equipment is essential to the successful functioning of the system.

NFPA 70, *National Electrical Code*®, and *NFPA 72*®, *National Fire Alarm Code*®, must be followed closely for all detection system wiring, component placement, and connections. Circuits between sensing devices and their controllers must be continuous with no splices and must be individually shielded.

GENERAL SYSTEM CONCERNS

Piping Methods

The piping methods associated with agent delivery to the hazard are as varied as the hazards they protect. The nozzles should be in very close proximity to the hazard with water in the piping and primed up to the nozzle, prepared for quick delivery of water to the hazard. One type of ultra-high-speed water spray system, the squib-actuated system, involves loosely capped nozzles, and/or a rupture disc at each nozzle, a preprimed piping system, and a deluge valve with an explosive squib (Figure 16.7.1). Another type, the solenoid-actuated system, involves pilot-actuated nozzles with a solenoid valve or system of solenoid valves installed on the pilot piping, which actuate upon receiving a signal from the detection system (Figure 16.7.2). A third type, possessing explosive squibs at each nozzle, is a variation of the squib-actuated system. Its distinguishing features (i.e., prepriming and squib actuation) will be covered in detail in this chapter.

Approaches to Detection

Two general design approaches, point protection and area protection, will apply to ultra-high-speed water spray system design. Point protection is the application of concentrated high-speed water spray onto a fixed point of ignition, such as a band saw blade for cutting solid munitions, and is accomplished by providing two or more counteropposed nozzles at positions as close as physically possible to the point of ignition (Figure 16.7.3). Area protection is the application of high-speed water spray over the area of a room or over the surface area of an object (Figure 16.7.4). In both cases, the nozzles must be as close to the intended target as possible to minimize the time for the water to travel from the nozzle to the target. Some hazards may be conducive to using the attributes of both point protection and area protection. This hybrid system is referred to as a combination system (Figure 16.7.5).

Nozzles and detectors should be placed no further than 36 in. (914.4 mm) from a point hazard and must be carefully coordinated with the process to avoid interference with the hazardous operation. Nozzles placed for point protection should have very narrow water spray angles for the efficient application of water density onto the point of hazard.

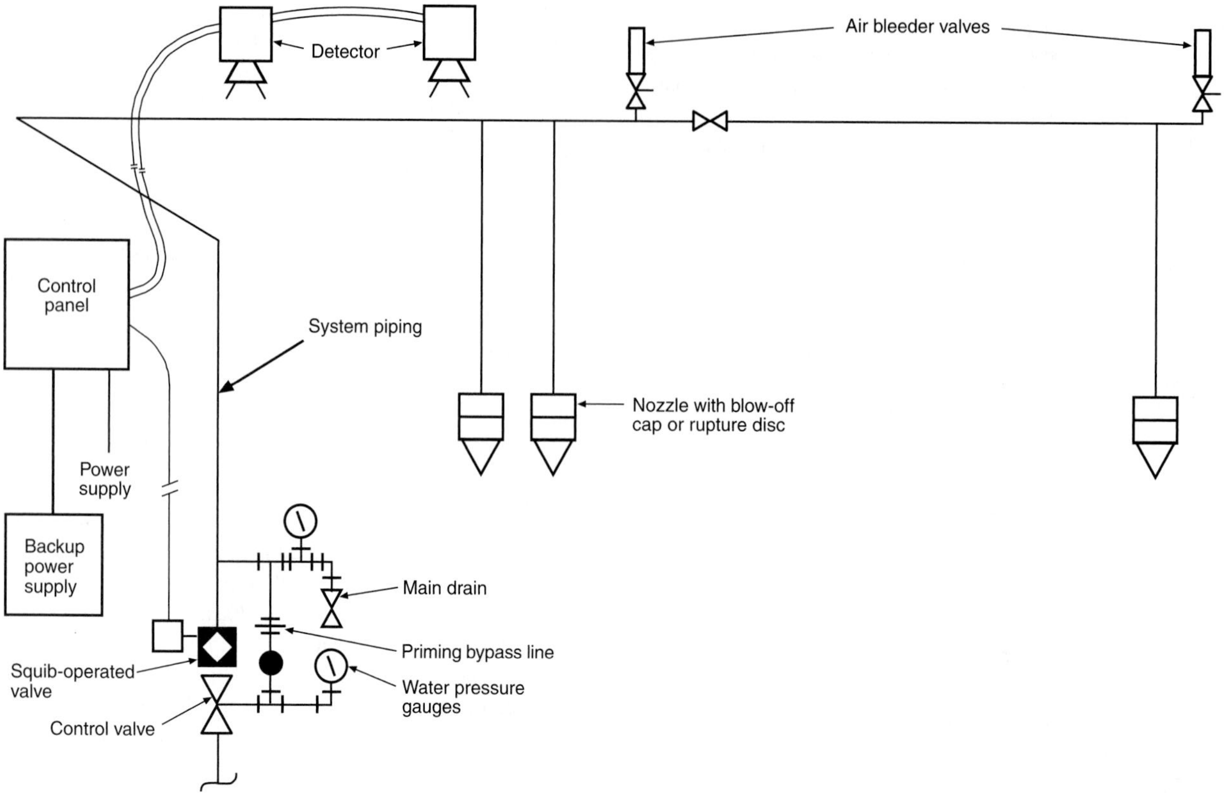

FIGURE 16.7.1 Squib-Actuated System

Nozzles spaced for an area hazard must be placed at a distance from the floor that permits the overlap of nozzle spray patterns on the floor or on the surface of interest. Although wide nozzle spray angles (about 120°) are likely to easily overlap, narrower spray angles (60° or 90°), spaced closely together, are more likely to provide efficient spray density, water velocity, and enhanced water travel time.

The process of detection, transfer of signal to the fire alarm control unit, interpretation of the signal, transmission of signal to the valve, and delivery of water to the hazard happens before one's senses are aware of a problem. It is not unusual for an installer to receive complaints of false trips after the installation of an ultra-high-speed water spray system. These occurrences may actually be real fires, undetectable by human senses. It is recommended that a diary of events be kept before and after system installation for analysis.

The first high-speed systems that protected munitions and propellant facilities were primarily preprimed deluge systems that used standard deluge valves, pneumatic detection, and enhanced pressurization. Response times for such systems were in the vicinity of 1 second. This type of system can still be used when it is desired that standard water spray deluge systems have an enhanced response time. The movement of the deluge valve clapper slows system actuation time considerably. However, improvements and innovations were developed to protect processes involving materials that require faster response times than the preprimed deluge system. The currently available ultra-high-speed water spray systems are covered in the sections that follow.

DETECTION SYSTEM SELECTION

In order to provide the best possible results in protecting munitions and other hazards requiring rapid-response technology, it is recommended that a four-step method be used to select a detection system:[3]

1. Choose a detector capable of reacting to the wavelengths expected to be encountered in a fire involving the hazardous material in question. For example, a UV detector will respond to a hydrogen fire, but an IR detector operating in the 4.4 micron range will not.
2. Survey the hazard area, the process, and the adjoining areas to determine sources of false signals that may exist. For example, if arc welding is expected to occur within the view of a detector, UV detectors must be either shielded from view or repositioned.
3. Determine elements that could interfere with the optimum operation of the detector. Dust or ice could severely hamper the detector's ability to function in accordance with its design parameters and will determine a detector's features or placement. Detectors with air shields to automatically clear dust from the detector lens are available.
4. Using test data or empirical results, ascertain the speed with which the detector is required to respond.

Two basic categories of flame detection systems are used as releasing systems for ultra-high-speed water spray systems. One type, UV detectors, responds to radiation in the range of 1850 to

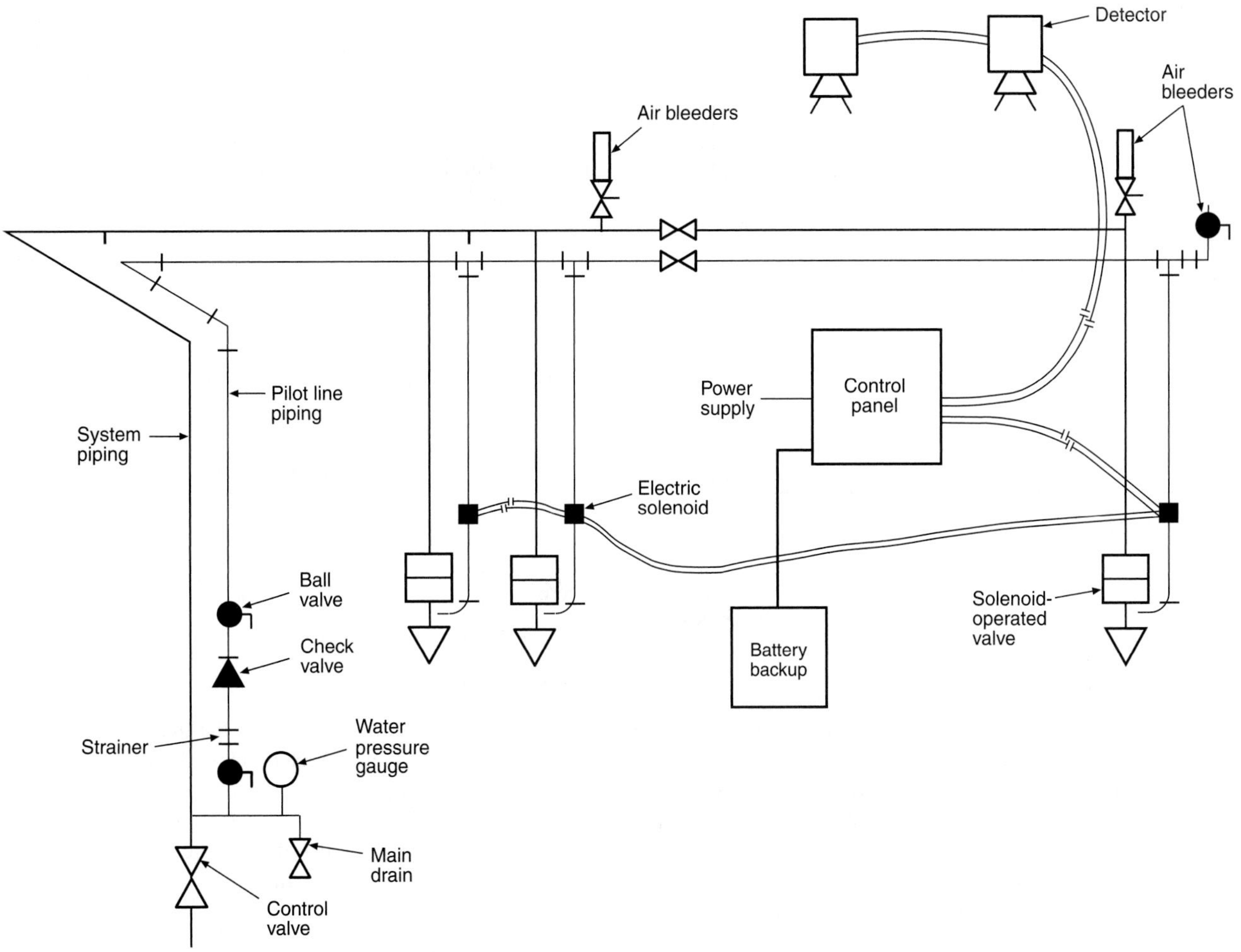

FIGURE 16.7.2 Solenoid-Actuated System

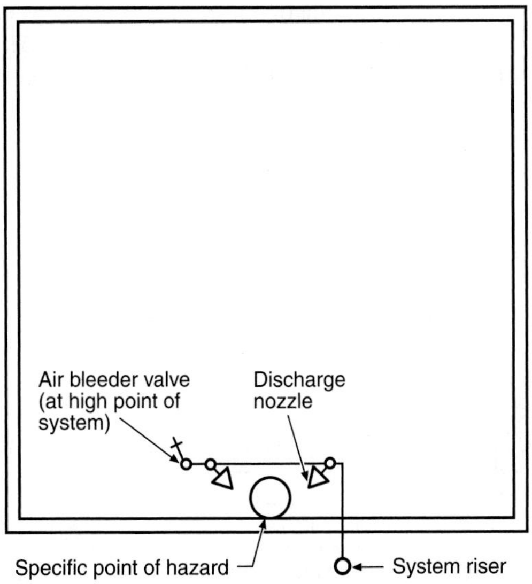

FIGURE 16.7.3 Local Point Application Design

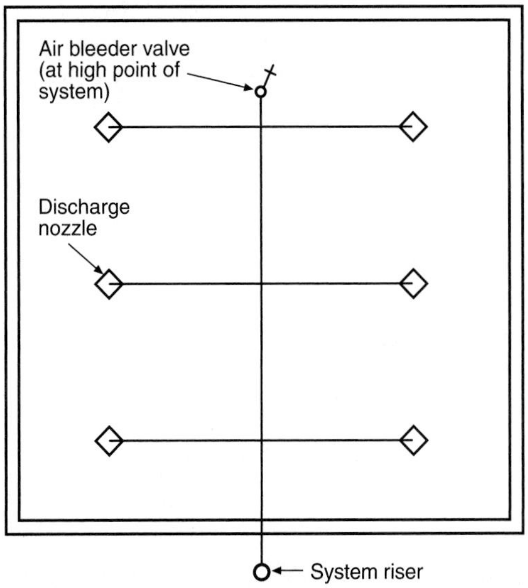

FIGURE 16.7.4 Area Application Design

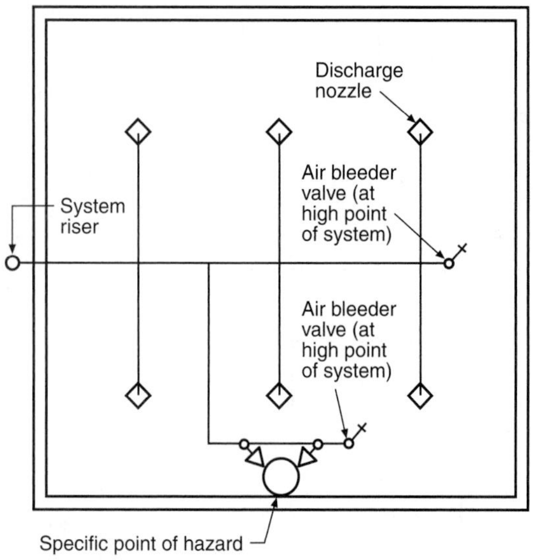

FIGURE 16.7.5 Combination Application

2850 angstroms (0.185 to 0.285 microns). Detection ranges are graphically shown on a radiation spectrum chart (Figure 16.7.6). The other type of flame detector is the IR detector.

Multiple-band optical detectors, such as dual-band or triple-band IR or UV detectors and dual-band UV/IR detectors, may also be used. A multiple-band IR detector, for example, searches a hazard for more than one band of IR radiation from the IR spectrum, providing the potential for a more reliable detection signal.

Note how the radiation spectrum chart shows an intersection between the IR detector sensitivity (between 0.8 and 1.0 microns) and the graph of solar radiation that reaches the earth. One can surmise by this intersection that an IR detector would be receptive to and would be adversely affected by sunlight radiation. This radiation spectrum correlation will strongly affect the manner in which IR detectors are used. UV detectors are not affected by sunlight, according to the graph, and can be located without regard to sun exposure. High-intensity lights and high-temperature bodies will affect IR detectors with no effect on UV detectors. However, arc welding, lightning, X-rays, and gamma rays will affect UV detectors more than IR detectors that have been properly aimed and shielded.

Since the two predominant types of ultra-high-speed system detectors (i.e., UV and IR) are searching for differing types of radiation and are affected by differing interfering media, their applications are generally quite different. UV detectors, being insensitive to sunlight, would be well suited for surveillance of an entire process area or a process requiring a wide angle of vision, whereas IR detectors would be better suited for close surveillance of a specific contact point within a processing machine or supervision of the interior of an enclosed vessel (Figure 16.7.7).

UV detectors are subject to the inverse square laws of optics, where detector sensitivity varies inversely with the distance between the detector and the energy source:

$$S = \frac{(\mathrm{K})pe^{cd}}{d^2}$$

where

S = Radiation power reaching the detector

K = Constant

p = Radiation power emitted by the fire, which is a function of the fuel characteristics and fire size

e = Base logarithm

c = Extinction coefficient of air, or the radiation energy absorbed or diffused by air, a function of humidity, dust, and so on

d = Lineal distance from the fire to the detector

From this famous law of physics, one can see that doubling the sight distance of the detector results in a dramatic reduction in the radiation received by the detector. Conversely, reducing the sight distance greatly increases the radiation received by the detector.

In cases where the point of ignition could be anywhere in a room, the wisest use of UV detectors is to provide area detection of the entire process by overlapping the area detection system

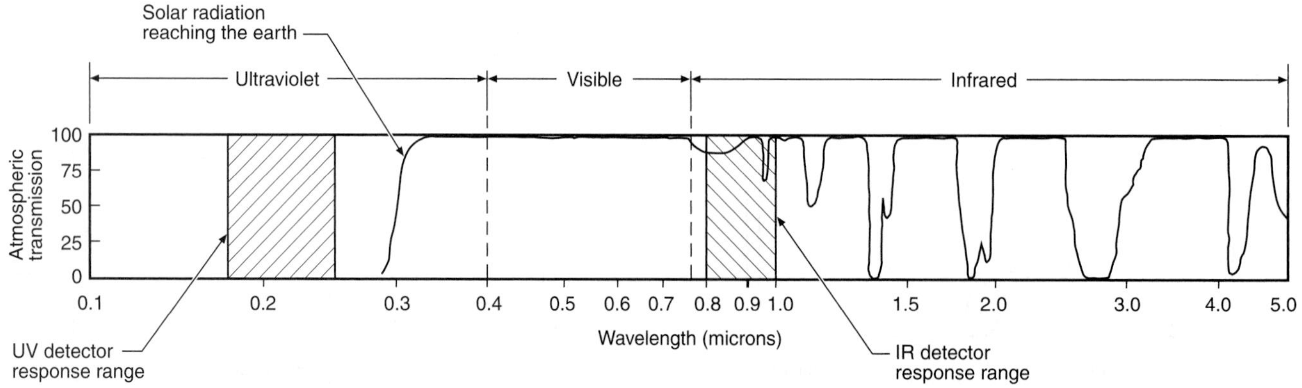

FIGURE 16.7.6 Radiation Spectrum Chart

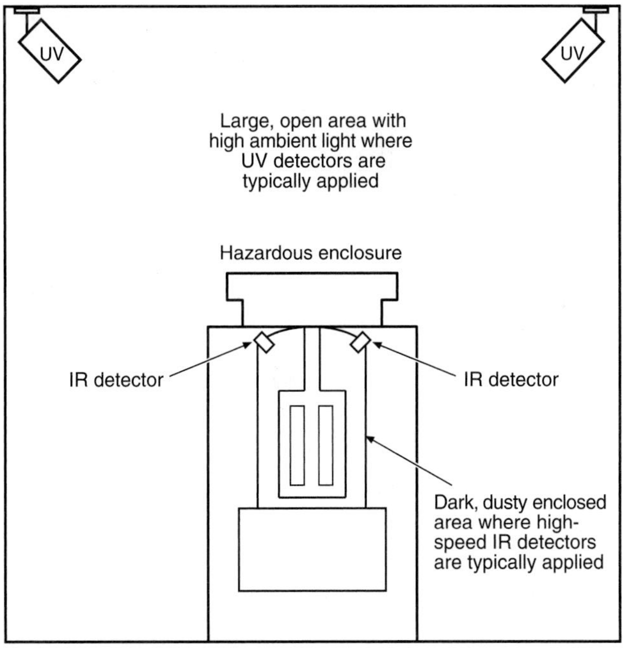

FIGURE 16.7.7 UV and IR Detectors

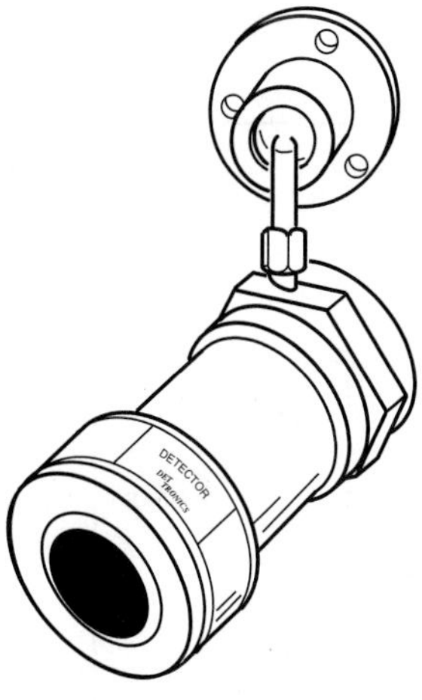

FIGURE 16.7.8 Ultraviolet Optical Detector on Swivel-Mount Base

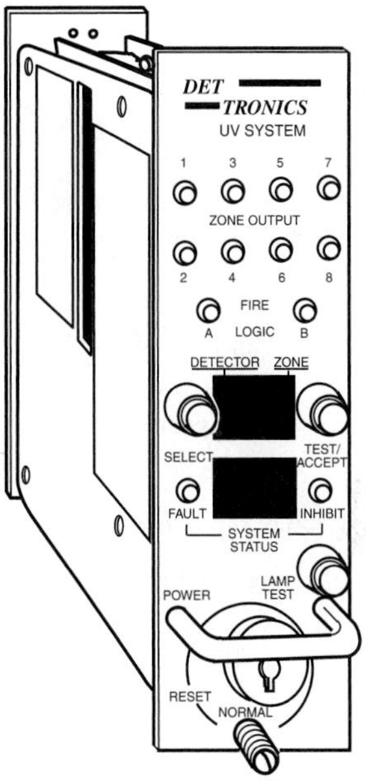

FIGURE 16.7.9 High-Speed Module

to cover all room areas, with additional detectors that closely view critical points in the process. For point protection, reliability increases dramatically when critical areas are viewed by overlapping cones of vision from counteropposed detectors in the same detection zone.

Because of their sensitivity to sunlight, IR detectors are best located in enclosed spaces, partially enclosed spaces, or spaces shielded from sunlight. Although IR detectors also obey the inverse square law, the hazard of receiving unwanted sunlight signals negatively affects their performance at extended detection distances. Shields are available to restrict the cone of vision of an IR detector to prevent unwanted actuation, and downward positioning reduces dust buildup on the lens.

The actuation or release apparatus for an ultra-high-speed suppression system consists of detectors (Figure 16.7.8), a specialized high-speed controller capable of monitoring and supervising up to eight detectors (Figure 16.7.9), a relay module to alert personnel and provide remote annunciation capability, and a detonator module that activates the squibs or solenoids that release an ultra-high-speed deluge system. Figure 16.7.10 illustrates the wiring of the detector and the controller shown in Figures 16.7.8 and 16.7.9. The modular control components are installed in a mounting cage and are served by a voltage converter that transforms ac building current into dc system current.

THE MUNITIONS MANUFACTURING PROCESS

The munitions manufacturing process is one of the most prominent applications for ultra-high-speed water spray systems and is among the most hazardous fire protection challenges that a system designer or contractor can encounter. A delay of only a few milliseconds can mean disaster. The stakes are frighteningly high, and munitions manufacturing personnel are routinely required to perform operations involving significant risk. The U.S. Army Operations Support Command and its army ammunition plants and depots have played a leading role in the development and improvement of ultra-high-speed water spray systems.

Ultra-high-speed water spray systems have been successfully employed to protect the manufacture of many types of munitions, including propellants, diazodinitropherol (DDNP), trinitrotoluene (TNT), tetranitromethylaniline (TETRYL), tetranitrocellulose-type explosives (RDX), C-4, black powder,

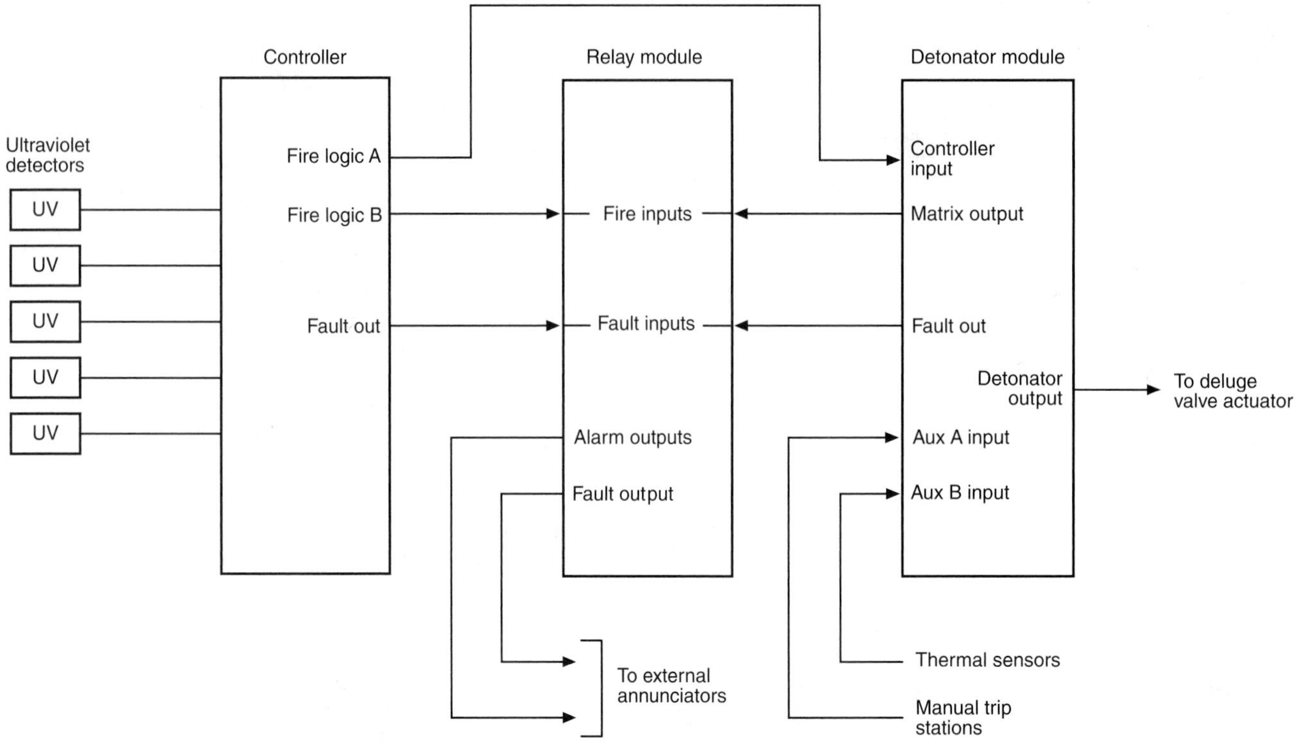

FIGURE 16.7.10 UV Block Diagram

pyrotechnics, fireworks, magnesium Teflon™ flares, and smoke-generating devices. Each commodity involves differing manufacturing processes and protection schemes.

Manufacturing Operations

In general, the 14 processes[1,4] that describe most munitions manufacturing operations include the following:

1. Weighing
2. Pressing
3. Pelletizing
4. Propellant loading
5. Melting
6. Extrusion
7. Mixing
8. Blending
9. Screening
10. Sawing
11. Granulating
12. Drying
13. Pouring
14. Machining

Each of these munitions manufacturing operations requires individual consideration and careful engineering to fully analyze the entire munitions manufacturing process and determine the proper and appropriate protection measures. In each case, the specifying engineer or designer must determine the objective of the system.

The three performance objectives that are to be considered in ultra-high-speed suppression system design are (1) life safety and personnel protection, (2) equipment protection and facility protection, and (3) total extinguishment or propagation cessation. The location and extent of protection and detection varies with the size of the operation, location of critical friction points, and the presence and location of the operating crew. A thorough risk analysis of the hazard is required and an evaluation of the financial and life safety effects of a catastrophic event in a processing area must be completed in advance of selecting the choice of objective or combination of objectives. If a catastrophic event would have a major effect on any objective, then prevention of such an event is a critical component of ultra-high-speed system design.

A strong consideration to be given in the choice of general area protection versus specific point protection is the mobility of the equipment. In many cases munitions processing machinery can be moved from one location to another, making protection at specific contact points impractical or impossible. It is recommended that a combination of area protection and point protection be provided wherever feasible and that protection for personnel be provided in all cases. Perhaps a way of solving the dilemma of frequently relocated point hazards is to provide area protection at the ceiling, supplemented by a portable ultra-high-speed water spray system, as discussed later in this chapter, for protection of the movable point hazard.

Weighing. If the munition is a powder, a special situation will arise as a result of the dust created by the operation. Ungrounded static charges could result in ignition of the dust. The detection system should be as close to the hazard as possible, while maintaining the ability to perform and observe the pouring operation. Nozzles should be placed in such a way as to wet down the entire operation, including the operator, with overlapping sprays from opposing angles and with as heavy a density as possible. Extra nozzles may be required at critical points in the process. Solid weighing processes will involve, in general, detectors and nozzles placed throughout the hazard area. By protecting the entire room, the pathways between operations will be supervised and protected by heavy-density water spray.

Pressing and Pelletizing. A major risk in pressing and pelletizing operations is associated with ignition of the munition at the contact points of the operation and propagation of flame to the bulk storage of the munition. Detection and protection must be located as close to the points of contact as possible. Normally, the operator's arms will be protected by water spray applied to the contact points. Strong consideration should also be given to adding nozzles for the protection of the entire machine and the operator. Also, the designer should ensure that the bulk storage of the commodity is physically isolated from the manufacturing operation, or is otherwise protected.

Propellant Loading. The fire protection objective in explosive propellant loading is to halt the flame front caused by an ignition of propellant, thereby preventing propagation from the loading area to the main hopper, preventing a deflagration in the hopper.

Area protection and detection is recommended for the loading area, the storage area, and the travel routes between the munitions operation, the storage area, and the loading area. Additional point protection is recommended for critical friction or contact points.

Melting. Kettles are used to melt munitions, employing steam or hot water as the predominant energy source. One or more detectors, placed as close to the kettle as possible, and nozzles directed over the exterior of the kettle, especially at the opening where materials are added, will be required. The close proximity of detection and nozzles with respect to the kettle is critical to successful fire protection during a melting operation.

Detectors are never placed within melt kettles. Such environments are conducive to severe fogging of the detector lenses, negating their value in a very short time. Furthermore, the temperature encountered within melt kettles often exceeds the upper operating limits of most detectors and will not permit the internal installation of detectors. For such applications, mount the optical detectors on the exterior of the melt kettle as close as physically possible.

Extrusion of Explosives, Pyrotechnics, and Propellants. Extrusion involves the process of pressing the propellant or pyrotechnic material through an opening or die to form it into a desired shape. The point of fire protection interest here is the opening through which the munition exits. Detection and nozzle placement close to this point should prevent any ignited munition from spreading to the bulk storage area of the machine. Personnel and machine protection should also be considered.

Mixing and Blending. Mixing and blending of munitions can take place in an open vat or in a closed container. The open mixing or blending process may be approached in a manner similar to the melting process. If the container is closed, the detector and nozzle should penetrate the enclosure, with appropriate precautions taken to avoid dust loading or obscuration of the detector and nozzle. Heat, mechanical damage, and dust must be considered when placing detectors or nozzles within closed containers.

Screening, Sawing, and Granulating. Common hazards to be considered in these processes are friction, dust, and sparks that can occur during these operations. Points of contact must be completely observed by detection and protected with point-protection ultra-high-speed water spray. Locating the nozzle as close to the point of contact as possible will enhance timely delivery of water to the critical point most likely to support ignition.

Drying, Pouring, and Machining. Drying operations are usually done in ovens or heating cabinets, with area nozzle protection over the surface area of the cabinets, especially where the operator opens the cabinet to remove or add items to be dried. Pouring requires point nozzle protection, and area nozzle protection is also often required. Machining operations require point nozzle protection similar to extrusion operations with area coverage also often required.

Choice of Agent for Munitions Manufacturing Protection

Water is the agent of choice in the protection of explosive munitions hazards for its ability to cool the combustible, insulate the exposed surfaces, dilute a hazardous material, knock down suspended dust, and cool the expanding flame front. Water is an inexpensive and readily available suppressant.

Munitions and propellants differ from most fire protection hazardous commodities in that they contain a built-in supply of their own oxidizer mixed in with the fuel. The oxidizer is needed to ensure rapid burning of the material on demand in tightly enclosed areas or oxygen-deficient atmospheres, such as rocket motor combustion chambers or artillery gun tubes. Most oxidizer additives in the munitions industry fall under the general classification of nitrates and chlorates, such as potassium nitrate and potassium chlorate.

In the choice of an agent for munitions manufacturing, the presence of this built-in oxygen supply effectively eliminates from consideration the commonly available smothering or blanketing agents, such as carbon dioxide. Halon clean agents and other gaseous suppressants typically fail to stop the flame front in munitions fires. These agents begin to chemically break down and, therefore, fail to provide the cooling necessary to inhibit propagation. It must, therefore, be concluded that the primary objective in munitions protection is cooling by using water, not unlike most hazards encountered by the fire protection engineer. By introducing a cooling agent in the early stages of a deflagration, one prevents the feedback of heat energy from spreading to unburnt fuel, thus effectively limiting and then ceasing combustion. Failure to apply water in the very early stages of munitions combustion could result in burrowing or flame propagation within a pile of munitions mixture covered by extinguished and water-soaked munitions material.[1]

Also to be considered are the combustion gases produced by burning munitions. There exists in munitions fires a point of no return, where the production of combustion gases creates a barrier sufficient to prevent water spray from reaching the fuel. This explains why sophisticated mechanical and electrical fire protection equipment, designed for response in a few milliseconds, is essential for the protection of munitions hazards. Retardation of ultra-high-speed fire suppression system response time from 100 milliseconds to 1 second or more can create a scenario whereby the deflagration reaches a point that the expanding flame front gets out of control, negating the effectiveness of the suppression system and resulting in the loss of the process.

An automatic sprinkler system should be specified for adjacent storage or operations areas if there is a possibility of a fire occurring in other materials that could result in a fire propagating to the munitions, such as a fire starting in combustible packaging material and spreading to a munitions item.

Flame Detection Devices

Flame detection is the detection method of choice for ultra-high-speed deluge systems. Two types of flame detectors in common usage are UV detectors and IR detectors, both consisting of a photoelectric cell and a photoconductive cell.

Ultraviolet Detectors (UV). UV detectors are designed to detect radiation falling within the ultraviolet wavelengths below 4000 angstroms (0.4 microns). Fires emitting radiation with wavelengths of this nature generally have high-intensity flames associated with diffusion flame combustion. Close proximity of the detector to the source of the combustion is critical to operation within its intended range of sensitivity.

Shielding or screening may be necessary to isolate the UV detector from unwanted signals, such as lightning and welding arcs. It should be noted that a UV detector is an efficient flame detector, but must see the fire to be effective. An anticipated fire that is preceded by or accompanied by significant quantities of thick or dark smoke may not be amenable for UV detection, since the smoke could prevent or delay the operation of a UV detector. UV detectors cannot see through Lexan shielding. It is, therefore, necessary to ensure that each area bounded by shielding is individually detected within the shielded zone.

A limitation to the use of UV detectors is the fogging or loading of the lens that can occur when these detectors are used in dusty or moist atmospheres, adversely affecting their reaction time. Unless special arrangements are provided, such as air shields to divert dust away from the lens, or a tightly controlled 24 hour maintenance and supervision program, UV detectors may be unsuitable for some dusty or greasy environments.

Infrared Detectors (IR). IR detectors are amenable for use at distances up to 50 ft (15.3 m), and respond to infrared radiation involving wavelengths from 8500 to 12,000 angstroms (0.8 to 1.2 microns). Using IR detectors at extended distances is generally not recommended for ultra-high-speed suppression systems for explosive hazards. There is, however, research currently under way on possibly using some of the newer IR detectors that show great promise as a possible detection source for ultra-high-speed water spray systems for specialized applications.

Some common heat sources that can be sources of false alarms for IR detectors include automobile headlights, direct or reflected sunlight, room lighting, heaters, lighted tobacco products, and matches. IR detectors may not be able to discriminate between a common heat source and a combustion scenario.

Most IR detectors have a built-in timing unit that can delay actuation by as much as 1 to 30 seconds. This length of delay is usually unsuitable for the detection of munitions fires. If IR detectors are used, the distance between hazard and detector must be kept to a minimum, effectively screening out most sources of unwanted signals, and the time delay must be eliminated or minimized. A special ultra-high-speed IR detector is available with the delay feature eliminated.

Detector Listing. Most UV and IR detectors are listed by Underwriters Laboratories Inc. (UL) and are approved by Factory Mutual Research Corporation (FMRC) for fire protection use. Although they are approved for both indoor and outdoor use, it is recommended that they not be used outdoors for ultra-high-speed detection, so that unwanted signals can be minimized. Sources of flickering light, such as lights mounted on operating or vibrating machinery, may be perceived as being a fire by the detector and should be screened or eliminated.

Multiband Detectors. Multiband IR/IR and UV/IR detectors are commercially available, and recently manufactured units have been found to provide rapid response times while lowering incidences of false actuation. Multiband detectors search for more than one band of spectral radiation and confirm receipt of such signals in advance of notification of the fire alarm control unit of a fire.

SQUIB-ACTUATED SYSTEMS

The squib-actuated ultra-high-speed deluge system is a preprimed deluge system with a squib-operated deluge valve, a system of piping preprimed with water, specially capped nozzles and/or rupture discs, and an ultra-high-speed flame detection system. Developed in the early 1960s, it was the first commercially available ultra-high-speed water spray system and continues to be in active use today.

It is recommended that this system be used for hazards such as ammunition loading, explosive powder drying operations, high-energy fuel processing, self-oxidizing fuel processing and storage, silane containment cells, explosive dust collecting and conveying operations, roll mills, and casting pits. Other hazards requiring enhanced reaction times may be suitable for the squib-actuated ultra-high-speed water spray system.

Preprimed Piping System

The preprimed piping system on a squib-actuated system is supplied by a priming bypass valve that provides a water head of up to a maximum of 12 psi (82.74 kPa) to the blow-off caps installed to hold back the pressurized priming water. Water pressure required to remove the blow-off caps will vary with the make and model of cap used. A wire retains the blow-off cap to the nozzle for ease of retrieval and to prevent it from falling into material or devices being protected. It is recommended that the nozzles be as close as possible to the hazard being protected, and directed toward the critical points of the hazard (Figure 16.7.11).

Allowing the water to be preprimed in the piping has a strong advantage over standard evacuated piping deluge systems. The time it would have taken for the water to travel from the deluge valve to the nozzle has been eliminated. This can be a significant difference, especially for systems requiring the deluge valve to be remote from the hazard. The preprimed aspect of this system requires that the hazard area and valve riser be heated. Heat tracing of the piping is not recommended because loss of power, improper tracing installation, cracking or crimping of the tracing wire, or other potential failures of the tracing would damage and compromise the ability of the system to function when required.

The priming static pressure that can be maintained on the blow-off caps for a squib-actuated system, without danger of accidental leakage, is 12 psi (82.74 kPa) or less, depending on the cap manufacturer. Rupture discs or other devices capable of maintaining a minimum system static pressure of 50 psi (344.75 kPa) are strongly recommended. The system must be hydraulically designed to ensure a minimum residual pressure of 50 psi (344.75 kPa) at each nozzle, with sufficient static pressure to allow for automatic removal of all blow-off caps or rupture of all rupture discs on system actuation (Figure 16.7.12).

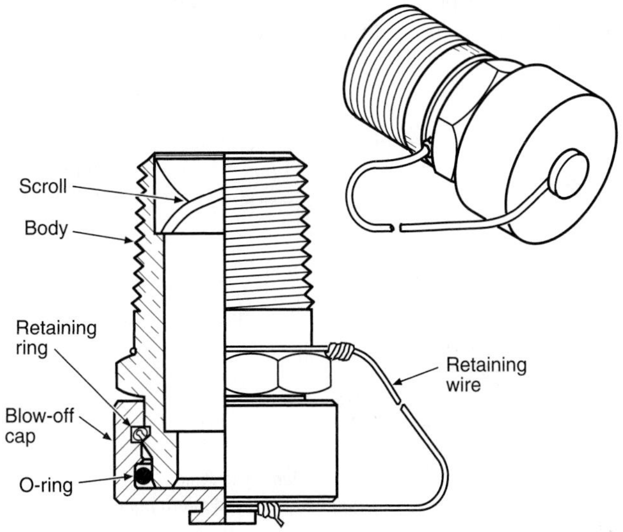

FIGURE 16.7.11 Nozzles and Blow-Off Caps

Squib-Actuated Valve

The squib-actuated valve is an electrically actuated valve with two explosive primers wired in parallel (Figure 16.7.13). The

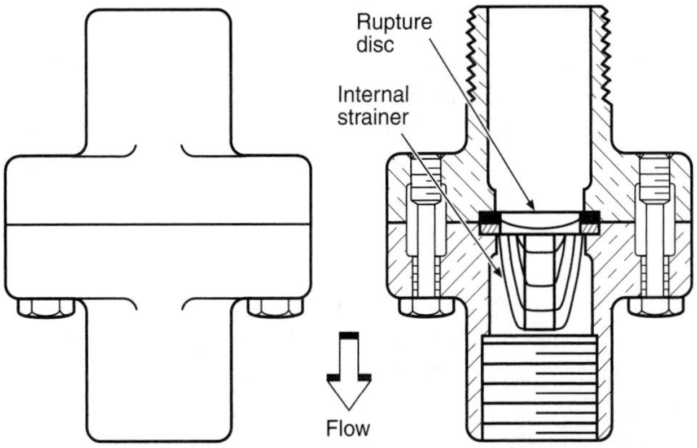

FIGURE 16.7.12 Rupture Discs

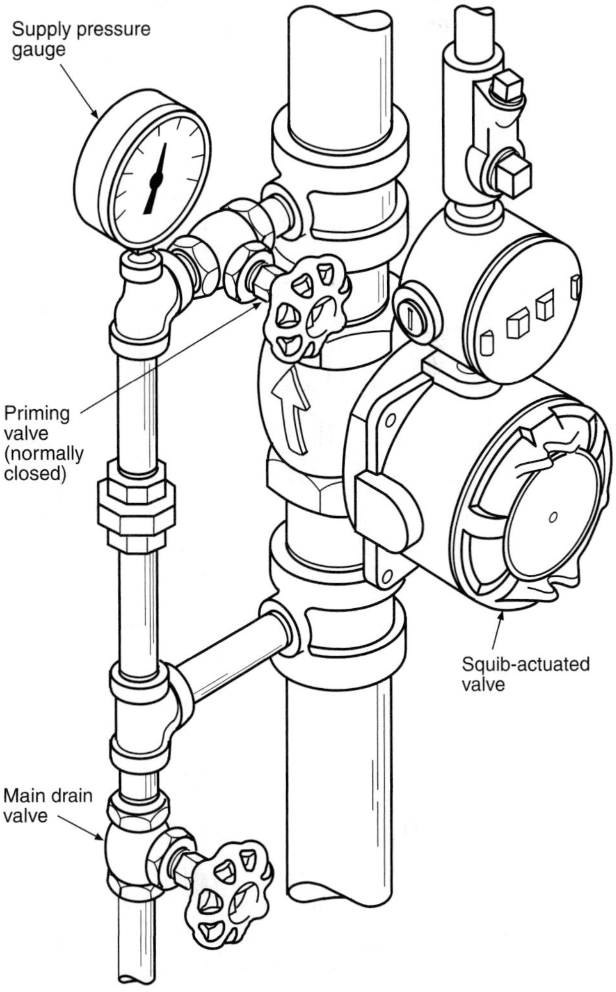

FIGURE 16.7.13 Squib-Actuated Valve

valve is intended to be installed vertically but will also function with increased response times in the horizontal position. The primers consist of 0.004 oz (0.12 g) of lead styphnate charge and actuate upon the receipt of an electric signal from the detection system.

The primers are designed so that the force of only one primer is needed to actuate the system. Firing of the primers shears a rod holding the clapper latch, allowing the plunger to rise, resulting in the rapid movement of the clapper and rapid pressurization of the priming water as water begins to flow through the valve. The blow-off caps are ejected or rupture discs broken once their inlet pressure exceeds their respective release pressure (Figure 16.7.14).

Although squib-actuated valves are rated for use in Class II (electrical rating) locations, it is recommended that the valve not be located directly adjacent to a hazardous process and in a nonhazardous area, if physically possible.

Squib-actuated valves are available for use with 2 in. (51 mm) and 2½ in. (64 mm) risers, and releases are available for 4 in. (102 mm) and 6 in. (152 mm) deluge valves. Increased system size has a very strong effect on the increasing of response time. A 500 gal (1893 L) water-holding capacity is recommended as the maximum system size, and best results would be obtained by subdividing the systems such that the number of nozzles served by one squib-actuated valve is between two and six nozzles with separate detection systems and suppression system actuation valves.

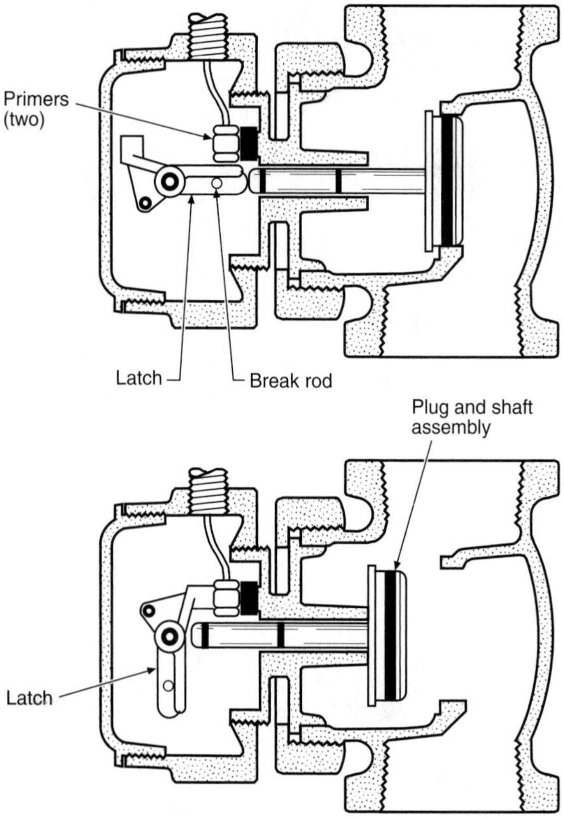

FIGURE 16.7.14 Squib-Actuated Valve Unlatching

Squib-Actuated Detection System

The detection system for a squib-actuated system (Figure 16.7.15) is ordinarily an optical flame detection system. These photoconductive cells monitor the hazard and can detect small amounts of radiant energy emitted by a fire in the hazard area. Such detectors are monitoring light within certain predetermined wavelengths normally associated with fire. Should the photoconductive cells receive more light than was specified to be ambient, the cells' resistance will change, sending a signal to an amplifier in the control panel. This amplifier increases the signal's strength and sends it to the primer for actuation. Signal transmission time is normally 2 or 3 milliseconds.

Normal actuation times for a squib-actuated system can vary with piping configuration, size of the system, distance from the valve to the nozzles, water pressure, and hazard conditions. Response times in the 100 millisecond range are possible for very small systems with risers very close to the hazard and with high water supply pressures.

Resetting a Squib-Actuated System

After operation, the two primers and primer holders are replaced, and a new break rod installed. Nozzles are then recapped or plugged or rupture discs replaced. Breakglasses must be replaced if the system was operated manually. The system is then reprimed by slowly opening the priming bypass valve and bleeding the air from bleeder valves located at high points in the piping system. Care must be taken to purge all air to ensure complete priming of the system. The control panel is then reset and returned to service. It is recommended that spare primers, holders, rods, blow-off caps, rupture discs, and breakglasses be kept in a convenient nearby location for ease of resetting. It is essential that the system be functionally tested and operated at least once a year to ensure that all parts are functioning properly and ready for use.

System Actuation Time

The piping in a preprimed deluge system must be sloped, with air bleed valves placed at the piping high points, to facilitate the

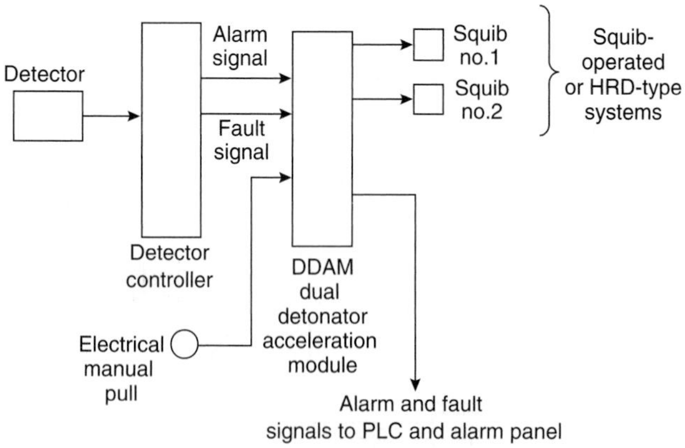

FIGURE 16.7.15 Squib-Operated Electrical Flow Diagram (Source: Pyrotech International)

removal of trapped air bubbles in the piping, which are known to have the effect of increasing response time.

Another major factor influencing actuation time is the system water supply pressure. When all other variables are held constant, the actuation time decreases with increasing water supply pressure. For example, if one could double the supply pressure from 50 to 100 psi (344.75 to 689.5 kPa), the actuation time would decrease by about 20 to 25 percent. Actuation times assume that the priming water is at rest at the nozzle orifices. The system pressure and the resulting enhanced actuation times, therefore, result from inertia effects and are effectively independent of pipe friction, head elevation, and nozzle orifice coefficients.

Other factors influencing the effectiveness of a squib-actuated system are the quantity of nozzles on the system, orifice diameter of the nozzles, length of piping from deluge valve to the nozzles, number of fittings on the supply and branch pipes, cap or disc blow-off pressure, and cross-sectional area of the supply pipe.

Actuation time for squib-actuated systems is shown in Figure 16.7.16. The valve unlatching time and cap blow-off time are strong functions of system pressure. The graph also shows that 4- and 6-in. (102- and 152-mm) squib-actuated valves take 3 milliseconds longer to unlatch than the 2- and 2½-in. (51- and 64-mm) valves.

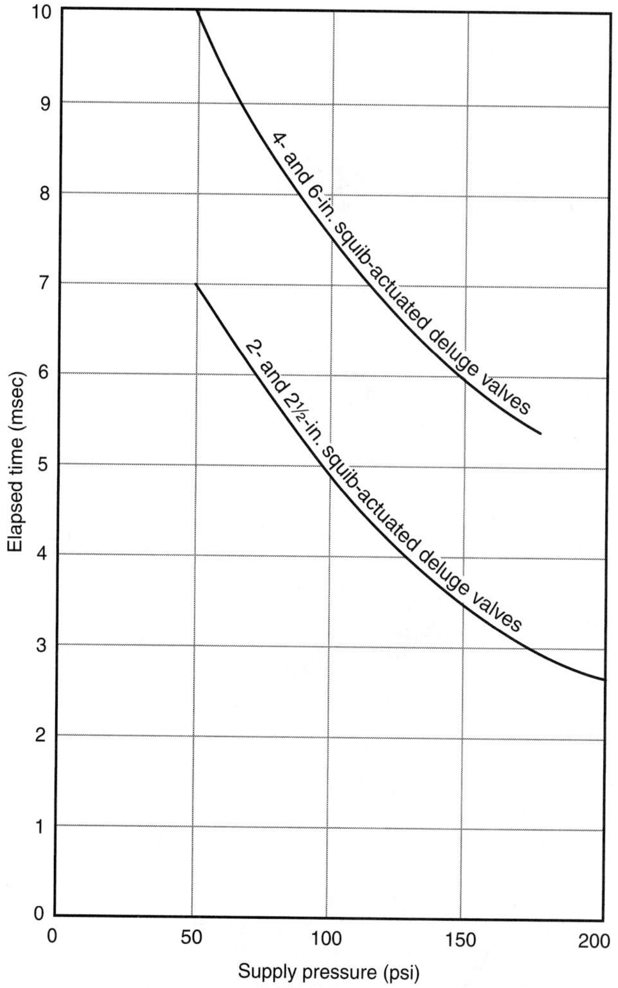

FIGURE 16.7.16 Valve-Unlatching Time

Most U.S. Army ammunition plants maintain static pressure for ultra-high-speed water spray systems in the range of 50 to 75 psi (344.75 to 517.13 kPa), usually supplied by elevated gravity tanks, to enhance actuation time.

Squib-Actuated Ultra-High-Speed Water Spray System Design

Recommendations for a squib-actuated ultra-high-speed water spray system design are as follows:

1. It is recommended that the squib-actuated valves be installed in the vertical position, even though a horizontal position is possible. Installation in the horizontal position could trap air, negatively affecting actuation time.
2. Care should be taken to make the pipe routing from squib-actuated valve to the nozzles as direct as possible, with as few fittings and bends as possible.
3. Slope all piping up to vent valves at piping high points to facilitate the elimination of air from the system. The pipe should be sloped as radically as possible, especially for smaller pipe sizes.
4. For point protection, position the nozzles into counter-opposed groups of no fewer than two nozzles for efficient delivery of water to a likely source of ignition. Counteropposition of the nozzles involves nozzles aimed from differing directions at a common point.
5. Ensure the highest possible water supply static pressure, enhancing system pressure with a surge (pressure) tank or an excess pressure pump if city or plant supply is insufficient. A minimum of 50 psi (344.75 kPa) static pressure is recommended.
6. Perform hydraulic calculations of the system to verify pipe sizes and ensure minimum nozzle discharge pressures of 50 psi (344.75 kPa). Densities must be calculated based on water that actually impinges on the hazard area. Unless the nozzles are wisely placed, the spray that impinges on areas of little consequence could be considerable, reducing the actual delivered density on the hazard area. Also care must be taken to overlap sprays as much as possible to supplement the lighter densities that are normally found along the outside perimeters of the conical spray patterns. For spot protection, it is recommended that the concept of average density (raw gal [L] available at nozzle divided by total ft^2 [m^2] of floor area covered) be replaced by experienced engineering evaluation of actual nozzle distribution to the hazard area in question. Each nozzle is required by NFPA 15 to discharge no less than 25 gpm (95 L/min) per nozzle for point protection, nor less than 0.50 gpm/ft^2 (20.37 L/min·m^2) for area protection. Some commodities, such as especially volatile pyrotechnics, may require densities as high as 3.0 gpm/ft^2 (122.24 L/min·m^2).

PILOT-ACTUATED SYSTEMS

Early Development

The first pilot-actuated nozzle was introduced in the early 1960s. This early system (Figure 16.7.17) has as its basis mechanical

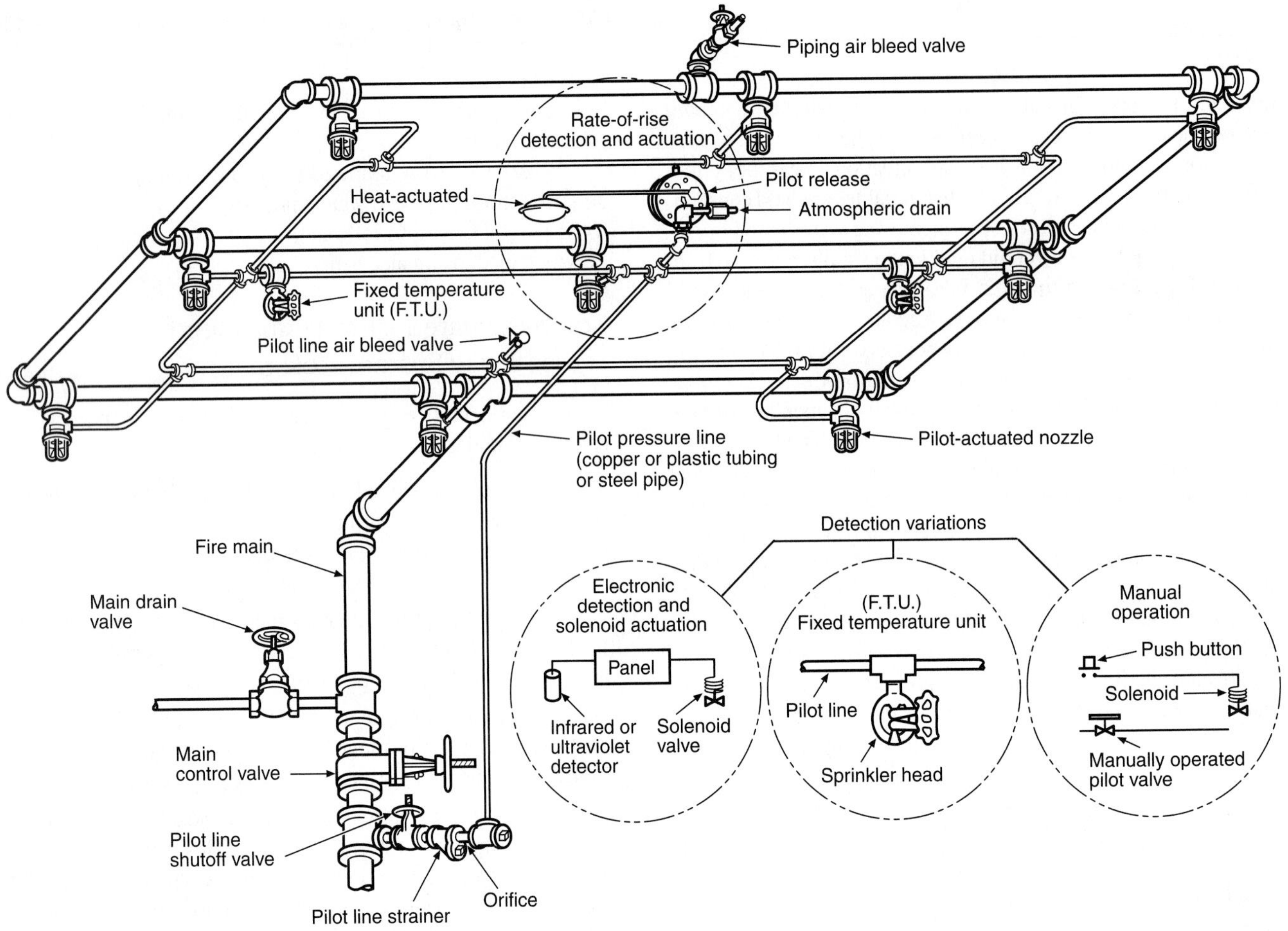

FIGURE 16.7.17 Early Pilot-Actuated System (Obsolete)

components similar to types in the present system. Each revision to the early concept was in the interest of speed, which became possible with the advent of more sophisticated electronic technology.

The first pilot-actuated nozzles had an integral deflector attached to the lower body with a male adapter for connection of a water spray nozzle. Today the integral deflector has been augmented by the addition of other bodies capable of accommodating a wide variety of water spray nozzles, allowing engineering flexibility. Each nozzle individually functions similarly to a wet-pilot-actuated deluge valve. In its earliest incarnation, the pilot-actuated nozzle was called the "aerospace" nozzle, as a result of its use in hyperbaric chambers for the space program[5] (Figure 16.7.18).

The standard detection arrangement for early systems was a system of pilot piping with a heat-actuated pilot release. This method was developed specifically for and became commonly employed with naval ship munitions magazine protection systems. The naval requirement for the early pilot-actuated system response was 150 milliseconds, with an operation time, measured from release of the pilot line to delivery of water, in the 10- to 20-millisecond range. The time that it took for the heat-actuated device to actuate and commence evacuation of the pilot line was not included in this time. The heat-actuated means of detection eventually gave way to ultraviolet electronic detection with solenoids on the pilot line as the method of choice, once the electronic detection and control technology became available.

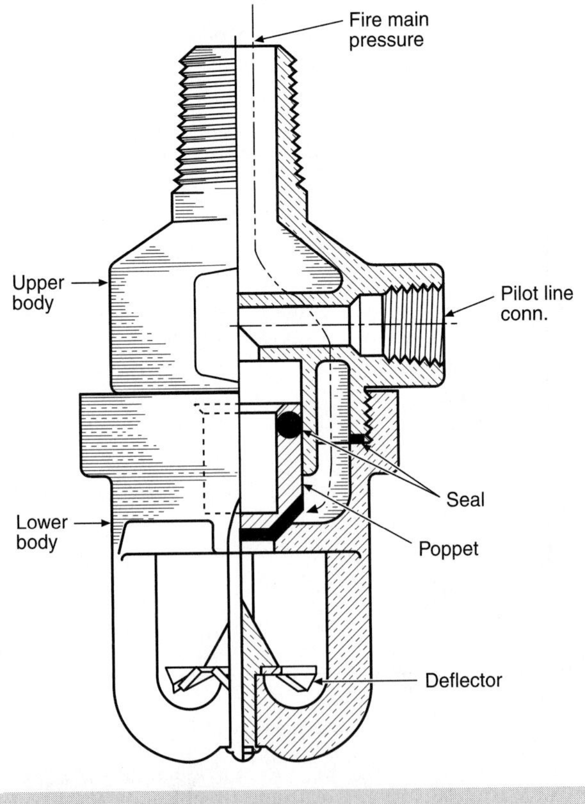

FIGURE 16.7.18 Early Pilot-Actuated Nozzle

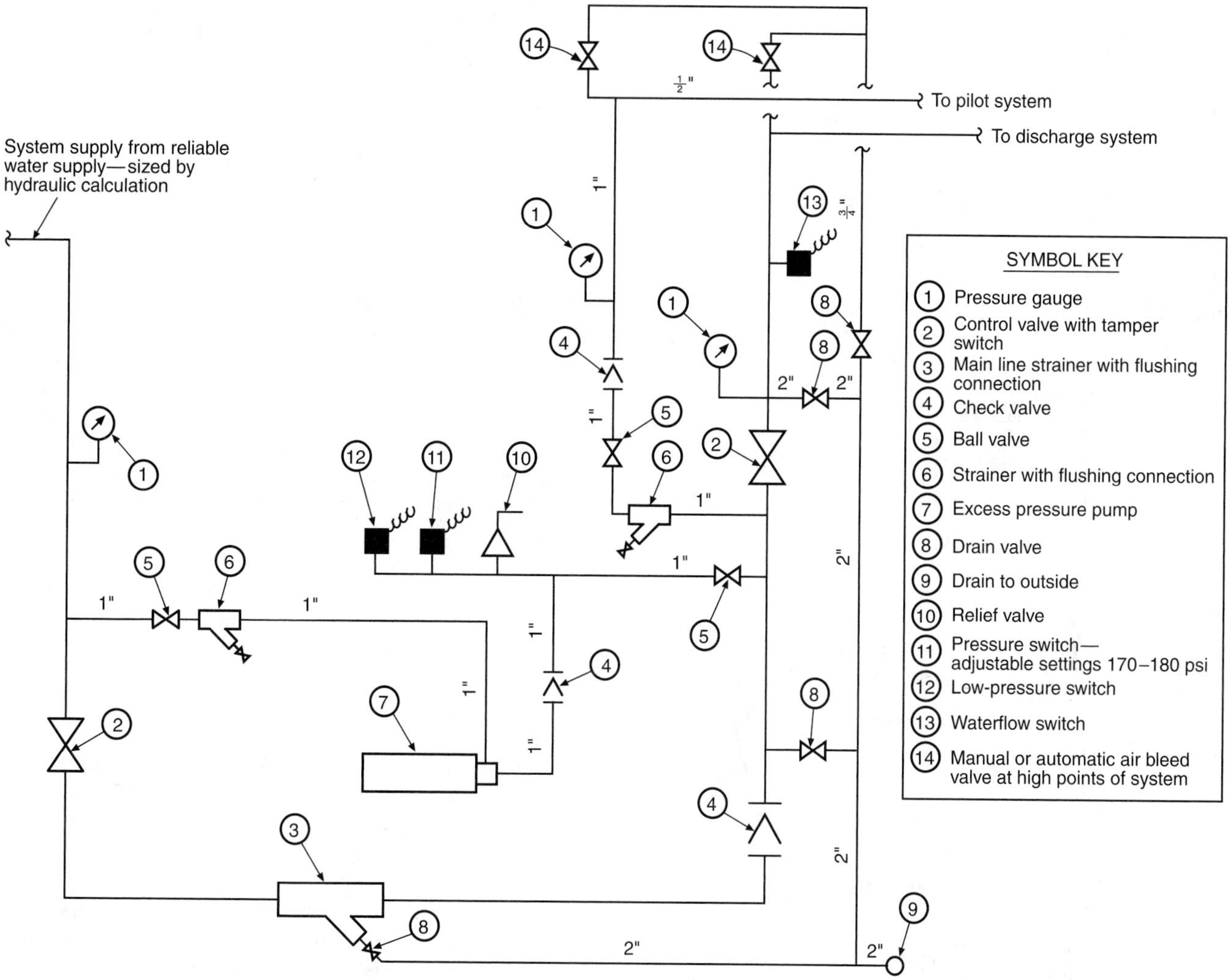

FIGURE 16.7.19 Control Riser Solenoid Operating System

What made the pilot-actuated system different was its positive priming at fire main pressure, its poppet-valve nozzle and pilot system, and simultaneous opening of all nozzles connected to one pilot line. The basic system in its earliest form had certain similarities to the pneumatically actuated deluge system and also bears a strong resemblance to a wet-pilot-actuated deluge system.

Pneumatic heat-actuated and eutectic heat-actuated devices are significantly slower than an electronic UV-actuated release system. With the development of more sophisticated circuit boards, microprocessors, high-speed release modules, solenoid improvements and other response time innovations, improvements in system actuation time were possible.

Current Arrangement

A fixed pilot-actuated ultra-high-speed water spray system consists of a primed discharge system with pilot-actuated nozzles; a hydraulic wet pilot system, supervised and discharged by high-speed solenoid valves; a UV or IR flame detection system; and a central fire alarm control unit with standby batteries and charger (Figures 16.7.19 and 16.7.20).

Discharge System. Although the pilot-actuated nozzle has been available for many years, recent developments in control modules and panels make the pilot-actuated system more amenable to hazards requiring extremely rapid response times. The pilot-actuated nozzle consists of a two-piece body, with ½ in., 1 in., or 1¼ in. (12.7 mm, 25.4 mm, 31.8 mm) male National Pipe Thread (NPT) threaded connection for attachment to the deluge piping system, a ¼ in. (6.4 mm) female inlet for connection to the pilot piping system, and an outlet for the insertion of water spray nozzles with male NPT connections.

The pilot-actuated nozzle is connected to two piping systems, discharge and pilot (Figure 16.7.21). The discharge piping system, normally filled with water to the nozzle, delivers the water for distribution to the hazard. The pilot piping system applies pressure onto a poppet valve in such a way that water in the discharge system, in its standby state, is prevented from flowing through the nozzle. The nozzles are located as close to the hazard as possible. Release of pilot pressure allows the deluge system to overcome the pressure differential, forcing the poppet valve up and initiating instantaneous discharge.

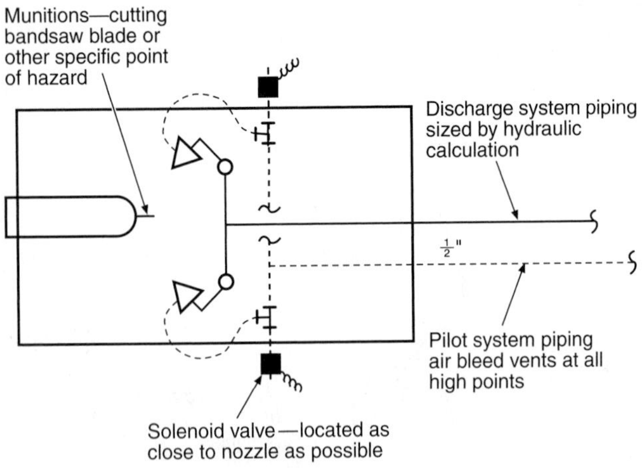

FIGURE 16.7.20 Plan View

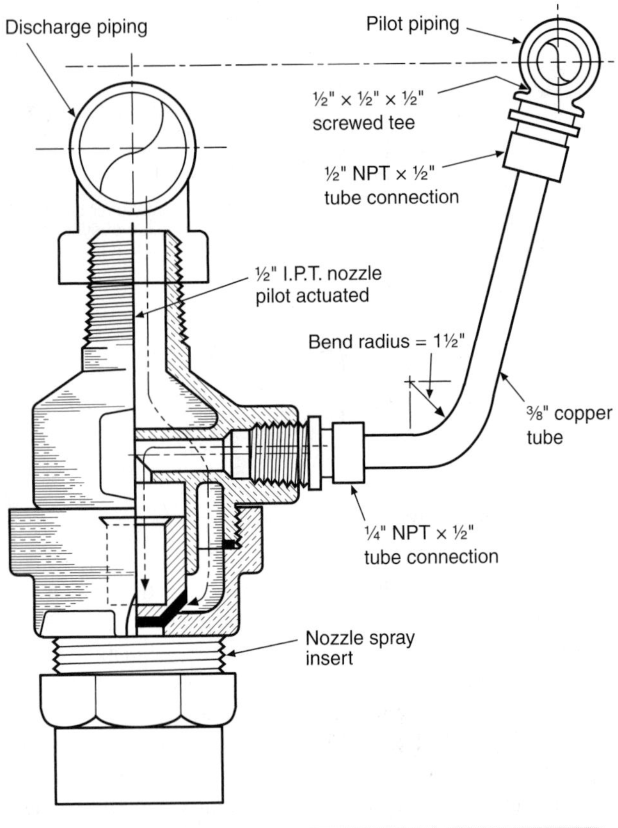

FIGURE 16.7.21 Pilot Connection

Pilot-actuated nozzles are capable of accepting inserts that allow custom designing of water application to the specific hazard in question. Discharge piping can be gridded when an area protection concept is employed. A strainer is required on the main riser of the discharge system to minimize debris that may accumulate between the poppet and the poppet seat and may cause leakage from the nozzle and possible system actuation. Sloping of the discharge system to air vents will serve to purge air from the discharge system and reduce system discharge time. Discharge and pilot piping is required by NFPA 15 to be sloped a minimum of 1 in. (25.4 mm) per 10 ft (3.1 m) of pipe.

Pilot System. The pilot system is monitored by normally closed two-way solenoid valves spaced throughout the system (Figure 16.7.22). Ideally, a solenoid valve should be provided for every pilot-actuated nozzle, but in certain cases one solenoid valve could control up to three nozzles. Engineering judgment must be exercised in determining a solenoid-to-nozzle ratio, since the response time increases as the distance between the pilot-actuated nozzle and the solenoid increases. Solenoids should be equipped with an enclosure-rated NEMA type 4 (watertight), NEMA type 7 (hazardous locations Class I, Group C or D), and NEMA type 9 (E, F, or G hazardous locations, Class II, Group E, F, or G). Detectors and detector housings should be rated for Class I and Class II locations.

It is essential that every effort be made to minimize air pockets in the pilot line, with piping radically sloped to air vents placed at all high points, facilitating the bleeding of air from the pilot system and enhancing the speed of reaction. The pilot line slope should be equal to or greater than the discharge piping slope, but should not be less than 1 in. (25.4 mm) per 10 ft (3.1 m) of pipe. For best results, keep branch lines and their associated pilot lines very short and slope them as radically as possible.

Air in the pilot line is of paramount concern because of its effect on the function of the pilot valve operation. The larger the air cushion, the longer the delay in response time. An automatic air vent is an option (Figure 16.7.23). To protect the solenoid orifices, a strainer must be installed on the pilot line feed.

The two systems of piping (i.e., pilot line and discharge) can be simultaneously pressurized by an excess pressure pump or some other pressure maintenance device, with static system pressure normally ranging from 170 to 180 psi (1172.2 to 1241.1 kPa), with a relief valve and pressure-limiting switch ensuring this range. An elevated gravity tank with a minimum static pressure of 75 psi (517.13 kPa) may provide acceptable response times. A specially designed orifice union in the pilot line maintains the pressure ratio necessary to keep the pilot-actuated nozzles open and allow smooth operation of all solenoid-

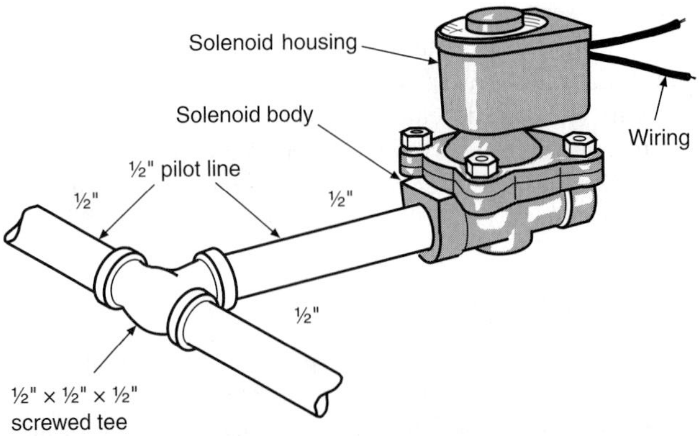

FIGURE 16.7.22 Solenoid Valve

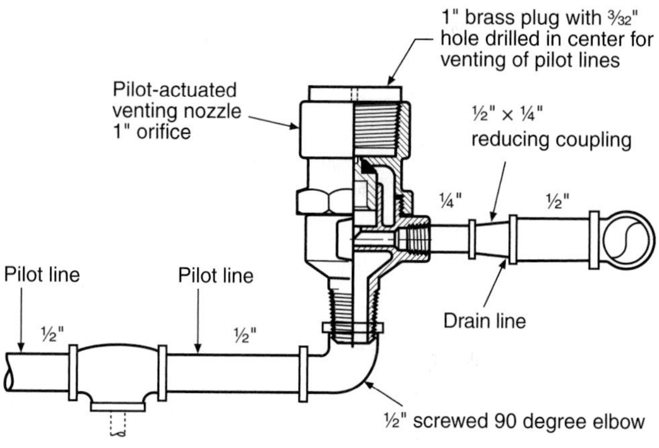

FIGURE 16.7.23 Automatic Pilot Vent

operated valves. The orifice retards the rush of pilot pressure so that the solenoids can exhaust enough water to permit full and even opening.

The Detection System. UV, IR/IR, and UV/IR detectors currently used on the pilot-actuated systems shown in Figures 16.7.24 and 16.7.25 comprise an extrasensitive detection tube housed in a stainless steel, brass, or aluminum explosionproof housing. The detector is mounted on a swivel base to give maximum field adjustment up to an angle of 240 degrees. Most UV and IR detectors have a field of vision between 80 and 90 degrees.

Flame detectors are installed as close to the points of anticipated hazard as practicable and angled and spaced so that all areas where the volatile substance might be found are observed by the detectors. Placement of detectors on an ultra-high-speed water spray system requires experienced judgment and thorough field inspection.

Fire Alarm Control Unit. The control unit, with its sensitive high-speed modules, is kept in a protected area remote from the hazard, usually an area classified safe for nonexplosion-proof equipment. Where it is necessary or required to install the control unit in the hazard area, it must be installed in a rated enclosure. The detector, module, and control unit system are specifically designed and customized for the hazard in question. The primary concern of each component is speed, and, as a result, the telemetry system is considerably faster than the systems of the early 1960s. The control system is designed to provide supervision over all electronic devices.

A fire alarm control unit that is placed outside or otherwise exposed to the elements must be installed within a weatherproof enclosure. It is possible that a weatherproof enclosure might be needed for an interior location if it is possible that roof leakage, sprinkler discharge, or other potential waterflow could enter the control unit.

The control unit should include a controller, high-speed modules, control relays, a lamp test push button, trouble silence switch, panel reset button, ac power fail light, waterflow lamp, tamper switch fault lamps, alarm lights, and indicators for special functions for pumps and tanks, with terminals for other functions, if required. The controller powers and monitors the ultraviolet detectors and their signals and notifies the high-speed modules of a trouble or fire signal from the detectors. The high-speed module receives a signal from the controller and will operate the high-speed solenoids on receipt of a fire signal, thus purging the pilot system of hydraulic pressure and opening the nozzles. An example of a currently manufactured ultra-high-speed water spray system module is the Response Acceleration Module (RAM), shown in Figure 16.7.25.

Control relays supervise gate valves, pressure switches, alarm bells or other notification appliances, and the control unit operation. Electrical contacts can be provided for customer functions, such as shutting down equipment. An automatic reset capability option allows the high-speed module to cease water

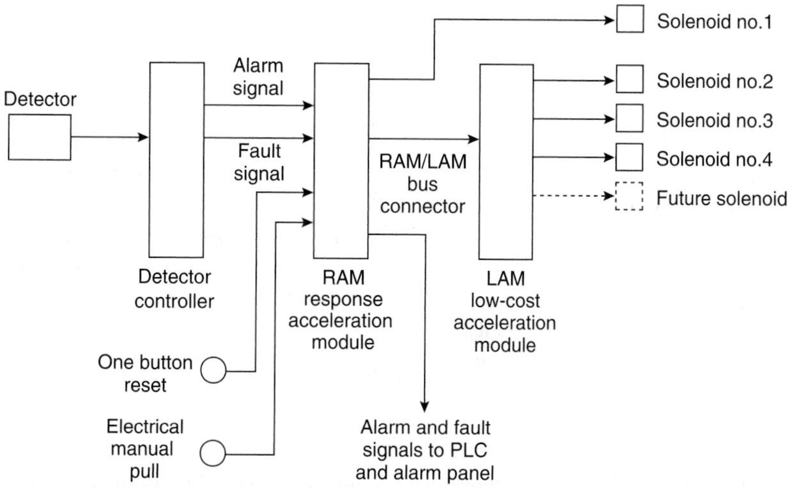

FIGURE 16.7.24 Pilot-Operated Electrical Flow Diagram (Source: Pyrotech International)

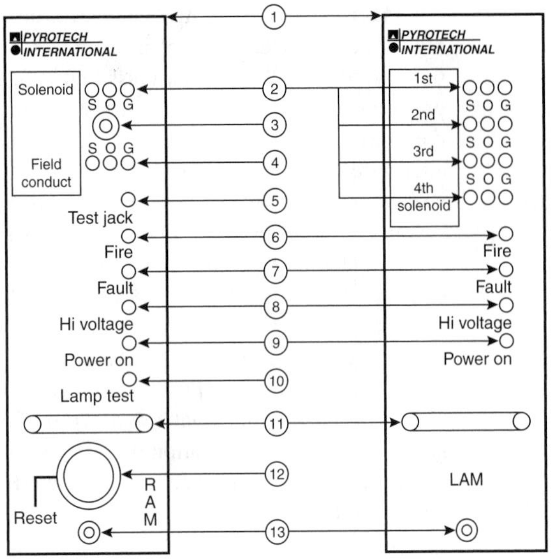

1. RAM/LAM frontplate
2. RAM/LAM short, open and ground solenoid status
3. RAM reset timing adjustment
4. RAM short, open and ground field alarm contact status
5. RAM response time test jack
6. RAM/LAM fire LED
7. RAM/LAM fault LED
8. RAM/LAM high-voltage LED (normally on)
9. RAM/LAM power on LED (normally on)
10. RAM lamp test button
11. RAM/LAM service handles
12. RAM reset/bypass key switch (normally in vertical position)
13. RAM/LAM fastener cap screw (4 mm)

FIGURE 16.7.25 RAM/LAM Frontplates (Response Acceleration Module) (Source: Pyrotech International)

distribution after a predetermined period of time (usually 2 minutes), provided that the detectors no longer view a hazard. Electric push buttons and LED indicators annunciate the control functions of the panel and display the status of the pilot-actuated system. The control unit should be equipped with a capability for resetting the solenoids automatically from the unit, eliminating lengthy system shutdowns.

A battery charger recharges the batteries when needed and rectifies the 120 V ac input power to 24 V dc for system use. Upon loss of primary 120 V ac power, the charger will transfer to the secondary 24 V dc battery supply.

Sequence of Operation for a Pilot-Actuated System

The flame detectors constantly view the hazard areas, searching for changes in light intensity. The status is reported to the controller for analysis. Light intensities are screened by the detectors' ability to recognize common signals, such as house lighting and sunlight. Physical screening may be necessary to prevent detector signals from such intermittent light sources as welding torches, lightning, or sun reflecting from the windshield of a car.

Upon detection of a valid signal, the controller, constantly interpreting system status, receives the signal. The signal is interpreted and relayed to the appropriate high-speed module. Indicator lights and indicating devices commence operation, and a signal is sent simultaneously to all the high-speed solenoids on the system.

The normally closed solenoids open, allowing water to flow through the solenoids, thus purging the pilot system of water and relieving the pilot pressure. The pressure drop allows the poppet valves in the pilot-actuated nozzles to move, allowing water to flow through the nozzle and onto the hazard, as shown in Figure 16.7.26 and Figure 16.7.27. The pilot-actuated nozzle insert directs the waterflow into a wide-, medium-, or narrow-angle spray. Minimum static pressure at each nozzle should be no less than 50 psi (344.75 kPa), with 180 psi (1241.1 kPa) strongly recommended.

Factors Influencing Speed of a Pilot-Actuated System

There are many variables that can enhance the speed of a pilot-actuated system, and all are considered in each engineered layout. For example, trapped air in the pilot line can be a significant hindrance to the hydraulic evacuation of the pilot line. To prevent this, the pilot line is sloped as radically as possible, with air-release vents, either manual or automatic, at all high points of the pilot system. It is a common practice to bleed air from the system after it is reset and repeat the process at the start of the next working day to ensure that all air is removed from the system.

Excess system volumetric capacity of a pilot-actuated system is a substantial contributor to increasing the response time of the system. It is important to maintain a maximum system volumetric capacity of less than 500 gal (1892.5 L), as required by NFPA 15. Where response times of less than 100 milliseconds are required, it may be necessary where possible to subdivide the systems such that the maximum number of nozzles on a single system is about 10. It is also advantageous to minimize the number of fittings and changes of water direction and to minimize the length of the feed main to the system.

The distance from the solenoid valve on the pilot line to the pilot connection of the pilot-actuated nozzle can be a major factor in the speed of evacuation of the pilot line. The ideal situation would be to place a solenoid on the pilot line adjacent to each nozzle. This would release the pilot pressure to the noz-

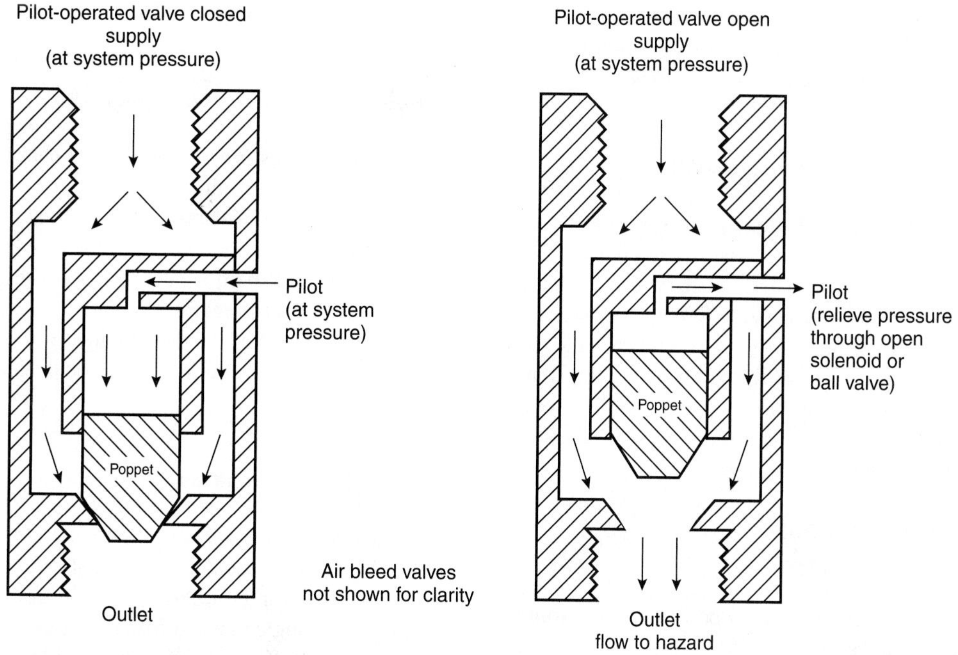

FIGURE 16.7.26 Modern Pilot Valve Operation (Source: Pyrotech International)

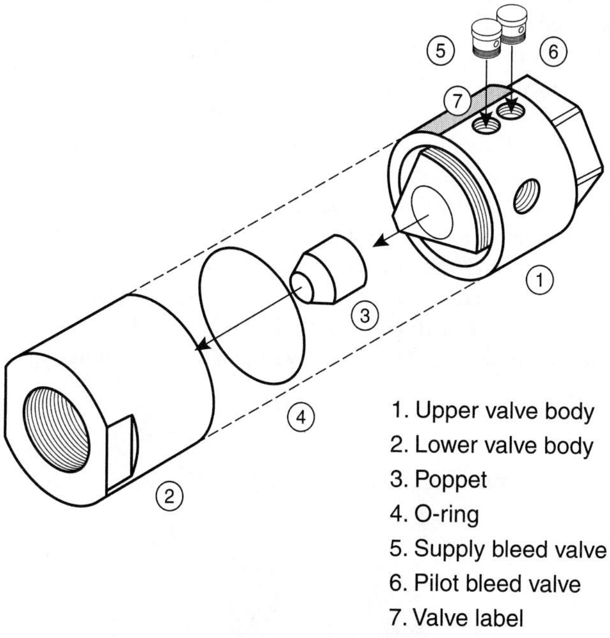

FIGURE 16.7.27 Pilot-Operated Valve (Source: Pyrotech International)

zle almost immediately, and evacuation of the entire pilot line would not become a factor. When large systems are necessary, it may be electronically impractical to provide a ratio of one solenoid per nozzle.

System pressure can be a major factor in response time. An excess pressure pump can be provided for each system or group of systems to maintain 170 to 180 psi (1172.2 to 1241.1 kPa) static pressure on the system piping and pilot line. Pressure of this magnitude at each nozzle provides the impetus for rapid evacuation of pilot pressure and rapid delivery of water to the hazard. Another alternative is the use of an elevated gravity tank that would provide a minimum of 75 psi (517.13 kPa) static pressure on the system. An orifice restriction device, either an orifice union or a drilled ball valve, is placed in the pilot line at the riser to maintain proper functioning of the pilot valves. Once the solenoids open, residual pressure drop in the pilot line is minimized by this restrictor, increasing the speed of pilot evacuation. The diameter of the pilot line can also be a factor in pilot evacuation. For short runs of pilot piping, ½ in. (12.7 mm) galvanized steel pipe is sufficient, with a very short run of ⅜ in. (9.5 mm) internal diameter copper piping for the nozzle pilot connections.

To increase the speed of solenoid actuation, the initial voltage provided to the solenoids from the panel, upon receipt of a signal from the detectors, should provide delivery of a high-voltage signal, enhancing the solenoid operating time. Although the voltage eventually levels off to 24 V dc, which is the normal control system operating voltage, the initial burst of energy may damage solenoids rated for less than the maximum voltage encountered.

No less than 25 gpm (95 L/min) per nozzle is required by NFPA 15 to be designed for point protection, nor less than 0.50 gpm/ft^2 (20.37 L/min·m^2) of exposed area for area protection. Point protection should be accomplished with no fewer than two counteropposed nozzles per point of likely ignition, and area protection should be accomplished with a nozzle spacing of between 30 and 60 ft^2 (2.8 and 5.6 m^2), depending on the configuration of the hazardous commodity or process.

Counteropposition of the nozzles involves nozzles aimed from differing directions at a common point. Some commodities, such as certain pyrotechnics, may require densities as high as 3.0 gpm/ft^2 (122.24 L/min·m^2).

Response Time for Pilot-Actuated Systems

Specifications written for pilot-actuated systems mandate a response time not to exceed 100 milliseconds, measured from presentation of an energy source to the detector to water discharge from the most distant pilot-actuated nozzle. Whenever possible, travel time for the water to hit its intended target should be included in the total response time. Research is ongoing that would evaluate and further define this time span.[1,6] The specifying engineer should evaluate test data and lower the required response time where warranted.

Method of Timing Response of a Pilot-Actuated System

The following procedure can be used to perform a functional time test of a pilot-actuated system:

1. Install a pressure switch on the nozzle being tested. Each nozzle on the system must be tested to ensure that the solenoids are functioning properly and that operation speeds are being maintained at each nozzle.
2. Slowly fill the system piping.
3. Bleed all air from the pilot system through air vent valves. Opening these valves too quickly may operate the system.
4. Close the air vent valves and record the static system pressure at the riser.
5. Connect the timer to the nozzle pressure switch and to the timing test jack on the RAM or high-speed module. High-speed photography is also an effective timing device.
6. Take three consecutive readings for each system.
7. Record the static pressure at the riser before and after each test.
8. A UV light source will be used to activate a UV detector for the system being tested. UV, IR, and UV/IR testing lamps for tripping ultra-high-speed water spray systems are commercially available.
9. An electrical impulse from the RAM time test jack will start the timers.
10. Two timers should be used in order to ensure accuracy.
11. The timers will be stopped by the water discharge reaching the pressure switch.
12. Record the test results, including residual pressure at the riser.
13. Reset the system at the control panel.

It has been found that when an ultra-high-speed water spray system has been discharged repeatedly, response times usually increase somewhat. This is the result of air bubbles created by the rapid movement of water through the piping collecting into pockets of air in critical segments of the piping system. When this phenomenon is identified through the observation of repeated declining response times, it may take several hours to permit air bubbles to migrate to positions in the piping where they can be completely expelled through the air bleeders.

Other Applications for Pilot-Actuated Systems

Although munitions provide the largest share of current pilot-actuated system applications, this system has been used with a preset timer to limit discharge to protect valuable commodities such as mail conveyors and chutes, ovens, and antique book storage facilities. Where enhanced system response is desired, but where a 100 millisecond response time is unnecessary, the system can be modified to resemble the early pilot-actuated system with thermal, pneumatic, or electric detection and standard control modules.

PORTABLE SYSTEMS

Portable ultra-high-speed water spray systems shown in Figure 16.7.28 have been created to supply cost-efficient, mobile, short-term protection for U.S. Army ammunition plants and other facilities requiring enhanced actuation times for exposed energetic materials.[7] This system is a portable, self-contained fire detection and suppression system capable of delivering water to the nozzles within 50 to 100 milliseconds from time of detection and can protect an area up to 100 ft^2 (9.3 m^2). The system features UV detection with a high-speed controller, a solenoid-actuated deluge valve, and a portable pressurized water storage tank that is capable of being temporarily cross-connected to a building water supply, if available.

Some portable ultra-high-speed water spray systems for use in explosive production facilities are supplied with 20 ft (6 m) extension hoses and are capable of reacting to a fire in less than 50 milliseconds. Reaction time interval is the time from the point of detection to flow at the nozzle. Because of their mobility, the portable units are well suited for use on short production runs where a fixed system is not practical. They can be rolled by one person and are designed with channels for forklift transport. Some units are of a size that allows them to be rolled through a

FIGURE 16.7.28 Portable Ultra-High-Speed Water Spray Systems (Source: Pyrotech International)

36 in. (91 cm) door with water tank capacity up to 100 gal (397 L) pressurized by a nitrogen bottle.

Units are provided with supervised ultraviolet detectors, solenoids, and pilot-operated valves, with tank pressure and water level also supervised. An integral power supply/charger and battery pack are normally provided. Electrical components should be housed in explosionproof enclosures with appropriate ratings. All necessary controls for normal operation (power switch and reset switch) are located on the outside of the explosionproof enclosure. The system could be reset with a switch or by means of automatic reset.

Applications for portable units include the following:

- Explosive or pyrotechnic spills, in which case the portable unit could be rolled into the hazard area and used to protect an area during the cleanup operation, where fixed fire protection may not normally be present
- Hazards for which there is not sufficient time or funding to install fixed fire protection quickly enough to satisfy the need
- Depot rework, where maintenance or operations often change and machinery is moved or replaced with different equipment. In some cases, fixed systems may not be practical from an operational, safety, or economic standpoint.
- Machining, milling, blending, or drying, where the portable unit could be attached to the machinery
- When the existing fixed system is shut down and production must go on; portable units can bridge the time involved in getting fixed systems back on line
- Cleanup and decontamination operations, when equipment is torn down or if there is fear of residual explosives. This presents one of the more hazardous conditions for operators at explosives facilities.
- Evaluation and burn testing of the design of fixed fire protection systems to prove the effectiveness of such configurations. This system would allow for easy modification and variations providing more comprehensive test results.
- Research, evaluation, and quality control laboratories. Hazards often vary in severity as do the processes and material to which the technicians are exposed. In most cases, the energetic material has known properties such as sensitivity to spark, friction, or impact. Sometimes in the case of experimental compounds the properties (possibly hazardous) are unknown. In either case, it would be advantageous to be able to roll in a portable unit to protect personnel and equipment. Processes in the laboratory environment are also quite likely to change, for example, blending, mixing, granulating, extruding, and drying. Changing operations (if hazardous) require an adaptable explosion or fire suppression system. Although personnel are more highly skilled and quantities often much smaller, the explosives laboratory can be a hazardous environment and in some cases warrants the use of such a system.
- Temporary depot and staging areas, possibly offshore or overseas, where fixed deluge systems could not have been considered possible because of installation time, lack of water supply, or varying processes
- Temporary storage protection for in-process work, in the situation of production overruns where surplus munitions ingredients must be stored and normal adequate fire protection is not available, or in the case of rejected production runs where the product must be stored until it can be reworked or destroyed
- Additional backup for existing systems or unforeseen changes in process

Additives can be included with the water supply. Antifreeze and wetting agents or water coloring may be added to help evaluate different spray patterns utilizing high-speed video (for added clarity). Possible advantages of water gels, "sticky water," could be tested.

Portable units can be moved to a shop or maintenance area for service, allowing them to leave the restricted (hazardous) area. Nozzles with different spray patterns can be adapted, moved, and configured depending on operation.

EXPLOSIVE SPHERE-HIGH-RATE-DISCHARGE (HRD) DEVICES

The explosive sphere-HRD-type device (Figure 16.7.29) is for rapid response deluge suppression in the munitions and explosives industries. It is an explosive squib-operated, high-pressure vessel (400 psi [27.579 bar]) with a rupture disk. It is compatible with all forms of high-speed detection and is actuated by the DDAM (Dual Detonator Acceleration Module) (Figure 16.7.30). Although the sphere-HRD-type device can achieve a reaction time under 15 milliseconds, it is limited to approximately 7 gal (26.5 L) of flow. For this reason, it is not a stand-alone device and must be used in conjunction with other rapid response deluge systems. These devices are often used for point protection.

When designing such systems, consideration must first be given to bringing explosive devices into a hazardous location to arm and reset the sphere. A source of high-pressure inert gas must also be available to prime the sphere-HRD-type device.

When a detector sends an alarm signal to the appropriate DDAM, the squib in the sphere-HRD-type device is detonated,

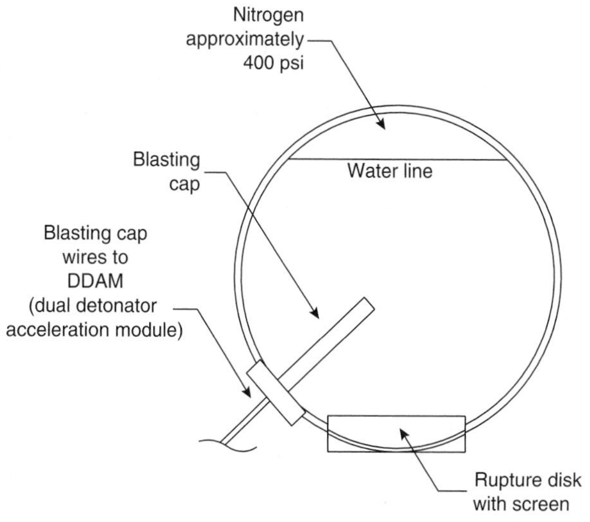

FIGURE 16.7.29 Explosive Sphere-HRD-Type Device (Source: Pyrotech International)

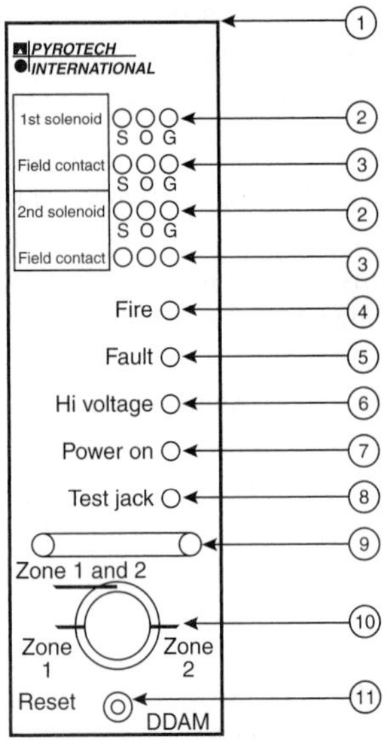

1. Frontplate
2. Short, open, and ground solenoid status or normal, open, and ground squib status
3. Short, open, and ground field alarm contact status
4. Fire LED
5. Fault LED
6. High-voltage LED (normally on)
7. Power on LED (normally on)
8. Response time test jack
9. Service handle
10. Reset/bypass key switch
11. Fastener cap screw (4 mm)

FIGURE 16.7.30 DDAM (Dual Detonator Acceleration Module) Frontplate (Source: Pyrotech International)

the rupture disk is broken, and the high-pressure chamber is emptied. Simultaneously, backup deluge is also discharged to the hazard. Even though the backup deluge may reset automatically, the sphere-HRD-type device must be reset manually. Sphere-HRD-type devices are squib actuated. Response time testing of the sphere-HRD-type device is best accomplished by the use of high-speed video.

EXPLOSION SUPPRESSION SYSTEMS

The first explosion suppression systems were introduced by the British in the late 1940s for protection of aircraft and were later extended to industrial use. Explosion suppression systems consist of a cylinder filled with a suppressing agent, a detection system, and a system of control circuitry. They can ordinarily be visually differentiated from ultra-high-speed water spray systems by their lack of system piping, by the existence of uniquely shaped agent containers, and by the use of a wide variety of agents, including water, that can be employed with such systems. Halon, which was once a commonly used agent for explosion suppression systems, has been scheduled for elimination by the Montréal Protocol.[8] A clean agent or halon substitute, in accordance with NFPA 2001, *Standard on Clean Agent Fire Extinguishing Systems,* may be required for a new explosion suppression system. Explosion suppression systems are designed in accordance with NFPA 69 to protect enclosed vessels or containers from rupture due to overpressurization resulting from a deflagration.

EXPLOSION VENTING

An enhancement to the effectiveness of an ultra-high-speed water spray system or an explosion suppression system is explosion venting. These passive vents are sometimes used in lieu of an ultra-high-speed water spray system or an explosion suppression system. Venting, however, will relieve pressure without any active effort to control the continued burning of the fuel in the hazard area. Care must be taken to avoid placing explosion venting louvers in a location where an operator or passerby could be injured by an explosion relief blast. NFPA 68, *Standard on Explosion Protection by Deflagration Venting,* should be used when designing an explosion venting system.

An alternative to a suppression system could be to provide no protection of any kind. In a facility with an enclosed and separated or isolated automatic process that is normally unoccupied, where vessels are manufactured with sufficient strength to withstand overpressurization resulting from a deflagration, or where there is enough process redundancy to avoid process stoppage, a firm may consider the option of no protection. Repair or replacement of a process area, the spreading of fire or blast damage to adjacent areas with a corresponding result of possible deaths or injuries, unfavorable publicity, and loss of income could prove to be significantly more costly than an ultra-high-speed suppression system or an explosion suppression system.

RESEARCH AND DEVELOPMENT

The Air Force Research Lab's (AFRL) Fire Research Group at Tyndall Air Force Base, Florida, has been working to invent a more effective deluge system capable of stopping high-velocity fires caused by deflagration of explosives, propellants, and pyrotechnic materials. Initially, a system similar to that described in the section on explosive sphere-HRD-type devices was used. Compared to the NFPA requirement of 100 millisecond response from detection to initiation of waterflow, AFRL's Advanced Fire Protection Deluge System (AFPDS) reduced response time to about 8 milliseconds (6 milliseconds detection time and 2 milliseconds initiation time) and put water on a fire 36 in. (0.9 m) away from the nozzles in 18 milliseconds. Close behind, backup water from a pressurized tank with solenoid-operated nozzles reached the fire in about 130 milliseconds. In 100 trials using ¼- to ½-lb (0.113- to 0.226-kg) samples of various pyrotechnic materials, most fires were extinguished by the initial water from the explosive sphere-HRD device, and the back-up water was redundant.

Effective as the AFPDS is on most propellants and pyrotechnic materials, it is not fast enough to stop fires from the fastest burning materials, exemplified by magnesium-Teflon pyrotechnic flare material. A new phototransistor-circuit flame detector was developed that cut detection time from 3 to 5 milliseconds to less than 1 millisecond, and a novel deluge system, the blast-initiated deluge system (BIDS), was developed that discharged water at nearly 500 ft/sec (152.4 m/sec). The heart of the BIDS consists of a steel cone set inside a steel cylinder (Figure 16.7.31). On detection of a fire, the controller sends an electrical signal to a small explosive charge fixed at the apex of the cone. Detonation of the charge causes a rapid rise in pressure inside the cone that forces the initial water out a burst disk and onto the fire. Holes in the side of the cone allow follow-on water

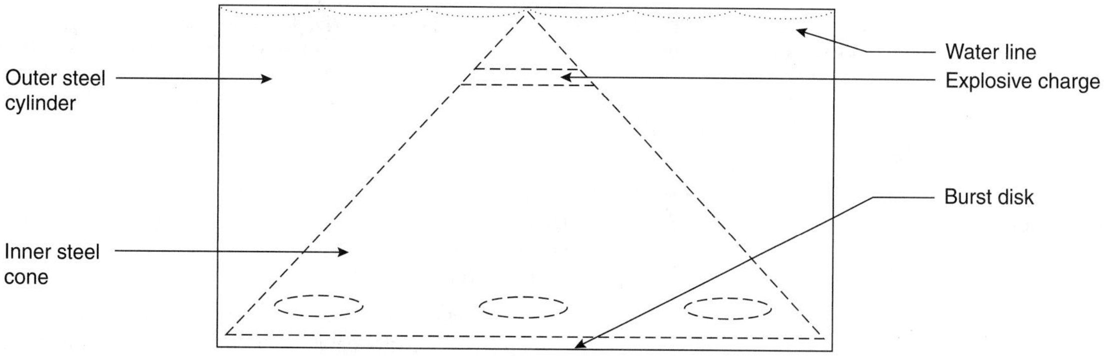

FIGURE 16.7.31 Blast-Initiated Deluge System (BIDS)

to flow through the cone and onto the fire. The BIDS reduced time from detection to water on a fire 36 in. (0.9 m) from the nozzle to 7 milliseconds, as compared to about 26 milliseconds for the AFPDS, and 130 milliseconds or longer for solenoid-activated systems. The BIDS extinguished 1 lb (0.453 kg) samples of magnesium-Teflon in an average of 15 milliseconds and 4 lb (1.81 kg) samples in 40 to 50 milliseconds, and significantly reduced heat flux levels.

SUMMARY

A major difference exists between ultra-high-speed water spray systems and explosion suppression systems. Even though both systems suppress explosive hazards, ultra-high-speed water spray systems are used predominantly for open machine protection or room area protection, whereas ultra-high-speed explosion suppression systems protect enclosed vessels. Although system names are sometimes used interchangeably, this chapter helps clarify correct terminology.

There is relatively little information available on practical testing of various munitions manufacturing explosive levels for differing munitions commodities and processes. However, years of successful field performance and experience, as well as system time and reliability testing demonstrate the effectiveness of ultra-high-speed water spray systems with respect to the suppression of munitions explosive hazards. Artificial retardation of the normal actuation times of ultra-high-speed water spray systems means the difference between extinguishment and total loss of control in the explosive process. A comparison of ultra-high-speed water spray systems is shown in Table 16.7.3.

BIBLIOGRAPHY

References Cited

1. Loyd, R. A., "Ultra-High-Speed Deluge Systems for Ordnance Operations," *Proceedings* of the Federal Fire Forum, November 3, 1989, National Institute of Standards and Technology, Gaithersburg, MD, 1989.
2. Goedeke, A. D., and Fadorsen, G. A., "Evaluation of State-of-the-Art High-Speed Deluge Systems Presently in Service at Various U.S. Ammunition Plants," Document WL-TR-93-3510, Wright Laboratory, Wright-Patterson AFB, Dayton, OH, Sept. 1993.
3. Detector Electronics Corporation, "Fire Detection System Selection Guide," Form 92-1002-01, Dector Electronics Corp, Minneapolis, MN, undated.
4. Fadorsen, G. A. "Ultra-High-Speed Fire Suppression for Explosives Facilities," American Chemical Society Symposium for Design Considerations for Toxic Chemical and Explosives Facilities, R. A. Scott and L. J. Doemeny (Eds.), 1987.
5. Ault, W. E., and Carter, D. I., "The Influence of Hyperbaric Chamber Pressure on Water-Spray Patterns," *Fire Journal,* Nov. 1967, pp. 48–49.
6. Loyd, R. A., "Design and Installation of Ultra-High-Speed Deluge Systems," *Proceedings* of the 24th Department of Defense Explosives Safety Seminar, August 27–30, 1990, St. Louis, MO, Department of Defense Explosives Safety Board, Alexandria, VA, 1990.
7. Loyd, R. A., "Portable Ultra-High-Speed Deluge Systems," *Proceedings* of the 23rd Department of Defense Explosives Safety Seminar, August 9–11, 1988, Atlanta, GA, Department of Defense Explosives Safety Board, Alexandria, VA, 1988.
8. Grant, C. C., "Halons and the Ozone Layer: An Overview," *Fire Journal,* Sep./Oct., 1989, pp. 59–81.

NFPA Codes, Standards, and Recommended Practices

Reference to the following NFPA codes, standards, and recommended practices will provide further information on ultra-high-speed water spray systems discussed in this chapter. (See the latest version of The NFPA Catalog *for availability of current editions of the following documents.)*

NFPA 13, *Standard for the Installation of Sprinkler Systems*
NFPA 14, *Standard for the Installation of Standpipe and Hose Systems*
NFPA 15, *Standard for Water Spray Fixed Systems for Fire Protection*
NFPA 18, *Standard on Wetting Agents*
NFPA 20, *Standard for the Installation of Stationary Pumps for Fire Protection*
NFPA 22, *Standard for Water Tanks for Private Fire Protection*
NFPA 24, *Standard for the Installation of Private Fire Service Mains and Their Appurtenances*
NFPA 25, *Standard for the Inspection, Testing, and Maintenance of Water-Based Fire Protection Systems*
NFPA 30, *Flammable and Combustible Liquids Code*
NFPA 61, *Standard for the Prevention of Fires and Dust Explosions in Agricultural and Food Processing Facilities*
NFPA 68, *Standard on Explosion Protection by Deflagration Venting*
NFPA 69, *Standard on Explosion Prevention Systems*
NFPA 70, *National Electrical Code®*
NFPA 72®, National Fire Alarm Code®

TABLE 16.7.3 Comparison of Squib-Operated, Pilot-Operated, Explosive Sphere-HRD, and Portable Deluge Systems

	Squib-Operated	*Pilot-Operated*	*Explosive HRD*	*Portable*	
Complete electrical supervision		*		*	Solenoids are supervised for shorts, opens, and grounds. On a squib-operated system the igniter wire can be supervised but condition of explosive is not known.
Response time not affected by air in supply pipe		*	NA	*	Due to low-pressure prime and the remote location of the valve, air in the piping of a squib-operated valve can cause slow and fluctuating response times.
No recurring cost or replacement parts needed after each firing		*		*	After firing of the squib-operated systems, disc or caps must be replaced and explosive devices reinstalled. Nitrogen or other inert gas must be accessible to recharge a sphere-type device.
Programmable automatic reset feature available		*		*	An optional automatic reset feature is available. This allows automatic system reset after a present time as long as no fire is present.
System does not require explosives for operation		*		*	Pilot-operated valves do not present the problem of bringing explosives (squibs) into the hazard area.
System can be reset and back on line in less than 30 seconds		*		*	Primac and HRD-sphere type devices may require caps, discs, squibs, blocks, or pins
Limited shelf life of components	*		*		Squibs have a shelf life and should be periodically replaced.
Requires pilot line piping		*		*	Pilot line connections are necessary for pilot-operated valves to function.
Mechanical manual operation available		*		*	Mechanical manual release is possible even in the event of total power failure (including loss of primary power and battery backup).
Each head acts as an individual deluge valve (safety through redundancy)		*		*	The system does not depend completely on one device for operation. Redundancy of solenoids and valves provides a more reliable system.
Response time not affected by system size		*	*	*	Since each nozzle can be considered an individual deluge valve, system size does not affect response time.
Compatible with all forms of detection	*	*	*	*	Systems can be interfaced with any of the available detection devices.
System can be preprimed with high pressure		*	*	*	Since valve is at the nozzle, a high-pressure prime can be accomplished.
Unlimited available water supply	*	*		*	HRD-type devices require backup systems to be in place. Portable deluge may be connected to existing supply. A backup system must be fast enough to provide full waterflow before HRD system empties (approximately 250 milliseconds).
Nozzles can be directed very close to the hazard	*	*		*	Due to the size of the HRD-type devices, it may be physically impossible to locate the HRD close to the hazard. Water travel time may greatly compromise safety.
Adapts to various response time test equipment	*	*		*	HRD-type systems can only be response time tested by use of high-speed video.
Contaminants discharged with deluge	*		*		Squib and HRD-sphere type systems may contain debris from rupture discs, blasting caps, and/or blasting cap holders.

NA = Not available.

Source: Pyrotechnic International.

NFPA 77, *Recommended Practice on Static Electricity*
NFPA 495, *Explosive Materials Code*
NFPA 2001, *Standard on Clean Agent Fire Extinguishing Systems*

References

Technical reports on ultra-high-speed water spray systems can be ordered from the Defense Technical Information Center, Cameron Station, Alexandria, VA, 22314. Phone 703-274-6733. Documents that are approved for public release are noted (APR). Documents that contain confidential or proprietary information and whose distribution is limited to government agencies only are noted (DL).

"Analysis of Mixer Bay Designs for Pyrotechnic Operations," No. AD-E401-602, Nov. 1986. (APR)

"Calculating Sprinkler Actuation Time in Compartments," Center for Fire Research, National Institute for Standards and Technology, Mar. 1984.

"Deluge Systems in Army Ammunition Plants," prepared by Science Applications, Inc., for the U.S. Army Munitions Production Base Modernization Agency, June 30, 1981.

"Design of a Deluge System to Extinguish Lead Azide Fires," No. AD-E400-204, Aug. 1978. (APR)

"Design of a Water Deluge System to Extinguish M-1 Propellant Fires in Closed Conveyors," No. AD-E400-216, Sept. 1978. (APR)

"Development of a Water Deluge System to Extinguish M-1 Propellant Fires," No. AD-E400-217, Sept. 1978. (APR)

"Dynamic Model of a Water Deluge System for Propellant Fires," No. AD-E400-315, May 1979. (APR)

"Engineering Guide for Fire Protection and Detection Systems at Army Ammunition Plants," Vol. I: Selection and Design, No. AD-E400-531, Dec. 1980. (APR)

"Engineering Guide for Fire Protection and Detection Systems at Army Ammunition Plants," Vol. II: Testing and Inspection, No. AD-E400-874, Dec. 1982. (DL)

"Evaluation of an Improved Fire Suppression System for Pyrotechnic Mixes," No. AD-E401-569, Sept. 1986. (DL)

"Evaluation of Pyrotechnic Fire Suppression Systems for Six Pyrotechnic Compositions," No. AD-E401-306, Mar. 1985. (APR)

"Feasibility Study to Develop a Water Deluge System for Conveyor Lines Transporting High Explosives," Tech. Report. No. 4889, Aug. 1975. (APR)

"Fire Suppression System Safety Evaluation," No. AD-E401-083, Dec. 1983. (APR)

"Guidelines for a Thermochemical Kinetics Computer Program," Los Alamos National Laboratory, LA-10361-MS, May 1895.

"Mathematical and Numerical Methods Used in Thermal Hazards Evaluation," Naval Weapons Center China Lake, NWC-TP-6510, Dec. 1986.

"Minutes of the Rapid Action Fire Protection Systems Seminar," U.S. Army Armament, Munitions, and Chemical Command, Oct. 23–24, 1984.

"On-Site Survey and Analysis of Pyrotechnic Mixer Bays," No. AD-E401-141, Feb. 1984. (APR)

"Technical Report on the Testing of Ultraviolet-Actuated Deluge Systems Utilizing Solid-State Controllers and Detonator-Actuated Valves to Extinguish Black Powder Fires," Day and Zimmerman, Lone Star Division, Nov. 1986.

"Water Deluge Fire Protection System for Conveyor Lines Transporting High Explosives," No. AD-E400-034, Dec. 1977. (APR)

Chapter 8

Water Mist Fire Suppression Systems

Jack R. Mawhinney

Chapter Contents

Key Terms

atomization, constant pressure system, declining pressure system, drop size distribution, enclosure effects, fire test protocols, flame cooling, local application, nozzles, oxygen displacement, positive displacement pump, radiant heat blocking, single fluid, spray momentum, thermal management, total flooding, tunnel fire protection, twin fluid, vapor dilution, water mist, water vapor

Interest in the use of very fine water sprays (water mist) in fire suppression systems has been intense for the last 15 years. The economic force behind this interest has been driven by two major fire protection needs. First, in the early 1990s the international maritime regulatory organizations mandated the installation of sprinkler systems on passenger ships. This mandate inspired a search for a system that could be considered equivalent to sprinklers but that would discharge less water, use smaller-diameter piping, have lower overall weight than a standard sprinkler system, and hopefully cost less. The second driving force was the need to find a replacement for ozone-depleting substances such as the halons, which had been used for decades to protect machinery spaces, flammable liquids rooms, computer rooms, and rooms for materials sensitive to water damage. The halon alternative search included the possibility of using water in applications where water was not previously considered practical. Thus, a technology that could minimize droplet size and application rate, enhance evaporation, and help reduce oxygen levels to extinguish hidden fires began to have marketable value.

Spurred by receptive market conditions, innovative fire suppression systems have been conceptualized, tested against specific fire scenarios, and installed as working systems. A large number of the world's passenger ships are now equipped with marine water mist systems. Much of the early work in developing fire tests and performance criteria occurred in Europe at laboratories such as SP in Sweden, SINTEF in Norway, VTT in Finland, and the Danish Fire Research Institute. In North America, practical research was conducted in Canada at the National Research Council National Fire Laboratory and in the United States by Hughes Associates, Inc., with U.S. Navy and Coast Guard support. In 1993, the National Fire Protection Association (NFPA) began work on a design and installation standard, NFPA 750, *Standard on Water Mist Fire Protection Systems,* to consolidate design concepts emerging from the research and development work. In the last decade a number of European companies have obtained approvals from North American listing agencies such as FM Global Research and Underwriters Laboratories (UL) for machinery spaces, turbine enclosures, and wet benches. Several North American fire protection manufacturers have developed specialized water mist equipment with their own nozzle designs. There are now formal fire test protocols not only for marine applications, such as machinery rooms, turbine enclosures, accommodations, public spaces, and service areas, but also for land-based applications involving very large machinery spaces, local application systems, light and ordinary hazard applications, and "wet benches" for electronics manufacturing. Although the marine market for water mist systems remains the strongest, there is a steady growth in land-based applications.

The first chapter on water mist technology appeared in the 18th edition of the *Fire Protection Handbook* released in 1997. Since then, the technology has advanced from "potential" to "actual." There are installed systems in process modules in the Alaskan oil fields and in heritage buildings, hotels, art galleries, and computer rooms worldwide. Experience with design, installation, commissioning, and maintenance of systems has advanced steadily. The handbook chapter has been revised to reflect the changes and advances made. It must be noted that the growing experience

Jack R. Mawhinney, P.E., FSFPE, is a senior engineer at Hughes Associates, Inc., based in Baltimore, Maryland. Prior to joining Hughes Associates in 1996, he was a senior research officer at the Institute for Research in Construction, National Research Council Canada.

has not changed one important factor in water mist system design. As indicated in the first edition, there still is no generalized "first principles" approach to design of water mist systems. Design criteria for each manufacturer's equipment are determined through full-scale fire testing to internationally recognized test protocols. The flux densities differ sufficiently among manufacturers so that one cannot enforce a single generic criterion on all manufacturers. Full-scale testing continues to be justified.

This chapter reviews the salient features of water mist fire protection systems. It discusses the general extinguishing mechanisms and the influence of fuel type and compartment conditions on effectiveness. The chapter provides details on the components, types of systems, calculation methods for single- and twin-fluid systems, pump selection and application of positive displacement pumps, and maintenance issues.

For related topics, see the following chapters in Section 16: Chapter 1, "Principles of Automatic Sprinkler System Performance"; Chapter 2, "Automatic Sprinklers"; and Chapter 3, "Automatic Sprinkler Systems."

APPLICATIONS OF WATER MIST SYSTEMS

Before discussing the details and general principles of water mist systems, it is instructive to review several applications of water mist systems. Some of the applications have been studied in detail by various technical groups seeking to develop consensus fire test protocols to set design criteria. Others were developed through ad hoc testing by a group interested in solving a specific problem. The following examples represent the proving ground for water mist fire suppression systems technology.

Machinery Spaces

Fires in machinery compartments involve diesel fuel and lubricating or hydraulic oil spills, ignited by hot engine parts, overheated bearings, or electrical arcing. Pool or spray hydrocarbon fires can be fast developing, very hot, and have the potential to cripple or destroy a ship. International shipping safety regulations, developed by the International Maritime Organization (IMO) and as written in the rules of SOLAS (Safety of Life at Sea), have for many years required that machinery spaces on large vessels be equipped with either CO_2 or halon fire suppression systems. With the phase-out of halon and increased awareness of the safety hazard that CO_2 represents, there is strong interest in finding an alternative fire suppression agent for machinery compartments on ships. Further incentive for improved suppression systems for machinery spaces comes from IMO regulation enacted in the 1990s that required all ships capable of carrying more than 36 passengers to be equipped with automatic sprinkler systems by 1997. Where the necessary pumps and water supplies must be provided for general sprinklering of the ship, the use of a water-based suppression system in lieu of a gaseous agent in the machinery space becomes economically viable. The requirement to retrofit existing ships with sprinkler systems raised concerns, however, about creating stability problems due to adding weight of piping or large volumes of water to the superstructure of a ship. Those potential problems could be addressed by water mist fire suppression systems that promise to use small-diameter piping and deliver minimum quantities of water.

The potential to use finely divided water sprays to suppress hydrocarbon pool and spray fires has been known for some time, at least since the 1950s.[1,2] Since 1990, a number of companies have developed water mist systems for marine machinery compartments, in which the primary fire hazard involves hydrocarbon spray or pool fires. The International Maritime Organization (IMO) test protocols and amendments dating from 1994 and 1996 established the baseline for machinery space water mist fire suppression systems (IMO MSC/Circular 668: Alternative Arrangements for Halon Fire Extinguishing Systems in Machinery Spaces and Pump-rooms).[3,4] The tests address liquid fuel fires in machinery compartments of 500 m^3, main diesel machinery in spaces up to 3000 m^3, and in larger-volume diesel machinery spaces on oil tankers and container ships. These test protocols are described in NFPA 750. There are 13 test scenarios involving shielded pool and spray fires of different size around a mockup of a diesel engine. There is a void space under the diesel mockup intended to simulate a bilge space with a shielded fire. There is also a 2 m by 2 m ventilation opening in the lower quarter of the test compartment. In order to pass the IMO test protocol a water mist system must extinguish all 13 of the test fires, from the largest 6 MW spray fire to the smallest pool fire (500 kW) within 15 minutes. The test fires involve both low- and high-flashpoint hydrocarbon fuels. One test involves a small wood crib and heptane igniter. Since 1999, the International Maritime Organization has issued test standard IMO MSC/Circular 913[5] for local application systems to protect specific equipment in large machinery spaces. In 2005, IMO produced MSC/Circular 1165,[6] which sets criteria for water mist systems for very large machinery spaces, for example, up to 3300 cubic meters. IMO MSC/Circular 1165 includes most of the fire tests used in MSC/Circular 668 but eliminates the need to extinguish the very smallest fire.

Experience has shown that extinguishing large fires in a compartment with limited ventilation is relatively easy.[7–9] A large fire consumes oxygen and generates enough heat to convert water droplets to water vapor, reducing the oxygen concentration in the compartment. The fire extinguishes itself due to oxygen starvation. Small fires are more difficult (take longer) to extinguish, because they do not consume the available oxygen fast enough (relative to the inflow through the ventilation opening), nor do they generate enough heat to evaporate much of the water mist.[7] For these reasons the IMO machinery compartment tests become increasingly difficult to pass as the compartment becomes larger and the fires become smaller. The IMO test protocol requires full extinguishment of all fires. Systems that have passed the IMO machinery space test protocol are permitted to utilize combinations of total flooding ceiling nozzles and screening nozzles over the ventilation opening, as well as the addition of a surfactant to the water supply. To a certain extent the successful system designs may be customized to pass the IMO test specifically. Some systems may be dependent on controlling the ventilation through the specific ventilation opening. If the actual application does not have such a well-defined ventilation opening, it is unknown whether the system would still achieve the same results. Furthermore, the IMO test structure does not include the clutter of overhead piping, cable trays, and ducts found in real machinery spaces. The extent to which the additional obstructions might increase extinguishment times is not evaluated by the test protocol.

The IMO regulations also require the installation of local application fire suppression systems on certain machinery space equipment, in particular, large diesel engines. The IMO MSC/Circular 913, Local Application test protocol[5] defines the performance requirements. For ships that utilize carbon dioxide for the engine room suppression system, the requirement to install the water-based local application system represents an additional cost. For passenger ships that utilize water mist to comply with the IMO requirements, the water supply and pumping capacity are already provided. The local application system represents only a small cost increase.

Both FM Global Research and Underwriters Laboratories (UL) have developed their own versions of the IMO test series. The FM Global Research and UL test programs differ from the IMO tests in certain ways. The FM Global Research and UL test protocols, for example, relax the requirement to extinguish the smallest pan fire in the bilge. The relaxation recognizes the level of control achieved by the suppression system—the small shielded fire can be approached and extinguished by hand.

Water mist systems have been installed in land-based machinery spaces in Alaska's North Slope. There are differences between machinery spaces on land and on ships. On ships, the concept of a single 2 m by 2 m ventilation opening is valid because of the nature of compartmentation on ships. In land-based facilities, the ventilation openings may be distributed differently. The designer must understand the conditions and the performance objectives of each test protocol in order to make an appropriate adaptation to a real installation.

Machinery compartment water mist systems can be characterized as follows:

- *Safety objectives.* Replace halon or CO_2 extinguishing agents. Extinguish all fires involving spilled or sprayed diesel fuel or hydraulic oils and provide cooling of hot gases using a limited amount of water. Fire sizes range between 0.5 and 10.0 MW. Extinguishment times must be within 15 minutes (IMO) or 30 to 60 minutes (UL or FM Global Research).
- *Mechanisms.* Mechanisms include convective cooling of flame, hot gases, and fuel; steam displacement of oxygen and dilution of air-fuel vapor mixtures; and blocking convective and radiant heat transfer to surfaces of unburned fuels and surrounding objects. The ability to ensure optimum conditions for any of the extinguishing mechanisms decreases as compartment size, ventilation, fuel complexity, and number of obstructions increase.
- *System features.* Deluge systems with open nozzles in grid at ceiling and sometimes at intermediate levels are used for flooding the total compartment with water mist. Local application systems around equipment also utilize open nozzles. Nozzles may be high- or low-pressure jet, twin-fluid, or impingement types and may be combined with other suppression systems (e.g., bilge foam systems) where control is beyond the capability of mist alone. A separate detection system is used for activation. Water supply is preferably fresh water, but systems are designed to permit switching to seawater after fresh-water supplies are depleted. Maritime regulations (IMO) require a minimum 30 minute water supply.
- *Industry acceptance.* Water mist systems are accepted worldwide by the International Maritime Organization (IMO) as a replacement for halon or CO_2 in marine machinery spaces. Maritime insurance societies such as Det Norske Veritas and Lloyd's inspect and commission the systems. For passenger cruise ships, which must be sprinklered throughout, water mist is frequently used to comply with Solas requirements for the machinery space. For cargo shipping, carbon dioxide systems are more widely used. The petroleum resource industries worldwide are using water mist systems in machinery spaces such as process modules at production sites.

BP Alaska, Phillips Petroleum, and ARCO Alaska have installed water mist systems in machinery modules on Alaska's North Slope as a replacement for halon 1301 systems. The designs of these land-based machinery space systems are based on IMO, FM Global Research, or UL protocols for machinery spaces.

Turbine Enclosures

Turbine enclosures are a type of machinery space. Unlike general machinery spaces, which may contain many potential fire sources, the source of fire in a turbine enclosure is limited to the turbine and its fuel lines. Large diesel or gas-driven turbines are standard equipment in offshore drilling platforms. Fuel line breaks may lead to spray fires or three-dimensional spill fires with pool fires in a bilge area under the turbine. The rotating turbine blades are susceptible to serious damage if the surrounding casing is cooled rapidly and contracts. For that reason, it was in the past considered dangerous to apply water to turbine fires, at least until the machine had stopped rotating. The turbines are enclosed in ventilation-controlled compartments. Halon 1301 and CO_2 total flooding systems have been the preferred method of providing automatic fire suppression for turbine enclosures.

Wighus et al.[7] confirmed the ability of a water mist fire suppression system to extinguish fires in a turbine enclosure. Subsequent test protocols have been developed by FM Global Research to address concerns about the use of water spray on hot turbines. The FM Global Research fire test protocol for turbines in enclosures incorporates a test to measure the rate of cooling of a thick metal plate. The test results in convective heat transfer coefficients for different segments of the heated plate. The heat transfer coefficients can then be used in a finite element analysis of the turbine casing to evaluate clearances between casing and turbine blades. As turbines are typically installed inside enclosures, the test protocols have been developed for enclosed conditions. A number of water mist equipment manufacturers have obtained FM Global Research listings for water mist systems in turbine enclosures up to 260 m^3. Other turbine enclosure test protocols exist in Europe and Australia. The manufacturers have adopted various strategies in order to pass the cooling test in the FM Global Research test protocol. These include orienting the nozzles to project the spray horizontally, parallel with the axis of the turbine, to minimize direct-spray impingement on the casing, or cycling the spray on and off for short intervals.

The turbine enclosure water mist system can be characterized as follows:

- *Safety objectives.* The safety objectives are to rapidly extinguish a fire involving spilled or sprayed diesel fuel on or under an operating diesel turbine, using a limited amount of water, and without damaging the turbine blades through thermal shock; provide cooling of hot gases in the compartment; and replace halon 1301 or CO_2.
- *Mechanisms.* Mechanisms include convective cooling of flame, hot gases, and fuel; steam displacement of oxygen and dilution of air/fuel vapor mixtures; blocking convective and radiant heat transfer to surfaces of unburned fuels and other objects; and cooling hot metal surfaces.
- *System features.* These include total compartment flooding systems with open nozzles on a preengineered piping system. Both low-pressure and high-pressure systems utilize stored water and compressed gas to deliver the water to the nozzles. Nozzle locations and orientation are important to overall performance. Cycling (on/off cycles) are sometimes used to minimize the cooling rate of the turbine casing. A separate heat or optical detection system is used to control release of the system and to activate interlocks. Water storage volume is based on either the FM Global Research minimum requirement for 10 minutes' duration or the NFPA 750 requirement for two complete discharges for preengineered systems (20 minutes).
- *Industry acceptance.* Norwegian and Australian petroleum industry operators and regulators accept water mist as an alternative to halon or CO_2 in turbine enclosures on offshore platforms. The Alaska North Slope oil field regulators also accept the use of water mist in land-based turbine enclosures. Most turbine manufacturers accept the use of water mist around their turbines provided they have passed the FM Global plate cooling test.

Marine Accommodation, Public Spaces, and Service Areas

The IMO maritime regulations that require installation of sprinkler systems on passenger-carrying ships have stimulated interest in developing water-based suppression systems that require less water than standard sprinklers, can use smaller-diameter piping, and be compatible with the water supplies, detection, and control systems on a ship. To that end, considerable effort has gone into developing water mist systems that operate in the same manner as sprinkler systems.

Test protocols have been developed by IMO to evaluate the use of water mist in crew's quarters and ship corridors.[10–12] Testing to date has focused on small cabins (i.e., 12 m^2 for crew's quarters, and 25 m^2 for luxury cabins). Unlike the water mist systems intended for application to Class B (hydrocarbon fuel) fires, the crew's quarters fire scenario involves Class A combustibles. Whereas large droplets are a disadvantage for hydrocarbon fires, they are beneficial to the extinguishment of Class A combustibles due to wetting of unburned fuel. Mist intended for suppression of Class A combustibles can have more large droplets than sprays intended for liquid fuel fires.

Water mist systems incorporating thermally released nozzles were recognized under IMO as equivalent to sprinklers for application in crew's quarters and passenger cabins.[10] Additional tests have been developed by IMO for the more severe fuel loading associated with shopping and service areas on ships.[11–14] The fire tests developed by IMO for the Class A hazards on ships have become the basis for generalized systems intended for land-based "light and ordinary hazard" and "residential" occupancies.[15,16]

The light and ordinary hazard occupancy applications of water mist systems can be characterized as follows:

- *Safety objectives.* The safety objectives are to save lives by suppressing and controlling fires in Class A combustibles and to prevent fire spread from the compartment of origin into adjacent compartments.
- *Mechanisms.* Mechanisms include wetting of wood, paper, cloth, and plastic fuels in furnishings and wall coverings; some steam displacement of oxygen; convective cooling of flame, hot gases, and fuel; and blocking convective and radiant heat transfer to surfaces of unburned fuels and other objects, thereby preventing flashover.
- *System features.* The system is similar to wet-pipe sprinkler systems with normally closed, fast-response, thermally activated nozzles. The nozzles produce a higher percentage of finer drops than standard sprinklers.
- *Industry acceptance.* As of 2006, almost all cruise ships are protected with marine water mist systems tested under the IMO test protocols for accommodation, public spaces, and service areas. The systems are recognized by most national coast guard authorities and marine classification societies.

Hotels, Heritage Buildings, and Galleries

Nonmarine applications of water mist systems include hotels, heritage buildings, and art galleries. The IMO test protocols for accommodation, public spaces, and service areas provide the design basis for many of these systems. Rooms with corridors on cruise ships are similar to rooms with corridors in land-based hotels. Since 2000, two hotels in the United Kingdom have been retrofitted with high-pressure water mist sprinkler systems for the purpose of increasing life safety. High-pressure water mist systems were selected because of the advantages of using small-diameter tubing and a small waterflow requirement compared to standard sprinklers. The water mist systems were cost competitive with standard sprinklers.

Water mist systems have been installed to protect remote heritage buildings in Norway and Finland. The 1000-year-old wood stave churches are located in remote areas with minimal or no water supply. There was a need to provide an automatic detection and suppression system that could protect the structures with a minimum amount of water and without damaging the icons painted with water-soluble paint on the wood walls. A water mist system was developed using nozzles at ceiling height to achieve flashover suppression by delivering enough water to take the heat out of the hot gas layer but not to wet the walls.[17,18] Supplementary nozzles with higher flow rates were mounted at floor level to extinguish the accelerant fires. Testing was performed in Norway to validate the concept, and

Norwegian authorities responsible for preservation of national treasures were pleased to have a means of protecting the structures.[19] The National Gallery of Art in Washington, DC, has installed a preaction, high-pressure water mist system in a series of galleries. The galleries are primarily period rooms with combustible walls or ceilings. A fire in these galleries would threaten all other areas of the gallery with smoke and fire damage. The combustible walls and ceilings were not considered to be irreplaceable because the woodwork could be recreated if damaged by water. The objective was to provide fire protection with minimal water use, so that other areas of the gallery would not be flooded or damaged. Water mist nozzles were selected to project spray horizontally along the underside of the ceiling in the concealed spaces above the ceiling and in wall cavities. The nozzles are thermally activated, although the fire pump unit does not start unless there is an alarm signal from at least two smoke detectors.

Water mist systems for hotels and heritage buildings can be characterized as follows:

- *Safety objectives.* For hotels, the objective is life safety, although property protection is also important. For remote heritage buildings and galleries, the objective is primarily property protection and heritage preservation.
- *Mechanisms.* Mechanisms used include cooling of hot gases near the ceiling to minimize the occurrence of flashover and direct wetting of Class A combustibles.
- *System features.* For hotels and galleries, high-pressure pump water supplies are used for a minimum 30 minute duration. For remote heritage buildings, compressed gas–driven systems with 10 minutes' stored water are used. Open nozzles on deluge systems for flashover suppression, thermally activated (automatic) nozzles on preaction systems for gallery protection, and automatic nozzles on wet-pipe systems for hotels are used. Preaction and deluge systems would also include the use of a supplemental fire or smoke detection system and interconnected alarm panel.
- *Industry acceptance.* Acceptance by authorities having jurisdiction (AHJ) in Europe is based on collaborative development work involving AHJ, design engineers, and manufacturers. Acceptance is growing rapidly in North America.

Electrical Equipment Rooms, Computer Rooms, and Wet Benches

Water mist has been viewed as a possible alternative to halon 1301 for use in electrical equipment rooms. Potential applications include telecommunications central office facilities, control rooms, and computer rooms. Developments in these areas are limited. There is strong interest worldwide in the use of water mist systems in control rooms, particularly since several European authorities mandated the removal of all halon systems. Consensus on a general design approach and performance objectives for water mist on fires in electronic equipment has not yet been reached.

Testing has been performed by the U.S. Navy and by manufacturers to demonstrate that water mist may be used on high-voltage electrical equipment if precautions are taken with regard to stand-off distances.[20] Electrical charge does not transmit through an atomized spray. Water mist may be used in switchboard compartments for 10 minutes or more before leakage currents reach dangerous levels.[21]

Although FM Global has shown support for the use of water mist for telecommunications central offices, general acceptance by end users has been slow in North America. Similarly, the use of water mist as a halon replacement for computer rooms has been mixed. The fundamental issue has to do with comparing the performance of total flooding gaseous clean agents that can penetrate into electronic cabinets with water mist that cannot extinguish fire inside a cabinet, at least not in a total compartment flooding mode.

One water mist manufacturer markets a water mist system intended to capture smoke in a computer room subfloor and direct it into tubes where it can be scrubbed of acidic gases. This computer room "smoke scrubbing" subfloor system has been approved by FM Global for the protection of computer room subfloors, not as a general computer room fire protection system. For general fire protection in the computer room above the subfloor, standard water mist nozzles are distributed according to light hazard spacing rules. In general, water mist may provide the level of protection afforded by sprinklers against Class A fire hazards in a computer room but with discharge of smaller volumes of water. The objective of extinguishing a small fire inside an electrical cabinet without causing extensive wetting of sensitive electronics can be better achieved with gaseous clean agents.

It should be stated that the subfloor "smoke scrubbing" takes place inside a 100-mm-diameter tube where thorough mixing and washout are possible. The system captures smoke from the subfloor in 100-mm-diameter tubes. A water mist nozzle placed inside the tube creates a positive differential pressure downstream of the nozzle and a negative differential pressure upstream of the nozzle relative to the pressure in the subfloor. In the positive-pressure end, nitrogen and very fine mist are pushed out of holes in the pipe into the subfloor. In the negative-pressure end of the pipe, air and smoke from the subfloor are drawn into the pipe. Nitrogen rises into the computer cabinets above the subfloor where it extinguishes small telltale fires inside a computer cabinet. For the smoke that is drawn into the scrubbing tube, the vigorous mixing causes soluble corrosive gases such as HCl to be washed out.

In contrast, it is not true that water mist has a general smoke-scrubbing benefit when injected into a smoky fire compartment from ceiling nozzles. Unfortunately, some water mist manufacturers make the general claim that water mist provides a smoke-scrubbing benefit, making it suitable for use in electronic spaces. This erroneous claim of generalized smoke-scrubbing benefit is promoted for electronic spaces, art galleries, highway tunnels, and buildings in general. In a study conducted for the U.S. Navy, Mawhinney et al. measured the optical density of smoke before and after passing through water mist screens.[22] The study noted that optical densities decreased as a result of the water mist but not enough to materially improve visibility. Furthermore, nonsoluble toxic gases in the smoke are not washed out, so the toxicity of smoke is not reduced by the water mist. Recently, an Austrian group claimed that water mist provided scrubbing benefits for fires in a highway tunnel—the perceived benefits include improved visibility and increased "breathability."[23] Such claims are not supported by experimentation and may lead to a dangerous misunderstanding of the benefits of water mist.

Wet benches are used for the manufacture of electronic computer chips. They are traditionally protected by carbon dioxide systems. The hazard includes confined spaces under the wet bench, vats of flammable liquid on the polypropylene surface of the work bench, and the collector hoods. Two water mist manufacturing companies have developed water mist systems for installation in wet benches. FM Global Research developed a test protocol for evaluation of the system.[24] The system consists of open nozzles in zones connected to a water storage cylinder connected to a cylinder of compressed gas. It is activated by optical detectors. Because of the high corrosivity of the etching acids used in the process, corrosion-resistant pipe and fittings are needed. One company manufactured a twin-fluid nozzle out of the equivalent of Teflon plastic to meet the corrosion-resistance requirement.

Water mist systems for electronic equipment, computer rooms, and wet benches can be characterized as follows:

- *Safety objective.* The safety objective is to provide property protection by extinguishing small fires and removing acid gases from smoke generated in subfloor areas.
- *Mechanisms.* Mechanisms include direct wetting of Class A combustibles in electrical wiring and normal combustible items found in computer rooms and washing out of soluble acid gases in subfloor smoke.
- *System features.* For computer rooms and electrical equipment rooms, closed nozzles equivalent to sprinklers are used. For subfloor smoke scrubbing, a custom-designed grid of large-diameter tubes for distribution and collection of the combined nitrogen/fine mist gas is used. Small water storage cylinders and cylinders of nitrogen gas provide a 10 minute operation of the subfloor system.
- *Industry acceptance.* Acceptance by authorities having jurisdiction in Europe is based on collaborative development work involving AHJ, design engineers, and manufacturers of water mist equipment. Consensus on test protocols and design criteria for water mist systems for computer rooms has not yet been reached. Wet bench systems have approval by FM Global.

Tunnels

Tunnels are likely to be an important direction of development for water mist fire protection systems in the next 10 years. Fire testing has been performed to evaluate the use of water mist against electrical cable fires in tunnels.[25] After a decade of serious highway and rail tunnel fires in Europe that resulted in heavy loss of life and financial losses totaling in the billions of dollars, the tunnel authorities in Europe have begun to lessen their reluctance to employ active water-based fire suppression systems in tunnels.[26,27]

In North America and Europe the fire protection strategies for highway tunnels have been based on providing ventilation to remove smoke and hot gases, using spall-resistant concrete, and providing traffic control and evacuation exits at certain distances along the tunnel. Water-based fire suppression systems were until recently viewed as undesirable, possibly because of incomplete risk evaluations. The body of opinion on which the designers of fire safety systems for tunnels have relied was reflected in NFPA 502, *Standard for Road Tunnels, Bridges, and Other Limited Access Highways.*[28] That standard also provided estimated fire sizes for different types of vehicles for use as design fires for designing ventilation systems and protective linings. Remarks in the Appendix to NFPA 502 gave dire warnings against the use of sprinklers or suppression systems.

A series of full-scale fire tests conducted in Norway in 2003 presented a challenge for the traditional design assumptions for fire safety in tunnels. The Runehamar Tunnel[29] fire tests demonstrated that a typical HGV lorry transporting furniture or foam mattresses could create a fire ranging from 75 to 200 MW. NFPA 502 suggested design fire size for a HGV is 30 MW. Ventilation systems designed on the basis of an assumed 30 MW fire are going to be ineffective against 150 MW fires. This fivefold underestimate in the size of the design fire for ventilation system design suggests that water-based suppression systems are in fact necessary in order to reduce the impact of fire in a tunnel to a level that the ventilation systems or other safety features can handle.

Since 2003 the tunnel fire safety authorities in Europe have realized that water-based active fire suppression systems may be essential to ensure the assumed (public expectation) minimum level of life safety in road tunnels. This change in attitude has motivated significant spending on the part of manufacturers of water mist fire suppression systems in full-scale testing. In the last 5 years, systems including high expansion foam, compressed air foam (CAF), and water mist have been tested. Fire testing of water mist systems has been and continues to be carried out at the Runehamar test tunnel in Norway, the IF tunnel research facility also in Norway,[30] the Hagerbach tunnel research facility in Switzerland,[31] and the San Pedro de Anes tunnel safety research facility in Spain.[32] Recently, contracts have been let to begin installation of water mist systems in several highway tunnels in Europe. One result of the extensive full-scale fire testing conducted to satisfy tunnel authorities will be some standardization of the performance objectives for the suppression system, against standard design fires, versus against very severe heavy goods vehicle fires such as identified in the Runehamar testing. Due to a lack of consensus among tunnel authorities in different countries as to how to set realistic performance objectives for a tunnel fire suppression system, there may be significant differences in the design features of systems developed by different manufacturers. The benefits of water mist in highway tunnels include cooling the gases to reduce the thermal threat to people, prevention of fire propagation beyond the first one or two vehicles involved, and reduced buoyant smoke spread. Reduced buoyancy makes it easier for existing ventilation equipment to function and for fire fighters to force smoke back into a tunnel as they try to approach the fire area. It should be noted that water mist applied generally from ceiling nozzles does not provide a smoke-scrubbing benefit. Although some soot is washed out of the smoke, the visibility does not improve sufficiently to improve existing conditions, and nonsoluble toxic gases such as CO are not removed.[33] Water mist can be used to cool tunnel ventilation fans so that they survive longer and continue to remove smoke from the tunnel.

Tunnels can be very long with limited space for equipment such as pumps and water reservoirs. The challenge of providing adequate flow and pressure of water to the mid-sections of a tunnel that might be 10 km or more in length presents a unique opportunity for water mist systems, which use smaller-diameter piping than traditional water-based suppression systems. Extensive full-scale fire testing of water mist systems in highway tunnels in the last 5 years has shown that water mist can provide satisfactory protection of life and property against even catastrophic fires in heavy goods vehicles. Cost-effective engineering designs to achieve the required waterflow rates at the three most remote zones in the tunnel have been realized.

Water mist systems for tunnels can be characterized as follows:

- *Safety objectives.* For electrical cable tunnels, the primary objective is property protection, although life safety is an issue for workers in the tunnel. For railway tunnels, both life safety and property protection are important. For highway tunnels, the property protection objective is to limit thermal damage to the tunnel lining to the area of a single burning vehicle and to prevent propagation of fire to adjacent vehicles. Reduced temperatures and smoke buoyancy will increase the effectiveness of ventilation systems in tunnels and make it easier for the fire fighters to enter the tunnel to fight the fire and aid rescue.
- *Mechanisms.* Mechanisms include direct wetting of Class A combustibles in electrical wiring or commodities carried in vehicles, cooling of hot gases; reduced smoke buoyancy, hence, smoke spread; and direct cooling of gases entering the smoke exhaust system to prolong functionality of equipment.
- *System features.* Features include generally high-pressure water mist systems with stainless steel tubing and several positive displacement pump stations, special detection systems, zoning of systems fixed to the tunnel, or systems fixed to a moving vehicle.
- *Industry acceptance.* Acceptance by local authorities having jurisdiction is on the basis of special fire testing directed by end users.

Aircraft Passenger Compartments

Starting in 1985, the Civil Aviation Administration (CAA) in the United Kingdom and the Federal Aviation Administration (FAA) in the United States, with the involvement of Transport Canada, Airbus, Boeing, and other aviation industry agencies, developed a fine water spray fire control system for aircraft passenger compartments.[34] The objective of this international research and development effort was to find a way to decrease the number of fatalities in air crashes that involve fuel spill fires (i.e., the postcrash fire scenario). The Manchester, United Kingdom, air crash of 1984 was the particular incident that sparked this interest. In that incident, the fatalities were not caused by the crash but by the fire from spilled fuel that engulfed the fuselage and spread into the passenger compartment. Aircraft are not at present equipped with fixed systems to protect against a postcrash fire.

The testing program verified that the aircraft passenger compartment water mist system met or exceeded the researchers' objectives for the postcrash fire scenario.[35] Having determined the details of the design, a cost-benefit study was conducted. The study concluded that the cost of outfitting a fleet of aircraft with passenger compartment water mist systems would be too high relative to the number of lives that would be saved to justify mandatory requirements for their installation.[34] As a result, both industry and regulatory partners in the aviation industry decided not to make it mandatory to install such systems on existing or new aircraft. Instead, focus has shifted to the problem of developing water mist systems for onboard cargo compartment fires during flight.

The aircraft passenger cabin water spray system can be characterized as follows:

- *Safety objective.* The primary safety objective is saving lives by protecting an aircraft passenger compartment from a postcrash, external fire threat and extending the survivable evacuation time.
- *Mechanisms.* Mechanisms include blocking convective and radiant heat transfer, cooling of hot fire gases, and wetting of fuels (plastic and cloth).
- *System features.* The system features zoned piping, automatic thermal activation of each zone, 3 minute supply of stored water in pressurized cylinders, single discharge, with limited duration of protection adequate for a well-defined performance objective.
- *Industry acceptance.* Developed through collaboration between aviation industry and regulatory authorities, the system has not been made mandatory on the basis of an unfavorable cost-benefit study.

SUMMARY OF WATER MIST SYSTEM FEATURES

From the preceding descriptions, it is evident that there are wide variations in the objectives, fire scenarios, system details, and levels of acceptance for water mist fire suppression systems. These can be summarized as follows:

Objectives

1. Protect lives and property in a compartment from external fire threat.
2. Control fire temperatures in a compartment to prevent flashover and fire spread to adjacent compartments.
3. Extinguish Class A and Class B fires.
4. Use water to provide protection where there was no previous protection (aircraft passenger compartments).
5. Use water where halon or CO_2 was previously used (Class B fires in machinery rooms).
6. Provide freedom from sprinkler system design constraints (e.g., allow use of smaller pipe sizes) with equivalent level of safety.

Fire Scenarios

1. Large external pool fire threatening to spread into a compartment

2. Liquid hydrocarbon fuels with high- and low-flashpoint liquids, in spray, spill, and pool fires, outdoors and in compartments
3. Class A combustibles (furniture, bedding, books on fixed shelving) in small compartments
4. Machinery compartments, underventilated liquid fuel fires
5. Large machinery compartments with obstructions, well-ventilated conditions, and small to large fire sizes
6. Tunnels with very large fuel loads of wood and plastic commodities on heavy goods vehicles or passenger vehicles

System Details

1. Low-pressure to high-pressure systems: 5 to 140 bar (75 to 2000 psi)
2. Single- and twin-fluid systems
3. Normally open nozzles, deluge-type systems, with separate detection system for activation
4. Normally closed, thermally activated nozzles
5. Continuous discharge
6. Repeated short discharges (cycling)
7. Declining pressure systems (gas driven)
8. Constant pressure systems (pump driven)

Levels of Acceptance

1. IMO full-scale fire test protocols, to be conducted by national laboratories, have been in place since 1996. Systems that meet the fire performance criteria in the IMO test protocols will be acceptable to national and international maritime authorities. Water mist is widely used on passenger ships, less so on commercial cargo ships.
2. FM Global Research approved a preengineered system for turbine enclosures in a compartment of fixed maximum dimensions. The performance evaluation includes not only the suppression effectiveness but also the performance of the detection system, effects of water on the equipment being protected, the performance of the detection/actuation equipment, flow duration, and sensitivity to partial dysfunction.
3. The components of water mist systems, including nozzles, pumps, actuators, gas cylinders, pressure control equipment, detection system panel, control valves, and so on, must meet IMO component testing criteria or be listed by Underwriters Laboratories Inc. (UL 2167) or FM Global Research (FM 5560 Test Protocols) for use in water mist systems.
4. Acceptance of water mist systems in land-based applications continues to grow. Authorities having jurisdiction are accepting more and more systems for industrial process modules, highway tunnels, hotels, and heritage buildings.
5. NFPA 750 describes what must be taken into account in full-scale fire test evaluations of water mist systems but defers to testing agencies to conduct those tests. If tests conducted by a credible laboratory demonstrate that the proposed design will meet the performance objectives, then it is expected that authorities having jurisdiction will accept the design.

Having reviewed the types of water mist systems that have achieved a level of recognition, the fundamental principles involved in extinguishing fires with water mist can be addressed. Ultimately, an understanding of the first principles governing the performance of water mist systems will allow the designer to adapt the range of misting technologies to the range of fire scenarios to meet a variety of system objectives.

GENERAL PRINCIPLES OF WATER MIST SYSTEMS

This section describes the general principles of water mist fire suppression systems technology and includes extinguishing mechanisms, spray characteristics, generic design elements, and methods of generating water mist. Extinguishing mechanisms are discussed first, as they are the basis on which the importance of specific spray characteristics can be appreciated. Technical details relating to spray characteristics are presented next. General principles governing the performance of water mist systems are outlined, and methods of generating water mist are described.

Extinguishing Mechanisms

A basic description of how water mist extinguishes fires was provided as early as 1955 by Braidech[1] and confirmed by Rasbash et al.[2] To quote Braidech:

> The extinguishing action of sprays of finely divided water applied to commonly encountered fires appears to be due predominantly to dilution of the air (oxygen) supply in the zone of burning with vapor (steam) resulting from evaporation of water droplets in the heated area surrounding the fire. The cooling effects of the water may also be important factors in extinguishment in many cases. In order to obtain extinguishment, the water droplets comprising the spray must be relatively small, and the amount of water applied must be adequate in relation to the specific fire.

Research conducted more than four decades later has not altered the accuracy of this description. The recent work has, however, suggested other processes that are involved and has identified the mechanisms that are most important for the design of effective fire suppression systems.

Figures 16.8.1 and 16.8.2 illustrate the mechanisms involved in extinguishing fire with mist. The mechanisms that act together to extinguish fire can be described as three primary and two secondary mechanisms.[36] The primary mechanisms are (1) heat extraction, (2) oxygen displacement, and (3) blocking of radiant heat. Wighus[7] and Hanauska and Back[37] described the mechanisms as "gas-phase cooling and steam inerting," making no reference to radiant heat attenuation. Although all three mechanisms are involved to some degree in every extinguishment, in tests conducted at the National Research Council, some fires were extinguished predominantly through heat extraction (cooling) and others predominantly through displacement of oxygen. The difference depends on whether the fire was poorly or well ventilated and on the properties of the fuel. The benefit of radiation attenuation in a compartment is evi-

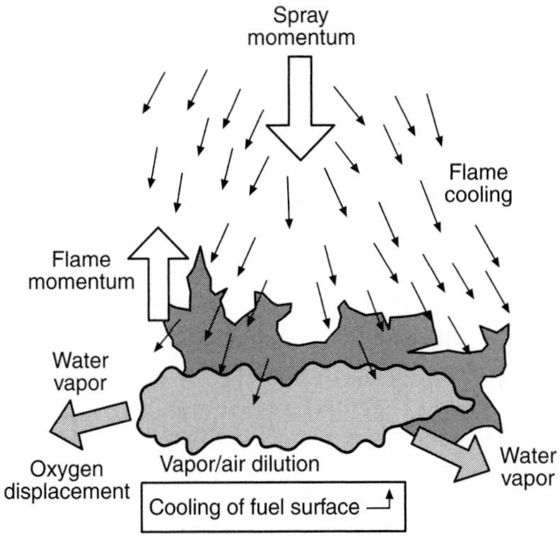

FIGURE 16.8.1 Interaction of Mist with Pool Fire Flame, Showing the Extinguishing Mechanisms

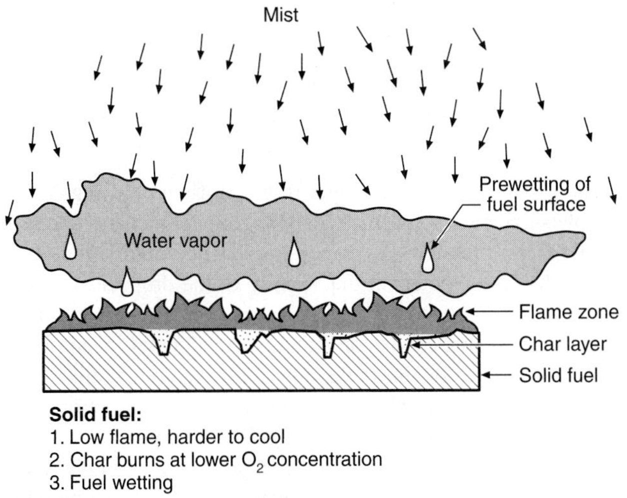

FIGURE 16.8.2 Flame on a Solid Fuel with Charring and Mist

dent in reduced thermal feedback to burning and unburned fuel surfaces. In the National Research Council of Canada (NRCC) experiments, however, radiation attenuation could not be identified as the dominant mechanism of extinguishment.

There are two secondary mechanisms that play a role in extinguishment, but it is difficult to quantify their importance. These are (1) vapor/air dilution, and (2) kinetic effects. The dilution of vapor/air mixtures by the mixing of water vapor and entrained air in the flammable vapor zone above a fuel surface can be deduced to have some effect on pool fires. Also, the velocity of the flame front in a flammable gas mixture may be inhibited (or accelerated) by the presence of small water droplets dispersed in a volume of flame, and this phenomenon may play a role in the extinguishment of spray fires and in inhibiting deflagrations.[38]

For engineering design of reliable water mist fire suppression systems, it may be sufficient to understand the three dominant mechanisms (i.e., heat extraction, oxygen displacement, and radiation attenuation). For scientific purposes, computer modelers need to consider all extinguishing mechanisms in order to develop algorithms to simulate the extinction of fire by mist. An ideal computer model would account for flame and fuel cooling, oxygen reduction, concentration changes in vapor/air mixtures at the fuel surface, reduced radiant feedback from flame to fuel surface, and possible kinetic effects caused by the interaction of mist with a moving flame front. Computational fluid dynamics (CFD) modeling to that level of detail is, at this time, in its early stages of development.[39–42] Recently zone models have been developed that predict extinguishing time based on oxygen depletion and cooling.[43] The mechanisms of extinguishment are described in detail in the sections that follow. Table 16.8.1 summarizes the points to be discussed.

Heat Extraction (Cooling). When water is applied to a fire, heat is absorbed in three areas: (1) from the hot gases and flames, (2) from the fuel, and (3) from the objects and surfaces in the vicinity of the fire. Cooling of the fuel and nearby objects contributes to reducing fire spread, but it does not necessarily require fine drop sizes. In fact, wetting and cooling of solid fuels are easier to achieve by using larger droplets (400 microns) and delivering more water than can usually be delivered as water mist.

Compared with coarser sprays, finely divided water sprays enhance the speed at which the spray extracts heat from the hot gases and flame. Reducing the drop size increases the surface area of the water mass and thereby increases the rate of heat transfer. The conversion of water droplets to steam absorbs heat. If sufficient heat is withdrawn, the gas-phase temperature of the flame can be dropped to a level that is below that necessary to sustain the combustion reaction, and flame will be extinguished. Theoretical considerations suggest that the combustion reaction in a diffusion flame will cease if the flame temperature drops below approximately 1600°K (1327°C).[1,2,36]

As for what constitutes "sufficient" heat absorption, various authors note that it is not necessary to absorb all of the heat given off by the fire at the rate of burning. Absorbing 30 to 60 percent may be enough to cause burning to stop.[44] An estimate of the minimum evaporation rate to extinguish a fire of a given heat release rate (HRR) is of little practical value, however, because extinguishment usually involves more than just flame cooling. The concurrent effect of oxygen reduction could mean the fire could be extinguished with only a fraction of the theoretical minimum required for flame cooling.

For liquid fuel fires, the evaporation of mist cools the flame, which, in turn, reduces the radiant heat flux to the surface of the fuel, resulting in a reduction in the evolution of flammable vapors. The combination of reduced flame temperature and reduced evolution of vapors results in a reduced burning rate and, in some cases, complete extinction. Fires in liquid fuels with flashpoints (FPs) above normal ambient temperatures, for example, diesel fuel (FP ~ 60°C), can be extinguished with relative ease by flame cooling and reduced radiation to the surface. Fires in liquid fuels with flashpoints below normal

TABLE 16.8.1 Mechanisms of Extinguishment by Water Mist and Their Application

Mechanism	*Principle of Application*
Primary	
Heat extraction	The drop size distribution, momentum, and mass flow rate delivered to the fire, after losses to interior surfaces and obstructions, must be sufficient to absorb a critical percentage of the heat released by the fire.
Oxygen displacement	Designed to: 1. Enclose fire to contain evaporated water 2. Use nozzle dynamics to force water vapor into the base of the fire
Radiant heat attenuation: 1. To unburned surfaces 2. To burning surfaces	Mist must: 1. Surround the fire 2. Penetrate the flame
Secondary	
Vapor/air dilution: 1. By water vapor 2. By entrained air	Significant for liquid fuel pool or spray fires. Must have enclosure or control of dynamic spray properties to distribute diluent over the fuel surface. Nozzle design may influence air entrainment, hence, dilution.
Kinetic effects: 1. Reduce flame velocity 2. Accelerate combustion reactions	Difficult to predict or control. Applies to deflagration control by reducing velocity of the flame front, hence, explosion overpressure. Unpredictable: mist may suppress or invigorate combustion.

ambient temperatures, for example, heptane (C_7H_{16}, FP ~ –4°C), are much harder to extinguish by cooling alone because temperatures cannot be reduced enough to reduce the vapor/air mixture above the surface of the fuel to below the lean flammability limit.[45] Any hot object or fragment of flame can cause reignition.

The cooling of flames above solid fuels also reduces the radiant heat flux to the fuel surface and the rate of pyrolysis of the fuel. As illustrated in Figure 16.8.2, however, with charring substances, the combustion reaction occurs within the carbon-rich porous zone that forms on the fuel surface.[46] Cooling of the diffusion flame above an established char zone may not suppress radiant feedback within the crevices of the char. Either water mist must be applied early in the fire, before a deep char zone has developed, or water droplets must penetrate the char zone and reach the actual interface between burning and unburned fuel. On the other hand, the flame height and plume velocities for glowing combustion are relatively low, so that the larger drop sizes in a spray may not be evaporated and will wet the fuel surface.

Extinguishment of solid fuels such as Class A combustibles, therefore, depends on the geometry of the fuel arrangement and the depth of the char layer. Exposed surfaces facing the source of the spray might be extinguished, whereas shielded surfaces (such as within a wood crib) will be almost impossible to extinguish by cooling alone.

Oxygen Displacement. Braidech et al.[1] concluded correctly in 1955 that the suppression effect of water mist "appears to be due predominantly to dilution of the air (oxygen) supply in the zone of burning with vapor (steam)." That is to say, oxygen displacement appears to play a stronger role than flame cooling. Water droplets expand approximately 1900-fold upon evaporation (at 95°C, 1 atm pressure). If evaporation occurs rapidly, the water vapor displaces the air in the vicinity of the drop. Injection of a finely divided water spray into a hot compartment results in rapid evaporation, expansion, and displacement of the air in the compartment by steam. If the amount of oxygen available for combustion is reduced below a critical level, the fire burns inefficiently and will be easier to extinguish by cooling.

The average temperature of the gases in the compartment limits the dilution of oxygen by water vapor in a suppression scenario.[42] As illustrated in Figure 16.8.3, the absolute concentration of water vapor that can be held in air at 60°C is 20 percent by volume—that is high enough to reduce the oxygen concentration in a compartment to about 16.8 percent, which begins to affect combustion. But at 45°C, the amount of water vapor in saturated air falls below 10 percent, which would only reduce the oxygen concentration to about 19 percent, which is not enough to extinguish the fire. This fact helps explain why water mist is more effective at extinguishing large fires than small fires in a given compartment. The higher the compartment temperature, the more water vapor dilutes the oxygen. It also explains why cycling sprays on and off, in closed compartments, reduces extinguishing time compared to systems with continuous discharge. More water is evaporated because of the increase in compartment temperature during the "off" stage of the cycle. Water mist is likely to act as gaseous extinguishing agent if the average compartment temperature is between 60 and 70°C. In a cooler compartment, the effectiveness of oxygen depletion is reduced. Flame and fuel cooling and wetting become the primary mechanisms of extinguishment.

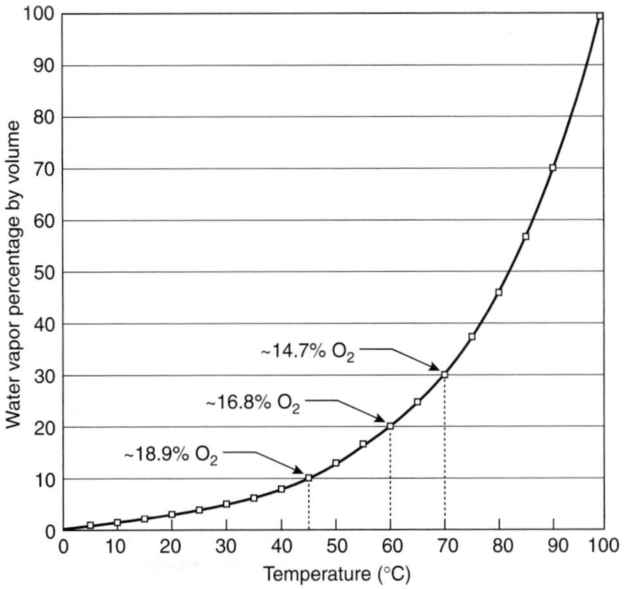

FIGURE 16.8.3 Relationship Between Gas Temperature and Volume Concentration of Water Vapor in Saturated Air. Approximate resulting oxygen concentration is indicated.

The Braidech et al.[1] study, as with most studies of the extinguishment of fires with water mist, concentrates on hydrocarbon pool fires with a few tests on wood cribs. Recent tests by Wighus et al.,[7,44] Mawhinney,[47] and Hanauska and Back[37] on diesel and heptane pool and spray fires confirmed that oxygen displacement ("steam inerting") was the dominant mechanism by which water mist extinguished the flames, both in compartments and in open-area pool fires. The confinement of heat allowed the water vapor concentration to build up so that hidden and shielded fires could be extinguished. Hanauska and Back[37] used a very fine spray with low momentum and flow rate to extinguish heptane pool and spray fires, after 30 to 50 seconds of mist application, in a 28 m^3 compartment. Fires in such enclosures can be extinguished with about one-tenth the mass flux of water needed for pool fires in open areas.[7,44] In open-area fire tests at National Research Council Canada (NRCC), extinguishment of pool fires could not be achieved unless the spray was oriented and applied with enough force to push water vapor created in the outer regions of a flame onto the fuel surface. The open-area fires required high-momentum sprays, properly oriented with respect to the plume direction. This fact suggests that the water vapor concentration at the fuel surface can be increased by either confining the fire in an enclosure or by using spray momentum to push the water vapor against the surface. In the NRCC plenum tests,[48] turbulent mixing alone did not bring about extinction if there was no component of the spray velocity directed toward the fuel surface.

The minimum amount of free oxygen needed to support combustion varies with the type of fuel. In general, hydrocarbon gases and vapors cease burning at oxygen concentrations below 13 percent, whereas charring solid fuels may burn with oxygen concentrations as low as 7 percent.[46] This explains why it is easier to extinguish hydrocarbon pool fires (diesel and heptane) than wood crib fires; the reduction in oxygen needed to extinguish a hydrocarbon flame is easy to obtain compared to that needed to arrest combustion in burning wood.

Figure 16.8.3 also explains why it is easier to extinguish large fires than small fires. The terms *small* and *large* refer to the size of the fire relative to the size of the enclosure. The observation is explained by the fact that a small fire has little effect on the average oxygen concentration in the enclosure (initially, at least), whereas the effect of a large fire on oxygen concentration is quickly evident. Compared to a small fire, a large fire generates more heat and creates a higher compartment temperature that in turn supports a higher absolute concentration of water vapor and reduces the average oxygen concentration more rapidly. To be useful in a compartment that cannot tolerate the damage that could be done by a small fire, perhaps due to flame impinging directly on a critical piece of equipment, careful thought must be given as to when or if it is necessary to extinguish small fires early.

Radiant Heat Blocking. Blocking radiant heat plays a role in stopping the fire from spreading to unignited fuel surfaces and reduces the vaporization or pyrolysis rate at the fuel surface. On a macro scale, radiation attenuation provided by water mist protects objects and personnel in a space from radiant heat damage, whether or not extinguishment occurs.

Theoretical work on radiation attenuation by water sprays[49,50] indicates that the attenuation of radiation depends on drop diameter and mass density of the droplets. As the concentration of drops with diameters smaller than 50 microns increases, the degree of attenuation of radiant heat increases.[49] This is one reason why water mists, having high concentrations of very fine drops, prove to be very effective at reducing radiant heat transfer. One question that arises is how much of the reduction in radiation to surfaces is due to the reduced size of the flame and what proportion is due to actual attenuation of radiant heat due to the presence of mist. Theoretical considerations suggest that mist or steam that enters the space between a flame and the fuel surface will reduce the radiant heat flux to that surface.[38] This is difficult to measure, but it is hypothesized that radiant heat from the flame could be absorbed by unevaporated droplets and steam, which reradiate at the lower temperature of the droplets or vapor. With some liquids, such as diesel fuel (FP ~ 60°C), this reduction in the heat flux to the fuel surface may reduce the vaporization rate of the liquid fuel and contribute to the extinguishment. Reducing energy transfer to the fuel surface reduces the rate of generation of volatile vapors.

Radiant heat attenuation between flame and fuel surface is important for computer modeling of fire suppression using computational fluid dynamics (CFD). In developing a CFD model of fire suppression using water mist, An et al.[51] calculated the heat release rate of a liquid pool fire, taking into account the coefficient of absorption of water vapor in each control volume. A reduction of radiant heat transfer to the fuel pan was predicted to measurably reduce the vaporization rate, hence, the heat release rate of the burning vapors. More experiments are needed to compare measurements of heat flux in this zone to predictions of radiant heat attenuation obtained using the CFD models.

Vapor/Air Mixture Dilution. Air and water vapor entrained in a water spray may dilute the vapor/air mixture to below the lean flammability limit. With diesel fuels (FP ~ 60°C), cooling of the flame reduces the thermal energy to the fuel surface, which in turn reduces the rate of evaporation. Coupled with a dilution of the vapors by the addition of entrained air, the vapor/air concentration falls below the lean flammability limit. In contrast, it is much harder to reduce a heptane/air mixture to below its lean flammability limit because of the low-flashpoint temperature (–4°C) and high vapor pressure of heptane. Dilution of pyrolized vapors emitted from solid fuels may also contribute to extinction and is referred to as a secondary mechanism because it is difficult to see how dilution alone could result in extinguishment. It requires uniform mixing of mist and entrained air throughout the space between the flame and the fuel surface to dilute all of the vapor/air mixture within the vaporization region. Mixing at fuel surfaces is often turbulent and nonuniform, so it is likely that there will always be some region of the vapor/air cloud that is in the flammable range.

For purposes of designing suppression systems, it is not yet feasible to quantify the relationship among the flammability limits of different fuels, the fuel vaporization rates, spray evaporation rate, and the mass flow rates of water mist and entrained air. A knowledge of dilution effects can, however, be used to explain differences in the effectiveness of water mist on different fuels as, for example, diesel and heptane. It should in principle be possible to calculate dilution effects on gas concentrations using computer field models based on computational fluid dynamics.

Kinetic Effects of Mist on Flames. A liquid pool fire is sometimes intensified by the application of water spray. A flare-up often occurs during the first moments of contact with the water mist, and it is evident in some fire tests that the burning rate is increased for longer periods. The general flare-up at the instant of application of water spray on liquid fuel fires is familiar to fire fighters. In many cases, the flare-up is followed by a quick knockdown and extinguishment of the flames. If the spray dynamics are insufficient to bring about extinguishment, the fire will continue to burn violently in spite of the mist.

The momentary intensification of the fire has been attributed by some authors to the effect of droplets striking the fuel surface and causing splashing and increased vaporization rate. Kokkala[52] referred to a "flame ball" that occurred when a sprinkler spray hit a hot, high-boiling-point liquid and explosively vaporized. In a study performed at WPI, the intensification of high-flashpoint oil fires on application of water spray was attributed largely to the disturbance of the fuel surface.[53] The same phenomenon was noted by Mawhinney[48] during suppression tests in which a fine water mist was applied from below a diesel pan fire in a direction concurrent with the fire plume, such that very few droplets could reach the surface of the diesel fuel. The visual evidence, supported by thermocouple readings, was that the flame within the plenum became violently turbulent and appeared to intensify during the time of application of the mist. One possible explanation for the observed intensification is that the turbulence acted to introduce more air into the combustion zone and thereby increased the burning rate of the fuel.

Mawhinney et al.,[36] at NRCC, measured the heat release rate of open-area heptane and diesel pan fires during the application of water mist. Figure 16.8.4 shows the measurements of heat release rate (HRR) during the suppression of a diesel pool fire and a heptane pool fire, respectively, using the same downward-oriented water spray in both cases. The HRR curves under suppressed conditions are plotted with the curves for unsuppressed fires in the same pans. In the case of diesel fuel, there is a brief spike in the HRR, followed by complete extinguishment within 60 seconds once the system is activated. For the heptane fire, a brief spike also occurred, followed by a partial suppression of the fire, and then by a continued increase in the burning rate of the heptane. The water spray failed to extinguish the fire, and turbulent flaming continued until the fuel was consumed. Over a portion of the burning time, the HRR of the fire with mist exceeded the HRR for the unsuppressed fire although, as expected, the overall burning time was reduced by the interval of intensified combustion. It is possible that the combustion process benefited from the additional air brought into the flame zone by the turbulent spray.

Jones and Thomas[38] report intensification of the rate of combustion in the use of water mists to quench gaseous explosions. The mist suppresses the maximum overpressure in an enclosed gaseous ignition, but the peak pressure may be attained sooner than for an unsuppressed explosion. Furthermore, the authors report that it is "never immediately obvious whether application of a water spray will quell or invigorate an explosion."

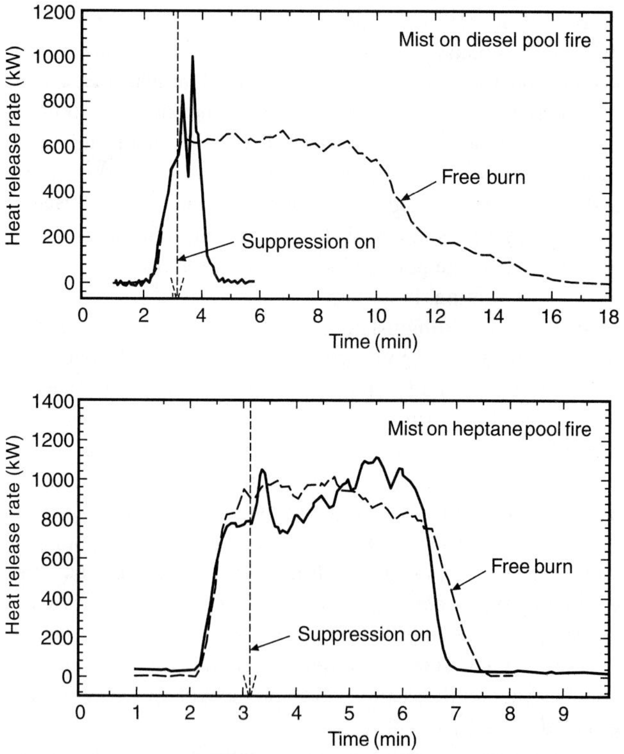

FIGURE 16.8.4 Momentary and Sustained Increases in the Heat Release Rate of Diesel and Heptane Pool Fires with Application of Water Mist

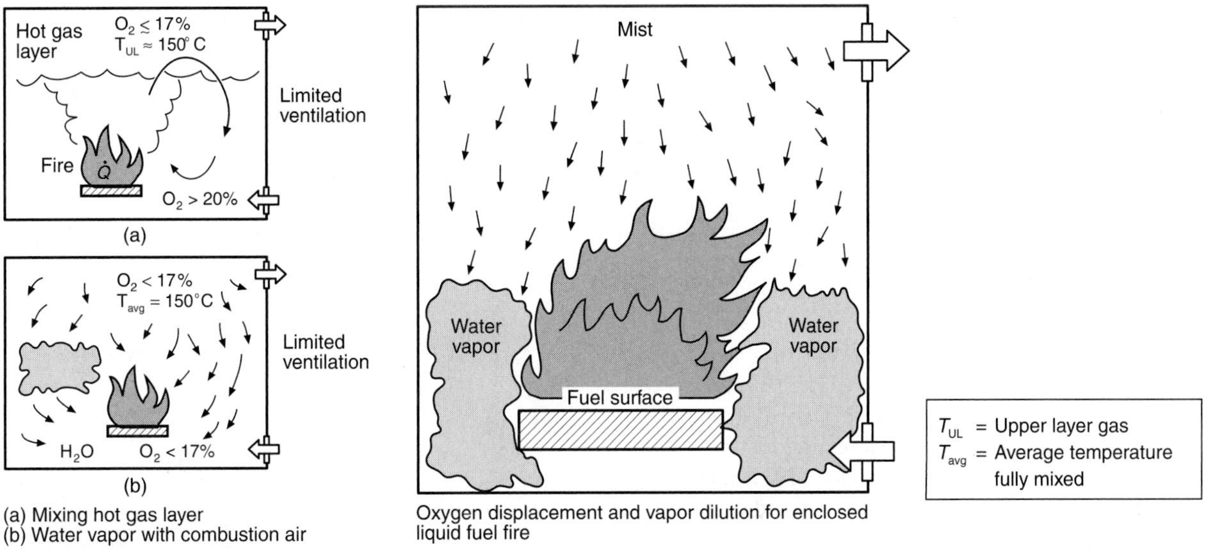

FIGURE 16.8.5 Enclosure Effects

The conflicting influences of cooling, inerting, dilution, and enhanced turbulence and fuel mixing lead to a degree of unpredictability in the effects of water mist on gas-phase burning.

There is reason to be concerned that a water mist system that is unable to extinguish a liquid fuel pool or spray fire could instead increase the heat release rate of the fire. Further research is needed to investigate the conditions under which flare-up or flame invigoration occurs.

Enclosure Effects. Enclosure effects enhance the performance of water mist systems. The enhanced performance can be attributed to restricted ventilation and heat entrapment. A fire in a small compartment reduces the average oxygen concentration in the compartment by several percentage points within the first few minutes of growth. Thus, a fire that is large enough to quickly reduce the average oxygen concentration in a compartment could be considered to be poorly ventilated. The addition of a small amount of water mist and resulting increase in water vapor further reduce the oxygen available to support combustion. Thus, an underventilated fire in an enclosure is "easier" to extinguish than a well-ventilated unenclosed fire.

Figure 16.8.5 illustrates how enclosure effects contribute to fire suppression with water mist. Heat from the fire trapped in the compartment evaporates the finest portion of the mist, so that the expanding water vapor pushes the air out of the compartment. Then oxygen-depleted, hot fire gases at the ceiling of the compartment are cooled by the mist and pushed down to floor level, mixing water vapor, oxygen-depleted air, and water drops with the fire. The combined effects of reduced combustion efficiency and flame cooling usually result in extinguishment. With enclosure effects, it is possible to extinguish even shielded fires with low-momentum sprays in heavily obstructed compartments. Where enclosure effects can be relied on, the flux density required for extinguishment can be as much as 10 times lower than that required for unconfined, well-ventilated fires.[7,44]

A phenomenon associated with enclosure effects can lead to very rapid pressure change between the fire compartment and the surrounding spaces. Water mist injected by a deluge system uniformly through the hot gas layer causes a rapid cooling of the gas layer. The accompanying volume change of the cooled gases creates a negative pressure inside the compartment relative to surrounding spaces. This is illustrated in Figure 16.8.6.[54] Depending on the temperature and depth of the hot layer, the rapid cooling results in an instantaneous volume reduction and

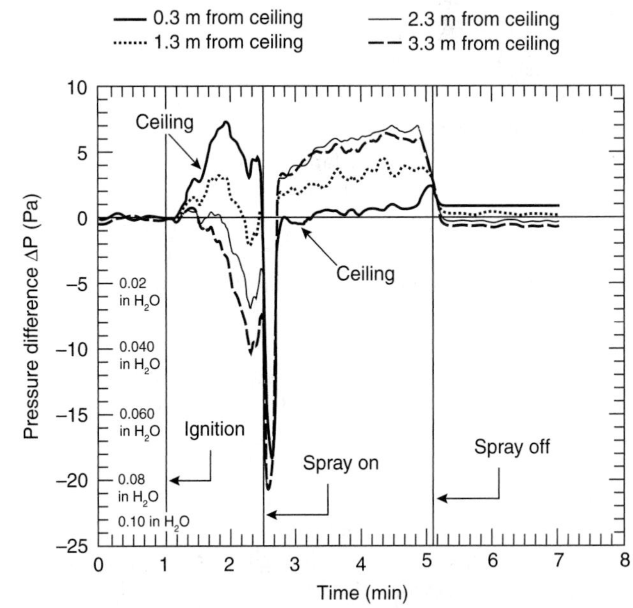

FIGURE 16.8.6 Generation of a Negative-Pressure Pulse in an Enclosure After the Injection of Water Mist into a Hot Gas Layer

negative pressure change that can suck in the windows or walls of a tight enclosure. The potential damage to a compartment is minimized by early release of the water mist system. If there is a delay in activation of the mist system, such as may occur with manual release of a local application system, the negative-pressure spike may be severe enough to damage the compartment ceiling, walls, windows, or doors.

In the case of an unconfined and, therefore, well-ventilated fire there are no enclosure effects to create conditions favorable to extinguishment. Water mist can achieve extinguishment only if the spray has strong enough momentum to push water droplets and vapor into the flame to the fuel surface. Thus, the absence of enclosure effects creates the need for a local application system. Local application systems typically have different spray characteristics, higher flow rates, and closer nozzle spacing than total-compartment application systems. Nozzle dynamics must compensate for the lack of confinement of vitiated gases, heat, and water vapor.

Time to Extinguishment. The time needed to extinguish a fire with water mist varies with the fuel type, compartment geometry, drop size distribution, momentum, and application rate of the water mist. Water mist extinguishes liquid fuel pool fires in 10 to 20 seconds, using small amounts of water. The top part of Figure 16.8.4, for example, shows a 600-kW, unenclosed diesel pool fire that was extinguished in less than 60 seconds by water mist. Such successes occur in circumstances in which all suppression properties act together (i.e., oxygen displacement, flame cooling, radiant heat blocking, and vapor dilution).

Rapid extinguishment is not characteristic of all water mist fire suppression systems, however. There are circumstances in which it can take several minutes to extinguish a fire without it being considered a failure. For example, the IMO machinery space test protocol requires extinguishment within 15 minutes. One example is where flame cooling cannot extinguish the fire immediately but, after several minutes, the buildup of water vapor in the compartment (an enclosure effect) combines with flame cooling to bring about extinguishment. With combustibles that form a char layer (e.g., fabric, wood, plastics, or electrical wiring), the fire may not be extinguished immediately. Fuel wetting begins to reduce the size of the fire and it is eventually extinguished. As long as the mist limits the heat release rate, causes the fire to progressively diminish in intensity, and cools the compartment, the level of fire control can be considered adequate.[55]

The relationships among fire size, compartment volume, and time to extinguishment are well described in work by Back et al.[56] Figure 16.8.7[56] shows test results for a series of machinery room fire tests conducted for the U.S. Coast Guard. The data were analyzed to develop a prediction for time to extinguishment as a function of fire size in different size compartments.[56] Fires were extinguished solely through the mechanism of oxygen depletion. It is evident from Figure 16.8.7 that smaller fires take longer to extinguish than larger fires and that increasing the compartment volume increases the time to extinguishment. For each size of compartment shown, there is a fire that is too small to extinguish (i.e., an "unextinguishable fire"). The size of the unextinguishable fire is a function of the size of the compartment. The relationship illustrates that there is a practical limit to what can be achieved through extinguishment by total flooding alone. That limit is reached when the unextinguishable fire is either too large to be extinguished by hand or when it is likely to do unacceptably severe damage to the contents of the space.

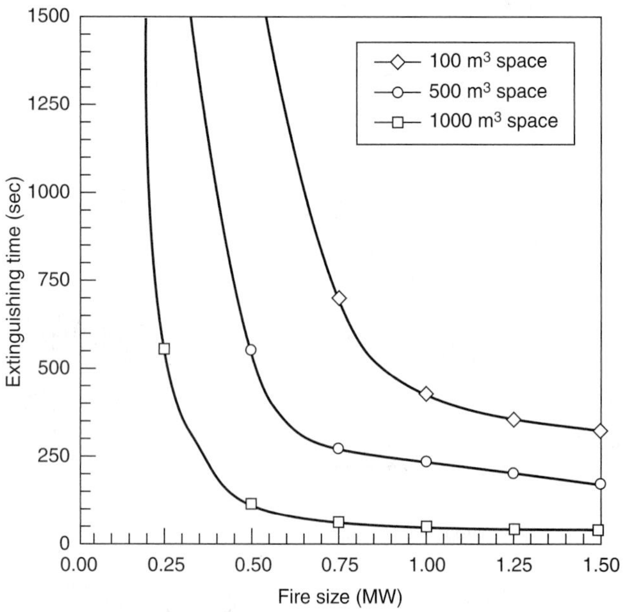

FIGURE 16.8.7 Relationship Between Fire Size, Enclosure Volume, and Time to Extinguishment of Fires in an IMO Machinery Room Test Enclosure

If the damage expected to be caused by the unextinguishable fire is unacceptably high, the system design must convert to a combination of total flooding and local application. It means that it is not sufficient to rely solely on the oxygen depletion mechanism of extinguishment. The other extinguishing mechanisms permitted by direct local application of spray must be unleashed.

Duration of Discharge. There are reasons to flow water from a system for a longer period of time than the minimum extinguishing time. First, extinguishment times vary even under controlled test conditions, and conditions in real compartments cannot be closely controlled. Second, with liquid fuel fires, reignition may occur if hot surfaces are not sufficiently cooled or if there is a remnant of flame in a shielded area. In principle, the flow should be sustained until it is confirmed that all fire has been extinguished and reignition will not occur. Such confirmation is difficult to obtain in real fire conditions. Practically, it is tempting to assign an arbitrary minimum flow duration, based on conservative assumptions about the probability of fire being extinguished. NFPA 750 recommends that the water supply be sized based on a 30 minute minimum flow duration. An exception is provided for preengineered systems, for which the minimum duration must be sufficient for two complete discharges. The length of one complete discharge is determined by the full-scale testing on which the listing was based. A second exception allows a fire protection engineer to use standard methods of fire hazard analysis to determine the appropriate design duration. The author's experience has been that a careful fire hazard analysis for a specific application invariably results in a decision to enforce the 30 minute minimum duration.

Spray Characteristics

The term *water mist* implies a very fine water spray that remains suspended in air for an extended period of time. The term reflects one of the qualities of a spray (i.e., the drop sizes are small) relative to rain or to sprinkler sprays, for example. This one characteristic of drop size is not the only characteristic of a spray that must be controlled in order to generate an effective fire suppression medium. There are three other characteristics that influence its effectiveness as an extinguishing agent: (1) the density of the spray (mass of suspended water per unit volume of space), (2) the velocity with which it is delivered to the seat of the fire, and (3) the quality of the water itself (which may contain dissolved additives to enhance suppression effectiveness). The following discussion includes all four characteristics of a water mist for fire suppression purposes:

1. Drop size distribution
2. Flux density
3. Spray momentum
4. Additives

Drop Size Distribution. It is difficult to discuss water mist without measuring and analyzing its most notable feature, the fact that it is made up of very small water drops. At the time of this writing, except for computer modeling, the drop size distribution of the spray cannot be used explicitly as a variable in the design of a water mist system. That stage awaits the results of further research work. The value in knowing the drop size distribution (and other characteristics) of a water spray lies in the fact that it relates directly to system performance: how spray is affected by obstructions, the dynamics of the spray interaction with the fire, and how extinguishment occurs. For computer modeling of the dynamics of suppression with water mist, a quantitative measure of the drop size characteristics of the spray is essential.

The term *drop size distribution* refers to the range of drop sizes contained in a representative sample of a spray or mist. There is a distribution of small and large drops, which varies with location in the spray as well as with time. For a continuous discharge, the distribution of drop sizes changes with distance from the source as drops collide, evaporate, or hit surfaces and fall out. For a short-duration discharge, the distribution measured at a point in space changes with time as the larger drops pass through quickly, leaving increasingly finer drops, which move at lower velocity.

There are a number of ways to present data about drop size distributions of sprays.[42,57,58] It is customary in some fields to refer to the size of particles in a spray by a single drop size parameter, such as a "Sauter Mean Diameter (SMD)" or "Volumetric Median Diameter (VMD)." Such terms reveal little about the *range* of drop sizes in a spray, however. It is important to know about the presence of larger-diameter drops in a spray to avoid splashing on the surface of a liquid fuel, for example, or perhaps to know about the potential to achieve fuel wetting.

NFPA 750 has adopted the cumulative percent volume (CPV) versus diameter curve to represent the distribution of drop sizes in a water mist. Reasons for this choice are that (1) the cumulative percent volume plot visually reveals the range of sizes, and (2) the volume distribution converts readily to mass distribution, which is the most relevant term for analyzing heat transfer and evaporation rates using computer modeling. Figure 16.8.8 illustrates cumulative percent volume curves, measured 3 ft (0.9 m) from the nozzle, for several nozzles used in water mist systems.[22] The weighted average CPV curves were obtained using the method described in NFPA 750.

Commercial software conforming to ASTM E799, *Standard Practice for Determining Data Criteria and Processing for Liquid Drop Size Analysis,* for particle size measurement,[57] provides output in several formats, one of which is the cumulative percent volume versus diameter curve. For comparison with other sprays, the "S" shape of the curve can be roughly

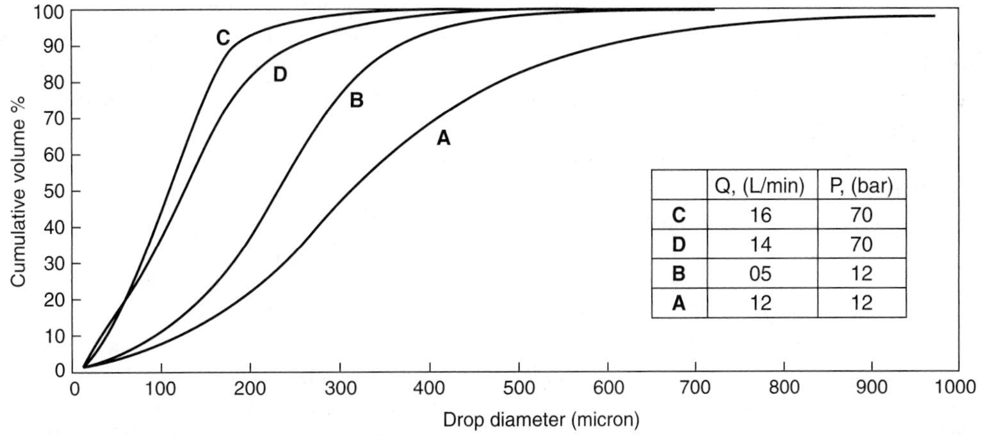

FIGURE 16.8.8 Statistically Weighted Cumulative Percent Volume Versus Drop Size Distribution Plots for Two Low-Pressure (A and B) and Two High-Pressure (C and D) Water Mist Nozzles

described using only three representative diameters: Dv0.1, Dv0.5, and Dv0.9. These parameters appear as standard output from a particle size analyzer conforming to ASTM E799. For a spray with a Dv0.9 of 400 microns, it means that "90 percent of the volume of a sample of the spray, at the sampling location, is contained in drops with diameters less than 400 microns." The cumulative percent volume distribution versus diameter curves can also be expressed as a mathematical function, which can be used in computer modeling of water spray/fire plume interactions.[42,58,59]

A method of obtaining a statistically representative measure of drop size distribution is described in the Appendix of NFPA 750. It is intended that the listing agency conduct drop size distribution measurements as part of component testing. The listing agency would then use the initial distribution readings as a baseline for ongoing checking for consistency in manufactured nozzles. The drop size distribution is measured 1 m from the nozzle, where the spray is expected to have the average properties of the spray elsewhere in the compartment. At that distance the cone is close to its maximum diameter, the entrained air has acquired a velocity, and the velocities of large- and small-diameter drops equalize.

This weighting approach, as described in NFPA 750, is necessary because individual readings may vary widely. If listing laboratories checked drop size distributions of manufacturers' nozzles annually, based on single point readings, they could see large variations that suggest changes in manufacturing quality, where in fact the variation could be due to the randomness of single point measurements. In contrast, a statistically blended curve will be more reproducible over time. Figure 16.8.8 shows statistically weighted cumulative percent volume distribution curves for two low-pressure and two high-pressure commercially available water mist nozzles.

Early research with fine water sprays was motivated by interest in using small drop sizes to enhance evaporation and heat extraction, using small volumes of water.[1,2] The research focused primarily on liquid fuel pool fires, for which the desired benefits are achievable with sprays that have most of the mass contained in drops of diameters of 400 microns or less.[48] Recent interest in using water mist for applications involving solid fuels, however, suggests that sprays with drop sizes greater than 400 microns need to be included. Drop sizes larger than 400 microns provide for fuel wetting, an important mechanism in extinguishing fires in solid fuels and charring substances. For that reason, the definition of water mist in NFPA 750 includes sprays for which 99 percent of the volume of the spray is contained in droplets less than 1000 microns in diameter ($Dv0.99 < 1000\ \mu$). Water mist systems, therefore, are applicable to a wide range of fire scenarios, including both liquid and solid fuels.

Classification of Water Sprays by Drop Size Distribution. The definition of water mist in NFPA 750 is so broad that some important differences in the qualities of sprays are disguised. It includes, for example, all water sprays used in NFPA 15, *Standard for Water Spray Fixed Systems for Fire Protection,* sprays produced by standard sprinklers operating at high pressure, and light mists suitable for greenhouse misting and HVAC humidification systems. In addition, the sprays referred to here are much coarser than what a meteorologist or physicist would view as a true mist.

The drop size distribution that will be most effective in one fire scenario will not necessarily be the best for a second scenario. There is no "one size fits all." The type of fuel (solid or liquid), the compartment dimensions, the velocity at which the mist is delivered, and the performance objective (e.g., temperature control versus extinguishment) collectively determine the most appropriate drop size distribution for a given application.

As a means of allowing distinctions to be made among coarser and finer sprays across the 1000 micron spectrum of the NFPA 750 definition of water mist, this chapter adopts a classification system that subdivides water mist into Class 1, 2, or 3 mists, according to their representative cumulative percent volume (CPV) versus diameter distribution curve (Figure 16.8.9).

This classification is introduced as a utilitarian necessity. It facilitates talking and thinking about sprays of significantly different character without referring to single-point parameters such as Sauter Mean diameter, volumetric, or numeric mean diameters. If a spray is reported as having a volumetric median diameter of 500 microns or a Sauter Mean diameter of 400 microns, the information is incomplete. Those single-point parameters do not tell us about the range of drop sizes in the spray or the steepness of the curve. Furthermore, it is difficult to say whether a 100-micron difference in volumetric mean diameter is significant in any way with respect to suppression effectiveness. The classifications of Classes 1, 2, and 3 set broad bands that describe the range of drop sizes and the relative steepness of the CPV curve. The classifications permit immediate visualization of the range of drop sizes in a spray.

The NFPA 750 committee agreed to delete reference to the spray classification system that was originally published in the Appendix of NFPA 750 in 1996 for the reason that some authorities having jurisdiction and specifying engineers imposed an interpretation on the system that Class 1 mists were superior in some way to Classes 2 and 3 mists. This misinterpretation of the meaning of spray drop size characteristics was used by some manufacturers to unjustifiably denigrate the products of their competitors. This misinterpretation of Classes 1, 2, and 3 sprays was damaging to some parties and to the promulgation of sensible engineering for water mist system design in general.

On the basis that the description of sprays as Class 1, 2, or 3 is of practical value to fire protection engineers working with water sprays, the classification system is described here. The boundaries defining the three classifications are shown in Figure 16.8.9.

A spray for which the $Dv0.9 \leq 200$ microns is a Class 1 mist, that is, $(^1Dv0.9) \leq 200$. This category includes the finest water mists. In general, one expects that the fineness of a spray is obtained at the expense of mass flow rate and spray velocity. As shown in Figure 16.8.8, however, there are a number of commercial water mist nozzles that produce Class 1 sprays at the same mass flow rate as Class 3 sprays and with a higher initial velocity.[22] Class 1 sprays can be generated at low pressures or high pressures with twin-fluid, single-fluid, pressure jet, and impingement nozzles and flashing of superheated water.

Again with reference to Figure 16.8.9, the CPV curve for a Class 2 mist falls in the range $200 < (^2Dv0.9) \leq 400$ microns.

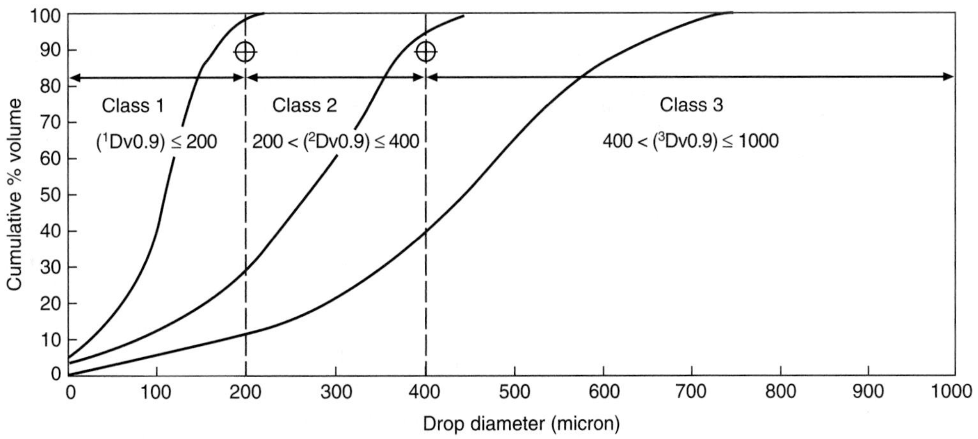

FIGURE 16.8.9 Classification of Drop Size Distributions—Classes 1, 2, and 3

Such sprays can be generated by low- and intermediate-pressure, pressure-jet nozzles; twin-fluid nozzles; and impingement nozzles.

A Class 3 mist has a CPV curve that lies in the range 400 < (^{3}Dv0.9) ≤ 1000 microns. Such sprays are typically generated by impingement nozzles of various sorts, including low- and intermediate-pressure, small-orifice nozzles. High mass flow rates are possible.

The relationship between drop size distribution and extinguishing capacity of a water mist is complex. In general, Class 1 and Class 2 mists are successful at extinguishing liquid fuel pool fires and spray fires without agitation of liquid pool surfaces. Class 3 sprays also extinguished pool fires. Class A fires can be extinguished with Class 1 mists if the velocity is high, the burning is surficial, or enclosure effects enhance the degree of oxygen reduction. This evidence confirms that drop size distribution alone does not determine the ability of a spray to extinguish a given fire. Factors such as fuel properties, enclosure effects, spray flux density, and spray velocity (momentum) are all involved in determining whether a fire will be extinguished. For this reason, NFPA 750 could not assign an optimum drop size distribution as a universal design variable for water mist systems for a specific hazard. Unlike with standard sprinklers, the flux density that successfully achieves the performance criteria of a fire test will vary depending on the drop size distribution, spray velocity, and mass flow rate of the nozzle.

Flux Density. The ability of water mist to extinguish a fire depends only partly on having the appropriate drop size and spray velocity. It also requires that the mass of water spray that interacts with the fire be sufficient to absorb a critical portion of the heat given off by the fire. Spray flux density is, therefore, an important characteristic of water mist for fire suppression systems. It can be expressed in *volume units* of gpm/ft^3 (L/min/m^3), although it is more practical to measure it as *area units* of gpm/ft^2 (L/min/m^2).

Expression of spray density in volume units is useful for the limited case of a total-flooding system in a compartment with no obstructions and nozzles with uniform distribution within their spray cones. With few exceptions, the flux density distribution of mist within a single spray cone is nonhomogeneous. When mixed with overlapping spray cones, air movement caused by the fire plume and the nozzles themselves and the deposition of mist on obstructions results in an unpredictable volume concentration of spray at any point in the compartment. It is, therefore, difficult to establish a meaningful correlation between volume concentration of mist and extinguishing effectiveness.

On the other hand, the average flux density in area units of gpm/ft^2 (L/min/m^2) can be measured easily using a grid of collection cups to measure the volume of liquid collected per unit of area per unit time. It is possible to relate success or failure to extinguish a fire to the flux density measured at that point (under nonfire conditions). It is, therefore, more useful to express flux density in area units, as a design variable, than to express it in volume units. Both representations are poor approximations of the actual flux density during extinguishment, however. That number is likely to vary dynamically with fire conditions and spray velocity and, therefore, can at best be used only as a rough design guide.

The density distributions from spray nozzles are far from uniform. Figure 16.8.10 shows an example of the flux density distribution on a plane 9.9 ft (3.0 m) below two SSC ¾ 7G5 nozzles, spaced 6.6 ft (2.0 m) apart, discharging 9.2 gpm (35 L/min) each.[60] These nozzles have been proposed for a "waterfog" system in a hydraulic equipment compartment on British (Royal Navy) submarines. At 100 psi (6.8 bar), the nozzles produce a Class 2 spray. The area covered by the spray cone at the level of collection was about 5 ft (1.5 m) square, for an area of 25 ft^2 (2.25 m^2). The nominal flux density for this array is calculated as the nozzle discharge divided by the coverage area of the spray cone at the plane of interest. In this case, the nominal flux density was 0.37 gpm/ft^2 (15.1 L/min/m^2). The measured flux density ranged from 0.42 gpm/ft^2 (17.2 L/min/m^2) directly below the nozzle, to 0.07 gpm/ft^2 (3 L/min/m^2) at the outer edge, and about 0.16 gpm/ft^2 (6.6 L/min/m^2) midway between the two nozzles. Thus, within a distance of less than 3.3 ft (1 m), the flux density distribution from these two nozzles ranged from 0.2 to 1.1 times the nominal flux density.

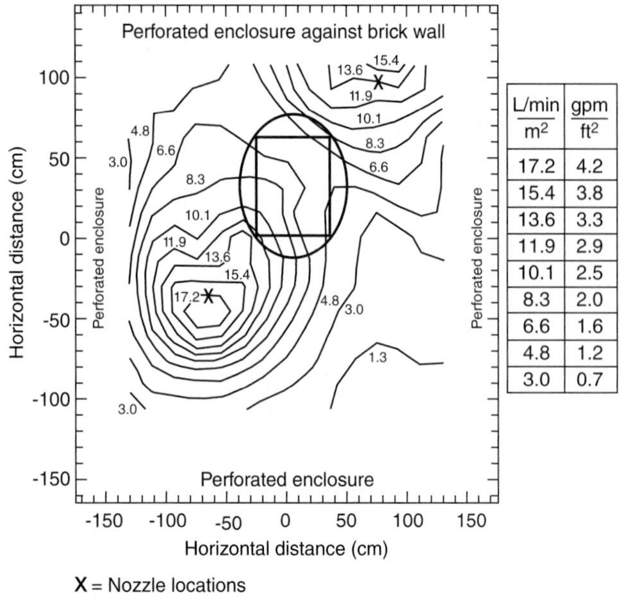

FIGURE 16.8.10 Actual Flux Density Measured 9.9 ft (3.0 m) Below Two SSC ¾ 7G5 Nozzles, Spaced 6.6 ft (2.0 m) Apart, Discharging at a Nominal Flux Density of 0.37 gpm/ft^2 (15.1 L/min/m^2)

The extinguishing effectiveness of these two nozzles on heptane and diesel fuel pan fires varied with fire location.[60] Directly beneath the nozzles, where both flux density and spray direction (momentum) were sufficient to overpower the fire plume, all fires were extinguished in less than 10 seconds. Placed midway between the nozzles, the diesel fires took longer to extinguish, and some heptane fires were not extinguished. Midway between nozzles, the overlapping spray cones create a zone of turbulence in which spray goes in all directions. The flux density of 0.16 gpm/ft^2 (6.6 L/min/m^2) would likely have been sufficient had the spray momentum been better aimed against the fire plume. The strong heptane fire plume could rise through the mist and deflect the rest of the spray cone.[59]

These results illustrate that the extinguishing effectiveness of water mist can only be related to actual, not nominal, flux density. Many nozzles concentrate a high percentage of the water spray into the center of the cone area. This occurs because a negative pressure develops in the inner core of a hollow-cone spray, which draws droplets from the outer fringes into the center. Further distortion of actual from nominal flux densities occurs because of obstructions. Obstructions scrub water mist from suspension, drastically reducing the flux density. Obstructions also deflect the spray randomly, reducing its momentum and rendering it less effective.

Spray Momentum. The difference between success and failure of a fire suppression test can often be attributed to variations in spray *momentum.* Three factors that constitute the momentum of the spray are (1) the spray velocity, (2) its direction relative to the fire plume, and (3) the mass of the water droplets transported into the flame or onto the fuel surface. Velocity is a vector quantity, which has both magnitude and direction. The more control that can be exercised over momentum, the greater the ability to control total water requirements, time to extinguishment, water damage, and overall system reliability.

The extinguishing capacity of water mist is the result of a complex interaction of fuel properties, enclosure effects, drop size distribution, flux density, and spray momentum. Of course, the velocity cannot be too great or liquid fuels could be displaced, worsening fire conditions. The efficiency of a spray generation method is highest when the maximum amount of the spray has the desired directional properties relative to the fire plume. Control over momentum, then, depends not only on the nozzle characteristics but also on the degree to which nozzles can be strategically positioned around the fire.

One very important aspect of the selection of a mist generation method is the degree of control it allows over the directionality of the spray produced. If oriented strategically, narrow-cone-angle sprays direct more of their flow toward the fire source than wide-angle-spray cones. This was demonstrated in a series of tests conducted by NIST[61] and at NRCC, involving fires in computer cabinets.[62] The fire was located between two parallel printed circuit boards in an array of circuit boards, as illustrated in Figure 16.8.11. The fires were extinguished only when the spray direction was close to parallel to the circuit boards. A single, wide-spray-angle nozzle mounted in an open space above the circuit boards could only extinguish fires in a narrow band on either side of the vertical axis of the cone, in which the spray could enter the narrow spaces between the circuit boards.[62] As the horizontal component of the spray increased toward the edges of the array, the spray could not penetrate the space between the circuit boards. Increasing the nozzle pressure and mass flow rate did not widen the effective zone: it simply increased its depth. When the wide-angle nozzle was replaced with a series of closely spaced, narrow-spray-angle nozzles, the effective zone was widened to include the entire cabinet. By converting from a "fan-shaped" distribution of spray to a linear distribution of parallel sprays, it became possible to extinguish fires between any of the circuit boards with very little water.

The experiment described here illustrates that controlling the directionality of the spray can be more important than controlling the drop size distribution or mass flow rate. Drop size distributions can vary by 100 microns (Dv0.9) or more and be apparently equally effective. Most water supply systems deliver more water than is needed for the minimum performance of a single nozzle, so there is no penalty for being overdesigned on flow rate. There is little to be gained by designing to narrow tolerances on those parameters. On the other hand, small modifications to the direction of application of the spray can mean the difference between success or failure to extinguish.

Additives. The chemical nature of the water supplied to the nozzles influences the performance of water mist as a fire suppressant. Experiments at NRCC demonstrated that the extinguishing effectiveness of a water mist was enhanced by addition of sodium chloride to the water.[48] Mist made with seawater (2.5% by weight sodium chloride solution) extinguished diesel fuel pan fires at lower flux densities, and 40 to 50 percent faster,

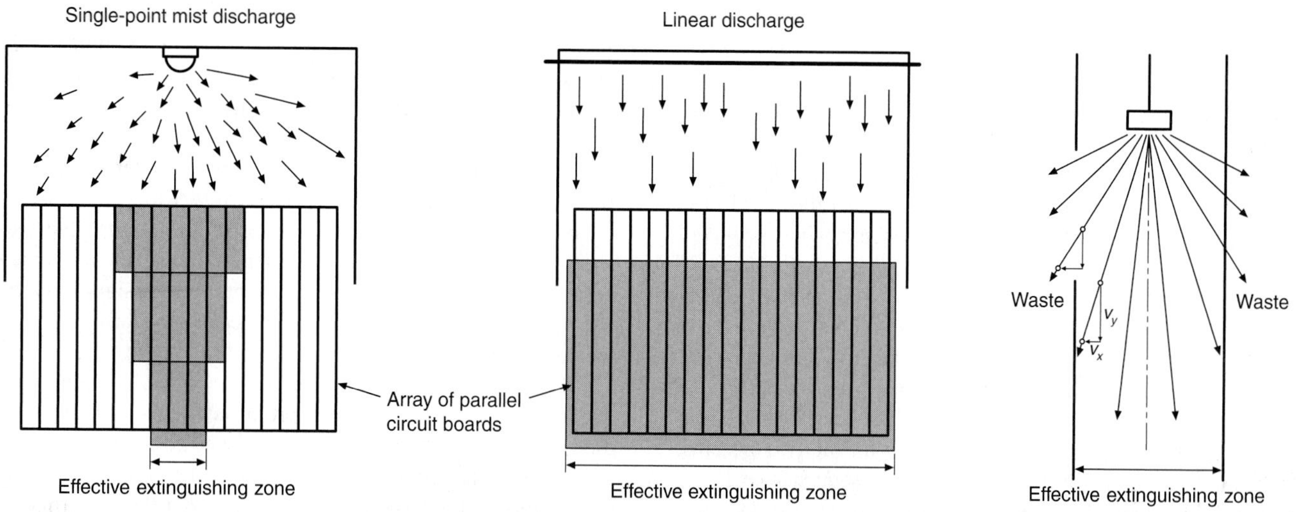

FIGURE 16.8.11 Effect of Controlling Spray Directionality or Momentum in Extinguishing Fires in Printed Circuit Boards

than mist made with fresh water. In addition, the seawater mist was less influenced by obstructions than fresh-water mist. One possible explanation for the improved performance is that dissolved alkali salts crystallize in the flame zone as drops evaporate. The salt crystals are small enough to be in the optimum effectiveness range of dry chemical extinguishing agents,[63] many of which are alkali salts. This hypothesis suggests that other alkali salts, which are better dry chemical fire suppressants than sodium chloride, could significantly improve the extinguishing effectiveness of water mist. Various products are already sold on the basis of their ability to enhance suppression effectiveness of water sprays.

The addition of a low percentage of a film-forming agent (e.g., 0.3% AFFF) greatly improves the effectiveness of water mist on hydrocarbon pool fires. This is particularly useful for suppressing spill fires in bilge areas that are sheltered from the water spray.

The chemicals that could be added to the water supply for a water mist system include antifreeze, film-forming agents, Class A or B foaming agents, surfactants, or emulsifiers to increase penetration of water into solid fuels, fire-retardant salts, biocides to prevent algae growth in stored water, and so on. The benefit provided by the additive may be offset by the introduction of secondary problems, for example, such as increased corrosivity or increased toxicity. The tolerance of equipment for increased corrosivity must be evaluated by the property owner/insurer on the basis of degree of corrosivity and the acceptable level of loss. Toxicity concerns, on the other hand, invoke government regulation. At the time of the aviation industry studies on aircraft passenger cabin water mist systems,[35] the U.S. surgeon general expressed concerns about the effects of inhalation of fine water spray on people. Those concerns were raised also by the U.S. Environmental Protection Agency (EPA) when water mist was being evaluated under the Significant New Alternatives Policy Program (SNAP) as a halon replacement. In response to the EPA concerns, the Halon Alternatives Research Committee (HARC), with the participation of the NFPA 750 committee, convened a health panel of medical experts to review data on this potential hazard.

The HARC Health Panel Report[64] concluded that water mist supplied by water, equivalent in quality to potable water (i.e., containing no additives other than those used in drinking water), or by natural seawater, poses no health risk to persons exposed to it, either under circumstances of a fire or due to nonfire actuation. The EPA found the panel's findings were credible and adopted its conclusions as the basis to a ruling. The resultant U.S. Federal Register regulation[65] recognizes that water mist systems supplied by potable water or natural seawater are "acceptable without restriction," as both a halon 1301 substitute in occupied spaces and as a streaming agent to replace halon 1211.

Water mist systems with additives are of interest for applications such as the engine compartments of vehicles and in machinery spaces. The EPA has accepted the use of water mist combined with a small percentage of a surfactant (water mist/Surfactant Blend A) for such applications in unoccupied areas.[65] Recent tests of surfactants used to improve suppression effectiveness by DuPont confirmed that their particular additive is not harmful to health.[66] Other additives, such as antifreeze, foaming agents, and fire-retardant salts, will be limited to unoccupied spaces unless the proponent provides EPA with the results of a medical peer review panel study addressing the toxicity question.

DESIGN OF WATER MIST SYSTEMS

The present level of understanding of the interaction of water mist with fire, obstructions, ventilation conditions, and compartment features is not sufficient to permit design of water mist systems by "first principles." Ideally, a first principles design would assume that there was a fixed relationship between the fire scenario, compartment geometry, ventilation, and application rate of water mist with a given drop size distribution. This relationship would hold regardless of the specific details of individual manufacturers' equipment. Such an ideal relationship has not been established for water mist systems. There is considerable variation in the design parameters associated with the systems of different manufacturers, even when they have supposedly optimized their systems to the same fire test protocol.[67] In the absence of a large empirical database of design criteria and of a set of general principles that applies to all water mist hardware, NFPA 750 requires that all water mist system designs be linked to formal fire tests. Testing has shown that the performance of water mist systems is dependent on the specific manufacturer's equipment, particularly the nozzle design. One manufacturer might pass a fire test program at a particular flow rate and nozzle spacing. Another might operate at a lower pressure but have a higher flow rate and closer nozzle spacing to pass the same test. If one calculates the average flux density for the two systems, they may differ by a factor of three![67] Consequently, it is not yet possible to see convergence between manufacturers' systems toward generic design criteria such as a consistent nominal flux density for a particular fire scenario. The criteria are dependent on the manufacturer's choice of equipment. It appears that barely perceptible differences in atomization, spray cone angle, and velocity influence the performance of the system. The only way to be sure that a particular manufacturer's water mist system will work in a given application is to conduct fire tests with the manufacturer's equipment.

If a water mist system is listed for an application, the system design criteria and performance objectives have been validated through fire tests conducted by a recognized testing laboratory. Table 16.8.2 shows a list of fire test protocols recognized in North America and Europe. Test protocols are intended to test the limits of performance of systems against a realistic range of conditions, including worst-case scenarios, and to establish agreed-on and measurable performance objectives. Considerable thought and experience go into achieving consensus on the test scenarios. In North America, end users of water mist technology tend to rely on third-party listings by Factory Mutual Research Corporation (FM Global Research) or Underwriters Laboratories (UL) to confirm suitability. In Europe end users are likely to accept the results of ad hoc or specially designed fire testing. It is always important that the test program put sufficient effort into looking for failure conditions, limits of applicability, and breadth of criteria for judging acceptability. Ad hoc tests will be very specific to an application. There are many ad hoc water mist test efforts that form the basis of design for water mist systems. Examples include local application systems;[68] high-voltage cable tunnels; railway tunnels;[69,70] heritage properties, libraries, and archival storage on fixed shelving,[71,72] electronic equipment rooms,[73] computer room underfloor areas;[74] aircraft cargo bays;[75] and outdoor transformers.[76] Many of the ad hoc test programs have the potential to become formal or consensus test protocols.

NFPA 750 describes a number of fire test protocols in detail. It should be noted that the criteria by which systems are deemed acceptable are decided by consensus of a committee. Successful performance does not necessarily mean extinguishment of the fire. For example, the IMO tests for accommodation spaces and public spaces on ships require only that the fire be controlled for a period of 10 minutes. At the end of 10 minutes, the fire is manually extinguished and a damage assessment made. Fire extent and damage to the test materials must be within certain limits. During that 10 minutes, the fire continues to burn, and if the water mist system is shut off, the fire will regrow. The IMO machinery space protocol, on the other hand, does require extinguishment of all fires, including small, hidden bilge fires. Both FM Global Research and UL have their own versions of the original IMO machinery space tests. They have listed systems without requiring extinguishment of the smallest shielded pan fire. Unfortunately, it is not certain that the designer and the end user will understand the significance of such differences for the application at hand.

It is not advisable to rely on a generalized listing without checking that the performance promised by the listing meets the end user's actual needs. The fire protection engineer must confirm that the application is similar to the conditions of the test protocol. He or she must also check that the performance criteria used to judge pass or fail in the test protocol are compatible with the end user's needs in the actual installation. In some cases the performance requirements of the listing may be lower than what the end user really needs. Measures to upgrade performance will be required. To determine exactly what upgrade measures might be required to raise the level of performance without doing further testing the designer will have to apply first principles of fire science.

A second problem with the current approach is that a simplified test protocol can never capture the details of all possible field conditions. For example, the IMO Machinery Space test compartment contains only a mockup of a large engine; it does not contain any of the ducts, cable trays, and overhead piping that may clutter a real machinery space. Yet the design spacing determined in the mockup is applied rigorously in all applications. Furthermore, the manufacturers may be able to fine-tune their systems to meet the narrow performance criteria of the test protocol. The tolerance for differences between the test arrangement and real spaces is not known. Rather than achieving better performance through more efficient mist nozzles, we may simply be peeling away the safety margin. Once installed in a real machinery compartment with more overhead clutter or different ventilation opening than the test setup, one manufacturer's system may be within a hair's breadth of losing control. Another manufacturer's system may be more tolerant of variances. It would be reassuring if we were not so entirely dependent on the formalized "design by fire testing" approach.

METHODS OF GENERATING WATER MIST

Methods to generate water mist range from simple to elaborate. Some of the more elaborate methods include high-speed spinning discs, ultrasonic vibrations, flashing and recondensation of superheated liquids, rapid release of dissolved gases, and explosives. For fire suppression purposes, the choice of method is narrowed by the fact that the mass flow rates and velocities needed to be effective are beyond the capacity of some methods. The methods that are practical for fire suppression systems are those that break up water into drops smaller than 1000 microns at mass flow rates and spray velocities

TABLE 16.8.2 Fire Test Protocols for Water Mist Fire Protection Systems as of May 2006

Agency	*Water Mist Fire Tests Protocol*
1. International Maritime Organization (IMO)	IMO MSC/Circular 668: Alternative Arrangements for Halon Fire Extinguishing Systems in Machinery Spaces and Pump-Rooms. a. Appendix A: Component Manufacturing Standards of Equivalent Water-Based Fire Extinguishing Systems (1994). b. Appendix B: Interim Test Method for Fire Testing Equivalent Water-Based Fire-Extinguishing Systems for Machinery Spaces of Category A and Cargo Pump-Rooms (1994). As amended in MSC/Circ. 728: Amendments to the Test Method for Equivalent Water-Based Fire-Extinguishing Systems for Machinery Spaces of Category A and Cargo Pump-Rooms contained in MSC/Circ. 668, Appendix B (June 1996). IMO Res. A.800 (19) Revised Guidelines for Approval of Sprinkler Systems Equivalent to that referred to in SOLAS Regulations II-2/12. a. Appendix 1—Component Manufacturing Standards for Water Mist Nozzles. b. Appendix 2—Fire Test Procedures for Equivalent Sprinkler Systems in Accommodation, Public Space and Service Areas on Passenger Ships (December 1995). MSC/Circ. 913, Guidelines for the Approval of Fixed Water Based Local Application Systems for Use in Category A Machinery Spaces, 4 June 1999. MSC/Circ. 914, Guidelines for the Approval of Alternative Fixed Water Based Fire-Fighting Systems for Special Category Spaces, 4 June 1999.
2. FM Global, Approval Standard for Water Mist Systems, Class Number 5560, May 2005	a. Appendix A, B, C: Fire Tests for Water Mist Systems for the Protection of Machinery Spaces, Special Hazard Machinery Spaces, Combustion Turbines with Volumes Up to and Including 2825 ft^3 (80 m^3) (respectively). b. Appendices D, E, F: Fire Tests for Water Mist Systems for the Protection of Machinery Spaces, Special Hazard Machinery Spaces, Combustion Turbines with Volumes Up to and Including 9175 ft^3 (260 m^3) (respectively). c. Appendix G: Fire Tests for Water Mist Systems for the Protection of Machinery Spaces and Special Hazard Machinery Spaces with Volumes Exceeding 9175 ft^3 (260 m^3). d. Appendix H: Fire Tests for Water Mist Systems for the Protection of Combustion Turbines with Volumes Exceeding 9175 ft^3 (260 m^3). e. Appendix I: Fire Tests for Water Mist Systems for the Protection of Light Hazard Occupancies. f. Appendix J: Fire Tests for Water Mist Systems for the Protection of Wet Benches and Other Similar Processing Equipment. g. Appendix K: Fire Tests for Water Mist Systems for the Protection of Local Applications. h. Appendix L: Fire Tests for Water Mist Systems for the Protection of Industrial Oil Cookers. i. Appendix M: Fire Tests for Water Mist Systems for the Protection of Computer Room Subfloors. j. Appendix N: Other Occupancies Which FM Global Has an Interest in Protecting with Water Mist Systems.
3. Underwriters Laboratories Inc., Northbrook, IL, USA	UL 2167, Proposed First Edition of the Standard for Water Mist Nozzles for Fire Protection Service, June 1998. a. Machinery Spaces b. Passenger Cabin Fire Tests c. Passenger Cabins Greater than 12 m^2 d. Public Space Fire Tests e. Residential Area Fire Tests f. Light Hazard Area Fire Tests g. Ordinary Hazard I and II Tests h. Nozzle Construction Design, Marking and Performance Requirements
4. Verband der Schadenversichen e.V. (VDS, Germany)	VDS 2498 Guidelines for Water Extinguishing Systems Requirements and Test Methods for Fine Spray Nozzles, 8/96 Edition. a. Fine Spray Nozzles for Cable Conduits

appropriate for full-scale fire scenarios, which can be protected against plugging and which reliably sustain that flow as long as required. The economics of providing the stored energy, or installing special pumps and piping systems, are also determinants in selection of a mist-generating technology for a given application.

Water mist nozzle designs involve one of three basic principles: (1) impingement of a jet of water on a deflector (impingement), (2) expulsion of a high-velocity jet from an orifice (pressure jet), or (3) use of compressed air or nitrogen to shear water into fine spray (twin-fluid or air-atomizing nozzles). All three methods have been used by manufacturers of spray nozzles. The innovations being made by manufacturers interested in fire suppression are intended to improve efficiency or to optimize some spray characteristics such as mass flow rate, spray velocity, drop size, or cone shape. NFPA 750 distinguishes among the pressure regimes at which mist-generating technologies operate by introducing terms for low-, intermediate-, and high-pressure systems. Low-pressure systems operate at pressures of 175 psi (12 bar) or less; intermediate-pressure systems involve pressures greater than 175 psi (12 bar) but less than 500 psi (34 bar); and high-pressure systems operate at pressures of 500 psi (34 bar) or greater. The operating range of low-pressure systems is similar to standard fire protection systems, such as sprinklers and standpipes. The requirements for pipe, fittings, valves, pumps, or hydraulic calculations can be met by conventional materials and installation practices. Pipe, fittings, and valves for intermediate-pressure systems are also commonly available, although there may be no listed centrifugal fire pumps that produce pressures in the range of 500 psi (34 bar). Therefore, there are some aspects of intermediate-pressure systems that lie outside of standard fire protection engineering experience. Special requirements are invoked with high-pressure systems for pipe, fittings, pumps, valves, pressure regulators, cylinders, and tanks. The technology of high-pressure systems, although new to fire protection engineering practice, is well developed in other industries, such as the hydraulics and offshore petroleum drilling industries.

The method of generating mist does not uniquely determine suppression capability. Matching the spray characteristics of drop size distribution, flux density, and spray momentum to the fire hazard is more important. The choice of mist-generating method does influence factors such as the cost-effectiveness and reliability of a system.

Impingement Nozzles

Impingement nozzles operate on the principle of a solid jet of water striking a deflector and breaking up into small drops. They include standard sprinklers, nozzles used in traditional (see NFPA 15) water spray and deluge systems, and nozzles used for a myriad of industrial applications. The jet velocity and the shape of the impingement surface determine the cone angle, drop size distribution, flux uniformity, and spray momentum. Figure 16.8.12 shows several types of impingement-style nozzles used in water mist systems.

Impingement nozzles operating at low pressures are simple in design and, therefore, cost less to construct than nozzles that require more precise machining. In 1992, NRCC[77] measured the spray characteristics of several commercially available impingement nozzles, including sprinkler-type deflector plates, spiral deflectors, and pin-type deflectors, operating at pressures less than 175 psi (12 bar). These nozzles produced Classes 2 and 3 sprays, with cone angles between 60 degrees and 120 degrees. The size and shape of the deflector determined the cone angle. The tests revealed that impingement nozzles have a limited axial spray projection distance because of the energy lost as the jet strikes the deflector. A slight tilt in the deflector plate will skew the spray distribution in one direction. Deflector supports can cause shadow effects, and irregularities in the impingement surface can magnify to large variation in the spray distribution patterns. These sprays controlled or extinguished fires, not only with Class A combustibles, but also in liquid fuel fires in enclosures, where enclosure effects made spray momentum less critical. Overall, the reduced forward spray momentum and irregular flux distribution, which were typical of the impingement nozzles tested, were limitations on their potential use in a water mist system for large machinery spaces.

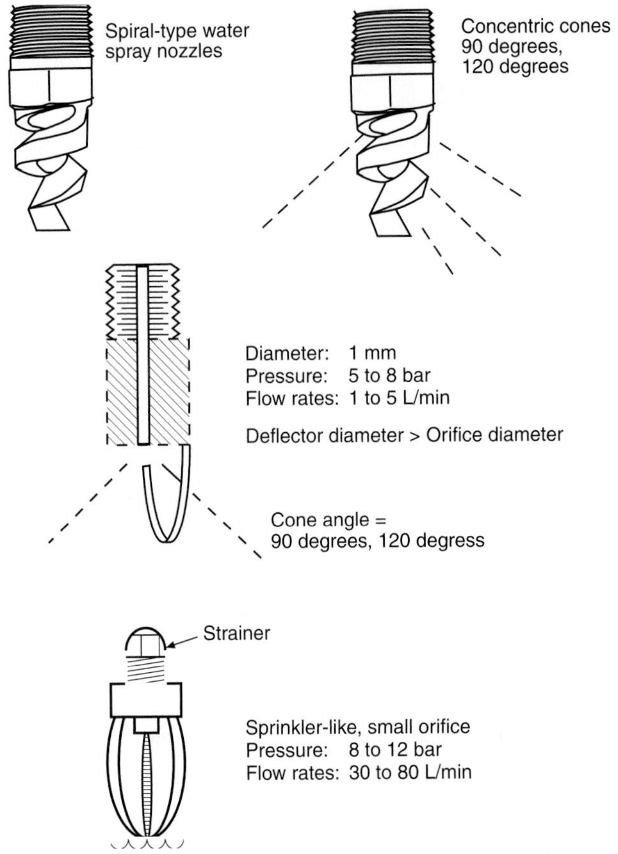

FIGURE 16.8.12 Several Types of Impingement Nozzles for Fine Sprays

The relationship between nozzle pressure and discharge rate for impingement nozzles is reliably calculated using the expression familiar to sprinkler system designers: where q is the discharge rate, P is the gauge pressure at the orifice, and k is a coefficient characterizing the nozzle.

Impinging Jets

The term *impinging jets* is used to describe a type of water mist nozzle that creates mist by forcing two thin jets of water to collide after exiting the orifice. Machining of the very small orifices must be very accurate to achieve correct alignment for collision of the jets. A German company has an impinging jet that creates a Class 2 mist at approximately 5 L/min at 175 psi (12 bar) operating pressure. It is an intermediate-pressure nozzle. The nozzle is used in turbine enclosure systems. It was tested in a cable tunnel fire scenario in New Zealand and performed very well.[25]

Pressure Jet Nozzles

Pressure jet nozzles work by pushing a jet of water through a relatively small-diameter orifice at a high velocity. As the jet leaves the orifice, complex physical events occur, involving the fluid viscosity and the jet diameter and velocity relative to the air.[58] The breakup of the thin jet of water into droplets begins within a few millimeters of the orifice. Figure 16.8.13 illustrates several pressure jet nozzles. The disintegration of the jet into droplets can be enhanced by inserting swirl devices in a chamber inside the nozzle to impart a rotation to the jet as it emerges from the orifice. If water is pushed through a narrow slot instead of a circular orifice, the jet takes the form of a sheet, which becomes unstable and disintegrates into droplets.

Individual pressure jet orifices can be assembled in groups on a single base or at intervals along a pipe (linear arrangement). Where several pressure jets are assembled in close proximity on a single base, the combined effect of all jets entrains air into the composite spray cone. The diameter of the fully developed composite cone is not a simple function of initial jet velocity and direction. The trajectory of drops from the individual jets is influenced by the pressure regime within the spray cone, which depends on the manner in which air is drawn toward the nozzle and entrained into the cone. With some nozzles, the spray cone may not become fully developed if free air movement to the back of the nozzle is restricted.

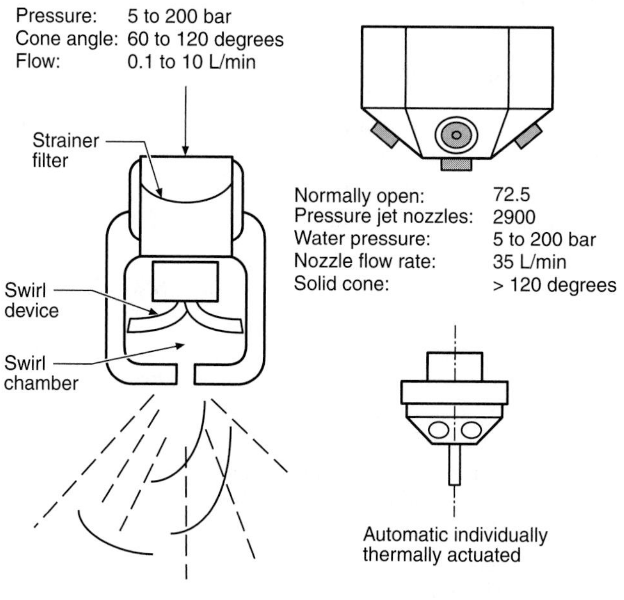

FIGURE 16.8.13 Pressure Jet Nozzles

Pressure jet nozzles operate over a wide range of pressures from 75 to 4000 psi (12 to 272 bar). Pressure jet nozzles require higher operating pressures than impingement nozzles. Up to a limit, the drop size distribution becomes finer as pressure increases. Often there is an upper limit, at which further increase in pressure has little effect on the drop size distribution. There may be incremental increase in mass flow rate or momentum but with no significant improvement in the coverage area of the spray cone. The listing agency will provide information about the operating pressure range needed to produce the desired spray qualities.

The relationship between pressure and flow from multi-orifice pressure jet nozzles follows the simple formula used for single-orifice nozzles, such as sprinklers. Again, the listing agency must provide information on how to calculate discharge rates as a function of pressure from pressure jet nozzles.

Twin-Fluid Nozzles

Twin-fluid nozzles are also referred to as air-atomizing nozzles. They combine compressed gas with a water stream to shear the water into fine droplets. The resulting mist can be directed through one or more orifices to shape a conical spray of any desired cone angle. Twin-fluid nozzles allow for efficient control over drop size distribution, cone angle, spray momentum, and discharge rate. Nozzle manufacturers have produced twin-fluid nozzles for a wide variety of industrial applications, including spray painting, agricultural spraying, and humidification systems. One company markets a twin-fluid nozzle based on a design developed by British Petroleum (BP) Ventures in the 1980s. This nozzle operates with compressed gas and water pressures in the 65- to 90-psi (4.5- to 6.2-bar) range. For fire protection systems (which may require many nozzles), it is an advantage to minimize the total required flow rate of compressed gas. Although typical industrial twin-fluid nozzles operate at air-to-liquid mass ratios (ALR mass) of 0.20 or greater, this particular water mist nozzle operates with ALR mass values of 0.05 to 0.10. Figure 16.8.14 illustrates the mixing arrangement for two types of twin-fluid nozzles.

The relationship between water discharge and atomizing medium (air) discharge from a twin-fluid nozzle cannot be characterized by the expression used for simple orifice nozzles. Because the air and water lines are joined (inside the nozzle), the pressure in one line works against the pressure in the other line. As air pressure increases, the airflow increases, which, in turn, forces a reduction in the waterflow and modifies the water system pressure. Conversely, if the water pressure is increased, it reduces the airflow.

Figure 16.8.15 shows a plot of atomizing medium and waterflow rates for a commercial twin-fluid nozzle. The term *air to liquid ratio* (ALR) is used to describe the balance of atomizing medium and liquid demand across the nozzle. To adjust a system in the field and to determine air and water discharge rates from manufacturers' data sheets, it is convenient to use the air-to-liquid pressure ratio, ALR_p. For comparing

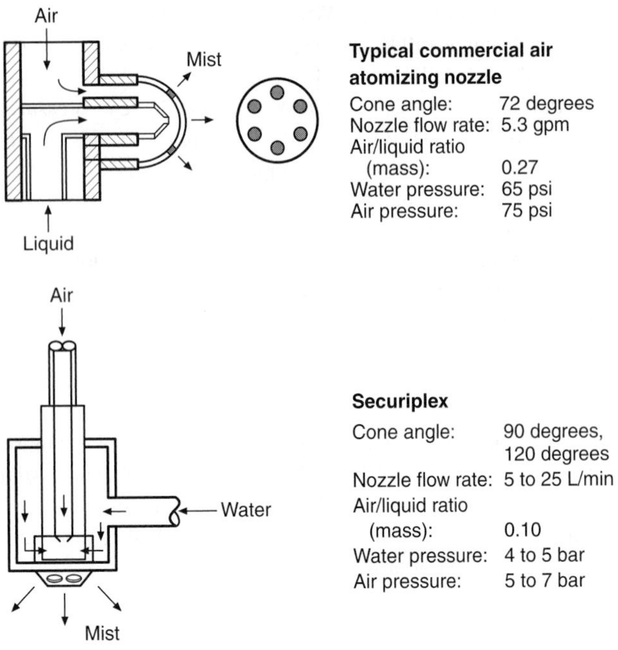

FIGURE 16.8.14 Two Designs for Twin-Fluid Nozzles

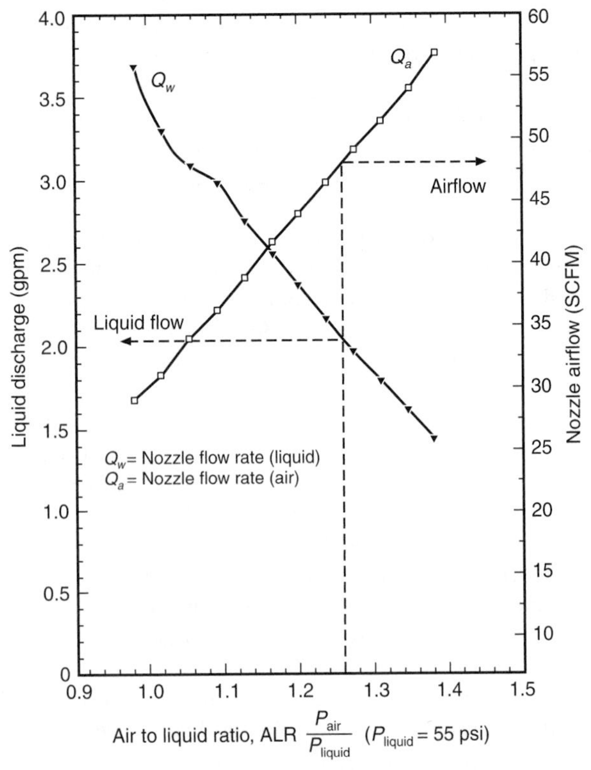

FIGURE 16.8.15 Air- and Waterflow Rates in Twin-Fluid Nozzles

the efficiencies of different nozzles and performing pneumatic system calculations to determine pipe sizes, pressure regulator settings, and the total quantity of compressed gas required for a system, it is better to work with an air-to-liquid ratio expressed in terms of mass flow rates, ALR_m. It is interesting to note that FM Global Loss Prevention Data Sheet 4-2, Water Mist Systems,[74] simply recommends calculating the pneumatic and the hydraulic piping separately to show that the nominal required flow can be delivered at an acceptable minimum pressure. The approach is simpler than the method described previously, and for some types of nozzles it may be sufficiently accurate for practical purposes. A functional discharge test of the installed system will be needed, however, as a final check on the system design.

$$ALR_p = \frac{P_a}{P_w} \qquad ALR_m = \frac{M_a}{M_w}$$

where

ALR_p = Air-to-liquid pressure ratio	ALR_m = Air-to-liquid mass ratio
P_a = Air pressure, gauge, psi (bar)	M_a = Mass of air per unit time, lb/min (kg/sec)
P_w = Water pressure, gauge, psi (bar)	M_w = Mass of water per unit time, lb/min (kg/sec)

The nozzle manufacturer should identify the range of air-to-liquid ratios (pressure and mass) over which the nozzle achieves the optimum spray characteristics. The total compressed gas demand of many nozzles in an open-nozzle system can be costly, so it is desirable to minimize the demand for atomizing medium. An efficient operating point for a twin-fluid nozzle is one that produces the desired spray characteristics at as low an ALR_m as possible (e.g., between 0.05 and 0.10).

Innovations in Mist Generation

The term *innovation* as used here applies to nozzles that incorporate unusual features to improve efficiency or to optimize some characteristic of the spray or that produce spray by a different physical mechanism than those described previously.

Combined Nitrogen and Water Discharge. One company has developed a two-stroke piston pump unit that is driven by compressed nitrogen. It has advantages for applications where electrical power for pumps may be unavailable. It is referred to as a GPU unit and has been listed for machinery spaces, turbine enclosures, and light hazard applications. At each stroke of the piston pump, either water or nitrogen gas is pushed into the piping. It is not clear how to do hydraulic calculations for a distribution system using this system. As the unit discharges air or nitrogen gas in one stroke and water on the next stroke, the flow of mixed gas and water in the piping system has unknown properties with respect to friction loss.

It may be undesirable to use the GPU system for nozzles at different elevations, as the balance of gas and water delivered from the nozzles is unpredictable. It is recommended to conduct a full discharge test of the system to ensure that the quantity of compressed gas is sufficient for the required duration of protection.

Linear Sprays. Water mist is usually delivered from nozzles with a 360° circular spray cone. Nozzles are distributed in a grid at ceiling level. This delivery pattern is typical of sprinkler systems and is suitable for most applications. Some applications, however, require that water mist be delivered to protect a well-defined geometry. Spray that is discharged in any direction other than that dictated by the fuel arrangement would be wasted. Fixed shelving in rows, cable trays, or electronic cabinets with parallel circuit boards are examples of applications in which circular distribution patterns lead to inefficient application of water. Placing small pressure jet orifices at close intervals along a tube creates a linear spray. The nozzle then is actually a length of tube with discharge orifices spaced along its entire length. The K-factor for such an elongated nozzle is different than for a conventional nozzle with orifices situated around a circular metal base. The discharge characteristic of a linear system is a function of the flow rate per orifice, the number of orifices per meter, the total length of each line, and whether water is supplied from one end or both ends.

Flashing of Superheated Water. The "flashing of superheated liquid" phenomenon is usually associated with gaseous fire suppression agents, but it occurs with water as well. A superheated liquid is one that is maintained by pressure in its liquid state at a temperature above its boiling point. When released suddenly from the pressurized container, the liquid partly flashes to vapor and partly disintegrates into spray by the shearing effect of rapidly expanding bubbles.[78–80] The pressure in the closed container is determined by the vapor pressure of the liquid at the given temperature. For water, standard steam tables indicate that at 348°F (176°C) the gauge pressure inside the container will be 118 psi (8 bar). This self-generated pressure is enough to discharge the water from the cylinder. The storage cylinder can be further pressurized by addition of compressed nitrogen, if necessary.

Once released to atmospheric pressure through a simple orifice, superheated water boils instantaneously. Tiny gas bubbles form, expand, and then explode in a powerful release of energy that fractures still-liquid water to small droplets. The rapid release of energy propels the mist throughout the compartment. The percentage of the water that flashes to vapor can be estimated from standard steam tables and could be as high as 14 percent at 348°F (176°C). The flashed water vapor promptly cools and condenses, forming an opaque fog of aerosol-sized (20 micron) water drops. These ultra-fine drops are the result of condensation, not the physical breakup of liquid water by mechanical energy. Within the cloud of white fog, the portion of the liquid that does not flash to vapor is distributed as a "rainout" of Class 1 mist ($^1Dv0.9 \leq$ 200 microns).[62,80]

The rapid generation of mist by the flashing process has been demonstrated to be effective in quenching dust explosions. For hydrocarbon pool fires in enclosures, tests conducted at NRCC[62] showed that the spray was no more effective than other Class 1 sprays. Research into the possible application of this technology continues.

Nano-Mist[81] is an ultra-fine mist with very uniform drop size distribution with a volumetric mean droplet diameter in the 10 micron range. The technology combines an ultrasonic transducer assembly and a process technology for aerosolization, extraction, and transport of mist. The throughput capacity of the mist generator is in the range of 0.25 Lpm (0.06 gpm). The opaque cloud of low-momentum mist can achieve suspended mass of water droplets in excess of 240 g/m^3 (0.015 lb/ft^3). No conventional water mist nozzle approaches that level of suspended water droplets. The Nano-Mist can be transported through smooth ducts to confined areas. In a series of tests conducted for the U.S. Navy to develop a hybrid system (nitrogen plus water mist),[82] Nano-Mist was tested in a mock computer-room subfloor (false deck) against telltale fires.[81] Various combinations of inert gas (nitrogen) and water mist were used to extinguish the test fires. The concentration of nitrogen needed to inert the space and extinguish the fires was first determined. Then water mist was added to the nitrogen. The water mist reduced the concentration of nitrogen needed to extinguish the fires by as much as 40 percent.[83] However, water mist itself could not extinguish the concealed fires in the subfloor. The Nano-Mist, however, was able to extinguish the telltale fires itself without addition of any nitrogen.

The Nano-Mist technology appears to be able to achieve the suspended mass of water droplets needed to bring about extinguishment of hydrocarbon fires if it can be delivered to the seat of the fire. As it is a low-momentum mist, it needs to be transported to the flame region by controlled air movement. Research and development work continues, seeking to increase the rate of generation of the mist to flow rates needed for large spaces, to improve the means of transporting the cloud to the flame area, and to reduce the cost of the ultrasonic generators.

Automatic, Nonautomatic, and Hybrid Nozzles

NFPA 750 introduces the terms *automatic, nonautomatic,* and *hybrid nozzles* to distinguish among three types of nozzles that are already on the market.

Automatic Nozzles. Automatic nozzles operate independently of other nozzles by means of a detection/activation device built into each nozzle. A heat-activated link or bulb is built into the nozzle that, when exposed to heat, releases and allows discharge from that single nozzle in exactly the same manner as a sprinkler. Automatic water mist nozzles use fast-response glass bulb elements, some of 2.5 mm diameter or less. The temperature ratings of the automatic nozzles are selected according to the application. Automatic water mist nozzles may also be referred to as "water mist sprinklers," as they are used in exactly the same manner as standard sprinklers.

Nonautomatic Nozzles. Nonautomatic nozzles are open nozzles used in deluge-type systems. Water mist systems intended for total compartment flooding are designed to discharge mist from all nozzles in the compartment. A separate detection system is required to detect the fire and release the system. Some local application systems in marine machinery space systems are permitted to be released manually. Once the main control valve is opened, water discharges from all nozzles. Nonautomatic nozzles for use in machinery spaces or aggressive environments are often equipped with blow-off caps to keep moisture and grime from getting into the nozzle orifices and piping. Release of water into the piping system creates enough force to dislodge the blow-off caps, allowing water to discharge freely.

Hybrid Nozzles. The term *hybrid nozzle* was introduced in NFPA 750 to recognize nozzles that were designed with a thermal element so that they would release if exposed to fire in the same manner as an automatic nozzle but which could also be released by a signal from a separate detection system. Hybrid nozzle hardware was developed for experimental work in the 1990s but has not been commercialized or undergone formal component testing associated with the official fire test protocols. It should be noted that the means of generation of Nano-Mist does not involve a nozzle as defined by NFPA 750. The ultrasonic generator, chamber, and associated delivery tubing might be viewed as a hybrid conception.

Choice of Mist-Generation Method

Full-scale fire testing has shown that it is not possible to say categorically that one mist-generation method is better than another with respect to fire suppression. Manufacturers working in different pressure ranges and employing different nozzle designs have all passed the IMO and FM Global Research machinery space and turbine enclosure tests. In general it can be stated that there is a tendency to favor higher rather than lower operating pressures. Nozzles that were at one time thought of as low-pressure nozzles require 185 psi (12.8 bar) minimum nozzle pressure. This means that the normal system operating pressure will be at a higher pressure, putting the system functionally in the intermediate-pressure range (12 to 34 bar). Only the twin-fluid system operates entirely in the low-pressure range for water pressure—the compressed gas provides the additional energy needed to produce a suitable spray. For manufacturers, the choice of mist-generation method for their product line is largely dictated by availability of unpatented technology and the ability to be cost competitive. The designer of water mist systems should be free to choose a mist-generation method according to the engineering merits and the cost of each.

Ultimately the best choice of mist-generation method will be determined by the following:

- Evidence of acceptable performance in a recognized fire test protocol relevant to the application
- Number of nozzles required at the manufacturer's spacing, hence, pipe and fitting materials and labor costs
- Total water demand—storage requirements, potential water damage, and environmental regulations for water retention
- Pump details—suction supply, pump capacity, power requirements, and emergency backup power
- Reliability considerations taking into account the ability to maintain water supply quality, compressed gas cylinder management, electrical circuit supervision, details of specific equipment, and degree of effort involved in scheduled maintenance tasks
- Cost

Reliability Considerations

Water mist systems incorporate a number of features that traditionally have been avoided in water-based fire protection systems. The use of small orifices increases the risk of nozzle plugging. The use of higher operating pressures than traditional sprinkler or water spray systems increases the risk of piping system failure. Control systems rely on electrical release of solenoid valves on compressed gas cylinders or on sectional control valves—a failure of the electrical control circuit will cause failure of the entire system. The use of positive displacement pumps to meet a variable system demand involves programming control logic in a programmable controller. Design procedures to calculate the correct storage volumes of compressed gas and water to deliver water to the nozzles at the specified pressure for the minimum discharge duration have not been fully developed. Design criteria for such systems are based on empirical testing. The use of multiple small storage reservoirs of water instead of a single large tank introduces concerns about maintaining the quality of stored water. The features unique to water mist systems introduce many potential failure modes. Measures must be taken in the design process and in ongoing maintenance to counter each identified failure possibility. Table 16.8.3 tabulates recommended countermeasures to improve system reliability.

DESIGN CALCULATIONS FOR WATER MIST SYSTEMS

Calculation Fundamentals

The calculation procedures for water mist systems range from fundamental methods for single-fluid, low-pressure systems to somewhat more complex methods for twin-fluid and high-pressure systems.

As for any engineered hydraulic system, the designer must select pipe sizes, confirm flows and pressures at discharge points, and determine total flow and pressure requirements for the system in order to select pumps and size storage reservoirs. Such calculations are done routinely for sprinkler systems and water spray systems. Water mist systems introduce problems

TABLE 16.8.3 Potential Failure Concerns and Suggested Countermeasures to Improve Reliability in Water Mist Systems

Potential Failure Concern	*Suggested Countermeasures to Improve Reliability*
Plugging of small orifices in nozzles and small-diameter passages in valves	• Set water quality standards = potable water. • Require screens or filters or both on inlet to storage tanks and on the outlet if algae growth could occur. • Treat stored water to prevent bacterial activity—either chlorination or bromination of UV light. Avoid chlorination where stainless steel tubing is used. • Provide screens on each individual nozzle. • Use corrosion resistant liners in water storage vessels. • Monitor water quality quarterly as part of regular maintenance. Drain and refill stored water cylinders semiannually. • Use corrosion-resistant pipe and fittings; mandate cleaning and flushing measures as installation practice and acceptance testing. • Use blow-off caps to prevent external grime from getting into open nozzles.
Start-up problems with positive displacement (PD) pumps (overcurrent trip)	• Modify NFPA 20 to specify controller design appropriate for PD pumps. • Conform to NFPA 20 with respect to duplicate power supplies and overcurrent protection.
Normally closed valves: Failure of electrical solenoid valves to release compressed gas or open sectional control valves	• Mandate emergency backup power supplies, apply process industry reliability standards, and ensure component testing as part of listing. • Duplicate release capability with hydraulic or pneumatic and manual release features. • Perform regular maintenance to check functionality of solenoid valves.
Normally open valves: Failure to identify a closed valve due to use of nonindicating type valves.	• Mandate use of open/closed indicators on all control valves. • Develop supervisory circuits and scheduled maintenance tasks to confirm water supply valves are open.
Inadequate capacity of stored gas to sustain discharge for the minimum duration	• Mandate calculation procedures to determine required capacity of compressed gas. • Confirm capacity of gas storage vessels by discharge test through system piping or test orifice with equivalent K-factor.
Accident while handling compressed gas cylinders	• Mandate safe handling and storage practices for compressed gas cylinders. • Secure support frames; provide minimum width of access aisle.
Loss of pressure in compressed gas cylinders due to slow leak	• Mandate electrical supervision of gas pressurized piping. • Mandate microleakage control on cylinder headers.
Failure of pressure regulator	• Require component testing of regulators and control valves as part of listing.
Install incorrect size of replacement cylinder	• Post specifications for all replacement cylinders on support rack.
Failure of stored water supply due to: — error in design calculation — loss of water from tank — deterioration in quality (algae growth) — tank corrosion	• Confirm correct capacity of water storage vessels by full discharge test through system piping or test orifice with equivalent K-factor. • Provide duplicate capacity of stored water. • Mandate supervision of water level or visual indicators. • Establish monthly, semiannual, and annual maintenance procedures to monitor water quality.
Failure of detection system for deluge and preaction systems	• Confirm functionality of all detectors, control panel, and interlocks at acceptance test.
Failure of interlocks to shut down ventilation and operate other ancillary devices	• Design and commission detection system to NFPA 72 and conduct regular maintenance as per industry standards.

that are not commonly encountered in calculations for sprinkler systems, however. For example, high-pressure systems may involve positive displacement pumps or stored pressure reservoirs with continuously declining pressure during the discharge. Twin-fluid systems involve the use of pressure-regulating and solenoid valves on both liquid and compressed gas lines. This section reviews some of the special calculation problems encountered in design of water mist systems.

Calculations Involving the Hazen-Williams Equation

NFPA 750 defines a low-pressure water mist system as one that operates at 175 psi (11.9 bar) or less. The operating range of low-pressure systems is similar to standard fire protection systems, such as sprinklers (see NFPA 13, *Standard for the Installation of Sprinkler Systems*), standpipes (see NFPA 14, *Standard for the Installation of Standpipe and Hose Systems*), and water spray systems (see NFPA 15, *Standard for Water Spray Fixed Systems for Fire Protection*). The requirements for pipe, fittings, valves, pumps, and hydraulic calculations, then, can be met by conventional materials and design practices. Based on this assumed similarity with sprinkler piping, NFPA 750 accepts the use of the Hazen-Williams equation to calculate pressure losses in piping provided that fluid velocity never exceeds 25 ft/sec (7.6 m/sec) (Table 16.8.4).

Values of the friction loss coefficient, *C*, used in the Hazen-Williams equation, are accurate only if the flow velocity is close to that at which the value of *C* was measured.[84] It is a matter of judgment as to what velocity is "too high" for the Hazen-Williams equation. American Water Works Association (AWWA) data, quoted in Titus,[84] list *C* factors measured at a velocity of 3 ft/sec (0.9 m/sec), yet it is standard practice in sprinkler calculations to accept velocities in sprinkler piping between 10 and 20 ft/sec (3.05 and 6.1 m/sec). Similarly, the tables of equivalent lengths for fittings and valves, used by sprinkler system designers, are based on fittings and valve types typical of sprinkler systems. Water mist systems may incorporate different types of fittings and valves, for which the Hazen-Williams–based equivalent length values commonly accepted for sprinkler piping will be incorrect.

Calculations Involving the Darcy-Weisbach Equation

The Hazen-Williams (H-W) equation contains no terms that allow one to change the temperature, density, or viscosity of the liquid. It assumes that the water contains no additives and is close to 60°F (15.6°C). The Darcy-Weisbach (D-W) equation does allow for variation in fluid properties, and for that reason it is widely used by mechanical engineers designing fluid systems.

TABLE 16.8.4 Hazen-Williams Equation for Calculation of Pressure Loss Due to Friction

U.S. Customary Units	*SI Units*
$p = \dfrac{4.52\,Q^{1.85}}{C^{1.85}d^{4.87}}$	$p_m = 6.05\left(\dfrac{Q_m^{1.85}}{C^{1.85}d_m^{4.87}}\right)10^5$
p = Frictional resistance, psi per foot of pipe	p_m = Friction resistance, bars per m of pipe
Q = Flow, gpm	Q_m = Flow, L/min
C = Friction loss coefficient	C = Friction loss coefficient
d = Actual internal diameter, in.	d_m = Actual internal diameter, mm

It also allows input of more detail to account for differences in pipe materials from standard sprinkler pipe and fittings. For water mist systems, if viscosity or water temperature departs significantly from typical sprinkler system water supply conditions, the Darcy-Weisbach equation should be used. NFPA 750 requires the use of D-W equation if fluid velocity exceeds 25 ft/sec (7.6 m/sec). The limiting velocity was selected after review of calculations comparing the agreement between H-W and D-W calculations and measured head losses in 1- to 3-in. (25- to 80-mm) diameter black steel pipe, over a range of velocities.[85] Table 16.8.5 shows the Darcy-Weisbach and related equations for use in calculating friction loss in pipe and tubing.

Most of the parameters in the Darcy-Weisbach equation will be known by the designer, such as the diameters and lengths of pipe (including equivalent lengths for fittings) and the density of the fluid. Density may vary according to water source (seawater or potable water) and the possible presence of additives such as wetting agents, fire retardant salts, or antifreeze. The flow rates (Q) will be determined by the nozzle characteristics, such as the K-factor. The unknown value f (friction factor) must be derived through a three-step process as follows:

1. Equation 2 in Table 16.8.5 is used to calculate the Reynolds number (Re).
2. Equation 3 in Table 16.8.5 is used to calculate the relative roughness factor

TABLE 16.8.5 Darcy-Weisbach and Associated Equations for Pressure Loss in Piping

U.S. Customary Units	*SI Units*
Darcy-Weisbach Equation: $\Delta p = 0.000216\,\dfrac{fL\rho Q^2}{d^5}$	Darcy-Weisbach Equation: $\Delta p_m = 2.252\,\dfrac{fL_m\rho_m Q_m^2}{d_m^5}$
Reynolds Number: $Re = 50.6\,\dfrac{Q\rho}{d\mu}$	Reynolds Number: $Re = 21.22\,\dfrac{Q_m\rho_m}{d_m\mu}$
Relative Roughness: $\textit{Relative roughness} = \dfrac{\varepsilon}{D}$	Relative Roughness: $\textit{Relative roughness} = \dfrac{\varepsilon_m}{d_m}$
Δp = Frictional loss, psi gauge	Δp_m = Frictional loss, bars gauge
f = Friction factor, psi/ft	f = Friction factor, bars/m
L = Length of pipe, ft	L = Length of pipe, m
ρ = Weight density of fluid, lb/ft³	μ = Absolute (dynamic) viscosity, centipoise (cP)
Q = Flow, gpm	Q = Flow, L/min
d = Internal pipe diameter, in.	d_m = Internal pipe diameter, mm
ε = Pipe wall roughness, ft	ρ = Weight density of fluid, kg/m³
D = Internal pipe diameter, ft	ε = Pipe wall roughness, mm
μ = Absolute (dynamic) viscosity, centipoise (cP)	

3. The Moody diagram (Figure 16.8.16) is used to obtain a value for the friction factor

Tables 16.8.6 and 16.8.7 provide values of water density dynamic viscosity and absolute roughness for use in solving equations 2 and 3. Once the Reynolds number and the relative roughness are determined, the values are located in the Moody diagram (see Figure 16.8.16). The intersection point for the Re and values is located on the diagram. A horizontal line is projected from the intersection point to the left axis of the Moody diagram, which provides a value for the friction factor

The value of *f* and other known parameters are then used in the equation in Table 16.8.5 to calculate a total pressure loss over each length of pipe. The value of *f* changes as flow quantities accumulate along the pipe length and as pipe diameters change across the system. From this point on the hydraulic calculation procedures are comparable to standard sprinkler calculations—discharges and pressure losses are accumulated over the entire piping network to provide an estimate of the total waterflow rate and pressure required at the water source (pump). Computerized calculation procedures based on the Darcy-Weisbach equations are available.

The equivalent length tables available in many NFPA standards are based on the Hazen-Williams equation and should be checked before being used with the Darcy-Weisbach equation.

The head losses incurred across valves and fittings not found in standard tables may be calculated using resistance coefficients (*K*) and equivalent lengths and flow coefficients, C_v.[86] Valve manufacturers should provide C_v values with data sheets on their valves.

Calculations for Declining Pressure Systems

Systems that utilize stored energy from compressed gas cylinders will operate in one of two ways. Low-pressure systems use a pressure regulator to sustain a constant pressure in the system 7piping. High-pressure systems do not regulate the pressure—all the gas is directed into the piping system, which instantly sees a high pressure that then decays steadily. In either case, the driving pressure in the compressed gas cylinders decreases throughout the discharge. The end of discharge is determined when the compressed gas can no longer deliver the minimum pressure to meet the minimum design flow condition.

For single-fluid systems, calculations to determine pipe sizing are the same as for any constant-pressure system. The engineering question of greater interest is how to determine the number of compressed gas cylinders needed to meet the flow/pressure/duration requirements of the water mist system. For the most part, systems utilizing compressed gas as a driving force are preengineered systems. The manufacturer has determined in

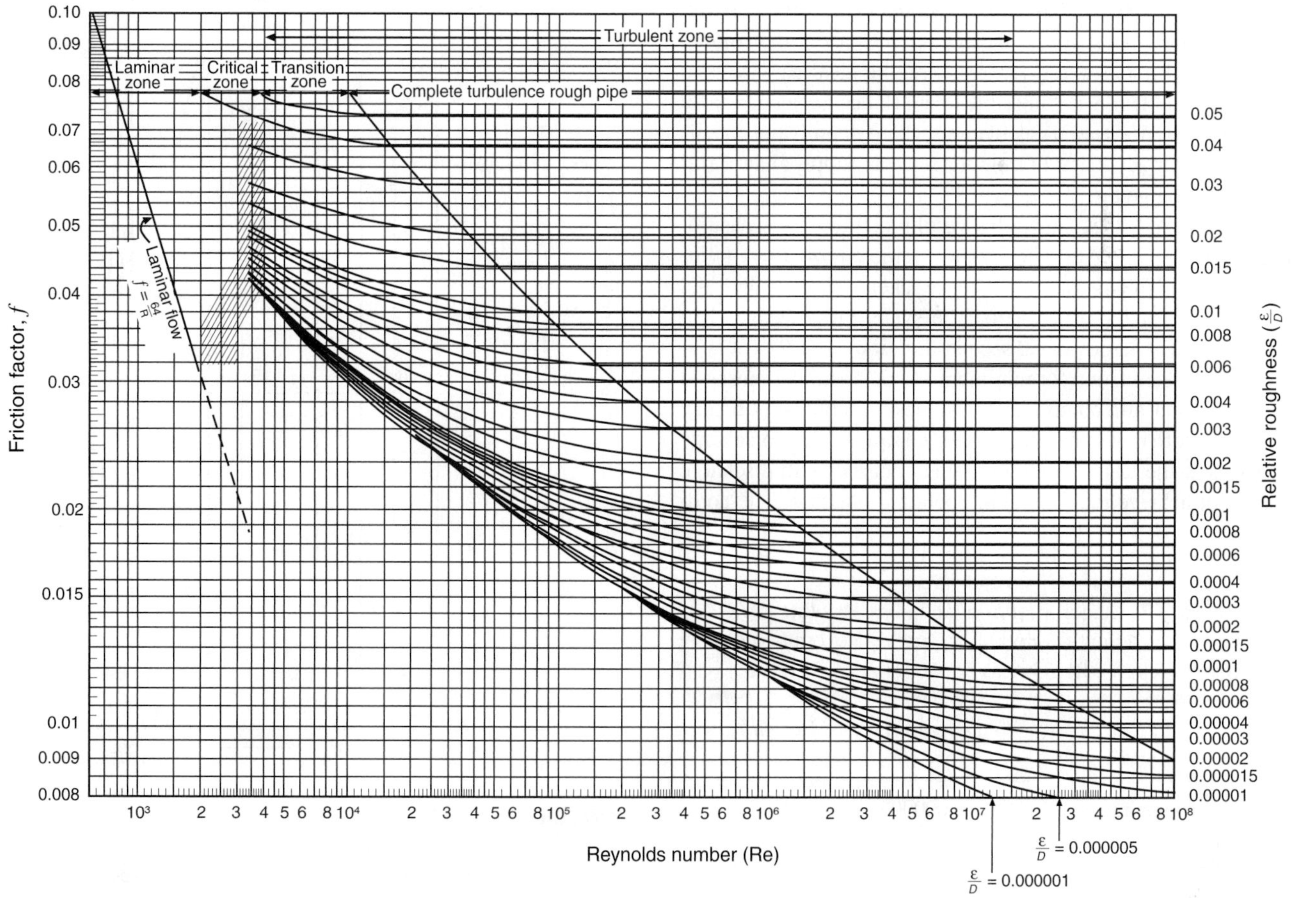

FIGURE 16.8.16 Moody Diagram

TABLE 16.8.6 Approximate Values of μ, Absolute (dynamic) Viscosity, and ρ for Clean Water, over the Temperature Range 40 to 100°F (4.4 to 37.8°C)

Temperature (°F)	*Temperature (°C)*	*Weight Density of Water (lb/ft³) p*	*Weight Density of Water (kg/m³) p_m*	*Absolute (dynamic) Viscosity, μ (centipoise)*
40	4.4	62.42	999.9	1.50
50	10.0	62.38	999.7	1.30
60	15.6	62.34	998.8	1.10
70	21.1	62.27	998.0	0.95
80	26.7	62.19	996.6	0.85
90	32.2	62.11	995.4	0.74
100	37.8	62.00	993.6	0.66

previous trials how many cylinders are needed to meet the design flow and the choice has been validated by the listing tests. However, if the number of nozzles increases and the piping layout is changed to adapt to an actual space, the compressed gas demand must be calculated. The designer is interested in knowing the length of time each nozzle will discharge in the pressure range needed for producing the design spray characteristics, the settings for pressure regulators, and how much water must be stored.

Practical calculation procedures for predetermining quantities of compressed gas cylinders for compressed gas–driven systems are not yet available. Manufacturers generally work out the gas requirements from basic assumptions about the volume of gas in a cylinder at a given pressure, the ideal gas law, and trial and error. If it is not possible to check design adequacy by reviewing the designer's calculations, there is no better means of confirming adequacy of compressed gas supply than a full system discharge test.

Figure 16.8.17A shows the results of pressure measurements taken at the hydraulically most remote nozzle in a twin-fluid system. The measurements were taken as part of the final acceptance test for the system. The system was designed to deliver six discharges of 50 second duration each. The manufacturer's specification for minimum nozzle operating pressure, for both water and compressed gas lines, was 66 psi (4.6 bar). The test plot shows that the system completed five discharge episodes at the desired pressure range, but the sixth discharge could not achieve the minimum operating pressure. The compressed gas supply was exhausted before the design duration was achieved. Adding one cylinder to the compressed gas bank extended the discharge to the minimum required duration.

In this case the manufacturer's method of estimating compressed gas requirements was inaccurate. The problem could be due to unavoidable imbalances in the system piping, so that more compressed gas than necessary was flowing through nozzles closest to the source. Thus, the characteristics of the pip-

TABLE 16.8.7 Recommended Values of Absolute Roughness or Effective Height of Pipe Wall Irregularities, for Use in Relative Roughness Equation

Pipe Material (new)	*Design Value of ε (ft)*	*Design Value of ε (mm)*
Copper, copper nickel, drawn tubing	0.000005	0.0015
Stainless steel, commercial steel, wrought iron	0.000150	0.0450
Galvanized iron	0.000500	0.1500

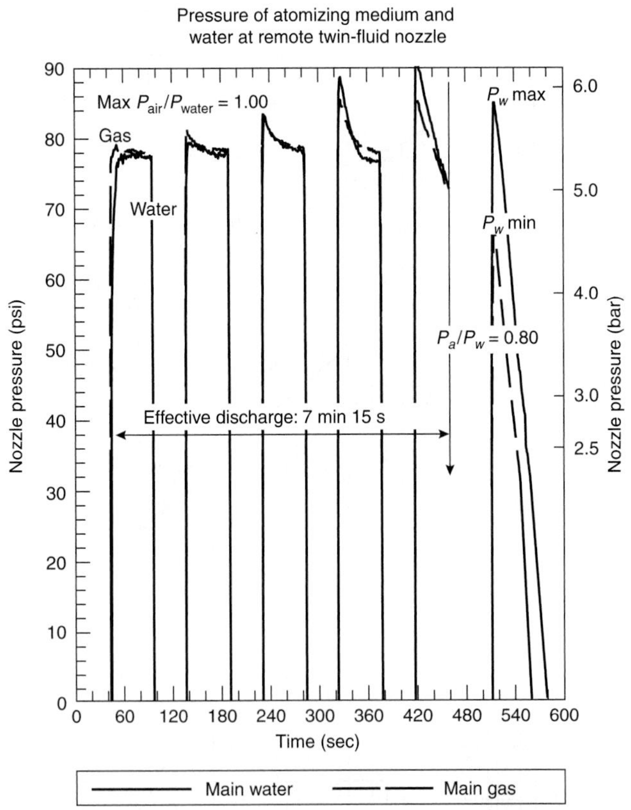

FIGURE 16.8.17A Discharge Test Results for a Twin-Fluid Water Mist System. Test objective was to confirm that the compressed gas supply was sufficient to sustain pressure greater than minimum 4.6 bar (66 psig) for 30 minutes. Pressures measured at remote twin-fluid nozzle.

ing system will directly affect the rate at which compressed gas supply is depleted. Since there were no calculations to confirm the adequacy of gas supply, the full discharge test was the only means of verification. In contrast, Figure 16.8.17B[87] shows the results of a full system discharge test of a gas-driven pump unit. The objective of the test was to ensure the adequacy of the compressed gas supply to achieve a 30 minute discharge duration, with the final system pressure not less than the end-of-discharge pressure in the FM approval test, which was 15 bar (215 psi).

Compressed gas cylinders are used on a variety of preengineered water mist systems. For all of these systems, the manufacturer is responsible for ensuring that the compressed gas supply is adequate for the design performance. Because industry practice is still founded in trial and error, it is highly advisable to verify design adequacy by means of a full system discharge test. The noise, sputter, and poor visibility in the compartment make it difficult to identify the end of discharge by visual observation. There must be actual measurements of nozzle pressure—the end of discharge is clearly identified when the nozzle pressure falls below its minimum operating pressure.

If circumstances do not permit a full system discharge for acceptance testing, the absence of a verifying calculation procedure is a serious problem. Such systems should be equipped with a test connection that simulates the system K-factor.

Calculations for Twin-Fluid Systems

Twin-fluid systems require sources of pressurized water and compressed gas in order for the nozzles to produce spray as required for fire suppression. The two "fluids" are delivered to the nozzles through two independent piping systems. The designer must calculate the pressure losses in each piping system in order to ensure that nozzles perform as intended and to determine the minimum storage quantities and pressure for each agent. The quantities of water and of compressed gas ("air") discharged at each nozzle depend on the air-to-liquid ratio (ALR) characteristics of the nozzle. If the air pressure is too high, it could prevent water from entering the nozzle. If the water pressure is too high, not enough air will enter the nozzle and the spray quality will deteriorate. Both air- and waterflow rates are very sensitive to the balance between their respective pressures. For that reason, summing the nominal flow rates of air and water is not the correct way to determine the required quantities of stored water or gas. Twin-fluid systems require special calculation procedures in order to ensure adequate nozzle performance, select pipe sizes, and determine agent storage requirements.

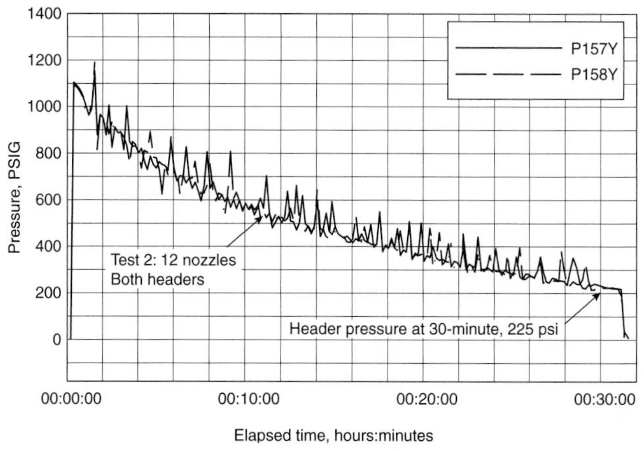

FIGURE 16.8.17B Results of Acceptance Test of a Decaying Pressure, Gas-Driven Pump System over a 30 Minute Discharge Period. Test objective was to confirm that the compressed gas supply was sufficient to sustain pressure greater than minimum 15 bar (215 psi) for 30 minutes. Pressures measured at pump discharge header.

One approach to the problem is to perform both the hydraulic and the pneumatic calculations simultaneously, checking to ensure that the gauge pressures, and pressure differences between liquid and compressed gas, at each nozzle, fall within a specified range. The listing information for a twin-fluid nozzle identifies the maximum and minimum operating pressures for both liquid and atomizing media. The designer's task is to select preliminary pipe sizes on both piping systems and then to work methodically through two sets of calculations, comparing the conditions at each nozzle. The H-W equation can be used for the water distribution piping. The calculations for the compressed gas line should follow standard engineering practice as described in references.[88] At any point, if the pressure/flow conditions exceed or fall outside of the desired operating range, an adjustment to the piping system should be made. After several iterations, it is possible to arrive at a reasonable estimate of total system demand.

The key step in the calculation procedure involves confirming that the ALR_m, that is, the mass ratio of the water discharge and the atomizing media discharge, at each nozzle, is within an acceptable range. That is,

$$ALR_m\ (\text{min}) < ALR_m\ (\text{actual}) < ALR_m\ (\text{max})$$

Figure 16.8.18 illustrates one model for this calculation procedure. Values for the water pressure and flow rate and air pressure and flow rate, at the most hydraulically remote nozzle, are set based on the manufacturer's recommended values. Flow rates must be converted from volumetric to mass units, for example, gpm to lb/min (L/min to kg/min), and SCFM to lb/min (m^3/min to kg/min). The ALR_m value (ALR_1 in Figure 16.8.18) is calculated. Then, for the given flow rates through the pipes supplying the most remote nozzle, the total pressure losses in each leg are calculated using the appropriate equations and added to the beginning pressures. The new pressures at the upstream nozzle (Pw_2 and Pa_2 in Figure 16.8.18) are used, with the manufacturer's nozzle data, as shown in Figure 16.8.15, to determine the new flow rates, Qw_2 and Qa_2. These values are converted to mass units to calculate ALR_{m2}. If ALR_{m2} is not within the acceptable range, then one of the pipe diameters should be increased or decreased and the calculation repeated. If it is within the acceptable range, the flows are accumulated and the calculation proceeds to the next nozzle until all nozzles have been included.

It is expected that manufacturers of twin-fluid systems will develop computerized methods for performing hydraulic and pneumatic calculations in combined piping systems. As noted earlier, FM Global accepts calculating the hydraulic and pneumatic piping independently.[74]

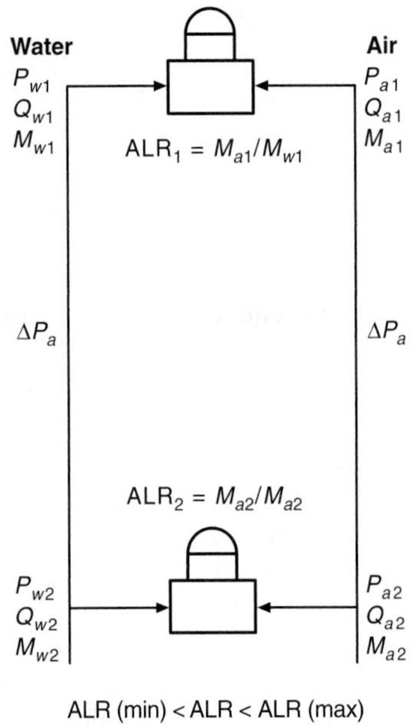

FIGURE 16.8.18 Simplified Air-to-Liquid Ratio Model

Calculations for High-Pressure Pump Systems

Water mist systems for large spaces or where a long duration of flow is needed require the use of pumps rather than compressed gas cylinders. For high-pressure systems, positive displacement (PD) pumps are normally used. Positive displacement refers to the fact that at each rotation of a gear or a piston, a fixed quantity of water is displaced. Although it is possible to use centrifugal pumps to generate high pressures, either by operating at very high speeds or by adding pumps in stages, it is more cost-effective to use PD pumps. The output pressure of a PD pump is limited only by the power of the motor and the strength of materials used. Centrifugal pump systems automatically vary both the pressure and discharge according to the demand of the fire suppression system. In contrast, PD pumps put out a constant Q but at varying pressure. Herein lies the engineering challenge: the hydraulic demand for a water mist system is seldom constant. Demand varies depending on the number of nozzles that open, as is the case when automatic nozzles are thermally released. It is also the case when several deluge systems of different sizes are supplied by a single pump source. The pump system must be able to supply both the largest and the smallest system demands. Calculations are needed to match the pump supply curve to the range of system demands and to develop a control program to manage the system.

The key to design involving PD pumps is to incorporate a pressure unloading valve, or unloader valve, with each pump. Figure 16.8.19 is an ISO symbol diagram showing a PD water mist pump assembly with unloader valves on each pump. The diagram shows two PD pumps driven by a single electric motor using direct-drive couplings at each end of the drive shaft.

An unloader valve incorporates a spring-operated valve and a check valve. When the system pressure exceeds the setting on the spring, the valve bypasses all output from the pump(s) that cannot be discharged by the system. The designer selects a pump with a specified volumetric output (L/min) at the set motor speed. The pump is coupled with an unloader valve that can "unload" up to the full output capacity of the pump. One approach is to design with one or more pumps to provide the desired Q output (equal to the maximum system demand) and a single large-capacity unloader valve. Several water mist pump manufacturers' systems are designed on this basis. In this case, the "pump curve" appears as shown in Figure 16.8.20, where the maximum pressure of the system is determined by the setting of the single unloader or pressure relief valve.

Another approach is to divide the total system demand among a number of small pumps, each with its own unloader valve and

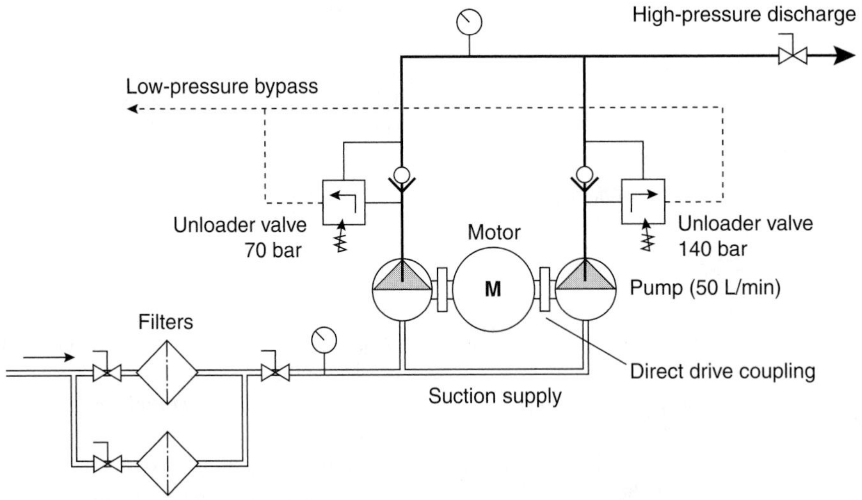

FIGURE 16.8.19 ISO Symbol Diagram of a High-Pressure Pump Assembly with Unloader Valves on Each Pump

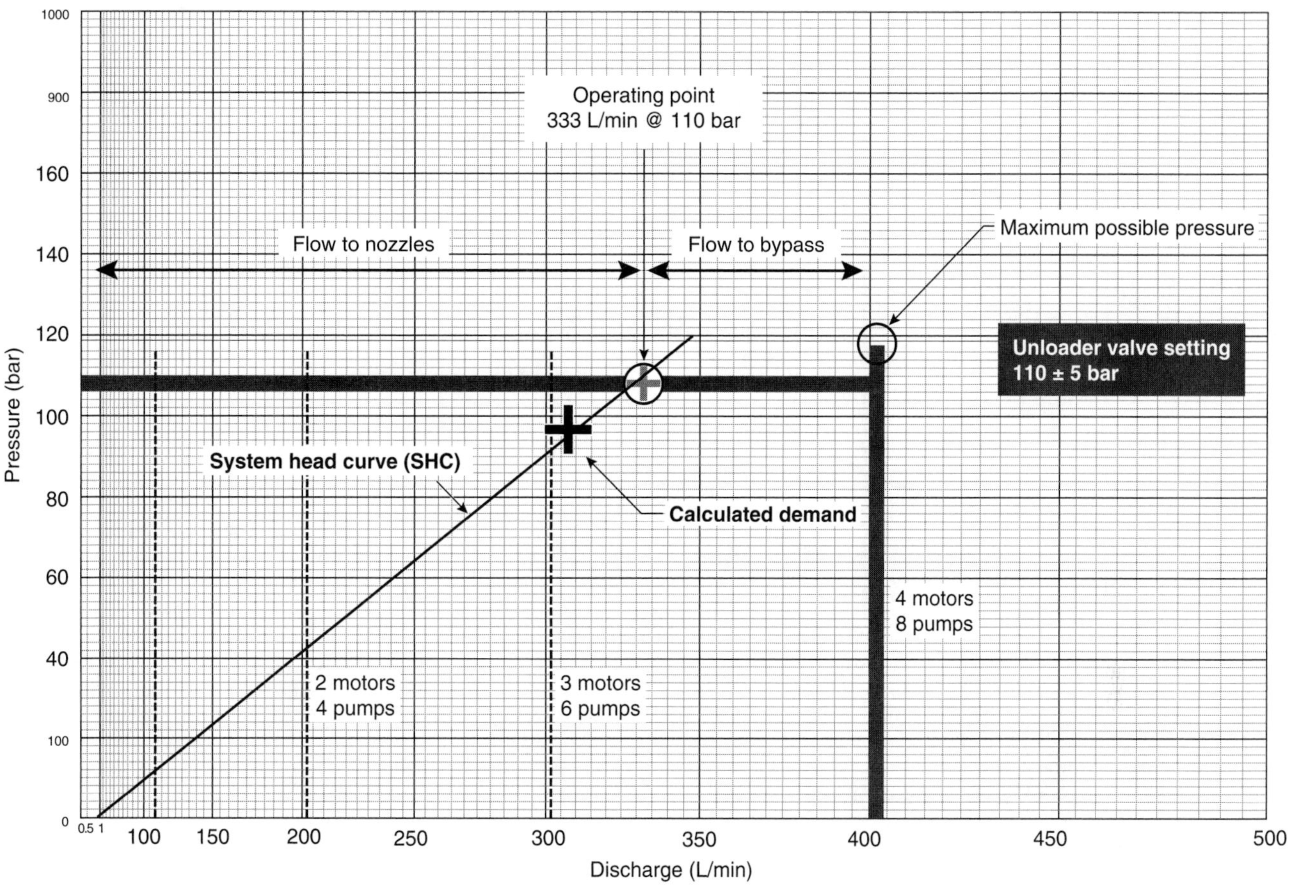

FIGURE 16.8.20 Composite Pump Curve for an 8 Pump Assembly with Single or Multiple Unloader Valves Set at 110 Bar

unique setting, and then bring different numbers of pumps on line as needed to match the demand. If one unloader valve is set at one-half the setting of the other unloader valve, the pump curve has a stepped appearance, as shown in Figure 16.8.21.

Suppliers of high-pressure water mist pumps and pump assemblies use both of these strategies. A German company uses a motor driving a single-piston pump of 120 L/min volumetric output at 1800 rpm as its basic unit. To meet larger demands several motor/pump combinations are connected in parallel to a common header. An unloader valve is connected to the common header—it is sized to pass the total output of all pumps connected to the header, for example, 120, 240, 360 L/min or more. Figure 16.8.20 illustrates the resulting pump curve. One difficulty presented by using a single large-capacity unloader valve is that, with small flows such as with a single water mist sprinkler flowing, the unloader valve may "chatter," causing uneven flow to the single nozzle. The arrangement is adequate for deluge-type water mist systems for which a relatively large flow rate is required, but it is less suitable for sprinkler-type water mist systems with automatic nozzles, in which only one or several nozzles will be opened. It should also be noted that settings on unloader valves may vary by 5 bar or more (75 psi) above or below the set pressure. It is imperative to test the installed equipment to determine the as-built capacity of the combination of pump(s) and unloader(s).

A European manufacturer of high-pressure water mist systems uses a different strategy. A piston pump with a volumetric output of about 50 L/min at 1800 rpm is used as the basic unit. A single electric motor may drive from one to four such pumps. Each pump is equipped with its own unloader valve, and each unloader valve can be set to different pressure. This approach allows the pump assembly to provide small flows at very high pressure and larger flows at a lower pressure, usually one-half the pressure of the lower flow regime. Figure 16.8.21 shows the two-step pump curve for the arrangement.

Each piston pump has an output of 13 gpm (50 L/min) discharge capacity at 1800 rpm. Assume, for example, that the largest demand on a system is 19.8 gpm (75 L/min), and the smallest demand is one nozzle at, say, 5.3 gpm (20 L/min). Both pumps would be required to meet the largest demand, at 70-bar pressure and some flow going to waste. The smallest demand of a single nozzle is less than the output of one pump. The unloader set at 70 bar will send all of its flow to the bypass, and the unloader set at 140 bar will allow 20 L/min to flow to the nozzle and the unused 30 L/min to bypass to waste. Even though the constant Q output of a single pump at 13 gpm (50 L/min) exceeds the smallest demand, the unloader valves allow partial output flows.

Table 16.8.8 displays the equations needed to design a PD pump system. Equation 1 calculates the power required of a motor to achieve a specified pressure/flow condition. Equation 2

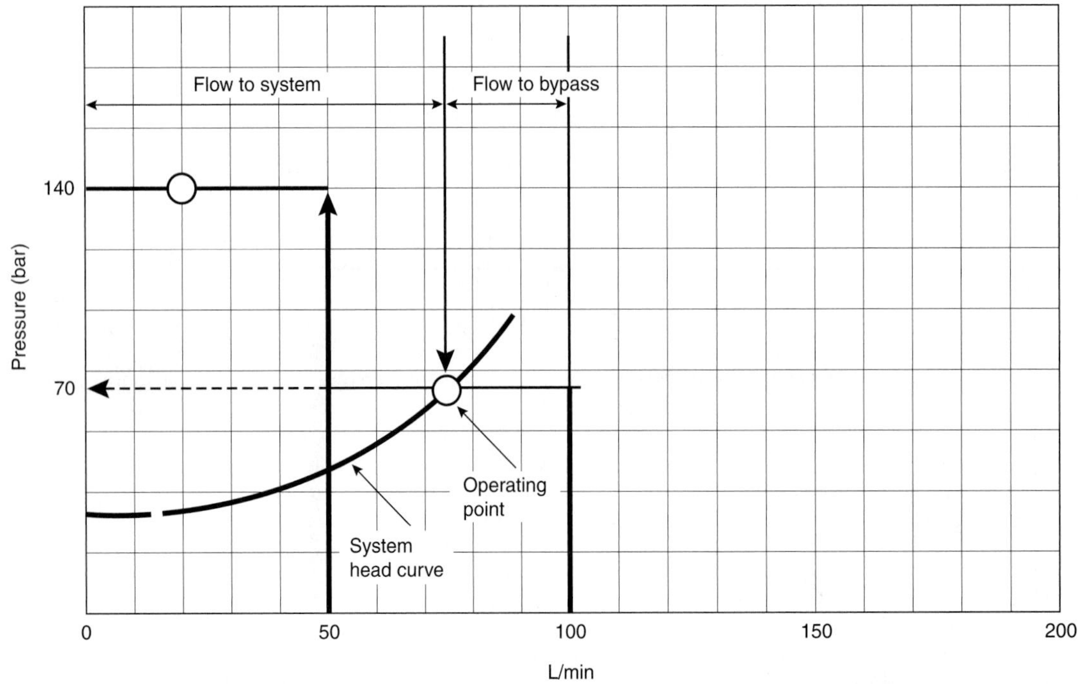

FIGURE 16.8.21 Composite Pump Curve for Two PD Pumps with Unloader Valves Driven by a Single Motor

TABLE 16.8.8 Basic Equations to Be Used in Design of PD Pump Assemblies

Pump Equations—Metric Units		*Pump Equations—U.S. Units*	
$kw = \dfrac{Ql \times H}{600 \times Em \times Ed}$	Eq. 1	$bHp = \dfrac{Qg \times P \times 2.31}{3960 \times Em \times Ed}$	Eq. 4
$H_{max} = \dfrac{kW \times 600 \times Em \times Ed}{Ql}$	Eq. 2	$P_{max} = \dfrac{bHP \times 3960 \times Em \times Ed}{Qg \times 2.31}$	Eq. 5
$\text{Amp} = \dfrac{kW \times 1000}{Em \times Pf \times V \times \sqrt{N}}$	Eq. 3	$\text{Amp} = \dfrac{bHP \times 746}{Em \times Pf \times V \times \sqrt{N}}$	Eq. 6
kW = Motor power, kW		bHP = Brake horsepower	
Ql = Discharge flow, L/min		Qg = Discharge flow, gal/min	
H = Discharge pressure, bar		P = Discharge pressure, psi gauge	
600 = Coefficient of 598.8 ~ 600		3960 = Coefficient for U.S. units	
Em = Efficiency of motor (0.88 to 0.92)		Em = Efficiency of motor (0.88 to 0.92)	
Ed = Efficiency of drive gear (<0.85)		Ed = Efficiency of drive gear (<0.85)	
Amp = Full load amp draw		Amp = Full load amp draw	
Pf = Power factor (~0.85 depends on motor)		Pf = Power factor (~0.85 depends on motor)	
V = Volts		V = Volts	
N = Number of phases in supply (N = 3)		N = Number of phases in supply (N = 3)	

calculates the maximum pressure that could be achieved using a specific motor with a specific PD pump. Equation 3 is used to calculate the full-load amp draw in order to size the electrical supply. All electrical equations assume 60 Hz frequency power.

Some very large water mist systems, such as those installed on cruise ships and in the oil and gas processing industry, make use of multiple assemblies of motors and PD pumps capable of providing specific flow rates to different zones. A controller is programmed to start a specified number of electric motors depending on which system is activated. Each system of nozzles will have its unique hydraulic characteristic, referred to as a system head curve (SHC). The SHC for any system is obtained by performing hydraulic calculations on the piping system to determine the total head losses at a given discharge rate. When the water supply is activated, the actual operating point can be determined by plotting the system head curve (SHC) for the piping system on the plot of pump curves. In Figure 16.8.21, which is a Cartesian plot, the SHC has an actual curve shape. When plotted on $N = 1.85$ hydraulic graph paper, as in Figure 16.8.20, the SHC is a straight line. For a complex assembly of multiple pumps and unloader-valve settings, the hydraulic plot looks like Figure 16.8.22.[89]

Figure 16.8.22 shows a plot of an assembly that includes 6 motors and 24 pumps. The assembly was designed to meet the different demands of many separate water mist systems in machinery modules of different sizes. The composite pump curve is determined by summing the number of motors, the number of pumps per motor, the volumetric capacity of each pump, and the settings on the unloader valves on individual pumps. The demand for each water mist system must be calculated separately and plotted on the graph. The SHC represented by the constant *K* line (dashed line) for the calculated point is projected to where it intersects the supply curve. This determines the operating point for the system and how many motors and pumps will be needed. A programmable controller is used to start the correct number of motors for a given water mist system demand. When a separate detection system calls for release of a water mist system in a given machinery module, the controller starts the number of motors needed to meet the precalculated demand. Figure 16.8.22 was used for acceptance testing to confirm that the PD pump system design for a large facility in Alaska was correct.[89]

As recommended by NFPA 750, when conditions permit, a full system discharge should be performed with recordings of critical pressures throughout the duration of the test. In the case shown, the actual measured operating point was above the calculated value, indicating either an error in the calculation or a significant difference between design and as-built piping. There

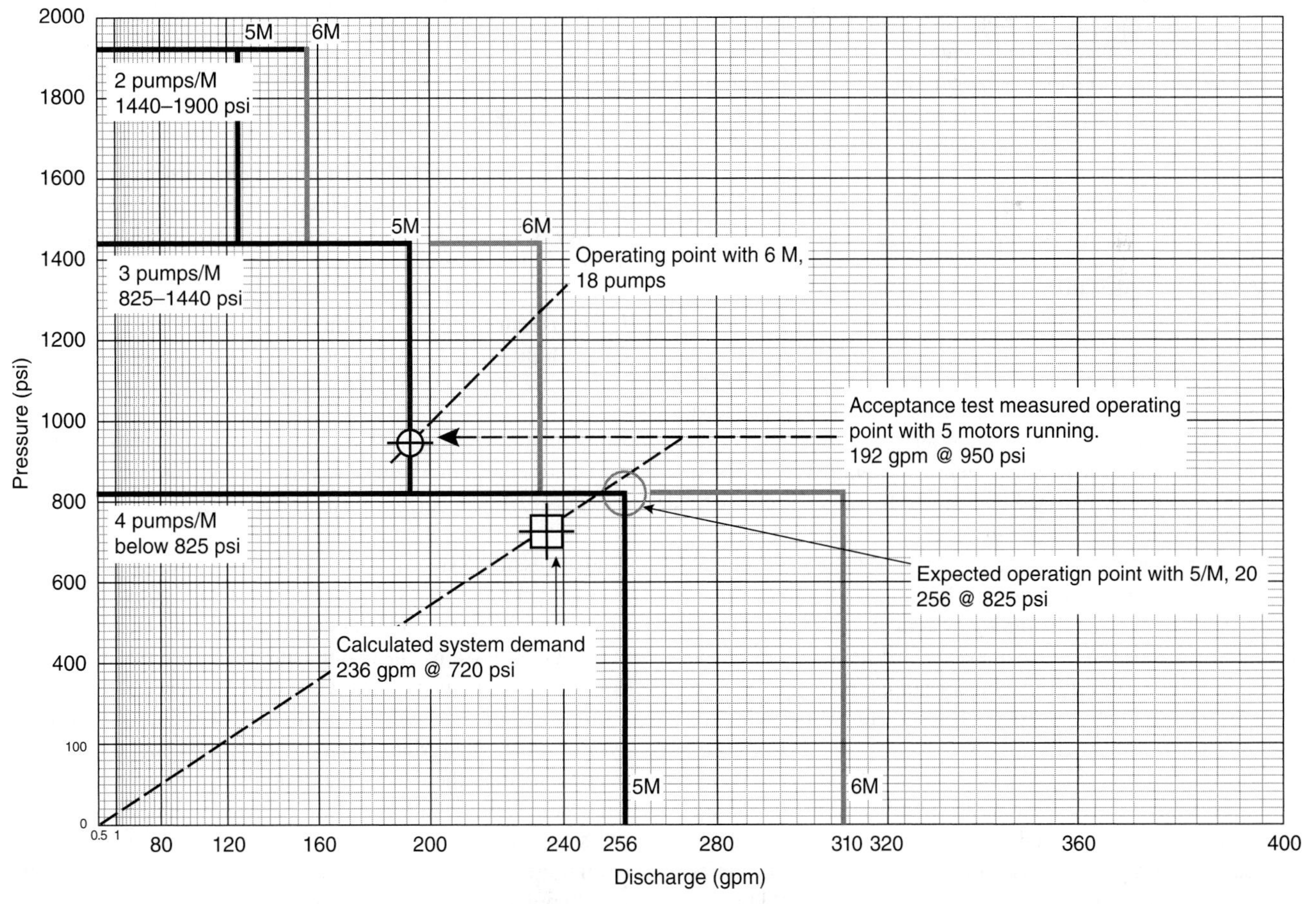

FIGURE 16.8.22 Hydraulic Diagram for Acceptance Test of a Water Mist System. Measured operating point indicates piping system is more restricted than calculated. Solution was to program system to operate six rather than five motors.

is a tendency to interpret a higher pressure on a system as corresponding to a higher discharge from the system. That interpretation only applies for a demand curve (i.e., a system head curve), for which a pressure increase corresponds to an increase in discharge. But a discharge pressure measured as part of a pump test represents the operating point of the system, where the demand curve intersects the supply curve. For a supply curve, a higher than expected pressure corresponds to a lower discharge rate. This principle applies for both centrifugal and PD pumps. Therefore, the operating point plotted in Figure 16.8.22 lies on the vertical portion of the pump curve above the lowest pressure setting of the fourth unloader, for which the total flow rate is *less than* the design flow rater for the system. In this case plotting the results of the full-system discharge test on the hydraulic graph sheet revealed the problem. After confirming that the hydraulic calculations were correct, the possible remedial actions were to (a) investigate the piping system to find and remove any restrictions, and (b) change the control program to start six motors instead of five motors for this system. In the particular case, the control program was changed to start another motor to increase the flow to at least the minimum design flow rate.

SYSTEM TYPES

NFPA 750 has introduced descriptive terms that classify water mist systems according to four basic characteristics of their design. The four parameters used as the basis of description are (1) system operation method, (2) operating pressure, (3) application, and (4) nozzle type. The reasons for classifying systems according to these four classifications are presented in the following sections.

System Operation Method

Systems may be described as deluge, dry-pipe, preaction, or wet-pipe systems. These descriptions are the same as those used for automatic sprinkler systems.

Deluge Systems. Deluge systems utilize open nozzles spaced throughout a compartment or around an object to be protected. Water is held out of the piping system by a *deluge* valve, which can be automatically released on a signal from a control panel. The system requires a separate fire detection system, which provides the signal to the control panel to release the water. Manual release features are always provided as well. When the deluge valve opens, water fills the piping system and discharges from all water mist nozzles simultaneously. The deluge system operation is widely used for machinery compartments and other applications where it is necessary to completely surround a fire with mist.

Dry-Pipe Systems. Dry-pipe systems utilize normally closed automatic nozzles on a closed piping system. The piping is pressurized with compressed gas. Some low-pressure water mist systems may use a differential-type dry-pipe valve held closed by the gas pressure. Such systems are then exactly equivalent to a standard dry-pipe sprinkler system. In the case of high-pressure water mist systems, there are no differential-type sectional control valves. The control valve is electrically activated and must be released by the fire alarm control panel (FACP). The signal to open the valve may come from a pressure sensor that responds to decreasing system pressure when an automatic nozzle is opened by heat. Pneumatic valves designed to open on a differential pressure are available.

Preaction Systems. A preaction system is similar to a dry-pipe system in that it utilizes closed nozzles on a piping system that contains no water. Water is prevented from entering the piping network by means of a valve that can be opened automatically by a control panel. A supplementary detection system is required to signal that there is a fire in the compartment and to open the valve. Water then enters and fills the piping, at which point the system operation is identical to a wet-pipe system. Water is not discharged until the heat is sufficient to actuate a nozzle. Just like a standard preaction sprinkler system, a low air pressure in the piping can be monitored to supervise the integrity of the piping system. A loss of air pressure would reveal a leak in the piping without resulting in a discharge of water.

Wet-Pipe Systems. A wet-pipe system consists of an array of closed nozzles on a piping network that is filled with water. Each nozzle is equipped with a thermal sensing element, like a sprinkler, which opens the nozzle when exposed to fire (hence, an *automatic* nozzle). As nozzles are opened by heat, water discharges immediately. This sprinkler-system-like configuration is suitable for many applications.

Operating Pressure

A second characteristic that differentiates system types is the range of operating pressure. Three categories have been defined by NFPA 750 as (1) low-pressure, (2) intermediate-pressure, and (3) high-pressure systems.

Low-Pressure System. In this water mist system the distribution piping is exposed to pressures of 175 psi (12.1 bar) or less.

Intermediate-Pressure System. In this water mist system the distribution system piping is exposed to pressures greater than 175 psi (12.1 bar) but less than 500 psi (34.5 bar).

High-Pressure System. In this water mist system the distribution system piping is exposed to pressures of 500 psi (34.5 bar) or greater. The working pressure regime of a water mist system is determined by the manufacturer's choice of nozzle. It is possible to create water mist with suitable spray characteristics in all three pressure regimes. With the exception of twin-fluid systems (and Nano-Mist), most commercial water mist systems operate in either the intermediate- or high-pressure range. Even if the nozzle is rated for 175 psi (12 bar) minimum operating pressure, which is the limit of low-pressure water mist, the operating pressure will by definition be higher than the minimum nozzle pressure; hence, it will be an intermediate-pressure system. Most of the advantages and disadvantages of high- versus low-pressure systems have already been discussed. In general, the use of high-pressure nozzles may increase spray velocity, which may translate to greater nozzle spacings and lower overall flow rates than low-pressure systems.

Although not introduced in NFPA 750, further distinction can be made between constant pressure systems and declining pressure systems. In general the distinction is between a pumped system versus one driven by cylinders of compressed gas. For water mist systems utilizing centrifugal-type pumps, or positive displacement pumps with a single unloader valve on the common header, the nozzle pressures remain approximately constant over the design area throughout the 30-minute discharge. In gas-driven systems, the nozzle pressure declines continuously over the duration of protection. In performing acceptance testing of declining pressure systems, the author has used the minimum pressure available at the end of the discharge in the approval test report as the criterion for minimum operating pressure.

Not all pumped systems are necessarily constant pressure systems, however. For marine water mist sprinkler systems utilizing pumps with a single unloader valve, a constant pressure system is designed on the basis of a minimum operating pressure at the most remote nozzle in a 180 m^2 (2000 ft^2) design area. The minimum operating pressure is the pressure that was used in the approval tests. For systems designed to use assemblies of positive displacement pumps with unloader valves on individual pumps, it is possible to design for at least two pressure regions, one higher than the other (see Figure 16.8.21). During the early stages of a fire, a few automatic nozzles may open. The pump assembly can deliver the required volume of water at a very high pressure. As more automatic nozzles open, the pump assembly can deliver the larger flow but at a lower pressure (determined by the pressure setting on the unloader valves). The system might be designed then for a design area of 100 m^2 (1100 ft^2) at 120 bar (1740 psi) and 180 m^2 (2000 ft^2) at 60 bar (870 psi). A similar concept of having to prove hydraulic capacity for two design conditions has been applied to sprinkler system designs in the past.[90]

Application

Three different types of applications are described in NFPA 750. These are (1) local, (2) total compartment, and (3) zoned applications.

Local Application. This configuration is used to protect a specific hazard or object. An example may be the protection of a piece of equipment in a large compartment. The system would be designed to discharge water mist directly onto the object. Figure 16.8.23 depicts a local application system.

Total Compartment Application. This type of system provides protection to all fire hazards and all areas in a compartment. The open nozzles are positioned in a grid so that water mist discharges approximately uniformly throughout the entire volume. Figure 16.8.24 illustrates a total compartment application system.

Zoned Application. This type of system is configured to discharge mist from portions of a larger system as required to control fire in a specific part of a compartment. It would be considered, for example, in circumstances where the water demand for a total compartment system (i.e., a deluge system), would be beyond the capability of the water supply. Zoning the water mist piping network, however, requires the installation of a detection system capable of pinpointing the exact location of the fire in the compartment or portion of a tunnel and a piping control system capable of opening or closing specific valves in the distribution network. Research focused on achieving accurate fire detection and location for zoning purposes continues.[91]

Figure 16.8.25 illustrates elements of a zoned application system. Clearly, water mist systems for tunnels must be zoned

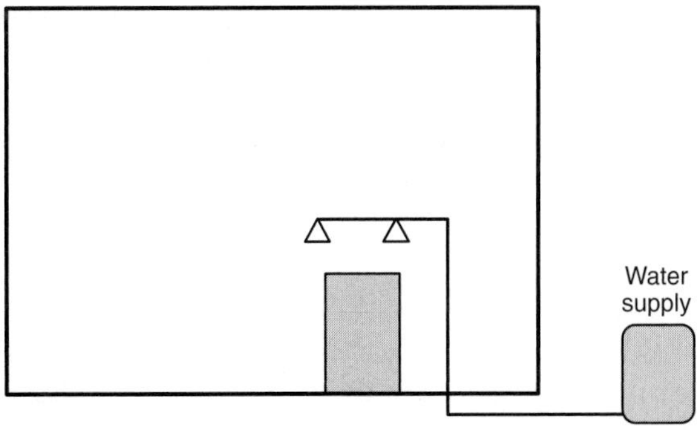

FIGURE 16.8.23 Local Application System

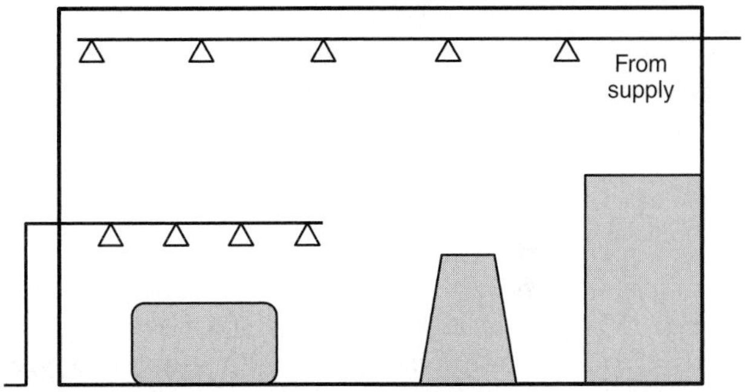

FIGURE 16.8.24 Total Compartment Application with Local Application System

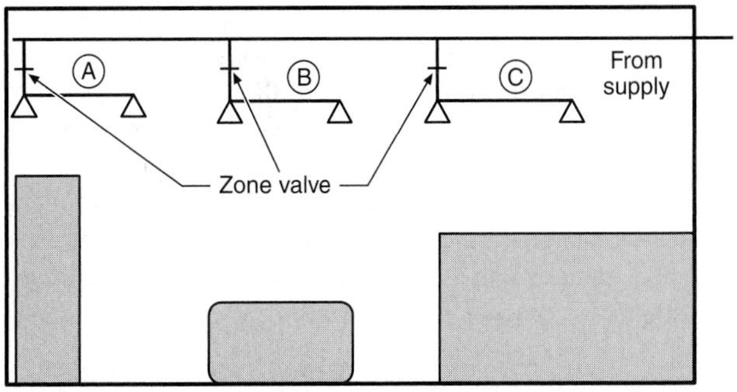

FIGURE 16.8.25 Zoned Application

in order to limit the total waterflow requirement. Typically, the design is based on the flow required for three zones—the zone where the fire is detected, plus one zone upstream and one zone downstream, to accommodate the possibility of a fire occurring at the boundary between two zones.

Nozzle Type

The nozzle type constitutes the fourth parameter for classifying water mist systems. Nozzles have been described as "open" or "closed" in previous text. Open nozzles have also been referred to as "nonautomatic" nozzles because they play no role in whether water is released. That is determined by the supplemental detection system. However, closed nozzles are designed with thermal sensing elements or other features that allow them to open, individually and automatically, in the presence of fire. Thus, NFPA 750 has adopted the terms (1) *nonautomatic,* (2) *automatic,* and (3) *hybrid* to describe the operation principle of types of nozzles. Characteristics of the types of nozzles are described elsewhere in this chapter.

SYSTEM COMPONENTS

As with all fire protection systems, water mist systems require their own unique set of hardware features, components, and materials. Basic components include but are not limited to pipe, fittings, valves, hangers, gas and water containers, nozzles, strainers, pumps, and detection system components.

The quality of system components and the overall reliability of water mist systems can be enhanced by using materials and components that comply with internationally recognized standards or material specifications. This is addressed in NFPA 750 by requirements for most components of systems to be listed for specific duty in water mist systems. The requirement of listing is particularly emphasized in North America. Marine authorities and European users have accepted water mist system technology on the basis of component testing done under the auspices of the International Maritime Organization (IMO) test protocols. The first water mist systems installed in North America contain components that were not listed at the time of installation but were part of systems being marketed internationally. Examples include pumps, motors, controllers, and the tubing clamps used on stainless steel tubing systems. As the acceptance of water mist systems increases, manufacturers continue to complete the North American listing requirements for their components.

It is important to ensure that all components in a water mist system, not just the water mist nozzles, are evaluated for functionality and reliability as part of the listing process. FM Global Approval standard number 5560 contains comprehensive requirements for listing of water mist system components, including positive displacement pump assemblies and controllers. Some additional design considerations for selection of pumps, detection, actuation and supervision of control equipment, and miscellaneous components are offered here.

Pumps

Pumps used to deliver the necessary flow and pressure to system pipe networks will be of the centrifugal type or the positive displacement type. The reliability of centrifugal fire pumps, pump drivers, and controllers are well regulated by NFPA 20, *Standard for the Installation of Stationary Pumps for Fire Protection.* Centrifugal pumps are suitable for use in low-pressure and possibly intermediate-pressure systems. They are not practical, however, for water pressures in the high-pressure regime (500 psi [34.5 bar]). High-pressure water mist systems utilize positive displacement (PD) pumps.

A number of issues relating to control of positive displacement pumps require close attention. For example, the controller functions necessary for an assembly of positive displacement pumps are not compatible with NFPA 20 requirements for fire pump controllers. Traditional centrifugal fire pump installations did not consider the need to operate many small motors, so each motor has its own controller. For multipump assemblies with many motors, there is one controller for the assembly, not for each motor. This difference invokes a need to modify requirements in NFPA 20 pertaining to locked rotor current and to permit timed shutdown of individual motors. The idea of starting and stopping individual motors in an assembly of motors conflicts with the basic practice of automatic start/manual stop for fire pumps. System features such as the electrical power supply connections, location and sizing of circuit breakers, and supervision are no different than conventional fire pump installations, and NFPA 20 should be followed. Acceptance testing of PD pump assemblies can prove problematic due to the difficulty of achieving accurate pressure setting on unloader valves. Variances of 5 bar (75 psi) or more over nominal settings are common; as a result the measured performance curve for the pump may not match its theoretical value. It is important to evaluate the adequacy of the PD pump or pump assembly on the as-built performance curve.

Table 16.8.9 compares technical features of centrifugal and PD pumps that should be taken into consideration by a designer of water mist systems (from NFPA 750).

Detection, Actuation, Alarm, and Control Equipment

Detection systems for water mist systems must be designed and installed in accordance with *NFPA 72, National Fire Alarm Code®* (CAN/ULC S524-M86 and S529-M87). The releasing device must also comply with these codes when appropriate. All the detection and control equipment used to activate a preaction system or a deluge system must work at the time of the fire. In addition to increasing the reliability of the system, evaluations and performance tests evaluate system controls to ensure that the possibility of inadvertent activation is minimized.

In the same manner that fire pumps require a specific set of features to be supervised, supervision of certain detection and control features is also necessary. System alarm, trouble signals, or both are necessary for critical parts of the electrical control system. These alarms include the following:

- System activation (alarm)
- Power failure (supervisory)
- Valve position (supervisory)
- Detector operation (alarm)
- Detector status (supervisory)

TABLE 16.8.9 Design Considerations for Centrifugal and Positive Displacement Pumps

Feature	*Centrifugal Pump*	*Positive Displacement Pump*
Ability to achieve high pressure	High pressure requires high speed and or multistage design.	High pressure limited only by the power of the driver (brake horsepower or kilowatts) and strength of materials.
Pressure and flow pulsation	Pressure and flow are smooth, varying only with system backpressure or pump speed. Pulsation dampers are unnecessary. Gauges and instruments can be directly mounted on piping or pump skid.	Pressure and flow are sinusoidal, varying with each plunger stroke or gear rotation. Pulsation damper in the suction piping can improve NPSH. Pulsation damper in the discharge piping can reduce vibratory stress to system and relief valve. Gauges and instruments should take their signals via flexible tubing or wiring and should not be mounted on the piping at the pump skid. *Note: Pulsation is not a problem at 1750 rev/min. Use of variable speed drivers in a PD pump system may introduce pulsation problems at slow motor speeds.*
Head curve	Flow from pump depends on backpressure from system. For any given pump speed, there is a maximum pressure that can be achieved. If operated at no-flow shutoff condition and maximum pressure, pump will vibrate and experience accelerated wear but will not fail catastrophically. Churning may heat water to boiling, but small bypass flow sufficient is to prevent boiling.	Flow from PD pump is proportional to pump speed and nearly independent of system backpressure. If flow from the pump is blocked partially or completely, discharge pressure will increase until full flow is forced past the blockage or something breaks. "Multistep pump curve" results when unloader valves are provided on each pump in a multipump assembly.
Relief valve	Not needed if the piping is designed to accommodate the maximum pressure achievable from the pump plus static suction head.	Pressure relief valve is needed. Relief valve must tolerate pressure pulsation produced by the pump.
Net positive suction head (NPSH)	Most centrifugal pumps used in fire service can tolerate a wide range of available NPSH. Ordinary design of suction piping is acceptable.	In general, PD pumps are more sensitive to NPSH than centrifugal pumps. Special care with the design of the suction piping must be taken to provide as much NPSH as possible.
Pump start-up	Conventional pump start-up strategies. Soft-start controllers.	Maximum pressure can be achieved with the first plunger stroke. Use of an unloader valve in the discharge piping is common. Manufacturers recommend motors with high starting torque. Constant torque motors required.
Strainers, sensitivity to dirty water	Silty water is not critical for pump flow passages. Some pumps have water lubricated surfaces that could be adversely affected. Strainer for the protection of water mist nozzles could be on suction or discharge side of the pump.	Silty or murky water is less critical for pump flow passages. Pumps are oil lubricated. Strainers and/or filters for the protection of water mist nozzles are required on the suction side of the pump. Strainers and filters reduce NPSH available. A suction booster pump may be required to meet minimum NPSH for pumps.
Foundation	Ordinary	Compared to centrifugal pumps additional rigidity and mass are helpful because of vibration caused by pulsating flow.
Pump motor link	Typically operate at motor speed. Close-coupled or direct drive via flexible coupling.	May operate at less than motor speed. Belt drive or geared speed reducer is typical. Pulsations and starting torque are considerations in the design of the speed reducer. Possible to have multiple pumps on one motor, with one pump driven directly by the shaft and the other(s) driven by chain drives.

Some systems may use pneumatic lines to activate system valves. These control lines should be protected against mechanical damage as well as fire damage. A means of supervising such pneumatic lines for integrity is necessary.

Water mist systems should also be equipped with a manual means of operation, for those situations in which the fire is discovered by people in the vicinity of the fire, prior to the fire being detected by the detection system. The manual means of activation should be independent of the automatic features, to the extent possible, to allow for the system to operate in the event of a catastrophic control failure. Manual releasing stations should be provided at the main system control valves or at other conspicuous areas within or near the protected hazard.

Miscellaneous Components

The discussion so far has centered on those components that are different than those used in similar types of water-based fire protection systems or special hazard systems.

Water mist systems may use a variety of valves that control everything from the discharge of the water to the discharge of the atomizing medium. Valves should be selected for their particular function and should be capable of sustaining the system pressure to which they will be subjected. All valves should be labeled as to the portion of the system that they control, and they should be supervised in the normal (open or closed) position.

Electrically activated sectional control valves are used on high-pressure systems. These valves can have very high head losses. Manufacturers should provide data on hydraulic performance of such valves to the designer. Electrically activated valves should be supervised. Special methods of supervision may be required where electrical valves operate on AC current. Where possible, valves should be of the indicating type and allow for manual release. Pressure-regulating devices will be found on any part of a system that may subject the valve, pipe, fitting, or nozzle to an operating pressure higher than the working pressure of the device.

Check valves may be necessary in a number of locations on water mist systems. Check valves should be installed in the following locations:

- At the point between the system piping and the system water supply
- On twin-fluid systems, in the pipe network, to prevent atomizing medium from entering the water supply pipe and to prevent the water supply from entering the atomizing medium

Pressure gauges are necessary to monitor key points within the system to verify that proper water pressure or atomizing medium pressure is available. These locations include the following:

- Pressurized side of all water and atomizing media connections
- Pressurized side of all system control valves
- Pressurized storage containers
- Suction side of all pumps

In general, the gauges are used to verify system status as part of a preventive maintenance program. Gauges should be selected such that they can withstand at least two times the working pressure associated with the particular system.

SYSTEM WATER SUPPLY AND ATOMIZING MEDIUM CONSIDERATIONS

Reliability of the water supply and atomizing medium is crucial to the performance of a water mist system. There are various engineering factors that affect reliability. For water, the major issues are whether it is free of silt or debris that could plug nozzles and free of bacteria that could cause algae growth in water storage vessels. For compressed gas media gas-driven systems, the major issue is whether the quantity is sufficient to meet the flow rate and duration required.

Water Supplies

For pumped water supplies there should be an automatic water supply to feed the pump. NFPA dictates that the supply should be at least equivalent to potable water, or natural seawater, with respect to particulates. Screens and filters are required on the supply connection to ensure that particulate matter in the water does not get into the piping and nozzles. Marine systems are equipped with a seawater connection, so that supply can be switched to a seawater source after the fresh-water supply is depleted. Seawater intakes typically draw marine life into the inlet. The IMO dirty water component test is intended to demonstrate that dirty water can be pumped through the screens and filters and not plug the nozzles.

Duration of water supply has been an interesting problem for end users. NFPA 750 requires a minimum supply duration of 30 minutes, except for preengineered systems with stored water supplies, for which there must be capacity to support two complete discharges of 10 minutes each. A problem has arisen in the field: FM Global Research and UL have listed systems for turbine enclosures and machinery spaces. These systems are expected to extinguish fire in less than 5 minutes and provide for 10 minute discharge time. The manufacturer has sold systems to end users with capacity for a 10 minute discharge duration, quoting the fact that the systems are FM approved. The FM Global Research approval documents state that discharge time shall be 10 minutes or the "coast down time of the turbine" (or by implication, the shutdown time of process lines containing hazardous fluids or gases). The systems installed provide only a 10-minute protection time. The installers have ignored the NFPA 750 requirement for either backup discharge or 30 minutes.

The NFPA 750 requirement for a minimum 30 minute discharge time should be observed in all cases. There may be circumstances where the facility is next door to a fire department where a 10-minute total capacity of the system is adequate. In many circumstances, however, 10 minutes is barely enough time for competent persons with necessary resources to react to the reality that a fire exists. To mobilize effective response in that time is unlikely. The fire test protocols for machinery spaces, for example, are based on fires in a compartment with a mockup of a diesel engine and bilge space. There are no overhead pipes, cable trays, or ducts in the test compartment. Real machinery spaces, in contrast, are filled with pipe, cable trays, and ducts. The clutter in a real machinery space is not simulated in the test compartment. Therefore, the performance of fire extinguishment in "less than 5 minutes" cannot be guaranteed in real spaces.

The time to extinguishment for a given fire size is a function of the fire size and compartment volume (see Figure 16.8.7). New FM Global Research test protocols for large machinery spaces (e.g., 1000 m^3) mandate minimum water supply durations of 60 minutes.

For pumped water supplies on high-pressure systems, it is sometimes necessary to utilize suction booster pumps on the suction supply to the fire pumps. The need arises because of the head losses created by the screens and filters that are required on the infeed to the pumps. Positive displacement pumps are particularly sensitive to low net positive suction head (NPSH) so attention to suction line details is necessary. Control over the additional pump must be worked into the control program to ensure that it operates when required.

In brief, water supplies for water mist systems must provide sufficient quantity (flow rate) at the pressure needed to supply pumps or refill reservoirs in a reasonable time. Minimum duration at design flow should be 30 minutes—shorter durations should only be considered for special cases after a fire protection engineering evaluation. Screens, strainers, and filters are needed to ensure the water is free from particulates that could plug the nozzles.

Water Quality

NFPA 750 mandates that water supplies for water mist systems must be at least equivalent to potable water or natural seawater with respect to particulates and dissolved minerals. Combined with the requirements for strainers and filters on the infeed piping and screens on individual nozzles, these measures were viewed as sufficient safeguards against plugging of nozzles. The requirements for corrosion-resistant pipe were also intended to minimize the possibility of scale in the piping. For systems utilizing a pumped water supply from a continuous source, the screening and filtering measurements are probably sufficient to avoid plugging of nozzles.

Many preengineered water mist systems involve water stored in vessels or pressure cylinders. It is possible that bacteria present in the stored water could result in algae growth in the tank. Filtering out the particulates during infill would not necessarily prevent bacterial activity in the stored water. Diligent maintenance is required to ensure the quality of stored water for water mist systems. Where there is a risk of *Legionella* bacteria in stored water, continuous ultraviolet treatment of the water should be provided. Equipment to achieve this is available.

Mandating the quality of the water supply is not sufficient to prevent plugging of nozzles. Cleaning of pipe and tubing and system flushing following installation are extremely important. High-pressure systems involving welded stainless steel piping have "purge paper" or "rice paper" inside the pipe after a weld is complete. The purge paper is used to provide a backing for argon gas used to minimize oxidation during the welding process. After the weld is complete, the purge paper remains inside the piping. For standard petroleum industry conditions, the purge paper is soluble in hydrocarbons and is usually flushed through the system. For water mist systems the purge paper becomes a jelly, and if it is not completely flushed from the piping it can stick to the inside of the pipe and plug the nozzles over an extended period of time. Extensive flushing of all branches of the piping system is essential to minimize future problems.

Plastic thread sealant tape such as Teflon tape should not be used on piping for water mist systems. Even with the greatest care in following good workmanship practices during installation, bits of Teflon tape appear on nozzle screens and will plug small orifices.

The important requirements with respect to water quality are as follows:

- Draw from a source with quality equivalent to potable water.
- Strain or filter water going into the system, including into storage reservoirs.
- Provide treatment for stored water to minimize possibility of algae or bacterial growth. (Do not use chlorination or bromination of water in systems with stainless steel pipe.)
- If necessary due to evidence of poor quality of stored water, provide screens or strainers on the outlet of stored water containers, sized to pass the design flow without excessive head losses even with partial blockage.
- Monitor water quality at regular intervals.

Atomizing Media

Twin-fluid systems require a supply of atomizing medium in addition to a reliable water supply. Air and nitrogen are the most commonly used compressed gases for water mist systems. The source of compressed gas must have the same level of reliability as the water supply. Two options are the use of dedicated compressed gas cylinders manifolded in banks and the use of plant air supplies in facilities that have the necessary capacity. If used, plant air supplies must be available on a continuous basis, not only while the plant is operating. Also, NFPA 750 limits moisture content to 25 ppm: plant air supplies may not always meet this quality standard. An air compressor that is listed for fire protection service may also be used as an acceptable supply of compressed gas. The unit should be connected to a backup power supply.

Compressed gas supplies must be monitored for high and low pressure and protected against physical or mechanical damage. Some of the supervisory functions expected on fire protection systems are difficult to achieve with gas cylinders. For example, the control valves on standard commercial gas cylinders are not of the indicating type. It is impossible to be certain that the valve has been opened without handling it. Vigilant system maintenance by qualified personnel is very important for the long-term reliability of water mist systems.

SYSTEM MAINTENANCE CONSIDERATIONS

A number of acceptance and commissioning tests must be performed once the installation of a system is completed. NFPA 750 specifies measures involved in the acceptance testing. These include a review of the design documentation, hydraulic calculations, working drawings, and the as-built installation. System piping is flushed and hydrostatically tested. All mechanical and electrical components are to be examined for correct installation and for functionality. Pumps are flow tested and, where possible, a system discharge test is carried out. Pumps are tested to confirm that they deliver the specified flow rate and pressure and that control features operate reliably. The acceptance tests are intended to identify the problems, which then must be corrected before the system is considered complete. The results of the acceptance tests must be recorded and kept with the system documentation. This basic documentation of all components of the system and acceptance test performance data is the basis on which the success of future maintenance practices rests.

After the acceptance testing, maintaining the reliability of the system depends on carrying out regular maintenance inspections. The owner or the tenant using the system is responsible for ongoing maintenance. NFPA 750 provides a table of recommended maintenance tasks to be carried out weekly, monthly, semiannually, or annually. The table in NFPA 750 was developed from common practices for similar fire protection systems involving pumps, compressed gas cylinders, water storage tanks, and detection and activation systems. Experience with installed water mist systems has increased since the time the table was drafted. A number of concerns specific to water mist systems have been discovered. The following list includes the most important concerns:

1. Water storage vessels must be equipped with a means of checking the level of water inside during a weekly or monthly inspection. Some high-pressure water storage cylinders do not have a means to confirm water levels. Some end users have installed weight scales to monitor the weight of the cylinders. If such cylinders are present in a system, extra measures to confirm water level should be implemented.
2. The quality of water in storage vessels should be checked for algae growth monthly or quarterly for the first year. A means of taking water samples should be provided. The vessels should be drained, flushed, and refilled at least quarterly or more frequently if water quality problems are identified by the monthly check.
3. Water mist systems make use of a variety of valves, some of which are not of the indicating type. It is not always possible to determine whether a critical valve is open or closed from external appearance. Key control valves that must be normally open should be of the indicating type.
4. Some valves on water mist systems are electrically activated. A manual means of operating the valve should be provided.
5. Systems involving the use of banks of compressed gas cylinders connected in parallel use a combination of pneumatic master and slave valves. Operation of the master valve triggers the release of all connected slave valves. Important differences between valves may not be evident to an inexpert maintenance person. Means of checking the readiness and functionality of pneumatic valves should be established. Valves should be marked to indicate whether they are the master or slave status.
6. An annual trip test should be conducted in all cases. If it is not possible to discharge water mist through the system nozzles, the discharge should be conducted through a test connection. The test connection should be designed to have the same K-factor as the actual piping system.
7. Confirmation of the adequacy of compressed gas supplies is best obtained by recording measurements of nozzle pressure throughout the discharge test. The minimum nozzle pressure must be sustained for the specified duration.

Table 16.8.10 is a modified version of the table in NFPA 750 specifying inspection frequencies. More complete discussion of maintenance requirements specific to the different types of water mist systems is provided in the NFPA handbook on inspection and maintenance of fire protection systems.[92]

SUMMARY

This chapter presents an overview of the history of development of water mist fire protection systems since 1990. Water mist fire suppression systems discharge less water, use smaller-diameter piping, and have lower overall weight than conventional water spray or sprinkler systems. Water mist can be used as a replacement for ozone-depleting substances such as halons and can be used in applications where water was not previously considered practical. Water mist fire suppression systems are used in a wide variety of marine-based and land-based applications, including machinery spaces on ships as well as land facilities, turbine enclosures in offshore drilling platforms, marine accommodation areas, electrical equipment rooms, tunnels, hotels, heritage buildings, and art galleries. The last five years have seen an intense effort to develop water mist systems for electrical cable, highway, and rail tunnels.

The objectives and characteristics of water mist systems are described for Class B fires in machinery spaces and turbine enclosures and for Class A fires in accommodation spaces, hotels, and heritage buildings. Use of water mist in electrical equipment rooms and computer rooms is discussed. The mechanisms by which water mist controls or extinguishes fire are described in detail, including flame cooling, evaporation of small droplets, enclosure effects, radiation attenuation, and others. Pressure fluctuations due to rapid cooling of a hot gas layer are described. The concept is established that water sprays must be described in terms of the range of drop sizes contained in the spray, not a single representative diameter. The chapter explains the role of spray momentum in allowing water mist to penetrate a strong fire plume or to penetrate a field of obstructions. The different types of nozzles, including impingement, pressure jet, and twin-fluid types, are described. Nozzles may be of the automatic type (thermally activated like sprinklers) or of the nonautomatic type (open nozzles). New technology involving ultra-fine mist (Nano-Mist) is referenced.

A section on hydraulic calculations for single-fluid and twin-fluid systems is presented. The chapter describes how positive displacement pumps are matched to variable-demand fire protection systems. The role of the unloader valve, which sends unused flow from the pump to a bypass, is explained. Acceptance testing of positive displacement pumps or pump assemblies must allow for variance in unloader valve settings.

TABLE 16.8.10 Recommended Inspection and Testing Frequencies for Water Mist Systems

Item	*Activity*	*Frequency*
Ambient conditions, temperature +4°C to 54°C in water tank/valve area	Check	Daily during extreme weather
Water tank (unsupervised)	Check water level	Weekly
Air receiver (unsupervised)	Check air pressure	Weekly
Dedicated air compressor (unsupervised)	Check air pressure	Weekly
Water tank (supervised)	Check water level	Monthly
Water tank	Check water quality	Monthly
Water tank	Drain, flush, refill	Quarterly first year
System strainer and filters	Inspect	Annually and whenever water has passed through it (after each refill)
Air receiver (supervised)	Check air pressure	Monthly
Dedicated air compressor (supervised)	Check air pressure	Monthly
Air pressure cylinders (unsupervised)	Check air pressure and indicator disk	Monthly
System operating components, including control valves (locked/unsupervised)	Inspect	Monthly
Air pressure cylinders (supervised)	Check air pressure and indicator disk	Quarterly
System operating components, including control valves	Inspect	Quarterly
Waterflow alarm and supervisory devices	Inspect	Quarterly
Initiating devices and detectors	Inspect	Semiannually
Batteries, control panel, interface equipment	Inspect	Semiannually
System strainers and filters	Inspect	Annually
Control equipment, fiber-optic cable connections	Inspect	Annually
Piping, fittings, hangers, nozzles, flexible tubing	Inspect	Annually

The chapter reviews the NFPA 750 classification of water mist systems as wet pipe, dry pipe, or preaction type; total compartment flooding, local application or zoned systems. The respective merits of low-, intermediate-, and high-pressure options are discussed; the concept of constant pressure water mist systems as opposed to declining pressure systems is introduced. Gas-driven systems are generally of the declining pressure type, but a water mist system utilizing assemblies of PD pumps may have a high-pressure mode and a lower-pressure design condition.

The importance of ensuring water quality to avoid potential plugging of small-orifice nozzles is highlighted. Issues relating to the supervision of certain equipment unique to water mist systems are raised. The chapter concludes with an overview of considerations pertaining to inspection testing and maintenance of water mist systems.

BIBLIOGRAPHY

References Cited

1. Braidech, M. M., Neale, J. A., Matson, A. F., and Dufour, R. E., "The Mechanism of Extinguishment of Fire by Finely Divided Water," Underwriters Laboratories Inc., for the National Board of Fire Underwriters, New York, 1955.
2. Rasbash, D. J., Rogowski, Z. W., and Stark, G. W. V., "Mechanisms of Extinction of Liquid Fuel Fires with Water Sprays," *Combustion and Flame,* Vol. 4, 1960, pp. 223–234.
3. IMO MSC/Circular 668, *Alternative Arrangements for Halon Fire-Extinguishing Systems in Machinery Spaces and Pump Rooms,* (a) Appendix A, "Component Manufacturing Standards of Equivalent Water-Based Fire-Extinguishing Systems," (b) Appendix B, "Interim Test Method for Fire Testing Equivalent Water-Based Fire-Extinguishing Systems for Machinery Spaces of Category A and Cargo Pump-Rooms," International Maritime Organization, London, UK, 1994.
4. IMO MSC/Circular 728, *Amendments to the Test Method for Equivalent Water-Based Fire-Extinguishing Systems for Machinery Spaces of Category A and Cargo Pump-Rooms* (Table updated October 30, 2006), Contained in MSC/Circular 668, Annex B, International Maritime Organization, London, UK, June 1996.
5. IMO MSC/Circular 913, *Guidelines for the Approval of Fixed Water-Based Local Application Fire-Fighting Systems for Use in Category A Machinery Spaces,* International Maritime Organization, London, UK, June 4, 1999.
6. IMO MSC/Circular 1165, *Revised Guidelines for the Approval of Equivalent Water-Based Fire-Extinguishing Systems for Machinery Spaces and Cargo Pump-Rooms,* International Maritime Organization, London, UK, June 10, 2005.
7. Wighus, R., Aune, P., Drangsholt, G., and Stensaas, J. P., "Fine Water Spray System—Extinguishing Tests in Medium- and Full-Scale Turbine Hood," *Proceedings* of the International Water Mist Conference, Swedish Testing Institute, Borås, Sweden, November 5–7, 1993.
8. Back, G. G., Beyler, C. L., DiNenno, P. J., Hansen, R., and Zalosh, R., "Full-Scale Testing of Water Mist Fire Suppression Systems in Machinery Spaces," Report No. CG-D-26-98, U.S. Coast Guard, Groton, CT, Oct. 1998.

9. "Evaluating the Extinguishing Effectiveness of the HI-FOG Fire Protection System in a Class 1 Machinery Space According to IMO MSC/CIRC 668," VTT Test Report No. RTE10310/98, Technical Research Centre of Finland (VTT), Espoo, Finland, Apr. 1998.
10. "Draft Test Protocol for Equivalent Sprinkler System for Cabin and Corridor Fires," International Maritime Organization, London, UK, July 1995.
11. Arvidson, M., Isaksson, S., and Tuomisaari, M., "Recommended Acceptance Criteria for Sprinkler Systems Equivalent to SOLAS II-2/12," SP Report 1995:20, Swedish National Testing and Research Institute, Borås, Sweden, 1995.
12. Arvidson, M., and Isaksson, S., "Equivalency Sprinkler Fire Tests," Nordtest Project 1152-94, SP Report 1995:19, Swedish National Testing and Research Institute, Borås, Sweden, 1995.
13. "Evaluating the Suppression Efficiency of the Hi-Fog Fire Protection System in Accommodation Areas on Passenger Ships According to IMO Res.A.800 (19)," VTT Test Report No. RTE10320/98, Technical Research Centre of Finland (VTT), Espoo, Finland, Aug. 1998.
14. IMO Res. A.800 (19), *Revised Guidelines for Approval of Sprinkler Systems Equivalent to That Referred to in SOLAS Regulations II-2/12,* (a) Appendix 1, "Component Manufacturing Standards for Water Mist Nozzles," (b) Appendix 2, "Fire Test Procedures for Equivalent Sprinkler Systems in Accommodation, Public Space and Service Areas on Passenger Ships," International Maritime Organization, London, UK, Dec. 1995.
15. "Proposed Draft Performance Requirements for Fine Water Spray Systems for the Protection of Light Hazard Occupancies," Factory Mutual Research Corporation (FM Global), Norwood, MA, 1997.
16. UL 2167, *Proposed First Edition of the Standard for Water Mist Nozzles for Fire Protection Service,* Underwriters Laboratories Inc., Northbrook, IL, June 1998.
17. Log, T., and Cannon-Brookes, P., "Water Mist Fire Protection of Historic Buildings and Museums," *Museum Management and Curatorship,* Vol. 14, 1995, pp. 283–298.
18. Log, T., "Flashover Suppression Using Fine Water Spray," INTERFLAM '96, Cambridge, UK, March 26–28, 1996.
19. Jensen, G., "A White Paper on Water Mist for Protection of Heritage," Interconsult ASSA, Trondheim, Norway, 2004, pp. 1–31.
20. Trevino, J. O., Fitch, W. E., and Forssell, E. W., "Electrical Hazards Represented by Marioff Hi-Fog Water Mist Systems Applied to Protect Electrical Spaces (Omega Point Laboratories, Inc. Tests.)," Hughes Associates, Inc., Baltimore, MD, 2004, pp. 1–38.
21. Gauthier, L. R., Jr., Bennett, J. M., et al., "The Effects of Water Mist Discharge on Energized LPD 17 Electrical Equipment in the Absence of Fire—Initial Studies," The Johns Hopkins University Applied Physics Laboratory, Washington, DC, 1999.
22. Mawhinney, J. R., DiNenno, P. J., and Williams, F. W., "Using Water Mist for Flashover Suppression on Navy Ships," Halon Technical Options Working Conference, Albuquerque, NM, April 27–29, 1999.
23. Muehlenbruch, G., "New Concept for Tunnel Fire Safety," *IWMA Newsletter,* Vol. 1/2000, International Water Mist Association, Vahldorf, Germany, Sept. 2000.
24. "Fire Performance Tests for Fine Water Spray Protection for Wet Benches and Other Processing Equipment," Factory Mutual Research Corporation, Norwood, MA, 1997.
25. Mawhinney, J. R., "Mercury Energy CBD Tunnel Project, New Zealand—Performance-Based Fire Testing of a Water Mist Fire Suppression System," *Proceedings* INTERFLAM '99, Interscience Communications, Edinburgh, UK, 1999.
26. Grant, G., and Southwood, P., "Development of an Onboard Fire Suppression System for Eurotunnel HGV Shuttle Trains," *Proceedings* INTERFLAM '99, Interscience Communications, Edinburgh, UK, June 1999.
27. Mawhinney, J. R., "Full-Scale Testing of an Onboard Hi-Fog Water Mist Fire Suppression System for Heavy Goods Vehicle Carriers in Railway Tunnels—August 1999 Fire Test Series," Client Report for Marioff Hi-Fog, Vantaa, Finland, 2000.
28. NFPA 502, *Standard for Road Tunnels, Bridges, and Other Limited Access Highways,* Appendix D, National Fire Protection Association, Quincy, MA, 2004.
29. Ingason, H., and Lönnermark, A., "Heat Release Rates from Heavy Goods Vehicle Trailer Fires in Tunnels," *Fire Safety Journal,* Vol. 40, 2005, pp. 646–668.
30. Mawhinney, J. R., "IF Tunnel Fire Test Series Report—Scoping Tests of a Prototype Hi-Fog Water Mist Fire Suppression System for Highway Tunnels," Client Report for Marioff Oy, Vantaa, Finland, Dec. 2002.
31. Mawhinney, J. R., "Approval Testing of a Hi-Fog Water Mist System for Protection of a Passenger Vehicle Highway Tunnel, Paris, France," Client Report HAI-5022-010-1, for Marioff Oy, Finland, Hagerbach Test Tunnel, Sargans, Switzerland, Oct. 7, 2005.
32. Mawhinney, J. R., and Ingason, H., "Full-Scale Fire Testing of Suppressed Heavy Goods Vehicle Fires in Road Tunnels," Client Report HAI 5022-010-2 for Marioff Oy, Finland, San Pedro de Anes Test Tunnel, Asturias, Spain, Feb. 2006.
33. Mawhinney, J. R., "A Critique of Claims of Smoke Scrubbing by Water Mist," *Proceedings* of the National Fire Protection Research Foundation, Fire Suppression and Detection Research Application Symposium, Tampa, FL, January 23–25, 2002.
34. "International Cabin Water Spray Research Management Group: Conclusions of Research Programme," CAA Paper 93012, Civil Aviation Authority, London, UK, 1993.
35. Hill, R. G., Marker, T. R., and Sarkos, C. P., "Evaluation and Optimization of an On-Board Water Spray Fire Suppression System in Aircraft," *Proceedings* of Water Mist Fire Suppression Workshop, NIST, Gaithersburg, MD, 1993.
36. Mawhinney, J. R., Dlugogorski, B. Z., and Kim, A. K., "A Closer Look at the Extinguishing Properties of Water Mist," in *Proceedings* of the International Association for Fire Safety Science (IAFSS) Conference, Ottawa, Canada, June 13–17, 1994.
37. Hanauska, C. P., and Back, G. G., "Halons: Alternative Fire Protection Systems, An Overview of Water Mist Fire Suppression Systems Technology," Hughes Associates, Inc., Columbia, MD, 1993.
38. Jones, A., and Thomas, G. O., "The Action of Water Sprays on Fires and Explosions," *Transactions* of the Institution of Chemical Engineers, Vol. 71, Part B, 1993, pp. 41–49.
39. Hadjisophocleous, G. V., Kim, A. K., and Knill, K., "Modeling of a Fine Water Spray Nozzle and Liquid Pool Fire Suppression," International Conference on Fire Research and Engineering, Orlando, FL, 1995, pp. 1–6.
40. Hadjisophocleous, G. V., and Knill, K., "CFD Modeling of Liquid Pool Fire Suppression Using Fine Water Sprays," Annual Conference on Fire Research, Gaithersburg, MD, 1994, pp. 71–72.
41. Hadjisophocleous, G. V., Cao, S., and Kim, A. K., "Modeling the Interaction Between Fine Watersprays and a Fire Plume," 4th International Conference on Advanced Computational Methods in Heat Transfer, Udine, Italy, July 1996.
42. Trelles, J., Mawhinney, J. R., and DiNenno, P. J., "Characterization of a High-Pressure Multi-Jet Water Mist Nozzle for the Purposes of Computational Fluid Dynamics Modeling," *Computational Simulation Models in Fire Engineering and Research—Proceedings,* Universidad de Cantabria, Cantabria, Spain, October 2004.
43. Back, G. G., Beyler, C. L., and Hansen, R., "A Quasi Steady-State Model for Predicting Fire Suppression in Spaces Protected by Water Mist Systems," Hughes Associates Report, *Fire Safety Journal,* Fall 2000.
44. Wighus, R., "Extinguishment of Enclosed Gas Fires with Water Spray," *Proceedings* of the 3rd International Symposium on Fire Safety Science, The University of Edinburgh, Edinburgh, Scotland, 1991.

45. Kanury, A. M., "Ignition of Liquid Fuels," *SFPE Handbook of Fire Protection Engineering,* 2nd ed., P. J. DiNenno et al. (Eds.), National Fire Protection Association, Quincy, MA, 1995.
46. Drysdale, D., *An Introduction to Fire Dynamics,* 1st ed., pp. 222–225, John Wiley and Sons, New York, 1985.
47. Mawhinney, J. R., "Water Mist Fire Suppression Systems for Marine Applications: A Case Study," *Proceedings* of IMAS 94: Fire Safety on Ships—Developments into the 21st Century, Institute of Marine Engineers, London, May 1994.
48. Mawhinney, J. R., "Characteristics of Water Mist for Fire Suppression in Enclosures," *Proceedings* of the Halon Alternatives Technical Working Conference, New Mexico Engineering Research Institute (NMERI), Albuquerque, NM, 1993.
49. Coppalle, A., Nedelka, D., and Bauer, B., "Fire Protection: Water Curtains," *Fire Safety Journal,* Vol. 20, 1993, pp. 241–255.
50. Ravigururajan, T. E., and Beltrav, M. P., "A Model for Attenuation of Fire Radiation through Water Droplets," *Fire Safety Journal,* Vol. 15, No. 2, 1989, pp. 171–181.
51. An, M. W., Sousa, A. C. M., and Venart, J. E. S., "Modeling of a Shipboard Waterfog Fire Suppression System," Report No. 991-1042-2045, University of New Brunswick, Fredericton, NB, 1994.
52. Kokkala, M. A., "Extinction of Liquid Pool Fires with Sprinklers and Water Sprays," Valtion Teknillinen Tutkimuskeskus, Statens Teniska Forskningscentral (Technical Research Centre of Finland), Espoo, Finland, 1989.
53. Ho, S. P., "Water Spray Suppression and Intensification of High Flash Point Hydrocarbon Pool Fires," [Ph.D. dissertation], Fire Protection Engineering, Worcester Polytechnic Institute, Worcester, MA, 2003.
54. "Draft Protection Requirements for Fine Water Spray Systems for the Protection of Combustion Machinery Spaces and Special Hazard Machinery Spaces—Class 5560," Factory Mutual Research Corporation (FM Global), Norwood, MA, 1997.
55. Mawhinney, J. R., "Engineering Criteria for Water Mist Fire Suppression Systems," *Proceedings* of Water Mist Fire Suppression Workshop, NIST, Gaithersburg, MD, 1993.
56. Back, G. G., Beyler, C. L., and Hansen, R., "The Capabilities and Limitations of Total Flooding Water Mist Fire Suppression System in Machinery Space Applications," *Fire Technology,* Vol. 36, No. 1, First Quarter, Feb. 2000.
57. ASTM E799, *Standard Practice for Determining Data Criteria and Processing for Liquid Drop Size Analysis,* American Society for Testing and Materials, W. Conshohocken, PA, 1992.
58. Lefebvre, A., *Atomization and Sprays,* Hemisphere Publishing Corporation, New York, 1989.
59. Hadjisophocleous, G. V., Kim, A. K., and Knill, K., "Physical and Numerical Modeling of the Interaction between Watersprays and a Fire Plume," National Research Council Canada, Ottawa, Canada, 1994.
60. Dlugogorski, B. Z., Mawhinney, J. R., Kim, A. K., and Crampton, G., unpublished laboratory data. National Fire Laboratory, National Research Council Canada, Ottawa, Canada, 1994.
61. Grosshandler, W., Lowe, D., Notarianni, K., and Rinkinen, W., "Protection of Data Processing Equipment with Fine Water Sprays," NISTIR 5514, National Institute of Standards and Technology, Gaithersburg, MD, 1994.
62. Mawhinney, J. R., Taber, B., and Su, J. Z., "The Fire Extinguishing Capability of Mists Generated by Flashing of Super-Heated Water," *Proceedings* of the American Institute of Chemical Engineers, 1995 Summer National Meeting, Boston, MA, July 30–August 2, 1995.
63. Ewing, C. T., Faith, F. R., Romans, J. B., and Hughes, J. T., "Extinguishment Properties of Dry Chemicals: Extinction Weights for Small Diffusion Pan Fires and Additional Evidences for Flame Extinguishment by Thermal Mechanisms," *Journal of Fire Protection Engineering,* Vol. 4, 1992, pp. 35–52.
64. Cortina, T. A. (Ed.), "Water Mist Fire Suppression System Health Hazard Evaluation: Response to Questions Posed by the US Environmental Protection Agency," Halon Alternatives Research Corporation, Washington, DC, Aug., 1995.
65. U.S. Environmental Protection Agency, "Protection of Stratospheric Ozone; Acceptable Substitutes for the Significant New Alternatives Policy (SNAP) Program," 40 CFR Part 82, *U.S. Federal Register,* Vol. 60, No. 145, July 28, 1995, p. 38731.
66. Pabon, M., "New Additive for Water Mist Systems on Class B Fires: Toxicological Study on Breathable Particles," Annual Meeting of International Water Mist Association, Berlin, Germany, September 29, 2005.
67. Mawhinney, J. R., and Back, G. G., "Bridging the Gap between Theory and Practice: Protecting Flammable Liquid Hazards Using Water Mist Fire Suppression Systems," Fire Suppression and Detection Research Application Symposium, Orlando, FL, February 25–27, 1998, National Fire Protection Research Foundation, National Fire Protection Association, Quincy, MA, 1998.
68. Back, G. G., "Coast Guard Tests for Local Application Protocols," Rpt No. CG-D-03-99, U.S. Coast Guard, Groton, CT, Feb. 1999.
69. Southwood, P., and Grant, G., "Eurotunnel's Full-Scale Fire Suppression Test Programme," International Conference on Tunnel Fires and Escape from Tunnels, May 5–7, 1999, Lyon, France.
70. Grant, G., and Southwood, P., "Development of an Onboard Fire Suppression System for Eurotunnel HGV Shuttle Trains." INTERFLAM '99, Edinburgh, UK, pp. 651–662.
71. Mawhinney, J. R., "A Linear Water Mist Fire Suppression System for Fixed Shelving in Archival Vaults," ICFRE 97, Gaithersburg, MD. Paper on file with the author.
72. Log, T., and Cannon-Brookes, P., "Water Mist for Fire Protection of Historic Buildings and Museums," *Museum Management and Curatorship,* Vol. 14, No. 3, 1995, pp. 283–298.
73. "Protecting Telephone Central Offices," *FMRC Update—A Progress Report from the Factory Mutual Research Corporation,* Vol. 6, No. 3, Factory Mutual Research Corporation, Norwood, MA, 1992, pp. 1–4.
74. FM Global Property Loss Prevention Data Sheet 4-2, *Water Mist Systems,* Jan. 2003
75. Blake, D., Marker, T., Hill, R., Reinhardt, J., and Sarkos, C., "Cargo Compartment Fire Protection in Large Commercial Transport Aircraft," *Proceedings* of the Fire Suppression and Detection Research Application Symposium, Research and Practice: Bridging the Gap, February 25–27, 1998, Orlando, FL, National Fire Protection Research Foundation, Quincy, MA, 1998, pp. 117–133.
76. Tuomisaari, M., and Kokkala, M., "Fire Suppression Tests of a Power Transformer in an Outdoor Installation with a Hi-Fog Fire Protection System," Research Report No. RTE10607/97, VTT Building Technology Centre, Espoo, Finland, 1997.
77. Mawhinney, J. R., and Carpenter, D. W., "Waterfog Fire Suppression System Project Full-Scale Fire Tests Summary Report," for Department of National Defense, Canada, Navy (DMEE 4–2), Client Report CR-A4007.4, National Research Council Canada, Ottawa, Canada, Mar. 1993.
78. Brown, R., and York, J. L., "Sprays Formed by Flashing Liquid Jets," *American Institute of Chemical Engineers Journal,* Vol. 8, No. 21, May 1962, pp. 149–153.
79. Sallet, D. W., Rod, S. R., Palmer, M. E., Nastoll, W., and Guhler, M., "Discharge of Flashing Liquid Through Tubes," *Proceedings* of the 2nd Multi-Phase Flow and Heat Transfer Symposium—Workshop, Miami Beach, FL, 1979.
80. Keary, J., and McGovern, F., "Characterization of a Heated Water Extinguishing System: Report Prepared for M. O'Connell," Department of Experimental Physics, University College Galway, Galway, Ireland, May 1994.
81. Forssell, E. W., Scheffey, J. L., et al., "False Deck Testing of NanoMist Water Mist Systems," Navy Technology Center for Safety and Survivability, Chemistry Division, Washington, DC, 2004, pp. 1–53.
82. Forssell, E. W., Scheffey, J. L., et al., "False Deck Development Testing of Hybrid Nitrogen–Water Mist Fire Suppression

Systems," Halon Options Technical Working Conference (HOTWC), New Mexico Engineering Research Institute (NMERI), Albuquerque, NM, 2004.
83. Forssell, E. W., Scheffey, J. L., et al., "False Deck Development Testing of Hybrid Nitrogen–Water Mist Systems—Interim Report (FY 2003)," Hughes Associates, Inc., Baltimore, MD, 2004, pp. 1–48.
84. Titus, J. J., "Hydraulics," *SFPE Handbook of Fire Protection Engineering,* 2nd ed., P. J. DiNenno et al. (Eds.), National Fire Protection Association, Quincy, MA, 1995.
85. Campbell, R. L., "Applicability of the Hazen-Williams Equation for Prediction of High Velocity Friction Loss in Fire Sprinkler Systems," University of Maryland, Department of Fire Protection Engineering, College Park, MD, 1997.
86. "Flow of Fluids Through Valves, Fittings, and Pipe," Technical Paper 410M, Crane Valves, St. Laurent, Quebec, Canada, 1986.
87. Mawhinney, J. R., "Final Report on Module 4932 Water Mist System Functional Checkout and Flow Test, December 16 and 18, 2003," Client Report for Veco Engineering, Anchorage, AK, Jan. 2004, p. 11.
88. ASME B31.1, *Power Piping,* American Society of Mechanical Engineers, New York, 2004.
89. Mawhinney, J. R., "A Review of Water Mist Fire Suppression Systems at the Phillips Alaska Alpine Site Central Facility, Prudhoe Bay, Alaska," Client Report CR 4814-1, by Hughes Associates, Inc., Baltimore, MD, Aug. 14, 2000.
90. Lougheed, G. D., Mawhinney, J. R., and O'Neill, J., "Full-Scale Fire Tests and the Development of Design Criteria for Sprinkler Protection of Mobile Shelving Units," *Fire Technology*, First Quarter, 1994, pp. 98–133 (NRCC-36140) (IRC-P-3387).
91. The Fire Protection Research Foundation, International Road Tunnel Fire Detection Research Project, National Fire Protection Association, Quincy, MA, Nov. 2003.
92. Mawhinney, J. R., "Inspection and Maintenance of Water Mist Systems," *Fire and Life Safety Inspection Manual*, 8th ed., R. E. Solomon (Ed.), National Fire Protection Association, Quincy, MA, 2002.

NFPA Codes, Standards, and Recommended Practices

Reference to the following NFPA codes, standards, and recommended practices will provide further information on water mist fire suppression systems discussed in this chapter. (See the latest version of The NFPA Catalog *for availability of current editions of the following documents.)*

NFPA 13, *Standard for the Installation of Sprinkler Systems*
NFPA 14, *Standard for the Installation of Standpipe and Hose Systems*
NFPA 15, *Standard for Water Spray Fixed Systems for Fire Protection*
NFPA 20, *Standard for the Installation of Stationary Pumps for Fire Protection*
NFPA 72®, National Fire Alarm Code®
NFPA 502, *Standard for Road Tunnels, Bridges, and Other Limited Access Highways*
NFPA 750, *Standard on Water Mist Fire Protection Systems*

Chapter 9

Water Spray Protection

Revised by

Kerry M. Bell

Chapter Contents

Key Terms

fixed water spray system, spray nozzle, water mist, water spray system, water supply

The term *water spray* refers to water that is discharged from specially designed nozzles or devices to produce a predetermined pattern, particle size, velocity, and density. The use of these designations cannot be taken as an indication of any specific discharge pattern or spray characteristics of the nozzles. NFPA 750, *Standard on Water Mist Fire Protection Systems,* has been developed to address the use of very fine water droplets from spray nozzles (see Section 16, Chapter 8, "Water Mist Fire Suppression Systems"). The primary distinction between a water spray and a sprinkler system is that of specific coverage versus general area coverage. Water spray systems have typically been provided to protect a specific piece of equipment with surface coverage. Water spray for fire protection has been called by various trade-name designations.

The discharge from water spray nozzles differs, generally, from the discharge from sprinklers. The pattern of the water spray discharged from spray nozzles onto a surface may be elliptical or circular, and the cross section of the projected discharge is conical. The water spray is forcefully directed onto the object or surface being protected. The pattern of spray nozzle discharge must carry water spray over the distance between the nozzle and the target, compensate for wind and draft conditions, and effectively hit the surface to be protected. The required discharge density in gpm/ft^2 (L/min/m^2) and complete coverage of the area to be protected are also essential elements.

Unlike most automatic sprinkler systems, water spray systems are usually of the deluge type. Generally, spray nozzles are not equipped with fusible operating elements. Spray nozzles may be equipped with internal pilot-pressure-controlled valves or with frangible or removable plugs or caps that will be displaced when the water spray deluge system is actuated. Pilot-pressure-controlled valves, plugs, or caps prevent corrosive atmospheres from entering the piping system. They may be used to retain water in the piping system for the purpose of speeding its delivery from the spray nozzles.

NFPA 15, *Standard for Water Spray Fixed Systems for Fire Protection,* is the standard applicable to water spray systems and should be consulted on details of system design and installation not covered in NFPA 13, *Standard for the Installation of Sprinkler Systems.*

This chapter covers the uses and applications of water spray systems for fire suppression, control, and extinguishment and describes the components of spray systems and the specialized uses of the systems. Because of the similarities between sprinkler systems and water spray systems, their water supply requirements, some of the equipment used in the systems, and the hydraulic calculations for determining water supplies, the chapters listed below should be consulted. The list includes chapters on releasing devices that can be used with water spray systems as well as protection of conveyor openings: Section 14, Chapter 2, "Automatic Fire Detectors"; "Section 15, Chapter 4, "Water Supplies for Sprinkler Systems"; Section 16, Chapter 3, "Automatic Sprinkler Systems"; Section 16, Chapter 7, "Ultra-High-Speed Water Spray Systems"; Section 16, Chapter 8, "Water Mist Fire Suppression Systems"; and Section 17, Chapter 3, "Characteristics and Hazards of Water and Water Additives for Fire Suppression."

Kerry M. Bell is a principal engineer at Underwriters Laboratories Inc. (UL) specializing in fire sprinkler and pump equipment. A member of NFPA, ASTM International, and SFPE, he is currently a member of NFPA's Residential Sprinkler Systems Committee and Sprinkler System Discharge Criteria and Technical Correlating Committee, chairman of the NFPA Technical Committee on Water Spray Fixed Systems, and vice-chairman of UL's Fire Council.

USES FOR WATER SPRAY PROTECTION

Generally, water spray can be used effectively to extinguish a fire, control a fire, protect exposures, and/or prevent a fire.

Extinguishment

Water spray extinguishes a fire by cooling it, smothering it with the steam produced, emulsifying or diluting some flammable liquids, or by a combination of these factors.

Controlled Burning

With its consequent limitation of fire spread, controlled burning may be applied if the burning combustibles cannot be extinguished by water spray or if extinguishment is not desirable.

Exposure Protection

Exposures are protected by applying water spray directly to the exposed structures or equipment to remove or reduce the heat transferred to them from the exposing fire. Water spray curtains mounted at a distance from the exposed surface are less effective than direct application.

Prevention of Fire

It is sometimes possible to use water spray to dissolve, dilute, disperse, or cool flammable or combustible materials before they are ignited by an exposing ignition source.

SPRAY SYSTEM DESCRIPTION AND APPLICATIONS

Fixed Water Spray Systems

A water spray system is a special fixed pipe system connected to a reliable supply of fire protection water and equipped with water spray nozzles for specific water discharge and distribution over the surface or area to be protected. The piping system is connected to a water supply through a deluge valve that can be actuated both automatically and manually to initiate the flow of water.

Automatic system actuation valves for spray systems can be actuated electrically by the operation of automatic detection equipment, such as heat detectors, relay circuits, and gas detectors, or mechanically by hydraulic or pneumatic systems, depending on the operating mode of the individual valves. Generally, each manufacturer of system actuation valves, most of which can do dual service in deluge systems, provides its own particular combination of system actuation valve, releasing mechanism, detection system, and supervisory service.

Water Spray Applications

Water spray can be used to protect the following types of materials or equipment:

- Ordinary combustible materials, such as paper, wood, and textiles, particularly to extinguish fires in such materials rather than control them
- Electrical equipment installations, such as transformers, oil switches, and rotating electrical machinery
- Flammable gases and liquids, particularly to control fires in these materials and to extinguish types of fires involving combustible liquids
- Flammable liquid and gas tanks, processing equipment, and structures, as protection against exposure fires
- Open cable trays and runs containing electrical cables or tubing

The nature of the equipment to be protected, the physical and chemical properties of the material involved, and the environment of the hazard should be considered when determining the design and effectiveness of the water spray system.

Examples of Systems

Fixed water spray systems are most commonly used to protect equipment from exposure fires in flammable liquid and gas tankage, piping, and equipment; in electrical equipment, such as transformers, oil switches, rotating machinery, and cable trays; in structural supports; and in conveyor systems and the openings in firewalls and floors through which they pass. The type of water spray required for any particular hazard will depend on the nature of the hazard and the purpose for which the protection is provided.

A water spray installation being tested at a group of liquefied petroleum gas tanks is shown in Figure 16.9.1. The spray keeps the tanks cool in case of fire, prevents the liquid contents from boiling away, and protects the tank shells against rupture due to localized high-temperature flame impingement. The spray system shown in Figure 16.9.1 is designed to give complete surface wetting with a specified water density, taking into consideration nozzle types, sizes, and spacing; the influence of wind and drafts; the probability of water rundown; the prevention of the formation of difficult-to-wet deposits of soot or carbon on surfaces; the overlap of water discharge patterns onto the surfaces; and the ability of the water supply to furnish adequate pressure to all of the nozzles. Ordinarily, it is neither

FIGURE 16.9.1 Water Spray Protection for LP-Gas Tanks

desired nor expected that water spray extinguish escaping liquefied petroleum gas. However, the cooling effect of the water on the tanks may reduce and control the rate of burning and reduce the severity of the exposure until the gas supply to the fire is exhausted or can be shut off.

Water spray protection for a group of oil-filled electric transformers is shown under test in Figure 16.9.2. A thick layer of crushed stone and subsurface drainage is provided around the base of the transformer installation to prevent the possibility of burning oil flowing beyond the ground area protected by the spray.

Due to the relatively high flashpoint and boiling point of transformer oil, transformer fires can be extinguished quickly by properly designed water spray systems. However, the metal surfaces of the transformer case and its structural supports must be protected from radiant heat while the burning transformer oil is being extinguished. Care must be taken to locate nozzles, piping, and supports the prescribed distances from electrically charged parts of the transformer installation, and direct application of water spray to electrically charged terminals or insulating bushings should be avoided. Electricity to the transformer should be shut off automatically before water spray is applied.

Water spray systems are also used to provide protection from fire damage for equipment and structures for the petroleum industry. API RP 2030, *Application of Fixed Water Spray Systems for Fire Protection in the Petroleum and Petrochemical Industries,* provides guidance for the petroleum and petrochemical industries in determining where these systems might be used.[1]

SPRAY SYSTEM NOZZLES AND PIPING

General Design Information

The practical location of the piping and nozzles with respect to the surface to which the spray is to be applied or to the zone in which the spray is to be effective is determined largely by the physical arrangement and protection needs of the installation requiring protection. Once the criteria are established, the size of the nozzles to be used, the angle of the nozzle discharge cone, and the water pressure needed can be determined.

FIGURE 16.9.2 Water Spray System for Oil-Filled Electric Power Transformers

The first factor to determine is the water density required to extinguish the fire or to absorb the expected heat from exposure or combustion. When this has been determined, a nozzle may be selected that will provide that density at a velocity adequate to overcome air currents and to carry the spray to the equipment to be protected. Each nozzle must have the proper angle of discharge to cover the area to be protected by the nozzle.

Determining the proper density needed for extinguishment requires considerable engineering judgment and, in the case of flammable or combustible liquids, depends on such characteristics of the fuel as vapor pressure, flashpoint, viscosity, water solubility, and specific gravity. The density varies between 0.2 and 0.5 gpm/ft^2 (8.1 to 20.4 L/min/m^2) of protected surface.

For exposure protection of vessels, a density of 0.25 gpm/ft^2 (10.2 L/min/m^2) should provide sufficient cooling to limit an exposure fire's heat input through the vessel walls to 6000 Btu/hr/ft^2 (18,930 W/m^2). The water density required for exposure protection of structural supports and miscellaneous equipment, such as cable trays and runs, pipe racks, transformers, and belt conveyors, varies from 0.1 to 0.3 gpm/ft^2 (4.1 to 12.2 L/min/m^2) of exposed surface area. NFPA 15 should be consulted for more details on required distribution densities.

When water spray is to be used to protect oil-filled electrical equipment, such as transformers and large switch gear, special care must be taken to provide safe electrical clearances. Special fixed water spray nozzles have been developed to provide adequate spray density and range to accommodate wind, along with a simplified piping arrangement that is spaced safely from energized electrical parts.

Selection and Use of Spray Nozzles

The selection of spray nozzles should take into consideration such factors as the character of the hazard to be protected, the purpose of the system, and the possibility of severe winds or drafts. In addition to different spray angles, droplet sizes, and velocities, spray nozzles are available in a variety of discharge patterns such as hollow cone, full cone, and flat discharge characteristics.

Nozzles of one type cannot be substituted for nozzles of another type when a water spray system is being repaired or nozzles are being replaced without taking into account the possibility of seriously compromising the effectiveness of the system. In general, the velocity, distribution, and size of water droplets affect the "reach" and coverage of the water spray pattern.

Some spray nozzles produce spray by giving the water streams a rotary motion in spiral passages inside the nozzles. These rotating streams are mixed internally with a center stream to project a solid cone of water spray from the nozzle. These nozzles are known as the internally impinging type (Figure 16.9.3). Another type of water spray nozzle uses the deflector principle of a sprinkler. The water-discharge orifice projects a solid, cylindrical stream of water onto a deflector that alters the stream into a conical distribution of water spray (Figure 16.9.4).

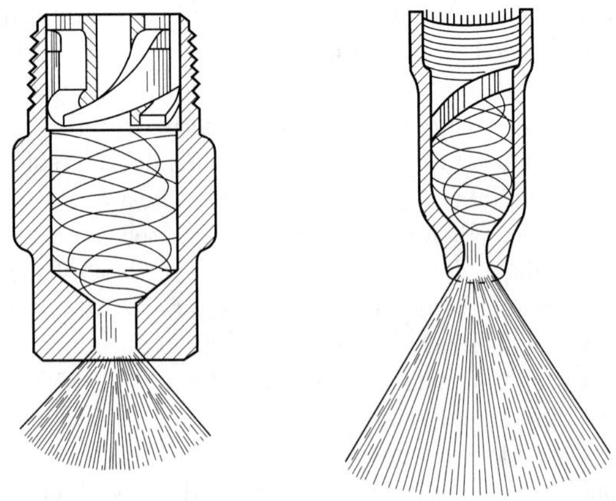

FIGURE 16.9.3 Water Spray Nozzles with Internal Spiral Water Passages

FIGURE 16.9.4 Water Spray Nozzle Using the Deflector Principles of the Standard Automatic Sprinkler

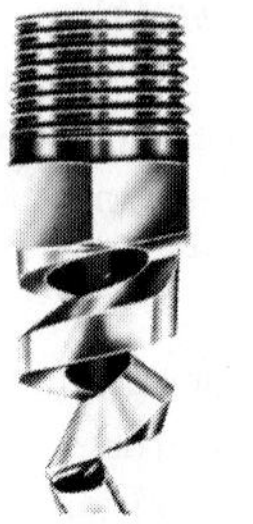

FIGURE 16.9.5 Spiral-Type Water Spray Nozzle

FIGURE 16.9.6 Flat-Spray-Type Water Spray Nozzle (Tyco Issue A) (Courtesy of Tyco Fire and Building Products)

A characteristically different type of water spray nozzle discharges water along the axis of a spiral of diminishing inside diameter. This spiral continuously peels off a thin layer of water from the surface of the cone, and this thin layer of water breaks into spray as it leaves the spiral (Figure 16.9.5). Another unique type of water spray nozzle discharges water in a flat or sheet-type pattern. A flat spray nozzle has a deflector that diverts the discharged water from the axis of the inlet pipe connection (Figure 16.9.6). This discharge characteristic can be useful in developing an overlapping, flat spray between adjacent nozzles. These nozzles are commonly used to protect windows and structures from exposure fires.

Pipe Sizes

Once the type of nozzle has been selected and the location and spacing to give the desired area coverage have been determined, hydraulic calculations are made to establish the appropriate pipe sizes and water supply requirements. Pipe sizes must be calculated hydraulically for each system so that the water at the spray nozzles will have adequate pressure to provide the necessary flow and spray pattern. A procedure for making the hydraulic calculations for a fixed pipe water spray system is given in the Appendix to NFPA 15.

Hydraulic calculations of water spray systems need to take into consideration the velocity head pressure in the calculations where the velocity pressure exceeds 5 percent of the total pressure at any junction point. When velocity pressures are high at a junction, the hydraulic principle in the tie fitting will not allow sufficient water to flow from the side outlet (acting much like a siphon). Ignoring the velocity pressure under these conditions can introduce a significant error, resulting in an actual nozzle pressure that is less than required. The 5 percent value used to determine whether velocity pressure needs to be considered can also be expressed in terms of velocity and total pressure. If $V \leq 2.7\ (P_T)^{1/2}$ then the velocity pressure does not need to be calculated, where V is the velocity (ft/sec) and P_T is the total pressure (psi).

Figure 16.9.7 shows a typical example of where the velocity head pressure needs to be included in the calculation as demonstrated by comparing calculations of the example configuration with (Figure 16.9.8) and without (Figure 16.9.9) veloc-

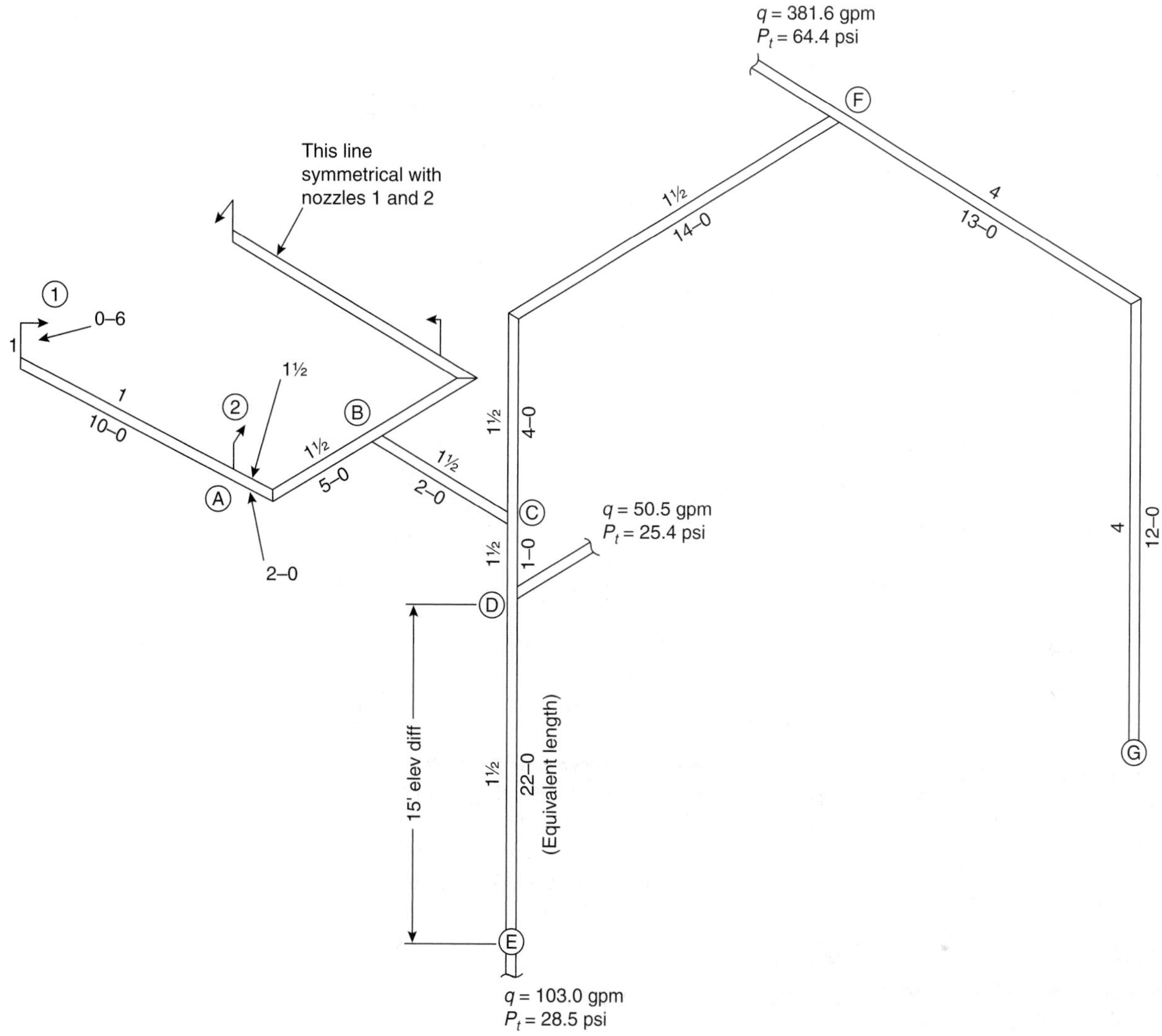

FIGURE 16.9.7 Water Spray System Used for Sample Calculation Shown in Figures 16.9.8 and 16.9.9

ity head pressures used in the calculations. Two methods exist to connect the system to a more balanced configuration, which include (1) increasing the pipe size upstream to reduce the effects of velocity pressure and (2) converting the side outlet tee fitting to a bullhead tee fitting (Figure 16.9.10).

WATER DEMAND AND SUPPLIES

Many factors govern the size of a water spray system, including the nature of the hazard or combustibles involved, the amount and type of equipment to be protected, the adequacy of other protection, and the size of the area that could be involved in a single fire. The size of the system needed may be minimized by taking advantage of possible subdivision by firewalls; by limiting the potential spread of flammable liquids with dikes, curbs, or special drainage; by installing water curtains or heat curtains; or by using a combination of these features.

The water demand will be heavy because water spray systems must perform as deluge-type systems with all nozzles open and because high densities of water are needed. Each hazard should be protected by its own water spray system to limit the cumulative demand on the water supply.

NFPA 15 advises that the size of a single water spray system be limited only by the available water supply so that the designed discharge rate will be calculated at the minimum pressures for which the nozzles are effective. Experience has shown that, in most installations, a single system should not exceed a design discharge rate of 3000 gpm (11,356 L/min). Separate hazard areas should be protected by separate systems.

Water Demand Rate

The water supply must be adequate to supply the operating water spray system(s) with the required gpm (L/min) at effective pressure. Water spray systems adjacent to the hazard initially protected may require additional water. The water supply

For all nozzles shown, K = 5.56; each nozzle covers 100.8 ft² at 0.25 gpm/ft² = 25.2 gpm minimum (Schedule 40 pipe used in example)

Nozzle I.D. and Location	*Flow in gpm*	*Pipe Size*	*Pipe Fittings and Devices*	*Equivalent Pipe Length*	*Friction Loss psi/ft*	*Pressure Summary*	*Normal Pressure*	*Notes*
			1-E	L 10.5		P_t 20.5	P_t	C = 120
1	q	1"		F 2.0	0.200	P_e +0.2	P_v	$P_t = (25.2/5.56)^2$
	Q 25.2			T 12.5		P_f 2.5	P_n	= 20.5 psi
				L		P_t 23.2	P_t	at A
	q			F		P_e	P_v	
	Q			T		P_f	P_n	
			1-T	L 0.5		P_t 20.5	P_t	$K = 25.2/\sqrt{21.7}$
2	q	1"		F 5.0	0.200	P_e +0.2	P_v	= 5.41
	Q 25.2			T 5.5		P_f 1.1	P_n	
				L		P_t 21.7	P_t	
	q			F		P_e	P_v	
	Q			T		P_f	P_n	
	26.1		1-E	L 7.0		P_t 23.2	P_t	$q_2 = 5.41\sqrt{23.2}$
A	q 25.2	1½"	1-T	F 12.0	0.092	P_e —	P_v ~0.4	P_v < 5% of Pt, no
	Q 51.3			T 19.0		P_f 1.7	P_n	correction required
			1-T	L 2.0		P_t 24.9	P_t	
B	q 51.3	1½"		F 8.0	0.333	P_e —	P_v	
	Q 102.6			T 10.0		P_f 3.3	P_n	
				L		P_t 28.2	P_t	at C
	q			F		P_e	P_v	
	Q			T		P_f	P_n	
				L 22.0		P_t 28.5	P_t	
E	q	1½"		F	0.335	P_e –6.5	P_v	
	Q 103.0			T 22.0		P_f 7.4	P_n	
				L 1.0		P_t 29.4	P_t 29.4	$q = 50.5(25.5/25.4)^{1/2}$
D	q 50.6	1½"		F —	0.702	P_e –0.4	P_v 3.9	P_v in to D from the
	Q 153.6			T 1.0		P_f 0.7	P_n 25.5	side assumed negligible
				L		P_t 29.7	P_t	
	q			F		P_e	P_v	
	Q			T		P_f	P_n	
	185.7		1-T	L 18.0		P_t 43.4	P_t 43.4	q from D =
C	q 102.6	1½"	1-E	F 12.0	2.250	P_e –1.7	P_v 15.2	$153.6(43.4/29.7)^{1/2}$
	Q 288.3			T 30.0		P_f 67.5	P_n 28.2	= 185.7 (see NFPA 15)
			1-E	L 25.0		P_t 109.2	P_t	$q = 381.6(109.2/64.4)^{1/2}$
F	q 496.9	4"		F 10.0	0.165	P_e +5.2	P_v ~2.9	P_v < 5% of Pt, no
	Q 785.2			T 35.0		P_f 5.8	P_n	correction required
				L		P_t 120.2	P_t	at G
	q			F		P_e	P_v	
	Q			T		P_f	P_n	
						P_t		

FIGURE 16.9.8 Hydraulic Calculation Worksheet of System Shown in Figure 16.9.7 with Velocity Pressure Included

For all nozzles shown, K = 5.56; each nozzle covers 100.8 ft^2 at 0.25 gpm/ft^2 = 25.2 gpm minimum

Nozzle I.D. and Location	*Flow in gpm*		*Pipe Size*	*Pipe Fittings and Devices*	*Equivalent Pipe Length*		*Friction Loss psi/ft*	*Pressure Summary*		*Normal Pressure*	*Notes*
				1-E	L	10.5		P_t	20.5	P_t	C = 120
1	*q*		1"		F	2.0	0.200	P_e	+0.2	P_v	$P_t = (25.2/5.56)^2$
	Q	25.2			T	12.5		P_f	2.5	P_n	= 20.5 psi
					L			P_t	23.2	P_t	at A
	q				F			P_e		P_v	
	Q				T			P_f		P_n	
				1-T	L	0.5		P_t	20.5	P_t	$K = 25.2/\sqrt{21.7}$
2	*q*		1"		F	5.0	0.200	P_e	+0.2	P_v	= 5.41
	Q	25.2			T	5.5		P_f	1.1	P_n	
					L			P_t	21.7	P_t	
	q				F			P_e		P_v	
	Q				T			P_f		P_n	
		26.1		1-E	L	7.0		P_t	23.2	P_t	$q_2 = 5.41\sqrt{23.2}$
A	*q*	25.2	1½"	1-T	F	12.0	0.092	P_e	—	P_v	
	Q	51.3			T	19.0		P_f	1.7	P_n	
				1-T	L	2.0		P_t	24.9	P_t	
B	*q*	51.3	1½"		F	8.0	0.333	P_e	—	P_v	
	Q	102.6			T	10.0		P_f	3.3	P_n	
					L			P_t	28.2	P_t	at C
	q				F			P_e		P_v	
	Q				T			P_f		P_n	
					L	22.0		P_t	28.5	P_t	
E	*q*		1½"		F		0.335	P_e	−6.5	P_v	
	Q	103.0			T	22.0		P_f	7.4	P_n	
					L	1.0		P_t	29.4	P_t	$q = 50.5(29.4/25.4)^{1/2}$
D	*q*	54.3	1½"		F	—	0.734	P_e	−0.4	P_v	= 54.3
	Q	157.3			T	1.0		P_f	0.7	P_n	
				1-T	L	18.0		P_t	29.7	P_t	*q* from B =
C	*q*	105.3	1½"	1-E	F	12.0	1.893	P_e	−1.7	P_v	$102.6(29.7/28.2)^{1/2}$
	Q	262.6			T	30.0		P_f	56.8	P_n	= 105.1
				1-E	L	25.0		P_t	84.8	P_t	$q = 381.6(84.82/64.4)^{1/2}$
F	*q*	437.9	4"		F	10.0	0.134	P_e	+5.2	P_v	= 437.9
	Q	700.5			T	35.0		P_f	4.7	P_n	
					L			P_t	94.7	P_t	at G
	q				F			P_e		P_v	
	Q				T			P_f		P_n	
					L			P_t		P_t	
	q				F			P_e		P_v	
	Q				T			P_f		P_n	
								P_t			

FIGURE 16.9.9 Hydraulic Calculation Worksheet of System Shown in Figure 16.9.7 with Velocity Pressure Not Included

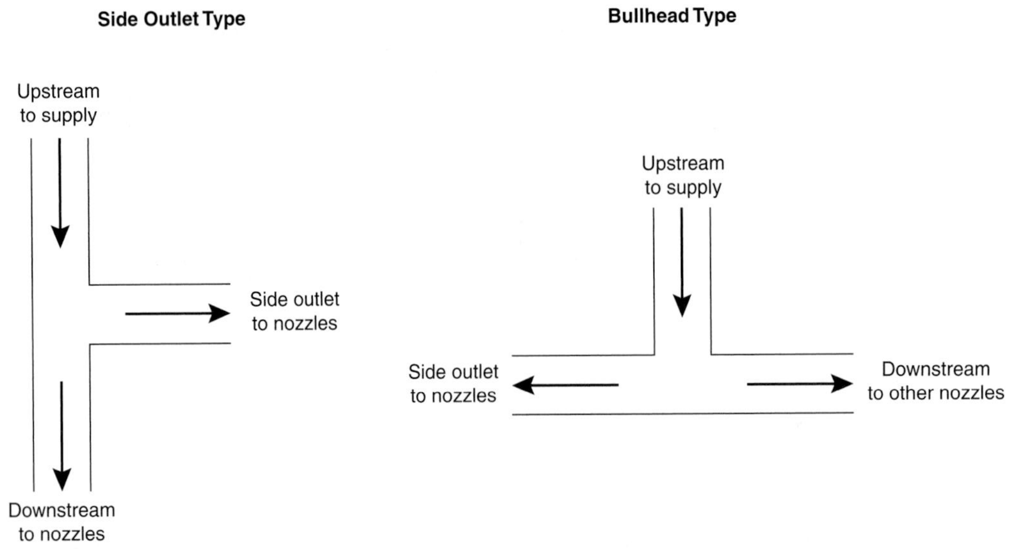

FIGURE 16.9.10 Tee Fittings—Side Outlet and Bullhead Types

should be able to supply hose streams simultaneously. The total required water supply pressure and flow rates should be considered when the system is designed. The duration of the discharge required varies according to the nature of the hazard, the purpose for which the system is designed, and other factors that can be evaluated only for each installation.

Waterflow demand is specified in terms of the density of a uniformly distributed spray measured in gpm/ft^2 (L/min/m^2) of area protected. The discharge rate per unit of area depends on whether the spray system is installed to extinguish a fire, to control a fire, or to protect an exposure, and on the characteristics of the materials involved.

Water Supplies

Fixed spray systems usually are supplied from one or more of the following:

- Connections from a reliable waterworks system of adequate capacity and pressure
- Automatic fire pumps with reliable power and a water supply of adequate capacity and reliability
- An elevated gravity tank of adequate capacity and elevation

The capacity of pressure tanks generally is not adequate to supply water spray systems. However, they may be acceptable as water supplies to small systems whose water and pressure requirements do not exceed the tank's capabilities.

OTHER CONSIDERATIONS AND MAINTENANCE

Strainers

Strainers are required in the supply lines of fixed piping spray systems to keep the nozzles from clogging where the waterways of nozzles are less than ⅜ in. (9.5 mm) or for systems in which the water is likely to contain obstructive material. The baskets of those selected should have a mesh small enough to protect the smallest water passages in the nozzles used. Figure 16.9.11 shows a Grinnell Model A strainer with a basket-type screen of corrosion-resistant metal. This particular strainer is available in 3 in., 4 in., 6 in., 8 in., and 10 in. sizes (1 in. = 25.4 mm). Water spray nozzles with very small water passages may have their own internal strainer, as well as a supply-line strainer to remove larger foreign material.

Drainage

Fixed water spray systems discharge large quantities of water. Special drainage and disposal facilities are important to control the spread of flammable or hazardous liquids to areas adjacent to the fire. Pitched floors, curbs, trenches, dikes, and sumps should be provided to direct the mixture of flammable or hazardous liquids and water runoff. These should be connected to a facility that separates flammable and hazardous liquids from the water. These liquids should be impounded in controlled areas until they can be disposed of safely.

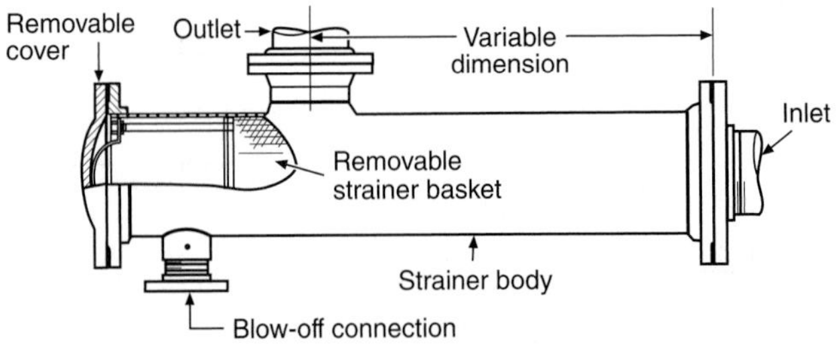

FIGURE 16.9.11 Grinnell Model A Strainer

Maintenance

It is important that fixed water spray systems be inspected and maintained on a regular basis. NFPA 25, *Standard for the Inspection, Testing, and Maintenance of Water-Based Fire Protection Systems,* provides specific requirements for periodic inspection, testing, and maintenance of water spray systems. Included in a scheduled inspection program are such items as strainers, piping, control valves, system actuation valves, heat-actuated devices, and spray nozzles, particularly those equipped with strainers. Flow tests are conducted frequently to ensure satisfactory operation. After the tests have been completed, it is necessary to clean all strainers and to check all valves to be sure the system is in normal operating condition.

Nozzles with blow-off caps or plugs are provided to protect the interior of the piping and the nozzles located in areas containing paint vapor, corrosive vapors, dusts, or other foreign matter. Other blow-off caps or plugs are attached to the nozzles to allow them to retain water in the piping system and, thus, reduce the time between the operation of the deluge valve and the discharge of water spray from the nozzles (Figure 16.9.12). Regular inspection and maintenance should confirm that caps and plugs are in place.

Specialized Systems Using Water

Specialized systems using water spray have been developed to fill particular fire control needs in the explosives industry. These systems are referred to as ultra-high-speed water deluge spray systems. (See Section 16, Chapter 7, "Ultra-High-Speed Water Spray Systems," for additional information on these systems.)

SUMMARY

Water spray systems primarily provide fire protection for specific hazards; that is, they are designed to protect specific hazards and equipment with surface coverage. This chapter addresses the applications of water spray systems in terms of fire suppression, control, and extinguishment and describes the components and specialized uses of water spray systems.

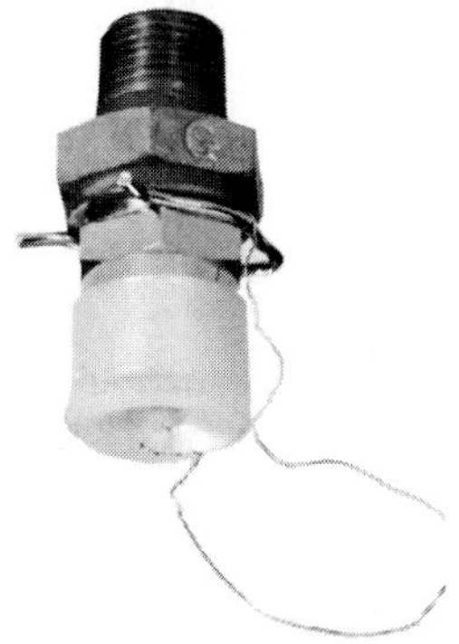

FIGURE 16.9.12 Grinnell Mulsifyre Nozzle with Blow-Off Cap

BIBLIOGRAPHY

Reference Cited

1. API RP 2030, *Application of Fixed Water Spray Systems for Fire Protection in the Petroleum and Petrochemical Industry,* American Petroleum Institute, Washington, DC, 2005.

NFPA Codes, Standards, and Recommended Practices

Reference to the following NFPA codes, standards, and recommended practices will provide further information on water spray protection discussed in this chapter. (See the latest version of The NFPA Catalog *for availability of current editions of the following documents.)*

NFPA 13, *Standard for the Installation of Sprinkler Systems*
NFPA 14, *Standard for the Installation of Standpipe and Hose Systems*
NFPA 15, *Standard for Water Spray Fixed Systems for Fire Protection*
NFPA 18, *Standard on Wetting Agents*
NFPA 20, *Standard for the Installation of Stationary Pumps for Fire Protection*
NFPA 22, *Standard for Water Tanks for Private Fire Protection*
NFPA 24, *Standard for the Installation of Private Fire Service Mains and Their Appurtenances*
NFPA 25, *Standard for the Inspection, Testing, and Maintenance of Water-Based Fire Protection Systems*
NFPA 30, *Flammable and Combustible Liquids Code*
NFPA 69, *Standard on Explosion Prevention Systems*
NFPA 70, *National Electrical Code®*
NFPA 72®, National Fire Alarm Code®
NFPA 80A, *Recommended Practice for Protection of Buildings from Exterior Fire Exposures*
NFPA 750, *Standard on Water Mist Fire Protection Systems*

References

Back, G. G., "Capabilities and Limitations of Total Flooding Water Mist Fire Suppression Systems for Protecting Flammable Liquid Hazards," *Proceedings* of Fire Suppression and Detection Research Application Symposium, Research and Practice: Bridging the Gap, February 23–25, 2000, Orlando, FL, National Fire Protection Research Foundation, Quincy, MA, 2000, pp. 424–436.

Bill, R. G., Jr., and Ural, E. A., "Water Mist Protection of Combustion Turbine Enclosures," *Proceedings* of 6th International Symposium, Fire Safety Science, July 5–9, 1999, Poitiers, France, International Association for Fire Safety Science, Boston, MA, 2000, pp. 457–468.

Boughen, D., "Success of Water Mist Systems," *Fire Supplement,* Vol. 91, No. 1118, 1998, p. 9.

Darwin, R. L., and Williams, F. W., "Overview of the Development of Water-Mist Systems for U.S. Navy Ships," *Proceedings* of Halon Options Technical Working Conference, April 27–29, 1999, Albuquerque, NM, HOTWC-99, 1999, pp. 373–380.

Gagnon, R. M., "Snuffing Hot Hazards," *Consulting-Specifying Engineer,* Vol. 26, No. 4, 1999, pp. 34–36.

Kim, A. K., "Water Mist," *Canadian Consulting Engineer,* Vol. 40, No. 3, 1999, p. 76.

LeBlanc, D. J., "Localized Protection of Flammable Liquid Hazards Utilizing Water Mist Nozzles with an AFFF Additive," *Proceedings* of Fire Suppression and Detection Research Application Symposium, Research and Practice: Bridging the Gap, February 23–25, 2000, Orlando, FL, National Fire Protection Research Foundation, Quincy, MA, 2000, pp. 437–447.

Liu, Z., and Kim, A. K., "Review of Water Mist Fire Suppression Technology. Part 2. Application Studies," *Journal of Fire Protection Engineering,* Vol. 11, No. 1, 2001, pp. 16–42.

Maranghides, A., and Sheinson, R. S., "NRL-Chesapeake Bay Detachment: Full-Scale Fire Test Platform," *Proceedings* of Halon Options Technical Working Conference, April 27–29, 1999, Albuquerque, NM, HOTWC-99, 1999, pp. 343–349.

Marker, T. R., and Reinhardt, J. W., "Water Spray as a Fire Suppression Agent for Aircraft Cargo Compartment Fires," DOT/FAA/AR-TN01/1, Federal Aviation Administration, Atlantic City International Airport, NJ, June 2001.

Mawhinney, J. R., and Back, G. G., III, "Bridging the Gap Between Theory and Practice: Protecting Flammable Liquid Hazards Using Water Mist Fire Suppression Systems," *Proceedings* of Fire Suppression and Detection Research Application Symposium, Research and Practice: Bridging the Gap, February 25–27, 1998, Orlando, FL, National Fire Protection Research Foundation, Quincy, MA, 1998, pp. 161–173.

Pepi, J. S., "Advances in the Technology of Intermediate Pressure Water Mist Systems for the Protection of Flammable Liquid Hazards," *Proceedings* of Halon Options Technical Working Conference, May 12–14, 1998, Albuquerque, NM, HOTWC-99, 1998, pp. 417–438.

Pepi, J. S., "Water Mist System Performance Trade-Offs with Flammable Liquid Hazards," *Proceedings* of Fire Suppression and Detection Research Application Symposium, Research and Practice: Bridging the Gap, February 24–26, 1999, Orlando, FL, National Fire Protection Research Foundation, Quincy, MA, 1999, pp. 219–232.

Slye, O. M., "Prevention and Suppression of Fires in Large Aboveground Atmospheric Storage Tanks," *Proceedings* of Fire Suppression and Detection Research Application Symposium, Research and Practice: Bridging the Gap, February 25–27, 1998, Orlando, FL, National Fire Protection Research Foundation, Quincy, MA, 1998, pp. 280–309.

Chapter 10

Standpipe and Hose Systems

Revised by
David R. Hague

Chapter Contents

Key Terms

automatic-dry standpipe system, automatic-wet standpipe system, fire department connection, manual-dry standpipe system, manual-wet standpipe system, semiautomatic-dry standpipe system, standpipe system, stationary fire pump, system demand

Standpipe systems are fixed piping systems with associated equipment that transports water from a reliable water supply to designated areas of buildings where hoses can be deployed for fire fighting. Such systems are typically provided in tall and large-area buildings.

Standpipe systems can significantly improve the efficiency of manual fire-fighting operations by eliminating the need for long and cumbersome hose lays from fire apparatus to a fire. Even in buildings that are protected by automatic sprinklers, standpipe systems can play an important role in building fire safety by serving as a backup for, and complement to, sprinklers.

The NFPA standard regulating the design, installation, and testing of standpipe systems is NFPA 14, *Standard for the Installation of Standpipe and Hose Systems* (references to NFPA 14 are based on the 2007 edition). Note that NFPA 14 does not cover where standpipe systems are required. Required installations are set forth in code documents, such as NFPA *101*®, *Life Safety Code*®; NFPA 1, *Uniform Fire Code*™; and model building codes, or they may be established by insurance regulations.

NFPA 13, *Standard for the Installation of Sprinkler Systems,* is a useful reference when considering hydraulically designed systems or combined sprinkler and standpipe systems. Other NFPA standards and recommended practices that may be helpful when dealing with standpipe systems are included in the bibliography at the end of this chapter.

For other information relevant to standpipe systems, see Section 15, Chapter 1, "Fixed Water Storage Facilities for Fire Protection"; Section 15, Chapter 6, "Water Distribution"; and Section 16, Chapter 11, "Care and Maintenance of Water-Based Extinguishing Systems."

STANDPIPE SYSTEM DESIGN CONSIDERATIONS

All standpipe systems share a common purpose of delivering water for manual fire fighting. However, system designs used to accomplish this purpose will vary. Whereas one system may involve a simple pipe network for conveying water from fire department apparatus to hose connections in a building, another may involve a fully automatic water supply and preconnected hoses.

Standpipe system designs are generally dictated by NFPA 14, but local, state, and model building codes and insurance standards may also have an influence. The requirements among these codes and standards vary, so it is essential for system designers to determine which codes and standards have been adopted by the regulating entity.

Because NFPA 14 is often recognized as the design standard for standpipe systems, the following discussion on design considerations focuses on the regulatory requirements in NFPA 14. In addition, model building code requirements and engineering and historical perspectives are also discussed.

The Design Process

The process of designing a standpipe system begins with determining the intended use, that is, whether it is for (1) full-scale fire fighting, (2) first-aid fire fighting, or (3) both. These three uses

David R. Hague, P.E., is a principal fire safety and systems engineer for NFPA. He serves as staff liaison for several water-based standards, including NFPA 14.

correspond with the three classes of standpipe systems—Class I, Class II, and Class III. Most aspects of system design, such as the required water supply, layout, and system components, are affected or dictated by the class of system.

Classes of Systems

Standpipe systems are designated as Class I, Class II, and Class III. Some sources refer to a fourth class of system called a "combined" system; however, combined systems are simply Class I or Class III standpipe systems that also supply water to a sprinkler system. Note that sprinkler systems with hose connections are not necessarily considered to be standpipe systems. Such systems are often regarded simply as sprinkler systems. The design of a combined system is similar to any other Class I or Class III system, except that the water supply and pipe sizes may be larger to accommodate the added sprinkler system demand.

Class I Systems. A Class I system provides 2½ in. (65 mm) hose connections at designated locations in a building for use by the fire department.

A Class I system is typically required in buildings that have more than three stories above or below grade because of the time and difficulty involved in laying hose from fire apparatus directly to remote floors. Class I systems are also sometimes required in malls because these occupancies contain areas that are difficult to access directly with hose from fire apparatus.

Class II Systems. A Class II system provides 1½ in. (40 mm) hose connections at designated locations in a building for first-aid fire fighting. These systems are generally intended for use by trained fire brigades before the fire department arrives, but they are occasionally provided for use by fire departments, as well. With Class II systems, a hose, a nozzle, and a hose rack are typically installed on each hose connection.

Class II systems are often required in large unsprinklered buildings. They may also be required to protect special hazard areas, such as exhibit halls and stages.

With respect to Class II standpipe systems, members of the fire protection community disagree about the desirability of having standpipe systems available for occupant use. Concerns focus on the ability of untrained occupants to safely use a 100-ft (30.5-m) long hose flowing up to 100 gpm (378 L/min) and on the wisdom of encouraging occupants to fight a fire instead of evacuating. These concerns have led to a trend of reducing the requirements for, or eliminating the installation of, standpipe systems with preconnected hoses. Consequently, the use of Class II systems is declining. The 2007 edition of NFPA 14 no longer recognizes "Building Occupant Use" of standpipes but refers to "Trained Industrial Fire Brigades."

Class III Systems. Class III systems combine the features of Class I and Class II systems. They are provided for both full-scale and first-aid fire fighting. These systems are generally intended for use by fire departments and fire brigades. Because of their multiple uses, Class III systems are provided with both Class I and Class II hose connections. This is sometimes accomplished by using 2½ in. (65 mm) hose valves with easily removable 2½- to 1½-in. (65- to 40-mm) adapters that are permanently chained to hose connections. Where Class III systems are required by code, the system may be provided with a 2½ in. (65 mm) hose value, a 2½ in. × 1½ in. (65 mm × 40 mm) reducer, and a cap and chain in lieu of providing hose.

Class III systems are sometimes used when both Class I and Class II systems are required and no useful purpose would be served by installing separate systems. Like Class II systems, the use of Class III systems is declining because of concerns about the safety and effectiveness of untrained occupants fighting fires.

Types of Systems

In addition to being subdivided into classes that delineate the intended use of a system (i.e., fire department use or industrial fire brigade use), standpipe systems are also classified by "type." These types delineate the basic characteristics of systems; that is, whether the piping will be filled with water or not (wet versus dry), and whether the water supply for fire fighting will be automatically available or not (automatic, semiautomatic, or manual).

Beginning with the 1993 edition of NFPA 14, standpipe system types were completely redefined. The result was the creation of five categories, as follows:

1. *Automatic-wet systems* have piping that is filled with water at all times and have an automatically available water supply capable of supplying the water demand necessary for fire fighting.

2. *Automatic-dry systems* have piping that is normally filled with pressurized air. These systems are arranged, through the use of devices such as a dry-pipe valve, to automatically admit water into system piping when a hose valve is opened, and they are connected to an automatically available water supply that is capable of supplying the water demand necessary for fire fighting.

3. *Semiautomatic-dry systems* have piping that is normally filled with air that may or may not be pressurized. These systems are arranged through the use of devices, such as a deluge valve, to admit water into system piping when a remote actuation device located at a hose station, such as a pull station, is operated. They also have a preconnected water supply that is capable of supplying the water demand necessary for fire fighting.

4. *Manual-dry systems* have piping that is normally filled with air, and these systems do not have a preconnected water supply. A fire department connection must be used to manually supply water for fire fighting.

5. *Manual-wet systems* have piping that is normally filled with water for the purpose of keeping the system full of water, thus avoiding "fill time" when the system is used. The water supply for these systems is typically provided by a small connection to domestic water piping, and it is not capable of supplying fire-fighting water demands. A fire department connection must be used to manually supply water for fire fighting.

In summary, wet systems have water-filled piping and dry systems do not. Automatic systems provide a water supply for fire fighting simply by opening a hose valve. Semiautomatic systems are connected to a water supply for fire fighting but require activation of a device at a hose valve in addition to opening the valve to get water. Manual systems do not have a preconnected water supply for fire fighting, and these systems must be manually supplied by connecting hoses from a fire department pumper truck to a fire department connection.

Design Restrictions Based on System Class and Type

NFPA 14 specifies several design limitations based on the type of system to be used.

Manual standpipe systems are not allowed to be used in high-rise buildings. This is partly to provide an increased level of safety in such buildings and partly in recognition of the fact that a sprinkler system will be required by building codes for high-rise buildings, almost surely necessitating a fire pump. In such applications, the standpipe and sprinkler systems are "combined" using common feed main piping precluding the use of dry systems. Once a pump is called for, it is considered reasonable to require that the pump be capable of supplying the standpipe system demand, given the marginal additional cost.

Manual systems are also prohibited for Class II and Class III systems, because systems with preconnected hose obviously need an available water supply to be of benefit in fighting incipient fires.

Dry systems are not allowed for most Class II or Class III systems because of the risk to untrained users that would be created by delaying the availability of water. Also, dry systems are allowed only in areas subject to freezing, because wet systems are considered more reliable. Dry standpipes have been known to perform unsatisfactorily in the past because open valves or severe leaks went undetected until the system was charged with water. The NFPA 14 committee considered this risk of failure avoidable for most cases by simply requiring system piping to be filled with water unless a risk of freezing is present.

System Layout

Number and Location of Hose Connections. The required number of hose connections is primarily based on a building's design. Codes and standards employ two approaches to determining hose connection locations. The first method, termed the "actual length" method, is used only for 1½ in. (40 mm) hose connections on Class II and Class III systems. This method locates 1½ in. (40 mm) hose connections such that enough are provided to reach all portions of the area served with a 100 ft (30.5 m) hose that has a nozzle with a 20- to 30-ft (6- to 9-m) reach. The 100 ft (30.5 m) length limit is required for ease of handling. Distances should be measured around partitions and obstructions for hose length and along unobstructed straight-line paths for nozzle reach.

Because standpipe systems with preconnected hose are usually intended for extinguishing incipient fires before the fire department arrives, 1½ in. (40 mm) hose stations should be located in central areas, such as corridors, where they are clearly visible and readily accessible. Figure 16.10.1 illustrates the actual length method for locating hose stations. In the actual length method (as illustrated on a partial floor plan), a maximum distance of 130 ft (39.5 m), consisting of 100 ft (30.5 m) of flexible hose-lay distance and 30 ft (9 m) of straight-line nozzle trajectory is the basis for locating the 1½ in. (40 mm) hose stations.

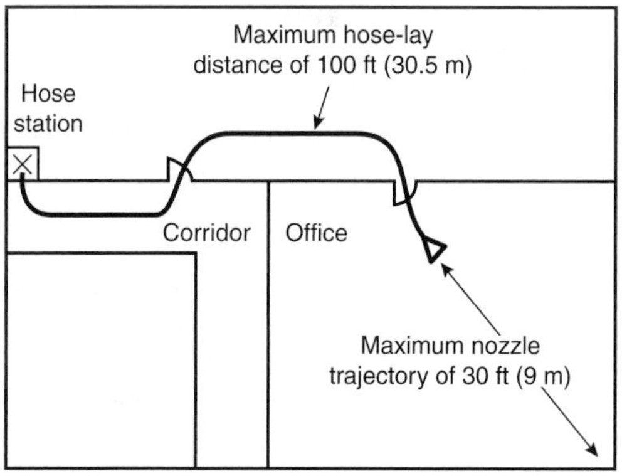

FIGURE 16.10.1 Actual Length Method for Locating Hose Connections

The second method, termed the "exit location method," is used for 2½ in. (65 mm) hose connections on Class I and Class III systems. This method locates connections based on a building's exiting system. Using this method, 2½ in. (65 mm) hose connections are located in exit stairs, at horizontal exits, and in exit passageways, as required by the building code. Because exits must be reasonably distributed within buildings to provide adequate egress, hose connections are considered to be adequately distributed when located at the points of egress from areas served. Figure 16.10.2 illustrates the exit location method for locating hose connections. In the exit location method, maximum travel distance to an exit (door), as established by the applicable building code, is the basis for locating required 2½ in. (65 mm) hose connections. Enclosed exit stairways are also

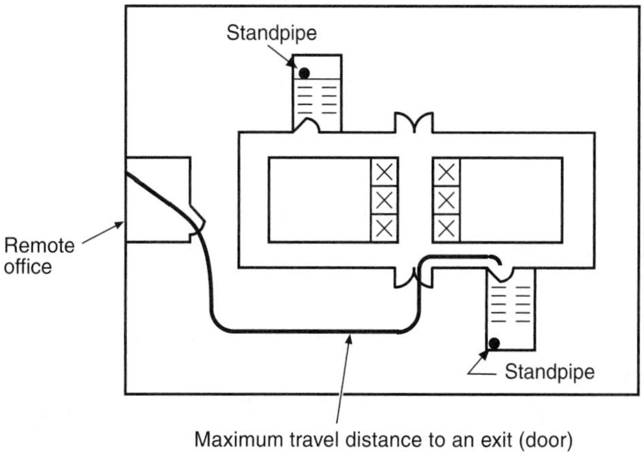

FIGURE 16.10.2 Exit Location Method for Locating Hose Connections

considered to be protected spaces and afford fire fighters an area to stage fire-fighting operations.

In early editions of NFPA 14, Class I hose connections were required to be located using the actual length method. In the 1993 and subsequent editions, the method specified is the exit location method. This switch was made because the actual length method encouraged locating hose connections in open-floor areas to meet distance requirements. Such locations are not advantageous to fire fighters because they may be obstructed by smoke or exposed to fire, preventing their use. NFPA 14 now recognizes that it is preferable to locate 2½ in. (65 mm) hose connections where they will be protected from a fire, such as within protected stair enclosures or on opposite sides of horizontal exits. This location allows fire fighters to connect to a system in relative safety and to have a charged hose available before entering a fire area.

Some have argued that extending hose from the inside of an exit enclosure compromises enclosure integrity and places occupants at risk during evacuation. However, NFPA 14 recognizes that the alternative is an unreasonable expectation of fire fighters to enter an area filled with smoke and heated gases to search for a hose connection, placing them in extreme danger. In addition, time lost while searching for a hose connection would prolong an uncontrolled fire, potentially posing a much greater threat to occupants.

It should be noted that NFPA 14 does permit additional 2½ in. (65 mm) hose connections to be required by local authorities when exit travel distances exceed 150 ft (46 m) in nonsprinklered buildings and 200 ft (61 m) in sprinklered buildings. This special option is provided because exit travel distance for occupants going out effectively equates to the maximum hose-lay distance for fire fighters going in, and deploying more than 200 ft (61 m) of charged hose is recognizably difficult. If additional connections outside of exit enclosures are considered necessary, they should be located only in areas protected by fire-resistive construction so that fire fighters will have a protected environment in which they can connect hoses.

For the purpose of locating standpipe outlets, the roof should be treated as an additional floor. Thus, for buildings with two or more standpipes, the building roof should be provided with two or more outlets. Beginning with the 2007 edition of NFPA 14, roof outlets can be omitted where the roof pitch is greater than 3 in 12. An additional outlet must be provided at the top of the standpipe for testing purposes. This outlet will permit flowing 500 gpm (1893 L/min).

Positioning of Hose Connections at Landings. One other aspect of locating 2½ in. (65 mm) hose connections that is worthy of discussion is the positioning of hose connections within stair enclosures. In earlier editions of NFPA 14, hose connections were required at floor levels within stair enclosures, positioning that actually hampered fire-fighting efforts.

The prior standards failed to recognize that fire departments typically use connections at the floor below the fire floor to leave the doorway to the fire floor uncongested and to give the fire fighters a safer location for connecting hoses. However, connecting hoses an entire story below the fire floor uses up valuable hose length, and connecting at a floor-level landing obstructs the adjacent doorway. The solution now included in NFPA 14 is to place connections at intermediate floor landings. This placement allows hoses to be connected somewhat below the fire floor while minimizing the additional hose length required to do so. It also avoids congestion problems associated with having hose connections located adjacent to exit doors and areas of wheelchair refuge within stairwells. Locating hose connections in this manner also prevents kinking hose, as it bends around doorways.

Interconnection of Piping. One last item to remember when laying out a system is that standpipes must be interconnected as close as possible to the source of supply, or at the top when gravity tanks are used. Interconnection of standpipes ensures that water supplies can service all portions of a system.

Water Supply and Piping Requirements

The class and type of system to be installed will dictate the required water supply. There are three aspects of water supplies that must be taken into account: (1) the minimum flow rate required, (2) the minimum pressure required, and (3) the type of supply to be used. In addition, the maximum pressure available may also be of concern.

Minimum Flow Rate and Minimum Pressure (System Demand). The minimum required flow and minimum required pressure are together referred to as the "system demand." The system demand for a standpipe system is a function of several variables:

1. The required flow rate and pressure at the hydraulically most remote hose connections
2. Required flow rates for additional standpipes
3. The water supply requirements for automatic sprinklers sharing common piping
4. Pressure losses from friction and changes in elevation between the water supply and the hydraulically most remote hose connection

Minimum flow rate and pressure requirements for standpipe systems are determined based on the class of system. According to NFPA 14, Class I and Class III systems are typically required to deliver 500 gpm (1893 L/min) for the first standpipe, plus 250 gpm (946 L/min) for each additional standpipe, up to a maximum of 1250 gpm (4731 L/min). The maximum flow is reduced to 1000 gpm (3785 L/min) for combined systems in recognition of the assistance provided by sprinklers even when sprinklers alone have been unable to control a fire. NFPA 14 also requires the water supply to be capable of providing the minimum flow rate for 30 minutes. This duration is intended to apply to automatic and semiautomatic supplies, and it assumes the fire department runs on a separate water source to supply the system using pumper trucks within 30 minutes. Figure 16.10.3 illustrates these design flow rate requirements for Class I and Class III systems.

With respect to pressure, NFPA 14 requires that a water supply for Class I and Class III systems be able to deliver a residual pressure of 100 psi (690 kPa) at the outlet of the topmost hose

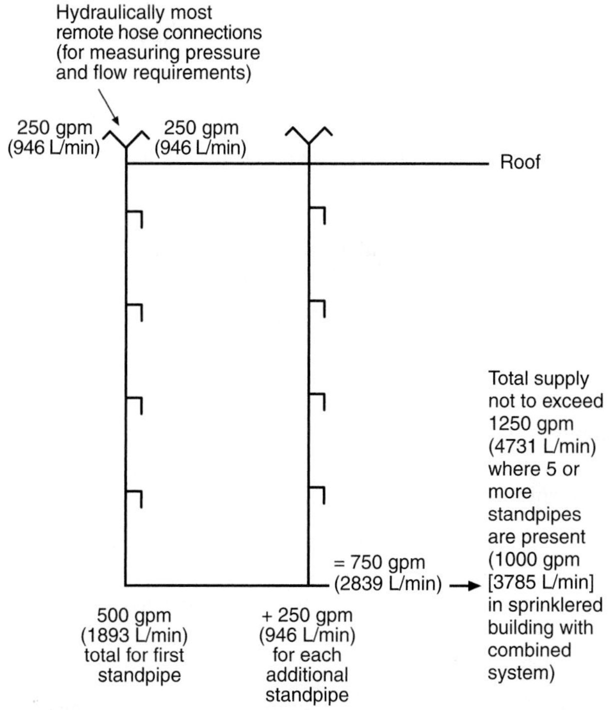

FIGURE 16.10.3 Basic Flow Rate Requirements for Class I and Class III Systems

TABLE 16.10.1 Pressure Limits for Standpipe System Outlets

Outlet Use	*Minimum Residual Pressure*	*Pressure-Regulating Device Required When Pressure Exceeds*[b]
1½ in. (40 mm) hose connection with preconnected hose	65 psi[a] (448 kPa)	100 psi (690 kPa)[c]
1½–2½ in. (40–65 mm) hose connection without preconnected hose	100 psi[a] (690 kPa)	175 psi (1207 kPa)[d]
Sprinkler system connection	per NFPA 13	175 psi (1207 kPa)[d]

[a]Measured at the hydraulically most remote hose connection while flowing at a rate specified by NFPA 14.
[b]Pressures in system piping should never exceed the rating of any system component.
[c]This is a residual pressure limit. Static pressure cannot exceed 175 psi (1207 kPa) before a pressure-regulating device is required.
[d]A setting of 165 psi (1138 kPa) can be used on a combined sprinkler/hose connection on combined systems while achieving acceptable flows and nozzles pressure. Set pressure-regulating device at 165 psi (1138 kPa) because NFPA 13 will require a relief valve set at 175 psi (1207 kPa).

connection on each standpipe. This pressure must be available while flowing 250 gpm (946 L/min) from each of the two topmost hose connections of the hydraulically most remote standpipe, plus 250 gpm (946 L/min) from each additional standpipe, up to the required maximum. Note that NFPA 14 no longer allows a reduction in the minimum pressure requirement.

For Class II systems, NFPA 14 requires that the water supply be capable of delivering 100 gpm (379 L/min) for 30 minutes. It must also be strong enough to maintain a residual pressure of 65 psi (448 kPa) at the outlet of the hydraulically most remote hose connection with 100 gpm (379 L/min) flowing.

In addition to minimum pressure and flow requirements, there are maximum pressure limits for hose connections as well. For a discussion on maximum pressure limits, see the subsection "Maximum Pressure and Zoning in Tall Buildings" later in this chapter.

See Table 16.10.1 for a summary of requirements.

Supplying System Demand for Standpipe Systems. For manual systems (described previously) the system demand must be supplied exclusively through the fire department connection. An automatic water supply is not required on such systems, and even where a manual-wet standpipe is combined with a sprinkler system, the standpipe demand does not have to be available via the preconnected water supply serving sprinklers.

History of Outlet Pressures and Fire-Fighting Nozzles. NFPA 14 was modified in the 1993 edition to increase the minimum outlet pressure for Class I and Class III outlets from 65 psi (448 kPa) to 100 psi (690 kPa) because of questions raised regarding the adequacy of a 65 psi (448 kPa) minimum design pressure on automatic and semiautomatic standpipes. From a performance perspective, the NFPA Committee on Standpipe and Hose Systems (NFPA 14 committee) agreed that the minimum pressure at any hose connection should be adequate to properly operate a fire nozzle while overcoming friction loss in a hose. From a design perspective, the establishment of a minimum design pressure for hose connections has proven difficult because nozzle operating pressures and friction losses in hoses vary, depending on the equipment used by each local fire department.

The concern over nozzle pressure originally became an issue when fog nozzles were introduced for fire fighting in the mid-1900s. Before fog nozzles, fire fighters used solid stream nozzles, which operated well at fairly low inlet pressures. As the use of fog nozzles became common, the fire protection community moved to increase the minimum pressure required at the hydraulically most remote hose connections on standpipe systems to accommodate the greater nozzle pressure required by fog nozzles. The NFPA 14 committee originally recommended a pressure of 65 psi (448 kPa), which was widely implemented. In establishing this pressure, the committee had tried to minimize the pressure required for standpipe system water supplies and assumed that nozzle designers and testing laboratories would establish criteria to ensure that fog nozzles would operate satisfactorily with a 65 psi (448 kPa) pressure at hose connections. Unfortunately, this assumption never materialized, and many later questioned the pre-1993 65 psi (448 kPa) minimum pressure requirement.

In reevaluating the minimum pressure requirement for the 1993 edition, the NFPA 14 committee decided that the minimum pressure required at standpipe hose connections must be chosen conservatively. This is because fog nozzle performance, unlike that of solid stream nozzles, varies significantly with respect to the minimum inlet pressure required to achieve satisfactory streams. Though some fire service fog nozzles operate satisfactorily with as little as 70 psi (483 kPa), others have discharge patterns that quickly deteriorate as the nozzle pressure drops below 100 psi (690 kPa). As a result of this inconsistency, the only pressure that will reasonably ensure satisfactory nozzle performance in all cases is the pressure at which nozzles are tested and rated, 100 psi (690 kPa). This is the residual test pressure for fog nozzles established by NFPA 1964, *Standard for Spray Nozzles.*

To deliver a pressure of 100 psi (690 kPa) at the nozzle, the pressure at the standpipe hose connection must exceed 100 psi (690 kPa) by a value great enough to offset friction loss in the hose connecting the nozzle to the outlet. Ideally, a design should provide an additional 25 psi (172 kPa) for this purpose. This is adequate to compensate for friction loss in (1) 200 ft (61 m) of 2½ in. (65 mm) rubber-lined hose flowing about 250 gpm (946 L/min), (2) 200 ft (61 m) of 2 in. (50 mm) rubber-lined hose flowing about 125 gpm (473 L/min), or (3) 150 ft (46 m) of 1¾ in. (45 mm) rubber-lined hose flowing about 100 gpm (379 L/min).

Based on the foregoing reasoning, the NFPA 14 committee contemplated requiring a 125 psi (862 kPa) minimum pressure at the most remote hose connection but eventually decided on 100 psi (690 kPa). At first glance, this figure appears inadequate for satisfactory streams, and an explanation of the committee's action is warranted. The basis of this figure is an assumption that a fire pump will typically be installed to supply an automatic standpipe and that a pump designed to deliver 100 psi (690 kPa) at the most remote outlet at full system demand will actually deliver 120 psi (827 kPa) or more at lower flows. This takes advantage of excess pressure at the low-flow end of a fire pump curve. (See NFPA 20, *Standard for the Installation of Stationary Pumps for Fire Protection.*)

The 120-plus psi (827 kPa) initial pressure was considered reasonably adequate to satisfy a 100 psi (690 kPa) nozzle inlet pressure plus friction loss in the connecting hose for the first one or two hose lines deployed, and it was assumed that if fire-fighting operations grew beyond this level, fire apparatus would be available to supply additional pressure to meet fire nozzle demands. Alternatively, smooth-bore nozzles could be deployed. If these assumptions are not valid for a particular installation, consideration should be given to exceeding the minimum pressure specified by NFPA 14 to accommodate fire-fighting needs.

Although the 100 psi (690 kPa) minimum design pressure now specified by NFPA 14 may seem excessive when compared to the 65 psi (448 kPa) pressure specified in the past, it is consistent with established fire-fighting practices. Fire departments for decades have used 100 psi (690 kPa) as the target nozzle pressure when pumping hoses supplying fog nozzles, and fire hoses supplying fog nozzles are routinely pumped by fire apparatus at 150 psi (1034 kPa) or more when such hoses are connected directly to such apparatus.

For hose connections on Class II or Class III systems with preconnected hoses installed, nozzles with operating pressures in the 50 psi (345 kPa) range should be specified. By purchasing low-pressure nozzles, the minimum pressure required at the hydraulically most remote hose connection with preconnected hoses can be limited to 65 psi (448 kPa).

For additional information regarding selection of fire nozzles for use with standpipe systems, see "Fire Department Operations Using Standpipe Systems" later in this chapter.

Type and Number of Water Supplies. Manual standpipe systems may be supplied exclusively by a fire department connection (FDC) with a reliable and adequate water source accessible nearby.

Automatic and semiautomatic standpipe systems require a minimum of one preconnected water supply that is capable of supplying the standpipe system's hydraulic demand for the minimum required duration. Several types of water supplies may be acceptable. These include:

1. Public waterworks systems, supplemented by a booster pump when higher pressures are required
2. Fire pumps connected to a reliable fixed water source
3. Pressure tanks
4. Gravity tanks

In addition to the primary water supply on an automatic or semiautomatic standpipe system, one or more FDCs with a reliable water source accessible nearby are required.

Special Water Supply Requirements. In some cases, special water supply requirements may be applicable. For example, buildings in active seismic areas are often required by local regulations to use in-house tanks and pumps to supply standpipe systems rather than relying on public water supplies, which are susceptible to earthquake-induced failure.

Water Supply for High-Rise Buildings. For high-rise buildings, two remotely located FDCs are required for each zone within the pumping range of fire apparatus in addition to the automatic water supply. Two FDCs reduce the possibility of having falling glass cut all supply hoses and interrupt the secondary water supply during a fire.

Very tall buildings with floors located above the pumping range of fire department apparatus require a permanent secondary water source instead of FDCs because failure of the primary supply would otherwise render a building completely unprotected. If the primary water supply uses a pump, the backup arrangement could consist of a second pump, driver, and controller, or, perhaps, high-level water storage with additional pumping capability. The point at which a system is beyond the capability of fire department apparatus depends on the apparatus's pump and the residual pressure available from the water source. A permanent secondary water source is needed, if the following is "true":

$$AP + RP \leq SD$$

where

AP = Apparatus pressure boost available from a fire department pumper measured at the system demand flow rate

RP = Residual pressure available from the public or private water supply measured at the system demand flow rate

SD = System demand pressure at the system demand flow rate, measured at the pumper truck outlet supplying the hose to the FDC

If the system demand exceeds the sum of the fire apparatus pressure boost and the residual supply pressure (or the rated service pressure of the fire hose that will supply the FDC), fire apparatus will not be able to adequately supply upper portions of the standpipe system, and a secondary water supply is necessary. As a rule of thumb, buildings exceeding 300 ft (91.5 m) in height should be evaluated to determine whether the pumping range of the fire department apparatus has been exceeded.

Water Supply and Fire Pumps for Sprinklered Mid-Rise Buildings. An issue that is often raised in the design of standpipe systems for sprinklered mid-rise buildings is whether the sprinkler demand, the standpipe demand, or both, must be supplied by the automatic water supply serving the sprinkler system. The issue can have a major cost impact on mid-rise buildings, because the sprinkler demand can often be supplied by the public water supply without the use of a pump, whereas the standpipe demand almost always requires a pump.

In the 1993 edition of NFPA 14, an effort was made to provide further guidance on this issue. Although the solution is not clearly stated in the document, the intent is clear.

NFPA 14 allows a Class I standpipe system to be a manual system in buildings that are not high-rise buildings (defined as buildings having the floor level of an occupied floor located 75 ft [23 m] or more above the lowest level of fire department access). By allowing such standpipe systems to be manual systems, NFPA 14 does not require an automatic water supply to meet the standpipe demand. Therefore, where such standpipes also serve sprinklers in a combined system, only the sprinkler system demand must be automatically supplied. The combined system, from a standpipe perspective, is merely a Class I manual-wet standpipe system.

Sizing Pipe. Two methods of sizing standpipe system piping are (1) the pipe schedule method and (2) the hydraulic method.

With the pipe schedule method, pipe sizes are prescribed by a schedule, in NFPA 14, based on the class of system and the height of the standpipe. However, pipe schedule systems are no longer common, because buildings with standpipe systems typically require sprinkler protection as well. Such buildings also make use of combined systems, which must be hydraulically designed.

With the hydraulic design method, pipe sizes are calculated so that a system will deliver the minimum required pressure and flow. Pipe sizes must be large enough to allow each water supply, including fire department apparatus, to deliver the required flow at the hydraulically most remote hose connection.

When performing a hydraulic design, the hydraulic characteristics of each water supply must be known. The procedure for determining the hydraulic characteristics of permanent water supplies such as pumps is fairly straightforward and is described in NFPA 20 and in other chapters of this handbook. The procedure for determining the hydraulic characteristics of fire apparatus supplying a standpipe system is similar. Lacking better information about local fire apparatus, a conservative design would accommodate a 1000 gpm (3785 L/min) fire department pumper performing at the level of design specifications set forth in NFPA 1901, *Standard for Automotive Fire Apparatus*. NFPA 1901 specifies that fire department pumpers must be able to achieve three pressure/flow combinations. These are 100 percent of rated capacity at 150 psi (1034 kPa) net pump pressure, 70 percent of rated capacity at 200 psi (1379 kPa) net pump pressure, and 50 percent of rated capacity at 250 psi (1724 kPa) net pump pressure. Therefore, a 1000 gpm (3785 L/min) pumper can be expected to deliver no less than 1000 gpm (3785 L/min) at 150 psi (1034 kPa), 700 gpm (2650 L/min) at 200 psi (1379 kPa), and 500 gpm (1893 L/min) at 250 psi (1724 kPa). Residual supply pressure on the suction side of a pump from a municipal or other pressurized water supply can also be added.

To perform a hydraulic design, one should determine the minimum required pressure and flow at the hydraulically most remote hose connection and calculate this demand back through system piping to each water supply, accumulating losses for friction and elevation changes and adding flows for additional standpipes and sprinklers at each point where such standpipes or sprinklers connect to the hydraulic design path. When considering fire apparatus as a water supply, flows must be calculated from system piping through the fire department connection and back through connecting hoses to the apparatus. If the pressure available at each supply source exceeds a standpipe system's pressure demand at the designated flow, the design is acceptable. Otherwise, the piping design or the water supply must be adjusted. For more information, see Section 15, Chapter 3, "Hydraulics for Fire Protection."

Maximum Pressure and Zoning in Tall Buildings. In tall buildings, standpipe systems are often divided into subsystems to limit system pressure by controlling the maximum height of a water column. These subsystems are called zones. The goal of zoning is to limit the pressure that can be developed in system piping and at hose connections to reduce the need for high-pressure fittings and pressure-reducing valves.

In the 1993 edition of NFPA 14, the previous height limitation was replaced by a pressure limitation of 350 psi (24.1 bar). Beginning with the 2007 edition, the pressure limitation was eliminated in favor of a performance requirement that limits pressure based solely on the pressure rating of the system components. This revision also introduced the concept of a master pressure-reducing valve (PRV) to control pressures at lower elevations on a standpipe system. Traditionally NFPA 14 required a separate pump for each zone of a standpipe system. The 2007 edition of NFPA 14 permits the use of a single high-pressure pump to serve all areas of a building and employing a master PRV to control pressures for the lower floors. See Figure 16.10.4 for master PRV applications. When a master PRV is used, certain restrictions on its use apply. They are as follows:

- A method to isolate the PRV must be provided to allow maintenance and repair.

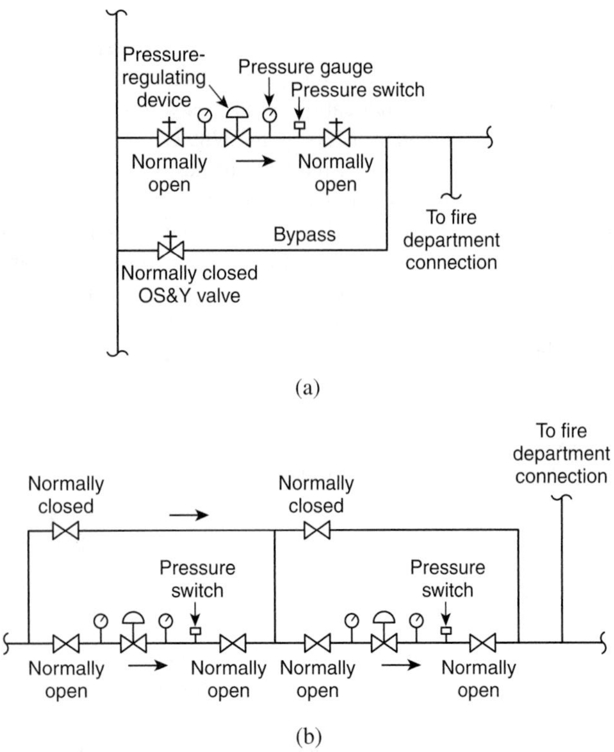

FIGURE 16.10.4 Two Examples of Master PRV Stations

- PRVs must be arranged so that failure of the device does not allow more than 175 psi (12.1 bar) to more than two hose connections.
- An equally sized bypass with a normally closed gate valve must be installed.
- The device must not be located more than 7 ft 6 in. (2.3 m) above the floor.
- Inlet and outlet pressure gauges must be provided.
- FDCs must be connected on the system side of the outlet isolation valve.
- A pressure relief valve must be provided in accordance with the manufacturer's recommendations.
- Remote monitoring for detecting failure of the PRV must be provided.

The maximum pressure in a standpipe system must always be limited based on the pressure ratings of system components. Fittings, valves, and pressure-regulating devices are usually the weakest links among system components with respect to pressure limits. Fittings often have a maximum pressure rating of 175 psi (1207 kPa); however, listed fittings are commonly available with pressure ratings of up to 350 psi (2413 kPa) or more. Listed valves and pressure regulating devices are also available with 350 psi (2413 kPa) or higher ratings. However, zone heights must be further limited if equipment with pressure ratings less than 350 psi (2413 kPa) is used.

Although the maximum zone height corresponding to a particular maximum system pressure can be calculated, zone height limits will be determined by trial and error in most cases. To determine whether a single zone can be used, a designer can lay out a system with one zone and calculate the required pressures and flows from hydraulic demand points back through system piping to the supply to determine the system demand. Assuming that the supply will be a pump, a single zone can be justified if a pump is available that would satisfy the hydraulic demand of the system without exceeding the system component pressure rating at churn, including residual supply pressure. If a pump cannot be found to meet these criteria, adjustments to the design or subdivision into zones can be made or a variable speed pump can be used.

Standpipe system pressures in the 350 psi (2413 kPa) range pose a danger to users and a risk of failure of sprinkler system components on combined systems. Therefore, pressure control devices are required when system pressure could exceed safety limits at hose or sprinkler connections.

The safety limits at hose connections are based on two criteria: (1) hose burst pressure and (2) handling. Hoses for fire department use are required to be tested periodically to 250 psi (1724 kPa) or more, according to NFPA 1962, *Standard for the Inspection, Care, and Use of Fire Hose, Couplings, and Nozzles and the Service Testing of Fire Hose*. NFPA 1962 requires preconnected standpipe hoses to be tested periodically to 150 psi (1034 kPa) or more.

Though a hose may not fail up to these pressures, experience indicates that 175 psi (1207 kPa) is about the maximum pressure on a hose that can be satisfactorily maneuvered by fire fighters and that 100 psi (690 kPa) is the maximum pressure that an untrained user should be expected to handle. Therefore, pressure-regulating devices are required to limit static and residual pressures to 175 psi (1207 kPa) at hose connections without preconnected hoses and to limit residual pressure to 100 psi (690 kPa) at hose connections with preconnected hoses.

The established pressure limit for sprinkler connections is also 175 psi (1207 kPa). This limit is the maximum pressure for which sprinklers are typically listed, and it provides a safety factor to prevent leakage. When higher pressure is expected at a sprinkler connection, both pressure-regulating and pressure relief valves are required. To allow a buffer between the pressure settings for the valves, regulating valves should be set at 165 psi (1138 kPa) and relief valves should be set at 175 psi (1207 kPa).

Table 16.10.1 summarizes the pressure for connections to a standpipe. Figures 16.10.5 and 16.10.6 illustrate sample multiple-zone systems. Note that, on multiple-zone systems, fire pumps may be used in series. In addition, two separate supply risers are always required for high zones supplied by pumps at lower levels so that a water supply can be maintained when one riser is out of service. Separate fire department connections are also required for each zone.

System Components

The selection of standpipe system components is determined largely by the class of system and the system layout. Particular attention should be given to ensuring that components are rated for pressures to which they may be subjected.

Piping and Fittings. Steel pipes assembled with welded joints, screwed fittings, flanged fittings, rubber-gasketed fittings, or a

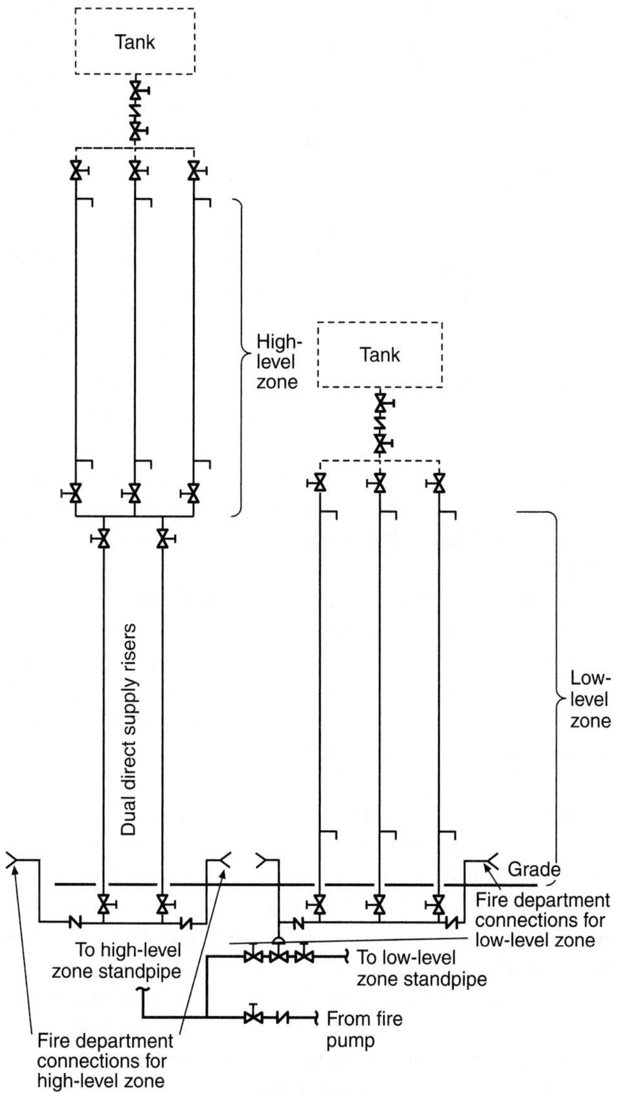

FIGURE 16.10.5 Major Components in a Multizone System with a Low-Level Pump

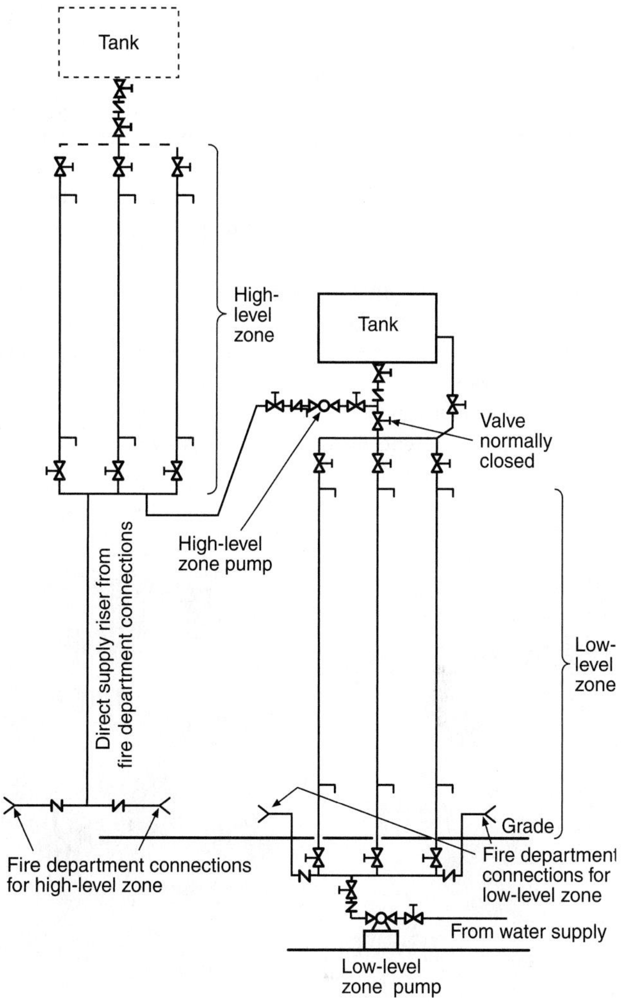

FIGURE 16.10.6 Schematic Diagram of Major Components in a Multizone System with a High-Level Pump

combination of these are the most common configurations of materials used for standpipe system piping and fittings. Piping should be capable of withstanding the maximum pressures that can be developed in a system.

Fittings are required to be rated to withstand either 175 psi (1207 kPa) or maximum system pressures, whichever is greater. When pressures are expected to exceed 175 psi (1207 kPa), extra-heavy fittings or fittings listed for greater pressures should be used for pressures up to 300 psi (2069 kPa), and specially designed fittings should be used for pressures exceeding 300 psi (2069 kPa).

Hose, Hose Racks, Nozzles, and Hose Cabinets. When preconnected hoses are required to be installed on Class II or Class III systems, lined hose must be used. Unlined linen hose has been phased out, because it is subject to rapid deterioration under moist or wet conditions. Usually, the size of choice is 1½-in. (40-mm) hose. However, the use of listed hoses smaller than 1½ in. (40 mm) is permitted by NFPA 14, in light-hazard occupancies when approved by the authority having jurisdiction. The allowance for smaller hose mounted on a reel recognizes that an untrained person might be more capable of using such equipment in the event of a fire. Similar equipment has been used in Europe for many years.

Preconnected hoses on Class II and Class III standpipes are generally limited to 100 ft (30.5 m) in length to minimize the difficulty that untrained users may have advancing a hose and to minimize kinking. Hoses are always required to be kept on compatible racks and should always be positioned in a readily accessible location within convenient reach of a person standing on the floor. Hoses should also be clearly visible and located in a place not likely to be obstructed. Where hoses are kept in cabinets or closets, the doors should have a glass panel or some other means to allow easy identification.

Preconnected hoses are required to be equipped with approved ⅜- or ½-in. (10- or 13-mm) open nozzles or combination spray/solid pattern nozzles. It is preferable to use nozzles that have operating pressures in the 50 psi (345 kPa) range. This range minimizes the pressure demand on the system and helps to ensure that hoses can be handled by industrial fire brigade members. Because nozzle shutoff valves complicate the operation of a hose, they are considered undesirable unless the users are trained.

For typical hose rack and valve connections, see Figure 16.10.7. A typical hose cabinet is shown in Figure 16.10.8.

Valves. Several different types of valves may be used as components of standpipe systems. These include gate valves, check valves, pressure-regulating valves, and hose valves. Like piping and fittings, valves must be capable of withstanding the maximum pressure that can be developed in a system. The following discussion highlights the most common valves and pressure control devices encountered.

FIGURE 16.10.7 Typical Hose Racks and Valve Connections (Source: Potter-Roemer, Inc.)

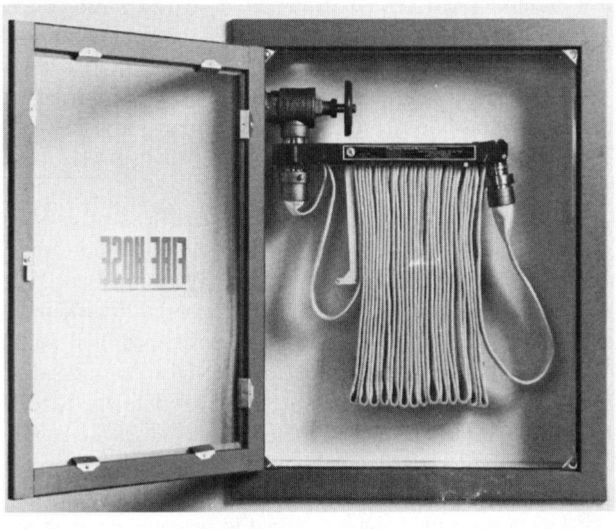

FIGURE 16.10.8 Typical Hose Cabinet

Starting at a permanent water supply, an indicating gate valve is required at each water source to allow isolation of any water source for servicing. Note that a gate valve is not permitted to be installed between a fire department connection and the standpipe system that it serves. This ensures the fire department's ability to pump into a system.

Next, each permanent water source should be protected by a check valve to prevent backflow. Check valves should also be installed between fire department connections and wet standpipe systems that they serve. These valves allow piping that is connected to fire department connections to normally be kept dry, when provided with automatic drain valves at low points. Keeping the FDC dry protects it from freezing and prevents the possibility of having FDC caps "thread-lock" if the internal clapper valves leak water back to the caps.

Moving farther into a system, gate valves should be installed at feed main connections to each standpipe to allow standpipes to be serviced independently without impairing protection to an entire building.

Drain valves also should be provided to allow individual standpipes, as well as an entire system, to be drained for servicing. Finally, each outlet from a standpipe system must terminate at a hose valve or at a sprinkler control valve on combined systems. When excessive pressures are expected at outlets, pressure-regulating devices are required.

Pressure-Regulating Devices. Pressure-regulating devices are used to limit system outlet pressures. Pressure-regulating devices used in standpipe systems can be categorized into three basic types: (1) pressure restricting, (2) pressure reducing, and (3) pressure control. Pressure-restricting devices reduce pressures in flowing conditions only. They do not compensate for changes in input pressure to maintain a constant discharge pressure, and they do not control pressure in static conditions. For these reasons, their use is limited to 1½ in. (40 mm) hose connections for limiting residual pressure to 100 psi (690 kPa) where the static pressure does not exceed 175 psi (1207 kPa). One example of a pressure-restricting device is an orifice plate. An orifice plate is a metal disk with a restricting orifice. Orifice plates may be inserted into connections to standpipe systems to reduce residual pressure on the downstream side. Though relatively inexpensive, orifice plates are generally undesirable because they do not maintain a steady discharge pressure, and because they can damage hoses if the pressure jet from an orifice strikes the inner wall of a hose. If used, orifice plates should always be installed at hose couplings to allow for easy removal.

The preferred devices for regulating excessive pressures are pressure control and pressure-reducing valves. These valves are designed to actively regulate outlet pressures in both static and flowing conditions, and they are required for outlets of systems where static pressure could exceed 175 psi (1207 kPa). Pressure control and pressure-reducing valves are preferred over pressure-restricting devices because hoses and sprinkler systems connected to standpipes are exposed to both static and flowing conditions; and uncontrolled static pressures can cause equipment failure and pose a danger to users.

Pressure control and pressure-reducing valves employ a mechanism that compensates for variations in inlet pressures by balancing water pressure in an internal chamber or chambers, typically against a spring. Pressure control valves, which are a type of pressure-reducing valve that is pilot operated, are considered by many to be the most reliable method of controlling pressure. Figure 16.10.9 illustrates one example of a pressure control valve. In the example shown, the outlet pressure is a function of the setting on the regulating spring. Often the outlet pressure is not field adjustable, and valves are preset at the factory for use at a specific floor level in a building. In such cases, it is critical to ensure that valves are installed at the intended location.

Standpipe systems with pressure-regulating devices are required to be designed such that each device may be tested, and routine testing must be conducted. To accommodate the need for testing pressure-regulating devices, standpipe systems using such devices must have a dedicated drainage system with connections at every other floor and a central means for measuring flow. Figure 16.10.10 shows one possible design of a floor valve assembly for such an arrangement. The case shown assumes a standpipe pressure in excess of 175 psi (1207 kPa) and a combined sprinkler and standpipe system with a directly connected drainage riser for pressure-regulating device testing. As an option, the drainage riser may simply have a hose connection at every other floor where a short piece of hose can be connected to the two closest pressure-regulating devices for testing.

Where system pressures are extreme, pressure relief valves, which reduce pressure by flowing water into a drain, may be provided as a backup to pressure-regulating valves. Pressure relief valves are commonly available in two types: (1) spring operated and (2) pilot operated. Pilot-operated valves are preferred because they respond more accurately to changes in system pressures; however, these valves may require increased maintenance to prevent excessive accumulation of debris in strainers.

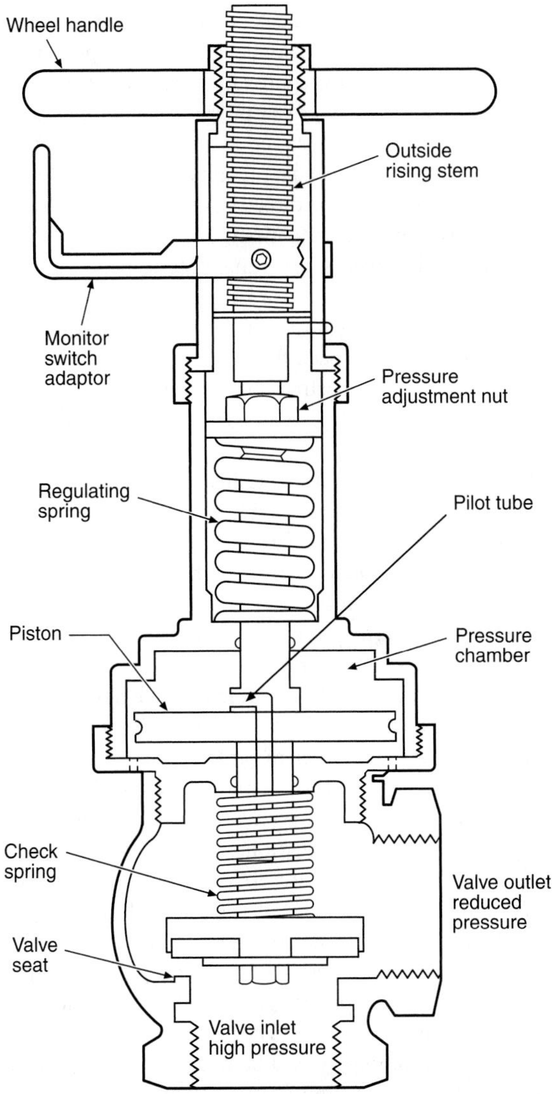

FIGURE 16.10.9 Cutaway of a Typical Pressure Control Valve

Fire Department Connections. (See the additional discussion under "Type and Number of Water Supplies" earlier in this chapter.) Fire department connections (FDCs) are required for all Class I and Class III systems. On manual standpipe systems, FDCs serve as the only water supply. On automatic and semiautomatic standpipe systems, they serve as an auxiliary water supply.

Fire department connections should be located where they are accessible to fire department vehicles and not more than 100 ft (30.5 m) from the nearest fire hydrant. They should not be obstructed by shrubbery, vehicles, or fences that limit visibility or access. For high-rise buildings, two or more connections, located remotely from each other, are required for each zone. This redundancy helps to ensure the fire department's ability to provide an uninterrupted water supply during a major fire. The concern is that falling glass from broken windows can cut supply hoses and prevent personnel from connecting new hoses to the affected FDC, and redundancy improves the chance of gaining access to at least one FDC in such cases.

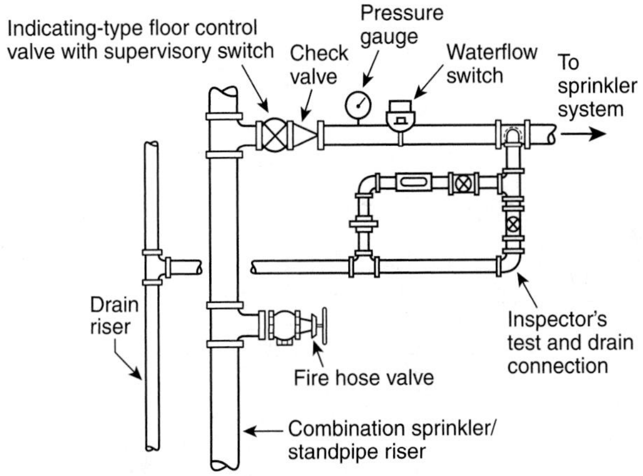

FIGURE 16.10.10 One Possible Arrangement for Valving at a Floor Connection for a Combined System (Not to Scale)

As a rule, most fire department connections are provided with one 2½ in. (65 mm) inlet for each 250 gpm (946 L/min) of design flow rate. Some fire departments require large-diameter inlets that are designed to connect to special high-pressure, large-diameter hoses. Even when large-diameter hoses are used, a second inlet is needed to allow for a backup hose that could be charged if the primary hose ruptures or separates from a coupling.

Another important issue that should not be overlooked is the size of the pipe connecting a fire department connection to system mains. This pipe should be sized to deliver the system demand, as discussed previously under "Sizing Pipe." It is preferable to use 4 in. (100 mm) or larger piping in all cases to avoid obstruction by debris.

Figure 16.10.11 illustrates a typical arrangement for a fire department connection on a wet standpipe system.

System Monitoring and Supervision Devices. To ensure the reliability and performance of standpipe systems, provisions must be made for monitoring system pressure and supervising control valves. Gauges should be provided at each water supply and at the top of each standpipe so that system pressure can be monitored.

Valve supervision can be accomplished by electrical or mechanical means. Supervision is generally required for water supply isolation valves, standpipe isolation valves, and similar valves that are capable of interrupting the water supply to large portions of a system. Supervision is necessary to ensure that the valves remain open at all times.

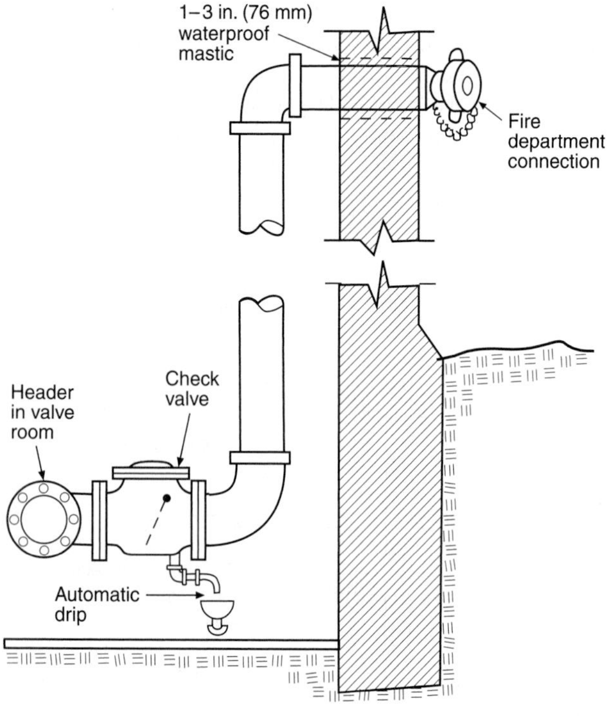

FIGURE 16.10.11 Typical Fire Department Connection for a Standpipe with Water-Filled Piping

Frequently, waterflow alarms are also specified for monitoring a system. This is usually limited to systems having preconnected hoses where immediate notification of waterflow is desired. Also, electronic supervision of hose cabinet doors may be provided where vandalism is a concern.

STANDPIPE SYSTEM INSTALLATION CONSIDERATIONS

Although a proper design establishes the groundwork for a reliable and usable standpipe system, the installation ultimately determines how well a system will perform. A few key considerations are discussed next.

Because most standpipe systems are hydraulically designed, it is essential that the installation conform to design drawings. This is especially true for combined standpipe and sprinkler systems that are based on hydraulically calculated designs. Because the installation of additional pipe or fittings has an adverse effect on hydraulic calculations, as will reductions in pipe sizes, plans should indicate that all such changes should be reported to the designer for approval. Plans should also caution installers of systems with preset pressure-regulating valves to ensure that the valves are installed at the proper floor levels.

To ensure operability and maintainability, it is preferable to label piping and indicate the direction of waterflow. Valve locations must also be clearly identified and accessible. Particular attention should be given to providing access space around hose connections, recognizing that fire fighters will be using large gloves when connecting hoses and operating valves. Twelve inches (0.3 m) of clear space from the valve handles and hose outlets to walls or other obstructions is desirable. Consideration should be given to installing hose valves at a 45 degree angle to prevent kinking the hose.

The key concerns for locating fire department connections are accessibility and visibility. Fire department connections should be clear of shrubbery, parking for vehicles, and other obstructions that could hinder their use. In addition, signs should be provided, preferably reflective, to indicate whether a connection serves standpipes, sprinklers, or both, and to indicate the area served by the connection.

During construction of a building that will have a standpipe system, it is important that the system be made operable before work progresses to a point where deployment of hoses from fire apparatus no longer provides an efficient means of fire fighting. Fire codes usually dictate the point at which standpipes must be made operable during construction.

Noncombustible structures often represent extreme fire hazards during construction because combustible shoring and a variety of ignition sources may be present. To provide protection during construction, the permanent system piping is typically used, along with a temporary fire department connection. At least one hose connection should be provided at each floor level, and all hose connections should be kept capped with an easily removable cap and protected from mechanical injury. Systems should be extended to keep pace with construction progress, and routine inspections should be scheduled to ensure that systems are kept operable.

COMMISSIONING OF STANDPIPE SYSTEMS

Because standpipe systems are essential fire safety systems, they must be routinely tested and inspected to verify that they perform to the original installation requirements and to ensure operational readiness. Testing should be conducted before system acceptance and at intervals adequate to verify reliability. Once accepted, inspection, testing, and maintenance of standpipe systems are regulated by NFPA 25, *Standard for the Inspection, Testing, and Maintenance of Water-Based Fire Protection Systems.* See Section 16, Chapter 11, for care and maintenance of water-based extinguishing systems.

Preinspection

Prior to conducting a performance test, the system should be inspected to verify that the installation is complete. This preliminary inspection should include the following:

- Location of control valves
- Method of valve supervision
- Verification of component type
- Valve identification/hydraulic data nameplate installed

Acceptance Tests

On completion of the inspection, the following tests should be conducted:

- Hydrostatic test
- Main drain test
- Pressure-regulating device test
- Alarm test
- Trip test for dry system (including water transit time)
- Trip test for semiautomatic system

The results of these tests are recorded on a form from NFPA 14 titled "Contractor's Material and Test Certificate for Above Ground Piping." The building owner should keep the form on file for the life of the system.

When standpipes are flow tested by flowing water at the roof level, a flow diffuser with a screen is recommended at the point of discharge to control the water stream and intercept any debris that may be ejected. Particular attention should be paid to the adequacy of the drainage route for water to avoid flooding the roof or other areas.

FIRE DEPARTMENT OPERATIONS USING STANDPIPE SYSTEMS

Preplanning

For standpipe systems to be effective, fire fighters must be trained in standpipe operations, and they should preplan to become familiar with systems that they will use. As part of the preplan, fire fighters should identify the locations of fire hydrants, fire department connections, water supply valves, pumps, tanks, and hose connections. The presence of orifice plates in hose connections or pressure-reducing or pressure control valves also should be noted. Fire departments also should develop standard operating procedures that assign personnel and apparatus responsibilities when using standpipe systems.

Equipment

To facilitate the use of standpipe systems, "standpipe packs" should be carried on responding fire apparatus. The packs should contain the equipment necessary to use standpipe system hose connections. Standpipe packs are typically carried on carts or in bags and contain between 100 and 200 ft (30.5 and 61 m) of hose, a nozzle, and miscellaneous tools and wrenches. A gated wye may also be carried to allow a second hose to be connected to a single hose connection. The length of hose carried should be based on local practices regarding which hose connections are expected to be used (at the fire floor or the landing below) and local building code requirements for locating hose connections. Probably the most versatile hose arrangement is one that includes 1¾- or 2-in. (45- or 50-mm) hose and a high-volume nozzle capable of flowing 200 gpm (757 L/min) or more. Such an arrangement can provide a flow capability comparable to a 2½ in. (65 mm) hose with a standard selectable flow fog nozzle when adequate pressure is available, but it is significantly easier to handle.

A fog nozzle that produces an effective pattern at operating pressures less than 100 psi (690 kPa) should be used to take maximum advantage of the pressure available. Use of piston-type automatic nozzles is not advised for standpipe systems because such nozzles may require high pressures to produce satisfactory steams. Some automatic nozzles require pressures in excess of 90 psi (621 kPa) to produce a reasonable fog pattern, and delivering this amount of pressure to the nozzle may prove difficult in some cases, particularly on older standpipe systems designed to provide only 65 psi (448 kPa) and to limit pressures to a maximum of 100 psi (690 kPa). Although low-pressure automatic nozzles designed to operate with inlet pressure in the 70 psi (483 kPa) range are available, the most reliable fog nozzle for use with standpipe systems is a selectable flow nozzle without an automatic piston.

In addition to standpipe packs, fire apparatus should also carry coiled or packed sections of 2½ in. (65 mm) hose for cases where large volumes of water are needed and the pressure available from a standpipe is limited. Such cases may occur in very tall buildings that have floor levels beyond the range of fire apparatus or where pressure regulating valves on a standpipe system have been improperly adjusted.

Operations

It is reasonable to expect the first fire-fighting crew on the scene of an incident in a building with a standpipe system to take a standpipe pack into the building when investigating the call. Meanwhile, an engine should connect to a fire department connection to supply the system. More than one supply hose should be connected to a system if a fire is discovered to prevent the water supply from being interrupted if a supply hose breaks. It is also preferable for additional apparatus to connect to a second

FDC, during major fires when more than one FDC is present. This connection reduces the risk of interruption of the water supply if glass breakage on upper floors makes conditions at some parts of a building's perimeter unsafe, perhaps cutting supply hoses.

When fire fighters determine that hoses are needed, they should select a hose connection located in a protected stairway enclosure, as opposed to a connection located in a corridor or open area (when such connections are present) because it is desirable to have a charged hose before entering a floor if smoke or flame is detected. In multiple-story buildings, a hose connection located at the intermediate landing below or one floor below a fire floor is often preferred over a connection at a fire floor because it provides additional space to spread a hose before charging it, and minimizes congestion at the fire floor entrance. It should be noted that using a hose connection on a lower level will create a need for additional hose to reach all areas on a fire floor, and by providing a gated wye preconnected in a standpipe hose line, fire fighters can add hose without having to shut off and disconnect an attack line. Fire fighters should also be aware that, depending on desired flows, they may have to remove pressure-restricting devices or adjust pressure-regulating valves if they are field adjustable.

The pressure to which a standpipe system should be charged varies from one fire department to another based on local preferences. Some departments use recommendations previously published in NFPA 13E, *Recommended Practice for Fire Department Operations in Properties Protected by Sprinkler and Standpipe Systems,* which suggested that the pressure at the FDC should be initiated at 100 psi (690 kPa) when smoothbore nozzles will be used at elevations of 100 ft (30.5 m) or less, and at 150 psi (1034 kPa) when fog nozzles will be used at elevations of 100 ft (30.5 m) or less. For elevations above 100 ft (30.5 m), 5 psi (34.5 kPa) should be added for each floor level above 100 ft (30.5 m). Other departments simply pump 150 psi (1034 kPa) plus 5 psi (34.5 kPa) for each floor level above grade. The latter method is more commonly used and should deliver adequate pressure for fog nozzles in most cases.

OUTSIDE HOSE SYSTEMS

Outside hose systems are not standpipe systems. Rather, they are appendages to a water supply. However, outside hose systems and standpipe systems have similar purposes. They both provide an efficient means for manually applying water to fires. Though not mandated by model building or fire codes, outside hose systems may be requested by insurance authorities or by owners as an additional safety measure to minimize potential fire losses. For a discussion of outside hose systems, see Section 15, Chapter 4, "Water Supplies for Sprinkler Systems."

SUMMARY

Standpipe systems deliver water for manual fire fighting. This chapter provided an overview of standpipe system design and installation considerations. The chapter also included a discussion of the testing and inspection of standpipe systems and fire department operations using standpipe systems. The chapter concluded with a brief description of the design and equipment considerations of outside hose systems.

BIBLIOGRAPHY

NFPA Codes, Standards, and Recommended Practices

Reference to the following NFPA codes, standards, and recommended practices will provide further information on standpipe and hose systems discussed in this chapter. (See the latest version of The NFPA Catalog *for availability of current editions of the following documents.)*

NFPA 1, *Uniform Fire Code*™
NFPA 13, *Standard for the Installation of Sprinkler Systems*
NFPA 13E, *Recommended Practice for Fire Department Operations in Properties Protected by Sprinkler and Standpipe Systems*
NFPA 14, *Standard for the Installation of Standpipe and Hose Systems*
NFPA 20, *Standard for the Installation of Stationary Pumps for Fire Protection*
NFPA 22, *Standard for Water Tanks for Private Fire Protection*
NFPA 25, *Standard for the Inspection, Testing, and Maintenance of Water-Based Fire Protection Systems*
NFPA 72®, National Fire Alarm Code®
NFPA *101®, Life Safety Code®*
NFPA 1901, *Standard for Automotive Fire Apparatus*
NFPA 1961, *Standard on Fire Hose*
NFPA 1962, *Standard for the Inspection, Care, and Use of Fire Hose, Couplings, and Nozzles and the Service Testing of Fire Hose*
NFPA 1963, *Standard for Fire Hose Connections*
NFPA 1964, *Standard for Spray Nozzles*

References

Bond, H., "Water for Fire Fighting in High-Rise Buildings," *Fire Technology,* Vol. 2, No. 2, pp. 159–163.
Bryan, J. L., *Automatic Sprinkler and Standpipe Systems,* 3rd ed., National Fire Protection Association, Quincy, MA, 1997.

Chapter 11

Care and Maintenance of Water-Based Extinguishing Systems

David R. Hague

Sprinkler systems are exceptionally reliable, such that the chance of dying in a fire is reduced by one-half to three-fourths when sprinklers are present. Statistics also indicate that property damage is reduced by one-half to two-thirds when sprinklers are present. This, of course, is only true for systems that have been designed, installed, and maintained properly. Maintenance procedures are critical, such as those required by NFPA 25, *Standard for the Inspection, Testing, and Maintenance of Water-Based Fire Protection Systems.*

This chapter covers the care and maintenance of sprinkler and water spray systems. It discusses the agencies involved in inspecting and testing these systems and the techniques they use. The chapter also covers sources of obstruction in sprinkler system pipes and methods for flushing and cleaning them, as well as sprinkler leakage and water damage.

For related topics, see Section 15, Chapter 1, "Fixed Water Storage Supplies for Fire Protection"; Section 15, Chapter 2, "Water Supply Requirements for Public Supply Systems"; Section 15, Chapter 5, "Microbiologically Influenced Corrosion in Fire Sprinkler Systems"; Section 16, Chapter 4, "Hanging and Bracing of Water-Based Systems"; Section 16, Chapter 8, "Water Mist Fire Suppression Systems"; and Section 16, Chapter 9, "Water Spray Protection."

Chapter Contents

Key Terms

automatic sprinkler system, central station, fire pump, microbiologically influenced corrosion (MIC), standpipe, unintended discharge, water-based fire protection, waterflow alarm, waterflow detector, water spray fixed system, water supply (private), water supply (public), zebra mussel

SYSTEM MAINTENANCE BASICS

Importance of System Maintenance

Care and maintenance includes more than the inspection and testing of system components. For effective protection, an evaluation of the factors that affect system performance should be made. These factors include such items as the following:

- Occupancy changes
- Process or material changes
- Building modifications such as relocated partitions or ceilings or the addition of mezzanines
- Modifications to the heating system exposing systems to potential freezing

To maintain the proper level of protection for a water-based extinguishing system, there are four areas of concern:

1. Adherence to a regular inspection schedule as determined by the needs of the system
2. Execution of any special investigations or tests that can assess the performance of the devices and equipment
3. Exercise of due diligence in the repair of devices and equipment
4. Assurance that all personnel involved in maintenance are properly trained to correctly execute the procedures for inspection, testing, and maintenance of equipment

David R. Hague, P.E., is a principal fire safety and systems engineer at NFPA.

Responsibility for Inspection, Testing, and Maintenance

Ultimately, the building owner is responsible for inspection, testing, and maintenance of fire protection systems. In the case of an absentee owner or where the complexity of the system is such that the building owner lacks the appropriate training and experience, that responsibility can be transferred to another qualified person or firm.

TYPES OF SPRINKLER SYSTEM INSPECTIONS

In addition to the indispensable inspection procedures followed by the property owner, other inspection services are available.

Insurance Company

In insured properties, extinguishing systems may be given special attention by the insurance carrier. Routine testing of sprinkler systems and devices at regular intervals is a service extended by some insurance companies. This service can benefit both the insurance carrier and the property owner. By these routine tests, the equipment can be shown to be in good operating condition or in need of repair or replacement. The purpose of these tests is also to verify reliability of the system to establish an insurance rate for the protected property.

Fire Department

Inspections are made of extinguishing system equipment by many fire departments at varying intervals. This type of inspection is principally done to make sure that valves are fully open for preplanning purposes and may not include the level of detail prescribed by NFPA 25. Inspections are customarily made by the fire department in the district where the property is located.

Sprinkler Contractor

Inspection and maintenance services are offered by sprinkler manufacturers, sprinkler contractors, and inspection service companies. This service provides periodic examinations and reports and is valuable to the property owner not only for a regular checkup of the sprinkler system and components but also for the valuable instruction that can be given to employees in the process. The inspection contract should include all components and systems needed for the proper protection of the property.

Central Station Supervision

Central station supervision of sprinkler alarm and control devices provided under contract is a valuable aid to any maintenance program. Reporting each incident involving waterflow or valve closure or other supervised events keeps a constant check on the condition of the equipment and encourages care on the part of the plant fire organization as well as the building owner.

All of the foregoing inspection procedures should follow the prescribed guidelines in NFPA 25 and *NFPA 72®, National Fire Alarm Code®*. For prescribed frequencies and sample report forms, see NFPA 25.

GENERAL MAINTENANCE OF SPRINKLERS AND SPRINKLER PIPING

Frequently, sprinklers are installed in areas that will subject them to harsh environments, causing loading (contamination), corrosion, exposure to high temperatures, and mechanical damage.

Frequency and Timing of Testing and Inspection

Testing Criteria. If sprinklers have generally performed satisfactorily through their service life, NFPA 25 requires testing of representative samples of installed sprinklers periodically to verify continued performance. The testing criteria for sprinklers are as follows:

- Sprinklers installed for 50 years must be tested, and tests must be repeated every 10 years thereafter.
- Sprinklers manufactured prior to 1920 must be replaced.
- Fast-response sprinklers must be tested after 20 years, with tests repeated every 10 years thereafter.
- High-temperature sprinklers (temperature ratings of 325°F [163°C] or greater) must be tested every 5 years.
- Dry-type sprinklers must be tested every 10 years.

The test sample should comprise 1 percent of the total number of sprinklers installed in the facility and should never be less than four sprinklers. Any sprinkler that shows signs of contamination (loading), corrosion, or paint (other than the paint applied by the manufacturer) should be replaced because the testing laboratory will not evaluate such sprinklers. See Figure 16.11.1 for an example of a loaded sprinkler. The test results will provide an indication of the service conditions that all sprinklers represented by the test sample are exposed to. Any sprinkler that fails the test requires that all sprinklers represented by the test sample be replaced. When removing or installing sprinklers, the manufacturer's instructions should be followed to minimize damage to the sprinkler.

Inspection procedures may be affected by their frequency as well as seasonal changes. The following are examples of inspections governed by seasonal effects.

Spring Inspection. When the danger of freezing temperatures (32°F [0°C]) has passed, spring inspections may be performed. Pertinent operations are as follows:

1. Open cold weather valves (it should be noted that these are prohibited for use on new systems).
2. Inspect, test, and reset dry-pipe valves.
3. Test water motor gongs.
4. Conduct waterflow tests.
5. Test fire pump.

Fall Inspection. At the approach of freezing weather, the system inspector(s) must perform the following functions:

FIGURE 16.11.1 Loaded Sprinkler

1. Close cold-weather valves and drain pipes exposed to freezing temperatures (drain valves on the exposed piping are left slightly open), and test the specific gravity of the solution in an antifreeze sprinkler system.
2. Check dry-pipe valves to make sure that the systems are holding air properly and that the pressure switches and water motor alarms are in order, check drains at the low points of the dry piping to ensure that they are properly clear of water, and check heating provisions for the dry-pipe valve enclosures.
3. Examine gravity tanks to verify that they are protected against freezing, and check that the employed heating system is in operating condition.
4. Check the condition of fire pump reservoirs and suction intakes from other water sources.
5. Carefully inspect buildings to make sure that cold air will not enter or unduly expose sprinkler piping to freezing.

Accumulation of Foreign Materials on Sprinklers

In many classes of properties, conditions exist that cause an accumulation of foreign material on automatic sprinklers. This accumulation is commonly known as loading. The operation of the sprinkler may be delayed or prevented by the loading effect.

Deposits on sprinklers tend to retard their operation as a result of the insulating effect of the loading material. If the deposit is hard, it may physically delay or prevent the sprinkler from operating. The best practice is to replace loaded sprinklers with new sprinklers rather than to attempt to clean the sprinkler. Attempts at cleaning, particularly in instances where deposits are hard, are likely to damage the sprinkler, thus rendering it inoperative or possibly causing leakage.

Deposits of light dust on sprinklers, such as may be found in woodworking plants and grain elevators, are less serious than hard deposits. Dust may be expected to partially delay the operation of sprinklers but ordinarily will not prevent the eventual discharge of water. Dust deposits can be blown or brushed off. Blowing by compressed air should not be undertaken where it can create a dust explosion or ignition hazard. When using a brush, make sure that it is soft to avoid possible injury to sprinkler parts. If these two methods prove unsatisfactory, then a damp, soft cloth may be used to clean the sprinkler. Water-solution cleaning liquids of caustic or acid type are likely to be destructive to sprinklers and should not be used for cleaning. Hot solutions of any kind should not be used.

Sprinklers are sometimes protected when ceilings or sprinkler piping are being painted by temporarily placing small, lightweight paper bags, plastic bags, or aluminum foil over them and securing them with rubber bands. Any such covering is likely to delay the operation of the sprinklers and should be removed immediately after the painting is completed. Should paint cover one of the sprinklers, the sprinkler should be replaced. There is no known method of adequately removing paint under the water cap or on the fusible link. Sprinklers that have been painted by anyone other than the manufacturer must be replaced with new sprinklers.

Sprinklers in spray booths present a special problem. To help minimize this problem, one acceptable solution is to conduct the spray process in a downward manner to avoid contaminating the sprinkler. Cleaning will be necessary; therefore, sprinklers must be installed in an easily accessible location. To facilitate the washing or wiping off of deposits, a light coating of a mild, soft soap should be used. Unless cleaning is done very carefully, deposits are likely to accumulate to such an extent as to interfere seriously with sprinkler operation. The use of paper, polyethylene, or cellophane bags to protect sprinklers in spray booths is fairly common and is permitted by NFPA 25 when the thickness of such bags does not exceed 0.0003 in. (0.008 mm).

Corrosion of Automatic Sprinklers

Corrosive conditions can make automatic sprinklers inoperative or delay the speed of operation. They can also seriously impede the waterways of spray nozzles, affecting the spray patterns of sprinklers. Corrosive vapors may seriously affect not only the heat-actuated element and the water-retaining mechanism of an automatic sprinkler but also may be severe enough to weaken or destroy other portions of the sprinkler. In most instances, such corrosive action is slow and chronic. Thus, the process must be monitored vigilantly. Illustrations of some typical corroded sprinklers are shown in Figure 16.11.2.

Some types of sprinklers are less susceptible than others to corrosive conditions. Nonferrous metal is used for some sprinkler parts, but special protective coatings are still necessary for sprinklers that are exposed to extreme corrosive conditions. Approved corrosion-resistant or special coated sprinklers

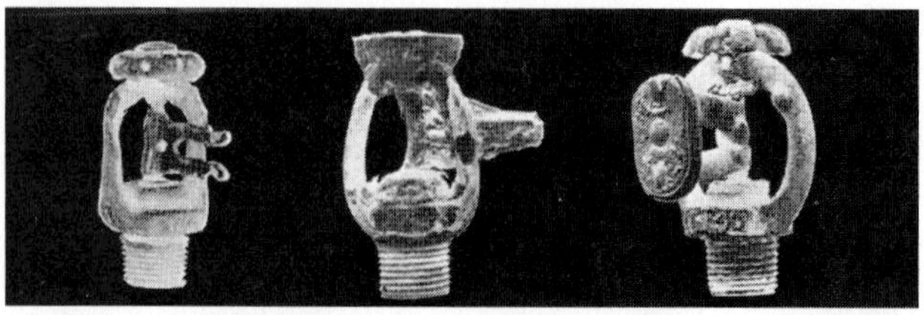

FIGURE 16.11.2 Examples of Corroded Automatic Sprinklers

FIGURE 16.11.3 Temporary Hose Connection from Hydrant

are needed in locations where chemicals, excessive moisture, or corrosive vapors exist.

Protection of Pipe against External Corrosion

Under some conditions, corrosive vapors may cause rapid deterioration of steel pipe and hangers. Proper protection can prevent the frequent replacement of these components. Cast-iron fittings are generally not affected by corrosive vapors.

In severe corrosive conditions where protective methods are not wholly satisfactory, copper or special alloy, noncorrosive pipe will yield the best results. Galvanized steel may offer the most economical method of obtaining a reasonably long life for the piping system. Galvanized piping systems have met with success in chemical plants, saltworks, or similar properties where severe corrosion exists. Stainless steel and copper piping have also been used in some cases.

Corrosion of existing equipment becomes a maintenance problem. The options available are replacement of the components or corrective measures, such as an application of a recognized protective coating.

Advance Preparations Before Shutoff

When maintenance or testing requires systems to be shut off, the work should be planned for a time when the least amount of hazard exists and when there is the least disruption. Both considerations lead to impairment during idle periods rather than during normal business operations. Therefore, work that requires system shutoff should be performed during weekends or other idle periods. A fire watch may be required to aid in the detection of any fire that might develop while the systems are shut down.

Sectional valves, rather than main valves, should be used to reduce to a minimum the number of systems removed from service and to take advantage of multiple water supplies. All personnel, materials, and tools should be on hand before the system is impaired.

If underground mains are involved, a tapping machine should be used when possible to avoid shutting off the water. If mains are to be opened, wood or other plugs or caps and clamps to close the ends of pipes should be available and ready to install. Emergency measures should be taken to maintain the maximum possible water supply. One possibility is to make a temporary hose connection from a hydrant that is still in service to the system riser(s) (Figure 16.11.3). Other options include the use of a domestic or industrial supply to the riser(s) (Figure 16.11.4). These connections are usually made to the nominal 2 in. (50 mm) drain with the drain valve and hydrant valve left open. Adapters for connecting 2½ in. (65 mm) hose to sprinkler systems should be kept on hand.

A formal procedure should be established and followed for closing valves, notifying the fire department and insurance companies, and making waterflow tests after the work is completed. Such impairment procedures will help to ensure that systems are out of service for a minimal period of time and that complete system protection is restored.

Emergency Measures for Maintaining Protection During Repairs or Alterations

The seriousness of having extinguishing systems shut off when a fire starts has been well documented. There is a danger if the water supply is shut off for extensions or alterations to piping, repairs due to accidental damage to sprinklers and spray nozzles, replacement of sprinklers after a fire, or maintenance or replace-

FIGURE 16.11.4 Temporary Hose Connection with Hose Connected to Sprinkler System Flushing Connection

ment of sprinklers and other system devices. When protection is interrupted, every effort must be made to limit the extent and duration of the interruption. A cardinal rule is to notify the fire department whenever an impairment exists so they will not place false reliance on the systems. Insurance companies also may request that building owners advise them when there is an interruption in protection, so that alternate means of protection can be arranged if necessary.

CARE AND MAINTENANCE OF SPECIFIC COMPONENTS

The following components are treated in relation to routine inspection, test, and maintenance programs. They are, however, independent of the organization performing the inspection and maintenance functions. These are in-house responsibilities and should be left in the care of trained and competent individuals.

Public and Private Water Supply Equipment

The inspection and testing of public water supplies and of private water-supply equipment, such as tanks and fire pumps, is covered elsewhere in Section 16. See NFPA 25 for a summary of valve and fire department connection inspection, testing, and maintenance.

Control Valves and Meters

Inspection and supervision of valves in fire protection systems is necessary because closed valves are the leading cause of unsatisfactory performance. The following paragraphs summarize some of the more salient points of valve inspection and supervision.

Service Valves. Service valves at private fire system connections to public systems are usually under the control of the water department and are seldom operated. Their condition is usually indicated adequately by waterflow tests made from the private protection system, as covered later in this chapter.

Meters. Meters in public water system connections are also generally under the control of the water department but are sometimes located in pits on the protected property.

Check Valves. Check valves in public water connections, where needed to prevent backflow into the public systems, are usually a part of the protection system for which the property owner is responsible. Tightness of check valves should be determined periodically by proper tests, depending on water supplies.

Check valves and any corresponding control valves should be properly arranged and located in accordance with the appropriate NFPA standards for sprinkler systems, water spray protection, or standpipe and hose systems.

Control Valves. All control valves should be readily accessible and unobstructed so they can be operated promptly and examined to see that they are open and in good operative condition, turn easily, and do not leak.

Pits for gate valves and check valves should be kept reasonably dry and clean, so that valves can be tested, examined, and maintained in good condition. Manhole covers should be kept clear of snow and ice. See Section 15, Chapter 2, "Water Supply Requirements for Public Supply Systems," for an example of a well-arranged check valve pit with access for inspection.

Each control valve should be numbered or otherwise identified at the valve and cataloged, giving location, use, or portions of the system controlled, on a plant fire inspection form or value chart. A plan showing valve locations should be posted at a central point known to plant and public fire officials.

Each valve should have a sign showing what it controls, with the legend "Must Be Open at All Times," or other proper wording. Underground valve sites should be shown by location and by distance markings on nearby buildings and on accurate plans of the property.

All control valves should be sealed or locked open, unless there is a central station supervisory service. Wrenches should be kept at post indicator valves or at locations where they are readily accessible.

For larger facilities or plants, there should be someone on premises at all times who knows the use and location of all the control and drain valves. This includes the person on watch or any others who may be on duty at night.

Sprinklers and Sprinkler Piping

In the inspection of the sprinkler system, the following eight categories should be considered.

Absence of Sprinklers. Observe whether there is any room or building from which sprinklers have been omitted. The following should be used as a basic checklist:

- Basement
- Lofts
- Show windows
- Concealed spaces
- Towers
- Under stairwells
- Under skylights
- Inside elevator shafts
- Vertical shafts
- Small enclosures, such as those for drying and heating
- Closets, unless open on top

Observe whether there are sprinklers under the following:

- Air ducts over 4 ft (1.3 m) in width
- Shelves
- Benches and tables
- Overhead storage racks
- Platforms or similar obstructions

Proper Clearance for Sprinklers. There are a few areas to review for clearance of sprinklers:

- Sprinklers cannot be obstructed by high-piled stock, walls, or partitions that might prevent free and proper water distribution.

- There must be a clear space of 18 in. (457 mm) below the deflectors of the sprinklers. This value is 36 in. (914 mm) for large-drop and ESFR sprinklers.
- Installation guidelines of special sprinklers have not been violated. This may include installation under certain construction types.
- Refer to NFPA 13, *Standard for the Installation of Sprinkler Systems,* for spacing recommendations for various occupancy classes, types of sprinklers, and construction factors.

Proper Position of Deflectors. The distance of deflectors from the ceiling or the bottom of beams or joists should conform to NFPA 13.

Proper Pitch of Dry-Pipe Systems. Note whether all pipes in a dry-pipe system have the proper pitch. This feature is of special importance, because water remaining in pockets or low points is likely to freeze and disable the system.

Proper Support of Piping. Are any hangers loose or pipes not properly supported? Observe whether sprinkler piping is used for any purpose unrelated to its function, such as hanging clothing. Sprinkler piping and hangers should never be used for such purposes.

Proper Sprinkler Installation. There are five areas to check for the proper installation of sprinklers:

- Sprinklers must be installed in the positions for which they are intended, in compliance with the rules for special application, whether they be pendent, upright, or sidewall types.
- Note the type and design of the sprinklers, the year of their manufacture, and the date of their installation.
- Are all sprinklers of the proper temperature rating? Ordinary-degree sprinklers should be substituted for high-degree sprinklers when the latter are unnecessary. Wherever the temperature around the sprinkler exceeds 100°F (37.8°C), substitute those sprinklers with intermediate-degree sprinklers.
- Are any sprinklers loaded or corroded? If so, remove immediately and replace with sprinklers of equal performance characteristics. In areas where corrosion is common, use sprinklers with the proper coating to decrease the likelihood of future corrosion.
- Sprinklers with coatings of paint, whitewashing, bronzing, or excessive deposits should be replaced immediately with new sprinklers.

A supply of extra sprinklers should be kept in a spare sprinkler cabinet so that any sprinklers that have operated or been damaged in any way can be replaced promptly. These sprinklers should correspond in type, style, and in temperature ratings to the sprinklers in the property. The cabinet should be situated in a cool, easily accessible location. The number of sprinklers stocked for replacement purposes is governed by the size and number of systems. Other considerations include the location of the protected property relative to the source of supply for replacement sprinklers and the number of sprinklers likely to be opened in the event of a fire.

The stock of spare sprinklers, under normal conditions, should be as follows:

System Size	*Number of Spares*
Up to 300 sprinklers	6 sprinklers
From 300 to 1000 sprinklers	12 sprinklers
More than 1000 sprinklers	24 sprinklers

For systems aboard vessels or in isolated locations, a greater number of sprinklers should be carried to permit restoring equipment to service promptly after a fire.

A sprinkler wrench should be kept in the sprinkler cabinet to be used for the removal and installation of sprinklers. This wrench should always be used for installing new sprinklers in order to minimize the chance of damaging the sprinkler.

System Waterflow Tests

NFPA 13 requires a water supply test of pipe and pressure gauges to be provided at locations that will permit flowing tests to be made to determine whether water supplies and connections are in order. A 2 in. (50 mm) drain at the sprinkler riser may suffice as a water supply test pipe. The valve of the water supply test pipe must be installed so that the valve may be opened wide for a sufficient time to ensure a proper test, without causing water damage. A similar main drain valve in a water spray system can serve the same purpose.

There should be provision for checking the system's gauge and its pressure recordings with an inspector's test gauge.

The pressure on the sprinkler system side of the alarm or check valves may be higher than that of the water supply, because any momentary high pressure on the supply will be transmitted to the system and retained by the check valves. This excess pressure is relieved when a waterflow test on the system side of such valves is made.

The drop in pressure below the normal static pressure with the 2 in. (50 mm) main drain pipe wide open should be noted, and general flow conditions evaluated. For instance, if the normal pressure is 50 psi (345 kPa), and if previous tests have shown a pressure drop to 45 psi (310 kPa) when the main drain valve is opened, it will be apparent that, if during a subsequent inspection the pressure drops to 35 psi (241 kPa) or lower, there is some obstruction to the flow, which should be investigated. Such a pressure drop could indicate a defect that should be located and remedied.

At each inspection, an individual flow test should be made for each water supply and each connection from a supply. This can be accomplished by closing all water supplies temporarily, except the one under test. Too much emphasis cannot be placed on the value of flow tests to determine whether there is any obstruction to full flow. It is mandatory that all water supplies be returned to service immediately after testing.

If there is a waterflow supervisory service, tests should not be made without first notifying the fire department, central station, or other alarm receiving facilities.

There should be a 1 in. (25 mm) test pipe having a test orifice of a size to simulate the flow of a single sprinkler at the remote point of each sprinkler system. This should be operated at least twice each year to make sure that there is free flow at good pressure and to test the waterflow alarm. In dry-pipe systems, this test pipe can also be used to trip the dry-pipe valve and determine water delivery time.

Dry-Pipe Sprinkler Systems

The best practice is to keep dry-pipe systems in the dry condition throughout the year. When water flows into sprinkler piping, rust scaling and other foreign materials tend to be carried into the smaller pipes. Accumulation and obstruction can occur due to the waterflow. Annual tripping of the dry-pipe valve to make the system wet may accelerate this condition.

When systems are wet, with the dry-pipe valve tripped, the waterflow alarm feature of the dry valve would have to be taken out of service.

Any old, obsolete, unapproved dry-pipe, or mechanically damaged valves should be replaced with the proper approved listed device. Instruction charts are provided for the maintenance of dry-pipe valves by the sprinkler manufacturing company and should be posted at or near the valves. All dry-pipe valves should be numbered and listed on inspection report forms.

The air pressure on each dry-pipe system should be checked at least once a week. A daily check is recommended for the first week after a dry-pipe valve is reset. If pressure is lost rapidly, requiring frequent replenishment of the air pressure, the piping system should be repaired and made tight. Air pressure higher than that called for by the valve manufacturer's instructions should be avoided as this may damage the gasketing on the valve or severely delay the operation of the valves.

Make sure that the priming water is maintained at the proper level above the dry-pipe valve.

Freezing of a dry-pipe valve may cause it to be inoperative. It is extremely important to make sure that adequate provisions are made for heating the valve enclosure or the room in which it is located, and that the heating equipment is safe and in proper working order.

Dry-pipe system piping should be thoroughly drained at all drum drips or low-point drains before freezing weather and kept clear of water during the winter. The freezing of a small amount of water in the piping may cause rupture of the piping or sprinklers and valve malfunction. Make sure that all low-point drains of the system are kept free of water and that the automatic drip or drain is clear and free to operate.

Dry-pipe valves should be examined externally at frequent intervals to detect evidence of deterioration. Thoroughly clean and reset each dry-pipe valve yearly during the warm weather. On such occasions, the valve body should be thoroughly washed out with warm water. Make sure that all small ports and piping leading to the alarm connections are free from obstructions.

Operating tests of dry-pipe valves and their quick-opening devices should be conducted annually. Such tests may be combined with the annual cleaning and resetting. Operating tests should also be conducted when any repairs, such as renewal of rubber gaskets, or the adjustment of gauges, alarm devices, connecting piping, and quick-opening devices, are performed.

When dry-pipe valves are tripped for testing purposes, the procedure should be such that only the minimum flow of water needed to trip the valve is admitted into the sprinkler riser. This can usually be done by opening the control valve only two to six turns and by closing it immediately after the dry-pipe valve trips.

Operating tests and servicing of dry-pipe valves, including quick-opening devices, should be conducted only by fully qualified personnel.

No grease or other sealing material should be used on seats of dry-pipe valves in an effort to stop leaks. Force should not be used to make dry-pipe valves tight.

Dry-pipe valves should carry a tag or card showing the date on which the valve was last tripped and the name of the organization making the test. Such tags are usually available from the installing company or the insurance company.

Quick-Opening Devices

The operation of quick-opening devices usually can be tested either with or without operating the dry-pipe valve. The manufacturer's instructions for testing and resetting the valve must be followed. If the device does not operate properly during a test, it can, if necessary, be removed and the sprinkler system kept in operation. The device can also be sent to the manufacturer for repair, adjustment, or replacement.

Pressure Gauges

Water and air pressure gauges should be tested for accuracy whenever the system valve is repaired or reset but not less frequently than every five years. Comparison with a calibrated gauge is considered sufficient for this test, or the gauge should be replaced if a calibrated gauge is not available.

Waterflow Alarm Devices

Vane-type waterflow alarm devices should be tested semiannually and pressure switches tested quarterly. Consideration should be given to the proper disposal of test water, particularly where freezing conditions exist. Water motor gongs in particular should never be tested in freezing weather.

Deluge and Preaction Systems

Complete charts are furnished by the installing contractor showing in detail the proper method of operating and testing thermostatically controlled systems. Only qualified persons, fully instructed with respect to the details and operation of such systems, should be employed in their repair and adjustment. It is highly advisable for the owner to arrange with the installing contractor to provide periodic inspection, testing, and maintenance of the equipment.

The automatic valves controlling the flow of water into these systems operate through the effect of fire temperatures on actuating devices. Ordinarily, when it is necessary to repair the actuating system of a preaction system, as distinguished from the piping system itself, the piping system can be temporarily converted to a wet system, and automatic sprinkler protection is, thus, maintained on a preaction system, provided there is no danger of freezing.

Sprinkler System Supervisory Systems

Central station, proprietary, remote station, fire alarm, and supervisory services for sprinkler systems interpret sprinkler system waterflow signals as fire alarms and immediately initiate occupant notification and fire department response. Signals of other types, such as valve supervision and pressure or temperature supervision, do not serve as fire alarms but initiate appropriate courses of action as prearranged between the supervisory service and the property owner. It is extremely important that these services be notified and any special arrangements made in advance of any inspection or tests of equipment that will cause a signal to be transmitted.

Fire Department Connections

Inspect each fire department connection regularly to make sure caps are in place, threads are in good condition, the ball drip or drain is in order, and the check valve is not leaking. A hydrostatic test should be conducted periodically on old fire department connection piping to ensure that it will withstand the required pressure.

Open Sprinkler Equipment

Outside or open sprinkler equipment should be tested once each year during warm weather. These tests should be coordinated with the authority having jurisdiction and, if desired, the fire department.

Before making operational tests, care should be exercised to make sure that all windows and doors through which water might enter are tightly closed. Proper precautions must be taken to prevent damage from obstruction or accumulation of water to sidewalks, streets, pedestrian ways, or adjoining buildings.

Determine by test whether the sprinklers and system piping are in good condition and free from obstruction. Any piping or sprinklers found clogged should be removed, cleaned, and replaced at once.

OBSTRUCTIONS IN PIPING

Obstructions in system piping or yard mains reduce or cut off the flow of water from all or part of the system, compromising the expected performance of the protection. Obstructed piping is a well-recognized cause of unsatisfactory sprinkler performance. One source of obstruction is foreign material in the water supply. Another is foreign material originating from the interior of the pipe itself. Figure 16.11.5 graphically illustrates an example of obstructions removed from the sprinkler system water supply piping.

Foreign material, such as sand, gravel, stones, and pieces of wood, may enter the underground mains as a result of the carelessness of workers when laying or repairing the mains.

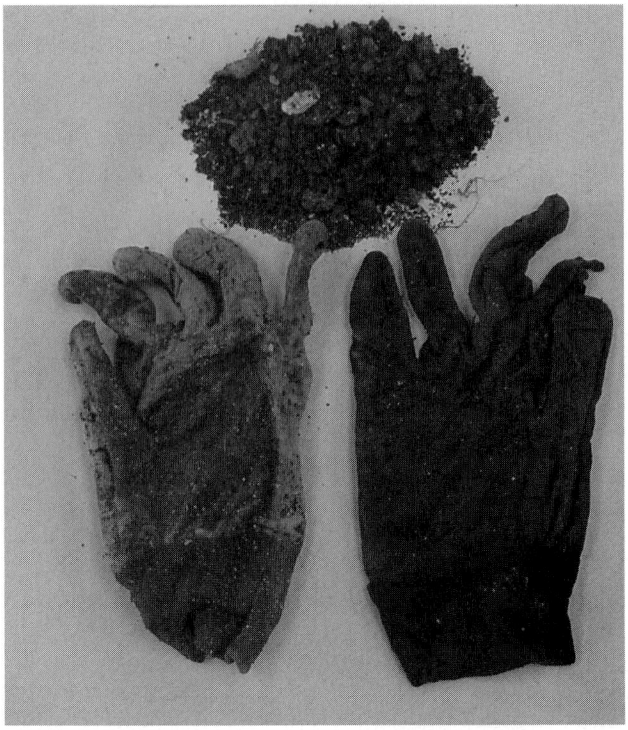

FIGURE 16.11.5 Work Gloves and Pipe Scale Recovered from Sprinkler System Water Supply Pipe

Sand, silt, or wood chips may also enter the mains through inadequately protected fire pump suction inlets. Sometimes when gravity tanks are cleaned, foreign material enters the discharge pipes unless preventive care measures are taken.

Keeping foreign material out of piping for water-spray systems is particularly critical. If the waterways in discharge nozzles are less than ⅜ in. (9 mm) in size or if it is suspected that the water is likely to contain obstructive material, then a strainer is required in the pipeline supplying the system. Small nozzles are prone to clogging if waterborne debris reaches them. Thus, it is imperative that strainers are maintained in good condition. Strainers used in fire protection systems should be approved and listed by a recognized testing laboratory for fire protection service. Strainers must be flushed through the flushing connection periodically, or in cases in which there is a substantial amount of obstructing material, the strainer basket must be removed and cleaned.

Scale and corrosion can form inside system piping. Dry sprinkler systems in particular are subject to the formation of scale because the condensation of moisture in the air supply reacts with the inner surface of the steel pipe. In many cases, dry systems are installed with galvanized pipe to prevent scaling. Untreated water from natural sources such as wells may contain salts that accelerate corrosion. Scale and corrosion can also affect wet-pipe systems.

Obstructing material can be distributed throughout a system when systems operate, during tests, or when systems are filled. The material may obstruct one or more fittings or a number of sprinklers, usually at the end of the branch line. The effective pipe diameter can also be reduced by pipe tuberculation when the water contains dissolved calcium and magnesium salts.

If the water is badly discolored during waterflow tests, or if gravel or stones are discharged with the water, foreign material is probably present in the piping. Finding foreign material in a fire pump suggests that there may be similar material downstream in the system piping. Finding foreign material when resetting dry-pipe valves or examining check valves indicates a possible serious impairment of the entire fire protection system.

Obstruction to the flow of water from sprinklers usually comprises concentrations of the lighter materials, such as silt, sand, and small pebbles, piling up in the ends of the cross mains and in the nearby branch lines, with the heaviest solids collecting near the system risers (Figure 16.11.6). There are some cases where the foreign material deposits extend so far back into the system from the ends of the cross mains that complete cleaning of the entire system is necessary. More often, however, a preliminary investigation will disclose that, although foreign material may cause complete obstruction of waterflow from sprinklers on branch lines connected to the ends of cross mains, there may be no obstruction at any point on branch lines farther back in the system.

OTHER SOURCES OF OBSTRUCTION

Microbiologically Influenced Corrosion (MIC)

Although generally considered to be a source of corrosion and pitting of pipe, microorganisms can colonize inside of piping systems to the extent that the effective diameter of the pipe is substantially reduced (Figures 16.11.7 and 16.11.8). This can have the same effect as other types of obstructing material by reducing the amount of waterflow through the system and plugging sprinklers.

MIC is caused basically by two types of microbes—aerobic, those requiring the presence of oxygen, and anaerobic, those not requiring the presence of oxygen. MIC can be recognized by the presence of orange or black tubercules and/or mud-like slime in steel pipe. MIC also affects copper systems and can be recognized by green or blue discoloration.

The most effective method to determine the presence of MIC is laboratory analysis of a water sample. Once the presence of MIC is confirmed, several treatment strategies can be employed, such as altering the residual chlorine, pH (acidity), temperature, and oxygen concentration of the water. It is important to note that altering the oxygen concentration of the water only affects aerobic microbes. The most common method of treatment is a permanently attached chlorine injection system, which automatically introduces chlorine into the sprinkler system any time waterflow occurs. Excessive flushing and flow testing of systems should be avoided to reduce the introduction of new microbes and renewed oxygen supplies to the piping system. (Section 15, Chapter 5, "Microbiologically Influenced Corrosion in Fire Sprinkler Systems," provides additional information on MIC.)

FIGURE 16.11.7 Typical Pinhole Formed by MIC

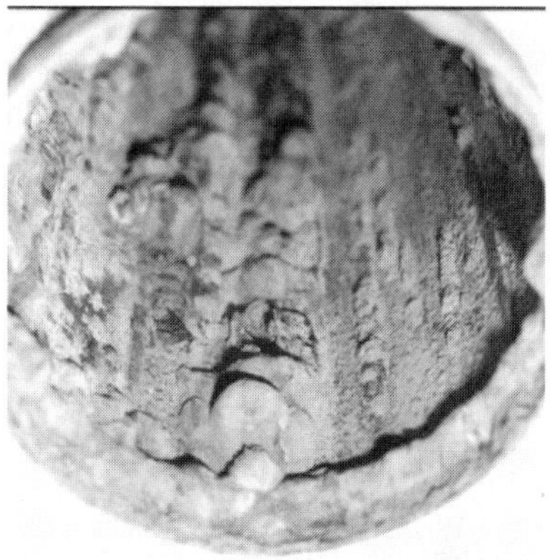

FIGURE 16.11.8 Substantial Obstruction of Pipe by MIC Colony

FIGURE 16.11.6 Silt Built Up in Feed Main Piping Obstructing the Waterway

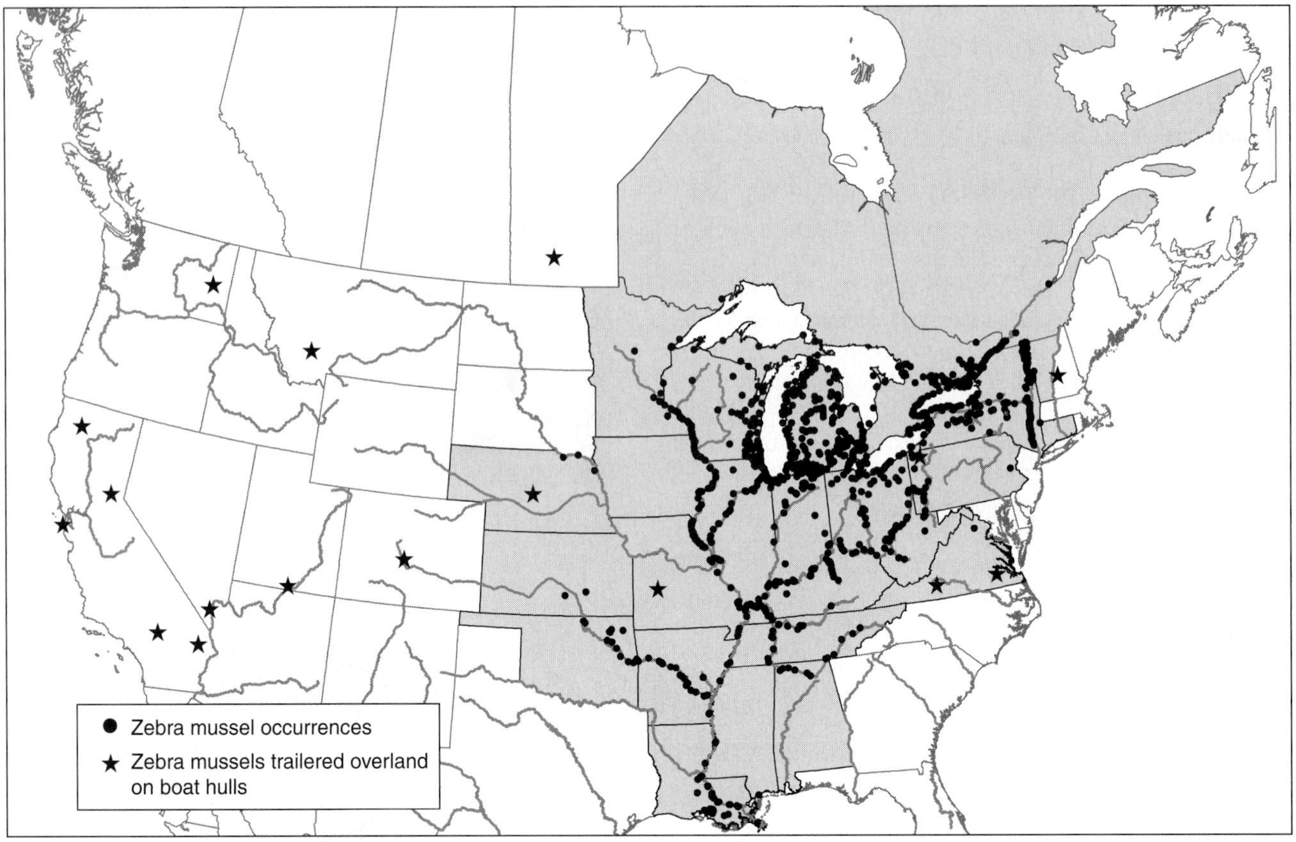

FIGURE 16.11.9 Zebra Mussel Sightings Distribution (*Dreissena polymorpha*) (Source: U.S. Geological Survey, Gainesville, Florida, June 13, 2005, http://www.unl.edu/nac/atlas/Map_Html/Ecosystem_Health/National/Current_zm_map/Current_zm_map.htm)

Zebra Mussels

Largely concentrated around the Great Lakes and Mississippi River areas (Figure 16.11.9), zebra mussels enter a sprinkler system through the water supply, particularly those systems that take their water from a natural body of water such as a lake or river. The mussels enter the pipe as larvae or young adults and colonize inside the piping, feeding from nutrients and oxygen in the water (Figures 16.11.10 and 16.11.11). As they continue to grow, they begin to obstruct waterflow to the system. The presence of zebra mussels is evidenced through the discharge of shells or live mussels during flow tests. An adult zebra mussel measures about ⅝ in. (16 mm) across the shell. Its name is derived from the distinct stripes on the shell resembling that of a zebra.

Treatment strategies for zebra mussels are similar to that for MIC, in other words, chlorination of water entering the system. Treatment with potassium in the range of 100 mg/L has shown promise; however, there are no commercially available systems at present.

Conditions Indicating Possible Obstructions in Piping

Evidence of possible obstruction in piping is given by any one of the following:

1. Plugging of test connections or discharge of dirty or colored water
2. Discharge of foreign material during routine water tests
3. Foreign material in dry-pipe valves, check valves, or fire pumps

FIGURE 16.11.10 One Inch Pipe Completely Obstructed by Zebra Mussels

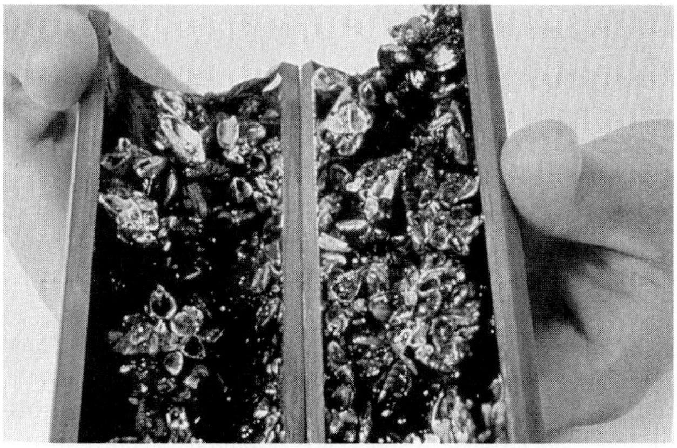

FIGURE 16.11.11 Two Inch Pipe Sample with Zebra Mussel Infestation

4. Obstructing material found in piping that is dismantled for building alterations
5. Defects found in fire pump suction screens when the water supply source is from open bodies of water
6. Repairs made to public water mains in vicinity
7. Underground piping not flushed before connection to systems
8. Plugged sprinklers or spray nozzles at time of fire
9. Old equipment, especially in dry-pipe systems

Investigation of Severity and Extent of Obstruction

An investigation of conditions must be made when evidence of foreign materials in systems is found or when obstructions are suspected. Where needed, cleaning or flushing procedures subsequently must be carried out to remove obstructing materials. Inspection and flushing methods outlined in this chapter are treated more completely in NFPA 25.

Flushing Feed Mains

Existing yard piping suspected of containing obstructing material should be thoroughly flushed through hydrants at dead ends of the system, blow-off valves, or groups of riser drains, by opening simultaneously as many outlets as possible and allowing the water to run until clean. If the water is supplied from more than one direction or through a looped system, divisional valves should be closed to produce a high-velocity flow through each single line.

It is usually desirable to learn the nature and extent of foreign material that may be in the piping. This can best be done by fastening burlap bags to the flowing outlets and examining the effluent remaining in the bag.

The connections to system risers should next be flushed through drain valves. If the foreign material is too large to pass through a main drain valve, some ingenuity must be used to procure a larger opening. Fire department connections can be used by removing the check valve. Flanged check valves or check valve covers or flanged fittings can be removed and a Siamese fitting can be substituted to facilitate such flushing.

Flushing System Piping

In choosing the critical points for examination, consideration should be given to the arrangement of the piping and the probable pattern of the flow of water when a system is rapidly filled (as in a dry-pipe system), or when a large flow of water from the system occurs due to operation of many sprinklers on a wet-pipe system.

After selection of the area in which the heaviest deposit of foreign material ordinarily would be expected, the investigation should take into consideration how much of the system's equipment in that area might be made ineffective by the obstructing material at the time of a fire. It is important that the preliminary investigation sufficiently indicates the extent of cleaning that may be required.

Flow Tests

Flow tests at critical points in a sprinkler system provide a positive means of determining the presence of foreign material in the system that may cause obstruction of flow from any of the sprinklers and also of indicating how much of the system is affected. To achieve this, valved hose connections are installed at the ends of two, three, or four branch lines on one side of and at the end of the affected cross main in the selected area. Flows are then taken simultaneously from these points and examined.

If obstruction occurs at any of the branch lines tested, additional tests may be necessary at points upstream on the system toward the system riser. Tests may next be extended to other floors to help make a judgment on the extent of cleaning operations that may be necessary for removing all foreign material that might cause obstructions.

Foreign deposits in sprinkler systems tend to be accumulated toward the ends of the cross mains and in the ends of branch lines. Of course, there will be exceptions to this general rule. For example, where highly corrosive material has been introduced into the system, severe corrosion and scaling of the interior surfaces of the piping will be evident uniformly throughout the system.

Visual Examination

The visual inspection of a system is a critical starting point of any flushing program. This first step will not tell the entire story of the condition of the piping; however, it can aid the trained person in an accurate determination of the piping condition. The visual examination encompasses the inspection of the interior and exterior of the piping, as well as the condition of and tuberculation in said piping.

The initial inspection should start by removing the end sprinklers at the upper- and lowermost portion of the system. Take extra care when removing any pendent sprinklers to check for sediment clogging the orifice.

The removal of the flushing connection is a simple method to determine the condition of the cross main.

Should these steps reveal the presence of obstructing material, and an internal inspection becomes necessary, the following should be used as a guideline:

1. Approximately 10 percent of the system should be examined when an internal inspection is recommended.
2. Remove
   a. Three to four endlines
   b. Riser nipples
   c. Elbows and tee feed for the cross main
3. Examine any areas where the water velocity decreases rapidly when draining the system piping.

If the internal inspection reveals substantial tuberculation and piping deterioration, a determination must be made by cost-efficiency analysis. The options available are flushing, whether it be by the hydropneumatic method or just with water, or the partial to total replacement of the affected area of the system.

The expense of flushing can be high when labor costs and materials are considered. Even though the system is flushed and back on line, the piping may have a shorter life expectancy than a new system.

EXTENT OF CLEANING REQUIRED

When preliminary tests show evidence of obstruction in sprinkler system piping, the next step is to undertake a cleaning program to remove the obstructing material. There are three levels of cleaning: (1) complete cleaning, (2) limited cleaning, and (3) flushing extremities only.

Generally, when obstruction occurs only in the branch lines at extremities of the system, only these areas of the system require flushing. If obstruction occurs at several test points, but indications are that free flows are available on the other lines back toward the riser, a limited cleaning procedure may be followed. If the obstruction is more extensive, then a complete cleaning procedure should be undertaken.

Before any cleaning efforts begin, written specifications or a flushing procedure covering the entire operation should be understood by all concerned. After completion of work, the sprinkler contractor or other party performing the cleaning operations should furnish a written report to those concerned indicating that all work has been completed in accordance with the approved procedure, that the specified examinations and tests have been made, and that the system has been left in normal condition.

Complete Cleaning

There are some cases where the foreign material is of such nature and extends so far back into the system from the ends of the cross mains that complete cleaning of the entire system will be necessary. In such cases, it is of prime importance that a plan of the piping system be prepared and be marked numerically to show the proper sequence of the cleaning operations, the size and length of hose to be used, the points where the hose is attached, and the number of flows to be made at each point.

Limited Cleaning

Where points of impairment can be identified as occurring within restricted areas rather than throughout the system, the limited cleaning procedure can be used. If these points exist in any appreciable amount but only in the ends of cross mains and in the branch lines connected at or near those points, not all branch lines need to be cleaned. The cleaning procedure may be limited to the branch lines at or near these points and to the cross mains on each floor.

Limited cleaning operations serve to minimize the time during which the sprinkler system is impaired. They lessen the interruption to normal activities within the premises where the cleaning operations are underway. Limited cleaning lowers the cost of the work as compared to more extensive cleaning. Because only a fraction of the total number of branch lines are being cleaned directly under the limited procedure, periodic flow tests should be made as the cleaning progresses in order to determine the effectiveness of the work.

Cleaning System Extremities Only

This method should be used only in cases in which obstruction of dry-pipe sprinkler system piping has been found to occur solely at the system extremities, and it relates to every floor protected, regardless of the number of floors. Extreme care should be exercised before this method is employed. Adequate examinations and flow tests are made to make certain that only the sprinklers located at the extremities of the system are subject to plugging. It should not be used where the deposits extend back into the cross main beyond the second branch line from the end of the cross main.

CLEANING METHODS

Generally, there are two methods used for cleaning sprinkler systems: (1) water flushing and (2) hydropneumatic. Convenience is a key factor that may make the hydropneumatic system preferable to the water flushing method. With the former, there is no open discharge of water outside the building, there is less interruption of plant operations, frequent filling and draining of the sprinkler system are unnecessary, there is considerably less pipe work, and a complete operation is performed at a single flush point.

Both methods are appropriate for complete cleaning and limited cleaning procedures. Good practice is to flush the underground piping and then to clean all private sources of water supply that might cause silting in the underground main. Both of these methods are thoroughly discussed in NFPA 25.

If it is anticipated that a sprinkler system may need periodic testing for obstruction or repeated flushing, a branch line tester may be installed permanently at the end of each branch line or between the last sprinkler and the end fitting on each branch line. The tester has a normally closed and capped outlet connection for hose. Turning a wrench fitting opens a passage to the outlet which has a 1 in. (25 mm) hose coupling thread. It is not necessary to remove the sprinkler when this type of device is used.

SPRINKLER LEAKAGE

The term *unintended discharge* is ordinarily used to describe leaks due to system component failure or damage, excluding fire conditions. Leaks, although infrequent, can occur in practically any portion of the system that has been damaged.

Unintended discharge from a properly designed, manufactured, and installed system should be very low because a sprinkler has undergone pressure testing during the commissioning process. Sprinkler pipe, fittings, and other components, including the sprinklers themselves, are rated for pressures far greater than are met with in practice. The supports are also designed to carry five times the weight of the pipe and water with a safety factor of 250 lb (113 kg). In some systems, the pipe supports are also intended to deal with the stress encountered during a seismic event. (See Section 16, Chapter 4, "Hanging and Bracing of Water-Based Systems.")

Automatic sprinkler systems protecting hazards vulnerable to water damage, such as computer equipment, works of art, valuable books, or important records, require an extra degree of attention due to the unusually severe consequences of any unintended discharge, which could occur, for example, if reasonable precautions are not taken against freezing, overheating, and mechanical damage. The use of single- or double-interlock preaction systems should be considered for these applications.

Mechanical Damage

Automatic sprinklers are designed to withstand at least 500 psi (3448 kPa) pressure without injury or leakage. If properly installed, there is little danger of the sprinkler breaking apart, unless it is physically damaged in some way. All of the listed sprinklers are very durable and will withstand considerable abuse. The frames can be bent somewhat, without opening the sprinkler.

When sprinklers are located in areas where they may suffer mechanical damage, they can be protected by commercially available metal guards (Figure 16.11.12).

The use of lift trucks or tractors in handling materials indoors must be carefully planned and supervised to avoid damaging sprinklers and sprinkler piping. Precautions should be taken where fast-response sprinklers are installed to reduce the chances of mechanical and environmental damage.

FIGURE 16.11.12 Metal Guard Protection Against Mechanical Injury

Freezing

The freezing of water in pipes is a common cause of trouble and the remedy in most cases is self-evident. Water expands slightly when it freezes, causing sprinklers to fail. When the ice melts, water is discharged. In other cases, the pipe or fittings may burst, causing more serious damage and more costly repairs. In some types of sprinklers, a moderate amount of freezing may not break the sprinkler open, but may cause it to leak at the seat after the ice has melted.

Some of the conditions that cause systems to freeze include the following:

1. Insufficient heat for severe weather conditions in certain portions, such as concealed spaces under roofs or blind attics, large open doorways for trucks or railway cars, entryways, or space under buildings
2. Windows left open during severely cold weather
3. Insufficient heat due to a shortage of heating fuel or power failure
4. Branch lines of dry-pipe systems not correctly pitched to drain
5. Feed mains or piping in unheated areas properly protected to prevent freezing
6. Freezing of tank risers due to lack of heat or lack of adequate protection; or obstructed circulating pipes of heating systems
7. Freezing of water in underground mains not buried deep enough

Overheating

"Overheating" is another potential cause of accidental discharge from sprinklers and is the term used when an automatic sprinkler operates as a result of abnormally high temperatures, without the presence of fire. This condition is usually caused by hot manufacturing processes, artificial heating, or lack of ventilation. It may result from a sudden increase in temperature that operates the thermal response element of the sprinkler, or from longer exposure to temperatures sufficiently high to cause gradual weakening of the element. In solder-type sprinklers, the latter condition, sometimes termed "cold flow" or "cold soldering," is indicated by partial separation of the soldered members.

In practice, there are a number of conditions that cause unsafe temperatures, such as the following:

1. Climatic conditions exceeding 100°F (41.3°C).
2. Ordinary temperature sprinklers located in close proximity to steam mains, unit heaters, or heating ducts. Temperatures higher than anticipated may occur after installation of sprinklers. Changes in heating methods, installation of unit heaters, or changes in manufacturing processes or equipment after sprinklers are installed can occur.
3. Changes in temperatures due to an occupancy change or processes that cause higher temperatures than contemplated.

These changes may be general or in isolated portions of a building.

4. In some cases, a fire that opens a number of sprinklers may weaken other sprinklers in that vicinity. This may not be apparent. Change all sprinklers in an area of fire influence and not just those that have opened.
5. Low-mass fusible linkage of quick-response sprinklers will enhance the negative influence as mentioned earlier. The installation and maintenance of this device requires great care.

NFPA 13 and NFPA 25 provide some information on sprinkler temperature ratings near unit heaters. Unit heaters should never be used without a careful study of conditions, and, in most cases, sprinklers near unit heaters must be replaced with a higher temperature rating in order to avoid unintended operation.

When conditions occur that require sprinklers higher than ordinary-degree rating, the maximum temperature at the sprinkler level must be determined and sprinklers of the correct temperature rating installed to avoid accidental discharge.

REDUCING WATER DAMAGE

It is evident that, if unintended waterflow occurs when there is no one in the building and no proper means of alarm notification to outsiders exists, the waterflow may continue for a considerable amount of time. This can result in serious damage to property, even with a small amount of water from just one leaking or flowing sprinkler.

Although security guard service is of value, it may not be adequate unless there is a sprinkler alarm device, which will notify the guard if water is flowing. Every sprinkler system should have a waterflow alarm device and properly located water motor gong to notify the proper personnel in case of fire or discharge of water due to inadvertent system discharge.

Large losses from sprinkler leakage or flow can result from lack of, or failure of, isolated sprinkler devices or the lack of waterflow alarms. Losses can also be attributed to the failure to promptly notify authorized person(s) who can investigate immediately and shut off the water if there is no fire. In some cases, water may run for many hours undetected.

Sprinkler supervisory service is of great value in the prompt discovery of system operation from a fire event. In addition, it is also useful to detect leakage from the system and in securing appropriate action to minimize the water loss.

WATER SPRAY SYSTEMS

Water spray systems are similar to sprinkler systems in that they contain a water supply, control valves, piping, hangers, and discharge devices. As such, these systems also require the same inspection, testing, and maintenance as sprinkler systems. However, water spray systems can have, in addition to these items, a detection system that is hydraulic, pneumatic, or electronic, other devices such as pipeline strainers (not normally found on sprinkler systems), and directional water spray nozzles. Each of these systems or devices requires special attention in order to maintain the operational status of the water spray system.

Strainers are usually present due to the small size of the orifice of the spray nozzles. They must be periodically flushed and/or cleaned to ensure that the perforations in the strainer basket are free of obstructing material. A small flushing connection, usually 2 to 2½ in. (50 to 65 mm) in diameter, is provided for this purpose. The strainer basket can be removed and cleaned when flushing is not sufficient for proper cleaning.

Water spray systems should be subject to a discharge test annually to verify automatic operation (if provided) of the systems and components and to verify proper orientation of spray nozzles (Figure 16.11.13). The nozzles used on these systems are directional type and are intended to directly impinge on the protected surface.

Some nozzles may be equipped with a protective cover, commonly referred to as a blow-off cap. It is important to ensure that the caps are in place before the test and that they are reinstalled following the discharge test. The cap prevents obstructing material, such as dirt or dust, from entering the system through the orifice of the nozzle (Figure 16.11.14).

FIGURE 16.11.13 Directional Spray Nozzle Testing (Source: NFPA 25 Handbook, 2002, Exhibit 10.3)

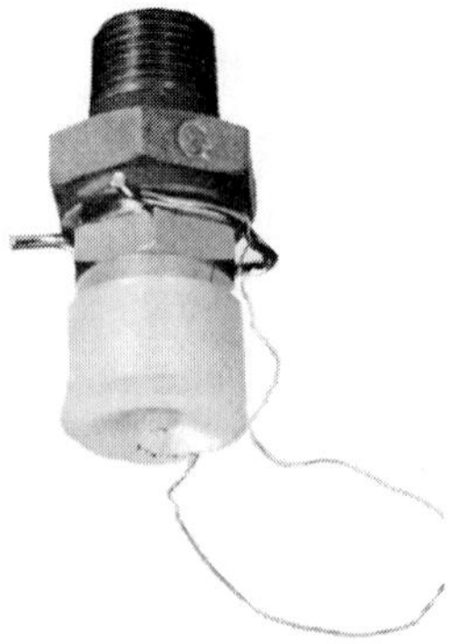

FIGURE 16.11.14 Nozzle with Blow-Off Cap (Source: NFPA 25 Handbook, 2002, Exhibit 10.6)

Pneumatic or hydraulic detection systems (pilot systems) also require some attention. Usually, a sprinkler with a fusible link is used as a thermal detector. These pilot sprinklers must be subject to the same inspection, testing, and maintenance as sprinklers installed in a common wet-pipe sprinkler system. They should be inspected to ensure that they are free of corrosion or contaminant loading.

Pneumatic systems rely on a source of compressed air. This can take the form of an air compressor, nitrogen cylinder, or plant air. In any case, the air supply should be inspected to determine its condition and operation, and any damaged or corroded parts should be replaced immediately.

Foam-Water Sprinkler and Foam-Water Spray Systems

In addition to the requirements for sprinkler and water spray systems, foam-water sprinkler and foam-water spray systems require special attention. These systems are equipped with a foam-proportioning system. The common types of proportioning systems are standard pressure, bladder tank, line, standard balanced pressure, and in-line balanced pressure type. Regardless of the proportioning system type, each component should be inspected quarterly for signs of corrosion or damage and to ensure that it is in good operating condition. In addition to inspection, at least every 10 years, the foam concentrate storage tank should be pressure tested to its working pressure. All components that are in contact with foam concentrate must be flushed and cleaned annually.

Foam-water sprinkler and foam-water spray systems are subject to an annual discharge test. During this test, a foam sample is taken and the proper concentration of foam is measured by refractometric or other methods to verify concentration of the foam-water solution. The results should be within 10 percent of the acceptance test results but not less than 10 percent below the minimum design standard. Foams are usually designed and listed for concentrations of 1, 3, and 6 percent. Following the discharge test, the foam concentrate tank must be refilled to capacity with adequate space remaining for expansion.

Standpipe Systems

Standpipe systems consist of pipe, fittings, valves, and sometimes hose intended to supply water for manual fire fighting in all areas of a building. A standpipe system eliminates the need to stretch long lengths of hose vertically and horizontally through a building to deliver water to a fire. There are three classes of standpipe systems—Class I provides a 2½ in. (65 mm) hose valve specifically for fire department use, Class II provides a 1½ in. (40 mm) hose valve, complete with hose and nozzles for building occupant use, and Class III is a combination of Classes I and II and may or may not include hose and nozzles. Standpipe systems may be automatic, providing a permanent water supply that is capable of supplying the required pressure and flow, or manual, relying on a fire department pumper to supply pressure and flow. Standpipe systems may also be wet or dry in cases in which the system may be subject to freezing temperatures.

Inspection of standpipe systems should begin at the water supply and continue throughout the entire system on a quarterly basis. This inspection, as for that of a sprinkler system, should reveal signs of damage, leaks, corrosion, or any condition that may impair system operation. Where building occupant hose is present, the hose should be removed from the rack or reel annually and inspected for evidence of vandalism. The hose should be free of obstruction and not damaged by mildew or abrasion of any kind. The hose should be reracked or rereeled in such a way that folds do not occur in the same position on the hose. Standpipe hose should be removed from the system for hydrostatic testing at five years and every three years thereafter.

Hose valves should be inspected quarterly to ensure that the handwheel is not missing or broken, the threads are not damaged, the valve is not leaking, and the cap is in place. In cases in which high pressures are present, the valve should be of the pressure-regulating type. Pressure-regulating hose valves are generally of two types—pressure reducing, which controls both static (nonflowing) and residual (flowing) conditions, and pressure restricting, which controls residual conditions only. Pressure-regulating devices should be flow tested every five years to verify that the pressure-reduction setting is correct. Valves that are not set properly should be reset; valves that are not adjustable should be replaced.

During commissioning, all standpipe systems must be hydrostatically tested at 200 psi (1379 kPa) for 2 hours, or 50 psi (345 kPa) in excess of the maximum anticipated static pressure, whichever is greater. Unless modifications to the piping system are made, no further hydrostatic testing is necessary. In the case of a manual dry-standpipe system, however, a hydrostatic test at five-year intervals is necessary to verify the piping system integrity. As defined in NFPA 14, *Standard for the Installation of Standpipe and Hose Systems,* a manual dry-standpipe system has no permanently attached water supply; the fire department is expected to supply waterflow and pressure through the fire department connection. Therefore, these systems must be hydrostatically tested periodically to confirm that they do not leak.

Standpipe systems of all types should be flow tested every five years at the most remote connection to reverify that the system can supply the required flow and pressure. Care should be exercised due to the potential high pressures involved and the proper disposal of test water should be considered.

WATER SUPPLIES

Private Fire Service Mains and Appurtenances

Since inspection of private fire service mains is not practical, flow tests should be conducted at least every five years. Flow test results should be compared to previous tests to reveal any sign of deterioration of the flow and pressure in the system. Should any deterioration be discovered, a complete investigation to determine the cause should be conducted.

Hydrants should be flushed annually by allowing full flow for at least one minute. Dry barrel hydrants should drain thoroughly in less than one hour. During this procedure, hydrants should be inspected for accessibility and operation, and hydrants should be lubricated.

Fire Pumps

A fire pump (when present) is a significant component of the system water supply. Therefore, it is imperative that fire pump equipment operates when needed. The lack of an inspection, testing, and maintenance program for a fire pump can result in costly repairs and system impairment.

Fire pumps should be inspected and tested on a weekly basis. The test is accomplished without flowing water. To begin the test, a pressure drop should be simulated by opening a valve on the fire pump sensing line. The pressure drop will cause the pressure switch in the pressure maintenance pump controller to start that pump. As system pressure continues to drop, the fire pump will start.

An electric pump should be run for a period of 10 minutes. During this time, several observations can be made. Of utmost importance, the casing relief valve should open, allowing a small discharge of water. This will cause an introduction of cool water into the fire pump casing, preventing overheating of the fire pump. The pump packing glands should be adjusted to provide a slight discharge of water. During the operation of the pump, other observations should be made such as unusual noise or vibrations and evidence of overheating. Suction and discharge pressures should be recorded and an inspection/operation test report filed (Figure 16.11.15).

A diesel pump should run for a period of 30 minutes. During operation, the following observations should be made and recorded: engine oil pressure, speed, water and oil temperature, and a check of the heat exchanger for cooling waterflow. Observations should be recorded and an inspection/operation report filed.

A diesel pump is operated for 30 minutes to allow the engine and cooling system to reach operating temperature. Another reason for the 30 minute operation time is to slowly consume fuel, since diesel fuel can become contaminated over time. By operating the engine weekly, diesel fuel will need to be replaced, thus avoiding problems with stale diesel fuel (Figure 16.11.16).

FIGURE 16.11.15 Electrically Driven Fire Pump

FIGURE 16.11.16 Diesel-Driven Fire Pump (Source: Mechanical Designs, Ltd.)

Fire pumps should be flow tested annually to verify that the pump is functioning properly. This test, identical to the initial commissioning test, is intended to discharge water through the pump at minimum, rated, and peak flows. The preferred test method is to discharge water through the fire pump test header and measure flow by means of a Pitot tube. The use of a flowmeter via a bypass is acceptable; however, once every three years, a test through the test header is necessary.

The results of the annual pump test should be recorded and compared to previous results. It is not the intent to reverify the fire pump curve each year; however, deterioration of performance should be recorded. The intent of the test is to verify that the pump is capable of supplying the maximum system demand.

Water Storage Tanks

Water can be stored in tanks for fire protection purposes, where no other source is available. The types of tanks used are described in Section 15, Chapter 1, "Fixed Water Storage Supplies for Fire Protection." Regardless of the type of tank in use, water tanks require inspection to ensure that they are in good condition.

All tanks should be inspected monthly to verify the correct water level and condition of the water. When installed in areas subject to freezing, tanks should be equipped with a heating system to maintain a minimum water temperature of 42°F (5.6°C). The heating system must be kept in operating condition to avoid the formation of ice that can cause an obstruction to the discharge pipe or cause tank walls to buckle. High and low water temperature alarms may be installed and should be kept in operating condition.

Steel tanks should be inspected for corrosion, including painting systems and cathodic protection where provided. Interior inspections should be done every five years by either a certified diver or by draining the tank completely and following confined space entry procedures.

SYSTEM IMPAIRMENT

When repair or modifications are necessary, a fire protection system may need to be taken out of service. To minimize this downtime, the building owner should appoint an impairment coordinator. The impairment coordinator should be familiar with the operation of the system, the tools and equipment necessary to make repairs, the operations affected by the repairs, and be thoroughly knowledgeable of the organizations that must be notified whenever a system is taken out of service. The impairment coordinator is responsible for supervising the impairment activity from system shutdown to restoration of service.

During any equipment shutdown, a lockout and/or tagout procedure should be in place. A tag should be posted on any valve that is closed (Figure 16.11.17). The tag should indicate that the system has been removed from service, the date, and person responsible for the procedure. Any electrical equipment, such as a fire pump, should be locked in the off position to avoid accidental start-up while the equipment is being serviced. Each tag or lock should be documented in the procedure and retrieved during restoration to service.

If systems must be taken out of service for extended periods of time, that is, four hours or more in a 24 hour period, additional safety procedures should be arranged. Consideration should be given to complete evacuation of the building, establishment of a temporary water supply, a fire watch, or an approved fire prevention program. In such cases, the building owner and the authority having jurisdiction should be consulted prior to system impairment.

Emergency impairments, such as replacement of sprinklers following a fire, leaks, or other service interruptions, should be supervised by the impairment coordinator following the same procedures for a preplanned impairment.

Restoration to service should include a complete inspection of the system to verify the following:

- Repairs are completed.
- All valves are returned to their normal operating position.
- Valve tags are retrieved and documented.
- The authority having jurisdiction, insurance and alarm companies, and all other interested parties are notified.

Closeout of the lockout/tagout program should be documented and filed.

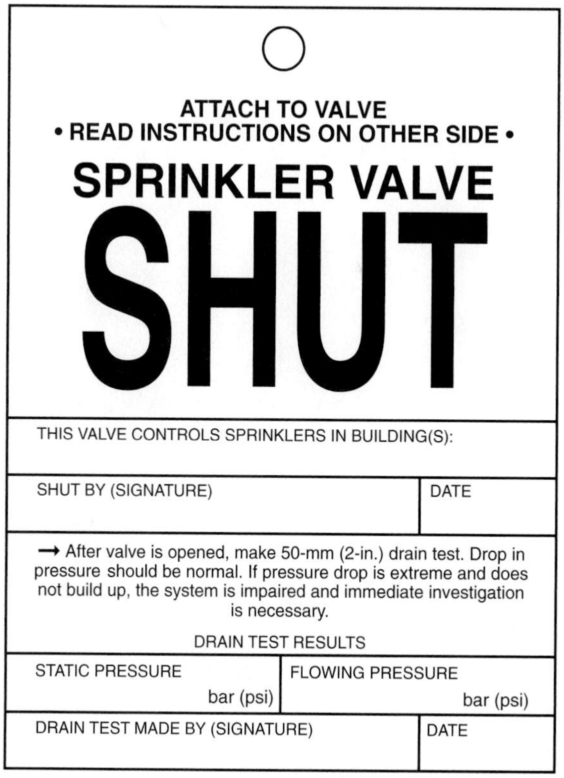
ATTACH TO VALVE
• READ INSTRUCTIONS ON OTHER SIDE •
SPRINKLER VALVE
SHUT

THIS VALVE CONTROLS SPRINKLERS IN BUILDING(S):

SHUT BY (SIGNATURE) | DATE

→ After valve is opened, make 50-mm (2-in.) drain test. Drop in pressure should be normal. If pressure drop is extreme and does not build up, the system is impaired and immediate investigation is necessary.

DRAIN TEST RESULTS

STATIC PRESSURE bar (psi) | FLOWING PRESSURE bar (psi)

DRAIN TEST MADE BY (SIGNATURE) | DATE

FIGURE 16.11.17 Sample Impairment Tag (Source: NFPA 25, 2008, Figure A.15.3.1)

SUMMARY

Of the leading causes of sprinkler system failures, 55 percent of those reported can be directly attributed to improper or lack of maintenance. NFPA 25, *Standard for the Inspection, Testing, and Maintenance of Water-Based Fire Protection Systems,* establishes a maintenance program that will improve sprinkler system performance. The standard devotes an entire chapter to valves, as water control valves account for 35.4 percent of unsatisfactory performance and defective dry-pipe valves account for 1.7 percent. Obstruction to water distribution accounts for 8.2 percent. A frozen system is responsible for 1.7 percent of unsatisfactory performance and, in general, 8.4 percent of sprinkler system failure is related to inadequate maintenance. (See *U.S. Experience with Sprinklers: Who Has Them? How Well Do They Work?* by Rohr.) By following the requirements of NFPA 25 and this chapter, the already excellent performance of fire protection systems can be improved.

BIBLIOGRAPHY

NFPA Codes, Standards, and Recommended Practices

Reference to the following NFPA codes, standards, and recommended practices will provide further information on the care and maintenance of water-based extinguishing systems discussed in this chapter. (See the latest version of The NFPA Catalog *for availability of current editions of the following documents.)*

NFPA 13, *Standard for the Installation of Sprinkler Systems*
NFPA 14, *Standard for the Installation of Standpipe and Hose Systems*
NFPA 25, *Standard for the Inspection, Testing, and Maintenance of Water-Based Fire Protection Systems*
NFPA 72®, National Fire Alarm Code®

References

Abell, J., "All Aboard," *Fire Prevention,* No. 307, Mar. 1998, pp. 22–25.

Bsharat, T., "Detection, Treatment, and Prevention of Microbiologically Influenced Corrosion on Water-Based Fire Protection Systems," National Fire Sprinkler Association, Patterson, NY, June 1998.

Bychowski, J. A., and Balingit, C., "Back-Flow Prevention for Today's Sprinkler Systems," *Consulting-Specifying Engineer,* Vol. 20, No. 4, 1996, pp. 54–56.

Cappers, M. A., "Investigation of Microbiologically Influenced Corrosion in Sprinkler Systems," *Proceedings* of Fire Suppression and Detection Research Application Symposium, Research and Development: Bridging the Gap, February 12–14, 1997, Orlando, FL, National Fire Protection Research Foundation, Quincy, MA, 1997, pp. 69–81.

Carson, W. G., and Klinker, R. L., *Fire Protection Systems: Inspection, Test, and Maintenance Manual,* 3rd ed., National Fire Protection Association, Quincy, MA, 2002.

Factory Mutual Research Corporation, *Loss Prevention Data Sheets, Nos. 2-11 through 2-95* (various titles); information on the care and maintenance of sprinkler system components (dry-pipe valves, quick-opening devices, deluge and preaction system valves, etc.), by manufacturers' names and model numbers (various dates).

Garlock, C., "Microbiolically Influenced Corrosion," *Sprinkler Age,* Vol. 20, No. 6, 2001, pp. 17–18.

Haagensen, D., "Microbiologically Influenced Corrosion of Fire Sprinkler Systems," *NFPA Journal,* Nov./Dec., National Fire Protection Association, Quincy, MA, 2000.

Hague, D. R., "Glass Bulb Technology," *Plumbing Systems and Design,* Vol. 3, No. 2, pp. 28–29.

Hague, D. R., *Inspection, Testing, and Maintenance of Water-Based Fire Protection Systems, The NFPA 25 Handbook,* National Fire Protection Association, Quincy, MA, 2002.

Hague, D. R., P.E., "Invasion of the Zebra Mussel," *NFPA Journal,* Mar./Apr., National Fire Protection Association, Quincy, MA, 1999, pp. 60–62.

Halton, B., and Allen, K., "Water Flow. Part 2. Fire Attack Hose," *Firehouse,* Vol. 26, No. 10, 2001, pp. 85–86.

Huggins, R. J., P.E., "Microbiologically Influenced Corrosion: What It Is and How It Works," *Sprinkler Age,* American Fire Sprinkler Association, Dallas, TX, 2000.

Lewis, D. P., et al., "A Method for Assessing the Risk of Zebra Mussel Dreissena Polymorpha Infestation in Industrial Fire Protection Systems," *Fire Technology,* Vol. 33, No. 3, 1997, pp. 214–229.

Lewis, D. P., et al., "Use of Potassium for Treatment and Control of Zebra Mussel Infestation in Industrial Fire Protection Water Systems," *Fire Technology,* Vol. 33, No. 4, 1997, pp. 356–371.

Mackenzie, N., "Sprinkler System Installations: Rules versus Reality," *Fire Safety Engineering,* Vol. 5, No. 6, 1998, pp. 23–26.

Marberg, P. A., Frantzich, H., Jonsson, R., Lundin, J., and Rantatalo, T., "Practical Design and Performance Based Regulations," *Fire Science and Technology,* Vol. 18, No. 1, 1998, pp. 33–42.

Mulligan, T. P., "Happy Land Fire: Have We Learned the Lessons?" *Fire Engineering,* Vol. 154, No. 8, 2001, pp. 89–91.

Parker, D., "Quake Protection on B.C.'s Coast," *Fire Fighting in Canada,* Vol. 45, No. 3, 2001, p. 56.

Puchovsky, M., "Peak Pump Performance," *NFPA Journal,* Vol. 94, No. 3, 2000, pp. 109–110.

Puchovsky, M. T., *Automatic Sprinkler Systems Handbook,* National Fire Protection Association, Quincy, MA, 1999.

Rohr, K. D., *U.S. Experience with Sprinklers: Who Has Them? How Well Do They Work?* National Fire Protection Association, Quincy, MA, 1998.

Schemel, C. F., and Budnick, E. K., "Pilot Study: Analyzing Fire Protection System Reliability Using Limited Databases. Quantifying the Effects of Inspection, Testing and Maintenance Frequencies on Selected Automatic Sprinkler Systems," *Proceedings* of Fire Suppression and Detection Research Application Symposium, Research and Development: Bridging the Gap, February 24–26, 1999, Orlando, FL, National Fire Protection Research Foundation, Quincy, MA, 1999, pp. 34–54.

Wolf, A., "NFPA 25: Inspection, Testing, Maintenance," *NFPA Journal,* Vol. 95, No. 3, 2001, pp. 72–75.

SECTION 17

Fire Suppression Systems and Portable Fire Extinguishers

Mark T. Conroy

Fire suppression systems and portable fire extinguishers are the subjects of Section 17 of the *Fire Protection Handbook*®. For this edition, two earlier chapters on halogenated agents and systems and direct halon replacement agents and systems have been combined to form one chapter entitled "Halon and Halon Replacement Agents and Systems." A new chapter on the application of gaseous agents for special hazards is also included.

Chapter 1, "Carbon Dioxide and Application Systems," presents the properties and extinguishing characteristics and limitations of carbon dioxide and its methods of application, as well as components, design considerations, and testing and maintenance of carbon dioxide systems.

Chapter 2, "Chemical Extinguishing Agents and Application Systems," contains information on the properties of both dry and wet chemicals that contribute to their use as extinguishing agents. The limitations; methods of application; system design; and the inspection, testing, and maintenance associated with these systems are addressed.

Water is the most widely used and most readily available extinguishing agent. Chapter 3, "Characteristics and Hazards of Water and Water Additives for Fire Suppression," discusses the properties of water as an extinguishing agent, including its advantages and limitations.

Foam is generated by proportioning foam concentrate with water; the resulting foam solution is used in fixed and portable fire extinguishing systems. Chapter 4, "Foam Extinguishing Agents and Systems," describes those agents and systems, along with their uses and limitations. Specialized foam fire-fighting vehicles are described.

Chapter 5, "Fire Extinguisher Use and Maintenance," provides basic information on matching extinguishers to hazards, types of extinguishers, and health and safety considerations.

Chapter 6, "Halon and Halon Replacement Agents and Systems," describes extinguishing mechanisms, flame suppression effectiveness, toxicity and environmental factors, thermophysical properties, and similar fundamental information.

Chapter 7, "Application of Gaseous Agents to Special Hazards Fire Protection," examines the key characteristics of special hazards that are particularly relevant to the use of gaseous fire extinguishing agents. This chapter also provides information aimed at evaluating a given fire hazard and selecting an appropriate gaseous extinguishing agent system to protect it.

The section concludes with Chapter 8, "Explosion Prevention and Protection." The contents of this chapter include a description of events leading to an explosion, explosion hazard analysis, explosion protection, deflagration prevention and suppression, and enclosure integrity and strength.

Mark T. Conroy is a senior fire protection engineer for Brooks Equipment Company of Charlotte, North Carolina.

Chapter 1

Carbon Dioxide and Application Systems

Thomas J. Wysocki

Chapter Contents

Key Terms

carbon dioxide, carbon dioxide hand hose line, electrical control panel, gas standpipe system, inerting, local application discharge nozzle, lockout, odorizer, total flooding system

Carbon dioxide (CO_2) has been used in fire extinguishing systems for nearly 100 years. The first systems were installed between 1910 and 1915 in Europe. CO_2 has no doubt safely extinguished more fires than any other gaseous fire-extinguishing agent. In the process, carbon dioxide systems have saved lives, maintained livelihoods, and prevented property damage. The benefits of carbon dioxide systems, properly applied, are enormous.

To gain the benefits of carbon dioxide extinguishing systems while minimizing risk to people, serious attention must be given to personnel safety in the design, installation, and maintenance of carbon dioxide systems. Training of personnel is essential.

This chapter will discuss the properties of carbon dioxide and its proper use in fixed fire-extinguishing systems; its limitations as a fire-extinguishing agent; life safety considerations; methods of application; system components; design considerations; and requirements for testing, maintenance, and training. NFPA 12, *Standard on Carbon Dioxide Extinguishing Systems,* provides guidance to those responsible for the purchase, design, installation, testing, inspection, operation, and maintenance of carbon dioxide systems.

Other chapters in the handbook that reference carbon dioxide systems include Section 9, Chapter 8, "Protection of Records"; Section 16, Chapter 7, "Ultra-High-Speed Water Spray Systems"; and Section 21, Chapter 10, "Marine Vessels."

USAGE

Carbon dioxide has been used for nearly a century to extinguish flammable liquid fires, gas fires, fires involving electrically energized equipment, and, to a lesser extent, fires in ordinary combustibles, such as paper, cloth, and other cellulosic materials. Carbon dioxide will suppress fire effectively in most combustible material. Exceptions are a few active metals and metal hydrides and materials, such as cellulose nitrate, that contain available oxygen. Furthermore, practical limitations of carbon dioxide are related to the physiological effects of carbon dioxide and to restrictions imposed by the hazard itself.

PROPERTIES OF CARBON DIOXIDE

Carbon dioxide has a number of properties that make it a desirable fire-extinguishing agent. It is noncombustible, it does not react with most substances, and it provides its own pressure for discharge from the storage container. Since carbon dioxide is a gas, it can penetrate and spread to all parts of a fire area. As a gas or as a finely divided solid called "snow" or "dry ice," it will not conduct electricity and, therefore, can be used on energized electrical equipment. It leaves no residue, thus eliminating cleanup of the agent itself.

Thomas J. Wysocki is a consultant with Guardian Services, Inc., in Frankfort, Illinois. He is active on several NFPA technical committees, including those covering carbon dioxide, halon fire-extinguishing systems, and clean agent halon alternative systems.

Thermodynamic Properties

At room temperature and pressure, carbon dioxide is a gas. It is easily liquefied by compressing and cooling, and, with further compressing and cooling, it can be converted to a solid. The effect of temperature changes on compressed carbon dioxide in a closed container is shown in Figure 17.1.1. Above the critical temperature of 87.8°F (31°C), irrespective of pressure, it is entirely gas. Between 87.8°F (31°C) and the temperature of the triple point, which is –69.9°F (–57°C), in a closed container, it is part liquid and part gas. Below the triple point, it is either a solid or a gas, depending on the pressure and temperature.

On the part of the curve between –69.9°F (–57°C) and the critical temperature of 87.8°F (31°C), carbon dioxide in a closed container may be a gas or a liquid. The pressure is related to the temperature, as long as both vapor (gaseous) and liquid states are present. As the temperature and pressure increase, the density of the vapor phase increases while the density of the liquid phase decreases. At 87.8°F (31°C), the density of the vapor becomes equal to the density of the liquid, and the clear demarcation between the two phases disappears. Above the critical temperature, high-pressure carbon dioxide exists only in a gaseous form.

When the temperature is reduced to –69.9°F (–57°C) at 75 psia (517 kPa), carbon dioxide may be present in vapor, liquid, and solid forms in equilibrium with each other. Hence, the term "triple point" to describe this condition. Below the triple point, only vapor and solid phases can exist. Thus, when liquid carbon dioxide is discharged to atmospheric pressure, a portion instantly flashes to vapor while the remainder is cooled by evaporation and converted to finely divided snow, or dry ice, at a temperature near –110°F (–79°C). The proportion of carbon dioxide converted to dry ice depends on the temperature of the stored liquid. Approximately 46 percent of the liquid stored at 0°F (–18°C) will be converted to dry ice, compared to approximately 25 percent for liquid stored at 70°F (21°C).

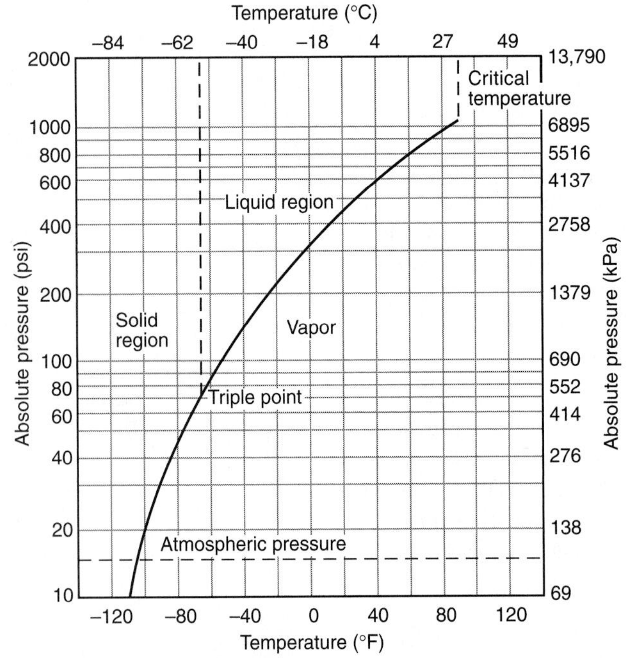

FIGURE 17.1.1 Effect of Pressure and Temperature Change on the Physical State of Carbon Dioxide

Storage

Liquid carbon dioxide may be stored in high-pressure cylinders with storage temperature varying with ambient temperature or in low-pressure refrigerated containers designed to maintain a storage temperature near 0°F (–18°C). Freezing (solidifying) in storage is not a problem. However, any substantial reduction in storage temperature—and corresponding storage pressure—could reduce the discharge flow rate below acceptable design limits. High-pressure systems normally are designed to operate properly with storage temperatures ranging from 32 to 120°F (0 to 49°C). Low-pressure systems, which normally operate at 0°F (–18°C), would not be affected unless the ambient temperature surrounding the storage container dropped to –10°F (–23°C) or lower for a prolonged time. Extreme climatic environments may require special design considerations to ensure proper operation. For low storage temperatures, high-pressure cylinders may require special "winterization" treatment, while low-pressure storage units may require heaters with circulation pumps.

Discharge Properties

A typical discharge of liquid carbon dioxide has a white, cloudy appearance due to finely divided dry ice particles carried along with the flash vapor. Because of the low temperature, some water vapor from the atmosphere will condense, creating additional fog that will persist for a time after the dry ice particles have settled out or sublimed.

Static Electricity

The dry ice particles produced during a discharge of carbon dioxide can carry a charge of static electricity. Static charge can also build up on ungrounded discharge nozzles. To prevent shock hazard to personnel or unwanted static discharge in a potentially explosive atmosphere, all discharge nozzles must be grounded. This is particularly important in the case of nozzles and playpipes used in hand hose line systems.

Vapor Density

Carbon dioxide gas has a density of one and one-half times the density of air at the same temperature. The cold discharge has a much greater density, which accounts for its ability to replace air above burning surfaces and maintain a smothering atmosphere when used in local application systems. When carbon dioxide is used for total flooding, the resulting mixture of carbon dioxide and air will be more dense than the ambient atmosphere.

Physiological Effects

Carbon dioxide is normally present in the atmosphere at a concentration of approximately 0.038 percent. It is present in humans and animals as a normal by-product of cellular respiration.

In the human body, carbon dioxide acts as a regulator of breathing, thus ensuring an adequate supply of oxygen to the system. Up to a point, an increase in carbon dioxide in the blood causes an increase in breathing rate. The maximum increase in respiration occurs when breathing 6 to 7 percent carbon dioxide in air. Higher concentrations of carbon dioxide slow down breathing. Finally, with 17 to 30 percent carbon dioxide in air, a narcotic effect takes over and stops breathing almost immediately—even with a sufficient supply of oxygen in the air. Death can result in a matter of minutes if prompt remedial action is not taken. Reduced oxygen supplies will cause a very much lower concentration of carbon dioxide to suppress breathing and cause death from asphyxiation. The exact concentration of carbon dioxide in air that will cause a decrease in respiration varies from person to person and is not constant even in the same person from time to time.

Six to 7 percent carbon dioxide is considered the threshold level at which harmful effects become noticeable in human beings. At concentrations above 9 percent, most people lose consciousness within a short time. Since the minimum concentrations of carbon dioxide in air used to extinguish fire far exceed 6 percent, adequate safety precautions must be designed into every carbon dioxide fire-extinguishing system.

The dry ice that is produced during a discharge can produce "burns," due to the extreme low temperature. Personnel should be warned not to handle any residual snow after a discharge.

EXTINGUISHING PROPERTIES OF CARBON DIOXIDE

The primary mechanism by which carbon dioxide extinguishes fire is oxygen reduction (smothering). The cooling effect of carbon dioxide is relatively small but does make some contribution to fire extinguishment, particularly when carbon dioxide is applied directly to the burning material.

Extinguishment by Smothering

In any fire, heat is generated by rapid oxidation of a combustible material. Some of this heat raises the unburned fuel to its ignition temperature, whereas a large part of the heat is lost by radiation and convection, especially in the case of surface burning materials. If the atmosphere that supplies oxygen to the fire is diluted with carbon dioxide vapor, the rate of heat generation is reduced until it is below the rate of heat loss. When the fuel is cooled below its ignition temperature, the fire dies out and is extinguished completely.

The minimum concentration of carbon dioxide needed to extinguish surface burning materials, such as liquid fuels, can be determined accurately, since the rate of heat loss by radiation and convection is reasonably constant. Table 17.1.1 lists the minimum concentrations of carbon dioxide for some common liquid and gaseous fuels as determined by the U.S. Bureau of Mines.[1] Minimum CO_2 concentrations for flammable liquid and gas hazards are based on inerting the air/fuel mixture. The theoretical minimum carbon dioxide concentration is the actual concentration of carbon dioxide required to extinguish and prevent fire in a given fuel. The minimum design concentration is

TABLE 17.1.1 Minimum Carbon Dioxide Concentrations for Extinguishment

Material	*Theoretical Minimum CO_2 Concentration (%)*	*Minimum Design CO_2 Concentration (%)*
Acetylene	55	66
Acetone	27*	34
Aviation gas grades 115/145	30	36
Benzol, benzene	31	37
Butadiene	34	41
Butane	28	34
Butane-I	31	37
Carbon disulfide	60	72
Carbon monoxide	53	64
Coal gas or natural gas	31*	37
Cyclopropane	31	37
Diethyl ether	33	40
Dimethyl ether	33	40
Dowtherm	38*	46
Ethane	33	40
Ethyl alcohol	36	43
Ethyl ether	38*	46
Ethylene	41	49
Ethylene dichloride	21	34
Ethylene oxide	44	53
Gasoline	28	34
Hexane	29	35
Higher paraffin hydrocarbons $C_nH_{2m}+2m-5$	28	34
Hydrogen	62	75
Hydrogen sulfide	30	36
Isobutane	30*	36
Isobutylene	26	34
Isobutyl formate	26	34
JP-4	30	36
Kerosene	28	34
Methane	25	34
Methyl acetate	29	35
Methyl alcohol	33	40
Methyl butene-I	30	36
Methyl ethyl ketone	32	40
Methyl formate	32	39
Pentane	29	35
Propane	30	36
Propylene	30	36
Quench, lubricating oils	28	34

Note: The theoretical minimum extinguishing concentrations in-air for the above materials were obtained from a compilation of Bureau of Mines Limits of Flammability of Gases and Vapors (*Bulletins* 503 and 627). Those marked with * were calculated from accepted residual oxygen values.

20 percent more than the theoretical minimum carbon dioxide concentration but is never less than 34 percent (per NFPA 12). It is difficult to obtain similar data for solid materials because the rate of heat loss by radiation and convection can vary widely, depending on shielding effects caused by the physical arrangement of the burning material. Design concentrations for hazards containing solid fuels have been determined from testing and experience. NFPA 12 gives design concentrations for a number of such hazards.

Extinguishment by Cooling

Although the temperatures involved in a carbon dioxide discharge may approach –110°F (–79°C), the cooling capacity of the carbon dioxide is quite small compared to an equal weight of water. The latent heat of 1 lb (0.4536 kg) of liquid carbon dioxide is about 120 Btu (126 kJ) from low-pressure storage and 64 Btu (67.5 kJ) from storage at 70°F (21°C). The cooling effect is most apparent when the agent is discharged directly on the burning material by "local application." A massive application quickly covering the entire surface area smothers the fire and helps cool the fuel.

LIMITATIONS OF CARBON DIOXIDE AS AN EXTINGUISHING AGENT

The use of carbon dioxide on general Class A fires is limited by its relatively low cooling capacity, compared to that of water, and by enclosures incapable of retaining an extinguishing atmosphere. True surface burning fires are extinguished easily because natural cooling takes place quickly. On the other hand, if the fire penetrates below the surface of the fuel and the mass of fuel provides a layer of thermal insulation that slows down the rate of heat loss (generally referred to as "deep-seated burning"), a higher concentration of carbon dioxide and a much longer holding time are needed for complete extinguishment. Some deep-seated fires may not be extinguished by carbon dioxide even after a long holding time. In such cases, carbon dioxide can be used to suppress open flaming and slow the propagation of the fire. This holding action should be maintained long enough to permit response by a properly equipped and trained fire brigade.

Carbon dioxide is not an effective extinguishing agent for fires involving chemicals that contain their own oxygen supply, such as cellulose nitrate. Fires involving reactive metals, such as sodium, potassium, magnesium, titanium, zirconium, and the metal hydrides, cannot be extinguished by carbon dioxide because the metals and hydrides decompose carbon dioxide.

METHODS OF APPLICATION

Two basic methods are used to apply carbon dioxide in extinguishing fires. One method is to discharge a sufficient amount of the agent into an enclosure to create an extinguishing atmosphere throughout the enclosed area. This is called "total flooding." The second method is to discharge the agent directly onto the burning material without relying on an enclosure to retain the carbon dioxide. This is called "local application." Other methods include hand hose lines, standpipe systems and mobile supply, extended discharge, and special applications.

Total Flooding

In total flooding systems, carbon dioxide is applied through nozzles designed and located to develop a uniform concentration of CO_2 in all parts of an enclosure (Figure 17.1.2). Calculation of the quantity of carbon dioxide required to achieve an extinguishing atmosphere is based on the volume of the room and the concentration of carbon dioxide required for the combustible materials in it.

The integrity of the enclosure is a very important part of total flooding, particularly if deep-seated fire potential exists in the hazard. If the room is tight, especially on the sides and bottom, the CO_2 extinguishing atmosphere can be retained for a long time to ensure complete control of the fire. If there are openings on the sides and bottom, however, the heavier mixture of carbon dioxide and air may leak out of the room rapidly. If the extinguishing atmosphere is lost too rapidly, glowing embers may remain and cause reignition when air reaches the fire zone. Therefore, it is important to close all openings to minimize leakage or to compensate for the openings by an extended discharge. Because of the relative weight of carbon dioxide, an opening in the ceiling helps to relieve internal air pressure during the discharge, with very little effect on leakage rate after the discharge.

Local Application

In local application systems, carbon dioxide is discharged directly on the burning surfaces through nozzles designed for this

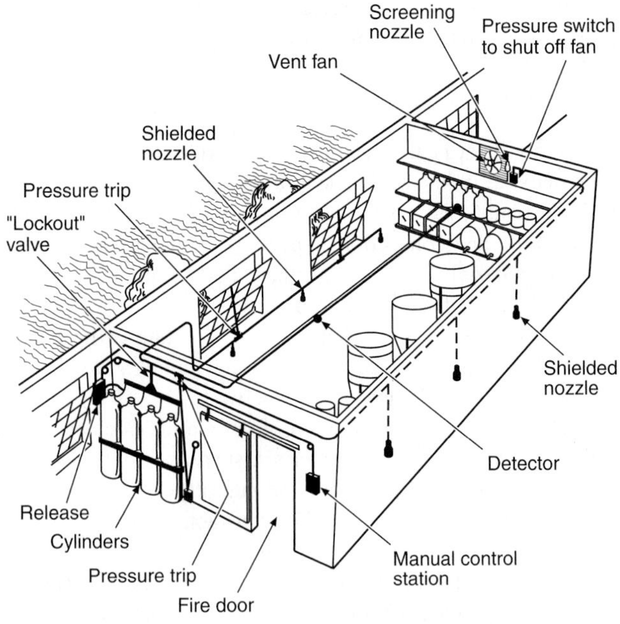

FIGURE 17.1.2 High-Pressure Carbon Dioxide System for Total Flooding

purpose. The intent is to cover all combustible areas with nozzles located so they will extinguish all flames as quickly as possible. Any adjacent area to which fuel or fire may spread also must be covered, because any residual fire could cause reignition after the carbon dioxide discharge ends (Figure 17.1.3).

Local application discharge nozzles usually are designed for relatively low velocity to avoid splashing and air entrainment. Automatic detection is a necessity to provide fast response and minimize heat buildup. Although not essential, an enclosure would help retain carbon dioxide in the fire area. Local application of carbon dioxide can also be used for fast fire knockdown in an enclosure where final total flooding can provide extinguishment.

Hand Hose Lines

Carbon dioxide systems can consist of hand hose lines permanently connected by means of fixed piping to a fixed supply of carbon dioxide. Such systems frequently are provided for manual protection of small localized hazards. Although not a substitute for a system with fixed nozzles, a hose line may be used to supplement a fixed system where the hazard is accessible for manual fire fighting, as well as to supplement portable equipment. There must be a sufficient carbon dioxide supply to permit the use of the hand hose line nozzle for at least 1 minute. Nozzles should be connected to a good electrical ground to permit static electrical charges produced by the carbon dioxide discharge to drain off. A wire-braided hose properly coupled to the discharge piping can provide a path to ground. Figure 17.1.4 shows a hand hose line system that offers flexibility for attacking fires.

FIGURE 17.1.3 Discharge of a Local Application Carbon Dioxide Extinguishing System (Source: Ansul Incorporated)

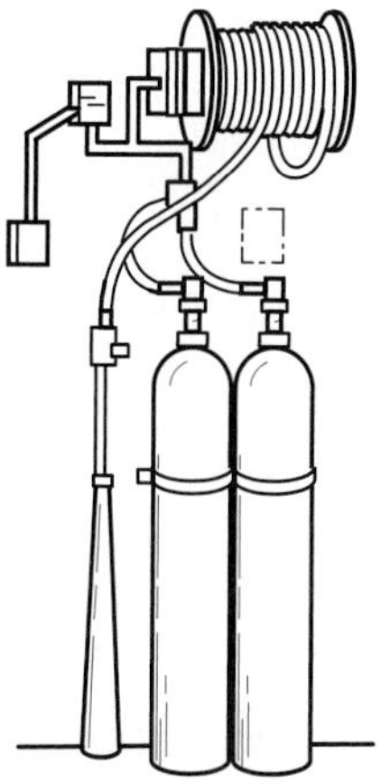

FIGURE 17.1.4 Carbon Dioxide Hand Hose Extinguishing System with Hose Mounted on a Reel

Standpipe Systems and Mobile Supply

Total flooding, local application, and hand hose line systems without a permanently connected carbon dioxide supply are known as gas standpipe systems. They are supplied by containers of carbon dioxide mounted on mobile units that can be moved and quickly coupled to a standpipe in case of fire.

Gas standpipe systems can be used as a supplement to complete fixed fire protection systems or as the only protection of hazards under certain circumstances. Mobile supplies may be equipped with hand hose lines for the protection of scattered hazards. If the possible fire damage that might occur while the mobile supply is moved to the scene and deployed is unacceptable, a fixed automatic system should be used.

Extended Discharge

An extended discharge of carbon dioxide is used when an enclosure is not tight enough to retain an extinguishing concentration as long as is needed. The extended discharge normally is at a reduced rate, following a high initial rate used to develop the extinguishing concentration in a reasonably short time. The reduced rate of discharge should be a function of the leakage rate, which can be calculated on the basis of leakage area, or of the flow rate through ventilating ducts that cannot be shut down.

Extended discharge is particularly applicable to enclosed rotating electrical equipment, such as generators, where it is difficult to prevent leakage until rotation stops. Extended discharge can be applied to ordinary total flooding systems, as well as to local application systems where a small hot spot may require prolonged cooling.

Special Applications

Carbon dioxide systems are sometimes used for inerting or purging to prevent fire or explosion. Carbon dioxide vapor is typically used in these applications. NFPA 69, *Standard on Explosion Prevention Systems,* gives guidance on these applications. Fire suppression in coal storage silos also can use carbon dioxide vapor. Low-pressure storage with an in-line vaporizer can conveniently supply the large quantities of carbon dioxide vapor typically required for these applications.

LIFE SAFETY CONSIDERATIONS

To gain the benefits of carbon dioxide extinguishing systems while minimizing risk to people, serious attention must be given to personnel safety. Personnel safety must be considered in the design, installation, maintenance, and use of carbon dioxide systems. NFPA 12 discusses personnel safety at length.

General Safety Considerations

The minimum design concentration for total flooding systems is 34 percent. This is well above the acceptable exposure threshold for personnel. Breathing such a concentration of CO_2 will cause almost immediate unconciousness followed by death in a matter of minutes if appropriate emergency rescue action is not begun immediately. All total flooding systems will produce lethal concentrations of carbon dioxide in the protected space. For such systems, predischarge evacuation is always required.

Local application systems produce high concentrations of carbon dioxide in the immediate vicinity of the fire hazard. Each local application system must be evaluated to determine if evacuation of personnel is necessary prior to the start of the discharge.

If the local application hazard is located in a large open space, the initial discharge of carbon dioxide generally presents little risk to personnel. Indeed if personnel are in the immediate vicinity of the fire, they are likely at risk from exposure to the fire itself. On the other hand, if the local application hazard occupies a large portion of the space, dangerous concentrations of carbon dioxide can build up quickly throughout the space, particularly at lower elevations within the space. Again the risk of exposure to uncontrolled fire must be weighed against the risk that the carbon dioxide discharge will endanger personnel before they can leave the area.

In all cases, both local application and total flood, migration of CO_2 from a discharge to adjacent low-lying spaces can produce dangerous concentrations of carbon dioxide, and if personnel are present in such spaces, such migration of CO_2 can present a danger to life. Suitable warning devices must be incorporated into the system.

Safety Guidance

NFPA 12 prohibits the use of total flooding carbon dioxide systems in normally occupied spaces with certain specific exceptions. NFPA 12 contains guidance as to the circumstances where the use of carbon dioxide total flooding systems in a normally occupied space could be permitted. Where a gaseous extinguishing agent is desired for a normally occupied space, the "clean agents" covered in NFPA 2001, *Standard on Clean Agent Fire Extinguishing Systems,* are generally recommended.

Arrangements to ensure evacuation before discharge must be made for all spaces protected by total flooding systems, including those that are not normally occupied but in which personnel might be present for maintenance or other purposes. If evacuation cannot be assured, the system should be locked out while personnel are within the space. Local application systems must be evaluated on a case-by-case basis, giving consideration to potential for hazardous concentrations within the enclosure containing the fire risk as well as potential for migration of CO_2 to adjacent low-lying areas.

Lockouts

NFPA 12 requires system "lockouts" to be provided for all systems except those where the dimensional characteristics of the space will prevent personnel from entering the space. The system must be locked out to prevent accidental or deliberate discharge when persons unfamiliar with the system and its operation are present in the protected space. Lockouts are also needed when personnel egress from a space is hampered (e.g., when persons are climbing ladders, working on scaffolds, or entering confined spaces).

NFPA 12 defines a system lockout as "a manually operated valve in the discharge pipe between the nozzles and the (carbon dioxide) supply which can be locked in the closed position to prevent flow of carbon dioxide to the protected area." Such a lockout will prevent both automatic and manual discharge. The emergency manual release required by NFPA 12 should *not* override the lockout. The lockout should be supervised to give an indication to those responsible for the system when the system is locked out. An adequate fire watch should be established to deal with any fire that might occur during a system lockout.

Alarms

NFPA 12 gives detailed guidance on the requirements for alarms that must be installed as part of a carbon dioxide system. In general, audible and visual predischarge alarms are required for all systems except hand hose lines. Personnel who will enter an area that could be made hazardous by discharged carbon dioxide must be trained as to the correct response to these alarms. For total flooding systems, every precaution must be taken to ensure that personnel in a protected area are evacuated before the area is flooded with carbon dioxide. This is the primary purpose of a predischarge alarm, which must provide a suitable time delay before the carbon dioxide discharge.

NFPA 12 requires that all total flood systems protecting enclosures which personnel could possibly enter be equipped with pneumatic predischarge time delays and pneumatic predischarge alarms. Both the time delays and alarms are typically powered by carbon dioxide from the system storage; neither the pneumatic time delay nor the pneumatic alarms depend on electrical power. Such pneumatic time delays and alarms are likewise required for local application systems, if the discharge will expose personnel to hazardous concentrations of carbon dioxide. The NFPA 12 standard gives details as well as specific exceptions for the pneumatic time delay and alarm requirement.

For systems that will produce a hazardous concentration of carbon dioxide throughout an enclosure, warning signs and discharge alarms must likewise be located outside each entryway to the enclosure. The purpose of these devices is to warn persons against entering the space containing a dangerous concentration of carbon dioxide.

Consideration should be given to any possibility that substantial volumes of carbon dioxide vapor could leak or flow into adjacent low-level areas, such as cellars, pits, or narrow hallways (i.e., spaces not included in the protected area). If this potential exists, alarms and warning signs should be extended to include these areas. Arrangements for safely ventilating all carbon dioxide–flooded spaces following a discharge must be made.

Odorizers, such as oil of wintergreen, are sometimes added to the carbon dioxide discharge to provide an olfactory indication of the presence of carbon dioxide. Odorizers are particularly useful to indicate that carbon dioxide has leaked from the protected area to adjoining areas.

Other Safety Features/Considerations

Manual controls for the system must be located to avoid confusion, and they must be clearly labeled with safe operating procedures. Avoid grouping manual controls for more than one hazard in order to avoid confusion. Self-contained breathing apparatus (SCBA) should be provided. This apparatus should be used by trained personnel to effect rescue of anyone who might be trapped in a carbon dioxide discharge.

Periodic maintenance is required to ensure proper function of these systems. Those doing maintenance must be thoroughly trained in the functions of the system. Whenever maintenance involves work on system controls, discharge valves, or other devices that could possibly initiate carbon dioxide discharge, personnel must be evacuated from areas where a discharge from the system could produce a dangerous concentration of carbon dioxide.

COMPONENTS OF CARBON DIOXIDE SYSTEMS

Components of a carbon dioxide system include the carbon dioxide supply, the piping system, the discharge nozzles, alarms, and control devices.

Carbon Dioxide Storage

The carbon dioxide supply may be stored in high- or low-pressure containers. Because of the differences in pressure, system design is influenced by the storage method.

High-Pressure Storage. High-pressure containers, usually cylinders, are designed to store liquid carbon dioxide at atmospheric temperature. Since the maximum pressure in the cylinder or other container is affected by the ambient temperature, it is important that the container be designed to withstand the maximum expected pressure. Figure 17.1.5 shows the change in gauge pressure with temperature.

Storage cylinders are designed, tested, and filled to applicable national codes and standards. In the United States the U.S. Department of Transportation (DOT) specifications apply. The maximum filling density permitted is equal to 68 percent of

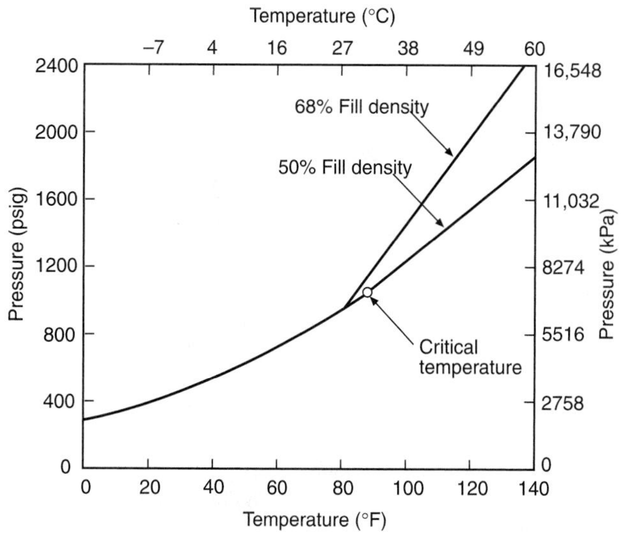

FIGURE 17.1.5 Variation in Pressure of Carbon Dioxide with Change in Temperature, Showing the Effect of Filling Density in High-Pressure Storage

the weight of water that the container can hold at 60°F (16°C). Standard cylinder capacities are 5, 10, 15, 20, 25, 35, 50, 75, 100, and 120 lb (2.3, 4.5, 6.8, 9.1, 11.3, 15.9, 22.7, 34, 45.4, and 54.4 kg) of carbon dioxide. Fire-extinguishing cylinders are fitted with an internal dip tube so that liquid will be discharged from the bottom when the cylinder is upright and the valve is opened.

Abnormally low storage temperatures adversely affect the rate of discharge. For this reason, NFPA 12 does not permit storage temperatures below 0°F (–18°C) for total flooding systems or below 32°F (0°C) for local application systems. Lower storage temperatures may be permitted only if the design includes special features to compensate for the reduced pressure. Techniques for "winterizing" cylinders are also available. Proper use of winterizing techniques can permit use of high-pressure storage at temperatures as low as –60°F (–51°C).

Low-Pressure Storage. Low-pressure storage containers are pressure vessels with a design working pressure of at least 325 psi (2240 kPa). These containers are maintained at a temperature of approximately 0°F (–18°C) by use of insulation and mechanical refrigeration. At this temperature, the pressure is approximately 300 psi (2069 kPa). A compressor, controlled by a pressure switch in the tank, circulates refrigerant through coils near the tank top. Tank pressure is controlled by condensation of carbon dioxide vapor by the coils. In the event of refrigeration failure, pressure-relief valves bleed off some of the vapor to keep the pressure within safe limits. This permits some of the liquid to evaporate, creating a self-refrigerating effect that reduces the pressure in the tank. Figure 17.1.6 shows a typical low-pressure container. Heaters with recirculating pumps are required if ambient temperatures will cool the tank contents below approximately –10°F (–23°C) (250 psi [1724 kPa] pressure level).

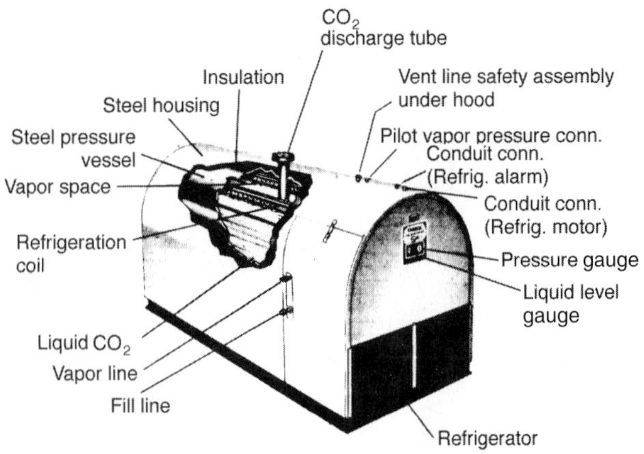

FIGURE 17.1.6 Low-Pressure Storage Unit—Carbon Dioxide Maintained at 0°F (–18°C) by Refrigeration; Pressure Is 300 psi (2069 kPa)

With low-pressure storage, it is common practice to protect multiple hazards from one central storage unit. The quantity of carbon dioxide discharged on a particular hazard is controlled by opening and closing the discharge valves in a preset timed sequence. Central low-pressure CO_2 storage units may have capacities ranging from less than 1 ton to 100 tons or more (1 ton is approximately 907 kg). For large hazards, the distance between hazard and storage may be several hundred feet (100 ft is approximately 30.5 m).

Piping System

Piping systems, normally empty, convey carbon dioxide from the storage container to open nozzles where there is a fire. Since the proper rate of flow is a critical requirement for fire extinguishment, it is important that the piping be designed and installed accurately. Minimum pressure in the pipeline must be kept well above the triple point pressure of 75 psia (5.2 bars). If the pressure of the flowing carbon dioxide falls below the triple point pressure, dry ice will form in the pipe and block orifices in the discharge nozzles, thus stopping the flow of carbon dioxide. NFPA 12 limits design nozzle pressures to a minimum of 300 psia (20.7 bars) for high-pressure storage and a minimum of 150 psia (10.3 bars) for low-pressure storage.

Carbon dioxide drawn from the bottom of the storage container enters the piping as a liquid. Friction causes loss in pressure. As pressure drops, the liquid boils, resulting in a mixture of liquid and vapor in the piping. The vapor increases in volume as the mixture passes through the piping, with a further drop in pressure. Thus, the flow is two-phase, a mixture of liquid and gas, a fact that pressure drop calculations must take into account.

NFPA 12 covers the calculation of carbon dioxide flow in some detail and provides pertinent equations and data tables. Although charts and tables are available for manual calculation of system piping, the use of available computer programs speeds and simplifies the design of piping systems.

The piping must be adequately supported to prevent movement during the discharge, and provision must be made for its contraction and expansion. Because liquid carbon dioxide is a refrigerant, it will substantially reduce the pipe temperature during discharge. Low-pressure liquid, in particular, starts at 0°F (–18°C) and may reach temperatures as low as –50°F (–46°C) in the piping before the discharge ends.

Valves and Operating Devices

Valves for controlling the discharge of carbon dioxide must withstand the maximum operating pressure, be absolutely bubbletight when closed, and be capable of both manual and automatic operation. Valves and allied devices, such as timers and pressure switches, must be listed or approved for use in carbon dioxide systems.

Discharge Nozzles

Many nozzle types are available for fire extinguishment applications. Nozzles used in total flooding simply may be orifices producing high-velocity jet streams, or they may be partially shielded to achieve reduced velocity or a specific discharge pattern. High-velocity types provide substantial mixing to ensure uniform concentration of carbon dioxide throughout an enclosure. Low-velocity types have a tendency to create high concentrations in the lower levels, which may be desirable under certain conditions.

Nozzle types used in local application systems normally are designed for relatively low discharge velocity. This helps to avoid splashing of liquid fuels and minimizes turbulence and air entrainment. All such nozzles must be tested for fire-extinguishing characteristics and listed or approved by a testing laboratory on the basis of test performance.

Figure 17.1.7 shows a typical performance curve for a nozzle designed for overhead mounting. The rate of discharge

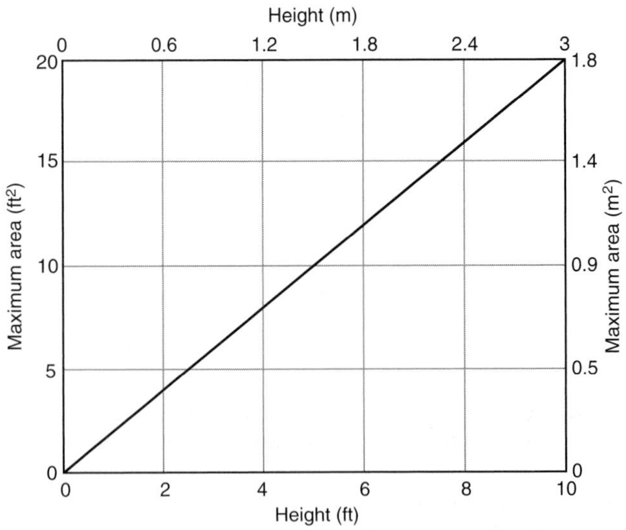

FIGURE 17.1.7 Listing or Approval Curve of a Typical Carbon Dioxide Nozzle Showing Maximum Area Versus Height or Distance from Liquid Surface

used is based on the height of the nozzle above the hazard or the fuel surface and is given in listing cards or approvals. (Testing is based on the maximum rate that will not splash liquid fuels.) The maximum fire area that the nozzle will extinguish also is based on the height above the hazard surface, using the design flow rate.

Performance information enables the system designer to select and properly locate the number of nozzles necessary to cover the entire fire area of the hazard. It also establishes the design flow rate that must be used on the hazard. The effective design flow rate must continue for a minimum of 30 seconds.

Figures 17.1.8 and 17.1.9 show typical performance curves for nozzles designed for mounting on the sides of open tanks containing flammable liquids. In such cases, the design flow rates are based on the area of coverage for the tankside nozzles or on the width of the hazard for linear nozzles mounted to extend the full length of one side. In each case, the design flow rate must be in the shaded area of the curves.

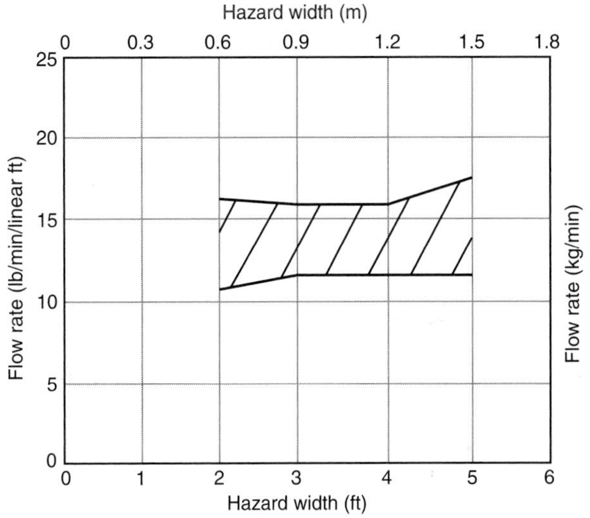

FIGURE 17.1.9 Typical Listing or Approval Curve of a Linear Carbon Dioxide Nozzle Showing Flow Rate Versus Hazard Width

System Controls

Most carbon dioxide systems incorporate three methods of actuation: automatic, normal manual operation, and emergency manual operation.

Automatic Actuation. Automatic actuation is an operation that does not require any human action. Generally, fire detectors that sense abnormal heat, smoke, or flame initiate automatic actuation. The detector, on sensing a fire condition, initiates a signal at an electrical control panel.

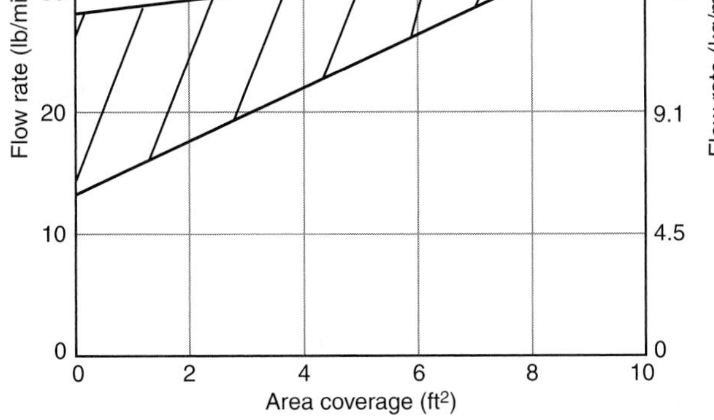

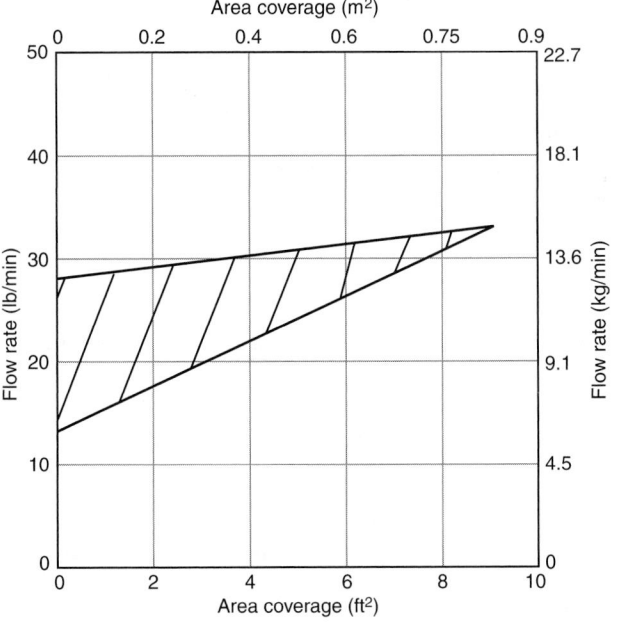

FIGURE 17.1.8 Typical Listing or Approval Curve of a Tankside Carbon Dioxide Nozzle Showing the Flow Rate Versus Area Coverage

Normal Manual Operation. Normal manual operation is actuation of the system requiring human action to initiate the operation. In modern carbon dioxide systems, normal manual operation is typically by a manual pull station connected to an electrical control panel.

Emergency Manual Operation. In emergency manual operation, the emergency manual release must function independently of electrical power and must be fully mechanical in nature. It can incorporate use of system carbon dioxide pressure to cause discharge. Emergency manual operation is intended for use only if both the automatic and normal manual operations have failed to cause a required discharge. Because most emergency manual operations cause immediate discharge of carbon dioxide without any alarm, it is essential that anyone who operates an emergency manual release be certain that the hazard area is evacuated and secured against entry of personnel prior to operation.

Control Panels

In modern carbon dioxide systems, fire detectors and manual electrical control stations (pull stations) are connected to an electrical control panel. Operation of a fire detector or pull station puts the control panel into an "alarm" condition. The control panel will cause a sequence of events leading to a discharge of carbon dioxide.

A relatively recent change to NFPA 12 requires pneumatic predischarge time delays and pneumatic predischarge alarms to be incorporated into most carbon dioxide systems. This is a retroactive requirement. Normally carbon dioxide from the system storage containers is used to power both the pneumatic time delays and the pneumatic audible alarms.

As part of the discharge sequence, the control panel opens a control valve to initiate carbon dioxide flow to the pneumatic predischarge time delay and pneumatic alarms. The control panel will also provide power to electrically operated alarm devices. After the pneumatic time delay has expired, the discharge of carbon dioxide begins. If the system uses high-pressure storage containers, the discharge will continue until the containers are emptied. If the system uses a low-pressure storage container, the discharge is continued for a predetermined length of time after which a control valve is shut, ending the discharge.

The control panel may also cause required equipment shutdown and fuel line shutoffs, control dampers and fans, and send alarm signals to personnel responsible for response to fire situations. It is essential that electrical control panels that are intended to control carbon dioxide systems be designed such that a system discharge will not occur without the required predischarge time delay and alarms. The sequence of operation for the carbon dioxide system must be documented in writing and maintained in a protective enclosure with the system.

When the system is in "standby" condition, the control panel supervises the interconnections between all electrically powered components necessary for control of the systems and life safety. Connections between the control panel and detectors, manual electrical release stations, system valve actuators, and alarms should be supervised. The control panel also monitors the condition of system lockout valves and electrical power sources.

Some older carbon dioxide systems used timer-driven cams to operate switches that controlled the various discharge functions. Totally pneumatic systems using pneumatic detection and control were also common. Many of these systems are still in service.

Alarms

Both audible and visual predischarge alarms are generally required for carbon dioxide systems. Various types of sirens or horns are used for audible alarm. NFPA 12 requires that most total flood systems and some local application systems be equipped with pneumatically powered predischarge time delays and pneumatically driven predischarge audible alarms. Existing systems which lack such pneumatic alarms are required by NFPA 12 to be retrofitted with them. Whatever type of audible device is used, its sound should be distinctive and capable of being heard above background noises. Strobe lights or rotating beacons are often used as visual alarms. It is essential that the alarms function to warn people against entry into all areas made hazardous by a carbon dioxide discharge for as long as the hazard exists or until the areas are secured against entry by personnel.

CARBON DIOXIDE SYSTEM DESIGN CONSIDERATIONS

To organize basic components into a carbon dioxide fire protection system, a number of factors must be considered. These include the quantity of stored carbon dioxide, the method of actuation, the location of predischarge alarms, ventilation shutdown, pressure venting, and anything else involved in ensuring safe, prompt, and effective fire extinguishment and personnel safety.

Quantity Requirements

The quantity of carbon dioxide required for extinguishment depends on the type of fire, the type of extinguishing system, and conditions in the fire area. Where continuous protection is required, the quantity of carbon dioxide on hand should be at least twice that needed for extinguishment. Detailed methods of determining the quantity required for extinguishment are covered in NFPA 12.

Total Flooding Systems. The design concentration for a given enclosure should be sufficient to extinguish fires in all the fuels that are present in the hazard. The minimum concentration used in total flooding systems is 34 percent carbon dioxide by volume. Minimum design concentrations for various liquids and gases are given in Table 17.1.1. NFPA 12 requires a 50 percent concentration for electrical wiring hazards, including small electrical machines; 65 percent for bulk paper and fur storage vaults; and 75 percent for dust collectors. These are specific hazards for which there is a background of test experience. Other materials should be tested to determine minimum carbon dioxide concentrations and holding time.

The quantity of carbon dioxide must be sufficient to achieve a minimum design concentration and to maintain it until the fire is extinguished or a trained and suitably equipped fire brigade responds to complete the extinguishment. A series of specific flooding factors has been established for surface fire hazards. These factors include an allowance for distributed leakage due to cracks around doors, porosity of the walls, and other small openings based on room size. The factors are greater for smaller rooms, because the anticipated leakage would be greater relative to volume (Table 17.1.2 and Figure 17.1.10).

Note: If a hazard requires a design concentration greater than 34 percent, the basic quantity of carbon dioxide needed would be calculated by multiplying the appropriate flooding factor from Table 17.1.2 by the conversion factor determined from Figure 17.1.10.

If the enclosure has obvious openings that cannot be closed, or ventilating systems that cannot be shut off in the event of a

TABLE 17.1.2 Flooding Factors to Achieve 34 Percent Design Concentration

	Volume Factor		
Volume of Space (ft^3)	*(ft^3/lb CO_2)*	*(lb CO_2/ft^3)*	*Calculated Quantity Not Less Than (lb)*
Up to 140	14	0.072	—
141–500	15	0.067	10
501–1,600	16	0.063	35
1,601–4,500	18	0.056	100
4,501–50,000	20	0.050	250
Over 50,000	22	0.046	2500

For SI units: 1 ft^3 = 0.0283 m^3; 1 lb = 0.454 kg.

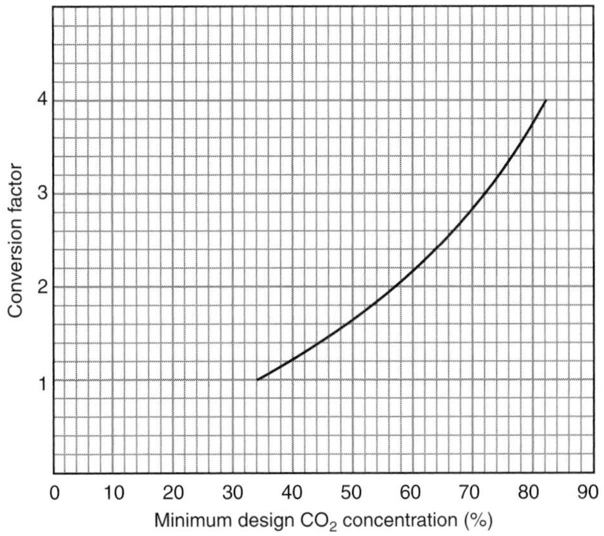

FIGURE 17.1.10 Minimum Design Carbon Dioxide Concentration Conversion Factors

fire, additional carbon dioxide must be added to the "basic quantity" calculated using the flooding factor and material conversion factor.

Surface burning fires, such as flammable liquid fires, are normally extinguished during a 1-minute carbon dioxide discharge. Leakage compensation must be in addition to the basic quantity.

Deep-seated fires require higher concentrations and much longer holding times. The rate of discharge must be high enough to develop a concentration of 30 percent in not more than 2 minutes, and the final design concentration must be achieved in not more than 7 minutes. Enclosures for deep-seated fires should be relatively tight, or it may be uneconomical to maintain the carbon dioxide design concentration. The basic quantity of carbon dioxide needed for deep-seated fire hazards is calculated using flooding factors given in NFPA 12. Some deep-seated fires can smolder for very long periods of time, even in the presence of a high carbon dioxide concentration. An example is fire in baled cotton stored in the cargo hold of a ship. For these fires, carbon dioxide may be used to suppress the open flaming and reduce the rate of fire spread. Complete extinguishment must be done by trained fire fighters using manual fire-fighting techniques. For such hazards, the carbon dioxide concentration should be maintained for sufficient time to permit response by a properly equipped and trained fire brigade.

Extended Discharge Systems. The most efficient way to compensate for leakage where the concentration must be maintained for a substantial time is to use an extended discharge at a reduced rate equal to the rate of leakage. The quantity of carbon dioxide required is based on the rate of discharge multiplied by the time that the concentration must be maintained. This is in addition to the quantity required to develop the design concentration.

Local Application Systems. These systems may be designed using either "rate-by-area" or "rate-by-volume" methods. When rate-by-area is used, the hazard is considered as a number of equivalent surface areas, each protected by a single nozzle. The rate of discharge from each nozzle is determined from listing information, and the total discharge rate for the system is the sum of the design rates required for each nozzle.

Where the hazard consists of three-dimensional irregular objects that cannot be reduced easily to equivalent surface areas, the rate-by-volume method may be used. In this case, the discharge rate of the system is based on the volume of an assumed enclosure entirely surrounding the hazard. Because this method is not as precise as the rate-by-area procedure, it usually results in more carbon dioxide discharge, unless the hazard is nearly enclosed with walls.

A discharge of vapor is not considered effective for local application. The liquid portion of the discharge should be continued for a minimum of 30 seconds, or longer if required for cooling. If a liquid fuel has an autoignition temperature lower than its boiling point (e.g., paraffin wax and some cooking oils), the mass of liquid can become "superheated" above its autoignition temperature. For such fuels, a minimum local application time of 3 minutes is required to permit the mass of liquid fuel to cool.

Additional carbon dioxide must be added to storage to compensate for any initial vapor discharge produced in cooling the piping. In high-pressure systems, only about 70 percent of the stored quantity will leave the storage cylinder as liquid. Therefore, the quantity calculated by rate and time must be increased by a factor of 1.4 to help ensure a 30 second liquid discharge.

Hand Hose Line Systems. The carbon dioxide supply depends upon the type and size of the hazard to be protected. As a practical matter, however, sufficient carbon dioxide should be available to counteract possible waste by inexperienced users. In any case, there should be sufficient carbon dioxide to permit operation of the system for at least 1 minute. The possible use of these hoselines by inexperienced personnel should be considered and enough carbon dioxide should be provided to permit extinguishment of a fire by such personnel. When more than one hose reel may possibly be used on a single hazard, sufficient carbon dioxide should be available to support the maximum number of hose reels that are likely to be used simultaneously for 1 minute.

Venting Requirements

When liquid carbon dioxide is discharged into a closed room, the atmosphere may shrink initially due to the sudden refrigerating effect. At a later flooding stage, the combined volume of the carbon dioxide and air may become greater than the initial room volume. Thus, although the first result may be to create a vacuum, or draw in air, the final result will be to increase the pressure or to exhaust the excess volume through vent openings. Actual air temperatures are greatly reduced during the discharge, but they soon return to normal as heat is absorbed from solid surfaces in the room.

Most ordinary rooms have sufficient leakage through cracks around doors and windows and through general porosity to prevent noticeable vacuum or pressure buildup. From the viewpoint of efficient total flooding, it is better to have major vent openings in or near the ceiling rather than near the floor.

In rooms that may be tightly sealed, a safe vent area can be estimated on the basis of calculated discharge flow rate and the strength of the enclosure:

$$X = \frac{Q}{1.3\sqrt{p}}$$

where

X = Vent area in in.^{2}

Q = Flow rate in lb/min

p = Allowable strength of the enclosure in lb/ft^2

For SI units:

$$X_m = \frac{239Q_m}{\sqrt{p_m}}$$

where

X_m = Vent area in mm^2

Q_m = Flow rate in kg/min

p_m = Allowable strength of the enclosure in kg/m^2

More information on room venting can be found in NFPA 12.

System Control

Total flooding and local-application carbon dioxide systems normally should be designed to operate automatically. The detection device may be any of the listed or approved devices that are actuated by heat, smoke, flame, flammable vapors, or other abnormal process conditions that could lead to a fire or explosion. Automatically operated systems are required to have an independent means of manual actuation (emergency manual operator).

It is essential that electrical control panels intended to control carbon dioxide systems be designed such that a system discharge will not occur without the required predischarge time delay and alarms. NFPA 12 requires pneumatically powered predischarge time delays for most total flood systems and some local application systems. Existing systems must be retrofitted with pneumatic time delays to meet the NFPA 12 requirements. If a control panel fails to discharge the carbon dioxide system, the emergency manual operator is available to cause a discharge independently of the control panel. An unwanted discharge without proper predischarge alarms may endanger life.

Whether supplemental to automatic actuation or the sole means of placing a system in operation, manual controls must be easy to operate, accessible in case of fire, and located close to the valves they control. Remote manual controls usually are located near an exit for a total flooding installation or near a hazardous area for local application installations. Instructions for safe operation of the manual controls must be prominently displayed at the control.

Marine Systems

Systems used on offshore platforms and marine vessels are subject to different regulations and design procedures. Quantity calculations, piping design, nozzle sizing, and system control requirements can vary from those discussed in this chapter. The guidance of the authority having jurisdiction over the vessel must be followed for such systems.

TESTING AND MAINTAINING CARBON DIOXIDE SYSTEMS

An elaborate fire protection system could be ineffective or even dangerous unless it is properly tested to demonstrate adequate performance and maintained in good working condition.

Acceptance Testing

No newly installed system should be accepted until it has been inspected properly and tested to prove performance in accordance with design specifications. The inspection should ascertain whether the system is installed in accordance with approved plans. The piping is particularly important, because any changes might affect the flow rates that were calculated on the basis of the pipe sizes shown on the plans.

NFPA 12 requires a "full discharge test" of all newly installed systems. The final proof of performance is to discharge the system and, for total flooding hazards, to measure the concentrations of carbon dioxide and the holding time in the fire zone. Local application systems cannot be subjected to concentration testing. Their effectiveness is judged by observation during the test discharge. NFPA 12 gives the minimum requirements for approval of new installations.

Figure 17.1.11 shows a local application discharge test on a printing press. The effectiveness of the local application discharge is judged by observation during the discharge test. It is helpful to videotape the discharge of large local application systems. This photo taken from such a videotape reveals that carbon dioxide coverage on the front press stations was inadequate. Post-test inspection showed that the left nozzle for the station was plugged.

FIGURE 17.1.11 Local Application Discharge Test on Printing Press (Source: Photo Courtesy of Guardian Services, Inc.)

Inspections

To maintain a system in proper operating condition, it is essential to conduct periodic inspections. At least once a month, the system must be inspected to verify its operational status. The status of the carbon dioxide supply should be checked at least weekly for low-pressure supplies, at 6 month intervals for high-pressure cylinders, and immediately after the system has operated. The entire system should be inspected annually. In particular, inspectors should look for changes in the scope of the hazard, changes in the condition of any enclosure, and other changes that could affect the adequacy of the fire protection system.

Maintenance

All operating devices should be tested annually. Although much of this testing can be accomplished without discharging the system, a partial discharge may be necessary in some cases. Any required maintenance found by testing should be performed without delay.

Training

Personnel must be made aware of the importance of the fire protection as well as the potential effects of exposure to high concentrations of carbon dioxide. Training should include how the system extinguishes fire, physiological effects of exposure to carbon dioxide, how the system is actuated, proper response to alarms (including a detailed evacuation plan), and proper safety precautions that are to be observed before manually actuating the system. New personnel should be trained before they are permitted to enter spaces that could be affected by a carbon dioxide discharge or areas where carbon dioxide system controls are located. Periodic "refresher" training courses should be mandatory.

Persons who are not normally associated with the protected hazard and adjoining spaces, but who are given temporary assignment there, must also be briefed on the safety issues related to the fire protection system, including proper response to alarms and evacuation procedures. This applies likewise to outsiders, such as construction and maintenance people.

SUMMARY

Carbon dioxide is a widely used fire-extinguishing agent that is especially effective on flammable liquid fires, gas fires, and fires involving electrically energized equipment. It can also be used on ordinary combustibles such as cloth and paper. Carbon dioxide has several properties that make it a desirable fire-extinguishing agent; for example, it is noncombustible, does not conduct electricity, and is easily spread in its gaseous form. Total flooding systems may not be effective in enclosures incapable of retaining an extinguishing concentration. The CO_2 should not be used on fires involving chemicals that contain their own oxygen supply or on fires involving reactive metals. A variety of methods can be used to apply carbon dioxide, including total flooding and local application systems. Because concentrations resulting from the discharge of a carbon dioxide system can endanger life, it is essential that safety features be installed and kept in operating condition and that personnel be properly trained with respect to system safety. These systems must be properly designed, tested, and maintained by trained personnel in order to ensure that the systems work effectively and safely.

BIBLIOGRAPHY

Reference Cited

1. Coward, H. W., and Jones, G. W., "Limits of Flammability of Gases and Vapors," *Bulletin* 503, USDI Bureau of Mines, Washington, DC, 1952.

NFPA Codes, Standards, and Recommended Practices

Reference to the following NFPA codes, standards, and recommended practices will provide further information on carbon dioxide and application systems discussed in this chapter. (See the latest version of The NFPA Catalog *for availability of current editions of the following documents.)*

NFPA 12, *Standard on Carbon Dioxide Extinguishing Systems*
NFPA 69, *Standard on Explosion Prevention Systems*
NFPA 2001, *Standard on Clean Agent Fire Extinguishing Systems*

References

"Carbon Dioxide Fire Extinguishing System Safety," USCG-NVIC-9-00, Coast Guard, Washington, DC, Mar. 17, 2000.

Cleary, T. G., and Donnelly, M. K., "Aircraft Cargo Compartment Fire and Nuisance Source Test in the FE/DE," *Proceedings* of 12th International Conference on Automatic Fire Detection "AUBE '01," March 25–28, 2001, Gaithersburg, MD, NIST SP 965, National Institute of Standards and Technology, Gaithersburg, MD, 2001, pp. 689–700.

Danbara, T., and Saito, N., "Effect of Inert Gas and Water Vapor on Flame Spread over Paper," *Report of National Research Institute of Fire and Disaster,* No. 86, Sept. 1998, pp. 28–34.

Hamilton, D., "Carbon Dioxide Again!" *Fire Safety Engineering,* Vol. 5, No. 3, 1998, pp. 10–12.

Hamins, A., Bundy, M., and Puri, I., "Supression of Low Strain Rate Flames by an Agent," *Proceedings* of 15th Joint Panel Meeting, U.S./Japan Government Cooperative Program on Natural Resources (UJNR), Fire Research and Safety, March 1–7, 2000, San Antonio, TX, NISTIR 6588, National Institute of Standards and Technology, Gaithersburg, MD, 2000, pp. 250–257.

Jackman, L., "Going Green: The Options," *Fire Prevention,* No. 316, Jan. 1999, p. 30.

Nichols, T. R., "Fire Suppression. Part 7: Local Application Systems," *Fire Safety Engineering,* Vol. 7, No. 6, 2000, pp. 32–33.

Skaggs, S. R., "Examining the Risks of Carbon Dioxide as a Fire Suppressant," *Proceedings* of Halon Options Technical Working Conference, HOTWC-98, May 12–14, 1998, Albuquerque, NM, 1998, pp. 261–268.

Tuomisaari, M., Baroudi, D., and Latva, R., "Extinguishing Smouldering Fires in Silos," VTT Publications 339, VTT-Technical Research Center of Finland, Espoo, Finland, 1998.

Chapter 2

Chemical Extinguishing Agents and Application Systems

James D. Lake

Although water is the most common fire extinguishing agent available, it is understood that for many types of fires water may not be the most effective, efficient, or even the safest agent to use. Flammable liquids, combustible metals, and various machining processes present special hazards that may best be protected by chemical extinguishing agents.

For the purposes of this chapter, chemical extinguishing agents are divided into two categories: dry and wet. Dry chemical fire extinguishing systems first appeared on the market in the mid-1950s, and wet chemical fire extinguishing systems began receiving listings for the protection of commercial cooking operations in the late 1960s. Both types of systems are addressed by the NFPA Technical Committee on Dry and Wet Chemical Extinguishing Systems, which outlines the two standards that address these systems: NFPA 17, *Standard for Dry Chemical Extinguishing Systems,* and NFPA 17A, *Standard for Wet Chemical Extinguishing Systems.*

This chapter contains information on the properties of both dry and wet chemicals that contribute to their use as extinguishing agents. The limitations, methods of application, system design, and the inspection, testing, and maintenance associated with these systems will also be addressed in this chapter.

Portable dry and wet chemical fire extinguishers are discussed in Section 17, Chapter 5, "Fire Extinguisher Use and Maintenance." For other related topics, see Section 9, Chapter 5, "Metalworking Processes."

Chapter Contents

Key Terms

dry chemical, dry chemical extinguishing system, fixed extinguishing system, flammable liquid fire, portable fire extinguisher, saponification, total flooding, wet chemical, wet chemical extinguishing system

OVERVIEW OF DRY CHEMICAL EXTINGUISHING AGENTS

Dry chemical is defined as a powder composed of very small particles, usually sodium bicarbonate–, potassium bicarbonate–, or ammonium phosphate–based with added particulate material supplemented by special treatment to provide resistance to packing and moisture absorption (caking) and to provide the proper flow capabilities. It is intended for application by means of portable extinguishers, hand hose line systems, or fixed systems.

Dry chemical extinguishing agents are commonly listed for use on Class B and Class C fires. However, ammonium phosphate–based agents may also be referred to as *multipurpose dry chemical* because they are listed for use on Class A, B, and C fires. Dry chemical extinguishing agents are not effective on Class D fires as the heat developed by combustible metals consumes the agent prior to extinguishment. Furthermore, application of multipurpose dry chemical may result in a violent reaction with some types of combustible metals. Therefore, the terms *dry chemical* and *multipurpose dry chemical* should not be confused with *dry powder* and *dry compound,* which identify powdered extinguishing agents developed primarily for use on Class D fires. See Section 9, Chapter 5, "Metalworking Processes," for a discussion on combustible metal fires.

James D. Lake is a senior fire protection specialist at NFPA and the staff liaison for the Technical Committee on Dry and Wet Chemical Extinguishing Systems. He also works with the Technical Committee on Venting Systems for Cooking Appliances.

The first dry chemical agents were borax- and sodium bicarbonate–based dry chemicals. Sodium bicarbonate eventually became the standard because of its greater effectiveness as a fire-extinguishing agent and was even modified to make it compatible with protein-based low-expansion foams for a dual agent attack in the 1960s. The mid-1960s saw the development of the monoammonium phosphate–based *multipurpose dry chemical;* the potassium bicarbonate–based *Purple K*, originally developed to be used with aqueous film forming foam (AFFF) in a dual system but is commonly used on its own for flammable liquid fires; and the potassium chloride–based *Super K*, which has extinguishing properties that are roughly equivalent to potassium bicarbonate but was developed as a dry chemical that would be compatible with protein-type foams.

As a group, dry chemical agents are noted for their efficiency in extinguishing fires in flammable liquids. They can also be used on fires involving some types of electrical equipment. Sodium bicarbonate– and potassium bicarbonate–based agents have certain limited applications in extinguishment of flash surface fires with ordinary combustibles, but the chemical requires water to put out deep-seated smoldering fires. Multipurpose dry chemical can be used on fires in flammable liquids, fires involving energized electrical equipment, and fires in ordinary combustible materials and seldom needs the help of water to completely extinguish fires in Class A materials.

In the late 1960s a urea-potassium bicarbonate–based dry chemical was developed in Great Britain but is not as widely used as the other agents.

Physical Properties

The principal base chemicals used in the production of currently available dry chemical extinguishing agents are sodium bicarbonate, potassium bicarbonate, potassium chloride, urea-potassium bicarbonate, and monoammonium phosphate. Various additives are mixed with these base materials to improve their storage, flow, and water repellency characteristics. The most commonly used additives are metallic stearates, tricalcium phosphate, or silicones, which coat the particles of dry chemical to make them free-flowing and resistant to the caking effects of moisture and vibration.

Because some of the additives in dry chemical agents may melt and cause sticking at higher temperatures, an upper storage temperature limit of 120°F (49°C) is recommended for dry chemical. (Temperatures up to 150°F [66°C] may be acceptable for very short durations.)

Most dry chemicals are alkaline (sodium bicarbonate, potassium bicarbonate, and potassium carbonate), one is neutral (potassium chloride), and the multipurpose type (monoammonium phosphate) is acidic. Inadvertent mixing of different base dry chemicals can initiate undesirable reactions, generating carbon dioxide gas and resulting in equipment failure or loss of discharge capability.

- *Sodium bicarbonate* is an odorless white crystalline powder that decomposes at 140°F (60°C), has a pH ranging from 8.3 to 8.6, is partly soluble in water, and is the mildest of all sodium alkalis. As an extinguishing agent, it commonly has a white or blue appearance. It is the original dry chemical extinguishing agent and may also be referred to as regular dry chemical. The production of sodium bicarbonate is more economical than any of the other dry chemicals, resulting in its being the most widely used of the group.
- *Potassium bicarbonate* is an odorless white powder that decomposes at 248°F (120°C), has a pH in the range of 8.4, and is not soluble in water. Purple K is given its characteristic hue by the addition of violet pigments during production.
- *Potassium chloride* is an odorless white crystal with a melting point of 1422°F (772°C), has a pH of 7, and is completely soluble in water. It was developed as a dry chemical that would be compatible with protein-type foams. Its extinguishing properties are about equal to those of potassium bicarbonate. One drawback is its tendency to cause corrosion after it has extinguished a fire.
- *Monoammonium phosphate* is a white crystal solid with a slight odor of ammonia. It has a melting point of 350°F (190°C) and is slightly soluble in water (0.04 oz/0.08 oz [1g/2.5mL]). As an extinguishing agent, it may have an off-white or yellow color.

Monoammonium phosphate is called a multipurpose dry chemical because it can be effective on Class A, B, and C fires. Ammonium salts interrupt the chain reaction of flaming combustion. The phosphate changes into metaphosphoric acid, a glassy fusible material, at fire temperatures. The acid covers solid surfaces with a fire-retardant coating. Therefore, this agent can be used on fires involving ordinary combustible materials such as wood and paper, as well as on fires involving flammable oils, gases, and electrical equipment. However, it may only control, but not fully extinguish, a deep-seated fire.

Toxicity. Dry extinguishing chemical agents are stable at both low and normal temperatures and are considered to be nontoxic and noncarcinogenic. However, other physiological conditions such as minor skin and respiratory irritations may occur on exposure to the agents. No chronic medical conditions have been reported from long-term exposure. The acute effects of exposure are irritation to mucous membranes, with the possibility of chemical burns of the skin, eyes, and mucous membranes lining the respiratory system. Moist skin may enhance this effect. In all cases, self-contained breathing apparatus (SCBA) should be worn to protect against smoke, fumes, and the dust created by fixed system discharge. Consult the appropriate material safety data sheets (MSDSs) for detailed information, instructions, and special precautions.[1]

Particle Size. Particles of dry chemical range in size from less than 10 microns up to 75 microns (1 micron = 0.000029 in.). Particle size has a definite effect on extinguishing efficiency, and careful quality control is necessary to prevent particles from exceeding upper and lower limits of this performance range. Each dry chemical has a unique size limiting factor, below which the particles completely decompose and vaporize, and above which the particles do not completely decompose or vaporize.[2] The best results are obtained by a heterogeneous mixture with a median particle size of 20 to 25 microns. Particle size also has an effect on the flow characteristics of dry chemical. Solid particles suspended in a gas stream present higher pressure losses than does gas alone. Coarse powders cause excessive surging, low flow rates, and will require larger expellant gas quantities. Fine powder will produce similar results but not to the same degree. Particle size is also responsible for the aerodynamic drag phenomenon (ADP). The momentum gained by larger particles will transport smaller particles to penetrate the updraft of a flame. Ordinarily, smaller particles would decompose or vaporize prior to penetration.[3] Underwriters Laboratories Inc. (UL) and Factory Mutual Research Corporation listings and ratings are based on the specified use of the particular type of dry chemical set forth by the equipment manufacturer.

Extinguishing Properties

When introduced directly to the fire area, dry chemical causes extinguishment almost at once. Fire tests on flammable liquids have shown potassium bicarbonate–based dry chemical to be more effective than sodium bicarbonate–based dry chemical in extinguishment. Similarly, monoammonium phosphate has been found equal to or better than sodium bicarbonate in extinguishment effectiveness.[4] The effectiveness of potassium chloride is about equivalent to that of potassium bicarbonate, and urea-potassium bicarbonate exhibits the greatest effectiveness of all the dry chemicals tested.

Smothering, cooling, and radiation shielding contribute to the extinguishing efficiency of dry chemical, but studies suggest that a chain-breaking reaction in the flame is the principal cause of extinguishment.[5]

Cooling Action. It cannot be substantiated that the cooling action of dry chemical is an important reason for its ability to promptly extinguish fires. The heat energy required to decompose dry chemicals plays an undeniable role in contributing toward their individual extinguishing abilities, but the effect, per se, is minor. To be effective, any dry chemical must be heat sensitive and, as such, absorb heat in order to become chemically active.[6]

Radiation Shielding. Discharge of dry chemical produces a cloud of powder between the flame and the fuel; this cloud shields the fuel from some of the heat radiated by the flame. Tests to evaluate this factor concluded that the shielding factor is of some significance.[6]

Smothering Action. For special applications, such as kitchen range, hood, duct, and fryer fire protection, the extinguishing mechanism for dry chemical is based on the process of saponification. Saponification is the process of chemically converting the fatty acid contained in the cooking medium to soap, or foam, and it accomplishes extinguishment by forming a surface coating that smothers the fire.[7]

The soap produced by saponification is readily broken down by exposure to heat. As a result, because dry chemicals do not offer a substantial cooling effect, the cooking medium may reflash after a brief period of time. It is due to this lack of cooling and the resultant potential for reflashing of the cooking medium that dry chemical extinguishing agents are no longer listed for the protection of commercial cooking operations. Wet chemical extinguishing agents are currently the only agents listed for the protection of this hazard.

For many years it was widely held that regular dry chemical extinguishing properties relied primarily on the smothering action of the carbon dioxide released when sodium bicarbonate was heated by fire. The carbon dioxide does undoubtedly contribute to the effectiveness of dry chemical, as does the like volume of water vapor released when dry chemical is heated. However, tests have not supported the belief that these gases are a major factor in extinguishment.

Chain-Breaking Reaction. The preceding extinguishing actions, when combined, exert a minimal effect. The rapidity of extinguishment is due to the interference of the dry chemical particles with the propagation of the combustion chain reaction, which reduces the concentration of "free" radicals present within the flames. To accomplish this, the dry chemical must become thermally decomposed.

The discharge of dry chemical into the flames prevents reactive particles from coming together and continuing the combustion chain reaction. The explanation is referred to as the chain-breaking mechanism of extinguishment.[8,9]

When multipurpose dry chemical is discharged into burning ordinary combustibles, the decomposed monoammonium phosphate leaves a sticky residue (metaphosphoric acid) on the burning material. This residue seals glowing material from oxygen, thus helping to extinguish the fire and prevent reignition.

USES AND LIMITATIONS OF DRY CHEMICAL SYSTEMS

Dry chemical is primarily used to extinguish flammable liquid fires. Because it is electrically nonconductive, it can also be used on flammable liquid fires involving live electrical equipment. Regular dry chemical extinguishers have been tested and found suitable for use on flammable liquid and electrical fires (Class B and C fires) by fire equipment testing laboratories.

Due to the rapidity with which dry chemical extinguishes flame, dry chemical is used on surface fires involving ordinary combustible materials (Class A fires). There are several areas in the textile industry, notably opener-picker rooms and carding rooms in cotton mills, where regular dry chemical has been used effectively. However, wherever regular dry chemical is provided for use on surface-type Class A fires, it should be supplemented by water spray for extinguishing smoldering embers or in case the fire gets beneath the surface. In some baled cotton storage areas, the tops of bales can be covered with regular dry chemical to prevent surface spread should fire break out. This preventive measure does not eliminate the need for automatic sprinkler protection in such areas. Because multipurpose dry chemical becomes sticky when heated, it is not recommended for textile card rooms or other locations where removal of the residue from fine machine parts may be difficult.

Dry chemical does not produce a lasting inert atmosphere above the surface of a flammable liquid; consequently, its use will not result in permanent extinguishment if reignition sources, such as hot metal surfaces or persistent electrical arcing, are present.

Dry chemical should not be used in installations where relays and delicate electrical contacts are located (e.g., in telephone exchanges and computer equipment rooms), as the insulating properties of dry chemical might render such equipment inoperative. Because some dry chemicals are slightly corrosive, they should be removed from all undamaged surfaces as soon as possible after fire extinguishment.

Specifications have been established by fire equipment testing laboratories to ensure the positive and consistent performance of dry chemical as an extinguishing agent. These specifications control moisture content, water repellency, electrical resistivity, storage at elevated temperatures, flow capability, caking resistivity, and abrasive action. The discharge characteristics of the device in which the dry chemical is to be used are also evaluated. Extinguishing effectiveness is determined by performance tests of the application to standard fires under conditions recommended by the manufacturer.

Dry chemical extinguishing systems can be used in those situations where quick extinguishment is desired and where reignition sources are not present. Dry chemical systems are used primarily for flammable liquid fire hazards, such as dip tanks, flammable liquid storage rooms, and areas where flammable liquid spills may occur. Systems have been designed for kitchen range hoods, ducts, and associated rangetop hazards, such as deep-fat fryers. However, due to its limited ability to prevent reflashing of a fire, no dry chemical agents or system has been able to meet the new listing criteria for the protection from these hazards. Where it is necessary to extinguish a flammable liquid or gas fire being fed by fuel under pressure, dry chemical hand hose line systems can be used, followed by closure of fuel shutoff valves.

Because dry chemical is electrically nonconductive, extinguishing systems using this agent can be used on electrical equipment that is subject to flammable liquid fires, such as oil-filled transformers and oil-filled circuit breakers. Dry chemical system protection is not recommended, however, for delicate electrical equipment, such as telephone switchboards and electronic computers. Such equipment is subject to damage by dry chemical deposit and, because of the insulating properties of the dry chemical, may require excessive cleaning to restore operation.

Regular dry chemical will not extinguish fires that penetrate beneath the surface or fires in materials that supply their own oxygen for combustion. Dry chemical may be incompatible with mechanical (air) foam unless the dry chemical has been specially prepared to be reasonably foam compatible.

Method of Application

Fixed systems are of two types: (1) total flooding and (2) hand hose line/local application. In total flooding applications, a predetermined amount of dry chemical is discharged through fixed piping and nozzles into an enclosed space or enclosure around the hazard (Figure 17.2.1). On actuation of the system by a heat detector, nitrogen is discharged into the 150 lb (68 kg) storage container and dry chemical is expelled through eight nozzles in the roof. Total flooding systems are applicable only when the hazard is totally enclosed or when all openings surrounding a hazard can be closed automatically, before or simultaneously when the system is discharged. In some instances, additional dry chemical can be included in the system design to compensate for unclosable openings. Total flooding can be used only where no reignition is anticipated, because the extinguishing action is transient.

FIGURE 17.2.1 A 15 ft by 24 ft (4.6 m by 7.3 m) Flammable Liquids Storage Building Protected by a Total Flooding Dry Chemical System

Hand hose line systems containing regular or ordinary dry chemical have been used to a limited extent for quick-spreading surface fires on ordinary combustible material. In such applications, the dry chemical system only stops or prevents a rapid surface spread, and must be supplemented by a water-type extinguishing device to put out deep-seated smoldering fires. Fixed systems containing multipurpose dry chemical are available and are suitable for the protection of ordinary combustibles, provided the dry chemical can reach all burning surfaces.

Hand hose line systems consist of a supply of dry chemical and expellant gas with one or more hand hose lines to deliver the dry chemical to the fire (Figure 17.2.2). Dry chemical systems of this type range from 125 to 3000 lb (57 to 1361 kg); the 3000 lb (1361 kg) system shown has six nitrogen cylinders and two 1 in. by 100 ft (25 mm by 30.5 m) hoses with shutoff nozzles. The hose stations are connected to the dry chemical container either directly or indirectly by means of intermediate piping. They can provide a large quantity of extinguishing agent for quick knockdown and extinguishment of relatively large fires, such as might be experienced at gasoline loading racks, flammable liquid storage areas, diesel and gas turbine locomotives, and aircraft hangars.

Figure 17.2.3 illustrates methods of dry chemical application.

System Design

Dry chemical systems are called either engineered or pre-engineered, depending on how the quantity of chemical, rate of flow, size and length of piping, and number and size of fit-

FIGURE 17.2.2 Dry Chemical Hand Hose Line System Consisting of an Expellant Gas Assembly, a Dry Chemical Storage Tank Assembly, and a Discharge Assembly (Source: Ansul Incorporated)

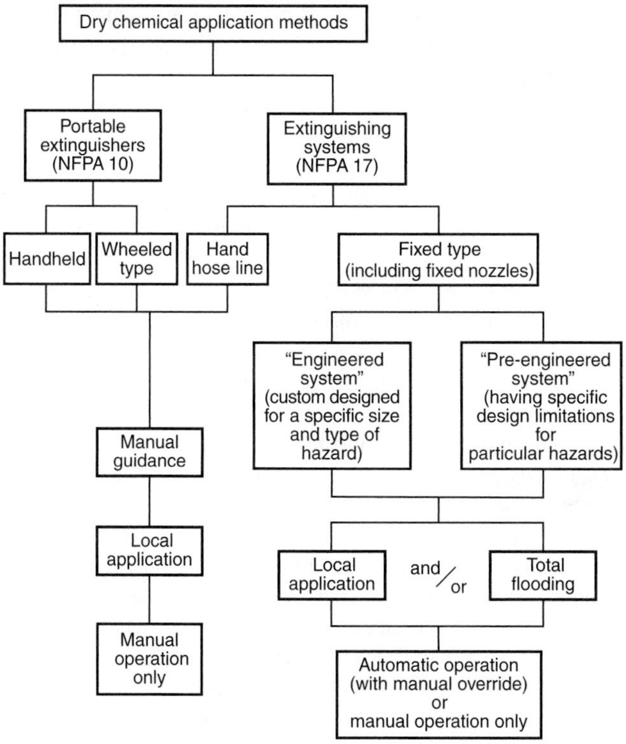

FIGURE 17.2.3 Methods of Dry Chemical Application

tings are determined. An engineered system is one in which individual calculation and design is needed to determine the flow rate, nozzle pressures, pipe sizes, quantity of chemical, and the number, types, and placement of nozzles for the hazard being protected. A pre-engineered system, sometimes called a package system, is one in which the size of the system (i.e., the quantity of chemical, pipe sizes, maximum and minimum pipe lengths, number of fittings, and number and types of nozzles) is predetermined by fire tests for specific sizes and types of hazards. Installation within these limits of hazard and system design ensures adequate flow rate, nozzle pressure, and pattern coverage without individual calculation (Figure 17.2.4).

In the past, pre-engineered systems were frequently used for kitchen range and hood fire protection, including deep-fat fryers. However, only alkaline dry chemicals (sodium bicarbonate, potassium bicarbonate, etc.) were used; multipurpose dry chemical was never used. It is important to note that dry chemical systems can remain in use provided the cooking equipment and the cooking medium have not changed from the time of the initial installation. Any changes in the system necessitate a change to a wet chemical system that has been listed in accordance with UL 300, *Standard for Fire Testing of Fire Extinguishing Systems for Protection of Restaurant Cooking Areas.*

Storage of Chemical and Expellant

Chemical agents are stored in pressure containers, usually of welded steel construction, either under atmospheric pressure until the system is actuated or under the pressure of the internally stored expellant gas.

Containers in which dry chemical is stored separately under atmospheric pressure are equipped with an expellant gas inlet, a moisture-sealed fill opening, and a dry chemical outlet. The gas inlet leads to an internal gas tube arrangement constructed so that, when it flows into the tank, it agitates and permeates the

FIGURE 17.2.4 A Double 30 lb (13.6 kg) Stored-Pressure Dry Chemical System with Pneumatic Release for Automatic Actuation. Each cylinder contains 30 lb (13.6 kg) of dry chemical pressurized to 350 psi (2413 kPa) with nitrogen.

powder, making it fluidlike. The dry chemical outlet is provided with a rupture disc or valve to permit buildup of proper operating pressure in the tank before the dry chemical can start to flow. The expellant gas assembly consists of a pressure storage vessel together with necessary valves, pressure regulators, and piping to deliver the expellant gas to the dry chemical storage tank at the correct pressure and rate of flow (see Figure 17.2.1). The expellant gas is usually dry nitrogen; however, dry air or other gases may be used. The volume and storage pressure of the expellant are dictated by the gas used and the requirements of the system. Containers in which dry chemical and the expellant gas are stored together are equipped with a moisture-sealed fill opening, a valve with integral discharge outlet and expellant gas charging inlet, and a pressure gauge.

It is desirable to locate the chemical expellant gas assemblies as near as practicable to the hazard to be protected. An area in which temperatures stay between –40 and +120°F (–40 and +49°C) is desirable to maintain the quality of the dry chemical.

System Actuation

Actuation of fixed systems is initiated by automatic mechanisms that incorporate sensing devices located in the hazard area and automatic, mechanical, or electrical releases that initiate the flow of the chemical, actuate alarms, and shut down process equipment. In systems with separate chemical and expellant gas containers, the flow of chemical is started by releasing the expellant gas, which pressurizes the chemical chamber to the point where the rupture disc in the container outlet operates. The chemical is then carried by the expellant gas through the distribution system to the hazard. In stored-pressure systems, however, the flow of chemical is started by merely opening the valve on the chemical chamber. If the expellant gas is used to pneumatically operate these devices, the gas shall be taken prior to its entry into the wet chemical tank.

Dry chemical systems have both automatic and manual methods of actuation. At least one manual actuator shall be provided for each system. It is important that the operating devices be designed, located, installed, or protected so that they are not subject to mechanical, environmental, or other conditions that could render them inoperative or cause inadvertent operation of the system. The automatic and manual means of system actuation must be separate and independent of each other so that a failure of one will not impair the operation of the other. Operation of any manual actuator is all that is required to operate the system. An easily accessible device for manual operation is required for all automatically operated systems.

A local signal is provided to indicate that the system has operated and is in need of recharging. The extinguishing system is also connected to the building fire alarm system, if one is provided, so that the actuation of the extinguishing system will sound the fire alarm throughout the building as well as provide the function of the extinguishing system.

System actuators are commonly mechanical and do not rely on electrical power for operation. However, it is permitted to have electrical actuators if there is a reserve power supply or the normal power supply is supervised. The means for mechanical actuator(s) shall be mechanical and shall not rely on electrical power for actuation.

When automatically actuated systems are used, consideration should be given to the reduced visibility and temporary breathing difficulty sometimes caused by quick discharge of large amounts of dry chemical in a restricted space. In all cases where there is a possibility that personnel may be stationed in such locations, suitable alarms and safeguards should be incorporated in the system to ensure adequate warning and prompt evacuation.

Operation of a hand hose line system requires two or, at the most, three steps. *Step one:* pressurizing the dry chemical chamber by opening the expellant gas valve (if the dry chemical and expellant gas containers are separate), or opening the main discharge valve if dry chemical is under stored pressure. *Step two:* operating the nozzle at the end of the hose line. *Step three:* if multiple hose stations are supplied by the same dry chemical supply, a distribution valve must be opened to direct the flow to the particular hose station to be used. It is extremely important to play out the hose fully (without kinks) to ensure the proper chemical discharge rate.

Fixed piping systems normally blow themselves clear. However, in hand hose line systems where the operator exercises control over the amount of dry chemical discharged, it is vital that all pipes and hose be independently blown clear before recharging to prevent blockage.

Distribution System

For fixed systems, the provisions for conveying the chemical to the hazard area and discharging it properly consist of piping or, for hand hose line systems, piping and hose lines or hose lines alone. Nozzles designed to emit wide, flat, or round streams in desired patterns are available to meet specific hazard requirements. Adjustable nozzles permitting an operator to vary the range and shape of the discharge are also available for use with hand hose line systems.

The piping and valving for dry chemical systems are of special design because dry chemical, while tending to behave as a fluid, has distinct flow characteristics.

Control of chemical flow starts at the chemical storage tank. In systems of separate dry chemical and expellant gas containers, expellant gas must be admitted to the tank in such a way as to properly fluidize the dry chemical while the pressure builds up equally throughout the entire volume of the tank before the dry chemical is released from the tank. Should the pressure increase too rapidly above the dry chemical, the powder will not be properly fluidized and, on release, the pressure drop in the piping or hose line will be excessive and result in a rate of dry chemical flow too low for proper extinguishing effectiveness.

If the expellant gas is permitted to channel to the outlet before the top of the dry chemical storage tank is properly pressurized, insufficient dry chemical will be carried by the flowing stream of gas, and the fire extinguishing effectiveness of the system again will be greatly reduced.

Pipe, Hose, and Fittings. After release from the storage tank, dry chemical is carried through the piping at high velocities by the expellant gas and is thrown to the wall of the piping by centrifugal force whenever the direction of flow is sharply altered, as by an elbow. Should an elbow be directly connected to a tee and lie in the same plane as the tee, it is obvious that the two branches of the tee will carry appreciably different proportions of gas and dry chemical. This condition is overcome by installing all tees in planes perpendicular to the planes of adjacent elbows, by allowing sufficient length of straight pipe between tees and elbows, or by inserting special venturi devices between tees and elbows to ensure proper redistribution of dry chemical in the stream of gas before the mixture enters the tee.

Another critical factor in dry chemical distribution system design is the pressure drop through various lengths of pipe, hose, or fittings. Consequently, the length and size of piping and hose, and the number and size of fittings, must be selected to provide the required rate of discharge and nozzle distribution. In pre-engineered systems, this is already ensured by virtue of the limitations established for piping and fittings. In engineered systems, this selection must be made on the basis of actual calculation of pressure drop and subsequent flow rate.

For engineered systems, pressure drop data have been obtained at various rates of flow for various sizes of pipe and fittings. In one manufacturer's system, the pressure drop through a standard elbow is equivalent to the pressure drop through 20 ft (6 m) of straight pipe of the same size.[10] Pressure drop through a tee is equivalent to that of 45 ft (14 m) of straight pipe of the same size.

Consideration must be given to the overall volume of the distribution piping. Excessive volume could result in agent remaining in the pipe due to insufficient pressure to move it through the system. Because these chemicals behave similarly to water in pipe, there is also a concern regarding hydraulic friction loss. Long runs and excessive numbers of elbow serve to reduce the velocity of the fluid as it travels through the pipe. Again, excessive pressure loss could result in agent being left in the piping and possibly resulting in an insufficient amount of agent being delivered to the fire.

Nozzles. Dry chemical agent is distributed through nozzles at predetermined flow rates and patterns depending on the hazard. Discharge nozzles are made of corrosion-resistant materials such as brass or stainless steel.

The selection of the proper types and sizes of nozzles for fixed systems is crucial to obtaining the proper coverage of the hazard. For example, total-flooding dry chemical agent nozzles are designed for a broadcast of turbulent agent flow. This is to achieve the fire-extinguishment mechanisms of smothering and shielding.[8] On the other hand, nozzles for local application, such as over deep fat fryers, are designed to get the liquid surface covered with agent while limiting the splashing effects, which could result in fire spread beyond the protected area. Consult the individual listing of the discharge nozzles to determine their intended use.

Due to the nature of the hazards protected and the extinguishing chemicals, it is necessary to protect the openings of discharge nozzles. Protection is provided against internal clogging by installing strainers in the distribution piping prior to the nozzles. Grease vapors, moisture, and other particles in the effluent from the processes may cause clogging at the nozzle or in the piping. For this reason, nozzles must have protective caps. These caps provide this protection and blow off or open when the system is discharged.

Nozzles for hand hose line systems may be of either a one- or two-position type. One-position nozzles provide a modified straight stream, whereas two-position nozzles provide a straight stream or a fan. Because the straight stream has a longer reach than the fan discharge, it is considered better for initial attack. The shorter, wider fan-shaped stream is usually preferred for a close-range attack to complete the extinguishment. However, the present state of the art seems to prefer the use of the modified straight stream only. It is more effective and less confusing in the hands of an experienced operator.

Quantity and Rate of Application of Dry Chemical

The quantity of chemical and rate of flow must be sufficient to create a fire-extinguishing concentration throughout all parts of the enclosure protected in a total flooding system, or over the specific fire area protected by a local application system. It must be realized that the fire-extinguishing concentration accomplished throughout an enclosure (total flooding) can occur only during discharge. Following discharge, dry chemical rapidly settles out and diminishes. This is in contrast to gaseous diffusion, where concentrations persist following discharge, such as in carbon dioxide and halon systems. Minimum rate of flow is critical because dry chemical will not extinguish a fire if applied too slowly. In local application systems, application at too high a rate may result in uneven discharge or complete discharge of chemical before extinguishment is accomplished.

Optimum quantities of chemical and application rates have been determined by experiment for engineered total flooding and local application systems. For pre-engineered systems, the maximum sizes of hazards that can be protected by the various sizes of systems within specific piping limitations have been determined.

The minimum flow rate in lb per second (kg/sec) is determined by multiplying the net volume in ft^3 (m^3) by 0.00125 (in SI units 0.020). These volume factors apply only to this manufacturer's equipment and are cited merely to illustrate a procedure used.[10] Quantities and flow rates determined in this manner are contingent on a nozzle arrangement that provides even distribution throughout the volume. The rates also assume that devices will be installed to close automatically all doors, windows, ventilators, or other openings through which dry chemical could escape from the enclosure.

In one manufacturer's pre-engineered total flooding system, a 1000 ft^3 (28 m^3) space not longer than 20 ft (6 m) can be protected by a 30 lb (14 kg) system with four nozzles and no more than 90 ft of ¾ in. pipe (27 m of 19 mm pipe), 13 elbows, three tees, and three venturi devices.[10] As with engineered systems, successful extinguishment is contingent on proper nozzle location, shutdown of ventilation, and the closing of all openings, such as doors and windows, in addition to closure of fuel valves.

Although simultaneous shutdown of ventilation with the actuation of a total flooding system is the normal procedure, one exception exists. This exception is the special case of kitchen range hood and duct protection wherein pre-engineered systems are specifically designed to provide extinguishment, regardless of whether the ventilation is operating. Actually, this latter type of system is a combination of both total flooding and local application.

Quantities of dry chemical and flow rates for engineered local application systems are obtained from graphs plotted from tests using different flammable liquid surface areas, weights of dry chemical, and rates of application. These graphs are available from the manufacturer. For pre-engineered local application systems, the limitations of hazard size, system size, and piping arrangement are established by test and used in the same manner as for total flooding systems. The minimum recommended quantity of dry chemical for hand hose line systems is sufficient to permit use of the system for 30 seconds. Capacities of hand hose line systems range from 125 to 2000 lb (57 to 907 kg), and as many as four hose lines can be operated from a single system. As with fixed systems, a minimum flow rate must be maintained to prevent surging or interruption of flow. Minimum rates are determined by the equipment manufacturer and depend on the equipment used.

WET CHEMICAL EXTINGUISHING AGENTS

Wet chemical fire extinguishing agents consist of organic or inorganic salts mixed with water to form an alkaline solution that is capable of being discharged through piping or tubing when under expellant gas pressure. They are extremely effective and are currently the only agents listed for suppression of fires in commercial cooking equipment (Figure 17.2.5), such as deep-fat fryers, griddles, range tops, and broilers, because of their ability to retain the separation of the oil from air for a sufficient time to allow complete cooling.

Physical Properties

Wet chemical extinguishing agents are typically a proprietary mixture consisting of potassium carbonate, potassium acetate, potassium citrate, or a combination, mixed in water and other additives such as phenolphthalein, phosphoric acid, and/or dyes. As they are already liquid in character, wet chemical agents do not require additives to enhance flow. Wet chemicals range in other physical properties depending on the mixture used. Table 17.2.1 shows the ranges of values in the common properties associated with wet chemicals.

Compatibility. Wet chemicals are incompatible with any reactive metals, electrically energized equipment, lime dust (CaO), chlorine triflouride (ClF_3), and any other material that is reactive with water. When in storage, it is also important that the containers be kept tightly closed and separated from acids.

Toxicity. Wet chemical extinguishing agents are stable at both low and normal temperatures and are considered to be nontoxic and noncarcinogenic. However, other physiological conditions such as minor skin and respiratory irritations may occur on exposure to the agents. No chronic medical conditions have been reported from long-term exposure. The acute effects of exposure are irritation to mucous membranes, with the possibility of chemical burns of the skin, eyes, and mucous membranes lining the respiratory system. Moist skin may enhance this effect. In all cases, self-contained breathing apparatus (SCBA) should be worn to protect against smoke, fumes created by fixed system discharge. Consult the appropriate material safety data sheets (MSDSs) for detailed information, instructions, and special precautions.[1]

Extinguishing Properties

When wet chemical extinguishing agents are sprayed on a grease fire, they interact immediately with the grease and saponify, forming a blanket of foam over the surface on which they are sprayed. This blanket extinguishes the fire by a combination of two primary methods: smothering and cooling.

(a)

(b)

FIGURE 17.2.5 Examples of Commercial Kitchen Cooking Equipment Protected by a Nozzle

TABLE 17.2.1 Characteristics of Wet Chemical Extinguishing Agents

Agent Property	*Value Range*
Storage life	12 years
Freeze point	10°F to –40°F –12°C to –40°C
Boiling point	215°F–230°F 102°C–110°C
Specific gravity	1.19–1.445
pH	7.8–13

Smothering Action. When wet chemical agent is applied to flammable liquid surfaces, the result is a rapid knockdown of flame and a spreading of foam on the fuel surface. This vapor-suppressing foam barrier extinguishes the flame by separating the liquid fuel and oxygen. The result is the inability of the flammable vapors from the fuel source to escape the surface and ignite. Because the primary use of wet chemical systems is for protection of commercial cooking equipment and this is a very localized protection area, it is critical that the fire be contained within the equipment involved. To achieve this end, wet chemical systems are specifically tested to determine that during the discharge process they do not splash burning grease.

Cooling Action. The effect of water vaporization by wet agents provides a cooling effect on the fuel. Furthermore, the application of the wet chemical solution and the resulting formation of foam on the surface of the fuel also provides a cooling effect, lowering the temperature of the flammable fuel, further decreasing flammable vapor release. Some wet chemical systems are designed to continue with an application of water through the nozzles after the wet chemical has been completely discharged. This serves to further cool the surrounding surfaces, thereby preventing reflash.

USES AND LIMITATIONS OF WET CHEMICAL EXTINGUISHING SYSTEMS

Commercial cooking operations have undergone major changes in recent years in two areas that have produced an increased challenge to chemical fire extinguishing systems.

First, there has been a change in the cooking medium from animal fats to vegetable oils. These newer cooking oils change their makeup after ignition. This change results in an ignition temperature that is considerably lower (50°F, or 28°C) than that of the original oil. Therefore, to prevent reflash of the oil, the entire volume of the oil must be cooled below the autoignition temperature. Vegetable oils also have less fatty acids than do animal fats. It is the fatty acids that interact with the alkaline solution of the chemical agent that produces the saponification that eventually smothers the fire. Because of the amount of fatty acids in animal fats, dry chemical agents were capable of producing a sufficient foam blanket to smother the fire. Vegetable oils, with their lower fatty acid content, do not provide as much of this catalyst and, therefore, the foam blanket is not as well developed. This results in the compromise of the smothering foam blanket and the potential for reflash of the fuel involved.

Second, new, energy-efficient cooking equipment allows the oils to retain their heat for greater lengths of time. The autoignition temperature of the majority of vegetable oils is 685°F (363°C), which is as much as 135°F (57°C) higher than that of animal fats. This temperature, combined with the ability of new cooking equipment to retain the heat, produces a fire that dry chemical agents cannot effectively suppress. Because heat breaks down the foam that is produced through saponification, it is also necessary to provide a sufficient cooling effect on the fuel. Dry chemical has limited saponification and cooling capabilities, and, as a result, is ineffective on present-day commercial cooking equipment fires. Wet chemical, because of the added cooling effect of its water base, is far more effective on these types of fire. As a result, only wet chemicals can be used to protect new commercial cooking systems in order to sufficiently saponify fats and oils. It is still possible for dry chemical systems to protect kitchen equipment that has not been changed since the original installation of the system.

Commercial cooking equipment is typically stainless steel, aluminum, or galvanized metal. As such, it is resistive to the corrosive effect of wet chemical agents. Caution must be exercised in the installation of other equipment near the cooking equipment as wet chemical extinguishing agents are not acceptable for use in areas where fires involve energized electrical equipment. However, wet chemical extinguishing agents may be used to protect other equipment within the commercial cooking exhaust system. The manufacturer's listed installation and maintenance manual should be consulted for the appropriate applications and limitations for which the specific wet chemical extinguishing system is considered satisfactory protection.

Methods of Application

Wet chemical is applied through fixed systems, but also may be applied in portable fire extinguishers that are used to provide additional support to the extinguishing system. The hardware components are similar to dry chemical systems insofar as there is an agent supply and expellant gas and an actuating method. The agent is delivered through piping to specially designed nozzles that atomize the solution and distribute the agent over the hazard area.

Wet chemical systems are local application systems. Local application systems are practical in those situations where the hazard can be isolated from other hazards so that fire will not spread beyond the area protected, and where the entire hazard can be protected. In this type of system, the nozzles are arranged to discharge directly onto the fire or burning surface such as deep-fat fryers, griddles, and stoves. It is especially critical in commercial cooking operations that the cooking equipment not be rearranged after the installation of the extinguishing system. Most wet chemical systems apply the agent through nozzles that are specifically designed to protect the equipment under them. It is therefore critical to note that any rearrangement of the cooking equipment after installation of the extinguishing system could result in unprotected surfaces. That being said, there are wet chemical systems available that are designed with overlapping spray patterns. The overlapping spray allows coverage of the entire space below exhaust hood, permitting greater flexibility in the location and relocation of equipment, provided it is always located under the hood.

System Design

Wet chemical systems are proprietary, pre-engineered systems. Pre-engineered systems are defined by predetermined flow rates, nozzle pressures, and quantities of agent required. They have specific pipe sizes and maximum and minimum pipe lengths. Further specifications are provided in the manufacturer's installation manual for flexible hose, the number of fittings, and the number and types of nozzles to be used. An important point is that pre-engineered systems are limited to the protection of hazards for which they have been specifically listed.

Part of the listing process requires the system to perform satisfactorily any one or number of types of commercial cooking equipment. UL 300 contains testing protocols deep-fat fryers, griddles, range tops, charbroilers, including gas radiant, electric charbroilers, lava, pumice or synthetic rock, natural charcoal, mesquite wood, upright and chain broilers and woks. The standard tests also include splash tests specifically for deep-fat fryers, range tops, and woks.

The objectives of these tests are to prove that the agent is effective in complete extinguishment. For deep-fat fryers, woks, and ranges, there is an additional objective that the agent prevents reignition for 20 minutes or until the temperature of the grease decreases at least 60°F (33°C) below its autoignition temperature, whichever takes longer. For other types of equipment, the agent must prevent reignition for 5 minutes.

Storage of Chemical and Expellant

Wet chemical extinguishing agents are typically stored in plastic containers up to 5 gal (19 L) in capacity. Attention should be given to the freeze point of the particular agent. The agent storage life is approximately 12 years. System tanks containing wet chemical range in size between 1.5 and 3 gal (5.7 and 11.4 L), depending on the manufacturer's design. To expel that agent, most systems use pressurized cartridges of nitrogen or carbon dioxide. To ensure proper operation, the temperature ranges for wet chemical systems are between 32 and 130°F (0 and 54°C). This range is not normally a problem as wet chemical systems are primarily used in indoors.

System Actuation

Wet chemical systems are actuated by either automatic or manual means. Automatic actuation is provided by fusible link or heat detector operation (Figure 17.2.6). It is critical that the detector devices be placed in the proper locations. To ensure this, NFPA 17A requires detectors above each appliance or group of appliances protected by a single nozzle. Detectors must also be installed in the duct entrance and another above the electrostatic precipitator if one is installed near the base of the duct.

Manual actuation occurs by the use of a listed manual pull station located adjacent to the means of egress from the room. Manual pull stations provide a backup source of system operation and must be clearly identified (Figure 17.2.7).

Part of the listing for these manual actuators states that they not require a force of more than 40 lb (178 N) or a movement of more than 14 in. (35.6 cm) to secure operation. All remote manual operating devices must be identified as to the hazard they protect.

Actuation of the system punctures the seal on the expellant gas cartridge, and the gas flows to the agent cylinder and expels the liquid through the discharge piping and nozzles. Wet chemical systems that use a secondary water application also have a pneumatically controlled waterflow valve that allows water to flow into the system after the wet chemical is totally expelled. This assists in the overall cooling effect of the wet chemical agent.

NFPA 17A requires that all sources of fuel and power to equipment that produces heat be shut down on activation of the system. Other sources of electrical power that may be exposed to the spray pattern of the system must also be shut down so as not to react with the wet chemical agent. To achieve this, actuation of the system also trips gas valves and electrical switches that interrupt fuel and power to any heat-producing appliances under the hood (Figure 17.2.8).

Distribution

Piping and fittings must be of noncombustible materials and compatible with the characteristics of wet chemical. Distribu-

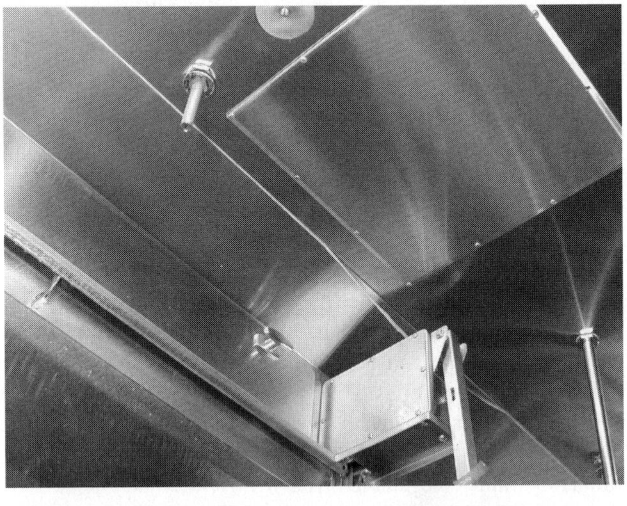

FIGURE 17.2.6 Typical Heat Detector Located in Exhaust Hood

FIGURE 17.2.7 Clearly Identified Manual Pull Station

FIGURE 17.2.8 Typical Gas Shut-Off Valve That Closes on Actuation of the Extinguishing System

tion piping should be either Schedule 40 black iron, chrome plated, or stainless steel. Galvanized piping is not used for the distribution piping. It is not necessary to calculate the flow rate, pressure drop, or nozzle pressure as the system has been pre-engineered for the specific protection and confirmed by testing by a listing laboratory. The manufacturer provides the necessary information on minimum and maximum piping limitations in the listing information and installation manual.

Nozzles

Discharge nozzles must be specifically listed for their intended use, and there may be many different nozzles manufactured for a given system (Figure 17.2.9). Each nozzle is designed to distribute the extinguishing agent in a specific pattern. It may not be possible to determine the type of nozzle from a cursory glance. Many of the nozzles appear to be identical; the differences are primarily in the tips of the nozzles that create the unique coverage characteristic. Nozzles carry permanent stampings that can be used to identify the type and spray pattern. This is very important when determining whether the system provides complete coverage. It is also critical that the nozzle be aimed in the

FIGURE 17.2.9 Wet Chemical Nozzles with Required Caps Protecting Against Clogging from Grease-Laden Vapors

proper direction. A specialized nozzle-aiming device is used for this purpose. This device clamps on the nozzle and uses a laser light that indicates the spray direction of the nozzles on the surface below. The nozzle can then be adjusted and tightened to hold the appropriate location.

Nozzles are typically chrome plated; however, they may constructed of any corrosion-resistant material such as brass or stainless steel. To prevent clogging, internal strainers or separate listed strainers are required to be located immediately upstream of the nozzle. Blow-off caps (either metal or rubber) are provided to protect the interior of the nozzle from clogging due to grease vapors, moisture, or other foreign materials.

Quantity and Rate of Application

The quantity and rate of application has been determined in the pre-engineering design process. Manufacturer's guidelines provide specific and detailed diagrams indicating the proper protection and coverage necessary for any component of the cooking operations, from the individual stove, wok, or broiler, to the hood and plenum areas, to the duct work. The quantity of extinguishing agent required is based on the number of flow outlets in the system. The number of nozzles in the system is then matched to the tank and cartridge requirements provided in the manufacturer's installation manual.

INSPECTION, TESTING, AND MAINTENANCE PROCEDURES FOR CHEMICAL SYSTEMS

Owners of chemical extinguishing systems should conduct monthly inspections to determine whether the system is in proper operating condition. This inspection is not intended to be detailed, but is rather a visual check of the system and should include determination of the following items:

- The extinguishing system is in its proper location.
- The manual actuators are unobstructed.
- The tamper indicators and seals are intact.
- The maintenance tag or certificate is in place.

- There is no obvious physical damage or condition that might prevent operation.
- There is no damage to, or obstruction of, fusible links or actuating devices.
- The pressure gauge(s), if provided, are in operable range.
- The nozzle blow-off caps are intact and undamaged.
- The hood, duct, and protected cooking appliances have not been replaced, modified, or relocated.

Systems subjected to process deposits (such as paint, dust, and grease) and corrosive conditions may require more frequent inspection of components. This inspection should be recorded in a report form and made available for review by the local authority having jurisdiction. Any deficiencies should be corrected immediately. For example, grease buildup on a link can severely delay the actuation of the system (Figure 17.2.10). Obstructed pull stations must be cleared to allow manual operation (Figure 17.2.11).

On a semiannual basis, routine maintenance, in addition to a more detailed inspection, should be performed. During this inspection, the hazard should be reviewed to determine whether it has been expanded or otherwise modified to extend beyond the capabilities of the system. A thorough examination of all system components is necessary. Each component should be inspected for wear, contaminant loading, corrosion, or any other condition that may render the component or system inoperable. The dry chemical agent is normally inspected at this time for evidence of caking. If caking is present, the dry chemical must be discarded and the system recharged in accordance with the manufacturer's instructions. In stored-pressure systems, the dry chemical must be checked every 6 years.

FIGURE 17.2.10 Grease Buildup on Link

FIGURE 17.2.11 Obstructed Pull Station

The distribution piping should be checked for obstructions during this procedure. This inspection can be accomplished by several means. If the system is small and accessible, the piping can be dismantled and inspected visually. If this is not practical, then purging with nitrogen or compressed air may be done. A full or partial discharge test may also be performed to verify the condition of the piping; however, all of the agent must be removed from the piping following the test to prevent caking and subsequent blockage of the pipe.

Periodically, a discharge test may be required during the performance of routine maintenance procedures. In this case, a "bag" test may be performed. During a bag test, the discharge nozzles are covered with a collection bag (a burlap bag or pillowcase) to retain discharged dry chemical. Following discharge of the system, the chemical should be weighed to determine the quantity of chemical contained. This can be compared to the amount required by the manufacturer's listed maintenance manual. Insufficient amounts may indicate possible piping obstructions.

Testing of wet chemical systems includes the operation of the detection system signals and releasing devices, including manual stations and other associated equipment. However, a discharge of the wet chemical normally is not part of this test.

The amount of expellant gas should be checked semiannually to ensure that there is sufficient gas to provide an effective discharge, and to automatically clean out the piping after the dry chemical has dissipated. In systems with separate expellant gas containers, this testing is accomplished by checking the pressure (if nitrogen) or weight (if carbon dioxide) against the manufacturer's recommended minimums. In stored-pressure systems, the pressure gauge is checked to see that it is in the operable range.

The inspection and maintenance of hand hose line systems will vary with the location and climate conditions. Equipment located in extremely hot or humid areas will require more frequent checking because the heat can cause cylinder pressure to increase and possibly cause leakage. Inspection of hand hose line systems consists primarily of checking the pressure of the expelling gas container, or the pressure of the unit itself (if it is of the pressurized type). It is also advisable to inspect all hose lines and nozzles to be sure that they are unobstructed and in good operating condition.

At least semiannually, maintenance should be conducted in accordance with the manufacturer's listed installation and maintenance manual. A trained person who has undergone the instructions necessary to perform the maintenance and recharge service should conduct maintenance of the system. This can be determined by requiring proof of training by the manufacturer.

As a minimum, maintenance should include a check to see that the hazard has not changed, and an examination of all detectors, the expellant gas containers, the agent containers, releasing devices, piping, hose assemblies, nozzles, signals, all auxiliary equipment, and the liquid level of all nonpressurized wet chemical containers.

It is also important to verify that the agent distribution piping is not obstructed. This verification will require the disassembly of all piping and conducting at least a partial discharge test in accordance with the instructions from the manufacturer. Other obstructions may occur in the conduit carrying the cable that activates the system. Grease can cause plugging and moisture can cause corrosion that will inhibit proper operation.

Special attention is given to the fixed temperature-sensing elements. NFPA 17 and NFPA 17A both require these components to be replaced at least annually from the date of installation.

After maintenance and testing occurs, the system should tagged or labeled, indicating the month and year the maintenance and testing has been performed and identifying the person performing the service.

Chemical containers, auxiliary pressure containers, valve assemblies, hoses, fittings (not including field piping), check valves, directional valves, manifolds, and hose nozzles, in addition to the dry chemical chambers and hose assemblies of both dry and wet chemical systems, must be hydrostatically tested every 12 years. The dry or wet chemical removed from the chambers should be discarded. Care must be exercised to ensure that all equipment tested is thoroughly dried prior to recharging. If there is no automatic, connected reserve supply, alternative fire protection should be provided.

SUMMARY

Both dry and wet chemicals are used to extinguish fires. Multipurpose dry chemical is used on fires in flammable liquids, fires involving energized electrical equipment, and fires in ordinary combustible materials. Dry chemical causes extinguishment primarily through the chain-breaking reaction and also through smothering, cooling, and radiation shielding. Wet chemical extinguishing agents are used for suppression of fires in commercial cooking equipment, such as deep-fat fryers, griddles, range tops, and broilers. Wet chemical causes extinguishment because of its ability to retain the separation of the oil from the air for a sufficient time to allow complete cooling.

The installation of a complete chemical extinguishing system requires that various factors be determined, including the method of application, storage of chemicals, system actuation, distribution system, and quantity and rate of application. The system must undergo a regimen of periodic inspection, testing, and maintenance to ensure proper operating condition.

BIBLIOGRAPHY

References Cited

1. "Material Safety Data Sheets Collection," Genium Publishing Corporation, Schenectady, NY, Aug. 1989.
2. Ewing, C. T., et al., "Extinguishing Class B Fires with Dry Chemicals: Scaling Studies," *Fire Technology,* Vol. 31, No. 1, 1995, pp. 17–43.
3. Ewing, C. T., et al., "Extinguishing Class A Fires with Multipurpose Chemicals," *Fire Technology,* Vol. 31, No. 3, 1995, pp. 195–210.
4. Guise, A. B., "Potassium Bicarbonate–Based Dry Chemical," *NFPA Quarterly,* Vol. 56, No. 1, 1962, pp. 21–27.
5. Haessler, W. M., *The Extinguishment of Fire,* rev. ed., National Fire Protection Association, Quincy, MA, 1974.
6. McCamy, C. S., Shoub, H., and Lee, T. G., "Fire Extinguishment by Means of Dry Powder," 6th Symposium on Combustion, Combustion Institute, Van Nostrand Reinhold, NY, 1956, pp. 795–801.
7. Kirk, R. E., and Othmer, D. E. (Eds.), *Encyclopedia of Chemical Technology,* 2nd ed., Interscience Publishers, New York, 1965.
8. Guise, A. B., "The Chemical Aspects of Fire Extinguishment," *NFPA Quarterly,* Vol. 53, No. 4, 1960, pp. 330–336.
9. Haessler, W. M., "Fire and Its Extinguishment," *NFPA Quarterly,* Vol. 56, No. 1, 1962, pp. 89–96.9.
10. Guise, A. B., and Lindlof, J. A., "A Dry Chemical Extinguishing System," *NFPA Quarterly,* Vol. 49, No. 1, 1955, pp. 52–60.

NFPA Codes, Standards, and Recommended Practices

Reference to the following NFPA codes, standards, and recommended practices will provide further information on chemical extinguishing agents and application systems discussed in this chapter. (See the latest version of The NFPA Catalog *for availability of current editions of the following documents.)*

NFPA 10, *Standard for Portable Fire Extinguishers*
NFPA 17, *Standard for Dry Chemical Extinguishing Systems*
NFPA 17A, *Standard for Wet Chemical Extinguishing Systems*

Reference

UL 300, *Standard for Fire Testing of Extinguishing Systems for Protection of Restaurant Cooking Areas*

Chapter 3

Characteristics and Hazards of Water and Water Additives for Fire Suppression

John A. Frank

Water is the most widely used and most readily available extinguishing agent. Water is readily available and inexpensive. Water also possesses many advantages over other liquids in fire-fighting characteristics. However, it is not the proper extinguishing agent for all types of fires. It has some disadvantages; for example, it freezes at 32°F (0°C). This chapter discusses the properties of water as an extinguishing agent, including its advantages and limitations.

The principles of fire extinguishment are discussed in Section 2, Chapter 1, "Physics and Chemistry of Fire"; Section 2, Chapter 7, "Theory of Fire Extinguishment"; and in Section 17, Chapter 8, "Explosion Prevention and Protection." The systems and devices used for the transportation and application of water as a fire-extinguishing agent are addressed in other chapters in this section of the handbook. For the use of water as a suitable extinguishing agent on specific materials, such as chemicals, flammable liquids, gases, and metals, see Section 6, Chapter 9, "Metals"; and Section 6, Chapter 12, "Flammable and Combustible Liquids." For related topics, see Section 9, Chapter 16, "Mining and Mineral Processing"; Section 15, Chapter 2, "Water Supply Requirements for Public Supply Systems"; Section 16, Chapter 8, "Water Mist Fire Suppression Systems"; Section 16, Chapter 9, "Water Spray Protection"; and Section 17, Chapter 4, "Foam Extinguishing Agents and Systems."

Chapter Contents

Key Terms

actual delivered density (ADD), Class A fire, Class A foam, Class B fire, Class C fire, Class D fire, extinguishing agent, fixed water spray system, fog stream, Iowa Flow Formula, ISO Flow Formula, NFA Flow Formula, ordinary combustible, required delivered density (RDD), water additive, water mist system, wetting agents

INTRODUCTION TO WATER

Water is the most widely used and most readily available fire-extinguishing agent. Water is inexpensive, abundant, and effective in fire suppression. Water is transportable and can be pumped from a source to the fire. Water is available from domestic water distribution systems (fire hydrants), streams and rivers, wells, ponds, lakes, swimming pools, and in some cases is taken from the ocean.

Water is a very effective agent for controlling and extinguishing combustion. Water is the most abundant and available substance on the earth's surface and exists in three states: (1) liquid (water), (2) vapor (steam), and (3) solid (ice).

Life safety considerations must be weighed when choosing an effective fire-extinguishing agent. Water as an agent is safe, nontoxic, relatively noncorrosive, and stable. Water (H_2O) remains stable when applied to a fire and does not, except in very special circumstances, break down into its basic elements of hydrogen (H) and oxygen (O), both of which would encourage fire growth. Water can be applied as an extinguishing agent with building occupants in compartments, unlike some

John A. Frank, P.E., is a loss prevention training leader with Swiss Re. He is the former chair of the NFPA Technical Committee on Water Additives for Fire Suppression and Vapor Migration and was formerly a fire protection specialist with the United States Air Force.

gaseous extinguishing agents, which could cause asphyxiation or adverse side effects.

PROPERTIES OF WATER

The physical properties that allow water to be an effective extinguishing agent are as follows:

1. At ordinary temperatures, water exists as a stable liquid. Water's viscosity in the temperature range of 34 to 210°F (1 to 99°C) remains consistent, which allows it to be transported and pumped.
2. Water has a high density, which allows it to be discharged from and projected from nozzles. Water's surface tension allows it to exist from small droplets to a solid stream.
3. The latent heat of fusion is the amount of energy required to change the state of water from solid (ice) at 32°F (0°C) to a liquid. Water absorbs 143.4 Btu per lb (333.2 kJ/kg) in this process.
4. The specific heat of water is 1.0 Btu per lb(°F) (4.186 kJ/kg(°C)). For example, raising the temperature of 1 lb (0.45 kg) of water 180°F (100°C) from 32°F (0°C) to 212°F (100°C) requires 180 Btu. Raising 1 kg of water from 0°C to 100°C requires 418.6 kJ.
5. Water is effective as a cooling agent because of its high latent heat of evaporation (changing water from a liquid to vapor), which is 970.3 Btu per lb (2260 kJ/kg) as described in Section 2, Chapter 1, "Physics and Chemistry of Fire." Some authors are giving "credit" to additional heat absorption from the steam as it is heated beyond the boiling point of water when water is applied in small droplets. The specific heat of steam is 2.01 kJ/kg(°C).[1]
6. Water expands in its conversion from a liquid state to a vapor state to 1600 to 1700 times the liquid volume. One gallon (3.8 L) of liquid (which occupies 0.1337 ft^2 [0.004 m^3]) produces over 223 ft^3 (6.3 m^3) of steam. Therefore, it follows that 1 gal (3.8 L) of water at room temperature applied to a fire and converted to steam (complete conversion) will absorb heat both in rising to the temperature at which it becomes a vapor and in the phase change from liquid to vapor. (For SI units: °F = °C × 9/5 + 32; 1 Btu = 1.055 kJ; 1 lb = 0.45 kg; 1 gal = 3.785 L; 1 ft^3 = 0.0283 m^3.)

Heat required to raise temperature of water to boiling:

- 212°F – 68°F (room temperature) = 144°F
- 144Δ°F × 1 Btu/lb × 8.33 lb (weight of 1 gal) = 1200 Btu

Heat required to change water from a liquid to a vapor:

- 970.3 Btu/lb × 8.33 lb (weight of 1 gal) = 8083 Btu
- Total heat absorbed is 1200 + 8083 = 9283 Btu/gal of water

Using SI units in the preceding example, the total heat absorbed by 1 kg of water raised from 20°C (room temperature) to its boiling point is 2594.9 kJ/kg of water. A figure of 2600 kJ/liter is commonly used.

Therefore, a fire department hose stream discharging at 100 gpm will absorb 928,300 Btu per minute in a complete conversion. The same fire department hose stream will create 22,300 ft^3 per minute of steam in a complete conversion. In SI units (using 2600 kJ/liter), this same hose stream (discharging 378.5 L/min) will absorb 984,100 kJ/min or 16,402 kJ/sec or 16.4 MW. Likewise, 631 cubic meters of steam will be created.

When reviewing the international literature recommended in this chapter, the reader is cautioned to carefully note the units being used. Minor differences may be noted due to unit conversions. Also note that the preceding example does not give credit to heat absorbed by the heating of steam above the boiling point of water. Some international authors are giving this credit in their suppression models if small water drops (e.g., smaller than 1 mm) are used. Some models also give credit to the observation that it is not necessary to absorb all of the heat released by diffusion flames. After these credits are applied, the models may then assign another factor that accounts for less than optimum performance, as discussed later in this chapter. As is the case with all models, it is essential that the user understand the model's inputs and outputs to make appropriate decisions.

EXTINGUISHING PROPERTIES

Water is a very effective extinguishing agent because of its ability to cool the fuel, remove or displace the oxygen supply, and separate/dilute the fuel source. See the discussion on the principles of fire in Section 2, Chapter 1, "Physics and Chemistry of Fire," and Section 2, Chapter 7, "Theory of Fire Extinguishment."

The dominant mechanism of extinguishment, or combination of mechanisms of extinguishment, depends on several interrelated factors, including the fuel's physical and chemical properties, the geometry of the compartment (if one exists), ventilation, ambient conditions, the form of the water applied (e.g., fog versus solid stream), and the application technique.

Knowledge of the influence of these factors and the interaction of the mechanisms of extinguishment vary widely with the extent of scientific research conducted on a given application method. Section 16, Chapter 8, "Water Mist Fire Suppression Systems," provides a good example of the extent of the body of knowledge that exists regarding the interactivity of these mechanisms for fixed water mist systems. For manually applied hose streams, see Grimwood et al.[2]

Extinguishing by Cooling

Water principally extinguishes solid fuel fires by cooling the fuel surface. In addition to the cooling of a solid fuel itself, water is effective as a cooling agent because of its high latent heat of evaporation (item 5 under properties). Water introduced to a fire promotes heat loss via the heat transfer from the fire to the water. When the heat loss exceeds the fire heat gain, the fuel surface will begin to cool until the flame can no longer exist at the surface. Water is an effective coolant for solid fuel surfaces.

Besides the direct cooling of a solid fuel, water can cool solid fuels indirectly by the reduction of the radiant heat flux from the flame, and from the hot upper gas layer (if present), to the fuel surface. This action reduces the rate of pyrolysis of the fuel, which reduces the heat release rate of the fire. This cooling results from the cooling effects of the water droplets and steam.

Conceptually, when the heat absorption rate of water approaches the total heat release rate of the fire, fire control begins. When the heat absorption rate of water exceeds the heat release rate of the fire, fire suppression and, ultimately, fire extinguishment are achieved. Other factors to consider in fire control and extinguishment include heat losses through openings and heat losses to walls, ceilings, and floors.

As discussed in Section 2, Chapter 7, "Theory of Fire Extinguishment," it is theoretically not necessary to absorb all of the heat being released, but only enough to effect the combustion reaction. Because of the difficulty of applying water in the manner described in Section 2, Chapter 7, the actual application needed for extinguishment may be 10 to 100 times the critical application rate. Mawhinney indicates that absorbing 30 to 60 percent of the heat released from a fire may be enough to extinguish the fire.[3] Some manual suppression models now account for this observation.

The amount of water required to extinguish a fire depends on the heat release rate [Btu/sec (kW)] of the fire. How quickly a fire is extinguished depends on how the water is applied, how much is applied, and in what form water is applied.

As shown in water mist applications, the smaller the droplet, the higher the rate at which water extracts heat from the fire and fire gases, resulting in using a lower volume of water. Grimwood[4] reports on the findings of Rasbash that a 2 mm droplet moving at 0.07 m/sec will extract heat at a rate of 167 kW/m^2 of droplet surface area. Decreasing the droplet size to 50 microns (0.05 mm) and increasing the velocity to 0.5 m/sec increased the heat transfer rate to 2500 kW/m^2 of droplet surface area. Calculations show that for many applications, the optimum diameter of a water droplet is in the range of 0.01 to 0.04 in. (0.3 to 1.0 mm), and that the best results are obtained when the droplets are fairly uniform in size. However, a water droplet approaching the fire can evaporate in the fire plume, thus only cooling the fire plume but not effectively cooling the fuel surface, which, as shown in Section 2, Chapter 7, "Theory of Fire Extinguishment," can be critical. The need for direct fuel surface cooling varies with the application. Actual delivered density (ADD) is the actual water application rate to a fire at the surface of the burning fuel. Research facilities at Underwriters Laboratories and FM Global are capable of measuring the ADD in warehouse applications. This figure is then compared to the required delivered density (RDD) for suppression. Fire suppression is achieved when the ADD > RDD.

The amount of water reaching a fire is affected by the fire's burning rate and associated upward plume velocity. The water droplets must overcome the effects of the upward momentum of the fire plume and air currents in order to reach the burning fuel and provide effective fuel cooling. For example, droplets, once produced at a sprinkler, are subject to high temperatures that evaporate the small droplets at the ceiling. If the small droplets survive the ceiling temperature, they may not have the mass or momentum to be able to penetrate the fire plume. Yao and Williams reported that 1 mm drops can penetrate a 20 ft/sec (6.1 m/sec) fire plume, 1.5 mm drops can penetrate a 30 ft/sec (9.1 m/sec) plume, and 2 mm drops can penetrate a 40 ft/sec (12.2 m/sec) plume, which occurs in high-challenge fires.[5] Drops smaller than 0.3 mm are found in some water mist applications. See Isman[6] for a complete discussion. For manual application from hose streams, see Clark[7,8] and Grimwood et al.[2]

As the preceding discussion indicates, the high heat absorption of a fine mist must be balanced against the need for water to reach the fuel surface to cool the fuel. The relative importance of these competing characteristics depends on several factors. These factors can be specifically accounted for in engineered systems. For example, engineered water mist systems emphasize general cooling whereas large drop sprinklers emphasize penetration of the fire plume to directly cool the pyrolyzing fuel.

For manual application from hose streams, the literature reports successful extinguishment from techniques that emphasize general cooling (as from a fog stream), from techniques that emphasize direct cooling of the fuel (as from a solid stream), and from various combinations of these techniques. As is the case with engineered systems, the high heat absorption characteristics of a fog stream must be balanced against the penetrating characteristics of a solid stream. Major texts discussing the advantages of solid stream applications are by Clark[7] and by Fornell.[9] A major text on fog streams entitled *The Safe and Effective Use of Fog Nozzles* was published in 2003.[10]

An application method known as fog attack or gas phase cooling has gained widespread acceptance in Europe and is gaining acceptance in Australia and the United States. A major text on this subject entitled *3D Fire Fighting, Training, Techniques, and Tactics* was published in 2005.[4] This text also gives a historical overview of all methods of manual application as well as where each is most effectively used. The limits of the fog attack technique are explained as well. See Grimwood[11,12] or http://www.firetactics.com.

Extinguishing by Smothering

When water is applied to a fire or a hot compartment surface, steam is formed. The dilution of the air (oxygen) supply around the fuel sources provides suppression by a smothering action. Suppression by this method is more effective if the steam and water droplets are confined around the fuel source. The steam and water droplets also continue to extinguish a fire by cooling as the water droplets continue to evaporate around the heated area of a fire.

Fires in ordinary combustibles are normally extinguished by the cooling effect of water—not by the smothering effect created by steam. Water mist systems, which may be used as an alternative to sprinkler systems or certain gaseous extinguishing systems, have been found to be effective in controlling *and* extinguishing fires by cooling and by smothering, as discussed in Section 16, Chapter 8, "Water Mist Fire Suppression Systems." The advantages and disadvantages of steam generation from manually applied water streams have been fiercely debated for many years.

Water may be used to smother a burning liquid when the liquid has a flashpoint above 100°F (37.8°C), a specific gravity greater than 1.0, and is not water soluble. To achieve this most effectively, a foam concentrate is added to the water to form a foam-water solution. The foam-water solution must then be applied gently to the surface of the flammable liquid. Water mist systems have been used to extinguish fires in liquids with a flashpoint below 100°F (37.8°C). Heptane is a common test liquid. In cases where oxygen is produced while a burning material decomposes, smothering by any agent is not possible.

Systems based on the use of industrial process steam are sometimes used in industrial ovens. Design applications are discussed in NFPA 86, *Standard for Ovens and Furnaces*, and in insurance company guidelines.

Extinguishing by Emulsification

An emulsion is formed when immiscible liquids are agitated together and one of the liquids is dispersed throughout the others. Extinguishment by this process can be achieved by applying water to certain viscous flammable liquids, since the effect of cooling the surfaces of such liquids prevents the release of flammable vapors. With some viscous liquids (such as No. 6 fuel oil), the emulsification is a froth that retards the release of flammable vapors. Care must be used on liquids of appreciable depth, however, because frothing may spread the burning liquids over the sides of the container. A relatively strong, coarse water spray is normally used for emulsification. A solid stream of water should be avoided, as it will cause violent frothing. These techniques are rarely used. Additives that promote emulsification are discussed later in this chapter.

Extinguishing by Dilution

Fires in water-soluble, flammable materials may, in some instances, be controlled or extinguished by dilution. The percentage of dilution necessary varies greatly, as does the volume of water and the time necessary for extinguishment. For example, dilution can be used successfully in a fire involving an ethyl or methyl alcohol spill if it is possible to get an adequate mixture of water and alcohol and if the mixture can be contained while it is being diluted. Details for ethyl alcohol can be found in FM Global Data Sheet 7–74 *Distilleries.*

Dilution is not a common practice when tanks are involved. The danger of overflow because of the amount of water required and the danger of frothing should the mixture become heated to the boiling point of water seldom make this form of extinguishment practical.

MANUAL APPLICATION RATES

In the United States, three methods are widely used to determine the manual water application rate needed to extinguish a fire. These are the Iowa Flow Formula, the National Fire Academy (NFA) Formula, and the Insurance Services Office (ISO) method. A fourth method—the Illinois Institute of Technology method—is not as widely used. (See Section 15, Chapter 2, "Water Supply Requirements for Public Supply Systems," for detailed information on the Illinois Institute method.) Although useful for fire service preplanning and for municipal water supply planning, none are readily adapted for fire protection engineering applications and performance-based design. The Iowa Flow Formula and the ISO formula are more fully discussed in Section 15, Chapter 2, "Water Supply Requirements for Public Supply Systems." See Burns and Phelps[13] for further information on the NFA formula. Grimwood et al.[14] introduced a tactical flow rate based on extensive analysis of international research as well as extensive practical experience in London. A detailed comparison of the tactical flow rate to the Iowa and NFA methods is also provided.

The Iowa State Method has scientific research behind it that emphasizes both the cooling effect of water and the smothering effect of steam. Measurements focused on the reduction of ceiling and compartment temperature. Fire protection engineering calculations are driven by heat release rates or their constituent components of the mass loss rate of the fuel and the heat of combustion of the fuel. The effect of the rate of cooling and steam smothering on these engineering parameters was not measured, which limits the usefulness of the method. Further, the formula is meant to be applied to the largest open area in a structure, not to partially involved areas. The amount of water needed for adjacent areas and for exposures is not addressed. For additional information see Clark,[7,8] Fornell,[9] and Royer.[15] Wiesman and Iowa State University Bulletin No. 18 should be read in their entirety.

The NFA formula was developed from the experience of structural incident scene commanders. The formula can be applied to partially involved structures; however, there is no method for fire protection engineers to determine a footprint of a fire that can be substituted into the percent involvement portion of the formula.

The ISO formula is based primarily on how much water (in increments of 250 or 500 gpm [946.25 to 1892.5 L/min]) is needed to contain a fully involved structure (or a predefined portion of a multistory facility) and to prevent fire spread to adjacent structures. It is not suitable to determine the manual application rate needed to extinguish a growing fire within a structure. For further information see Hickey.[16]

It may seem desirable to use knowledge of the heat absorption rate of water and knowledge of the heat release rate of a fire to determine if the flow rate is adequate. This is being discussed more and more in the international literature. As previously discussed, a 100 gpm (378.5 L/min) stream will absorb 928,300 Btu per min (16.4 MW) in a complete conversion. The same 100 gpm (378.5 L/min) hose stream will create 22,300 ft^3/min (631 m^3/min) of steam in a complete conversion. The difficulty in applying this knowledge to fire protection engineering problems is based on the compound effect of the following unknowns:

- The amount of water that is converted to steam
- The amount of water that reaches the flame
- The amount of water that actually reaches the fuel surface
- The combined effect of steam's smothering and cooling
- The criticality of water reaching and cooling the fuel surface versus general area cooling for the given fire
- The amount of heat that must be removed to cause a collapse of the combustion reactions

Kimball observed that two to four times the flow rate suggested by the Iowa State study tends to be used.[17] Recently, factors have been introduced to account for the unknowns listed previously. When reviewing such factors, it is important not to mix the reduction factors with the theoretical heat absorption in other models. This is because, as discussed earlier in this chapter, some heat absorption models give additional credits for heat absorption as the steam is heated beyond the boiling point of water and for the observation that it is not theoretically necessary to absorb 100 percent of the heat that is being released. Table 17.3.1 gives some of the values used in the international literature.

OPACITY AND REFLECTIVITY

Tests conducted at Underwriters Laboratories Inc. (UL), using water spray to provide exposure protection to a sheet metal surface from a gasoline fire, indicate that when the spray is applied as a thin film of water over the sheet metal, the temperature of the metal was contained within limits that protected the metal from significant damage. This did not occur, however, when the water spray was adjusted so that it did not touch the sheet metal, but it did provide a water curtain between the metal and the fire. In this latter case, the temperature of the metal was three to four times greater than when the water flowed over the metal. These tests indicate that, because of its lack of opacity, water does not prevent the passage of radiant heat very well. The principal value of water used to protect exposures is from the cooling obtained by evaporation of a water film on the exposed surfaces.

NFPA 13, *Standard for the Installation of Sprinkler Systems,* calls for outside sprinklers for protection against exposure fires to be positioned so that the water will thoroughly wet exposed glass windows and run down over the window sash

TABLE 17.3.1 Literature Values for Heat Absorption Efficiency of Water Applied by Fire Fighters

Researcher	*Reference*	*Efficiency (%)*	*Theoretical Heat Absorption Used (MW per kg/sec) (Same as L/sec)*[a]	*Conditions/Comments*
Barnett[b]	Draft SFPE *Engineers Guide to Fire Department Intervention* citing New Zealand Fire Engineering Guide and National Research Council of Canada	33	2.6	Based on first principles of heat absorption. The 33% factor includes an increase over heat absorption efficiencies alone to account for the effect of steam
Grimwood et al.[c]	*3D Fire Fighting, Training, Techniques, and Tactics*	32	2.6	Heat absorption a rounded conversion from 9.8 MW/gal/sec. Applies to direct attack
Särdqvist[d]	*An Engineering Approach to Fire-Fighting Tactics,* Sweden	40	2.6	Standard smooth bore nozzle (7 mm or 14 mm) at short range and well placed
Särdqvist	*An Engineering Approach to Fire-Fighting Tactics,* Sweden	30	2.6	Standard smooth bore nozzle (22 mm) or large-capacity nozzle at long range and well placed
Särdqvist	*An Engineering Approach to Fire-Fighting Tactics,* Sweden	20	2.6	Monitor nozzle at long range and well placed
Särdqvist	*An Engineering Approach to Fire-Fighting Tactics,* Sweden	20	10.8	Interior use of Swedish design fog nozzles producing droplets smaller than 1 mm
Zhao, Beck, and Kurban[e]	*Fire Brigade Intervention Model for Residential Buildings in Australia*	5	10.5	Exterior stream
Zhao, Beck, and Kurban	*Fire Brigade Intervention Model for Residential Buildings in Australia*	15	10.5	Interior stream

[a]Note: The 10+ MW values are extinction capacity based on not removing 100% of the heat. Steam heat absorption also credited.

[b]*Engineers Guide to Fire Department Intervention*, Society of Fire Protection Engineers, Bethesda, MD, 2005 draft, pp. 45–46, 50. This information will likely be more accessible in this guide once it is published than in the original sources.

[c]Grimwood, P., Hartin, E., McDonough, J., and Raffel, S., *3D Fire Fighting, Training, Techniques, and Tactics*, Fire Protection Publications, Stillwater, OK, 2005, p. 89.

[d]Särdqvist, S. *An Engineering Approach to Fire-Fighting Tactics*, Lund Institute of Technology, Lund, Sweden, 1996, pp. 52–55.

[e]Zhao, L., Beck, V., and Kurban, N., *Fire Brigade Intervention Model for Residential Buildings in Australia*, Victoria University of Technology, Melbourne, Australia. No date, appears to have been published in 1998 or 1999, pp. 8–9.

and the glass, wetting the entire window as much as possible. Similar recommendations require that as much of the cornice as possible be wetted when cornice sprinklers are installed. These recommendations reflect the experimental evidence.

In England, tests measured the transmission of radiant heat through water sprays from two types of nozzles.[18] The tests proved that the transmission of this kind of heat depends mostly on nozzle design, and that, with certain nozzles, a water curtain of low transmission could be produced for waterflows comparable to those of sprinkler installations. Fire fighters have, of course, used water curtains in situations where it was too hot or dangerous for them to remain exposed to flames and heat.

WATER AS AN EXTINGUISHING AGENT

It is recognized that fires involving various fuels and materials react differently to various extinguishing agents and that water is *not* the best agent for all types of fuels.

Water is not suitable for all types of fires. There are four typical classifications of fire: (1) Class A—ordinary combustibles, (2) Class B—flammable and combustible liquids, (3) Class C—electrical, and (4) Class D—combustible metals. A fifth class, Class K, has been added for cooking oils. Water is most effective and most commonly used for Class A fires. Water is not appropriate or the most desirable agent of choice for Class B, Class D, or Class K fires. (Water mist systems have been successful on tests of some Class B and Class K fires.) Using water for Class C fires must be considered carefully before the water is applied. Water may not be an acceptable agent where collateral water damage is deemed unacceptable.

A good reference to consult for recommendations on use of water on specific materials where problems could be encountered is the NFPA *Fire Protection Guide to Hazardous Materials.*[19]

Water applied to fires by certain types of water mist fire suppression systems has been found to be effective with fires involving flammable liquids and live electrical equipment. Water mist systems can be used to protect shipboard engine enclosures, valuable artwork, and computer room subfloors. Water mist is especially effective in confined spaces when a detection system operates the water mist fire suppression system. Water mist systems are also an attractive option for applications where the storage or discharge of water is to be minimized. Direction on the use of water mist as a suppression system is given in NFPA 750, *Standard on Water Mist Fire Protection Systems.* More information can be found in Section 16, Chapter 8, "Water Mist Fire Suppression Systems."

Water can be used in some instances for fires involving chemicals and combustible metals, where the quantity of water can overcome some adverse chemical reactions and extinguish the fire.

The following possible personnel hazards must be considered when choosing water as the extinguishing agent: (1) exposure and/or inhalation of steam in all fires, (2) electrocution or shock injury in electrical fires, and (3) adverse or explosive reactions in chemical and combustible metal fires.

Wetting Agents

Information in this section is based on NFPA 18, *Standard on Wetting Agents.* Wetting agents are compounds that are added to water to change some or all of the water's characteristics, for example, surface tension or viscosity. Experience as well as testing indicates that the addition of a proper wetting agent to water will, when properly applied, increase the extinguishing efficiency of that water with respect to quantity used and time to achieve fire control or suppression. The value of such a factor may well become important, especially in rural areas where adequate quantities of water are not always available for fire fighting.

Certain types of fires, such as those in baled cotton, stacked hay, some rubber compounds, and some flammable liquids that do not ordinarily respond to treatment with water may be extinguished when a proper wetting agent is used. This may be attributed to an increase in the penetrating, spreading, and emulsifying capability of water due to lowered surface tension. This decrease in surface tension can be described as a disruption of the forces holding the surface film of water together, permitting it to flow and spread uniformly over solid surfaces. The treated water possesses the ability to penetrate into small openings and recesses that nontreated water would flow over by the simple bridging action of the surface film. The treated water exhibits not only penetrating and spreading qualities but also increased absorptive speed and superior adhesion to solid surfaces.

Some wetting agents have foaming characteristics when mixed with water and air. The foam retains the wetting and penetrating characteristics of the wetting agent and provides an efficient smothering action for the extinguishment of Class A and some Class B fires. It also provides a fluid insulation for protection against fire exposure. The foam produced in this manner has the additional advantage of breakdown at approximately 175°F (79.4°C), then returns to its original liquid state and retains the penetrating and wetting qualities.

Although wetting agents can be used on some Class B fires, they do not perform as well as foam and in many cases the performance of a wetting agent on Class B fires may be unsatisfactory with respect to extinguishment or burnback resistance. A wetting agent that has been listed for Class B fires by UL has not undergone testing as rigorous as the testing required to be listed as a foam under UL 162, *Foam Equipment and Liquid Concentrates.*

There are numerous chemicals that fulfill the primary function of a wetting agent, which is to lower the surface tension of water. However, very few of these chemicals are suited to fire protection because their application is complicated by hazard considerations, such as toxicity, corrosive action on equipment, and stability in water.

Wet water is water plus a wetting agent. Wet water has the same limitations as water on fires in chemicals that react with water. The use of wet water on flammable and combustible liquid fires is not common. Wet water should not be used on flammable or combustible liquid fires if the liquids are water soluble, such as the alcohols, glycols, and some ketones.

Because of its conductivity, the application of wet water solutions on live electrical equipment requires the same precautions as application of water on Class C (electrical) fires. Wet water applied by spray or fog might be used with caution due to its penetrating characteristics. Wet water may have more harmful effects on motors, transformers, and similar equipment than plain water. Any electrical equipment that has been penetrated by wet water should be thoroughly flushed and cleansed before it is returned to service.

A specific use of wet water is to penetrate combustible materials. One objective is to use less agent than if plain water were used, especially in Class A fuels with the potential for a deep-seated fire. This increased water absorption can increase the potential for structural or commodity collapse if too much agent is absorbed, thereby increasing the weight of the commodity.

Wetting agents may be either premixed with water or added to the water through suitable proportioning equipment at the time the water is being used. Mixing wetting agents from different manufacturers, or mixing a wetting agent with mechanical or chemical foam concentrates, is not recommended. Distinction must be made between wetting agents and wetting-agent foams and other detergent-type foams (high-expansion foam) and film-forming foam agents. Guidance for the use of wetting agents is given in NFPA 18, *Standard on Wetting Agents.*

Class A Foam

Water additives known as Class A foams have become extremely popular in recent years. Fornell describes seven advantages of Class A foam over water alone.[20] Colletti and Liebson should be read in their entirety. Also see NFPA 1150, *Standard on Foam Chemicals for Fires in Class A Fuels,* and NFPA 1145, *Guide for the Use of Class A Foams in Manual Structural Fire Fighting.*

Modern Water Additives

Manufacturers have developed water additives that appear to be much more effective on Class A and Class B fires than traditional wetting agents. These manufacturers often promote the environmental benefits of their agents as well. As of this writing, the Technical Committee on Water Additives for Fire Suppression and Vapor Mitigation is working on a new document, NFPA 18A, *Standard on Water Additives for Fire Control and Vapor Mitigation.* The challenge before the committee was how to quantify the improvements that these agents purport to offer. The proposed standard will provide quantifiable performance requirements. These requirements can be compared to other agents for the intended use.

For example, an agent meeting the minimum requirements of NFPA 18A is required to be applied at a greater density than a UL-listed Aqueous Film Forming Foam (AFFF) to extinguish a Class B fire. But the NFPA 18A agent may have additional listings and capabilities that AFFF does not have. Specifically, NFPA 18A requires that agents demonstrate improved performance over water on Class A fires.

Agents listed under NFPA 18A have the option of being listed for long-term vapor mitigation and for use on three-dimensional (flowing) fuel fires. AFFF is not listed for these applications. Agents listed under NFPA 18A must meet the requirements of UL 162 if they are intended to be used on Class B fuels in extreme depth such as tank fires. Some agents that would be covered under the NFPA 18A agent have found a niche market in the protection of Powder River Basin coal at power plants and have become the standard in that industry. Powder River Basin (PRB) coal refers to low-sulfur coal. Its name comes from the region along the Montana-Wyoming border where it is mined. Powder River Basin coal is a greater fire protection challenge than more traditional coals and warrants extra fire protection precautions. For more information visit the Powder River Basin coal users group at http://www.prbcoals.com. For related topics, see Section 9, Chapter 16, "Mining and Mineral Processing."

Additional information on the differences between agents covered under NFPA 18A and traditional Class B foams can be found in the annex of NFPA 18A. It is up to the user to carefully evaluate the intended application(s), the cost and amount of agent needed to meet those needs, and potential environmental impact before selecting the agent that best meets those needs.

Two additives, along with two types of aqueous film-forming foam and a film-forming fluoroprotein foam, were tested in sprinkler and water mist systems by the UK Royal Navy. Liu and Kim reported that "test results showed that all five types of additives improved the performance of both sprinklers and water mist but such improvement was much more significant for water mist."[21]

WATER AND FLAMMABLE AND COMBUSTIBLE LIQUIDS—CLASS B FIRES

Care must be exercised when using water as an extinguishing agent with Class B (flammable and combustible liquid) fires. Water density can create problems with flammable and combustible liquids. When the liquid is lighter (specific gravity less than 1.0) than water, the water can submerge beneath the liquid and can cause the flammable or combustible liquid to flow from its containment, spreading the fire. With crude oil, water can submerge to the bottom of the container and cause the crude oil to "boil over." Other hazards are slopover and frothover. (See Section 6, Chapter 12, "Flammable and Combustible Liquids.") Water is immiscible with hydrocarbon fuels, does not provide an effective coating of the fuel surface, and does not dilute the flammable or combustible mixture below the flammable limits. However, when properly mixed with certain types of foam concentrate, water is an effective fire-suppressing agent for certain types of flammable and combustible liquids.

Heavy fuel oil, lubricating oil, asphalt, and other high-flashpoint liquids do not produce flammable vapors unless heated. Once ignited, the heat of the fire will cause pyrolysis for continued burning. If water in spray form is applied to the surface of such high-flashpoint burning liquids, cooling will slow down the rate of pyrolysis enough that it may extinguish the fire. If water is applied to high-flashpoint burning liquids by means of a coarse spray, extinguishment may be obtained by emulsification.

Foam concentrate used for flammable and combustible liquids are commonly called Class B foams to distinguish themselves from the previously discussed Class A foams. Fire department pumpers are now commonly equipped with one tank for Class A foam and another for Class B foam.

Fire-fighting foam for Class B liquids is (1) an aggregate of air-filled bubbles forming from aqueous solutions (water and foam concentrate) and (2) lower in density than flammable liquids. It is used principally to form a cohesive floating blanket on flammable and combustible liquids and prevents or extinguishes fire by limiting the amount of air and cooling the fuel. It also prevents reignition by suppressing formation of flammable vapors. (See Section 17, Chapter 4, "Foam Extinguishing Agents and Systems.")

Fire-fighting foams for Class B liquids consist of a combination of water, foam concentrate, and air. Low-expansion-type foams typically utilize a ratio of 1, 3, or 6 percent concentrate to 99, 97, or 94 percent water, respectively, to make a foam-water solution. Water remains the principal component in fire-fighting foams.

The ability of water without additives (foaming agents) to extinguish a fire is limited on low-flashpoint flammable liquids, such as Class I flammable liquids (flashpoints below 100°F [37.8°C]), as defined in NFPA 30, *Flammable and Combustible Liquids Code.* Sprinklers and water spray are usually effective in extinguishing fires in combustible liquids with flashpoints of 200°F (93.3°C) and higher, in flammable liquids with a specific gravity greater than 1.0, and in water-soluble liquids. Water can be effective with high-flashpoint hydrocarbon fires when introduced as a high-velocity spray causing penetration of the droplets and cooling of the surface layer.[22] If water does not evaporate and cool the fuel surface, it can accumulate and submerge and can displace the hydrocarbon. Control of fire, but not extinguishment, is possible in low-flashpoint (under 200°F [93.3°C]) flammable liquids. Any water that reaches the surface of a burning, low-flashpoint flammable liquid in a tank may sink and cause the tank to overflow. In the case of a spill fire, the water may cause the fire to spread. Special handling of certain types of water spray nozzles can result in extinguishment of fires in these liquids or, at a minimum, effective fire control.

Water can be used as an effective cooling agent in Class B fires; it can also (1) protect against flame-exposure of the storage container and (2) protect exposures as a cooling agent.

See Section 6, Chapter 12, "Flammable and Combustible Liquids," for characteristics and fire preventive methods for Class B fires.

WATER AND LIVE ELECTRICAL EQUIPMENT—CLASS C FIRES

Water in its natural state contains impurities that make it conductive. If water is applied to fires involving live electrical equipment, a continuous circuit might be formed that would conduct electricity back to the user and cause a shock, especially if there are high voltages or potentials. Foam-type extinguishing agents are also conductive. The amount of current, rather than the voltage, determines the extent of the shock. Conductivity of water when used on live electrical equipment depends on several variables:

1. The voltage and amount of current flowing
2. The "breakup" of the stream as a result of the nozzle design, the pressures used, and the wind conditions. This breakup influences the conductivity of the stream because the air spaces formed between the droplets interrupt the electrical path to ground. Water spray nozzles and combination straight-stream spray nozzles (in the spray position) provide for effective dispersion of the water droplets. The hazards of these are less than those of solid streams of water.
3. The purity of the water and the relative resistivity of the water
4. The length and cross-sectional area of the water stream
5. The resistance to ground through a person's body as influenced by location (whether on wet ground or not), skin moisture, the amount of current the body can endure, the length of exposure to the current, and other factors, such as protective clothing.
6. The resistance to ground through the hose

Conductivity and Hazard of Shock

There is some danger to fire fighters directing streams of water onto wires of less than 600 V to ground from a distance likely to be encountered under ordinary fire-fighting conditions. It is more dangerous if fire fighters, standing either in puddles of water or on moist surfaces, come into contact with live electrical equipment. In such cases, the fire fighters' bodies complete an electrical circuit, and the current from the electrical equipment relayed through their bodies is more readily grounded than if it were conveyed through dry, nonconductive surfaces. Rubber boots often contain enough carbon black to permit the passage of current through the body and do not provide reliable protection.

Research conducted by UL on electric fences indicates that there are differences in the electric current to which individuals may be safely subjected and that the maximum continuous (uninterrupted) current to which an individual may be safely subjected is 5 mA (milliamperes) AC applied on the surface of the body.[23]

Impurities in water (mostly the mineral content) also affect its conductivity. Tests of the resistivity of public water supplies in Indiana showed results ranging from 710 to 5400 ohms per cm^3; the lowest values were found in supplies from deep wells. The resistivity of deep well supplies ranged from 1000 to 2000 ohms per cm^3; and the resistivity of river waters was about 4000 ohms per cm^3. In tests conducted by the Commonwealth Edison Company in cooperation with the Chicago Fire Department, the resistivity of Chicago River water ranged from 1671 to 2393 ohms per cm^3.[24] At the time the tests were made, the normal hydrant water in the Chicago area had a resistivity of about 3800 ohms per cm^3.

Safe Distances from Live Equipment

From time to time, authorities have tried to determine safe distances between nozzles and live electrical equipment. The bibliography at the end of this chapter cites more papers on this subject.

The conductivity of water streams varies according to the type of equipment from which they are expelled, such as

(1) handheld or manually supported solid-stream nozzles, (2) handheld water spray (water fog) nozzles, (3) fixed water spray systems for fire protection services, and (4) plain water and water-solution portable fire extinguishers.

Data available on the minimum safe distances between manually supported solid-stream hose lines and live electrical equipment carrying voltages higher than 600 V are not entirely consistent because the results of different tests vary. These variations may be attributed to the different testing methods used, the variances in the purposes of the tests, the limitations of the tests caused by the physical circumstances and available equipment, and the fact that the same voltages were not used in all of the tests.

Data from the American Insurance Services Group (AISG), a unit of Insurance Services Offices, Inc. (formerly AIA), was published in the 18th and earlier editions of this handbook. At AISG's request, this information was removed from the 19th edition of this handbook because the data are based on an AIA bulletin that is no longer in print and is considered obsolete. AISG does not recommend the information published in Table 6-1A in the 18th edition of this handbook. Some limited tests made in 1958 by the Hydroelectric Power Commission of Ontario, in cooperation with the Office of the Fire Marshal of Ontario, Canada,[25] resulted in recommendations for minimum safe distances from live electrical equipment for a ⅝ in. (16 mm) solid-stream nozzle (Table 17.3.2). The report recommends that solid streams greater than ⅝ in. (16 mm) should not be used near live electrical equipment, but the tests were limited to a maximum stream distance of 30 ft (9.1 m). Larger nozzles might produce sufficient stream dispersion over longer distances, which would permit their use.

The results of tests made in 1934 for the Fire Brigade of Paris, France, present perhaps the most comprehensive guide[26] (Table 17.3.3). The distances are based on preventing the transmission of a 1 mA current to a fire fighter in contact with a nozzle or hose. The tests covered only voltages to ground ranging from 115 to 150,000 V, and the groupings of the voltages do not correspond to current standard U.S. voltages. The maximum size of the nozzle used is also nonstandard in the United States.

The preceding information indicates that definite shock hazards exist unless adequate distances are maintained, and these distances can only be estimated from the available data. It is difficult for fire fighters in the field to know precisely what electrical potentials exist in any given situation. For this reason, and those given next, it is best, whenever possible, to use water spray streams rather than solid streams.

As noted previously, water spray reduces the conductivity hazard. The design of the nozzle and the characteristics of the spray determine the amount of leakage current that can actually flow in the stream, and each nozzle should be tested to determine precisely the characteristics it possesses. Tests on various commercial water spray nozzles indicate that a minimum

TABLE 17.3.2 Limit of Safe Approach to Live Electrical Equipment

Voltage to Ground	*Voltage Between Conductors*	⅝ in. (16 mm) Solid-Stream Nozzle:[a] Minimum Safe Distance	
		ft	*m*
2,400	4,160	15	4.6
4,800	8,320	20	6.1
7,200	12,500	20	6.1
8,000	13,800	20	6.1
14,400	24,900	25	7.6
16,000	27,600	25	7.6
25,000	44,000	30	9.1
66,000	115,000	30	9.1
130,000	230,000	30	9.1

[a]Nozzle pressure 100 psi (690 kPa) water resistance 600 ohms per in.^{3}.

Source: Fitzgerald, G. W. N., "Fire Fighting Near Live Electrical Apparatus," Research Division Report No. 58160, Hydro-Electric Power Commission of Ontario, Canada, 1958.

TABLE 17.3.3 Minimum Safe Distances Between Hose Nozzles and Live Electrical Equipment Recommended for the Paris, France, Fire Brigade

Voltage to Ground	*Voltage Between Conductors*	Diameter of Nozzle Orifice — ¼ in. (6 mm) — Safe Distance		¾ in. (19 mm)		1¼ in. (32 mm)	
		ft	*m*	*ft*	*m*	*ft*	*m*
115	230	1.6	0.50	3.3	1.00	6.6	2.00
460	480	2.5	0.75	9.8	3.00	16.4	5.00
3,000	5,195	6.6	2.00	16.4	5.00	32.8	10.00
6,000	10,395	8.2	2.50	19.7	6.00	39.4	12.00
12,000	20,785	9.8	3.00	21.4	6.50	49.2	15.00
60,000	103,820	14.8	4.50	39.4	12.00	72.2	22.00
150,000	259,800	19.7	6.00	49.2	15.00	82.0	25.00

Source: Buffet, "Peut-on Employer les Lances d'Incendie sur des Conducteurs Electriques?" 1934.

distance of 4 ft (1.2 m) should be maintained for voltages to ground up to about 10 kV. This distance is actually no greater than is sensible to prevent personnel from getting dangerously close to live electrical equipment. Distances should be increased when attacking fires involving live electrical equipment operating above this voltage. Figure 17.3.1 shows the results of four researchers, as analyzed by the U.K. Fire Offices' Committee, Joint Fire Research Organization.[27]

The Toledo Edison Company conducted tests in which water was discharged onto a screen at a potential to ground of 80,500 V (equivalent to a system or line voltage of 138 kV phase-to-phase). As a consequence, the Edison Electric Institute in 1967 adopted the following safety rules. (The distances in these rules will limit leakage currents to less than 1 mA):

1. Using all handheld water spray nozzles, the minimum approach distance is 10 ft (3 m).
2. Using handheld, 1½-in. (38-mm) straight (solid) stream nozzles, the minimum approach distance is 20 ft (6 m).
3. Using handheld, 2½-in. (64-mm) straight (solid) stream nozzles, the minimum approach distance is 30 ft (9 m).

When combination straight-stream spray nozzles are used on live electrical equipment, fire fighters should be sure they have the desired spray pattern before applying the stream. The use of spray nozzles on "applicators" increases the possibility of accidental contact between the nozzle and live electrical equipment, and most authorities recommend that they not be used.

Clearance from Fixed Water Spray Systems

Fixed water spray systems are used extensively to protect high-value and/or critical electrical equipment, such as transformers, oil switches, and motors. These systems are designed to provide effective fire control, extinguishment, prevention, or exposure protection. NFPA 15, *Standard for Water Spray Fixed Systems for Fire Protection,* gives installation recommendations for such systems and includes a table of recommended clearances between water spray equipment and unenclosed or uninsulated live electrical components at other-than-ground potential (Table 17.3.4). Modern practice is to coordinate the required clearance

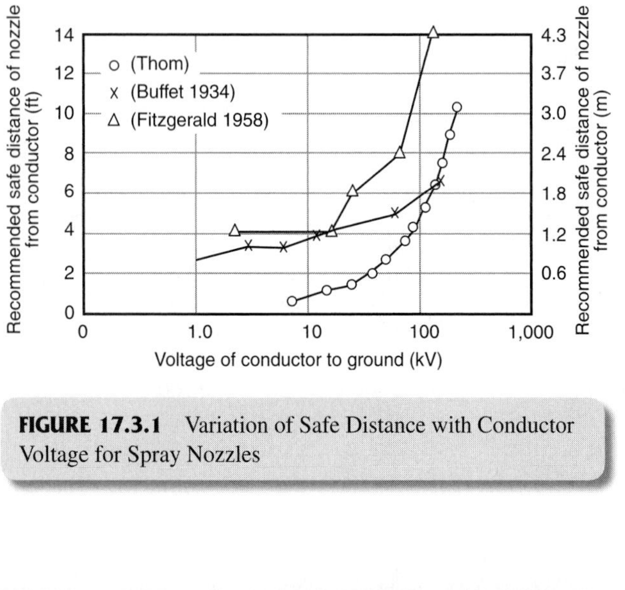

FIGURE 17.3.1 Variation of Safe Distance with Conductor Voltage for Spray Nozzles

TABLE 17.3.4 Clearance from Water Spray Equipment to Live Uninsulated Electrical Components

Nominal System Voltage (kV)	*Maximum System Voltage (kV)*	*Design BIL (kV)*	Minimum* Clearance	
			in.	*mm*
To 13.8	14.5	110	7	178
23.0	24.3	150	10	254
34.5	36.5	200	13	330
46.0	48.3	250	17	432
69.0	72.5	350	25	635
115.0	121.0	550	42	1067
138.0	145.0	650	50	1270
161.0	169.0	750	58	1473
230.0	242.0	900	76	1930
		1050	84	2134
345.0	362.0	1050	84	2134
		1300	104	2642
500.0	550.0	1500	124	3150
		1800	144	3658
765.0	800.0	2050	167	4242

Note: BIL values are expressed as kilovolts (kV), the number being the crest value of the full wave impulse test that the electrical equipment is designed to withstand. For BIL values that are not listed in the table, clearances can be found by interpolation.

*For voltages up to 161 kV, the clearances are taken from NFPA 70, *National Electrical Code.* For voltages 230 kV and above, the clearances are taken from Table 124 of ANSI C2, *National Electric Safety Code.*

Source: NFPA 15, *Standard for Water Spray Fixed Systems for Fire Protection*, Table 6.1.2.2, 2007, p. 15-13.

with the electrical design. The basic insulation level (BIL) values of the equipment are used as the basis, although the clearance between uninsulated live parts of the equipment and any portion of the water spray system should not be less than the minimum clearances provided elsewhere for electrical system insulation on any individual component (the minimum unshielded straight-line distance from the exposed electrical parts to nearby grounded objects). The BIL (expressed in kilovolts [kV]) is the crest value of the full wave impulse test. (See Section 16, Chapter 9, "Water Spray Protection.")

Portable Extinguishers and Hazard of Shock

Water-based or water-solution portable fire extinguishers are not recommended for use on live electrical equipment, that is, Class C fires. NFPA 10, *Standard for Portable Fire Extinguishers,* recommends that extinguishers specifically tested for use on Class C fires be used for such fires. When electrical equipment is de-energized, water-based extinguishing agents and extinguishers for Class A or B fires may be used safely. Conductivity tests of portable fire extinguishers containing water indicate that soda-acid (now discontinued), loaded-stream (now discontinued), foam, and antifreeze solution extinguishers, all of which produce solid streams and have a short range, are particularly hazardous. One test involving an antifreeze solution extinguisher showed a current of 157 mA for a potential of 1 kV with a 3⁄32 in. (2.4 mm) stream at a distance of 1 ft (0.3 m). To reduce the current to below 1 mA, it would be necessary to use the device from a distance at which the stream is dispersed; it is generally agreed that for such extinguishers the minimum distance should be 4 ft (1.2 m) for voltages up to 1 kV. Extinguishers containing plain water might, in theory, be used at shorter distances, but it is best to maintain a 4 ft (1.2 m) distance if it is necessary to use this kind of extinguisher.

Water on Electrical, Electronic, and Computer Equipment

Automatic sprinkler protection and water spray fixed systems are valuable for fire control, even where electrical, electronic, or computer equipment may be present. There should be little concern about the possibility of shock or of the water causing excessive damage to the equipment. Experience has proved that, if a fire activates sprinklers, the sprinklers, if properly installed and maintained, provide effective protection, with regard to electrical shock, with no measurable increase in damage to the equipment, as compared with the damage done by heat, flame, smoke, and the manual hose streams.[28]

NFPA 75, *Standard for the Protection of Information Technology Equipment,* recognizes the importance of automatic sprinkler protection in computer rooms. It recommends that, where sprinklers are installed to protect electronic computer equipment, the power to the equipment should be disconnected prior to the application of water.

WATER AND COMBUSTIBLE METALS—CLASS D FIRES

The reaction between water and combustible metals ranges widely from minor reactions to an explosive reaction. In some instances, water can be used to overcome some adverse chemical reactions if a large quantity is applied. As a rule, water should not be used on fires involving combustible metals, for example, magnesium, titanium, metallic sodium, and hafnium, or on metals that are combustible under certain conditions, for example, calcium, zinc, and aluminum. However, water can be utilized to protect exposures as a cooling agent. NFPA 484, *Standard for Combustible Metals*, specifies when sprinklers may and may not be used when magnesium is present.

USE OF WATER ON SPECIAL HAZARDS

Although water is generally a universal extinguishing agent, there are certain prohibitions and precautions that must be observed when it is applied manually on some burning materials that either react chemically or explosively on contact with water. In other instances, the mechanical action of applying water must be carefully monitored to avoid creating conditions that intensify the hazard rather than controlling it.

The following paragraphs give guidance on using water on different materials that can present problems if water is used arbitrarily as an extinguishing agent. See Section 6, "Characteristics of Materials and Products," for specific information on chemicals and gases.

Chemical Hazards

As a general rule, water should not be used on materials that react with water and may release oxygen, flammable gases, and heat. Examples include alkalies, anhydrides, carbides, hydrides, nitrates, and peroxides (organic and inorganic) to list a few. When wet, certain materials, such as unslaked lime, will heat spontaneously over a period of time if heat cannot be dissipated due to storage conditions.

Radioactive Metals

Water should not be used continuously on radioactive metals. The requirements for fire protection for radioactive metals are generally consistent with their nonradioactive counterparts (for all practical purposes, radioactivity does not influence, nor is it influenced by, the fire properties of a metal). Control of contaminated runoff water is a complicating factor in using water on radioactive metals.

Flammable Gases

In gas-fire emergencies, water is generally used for the control of heat from the fire while efforts are made to shut off, or stop, the flow of escaping gas. Water in the form of spray applied from hose lines or monitor nozzles, or by fixed water spray systems, is commonly used for dispersement or dilution of concentrations of flammable gases.

WATER ADDITIVES FOR SPECIALIZED USES

Freezing Temperatures and Antifreeze Additives

Because water freezes at 32°F (0°C), its use as an extinguishing agent is limited in climates or situations where freezing temperatures are encountered. There are several methods commonly used to prevent problems of freezing. These include using dry-pipe sprinkler systems instead of wet-pipe systems, circulation or heating tank water supplies held for fire protection purposes, adding freezing-point depressants to the water, or a combination of these.

The water-soluble freezing-point depressant most widely used in fire equipment is calcium chloride with a corrosion-inhibitor additive. Calcium chloride solutions are not used when fire protection systems are supplied by public water connections. Sodium chloride (common salt) is unsatisfactory because of its limited ability to depress the freezing point of water and its highly corrosive attribute.

Antifreeze Additives for Sprinkler Systems

Chemically pure glycerine (U.S. Pharmacopoeia 96.5 percent grade) or pure propylene glycol can be used to depress the freezing point of water in portions of water suppression systems connected to public water supplies, if authorized by local health or water authorities. Diethylene glycol, ethylene glycol, or calcium chloride, as well as glycerine or propylene glycol, can be used for the same purposes where public water is not connected to the system. Both ethylene and diethylene glycol are poisonous and cannot be permitted to contaminate drinking water.

Antifreeze Additives for Water-Type Extinguishers

Alkali-metal salt solutions provide protection against freezing temperatures as low as –40°F (–40°C). Only the antifreeze solutions specified by the manufacturers should be used. Glycol solutions should not be used in extinguishers because the amount required to protect against freezing would be high; a 52.5 percent solution of ethylene glycol would be needed to depress the freezing point to –40°F (–40°C). Such amounts will alter the effectiveness of the extinguisher and may also lead to complications if the water should "boil off" and leave a strong concentration of the glycol, which, under certain conditions, could be ignited.

Efforts have been made to develop other additives that can be mixed with water to lower the freezing point to –65°F (–54°C). This work has been largely stimulated by increased activity in extremely low-temperature areas, with most of the research being done by the U.S. armed forces. To date, formulas of lithium chloride, lithium chloride–calcium chloride, and lithium chloride–anhydrous sodium chromate have been used successfully. No commercial use of these solutions is known; however, the U.S. Naval Research Laboratory has developed a lithium chloride solution for fire extinguishers exposed to low temperatures of –65°F (–54°C).

Additives to Modify Flow Characteristics

Friction loss in fire hose is always an obstacle for fire fighters. The longer the hose or the more water pumped through it, the greater the pressure loss. With a smooth fire hose lining, most of the pressure loss is the result of friction between particles of water generated by the turbulence in the flowing stream. When flow is either smooth or laminar, the friction loss tends to be very low with a slow stream of water. However, the amount of water delivered under laminar flow is generally too low for fire fighting. Fire fighting requires high-velocity streams that generate turbulence, which, in turn, results in friction between water particles. This friction accounts for about 90 percent of the pressure loss in fire hose. The friction between the flowing water and the interior hose wall accounts for only 5 to 10 percent of the loss.

Until 1948 it was generally believed that not much could be done to reduce friction loss. At the time, trace quantities of certain polymers were found to reduce friction loss of turbulent streams. Most researchers report that linear polymers (i.e., polymers that form a single straight-line chemical chain with no branches) are the most effective in reducing turbulent frictional losses. Of these, the poly-chain (polyethylene oxide) is the most effective. Friction-reducing efficiency is a direct function of polymer linearity.

Poly-chain synthetics are nontoxic, have no effects on plants or marine life, and will degrade in sunlight. A poly-chain synthetic is a long linear chain, high-molecular-weight polymer, and is two to three times more effective as a friction-reduction agent than other materials tested to date. It is an odorless, opaque, white slurry that weighs 9.1 lb per gal (1.1 kg/L) and must be kept within 0 to 120°F (–17 to 49°C). When it is injected into the hose stream, it dissolves completely and does not separate. It is compatible with all fire-fighting equipment and is useful in both fresh and salt water. One gallon (2.6 L) of additive treats 6000 gal (22,710 L) of water and achieves at least a 40 percent greater water delivery.

Tests conducted by the New York City Fire Department and Union Carbide Corporation found that a 1½ in. (38 mm) hose with an additive delivered 250 gpm (946 L/min), or as much as a 2½ in. (64 mm) hose without the additive. With the additive, a 2½ in. (64 mm) hose was able to deliver more water than a 3 in. (76 mm) hose, and nearly as much water as a 3½ in. (89 mm) hose. These tests also showed that the additive nearly doubled the nozzle pressure. The stream's reach was increased by nearly 30 percent, and the stream was more coherent.

The author is unaware of any fire departments that are currently using these additives. Certainly, they are not in widespread use.

Additives to Increase Water's Viscosity

The relatively low viscosity of water makes it tend to run off solid fuel surfaces quickly and limits the ability to blanket a fire by forming a barrier at the surface. Additives make the use of water more effective on certain types of fires. Most applications of viscous water have been directed at fighting forest fires.

Viscous water has had several thickening agents added to it. In proper proportions, viscous water has the following advantages over nontreated water: ability to cling and adhere to the fuel surface; provide a continuous coating over the fuel surface; provide a layer thicker than water; absorb heat proportional to the amount of water present; project farther when discharged from a nozzle; and resist movement due to wind and air currents.

Viscous water has the following disadvantages over water: it does not penetrate the fuel as well as water, it creates a higher friction loss in fire hose or piping, increases the water droplet size, makes surfaces slippery and difficult to walk on, and requires mixing prior to use.

The author is unaware of any systems currently using this additive. Certainly, they are not in widespread use.

CARE IN USE OF WATER AS AN EXTINGUISHING AGENT

There are numerous factors that must be considered before using water as an extinguishing agent, as this chapter has already discussed. It must be considered if the use of water will cause the fire to grow or spread, whether there will be a chemical reaction causing harm, or if live electrical equipment can endanger personnel.

Fire fighters must also consider water runoff when using water-based fire extinguishing agents. Water can carry pollutants from a fire to a water supply or cause groundwater contamination. When using water to extinguish hazardous materials fires, such as pesticides and flammable liquids, some of the fuel will be carried off by the water vapor (steam), some of the water may be absorbed by the fuel, and some fuel may be carried by the runoff water.

SUMMARY

Water is the most widely used extinguishing agent because it is readily available and because of its ability to cool, to remove and displace the oxygen supply, and to separate/displace the fuel source. Although water is highly effective on Class A fuels, it is not usually the agent of choice on Class B, C, D, or K fires.

Several additives are available to improve water's performance. The most common are Class A and B foams, and an emerging class of additives collectively known as water additives for fire control and vapor mitigation.

Care must be exercised before using water on fires involving energized electrical apparatus, hazardous materials (including flammable and combustible liquids), and combustible metal fires. The effect of contaminated runoff on the environment should always be considered.

BIBLIOGRAPHY

References Cited

1. Särdqvist, S., *An Engineering Approach to Fire-Fighting Tactics,* Lund Institute of Technology, Lund University, Lund, Sweden, 1996, p. 52.
2. Grimwood, P., Hartin, E., McDonough, J., and Raffel, S., *3D Fire Fighting, Training, Techniques, and Tactics,* Fire Protection Publications, Stillwater, OK, 2005.
3. Mawhinney, J. R., Dlugogorski, B. Z., and Kim, A. K., "A Closer Look at the Fire Extinguishing Properties of Water Mist," *Fire Safety Science—Proceedings* of the 4th International Symposium at the Ottawa Congress Centre, Ottawa, Ontario, Canada, T. Kashiwagi (Ed.), International Association of Fire Safety Science, London, UK, 1994, p. 514.
4. Grimwood, P., *3D Fire Fighting, Training, Techniques, and Tactics,* Fire Protection Publications, Stillwater, OK, 2005, p. 76.
5. Yao, C., and Marsh, W., "Early Suppression—Fast Response: A Revolution in Sprinkler Technology," *Fire Journal,* Vol. 78, No. 1, 1984, pp. 42–44, 46.
6. Isman, K., "Which Sprinkler to Choose?" *Fire Protection Engineering,* No. 9, Winter 2001, pp. 25–36.
7. Clark, W. E., *Firefighting Principles and Practices,* Fire Engineering Books & Videos, Saddle Brook, NJ, 1991, pp. 29–49.
8. Clark, W. E., "Fighting Fire with Water: Using Water Wisely," *Fire Engineering,* Vol. 148, No. 9, 1995, pp. 33–34, 38, 40.
9. Fornell, D. P., *Fire Stream Management Handbook,* Fire Engineering, Saddle Brook, NJ, 1991, pp. 33–75.
10. Wiseman, J., and Bertrand, J., *The Safe and Effective Use of Fog Nozzles,* PennWell Corporation, Tulsa, OK, 2003.
11. Grimwood, P., *Fog Attack, Firefighting Strategy & Tactics—An International View,* FMJ International Publications Limited, UK, 1992, pp. 65–98.
12. Grimwood, P., "'New Wave' 3-D Water Fog Tactics: A Response to Direct Attack Advocates," *Fire Engineering,* Vol. 153, No. 10, 2000, pp. 89–99.
13. Burns, E., and Phelps, B., "Redefining Needed Fire Flow for Structure Fires," *Fire Engineering,* Vol. 147, No. 11, 1994, pp. 22–26.
14. Grimwood, P., Hartin, E., McDonough, J., and Raffel, S., *3D Fire Fighting, Training, Techniques, and Tactics,* Fire Protection Publications, Stillwater, OK, 2005, pp. 91–97.
15. Royer, K., "Iowa Rate of Flow Formula, for Fire Control," *Fire Engineering,* Vol. 148, No. 9, 1995, pp. 40–43.
16. Hickey, H., *ISO Fire Suppression Rating Schedule Handbook,* Society of Fire Protection Engineers, Bethesda, MD, 1993.
17. Kimball, W., *Fire Attack 2,* National Fire Protection Association, Quincy, MA, 1968, pp. 125–126.
18. Heselden, A. J. M., and Hinkley, P. L., "Measurement of the Transmission of Radiation through Water Sprays," Fire Research Note No. 520, Department of Scientific and Industrial Research and Fire Offices' Committee, Joint Fire Research Organization, Boreham Wood, Herts, UK, 1963.
19. NFPA, *Fire Protection Guide to Hazardous Materials,* National Fire Protection Association, Quincy, MA, 2001.
20. Fornell, D. P., *Fire Stream Management Handbook,* Fire Engineering, Saddle Brook, NJ, 1991, pp. 308–309.
21. Liu, Z., and Kim, A., "Review of Water Mist Suppression Technology: Part II—Application Studies," *Journal of Fire Protection Engineering,* Vol. 11, No. 1, 2001, p. 21.
22. Drysdale, D., *An Introduction to Fire Dynamics,* 1st ed., John Wiley and Sons, New York, 1985, p. 224.
23. UL, "Electric Shock as It Pertains to the Electric Fence," Bulletin of Research No. 14, Underwriters Laboratories Inc., Northbrook, IL, 1939.
24. Commonwealth Edison Co., "Conductivity of Electricity through Various Sizes and Types of Fire Streams," 1947. (An engineering report of tests conducted in cooperation with the Chicago Fire Department.)
25. Fitzgerald, G. W. N., "Fire Fighting Near Live Electrical Apparatus," Research Division Report No. 58160, Hydro-Electric Power Commission of Ontario, Canada, 1958.
26. Buffet, "Peut-on Employer les Lances d'Incendie sur des Conducteurs Electriques?" 1934.
27. O'Dogherty, M. J., "The Shock Hazard Associated with the Extinction of Fires Involving Electrical Equipment," Fire Research Technical Paper No. 13, Ministry of Technology and Fire Offices' Committee, Joint Fire Research Organization, 1965. (Published by Her Majesty's Stationery Office.)
28. Keigher, D. J., "Water and Electronics Can Mix," *Fire Journal,* Vol. 62, No. 6, 1968, pp. 68–72.

NFPA Codes, Standards, and Recommended Practices

Reference to the following NFPA codes, standards, and recommended practices will provide further information on water and water additives for fire suppression discussed in this chapter. (See the latest version of The NFPA Catalog *for availability of current editions of the following documents.)*

NFPA 10, *Standard for Portable Fire Extinguishers*
NFPA 11, *Standard for Low-, Medium-, and High-Expansion Foam*
NFPA 13, *Standard for the Installation of Sprinkler Systems*
NFPA 15, *Standard for Water Spray Fixed Systems for Fire Protection*
NFPA 16, *Standard for the Installation of Foam-Water Sprinkler and Foam-Water Spray Systems*
NFPA 18, *Standard on Wetting Agents*
NFPA 18A, *Standard on Water Additives for Fire Control and Vapor Mitigation*
NFPA 30, *Flammable and Combustible Liquids Code*
NFPA 70, *National Electrical Code®*
NFPA 75, *Standard for the Protection of Information Technology Equipment*
NFPA 86, *Standard for Ovens and Furnaces*
NFPA 484, *Standard for Combustible Metals*
NFPA 750, *Standard on Water Mist Fire Protection Systems*
NFPA 1145, *Guide for the Use of Class A Foams in Manual Structural Fire Fighting*
NFPA 1150, *Standard on Foam Chemicals for Fires in Class A Fuels*

Chapter 4

Foam Extinguishing Agents and Systems

Joseph L. Scheffey

Chapter Contents

Key Terms

alcohol-type foaming agent, aqueous film-forming foam, chemical foam, crash-rescue vehicle, film-forming fluoroprotein (FFFP) agent, fire-fighting foam, foam extinguishing agent, high-expansion foaming agent, low-temperature foaming agent, protein foaming agent

Fire-fighting foams are used in fixed and portable fire extinguishing systems. They are used primarily to combat flammable and combustible liquid fuel fires. Aqueous foam solutions, created using foam concentrate mixed with water, are expanded with air to create foam. Foam is used to suppress liquid fuel vapors and cool the liquid surface. There are many NFPA standards and guidelines that address foam application for tank/dike protection, aviation spill hazards, aircraft hangar protection, and liquid warehousing applications.

Foams vary in terms of their chemical makeup, which affects the required rate of application and appropriateness for use on particular liquid fuel hazards. For example, protection of polar solvent hazards requires specially formulated alcohol-type concentrate (AR). High-expansion foams can, in some cases, be used to protect both Class A and Class B fire hazards; they are particularly suited as a flooding agent for large spaces. Foams may be tailored for combined use with dry chemical agents. This provides for both two-dimensional pool and three-dimensional spilling fuel fire scenarios.

Foam is generated by proportioning foam concentrate with water. Various fixed and portable proportioning devices are used. Discharge devices include nozzles, foam monitors, and sprinklers. Tank protection requires special nozzle and distribution systems. Specialized foam fire-fighting vehicles are described.

For related topics, see Section 7, Chapter 2, "Storage of Flammable and Combustible Liquids"; Section 13, Chapter 7, "Aircraft Rescue and Fire Fighting (ARFF)"; and Section 16, Chapter 1, "Principles of Automatic Sprinkler System Performance."

USES AND LIMITATIONS OF FIRE-FIGHTING FOAMS

Low-expansion foam is used principally to extinguish burning flammable or combustible liquid spill or tank fires by application to develop a cooling, coherent blanket. Foam is the only permanent extinguishing agent used for fires of this type. Its application allows fire fighters to extinguish fires progressively. A foam blanket covering a tank's liquid surface can prevent vapor transmission for some time, depending on the stability and depth of the foam. Fuel spills are quickly rendered safe by foam blanketing. The blanket may be removed after a suitable period of time; typically it has no detrimental effect on the product with which it comes into contact.

Foams can be used to diminish or halt the generation of flammable vapors from nonburning liquids or solids and may be used to fill cavities or enclosures where toxic or flammable gases may collect.

Foam is of great importance where aircrafts are fueled and operated. Sudden, large fuel spills resulting from aircraft accidents or malfunction require rapid foam application. Hangar fire protection is best accomplished by properly designed foam systems.

Increasingly, warehouses and buildings storing large quantities of combustible and flammable liquids are protected by foam-water sprinkler systems. The protection required is a function of the

Joseph L. Scheffey, P.E., is director of fire protection research and development at Hughes Associates, Inc., in Baltimore, Maryland.

type and quantity of liquid stored, building height, and storage configuration.

Foams of the medium- or high-expansion type (20 to 1000 times) may be used to fill enclosures such as basement room areas or holds of ships where fires are difficult or impossible to reach. Here foams act to halt convection and access to air for combustion. Their water content also cools and diminishes oxygen by steam displacement. Foams of this type (with expansion ratios of 400 to 500) may be used to control liquefied natural gas (LNG) spill fires and help disperse the resulting vapor cloud.

Many foams are generated from solutions with very low surface tension and penetration characteristics. Foams of this type are useful where Class A combustible materials are present. In such instances, the water solution draining from the foam cools and wets the solid combustible.

Foam breaks down and vaporizes its water content under attack by heat and flame. It therefore must be applied to a burning liquid surface in sufficient volume and rate to compensate for this loss, with an additional amount applied to guarantee a residual foam layer over the extinguished liquid. Foam is unstable and may be broken down easily by a physical or mechanical force, such as a water hose stream. Certain chemical vapors or fluids may also destroy foam quickly. When certain other extinguishing agents are used in conjunction with foam, severe breakdown of the foam may occur. Turbulent air or violently uprising combustion gases from fires may divert foam from the burning area.

The mechanisms of foam fire extinguishment on two-dimensional hydrocarbon fuel fires have not been fully developed. Recent theoretical and preliminary experimental work has attempted to correlate foam extinguishment with fundamental fluid spread mechanisms. More research is required to develop foam suppression theory.

Foam solutions are conductive and therefore not recommended for use on electrical fires. If foam is used, a spray is less conductive than a straight stream. However, because foam is cohesive and contains materials that allow water to conduct electricity, foam spray is more conductive than water spray.

Engineering design requirements and recommended application methods must be followed for successful use of foams. These requirements can be found in NFPA 11, *Standard for Low-, Medium-, and High-Expansion Foam;* NFPA 16, *Standard for the Installation of Foam-Water Sprinkler and Foam-Water Spray Systems*; and NFPA 403, *Standard for Aircraft Rescue and Fire-Fighting Services at Airports*. Additionally, NFPA codes and standards, such as NFPA 30, *Flammable and Combustible Liquids Code*, and NFPA 409, *Standard on Aircraft Hangars*, provide application rate and installation details on special hazard systems.

In general, the following criteria for the hazardous liquid must be met for a foam to be fully effective:

1. The liquid must be below its boiling point at the ambient conditions of temperature and pressure.
2. Care must be taken in application of foam to liquids with a bulk temperature higher than 212°F (100°C). At these fuel temperatures and above, foam forms an emulsion of steam, air, and fuel. This may produce a fourfold increase in volume when applied to a tank fire, with dangerous frothing or slopover of the burning liquid.
3. The liquid must not be unduly destructive to the foam used, or the foam must not be highly soluble in the liquid to be protected.
4. The liquid must not be water reactive.
5. The fire must be a horizontal surface fire. Three-dimensional (falling fuel) or pressure fires cannot be extinguished by foam unless the hazard has a relatively high flashpoint and can be cooled to extinguishment by the water in the foam.

TYPES OF FOAM

A number of types of foaming agents are available, known as foam concentrates, some of which are designed for specific applications. Some are suitable for extinguishing all types of flammable liquids, including water-soluble and foam-destructive liquids. Descriptions of the common types of foam follow.

Aqueous Film-Forming Foam Agents (AFFF)

Aqueous film-forming foam agents are composed of synthetically produced materials that form air-foams similar to those produced by the protein-based materials. In addition, these foaming agents are capable of forming water solution films on the surface of flammable hydrocarbon liquids, hence the term *aqueous film-forming foam (AFFF)*. AFFF concentrates are available for proportioning to a final concentration of 1 percent, 3 percent, or 6 percent by volume, with either fresh water or seawater.

The air-foams generated from AFFF solutions possess low viscosity, have fast spreading and leveling characteristics, and, like other foams, act as surface barriers to exclude air and halt fuel vaporization. These foams also develop a continuous aqueous layer of solution under the foam, maintaining a floating film on hydrocarbon fuel surfaces to help suppress combustible vapors and cool the fuel substrate. This film, which can also spread over fuel surfaces not fully covered with foam, is self-healing following mechanical disruption and continues to spread as long as there remains a reservoir of nearby foam. Film effectiveness may be reduced on hot surfaces and aromatic hydrocarbons. To ensure fire extinction, an AFFF blanket should cover the fuel surface entirely, as with other types of foam.

AFFF fluidity and film strength on kerosene makes it particularly suitable for jet aircraft fuel spill fire fighting.

AFFF concentrates contain fluorinated, long-chain synthetic hydrocarbons with particular surface-active properties.

Because of the extremely low surface tension of the solutions draining from AFFF, these foams may be useful under mixed-class fire situations (Classes A and B), where deep penetration of water is needed in addition to the surface-spreading action of foam itself.

Foam-generating devices yielding stable, homogeneous foams are not necessarily needed in the employment of AFFF. Less sophisticated foaming devices, such as water spray nozzles and sprinklers (unlike with most other foaming agents), may be used because of the inherent rapid and easy foaming capability of AFFF solutions. However, such foams drain relatively rapidly, and they may provide less burnback resistance compared to protein-based foams. AFFF also may be used, without compatibility problems, in conjunction with dry chemical agents. Although AFFF concentrates must not be mixed with other types of foam concentrates, foams made from them do not break down other types of foams in fire-fighting operations. The normal-use temperature range for these agents is 35 to 120°F (1.7 to 49°C).

Fluoroprotein (FP) Foaming Agents

The concentrates used for generating fluoroprotein foams are similar in composition to protein foam concentrates, but, in addition to protein polymers, they contain fluorinated surface active agents that confer a "fuel shedding" property to the foam generated. This makes them particularly effective for fire-fighting conditions where the foam becomes coated with fuel, such as in the method of subsurface injection of foam for tank fire fighting, and nozzle or monitor foam applications where the foam may often be plunged into the fuel. Fluoroprotein foams are very effective for in-depth crude petroleum or other hydrocarbon fuel fires because of this fuel shedding property. In addition, these foams demonstrate better compatibility with dry chemical agents than do the regular protein-type foams. They also possess superior vapor securing and burnback resistance characteristics. Fluoroprotein-type concentrates are available for proportioning to a final concentration of either 3 percent or 6 percent by volume, using either fresh water or seawater. They are nontoxic and biodegradable after dilution. The normal-use temperature range for these agents is 20 to 120°F (–7 to 49°C).

Film-Forming Fluoroprotein (FFFP) Agents

Film-forming fluoroprotein (FFFP) agents are composed of protein together with film-forming fluorinated surface-active agents, which make them capable of forming water solution films on the surface of most flammable hydrocarbons and conferring a fuel-shedding property to the foam generated.

Air-foams generated from FFFP solutions have fast-spreading and leveling characteristics and, just as other foams, act as surface barriers to exclude air and prevent vaporization. Like AFFF, they generate a self-healing, continuous floating film on hydrocarbon fuel surfaces that helps suppress combustible vapors. However, to ensure fire extinction, an FFFP blanket, as with other types of foam, should cover the entire fuel surface.

Because of the rapid and easy foaming capability of FFFP solutions, water spray devices may be used in many situations. However, the foams produced drain rapidly and may have less burnback resistance compared to protein-based foams.

Film-forming fluoroprotein-type concentrates are available for proportioning to a final concentration of either 3 or 6 percent by volume, using either freshwater or seawater. They may be used in conjunction with dry chemical agents without compatibility problems.

Protein (P) Foaming Agents

Protein-type air-foams use aqueous liquid concentrates proportioned with water for their generation. These concentrates contain high-molecular-weight natural proteinaceous polymers derived from a chemical digestion and hydrolysis of natural protein solids. The polymers give elasticity, mechanical strength, and water retention capability to foams generated from them. The concentrates also contain dissolved polyvalent metallic salts, which aid the protein polymers in their bubble-strengthening capability when the foam is exposed to heat and flame. Protein-type concentrates are available for proportioning to a final concentration of either 3 or 6 percent by volume, using either freshwater or seawater. In general, these concentrates produce dense, viscous foams of high stability, high heat resistance, and good resistance to burnback, but they are less resistant to breakdown by fuel saturation than are AFFF and fluoroprotein foams. They are nontoxic and biodegradable after dilution. The normal-use ambient temperature range for these concentrates is 20 to 120°F (–7 to 49°C).

Low-Temperature Foaming Agents

This type of foam concentrate is protected for storage and use at low temperature by the inclusion of freezing-point depressants. Low-temperature foaming agents may be used at ambient temperatures as low as –20°F (–29°C). They are available for use at either 3 or 6 percent by volume concentration in either freshwater or seawater, and may be of the AFFF or protein-based type.

Alcohol-Type Foaming Agents (AR)

Air-foams generated from ordinary agents are subject to rapid breakdown and loss of effectiveness when they are used on fires that involve fuels that are water soluble, water miscible, or of a "polar solvent" type. Examples of this type of fuel are alcohols, enamel and lacquer thinners, methyl ethyl ketone, acetone, isopropyl ether, acrylonitrile, ethyl and butyl acetate, and the amines and anhydrides. Even small amounts of these substances mixed with common hydrocarbon fuels, such as gasohol, may cause rapid breakdown of ordinary fire-fighting foams.

Therefore, certain special foaming agents, called alcohol-type concentrates, have been developed. These alcohol-resistant (AR) concentrates are proprietary compositions of several types, some containing a protein, fluoroprotein, or an aqueous film-forming foam concentrate base. The most common are usually described as polymeric alcohol-resistant AFFF concentrates which produce foams suitable for application to spill or in-depth fires of either hydrocarbon or water-miscible flammable liquids by any foam-generating device. They exhibit AFFF characteristics on hydrocarbons and produce a floating gel-like mass for foam buildup on water-miscible fuels. Agents of this type have no transit time limitations. Normal-use temperatures for any of the alcohol-type agents are 35 to 120°F (1.7 to 49°C).

Medium- and High-Expansion Foaming Agents

Medium- and high-expansion foams are agents for control and extinguishment of Class A and some Class B fires, and are particularly suited as a flooding agent for use in confined spaces. The foam is an aggregation of bubbles, mechanically generated by aspiration or a blower-fan, which forces air or some other gas through a net or screen that is wetted by an aqueous solution of surface-active foaming agents. Under proper conditions, fire-fighting foams of expansions from 20:1 up to 1000:1 can be generated.

Medium- or high-expansion foam is a unique vehicle for transporting wet foam masses to inaccessible places, for total flooding of confined spaces, and for volumetric displacement of vapor, heat, and smoke. Tests have shown that when used under certain circumstances in conjunction with water from automatic sprinklers, the foam will provide more positive control and extinguishment than either extinguishing agent by itself. Optimum efficiency in any one type of hazard is dependent on the rate of application and the foam expansion and stability.

Liquid concentrates for producing medium- and high-expansion foams consist of synthetic hydrocarbon surfactants of a type that will foam copiously with a small input of turbulent action. They are generally used in approximately 2 percent proportion in water solution. Medium-expansion foam may also be generated from solutions of fluoroprotein, protein, or AFFF concentrates at 3 or 6 percent proportion.

Medium- or high-expansion foams are particularly suited for indoor fires in confined spaces. Their use outdoors may be limited because of the effects of weather. These foams have several effects on fires:

1. When generated in sufficient volume, they can prevent the air necessary for continued combustion from reaching the fire.
2. When forced into the heat of a fire, the water in the foam is converted to steam, which reduces the oxygen concentration by diluting the air.
3. The conversion of the water to steam absorbs heat from the burning fuel. Any hot object exposed to the foam will continue breaking down the foam, converting the water to steam, and being further cooled.
4. Because of its relatively low surface tension, foam solution not converted to steam will tend to penetrate Class A materials. However, deep-seated fires may require overhaul.
5. When accumulated in depth, high-expansion foam can provide an insulating barrier for protection of exposed materials or structures not involved in a fire, thereby preventing fire spread.

Research has shown that using air from inside a burning building to generate high-expansion foam has an adverse effect on the volume and stability of the foam produced. Combustion and pyrolysis products, when they react chemically with the foaming agent, can reduce the volume of foam produced and increase the drainage rate. The high temperature of the air breaks down the foam as it is generated. Physical disruption also takes place, apparently caused by vapor and solid particles from the combustion process. These factors that cause foam breakdown may be compensated for by higher rates of foam generation.

Entry to a foam-filled passage must not be attempted without use of self-contained breathing apparatus. The foam mass also reduces vision and hearing, and lifelines must be used for personnel entering the foam.

Foam of approximately 500:1 expansion can be successfully used for control of fires and reduction of vaporization from LNG spills. As water slowly drains from the foam in small amounts, it forms a thin ice layer which floats on the LNG and supports the high-expansion foam blanket. Fixed and portable high-expansion foam facilities of this type have been provided for LNG storage and manufacturing plants.

Other Synthetic Hydrocarbon Surfactant Foaming Agents

There are many synthetically produced surface active compounds that foam copiously in water solution. When these are formulated properly, they may be used as wetting agents or as fire-fighting foams and employed in much the same manner as other types of foam (see NFPA 18, *Standard on Wetting Agents*).

Hydrocarbon surfactant foam liquid concentrates are employed in 1 to 6 percent proportions in water. When these solutions are used in conventional foam-making devices, the resulting air-foam possesses low viscosity and spreads quickly over liquid surfaces. Its fire-fighting characteristics depend on (1) the volume of the foam layer on the burning surface, which halts access to air and controls combustible vapor production; and (2) the minor cooling effect of the water in the foam, which becomes available due to a relatively rapid breakdown of the foam mass. This water solution does not possess film-forming characteristics on the flammable liquid surface although, under some conditions, it may produce a temporary water emulsion due to its wetting agent or "detergent-type" properties. Because of the low surface tension and wetting properties of the water solutions of these foams, they also may be used as extinguishing agents for Class A fires, although they were primarily developed with medium- or high-expansion foam in mind.

Synthetic hydrocarbon surfactant foams are generally less stable than other fire-fighting foams. Their water solution content drains away rapidly, leaving a bubble mass which is highly vulnerable to fuel heat or mechanical disruption. Usually these foams must be applied at higher rates than other fire-fighting foams to achieve extinction. Many formulations of this type of foam concentrate break down other foams if used simultaneously or sequentially.

Caution should be used when using wetting agents described in NFPA 18 for Class B situations. The test criteria used to classify the wetting agent for use on Class B fires may be significantly different than that used to classify AFFF, fluoroprotein, and protein foams. Fire suppression of Class A, B, and D fires using wetting agents is the subject of ongoing investigation.

Foams for Vapor Suppression

Fire-fighting foams may be used to suppress vapors from unignited flammable liquids for which the foams are proven extinguishing agents. To ensure good vapor suppression, the foam must be applied gently, so as to not mix fuel with the foam, and must cover the entire fuel surface. Care should be taken not to agitate the fuel during foam application, because static spark ignition of volatile hydrocarbons can result from plunging and turbulence from a foam or water stream.

There are flammable, toxic, or otherwise hazardous liquids on which fire-fighting foams are unstable and are therefore unsuitable for use either for fire fighting or vapor suppression. Special vapor-mitigating foams have been developed that are relatively stable on many hazardous liquids; one type is an alcohol-resistant fire-fighting foam of the low-expansion type, which can be additionally stabilized to enhance its effective foam life and stability on toxic, flammable, or corrosive liquids. Other types are medium-expansion foams especially formulated to be stable on either acidic or alkaline hazards. These medium-expansion foams are not effective fire-fighting foams.

In general, vapor-mitigating foams should be applied to spills of toxic liquids only by trained personnel wearing suitable protective gear. These foams require special engineering consideration, and, to date, no standards have been developed for their use. The manufacturers should be consulted for use, limitations, and application data.

Chemical Foam Agents and Powders

These foam-producing materials have become obsolete because of the superior economics and ease of handling of the liquid foam-forming concentrates previously discussed. Chemical foam is formed from the chemical reaction in aqueous solution between aluminum sulfate ("A," acidic) and sodium bicarbonate ("B," basic) which also contains proteinaceous foam stabilizers. Foam is formed by the generation of carbon dioxide gas trapped in the bubbles of the foaming solution.

GUIDELINES FOR FIRE PROTECTION WITH FOAMS

The following general rules apply to the application and use of ordinary air-foams:

1. The more gently the foam is applied, the more rapid the extinguishment and the lower the total amount of agent required.

2. Successful use of foam is also dependent on the rate at which it is applied. Application rates are described in terms of the amount by volume of foam solution reaching the fuel surface (in terms of total area) every minute. If the foam has an expansion rate of 8:1, an application rate of 0.1 gpm/ft^2 (4.1 Lpm/m^2) will provide 0.8 gal/ft^2 (32.8 L/m^2) of finished foam every minute. Increasing the foam application rate over the recommended minimum will generally reduce the time required for extinguishment. However, little time advantage is gained if application rates are increased more than three times the minimum recommended. If application rates are less than the minimum, extinguishment time will be prolonged or may not be accomplished at all. If application rates are so low that the rate of foam loss by heat or fuel attack equals or exceeds the rate of foam application, the fire will not be controlled or extinguished.

3. The minimum recommended application rate is the rate found by test to be the most practical in terms of speed of control and amount of agent required. The general curve in Figure 17.4.1 illustrates the rate-time relationship for foam application to a hazard. The curve may be displaced right or left depending on fuel, method of application, and type of foam concentrate; hence, the need for carefully engineered systems based on the appropriate standard and actual test information.

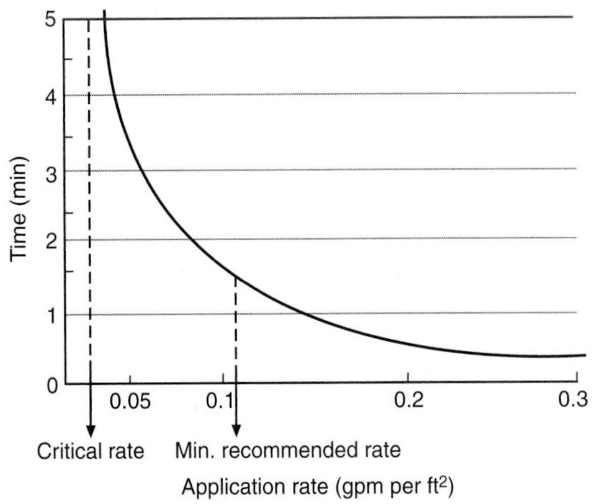

FIGURE 17.4.1 General Relationship of Foam Application Rate to Time of Application Necessary for Extinction (1.0 gpm/ft^2 equals 40.7 Lpm/m^2)

4. In general, air-foams will be more stable when they are generated with water at ambient temperature. Preferred water temperatures range from 35 to 80°F (1.7 to 27°C). Either freshwater or seawater may be used. Water containing known foam contaminants, such as detergents, oil residues, or certain corrosion inhibitors, may adversely affect foam quality.

5. Foams are adversely affected by air containing certain combustion products. Although the effect is minor with ordinary air-foam and ordinary hydrocarbon fuels, it is desirable to locate fixed foam-makers on the sides of, rather than directly over, the hazard.

6. Recommended pressure ranges should be observed for all foam-making devices. Foam quality will deteriorate if these limits (high and low) are exceeded.

7. Many air-foams are adversely affected by contact with vaporizing liquid extinguishing agents, their vapors, and by some dry chemical agents.

FOAM-GENERATING METHODS

The process of producing and applying fire-fighting air-foams to hazards requires three separate operations, each of which consumes energy. They are (1) the proportioning process, (2) the foam generation phase, and (3) the distribution method. A flow diagram illustrating the relationship of the three operations is given in Figure 17.4.2.

In general practice, air-foam generation and distribution occur nearly simultaneously within the same device. There are also many types of proportioning. In certain portable devices, all three functions are combined into a single device. The design and performance requirements of foam systems dictate the choice of types of proportioning, generating, and distributing equipment for the protection of specific hazards.

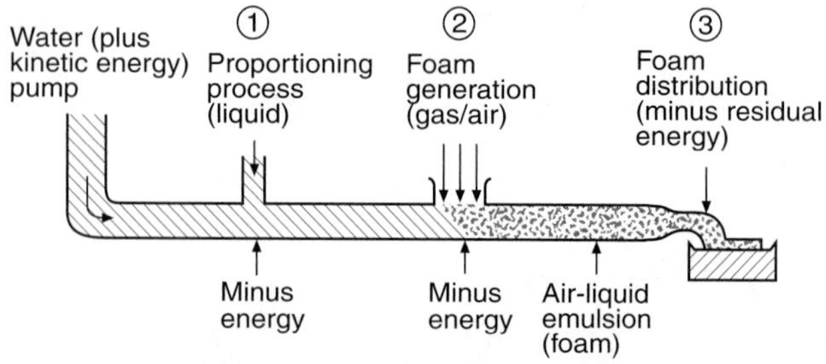

FIGURE 17.4.2 Steps in Air-Foam Generation

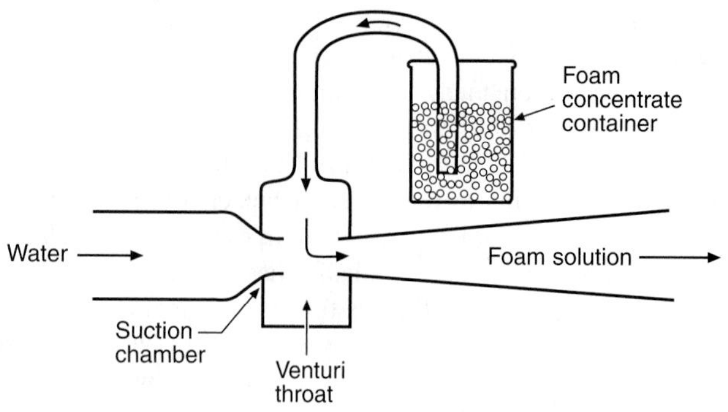

FIGURE 17.4.3 Venturi Induction (In-Line) Proportioner

Foam Concentrate Proportioners

It is very important that foam concentrate be proportioned accurately into the water stream. Proportioning equipment, foam concentrate, and discharge equipment must be matched to produce the proper solution concentration at system design operating pressures. If proportioning is low, the foam will be relatively weak and unstable; if too high, the foam may be stiff and concentrate will be wasted, thus reducing effective system operating time.

So that a predetermined volume of liquid foam concentrate may be mixed with a water stream to form a foam solution of fixed concentration, the following two general methods are used:

1. Methods that use the pressure energy of the water stream by venturi action and orifices to induct concentrate
2. Methods that use external pumps or pressure heads to inject concentrate into the water stream at a fixed ratio to flow

Figures 17.4.3 and 17.4.4 illustrate the general principles of the two different proportioning methods. Figure 17.4.5 shows a section view of a proportioner. Specific system designs of proportioning equipment are given below.

The Nozzle Eductor. This type of foam concentrate proportioner is of simple design and is widely used in portable foam-making nozzles where foam concentrate is available in 5 gal (19 L) pails or drums as shown in Figure 17.4.6. Incorporating a modified venturi within the foam-making nozzle section, the nozzle eductor drafts concentrate from a portable container through a pickup tube. By using a properly sized orifice or pipe section at the low-pressure cavity, the concentrate is mixed in proper proportion to the fixed flow and operating pressure of the nozzle and foam generation proceeds.

In-Line Eductor. This type of proportioner educts or drafts foam concentrate from a container or tank by venturi action, using the operating pressure of the hose water stream on which it is installed, and injecting concentrate into that flow of water. Its correct operation is very sensitive to waterflow and pressure. Changes in either of these factors from those for which the eductor was designed will result in incorrect proportioning. Distances of more than 6 ft (1.8 m) elevation from the eductor to the lowest liquid level of the foam concentrate container also may result in incorrect proportioning. Foam-generation devices and

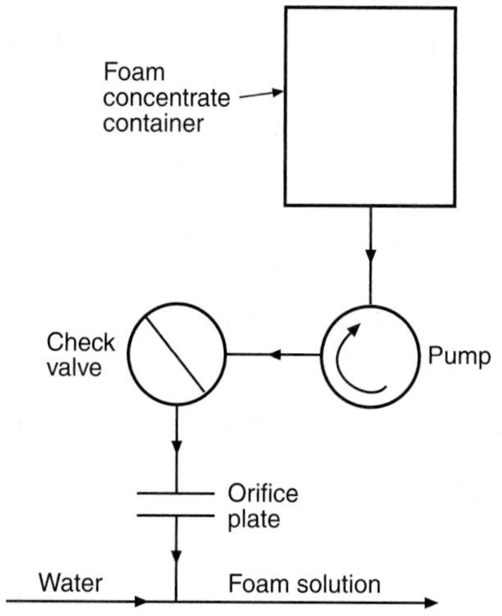

FIGURE 17.4.4 Foam Concentrate Pump Proportioner

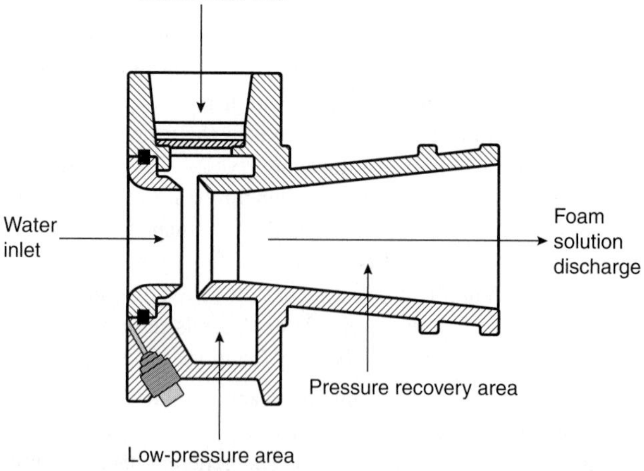

FIGURE 17.4.5 Section of Proportioner (Source: Ansul Incorporated)

FIGURE 17.4.6 Air-Foam Nozzle with Built-In Eductor

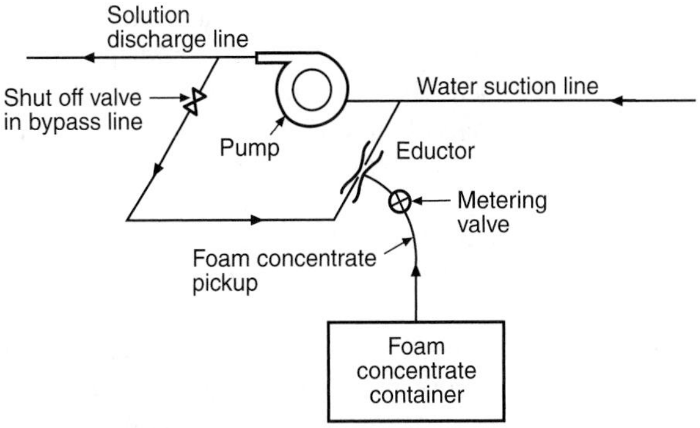

FIGURE 17.4.7 Around-the-Pump Proportioner

maximum downstream lengths of hose recommended for each eductor must be carefully adhered to. This proportioning device may be used in the hose line leading to the foam-generation device. An eductor of this type may also be installed at the foam concentrate tank in a fixed system or at the pump discharge of a mobile pumper.

Some designs of this proportioning device incorporate metering valves in the foam concentrate intake line so various volume percentages of concentrate in the water stream may be obtained. A check valve is usually placed in this intake so that water cannot flow back into the foam concentrate container if a blockage occurs or a valve is closed in the downstream hose. The use of this eductor requires an allowance for a pressure loss of approximately 30 percent in the system or layout.

Around-the-Pump Proportioner. This type of proportioner also operates on the venturi principle, except that this proportioner must be situated at the pump and connected to both suction and pressure sides. Its advantage is that pressure recovery of the venturi action is attained, and pump delivery pressures to the foam-making device or devices downstream require no compensation for pressure loss except for that in the layout hose length. The net delivery volume of the pump will be decreased by 10 to 40 gpm (38 to 150 Lpm) in this method of proportioning (Figure 17.4.7). The small portion of the pump discharge flows through a bypass line to the suction side of the pump. A venturi eductor in this line produces a negative pressure on the foam concentrate pickup line from the foam concentrate container. Foam concentrate is led to the eductor, where it mixes with water and is delivered to the suction side of the pump.

Multiple foam-makers may be supplied with foam solution by this type of proportioner when it is supplied with a multiported metering valve designed for the required flows.

Pressure Proportioning Tank. This type of proportioner may consist of one tank or of two tanks separately connected to the water and foam solution lines. The tank or tanks in the system may each be fitted with a flexible diaphragm or bladder to separate the "driving" water from foam concentrate. Tanks may rely simply on differences in density of the two liquids to retard mixing during operation (without diaphragm or bladder) when proportioning protein or fluoroprotein concentrate.

The principle of this device is simple. A small amount of the flowing water volumetrically displaces foam concentrate into the main water stream. The design pressure of the vessel must be above the maximum static water pressure encountered in the system.

Water is allowed to enter the foam tank from the main stream with as little friction loss as possible. An orifice meters liquid in the tank into the low-pressure area. Advantages of this system are its low-pressure drop, automatic proportioning over range of flows and pressures, and its freedom from external power. Its disadvantages are a long refill time (since it is a "batch" method, the tank must be drained of its driving water and the tank or the bladder refilled with concentrate) and an economic limit on size.

Coupled Water Motor-Pump Proportioner. This proportioner consists of two positive displacement rotary pumps mounted on a common shaft. Water delivered to the larger pump (motor) causes it to drive the smaller pump, which is used to draft concentrate from a container and deliver it (at line pressure) to the water discharge line from the larger pump. By proportioning the sizes of the two pumps, the correct volume of concentrate is delivered to the water stream.

This proportioner is manufactured in only two sizes for water throughputs of 60 to 180 gpm (227 to 680 Lpm) and 200 to 1000 gpm (757 to 3800 Lpm). Both sizes are designed for proportioning foam concentrates recommended for use at 6 percent concentration. A pressure drop of 25 to 30 percent in the water stream supplied to the device is required for its operation.

Balanced Pressure Proportioner. Foam proportioning into the water line supplying a foam suppression system can be accomplished by using a balanced pressure or positive-pressure injection-type proportioning system. These two methods provide the widest variations for operating flows, pressures, and operating ranges for systems having single and multiple supplies to protected areas. Although these systems are widely used for fixed systems, they may also be used in mobile apparatus as shown in Figure 17.4.8. The following sections describe installations for fixed systems. Figure 17.4.9 shows a representative skid-mounted balanced pressure proportioner unit.

Balanced Pressure System Utilizing a Foam Concentrate Pump for a Single Injection Point. This method, illustrated in Figure 17.4.10, uses a separate pump for supplying foam concentrate that is delivered in the correct proportions into the flowing water. Foam concentrate to water percentage equals 1 percent (1:99), 3 percent (3:97), or 6 percent (4:96) for Class B foams protecting flammable liquids. Usually a modified venturi type proportioner that includes a fixed metering orifice is used at the injection point of foam concentrate into the water stream. A pressure-balancing valve senses the water and foam pressures entering the modified venturi during flowing conditions. The balancing valve maintains equal water and foam pressures entering the venturi device by sensing the water pressure and relieving the higher-pressure foam concentrate supply back to the foam tank reservoir. The foam pressure at the entry point to the metering orifice is maintained equal to the water pressure at all flowing conditions of the system. The modified venturi creates a low-pressure point. This metering pressure drop at the foam concentration entry point allows the concentrate to enter the water stream and mix as a solution, supplying the discharge devices in the protected area. As waterflow increases to system, the metering pressure drop increases, thereby maintaining proper proportions of foam concentrate to water.

Balanced Pressure System Using Diaphragm Bladder Tank for Single Injection Point. This simple system, illustrated in Figure 17.4.11, uses water power to operate. The system consists of a pressure vessel-type steel tank that includes a reinforced rubber bladder inside that is shaped to fit the inside geometry of the tank vessel. Foam concentrate is contained inside the bladder, and water is supplied to the outer shell of the bladder. As the water compresses the bladder, foam concentrate is forced out of the tank and supplied to the modified venturi proportioner and metering orifice in the same manner as used for the foam concentrate pump system described previously. As the waterflow increases through the venturi, a metering pressure loss is created. When this pressure loss reaches a point equal to the pressure loss in the supply and discharge piping of the foam concentrate tank, the proper foam concentrate flow will occur. This provides the proper solution mixture of foam water required to extinguish the fire at 1 percent (1:99), 3 percent (3:97), or 6 percent (6:94). The height of proportioner above the tank top must be considered in the friction loss calculations, as it will directly affect the foam concentrate percentage accuracy. This type of system proportions lean (lower foam concentrate than needed) below the approved or listed minimum flow rates. Consideration should be used before applying this system below these flow rates: the listed minimum flow rates should fall within the operating limits of the application. AFFF or nonviscous foam concentrates are generally acceptable considering the initial operation of the system discharge device. Most alcohol-resistant foam concentrates are very viscous and create much higher friction loss in foam concentrate piping. The higher friction loss results in a much higher minimum flow rate where the desired percentage of foam to water is developed. This is critical in closed sprinkler systems where initial operation of sprinklers will not result in enough flow to produce proper foam water so-

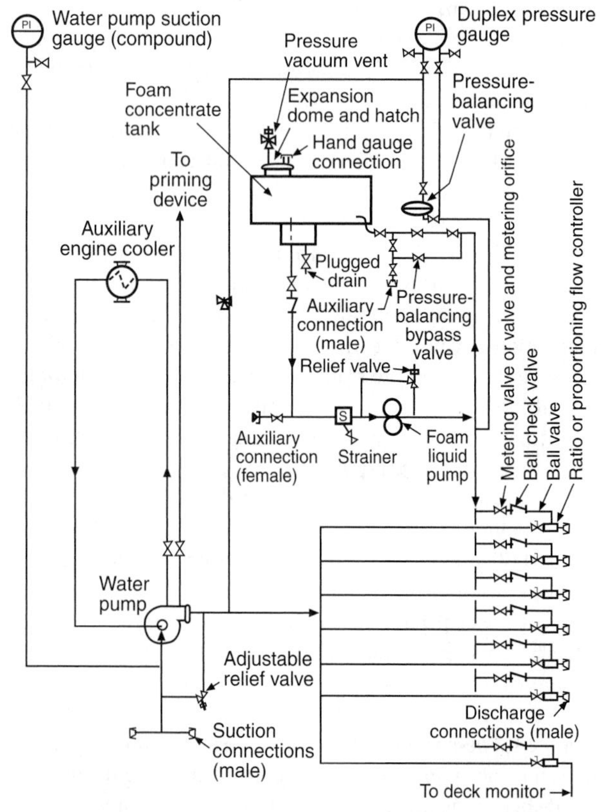

FIGURE 17.4.8 Balanced Pressure Proportioning for Mobile Equipment

FIGURE 17.4.9 Skid-Mounted Balanced Pressure Proportioner (Source: Ansul Incorporated)

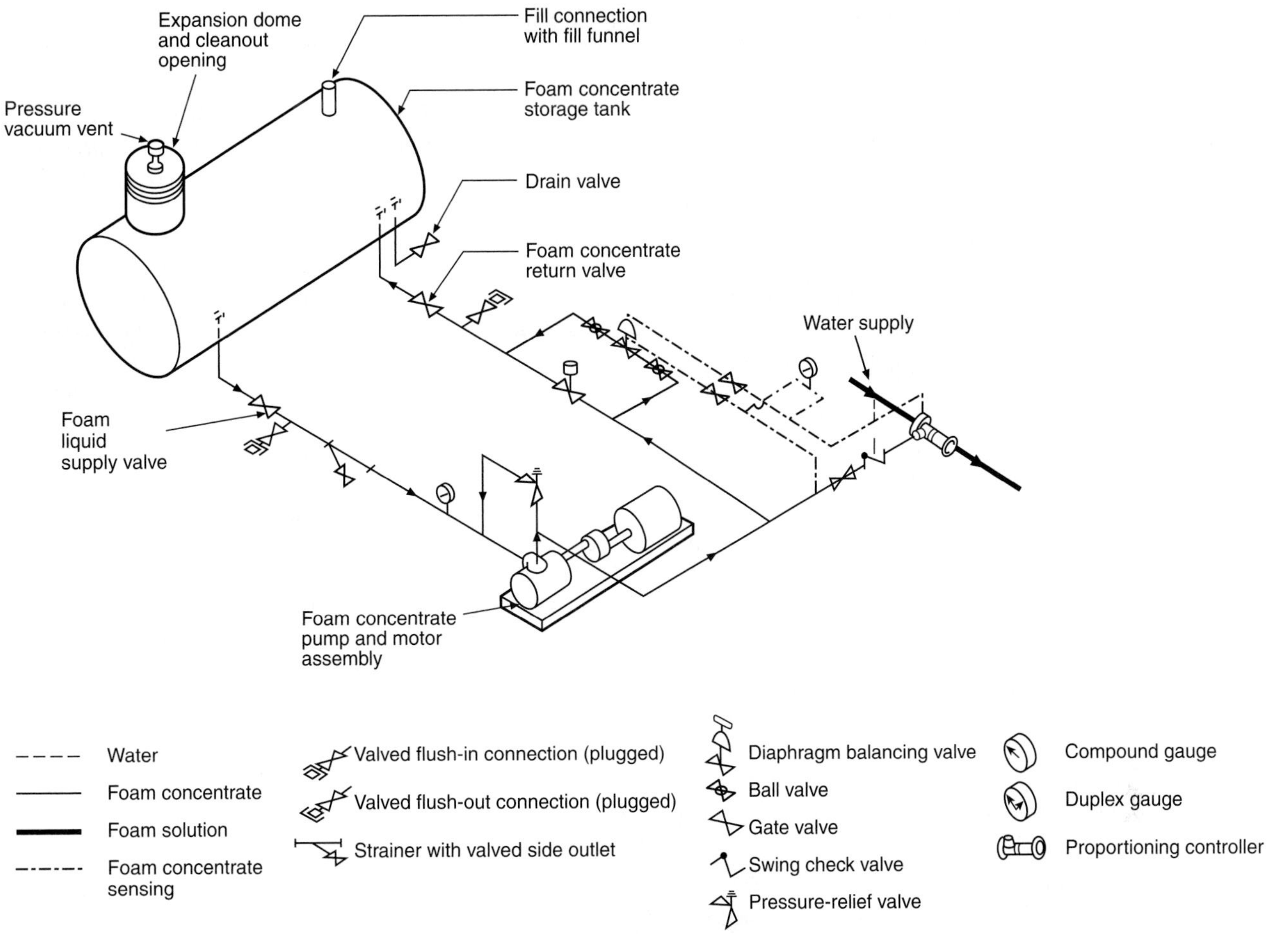

FIGURE 17.4.10 Balanced Pressure Proportioning with Single Injection Point

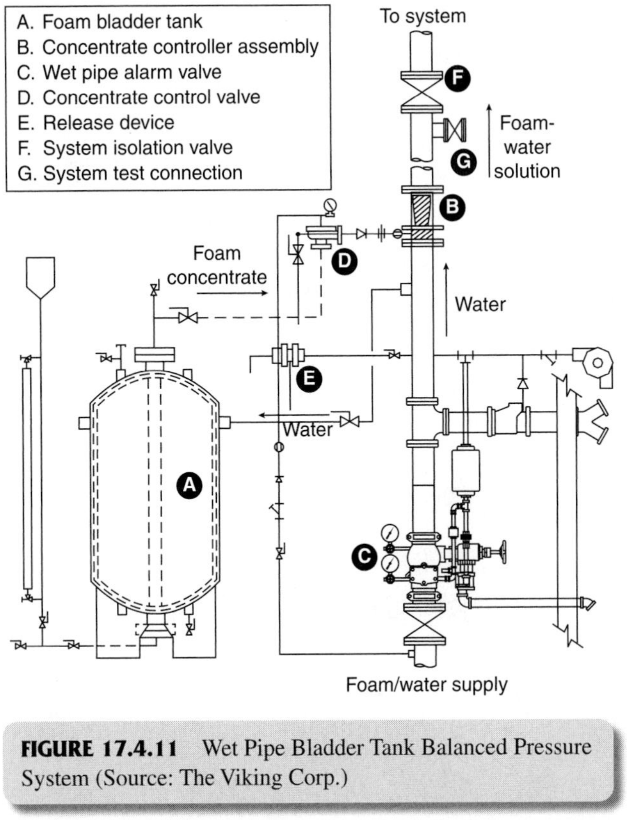

FIGURE 17.4.11 Wet Pipe Bladder Tank Balanced Pressure System (Source: The Viking Corp.)

lution to extinguish a flammable liquid fire. In a deluge system, the proportioner should be sized to meet the desired hydraulic characteristics of the application.

Balanced Pressure System Using Positive Pressure Foam Injection and In-Line Balanced Pressure Proportioners (ILBP). Balanced pressure proportioning systems using positive-pressure foam injection and an ILBP device use two basic methods of foam concentrate supply (Figures 17.4.12, 17.4.13, 17.4.14, and 17.4.15). Foam concentrate can be supplied from a bladder tank or a foam concentrate pump as long as it is being supplied at a higher pressure than the water supply at the point of foam injection to the system.

In a bladder tank system, concentrate proportioning is accomplished by installing a pilot-operated pressure control valve (POPCV) upstream of the ILBP assembly (see Figures 17.4.12 and 17.4.13). The POPCV is adjusted to a lower outlet pressure differential that meets the required difference to operate the ILBP balancing valve (note: this differential is manufacturer dependent). The water supply to the bladder tank is taken upstream of the POPCV, which provides a higher outlet pressure of foam concentrate being supplied to the ILBP proportioner assembly (Figure 17.4.16). The ILBP balancing valve senses the water supply pressure entering the modified venturi proportioner device and lowers the foam concentrate pressure entering the metering orifice to that equal to the water pressure entering the venturi proportioner. When the water pressure equals the foam concentrate pressure and the waterflow is such that the proper metering pressure drop is created across the venturi, the proper percentage of foam concentrate is injected into the water supply, thereby delivering the proper foam solution to the protected area.

Since this is a positive injection system, foam solution percentage will be rich (i.e., higher foam concentrate than needed) at lower flow rates. For example, this phenomemon will occur in a closed sprinkler system during the initial operation of several sprinklers. Also, the minimum listed flow rates for this type of system, compared to the balanced pressure bladder tank system, are typically much lower when alcohol-resistant foam concentrates are used.

In some installations, the total water supply pressure available is not adequate to create the proper pressure differential to allow the system to proportion within its operating limits. A foam concentrate pump can be used to supply the foam concentrate at a higher pressure than the water supply pressure at the point of foam injection to the system. Positive displacement foam pumps are generally used to supply the higher foam concentrate pressure. Accurate supply is maintained by using a pressure-relief-type valve in the foam supply line. The relief is piped back to the foam supply tank and is set to supply adequate pressure at the full range of system operating conditions (Figure 17.4.17).

A positive-pressure foam system using a bladder tank with POPCV or foam concentrate pump can supply multiple system proportioning points from a single foam supply source. Also, a longer distance from the foam concentrate supply is feasible. Large variations in system pressure are tolerable with the same accuracy of foam proportioning throughout the system. Multiple discharge devices and system sizes are adaptable to a single foam concentrate supply source.

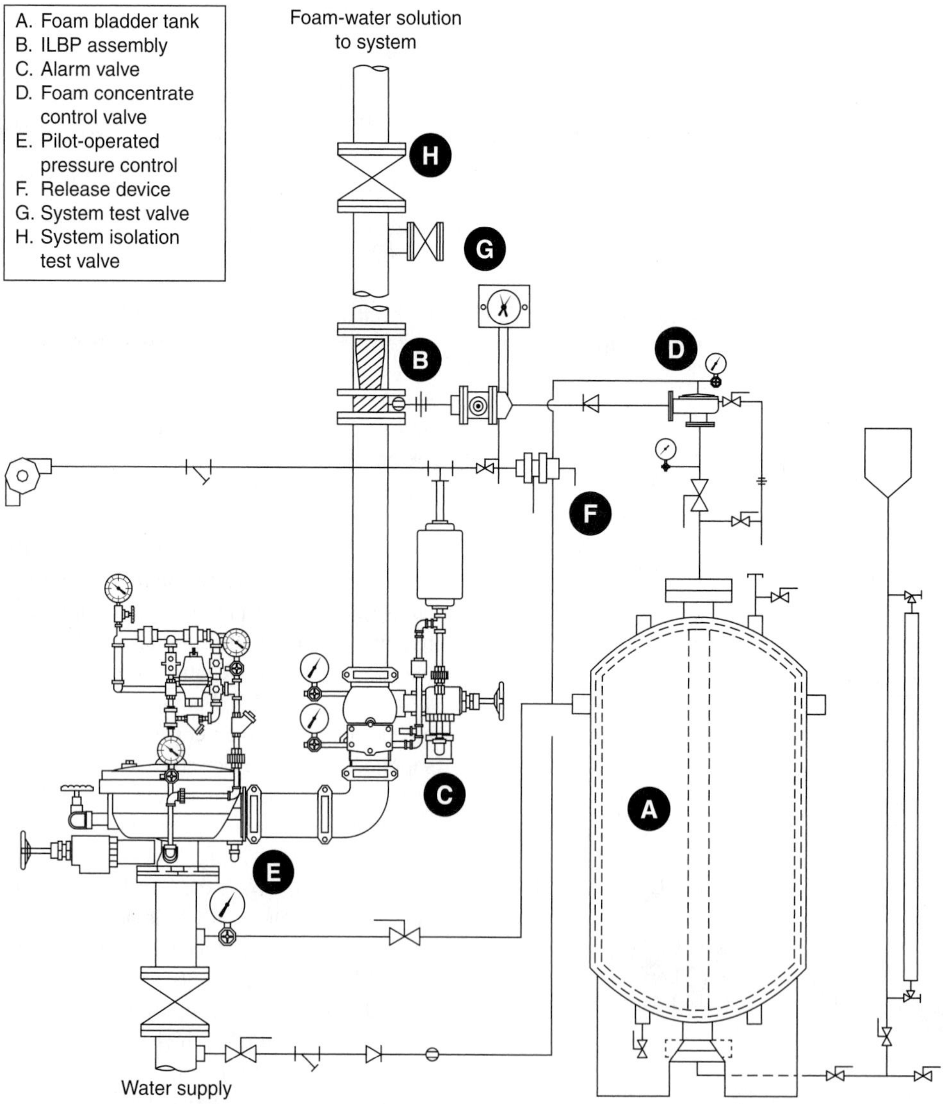

FIGURE 17.4.12 Wet Pipe Low-Flow Foam Proportioning System Bladder Tank Foam Supply (Source: The Viking Corp.)

Advantages and Disadvantages of Various Balanced Pressure Proportioning Systems. The different balanced pressure proportioning systems have advantages and disadvantages, depending on the particular design. The balanced pressure system with foam concentrate pump for single injection point has the following advantages and disadvantages:

Advantages

1. Foam concentrate can be pumped longer distances and the balancing valve can be kept adjacent to proportioner.
2. Foam supply can be replenished on the run by adding to the atmospheric tank.
3. The system will proportion at the correct percentage at lower flow rates due to less effect by friction loss.

Disadvantages

1. Maintenance and reliability requirements are relatively greater.
2. The cost is relatively high.
3. A backup power supply is required for electric systems.

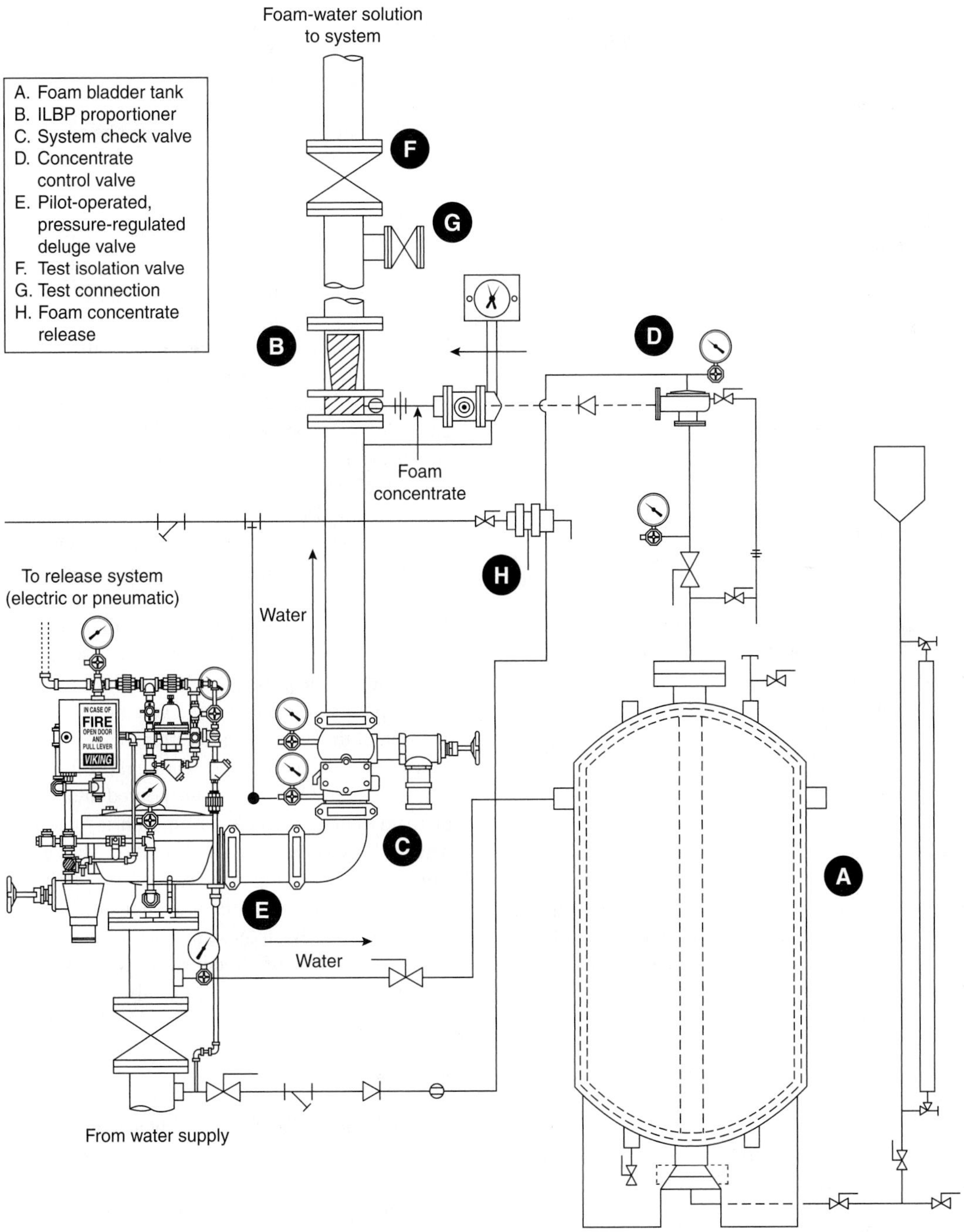

FIGURE 17.4.13 Low-Flow Preaction System with Bladder Tank (Source: The Viking Corp.)

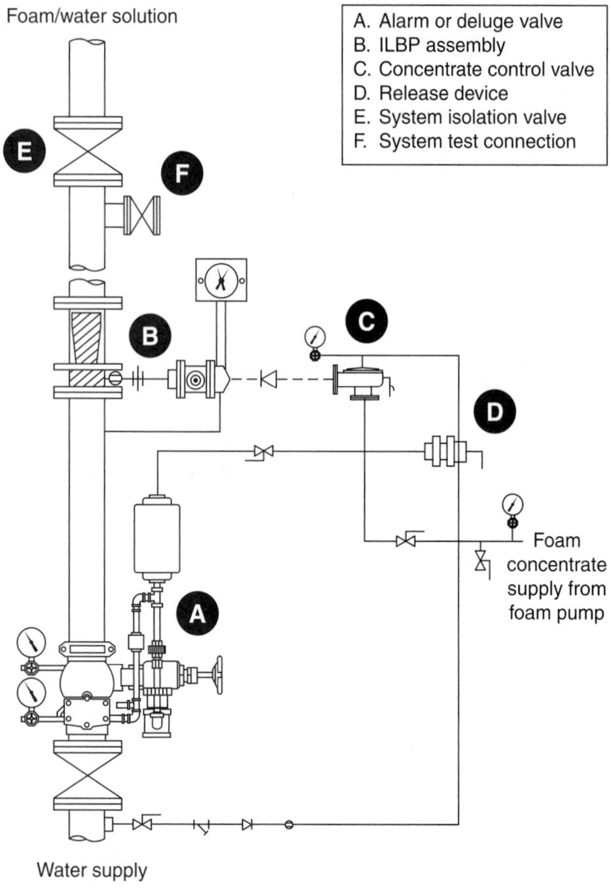

FIGURE 17.4.14 Wet Pipe Low-Flow System, Foam Supply from Foam Pump (Source: The Viking Corp.)

4. The balanced pressure proportioning systems require more space than other systems.
5. The system is limited to a single point of foam injection.

The balanced pressure system with bladder tank has the following advantages and disadvantages:

Advantages

1. No electrical power is required for the water-powered design.
2. Costs are lower for smaller systems and deluge applications.
3. Pre-engineered systems and foam storage are available.
4. Retrofitting into an existing system is relatively easy.
5. Maintenance costs are relatively low.

Disadvantages

1. Refill during a fire condition is not easy.
2. The bladder tank must be installed adjacent to proportioning equipment.
3. Proportioning of foam at low flows is lean, that is, has a lower concentrate percentage than needed or below listed rates.
4. The application is limited to a single proportioning source. (It is difficult to balance various flows that may be required in a multi-injection point system.)

The balanced pressure system with positive foam injection bladder or foam pump has the following advantages and disadvantages:

Advantages

1. The system can handle variable-pressure applications with the bladder tank design discharging a constant supply.
2. Multiple proportioning points and sizes can be accommodated from a single foam supply source.
3. Foam concentrate can be supplied a long distance to multiple points.
4. A wide flow range is available.
5. In closed head sprinkler systems, foam is supplied at the first sprinkler operation.
6. Multiple discharge devices and multiple areas of protection can be supplied.
7. Pressures and proportioning can be adjusted at the point of application.

Disadvantages

1. Refill during a fire condition is not easy.
2. Higher relative cost proportioning assembly compared to the system with only an injection pump or bladder.

Variable Orifice, Variable Flow Demand Proportioner. This type of balanced pressure system uses a specially designed, flow-sensitive, moveable piston section in the water supply that controls a variable orifice in the foam concentrate line. A pump supplies concentrate at monitored pressures to the metering orifice, which changes in size proportionally to the system demand for foam solution. The device is especially designed for large-capacity systems. Its design provides accurate proportioning over ranges of flow of water of approximately 2.3 to 1.

Premixed Foam Solution. This method of proportioning is a batch type of mixing of concentrate with water, usually in a container that can be pressurized. The measured volume of concentrate is poured into a measured volume of water to yield a foam solution of the recommended strength; for example, for a 3 percent solution in a container that holds 100 gal (378.5 L) of liquid, 97 gal (367 L) of water are poured into it and 3 gal (11.5 L) of foam concentrate are mixed with it to give a solution of 3 percent by volume. The final solution mixture is then educted from a tank to a pump or placed in a pressurizing vessel.

Some foam concentrates are not suitable for storage in premixed solution. Even those that are formulated for this use may show gradual loss of effectiveness. Manufacturers' recommendations should be followed carefully.

Portable Aspirating Equipment and Systems

Because of the difficulties associated with pumping or transporting generated foam in pipes or hoses and the familiarity of fire fighters with nozzles, the earliest designs of air-foam generators were devised to be used in much the same manner as water nozzles. They incorporated a crude venturi design whereby a jet or jets of foam solution enter an open contracted portion of a large-diameter foam tube. This action lowers the atmospheric

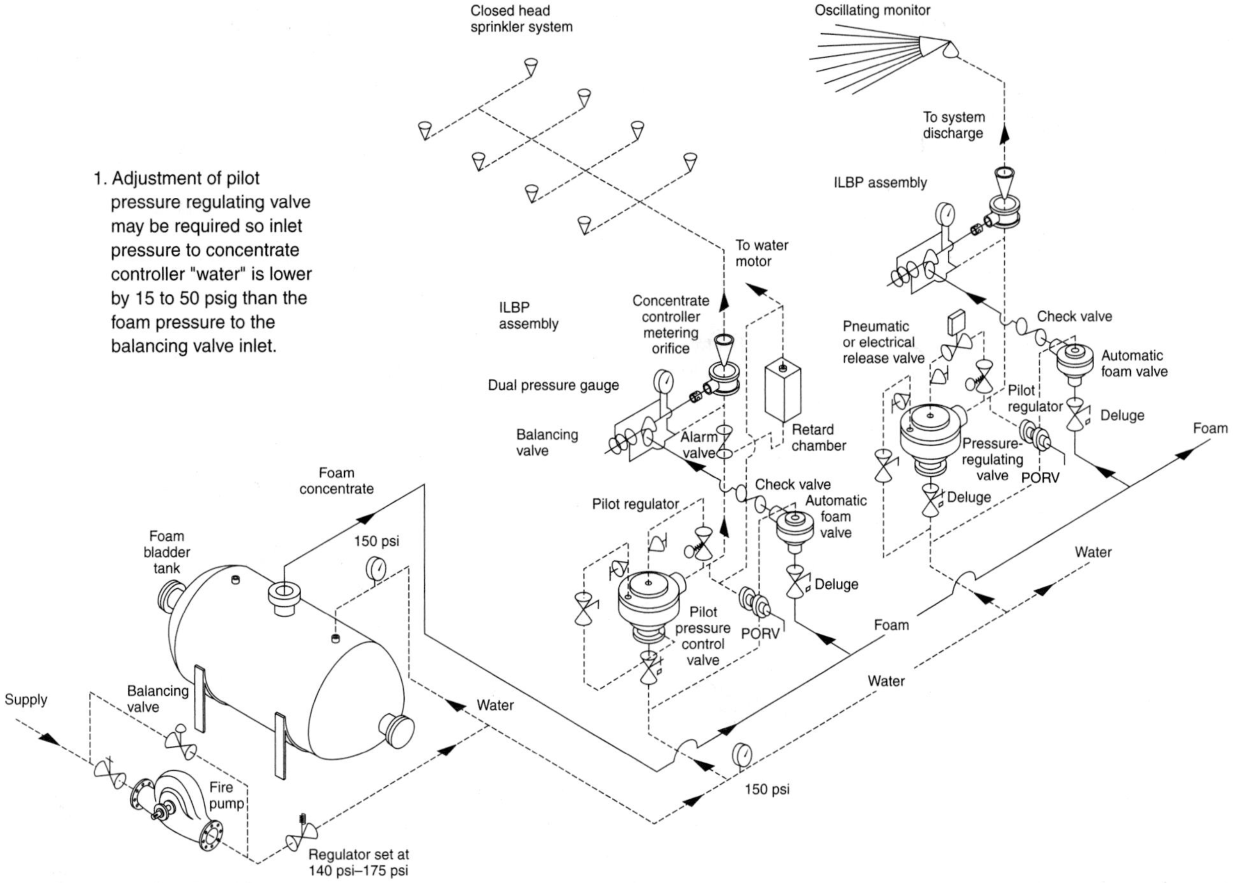

FIGURE 17.4.15 Low-Flow Foam System Schematic with Multiple Discharge Areas (Source: The Viking Corp.)

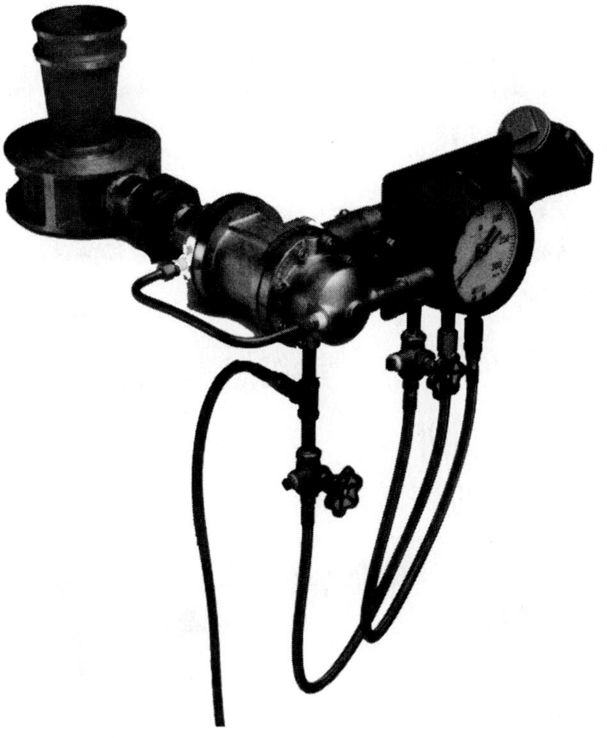

FIGURE 17.4.16 ILBP Assembly (Source: The Viking Corp.)

pressure surrounding the jets, and air is drawn or aspirated into the throat of the tube. Downstream of the contracted portion of the tube, a high turbulence and mixing of air and foam solution occurs. This turbulence may be increased by internal turbulence-accelerating devices, such as screens or baffles. The kinetic energy of the fluid contributes to this mixing action so that a useful, stable foam exits the tube at a relatively low pressure (Figure 17.4.18).

The basic design principles of this method of producing air-foam have been changed in many ways to yield, for many purposes, foams with greatly differing characteristics. However, all types of nozzles incorporating foam solution jets leading into free air-mixing cavities, followed by discharge apertures of one kind or another, use the aspirating action for making foam.

Hose Line Foam Nozzle. This is the most widely used portable, air-aspirating foam device for flammable liquid fire fighting. It is manufactured in a variety of capacities up to approximately 350 gpm (1325 Lpm) (Figure 17.4.19). Supplied with foam solution from a proportioner or by means of a pickup tube, it is used for combating fires resulting from spills of flammable liquid, or fires in tanks or fuel pits. To provide a variety of foam stream patterns that may be needed for the extinguishment operation, these nozzles often contain built-in devices that allow continuous foam pattern variation from a solid, straight stream to an inverted, filled umbrella shape (Figure 17.4.20). As with water streams, foam is employed in a solid, straight stream for range or reach. A flat or wide "bushy" shape is used for gentle

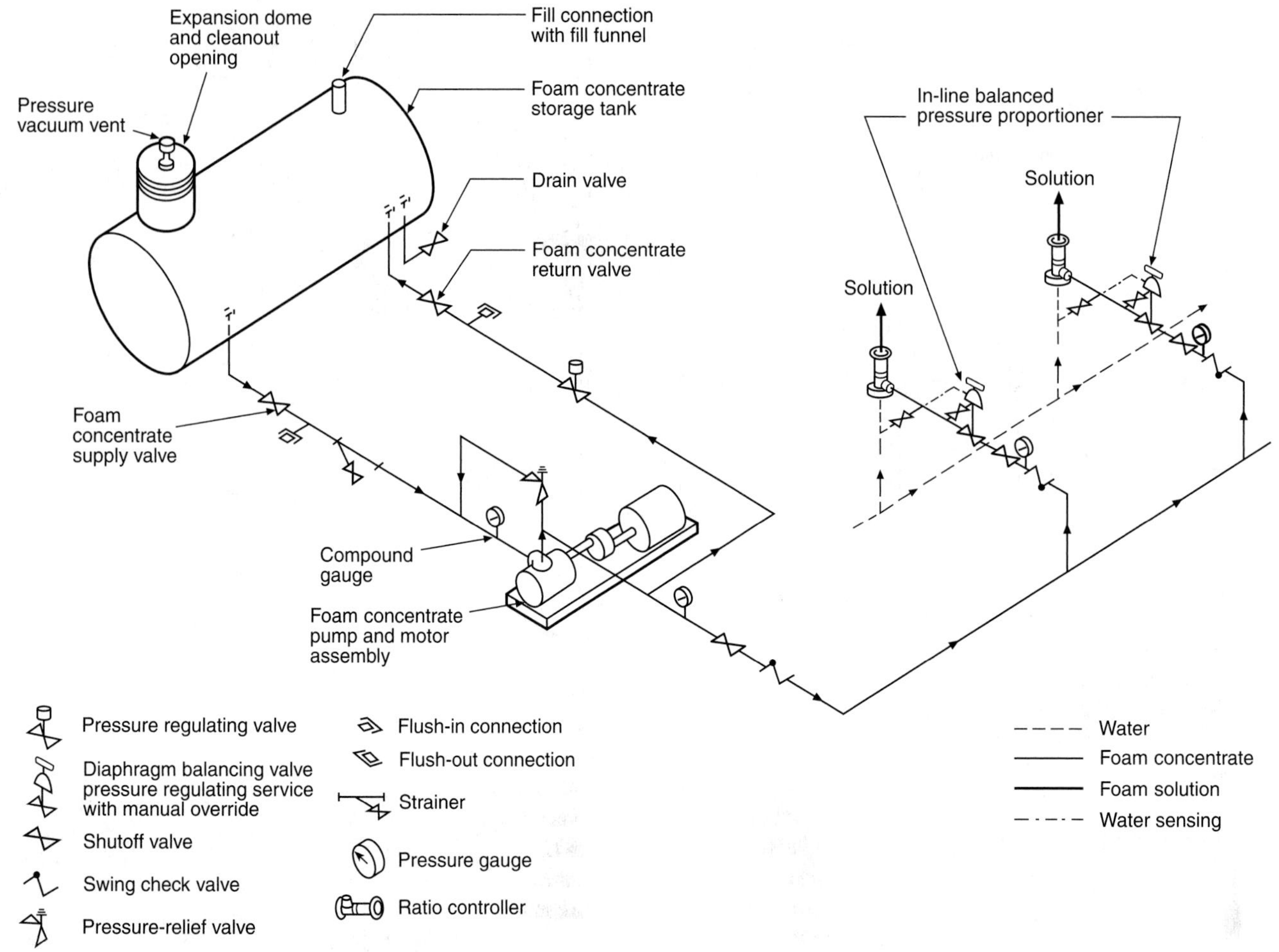

FIGURE 17.4.17 Balanced Pressure Proportioning with Multiple Injection Points

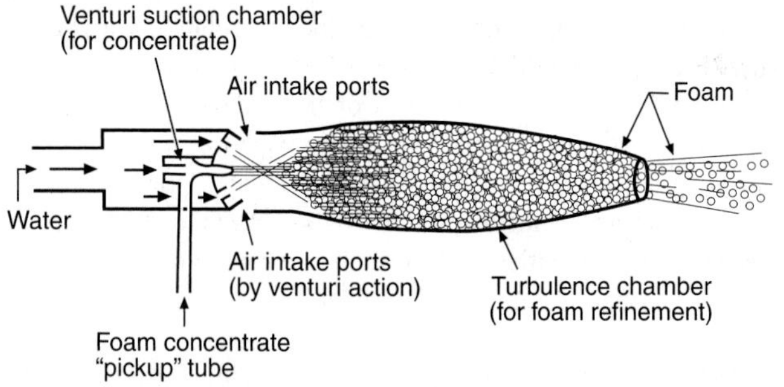

FIGURE 17.4.18 Aspirating Foam-Maker with a Concentrate Pickup Tube

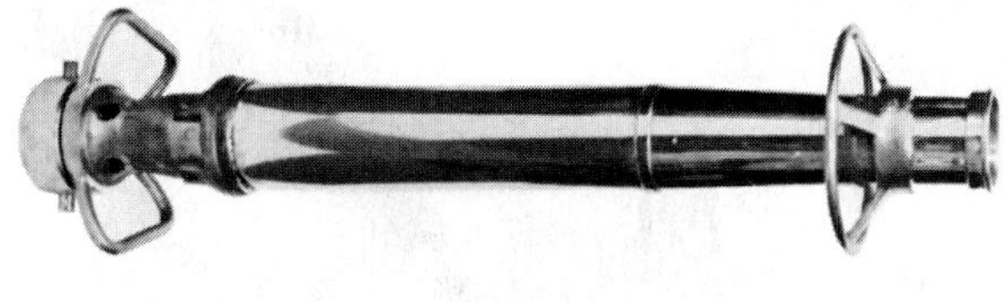

FIGURE 17.4.19 Hose Line Foam Nozzle

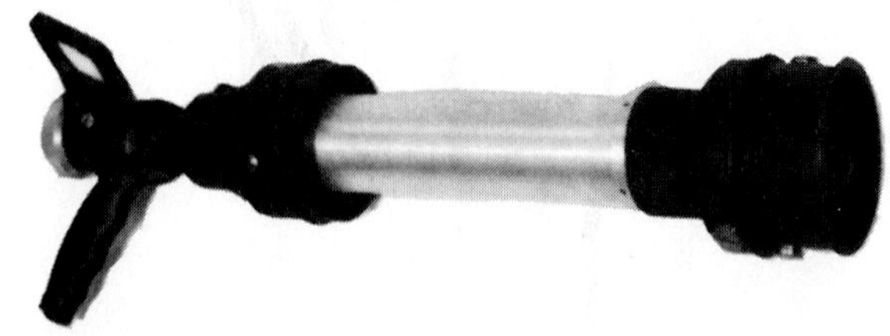

FIGURE 17.4.20 Adjustable Hose Line Foam Nozzle (Source: Kidde Fire Fighting)

"snowstorm" application on the burning fuel surface, and a very wide, circular "bushy" shape is used for radiance shielding of the operator during fire extinguishment or penetration into the fire area.

Another type of hose line foam nozzle is especially designed for quick, portable, one-person use during emergency operations from airport crash-rescue vehicles. Customarily called a handline foam nozzle, it is equipped with a foam pattern changing device, and some types are supplied with a valve control for converting the water or solution stream into a water spray for cooling purposes.

Foam and Foam-Water Monitors. In large-scale fuel-fire fire-fighting operations, it may become necessary to position a foam-making nozzle with a high discharge rate at an advantageous position for continuous application of foam to one point or over an area. Devices for this purpose are available in a variety of types, for example, as part of mobile truck apparatus, on a trailer, wheeled, or permanently mounted. The foam pattern change is accomplished by moving a deflector into the foam stream or by opening or closing the "jaws" at the exit end of the large tube.

This equipment has largely been replaced with non-air-aspirating monitor nozzles. Non-air-aspirating monitors are effective devices for extinguishing hydrocarbon pool fires.

High Back-Pressure Foam-Maker. Certain circumstances necessitate that foam be generated and supplied under pressure for transmission in pipes under a definite pressure head. The subsurface foam injection method for fuel tank fire extinguishment requires this type of foam-maker. The high back-pressure foam-maker, or "forcing foam-maker," is a venturi device that is carefully designed to make foam by air aspiration and to supply it under pressure at a carefully selected ratio (from 2:1 to 4:1) of air-to-foam solution. Approximately 20 to 40 percent of the inlet pressure is recoverable. In use, this foam device is usually brought to the fixed piping foam inlet, installed, and then supplied with foam solution by a portable or mobile pumper, or it may be permanently installed as part of a fixed system (Figure 17.4.21).

Medium- and High-Expansion Foam-Generating Devices. There are two principal methods used for the generation of these types of fire-fighting foams. One method uses a modified venturi action with air aspiration flow, whereas the other requires use of a blower and screen to form the finished foam. The latter system produces high-expansion foam containing sufficient residual kinetic energy to enable it to be forced through large tubes and passageways.

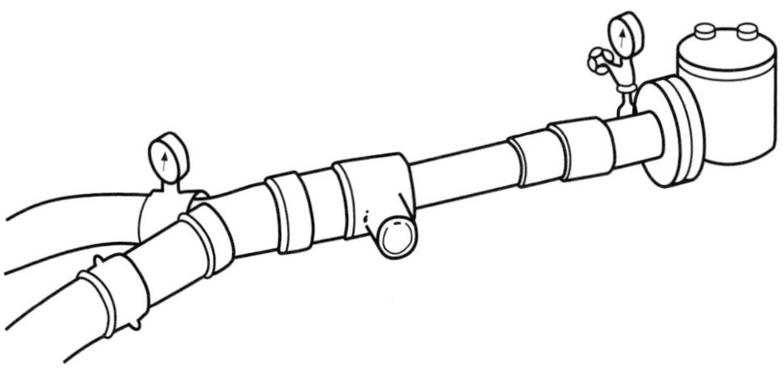

FIGURE 17.4.21 High Back-Pressure-Type (or Forcing-Type) Foam-Maker

Figure 17.4.22 illustrates the operating principles of high-expansion foam-generating devices.

Water Fog or Spray Nozzles and Monitors. Several types of adjustable water fog or spray nozzles for portable use provide an acceptable fire-fighting foam of adequate characteristics when supplied with certain foam concentrates. The most universal design of these is shown in Figure 17.4.23. An adjustable water spray monitor nozzle designed for this purpose is shown in Figure 17.4.24.

These portable water spray nozzles are used with aqueous film-forming foam (AFFF) solutions for combating flammable liquid tank and spill fires and are used in this manner on crash-rescue vehicles. The foam resulting from the discharge of AFFF solution devices that do not aspirate air is generally fast draining and may not impart the same degree of burnback resistance as the foam produced from AFFF agents when foam-generating devices of an air-aspirating type are used.

Foam monitors using AFFF can be either air-aspirating or non-air-aspirating. Non-air-aspirating monitor nozzles have the advantage of increased stream reach compared to air-aspirated devices. Combined with the rapid-fire knockdown characteristics of AFFF, these monitors are very effective for large hydrocarbon pool fire suppression. In particular, foam monitors are effective in aviation fire protection, both as turrets on aircraft rescue and fire-fighting vehicles and in fixed systems protecting aircraft hangars (Figure 17.4.25).

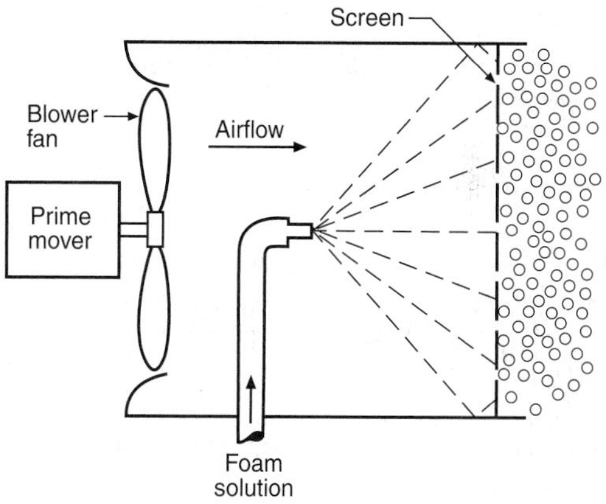

FIGURE 17.4.22 Fan-Blower-Type High-Expansion Foam-Generator

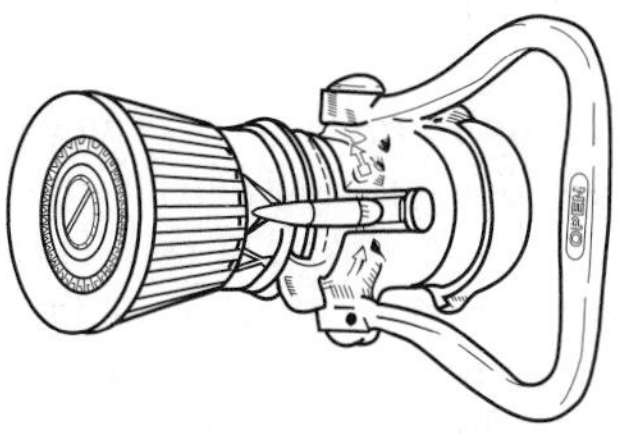

FIGURE 17.4.23 Variable-Pattern Water Fog Nozzle Foam-Maker for Use with AFFF

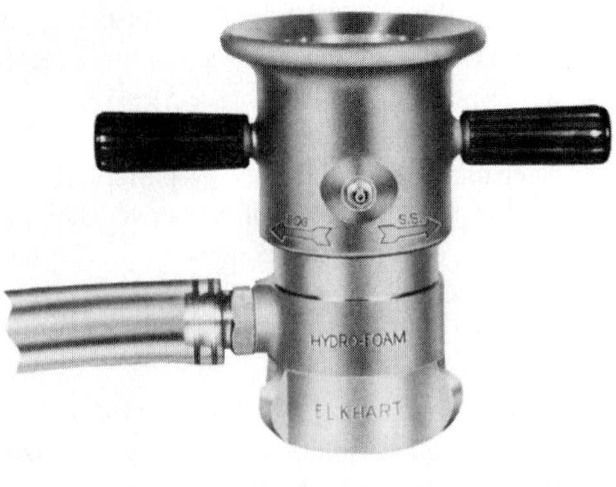

FIGURE 17.4.24 Adjustable 350 to 500 gpm (1325 to 1893 Lpm) Water Spray Foam Monitor Nozzle (Source: Elkhart Brass Mfg. Co.)

FIGURE 17.4.25 Foam Monitor (Source: Ansul Incorporated)

Foam-Generating Equipment

Where flammable liquid fire protection is required for permanently installed hazards, such as fuel storage tanks or dip tanks containing flammable or combustible liquids, air-foam-generating and distributing devices are installed integrally with the hazard. These fixed devices, which are piped to a source of foam solution, may be arranged for manual control or automatic activation by fire detectors in the event of fire.

Open Dip Tank, Quench Tank System. This system consists of a small, aspirating foam-maker supplied by a water line and foam concentrate educted to the foam-maker. Foam discharges into a mixing box, which also acts as a surface distributor for gentle foam application.

Foam Chambers for Large Fuel Storage Tanks. Fire protection of large outdoor fuel storage tanks requires that several foam chambers with foam-makers be installed at equally spaced positions slightly below the curb angle on the top periphery of the tanks. These chambers are connected to lines on the ground that supply foam solution to each foam-maker simultaneously in case of ignition of the flammable contents of the tank. Frangible seals at the discharge outlet of the foam chamber prevent vapor from entering the foam piping. These seals are designed to burst when foam pressure is applied. A screen for the air inlet to the aspirating foam-maker prevents clogging from foreign matter, such as bird nesting material. A universal or swing pipe joint is installed at ground level in the foam solution inlet pipe to prevent fracturing of the supply piping if an explosion precedes a tank fire (Figure 17.4.26).

Internal Tank Foam Distributing Devices. A prime requirement for efficient fuel tank extinguishment by topside foam devices has always been that the foam must be applied to the burning surface without undue plunging into the fuel or allowing the foam to become coated with burning fuel. This gentle application of foam must be accomplished at any level of the contents of the tank. Many devices have been developed to gently apply foam from one point, regardless of burning fuel level. These devices are required for some alcohol-type foams. Alternatively, foam discharge into a tank may be deflected to run down the inside tank shell to the burning fuel surface.

Central "Foam House" Distributing Systems. These systems, as shown in Figure 17.4.27, consist of an enclosure housing a foam concentrate supply tank and a proportioning device of an automatic or balanced pressure type. Foam solution is supplied under adequate pressure from this foam house to the piping system and controlled by appropriate valves so that the foam chambers with foam-makers on the burning tank receive foam solution.

Semifixed systems of similar design are more frequently used with mobile foam concentrate supply from foam trucks. The truck proportions and pumps foam solution to the pipe laterals feeding the foam-makers from a safe location outside the dike.

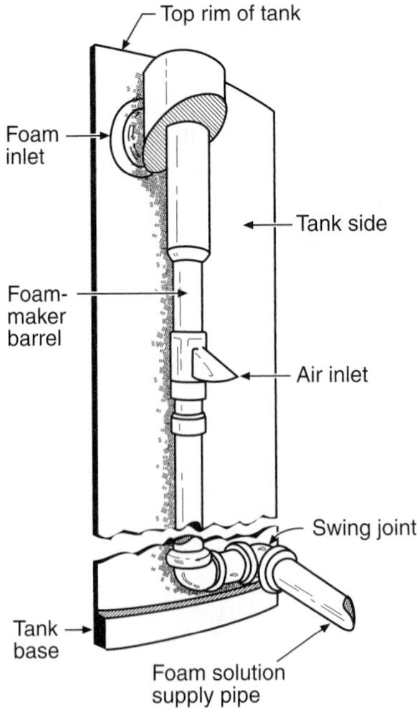

FIGURE 17.4.26 Air-Foam Chamber at Top of Storage Tank

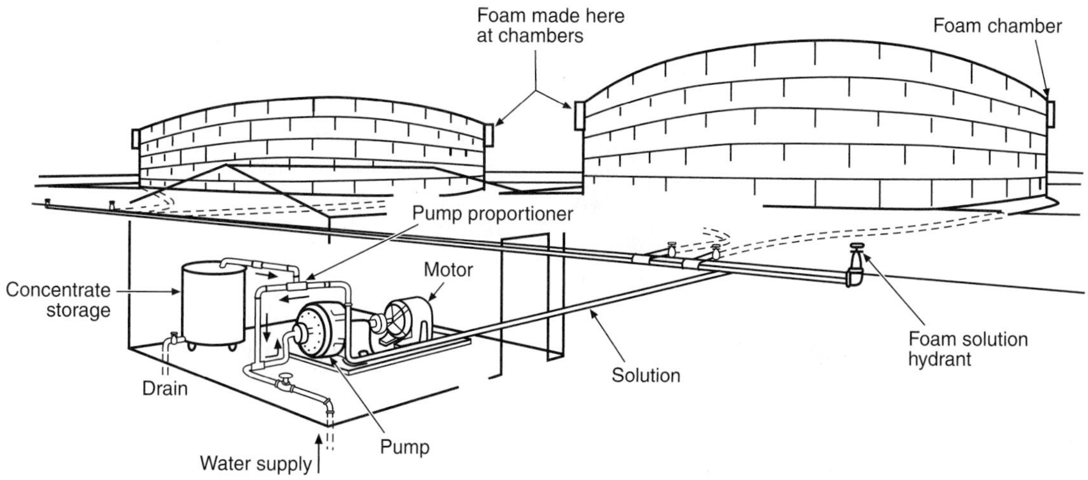

FIGURE 17.4.27 Schematic Arrangement of Foam Protection for Storage Tanks

Intermediate Back-Pressure System. Although this system of tank protection is similar to the preceding central foam house distributing systems, it utilizes strong and well-braced foam-delivery pipes on the side of the tank, which act as supports to prevent buckling of the tank from heat. This system also uses a foam truck to proportion and pump foam solution to the piping outside the dike or firewall of the burning tank.

Subsurface Foam-Injection Systems. The problems inherent with the application of foam from above the burning surface (topside) are sometimes difficult to combat. Problems may consist of explosion or fire damage to the foam-makers or tankside piping, forceful upward fire-drafted air currents that prevent the falling foam from reaching the burning surface, hazard to workers attempting to erect portable foam distributing devices near the burning tank, or inability of foam applied from the periphery of a large tank (greater than about 200 ft [61 m] in diameter) to flow and form a complete center seal during fire attack.

The obvious solution to these problems is to apply foam from the underside of the fire, causing it to come up through the contents of the tank. The subsurface foam-injection system accomplishes this by injecting foam under the pressure of the head of fuel in the tank, using the high back-pressure foam-maker referred to previously in this chapter.

Entry of foam may be provided at several points at the base of the tank (base injection), or it may be accomplished by means of the product line. Where large tanks are involved, a branched pipe foam distributor may be installed on or slightly above the floor of the tank above any expected water level and connected to a central foam-injection point outside the tank.

Mobile foam concentrate proportioning equipment is used with these systems, pumping from a protected position outside the tank dike (Figure 17.4.28).

Subsurface application of foam is recommended only for protection of cone-roof tanks containing hydrocarbon fuels. It is not recommended for use on floating-roof tanks or for protection of polar or water-miscible fuels.

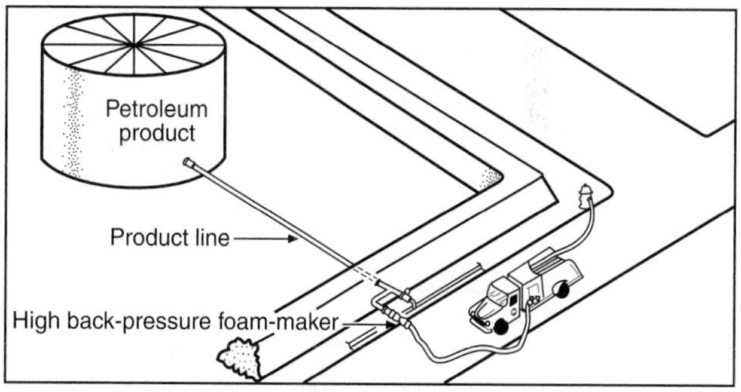

FIGURE 17.4.28 Semifixed Subsurface Foam Installation

These topside and subsurface injection systems require careful design. Their minimum installation requirements are found in NFPA 11.

Portable Foam Devices for Tank Protection. Mobile foam monitors of high-capacity discharge (foam cannon) may be used to direct a stream of foam over the open top rim of a burning tank so foam will fall into the burning area. These devices waste foam because of crosswinds, fire updrafts, and inability to place the equipment in an advantageous position. A foam-application rate 60 percent higher, therefore, must be included in the design; details are contained in NFPA 11. Nozzles of this type also are used to extinguish fires in the overflow space inside the dike surrounding the tank. Care is needed in directing the foam stream from such devices, as shown in Figure 17.4.29.

In recent years, mobile foam monitors with capacities up to 4000 gpm (15,144 Lpm) have been developed and used successfully for extinguishment of hydrocarbon fires in tanks up to 195 ft (60 m) in diameter.[1] Careful planning is required to ensure availability of adequate waterflow and pressure, foam concentrate, proportioning equipment, trained personnel, and safe accessibility to the hazard when relying on such devices.

FIGURE 17.4.29 Portable (Trailer) Foam Monitor (Cannon) (Source: Kidde Fire Fighting)

Other Considerations for Fuel Storage Tanks. The floating-roof storage tank has a good chance of freedom from fire; consequently, fixed foam systems are usually not required for their protection. Under certain circumstances, however, there may be a need for a foam-flooding system to flood the rim area.

As indicated by its name, the "covered" floating-roof tank is totally enclosed above the floating roof with a properly vented steel roof. Usually Class IB flammable liquids, such as gasolines and crudes, are stored in "open top" or covered floating-roof tanks. During storage operations, there is no vapor space between the bottom of the floating roof and the stored product surface. However, during periods of initial fill, a flammable vapor space will exist until the floating roof is buoyant. In the case of covered floating-roof tanks, the space between the fixed and the floating roof will be within the flammable range during periods of initial fill and longer, depending on atmospheric temperatures, wind, and vapor pressure of the stored product. Class II and III combustible liquids are usually stored in fixed-roof tanks.

In an open-top floating-roof tank, a rim of fire is all that can be expected. Rim fires may be caused by atmospheric disturbances, such as lightning, but usually do not occur if the floating roof is bonded properly to the shell as specified in NFPA 780, *Standard for the Installation of Lightning Protection Systems.* Rim fires due to atmospheric disturbances do not occur in covered floating-roof tanks because of the "Faraday effect" of the fixed roof. Rim fires may occur in either type of floating-roof tank due to a serious exposure fire.

Fixed foam fire protection for the open top floating-roof consists of aspirating-type foam-makers installed in such a way that when supplied with foam solution, their foam discharge floods the annular area covered by the seal around the tank periphery. A metal foam dam may be needed to restrict the foam to this area. Further details of such construction are contained in the Appendix to NFPA 11.

When foam protection is desired for covered floating-roof tanks, a foam system similar to those described for fixed-roof tanks may be provided. Subsurface injection systems are not recommended for open top or covered floating-roof tanks because of the possibility of tilted or sunken roofs resulting in improper foam distribution.

Fixed foam systems employing foam spray nozzles or monitors are used to protect large oil-water separators, pump areas, and oil piping manifolds. Fixed foam systems are not generally used to protect tank diked areas. Large wheeled monitors or trailer-mounted foam cannons, as shown in Figure 17.4.29, are used for this purpose.

Other Hazards. Certain hazardous areas, for example, aircraft hangars, may require additional foam-making and distributing devices, such as foam monitors mounted near floor level. Often these devices are provided with an automatic oscillator so that foam is continually distributed over the floor to extinguish burning spilled fuel under obstacles, such as aircraft wings. These are typically combined with air-aspirating or non-air-aspirating sprinklers installed at the roof of the hangar. Application rates for non-air-aspirating AFFF sprinklers are lower than air-aspirating sprinklers, in recognition of the fire plume penetration capability of AFFF discharged from ordinary sprinklers. NFPA 409 provides design details for overhead and low-level foam systems.

NFPA 409 also recognizes low-level AFFF application, combined with water-only sprinklers at the ceiling. A recently developed low-level AFFF nozzle can be installed in the floor

FIGURE 17.4.30 Low-Level AFFF Nozzle Installed in Aircraft Hangar Floor (Source: The Viking Corp.)

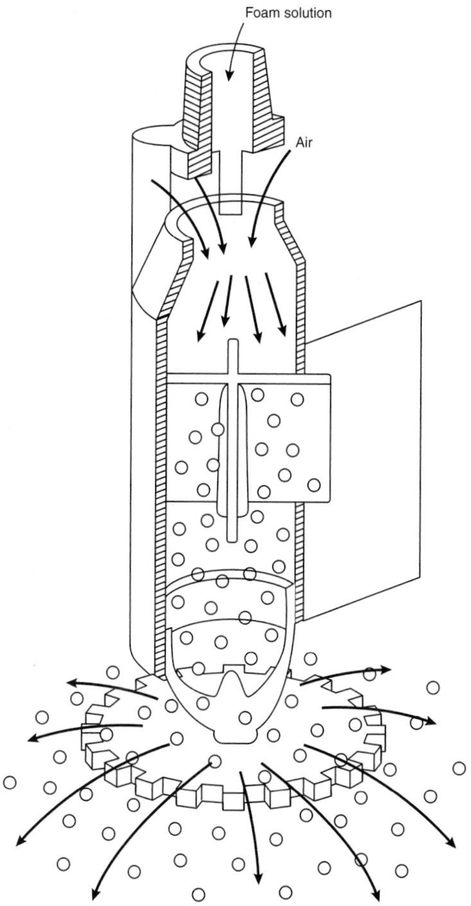

FIGURE 17.4.31 Air-Aspirating Foam Sprinkler (Source: Ansul Incorporated)

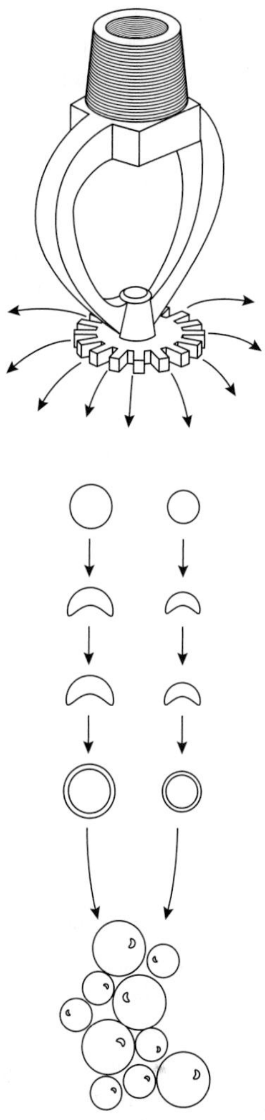

FIGURE 17.4.32 Non-Air-Aspirating Sprinkler (Source: Ansul Incorporated)

of a hangar (Figure 17.4.30). This design reduces AFFF spray to aircraft in the event of a false discharge.

Fixed foam systems are used to protect petroleum piers and wharves where products and petroleum crude are handled. Foam monitors of 1000 gpm (3800 Lpm) and greater capacity are mounted on towers and remotely operated to cover both the pier and the tanker deck in the pipe manifold area. Below deck, foam spray systems or oscillating monitors are installed to keep the pier tenable in the event of a spill fire floating on the water surface under the pier.

Fixed systems consisting of automatically operated combinations of foam spray systems and foam monitors are often installed to protect chemical processing plants. Alcohol-resistant foams are usually required. In these designs, where there may be a high risk, process vessels, pumps, and piping often are all included within the foam distribution pattern for overall protection. The system can be automatically activated by heat or fire detectors. See NFPA 11 for design of foam spray systems.

Foam-Water Sprinkler Systems. In areas where flammable and combustible liquids are processed, stored, or handled, water discharge may have limited effectiveness for controlling or extinguishing large spill fires. The effectiveness of water in these applications is a function of many variables, including fuel type, storage container, fuel configuration and geometry, height of the facility, and the level of acceptable risk. NFPA 30 recognizes both water and AFFF protection for indoor storage of liquids.

Sprinklers or nozzles used to protect liquid hazards may be air-aspirating or non-air-aspirating devices. Figures 17.4.31 and 17.4.32 show examples of both types of sprinklers. Air-aspirating sprinklers, such as that shown in Figure 17.4.31, were developed for use with protein-based foam in deluge sprinkler applications. Foam solution is discharged through the device, aerated, and applied through the open sprinkler or nozzle to the hazard. Detection systems are often provided to actuate the system automatically. The design area is the entire area of the deluge system.

Although AFFF can be effectively applied using air aspirating deluge sprinklers, it can also be discharged through traditional water sprinklers. Research was performed by the Factory Mutual Research Corporation related to aircraft hangar fire protection.[2] This research demonstrated that AFFF discharged through non-air-aspirating standard sprinklers was at least as effective in extinguishing large spill fires as AFFF discharge from air-aspirating sprinklers. The effectiveness of the standard sprinklers was attributed to more effective plume penetration by higher-density foam particles. Figure 17.4.32 shows an example of a non-air-aspirated sprinkler.

Standard sprinklers used with AFFF may be open for use in a deluge system, or closed where the use is similar to a standard closed sprinkler system. For example, NFPA 409 recognizes the use of open standard sprinkler AFFF systems installed at the ceiling of aircraft hangars. NFPA 30 requires the use of closed sprinklers where AFFF is used. The sprinkler temperature rating, response characteristics, and application rate are specified based on test data for a specific hazard.

Air-aspirating foam sprinklers and standard sprinklers used to discharge AFFF are tested in accordance with UL 162.[3] Systems are listed for use by the combination of foam concentrate, proportioning system, and discharge device. For example, a vendor's foam sprinkler design may consist of 3 percent AFFF concentrate using a balanced pressure proportioner discharging through a standard sprinkler. Additionally, foam sprinkler or spray nozzles must have essentially the same discharge pattern when water is discharged. This dual capability affords the system Class A and B extinguishing capability.

Fundamental design requirements can be found in NFPA 16. Listing of system components is required in accordance with UL 162. Listing requirements vary as a function of discharge device (air-aspirating and non-air-aspirating sprinkler), type of fuel (miscible and nonmiscible hydrocarbons), extinguishment time, and burnback resistance. Only AFFF and FFFP can be used through standard orifice sprinkler and spray systems. These agents must extinguish test fires at an application rate of 0.10 gpm/ft^2 (4.1 Lpm/m^2). Standard orifice (½ in. [12.7 mm]) and large orifice ($^{17}/_{32}$ in. [13.5 mm]) sprinklers are recognized. Air-aspirated foam-water sprinklers using protein or flouroprotein foam are tested at 0.16 gpm/ft^2 (6.6 Lpm/m^2). It should be recognized that NFPA 16 requires a minimum design application rate of 0.16 gpm/ft^2 (6.6 Lpm/m^2) for all foam agents. Other standards, such as NFPA 409 and NFPA 30, provide specific requirements for the particular hazards.

Application rates required to protect polar solvents using alcohol-type foams are generally greater than those required for nonmiscible hydrocarbons. The sprinkler design must meet the minimum application rate in the UL listing for the polar solvent being protected. Where polar solvents in containers are protected in warehouses, other factors may impact minimum design application rates. For example, the lowest design application rate currently permitted in NFPA 30 for indoor storage is 0.30 gpm/ft^2 (12.3 Lpm/m^2).

Fixed systems using foam-water or standard sprinklers require associated foam concentrate tanks, proportioners, and suitable pumps to supply the system with foam solution. NFPA 16 is the installation standard that provides fundamental design requirements. Other standards may require specific additional features. For example, NFPA 30 requires that foam solution be discharged when four closed AFFF sprinklers have operated. This requires a system that can proportion at the low end of the flow range, such as the positive pressure ILBP system discussed earlier.

DELIVERING FOAM FROM VEHICLES

The majority of the mobile fire protection vehicles using foam consist of airport crash-rescue trucks and industrial foam trucks used at oil refineries and petrochemical plants. Many of these vehicles are also equipped to discharge dry chemical in combination with foam. These have combined, or "twinned," agent equipment and are described later in this chapter.

Crash-Rescue Trucks

Mobile foam trucks, developed by military and municipal authorities in the United States and other countries, are large, custom-designed vehicles with oversize running gear that allows them to travel over all types of terrain. The trucks carry their own water supply as well as foam concentrate. Automatic balanced pressure proportioning is usually provided, although in some designs an around-the-pump proportioning system is used. The trucks are equipped with separate engine-driven water pumps and foam concentrate pumps so that the turret monitor nozzles and roadway foam nozzles can be discharged while the truck is in motion. Recent designs accomplish this using one or two engines for all necessary power requirements. Crash-rescue trucks are equipped with large-capacity, adjustable foam monitors of 500- to 1500-gpm (1900- to 5700-Lpm) discharge, depending on truck size. The foam monitors are usually installed on top of the cab with remotely operated controls. The trucks are also equipped with portable handlines. Although limited, their supply of foam concentrate and water is sufficient for fire fighters to form a passageway for access to a burning aircraft for rescue. Their primary purpose is rescue of people and not necessarily a total extinguishment of fire. Aircraft crash-rescue foam vehicles are specially designed and require special attention to detail in their fabrication and performance requirements. NFPA 414, *Standard for Aircraft Rescue and Fire-Fighting Vehicles,* provides standards for such vehicles.

Industrial Foam Truck Design

Foam trucks are manufactured by vendors who make a specialty of this design and by some vendors of fire department pumpers. Generally, using NFPA 1901, *Standard for Automotive Fire Apparatus,* as a design basis, these trucks are fabricated on a suitable commercial or custom truck chassis. In the United States, they are available with water pumps in sizes from 750 to 2000 gpm (2839 to 7570 Lpm), using gasoline or diesel engine drives.

Balanced pressure proportioning is provided for maximum flexibility and simplification. A positive-displacement-type foam concentrate pump takes suction from a 500- to 1000-gal (1900- to 3800-L) foam concentrate storage tank. The foam concentrate pump is driven by a power takeoff or hydraulic motor. The water pump is driven by a transfer gear from the main drive shaft behind the transmission. A metering valve at each truck outlet can vary foam proportioning from 3 to 6 percent.

In addition to the foam concentrate, each foam truck usually is equipped with a 500- to 1000-gpm (1900- to 3800-Lpm) monitor and carries fire hose, foam nozzles and adjustable water spray nozzles, hose adapters, and other accessories. The maximum truck height is limited to permit passage beneath overhead obstructions. When the truck is equipped with a large-capacity nozzle on a telescopic or articulated boom, a second power take-off is used to power the boom hydraulic system.

Foam trucks for special hazard application, instead of fixed foam systems, are popular for refinery and petrochemical plant use. Their advantages are as follows:

1. Capability of discharging their maximum capacity at any hazard in the plant rather than only to the limited areas covered by a fixed system.
2. Improved reliability because their equipment is easily maintained; thus, operating procedures can be simplified and fire fighters can be trained more easily to use the equipment.

Industrial foam trucks are used to extinguish spill fires in process areas, piping runs, and tank diked areas, as well as in fighting tank fires. Their 500- to 1000-gpm (1900- to 3800-Lpm) foam-water monitors and 1½ in. (38 mm) and 2½ in. (64 mm) handlines are used for fighting major spill fires. Designs that are equipped with monitor nozzles on articulated or telescopic booms enable the operator to discharge foam at various elevations in and around process equipment. In some cases, a tank fire can be extinguished with this equipment. Figure 17.4.33 illustrates a typical industrial foam truck. Figure 17.4.34 illustrates a typical foam truck with a telescopic boom, ladder, and basket. The foam trucks with booms may or may not be equipped with a ladder and/or basket.

COMBINED AGENT OR "TWINNED" EQUIPMENT

The capability of dry chemical agent (especially potassium-salt-types) for very fast flame control and three-dimensional flowing fuel extinguishment is well documented. However, dry chemicals have no cooling or vapor-suppressing capability, and reflash can occur. With dry-chemical-compatible foam concentrates, it is possible to apply a coating of vapor-securing foam to

FIGURE 17.4.33 A Typical Industrial Foam Truck (Source: Motiva Enterprises LLC)

FIGURE 17.4.34 Foam Truck with Telescopic Boom and Nozzle with Ladder and Basket (Source: Kidde Fire Fighting)

a burning fuel surface that has been freshly extinguished by the chemical action of dry chemical discharges.

The logical extension of these developments has been incorporated into portable and mobile devices with dual-trigger valve nozzles and monitor nozzles discharging AFFF and dry chemical. Figure 17.4.35 illustrates a type of twinned agent nozzle where dry chemical is entrained in the foam stream. Figure 17.4.36 shows a twin agent unit consisting of a dry chemical agent tank and an AFFF solution tank for dual agent application. The use of this combined agent attack allows three-dimensional as well as spill fire extinguishment of flammable liquid with both speed and freedom from reignition. The fire-fighting vehicle shown in Figure 17.4.37 is for aircraft crash-rescue purposes and for extinguishment on freeways or in plants, using combined agents.

In use, the twinned hose from the hose reel supplies dry chemical and AFFF to a dual nozzle for one-person operation. Similarly, the turret nozzles at the front of the vehicle discharge dry chemical from the upper nozzle and AFFF from the lower. With a sweeping motion, the flames are controlled with the dry chemical, quickly followed by a vapor-securing, cooling layer of foam to prevent reflash. This rapid action halts

FIGURE 17.4.35 Twinned Agent Nozzle (Source: Crash Rescue Equipment Service)

FIGURE 17.4.36 Twin Agent Unit Consisting of One Dry Chemical Agent Tank and One AFFF Solution Tank for Dual Agent Application (Source: Ansul Incorporated)

FIGURE 17.4.37 A Combined-Agent Vehicle (Source: Emergency One, Inc., and Kidde Fire Fighting)

flame radiation and makes advancement over the fire area safe and cool.

A design especially for petroleum refinery plant protection involves the combined agent concept in a triple-use arrangement consisting of a 2000 lb (908 kg) dry chemical tank, a 200 gal (757 L) AFFF premixed solution tank, nitrogen bottles for pressurization of both tanks, a 500 gal (1900 L) foam concentrate tank, a 1500 gpm (5700 Lpm) water pump, and balanced pressure proportioning up to 2000 gpm (7600 Lpm). Two monitors mounted behind the truck cab are twinned for operation as a unit and consist of a 50 lb/sec (23 kg/sec) dry chemical turret nozzle and a 500 gpm (1900 Lpm) AFFF or foam nozzle as shown in Figure 17.4.38. A different configuration uses three monitors mounted behind the truck cab—twinned 50 lb/sec (23 kg/sec) dry chemical and 180 gpm (680 Lpm) AFFF nozzles, and one adjacent 1000 gpm (3800 Lpm) adjustable foam monitor. In addition, the truck carries two hose reels, each with 100 ft (30.5 m) of twinned hose, and hose nozzles for dry chemical and AFFF arranged for twinned operation. The hose reels are equipped with an electric motor rewind. Foam nozzles, adjustable water fog nozzles, fire hose, and other accessories are carried on the truck.

FIGURE 17.4.38 Triple-Agent Truck (Source: Kidde Fire Fighting)

The dry chemical turret nozzle will extinguish three-dimensional or pressure fires at a distance of 100 ft (30.5 m) and spill fires at a distance of approximately 150 ft (46 m). In addition, for long-range operation with lengthy duration, the 1000 gpm (3800 Lpm) foam-water monitor has a range of more than 200 ft (61 m). The truck is capable of fighting fires in fixed-roof oil storage tanks with a maximum diameter of 160 ft (49 m). The proportioning system is designed to permit an external tank, such as a tank truck or trailer, to be used for foam concentrate supply without interrupting foam solution proportioning.

Twinned agent hose reels are often used on offshore oil platforms for equipment protection and in naval shipboard engine rooms. These systems have suitably sized potassium bicarbonate (Purple K) dry chemical containers that are pressurized by nitrogen when put into operation and AFFF central pumped systems using balanced pressure proportioning. Similar twinned agent skid-mounted systems are used in refineries and petrochemical plants.

MEDIUM- AND HIGH-EXPANSION FOAM-GENERATING EQUIPMENT AND SYSTEMS

Medium- or high-expansion foam is an aggregation of bubbles resulting from the mechanical expansion of a foam solution by air or by other gases, with expansion ratios in the range of from 20:1 to approximately 1000:1. There are three types of systems: (1) total flooding, (2) local application, and (3) portable.

The foam generators for these systems are of two types: (1) aspirator and (2) blower. The portable or fixed aspirator-type device utilizes jet streams of water-foam solution, entraining suitable amounts of air to produce foam. With the blower-type device, foam solution is discharged onto a screen through which an air stream, developed by a fan or blower, is passing. As the air passes through the screens wetted with the foam solution, large masses of bubbles or foam are formed. The blower may be powered by a hydraulic or water motor, compressed air or gas, an electric motor, or an internal combustion engine.

System Design and Use

Detailed design information on medium- and high-expansion foam systems can be found in NFPA 11.

Basically, medium- and high-expansion foam systems are used to control or extinguish fires involving surface fires in flammable and combustible liquids and solids, and deep-seated fires involving solid materials subject to smoldering. Three-dimensional fires in flammable liquids (falling or flowing under pressure) with flashpoints below 100°F (38°C) generally cannot be extinguished with this technique, although they may be kept under control. The following are key factors to consider in determining the design adequacy of medium- and high-expansion foam systems:

1. The quality and adequacy of water supply, the adequacy of supply of foam liquid concentrate, and the source of the air supply
2. Suitability of the generator and foam delivery system (piping, fittings, valves, ducts)
3. Needed submergence volume and time as influenced by the space being protected, the nature of the hazards involved, leakage of the foam, and similar factors
4. If outdoors, the effect of wind, because some of the foam may be dissipated by air currents

High-expansion foam may be useful in controlling LNG fires and unignited spills by forming an ice layer on the liquid and by helping disperse the vapor cloud.

Total Flooding Systems

A total flooding system may be used where there is an enclosure surrounding the hazard being protected that will permit the required amount of medium- or high-expansion foam to be built up to extinguish or control the fire. Examples of such enclosures are rooms, vaults, pits, and basement areas. Even an entire building may be so protected where the foam generators are of sufficient capacity and steps are taken to ensure effective distribution and retention of the foam. Since the efficiency of the system depends on the development and maintenance of a suitable quantity of foam within the particular enclosure, leakage of the foam from the enclosure must be avoided. Thus, it is important that doorways or windows be designed to close automatically, with consideration being given to the evacuation of personnel. High-level venting is required for the air that is displaced by the foam.

For adequate protection, sufficient high-expansion foam must be discharged at a rate to fill the space to an effective depth above the hazard before an unacceptable degree of damage occurs. The depth of the foam above the hazard will vary, depending on the type of materials creating the hazard. Generally, the minimum depth above the hazard should be 2 ft (0.6 m). The time allowed to cover the hazard will likewise vary depending on the type of material involved, construction features, and whether the enclosure also has an automatic sprinkler system or similar protection. Consideration has to be given to the disintegration of the foam by the heat of the fire, by normal foam shrinkage, by leakage around doors and windows and through unclosable openings, and by the effects of sprinkler discharge where sprinkler protection is provided.

Local Application Systems

Local application systems can be used where total flooding systems may be impractical or unnecessary. Such hazards may be indoors or outdoors, where air currents are not likely to be severe. These systems are best adapted to the protection of flammable or combustible liquids in dip tanks and associated drainboards, and for pits and trenches. Medium- or high-expansion foam may be used for extinguishing spill fires where it is feasible to apply the foam from fixed or portable nozzles at adequate rates of discharge to develop a foam blanket to achieve complete extinguishment.

Compressed Air Foam Systems

Unlike traditional foam systems in which air aspiration occurs at or near the discharge device, compressed-air foam (CAF) systems inject air prior to the discharge device. Foam is generated by injecting air under pressure into a foam solution stream. As solution moves through a hose or piping system, foam is produced by the combined momentum of the foam solution and the injected-air stream in the hose or pipe.

CAFs for mobile fire fighting have been used primarily as Class A fire-fighting agents. There are mobile systems that are designed for use on Class B fire hazards; sometimes these Class B CAFs are combined with a secondary agent such as Purple K. AFFF foam concentrate is generally used in these systems.

CAF in fixed-pipe systems is a recent development. As with the mobile systems, AFFF is used as the foam concentrate. In one listed/approved system, the AFFF is proportioned at 2 percent compared to 3 percent for traditional foam sprinkler systems. Also, the effective application rate (foam solution, gpm/ft^2 [Lpm/m^2]) is lower than similarly listed low-expansion foam sprinkler systems. NFPA 11 recognizes this system and provides design and installation requirements. The primary advantage of CAF systems is for situations in which there is an extremely limited water supply.

Precautions to Be Observed with Medium- or High-Expansion Foam

Medium- or high-expansion foam is normally nontoxic to persons who may be trapped in a space filled with it, since the air entrained in the foam is generally not contaminated. However, because of the foam bubbles, some difficulty may be experienced in breathing, and breathing discomfort will increase with reduction of foam expansion. Air is usually taken from a clean source, but where products of combustion are introduced, the foam quality may be substandard because of the contaminants present and the temperature of the heated air. Entering a foam-filled space should be avoided unless adequate precautions are taken because loss of vision and disorientation introduce life and injury hazards. A coarse water spray may be used to "cut" a path in the foam. Personnel should wear self-contained breathing apparatus and employ a lifeline when entering an area filled with high-expansion foam.

FOAM EQUIPMENT TESTING AND SURVEILLANCE

The continued effective emergency performance of foam equipment depends entirely on fully adequate maintenance procedures, with periodic testing where possible. The many variations in system design and equipment applications for hazards requiring foam make it impossible to establish anything other than general procedures for periodic inspection. Because air-foam concentrates, foam equipment, and fire protection systems are subject to change, variation, and even malfunction over long unattended spans of time, they must be kept adequate for the purpose for which they are designed.

Foam Concentrate Surveillance

Because all air-foam concentrates are water solutions of organic and inorganic chemicals of one sort or another, they must be carefully observed for changes in constitution and characteristics. They must be stored in shipping containers and in storage tanks according to the manufacturer's recommendations. Exposure to extreme heat, cold, or contamination, or mixing with other materials must be avoided. Sedimentation or precipitate formation in containers or tanks of concentrate should be carefully checked periodically. The manufacturer or the manufacturer's representative is best qualified to test and determine the extent of reliability of foam concentrates under questionable conditions of deterioration. Foam concentrates should be tested at least annually.

Equipment Testing

The performance of all foam equipment under emergency conditions is best guaranteed by the initial acceptance test and periodic inspection of the equipment. Original design specifications of fixed installations should include provision for periodic testing of proportioners, pumps, and other ancillary equipment, without the trial distribution of foam to the hazard being protected.

Problems of corrosion, clogged orifices, sticky valves, and electric circuitry malfunction may be detected by suitable means without full system activation.

In the absence of an actual fire, and without full system activation, the complete testing of foam equipment performance for fire protection adequacy may be accomplished by various means. In the absence of an actual fire, complete testing may be accomplished by several physical test methods. However, because these tests are similar in nature to "fingerprint" tests, their results can only be interpreted by comparison with similar tests conducted at the installation acceptance of the equipment or as provided for under the performance guarantee of the manufacturer.

Foam equipment performance can be tested for the following physical characteristics of foam:

1. The dimensions of the discharge pattern or patterns of the device or system
2. The percent concentration of foam concentrate in the finished foam solution
3. The degree of expansion of the finished foam
4. The rate at which water drains from the foam, for example, 25 percent drainage time. This correlates with its viscosity or rate of spreading over fuel surfaces
5. Film-forming capacity of the foam concentrate

The preceding tests require specially designed test equipment and standardized techniques. They require qualified operators and may or may not be carried out easily in the field. Detailed information concerning the equipment required, methods used, and some interpretations of the test results can be found in the Appendices of NFPA 11 and NFPA 412, *Standard for Evaluating Aircraft Rescue and Fire-Fighting Foam Equipment,* which includes tests for foam discharge patterns, AFFF-type foams, and protein-based foams.

The test for the concentration of the foam concentrate is very important because it indicates the efficiency of operation of the concentrate proportioning device in the system. It is performed easily in the field with a hand refractometer and volume-measuring device or portable electrical conductivity meter.

ENVIRONMENTAL ISSUES

The use of fire-fighting foams is essential for the control of flammable liquid fire threats. The ability of foam to rapidly extinguish flammable liquid fires has contributed to life safety and property conservation. However, with the increasing global environmental awareness, fire-fighting foams are being scrutinized for their potential environmental impact. The primary concerns are toxicity, biodegradability, persistence, treatability in wastewater treatment plants, and nutrient loading.

Discharge Scenarios

In order to assess the impact of foam on the environment, likely discharge scenarios should be considered. These scenarios include the following:

1. Uncontrolled fire situations
2. Potential hazardous situations (e.g., unignited fuel spills)
3. Fire-fighting training evolutions
4. Fixed or mobile vehicle suppression system discharge
   - Intentional system test
   - Inadvertent discharge

Under many fire-fighting situations, control of foam and water/fuel effluent will be difficult. Control and extinguishment are usually of paramount importance, and rapid control by foam can substantially reduce the potential total effluent from an incident. Where possible, blocking of sewer drains, along with the use of portable dikes or booms, can be used to implement mitigation strategies.

Training scenarios provide greater opportunities to control foam flow, particularly by means of collection. New training techniques, using simulated pool fires and simulated foams, are available.

System tests can also be performed, to a certain extent, with the use of simulants. Alternatively, small amounts of foam can be flowed and contained for proper disposal in accordance with local regulations and manufacturer's recommendations. Inadvertent system discharges may be handled by preplanned, engineered containment strategies or by portable containment devices, where containment is deemed appropriate.

Environmental Properties and Concerns

Fluorochemical surfactants in film-forming foams can exhibit characteristics having undesirable environmental impact. Of particular concern to the U.S. Environmental Protection Agency (EPA) are chemicals that are persistent, bioaccumulative, and potentially toxic (PBT). A major producer of AFFF, which was produced using the electrochemical fluorination process, has an agreement with the EPA to no longer manufacture a range of products that uses perfluoroctanyl sulfonate (PFOS) chemistry. This decision was based on data that suggest that these chemicals can exhibit a degree of toxicity and bioaccumulation not previously identified in addition to their known persistence to resist biodegradation. Other manufacturers of AFFF use a different process (e.g., telemerization) to produce fluorosurfactants used in their AFFF. Environmental characteristics of these agents have been under study by the industry and the EPA. Telmer-based agents have been found to be persistent but are not generally considered to be significant environmental toxins. Although there was concern that telemer-based AFFF could break down in the environment to perfluoroctanoic acid (PFOA) and would eventually be regulated by the EPA, the EPA decided that AFFF is not likely to be a source of PFOA. There are currently no restrictions on the production or sale of telemer-based AFFF in the United States. Users of AFFF should monitor these regulatory activities to determine the potential impact of regulations that may restrict the future use of AFFF and FFFP.

Foam solutions generally have a high biological oxygen demand (BOD); that is, they extract high levels of oxygen to break down. This is an issue both in the natural environment and where foam is discharged to wastewater treatment plants.

Foaming can occur in natural waterways and in treatment plants. In wastewater plants, foaming can cause bubbles to trap activated sludge, upsetting the normal operation of the plant. Before discharge of foam to a wastewater treatment plant, the plant operator should be contacted to discuss the type of foam, estimated BOD, total volume, and time over which the foam may be discharged to the plant. This should be done, where possible, as part of the emergency planning process.

In sufficient concentrations, foam may affect aquatic life. Where sufficiently diluted, foam solutions may not have an impact on aquatic life; however, localized concentrations in streams or ponds may create levels that are toxic to fish. Under emergency conditions, attempts should be made to prevent discharge to waterways (recognizing the primary concern of controlling the fire). Under controlled discharge conditions, prevention of foam discharge to natural waterways is appropriate.

The U.S. EPA requires reporting of certain releases of chemicals in broadly defined categories. The glycol ether category of chemicals was placed on the list of hazardous air pollutants under the 1990 Clean Air Act Amendments. These chemicals are used as solvents in certain fire-fighting foams. Although the EPA had originally assigned no reportable quantity for any glycol ethers, these chemicals still were designated as hazardous substances under the Comprehensive Environmental Response Compensation and Liability Act (CERCLA). In a 1995 clarification, the EPA decided not to assign reportable quantities to several broad categories of glycol ethers, including the commonly used butyl carbitol. As a result, fire-fighting foams containing solvents within the glycol ethers category no longer require reporting under CERCLA when discharged. Several manufacturers have replaced glycol ether solvents with alternative solvents that have less environmental impact. Manufacturers should be consulted regarding environmental aspects in general and for responsible use guidance.

Disposal Alternatives

The uncontrolled release of foam solutions to the environment should be avoided. Alternative disposal options include the following:

1. Discharge to a wastewater treatment plant with or without pretreatment
2. Discharge to the environment after pretreatment
3. Solar evaporation
4. Transportation to a wastewater treatment plant or hazardous waste facility

When foam is collected, any fuel from a fire should be separated. Dilution with water may be required before discharging foam to a wastewater treatment plant. Defoamers or other pretreatments may also be required. Any discharge to a wastewater treatment plant should be coordinated in advance with the treatment facility personnel. Foam manufacturers can advise on proper disposal techniques for specific circumstances.

SUMMARY

Fire-fighting foam is an effective agent for combating flammable and combustible liquid fuel fires. Various types of foam are applied in different manners, but all act to suppress flammable vapors and cool fuel surfaces to extinguish fires. Foam may have low- or high-expansion ratios. Foam may be proportioned using various methods in both fixed and mobile systems. Foam agents are used to combat fires in various hazards, including tank farms, airfields, aircraft hangars, and flammable liquid hazards. Foam may be discharged through fixed nozzles, sprinklers, hose line nozzles, and monitors.

BIBLIOGRAPHY

References Cited

1. American Petroleum Institute, "Interim Study: Prevention and Suppression of Fire in Large Aboveground Atmospheric Storage Tanks," API Publication 2021A, Washington, DC, July 1998.

2. Breen, D. E. "Hangar Fire Protection with Automatic AFFF Systems," *Fire Technology,* Vol. 26, No. 1, 1990, pp. 41–50.
3. UL 162, *Foam Equipment and Liquid Concentrates,* 7th ed., Underwriters Laboratories Inc., Northbrook, IL, Mar. 29, 1999.

NFPA Codes, Standards, and Recommended Practices

Reference to the following NFPA codes, standards, and recommended practices will provide further information on foam extinguishing agents and systems discussed in this chapter. (See the latest version of The NFPA Catalog *for availability of current editions of the following documents.)*

NFPA 11, *Standard for Low-, Medium-, and High-Expansion Foam*
NFPA 16, *Standard for the Installation of Foam-Water Sprinkler and Foam-Water Spray Systems*
NFPA 18, *Standard on Wetting Agents*
NFPA 30, *Flammable and Combustible Liquids Code*
NFPA 403, *Standard for Aircraft Rescue and Fire-Fighting Services at Airports*
NFPA 409, *Standard on Aircraft Hangars*
NFPA 412, *Standard for Evaluating Aircraft Rescue and Fire-Fighting Foam Equipment*
NFPA 414, *Standard for Aircraft Rescue and Fire-Fighting Vehicles*
NFPA 780, *Standard for the Installation of Lightning Protection Systems*
NFPA 1901, *Standard for Automotive Fire Apparatus*

References

Back, G. G., Williams, F. W., Gott, J. E., Parker, A. J., Scheffey, J. L., and Tabet, R. J., "Effects of Water Sprinklers on the Performance of Low-Level AFFF Hangar Fire Suppression Systems," NRL/MR/6180-00-8456, Naval Research Laboratory, Washington, DC, May 22, 2000.

Carey, W. M., "Knockdown, Exposure and Retention Tests. National Class A Foam Research Project Technical Report. Phase 1," Technical Report, Underwriters Laboratories Inc., Northbrook, IL, National Fire Protection Research Foundation, Quincy, MA, Dec. 1993.

Carey, W. M., "Structural Fire Fighting: Room Burn Tests. National Class A Foam Research Project Technical Report. Phase 2," Technical Report, Underwriters Laboratories Inc., Northbrook, IL, National Fire Protection Research Foundation, Quincy, MA, Dec. 1994.

Center for Chemical Process Safety, *Guidelines for Safe Warehousing of Chemicals,* CCPS, American Institute of Chemical Engineers, New York, 1998.

"Chevron Firefighting Foam Test Report," American Petroleum Institute, Washington, DC, by the Chevron Foam Concentration Team, May 8, 2001.

Crampton, G., and Kim, A., "The Comparison of the Fire Suppression Performance of Compressed-Air Foam with Foam Water Sprinklers on Free-Flowing Heptane Spill Fires," Research Report RR-174, National Research Council Canada, Ottawa, Canada, Sept. 2004.

Crampton, G. P., Kim, A. K., and Richardson, J. K., "A New Fire Suppression Technology," *NFPA Journal,* July/Aug. 1999.

Darley, P. C., "Use of Class 'A' Foam and Compressed Air Foam Systems (CAFS) in Firefighting," Foam Applications for Wildland and Urban Fire Management, Vol. 7, No. 2, 1995, pp. 15–22.

Darwin, R. L., Ottman, R. E., Norman, E. C., Gott, J. E., and Hanauska, C. P., "Foam and the Environment: A Delicate Balance," NFPA Fire Journal, Vol. 89, No. 3, 1995, pp. 67–73.

Darwin, R. L., and Williams, F. W., "A Review of the Performance of AFFF Systems Serving Helicopter Decks on U.S. Navy Surface Combatants," NRL/MR/6180—01-8546, Naval Research Laboratory, Washington, DC, Apr. 23, 2001.

Department of the Army, "Engineering and Design Containment and Disposal of Aqueous Film-Forming Foam Solution," ETL 1110-3-481, U.S. Army Corps of Engineers, Washington, DC, Mar. 31, 1997.

Fire Extinguishing Agent, Aqueous Film Forming Foam (AFFF) Liquid Concentrate, Six Percent for Fresh and Sea Water, Military Specification MIL-F-24385 (NAVY), Naval Sea Systems Command, Washington, DC.

Guide for Fighting Fires in and Around Petroleum Storage Tanks, API Publication 2021, 3rd ed., American Petroleum Institute, Washington, DC, 1991.

Jackson, E., "Aqueous Film Forming Foam Fixed System Applications," *Flammable and Combustible Liquids Symposium: Book of Abstracts,* Society of Fire Protection Engineers, Bethesda, MD, Sept. 2004, pp. 43–47.

Kim, A. K., and Dlugogorski, B. Z., "Effective Fixed Foam System Using Compressed Air," Proceedings of the National Institute of Standards and Technology (NIST) and Society of Fire Protection Engineers (SFPE) International Conference on Fire Research and Engineering, September 10–15, 1995, Orlando, FL, SFPE, Boston, 1995, pp. 71–76.

Lattimer, B. Y., Hanauska, C. P., Scheffey, J. L., and Williams, F. W., "The Use of Small-Scale Test Data to Characterize Some Aspects of Fire Fighting Foam for Suppression Modeling," *Fire Safety Journal,* Vol. 38, 2003, pp. 117–146.

Persson, B., Loennermark, A., Persson, H., Mulligan, D., Lancia, A., and Demichela, M., "FOAMSPEC: Large Scale Foam Application. Modeling of Foam Spread and Extinguishment," SP Report 2001:13, Swedish National Testing and Research Institute, Boras, Sweden, 2001.

Purvis, F., "Recent Developments in 1 × 3 Alcohol Resistant Aqueous Film Forming Foam Concentrates," *Flammable and Combustible Liquids Symposium: Book of Abstracts,* Society of Fire Protection Engineers, Bethesda, MD, September 2004, pp. 52–55.

Reese, S., "Foam Use in Aircraft Hangars," *NFPA Journal,* Vol. 94, No. 4, 2000, pp. 79–81.

Scheffey, J. L., "Foam System Calculations," *SFPE Handbook of Fire Protection Engineering,* 3rd ed., National Fire Protection Association, Quincy, MA, 2002.

Scheffey, J. L., "Foam Agents and AFFF System Design Considerations," *SFPE Handbook of Fire Protection Engineering,* 3rd ed., National Fire Protection Association, Quincy, MA, 2002.

Scheffey, J. L., Wright, J., and Sarkos, C., "Analysis of Test Criteria for Specifying Foam Firefighting Agents for Aircraft Rescue and Firefighting," FAA Technical Report, DOT/FAA/CT-94/04, FAA Technical Center, Atlantic City, NJ, Aug. 1994.

Scheffey, J. L., Darwin, R. L., and Leonard, J. T., "Evaluating Fire-Fighting Foams for Aviation Fire Protection," *Fire Technology,* Vol. 31, No. 3, 1995, pp. 224–243.

Timms, G., and Hagger, P., "Foam Concentration Measurement Techniques," Fire Technology, Vol. 26, No. 1, 1990, pp. 41–50.

UL Fire Protection Equipment Directory 2006, Underwriters Laboratories Inc., Northbrook, IL, 2006.

UL 162, *Foam Equipment and Liquid Concentrates,* 7th ed., Underwriters Laboratories Inc., Northbrook, IL, Mar. 29, 1999.

Chapter 5

Fire Extinguisher Use and Maintenance

Mark T. Conroy

Chapter Contents

Key Terms

AFFF fire extinguisher, carbon dioxide fire extinguisher, Class A fire, Class B fire, Class C fire, Class D fire, Class K fire, Classification of Hazards for Portable Fire Extinguishers, dry chemical fire extinguisher, dry powder fire extinguisher, halogenated agent fire extinguisher, portable fire extinguisher, water-based fire extinguisher

Before choosing an extinguisher, it is important to know the nature of the fuels present, who will use the extinguisher, the physical environment in which the extinguisher will be placed, and whether any chemicals present in the area will react adversely with an extinguishing agent. When choosing from among various extinguishers, one should consider whether it is effective on the specific hazards present, whether it is easy to operate, and what maintenance and upkeep it requires.

Related information can be found in the following chapters in this section: Section 17, Chapter 1, "Carbon Dioxide and Application Systems"; Section 17, Chapter 2, "Chemical Extinguishing Agents and Application Systems"; Section 17, Chapter 3, "Characteristics and Hazards of Water and Water Additives for Fire Suppression"; and Section 17, Chapter 4, "Foam Extinguishing Agents and Systems." See also Section 6, Chapter 9, "Metals."

MATCHING EXTINGUISHERS TO HAZARDS

By far the most important consideration when selecting extinguishers is the nature of the area to be protected. NFPA 10, *Standard for Portable Fire Extinguishers,* classifies fires as either Class A, Class B, Class C, Class D, or Class K, according to the fuel involved:

- Class A fires are fires in ordinary combustible mateirals, such as wood, cloth, paper, rubber, and many plastics.
- Class B fires are fires in flammable liquids, combustible liquids, petroleum greases, tars, oils, oil-based paints, solvents, lacquers, alcohols, and flammable gases.
- Class C fires are fires that involve energized electrical equipment.
- Class D fires are fires in combustible metals, such as magnesium, titanium, zirconium, sodium, lithium, and potassium.
- Class K fires are fires in cooking applicances that involve combustible cooking media (vegetable or animal oils and fats).

Extinguishers are classified for use on one or more of these types of fires.

In addition, the relative hazard in a building varies according to its fire load, or the amount of combustibles it contains. NFPA 10 establishes three types of hazards. A light, or low, hazard exists when there are few combustibles. Light-hazard occupancies include offices, churches, schoolrooms, assembly halls, and so on. An ordinary, or moderate, hazard exists when the combustibles present are substantial but ordinary in nature or where there are small quantities of combustibles capable of rapid fire growth. Examples of ordinary-hazard occupancies are mercantile storage and display areas, auto showrooms, and parking garages. Some offices, schools, and so on can contain a sufficient amount of combustible materials to be classified as ordinary hazard. An extra, or high, hazard exists in areas where there are substantial quantities of on-site combustibles whose nature or configuration could readily support rapid fire growth and large fire size, such as woodworking areas, aircraft servicing areas, and warehouses with high-piled combustibles.

Mark T. Conroy is a senior fire protection engineer for Brooks Equipment Company of Charlotte, North Carolina.

Hazard type is an important factor when selecting extinguishers. For example, a 2½ gal (9.5 L) water extinguisher with a 2-A rating is only suitable in low- and moderate-hazard areas. In a high-hazard area, an extinguisher with a minimum rating of 4-A is needed.

Class-A-rated extinguishers are used most often for ordinary building protection. Among the agents classified for Class A use are water, loaded stream, aqueous film-forming foam (AFFF), film-forming fluoroprotein foam (FFFP), multipurpose (ammonium-phosphate-base) dry chemical, and halogenated agent types. Due to the environmental problems associated with halons, however, they are no longer being produced and their use is being discouraged except in specific circumstances. Extinguishers containing halogenated agents called halocarbons have been introduced to replace halon extinguishers.

Class-A-rated extinguishers are sometimes not the only type needed for building protection. In most areas of a restaurant, for example, the principal combustibles are wood, paper, and fabrics. In the kitchen, however, the hazard of greatest concern is cooking media (vegetable oils and fats), which requires a Class-K-rated extinguisher. In hospitals, there is a general need for Class-A-rated extinguishers in rooms, corridors, and offices, but Class-B:C-rated extinguishers should be placed in laboratories, generator rooms, and areas where anesthetics are stored or used. In short, the extinguishers in any one area should correspond to the hazards of that area.

Class B fires are fires in flammable liquids. Class-B-rated extinguishing agents include carbon dioxide, dry chemicals, AFFF, FFFP, and halogenated agent types. There are three general types of flammable liquids fires: (1) fires in liquids of appreciable depth (deeper than ¼ in. [6.4 mm]), such as those in industrial dip tanks and quench tanks; (2) spill fires or running fires in liquids of a depth of ¼ in. (6.4 mm) or less; and (3) pressurized flammable liquid or gas fires from damaged vessels or product lines. Portable fire extinguishers should not be relied on when the surface area of an indoor open tank is in excess of 10 ft^2 (1 m^2); fires in such areas can give off so much heat and smoke that it is dangerous for anyone to remain in the area.

Pressurized flammable liquids and pressurized gas fires present special hazards. Only dry chemical type extinguishers have proved to be effective. In addition, special nozzles and higher rates of agent application are often required. Extinguishers for these types of fires should therefore be selected on the basis of manufacturers' recommendations. *No* attempt should be made to extinguish these fires unless there is reasonable certainty that the source of fuel can be shut off promptly.

Class-C-rated extinguishers contain extinguishing agents that are considered electrically nonconductive to the extinguisher operator while being discharged and are therefore preferred for fires in charged electrical equipment. They should be chosen based on the materials used in constructing the electrical equipment, the degree of agent contamination that can be tolerated, and the types of other combustibles in the area. Of these, the first is particularly important. For example, a power panel will contain more Class A insulating materials than an oil-filled transformer will, which will contain mostly Class B material. The agents classified for Class C use include carbon dioxide, dry chemicals, and the halogenated agent types.

Class D fires are fires in combustible metals. These require special extinguishing agents, known as dry powder.

Once an area has been analyzed for hazards, appropriate extinguishers can be chosen. For the Class A fire, three basic types of extinguishers can be used: water-based extinguishers, multipurpose (ammonium-phosphate-base) dry chemical extinguishers, or halogenated agent extinguishers. For Class B fires, there are carbon dioxide, dry chemical, halogenated agent, and AFFF and FFFP extinguishers. (Some small extinguishers are rated less than 5-B and, as indicated by their omission from Table 17.5.1, are not permitted as a required extinguisher.) For Class C fires there are carbon dioxide, dry chemical, or halogenated agent extinguishers. Water mist extinguishers have recently been reconsidered for use in the vicinity of live electrical equipment. The various types of extinguishing agents for Class D combustible metal fires are discussed separately. (See Section 6, Chapter 9, "Metals.")

AVAILABLE PERSONNEL—EASE OF USE

Before extinguishers are selected, consideration should be given to who will use them. Evaluation should include the potential user's physical abilities, reactions under stress, and previous training. Many firms have standardized their extinguishers so that employees need only learn one set of instructions. In companies employing trained fire brigades, there may be more variation.

An individual's emotional reaction to a fire will be greatly influenced by his or her familiarity with the extinguisher, experience in using it or observing its use, and self-confidence. Training is, therefore, very important. Many companies have employees practice with extinguishers when the units are scheduled for recharging. Employees should be adequately trained so they will not jeopardize their own safety and safety of others.

Sometimes, the size or weight of an extinguisher is important. Some extinguisher models have lightweight shells or use agents with more extinguishing capacity per unit of weight. A very common fire extinguisher holds 2½ gal (9.5 L) of water and weighs about 30 lb (13.6 kg). The weight of many extinguishers varies. For example, one manufacturer offers two dry chemical extinguishers with a rating of 40-B:C. The sodium-bicarbonate-based model has a 20 lb (9.1 kg) capacity and weighs 27 lb (12.3 kg), but the potassium-bicarbonate-based model has a 9 lb (4.1 kg) capacity and weighs only 14 lb (6.4 kg).

PHYSICAL ENVIRONMENT

Still another factor that influences extinguisher selection is the area in which the extinguishers will be placed. Is the extinguisher affected by extreme temperatures, for example? ANSI standards require evaluation of water-based extinguishers at temperatures between 40 and 120°F (4 and 49°C) and all other types between –40 and 120°F (–40 and 49°C).

Performance Standards for Fire Extinguishers:[1]

(a) Carbon Dioxide Types. ANSI/UL 154, *Standard for Carbon Dioxide Fire Extinguishers;* CAN/ULC-S503-M90, *Standard for Carbon Dioxide Hand and Wheeled Fire Extinguishers*

(b) Dry Chemical Types. ANSI/UL 299, *Standard for Dry Chemical Fire Extinguishers;* CAN/ULC-S504-M86, *Standard for Dry Chemical and Dry Powder Hand and Wheeled Fire Extinguishers*

TABLE 17.5.1 Characteristics of Extinguishers

Extinguishing Agent	*Method of Operation*	*Capacity*	*Horizontal Range of Stream*	*Approximate Time of Discharge*	*Protection Required below 40°F (4°C)*	*UL or ULC Classifications*[a]
Water	Stored-pressure	6 L	30 to 40 ft	40 sec	Yes	1-A
	Stored-pressure or pump	2½ gal	30 to 40 ft	1 min	Yes	2-A
	Pump	4 gal	30 to 40 ft	2 min	Yes	3-A
	Pump	5 gal	30 to 40 ft	2 to 3 min	Yes	4-A
Water (wetting agent)	Stored-pressure	1½ gal	20 ft	30 sec	Yes	2-A
	Stored-pressure	25 gal (wheeled)	35 ft	1½ min	Yes	10-A
	Stored-pressure	45 gal (wheeled)	35 ft	2 min	Yes	30-A
	Stored-pressure	60 gal (wheeled)	35 ft	2½ min	Yes	40-A
Loaded stream	Stored-pressure	2½ gal	30 to 40 ft	1 min	No	2-A
	Stored-pressure	33 gal (wheeled)	50 ft	3 min	No	20-A
Water mist	Stored-pressure	6 L	NA	60 to 70 sec	Yes	2-A:C
	Stored-pressure	2½ gal	NA	70 to 80 sec	Yes	2-A:C
AFFF, FFFP	Stored-pressure	2½ gal	20 to 25 ft	50 sec	Yes	3-A:20 to 40-B
	Stored-pressure	6 L	20 to 25 ft	50 sec	Yes	2-A:10-B
	Nitrogen cylinder	33 gal	30 ft	1 min	Yes	20-A:160-B
Carbon dioxide[b]	Self-expelling	2½ to 5 lb	3 to 8 ft	8 to 30 sec	No	1 to 5-B:C
	Self-expelling	10 to 15 lb	3 to 8 ft	8 to 30 sec	No	2 to 10-B:C
	Self-expelling	20 lb	3 to 8 ft	10 to 30 sec	No	10-B:C
	Self-expelling	50 to 100 lb (wheeled)	3 to 10 ft	10 to 30 sec	No	10 to 20-B:C
Regular dry chemical (sodium bicarbonate)	Stored-pressure	1 to 2½ lb	5 to 8 ft	8 to 12 sec	No	2 to 10-B:C
	Cartridge or stored-pressure	2¾ to 5 lb	5 to 20 ft	8 to 25 sec	No	5 to 20-B:C
	Cartridge or stored-pressure	6 to 30 lb	5 to 20 ft	10 to 25 sec	No	10 to 160-B:C
	Stored-pressure	50 lb (wheeled)	20 ft	35 sec	No	160-B:C
	Nitrogen cylinder or stored-pressure	75 to 350 lb (wheeled)	15 to 45 ft	20 to 105 sec	No	40 to 320-B:C
Purple K dry chemical (potassium bicarbonate)	Cartridge or stored-pressure	2 to 5 lb	5 to 12 ft	8 to 10 sec	No	5 to 30-B:C
	Cartridge or stored-pressure	5½ to 10 lb	5 to 20 ft	8 to 20 sec	No	10 to 80-B:C
	Cartridge or stored-pressure	16 to 30 lb	10 to 20 ft	8 to 25 sec	No	40 to 120-B:C
	Cartridge or stored-pressure	48 to 50 lb (wheeled)	20 ft	30 to 35 sec	No	120 to 160-B:C
	Nitrogen cylinder or stored-pressure	125 to 315 lb (wheeled)	15 to 45 ft	30 to 80 sec	No	80 to 640-B:C
Super K dry chemical (potassium chloride)	Cartridge or stored-pressure	2 to 5 lb	5 to 8 ft	8 to 10 sec	No	5 to 10-B:C
	Cartridge or stored-pressure	5 to 9 lb	8 to 12 ft	10 to 15 sec	No	20 to 40-B:C
	Cartridge or stored-pressure	9½ to 20 lb	10 to 15 ft	15 to 20 sec	No	40 to 60-B:C
	Cartridge or stored-pressure	19½ to 30 lb	5 to 20 ft	10 to 25 sec	No	60 to 80-B:C
	Cartridge or stored-pressure	125 to 200 lb (wheeled)	15 to 45 ft	30 to 40 sec	No	160-B:C
Multipurpose/ABC dry chemical (ammonium phosphate)	Stored-pressure	1 to 5 lb	5 to 12 ft	8 to 10 sec	No	1 to 3-A[c] and 2 to 10-B:C
	Stored-pressure or cartridge	2½ to 9 lb	5 to 12 ft	8 to 15 sec	No	1 to 4-A and 10 to 40-B:C
	Stored-pressure or cartridge	9 to 17 lb	5 to 20 ft	10 to 25 sec	No	2 to 20-A and 10 to 80-B:C

(continued)

TABLE 17.5.1 Continued

Extinguishing Agent	*Method of Operation*	*Capacity*	*Horizontal Range of Stream*	*Approximate Time of Discharge*	*Protection Required below 40°F (4°C)*	*UL or ULC Classifications*[a]
Multipurpose/ABC dry chemical (ammonium phosphate) *(continued)*	Stored-pressure or cartridge	17 to 30 lb	5 to 20 ft	10 to 25 sec	No	3 to 20-A and 30 to 120-B:C
	Stored-pressure or cartridge	45 to 50 lb (wheeled)	20 ft	25 to 35 sec	No	20 to 30-A and 80 to 160-B:C
	Nitrogen cylinder or stored-pressure	110 to 315 lb (wheeled)	15 to 45 ft	30 to 60 sec	No	20 to 40-A and 60 to 320-B:C
Dry chemical (foam-compatible)	Cartridge or stored-pressure	4¾ to 9 lb	5 to 20 ft	8 to 10 sec	No	10 to 20-B:C
	Cartridge or stored-pressure	9 to 27 lb	5 to 20 ft	10 to 25 sec	No	20 to 30-B:C
	Cartridge or stored-pressure	18 to 30 lb	5 to 20 ft	10 to 25 sec	No	40 to 60-B:C
	Nitrogen cylinder or stored-pressure	150 to 350 lb (wheeled)	15 to 45 ft	20 to 150 sec	No	80 to 240-B:C
Dry chemical (potassium bicarbonate urea based)	Stored-pressure	5 to 11 lb	11 to 22 ft	18 sec	No	40 to 80-B:C
	Stored-pressure	9 to 23 lb	15 to 30 ft	17 to 33 sec	No	60 to 160-B:C
	Nitrogen cylinder or stored-pressure	175 lb (wheeled)	70 ft	62 sec	No	480-B:C
Wet chemical	Stored-pressure	3 L	8 to 12 ft	30 sec	No	K
	Stored-pressure	6 L	8 to 12 ft	35 to 45 sec	No	K
	Stored-pressure	2½ gal	8 to 12 ft	75 to 85 sec	No	K
Halon 1211 (bromochloro-difluoromethane)	Stored-pressure	0.9 to 2 lb	6 to 10 ft	8 to 10 sec	No	1 to 2-B:C
	Stored-pressure	2 to 3 lb	6 to 10 ft	8 to 10 sec	No	5-B:C
	Stored-pressure	5½ to 9 lb	9 to 15 ft	8 to 15 sec	No	1-A:10-B:C
	Stored-pressure	13 to 22 lb	14 to 16 ft	10 to 18 sec	No	2 to 4-A and 20 to 80-B:C
	Stored-pressure	50 lb	35 ft	30 sec	No	10-A:120-B:C
	Stored-pressure	150 lb (wheeled)	20 to 35 ft	30 to 44 sec	No	30-A:160 to 240-B:C
Halon 1211/1301 (bromochloro-difluoromethane bromotrifluoro-methane) mixtures	Stored-pressure or self-expelling	0.9 to 5 lb	3 to 12 ft	8 to 10 sec	No	1 to 10-B:C
	Stored-pressure	9 to 20 lb	10 to 18 ft	10 to 22 sec	No	1-A:10-B:C to 4-A:80-B:C
Halocarbon type	Stored-pressure	1.4 to 150 lb	6 to 35 ft	9 to 23 sec	No	1-B:C to 10-A:80-B:C

Note: Halon should be used only where its unique properties are deemed necessary.
[a]UL and ULC ratings checked as of July 24, 1987. Readers concerned with subsequent ratings should review the pertinent lists and supplements issued by these laboratories: Underwriters Laboratories Inc., 333 Pfingsten Road, Northbrook, IL 60062, or Underwriters Laboratories of Canada, 7 Crouse Road, Scarborough, Ontario, Canada M1R 3A9.
[b]Carbon dioxide extinguishers with metal horns do not carry a C classification.
[c]Some small extinguishers containing ammonium phosphate–based dry chemical do not carry an A classification.
NA = Not available.
Source: Modified from NFPA 10, *Standard for Portable Fire Extinguishers,* Table H.2, 2007, p. 10-50.

(c) Water Types. ANSI/UL 626, *Standard for 2½-Gallon Stored-Pressure, Water-Type Fire Extinguishers;* CAN/ULCS507-92, *Standard for 9 Litre Stored Pressure Water Type Fire Extinguishers*
(d) Halon Types. ANSI/UL 1093, *Standard for Halogenated Agent Fire Extinguishers;* CAN/ULC-S512-M87, *Standard for Halogenated Agent Hand and Wheeled Fire Extinguishers*
(e) Film-Forming Foam Types. ANSI/UL 8, *Standard for Foam Fire Extinguishers*
(f) Halocarbon Type. ANSI/UL 2129, *Standard for Halocarbon Agent Fire Extinguishers*

If extinguishers are installed in areas subject to higher or lower temperatures, they should be listed for those areas or put in an enclosure where the proper temperature is maintained. Some stored-pressure extinguishers for Class B fires use nitrogen rather than carbon dioxide as the pressurizing force. For units that must perform in temperatures as low as –65°F (–54°C), nitrogen pressurization is used.

Other conditions that may affect extinguisher performance are direct sunlight, snow, rain, airborne debris, and corrosive fumes. If extinguishers must be placed outdoors, installing them in cabinets and sheltered areas or placing a protective cover over them will help prevent damage or premature deterioration (Figures 17.5.1 and 17.5.2).

Corrosives can cause extinguishers to fail, and extinguishers capable of withstanding corrosive conditions are listed separately. For example, extinguishers that may be used in salt-air atmospheres appear under the heading "Marine Type, USCG." Where corrosive fumes exist at industrial sites, special analysis should be made before extinguishers are chosen.

Extinguishers may also be affected by the vibration found in places such as a drop forge or hammer mill, trains, vehicles, and power boats. In such cases, they should be of rugged design, mounted securely, and inspected at frequent intervals.

FIGURE 17.5.1 Cover Used to Protect Extinguishers That Are Mounted Outside from Substances That Would Interfere with Operation (Source: Ansul Incorporated)

HEALTH AND OPERATIONAL SAFETY CONSIDERATIONS

Potential health hazards should always be considered when selecting extinguishers. Manufacturers normally provide prominent labels of caution on extinguishers that could produce toxic vapors or decomposition vapors. Sometimes, however, the danger resides not in the extinguisher but in the area in which it will be used. Useful safeguards include posting warning signs at the entries to confined areas, providing extinguishers with long-range nozzles, installing special ventilation, or supplying employees in the area with self-contained breathing apparatus.

Most water-based extinguishers are rated only for Class A fires. AFFF and FFFP models are also rated for Class B fires. Class K fire extinguishers have water additives intended for fires

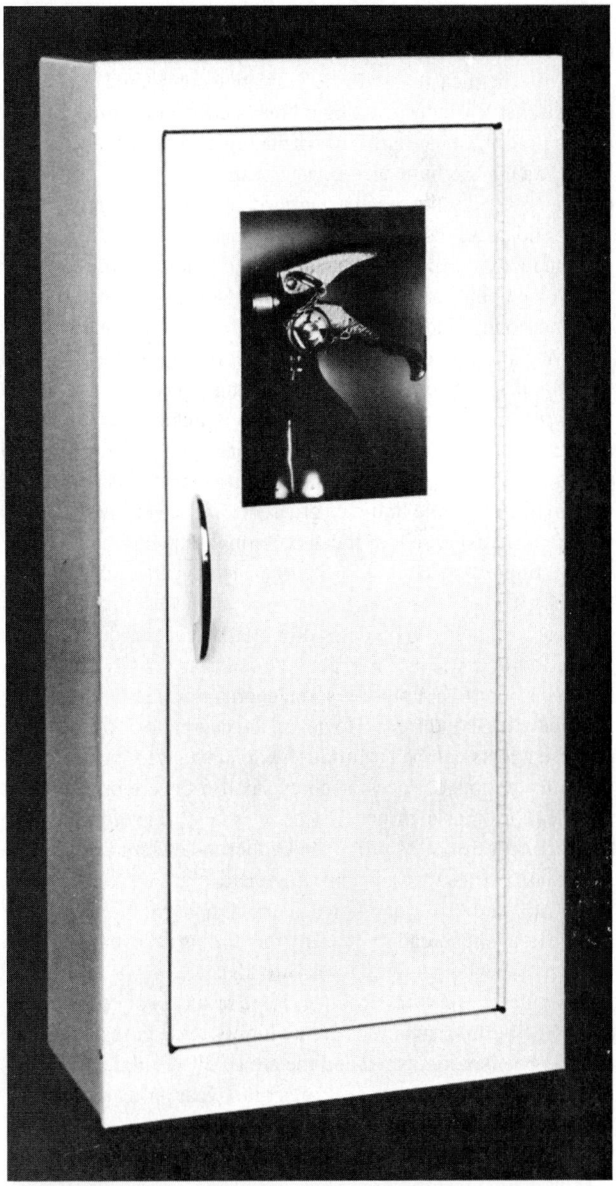

FIGURE 17.5.2 Surface-Mounted Extinguisher Cabinet with a Hinged Door (Source: Larsen's Manufacturing Company)

in commercial fryers. If the nonfoam/water types are used on Class B fires, the fire may flare up, spread, or injure the operator in some way. If water-based extinguishers are used on fires in or near live electrical equipment, the water stream may transmit an electric shock to the operator.

Although carbon dioxide is not itself toxic, it will not support life when used in concentrations high enough to extinguish a fire. (See Section 17, Chapter 1, "Carbon Dioxide and Application Systems.") If a carbon dioxide extinguisher is used in an unventilated area, it dilutes the oxygen supply, and those remaining in the area may become unconscious or even die if they do not receive oxygen. In addition, the thick cloud of condensing water vapor that forms upon discharge may cause persons to become disoriented.

Older carbon dioxide extinguishers may have metal horns that transmit a shock to the user when the horns touch live electrical equipment. These metal horns should be replaced with nonmetallic horns. Occasionally, the operator may receive a shock even when no contact has been made; these result from built-up static electricity and are generally more annoying than hazardous.

Dry chemical extinguishers are not considered toxic, but their discharge can be irritating if breathed for a long time. Monoammonium phosphate is the most irritating, followed by potassium-based agents. Sodium bicarbonate is the least irritating. If dry chemicals are discharged in a confined area, they may reduce visibility and cause disorientation. Because dry chemical agents are nonconductors, deposits left on electrical contacts can reduce or negate the ability of the contacts to conduct. They may also clog air conditioning and air cleaning filters if discharged nearby.

Multipurpose dry chemical (ammonium-phosphate-base) is acidic and, if mixed with even a small amount of water, will corrode some metals unless all agent residues are removed promptly and thoroughly. Finally, the initial discharge of agent from an extinguisher has considerable force. If it is aimed at close range at a small flammable liquid or grease fire, it can cause the fire to spread extensively before it can be brought under control.

Extinguishers containing halogenated agents such as halons (Halon 1301 or Halon 1211 or a mixture of these) or halocarbons (halocarbon agents include hydrochlorofluorocarbon [HCFC], hydrofluorocarbon [HFC], perfluorocarbon [PFC], and fluoroiodocarbon [FIC]) present some degree of toxicity under normal operating conditions. However, the decomposition products of these agents can be hazardous. When using these extinguishers in unventilated places, such as small rooms, closets, motor vehicles, or other confined spaces, it is best to avoid breathing the vapors or the gases produced by thermal decomposition.

Class D fires involving burning metal chips can be scattered if the full force of a dry powder extinguisher is used at close range. To avoid spreading the fire, the discharge lever should be squeezed slowly, beginning at a safe distance.

Virtually every fire produces toxic products of combustion, and some burning materials create highly toxic gases. Until the fire has been extinguished and the area well ventilated, it is important either to stay out of the area or to wear protective breathing apparatus.

OPERATION AND USE

Whether an extinguisher is effective often depends on who is using it. One person may be able to extinguish a fire that someone else, using the same equipment, may not. Many extinguishers discharge their entire contents in 8 to 15 seconds, leaving little time for experimentation. Occasionally, improper use of an extinguisher injures the operator and delays extinguishment.

There are several kinds of extinguishers. Because differences exist among extinguishers, it is imperative that people be trained to use them properly. Ideally, this includes the general public. In any case, fire fighters and others responsible for fire protection, such as industrial fire brigades, should be trained thoroughly in the operation and use of extinguishers.

Currently, listed fire extinguishers are classified into six major groups, based on the extinguishing medium each contains. They are (1) water-type, (2) carbon dioxide, (3) halogenated agent, (4) dry chemical, (5) foam, and (6) wet chemical. Dry powder for Class D fires receives special testing and listing based on specific combustible metals. Additionally, special extinguishers containing wet chemical are tested and listed for cooking oil fires that could occur in commercial fryers. Information about each of these can be found in the following subsections and in Table 17.5.1.

In addition, extinguishers that are no longer manufactured may still be found in some areas. Some information on them is provided under the heading "Obsolete Extinguishers."

Water-Based Extinguishers

Water-based extinguishing agents include water, antifreeze, loaded stream, wetting agent, wet chemical, and foam. All except AFFF, FFFP, and wet chemical are for use on Class A fires only. Antifreeze, loaded stream, AFFF, wetting agent, and wet chemical all use water as a base to which chemicals are added to improve the extinguisher's performance. Both antifreeze and loaded stream models are specially treated to withstand low temperatures; the additive in loaded stream extinguishers is an alkali metal-salt solution. In wetting agents, a material is added to reduce the surface tension of the water so that it will spread and penetrate better. Wet chemicals include, but are not limited to, aqueous solutions of potassium acetate, potassium carbonate, potassium citrate, or combinations of these materials.

Originally, water-based extinguishers were of three basic designs: (1) stored-pressure, (2) pump tank, and (3) inverting. In 1969, however, the manufacture of all inverting extinguishers was discontinued. Consequently, the soda-acid and foam agents used exclusively in inverting extinguishers also became obsolete. The two designs that remain, stored-pressure and pump tank, are discussed later.

If ordinary, or nonfoam, water-based extinguishers are used on flammable liquids or electrical fires, they can spread the fire, injure the operator, or both. After activating an extinguisher, the operator should point the stream at the base of the flames and work from side to side or around the fire. When flames are high, the range of the stream (about 30 ft [9 m]) should be used to best advantage. As the flames diminish, it is possible to move closer and change the solid stream to a spray by holding a fingertip over the end of the nozzle. A spray stream is more effective on burning embers. Deep-seated smoldering or glowing areas should be wetted thoroughly. If necessary, a hand tool should be used to poke apart burning materials to do this.

Stored Pressure. For the capacities, ratings, discharge times, stream range, and temperature requirements of the various stored-pressure water-based extinguishers available, see Table 17.5.1. The most common stored-pressure water-based extinguisher contains 2½ gal (9.5 L) and weighs about 30 lb (13.6 kg). It can be operated intermittently, is rechargeable, and has a comparatively long stream range and discharge time. It consists of a single chamber that contains both the agent and expellant gas. The head assembly includes a siphon tube, a combination carrying handle/operating lever, a discharge valve, an air valve and pressure gauge, a discharge hose, and a nozzle (Figure 17.5.3). The extinguisher is pressurized with air or inert gas by means of an automobile-tire-type valve. Charging pressures range from 90 to 125 psi (620 to 862 kPa). A "fill mark" is stamped on many older stored-pressure water-based extinguishers about 6 in. (152.4 mm) from the top; when refilling, this level should never be exceeded. Some models use a special tube device to prevent overfilling.

In most models, the operating lever is locked by a ring pin that prevents accidental discharge. To activate the extinguisher, set it on the ground. Hold the combination handle loosely in one hand and pull out the ring pin or release a small latch with the other hand. Then grab the hose in one hand and squeeze the discharge lever with the other.

Pump Tanks. Two different types of pump tanks are available: one is cylindrical, and the other is made to be used as a backpack. The sizes, ratings, discharge times, stream ranges, and weather requirements of the various pump tanks are given in Table 17.5.1. The cylindrical model has carrying handles either attached to the container or built into the pump handle, and the water is discharged by a built-in, hand-operated vertical piston pump with an attached short rubber hose. The pump is double-acting and discharges water on both the up and the down strokes (Figure 17.5.4). The cylindrical models are available with copper, steel, or plastic shells.

To operate a cylindrical pump tank, place it on the ground and put one foot on the extension bracket at the base to steady the unit. To force water through the hose, pump the handle up and down. Cylindrical pump tanks have two characteristics that may be slight disadvantages: (1) to move the extinguisher, the operator must stop pumping, and (2) the force, range, and duration of the stream are dependent, in part, on the operator.

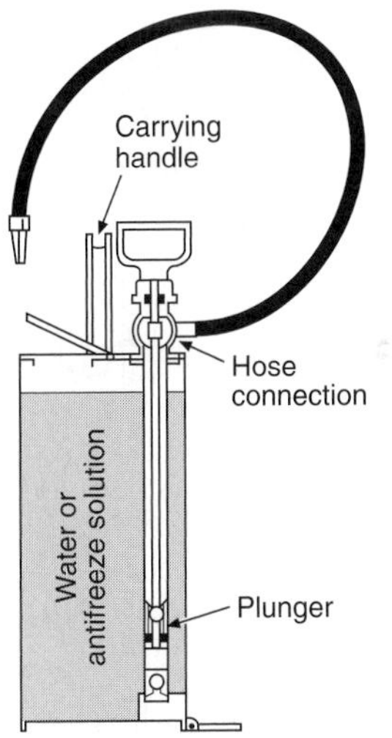

FIGURE 17.5.4 Cylindrical Pump Tank Fire Extinguisher

Cylindrical pump tanks can be filled with either plain water or antifreeze charges recommended by the manufacturer. Common salt or other freezing depressants might corrode the extinguisher or damage the pump assembly. Copper- or plastic-shell models do not corrode as easily as steel and are recommended for use with antifreeze.

Backpack pump tanks are used chiefly for fighting outdoor brush and wildland fires. As the name implies, they are carried on the operator's back. The most common backpack pump tank holds 5 gal (19 L) and weighs about 50 lb (23 kg) when full (Figures 17.5.5 and 17.5.6). Although listed, backpack pump tanks do not have a designated rating. Generally, the tank is filled with plain water, though antifreeze agents, wetting agents, and other special water-based agents may be used. The tank may be made of fiberglass, stainless steel, galvanized steel, or brass, or it may be a flexible water bag. Some models have a large opening with a tight-fitting filter that allows speedy refilling and prevents foreign matter from entering and clogging the pump.

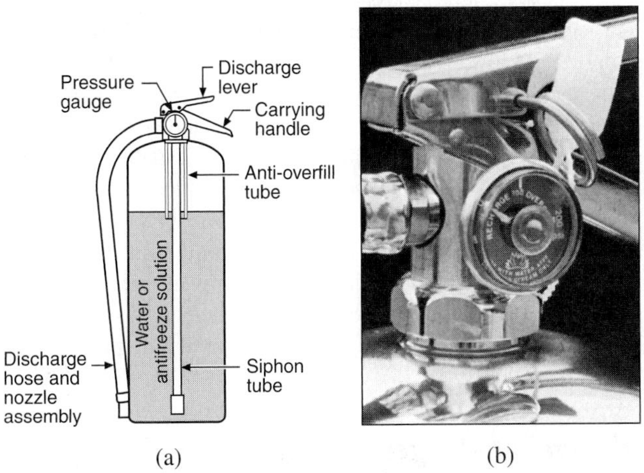

FIGURE 17.5.3 (a) Stored-Pressure Water Fire Extinguisher; (b) Close-Up of Head Assembly (Photo courtesy of Badger Fire Protection)

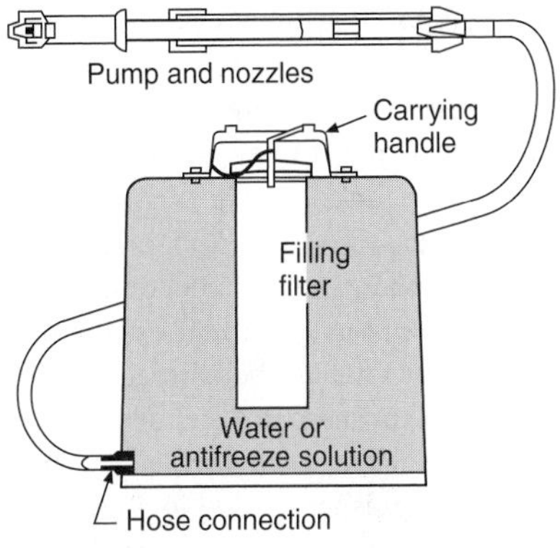

FIGURE 17.5.5 Backpack Pump Tank Fire Extinguisher

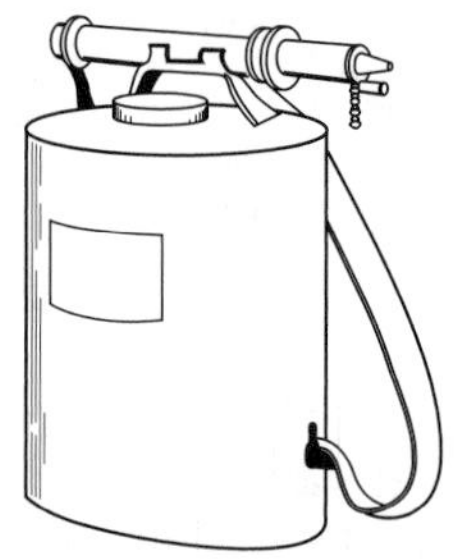

FIGURE 17.5.6 Backpack Pump Tank Fire Extinguisher with 5 gal (19 L) Tank Made of Fiberglass and with Trombone-Type Pump Action at Nozzle

This design also permits refilling from sources such as ponds, lakes, and streams.

The most common backpack pump tank has a trombone-type, double-acting piston pump connected to the tank by a short length of rubber hose. To discharge the device, the operator holds the pump in both hands and moves the piston back and forth. Other models have compression pumps mounted on the right side of the tank. In these, the expellant pressure is built up with about ten strokes of the handle and then maintained by slow, easy pumping. The left-hand controls discharge by means of a lever-operated shutoff nozzle at the end of the hose.

Water Mist. The water mist extinguisher is a fairly recent development. Currently it is available in the 2½ gal (9.5 L) size, and it is similar to the stored-pressure water extinguisher, but has a wand with a special nozzle, which disperses the water into a fine spray. The wand allows the operator to stand at a safe distance from the fire and deliver the low velocity water mist to the burning materials. The mist does not conduct electricity, but operators need to be cautious if pooling of the water occurs near energized electrical equipment, since pooled water will conduct electricity. Besides the advantage of being nonconductive while in a mist, the water can cool and soak the burning materials, helping to extinguish the fire and prevent reflash.

Carbon Dioxide Extinguishers

Carbon dioxide is a compressed gas agent and is commonly referred to as CO_2. Although rated for use on Class B and C fires, it is often effectively used on small Class A fires.

Carbon dioxide prevents combustion by displacing the oxygen in the air surrounding a fire and by cooling the fuel. Its principal advantage is that it does not leave a residue, a consideration that may be important in laboratories and in areas in which food is prepared or electronic equipment is present. The rapid expansion and pressure reduction of the pressurized liquid carbon dioxide in the cylinder results in the cooling and refrigeration effect. However, carbon dioxide extinguishers have a relatively short range because the agent is expelled in the form of a gas/snow cloud; they are also affected by wind or drafts. If a carbon dioxide extinguisher is used in a confined or unventilated area, precautions should be taken so that people are not overcome from lack of oxygen. For the various sizes, stream ranges, discharge times, temperature requirements, and ratings of carbon dioxide extinguishers available, see Table 17.5.1.

In all carbon dioxide extinguishers, the agent is retained as a liquid at 800 to 900 psi (5516 to 6205 kPa) at temperatures below 88°F (31°C), and is self-expelling. The extinguisher design consists of a pressure cylinder, or shell; a siphon tube and valve for releasing the agent; and a discharge horn or horn-hose combination. The siphon tube extends from the valve almost to the bottom of the shell, so that normally only liquid carbon dioxide reaches the discharge horn until about 80 percent of the content has been released. The remaining 20 percent enters the siphon tube as a gas. The rapid expansion from liquid to gas when most of the carbon dioxide is discharged converts about 30 percent of the liquid into a very cold "snow" or "dry ice," which then sublimes into a gas.

To operate a carbon dioxide extinguisher, hold it upright by its carrying handle, remove the locking pin, and squeeze the operating lever (Figure 17.5.7). In smaller portable models, the discharge horn often is connected to the valve assembly by a metal tube/swing joint connector, and the models may be operated with one hand. Larger portable models require two hands, and their discharge horns are attached to a length of hose. Wheeled extinguishers have a cylinder valve with a locking ring pin, a long hose of 15 to 40 ft (4 to 12 m), and a projector that consists of a horn, a long handle, and a control valve. Once the cylinder valve has been opened, the operator controls the discharge with the valve on the projector handle.

Care should be taken not to touch the discharge horn during operation, because it can become extremely cold. If carbon dioxide extinguishers are used in subzero temperatures, the valve must remain open at all times or the discharge may become blocked unless a special low-temperature charge has been added.

Because carbon dioxide extinguishers have a limited range and are affected by draft or wind, they should be applied as close to the base of a fire as possible. Agent should be applied even after the flames have been extinguished to allow time for cooling and to prevent reflash. Due to the relatively short discharge range, carbon dioxide extinguishers are of limited effectiveness on large Class B fires. For flammable liquid fires, the usual method is to begin at the near edge and sweep from side to side toward the back of the fire. However, there is another method called "overhead application." In this method, the discharge horn is pointed downward at an angle of about 45 degrees toward the center of the burning area. Usually, the horn is not moved, and the agent spreads out in all directions. The side-to-side sweeping method may give better results on spill fires, while the overhead method may be best for confined fires.

For fires involving electrical equipment, the discharge should be directed at the source of the flames. It is important to deenergize the equipment as soon as possible to prevent possible reignition.

Halogenated Agent Extinguishers

Halogenated agents fall into two categories. These categories are (1) halons, which include bromochlorodifluoromethane (Halon 1211), bromotrifluoromethane (Halon 1301), and mixtures of

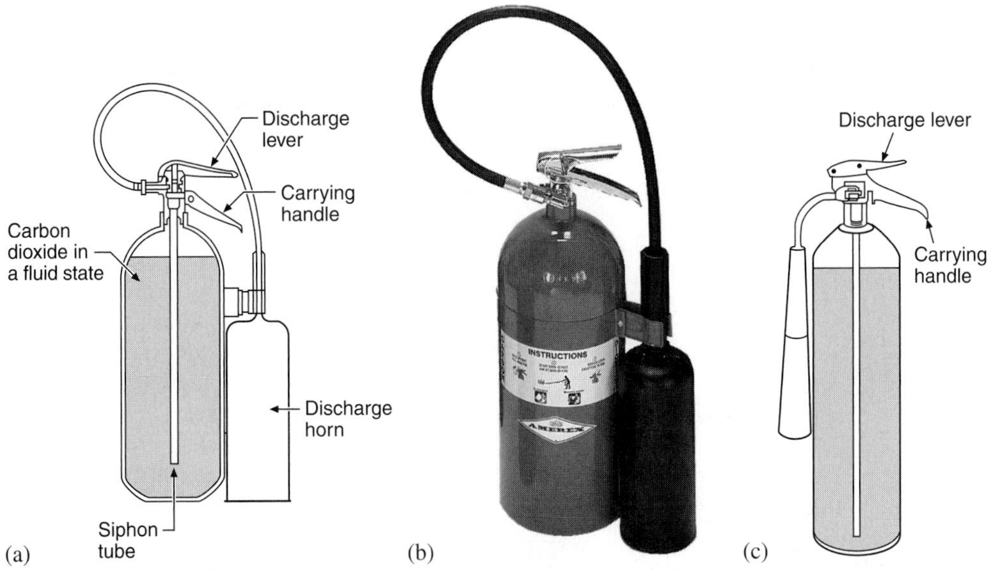

FIGURE 17.5.7 Carbon Dioxide Fire Extinguisher (Photo courtesy of Amerex)

Halon 1211 and Halon 1301; and (2) halocarbons, which include hydrochlorofluorocarbon (HCFC), hydrofluorocarbon (HFC), perfluorocarbon (PFC), and fluoroiodocarbon (FIC) (Figure 17.5.8). These extinguishing agents are often called "clean agents" because they leave no residue.

Halogenated agents not only leave no residue, but are virtually noncorrosive and nonabrasive, and are effective on Class A and B fires. With the exception of Halon 1301, these extinguishing agents are streaming agents because they discharge as a liquid stream from the extinguisher. Because of their physical properties, they need no cold weather protection. When halogenated agents are used on a fire, the decomposition products are a concern to the user and people in the area as the products are toxic. Normally, only small quantities of these chemicals are formed, and, as a warning of their presence, they give off an acrid odor. Using a halogenated agent extinguisher on a large intense fire such as a large flammable liquid spill fire will produce large quantities of decomposition products. Although halogenated agents are retained under pressure in a liquid, a booster charge of nitrogen or inert gas is added to ensure proper operation.

The most common application for halogenated agent extinguishers is for the protection of delicate electronic equipment such as in computer rooms. Since there are production restrictions on the chemical Halon 1211 due to environmental concerns, the halocarbon agent extinguishers have been installed where Halon 1211 was previously the preferred extinguishing agent. Due to these concerns, Halon 1211 use is being discouraged except in specific circumstances. Halon 1211 should never be inadvertently discharged into the atmosphere or used for training purposes.

Dry Chemical Extinguishers

There are two basic kinds of dry chemical agents: (1) ordinary dry chemicals, which are rated B:C and include sodium bicarbonate, potassium bicarbonate (Purple K), urea-potassium-bicarbonate (Monnex®), and potassium-chloride-based agents; and (2) multipurpose dry chemical, ammonium-phosphate-based agent, which achieves the A:B:C rating. There are also two basic designs of dry chemical extinguishers: one uses a separate pressurized cartridge or cylinder of gas to expel the agent *(cartridge- or cylinder-operated extinguisher),* and the other pressurizes the agent chamber for the same purpose (stored pressure extinguisher). The stored-pressure is the most widely used. It is best suited to areas where infrequent use is anticipated and where skilled personnel with professional recharge equipment are available. By contrast, the cartridge-operated type can be refilled quickly in remote locations without special equipment.

The size, rating, and method of operation of any particular extinguisher depends both on its design and on the agent. Table 17.5.1 gives specific information on the capacities, ratings, discharge times, and stream ranges of the dry chemical extinguishers now available.

In areas where Class A:B:C protection is needed, water-based extinguishers may be omitted if multipurpose dry chemical extinguishers are installed. However, they are not replacements for water-based extinguishers under all conditions.

When choosing a dry chemical extinguisher for Class C protection, it is important to remember that potassium chloride and ammonium phosphate are more corrosive than the other dry chemicals.

The various dry chemical extinguishers possess certain common characteristics. Dry chemical extinguishers can be discharged while being carried, and all can be stopped from discharging momentarily to conserve the agent. Dry chemicals also can be used simultaneously with water, either straight stream or spray. Special long-range nozzles may be necessary for some very hazardous areas, such as those with pressurized gases and flammable liquids. Dry chemicals are dispersed less easily by wind than carbon dioxide, though dry chemicals can be more

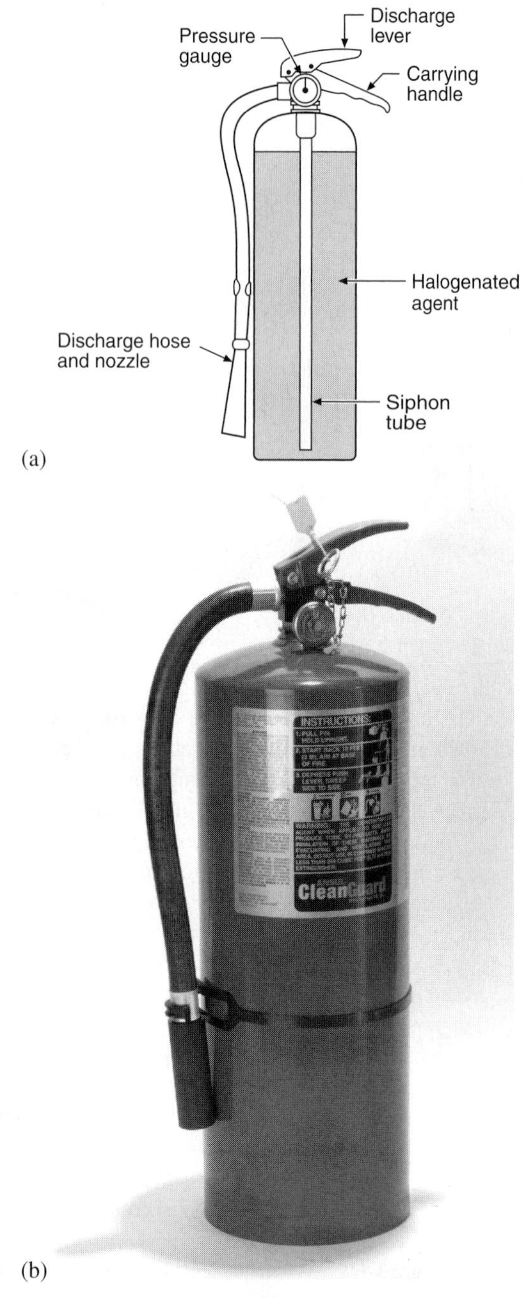

FIGURE 17.5.8 Halogenated Agent Stored-Pressure Fire Extinguisher (Source: *NFPA Guide to Portable Fire Extinguishers,* NFPA, 2003, Figure 1-29. Reproduced courtesy of Jones and Bartlett Publishers.)

effective during windy conditions if the wind is at the operator's back.

If dry chemicals are used on wet, energized electrical equipment, such as rain-soaked utility poles, high-voltage switch gear, and transformers, electrical leakage problems may be aggravated. The combination of dry chemical with moisture provides an electrical path that can keep insulation from being effective. In such cases, all traces of dry chemical should be removed after the fire has been extinguished.

Although all dry chemicals are treated for water repellancy, they may harden if exposed to water. It is therefore important to avoid exposing them to any moisture during storage, handling, and recharging. Manufacturers' specifications must be followed carefully.

Ordinary dry chemicals are rated for use on Class B:C fires, but they may be used on Class A fires to knock down flames rapidly until something more suitable can be obtained. When used on flammable liquid fires, the stream should be directed at the base of the flame. Attack the fire near the edge, and move the discharge toward the back of the fire while sweeping the nozzle from side to side. Do not direct the initial discharge directly at the burning surface at close range (less than 5 to 8 ft [1.5 to 2.4 m]), because the high velocity of the stream may splash and spread the burning material.

Multipurpose dry chemical extinguishers should be used in exactly the same manner as ordinary dry chemical agents on Class B fires. On Class A fires, the multipurpose agent softens and sticks to hot surfaces. In this way, it forms a coating that smothers and isolates the fuel from the fire. The agent itself has little cooling effect and cannot penetrate below the burning surface. For this reason, it may be hard to extinguish deep-seated fires unless the agent is discharged below the surface or the material is broken apart and spread out.

Dry chemicals extinguish fires by interfering with the propagation of the combustion chain reaction, which reduces the concentration of "free" radicals present within the flames. The dry chemical thermally decomposes and prevents the flaming process from continuing. In other words, discharge of dry chemical into the flames prevents reactive particles from coming together and continuing the combustion chain reaction.

Cartridge-Operated Extinguishers. Cartridge-type dry chemical extinguishers have a chamber in which the agent is kept at atmospheric pressure; the chamber has a large opening at the top through which the extinguisher may be filled. Attached to the side of the extinguisher, on most models, is a small cartridge of propellant gas, either carbon dioxide or nitrogen, threaded into a puncture valve and gas tube assembly. The agent is discharged through a hose attached to the bottom edge of the shell, and the discharge is controlled by a squeeze-grip nozzle at the end of the hose (Figure 17.5.9). Cartridge-operated extinguishers should be recharged once they have been pressurized. Even if no agent has been released, the propellant gas can leak away in several hours.

To activate a cartridge-operated extinguisher, hold it upright or place it on the ground. Remove the nozzle from its holder, and hold it in one hand while first pushing down the puncture lever before squeezing the nozzle. Pushing the puncture lever releases the propellant from the cartridge and pressurizes the agent cylinder. On some models, it may be necessary to remove a locking pin before pushing the puncture lever. This operation requires two hands, one to hold the device and the other to release and direct the discharge. Do not stand directly over the extinguisher when pressurizing it.

Stored-Pressure Extinguishers. Dry chemical extinguishers with this expellant method are available in both rechargeable and disposable shell models. Most disposable models have a

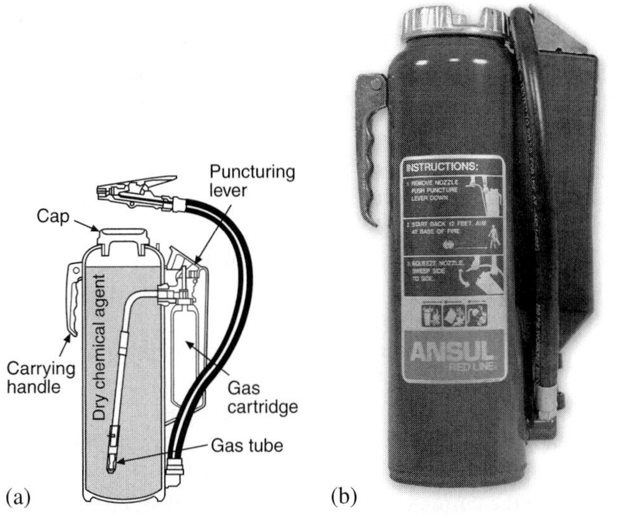

FIGURE 17.5.9 Cartridge-Operated Dry Chemical Fire Extinguisher (Photo courtesy of Ansul Incorporated)

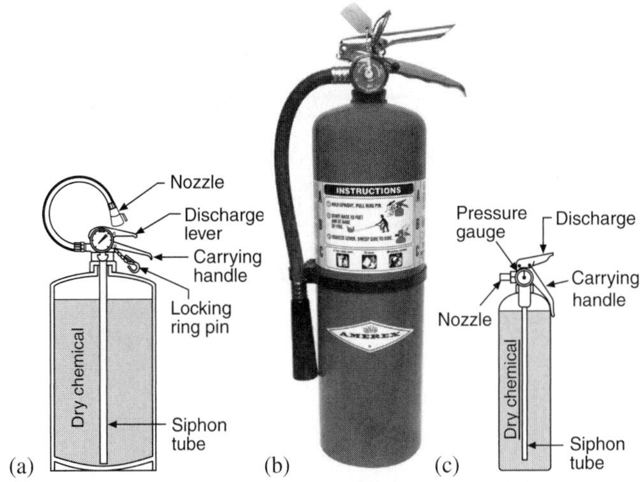

FIGURE 17.5.10 Stored-Pressure Dry Chemical Fire Extinguisher (Photo courtesy of Amerex)

disposable, factory-sealed cylinder containing agent and propellant gas that is threaded into the valve and nozzle assembly. Some small models are designed so that the entire device can be discarded after use. Once this type of device has been used, it should be replaced, even if only a small amount of agent has been discharged, because the propellant gas will leak, leaving no pressure to discharge to agent.

Rechargeable stored-pressure extinguishers come in two types. In both, the agent and the propellant gas are in the extinguisher shell. When the extinguisher is activated, the agent is forced up the siphon tube, where its release is controlled by the operator. One type of extinguisher has a threaded valve assembly and combination carrying handle/operating lever that screws into an opening on the top of the shell. To activate it, release the locking device and squeeze the operating lever (Figure 17.5.10). On smaller sizes of this extinguisher, only one hand is needed to operate the device because the nozzle is part of the valve assembly. Larger sizes require two hands for operation, one to squeeze the lever and carry the device, and the other to direct the agent discharge from the hose.

The other rechargeable stored-pressure dry chemical extinguisher (pre-1975) has a release lever and a hose attached to the cap assembly that covers the fill opening. The hose has a squeeze-grip nozzle for controlling the discharge. To activate it, pull the ring pin and push down the release lever. The agent will travel down the hose to the nozzle, where its discharge can be controlled by squeezing the nozzle. Two hands are needed to operate this extinguisher, one to carry the extinguisher, and the other to release and aim the discharge stream.

Dry Powder Extinguishers

Dry powder extinguishers are intended for use on Class D fires, which involve combustible metals. The agent and method of application should be chosen according to manufacturers' recommendations. The agent may be applied to the fire from an extinguisher or with a scoop and shovel, depending on the type of both agent and metal. In any case, the agent should be applied so that it covers the fire and provides a smothering blanket. More agent may be necessary on hot spots. Care should be taken not to scatter the burning material, which should be left undisturbed until it has cooled.

If there is a fire in finely divided combustible metal or combustible metal alloy scrap that is wet, or if such a fire is wetted with water or water-soluble machine lubricants, the metal may burn rapidly and violently. Such fires may become so hot that it is impossible to get close enough to apply extinguishing agent. If burning metal is on a combustible surface, it should be covered with dry powder. Then a 1- or 2-in. (25- or 50-mm) layer of powder should be spread out nearby, and the burning metal shoveled into it.

One cartridge-operated portable (30 lb [13.6 kg]) dry powder extinguisher currently is available (Figure 17.5.11). Wheeled models are available in 150- and 350-lb (68- and 159-kg) sizes. The extinguishing agent is sodium chloride with additives that render it freeflowing. Thermoplastic material also is added to bind the sodium chloride particles into a solid crust when applied to a fire. With the nozzle fully open, the portable model has a range of 6 to 8 ft (1.8 to 2.4 m).

The method of agent application depends on the type, quantity, and physical form of the burning metal. If the fire is very hot, discharge should begin at the maximum range with the nozzle fully open. Once control is established, the nozzle should be partly closed to produce a soft, heavy flow so that complete coverage can be accomplished at close range. More complete details should be obtained from the manufacturer.

In bulk form, dry powder agents are available in 40- or 50-lb (18- or 23-kg) pails and 350 lb (159 kg) drums. The two most common agents are sodium chloride and G-1 powder. The latter consists of graded, granular graphite to which compounds containing phosphorous have been added. The sodium chloride can be used in an extinguisher or applied by hand. The G-1 agent must be applied by hand. When G-1 is applied to a metal fire, the heat of the fire causes the phosphorous compounds to generate vapors that blanket the fire and prevent air from reaching the

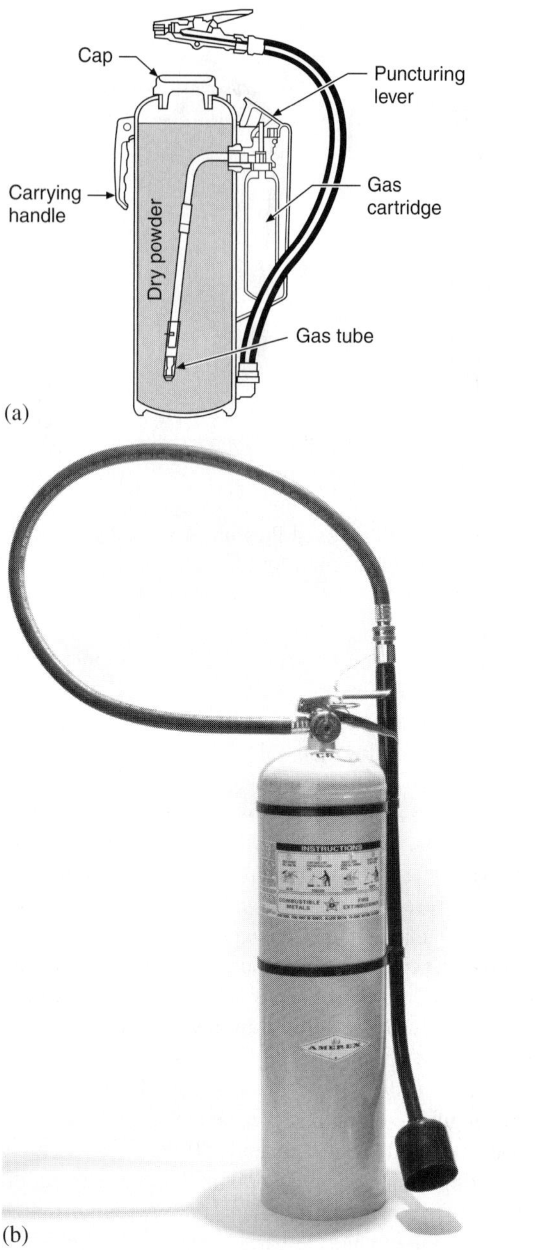

FIGURE 17.5.11 Dry Powder Extinguishers: (a) Cartridge-Operated Extinguisher; (b) Stored-Pressure Extinguisher (Photo source: *NFPA Guide to Portable Fire Extinguishers,* NFPA, 2003, Figure 1-39. Reproduced courtesy of Jones and Bartlett Publishers.)

burning metal. The graphite, being a good conductor of heat, cools the metal.

Aqueous Film-Forming Foam (AFFF) and Film-Forming Fluoroprotein Foam (FFFP) Extinguishers

AFFF and FFFP are extinguishing agents that contain an aqueous film-forming surfactant. When added to water, AFFF and FFFP form solutions that create a foam when discharged through an aspirating nozzle. On Class A fires, these agents both cool and penetrate to reduce temperatures below the ignition level. On Class B fires, they act as a barrier to exclude oxygen from the surface of the fuel.

AFFF and FFFP currently are available in 2½ gal (9.5 L) stored-pressure models rated at 3-A:20-B. They discharge their contents in approximately 50 seconds and have a range of 20 to 25 ft (6 to 8 m). They should be installed only in areas not subject to temperatures below 40°F (4°C). There is also a 33 gal (125.4 L) unit with 20-A:160-B ratings.

These types of extinguishers closely resemble the stored-pressure water extinguisher, except for their special aspirating nozzles (Figure 17.5.12). On flammable liquid fires of appreciable depth, the best results are obtained when the discharge is played against the inside of the back wall of the vat or tank just above the burning surface, which should permit the natural spread of the foam back over the burning liquid. If this is not possible, the operator should stand far enough away from the fire to allow the foam to fall lightly on the burning surface instead of splashing it into the burning liquid. Where possible, the operator should walk around the fire while directing the stream to get maximum coverage during discharge. For flammable liquid spill fires, the foam may be flowed over a burning surface by bouncing it off the floor just in front of the burning area. The operator should never turn his or her back on the fire, as unburned fuel may reignite. For fires in ordinary combustibles, the foam may be used to coat the burning surface directly. Foam is not effective on flammable liquids and gases escaping under pressure, nor is it suitable for fires involving ethers, alcohols, esters, acetone, lacquer thinners, carbon disulfide, and other flammable liquids that either break down or penetrate the foam blanket.

OBSOLETE EXTINGUISHERS

In 1969, the manufacture and testing of all inverting-type extinguishers—soda acid, chemical foam, and cartridge-operated water and loaded stream—was halted in the United States. It was not only the difficult and unorthodox "upside-down" method of actuation that brought about the discontinuance of these extinguishers. Of greater importance was the fact that, after 10 to 15 years, many inverting types tended to fail the minimum test pressure requirements of NFPA 10 (original factory test pressure). When pressurized, the failure record, including hydrostatic test failures, was alarmingly high. Since the inverting types are not normally pressurized, potential failures generally are not evident until the time of operation or hydrostatic testing.

When inverted, normal operating pressures are about 100 psi (690 kPa). Should the discharge elbow or hose become blocked, however, pressures in excess of 300 psi (2069 kPa) may occur. Container failures can injure the operator seriously.

NFPA 10 was revised in 1978, and stated that extinguishers with copper or brass shells joined by soft solder or rivets could no longer be hydrostatically tested, which would result in their removal from use within five years of the latest hydrostatic test date. Reliability and safety of this type of construction could not be determined by standard hydrostatic test procedures.

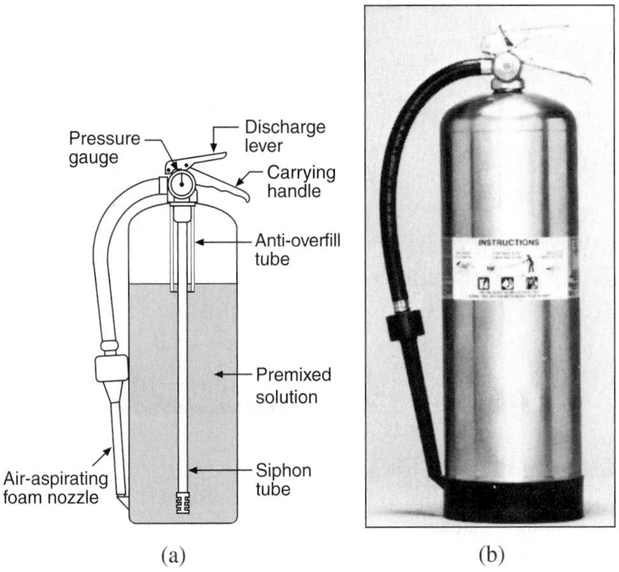

FIGURE 17.5.12 Aqueous Film-Forming Foam (AFFF) Extinguisher (Photo courtesy of Amerex)

In 1978, NFPA 10 called for the removal from service, by or before 1983, of all riveted and soft-solder copper and brass shell extinguishers of the inverting type. The one exception is stainless-steel shells and brass shells that are brazed, as opposed to soft-soldered. Also in 1978, stored-pressure water and/or antifreeze fiberglass shell types were required to be removed from service immediately because they had been recalled by the manufacturer. The following types of fire extinguishers are considered obsolete and should be removed from service:

- Soda acid
- Chemical foam (excluding film-forming agents)
- Vaporizing liquid (e.g., carbon tetrachloride)
- Cartridge-operated water
- Cartridge-operated loaded stream
- Copper or brass shell (excluding pump tanks) joined by soft solder or rivets
- Carbon dioxide extinguishers with metal horns
- Solid charge–type AFFF extinguishers (paper cartridge)
- Pressurized water fire extinguishers manufactured prior to 1971
- Any extinguisher that must be inverted to operate
- Any dry chemical extinguisher with a stainless steel shell
- Any stored pressure extinguisher manufactured prior to 1955
- Any extinguisher with a 4B, 6B, 8B, 12B, or 16B fire rating
- Stored-pressure water extinguishers with fiberglass shells (pre-1976)
- Any extinguisher that can no longer be serviced in accordance with the manufacturer's maintenance manual

Vaporizing liquid extinguishers with CCl_4 (carbon tetrachloride) and CBM (chlorobromomethane) became obsolete in the late 1960s. The toxic properties of these agents expose the operator to unwarranted health hazards, and their use was supplanted by safer, more effective extinguishers. In 2007, NFPA 10 called for the removal from service, at the next six-year maintenance interval or the next hydrostatic test interval, all dry chemical stored pressure extinguishers that were manufactured prior to October 1984.

DISTRIBUTION OF FIRE EXTINGUISHERS

No matter how carefully extinguishers are chosen to match the hazards of an area and the ability of the people who will use them, they will not be effective unless they are readily available. Sometimes extinguishers are kept at hand, as in welding operations, but, more often, one has to travel from the fire to the extinguisher and back before beginning to put out the fire. In such cases, travel distance to the nearest extinguisher is very important. Travel distance is the actual distance around partitions, through doorways and aisles, and so on that someone must walk to reach the extinguisher.

When placing extinguishers, select locations that provide uniform distribution, easily accessible and relatively free from temporary blockage, near normal paths of travel, near exits and entrances, free from the potential of physical damage, and readily available.

Mounting Extinguishers

If an extinguisher falls, it may injure someone or be so damaged that it must be replaced. Extinguishers should be mounted on walls or columns by securely fastened hangers so that they are supported adequately. Some extinguishers are mounted in cabinets or wall recesses. The operating instructions should always face outward, and the extinguisher should be placed so that it can be removed easily. Cabinets should be kept clean, dry, and ventilated if installed in outdoor locations.

Where extinguishers may become dislodged, brackets specifically designed to cope with this problem are available. In areas where they are subject to physical damage, such as warehouse aisles, protection from impact is important. In large open areas, such as aircraft hangars, extinguishers may be mounted on moveable pedestals or wheeled carts. To maintain some pattern of distribution and specify intended placement, locations should be marked on the floor.

NFPA 10 specifies floor clearance and mounting heights, based on extinguisher weight, as follows:

1. Extinguishers with a gross weight not exceeding 40 lb (18 kg) should be installed so that the top of the extinguisher is not more than 5 ft (1.5 m) above the floor.
2. Extinguishers with a gross weight greater than 40 lb (18 kg), except wheeled types, should be installed so that the top of the extinguisher is not more than 3½ ft (1 m) above the floor.
3. In no case can the clearance between the bottom of the extinguisher and the floor be less than 4 in. (100 mm).

When extinguishers are mounted on industrial trucks, vehicles, boats, aircraft, trains, and so on, special mounting brackets, available from the manufacturer, should be used. It is also important that the extinguisher be located at a safe distance from the hazard so that it will not become involved in the fire.

Extinguisher Distribution for Class A Combustibles

Table 17.5.2 is a guide to determining the minimum number and rating of extinguishers for Class A fires needed in any particular area. Sometimes extinguishers with ratings higher than those indicated in Table 17.5.2 may be necessary because of process hazards, building configuration, and so on, but in no case should the recommended maximum travel distance be exceeded.

The first step when calculating how many Class A extinguishers are needed is to determine whether an occupancy is light-, ordinary-, or extra-hazard, according to NFPA 10. Next, the extinguisher rating should be matched with occupancy hazard to determine the maximum area that an extinguisher can protect. The maximum travel distance, or actual walking distance, allowed for Class A extinguishers is 75 ft (23 m).

The figure of 11,250 ft^2 (1044 m^2) in Table 17.5.2 is used instead of 12,000 ft^2 (1115 m^2), which would appear to be a normal progressive increment. This is because the largest square inside a circle with a 75 ft (23 m) radius would be 106 ft × 106 ft (32 m × 32 m), or 11,250 ft^2 (1044 m^2). Because buildings are usually rectangular, this is the largest open area one can have and still comply with the 75-ft (23-m) travel distance rule (Figure 17.5.13).

The area that can be protected by one fire extinguisher with a given A rating is shown in Table 17.5.3. These values are determined by multiplying the maximum floor area per unit of A shown in Table 17.5.3 by the various A ratings until a value of 11,250 ft^2 (1044 m^2) is exceeded.

NFPA 10 also provides that up to half of the complement of extinguishers for Class A fires, as specified in Table 17.5.2, may be replaced by uniformly spaced small-hose (1½ in. [38 mm]) stations. However, the hose stations and extinguishers should be located so that the hose stations do not replace more than every other extinguisher.

The following examples illustrate the number and placement of extinguishers according to occupancy hazard and extinguisher rating. The sample building is 150 ft by 450 ft (46 m by 137 m), which gives a floor area of 67,500 ft^2 (6270 m^2). Although several different ways of placing extinguishers are given, a number of other locations could have been used with similar results.

The first example demonstrates placement at the maximum protection area limits (11,250 ft^2 [1044 m^2]) allowed per extinguisher in NFPA 10 for each class of occupancy. Installing extinguishers with higher ratings will not affect distribution or placement.

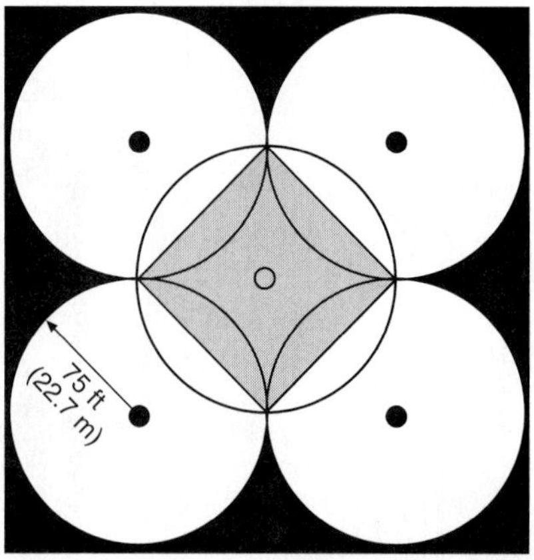

FIGURE 17.5.13 Maximum Extinguisher-Protected Area. The shaded square shows the maximum area (11,250 ft^2 [1044 m^2]) that an extinguisher can protect within the limits of a 75 ft (23 m) radius.

TABLE 17.5.2 Fire Extinguisher Size and Placement for Class A Hazards

	Light (Low) Hazard Occupancy	*Ordinary (Moderate) Hazard Occupancy*	*Extra (High) Hazard Occupancy*
Minimum rated single extinguisher	2-A[a]	2-A[a]	4-A[b]
Maximum floor area per unit of A	3,000 ft^2	1,500 ft^2	1,000 ft^2
Maximum floor area for extinguisher	11,250 ft^2	11,250 ft^2	11,250 ft^2
Maximum travel distance to extinguisher	75 ft	75 ft	75 ft

[a]Up to two water-type extinguishers, each with 1-A rating, can be used to fulfill the requirements of one 2-A rated extinguisher.
[b]Two 2½ gal (9.46 L) water-type extinguishers can be used to fulfill the requirements of one 4-A rated extinguisher.
For SI units: 1 ft = 0.305 m; 1 ft^2 = 0.0929 m^2.
Source: NFPA 10, *Standard for Portable Fire Extinguishers,* Table 6.2.1.1., 2007, p. 10-11.

TABLE 17.5.3 Maximum Area in Square Feet to Be Protected per Extinguisher

Class A Rating Shown on Extinguisher	*Light (Low) Hazard Occupancy*	*Ordinary (Moderate) Hazard Occupancy*	*Extra (High) Hazard Occupancy*
1-A	—	—	—
2-A	6,000	3,000	—
3-A	9,000	4,500	—
4-A	11,250	6,000	4,000
6-A	11,250	9,000	6,000
10-A	11,250	11,250	10,000
20-A	11,250	11,250	11,250
30-A	11,250	11,250	11,250
40-A	11,250	11,250	11,250

Note: 11,250 ft^2 is considered a practical limit.
For SI units: 1 ft^2 = 0.0929 m^2.
Source: NFPA 10, *Standard for Portable Fire Extinguishers,* Table E.3.4, 2007, p. 10-43.

EXAMPLE 1:

	4-A	Extinguishers for light-hazard occupancy
$\frac{67{,}500}{11{,}250} = 6$	10-A	Extinguishers for ordinary-hazard occupancy
	20-A	Extinguishers for extra-hazard occupancy

This placement along outside walls would not be acceptable because it clearly violates the travel distance rule (Figure 17.5.14). Instead, relocation and/or additional extinguishers are needed.

Example 2 is for fire extinguishers having ratings that correspond to protection areas of 6000 ft^2 (557 m^2). Example 3 is for extinguishers having the minimum ratings permitted by Table 17.5.2 with corresponding minimum protection areas. As the number of lower-rated extinguishers increases, meeting the travel distance requirement generally becomes less of a problem.

EXAMPLE 2:

	2-A	Extinguishers for light-hazard occupancy
$\frac{67{,}500}{6{,}000} = 12$	4-A	Extinguishers for ordinary-hazard occupancy
	6-A	Extinguishers for extra-hazard occupancy

EXAMPLE 3:

$\frac{67{,}500}{6{,}000} = 12$	2-A	Extinguishers for light-hazard occupancy
$\frac{67{,}500}{3{,}000} = 23$	2-A	Extinguishers for ordinary-hazard occupancy
$\frac{67{,}500}{4{,}000} = 17$	4-A	Extinguishers for extra-hazard occupancy

Extinguishers could be mounted on exterior walls or, as shown in Figure 17.5.15, on building columns or interior walls, and conform to both distribution and travel distance rules.

The arrangement illustrated in Figure 17.5.16 shows extinguishers grouped together on building columns or interior walls in a manner that still conforms to distribution and travel distance rules.

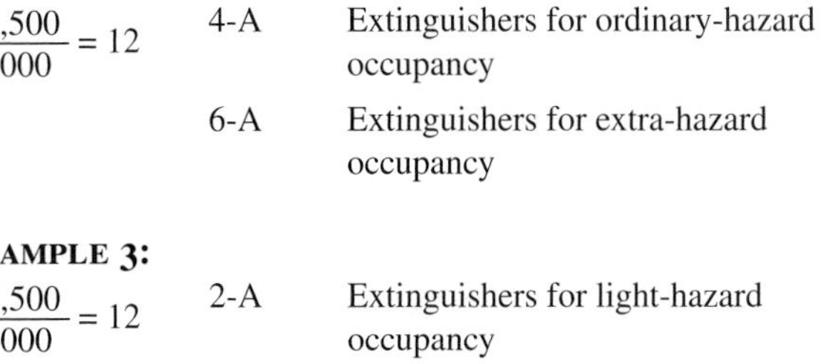

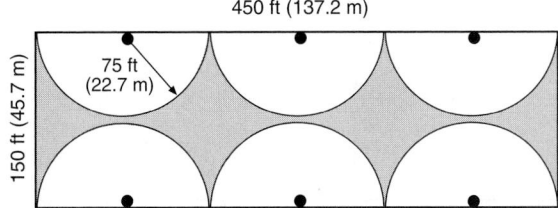

FIGURE 17.5.14 Diagrammatic Representation of Extinguishers Located Along Outside Walls of a 150 ft × 450 ft (46 m × 137 m) Building. The large dots represent extinguishers. The shaded areas indicate "voids" that are farther than 75 ft (23 m) from the nearest extinguisher.

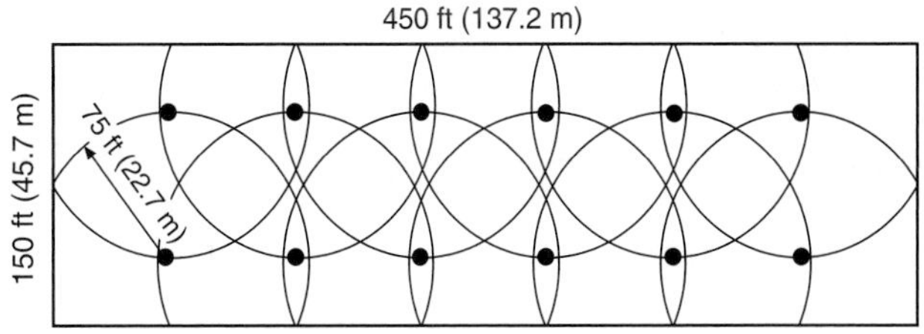

FIGURE 17.5.15 Configuration of 12 Extinguishers Mounted on Building Columns or Interior Walls, Meeting Requirements for Travel Distance and Extinguisher Distribution

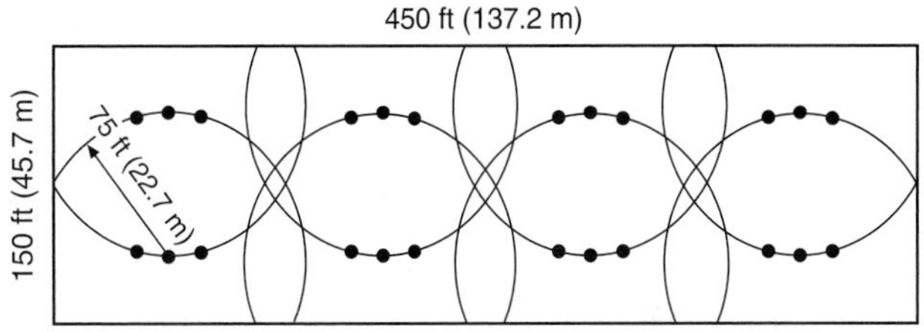

FIGURE 17.5.16 Extinguishers Grouped Together

Extinguisher Distribution for Class B Combustibles

Class B fire hazards fall into two distinct categories. The first includes liquids ¼ in. (6.4 mm) deep or less, and the other includes liquids deeper than ¼ in. (6.4 mm).

In areas where liquids do not reach an appreciable depth, extinguishers should be provided according to Table 17.5.4. The reason the basic maximum travel distance to Class B extinguishers is 50 ft (15 m), as opposed to 75 ft (23 m) for Class A extinguishers, is that flammable liquid fires reach their maximum intensity almost immediately, and thus the extinguisher must be nearer to hand. With lower-rated extinguishers, the travel distance is reduced to 30 ft (9 m).

Even though Table 17.5.4 specifies maximum travel distances to extinguishers for Class B fires, judgment should be used when actually placing the devices. The closer the extinguisher to the hazard, the better—up to the point at which a fire might damage or obstruct access to the device.

When flammable liquids reach an appreciable depth, the extinguisher's rating number, except for foam types, should be at least twice the number of square feet (m^2) of surface area of the largest tank in the area, assuming that other requirements are met. The travel distances specified by Table 17.5.4 should also be used to locate extinguishers for protection of spot hazards. Sometimes, one extinguisher can be installed to provide protection against several different hazards, provided that travel distances are not exceeded.

Where there are open process tanks of flammable liquids with surface areas greater than 10 ft^2 (1 m^2), complete dependence should not be placed on fire extinguishers. It is often advisable to consider installing fixed fire protection systems for

TABLE 17.5.4 Fire Extinguisher Size and Placement for Class B Hazard Excluding Protection of Deep-Layer Flammable Liquid Tanks

Type of Hazard	*Basic Minimum Extinguisher Rating*	Maximum Travel Distance to Extinguishers *ft*	*m*
Low	5-B	30	9
	10-B	50	15
Moderate	10-B	30	9
	20-B	50	15
High	40-B	30	9
	80-B	50	15

these tanks because of the potential size and intensity of the fire which could occur. If a fixed protection system suitable for Class B fires is installed, then the extinguisher requirement may be waived for the hazard, or hazards, it protects, though not for the complete structure or any other special hazards in the area. Portable extinguishers can be useful even when fixed protection systems have been installed, in case a burning tank spills liquid outside the range of the fixed equipment or a fire begins adjacent to a tank rather than in it.

Pressurized flammable liquids and gases are not stored in open containers, and it is not possible to select extinguishers for them according to the square foot (m^2) requirements. Instead, extinguishers with special nozzles and rates of agent application should be chosen. The manufacturers of these specialized extinguishers usually recommend what equipment they are suited for. In general, however, no attempt to extinguish pressurized fuel fires should be made unless the source of fuel can be shut off promptly. As before, the travel distances to portable extinguishers should not exceed those specified by Table 17.5.4.

Because Class B fires can become so intense so quickly, the flow rate and the duration of discharge of an agent are very important. For these reasons, NFPA 10 does not permit substituting two or more extinguishers of lower rating for the minimum ratings given in Table 17.5.4, except for certain foam extinguishers. The exception permits the substitution because foam progressively "secures" a fire, and the foam from one extinguisher is effective during the time it takes to bring other units into operation. With carbon dioxide and dry chemical extinguishers, however, four extinguishers rated 5-B are not equal to one extinguisher rated 20-B; the larger extinguisher has a higher flow rate in pounds per second (kg/sec) and a longer continuous discharge time than the smaller models.

Wheeled extinguishers with ratings from 20-B to 480-B are available. They are designed chiefly for outdoor fire fighting and should be used only by trained employees. They should be distributed according to the 50 ft (15 m) travel distance rules of Table 17.5.4, though longer travel distances may be authorized by the authority having jurisdiction.

A sample problem from NFPA 10 for protection by portable extinguishers follows.

Sample Problem. A light-occupancy office building is to be protected by portable fire extinguishers. The floor area is 11,100 ft^2 (1031 m^2) and of unusual design (Figure 17.5.17).

The most common fire extinguisher selections would be 2½ gal (9.5 L) stored-pressure water models rated 2-A. According to Table 17.5.2 (Table E-3.4 from NFPA 10), two fire extinguishers are needed (11,100/6000 = 2). Travel distance requirements are 75 ft (23 m) maximum.

The two units are placed at points 1 and 2, and a check is make on the travel distance requirement. Because of the area's unusual shape, it is found that the shaded areas exceed the 75 ft (23 m) distance. Two additional fire extinguishers (at points 3 and 4) are needed. The additional fire extinguishers afford more flexibility in placement, and alternative locations are indicated. It is important to consider any partitions, walls, or other obstructions in determining the travel distance.

As an additional item, consider that Area A contains a small printing and duplicating department that uses flammable liquids. This area is judged to be an ordinary Class B hazard. A 10-B:C or 20-B:C fire extinguisher should be specified to protect this area.

There are now two alternatives to be considered. First, a fifth fire extinguisher, either carbon dioxide or ordinary dry chemical, with a rating of 10-B:C or 20-B:C could be specified. Second, the water fire extinguisher at point 2 could be replaced with a multipurpose dry chemical fire extinguisher that has a rating of at least 2-A:10-B:C. It should be located near point 2, keeping in mind the 75 ft (23 m) travel distance for the 2-A protection and the 30 ft or 50 ft (9.1 m or 15.25 m) travel distance required for the Class B protection that this fire extinguisher provides.

Extinguisher Distribution for Class C Fires

Extinguishers for Class C fires are required wherever there is live electrical equipment. This sort of extinguisher contains a nonconducting agent, usually carbon dioxide, dry chemical, or a halogenated agent.

Once the power to live electrical equipment is cut off, the fire becomes a Class A or Class B fire, depending on the nature of the burning electrical equipment and the burning material in

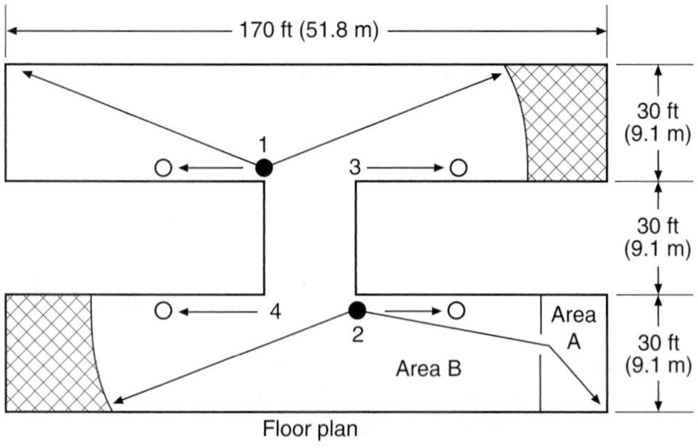

FIGURE 17.5.17 Floor Plan

the vicinity. Extinguishers for Class C fires should be selected according to the size of the electrical equipment; the configuration of the electrical equipment, particularly the enclosures of units, which influence agent distribution; and the range of the extinguisher's stream. At large installations of electrical equipment where continuity of power is critical, fixed fire protection is desirable. But even when fixed fire protection is present, it is recommended that some Class C extinguishers be provided to handle incipient fires.

Class D Extinguisher Distribution

It is particularly important that the proper extinguishers be available for Class D fires. Because the properties of combustible metals differ, even an agent for Class D fires may be hazardous if used on the wrong metal. Agents should be chosen carefully according to the manufacturers' recommendations. The amount of agent needed is normally figured according to the surface area of the metal, plus the shape and form of the metal, which could contribute to the severity of the fire and cause "bake-off" of the agent. For example, fires in magnesium filings are more difficult to put out than fires in magnesium scrap, and more agent is needed for magnesium filings. The maximum travel distance to all extinguishers for Class D fires is 75 ft (23 m).

INSPECTION AND MAINTENANCE OF FIRE EXTINGUISHERS

Once a fire extinguisher has been purchased, it becomes the responsibility of the purchaser or an assigned agent to maintain the device. Adequate maintenance consists of periodically inspecting each extinguisher, recharging each extinguisher following discharge, and performing periodic hydrostatic tests or as needed.

A fire equipment servicing agency is considered the most reliable way for the general public to maintain extinguishers, but large industries often train employees to handle this maintenance themselves. Many jurisdictions require service technicians to be licensed. Carson[2] provides checklists for periodic inspection and maintenance of fire extinguishers.

Inspection Considerations

An inspection is a quick check that visually determines whether the fire extinguisher is properly placed and will operate. The purpose of an inspection is to give reasonable assurance that the extinguisher is fully charged and will function effectively if needed. An inspection should determine that the extinguisher is in its designated place, is conspicuous, is not blocked in any way, has not been activated and partially or completely emptied, has not been tampered with, and has not sustained any obvious physical damage or been subjected to an environment that could interfere with its operation, such as corrosive fumes. If the extinguisher is equipped with a pressure gauge and/or tamper indicators, the inspection should show conditions to be satisfactory. In addition, the maintenance tag can be checked to determine the date of the last thorough maintenance check.

In order to be effective, inspections must be frequent, regular, and thorough. In a small building with few extinguishers, the manager, property owner, or some designated person could check extinguishers at the beginning of each workday. If a building is large enough to employ security guards or a surveillance service, extinguishers should be inspected at least once during each 8 hour shift. In industrial plants, the plant fire brigade or fire inspector often inspects extinguishers either daily, weekly, or monthly. The maximum time period between inspections is 30 days.

An individual evaluation must be made of each property to determine how frequently inspections should be made. If a particular operation is fire prone or is crucial to the use of the property, more frequent inspections should be made. For example, if all the products manufactured in a particular industrial plant had to be painted, a fire in the painting room could be disastrous, so inspections should be very frequent.

It is important to consider the nature of the hazards present that influence the potential use of the extinguisher: the exposure of the extinguisher to tampering, vandalism, and malicious mischief; extraordinary weather conditions; the likelihood of accidental damage to the extinguisher; and the possibility of visual or physical obstructions to the accessibility of extinguishers.

Manual Inspection Alternative

An alternative to a manual inspection of extinguishers is to have them electronically monitored. These extinguisher monitoring systems have gained acceptance and are now routinely used to check the condition of extinguishers. Typically, extinguishers are connected to a fire alarm system and are electronically monitored to ensure that they are in their designated places. Such electronic monitoring can also verify that there are no obstructions to accessing the extinguishers and that the pressure gauge is in its operable range. This alternative is desirable for locations where the extinguishers were previously neglected or where there is a problem of theft.

Maintenance Considerations

Maintenance, as distinguished from inspection, means a complete and thorough examination of each extinguisher. A maintenance check involves examining parts, cleaning and replacing any defective parts, and reassembling, recharging, and, where appropriate, pressurizing the extinguisher.

Maintenance checks sometimes reveal the need for special testing of extinguisher shells or other components. For example, they may reveal that the extinguisher container should be hydrostatically tested or even replaced.

Frequency. Maintenance should be performed periodically, but at least once every 12 months, after each use, or when an inspection shows that the need is obvious. If an inspection reveals evidence of serious damage by corrosion, for example, the extinguisher should be subjected to a thorough maintenance check, even though it may have undergone one recently. Similarly, if an inspection shows evidence of tampering, agent leakage, or physical damage, a complete maintenance check should be initiated. NFPA 10 contains specific details related to maintenance.

Tags and Tamper Seals. For many years, extinguisher tags have been used as a convenient means for recording maintenance checks. For routine maintenance, a tied-on tag or pressure-sensitive label is used to record the date and the inspector's initials. Newer technology using bar code readers also can be used. Tamper seals also should be used. Lead and wire seals were used commonly until plastic seals were introduced in 1972. As long as the seal remains intact, one can be reasonably sure that the extinguisher has not been used. However, it is important to note that a stored-pressure extinguisher can develop a leak and lose its pressure even though the tamper indicator remains intact or the pressure gauge reads normal. During annual maintenance, the tamper seal is removed by operating the pull pin or locking device. This is done to ensure that they operate freely. A new tamper seal is then installed.

A neck ring collar is installed on an extinguisher following servicing, which necessitates the removal of the extinguisher valve assembly. This is used to verify if the extinguisher was depressurized and the valve was removed. The collar design also necessitates the removal of the valve before the collar can be attached to the extinguisher. The collar design permits the date to be recorded. The collar provides the authorities having jurisdiction with convenient visual proof that the extinguisher was disassembled. Figure 17.5.18 provides a guide to the design of a "Verification of Service" collar.

Maintenance Operations

In any operational test of a portable fire extinguisher, there are three basic items that need to be checked: (1) the mechanical parts of the device—that is, the extinguisher shell and other component parts; (2) the amount and condition of the extinguishing agent; and (3) the condition of the means for expelling the agent.

A record of the date of purchase, as well as maintenance dates, should be kept for each extinguisher. A separate record is also desirable and should include the maintenance date and the name of the person or agency performing the maintenance; the date last recharged and the name of the person or agency performing the recharge; the hydrostatic retest date and the name of the person or agency performing the hydrostatic test; description of dents remaining after passing a hydrostatic test; and the date of the six-year maintenance for certain stored-pressure dry chemical and halogenated agent extinguishers.

Individuals who own extinguishers might neglect them if there is no planned periodic follow-up program. It is recommended that owners become familiar with their extinguishers so that they can detect telltale signs which suggest the need for maintenance. An alternative is to have the dealer from whom the extinguisher was purchased establish an annual follow-up maintenance program.

On properties where extinguishers are maintained by the occupant, a supply of recharging materials should be kept on hand. When recharging extinguishers other than those with plain water, use only those recharging materials specified on the extinguisher's nameplate. Other recharging materials may impair the efficiency of the extinguisher or cause it to malfunction and injure the operator. Special precautions are necessary for certain types of extinguishers, and they are discussed elsewhere in this chapter.

NFPA 10 has an appendix with a checklist of items that require maintenance. The checklist is divided into two sections. One section of the checklist is arranged to pinpoint the mechanical parts common to most extinguishers. The other section addresses agent and expelling means.

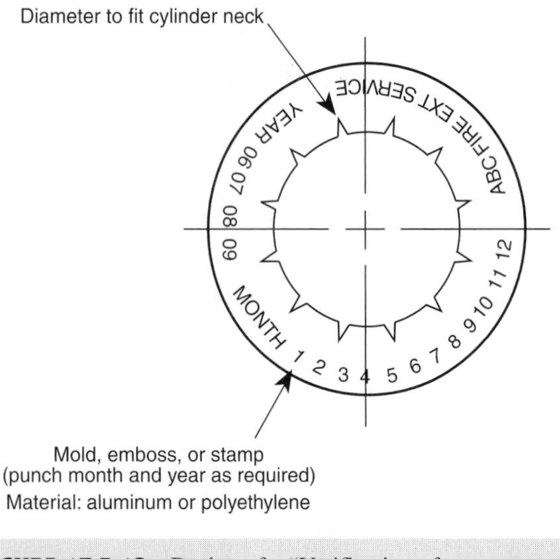

FIGURE 17.5.18 Design of a "Verification of Service" Collar

Inspection and Maintenance of Water-Type Extinguishers

Inspection and maintenance for stored-pressure models is too often thought of as quite simple. Unless the extinguisher has been used or a routine inspection reveals a defect, maintenance is sometimes left until the five-year hydrostatic test is performed. This practice can result in failures and malfunctions. The principal items that need to be checked during an inspection are a loose, worn, or damaged hose; a plugged nozzle; a dented shell; a damaged indicator gauge; and a damaged or jammed ring pin. Normal maintenance service, as specified in NFPA 10, should be performed annually.

Mechanical pump extinguishers, such as pump tanks and backpacks, are easy to inspect and maintain. The tanks containing the water or antifreeze solution must be checked to ensure they are in good condition, have not been weakened by corrosive action, and do not contain sediment that might block the stream during the pumping operation. If the device has not been used in the last 12 months, the liquid should be removed from the tank and the tank should be flushed and filled with new liquid. Pumps require lubrication from time to time. They should be checked annually to ensure that the plungers are in proper condition, that seals and washers have not deteriorated, and that hoses are not clogged. Antifreeze solutions need to be checked to ensure that they are not contaminated and can withstand the temperatures in the area.

Inspection and Maintenance of Dry Chemical Extinguishers

Dry chemical extinguishers should be inspected monthly, and they should also undergo normal annual maintenance. The quantity of agent for a cartridge-operated model can be checked by weighing or by removing the fill cap and checking it visually. The gas cartridge also can be checked by weighing. On stored-pressure models, the pressure gauge will indicate if adequate pressure is maintained, and the agent quantity can be checked by weighing.

Dry chemical extinguishers should be refilled promptly after use, even if they have been discharged only partially. When refilling, extreme caution must be taken to ensure that no water, moisture, or foreign material enters the cylinder. Even though dry chemical agents are treated for moisture repellency, they can eventually harden if moisture is present. When these extinguishers are hydrostatically tested, they must be dried thoroughly so that no trace of water or moisture remains. Before new agent is added, all of the unused agent should be removed by dumping or vacuuming, and any residue should be removed from the hose.

An extinguisher containing a Class B:C dry chemical (bicarbonate-base or potassium chloride) should not be refilled with a Class A:B:C agent (monoammonium-phosphate-base). Mixing different dry chemical agents can result in malfunction, damage to the extinguisher, or both. The bicarbonate-based agent is chemically alkaline and will react with the acidic ammonium phosphate. This reaction is aggravated by exposure to heat or the presence of moisture in amounts as small as 0.1 percent. One result is caking of the agent; another possible result is the internal corrosion of the extinguisher. Under certain conditions, the reaction will cause excess pressure to build up within the shell, which may damage or rupture the extinguisher.

Substituting another manufacturer's dry chemical of the same type is not recommended unless it has the same chemical and physical characteristics, or has been tested and found to give equivalent performance. The problems involved in substitution include the following:

1. An altered flow rate of the dry chemical, which could influence extinguishing efficiency
2. The amount of agent that could be placed in the extinguisher, which could influence discharge time
3. Incompatibility of one dry chemical to another, including chemical reactions, caking, and jamming of hose or nozzles. The flow rate can change with the particle size and density of the agent. A discharge nozzle designed to dispense one dry chemical efficiently might well be less efficient for another. An extinguisher designed to hold a given weight of one formula may not hold the same amount of another. Dip tubes, hoses, or valves could become plugged.

Recharge operations for the cartridge-operated models are relatively easy. The rubber sleeves on the gas tube should be checked for cracking or overstretching, and the gasket and gasket seats on the shell and cap should be wiped clean. The cap should be screwed on handtight. When replacing the cartridge, care should be taken that the threads are not dirty, cross-threaded, or otherwise damaged. For stored-pressure models, the entire valve body, stem, and "O" ring should be carefully wiped clean and blown out with dry nitrogen to get rid of all traces of agent residue which might cause a pressure leak.

Nitrogen gas used for pressurizing should be of the standard industrial grade, with a dew point of –60°F (–51.1°C) or lower so that it is free of moisture. Once the extinguisher has been pressurized, it should be given a leak test or allowed to stand for about 12 hours and then checked for leaks before it is returned to service.

Some stored-pressure extinguishers are factory-sealed and are not rechargeable. No effort should be made to recharge these units in the field. Normally, the shell of the extinguisher is discarded following use; only the valve and nozzle assembly are retained. Refill units should be obtained from the manufacturer, and detailed instructions for replacement are included on the extinguisher nameplate.

The general inspection and maintenance procedures for dry powder (Class D) extinguishers are the same as for cartridge-operated dry chemical extinguishers.

Inspection and Maintenance of Carbon Dioxide Extinguishers

Weighing is the only way to determine whether carbon dioxide extinguishers are fully charged. They should be weighed at least semiannually for loss of weight and inspected for deterioration and/or physical damage. The full and empty weights are stamped on the valve assembly. Any carbon dioxide extinguisher that has a weight loss of 10 percent or more should be recharged and tested for leaks. Recharging is generally done by an extinguisher servicing company. Should on-site recharging be desirable, however, the manufacturer should be contacted for assistance in setting up a recharging station.

Recharging extinguishers with carbon dioxide from dry-ice converters is no longer permitted due to the high potential for moisture in the carbon dioxide. The vapor phase of carbon dioxide must not be less than 99.5 percent carbon dioxide. The water content of the liquid phase must not be more than 0.01 percent by weight (–30°F [–34.4°C] dew point). The oil content of the carbon dioxide must not exceed 10 ppm by weight.

Specific recommendations are given for such recharging in NFPA 10. The required source of carbon dioxide is a low-pressure carbon dioxide supply (300 psi at 0°F [206.8 kPa at –17.8°C]), either directly from the source or through dry cylinders used as intermediaries. It cannot be emphasized too strongly that internal moisture can seriously corrode an extinguisher, and that moisture is most easily introduced into a cylinder either during recharging or following a hydrostatic test.

Inspection and Maintenance of Halogenated Agent Extinguishers

The general inspection and maintenance procedures for halogenated agent extinguishers are similar to the requirements for other extinguishers. They are physically similar to stored-pressure dry chemical extinguishers. The specific requirements of each manufacturer should be followed.

Hydrostatic Testing of Extinguishers

The purpose of hydrostatic testing of portable fire extinguishers that are subject to internal pressures is to protect against unexpected, in-service failure. Such a failure may be due to undetected internal corrosion caused by moisture in the extinguisher; external corrosion caused by atmospheric humidity or corrosive vapors; damage caused by rough handling, which may or may not be obvious by external inspection; repeated pressurizations; manufacturing flaws in the construction of the extinguisher; improper assembly of valves or safety relief discs; or exposure of the extinguisher to abnormal heat, as during a fire.

NFPA 10 requires that hydrostatic pressure tests be performed on extinguishers according to Table 17.5.5. The first hydrostatic retest may be conducted between the fifth and sixth year for those with a designated test interval of five years. However, carbon dioxide types require a strict five-year interval according to federal law. Hydrostatic tests also should be conducted immediately upon discovery of any mechanical injury or corrosion to the extinguisher shell.

In the United States, various U.S. Department of Transportation (DOT) rules apply to specific types of cylinders used for fire extinguishers. Title 49 of the *Code of Federal Regulations* calls, with some exceptions, for the hydrostatic retesting every five years of compressed-gas cylinders offered for interstate transportation in a charged condition. Paragraph 173.34(e) calls for periodic retesting of DOT compressed-gas cylinders whether or not the cylinders are shipped interstate.

Many different DOT specification cylinders are used for dry chemical extinguishers, including Types DOT-4B and DOT-4BA. The requirements for these types are peculiar to them.

The preferred method of hydrostatic testing of compressed-gas cylinders is the water-jacketed, volumetric expansion method recommended in NFPA 10. The guide to follow in conducting this type of test is Pamphlet C-1, "Methods for Hydrostatic Testing of Compressed Gas Cylinders," published by the Compressed Gas Association, Inc. (CGA).[3] For visually evaluating the condition of cylinders made to DOT specifications, CGA's Pamphlet C-6, "Standards for Visual Inspection of Steel Compressed Gas Cylinders,"[4] is helpful.

Procedures for testing extinguishers other than compressed-gas extinguishers or affixed compressed-gas cylinders are detailed in NFPA 10. Table 17.5.6 gives the basic data on the hydrostatic test pressure requirements. Figures 17.5.19 and 17.5.20 illustrate equipment used in hydrostatic testing work.

It is not necessary to hydrostatically test certain extinguishers, such as pump tanks, backpacks, and similar devices. Factory-sealed, nonrefillable, disposable fire extinguishers cannot be hydrostatically tested. When such extinguishers are damaged, they must be replaced.

Proper hydrostatic testing requires competent personnel and suitable testing equipment and facilities. The preparation for testing and the removal of all traces of water and moisture with special drying equipment after testing are very important and reinforce the recommendation that only those experienced in this type of work should undertake such servicing. The DOT requires that agencies testing carbon dioxide extinguishers hydrostatically be certified by the DOT.

Extinguisher hoses of certain types also need to be hydrostatically tested, and the details of these tests can be found in NFPA 10.

Because hydrostatic test results are of major importance, they must be recorded on the extinguisher. For high-pressure cylinders and cartridges passing a hydrostatic test, the month and year is stamped into the cylinder, in accordance with CGA Pamphlet C-1, or the Canadian Transport Commission regula-

TABLE 17.5.5 Hydrostatic Test Interval for Extinguishers

Extinguisher Type	*Test Interval (Years)*
Stored-pressure water loaded stream and/or antifreeze	5
Wetting agent	5
AFFF (aqueous film-forming foam)	5
FFFP (film-forming fluoroprotein foam)	5
Dry chemical with stainless-steel shells	5
Carbon dioxide	5
Wet chemical	5
Dry chemical, stored-pressure, with mild steel shells, brazed brass shells, or aluminum shells	12
Dry chemical, cartridge or cylinder operated, with mild steel shells	12
Halogenated agents	12
Dry powder, stored pressure, cartridge- or cylinder-operated, with mild steel shells	12

TABLE 17.5.6 Hydrostatic Test Pressure Requirements

Carbon dioxide extinguishers Carbon dioxide and nitrogen cylinders (used with wheeled extinguishers)	5/3 service pressure stamped on cylinder
Carbon dioxide extinguishers with cylinder specification ICC3	3000 psi (20,685 kPa)
All stored-pressure	Factory test pressure not to exceed 3 times the service pressure
Carbon dioxide hose assemblies	1250 psi (8619 kPa)
Dry chemical and dry powder, water, foam, halogenated agent hose assemblies	300 psi (2068 kPa) or at service pressure, whichever is higher

Note: The factory test pressure is the pressure at which the shell was tested at time of manufacture. This pressure is shown on the nameplate.
The service pressure is the normal operating pressure as indicated on the gauge and nameplate.

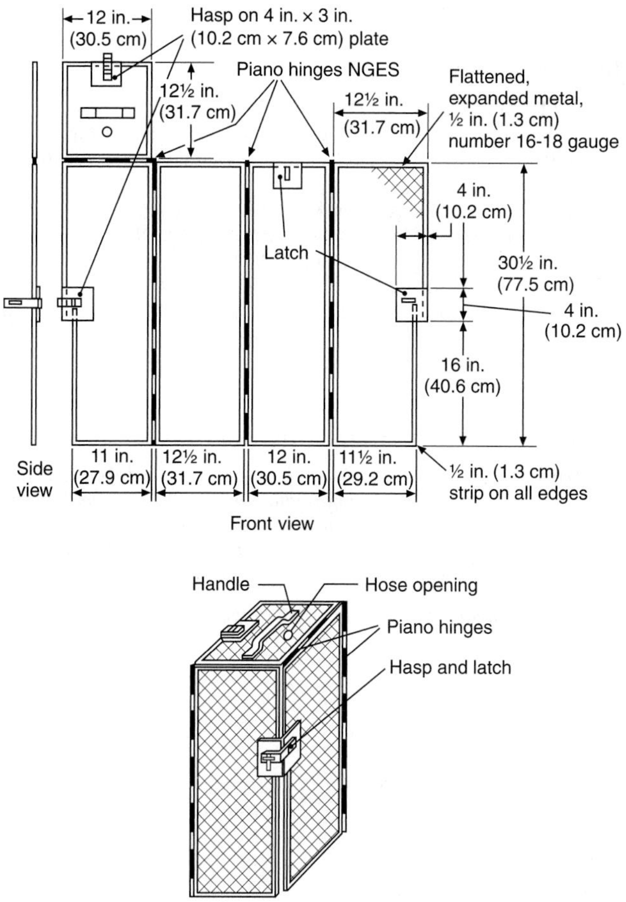

FIGURE 17.5.19 Low-Pressure Portable Hydrostatic Test Cage Used for Hydrostatic Tests of Low-Pressure Cylinders. Cage is not used for hydrostatic testing of high-pressure cylinders. Cage should not be anchored to floor during testing. Such cages can be made by any metal fabricator. For SI units: 1 in. = 25.4 mm.

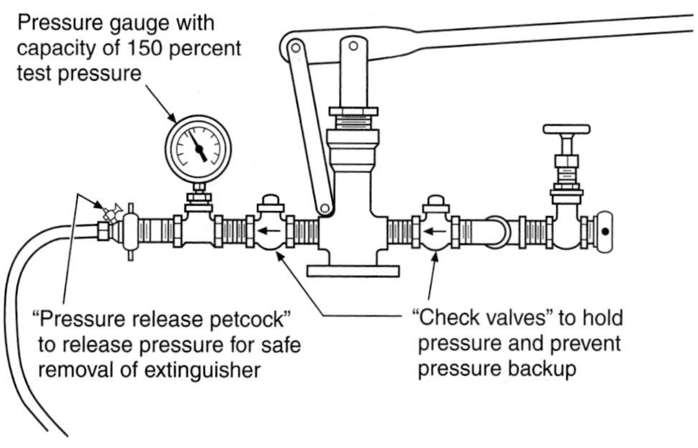

FIGURE 17.5.20 Hydrostatic Hand Pump

tions. It is important that the recording, or stamping, be placed only on the shoulder, top head, neck, or footing (when so provided) of the cylinder. For low-pressure cylinder extinguishers, the test information should be recorded on metal or some equally durable material. The label should be affixed by a heatless process to the shell and should be self-destructive if removal is attempted (Figure 17.5.21.) The label must include the following information:

1. The month and year the test was performed, indicated by a perforation, such as by a hand punch
2. The test pressure used
3. The name or initials of the person performing the test, and the name of the agency performing the test

Above all, remember the following: Allow only competent personnel with proper equipment and facilities to do the testing. Do not use air or gas for pressure testing because a violent rupture may occur in cases of failure. Place any extinguisher undergoing a test in a protective cage before applying the test pressures. Remove all traces of moisture from dry chemical, carbon dioxide, halogenated agent, and dry powder extinguishers before refilling after each test; a heated air stream not exceeding 150°F (65°C) is recommended for such drying. Destroy any extinguisher shell that fails a hydrostatic test—do not attempt to repair it.

Do not hydrostatically test any cylinder or shell if it has one or more of the following conditions:

1. Repairs by soldering, welding, brazing, or use of patching compounds; for welding or brazing on mild steel shells, consult the manufacturer of the extinguisher
2. Damaged cylinder or shell threads
3. Pitting caused by corrosion, even under the removable nameplate band assemblies
4. Burns from a fire
5. Calcium chloride agent in a stainless steel extinguisher

Destroy any such cylinder or shell.

Extinguisher Maintenance Services

Fire extinguisher maintenance, particularly hydrostatic testing, is a specialized activity and should be performed by competent, dependable people. Fire extinguishers are provided to protect life and property; this means that there should be no doubt as to

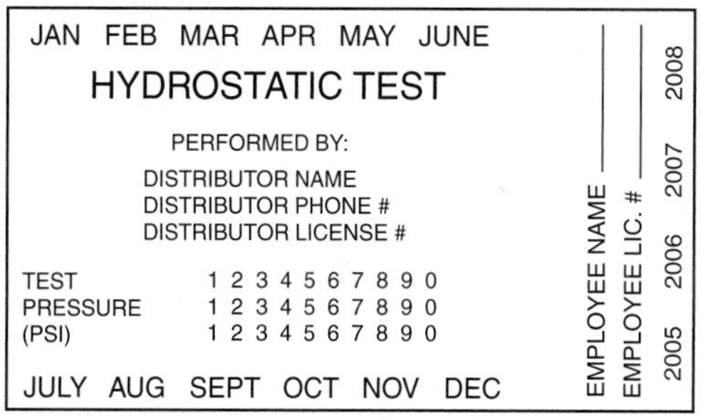

FIGURE 17.5.21 Typical Hydrostatic Test Label

their reliability or safe use in an emergency. Extinguisher owners are thus urged to seek out the services of reliable fire extinguisher maintenance firms. Such firms should be able to show proof that they are competent, that their facilities are adequate, and that they are licensed or registered in accordance with any local or federal law.

SUMMARY

Extinguishers are available in a number of different forms and use a variety of extinguishing agents, including water, carbon dioxide, halogenated agents, dry chemicals, dry powders, and foam. Extinguishers are classified for use on one or more types of fire, known as Class A, Class B, Class C, Class D, and Class K fires. In addition to the class of fire, the selection of the extinguisher should take into account the hazard level of the area being protected, the physical environment, the ease of operation and maintenance, and safety considerations. In order to provide effective fire protection, extinguishers must be distributed, mounted, maintained, and tested properly.

BIBLIOGRAPHY

References Cited

1. NFPA 10, *Standard for Portable Fire Extinguishers,* Section 1.3.1(2), "Classification, Ratings, and Performance of Fire Extinguishers: Performance Standards," National Fire Protection Association, Quincy, MA, 2002, p. 10-4.
2. Carson, W. G., and Klinker, R. L., *Fire Protection Systems, Inspection, Test, & Maintenance Manual,* 3rd ed., National Fire Protection Association, Quincy, MA, 2001.
3. *Methods for Hydrostatic Testing of Compressed Gas Cylinders,* Pamphlet C-1, Compressed Gas Association, Chantilly, VA, 1996.
4. *Standards for Visual Inspection of Steel Compressed Gas Cylinders,* Pamphlet C-6, Compressed Gas Association, Chantilly, VA, 2001.

NFPA Codes, Standards, and Recommended Practices

Reference to the following NFPA codes, standards, and recommended practices will provide further information on fire extinguisher use and maintenance discussed in this chapter. (See the latest version of The NFPA Catalog *for availability of current editions of the following document.)*

NFPA 10, *Standard for Portable Fire Extinguishers*

SECTION 17

Chapter 6

Halon and Halon Replacement Agents and Systems

Revised by

Philip J. DiNenno ❑ Gary M. Taylor

Chapter Contents

Key Terms

application fire extinguishing systems, carbon dioxide, clean fire extinguishing agents, clean fire suppression agents, explosion suppression, halogenated extinguishing agents, halon, safety factors, total flooding fire extinguishing systems

Clean fire-extinguishing agents include halogenated and inert gas fire suppressants. Halon and halon replacement clean agents including inert gases are used to provide total flooding fire-extinguishing systems that do not result in lethal conditions for any occupants of a protected space inadequately exposed when properly designed and installed. Although some clean agents cannot be used in occupied areas due to toxicity concerns, the primary distinction today between clean agents and carbon dioxide is the toxicity of the gases. Whereas carbon dioxide is used in fire-extinguishing concentrations far in excess of fatal limits, clean agents are generally used in occupied areas in fire-extinguishing concentrations below toxic thresholds.

Halogenated extinguishing agents are hydrocarbons in which one or more hydrogen atoms have been replaced by atoms from the halogen series: fluorine, chlorine, bromine, or iodine. This substitution confers not only nonflammability but also flame extinguishment properties to many of the resulting compounds. Halogenated agents are used both in portable fire extinguishers and in extinguishing systems. Streaming agents, such as Halon 1211 and 2402, have most often been used in manually applied fire equipment and local application-type fixed systems. Halon 1301 has most often been used in total flooding-type fixed systems.

Halons have been identified as stratospheric ozone-depleting substances. In fact, halons have been identified as the most potent of all ozone-depleting substances. The Montreal Protocol on Substances That Deplete Stratospheric Ozone is an international agreement to control the production and trade of ozone-depleting substances. The agreement has been signed by over 140 countries and is administered by the United Nations Environment Programme.

Production of Halons 1301, 1211, and 2402 ceased in developed countries on January 1, 1994, and is currently being phased out in the last developing country that produces halons. Many halon systems remain in use worldwide and, consequently, this chapter discusses Halons 1211, 1301, and 2402. The transition to other forms of fire protection for applications that historically used halons is well underway.

Recycled halons, recovered from less critical applications, now serve as a source of supply for those specialized applications such as mobile military equipment, aviation applications, and explosion prevention applications that remain dependent on halons.

See also Section 2, Chapter 7, "Theory of Fire Extinguishment"; Section 17, Chapter 1, "Carbon Dioxide and Application Systems"; Section 17, Chapter 7, "Application of Gaseous Agents to Special Hazards Fire Protection"; and Section 17, Chapter 8, "Explosion Prevention and Protection."

Philip J. DiNenno, P.E., is president of Hughes Associates, Inc., chair of the NFPA Standards Council, and has been heavily involved in the testing and development of halon replacement chemical and alternative fire suppression technologies.

Gary M. Taylor is a professor in fire protection engineering technology at Seneca College, Toronto; past chair of the NFPA Standards Council; and former chair of the NFPA Technical Committee on Halogenated Extinguishing Agent Systems.

BACKGROUND AND DEFINITIONS

Background

The use and development of halogenated fire-extinguishing agents have evolved over many years. The first member of this family of chemicals was carbon tetrachloride (Halon 104). Use as a fire extinguishant probably occurred before 1900, and by 1910 portable fire extinguishers, tested by independent agencies, had appeared. The growing popularity of the automobile and other uses of internal combustion engines signaled an increasing need for fire extinguishants suitable for use on flammable liquids fires.

By 1917, there were discussions regarding the possible effects that carbon tetrachloride could have on the human system. In 1919 the first known deaths due to carbon tetrachloride use occurred. Two men working on the construction of a submarine were killed. One man's clothing caught fire, and the other man extinguished the fire with a carbon tetrachloride agent fire extinguisher. Both were overcome by the fumes and later died. During the 1920s, the discussions regarding the toxicity of carbon tetrachloride continued with particular attention to the possibility that freezing point depressants and impurities were contributing factors.

Methyl bromide (Halon 1001) gained popularity after it was discovered in the late 1920s. Due to its high toxicity, it was never popular for use in portable extinguishers, although it was used in British and German aircraft and ships during World War II. During World War II, Germany developed bromochloro-methane (Halon 1011) to replace methyl bromide. In 1947 a report by Underwriters Laboratories Inc. (UL) showed that the toxicities of carbon tetrachloride (Halon 104) and bromochloro-methane (Halon 1011) were comparable, but bromochloro-methane was a more efficient fire-extinguishing agent.

In the post–World War II era, the addition of stearate to sodium bicarbonate–based dry chemicals provided improved flow and moisture repellency characteristics to sodium bicarbonate–based dry chemicals. This, in turn, encouraged the use of portable dry chemical fire extinguishers as an alternative to vaporizing liquid extinguishers that used early halons as extinguishants.

By the 1950s the era of the early halons (Halons 104, 1001, and 1011) was ending. Increased popularity of dry chemicals had decreased the need for widespread use of these early halons, and growing concerns with their toxic effects resulted in their "official" death by the 1960s.

In 1947, the Purdue Research Foundation conducted a systematic evaluation of more than 60 new candidate extinguishing agents. Simultaneously, the U.S. Army Corps of Engineers undertook toxicological studies of these same compounds. As a result, four halons were selected for further study: dibromodifluoromethane (Halon 1202), bromochlorodifluoromethane (Halon 1211), bromotrifluoromethane (Halon 1301), and dibromotetrafluoroethane (Halon 2402). Testing showed that Halon 1202 was the most effective fire extinguishant, but it was also the most toxic. Halon 1301 ranked second in fire-extinguishing effectiveness and least toxic. As a direct result of this program, a portable fire extinguisher employing Halon 1301 was developed by the U.S. Army, primarily for use inside armored personnel carriers and tanks. The U.S. Air Force selected Halon 1202 for military aircraft engine protection, and the U.S. Federal Aviation Administration approved the use of Halon 1301 for commercial aircraft engine fire protection.

In the 1960s attention began to focus on the use of Halon 1301 as a total flooding extinguishant for the protection of computer rooms. For the next 25 years, Halon 1301 grew in popularity as an agent for use in fixed fire protection systems, primarily for the protection of vital electronics facilities, such as computer rooms and communications equipment rooms. Other significant applications for Halon 1301 systems include protection for museums, shipboard machinery spaces, and pipeline pumping stations.

In 1966, NFPA organized a Technical Committee on Halogenated Fire Extinguishing Agent Systems to develop standards covering installation, maintenance, and use of such systems. NFPA 12A, *Standard on Halon 1301 Fire Extinguishing Systems,* and NFPA 12B, *Standard on Halon 1211 Fire Extinguishing Systems* (discontinued), were approved in the early 1970s. NFPA 12CT was a tentative standard for Halon 2402; however, the standard was never adopted as a full standard due to lack of acceptance of this agent by users of NFPA standards. Halon 2402 has been employed extensively within the Russian federation as both a total flooding system agent and a streaming agent for use in portable fire equipment. There is limited experience with Halon 2402 in the United States; therefore, it cannot be treated as extensively as the other agents in this handbook.

In 1972, following extensive testing by several major companies on the effects of Halon 1301 decomposition products on electronic equipment, the NFPA Committee on Electronic Computer/Data Processing Equipment recognized Halon 1301 total flooding systems as suitable for protection of electronic computer/data processing equipment. With suitable precautions, such as time delays, Halon 1211 total flooding systems have been used in Europe.

The regulation of Halon 1301 under the Montreal Protocol on Substances That Deplete Stratospheric Ozone and its amendments culminated in the phaseout of production of halons in the developed countries on December 31, 1993. This regulation engendered tremendous research and development efforts across the world in a search for replacements and alternatives. There are currently over 12 commercialized total flooding, clean agent alternatives to Halon 1301, and development continues on others. In addition to clean agent total flooding gaseous alternatives, new technologies, for example, water mist and fine solid particulate, are being introduced. This chapter focuses on total flooding clean agent halon replacements.

The primary design and installation standard used in North America is NFPA 2001, *Standard on Clean Agent Fire Extinguishing Systems.* The first edition of the standard was published in 1994. The third and current edition was issued in February 2000. The first International Standards Organization (ISO) standard, ISO Standard 14520—Parts 1 through 15—was issued in 2000.[1]

Clean Agents Defined

Clean fire suppression agents are defined as fire extinguishants that vaporize readily and leave no residue.[1] Clean agent halon replacements fall into two broad categories: (1) compounds and (2) inert gases and mixtures. Halogenated agents include compounds containing carbon, hydrogen, bromine, chlorine, fluorine, and iodine. They are grouped into seven categories, as displayed in Table 17.6.1.

Table 17.6.2 summarizes currently available clean fire suppression agents included in NFPA 2001.

Although the characteristics of halocarbon clean agents vary widely, they share several common attributes:

- All are electrically nonconductive.
- All are clean agents; they vaporize readily and leave no residue.
- All are liquefied gases or display analogous behavior (e.g., compressible liquid).
- All can be stored and discharged from typical Halon 1301 hardware (with the possible exception of HFC-23, which more closely resembles 600 psig [40 bar] superpressurized halon systems).
- All (except HFC-23) use nitrogen superpressurization in most applications for discharge purposes.
- All are less efficient fire extinguishants than Halon 1301 in terms of storage volume and agent weight; the use of most of these agents requires increased storage capacity.
- All are total flooding gases after discharge; many require additional care relative to nozzle design and operating pressure to ensure mixing.
- All produce more decomposition products than Halon 1301, given similar fire type, fire size, and discharge time.

TABLE 17.6.1 Categories of Clean Agent Fire Suppression Agents

Category	*Compounds*
Halon	Chlorine, bromine, or fluorine and hydrogen and carbon
Hydrofluorocarbons (HFC)	Fluorine, hydrogen, and carbon
Hydrochlorofluorocarbon (HCFC)	Fluorine, chlorine, carbon, and hydrogen
Perfluorocarbons	Carbon and fluorine
Fluoroiodocarbon (FIC)	Carbon, fluorine, and iodine
Fluoroketones (FK)	Carbon, fluorine, and oxygen
Hydrobromofluorocarbon (HBFC)	Bromine, fluorine, and carbon

Inert gas alternatives include nitrogen and argon, and blends of these. One inert gas replacement has a small fraction of carbon dioxide. Carbon dioxide is not an inert gas because it is physiologically active and fatal at low concentrations (approximately 9 percent). Inert gas clean agents are stored as pressurized gases and, hence, require substantially greater storage volume. They are electrically nonconductive, form stable mixtures in air, and leave no residue.

EXTINGUISHING MECHANISMS

Halocarbon clean agents extinguish fires by a combination of chemical and physical mechanisms, depending on the compound. Chemical suppression mechanisms of HBFC and HFIC compounds are similar to Halon 1301; that is, the Br and I species scavenge flame radicals, thereby interrupting the chemical

TABLE 17.6.2 Clean Fire Extinguishing Agents in NFPA 2001

FC-2-1-8	Perfluoropropane	C_3F_8
FC-3-1-10	Perfluorobutane	C_4F_{10}
FIC-13I1	Trifluoroiodide	CF_3I
FK-5-12mmy2	Dodecafluoro-2-methylpentan-3-one	$CF_3CF_2C(O)(CF(CF_3)_2)$
HCFC Blend A	Dichlorotrifluoroethane HCFC-123 (4.75%) Chlorodifluoromethane HCFC-122 (82%) Chlorotetrafluoroethane HCFC-124 (9.75%) Isopropeny-1-methylcyclohexene (3.75%)	$CHC_{12}CF_3$ $CHCIF_2$ $CHCIFCF_3$
HCFC-124	Chlorotetrafluoroethane	$CHCIFCF_3$
HFC-125	Pentafluoroethane	CHF_2CF_3
HFC-227ea	Heptafluoropropane	CF_3CHFCF_3
HFC-23	Trifluoromethane	CF_3CHFCF_3
HFC-236fa	Hexafluoropropane	$CF_3CH_2CF_3$
IG-01	Argon	Ar
IG-100	Nitrogen	N_2
IG-541	Nitrogen (52%) Argon (40%) Carbon dioxide (8%)	N_2 Ar CO_2
IG-55	Nitrogen (50%) Argon (50%)	N_2 Ar

chain reaction. Other replacement compounds suppress fires primarily by extracting heat from the flame reaction zone, reducing the flame temperature below that which is necessary to maintain sufficiently high reaction rates by a combination of heat of vaporization, heat capacity, and the energy absorbed by the decomposition of the agent.

Burgess et al.[2] performed kinetic simulations on a range of fluorinated compounds (CF_4, CF_3H, CF_2H_2, CF_3-CF_3, CF_3-CF_2H, and CF_3-CFH_2) for chemical kinetic fire suppression effects of fluorine compounds. Of the agents examined, only CF_3H was seen to have any chemical effect on flame suppression. They concluded that the differences in flame suppression properties can be explained by differences in heat capacity and relative amounts of heat release during agent combustion. Battin-LeClerc et al.[3] indicate that, while clearly some noncatalytic flame inhibition may occur with FC and HFC compounds, this effect is expected to be limited. Richter et al.[4] draw similar conclusions, owing to the inability of fluorine atoms to be continuously recycled in the flame, as occurs with bromine.

Oxygen depletion also plays an important role in reducing flame temperature. The energy absorbed in decomposing the agent by breaking fluorine and chlorine bonds is quite important, particularly with respect to decomposition production formation. There is undoubtedly some degree of "chemical" suppression action in flame radical combustion with halogens, but it is considered to be of minor importance because it is not catalytic.

The lack of significant chemical reaction inhibition in the flame zone by HCFC, HFC, and FC compounds results in higher extinguishing concentrations relative to Halon 1301. The importance of the energy sink, represented by breaking halogen species bonds, results in higher levels of agent decomposition relative to Halon 1301.

Inert gas agents suppress flames by reducing the flame temperature below the threshold necessary to maintain combustion reactions. This flame supression is done by reducing the oxygen concentration and by raising the heat capacity of the atmosphere supporting the flame. For example, the addition of a sufficient quantity of nitrogen to reduce the oxygen concentration below 12 percent (in air) will extinguish flaming fires. The agent concentration required (and, hence, the minimum oxygen level) is a function of the heat capacity of the inert gas added. Hence, there are differences in minimum extinguishing concentrations between inert gases.

The differences between argon and nitrogen are clearly shown in Table 17.6.2, with nitrogen extinguishing concentrations in the range of 30 percent (14.6 percent O_2) and argon extinguishing concentrations of 41 percent (12.3 percent O_2). Inert gas blends with more nitrogen than argon will have lower minimum extinguishing concentrations. When one considers nitrogen as the primary inert gas in examining oxygen concentrations at extinction in fire experiments, the minimum oxygen concentration at extinction can be as low as 12 percent, or a 42.5 percent "agent" concentration.[5,6]

FLAME SUPPRESSION EFFECTIVENESS

Flame suppression effectiveness of total flooding halon replacement agents has been evaluated in a number of ways. The predominant small-scale test method for establishing flame extinguishing concentrations for liquid and gaseous fuels is the cup burner.

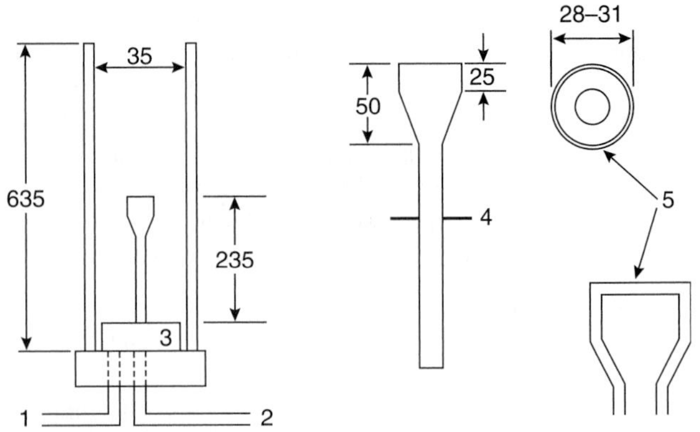

FIGURE 17.6.1 ISO Standard Cup Burner Apparatus (Source: ISO 14520-1, "Gaseous Fire Extinguishing Systems—Physical Properties and System Design, Part 1: General Requirements," International Organization for Standardization, Geneva, Switzerland, 2005. Copyright International Organization for Standardization.)

Figure 17.6.1 is a schematic of the standardized ISO cup burner.[1] A small laminar flame is established above a "cup" of fuel surrounded by a cylindrical chimney. An air/agent mixture flows up the chimney surrounding the flame. The minimum concentration of agent (in air) at which the flame is extinguished is the minimum extinguishing concentration (MEC). There are many variations of the basic device as used by different laboratories; these variations include cup and chimney diameter, different mixing and measuring methods, chimney height, and agent/air mixture velocity past the flame.[7]

Table 17.6.3 gives the most recent heptane cup burner values vetted on a consensus basis and contained in the ISO series of documents. These data are the best available consensus values for the MEC for heptane. There have been substantial differences between MEC values published in the past. These differences are largely due to the use of more standardized test devices, different test procedures, and operator error.

TABLE 17.6.3 Minimum Class B Extinguishing Concentration

Agent	*ISO Class B Extinguishing Concentration (%)*
HFC-227ea	6.9
HFC-125	9.3
HFC-23	12.6
FK-5-1-12	4.5
IG 541	31.7
IG 55	36.5
IG 01	39.5
IG 100	33.6

Minimum extinguishing concentrations for Class A fuels are determined as part of the third-party approval process. They are based on standardized tests of plastic sheet array. There are substantial differences between Class A extinguishing concentrations developed for use in NFPA 2001 versus those required in ISO 14520. The differences are largely based on the details of the test, such as ignition pan size and preburn, but are also substantially affected by the allowable extinguishment time. Both UL and FM and, therefore, NFPA 2001 allow a much longer extinguishment time (600 seconds) than the 180 seconds presented by ISO. This partially explains the substantially higher Class A extinguishing concentrations obtained under ISO 14520, as seen in Table 17.6.4.

Wickham[8] has provided comparative values for cost and footprint of halon and halon replacement systems for use in marine applications. These comparisons are given for weight, footprint, and cost in Tables 17.6.5, 17.6.6, and 17.6.7, respectively.

Note that all clean agent alternatives require at least 50 percent more agent by weight as a consequence of the elimination of bromine in the compounds and subsequent level of catalytic recombination of flame radicals. These data should be taken as representative values, as there are variations among hardware manufacturers. The storage volume equivalent does not translate directly to a required area or volume for storage cylinders. The relative "footprint" of these storage volume equivalents will vary with the volume of the space protected and the maximum storage cylinder size offered by a manufacturer for a particular gas.

EXPLOSION INERTING

One of the most important application areas of total flooding fire suppressants is explosion inertion. The inerting concentration of an agent is the concentration required to prevent unacceptable pressure increases in a premixed fuel/air/agent mixture subjected to an ignition source. Inertion concentrations are typically measured in small laboratory-scale spheres with an electric spark initiator.

The measured inerting concentration of an agent is dependent on the details of the test apparatus used, particularly the ignition source strength and "allowable" pressure rise. The "allowable" pressure rise is a surrogate measurement of the distance the flame front travels inside the constant volume sphere prior to suppression. Inerting concentrations are not appropriate for use in deflagration or detonation (explosion) suppression.

Small-scale sphere data are used to develop flammability diagrams for various fuel/oxidizer/agent concentrations. The chapter on flammability limits by Beyler in the *SFPE Handbook of Fire Protection Engineering* gives an excellent introduction to the subject.[9] A wealth of data on flammability limits for inert gases, such as nitrogen and argon, and for a variety of fuels is available in the combustion literature.

Table 17.6.8 provides inerting concentration data for several agents and fuels taken from small-scale inertion spheres. There are some substantial differences in results. Ignition source type and strength as important variables with differences of approximately 40 percent for Halon 1301 inerting concentrations are reported. Figure 17.6.2 shows flammability diagrams[10] derived from small-scale inertion data along with points taken from a large-scale 795 ft^3 (22.5 m^3) explosion vessel. Although the small- to large-scale agreement is reasonable, there are scale effects.

Explosion suppression systems employ rapid delivery of agent following very early detection of an ignition. Such systems employ significantly higher agent quantities (than flame suppression or inertion) delivered at higher rates. The total agent delivery time is on the order of 100 millisecond.

Explosion suppression systems must be specifically designed for a particular application. There are no generic design requirements or standards currently available for such systems.

Senecal et al.[11,12] report on explosion suppression testing for occupied armored fighting vehicles and aerosol filling rooms. Results were obtained on premixed fuel droplet sprays. In contrast to flame suppression or inerting, suppression or deflagration requires significantly more agent. The aerosol filling room tests employed 44.1 lb (20 kg) of HFC-227ea, FC-3-1-10, HFC-236fa, and 22 lb (10 kg) of water in a 2827 ft^3 (80 m^3) test room to suppress a 3.2 oz. (90 g) propane release in a simulated aerosol fill station. Suppression of the propane-air deflagration was achieved, and the maximum flame front extension was approximately 4 ft (1.22 m). Suppression tests of heated diesel fuel droplet cloud deflagrations were conducted in simulated armored fighting vehicle crew compartments.

Table 17.6.9 summarizes typical data for flame suppression, inertion, and deflagration suppression concentrations. Note that these values are for comparison purposes only. They should not be used in any way for design purposes.

Suppression of detonations requires substantially higher agent concentrations. An excellent discussion is given in "Review of the Use of Carbon Dioxide Total Flooding Fire Extinguishing Systems." [8]

TOXICITY[13]

Background

Toxicology tests are performed based on (1) the duration and frequency of the exposure and (2) determination of specific biological effects.[14] The studies examining duration and frequency are divided into four categories:[15]

1. Acute: less than 24 hour exposure
2. Subacute: 1 month or less of exposure
3. Subchronic: 1- to 3-month exposure
4. Chronic: more than 3 months of exposure

The specific biological effects examined are many, but for the purposes of halocarbon fire-fighting agents, the following are the most common:

1. Inhalation toxicity
2. Developmental toxicity
3. Reproductive toxicity
4. Genetic toxicity
5. Cardiotoxicity
6. Central nervous system (CNS) effects

TABLE 17.6.4 Summary of the Class A and Class B Extinguishing Concentrations for Various Agents and Equipment Manufacturers

			UL				ISO						
			Class B		Class A		Class B		Class A			Plastic Sheet	
Agent	*Trade Name*	*Equipment Manufacturer*	*Test*	*Design*	*Test*	*Design*	*Test*	*Design*	*Min (95% of Class B)*	*Test*	*Design*	*Test*	*Design*
HFC-227ea	FM-200, FE-227	A	6.7	8.7	—	—	—	—	—	—	—	—	—
		B	6.7	8.7	—	—	—	—	—	—	—	—	—
		C	6.7	8.7	—	—	—	—	—	—	—	—	—
		D	6.7	8.7	5.2	6.2	—	—	—	—	—	—	—
		E	6.7	8.7	5.4	6.5	—	—	—	—	—	—	—
		F	6.6	8.6	—	—	6.9	9.0	8.5	6.1 (4.9 wood crib)	7.9	6.1	7.9
HFC-125	FE-25	A	—	—	6.7	8.0	—	—	—	—	—	—	—
		B	—	—	—	—	—	—	—	8.6 (6.7 wood crib)	11.2	8.6	11.2
		—	8.7	11.3	—	—	9.3	12.1	11.5	—	—	—	—
	NAF-S-125	C	8.7	11.3	6.7	8.0	—	—	—	6.7	8.7	6.7	8.7
HFC-23	FE-13	A	—	18	—	18	—	—	—	—	—	—	—
		B	12.9	16.8	—	—	12.6	16.4	15.6	12.5 (10.5 wood crib)	16.3	12.5	16.3
FK-5-1-12	Novec-1230	A	4.5	5.9	3.5	4.2	—	—	—	—	—	—	—
		B	4.5	5.9	—	—	4.5	5.9	5.6	4.1 (3.4 wood crib)	5.3	4.1	5.3
IG-541	Inergen	—	28.9	37.6	28.5	34.2	31.7	41.2	39.1	30.7 (28.2 wood crib)	36.5	30.7	39.9
IG-55	Argonite	—	—	—	—	—	36.5	47.5	45.1	31 (28.7 wood crib)	40.3	31.0	40.3
IG-01	Argon	—	—	—	—	—	39.2	51.0	48.4	32.2 (30.7 wood crib)	41.9	32.2	41.9
IG-100	Nitrogen	—	—	—	—	—	33.6	43.7	41.5	31.0 (30 wood crib)	40.3	31.0	40.3

TABLE 17.6.5 Percent Weight Comparisons of Systems in 500–5000 m³ Range of Volumes

Agent	Percentage Additional Weight When Compared to a Halon 1301 System *500 m³*	*1000 m³*	*3000 m³*	*5000 m³*
Halon 1301	0	0	0	0
Carbon dioxide	150	163	200	186
FE-13	200	188	219	211
FM-200	50	38	48	36
Novec 1230	50	50	71	58
Inergen	400	450	529	497
Water mist	625	613	671	522

TABLE 17.6.6 Percent Footprint Comparisons of Systems in 500–5000 m³ Range of Volumes

Agent	Percentage Additional Weight When Compared to a Halon 1301 System *500 m³*	*1000 m³*	*3000 m³*	*5000 m³*
Halon 1301	0	0	0	0
Carbon dioxide	84	82	118	99
FE-13	105	94	122	107
FM-200	20	20	19	6
Novec 1230	20	20	43	19
Inergen	327	365	459	404
Water mist	1119	889	1030	636

TABLE 17.6.7 Percent Cost Comparisons of Systems in 500–5000 m³ Range of Volumes

Agent	Percentage Additional Weight When Compared to a Halon 1301 System *500 m³*	*1000 m³*	*3000 m³*	*5000 m³*
Halon 1301	0	0	0	0
Carbon dioxide	108	140	200	204
FE-13	315	406	553	585
FM-200	202	267	351	361
Novec 1230	259	368	513	515
Inergen	277	330	449	460
Water mist	1032	723	478	376

The separation into categories is based on experience that acute exposure toxicity and chronic exposure toxicity can be significantly different. For example, the acute (single) exposure toxicity for organic solvents is typically central nervous system disturbances that are reversible once the exposure ends. Chronic (repeated, long-term exposure) toxicity for organic solvents can include liver damage and cancer, which are not considered reversible. Each chemical may cause different specific acute

TABLE 17.6.8 Inerting Concentrations for Various Agents

Fuel	*Agent*	*Volume Percent Inerting Concentration*
i-Butane	HFC-227ea	11.3
	HCFC Blend A	18.4
	IG-100	40.0
1-Chloro-1, 1-difluoro-ethane (HCFC-142b)	HFC-227ea	2.6
1.1-Difluoroethane (HFC-152a)	HFC-227ea	8.6
	HCFC Blend A	13.6
Difluoromethane (HFC-32)	HFC-227ea	3.5
	HCFC Blend A	8.6
Ethane	IF-100	44.0
Ethylene oxide	HFC-227ea	13.6
Hexane	IG-100	42.0
Methane	HFC-125	14.7
	HFC-227ea	8.0
	HFC-23	20.2
	HCFC Blend A	18.3
	IG-100	37.0
	IG-541	43.0
Pentane	HFC-227ea	11.6
	IG-100	42.0
Propane	FC-3-1-10	10.3
	FC-3-1-10	9.9
	FC-5-1-14	7.3
	FIC-1311	6.5
	HFC-125	15.7
	HFC-227ea	11.6
	HFC-23	20.2
	HFC-23	20.4
	HCFC Blend A	18.6
	IG-541	49.0
	IG-100	42.0

TABLE 17.6.9 Comparison of Concentrations for Flame Extinguishment, Inerting, and Deflagration Suppression

	Volume Percentage		
Agent	*Typical Value Flame Suppression*	*Inerting Concentration in Propane*	*Diesel Fuel Droplet Deflagration Suppression*
Halon 1301	3.0	6–7	12
FC-3-1-10	5.5	10.3	8
HFC-227ea	5.8	~12	11
HFC-23	12.0	20.2	—
IG-541	29.0	49.0	—

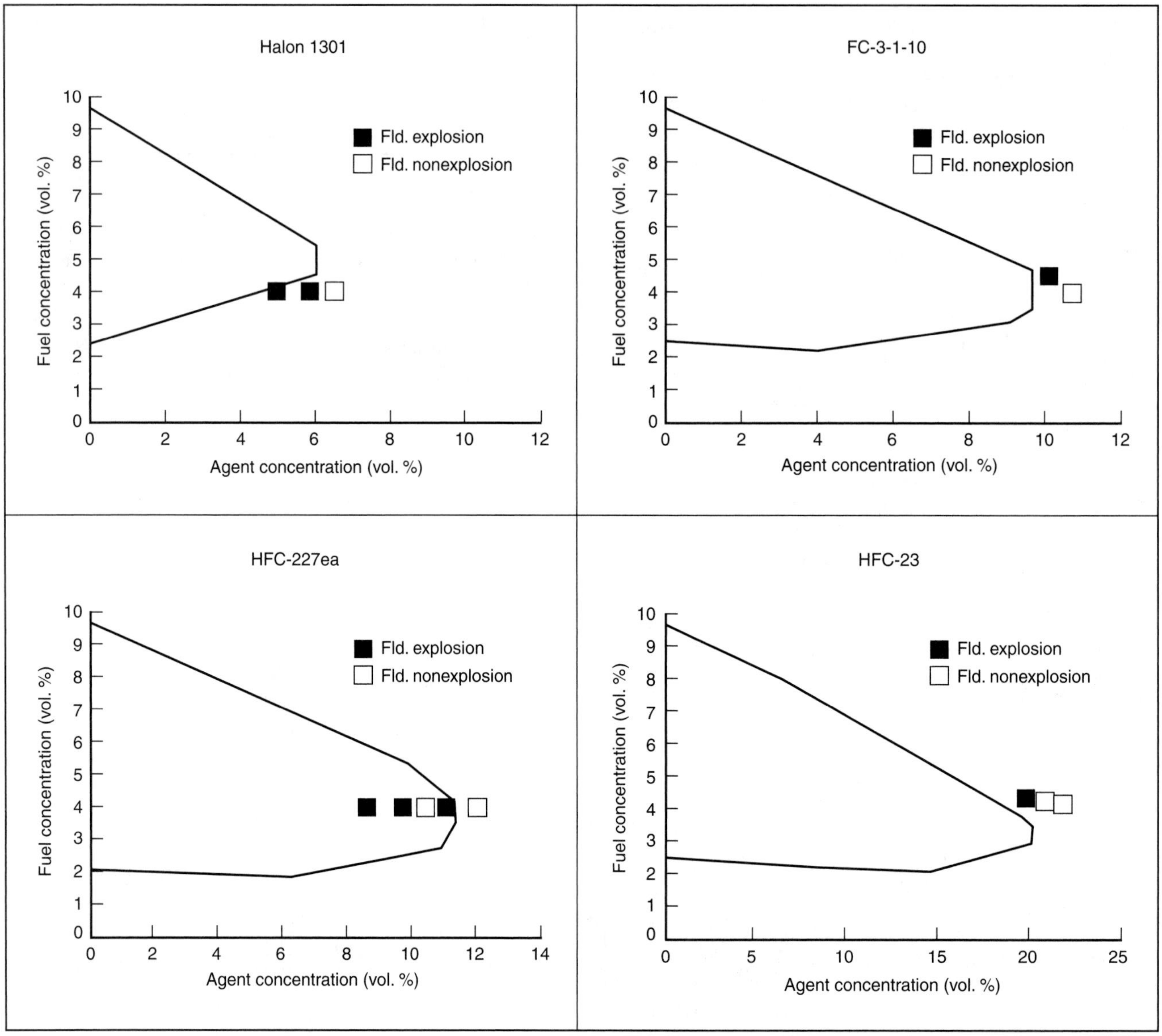

FIGURE 17.6.2 Small-Scale Flammability Diagrams for Propane and Several Replacement Agents. Squares denote explosion/no explosion points in large-scale 792 ft^3 (22.5 m^3) chamber. (Source: Moore, T. A., "Large-Scale Inertion Evaluation of NFPA 2001 Agents," *Proceedings* of the 1993 International CFC and Halon Alternatives Conference, Washington, DC, October 20–22, 1993)

and chronic toxicity problems that need to be addressed. These include cancer, birth defects, liver toxicity, heart toxicity, and so on.[15] Different chemicals within the same family may cause different effects or similar effects over a wide range of concentrations. Lastly, the route of exposure is examined. For gaseous fire-fighting agents, inhalation studies are required.

A series of tests is required, beginning with the acute studies. This is done to build on the results from previous shorter-term studies. One important reason is to establish the correct exposure concentrations for testing. An improper dosage could cause the invalidation of a long-term test halfway or more through the study; that is, too many test specimens may die from an excessive test dosage. An equally important reason is to preclude running expensive, longer-term chronic studies when the shorter-term studies do not suggest any need. The shorter-term studies can be used as screens to give indications, but not direct results, for the type of toxicity problems that longer-term tests may need to address. The toxicology series is not a "cookbook" process. Professional toxicologists must evaluate the results through each step of the process and make educated decisions on the next phase of testing.

A minimum set of tests required by the U.S. Environmental Protection Agency (EPA) under the Significant New Alternatives Policy (SNAP) program would likely include:[16]

1. Acute toxicity "range finder," for example, limit or LC_{50} test
2. Cardiac sensitization test

3. Developmental and reproductive toxicity
4. 4- or 13-week subchronic test
5. Genetic toxicity screening test (such as Ames test)
6. Thermal decomposition product test

As noted, acute toxicity studies are usually the first to be done. These tests provide information on acute lethality. For inhalation toxicity this is called the LC_{50} and is the concentration at which 50 percent of the animals die within 14 days of the exposure. This study is usually a single 4 hour exposure and generally performed with mice and rats.

Subacute studies are the lowest tier of the repeated exposure tests. They are used to (1) discover specific toxicity problems above the acute effects and (2) refine the proper doses for follow-up tests. Subacute studies generally run 14 days.

Subchronic studies are used to (1) establish final dosage data to be used in chronic studies and (2) identify further the specific toxicity concerns of long-term exposures. These studies are usually performed for 90 days on one or two species.

Chronic studies are generally performed in the same way as subchronic tests, except that the exposure is increased beyond 3 months and up to 2½ years. Often chronic studies incorporate carcinogenicity (cancer) tests to preclude running separate tests.

Developmental and reproductive toxicity studies are designed to look at the adverse effects on the reproductive system and on offspring. Developmental tests examine the effects on a developing organism any time during its life span as the result of repeated exposure by either parent before conception or during pregnancy and postnatally until puberty. Reproductive toxicology is a multigenerational study concerned with the adverse effects to the reproductive system that may be passed on to the first-generation and second-generation offspring by either parent. The specific study of defects caused between conception and birth is called teratology.

Genetic toxicity studies examine mutangenic potential, that is, the capability of a chemical to cause changes in the genes of a cell. These studies are also effective as screens and tests for the potential to cause cancer. Two of the most common tests used for halocarbon agents are (1) the Ames test and (2) the micronucleus test. The Ames test examines the ability of the chemical to cause changes or mutations in the genes of a cell. The micronucleus test studies look at chromosome aberrations. Both screens are used as indicators of the potential to cause cancer. Results of these screens are used to decide whether longer-term cancer studies, other genetic toxicity studies, or developmental and reproductive studies are required.

Beyond the preceding tests, specific toxicology concerns may warrant requiring other, less standard, toxicity studies. Such is the case for halocarbons where they have been found to depress the heart rate. In the presence of adrenaline, the heart can experience mild conditions of an irregular heartbeat to severe conditions of a full heart attack. This effect was first seen with chloroform when it was widely used as an anesthetic. The test developed to assess this type of cardiotoxicity is called "cardiac sensitization."

The data gathered from these tests on nonhuman species are only an indication of the toxicity for humans. Toxicologists use these studies to do risk assessments to predict the toxicity of a chemical or specific mixture of chemicals in a particular exposure scenario. The acute tests are used to establish limits for single or very infrequent exposures. For example, acute toxicity is used in determining the effects that can be expected when a fire suppression system is discharged. Subchronic and chronic studies are used to establish limits for repeated exposures for workers who are subjected to the halocarbon on a more frequent basis, such as production plant workers and maintenance personnel who fill/refill cylinders.

The EPA requires, as a minimum for halocarbon fire suppression agents, cardiac sensitization and developmental toxicology studies to set acute exposure limits. To set worker/manufacturer exposure limits, the EPA uses, as a minimum, genetic toxicology, 90-day subchronic and developmental toxicology studies.[16]

Although all halocarbon agents are tested for long-term health hazards, the primary end point is acute, or short-term, exposure. The primary acute toxicity effects of the halocarbon agents described in this chapter are anesthesia and cardiac sensitization. For inert gases, the primary physiological concern is reduced oxygen concentration.

Halocarbon Agents

Cardiac sensitization is the primary short-term "acute" toxicity problem for fire suppression applications. *Cardiac sensitization* is a term describing the sudden onset of cardiac arrhythmias in the presence of a concentration of an agent caused by sensitization of the heart to epinephrine. The presence of epinephrine is critical to the onset of arrhythmias. This is important in fire protection applications due to the increased production of epinephrine by the body under stress.

The toxicity end points used to describe cardiotoxicity and allowable exposure levels are no observed adverse effect level (NOAEL) and the lowest observed adverse effect level (LOAEL). The NOAEL is the highest concentration of an agent at which no "marked" or adverse effect occurred. The LOAEL is the lowest concentration at which an adverse effect was measured.

The procedures used to evaluate cardiac sensitization vary somewhat. The procedure involves intravenous dosing of male beagles with epinephrine for 5 minutes. Continuous inhalation exposure to the agent follows for 5 minutes. Following this inhalation exposure, the dog is dosed again with epinephrine and monitored for 5 minutes to determine the effect of the agent and epinephrine. The protocol is performed at higher doses until an effect occurs.

Effects are monitored by electrocardiograph (ECG) measurements. An adverse effect is generally considered to be the appearance of five or more arrhythmias or ventricular fibrillation. The data from these tests are evaluated by medical experts, and the appropriate NOAEL and LOAEL values are reported by the EPA under the SNAP program.

There is no direct correlation between the experimental results from dogs to humans. It is generally accepted due to the combination of the high doses of epinephrine in the tests and the similarity in cardiovascular function between dogs and humans that the results can be applied to humans. It is believed that the results of these tests are conservative with respect to direct application of the results to humans in typical fire suppression applications.

In addition to the short-term chronic exposure limits of interest in fire suppression system design, the EPA evaluates longer-term inhalation data for these compounds. Table 17.6.10 summarizes NOAEL, LOAEL, and LC_{50} values. Note that the LC_{50} values greatly exceed the NOAEL.

The use of halocarbon agents in occupied areas is generally subject to the constraint that the design concentration must be less than the NOAEL. In the 1996 edition of NFPA 2001, an exception allows the use of total flooding gases up to LOAEL for Class B hazards where a predischarge alarm and time delay are provided and where acceptable to the authority having jurisdiction. The rationale for the exception is based on (1) the conservative nature of NOAEL/LOAEL, (2) consistency with EPA guidelines, and (3) positive benefit of higher agent concentrations in certain flammable/combustible liquid hazards. Although it is recommended that all systems employ predischarge alarms and that personnel evacuate prior to system actuation, it is understood that inadvertent discharges and short-term exposures will occur, hence the limitation. It is expected that emergency exposures for up to several minutes at or below the NOAEL and possibly the LOAEL are reasonably safe. In no case should systems be designed or installed where intentional exposure of any duration is anticipated.

In the 2000 edition of NFPA 2001, the exposure limits for halocarbon agents have been modified. Physiologically based pharmacokinetic modeling (PBPK) for evaluation of acute exposure to halocarbon agents has been used to establish alternative exposure limits for halogenated agents. PBPK modeling attempts to account for the time-dependent uptake rate of halocarbons in the body and establishes exposure limits based on the rate of uptake.[17–22] The limits are based on the concentration of agent and the time at which the concentration of agent in the blood equals that of the LOAEL. Typical PBPK results for safe exposure times for HFC-227ea and HFC-125 are given in Table 17.6.11. Note exposure above the NOAEL limits and up to the LOAEL is permitted.

These limits were derived and supported by the EPA, which has the primary regulatory authority for health and toxicity associated with halon replacements. The use of the PBPK approach partially accounts for the differences between laboratory animal tests and humans. The laboratory results form the basis of the end points (LOAEL) and are still conservative due to the nature of epinephrine dosage used during the animal tests.

TABLE 17.6.10 Toxicity Data for Halocarbon Clean Agent Fire Suppression

Designation	*Formula*	*NOAEL Percentage V/V$_a$*	*LOAEL Percentage V/V$_a$*	*LC_{50} or $ALC_{b,c}$ Percentage*
FC-3-1-10	C_4F_{10}	40	>40_d	>80
HFC-227ea	C_3F_7H	9.0	>10.5	>80
HFC-23	CHF_3	50	>50_d	>65
HCFC-124	C_2HClF_4	1	2.5	23–29
HFC-125	CH_2HF_5	7.5	10.0	>70
FK-5-1-12		10	>10	

TABLE 17.6.11 Exposure Limits Derived from PBPK Modeling for HFC-227ea and HFC-125

HFC-227ea Concentration			HFC-125 Concentration		
Percentage v/v	*ppm*	*Human Exposure Time (min)*	*Percentage v/v*	*ppm*	*Human Exposure Time (min)*
9.0	90,000	5.00	7.5	75,000	5.00
9.5	95,000	5.00	8.0	80,000	5.00
10.0	100,000	5.00	8.5	85,000	5.00
10.5	105,000	5.00	9.0	90,000	5.00
11.0	110,000	1.13	9.5	95,000	5.00
11.5	115,000	0.60	10.0	100,000	5.00
12.0	120,000	0.49	10.5	105,000	5.00
			11.0	110,000	5.00
			11.5	115,000	5.00
			12.0	120,000	1.67
			12.5	125,000	0.59
			13.0	130,000	0.54
			13.5	135,000	0.49

Inert Gas Agents

Inert gas agents are effectively physiologically inert. The primary physiological problem with these agents is the reduced oxygen concentration caused by the high agent design concentrations. One inert gas blend employs a low concentration of CO_2 (which is not physiologically inert) in order to counter the effects of the reduced oxygen concentration. The mechanism of this effect is discussed in "Research Basis for Improvement of Human Tolerance to Hypoxic Atmospheres in Fire Prevention and Extinguishment."[23]

The EPA had previously determined that inert gases can be used in concentrations up to 43 percent in normally occupied areas subject to similar limits placed on halocarbon agents when used at the NOAEL. This usage results in a residual oxygen concentration of 12 percent. The analog to the LOAEL is 52 percent agent concentration with a 10 percent residual oxygen concentration. NFPA 2001 requirements mirror the EPA limitations at 43 percent agent concentration with the exemption permitting use up to 52 percent concentration for Class B hazards. There appears to be a growing consensus among independent toxicologists that inert gases could be safely used up to 52 percent concentration for a 5-minute exposure time.

This consensus was further developed in the 2000 edition of NFPA 2001. The current limitations on exposure limits for inert gases are as follows:

> For gas concentrations up to 43 percent (a residual oxygen concentration of 12 percent), exposure time is limited to 5 min. For agent concentrations between 43 and 52 percent (12 and 10 percent residual oxygen concentration), the exposure time is limited to 3 min. For concentrations between 52 and 62 percent (10 and 8 percent residual oxygen concentration), exposure time is limited to 30 s. For concentrations above 62 percent (above 8 percent residual oxygen concentration) exposure must be avoided.

There is strong indication that small concentrations of CO_2 added to inert gases (such as IG-541) substantially reduce hypoxic effects and improve human performance at low oxygen levels. Regulatory authorities have not yet differentiated between such agents and other inert gases or blends.[23]

ENVIRONMENTAL FACTORS

Two main environmental impacts need to be considered with respect to halocarbon extinguishing agents: (1) ozone depletion and (2) global warming.[24] Another environmental factor, atmospheric lifetime, can be considered in the discussion of each of these environmental impacts. It is also a "stand-alone" environmental concern that needs to be addressed. International, national, state, and local governments currently regulate halocarbon fire-fighting agents based on their effect on ozone depletion. However, the U.S. EPA also takes into account atmospheric lifetimes and global warming potentials in the implementation of its SNAP program under Section 612 of the Clean Air Act, as amended in 1990. Although no specific national environmental regulations cover global warming and atmospheric lifetimes, the consideration of these issues in the EPA's implementation of existing regulations makes these issues of concern.

Ozone Depletion

Ozone (O_3) is a naturally occurring gas that is found in the atmosphere. Most naturally occurring ozone is created by the reaction of O_2 with ultraviolet (UV) light coming from the sun.

$$O_2 + UV \rightarrow O + O$$

$$O + O_2 \rightarrow O_3$$

The UV light causes this reaction to occur. Ozone is also created in nature when the high energy output from lightning initiates a similar reaction.

Ozone is also formed by a number of manufactured sources, mainly as a result of air pollution. When carbon monoxide, methane, and other hydrocarbons meet nitrogen oxide (e.g., from car exhaust) and ordinary sunlight, ozone is produced.[25] It is also produced by laser printers and electrical motors, and is responsible for the pungent odor often associated with the devices. Man-made ozone is often called "smog" and is a considerable health risk.

With respect to the environment, an important difference exists between naturally occurring and man-made sources of ozone. Man-made ozone is produced in the region of our atmosphere called the troposphere. This is the portion that starts at the earth's surface and extends 3.7 to 10.6 mi. (6 to 17 km) above the surface. (The thickness of this region is different at the poles versus the equator.) Naturally occurring ozone is produced primarily in the stratosphere. The stratosphere is the region directly above the troposphere and extends to approximately 31 mi (50 km) above the earth's surface.[26] The ozone produced in the stratosphere by the reaction described earlier is what is known as the "ozone layer" and serves a very important purpose. Ozone absorbs the UV-b portion of the total UV in sunlight and prevents it from entering further into the atmosphere. This absorption has two net effects: (1) it lowers the amount of harmful UV-b that plants and animals are exposed to and (2) it prevents more ozone from being created naturally in the troposphere.

Over about the last decade, the United States has begun to give "ozone alerts," typically as part of daily weather reports. The ozone referred to by these alerts is tropospheric ozone and does not refer in any way to stratospheric ozone or ozone depletion. There are, however, concerns with tropospheric ozone. These concerns will be addressed along with the discussion of global warming.

Halons, HCFCs, and other halocarbons containing chlorine or bromine have been shown to cause the destruction of stratospheric ozone. The characterization of stratosphere ozone destruction is not a measure of the exact amount of ozone destroyed. Instead, it is the relative amount of ozone destroyed as compared with an arbitrary standard. The standard chosen is CFC-11, which has been assigned an ozone depletion potential (ODP) of 1. ODP of all other halocarbons relates to their relative effect on the destruction of ozone as compared with CFC-11. Halon 1301 has an ODP of 13, meaning it will destroy 13 times as much ozone as CFC-11 on a pound-for-pound (kilogram-for-kilogram) basis. A compound having an ODP of 0.1 would have 10 percent of the relative ozone-depleting effects of CFC-11. All ODP values are based on mass (weight) and not on moles (numbers of molecules).

Atmospheric Lifetimes

When one thinks of a chemical species lifetime, the term *half-life* is often used. This usage is most common in the nuclear field where calculations are made to determine how long it takes a species to decay to half its original concentration. Atmospheric lifetime values used in the determination of ozone depletion and global warming potentials are *not* half-lives. They are $^1/_e$ lifetimes, sometimes called *e*-folding lifetimes.

It has been determined that greenhouse gases break down in the atmosphere according to the following equation:

$$C = C_0 e^{-kt}$$

where

C = Concentration at time t

C_0 = Initial concentration at time

k = An experimentally determined rate constant (units = 1/time)

A mathematical manipulation can be made to express this equation as a function of more readily quantifiable terms and is accomplished by defining the atmospheric lifetime, L, as an *e*-folding lifetime, or the time it takes for the ratio of $C{:}C_0$ to be equal to $^1/_e$ (e is the base of the natural logarithm system and has a numerical value of approximately 2.718). The resulting equation is as follows:

$$C = C_0 e^{-t/L}$$

Although the term *half-life* is most commonly used when describing the decay of a species concentration, the use of the *e*-folding lifetime allows for quantification of concentration in terms of a compound's atmospheric lifetime, as previously shown. A half-life refers to the time it takes for half a given amount of compound to be broken down in the atmosphere; thus, the ratio $C{:}C_0$ is equal to $^1/_2$. Using an *e*-folding lifetime, the ratio is equal to $^1/_e$ or 0.368. After one lifetime, the concentration will be equal to 0.368 times its original value. After two lifetimes, the concentration will be 0.135 or $(0.368)^2$ its original value. After three lifetimes, the concentration will be 0.0498 or $(0.368)^3$ times its original value, and so on.

An important factor when using the preceding equation to solve for concentration as a function of time is that, no matter what value is used for time, the concentration never equals zero. Some portion will always exist in the atmosphere. When the atmospheric lifetime is small, the concentration over hundreds of years may become negligible. When the atmospheric lifetime is very large, on the order of tens of thousands of years, the concentration in the atmosphere may not be negligible.

The environmental concern is one of "what if" The halocarbons were believed to be "safe" for many years after their release into the atmosphere began. It was not until many years later that they were linked to ozone depletion. There is a concern that these other halocarbons, or other compounds, may cause other environmental impacts that yet are unknown. If the atmosphere is filled with these chemicals and they exist in appreciable amounts for hundreds, thousands, and millions of years, what then? Might the damage we do to our environment be more than humans can cope with? Nature can probably overcome this impact, but it may take tens of millions of years. This is a short time frame for nature but not for man. Current implementation of the EPA SNAP program places restrictions on perfluorocarbons that have very large or "outlying" atmospheric lifetimes as compared with the rest of the halocarbons. This restriction is not based on any known or anticipated environmental problem. It is a response to the "what if" concerns raised previously.

Global Warming Potential

A basic understanding about the earth's climate and atmosphere is needed to understand what global warming potential (GWP) is and how to attempt its measurement.

The atmospheric region closest to Earth, the troposphere, represents approximately 81 percent of the earth's atmosphere. It is made up mainly of nitrogen (N_2) and oxygen (O_2), representing 99 percent of its composition. The remaining 1 percent is made up of mostly argon, with smaller amounts of water, 0.2 percent; and CO_2, 0.03 percent (300 parts per million by volume [ppmv]). The atmosphere also contains several compounds in very small amounts known as "trace gases." These are methane, nitrous oxide, carbon monoxide, hydrogen, ozone, and halocarbons, which are so dilute that they are measured in parts per billion by volume (ppbv).

Weather and climate are not the same. Weather is the short-term, day-to-day conditions of temperature, humidity, rainfall, winds, and so on.[27] Climate is the long-term condition averaged over many years. Based on the climate of a region, particular weather is expected or predicted. Many factors determine a region's climate. These are a complex interaction of both natural and man-made activities. The biggest factor on the overall behavior of the earth's climate is the sun. The sun's energy hits Earth more at the tropics and equator than at the poles. Driven by diffusion principles, Earth distributes heat away from the tropics, which leads to the major wind and ocean currents.

Estimates of the average temperature of Earth's atmosphere have been made, assuming two theoretical conditions. The first assumes no atmosphere at all, and the second assumes an atmosphere made up solely of N_2 and O_2 (normally representing 99 percent of our atmosphere). In both cases, models have predicted that the earth's surface would be some 91°F (33°C) cooler than it is. The temperature difference is believed to be a direct result of the very small amounts of trace gases, water vapor, and CO_2. These act very much like the glass on a greenhouse that lets the sunlight in but helps to prevent the heat from escaping—hence, the terms *greenhouse effect* and *greenhouse gases.* A greenhouse gas is defined as any gas that absorbs infrared (IR) radiation.

It should not be surprising that certain constituents in the air can cause it to stay warmer. For example, it is common knowledge that the temperature on a hot, humid night does not drop as much as on a less humid night. During the winter, a clear night will have a larger drop in temperature than a cloudy night. In both cases, the difference is due to the water vapor present in the air. In fact, water is the largest contributor to the natural greenhouse effect, followed by CO_2.

Climate change and global warming are not synonymous. Climate change includes cooling and warming of the atmosphere. Global warming only deals with the aspects of climate change that result in warming of the atmosphere.

It is estimated that about one-third of the total solar radiation is reflected off earth's atmosphere. Most of the remaining two-thirds passes through the atmosphere and is absorbed by the earth's surface, causing it to warm.[28] The earth cools itself by releasing heat, or IR. In order for a balance to be maintained, the solar radiation coming in must equal the radiation going out. If more radiation entered the atmosphere than left, the earth would be constantly getting warmer. The opposite would be true if more radiation left earth than came in; that is, the earth would be constantly getting cooler.

O_2 and N_2 are transparent to IR, meaning that these compounds easily let IR radiation or heat pass through. Greenhouse gases are not transparent to IR—they absorb it. Their ability to absorb IR is finite, however, and some of what they absorb is reradiated out of the atmosphere. The IR reradiated is what is important. For a given concentration of greenhouse gases, reradiation depends on two factors: (1) how much IR comes in and (2) the temperature of the gas. Given the premise that the atmosphere wants to establish an equilibrium, the IR from the earth's surface and the amount reradiated from these gases want to be equal. Because the IR coming from the earth's surface does not change, the only remaining variable to affect the equilibrium is temperature. The atmosphere will heat until the IR balance is achieved. As stated previously, this has been predicted as a 91°F (33°C) rise in the temperature of the atmosphere.

On a day-to-day basis, the premise that the solar radiation is equal to the sum of IR radiated from the earth's surface and the IR reradiated from the greenhouse gases is not necessarily true. Daily, weekly, monthly, and yearly changes in weather are always occurring. Nevertheless, over the years, the averages are very close to equal and have resulted in a stable climate. To understand the greenhouse effect, scientists studying the climate have developed the concept of *radiative forcing.* They define radiative forcing as anything that will cause the energy balance at the top of the troposphere to no longer be in balance. Put another way, it is when radiation in and the radiation out of the top of the troposphere are not equal. This unbalanced radiation forces the climate to adapt, hence the term *radiative forcing.* The theory is that the climate will change to equalize the incoming and outgoing radiation. Any condition that results in a positive radiative forcing will cause a rise in the average temperature and, therefore, is responsible for global warming. Any condition that results in a negative radiative forcing will cause a drop in the average temperature and, therefore, is responsible for global cooling.[28]

To estimate the amount of global warming expected from a release of a particular greenhouse gas, a scale was developed by the International Panel on Climate Change (IPCC), based on the idea of radiative forcing. This scale is called the global warming potential (GWP) and relates to positive radiative forcing that will cause the atmosphere to heat up. The GWP is the cumulative amount of radiative forcing between the present and some future time caused by a unit mass (weight) of a compound, as compared with the same unit mass (weight) of an arbitrary standard. CO_2 is the most common reference, and 20 year, 100 year, and 500 year time periods, or horizons, are the most common time references cited in the literature.[28] The choice of time horizons is a policy issue and not a technical one.[29]

Since the GWP is a cumulative effect, summed year by year over a given time horizon, the quantity present in the atmosphere must be known year by year over that horizon. The atmospheric lifetime is used to perform these calculations. GWPs are also affected by the specific IR-absorbing capabilities of the chemical. Analogous to ODPs, GWPs are not exact numbers showing the precise effect on global warming. A 100 year horizon GWP of 6200 for Halon 1301 means that 1 lb (0.454 kg) of Halon 1301 will cause as much global warming as 6200 lb (2812 kg) of CO_2. A 500 year horizon GWP for methylene chloride of 0.3 means that 1 lb (0.454 kg) of methylene chloride will cause the same warming as 0.3 lb (0.14 kg) of CO_2.

GWPs are used to determine the future global warming contribution of a substance *over a given time* by multiplying the weight of the greenhouse gas by a specific time-horizon-GWP. The resultant number can be compared with others to decide which will have the least (or greatest) impact *over that time horizon.* Emitting a large quantity of a small GWP greenhouse gas may cause less global warming than a small release of a very large GWP greenhouse gas over a certain time horizon. Different time horizons may lead to different results.

The choice of which time horizon to use is a policy issue and not a technical one. A standard measure to predict future global warming commitments was developed as a tool to help policy makers and regulators in making decisions of which greenhouse gases would provide the biggest "bang for the buck." Currently, there is no standard in choosing a time horizon. In the future, however, this may change. It is also possible that different time horizons will be used for different greenhouse gases.

Environmental Regulation of Halon Replacements

The evaluation of clean agent fire suppressants includes a consideration of environmental factors. International, national, and local government regulations control the use of any alternatives in this regard. The primary environmental consideration is ODP. This is a measure of a chemical's ability to deplete stratospheric ozone with CFC-11 as a basis with an ODP of 1. All chemicals with a nonzero ODP are subject to phaseout under the Montreal Protocol and its amendments. Table 17.6.12 summarizes environmental impact data for halocarbon alternatives. Note that FC and HFC compounds have zero ozone depletion potential. One relatively recent advance has been the development of the Fluoroketone FK-5-1-12, a halogenated agent with essentially zero GWP.[30] This agent pressures many of the advantages of a halogenated agent but with an environmental impact similar to inert gases.

In the United States, the EPA has the responsibility for regulating the use of halon replacements. Through the SNAP

TABLE 17.6.12 Environmental Factor for Clean Agents

Designation	*ODP*	*GWP (100 years)*	*Atmospheric Lifetime (years)*
Halon 1301	12.000	7,030	LS
HFC-227ea	0.000	2,900	34.2
HFC-23	0.000	14,310	270
HFC-125	0.000	3,450	29
FK-5-1-12	0.000	Extremely low	0.038
Inert gas	0.000	0	NA

program, the EPA may prohibit or restrict the use of halon replacements on the basis of certain environmental factors or toxicity. There are two basic types of restrictions given to date: (1) restrictions on use in occupied versus unoccupied areas and (2) use restrictions (e.g., HCFC-22, HCFC-124, CF_3I) related to high atmospheric lifetime (e.g., C_4F_{10}, C_3F_8). The EPA periodically updates this list as new agents are proposed or as new data become available. It is relatively common to have NOAEL/LOAEL values updated, usually increased, as additional data become available. Such updates may change the acceptability of an agent for use in occupied areas.

HFCs and PFCs are part of the basket of industrial gases (also including methane, sulfurhexafluoride, and nitrous oxide) included in the Kyoto Protocol and may therefore be subject to emission controls in signatory nations. Currently, HFCs and PFCs represent less than 2 percent of greenhouse gas emissions on a carbon equivalency basis. Some PFCs were briefly used as fire extinguishants.

THERMOPHYSICAL PROPERTIES

Tables 17.6.13 and 17.6.14 give thermophysical properties of clean agent replacement update from NFPA 2001, in U.S. custom and SI units, respectively.

Representative isometric diagrams for various clean agents are given in Figures 17.6.3, 17.6.4, and 17.6.5 for HFC-227ea, HFC-23, and IG-541, respectively. The features of a typical isometric diagram for a liquefied halocarbon, superpressurized to 360 psig, can be seen in Figure 17.6.3. The importance of an isometric diagram is that it determines the maximum fill density for an agent in a cylinder with a fixed pressure rating. The basic rule is that the cylinder must not become liquid full at 130°F (54°C) (for U.S. DOT) and/or the pressure developed at 130°F (54°C) must not exceed 5⁄4 cylinder design pressure. The pressure developed is a function of the agent, the superpressurization level, and the temperature. For 360 psig (at 70°F) cylinders, pressure is limited to 5⁄4 of the design working pressure of 500 psig at 130°F. For HFC-227ea, as seen in Figure 17.6.5, this yields a maximum fill density of 72 lb/ft^3. The 360 psig pressurization level is not based on characteristics of halon replacement halocarbons but is a vestige of standard Halon 1301 systems.

Figure 17.6.4 is an isometric diagram for HFC-23. HFC-23 is not pressurized with nitrogen. At a maximum fill density of 54 lb/ft^3, it has a vapor pressure of 609 psi at 70°F. Above its critical point of 78.6°F, there is no distinction between liquid

TABLE 17.6.13 Thermophysical Properties of Clean Halocarbon Agents (U.S. Customary Units)

	Units	*FK-5-1-12mmy2*	*HCFC Blend A*	*HFC-125*	*HFC-227ea*	*HFC-23*	*IG-541*	*IG-55*	*IG-01*
Molecular weight	NA	316.04	92.90	120.2	170.03	70.01	34.0	33.95	39.9
Boiling point at 760 mm Hg	°F	120.02	−37.0	−55.3	2.6	−115.7	−320	−310.2	−302.6
Freezing point	°F	−162.4	<−161.0	−153	−204	−247.4	−109	−327.5	−308.9
Critical temperature	°F	335.6	256.0	158.8	215.0	78.6	—	−210.5	−188
Critical pressure	psia	270.44	964	521	422	701	—	602	711
Critical volume	ft^3/lbm	0.0251	0.0280	0.0281	0.0258	0.0305	NA	NA	NA
Critical density	bm/ft^3	39.91	36.00	35.68	38.76	32.78	NA	NA	NA
Specific heat, liquid at 77°F	Btu/lb-°F	0.2634	0.30	0.301	0.2831	0.370	NA	NA	NA
Specific heat, vapor at constant pressure (1atm) and 77°F	Btu/lb-°F	0.2127	0.16	0.191	0.1932	0.176	0.195	0.187	0.125
Heat of vaporization at boiling point of 25°C	Btu/lb	40.1	97.0	70.8	57.0	103.0	94.7	77.8	70.1
Thermal conductivity of liquid at 77°F	Btu/h ft °F	0.033	0.052	0.0376	0.040	0.0450	NA	NA	NA
Viscosity, liquid at 77°F	lb/ft hr	1.27	0.508	0.351	0.443	0.201	NA	NA	NA
Relative dielectric strength at 1 atm at 734 mm Hg 77°F (N_2 = 1.0)	NA	2.8	1.32	0.995 at 70°F	2.00	1.04	1.03	1.01	1.01
Solubility of water in agent at 70°F	NA	<0.001	0.12% by weight	0.07% by weight at 77°F	0.06%	500 ppm at 50°F (10°C)	0.015%	0.006%	0.006%
Vapor pressure at 77°F	psi	—	1.37	199	66.4	686.0	2207	NA	NA

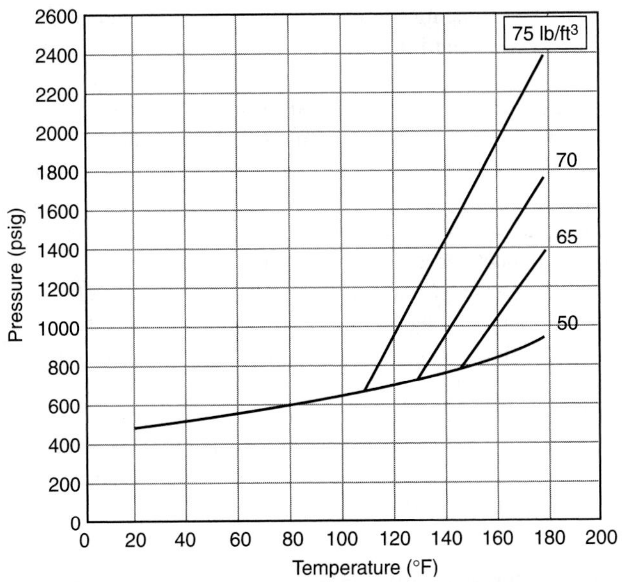

FIGURE 17.6.3 Isometric Diagram of HFC-227ea, Pressurized to 360 psig with N_2 at 70°F. For SI units: 1 lb per ft³. (Source: Sheinson, R. S., et al., "Halon 1301 Replacement Total Flooding Fire Testing, Intermediate Scale," *Proceedings* of Halon Options Technical Working Conference 1994, Albuquerque, NM, May 3–5, 1994, pp. 43–53)

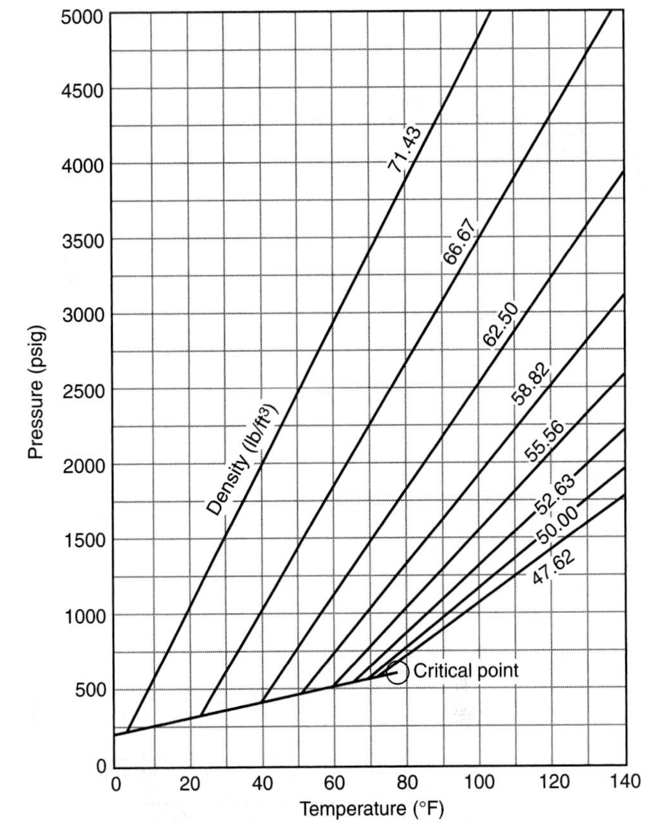

FIGURE 17.6.4 Isometric Diagram of HFC-23. For SI units: 1 lb per ft³.

TABLE 17.6.14 Physical Properties of Clean Halocarbon Agents (SI Units)

	Units	*FK-5-1-12mmy2*	*HCFC Blend A*	*HFC-125*	*HFC-227ea*	*HFC-23*	*IG-541*	*IG-55*	*IG-01*
Molecular weight	NA	316.04	92.90	120.2	170.03	70.01	34.0	33.95	39
Boiling point at 760 mm Hg	°C	49	–38.3	–48.5	–16.4	–82.1	–196	—	—
Freezing point	°C	–108	<–107.2	–102.8	–131	–155.2	–78.5	—	—
Critical temperature	°C	168.66	124.4	66.0	101.7	25.9	—	—	—
Critical pressure	kPa	1865	6647	3595	2912	4836	—	—	—
Critical volume	cc/mole	494.5	162	210	274	133	NA	NA	NA
Critical density	kg/m³	639.1	577	571	621	525	NA	NA	NA
Specific heat, liquid at 25°C	kj/kg °C	1.103	1.256	1.260	1.184	1.549	NA	NA	NA
Specific heat, vapor at constant pressure (1 atm) and 25°C	kj/kg °C	0.891	0.67	0.800	0.8082	0.737	0.574	—	—
Heat of vaporization at boiling point of 25°C	kj/kg °C	93.2	225.6	164.7	132.6	239.6	220	—	—
Thermal conductivity of liquid at 25°C	W/m °C	0.057*	0.900	0.0651	0.069	0.0779	NA	NA	NA
Viscosity, liquid at 25°C	Centipoises	0.524	0.21	0.145	0.184	0.083	NA	NA	NA
Relative dielectric strength at 1 atm at 734 mm Hg 25°C (N2=1.0)	NA	2.8	1.32	0.955 @ 70°F	2.00	1.04	1.03	1.01	1.0
Solubility of water in agent at 21°C	NA	<0.001	0.12% by weight	0.07% by weight at 77°C	0.06% by weight	500 ppm at 50°F (10°C)	0.015%	0.006%	0.0
Vapor pressure @ 25°C	kPa	—	948	1371	457.7	4730	15200	NA	NA

*3M estimated values.

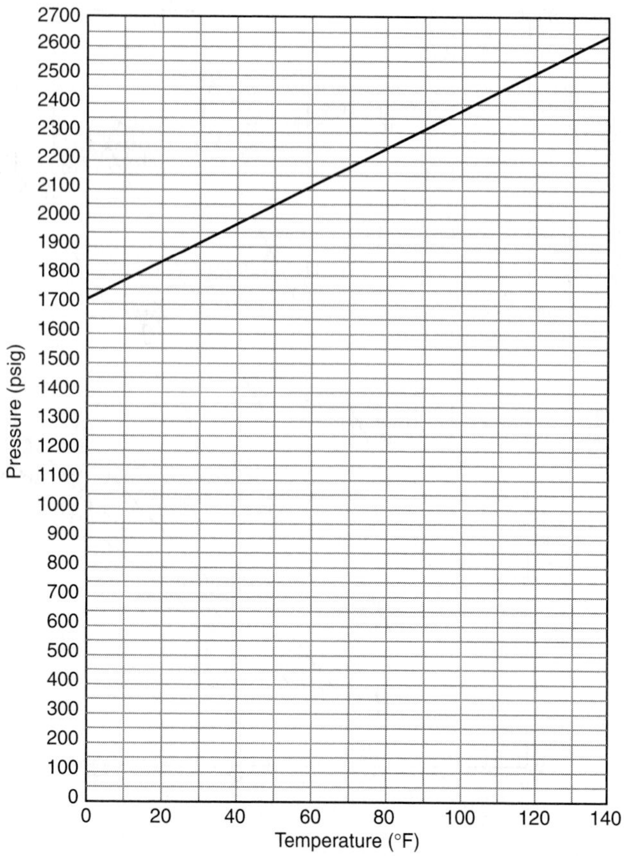

FIGURE 17.6.5 Isometric Diagram of Inert Gases and Blends Treated as Ideal Gases Pressurized to 2175 psig at 70°F

and gas with no liquid/gas separation in the cylinder. Further, compression does not result in formation of a liquid phase. Since it is not possible for the cylinder to be "liquid" full at 130°F, the pressure developed at a maximum fill density of 54 lb/ft^3 must be less than $^5\!/_4$ of the container design level working pressure of 1800 psi or 2250 psig, as shown in the graph. Below the critical temperature, the agent will exist as a liquid with a vapor or gas phase above it.

Figure 17.6.5 is a typical isometric diagram for inert gases exhibiting ideal gas law behavior at the pressures and temperatures of interest. Because these are compressed gases only, there is no fill density variation, only a linear relationship between temperature and pressure.

APPLICATION SYSTEMS

An application system consists of a supply of agent, a means for releasing or propelling the agent from its container, and one or more discharge nozzles to apply the agent into the hazard or directly onto the burning object. A system may also contain other elements, such as one or more detectors, remote and local alarms, a piping network, mechanical and electrical interlocks to close fire doors and to shut down ventilation, directional control valves, installed reserve agent supplies, and so on. The extent of the auxiliary functions of a system is usually dependent on the nature of the hazard in keeping with the desires and resources of the user.

A system is usually a fixed or stationary apparatus, but some portable or mobile systems have been designed. A portable or mobile system may be moved from one hazard to a similar one, but it is placed in a stationary position while it is in service. In this regard, all systems may be considered to be "fixed" but not necessarily permanently placed.

Halogenated clean agent systems are broadly classified by their method of applying agent to the hazard. The two main types are (1) total flooding and (2) local application systems. Another category, called "specialized systems," includes those systems that are designed to protect special or unique hazards and that have been tested and approved under these specific conditions. There are no NFPA design and installation standards for local application clean agent systems.

Total Flooding Systems

These systems protect enclosed, or at least partially enclosed, hazards. A sufficient quantity of extinguishing agent is discharged into the enclosure to provide a uniform fire-extinguishing concentration of agent throughout the entire enclosure. Examples of total flooding systems using halogenated agents are found in computer rooms, electrical switchgear rooms, magnetic tape storage vaults, and electronic control rooms; storage areas for artwork, books, and stamps; aerosol filling rooms; machinery spaces in ships; cargo areas in large transport aircraft; processing and storage areas for paints, solvents, and other flammable liquids; and so on.

Total flooding systems may be further distinguished by their method of design or installation. An engineered system is custom designed for a particular hazard, using components that are approved or listed only for their broad performance characteristics. Components may be arranged into an almost unlimited variety of configurations.

In preengineered systems, the number of components and configurations are determined in advance and included in the description of the system's approval or listing. Although the degree of preengineering can differ from one system to another, the following limits of components and configurations must be considered:

1. Maximum number of cylinders per manifold
2. Maximum and minimum size and length of piping
3. Maximum and minimum size and number of elbows, tees, and discharge nozzles
4. Container volume, fill density, and level of nitrogen superpressurization

Modular systems consist of single containers connected to discharge nozzles with minimal piping. A group of container-nozzle assemblies may be distributed throughout the protected area and interconnected electrically. Modular systems permit a more attractive and less expensive initial installation but often result in higher maintenance costs.

Central storage systems locate all agent containers in one centralized location. The agent can be stored in multiple tanks connected by a manifold arrangement or in a single bulk storage tank. A piping network distributes the agent to the various discharge nozzles. Ease of maintenance is the primary advantage of central storage systems.

Local Application Systems

As the name implies, these systems discharge extinguishing agent in such a manner that the burning object is surrounded locally by a high concentration of agent to extinguish the fire. In local application systems, neither the quantity of agent nor the type or arrangement of discharge nozzles is sufficient to achieve total flooding of the enclosure containing the object. Often, too, a local application system is required because the enclosure itself may not be suitable to provide total flooding. Examples of areas protected by local application are printing presses, dip and quench tanks, spray booths, oil-filled electric transformers, vapor vents, and so on. The protected object is not enclosed; therefore, discharge nozzles and rate of application must be capable of enveloping the object. The agent supply must be sufficient to maintain flow for the required time of protection, usually several minutes. Nozzle design is critical and must be determined by extensive testing.

Because of its lower volatility, Halon 1211 is well suited for local application systems. The lower volatility, plus a high liquid density, permits the agent to be sprayed as a liquid and, thus, propelled into the fire zone to a greater extent than is possible with other gaseous agents. Halon 2402 also is well suited for local application systems.

The material relating to local application systems, in NFPA 12B, was largely theoretical and intended for use by equipment manufacturers and testing laboratories in designing and evaluating components for local application systems. The component of overriding importance was the discharge nozzle, and its performance characteristics must be known with a high degree of reliability.

USE CONSIDERATIONS FOR CLEAN AGENT SYSTEMS

Advantages and Disadvantages

The primary advantages of total flooding clean agent systems are (1) the ability to extinguish shielded, obstructed, or three-dimensional fires in complex geometries; (2) the ability, through the use of appropriate detector-based actuation, to extinguish fires at a very early stage, well before direct or indirect fire/smoke damage occurs; and (3) the ability to cause no collateral damage due to agent discharge. These three technical attributes drive much of the usage of these agents in both flammable and combustible liquid hazards (e.g., shipboard engine rooms, pump rooms, etc.) and electronics equipment areas.

There are, however, the following technical disadvantages with respect to the use of clean agents:

1. They require a reasonably intact enclosure with the doors closed and external ventilation secured prior to discharge.
2. These agents provide virtually no cooling. This is an important consideration for situations in which large fires with long preburn times are expected.
3. Electrical power to wire/cable and equipment must be secured, or sufficiently high agent concentrations and hold times must be provided to ensure extinguishment at the expected electrical power density in the cable.
4. All elements of the detection, control, actuation, release, and distribution system must perform as designed. This requirement places increased reliance on both acceptance testing and postinstallation maintenance and test.

Use Recommendations

The decision to use total flooding clean agents is a relatively complex risk management decision. There are several recommendations on the use of these systems in the context of an overall fire protection program. The following are some commonsense recommendations:

1. In general, it does not make sense to protect a hazard area with a total flooding gas system within a building in which all other areas are not protected. Consider the case of a sensitive electronics facility within an office building. The probability of a fire occurring outside the space is at least equal to, and probably greater than, a fire occurring inside the space. Given the cost of protecting the electronics space, the cost/benefit of providing alternative protection (for example, automatic sprinklers) in the remainder of the building is much lower. For a fixed investment, it makes more sense to protect areas outside the electronics area first. As a general rule, never protect an area with a clean agent total flooding system unless the remainder of the building is adequately protected. Notable exceptions to this rule are cases in which the only or predominant fire hazard is in the space to be protected with a clean agent.

2. In facilities where the room or enclosure geometry changes frequently, sufficient administrative control of such modifications is required to ensure a clean agent total flooding system is not rendered inoperable or useless by changes in partitioning, modifications to detection equipment, and so forth. Although the same can be said for other types of fire protection, total flooding gas systems are particularly vulnerable to enclosure volume changes, enclosure integrity, and the integrity of the originally designed and installed detection, actuation, and control system.

3. Wherever possible, individual fire suppression equipment item failures should be anticipated and accounted for in the design. Examples include the use of higher design concentration to account for floodable volume changes or leakage changes, the addition of an extra cylinder to account for valve actuation failure, and provision of very early warning sampling detectors to permit human intervention prior to discharge.

4. Given the cost of halon replacement clean agent systems, it is expected that one significant use area will be in critically important sensitive electronics facilities. Substantial additional risk reduction at very high benefit/cost ratios may be realized by protecting these facilities with *both* clean agent total flooding systems and, at a relatively low incremental cost,

standard wet-pipe automatic sprinklers. Because both systems are designed to perform at different levels, the provision of an additional wet-pipe sprinkler system can be viewed as a backup system to the total flooding gas system. Although one expects higher direct and indirect damage levels in sensitive electronics, due to the difference in actuation time of sprinklers, they are relatively inexpensive and a reliable means of preventing excessively large losses in the event of the primary system (i.e., clean agent system) failure. For a typical 8 ft (2.4 m) high compartment, the additional cost of providing a simple wet-pipe sprinkler system as a secondary system can be as low as 5 percent of the installed clean agent system cost.

Clean agent total flooding systems can offer unequaled performance for the very early extinguishment of fires, which is critical in certain electronics facilities and the suppression of three-dimensional flammable liquid fires. However, the system must function as designed through the life of the facility. In the case of these total flooding gases, the system includes not only the detection, alarm, and suppression system but also the hazard enclosure, doors, dampers, ventilation/fans, and electrical power isolation. A study of existing clean agent system installations undertaken by Taylor/Wagner, Inc., indicated that within 5 years of initial installation, over 50 percent of the systems no longer met design requirements due to changes in the configuration of the protected space. The consequences included inability to achieve design concentration or the possibility of achieving concentrations that would have exceeded human exposure limits. The need to control and maintain this "system" cannot be overstated. See also Section 17, Chapter 7, "Application of Gaseous Agents to Special Hazards Fire Protection."

CLEAN AGENT SYSTEM DESIGN

The basic process of designing a total flooding gaseous extinguishing system involves the following:

1. Determine the design concentration
2. Determine the total agent quantity
3. Establish the maximum discharge time
4. Select piping material and thickness consistent with pressure rating requirements
5. Design piping network and select nozzles to deliver required concentration at required discharge time to ensure mixing
6. Evaluate compartment over/underpressurization and provide venting if required
7. Establish minimum agent hold requirements and evaluate compartments for leakage

These attributes apply only to the mechanical design of the system.

The detection and actuation system is a critical and integral part of a clean agent system design. The detection system should be designed to actuate the system, with appropriate predischarge alarms, before unacceptable thermal or nonthermal damage occurs. This is particularly important relative to the thermal decomposition in which products of halocarbon clean agents are a concern. Section 14, Chapter 2, "Automatic Fire Detectors," provides engineering methods and calculation procedures for this purpose.

In addition to the detection, actuation, and alarm system, the enclosure itself is critical in the design of any total flooding gaseous suppression system. The most important considerations are that the enclosure's integrity is sufficient to prevent (1) preferential agent loss during discharge and (2) excessive agent/air mixture loss after discharge to ensure adequate hold time.

As a general rule, all openings, notably doors and ventilation fans and/or openings, must be secured prior to discharge in conjunction with the detection and alarm system. System installation in rooms with unenclosable openings should not be attempted with these agents unless sufficient test data are available to ensure adequate concentrations. Some enclosures, such as very tightly sealed low electromagnetic field (EMF) emission electronics spaces, require additional care to avoid compartment damage due to overpressurization or underpressurization during agent discharge.

Design Concentrations

Design concentrations for various agents and fuel combinations are generally determined by a combination of small-scale testing, large-scale testing, independent laboratory approval of hardware, and addition of design safety factors.

Historically, minimum design concentrations for Halon 1301 were set by the cup burner extinguishing concentration plus a 20 percent safety factor. A minimum Halon 1301 design concentration of 5 percent was also established for all applications. For *n*-heptane, the cup burner value was approximately 3 percent; with a 20 percent safety factor, a design concentration of 3.6 percent is obtained. At the minimum design concentration set by NFPA 12A of 5 percent, a 66 percent safety factor was achieved. For fuels with cup burner extinguishing concentrations greater than 4.2 percent, the safety factor remained at 20 percent.

The basic requirement for determining the design concentration of clean agents in NFPA 2001 is twofold. First, the minimum extinguishing concentration as determined by the cup burner must be established. After this minimum is established by the *system* manufacturer, full-scale third-party approval testing is conducted using the manufacturer's hardware on *n*-heptane, wood crib, and selected flammable liquids. These tests are performed at the cup burner minimum extinguishing concentration, not the design concentration. Further, they are conducted with flooding factors lower than utilized in design. Hence, the minimum set by the cup burner or equipment manufacturer, whichever is higher, is tested in full scale as part of the approval/listing process for the agent/system combination. Often hardware manufacturers will establish a minimum concentration greater than the cup burner value to account for nozzle efficiency.

Reliance on the cup burner to set a minimum value is supported by the observation that no full-scale test known to the author conducted at the cup burner concentration plus 80 percent safety factor has failed to extinguish a flammable liquid fire in an enclosure. It is critical to recognize that, in real system design, the agent and the hardware delivering it, particularly the nozzle, are not independent. They must be taken as a system and designed and installed per the listing/approval guidelines and limitations.

There has been some full-scale test work that indicates that the 20 percent safety factor may be insufficient for certain applications, depending on the performance required of the system. Sheinson noted significant improvement in extinguishing time performance with a safety factor of 40 percent.[31] Brockway noted similar results with no performance improvement beyond a safety factor of 40 percent.[32]

It has also been noted by several investigators that higher safety factors result in lower thermal decomposition products.[31–33] None of the previously referenced investigations utilized listed or approved hardware for the specific agents tested; as in most cases, the tests were performed before such hardware was available.

There was an exception in the first edition of NFPA 2001 to the general rule that a minimum extinguishing concentration be established by the cup burner method. It was alleged that reliable cup burner data were not available for HCFC Blend A due to two facts: (1) the agent was a blend and (2) one of the blend components heats at a low vapor pressure. In the case of this agent, a minimum extinguishing concentration of 7.2 percent and, hence, a design concentration of 8.4 percent was established through limited full-scale testing. Since at the time insufficient data were available to evaluate the claim, the exception that requires full-scale testing at minimum extinguishing concentration consistent with UL 1058, *Halogenated Agent Extinguishing Systems Units,* was invoked. Since that time, reliable cup burner data were obtained for the blend from several laboratories. The data are consistent with MEC values for the blend components, primarily HCFC-22. Furthermore, some full-scale testing has indicated that the design concentration of 8.6 percent may be inadequate.[34] This exception was removed in the second edition of NFPA 2001. The current requirement for Class B fires is that the cup burner concentration for the worst-case fuel in the protected enclosure forms the MEC basis for that hazard.

It is important to recognize that the use of *n*-heptane cup burner values as a minimum for design concentration has no technical basis. With Halon 1301, *n*-heptane was a reasonable "worst case" fuel, but such is not the case with the replacements. It is important, therefore, that the design concentration be based on the "worst case" or fuel requiring the highest design concentration when designing systems for flammable or combustible liquid risks.

Extinguishing concentrations for Class A fuels were traditionally developed using wood cribs as part of the equipment listing/approval process. Further, the minimum Class A extinguishing concentration used for design purposes was required to be greater than or equal to the minimum extinguishing concentration for heptane. Recently, additional tests utilizing plastic sheet arrays of polymethylmethacrylate (PMMA), acrylonitrile-butadiene-sytrene (ABS), and polypropylene (PP) have been required.[35,36]

The test consists of an array of four sheets of polymer, 200 mm x 4000 mm × 10 mm thick, oriented vertically, forming three vertical channels. The array is enclosed on two sides and the top and surrounded by an additional baffle arrangement as shown in Figure 17.6.6. The array is tested in a minimum 100 m^3 compartment. The fuel is ignited by a small heptane pan, and the entire array is subjected to a 210-second preburn time.

Clean agent systems are widely used in electronic equipment areas where fires involving electrically energized cables and equipment are often encountered. Extinguishment tests involving PMMA heated externally with nichrome wire indicated

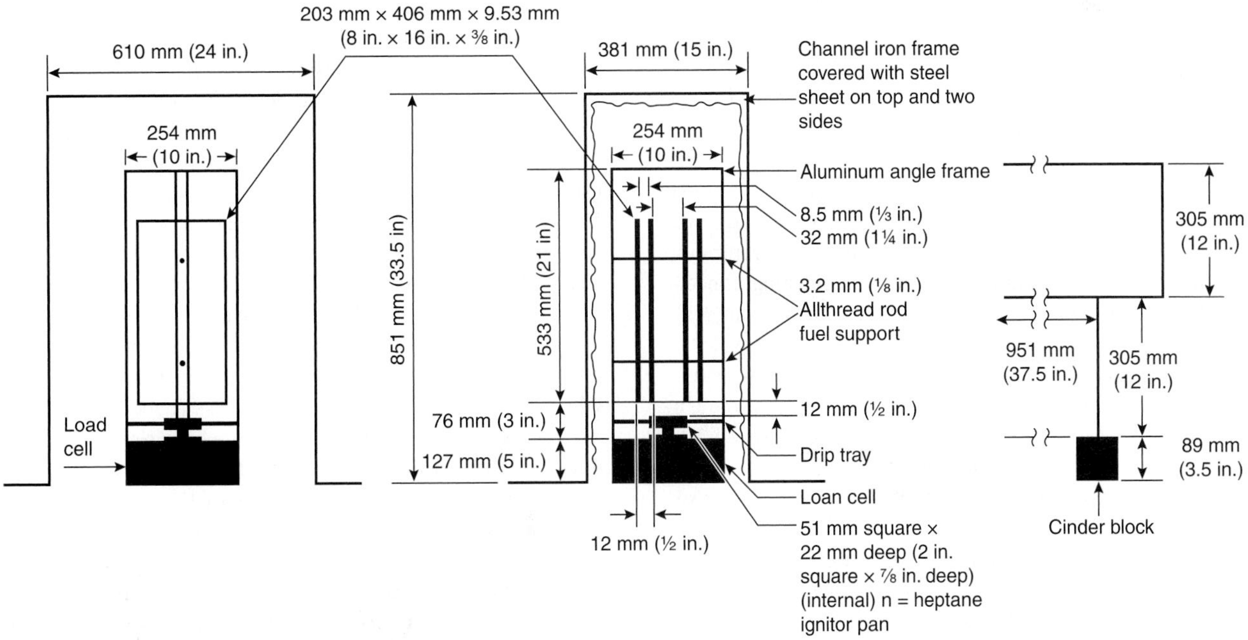

FIGURE 17.6.6 Four-Piece Modified Plastic Setup

that agent concentrations substantially higher than those typical for plastic fuels were required. For example, extinguishing concentrations of 9.5 percent, 9.0 percent, and 20 percent were required for FC-3-1-10, HFC-227ea, and HFC 23, respectively.

Extinguishment tests on actual wire and cable materials were reported by McKenna et al.[37] Three types of tests were conducted: ohmic heating, conductive heating, and printed wiring board arcing. The ohmic heating tests involved deliberate electrical overheating of the conductor. Under severe overcurrent conditions, all cable assemblies were extinguished at 5.8 percent, a typical Class A extinguishing concentration. The one exception was the 18 AWG polyethylene coaxial cable, which is generally not used in power applications. The striking difference between these results and those discussed earlier for PMMA probably lies in the fire-retardant nature of real electrical wire and cable assemblies. Results for cable assemblies heated at the ends by conduction, a situation simulating an overheated connection, showed results similar to the ohmic heating tests for Hypalon and PVC cables. There has, however, been no systematic evaluation of grouped electrical cables or high-voltage cables. Cable arrays with long preburn times have been demonstrated to require substantially higher agent concentration than for surface fires in the case of Halon 1301 and carbon dioxide.

Given the widespread use of clean agents in areas involving continuously energized equipment and recognizing the significant gaps in knowledge of required extinguishing concentration, the ISO standard[2] has required an extinguishing concentration no less than 95 percent of the heptane extinguishing concentration when any of the following conditions apply:

1. Cable bundles greater than 100 mm in diameter
2. Cable trays with a fill density greater than 20 percent of the tray cross section
3. Horizontal or vertical stacks of cable trays (closer than 250 mm)
4. Equipment energized during the extinguishment period in which the collective power consumption exceeds 5 kW

The issue of inadequate design concentration is exacerbated by the relatively recent decline in extinguishing concentration achieved in the Class A polymeric sheet tests. Additional uncertainty in the Class A extinguishing concentration was seen in Table 17.6.3, in which minimum required concentration is a function of system hardware. The extinguishing concentration for total flooding systems should be system and scale independent.

There has been no systematic evaluation of these agents under so-called "deep-seated" fire scenarios. However, the Underwriters Laboratories Inc. (UL) and FM Global Research listing procedures require testing on wood cribs subsequent to long preburn times (approximately 5 minutes). Under these tests, surface oxidation and char reactions do occur.

Design concentrations for fire scenarios involving long preburn times in thick arrays of cellulosic fuels may require additional testing. For most applications in which incidental quantities of cellulosic materials may be involved and preburn times have relatively short (5 minute) time frames (i.e., automatic actuation), the flame extinguishing concentrations for Class A fuels that are less than, or equal to, that of *n*-heptane can be used.

IG-541 is used at 37.5 percent minimum design concentration where Class A materials are involved. IG-55 may have slightly higher minimum design concentrations; IG-01 (argon) should have substantially higher MEC.

The minimum design concentration is a function of the fuel, the agent, and the delivery system. Design concentrations for specific hazards must be determined in accordance with the system manufacturer's approval or listing.

Safety Factors

The safety factor requirement in NFPA 2001 used for developing design concentrations should be considered a minimum. It can reasonably be expected to account for minor errors arising from the design and installation process, such as errors in room volume calculations, cylinder filling/agent weight, and cup burner MEC values.

The 20 percent minimum safety factor required in previous editions of NFPA 2001 has been increased under certain conditions. Systems protecting Class B or any system exclusively operated by manual means now requires a 30 percent safety factor. The ISO standard requires a minimum safety factor of 30 percent for all systems. The increase in safety factor resulted from a combination of theoretical analysis and fire testing. The ISO standard requires a 30 percent safety factor in all cases.

Analysis by Schlosser[38] indicated that the probability of failure of a system was reduced from approximately 15 percent to 10 percent when the safety factor increased from 20 percent to 30 percent. In addition to these data, the variation in cup burner values used as a basis for design concentration was significant due in part to a lack of standardization in the method. Some full-scale test results[39] also indicated a need for higher design concentrations.

The safety factor was also increased in response to increasing uncertainty concerning the determination of extinguishing concentrations for Class B fuels by the cup burner method. One concern was the observed increase in extinguishing concentration for inert gases as the cup burner flow rate was increased. VdS also reported a significant increase in extinguishing concentration for inert gases as the cup burner was increased in size.[40] The extinguishing concentration for all agents was observed to increase when the fuel pan was either thin-gauge metal or allowed to heat excessively. In addition to these small-scale test observations, difficulties were observed in full-scale tests in which long preburn times (for both Class A and Class B fuels) and compartment venting schemes may have resulted in higher than expected extinguishing concentrations.[41]

The increase in the safety factor was, therefore, judged prudent for application to future system installations. There is no evidence whether or not systems designed and installed prior to these changes are adequate. There have been no reported incidents in which an existing system failed to extinguish a fire using the 20 percent safety factor.

In addition to increased safety factors, the concept of design factors was introduced into the 2000 edition of NFPA 2001. A design factor is used to increase the agent quantity for a specific installation or design that has attributes for which the minimum safety factor may not be sufficient. The only variable for which design factors have been quantified is for systems with multiple flow splits protecting more than four enclosures simultaneously. The motivation for a design factor in these very rare cases is the uncertainty in the split of agent mass flow at unbalanced tee junctions and the compounding of that error with more than four tees in series.

Table 17.6.15 gives the required additional design quantity or design factor for systems with a large number of unbalanced flow divisions at tee splits. Note that the inert gas factor is always less than the halocarbon agent factor, reflecting the higher calculation uncertainty due to the complex two-phase behavior at flow splits for the halocarbon agents.

Consideration should be given to increasing the safety factor and, hence, the minimum design concentration when any of the following conditions apply:

1. When the nozzle is installed at or near its maximum listed ceiling height or area coverage
2. For the protection of combustible or flammable liquid hazards when limiting the quantity of thermal decomposition products (for halocarbon agents) and/or rapid (less than 15 seconds) extinguishment times are required
3. When a large number of highly imbalanced flow splits occurs in a piping network protecting large and small enclosures simultaneously (use design factors approach)
4. When the floodable room volume is highly variable (e.g., record storage), unless the maximum floodable volume is used
5. Where unenclosable openings exist or pressure-relief vents are provided and located such that excessive agent loss during discharge will occur
6. When excessive postdischarge agent leakage is expected

TABLE 17.6.15 Design Factors for Piping Tees

Design Factor Tee Count	*Halocarbon Design Factor*	*Inert Gas Design Factor*
0–4	0.00	0.00
5	0.01	0.00
6	0.02	0.00
7	0.03	0.00
8	0.04	0.00
9	0.05	0.01
10	0.06	0.01
11	0.07	0.02
12	0.07	0.02
13	0.08	0.03
14	0.09	0.03
15	0.09	0.04
16	0.10	0.04
17	0.11	0.05
18	0.11	0.05
19	0.12	0.06

Increasing the safety factor or design concentration is not warranted in many applications and may not substantially improve the reliability or performance of the system. For example, increasing the safety factor will not improve system reliability if doors are not closed. The design safety factor is not a panacea and cannot be used in lieu of other system design requirements.

Agent Quantity

Once the design concentration is established, the quantity of agent necessary to achieve that concentration is determined. The quantity of halocarbon agent necessary is determined by the following equation:

$$w = \frac{V}{S}\left(\frac{C}{100 - C}\right) \tag{1}$$

where

w = Specific weight of agent required

V = Net volume of protected space

C = Design concentration (%)

S = Specific volume (ft^3/lb or m^3/kg), and is determined by

$$S = k_1 + k_2(T) \tag{2}$$

where

T = Minimum ambient temperature of the protected space

k_1 and k_2 are constants

Values for k_1 and k_2 used in Equation 2 are given in Table 17.6.16.

The flooding factor in Equation 1 implies that the agent/air mixture "lost" during discharge is well mixed and has an agent concentration of C. This formula makes no assumption regarding leakage of the enclosure. During UL/FMRC approval testing, the agent is evaluated with a flooding factor of (C/100), essentially assuming that losses during discharge are 100 percent air.

For inert gases, the following formula is used:

$$X = 2.303\,\frac{V}{S}\log\left(\frac{100}{100 - C}\right)V_s \tag{3}$$

where

X = Volume of inert gas required at 70°F (21°C)

V_s = Specific volume at 70°F (21°C)

V = Net protected hazard volume

S = Specific volume at ambient temperature in protected volume (from Equation 2)

The flooding factor used here is derived assuming that leakage from the compartment during discharge occurs with a varying concentration of agent from zero to C from beginning to end of discharge. It is identical to the expression used in CO_2 system

TABLE 17.6.16 Specific Volume Constants

Generic Name	*Trade Name*	k_1 *English Units*	k_2 *English Units*	k_1 *SI Units*	k_2 *SI Units*
Halocarbons					
Halon 1301	Halon 1301	2.206200	0.0050460	0.1478	0.0005700
HFC-23	FE-13	4.730200	0.0106990	0.3168	0.0011942
HFC-125	FE-25	2.722000	0.0063760	0.1828	0.0007085
HFC-227ea	FM 200	1.879775	0.0046625	0.1268	0.0005133
HFC-236fa	FE-36	2.097800	0.0051400	0.1413	0.0005800
FK-5-1-12	Novec-1230	0.985600	0.0024410	0.0664	0.0002743
Inert Gases					
IG-01	Argotec	8.40299	0.0182810	0.56120	0.0020540
IG-55	Argonite	9.88090	0.0214956	0.65979	0.0024134
IG-100	NN-100	11.97600	0.0260600	0.79970	0.0029270
IG-541	Inergen	9.85800	0.0214300	0.65900	0.0024100

design. It assumes that the displaced atmosphere is freely vented from the enclosure.

Discharge Time

The maximum discharge time permitted for halocarbon clean agent systems is 10 seconds. This discharge time is taken to be the point at which all liquid agent has cleared the nozzle. The total discharge time will be longer as agent vapor and nitrogen are expelled from the system.

The 10-second discharge time limitation for halocarbon agents is designed to aid the following four objectives:

1. Provide high flow rates through nozzles to ensure adequate mixing of agent with air inside the enclosure
2. Provide sufficient velocity through pipes to ensure homogeneous flow of liquid and vapor
3. Limit the formation of agent thermal decomposition products
4. Minimize direct and indirect fire damage, particularly in fast-developing fire scenarios

The most important of these objectives relative to discharge time is the minimization of agent thermal decomposition product formation. Items 1 and 2 alone are determined by the piping system design.

The discharge time requirement for inert gases is currently 60 seconds. Longer discharge times are typically used for these systems in Europe. The primary reasons to constrain the discharge time of inert gas agents that form no decomposition products are to limit the direct and indirect fire damage and to minimize the length of time that the fire burns in a depleted oxygen atmosphere. As more information is developed on the effect of discharge time on inert gas agent performance, this 60 second limit may be increased for certain applications.

In some applications, such as flammable liquid hazards and explosion inerting, it is necessary to discharge the agent quickly to minimize direct fire damage or to ensure that the agent concentration is achieved prior to the lower explosive limit (LEL) being reached.

Thermal Decomposition Products

All of the halocarbon replacement agents form higher levels of decomposition products than Halon 1301 under similar conditions. For a given fuel, the primary variables determining the level of decomposition products are (1) the size of the fire at the time of discharge, (2) the time required to reach an extinguishing concentration in the compartment, and (3) the agent design concentration.

The dependence of thermal decomposition product formation on discharge time and fire size has been extensively evaluated.[31–33,42–46] Figure 17.6.7 is a plot of peak HF concentration as a function of fire size to room volume ratio. The data encompass room scales of 1.2 to 972 m^3. The 526 m^3 results are from USCG testing; the 972 m^3 results are based on Naval Research Laboratory testing.

These fires include diesel and *n*-heptane pool and spray fires. The design concentrations in all cases, except HCFC Blend A (at 8.6 percent), are at least 20 percent above the cup burner value. For fires in which the extinguishment times were greater than 17 seconds, the extinguishment time is noted in braces. Note that excessively high extinguishment times (greater than 60 seconds), generally an indication of inadequate agent concentrations, yield qualitatively higher HF concentrations. In addition, Halon 1301 will yield bromine or bromine acids as well as HF. Likewise, HCFC Blend A will produce HCl in addition to HF.

The quantity of HF formed is approximately three to eight times higher for all halocarbon replacements relative to Halon 1301. There may be differences between the various HFC/HCFC compounds tested, but it is not clear from these data whether (1) such differences occur, (2) the differences are attributable to agent mixing and distribution, or (3) the differences are attributable to locally high velocities or concentrations of agent from the nozzle. In all of the data reported, the fire source, *n*-heptane pans of varying sizes, was baffled to prevent direct interaction with the agent jet.

Whereas these results are based on flammable and combustible liquid fires, solid polymeric fires of similar size will

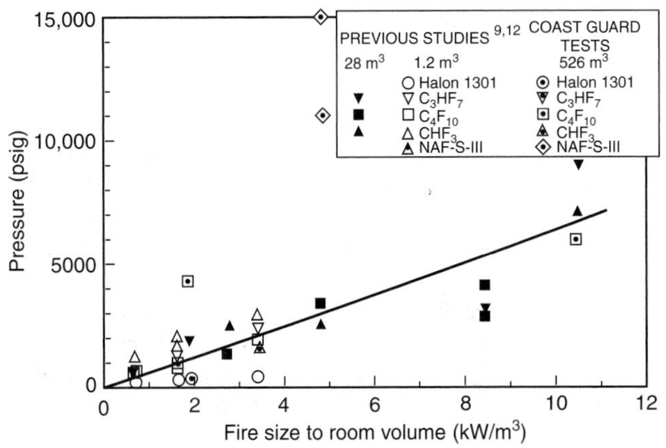

FIGURE 17.6.7 Maximum HF Concentration Resulting from Extinguishment of Test Fires with Nominal 10 sec Discharge Times with Data from U.S. Coast Guard Research and Development Testing and from Naval Research Laboratory Testing. For U.S. customary units: 1 ft^3 = 0.0283 m^3. (Sources: Back, G. G., et al., "Full-Scale Machinery Space Testing of Gaseous Halon Alternatives," USCG R&D Center, Groton, CT, Sept. 1994; Forssell, E. W., and DiNenno, P. J., "Evaluation of Alternative Agents for Use in Total Flooding Fire Protection Systems," Contract NAS 10-1181, National Aeronautics and Space Administration, John F. Kennedy Space Center, FL, Oct. 1994)

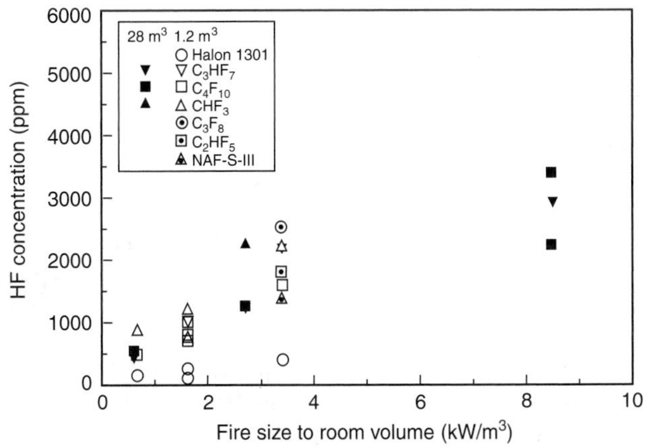

FIGURE 17.6.8 Average HF Concentration Resulting from Extinguishment of n-Heptane Fires with Nominal 15 sec Total Discharge Time. For U.S. customary units: 1 ft^3 = 0.0283 m^3. (Source: Forssell, E. W., and DiNenno, P. J., "Evaluation of Alternative Agents for Use in Total Flooding Fire Protection Systems," Contract NAS 10-1181, National Aeronautics and Space Administration, John F. Kennedy Space Center, FL, Oct. 1994)

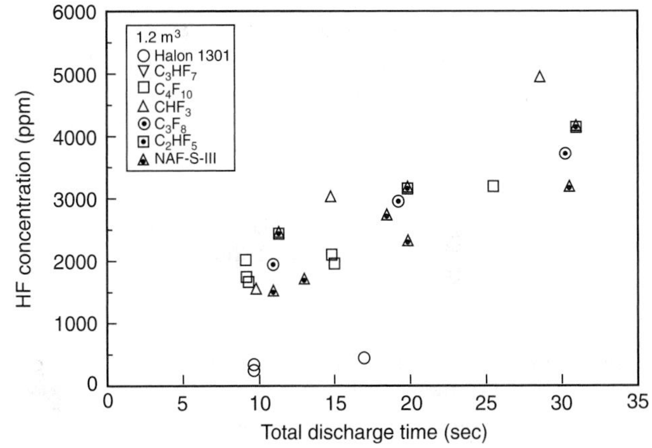

FIGURE 17.6.9 Maximum HF Concentration Resulting from Extinguishment of 4.0 kW n-Heptane Fires. For U.S. customary units: 1 ft^3 = 0.0283 m^3. (Source: Forssell, E. W., and DiNenno, P. J., "Evaluation of Alternative Agents for Use in Total Flooding Fire Protection Systems," Contract NAS 10-1181, National Aeronautics and Space Administration, John F. Kennedy Space Center, FL, Oct. 1994)

generally produce lower HF concentrations. Figure 17.6.8 reports 10-minute average HF concentration data for the 1.2 and 29 m^3 enclosures as opposed to the peak values shown in Figure 17.6.7. These 10 minute average values show HF concentrations 50 percent (or less) of the peak values.

Figure 17.6.9 shows the dependence of the quantity of decomposition products formed on the discharge time. Increased discharge time will also result in longer extinguishment times. The relationship is approximately linear with a doubling in discharge time resulting in a 100 percent increase in HF production. Clearly, increasing the amount of time the flame is exposed to a subextinguishing concentration of agent will increase the amount of agent decomposition expected.

Sheinson[47] has shown that increasing the design concentration of HFC-227ea from 8 percent (approximately 1.2 × cup burner) to 9.8 percent (1.8 × cup burner) results in a decrease in peak HF concentration from 8000 ppm to 2500 ppm for real-scale large combustible liquid fires. He also found HF concentrations 4 to 5.5 times higher than the peak HF concentration of Halon 1301 under similar conditions. He did not report HBr or bromine formation in these tests.

Although other thermal decomposition products have been identified in some cases, it appears that HF is the primary decomposition product of interest relative to human safety and equipment damage.

One of the characteristics of HF, like HCl, is that it is an irritant gas, detectable at very low concentrations; however, there is a very large difference between the human detection threshold, the severe sensory irritant threshold, and the ALC (approximately two and three orders of magnitude, respectively).

Fire sizes necessary to generate short-term lethal concentrations of HF in an enclosure (on the order of 1000 ppm) are large enough in some cases that the hazard posed to personnel in the protected space during a discharge in a fire incident is primarily from the fire and its effects rather than the secondary impact of agent decomposition products. This outcome, however, should be verified for a particular application under a range of fire scenarios using engineering methods discussed by Hanauska et al.[48,49]

The impact of decomposition products on electronic equipment is another area of concern. There are not sufficient data at present to predict the effects of a given HF exposure scenario on all electronic equipment. Several evaluations of the impact of HF on electronic equipment have been performed relative to the decomposition of Halon 1301, where decomposition products include HF and HBr. One of the more notable evaluations was a NASA study where the space shuttle *Orbiter* electronics were exposed to 700, 7000, and 70,000 ppm HF and HBr. In these tests, exposures up to 700 ppm HF and HBr caused no failures. At 7000 ppm, severe corrosion was noted; there were some operating failures at this level.

Dumayas[50] exposed IBM-PC-compatible multifunction cards to environments produced by a range of fire sizes as part of an evaluation program on halon alternatives. He found no loss of function of these boards following a 15 minute exposure to a postfire extinguishment atmosphere up to 5000 ppm HF, with unconditioned samples stored at ambient humidity and temperature conditions for up to 30 days. Forssell et al.[51] exposed multifunction boards for 30 minutes in the postfire extinguishment environment; no failures were reported up to 90 days posttest. HF concentrations up to 550 ppm were evaluated.

Although no generic rule or statement can be made at this time, it appears that short-term damage resulting in electronic equipment malfunction is not likely for exposures of between 500 and 1000 ppm HF for up to 30 minutes. This outcome, however, is dependent on the characteristics of the equipment exposed, postexposure treatment, exposure to other combustion products, and relative humidity. Important equipment characteristics include its location in the space, existence of equipment enclosures, and the sensitivity of the equipment to damage.

All HCFC, PFC, and HFC clean agents form more decomposition products than Halon 1301, given similar fire sizes and discharge times. The primary variable controlling the quantity of decomposition products is the size of the fire at the time of agent discharge. Through evaluation of the fire size at the time of system actuation, the potential hazard posed can be adequately managed.

Hanauska et al. have indicated that the degree of decomposition products in electronic applications of agents can be safely managed when automatic detection and actuation are provided. Full-scale testing with typical Class A fuel packages in conjunction with typical detection system installation[51] has shown that the level of decomposition products is acceptable in typical computer/electronics spaces. For installation in hazard areas where very rapidly developing large fires are likely, the degree of thermal decomposition formation should be evaluated in the context of the hazard posed by the fire and the performance of alternative fire protection systems.

The production of HF and other agent decomposition products forms a potential hazard for occupants. Table 17.6.17, from *Toxicology of Substances in Relation to Major Hazards: Hydrogen Fluoride,*[52] summarizes potential health effects in healthy individuals. Note that exposure above 200 ppm may begin to impair escape particularly at exposure times exceeding 5 minutes.

Emergency Response Planning Guidelines (ERPG) values, developed by the American Industrial Hygiene Association, for 10 minute exposures are as follows: ERPG-2, a level at which mitigating steps such as evacuation should be taken is 50 ppm; and ERPG-3, the maximum nonlethal exposure concentration for 10 minutes is 170 ppm. The ERPG values are in contrast to an analysis by Melchrum, which indicates a dose of 12,000 ppm/

TABLE 17.6.17 Potential Human Health Effects of Hydrogen Fluoride in Healthy Individuals

Exposure Time (min)	*Hydrogen Fluoride (ppm)*	*Reaction*
2	<50	Slight eye and nasal irritation
	50–100	Mild eye and upper respiratory tract irritation
	100–200	Moderate eye and upper respiratory tract irritation; slight skin irritation
	>200	Moderate irritation of all body surfaces; increasing concentration may be escape impairing
5	<50	Mild eye and nasal irritation
	50–100	Increasing eye and nasal irritation; slight skin irritation
	100–200	Moderate irritation of skin, eyes, and respiratory tract
	>200	Definite irritation of tissue surfaces; will cause escape impairment at increased concentrations
10	<50	Definite eye, skin, and upper respiratory tract irritation
	50–100	Moderate irritation of all body surfaces
	100–200	Moderate irritation of all body surfaces; escape-impairing effects likely
	>200	Escape-impairing effects will occur; increasing concentrations can be lethal without medical intervention

Source: *Toxicology of Substances in Relation to Major Hazards: Hydrogen Fluoride,* Health and Safety Executive Information Centre, U.K., 1993.

min based on 1 percent lethality in exposed animals. Additional health effect and risk assessment data have been reported.[53–56]

For large flammable or combustible liquid fire hazards utilizing manual system operation, the concentration of thermal decomposition products may be high enough to preclude entry into the space without special precautions. The use of an inexpensive water spray, wash-down cooling system in conjunction with a gaseous suppressant will provide substantial cooling, a reduction in the total decomposition products generated, and a reduction in the postdischarge decomposition product concentration due to scrubbing. Although the enhanced cooling would benefit all total flooding gases, the reduced decomposition product potential applies only to halocarbons. The provision of such a system would permit more rapid reentry into the space and may be of particular benefit for shipboard engine room protection.

Hydraulic and System Discharge Characteristics

All of the halocarbon replacement agents will exhibit two-phase flow behavior. Since all, except HFC-23, are used in cylinders pressurized to 360 or 600 psig (2482 or 4137 kPa) with nitrogen, they are also multiple component flows. Inert gases and blends will be single-phase compressible fluid flow problems. Most of the following discussion will not apply to inert gas systems; the testing and approval of flow calculations are similar with emphasis placed on flow parameters relevant to compressible gas flow, ignoring phase separation issues such as the orientation. As in the case of engineered Halon 1301 systems, all flow calculation procedures used must be listed or approved by a third-party laboratory and within the limitations of the flow calculation method determined during the engineered system approval process.

The characteristics that differentiate two-phase pipe flow from incompressible fluid (e.g., water) pipe flow is the existence of gas and liquid phases simultaneously in the pipe network. This coupled with the relatively short flow times results in significant challenges to correctly predicting the flow. Among the important factors are the change in density of the fluid with pressure, the release of nitrogen in the cylinder and pipe as the fluid pressure and temperature change, differences in agent mass delivered caused by the flow time imbalances between nozzles, and preferential distribution of phases (and subsequently agent mass) at tee splits.

The need for accurate flow predictions is driven by the following three design requirements:

1. Control of agent discharge time
2. Maintenance of adequate nozzle flow and pressure to ensure agent distribution and mixing at the listed coverage area
3. Delivery of adequate, but not excessive, agent quantities to different rooms within the same protected area, when such rooms are flooded simultaneously

In addition, agent flow rate and thermodynamic state properties are necessary for estimating compartment pressurization levels during agent discharge.

For preengineered systems, limits on discharge time and nozzle pressure are built into the limits on piping system geometry. Agent distribution is handled by constraining preengineered systems to balanced flow conditions (i.e., the same agent mass is distributed from each nozzle). For adequate design of preengineered systems, accurate methods for predicting these elements are required.

Figure 17.6.10 is an idealized plot of cylinder and nozzle pressure during discharge.

Testing and Approval of Design Methods

The approval or listing of a clean agent flow calculation procedure including inert gases is part of the approval granted for engineered systems. Since some aspects of two-phase flow calculations are empirically based (e.g., flow regime, pressure drop, flow splits) and all calculation procedures have some bounds on their validity, testing is performed to verify the predictions and establish the limits of the calculation procedure. These limitations are crucial in helping to ensure that system designs do not exceed verified limits of calculation.

One of the most rigorous approval procedures used in verifying design methods is outlined by Underwriters Laboratories Inc. UL 1058, *Halogenated Agent Extinguishing Systems Units,* was used for evaluating engineered Halon 1301 systems, but the same approach is taken for all clean agent alternatives. Design method limitations are described by the following 10 parameters, and tests are required to verify the accuracy of the calculation procedure at all of these limits (some of these parameters will not apply to inert gas systems):[35,36]

1. Percent of agent in piping (maximum)
2. Minimum and maximum discharge times
3. Minimum pipeline flow rates
4. Variance of piping volume to each nozzle

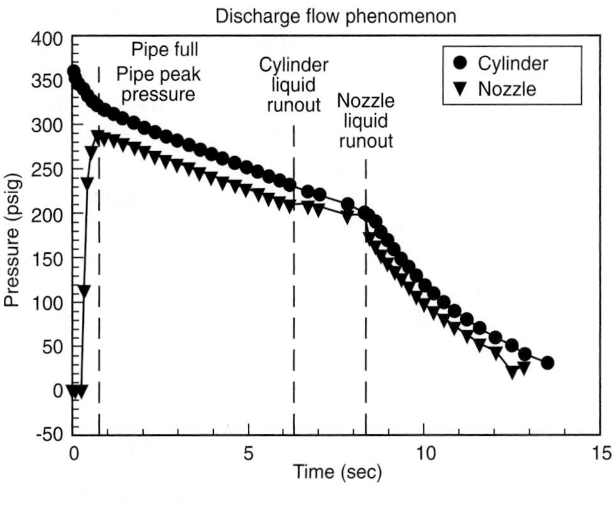

FIGURE 17.6.10 Idealized Cylinder and Nozzle Pressure Time Curves for Halocarbon Agents. For SI units: 1 psi = 6.895 kPa.

5. Maximum variance of nozzle pressures within a piping arrangement
6. Maximum ratio of nozzle diameter to inlet pipe diameter
7. Arrangement most likely to exhibit vapor time–imbalance condition at nozzle
8. All types of tee splits, including through tees, bullhead tees, and tee orientation (vertical versus horizontal)
9. Minimum and maximum container fill density
10. Minimum and maximum flow split for each type of tee

These parameters are related to the important attributes of the agent discharge process previously discussed. Full-scale testing is performed to evaluate the performance of the design method. The limits on flow calculation method performance are as follows:

1. Actual versus predicted discharge time (second)
2. Actual versus predicted nozzle pressure (percent)
3. Actual versus predicted mass flow through a nozzle (percent)

The accuracy limits required for mass flow rate through a nozzle, particularly the –5 percent allowable variation, are quite challenging given the complex nature of the problem. This allowable variation points to an area where increased agent quantity (or safety factor) may be appropriate. For networks in which a small fraction of the total agent flow is directed to a simultaneously protected but segregated enclosure *and* a large number of tees or flow splits are involved, the provision of additional agent to provide an allowance for the mass flow accuracy through greater than five or six tees should be considered. This is generally not a problem when all of the agent is discharged into the same enclosure.

Testing in conjunction with a particular manufacturer's hardware is important. Two critical hardware-dependent verifications are (1) ensuring that pressure drop through a particular valve assembly is calculated properly and (2) evaluating the nozzle orifice discharge coefficient.

In order to preserve a 10-second discharge time, the mass flow rate of these clean agents must be higher than Halon 1301. The increased density of some of the alternative agents in the piping, caused by lower vapor pressures and nitrogen solubility differences, may result in high enough mass flow rates to retrofit existing Halon 1301 systems. Although agent cylinders and nozzles will require changeout, it is often possible to preserve the existing Halon 1301 pipe network and often requires the use of lower fill density cylinders to increase the average system pressure throughout the discharge time. Any such retrofit using existing Halon 1301 piping must be carefully evaluated with respect to hydraulic performance with particular care given to preserving minimum required nozzle pressures and flow divisions at tees.

Nozzle Area Coverage and Height Limitations

One of the most important requirements of a gaseous total flooding fire suppression system is the ability of the system to deliver a uniform concentration of agent throughout the protected enclosure. The nozzle design and minimum nozzle pressure are critical in ensuring this distribution of agent. The performance of the nozzle is evaluated by full-scale approval testing.[57,58] The basic testing performed to evaluate nozzles is as follows:

1. Establish minimum nozzle pressure and maximum nozzle height by ensuring extinguishment of *n*-heptane fires located throughout a space with a height equal to the maximum allowable at the minimum allowable nozzle pressure.
2. Establish maximum nozzle coverage area by extinguishing tests in a plenum at the minimum height (generally less than 1.6 ft [0.5 m]) at the maximum nozzle coverage area (on the order of 1076 ft^2 [100 m^2]) and minimum nozzle operating pressure.

There are substantial differences among hardware manufacturers relative to minimum nozzle pressure, maximum ceiling height, and maximum average coverage. All nozzle orientations should be evaluated. In general, maximum nozzle heights are on the order of 13 to 16 ft (4 to 5 m), nozzle area coverage on the order of 97 to 108 ft^2 (9 to 10 m^2), and minimum nozzle pressures between 3 and 6 bar. It is critical to ensure that the nozzle spacing, height, and minimum pressure limits are not exceeded for a particular manufacturer's hardware in a specific design.

The flow, mixing, and distribution of an agent from a nozzle into an enclosure can be predicted theoretically for relatively simple nozzle designs by using sophisticated computer models.[59] Further development of such methods for complex nozzle designs and compartment geometries may eventually form the basis of a design procedure. At present, however, the primary means of ensuring adequate nozzle performance is the hardware approval process and real-scale testing.

Since many of the halocarbon replacements have lower vapor pressures than Halon 1301, there is often a much higher percentage of liquid at the nozzle. This makes the task of vaporizing and mixing the agent in the compartment more difficult. In general, nozzle designs used for Halon 1301 systems are not adequate for the halocarbon replacement agents. Due to the increased liquid fraction at the nozzle, it is critical to ensure that no unenclosed openings exist along the trajectory of the nozzle orifices. This may result in significant preferential loss of agent through these openings. This further emphasizes the need for third-party approval testing of nozzle performance. In any retrofit situation, the nozzles will need to be replaced even if the piping is adequately sized to deliver adequate agent flow rates.

Compartment Pressurization

The rapid discharge of agent into a compartment will cause rapid changes in the compartment pressure. Depending on the agent and rate of discharge, the initial pressure change may be negative. Figure 17.6.11 is a plot of compartment pressure versus time for the discharge of HFC-227ea into a 989 ft^3 (28 m^3) room with a 56 $in.^2$ (360 cm^2) leakage area.[44] Immediately after discharge, the pressure in the compartment drops below ambient to a minimum of –0.3 kPa; at approximately 1.5 seconds after discharge starts, the pressure begins to increase to a maximum of approximately 0.14 kPa after nozzle liquid runout. Similar results were obtained for FC-3-1-10. HFC-23 discharge exhibited much higher compartment overpressurization without the

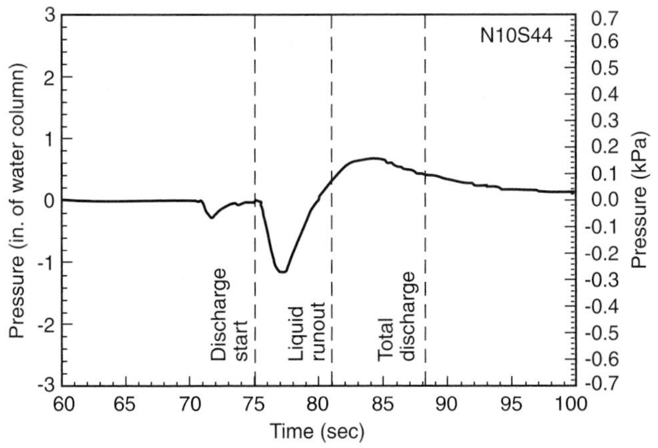

FIGURE 17.6.11 Pressure Measured in 989 ft^3 (28 m^3) Enclosure During HFC-227ea Discharge with Nominal 15 sec Discharge Time and 10 in. (254 mm) Pan of *n*-Heptane (Source: Forssell, E. W., and DiNenno, P. J., "Evaluation of Alternative Agents for Use in Total Flooding Fire Protection Systems," Contract NAS 10-1181, National Aeronautics and Space Administration, John F. Kennedy Space Center, FL, Oct. 1994)

marked initial negative pressure. The maximum overpressure for HFC-227ea and FC-3-1-10 discharge was similar to that of Halon 1301. Inert gas agents will, in general, result in positive pressure throughout the discharge.

As the halocarbon agent is discharged into the space, it vaporizes rapidly, cooling the compartment and lowering the pressure. As the agent/air mixture gains heat from the walls or other objects in the space, the pressure recovers and, as additional agent is added, the pressure increases over ambient as mass is added to the compartment.

The expected maximum and minimum compartment pressure during discharge will be a function of the following:

1. Thermodynamic state of the agent at the nozzle (determined by the agent and piping arrangement)
2. Nozzle design
3. Compartment volume and wall surface area
4. Size of fire
5. Initial conditions in space
6. Leakage area from compartment
7. Agent flow rate

For inert gases, significant compartment overpressurization can occur during discharge, unless adequate free vent area is provided. Calculation of required open area for venting is a part of the design manual for IG-541 systems.[60]

No generalized design procedure for calculating under/overpressurization has been established. Forssell and DiNenno[44] have developed a procedure for estimating the compartment pressure as a function of agent, agent flow rate, agent thermodynamic state at the nozzle, compartment volume, and surface area and leakage area. For inert gases utilizing relatively high agent concentrations, the required vent area calculation used for CO_2 systems is often used.

One area of concern with respect to vents is the possibility of preferential leakage of agent (as opposed to leakage of an agent/air mixture). This leakage can occur when an unencloseable opening or vent opening during discharge is located where a jet (from the nozzle) with a high agent concentration directly impinges on the opening. In this case, the possibility of higher than expected (in the flooding factor assumption) agent losses during discharge may occur. This outcome is particularly important for small rooms or areas with high wall area/room volume ratios and is probably more a problem for liquified halocarbon agents. Direct impingement by horizontal projection nozzles is most problematic where vents are located high on the walls.

Note that this preferential agent loss will not occur with the distributed leakage normally found in a room. A simple fix is to baffle any unenclosable opening or vent opening so that direct impingement by a nozzle jet on the opening is avoided. Ductwork attached to the relief vent discharge will also help prevent excessive agent loss.

Agent Hold Time and Leakage

Traditionally, total flooding gas systems were required to maintain a minimum concentration for a specified time period (10–20 minutes) after discharge. The minimum required hold time was a function of the following:

1. Soak time required for deep-seated Class A fuels
2. Response time of emergency personnel
3. Time required to prevent reflash due to presence of hot surfaces and other reignition sources, particularly in flammable and combustible liquid applications

Currently, there is no specified minimum hold or soak time for clean agents. The variables described earlier will vary among installations, and there is no significant database on the performance of these agents on "deep-seated" fires other than wood cribs. The designer will be required to specify the minimum soak time consistent with the requirements of the hazard being protected. A practical minimum of 10 minutes is generally recommended, with some applications requiring substantially longer hold times.

The ability of a compartment to maintain adequate agent concentration is a function of the leakage of the compartment. Historically, leakage testing was done with Halon 1301 through the use of discharge tests. Discharge testing for this purpose was rendered unnecessary by the introduction of door fan pressurization leakage tests. Annex B of NFPA 2001 describes a complete procedure for evaluating agent hold time as a function of compartment leakage measured by the door fan pressurization method.

The only difference between alternative agents and Halon 1301, in this regard, is the density of the agent/air mixture that is the driving force for leakage in quiescent environments. The mixture density can be estimated as follows:[1]

All agents, except inert gases, have higher mixture densities than Halon 1301 at 5 percent when used at their design concentrations. This will require slightly more leaktight enclosures to maintain the same hold time.

Note that IG-541 and IG-55 have densities very close to air. Such densities will result in excellent concentration retention or, conversely, relatively high allowable leakage areas, minimizing problems associated with leak integrity testing and required hold time.

Based on actual room testing with halogenated agents, the allowable leakage area calculated from the enclosure integrity test procedure given in Annex B of NFPA 2001 will be conservative. The actual hold time can be expected to be quite longer than the calculated hold time. This conservatism arises from the necessary, conservative simplifying assumption that the total equivalent leakage area measured by the door fan is evenly distributed at the top and bottom of the enclosure being tested.

Recent work by Dewsbury and Whitely[61,62] and Klocke[63] indicates interface between the air and the agent/air mixture may result in shorter than expected agent retention times due to the development of a wide interface of a subextinguishing concentration mixture of the agent. This more conservative method as modified has been adapted by ISO.

SUMMARY

A wide range of inert gas and halocarbon total flooding clean agents has been introduced over the past several years. More will be commercialized in the near future. The use of an agent must be consistent with applicable environmental regulations. The selection of an agent is driven by its fire performance characteristics; agent and system space and weight concerns; toxicity, particularly for use in occupied areas; and the availability of approved system hardware.

The design of clean agent systems must be carefully done in accordance with third-party listing and approval limitations on both agent and hardware. Given the relative lack of experience with systems employing these new agents, particular care in design, installation, inspection, testing, and maintenance is warranted. Design and installation standards, such as NFPA 2001 and the associated hardware approval standards, form the minimum requirements for these new technologies.

As generalized design methods and more detailed requirements evolve, the ability to design and install systems on a performance basis will increase. A critical part of the installation process is postinstallation inspection and testing. NFPA 2001 contains requirements for the approval and postinstallation inspection and test of clean agent systems. Bearing in mind the relative complexity of these systems and the importance of the detection system and enclosure integrity, postinstallation inspection and testing should be rigorously performed.

BIBLIOGRAPHY

References Cited

1. ISO 14520-1, "Gaseous Fire Extinguishing Systems—Physical Properties and System Design, Part 1: General Requirements," International Organization for Standardization, Geneva, Switzerland, 2005.
2. Burgess, D., et al., "Kinetics of Fluorine-Inhabited Hydrocarbon Flames," *Proceedings* of the Halon Options Technical Working Conference 1994, Albuquerque, NM, May 3–5, 1994, pp. 489–500.
3. Battin-LeClerc, F., et al., "The Chemical Inhibiting Effect of Some Fluorocarbons and Hydrofluorocarbons Proposed as Substitutes for Halons," *Halon Replacements: Technology and Science,* A. W. Miziolek and W. Tsang (Eds.), American Chemical Society, Washington, DC, 1995, pp. 289–303.
4. Richter, H., et al., "Flame Inhibition of Current Fire Extinguishers and of Potential Substitutes," *Halon Replacements: Technology and Science,* A. W. Miziolek and W. Tsang (Eds.), American Chemical Society, Washington, DC, 1995, pp. 304–320.
5. Brown, R., and Bailey, J. L., "Effect of Pressure and Oxygen Concentration on Pan Fires in an Enclosed Space," NRL Ltr. Rpt. Ser. 6180-25, Naval Research Laboratory, Washington, DC, Feb. 20, 1992.
6. Morehart, J. H., Zukowski, E. E., and Kubota, T., "Characteristics of Large Diffusion Flames Burning in a Vitiated Atmosphere," *Fire Safety Science—Proceedings* of the 3rd International Symposium, Elsevier Science Publishers, New York, 1991, pp. 575–583.
7. Moore, T. A., "Cup Burner Analysis," *Halon Substitute Program Review,* Albuquerque, NM, May 14, 1993.
8. Wickham, R. T., "Review of the Use of Carbon Dioxide Total Flooding Fire Extinguishing Systems," Wickham Associates prepared for U.S. EPA, Aug. 8, 2003.
9. Beyler, C. L., "Flammability Limits of Premixed and Diffusion Flames," *SFPE Handbook of Fire Protection Engineering,* 2nd ed., P. J. DiNenno et al. (Eds.), National Fire Protection Association, Quincy, MA, 2002.
10. Moore, T. A., "Large-Scale Inertion Evaluation of NFPA 2001 Agents," *Proceedings* of the 1993 International CFC and Halon Alternatives Conference, Washington, DC, October 20–22, 1993.
11. Senecal, J. A., "Explosion Protection in Occupied Spaces: The Status of Suppression and Inertion Using Halon and Its Descendants," *Proceedings* of the 1993 International CFC and Halon Alternatives Conference, Washington, DC, October 20–22, 1993, pp. 767–772.
12. Senecal, J. A., Ball, D. N., and Chattaway, A., "Explosion Suppression in Occupied Spaces," *Proceedings* of the Halon Options Technical Working Conference 1994, Albuquerque, NM, May 3–5, 1994, pp. 79–86.
13. Verdonik, D., "Introduction to Fire Suppression Agent Toxicology," Hughes Associates, Inc., Baltimore, MD, 1995.
14. *Casarett and Doull's Toxicology: The Basic Science of Poisons,* 4th ed., M. O. Amdur, J. Doul, and C. D. Klaassen (Eds.), Pergamon Press, Elmsford, NY, 1991.
15. Skaggs, S. R., Moore, T. A., and Tapscott, R. E., "Toxicological Properties of Halon Substitutes," *Halon Replacements: Technology and Science,* A. W. Miziolek and W. Tsang (Eds.), American Chemical Society, Washington, DC, 1995, pp. 99–109.
16. Rubenstein, R., "Halon Alternatives in Health Effects Assessment," *Proceedings* of the Halon Options Technical Working Conference 1995, Albuquerque, NM, May 9–11, 1995.
17. Vinegar, A., and Jepson, G. W., "Cardiac Sensitization Thresholds of Halon Replacement Chemicals Predicted in Humans by Physiologically-Based Pharmacokinetic Modeling," *Risk Analysis,* Vol. 16, No. 4, 1996.
18. Vinegar, A., Jepson, G. W., and Overton, J. H., "PBPK Modeling of Short Term (0 to 5 min) Human Inhalation Exposures to Halogenated Hydrocarbons," *Inhalation Toxicology,* Vol. 10, 1998, pp. 411–429.
19. Vinegar, A., "Performance of Monte Carlo Simulations of Exposure to HFC-227ea," ManTech Environmental Technology, Inc., Dayton, OH, Feb. 1999.
20. Vinegar, A., Jepson, G. W., Cisneros, M., Rubenstein, R., and Brock, W. J., "Setting Safe Exposure Limits for Halon Replacement Chemicals Using Physiologically Based Pharmacokinetic Modeling," *Inhalation Toxicology,* in press.
21. Vinegar, A., and Jepson, G., "Pharmacokinetic Modeling for Determining Egress from Exposure to Halon Replacement Chemicals," *Proceedings* of Halon Options Technical Working Conference—1998, New Mexico Engineering Research Institute, Albuquerque, NM, May 12–14, 1998.
22. Vinegar, A., and Jepson, G., "Ephinephrine Challenge for Cardiac Sensitization Testing Versus Endogenous Ephinephrine," *Proceedings* of the Halon Technical Working Conference—1999, New Mexico Engineering Research Institute, Albuqueque, NM, April 27–29, 1999.

23. "Research Basis for Improvement of Human Tolerance to Hypoxic Atmospheres in Fire Prevention and Extinguishment," EBRDC Report 10.30.92, Environmental Biomedical Research Data Center, Institute for Environmental Medicine, University of Pennsylvania, Philadelphia, PA, Oct. 1992.
24. Verdonik, D., "Understanding the Environmental Impact of Halocarbon Fire Suppression Agents," Unpublished Report, Hughes Associates, Baltimore, MD, 1995.
25. *Reporting on Climate Change: Understanding the Science,* National Safety Council of the Environmental Health Center, Washington, DC, Nov. 1994.
26. *A Matter of Degrees: A Primer on Global Warming,* Ministry of Supply and Services, Ottawa, Canada, 1993.
27. Schlesinger, M. E., "Greenhouse Policy," *Research and Exploration—National Geographic Survey,* Vol. 9, No. 2, Spring 1993.
28. *Climate Change 1994 Radiative Forcing of Climate Change and an Evaluation of the IPC 1992 Emission Scenarios,* Intergovernmental Panel on Climate Change, Cambridge, Cambridge University Press, London, UK, 1994.
29. Telcom with Dr. Tapscott, 1996.
30. Intergovernmental Panel on Climate Change (IPCC) Special Report on Safeguarding the Ozone Layer and the Global Climate System, Issues Related to Hydrofluorocarbons and Perfluorocarbons, United Nations Environment Programme/World Meteorological Organization (UNEP/WMO), Geneva, Switzerland, 2005.
31. Sheinson, R. S., et al., "Halon 1301 Replacement Total Flooding Fire Testing, Intermediate Scale," *Proceedings* of Halon Options Technical Working Conference 1994, Albuquerque, NM, May 3–5, 1994, pp. 43–53.
32. Brockway, J. C., "Recent Findings on Thermal Decomposition Products of Clean Extinguishing Agents," 3M Report presented to NFPA 2001 Committee, Ft. Lauderdale, FL, Sept. 19–22, 1994.
33. Moore, T. A., et al., "Intermediate Scale (645 ft^3) Fire Suppression Evaluation of NFPA 2001 Agents," *Proceedings* of Halon Options Technical Working Conference 1993, Albuquerque, NM, May 11–13, 1993, pp. 115–128.
34. Back, G. G., et al., "Full-Scale Machinery Space Testing of Gaseous Halon Alternatives," United States Coast Guard R&D Center, Groton, CT, Sept. 1994.
35. UL 2166, "Halocarbon Clean Agent Extinguishing System Units," Underwriters Laboratories, Northbrook, IL, 1999.
36. UL 2127, "Inert Gas Clean Agent Extinguishing System Units," Underwriters Laboratories, Northbrook, IL, 1999.
37. McKenna, L. A., et al., "Extinguishment Tests of Continuously Energized Class C Fires," *Halon Options Technical Working Conference—1998,* New Mexico Engineering Research Institute, Albuquerque, NM, May 12–14, 1998.
38. Schlosser, I., "Reliability and Efficacy of Gas Extinguishing Systems," *Proceedings* of Conference on Fire Extinguishing Systems, VdS, Cologne, Germany, December 1–2, 1998.
39. "Halon Alternatives, A Report on the Fire Extinguishing Performance Characteristics of Some Gaseous Alternatives to Halon 1301, LPR6: July 1996," Loss Prevention Council, Hertfordshire, UK, 1996.
40. Schlosser, I., et al., "CEA-R&D-Project Extinguishing Behavior of Inert Gases, Final Report," VdS, Cologne, Germany, 1999.
41. "Halon Alternatives, A Report on the Fire Extinguishing Performance Characteristics of Some Gaseous Alternatives to Halon 1301, LPR6: July 1996," Loss Prevention Council, Hertfordshire, UK, 1996.
42. Sheinson, R., et al., "Large-Scale (840 m^3) HFC Total Flooding Extinguishment Results," *Proceedings* of the Halon Options Technical Working Conference 1995, Albuquerque, NM, May 9–11, 1995, pp. 637–648.
43. Hansen, R., et al., "USCG Full-Scale Shipboard Testing of Gaseous Agents," *1994 International CFC and Halon Alternatives Conference Proceedings,* Washington, DC, October 24–25, 1994, pp. 386–394.
44. Forssell, E. W., and DiNenno, P. J., "Evaluation of Alternative Agents for Use in Total Flooding Fire Protection Systems," Contract NAS 10-1181, National Aeronautics and Space Administration, John F. Kennedy Space Center, FL, Oct. 1994.
45. Forssell, E., et al., "Hazard Assessment of Thermal Decomposition Products of FM-200™ in Electronics and Data Processing Facilities," Hughes Associates, Inc., Baltimore, MD, Jan. 6, 1995.
46. DiNenno, P. J., et al., "Thermal Decomposition Testing of Halon Alternatives," *Proceedings* of the Halon Alternatives Technical Working Conference 1993, Albuquerque, NM, May 1993.
47. Sheinson, R., "The US Navy Halon Total Flooding Replacement Program: Laboratory through Full Scale," *Halon Replacements: Technology and Science,* A. W. Miziolek and W. Tsang (Eds.), American Chemical Society, Washington, DC, 1995, pp. 175–189.
48. Hanauska, C. P., "Hazard Assessment of HFC Decomposition Products," presented at 1994 International CFC and Halon Alternatives Conference, Washington, DC, October 1994.
49. Hanauska, C. P., et al., "Hazard Assessment of Thermal Decomposition Products of Halon Alternatives," *Proceedings* of the Halon Alternatives Technical Working Conference 1993, Albuquerque, NM, May 1993.
50. Dumayas, W. A., "Effect of HF Exposure on PC Multifunction Cards," Senior Research Project, Department of Fire Protection Engineering, University of Maryland, College Park, MD, 1992.
51. Forssell, E. F., et al., "Draft Report: Performance of FM-200 on Typical Class A Computer Room Fuel Packages," Hughes Associates, Inc., Columbia, MD, Oct. 1994.
52. Meldrum, M., *Toxicology of Substances in Relation to Major Hazards: Hydrogen Fluoride,* Health and Safety Executive (HSE) Information Centre, Sheffield, UK, 1993.
53. Dalby, W., "Evaluation of the Toxicity of Hydrogen Fluoride at Short Exposure Times," Stonybrook Laboratories, Inc., Pennington, NJ, sponsored by the Petroleum Environmental Research Forum (PERF), PERF Project 92-90, 1996.
54. Machle, W., and Kitzmiller, K. R., "The Effects of the Inhalation of Hydrogen Fluoride, II. The Response Following Exposure to Low Concentrations," *Journal of Industrial Hygiene and Toxicology,* Vol. 17, 1935, pp. 223–229.
55. Machle, W., Tharnann, F., Kitzmiller, K. R., and Cholak, J., "The Effects of Inhalation of Hydrogen Fluoride, I. The Response Following Exposure to High Concentrations," *Journal of Industrial Hygiene and Toxicology,* Vol. 16, 1934, pp. 129–145.
56. Brock, W. J., "Hydrogen Fluoride: How Toxic Is Toxic? (A Hazard and Risk Analysis)," *Proceedings* of the Halon Options Technical Working Conference—1999, New Mexico Engineering Research Institute, Albuquerque, NM, April 27–29, 1999.
57. UL 2166, "Standard for Halocarbon Clean Agent Extinguishing System Units," Underwriters Laboratories, Northbrook, IL, Mar. 31, 1999.
58. UL 2127, "Standard for Inert Gas Clean Agent Extinguishing System Units," Underwriters Laboratories, Northbrook, IL, Mar. 31, 1999.
59. Bird, E. B., et al., "Development of Computer Model to Predict the Transient Discharge Characteristics of Halon Alternatives," *Proceedings* of the Halon Options Technical Working Conference 1994, Albuquerque, NM, May 1994.
60. Ansul Co., "Inergen System Design Installation and Maintenance Manual," Ansul Co., Westminster, MA, July 1994.
61. Dewsbury, J., and Whitely, R. A., "Review of Fan Integrity Testing and Hold Time Standards," *Fire Technology,* Vol. 36, No. 4, 2000, pp. 249–265.
62. Dewsbury, J., and Whitely, R. A., "Extensions of Hold Time Standards," *Fire Technology,* Vol. 36, No. 4, 2000, pp. 266–278.
63. Klocke, M., "Door Fan Test," *Proceedings*—VdS Congress on Fire Extinguishing Systems, VdS, Cologne, Germany, December 1998.

NFPA Codes, Standards, and Recommended Practices

Reference to the following NFPA codes, standards, and recommended practices will provide further information on halon replacement discussed in this chapter. (See the latest version of The NFPA Catalog *for availability of current editions of the following documents.)*

NFPA 12A, *Standard on Halon 1301 Fire Extinguishing Systems*
NFPA 2001, *Standard on Clean Agent Fire Extinguishing Systems*

Chapter 7

Application of Gaseous Agents to Special Hazards Fire Protection

Jeff L. Harrington

Chapter Contents

Key Terms

automatic sprinkler system, clean agent, design fire scenario, gaseous fire-extinguishing agent, halogenated agents, inert clean agent, performance-based design, special hazard

For purposes of this chapter, a *special hazard* is defined as a fuel array that for one or more reasons cannot be effectively protected by standard spray sprinklers.

Many alternatives to standard spray sprinklers have been developed to protect special hazards, each having certain characteristics uniquely suited to effectively protect the specific aspects of certain special hazards. Special hazard fire protection systems employ every known fire extinguishant, including water.

This chapter examines the key characteristics of special hazards that are particularly relevant to the use of gaseous fire-extinguishing agents (i.e., carbon dioxide, Halon 1301 and clean agents). *Gaseous fire-extinguishing agents* are chemicals or chemical compounds that are discharged on or about a fire hazard in their gaseous phase.

Until the late 1980s, there were two predominant gaseous agents to choose from to protect significant mission-critical hazards that required either a local application approach (carbon dioxide) or total flooding approach (Halon 1301 and carbon dioxide). However, since the advent of the Montreal Protocol and the U.S. Clean Air Act of 1990, production of new Halon 1301 has ceased. Chlorofluorocarbon (CFC) agents, including Halon 1301, have been identified as contributors to depletion of the ozone layer and targeted for phaseout. However, many new Halon 1301–like gaseous agents have been developed, and regulations have emerged aimed at safeguarding human health from exposure to gaseous fire extinguishants.

Halon 1301 is no longer manufactured in most industrialized nations and new fire-extinguishing systems that employ Halon 1301 are generally not allowed except for certain specific national defense applications. Halon 1301 is, however, still in use in existing systems and recycled Halon 1301 is readily available to refill them should they discharge for any reason.

NFPA 2001, *Standard on Clean Agent Fire Extinguishing Systems,* lists 13 gaseous extinguishing agents that have been developed with the hope of filling, at least in part, the market once held solely by Halon 1301. Nine of these agents are halocarbon chemical compounds or mixtures of them, and four are inert gases or mixtures of them.

For new systems, how does one choose the optimal gaseous agent for a particular fire hazard? Should it be carbon dioxide, one of the nine halocarbons, or one of the four inert agents? This chapter provides information aimed at helping to evaluate a given fire hazard and select one or more gaseous extinguishing agents that can provide an optimum fire protection solution for that hazard.

Also provided is information that will assist in effectively and safely maintaining existing Halon 1301 systems in service, so they will continue to provide effective fire protection that is safe for personnel in close proximity.

See also Section 2, Chapter 7, "Theory of Fire Extinguishment"; Section 3, Chapter 11, "Overview of Performance-Based Fire Protection Design"; Section 17, Chapter 1, "Carbon Dioxide and

Jeff L. Harrington is president and CEO of Harrington Group, Inc., a fire protection engineering and consulting firm. Mr. Harrington is the chair of the NFPA Technical Committee on Gaseous Fire Extinguishing Systems and a fellow of the Society of Fire Protection Engineers.

Application Systems"; and Section 17, Chapter 6, "Halon and Halon Replacement Agents and Systems."

FUNDAMENTALS OF SPECIAL HAZARDS

Fire and Fuel Classification

The performance objective of any special hazard fire-extinguishing system, of course, is to effectively extinguish the fire. It is critical, therefore, to select an extinguishing agent that is well suited to this task.

The nature of a potential fire is influenced by the type of fuel as classified in accordance with the definitions given in NFPA 10, *Standard for Portable Fire Extinguishers.* These definitions are summarized in Table 17.7.1 and are also discussed in Section 17, Chapter 5, "Fire Extinguisher Use and Maintenance."

Applicability of Sprinklers

In general practice, if standard spray sprinklers discharging plain water can adequately protect a fuel array using an occupancy hazard fire control approach, then that fuel array is not considered a special fire hazard. An occupancy hazard fire control approach, in general, utilizes standard spray sprinklers at the ceiling in a rectangular pattern, and is further detailed in NFPA 13, *Standard for the Installation of Sprinkler Systems.*

Class A fuel arrays are commonly protected by standard spray sprinklers discharging plain water, usually using the occupancy hazard fire control approach. An administrative office area is an example of this. This same approach is used to protect small Class B fuel arrays such as might be stored in a cleaning supply closet within the administrative office area. Certain Class C fuel arrays can also be protected using this approach. NFPA 13 requires sprinkler protection in electrical rooms, while allowing exemption from this requirement if certain conditions are satisfied.

If for any reason a fuel array is considered unsuitable for sprinkler protection using the occupancy hazard fire control approach and plain water, then it is often deemed to be a special hazard. In some instances, a water-based sprinkler system may be considered inappropriate for a particular fuel array because the water by itself may be ineffective or could cause unacceptable collateral damage. An example of the former is a flammable liquid pool array where plain water may not be an effective flame extinguishant. An example of the latter is a highly critical computer operations hub where water may result in significant collateral damage and extensive interruption of critical operations.

Standard spray sprinklers should never be used to protect Class D fuels because water is not an effective extinguishant and can cause violent reactions. Class K fuel arrays are normally protected by wet chemical extinguishants. Sprinklers can be used effectively, but a special design method is needed.

In summary, a special fire hazard might consist of a fuel array that meets the definition of any one, or a combination of, the standard classifications of Class A, B, C, D, or K. The hazard will need to be protected as a special fire hazard if it possesses one or more characteristics that make it unsuitable for protection by standard spray sprinklers using the occupancy hazard fire control approach and plain water.

Gaseous fire-extinguishing agents, among other options, are often considered and chosen as the primary fire extinguishant to protect certain special fire hazards where they can be effective, and where water is deemed inappropriate or used as a secondary protection method.

TABLE 17.7.1 Fire Classification and Fuel

Fire Classification	*Fuel*
Class A	Ordinary combustible materials, such as wood, cloth, paper, rubber, and many plastics
Class B	Flammable liquids, combustible liquids, petroleum greases, tars, oils, oil-based paints, solvents, lacquers, alcohols, and flammable gases
Class C	Energized electrical equipment
Class D	Combustible metals, such as magnesium, titanium, zirconium, sodium, lithium, and potassium
Class K	Combustible cooking media (vegetable or animal oils and fats)

Examples of Special Hazards Protected by Gaseous Agents

Examples of special hazards protected by gaseous agents include the following:

- Aircraft engine nacelles
- Cargo holds
- Computer data centers
- Dip tanks and coating machines
- Electrical equipment cabinets
- Electrical transformers and transformer vaults
- Engine rooms aboard ships
- Flammable liquid storage rooms
- Gas and oil processing facilities
- Hot oil industrial food fryers
- Industrial ovens
- Machine lube oil pits
- Offshore oil platforms
- Printing presses
- Process control room
- Steel rolling mills
- Telecommunications centers
- Turbine generator lube and seal oil systems
- Valuable electronic media storage vault
- Valuable paper records storage vault
- Wave soldering machines

Note that several of these examples are covered in more detail in relevant chapters of Section 8 ("Special Equipment") and Section 9 ("Processes and Facilities").

CHARACTERISTICS OF SPECIAL HAZARDS

The choice of the most appropriate fire-extinguishing agent for a special fire hazard depends on its specific characteristics. The most influential hazard characteristics commonly evaluated when making this choice include fuel properties, dimensional orientation, enclosure around the hazard, physical location, and occupancy.

Fuel Properties

Fuel properties that are particularly germane to special hazards fire protection include class and form of fuel and the presence of an oxidizer.

Classification of Fuel. Careful identification of the fuel related to the hazard being protected is a key first step in selecting an appropriate gaseous fire-extinguishing agent. One should collect as much information as possible, including the elemental materials involved, such as wood, paper, plastic, chemical, and so on. Then the fuel array should be classified using the system previously described (Class A, B, C, D, or K).

If the hazard involves electronic equipment, such as data processing or telecommunications equipment, determine whether power to the equipment will be interrupted prior to agent discharge, in which case the fuel classification might well be Class A (surface burning). Otherwise, the fuel classification would more accurately be Class C (energized electrical).

Class A—Surface Flame or Smoldering Combustion Tendency. Class A fuel arrays often burn with a predominant surface flame and negligible smoldering combustion. Materials made of plastic or rubber often produce this type of fire, which is often referred to as a Class A surface fire. A surface flame propagates in the gas phase in close proximity to the fuel surface, but not actually in contact with it.[1] Heat from the flame vaporizes the solid or liquid fuel just ahead of the flame front. The flame then ignites the vaporized fuel at the lower flammability range of the vapor mixture, and the flame advances, vaporizing more solid or liquid fuel in a continuing process. Surface-type flame spread can occur in solid, liquid, or gas fuels.

In Class A fuel arrays comprising cellulosic material in fibrous or particulate form, smoldering may be the predominant form of combustion, either in the absence of any surface flaming or after the surface flaming has subsided. Smoldering is a form of combustion without flame that occurs in fuel comprising finely divided fibers or particles that have a relatively large surface area to mass ratio.[2] Wood, pressed fiber insulation board, corrugated paper board, paper, and natural textile fabrics are examples of cellulosic materials or products that will produce significant smoldering combustion. The fuel aggregate must be permeable, allowing oxygen transport to the combustion reaction zone below the surface of the fuel. The fuel aggregate must also be dense enough to form an effective insulation layer that slows down heat losses from the reaction zone. Smoldering combustion can occur only in solid fuels.

Class C—Energized Electrical Equipment. Many special hazards protected by gaseous fire-extinguishing systems involve electrically energized equipment. Examples include telecommunication switches, satellite uplink transmitters, data processing equipment, and industrial process control rooms. When a fire in such hazards results in interruption of power to the equipment, the fuel is immediately converted from a Class C to a Class A–type hazard. The polymeric materials used in electric cable insulation and printed circuit boards are inherently Class A materials. When these materials burn, the flame is predominantly a surface burning phenomenon. Extinguishing a surface burning fire in Class A materials with gaseous agents is a relatively straightforward process.

These same materials are considered Class C fuel if the electrical power is not interrupted during the extinguishing process. One can easily conclude that fires in Class C fuels are more difficult to extinguish and prevent rekindling due to the presence of a persistent electrical energy input, which can add heat to the combustion zone. Various building and fire codes that may apply to a particular project could require electrical equipment to be de-energized prior to agent discharge, effectively converting the Class C fire into a Class A surface fire. Examples are found in NFPA 70, *National Electrical Code®*, and NFPA 75, *Standard for the Protection of Information Technology Equipment.*

Form of Fuel. For a given special fire hazard, the fuel array may be in solid, liquid, or gas form, or a combination of these forms. The fuel form plays a major role in determining the nature of the fire hazard. For example, solid cellulosic fuels can foster smoldering combustion that spreads very slowly with no visible flame. A flammable liquid pool, on the other hand, can produce a surface fire that spreads very rapidly with a high heat release rate. The fire characteristics, which are determined by the fuel characteristics, will influence the most appropriate choice of gaseous extinguishing agent.

Gaseous extinguishing agents are also suitable as inerting agents when a fuel exists in gaseous form. Such an atmosphere can be inerted by certain gaseous agents to prevent a fire or explosion.

Presence of Oxidizer. NFPA 430, *Code for the Storage of Liquid and Solid Oxidizers,* defines an oxidizer as any material that readily yields oxygen or other oxidizing gas, or that readily reacts to promote or initiate combustion of combustible materials and can undergo a vigorous self-sustained decomposition due to contamination or heat exposure. Generally, gaseous extinguishing agents are not suitable for use on hazards that contain oxidizers.

Dimensional Orientation

Gaseous extinguishing agents are particularly well suited to protect hazards that have three-dimensional fuel characteristics or where the fuel may be shielded. An example of this is a computer cabinet where the fuel is located inside a closed cabinet in the form of printed circuit boards and electric cable insulation. A gaseous extinguishing agent can flood the area surrounding the cabinet and permeate the cabinet interior through gaps and holes in concentrations sufficient to surround the fuel and extinguish a fire inside.

Enclosure Around the Hazard

Many fire hazards are surrounded partially or completely by an enclosure, such as a room. If the enclosure is complete, and any openings can be effectively closed, then the hazard may be protected by a total flooding gaseous extinguishing system. If the enclosure cannot be effectively sealed to accommodate total flooding, then partial flooding or local application systems using gaseous agents may be possible. Where no enclosure exists, and the hazard is not concealed or shielded, gaseous extinguishing agents might be applied as local applications or they simply may not be the most suitable choice.

Total Flooding Application. A total flooding configuration is one where the fire hazard being protected is surrounded completely by an enclosure, usually consisting of a floor, four walls and ceiling. A total flooding extinguishing system is designed to quickly fill the entire enclosure with a concentration of agent sufficient for fire extinguishment. The system should also be designed to maintain the concentration for a period of time to prevent rekindling and enable a manual emergency response.

Total Flooding Enclosure Integrity. When a total flooding gaseous extinguishing system discharges into an enclosure with no fire present, rapid pressure changes occur, that exert significant forces on the enclosure boundaries. With a fire present, the pressure forces produced will likely be even greater.[3] The enclosure construction elements must be capable of withstanding the peak pressures produced during agent discharge, or damage to the enclosure—and even catastrophic failure—could occur. This could in turn lead to failure of the fire protection system to extinguish the fire. Any failure of the enclosure's integrity could also endanger personnel in the immediate vicinity.

Evaluation of Peak Pressures During Agent Discharge. The discharge of halocarbon agents, both halocarbon clean agents and Halon 1301, causes an initial drop in pressure within the enclosure followed by a temporary rise in pressure. Shortly after the completion of agent discharge, the enclosure pressure reaches equilibrium, just slightly above the pressure value prior to discharge. The enclosure pressure changes during halocarbon agent discharge are shown schematically in Figure 17.7.1. (Note that the graphic does not, however, apply to HFC-23 [FE-13].)

The discharge of inert clean agents and carbon dioxide causes a positive pressure change within the enclosure. This pressure change can be quite large, exceeding the strength of most common enclosure elements. Thus, inert clean agent and carbon dioxide total flooding extinguishing systems will normally require the installation of enclosure pressure relief vents to protect the integrity of the enclosure during agent discharge. The enclosure pressure changes during inert agent discharge are shown graphically in Figure 17.7.2.

Evaluation of Enclosure Strength. During the development of heptafluoropropane (HFC 227ea), several studies evaluated various aspects of the enclosure pressure dynamics during agent discharge and the inherent strength of various construction elements to resist these pressure forces.[3] These studies found that the enclosure walls for the majority of total flooding applications using HFC 227ea are either gypsum wallboard on studs or masonry units such as concrete block and/or brick. Findings from these studies of particular interest follow:

- The peak pressures developed during agent discharge ranged from –8 psf (–383 Pa) to 8 psf (383 Pa).
- The peak pressures developed in an enclosure with gypsum wallboard on studs was less than that developed with walls of concrete block, because gypsum wallboard on studs flexes in response to pressure changes, which dampens peak pressure development. Concrete block walls do not flex, thus enabling peak pressure magnitudes to be greater.

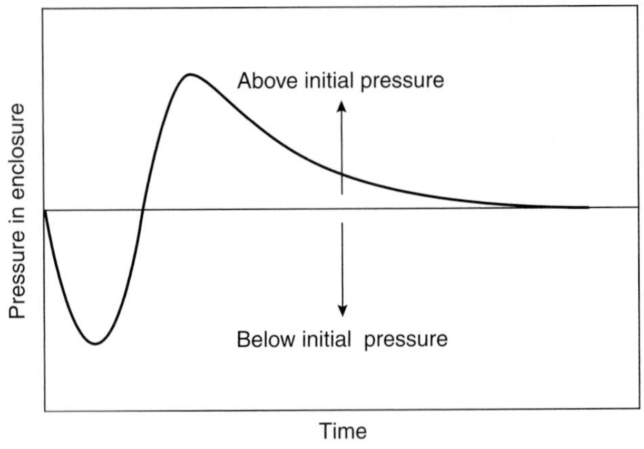

FIGURE 17.7.1 Variation in Room Pressure During Halocarbon Agent Discharge (Source: *Room Pressure Venting Guideline with FM-200®—Application Guide,* 93-1001, Fenwal Protection Systems, Ashland, MA, Dec. 2003)

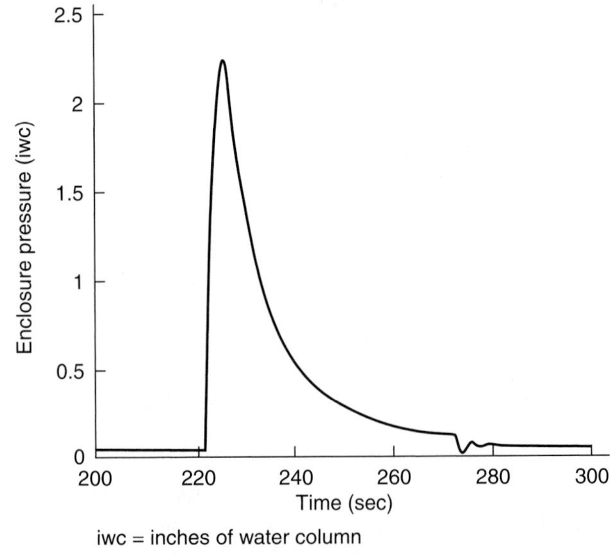

FIGURE 17.7.2 Variation in Room Pressure During Inert Agent Discharge (Source: Robin, M. L., Forssell, E. W., and Sharma, V., "Pressure Dynamics of Clean Agent Discharges," Halon Options Technical Working Conference, 2005)

- The metal studs most commonly used in gypsum wallboard construction can resist a peak pressure of over 25 psf (1197 Pa) before reaching their yield strength. This value can vary depending on such variables as wall height and stud spacing.
- The wood studs most commonly used in gypsum wallboard construction can resist a peak pressure of about 11 psf (527 Pa) before reaching their maximum tensile strength. This value can vary depending on such variables as wall height and stud spacing.
- Additional investigation is warranted on other construction materials and assemblies commonly used in protected enclosures, such as concrete, other masonry units, doors, and windows.
- For very tight enclosures, that is, those with predicted agent retention times significantly exceeding 10 minutes, and for enclosures significantly higher than 12 ft (3.7 m), the pressures developed during agent discharge could reach or exceed the maximum strength of the construction elements.

It is advisable to consult a qualified structural engineer for assistance with the determination of enclosure strength. Likewise, the gaseous extinguishing system manufacturer should be consulted to assist with the determination of peak discharge pressure values. Once the peak pressure load and enclosure strength values are determined, the need for enclosure relief venting or strengthening the enclosure should be evaluated.

Partial Flooding Application. A partial flooding configuration is one where the fire hazard being protected is surrounded only partially by an enclosure. An example of this is a flight simulator. Flight simulators are large boxes elevated above the floor on sophisticated hydraulically operated supports. The hydraulic oil system is usually located on the floor directly beneath the simulator box. Because a hydraulic oil fire could endanger the occupants of the box during simulation exercises, a partial height wall is constructed beneath the box, completely surrounding the hydraulic oil equipment and completely sealed to the floor, gastight. This partial enclosure is then equipped with an automatic gaseous extinguishing system that will flood the partial enclosure like filling a bathtub. The burning fuel will be submerged in an extinguishing concentration of gaseous agent and the fire will be extinguished.

Local Application. Where the fire hazard being protected is not surrounded by an enclosure, a local application extinguishing system is designed to discharge extinguishing agent in predominantly liquid form directly onto the burning fuel surfaces in sufficient quantity to extinguish the fire and very often cool the fuel. See "Carbon Dioxide" later in this chapter under the section "Local Application Capability" for more information. A printing station on a large commercial printing press is an example of a fire hazard that is commonly protected with a local application gaseous extinguishing system.

Physical Location

The physical location of a hazard to be protected has an influence on the most suitable fire-extinguishing system for the application. Gaseous clean agent systems have been employed in just about every location imaginable with great success. For example, gaseous agent systems protect engine and machinery spaces on cargo ships, gas compressor rooms at the North Slope in Alaska, telecommunication rooms at the top of air traffic control towers, and cargo compartments on commercial aircraft. Carbon dioxide systems have also been used in many of these same locations.

The physical location of the hazard should be carefully evaluated. Different variables associated with the hazard location may favor the use of one gaseous agent over another. For example, some locations may experience extreme low or high temperatures. Others may be relatively remote, providing a challenge to the process of refilling and restoring a system to full operation following a system discharge. These and other factors related to hazard location can favor one gaseous extinguishant over others.

Occupancy

One clear objective of the NFPA standards addressing gaseous extinguishing agents is to design and install systems in a manner that prevents human exposure to the extinguishing agent. This objective was emphasized with EPA involvement in the process to find safe new alternatives for fire protection halons such as Halon 1301 and Halon 1211 that were deemed harmful to the stratospheric ozone layer. All gaseous agents currently used, other than Halon 1301 and Halon 1211, are included in the Safe New Alternatives Policy Program (SNAP), EPA's program to evaluate and regulate substitutes for ozone-depleting chemicals being phased out under the stratospheric ozone protection provisions of the U.S. Clean Air Act.

EPA has stated, "The Administrator has determined a large number of alternatives that exist to reduce overall risk to human health and the environment. The purpose of the program is to allow a safe, smooth transition away from ozone-depleting compounds by identifying substitutes that offer lower overall risks to human health and the environment." It is clear that EPA intends not only to reduce environmental risk, but also human health risk.

NFPA 12, *Standard on Carbon Dioxide Extinguishing Systems,* NFPA 12A, *Standard on Halon 1301 Fire Extinguishing Systems,* and NFPA 2001 provide various requirements to reduce human health risks from potential exposure to the gaseous agents listed in these standards. Table 17.7.2 presents several definitions related to occupancy and human health exposure.

In general, requirements in the standards are designed to provide protection against human exposure to the gaseous agents in direct proportion to the likelihood of human occupancy in the protected room or space. The risk of human exposure to the agent is relatively high in a space that is "normally occupied" and relatively low in a space that is "unoccupiable."

TYPES OF GASEOUS AGENTS

Although there are many gaseous fire-extinguishing agents to choose from for a given application, the three main types of gaseous agents are clean agents, carbon dioxide, and Halon 1301. NFPA publishes design, installation and maintenance standards for each type in NFPA 2001, NFPA 12, and NFPA 12A respectively.

TABLE 17.7.2 Human Health Exposure Terms and Definitions Related to Occupancy

Term	*Definition*
Normally occupied area	An area that is intended for occupancy
Normally occupied	An enclosure where, under normal circumstances, persons are present
Normally unoccupied	An area or space not normally occupied by people that could be entered occasionally for brief periods
Unoccupiable	An enclosure that cannot be occupied due to dimensional or other physical constraints

Clean Agents

Clean agents are in the gaseous state in the vicinity of the fire hazard. As gases, they quickly surround the fuel and permeate the fire, even if physical barriers or complex fuel geometries exist. They are electrically nonconductive and leave no residue.

Clean agents were developed and commercialized in direct response to the phaseout of Halon 1301 initiated by the Montreal Protocol. The Montreal Protocol was adopted into U.S. law through the Clean Air Act of 1990. The aim of the Montreal Protocol was to reduce the emissions of chemicals that destroy stratospheric ozone. Compounds that contain bromine and, to a lesser extent, chlorine, were known to be especially detrimental to the ozone layer. Clean agents are addressed in NFPA 2001 as well as several other international standards.

Clean agents are categorized into two chemical groups, halocarbon and inert.

Halocarbon compounds are chemicals in which one or more carbon atoms are linked by covalent bonds with one or more halogen atoms: fluorine, chlorine, bromine, or iodine. Nine halocarbon agents are currently listed in NFPA 2001. None of these contain bromine, and only two contain chlorine. All contain fluorine and one contains iodine. See Table 17.7.3.

Inert clean agents consist of one of several naturally occurring inert chemicals, or mixtures of them. Four inert agents are currently listed in NFPA 2001 (see Table 17.7.4).

Carbon Dioxide

Carbon dioxide is a naturally occurring atmospheric gas. At normal room temperature and atmospheric pressure, carbon dioxide is a gas. Under certain conditions of temperature and pressure, carbon dioxide forms a liquid. For fire protection systems, it is stored as a liquid in steel containers, either by applying high pressure or by cooling the gas and applying a lower pressure.

Halon 1301

Halon 1301 is a halocarbon compound that contains bromine, and has, therefore, been deemed harmful to the stratospheric ozone layer. The Montreal Protocol targeted Halon 1301 for phaseout. Many countries have ceased production of Halon 1301 and prohibit its use in new fire-extinguishing systems. For example, the U.S. Clean Air Act of 1990 required that no new Halon 1301 be manufactured after January 1, 1994.

TABLE 17.7.3 Halocarbon Clean Agents Listed in NFPA 2001

Halocarbon Clean Agents	*Chemical Name*	*Chemical Formula*
FC-3-1-10	Perfluorobutane	C_4F_{10}
FK-5-1-12[a]	Dodecafluoro-2-methylpentan-3-one	$CF_2CF_2C(O)CF(CF_3)_2$
HCFC Blend A[b]	Dichlorotrifluoroethane HCFC-123 (4.75%)	$CHCl_2CF_3$
	Chlorodifluoromethane HCFC-22 (82%)	$CHClF_2$
	Chlorotetrafluoroethane HCFC-124 (9.5%)	$CHClFCF_3$
	Isopropenyl-1-methylcyclohexene (3.75%)	
HCFC-124	Chlorotetrafluoroethane	$CHClFCF_3$
HFC-125	Pentafluoroethane	CHF_2CF_3
HFC-227ea	Heptafluoropropane	CF_3CHFCF_3
HFC-23	Trifluoromethane	CHF_3
HFC-236fa	Hexafluoropropane	$CF_3CH_2CF_3$
FIC-13I1	Trifluoroiodide	CF_3I

Note: Other agents could become available at later dates.
[a]The full analogous ASHRAE nomenclature for FK-5-1-12 is FK-5-1-12mmy2.
[b]Composition of HCFC Blend A is given in percent by weight.

TABLE 17.7.4 Inert Clean Agents Listed in NFPA 2001

Inert Clean Agents	*Chemical Name*	*Chemical Formula*
IG-01	Argon	Ar
IG-100	Nitrogen	N_2
IG-541	Nitrogen (52%)	N_2
	Argon (40%)	Ar
	Carbon dioxide (8%)	CO_2
IG-55	Nitrogen (50%)	N_2
	Argon (50%)	Ar

Notes:
1. Other agents could become available at later dates.
2. Composition of inert gas agents are given in percent by volume.

CHARACTERISTICS OF GASEOUS AGENTS

Common Characteristics

All gaseous extinguishing agents share certain properties that are considered generally advantageous for special hazard fire-extinguishing applications. These include the following:

- They are applied to the hazard in gaseous form that is electrically nonconductive and leaves no residue.
- As a gas, these agents are able to extinguish fires even in the presence of physical barriers or obstructions.
- They are able to surround and penetrate three-dimensional fuel arrays.
- They are able to totally flood an enclosure about a hazard and be held at a design concentration to extinguish a fire.
- They are able to inert an enclosed volume for a period of time to prevent a fire or explosion from occurring.
- They do not cause direct collateral damage to equipment or materials in the protected area.

Specific Characteristics

It is important to carefully evaluate the specific characteristics of one or more gaseous extinguishing agents when looking for the optimal choice for a specific fire hazard. The characteristics most relevant to this task are the following:

- Fire extinguishing effectiveness
- Health and safety
- Environmental impact
- Cost
- Temperature range
- Collateral damage (direct or indirect)
- Availability for recharge
- Discharge pressure effects
- Local application capability

Table 17.7.5 summarizes these characteristics for each type of gaseous agent. The following sections discuss some of these characteristics in more detail.

Fire Extinguishing Effectiveness

For a given halocarbon clean agent, care must be taken to apply the minimum extinguishing concentration value for the actual Class A or B hazard to achieve the desired extinguishing effectiveness.

Class A Deep-Seated Fires. There are no standardized tests to determine the minimum extinguishing concentrations for Class A deep-seated fires. NFPA 2001 cautions that deep-seated Class A fires may require substantially higher design concentrations and longer holding times than for surface burning Class A fires. No quantified recommendations are provided by the standard. The designer should seek guidance from the system manufacturer where deep-seated Class A fires may be a concern.

Class C Fires. NFPA 2001 addresses Class C fire hazards only briefly by stating that the minimum design concentration for Class C fires should be no less than that for Class A surface-type fires. Additional guidance is provided in Annex A, which suggests that higher initial design concentrations and extended agent discharge be considered when electrical equipment cannot be de-energized. Testing of certain halocarbon clean agents on Class C fires has revealed the following:

- After initial flame extinguishment, the flame can rekindle due to the persistence of the heat energy source via the continuation of electrical energy to the fuel array.[4]
- Flame rekindling can be prevented by raising the design concentration above the minimum value required for Class A surface-burning type fires.[5,6]
- The minimum extinguishing concentration for a particular halocarbon agent is dependent on numerous variables, including the form of electrical heat energy (i.e., electric arc, ohmic, or conductive), the absence or presence of a pilot ignition source, the quantity of electric energy involved, and so forth.

Only a few of the many possible combinations of variables have been tested for some of the available halocarbon agents. Although these tests are not sufficient to be conclusive for all possible configurations of Class C hazards, two definitive recommendations are offered regarding Class C fires as follows:

- Make every possible effort to arrange for electric energy to be interrupted prior to or during agent discharge.
- If it is not possible to interrupt electric energy, consider increasing the quantity of agent for the hazard to compensate for the continuous energy being supplied to the hazard, seeking guidance from the system manufacturer.

Health and Safety

As seen in Table 17.7.5, the four types of agents vary in safety for use in normally occupied spaces. Clean agents are assigned several values used to help determine the relative health risk in the event of human exposure to a clean agent. One such value is termed "No Observed Adverse Effect Level" (NOAEL) and the other, "Lowest Observed Adverse Effect Level" (LOAEL). In the case of halocarbon clean agents, the LOAEL value is the

TABLE 17.7.5 Characteristics of Types of Gaseous Agents

	Halocarbon Clean Agents	*Inert Clean Agents*	*Carbon Dioxide*	*Halon 1301*
Fire Extinguishing Effectiveness				
For Class A and B fuels[a]	Excellent	Excellent	Excellent	Excellent
Additional agent needed for extinguishment for Class C fires	Sometimes[b]	Sometimes[b]	No	Sometimes[b]
For Class D and K fuels	May not be effective	May not be effective	May not be effective	May not be effective
Health and Safety[c]				
Primary health risk	Cardiac sensitization leading to heart arrhythmia and possibly death	Hypoxia	Death from asphyxiation	Cardiac sensitization leading to heart arrhythmia and possibly death
Considered safe for use in normally occupied spaces	Yes, when the design concentration is less than or equal to the agent's NOAEL value[d]	Yes, when the design concentration is less than or equal to the agent's NOAEL value	Only at low design concentrations	Yes, when the design concentration is 7% or less and human exposure can be limited to 15 minutes or less
Environmental Impact				
Approved for use by U.S. Environmental Protection Agency	Yes[e]	Yes[e]	Yes[e]	Generally, new systems are not allowed except in certain applications deemed essential to national defense[f]
Ozone depletion potential (ODP)	ODP = 0 for most systems and agents	ODP = 0 for all systems and agents	ODP = 0	Highest ODP of any man-made ozone-depleting substance
Global warming potential and atmospheric lifetime characteristics	Vary among agents; the impact of each agent should be evaluated individually	One agent contains a small percentage of CO_2 (see next column)	Regulated in some countries as a contributor to global warming	Has characteristics that can contribute to global warming
Cost				
Generalized system cost[g]	Agent = 25.0%; mechanical = 12.5%; electrical = 12.5%; labor = 50%	Agent = 5% mechanical = 22.5% electrical = 12.5% labor = 60%	System cost varies greatly and cannot be generalized	New systems are generally not allowed[h]
Cost of fire-resistant enclosure[i]	Can be substantial[i]	Can be substantial[j]	Can be substantial[k]	NA
Cost impact of proximity of hazard to agent refill supply	Consider a connected reserve supply of agent if the refill time from the closest supply sources is considered excessive or unacceptable	Consider a connected reserve supply of agent if the refill time from the closest supply sources is considered excessive or unacceptable	Consider a connected reserve supply of agent if the refill time from the closest supply sources is considered excessive or unacceptable	Consider a connected reserve supply of agent if the refill time from the closest supply sources is considered excessive or unacceptable
Cost impact of cylinder footprint size	Relatively small	Relatively large	Relatively large (for cylinders or tanks)	NA
Cost impact of distance between agent storage and protected hazard	Limited; increasing distance increases cost	Limited; increasing distance increases cost	Limited, but to a lesser degree than with clean agents	NA

TABLE 17.7.5 Continued

	Halocarbon Clean Agents	*Inert Clean Agents*	*Carbon Dioxide*	*Halon 1301*
Extra tall enclosure configuration may require additional levels of discharge nozzles.	Yes	Yes	Yes	NA
Temperature Range[l]				
Typical storage temperature range	32°F (0°C) to 130°F (54.4°C)	32°F (0°C) to 130°F (54.4°C)	0°F (–17.8°C) to 130°F (54.4°C) for total flooding systems[m] 32°F (0°C) to 120°F (48.9°C) for local application systems	32°F (0°C) to 130°F (54.4°C)
Temperature range for flow calculation programs	60°F (15.6°C) to 80°F (26.7°C)	60°F (15.6°C) to 80°F (26.7°C)	NA	60°F (15.6°C) and to 80°F (26.7°C)
Collateral Damage				
Contains fluorine or other substances which form potentially harmful acid gases upon breakdown.	Contain fluorine (F), which breaks down during the fire extinguishing process to form hydrogen fluoride (HF)	No	No	Contains bromine (Br) and fluorine (F), which break down during the fire extinguishing process to form hydrogen bromide (HBr) and hydrogen fluoride (HF)
Availability for Recharge[n]				
Worldwide availability of agent	Varies with agent	Varies with agent	Widely available throughout the world	Recycled Halon 1301 is readily available around the world and can be obtained at reasonable cost to recharge existing systems that have discharged
Discharge Pressure Effects in a Protected Enclosure[o]				
General guidance	Evaluate extremely tight or tall enclosures carefully	Evaluate all enclosures carefully	Evaluate all enclosures carefully	Evaluate extremely tight or tall enclosures carefully
Initial pressure effects	Momentary negative pressure spike followed by a momentary positive pressure spike	Momentary positive pressure spike	Momentary positive pressure spike	Momentary negative pressure spike followed by a momentary positive pressure spike (similar to halocarbon clean agents)
Enclosures generally strong enough to withstand pressure spikes without damage	Yes, in most cases	Usually not	No, in most cases	Yes, in most cases

(continued)

TABLE 17.7.5 Continued

	Halocarbon Clean Agents	*Inert Clean Agents*	*Carbon Dioxide*	*Halon 1301*
Considerations for extremely tight (low vent to volume ratio) or tall enclosures	Could be damaged, especially tall, brittle walls, such as those constructed of concrete block, brick, or clay tile. Evaluate carefully and provide pressure relief venting if necessary.	Must provide pressure relief venting	Must provide pressure relief venting	Could be damaged, especially tall, brittle walls, such as those constructed of concrete block, brick, or clay tile. Evaluate carefully and provide pressure relief venting if necessary.
Local Application Capability	Very limited	Very limited	Yes	Very limited

[a]Additional extinguishing agent needed for smoldering combustion (deep-seated fires) involving Class A fuels.
[b]Additional agent is needed in certain Class C fires (i.e., the required agent quantity generally increases as the electrical energy and related heat energy input to the fire increases).
[c]General guidance during system maintenance is to avoid human exposure.
[d]PBPK (physiologically based pharmacokinetic) modeling can be used to determine safe use in normally occupied spaces above the NOAEL value.
[e]Listed as acceptable alternative to Halon 1301 in EPA's SNAP program.
[f]Existing systems are allowed to remain in service in the United States; however, some countries have required that they be decommissioned.
[g]Cost of detection system increases as size of fire to be detected decreases.
[h]The costs associated with Halon 1301 systems are related to maintenance of existing systems.
[i]On rare occasions, may need to protect the enclosure from damage due to overpressure during agent discharge (total flooding systems).
[j]Usually need to protect the enclosure from damage due to overpressure during agent discharge (total flooding systems).
[k]Always need to protect the enclosure from damage due to overpressure during agent discharge (total flooding systems).
[l]For typical operating temperature range, see manufacturer's listing or approval documentation.
[m]When used outside of this temperature range, agent quantity must be adjusted.
[n]Each location needs to be evaluated for ability to recharge.
[o]Postdischarge pressure inside the enclosure reaches an equilibrium point just slightly higher than the original starting point.
NA = Not applicable.

lowest agent concentration by volume percent in air where adverse health effects were first noticed in animals being tested, which in these tests were beagle dogs. The adverse health effect observed is the onset of heart arrhythmia.

In the case of inert clean agents, the LOAEL value is the agent concentration by volume percent in air where adverse health effects are expected to occur in humans as determined by a panel of experts organized by the EPA. The panel reviewed pertinent literature regarding adverse health effects in humans exposed to hypoxic (low oxygen concentration) atmospheres and drew conclusions based on this existing body of knowledge. All inert agents are considered to be the same in relation to the determination of an appropriate LOAEL and NOAEL value.

Halocarbon Clean Agents. Table 17.7.6 provides the NOAEL and LOAEL values for the halocarbon clean agents.

Table 17.7.7 provides safe exposure limits in the unlikely event that halocarbon clean agent is discharged while one or more persons are still in the protected area.

The following example is presented to help illustrate the criteria in Tables 17.7.5 and 17.7.7 related to the use of PBPK data. Halocarbon clean agent X is proposed for use in a normally occupied space at a design concentration of 10 percent. The NOAEL value for this agent is 8 percent and the LOAEL value is 9.5 percent. Under the original human exposure rules, this proposed design could only be used for a space not normally occupied because the design concentration exceeds the LOAEL

TABLE 17.7.6 NOAEL and LOAEL Values for Halocarbon Clean Agents

Halocarbon Clean Agent	*NOAEL (Agent % by Volume)*	*LOAEL (Agent % by Volume)*
FC-3-1-10	40.0	>40.0
FK-5-1-12	10.0	>10.0
HCFC Blend A	10.0	>10.0
HFC Blend B	5.0	7.5
HCFC-124	1.0	2.5
HFC-125	7.5	10.0
HFC-227ea	9.0	>10.5
HFC-23	30.0	>30.0
HFC-236fa	10.0	15.0
FIC-13I1	0.2	0.4

TABLE 17.7.7 Safe Exposure Limits for Halocarbon Clean Agents

Agent Design %	*Occupancy*	*Exposure Time Limit*	*Comments*
≤ NOAEL	Normally occupied	Up to 5 minutes	No PBPK data needed
> NOAEL and LOAEL	Normally occupied	PBPK model limit corresponding to design concentration and 5 minute exposure	PBPK data needed
> NOAEL and LOAEL	Normally occupied	PBPK model limit corresponding to design concentration and *less than* 5 minute exposure	Conditions: 1. Authority having jurisdiction (AHJ) approval 2. Egress time calculations 3. Adhere to PBPK model exposure time limitation
> LOAEL	Not occupied	PBPK model limit corresponding to the design concentration	PBPK data needed
≤ LOAEL	Not occupied	Up to 60 seconds	No PBPK data available
> LOAEL	Not occupied	Up to 30 seconds	No PBPK data available

value. Furthermore, the design would have to ensure that occupants of the room would evacuate before agent discharge.

Application of the PBPK model allows additional flexibility. The PBPK model needs, as input, the arterial blood level measured in the beagle dog that experienced a heart arrhythmia at the LOAEL concentration of 9.5 percent. This value is loaded into the PBPK model, as is the desired design concentration of 10 percent. The PBPK model calculates the human exposure time that will allow the human arterial blood concentration of agent to reach the same level as the input value from the dog. The result is 6 minutes.

In this example, the PBPK model determines that a human being can be safely exposed to an agent concentration of 10 percent for up to 6 minutes. The second row of Table 17.7.6 applies to this case. This result indicates that the proposed design is safe for use in normally occupied spaces, and no special approvals are needed nor do any special conditions apply. The system design must limit human exposure to 5 minutes, even though the PBPK model predicts that 6 minutes is safe.

Altering this example slightly will illustrate other provisions in the safe exposure rules. Assume that the PBPK model determines that a human being can safely be exposed to an agent concentration of 10 percent for only 3 minutes. For this case, the third row of Table 17.7.7 applies. Special conditions must be satisfied to allow this proposed design to be used in a normally occupied space. Egress calculations must be performed to demonstrate that all occupants of the space can egress within 3 minutes corresponding to the PBPK model result. Widely accepted calculation methods are available and applicable for this purpose.[7–9] Furthermore, special approval from the authority having jurisdiction (AHJ) must be obtained.

Design concentrations greater than the NOAEL may be used in normally occupied spaces using PBPK modeling results corresponding to a minimum safe human exposure time of 5 minutes.

Halocarbon clean agents are considered conditionally safe for use in normally occupied spaces when design concentration exceeds the agent's NOAEL value using PBPK modeling results corresponding to a human exposure time of less than 5 minutes. This requires special approval by the AHJ. See Section 17, Chapter 6, "Halon and Halon Replacement Agents and Systems," for more information on PBPK modeling.

Inert Clean Agents. Table 17.7.8 provides the NOAEL and LOAEL values for the inert clean agents.

Table 17.7.9 provides safe exposure limits in the unlikely event that an inert clean agent is discharged while one or more persons are still in the protected area.

TABLE 17.7.8 NOAEL and LOAEL Values for Inert Clean Agents

Inert Clean Agent	*NOAEL (Agent % by Volume)*	*LOAEL (Agent % by Volume)*
IG-01	43.0	52.0
IG-100	43.0	52.0
IG-541	43.0	52.0
IG-55	43.0	52.0

TABLE 17.7.9 Safe Exposure Limits for Inert Clean Agents

Agent Design %	*Oxygen %*	*Occupancy*	*Exposure Time Limit*
≤ 43	≥ 12	Normally occupied	Up to 5 minutes
> 43 and ≤ 52	≥ 10 and < 12	Normally occupied	Up to 3 minutes
> 52 and ≤ 62	≥ 8 and < 10	Not occupied	Up to 30 seconds
> 62	< 8	Not occupied	No exposure allowed

Carbon Dioxide. At a concentration of about 9 percent, most humans will become unconscious. At 25 percent to 30 percent, respiration will suddenly stop and death will soon follow.

Collateral Damage

Halocarbon clean agents and Halon 1301 contain fluorine (F), which breaks down during flame extinguishment and forms hydrogen fluoride. Hydrogen fluoride (HF) is a weak acid that in small concentrations can cause mild irritation in exposed humans in the upper respiratory tract and eyes. HF in sufficiently high concentrations can be debilitating to humans and cause damage to exposed equipment.

Availability for Recharge

The many halocarbon clean agents and several inert clean agents differ in their availability for recharging a system after it has discharged. Some are widely available throughout the world. Some are not as widely available and may require a significant amount of time to accomplish a system recharge.

Discharge Pressure Effects in a Protected Enclosure

In the case of Halon 1301 systems with extremely tight or tall enclosures, enclosure damage due to pressure spikes during total flooding system discharge has been rare. This is due in large part to the fact that Halon 1301 enclosures have a relatively high vent to volume ratio. That is, they are much leakier than enclosures that are protected by halocarbon or inert clean agents.

Local Application Capability

Halocarbon Clean Agents. Historically, halocarbon clean agents have been used primarily in total flooding applications. NFPA 2001 applies only to total flooding systems. Local application systems are, therefore, excluded. One halocarbon agent has been developed for use in hazard-specific local application and partial-flooding applications. These systems are typically proven by individual test to the satisfaction of the purchaser or approval authority.

Inert Clean Agents. Inert clean agents discharge from the nozzles as a gas with no liquid component. It is very difficult to direct this gaseous discharge precisely for any distance from the nozzle. Inert clean agents, therefore, have not been developed for local application use.

Carbon Dioxide. Carbon dioxide is stored in liquefied form inside pressure containers. In high-pressure systems, carbon dioxide is stored at 70°F (21°C) at a pressure of 850 psi (5860 kPa). In low-pressure systems, the carbon dioxide is stored at a controlled low temperature of 0°F (–18°C). At this temperature the pressure in the container is 300 psi (2068 kPa). As carbon dioxide liquid flows from the storage containers to the discharge nozzles, it absorbs heat and begins to gasify. It does not fully gasify in the pipe network; therefore, a portion of the discharge from the nozzles is still in liquid form. This characteristic enables carbon dioxide to be configured in local applications systems and to protect hazards that are partially enclosed or completely unenclosed.

Halon 1301. Halon 1301 gasifies in very close proximity to the discharge nozzles; therefore, it is not well suited for use in local application systems. Local application systems using Halon 1301 have been very uncommon. Those that exist now, or existed in the past, most likely were protecting hazards with enclosures that had uncloseable openings making it impossible for the agent to be retained for at least 10 minutes, as was commonly required of total flooding applications. These systems are typically proven by individual test to the satisfaction of the purchaser or approval authority.

PERFORMANCE-BASED ANALYSIS IN AGENT SELECTION

Steps in Performance-Based Analysis and Design

The *SFPE Engineering Guide to Performance-Based Fire Protection: Analysis and Design*[10] offers an excellent performance-based engineering methodology that can easily be adapted to the process of selecting clean agents. The *Guide* defines performance-based design as follows:

> An engineering approach to fire protection design based on (1) agreed upon fire safety goals and objectives, (2) deterministic and/or probabilistic analysis of fire scenarios, and (3) quantitative assessment of design alternatives against the fire safety goals and objectives using accepted engineering tools, methodologies, and performance criteria.

Performance-based analysis and design offers a number of benefits over other design methods, including maximized value, reliability, and effectiveness. The process of performance-based analysis and design, as detailed in the guide, includes eight generic steps, preceded by a preliminary unnumbered step of identifying stakeholders. Table 17.7.10 lists those steps and presents the first two steps of an example related to gaseous agent selection for a generic corporate data center that incorporates sophisticated electronic data processing and telecommunications equipment. It also contains some limited administrative office space for occupants with responsibilities for the operations. The operations are contained within a single room on the first floor of a two-story building of noncombustible construction. The room is fully sprinklered using a double-interlock preaction configuration. The data center room is cut off from surrounding spaces by 1 hour fire rated, full-height walls, and contains an 18-in. (46-cm) raised access floor and a suspended acoustical ceiling at the 10 ft elevation. The room covers 20,000 feet^2 (1858 m^2) and is occupied by 18 persons during the day shift, 8 persons during the evening shift, and 3 persons during the night shift. All occupants are well-trained, full-time employees of the end user. All occupants are capable of self-preservation without assistance.

TABLE 17.7.10 Steps in Performance-Based Analysis and Initial Application to Gaseous Agent Selection

Step	*Activity*
1	Define the project scope. Select the optimum gaseous extinguishing agent for this corporate data center.
2	Identify the project goals and prioritize them. a. Minimize interruption of the company's business operations where such interruption would harm a customer's business, harm a customer's relationship with the company, harm the company's brands, or otherwise prevent accomplishment of the mission. b. Prevent loss of life or serious injury to building occupants and emergency responders. c. Minimize damage to the company's physical assets.
3	Define the project objectives.
4	Develop the performance criteria.
5	Develop design fire scenarios.
6	Develop trial designs.
7	Evaluate and modify the trial designs.
8	Select the final design.

Stakeholder Identification

The purpose of the preliminary step is to identify key stakeholders so that all primary system performance objectives can be identified and evaluated.

Step 1: Define the Project Scope

The project scope defines the boundaries of the performance-based analysis or design. If the scope of the project were more complex, it would be advisable to identify all of the stakeholders and solicit their input in defining project scope. Developing a consensus of the stakeholders relative to the project scope will improve the quality and overall acceptance of the results. The guide defines stakeholder as "one who has a share or interest in an enterprise. Specifically, an individual (or representative) interested in the successful completion of a project."

A list of stakeholders typical to a gaseous extinguishing system design project might include, but not necessarily be limited to, the following:

- Business owner (end user)
- Design team
- AHJs (building, fire, insurance)
- Construction team (construction manager, general contractor, subcontractors)
- Gaseous extinguishing agent and system manufacturers

Step 2: Identify and Prioritize the Project Goals

One or more of three general goals is commonly assigned to most fire protection analysis or design projects: (1) prevent loss of life or serious injury due to fire or its effects, (2) minimize loss of property due to fire or its effects, and (3) minimize interruption of business operations due to fire or its effects (also referred to as mission preservation).

All three of these general fire protection goals are applicable to most projects that consider the use of gaseous extinguishing agents. In the performance-based example that follows, the goal of minimizing business interruption is considered by the stakeholder group to be the biggest challenge (see Table 17.7.10). Therefore, this goal is listed first. Gaseous extinguishing agents, for example, are widely used to protect operations that utilize computerized electronic data processing, telecommunications, and broadcasting equipment. It is paramount to keep interruptions to such operations to an absolute minimum in the event of a fire. Preserving the mission is critical. Accomplishing this goal will usually also substantially achieve the second goal of preventing loss of life or serious injury. Protecting people is always important. For many gaseous extinguishing agent applications, such as those mentioned above, the expected fires are relatively low-energy fires that are not likely to threaten the occupants in the immediate surrounding areas before they are able to escape safely. However, gaseous extinguishing agents are also commonly employed to protect hazards involving flammable or combustible liquids, such as engine rooms on ships, where fast large fires are expected.

Step 3: Define the Project Objectives

This step involves identification of the stakeholder objectives to meet the project goals. The various stakeholders might define these objectives in different terms; however, they should be clear and agreed to by all stakeholders. In the example begun in Table 17.7.10, there are multiple goals. Table 17.7.11 presents hypothetical stakeholder and design objectives related to those multiple goals, as well as performance criteria.

Minimize Interruption of the Company's Business. For example, the company can establish an objective to limit interruption of telecommunication operations to no more than 4 hours. The insurance stakeholder may state an objective to limit interruption

TABLE 17.7.11 Hypothetical Objectives and Performance Criteria

Stakeholder Objective	*Design Objective*	*Performance Criteria*
Minimize interruption of the company's business operations where such interruption would harm a customer's business, harm a customer's relationship with the company, harm the company's brands, or otherwise prevent accomplishment of the mission.		
1. Limit interruption of all critical telecommunications operations to no more than 4 hours. 2. Limit interruption of all noncritical telecommunications operations to 48 hours. 3. Maintain power to all critical telecommunications equipment during a fire to minimize interruption of operations and customer services.	1. Limit damage to all critical equipment from a fire, fire effects, and suppression effects to one, or several, individual components that can be replaced or restored to full service in less than 4 hours. 2. Limit damage to all noncritical telecommunications equipment from a fire, fire effects, and suppression effects to equipment, or equipment components, that can be replaced or restored to full service in less than 48 hours. 3. Supply power to all critical telecommunications equipment independently from any manual or automatic emergency power off (EPO) systems. The gaseous extinguishing agent must be capable of extinguishing fires in energized electrical equipment.	1. Extinguish the fire at or below 2 kW (1.9 Btu/sec).* 2. Limit the production of halide acids to a concentration within the protected space of 200 ppm or less. 3. Extinguish a fire in energized electrical equipment and prevent re-ignition for the specified hold time or at least 10 minutes.
Prevent loss of life or serious injury to building occupants and emergency responders.		
1. No loss of life and no serious injuries to occupants of the protected enclosure from fire or products of combustion. 2. No loss of life and no serious injuries to occupants of the surrounding areas from fire or products of combustion. 3. No loss of life and no serious injuries to occupants of the protected enclosure from direct exposure to the gaseous extinguishing agent or its decomposition products. 4. No loss of life and no serious injuries to occupants of the surrounding areas from direct exposure to the gaseous extinguishing agent or its decomposition products. 5. Minimize short-term and long-term harm to the natural environment from the gaseous extinguishing agent or arising from the process of accomplishing final fire extinguishment.	1. The smoke layer and radiation heat flux from all feasible and reasonably conservative design fire scenarios must not cross thresholds harmful to the occupants of the protected space before they are able to exit the space. 2. The smoke layer, and radiation heat flux, from all feasible and reasonably conservative design fire scenarios must not cross thresholds harmful to the occupants of the areas surrounding the protected space before they are able to exit these areas to the building exterior. 3. The gaseous extinguishing agent selected must not be harmful to the occupants of the protected space in the required design concentration, and must not produce acidic decomposition products during the extinguishing process that could be harmful to an occupant inadvertently remaining in the protected space following gaseous extinguishing agent discharge. 4. The gaseous extinguishing agent selected must not be harmful in the required design concentration	1. The design concentration for the gaseous extinguishing agent for Class C fires (energized electrical equipment) must be at or below the level corresponding to a maximum 5-minute human exposure time as defined in NFPA 2001. 2. Extinguish the fire at or below 2 kW (1.9 Btu/sec). 3. Limit the production of halide acids to a concentration within the protected space of 200 ppm or less 4. The negative and positive pressure changes during the discharge of the gaseous extinguishing agent must be controllable to a magnitude of 5 psf (239 Pa) or less. 5. The gaseous extinguishing agent must have an ozone depletion factor (ODP) of 0, a relatively low atmospheric lifetime and global warming potential, and must not contain HFC compounds, or carbon dioxide.

TABLE 17.7.11 Continued

Stakeholder Objective	*Design Objective*	*Performance Criteria*
	to the occupants of the areas surrounding the protected space, and must not produce acidic decomposition products during the extinguishing process that could be harmful to occupants that remain in the building following gaseous extinguishing agent discharge. The integrity of the enclosure construction surrounding the protected area must remain during and following gaseous extinguishing agent discharge. 5. The selected gaseous extinguishing agent must be approved for use in normally occupied spaces by the U.S. EPA's SNAP program, and must not be targeted for reduction or phaseout in the Kyoto Protocol.	
Minimize damage to the company's physical assets.		
Minimize the loss of physical assets (real and personal property) to no more than $1,000,000.	Limit damage to all critical equipment from a fire, fire effects, and suppression effects to one, or several, individual components that can be replaced in less than 4 hours, or noncritical equipment components that can be replaced in less than 48 hours. Do not allow an entire piece of equipment, equipment cabinet, or equipment rack to be destroyed by a fire or fire effects.	1. Extinguish the fire at or below 2 kW (1.9 Btu/sec).* 2. Limit the production of halide acids to a concentration within the protected space of 200 ppm or less. 3. Extinguish a fire in energized electrical equipment and prevent reignition for the specified hold time or at least 10 minutes.

*For more information, see Meacham, B. J., "Factors Effecting the Early Detection of Fire in Electronic Equipment and Cable Installations," *Fire Technology,* first quarter 1993.

of telecommunication operations to no more than 24 hours. By selecting a final limit of 4 hours, both stakeholders are satisfied.

Once the consensus stakeholder objectives have been identified, the design engineer translates them into concise design objectives. Design objectives are stated in terms that can be subsequently quantified in fire protection engineering terms and used to develop specific performance criteria.

For the goal of minimizing business interruption, the third stakeholder objective of maintaining power usually does not find easy consensus among all stakeholders. Typically the end user and the insurance authority might be in agreement that electric power should not be interrupted to critical equipment. The building and fire code authorities might prefer automatically interrupting power to all equipment prior to application of the gaseous extinguishing agent. After negotiations, the building and fire code authorities may agree to allow power to remain uninterrupted. The design engineer may assist in reaching consensus on this objective by offering to select and design a gaseous extinguishing agent system such that it is capable of extinguishing fires in electrical equipment that remains continuously energized.

Prevent Loss of Life or Serious Injury. The fifth stakeholder objective for this goal is to minimize harm to the natural environment. Normally, only the end user stakeholder would identify an objective such as this. The other stakeholders might easily reach consensus to include this objective, since it likely will not conflict with their interests. Some end users have set such objectives to achieve harmony with their corporation's environmental policies. It is shown here to illustrate that environmental factors can be a strong determining factor in the selection process of a gaseous extinguishing agent and should always be considered in the performance-based analysis process.

Step 4: Define the Performance Criteria

Performance criteria for the gaseous extinguishing agent must be developed that will satisfy the design objectives (listed in

Step 3) and be used to evaluate the trial designs (candidate gaseous extinguishing agents). Table 17.7.11 presented sample performance criteria for the hypothetical example.

Step 5: Define the Design Fire Scenarios

The purpose of a gaseous extinguishing system is to extinguish a fire. It is therefore necessary for the design engineer to analyze the possible fire scenarios that are plausible for the protected space. These are then reduced to a reasonable number and called *design fire scenarios* that represent the boundaries of the conditions present. Only then is it possible for the design engineer to begin evaluating possible gaseous extinguishing agents for selection.

Possible fire scenarios should address the heat sources and fuel involved in fire ignition and growth. They should address the building construction, service equipment, and spatial relationships that might influence or be affected by the fire. They should address the human element, such as the number and distribution of occupants, their emergency response training and commitment, and their physical and psychological conditions related to self-preservation abilities.

Listed below are summaries of possible fire scenarios for the example of the corporate data center used to illustrate performance-based analysis and design, as summarized in Table 17.7.10.

Possible Fire Scenario 1. An electric drive motor in a high-speed data storage unit overheats due to an internal failure. Insulation on the internal windings ignites, leading to a fire that spreads to adjacent combustibles inside the equipment enclosure.

Possible Fire Scenario 2. A manufacturer's defect on a printed circuit board inside a telecommunications equipment module within an equipment rack leads to localized overheating and ignition of the board. The fire spreads to adjacent boards until it involves the entire module, and then spreads until it involves the entire rack.

Possible Fire Scenario 3. Two electrical extension cords are connected to a wall outlet and extended to a nearby work desk module where four workers share its power simultaneously. The two cords are draped over the top of an open box of paper forms. Their interconnection point is only partially engaged and is resting on top of the paper forms. The connection point overheats and ignites the box and the paper forms. Initially, this fire is a Class A surface fire but, if not extinguished early, has the potential to become a deep-seated Class A fire. The fire could then spread to involve the entire box of forms and begin heating adjacent racks of telecommunications components.

Possible Fire Scenario 4. An electrical fault in a power circuit within a data processing equipment enclosure results in sustained electrical arcing, which is not interrupted by the circuit fault protection device. The heat from the continuous arcing ignites cable insulation that spreads to other cables and combustible components within the equipment cabinet. If not extinguished early, this fire could spread to fully involve the original equipment cabinet and spread to adjacent equipment and other combustibles. Ultimately, the spreading fire would have enough energy to activate the sprinkler system in the room. This is a Class C fire. It would become a Class A surface fire on interruption of electrical power to the equipment involved.

The preceding fire scenarios are just a few representative examples of the relatively large number of those possible for such an operation. The full range of possible fire scenarios must be identified, then reduced to a smaller, more manageable number of design fire scenarios, which will be used to evaluate trial designs to select a final, optimized design. For this example, the four possible fire scenarios are narrowed down to a single design fire scenario, which will be used to evaluate the suitability of the trial designs. In this case the design fire scenario 5 is the same as possible fire scenario 4.

Step 6: Develop Trial Designs

Trial designs should be developed that have the potential to achieve the performance criteria. The design fire scenarios are used to test the effectiveness of each trial design, with the results being analyzed to help narrow the trial designs to one or two that are most effective. Applying this process to the task of selecting a gaseous extinguishing agent is relatively simple, since it involves only one of the several subsystems that are part of a complete gaseous extinguishing agent fire-extinguishing system. In the context of this example, a single agent is a trial design. Multiple trial designs (i.e., agents) should be considered. Each agent should be evaluated to ensure it meets the stated goals and objectives.

Step 7: Evaluate and Modify the Trial Designs

The trial designs should be evaluated to determine if they satisfy the performance criteria when challenged by the design fire scenarios. If a trial design is successful, the next trial design would be evaluated, and so on. If a trial design is not successful, it might be modified and retested or eliminated from consideration. In this manner, all trial designs are optimized (i.e., evaluated, modified, or eliminated) until one or more acceptable designs are developed.

Step 8: Select the Final Design

The acceptable designs should be further evaluated and one chosen as the final design. All performance criteria should be reviewed and compared to the capabilities of each acceptable design. Secondary criteria that are important to any stakeholder should also be evaluated in an effort to identify the design that is optimal for this particular project. Considerations include availability of agent, agent storage and space requirements, cost of system, complexity of system, and life cycle costs of the system.

SUMMARY

Until the late 1980s, there were predominantly two gaseous agents to choose from to protect significant mission-critical hazards that required either a local application approach (carbon dioxide) or total flooding approach (Halon 1301 or carbon dioxide). Since the advent of the Montreal Protocol and the U.S. Clean Air Act of 1990, several new gaseous agents have been developed, and regulations have emerged aimed at safeguarding human health relative to exposure to gaseous fire extinguishants.

Fire hazards and gaseous fire extinguishants possess certain characteristics that make it possible to optimize the selection of one or more agents to protect a given fire hazard. A performance-based decision methodology was developed that can provide a consistent and repeatable framework for the selection of gaseous extinguishants and systems optimized for a particular hazard.

The performance-based analysis and design process illustrated in this chapter summarized the steps necessary to selecting a gaseous extinguishing agent that is best suited for the example project. The gaseous extinguishing agent must have the capability to enable all primary, and some secondary, performance criteria to be achieved, assuming that the remaining subsystems are properly designed and installed.

The examples used to illustrate the performance-based analysis and design process were greatly oversimplified. The reader is encouraged to review the *SFPE Engineering Guide to Performance-Based Fire Protection: Analysis and Design* in detail and study the many design variables that influence the performance of gaseous agent fire-extinguishing systems using each of the available gaseous extinguishing agents. Each of them have performance strengths and weaknesses that, when properly evaluated, would result in one or more agents being an acceptable candidate for each particular application.

BIBLIOGRAPHY

References Cited

1. Quintiere, J., "Surface Flame Spread," *SFPE Handbook of Fire Protection Engineering,* 3rd ed., P. J. DiNenno et al. (Eds.), National Fire Protection Association, Quincy, MA, 2002.
2. Ohlemiller, T. J., "Smoldering Combustion," *SFPE Handbook of Fire Protection Engineering,* 3rd ed., P. J. DiNenno et al. (Eds.), National Fire Protection Association, Quincy, MA, 2002.
3. Robin, M. L., Harry, L. D., Meltzer, J. S., and Calciano, D. L., "Development of Room Pressure in the Discharge of FM-200®, Compared to the Strength of Various Structural Components," Halon Options Technical Working Conference, 1997.
4. Driscoll, M. R., and Rivers, P. E., "Clean Extinguishing Agents and Continuously Energized Circuits: Recent Findings," Halon Options Technical Working Conference, 1997.
5. Flamm, J., Niemann, R., and Bengston, G., "Continuing the Examination and Comparison of Existing Halon Alternatives in Preventing Re-Ignition on Continuously Energized Fires," Halon Options Technical Working Conference, 1995.
6. McKenna, L. A., Gottuk, D. T., and DiNenno, P. J., "Extinguishment Tests of Continuously Energized Class C Fires," Halon Options Technical Working Conference, May 12–14, 1998.
7. Fahy, R. F., "Calculation Methods for Egress Predictions," *Fire Protection Handbook,* 19th ed., A. E. Cote (Ed.), National Fire Protection Association, Quincy, MA, 2003.
8. Proulx, G., "Movement of People: The Evacuation Timing," *SFPE Handbook of Fire Protection Engineering,* 3rd ed., P. J. DiNenno et al. (Eds.), National Fire Protection Association, Quincy, MA, 2002.
9. Nelson, H. E., and Mowrer, F. W., "Emergency Movement," *SFPE Handbook of Fire Protection Engineering,* 3rd ed., P. J. DiNenno et al. (Eds.), National Fire Protection Association, Quincy, MA, 2002.
10. Custer, R. L. P., and Meacham, B. J., *SFPE Engineering Guide to Performance-Based Fire Protection: Analysis and Design of Buildings,* National Fire Protection Association, Quincy, MA, 2000.

NFPA Codes, Standards, and Recommended Practices

Reference to the following NFPA codes, standards, and recommended practices will provide further information on the application of gaseous agents to special hazards, as discussed in this chapter. (See the latest version of The NFPA Catalog *for availability of current editions of the following documents.)*

NFPA 10, *Standard for Portable Fire Extinguishers*
NFPA 12, *Standard on Carbon Dioxide Extinguishing Systems*
NFPA 12A, *Standard on Halon 1301 Fire Extinguishing Systems*
NFPA 13, *Standard for the Installation of Sprinkler Systems*
NFPA 17, *Standard for Dry Chemical Extinguishing Systems*
NFPA 17A, *Standard for Wet Chemical Extinguishing Systems*
NFPA 72®, National Fire Alarm Code®
NFPA 75, *Standard for the Protection of Information Technology Equipment*
NFPA 430, *Code for the Storage of Liquid and Solid Oxidizers*
NFPA 2001, *Standard on Fire Clean Agent Extinguishing Systems*

Chapter 8

Explosion Prevention and Protection

Erdem A. Ural ❑ Henry W. Garzia

Chapter Contents

Key Terms

deflagration, dust explosion, explosibility, explosion, explosion control, flame arrester, flame front diverter, flammable limit, flammable mixture, fuel control, hazard analysis, ignition control, inert gas, limiting oxidant concentration (LOC), minimum ignition energy (MIE)

In literature, the word *explosion* is used to express a number of different chemical or physical processes. Some of these processes are outlined in Section 2, Chapter 8, "Explosions." This chapter focuses only on deflagrations where, by definition, the combustion reaction front propagates through a nearly premixed fuel-air mixture at a velocity less than the speed of sound in the unburnt mixture. The fuel may be in the form of a gas, vapor, dust, mist, or a combination. The definition provided in NFPA 68, *Standard on Explosion Protection by Deflagration Venting,* and NFPA 69, *Standard on Explosion Prevention Systems,* further limit the meaning of the word *explosion* to "the bursting or rupture of an enclosure or a container due to the development of internal pressure from a deflagration."

For related topics, see Section 2, Chapter 8, "Explosions"; Section 6, Chapter 8, "Dusts"; Section 9, Chapter 7, "Storage and Handling of Grain Mill Products"; and Section 18, Chapter 6, "Deflagration (Explosion) Venting."

EVENTS LEADING TO AN EXPLOSION

Explosions often have catastrophic consequences. Fortunately, explosions occur only when a number of preceding events take place almost simultaneously. Table 17.8.1 lists a generic chain of events that can lead to an explosion. Examples of the hazard tests to characterize the material, equipment, or process, as well as the possible means of engineering intervention that can be used to break the chain are also listed in Table 17.8.1. It should be pointed out that the generic list provided in Table 17.8.1 might not cover all possible processes and that not all steps listed play a key role in each situation.

Unless dust is kept suspended in the air by design, most dust explosions start with a disturbance that raises dust into suspension. The disturbance could be as simple as the rupture of a compressed air line, a mechanical jolt to beams where dust layers have accumulated, or a small explosion somewhere else in the plant. Once subjected to the disturbance, the amount of dust removed from the deposit is a property of the dust and how the layer was formed.[1] These steps obviously do not play a role in gas or vapor explosions.

Once the fuel is released into an enclosure, it mixes with air and forms flammable volumes. The size of the flammable volume is controlled by the fuel supply rate and the ventilation/recirculation conditions inside the enclosure; it directly affects the severity of the explosion, if ignited. Therefore, control of the fuel supply rate and proper ventilation are frequently practiced methods of explosion prevention or protection.

A flammable fuel-air mixture can be ignited by a number of possible ignition sources. In critical applications, credible strength of ignition sources can be evaluated and compared to the

Erdem A. Ural is an independent explosion protection/investigation consultant for Loss Prevention Science and Technologies, Inc., in Stoughton, Massachusetts. Previously, he worked at FM Global and Fenwal. He is chair of the ASTM E27.04 Subcommittee on Ignitability and Flammability of Chemicals, a member of the NFPA Technical Committee on Explosion Protection Systems, and the chair of the American Institute of Chemical Engineers (AIChE) Committee on Loss Prevention.

Henry W. Garzia is the systems design manager of the Industrial Explosion Protection Group of Fenwal Protection Systems. He is a member of the NFPA Technical Committee on Handling and Conveying of Dusts, Vapors, and Gases.

TABLE 17.8.1 Generic Chain of Events That Can Lead to an Explosion

Steps of Explosion (Gas, Vapor, Dust, Mist)	*Material/Enclosure/Process Hazard Characterization*	*Possible Means of Engineering Intervention*
Disturbance	Maximum credible leak size	Avoid disturbances
	Maximum credible pressure	Redirect disturbances to a safe location
Entrainment of dust deposits	Particle size distribution	Eliminate/limit dust deposits (refer to p. 17-150, "Housekeeping")
	Critical shear stress	Spray dust deposits (with oil or water)
Fuel dispersion	Turbulence inside enclosure	Minimize fuel source
	Ventilation/recirculation	Improve ventilation
	Localization of flammable mixtures	
Mixture flammability	LFL and UFL for gases and vapors	Fuel control (refer to p. 17-149, "Fuel Control")
	MEC for dusts	Oxygen control
	Limiting oxygen concentration	
Credible ignition sources	Open flames	Eliminate ignition sources (refer to p. 17-150, "Ignition Source Control")
	Heated volumes or surfaces	
	Static electricity	
	Lightning	
	Stray currents	
	Mechanical sparks, friction, impact and vibration	
Material ignitability	Electrostatic ignition (MIE)	Material additives
	Hot surface ignition	Change particle size distribution
	Hot volume ignition temperature	
Material reactivity	Peak pressure	Material additives
	Peak rate of pressure rise	Change particle size distribution
	Burning velocity	
	Deflagration-to-detonation transition propensity	
Flame propagation	Turbulent flame speeds	Arrest flame propagation
	Flame accelerations induced by geometry	Explosion suppression (refer to p. 17-155, "Deflagration Suppression")
		Explosion isolation (refer to p. 17-157, "Deflagration Isolation")
Pressure development	Heat released by combustion	Pressure containment (refer to p. 17-154, "Pressure Containment")
		Explosion suppression (refer to p. 17-155, "Deflagration Suppression")
	Heat lost by radiation/convective cooling	Explosion venting
	Mass lost by venting	
Damage to	Mechanical damage due to overpressure	Improved mechanical design
People	Projectiles	Projectile control
Equipment	Thermal damage (people are vulnerable)	Thermal protection (passive or active)
Physical		
Plant	Chemical damage	
Environment	Environmental damage	

ignition requirement of the fuel-air mixtures. Such an exercise may reveal whether elimination of ignition sources is a viable prevention method for the particular application.

Once ignition takes place, the reaction front (flame) moves toward the unburnt fuel-air mixture with a well-defined velocity, called the burning velocity. If the enclosure is practically unvented, the maximum explosion pressure is related to the heat of combustion of the fuel-air mixture. Fully confined deflagrations commonly develop pressures in the range of seven to ten times the initial absolute pressure, or 100 to 140 psig (7 to 10 barg). If the enclosure has large openings, then the maximum explosion pressure is also related to the burning velocity and the maximum flame surface area. Pre-existing turbulence conditions inside the enclosure, turbulence induced by flame propagation, and the geometry of the enclosure can increase both the burning velocity and the maximum flame surface area.

Process enclosures are seldom designed for pressure containment. Pressures at which enclosure failure occurs can be quite low, particularly for enclosures of rectangular sheet metal construction. These can fail completely at internal pressures of a few pounds per in.^{2} (psi [1 psi = 6.895 kPa]). Typically, buildings can tolerate only a fraction of 1 psi pressure. Active and passive suppression and isolation methods can be used to limit the extent of flame propagation and magnitude of the pressure increase caused by an explosion.

If allowed to proceed uncontrollably, an explosion can cause harm to the physical plant, to people, and to the environment. In addition to the pressure damage considered in the NFPA 68/69 definition, an explosion can do the following:

- Hurt people (by skin burns,[2] eardrum rupture, lung collapse, body translation, toxic unburnt/burnt material)
- Create projectiles and fireballs that can lead to domino effects
- Pollute the environment
- Interrupt production
- Start fires

EXPLOSION HAZARD ANALYSIS

Conducting a thorough and competent process hazard analysis is perhaps the most important task of any explosion prevention or protection project. Such an analysis should consider the entire process chain, all the buildings, enclosures, and interconnections. The process analysis generally includes, but is not limited to, review of the general scope of work, process design criteria, process description, material flow diagrams, bases for fire and explosion protection methods and systems, basis for the physical and chemical properties of the process materials, equipment layouts, detailed mechanical drawings and specifications, supporting engineering calculations, and process and instrumentation diagrams. This analysis should consider startup, normal operation, normal shutdown, temporary operations, and emergency shutdowns. The analysis should also consider the hazards that can be created by the explosion prevention and protection systems. It is essential to update this analysis periodically, as well as each time changes are made to the process and to the protection systems. A detailed description of the explosion hazard analysis is beyond the scope of this chapter. Examples can be found in *Guidelines for Hazard Evaluation Procedures*, American Institute of Chemical Engineers, 1992.[3]

Figure 17.8.1 shows a simplified flowchart for dust explosion prevention and protection philosophy, adapted from material in R. K. Eckhoff's *Dust Explosions in the Process Industries.*[4] Within each appropriate box, the relevant ASTM E27 test method that can be used to characterize material hazard properties is listed. Standardized tests are often performed to characterize the hazard properties of materials. A comprehensive menu of such tests can be assembled from the standards of ASTM (American Society for Testing and Materials International), CEN (European Committee for Standardisation [Comité Européen de Normalisation]), CENELEC (European Committee for Electrotechnical Standardization [Comité Européen de Normalisation Electrotechnique]), DIN (German Institute for Standardization [Deutsches Institut für Normung]), VDI (Association of German Engineers [Verein Deutscher Ingenieure]), IEC (International Electrotechnical Commission), ISO (International Organization for Standardization), NFPA (National Fire Protection Association), and the UN (United Nations). Although a comprehensive review of the tests used to characterize material flammability, ignitability, and explosibility is beyond the scope of this chapter, a tabulation of the ASTM tests pertaining to explosion prevention and protection and simplified conceptual descriptions of key test methods are provided. A more detailed description can be found in "The Role of ASTM E27 Methods in Hazard Assessment."[5]

Fuel-Air Mixture Flammability

The classic notion of the "fire triangle" is that an ignition source must come together with both fuel and oxidant, the latter usually being atmospheric oxygen, in order to initiate and sustain a fire. This representation, although convenient, oversimplifies the more complex requirements needed to sustain a deflagration, particularly regarding fuel and oxygen concentration requirements. A flammability diagram can be used to illustrate, in composition space, the boundary that divides mixtures of fuel, oxygen, and inert components into flammable and nonflammable regions. Figure 17.8.2 is an example of one of the several types of such representations.

The three-component (ternary) diagram is plotted as a triangular graph, with each corner representing fuel, oxidant, or inert gas. Where appropriate, the oxidant may be taken as air, or other separately managed stream containing the oxidizing species, and the inert gas as only added inert components not associated with atmospheric air. Only two components are plotted in some diagrams, the concentration of the third being determined by the difference from 100 percent. The lower and upper flammable limits are two limiting points on such a diagram for compositions having no added inert component. (See Bodhurtha,[6] Lewis,[7] and Strehlow[8] for more detailed discussions on flammability.)

Dust-air mixtures also display a lower flammability limit (often called the minimum explosible concentration [MEC]), which is comparable in magnitude (on the order of 50 g/m^3) to that for gases and vapors. An extensive compilation of MEC data for generic dust samples can be found in Eckhoff.[4] Although

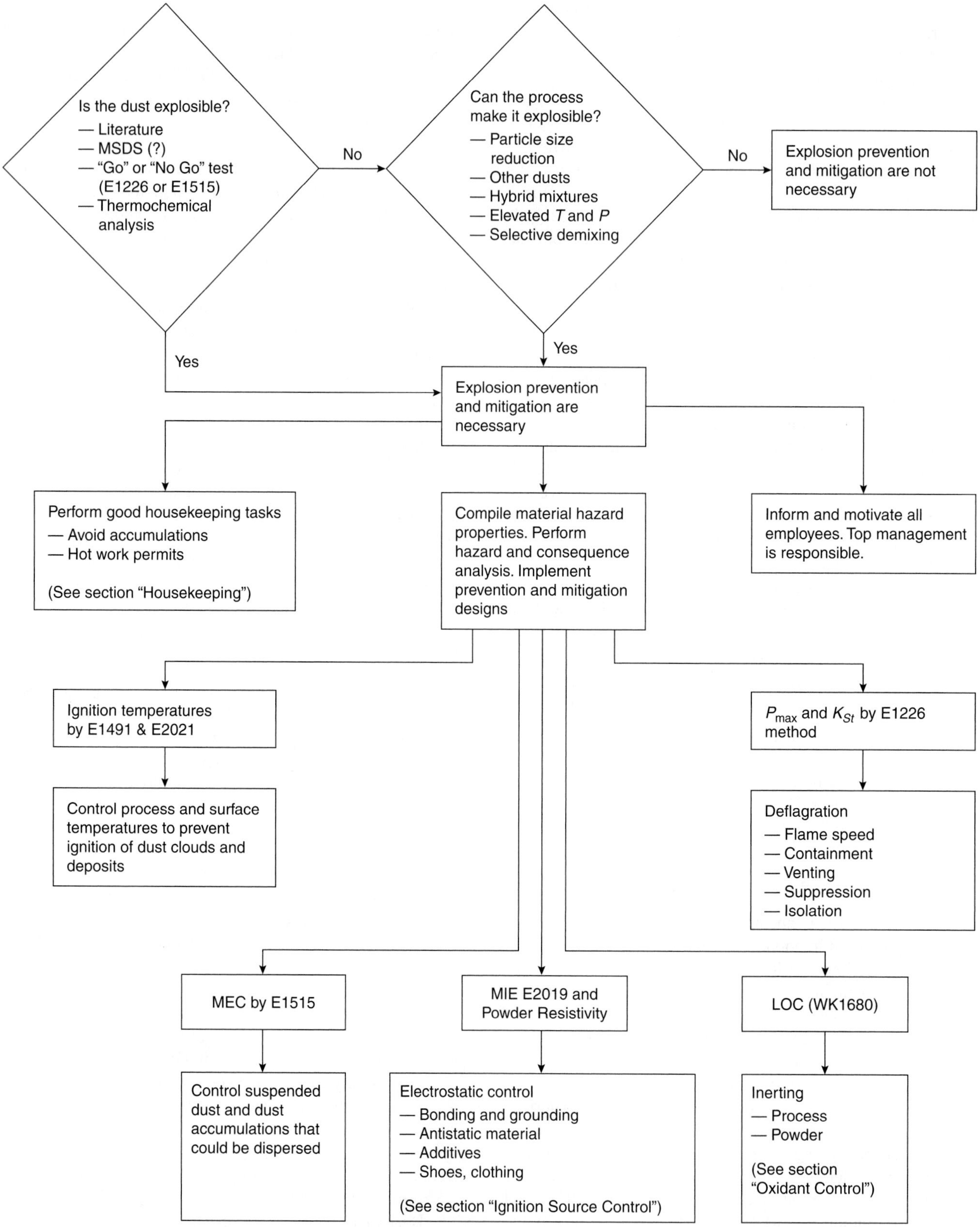

FIGURE 17.8.1 Dust Explosion Protection Philosophy. LOC = Limiting oxygen concentration. WK1680 = The ASTM draft standard for limiting oxidant concentration determination of dust samples. (Source: Adapted from Eckhoff, R. K., *Dust Explosions in the Process Industries,* Butterworth, Heinemann, Boston, 1991)

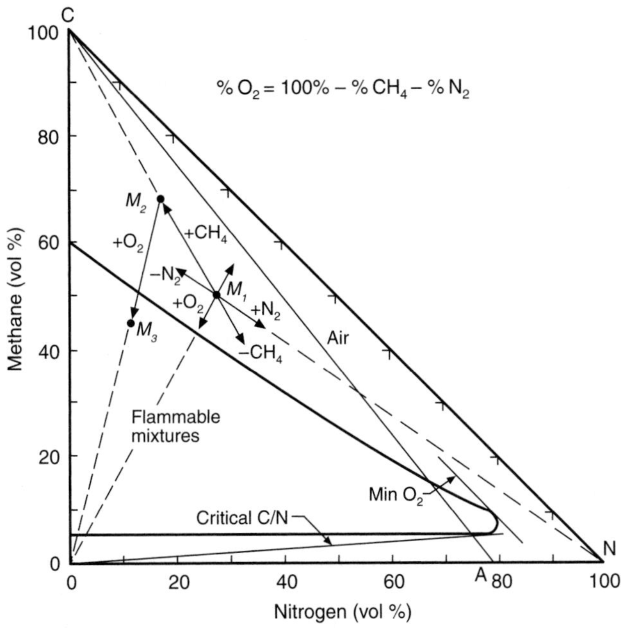

FIGURE 17.8.2 Flammability Diagram for Methane-Air-Oxygen System in Triangular Format (Source: Zabetakis, M. G., "Flammability Characteristics of Combustible Gases and Vapors," Bulletin 627, U.S. Bureau of Mines, Washington, DC, 1965)

sometimes academically debated, there is no practical upper flammability limit for dust-air mixtures because such high concentrations are difficult to produce and control.

An important part of deflagration prevention is maintaining atmospheres in process volumes that are nonflammable. This may be achieved by using any of several techniques, either singly or in combination. These include reduction of airborne concentrations of gaseous, dusty, or misted fuels. Alternatively, the concentration of the oxidant may be reduced. Finally, a nonflammable component, such as inert gas, may be added to the atmosphere. Thus, the composition of the atmosphere within a process volume that has the potential to be in the flammable range is controlled to prevent this condition.

Flammability properties of materials generally depend on temperature and pressure.[9] In the case of dusts, particle size distribution and moisture content can also play a significant role.

Fuel-Air Mixture Ignitability

Ignition of a flammable mixture occurs when a critical mass is heated to a temperature above the ignition temperature of the mixture. For example, all incandescent sparks (e.g., mechanical, electrical, electrostatic) have sufficiently high temperatures to cause ignition, but may lack sufficient energy to heat a minimal propagating mass to its ignition temperature.[10,11] A hot process surface may have a temperature below that required for prompt ignition, but may have large energy content. Dust deposits on such surfaces can be subject to accelerated self-heating and eventual ignition.

As illustrated in Table 17.8.2, there are a number of test methods to characterize the ignition propensity of gases, vapors, and dusts. It is important to note that the minimum ignition energy or minimum autoignition temperature depends not only on the material and the test sample, but also on the details of the test setup. Therefore, when using ignitability data for safety analysis, one should be careful to consider the relevance of the test setup and test conditions to the safety threats being considered.

Table 17.8.3 shows the minimum ignition energy (MIE) of selected gases and vapors in air at 1 atmosphere and 25°C. The MIE for gases and vapors is seen to vary from a fraction of a millijoule (mJ) to joules (J). In pure oxygen, MIE can be an order of magnitude or smaller than that in air.

Table 17.8.4 lists the MIE of dust clouds of selected materials. Since the dust cloud MIE is a strong function of the particle size distribution, particle size distribution as well as the median particle size of the samples are included in the table. A theoretical analysis included in Eckhoff[4] predicts MIE to be proportional to the cube of the median particle size. One of the authors' experience suggests that the relationship is more complex and probably involves additional parameters further characterizing the quantity of the fines. That is why the data in Table 17.8.4 do not seem to support a strong empirical correlation to the cube of the median particle size. In fact, the cubic relation becomes prominent when the data from samples with narrow particle size distributions are analyzed (Figure 17.8.3). A didactic composite diagram of ignition energies of various materials and types of ignition source that may ignite them has been reproduced in Figure 17.8.4.

Fuel-Air Mixture Explosibility

The most commonly used parameters are the maximum unvented explosion pressure, P_{max}, and volume scaled maximum rate of pressure rise, K. The latter parameter is defined as

$$K = V^{1/3}(dP/dt)_{max} \qquad (1)$$

where V denotes the volume of the test vessel. K is often used with the subscript St (abbreviation of the German word *staub*)

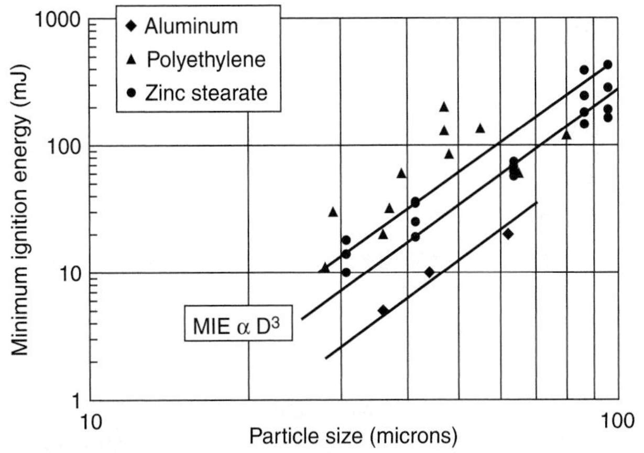

FIGURE 17.8.3 Round Robin MIE Data Showing the Effect of Particle Size

TABLE 17.8.2 ASTM Test Methods Characterizing Material Hazard Potential Pertaining to Explosion Prevention and Protection

ASTM Designation	*Title*
E476	Standard Test Method for Thermal Instability of Confined Condensed Phase Systems (Confinement Test)
E487	Standard Test Method for Constant-Temperature Stability of Chemical Materials
E502	Standard Test Method for Selection and Use of ASTM Standards for the Determination of Flashpoint of Chemicals by Closed Cup Methods
E537	Standard Test Method for Assessing the Thermal Stability of Chemicals by Methods of Thermal Analysis
E582	Standard Test Method for Minimum Ignition Energy and Quenching Distance in Gaseous Mixtures
E659	Standard Test Method for Autoignition Temperature of Liquid Chemicals
E680	Standard Test Method for Drop Weight Impact Sensitivity of Solid-Phase Hazardous Materials
E681	Standard Test Method for Concentration Limits of Flammability of Chemicals (Vapors and Gases)
E771	Standard Test Method for Spontaneous Heating Tendency of Materials
E918	Standard Practice for Determining Limits of Flammability of Chemicals at Elevated Temperature and Pressure
E698	Standard Test Method for Arrhenius Kinetic Constants for Thermally Unstable Materials
E1226	Standard Test Method for Pressure and Rate of Pressure Rise for Combustible Dusts
E1231	Standard Practice for Calculation of Hazard Potential Figures-of-Merit for Thermally Unstable Materials
E1232	Standard Test Method for Temperature Limit of Flammability of Chemicals
E1491	Standard Test Method for Minimum Autoignition Temperature of Dust Clouds
E1515	Standard Test Method for Minimum Explosible Concentration of Combustible Dusts
E1981	Standard Guide for Assessing the Thermal Stability of Materials by Methods of Accelerating Rate Calorimetry
E2012	Standard Guide for Preparation of Binary Chemical Compatibility Chart
E2019	Standard Test Method for Minimum Ignition Energy of a Dust Cloud in Air
E2021	Standard Test Method for Hot-Surface Ignition Temperature of Dust Layers
E2046	Standard Test Method for Reaction Induction Time by Thermal Analysis
E2079	Standard Test Methods for Limiting Oxygen (Oxidant) Concentration in Gases and Vapors
D56 D92 D93 D1310 D3278 D3828 D3934 D3941 D4206	Miscellaneous open cup and close cup flashpoint tests
D323 D2879 E1194 E1719 E1782	Miscellaneous vapor pressure tests
WK1680	ASTM draft Standard for Limiting Oxygen Concentration Determination of Dust Samples

for dusts and G for gases and vapors. ASTM E1226[12] provides a standard test method for the determination of K_{St} and P_{max} values for dust-air mixtures. An extensive compilation of K_{St} and P_{max} data for generic dust samples can be found in Eckhoff.[4] The K_{St} value is theoretically (e.g., see Ural[13]) proportional to an equivalent turbulent burning velocity for dust-air mixtures.

Although the simple one-third power correction seen in the K definition (Eq. 1) adequately accounts for the effect of the test volume in dust explosions, the prediction of the volume dependence of the maximum rate of pressure rise is complicated by other flame acceleration mechanisms in gas explosions. Nevertheless, K_G values have long been used in explosion protection technology. Although a standard test method for K_G and burning

TABLE 17.8.3 Minimum Ignition Energy of Selected Gases and Vapors in Dry Air at 1 atm and 25°C

Fuel	*MIE (mJ)*
Hydrogen	0.016
Acetylene	0.017
Methanol	0.14
Methane	0.21
Ethane	0.24
Propane	0.24
n-Butane	0.25
n-Pentane	0.28
Acetaldehyde	0.37
Isopropyl alcohol	0.65
Acetone	1.15
Isooctane	1.35
Neopentane (2,2-dimethyl propane)	1.57
Ethylamine	2.40
Ammonia	680
Methylene chloride	>1000

Source: Adapted from Britton, L. G., *Avoiding Static Ignition Hazards in Chemical Operations, A CCPS Concept Book,* American Institute of Chemical Engineers, New York, 1999.

velocity is not yet available, Annex C of NFPA 68 (2007 edition) provides some data and guidance for testing.

DEFLAGRATION PREVENTION

Oxidant Control

The process of reducing the concentration of an oxidant beyond the flammable zone is also called inerting. Materials other than oxygen can act as oxidants. The selection of a gas for inerting a process atmosphere will be influenced by several factors such as inert gas effectiveness, availability, cost, process conditions, distribution requirements, and toxicity. The heat capacity of a gas is the most important inerting property. This is because a nonflammable condition is achieved when the heat capacity of a fuel-oxygen-inert gas mixture is elevated above about 250 J/mol-K of oxygen in the mixture. Thus, the higher the heat capacity of the inert gas, the lower the quantity required to achieve an inert mixture. Certain halogenated hydrocarbons used in total flooding fire protection systems have also been shown to be useful in inerting flammable atmospheres. Table 17.8.5 shows data on several inert gases.

Minimum inerting concentration for a specific fuel/oxidant/inert system can be determined by performing the limiting oxygen concentration (LOC) tests described by Frurip et al.[5] The LOC depends on the temperature, pressure, and fuel concentration as well as the type of diluent and should be determined at the worst case conditions.

LOC of dust samples can be determined using the ASTM standard draft WK1680. It is prudent to use a sufficiently strong chemical ignition source for dusts to avoid the ignitability effects on the LOC determination. Hence, some of the old LOC values, if they were obtained using spark ignition, may be considered suspect. Some references provide LOC data tabulations. These values should be used with care, since the LOC of dusts depends on the particle size distribution.

Where the fuel is gas or vapor, ASTM E2079 is the contemporary test method of choice. Unfortunately, most data listed in reference publications were obtained decades ago, using flammability tubes. Preliminary results of the ASTM E2079 round robin tests for gases and vapors revealed that the LOC data obtained using different test methods and listed in a majority of reference publications are nonconservative. The old Bureau of Mines data were obtained mostly in a 5 cm diameter flammability tube. This diameter may be too small to mitigate the flame quenching influence, thereby impeding accurate determination of the LOC of most fuels. The 4 L minimum volume specified in ASTM E2079 would correspond to a diameter of at least 20 cm. As a result, some LOC values determined using this standard are

TABLE 17.8.4 MIE Data for Selected Dust Samples in Air

	Particle Size Distribution						
	Weight % < Size (microns)						
Material	*500*	*125*	*71*	*32*	*20*	*Median (microns)*	*MIE (mJ)*
Sulfur			97	85	71	12	<1
Toner			100	96	48	21	<1
Dimethyl terepthalate				60		27	2
Ferrocene		71	33			95	5
Calcium stearate	100	43	25			145	12
Fructose (from filter)	99	39	17			150	<1
Fructose	92	15				200	180
Fructose	81					400	>4000
Silicon			99	98	97	<10	54
Wood dust	58	57	55	43	39	80	7
Wood dust			90	47	7	33	100

Source: Adapted from Eckhoff, R. K., *Dust Explosions in the Process Industries,* Butterworth, Heinemann, Boston, 1991.

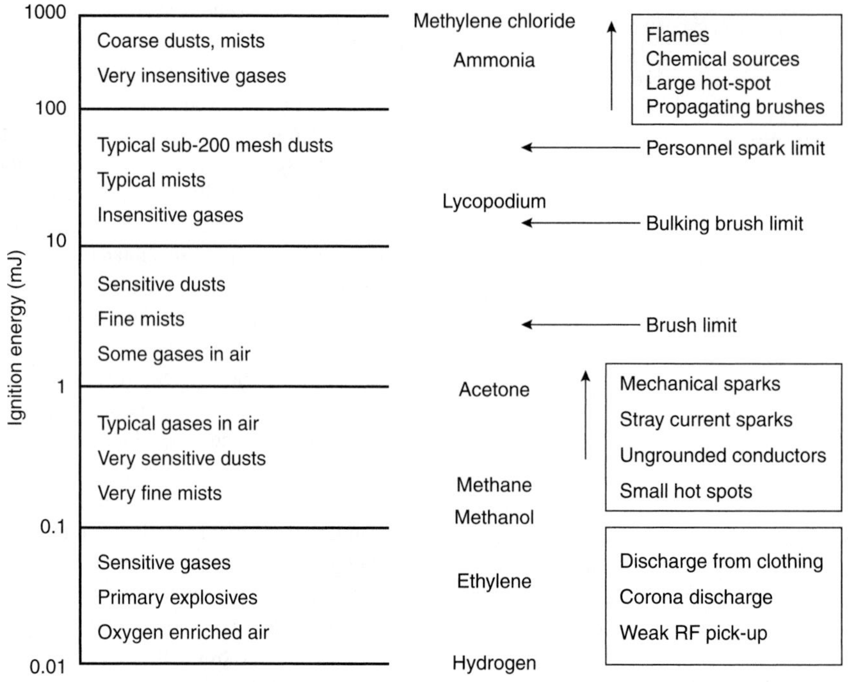

FIGURE 17.8.4 Ignition Energies of Various Materials and Types of Ignition (Source: Britton, L. G., *Avoiding Static Ignition Hazards in Chemical Operations, A CCPS Concept Book,* American Institute of Chemical Engineers, New York, 1999)

approximately 1 percent by volume oxygen lower than the previous values measured in the flammability tube, and a few are even up to 2 percent by volume lower. The lower LOC values obtained in larger chambers are more appropriate for use in fire and explosion hazard assessment studies. A data comparison can be found in Table 17.8.6.

If inerting is used as the primary means of explosion protection, several safety margins are applied to the LOC in order to arrive at the design inerting concentration. Such safety margins are selected to address factors such as mixture nonuniformities, temperature/pressure fluctuations, concentration measurement/alarm system accuracy, response time, and the consequences of false alarms. Where total inerting cannot be achieved due to technical or financial constraints, partial inerting may be considered in conjunction with other explosion prevention and protection methods. Even above the LOC, reduced oxygen concentration generally narrows the combustible range, reduces explosibility parameter *K,* and increases MIE.

TABLE 17.8.5 Heat Capacities of Inert Gases (Values at 25°C)

Gas	C_p *(J/mol-K)*
Argon	20.9
Nitrogen	28.4
Steam	35.4 at 100°C
Carbon dioxide	37.5
HFC 23 (CHF_3)	51.6
HFC 227ea (CF_3CHFCF_3)	137
FC 3-1-10 (C_4F_{10})	191

For U.S. units: 77°F = 25°C; 212°F = 100°C.

TABLE 17.8.6 Effect of Test Enclosure on LOC Values When Using Nitrogen as Diluent

	Flammability Tube, 5 cm Diameter	*120 L Sphere, 60 cm Diameter*
Hydrogen, H_2	5.0	4.6
Carbon monoxide, CO (at high humidity)	5.5	4.8
Methane, CH_4	12.0	11.0
Ethylene, C_2H_4	10.0	8.5
Propane, C_3H_8	11.5	10.6

Sources: Flammability tube data from J. M. Kuchta, "Investigation of Fire and Explosion Accidents in the Chemical, Mining, and Fuel-Related Industries," Bulletin 680, U.S. Bureau of Mines, 1985. 120 L chamber data from Isaac Zlochower, National Institute for Occupational Safety and Health, Pittsburgh Research Laboratory, 2005, unpublished and not peer-reviewed. The data were obtained in accordance with ASTM test method E2079, at 1 atm and at 20 to 30°C on N2 air-fuel mixtures. Electric spark was created by the discharge of a 1300 μF capacitor, initially charged to 300 V, through 15 kV transformer. The standard criterion (i.e., minimum 1 psi or 7% absolute pressure rise) was used to detect ignition.

Nitrogen is commonly used as an inerting gas. It may be obtained from cryogenically stored liquefied gas. Catalytic combustion of ammonia in air followed by water condensation results in a relatively pure grade of nitrogen for process inerting. Carbon dioxide is somewhat more effective than nitrogen due to its higher heat capacity. It can be stored as a liquefied compressed gas in cylinders or kept in low-pressure refrigerated tanks for use on demand. Flue gas from a combustion system is a mixture of carbon dioxide and nitrogen, usually saturated with water vapor and having a low oxygen concentration. Flue gas is commonly used to inert storage tanks when offloading oil from ships. Carbon dioxide should not be used as an inerting gas for certain refractory metals. Examples are magnesium, silicon, and zirconium. In such cases, it may be necessary to use a noble gas, such as argon, for inerting. Examples of the LOC values for a variety of gases, metals, and carbonaceous dusts can be found in the 2008 edition of NFPA 69, *Standard on Explosion Prevention Systems.*

Since oxygen is essential to sustain life, inerting systems present an inherent risk to personnel safety. It is important to follow the OSHA regulations when entrance is required to the protected equipment. External leakage to other areas that are unventilated can present a hidden risk and must be kept in mind. Adverse health effects of selected gases used for inerting, as well as the corresponding inerting concentrations, can be found in NFPA 2001, *Standard on Clean Agent Fire Extinguishing Systems.*

Methods of Inert Gas Application. Inert gas can be applied in three ways: using batch methods, using the continuous methods described below, or using a combination of the two.

Batch Methods. In vacuum purging, the pressure in the process unit is reduced from its initial value, P_1, to a lower pressure, P_2. Inert gas is then added to return the vessel to P_1. If the gas within the process volume is assumed to be well-mixed, then the fraction of original gas remaining after one such purge cycle will be

$$X = \frac{P_2}{P_1} \tag{2}$$

In *pressure purging,* a volume is pressurized from P_1, to a higher pressure, P_2, by addition of purge gas and then vented back to the initial pressure, P_1. The fraction of original gas remaining after each such cycle will be

$$X = \frac{P_1}{P_1 + P_2} \tag{3}$$

The fraction of original gas remaining after n cycles by either batch purge method is

$$X(n) = X^n \tag{4}$$

Continuous Methods. Some enclosures, such as solvent storage tanks, are under continuous use or are not suited to batch purge methods due to structural considerations. Such tanks "breathe" on addition or removal of liquid contents or when their internal temperature changes due to climatic variations. In *fixed-rate* purging, inert gas is added continuously at the maximum anticipated demand rate. This method has the advantage of being simple to monitor and control but at the expense of purge gas consumption and, perhaps more important, results in carrying product vapors out of the enclosure.

Variable-rate purging may involve elements of both pressure demand and load demand gas addition. A small rate of continuous inert gas addition may be used together with pressure monitoring to determine when automatic addition of gas is required to make up for vapor space cooling. Addition of inert gas may also be increased on removal of liquid contents of a tank.

Purging enclosures of volatile liquids can be regulated under Title IV of the U.S. Clean Air Act Amendments of 1990. The capture and recovery, recycling, or incineration of process gas emissions has become common. Vapor recovery systems need consideration with respect to possible explosion risks that may be present. The U.S. Coast Guard has promulgated rules on operation of marine vapor recovery systems pertaining to explosion prevention and control.[14]

Fuel Control

Effective explosion prevention can be ensured if combustible materials are excluded from spaces to be protected. Four aspects of minimizing risks associated with combustibles are (1) containment, (2) ventilation, (3) purging, and (4) housekeeping.

(1) Containment. Special considerations are necessary for each class of combustible material. For example, cylinders and tanks of flammable compressed gases must be properly stored or located to ensure valves and other appurtenances are not subject to accidental damage. Containers and tanks of flammable and combustible liquids need periodic inspection to verify tightness of closures and the absence of damage or corrosion. Filter bags in dust collectors need periodic inspection to locate and replace damaged elements that can allow passage of combustible dusts. It is recommended that conformance be maintained with materials handling and storage requirements as outlined in NFPA codes (such as NFPA 30, *Flammable and Combustible Liquids Code,* NFPA 484, *Standard for Combustible Metals,* and NFPA 654, *Standard for the Prevention of Fire and Dust Explosions from the Manufacturing, Processing, and Handling of Combustible Particulate Solids*) and other codes and practices pertaining to specific flammable and combustible materials.

(2) Ventilation. Where the presence of flammable gases or combustible dusts may be possible as a result of normal operations or upset conditions their concentrations can be kept to a minimum or excluded altogether by general area or localized ventilation techniques. Continuous introduction of clean air to a room may be used to either continually sweep away contaminants or to maintain a room or process space under constant positive pressure to exclude entry of flammable materials. Appendix D of NFPA 69 contains guidance on the concentration control design of ventilation systems, and NFPA 91, *Standard for Exhaust Systems for Air Conveying of Vapors, Gases, Mists, and Noncombustible Particulate Solids,* provides guidance on the physical installation of such systems. An improperly designed dusty operation ventilation system can create dust deposits in most unexpected locations and set the stage for devastating secondary explosions as in the West Pharmaceutical explosion on January 29, 2003.

(3) Purging. Purging is used to prevent development of ignitable atmospheres in enclosures or equipment. Specific methods are recommended for maintaining safe atmospheres inside electrical equipment enclosures. Type X, Type Y, and Type Z purging pertain to reducing the classifications within enclosures from Division 1 to nonhazardous, Division 1 to Division 2, and Division 2 to nonhazardous, respectively. The details of these purging methods can be found in NFPA 496, *Standard for Purged and Pressurized Enclosures for Electrical Equipment.*

(4) Housekeeping. This is the most obvious yet often the most difficult method of dust explosion prevention. Good practices adopted into NFPA 654 include minimizing dust emission from equipment, from operations, and from cleaning activities, and setting up regularly scheduled thorough cleaning procedures to reduce the probability of primary or secondary dust explosions fueled by dust accumulations. NFPA 654 also provides guidance on housekeeping requirements when they are employed in conjunction with the ignition control method described later in the next section and as shown in Table 17.8.7.

Ignition Source Control

Ignition control techniques can be used successfully to reduce the frequency of fires and explosions. However, ignition control must almost always be used in conjunction with another explosion prevention and protection method. This is because the means by which flammable atmospheres can become ignited are diverse and readily available in industrial settings. Although it is often true that the ignition source of a given event cannot be identified with certainty after the fact, due to the generalized destruction of the scene, a number of important mechanisms of deflagration initiation are recognized and should be carefully considered when conducting a hazard analysis.

Mechanical Sparks. A survey of 357 dust explosions between 1965 and 1980 revealed that, in 29 percent of the cases, the source of ignition was mechanically generated by sparks.[15] It has been shown[16] that sparks generated by grinding handheld steel can have sufficient energy to ignite organic dust clouds. This clearly points to the ignition energy potential when high-

TABLE 17.8.7 Guidance for Area Electrical Classification

Depth of Dust Accumulation (in.)	*Frequency*	*Housekeeping Requirement*	*Area Electrical Classification*
Negligible[a]	NA	NA	Unclassified (general purpose)
Negligible to < 1/32[b]	Infrequent[c]	Clean up during same shift.	Unclassified (general purpose)
Negligible to < 1/32[b]	Continuous/frequent[d]	Clean as necessary to maintain an average accumulation below 1/64 in.[e]	Unclassified; however, electrical enclosures should be dusttight[f,g]
1/32 to 1/8	Infrequent[c]	Clean up during same shift.	Unclassified; however, electrical enclosures should be dusttight[f,g]
1/32 to 1/8	Continuous/frequent[d]	Clean as necessary to maintain an average accumulation below 1/16 in.	Class II, Division 2
> 1/8	Infrequent[c]	Immediately shut down and clean.	Class II, Division 2
> 1/8	Continuous/frequent[d]	Clean at frequency appropriate to minimize accumulation.	Class II, Division 1

[a] Surface color just discernible under the dust layer.
[b] 1/32 in. is approximately the thickness of a typical paper clip.
[c] Episodic release of dust occurring not more than about two or three times per year.
[d] Episodic release of dust occurring more than about three times per year or continuous release resulting in stated accumulation occurring in approximately a 24 hour period.
[e] It has been observed that a thickness of about 1/64 in. of a low-density dust is sufficient to yield a small puffy cloud with each footstep.
[f] For example, National Electrical Manufacturers Association (NEMA) 12 or better. Note: Ordinary equipment that is not heat producing, such as junction boxes, can be significantly sealed against dust penetration by the use of silicone-type caulking. This can be considered in areas where fugitive dust is released at a slow rate and tends to accumulate over a long period of time.
[g] Guidance to be applied for existing facilities. For new facilities, it is recommended that the electrical classification be at least Class II, Division 2.
For SI units, 1 in. = 25.4 mm.
NA = Not available.

Source: NFPA 654, *Standard for the Prevention of Fire and Dust Explosions from the Manufacturing, Processing, and Handling of Combustible Particulate Solids,* Table A.6.6.2, 2006, p. 654-24.

energy systems—for example, coal pulverizers or mills of the rolling, hammer, and pin type—cause grinding action on metal or other spark-inducing materials. Where tramp metal is a recognized hazard, the use of magnetic separators is recommended.

Fires. Unexpected open flaming due to ignition of accumulated dust can serve to ignite an ambient dust cloud. There are several mechanisms of causing such fires. Their risk of occurrence can be reduced by both understanding the ignition characteristics of the material being processed and by preventing the accumulation of materials susceptible to ignition by the given mechanism.

Hot Surfaces. Accumulated dust on a motor housing, transformer, high-pressure steam pipe, or other like hot surface can lead to slow pyrolysis of the solids, which can then ignite. The ignition probability is related to the surface temperature, dust layer thickness, and the thermal stability of the dust. A method of characterizing surface ignition temperature for dusts is available.[17] Approved equipment will be marked to indicate the operating temperature. The temperature of equipment operating in Class I or II (discussed later) environments must not exceed the ignition temperature of the gas or dust to which it is exposed. NFPA 497, *Recommended Practice for the Classification of Flammable Liquids, Gases, or Vapors and of Hazardous (Classified) Locations for Electrical Installations in Chemical Process Areas,* provides ignition temperature data on vapors and gases, whereas NFPA 499, *Recommended Practice for the Classification of Combustible Dusts and of Hazardous (Classified) Locations for Electrical Installations in Chemical Process Areas* provides similar data for dusts.

Autoignition. Dusts layers exposed to continuous uniform elevated temperature, or even ambient temperatures, can also undergo self-heating and ignite.[9,10] The temperatures at which autoignition of bulk dusts occurs are much lower than for surface ignition, above, and are dependent on the volume of the heated dust. A small-scale method for characterizing the self-heating tendency of dusts was developed by the U.S. Bureau of Mines.[18] Another method is recommended by the United Nations (originally by the U.S. Department of Transportation) for determination of packaging classification of self-heating materials for purposes of road shipment.[19]

Mechanical Impact. Some materials may be subject to immediate ignition due to sudden mechanical impact. The ASTM E680 drop hammer test method can be used to characterize materials in this regard.[20]

Friction. Frictional heating of combustible materials is possible where moving components are found. Rotating drums and moving belts in bucket elevators are an example of a system that requires special consideration. Regular lubrication of bearings is essential. Use of belt-alignment devices is mandated in some cases.[21]

Embers. Wood-processing operations, such as grinding, sanding, and cutting, can produce glowing wood particles that can be conveyed to a dust collector. Such embers can lead to ignition of a wood–dust layer in which it becomes embedded. Spark detection and extinguishing systems, described in NFPA 69, may be appropriate in such operations.

Electrical Equipment. Electrical motors, switches, lights, heaters, and similar high-current devices may be powerful ignition sources. Such equipment can be constructed for use in hazardous atmospheres and is rated with respect to the type of atmosphere in which it is suited for use. A synopsis of one of the rating systems is given next:

Class I	*Groups*	
Flammable gases	A	(acetylene)
	B	(hydrogen)
	C	(ethylene)
	D	(propane)
Class II	*Groups*	
Combustible dusts	E	(metal dusts)
	F	(carbonaceous dusts, e.g., coal, charcoal, coke, etc.)
	G	(flour, grain, wood, plastics, chemicals)
Class III		
Combustible fibers		
Division 1	Flammable gases or combustible dusts may be present at ignitable concentrations, under normal operating conditions.	
Division 2	Where hazardous materials may be handled, processed, or used; ignitable atmospheres not normally present due to containment or ventilation of hazardous materials; areas adjacent to Division 1 locations.	

The examples given in the preceding groups are representative only. Flammable gases are classified according to the maximum experimental safe gap (MESG), which prevents flame passage, and the minimum igniting current ratio, MIC. NFPA 70, *National Electrical Code®,* determines the group designations whereas NFPA 497 defines the MESG and MIC values for each group. MESG and MIC are determined by tests.[22] Thus, a motor rated as Class I, Division 1, Group D would be rated for use in an environment where a propane-like gas was likely to be present.

Unrated electrical equipment can be employed in hazardous areas, provided such equipment is contained in a pressurized or purged enclosure. The requirements for this approach are given in NFPA 496. Various purging methods are described that can render the classification within an enclosure from Division 1 to nonhazardous (Type X purging); from Division 1 to Division 2 (Type Y purging); and from Division 2 to nonhazardous (Type Z purging).

Electrostatic Ignition. Conveyance of liquids or dusts leads to electron transfer at the boundary of the moving material and a duct or pipe. The flow of electric charge in this manner is called a *streaming current,* I_s. The discharge of the moving material from the conduit to a receiving point (tank or drum for liquids; bin or pile for solids), of capacitance C, results in charge separation and the development of an electric potential difference, V. The accumulated charge, Q, if not allowed to dissipate or *relax,* will have a stored energy of $E = QV/2 = CV^2/2$. Potentials exceeding 350 V and stored energies exceeding 0.1 mJ are considered hazardous in flammable gas areas. MIE of dust clouds vary widely, but can be less than 10 mJ. Most dusts of organic composition have MIEs in the range of 10 to 100 mJ. Charge potentials of several thousand volts and stored energies sufficient to ignite dust clouds are readily achieved in some solids transfer operations.

Ignition of flammable atmospheres by electrostatic discharges can be avoided by first recognizing process operations that can lead to charge separation. One can then provide conduction paths to maintain process components at low or zero electric potential. Resistance to ground should not exceed 100,000 Ω from any component. It is important to consider all components in a system. A section of pipe may be connected to a system by bolted flanges but electrically insulated by nonconductive gaskets. Such a component has the characteristics of a capacitor and can hold an electric charge. *Bonding* of electrically isolated process components is achieved by connecting a wire between them (see NFPA 70 for guidance). *Grounding* of the bonded components to an earth ground provides a conduction path that prevents charge accumulation. Britton,[11] Jones,[23] Glor,[24] Louvar,[25] and Pratt[26] should be consulted for a more complete discussion of electrostatic hazards. A consensus standard is not available for the control of electrostatic ignition sources. As a result, most companies develop their internal standards. Figure 17.8.5 and Table 17.8.8 show an approach used by Ciba Specialty Chemicals (see Hoppe et al.[10]) for this purpose.

Combined Mechanisms. In any given ignition scenario it is possible that multiple ignition mechanisms were involved. For example, an unlubricated bearing (*friction, hot surface*) in the tension roll in the boot (bottom) section of a bucket elevator conveying grain could generate a smoldering mass of grain dust (*ember*). The burning matter could become dislodged and fall into the general mass of moving grain and be conveyed in a bucket into an upper section of the elevator, during which time

TABLE 17.8.8 Additional Safety Measures Required for Large Containers (Volume > 2 m^3) Where Combustible Powders Are Handled or Stored in the Absence of Flammable Gases or Vapors

Minimum Ignition Energy, MIE (mJ)	*Volume Resistivity (ρ_V) of Powder (MΩ-m)*	*Safety Measures*
MIE < 10 mJ	Any value	All parts of the installation must be conductive and grounded All containers must be conductive or dischargeable and grounded Apply additional explosion protection measures (e.g. inerting, venting, suppression) OR Seek expert advice
10 mJ < MIE < 1000 mJ	10,000 MΩ-m < ρ_V	Use only conductive or dischargeable containers which are grounded, AND Apply additional explosion protection measures (e.g. inerting, venting, suppression) OR Seek expert advice
	1 MΩ-m < ρ_V < 10,000 MΩ-m	Use only conductive or dischargeable containers which are grounded, OR Restrict the filling rate to 5 kg/sec OR Apply additional explosion protection measures (e.g. inerting, venting, suppression) OR Seek expert advice
	ρ_V < 1 MΩ-m	All parts of the installation must be conductive and grounded All containers must be conductive or dischargeable and grounded
1,000 mJ < MIE	Any value	Electrostatic ignition unlikely

Notes: Containers capable of discharge: The leakage resistance from any point to ground must be less than 100 MΩ.
Conductive containers: maximum leakage resistance less than 1 MΩ.

Source: CIBA methodology adapted from Hoppe, T., Jaeger, N., and Terry, J., "Safe Handling of Combustible Powders During Transportation, Charging, Discharging, and Storage," 8th International Colloquium on Dust Explosions, Schaumburg, IL, September 21–25, 1998.

its extent of burning increases. At some moment the ember becomes a flaming mass (*open flame*), and encounters a dust cloud with a concentration greater than its lower explosible limit, thus initiating a deflagration. The pressure developed by the primary deflagration could rupture the elevator leg enclosure. The escaping pressurized blast of gases could cause grain dust on nearby surfaces to become airborne and ignited (*flame jet ignition*). An ensuing secondary deflagration would likely involve

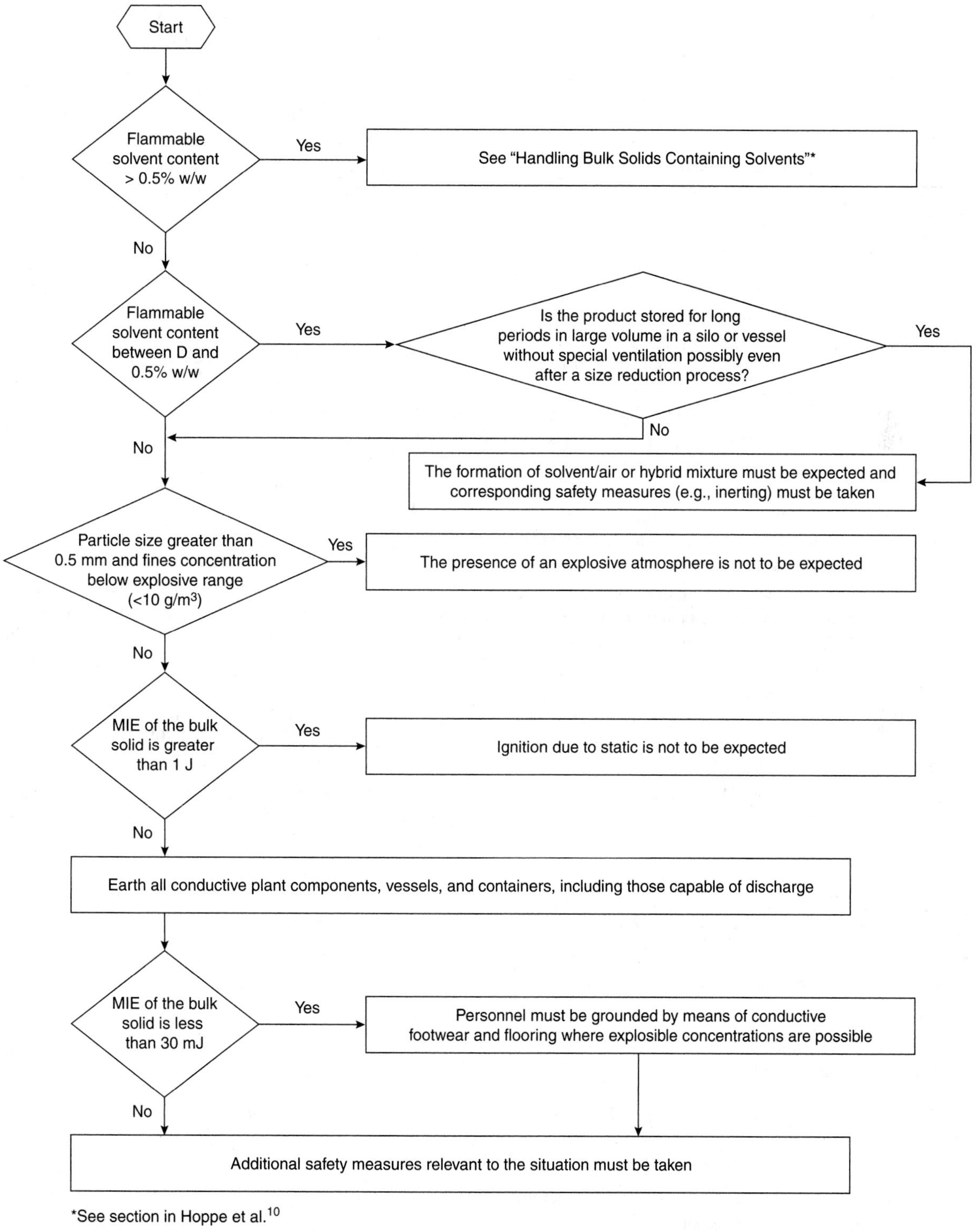

FIGURE 17.8.5 Decision Tree Used to Evaluate Electrostatic Ignition. (Source: Hoppe, T., Jaeger, N., and Terry, J, "Safe Handling of Combustible Powders During Transportation, Charging, Discharging, and Storage," 8th International Colloquium on Dust Explosions, Schaumburg, IL, September 21–25, 1998, pp. 253–263)

a much larger mass of fuel and air and lead to generalized pressure damage to the facility. Due to failure of a grease fitting, the plant could be substantially damaged. This example does not represent any particular event. Rather, it is a synthesis of many similar actual events that have occurred.

ENCLOSURE INTEGRITY AND STRENGTH

The explosion prevention methods discussed in the previous section and those that will be discussed in the next section rely on the premise that the enclosures will remain intact throughout the prevention and protection missions. This is achieved by determining the loads and by determining the strength of each enclosure and interconnecting piping.

Loads on the Enclosure

Explosion prevention techniques generally impose little or no additional loads on the enclosure, beyond the loads (such as weight, seismic loads, process fluctuations) considered in the conventional design. On the other hand, there are cases where such loads can be considerable. For example, batch methods of inerting create repeated overpressure or vacuum loads by design. A malfunction in an inerting system can conceivably exceed the design loads by a great margin.

The deflagration loads that a protected enclosure experiences are generally significant. For example, a 10 barg (150 psig) overpressure for an explosion containment application, and 0.3 barg (5 psig) overpressure for an explosion venting or explosion suppression application are not uncommon. These loads must be characterized as a part of the explosion protection system design.

Enclosure Strength

Explosion protection standards allow two separate approaches towards the enclosure strength determination. Calculations or design can be based on either of the following:

- Preventing rupture of the vessel enclosure (the ultimate strength of the vessel enclosure), but allowing permanent deformation (also called explosionproof/shock-resistant)
- Preventing permanent deformation (the yield strength of the vessel enclosure, which is also called explosion-pressure/shock-resistant) from internal positive overpressure

NFPA 69 allows loads up to two-thirds of yield or ultimate strength for containment design. If venting is chosen as the protection method, NFPA 68 also allows the same fraction, based on a dynamic loading factor. When enclosures are designed and constructed according to the ASME Boiler and Pressure Vessel Code or similar codes, NFPA 68 and 69 both allow deflagration loading to the same two-thirds fraction of yield or ultimate strength. Since pressure vessel codes include a larger inherent safety factor, this means that the anticipated deflagation loading (i.e., pressure) can be greater than the stamped maximum allowable working pressure (MAWP). The ASME Boiler and Pressure Vessel Code recognizes the NFPA methodology as acceptable for deflagration applications.

EXPLOSION PROTECTION

As used in this chapter, *explosion protection* means the measures adopted to control and mitigate the effects of ignition of the contents of a process volume that may be capable of propagating a deflagration. Thus, although appropriate explosion prevention measures may have been implemented, it is assumed at this point that these steps have only reduced the probability of initiating a deflagration and not eliminated such a possibility altogether. Whether the probability of the occurrence of a deflagration is now so small as to constitute a risk of acceptable magnitude is a matter for evaluation using the methods of risk and consequence analysis, which is beyond the scope of this chapter.

There are essentially only four strategies available as explosion protection options: (1) pressure containment, (2) deflagration venting, (3) deflagration suppression, and (4) deflagration isolation.

Pressure Containment

Equipment can be designed to contain the full brunt of the explosion load for pressure containment. This approach may be required if no emission of vessel contents is tolerable (for concerns relating to toxicity, environmental pollution, or public perception). In some cases, design for pressure containment (DPC) may be the most economical approach.

The use of pressure relief vents on vessels in some processes may be impractical. Where the safety strategy is to allow a possible deflagration to occur, but be contained, the process vessel must be constructed to be able to contain the pressurized gases with no equipment damage or with limited acceptable damage. No credit is taken for pressure relief devices on the vessel. The design pressure to which the vessel must be fabricated is determined by the maximum anticipated deflagration pressure, P_{Cont}, that may develop in the enclosure. This is the maximum deflagration pressure of the combustible material that is used. If the enclosure is operating at atmospheric temperature and pressure, P_{Cont} is equal to the P_{max} determined for standard initial temperature and pressure from either closed vessel test series (e.g., ASTM E1226) or from equilibrium calculations. When the operating temperatures and pressures are different from standard conditions, the pressure load to be contained, P_{Cont}, can be estimated using the following simple equation:

$$P_{Cont} = [(P_{max} + 1) \times (P_i + P_{std}) - P_{std}] \times \frac{298}{273 + T_i} \quad (5a)$$

where

P_i = Initial pressure (gauge in units consistent with other pressure values)

T_i = Initial temperature (°C)

P_{std} = 1 atm = 14.7 psia, standard pressure

T_{std} = 25°C = 298 K, standard temperature

Vessels designed and constructed for pressure containment must conform to the ASME *Boiler and Pressure Vessel Code,* Section VIII, Division I. The design pressure for deflagrations may be calculated, using Equation 5a, to result in a vessel of sufficient strength to either not deform at the maximum deflagration pressure or to deform but not rupture. Accordingly, the maximum allowable working pressure, P_{MAWP}, of the enclosure is selected using the following equations:

$$P_{\mathrm{MAWP}} \geq \frac{3}{2}\left(\frac{P_{\mathrm{Cont}}}{F_u}\right) \tag{5b}$$

or

$$P_{\mathrm{MAWP}} \geq \frac{3}{2}\left(\frac{P_{\mathrm{Cont}}}{F_y}\right)$$

where

F_u = Ratio of ultimate stress of the enclosure to the allowable stress of the materials of construction of the enclosure per the ASME Boiler and Pressure Vessel Code

F_y = Ratio of the yield stress of the enclosure to the allowable stress of the materials of construction of the enclosure per the ASME Boiler and Pressure Vessel Code

For vessels constructed of carbon steel or low-alloy stainless steel, F_u and F_y are approximately 3.5 and 1.75, respectively. See NFPA 69 for further details.

Design for pressure containment requires further consideration of the eventual release of the pressurized gases. If the vessel is truly leaktight, then pressure reduction will occur as the products of combustion cool, and vacuum may develop. Alternatively, pressurized gases will flow through process openings or pressure relief devices. The essential point here is that hot combustion gases should be prevented from passing to other process units where adverse consequences may occur due to initiation of a fire or another deflagration. Techniques for using deflagration isolation systems to prevent deflagration propagation to interconnecting piping and equipment are discussed later in this chapter.

Deflagration Venting

Deflagration venting is widely used to direct expanding gases and overpressure out of a vessel to a safe location. This protection option may be appropriate when material toxicity and environmental contamination are not a concern and when a safe vent discharge location is available. When appropriate, venting is often the low-cost protection option.

A simplified theory of explosion venting is provided by Ural.[13] The explosion pressure rise is created by the burnt gases heated by the combustion energy. Where vent openings are provided, developing explosion overpressure pushes both unburnt and burnt mixtures outside the enclosure, thereby reducing the maximum pressure.

The simplest postignition method of explosion protection is deflagration venting. Pressure development within a process enclosure in which a deflagration occurs is prevented from attaining damaging levels by allowing the enclosure contents to be ejected, in a controlled way, to a safe location. It is the control and safety aspects of a vented deflagration that differentiate it from an explosion.

A detailed discussion of the design and use of deflagration vents is given in Section 18, Chapter 6, "Deflagration (Explosion) Venting," and in NFPA 68. Venting reduces the maximum deflagration pressure in the protected enclosure to reduced pressure, P_{red}. Documents such as NFPA 68, VDI 3673, and European Standard EN 14491, provide correlations to calculate P_{red} for a given vent opening area and vice versa. These documents and the equations are publicly available and hence subject to thorough peer review and contribution. This approach also allows calculation and verification of proper vent size by any of the stakeholders, including vendors, owner/operators, and authorities having jurisdiction (AHJ).

Deflagration Suppression

Deflagration suppression may be the preferred approach when the consequences of employing other prevention and protection options are unacceptable. Process equipment may be too large to economically construct for DPC, venting may not be possible due to the location or contents of the vessel, or mechanical isolation of the process system may have unacceptable secondary consequences in a complex plant.

Deflagration suppression is the only one of the four explosion protection methods that terminates the combustion process before most of the fuel-air mixture is consumed. Because of this, explosive fuel-air mixture may still exist in the protected enclosure after the suppression system operates as intended, if the suppressant can settle out or condense after discharge. The utility of this approach is that it provides protection in special applications where other methods cannot meet the requirements imposed by the hazard. For example, venting may be inappropriate where toxic or noxious materials are concerned or where equipment vents cannot be discharged to a safe location. Isolation methods, on the other hand, are designed to protect adjacent process units, not the unit where ignition has occurred. Containment is applicable only where the vessel has sufficient pressure resistance.

Deflagration Suppression Defined. Deflagration suppression systems are active systems similar to fire protection systems. These systems typically comprise deflagration detectors (pressure or optical), a control/alarm panel, and suppressors containing the suppressant to be applied. Because a deflagration grows much more rapidly than a fire, the overall system response time is one of the key design parameters. Detection time, suppressor response time, suppressor discharge time, and suppressant travel time in the enclosure all contribute to the overall system response time. The principle of operation is that, once detection of ignition has occurred, the extinguishing agent is delivered to and distributed within the protected volume more rapidly than the rise in demand for the agent (to achieve extinguishment) by the growing flame ball. Deflagration suppression systems reduce the pressure in the protected enclosure to P_{red}, which comprises the sum of the two contributors: pressure rise due to partial burning of the contents prior to total extinguishment and pressure rise created by the agent injection. Using proprietary calculation procedures, a suppression system designer tries to control the suppressant delivery time, nominal concentration, and dispersion uniformity in the protected enclosure by specifying the number of suppressors, their volumes, and discharge cross-sections to achieve desired P_{red}. Increasing the number of suppressors effectively increases the suppressant discharge area, hence decreasing the delivery time and the reduced pressure. Increasing the number of suppressors also improves the suppressant uniformity in the protected enclosure. If the total rise in pressure that occurs in a vessel during suppression, P_{red} (reduced pressure), is less than the pressure strength of the equipment, then the suppression is considered successful.

Explosibility. Combustion of a flammable mixture in a closed vessel results in a rapid rise in pressure (Figure 17.8.6). Key characteristics of closed-vessel combustion are the maximum pressure attained, P_{max}, and the maximum rate of pressure rise, that is, the $(dP/dt)_{max}$ developed during the event.

The principal quantitative measure of the explosibility of a combustible material is characterized with parameter K_G for gases and K_{St} for dusts as shown previously in Equation 1.

A typical set of data points obtained in evaluating the explosibility of a dust is illustrated in Figure 17.8.7. The term *index of explosibility* is sometimes applied to K_{St}. Explosibility is dependent on chemical composition and, for dusts, physical parameters such as moisture content, particle size, and shape. The K_{St} value of a dust has been found to be nearly invariant with $V^{1/3}$ for vessels 20 L or larger in size. For this reason, it is important that K_{St} values be determined according to an approved standard that employs a vessel of at least 20 L volume.[12]

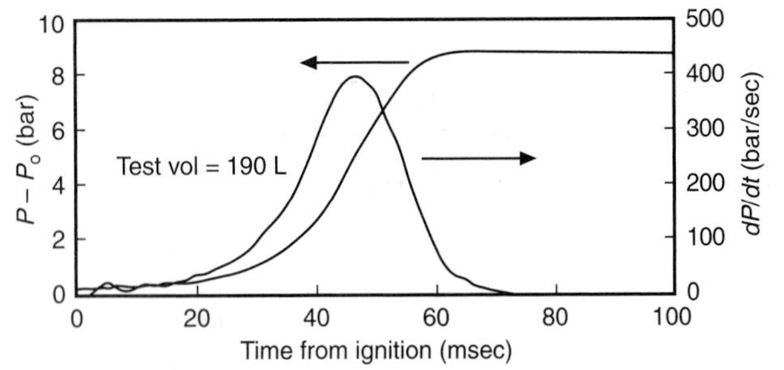

FIGURE 17.8.6 Pressure and *dP/dt* versus Time at 750 g/m³ for Closed-Vessel Deflagration of a Proprietary Corn Starch Product. (Courtesy of Kidde-Fenwal, Inc.)

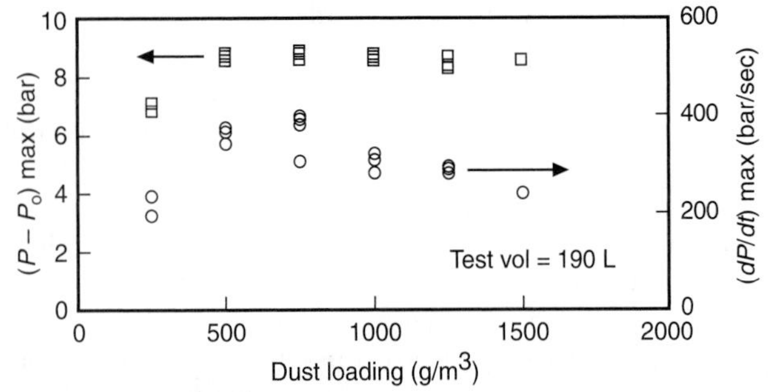

FIGURE 17.8.7 Typical P_{max} and $(dP/dt)_{max}$ Data Obtained in Determination of Explosibility of a Combustible Dust (Corn Starch) (Courtesy of Kidde-Fenwal, Inc.)

It can be shown that the K_{St} value may be used to estimate the effective burning velocity in a flammable dust–air mixture.[13] Thus, the explosibility of a mixture can be related to a burning rate, which can then be compared to the agent delivery characteristics of a suppression system.

Active Deflagration Suppression Systems. Deflagration suppression is a special case of fire extinguishment and may be viewed as a competition between a rapidly rising heat release rate from the combustion zone and the rate of agent delivery. A deflagration will be suppressed when the unburned fuel-air mixture has been rendered noncombustible due to the addition of agent and the flame front has been cooled to the point of extinguishment.

At the onset of ignition there is some minimum uniform concentration of agent that can render the protected space noncombustible; that is the inerting concentration. As deflagration proceeds, larger and larger quantities of agent are required, because the unburned material must be inerted and the burning volume must be quenched. Therefore, the amount of agent that must be dispersed within the protected space to achieve suppression increases with time as the deflagration propagates. Should delivery of agent be delayed too long, the deflagration will pass beyond the point of suppressibility. The result may be the attainment of unprotected deflagration pressures, or even higher pressures. For each application, deflagration suppression system manufacturers resort to propretary design methodologies or test data to ensure adequate system performance. Pressure-time traces of suppressed and unsuppressed deflagrations of a fast-burning dust are shown in Figure 17.8.8. The test was conducted in a 67 ft³ (1.9 m³) vessel. A sodium-bicarbonate-based agent was used. This particular case would be considered successful suppression only if the protected equipment could tolerate 8 psig (0.55 bar) over pressure.

Elements of a Suppression System. A deflagration suppression system consists of components for detection, extinguishment, and control/supervision. To ensure suppression success, deflagrations must be detected at a very early (incipient) stage

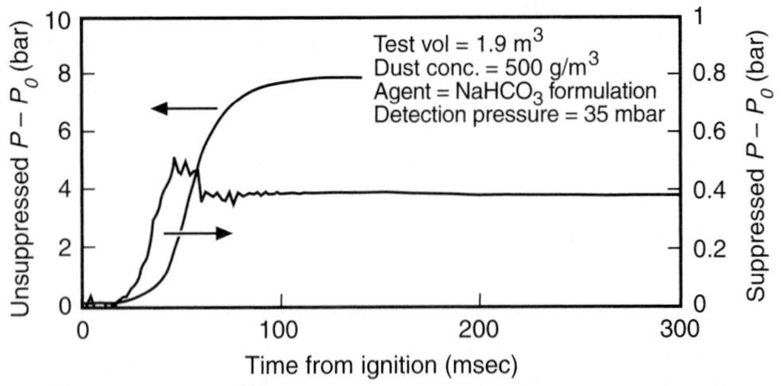

FIGURE 17.8.8 Pressure-Time Traces of Unsuppressed and Suppressed Deflagrations of a Combustible Processed Cellulosic Dust Having a K_{St} Value of 310 bar • m/sec (Courtesy of Kidde-Fenwal, Inc.)

when the volume of the burning material is much smaller than the protected enclosure volume. For this purpose, special pressure detectors, rate-of-pressure-rise detectors, or optical flame detectors are used. Optical detectors, employing ultraviolet (UV) or combination UV and infrared (IR) radiation sensors, are preferred in unenclosed environments with nonabsorbing UV atmospheres. Examples of such environments are solvent storage and pump rooms and aerosol can filling rooms. Pressure and rate-of-pressure-rise detectors are employed in closed process equipment, particularly where dusty atmospheres prevail. Multiple detectors and appropriate detection logic are essential to avoid false actuations.

Extinguishers are of the high-rate-discharge (HRD) type, charged with agent and propelling gas, usually nitrogen. The nitrogen overpressure is normally in the range of 300 to 900 psig (20 to 60 bar), depending on the manufacturer. Explosively or electrically operated high speed valves, usually 13/16 to 6 in. (30 to 300 mm) in diameter, ensure the high rate of agent delivery necessary for effective suppression. Several types of extinguishing agents are employed, usually selected from among the following:

- Water, with or without additives
- Dry chemical formulations, usually based on sodium bicarbonate or monoammonium phosphate. Other extinguishing powders have also been used.
- Halocarbons (halogenated hydrocarbons). Halon 1301, although no longer manufactured, will continue to be available on a market basis, subject to changes in regulations, for suppression systems meeting critical-use criteria. Chlorobromomethane (Halon 1011) has been used widely, but has come under regulation as an ozone-depleting substance and can no longer be used without special permission from the EPA.* Research continues on the use of environmentally friendly fluorocarbons and hydrofluorocarbons in explosion protection applications.[27]

Extinguishing mechanisms, wherein each agent works as a combination of thermal quenching (100 percent in the case of water) and chemical inhibition, are beyond the scope of this chapter. The selection of agent is usually based on several considerations, such as effectiveness, toxicity, product compatibility, residual inerting, and volatility. Dry chemical agents are most commonly specified in deflagration suppression applications. Distribution of agent within the protected volume is aided by use of nozzles. These may be fixed in position, or of the "pop-out" type that remains recessed until projected into the process volume by the momentum of the discharging suppressant.

*Halon 1011 is environmentally much more benign than Halon 1301. For example, the ozone depletion potential (ODP) of Halon 1011 is a factor of 75 smaller than that of Halon 1301 (i.e. 0.01 for 1011 versus 13.00 for 1301). Similarly, the atmospheric lifetime of Halon 1011 is a factor of 250 smaller than that of Halon 1301 (i.e., 0.23 year for 1011 versus 65 years for 1301). The atmospheric lifetimes of the second generation clean agents (HFC-125, HFC-227ea, and HFC-236fa) range from 36 to 250 years. Therefore, these agents tend to contribute to global warming problems although their ODP is zero, and thus face potential environment regulations limiting their use.

A suppression system is controlled using an electronic power supply having battery backup power. This unit supervises the suppression system circuitry to ensure integrity of the system and supplies the current to explosively or electrically operated valve actuators employed on the extinguishers. Normally the process equipment being protected by the suppression system is automatically shut off on detection of an incipient deflagration. An example of a process layout protected by a deflagration suppression system is shown in Figure 17.8.9.

The protection afforded by a deflagration suppression system depends on several factors, including the size and shape of the protected volume; the explosibility of the material being processed; the initial turbulence scale and intensity; the number, size, and location of HRD extinguishers; and the means, sensitivity, and location of detection devices. The pressure–time profile for a suppressed deflagration of a combustible processed cellulosic dust was shown in Figure 17.8.8.

Deflagration suppression systems are active systems that require periodic inspection and maintenance. The use of deflagration suppression systems is discussed in NFPA 69.

Deflagration Isolation

Deflagration isolation is the strategy of preventing a deflagration initiated in one location from passing to another location where personal injury or additional damage may occur. *It is well known* that deflagration waves allowed to propagate into interconnecting piping and equipment can create much more powerful explosions than the initial explosion. A deflagration may transition to detonation if it is allowed to enter into unprotected piping or equipment. Process equipment such as mills, spray dryers, dust collectors, blowers, and vacuum pumps are regularly connected together by piping, ducts, chutes, or conveyors. (For convenience, such systems will be referred to here simply as "pipes.")

Ducting and Piping. An explosion beginning at one point in the process can propagate through these interconnections to other parts of the process, both upstream and downstream. Generally, isolation techniques are necessary unless a qualified risk analysis is performed and a determination is made based on both probability and consequence that the risk is acceptable. Flame propagation inside ducting or piping is somewhat unpredictable for dusts. Tests have shown that propagation is much less likely under certain conditions. Piping of less than 100 mm (4 in.) in diameter is far less likely to provide a conduit for flame spread than piping of larger diameters.

Dense phase pneumatic transfer (air velocity down near 600 ft/min, and solids loading ratio* greater than 30) is also much less likely to provide a conduit for flame spread propagation than dilute phase pneumatic transfer (air velocity in the region of 2200–3600 ft/min [11–18 m/sec] and solids loading ratio less than 15). As reported by Pineau[28] it is not uncommon for propagation to occur as infrequently as one time in

*Solids loading ratio is the ratio of average solid mass to air mass in the transfer line.

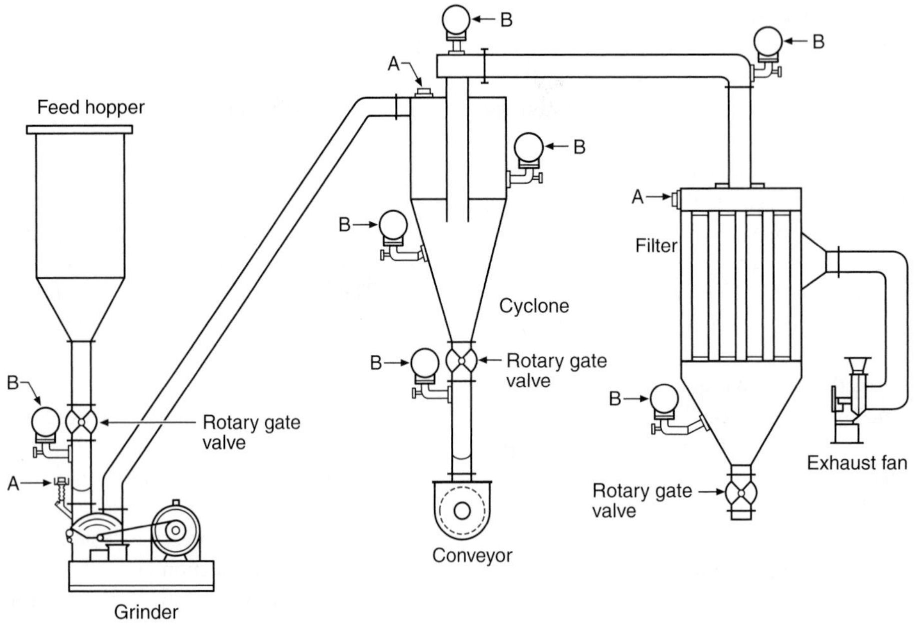

FIGURE 17.8.9 Deflagration Protection System for a Typical Grinding Plant. Deflagration detectors (A) actuate high-rate-discharge extinguishers (B).

ten in controlled experiments for 150 mm piping, even for dilute phase systems. Compared to other dusts, metal dusts and other high K_{St} dusts are more likely to propagate deflagrations through smaller diameter pipes. For interconnected vessels that are relatively close together, measures to reduce P_{red} for each interconnected vessel, taking into account that propagation could occur, would not necessarily eliminate the need for isolation techniques.

Flammable gases and combustible dusts are commonly conveyed between process units in pipe or duct systems. Dust or powdered materials are frequently transported together with air in dilute or dense phase conveying. Combustible vapors may be transported, by design or by accident, in a flammable state. A pipe carrying flammable mixtures can, should ignition occur at one end, act as a fuse. The ignited mixture can propagate flame through the pipe, leading to ignition of a process unit at the other end. Flame propagation, if possible, should be blocked near the point of ignition. Otherwise, the speed at which a flame propagates in the pipe will steadily increase. If the mixture composition is in the detonable range, the flame front can undergo deflagration to detonation transition, developing pressures of about 25 times the initial pressure and reflected pressures (that experienced by an object in the flow path) of up to 50 times the initial pressure.[29] Alternatively, pressure development and flame speeds can be limited with explosion vents placed in accordance with Chapter 9 of NFPA 68. Nevertheless, the flame front can still propagate, though at a moderate speed, through the entire length of the pipes.

Prevention of flame propagation through pipe systems is an important aspect of total protection of a process plant. Isolation methods can be used to interrupt or mitigate flame propagation, deflagration pressure, pressure piling that may lead to blast and shock formation, and flame jet ignition between items of equipment. Each isolation technique has unique application limitations. Some of these limitations are summarized in Table 17.8.9 and are discussed below.

Passive Isolation Devices. Passive protection devices include material chokes (rotary valves), flame front diverters, passive float valves (explosion check valves), static dry flame arresters, and hydraulic-type (liquid seal) flame arresters.

Flame Arresters. Flame arresters are constructed so as to cause the gas flow to pass through small passageways to prevent flame propagation due to thermal quenching. The maximum experimental safe gap (MESG), through which a flame cannot pass, can be determined using a device such as the Westerberg explosion test vessel.[30] These devices are not suitable for dust or saturated vapor service.

Flame arresters are normally placed at the end of a pipeline near a potential source of ignition. Special requirements are placed on flame arresters intended for use at a significant distance from the pipe end, for example, mounted in-line. NFPA 69 includes requirements for installation of in-line flame arresters. The U.S. Coast Guard has promulgated testing requirements for arresters that, when located in mid-pipe positions, may be challenged by a detonation. These requirements have been adopted in ANSI/UL 525, *Standard for Safety Flame Arresters.*[31]

Flame Front Diverters. Pressure piling and flame jet ignition through interconnecting piping can be controlled by means of a flame front diverter. The basic operating principle of this device is to vent the deflagration at a point where the flow direction is typically changed by 180 degrees. Figure 17.8.10 shows

TABLE 17.8.9 Isolation Features of Pipe and Duct Protection Systems

Isolation System	*Type*	*Fuel Type*	*Deflagration Isolation*	*Ignition Source Isolation*	*Flow (Pressure) Isolation*
Chemical barrier	Active	Dust, gas	Yes	Yes	No
Mechanical valve	Active	Dust, gas	Yes	Yes	Yes
Actuated float valve	Active	Gas	Yes	Yes	Yes
Actuated pinch valve	Active	Dust, gas	Yes	Yes	Yes
Rotary valve	Passive	Dust	Yes	*	Yes
Flame arrester	Passive	Gas	Yes	Yes	No
Flame front diverter	Passive	Dust	No	No	Yes
Liquid seal	Passive	Gas	Yes	Yes	No
Float valve	Passive	Gas	Yes	Yes	Yes

*Rotary valves are capable of preventing flame front passage under certain conditions but do not always prevent the passage of burning embers.

several flame front diverter designs. Due to the inertia of the fast flow caused by the deflagration, the flow will tend to maintain its *upward* direction rather than making a sharp turn, as it would when the velocity is low (at normal conditions). When the high-speed deflagration flame continues *upward,* it pushes open either a hinged cover or bursts a rupture disk located at the top of the diverter, allowing the flame to be released to the atmosphere. Some flame front diverters have demonstrated the ability to prevent flame propagation. In most cases, tests have indicated that diverters were not completely effective in preventing flame propagation. Where this has occurred, however, the deflagration severity was reduced; pressure piling did not occur or was less severe.

Siwek[32] discusses some design details concerning flame front diverters. More information about flame front diverters is presented in books by Bartknecht[15] and Eckhoff.[4] Bartknecht

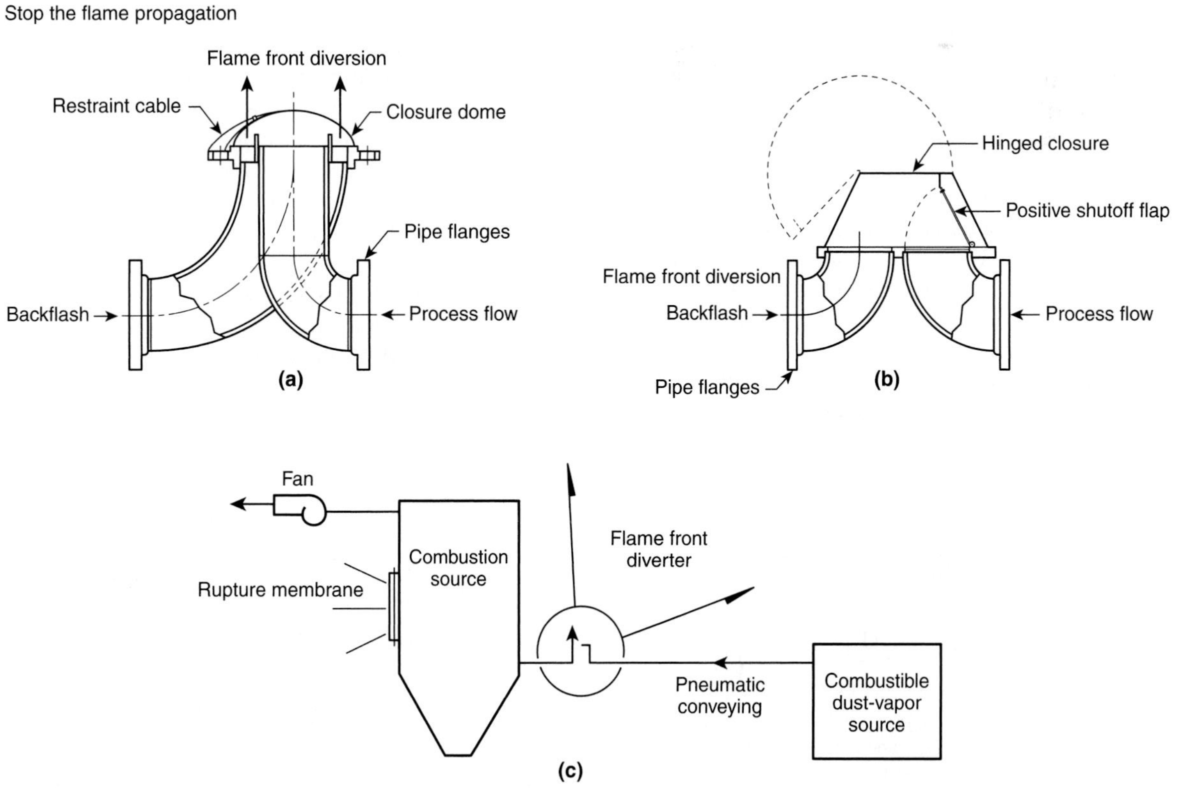

FIGURE 17.8.10 Typical Application and Design of Flame Front Diverters

recommends not using a flame front diverter as the only means of isolation if it is intended to stop flame propagation. Before flame front diverters are specified, they should be tested for the intended application.[32]

Passive Float Valves. A deflagration in pipe can generate flow velocities well in excess of the process flow velocities. Not unlike common check valves in hydraulic systems, passive float valves are designed to close at a specific flow rate, or a rated pressure differential, resulting from the deflagration. Therefore, the deflagration must develop a minimum strength pressure wave in the upstream piping. The valve float seals against a valve seat on closing and is held in place by a retaining device. The float valve remains closed until manually reset. A schematic drawing of a typical flow-actuated passive float valve and its internals is shown in Figure 17.8.11. The float valve typically functions in both directions.

A potential problem with this valve is that an elastomeric seat, if used, could be adversely affected in high-temperature environments. Another possible problem is that powder coating on the seal surfaces can prevent a tight seal, and flame breakthrough is then possible. Since a certain minimum pressure differential is required to close the float valve, the propagation of an explosion through a pipe will not be stopped if its pressure is lower than the minimum actuation pressure of the float valve. The placement of flow-actuated float valves requires a determination of the minimum and maximum distances from the origin of the explosion. Placement at the minimum distance ensures that the float valve closes before flame arrival. Placement at the maximum distance ensures that detonation does not develop in the vicinity of the float valve and that the pressure does not exceed the design pressure of the float valve. These distances are usually recommended by the valve vendor and are affected by the explosibility of the fuel, the pipe diameter, and the expected minimum and maximum P_{red} in the upstream enclosure.

Rotary Valves. Rotary valves are commonly used in process design to maintain pressure differences between interconnecting equipment. They need special operational and mechanical features to perform explosion isolation. If an explosion occurs, the rotary valve has to be automatically stopped to avoid transport of glowing and/or burning material to downstream equipment where it could cause a secondary fire or act as an ignition source to ignite a dust cloud and cause a deflagration.[15]

There are two different isolation concepts from which to chose, either flame quenching by maintaining close clearances or material blocking by maintaining a product layer above the valve. If the close clearance concept is chosen, it is important that actual clearance of such rotary valves is measured before installation and monitored using a preventive maintenance program such that the design clearance is not exceeded due to wear. If the material blocking concept is chosen, it is important that the hopper or vessel located upstream of the valve have a minimum inventory of solids to prevent flames passing through the solids due to the pressure wave from an explosion in the hopper/vessel. To maintain this minimum height of solids in the hopper upstream of the rotary valve, low-level sensors are provided which are interlocked to shut down the rotary valve before the hopper goes empty, thereby maintaining a level of solids above the rotary valve. This level of solids is intended to act as a seal to prevent flame and pressure transfer through the valve. A manual bypass should be provided for the low-level sensor/interlock to allow emptying of the hopper when necessary. However, the rotary valve can still significantly mitigate explosion propagation, even if total isolation is not achieved, by significantly reducing transmission of pressure. Figure 17.8.12 shows a typical rotary valve.

Hydraulic-Type (Liquid Seal) Deflagration Arresters. When an explosive mixture flows through a hydraulic arrester, it is separated into single isolated gas bubbles which rise due to buoyancy. Because of the formation of isolated bubbles continuous channels for the passage of the igniting flame do not exist. If an ignition occurs on the side of the device where the single bubbles reach the surface of the liquid, flame propagation can be blocked. This is the usual direction when hydraulic arresters are applied. In the opposite case, that is, if ignition occurs at the upstream side, separation into single gas bubbles will still take place, but the efficiency of the protection will be low, since the combustion process can be transferred to the surface of the liquid. Typical hydraulic deflagration arrester designs are seen in Figure 17.8.13.

Active Isolation Systems. The design of an active isolation system is based on the relative timing of three key processes: the time required for the detection of an explosion, the time

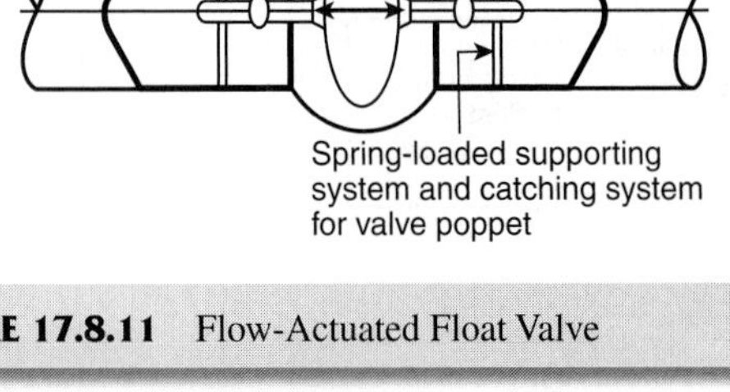

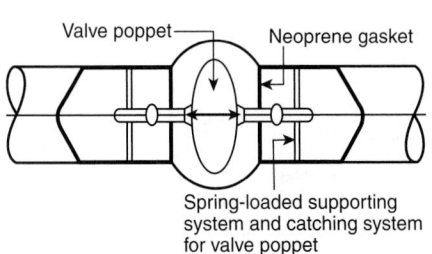

FIGURE 17.8.11 Flow-Actuated Float Valve

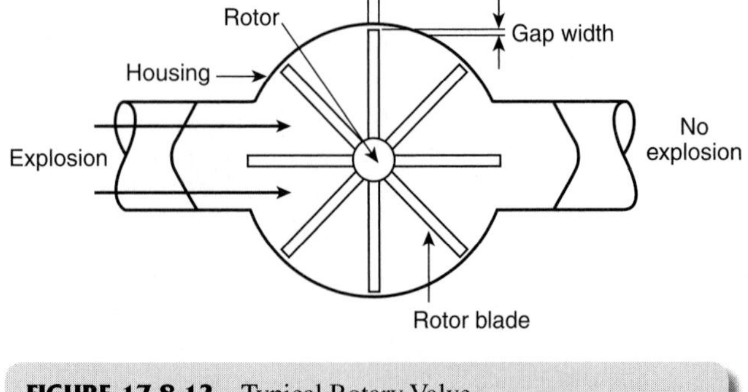

FIGURE 17.8.12 Typical Rotary Valve

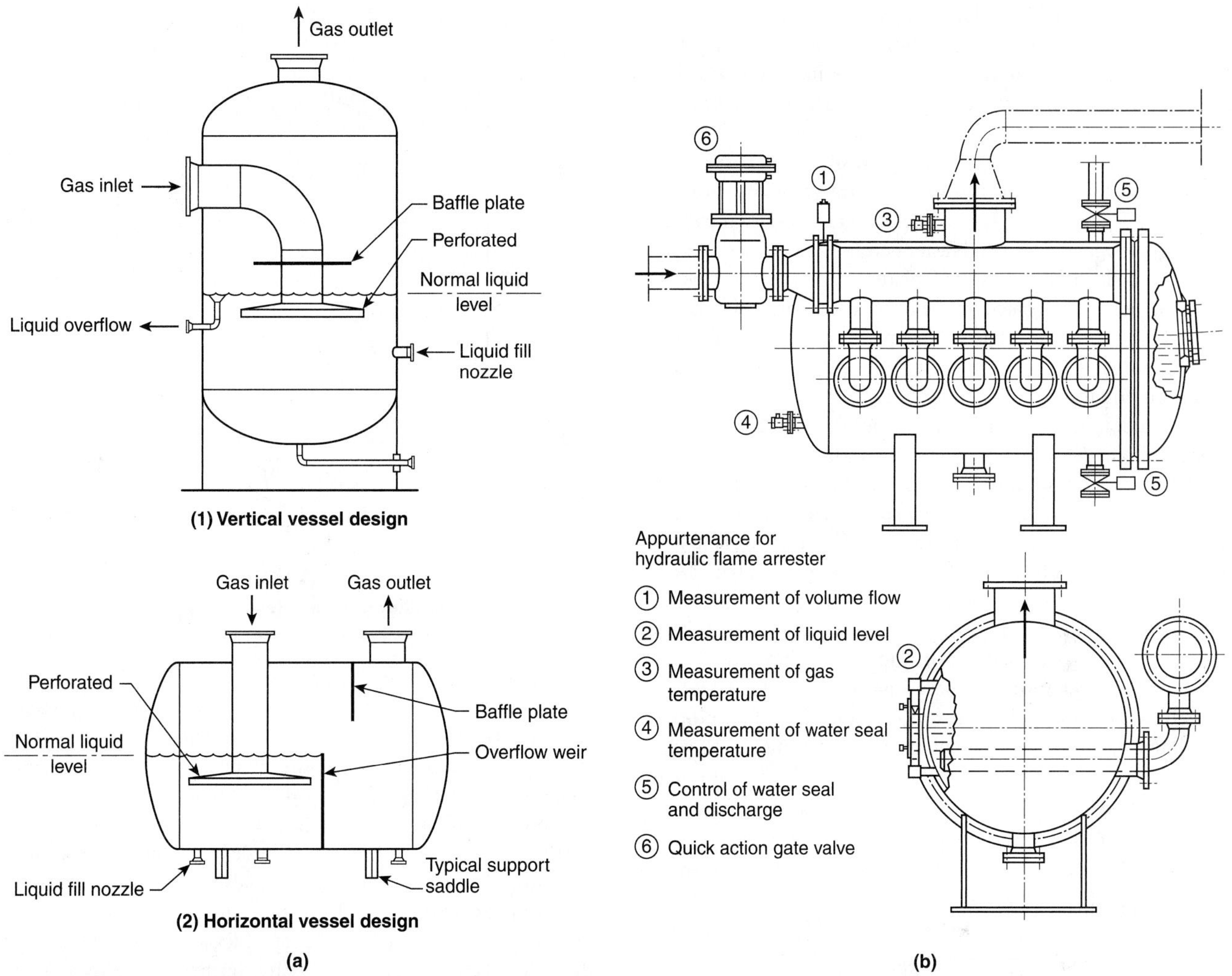

FIGURE 17.8.13 (a) Bubble Screen Hydraulic Flame Arrester; (b) Sparge Tube Hydraulic Arrester

required for the creation of a barrier, and the time it takes for the propagating flame front to reach that barrier. If the flame front can reach the barrier location before a complete barrier is established, then the isolation fails as the flame will travel beyond the barrier location. In such cases, the barrier needs to be placed further downstream to catch the flame front, assuming the pipe is sufficiently long, and the required distance is not too long to promote pressure piling and transition into detonation.

Since the protection is deployed only after the detection of an explosion, the design, fabrication, specification, and installation of these systems pose unique challenges. Establishment of an adequate barrier before the arrival of the flame front is the key to successful protection. The hardware-specific barrier establishment time is one side of this inequality and is carefully controlled as a part of the manufacturing and service quality programs. On the other side of the inequality is the time from the moment of detection to the moment the flame front arrives at the barrier location. Flame travel time is calculated from the three contributors to the flame speed: air velocity in the pipe prior to the explosion, air velocity induced by the explosion pressure rise upstream, and flame acceleration through the pipe. In addition to other occupancy specific parameters, the system design considers both strongest credible explosions, to specify a minimum distance between the possible ignition location and the barrier location, and weakest credible explosions, to ensure detectability.

The time required to create a barrier is the most straightforward to determine when compared to the others and depends on the type of isolation process. For chemical isolation, the time is determined by factors such as the time to initiate discharge, the discharge velocity, and duct diameter. The discharge velocity is affected by the gas pressure used to propel the agent as well as the length and diameter of the discharge piping. Mechanical isolation (fast-acting valves) is characterized by the time required for valve closure, which depends on the closure energetics and duct diameter. Float and pinch valves have similar dependencies. Detection is most often based on the system reaching a preset pressure or a pressure rate of rise. This requires a finite and not insignificant amount of time.

The time required for detection is dependent primarily on the preset conditions, the vessel volume, and the K_{St} or K_G. The detection time will increase as the volume increases and will decrease as K_{St} (K_G) increases. For example, a dust with a low K_{St} in a large volume will take considerably more time for pressure detection than a high K_{St} dust in a small volume. Similarly, ignition near the pipe inlet will be difficult to detect before it is too late. The effect of delayed detection can be to allow the flame to propagate farther and faster before isolation is initiated, and may result in failure of the isolation performance. Optical detection, normally located on the duct close to the inlet, is not affected in this manner. It does, however, require that the flame enter the duct in order to be detected. Optical detection can also be challenging for dust service.

Prediction of the flame propagation time is the most challenging among the three processes. It is well known that flames accelerate in ducts so that flame speed or burning velocity increases as the flame travels. Flame speed and acceleration are affected strongly by fuel characteristic (K_{St}, K_G), turbulence, elbows and other obstructions in the duct, conveyance flow velocity, and the reduced pressure in the primary enclosure. A scientifically valid and universally accepted methodology to predict flame speed and acceleration inside industrial pipes does not exist. As a result, the active isolation system manufacturers have no choice but to resort to using simplified proprietary flame acceleration correlations based on limited data sets. Additional information can be found in Vogl[33], Chatrathi and Going[34], Siwek and Moore[35], Roser et al.[36], Chatrathi et al.[37], Moore and Spring[38], and Pineau[39].

Active protection systems include the following:

- Actuated float valves
- Actuated pinch valves
- Automatic fast-acting mechanical valves
- Chemical isolation systems

Actuated Float Valves. Actuated float valves are similar to the passive float valves described previously. In order to achieve satisfactory performance when low explosion overpressures are expected, these valves are equipped with pneumatic means (such as pressurized gas or gas generator) to effect rapid closure. The system detectors and the control panel logic determines when to close actuated float valves. The actuated float valve typically functions in a single direction.

Actuated Pinch Valves. The valve trim (internals) is an elastomer pinch surrounded by a gas chamber. In the event of a deflagration, an electrical signal is sent from a sensor, typically mounted on a deflagration relief device, to an air tank mounted integral to the valve. The gas tank discharges gas to the chamber surrounding the elastomer pinch and compresses it, which pinches off flow in the pipeline. Because the pinch has relatively little mass, it is both very fast acting and imparts low shock to the piping. The pinch, however, may be adversely affected by sustained high temperatures such as might be encountered in a fire. A schematic of a pinch valve can be found in Figure 17.8.14.

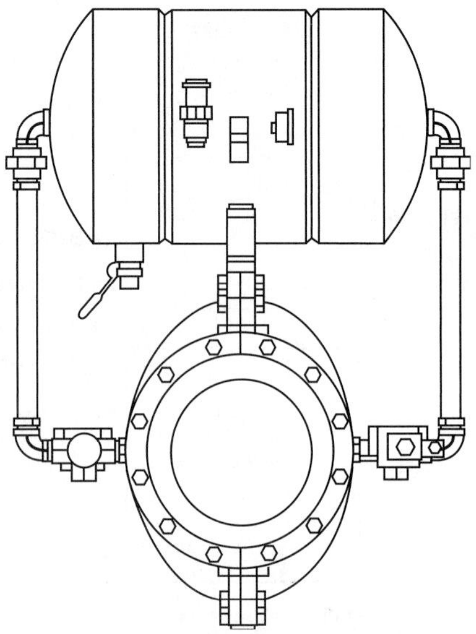

FIGURE 17.8.14 Pinch Valve

Automatic Fast-Acting Mechanical Valves. Positive mechanical isolation of a pipe system is another way to prevent passage of flames or pressure pulses from communicating between process units. Automatic fast-acting mechanical valves are actuated (closed) on a signal from a detector (sensor) in the pipeline between two items of interconnected process equipment. The detector sends a signal to a control device which is relayed to the valve-closure mechanism. Originally this was a compressed gas cylinder which then discharged the compressed gas to a piston-cylinder assembly at the top of the valve, thereby closing the gate. The propellant is generally nitrogen at 33 to 60 barg. The valve separating the compressed gas and the piston must be rapidly opened. Mechanisms for this include rapid pressurization of a rupture disk by pyrotechnical (detonator) devices. In some systems, gas-generating devices have replaced the pyrotechnics. Alternately, gas generators alone have been used to generate the pressure required to rapidly close the valve gate. Plant-air actuated valves are also available. Fast-acting slide gate isolation valves are shown in Figure 17.8.15 and can be mounted in vertical, horizontal, or inclined piping. With this type of valve, the pipe area is completely open and can be built without pockets and dead corners, so that dust will not settle out or accumulate. Special dampers absorb the substantial forces from the closing device and prevent the slide from springing back after closure.

Arrangements of isolation valve systems are shown in Figure 17.8.15 and Figure 17.8.16. A flame sensor is located at a sufficient distance from the valve such that, on detection of flame, the valve has adequate time to close. Fast-closing valves have been tested successfully in these applications to detect and intercept detonations in progress.[40]

Chemical Isolation Systems. Rather than completely blocking a pipe or duct by a valve, an alternative approach is to discharge a chemical extinguishing medium (suppressant) into the pipe,

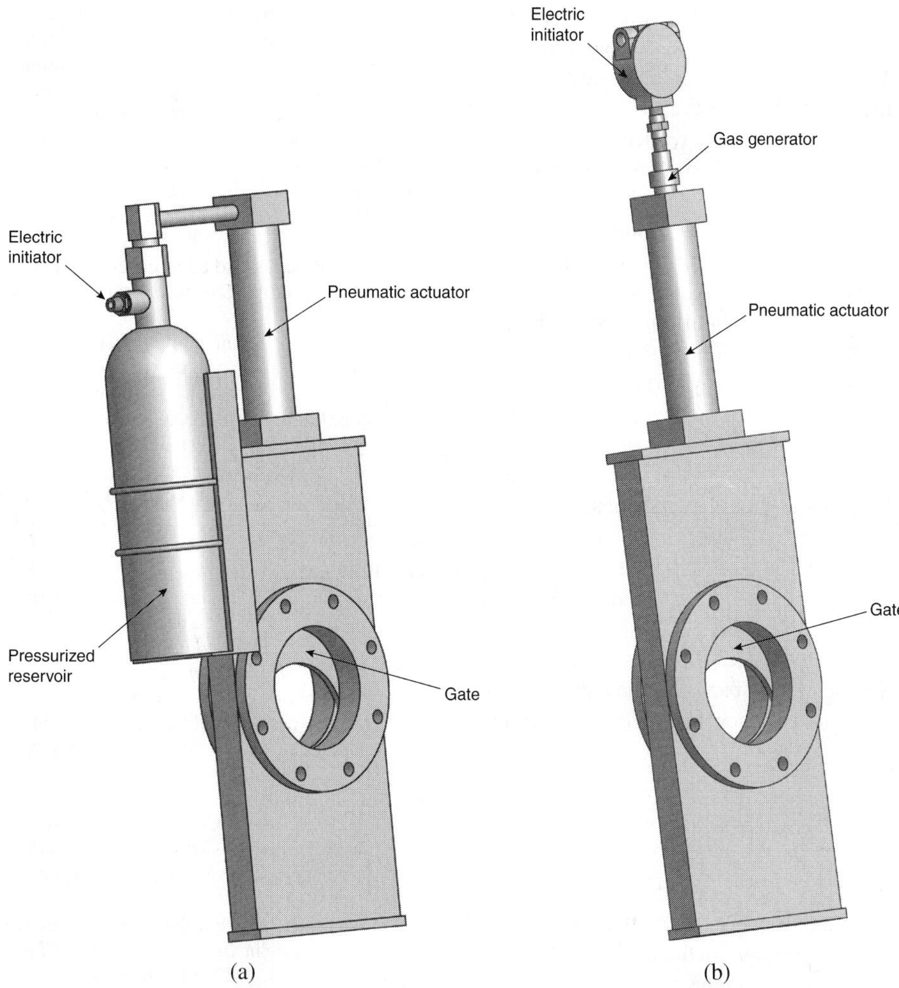

FIGURE 17.8.15 Examples of Automatic Fast-Acting Mechanical Valves

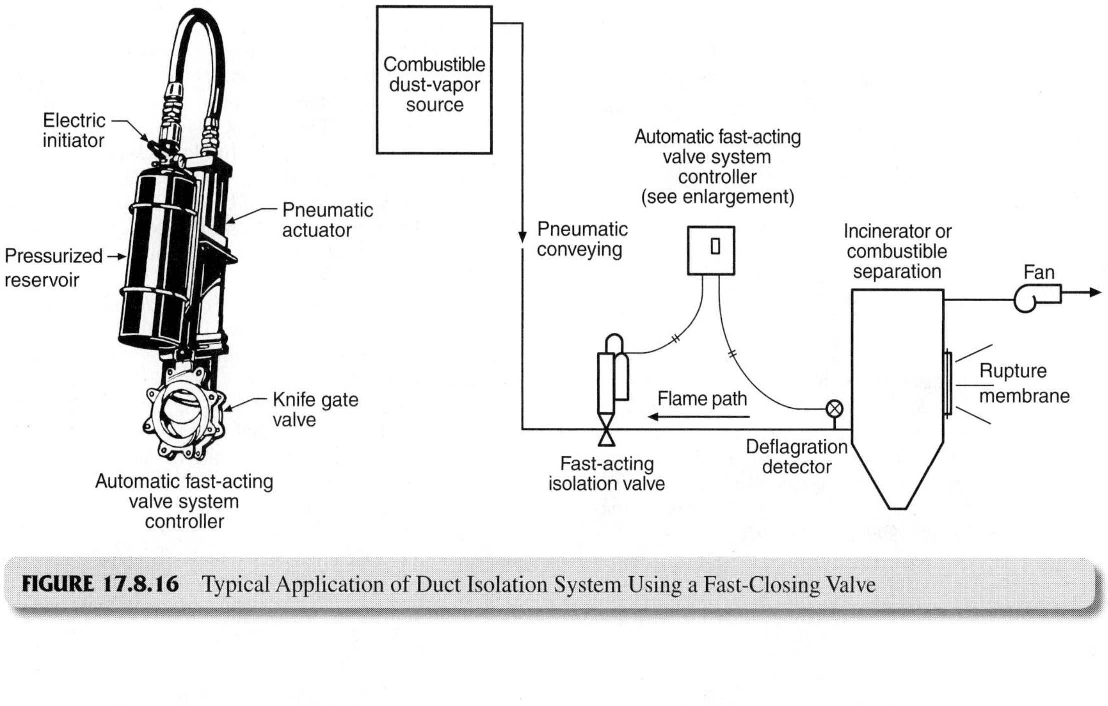

FIGURE 17.8.16 Typical Application of Duct Isolation System Using a Fast-Closing Valve

forming a nonflammable zone. These systems require special consideration in high P_{red} applications, where the induced flow velocity in the pipe can be quite high. As the injected suppressant is free to move with the induced flow, the intended nonflammable zone can be displaced or may have reduced suppressant concentration. Extinguishing compounds such as sodium bicarbonate or ammonium dihydrogen phosphate, chemicals commonly used in fire extinguishers, have been found to be very effective.[41] Halogenated hydrocarbons with low boiling points may be particularly useful, as they provide complete vapor blocks in pipes. Examples of chemicals of this type are HFC-23, HFC-125, HFC-227ea, and HFC-236fa. Halogenated agents leave no residue after discharge, but may form halogen acids upon interacting with flame and hot products of combustion. These acids may be harmful to mechanical components as well as to personnel. Additionally, due to their high global warming potential, these agents face environmental regulations limiting their use. Both dry chemical and gaseous agents have been used successfully in industrial pipe and duct explosion protection systems applications. Applications where chemical barriers are used are often similar to the example shown for fast-acting valves in Figure 17.8.15, where an agent bottle is used in place of a valve to create an inert chemical barrier in the pipe or duct. Chemical isolation systems must be specifically engineered for each application.

SUMMARY

The purpose of this chapter was to provide basic guidance in the prevention of deflagrations and to outline the more commonly employed explosion protection methods. The subject of explosion prevention was presented in the context of deflagration prevention through control or elimination of flammable atmospheres and ignition sources. Careful application of steps to prevent deflagrations is no guarantee that such events will not occur, but only that their likelihood is reduced. Additional protection is afforded through use of any of several explosion mitigation methods. These techniques come into play once ignition has occurred and serve to vent, contain, or redirect the expanding combustion gases, or suppress the combustion process itself. The reader is urged to consult other chapters in this handbook that are relevant to the fundamentals of fires, explosions, and extinguishing systems, and the literature cited at the end of this chapter.

BIBLIOGRAPHY

References Cited

1. Ural, E. A., "Dust Entrainability and Its Effect on Explosion Propagation in Elongated Structures," *Plant/Operations Progress,* Vol. 11, No. 3, 1992, pp. 176–181.
2. Ural, E. A., "Personnel Protection Against Heat Exposure from a Deflagration via a Rapid One-Time Surface Wetting," *Proceedings* of the Halon Options Technical Working Conference, Albuquerque, NM, April 27–29, 1999, pp. 301–307.
3. AIChE/CCPS, *Guidelines for Hazard Evaluation Procedures,* 2nd ed., Center for Chemical Process Safety, American Institute of Chemical Engineers, New York, 1992.
4. Eckhoff, R. K., *Dust Explosions in the Process Industries,* 3rd ed., Gulf Professional Publishing, Boston, 2003.
5. Frurip, D., Britton, L., Fenlon, W., Going, J., Harrison, K., Niemeier, J., and Ural, E. A., "The Role of ASTM E27 Methods in Hazard Assessment," 38th Loss Prevention Symposium, April 25–29, 2004, New Orleans, LA, American Institute of Chemical Engineers, 2004.
6. Bodurtha, F. T., *Industrial Explosion Prevention and Protection,* McGraw-Hill, New York, 1980.
7. Lewis, B., and von Elbe, G., *Combustion, Flames and Explosions of Gases,* 3rd ed., Academic Press, Orlando, FL, 1987.
8. Strehlow, R. A., *Combustion Fundamentals,* McGraw-Hill, New York, 1984.
9. Ural, E. A., "Flammability Potential of Selected Halogenated Fire Suppression Agents and Refrigerants at Room Temperature and Elevated Pressure," 36th Annual Loss Prevention Symposium, March 10–14, 2002, New Orleans, LA, American Institute of Chemical Engineers, 2002.
10. Hoppe, T., Jaeger, N., and Terry, J., "Safe Handling of Combustible Powders During Transportation, Charging, Discharging, and Storage," 8th International Colloquium on Dust Explosions, Schaumburg, IL, September 21–25, 1998.
11. Britton, L. G., *Avoiding Static Ignition Hazards in Chemical Operations, A CCPS Concept Book,* American Institute of Chemical Engineers, New York, 1999.
12. ASTM E1226, *Standard Test Method for Pressure and Rate of Pressure Rise for Combustible Dusts,* American Society for Testing and Materials, W. Conshohocken, PA, 1994.
13. Ural, E. A., "A Simplified Development of a Unified Dust Explosion Vent Sizing Formula," *Process Safety Progress,* Vol. 20, No. 2, 2001, pp. 136–144.
14. "Marine Vapor Control Systems," 33 CFR Part 154, *Federal Register,* June 21, Coast Guard/Department of Transportation, Washington, DC, 1990, pp. 25428–25451.
15. Bartknecht, W., *Dust Explosions,* Springer-Verlag, Berlin, Germany, 1989.
16. Bruderer, R. E., "Ignition Properties of Mechanical Sparks and Hot Surfaces in Dust/Air Mixtures," *Plant Operations Progress,* Vol. 8, No. 3, 1989, pp. 152–164.
17. ASTM E2021, *Standard Test Method for Hot Surface Ignition Temperature of Dust Layers,* American Society for Testing and Materials, W. Conshohocken, PA, 2001.
18. Dorsett, H. G., et al., "Laboratory Equipment and Test Procedures for Evaluating Explosibility of Dusts," RI 5624, U.S. Bureau of Mines, U.S. Department of the Interior, Washington, DC, 1960.
19. Recommendations on the Transport of Dangerous Goods, Manual of Tests and Criteria, United Nations, 2003.
20. ASTM E680, *Standard Test Method for Drop Weight Impact Sensitivity of Solid-Phase Hazardous Materials,* American Society for Testing and Materials, W. Conshohocken, PA, 1992.
21. "Grain-Handling Facilities, Inside Bucket Elevators," 29 CFR 1910.272(b)(2)(p)(6)(i), Occupational Safety and Health Administration, U.S. Department of Labor, Washington, DC, Apr. 1, 1991.
22. IEC, "Electrical Apparatus for Explosive Gas Atmospheres," *Publication 79–1A,* International Electrotechnical Commission, Geneva, Switzerland, 1975.
23. Jones, T. B., and King, J. L., *Powder Handling and Electrostatics,* Lewis Publishers, Chelsea, MI, 1991.
24. Glor, M., *Electrostatic Hazards in Powder Handling,* John Wiley & Sons, New York, 1988.
25. Louvar, J. F., "Fundamentals of Static Electricity," Paper 12a, *Proceedings* of the 28th Annual Loss Prevention Symposium, American Institute of Chemical Engineers, Atlanta, GA, April 1994.
26. Pratt, T. H., "Static Electricity in Pneumatic Transport Systems: Three Case Histories," *Process Safety Progress,* Vol. 13, No. 3, 1994, pp. 109–113.
27. Grigg, J. P., Chattaway, A., and Ural, E. A., "Evaluation of Advanced Agents by Kidde," *Proceedings* of the Halon Options Working Conference, Albuquerque, NM, 2001.

28. Pineau, J. P., "Dust Explosions in Vessels Connected to Ducts," VDI-Berichte No. 494, 1984.
29. Nettleton, M. A., *Gaseous Detonations: Their Nature, Effects, and Control,* Chapman and Hall, London, UK, 1987.
30. Dufort, B. E., and Westerberg, W. C., "An Investigation of Fifteen Flammable Gases or Vapors with Respect to Explosion-Proof Electrical Equipment," Bulletin of Research No. 58, Underwriters Laboratories Inc., Northbrook, IL, 1969.
31. ANSI/UL 525, *Standard for Safety Flame Arresters,* Underwriters Laboratories Inc., Northbrook, IL, 1994.
32. Siwek, R. "A Review of Explosion Isolating Techniques," *Proceedings* of the 2nd World Seminar on the Explosion Phenomena and on the Application of Explosion Protection Techniques in Practice, March 4–8, 1996, Ghent, Belgium.
33. Vogl, A., "Flame Propagation in Pipes of Pneumatic Conveying Systems and Exhaust Equipment," *Process Safety Progress,* Vol. 15, No. 4, 1996, p. 219.
34. Chatrathi, K., and Going, J., "Pipe and Duct Deflagrations Associated with Incinerators," *Process Safety Progress,* Vol. 15, No. 4, 1996, p. 237.
35. Siwek, R., and Moore, P. E. "Design Practice for Extinguishing Barrier Systems, *Process Safety Progress,* Vol. 16, No. 4, 1997, p. 244.
36. Roser, M., Vogl, A., Radandt, S., Malalasekera, W., and Parkin, R., "Investigations of Flame Front Propagation Between Interconnected Process Vessels," *Journal of Loss Prevention in the Process Industries,* Vol. 12, 1999, pp. 421–436.
37. Chatrathi, K., Going, J., and Grandestaff, W., "Flame Propagation in Industrial Scale Piping," *Process Safety Progress,* Vol. 20, No. 4, 2001, pp. 286–294.
38. Moore, P., and Spring, D., *Design of Explosion Isolation Barriers,* IChemE Symposium Series No. 150, 2004, pp. 1–20.
39. Pineau, J. P., "Mechanisms of the Propagation of Dust Explosions in Elongated Vessels," Seminar Course on Dust Explosion Venting, London, October 1987.
40. Senecal, J. A., and Meltzer, J. S., "Barrier Detonation Arresting Systems," American Petroleum Institute's Marine Technical-Environmental Conference, Chantilly, VA, January 1992.
41. Chatrathi, K., and DeGood, R., "Explosion Isolation Systems Used in Conjunction with Explosion Vents," *Plant/Operations Progress,* Vol. 10, No. 3, 1991, pp. 159–163.

NFPA Codes, Standards, and Recommended Practices

Reference to the following NFPA codes, standards, and recommended practices will provide further information on explosion prevention and protection discussed in this chapter. (See the latest version of The NFPA Catalog *for availability of current editions of the following documents.)*

NFPA 30, *Flammable and Combustible Liquids Code*
NFPA 68, *Standard on Explosion Protection by Deflagration Venting*
NFPA 69, *Standard on Explosion Prevention Systems*
NFPA 70, *National Electrical Code®*
NFPA 91, *Standard for Exhaust Systems for Air Conveying of Vapors, Gases, Mists, and Noncombustible Particulate Solids*
NFPA 484, *Standard for Combustible Metals*
NFPA 496, *Standard for Purged and Pressurized Enclosures for Electrical Equipment*
NFPA 497, *Recommended Practice for the Classification of Flammable Liquids, Gases, or Vapors and of Hazardous (Classified) Locations for Electrical Installations in Chemical Process Areas*
NFPA 499, *Recommended Practice for the Classification of Combustible Dusts and of Hazardous (Classified) Locations for Electrical Installations in Chemical Process Areas*
NFPA 654, *Standard for the Prevention of Fire and Dust Explosions from the Manufacturing, Processing, and Handling of Combustible Particulate Solids*
NFPA 2001, *Standard on Clean Agent Fire Extinguishing Systems*

SECTION

18

Confining Fires

Robert J. Vondrasek

The *Fire Protection Handbook*® emphasizes the notion that fire safety must be addressed through system design and analysis of all elements and their relationships to each other. Nowhere is this more essential than in the decisions that determine strength, location, and other features of barriers, surfaces, and spaces in buildings. Confining fires is an important aspect of building fire protection. The six chapters of Section 18 describe construction features, built-in equipment, and techniques for confining or containing fire and fire products to within the barrier of the area where the fire began.

Chapter 1, "Confinement of Fire in Buildings," is an overview chapter that discusses barriers (such as fire doors, fire partitions, and fire walls) that are intended to limit the spread of fire.

Chapter 2, "Interior Finish," reviews the effect of interior finish materials on fire growth, examines the method of application of interior finishes and the effect on fire behavior, and summarizes various fire tests of interior materials.

Chapter 3, "Smoke Movement in Buildings," gives information on the techniques used to evaluate the physical characteristics of smoke and assess its movement in both short and tall buildings. It also covers the approaches that can be used to limit the hazard of smoke in buildings. Chapter 4, "Venting Practices," discusses venting theory, venting in industrial buildings, and automatic heat and smoke venting in sprinklered buildings.

In earlier editions of this handbook, the topic of penetration sealing was covered in a chapter on building services. This edition features an entire chapter on the topic: Chapter 5, "Penetration Sealing." Included are discussions of through-penetration/firestop systems, perimeter fire containment systems, and joint systems.

The section concludes with Chapter 6, "Deflagration (Explosion) Venting." The chapter presents the fundamentals of deflagration, detonation, pressure effects, and explosion venting.

Robert J. Vondrasek, P.E., is a vice-president of NFPA.

Chapter 1

Confinement of Fire in Buildings

Revised by
Hossein Davoodi

Chapter Contents

Key Terms

atria, compartmentation, concealed space, fire barrier, fire blocking, fire confinement, fire door, fire load, fire model, fire partition, fire plume, fire resistance, fire severity, fire spread, firestop, fire wall, Stefan-Boltzman constant, stoichiometric combustion, temperature-time curve

People and property not directly exposed to a fire can be protected by confining heat and smoke to the area of origin until the fire either is extinguished or burns itself out. People can also be protected by delaying the spread of fire and smoke until the occupants can be relocated to a place of safety.

Throughout building codes and standards, several terms are used to represent fire separation barriers, including *fire partition* and *fire barrier.* This chapter discusses barriers that are intended to limit the spread of fire. Smoke movement in buildings is discussed in Section 18, Chapter 3, "Smoke Movement in Buildings," and smoke and heat venting in Section 18, Chapter 4, "Venting Practices." The same barriers used to prevent the spread of fire will almost always be the bulwark of systems designed to prevent the spread of smoke. To be contained, a fire must be bounded by barriers that limit the transmission of heat and hot gases. Such barriers must maintain their continuity and stability under the thermal and physical forces of a fire and during the structural distortions and collapse that sometimes occur within the fire area.

The fire resistance required of a barrier depends on its intended purpose and on the expected severity of the fire to which it may be exposed. In most cases, the temperature history of the fire provides an approximate but adequate description of fire severity. If the purpose of the barrier is to limit probable fire size independent of any fire suppression actions, the barrier must then withstand the maximum expected fire that would occur during a burnout of combustibles inside the fire zone. However, if the purpose of the barrier is to contain the fire until occupants are evacuated and the fire department gains access, the time necessary for these actions determines the time that the barrier must hold back the fire, unless the fire is expected to largely burn itself out first.

Properly designed and constructed barriers that satisfy fire endurance test criteria are assigned a fire resistance rating that is measured in hours or fractions thereof. Any breach or unprotected opening in a fire barrier will negate its fire resistance rating and may indeed contribute to rapid fire spread through the barrier.

See also Section 2, Chapter 5, "Basics of Fire Containment"; Section 3, Chapter 5, "Introduction to Fire Modeling"; and Section 6, Chapter 3, "Concepts and Protocols of Fire Testing."

FIRE SEVERITY

The fire severity to which a barrier can be exposed is related to the intensity of a fully developed fire in the space adjacent to the fire barrier. For a room fire, a fully developed fire would be a postflashover fire; however, in large open volumes, such as those found in many industrial plants, a fully developed fire may occur in one area without flashover of the entire volume. It is the fully developed fire that first imposes extensive thermal and physical stresses on fire barriers. The initial possibility of barrier penetration occurs prior to full development. A typical developing fire is characterized by a flame front moving over a surface and/or flames localized to a stationary source.

Hossein Davoodi is a senior fire protection engineer in the Building Fire Protection and Life Safety division at the National Fire Protection Association.

Although such a fire does not massively attack fire barriers, it can spread through faults or openings in the barrier and cause local destruction of barrier fire resistance.

A growing fire may or may not continue to flashover or become a fully developed area-wide fire. Unless it reaches these stages, it is unlikely to threaten fire-resistive barriers except through unprotected openings or serious defects in the construction of the barrier system.

Flashover of an enclosure is likely to occur if the temperature of the upper gas layer reaches approximately 1100°F (600°C). Full-scale fire experiments and energy balance analysis of room fires have shown that the temperature of this upper gas layer depends on the heat released by the burning fire, ventilation of the enclosure, dimensions of the enclosure, and the type of finish material lining the enclosure.[1] These factors are also interdependent with each other to some degree. The larger the enclosure, the higher the heat release necessary to produce the upper gas temperature needed for flashover. The more heat lost through walls, doors, and windows, the larger the fire and/or longer the time needed to produce flashover. Conversely, the greater the combustibility of the enclosure lining, the smaller the fire needed to produce flashover. The combustibility of the lining, or interior finish, is particularly significant. Interior finish in an enclosure can reduce the rate of heat release in the enclosure to below the value necessary for flashover as well as reduce the preburn time before flashover. A practical difficulty in estimating the likelihood of room flashover is in determining a value for the heat-release rate possible from the room contents. Typical heat-release rates from some common furnishings have been summarized from full-scale experimental data.[2] These data can be used in calculating the likelihood of flashover in a particular room.

Combustion

The intensity and duration of a fully developed fire depend on the quantity of combustibles available, their burning rates, the geometry of the material, room geometery, and the air available for combustion. Fire intensity will also be somewhat lower when walls and ceilings absorb significant amounts of energy rather than act primarily as insulation or radiation barriers.

The burning rate of a fully developed fire involving a specific material or grouping of similar materials is determined by either (1) the fuel surface area available to participate in the combustion reaction or (2) the amount of oxygen available for combustion. These are referred to as fuel-surface-controlled and ventilation-controlled combustion, respectively. The maximum rate of heat transfer into fire separation barriers occurs at the point where the ventilation is just sufficient so that combustion is controlled at the fuel surface (*stoichiometric combustion*).[3] At higher ventilation rates, more heat is removed from the fire by the excess air. At lower ventilation rates, the combustion heat-release rate is less, and more unburned pyrolysis products and fuel particles are vented outside the fire area. Burning of unburned pyrolysis products outside fire compartment windows can increase the threat of floor-to-floor and building-to-building fire spread.

The possibility of failure of fire separation barriers can exist long after the fully developed fire begins to decay. However, in many real fires, this threat is mitigated by fire suppression activities. The decay in air temperature in a fire room has been reported as 27 to 36°F (15 to 20°C) per minute after fully developed fires of 10- to 15-minute duration. Other data indicate a decay rate of 18°F (10°C) per minute for longer-duration fires.[4] Cooling can be even slower in large debris piles. Fire endurance testing in the United States does not simulate a fire decay period, although the decay period is simulated by some European testing and has been proposed in U.S. testing. Research has proposed that short-duration, high-temperature fires, followed by temperature decay, should be considered.

Poorly ventilated fires that are encountered in spaces such as basements, ship holds, or enclosed interior rooms can produce sufficient heat over a long period of time to penetrate fire separation barriers. These fires start with or reach flaming combustion and, as the air in the space is consumed, revert to a state of mixed smoldering and glowing combustion with isolated or intermittent flaming. However, at present, there are no adequate experimental data or theoretical approach capable of reliably estimating the effect of these fires on fire-resistive barriers.

Standard Temperature-Time Curve

Fire-resistive barriers are evaluated in a testing furnace by exposure to a fire whose severity follows a time-varying temperature curve known as the standard temperature-time curve. The specified temperature-time history is tabulated in NFPA 251, *Standard Methods of Tests of Fire Resistance of Building Construction and Materials,* and illustrated in Figure 18.1.1. The standard temperature-time curve was adopted by the ASTM in 1918 and has been the basis of almost all fire-resistive testing ever since.

Following adoption of the curve, the National Institute of Standards and Technology (NIST), formerly the National Bureau of Standards (NBS), conducted a number of full-scale fire tests to determine how actual building fires compared with the temperatures represented on the curve.[5,6] The tests included two actual buildings that were allowed to burn to destruction and a series of fires in fire-resistive test buildings containing

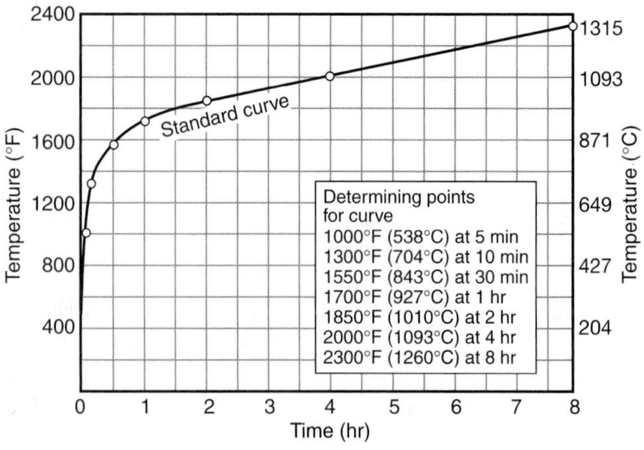

FIGURE 18.1.1 Standard Temperature-Time Curve

contents representative of office, record room, and household occupancies.

The principal variable considered in these occupancy fire tests was the amount of combustible materials present, which is defined as the fire load. Although the ventilation in the test buildings was not reported, the windows were equipped with steel shutters that could be adjusted to control ventilation and maximize fire severity. The quantitative importance of ventilation on fire severity was not identified until the 1950s. These tests conducted by NIST provided quantitative data on the temperature history of fires that were representative of various occupancies and fire load at that period of time. Fire load was expressed as the weight of ordinary combustibles in the room divided by the floor area of the room. Loading is the average amount of ordinary combustible material per square foot (m^2) of floor area. The temperature history of the fully developed fires in three test occupancies was approximately bounded by the standard temperature-time curve.

NIST developed the concept of equivalent fire severity to define the severity of actual fires that had various temperature histories. This concept states that the area above a baseline under the temperature-time curve of a test fire, which is expressed in degree hours, is an approximate representation of the severity of a fire involving ordinary combustibles. The baseline used represents the temperature the materials can be exposed to without impairing their fire-resistive capabilities. Two fires with differing temperature histories are considered to have equivalent severity when the areas under their temperature-time curves are similar. This concept permitted comparison of any fire test data to the standard temperature-time curve by relating the area under the test curve to the area under the standard curve.

TABLE 18.1.1 Estimated Fire Severity for Offices and Light Commercial Occupancies

Total Combustible Content, Including Finish, Floor, and Trim		Heat Potential Assumed*		*Equivalent Fire Severity Approximately Equivalent to That of Test Under Standard Curve for the Following Periods*
(lb/ft²)	*(kg/m²)*	*(Btu/ft²)*	*(MJ/m²)*	
5	24	40,000	454	30 min
10	49	80,000	909	1 hr
15	73	120,000	136	1½ hr
20	98	160,000	1820	2 hr
30	147	240,000	2730	3 hr
40	196	320,000	3640	4½ hr
50	245	380,000	4320	7 hr
60	290	432,000	4910	8 hr
70	340	500,000	5680	9 hr

Note: Data apply to fire-resistive buildings with combustible furniture and shelving.
*Heat of combustion of contents taken at 8000 Btu/lb up to 40 lb/ft²; 7600 Btu/lb for 50 lb; and 7200 Btu for 60 lb and more to allow for relatively greater proportion of paper. The weights contemplated by the table are those of ordinary combustible materials, such as wood, paper, or textiles.
For SI units: 1 lb/ft² = 4.88 kg/m²; 1 Btu/ft² = 1.14 J/m².

FIRE LOADS

Relationship of Fire Load and Fire Severity to Fire Resistance Requirements

The original concepts of fire severity and fire load are very important even though they are technically obsolete. These concepts are the basis for many of the fire resistance requirements of building codes and for government agencies. In many cases, this original fire severity/fire load relationship was more severe than is indicated by more accurate analysis. Such results are conservative since the resultant error is on the safe side.

Analysis of NIST tests developed an approximate relationship between fire loading and an exposure to a fire severity equivalent to the standard temperature-time curve. The weight per square foot (m^2) of ordinary combustibles (wood, paper, and similar materials with a heat of combustion of 7000 to 8000 Btu per lb [16.282 to 18.608 MJ/kg]) was related to hourly fire severity, as described in Table 18.1.1.

The fire severity/fire load relationship was the first method developed to predict the severity of a fire that would be anticipated in various occupancies. It was used to determine resistance required of fire barriers as well as structural components. Although the technique has its limitations, the fire severity/fire load relationship still provides an approximate but conservative estimate of the probable maximum fire severity with combustibles having a high heat-release rate and when fire conditions can produce temperatures significantly higher or lower than the standard temperature-time curve.

Fire load is a measure of the maximum heat that would be released if all the combustibles in a given fire area burned. Maximum heat release is the product of the mass of each combustible multiplied by its heat of combustion. In a typical building, the fire load includes combustible contents, interior finish, floor finish, and structural elements. Fire load is commonly expressed in terms of the average fire load, which is the equivalent combustible weight divided by the fire area in square feet (m^2).

Equivalent combustible weight is defined as the weight of ordinary combustibles having a heat of combustion of 8000 Btu/lb (18,608 kJ/kg) that would release the same total heat as the combustibles in the space. For example, the equivalent weight of 10 lb/ft² (48.8 kg/m²) of a plastic with a heat of combustion of 12,000 Btu/lb (27,912 J/kg) would be

$$10 \text{ lb/ft}^2 \times 12{,}000 \text{ Btu/lb} = 120{,}000 \text{ Btu/ft}^2$$

$$120{,}000 \text{ Btu/ft}^2 \div 8000 \text{ Btu/lb ordinary combustibles} = 15 \text{ lb/ft}^2$$

or

$$48.8 \text{ kg/m}^2 \times 27.9 \text{ MJ/kg} = 1365 \text{ MJ/m}^2$$

$$1365 \text{ MJ/m}^2 \div 18{,}608 \text{ MJ/kg} = 75.36 \text{ kg/m}^2$$

Technically accurate methods for calculating the actual fire severity and fire resistance requirements are available for many common building-occupancy-contents combinations. Technical

TABLE 18.1.2 Characteristic Fire Loads in Office Buildings

	Government Buildings			Private Buildings		
		Total Fire Load (lb/ft²)			Total Fire Load (lb/ft²)	
Room Use	*No. of Rooms Sampled*	*Mean*	*Std. Dev.*	*No. of Rooms Sampled*	*Mean*	*Std. Dev.*
General	342	7.3	4.4	479	7.7	4.3
Clerical	77	5.8	5.2	146	6.8	4.0
Lobby	15	2.6	1.4	45	5.0	4.2
Conference	39	4.2	6.1	57	5.9	4.6
File	10	17.9	11.9	20	16.2	12.9
Storage	35	11.7	19.2	77	13.2	11.7
Library	2	30.2	7.8	10	23.6	10.8

Note: Fire in steel enclosures. Weight of combustibles was converted to an equivalent weight of combustibles having a heat of combustion of 8000 Btu/lb.
For SI units: 1 lb/ft² = 4.88 kg/m².

limitations are primarily related to availability of input data rather than the analytical tools. These methods have been accepted to varying degrees under performance-based building codes adopted in some countries. Such analytical approaches have not yet been widely or routinely accepted by code authorities in the United States. However, third-party reviews are opening up opportunities for this alternative.

Occupancy Fire Loads

A number of surveys have identified the fire loads found in various occupancies[5,7,8] (Tables 18.1.2 and 18.1.3).

Data from some fire load surveys as well as the inherent nature of combustible contents likely to be encountered suggest that the dispersion of fire load within a certain class of rooms can be approximated by either a normal or moderately skewed frequency distribution curve (Figure 18.1.2). The standard deviation, included in Tables 18.1.2 and 18.1.3, can be used to determine the probability that a particular fire load value will not be exceeded in a class of rooms. A fire load that is one standard deviation above the mean value of a normal distribution curve would represent an upper boundary for 84.13 percent of the fire loads in rooms of that class. Two standard deviations above the mean would bound 97.73 percent of the fire loads in that class of rooms, and three standard deviations, 99.86 percent of the fire loads. Thus, if a fire barrier were to be designed on the basis of two standard deviations above the mean, there would be a 97.73 percent probability that this fire load would not be exceeded in a similar room.

The above percentages consider that the distribution of fire loads is perfectly normal. If the distribution is more accurately defined by a moderately skewed curve, the percentages represent only close approximations.

Derated Fire Loads

Ordinary combustibles that are completely or largely enclosed in steel containers will not burn completely during a room fire and, therefore, will not contribute a full 8000 Btu/lb (18.608 MJ/kg) to the fire load. The General Services Administration (GSA) has developed guidelines for determining a derated fire load for office buildings, which can be applied to other occupancies having similar classes of combustibles.[9] The total contents fire load is divided into three categories: (1) weight of materials completely enclosed in containers, such as steel desks or file

TABLE 18.1.3 Typical Fire Loads

Type of Room	*Contents Fire Load (lb/ft²)*	*Standard Deviation (lb/ft²)*
Living room	3.9	1.13
Family room	2.7	0.65
Bedroom	4.3	1.15
Dining room	3.6	1.02
Kitchen	3.2	0.77
Hospital patient room	1.2	0.36
Nursing home patient room	2.6	0.62

For SI units: 1 lb/ft² = 4.88 kg/m².

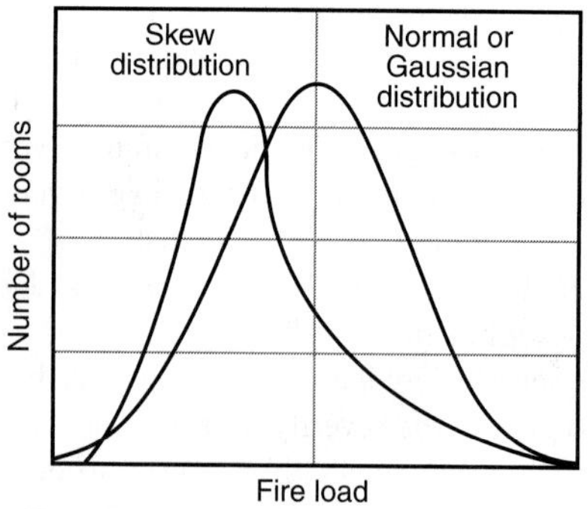

FIGURE 18.1.2 Expected Distributions of Sample Fire Loads

cabinets, (2) weight of materials enclosed on five sides, such as in a steel bookcase, and (3) weight of free combustibles.

Completely enclosed combustibles will be heated by the room fire and pyrolyze, and the escaping pyrolysis products will burn. Therefore, the heat that the enclosed combustibles release depends on the extent to which they are *pyrolyzed.* This is related to the intensity and duration of the room fire, which in turn is related to the total combustibles in the room. The extent to which the enclosed contents are derated is determined by considering the ratio of the total weight of enclosed combustibles to the total weight of all combustibles in the room. Thus,

$$F_T = W_E + W_{PE} + W_{FE}$$

A derating factor is assigned to W_E as tabulated:

Ratio W_E/F	*Derating Factor, K*
Under 0.5	0.4
0.5 to 0.8	0.2
Over 0.8	0.1

Ordinary combustibles enclosed on five sides by steel, such as in a bookcase, are derated to 75 percent of their weight.

The total derated fire load is given by the following equation:

$$F_{DR} = K_{WE} + 0.75W_{PE} + W_{FE}$$

The specific fire load is then computed by dividing by the floor area.

This derating procedure can be applied if other than ordinary combustibles are included in the fire load. The total weight of other combustibles must be expressed in terms of an equivalent weight of ordinary combustibles that would release the same total heat in burning. This is accomplished by multiplying the weight of the other combustibles by the ratio of their heat of combustion in Btu/lb, to 8000 Btu/lb (19 MJ/kg), the heat of combustion of ordinary combustibles.

British Fire Loading Studies

The British also have graded building occupancies according to hazard. Three classifications—low, moderate, and high fire loads—were defined in terms of Btu/ft^2 (J/m^2).

Occupancies of Low Fire Load. The fire load of an occupancy is described as low if it does not exceed an average of 100,000 Btu/ft^2 (1134 MJ/m^2) of net floor area of any compartment, or an average of 200,000 Btu/ft^2 (2268 MJ/m^2) in limited isolated areas, provided that storage of combustible material necessary to the occupancy may be allowed to a limited extent if separated from the remainder and enclosed by appropriate-grade fire-resistive construction. Examples of occupancies of normal low fire load are retail shops, factories, and workshops.

Occupancies of Moderate Fire Load. The fire load of an occupancy is described as moderate if it exceeds an average of 100,000 Btu/ft^2 (1134 MJ/m^2) of net floor area of any compartment but does not exceed an average of 200,000 Btu/ft^2 (2268 MJ/m^2), or an average of 400,000 Btu/ft^2 (4540 MJ/m^2) in limited isolated areas, provided that storage of combustible material necessary to the occupancy may be allowed to a limited extent if separated from the remainder and enclosed by fire-resistive construction of an appropriate grade. Examples of occupancies of moderate fire load are retail shops, factories, and workshops.

Occupancies of High Fire Load. The fire load of an occupancy is described as high if it exceeds an average of 200,000 Btu/ft^2 (6 MJ/m^2) of net floor area but does not exceed an average of 400,000 Btu/ft^2 (4540 MJ/m^2) of net floor area, or an average of 800,000 Btu/ft^2 (9080 MJ/m^2) in limited isolated areas. Examples of occupancies with normal high fire load are warehouses and other buildings used for the bulk storage of commodities of a recognized nonhazardous nature.

Other Fire Loading Studies

Fire loading studies have been conducted in other countries. Results of some of these studies are summarized in Tables 18.1.4 through 18.1.6.

EFFECT OF VENTILATION

The burning rate of fully developed fires may depend on the available fuel surface area or on the air available for combustion. When ample air is available, the burning rate of a fire depends on the exposed surface area and on the properties of the combustible itself. Fully developed fires involving ordinary residential furnishings burn at a rate *R,* which can be approximated by the following equation:

$$R = 0.09A_f \text{ (lb/min)}$$

TABLE 18.1.4 Mean Values of Fire Load and Fire Load Density for the Various Homes

Home Type	*Mean Fire Load (MJ)*	*Mean Fire Load Density Based on Floor Area of 22 m^2 (MJ/m^2)*	*Number of Samples*
Apartment	12,000	550	6
3 story townhome	11,000	500	5
2 story semidetached	10,000	450	4
2 story detached	11,000	500	33
3 story detached	11,000	500	4
2 story townhome	10,000	450	6
Bungalow	10,000	450	13
Duplex	7,000	300	2

Source: Table 2, "Mean Values of Fire Load and Fire Load Density for the Various Homes," *A Pilot Study of Fire Loads in Public Homes,* Institute for Research in Construction, National Research Council Canada, Research Report, No. 159, Mar. 9, 2004.

TABLE 18.1.5 Published Fire Load Densities for Residential Occupancies

Fire Load Density (MJ/m²)	*Country*	*Reference*	*Notes*
450	United States	8	Survey of basement recreation rooms in 200 single-family detached homes
500	United States	8	Survey of 70 residential recreation rooms
400, 800, 1200	New Zealand	9	Recommended in the New Zealand building code
600	Sweden	11	—
724	New Zealand	12	—
670	Japan	13	Survey of 214 homes
600, 500	Canada	—	This survey (mean values for main floor and basement living rooms in 74 homes)

Source: Table 4, "Published Fire Load Densities for Residential Occupancies," *A Pilot Study of Fire Loads in Public Homes,* Institute for Research in Construction, National Research Council Canada, Research Report, No. 159, Mar. 9, 2004.

TABLE 18.1.6 Fire Load Classifications (MJ/m²) for Different Occupancies

	Fire Load Density			
		Fractile[a] MJ/m²		
Occupancy	*Average MJ/m²*	*80%*	*90%*	*95%*
Dwelling	780	870	920	970
Hospital	230	350	440	520
Hospital storage	2000	3000	3700	4400
Hotel Bedroom	310	400	460	510
Offices	420	570	670	760
Shops	600	900	1100	1300
Manufacturing	300	470	590	720
Manufacturing and storage[b]	1180	1800	2240	2690
Libraries	1500	2250	2550	—
Schools	285	360	410	450

[a]The 80% fractile is the value that is not exceeded in 80% of the rooms or occupancies.
[b]Storage of combustible materials at less than 150 kg/m².
Source: Table 5.2.2, Draft Irish National Annex, I.S.EN 1991-1-2: 2002 Actions of Structures, Part 1-2, General Actions on Structures Exposed to Fire, National Standards Authority of Ireland.

where A_f is the exposed fuel surface in ft² (m²).[10] For the general case, the equation becomes

$$R = W_f A_f$$

where W_f = surface rate of burning of the fuel, lb/ft² (kg/m²) of exposed surface per minute.

Typical furniture found in homes and offices has a surface-area-to-weight ratio between 0.55 and 0.90 lb/ft² (2.7 and 44 kg/m²).[11] Loose combustibles, cellular material, hanging clothes, and similar materials have much higher surface-to-weight ratios and are associated with more rapidly developing fires.

When a fire cannot get sufficient air to maintain the burning rate associated with fuel-surface-controlled (stoichiometric) combustion, it will burn at a ventilation-controlled rate. The burning rate for fully developed fires with ordinary combustibles to which air is supplied through broken windows or a doorway is approximated by the following equation:

$$R = 0.62 A_o H_o^{1/2} \text{ (lb/min)}$$

where

A_o = The opening area in ft² (m²)

H_o = The height of the opening in ft (m)[12]

Airflow into the fire, through a single opening, has been found to be approximately equal to the following equation:

$$\dot{m} \simeq 5.06 C_D A_o H_o^{1/2} \text{ (lb/min)}$$

where C_D = the orifice coefficient, normally about 0.5 to 0.7.[13]

Where there are multiple openings or a window wall, the flow is less than predicted by the area, and a coefficient of about 0.35 is recommended.

The maximum fire intensity, from the standpoint of rate of heat input into barriers, occurs at a ventilation rate just sufficient to sustain a surface burning fire. This can be expressed in the following equation:

$$W_f A_f = 5.06 C_D W_a A_o H_o^{1/2}$$

where W_a is the weight of fuel each pound (kg) of air will burn completely. Typical values of W_a are presented in Table 18.1.7.[13]

The preceding relationships assume that wind is not a factor in ventilation. In addition, if the ventilating opening is an interior door, such as from a corridor, adequate combustion air must be available for the fire.

Considerable ventilating area is required for a fully developed fire to burn at a fuel-surface-controlled rate (stoichiometric combustion). For example, over one-fourth of the wall area would have to be open in a 20 ft × 20 ft (6.1 m × 6.1 m) room with an 8 ft (2.4 m) ceiling and an exposed combustible surface of 800 ft² (74.3 m²) of ordinary combustibles. Most building fires will be ventilation controlled during the period when containment is critical from the initial well-developed phase until the start of decay. A fully developed fire can change from

TABLE 18.1.7 Fuel Consumed by 1 Pound of Air at a Stoichiometric Fuel/Air Ratio

Combustible	*lb fuel/lb air*	*g fuel/kg air*
Wood	0.175	175
Polyethylene	0.069	69
Polystryene	0.076	76
Polyurethane	0.135	135
Benzene	0.076	76
Methane	0.060	60

a ventilation-controlled to fuel-surface-controlled fire as ventilation changes (such as when windows break out). Fires in modern buildings that have large glass windows may burn at ventilation-controlled rates.

FIRE MODELING

A number of mathematical models have been developed that include calculations of the temperature history of fully developed room fires as a function of ventilation, fuel, and the walls and ceiling of the room.[3,4,11,13–18] Fire models are increasingly being used in design as well as the evaluation of hazards and reconstruction of incidents. An extensive and expanding database is available that provides histories of heat release rates for combustible contents and finishes as well as the physical and thermal properties of construction materials. The most widely used models in the United States are classified as zone models and exemplified by the Consolidated Firegrowth and Smoke Transport (CFAST) component of HAZARD.[16] Zone models are available with varying degrees of complexity and can be run on personal computers. A typical assumption of zone models is the filling of the fire compartment from the top down with hot gases of a uniform temperature. An advantage of zone-based models is their ability to address smoke spread and a variety of fire-growth profiles. Field models do not make such assumptions but use computational fluid dynamics; this requires numerical solution of the differential equations describing the principles of conservation of mass, energy, momentum, and species. Field models examine a fire in two or three dimensions, breaking the compartment into thousands of cells or elements. Performing these calculations demands the use of powerful computers beyond the capabilities of most personal computers. Network flow models such as CONTAM2.4 are used to evaluate airflow paths composed of doorways, window vents, ducts, and leaks in buildings. These systems are often used to evaluate smoke management systems.

Calculations can also be made that yield the temperature rise on the unexposed wall and ceiling surfaces. Such calculations are meaningful only on the types of barriers that have extensive fire test and actual fire experience, because temperature rise is only one of the ways a fire barrier can fail. Mathematically modeling other failures can be difficult with many common constructions. In determining fire severity, this technique represents an improvement over the single-parameter fire load concept; however, it also is an approximation and has definite limitations.

All fire models have limitations and require some assumptions just as do all other engineering models used to design buildings and building systems. For example, the assumption that the temperature is uniform in the fire room is associated with the less complex postflashover fire models. The turbulence associated with a postflashover fire is assumed to mix the hot gases so that no appreciable temperature gradients exist. In fire models, this assumption is used to calculate mass airflow into the room, heat transfer from the room to walls and ceiling, and pyrolysis of the fuel. This assumption is an approximation, because temperature differences of between 250 and 500°F (139 and 278°C) have been measured within a room during postflashover fires; larger differences could be encountered in larger compartments.[19–21]

The maximum intensity of postflashover room fires occurs when the ventilation is just sufficient to permit fuel-surface-controlled (stoichiometric) combustion.[3] At either higher or lower ventilation levels, the maximum fire temperature is lower.[4] At higher ventilation levels, the fire duration will be shorter, and at lower levels, it will be longer. The ventilation necessary to sustain fuel-surface-limited (stoichiometric) combustion will depend on the combustibles in the room, their exposed surface area, surface burning rate, and the amount of air each pound (kg) of fuel requires for combustion. More ventilation would be needed to sustain fuel-surface-controlled (stoichiometric) combustion if a room contains blocks of foam rubber than if it contains an equivalent fire load of ordinary furnishings. The effect ventilation area has on the temperature of a fully developed room fire is qualitatively shown in Figure 18.1.3.

The majority of experimental fires, which form the basis for the previously described relationships, have emphasized one-room fires, fuel consisting of either ordinary household and business furnishings or wood cribs, fuel loads under 10 lb/ft^2 (48.8 kg/m^2), and at least a level of ventilation provided by an open door or large window representing 10 to 15 percent of the room area. The results of these fires have shown the following:

1. Fire room temperatures may rise much faster than the standard temperature-time curve, remain above the curve for a period of time, and then drop below it.
2. Within a normal ventilation range of about 10 to 15 percent of room area on the low end and 25 to 30 percent on the

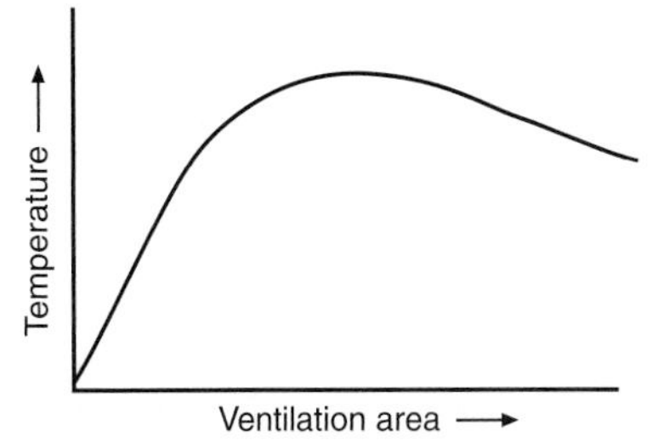

FIGURE 18.1.3 Typical Fully Developed Fire Temperature-Ventilation Curve

high end, the maximum fire temperature depends primarily on fire load, which, in turn, is related to the exposed fuel surface area.

3. Maximum fire temperatures involving ordinary furnishings generally range between 1400 and 1800°F (760 to 982°C). However, ordinary combustible materials with a very high exposed fuel surface area of 8 ft^2/ft^2 (0.74 m^2/m^2) of floor area can result in maximum fire room temperatures over 2000°F (1093°C).

Temperature histories of some typical small room fires in which ventilation was provided by an open corridor door are illustrated in Figure 18.1.4.

Higher temperatures associated with the large fuel surface areas of wood cribs are shown in Figure 18.1.5;[22] the fuel surface area was about 1000 ft^2 (93 m^2) for the 10 lb/ft^2 (48.8 kg/m^2) fire loading.

For more information on fire modeling, see Section 3, Chapter 5, "Introduction to Fire Modeling." For an overview of fire modeling, also see the *SPFE Handbook of Fire Protection Engineering*[23] and *SFPE Engineering Guide to Performance-Based Fire Protection Analysis and Design of Buildings.*[24]

FIRE SPREAD

Fire spread rarely occurs by heat transfer through, or structural failure of, walls and floor/ceiling assemblies. The common mode of fire spread in a compartmented building is through open doors, unenclosed stairways and shafts, unprotected penetrations of fire separation barriers, and nonfirestopped combustible concealed spaces. Even in buildings of combustible construction, the common gypsum board or lath-on-plaster protecting wood stud walls or wood joist floors provides 25 to 30 minutes of resistance to a fully developed fire, as determined by a standard fire test.[25] When such barriers are properly constructed and maintained and have protected openings, they will normally contain fires of maximum expected severity in light-hazard occupancies. However, no fire barrier will reliably protect against fire spread if it is not properly constructed and maintained and openings in the barrier are not protected.

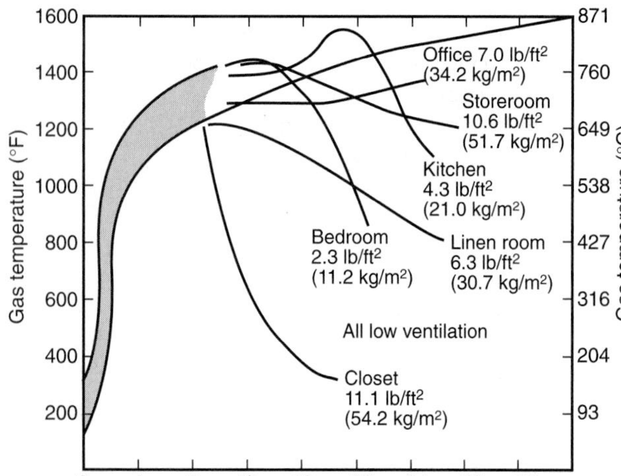

FIGURE 18.1.4 Gas Temperature at Ceiling of Burning Room

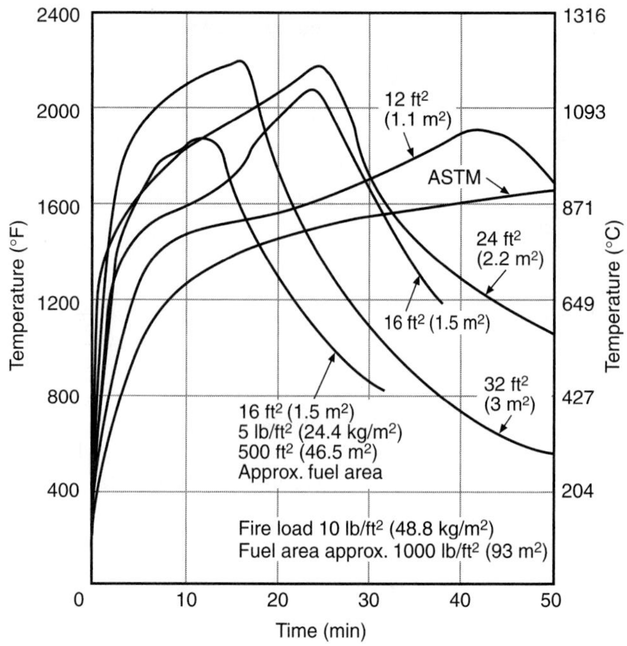

FIGURE 18.1.5 Effect of Window Area on Average Fire Room Temperature

Although typical wall and floor-ceiling constructions generally have adequate inherent fire resistance in light-hazard occupancies, there are practical advantages in requiring rated fire-resistive assemblies in new construction. Materials and construction methods required for fire-rated assemblies provide quality controls not found in typical construction.

Fire can spread horizontally and vertically beyond the room or area of origin and through compartments or spaces that do not contain combustibles. Heated unburned pyrolysis products from the fire will mix with fresh air and burn as they flow outward. This results in extended flame movement under noncombustible ceilings, up exterior walls, and through noncombustible vertical openings. This is a common way fire spreads down corridors and up open stairways and shafts. Similar phenomena have been observed in flame spread underneath the ceiling in industrial and storage buildings. Combustible interior finish in corridors and vertical openings, which by itself may be incapable of propagating flames, will be heated and may produce pyrolysis products. These products add to those from the main fire and increase the intensity and length of flames.

Once a room fire becomes fully developed, fire can spread very quickly to adjacent rooms in the absence of any fire separation barriers. When a building contains similar size rooms, the total volume of the rooms involved in fully developed fires tends to increase at an exponential rate.[26] This is illustrated in Figure 18.1.6, which shows the form of percentage increase in total fire volume, based on the initial room volume as a function of time after the initial room flashed over.

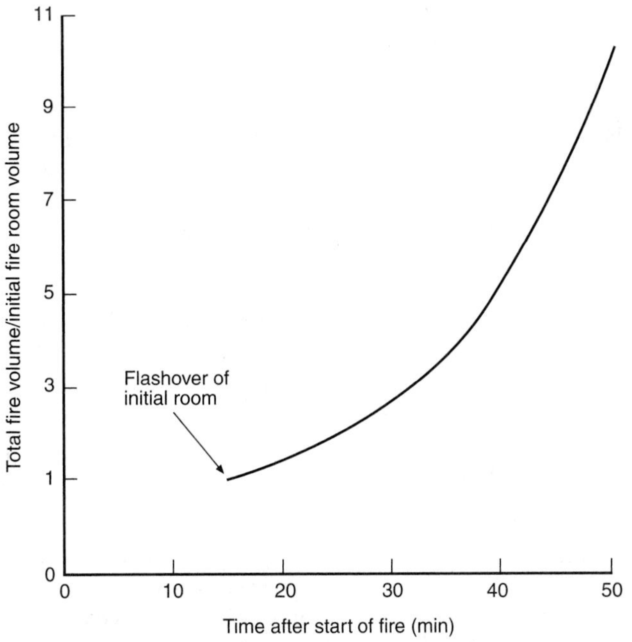

FIGURE 18.1.6 Exponential Fire Volume Increase for a Room Flashover Time of 15 Minutes

Floor-to-floor fire spread along the outside of a building is not a common occurrence, but it can and does occur, such as in the Hilton Hotel fire in Las Vegas, Nevada, in 1981. Glass panes normally break when heated to 550 to 600°F (288 to 316°C), although some breakage may occur at lower temperatures.[27] Glass breakage is actually the result of thermal stress induced by heating the area of the glass panel faster than the area of the frame.[28] The hazard is greater in high-rise buildings because of fire-fighting difficulties and because there are more floors to which fire can spread. Wide spandrels and projections, such as balconies, will reduce the risk of, although not necessarily prevent, external fire spread.

Whether a barrier will or will not contain a fire can be considered as a probability and reliability problem that parallels reliability problems encountered in the operation of electronic, electrical, and mechanical equipment. Using this analogy, barrier failures can be considered to fall into one of three categories: (1) early failures, (2) random failures, and (3) degradation failures. Early failures would be the result of occurrences such as a door not closing or an opening not being protected. Random failures would be the result of faults in materials or construction, a fire of unexpected severity, or design weaknesses not identified by standard testing methods. Random failure probabilities typically follow an exponential law and would predominate until barrier thermal degradation became a factor. Degradation failures would be similar to wear-out failures encountered in electronic, electrical, and mechanical equipment. The probability of a wear-out failure typically follows a normal or Gaussian distribution law, and the probability of barrier degradation failures should be similarly distributed. This technique of considering the three categories of barrier failure probability permits a more realistic comparison to be made between compartmentation and other protective measures. It is also apparent from this analogy that a barrier having a certain fire-resistive rating is not necessarily twice as reliable as one having one-half that rating.

Concealed Spaces

Buildings may contain a wide variety of concealed spaces behind walls, above suspended ceilings, in utility chases, behind soffits, under computer room floors, in attics, and elsewhere. The spaces range in size from 1⅝ in. (41.3 mm) stud spaces to full floor height interstitial spaces. Fires in concealed spaces burn out of sight of building occupants, and detection is frequently delayed. Manual fighting of concealed-space fires can be very difficult because of limited accessibility and inherent venting problems. Vertical concealed spaces also can act as flues to spread fire and hot gases.

Fire development and spread in combustible concealed spaces have long been a cause of large losses in fires. The fire may originate in, or spread into, a combustible concealed space and burn for a long time, spreading throughout the concealed volume. The disastrous Beverly Hills Supper Club and MGM Grand Hotel fires both originated in combustible concealed spaces.[29,30] Fires in horizontal concealed spaces, such as cock lofts, attics, interstitial spaces, and soffits, can spread undetected until they either burn through the floor or roof above or cause parts of the ceiling below to drop. At that time, a fresh air supply, preheated combustible materials, and hot pyrolysis products can combine to produce a rapidly developing fire, which may break out of the concealed space over a wide area. Vertical fire spread inside walls and chases can spread fire between floors and into attic spaces where it mushrooms out horizontally. The rapid vertical spread of fire was quantitatively demonstrated during several full-scale fire tests in wood-frame housing in the Bushwick section of Brooklyn, New York. In one test, temperatures in excess of 1500°F (816°C) were recorded at the top of a 32 ft (9.75 m) shaft 1 minute after a fire was started at the bottom.[31]

Flame spread through horizontal noncombustible concealed spaces is rarely a hazard unless the space contains a significant amount of combustible materials, such as communications or electrical cable trays, plastic pipe, cellular foam insulation, and insulation with a combustible vapor barrier. Isolated combustible items are not likely to propagate fire horizontally; however, they may when grouped together. For example, grouped electrical cables in trays may spread a fire, although any fire spread will be slow and not likely to extend very far from the ignition source; one exception is foam-insulated coaxial cable.[32] This does not mean that such combustibles will not assist in fire spread when they are preheated by hot fire gases from another source. Movement of flame through a noncombustible ceiling plenum space was reported as contributing to the horizontal spread of fire in One New York Plaza.[33] The interstitial space contained a number of electrical communications cables and exposed foam plastic insulation on the inside of the exterior walls. Insulation installed with a combustible vapor barrier exposed can spread fire even if its fuel contribution is very small.

Electrical cables that are difficult to ignite are available and being used in nuclear power plants. New materials have been developed to meet stringent fire resistance requirements for use in life safety applications. One such application is fire-resistant cables for emergency power supply lines. In tests, fire-resistant cables did not propagate fire horizontally, except in a multiple-stacked tray configuration.[34] Tests have also shown that use of fire-retardant coatings can be effective in inhibiting horizontal fire spread; however, there were major performance differences among the products tested.[35] Although some combustibles do not pose a serious threat of horizontal fire spread in noncombustible concealed spaces, they are likely to pose a serious threat of spread in vertical concealed spaces.

Vertical Openings

Unprotected vertical openings have been responsible for many large loss-of-life fires. These openings can act as a chimney—smoke, hot gases, and burning pyrolysis products flow up under the stack effect and then mushroom out horizontally. Because of their function, openings such as elevator shafts, stairways, laundry chutes, and air shafts cannot be cut off at floor levels. Vertical openings are enclosed with fire-rated walls to prevent fire spread and, in the case of vertical exitways, to provide a safe path of egress for occupants and access for fire department personnel. Vertical interior exitways are often the only avenue of escape to the outside or to adjacent floors for building occupants. NFPA *101*®, *Life Safety Code*®, provides a comprehensive treatment of exits in general and for various types of occupancies involving both new and existing buildings. Detailed requirements are given for enclosing walls, doors, stairs, ramps, escalators, and other components of an exit system.

Shafts containing power, communications cable, combustible ducts or pipes, and other combustible materials should normally be enclosed and often firestopped at each floor. The reliability of the protection of combustible material penetrations through enclosure walls will normally be lower than for noncombustibles. If fire enters a vertical shaft containing combustible materials, it can spread rapidly upward, generate considerable smoke, and possibly spread to other floors.

Room or Suite Compartmentation

The goals of compartmentation in confining a fire to the room or suite of rooms of origin are generally the following:

1. Segregate a space that has a higher fire hazard than the surrounding area. This is commonly found around rooms or suites used for storage, trash, flammable liquids, furnaces, laboratories, maintenance, and shops such as woodworking or painting.
2. Compartmentation is also used to protect locations of high value or critical operations from a fire in the surrounding area. Computer rooms, control rooms, vaults, record rooms, and high-value storage areas are often protected from a fire involving the rest of the building.
3. Minimize risk of loss of an occupant of one space as a result of a fire in space controlled by another. This is common in apartments, office suites, motel/hotel rooms, row houses, and other multitenant buildings.

An added benefit is that compartmentation limits the size of the fire, which limits the amount of smoke that will be generated and facilitates fire suppression.

Properly designed and installed compartmentation has been successful in limiting many fires to the unit of origin. In a number of high-rise fires, occupants who were unable to escape safely through corridors were able to "sit out" a major fire in an apartment adjacent to theirs.[36] A common cause of "failure" of this level of compartmentation has been a door that did not have a closer or was left open.

When a single room is compartmented, there may be insufficient ventilation for a fire to develop fully unless a window is open or happens to break. Occasionally such fires will completely self-extinguish.

Protection of Corridors

Fire-resistive corridor partitions may be required to (1) protect the means of access to an exit for sufficient time to permit occupant evacuation or (2) provide a protected means of access to the fire department personnel. In addition, when used in conjunction with room-to-room or suite-to-suite fire-resistive separation, the corridor wall forms an element in preventing fire spread.

Corridor partitions in nonsprinklered buildings typically are required to have a 1-hour fire resistance rating, and codes may require the partition to extend from the floor to the underside of the floor above. Either automatic or self-closers are generally required on doors opening into the corridor. Since smoke entering the corridor is a significant problem, as the corridor provides access to the exits, automatic door closers, if used, are generally actuated by smoke detectors. Additional information on corridor doors can be found later in this chapter where protection for openings is discussed. Corridor walls that resist the passage of smoke have become common applications in some occupancies that are fully or completely sprinkler protected. These walls generally do not have a specified fire resistance rating. Their intent is strictly to restrict movement of smoke beyond the barrier.

Building Separation

Walls separating two buildings or dividing a building into separate fire areas limit the maximum probable property loss and also can divide one building into what is legally two or more buildings to comply with the height and area limits of building codes. Stability becomes a very important consideration in this class of wall. Although all fire separation walls must maintain their stability under fire exposure for their rated duration, walls separating buildings or dividing a building into two fire areas must maintain stability during a complete burnout on either side, which is often accompanied by structural collapse of the burned-out side.

If at least one of the buildings has a fire-resistive frame—such as reinforced concrete or protected steel—panel walls built in along a column line can provide fire separation. The frame must have sufficient resistance to withstand a fire of the maximum expected severity for that building. Care must be taken so that the floor construction will not adversely affect stability of the wall under fire exposure. In buildings of Type V (wood frame), Type IV (heavy timber), or Type III (ordinary) construction, the combustible framing members can be tied into the fire wall so that they are self-releasing in case of collapse. The wall then remains supported by the framing on the unexposed side. The use of self-releasing framing is considered to have been generally successful in combustible construction but has questionable reliability in steel-framed buildings. Caution must be exercised in the design of these fire walls because some methods of framing combustible members into the wall will lower its fire resistance.

Freestanding fire walls are most commonly used in one- or two-story industrial and storage buildings of unprotected steel-frame construction. The maximum height is generally limited by economic considerations. A freestanding fire wall is entirely self-supporting under vertical loads and is not directly connected to the building framing. The adjacent building framing can provide support under horizontal loading. During a fire, the wall must be capable of acting as a cantilever to withstand all horizontal forces directed toward the fire side. Freestanding fire walls should be designed to withstand at least a 5 lb/ft^2 (24.5 kg/m^2) uniform lateral loading without any support from the framing on either side.[37]

Tension stress in mortar joints limits the height of unreinforced 12 in. (0.3 m) concrete block walls to 15 ft (4.6 m). Higher walls either require massive construction, which is rarely practical, or reinforcement. A common reinforcement technique is installation of vertical steel bars, anchored to the foundation, within hollow masonry units that are then filled with concrete. Reinforced pilasters can also be built into the wall at periodic points along the perimeter. A typical freestanding fire wall is illustrated in Figure 18.1.7.

Freestanding fire walls have very definite limitations under horizontal forces, which may preclude or restrict their use. They are particularly vulnerable to collapse under seismic loads and wind forces received by exterior walls. Additional support must be provided if the walls are temporarily used as an exterior wall or become an exterior wall as a result of a fire. Piping, conveyors, and similar items whose collapse in a fire will exert a horizontal pull should not pass through freestanding fire walls. Where they must, means should be provided to allow the penetrating items to break away without impacting the wall.

Fire walls in steel-frame buildings may be tied into the building structure so the forces of collapse on one side are resisted by the framing on the other side. The wall may be built along a column line and the columns and horizontal framing tied into the wall. The columns and framing in the wall line must be protected so that they have the same fire resistance as the wall. The walls have to be located in the framing so that the strength of framing on one side will be capable of withstanding the pull of collapsing framing on the other side. The construction of a typical tied fire wall is shown in Figure 18.1.8.

Fire separation between buildings can also be provided by two blank exterior walls of adequate fire resistance and located very close together. Each wall is tied to the frame in its building; collapse of the frame pulls the wall in, leaving the other wall to resist the fire.

Pipes, conveyors, cable trays, and similar through-penetrations of fire walls can present special problems in seismic areas. The need for mobility may conflict with opening protection

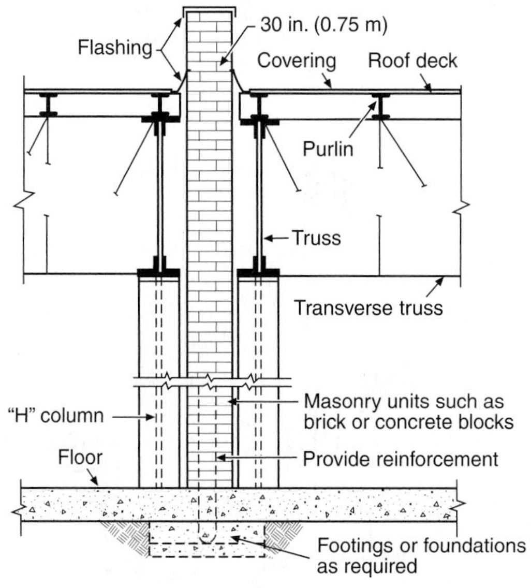

FIGURE 18.1.7 Typical Freestanding Fire Wall, Used at Expansion Joints or at Joints Between Buildings

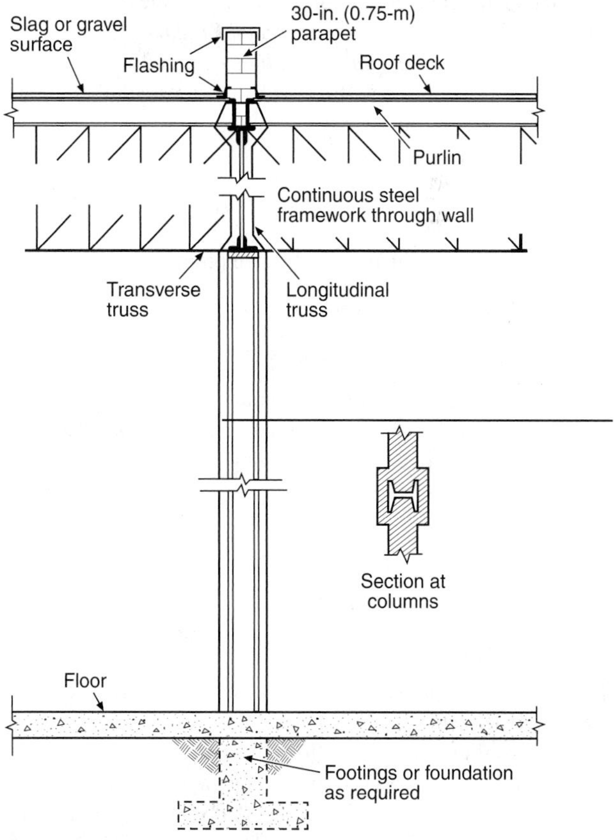

FIGURE 18.1.8 Typical Tied Fire Wall, Used with Continuous Building Framework

criteria. The complexity of the problem depends on whether the systems are to be designed to protect against one hazard at a time (fire or earthquake) or whether the simultaneous or consecutive occurrence of earthquake and fire should be considered in protection. See NFPA 221, *Standard for High Challenge Fire Walls, Fire Walls, and Fire Barrier Walls,* for minimum requirements for walls that separate buildings or subdivide buildings and prevent the spread of fire.

Fire Plumes Above Roofs

Fire walls must extend through and above a combustible roof to reduce the risk of fire spread over the top of the wall. Codes and standards typically call for fire walls to have a parapet 18 to 36 in. (0.46 to 0.9 m) above a combustible roof. The parapet minimizes the risk of direct flame spread over the fire wall and reduces the risk of fire spread by radiant heat from flames above the roof. The risk of direct flame spread over an 18 to 36 in. (0.46 to 0.9 m) high parapet is very low. However, risk of fire spread by radiant heat depends on the ease of combustibility of the roof surface, the height of the parapet, the dimensions of the fire plume through the roof of the fire zone, the wind velocity, and, if the roof covering is resistive to ignition by radiant heat, its insulating properties and the duration of the exposing fire. If a roof surface is combustible, the risk of fire spread by radiant heat past a parapet can be quite high.

The threat of fire spread by radiant heat over a parapet can be calculated using the thermal radiation values identified in Annex A of NFPA 80A, *Recommended Practice for Protection of Buildings from Exterior Fire Exposures,* and the plume dimensions.[38] Standard heat-transfer procedures can then be applied, using the formula:

$$I = I_o \Phi$$

where

I_o = Radiating intensity of the fire plume

Φ = Configuration factor or view factor

I = Unit incident radiation on the exposed surface

Instead of using the referenced radiant intensities, the average temperature of the plume flames can be estimated and the radiation calculated using the following relation:

$$I = \sigma T^4 \Phi$$

where

σ = Stefan-Boltzman constant

T = Absolute temperature

This assumes the flame plume is sufficiently thick so that it radiates as a black body.

The configuration factor for plume-roof relationships can be calculated using the formula found in a cited reference.[39] The effect of wind velocity, which deflects the fire plume, must be accounted for in calculation of the configuration factor. At high winds, a fire plume can be deflected such that it is almost horizontal above a burning roof. However, in high winds, a fire plume also tends to break up and is expected to be cooled by excess air. The angle of the fire plume selected is a matter of professional judgment; use of 45 degrees is considered reasonable by some engineers.

If the roof surface is combustible, the value of the incident thermal radiation calculated will indicate whether ignition of the roof is expected. If the surface is noncombustible or resistive to ignition by radiant heat, it is then necessary to calculate the temperature of the combustible subsurface material to which heat will be transferred from the surface. This is an unsteady-state heat transfer problem readily solved by standard numerical procedures.

A simple example of the calculation of incident thermal radiation can be used to illustrate the method of analysis. For the example, consider a 12 ft (3.7 m) high and 60 ft (18.3 m) wide frame building with a wood-surfaced roof. The building is subdivided by a masonry fire wall with a 3 ft (0.9 m) parapet (Figure 18.1.9).

The expected height of flames above the roof would be about 1.4 times the height of the building, or approximately 17 ft (5.2 m).[39] Assuming a flame temperature of 1400°F (760°C), the thermal radiation from the fire plume would be about 5.8 Btu/ft^2/sec (66 kW/m^2). In a moderate wind, a fire plume deflection of 45 degrees is possible. The maximum configuration factor would be about 0.3 and the incident radiation on the wood roof surface about 1.75 Btu/ft^2/sec (20 kW/m^2).

At an incident radiation of 1.1 Btu/ft^2/sec (12.5 kW/m^2), a wood roof can be sufficiently heated so that a small burning brand will ignite it;[40] this is referred to as pilot ignition. Since in the example the incident thermal radiation is well above that required for pilot ignition, flame spread over this fire wall is to be expected if the wind deflects the fire plume toward the exposed roof.

Fire-Resistive Wall Requirements for Structural Stability

Fire-rated wall requirements may be intended to ensure structural stability rather than to provide a fire barrier. In many cases,

FIGURE 18.1.9 Fire Plume Exposing a Wood Roof over a Parapeted Fire Wall

for example, hourly rated exterior bearing walls are permitted to have unlimited unprotected window areas; it is obvious that the rating refers to structural stability rather than provision of a fire barrier. Required fire ratings of interior bearing walls may or may not be intended to provide a fire barrier. Interior bearing walls with an hourly rating for fire separation do require protection of all openings; however, interior bearing walls that have an hourly rating only for structural stability purposes would not need opening protection. Caution must be exercised in selecting the proper hourly rating for interior bearing walls intended for structural stability only. A barrier separation wall is exposed to fire on only one side, where an interior bearing wall that would be providing only structural stability could be exposed to fire on both sides. The same hourly rating wall will not provide the same protection in both cases.

Fire-resistive walls of a high hourly rating are occasionally improperly specified to separate areas for protection against an explosion hazard rather than a long-duration fire. The fire resistance of a wall has no relationship to its ability to withstand explosion forces. A wall with a 1 hour rating may withstand explosion overpressures better than a wall with a 4 hour rating; no conventional wall will remain in place unless the explosion pressure is limited by venting or suppression.

PROTECTION OF OPENINGS

The protection for openings in a fire-rated wall generally has less resistance to fire spread than is provided by the wall. This is allowable because (1) easily ignited combustibles are not normally found against doors and other opening protection constructions, and (2) fire suppression forces can usually extinguish small localized fires that may spread past the wall. However, because openings do reduce the effectiveness of a fire barrier, fire doors generally cannot occupy more than 25 percent of the linear length of any fire separation wall. Clearances may be required in front of and to the sides of the opening to compensate for the differences between a wall rating and door rating.

Factors that reduce the fire resistance of opening protection as compared to resistance of walls include the following:

1. There is no maximum temperature-rise limitation on the unexposed sides of most types of fire doors. The unexposed side of steel doors may actually glow red during fire testing. When there is a limit to, or listing of, a temperature rise on a fire door, it applies only to the temperature rise during the initial 30 minutes of the fire test. (Temperature-rise limits are often specified in building codes for doors on exit stair enclosures.) Fire doors also buckle during the fire tests and are permitted to move out of their frames in a direction perpendicular to the plane of the door as much as 2.88 in. (73 mm). Some flaming is also permitted on unexposed sides of fire doors during the test procedures.

2. Requirements for the protection of duct penetrations place no limit on the temperature rise on the duct itself on the unexposed side of the wall.

3. Piping, cable trays, and conduit can penetrate fire walls and, although the opening must be firestopped, the temperature rise on the metal penetration itself would normally be above the 250°F (121°C) average or 325°F (161°C) single-point temperature-rise limit required of the wall. However, some codes require use of through-penetration firestopping systems that have a temperature-rise limitation on the penetrating item also.

4. The standard fire test furnace is operated at a pressure rating so that a neutral plane is established with the tested assembly. As a result of research studies, ASTM modified the test standards for fire doors and fire windows to require positive pressure testing of some elements. The neutral plane is established based on the assembly being tested. For example, within the first 5 minutes of the window test, the neutral plane is established so that at least the upper two-thirds of the window assembly is under positive pressure.

5. Vision panels and fire windows may transmit heat by both conduction and radiation.

6. Doors can become large radiators during early fire tests.

Thermally induced distortions of between 4 and 5 in. (102 and 127 mm) were observed on some foreign tests of swinging steel fire doors.[41] Considerably smaller distortions were noted with wood and insulated metal swinging doors. However, wood doors were noted as being more likely to fail by localized carbonation at hinges, locks, and knobs. Rolling steel fire doors generally do not deform appreciably during a fire. Large distortions of some rated fire doors, both wood and metal, were also reported in "Project Corridor," a series of fire tests conducted by the California State Fire Marshal in a simulated light-hazard occupancy.[42] In some countries, extensible bolts and latches are added to swinging steel fire doors so that the door is held in the frame at five or six points. Distortions of this type of door were reported to be under 1 in. (2.54 mm) during a standard fire test.[39]

However, the most common failure mode of fire doors observed in actual fires is not closing. This has occurred because of lack of maintenance; physical damage to the closer, door, guides, or tracks; blockage in the doorway; and other faults. Reliable fire door performance cannot be ensured unless doorways are kept clean and doors maintained in operating condition, as specified in NFPA 80, *Standard for Fire Doors and Other Opening Protectives,* and the manufacturer's instructions. Some common faults often observed on swinging fire doors include inoperative latches and improperly adjusted closing devices. Overhead and sliding doors that are not used regularly are particularly susceptible to track and guide damage. The closing mechanism on overhead doors is a more complicated and less visible mechanism than the closing mechanism on most other fire doors. Inspection, testing, and proper preventive maintenance are always essential.

Fire doors, windows, and shutters are the most widely used and accepted means of protecting openings in fire-resistive walls. Suitability of these closures is determined through tests by recognized testing laboratories, and untested doors cannot be relied on for effective protection. Fire door assemblies for the protection of openings depend on the use of labeled fire doors and frames (where frames are required) and listed or labeled hardware. Hardware for fire doors is referred to as "builder's hardware," which includes fire exit hardware and fire door hardware.

Doors must be installed in a properly constructed wall and floor so that fire cannot spread below, around, or above the door. Special noncombustible sills are required for door openings in buildings with combustible floors, except for openings protected by 20 or 30 minute doors. However, combustible floor coverings may extend through openings protected by fire doors rated at 1½ hours or less if the cover has a critical radiant flux of 0.22 W/cm^2 or greater. Critical radiant flux is to be determined per NFPA 253, *Standard Method of Test for Critical Radiant Flux of Floor Covering Systems Using a Radiant Heat Energy Source.* In general, the critical radiant flux for vinyl sheet and flooring, wool carpet, and some synthetic carpets will exceed 0.22 W/cm^2. Combustible floor coverings may not extend through openings required to be protected by 3-hour or higher-rated doors.

Classification of Openings, Doors, and Windows

Fire doors are now rated according to the duration of fire exposure and, optionally, the temperature rise on the unexposed surface after 30 minutes, when tested as per NFPA 252, *Standard Methods of Fire Tests of Door Assemblies.* Doors are rated as 4 hour, 3 hour, 1½ hour, 45 minute, 30 minute, and 20 minute. Temperature rises are listed at 250, 450, and 650°F (121, 232, and 343°C); absence of a temperature rating indicates a rise of over 650°F (343°C) on the unexposed surface of the door after 30 minutes of testing. There is no temperature rise limitation for most types of fire doors. Fire doors tested under NFPA 252 are exposed to a standard temperature-time curve and a hose stream test. The hose stream test is not always required by the authority having jurisdiction for 20 and 30 minute doors. Those doors that are fire tested without a hose stream test indicate this fact on the label. The categories in which fire doors are classified are also identified on the label; these include access, bullet-resisting, chute, curtain, dumbwaiter, freight elevator, rolling steel, service counter, sliding, special-purpose, and swinging-type doors.

Existing fire doors and windows may be classified by an hourly rating designation, an alphabetical letter designation, or a combination of these. At one time the alphabetical letter designation was one method commonly employed to classify the opening for which the fire door is considered suitable. Traditionally, the relationship between the alphabetical designation and its use was as follows (from NFPA 80, Appendix E):

1. Class A—Openings in fire walls and in walls that divide a single building into fire areas
2. Class B—Openings in enclosures of vertical communications through buildings and in 2 hour rated partitions providing horizontal fire separations
3. Class C—Openings in walls or partitions between rooms and corridors having a fire resistance rating of 1 hour or less
4. Class D—Openings in exterior walls subject to severe fire exposure from outside the building
5. Class E—Openings in exterior walls subject to moderate or light fire exposure from outside the building

The alphabetical classification of the opening does not apply to the closure; however, in actual practice, the distinction between opening classification and door classification was rarely maintained. A 3 hour door for use in a Class A opening was commonly called a Class A door.

Building codes and NFPA 80 commonly specify a door by its fire-protection rating instead of by the classification of opening to be protected. Fire doors are now available with ½ hour and ⅓ hour ratings, which do not fall within the specified protection criteria for the classes of opening. The following paragraphs summarize current application of doors, windows, and shutters for openings in fire-resistive walls.

Four and Three Hour Fire Doors. Openings in walls separating buildings or dividing a building into different fire areas are generally protected by 4 or 3 hour fire doors. Many codes only require 3 hour fire doors in separation walls required to have a fire resistance of 3 hour or more. However, some authorities require two 3 hour fire doors, one on each side of the opening, whenever a wall is required to have a fire resistance of 4 hours. Four-hour fire door listings are relatively recent, and their availability may not be reflected in all codes.

One-and-One-Half Hour Fire Doors. Openings in 2 hour enclosures of vertical openings in buildings are protected by 1½ hour fire doors. Many codes also permit the use of 1½ hour fire doors to protect openings in walls separating buildings or dividing buildings into different fire areas when the wall is only required to have a fire resistance of 2 hours. One-and-one-half hour fire doors are used in walls required to have a 2 hour fire resistance to enclose hazardous areas.

One-and-One-Half Hour Fire Doors and Shutters. Openings in exterior walls that can be subjected to severe fire exposure from outside the building are protected by 1½ hour fire doors and shutters.

One Hour Fire Doors. Openings in 1 hour enclosures of vertical openings in buildings, such as stairs, shafts, and exit enclosures, are protected by 1 hour fire doors.

Three-Quarter Hour Fire Doors. Openings in room partitions and walls around some hazardous areas are protected by ¾ hour fire doors. Sometimes they are also permitted in partitions that subdivide floors of a building. Although ¾ hour fire-rated doors are for use in 1 hour corridor partitions, many codes permit installation of other types of doors, such as ½ or ⅓ hour fire-rated or 1¾ in. (45 mm) solid-bonded wood-core doors. Either automatic closers or self-closers are generally required on corridor doors. Since control of smoke is also necessary to protect a corridor as an access to an exit, automatic closers are generally actuated by smoke detectors.

Three-Quarter Hour Fire Doors and Shutters. Openings in exterior walls subject to a moderate or light fire exposure from outside the building are protected by ¾ hour fire doors and shutters.

Three-Quarter Hour Fire Windows. Openings in corridor or room partitions or in exterior walls subject to a moderate or light external fire exposure can be protected by ¾ hour fire windows.

One-Half Hour and One-Third Hour Fire Doors. Doors with these ratings are for use where control of smoke is a primary consideration. They are also used for the protection of openings in partitions between a habitable room and a corridor when the wall is constructed to have a fire-resistance rating of not more than 1 hour or across corridors where a smoke partition is required. Some codes permit the use of 1¾ in. (45 mm) solid-bonded wood-core doors in corridor, room, and smoke-stop partitions that are required to have a fire resistance of not more than 1 hour. These doors cannot be used for corridor doors to hazardous areas or to protect openings in enclosures of vertical openings in buildings.

Types of Doors

There are several types of construction for fire doors, which are described in the following paragraphs.

Composite Doors. These are of the flush design and consist of a manufactured core material with chemically impregnated wood-edge banding and untreated wood-face veneers or laminated plastic faces or are surrounded by and encased in steel.

Hollow Metal Doors. These are of formed steel of the flush and paneled designs of 20 gauge or heavier steel. These doors may include a honeycomb core.

Metal-Clad Doors. These are of flush and paneled design consisting of metal-covered wood cores or stiles and rails and insulated panels covered with steel of 24 gauge or lighter.

Sheet-Metal Doors. These are of formed 22 gauge or lighter steel and of the corrugated, flush, and paneled designs.

Rolling Steel Doors. These are of the interlocking steel-slat design or plate-steel construction.

Tin-Clad Doors. These are of two- or three-ply wood-core construction, covered with 30 gauge galvanized steel or terneplate (maximum size 14–20 in. [0.36–0.51 m]) or 24 gauge galvanized steel sheets not more than 48 in. (1.2 m) wide.

Curtain-Type Doors. These consist of interlocking steel blades or a continuous formed-spring steel curtain in a steel frame.

Wood-Core Doors. These doors consist of wood, hardboard, or plastic-faced sheets bonded to a wood block or wood particleboard core material with untreated wood edges.

Unrated Door Protection

The fire resistance of existing doors can be improved by coating the doors with an intumescent paint, although no formal fire resistance rating for such a door has been established. This method is not commonly accepted in the United States, although it has been used in England. Intumescent paint is listed for reducing flame spread, not for improving fire resistance. However, tests conducted by NBS showed that a single layer of intumescent paint, 7 to 8 mil (0.18 to 0.20 mm) thick, significantly delayed char penetration into a soft wood joist.[43] Ordinary wood-panel doors, in which both door and frame were coated with two layers of intumescent paint, withstood fully developed room fires similarly to 1¾ in. (44.5 mm) thick solid-core wood doors in simulated nursing home room fires.[19] In another test, a wood-panel door was protected with gypsumboard on the thin panel and intumescent paint on the remainder of the wood. This upgraded door withstood a standard fire test, modified to simulate the positive pressure of a room fire, longer than a 20 minute rated fire door.[44] However, there is no fire protection rating assigned to any upgraded fire doors; it is entirely up to the authority having jurisdiction whether or not this upgraded door is acceptable for improving the fire safety in existing buildings.

Glazing for Fire Doors, Windows, and Walls

Glazing materials are available for use in fire-rated doors, windows, and walls; they are used as vision panels in fire doors and as windows in fire-rated corridor walls. In addition, they are frequently used in smoke-stop barriers and to enclose open stairways in older buildings.

Wired glass was historically the only transparent material that could be used in fire-rated doors and windows. It is a glass sheet containing an imbedded net of steel that helps distribute heat, lowers thermal stresses, and increases the strength of the assembly. When exposed to a fire, the glass starts cracking after a minute or two but does not open up. The glass begins to weaken when heated to about 1470°F (799°C) and gradually starts to soften. At about 1600°F (871°C) it deforms so badly that it will drop out.[39] Its normal 45 minute fire resistance rating corresponds to 1638°F (892°C) on the standard temperature-time curve. In actual fires, the endurance of wired glass is temperature dependent; if it is never heated above the temperature at which it weakens, it could remain in place for an extended period of time. Wired glass has been the most economical fire protection–rated glazing material.

Clear fire protection–rated glazing has been developed as an alternative to wired glass and to provide a higher hourly fire rating than had been possible with wired glass. These products include fire protection–rated glass and transparent ceramics as well as fire resistance–rated glass. The clear glazing provides more architectural freedom to achieve openness while still meeting building codes' often increased compartmentation requirements. Clear fire protection–rated glazing materials that also can provide security protection are available.

Glazing materials for use in fire-rated windows, doors, frames, and sidelights are tested in accordance with NFPA 257, *Standard on Fire Test for Window and Glass Block Assemblies.* This test includes exposure to a standard temperature-time curve fire on one side for the rated period of time, plus the hose stream test. There also are fire-resistant glazing materials that are suitable for use in specific wall and partition assemblies. These are tested in accordance with NFPA 271, *Standard Method of Test for Heat and Visible Smoke Release Rates for Materials and Products Using an Oxygen Consumption Calorimeter.* This test includes the same temperature-rise limitation on the unexposed surface of the glazing material as on the wall.

Vision panels are permitted in fire doors rated at 3 hours or less. However, vision panels in 3 hour fire doors and fire doors with a 1½ hour rating used in protecting severe exterior exposures must be tested as a component of the door assembly in accordance with NFPA 252. These vision panels are limited to 100 in.^{2} (0.065 m^2) or less. Wired glass may not be used in 3 hour fire doors or 1½ hour doors used for severe exposure protection. Vision panels used in 1½ hour and 1 hour fire-rated doors is limited to the maximum area tested. In ¾ hour rated doors and windows and 20 and 30 minute doors, wired glass is limited to 1296 in.^{2} (0.84 m^2) per light with a maximum dimension of 54 in. (1.37 m). In all applications, the maximum exposed area and area per light for glazing material other than wired glass are listed individually for each product.

Glazing materials used in fire doors, windows, sidelights, and commercial lights must also meet applicable safety standards if these are subject to human impact. These current standards include the U.S. Consumer Product Safety Commission (CPSC) *Safety Standard for Architectural Glazing* and the less stringent, in terms of impact resistance, ANSI Z79.1, *Safety Performance Specifications and Methods of Test for Safety Glazing Materials Used in Buildings.* Wired glass is specifically exempt from the CPSC standard but not the ANSI standard.

Glazing materials in fire doors, windows, and frames are commonly installed on the job site and not provided by the manufacturer of the fire door. The door manufacturer provides grooves in the door for the glazing, and the glazing manufacturer or distributor supplies the glazing in the necessary light sizes. NFPA 80 requires each light to have a visible listing mark when installed. This mark may be the only way to identify whether the glazing installed is clear fire protection–rated material or ordinary commercial glass. Installation and caulking requirements are very specific and specified in the individual listings. Grooves and installation methods and materials used for wired glass will generally not be suitable for use with other glazing materials.

Vision panels and windows differ from a solid wall primarily in the transmission of radiant heat. Conductive heat transmission is also increased, but high conductive heat transmission is also found in doors, door and window hardware, and frames. The intensity of radiant heat, I, to which a combustible or person would be exposed through a wired-glass panel from a fully developed room fire, is given by the following formula:

$$I = k\Phi I_0$$

where k is the transmissivity of the window, Φ is the configuration factor, and I_o is the radiant intensity of the exposing fire. This equation may be used for U.S. customary or SI units, as long as their use is consistent.

A radiant intensity of 5 Btu/ft^2/sec (57 kW/m^2) has been measured for a room fire involving ordinary residential furnishings with average ventilation, such as an open door.[45] Measurements of well-ventilated fires in light-hazard occupancies indicate a peak radiant intensity of 7.4 Btu/ft^2/sec (84 kW/m^2).[30] Transmissivity of glass windows is reported to range from 0.4 to 0.6.[40] These values of transmissivity are reasonable for the early period of fire exposure; as the glazing is exposed to the fire for a period of time, its transmissivity will be reduced. The configuration factor can be determined from any specific situation for graphs found in most heat-transfer texts.

If wood on the unexposed side of the wired glass is exposed to a radiant intensity above 3 Btu/ft^2/sec (34 kW/m^2), autoignition may occur. Most synthetic materials will require a higher level of radiant heat intensity for autoignition.

When wired-glass panels are installed in walls on a dead-end corridor or other location in which building occupants have no alternative escape path, the heat radiated through the glass may prevent escape. If persons moving past the glass absorb sufficient heat to cause severe pain, their ability to escape could be impaired. The human threshold of severe pain for exposure to radiant heat depends on both the intensity and the time over which it is received. Experimental data that have defined this limit[46] can be approximated by the following equation:

$$Q_{max} = 2.3t^{0.25} \leq 45 \text{ sec}$$

where Q_{max} is the total heat absorbed by the skin in Btu/ft^2 (W/m^2) over t seconds at the threshold of severe pain. As a person moves past the wired-glass panel, the view factor, Φ, will change. The absorbed heat can be calculated by determining Φ for a number of points along the person's path and using a stepwise integration over the time required to move past each point. The normal walking speed used in exit calculations is 3.5 ft/sec (1.07 m/sec).[9] If the total heat absorbed exceeds the limits in the equation, the escape of occupants past the wired-glass panels may be impaired.

Fire Blocking and Firestop Protection

The term *fire blocking* is used to describe both barriers to restrict the spread of fire in concealed spaces. Materials used to fill gaps around penetrations in walls and ceilings are called firestop devices or systems.

In wood-frame construction, the normal fire block inside walls and ceiling spaces is a 2 in. (50.8 mm) thick (nominal) piece of lumber. However, for other applications, fire blocking should normally be noncombustible and have a sufficiently high melting point so that it will remain in place under fire exposure. Gypsum board, sheet metal, plaster, brick, cement grout, mineral fiber insulation, fire blocking, and ceramic fiberboards are all examples of commonly used fire blocking. Firestop systems protect penetrations of fire-rated walls and floors by noncombustible pipe or tube, and conduit has commonly been provided by filling the annular space around the penetrant with a noncombustible material, such as cement grout, mineral wool, cement plaster, and so forth. This type of firestop system is regarded as having performed effectively in actual fires. However, lack of firestop systems[29,30] or improperly protected openings, such as the combustible foam plastic used at Brown's Ferry Nuclear Plant,[47] have been responsible for a number of serious fire losses.

Considerable attention and research have been directed toward wall and floor penetrations by plastic drain, waste, and vent

(DWV) pipes.[48–51] Full-scale tests have shown that the integrity of a 2 hour fire-resistive chase enclosure could be maintained by encasing the pipe in an 18 in. (0.46 m) steel sleeve and penetrating the chase at a 45 degree downward angle. These results were applicable to 3 in. (76 mm) laterals of both PVC and ABS DWV pipe. Unless otherwise tested and approved, chases should be firestop protected at each floor. In many buildings, much of the plumbing is installed in wall cavities. Use of plastic DWV pipe inside fire-resistive wall assemblies has been extensively tested, and a number of methods of protection that will not compromise the fire resistance or create a risk of vertical fire spread have been identified.

Cable-tray penetrations present another challenge; the size of the penetrant is large and contains a mixture of combustible and noncombustible material. Research and development programs were sponsored by the Nuclear Regulatory Commission (NRC) on firestops for use in nuclear power plants. The results of these programs, plus work by suppliers, led to new firestop products.

Building codes require approved and tested firestops wherever conduit, pipe, cables, or other utilities pass through fire-rated—and sometimes non-fire-rated—walls, floors, and ceilings. These firestop products can be qualified under either ASTM E814, *Standard Test Method for Fire Tests of Through-Penetration Fire Stops,* or under a fire exposure corresponding to ASTM E119, *Standard Test Method for Fire Tests of Building Construction and Materials.* The test furnace must be operated at a specified positive pressure, such as 0.01 or 0.03 in. of water column (2.5 or 7.5 pascal). Currently, neither of these tests evaluates smoke spread.

There are two types of tested firestop protection: (1) through-penetration firestop devices and (2) through-penetration firestop systems. The firestop devices are manufactured products used primarily for protecting cable and poke-through penetrations. Through-penetration firestop systems are field-installed constrictions for protecting penetrations of floors or walls by conduit, pipe, duct, cable, cable trays, and so forth. The basic standard used to investigate these firestops is UL 1479, *Standard for Safety Fire Tests of Through-Penetration Firestops,* which is based on ASTM E814.

ASTM E814 was developed for evaluating firestops that are installed to prevent spread of fire through an opening where cable trays, pipe, conduits, ducts, and so on, pass through a wall or floor. This standard was first published in 1981. The ASTM E814 test has many similarities to ASTM E119, but it can be conducted on a much smaller scale and at a documented positive pressure. In addition, all test items are subject to a hose stream test similar to that required for some constructions tested under ASTM E119. ASTM E119 requires testing of at least a 100 ft^2 (9.3 m^2) sample of a wall and a 180 ft^2 (16.2 m^2) sample of a floor. A wall or floor sample less than 9 ft^2 (0.83 m^2) can be used in ASTM E814. The ASTM E814 furnace is heated to follow the temperature history of ASTM E119. There is no standard "aging" test for the new firestop materials; one proprietary product recently was recalled because its reliability apparently deteriorated with age.

Two types of hourly time ratings are established for a tested firestop: F and T. The conditions for these ratings are broader. The F rating is a measure of the ability of the firestop system to maintain its physical integrity under the fire exposure and hose stream tests and to prevent occurrence or passage of flame on the unexposed surface. The T rating is intended to measure whether combustible materials on the unexposed side of a fire barrier would be ignited by conduction of heat through the firestop material or along the penetrating conduit or pipe. The same maximum temperature limit is used in the ASTM E814 test as in the ASTM E119 test. The hourly F or T rating is the duration of the fire test that the through-penetration firestop system passed.

The T rating achieved can be less than the F rating; there is nothing similar to this in the ASTM E119 test. If the temperature limit is reached before the completion of a successful test for an F rating, the T rating will be based on the time at which the temperature limit was reached. However, the F rating assigned would be the total hourly duration of the successful test. Building codes that require firestop systems tested under ASTM E814 differ as to if and when a T rating is necessary.

There are many types of listed through-penetration firestop system constructions, ranging from relatively simple to complex arrangements. A typical through-penetration firestop system requires installation of both a form and a fill material. The form material is generally a ceramic fiber mat; a hole the size of the penetrating conduit (or pipe) is cut in it and the form is slipped over the conduit into the opening in the wall or floor. The form material serves to place and restrain the fill material that is installed in the annular space around the conduit to a specified thickness. Fill materials include one- and two-part foams, silicone elastomers, proprietary caulking and grouting materials, and specific proprietary cementitious mixtures.

Some through-penetration firestop systems also require use of an additional filling material, such as ceramic fibers, and some only require a single material, such as a proprietary caulk or grout. There are a number of through-penetration firestop systems that are much more complex and require additional features, such as sleeves, special supports to retain the system in the opening, and insulation on the conduit or pipe extending out from the surface of the floor or wall.

Some of these systems permit penetrating items to be easily removed or replaced. This facilitates future additions of pipe, tube, or cable through the penetration opening. However, restoration of the integrity of the original firestop may or may not be possible under the conditions of the system's listing by a testing laboratory. Any additions or changes that require removal and restoration of a through-penetration firestop system have to be tightly controlled so that (1) the restoration is performed in an approved manner, (2) the allowable number of penetrating items is not exceeded, (3) only permitted penetrants are installed, and (4) adequate clearances are maintained among penetrating items and between penetrating items and the sides of the opening.

Some designs for curtain walls, particularly in high-rise buildings, offer the danger of vertical spread of fire behind the curtain walls for the entire height of the building. This can occur when the panels of a curtain wall do not rest tightly for their full length on a floor slab. Rather, there is a continuous relieving angle attachment between the panels and the floor slab, creating vertical flue spaces between the panels and the end of the floor slab. Where fire blocking is not inherent in the design, it is necessary to fill this space with appropriate fire block materials. This arrangement is generally less satisfactory because of the tendency for both expansion and contraction of the exterior wall and the likelihood of maintenance operations causing unplanned openings through and around the firestopping.

Atria

Atria, which are common in many new buildings, depart from the traditional compartmentation concept of fire containment by enclosing all vertical openings. Alternative arrangements must be provided in atrium buildings to achieve the same level of protection found in buildings using the traditional compartmentation concept. The occupancy should be one in which a rapidly spreading fire would not be encountered, and all occupants should be expected to be aware of any hazards before they are endangered, and in time to move to a place of safety if necessary.

Fire protection in atrium buildings is generally provided by a combination of methods, such as compartmentation, ventilation, automatic suppression, and contents and material control. NFPA *101* requires atria in new construction to be separated from adjacent spaces by fire barriers having at least a 1 hour fire resistance rating. However, as many as three levels of a building may open directly to the atrium without the need for a fire-resistive barrier. As an alternative where 1 hour barriers are normally required, glass walls may be used, provided there are sprinklers spaced 6 ft (1.8 m) apart and not more than 1 ft (0.3 m) from the glass along both sides of the glass wall. The sprinklers must be located to ensure that the glass surface is wet when the sprinklers operate. Sprinklers are not required on the atrium side of the glass wall if there is no walkway or other floor area on that side above the main floor level.

Large-volume atria will dilute fire gases and, with proper ventilation, direct their flow safely to the outside. Small atria may not have the capacity to dilute fire gases, although if they are properly designed and ventilated, fire gases can be channeled to the outside and the risk of horizontal fire spread minimized.

SUMMARY

Barriers can protect people and property by confining a fire to its area of origin until it either is extinguished or burns itself out. Fire resistance ratings of barriers are based on fire endurance tests and are measured in hours or fractions thereof. The basis for almost all fire-resistive testing is the standard temperature-time curve.

The concepts of fire severity and fire load, although technically obsolete, are still used to make conservative estimates of the maximum severity of a fire. Fire load is a measure of the maximum heat that would be released if all the combustibles in a given area burned. Fire modeling is based on mathematical models that calculate the temperature history of room fires as a function of ventilation, fuel, and the walls and ceiling of the room. The most widely used models in the United States are zone models, exemplified by the CFAST component of HAZARD.

Several aspects of a building can affect fire spread, among them concealed spaces, vertical openings, compartmentation, fire-resistive corridor partitions, fire walls, and the protection of openings in the fire walls.

BIBLIOGRAPHY

References Cited

1. McCaffrey, B. J., et al., "Estimating Room Temperatures and the Likelihood of Flashover Using Fire Data Correlations," *Fire Technology,* Vol. 17, No. 2, 1981, pp. 98–119.
2. Quintiere, J. G., "A Simple Correlation for Predicting Temperature in a Room Fire," NBSIR 832712, U.S. Department of Commerce, National Bureau of Standards, Gaithersburg, MD, 1983.
3. Berry, D. L., and Minor, E. E., "Nuclear Power Plant Fire Protection—Fire Hazards Analysis (Subsystems Study Task 4)," Report NUREG/CR-0654, SAND 79-0324, Sandia National Laboratories, Albuquerque, NM, 1979.
4. Lie, T. T., "Characteristic Temperature Curves for Various Fire Severities," *Fire Technology,* Vol. 10, No. 4, 1974, pp. 315–326.
5. Ingberg, S. H., "Fire Tests of Office Occupancies," *NFPA Quarterly,* Vol. 20, No. 3, 1927, pp. 243–252.
6. Ingberg, S. H., "Tests of the Severity of Building Fires," *NFPA Quarterly,* Vol. 22, No. 1, 1928, pp. 43–61.
7. Culver, C. G., "Characteristics of Fire Loads in Office Buildings," *Fire Technology,* Vol. 14, No. 1, 1978, pp. 51–60.
8. Campbell, J. A., "Fire Safety Systems Analysis Data Base," reported at NFPA Fall Meeting, Montreal, Quebec, Canada, 1978.
9. "Handbook, Building Firesafety Criteria," PBS P5920.9, Change 6, General Services Administration, Washington, DC, 1977.
10. Waterman, T. E., et al., "Prediction of Fire Damage to Installations and Built-up Areas from Nuclear Weapons," Final Report—Phase III, Experimental Studies, Appendices A–G, Contract No. DCA-8, National Military Command System Support Center, Washington, DC, 1964.
11. Harmanthy, T. Z., "Design of Buildings for Fire Safety—Part I," *Fire Technology,* Vol. 12, No. 2, 1976, pp. 95–108.
12. Heselden, A. J. M., et al., "Burning Rate of Ventilation-Controlled Fires in Compartments," *Fire Technology,* Vol. 6, No. 2, 1970, pp. 123–125.
13. Babrauskas, V., and Williamson, R. B., "Post-Flashover Compartment Fires," Report UCB FRG 75-1, Fire Research Group, University of California, Berkeley, CA, 1975.
14. Kawagoe, K., "Estimation of Fire Temperature-Time Curve in Rooms," *Building Research Paper No. 29,* Ministry of Construction, Japanese Government, Tokyo, Japan, 1967.
15. Miller, H. E., and Emmons, H. W., "Documentation for the Fifth Harvard Computer Fire Code," Home Fire Project Technology Report No. 45, Harvard University, Cambridge, MA, 1981.
16. Bukowski, R. B., Peacock, R. D., Jones, W. W., and Forney, C. L., "Technical Reference Guide for the HAZARD I Fire Hazard Assessment Method," *Handbook 146,* Vol. II, National Institute of Standards and Technology, Gaithersburg, MD, 1989.
17. Davis, W. D., and Cooper, L. Y., "Estimating the Environment and the Response of Sprinkler Links in Compartment Fires with Draft Curtains and Fusible-Link-Actuated Ceiling Vents, Part II: User Guide for the Computer Code LAVENT," NISTIR 89-4122, National Institute of Standards and Technology, Gaithersburg, MD, 1989.
18. Mitler, H. E., and Rockett, J. A., "User's Guide to FIRST, A Comprehensive Single-Room Fire Model," NISTIR 89-4122, National Institute of Standards and Technology, Gaithersburg, MD, Sept. 1987.
19. "Fire Tests in a Nursing Home Patient Room," Report HEW, Contract HSA 105-74-116, American Health Care Association, Washington, DC, 1975.

20. Zinn, B. T., et al., "Fire Spread and Smoke Control in High-Rise Fires," *Fire Technology,* Vol. 10, No. 1, 1974, pp. 35–53.
21. Christian, W. J., and Waterman, T. E., "Characteristics of Full-Scale Fires in Various Occupancies," *Fire Technology,* Vol. 7, No. 3, pp. 204–218.
22. "Fire Severity at the Exterior of a Burning Building," Report 67NK5227A, American Iron and Steel Institute, Washington, DC, 1975.
23. DiNenno, P. J., et al., *SFPE Handbook of Fire Protection Engineering,* 3rd ed., National Fire Protection Association, Quincy, MA, 2002.
24. Rosenbaum, E. R., et al., *SFPE Engineering Guide to Performance-Based Fire Protection Analysis and Design of Buildings,* National Fire Protection Association, Quincy, MA, 2000.
25. "Fire Resistance Ratings of Less Than One Hour," National Board of Fire Underwriters, New York, 1956.
26. Waterman, T. E., "Experimental Structural Fires," Report J6269, Contract DAHC 20-72-C-0290, DCPA Work Unit 2562B, IIT Research Institute, Chicago, IL, 1974.
27. Roytman, M. Y., *Principles of Fire Safety Standards for Building Construction,* Construction Literature Publishing House, Moscow, USSR, 1969; TT-71-58002, National Bureau of Standards, Amerind Publishing Co., PVT Ltd., New Delhi, India, 1975.
28. Cuzillo, B. R., and Pagni, P. J., "Thermal Breakage of Double-Pane Glazing by Fire," *Journal of Fire Protection Engineering,* Vol. 9, No. 1, 1998, pp. 1–11.
29. Best, R. L., "Tragedy in Kentucky," *Fire Journal,* Vol. 72, No. 1, 1978, pp. 18–35.
30. Best, R. L., and Demers, D., "Fire at the MGM Grand," *Fire Journal,* Vol. 76, No. 1, 1982, pp. 19–37.
31. DeCicco, P. R., "What to Do with Existing Row-Frame Residential Buildings," *Fire Journal,* Vol. 70, No. 6, 1976, pp. 23–31.
32. Riches, W. M., *Full-Scale Horizontal Cable Tray Fire Tests,* Fermi National Accelerator Laboratory, Batavia, IL, 1988.
33. Powers, W. R., "One New York Plaza Fire," New York Board of Fire Underwriters, New York, 1970.
34. Kamerus, L. J., "A Preliminary Report on Fire Protection Research Program (July 6, 1977 Test)," SAND 77-1424, Sandia National Laboratories, Albuquerque, NM, 1977.
35. Kamerus, L. J., "A Preliminary Report on Fire Protection Research Program Fire Barriers and Fire-Retardant Coating Tests," NUREG CR-0381, SAND 78-1456, Sandia National Laboratories, Albuquerque, NM, 1978.
36. Watrous, L. D., "Fire in a High-Rise Apartment Building, Hawthorne House, Chicago," *Fire Journal,* Vol. 63, No. 3, 1969, pp. 5–11.
37. "MFL Fire Walls: Barriers Against Destruction," *Factory Mutual Record,* Factory Mutual Research Corp., Norwood, MA, 1982, p. 13.
38. Pingree, D., "Looking at Fire Hazards: The Height of Flames Above a Roof," *Fire Journal,* Vol. 62, No. 3, 1968, pp. 24–27, 32.
39. Hamilton, D. C., and Morgan, W. R., *Radiant-Interchange Configuration Factors,* Technical Note 2836, National Advisory Committee for Aeronautics, Washington, DC, 1952.
40. Law, M., "Heat Radiation from Fires and Building Separation," *Technical Paper No. 5,* Joint Fire Research Organization, Her Majesty's Stationery Office, London, UK, 1963.
41. Bushev, V. P., et al., *Fire Resistance of Buildings,* Construction Literature Publishers, Moscow, USSR, 1970; IT 73-52030, National Bureau of Standards, Amerind Publishing Co., PVT Ltd., New Delhi, India, 1978.
42. Reagan, R., et al., "Project Corridor, Fire and Life Safety Research," *Western Fire Journal,* Bellflower, CA, 1974.
43. "A Compendium of Fire Testing," Feedback, Operation Breakthrough, Vol. 5, HUD-PDR-28-3, U.S. Department of Housing and Urban Development, Washington, DC, 1976.
44. Fisher, F. L., et al., "A Study of Potential Post-Flashover Fires in Wheeler Hall and the Results from a Full-Scale Fire Test of a Modified Wheeler Hall Door Assembly," Report UCX 77-3, Fire Research Laboratory, University of California, Berkeley, CA, 1977.
45. Battelle Columbus Laboratories, "Space Age Contribution to Residential Fire Safety," *Fire Journal,* Vol. 68, No. 2, 1974, pp. 18–25.
46. Buettner, K., "Effects of Extreme Heat on Man, III: Surface Temperature, Pain, and Heat Conductivity of Living Skin in Experiments with Radiant Heat," Project 21–26–002, Report No. 3, USAF School of Aviation Medicine, Randolph, TX, 1951.
47. Hanauer, S. H., Collins, H. E., Levine, S., Minners, W., Moore, V. A., Panciera, V. W., and Sayfirt, K. V., "Recommendations Related to Brown's Ferry Fire," Report by Special Review Group, NUREG-0050, U.S. Nuclear Regulatory Commission, Washington, DC, Feb. 1976.
48. Atwood, P. C., "Penetration of Fire Partitions by Plastic Pipe," *Fire Technology,* Vol. 16, No. 1, 1980, pp. 37–62.
49. Benjamin, I. A., and Parker, W. J., "Fire Spread Potential of ABS Plastic Plumbing," *Fire Technology,* Vol. 8, No. 2, 1972, pp. 104–119.
50. McGuire, J. H., "Penetration of Fire Partitions by Plastic DWV Pipe," *Fire Technology,* Vol. 9, No. 1, 1973, pp. 5–14.
51. Williamson, R. B., "Installing ABS and PVC Drain, Waste, and Vent Systems in Fire-Resistant Buildings," *Fire Journal,* Vol. 73, No. 2, 1979, pp. 36–45.

NFPA Codes, Standards, and Recommended Practices

Reference to the following NFPA codes, standards, and recommended practices will provide further information on the methods for confinement of fire in buildings discussed in this chapter. (See the latest version of The NFPA Catalog *for availability of current editions of the following documents.)*

NFPA 80, *Standard for Fire Doors and Other Opening Protectives*
NFPA 80A, *Recommended Practice for Protection of Buildings from Exterior Fire Exposures*
NFPA *101*®, *Life Safety Code*®
NFPA 221, *Standard for High Challenge Fire Walls, Fire Walls and Fire Barrier Walls*
NFPA 251, *Standard Methods of Tests of Fire Resistance of Building Construction and Materials*
NFPA 252, *Standard Methods of Fire Tests of Door Assemblies*
NFPA 253, *Standard Method of Test for Critical Radiant Flux of Floor Covering Systems Using a Radiant Heat Energy Source*
NFPA 257, *Standard on Fire Test for Window and Glass Block Assemblies*
NFPA 271, *Standard Method of Test for Heat and Visible Smoke Release Rates for Materials and Products Using an Oxygen Consumption Calorimeter*

References

ASTM E119, *Standard Test Methods for Fire Tests of Building Construction Methods,* ASTM International, W. Conshohocken, PA, 2005.
ASTM E2010-01, *Standard Test Method for Positive Pressure Fire Tests of Window Assemblies,* American Society for Testing and Materials, W. Conshohocken, PA, 2001.
ASTM E2074-00e1, *Standard Test Method for Fire Tests of Door Assemblies, Including Positive Pressure Testing of Side-Hinged and Pivoted Swinging Door Assemblies,* American Society for Testing and Materials, W. Conshohocken, PA, 2000.
ASTM E814, *Standard Test Method for Fire Tests of Through-Penetration Fire Stops,* ASTM International, W. Conshohocken, PA, 2002.
UL 1479, *Fire Tests of Through-Penetration Firestops,* Underwriters Laboratories, Northbrook, IL, 2006.

Chapter 2

Interior Finish

Revised by
Marcelo M. Hirschler

Chapter Contents

Key Terms

cone calorimeter, critical radiant flux test, flame spread index, flashover, flooring radiant panel test, full-scale test, interior finish material, interior lining material, lateral ignition and flame spread test (LIFT), methenamine pill test, room corner test, smoke density chamber test, smoke developed index, Steiner tunnel test, trim material

The best fire protection strategy for buildings is one that limits fires to a small size. In instances where fires eventually do become large, the fire growth rate must be slow enough to give occupants time to react or to give emergency responders enough time to respond and combat the fire manually and to rescue trapped victims while the fire is still limited in size.

Fires need to be limited in size because fire hazard is related to fire size. A material's burning rate—measured by its heat release rate—is the single most important parameter affecting fire hazard, because burning rates determine fire size. Burning rates directly affect temperature rise and the mass loss rate. Furthermore, mass loss and heat release also control the amount of smoke (and soot) released into a given volume, which determines visibility and thus the ease of escape or rescue of fire victims. Moreover, in a given volume, heat release and mass loss rates also affect the amounts of toxic products generated, which determines toxic hazard.

Large fires in buildings always represent an acute threat to occupants, irrespective of what is burning; and the faster a fire grows to a large size, the greater the threat. Any building material, furnishing, or content will have undesirable fire properties if its presence could cause a fire that would otherwise stay small to become large. For that reason, the use of furnishings and contents, especially including interior finish, with superior fire performance is a way to passively protect building occupants from the dangers of fire. Once a room fire has progressed so that the upper layer temperature approaches 1112°F (600°C) and that layer becomes thick, descending toward the lower portion of the room, all combustible furnishings and combustible room contents may be ignited, leading to flashover or full room fire involvement. Although some fires involve extended periods of slow, undetected fire development, fires that cause large life loss or high property loss nearly always grow rapidly to large size. Such fires typically reach flashover, or full room involvement, within minutes of having been small and easy to control. Therefore, prevention of flashover is a key strategy for lowering fire hazard. NFPA 555, *Guide on Methods for Evaluating Potential for Room Flashover,* is a guide for considering ways to prevent flashover.

Building interior finishes, principally wall and ceiling linings, can have a major impact on both fire growth and ultimate fire size. Interior wall and ceiling linings may act like fuses, spreading flames away from fire origin to involve other objects, causing the fire to grow to large size. Interior finishes may also provide a large, unbroken surface over which flame spreads. As the flame spreads to involve greater surface area, a fire's rate of heat release, and, therefore, the fire size increases. If the interior finish exhibits poor fire performance, the flames from the interior finish may release sufficient energy to cause the formation of a hot gas layer. Combustible interior finishes, such as low-density fiberboard ceilings, wood paneling, textile wall coverings, and combustible floor coverings, have been found in the past to be significant factors in many major fires, including some that became multiple death fires.[1–11] In recent years there have been fewer cases where interior finish has led to fire fatalities, but interior finish is still a major fire problem. The NFPA Fire Analysis and Research Division publishes yearly reports on fire loss statistics and the 2005 report[12] shows that interior finish was responsible for being the item first ignited in 22,900 fires in homes annually between 1999 and 2002 (just over 6% of the total) , which resulted in 261 civilian annual fire fatalities (just under 9% of the total). Worldwide, relatively recently there have been two major nightclub fires with multiple fatalities that were primarily associated with the use of inadequate interior finish materials, which were the items first ignited: the West Warwick, Rhode Island, fire on February 20, 2003, caused 100 fatalities [13,14] and the Buenos Aires, Argentina, fire on December 30, 2004,

Dr. Marcelo M. Hirschler is a consultant with GBH International in Mill Valley, California.

caused 193 fatalities.[15] In both fires, there were multiple code violations and other issues.

Interior finishes are regulated by codes, including NFPA *101*®, *Life Safety Code*®, and by *NFPA 5000*®, *Building Construction and Safety Code*®, to slow initial fire growth and to reduce the likelihood of fire growing to a large size. In fact, the sections addressing interior finish in NFPA *101* and in *NFPA 5000* (Chapter 10 in both codes) are correlated, and both are under the jurisdiction of the same NFPA technical committee, the Technical Committee on Furnishings and Contents.

This chapter reviews the effect of interior finish materials on fire growth. In order to properly evaluate the fire performance of interior finish materials, the fire tests to be used must be suitable for that use. Thus, after broadly looking at what interior finish and interior floor finish entails, the fire tests that can be used for evaluation of interior wall, ceiling, and floor finish materials will be addressed. This chapter then examines ways in which fire behavior requirements can be amended for certain specific interior finish materials to ensure that each type of material can be used safely. This chapter examines the method of application of interior finishes and the effect this can have on fire behavior. This chapter also contains some discussion of decorative materials, mainly by contrast to interior finish materials, and with an indication of the unique issues associated with them.

See also Section 3, Chapter 5, "Introduction to Fire Modeling"; Section 6, Chapter 1, "Fire Hazards of Materials"; and Section 6, Chapter 3, "Concepts and Protocols of Fire Testing."

INTERIOR FINISH AND TRIM CONCEPTS

Most codes, such as NFPA *101* or *NFPA 5000,* define interior wall and ceiling finishes as "the exposed surfaces of walls, ceilings, and floors within buildings" with the following explanation: "Interior finish is not intended to apply to surfaces within spaces, such as those that are concealed or inaccessible. Furnishings that, in some cases, might be secured in place for functional reasons should not be considered as interior finish." Thus, interior finish are those materials or assemblies of materials that form the exposed interior surfaces of walls and ceilings in a building. Interior wall finishes also include the interior finish of columns, fixed or movable walls, and fixed or movable partitions. Interior finish materials include materials such as wood, plaster, wallboard, acoustical tile, wall and ceiling coverings, plastics (including light-transmitting plastics), and insulating materials. Interior finish materials also include interior floor finishes, which tend to be a less severe fire problem, because heat and smoke rise in a fire. Interior floor finishes are the exposed floor surfaces of buildings (floors, ramps, stair treads and risers, and other walking surfaces) and include floor coverings, such as carpets and floor tiles, that may be applied over, or in lieu of, a finished floor. The term *interior lining* or *lining material* is used by the international fire community to define interior finish and the role of interior surfaces in the growth of fire in the room of origin. The term *interior lining* is not gaining very wide acceptance in North America and is unlikely to replace the term *interior finish,* at least in the near future.

There is some variability in the way interior finish regulations are applied. For example, some regulatory officials consider countertops and building cabinets as interior finish, and they are explicitly regulated as such in many transportation environments. It is sometimes difficult to differentiate between interior finishes and furnishings. Furnishings, although in some cases fastened in place, are not normally considered interior finish. For example, fixed plastic-covered restaurant "booth" seating and permanently mounted work counters and cabinets at a nursing station in a health care facility are not usually classified as interior finish.

Interior trim represents the picture moldings, baseboards, handrails, door and window frames, and similar decorative or protective materials used in fixed applications. Interior trim is ordinarily regulated as an interior finish. However, the requirements for trim and other incidental finish materials (like doors) are more lenient than those for the remainder of the wall and ceiling interior finish, when the trim or incidental finish is less than 10 percent of the aggregate wall and ceiling area. The "10 percent rule" is intended to be based on the trim or incidental finish being uniformly distributed and lacking sufficient continuity to allow flames to spread over any significant surface area. Concentration of the trim in one area, so that the trim forms one "fuel package," would violate the principle underlying the "10 percent rule."

Movable walls, folding partitions, and flexible or folding door assemblies are all normally treated as interior finishes. Movable partitions, used for example as a portion of office furnishings or work stations, are regulated as interior finish. Office cubicle partitions and work stations are sometimes formed of textile materials mounted over various substrates. Full-scale tests at the National Institute of Standards and Technology (NIST) involving office work stations consisting of computer terminals, 5 ft (1.5 m) high partitions of textile covering over fiberglass on metal frames, wood desks, and typical office contents revealed that fires involving such work stations may reach large sizes in 300 to 600 seconds.[16,17]

FIRE TESTS FOR INTERIOR WALL AND CEILING FINISH MATERIALS

The nature of interior finish materials and the fire environment to which they may be exposed vary so widely that development of a fire test becomes highly complex. The following three factors must be taken into account:

1. The start and growth of fire in a building is affected by the ignition source, space geometry, ventilation, and by the nature, amount, and location of other processes and materials in the building.
2. There are many time-varying events associated with fires, such as oxygen concentration, rate of heat release, and effects caused by protection systems.
3. Materials vary in form, composition, density, and application.

With these variables in mind, the difficulty in designing a test that will provide a basis for predicting performance under a specific fire exposure becomes obvious. Equally obvious is the impracticality of designing tests to represent all fire conditions. A test designed to represent a "typical" fire or to expose materials to one set of "standard test" conditions may not provide a reliable basis for predicting real-life performance of all materials tested. Thus, there is a constant search for improved test methods that will provide a range of results for a variety of fire conditions.

However, the traditional test for interior finish fire performance, which is NFPA 255, *Standard Method of Test of Surface*

Burning Characteristics of Building Materials (Steiner tunnel test, which also has equivalent designations ASTM E84 and UL 723), is still being widely used in the United States. In recent versions of codes alternative testing of interior finish materials is permitted by the use of a room-corner test: NFPA 286, *Standard Methods of Fire Tests for Evaluating Contribution of Wall and Ceiling Interior Finish to Room Fire Growth.* The major reason for using the room-corner test is that it assesses interior finish in a realistic room scenario and measures the key fire property, heat release,[18] and therefore results of room-corner tests are more reliable than results of tunnel tests. The Steiner tunnel test has been found to be an adequate fire test for traditional building materials and for materials that are not very thin and that remain in place during the test. However, many modern interior finish materials and systems are more complex than that and may not be suitably assessed by the Steiner tunnel fire test. A discussion on fire testing of interior finish was published recently.[19]

The use of bench-scale test data to predict product behavior through the use of models has been under study for many years, but there is no agreement yet in the United States on using such tests for regulatory purposes. Use of data from bench-scale tests, such as the cone calorimeter and the lateral ignition and flame spread test (LIFT apparatus),[20,21] to predict product behavior under a variety of circumstances may result in improved regulation of interior finish materials in the future. The models are fairly adequate in linking the actual fire hazard associated with the use of a product in a specific situation to regulatory limits.[22–26] This future form of regulation must be contrasted with the current regulation of interior finishes using the traditional standardized procedure (NFPA 255) or the more modern heat release tests (such as NFPA 286) in which the behavior of one product is simply compared with another. At present, this is still a practical approach for building regulation; however, one should understand that good behavior in a standardized test (such as NFPA 255) does not necessarily ensure good behavior in an actual fire, particularly when dealing with nontraditional materials and with complex systems. For example, it has been industry practice to evaluate movable partitions as an assembly in the Steiner tunnel test. There is concern that the NFPA 255 flame spread indices may not be suitable to predict the performance of certain movable or fixed partitions in fires without the benefit of adding supplemental restrictions such as the presence of sprinklers or limiting the height of the partition. Similarly, products such as foam plastic insulation have been identified, in building and fire codes, as materials for which NFPA 255 test protocol is not appropriate.

Steiner Tunnel Test

The 25 ft (7.62 m) Steiner tunnel test, also known as NFPA 255, ASTM E84, and UL 723, was developed by A. J. Steiner at Underwriters Laboratories Inc.[27–30] After a series of fatal fires, the need for a method of controlling interior finishes was recognized and the use of the tunnel test proposed. The method was adopted by the American Society for Testing and Materials (ASTM, now ASTM International) as a tentative standard in 1950 and as an official standard in 1958 (as ASTM E84). NFPA adopted the test method tentatively in 1953 and officially in 1958 as NFPA 255. In both organizations it has been revised periodically.

Figures 18.2.1 and 18.2.2 show the general appearance and basic layout of the tunnel test apparatus. A detailed description can be found in NFPA 255. In summary, a 20- to 24-in. (508- to 610-mm) wide by 24-ft (7.3-m) long test specimen (normally up to 0.15 m thick) is placed face down on a ledge at the top of the furnace to form the ceiling of the test chamber. A gas burner projects a 4½-ft (1.4-m) long flame (89 kW intensity) onto the underside of the test specimen while air flows through the tunnel at a controlled linear air velocity of 240 ft/min (approximately

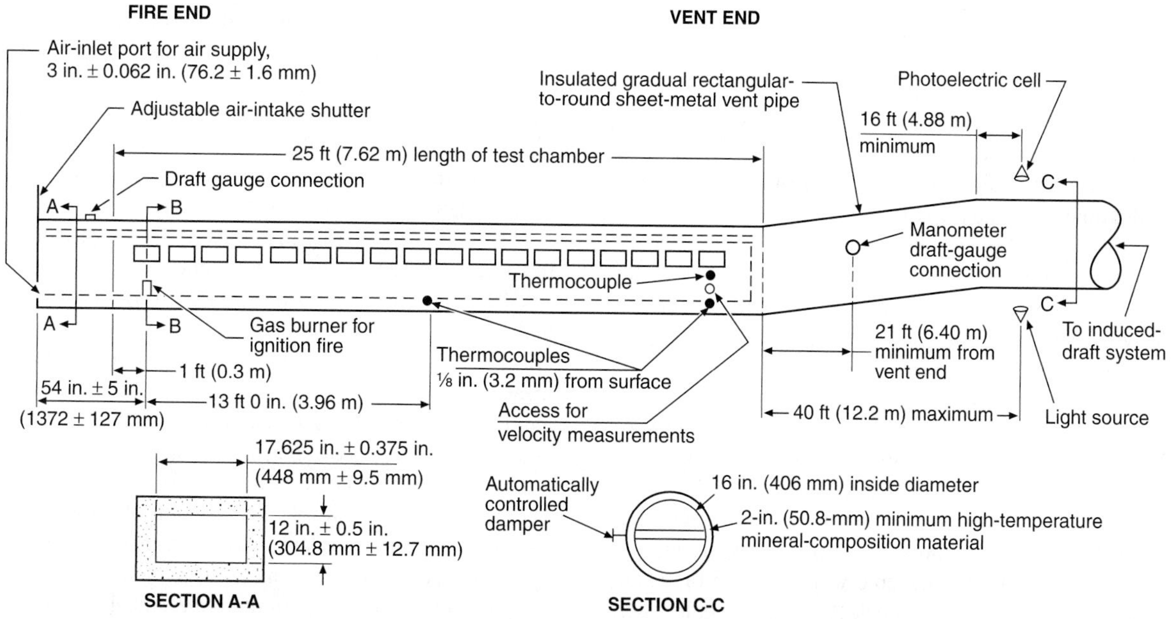

FIGURE 18.2.1 Steiner Tunnel Test Apparatus Used for the Fire Hazard Classification of Building Materials

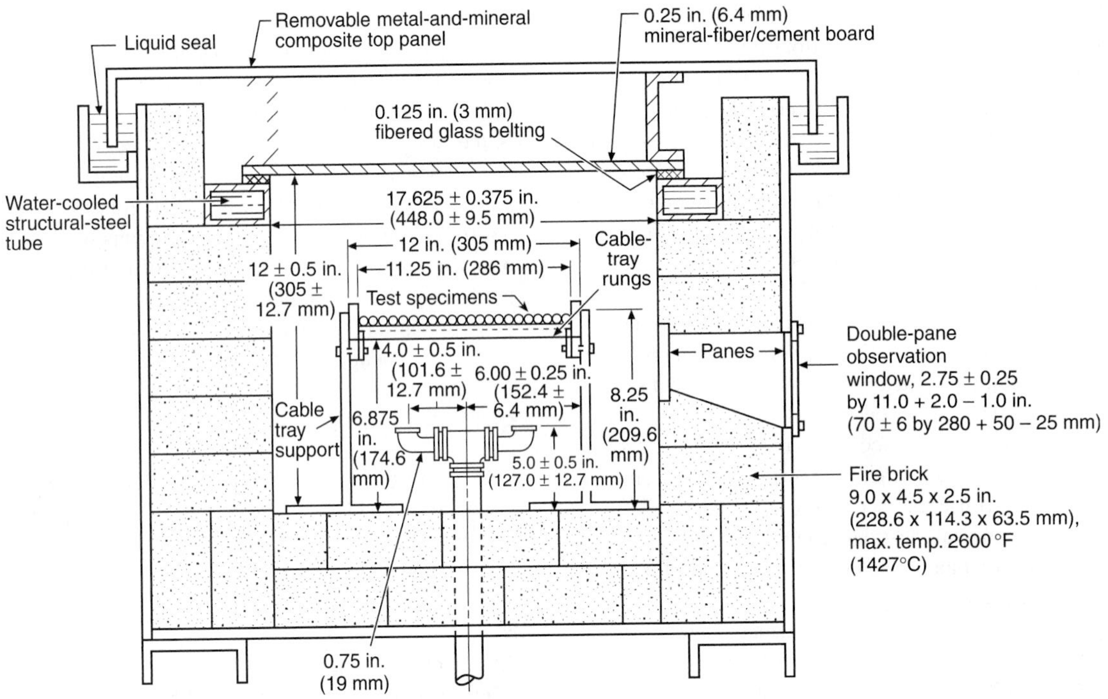

FIGURE 18.2.2 Cross-Sectional View of the Steiner Tunnel Test Apparatus

73 m/min). Flame spread over the face of the test specimen is observed through windows in the side of the "tunnel." Flame propagation is recorded as a function of time over the 10 minute test duration. The record of flame propagation versus time is used to calculate a flame spread index, by comparison with two standard reference materials. Red oak flooring is arbitrarily assigned a flame spread index of 100 and a cementitious board material is assigned a flame spread index of 0. According to the test standard, red oak flooring spreads flame 24 ft (7.3 m) to the end of the test specimen in 5½ minutes ± 15 seconds. The flame spread indices of products are calculated on the basis of a graph of flame spread versus time. The lower the flame spread index, the better the presumed performance. However, as stated above, there is not necessarily a correlation between the measured flame spread index and product behavior in actual fires. NFPA 255 simply provides a basis for comparing one product with another under a standardized set of test conditions.

The reduction in light across the tunnel exhaust caused by smoke generated during the test is measured by a photometer system consisting of a lamp and photo cell. The attenuation of light by the passing smoke and particulate is used to compute a smoke developed index. The smoke developed index for a test specimen is determined by comparing the reduction in light caused by the smoke from red oak flooring to the reduction of light by smoke from a test specimen. Red oak flooring is arbitrarily assigned a value of 100 and the cementitious board material is assigned a smoke developed index of 0. Therefore, a product achieving a 450 smoke developed index produces a curve of light attenuation versus time which has 4.5 times the area of the curve produced by red oak flooring (in comparison with the results for the cementitious board). In simplistic terms, one may think of a product having a 450 smoke developed index as one that produces 4.5 times the amount of smoke that red oak flooring generates during a 10 minute tunnel test.

Factors Affecting Test Results. Products should be tested as proposed for use. For example, the use of high-temperature mortar cement to mount a thin wall covering to an inorganic reinforced cement board substrate may result in artificially good test performance, but such an assembly is not likely to simulate actual installation practices. A product installed in a manner different from that used in testing may perform differently and, in some cases, unsatisfactorily. To illustrate, products that are to be installed over gypsum board with adhesives, such as vinyl wall covering, must be tested over gypsum board, because the paper facing on the gypsum board and the adhesives used can affect fire behavior. ASTM has issued two standard practices which address mounting and testing some materials: pipe and duct insulation materials (ASTM E2231[31]) and vinyl and paper wall and ceiling covering materials (ASTM E2404[32]) and is in the process of developing other practices.

The significance of adhesives has been briefly addressed in the previous paragraph: its fire performance can significantly affect the flame spread index and the smoke developed index measured in the tunnel test. Products should be tested with fastening details that represent conditions of actual use. NFPA *101* and *NFPA 5000* require that interior finish materials be tested as they are to be installed. For example, Paragraph 10.2.1.1 of NFPA *101* (2006) states, "Classification of interior finish materials shall be in accordance with tests made under conditions simulating actual installations, provided that the authority having jurisdiction shall be permitted to establish the classification of any material on which a rating by standard test is not available, unless otherwise provided." This idea is reinforced in the test method itself. For another example, Paragraph 4.2.1.3 of NFPA 255 (2006) states, "The specimen shall be representative of the material for which test results are desired."

Specimen thickness can also affect flame spread. Thinner sections of the same material often will spread flame more rapidly than thicker sections. For example, data show that the flame spread rate remains constant for an acrylic sheet (polymethyl methacrylate or PMMA) with a thickness greater than approximately ⅜ in. (9.5 mm).[33] Decreasing thickness increases the rate of flame spread for that acrylic sheet. These findings indicate that products to be used in varying thicknesses must be tested at the thickness at which they are to be used. Similarly, products that are offered in different densities should be tested in a range of densities.

Other mounting details can be important too. Thermally thin products, such as wood paneling with thickness of ¼ in. (6.4 mm) or less, that are tested when directly applied to an inorganic-reinforced cement board (as noted earlier) may behave differently if they were installed over furring strips with air space. The installation of paneling with air space will likely result in a greater tendency for surface flame spread. Similarly, where a product is to be applied in multiple layers, it should be tested in the maximum thickness intended for use. For example, a wall covering tested by itself may perform satisfactorily, but multiple layers of the same product applied to a wall covering may spread flame and, in recent years, multiple layers of wall coverings applied to gypsum board have contributed to flame propagation in a number of fires where multiple lives were lost.

As discussed throughout this section, the tunnel test is not able to adequately evaluate certain types of materials. Some materials, such as foam plastic insulation, can achieve a low flame spread index and still spread flames readily in actual fires. A research program involving textile wall coverings demonstrated that NFPA 255 is often unable to evaluate textile wall coverings properly.[34]

One should be suspicious of tunnel results for lightweight materials with low thermal inertia and for thermoplastic materials that drip to the floor of the tunnel during testing. When questions arise about the fire performance of a material or product, the product should be evaluated on a full-scale basis, using an ignition source simulating the type of fire likely to be encountered in actual use. Products should be mounted in a manner that is representative of the conditions of actual use, as it has been shown that often each layer of a system may "pass" a certain set of fire test criteria, but the entire system will perform much worse.

Application of Tunnel Test Results. NFPA *101* and *NFPA 5000* classify interior finish materials using flame spread and smoke developed indices. It is recognized that considerable variability exists in tunnel data, and precise values are not likely to be obtained in replicate tests. Further, small differences in indices (10 to 20 points, for example) are not likely to be discernible in terms of actual fire behavior. Accordingly, flame spread indices are usually rounded to the nearest whole number divisible by 5.

Classification	*Flame Spread Index*	*Smoke Developed Index*
A	0–25	0–450
B	26–75	0–450
C	76–200	0–450

Interior wall and ceiling finish classifications are based mainly on flame spread index with a single smoke developed index limit value of 450, which is common to all classifications.

Flame spread indices are used to provide information on the rate of flame spread across the surface of a material. Heat transfer would be the principal hazard associated with flame spread and would only affect a person who was in close proximity to the fire. As a consequence, different classes of interior finish materials are specified within a building, depending on location. For example, exit enclosures in which travel paths are severely restricted have the most severe flame spread index limitations, since individuals in such a location would be restricted in their travel paths and, therefore, might not be able to avoid the heat from the flame.

A smoke developed index of 450 is used for all interior finish classifications. The smoke developed indices assess product behavior in terms of obscuration of exit paths and loss of visibility by smoke. Smoke interferes with visibility on the basis of the accumulated soot and other particles within a given volume. The smoke level will depend on both time and rate of smoke production. A product that has a low smoke developed index would be expected to maintain visibility in egress paths for a longer period of time than a material with a high smoke developed index. The same smoke developed index criterion is used for all three classifications (i.e., classes A, B, and C). The recommended 450 limit acknowledges that smoke affects visibility both in the immediate vicinity of the fire and in remote areas as well. Large buildings can be quickly filled with smoke as the result of a fire. An upper limit has been established that is applicable to interior finishes, regardless of where the materials are installed.

The smoke developed index limit of 450 was originally developed from research conducted by Underwriters Laboratories Inc. (UL).[35] In this research, products were burned in the NFPA 255 "tunnel test" and the smoke discharged into a 5000 ft^3 (141.5 m^3) room. The room was equipped with illuminated exit signs. The time required for exit signs to be obscured was recorded and compared to the smoke developed index for the different materials tested. The UL report stated that materials with smoke developed index values above 325 showed "good" to "marginal" visibility in a few cases, whereas other materials produced conditions of "marginal" to "obscuration" in the 6-minute period. The 450 limit has been used for many years and has long been thought to set a "reasonable" limit for smoke developed index values in rooms. The 450 smoke developed index limit takes into account both the time required to produce the smoke and the effect of the smoke on vision distance.

There is no direct relationship between flame spread index and smoke developed index. In the UL report referenced above,[35] for example, one material had a flame spread index of 490 and a smoke developed index of 57, whereas another had a flame spread index of 44 and a smoke developed index of 1387.

The smoke developed index from NFPA 255 is determined solely on the basis of obscuration of light. It should be recognized that, in some cases, smoke may also act as an irritant, further affecting visibility, and the smoke may, in addition, have a debilitating effect on persons attempting to escape. The irritability and other physiological effects are not evaluated by the 450 smoke developed index limit.

Different classes of interior finish materials are specified, depending on location within a building and on the occupancy involved. Interior finish restrictions are less stringent for a general office area, for example, than would be the case for an exit stair enclosure or exit access corridor. Similarly, occupancies having less capable occupants have stricter interior finish requirements than occupancies used by mobile and alert occupants. For example, the interior finish restrictions for health care facilities are quite restrictive, due to the inability of hospital patients to take action for their own self-preservation.

The limits on interior finish are set forth in the 2006 editions of NFPA *101* and *NFPA 5000*. The limits for interior wall

TABLE 18.2.1 *Life Safety Code* (2006) Requirements (Classes) for Interior Wall and Ceiling Finish[a,b]

Occupancy	*Exits*	*Exit Access Corridors*	*Other Spaces*
Assembly—new			
>300 occupant load	A	A or B	A or B
≤300 occupant load	A	A or B	A, B, or C
Assembly—existing			
>300 occupant load	A	A or B	A or B
≤300 occupant load	A	A or B	A, B, or C
Educational—new	A	A or B	A or B; C on low partitions[c]
Educational—existing	A	A or B	A, B, or C
Day-care centers—new	A	A	A or B
Day-care centers—existing	A or B	A or B	A or B
Day-care homes—new	A or B	A or B	A, B, or C
Day-care homes—existing	A or B	A, B, or C	A, B, or C
Health care—new	A	A; B on lower portion of corridor wall[c]	A; B in small individual rooms[c]
Health care—existing	A or B	A or B	A or B
Detention and correctional—new (sprinklers mandatory)	A or B	A or B	A, B, or C
Detention and correctional—existing	A or B	A or B	A, B, or C
One- and two-family dwellings and lodging or rooming houses	A, B, or C	A, B, or C	A, B, or C
Hotels and dormitories—new	A	A or B	A, B, or C
Hotels and dormitories—existing	A or B	A or B	A, B, or C
Apartment buildings—new	A	A or B	A, B, or C
Apartment buildings—existing	A or B	A or B	A, B, or C
Residential board and care		(See Chapters 32 and 33 of NFPA *101*)	
Mercantile—new	A or B	A or B	A or B
Mercantile—existing			
Class A or Class B stores	A or B	A or B	Ceilings: A or B; walls: A, B, or C
Class C stores	A, B, or C	A, B, or C	A, B, or C
Health care—new			
Business and ambulatory	A or B	A or B	A, B, or C
Health care—existing			
Business and ambulatory	A or B	A or B	A, B, or C
Industrial	A or B	A, B, or C	A, B, or C
Storage	A or B	A, B, or C	A, B, or C

Notes:
1. Class A interior wall and ceiling finish—flame spread index 0–25, (new applications) smoke developed index 0–450.
2. Class B interior wall and ceiling finish—flame spread index 26–75, (new applications) smoke developed index 0–450.
3. Class C interior wall and ceiling finish—flame spread index 76–200, (new applications) smoke developed index 0–450.
4. Automatic sprinklers: The annex of NFPA *101* states that where a complete standard system of automatic sprinklers is installed, interior wall and ceiling finish with a flame spread rating not exceeding Class C is permitted to be used in any location where Class B is required and with a rating of Class B in any location where Class A is required. These provisions do not apply to new detention and correctional occupancies.
5. Exposed portions of structural members complying with the requirements for heavy timber construction are permitted.

[a]*Life Safety Code* requirements for interior wall and ceiling finish materials apply as shown in this table where specified elsewhere in the *Life Safety Code* for specific occupancies (see Chapter 7 and Chapters 11 through 42), unless otherwise specified in the sections addressing individual materials.

[b]Note that everywhere that a Class A, Class B, or Class C interior wall or ceiling finish material is required, a material that has been tested by NFPA 286 and complies with the appropriate criteria is also permitted.

[c]See corresponding chapters for details.

and ceiling finish are summarized in Table 18.2.1 and those for interior floor finish are summarized in Table 18.2.2. As noted in footnotes to the tables, automatic fire suppression, such as automatic sprinklers, will significantly mitigate the hazard associated with a fire, including one associated with interior finish materials. Accordingly, codes often allow materials, including interior finish materials, to comply with a less severe fire performance classification when the area is fully provided with protection from automatic sprinkler systems, in accordance with the appropriate system, namely either NFPA 13, *Standard for the Installation of Sprinkler Systems,* NFPA 13D, *Standard for the Installation of Sprinkler Systems in One- and Two-Family Dwellings and Manufactured Homes,* or NFPA 13R, *Standard for the Installation of Sprinkler Systems in Residential Occupancies up to and Including Four Stories in Height.* The code will explicitly discuss these trade-offs. Accordingly, the informational annexes of NFPA *101* and *NFPA 5000* talk about allowing interior finish materials to drop one classification when automatic sprinkler systems are provided. For example, if the code normally requires a Class A interior finish and automatic sprinklers are installed, then a Class B interior finish is normally allowed. This trade-off is not written in code language and is different from the one incorporated into the International Building Code, for example.

Room-Corner Test

Seeking a more realistic assessment of the hazard of interior finishes, several laboratories started conducting room-corner tests around 1970. These originally comprised an 8 ft (2.44 m) high corner construction with 2 to 4 ft (0.1 to 1.22 m) long wing walls. A simulated ceiling of the same material was provided. A wood crib placed in the corner at floor level was used for ignition. The degree of flame spread and the rate and amount of smoke developed were the primary observations. Interest in the rapidity of flame spread across the surface of what was considered low-flame-spread cellular plastics in actual fires reinforced the use of the corner test. Large-scale corner tests conducted by Factory Mutual Research (now FM Global) and UL (Underwriters Laboratories) have used corners up to 25-ft (7.6-m) high with wing walls up to 50-ft (15.4-m) long to determine the burning characteristics of cellular plastics and the effectiveness of protective measures such as automatic sprinkler protection or thermal barriers.[36] Results have reinforced the premise that fire hazard cannot be fully judged on the basis of a traditional fire test method.[37]

Building codes and NFPA *101* now specify the use of room-corner tests for judging the flammability behavior of certain interior finishes. NFPA *101* and *NFPA 5000,* for example, use NFPA 265, *Standard Methods of Fire Tests for Evaluating Room Fire Growth Contribution of Textile Coverings on Full Height Panels and Walls,* to evaluate the performance of textile and expanded vinyl wall coverings. In the 1980s, researchers at the University of California–Berkeley Fire Research Laboratory showed that wall coverings with NFPA 255 (ASTM E84) ratings as low as 15 sometimes performed poorly, producing flashover in room-corner tests.[34–38] It was determined that room-corner tests (such as NFPA 265) provide a better indication of the hazard presented by these particular wall coverings than do the

TABLE 18.2.2 *Life Safety Code* (2006) Requirements (Classes) for Interior Floor Finish[a]

Occupancy	*Exits*	*Exit Access Corridors*
Assembly—new		
>300 occupant load	I or II	I or II
≤300 occupant load	I or II	I or II
Assembly—existing		
>300 occupant load		
≤300 occupant load		
Educational—new	I or II	I or II
Educational—existing		
Day-care centers—new	I or II	I or II
Day-care centers—existing		
Day-care homes—new	I or II	
Day-care homes—existing		
Health care—new	I or II	I or II
Health care—existing		
Detention and correctional—new (sprinklers mandatory)	I or II	I or II
Detention and correctional—existing	I or II	I or II
One- and two-family dwellings and lodging or rooming houses		
Hotels and dormitories—new	I or II	I or II
Hotels and dormitories—existing	I or II[b]	I or II[b]
Apartment buildings—new	I or II	I or II
Apartment buildings—existing	I or II[b]	I or II[b]
Residential board and care	(See Chapters 32 and 33 of NFPA *101*)	
Mercantile—new	I or II	
Mercantile—existing		
Class A or Class B stores		
Class C stores		
Health care—new		
Business and ambulatory	I or II	
Health care—existing		
Business and ambulatory		
Industrial	I or II	I or II
Storage	I or II	

Notes:

1. Class I interior floor finish—critical radiant flux, not less than 0.45 W/cm^2.
2. Class II interior floor finish—critical radiant flux, not more than 0.22 W/cm^2 but less than 0.45 W/cm^2.
3. Automatic sprinklers: The annex of NFPA *101* states that where a complete standard system of automatic sprinklers is installed, Class II interior floor finish is permitted to be used in any location where Class I is required, and no critical radiant flux rating is required where Class II is required. These provisions do not apply to new detention and correctional occupancies.

[a] *Life Safety Code* requirements for interior floor finish materials apply as shown in this table where specified elsewhere in the *Life Safety Code* for specific occupancies (see Chapter 7 and Chapters 11 through 42), unless otherwise specified in the sections addressing individual materials.

[b] See corresponding chapters for details.

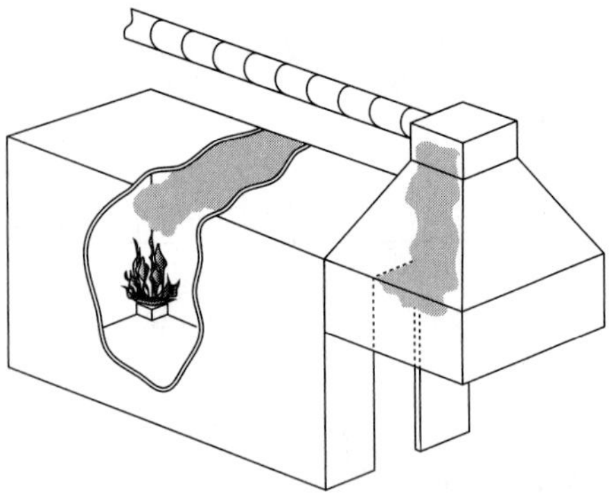

FIGURE 18.2.3 Schematic of Modern Room-Corner Test Apparatus

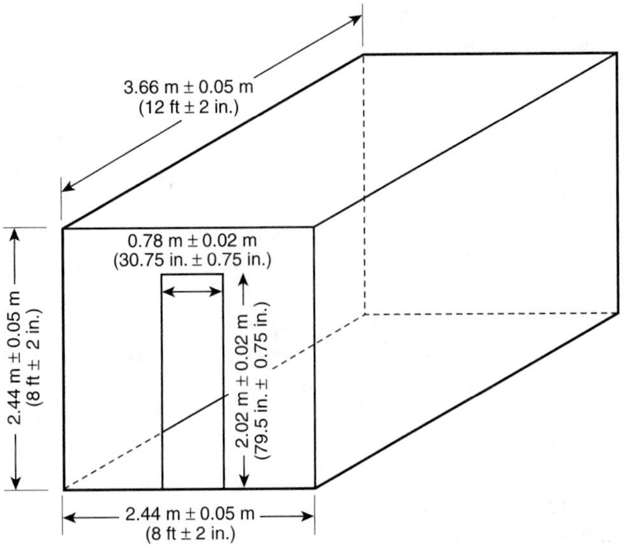

FIGURE 18.2.4 Interior Fire Test Room Dimensions and Interior Doorway Dimensions (Source: Figure 4.2.1, NFPA 286, *Standard Methods of Fire Tests for Evaluating Contribution of Wall and Ceiling Interior Finish to Room Fire Growth,* 2006 ed.)

NFPA 255 flame spread indices. The general layout of modern room corner tests is shown in Figure 18.2.3.

The NFPA 265 test method consists of an 8-ft (2.44-m) wide by 12-ft (3.66-m) long by 8-ft (2.44-m) high room with a single door opening (Figures 18.2.4 through 18.2.6). Products are mounted on three walls, opposite the room door. A diffusion burner is positioned near the corner of the room and provides the required fire exposure. The smoke from the room is collected in a hood and duct exhaust system where instrumentation is used to determine heat release rate (through oxygen depletion) and smoke release (as optical density). Heat flux and temperature measurements are also, optionally, made within the room. Key visual observations are the extent of flame spread and the occurrence of flashover. In NFPA 265, the burner (placed 2 in. [51 mm] away from each wall, near a corner) provides 5 minute, 40 kW fire exposure (which simulates a "waste basket"–sized fire exposure) followed by a 10 minute, 150 kW exposure. A key issue is the fact that the 150 kW burner flame does not reach the

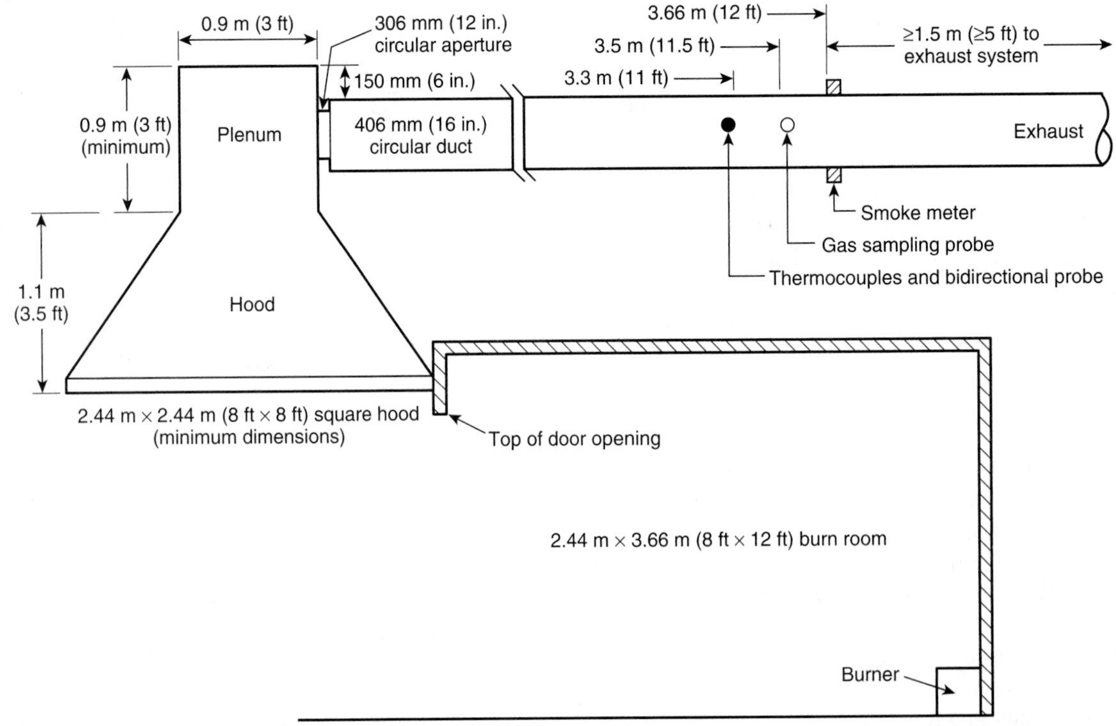

FIGURE 18.2.5 Canopy Hood and Exhaust Duct (Source: Figure 7.2.1, NFPA 286, *Standard Methods of Fire Tests for Evaluating Contribution of Wall and Ceiling Interior Finish to Room Fire Growth,* 2006 ed.)

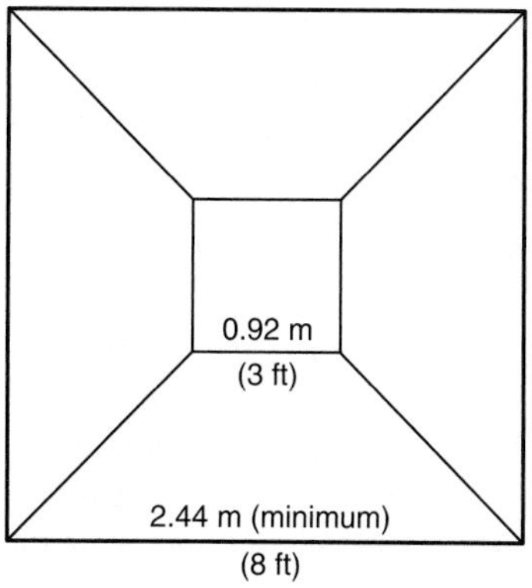

FIGURE 18.2.6 Plan View of Canopy Hood (Source: Figure 7.2.1.3, NFPA 286, *Standard Methods of Fire Tests for Evaluating Contribution of Wall and Ceiling Interior Finish to Room Fire Growth,* 2006 ed.)

ceiling, and the test method is, therefore, not applicable to ceiling coverings. Thus, although the fire exposure specified within NFPA 265 is believed to be appropriate for wall coverings, ceiling coverings are not adequately evaluated by this procedure since the burner placement and 150 kW output (assuming no involvement of a wall test specimen) produces a flame that does not reach the ceiling. The codes set limits for products tested in accordance with NFPA 265, which is for textile and expanded vinyl wall coverings only. The 2006 editions of the codes require that materials tested using the complete NFPA 265 test (also known as Protocol B, namely not the screening test) must meet the following test criteria:

1. Flame shall not spread to the ceiling during the 40 kW exposure.
2. During the 150 kW exposure, flame shall not spread to the outer extremities of the sample on the 8 ft × 12 ft (2.44 m × 3.66 m) wall and flashover shall not occur.

For ceiling coverings and for other interior finish materials, the codes use a different burner placement and output, as detailed in NFPA 286. The NFPA 286 test places the test specimen on the three walls of the room (just like the NFPA 265 test) but also covering the entire ceiling. The test uses a 5 minute, 40 kW initial exposure, followed by a 10 minute, 160 kW exposure, with the burner flush against both walls in the corner. The 160 kW exposure (even absent any contribution by the products undergoing test) will result in burner flames hitting the ceiling and turning to expose the underside of the ceiling for 18 to 24 in. (457 to 610 mm). The direct flame exposure to the ceiling is considered necessary to adequately evaluate ceiling finish. The codes also set limits for products tested in accordance with NFPA 286 (all interior finish materials). Interior finish materials tested by NFPA 286 must meet the following test criteria:

1. Flames shall not spread to the ceiling during the 40 kW exposure.
2. During the 160 kW exposure, flame shall not spread to the outer extremities of the sample on the 8 ft × 12 ft (2.44 m × 3.66 m) wall and flashover shall not occur.
3. The peak heat release rate throughout the test shall not exceed 800 kW.
4. For new installations, the total smoke released throughout the test shall not exceed 1000 m^2.

Clearly the room-corner test is a much more suitable way of assessing fire performance than the NFPA 255 tunnel test. However, the codes admit the NFPA 286 room-corner test results based on the premise that materials that don't cause flashover (or high smoke release) in the room-corner test are known to also have flame spread indices of less than 200 and smoke developed indices of less than 450 in the Steiner tunnel test. This is excellent as far as it goes, but needs refinement. The Steiner tunnel test is very likely to give falsely favorable results (in fact, that happens often with materials that melt and drip and with materials that are thin films) but it rarely gives falsely unfavorable results (meaning that a high flame spread index, or FSI, is almost always indicative of a material with mediocre or poor fire performance). The room-corner test results are potentially much more suitable to classification of materials, because the heat release rate history is obtained in the test. However, the fact that the heat release rate history is not used for code classification purposes results in some inconsistencies occurring when comparing results from both tests. Therefore, it would be important to use the heat release rate history in the room-corner test and not just whether flashover does or does not occur, and the codes have started in that direction by requiring a peak heat release rate not exceeding 800 kW and not just the absence of flashover. Work based on a survey of published data[19] analyzed the comparative fire performance of 25 materials tested in the Steiner tunnel and in the room-corner test, the following points illustrate the problem:

- Five materials had an FSI of 200 or less (i.e., Class A, B, or C) in the Steiner tunnel and yet led to flashover in the room-corner test. The Steiner tunnel test classifies them as acceptable and the room-corner test as unacceptable.
- Fourteen materials had an FSI of 25 or less (i.e., Class A) in the Steiner tunnel and released less than 400 kW in the room-corner test. Both tests consider them satisfactory materials.
- Two materials had an FSI of greater than 25 but not exceeding 75 (i.e., Class B) in the Steiner tunnel and also released less than 400 kW in the room-corner test. The Steiner tunnel test classifies them as Class B and yet the codes would allow such materials to be used instead of Class A materials.
- Two materials had an FSI of 25 or less (i.e., Class A) in the Steiner tunnel and released more than 400 kW but less than flashover in the room-corner test. The codes classify the materials as Class A but these materials are clearly less fire safe than those that release less than 400 kW.
- Two materials had an FSI of 200 or less (i.e., Class C) in the Steiner tunnel and heat release very close to but less than flashover in the room-corner test. The Steiner tunnel test classifies them as Class C and the codes consider them equivalent to Class A materials.

In terms of smoke release by interior wall and ceiling finish, the question has been posed whether it is necessary to test for smoke release if a material shows excellent fire performance in the room-corner test, or is it enough to just develop low heat release products? Recent work[19] shows that of five series of tests conducted in room-corner tests (two in Europe and three in the United States), with a total of 84 materials tested, systematically some 10 percent of the materials (in fact 10 of the 84) give low heat release but very high smoke release. Therefore, it is important to also assess smoke release of interior wall and ceiling finish in a large-scale test. Thus, a smoke release criterion is included in the codes for use with the NFPA 286 room-corner test. The code requirements, total smoke release (TSR) of 1000 m^2 in the NFPA 286 room-corner test, is roughly equivalent to the 450 smoke developed index (SDI) criterion used for the Steiner tunnel test.

A different version of the room-corner test procedure was developed as the result of a research project sponsored by the National Association of Garage Door Manufacturers.[39,40] It is referenced in the 2006 editions of building codes such as *NFPA 5000®, Building Construction and Safety Code®*, for the regulation of foam plastic–insulated garage doors in commercial applications. This room-corner test method and associated regulatory limits are particularly notable in that heat release and smoke release limits have been developed that are linked to the actual fire hazard. The heat release rate and smoke limits eliminate the need for subjective judgments of product behavior required by the older editions of room-corner tests.

If foam or cellular plastics are to be used exposed within a building, the application should be substantiated on the basis of tests that are representative of the conditions of actual use. Room-corner tests, such as NFPA 265, NFPA 286, and ISO 9705[41] or ASTM E2257,[42] have been used to evaluate foam plastic insulation materials. They all use a gas diffusion burner as the fire source, with ISO 9705 or ASTM E2257 being the most severe one (the ignition source is 100 kW for the first 10 minutes and 300 kW for the next 10 minutes).

Full-scale test procedures, like room-corner tests, allow products to be evaluated because they will be installed using an ignition source representative of those likely to be encountered during actual use. Accordingly, results of room-corner fire tests are more indicative of product behavior during actual fires than are traditional tests, such as NFPA 255. Codes exempt materials tested in accordance with an appropriate room-corner test from classification in accordance with NFPA 255. In other words, the codes allow products shown to perform acceptably by a room-corner fire test to be used as interior finish in those locations otherwise requiring Class A, B, or C materials. Furthermore, the data from room-corner fire tests is also suitable for use as input into fire models for performance-based design.

Other Flame Spread Tests

Attempts have been made to develop a smaller scale test that could be used in place of the nominally 25 ft (7.6 m) long "tunnel" test. The advantages of such a method are obvious: less space required for the equipment, smaller specimens needed, and lower costs. The Forest Products Laboratory developed a reduced-scale version of the tunnel. The reduced-scale tunnel was 8 ft (2.4 m) long and used flame spread observations as a function of time to determine flame spread ratings. The 8 ft (2.4 m) tunnel test was adopted by ASTM in 1968 as ASTM E286[43] and withdrawn by ASTM in 1991.

A radiant panel apparatus was developed at the National Bureau of Standards (NBS), now NIST. The radiant panel apparatus uses a much smaller test specimen of 6 in. by 18 in. (152 mm by 457 mm) and measures hazard in terms of both flame spread and, potentially, heat release rate after ignition. The test method was adopted as a standard by ASTM in 1967 as ASTM E162.[44] In the radiant panel test, *Standard Test Method for Surface Flammability of Materials Using a Radiant Heat Energy Source,* the specimen is positioned at an angle of 30° to vertical in front of a gas-fired, porous, refractory, vertical panel. The specimen slants toward the radiant panel at the top and a small pilot flame at that location ignites flammable gases released from the surface of the specimen. Air is drawn over the surface of the specimen at a controlled rate by a fan in the hood under which the equipment is located. The rate of flame travel from the top of the specimen to the bottom is noted, as are temperatures that develop in the stack. The amount of smoke generated can be measured by weighing deposits on a filter located in the stack. The test is continued for 15 minutes or until surface flaming reaches the lower edge of the specimen. This radiant panel apparatus is available commercially and is used in many research, commercial, and industrial laboratories. The results of tests are expressed on a scale and reported as the "radiant panel index." In the radiant panel, the air flow is against or across the direction of flame travel. This provides a clear definition of the interfacial burning. With the Steiner tunnel test (NFPA 255), the flame travel and airflow coincide, and, with some materials, the flame front may be several feet in front of the interfacial burning (see Figure 18.2.3).

ASTM E162 was not originally intended for regulatory use and is not used in codes (building code, fire code, or life safety code) as a substitute for evaluating products in accordance with the Steiner tunnel test, such as NFPA 255. It is, however, used for some transportation vehicles and for manufactured housing. In the case of rail transportation vehicles, both the Federal Railroad Administration[45,46] and NFPA 130, *Standard for Fixed Guideway Transit and Passenger Rail Systems,* require that lining materials pass the ASTM E162 test, with radiant panel indices ranging from 25 to 100, depending on the application. ASTM E162 is also used in NFPA 1192, *Standard on Recreational Vehicles,* for assessing the flame spread performance of cabinet door and drawer faces, exposed cabinet bottoms and end panels, and tub/shower walls in recreational vehicles, and in NFPA 501, *Standard on Manufactured Housing,* as an alternative to the Steiner tunnel test to assess flame spread performance of interior finish materials in manufactured housing; for both applications a radiant panel index of 200 is required.

Smoke Density Chamber Test

A "bench test" for measuring smoke generation, the smoke density chamber, has been available for many years. Described in ASTM E662,[47] it measures the specific optical density of smoke generated in a chamber from test specimens up to 1 in. (25.4 mm) thick. Despite the existence of a clause in ASTM E662 that intends to limit the test procedure for use as a research and development tool, it is actually widely used for regulatory purposes (including its use for lining materials in trains by the Federal Railroad Administration[45,46] and in airplanes by the

Federal Aviation Administration[48]) but not normally for interior finish in codes. A variation of the test (ASTM E1995,[49] also known as NFPA 270, *Standard Test Method for Measurement of Smoke Obscuration Using a Conical Radiant Source in a Single Closed Chamber,* and ISO 5659-2[50]) is used for regulating interior finish in ships by the International Maritime Organization (IMO), the U.S. Coast Guard, and NFPA 301, *Code for Safety to Life from Fire on Merchant Vessels.* ASTM E1995 differs from ASTM E662 mainly in that the burner is a conical heater and the sample is tested horizontally. The smoke density chamber test is known to have numerous shortcomings. The method involves a closed, static chamber, whereas smoke transfer in actual fires is dynamic. The chamber is closed, and oxygen-deficient atmospheres can develop that may artificially affect the burning behavior of the products being tested. Deposits of soot on wall surfaces and optics can affect measurements. In summary, numerous questions exist as to the relevance of data from ASTM E662 to the behavior of products in actual fires.

FIRE TESTS FOR INTERIOR FLOOR FINISH MATERIALS

Fire tests for interior finishes were developed primarily with wall and ceiling finishes in mind, long before carpeting became popular as an interior floor finish. Official attention was directed toward a possible hazard with soft floor coverings in 1960 and 1961 as a result of a series of small fires in the Washington, D.C., area.[51] A well-publicized dwelling fire on the West Coast in 1967, followed by the Harmer House Nursing Home fire in Ohio in 1970, focused attention on carpet floor coverings, although carpets were a contributing, rather than a causative, factor in these incidents.[52,53]

In 1965, the Public Health Service of the U.S. Department of Health, Education, and Welfare issued a directive setting flame spread limits on floor coverings in federally funded hospitals, citing the Steiner tunnel test as the test method. In the Steiner tunnel test, a floor covering would be mounted upside down and on the ceiling of the apparatus. Since neither the mounting nor location correctly simulated an actual installation, it is not surprising that the tunnel test was ultimately judged to be inadequate for floor coverings. Moreover, the Steiner tunnel cannot assess ignitability and its fuel source is not appropriate to assess slow flame spread. It was also found to be inadequate for carpets made with synthetic fibers of the type that melt, drip, or delaminate when exposed to elevated temperatures. As a further deficiency, carpets with separate underlayments could not be effectively tested in the tunnel. Thus, the need for a test specifically designed for interior floor finishes was clearly identified.

In 1969, UL started work on a new test for floor coverings with the test specimens mounted in a floor position.[54] The program was sponsored by the U.S. Public Health Service and resulted in what became known as UL Subject 992, the floor covering chamber test. In essence, UL Subject 992 is an 8 ft (2.44 m) version of the Steiner tunnel, with the test specimen mounted on the floor of the tunnel and with appropriate modifications in heat input, burner design, airflow, and other test specifications. This test never gained widespread acceptance and is no longer used.

Methenamine Pill Test

NIST (formerly NBS) developed the methenamine pill test as a means of preventing the use of highly flammable carpet floor coverings. The pill test was adopted by the federal government in 1970 as DOC FF-1-70 (Federal Register 1970a) for carpets and DOC FF-2-70 for rugs[55–57] and was also adopted by ASTM as ASTM D2859.[58] In this test, eight 9 in. (229 mm) square sections of a carpet are conditioned to drive off excess moisture, brought to room temperature in a desiccator, and tested. Each specimen, in turn, is placed on the bottom of a 1 ft (0.3 m) enclosed cube, which is open at the top. The specimen is held in place by a 9 in. (229 mm) square metal plate having an 8 in. (203 mm) circular cutout. A methenamine tablet is placed at the center of the circle and lighted. The pill produces a candlelike flame for about 100 seconds. A specimen fails if the flame advances to within 1 in. (25.4 mm) of the metal ring in the hold-down plate. At least seven of the eight specimens must pass the test to meet the established criteria. All carpet manufactured for sale in the United States has been required, since April 1971, to pass this test (Figure 18.2.7).

Although the pill test is a small-scale test, the results have large implications in terms of floor covering performance. It has been shown that the pill test provides adequate "first to ignite" protection for carpet located in rooms.[59,60] Experiments conducted at NIST[61,62] revealed that carpet and floor coverings were unlikely to be involved in a fire or propagate flame in rooms until room fires approach or exceed flashover unless the fire started at the floor level. As a consequence, little additional safety is to be gained by regulating floor coverings within rooms beyond the pill test. These findings were used, in part, to establish the current code restrictions for floor coverings.

Experience has shown that many flooring materials (traditional floor finishes such as wood flooring or resilient materials) will not ignite unless exposed to an ignition source of well over 1 kW/m^2, but that some carpetlike or loose-fill materials may ignite at lower heat fluxes. A study of precision of the flooring radiant panel test method (ASTM E648,[63] NFPA 253, *Standard Method*

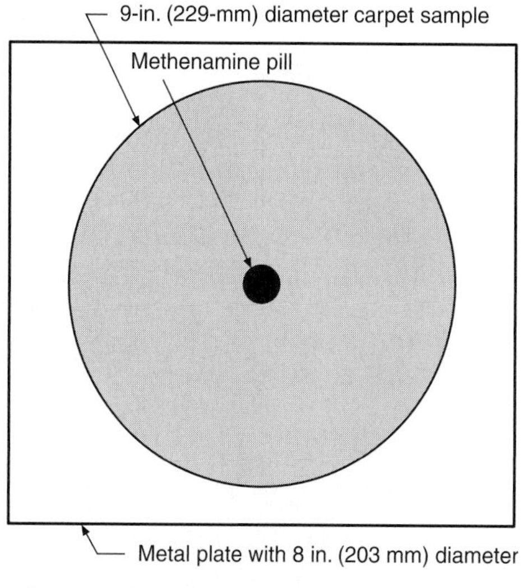

FIGURE 18.2.7 Methenamine Pill Test

of Test for Critical Rdiant Flux of Floor Covering Systems Using a Radiant Heat Energy Source) found carpets with critical radiant heat fluxes well under 2 kW/m^2.[64] The minimum critical radiant flux of a product that will still pass the pill test has been determined to be 0.4 kW/m^2.[61] Therefore, as stated above, all carpets sold in the United States must meet the "methenamine pill" test, which ensures that flame spread will be minimal.

Flooring Radiant Panel Test or Critical Radiant Flux Test

Floor coverings having modest resistance to flame spread are unlikely to become involved in the early growth of a fire within a room. Thus, regulation of floor coverings is generally where specified by the code or where a need is indicated by some unusual product. It has been shown that floor coverings will tend to propagate flame only under the influence of a sizable exposure fire (often after flashover). Corridor floor coverings, for example, may spread flame when subjected to radiant heat from the hot gases discharging from the doorway of a fully fire-involved room.[65,66] The fire discharges flame and hot gases into the upper level of the corridor, which results in radiant heat energy transfer to the floor. The level of energy radiating onto the floor is a significant factor in determining whether progressive flaming will occur. Corridors with combustible wall and ceiling finishes would be expected to produce a potentially greater fire hazard. Experimental results suggest that floor coverings would contribute much less to fire spread than wall or ceiling finish in the initial growth of fires.[67]

Codes specify the use of the flooring radiant panel test for floor coverings in exits and corridors of certain occupancies. The flooring radiant panel test consists of a closed chamber having a radiant panel inclined at a 30° angle from a 39 in. (1000 mm) long test specimen. The test specimen is exposed to radiant heat that ranges from approximately 11 kW/m^2 to 1 kW/m^2. Flame spread over the face of the floor covering specimen is initiated by flames from a gas burner (Figure 18.2.8). The test determines the minimum energy required for a floor covering to spread flame. The flooring radiant panel test simulates conditions that have been observed and defined in large-scale corridor experiments, particularly when there is little or no combustible wall or ceiling finish. The test method assesses the critical incident flux required for continued flame propagation. It does so by determining the distance between the igniter and the point where flame propagation stops, and obtaining the heat flux from a calibration curve of heat flux versus distance. The flooring radiant panel measures the minimum energy required to be impinged on floor coverings to sustain flame propagation. The minimum value required to

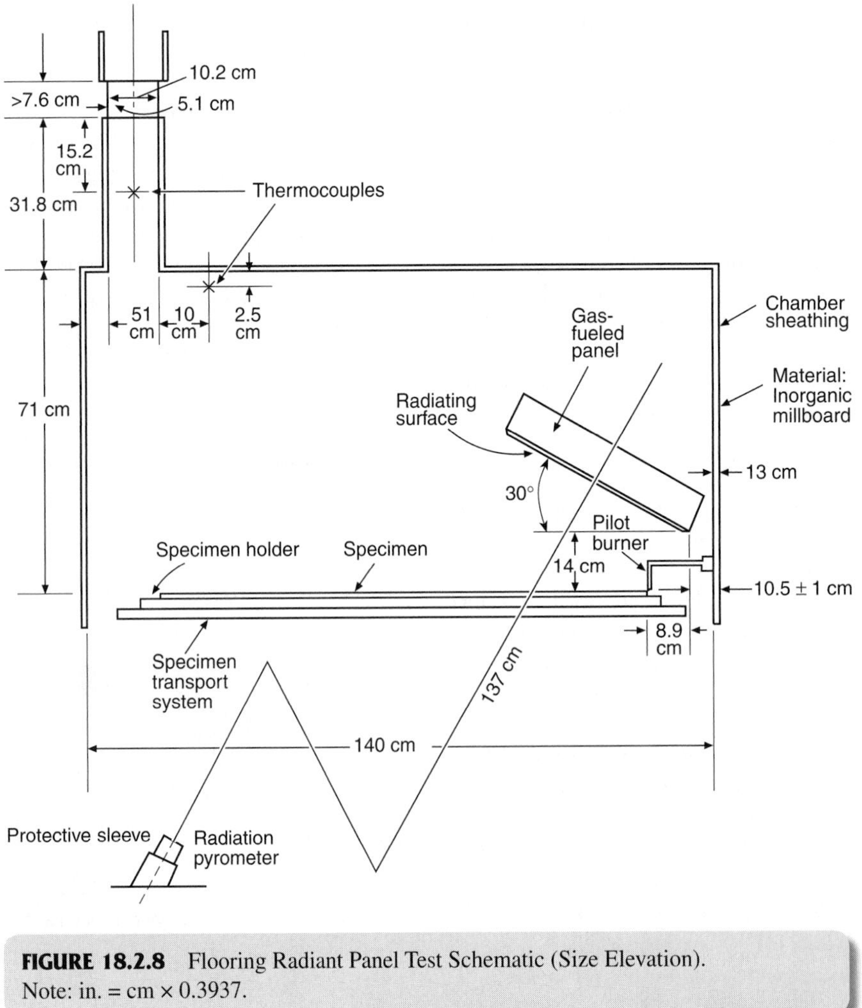

FIGURE 18.2.8 Flooring Radiant Panel Test Schematic (Size Elevation). Note: in. = cm × 0.3937.

sustain flame propagation is termed *critical radiant flux.* The higher the critical radiant flux, the better the performance. In summary, the flooring radiant panel test is used for evaluating the fire performance of a floor covering in a building in areas where risks need to be especially minimized. Floor coverings in open building spaces and in rooms within buildings generally merit no further regulation, provided the floor covering is at least as resistant to flame spread as a material that will meet the federal flammability standard FF-1-70/ASTM D2859 methenamine pill test. Therefore, most codes regulate interior floor finish to be tested with the flooring radiant panel (ASTM E648, NFPA 253).

The codes classify interior floor finishes on the basis of critical radiant flux and group them into the following two classes:

- *Class I.* A minimum critical radiant flux of 0.43 Btu per ft^2 per second (0.45 W/cm^2)
- *Class II.* A minimum critical radiant flux of 0.19 Btu per ft^2 per second (0.22 W/cm^2)

See Table 18.2.2 for assignment of the two classes of floor finishes to the various occupancies identified in NFPA *101.*

The flooring radiant panel test requires test specimens to be representative of the product to be installed. Where carpet is to be loose-laid over concrete, for example, it should be tested over a thick, high-density inorganic reinforced cement board that simulates concrete. Where carpet, with or without integral pad, is to be bonded to concrete, an adhesive should be used, following the manufacturer's directions as to the type and application rate. The use of a separate underlayment (pad) will normally lower the critical radiant flux of a test specimen and, therefore, increase the tendency for flame spread. Research at NIST[68] has shown that underlayment lowers the critical radiant flux of a test specimen due to the insulative effect of the underlayment. The flooring radiant panel test formerly allowed a manufacturer of carpet to test over a "standard" pad or the actual underlayment proposed for use. Research at NIST has shown that using what was formerly considered the standard pad—a rubber-coated jute and animal hair or fiber pad a minimum of ⅜ in. (9.5 mm) thick and weighing 50 oz/yd^2 (1.86 kg/m^2)—is likely to yield lower critical radiant flux values than those associated with other underlayments in use.[68,69] If the manufacturer tests a carpet over the "standard pad," NFPA 253 allows the results to be applied to any carpet/underlayment combination. Alternatively, if the manufacturer chooses to test using the actual pad proposed for use, the results would be valid only for the actual combination tested.

Floor coverings are not generally regulated on the basis of smoke generation in codes. Regulation of floor coverings on the basis of smoke is usually not considered necessary. Floor coverings will not normally spread flame until after a fire grows to large size and most fires will be so large and the smoke production so great when floor coverings become involved that the minimal benefits achieved by imposing smoke limits on floor coverings would not generally warrant such regulation. Nevertheless, some jurisdictions and many transport environments (including trains and ships) establish criteria for floor finishes based on a test for smoke generation. In such instances, the ASTM E662 test method has been used for trains (and for some building regulations) and the ISO 5659-2 test method has been used for ships. These test methods provide procedures for measuring the specific optical density of smoke generated in a closed chamber, as discussed previously.

TYPES OF INTERIOR FINISH

The types of interior finish materials are numerous and include such commonly used materials as plaster, gypsum wallboard, wood, plywood paneling, fibrous ceiling tiles, several different plastic products, and a variety of wall coverings. Collectively, these finishes serve several functions: aesthetic, acoustical, and insulating, as well as protecting against wear and abrasion.

Wall and ceiling finish classification needs to be based on test specimens that are representative of actual installations (particularly in terms of the various layers involved and of components such as adhesives). Building, fire, and life safety codes single out certain specific interior finish materials. The interior finish materials singled out are very thin materials, structural members, textile wall and ceiling coverings, expanded vinyl wall and ceiling coverings, foam plastic insulation, interior trim (foam plastic or otherwise), light-transmitting plastics, wall base, metal panels, and fire retardant coatings (not discussed in building codes). NFPA *101* also has a specific reference to the fact that decorations and furnishings not meeting the definition of interior finish should not be tested by the test methods for interior finish. Electrical nonmetallic raceways are normally considered a subset of interior trim.

Very Thin Materials

Codes exempt very thin materials applied directly to the surface of walls and ceilings in a total thickness of less than 1⁄28 in. (0.9 mm) from testing as interior finish "if they meet the requirements of Class A interior wall or ceiling finish when tested in accordance with the Steiner tunnel test, using fiber cement board as the substrate material." This exemption for 1⁄28 in. thin materials that attain a flame spread index of 25 or less applies to products such as gypsum wallboard, single layers of paints, and thin paper, vinyl, or textile wall coverings. The exception for thin materials is based on the understanding that thin coverings secured to a substrate will tend to behave like the substrate. Thin coverings, such as paint on steel and paper over gypsum, will not generally spread flames or contribute to fire growth during the developing stage of a fire. However, thicker coverings, such as multiple layers of a wall covering or paint, can contribute to rapid fire growth.

Structural Members

Exposed portions of structural members complying with the requirements for Type IV(2HH) construction are exempt from testing and classification as interior finish in codes.

Textile Wall and Ceiling Coverings

Some textile wall and ceiling coverings are able to achieve good flame spread indices (less than 25) when tested in accordance with NFPA 255, and yet these same textile wall coverings in room-corner tests sometimes propagate flame and cause fires to grow to full-room size, that is, flashover, within minutes.[34] The codes mandate three options for textile wall coverings: (a) automatic suppression (sprinklers) as well as a Class A performance in the Steiner tunnel test, (b) satisfactory behavior in the NFPA 265 room-corner test, or (c) satisfactory behavior in the NFPA 286 room-corner test. Since the ignition source of the NFPA 265 room-corner test does not reach the ceiling, textile ceiling coverings are allowed only options (a) or (c) and not (b). Satisfactory performance in accordance with NFPA 265 requires (a) no flame spread to the ceiling during the initial exposure, (b) no flame spread to the extremities of the sample, and (c) no flashover. Satisfactory performance in accordance with NFPA 286 is more difficult to achieve, because it requires two additional criteria: heat release rate not exceeding 800 kW and total smoke release not exceeding 1000 m^2. Since NFPA *101* applies to existing buildings, textile wall or ceiling coverings are not allowed to be tested by NFPA 286.

Expanded Vinyl Wall and Ceiling Coverings

Expanded vinyl wall or ceiling coverings are another example of products that may attain good flame spread indices in the Steiner tunnel test and yet perform unsatisfactorily in an actual fire. The codes establish special criteria for the use of expanded vinyl wall and ceiling coverings, similar to the requirements for textile coverings. The code also allows the use of expanded vinyl wall coverings for walls (but not ceilings) if the wall covering has been tested to the less severe room-corner test in NFPA 265.

Foam Plastic Insulation

The development of certain types of cellular plastics in board, poured-in-place, and sprayed-on foam has yielded lightweight materials with exceptional thermal insulation. The incorporation of fire retardants into some cellular plastic products makes it possible for them to meet the NFPA 255–related requirements for interior finishes. As a result, cellular plastics, particularly the sprayed-on type, have been used as exposed insulation. Rapid fire spread in several widely publicized fires (including the two nightclub fires described earlier[13–15]) involving exposed cellular polyurethane and polystyrene materials resulted in recommendations for protection of such surfaces against ignition and fire spread by the use of 15-minute thermal barriers.[70,71] NFPA *101* and *NFPA 5000* state that cellular or foam plastic materials are not allowed for use as interior finish unless actual fire tests substantiate, on a reasonable basis, their combustibility characteristics for the intended use.

Interior Trim

Codes also state that interior trim (for example around doors or windows or as chair rails) materials (other than cellular or foam plastics) must comply with an NFPA 255 flame spread index classification of Class C, without smoke developed index limitation, provided they do not exceed 10 percent of the aggregate wall or ceiling area. The rationale for this requirement is that typical wood products exhibit a Class C flame spread index classification. On the other hand, cellular or foam plastics may be used as interior trim only if they meet three criteria: (1) they do not exceed 10 percent of the aggregate wall or ceiling area, (2) the density is not less than 20 lb/ft^3 (320 kg/m^3) and they are no more than ½ in. (12.7 mm) thick and 4 in. (102 mm) wide, and (3) they comply with a NFPA 255 Class B flame spread index without the smoke developed index limitation. The exception for "plastic trim" is based on the assumption that the fire performance of the foam plastic trim will be comparable or better than that of traditional wood products. The required Class B flame spread index is better than the flame spread index achieved by most wood materials. A minimum density of 20 lb/ft^3 (320.4 kg/m^3) is set to prohibit the use of lightweight foam plastics, which typically have densities of 1 to 3 lb/ft^3 (16 to 48 kg/m^3). The width and thickness limits are to restrict the combustible mass. The concept of the "10 percent rule," which applies the same way for foam plastic as for other trim, has already been discussed in the section on concepts.

Electrical Nonmetallic Raceways. Electrical nonmetallic raceways are a special case of interior trim. Raceways are not normally regulated as interior finish. However, concerns have been expressed about the potential contribution of a sizable number of raceways mounted along a wall or ceiling. If the raceways collectively form a substantial surface area over which fire may spread, they could behave like combustible interior finish. Where the authority having jurisdiction judges that a potential hazard exists because of the number, area exposed, or type of material involved, NFPA *101* and *NFPA 5000* currently require nonmetallic raceways to attain a flame spread index of 25 or less when tested "in the form in which they are used." Similar to foam plastic trim, when the raceway constitutes less than 10 percent of the wall area, the smoke index is not limited.

Light-Transmitting Plastics

Light-transmitting plastics are permitted for use if they meet several small-scale fire test criteria and meet other severe area limitations.

Wall Base

Interior floor trim material used at the junction of the wall and the floor to provide a functional or decorative border, and not exceeding 6 in. (150 mm) in height, is permitted for use by NFPA *101* and *NFPA* 5000 if it meets the interior wall finish requirements for its location or the requirements for Class II interior floor finish.

Metal Panels

Listed factory-finished NFPA 255 Class A metal ceiling and wall panels are permitted by NFPA *101* and *NFPA 5000* to be finished with one additional application of paint and to be used in areas where Class A interior finishes are required. The total paint thickness is not allowed to exceed 1⁄28 in. (0.90 mm).

Fire-Retardant Coatings

Fire-retardant coatings are permitted by NFPA *101* if they are maintained to retain the effectiveness of the treatment under service conditions encountered in actual use.

Decorations and Furnishings

Free-hanging draperies that cover most or all of a wall surface have, on occasion, been subject to the requirements for interior finish but are considered decorations by NFPA *101* and fire codes and are not addressed by building codes such as *NFPA 5000.* The traditional test for interior finish combustibility, NFPA 255, does not adequately assess the fire behavior of such products. Free-hanging drapery materials are more properly evaluated by NFPA 701, *Standard Methods of Fire Tests for Flame Propagation of Textiles and Films,* although the test is less severe than NFPA 255. When applied to a solid backing, such as gypsum wallboard, a drapery material needs to be considered as a textile wall covering and would be evaluated as interior finish (textile wall or ceiling covering, as appropriate). Other decorations and furnishings are often also required to meet the fire performance of NFPA 701, for example in NFPA *101.* However, when these are stand-alone decorations, they are no longer associated with interior finish and are often not regulated.

ROLE OF INTERIOR FINISH IN FIRES

Most building fires begin when decorative materials, furnishings, or waste accumulations ignite. Interior finishes are less often the first items ignited. For example, in 1999–2002 home fires, interior finish on walls, floors, or ceilings was cited as the first item ignited in only about 6 percent of fires, about 9 percent of civilian fire deaths, about 6 percent of civilian fire injuries, and about 10 percent of direct property damage from fires.[15] When interior finish is ignited, typical heat sources are equipment installed adjacent to interior finish (e.g., wiring, switches, receptacles, outlets, cords and plugs, fireplaces, chimneys or flues), equipment placed near interior finish (e.g., stoves, space heaters, water heaters, dryers, furnaces), equipment used near interior finish (e.g., torches), and open flame sources (e.g., matches, lighters, candles) used by adults or children to intentionally or unintentionally start a fire. Once a fire has started and intensified, however, the interior finish can become involved and contribute extensively to the spread and growth of fire. For example, multiple layers of wall coverings contributed to fire growth in the multideath fires at the Holiday Inn in Cambridge, Ohio, in 1979,[72] and at an office building in Atlanta, Georgia, in 1989.[7] Similarly, the use of non-fire-retarded wood paneling as interior finish in corridors, stairways, or exits (which does not comply with code requirements) often leads to an enhancement of the heat release in the fire; 0.25 inch luan paneling, 0.125 inch plywood paneling, and heart pine boards mounted on furring strips contributed to the severity of fires in a fraternity dormitory in Berkeley, California, in 1990; in a board-and-care facility fire in Detroit, Michigan, in 1992; and in a fraternity house fire in Chapel Hill, North Carolina, in 1996, respectively.[10,11,73,74]

Mechanisms

Interior finish affects fire hazard in four ways: (1) affecting the rate of fire buildup to flashover conditions, (2) contributing to fire extension by flame spread over its surface, (3) adding to the intensity of a fire by contributing additional fuel, and (4) producing smoke and toxic gases that can contribute to life hazard and property damage.[75] From a fire safety standpoint, the most desirable interior finish is one made of a relatively dense and noncombustible material that is a good conductor of heat, does not speed up flashover, does not add fuel to the fire, provides no path for surface flame spread, and produces little or no smoke or toxic gases. Materials that exhibit high rates of flame spread, contribute substantial quantities of fuel to a fire, or produce hazardous quantities of smoke or toxic gases are undesirable.

Interior Finish Materials and Flashover

Combustible interior finish in an enclosure can reduce the heat release rate necessary for flashover and can reduce the time to flashover. Flashover is caused by thermal radiation feedback from the ceiling and upper walls, which have been heated by the fire. This radiation feedback gradually heats the contents of the fire area. When all the combustibles in the space have become heated to their ignition temperatures, simultaneous ignition occurs. Interior finish plays an important role in the occurrence of flashover; that is, an insulating interior finish that lowers heat transfer to upper walls or ceilings can reduce both the time and the rate of heat release required to reach flashover. Any interior finish material that is combustible will contribute fuel to an existing fire, but those with better fire performance are likely to have minimal effects. Considering the nature of thermal radiation, the size and shape of the space in which the fire occurs becomes a critical factor.[76] In some corridor tests conducted by NIST, rapid spread of flame over one or more surfaces was found,[77] an obviously undesirable feature unlikely to be found with materials that meet the NFPA 286 room-corner test.

Once a room fire reaches full involvement, or flashover, heat, smoke, and combustion gases escape through openings to adjoining spaces. In those cases, the ignition of combustible interior finish may become a significant factor in the spread of fire to other areas. Several full-scale fire tests have demonstrated that heat, smoke, and combustion gases from burning furnishings are often sufficient to create a threat to the life safety of persons unable to evacuate the room of fire origin, without any contribution from combustible interior finishes if the interior finish materials have adequate fire performance.[78,79] However, even in such a case, the life safety of occupants remote from the fire and, in addition, potential property damage may be affected by the nature of the interior finishes. It is critical, therefore, to ensure proper fire performance of interior finish.

METHODS OF APPLICATION

The method of applying an interior finish both in actual practice and during the fire test can have a large effect on its fire behavior. For this reason, the manufacturer's specifications for material application should be strictly followed. Special attention must be paid to fastening details, including the type and application of adhesives and the number of coats and the application rate of any fire-retardant coatings. Application details are equally important in repair or replacement of interior finishes. Any new material used in retrofit must meet the code requirements in effect at the time of the retrofit.

The substrate material to which surface finishes are attached plays an important role in the flame spread behavior of thin products.[80] A thin combustible finish applied to a noncombustible substrate may sometimes present little hazard. The same finish material on a combustible backing could constitute a much more serious hazard. In the former situation, the substrate will not ignite and, thus, will absorb heat during early fire development. In the latter case, both the surface finish and the backing material may ignite and the system will spread flames much more rapidly than either material would alone.

A particularly important case is that of paints. Testing[81] has shown that adding up to two layers of paint with a dry film thickness of about 0.007 in. (0.18 mm) will not change the fire properties of surface-covering systems. Testing has also shown that the fire properties of the surface-covering systems are highly substrate-dependent and that thin coatings generally take on the characteristics of the substrate. When exposed to fire, the potential for partial delamination, bubbling, and blistering of paint has been shown to result in an accelerated rate of flame spread.

The adhesive used is also a crucial factor in the fire behavior of interior finishes. The best performance is likely when an intimate bond is maintained between the face product and the substrate. However, adhesives can, and often do, also contribute fuel to a fire, and too much adhesive or the use of a highly flammable or inappropriate adhesive may result in faster flame propagation. The failure in bond between a surface finish and a substrate can also result in poor performance. Adhesives that soften at moderate temperatures may allow wall and ceiling finishes to drop or partially peel away during the growth stage of a fire. Perhaps the "worst case" for an interior finish is where partial release or partial delamination occurs. In such a case, the material separates from the substrate but remains in position. This not only increases the susceptibility of the surface material to ignition but it also exposes the substrate material, which, if combustible, adds fuel to the fire.

Some interior finishes, such as polystyrene ceiling tiles, achieve acceptable performance in an entirely different manner. They are designed to fall away early in a fire, thereby avoiding fire exposure. Satisfactory performance for such products results from evading flame during the fire growth phase. However, if the products fall or delaminate too early in a fire, they may interfere with persons attempting to escape. Where interior finish materials may fall or delaminate at relatively low temperatures and where the products involved have a significant mass, the behavior of such products should be assessed in terms of their impact on occupants and their effect on potential evacuation. Some building codes specify that wall and ceiling finishes should not become detached when exposed to elevated temperatures of 175 to 300°F (79 to 149°C) for a specified time interval, usually 30 minutes.

Thermally thin products, such as wood paneling 0.25 in. (6.4 mm) thick or less, will tend to spread flame more rapidly when the paneling is installed over studs or furring strips with air space than would be the case if installed over a solid substrate, such as cement board or gypsum board. As a consequence, in such cases some codes require that Class B and C interior finish materials less than 0.25 in. (6.4 mm) thick be permitted for use only when applied over a substrate of noncombustible material. Concern also exists about the possibility of flame spread over concealed surfaces of combustible interior finish materials where air space exists behind the finish. Building codes have application sections that restrict the application of interior finishes over air space in noncombustible assemblies. Interior finishes installed over an air space are restricted to products having a Class A flame spread index on both faces. Building codes regulate concealed spaces created by furring strips by requiring either firestopping or that the space be filled with inorganic or Class A materials.

The use of sprayed-on materials for interior finishes has proliferated. Some of these materials are coatings that are inherently fire safe. Other materials, however, especially the sprayed-on cellular or foam plastics used for insulation or decorative effects, may readily spread flames. The use of such products should be permitted only if fire behavior can be substantiated by large-scale tests conducted under actual fire conditions.

FULL-SCALE TESTS

Many large-scale fire tests have been conducted using existing buildings slated for demolition or available for other reasons. When carefully planned, such tests can add significantly to knowledge about the growth and spread of fire in buildings.

One of the first of these tests was conducted in Great Britain in 1949, under the auspices of the Fire Research Station (now Building Research Establishment).[82] Two 2 story dwellings were used, one with cellulose fiber insulation board lining and the other with plasterboard over fiberboard. One test was conducted in each house, both with real or simulated furnishings, with the bedroom doors open. Another test was conducted in each house with the doors closed. With both types of lining, temperatures in the living room, which was the room where the fire was started, became intolerable within a few minutes. As in many other tests and actual fires, the value of the closed door also was clearly demonstrated in decreasing fire hazard in bedrooms.

In 1958, the Division of Building Research of the National Research Council of Canada (NRCC) conducted a series of full-scale tests, known as the "St. Lawrence Burns," in six dwellings and two larger buildings.[83] Again, the one objective was to study fire spread as it would affect the life safety of the occupants of the second-floor bedroom behind open and closed doors. All dwellings became "smoke logged" within 6 minutes of the ignition of the wood cribs, regardless of the type of interior finish. Temperatures and gaseous combustion products developed much faster in the dwellings with combustible finishes and in those tests in which the bedroom doors were open.

Many large buildings scheduled for demolition were partially burned under the auspices of the Illinois Institute of Technology (ITT) Research Institute. In those tests and in extensive room/corridor tests, much information was developed relative to fire spread, flashover phenomena, and factors affecting life safety in fires.

The Office of the State Fire Marshal in California sponsored a series of tests in unused buildings at Camp Parks in the early 1970s. The objective was to develop criteria for egress facilities, particularly corridors. The final report includes a discussion of the reaction and interaction of wall, ceiling, and floor finishes.[84] Precedent for the full-scale corridor burns was established earlier in 1959 and 1960 by the City of Los Angeles (CA) Fire Department. Final reports on the Los Angeles tests were published in two volumes by NFPA.[85,86]

Furnished room burnout and corridor tests conducted at the Forest Products Laboratory of the U.S. Department of Agriculture compared the relative importance of room furnishings versus room finishes.[78] A conclusion was reached that lethal levels of combustion products usually developed from burning furnishings before the wall finishes were seriously involved; this was supported by later work at Southwest Research Institute.[79] These and other studies recognize that once a fire is well established, it is highly probable that all combustibles in the room will become involved. Thus, the attainment of flashover, which is often associated with full room involvement in fire statistics, is an indication that life is untenable in the room of fire origin. It is also recognized that early detection, containment, and extinguishment in the room of fire origin is important, not only for early evacuation from the fire area, but also for the safety of persons elsewhere in the building and for the protection of the building itself.

Full-scale experiments have also been conducted to determine how the location and area of a wall finish affects the spread of fire in a corridor.[87] A series of experiments were conducted in a 6-ft (1.83-m) wide by 8-ft (2.44-m) high by 55-ft (16.76-m) long corridor exposed to hot gases from a burner. The corridor ceiling and upper walls were exposed to temperatures of approximately 1450°F (788°C). Corridor ceiling finish materials had flame spread indices between 0 and 25, whereas the wall coverings had a flame spread index of 90. These experiments revealed that ceiling interior finish plays an important role in flame spread behavior of walls. It was determined that wall coverings with a flame spread index of 90 could be used safely with ceiling finish materials having a flame spread index of no more than 25 when the wall covering was limited to the lower 4 ft (1.2 m) of wall surface. Most test configurations using material with a flame spread index of 90 covering the full height of the corridor walls and with ceiling finish materials having a flame spread index of 25 resulted in rapid flame propagation and unsafe conditions. It was deduced that some Class A (FSI < 25) ceiling materials increased flame spread mainly due to the fact that they were better insulators than materials with a zero flame spread index. In other words, the ceiling finish material influenced flame spread over walls by its resistance to heat transfer. This was a unique and unusual situation. These full-scale experiments support the application of materials with flame spread indices greater than those normally allowed when such interior finishes, such as a wainscot, are located in the lower portion of a wall. Codes occasionally recognize this principle and allow Class C materials as a corridor wall finish where Class B is normally required, for example, in health care occupancies, as long as the interior finish does not exceed 4 ft in height and is restricted to the lower half of the wall.

From 1979 to 1980, the U.S. Fire Administration sponsored a series of 75 tests to evaluate the performance of residential sprinklers in single-family and mobile homes. These tests showed the rapid buildup of heat and toxic gases that was possible with ordinary-hazard furnishings, particularly when the fire was ignited in the corner of the room or near curtains. There was a significant difference in the levels of combustion products and the times to reach those levels between fires in noncombustible interior finish and combustible interior finish.[88]

Room fire tests were commonly used in the 1980s for research purposes to evaluate interior finishes, wall coverings, and room furnishings. To help make sense of the proliferation of testing procedures, ASTM E603, *Standard Guide for Room Fire Experiments*,[89] and ASTM E2067, *Standard Practice for Full-Scale Oxygen Consumption Calorimetry Fire Tests*,[90] were developed. The ASTM E603 guide provides information on how room fire tests can be implemented and what combustion parameters are measured. Testing instrumentation may include, but is not limited to, oxygen, carbon dioxide, carbon monoxide, and other gas measurements; rate of heat release; heat flux; flame spread; temperature; air velocity profiles; mass loss rates; and smoke optical densities. The subsequent ASTM E2067 practice goes into considerably more detail but addresses mainly the tests that are intended to make heat release measurements rather than demonstration-type tests; it is a companion to ASTM E603.

See also Section 6, Chapter 3, "Concepts and Protocols of Fire Testing."

SUMMARY

Building interior finish materials can have a significant effect on fire growth and, ultimately, fire size. Interior finish materials can affect the rate of fire buildup to full room involvement and flashover, contribute to fire extension, add to the intensity of a fire, and produce smoke and toxic gases.

Several tests have been developed to try to predict the behavior of interior finish products in a fire. The Steiner tunnel test (NFPA 255 or ASTM E84) is used to calculate the flame spread index and smoke developed index of an interior wall or ceiling finish material, based on flame spread over the face of the test specimen. Room-corner tests are used to determine the probability of flashover and the heat release rate (measured through oxygen depletion) and smoke release in a room in which finish products are mounted on three walls forming a corner (and usually also on the ceiling). Fire testing of interior finish as conducted today is probably adequate to eliminate the poorest performers (both in terms of heat release, or flame spread, and smoke release). However, the emphasis on the supremacy of the Steiner tunnel test for all interior wall and ceiling finish materials means that the full capabilities of the room-corner test, including the actual heat release rates measured, are not being used, and improvements in that area would be welcome.

Fire tests for interior floor finishes include the methenamine pill test, which is a required safety test for all carpet manufactured for sale in the United States, and the critical radiant flux test, which measures the minimum energy required to be impinged on a floor covering to sustain flame propagation.

In addition to controlled laboratory tests, many large-scale fire tests of interior finishes have been conducted by various research organizations on buildings slated for demolition. Such tests yield important data concerning the behavior of interior finishes and furnishings in a fire.

BIBLIOGRAPHY

References Cited

1. Isner, M. S., "3 Die, 8 Injured in Athletic Club Fire," *Fire Journal,* Nov./Dec. 1992.
2. Coté, R., and Timoney, T., "Boarding House Fire Causes Fifteen Deaths," *Fire Journal,* Jan. 1985.
3. "Investigation Report on the Las Vegas Hilton Hotel Fire," *Fire Journal,* Jan. 1982.

4. Bukowski, R. W., "Analysis of the Happy Land Social Club Fire with Hazard I," *Fire and Arson Investigator,* Vol. 42, No. 3, 1992.
5. Hall, J. R., Report prepared for the House Subcommittee on Science, Research, and Technology on H. R. 94, the Hotel and Motel Firesafety Act of 1989, National Fire Protection Association, Quincy, MA, Mar. 2, 1989.
6. Klem, T., "Investigation Report on the DuPont Plaza Hotel Fire," National Fire Protection Association, Quincy, MA, 1987.
7. Isner, M. S., "Five Die in High-Rise Office Building Fire," *Fire Journal,* Vol. 84, No. 4, 1990.
8. Wolf, A., "Fraternity Fire Kills Five," *NFPA Journal,* Sept./Oct. 1996.
9. Isner, M. S., "Stadium Fires Demonstrate Unique Protection Problems," *NFPA Journal,* July/Aug. 1994.
10. Isner, M. S., "10 Die in Detroit Board and Care Facility," *NFPA Journal,* Jan./Feb. 1993.
11. Isner, M. S., "Fire Investigation Report, Fraternity House Fire—Berkeley California," National Fire Protection Association, Quincy, MA, 1991.
12. Rohr, K. D., *The U.S. Home Product Report (Products First Ignited in U.S. Home Fires),* NFPA Fire Analysis and Research Division, Quincy, MA, Apr. 2005.
13. Grosshandler, W. L., "Station Nightclub Fire Investigation Status Report," National Institute of Standards and Technology, Gaithersburg, MD, Oct. 2004.
14. Grosshandler, W. L., Bryner, N., Madrzykowski, D., and Kuntz, K., "Report of the Technical Investigation of the Station Nightclub Fire," NIST NCSTAR 2, National Institute of Standards and Technology, Gaithersburg, MD, June 2005.
15. Alvarez, E. D., "Incendio en la Disco Cromagnon [Fire at the Cromagnon Discotheque]," *NFPA Journal Latino,* June 2005, pp. 18–22.
16. Madrzykowski, D., and Vettori, R., "A Sprinkler Fire Suppression Algorithm for the GSA Engineering Fire Assessment System," NISTIR 48, 33, Building and Research Laboratory, National Institute of Standards and Technology, Gaithersburg, MD, May 1992.
17. Belles, D. W., "Designing Fire Safe Interiors," *NFPA Journal,* July/Aug. 1992.
18. Babrauskas, V., and Peacock, R. D., "Heat Release Rate: The Single Most Important Variable in Fire Hazard," *Fire Safety Journal,* Vol. 18, 1992, pp. 255–272.
19. Hirschler, M. M., "Fire Testing of Interior Finish," *Journal of Fire Protection Engineering,* Vol. 24, Fall 2004, pp. 16–24.
20. ASTM E1354, *Standard Test Method for Heat and Visible Smoke Release Rates for Materials and Products Using an Oxygen Consumption Calorimeter,* American Society for Testing and Materials, W. Conshohocken, PA.
21. ASTM E1321, *Standard Test Method for Determining Material Ignition and Flame Spread Properties,* American Society for Testing and Materials, W. Conshohocken, PA.
22. Hirschler, M. M., "Use of Heat Release Rate to Predict Whether Individual Furnishings Would Cause Self Propagating Fires," *Fire Safety Journal,* Vol. 32, 1999, pp. 273–296.
23. Hirschler, M. M., "Flammability and Fire Performance of Polymers," Chapter 26 in *Comprehensive Desk Reference of Polymer Characterization and Analysis,* American Chemical Society, R. Brady (Ed.), American Chemical Society, Washington, DC, 2003, pp. 700–738.
24. Finley, G., Janssens, M. L., and Hirschler, M. M., "Room Fire Testing—Recent Experiences and Implications," Fire and Materials Conf., San Antonio, TX, February 22–23, 1999, Interscience Communications, London, UK, pp. 83–94.
25. Hirschler, M. M., and Janssens, M. L., "Smoke Obscuration Measurements in the NFPA 265 Room-Corner Test," Fire and Materials Conf., San Antonio, TX, February 22–23, 1999, Interscience Communications, London, UK, pp. 179–198.
26. Janssens, M. L., Dillon, S. E., and Hirschler, M. M., "Using the Cone Calorimeter as a Screening Tool for the NFPA 265 and NFPA 286 Room Test Procedures," Fire and Materials Conf., San Francisco, CA, January 22–24, 2001, Interscience Communications, London, UK, pp. 529–540.
27. Steiner, A. J., "Burning Characteristics of Building Materials," *Fire Engineering,* May 2, 1951.
28. Underwriters Laboratories Inc., "Fire Hazard Classification of Building Materials," *Bulletin of Research,* No. 32, Chicago, IL, Sept. 1947.
29. Steiner, A. J., *Building Officials Conference of America Yearbook,* Building Officials Conference of America, Chicago, 1949–1950, pp. 115–116.
30. Wilson, J. A., "Surface Flammability of Materials: A Survey of Test Methods and Comparison of Results," ASTM STP No. 301, American Society for Testing and Materials, W. Conshohocken, PA, 1961.
31. ASTM E2231, *Standard Practice for Specimen Preparation and Mounting of Pipe and Duct Insulation Materials to Assess Surface Burning Characteristics,* American Society for Testing and Materials, W. Conshohocken, PA.
32. ASTM E2404, *Standard Practice for Specimen Preparation and Mounting of Paper or Vinyl Wall or Ceiling Coverings to Assess Surface Burning Characteristics,* American Society for Testing and Materials, W. Conshohocken, PA.
33. Drysdale, D., *Introduction to Fire Dynamics,* John Wiley and Sons, New York, 1985, pp. 234–235.
34. Belles, D. W., Fisher, F. L., and Williamson, R. B., "How Well Does ASTM E 84 Predict Fire Performance of Textile Wallcoverings?" *Fire Journal,* Vol. 82, No. 1, 1988.
35. Underwriters Laboratories Inc., "Study of Smoke Ratings Developed in Standard Fire Tests in Relation to Visual Observations," *Bulletin of Research,* No. 56, Apr. 1965.
36. Christian, W. J., and Waterman, J. E., "Fire Behavior of Interior Finish Materials," *Fire Technology,* Vol. 6, No. 3, 1970, pp. 165–178.
37. Maroni, W. F., "Large-Scale Fire Tests of Rigid Cellular Plastic Wall and Roof Insulations," *Fire Journal,* Vol. 67, No. 6, 1973, pp. 24–30.
38. Fisher, F. L., MacCracken, W., and Williamson, R. B., "Room Fire Experiments of Textile Wall Coverings, A Final Report of All Materials Tested Between March 1985 and January 1986," ES-7853, Service to Industry Report No. 86-2, Fire Research Laboratory, University of California, Berkeley, 1986.
39. ANSI/DASMA 107, *Room Fire Test Standard for Garage Doors Using Foam Plastic Insulation,* Door and Access Systems Manufacturers Association, Cleveland, OH, 1997.
40. Belles, D. W., "Regulating Foam Plastic Insulated Garage Doors," *Building Standards,* ICBO, Jan.–Feb. 1995.
41. ISO 9705, *Fire Tests—Full-Scale Room Test for Surface Products,* International Organization for Standardization, Geneva, Switzerland, 1993.
42. ASTM E2257, *Standard Test Method for Room Fire Test of Wall and Ceiling Materials and Assemblies,* American Society for Testing and Materials, W. Conshohocken, PA.
43. ASTM E268-1985, *Standard Test Method forSurface Flammability of Building Materials Using an 8 ft (2.44 m) Tunnel Furnace,* American Society for Testing and Materials, W. Conshohocken, PA, 1985 (withdrawn 1991).
44. ASTM E162, *Standard Test Method for Surface Flammability of Materials Using a Radiant Heat Energy Source,* American Society for Testing and Materials, W. Conshohocken, PA.
45. 49 CFR Part 238 et al., "Passenger Equipment Safety Standards; Final Rule," *Federal Register,* Vol. 67, No. 122, Federal Railroad Administration, Dept of Transportation, Washington, DC, June 25, 2002, pp. 42892–42912.
46. 49 CFR Part 216 et al., "Passenger Equipment Safety Standards: Final Rule," *Federal Register,* Vol. 64, No. 91, Federal Railroad Administration, Dept. of Transportation, Washington, DC, May 12, 1999, pp. 25539–25705.
47. ASTM E662, *Standard Test Method for Specific Optical Density of Smoke Generated by Solid Materials,* American Society for Testing and Materials, W. Conshohocken, PA.
48. Federal Aviation Administration, *Aircraft Materials Fire Test Handbook,* http://www.fire.tc.faa.gov/handbook.stm.
49. ASTM E1995, *Standard Test Method for Measurement of Smoke Obscuration Using a Conical Radiant Source in a Single Closed*

Chamber, with the Test Specimen Oriented Horizontally, American Society for Testing and Materials, W. Conshohocken, PA.
50. ISO 5659-2, *Fire Tests—Determination of Specific Optical Density by a Single-Chamber Test,* International Organization for Standardization, Geneva, Switzerland, 1994.
51. Yuill, C. H., "Floor Coverings: What Is the Hazard," *Fire Journal,* Vol. 61, No. 1, 1967, pp. 11–19.
52. "Fire in Acrylic Carpeting," *Fire Journal,* Vol. 62, No. 2, 1968, pp. 13–14.
53. Sears, A. B., Jr., "Nursing Home Fire, Marietta, Ohio," *Fire Journal,* Vol. 64, No. 2, 1970, pp. 5–9.
54. UL, "Standard Method of Test for Flame Propagation Classification of Flooring and Floor Covering Material," Subject 992, Underwriters Laboratories Inc., Northbrook, IL, Feb. 1971.
55. "Carpets and Rugs—Notice of Standard," *Federal Register,* Vol. 35, No. 74, 1970.
56. "Small Carpets and Rugs—Notice of Standard," *Federal Register,* Vol. 35, No. 251, 1970.
57. 16 CFR 1630, *Standard for the Surface Flammability of Carpets and Rugs,* Chapter II, Part 1630, Consumer Product Safety Commission, Washington, DC, 2000.
58. ASTM D2859, *Standard Test Method for Ignition Characteristics of Finished Textile Floor Covering Materials,* American Society for Testing and Materials, W. Conshohocken, PA.
59. Benjamin, I. A., and Adams, C. H., "The Flooring Radiant Panel Test and Proposed Criteria," *Fire Journal,* Vol. 70, No. 2, 1976.
60. Benjamin, I. A., and Davis, S., "Flammability Testing for Carpet," NBSIR 78-1436, Center for Fire Research, National Bureau of Standards, Gaithersburg, MD, Apr. 1978.
61. Tu, K.-M., and Davis, S., "Flame Spread of Carpet Systems Involved in Room Fires," NBSIR 76-1013, Center for Fire Research, National Bureau of Standards, Gaithersburg, MD, June 1976.
62. Davis, S., Unpublished Series of Experiments, Fire Standards Research—Furnishings 4927677, Program: Fire-Control-Furnishings, Center for Fire Research, National Bureau of Standards, Gaithersburg, MD, Jan. 11, 1977.
63. ASTM E648, *Standard Test Method for Critical Radiant Flux of Floor-Covering Systems Using a Radiant Heat Energy Source,* American Society for Testing and Materials, W. Conshohocken, PA.
64. Lawson, J. R., "Fire Tests and Flooring Materials," *Proceedings* of the 2nd Fire and Materials Conf., September 22–23, 1992, Arlington, VA, Interscience Communications, London, UK, pp. 253–262.
65. Hartzell, L. G., "Development of a Radiant Panel Test for Flooring Materials," *Journal of Fire and Flammability,* Consumer Product Flammability Supplement, Vol. 1, Dec. 1974, pp. 305–353.
66. Adams, C. H., and Davis, S., "Development of the Flooring Radiant Panel Test as a Standard Test Method," NBSIR 79-1954, Center for Fire Research, National Bureau of Standards, Gaithersburg, MD, Mar. 1980.
67. McGuire, J. H., "The Spread of Fire in Corridors," *Fire Technology,* Vol. 4, No. 2, 1968, pp. 103–108.
68. Alderson, S., and Breden, L., "Evaluation of the Fire Performance of Carpet Underlayments," NBSIR 76-1018, Center for Fire Research, National Bureau of Standards, Gaithersburg, MD, Sept. 1976.
69. Benjamin, I. A., and Adams, C. H., "Proposed Criteria for Use of the Critical Radiant Flux Test Method," NBSIR 75-950, Center for Fire Research, National Bureau of Standards, Gaithersburg, MD, Dec. 1975.
70. "Disclosure Requirements and Prohibitions Concerning the Flammability of Plastics," Federal Trade Commission, Washington, DC, Aug. 1974.
71. "Fire Safety Guidelines for Use of Rigid Urethane Foam Insulation in Building Construction," *Urethane Safety Group Bulletin,* The Society of the Plastics Industry, New York, May 1974.
72. Demers, D. D., "Familiar Problems Caused Ten Deaths in Hotel Fire," *Fire Journal,* Vol. 74, No. 1, 1980.
73. Chubb, M., "Ten-Fatality Board and Care Facility Fire, Detroit, Michigan," Report 066, United States Fire Administration, Federal Emergency Management Agency, Washington, DC, June 2, 1992.
74. "Fire Investigation Summary, Chapel Hill, NC, Fraternity House Fire, May 12, 1996," National Fire Protection Association, Quincy, MA, 1996.
75. Christian, W. J., "The Effect of Structural Characteristics on Dwelling Fire Fatalities," *Fire Journal,* Vol. 68, No. 1, 1974, pp. 22–28.
76. Waterman, T. E., "Room Flashover-Model Studies," *Fire Technology,* Vol. 8, No. 4, 1972, pp. 316–325.
77. "NBS Corridor Fire Tests: Energy and Radiation Models," NBS Technical Note 794, National Bureau of Standards, Washington, DC, Oct. 1973.
78. Bruce, H. D., "Experimental Dwelling Room Fires," Report No. 1941, U.S. Department of Agriculture, Forest Products Laboratory, Madison, WI, Apr. 1959.
79. Pryor, A. M., "Full-Scale Fire Tests of Interior Wall Finish Assemblies," *Fire Journal,* Vol. 63, No. 2, 1969, pp. 14–20.
80. Waksman, D., and Ferguson, J. B., "Fire Tests of Building Interior Covering Systems," *Fire Technology,* Vol. 10, No. 3, 1974.
81. Waksman, D., and Ferguson, J., "Fire Tests of Building Interior Covering Systems," Institute for Applied Technology, National Bureau of Standards, *NFPA Fire Technology,* Aug. 1974.
82. "British Fire Tests of Fiberboard," *NFPA Quarterly,* Vol. 45, No. 3, 1952, pp. 218–224.
83. Shorter, G. W., et al., "The St. Lawrence Burns," *NFPA Quarterly,* Vol. 53, No. 4, 1960, pp. 300–316.
84. "Project Corridor: Fire and Life Safety Research," *Western Fire Journal,* North Highlands, CA, 1974.
85. "Operation School Burning: Official Report on a Series of School Fire Tests Conducted April 16 to June 30, 1959, by the Los Angeles Fire Department," National Fire Protection Association, Quincy, MA, 1959.
86. "Operation School Burning, No. 2: Official Report on a Series of Fire Tests in an Open Stairway, Multi-Story School Conducted June 30, 1960 to July 30, 1960, and February 6, 1961, by the Los Angeles Fire Department," National Fire Protection Association, Quincy, MA, 1961.
87. Waterman, T. E., and Christian, W. J., "Flame Spread in Corridors: Effect of Location and Area of Wall Finish," *Fire Journal,* July 1971, pp. 352–355.
88. Cote, A. E., and Moore, D., "Field Test and Evaluation of Residential Sprinkler Systems," National Fire Protection Association, Quincy, MA, 1981.
89. ASTM E603, *Standard Guide for Room Fire Experiments,* American Society for Testing and Materials, W. Conshohocken, PA.
90. ASTM E2067, *Standard Practice for Full-Scale Oxygen Consumption Calorimetry Fire Tests,* American Society for Testing and Materials, W. Conshohocken, PA.

NFPA Codes, Standards, and Recommended Practices

Reference to the following NFPA codes, standards, and recommended practices will provide further information on interior finish discussed in this chapter. (See the latest version of The NFPA Catalog *for availability of current editions of the following documents.)*

NFPA 1, *Uniform Fire Code™*
NFPA 13, *Standard for the Installation of Sprinkler Systems*
NFPA 13D, *Standard for the Installation of Sprinkler Systems in One- and Two-Family Dwellings and Manufactured Homes*
NFPA 13R, *Standard for the Installation of Sprinkler Systems in Residential Occupancies up to and Including Four Stories in Height*
NFPA *101®*, *Life Safety Code®*
NFPA 130, *Standard for Fixed Guideway Transit and Passenger Rail Systems*
NFPA 253, *Standard Method of Test for Critical Radiant Flux of Floor Covering Systems Using a Radiant Heat Energy Source*
NFPA 255, *Standard Method of Test of Surface Burning Characteristics of Building Materials*
NFPA 265, *Standard Methods of Fire Tests for Evaluating Room Fire Growth Contribution of Textile Coverings on Full Height Panels and Walls*
NFPA 286, *Standard Methods of Fire Tests for Evaluating Contribution of Wall and Ceiling Interior Finish to Room Fire Growth*

NFPA 301, *Code for Safety to Life from Fire on Merchant Vessels*
NFPA 501, *Standard on Manufactured Housing*
NFPA 555, *Guide on Methods for Evaluating Potential for Room Flashover*
NFPA 701, *Standard Methods of Fire Tests for Flame Propagation of Textiles and Films*
NFPA 1192, *Standard on Recreational Vehicles*
NFPA 5000®, Building Construction and Safety Code®

References

Babrauskas, V., "Estimating Room Flashover Potential," *Fire Technology,* Vol. 16, No. 2, 1980, pp. 94–104.

Benichou, N., and Sultan, M. A., "Fire Resistance of Lightweight Wood-Framed Assemblies," *Fire Technology,* Vol. 36, No. 3, 2000, pp. 184–219.

Bisby, L. A., Green, M. F., Kodur, V. K. R., "Fire Behavior of FRP Wrapped Reinforced Concrete Columns," *Proceedings* of the Structural Faults and Repair Conference, July 2001, London, UK, 2001, pp. 1–14.

Bukowski, R. W., et al., "Fire Risk Assessment Method: Case Study 4, Interior Finish in Restaurants," NISTIR 90-4246, National Institute of Standards and Technology, Gaithersburg, MD, National Fire Protection Association, Quincy, MA, Benjamin/Clarke Associates, Inc., Kensington, MD, National Fire Protection Research Foundation, Quincy, MA, May 1990.

Bukowski, R. W., Peacock, R. D., Reneke, P. A., Averill, J. D., and Markos, S. H., "Development of a Hazard-Based Method for Evaluating the Fire Safety of Passenger Trains," *Proceedings* of 8th International INTERFLAM Conference, INTERFLAM '99, June 29–July 1, 1999, Edinburgh, UK, Interscience Communications Ltd., London, UK, 1999, pp. 853–864.

Castino, G. T., et al., "Flammability Studies of Cellular Plastics and Other Building Materials Used for Interior Finish," UL Report, Underwriters Laboratories Inc., Northbrook, IL, 1975.

Cullis, C. F., and Hirschler, M. M., "The Combustion of Organic Polymers," Oxford University Press, Oxford, UK, 1981.

Debanne, S. M., Hirschler, M. M., and Nelson, G. L., "The Importance of Carbon Monoxide in the Toxicity of Fire Atmospheres," *Fire Hazard and Fire Risk Assessment,* ASTM STP 1150, M. M. Hirschler (Ed.), American Society for Testing and Materials, Philadelphia, PA, 1992, pp. 9–23.

Gann, R. G., Babrauskas, V., Peacock, R. D., and Hall, J. R., "Fire Conditions for Smoke Toxicity Measurement," *Fire and Materials,* Vol. 18, 1994, pp. 193–199.

Grexa, O., Janssens, M., and White, R., "Analysis of Cone Calorimeter Data for Modeling of the Room/Corner Tests on Wall Linings," *Proceedings* of the 4th International Conference and Exhibition on Fire and Materials, November 15–16, 1995, Crystal City, VA, 1995, pp. 63–71.

Hirschler, M. M., "Can the Cone Calorimeter Be Used to Predict Full Scale Heat and Smoke Release Cable Tray Results from a Full Scale Test Protocol?" *Proceedings* of 9th International INTERFLAM Conference, INTERFLAM 2001, September 17–19, 2001, Edinburgh, UK, Interscience Communications Ltd., 2001, pp. 137–148.

Hirschler, M. M., "Experience in Full Scale Fire Testing of Consumer Products," 10th European Meeting on Fire Retardancy and Protection of Materials, Federal Institute for Materials Research and Testing, Berlin, Germany, September 7–9, 2005.

Hirschler, M. M., "Fire Retardance, Smoke Toxicity and Fire Hazard," *Proceedings* of Flame Retardants '94, British Plastics Federation, Interscience Communications, London, UK, January 26–27, 1994, pp. 225–37.

Hirschler, M. M., "Flammability and Fire Performance," *PVC Handbook,* C. E. Wilkes, J. W. Summers, and C. A. Daniels (Eds.), Carl Hanser, Cincinnati, OH, 2005, Chapter 13, pp. 419–481.

Hirschler, M. M. (Editor-in-chief), Debanne, S. M., Larsen, J. B., and Nelson, G. L., *Carbon Monoxide and Human Lethality—Fire and Non-Fire Studies,* Elsevier, London, UK, 1993.

Hsiung, K. H., "Study of the Alternative Fire Control Performance Between the Interior Finishing and Sprinkler System Based on Equivalency Concept," *Proceedings* of FORUM 2000 Symposium, Fire Research Development and Application in the 21st Century, October 23–24, 2000, Taipei, Taiwan, 2000, pp. 1–20.

Isner, M. S., and Bielen, R. P., "Bulk Retail Store Fire, Albany, GA, April 16, 1996," NFPA Fire Investigation Report, National Fire Protection Association, Quincy, MA, 1997.

Isner, M. S., and Foley, S. N., "Carpet Store Fire, One Fire Fighter Fatality, Branford, CT, November 28, 1996," NFPA Fire Investigation Report, National Fire Protection Association, Quincy, MA, 1997.

Janssens, M. L., *Introduction to Mathematical Fire Modeling,* CRC Press, Boca Raton, FL, 2000.

Karlsson, B., "Models for Calculating Flame Spread on Wall Lining Materials and the Resulting Heat Release Rate in a Room," *Fire Safety Journal,* Vol. 23, No. 4, 1994, pp. 365–386.

Karlsson, B., and Magnusson, S. E., "Combustible Wall Lining Materials: Numerical Simulation of Room Fire Growth and the Outline of a Reliability Based Classification Procedure," *Proceedings* of the 3rd International Symposium on Fire Safety Science Safety Science, Elsevier Applied Science, New York, 1991, pp. 667–678.

Kodur, V. R., Benichou, N., and Sultan, M. A., "Behavior of Load-Bearing Wood-Stud Shear Walls Exposed to Fire," *Proceedings* of 9th International INTERFLAM Conference, INTERFLAM 2001, September 17–19, 2001, Edinburgh, UK, Interscience Communications Ltd., 2001, pp. 1369–1374.

LeTallec, Y., Sainrat, A., LeSant, V., Briggs, P., Messa, S., and Breulet, H., "FIRESTARR Project: Fire Protection of Railway Vehicles," *Proceedings* of 7th International Conference and Exhibition, Fire and Materials 2001, January 22–24, 2001, San Antonio, TX, Interscience Communications Ltd., London, UK, 2001, pp. 53–66.

Parker, W. J., "An Investigation of Fire Environment in the ASTM E84 Tunnel Test," NBS Technical Note 945, National Bureau of Standards, Gaithersburg, MD, Aug. 1977.

Quintiere, J. G., Haynes, G., and Rhodes, B. T., "Applications of a Model to Predict Flame Spread over Interior Finish Materials in a Compartment," *Journal of Fire Protection Engineering,* Vol. 7, No. 1, 1995, pp. 1–13.

Quintiere, J. G., Hopkins, M., and Hopkins, D., Jr., "Room-Corner Fire Prediction for Textile Wall Materials," *Proceedings* of the International Conference on Fire Research and Engineering, September 10–15, 1995, Orlando, FL, Society of Fire Protection Engineers, Boston, 1995, pp. 272–277.

Sheratt, J., and Drysdale, D., "Effect of the Melt-Flow Process on the Fire Behavior of Thermoplastics," *Proceedings* of 9th International INTERFLAM Conference, INTERFLAM 2001, September 17–19, 2001, Edinburgh, UK, Interscience Communications Ltd., 2001, pp. 149–159.

Shields, T. J., Silcock, G. W. H., Moghaddam, A. Z., Azhakesan, M. A., and Zhang, J., "Comparison of Fire Retarded and Non-Fire Retarded Wood-Based Wall Linings Exposed to Fire in an Enclosure," *Fire and Materials,* Vol. 23, No. 1, 1999, pp. 17–25.

White, R. H., Dietenberger, M. A., Tran, H., Grexa, O., Richardson, L., Sumathipala, K., and Janssens, M. L., "Comparison of Test Protocols for Standards Room/Corner Tests," *Proceedings* of the 5th International Conference on Fire and Materials, San Antonio, TX, 1998, Interscience Communications, London, UK, 1998, pp. 77–88.

Wickstrom, U. (Programme Manager), *Proceedings* of the International EUREFIC Seminar 1991, September 11–12, 1991, Copenhagen, Denmark, Interscience Communications, London, UK, 1991.

Wickstrom, U., and Goransson, U., "Full-Scale/Bench-Scale Correlations of Wall and Ceiling Linings," *Fire and Materials,* Vol. 16, No. 1, 1992, pp. 15–22.

Wickstrom, U., and Goransson, U., "Full-Scale/Bench-Scale Correlations of Wall and Ceiling Linings," *Heat Release in Fires,* Elsevier Applied Science, NY, 1992, Chapter 13, pp. 461–477.

Williamson, R. B., and Baron, F. M., "A Corner Fire Test to Simulate Residential Fires," *Journal of Fire and Flammability,* Vol. 4, 1973, pp. 99–105.

Chapter 3

Smoke Movement in Buildings

James A. Milke ■ John H. Klote

Chapter Contents

Key Terms

atria, buoyancy, compartmentation, dilution, pressurization, smoke (cool), smoke (hot), smoke movement, smoke production, stack effect, wind effect

Smoke is inherent in all fires and contains dangerous products of combustion that have critical influences on life safety, property protection, and operations by fire fighters in buildings. In some fires, the volume of visible smoke is so great that it may fill an entire building and obscure visibility at street level to such an extent that it is difficult to identify the fire-involved building. In other incidents, the volume of visible smoke generated may be considerably less, although the danger to life is not necessarily diminished because of the presence of invisible airborne products of combustion.

This chapter gives information on the techniques used to evaluate the physical characteristics of smoke and assess its movement in both short and tall buildings. Information on smoke properties and the forces inducing movement are used as a basis for designing smoke-control systems. The approaches that can be used to limit the hazard of smoke in buildings are also covered.

This chapter provides a general background on the subject, including a discussion of relationships, and selected equations useful in understanding smoke movement and smoke management in buildings. Detailed design information is available from a number of sources. The book by Klote and Milke,[1] *Design of Smoke-Management Systems,* provides a consolidation and systematic presentation of data and calculations necessary for the design of systems to manage smoke movement. Specific design information is provided in that publication for pressurized stairwells, pressurized elevators, zoned smoke control, and smoke management in large spaces, including atria and shopping malls. Klote and Milke each have written chapters in the third edition of the *SFPE Handbook of Fire Protection Engineering,*[2] which summarize much of the general information from the book by those two authors. First published in 1988, NFPA 92A, *Standard for Smoke-Control Systems Utilizing Barriers and Pressure Differences,* provides additional recommendations for stairwell pressurization systems and zoned smoke-control systems, including suggested levels of pressurization for such systems in sprinklered and unsprinklered buildings. NFPA 92B, *Standard for Smoke Management Systems in Malls, Atria, and Large Spaces,* first published in 1991, is a technical guide for the design of smoke management systems in shopping malls, atria, and other large-volume spaces.

For related topics see, Section 3, Chapter 5, "Introduction to Fire Modeling"; Section 3, Chapter 6, "Applying Models to Fire Protection Engineering Problems and Fire Investigations"; Section 3, Chapter 9, "Closed Form Enclosure Fire Calculations"; Section 10, Chapter 4, "Air-Conditioning and Ventilating Systems"; and Section 18, Chapter 4, "Venting Practices."

James A. Milke, Ph.D., P.E., is an associate professor in the department of fire protection engineering at the University of Maryland. He is a fellow of SFPE and is past chair of the NFPA Smoke Management Systems Committee.

John H. Klote, D.Sc., P.E., is a consultant specializing in smoke management and was the head of building fire physics at NIST. He is a fellow of SFPE and a fellow of ASHRAE. Dr. Klote is a member of the NFPA Smoke Management Committee.

DESCRIPTION OF SMOKE

As a fire burns, it generates heat and also generates products of combustion as a result of the chemical reactions associated with the combustion process. These products of combustion include the following:

1. Gases, such as carbon dioxide, carbon monoxide, water vapor, and possibly many others depending on the fuel
2. Solids, such as "soot," and liquids

A major portion of the heat generated by a fire remains in the mass of combustion products generated by the fire. This mass expands, is lighter than the surrounding air, and rises as a plume. The rising plume is turbulent and, because of this, entrains large quantities of air from the surrounding atmosphere into the rising gases, as indicated in Figure 18.3.1. This entrainment has the following effects:

1. Increases the total mass and volume of the plume
2. Cools the plume by mixing the cool entrained air with the rising hot gases; normally, the rising plume is hotter at its center and cooler toward the edges where cooler air is entrained
3. Dilutes the concentration of fire products in the plume

Smoke is defined in NFPA 92A and 92B as "The airborne solid and liquid particulates and gases evolved when a material undergoes pyrolysis or combustion, along with the quantity of air that is entrained or otherwise mixed into the mass."[1,2]

SMOKE PRODUCTION

The volume of combustion products contained in a rising plume is relatively small compared to the volume of air in the total mixture. Consequently, the volume of smoke produced by a fire approximates the volume of air drawn or entrained into the rising plume. Figure 18.3.1 illustrates the process.

In situations in which the height of the plume, measured from the top of the fire to the level of the smoke layer, is greater than the height of the solid body of flame, reasonably accurate estimates of the rate of smoke production can be obtained using empirical formulas.[3,4]

In general, the equations given in this chapter should be used where the fire is small compared to the height of the space involved. Alternatively, where this is not true, approaches such as those contained in Section 18, Chapter 4, "Venting Practices"; Section 3, Chapter 5, "Introduction to Fire Modeling"; and Section 3, Chapter 9, "Closed Form Enclosure Fire Calculations" are more appropriate.

The following equation is based on research conducted at Factory Mutual Research (FMR) and is the equation used for smoke production in NFPA 92B. The rate of smoke production (i.e., mass entrainment rate) can be estimated as[5]

$$\dot{m} = 0.071k^{2/3}Q_c^{1/3}z^{5/3} + 0.0018Q_c \quad (1)$$

where

$\dot{m}$ = Mass flow in plume at height z (kg/sec)

k = Wall factor (Figure 18.3.2)

Q_c = Convective heat release rate of fire (kW)

z = Height above top of fuel (m)

Equation 1 is the same as the corresponding equation in NFPA 92B for the value of $k = 1$. Equation 1 includes a series of assumptions, the most important of which are the following:

1. The tip of the flame is a significant distance below the bottom of the smoke layer as is often the case in malls and atria. The formula is less accurate in spaces with a low ceiling relative to the height of the fire involved. In such cases, see NFPA 92B for the applicable equation.

2. The fire bed itself covers an area whose length and width are reasonably approximate to each other. The original formula is based on the assumption of a circular fire. The degree of error in the formula increases as the ratio of length to width increases.

3. The ceiling is sufficiently high so that a correction for the "virtual origin" of the fire is unnecessary (see Klote and Milke[1] for a description of virtual origin). This is true where the fire is small compared to the height of the space involved, as is the case for small fires in rooms or for design applications involving atria or other large-volume spaces.

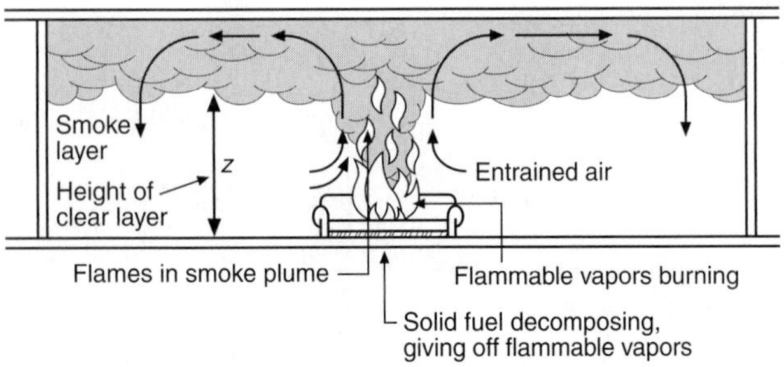

FIGURE 18.3.1 Production of Smoke from a Fire

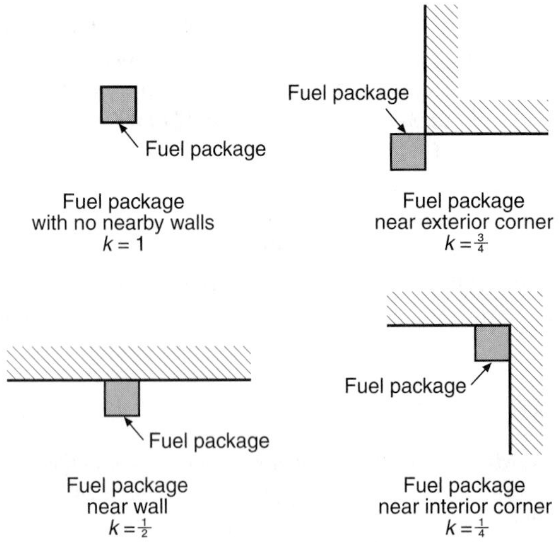

FIGURE 18.3.2 Wall Factors for Fuel Package Locations

Flame Height

A reasonable estimate of the visible flame height[6] can be obtained from the equation:

$$z_f = 0.166(Q/k)^{0.4} \quad (2)$$

where

z_f = Mean flame height (m)

Q = Heat release of the fire (kW)

k = Wall factor (see Figure 18.3.2).

Equation 2 is the same as the corresponding equation in NFPA 92B for the value of $k = 1$. The convective portion of the heat release rate, Q_c, can be expressed as

$$Q_c = \xi Q \quad (3)$$

where ξ is the convective fraction of heat release. The convective fraction depends on the heat conduction through the fuel and the radiative heat transfer of the flames, but a value of 0.7 is often used for ξ. The results of Equation 3 for a convective fraction of 0.7 are shown graphically in Figure 18.3.3.

Average Plume Temperature

Detailed engineering equations for fire plumes have been presented.[5,6] The average temperature of a fire plume is needed to express the rate of smoke production as a volumetric rate rather than as a mass rate (as in the previous section).

$$T_p = \frac{Q_c}{\dot{m}C_p} + T_o$$

where

T_p = Average plume temperature (°C)

$\dot{m}$ = Mass flow in plume at height z (kg/sec)

Q_c = Convective heat release rate of fire (kW)

C_p = Specific heat of plume gases, 1.00 kJ/kg°C

T_o = Ambient temperature (°C)

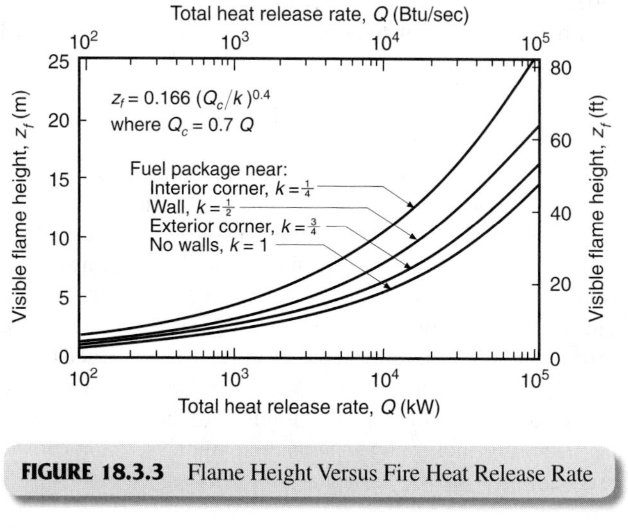

FIGURE 18.3.3 Flame Height Versus Fire Heat Release Rate

The average plume temperature decreases with increasing height above the fuel. This can be realized by recalling that the mass flow in the plume increases with the clear height, z.

The average plume temperature should not be confused with the centerline plume temperature. The plume centerline temperature is greater than the average plume temperature. Where the average plume temperature is approximately equal to the ambient temperature, the buoyancy of the plume is relatively weak. Because the mass entrainment equation (Equation 1) is for a strongly buoyant plume, the correlations may yield answers with significant errors in cases where the plume has low buoyancy. This topic needs further study, but in the absence of better data, it is recommended that the plume equations not be used when the average temperature increase is small—less than 4°F (2°C). The average temperature rise of a plume for a fuel package with no nearby walls is shown in Figure 18.3.4.

Volumetric Plume Flow

The volumetric flow rate of a plume is

$$\dot{V} = 1.51\dot{m}(T_p + 460)$$

where

$\dot{V}$ = Volumetric flow rate of plume at height z (ft³/min)

$\dot{m}$ = Mass flow in plume at height z (lb/sec)

T_p = Average temperature of plume gases at height z (°F)

In SI units, this equation is

$$\dot{V} = \frac{\dot{m}(T_p + 273)}{353}$$

where

$\dot{V}$ = Volumetric flow rate of plume at height z (m³/sec)

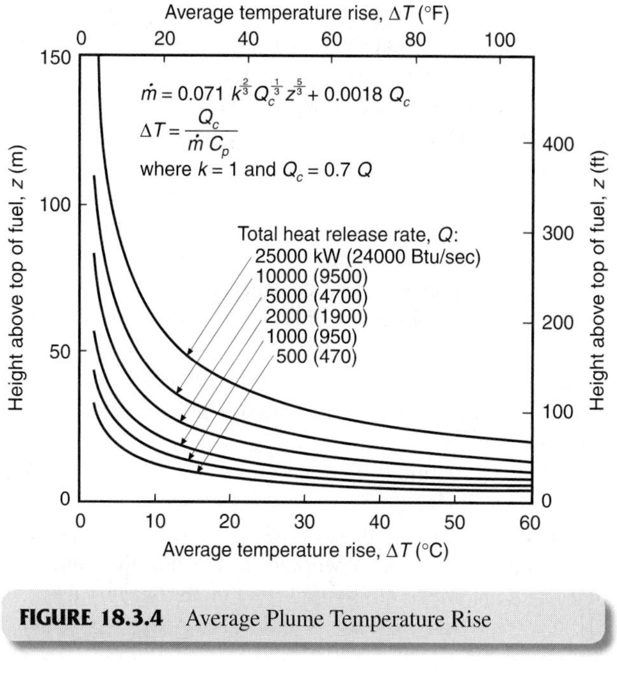

FIGURE 18.3.4 Average Plume Temperature Rise

$\dot{m}$ = Mass flow in plume at height z (kg/sec)

T_p = Average temperature of plume gases at height z (°C)

HAZARD OF SMOKE

Smoke can adversely affect people, property (including the building structure and contents), and mission continuity. The effect of exposure to smoke is dependent on the magnitude of the properties of the smoke (concentration of various gases, visibility reduction, temperature, and radiant flux) and the duration of the exposure.

People who are exposed to smoke may be harmed as a result of exposure to toxic gases, elevated temperature, or radiant energy. The toxic effects of the gases in smoke are described in Purser[7] and Klote and Milke.[1] For short duration exposures (on the order of 1 to 2 minutes), a carbon monoxide concentration of 0.1 to 0.8 percent may cause humans to become incapacitated while walking or being involved in a similar level of activity.

Exposure to radiant energy from a smoke layer at a temperature of at least 320°F (160°C) for a short duration (5 to 10 seconds) may be sufficient to inflict pain, considering the smoke to be a black body. Such a smoke layer temperature will provide a radiant heat flux of approximately 2 kW/m^2 (20 Btu/sft^2). Alternatively, people can typically tolerate being submerged in a smoke layer up to 212°F (100°C) for approximately 10 minutes.

A reduction of visibility by smoke may cause people evacuating to become disoriented or reduce their walking speed, thereby increasing the amount of time required for evacuation. Klote and Milke[1] describe the relationship between visibility and movement speed based on the work by Jin.[8] In addition, a reduction of visibility may increase the susceptibility of building occupants to trip over obstructions or fall over balcony railings.[9] A review of tenability analysis methods is provided by Purser as well as Milke, et al.[10]

Building contents can be affected by exposure to corrosive gases, particulate matter, and the elevated temperature of smoke. Electronic components may be damaged by temperatures and gas concentrations well below that needed to harm humans. Electronic equipment and data storage media are particularly sensitive to elevated temperature, being damaged at temperatures as low as 104°F (40°C) for diskettes and 176°F (80°C) for computer hardware. Smoke may contain several corrosive components, either as gases or absorbed into solid particles. Electronic equipment can be damaged by exposure to smoke containing only 0.01 percent of HCl or 0.1 percent of HF, especially if restoration activities are not initiated promptly after the incident. Contamination of food and pharmaceuticals is generally acknowledged, given exposure to smoke of virtually any concentration.

Mission continuity may be threatened following a fire, while a building or portion thereof is closed for restoration. This results in loss of revenue for the building owner, temporary unemployment of workers in the building, and loss of service of the facility to the community, among other effects.

PRINCIPLES OF SMOKE MOVEMENT

Smoke moves from an area of high pressure to one of low pressure. Pressure differences from one space to another may be caused by buoyancy from the fire, stack effect, wind, and forces from building heating, ventilating, and air-conditioning (HVAC) systems. Where multiple effects are present, smoke movement will depend on a combination of effects, one of which may be dominant.

Hot Smoke Versus Cool Smoke

The temperature of hot smoke results in the smoke being naturally buoyant. As such, the movement of hot smoke is directed toward the ceiling while clean (or at least less polluted) air is drawn in through the lower portion of the space. Hot smoke may be transported to adjacent rooms or corridors, depending on the level of energy produced by the fire and the size of connecting openings, such as open doors. Industrial and warehouse smoke and heat venting are effective smoke management methods because hot smoke is particularly buoyant.

As smoke is transmitted from the area of fire origin, it is cooled by the entrainment of air, heat transfer from the smoke body to surrounding walls and ceiling, and by radiant energy losses to all surroundings. When smoke from a fire flows through a relatively small crack, the entrainment of cool air on the unexposed side tends to cool the smoke very quickly. When the leakage is through larger openings, there may be less entrainment relative to the mass of smoke movement at such junctures and, therefore, cooling will be slower.

Where mixing and other forms of heat transfer have significantly reduced the temperature of the smoke, the effect of the buoyancy force is moderated. In such cases, stack effect, wind, and the mechanical HVAC or other air-movement systems become the primary controlling forces affecting smoke movement. Consequently, the movement of cool smoke is essentially the same as the movement of any other pollutant.

When hot smoke is transported from one area of a building to another through a confined passageway, such as a duct, shaft, or stairwell, there will be little or no cooling due to entrainment. In such cases, cooling will be limited to heat lost by conduction from the moving smoke through the shaft material. Often, this loss is modest, and hot smoke can be transported significant distances with only minor cooling by such confined passageways.

Smoke Movement in Tall Buildings

Smoke can behave very differently in tall buildings than in low buildings. In low buildings, the influences of the fire, such as heat, convective movement, and fire pressures, are generally the major factors that cause smoke movement. Smoke removal and venting practices reflect this behavior. In tall buildings, these same factors are complicated by the stack effect, which is the vertical natural air movement through the building caused by the differences in temperatures and densities between the inside and outside air. Stack effect in tall buildings can become an important factor in smoke movement and in building design features used to combat that movement.

The predominant factors that cause smoke movement in tall buildings are stack effect, the influence of external wind forces, and the forced air movement within the building. The next two parts of this chapter describe theoretical natural air movement, which is affected by the stack effect and external wind forces. Forced air movement caused by the building air-handling equipment is presented in Section 18, Chapter 4, "Venting Practices," and Section 10, Chapter 4, "Air-Conditioning and Ventilating Systems," and is not discussed here except to note that air movement can be influenced significantly by the mechanical systems of the building. Many smoke management systems use emergency operation of the mechanical systems.

Flow Through Openings

Where a pressure difference exists across a crack, gap, or other opening, a flow will result from the higher pressure side to the lower pressure side. The *orifice equation* is commonly used to describe such flow:

$$\dot{V} = CA\sqrt{\frac{2\Delta P}{\rho}}$$

where

$\dot{V}$ = Volumetric flow rate through the path (m^3/sec)

C = Dimensionless flow coefficient

A = Flow area (also called leakage area) (m^2)

ΔP = Pressure difference across path (Pa)

ρ = Density of gas in path (kg/m^3)

In the context of flows through gaps around doors and through construction cracks, the coefficient C is generally 0.6 to 0.7. For standard air density of $\rho = 0.075$ lb/ft^3 (1.20 kg/m^3) and for $C = 0.65$, the flow equation above can be expressed as

$$\dot{V} = 2610A\sqrt{\Delta P}$$

where

$\dot{V}$ = Volumetric flow rate through the path (ft^3/min)

A = Flow area (also called leakage area) (ft^2)

ΔP = Pressure difference across path (in. of water)

In SI units, this equation is

$$\dot{V} = 0.839A\sqrt{\Delta P}$$

where

$\dot{V}$ = Volumetric flow rate through the path (m^3/sec)

A = Flow area (also called leakage area) (m^2)

ΔP = Pressure difference across path (Pa)

Stack Effect

Under normal conditions, stack effect can account for a major part of the natural air movement in buildings. During a fire, stack effect is often responsible for the wide distribution of smoke and toxic gases in high-rise buildings. "Normal" stack effect, present when the indoor air temperature is greater than the outdoor air temperature, is characterized by a strong draft from the ground floor to the roof of a tall building. The magnitude of this stack effect is a function of the building height, the airtightness of the exterior walls, the air leakage between floors of the building, and the temperature difference between the inside and outside of the building.

To illustrate the principle of stack effect, consider the schematic of a box with a single opening near the bottom and another near the top, as shown in Figure 18.3.5. The theoretical natural draft between the two openings is caused by the difference in weight of the column of air within the box and that of a corresponding column of air of equal dimensions outside the box. The magnitude of the theoretical natural draft may be computed by using the following formula:

$$\Delta P = 2.96HB_o\rho\left(\frac{1}{T_o} - \frac{1}{T_i}\right)$$

where

ΔP = Theoretical pressure difference (in. of water)

H = Vertical distance between the inlet and the outlet (ft)

B_o = Barometric pressure (in. of mercury)

T_o = Temperature of outside air (°F)

T_i = Temperature of inside air (°F)

ρ = Density of air at 0°F and 1 atmosphere pressure (lb/ft^3)

Assuming values of $B_0 = 29.9$ in. and $\rho = 0.0862$ lb/ft^3, this expression reduces to

$$\Delta P = 7.63H\left(\frac{1}{T_o} - \frac{1}{T_i}\right)$$

Vertical air movement in a building is caused by this natural draft, or stack effect. The magnitude of the stack effect depends on the difference between the inside and outside temperatures

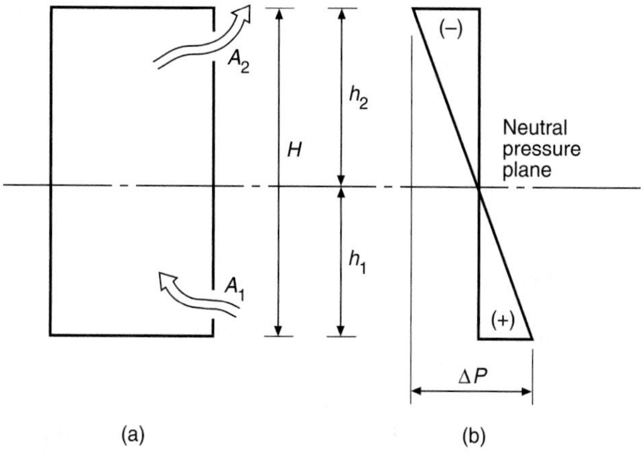

FIGURE 18.3.5 Air Movements Caused by (a) Pressure and (b) Location of Neutral Pressure Plane in a Structure Without Horizontal Barriers and With the Two Openings Shown

and on the vertical distance between openings. If the inside and outside temperatures are equal ($T_i = T_o$), no natural air movement takes place. When T_o is less than T_i, the air moves vertically upward, with the lower opening acting as the inlet and the upper opening as the outlet. A reverse stack effect occurs when T_o is greater than T_i. In this case, the upper opening is the inlet and the lower opening becomes the outlet.

Part (b) of Figure 18.3.5 illustrates the pressures that cause these movements. In this figure, if T_o is assumed to be equal to T_i, the exterior pressure will be greater than the interior pressure at the lower opening. Consequently, outside air is forced into the building at that location. Because the outside pressure at the upper opening is lower than the inside pressure, a negative pressure difference at that location is present, which forces the inside air to the outside. Based on basic engineering principles, the pressure distribution between these two locations is assumed to be linear.

If an opening were present in the exterior wall in a region of positive pressure, air would flow into the building. An opening in a region of negative pressure would cause air to flow out of the building. The neutral pressure plane indicates where inside and outside pressures are equal. If there were an opening at this level, air would move neither inward nor outward. The location of the neutral pressure plane in a structure without horizontal barriers and with the two openings shown in Figure 18.3.5 can be determined from the following relationship:

$$\frac{h_1}{h_2} = \frac{A_2^{\,2} T_o}{A_1^{\,2} T_i}$$

where

h_1 and h_2 = Distances from the neutral pressure plane to the lower and upper openings, respectively

A_1 and A_2 = Cross-sectional areas of the lower and upper openings, respectively

T_i and T_o = Absolute temperatures of the air inside and outside the building, respectively

The magnitude of the pressures created by stack effect are described by the equation

$$\Delta p = 7.63H\left(\frac{1}{T_o} - \frac{1}{T_i}\right)$$

where

Δp = Pressure difference (in. of water)

T_o = Temperature of outside air (°F)

T_i = Temperature of inside air (°F)

Examination of Figure 18.3.6 illustrates the significant differences between tall and short buildings with regard to air movement by stack effect. For example, assume that a fire develops a pressure of 0.06 in. of water (15 Pa) in a compartment, the outside temperature is 50°F (10°C) lower than the inside temperature, and the fire occurs at the same level as the lower opening. The curve T_i ± 50°F (10°C) indicates that if the upper outlet were approximately 40 ft (12 m) above the fire, the inlet stack pressure would balance the pressure caused by the fire. A building taller than 40 ft (12 m) would create a greater stack pressure, and, theoretically, the outside air would move into the building.

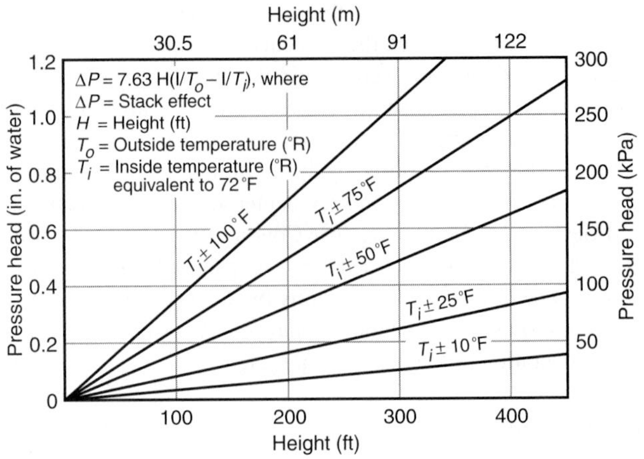

FIGURE 18.3.6 Stack Effect Due to Height and Temperature Difference (°C = [°F – 32] × 5/9)

Influence of Floors and Partitions

The theoretical draft described by Figure 18.3.5 and the net pressure difference present in real buildings is modified by the presence of floors and partitions. These barriers impede the free movement of air, although a significant flow can take place through openings in the assemblies.

The magnitude and location of the leakage areas in a building naturally vary with the building's function and type of construction. The National Research Council of Canada (NRCC) conducted studies of airtightness for major separations on four buildings ranging from 9 to 44 stories high. The measurements were used for computer modeling of the air movement for a simulated 20 story building with a floor plan dimension of 120 ft by 120 ft (36 m by 36 m) and a floor to floor height of 12 ft (3.6 m).[11] The data from the NRCC are given in Table 18.3.1 in the form of a ratio of the net leakage area to the surface area of the building component.

These leakage areas are sufficient to allow substantial air movement throughout the building. Most of the air will flow into vertical shafts, such as stairwells and elevator shafts. Some will flow vertically from floor to floor through the minor openings in the floor-ceiling assembly. This floor-to-floor movement is always caused by a pressure differential between the floors.

Part (a) of Figure 18.3.7 illustrates the pressure difference characteristics of a building in which stack effect causes air movement. The slopes of the pressure lines represent differences between any two regions at the same height. Airflow from one region to another is illustrated by the airflow directions represented by the arrows in Part (b) of Figure 18.3.7.

Wind Effects

Wind is another important factor influencing the movement of smoke. Again, tall and short buildings behave somewhat dif-

TABLE 18.3.1 Typical Leakage Areas for Walls and Floors of Commercial Buildings[a]

Construction Element	*Tightness*	*Area Ratio*[b]
		A/A_w
Exterior building walls (includes construction cracks, cracks around windows and doors)	Tight	0.50×10^{-4}
	Average	0.17×10^{-3}
	Loose	0.35×10^{-3}
	Very Loose	0.12×10^{-2}
Stairwell walls (includes construction cracks but not cracks around windows or doors)	Tight	0.14×10^{-4}
	Average	0.11×10^{-3}
	Loose	0.35×10^{-3}
Elevator shaft walls (includes construction cracks but not cracks around doors)	Tight	0.18×10^{-3}
	Average	0.84×10^{-3}
	Loose	0.18×10^{-2}
		A/A_f
Floors (includes construction cracks and gaps around penetrations)	Tight[c]	0.66×10^{-5}
	Average	0.52×10^{-4}
	Loose[c]	0.17×10^{-3}

[a]Flow area ratios for $C = 0.65$ at 0.3 in. H_2O (75 Pa).

[b]A is flow area, A_w is wall area, and A_f is floor area. Values of area ratios based on pressurization measurements in buildings by Tamura and Wilson,[12] Tamura and Shaw,[13–15] and Shaw, Reardon, and Cheung.[16]

[c]Values extrapolated from average floor tightness based on range of tightness of other construction elements.

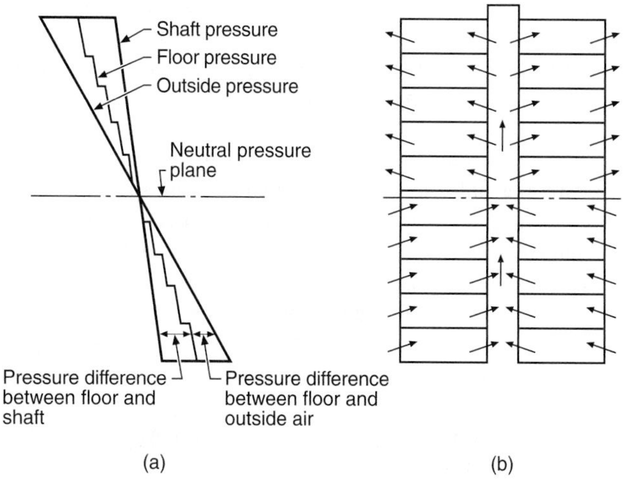

FIGURE 18.3.7 Pressure Difference Characteristics of a Building in Which Stack Action Causes Air Movement

ferently in this regard. Figure 18.3.8 illustrates the air pressure distribution along the four sides and the roof of a building. The plan view of the pressures shows that the windward wall is subjected to an inward pressure, whereas the leeward wall and the two side walls have an outward pressure, or suction. The flat roof has an upward pressure, with the maximum amount occurring at the windward edge.

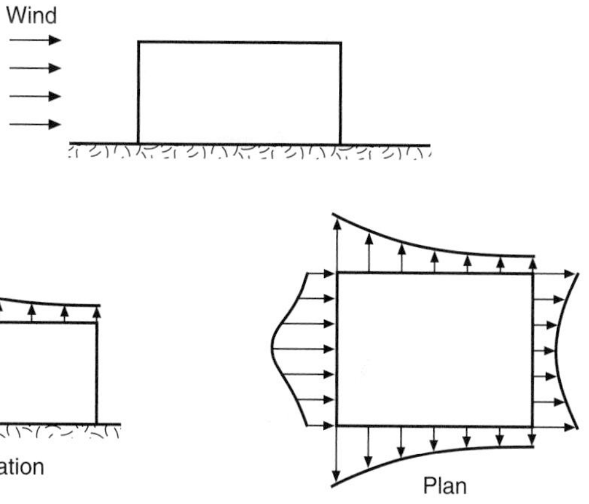

FIGURE 18.3.8 Air Pressure Distribution Along the Four Sides and Roof of a Building

These pressures are caused by the movement of a mass of air over and around the structure. A short, wide building will cause the major volume of air to move over the roof, with correspondingly less air movement around the sides. A tall, narrow building, on the other hand, will cause the major volume of air to follow the path of least resistance around the building, with less movement over the top. The velocities of these movements are the primary cause of the amount and directions of the pressures on the building.

Wind velocities and direction vary over any face of a building. The following are the most important effects:

1. *Wind velocity.* The higher the wind velocity, the greater the effects of the following two influences.
2. *Ground effect.* Unless influenced by unusual arrangements of structures or terrain, the friction and turbulence that occur as air moves over the ground result in the lowest velocity at ground level, which increases with increasing height.
3. *Structures.* Buildings and other artificial or natural features, such as trees, can produce localized effects that can increase, decrease, or alter the direction of wind forces.

The effect of wind pressures and suctions modifies the natural air movement within a building. For example, the negative pressure on the roof of a tall building can have an aspirating effect on a vertical shaft opened at the roof level. This can cause the observed draft to exceed the theoretical draft shown in Figure 18.3.9. Note how the neutral pressure plane changes location throughout the building in the presence of significant wind.

Horizontal pressures and suctions cause the neutral planes in exterior walls to move. Positive wind pressure tends to raise the neutral pressure plane, whereas negative pressure lowers it. Figure 18.3.9 illustrates the influence of wind action on air movement in a building.

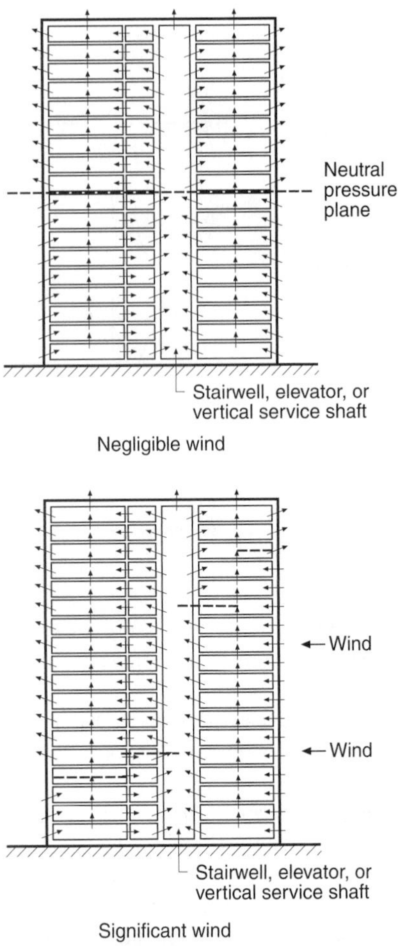

FIGURE 18.3.9 Influence of Wind Action on Air Movement in a Building

SMOKE MANAGEMENT

The term *smoke management,* as used in this section, includes all methods that can be used alone or in combination to modify smoke movement for the benefit of occupants or fire fighters or to reduce property damage. Compartmentation, dilution, airflow, pressurization, and buoyancy of the smoke itself can be used alone or in combination to manage the hazard of smoke in fires.

Compartmentation

Barriers such as walls, partitions, floors, and doors with sufficient fire resistance to remain effective throughout a fire exposure have a long history of providing protection against fire spread. These same barriers provide some level of smoke protection to spaces remote from the fire. Many codes, such as NFPA *101*®, *Life Safety Code*®, and NFPA 105, *Standard for the Installation of Smoke Door Assemblies and Other Opening Protectives,* provide specific criteria for the construction of smoke barriers, including doors and smoke dampers in these barriers. The amount of smoke leakage through such barriers depends on the size and shape of the leakage paths in a barrier and on the pressure difference across the leakage path.

There is no formalized analytical method for determining the rate of smoke leakage through barriers and the resulting levels of hazard in areas to be protected. A first-order approximation of the leakage can be made using the equation for flow through an opening. Typical leakage areas for barriers are listed in Table 18.3.1. Estimates of the leakage areas for gaps around doors can be obtained by considering the dimensions of paths around doors. Where multiple leakage paths are present, an effective leakage area can be determined following the methods in Klote and Milke.[1] In lieu of using the simple algebraic equation, fire and smoke transport models can address the smoke leakage through barriers (though these still require information to be provided concerning the size of the leakage paths). Full appraisal of the impact of such leakage requires knowledge of the smoke toxicity or an assumed design value of the acceptable smoke concentration in protected spaces. More effort is needed to increase the understanding of the capabilities and reliability of passive barriers in order to maximize the usefulness of this oldest and most fundamental method of smoke management.

Dilution

Dilution of smoke is sometimes referred to as smoke purging, smoke removal, smoke exhaust, or smoke extraction. Dilution can be used to maintain an acceptable smoke concentration in a compartment subject to smoke infiltration from an adjacent space. This can be effective if the rate of smoke leakage is small compared to either the total volume of the safeguarded space or the rate of purging air supplied to and removed from the space. Dilution also can be beneficial to the fire service for removing smoke after a fire has been extinguished. Sometimes, when doors are opened, smoke will flow into areas intended to be protected. Ideally, doors will be open only for short periods during evacuation. Smoke that has entered spaces remote from the fire can be purged by supplying outside air to dilute the smoke.

Some expectations may be unrealistic regarding what dilution can accomplish in the fire space. There is no theoretical or experimental evidence that using a building's HVAC system for smoke dilution will result in any significant improvement in tenable conditions within the fire space. Even though HVAC systems promote a considerable degree of air mixing within the spaces they serve, building fires produce very large quantities of smoke. As such, dilution of smoke by an HVAC system in the fire space does not usually result in any practical improvement in the tenable conditions of that space. Thus, smoke-purging systems intended to improve hazard conditions should not be used within a fire space or in spaces connected to a fire space by large openings.

The following is a simple analysis of smoke dilution for spaces in which there is no fire. At time zero ($t = 0$) a compartment is contaminated with some concentration of smoke, and no further smoke flows into or is generated within the compartment. In addition, the contaminant is considered uniformly distributed throughout the space. The concentration of contaminant in the space can be expressed as

$$a = \frac{1}{t} \log_e \left(\frac{C_o}{C} \right)$$

where

C_o = Initial concentration of contaminant

C = Concentration of contaminant at time t

a = Dilution rate in number of air changes per minute

t = Time after smoke stops entering space or time after which smoke production has stopped (minutes)

e = Constant, approximately 2.178

The concentrations C_o and C must be expressed in the same units, and they can be any units appropriate for the particular contaminant being considered. McGuire, Tamura, and Wilson[17] evaluated the maximum levels of smoke obscuration from a number of fire tests and a number of proposed criteria for tolerable levels of smoke obscuration. Based on this evaluation, they stated that the maximum levels of smoke obscuration are greater by a factor of 100 than those relating to the limit of tolerance. According to their observation, an area can be considered "reasonably safe" with respect to smoke obscuration if its atmosphere will not be contaminated to an extent greater than 1 percent by the atmosphere prevailing in the immediate fire area. Because a toxicity analysis can be somewhat involved and dilution will reduce concentrations of toxic smoke components as well as improve visibility, a first-order analysis can be done on a basis of smoke obscuration.

EXAMPLES: Smoke purging after the fire is extinguished.

1. After the fire department puts out a fire, the smoke must be cleared quickly so that an inspection can be made to determine if the fire is completely out. If the smoke HVAC system is capable of a dilution rate of six air changes per hour, how long will it take to reduce the smoke concentration to 1 percent of the initial value? The dilution rate, a, is 0.1 change per minute, and C_o/C is 100. $t = 1/10 \log_e(100) = 46$ minutes to purge smoke to 1 percent of initial value.

2. Considering the fire department's desire to inspect the area quickly, such a long purging time will probably be excessive. If the fire department wants the space to be purged in 10 minutes, what dilution rate is needed? The dilution time, t, is 10 minutes, and C_o/C is 100. $a = 1/10 \log_e(100) = 46$ change per minute (28 changes per hour).

In reality, it is impossible to ensure that the concentration of the contaminant is uniform throughout the compartment. Because of buoyancy, it is likely that higher concentrations would tend to be near the ceiling. Therefore, an exhaust inlet located near the ceiling and a supply outlet located near the floor would probably dilute smoke even faster than indicated by the preceding equations. Caution should be exercised in locating the supply and exhaust points to prevent the supply air from blowing into the exhaust inlet and thus short-circuiting the dilution operation.

Pressurization

Systems using pressurization produced by mechanical fans are referred to as smoke-control systems in NFPA 92A. Pressurization results in airflows of high velocity in the small gaps around closed doors and in construction cracks, thereby preventing smoke backflow through these openings. The pressurization systems most commonly used are pressurized stairwells and zoned smoke control. Elevator smoke control is rarely used, though interest in elevator smoke control may rise with the increasing interest in using the elevators as part of the means of egress for all or part of the building population. A public domain computer program, CONTAM,[18] may be applied to assess the pressure differences provided by a smoke-control system.

Many pressurized stairwells are provided with the goal of maintaining a tenable environment within the escape route in the event of a building fire. As such, a pressurized stairwell is designed to limit the amount of smoke migration into the stairwell, though not necessarily to keep the stairwell perfectly smoke-free. The following are the three major design concerns with pressurized stairwells:

1. Varying pressure differences that occur over the stairwell height
2. Large pressure fluctuations caused by doors being opened and closed
3. Location of supply air inlets and fans

Intuitively, it might appear that the pressure differences from the stairwell to the building would be approximately the same over the height of the stairwell. Unfortunately, this is not the case. For a building without vertical leakage through floors or shafts other than the stairwell, the pressure profile is linear. Of course, actual buildings have other shafts (elevators, pipe chases, etc.) and also have floor assemblies that are not airtight. However, this case is useful because it represents the most challenging situation to formulate a design. Its minimum pressure difference is less than that for buildings with more realistic leakage configurations and its maximum pressure difference is greater than that for other leakage configurations. A solution in the form of an algebraic equation exists to determine the pressure differences in a pressurized stairwell, neglecting vertical air movement in the building. In contrast, computer analyses are required to include the effects of more complicated building leakage arrangements.

When a door is opened in a pressurized stairwell, the pressure difference across the remaining closed doors can drop substantially. The two classes of design concepts that have been used to deal with this problem are overpressure relief and feedback control. An overpressure relief system that has gained attention as being simple and cost-effective is the "Canadian system." The essential features of this system are that air is supplied by one or more fans at relatively constant flow rates, and the ground-floor exterior stairwell door opens automatically when the system activates. This system eliminates the source of the most severe pressure fluctuations—the opening and closing of the exterior door.

There is concern about locating supply air inlets near the exterior ground-floor doors of the stairwell. If a supply inlet is located near this door, it is possible that much of the supply air will flow directly through the exterior doorway when it is opened, thus compromising the stairwell pressurization system. It is believed that locating inlets only one floor away from exterior doors eliminates this potential.

In the late 1960s, the concept of the "pressure sandwich" or "zoned smoke control" evolved. This consisted of exhausting the fire floor and pressurizing surrounding floors to limit smoke movement to the fire floor by creating pressure differences between floor levels. According to the concept of zoned smoke control, a building can be divided into a number of smoke zones, each separated from the others by partitions and floors. A smoke-control zone can consist of one floor, more than one floor, or part of a floor. In the event of fire, pressure differences and airflows produced by mechanical fans can be used to restrict smoke spread to the zone in which the fire began, or the smoke zone. One of the factors affecting successful performance of a zoned smoke control system is accurate identification of the zone of fire origin. As such, fire alarm initiating devices used to actuate a zoned smoke control system need to be carefully selected. Failure to identify the correct fire zone, such as a case where a manual pull station is activated outside the fire zone, may result in a positive pressurization of the fire zone, which may encourage smoke spread to other zones.

When using zoned smoke control, careful integration of smoke zones, barriers, and the initiating devices is required. Physical barriers (walls or floors) must coincide with the spatial definition of the smoke control zone. Where HVAC equipment is used to supply and exhaust air, the HVAC zones must agree with the smoke zones. If fire alarm initiating devices or sprinkler waterflow alarms are used to actuate the zoned smoke-control system, the zones for these systems must coincide with the smoke-control zones.

As a caution, the design of zoned smoke-control systems is not intended to improve conditions in the fire zone. The concentration of smoke in this zone may render it untenable. Accordingly, in zoned smoke-control systems, building occupants should evacuate the zone in which the fire occurs as soon as possible after the fire has been detected.

Airflow

Airflow has been used extensively to manage smoke from fires in subway, railroad, and highway tunnels. Large flow rates of air are needed to control smoke flow, and these flow rates can supply additional oxygen to the fire. Because of the need for complex controls and large airflows, airflow is not used as extensively in buildings. The control problem consists of having very small flows when a door is closed, and then having those flows increase significantly when that door opens.

Thomas[19] determined that airflow in a corridor in which there is a fire can almost totally prevent smoke from flowing upstream of the fire. As illustrated in Figure 18.3.8, the smoke forms a surface that slopes into the direction of the oncoming airflow. Molecular diffusion is believed to result in the transfer of trace amounts of smoke, producing only an odor of smoke, but no hazard upstream. There is a minimum velocity below which smoke will flow upstream, and Thomas[19] developed the following empirical relation for this critical velocity. This relation, evaluated at an air density of 0.081 lb/ft^3 (1.3 kg/m^3) and temperature of 81°F (27°C), is

$$V_k = 5.68\left(\frac{E}{W}\right)^{1/3}$$

where

V_k = Critical air velocity to prevent smoke backflow (ft/min)

E = Energy release rate into corridor (Btu/hr)

W = Corridor width (ft)

This relation can be used when the fire is located in the corridor or when the smoke enters the corridor through an open doorway, an air transfer grille, or some other opening. Although the critical velocities calculated from the above equation are approximate, these critical velocities are indicative of the kind of velocities required to prevent smoke backflow from fires of different sizes.

EXAMPLES: Rough estimates of airflow for a doorway.

1. Thomas[19] indicated that his relationship for critical velocity can be used to obtain a rough estimate for doorways. A room fully involved in fire could have an energy release rate on the order of 8 × 10^6 Btu/hr. What estimate of critical velocity is obtained from the Thomas equation for a door 3 ft (0.9 m) wide?

$$V_k = 5.68\ (8 \times 10^6/3)^{1/3} = 800 \text{ ft/min}$$

If the door has an area of 20 ft^2 (1.9 m^2), this would amount to a flow of 1600 ft^3/min (0.76 m^3/sec).

2. Consideration of a smaller fire, such as a wastebasket fire, may be appropriate for many situations. What flow rate does the Thomas relation indicate is needed to prevent backflow for the door in Example 1? A wastebasket fire has a peak energy release rate near 0.5 × 10^6 Btu/hr (146 kW).

$$V_k = 5.68\ (0.5 \times 10^6/3)^{1/3} = 300 \text{ ft/min (1.5 m/sec)}$$

For a door area of 20 ft^2 (1.9 m^2), this would amount to a flow of 6000 ft^3/min (2.8 m^3/sec).

In any smoke management design with airflow, the effect of providing a significant quantity of fresh air to the fire needs to be considered. Also, the airflow must be exhausted at some point downstream.

Buoyancy in Large Spaces

Buoyancy of hot combustion gases is employed in both fan-powered and nonpowered smoke management systems for large-volume spaces. The spaces where such systems are employed include atria, arcades, covered shopping malls, sports arenas, and exhibition halls. In general, these buoyancy systems are used for spaces with floor to ceiling heights of at least 33 ft (10 m) and may be much greater. The following approaches can be used to manage smoke in large spaces.[20,21]

Smoke Filling. This approach consists of allowing smoke to fill the large-volume space while occupants evacuate the atrium. This approach applies only to spaces where the smoke-filling time is sufficient for both decision making and evacuation. Evacuation time can be estimated by people movement analysis.[22,23] Smoke-filling time can be estimated by computer fire models or by the filling time equations in NFPA 92B.

Unsteady Clear Height with Upper Layer Exhaust. This approach consists of providing a sufficient exhaust rate of smoke from the top of the atrium to delay the descent of the smoke layer to permit occupants to have sufficient time for decision making and evacuation. This approach requires an analysis of people movement and analysis of the smoke-filling process with a fire model.

Steady Clear Height with Upper Layer Exhaust. This approach consists of exhausting smoke from the top of the atrium in order to achieve a steady clear height for a steady fire (Figure 18.3.10). Design analysis of this system is based on the fact that the mass flow of smoke entering the upper smoke layer equals that of the exhaust. For a fuel package away from walls, the exhaust airflow rates are shown in Figure 18.3.11.

Design Considerations

The design of exhaust systems for large-volume spaces includes more than the overall exhaust rate needed. Additional items include makeup air supply, stratification, and plugholing.

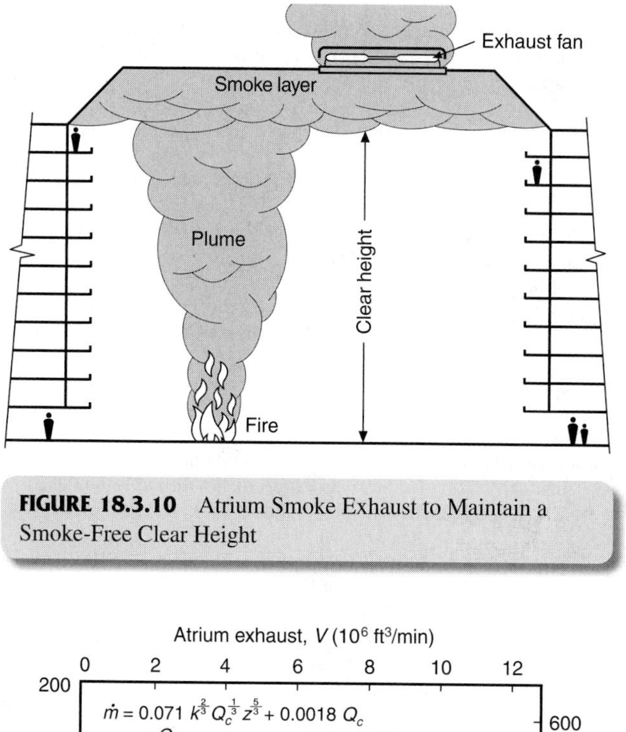

FIGURE 18.3.10 Atrium Smoke Exhaust to Maintain a Smoke-Free Clear Height

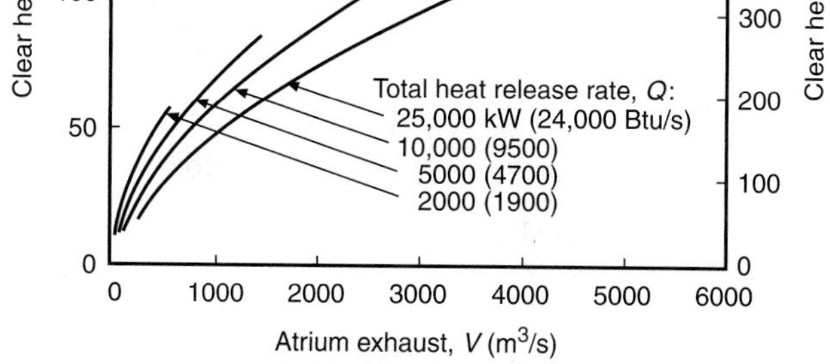

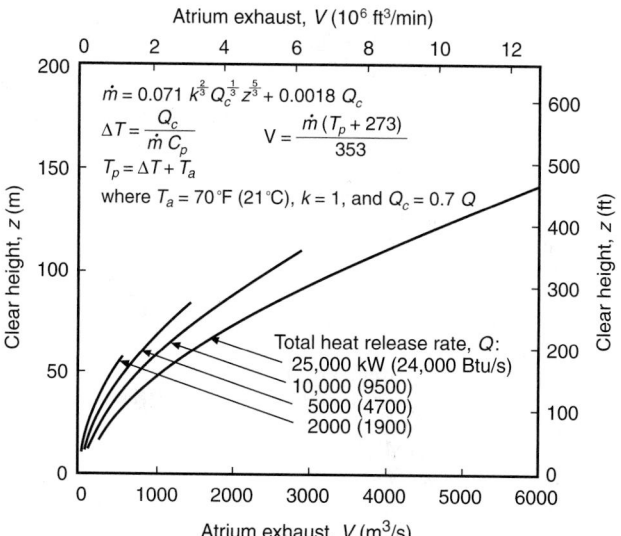

FIGURE 18.3.11 Atrium Exhaust Needed to Maintain a Clear Height for Various Heat Release Rates

The makeup air supply needs to be provided at a relatively low velocity (200 fpm [1 m/sec] or less at the fire) to avoid disrupting the plume and increasing entrainment of air in the plume. In addition, the makeup air supply should be distributed around the entire perimeter of the design fire to avoid tilting the flames or increasing the turbulence of the plume. If the makeup air velocity is provided at too great a speed or from one side only, the exhaust capacity may not be sufficient for the system to perform as intended.

Stratification of the smoke layer below the ceiling will delay or prevent actuation of ceiling-mounted smoke detectors and sprinklers. The solar load on an atrium often results in the formation of a layer of hot air under the ceiling. Stratification is expected if the temperature of the rising smoke plume is less than the surrounding air. If stratification of the smoke occurs at an intermediate height, smoke will not be able to reach ceiling-mounted smoke detectors, delaying or preventing smoke detection. This problem can be overcome by using projected beam detectors, as discussed in NFPA 92B.

Plugholing relates to the situation where a hole is "punched" through the smoke layer by a relatively high-velocity exhaust fan. The condition necessary for plugholing can be identified using calculations in NFPA 92B. If plugholing occurs, some of the exhaust capacity of the fan will be utilized to exhaust the "clean" air from below the smoke layer that is pulled through the hole in the smoke. As such, the efficiency of the exhaust system will decrease and the smoke layer will descend, perhaps to unacceptable levels.

Computational Tools for Design

NFPA 92B recognizes the following types of computational tools that can be used for analysis of smoke management systems in large-volume spaces: (1) scale modeling, (2) algebraic equations, and (3) compartment fire models. These tools can be used singularly or in combination. In scale modeling, a scale model of a building is made, and the design fire and results of the modeling are scaled in accordance with established scaling laws. Chapter 6 of NFPA 92B lists the algebraic equations that can be used for analysis of smoke management systems in large-volume spaces. Compartment fire models consist of zone fire models and computational fluid dynamics (CFD).

The algebraic equations and the zone fire models are based on the following assumptions: (1) a smoke plume rises from the fire, (2) the plume entrains air from the surroundings as it rises, (3) a smoke layer forms under the ceiling, (4) the concentration of contaminants is uniform throughout the smoke layer, (5) the smoke temperature is uniform throughout the smoke layer, and (6) the transition between the smoke layer and the room air is a plane. While the last three assumptions are not completely realistic, they are considered to be justified by the proven utility of the algebraic equations and the zone fire models.

If the algebraic equations are not applicable for a particular space of design fire, then computer fire models need to be applied to develop the design parameters of the system. When algebraic equations and the zone fire models are used for analysis of atrium smoke control, specific calculations need to be made concerning plugholing, and the makeup air velocity needs to be 200 fpm (1 m/sec) or less.

Computer fire models include the ASET,[24] ASET-B,[25] the BRI Model,[26] FIREFORM,[27] CCFM,[28] and CFAST.[29] The University of Maryland has made modifications to CCFM, specifically for atrium smoke management design.[30] Joglar-Billoch and Mowrer[31] have developed a model, FIRE-MD, to assess the impact of either mechanical or natural ventilation on the smoke layer position or properties. Descriptions of zone models are provided by Bukowski,[32] Friedman,[33] Jones,[34] Mitler and Rockett,[35] and Quintiere.[36] Klote[37] provides an overview of atrium smoke management and the public domain computer program, Atrium Smoke Management Engineering Tools (ASMET).

Zone fire models are best applied in cases where the changes in the geometry with respect to height are minimal. Further, because of the homogeneous smoke layer assumption that is part of the zone models, the zone models may not be appropriate for spaces with very large open areas or where horizontal spread needs to be modeled. In such cases, the computational fluid dynamics (CFD) models are more appropriate.

CFD models consist of dividing the large volume space into a large number of cells and solving the governing equations for each cell to obtain the flows and temperatures throughout the space. It is not unusual for atrium applications to consist of hundreds of thousands of cells. CFD models have the ability to realistically simulate smoke flow, and they can be used to evaluate tenability. There are a number of general purpose CFD models suitable for smoke management analysis. The fire dynamic simulator (FDS) model was developed at NIST specifically for fire application, and a number of projects have been conducted to verify FDS.[38] Because CFD models realistically simulate smoke flow, they can simulate plugholing without other algebraic equations, and CFD can simulate the consequences of exceeding the 200 fpm (1 m/sec) limit on makeup air.

SUMMARY

Smoke is defined as the "airborne solid and liquid particulates and gases" resulting from a fire, "along with the quantity of air that is . . . mixed into the mass." Smoke, whether or not it is highly visible, can contain dangerous products of combustion and pose a considerable threat to life and property.

Smoke moves from areas of high pressure to areas of lower pressure. Factors that affect smoke movement include the temperature of the smoke, the height of the building involved, the existence of openings in the building, stack effect, and wind. Smoke management methods use compartmentalization, dilution, airflow, pressurization, and buoyancy of the smoke itself to control the smoke hazards of fires.

BIBLIOGRAPHY

References Cited

1. Klote, J., and Milke, J., "Principles of Smoke Management," ASHRAE/SFPE, Atlanta, GA, 2002.
2. Klote, J. H., "Smoke Control," *SFPE Handbook of Fire Protection Engineering,* 3rd ed., P. J. DiNenno, et al. (Eds.), National Fire Protection Association, Quincy, MA, 2002.
3. Thomas, P. H., et al., "Investigations into the Flow of Hot Gases in Roof Venting," *Fire Research Technical Paper No. 7,* Joint Fire Research Organization, London, UK, 1963.
4. Butcher, E. G., and Parnell, A. C., *Smoke Control in Fire Safety Design,* E. and F. N. Spon, London, UK, 1979.
5. Heskestad, G., "Engineering Relations for Fire Plumes," *SFPE Technology Report 82–8,* Society of Fire Protection Engineers, Boston, 1982.
6. Heskestad, G., "Fire Plumes," *SFPE Handbook of Fire Protection Engineering,* 3rd ed., P. J. DiNenno, et al. (Eds.), National Fire Protection Association, Quincy, MA, 2002.
7. Purser, D. A., "Toxicity Assessment of Combustion Products," *SFPE Handbook of Fire Protection Engineering,* 3rd ed., P. J. DiNenno, et al. (Eds.), National Fire Protection Association, Quincy, MA, 2002.
8. Jin, T., "Visibility and Human Behavior in Fire Smoke," *SFPE Handbook of Fire Protection Engineering,* 3rd ed., P. J. DiNenno, et al. (Eds.), National Fire Protection Association, Quincy, MA, 2002.
9. Morehart, J., "Sprinklers in the NIH Atrium: How Did They React During the Fire Last May?" *Fire Journal,* Vol. 83, No. 1, 1989, pp. 56–57.
10. Milke, J. A., Hugue, D. E., Hoskins, B. L., and Carroll J. P., "Tenability Analyses in Performance-Based Design," *Fire Protection Engineering,* Vol. 28, 2005, pp. 50–56.
11. Tamura, G. T., "Computer Analysis of Smoke Movement in Tall Buildings," paper presented at the ASHRAE Annual Meeting, American Society of Heating, Refrigerating, and Air Conditioning Engineers, Atlanta, GA, June 1969.
12. Tamura, G. T., and Wilson, A. G., "Pressure Differences for a Nine-Story Building as a Result of Chimney Effect and Ventilation System Operation," *ASHRAE Transactions,* Vol. 72, No. 1, 1966, pp. 180–189.
13. Tamura, G. T., and Shaw, C. Y., "Studies on Exterior Wall Tightness and Air Filtration of Tall Buildings," *ASHRAE Transactions,* Vol. 82, No. 1, 1976, pp. 122–134.
14. Tamura, G. T., and Shaw, C. Y., "Air Leakage Data for the Design of Elevator and Stair Shaft Pressurization Systems," *ASHRAE Transactions,* Vol. 82, No. 2, 1976, pp. 179–190.
15. Tamura, G. T., and Shaw, C. Y., "Experimental Studies of Mechanical Venting for Smoke Control in Tall Office Buildings," *ASHRAE Transactions,* Vol. 86, No. 1, 1978, pp. 54–71.
16. Shaw, C. Y., Reardon, J. T., and Cheung, M. S., "Changes in Air Leakage Levels of Six Canadian Office Buildings," *ASHRAE Journal,* American Society of Heating, Refrigerating, and Air Conditioning Engineers, Atlanta, GA, Vol. 35, No. 2, 1993, pp. 34–36.
17. McGuire, J. H., Tamura, G. T., and Wilson, A. G., "Factors in Controlling Smoke in High Buildings," *Symposium* on Fire Hazards in Buildings, ASHRAE Semiannual Meeting in San Francisco, CA, 1970, pp. 8–13.
18. Walton, G. N., Dols, W. S., *CONTAM 2.4, User Guide and Program Documentation,* NISTIR 7251, National Institute of Standards and Technology, Gaithersburg, MD, 2005.
19. Thomas, P. H., "Movement of Smoke in Horizontal Corridors Against an Airflow," *Institute of Fire Engineers Quarterly,* Vol. 30, No. 77, 1970, pp. 45–53.
20. Milke, J. A., "Smoke Management in Covered Malls and Atria," *SFPE Handbook of Fire Protection Engineering,* 3rd ed., P. J. DiNenno, et al. (Eds.), National Fire Protection Association, Quincy, MA, 2002.
21. Milke, J. A., "Effectiveness of High-Capacity Smoke Exhaust in Large Spaces," *Journal of Fire Protection Engineering,* Vol. 13, No. 3, 2002, pp. 111–128.
22. Nelson, H. E., and MacLennan, H. A., "Emergency Movement," *SFPE Handbook of Fire Protection Engineering,* 3rd ed., P. J. DiNenno, et al. (Eds.), National Fire Protection Association, Quincy, MA, 2002.
23. Pauls, J., "Movement of People," *SFPE Handbook of Fire Protection Engineering,* 3rd ed., P. J. DiNenno, et al. (Eds.), National Fire Protection Association, Quincy, MA, 2002.

24. Cooper, L. Y., "ASET: A Computer Program for Calculating Available Safe Egress Time," *Fire Safety Journal,* Vol. 9, 1985, pp. 29–45.
25. Walton, W. D., "ASET-B: A Room Fire Program for Personal Computers," NBSIR 85-3144-1, National Bureau of Standards, Washington, DC, 1985.
26. Tanaka, T., "A Model of Multiroom Fire Spread," NBSIR 83-2718, National Bureau of Standards, Washington, DC, 1983.
27. Nelson, H. E., "FIREFORM: A Computerized Collection of Convenient Fire Safety Computations," NBSIR 88–3308, National Bureau of Standards, Washington, DC, 1986.
28. Cooper, L. Y., and Forney, G. P., "Fire in a Room with a Hole: A Prototype Application of the Consolidated Compartment Fire Model (CCFM) Computer Code," Presented at the 1987 Combined Meetings of Eastern Section of Combustion Institute and NBS Annual Conference on Fire Research, Gaithersburg, MD, 1987, pp. 1–4.
29. Peacock, R. D., Forney, G. P., Reneke, P., Portier, R., and Jones, W. W., "CFAST: The Consolidated Model of Fire Growth and Smoke Transport," NIST Technical Note 1299, National Institute of Standards and Technology, Gaithersburg, MD, 1993.
30. Milke, J. A., and Mower, F. W., "Computer-Aided Design for Smoke Management in Atria and Covered Malls," *ASHRAE Transactions,* Vol. 100, Part 2, 1994.
31. Joglar-Billoch, F., "A Methodology for Fire Risk and Hazard Assessment," Ph.D. thesis, University of Maryland, College Park, 2000.
32. Bukowski, R. W., "Fire Models, the Future Is Now!" *NFPA Journal,* No. 85, Vol. 2, 1991, pp. 60–69.
33. Friedman, R., "An International Survey of Computer Models for Fire and Smoke," *Journal of Fire Protection Engineering,* Vol. 4, No. 3, 1992, pp. 81–92.
34. Jones, W. W., "A Review of Compartment Fire Models," NBSIR 83–2684, National Bureau of Standards, Washington, DC, 1983.
35. Mitler, H. E., and Rockett, J. A., "How Accurate Is Mathematical Fire Modeling?" NBSIR 86–3459, National Bureau of Standards, Washington, DC, 1986.
36. Quintiere, J. G., "Fundamentals of Enclosure Fire 'Zone' Models," *Journal of Fire Protection Engineering,* Vol. 1, No. 3, 1989, pp. 99–119.
37. Klote, J. H., "Method of Predicting Smoke Movement in Atria with Application to Smoke Management," NISTIR 5516, National Institute of Standards and Technology, Gaithersburg, MD, 1994.
38. McGrattan, K., *Fire Dynamics Simulator (Version 4)—Technical Reference Guide,* NIST Special Publication 1018, National Institute of Standards and Technology, Gaithersburg, MD, 2004.

NFPA Codes, Standards, and Recommended Practices

Reference to the following NFPA codes, standards, and recommended practices will provide further information on smoke movement in buildings discussed in this chapter. (See the latest version of The NFPA Catalog *for availability of current editions of the following documents.)*

NFPA 92A, *Standard for Smoke-Control Systems Utilizing Barriers and Pressure Differences*

NFPA 92B, *Standard for Smoke Management Systems in Malls, Atria, and Large Spaces*

NFPA *101®*, *Life Safety Code®*

NFPA 105, *Standard for the Installation of Smoke Door Assemblies and Other Opening Protectives*

NFPA 204, *Standard for Smoke and Heat Venting*

References

Cooper, L. Y., "The Development of Hazardous Conditions in Enclosures with Growing Fires," NBSIR 82–2622, National Bureau of Standards, Washington, DC, 1982.

Hadjisophocleous, G. V., Lougheed, G. D., and Cao, S., "Numerical Study of the Effectiveness of Atrium Smoke Exhaust Systems," *ASHRAE Transactions,* Vol. 104, 1999.

Klote, J. H., "An Overview of Atrium Smoke Management," *Fire Protection Engineering,* No. 7, Summer 2000, pp. 24–34.

Lougheed, G. D., and Hadjisophocleous, G. V., "Investigation of Atrium Smoke Exhaust Effectiveness," *ASHRAE Transactions,* Vol. 103, 1997, pp. 1–15.

Lougheed, G. D., Hadjisophocleous, G. V., McCartney, C., and Taber, B. C., "Large-Scale Physical Model Studies for an Atrium Smoke Exhaust System," *ASHRAE Transactions,* Vol. 104, 1999.

Milke, J. A., "Using Models to Support Smoke Management System Design," *Fire Protection Engineering,* No. 7, Summer 2000, pp. 17–22.

Mowrer, F. W., Milke J. A., and Torero, J. L., "Comparative Driving Forces for Smoke Movement in Buildings," *Journal of Fire Protection Engineering,* Vol. 14, No. 4, 2004, pp. 237–265.

Tamura, G. T., and Shaw, C. Y., "Studies on Exterior Wall Air Tightness and Air Infiltration of Tall Buildings," *Transactions of the American Society of Heating, Refrigerating, and Air Conditioning Engineers,* Vol. 82, Part 1, 1976, pp. 122–134.

Tamura, G. T., and Shaw, C. Y., "Air Leakage Data for the Design of Elevator and Stair Shaft Pressurization Systems," *Transactions of the American Society of Heating, Refrigerating, and Air Conditioning Engineers,* Vol. 83, Part II, 1976, pp. 179–190.

Tamura, G. T., and Shaw, C. Y., "Experimental Studies of Mechanical Venting for Smoke Control in Tall Office Buildings," *Transactions of the American Society of Heating, Refrigerating, and Air Conditioning Engineers,* Vol. 86, Part I, 1978, pp. 54–71.

Tamura, G. T., and Wilson, A. G., "Pressure Differences for a Nine-Story Building as a Result of Chimney Effect and Ventilation System Operations," *Transactions of the American Society of Heating, Refrigerating, and Air Conditioning Engineers,* Vol. 72, Part I, 1966, pp. 180–189.

Tamura, G. T., and Wilson, A. G., "Pressure Differences Caused by Chimney Effect in Three-Story-High Buildings," *Transactions of the American Society of Heating, Refrigerating, and Air Conditioning Engineers,* Vol. 73, Part II, 1967.

Chapter 4

Venting Practices

Gunnar Heskestad

Chapter Contents

Key Terms

curtain boards, curtained area, curtained compartment, General Motors fire, LAVENT, Livonia fire, unit vents, vent areas, venting

The importance of the buoyant properties of heat and smoke was realized at an early date, as evidenced by an NFPA standard adopted in 1903 that called for smoke vents over theater stages and in the ceilings of theater auditoriums. However, until the advent of effective artificial lighting, buildings were generally small enough so that windows provided adequate smoke venting, other than venting of fire through the roof.

The main body of this chapter covers venting practices as they would be applied to nonsprinklered buildings, based on NFPA 204, *Standard for Smoke and Heat Venting* (formerly 204M). An addendum to the chapter (in which the several different approaches are incorporated) discusses the current state of the technology involving the sprinkler/vent issue.

See also Section 10, Chapter 4, "Air-Conditioning and Ventilating Systems"; and Section 18, Chapter 6, "Deflagration (Explosion) Venting."

HISTORICAL BACKGROUND

Large undivided floor areas present extremely difficult fire-fighting problems, since fire fighters must enter these areas to fight fires in central portions of the building. If fire fighters are unable to enter because of the accumulation of heat and smoke, fire-fighting efforts may be reduced to ineffective application of hose streams to perimeter areas while fire consumes the interior (Figure 18.4.1). Venting through roof openings can mitigate the accumulation of heat and smoke, enabling fire fighters to reach the origin or seat of the fire. In addition, venting provides occupants with the opportunity to travel to a safe area and, furthermore, can reduce damage to buildings and contents due to smoke and hot gases.

Great impetus to the subject of smoke and heat venting was provided by the General Motors fire at Livonia, Michigan, in 1953, when fire spread horizontally under an unvented metal roof, with 34 acres (137,600 m^2) of undivided area. Fire protection engineers were in general agreement that this fire could have been greatly reduced if there had been effective roof venting. The General Motors fire led to a new approach to the subject by the NFPA Committee on Building Construction, which prepared NFPA 204M, adopted by NFPA in May 1961. In 1968, the venting guide was expanded to include a new section on inspection and maintenance.

A reconfirmation action failed in 1975, as concerns had surfaced over use of NFPA 204M in conjunction with automatically sprinklered buildings. Because of this controversy, work on a revision of NFPA 204M continued at a slow pace but concluded with the 1982 edition.

The 1982 edition of NFPA 204M distinguished between unsprinklered and sprinklered buildings. The unsprinklered part was considered to represent a major advance in engineered smoke and heat venting. The sprinklered part, limited to a single chapter (Chapter 6), did not recognize that venting is necessarily desirable in a sprinklered building and did not offer a design basis, pending the resolution of some technical questions.

No changes were made for the 1985 edition of NFPA 204M, except for a limited revision of Chapter 6 dealing with venting of sprinklered buildings. Reference was made to new test data on deploying vents in a test building with automatic sprinklers. However, the new data did not permit conclusions to be developed whether sprinkler control was impaired or enhanced by the presence of automatic roof vents of typical spacing and area.

Gunnar Heskestad, Ph.D., retired from FM Global in 2004 as an assistant vice-president and consulting research scientist. He has specialized in fluid mechanics and heat transfer of fire with application to fire protection.

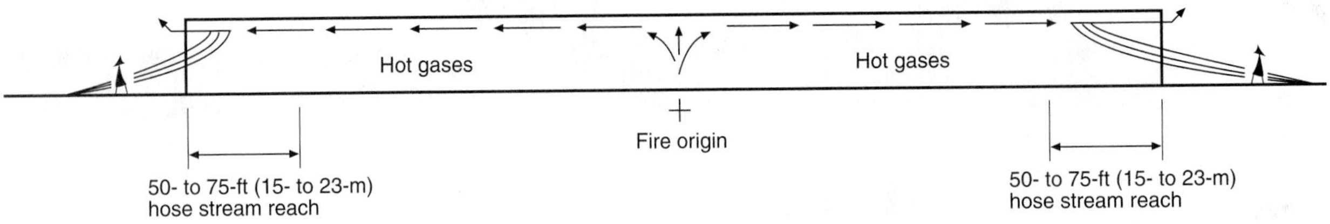

FIGURE 18.4.1 Behavior of Hot Gases in a Flat-Roofed Building

Changes for the 1991 edition of NFPA 204M again focused on Chapter 6. While the two previous editions had stated that a generalized design basis had not been developed and was not available for using sprinklers and vents together for hazard control, the 1991 edition stated that such a design basis "has not been universally recognized" and did not offer one. Furthermore, words were added to the effect that the concern for combining sprinklers and vents relates to "occupancies that present a high challenge to sprinkler systems." As in previous editions, "the designer is encouraged to use the available tools and data referenced in the document for solving problems peculiar to a particular type of hazard control."

The 1998 edition, designated NFPA 204, represented a significant revision. Tables in the previous editions that listed vent areas were deleted, and, instead, engineering equations and referenced computer models provided the designer with the tools to develop vent designs based on performance objectives. The engineering equations were updated based on new research and did not assume that the base of the fire and the so-called virtual origin coincided with the floor level, a simplifying assumption used in preceding editions (NFPA 204M). Additional data on heat release rate were presented, together with a new chapter dealing with techniques for estimating heat release rates of untested fuel arrays. As before, there was a single chapter devoted to sprinklered buildings (Chapter 8). The new chapter was little changed from Chapter 6 of the preceding edition, except for recognizing *curtain boards,* usually part of a venting system, as potentially detrimental to the outcome of sprinklered fires. In addition, there was reference to a new series of large-scale fire tests that the designer may consult.

The 2002 edition of NFPA 204 was converted from a guide to a standard, thus implementing mandatory requirements and updated language. The document was also updated to meet NFPA *Manual of Style* requirements. The only significant technical change is the treatment of venting for sprinklered buildings, presented in Chapter 11, "Venting in Sprinklered Buildings." This chapter is a single-paragraph statement: "Where provided, the design of venting for sprinklered buildings shall be based on a performance analysis acceptable to the authority having jurisdiction, demonstrating that the established objectives are met." An annex includes objectives that may be selected for the design, a review of research as in the preceding edition, subsequent research, and design considerations for venting of sprinklered buildings. Subsequent research (reviewed in this chapter under the heading "FPRF Program" in the Addendum) was deemed to be inconclusive as to benefits of automatic venting in sprinklered buildings. The design considerations are based on preventing automatic vents and draft curtains from interfering with sprinkler control of a fire, subject to the overall guide: "Draft curtains and open vents of venting systems should not adversely affect sprinklers that are capable of discharging water onto the fire, either in time of operation or in the water discharge pattern."

The technical questions that remain unresolved in application of venting to sprinklered buildings are related to the effects of (1) sprinkler discharge on venting effectiveness; (2) fresh air introduced into the building on the burning process and the water demand of the sprinkler system; and (3) curtain boards on the operation of sprinklers. Sprinkler discharge will cool the fire gases, perhaps to the extent that the vent discharge is reduced, hence reducing venting effectiveness. Additionally, the sprinkler sprays will entrain ambient smoke and air, transporting smoke to the floor level and possibly drawing gas from the vent exhaust wherever nozzles are located close to vents, further reducing venting effectiveness. Unless the building is very large, fresh air flowing into the building and replacing smoke escaping through the vents will increase the oxygen concentration in the fire space. The increased oxygen concentrations may cause a more vigorous fire than would otherwise exist, with the possible outcome of an increased number of operating sprinklers, in some cases overtaxing the water supply. Curtain boards may prevent or delay the operation of sprinklers capable of delivering water to the fire or interfere with the discharge of such sprinklers. Against these possible adverse effects must be balanced the likelihood that some improvement in visibility for fire fighting will result in many cases and the possibility that the number of operating sprinklers may sometimes be reduced because of the cooling effect of vent flows.

Many of the problems of combining sprinklers and vents may not appear if all the vents in the fire area are gang operated the moment a predetermined number of sprinklers have operated. Limited experiments on model scale[1] showed that opening all the vents in a test building at the moment of the *first* sprinkler operation could reduce the total number of sprinkler operations, compared to the corresponding unvented fire, and also prevent the total loss of visibility through the smoke which occurred in the corresponding unvented fire. Requiring more than one sprinkler to operate before the vents are opened, ideally all sprinklers that are capable of delivering water to the fire, would be a conservative approach for ensuring that sprinkler effectiveness is not compromised. Alternatively, prior to gang operation of the vents at the first sprinkler operation, any vent located within a small distance of the initial fire (to be determined) may be blocked from opening by signal from a fire proximity sensor. Experimental studies would be needed to confirm feasibility and establish design information.

Essential features specified in NFPA 204 include roof vents actuated by heat or smoke, curtain boards to confine heat and prevent lateral fire spread, and openings for fresh air makeup at low levels (Figure 18.4.2). Two general classes of fires are considered: (1) limited growth fires, which are not expected to grow past a predictable maximum size, and (2) continuous growth fires, which can be expected to grow indefinitely until intervention by fire fighters. Guidance to vent design is based on engineering equations (hand calculations) or the use of the computer model LAVENT (or equivalent). Mechanical exhaust at ceiling apertures is treated as an option to natural ventilation at roof vents and is deemed a highly favorable option in sprinklered occupancies because of near immunity to adverse effects on venting efficiency of cooled fire gases and entrained fire gases by nearby sprinklers. The provisions of NFPA 204 may be applied to one-story buildings or to the top story of multiple-story buildings. With mechanical exhaust, lower stories of multiple-story buildings can also be vented.

INDUSTRIAL BUILDING VENTILATION

Although any opening in a roof will reduce some heat and smoke, building designers and fire protection engineers cannot rely on casual inclusion of skylights, windows, or monitors as adequate means of venting. Standards now exist (FM Approvals, Underwriters Laboratories Inc. [UL], etc.) that include design criteria and test procedures for unit vents and also call for simulated fire tests as well as engineering analysis.

Unit Vents

Unit vents are relatively small, usually 16 to 100 ft^2 (1.49 to 9.29 m^2) in area. Automatic unit vents are of two types, based on manner of operation—fusible link or drop-out plastic (Figure 18.4.3). The fusible link type consists of a metal housing with lids that depend on a temperature-rated fusible link to trip the lid mechanism, but alternative modes of operation are possible, for example, by heat or smoke detectors. The drop-out plastic type depends on a temperature-sensitive, transparent or translucent, thermoplastic dome that deforms from its setting and falls out of the roof. Vents designed for manual operation are constructed with metal lids to resist elevated fire temperatures and may be opened from the floor with wires and cables. These units can also be modified for automatic operation.

Vents may be a single unit, in which the entire unit opens fully with a single sensor, or multiple units in rows, clusters, groups, or other arrays that will satisfy the venting requirements for the specific hazard.

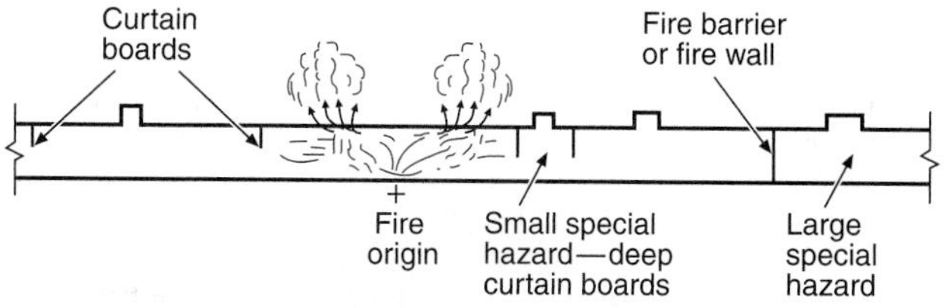

FIGURE 18.4.2 Behavior of Combustion Products Under Vented and Curtained Roof

FIGURE 18.4.3 Building with Roof Vents

Mechanical roof ventilators actuated by fire conditions are possible—and often preferable—alternatives to roof vents based on natural ventilation, especially in lower stories of multiple-story buildings. These ventilators must be capable of functioning under expected high-temperature fire conditions.

Curtain Boards

In large-area buildings, unless vented areas are subdivided by means of walls or partitions, curtain boards are important for prompt and positive actuation of vents because they bank up heat in the curtained area. They also limit the spread of heat and smoke beneath the ceiling during the design duration of the venting system. Curtain boards can be made from any substantial noncombustible material that will resist the passage of smoke.

The depth of curtain boards would normally be selected to correspond with the design depth of the smoke layer. However, the depth should not be less than 20 percent of the ceiling height, to prevent spillage of smoke under the curtain, where depth and ceiling height are referenced to the center of the lowest roof vent. It would rarely be desirable to have the curtain extend below 10 ft (3 m) from the floor. Around special hazards, the curtain should preferably extend down to this limit (Figure 18.4.4). Equipped

FIGURE 18.4.4 Deep Curtain Boards Around a Special Hazard (a Heat-Treating Department)

with proper venting, a noncombustible curtain board extending down from a ceiling around special hazards will prevent smoke and heat from mushrooming throughout the facility.

The distance between curtain boards should not exceed eight times the ceiling height, to ensure that vents remote from the fire will be effective within the curtained compartment. Smaller curtained areas may be desirable where occupancies are particularly vulnerable to damage. However, it is important that the distance between curtain boards not be less than two times the ceiling height, unless the curtain boards extend down to a depth of at least 40 percent of the ceiling height. The increased curtain depth is needed for these small curtain spacings to prevent significant spillage of fire gases underneath the curtain because of the close proximity of the fire.

Dimensioning and Spacing of Vents

When the area of an individual vent becomes sufficiently large, there is a possibility that a core of clear air from beneath the smoke layer will be included in the exhaust from the vent, which reduces the effectiveness of the vent. To prevent inclusion of clear air, called *plugholing,* the area of a unit vent or cluster of vents should not exceed $2d^2$, where d is the design depth of the smoke layer or curtain board. In the case of a row of unit vents or a monitor vent, the width of the row or monitor should not exceed d.

A large number of small vents on close spacing is preferable to a small number of large vents on wide spacing. This ensures early operation of the first vents in a fire, reducing the likelihood of initial smoke excursions beyond the curtained area above the fire. In no case should the vent spacing in a rectangular matrix exceed $4H$, where H is the ceiling height measured from the floor to ceiling for flat roofs, and from the floor to the center of the vent for sloped roofs. Alternatively, in a nonrectangular vent matrix in plan, the distance between any point on the floor and the nearest vent should not exceed $2.8H$ (the diagonal of a square whose side is $2H$). (The maximum vent spacings indicated in the 2002 edition of NFPA 204 are incorrect representations of the original formulation in NFPA 204M, 1982 edition.)

The total vent area for each curtained compartment under the ceiling depends on the severity of the expected fire and is discussed later in this chapter.

Fresh Air Makeup

Openings must be provided at or near floor level to allow the introduction of makeup air. This is critical in today's tightly constructed and insulated buildings. The total area of these openings must normally be at least as great as the largest installed vent area for a curtained compartment; otherwise, the inlets may effectively throttle the vent flow. The vent flow equation in NFPA 204 indicates the degree to which the vent flow rate is reduced by limiting the inlet opening area. If doors and windows below the designed smoke layer cannot meet the total required inlet area, special air inlet provisions are necessary.

It is essential that a dependable means be provided for admitting inlet air within approximately one minute after the first vent opens. If prompt air inlet is not provided, the entire building may quickly fill with smoke, which will clear slowly at lower levels (in the design clear layer) in response to the fully developed vent flow after the air inlets have been actuated.

Fire Characterization*

Each curtained compartment or the ceiling area of buildings requiring no curtain boards must be furnished with a total installed vent area (or exhaust capacity in case of mechanical ventilation) sufficient to vent fires of the expected severity. In addition to the expected fire severity, the installed vent area (or exhaust capacity) will depend on the depth of the curtain boards or design depth of the smoke layer. Furthermore, unless the occupancy or hazard is such that the expected fire will peak or level off at a predictable maximum size, the installed vent area (or exhaust capacity) will also depend on the minimum clear visibility design time as measured from the time the vents first operate. The fire severity is expressed differently according to the class of the fire, which for purposes of calculating vent areas is classified as either a limited-growth or a continuous-growth fire.

Limited-Growth Fires. These are fires that are not expected to grow past a predictable maximum size in terms of heat release rate, expressed in Btu per second or kW. Special-hazard fires can be assigned to this class, as can fires in occupancies with concentrations of combustibles separated by sufficiently wide aisles. The minimum aisle width to prevent lateral spread (by radiation), W_{min}, can be estimated from an equation[2] for radiant flux from a fire and a (conservatively low) value for the ignition flux of most materials (1.8 $Btu/ft^2/sec$ or 20.4 kW/m^2):

$$W_{min}(\text{ft}) = 0.13\ [Q\ (\text{Btu/sec})]^{1/2} \qquad (1)$$

For example, if the predicted maximum fire size is 30,000 Btu/sec (31,600 kW), the aisle width should be at least 24 ft (7.3 m). Table 18.4.1 contains examples of heat release data, expressed as Btu per second per ft^2 of floor area. To obtain heat release in Btu per second, a number in the table is multiplied by the floor area underneath the combustible.

Continuous-Growth Fires. These are fires that can be expected to grow indefinitely until intervention by fire fighters (Figure 18.4.5). Starting after an incubation period, the heat release rate of these fires grows continuously, proportional to the square of time, sometimes referred to as "t-squared fire growth." The growth time of a given fire is defined as the interval of time between the effective ignition time and the time when the fire reaches an intermediate energy release rate of 1000 Btu/sec (1054 kW). Any reference heat release rate

*The theory and application of venting outlined in this chapter are presented in U.S. customary units. These units reflect the system used in the original research and are consistent with the background materials contained in NFPA 204. For those more familiar with SI units, quantities such as curtain board depth (in m) and heat release rate (in kW) should be converted to the appropriate conventional units (ft and Btu/sec, respectively), using the conversion factors given at the end of this footnote and at various points throughout the text. After conversion, design data should be inserted in unit-dependent formulas to calculate vent areas and mass flow rates. 1 ft = 0.305 m; 1 Btu/sec = 1.054 kW.

TABLE 18.4.1 Heat Release Rates of Some Limited-Growth Fires*

	Btu/sec/ft² of Floor Area
1. Wood pallets, stacked 1½ ft high (6–12% moisture)	120
2. Wood pallets, stacked 5 ft high (6–12% moisture)	340
3. Wood pallets, stacked 10 ft high (6–12% moisture)	600
4. Wood pallets, stacked 15 ft high (6–12% moisture)	900
5. Mailbags, filled, stored 5 ft high	35
6. Cartons, compartmented, stacked 15 ft high	200
7. PE letter trays, filled, stacked 5 ft high on cart	750
8. PE trash barrels in cartons, stacked 15 ft high	260
9. FRP shower stalls in cartons, stacked 15 ft high	110
10. PE bottles packed in Item 6	550
11. PE bottles in cartons, stacked 15 ft high	170
12. PU insulation board, rigid foam, stacked 15 ft high	170
13. PS jars packed in Item 6	1300
14. PS tubs nested in cartons, stacked 14 ft high	450
15. PS toy parts in cartons, stacked 15 ft high	180
16. PS insulation board, rigid foam, stacked 14 ft high	280
17. PVC bottles packed in Item 6	300
18. PP tubs packed in Item 6	380
19. PP and PE film in rolls, stacked 14 ft high	540
20. Methyl alcohol	65
21. Gasoline	200
22. Kerosene	200
23. Diesel oil	170

Note: PE = polyethylene; PS = polystyrene; PVC = polyvinyl chloride; PP = polypropylene; PU = polyurethane; FRP = fiberglass-reinforced polyester.
For SI units: 1 ft = 0.31 m; 1 ft^2 = 0.093 m^2; 1 Btu/sec = 1.054 kW.
*Heat-release rate per unit floor area of fully involved combustibles, assuming 100 percent combustion efficiency.

could have been chosen with a corresponding change in the growth time. The rate 1000 Btu/sec (1054 kW) was chosen for convenience. Mathematically, t-squared fire growth can be expressed as

$$Q \text{ (Btu/sec)} = 1000(t/t_g)^2 \qquad (2)$$

where t is the time in seconds from the effective ignition time and t_g is the growth time in seconds. Table 18.4.2 contains examples of growth times for continuous-growth fires.

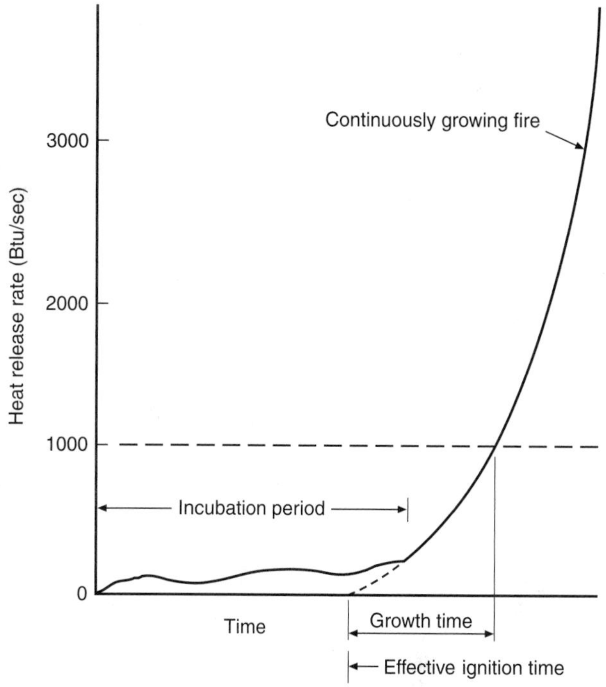

FIGURE 18.4.5 Conceptual Illustration of Continuous Fire Growth

INSTALLED VENT AREA

Limited-Growth Fires

Using the theory for air entrainment in fire plumes and gas flow through roof vents presented in NFPA 204, required vent areas can be calculated. Results for the minimum recommended curtain depth, 20 percent of the ceiling height, are presented in Figure 18.4.6 for vent area per curtained compartment (in ft^2) versus expected maximum heat release rate (in Btu/sec) of the combustibles underneath the curtained compartment. These curves have been adopted from the 1991 edition of NFPA 204M, which employed the assumption that the base of the fire and the so-called "virtual origin" were both at the floor level. The simplified curves are useful for illustrating results of venting calculations and issues. Several ceiling heights in the range 15 ft to 60 ft (4.6 m to 18.3 m) are represented. An aerodynamic discharge coefficient of 0.6 has been assumed, which is normal for commercial unit vents. If the discharge coefficient is different from 0.6, the recommended vent areas need to be multiplied by the ratio of 0.6 to the actual discharge coefficient.

For each ceiling height in Figure 18.4.6, the respective curve begins at a heat release rate where vents operated by fusible links rated at 100°F (37.8°C) to 220°F (104°C) above ambient are first expected to operate promptly. Furthermore, for each ceiling height, the respective curve terminates near a heat-release rate, Q_{feasible}, beyond which the feasibility of roof venting, using the present approach, might be questioned. Q_{feasible} can be estimated from the equation

$$Q_{\text{feasible}} \text{ (Btu/sec)} = 1130(H - d)^{5/2} \qquad (3)$$

TABLE 18.4.2 Growth Times of Some Continuous-Growth Fires*

	Growth Time (sec)
1. Wood pallets, stacked 1½ ft high (6–12% moisture)	160–320
2. Wood pallets, stacked 5 ft high (6–12% moisture)	95–190
3. Wood pallets, stacked 10 ft high (6–12% moisture)	80–120
4. Wood pallets, stacked 16 ft high (6–12% moisture)	75–120
5. Mail bags, filled, stored 5 ft high	190
6. Cartons, compartmented, stacked 15 ft high	60
7. Paper, vertical rolls, stacked 20 ft high	17–27
8. Cotton (also Pe, Pe/Cot Acrylic/Nylon/Pe), garments in 12-ft-high rack	22–43
9. "Ordinary combustibles" rack storage, 15–30 ft high	40–270
10. Paper products, densely packed in cartons, rack storage, 20 ft high	470
11. PE letter trays, filled, stacked 5 ft high on cart	190
12. PE trash barrels in cartons, stacked 15 ft high	55
13. FRP shower stalls in cartons, stacked 15 ft high	85
14. PE bottles packed in Item 6	85
15. PE bottles in cartons, stacked 15 ft high	75
16. PE pallets, stacked 3 ft high	150
17. PE pallets, stacked 6–8 ft high	32–56
18. PU mattress, single, horizontal	120
19. PU insulation board, rigid foam, stacked 15 ft high	8
20. PS jars packed in Item 6	55
21. PS tubs nested in cartons, stacked 14 ft high	110
22. PS toy parts in cartons, stacked 15 ft high	120
23. PS insulation board, rigid foam, stacked 14 ft high	7
24. PVC bottles packed in Item 6	9
25. PP tubs packed in Item 6	10
26. PP and PE film in rolls, stacked 14 ft high	40
27. Distilled spirits in barrels, stacked 20 ft high	25–40

Note: Pe = polyester; Cot = cotton; PE = polyethylene; PS = polystyrene; PVC = polyvinyl chloride; PP = polypropylene; PU = polyurethane; FRP = fiberglass-reinforced polyester.
For SI units: 1 ft = 0.305 m.
*Growth times of developing fires in various combustibles, assuming 100 percent combustion efficiency.

where H is the ceiling height and d is the curtain depth ($0.2H$ in this case). At $Q_{feasible}$, the fire may become controlled by the ventilation rate allowed by the roof vents. Ventilation-controlled fires do not support a clear layer. Venting at heat release rates greater than $Q_{feasible}$ to maintain a clear layer

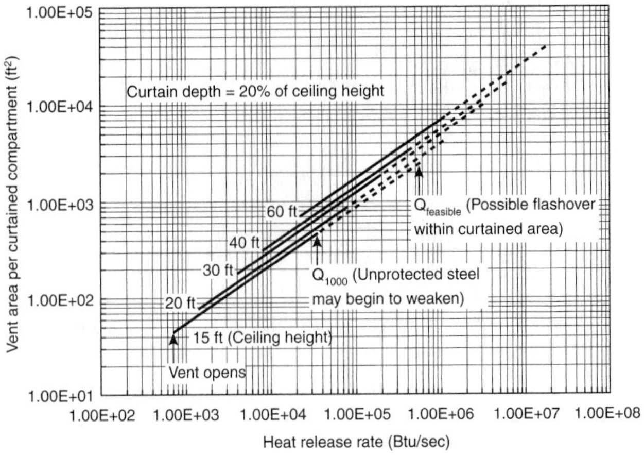

FIGURE 18.4.6 Limited Fire Growth: Recommended Vent Areas for Each Curtained Compartment for Various Maximum Heat Release Rates (Btu/sec)

would require larger vent areas than indicated in Figure 18.4.6.

Along the dashed segments of the curves in Figure 18.4.6, gas temperatures in excess of 1000°F (538°C) may be reached; unprotected structural steel may begin to lose strength and the possibility of flashover exists within the curtained area. The lowest rate of heat release at which this may occur, Q_{1000}, has been estimated from the equation

$$Q_{1000}\ \text{(Btu/sec)} = 69(H - d)^{5/2} \qquad (4)$$

where, in the case of Figure 18.4.6, $d = 0.2H$.

For curtain depths greater than 20 percent of the ceiling height, the vent areas read from Figure 18.4.6 may be multiplied by the factors indicated in Table 18.4.3. New values for $Q_{feasible}$ and Q_{1000} can be calculated using Equations 3 and 4, respectively, by inserting the appropriate values of H and d.

Continuous-Growth Fires

Required vent areas for each curtained compartment for fires in this class depend on ceiling height (H), growth time, spacing of

TABLE 18.4.3 Multiplication Factors for Vent Areas in Figure 18.4.6 for Curtain Depths Other Than 20 Percent of Ceiling Height

Curtain Depth as Percent of Ceiling Height	*Multiplication Factor*
30	0.71
40	0.53
50	0.40
60	0.29
70	0.20
80	0.13

curtain boards (S_c) vent spacing, and means of vent actuation. They also depend on the desired minimum clear visibility time from the time the first vents operate. The minimum clear visibility design time will facilitate such activities as locating the fire, appraising the severity and extent of the fire, evacuating the building, and making an informed decision on deployment of personnel and equipment to be used for fire fighting.

Table 18.4.4 has been adapted from the 1991 edition of NFPA 204M (base of fire and virtual origin at floor level), and the values are limited to the minimum recommended curtain depth, 20 percent of the ceiling height. Table 18.4.4 lists vent areas per curtained compartment for vents spaced at no more than one-half the curtain board spacing. For other than square curtains, the spacing S_c is interpreted as the largest spacing defined by the curtained area. The tabulated areas are approximate, pertaining to vents that are operated by heat-responsive devices of an average response-time index (RTI) of 520 $(\text{ft·sec})^{1/2}$ [287 $(\text{m·sec})^{1/2}$] and rated between 100°F (37.8°C) and 220°F (104°C) above ambient temperature.[3,4] Each entry in the table gives the range of vent areas in 1000 ft^2 (92.9 m^2) associated with the selected range of temperature ratings. Boxed entries are not possible (since the vent areas exceed the largest possible curtained area of $S_c \times S_c$); however, these entries may be needed for curtain depths greater than 20 percent of ceiling height, as treated later in this chapter.

TABLE 18.4.4 Vent Areas for Curtained Compartments*

Ceiling Height, H	*Growth Time (sec)*	$S_c = 2 \times H$			$S_c = 4 \times H$			$S_c = 8 \times H$		
		5 min	*10 min*	*15 min*	*5 min*	*10 min*	*15 min*	*5 min*	*10 min*	*15 min*
15 ft	20				(1.9–2.1)			(2.2–2.5)		
	40	0.87–0.97			(0.98–1.1)	(1.8–2.0)		(1.1–1.4)	(2.0–2.3)	
	80	(0.44–0.52)	(0.82–0.90)		(0.52–0.64)	(0.90–1.0)	(1.3–1.4)	(0.64–0.83)	(1.0–1.2)	(1.5–1.7)
	150	0.25–0.32	(0.43–0.50)	(0.63–0.70)	0.31–0.41	(0.50–0.60)	(.70–.80)	(0.41–0.58)	(.60–.77)	(0.81–0.98)
	300	0.15–0.20	0.23–0.29	0.32–0.38	0.20–0.28	0.28–0.36	0.37–0.46	0.27–0.41	0.36–0.51	(0.46–0.61)
	600	0.10–0.14	0.13–0.18	0.17–0.23	0.13–0.21	0.17–0.25	0.21–0.29	0.20–0.34	0.24–0.38	0.29–0.43
20 ft	20	2.2–7.3			(2.5–2.7)			(2.7–3.2)		
	40	(1.1–1.2)	2.1–2.2		(1.2–1.5)	(2.2–2.5)	(3.3–3.6)	(1.5–1.8)	(2.5–2.9)	(3.6–4.0)
	80	0.56–0.68	(1.0–1.1)	1.5–1.6	0.68–0.86	(1.1–1.3)	(1.6–1.8)	(0.87–1.2)	(1.3–1.6)	(1.8–2.1)
	150	0.34–0.43	0.55–0.65	(0.77–0.88)	0.43–0.58	0.64–0.80	(0.88–1.0)	0.58–0.83	(0.80–1.1)	(1.0–1.3)
	300	0.21–0.29	0.30–0.39	0.40–0.50	0.28–0.41	0.38–0.52	0.48–0.63	0.40–0.65	0.51–0.76	0.62–0.88
	600	0.14–0.22	0.19–0.27	0.23–0.32	0.20–0.33	0.25–0.38	0.30–0.44	0.32–0.56	0.37–0.61	0.42–0.67
30 ft	20	(2.9–3.2)	5.6–6.0		(3.2–3.8)	(6.0–6.6)		(3.8–4.6)	(6.7–7.6)	
	40	1.5–1.8	(2.7–3.0)	4.0–4.3	(1.8–2.2)	(3.0–3.4)	(4.3–4.8)	(2.2–2.9)	(3.5–4.2)	(4.8–5.6)
	80	0.82–1.0	1.4–1.6	(2.0–2.2)	1.0–1.4	1.6–2.0	(2.2–2.6)	1.4–2.0	(2.0–2.6)	(2.6–3.2)
	150	0.51–0.71	0.78–0.99	1.1–1.3	0.68–0.99	0.96–1.3	1.3–1.6	0.97–1.5	1.3–1.8	(1.6–2.2)
	300	0.34–0.53	0.47–0.66	0.59–0.80	0.48–0.77	0.61–0.91	0.74–1.1	0.74–1.3	0.88–1.4	1.0–1.6
	600	0.26–0.44	0.32–0.50	0.38–0.57	0.38–0.67	0.44–0.74	0.50–0.81	0.62–1.2	0.69–1.2	0.76–1.3
40 ft	20	(3.6–4.1)	6.7–7.3	10–11	(4.1–4.9)	(7.4–8.2)	(11–12)	(5.0–6.3)	(8.3–9.7)	(12–13)
	40	1.9–2.3	(3.3–3.8)	(4.8–5.3)	2.3–3.0	(3.8–4.5)	(5.3–6.1)	(3.0–4.1)	(4.5–5.6)	(6.1–7.3)
	80	1.1–1.5	1.7–2.1	2.4–2.8	1.4–2.0	2.1–2.7	2.8–3.4	2.0–3.0	2.7–3.7	(3.4–4.5)
	150	0.72–1.1	1.0–1.4	1.4–1.8	0.98–1.5	1.3–1.9	1.7–2.2	1.5–2.4	1.8–2.8	2.2–3.2
	300	0.51–0.84	0.66–1.0	0.81–1.2	0.74–1.3	0.89–1.4	1.1–1.6	1.2–2.2	1.4–2.3	1.5–2.5
	600	0.41–0.74	0.48–0.81	0.55–0.89	0.61–1.1	0.69–1.2	0.77–1.3	1.1–2.0	1.1–2.1	1.2–2.2
60 ft	20	4.9–5.9	(8.9–10)	(13–14)	5.9–7.4	(10–12)	(14–16)	(7.5–10)	(12–14)	(16–19)
	40	2.8–3.6	4.6–5.5	6.5–7.4	3.5–4.8	5.4–6.7	(7.3–8.8)	4.8–7.0	(6.7–9.1)	(8.7–11)
	80	1.7–2.5	2.5–3.4	3.4–4.3	2.3–3.5	3.2–4.4	4.1–5.4	3.4–5.6	4.3–6.6	5.2–7.6
	150	1.2–2.0	1.6–2.4	2.1–2.9	1.7–2.9	2.2–3.4	2.6–3.9	2.8–4.9	3.2–5.4	3.7–5.9
	300	0.95–1.7	1.2–1.9	1.3–2.1	1.4–2.6	1.6–2.8	1.8–3.1	2.4–4.6	2.6–4.8	2.9–5.1
	600	0.82–1.6	0.92–1.7	1.0–1.8	1.3–2.4	1.4–2.6	1.5–2.7	2.2–4.4	2.3–4.5	2.5–4.6

Notes:
1. Vents are assumed to be spaced at one-half of the curtain board spacing.
2. Curtain depth assumed at 20 percent of ceiling height.
3. Each entry is the vent-area range (in 1000 ft^2) associated with heat-responsive devices rated between 100 and 220°F (37.8 and 104°C) above ambient temperature.
4. No entries: Heat release rates greater than Q_{feasible}.
5. Entries boxed-in: Not possible, but needed for curtain depths greater than 20 percent.
6. Entries in parentheses: Correspond to levels of heat release greater than Q_{1000}.

For SI units: 1 ft = 0.305 m; 1 ft^2 = 0.093 m^2.

*Vent area (in 1000 ft^2) per curtained compartment for heat-responsive device-operated vents with various curtain board spacings (S_c) and minimum clear-visibility design times (5, 10, or 15 min).

Where values are not given, heat-release rates are greater than $Q_{feasible}$, as given in Equation 3; the vent area associated with $Q_{feasible}$ is $A_{feasible}$, which has been calculated from the following equation from the 1991 edition of NFPA 204M:

$$A_{feasible}\ (ft^2) = 8.5(H - d)^{5/2}/d^{1/2} \quad (5)$$

where, in the case of Table 18.4.4, $d = 0.2H$. Entries in parentheses in the table correspond to levels of heat release greater than Q_{1000}, as given in Equation 4. The vent area associated with Q_{1000} is A_{1000}, which has been calculated from the following equation from the 1991 edition of NFPA 204M:

$$A_{1000}\ (ft^2) = 1.6(H - d)^{5/2}/d^{1/2} \quad (6)$$

where, in the case of Table 18.4.4, $d = 0.2H$.

To illustrate the use of Table 18.4.4, consider an installation with heat-responsive devices rated approximately 100°F (37.8°C) above ambient, a ceiling height of 20 ft (6.1 m), a growth time of approximately 150 seconds, a (square) curtain spacing of 80 ft or 24.4 m ($S_c = 4 \times H$), a curtain depth of 4 ft or 1.2 m (4/20 = 20 percent of ceiling height), and a minimum clear visibility time of 10 minutes. In Table 18.4.4, the lower limit 100°F (37.8°C) of the appropriate entry indicates a vent area per curtained compartment of 0.64 × 1000 = 640 ft² (59.5 m²) for this case.

The recommended vent area for each curtained compartment is reduced if larger curtain depths than minimum (20 percent of ceiling height) are installed. The reduced areas are calculated by multiplying the values listed in Table 18.4.4 by the appropriate multiplication factor listed in Table 18.4.3. To determine if Note 4 or 6 from Table 18.4.4 applies to the newly derived values for vent area, the value of $A_{feasible}$ associated with $Q_{feasible}$ is calculated from Equation 5, and the value of A_{1000} associated with Q_{1000} is calculated from Equation 6. Note 4 applies if a vent area is larger than $A_{feasible}$, and Note 6 applies if a vent area is larger than A_{1000}.

Vent areas for each curtained compartment should be distributed among individual vents within the constraints discussed in the subsection "Dimensioning and Spacing of Vents," earlier in this chapter. In some cases, the calculated number of vents may be so large that the vent spacing will be considerably smaller than the design spacing for vents assumed in Table 18.4.4 (½S_c) The closer vent spacing implies earlier operation of the first vents than is the case for the designs of Table 18.4.4. Earlier operation, such as that provided by an auxiliary fire detection system, would provide extra clear visibility times beyond the values of 5, 10, and 15 minutes selected in Table 18.4.4. The extra time available with vents spaced at less than ½S_c may be considered to represent a safety factor.

Selection of Design Basis

The vent area in a curtained compartment need not exceed the vent area recommended for the largest limited-growth fire predicted for combustibles beneath the curtained area. Using sufficiently small concentrations of combustibles and minimum aisle widths according to Equation 1, it may be possible to satisfy the venting needs using smaller vent areas than required by a continuous-growth fire vent design. For example, in the illustration discussed previously for the use of Table 18.4.4, the continuous-growth fire vent design for a growth time of 150 seconds led to a required vent area for each curtained compartment of 640 ft² (59.5 m²). A limited-growth fire vent design for a 50 ft² (4.7 m²) floor area concentration at 200 Btu/sec per ft² (2271 kW/m²) (if that is the heat release rate per unit floor area of the combustible considered) involves a total heat release rate per fuel concentration of 10,000 Btu/sec (10,540 kW) and a minimum aisle width of 14 ft (4.3 m), according to Equation 1. For the relevant vent parameters of a ceiling height of 20 ft (6.1 m), curtain depth at 20 percent of ceiling height, and heat release rate of 10,000 Btu/sec (10,540 kW), Figure 18.4.6 indicates a vent area per curtained compartment of 250 ft² (23.2 m²), which is considerably smaller than the 640 ft² (59.5 m²) vent area according to the design for continuous-growth fire. Of course, the combustible and floor area concentrations must be carefully controlled when limited-growth fire vent designs are selected. Furthermore, designs incorporating heat release rates greater than Q_{1000} are risky, since the fire may flash over to all the combustibles under the curtained area. Such designs should be based on the potential heat release rate of all the combustibles under the curtained area and should not be attempted at all if the resulting heat release rate approaches $Q_{feasible}$. For continuous-growth fires, designs giving vent areas greater than A_{1000} cannot be recommended because of the flashover potential.

Mechanical Ventilators

For mechanical venting systems capable of functioning under the expected fire exposure, recommended exhaust capacities per curtained compartments are obtained by simple conversion from the recommended vent areas per curtained compartment. The conversion depends on the depth of the curtain board or the design depth of the smoke layer, according to Table 18.4.5. To avoid plugholing (i.e., inclusion of clear air from below the smoke layer in the vent flow), the exhaust flow (SCFM) for a vent should not exceed a maximum rate:

$$SCFM_{max} = 452 d^{5/2} \left[\frac{T_o}{T_s} \left(1 - \frac{T_o}{T_s} \right) \right]^{1/2} \quad (7)$$

TABLE 18.4.5 Conversion from Vent Area of Gravity Vents to Equivalent Mechanical Exhaust Capacity

Curtain Depth (ft)	*Mechanical Exhaust Capacity per Unit Area of Gravity Vent (SCFM*/ft²)*
6	354
8	409
10	457
12	501
16	578
20	647
24	708

For SI units: 1 ft = 0.305 m; 1 ft² = 0.093 m².
*SCFM = Standard cubic ft per min (standard temperature and pressure).

where d is the depth of the smoke layer (ft), T_0 is the ambient temperature (°R), and T_s is the smoke layer temperature (°R).

ELEMENTS OF VENTING THEORY

To stop the descent of a smoke layer, the mass flow rate of hot gas out of the vents, $\dot{m}_v$, must match the mass injection rate of gas by the fire plume at the interface with the smoke layer, $\dot{m}_P$ (Figure 18.4.7). Therefore, expressions are needed for the vent flow and for the plume flow.

Vent Flow

The vent flow for sufficiently large area of inlet opening (see NFPA 204 for effect of restricted inlet area) can be calculated from the following equation:[5,6]

$$\dot{m}_v = (2\rho_o^2 g)^{1/2} \left[\frac{T_o(T_s - T_o)}{T_s^2} \right]^{1/2} A_v d^{1/2} \qquad (8)$$

where $\dot{m}_v$ is the mass flow rate through the vent (lb/sec or kg/sec); ρ_o is the density of the ambient air (lb/ft^3 or kg/m^3); g is the acceleration of gravity (ft/sec^2 or m/sec^2); T_o is the ambient temperature (°R or K); T_s is the smoke layer temperature (°R or K); A_v is the aerodynamic vent area (ft^2 or m^2); and d is the depth of the smoke layer (ft or m), generally interpreted as the height of the center of the vent above the smoke interface.

The aerodynamic vent area, A_v, is always smaller than the geometric vent area. For simple apertures, A_v may be taken as 0.6 times the geometric through-flow area.

The temperature function $\left[\frac{T_o(T_s - T_o)}{T_s^2} \right]^{1/2}$ can be approximated at 0.50 for smoke layer temperatures in the range of 275 to 1400°F (135 to 760°C), which covers most vent applications. Then Equation 8 becomes simply

$$\dot{m}_v = (\rho_o^2 g)^{1/2} A_v d^{1/2} \qquad (9)$$

To prevent air from the clear layer below from being entrained in the vent exhaust (plugholing), the area of the vent should not exceed $2d^2$.[7] If the vent is long and narrow, an analogous requirement would be that the width of the vent not exceed d.

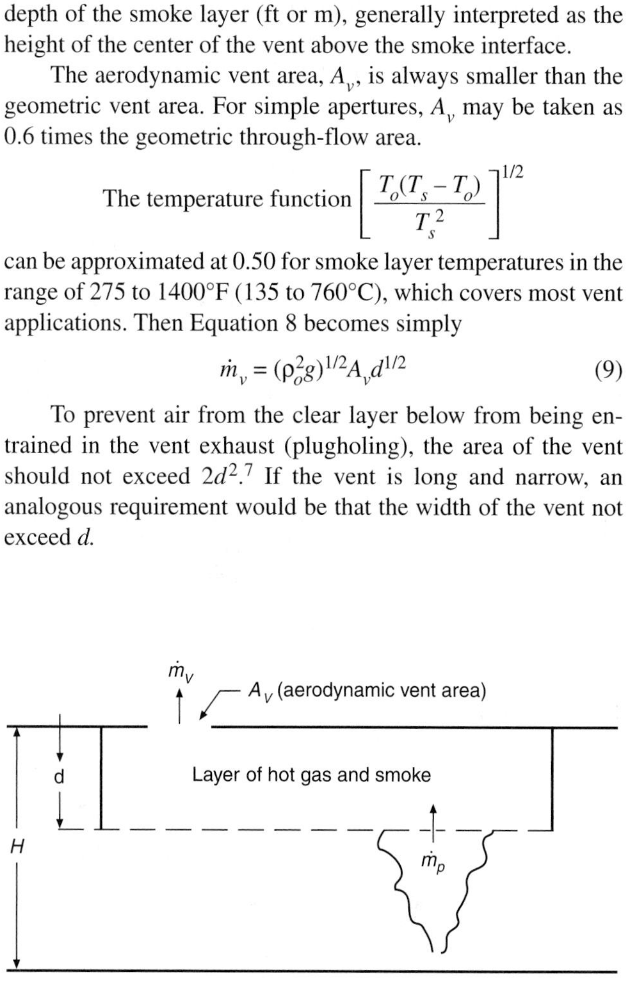

FIGURE 18.4.7 Schematic of a Venting System

Plume Flow

The mass flow rate injected into the smoke layer by the fire plume is practically equal to the air entrainment rate of the plume from the clear layer; the contribution of the fire source itself is small in comparison. The equations presented here are based on the updated engineering relations of NFPA 204, rather than the simplified equations of the 1991 edition of NFPA 204M.

The plume flow, $\dot{m}_p$, is calculated according to either of two equations, depending on whether the mean flame height is below the smoke layer (interpreted as below the curtain boards) or has entered the smoke layer (interpreted as at or above the bottom of the curtain boards). The mean flame height is calculated from

$$L = -1.02D + 0.79Q^{2/5} \qquad (10)$$

where

L = Mean flame height above the base of the fire (ft)

D = Base diameter of fire (ft)

Q = Total heat release rate (Btu/sec)

When the mean flame height is below the smoke layer ($L < H - d$) the plume flow into the smoke layer is calculated from

$$\dot{m}_p = 0.022Q_c^{1/3}(H - d - z_0)^{5/3}[1 + 0.20Q_c^{2/3}(H - d - z_0)^{-5/3}] \qquad (11)$$

where

$\dot{m}_p$ = Mass flow rate into the smoke layer (lb/sec)

Q_c = Convective heat release rate (approx. 0.7 Q) (Btu/sec)

z_0 = Height of virtual origin above base of fire (below the base if negative) (ft) calculated from

$$z_0 = 0.28Q^{2/5} - 1.02D \qquad (12)$$

When the mean flame height reaches into the smoke layer ($L \geq H - d$),

$$\dot{m}_p = 0.0130Q_c(H - d)/L \qquad (13)$$

Note that when the flames are just entering ($L = H - d$),

$$\dot{m}_p = 0.0130Q_c \qquad (14)$$

For continuous-growth fires, the instantaneous fire diameter D in Equations 10 and 12 can be calculated from the instantaneous heat release rate, Q, and data on the heat release rate per unit floor area, Q'' (according to listings such as Table 18.4.2):

$$D = \left(\frac{4Q}{\pi Q''} \right)^{1/2} \qquad (15)$$

Required Vent Area

For $L < H - d$, the expression for $\dot{m}_p$ in Equation 11 is set equal to the expression for $\dot{m}_v$ in Equation 9 and solved for A_v, the aerodynamic vent area. For $L \geq H - d$, the expression for $\dot{m}_p$ in Equation 13 is set equal to the expression for $\dot{m}_v$ in Equation 9 and solved for A_v. The aerodynamic vent area, A_v, is divided by the vent discharge coefficient, usually 0.6, to establish the geometric vent area.

For continuous-growth fires, the vent area is calculated for the fire conditions prevailing at the time $t = t_d + t_r$, where t_d is the detection time (often, but not necessarily, the actuation time of the first vent) and t_r may be selected to correspond to various critical events ("clear-visibility time" in context of Table 18.4.4):

1. Arrival of emergency response team
2. Arrival of fire fighters from the public fire department
3. Completion of evacuation
4. Other critical events

Detection times (t_d) for heat responsive devices (fusible links, heat detectors) can be calculated for t-squared fires, using a thermal response equation for heat responsive devices[3,4] together with generalized data on gas temperatures and velocities under flat ceilings.[8]

Limiting Heat Release Rates

Q_{1000} was defined in conjunction with Equation 4 as the heat release rate at which gas temperatures in excess of 1000°F (538°C) may be reached with possible weakening of structural steel and potentials for flashover within the curtained areas. The expression for Q_{1000} was derived first using Equation 13, with substitution for L from Equation 10 (suppressing $-1.02D$, which usually makes a relatively small contribution to the calculated value of L, and setting $Q_c = 0.7Q$), to obtain $\dot{m}_p$ expressed as

$$\dot{m}_p\,(\text{lb/sec}) = 0.0143(H - d)Q_c^{3/5} \tag{16}$$

where Q_c is in Btu/sec, and H and d are in ft.

The average temperature rise in the smoke layer, ΔT_s (°F), follows from

$$\dot{m}_p c_p \Delta T_s = \lambda Q_c \tag{17}$$

where c_p (Btu/lb/°F or kJ/kg/K) is the specific heat of air and λ is the surviving fraction of convective heat after heat loss to the ceiling and walls. With substitution of Equation 16 for $\dot{m}_p$, $c_p = 0.24$ Btu/lb/°F (1.00 kJ/kg/K) and $\Delta T = 1000$°F (538°C) in Equation 17, the resulting expression can be solved for Q_c. The result is Equation 4 if it is assumed $\lambda = 0.63$ which is a realistic convective fraction.[9]

Q_{feasible} was described in conjunction with Equation 3 as a heat release rate beyond which the feasibility of roof venting, using the present approach, might be questioned because of the onset of ventilation control of the burning process. Ventilation-controlled fires do not support a clear layer as, for example, in the case of the typical, flashed-over room fire. According to experiments on wood crib fires in enclosures, vented through doors or windows,[10] ventilation control appears to set in when the so-called ventilation parameter, $A_w\sqrt{h_w}$, in ratio to the mass burning rate, R, is less than 266 ft$^{5/2}$/lb/sec, where A_w is the window (or door) area, and h_w is the window (or door) height. Generalized to any combustible, the limiting ratio might be expressed as $A_w\sqrt{h_w}$ in ratio to the stoichiometric air requirement associated with the mass burning rate, Rr, where r is the stoichiometric mass ratio, air to combustible (assumed at 5.5 for wood). Now, the ventilation parameter, $A_w\sqrt{h_w}$, is proportioned to the mass flow rate of air through a window or door opening, $\dot{m}_v$:[11]

$$\dot{m}_v\,(\text{lb/sec}) = 0.064 A_w\sqrt{h_w}. \tag{18}$$

where A_w is in ft^2, and h_w is in ft.

The limiting condition for ventilation control can, therefore, be expressed in terms of the mass venting rate of air in ratio to the stoichiometric air requirement, $\dot{m}_v Rr$, which turns out to be approximately 3. Using the fact that Rr can be written $Q/(\Delta H_c/r)$, where Q is the heat release rate and ΔH_c is the heat of combustion, the limiting mass rate ratio can be converted to a limiting heat release rate:

$$Q = \frac{1}{3}\dot{m}_v(\Delta H_c/r) \tag{19}$$

In application to roof vents, $\dot{m}_v$ can be expressed as in Equation 9. Furthermore, $\Delta H_c/r$ is quite constant among common combustibles. Substituting Equation 9 and taking $\Delta H_c/r =$ 1328 Btu per lb (3086 kJ/kg), Equation 19 becomes:

$$Q\,(\text{Btu/sec})\ 133 A_v d^{1/2} \tag{20}$$

where A_v is in ft^2, and d is in ft.

In the simplified venting approach of the 1991 edition of NFPA 204M, an equation for A_v was presented (Equation 12 in that edition), applicable to heat release rates above a lower limit likely to be exceeded in all practical cases. When this equation is combined with Equation 20, the result is the expression for Q_{feasible} in Equation 3.

SUMMARY

Adequate venting in a building is necessary to prevent the buildup of heat and smoke during a fire, which can severely hamper fire-fighting efforts. Ventilation in industrial buildings is accomplished by the use of unit vents or mechanical ventilators and curtain boards. Unit vents are manufactured specifically to provide ventilation during a fire. Curtain boards contain smoke and heat, and the buildup of heat in the curtained area actuates the venting system. The required vent areas in a building are calculated on the basis of limited-growth fires, which involve maximum heat release rates, versus continuous growth fires, which involve growth times. Information is provided to calculate mechanical exhaust rates equivalent to required vent areas.

BIBLIOGRAPHY

References Cited

1. Heskestad, G., "Model Study of Automatic Smoke and Heat Vent Performance in Sprinklered Fires," Technical Report FMRC 21933, Factory Mutual Research Corporation, Norwood, MA, 1974.
2. Alpert, R. L., and Ward, E. J., "Evaluation of Unsprinklered Fire Hazards," *Fire Safety Journal,* Vol. 7, 1984, pp. 127–143.
3. Heskestad, G., and Smith, H. F., "Plunge Test for Determination of Sprinkler Sensitivity," Technical Report FMRC 3A1E2. RR, Factory Mutual Research Corporation, Norwood, MA, 1980.
4. Heskestad, G., and Bill, R. G., Jr., "Modeling of Thermal Responsiveness of Automatic Sprinklers," *Fire Safety Science—*

Proceedings of the Second International Symposium, 1989, Hemisphere Publishing Corporation, New York, pp. 603–612.
5. Thomas, P. H., et al., "Investigations into the Flow of Hot Gases in Roof Venting," Fire Research Technical Paper No. 7, Department of Scientific and Industrial Research and Fire Offices' Committee, Joint Fire Research Organization, Her Majesty's Stationery Office, London, UK, 1963.
6. Thomas, P. H., and Hinkley, P. L., "Design of Roof-Venting Systems for Single-Story Buildings," Fire Research Technical Paper No. 10, Department of Scientific and Industrial Research and Fire Offices' Committee, Joint Fire Research Organization, Her Majesty's Stationery Office, London, UK, 1964.
7. Thomas, P. H., and Hinkley, P. L., "Design of Roof-Venting Systems," Department of Scientific and Industrial Research and Fire Offices' Committee, Joint Fire Research Organization, Her Majesty's Stationery Office, London, UK.
8. Heskestad, G., and Delichatsios, M. A., "Update: The Initial Convective Flow in Fire," *Fire Safety Journal,* Vol. 15, 1989, pp. 471–475.
9. Heskestad, G., "Volume Expansion Pressures and Global Heat Transfer in Compartment Fires," *Twenty-Fourth Symposium (International) on Combustion,* The Combustion Institute, Pittsburgh, PA, pp. 1753–1760, 1992.
10. Croce, P. A., "Modeling of Vented Enclosure Fires, Part I: Quasi-Steady Wood-Crib Source Fire," Technical Report FMRC 7A0R5.GU, Factory Mutual Research Corporation, Norwood, MA, 1978.
11. Harmathy, T. Z., "Ventilation of Fully-Developed Compartment Fires," *Combustion and Flame,* Vol. 37, 1980, pp. 25–39.

NFPA Codes, Standards, and Recommended Practices

Reference to the following NFPA codes, standards, and recommended practices will provide further information on venting practices discussed in this chapter. (See the latest version of The NFPA Catalog *for availability of current editions of the following documents.)*

NFPA 204, *Standard for Smoke and Heat Venting*

ADDENDUM

AUTOMATIC HEAT AND SMOKE VENTING IN SPRINKLERED BUILDINGS

This addendum supplements the venting practices in this chapter as written by Dr. Heskestad. It presents in summary the various views on the controversial and unresolved subject of automatic venting in sprinklered buildings. The history of research testing on the subject is traced. Original contributors (sixteenth edition, 1986) include Ernest E. Miller, Thomas E. Waterman, and Edward J. Ward.* The author has expanded the section "New Sprinkler/Vent Research," which he wrote for the eighteenth edition of the *Fire Protection Handbook,* with material on additional research included in the nineteenth edition ("FPRF Program") and new material for this edition from the literature ("New Analysis of Past Studies").The updated section is headed "More Recent Sprinkler/Vent Research and Analysis".

*Ernest E. Miller was an executive engineer with Industrial Risk Insurance (IRI) at the time he contributed his views. Thomas E. Waterman was employed by the IIT Research Institute and conducted the IITRI test series of 1980–1981. Edward J. Ward was employed by Factory Mutual Research Corporation.

Differing Views

There has been controversy for more than four decades over automatic venting for sprinklered buildings.

Proponents of automatic venting in sprinklered buildings claim that venting will aid manual fire fighting by delaying loss of visibility, reduce the risk of structural failure by venting gases with dangerously high temperatures, vent the equivalent of an unsprinklered fire if the installed sprinklers are defeated by human failure or mechanical damage, and substitute for manual roof venting by fire service personnel.

Opponents believe that, in some cases, venting may be detrimental because it draws in fresh makeup air, keeping oxygen levels higher than they would be otherwise, causing more vigorous combustion with an increase in fuel consumption, and creating potential for loss of sprinkler control. They also believe sprinkler discharge will cool the fire gases, perhaps to the extent that the vent discharge is reduced, hence reducing venting effectiveness. Further, the sprinkler sprays will entrain ambient smoke and air, transporting smoke to the floor level and possibly drawing gas from the vent exhaust wherever sprinklers are located close to vents and further reducing venting effectiveness. Additionally, opponents see little, if any, evidence from research testing of the benefit to fire control obtained from the use of vents in a sprinklered building and believe that the high cost of installation does not justify their use.

Sprinkler/Vent Research

Research testing on the subject includes large-scale tests, FMRC model study, other FMRC large-scale testing, and IITRI full-scale venting research testing.

Large-Scale Tests. In 1956 Factory Mutual Research Corporation (FMRC), now FM Global, ran a series of large-scale tests from which it concluded that the effects of venting in sprinklered buildings are different from those in unsprinklered buildings. The research project[1] was conducted in a 120- by 60-ft (36.6- by 18.3-m) test building equipped with 5 ft (1.5 m) draft curtains and vent areas ranging up to 32 ft^2 (3 m^2) within a curtained area of 2280 ft^2 (212 m^2). This is a vent ratio of about 1:70—that is, 1 ft^2 (0.093 m^2) of vent area for every 70 ft^2 (6.5 m^2) of floor area. A 5-gal/min (18.9-L/min) gasoline spray fire was used as the exposure, and protection consisted of 160°F (71°C) automatic sprinklers installed on a 10 ft by 10 ft (3 m by 3 m) spacing.

The tests in the series were conducted using various combinations of vents, draft curtains, and sprinklers. Six of these were sprinklered tests (Table 18.4.6).

Comparison of average temperatures indicates that vents contributed significantly to temperature reductions in the unsprinklered tests in the series; however, they were of marginal value in the sprinklered tests. The greatest reduction in sprinkler operation was attributed to increased sprinkler discharge.

FMRC Model Study. In the early 1970s, an FMRC study was conducted.[2] The objective was to investigate experimentally the performance of automatic heat and smoke vents in sprinklered

TABLE 18.4.6 FMRC Test Results

Test Number	*Curtain ft (m)*	*Vent ft^2 (m^2)*	*Sprinkler Discharge gpm (L/min)*	*Number of Sprinklers Operated*
1	None	None	15 (57)	48
2	None	32 (3.0)	15 (57)	44
3	5 (1.5)	32 (3.0)	15 (57)	24
4	5 (1.5)	16 (1.5)	15 (57)	24
5	5 (1.5)	None	15 (57)	28
6	5 (1.5)	None	25 (95)	15

fires in one-story buildings, principally in terms of sprinkler water demand, but also in terms of visibility conditions and fuel consumption. The study was performed at FMRC's Norwood, Massachusetts, laboratory and involved a 1:12.5 scale model of FMRC's fire test facility at West Gloucester, Rhode Island. Automatic, individually fused vents on 50 ft (15.2 m) spacing were employed, often in combination with a draft curtain encompassing a 10,000 ft^2 (929 m^2) curtained area.

Of primary interest were venting installations conforming to recommendations of standards-setting groups that were state of the art at the time. For a fire in cellulosic material that opened about fifty 212°F (100°C) sprinklers at a density of 0.27 gpm per ft^2 [11 (L/min)/m^2], distributed vents alone (without draft curtains) had no effect on the water demand but delayed loss of visibility from 13.1 to 15.7 minutes and increased fuel consumption by 31 percent. Vents and draft curtains caused a 35 percent increase in water demand relative to the unvented fire, delayed loss of visibility from 13.1 to 20.2 minutes, and increased fuel consumption by 66 percent.

Favorable effects of venting were observed for a series of large, heptane fires that opened an average of 112 sprinklers at 0.27 gpm per ft^2 [11 (L/min)/m^2]. Vents alone reduced the water demand by 8 percent and markedly improved visibility conditions; vents and draft curtains reduced the water demand by 18 percent but did not improve visibility conditions as much as without draft curtains.

The test results were based on ignition points that were equidistant from the four nearest vents in the vent matrix. Experiments with ignition directly under a vent indicated that some reduction in water demand could be expected for fires that opened fifty sprinklers or less. It was concluded, however, that for randomly started fires, less than about 13 percent of the fires would benefit, respective to water demand, from closeness to a nearby vent.

Critics counter that the 0.08-scale-model experiments, although carefully designed and executed, incorporated numerous uncertainties. Of particular concern was modeling of a full-scale fuel bed (rack storage configuration), by using ½-in. (12.7-mm) thick triwall cardboard. Some 10 years later, the modeling of room fire development has proceeded to an advanced state in all respects, except for the burning fuel; both analytical and experimental models address only the simplest of fuel configurations. Yet the model study assumed that both flame spread and burning rate of the fuel bed were modeled under conditions of depleted oxygen and impacting water droplets.

The FMRC model study was also criticized because of the configuration of the water discharge devices that were used. The study pioneered the use of nondescript miniature nozzles (representing sprinklers) arranged to be operated in small open-head deluge systems of groups of five to eleven nozzles controlled by individual sensors. Critics claim this arrangement magnified the known imprecision in measuring comparative sprinkler performance. It required multiplying the normal spread experienced in full-scale sprinkler operation by a variable factor of 5 to 11. Due to the small deluge systems, which operated as groups, sprinkler skipping occurred in units of five or more open nozzles, rather than the skipping of individual sprinklers as would be customary in full-scale fire research.

Lastly, the critics agreed that, although up to three times as much combustible material was consumed in the vented tests as compared to the unvented tests, the implication of detriment was improper. They claimed the explanation for the increased fuel consumption in the vented tests lies in the customary manner of conducting fire tests involving sprinklers. The test fires are allowed to continue far beyond sprinkler control to give the fires every opportunity to escape. During the additional minutes of these tests, the oxygen reduction in the unvented tests limited the fuel consumption, whereas oxygen remained abundant in the vented tests and resulted in greater fuel consumption. Since sprinkler-controlled fires continue to smolder and burn, it was felt that the reported increased fuel consumption was attributable to more complete burning of the rubble and did not represent increased fire damage. Had the fires spread to involve a significantly larger area, additional sprinklers would have operated.

Other FMRC Large-Scale Testing. More than 80 full-scale rack storage tests were conducted between 1968 and 1975. Only three tests employed perimeter ventilation (not to be confused with roof venting directly over a fire) and only one of these three (No. 72) was identical to two other tests (Nos. 65 and 66), except for the ventilation variable. Results of these tests are given in Table 18.4.7.

Comparing Test Nos. 65 and 66 to Test No. 72, researchers discovered that venting caused a dramatic detriment to the performance of the sprinklers. However, it is pointed out that Test No. 72 had a significantly different initial fire growth behavior compared to the other tests, which may have affected the outcome. FMRC's position on the effects of ventilation in these tests is that they are not conclusive.

TABLE 18.4.7 Rack Storage Tests

Test Number	*Ventilated*	*Number of Ceiling Sprinklers Operated*
65	No	45
66	No	48
72	Yes	92

Venting proponents argue that, although the influence of venting was inconclusive because the perimeter windows were too remote, the ventilated tests maintained visibility for 48:40 and 33:00 (minutes:seconds), as compared to 10:30 and 18:00 for the unventilated tests.

Venting opponents claim the effect of ventilation on fire control was best demonstrated during FMRC's large-scale fire testing of rubber tires in 1970. This test was made to evaluate sprinkler protection for automobile tires stored in portable steel racks. Storage was located in a single pile 35 ft by 50 ft by 18 ft (11 m by 15 m by 5.4 m) high. Protection consisted of 286°F (141°C), ½ in. (12.7 mm) sprinklers, spaced 50 ft^2 (4.6 m^2), each with a controlled discharge of 0.6 gal per minute per ft^2 [24.4 (L/min)/m^2]. There was no ventilation at the start of the test.

The fire was started at the base of a rack. The first sprinkler operated 2 minutes and 15 seconds after ignition. By 8 minutes and 20 seconds, 43 sprinklers had operated and controlled the fire. Only one additional sprinkler operated at 28 minutes. The fire remained under control until 60 minutes into the test, when all doors and windows were opened to ventilate the building and sprinklers were left on. The fire then began to spread and grow in intensity. At 117 minutes, when it was apparent that sprinklers were failing to control the fire, all doors and windows were closed. A total of 95 sprinklers operated, and water was discharged for over 5 hours. Only the ninety-fifth sprinkler operated after doors and windows were closed, and that was at 118 minutes, 1 minute after closure.

Critics reappraised the ventilated rubber tire fire test[3] and contended that the loss of initial sprinkler control was not due to remote window ventilation, as reported. Ceiling temperature gradients revealed that during the hour delay before hose extinguishment of the sprinkler-controlled fire was attempted, the fire had burrowed to the other end of the pile where sprinklers were not operating and had erupted with great intensity. The tightly stacked tires, stored on tread, formed horizontal tunnels that offered avenues of fire spread that were sheltered from sprinkler discharge.

IITRI Full-Scale Venting Research Testing. In 1977, the IITRI was commissioned by the intra-industry Fire Venting Research Committee to review past research and fire experience related to vent/sprinkler interactions in large-area single-story structures. Based on IITRI's review and other considerations, the committee ultimately funded some 45 large-scale segment experiments in 1980–1981.[4] The experiments were conducted in a 75 ft by 25 ft by 17 ft (23 m by 7.6 m by 5.2 m) high portion of IITRI's fire laboratory. Fires were placed in a corner to represent one-quarter of a larger fire in the center of a 150 ft by 50 ft (46 m by 15.2 m) room. To simulate the test area as part of an even larger area, two garage doors on the wall farthest from the fire were partially opened to represent a draft curtain. The area beyond the curtains was also enclosed by vertical air stacks to minimize extraneous wind effects.

To allow variations in vent area, two pairs of automatic roof vents were installed in the laboratory roof. A diagonal sprinkler pattern was chosen to eliminate aisles between sprinklers that were located between the test fires and the vents. Experiments were conducted using propane diffusion burners or stacked pallets as the fuel source. For each fuel source, fire size and sprinkler water supply pressure were varied until a condition of "marginal" sprinkler control was achieved. Then, vent areas were varied to assess effects of venting on sprinkler performance (number of operating sprinklers and temperature levels at various locations). The laboratory size and excessive recirculation of smoke due to the substitution of vertical stacks for added rooms precluded useful measures of smoke obscuration.

Propane-source fires produced results suggesting a slight reduction in water demand for vented fires when either 165 or 286°F (74 or 141°C) sprinklers were employed (vents were operated either with 165°F [74°C] links or by simulated smoke detector or waterflow switch actuation).

All pallet fire experiments employed 165°F (74°C) sprinklers and the same vent arrangement previously described. These experiments demonstrated that, under marginal sprinkler protection, the configuration of the test facility was extremely sensitive to variations in fire intensity from any cause. Once this possibility appeared, a final series of 10 "replicate" experiments was conducted, alternating between vented and unvented configurations. These experiments proved to produce widely varying results, apparently independent of the presence of automatic venting. The number of operating sprinklers varied from 7 to 22 per test, and the pattern of sprinkler operating times appeared unrelated to the time that vents opened. Other measured factors (temperature, O_2) varied in the same way. Although the number of operating sprinklers varied widely in these experiments with marginal sprinkler control, 84 sprinklers operated in the five unvented tests and 85 in the five vented tests. Earlier tests at higher water supply pressures produced good replication, independent of venting.

On the basis of the IITRI experiments, the test sponsors concluded that automatic roof venting did not detract from current state-of-the-art automatic sprinkler performance. Likewise, no particularly significant benefit to sprinkler performance was noted. Thus, it was suggested that automatic vents, if used in sprinklered properties, will perform the following functions:

1. Vent unsprinklered fires, if installed sprinklers are defeated by human failure or mechanical damage
2. Substitute for manual roof venting on arrival of fire service personnel

Primarily on the basis of the first listed application, the researchers recommended that, where they are used for sprinklered properties, the design and installation of automatic roof vents follow guidance provided by NFPA 204 for unsprinklered properties, until further research, testing, or experience suggests more beneficial alternative configurations.

Critics of the IITRI research effort do not agree that the experimental results support the main conclusion of the investigation, which is that automatic roof vents do not impair sprinkler control of fires capable of growth.[5] The critics also claim that the finding that automatic roof vents do not impair the ability of 165°F (74°C) sprinklers to control fires capable of growth contradicts the other studies described here, which have indicated that the increased availability of oxygen associated with open vents may lead to increased fire intensity (of fires capable of growth), water demand, and consumption of combustibles.

The critics concluded that the reported results do not justify the overall conclusions and recommendations of the IITRI researchers. Their critique suggested the investigation suffered from a number of defects: (1) situations claimed to be unvented were not; (2) one of the most important principles of venting was violated (i.e., the provision of adequate openings for inlet air); and (3) inadequate control was exercised over the experimental conditions to the extent that major variations observed in fire behavior could not be attributed to the parameter under study.

Conclusions of the Research

The proponents of automatic venting in a sprinklered building cite the IITRI research work as substantiation of the merit of vents in sprinklered buildings. On the basis of those data, they believe that automatic roof venting can provide two major contributions to 165°F (74°C) sprinkler-protected (large one-story) properties:

1. Perform as vents in unsprinklered properties should installed sprinklers be defeated by human failure or mechanical damage.
2. Substitute for manual roof venting on arrival of the fire services.

The opponents of automatic venting in a sprinklered building believe that the high installation cost of vents is difficult to justify when one considers the limited benefits and possible detriment. They are not cost-effective because it is unlikely that a large loss will be averted solely due to the presence of vents when automatic sprinkler protection is inadequate or impaired.

Venting may or may not be detrimental, depending on many factors, such as the location of the fire origin in relation to the location of vents. More often than not, vents will increase the water demand.[2] Even when automatic vents result in some improvement, the improvement is not required for sprinklers to gain control. Vents can also create conditions that will inhibit or prevent sprinkler control.[5]

Installing automatic vents in unsprinklered buildings is acceptable. It would certainly be more beneficial to the building owner, however, to install sprinklers rather than vents to obtain active rather than passive fire control.

Installing manual vents in a sprinklered building is also acceptable, if desired by the building owner. These vents can be used during manual overhaul or at locations that would be expected to produce dense smoke. However, a similar effect can be achieved by venting through windows, by fire fighters cutting holes in the roof, or by ventilation equipment or smoke exhausters.

Through NFPA's consensus-making standards process, NFPA members agreed to the following statements for the 1985 edition of NFPA 204M:

> A series of tests was conducted to increase the understanding of the role of automatic roof vents simultaneously employed with automatic sprinklers [Section 6-5(c)]. The data submitted did not permit consensus to be developed as to whether sprinkler control was impaired or enhanced by the presence of automatic (roof) vents of typical spacing and area. (Section 6-3)
>
> While the use of automatic venting in sprinklered buildings is still under review, the designer is encouraged to use the available tools and data referenced in this document for solving problems peculiar to a particular type of hazard control. (Section 6-4)

Even though the issue has been argued for years, proponents maintain venting critics have been unable to cite a single fire in which automatic venting was blamed for loss of fire control by sprinklers. Thus, to proponents it is paradoxical that fire research, which is typically motivated only by adverse fire experience, should be the sole basis of suspecting venting to be a detriment. They urge that serious students of venting should obtain and carefully examine this research and compare it with related research, both direct and indirect.

More Recent Sprinkler/Vent Research and Analysis

Ghent Experiments. During the latter part of 1989, the Fire Research Station of the Building Research Establishment (U.K.) and Colt International (together with Verband der Sachversicherer eV and City of Ghent Fire Brigade) undertook a collaborative test program in a unique test building constructed in Ghent, Belgium, the Multifunctioneel Trainingcentrum.[6] The main objective was to validate a theoretical model for predicting the effect of venting on sprinkler operations, but the direct data are being generally used to assess the efficacy of venting in sprinklered buildings.

The test building in Ghent is designed for fire service training purposes and incorporates a hall of the dimensions 164 ft × 59 ft × 33 ft high (50 m × 18 m × 10 m). For the tests, a 10-ft (3.1-m) deep draft curtain was hung from the ceiling, creating a curtained, flat-ceiling area of 89 ft × 59 ft (27 m × 18 m) under which test fires were burned. A total of 20 roof vents, each with an area of 18 ft^2 (1.67 m^2), were installed in this area, centered on a grid measuring 15.9 ft × 14.8 ft (4.85 m × 4.5 m). Sprinklers on a spacing of 12 ft × 8 ft (3.7 m × 2.4 m) were also installed in this area (temperature rating of 155°F [68°C]). The ceiling area on the other side of the draft curtain was provided with 20 roof vents that were always open. A total of 16 inlet vents were installed at ground level in the sides of the building, each having an aerodynamic free area of 33.7 ft^2 (3.1 m^2). As fire sources were used, *n*-hexane floated on water near the floor level. One source had a steady output of 5100 Btu/s (5.4 MW). The other source provided an exponentially growing heat release rate (roughly equivalent to a continuous-growth fire of 50 seconds growth time) until the first sprinkler operated, at which time the heat releaser rate was leveled off (8700 to 12,300 Btu/sec [9.2 to 13.0 MW]).

Note that the vents were very closely spaced (although not all of the vents were used in all the tests) and, furthermore, that the building space on the side of the draft curtain away from the fire was amply ventilated, which may have been factors in the outcome. Other unusual features were that the vents were in effect short chimneys about 5 ft (1.5 m) high and, when venting was used, the vents were open from the start of the test.

The first test series involved the steady fire source. Combinations of 0, 1, and 5 operating sprinklers (at approximately 30 psi [2 bar]) with 0, 10, and 20 open vents were investigated.

With no sprinklers operating, the ceiling gas temperatures decreased significantly with the number of open vents, from 220°F (104°C) to 153°F (67°C) at a 20 ft (6 m) radius from the fire axis when conditions changed from no vents to 20 open vents. With 5 sprinklers operating, the drop in gas temperature at the same location was from 203°F (95°C) with no vents to 130°F (54°C) with 20 open vents. Extensive temperature, velocity, and CO_2 concentration data were recorded.

The second test series involved the growing-fire source and automatic operation of the sprinklers. The number of open vents in a test were mostly 0, 10, or 20, but a few tests were conducted using special patterns of 9 and 16 open vents. The water supply in the first tests was very weak. For the test providing data for this review, the water supply was boosted with a fire pump, yielding a pressure of about 88 psi (6 bar) for one open sprinkler, decaying to about 15 psi (1 bar) for 40 open sprinklers (roughly linear decay with number of open sprinklers). The time of the first sprinkler operation ranged from an average of 148 seconds for no open vents to an average of 160 seconds for 20 open vents. Subsequent sprinkler operations depended on the particular test scenarios, that is, the original, Scenario A, where the fire size was maintained constant to the end of the test at the value when the first sprinkler operated (leading to operations of all installed sprinklers with no open vents), or the revised, Scenario B, where the fire size was maintained constant for 30 seconds and then reduced by 20 percent. In Scenario B, an initial group of 6 sprinklers operated within an interval of 60 seconds for both 10 and 20 open vents, compared to an initial group of 9 sprinklers in the same interval with no vents. With 20 open vents, only one additional sprinkler operated (no additional operations for 10 open vents). With no vents, additional sprinkler operations began about 2 minutes after the first sprinkler operated, accumulating to a final total, nearly 6 minutes from ignition, of 37 sprinklers.

With respect to the issue of visibility through smoke, the report offers the following observation: "In the experiments with growing fires and the pumped supply, the water pressure was higher and the number of operating sprinklers greater than in the experiments with steady fires. There was then some tendency for the fire gases to be pulled down in both vented and unvented experiments." On other issues, the experiments provided no evidence that the flow through the vents was affected by the wind (wind speeds up to 26 ft/sec [7.8 m/sec]), and there were no observable effects of nearby sprinklers on the vent flow (nearest sprinkler about ¾ vent width from any part of the vent opening). The author often finds fair agreement between his theory and the experimental results but identifies areas needing further study, which are issues beyond the scope of this review.

On the effect of venting on sprinkler operations, the report concludes that (1) the prior opening of vents will have little effect on the operation of the first sprinkler with fast growing fires; (2) venting substantially reduced the total number of sprinkler operations; and (3) there was no indication that venting could increase the total number of sprinkler operations.

These conclusions of the report are deemed, by this reviewer, to be highly dependent on the special circumstances of the experiments, primarily (1) the use of a fire source that did not respond in heat output to the sprinkler spray per se, and (2) the fact that even unvented fires were supplied with unvitiated air, arriving from the adjacent, amply ventilated part of the building.

Further to the issue of responsiveness of the fire source to sprinkler spray, Gustafsson[7] observed from the sprinkler operation maps in the report that, in vented tests, sprinklers near the fire source often were delayed or did not operate altogether. Gustafsson makes the point very strongly: "It is clearly seen that the effect of ventilation on the operation of sprinklers was strong and detrimental in all cases. It must be appreciated that prevented or substantially delayed operation of any sprinkler close to, or directly above, the fire must be avoided."

Additional research and testing will be needed before definitively establishing the benefits and detriments of automatic venting in a sprinklered building.

FPRF Program. Large-scale tests to study the interaction of sprinklers, roof vents, and draft curtains were organized by the Fire Protection Research Foundation (FPRF), formerly known as the National Fire Protection Research Foundation (NFPRF), and reported in 1998 by McGrattan et al.[8] The tests were conducted in a building provided with a free-hung test ceiling underneath a fixed ceiling provided with exhaust to an abatement system, which made the tests difficult to interpret for field applications.

The 120 ft by 120 ft (36.6 m by 36.6 m) test building employed a 100 ft by 100 ft (30.5 m by 30.5 m) free-hung ceiling at a height of 27 ft (8.2 m) above the floor, underneath which the fires were burned. Smoke exhausted above the free-hung ceiling to a smoke abatement system, and makeup air entered through duct openings at four locations around the building perimeter, 10 ft (3.1 m) above the floor. Roof vents (4 ft by 8 ft [1.2 m by 1.2 m]), normally operated by fusible links, were installed on 50 ft by 50 ft (15.3 m by 15.3 m) spacing within a 70 ft by 75 ft (21.4 m by 22.9 m) draft-curtained area. Some tests were run without draft curtains.

A series of tests employed *heptane spray fires* with *t*-squared growth to a constant heat release rate of 10 MW in 75 seconds. Smoke exhaust and air supply for the test building were held constant at 24,000 scfm (13.6 kg/sec). Unless a fire was ignited directly under a roof vent, roof venting had no significant effect on sprinkler operations or near-ceiling gas temperatures. Ignitions directly under an automatic roof vent decreased the number of operated sprinklers compared to tests without vents. When 6-ft (1.8-m) deep draft curtains were installed (depth corresponding to 22 percent of the ceiling height), the number of sprinkler operations was considerably larger than without curtains.

Five tests were conducted with a 19-ft (5.8-m) high array of *cartoned plastic commodity.* In these tests, smoke exhaust and air supply for the test building were at a constant 60,000 scfm (34.1 kg/sec), requiring a velocity of make-up air at the building perimeter duct openings of 13 fps (4.0 m/sec). Three of the tests operated 20 to 23 sprinklers, with a potentially higher upper limit since sprinklers operated to the edge of the test ceiling. The remaining two tests operated 5 to 7 sprinklers. This large span was attributed[8] to variability in the initial fire growth and not to any variables under study. One of the tests with ignition near a draft curtain resulted in much larger fuel consumption than the other tests, attributed[8] to fire spread under the draft curtain. In a test in which four vents were opened manually at the same time as the first sprinkler operated, vent flow rate was one-third the expected rate, attributed[8] to reduction in gas temperatures by the sprinklers.

In the test in which four vents were opened manually (series of five tests), the total vent flow rate is estimated from the report[8] to have been only one-quarter the flow rate of the smoke abatement system for these tests (60,000 scfm [34.1 kg/s]). Hence any observations on smoke behavior would be difficult to interpret for field applications. Furthermore, differences in oxygen vitiation and their effects on combustion, vented versus unvented cases, would be much smaller than in many field situations.

The FPRF tests can be summarized as follows:

1. In the heptane spray fires, venting had no significant effect on sprinkler operations unless a fire was ignited directly under a vent, in which case the number of sprinkler operations decreased.
2. When a draft curtain was installed in the heptane spray fires, the number of operating sprinklers increased.
3. In five tests with the cartoned plastic commodity, three tests operated 20 to 23 sprinklers and two tests operated 5 to 7 sprinklers, attributed to variability in the initial fire growth and not to any of the variables under study.
4. One of the tests with ignition near a draft curtain consumed much more fuel than the other tests did, attributed to fire spread under the draft curtain.
5. Effects of venting through roof vents on smoke obscuration could not be determined because of the dominant effect of the building smoke abatement system.

New Analysis of Past Studies

In January 2001 Beyler and Cooper presented a review of past studies deemed to have some relevance to assessing combined use of sprinklers and smoke/heat vents.[9] The authors conclude that (1) venting clearly does not have a negative effect on sprinkler performance, (2) venting limits spread of combustion products, and (3) venting remains a valuable aid to manual control of the fire in the event the sprinklers do not operate. In a letter to the editor following the publication of this paper, Heskestad[10] argues the view that the first two of the authors' conclusions are performance measures that are not met, or not well met, by current technology, based on the studies cited by the authors. With respect to the third conclusion, Heskestad refers to the FM Global position that venting, installed as a backup to an automatic sprinkler system that is inadequate or impaired, is not cost effective because it is unlikely a large loss will be averted solely due to the presence of vents.

Beyler and Cooper[9] recommend that design practice move to methods that ensure early operation of vents, that vent operation be ganged, and that draft curtains be placed over aisles rather than over storage. It is agreed that this recommendation may lead to much improved technology (as reflected in the next-to-last paragraph of the section headed "Historical Background"), but it will require a significant research effort.

ADDENDUM SUMMARY

Automatic venting in sprinklered buildings is a controversial and unresolved subject. Proponents contend that venting will delay loss of visibility, reduce the risk of structural failure by venting gases with dangerously high temperatures, offset problems caused by failure of the sprinkler system, and substitute for manual roof venting by fire fighters. Opponents claim that venting may be detrimental by drawing in fresh makeup air, thus raising oxygen levels and causing more vigorous combustion. Opponents also believe that sprinkler operation would reduce the effectiveness of automatic vents to the point where installation costs would not justify their use.

Research on this dispute has included a large-scale test run by FMRC in 1956, the FMRC model study conducted in the 1970s, more than 80 full-scale rack storage tests carried out by FMRC between 1968 and 1975, and IITRI full-scale testing in 1977. The results of that research failed to resolve the issue, and consensus is yet to be reached. More recent research involves a collaborative test program in Ghent, Belgium, and large-scale tests organized by the FPRF to study the interaction of sprinklers, roof vents, and draft curtains. Again, the results of the research were not conclusive as to the definitive benefits and detriments of automatic venting in sprinklered buildings. A fresh review of past research has suggested benefits, but its conclusions have been challenged.

ADDENDUM BIBLIOGRAPHY

References Cited

1. FMRC, "Heat Vents and Fire Curtains, Effect on Operation of Sprinklers and Visibility," Factory Mutual Research Corporation, Norwood, MA, 1956.
2. Heskestad, G., "Model Study of Automatic Smoke and Heat Vent Performance in Sprinklered Fires," Technical Report FMRC 21933, 1974, Factory Mutual Research Corporation, Norwood, MA, 1974.
3. Miller, E. E., "Reappraisal of Ventilated Rubber Tire Fire Tests," *Fire Venting Mini-Study No. 8,* Industrial Risk Insurers, Chicago, IL, 1982.
4. Waterman, T. E., "Fire Venting of Sprinklered Buildings," *Fire Journal,* Vol. 78, No. 2, 1984, pp. 30–39, 86. (Also see "Letters to the Editor," *Fire Journal,* Vol. 78, No. 5, 1984, p. 6.)
5. Heskestad, G., "Review of 'Fire Venting of Sprinklered Buildings by T. E. Waterman, et al.,' Interoffice Correspondence to E. J. Ward," Factory Mutual Research Corporation, Norwood, MA, 1983. (Also see "Letters to the Editor," *Fire Journal,* Vol. 78, No. 5, 1984, p. 6.)
6. Hinkley, P. L., et al., "Experiments at the Multifunctioneel Trainingcentrum, Ghent, on the Interaction Between Sprinklers and Smoke Venting," Fire Research Station, Building Research Establishment, Borehamwood, Hertfordshire, UK, 1992.
7. Gustafsson, N. E., "Smoke Ventilation and Sprinklers—A Sprinkler Specialist's View," Seminar at the Fire Research Station, Borehamwood, Hertfordshire, UK, 1992.
8. McGrattan, K. B., Hamins, A., and Stroup, D., "International Fire Sprinkler-Smoke and Heat Vent-Draft Curtain Fire Test Project, Large Scale Experiments and Model Development," Technical Report, National Institute of Standards and Technology, prepared for National Fire Protection Research Foundation, September 1998.
9. Beyler, C. L., and Cooper, L. Y., "Interaction of Sprinklers with Smoke and Heat Vents," *Fire Technology,* Vol. 37, 2001, pp. 9–35.
10. Heskestad, G,. Letter to the Editor, *Fire Technology,* Vol. 38, 2002, pp. 207–210.

Chapter 5

Penetration Sealing

John E. Kampmeyer

Chapter Contents

Key Terms

Browns Ferry nuclear power plant fire, fire barrier, fire containment, fire resistance, firestop, health care facility, penetration sealing

As construction for new buildings or renovations to existing buildings are planned, it is important to include fire containment penetration sealing systems, which include through-penetration firestop systems, perimeter fire containment systems, and joint systems. These systems must be properly installed to contain fires and smoke and prevent their spread.

A series of tests has been developed for testing materials in combination with various fire barrier constructions, so that today, the Underwriters Laboratories (UL) Fire Resistance Directory devotes 2975 pages in two volumes to sealing of penetrations. These are divided into the following three categories:

1. *Through-penetration firestop systems.* Used to seal openings where mechanical or electrical systems pass through rated walls or floors
2. *Perimeter fire containment systems.* Used to seal openings between floors and curtain walls
3. *Joint systems.* Used to seal openings where two elements of construction come together such as joints where two walls meet or where two different floor systems meet

For related topics, see Section 12, Chapter 8, "Effect of Building Construction and Fire Protection Systems on Fire Fighter Safety"; Section 18, Chapter 1, "Confinement of Fire in Buildings"; and Section 18, Chapter 3, "Smoke Movement in Buildings."

HISTORICAL BACKGROUND

Prior to 1975, sealing of penetrations through fire-resistant assemblies was relatively simple. Once an opening was made through a fire barrier and a pipe, conduit, or other similar penetrating service was installed, the annular space was filled with a noncombustible material such as mineral wool, fiberglass, or asbestos (before asbestos was known to be a carcinogen).

On March 22, 1975, workers at the Browns Ferry nuclear power plant in northern Alabama were using a candle to check for air leaks at openings in a wall where trays of electrical cables pass from one room to another. As a worker held a candle near one of the openings, the flow of air through it drew the flame toward polyurethane foam that had recently been installed to seal the openings. The foam ignited and fire spread along the cables, shorting out backup safety systems as the cable insulation burned off.[1]

This fire demonstrated that it was not only important to properly seal penetrations to limit the spread of fire, but also to limit the spread of smoke. Previously used materials were found to be inadequate for this purpose. One of the first materials used to provide safer sealing of penetrations was silicone room temperature vulcanizing (RTV) foam, which can withstand high temperatures and confine hazards such as smoke, fire, and gases.

John E. Kampmeyer, P.E., FSNPE, FASHRAE, has practiced both mechanical and fire protection engineering since 1961. He is a senior project engineer at Triad Fire Protection Engineering Corp. in Springfield, Pennsylvania. Mr. Kampmeyer is chairman of NFPA's AEBO Section, a member of the *NFPA 5000*® Technical Committee, and a member of the Smoke Management Committee. He also teaches short courses in fire protection systems, smoke control, mechanical codes, and energy codes.

THROUGH-PENETRATION FIRESTOP SYSTEMS

Through-penetration firestop systems represent the majority of the systems contained in the Underwriters Laboratories Directories. Each system deals with a specific firestop material, penetrating element, and construction system. In order to apply the systems, there are a number of steps that must be developed.

Determining the Fire Barrier Location and Rating

The first step in determining the proper firestop method to be used is to identify the location of the fire barriers and their hourly rating. In new construction projects, these are generally shown on the architectural drawings or, in the case where a fire protection engineer is part of the design team, a separate set of fire barrier drawings may be provided which show their locations and hourly ratings.

In existing construction, there may be little or no guidance from drawings. It will be necessary to study the building and the local building code to determine the locations of fire barriers. In multistory buildings, each floor is generally separated by 1 or 2 hour rated construction, although it could be greater in some cases. Shafts and stairs are generally separated by 1 or 2 hour rated construction depending on the height of the building. Boiler rooms, incinerator rooms, storage rooms over 100 ft^2 (9.3 m^2), paint shops, and maintenance shops will often be separated by 2 hour rated construction. Enclosed corridors used for access to exits, separations between tenants, and separations between dwelling units generally carry a 1 hour rating, although in some cases these may be nonrated partitions in buildings that are provided with automatic sprinklers. Storage rooms under 100 ft^2 (9.3 m^2), trash chute access rooms, linen chute access rooms, and laboratories are examples of rooms which may be separated by 1 hour rated construction.

Health Care Occupancies

Health care occupancies such as hospitals and nursing homes have an additional requirement for smoke barriers to separate floors, so that patients can be moved to an area protected from smoke in the event of fire. Unlike other occupancies, these smoke barriers must also carry a 1 hour fire resistance rating, and penetrations through them must be protected with through-penetration firestop systems. One method which may be used, although not always accurate (since rated assemblies may have been used because they were available but not required), is to look for labels on doors and door frames which contain hourly ratings. Generally, the ratings of fire doors are as listed in Table 18.5.1.

F, T, and L Ratings

Firestop systems are tested in accordance with either ASTM E814, *Standard Test Method for Fire Tests of Through-Penetration Fire Stops*[2] or UL 1479, *Fire Tests of Through-Penetration Firestops.*[3] These tests yield three ratings which are used in the published listings for the systems:

TABLE 18.5.1 Fire Door Ratings

Door Rating	*Wall Rating*
20 min	½–1 hr
¾ hr	1 hr
1 hr	1 hr
1½ hr	1½–2 hr
3 hr	3–4 hr

- *F rating.* Evaluates the time that the system will withstand the passage of flame expressed in hours
- *T rating.* Evaluates the time that the system will limit the temperature on the unexposed side to not more than 325°F (163°C) expressed in hours
- *L rating.* Evaluates the air leakage through the system at ambient and/or 400°F (204°C) at an air pressure differential of 0.30 in. of water (74.6 Pa) expressed in cubic feet per minute per square foot of opening (cfm/ft^2); the test for L ratings is not a requirement of ASTM E814 and is optional in UL 1479.

Both the 2006 edition of *NFPA 5000®, Building Construction and Safety Code®,* and the 2006 edition of the ICC *International Building Code* (IBC)[4] require that penetrations through all fire barriers be protected with a through-penetration firestop system having an F rating equal to the hourly rating of the assembly. NFPA places the additional requirement that the F rating cannot be less than 1 hour. There is an exception in both codes: where the penetrating items are 6 in. diameter (152 mm) maximum steel, copper, or cast iron pipes, the annular spaces can be filled with grout to the full depth of the assembly. The T rating is not required for these assemblies, because they are generally located above any combustible materials which could come in contact with the penetrating item.

For horizontal fire barriers (floors and floor/ceiling assemblies), both building codes require additionally that the T rating of the through-penetration firestop system be equal to the hourly rating of the assembly, except where the penetration is contained within a fire-rated wall or partition assembly. The additional T rating requirement is in recognition of the fact that many vertical pipes may come in contact with combustible materials that are on the floor of the areas where the penetration firestop system is located. If it can be assured that there will be no combustibles near the piping, NFPA allows that the T rating requirement may be dropped.

Neither of the building codes call for an L rating on smoke barriers at the present time. The only reference to a pressure differential is in the IBC, which requires the firestop system to be tested under a differential pressure of 0.01 in. of water (2.484 Pa). The ASTM E814 and UL 1479 standards require a 0.01 in. of water (2.484 Pa) positive pressure as a minimum for all through-penetration firestop system tests. This is done to assure that the system will withstand a fire pressure attempting to push the heat through it. It is typically more of an issue with nonmetallic penetrating items, where the fire could push through burned-off sections, penetrating piping or conduits.

Firestop System Selection

Once the required hourly ratings for the through-penetration firestop system have been determined, the search for a specific system begins. Note that the term "system" and not "product" has been used. In order to determine the proper application of any product, it is necessary to know more about the construction of the fire barrier as well as the penetrating item. These three elements, fire barrier, penetrating item, and firestop product go together to form a system that makes up the through-penetration firestop. The testing laboratories list thousands of systems, each of which is specific to a type of construction, hourly rating, and manufactured product(s). On the surface, this appears to be a formidable task. In order to solve these difficulties, it is necessary to consider the elements of the construction described in the sections that follow.

Type of Fire Barrier Designation. The first consideration is the configuration of the fire barrier being penetrated. Is the barrier a floor (or horizontal barrier) requiring protection from vertical fire spread or is it a wall (or vertical barrier requiring protection from horizontal fire spread)?

Fire Barrier Construction Type. The second consideration is the type of construction used to create the fire barrier. Some examples follow, each having different firestop systems associated with it:

- Concrete floors of varying thicknesses
- Framed floors
- Steel
- Floor/ceiling assemblies consisting of layers of construction materials with horizontal spaces for ductwork, piping, and wiring
- Concrete or masonry walls of varying thickness
- Framed walls
- Bulkheads in marine vessels
- Composite walls

A through-penetration firestop system tested for a concrete block wall may not be applicable to a wall constructed of metal studs and drywall.

Penetrating Item Designation. The last consideration is the general type of penetrating item through the rated assembly, examples of which are the following:

- No penetrating item where a void in construction is to be sealed
- Metallic pipe, conduit, or tubing
- Nonmetallic pipe, conduit, or tubing
- Electric cables
- Cable trays with electric cables
- Insulated pipes
- Miscellaneous electrical items such as bus ducts
- Miscellaneous mechanical penetrating items, including air ducts
- Combinations of penetrating items including any combination of items listed above

Each of the systems will be listed for a particular size of penetrating item and the specific material of the penetrating item. For example, a system may be listed for steel pipes up to 24 in. (0.61 m) and copper pipes up to 6 in. (152.4 mm) with 2 in. (50.8 mm) or less insulation in diameter, whereas another system is listed for steel or copper pipes up to 4 in. (101.6 mm) with 1 in. (25.4 mm) or less insulation.

These systems illustrate a major problem facing designers in finding systems for floor penetrations using metallic pipes. It is difficult to get T ratings that will equal the F rating. This is because the metal transmits heat through the fire barrier at a greater rate than either the fire barrier construction or the firestop sealant, resulting in less time to reach the 325°F (163° C) maximum temperature. Generally, it will be necessary to use insulation on the piping and the result will probably be an F rating greater than needed for the particular fire barrier. This is generally not as great a problem when using nonmetallic piping because of the lower heat transmission rate.

Thus, the search can be narrowed down to 1000 to 2000 possible choices. Each of these choices is very specific as to the size and type of penetrating items, as well as the details of the construction of the floor or wall being penetrated. It is necessary to study these details to be certain that the construction details in the listing meet the details of the fire barrier being penetrated before choosing a system to be used.

In summary, to select the appropriate firestop sealant for a particular project you need to determine the following:

- Fire resistance rating of the construction being penetrated
- Type of pipe, conduit, or other item being using to penetrate the fire barrier
- Type of penetrated construction—floor, wall, or both
- F, T, and L ratings required or desired
- Construction details and materials of the rated construction

PERIMETER FIRE CONTAINMENT SYSTEMS

Building Construction and Fire Resistant Materials

Perimeter fire containment systems were developed as the result of the increased use of exterior curtain wall construction in buildings, particularly high-rise buildings. In typical building construction used prior to the turn of the twentieth century, the exterior walls were either load bearing or were supported on the floor slabs and extended between the floors (See Figure 18.5.1). In the late nineteenth century and early twentieth century, lightweight panelized systems were developed that could cover the exterior of the building more economically but covered the edge of the floor slab only, leading to the term "curtain wall" construction.[5] In this construction, the floor slab does not extend to the exterior wall but is separated by a nonrated vertical construction, which extends unbroken past the edge of the slab, creating a void through which fire can pass from floor to floor (Figure 18.5.2).

Early methods employed to firestop these voids involved the use of fibrous fire retardant materials such as mineral wool. These materials provided an effective method of restricting

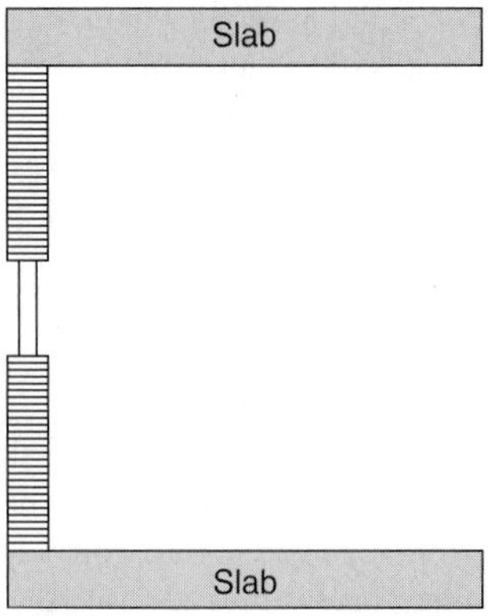

FIGURE 18.5.1 Floor Slabs in Typical Building Construction Before 1900

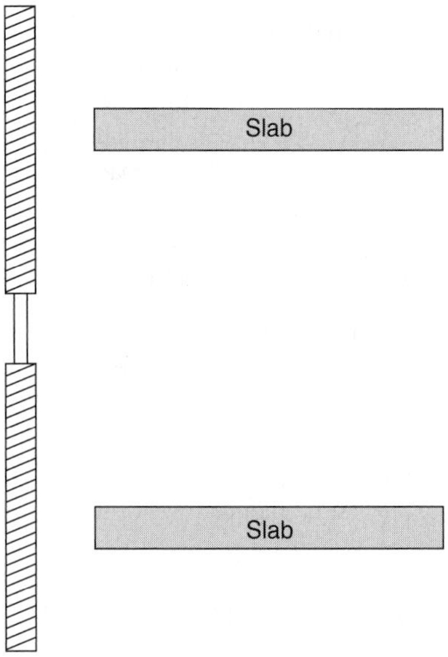

FIGURE 18.5.2 Floor Slab for Curtain Wall Construction

flame passage between floors, but were not effective in controlling the movement of smoke. Therefore, elastomeric sealants were developed that, in conjunction with fire-resistant materials, could effectively limit the spread of both flame and smoke between floors.

Testing and Ratings

Systems designed to protect curtain wall construction are tested in accordance with ANSI/UL 2079, *Tests for Fire Resistance of Building Joint Systems,*[6] using test methods and conditions given in NFPA 285, *Standard Fire Test Method for Evaluation of Fire Propagation Characteristics of Exterior Non-Load-Bearing Wall Assemblies Containing Combustible Components.*

Integrity Rating and Insulation Rating. Just as fire resistance ratings are given for through-penetration firestop systems, two fire resistance ratings are given in hours for perimeter fire containment systems: integrity rating and insulation rating. The integrity rating is analogous to the F rating on firestop systems and is a measure of the system's ability to limit the spreads of flame through the construction. The insulation rating is analogous to the T rating on firestop systems and is a measure of the system's ability to limit the temperature 1 in. (2.54 cm) above the fill material to 325°F (163°C). Where space between the slab and the curtain wall exceeds 6 in. (15.24 cm), there is an additional restriction on the insulation rating that the temperature will not rise more than 250°F (121.1°C) above the starting temperature.

Maximum Linear Opening Width Rating. A third listing for perimeter fire containment systems is the maximum linear opening width. This places a limitation on the width of the protected space between the slab and the curtain wall. Where the system is subject to movement, the components of the system are cycled prior to the fire test for 500 or 100 complete movement cycles at a minimum rate of 1, 10, or 30 cycles per minute. This results in the system being given a Class I, II, and/or III designation as shown in Table 18.5.2.

Using these tests, the joints are assigned a nominal joint width and a percentage factor for either compression or extension. From these, the minimum and maximum allowable joint widths are calculated using the formulae:

$$W_{min} = W_{nom}\,[1 - (\%\ \text{Exp}/100)] \qquad (1)$$

where

W_{min} = Minimum joint width (in.)

W_{nom} = Nominal joint width (in.)

% Exp = Percent movement capability in the compression direction

and

$$W_{max} = W_{nom}\,[1 - (\%\ \text{Comp}/100)] \qquad (2)$$

where

W_{max} = Maximum joint width (in.)

W_{nom} = Nominal joint width (in.)

% Comp = Percent movement capability in the extension direction

Movement Capabilities Rating. When a system has capabilities of resisting shear movement, the system is given a movement capabilities rating expressed in percent vertical shear. From this

TABLE 18.5.2 System Movement Capabilities

Movement Class	*Mininum Number of Cycles*	*Minimum Cycling Rate (cycles per minute)*
Class I	500	1
Class II	500	10
Class III	100	30

data, the maximum vertical shear the system can withstand can be calculated from the formula:

$$\text{Shear} = W_{nom}\,(\%\ \text{Shear}/100) \qquad (3)$$

where

Shear = Vertical shear movement

W_{nom} = Nominal joint width (in.)

% Shear = Percent in shear movement

Leakage Rating. There is a fifth rating, leakage rating, which is optional and not part of every listing. This rating determines the amount of air leakage in cfm per lineal foot through the joint at ambient temperatures and/or 400°F (204°C). The test is conducted at a differential pressure of 0.20 in. of water (49.8 Pa) and provides an indication of the amount of smoke which could be transmitted through the joint.

Curtain Wall Penetration Protection

When evaluating curtain wall penetration protection, there are two considerations which must be investigated: movement capabilities and maximum clearance.

Movement Capabilities. It must be determined whether the through-penetration fire stop system is static (i.e., the system does not have movement capabilities) or dynamic (i.e., the system has movement capabilities).

Maximum Clearance. This system will be listed for varying maximum clearance distances between the curtain wall and perimeter of the floor. The following are the usual ranges of clearances:

Less than or equal to 2 in. (50.8 mm)
Greater than 2 in. (50.8 mm) and less than or equal to 6 in. (152.4 mm)
Greater than 6 in. (152.4 mm) and less than or equal to 12 in. (304.8 mm)

JOINT SYSTEMS

Testing and Ratings

Fire resistance rated construction is tested and rated to provide a barrier which can resist the passage of fire and smoke for the period given in the hourly rating of the construction. However, the mating of two construction elements creates a space through which fire, heat, and/or smoke can pass, thereby reducing the effectiveness of the fire-resistant barrier. Joint systems protect these gaps. These systems are tested per ANSI/UL 2079, *Tests for Fire Resistance of Building Joint Systems.*

Similar to perimeter fire containment systems, systems with movement capabilities are tested by cycling the components of the system prior to the fire test under one of three conditions. The movement class, minimum number of cycles, and minimum cycling rate per minute are the same as those shown in Table 18.5.2.

Using these tests, the joints are assigned a nominal joint width and a percentage factor for either compression or extension. From these, the minimum and maximum allowable joint widths are calculated using the formulae:

$$W_{min} = W_{nom}\,[1 - (\%\ \text{Exp}/100)] \qquad (4)$$

where

W_{min} = Minimum joint width (in.)

W_{nom} = Nominal joint width (in.)

% Exp = Percent movement capability in the compression direction

and

$$W_{max} = W_{nom}\,[1 - (\%\ \text{Comp}/100)] \qquad (5)$$

where

W_{max} = Maximum joint width (in.)

W_{nom} = Nominal joint width (in.)

% Comp = Percent movement capability in the extension direction

As was the case with perimeter fire containment systems, there is an optional L (leakage) rating, which determines the amount of air leakage in cfm per lineal foot through the joint at ambient temperatures and/or 400°F (204°C). The test is conducted at a differential pressure of 0.3 in of water (74.6 Pa), and provides an indication of the amount of smoke which could be transmitted through the joint.

There is an L rating which is the same as for through-penetration firestop systems. This evaluates the air leakage through the system at ambient and/or 400°F (204°C) at an air pressure differential of 0.3 of water (74.6 Pa). and is expressed in cubic feet per minute per square foot of opening (cfm/ft^2). The test for L ratings is optional in ASI/UL 2079.

Factors to Consider Before Beginning Construction

When evaluating joint systems, there are three factors to consider: arrangement of construction elements, movement capabilities designation, and maximum clearance.

Arrangement of Construction Elements. Several types of joint systems can be used depending on the particular construction arrangement as follows:

- Floor-to-floor (typically at expansion joints in floors)
- Wall-to-wall (typically at expansion joints or corner joints in walls)
- Head of wall
- Bottom of wall

Movement Capabilities Designation. A decision must be made on whether the through-penetration fire stop system is static (i.e., the system does not have movement capabilities) or dynamic (i.e., the system has movement capabilities).

Maximum Clearance. This system will be listed for varying maximum clearance distance between the curtain wall and perimeter of the floor. The following are the usual ranges of clearances:

Less than or equal to 2 in. (50.8 mm)
Greater than 2 in. (50.8 mm) and less than or equal to 6 in. (152.4 mm)
Greater than 6 in. (152.4 mm) and less than or equal to 12 in. (304.8 mm)
Greater than 12 in. (304.8 mm) and less than or equal to 24 in. (61 m)
Greater than 24 in. (0.61 m)

A further complication is introduced when a floor-to-floor joint system is considered. This is the situation which is often represented by expansion joints in concrete floors. Not only will the joint require consideration of its movement, it is often necessary to consider the probability of smoke movement through the joint. Therefore, these systems also carry L ratings.

SUMMARY

The Browns Ferry nuclear power plant fire of 1975 demonstrated that building construction must be properly sealed to limit the spread of both fire and smoke. Because materials used before 1975 to seal penetrations were found to be inadequate, new sealing materials were developed along with a series of tests for rating the use of these materials in combination with various fire barrier constructions. The initial concentration was on sealing of pipes and conduits penetrating fire barriers. However, the sealing of joints around pipes and conduits and in joints between elements of fire resistance rated construction has come a long way from the simple selection of a "fire caulk" and then using it to plug up the opening. The sealing of joints requires consideration of a number of factors including the following:

- Desired fire resistance rating
- Maximum allowable opening width
- Nature of the item penetrating to fire resistance rated construction where applicable
- Allowable temperature rise where applicable
- Need for the system to resist movement
- Need for the system to resist the passage of smoke as well as fire

This chapter outlines three categories of sealing penetration systems: through-penetration firestop, perimeter fire containment, and joint. The chapter describes steps for determining which firestop method should be used, the unique sealing requirements of different types of facilities, rating systems, and building codes, standards and regulations for the application of penetration sealing.

BIBLIOGRAPHY

References Cited

1. Nuclear Energy Institute Fact Sheet, Nuclear Energy Institute, Washington, DC, July 2003.
2. ASTM E814, *Standard Test Method for Fire Tests of Through-Penetration Fire Stops,* American Society for Testing and Materials (ASTM), W. Conshohocken, PA, 2006.
3. ANSI/UL 1479, *Fire Tests of Through-Penetration Firestops,* Underwriters Laboratories (UL), Northbrook, IL, 2003, revised 2006.
4. *The International Building Code,* 2006 edition, International Code Council, Falls Church, VA.
5. Ochshorn, J., "Curtain-Wall Systems in 20th-Century Architecture," *Encyclopedia of Twentieth Century Architecture,* Fitzroy Dearborn (Taylor and Francis) Publishers, 2003.
6. ANSI/UL 2079, *Tests for Fire Resistance of Building Joint Systems,* Underwriters Laboratories (UL), Northbrook, IL, 2004, revised 2006.

NFPA Codes, Standards, and Recommended Practices

Reference to the following NFPA codes, standards, and recommended practices will provide further information on penetration sealing discussed in this chapter. (See the latest version of The NFPA Catalog *for availability of current editions of the following documents.)*

NFPA 285, *Standard Fire Test Method for Evaluation of Fire Propagation Characteristics of Exterior Non-Load-Bearing Wall Assemblies Containing Combustible Components*
NFPA 5000®, Building Construction and Safety Code®

Chapter 6

Deflagration (Explosion) Venting

Richard F. Schwab

Chapter Contents

Key Terms

combustible dust, deflagration, detonation, enclosure, explosion venting, fireball, flammable gas, pressure effect

The first document by NFPA concerning explosion (deflagration) venting was NFPA 68-T, *Standard on Explosion Venting,* tentatively adopted by NFPA in 1945. The *Guide for Explosion Venting,* tentatively adopted by NFPA in 1954, brought together the best available, albeit sparse, information on the design and utilization of vents to limit pressures developed by "explosions." The 2007 edition of NFPA 68 is titled *Standard on Explosion Protection by Deflagration Venting.*

NFPA 68 clearly differentiates the terms *deflagration, detonation,* and *explosion.* A *deflagration* is defined as the propagation of combustion zone from the ignition point at less than the speed of sound in the unreacted medium. A *detonation* results when the combustion zone proceeds at greater than the speed of sound. An *explosion* is the bursting of an enclosure or container due to the development of internal pressure. The standard refers to cases in which vents are designed to relieve pressures developed by the combustion process proceeding at less than the speed of sound as explosion (deflagration) venting. Detonations cannot be vented.

Unfortunately, the data available in 1954 was primitive and without theoretical basis. It was customary at the time to express vent area in terms of vent ratios (square feet/cubic feet of enclosure volume). Very little regard was given to the strength of the enclosure and its effect on vent sizing, although it was recognized that a strong enclosure or a heavy building did not need as much vent area as a weak enclosure or building. It was qualitatively recognized that the rate of pressure rise had an effect on the size of vent required for a given enclosure; that is, a combustible or flammable gas showing test data with high rates of pressure rise required a larger vent ratio than those with lower rates of pressure rise. Also, increasing the mass of the vent closure was undesirable because it slowed down the opening of the closure, resulting in the buildup of destructive pressures within the enclosure.

This unfortunate state of affairs prevailed into the late 1960s and early 1970s, when work done at the U.S. Bureau of Mines and more extensive work done in Great Britain, Germany, and Switzerland increased the pool of knowledge to the extent that the 1974 edition of NFPA 68, *Guide for Venting of Deflagration,* was issued. Bartknecht provides additional historical information on the development of deflagration venting.[1]

For related topics, see Section 2, Chapter 8, "Explosions"; Section 6, Chapter 15, "Explosives and Blasting Agents"; Section 17, Chapter 8, "Explosion Prevention and Protection"; and Section 18, Chapter 4, "Venting Practices."

FUNDAMENTALS OF DEFLAGRATIONS

The following conditions are necessary to initiate a deflagration:

- A fuel concentration between upper and lower combustible limits
- Sufficient oxidant (usually air) to support combustion
- An ignition source of sufficient energy to ignite the combustible mixture

Richard F. Schwab, P.E., is a fellow of the American Institute of Chemical Engineers and of the Society of Fire Protection Engineers. He is retired manager of process safety and loss prevention at Honeywell International (formerly Allied-Signal, Inc.) in Morristown, New Jersey.

Once a deflagration has been initiated, the associated pressure needs to be characterized. The deflagration pressure in the enclosure generally follows the gas law equation, which can be expressed as follows:

$$P = \frac{n \times R \times T}{V} \quad (1)$$

where

R = Universal gas constant

P = Pressure

T = Absolute temperature

V = Volume

n = Number of moles of gases generated by the deflagration

The maximum deflagration pressure P_{max} and the maximum rate of pressure rise $(dP/dt)_{max}$ are determined by test. For most fuel, the maximum deflagration pressure is 6 to 10 times the absolute pressure at the time of the ignition.

The fundamental basis for deflagration venting theory is the so-called cubic law that can be stated as follows:

$$K = \left(\frac{dP}{dt}\right) \times V^{1/3} \quad (2)$$

The deflagration index K is computed from the maximum rate of pressure rise in a closed vessel multiplied by the cube root of the enclosure volume. It should be noted that the deflagration index is not a constant, although it has been referred to as such in some of the older literature. The deflagration index for gases is K_G; for dusts it is K_{St}. The maximum rate of pressure rise occurs at an optimum concentration. If the optimum concentration is either not reached or exceeded, the rates of pressure rise are less than the optimum. Further, the energy of the ignition source affects the rate of pressure rise. If the energy is less than standard test method requirements, then the rate of pressure rise will be lower.

Test methods are usually used by laboratories to measure these factors; the determination of optimum concentration requires a series of tests over a range of concentrations. The ignition energy used is high to ensure that the rate of pressure rise is at its maximum.

Table 18.6.1 provides values for the key factors, P_{max} and K_G, for some common flammable materials.

Three hazard classes have been defined for dusts based on the magnitude of the dust deflagration index, K_{St}. Table 18.6.2 displays three hazard classes for dust deflagrations

Fuel

Any mixture that is capable of reacting with an oxidizing medium (which in most cases is air) can be classified as a fuel. The fuel can exist in the gaseous, liquid, or solid state. Liquid fuels are dispersed in air as fine mists, solid fuels are dispersed in air as dusts, and hybrid mixtures can be mixtures of dusts and flammable or combustible gases (or mists) very similar to gaseous fuels.

The concentration of a gaseous fuel is usually expressed in volume percent (vol%) or mole percent (mol%) and concentrations of combustible dusts and mists are expressed as mass per unit volume, such as grams per cubic meter (g/m^3) or ounces per cubic foot (oz/ft^3).

TABLE 18.6.1 Typical Flammability Parameters of Gases Measured in a 5 L Sphere (0.005 ft^3) with an Ignition Energy of 10 J

Flammable Material	P_{max} *(bar)*	K_G *(bar-m/sec)*
Acetophenone[a]	7.6	109
Acetylene	10.6	1415
Ammonia[b]	5.4	10
β-Napthol	4.4	56
Butane	8.0	92
Carbon disulfide	6.4	105
Diethyl ether	8.1	115
Dimethyl formamide[a]	8.4	78
Dimethyl sulfoxide[a]	7.3	112
Ethane[a]	7.8	106
Ethyl alcohol (ethanol)	7.0	78
Ethyl benzene[a]	7.4	96
Hydrogen	6.8	550
Hydrogen sulfide	7.4	45
Isopropanol[a]	7.8	83
Methane	7.1	55
Methanol[a]	7.5	75
Methylene chloride	5.0	5
Methyl nitrite	11.4	111
Neopentane	7.8	60
Octanol[a]	6.7	95
Octyl chloride[a]	8.0	116
Pentane[a]	7.8	104
Propane	7.9	100
South African crude oil	6.8–7.6	36–62
Toluene	7.8	94

Note: The method for developing K_G values has not been standardized. See NFPA 68 (2007) Paragraph E.2 and Bartknecht.[1]
[a]Measured at elevated temperatures and extrapolated to 25°C (77°F) at normal conditions.
[b]E = 100–200 J.
[c]200°C (392°F).
Source: Bartknecht.[1]

TABLE 18.6.2 Hazard Classes of Dust Deflagrations

Hazard Class	K_{St} *(bar-m/sec)**	P_{max} *(bar)**
St-1	≤200	10
St-2	201–300	10
St-3	>300	12

*K_{St} and P_{max} are determined in approximately spherical calibrated test vessels of at least 20 L capacity per ASTM E1226, *Standard Test Method for Pressure and Rate of Pressure Rise for Combustible Dusts.*
Source: NFPA 68, *Standard on Explosion Protection by Deflagration Venting,* 2007 ed., Table B.1.

Flammable Gas

The flammable gas must be present in air (the oxidizing media) between the lower and upper flammable limits (LFL and UFL).

LFL is the lowest concentration of material that will propagate a flame from an ignition source through a mixture of flammable gas or combustible dust dispersion with a gaseous oxidizer; LFL is also known as the minimum explosible concentration. UFL, on the other hand, is the highest concentration of material that will propagate a flame from an ignition source through a mixture of flammable gas or combustible dust dispersion with a gaseous oxidizer. Ignition can occur between the lower and upper flammable limits. The maximum deflagration pressure of a flammable gas in a particular oxidizing medium is determined by test and is generally on the fuel rich side of the stoichiometric mixture. The concentration at which the maximum rate of pressure rise $(dP/dt)_{max}$ and the maximum pressure P_{max} occur can differ slightly. These experimental values are used to calculate K_G values according to Equation 2.

Combustible Dust

Solid particulates smaller than 0.017 in. (420 μm) capable of passing through a U.S. No. 40 standard sieve are classified as dusts. The fineness of the dust is characterized by the particle size distribution. Generally speaking, the maximum rate of pressure rise increases with a decrease in dust particle size, along with the maximum pressure. The experimental K_{St} of a combustible dust sample is determined by the optimum rate of pressure rise at the optimum concentration multiplied by the cube root of the test enclosure volume as shown in Equation 2.

The minimum ignition energy of the dust cloud decreases as the particle size decreases. Experimental data shows this trend, though it is generally not extensively reported. Particle shape also has an effect on the combustion characteristics of dusts. Dust particles with an irregular shape, such as those that would be obtained from polymer dust generated in a hammer mill, have different combustion characteristics from a dust with a spherical shape, such as those that would be obtained from a similar polymer generated by a suspension polymerization process, even though the general particle size distribution of the two may be similar. The irregularly shaped dust particles of the hammer mill product show a higher rate of pressure rise. This is one of the reasons for testing sample dusts coming from a particular process and not trying to extrapolate dust test data from a completely unrelated process even though particle size distribution may appear to be similar.

The lower combustible limit of a dust-air mixture, also called the minimum explosible concentration (MEC), exists along with the upper limit, although upper combustible limit numbers are of no practical value for designing a viable explosion protection system. The upper combustible limit is usually not reported.

Burning Velocity and Flame Speed

The burning velocity is the rate of flame propagation relative to the unburned gas that is ahead of it. The fundamental burning velocity, S_u, is the burning velocity of a laminar flame under stated conditions of composition, temperature, and pressure of the unburned gas. Table 18.6.3 lists typical fundamental burning velocities of flammable gases in air.

Flame speed is the speed of a flame front relative to a fixed reference point. Its minimum value is equal to the fundamental burning velocity times the expansion factor equal to the ratio of the density of the unburned gas to the density of the burned gas. Flame speed is influenced by the degree of turbulence in the gas-air mixture, which can be induced by obstructions in the flame path, volume of the enclosure, ignition energy, temperature of the mixture, and so on, and cannot be determined by the properties of the flammable gas mixture alone.

Hybrid Mixtures

The addition of a flammable gas to a dust-air mixture is called a hybrid mixture. The presence of a flammable gas in a dust-air mixture reduces the LFL and the ignition energy required to initiate the deflagration. This effect can occur even though flammable gas is below its LFL (when considered alone as a flammable gas-air mixture) and the dust is below its LFL (MEC). The addition of the flammable gas to a combustible dust cloud will increase the effective K_{St} value, which means that the required vent area will have to be increased (Figure 18.6.1).

Introduction of an inert gas into the fuel-air mixture will reduce the rate of pressure rise and the maximum pressure attained. If it is desired to take these effects into account when designing the deflagration vents, the effects on the rate of

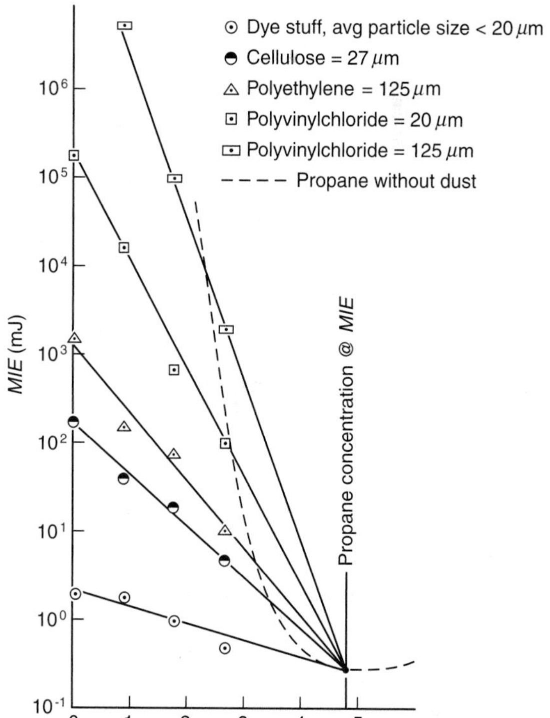

FIGURE 18.6.1 Lowest Minimum Ignition Energy (MIE) of Hybrid Mixtures Versus Propane Content

TABLE 18.6.3 Fundamental Burning Velocities of Selected Gases and Vapors

Gas	*Fundamental Burning Velocity (cm/sec)*	*Gas*	*Fundamental Burning Velocity (cm/sec)*	*Gas*	*Fundamental Burning Velocity (cm/sec)*
Acetone	54	Cyclohexane	46	Methyl alcohol	56
Acetylene	166	methyl-	44	1,2-Pentadiene	61
Acrolein	66	Cyclopentadiene	46	(ethylal lene)	
Acrylonitrile	50	Cyclopentane	44	*cis*-1,3-Pentadiene	55
Allene (propadiene)	87	methyl-	42	*trans*-1,3-Pentadiene	54
Benzene	48	Cyclopropane	56	(piperylene)	
,n-butyl-	37	*cis*-1,2-dimethyl-	55	2-methyl-(cos or trans)	46
,tert.obutyl-	39	*trans*-1,2-	55	1,4-Pentadiene	55
,1,2-dimethyl-	37	dimethyl-		2,3-Pentadiene	60
1,2,4-trimethyl-	39	ethyl-	56	*n*-Pentane,	46
1,2-Butadiene	68	methyl-	58	2,2-dimethyl-	41
(methylallene)		1,1,2-dimethyl-	52	2,3-dimethyl-	43
1,3-Butadiene	64	*trans*-Decalin	36	2,4-dimethyl-	42
2,3-dimethyl-	52	(decahydro-		2-methyl-	43
2-methyl-	55	naphthalene)		3-methyl-	43
n-Butane	45	*n*-Decane	43	2,2,4-trimethyl	41
2-cyclopropyl-	47	1-Decene	44	1-Pentene	50
2,2-dimethyl-	42	Diethyl ether	47	2-methyl-	47
2,3-dimethyl-	43	Dimethyl ether	54	4-methyl-	48
2-methyl-	43	Ethane	47	*cis*-2-Pentene	51
2,2,3-trimethyl-	42	Ethane (ethylene)	80	1-Pentene	63
Butanone	42	Ethyl acetate	38	4-methyl-	53
1-Butene	51	Ethylene oxide	108	2-Pentyne	61
2-cyclopropyl-	50	Ethylenimine	46	4-methyl-	54
2,3-dimethyl-	46	Gasoline	40	Propane	46
2-ethyl-	46	(100-octane)		2-cyclopropyl-	50
2-methyl-	46	*n*-Heptane	46	1-deutero-	40
3-methyl-	49	Hexadecane	44	1-deutero-2-methyl-	40
2,3-dimethyl-	44	1,5-Hexadiene	52	2-deutero-2-methyl	40
2-butene		*n*-Hexane	46	2,2-dimethyl-	39
2-Buten 1-yne	89	1-Hexene	50	2-methyl-	41
(vinylacetylene)		1-Hexyne	57	2-cyclopropyl	53
1-Butyne	68	3-Hexyne	53	2-methyl-	44
3,3-dimethyl-	56	Hydrogen	312	Propionaldehyde	58
2-Butyne	61	Isopropyl alcohol	41	Propylene oxide	82
Carbon disulfide	58	Isopropylamine	31	(1,2-epoxypropane)	
Carbon monoxide	46	Jet fuel, grade JP-1	40	1-Propyne	82
Cyclobutane	67	(average)		Spiropentane	71
ethyl-	53	Jet fuel, grade JP-4	41	Tetrahydropyran	48
isopropyl-	46	(average)		Tetralin (tetra-	39
methyl-	52	Methane	40	hydronaphthalene)	
methylene	61	diphenyl-	35	Toluene (methylbenzene)	41

pressure rise and the maximum pressure must be determined experimentally.

Introduction of an inert gas into a combustible dust-air cloud affects the rate of pressure rise (which will decrease) and the maximum pressure attained (which will decrease) after ignition of the cloud. When considering this technique for reducing the hazard of combustible dust, additional problems concerning the possibility of segregation of inert material from the combustible material must be considered. See Bartknecht,[1] Eckhoff,[2] and NFPA 68.

FUNDAMENTALS OF DEFLAGRATION VENTING AND ENCLOSURE DESIGN CONSIDERATIONS

Deflagration venting is intended to limit the amount of damage to a protected enclosure. It is not a preventative measure. It presupposes that a combustible mixture will occur in the enclosure and that it will ignite. Properly designed venting will limit the damage to a predetermined acceptable level. Some users will accept a permanently deformed enclosure, while others will only accept elastic deformation. Accepting permanent deformation means that while the enclosure will not rupture during the event, a rectangular box might well become somewhat spherical and unserviceable. The user must weigh the probability of the event against the potential for lost productivity.

A deflagration vent is an opening in an enclosure through which material expands and flows, thus relieving pressure. If no venting is provided, the maximum pressures developed during the deflagration are typically 6 to 10 times the initial absolute pressure. In most cases it may be impractical to construct an enclosure that can withstand or contain such pressures. The reduced pressure P_{red} is the maximum pressure developed in a vented enclosure during a vented deflagration.

The rate of pressure rise is the most important parameter that is used in the design of deflagration venting. A rapid rate of pressure rise means that only a short time is available for successful venting, whereas a slower rate of pressure rise allows the venting to proceed more slowly while remaining effective. It also follows that, all other factors being equal, the more rapid rate of pressure rise requires the greater area for effective venting.

The vents provided are intended to limit the buildup of pressure within the enclosure so that damage to the enclosure does not occur or is limited to acceptable levels. As the vent area increases, the reduced pressure for a given static activation pressure of the vent closure decreases. Open vents are more effective than covered vents. Lightweight closures are more responsive than heavy closures. Damage can result if a deflagration occurs in an enclosure that is too weak to withstand the pressure of a deflagration. An ordinary masonry wall of 8 in. (20 cm) brick or concrete block cannot withstand a pressure difference greater than 0.5 psi (0.035 bar).

Since the pressure development during deflagration is rapid, it could be experienced as a dynamic load by the enclosure (building) rather than a static load. Therefore, a suitable design safety factor is applied to P_{red} in the absence of detailed structural response analysis.

Common design standards allow P_{red} to be selected for up to two-thirds of the enclosure strength (see Taminini and Valiulis[3] and NFPA 68). NFPA 68 should be consulted for specific guidance for enclosure design pressure requirements when permanent deformation can or cannot be accepted.

Flames and pressure waves that emerge from an enclosure during the venting process must be taken into account to ensure that they do not ignite nearby combustible material or injure personnel who may be exposed to their effects.

Enclosure Length to Diameter

In NFPA 68, the combustion process in an enclosure involves the ignition of a combustible with an oxidant where the length/diameter (*L*/*D*) ratio is 2 or less. If the *L*/*D* ratio is greater than 2, modifications in the calculation, leading to an increase in the necessary vent area, must be taken into account for the venting design. The P_{red} developed within an enclosure decreases as the available vent area for the enclosure increases. If the enclosure is small and relatively symmetrical, then one large vent can be effective; however, for large enclosures, it is recommended that the vents be distributed over the surface area of the enclosure to the greatest extent possible.

The *L*/*D* of an elongated enclosure is determined based on the general shape of the enclosure, the location of the vent, the shape of any hopper extensions, and the furthest distance from the vent at which the deflagration could be initiated. The calculation involves the worst case flame path length to the farthest side of the vent and an effective diameter of the enclosure. The position of the vent along the enclosure can change the effective *L*/*D*. In this way a single vent located midway along the central axis of an elongated vessel would result in a smaller *L*/*D* than the same vent located at one end of the vessel. In no case can the effective *L*/*D* of an enclosure be less than 1, meaning that as the vents get closer together along the central axis, at some point the controlling flame path length would become, for instance, the diameter of the cylindrical enclosure. Detailed explanation of this approach can be found in NFPA 68.

Effect of Vent Duct Length

When a vent duct is added to the vent closure to direct the vented combustion gases to a safe outside area, this introduces a resistance to the relief of the vented gases from the enclosure and must therefore be taken into account. This basically means that the size of the vent area must be increased to accommodate this restriction. Different equations are used to determine the vent duct effect for gases as compared to dusts. In general, the solution for required vent area with a vent duct is trial and error and the calculations limit the length of the vent duct. This solution is iterative (trial and error). The following equations are to be used for this iterative calculation:

$$A_{vf} = A_{v4} \times (1 + 1.18 \times E_1^{0.8} \times E_2^{0.4}) \times \sqrt{\frac{K}{K_0}} \qquad (3)$$

where

A_{v4} = Vent area after adjustment for turbulence (m^2)

A_{vf} = Vent area required when duct is attached to the vent opening (m^2)

K_0 = 1.5, the resistance coefficient value assumed for the test configurations that generated the data used to validate the basic dust venting equations

$$E_1 = \frac{A_{vf} \times L_{duct}}{V} \qquad (4)$$

where

L_{duct} = Vent duct overall length (m)

$$E_2 = \frac{10^4 \times A_{vf}}{(1 + 1.54 \times P_{stat}^{4/3}) \times K_{St} \times V^{3/4}} \qquad (5)$$

where

P_{stat} = Nominal static opening pressure of the vent cover (bar)

V = Enclosure volume (m^3)

$$K \equiv \frac{\Delta P}{{}^1\!/_2 \times \rho \times U^2} = K_{inlet} + \frac{f_D \times L}{D_h} + K_{elbows} + K_{outlet} + \ldots \qquad (6)$$

where

K = Overall resistance coefficient of the vent duct application

K_{inlet}, K_{elbows}, K_{outlet} = Resistance coefficients for fittings

U = Fluid velocity (m/sec)

D_h = Vent duct hydraulic diameter (m)

f_D = D'Arcy friction factor for fully turbulent flow (see NFPA 68 Annex)

ρ = Fluid density × $1/G_c$

Note: In this chapter pressure is expressed as bar gauge (bar g) unless it is otherwise noted as bar absolute (bar a). It is recommended that NFPA 68 (2007) be consulted for details describing this calculation.

Enclosure Strength

The vent designed for an enclosure according to NFPA 68, whether for a high strength enclosure or a low strength enclosure, is intended to allow the deflagration pressure P_{red}, to attain two-thirds the strength of the enclosure without rupturing the enclosure. In all cases

$$P_{red} \leq \frac{P_{es}}{\text{DLF}} \tag{7}$$

where

P_{red} = Maximum pressure developed during venting (bar [psi])

P_{es} = Enclosure strength evaluated bases on static pressure calculations for either deformation or burst (bar [psi])

DLF = X_m/X_s

X_m = Maximum dynamic deflection

X_s = Static deflection or, in other words, the displacement produced in the system when the peak load is applied statically

In the absence of detailed structural response analysis, a conservative value of DLF = 1.5 is used and design is based on the weakest structural element of the enclosure.

Two alternative conditions apply to the concept of enclosure strength, presuming that the enclosure is a ductile design, that is, designed to be somewhat elastic or deform without rupture under pressure:

- Permanent deformation, but not rupture, of the enclosure can be accepted.
- Permanent deformation of the enclosure cannot be accepted.

When the enclosure is a pressure vessel designed according to ASME or similar code, the allowable P_{red} is greater than the maximum allowable working pressure (MAWP) for the vessel. The ASME code specifically allows the NFPA 68 method for determining the allowable reduced pressure P_{red} during a deflagration.

If permanent deformation, but not rupture, of the enclosure can be accepted,

$$P_{red} \leq \left(\frac{2}{3}\right) \times F_u \times P_{\text{MAWP}} \tag{8}$$

If permanent deformation of the enclosure cannot be accepted,

$$P_{red} \leq \left(\frac{2}{3}\right) \times F_y \times P_{\text{MAWP}} \tag{9}$$

where

P_{red} = Maximum pressure developed in a vented enclosure (bar [psi])

F_u = Ratio of the ultimate stress of the enclosure to the allowable stress of the enclosure per ASME *Boiler and Pressure Vessel Code*[4]

P_{MAWP} = Enclosure design pressure [bar (psi)] according to ASME *Boiler and Pressure Vessel Code*

F_y = Ratio of the yield stress of the enclosure to the allowable stress of the materials of construction of the enclosure per ASME *Boiler and Pressure Vessel Code*

Note: The ASME *Boiler and Pressure Vessel Code* contains data on the ultimate and yield stresses for various materials of construction plus the allowable stress. The ratios can be calculated from this information. It is anticipated that ambient conditions will apply when applying Equations 8 and 9.

Venting of Gas or Mist Deflagrations in Low Strength Enclosures

A low strength enclosure is capable of withstanding a P_{red} of not more than 1.5 psi (0.1 bar g).[5,6]

$$A_v = \frac{C \times A_S}{P_{red}^{1/2}} \tag{10}$$

where

A_v = Vent area (m² or ft²)

C = Venting parameter, in units consistent with P_{red}

A_S = Internal surface area of the enclosure (m² or ft²)

P_{red} = Maximum pressure developed in a vented enclosure during a deflagration (bar [psi])

The venting parameter shall be defined by the following equations for fundamental burning velocity (less than 60 cm/sec):

For C (bar$^{1/2}$):

$$C = 1.57 \times 10^{-5} \times (S_u)^2 + 1.57 \times 10^{-4}(S_u) + 0.0109 \tag{11}$$

where S_u is fundamental burning velocity (less than 60 cm/sec).

For C (psi$^{1/2}$):

$$C = 6.1 \times 10^{-5} \times (S_u)^2 + 6.1 \times 10^{-4}(S_u) + 0.0416 \tag{12}$$

Figure 18.6.2 shows the venting parameter as a function of fundamental burning velocity.

In contrast to the earlier editions of NFPA 68, the available data on fundamental burning velocity can now be used to determine venting parameters for more individual fuels. This introduces the need to understand the potential range of fuels that could be present in the enclosure. The designer should consider the material with the highest fundamental burning velocity when designing the vent.

Venting Gas Deflagrations in High Strength Enclosures

The recommended equation for venting enclosures with an *L*/*D* of 2 or less is

$$A_v = \{[(0.127) \times \log_{10}(K_G) - (0.0567)] \times P_{red}^{-0.582}\} \times V^{2/3} + [(0.175) \times P_{red}^{-0.572}(P_{stat} - 0.1)] \times V^{2/3} \quad (13)$$

where

$K_G \leq 550$ bar-m/sec

$P_{red} = 2$ bar and at least 0.5 bar $> P_{stat}$

$P_{stat} \leq 0.5$ bar

$V \leq 1000\ m^3$

For *L*/*D* values from 2 to 5 and for P_{red} no higher than 2 bar, the vent area A_V calculated from Equation 13 should be increased as follows:

$$\Delta A = \frac{A_v \times K_G \left(\frac{L}{D} - 2\right)^2}{750} \quad (14)$$

where *D* is the hydraulic diameter. For noncircular cross sections it is determined by 4(*A*/*p*), where *A* is the cross sectional area normal to the longitudinal axis of the space and *p* is the perimeter of the cross section.

In the case where the vent mass is greater than that calculated in Equation 15

$$M_T = \left(6.67 P_{red}^{0.2} \times n^{0.3} \times \frac{V}{K_G^{0.5}}\right)^{1.67} \quad (15)$$

where

n = Number of panels

M_T = Threshold mass (kg/m²)

P_{red} = Vented pressure (bar)

K_G = Gas deflagration index (bar-m/sec)

$V > 1\ m^3$

If the vent mass is within the above constraints and greater than M_T calculated, then Equation 16 is used to determine the incremental vent area to maintain the desired P_{red}.

$$\Delta A_i = A_v \times (0.0075) \times M^{0.6} \times \frac{K_G^{0.5}}{n^{0.3}} \times V \times P_{red}^{0.2} \quad (16)$$

where

M = Mass of vent panel (kg/m²) ≤ 40 kg/m²

A_v = Vent area calculated by Equation 12

$V > 1\ m^3$

If K_G is less than 75 bar-m/sec, use $K_G = 75$ in the equation.

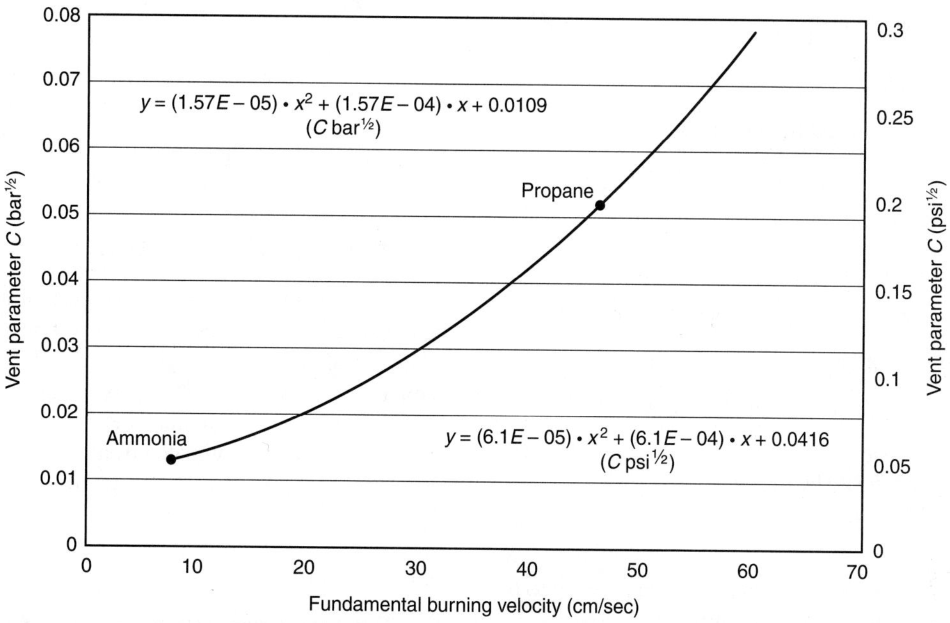

FIGURE 18.6.2 Venting Parameter as a Function of Fundamental Burning Velocity (Source: NFPA 68, *Standard on Explosion Protection by Deflagration Venting,* 2007 ed., Figure 7.2.2.2)

When dealing with enclosures that require ducts to carry the forces of the deflagration and the fireball to a safe location, several problems introduced by using ducts have to be considered. For example, the introduction of ducts results in an increase of pressure inside the enclosure being vented. Consequently, the forces of reaction on the enclosure being vented (dust collector, silo, etc.) must be taken into account, along with considering where the fireball that will be emitted from the ductwork will be vented.

In a situation in which a vent duct is installed after the vent closure to direct the discharge of the gases to an outside safe location, a pressure drop occurs that must be taken into account. The way to do this is to increase the area of the vent. The ductwork leading to the discharge point must be as short and straight as possible. This is the intent of NFPA 68.

NFPA 68 also intends to keep the mass of the vent closure as low as possible. Where vent panels with insulation are needed to prevent heat loss, this need requires a higher vent mass and can affect the achieved P_{red}. It is the intention of NFPA 68 to encourage keeping the relieving panels as light as possible and keeping the relieving ductwork as short and direct to a safe location as possible.

Venting of Deflagrations of Dusts and Hybrid Mixtures

Equation 17 is intended to apply to the design of vents for dust deflagration and hybrid mixtures for high-strength—greater than 1.5 psi (0.1 bar)—enclosures. The recommended design equations for the dust deflagration and the hybrid mixture deflagration for high-strength enclosures are given next. The *L/D* ratio of the design equation is limited to 2 or less. With the initial pressure before the ignition being 1 bar (absolute ±0.2 bar)

$$A_{vo} = 1 \times 10^{-4} \times (1 + 1.54 \times P_{stat}^{4/3}) \times K_{St} \times V^{3/4} \left(\frac{P_{max}}{P_{red}} - 1\right)^{0.5} \tag{17}$$

where

A_{vo} = Vent area calculated from Equation 17 (m^2)

P_{stat} = Nominal static burst pressure of the vent (bar)

K_{St} = Deflagration index (bar-m/sec)

V = Enclosure volume (m^3)

P_{red} = Reduced pressure after vent operation (bar)

P_{max} = Maximum deflagration pressure (bar)

The following limitations must also apply to Equation 17:

- $5 \text{ bar} \le P_{max} \le 12 \text{ bar}$
- $10 \text{ bar-m/sec} \le K_{St} \le 800 \text{ bar-m/sec}$
- $0.1 \text{ m}^3 \le V \le 10{,}000 \text{ m}^3$
- $P_{stat} \le 0.75 \text{ bar}$

In cases where *L/D* is greater than 2 but less than or equal to 6, the calculated A_{v1} is determined by Equation 18:

$$A_{v1} = A_{vo}\left[1 + 0.6 \times \left(\frac{L}{D} - 2\right)^{0.75} \times \exp(-0.95 \times P_{red}^2)\right] \tag{18}$$

For the case where we have a top-fed bin, hopper, and silo the *L/D* can be increased to 8.

Effects of Initially Elevated Pressure

In the case where we have a combustible dust cloud in an enclosure that is pressurized at greater than 0.2 bar, deflagration vents can only be used when the following conditions are met:

- Vent duct length *L/D* is to be ≤ 1
- $M \le M_T$ (threshold mass, kg/m^2) and $M < 40 \text{ kg/m}^2$
- V_{axial} and $v_{tan} < 20$ m/sec
- No allowance for partial volume
- $0.2 \text{ bar} < P_{initial} < 4.0 \text{ bar}$
- Use Equation 19 to calculate the needed vent area

$$A_{vep} = \frac{A_{v1}}{A_{vo}} \cdot 10^{-4} \cdot \left[1 + 1.54 \cdot \left(\frac{P_{stat} - P_{initial}}{1 + P_{effective}}\right)^{4/3}\right] \cdot K_{St} \cdot V^{3/4} \cdot \sqrt{\frac{1}{\pi_{effective}} - 1}^{\,0.5} \tag{19}$$

where

A_{vep} = Vent area (m^2)

P_{stat} = Static burst pressure of the vent (bar)

$P_{initial}$ = Enclosure pressure at the moment of ignition (bar)

$P_{effective} = \frac{1}{3} P_{initial}$ (bar)

K_{St} = Deflagration index (determined at atmospheric pressure) (bar-m/sec)

V = Enclosure volume (m^3)

$\pi_{effective} = (P_{red} - P_{effective}) / (P^E_{max} - P_{effective})$

P_{red} = Reduced pressure (bar)

P^E_{max} = Maximum pressure of the unvented deflagration at initially elevated pressure (bar) $[(P_{max} + 1)(P_{initial} + 1)/(1 \text{ bar-abs} - 1)]$

P_{max} = Maximum pressure of the unvented deflagration initially at atmospheric pressure (bar)

Discharge of Fireballs from Explosion Vents

When flammable gas, combustible dust, or a hybrid mixture is ignited in a vented enclosure, consideration must be given to the discharge of the resultant fireball and its effects. See NFPA 68 for similar treatment of fireball effects for gases. In the case of dust deflagration or hybrid mixture, the distance which this expected fireball will travel is estimated from the following equation:

$$D = K\left(\frac{V}{n}\right)^{1/3} \tag{20}$$

where

D = Axial distance (front) from the vent (ft or m)

K = Flame length factor ($K = 10$ for metal dusts; $K = 8$ for chemical and agricultural dusts)

V = Volume of vented enclosure (m^3 or ft^3)

n = Number of evenly distributed vents

The axial distance calculated by Equation 20 shall be limited to 200 ft (60 m).

In the case of a vented gas or vapor deflagration the equation is

$$D = 3.1\left(\frac{V}{n}\right)^{0.402} \quad (21)$$

where

D = Axial distance (front centerline) from vent (m)

V = Volume of the vented enclosure (m^3)

n = Number of evenly distributed vents

The hazard zone measured radially (to the sides, measured from the centerline of the vent) shall be calculated as one-half D.

In the case where it is necessary to vent an enclosure containing a combustible dust or a hybrid mixture internally into a building through a flame-arresting and particulate retention device, the resulting pressure increase in an unvented building is estimated to be

$$\Delta P = 1.47 \times P_o \times \left(\frac{V_1}{V_o}\right) \quad (22)$$

where

V_o = Free volume of the building

V_1 = Volume of the protected equipment

P_o = Ambient pressure (14.7 psia or 1.013 bar absolute)

ΔP = Pressure rise in the building (in same units as P_o)

External Pressure Effects

When a deflagration is vented from an enclosure, pressure effects are created in the atmosphere external to the enclosure. These effects are due to the vented products and in the case of a dust explosion are the further effects of the combustion of the unburned dusts and the gases external to the enclosure. NFPA 68 allows the designer to calculate the maximum external pressure that will be seen when an explosion vent opens, where those pressure effects will be seen as a function of the distance from the vent opening, and the distance that the fireball travels from that vent opening.

NFPA 68 allows a designer to calculate the maximum external pressure effects as follows:

$$P_{max,a} = 0.2 \times P_{red} \times A_v^{0.1} \times V^{0.18} \quad (23)$$

where

$P_{max,a}$ = External pressure

A_v = Vent area (m^2)

V = Volume of the vented enclosure (m^3)

Once this is known, the designer can estimate the pressure at any point from the vent knowing the distance that the fireball will travel from the vent. The pressure at any point from the vent can be estimated from the following equation:

$$P_{max,r} = P_{max,a} \times \left(\frac{0.20D}{r}\right) \quad (24)$$

where

D = Axial distance traveled by the fire ball from the vent (m) (Equation 20)

$P_{max,r}$ = Maximum external pressure

r = Distance from vent $\geq 0.2D$ (m)

SUMMARY

Explosion venting is a damage limiting protection technique. It is intended to protect an enclosure against damaging pressures generated by a deflagration within the enclosure by safely venting these pressures to a safe location. The chapter discusses the design techniques used to accomplish this objective.

Deflagration is the propagation of combustion zone from the ignition point at less than the speed of sound in the unreacted medium. Three conditions are necessary to initiate a deflagration: a fuel concentration between the upper and lower combustible limits, sufficient oxidant (usually air) to support combustion, and an ignition source of sufficient energy to ignite the combustible mixture (e.g. flammable gases, combustible dusts, or hybrid mixtures). An explosion (deflagration) vent is an opening in an enclosure through which material expands and flows, thus relieving pressure.

BIBLIOGRAPHY

References Cited

1. Bartknecht, W., *Explosions Schutz, Grundlagen und Anwendung,* Springer Verlag, Berlin, Germany, 1993.
2. Eckhoff, R. K., "Partial Inerting—An Additional Degree of Freedom in Dust Explosion Protection," *Journal of Loss Prevention,* Vol. 17, 2004, pp. 187–193.
3. Taminini, F., and Valiulis, J. V., "Improved Guidelines for the Sizing of Vents in Dust Explosions," *Journal of Loss Prevention,* Vol. 8, No. 1, 1996, pp. 105–118.
4. *ASME Boiler and Pressure Vessel Code,* American Society of Mechanical Engineers International, New York, 2004.
5. Swift, I., and Epstein, M., "Performance of Low Pressure Explosion Vents," Paper 84d, 20th Annual Loss Prevention Symposium, AIChE Spring National Meeting, April 6–10, 1986, New Orleans, LA.
6. Swift, I., "Venting Deflagrations—Theory and Practice," *Plant Operations Progress,* Vol. 3, No. 2, 1984, pp. 89–93.

NFPA Codes, Standards, and Recommended Practices

Reference to the following NFPA codes, standards, and recommended practices will provide further information on deflagration (explosion) venting discussed in this chapter. (See the latest version of The NFPA Catalog *for availability of current editions of the following documents.)*

NFPA 68, *Standard on Explosion Protection by Deflagration Venting*
NFPA 69, *Standard on Explosion Prevention Systems*

References

Alexiou, A., Andrews, G. E., and Phylaktou, H., "A Comparison Between End Vented and Side Vented Gas Explosions in Large L/D Vessels," *Transactions of the Institution of Chemical Engineers,* Vol. 75, Part B, 1997, pp. 9–13.

Barton, J., *Dust Explosions—Prevention and Protection,* Institution of Chemical Engineers, Rugby, Warwickshire, UK, 2002.

Eckhoff, R. K., *Dust Explosions in the Process Industries,* 3rd ed., Gulf Professional Publishing (Elsevier), Burlington, MA, 2003.

Hattwig, M., and Steen, H., *Handbook of Explosion Prevention and Protection,* Wiley-VCH, Weinheim, Germany, 2004.

Holbrow, P., Hawksworth, S. J., Tyldesley, A., "Thermal Radiation from Vented Dust Explosions," *Journal of Loss Prevention,* Vol. 13, 2000, pp. 467–475.

Howard, W. B., and Karabinis, A. H., "Tests of Explosion Venting of Building," *Plant Operations Progress,* Jan. 1982, pp. 51–68.

Lunn, G. A., Nicol, A. M., Collins, P. D., and Hubbard, N. R., "Effects of Vent Ducts on the Reduced Pressures from Explosions in Dust Collectors," *Journal of Loss Prevention in the Process Industries,* Vol. 11, 1998, pp. 109–121.

Siwek, R., "New Findings on Dust Explosions," 9th International Symposium on Loss Prevention and Safety Promotion in the Process Industries, May 4–8, 1998, Barcelona, Spain.

Taminini, F., "An Improved Correlation of Experimental Data on the Effects of Ducts in Vented Dust Explosions," *Journal of Loss Prevention in the Process Industries,* 1995, pp. 243–243.

Taminini, F., "The Use of Models in the Development of Explosion Protection Guidelines," 9th International Symposium on Loss Prevention and Safety Promotion in the Process Industries, May 4–8, 1998, Barcelona, Spain, pp. 305–331.

Taminini, F., and Valiulis, J. V., "A Correlation for the Impulse Produced by Vented Explosions," *Journal of Loss Prevention,* Vol. 13, 2000, pp. 277–289.

Taminini, F., and Valiulis, J. V., "Dust Explosion Vent Sizing TechnologyImplemented by FM Loss Prevention Consultants Worldwide," *Internet Conference on Process Safety,* January 27–29, 1998.

Ural, E. A., "A Simplified Development of a Unified Dust Explosion Vent Sizing Formula," *AIChE Loss Prevention Symposium,* April 22–26, 2001, Houston, TX.

Valiulus, J. V., Taminini, F., and Zalosh, R. G., "Experiments on the Propagation of Vented Dust Explosions to Connected Equipment," AIChE Loss Prevention Symposium, March 9–11, 1998, New Orleans, LA.

VDI 3673, "Pressure Venting of Dust Explosions," Verein Deutsche Ingenieure, Dec. 2002.

SECTION

19

Structural Fire Protection

Milosh T. Puchovsky

Fire can present a significant challenge to the structural integrity of buildings. Section 19 of the *Fire Protection Handbook*® provides information on protecting structural elements from fire. A new chapter in the section describes techniques for calculating structural fire resistance.

Chapter 1, "Types of Building Construction," identifies the basic types of building construction in terms of their anticipated performance during a fire. It also addresses fire protection of building elements; the value of exterior walls, interior walls, and partitions; floor framing systems; trusses; floor/ceiling assemblies; and roof framing and coverings.

The first part of Chapter 2, "Structural Integrity During Fire," describes common fire resistance test procedures. The chapter also introduces methods of calculating fire endurance (resistance) ratings, the behavior of building materials at elevated temperatures, and design approaches for structural integrity in a fire.

Chapter 3, "Structural Fire Safety in One- and Two-Family Dwellings," addresses the structural elements of one- and two-family dwellings and manufactured homes as they affect fire safety.

Chapter 4, "Analyzing Structural Fire Damage," reviews building types and structural systems before providing guidance on evaluating fire-damaged structures and specific materials. The chapter also considers fire during construction.

The section concludes with a new chapter: Chapter 5, "Approaches to Calculating Structural Fire Resistance." The chapter provides an overview of structural fire resistance calculation techniques and includes information on alternative approaches to fire resistance and selecting a design fire for structural analysis.

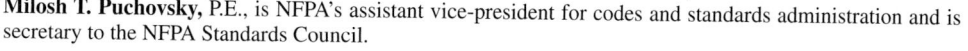

Milosh T. Puchovsky, P.E., is NFPA's assistant vice-president for codes and standards administration and is secretary to the NFPA Standards Council.

Types of Building Construction

Revised by

Peter J. Gore Willse

Chapter Contents

Key Terms

building construction (types of), combustible construction, construction (Type I), construction (Type II), construction (Type III), construction (Type IV), construction (Type V), fire-resistive construction, floor framing system, heavy timber construction, noncombustible construction, ordinary construction, roof, structural element, truss, wood frame construction

A well-established means of codifying the performance of a building's structural elements during a fire is to classify them by types of construction, based on the materials used for the structural elements and the degree of fire resistance afforded by each element.

In early codes, only two classifications of construction were identified: fireproof and nonfireproof. The term *fireproof* was replaced by the term *fire resistive,* because it was recognized that no material or building is totally fireproof and that the building contents can produce a significant fire without involving the structure. It is possible, however, to design buildings that will resist a fire without suffering serious structural damage. Appropriate fire-resistive design, balanced against anticipated fire severity, is the objective of structural fire protection requirements in modern codes.

Several distinct types of construction that use combustible framing were originally classified based on the materials—masonry or wood—used in the exterior wall construction and the type and size of the framing members (i.e., heavy timber versus conventional framing). As fire resistance ratings for construction assemblies were recognized in building codes, subclassifications of building types were added for both noncombustible and combustible types of construction, based on the degree of fire resistance provided.

Code regulations governing the size, area, and height of buildings and their allowable uses are usually predicated on the relative fire load and other factors represented by the occupancy and the construction materials used in the building.

This chapter identifies the basic types of building construction in terms of their anticipated performance during a fire. These construction types are recognized in NFPA 220, *Standard on Types of Building Construction,* and in the model building codes. It also recognizes the current classification system of building construction equated with the traditional descriptive terms used to identify building types (e.g., *fire resistive, noncombustible, ordinary, frame,* etc.) that no longer are prime references to construction types. It also addresses fire protection of building elements; the value of exterior walls, interior walls, and partitions; floor framing systems; trusses; floor/ceiling assemblies; and roof framing and coverings.

For related topics, see the following: Section 1, Chapter 2, "Fundamentals of Structurally Safe Building Design"; Section 12, Chapter 1, "Planning for Public Fire-Rescue Protection"; Section 18, Chapter 1, "Confinement of Fire in Buildings"; Section 19, Chapter 2, "Structural Integrity During Fire"; and Section 19, Chapter 4, "Analyzing Structural Fire Damage."

CONSTRUCTION CLASSIFICATIONS

U.S. Classifications

The construction types currently identified by NFPA and the International Code Council (ICC) fall into ten subtypes in the NFPA system and nine subtypes in the ICC system. Subtypes are derived from

Peter J. Gore Willse, P.E., is the director of research at Global Asset Protection Services, Avon, Connecticut. He chairs the Technical Committee on Structures, Construction, and Materials and is a member of the Technical Committee on Building Construction.

five fundamental construction types, in almost every case: (1) fire resistive, (2) noncombustible, (3) ordinary (exterior protected), (4) heavy timber, and (5) wood frame. The previously published Standard Building Code (SBC) used six construction types. These descriptive names, while still referenced, no longer define the construction types as precisely as needed. The names are helpful, however, in tracing the development of building types.

ICC was formed by Building Officials and Code Administrators (BOCA), International Congress of Building Officials (ICBO), and Southern Building Code Congress International (SBCCI). The 2000 ICC International Building Code (IBC) was meant to succeed the building codes of these organizations. However, earlier editions of their building codes are still being adopted in some places—for example, California. Drawing on its experience with addressing structural fire protection, NFPA has also developed a building code as documented in NFPA 220 and NFPA *101®*, *Life Safety Code®*.

Classification Notation

To achieve better uniformity of building construction classifications, the Model Codes Standardization Council (MCSC) established a committee in 1972 to study the classifications and fire resistance requirements for the types of construction used in the model building codes and to develop recommendations for the model building code organizations.

As a result of the MCSC comparative study, its successor, the Board for the Coordination of the Model Codes (BCMC) proposed that the basic types of construction now recognized in the codes be continued but that they be reordered to some degree and be divided into two groups: (1) noncombustible and (2) combustible. It was also proposed that the identifying names for types of construction, such as *fireproof, ordinary, heavy timber,* and so on, be dropped because current design methods and architecture no longer follow the concepts in use when the named building types were established. The classifications proposed are shown in Table 19.1.1. These are the classifications recognized in NFPA 220 and *NFPA 5000®*, *Building Construction and Safety Code®*.

The MCSC also concluded that to rationally compare the various types of construction, a notational system was needed to identify the fire resistance required for three basic elements of the building. These elements are: (1) the exterior wall, (2) the primary structural frame, and (3) the floor construction. A three-digit notation was developed, as follows:

1. *First digit.* Hourly fire resistance requirement for exterior-bearing wall fronting on a street or lot line
2. *Second digit.* Hourly fire resistance requirement for structural frame or columns and girders supporting loads from more than one floor
3. *Third digit.* Hourly fire resistance requirement for floor construction

A comparison of types of construction, based on the MCSC notational system, as found in five building codes, is shown in Table 19.1.2.

For heavy timber construction, the notation *H* and not a digit was used for the structural frame and floor construction designations. Heavy timber construction is unique because it is identified by detailed requirements relating mainly to the size of structural members and their connections. Properties such as combustibility or fire resistance are not specifically included in the requirements for heavy timber construction, except that exterior walls are required to be of noncombustible construction.

Thus, for example, a "332" building would have 3 hour fire-resistant exterior bearing walls, a 3 hour fire-resistant structural frame, and 2 hour fire-resistant floor construction, and would correspond to the *NFPA 5000* Type I (332) building, the BOCA National Building Code Type 1B building, the ICBO Uniform Building Code Type I FR (fire resistive) building, the SBCCI Standard Building Code Type II building, and the ICC International Building Code Type 1A.

A standard nomenclature was also developed for identifying and defining the structural elements in buildings as they relate to fire resistance. For example, it was found in reviewing various codes and fire protection standards that floor construction was referred to by such terms as "floors," "floor assemblies," "floor and ceiling assemblies," and "floor deck construction." If codes agree, for example, that "floor construction" includes the floor deck and all structural elements directly supporting the loads from the floor, as recommended by MCSC, then some misinterpretation of a code's intent would be avoided.

TABLE 19.1.1 Model Codes Standardization Council Recommended Types of Construction

	Noncombustible	
	Type I (443)	Type II (222)
	Type I (332)	Type II (111)
		Type II (000)
	Combustible	
Type III (211)	Type IV (2HH)	Type V (111)
Type III (200)		Type V (000)

TABLE 19.1.2 Comparison of Construction Types (Based on the MCSC National System)

NFPA 220	I (443)	I (332)	II (222)	II (111)	II (000)	III (211)	III (200)	IV (2HH)	V (111)	V (000)
UBC	—	I FR	II FR	II 1-hr	II N	III 1-hr	III N	IV HT	V 1-hr	V-N
BNBC	1A	1B	2A	2B	2C	3A	3B	4	5A	5B
SBC	I	II	—	IV 1-hr	IV unp	V 1-hr	V unp	III	VI 1-hr	VI unp
IBC	—	1A	1B	IIA	IIB	IIIA	IIIB	IVHT	VA	VB

International Perspective

With regard to building construction in Australia, Belgium, Canada, Denmark, Finland, France, Germany, Great Britain, Italy, Japan, Netherlands, New Zealand, Norway, Russia, Sweden, Switzerland, and the United States, time temperature curves used to conduct fire resistance tests for building materials are virtually identical for the first 2 hours. After that period of time, most countries use a slightly similar curve, except for Japan, which uses a less severe exposure after 2 hours. Some countries limit heat transmission as a requirement for fire doors. In most cases this is not a requirement in the United States, and when it is a requirement, it is for only the first 30 minutes of the test. Two other building construction-related differences are that fire departments tend to be more aggressive in the United States than they are in most European countries and that there are many more unsprinklered properties outside the United States than there are within the United States.

Construction type classification in building codes is more of a convenience than a necessity. The National Building Code of Canada (NBCC) does not classify buildings in the traditional manner as do United States codes but rather specifies fire-resistive requirements for the structural components of a building, depending on its occupancy and its story height and floor area. In this code, two basic types of construction (i.e., combustible and noncombustible) are recognized. These are further subdivided by the characteristics of the materials used in construction under fire conditions.

CLASSIFICATION OF BUILDING CONSTRUCTION TYPES

Following the completion of the MCSC recommendations in 1974, a number of changes were adopted to the requirements for types of construction to agree with the MCSC classifications. However, it was recognized that some conflicts still remained among building codes. In 1975, the BCMC established a committee to develop more detailed recommendations for types of construction.

In 1980 the committee's recommended definitions of types of construction and fire resistance requirements were finalized. The requirements are based on five basic types of construction. Two are identified as noncombustible construction (Types I and II) and three as combustible construction types (Types III, IV, and V). Table 19.1.3 gives the fire resistance requirements for the structural frame, interior bearing walls, floor construction, and roof construction of the five basic types of construction. The table lists the building components that are essential to the stability of the building as a whole and comprise the "structural frame." The members of floor or roof panels that have no connection to the columns are considered part of the floor or roof construction and are not classified as a part of the structural frame.

Some of the terminology used to describe and classify building construction types is presented as follows:

- *Fire resistance rating.* The time, in minutes or hours, that materials or assemblies have withstood a fire exposure as determined by tests, or methods based on tests, as prescribed by the applicable building code. Applicable test methods include NFPA 251, *Standard Methods of Tests of Fire Resistance of Building Construction and Materials,* ASTM E119, *Standard Test Methods for Fire Tests of Building Construction and Materials,* or UL 263, *Standard for Fire Tests of Building Construction and Materials.* Where other methods such as calculation procedures are used to determine fire resistance, the calculations are to be based on the fire exposure and acceptance criteria specified in standardized test procedures such as NFPA 251. Standardized calculation methods include ASCE/SFPE 29, *Standard Calculation Methods for Structural Fire Protection,* and ACI 216.1/TMS 0216.2, *Standard Method for Determining Fire Resistance of Concrete and Masonry Assemblies.* The referenced test methods and associated calculation methodologies are useful in comparing the fire resistance of building materials but are not necessarily indicative of how the building materials might perform in an actual building fire. See Section 19, Chapter 2, "Structural Integrity During Fire," for more information on how the fire performance of building materials is determined.
- *Noncombustible material.* A material that, in the form in which it is used and under the conditions anticipated, will not ignite, burn, support combustion, or release flammable vapors when subjected to fire or heat. Materials that are reported as passing ASTM E136, *Standard Test Method for Behavior of Materials in a Vertical Tube Furnace at 750 Degrees C,* shall be considered noncombustible materials.
- *Limited-combustible material.* Refers to a building construction material not complying with the definition of noncombustible material that, in the form in which it is used, has a potential heat value not exceeding 3500 Btu/lb (8141 kJ/kg) where tested in accordance with NFPA 259, *Standard Test Method for Potential Heat of Building Materials,* and includes either of the following: (1) materials having a structural base of noncombustible materials, with a surfacing not exceeding a thickness of 1/8 in. (3.2 mm) that has a flame spread index not greater than 50; and (2) materials, in the form and thickness used, having neither a flame spread index greater than 25 nor evidence of continued progressive combustion, and of such composition that surfaces that would be exposed by cutting through the material on any plane would have neither a flame spread index greater than 25 nor evidence of continued progressive combustion, when tested in accordance with NFPA 255, *Standard Method of Test of Surface Burning Characteristics of Building Materials.* Materials subject to increases in combustibility or to a flame-spread index beyond the limits herein established through the effects of age, moisture, or other atmospheric conditions are considered combustible.
- *Combustible material.* A material that, in the form in which it is used and under the condition anticipated, will ignite and burn. It is further described as a material that does not meet the definition of noncombustible material or limited-combustible material.

Type I Construction

Type I construction (formerly referred to as fire resistive) is construction in which the structural members are noncombustible

TABLE 19.1.3 Fire Resistance Ratings for Type I Through Type V Construction (hr)

	Type I		Type II			Type III		Type IV	Type V	
	442	*332*	*222*	*111*	*000*	*211*	*200*	*2HH*	*111*	*000*
Exterior Bearing Walls										
Supporting more than one floor or columns or other bearing walls	4	3	2	1	0	2	2	2	1	0
Supporting one floor only	4	3	2	1	0	2	2	2	1	0
Supporting a roof only	4	3	1	1	0	2	2	2	1	0
Interior Bearing Walls										
Supporting more than one floor or columns or other bearing walls	4	3	2	1	0	1	0	2	1	0
Supporting one floor only	3	2	2	1	0	1	0	1	1	0
Supporting roofs only	3	2	1	1	0	1	0	1	1	0
Columns										
Supporting more than one floor or columns or other bearing walls	4	3	2	1	0	1	0	H	1	0
Supporting one floor only	3	2	2	1	0	1	0	H	1	0
Supporting roofs only	3	2	1	1	0	1	0	H	1	0
Beams, Girders, Trusses, and Arches										
Supporting more than one floor or columns or other bearing walls	4	3	2	1	0	1	0	H	1	0
Supporting one floor only	2	2	2	1	0	1	0	H	1	0
Supporting roofs only	2	2	1	1	0	1	0	H	1	0
Floor-Ceiling Assemblies	2	2	2	1	0	1	0	H	1	0
Roof-Ceiling Assemblies	2	1½	1	1	0	1	0	H	1	0
Interior Nonbearing Walls	0	0	0	0	0	0	0	0	0	0
Exterior Nonbearing Walls	0	0	0	0	0	0	0	0	0	0

Note: See applicable building requirements for more information.
H = Heavy timber members.
Source: *NFPA 5000®*, *Building Construction and Safety Code®*, Table 7.2.11, 2006, p. 5000-89.

and have a fire resistance as specified in Table 19.1.3. This classification is divided into two subtypes, Type I (442) and Type I (332). Reductions in the hourly rating might be permitted by the applicable building code. The basic difference between the subtypes is in the level of fire resistance specified for the structural frame. The fire resistance requirements for Type I (442 and 332) construction were selected because they provide reasonable fire safety for the structure for occupancies with moderate- and low-combustible contents. In occupancies with higher fire loads and hazardous uses, fire resistance may be supplemented by additional protection, usually including an automatic fire-extinguishing system. Even in occupancies with moderate fire loads, such as in mercantile and in some factory industrial and storage uses, supplementary fire safety precautions are usually required. These include restrictions on the building size or requirements for automatic fire-extinguishing equipment.

In Type I construction, only noncombustible or limited-combustible materials are permitted for the structural elements of the building. This regulation is well accepted and appears in practically every modern building code. Obviously, if combustible structural materials were allowed in noncombustible building types, the whole concept of their allowable use (height and area) would become meaningless. However, for practical reasons, the use of some combustible materials in Type I and Type II buildings are permitted for other than structural components. Roof coverings, some types of insulating materials, and limited amounts of interior finish and flooring do not add significantly to the fire hazard or fire load if these materials are properly regulated and qualified by fire tests.

Some codes have attempted to regulate combustible materials by using two or three alternatives that allow for the acceptance of materials having relatively low fuel content and surface burning characteristics. The purpose of this definition was to recognize certain materials or nonhomogenous assemblies containing limited amounts of combustible materials, such as gypsum wallboard which, although covered with paper, is used as a fire-resistive material. These alternate definitions include limits on surface flame spread rating (per NFPA 255) and on the heat content (per NFPA 259)—the latter being 3500 Btu per lb (8050

J/kg) for limited-combustible material, somewhat less than half that of untreated wood.

Rather than complicate the definition for the accommodation of certain materials, a more fundamental approach is to define limited uses and combustibility characteristics of materials that may be acceptable in buildings of Type I construction. This approach was followed in the NBCC and by the BCMC committee in its recommendations for the allowable kinds and extent of use of combustible material in the construction of Type I and II buildings.

Type II Construction

Type II construction (formerly referred to as noncombustible construction) is a construction type in which the structural elements are entirely of noncombustible or limited-combustible materials. Type II construction can be further classified as protected—Type II (222) or Type I (111)—in which the structural members have some degree of fire resistance, either 2 hour or 1 hour, or unprotected—Type II (000)—in which the structural members have no fire resistance rating. An example of protected construction is structural steel with spray-on fire proofing applied. Applicable building codes typically include additional provisions for exterior structural bearing walls of Type II construction.

The fire resistance required in Type II (222 or 111) construction will afford adequate fire safety for residential, educational, institutional, business, and assembly occupancies, without supplementary restrictions. Height limits, however, are commonly prescribed for this type of construction. When used for other occupancies involving a greater fire loading, additional fire safety precautions are usually required, such as more stringent area limitations and automatic fire-extinguishing equipment. In occupancies with a low fire load attributed to contents, the absence of fuel in noncombustible construction not only helps prevent the spread of fire but also reduces potential risk of a fire starting within the structure itself.

The limitation on combustible material is valuable because it acts to prevent fire from spreading through concealed spaces or involving the structure itself. Because of this attribute, a fire in a building of Type I and Type II construction can be controlled more readily (Figure 19.1.1). Requirements for exterior walls of Type II construction are specified by the applicable building code or standard that is used by the authority having jurisdiction (AHJ).

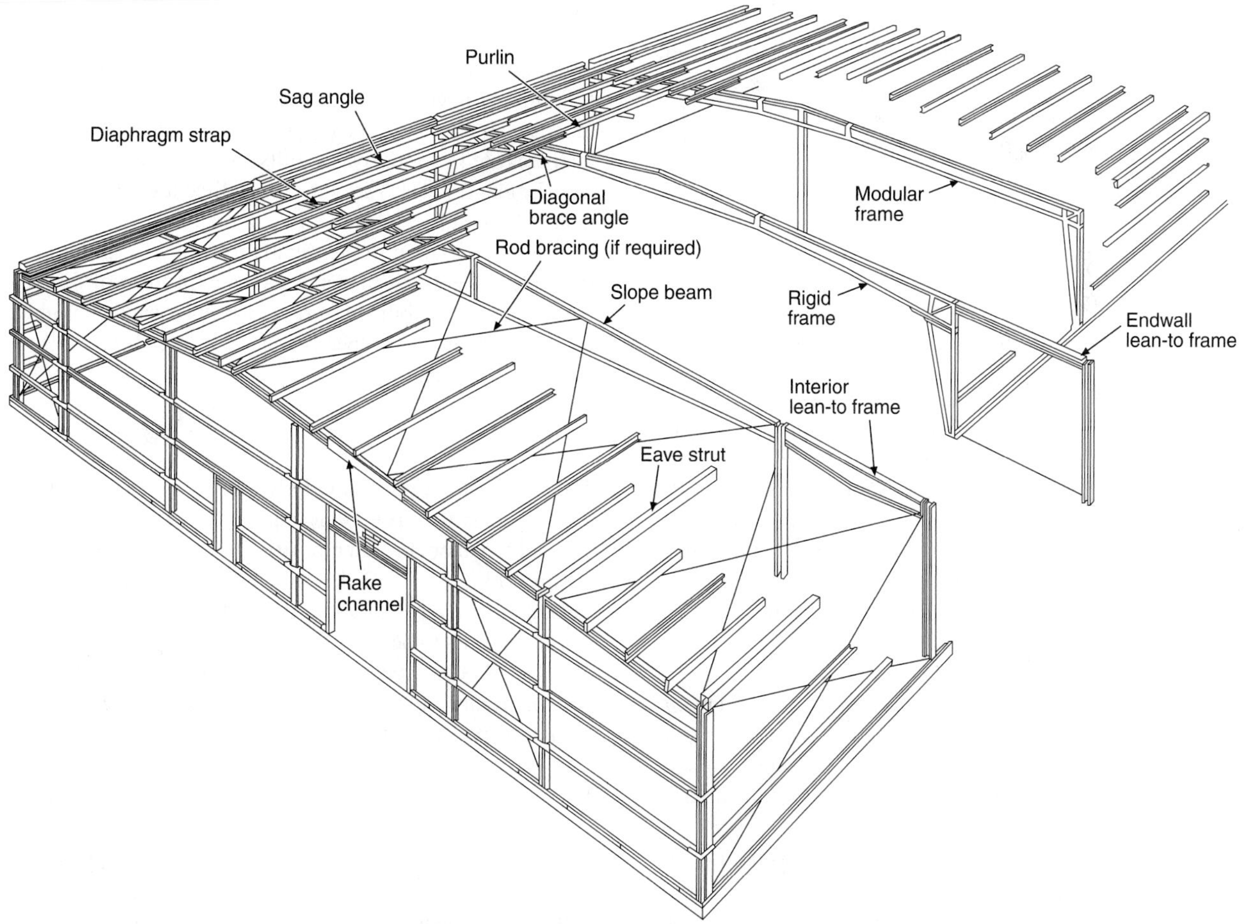

FIGURE 19.1.1 Framing System Representative of Type II (Noncombustible, Unprotected) Construction, Showing Preengineered Pitched Roof and Lean-To Framing with Structural Elements of Unprotected Steel

Type III Construction

Type III construction (formerly referred to as exterior protected or ordinary construction) is a construction type in which all or part of the interior structural elements may be of noncombustible, limited-combustible, or approved combustible materials as permitted by the applicable building code. The exterior walls are required to be of noncombustible or limited-noncombustible materials possessing a fire resistance rating in accordance with the applicable building code. Type III construction is further divided into protected and unprotected subtypes. Protected construction, Type III (211), has a 1 hour fire resistance for the floors and structural elements. Type III (200) construction has no fire resistance for the floors or structural elements. Whether or not fire resistance is provided, it is essential that all concealed spaces be properly fire blocked in buildings of combustible construction. This must be done with care in all furred spaces, partitions, ceiling spaces, and attics. Codes are very specific as to the materials used for fire blocking and the locations where it is required. To be effective, fire blocking must completely close off and subdivide the combustible construction into limited areas, thereby restricting the spread of fire and hot gases and allowing additional time for detection and evacuation of the building or area involved.

The 1 hour fire resistance provided in Type III (211) construction offers a measure of safety for fire fighting and evacuation before the construction itself becomes involved. However, combustible parts of any fire-rated assembly are likely to be burning actively before the end of the rated time period. For this reason, that portion of the fire load represented by combustible structural elements must be considered as part of the total potential fire load, whether or not the construction is protected.

Type IV Construction

Type IV construction (formerly referred to as heavy timber) is a construction type in which structural members—that is, columns, beams, arches, floors, and roofs—are basically of unprotected wood (solid or laminated) with large cross-sectional areas, with minor exceptions. No concealed spaces are permitted in the floors and roofs or other structural members. NFPA 220 and most model building codes are specific in the minimum dimensions permitted for the various wood structural members and minimum fire-resistive ratings required for interior columns, arches, beams, girders, and trusses of materials other than wood that may be permitted as acceptable alternatives to wood members (Table 19.1.4).

Walls, both interior and exterior, including structural members framed into them, can be of noncombustible or limited-combustible materials acceptable to the code being applied. Brick and stone were the traditional materials used in early heavy timber, or "mill," construction.

During a fire, heavy timber construction resists failure longer than a conventional wood frame structure because the structural members are larger, have a smaller surface to mass ratio, and take longer to burn. As the wood member burns, a layer of char develops, which acts like insulation and slows down the rate of burning. The large wood members, therefore, can continue to carry their structural loads due to the mass of unburned wood.

TABLE 19.1.4 Recommended Nominal Dimensional Requirements for BCMC Type IV (2HH) Construction

	Supporting Floors	*Supporting Roofs*
Columns	8 in. × 8 in.	6 in. × 8 in.
Beams and girders	6 in. × 10 in.	4 in. × 6 in.
Arches	8 in. × 8 in.	6 in. × 8 in., 6 in. × 6 in., 4 in. × 6 in.
Trusses	8 in. × 8 in.	4 in. × 6 in.
Floors	3 in. T & G or 4 in. on edge w/1-in. flooring	
Roofs		2 in. T & G or 3 in. on edge or 1⅛ in. plywood

Note: T & G = tongue and groove.
For SI units: 1 in. = 25.4 mm.

Heavy timber construction is more properly considered a building system, not just a construction type using large-size framing members. It was developed during the mid-1800s by insurance interests for the purpose of reducing fire losses in the many textile factories, paper mills, and storage buildings in the New England states. Through the intelligent use of combustible materials of sufficient mass, the absence of concealed spaces, and by paying attention to details to avoid sharp corners and ignitable projections, the chance of rapid spread of fire is lessened and the probability of serious structural damage is reduced. Examples of heavy timber construction are shown in Figures 19.1.2 and 19.1.3.

Type V Construction

Type V construction (formerly referred to as wood frame) is a type of construction in which the structural members are entirely of wood or any other material permitted by the code being applied (Figure 19.1.4). Depending on the exterior horizontal separation to adjacent buildings, the exterior walls may or may not be required to be fire resistive.

Type V construction is probably more vulnerable to fire, both internally and externally, than any other building type. Accordingly, it is essential that greater attention be given to the details of construction of this basically light wood-frame building. Fire blocking in exterior and interior walls at ceiling and floor levels, in furred spaces, and other concealed spaces can retard the spread of fire and hot gases in these vulnerable areas. Type V construction is subdivided into two subtypes: Type V (111) construction, which has 1 hour fire resistance throughout, including the exterior walls; and Type V (000) construction, which has no fire protection or fire resistance requirements, except for the exterior walls when horizontal separation is less than 10 ft (3 m).

FIGURE 19.1.2 Elements of a Building of Type IV (Heavy Timber) Construction. Note the large size of the columns and beams and the absence of concealed spaces. The exterior nonbearing wall at far left is of lightweight corrugated steel.

FIGURE 19.1.3 A Variation of Type IV (Heavy Timber) Construction with Haunched Arches of Laminated Wood (Glue-Laminated Construction) and Beams Anchored to Arches by Steel Hangers

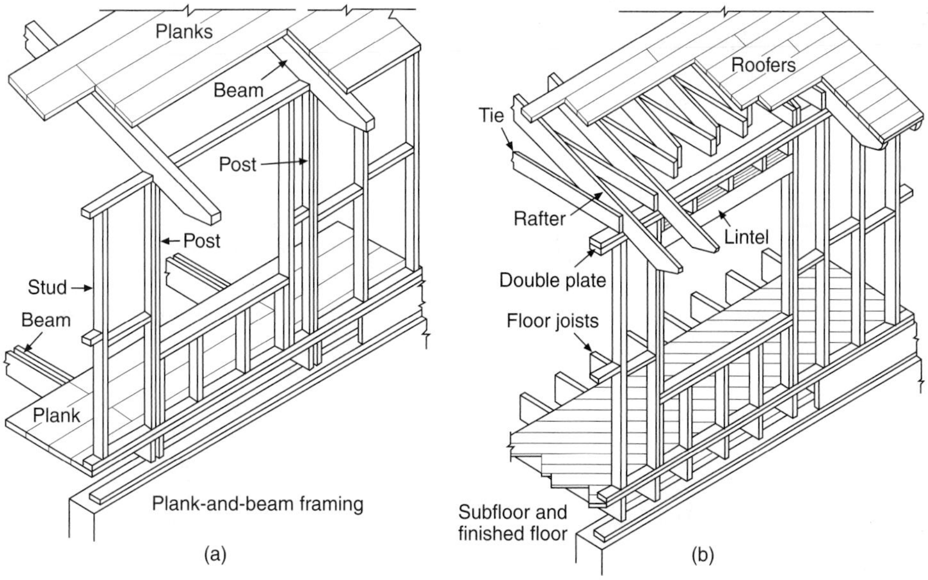

FIGURE 19.1.4 Two Variations on Basic Type V (Wood Frame) Construction: (a) Plank-and-Beam Framing in Which a Few Large Members Replace Many Small Members Used in Typical Wood Framing, (b) Conventional Wood Framing (Western or Platform Construction). Fire blocking is essential in concealed spaces.

Mixed Types of Construction

Where two or more types of construction are used in the same building, it is generally recognized that the requirements for occupancy or height and area would apply for the least fire-resistive type of construction. However, in cases where each building type is separated by adequate fire walls or area separation walls (see NFPA 221, *Standard for High Challenge Fire Walls, Fire Walls, and Fire Barrier Walls*) having appropriate fire resistance, each portion may be considered as a separate building.

Another general limitation included in some codes prohibits construction types of lesser fire resistance to support construction types having higher required fire resistance. In the event of a fire, the risks of a major structural collapse are generally too great to permit this type of design. This limitation does not necessarily apply where construction supports nonbearing separating partitions that provide protection for exit corridors or tenant spaces.

FIRE PROTECTION OF BUILDING ELEMENTS

Fire protection of structural elements is provided for two reasons: (1) to minimize the likelihood that the structural member will contribute to the fuel load, and (2) to ensure that the structural elements will maintain their integrity when exposed to fire. Loss of integrity of the building structure (total or partial collapse) will render fire-fighting measures less effective. Protection of other building elements, such as non-load-bearing interior walls, is also desired under certain conditions to mitigate the spread of fire within or into the building. See Section 19, Chapter 2, "Structural Integrity During Fire," for further discussion.

There are two groups of building elements: (1) load-bearing and (2) non-load-bearing. Load-bearing elements are those that support significant loads other than their own weight. Non-load-bearing elements support only limited loads in addition to their own weight. Removal of non-load-bearing elements would have no effect on the structural behavior of the building as a whole. Table 19.1.5 lists the structural elements that are common to most buildings, separated into these two general categories.

Building codes provide requirements for both structural loads and superimposed live loads. Structural failures are generally the result of application of unanticipated loadings. In a fire situation, "loads" are induced by heat which may cause thermal stresses. These stresses may be increased if the members are in any way restrained against expansion. Also, heat from fire may cause a loss of strength and increase in deflection, if not actual consumption of the member. Although restraint in some designs may offset any loss in strength, there is the increased likelihood of collapse in the event of a protracted fire. Properly designed and constructed assemblies having a fire resistance adequate for the exposure will retain adequate strength during fire exposure and continue to resist collapse.

TABLE 19.1.5 Structural Elements of a Building

Load-Bearing Elements	*Non-Load-Bearing Elements*
Compressively stressed columns	Curtain or panel walls
Walls, exterior or interior	Partitions
Flexurally stressed beams, girders, trusses, floors, roofs	Ceilings

Columns serve to carry building loads to the foundation where the loads are distributed to the supporting ground or rock. The material of the column is established by the type of construction—steel or reinforced concrete if noncombustible, or wood, including heavy timber designs, if combustible. In a fire, interior columns are the most severely exposed of any structural members, as they may be enveloped in fire on all sides.

WALLS

Building walls may serve one or more functions and they may be either bearing or nonbearing and exterior or interior. The following brief definitions describe the general functions that walls may serve:

Bearing wall: A wall that supports significant vertical loads in addition to its own weight

Cavity wall: A wall of two parallel wythes (vertical wall of bricks or concrete blocks) with an air space between them. The wythes are connected by metal ties.

Curtain wall: An exterior wall supported by the structural frame of the building. Also called a panel wall.

Exterior wall: A wall that forms a boundary to a building and is usually exposed to the weather

Faced wall: A wall composed of two different masonry materials: (1) the facing wythe and (2) the backup wythe, which are bonded together to act as a single unit

Fire partition or *fire barrier wall:* An interior wall that serves to restrict the spread of fire, but does not qualify as a fire wall

Fire wall: A wall of sufficient fire resistance, durability, and stability to withstand the effects of an uncontrolled fire exposure, which may result in collapse of the structural framework on either side. Openings in the wall, if allowed, must be protected.

Hollow wall: A wall of two parallel wythes, with an air space between them, but without ties to hold the wythes together

Nonbearing wall: A wall that supports only limited loads in addition to its own weight

Parapet wall: A portion of an exterior, fire, or party wall that penetrates through and extends above the roof line

Partition: An interior wall, not more than one story in height, that separates two areas in the same building but is not intended to serve as a fire barrier

Party wall: A wall that lies on a common lot line for two buildings and is common to both buildings. These walls may be constructed with a wide range of materials or assemblies.

Sandwich wall: A nonbearing wall whose outer faces enclose an insulating core material

Shaft wall: An interior wall that separates a vertical opening for a stairway, elevator, duct space, and so on, and connects two or more floors

EXTERIOR WALLS

The primary function of all exterior walls is to protect the inside of the building from the elements, such as heat and cold, water, wind, and windblown dust and dirt. In addition, some exterior walls may support floor and roof framing systems and may include portions that support girders or beams.

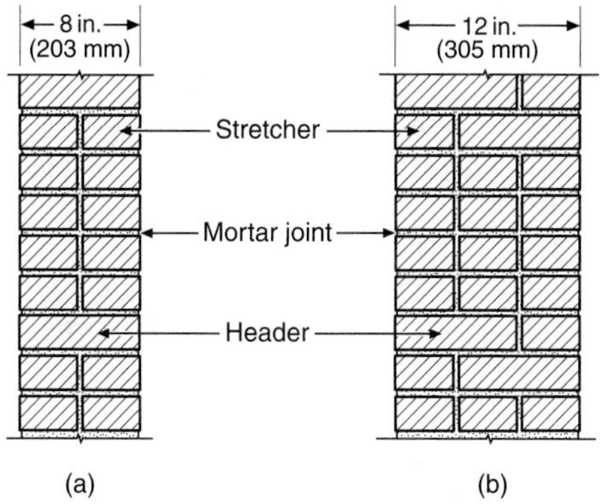

FIGURE 19.1.5 Typical Types of Wall and Partition Assemblies: (a) 8 in. (203 mm) Brick Bearing Wall, (b) 12 in. (305 mm) Brick Bearing Wall

The fire resistance required for exterior walls is determined not only by the type of construction but also by the distance the wall is set back from a lot line or an exposing structure. The greater that distance, the less severe the exposure and, hence, the less fire resistance that would be needed. NFPA 80A, *Recommended Practice for Protection of Buildings from Exterior Fire Exposures,* may be used to determine acceptable combinations of separation distance and exterior wall fire resistance or active protection.

Load-Bearing Exterior Walls

Load-bearing exterior walls are generally constructed of either masonry units (such as stone, brick, concrete block, or a combination of these materials) or concrete. Brick veneer is sometimes used as a facing in wood or metal-stud wall construction. In this case, the studs support the applied loads, while the veneer provides an attractive, useful exterior surface. Veneers are also used as the exterior face of cavity walls. Figures 19.1.5, 19.1.6, 19.1.7, 19.1.8, and 19.1.9 illustrate some common forms of exterior wall construction.

Exterior walls of reinforced concrete are poured-in-place, precast, or tilt-up type. Masonry veneers are sometimes used as the exposed surface of reinforced concrete walls. The brick veneer is tied to the concrete by metal ties fastened to the concrete and set into the mortar bed joints of the masonry. If the walls are load-bearing, the reinforced concrete is designed to support all of the applied loads.

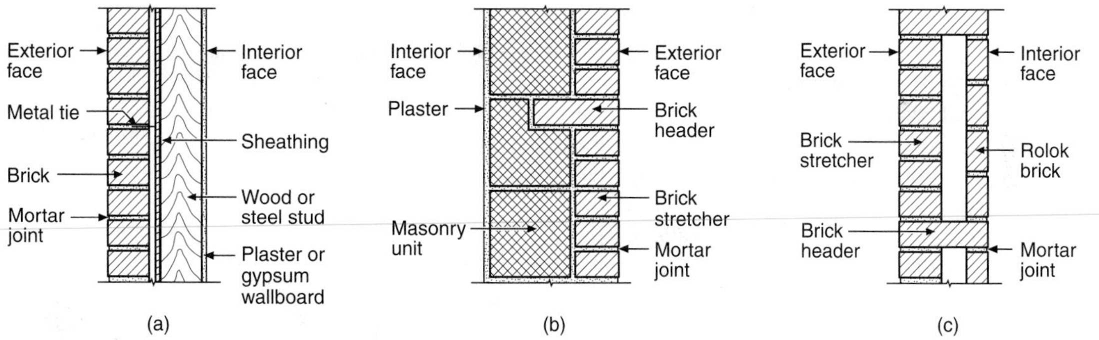

FIGURE 19.1.6 Typical Types of Wall Assemblies: (a) Exterior Brick Veneer on Wood-Frame Wall, (b) 12 in. (305 mm) Exterior Faced or Veneered Wall, (c) 8 in. (203 mm) Exterior Hollow Rolok Bak® Brick Wall

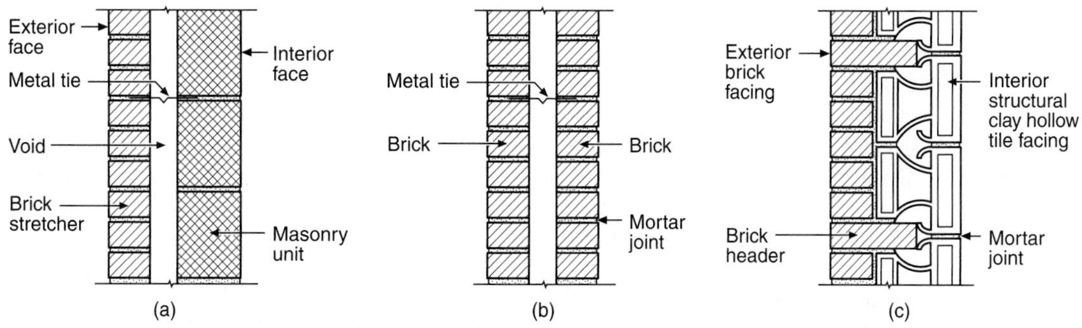

FIGURE 19.1.7 Typical Types of Wall Assemblies: (a,b) Two Examples of Exterior Nonbearing Cavity Walls, (c) 12 in. (305 mm) Exterior Bearing Wall

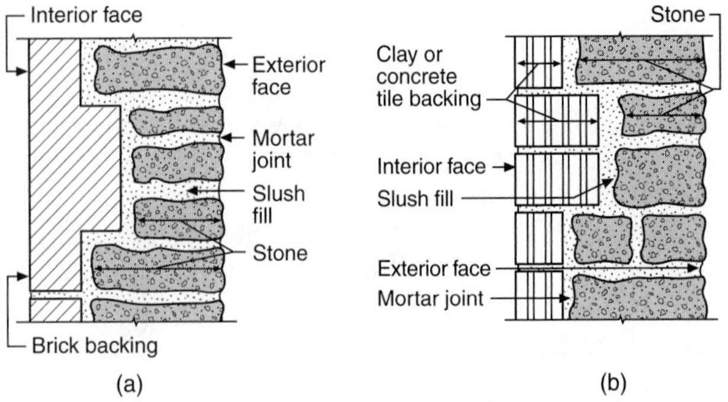

FIGURE 19.1.8 Stone-Faced Wall Assemblies: (a) with Brick Backing, (b) with Tile

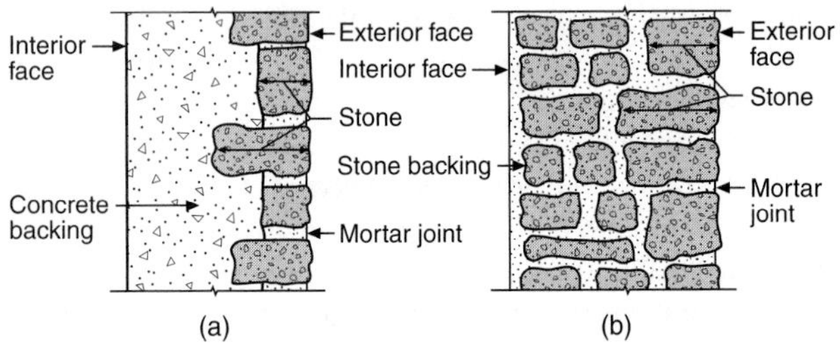

FIGURE 19.1.9 (a) Wall of Concrete Backing and Stone Face, (b) Solid Stone Wall

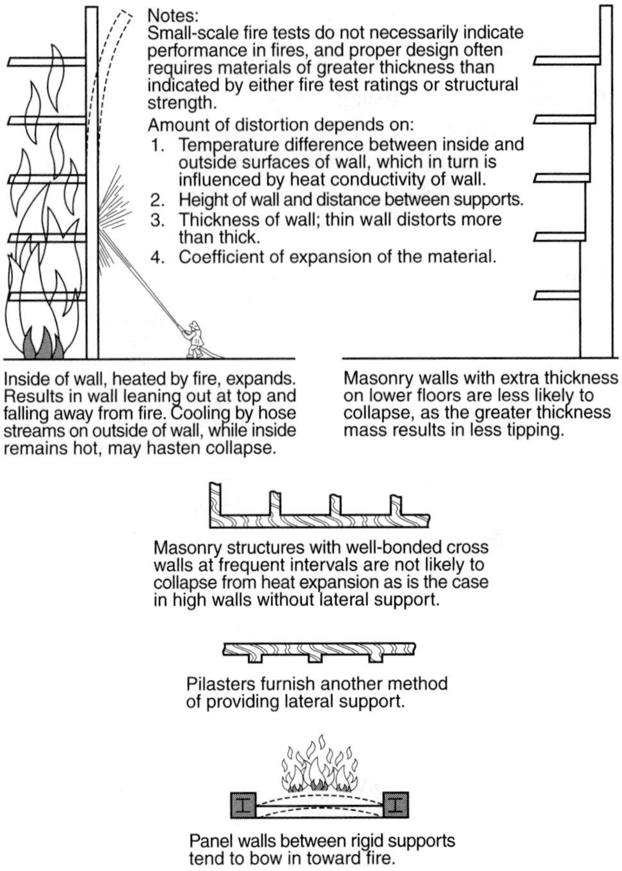
Notes:
Small-scale fire tests do not necessarily indicate performance in fires, and proper design often requires materials of greater thickness than indicated by either fire test ratings or structural strength.
Amount of distortion depends on:
1. Temperature difference between inside and outside surfaces of wall, which in turn is influenced by heat conductivity of wall.
2. Height of wall and distance between supports.
3. Thickness of wall; thin wall distorts more than thick.
4. Coefficient of expansion of the material.
Inside of wall, heated by fire, expands. Results in wall leaning out at top and falling away from fire. Cooling by hose streams on outside of wall, while inside remains hot, may hasten collapse.
Masonry walls with extra thickness on lower floors are less likely to collapse, as the greater thickness mass results in less tipping.
Masonry structures with well-bonded cross walls at frequent intervals are not likely to collapse from heat expansion as is the case in high walls without lateral support.
Pilasters furnish another method of providing lateral support.
Panel walls between rigid supports tend to bow in toward fire.

FIGURE 19.1.10 Heat Expansion Effects on Ordinary Masonry Walls

Exterior masonry walls may be non-load-bearing, that is, essentially supporting only their own weight. The floor and roof framing is supported by columns that transfer the loads to the foundation. Usually each story of the exterior wall is supported on spandrel beams, which frame into the columns. Some of the structural difficulties experienced with masonry walls in fires are illustrated in Figure 19.1.10.

Openings in Exterior Walls

Openings such as doors and windows in masonry walls must have supports to carry the weight of the wall structure above the openings. These supports, called lintels, can be constructed of several materials, including steel shapes, precast concrete beams, and stone or brick arches. Figures 19.1.11 and 19.1.12 illustrate several types of lintels. Steel lintels used in fire-resistive walls should have a fire-protective covering, such as concrete, or a spray-applied cementitious or mineral coating to prevent failure of the lintel and wall section above the opening. Openings may need to be limited in size and number when the exterior wall is close to the lot line. Openings that are protected do not have fire resistance as such but can impede the spread of fire. See the section entitled "Protection of Openings" in Section 18, Chapter 1, "Confinement of Fire in Buildings."

Openings for which protection (windows, doors) does not have the insulating value as that of the fire barrier wall or fire wall may hamper egress, cause personal injury in a fire, or allow autoignition of combustibles located near the unexposed face of

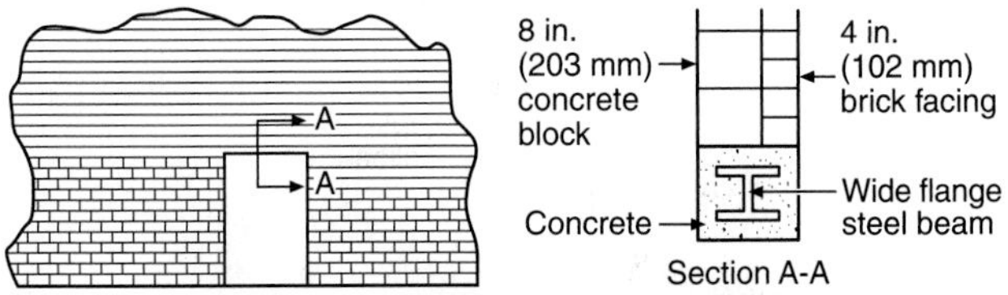

FIGURE 19.1.11 Lintels in Brick-Faced, Concrete Block Wall

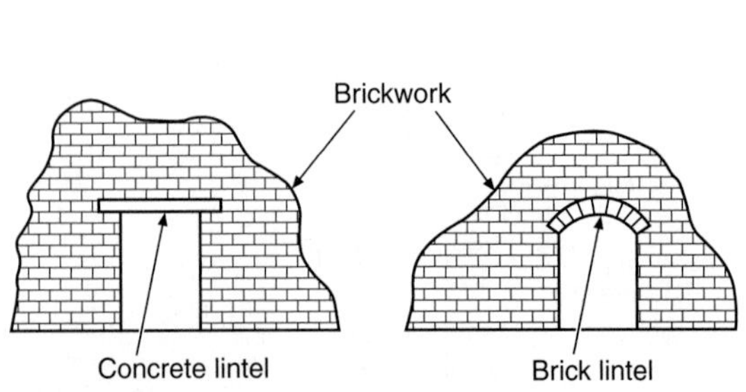

FIGURE 19.1.12 Use of Concrete and Brick Lintels in Masonry Walls

the opening. Maintaining a minimum separation distance (perpendicular to the face of the opening) equal to the maximum dimension of the opening will help prevent this.

Curtain Walls

Most multistory buildings consist of a protected steel or reinforced-concrete frame (columns, girders, and beams). The building envelope may be enclosed with nonbearing walls supported at each level. These walls are often identified as either curtain or panel walls. Many materials and types of construction are used for curtain walls. Aluminum and stainless steel curtain walls are, by far, the most common, but copper and copper alloys, carbon steel, galvanized metals, porcelain enamel finish, concrete, glass, and plastics are also used. Large window areas are common in this type of wall. Figure 19.1.13 shows an example of contemporary curtain wall construction.

A complete curtain wall assembly may consist of a panel with finished outside and inside surfaces, insulation, and means of attachment to the building frame. However, this type is not used as frequently as is a metal or glass skin assembly reinforced by conventional construction. Curtain walls are required to have fire resistance ratings up to 2 hours, depending on the separation distance between the wall and a lot line or exposing structure. Secure fastening of curtain walls is important for many reasons, including stability during fire exposure. Curtain walls are generally bolted to clips attached to the columns, spandrel, or floor slab. There is usually a space between the outer end of the floor slab and the inside face of the curtain wall. Unless adequately fire blocked, this space may act as a route for vertical fire spread for the entire height of a building.

Parapet Walls

A parapet wall is an extension of the wall construction above the roof line. The parapet on a fire wall helps to prevent a fire from spreading across the roof over the fire wall and can aid manual fire fighting. Where walls extend only a few inches above the roof, ignition of an adjoining roof is more likely to occur, depending on wind direction and velocity and the type of the roof covering. NFPA 220, *NFPA 5000,* GAP Guideline GAP 2.2.1, and FM Global Data Sheet 1-22,[1] for example, specify a parapet height of 30 in. (762 mm). Many building codes permit lesser heights, and in large sections of the country, 18 in. (457 mm) parapets are considered standard. The higher the parapet, the greater the degree of safety, but considerations of expense and appearance often dictate overall compromises.

Fire may also extend around the ends of fire walls where the exterior walls of the building on both sides of the fire wall are combustible. There are two methods of minimizing this danger: (1) extend the fire wall several feet out beyond the wall of the building or (2) provide blank fire-resistive exterior wall construction at each end of the wall (Figure 19.1.14 and Table

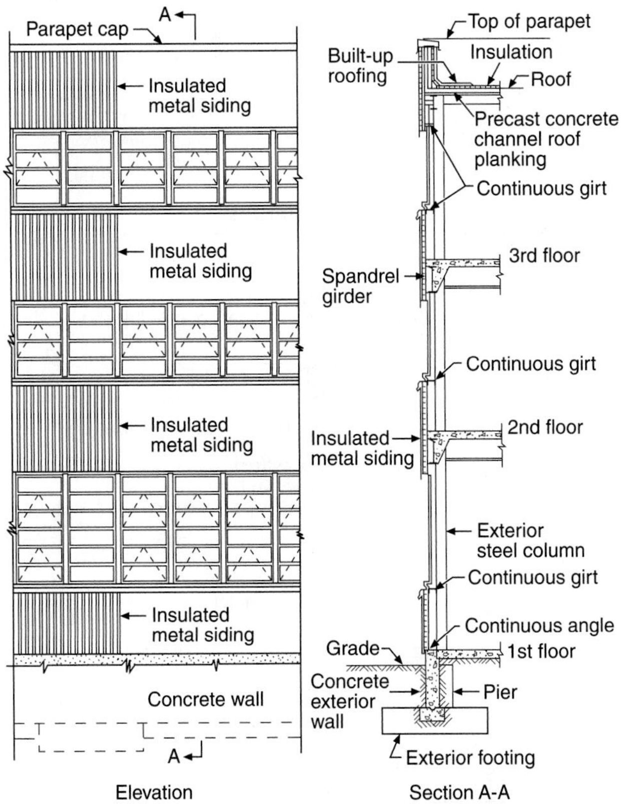

FIGURE 19.1.13 Elevation of Typical Bay of Steel Frame Curtain Wall Construction

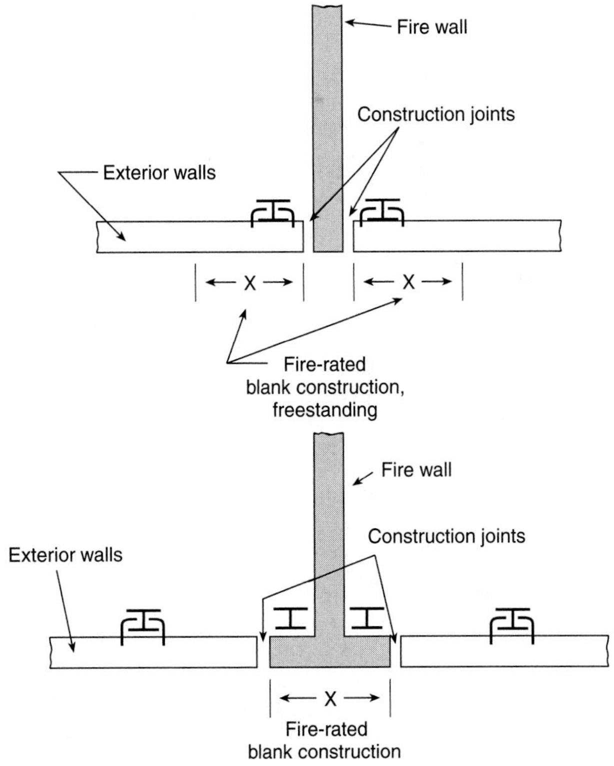

FIGURE 19.1.14 End Wall Exposure Protection: (a) End Walls Tied to Structural Framing, (b) End Walls Not Tied to Structural Framing (see Table 19.1.6)

19.1.6). The fire resistance rating of the end walls should be from the outside and should be a minimum of 1 hour but not more than 2 hours less than that of the fire wall. Where combustible roofs or cornices project beyond the walls of the building, fire walls should be extended to form a break in such combustible construction, as shown in Figure 19.1.15. Otherwise effective fire walls have failed because wood platforms or projecting canopies along the sides of buildings have spread fire from one fire area to another.

INTERIOR WALLS AND PARTITIONS

Interior walls and partitions used for building corridors or rooms may be either bearing or nonbearing. Bearing partitions are common in the older, wall-bearing construction systems and are also employed with industrialized building systems, particularly those of precast concrete. Newer construction tends to use nonbearing partitions.

The need for open space flexibility in modern construction has led to floor and interior partition design that allows nonbearing partitions to be installed at any location. These moveable partitions are often made of steel studs and gypsum board, and they may be installed, then dismantled and reinstalled at another location when occupancy needs change. Normally, moveable partitions extend only from the floor to the underside of the ceiling.

Interior partitions, particularly non-load-bearing partitions, can be installed with a number of other different materials. Wood stud and gypsum board or plaster is another very common type of partition. Partitions constructed of masonry units, such as concrete block, structural clay tile, terra cotta, and gypsum block are or have been commonly used in a wide variety of buildings and are more permanent. Figure 19.1.16 shows typical partition constructions.

Properly designed interior partitions can act as barriers to the spread of fire. To protect certain areas more completely than would be possible with ordinary partitions, wall assemblies possessing a fire resistance rating such as fire walls or fire barrier

TABLE 19.1.6 Length of End Wall Protection

Height of Exposing Area (ft [m])	*Length of End Wall Protection* (ft [m])*
Up to 40 (12.2)	6 (1.8)
41 to 70 (12.3)	10 (3.1)
71 (21.6) and over	14 (4.3)

*Protection should consist of blank, fire-rated construction.

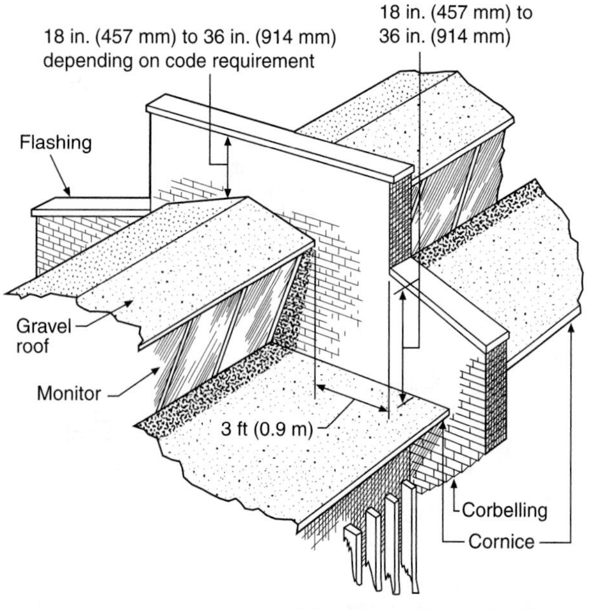

FIGURE 19.1.15 Fire Wall Installation on Building with Combustible Roof and Monitor

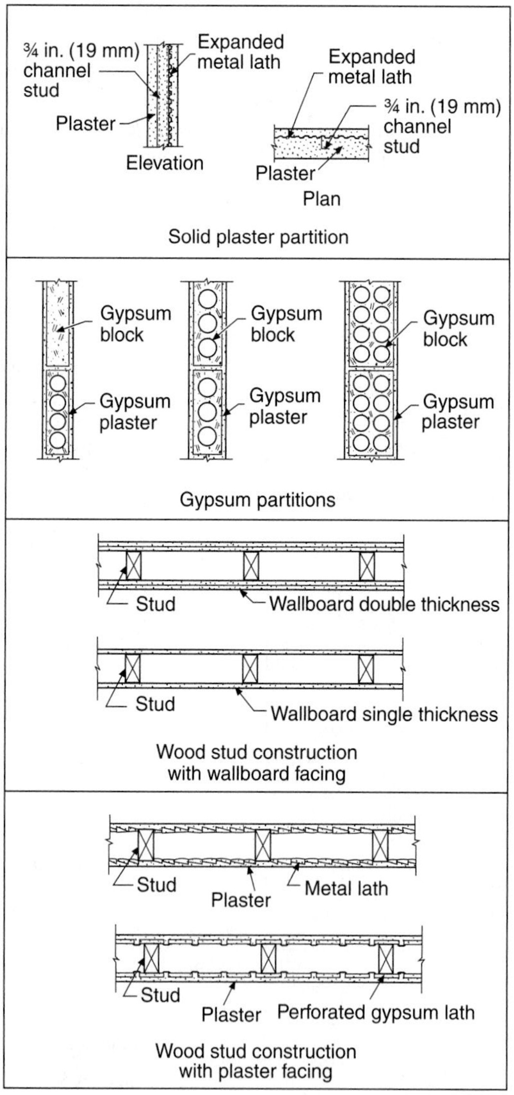

FIGURE 19.1.16 Typical Interior Wall and Partition Constructions

walls are constructed. Fire partitions may also be referred to as fire barrier walls; however, they are often incorrectly called fire walls.

Fire Walls and High Challenge Fire Walls

Fire walls and high challenge fire walls are interior walls providing a fire separation between areas of the same building. These walls are fire resistive, of noncombustible construction, often self-supporting, and cannot be readily modified to meet changing building needs. They are designed to maintain structural integrity, even in cases of complete collapse of the structure on either side of the fire wall. They are constructed of reinforced concrete, concrete block, prestressed concrete, and sometimes brick. Concrete or masonry walls generally require some type of steel reinforcement to withstand heat expansion effects. Adequate cover thickness of concrete must be provided over steel reinforcement. This is particularly important in the case of prestressed concrete walls. When designing prestressed concrete walls, refer to *Design for Fire Resistance of Precast Prestressed Concrete.*[2] Also, they may be buttressed by pilasters if of considerable height or length. In fire-resistive buildings, structure-supported fire division walls may be used, provided the structure has equal or greater fire resistance than that of the wall. Requirements for fire walls can be found in NFPA 221 and *NFPA 5000.*

Fire Barrier Walls

Usually, a fire barrier wall (or fire partition) subdivides a floor or an area and is erected to extend from the floor to the underside of the floor or roof above. Fire partitions may be constructed of noncombustible, limited-combustible, or protected combustible materials, and should be attached to and supported by structural members having fire resistance at least equal to that of the partition. A fire barrier wall normally possesses somewhat less fire resistance than a fire wall and does not extend from the basement through the roof, as does a fire wall. The fire resistance ratings for such partitions range from a half hour to as much as 4 hours. Requirements for fire barrier walls are less involved than those for fire walls and are also contained in NFPA 221 and *NFPA 5000.*

FLOOR FRAMING SYSTEMS

Floor framing systems typically include not only the flooring assembly but also its supporting beams, girders, or trusses. Beams and girders are nearly always an integral part of the floor system, whereas trusses may serve other purposes (and, hence, are discussed separately). The range of different types of floor framing systems that include beams and girders and the variety of components that may be included in a given assembly is best portrayed through drawings. Figures 19.1.17 through 19.1.27 are typical of many designs that are currently used.

Types of Floor Systems

Steel and Reinforced-Concrete Floor Assemblies. Figures 19.1.17 and 19.1.18 are generalized framing plans for steel and reinforced-concrete floor assemblies. The steel beams shown in Figure 19.1.17 support the floor assembly and are, in turn, supported by girders. Interior girders support beams on both sides. Girders are often concealed within partitions where their depth is not apparent, and they can directly support the weight of partitions in the space above. The girders frame into steel columns. Figure 19.1.18 illustrates a slab beam girder column system cast

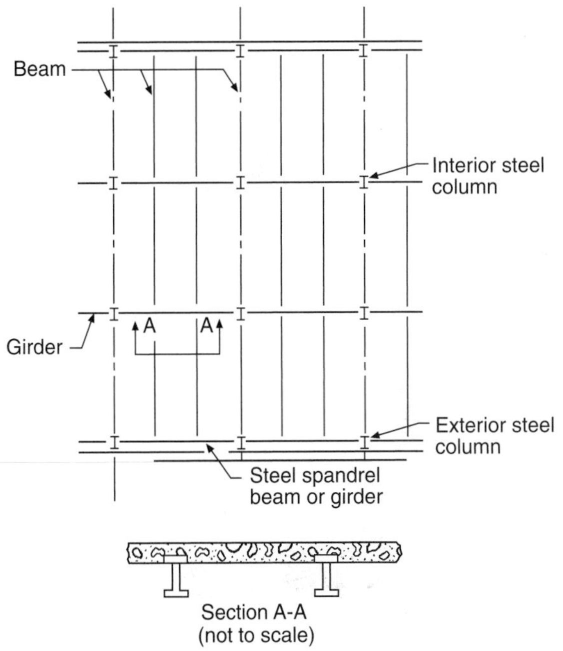

FIGURE 19.1.17 Portion of Floor Plan of Steel Frame Structure

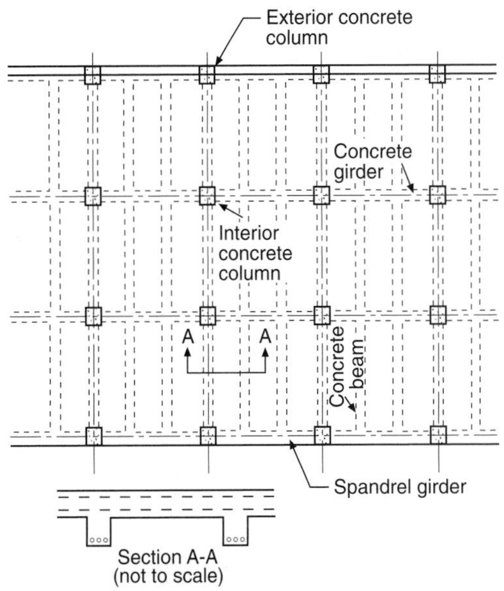

FIGURE 19.1.18 Portion of Floor Plan of Reinforced Concrete Beam and Girder Construction

monolithically (no joints) of reinforced concrete. The functions of the various components are the same as those described for the steel frame.

The floor slab supported by the steel beams shown in Figure 19.1.17 need not be of reinforced concrete. Alternative types of deck are the composite decks shown in Figures 19.1.19 and 19.1.20. This type of floor system offers many construction advantages. The metal deck acts as a form for the concrete and remains in place after curing. In addition, the cellular panels can be used for building service raceways where desired. The cellular panels can carry all three basic building services—power, telephone, and data transmission lines. A feature of this floor system is that the steel deck also acts as the tensile reinforcement of the concrete floor slab. A spray-applied fire-resistive coating on the steel deck underside may be required in some cases.

Another floor deck modification is to replace the reinforced-concrete floor slab with a precast concrete system. Figure 19.1.21 illustrates three common precast concrete floor slabs. The precast concrete planks generally have voids through their length that reduce the weight of the planks and act as building service raceways. The planks may be supported by either steel beams or reinforced concrete beams.

Open-web joists, which are lightweight prefabricated trusses, may replace steel beams as the intermediate flexural framing and are a very common type of construction both for floors and roofs. The spacing of floor joists is approximately 2 ft (0.61 m), and generally about 6 ft (1.8 m) for roof joists. Figure 19.1.22 illustrates this type of construction.

Because the spacing of the joists is so close, the floor slab can be thinner and still support the same load. Corrugated steel forms with 2½ in. (64 mm) of concrete as a wearing surface is a

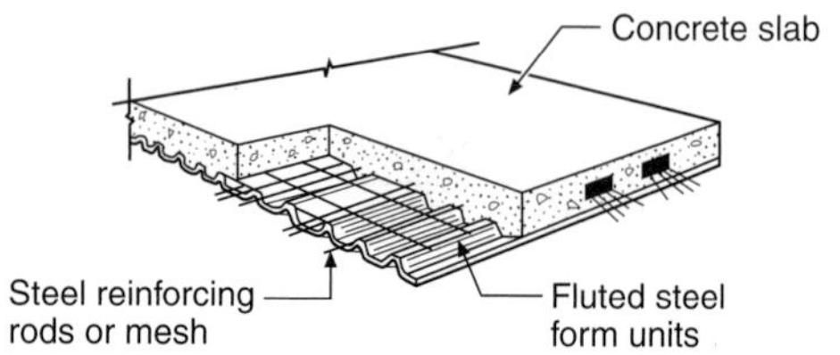

FIGURE 19.1.19 Concrete Floor Construction Showing Composite Floor Assembly

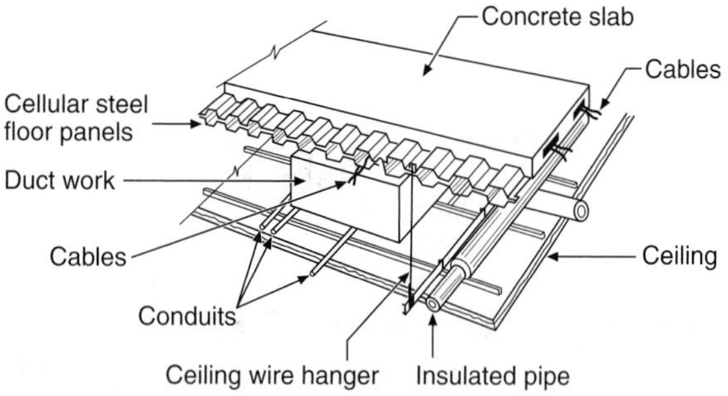

FIGURE 19.1.20 Concrete Floor Poured over Light Gauge Cellular Floor Panels

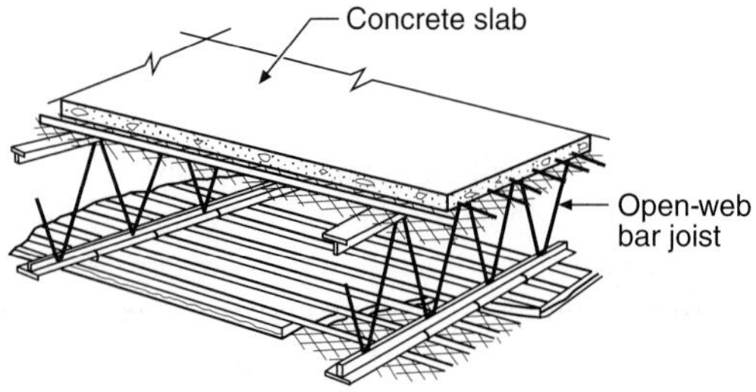

FIGURE 19.1.22 Concrete Floor Construction Showing Open-Web Steel Joist

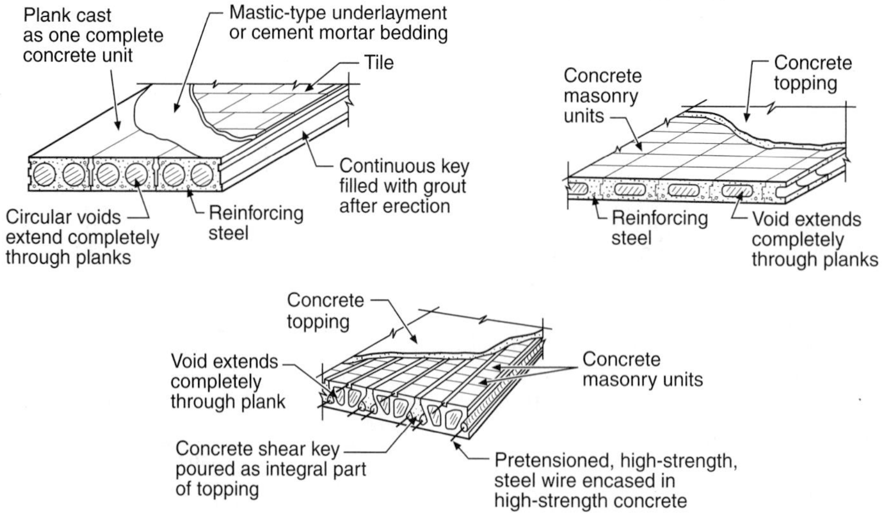

FIGURE 19.1.21 Three Precast Concrete Floor Slabs

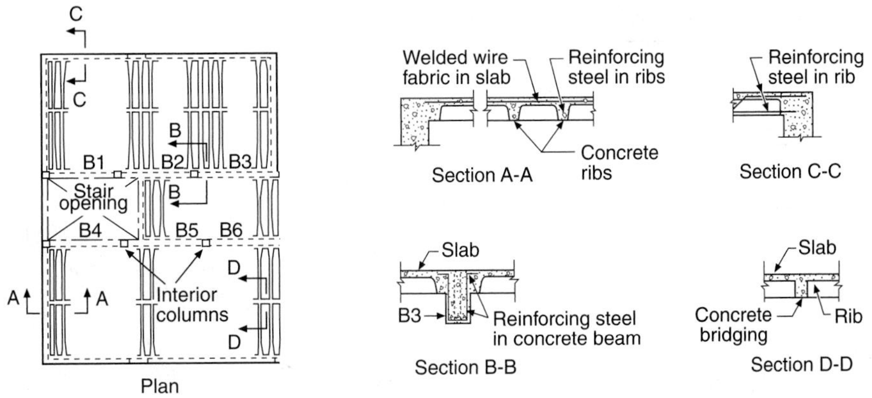

FIGURE 19.1.23 Partial Plan of a Concrete Joist Floor with Four Sectional Views

typical design. The corrugated deck acts as a form for the concrete and contributes to the support of live loads. Lightweight concrete is often used in place of normal-weight concrete to reduce the dead load.

Similarly, the reinforced concrete beams shown in Figure 19.1.18 may be spaced more closely together, permitting both a thinner floor slab and smaller beams. This type of construction is generally called a ribbed reinforced-concrete system or a concrete joist system. The ribbed system can be either cast in place or precast. Figure 19.1.23 illustrates the concrete joist floor, while Figure 19.1.24 illustrates two of the more common forms of ribbed precast systems. In each illustration, the ribs are the intermediate flexural framing.

The two-way flat slab is an increasingly popular floor system. Two-way reinforced-concrete slabs, used since the turn of the century, include reinforcement placed in two directions. The slab performs the functions of deck, intermediate flexural framing, and primary flexural framing. The underside of the slab may be either flat or ribbed in two directions. Figures 19.1.25 and 19.1.26 illustrate two different forms of this type of construction.

Wood Floor Systems. Wood floor systems can be designed to perform the same functions as the basic model in Figure 19.1.17. If the reinforced-concrete deck were replaced with heavy wood planking 2 in. (51 mm) or more in thickness, and

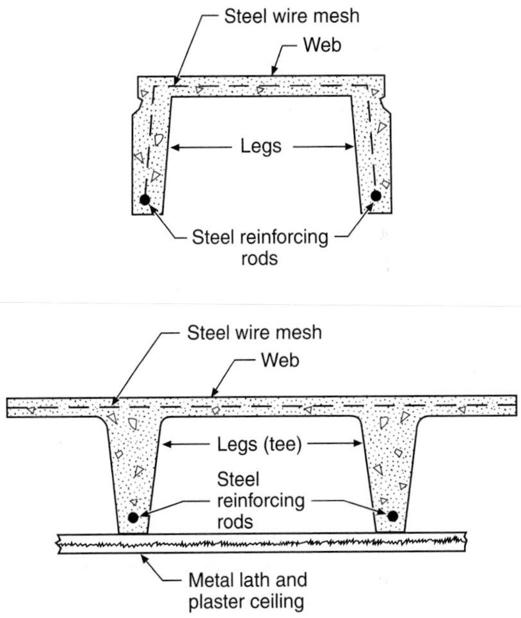

FIGURE 19.1.24 Sections Through Channel and Double-Tee Concrete Slabs. The slab at bottom shows a metal lath and plaster ceiling attached directly to the ribs of the slab. These slabs may be used as part of floor or roof framing systems.

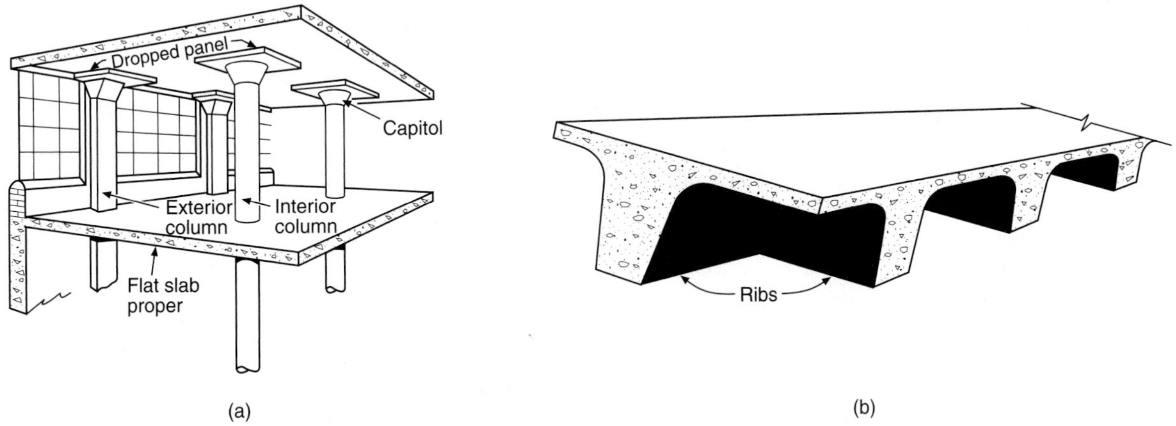

FIGURE 19.1.25 Two Types of Two-Way Flat Slabs: (a) Flat Underside, (b) Two-Way Ribbed Underside

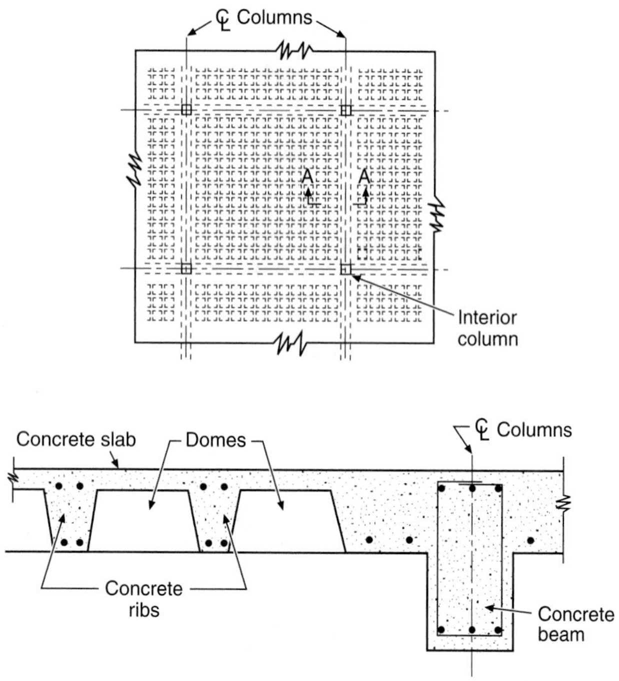

FIGURE 19.1.26 Partial Typical Interior Two-Way Ribbed Floor Slab with Section View A-A

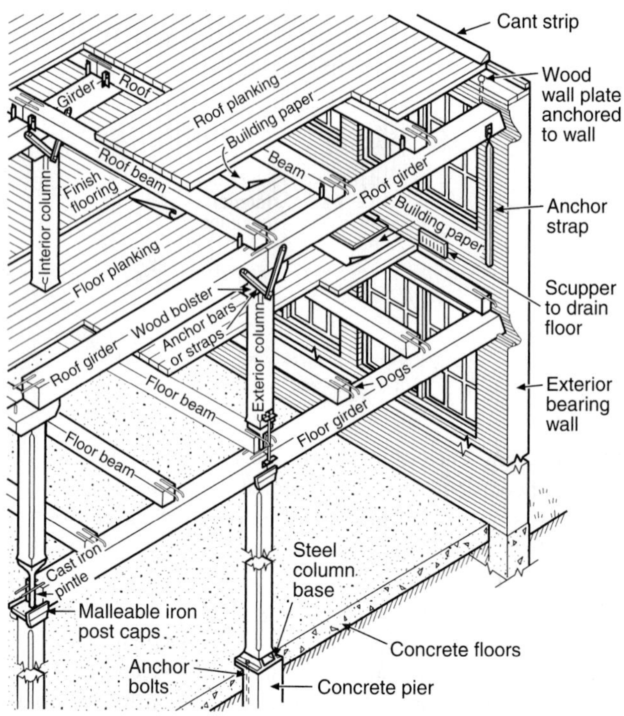

FIGURE 19.1.27 Components of a Heavy Timber Building Showing Floor Framing and Identifying Components of a Type Known as Semimill

the steel beams, girders, and columns with large wood members with a minimum dimension of 6 in. (152 mm), the basic form would be that of mill construction. This construction, shown in Figure 19.1.27, was quite common for industrial buildings and warehouses during the nineteenth century. The general design is still used in locations where wood has aesthetic appeal.

Lightweight, wood-frame construction is usually used in buildings of limited size. Floor joists in such construction are normally spaced 16 in. (406 mm) on center, and the vertical supports are often 2 in. by 4 in. (51 mm by 102 mm) or 2 in. by 6 in. (51 mm by 152 mm) wall-bearing studs, again spaced 16 in. (406 mm) on center. The stud walls may extend only from floor to floor in platform framing (Figure 19.1.28), or they may be extended continuously for two or three floors, a type of framing identified as balloon construction (Figure 19.1.29).

Wood-frame construction has little fire resistance because flames and hot gases can penetrate into the spaces between the joists or the studs. Fire blocking must be installed at critical locations throughout the building to prevent the rapid vertical and horizontal spread of fire. Fire blocks are normally made of wood blocks or noncombustible material. Figures 19.1.29 and 19.1.30 illustrate critical locations for fire blocking in balloon frame and in platform frame construction; Figure 19.1.31 shows the fire blocking for these constructions in greater detail.

Watertightness and Drainage of Floors

In addition to the effectiveness of floor framing systems as barriers to fire spread, there is another consideration involving floors in multistory buildings that can have a bearing on their performance in fires. This consideration is the degree of wa-

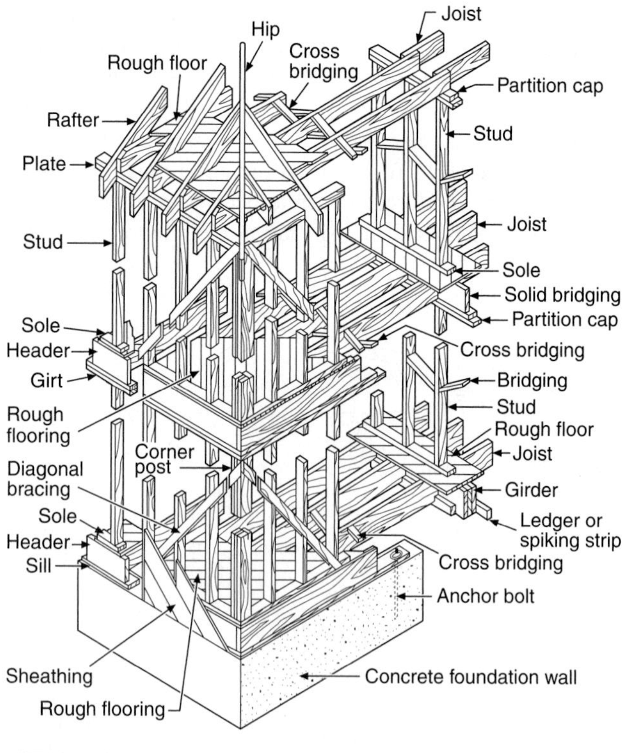

FIGURE 19.1.28 Wood-Frame Platform Construction Common to Dwellings with Structural Members Identified

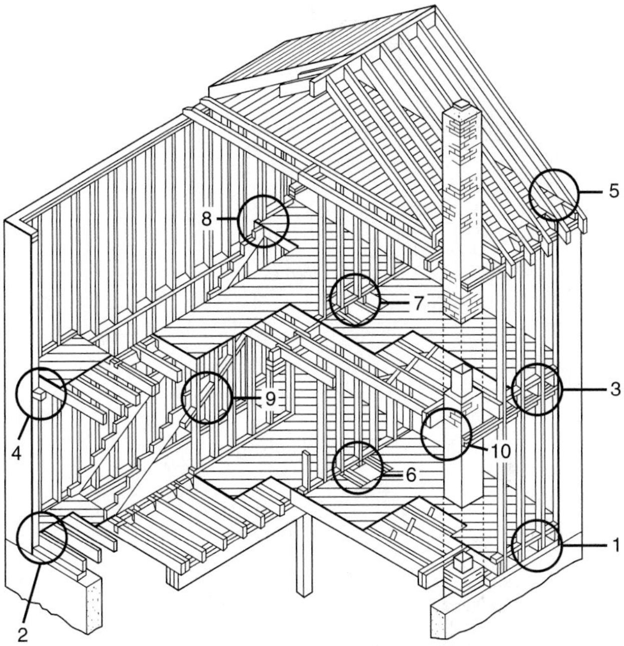

FIGURE 19.1.29 Wood Balloon Frame Construction Showing Points to Be Fire Blocked. Expanded views of points are shown in Figure 19.1.31.

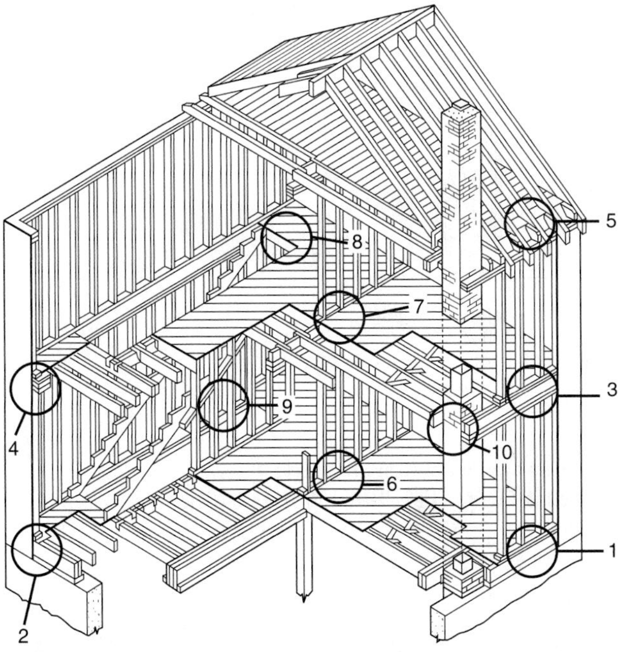

FIGURE 19.1.30 Wood Platform Frame Construction Showing Points to Be Fire Blocked. Expanded views of points are shown in Figure 19.1.31.

tertightness of construction and drainage arrangements for the floors. Massive quantities of water are sometimes needed on fires in unsprinklered buildings of combustible construction or buildings of noncombustible construction with significant occu-

TABLE 19.1.7 Sizes for Scuppers and Drains

Floor Areas	*Number of 4 in. (102 mm) Scuppers or Drains*
500 ft^2 (46 m^2) or less	2
750 ft^2 (70 m^2)	3
1000 ft^2 (93 m^2)	3

Note:
Additional scuppers for areas over 1000 ft^2 (93 m^2):
For Extra-Hazard Occupancies, Group 1 or 2 (quantity and combustibility of contents is very high), or floors of questionable watertightness, or contents especially subject to water damage—one scupper for each additional 500 ft^2 (46 m^2).
For Ordinary-Hazard Group 2 Occupancies (quantity and combustibility of contents is moderate) with watertight floors—one scupper for each additional 1000 ft^2 (93 m^2) or fraction thereof.
For Ordinary-Hazard Occupancies Group 1, or Light-Hazard Occupancies (quantity and combustibility of contents is low) with strictly watertight floors—one scupper for each additional 2000 ft^2 (186 m^2) or fraction thereof.

pancy fuel loads. Without good drainage and/or waterproofing arrangements, water could pose the threat of increased water damage on floors below.

Where acceptable, one inexpensive method of drainage is to provide scuppers in the exterior walls. Floor drains connected to ample size headers or a combination of scuppers and floor drains may be used. The number of scuppers or drains is dependent upon the hazard and the amount of water likely to be used. For average conditions, the recommendations in Table 19.1.7[3] are considered good practice.

Waterproofing techniques, such as waterproof membranes, hot mastics, asphalt emulsions, cementitious surfacings, and so on, are available that can be applied to the floors depending on the basic type of floor construction in question. The intent of these applications is to provide a watertight barrier on the floor itself, which extends up 4 to 6 in. (100 to 150 mm) at walls and columns. Water impounded by these protective measures must be carried off before its weight becomes a loading threat to the building.

TRUSSES

Where large areas must be column free or where special occupancy requirements may warrant, trusses may be used for purposes other than roof support. Three such applications are identified as (1) transfer trusses, (2) staggered trusses, and (3) interstitial trusses.

Transfer Trusses

Load transfer trusses create a clear space on a lower floor by directly supporting the loads from columns above the truss or, at times, from tension members below. This design allows large, column-free areas for auditoriums, ballrooms, and so on, at any level in a multistory building. Since transfer trusses carry loads from more than two floors, building codes generally require that the fire protection be provided by individual protection for each of the truss elements, or by complete enclosure of the truss (for its entire height and length) with envelope protection.

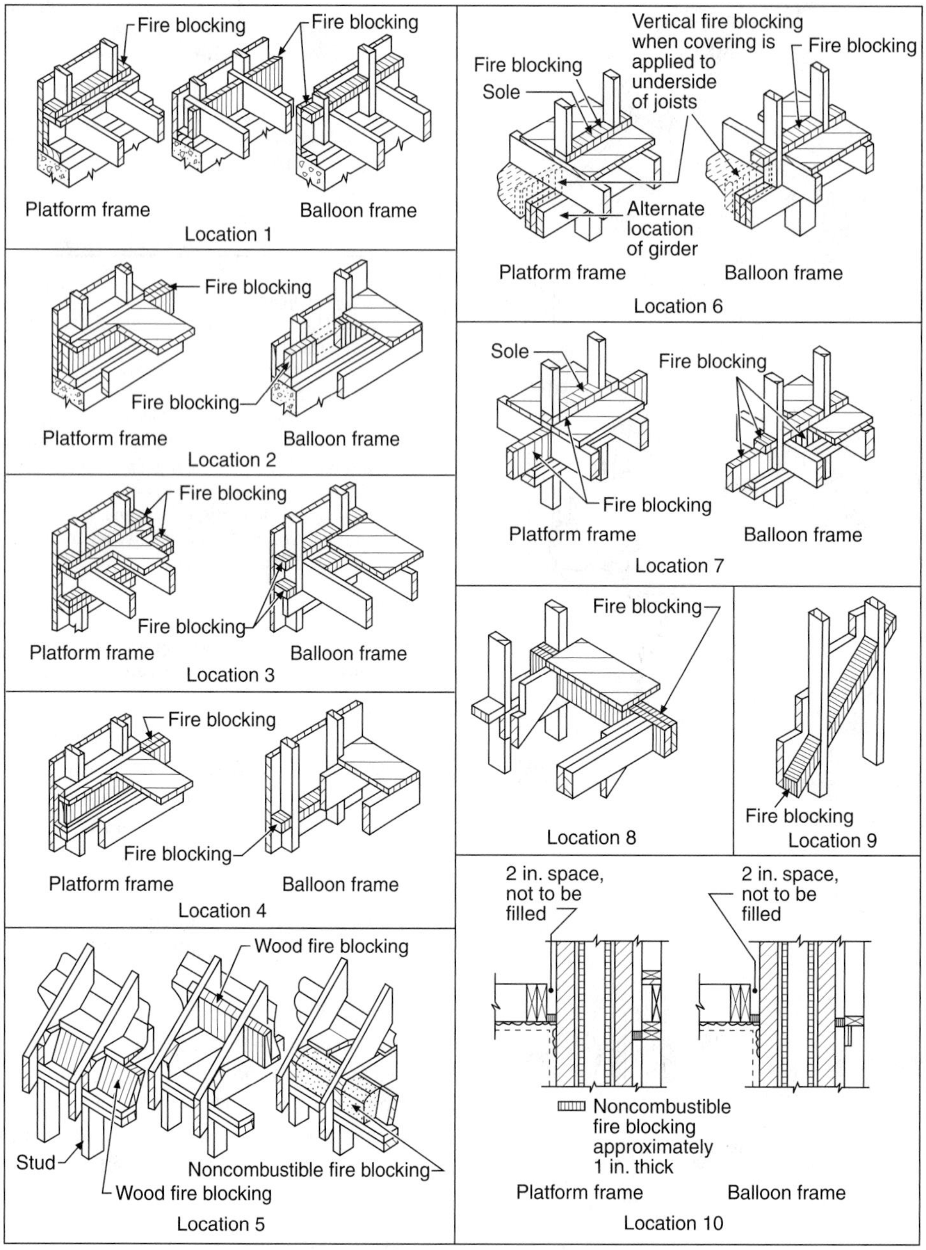

FIGURE 19.1.31 Details of the Application of Fire Blocking to Platform and Balloon Framing. Location numbers coincide with locations circled in Figures 19.1.29 and 19.1.30. For SI units: 1 in. = 25.4 mm.

Staggered Trusses

The staggered truss system is primarily intended for high-rise residential buildings. Typically, in a staggered truss design, story-high trusses span the full building width at alternate column lines on each floor. These trusses are supported only on the two rows of exterior columns. Thus, the interior of the building is column free; at any given elevation, floor construction is alternately supported on the top and bottom chords of adjacent trusses.

It is characteristic of staggered truss applications that these trusses are enclosed in wall construction that separates individual apartments or hotel/motel guest rooms. There may be a control opening in the truss that permits passage space for a corridor. Since staggered trusses are usually enclosed in walls, the entire wall assembly must have a fire resistance required for this condition.

Interstitial Trusses

The interstitial truss concept was first developed to solve the functional needs of hospitals. Although steel trusses in interstitial framing systems are quite deep (on the order of 8 ft [2.5 m] in height), they do not extend from floor to floor as do staggered trusses. The top chords support the floor above, while the bottom chords support a suspended ceiling system and a walking surface for maintenance purposes. As such, interstitial trusses are analogous to very deep open-web steel joists.

The interstitial space thus created provides a convenient location for the complex mechanical and electrical systems that are necessary components of a modern hospital. Direct access for maintenance, renovation, and replacement of the various system components within these interfloor spaces is provided without significant interference with normal operations.

Because each interstitial truss supports only one floor, all three conventional fire protection methods for trusses are permitted by the model building codes. However, because of practical considerations, individual protection of each truss element or ceiling membrane protection are the methods most widely used.

FLOOR/CEILING ASSEMBLIES

Ceiling components are important elements in the performance of a fire-resistive floor/ceiling assembly. In the event of fire within a room, the ceiling acts as a barrier to protect the structural framing above it. The degree of protection, of course, depends on the type of material, its installation, and its completeness. Combustible ceilings or ceilings that do not remain in place when subjected to the pressures and temperatures of a fire do not provide a significant degree of protection. It is important to note that the membrane ceiling is one part of the floor/ceiling assembly. The entire assembly, acting together, provides the designated fire resistance. The ceiling itself has insufficient fire resistance.

Ceilings may be applied directly to or suspended from the underside of the floor framing. Figure 19.1.24 illustrates a ceiling connected directly to the floor framing system; Figure 19.1.20 shows a ceiling suspended from the floor slab. It is also common to apply a fire-protective material, such as a plaster or sprayed mixture, directly to the bottom surface of the floor slab. Figure 19.1.32 illustrates a floor slab with plaster applied directly to the steel floor deck.

There are several types of suspended membrane ceilings in common use. One type consists of a lay-in system in which the ceiling panels are supported by an exposed metal grid. Another common type of membrane has the metal grid concealed by recesses in the edges of the ceiling panels. Suspended membrane ceilings may also consist of traditional lath and plaster or permanently secured gypsum wallboard with finished joints. Both of these latter systems can be either suspended below or attached directly to the basic subflooring system.

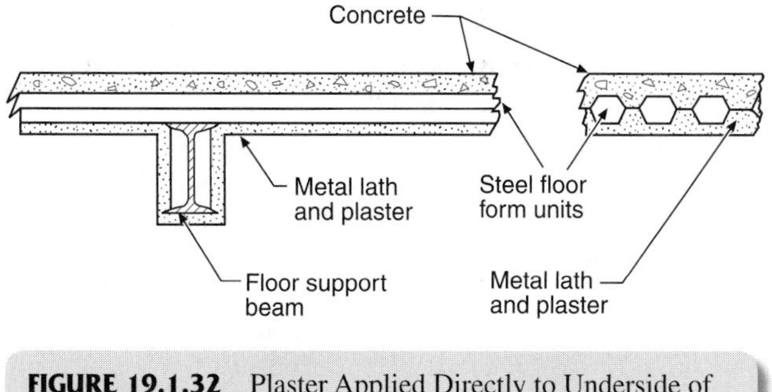

FIGURE 19.1.32 Plaster Applied Directly to Underside of Floor Slab Construction

In the variety of arrangements currently used, the space above the ceiling may be of combustible construction and may also contain other combustible materials, such as duct insulation, wire insulation, and vapor seals. Air-handling systems may use ducts or the void space itself (plenum) as a means of supplying, exhausting, or recirculating air, but associated materials must meet stringent requirements for combustibility and smoke evolution.

The material used for the membrane ceiling is important. Gypsum plaster and lath were a common construction of early membranes. Today special mineral tile formulations are generally used for acoustical panel systems that will not warp during fire exposure. The support framing is designed to accommodate thermal expansion with a minimum of distortion, so that the ceiling panels stay in place.

If lighting fixtures and duct openings are included in membrane ceilings that are part of fire-rated assemblies, they both must be of suitable design and properly spaced, and they often require shielding to reduce heat transmission into the ceiling space. Fire test performance is based on specific lighting fixtures and spacing, so indiscriminate substitution of lighting fixtures can cause premature failure. If air duct openings are installed in a membrane-type ceiling, they should be suitably protected or dampered, as determined by a fire test on the ceiling assembly that incorporates the air-handling components.

ROOF FRAMING

The design and construction of roof framing follow the general pattern for floor framing systems—both must support vertical loads and distribute these loads to walls or columns. Roof loads are usually smaller than floor loads. In addition, architectural considerations may demand longer spans than floor framing, and the shape of the roof need not be flat.

The roof deck and covering may be supported by steel or wood joists or by a truss where a longer span is needed. Roof trusses can be made to conform to any roof shape, whether flat, pitched, or curved.

Open-web steel or wood joists are often used in flat roof construction. An open-web joist is merely a lightweight, parallel chord truss. Open-web steel joists are typically used to support 1½-in. (38-mm) deep steel deck and are usually spaced about 6 ft (1.8 m) on center. This close spacing allows the roof deck to be designed to span between the joists. Figure 19.1.33 illustrates this type of roof framing.

In single-story buildings that require a large open space, rigid frames are sometimes used both as columns and roof supports. The portion spanning the roof is rigidly connected to columns on opposite sides of the building to form a single member. The frame itself may provide for a sloping roof. Figure 19.1.34 shows a rigid frame structure.

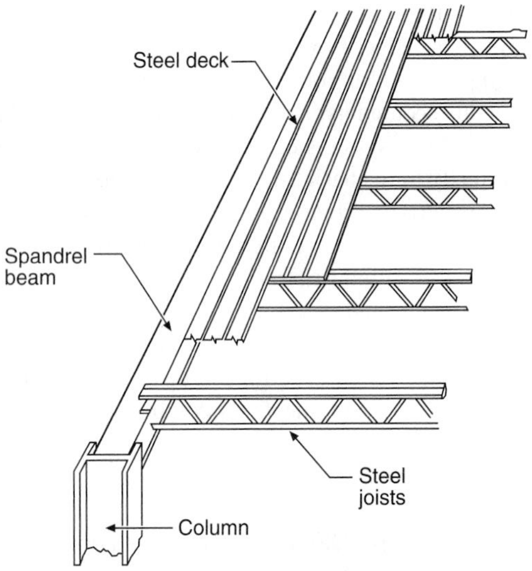

FIGURE 19.1.33 Long-Span Joist Framing

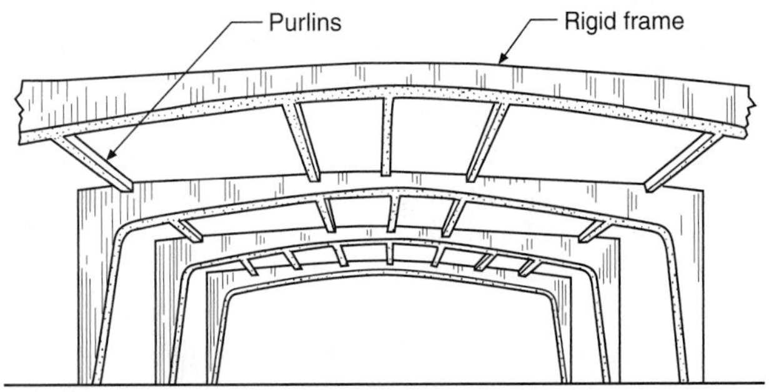

FIGURE 19.1.34 Rigid Frame

Flat slab and ribbed concrete slab systems may be used for roof construction in buildings in which that is the predominant type of framing. Other systems utilizing long-span prestressed concrete double-tee or channel sections are also common. These units serve both as support and as the deck (see Figure 19.1.24).

Roof decks may also consist of precast reinforced concrete planks fastened to the structural steel supports by galvanized metal clips, as shown in Figure 19.1.35. These planks are manufactured in three general shapes: (1) square edge, (2) channel slab, and (3) tongue and groove. To reduce weight they may be fabricated with aerated concrete using lightweight aggregates.

ROOF COVERINGS

In resistance to ignition and burning from exterior fire exposure, roof coverings range from combustible wood shingles with no fire-retardant treatment to built-up or prepared coverings that are effective against severe external fire exposure. Insofar as well-designed roof coverings can protect buildings from exposure fires, the likelihood of fire spread from one building to another can be reduced considerably.

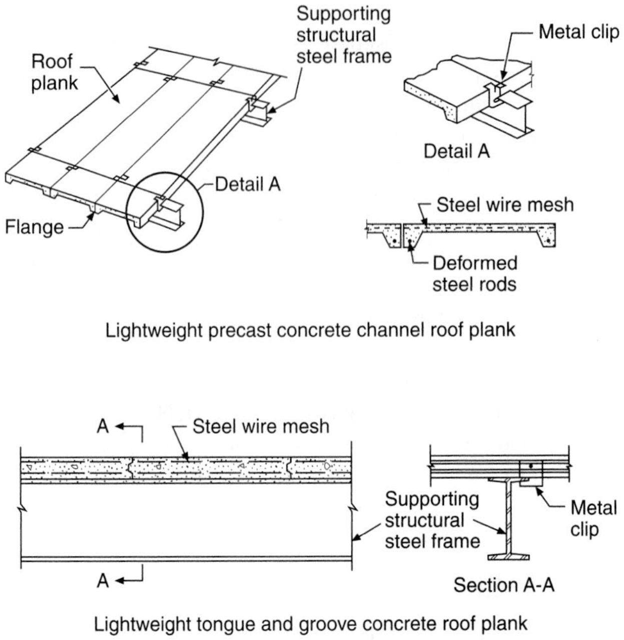

FIGURE 19.1.35 Lightweight Precast Concrete Planks

Fire performance for any given roof assembly subjected to exterior fire exposure is not necessarily the same as that for interior fire exposure. The presence of pea stone gravel, large stone ballast, concrete paver blocks, or some coatings such as fibrated aluminum or asphalt emulsions on top of roof coverings can greatly enhance resistance to exterior fire exposure.

Fire-Retardant Roof Coverings

The test standard for roof coverings is NFPA 256, *Standard Methods of Fire Tests of Roof Coverings.* The three classes of roof coverings that rank resistance to exterior fire exposure are the following:

Class A Coverings. Class A coverings include roof coverings that are effective against severe fire exposures. These coverings are not readily flammable, do not carry or communicate fire, afford a fairly high degree of fire protection to the roof deck, do not slip from position, and possess no flying brand hazard.

Class B Coverings. Class B coverings include roof coverings that are effective against moderate fire exposures. These coverings are not readily flammable, do not readily carry or communicate fire, afford a moderate degree of fire protection to the roof deck, do not slip from position, and possess no flying brand hazard; however, they may require repairs to maintain their fire retardant properties.

Class C Coverings. Class C coverings include roof coverings that are effective against light fire exposure. These coverings are not readily flammable, afford at least a slight degree of fire protection to the roof decks, do not slip from position, and possess no flying brand hazard; however, they may require repairs or renewals to maintain their fire-retardant properties.

Building codes commonly require Class A or B coverings within the fire limits of cities or wherever fire-resistive construction is required. Class C roofing is appropriate for other buildings. Many cities specify Class C as the minimum standard for roofing. Fire testing laboratories classify metal deck roof assemblies by type of construction (Table 19.1.8).[4]

Built-Up and Prepared Coverings

Fire-retardant roof coverings fall within one of several groups. One is the built-up covering which, as the name implies, consists of several layers of materials applied or "built up" on the roof decks according to specifications. What is known as a "tar and gravel" roof is actually a built-up roof covering consisting of several layers of roofing felts and insulating panels or sheets bonded together by hot or cold cements and topped with roofing gravel (Figure 19.1.36).

Another group (prepared coverings) includes fire-retardant shingles and sheet coverings, which can be applied only to roof decks capable of receiving and retaining nails and which are sloped sufficiently to permit drainage (Figure 19.1.37). In some instances, however, the slope must not exceed a specified maximum in order to qualify for Class A, B, or C fire-retardant rating. Asphalt organic felt shingles (i.e., "composition" roofs) are a common example of prepared roof coverings and are frequently used on dwellings.

Prepared roof coverings also include such noncombustible coverings as brick, concrete, tile, and slate. Tables 19.1.8 and 19.1.9 list various types of prepared and built-up roof coverings, respectively, and their fire-retardant classifications. Any roof covering can be used for a less severe exposure than the one for which it is listed.

In addition to the built-up roof coverings described in Table 19.1.9, there are several other types consisting of organic felt, glass fiber, aluminum, steel, and tile applied in a special manner with special listed proprietary securements that are listed by testing laboratories. Single-ply membranes are a very popular type of roof covering. Exterior fire exposure ratings for these coverings are dependent on the type of material, whether it is fire retardant, the type of insulation directly below, and the presence of a coating or topping. Such classifications can be found in publications by fire testing laboratories.

Wood Shingles

Untreated wood shingles may be readily ignited by small sparks from chimneys or exposure fires, by radiated heat, or by burning brands. Burning shingles themselves also produce brands, which may be carried by the wind to start other fires. Age and humidity increase the susceptibility of wood-shingled roofs to ignition.

Treatment of wood shingles in place with fire-retardant coatings has not proved practical to date. Ordinary flame-resistant treatments lose their effectiveness with continued exposure to the weather. Wood shingles impregnated with a fire-retardant solution are more durable. Shingles of this type have been tested and carry a Class B or C rating.

Untreated wood shingle roofs are prohibited by law in the congested sections of practically all large cities, and a very large number of cities and towns prohibit their use altogether within municipal limits.

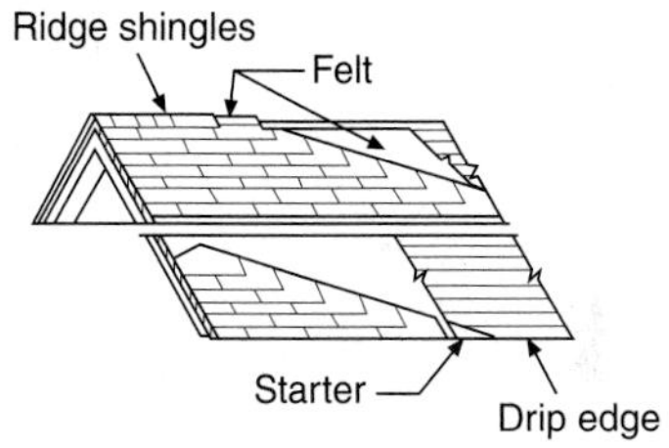

FIGURE 19.1.37 Installation of a Typical Prepared Roof Covering

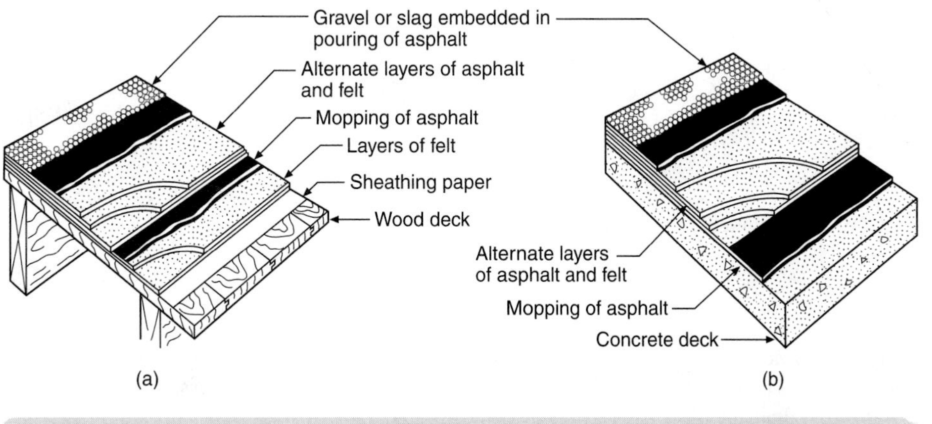

FIGURE 19.1.36 Typical Built-Up Roof Coverings with Hot Asphalt Mopping or Coal Tar Pitch Between Each Two Layers: (a) 5 Ply Built-Up Roof over Wood, (b) 4 Ply Built-Up Roof over Concrete

TABLE 19.1.8 Some Typical Prepared Roof Coverings

Roof Covering[a]	*Minimum/ Maximum Roof Slope, in. per ft*	*Class A*	*Class B*	*Class C*
Brick Concrete Tile Slate	Minimum required for drainage/ unlimited	Brick, 2¼ in. thick Reinforced Portland cement, 1 in. thick Concrete or clay floor or deck tile, 1 in. thick Flat or French-type clay or concrete tile, ⅜ in. thick with 1½ in. or more end lap[b] and head lock, spacing body of tile ½ in. or more above roof sheathing, with underlay of one layer of Type 30 or two layers of Type 15 asphalt-saturated organic felt Clay or concrete roof tile, Spanish or Mission pattern, 7/16 in. thick, 3 in. end lap,[b] same underlay as above Slate, 3/16 in. thick, laid American method		
Metal roofing	12/unlimited	Sheet roofing of 16 oz copper or of 30 gauge steel or iron protected against corrosion—limited to noncombustible roof decks or noncombustible roof supports when no separate roof deck is provided	Sheet roofing of 16 oz copper or of 30 gauge steel or iron protected against corrosion or shingle-pattern roofings with underlay of one layer of Type 30 or two layers of Type 15 asphalt-saturated organic felt[b]	Sheet roofing of 16 oz copper or of 30 gauge steel or iron, protected against corrosion, or shingle-pattern roofings, either without underlay or with underlay of rosin-sized paper
	¼ (standing seam) or ½ (lap seam)/ unlimited	Standing or lap seam metal panel with glass fiber batts below on steel purling or joints		Zinc sheets or shingle roofings with an underlay of one layer of Type 30 or two layers of Type 15 asphalt-saturated organic felt[b]
Organic felt (previously referred to as *rag felt*) sheet coverings	¼/unlimited			Sheet coverings of asphalt organic felt either grit surfaced or aluminum surfaced
Organic felt (previously referred to as *rag felt*) shingle covering, with special coating	Sufficient to permit drainage[c]	Mineral surfaced, two or more thicknesses	Mineral surfaced, two or more thicknesses	
Organic felt (previously referred to as *rag felt*) shingle coverings	Sufficient to permit drainage[c]	Mineral surfaced, two or more thicknesses	Mineral surfaced, two or more thicknesses	Mineral surfaced shingles, one or more thicknesses

TABLE 19.1.8 Continued

Roof Covering[a]	*Minimum/ Maximum Roof Slope, in. per ft*	*Class A*	*Class B*	*Class C*
Asphalt glass fiber mat shingle coverings	Sufficient to permit drainage[c]	Mineral surfaced, two or more thicknesses	Mineral surfaced, one or more thicknesses	Mineral surfaced shingles, one or more thicknesses
Asphalt glass mat sheet covering	Sufficient to permit drainage[c]			Mineral surfaced
Fire-retardant treated red cedar wood shingles and shakes				Treated shingles or shakes, one or more thicknesses; shakes require at least one layer of Type 15 felt underlayment

Note: Roofing materials containing asbestos are no longer used in the United States; however, they may still be encountered in existing construction.

[a]Prepared roof coverings as classified as applied over square-edge wood sheathing of 1 in. nominal thickness, or the equivalent, unless otherwise specified. See footnotes (built-up roof coverings) to Table 19.1.9. Laid in accordance with instruction sheets accompanying package. Limited to decks capable of receiving and retaining nails. Prepared roofings are labeled by Underwriters' Laboratories to indicate the classification when applied in accordance with direction for application included in package.

[b]*End lap* means the overlapping length of the two units, one placed over the other. *Head lap* in shingle-type roofs is the distance a shingle in any course overlaps a shingle in the second course below it. However, with shingles laid by the Dutch-lap method, where no shingle overlaps a shingle in the second course below, the head lap is taken as the distance a shingle overlaps one in the next course below.

[c]Typically ¼ in. per ft.

For SI units: 1 in. = 25.4 mm; 1 ft = 0.305 m; 1 oz = 0.0284 kg; 1 lb = 0.454 kg.

ROOF DECK INSULATIONS AND VAPOR BARRIERS

Since the 1953 General Motors fire at Livonia, Michigan, major attention has been paid to the combustibility of insulated metal roof decks. In that fire, the asphalt mopping in the felt vapor barrier beneath the insulation on the 1,502,500 ft^2 (139,582 m^2) flat steel-deck roof melted and vaporized. Asphalt vapor under pressure entered the building through the joints in the steel deck and burned inside. As a result of this and similar fires, research was conducted to find a solution to the problem.

The combustibility of a roof was historically determined by the physical characteristics of the roof deck and its supporting structure, with no consideration given to the combustibility of the roof insulation and covering. Thus, combustible fiberboard insulation and asphalt-impregnated felt roof covering normally were not considered to affect the classification of a noncombustible roof deck on noncombustible supports. Large-scale fire tests, confirmed by actual fire experience, however, have shown that under certain conditions some metal deck assemblies can contribute to an interior fire.[4]

A series of full-scale tests was conducted in 1955 at Factory Mutual Research (FMR) testing facilities to compare the performance of various metal roof deck constructions with respect to fire propagation along the underside of the deck. The tests were run in cooperation with the Metal Roof Deck Technical Institute (now Steel Deck Institute) and the Insulation Board Institute, and the results were published in a technical report.[5] With the insulation or vapor barriers adhered to the metal deck with complete moppings of asphalt, it was shown that the asphalt contributed a significant amount of fuel when exposed to the heat of an intensive interior fire below the deck (Figure 19.1.38). The asphalt was vaporized by the heat of the fire below and, unable to escape upward through the roof covering, was forced down through the joints in the deck, when it ignited and contributed to the spread of fire under the roof deck. This type of assembly is called combustible or a Class 2 steel deck. Because of poor wind-loss experience, FM Global no longer recommends using adhesives to secure above-deck components to steel decks. However, other combinations of combustible above-deck components (such as vapor barriers, insulation, and roof covers) may create a Class 2 steel-deck assembly.

Recognized fire testing laboratories now list metal roof deck construction and components that will not contribute significantly to an interior fire and that meet certain performance standards. Such assemblies are called noncombustible, fire-classified, or Class 1 steel decks.

Metal roof deck constructions use both combustible and noncombustible insulation fastened with mechanical fasteners to the upper surface of the deck. Prior to the early 1980s, asphalt was accepted as an adhesive to secure certain insulation to steel decks if it was applied in strips (with a mechanical applicator), and if the total amount used between the deck and the insulation did not exceed 12 to 15 lb per 100 ft^2 (5.4 to 6.8 kg/9.3 m^2) of roof area.

There is no restriction on the use of asphalt in conventional built-up roofing used above the insulation. When a vapor

TABLE 19.1.9 Built-Up Roof Coverings

*Roof Covering**	*Minimum/ Maximum Roof Slope, in. per ft*	*Class A*	*Class B*	*Class C*
Asphalt organic felt, bonded with asphalt and surfaced with 400 lb of roofing gravel or crushed stone, or 300 lb of crushed slag per 100 ft² of roof surface, on coating of hot mopping asphalt	¼/2	4 (plain) or 5 (perforated) layers of Type 15 felt 1 layer of Type 30 felt and 2 layers of Type 15 felt 1 layer of Type 15 felt and 2 layers of Type 15 or 30 cap or base sheets 3 layers of Type 15 or 30 cap or base sheets 3 layers of Type 15 felt—limited to noncombustible decks	4 layers of perforated Type 15 felt 3 layers of Type 15 felt 2 layers of Type 15 or 30 cap or base sheets	
Organic felt bonded with tar and surfaced with 400 lb of roofing gravel or crushed stone, or 300 lb of crushed slag per 100 ft² of roof surface on a coating of hot mopping tar	¼/2	4 layers of Type 15 organic felt 3 layers of Type 15 organic felt	3 layers of Type 15 organic felt	
Steep tar organic felt	¼/2	4 layers of Type 15 tar-saturated organic felt, bonded with steep coal-tar pitch, surfaced with 275 lb of ⅝ in. crushed slag per 100 ft² of roof surface on steep coal-tar pitch		
Asphalt organic felt, plain or perforated, bonded and surfaced with a cold application coating	¼/12			3 layers of Type 15 felt 1 layer of Type 30 felt and 1 layer of Type 15 felt 2 layers of Type 15 or 30 cap or base sheets 2 layers of Type 15 felt and 1 layer of Type 15 or 30 cap or base sheets

Note:

From the standpoint of relative effectiveness of the different types of wood sheathing, the tongue-and-groove boards and ¾ in. moisture-resistant plywood give better results in the brand and flame tests than square-edge sheathing with boards spaced about ¼ in. apart. For classifications based on square-edge sheathing, tongue-and-groove or plywood sheathing can be substituted. Square-edge sheathing boards should be butted together as closely as possible. Reference to ¼ in. spacing is to indicate fire test procedure intended to simulate actual conditions after shrinkage of boards due to age or other reasons.

The minimum weight of cementing material between separate layers of felt is considered to be 25 lb per 100 ft² of roof surface.

Types 15 and 30 felts are defined as saturated felts weighing a minimum of 14 lb and 28 lb per 100 ft² of the finished materials, respectively. Where saturated felts are referred to be weight, the weight is minimum and is expressed in pounds per 100 ft² of the finished material.

Materials intended for built-up roof coverings are labeled by Underwriters Laboratories. The classifications indicated are of generally accepted combinations.

*Built-up roof coverings are classified as applied over square-edge wood sheathing of 1 in. nominal thickness, or the equivalent, unless otherwise specified.

For SI units: 1 in. = 25.4 mm; 1 ft = 0.305 m; 1 ft² = 0.0929 m²; 1 lb = 0.454 kg.

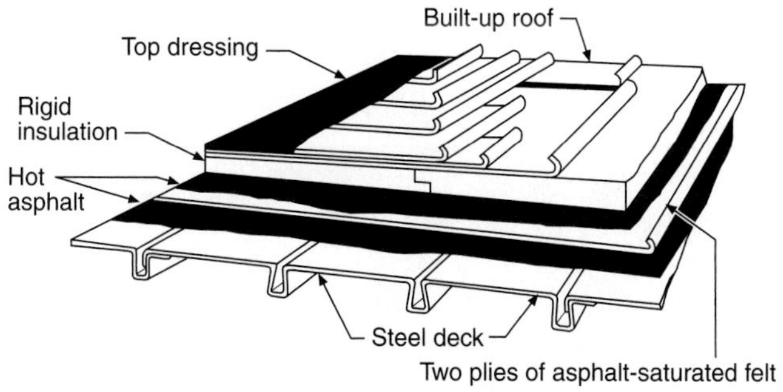

FIGURE 19.1.38 Typical Built-Up Roof Covering with a Combustible Vapor Barrier Adhered to the Roof Deck and to Roof Insulation by a Combustible Adhesive

barrier is used between the deck and the insulation, a listed, noncombustible, or material with limited fuel contribution is recommended. Testing laboratories list various manufacturers of acceptable vapor barriers and adhesives.

FM Global divides insulated metal deck roof assemblies into two classes. Class 1 construction is any insulated steel roof deck construction having a combination of above-deck components that will not contribute significantly to an interior fire and that will meet or equal FMR performance standards. Class 2 construction is any insulated metal roof deck construction using a combination of above-deck components which, when exposed to fire locally, will produce sufficient heat release to allow a self-propagating fire on the underside of an unprotected deck.

Constructions that are found acceptable to FM are listed by FM Global Research.[6] Underwriters Laboratories list those roof deck constructions that have been tested in the UL Building Construction Directory or online at http://database.ul.com.

SUMMARY

Building construction is classified based on the materials used for the structural elements and the degree of fire resistance afforded by each element. In the United States, construction is classified according to subtypes derived from five fundamental construction types: Type I, formerly referred to as fire-resistive construction; Type II, formerly referred to as noncombustible construction; Type III, formerly referred to as exterior protected combustible or ordinary construction; Type IV, formerly referred to as heavy-timber construction; and Type V, formerly referred to as wood-frame construction.

The classification of construction recommended by the MCSC and the BCMC comprises two major groups, noncombustible and combustible, with subtypes based on the fire resistance of the three basic elements of a building: the exterior wall, the primary structural frame, and the floor. The designs of exterior walls, interior walls and partitions, floor framing systems, trusses, floor/ceiling assemblies, roof framing, roof coverings, and roof deck insulations and vapor barriers also play an important role in the fire safety of a building.

BIBLIOGRAPHY

References Cited

1. FM Global Loss Prevention Data Sheet 1-22, *Maximum Foreseeable Loss Fire Walls and Space Separation,* FM Global, Johnston, RI, 2001.
2. *Design for Fire Resistance of Precast Prestressed Concrete,* 2nd ed., Prestressed Concrete Institute, Chicago, IL, 1989.
3. FM Global Loss Prevention Data Sheet 1-24, *Protection Against Liquid Damage,* FM Global, Johnston, RI, 2001.
4. ASTM E108-2005, *Standard Test Methods for Fire Tests of Roof Coverings,* ASTM International, W. Conshohocken, PA, 2005.
5. "Insulated Metal Roof Deck Fire Tests," Factory Mutual Research Corp., Norwood, MA, 1955.
6. "Approval Guide," Building Materials Volume, FM Global Research, Norwood, MA (published annually).

NFPA Codes, Standards, and Recommended Practices

Reference to the following NFPA codes, standards, and recommended practices will provide further information on types of building construction discussed in this chapter. (See the latest version of The NFPA Catalog *for availability of current editions of the following documents.)*

NFPA 80, *Standard for Fire Doors and Other Opening Protectives*
NFPA 80A, *Recommended Practice for Protection of Buildings from Exterior Fire Exposures*
NFPA *101®*, *Life Safety Code®*
NFPA 220, *Standard on Types of Building Construction*
NFPA 221, *Standard for High Challenge Fire Walls, Fire Walls, and Fire Barrier Walls*
NFPA 251, *Standard Methods of Tests of Fire Resistance of Building Construction and Materials*
NFPA 252, *Standard Methods of Fire Tests of Door Assemblies*
NFPA 255, *Standard Method of Test of Surface Burning Characteristics of Building Materials*
NFPA 256, *Standard Methods of Fire Tests of Roof Coverings*
NFPA 259, *Standard Test Method for Potential Heat of Building Materials*
NFPA 285, *Standard Fire Test Method for Evaluation of Fire Propagation Characteristics of Exterior Non-Load-Bearing Wall Assemblies Containing Combustible Components*
NFPA 703, *Standard for Fire Retardant–Treated Wood and Fire-Retardant Coatings for Building Materials*
NFPA 5000®, Building Construction and Safety Code®

Chapter 2

Structural Integrity During Fire

Revised by
Richard J. Davis

Chapter Contents

Key Terms

ceiling assembly, fire barrier, fire endurance, fire resistance, fire test, floor assembly, glass, gypsum, partition, prestressed concrete, reinforced concrete, roof assembly, structural assembly, structural frame, structural integrity, structural steel, timber, wall, wood

The selection of building materials and the design of the details of construction always play an important role in overall building fire safety. Two important fire safety considerations regarding the building structure are to minimize the likelihood of collapse of the structural frame during a fire and to ensure that fire barriers remain intact to prevent ignition and fire spread to adjoining spaces.

The following are the three general approaches to structural frame and barrier design for fire resistance that are in use or under development today:

1. Standard fire resistance testing combined with building code requirements
2. Analytical calculations to determine the resistance to a standard fire test exposure as a substitute for laboratory testing
3. Analytical structural fire engineering design methods based on real fire exposure characteristics

The traditional method of treating the structural aspects of fire protection is through building code requirements. Codes generally require structural frames and barrier assemblies to be selected based on ratings determined through standardized laboratory fire resistance tests (approaches 1 and 2 above).

Classification of building construction with regard to fire resistance requirements is an approach that has the principal advantage of being relatively easy to incorporate into the design process and to administer from a code enforcement viewpoint. It has a major disadvantage of being unable to represent the performance of the structural member or fire barrier under the broad range of "real world" fire loads. In other words, code compliance alone is not sufficient to ensure performance success of the barriers or structural frame in an actual fire. Studies that correlate building code requirements and fire test results with field performance need to be further pursued.

Although the century-old approach for determining fire resistance can be criticized for its shortcomings, it is the only method universally accepted in U.S. building codes today. The first part of this chapter describes the fire resistance test procedures common in building construction today. Latter parts of the chapter discuss methods of calculating fire-endurance (resistance) ratings and the behavior of building materials at elevated temperatures. The chapter concludes with a brief discussion of some of the more advanced approaches to designing for structural integrity in a fire.

For related topics, see Section 6, Chapter 3, "Concepts and Protocols of Fire Testing"; Section 18, Chapter 1,"Confinement of Fire in Buildings"; Section 19, Chapter 1, "Types of Building Construction"; Section 19, Chapter 4, "Analyzing Structural Fire Damage"; and Section 19, Chapter 5, "Approaches to Calculating Structural Fire Resistance."

Richard J. Davis, P.E., FSFPE, is an assistant vice-president and senior engineering technical specialist at FM Global in Norwood, Massachusetts, and is a member and retired chair of the NFPA Technical Committee on Construction and Demolition and a member of the NFPA Technical Committees on Building Construction; Structures, Construction and Materials; Fire Tests; and Smoke Management.

FIRE RESISTANCE TESTING

The fire resistance rating of the beams, girders, columns, and other members that comprise the structural frame and the fire resistance rating of the walls, partitions, floor/ceiling assemblies, and roof/ceiling assemblies that serve as fire barriers serve as the basis for classifying building construction and codifying frame and barrier capabilities. This part of the chapter describes the history and procedure for standardized fire testing and discusses the interpretation of laboratory fire test results.

History of Fire Resistance Tests

One review of fire test methods for building constructions refers to tests on metal and masonry conducted in Germany as early as 1884–1886.[1] The first large-scale fire tests in this country are reported to have been conducted on masonry arches in Denver, Colorado, in 1890. These were followed by tests in New York City in 1896.

Efforts to establish an acceptable test procedure were initiated by Professor Ira H. Woolson of Columbia University and Rudolph P. Miller, Chief Engineer, Building Bureau, New York City. Preliminary tests by the bureau, "necessitated by the rapid development of the skyscraper," led to the development of a test furnace (using railroad ties as fuel). This provided a means of establishing hourly fire ratings for floor constructions.

After the Baltimore, Maryland, conflagration of 1905, the American Society for Testing and Materials (ASTM) established a committee to standardize the test method, with Woolson as chairman and Miller as secretary. A test method for floor constructions was proposed in 1906 and adopted by ASTM in 1907. A procedure for testing wall and partition constructions was proposed in 1908 and adopted in 1909.[2]

These standards were presented to the NFPA Committee on Fire-Resistive Construction for consideration in 1914. In 1916, a joint committee composed of representatives from eleven engineering societies, including NFPA, was organized to revise and update the standard. This was done, and the revised standard test method controlled by a standard time-temperature curve was adopted subsequently by NFPA, ASTM, and the American Engineering Committee (now the American National Standards Institute [ANSI]). NFPA 251, *Standard Methods of Tests of Fire Resistance of Building Construction and Materials,* was adopted by NFPA as a tentative standard in 1917 and advanced to official standard status in 1918. Time-temperature curves and testing procedures developed in other countries follow the same general pattern, with minor differences. See Section 19, Chapter 5, "Approaches to Calculating Structural Fire Resistance," for discussion of international approaches.

Fire Test Procedures

Fire test procedures usually require that columns, floors, partitions, walls, and other structural elements be loaded in a manner calculated to develop, as nearly as practicable, the theoretical working stresses expected by the structural design. Separate test procedures are provided for load-bearing and non-load-bearing arrangements and for arrangements involving restrained and unrestrained beams and girders.

The Appendices to NFPA 251 contains detailed specifications for test procedures, a guide to the determination of restraint required, if any, and a suggested report form. The standard specifies in detail the preparation and conditioning of the test specimens.

Acceptance criteria are specific for the assembly or structural element tested based on predetermined conditions of test (load or no load, restrained or unrestrained). The criteria include the following:

1. Failure to support load
2. Temperature increase on the unexposed surface 250°F (121°C) above ambient
3. Passage of heat or flame sufficient to ignite cotton waste
4. Excess temperature (as specified) on steel members
5. Failure under hose streams (walls and partitions)

The end restraint conditions during the fire test influence significantly the test results and, consequently, the ratings. Appendix E of NFPA 251 defines a restrained condition as one in which expansion at the supports of a load-carrying element is prevented during the test. A restrained condition is intended to account for some degree of rotational restraint at the ends of the element in addition to prestressing some parts of the assembly. An unrestrained condition is one in which the load-carrying element is free to expand and rotate at its supports.

One justification for incorporating two differing means of end restraint is to simulate simple (statically determinant) and continuous (statically indeterminant) conditions. Figure 19.2.1 illustrates simple and continuous arrangements. All else being

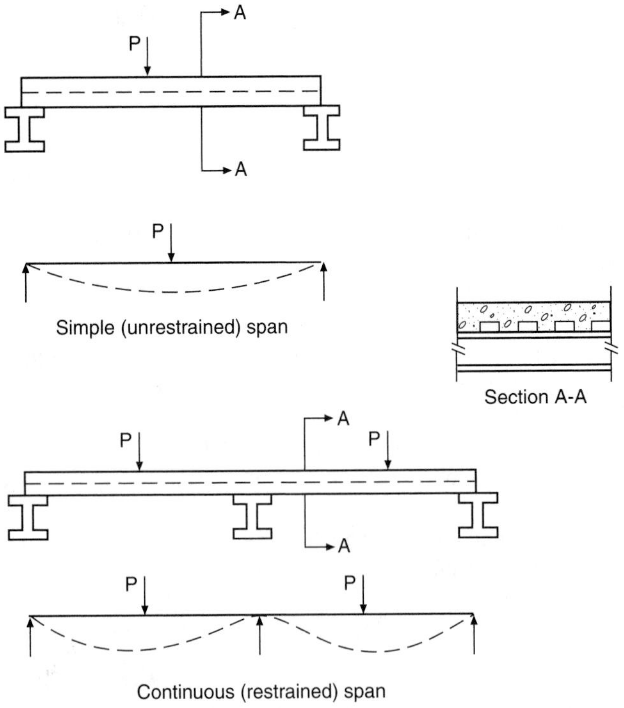

FIGURE 19.2.1 Influence of Structural Continuity on Collapse Mechanisms

equal, continuous span construction is inherently stronger than simple span construction. It is possible to calculate the increase in load-carrying capacity of statically indeterminant structural members. However, the amount of increased strength in an indeterminant structure can be quite variable, depending on the type of construction materials used, the location of structural members within the structure, the degree of indeterminance, the loading conditions, and the details of construction.

Requirements to evaluate structural members based on restrained and unrestrained conditions were introduced in standardized fire testing in 1970. The degree of restraint for structural members and assemblies tested and accepted for building construction prior to 1970 is unknown.

Fire Resistance Ratings

Fire resistance ratings represent the time duration the structural member or assembly withstood the fire test without failure. Although the actual time is recorded to the nearest integral minute, fire resistance ratings are given in standard intervals. The usual fire resistance ratings for all types of structural members and assemblies are 15 minutes, 20 minutes, 30 minutes, 45 minutes, 1 hour, 1½ hours, 2 hours, 3 hours, and 4 hours. Therefore, a 1 hour rating indicates that the assembly withstood the standard test for 1 hour or longer. A 2 hour rating indicates that the assembly withstood the standard test for a minimum of 2 hours without failure of any of the criteria listed in the fire test protocol.

Some agencies in the United States that test assemblies of building construction materials for fire resistance are Underwriters Laboratories Inc. (UL), Omega Point, Southwest Research Institute, and Intertek Testing. A number of other organizations have furnaces or equipment for conducting fire tests of various special assemblies. Some of these include the Forest Products Laboratory at Madison, Wisconsin; University of California at Berkeley; Armstrong Cork Co., Lancaster, Pennsylvania; and the National Gypsum Co., Buffalo, New York. Some of these test facilities may not conform to the specifications described in NFPA 251. Consequently, those facilities may be used more for research purposes rather than for establishing fire resistance ratings.

The results of fire tests conducted by Underwriters Laboratories Inc., Omega Point, Southwest Research Institute, and Intertek Testing are published in company directories, which are now available in electronic as well as in print formats. The *Fire Resistance Directory* is published by UL. Omega Point, Southwest Research Institute, and Intertek Testing each have their own *Directory of Listed Products.* FM Approvals has access to a facility to conduct the tests and publishes the results in its *Approval Guide.* These guides and directories have illustrations of building assemblies that have met the test criteria for specific fire resistance hourly ratings.

The results of fire tests conducted by governmental agencies have been published in various reports and technical papers. Those issued by the National Institute of Standards and Technology (NIST) may be consulted in many depository libraries, and lists of those available may be obtained from NIST. In Canada, there are facilities at the Underwriters Laboratories of Canada in Toronto and the Building Research Division of the National Research Council of Canada in Ottawa. Throughout the world, many well-equipped fire-testing laboratories are making significant contributions to the literature and to the development of international fire test standards.

In Europe, there are a number of public and private facilities available. Some of the facilities that have furnaces include the Centre Technique Industriel da la Construction, Metz, France; Netherlands Organization for Applied Scientific Research, Ja Delft, Netherlands; Danish Institute of Fire and Security Technology, Hvidovre, Denmark; Federal Institute for Materials Research and Testing, Berlin, Germany; University of Ghent, Ghent, Belgium; Warrington Fire Research Center, Warrington, UK; Timber Research and Development, Buckinghamshire, UK; Swedish National Testing and Research Institute, Borås, Sweden; VTT Technical Research Centre of Finland, Espoo, Finland; and The Foundation for Scientific and Industrial Research at the Norwegian Institute of Technology, Trondheim, Norway. The bulletins and reports of the British Ministry of Technology on the subject are obtainable by purchase from H. M. Stationery Office or the British Information Services, New York. Throughout the world, many well-equipped fire-testing laboratories are involved with determining structural fire resistance.

Building codes may include tabulations of construction assemblies that will be accepted as meeting code requirements for terms of fire test results and may include tabulations of construction forms that will be accepted as meeting code requirements for specific fire resistance ratings. Such tables are usually based upon fire test data, but some include ratings determined by experience, judgment, and extrapolation of specific test data.

Not included are the many useful data sheets and summaries published by trade associations of the building materials manufacturers. These sources are not cited because they are so numerous and because the information published either pertains to the products of a specific manufacturer or consists of tabulated ratings for a single type of construction material.

The number of test facilities in use today and the variety of published test results make it almost impossible to tabulate in a single useful form all the data on the various assemblies that have been tested. Users of this handbook are urged to consult the fire resistance directories and reports mentioned previously for the specifics on design specifications for assemblies that have been tested and for which fire resistance ratings have been assigned.

As a matter of information and to illustrate the scope of testing activities, tabular compilations of test results or representative assemblies will be found later in this chapter. They are included in this handbook to help give an understanding of basic requirements for test specimens and how the results of tests are recorded. In addition, the information contained in the tables can be useful in identifying, within reasonable limits, the fire resistance capabilities of assemblies as they are found in the field and for which precise data on their fire resistance are not available or are no longer available. The tables are not presented as references for design but to familiarize handbook users with the type of test information available.

Variations in Test Results

The standard fire test attempts to provide a relative measure of fire performance of comparable assemblies under uniform fire exposure conditions. It does not consider suitability for use after the fire. Many effects from fire tests are observed indirectly, if at all. For example, the temperature gradient through a wall or floor slab results in internal strains and deflections. The strains may cause spalling or other disruptions, and distortions may be severe enough to crack floor slabs and walls, sometimes leading to collapse or excessive heat transmission. The greater the area exposed, the more serious are the results of unequal expansion. General deterioration of the test specimen is not considered when determining the fire resistance rating, except when it contributes to the failure of the test specimen.

It should be recognized that the fire resistance rating is the amount of time the member of assembly withstood a standard laboratory fire test. It is not necessarily the time duration the assembly will perform without failure under actual fire conditions. For example, a 2 hour assembly can withstand failure for at least 2 hours when subjected to the standard fire test exposure. Under actual field conditions, the same assembly may fail in a considerable shorter or longer time duration. One of the major misconceptions in fire protection is the belief that an assembly rating indicates the time that the assembly will survive an actual fire. Rather, it is the time the assembly survived, without failure, the fire test exposure. Differences between the standard test and field conditions can be substantial.

The fact that test-time duration and field performance may be vastly different is not intended to demonstrate that fire resistance ratings do not have value or purpose. Over the years this procedure has resulted in improved fire performance of code-complying buildings. However, one must understand the limitations of the procedure so that unrealistic reliance is not placed on the construction.

Although the test standard specifies the preparation and conditioning of specimens, there are many opportunities for differences between a test specimen and an actual structural element in the field. The test specimen may be superior in both materials and workmanship to those found in the field; the test specimen is usually smaller than the construction assembly it represents. Restraints to thermal expansion may be of different magnitudes. Therefore, discretion in the interpretation of fire test results is in order. Differences in the results of fire tests on apparently equal test specimens of building constructions arise from many factors, such as undetermined differences in the quality of materials, workmanship, moisture content, and test procedures. While the standard method of test requires that materials in the specimen and the workmanship be representative of those in actual buildings, considerable variation in field practice can occur.

The test method permits the intensity of the fire exposure to deviate as much as 10 percent (formerly 15 percent) from that prescribed as standard and requires adjustment in the reported results to correct for such deviations only for tests of ½ hour duration or greater. The effects of several of the variables encountered in fire testing procedures are found in the technical reports listed in the bibliography at the end of the chapter.

The character and proportions of aggregates and binders have an important influence on the results of fire resistance tests. For example, gypsum plaster with lightweight aggregates, mixed with 2 to 3 ft^3 (0.057 to 0.085 m^3) to each 100 lb (45 kg) of gypsum, provides fire resistance from 10 to 70 percent greater than equal thicknesses of sanded gypsum plaster. The use of such aggregate in specific constructions should be adopted only after consulting the publication of ratings based on tests in which these aggregates have been used.

Vermiculite aggregate plaster, if too wet when applied, may be subject to shrinkage cracks. Such cracks, if they develop, are likely to occur within a short time. Some expanded perlite aggregates tend to absorb atmospheric moisture and may show destructive expansion after a few years. There may be considerable variation in this effect, as perlite is a natural volcanic glass or rock from many sources and varies in composition.

Finishing lime produced from dolomite contains magnesium oxide. That which is designated as "normal" finishing hydrate may not be sufficiently hydrated, and sometimes subsequent gradual hydration results in destructive expansion. Plasters containing such lime are subject to rapid destruction in the event of fire. This difficulty is avoided with lime hydrated under high temperature and pressure and known as "special" or "autoclaved" lime.

So-called stabilized gypsum plaster containing a small percentage of the normal hydrated lime may similarly be subject to deterioration with age and, in tests, may not provide the fire resistance to be expected from such constructions.

The effects mentioned are not such as to preclude the use of these materials where long life is not a factor or where adequate guarantees are provided. They are merely illustrations of the variability in test results that can occur as a result of differences in materials.

Although standard fire tests are made on fairly large specimens representative of building constructions or assemblies, they do not necessarily produce heat-expansion effects similar to those of fires in buildings having larger wall or floor areas. It may be necessary to specify thickness of construction or lateral support in addition to rated fire resistance to guard against the adverse effects of heat expansion or temperature gradients.

In addition to the material variation noted, construction differences may be even more significant. For example, a test does not provide full information on performance of assemblies constructed with components or lengths other than those tested. Performance is often reduced when the spans are increased. Also, approving "or equal" clauses in construction specifications need to be thoroughly evaluated. Sometimes substitutions in materials are approved for components that have not been listed with the assembly. Consideration also needs to be given to the connection methods used in constructing the various elements of the assembly.

The standard test does not incorporate information regarding the effect on fire resistance of conventional openings in the assembly, such as electrical receptacle outlets, pipe chases, and so on. Poke-through construction for electrical services or piping often is not patched properly. Transfer grilles, windows, and other penetrations are often incorporated into barriers without considering their impact on fire resistance.

The factors noted above, in addition to the many deviations to plans and specifications during and after construction, significantly affect the fire resistance of members and assemblies. Often the code calls for—and the designer may think he or she is providing—a specified fire resistance, only to have that resistance reduced because of inattention to penetrations and important details of construction.

FIRE RESISTANCE TESTS OF STRUCTURAL ASSEMBLIES

Structural Frame Systems

The fire resistance rating of structural framing members, such as beams, girders, and columns, may be achieved in several ways. Generally, the members are protected by encasing them in a material with sufficient insulating qualities to prevent excessive thermal penetration or by providing a membrane protection that delays thermal penetration to the members. The general behavior of reinforced concrete, structural steel, and barrier assemblies are described in the following paragraphs. Illustrative fire resistance ratings are shown in tabular form later in this chapter.

Reinforced Concrete Systems

Reinforced concrete construction has exhibited good performance with regard to its ability to withstand structural collapse. Because concrete has a low thermal conductivity and a low thermal capacity, it provides an effective cover for reinforcing steel. For example, Figure 19.2.2 shows the temperature gradient in a 6 in. (152 mm) slab after a 2 hour fire exposure.[3] Although undoubtedly the moisture in the concrete greatly influences the values, the significant feature is the fact that the temperatures vary considerably throughout the thickness, even after a considerable time exposure.

This feature provides some insight into one reason that reinforced-concrete systems usually perform comparatively well during fire exposure. Consider, for example, a continuous, monolithic reinforced-concrete beam or slab, as shown in Figure 19.2.3. Considering the temperature gradient of Figure 19.2.2, it will take some time before the tension steel at midspan is affected. Even after the tension steel at midspan reaches its yield value, the steel reinforcement in the negative moment region near the top of the beam or slab over the supports has not been seriously affected because of the insulating effect of the concrete and the moisture.

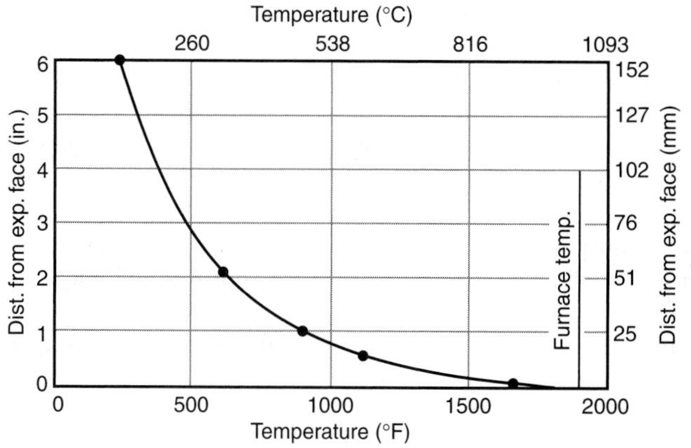

FIGURE 19.2.2 Thermal Gradient in a 6 in. Slab After 2 Hour Fire Exposure. For SI units: 1 in. = 25.4 mm; °C = 5/9 (°F – 32).

Continuous (restrained) construction of this type has inherent capabilities far greater than statically determinant (simple unrestrained) construction. Considerable stress redistribution can take place before collapse will occur. It takes time before excessive rotation will develop at all the necessary locations, causing structural collapse of the restrained member. Although the member is weakened by the fire, structural stability against collapse will remain for a considerable period of time.

The level of stress in a reinforced-concrete member exposed to the elevated temperatures of a fire has a significant influence on its fire resistance. A series of tests was conducted on 15 in. × 15 in. (381 mm × 381 mm) columns with four number-nine reinforcing bars.[3] Each column was loaded at a different percentage of the design load. Table 19.2.1 illustrates the effects of stress level on the fire resistance of reinforced-concrete columns. It can be seen that the magnitude of stress during a fire causes significant reductions in capacity. This is attributed primarily to the reduction in the mechanical properties of steel and concrete at elevated temperatures.

Steel Construction

The popularity of steel-frame building construction is due to its high strength, ease of fabrication, and ensured uniformity of quality. Exposed structural steel, however, is vulnerable to fire

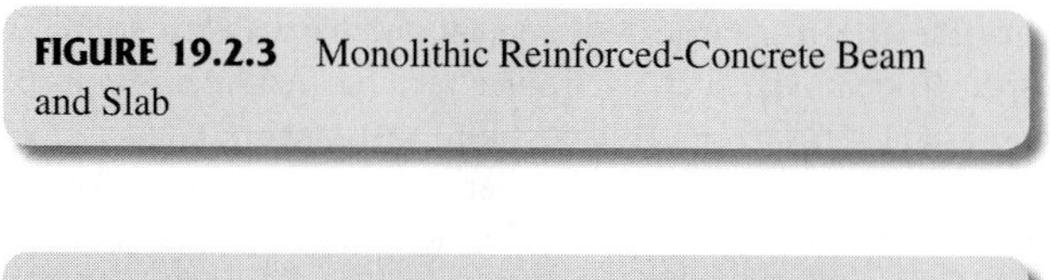

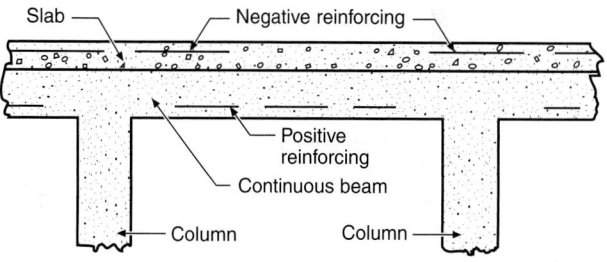

FIGURE 19.2.3 Monolithic Reinforced-Concrete Beam and Slab

TABLE 19.2.1 Influence of Stress on Fire Resistance of Concrete Columns

Applied Load (% Design Load)	*Fire Resistance (min)*
150	68
100	124
75	198
50	248
30	358

damage. In order to possess fire resistance, it must be protected from high temperatures encountered in fires with other materials. Protection for steel beams, girders, and columns, such as encasements of concrete, clay, tile, masonry, or gypsum blocks, has been generally superseded by plastered or sprayed-on applications applied either to a furred plaster base, such as expanded metal lath, or directly to the surface of the member to be protected. The applications may be conventional plasters of portland or gypsum cements combined with appropriate aggregates, or one of the many combinations of mineral fibers with binders. Gypsumboard encasement is a popular technique for protecting steel structural elements. Deliberate efforts must be taken to ensure that the materials used to protect the steel members from fire are maintained and not removed for the installation of hangers, supports, and other purposes.

Barrier Systems (Walls and Partitions)

Exterior walls, interior partitions, floors, and floor/ceiling assemblies are components that define the functional layout of rooms and spaces in a building. In the normal functional use of a building, these components are used to provide privacy, security, protection from the elements, and noise control. They can also provide fire protection by delaying or preventing heat and particles of combustion from spreading throughout the building.

The effectiveness of a barrier in preventing fire spread depends on several factors. One is fire severity, which is influenced by the fuel in the space, as well as the size and location of openings, the size of the room, and the thermal properties of the wall and ceiling construction. The fire severity represents the thermal load applied to the barrier surface. The performance of the barrier is affected by the materials of construction, as well as other factors such as the applied structural loads, the details at connections, and the dimensions. Of even greater importance is the effect of openings and penetrations in the barrier. The most common cause of fire spread from one room to an adjacent room is through unprotected openings in barriers. Information on protection of openings can be found in NFPA 80, *Standard for Fire Doors and Other Opening Protectives.* Often code requirements and expensive constructions are rendered ineffective because of lack of attention to the details of opening protection.

Building codes through construction classifications identify the fire resistance requirements of barriers. In addition, special locations, such as around vertical shafts, are required to provide specific resistances. Fire resistance ratings are determined by subjecting the barrier assembly to a standard fire test, as described in NFPA 251. The length of time the assembly withstands the laboratory fire without failure describes the fire resistance and is similar to how ratings are obtained for structural building elements. Both combustible and noncombustible barriers can obtain fire resistance ratings in the standard fire test.

The limitations expressed earlier in this chapter with regard to the interpretation of the fire resistance time durations also apply here. That is, the time durations reflect laboratory times and are not necessarily the values to be expected in a real fire. For example, one should not expect a 2 hour barrier assembly to withstand an actual building fire for 2 hours. Failure could occur earlier or later, depending on construction details.

Many fire tests are stopped arbitrarily before an end-point criterion has been attained. In some cases, the indications are that, had the test been continued, the construction would have qualified for a higher fire resistance rating than that assigned to it. For a more detailed discussion of fire barrier systems, see Section 18, Chapter 1, "Confinement of Fires in Buildings," NFPA 221, *Standard for High Challenge Fire Walls, Fire Walls, and Fire Barrier Walls,* and *NFPA 5000®, Building Construction and Safety Code®*.

Floor/Ceiling Assemblies

The fire resistance of floor/ceiling assemblies is important in the prevention of flame movement vertically from floor to floor. Fire resistance ratings from the standard fire test are determined from unpenetrated assemblies. The anticipated fire resistance may be reduced greatly or eliminated in building construction when holes and poke-throughs are not protected adequately or when details do not conform to the tested assembly.

The method of attaching ceilings is a major factor in determining the fire resistance of floors. For example, the nailing of gypsum lath, metal lath, or gypsum wallboards to the soffits of wood joists is often critical in plaster construction. The longer, thinner nails, particularly those with cement coatings, conduct less heat to char the wood surrounding them than do the common types of wire nails. Similarly, the integrity of suspended ceilings must be maintained to reduce the likelihood of premature failure on some assemblies. Details such as attention to expansion of the supporting framework are essential to preventing premature ceiling failures.

Self-tapping screws, made particularly for the attachment of gypsumboard, offer greater holding power and less damage to the core materials than do nails. Such screws can be used to attach wallboards to either wood or cold-rolled channels without previous drilling.

Consideration must also be given to the character of the plaster base with respect to loosening of plaster mixes from the base on application of heat sufficient to char combustible surfaces. The use of wire or, better yet, wire fabric to reinforce the plaster mixes applied to such plaster bases ensures increased fire resistance. Clearances for longitudinal expansion of metal furring members are required to prevent damage from buckling. The tendency of certain plaster bases and plaster mixes to expand or contract with changes in atmospheric humidity should also be given consideration where resultant cracking might affect the fire resistance of structures incorporating such plaster.

Suspended ceilings with openings for air diffusers and light troughs should be designed so that such openings are not points of vulnerability to fire. Continuous construction above recesses for lighting fixtures and properly designed self-closing dampers for air ducts provide protection.

Roof/Ceiling Assemblies

Roof/ceiling assemblies are tested and rated in a manner similar to the floor/ceiling assemblies. The results are generally comparable. However, it should be noted that roof assemblies often have a given thickness of insulation in place at the test. If additional thicknesses of insulation are desired, the fire resistance rating may be reduced.

ILLUSTRATIVE FIRE RESISTANCE RATINGS FOR STRUCTURAL FRAME AND BARRIER CONSTRUCTIONS

Fire resistance testing has produced a large amount of performance data. To illustrate the effect of materials and construction materials on the fire resistance rating of assemblies and structural members, several graphs and tables are included. These graphs and tables can be used to give guidance on the needs to achieve fire resistance ratings and to provide a basis for interpretations of the fire resistance of construction encountered in field evaluations.

TABLE 19.2.2 Reinforced-Concrete Beams and Girders of Medium Size

Concrete Grade[a]	*Protective Cover of Reinforcement (in.)*	*Fire Resistance Rating*[b] *(hr)*
	¾	1
	1	2
1	1¼	3
	1½	4
	¾	½–1[c]
	1	1–2[c]
2	1½	2–3[c]
	2	2–4[c]

[a]For lightweight concrete having an oven-dried density of 110 pcf or less, the cover shown for concrete Grade 1 may be reduced 25 percent.
[b]May be increased if some bars are better protected by being away from corners or in an upper layer or if beam is large. Should be decreased if beam is small.
[c]Variable depending on spalling characteristics of aggregate. The use of mesh to hold cover in place will give ratings about as high as for concrete of Grade 1.
For SI units: 1 in. = 25.4 mm.

Reinforced-Concrete Members

The details of construction and the kind of aggregates affect the fire resistance of concrete structures. The fire resistance ratings for reinforced concrete beams are given in Table 19.2.2 and for prestressed concrete girders, beams, joists, and slabs in Table 19.2.3. As the cold-drawn, high-strength steel tendons used in prestressed concrete are more adversely affected by high temperatures than normal reinforcement steel, these tendons require a thicker protective cover than is required in conventional reinforced concrete. The fire resistance of reinforced concrete columns is shown in Table 19.2.4.

Structural Steel Members

As previously noted, fire resistance generally is provided for structural steel by encasing the members in concrete, lath and plaster, gypsumboard, or spray-applied cementitious or material fiber coatings. Another common method of providing fire resistance is by installing a membrane barrier to delay or prevent the heat from raising the temperature of the steel to critical failure temperatures. Table 19.2.5 gives minimum thicknesses of portland cement encasement for steel beams, whereas Tables 19.2.6 and 19.2.7 illustrate the influence on the fire resistance of columns for various methods of encasement. Figures 19.2.4 and 19.2.5 illustrate different methods of encasement for steel columns. Figure 19.2.6 provides a means to estimate the necessary encasing requirements for steel columns.

TABLE 19.2.3 Prestressed Concrete Girders, Beams, Joists, and Slabs (Grade 1 Concrete)

Type of Unit	*Condition of Restraint*	*Cross-Sectional Area (in.²)*[b]	Cover for Fire Rating Shown (in.)[a]			
			1 hr	*2 hr*	*3 hr*	*4 hr*
Girders, beams, and joists	Unrestrained	40 to 150	2	2.5	—	—
		150 to 300	1.5	2.5	3.5[c]	—
		Over 300	1.5	2.25	3[c]	4[c]
	Axially restrained	40 to 150	1.5	2	—	—
		150 to 300	1	1.5	2	—
		Over 300	1	1.5	1.5	2
Slabs, solid or covered,	Unrestrained		1	1.5	2	2.5
with flat undersurface	Biaxial restraint		0.75	1.25	1.5	2

Note: Data in this table are based on 67 standard ASTM fire tests.
[a]Cover for an individual steel tendon is measured to the nearest exposed surface. For several tendons in the same member having different concrete covers, the minimum cover may be reduced slightly. The covers shown may be reduced 25 percent for lightweight concrete having an over-dried density of 110 pcf or less. For Grade 2 concrete, the cover may need to be increased.
[b]In computing the cross-sectional area of joists, the area of the flange must be added to the area of the stem, but the total width of the flange so used must not exceed three times the width of the stem.
[c]Provide against spalling of the cover by means of a light, 2-in., U-shaped mesh, covered about 1 in.
For SI units: 1 in. = 25.4 mm; 1 in.² = 645 mm².

TABLE 19.2.4 Fire Resistance of Reinforced-Concrete Columns*

Column				Concrete			Reinforcement							
	Section		Load	Aggregates		Mix	Vertical			Lateral		Concrete Cover	Fire Resistance	
No.	*(in.)*	*Area (in.²)*	*in 1000 lb*	*Fine*	*Coarse*	*Cement Fine Coarse*	*Number*	*Bar Size No.*	*(in.²)*	*Diam. (in.)*	*Spacing (in.)*	*Thickness*	*hr*	*min*
70	16 × 16	256	101	Fox River sand	Chicago limestone	1:2:4	4	9	4.00	¼	12	2¼	8 (13+	40 —)
71	16 × 16	256	101	Long Island sand	New York trap rock	1:2:4	4	9	4.00	¼	12	2¼	7	22
72	17 dia	227	107.5	Fox River sand	Chicago limestone	1:2:4	6	9	6.00	¼	12	2½	8 (12+	04 —)
73	17 dia	227	107.5	Long Island sand	New York trap rock	1:2:4	6	9	6.00	¼	12	2½	7	57
74	17 dia	227	129	Fox River sand	Chicago limestone	1:2:4	6	6	2.64	¼	1½	2¼	8 (13+	06 —)
75	17 dia	227	129	Long Island sand	New York trap rock	1:2:4	6	6	2.64	¼	1½	2¼	8	02
25	16 × 16	256	92	Pittsburgh sand	Pittsburgh gravel	1:2:4	4	8	3.16	¼	12	1½	4 (6	— 30)
44	16 × 16	256	92	Long Island sand	Pure quartz gravel	1:2:4	4	8	3.16	¼	12	1½	4 (6	— —)
51	16 × 16	256	92	Pittsburgh sand	Blast furnace slag	1:2:4	4	8	3.16	¼	12	1½	4 (8	— —)
56	16 × 16	256	92	Pittsburgh sand	New Jersey trap rock	1:2:4	4	8	3.16	½	12	1½	4 (7	— —)
7	18 dia	254	99.75	Pittsburgh sand	Pittsburgh gravel	1:2:4	8	6	3.52	¼	12	1½	5 (6	— —)
2	18 dia	254	141	Pittsburgh sand	Pittsburgh gravel	1:2:4	8	6	3.52	3/16	2	1½	4	—
48	18 dia	254	141	Pittsburgh sand	Blast furnace slag	1:2:4	8	6	3.52	3/16	2	1½	4 (10+	— —)
85	18 dia	254	141	Elgin, IL, sand	Elgin, IL, sand	1:2:4	8	6	3.52	3/16	2	1½	4 (12+	— —)
12	18 dia	254	81	Pittsburgh sand	Pittsburgh gravel	1:2:4	None	—	—	—	—	—	4	—
33	12 dia	113	51	Pittsburgh sand	Pittsburgh gravel	1:2:4	4	5	1.24	¼	2⅛	1½	Avg. 3	of 2 —

*Column Nos. 70 to 75 tested at UL. Test No. 70 of the group was stopped at 8 hours 40 minutes; others at failure or at 8 hours, and all loaded to failure at end of fire exposure (NBS Tech. Paper 184). All other columns tested at NBS Laboratory at Pittsburgh, PA. The fire endurance test of Col. No. 7 stopped at 5 hours, all others of series stopped at 4 hours. Figures in parentheses are estimates of fire resistance if tests had continued to failure (NBS Tech. Paper 272).

For SI units: 1 in. = 25.4 mm; 1 in.² = 645 mm²; 1 lb = 0.45 kg.

TABLE 19.2.5 Concrete Protection for Steel Beams (All re-entrant portions filled)

Fire Resistance Rating		Thickness of Concrete Protection (in.)							
		Grade 1 Size of Member (Flange Width)				Grade 2 Size of Member (Flange Width)			
hr	*min*	*2 to 3¾ in.*	*4 to 5¾ in.*	*6 to 7¾ in.*	*8 in. and over*	*2 to 3¾ in.*	*4 to 5¾ in.*	*6 to 7¾ in.*	*8 in. and over*
4	—	4	3¼	2½	2	4¾	3¾	3	2½
3	—	3½	2½	2	1½	4	3	2½	2
2	—	2½	2	1½	1	3	2½	1¾	1¼
1	30	2	1½	1	1	2½	1¾	1¼	1
1	—	1½	1	1	1	1¾	1¼	1	1

Note: Protective concrete having thickness one-fourth of flange width or less must have steel wire reinforcement spaced nor more than four times the thickness of the concrete covering the flange.
For SI units: 1 in. = 25.4 mm.

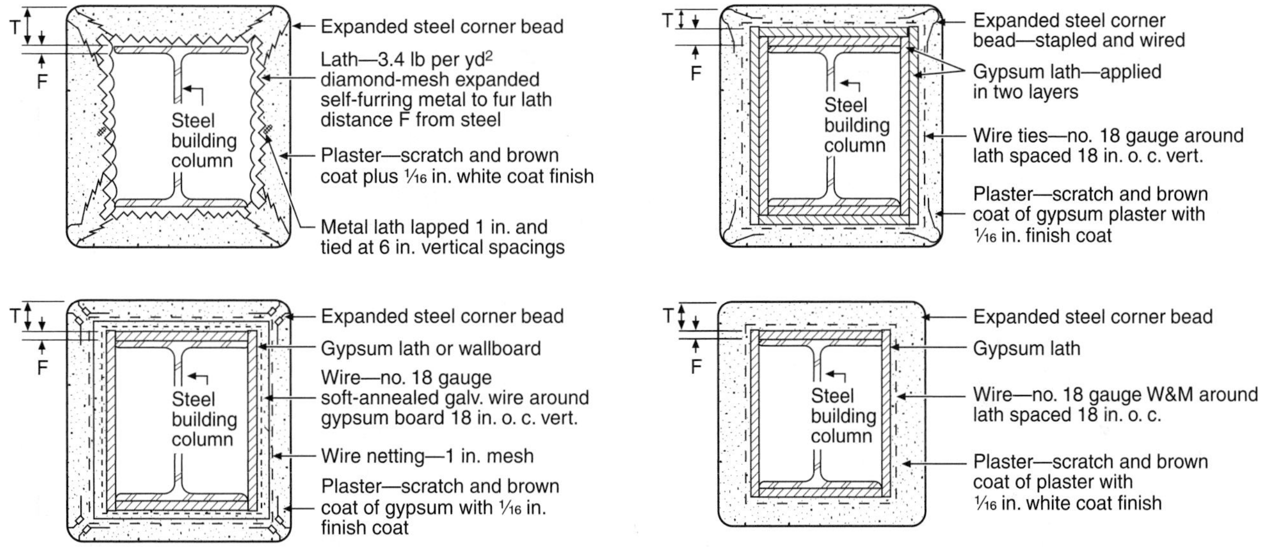

FIGURE 19.2.4 Typical Steel Column Protection of Lath and Plaster Assemblies. For SI units: 1 in. = 25.4 mm; 1 lb = 0.454 kg.

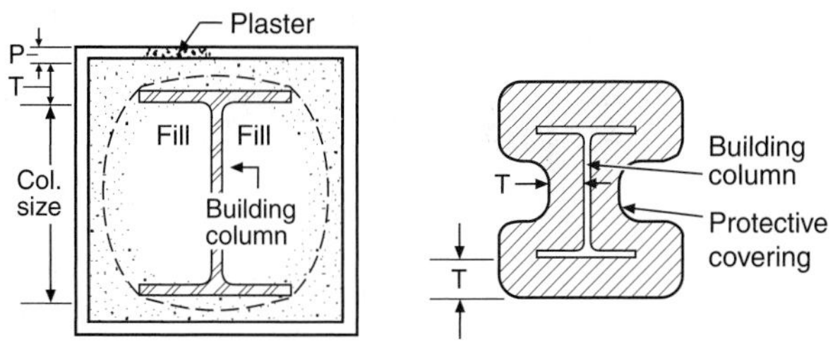

FIGURE 19.2.5 Typical Steel Column Protection of Concrete, Masonry, or Sprayed Fibers

Floor/Ceiling Assemblies

Fire resistance for floor/ceiling assemblies of reinforced concrete, structural steel, and wood can be achieved in several ways. For example, Figure 19.2.7 illustrates the influence of floor thickness and aggregate type on the fire resistance of reinforced-concrete slabs, whereas Table 19.2.8 shows the fire resistance for several types of concrete floor constructions. Table 19.2.9 shows the test results for structural steel joist floor and roof constructions, and Table 19.2.10 provides some data on the fire resistance of steel-formed concrete floor systems.

TABLE 19.2.6 Fire Resistance of Steel Columns with Lath and Plaster Protective Coverings

Metal Column					Protective Covering							Fire Resistance Rating		
					Type of Covering									
					Plaster									
Type of Section	*Size (in.)*	*Weight per Lin Ft (lb)*	*Area of Metal (in.²)*	*Design*	*Type*	*Aggregate*	*Mix, Volumes*	*Thickness T^b (in.)*	*Furring T^b (in.)*	*Bond of Covering*	*Total Area of Materials (in.²)*	*hr*	*min*	*Notes*
H	6	44	13	—	Portland cement and lime	Sand	1:1/10:2½	⅞	1	Metal lath	40	—	45	Metal lath furred out
H	6	31	9	—	Two thicknesses of above	Sand	1:1/10:2½	⅞ + ⅞	1 & 1	Metal lath	80	1	30	Metal lath furred out
H	10	49	14.5	A	Gypsum-cement mixture	Lightweight[a]	Mill mix	1¾	⅜	Wire fabric	125	3	25	
H	10	49	14.5	A	Gypsum	Lightweight[a]	Mill mix	1⅞	⅝	Metal lath	125	4	—	½-in. channel behind lath
H	10	49	14.5	A	Gypsum	Lightweight[a]	1½:2 1½:3	1¾	⅜	Metal lath	125	4	—	Self-furring lath
H	10	49	14.5	A	Gypsum	Lightweight[a]	1½:2 1½:3	1⅜	⅜	Metal lath furred out	102	3	—	Self-furring lath
H	10	49	14.5	A	Gypsum	Lightweight[a]	1½:2 1½:3	1	⅜	Metal lath	78	2	—	Self- furring lath
H	10	49	14.5	B	Gypsum	Lightweight[a]	½:3½ ½:4	2⅛	½	18-gauge wire and wire fabric	145	4	—	Gypsum
H	10	49	14.5	C	Gypsum	Lightweight[a]	1½:2 1½:3	1½	1	18-gauge wire and wire fabric	140	4 to 15 4 to 40		Gypsum lath
H	10	49	14.5	B	Gypsum	Lightweight[a]	1½:2½	1½	½	18-gauge wire and wire fabric	110	3	40	Gypsum lath
H	10	49	14.5	D	Gypsum	Lightweight[a]	1:2½	½	⅜	18-gauge wire ties	53	1	20	Perforated gypsum lath
H	10	49	14.5	D	Gypsum	Lightweight[a]	1:2½	⅝	⅜	18-gauge wire ties	60	1	30	Perforated gypsum lath
H	10	49	14.5	D	Gypsum	Lightweight[a]	1½:2 1½:3	1	⅜	18-gauge wire ties	80	2	15	Perforated gypsum lath
H	10	49	14.5	D	Gypsum	Lightweight[a]	1½:2 1½:3	1½	⅜	18-gauge wire ties	104	2	30	Perforated gypsum lath
O	7	51	15.5	—	Portland cement and lime	Sand	1:1/10:2½	1¼	⅞	⅞-in. rib lath	70	2	45	Metal lath on cast column

[a]Lightweight aggregate can be either perlite or vermiculite.
[b]Dimensions as shown in Figure 19.2.4.
For SI units: 1 in. = 25.4 mm; 1 in.² = 645 mm²; 1 ft = 0.305 m; 1 lb = 0.454 kg.

TABLE 19.2.7 Fire Resistance of Steel Columns Encased with Concrete, Masonry, or Sprayed Fibers

Steel Column			Protective Covering							Fire Resistance Rating		
Type of Section	*Size (in.)*	*Weight per Lin Ft (lb)*	*Design*	*Type of Covering*	*Thickness Outside Steel TI (in.)*	*Reentrant Portion Filled*	*Plaster Thickness (in.)*	*Section Area of Solid Material (in.²)*	*Bond of Covering*	*hr*	*min*	*Notes*
H	8[e]	34		None	0	No	0	8	—	—	10	Bare column
H	6[e]	20	E	Siliceous gravel concrete, 1:2½:3½ mix	2	Yes	0	100	8 gauge wire spiral 8 in. pitch	3	30	NBS test
Plate and angle	6[e]	34	E	Trap rock or cinder concrete, 1:6 mix[a]	2	Yes	0	130	6 gauge wire spiral	3	45	UL test
H	8[e]	34	E	Limestone concrete, 1:6 mix[a]	2	Yes	0	144	6 gauge wire spiral	6	30	UL test
H	8[e]	34	E	Limestone concrete, 1:6 mix[a]	4	Yes	0	256	6 gauge wire spiral	7	30	UL test
H	8[e]	34	E	Trap rock, granite, cinders, 1:6 mix[a]	4	Yes	0	256	6 gauge wire spiral	7	—	UL test
Plate and angle	6[e]	34	E	Gypsum concrete[b]	2	Yes	½	114	4 in. mesh fabric	6	30	NBS test gypsum plaster
Plate and angle	6[e]	34	E	Gypsum block	2	No	½	107	1 by ⅛ in. O clamps Block bond	4	—	NBS test gypsum plaster
Plate and angle	6[e]	34	E	Cinder block	3¾	Yes	¾	240	Brick bond	7	—	NBS test gypsum plaster
H	8[e]	34	E	Common brick	4¼	Yes	0	270	Wire ties	7	—	UL test
H	8[e]	34	E	Semi-fire clay hollow tile	2	No	0	96	Wire ties	1	30	UL test
H	8[e]	34	E	Semi-fire clay hollow tile	4	No	0	158	No special adhesive	1	30	UL test
H	10[e]	49	F	Sprayed mineral fiber[c]	2¼	Yes	—	164	Special adhesive	5	—	
H	10[e]	49	F	Sprayed mineral fiber[c]	3⅜	Yes	—	238	Special adhesive	5	—	
H	8[e]	28	F	Sprayed mineral fiber[c]	2	Yes	—	44	No special adhesive	5	—	
I	8[e]	28	F	Sprayed asbestos fiber[c]	2	Yes	—	38	No special adhesive	3	—	
	8[e]	35	E	Sprayed asbestos fiber[c]	1	Yes	—	90	No special adhesive	2	—	
	8[e]	35	E	Sprayed asbestos fiber[c]	1¾	Yes	—	98	No special adhesive	4	—	
	8[e]	35	E	Sprayed asbestos fiber[c]	1⅞	Yes	—	120	No special adhesive	4	—	
I	8[e]	28	F	Sprayed asbestos fiber[c]	1½	Yes	—	28	—	2	—	UL test
O	7.6[f]	24		None (bare steel pipes filled with concrete)[d]	0	Yes	0	46		—	35	UL test

[a]Concrete mix—1 part cement to 6 parts total aggregate including sand and coarse aggregate.
[b]Gypsum concrete—7 parts gypsum stucco to 1 part wood shavings, by weight.
[c]Mineral fibers, with bonding agent as required, sprayed on to all surfaces of column shaft to thicknesses indicated. (Thickness different on account of characteristics of fiber and binder.)
[d]Concrete-filled columns require vent holes to prevent explosion in the event of fire.
[e]Approximate depth, flange width per Table 19.2.5.
[f]Inside diameter.
For SI units: 1 in. = 25.4 mm; 1 in.^{2} = 645 mm^2; 1 ft = 0.305 m; 1 lb = 0.454 kg.

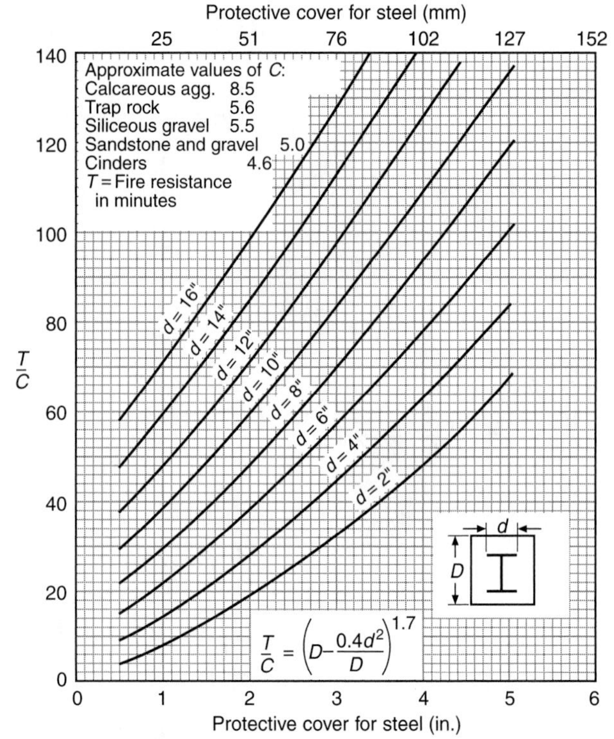

FIGURE 19.2.6 Encasing Requirements of Steel Columns and Other Free-Standing Steel Members. For SI units: 1 in. = 25.4 mm.

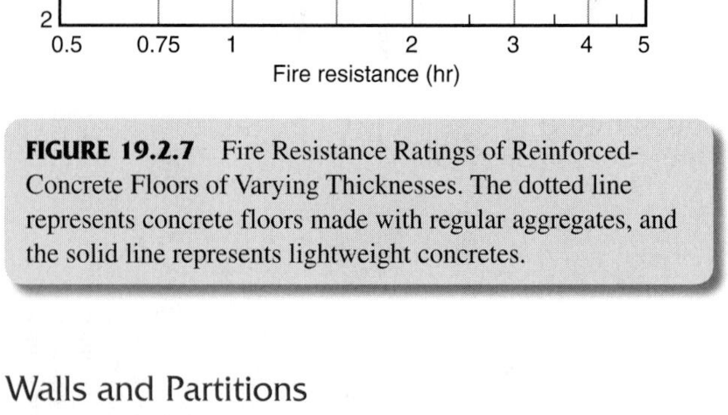

FIGURE 19.2.7 Fire Resistance Ratings of Reinforced-Concrete Floors of Varying Thicknesses. The dotted line represents concrete floors made with regular aggregates, and the solid line represents lightweight concretes.

Walls and Partitions

Walls and partitions are commonly constructed of masonry, wood, or metal studs faced with fire-resistant materials. Table 19.2.11 gives the fire resistance of load-bearing brick or clay tile walls. Figure 19.2.8 shows a graph that allows the fire resistance of burned clay brick walls to be estimated. Tables 19.2.12 and 19.2.13 provide fire resistance ratings for wood stud walls, whereas Figure 19.2.9 gives the fire resistance of stud walls

TABLE 19.2.8 Concrete Floor Constructions

Materials	Fire Resistance Rating *hr*	*min*
Reinforced Concrete (free or partly restrained, 1500–2500 psi)		
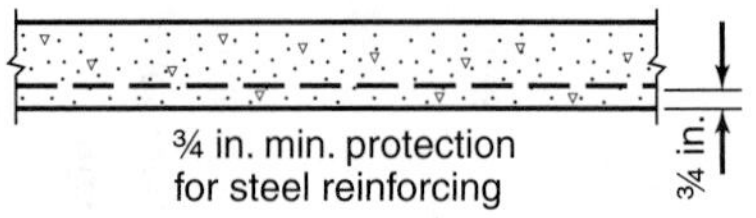		
3 in. thick	—	45
4 in. thick	1	15
6 in. thick, 1 in. minimum protection for steel	2	—
Reinforced Concrete on Precast Joists		
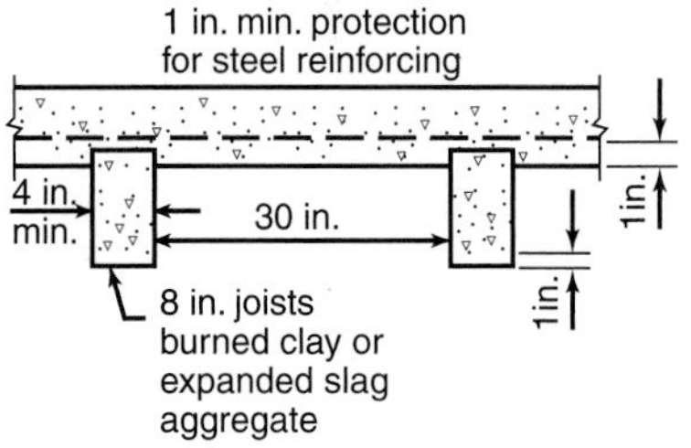		
Reinforced concrete, 1:3½:4, 3 in. thick, no ceiling	45	—
Reinforced concrete, 1:3½:4, 3 in. thick, ceiling of gypsum wallboard ½ in. thick, nailed to wood, strips wired to joists	1	—
Combination of Tile and Concrete Floors		
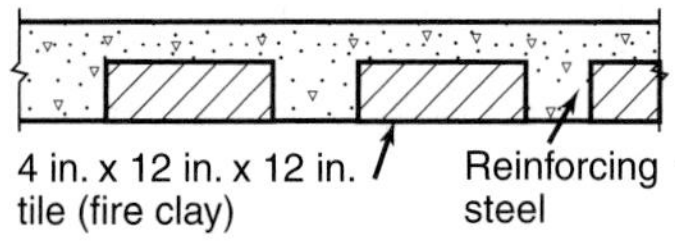		
Concrete 2 in. or 1½ in. thick, and fire clay tile 6 in. or 4 in. thick, no ceiling finish	1	—
Concrete 1½ in. thick, and tile 4 in. thick with gypsum-sand plaster ceiling finish, 1:3 mix, ⅝ in. thick	1	30
Concrete 2 in. thick, and fire clay tile 6 in. thick with gypsum plaster ceiling finish, 1:3 mix, ⅝ in. thick	2	—
Concrete 2½ in. thick, limestone aggregate 4 in. thick, expanded slag concrete tile	3	—
Reinforced Concrete Ribbed Slab		
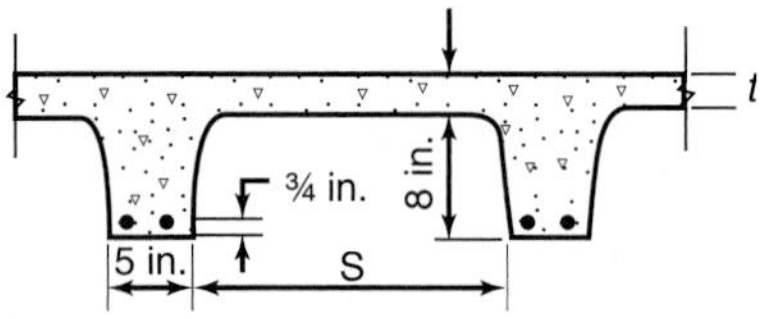		
Concrete, ribbed slab, limestone aggregate, t = 1½ in., S = 20 in.	—	20
Concrete, ribbed slab, limestone aggregate, t = 2½ in., S = 20 in.	—	45
Same with metal lath and ⅞ in. gypsum-sand plaster ceiling, 1:2, 1:3 mix	2	30
Concrete, ribbed slab, limestone aggregate, t = 3 in., S = 30 in.	1	—

For SI units: 1 in. = 25.4 mm; 1 psi = 6.89 kPa.

TABLE 19.2.9 Steel Joist Floor or Roof Constructions

Joists: Type	Joists: Depth (in.)	Floor Slab	Thickness (in.)	Furring	Ceiling Kind	Thickness (in.)	Fire Resistance Rating (hr)	Fire Resistance Rating (min)
I or S[a]	8	T & G wood flooring on 2 in. by 2 in. wood strips	25/32	3.4 lb metal lath	Gypsum—sand plaster	¾	—	45[b]
I or S[a]	8	T & G wood flooring on 2 in. by 2 in. wood strips	1⅝	3.4 lb metal lath	Gypsum—sand plaster	¾	1[b]	—
I or S[a]	8	Reinforced concrete, precast concrete, or gypsum planks	2	3.4 lb metal lath	Gypsum—sand or portland cement-sand plaster	¾	1	—
S	8	Reinforced concrete or precast gypsum tile	2¼	3.4 lb metal lath	Gypsum—sand plaster, 1:2; 1:3 mix	¾	2	—
S	10	Reinforced concrete or reinforced gypsum tile or planks	2	3.4 lb metal lath	Neat[h] gypsum, or gypsum-vermiculite plaster, 1:2; 1:3	1¾	2	30
S	10	Reinforced concrete	2½	3.4 lb metal lath	Gypsum—sand plaster	⅞	2	30
		Reinforced concrete	2½	3.4 lb metal lath	Gypsum-perlite of gypsum-vermiculite plaster, 1½:2; 1½:3	¾	3	—
S	8	Reinforced concrete perlite or vermiculite aggregate	2½	3.4 lb metal lath	Gypsum-perlite or gypsum-vermiculite plaster, 1½:2; 1½:3	¾	3	—
S	10	Reinforced concrete, 1:2:4 gravel aggregate	2½	3 lb metal lath	Gypsum-vermiculite or gypsum-perlite plaster,1½:2; 1½:3	1	4	—
S	10	Reinforced concrete, 1:2:4 gravel aggregate	2	Gypsum lath[c]	Gypsum-perlite or gypsum-vermiculite plaster, 1½:2½	⅝	1	—
S	10	Reinforced concrete, 1:2:4 gravel aggregate	2	Gypsum and wires[c,d]	Gypsum-perlite or gypsum-vermiculite plaster, 1½:2½	½	2	—
S	10	Reinforced concrete, 1:2:4 gravel aggregate	2	Gypsum[c,e]	Gypsum-vermiculite or perlite plaster, 1½:2; 1½:3	1	4	—
S	10	Reinforced concrete, 1:2:3.4 gravel	2½	Gypsum and wires[c,d]	Sprayed-on mineral fiber	¾	3	—
S	10	Reinforced concrete, 1:2.5:3.5 gravel	2	Special Z section[f]	Special acoustical tiles (see UL list)	⅝	2	—
S	12	Reinforced concrete, gravel aggregate	2	Nailing channels 16 in. o.c. 2¾ in. × ⅞ in.	Type X[g] wallboard	⅝	1	30
S	12	Reinforced concrete, 1:3:3⅔ gravel aggregate	2	26 gauge 14 in. o.c. channels	Type X[g] wallboard applied with No. 6 by 1 in. wallboard screws	⅝	1	30
S	10	Reinforced concrete, 1:2:4 gravel aggregate	2	25 gauge nailing channels 16 in. o.c.	Gypsum wallboard applied with 1¼ in. long barbed nails ⅜ in. diam. head	⅝	1	—

[a]I-beam or open-web type joists.
[b]Combustible construction.
[c]All gypsum lath ⅜ in. perforated type.
[d]Gypsum lath and No. 20 gauge wires attached to nailing channels. Wires attached diagonally to reinforce and support lath and plaster.
[e]1 in. hexagonal mesh wire fabric to reinforce plaster and hold up lath and plaster.
[f]Special No. 25 gauge galvanized steel Z runners 12 in. o.c.
[g]Type X gypsum wallboard designates gypsum wallboard with a specially formulated core that provides greater fire resistance than regular gypsum wallboard of the same thickness.
[h]Unsanded wood-fiber plaster.
For SI units: 1 in. = 25.4 mm; 1 lb = 0.454 kg.

TABLE 19.2.10 Floors of Concrete on Steel Floor and Form Units (Plaster or Sprayed-On Fire Protective Covering)

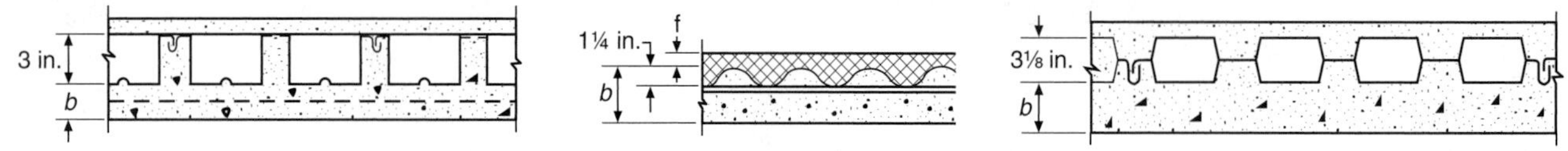

Type A | Type B | Type C

Type of Floor Unit	*Thickness of Floor (in.)*	*Furring*	*Protective Covering Material*	*Application*	*Thickness (in.)*	Fire Resistance Rating *hr*	Fire Resistance Rating *min*
A	5⅝	None	Mineral fibers applied to floor units	Sprayed	½ to 2	5	—
C	5½	None	Same	Sprayed	1½	5	—
A	5⅝	None	Vermiculite or perlite acoustical plastic	Sprayed	1¹⁄₁₆ to 3¹⁄₁₆	4	—
B	4½	None	Same	Sprayed	4	—	—
B	4½	[a]	Gypsum-vermiculite or perlite plaster	Troweled or sprayed	⅜ to 1⅝	4	—
C	4	None	Mineral fiber applied to floor units	Sprayed	¾	3	—
A	5⅝	None	Vermiculite acoustical plastic, cellular floor units	Sprayed	½ to 2	2	—
B	5¼	None	None[b]	—	—	2	—
B	4¼	None	None[c]	—	—	1	—
A	8	[d]	Gypsum-vermiculite or perlite plaster, 100 lb gypsum to 2 ft^3 for scratch coat and 3 ft^3 for browncoat plaster, white finish ¹⁄₁₆ in.	Troweled	⅜	4	—
A	8	[d]	Same	Troweled	1	5	—
A	6⅝	[e]	Acoustical tiles, T & G edges with saw kerfs	Sheet metal clips	¾	4	4

[a]Expanded metal lath tack welded or tied to bottom of corrugated steel floor units.
[b]Floor slab, limestone concrete, 5¼ in. thick.
[c]Floor slab, limestone concrete, 4¼ in. thick.
[d]24 gauge, 3.4 lb, ⅜ in. mesh expanded metal lath suspended 2½ to 7½ in. below floor units.
[e]Special furring system to which acoustical tiles are clipped 10¾ in. below floor units.
For SI units: 1 in. = 25.4 mm; 1 lb = 0.454 kg; 1 ft^3 = 0.0283 m^3.

TABLE 19.2.11 Load-Bearing Brick and Clay Tile Walls

Material	*Wall Thickness (in.)*	*Solid Content of Walls (percent)*	Hollow Units: *Number of Cells in Wall Thickness*	Hollow Units: *Thickness of Shells of Unit (in.)*	Fire Resistance Ratings (hr) — Combustible Members Framed 4 in. into Wall: *No Plaster*	Combustible Members Framed 4 in. into Wall: *Plaster on Two Sides*	No Combustible Members Framed into Wall: *No Plaster*	No Combustible Members Framed into Wall: *Plaster on Two Sides*
Brick, clay, or shale	12	90 to 100	—	—	8	9	10	12
	10[a]	72	2 in. cavity	—	2	2½	5	7
Load-bearing hollow tile (not partition tile)	8	90 to 100	—	—	2	2½	5	7
	4[b]	90 to 100	—	—	—	—	1	1½
	12	45	3	0.7	2½	3½	3	6
	12[c]	48	4	⅝	2½	4	5	7½
	10[a]	36	2 + 2 in. cavity	—	—	1¼	—	4
	8	48	3 or 4	—	1	1¾	2½	3½
	8	40	2	—	¾	1½	2	3
	6[b]	40	2	⅝	—	—	¾	1½

[a]Cavity wall with metal ties across cavity.
[b]Non-load-bearing wall restrained in all edges.
[c]Two units, 8 in. by 12 in. by 12 in. 6-cell and 3¾ in. by 12 in. by 12 in. 3-cell tiles, in wall thickness.
For SI units: 1 in. = 25.4 mm.

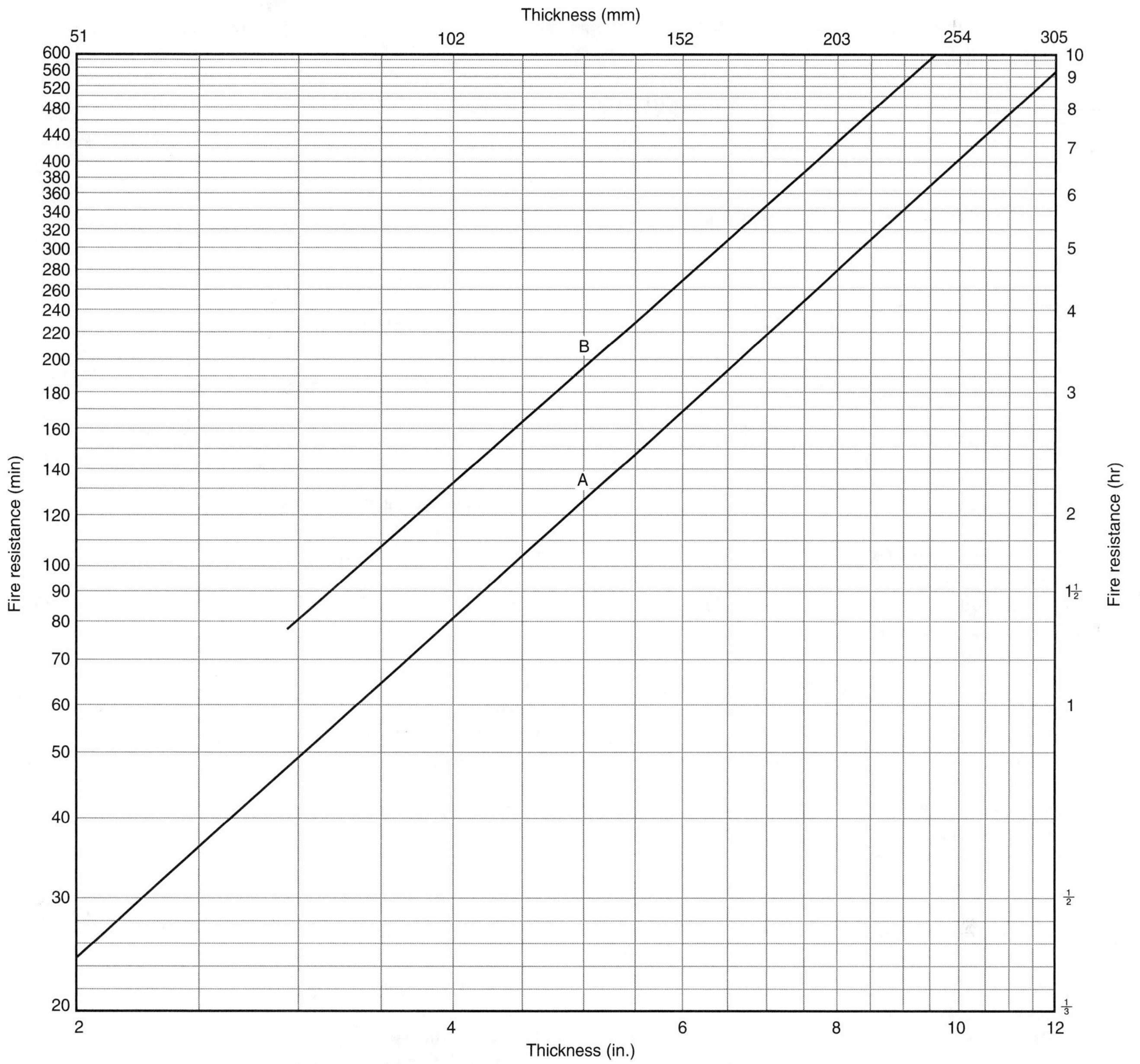

FIGURE 19.2.8 Fire Resistance of Burned Clay Brick Walls: (A) Unplastered; (B) Plastered Both Sides

faced with common construction materials and can be used to estimate quickly and conveniently. Table 19.2.14 and Figure 19.2.10 are very useful descriptions of the fire resistance of solid, non-load-bearing partition materials.

CALCULATING FIRE ENDURANCE

As previously noted, the traditional approach to structural fire protection is by specification of fire resistance ratings through building and safety regulations. Structural members and assemblies are evaluated to the standard fire test (NFPA 251) to establish fire resistance ratings.

Over the past five decades, a substantial amount of research has been conducted on behavior of structural elements in fires. One development is the use of computer models to approximate compartment fire behavior, heat transfer, and structural performance at elevated temperatures. These models utilize scientific research on mechanical and thermal properties of materials at elevated temperatures with some having undergone a degree of validation. This research and computer model application resulted in a broader range of predictions of structural behavior in fires than has been possible with only the traditional code and standard fire test procedures.

A fairly recent development occurred in 1999 when the American Society of Civil Engineers (ASCE) and the Society of Fire Protection Engineers (SFPE) published a jointly developed standard intended for the calculation of fire resistance of structural elements. ASCE/SFPE 29, *Standard Calculation Methods for Structural Fire Protection,* provides the methods of

TABLE 19.2.12 Wood Stud Walls and Partitions (Combustible) (Bearing and nonbearing: 2 in. by 4 in. studs spaced 16 in. on center, firestopped)

Plasterless Types of Construction

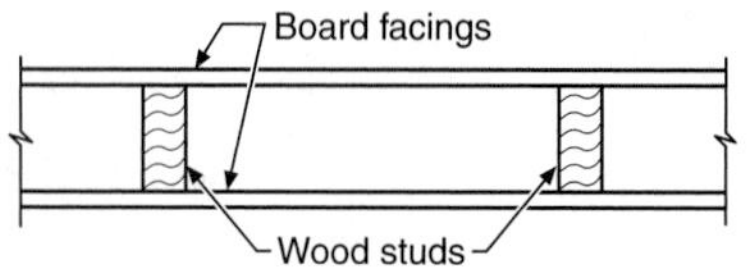

Material	Fire Resistance Rating: Partition Hollow *hr*	Partition Hollow *min*	Partition Filled with Mineral Wool* *hr*	Partition Filled with Mineral Wool* *min*
The following are applied to both sides of studs:				
Sheathing boards (tongue-and-groove) ¾ in. thick	—	20	—	35
Gypsum wallboard, ⅜ in. thick	—	25	—	—
Gypsum wallboard, ½ in. thick (non-load-bearing only for mineral wool filled)	—	40	1	—
Gypsum wallboard, ⅜ in. thick, in two layers each face	1	—	—	—
Gypsum wallboard, ½ in. thick, in two layers each face	1	30	—	—
Gypsum wallboard, ½ in. thick, Type X, one layer each face	—	45	—	—
Gypsum wallboard, ⅝ in. thick, Type X, one layer each face	1	—	—	—
Gypsum wallboard, ⅝ in. thick, Type X, on fire retardant wood fibreboard, ½ in. thick	1	—	—	—
Fir plywood, ¼ in. thick	—	10	—	—
Fir plywood, ⅜ in. thick	—	15	—	—
Fir plywood, ½ in. thick	—	20	—	—
Fir plywood, ⅝ in. thick	—	25	—	—
Cement-asbestos board, 3/16 in. thick	—	10	—	40
Cement-asbestos board, 3/16 in. thick, on gypsum wallboard, ⅜ in. thick	1	—	—	—
Cement-asbestos board, 3/16 in. thick, on gypsum wallboard, ½ in. thick	1	25	—	—

Plaster and Lath Construction

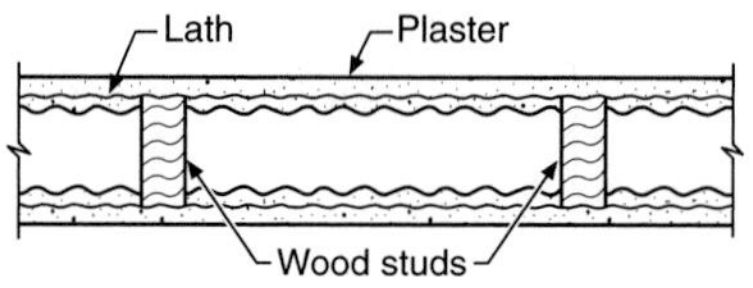

Material	Fire Resistance Rating: Partition Hollow *hr*	Partition Hollow *min*	Partition Filled with Mineral Wool* *hr*	Partition Filled with Mineral Wool* *min*
The following are applied to both sides of studs:				
Gypsum-sand plaster, 1:2, 1:3, ½ in. thick on wood lath	—	30	1	—
Lime-sand plaster, 1:5, 1:7.5, ½ in. thick on wood lath	—	30	—	45
Gypsum-sand plaster, 1:2, 1:2, ½ in. thick on ⅜ in. perforated gypsum lath	1	—	—	—
Gypsum-sand plaster, 1:2, 1:2, ¾ in. thick on metal lath	1	—	1	30
Gypsum lath, ½ in. thick, Type X, and ⅛ in. gypsum-sand plaster, each face	1	—	—	—
Gypsum wallboard, ½ in. thick, Type X, and 1/16 in. gypsum plaster, each face	1	—	—	—
Portland cement-lime-sand plaster, 1:1/30: 2, 1:1/30:3 and asbestos-fiber plaster, ⅞ in. thick on metal lath	1	—	—	—
Gypsum-vermiculite, or perlite plaster, 100 lb gypsum to 2½ ft^3 aggregate, ½ in. thick on ⅜ in. perforated gypsum lath	1	—	—	—
Gypsum perlite plaster, 1:2, ¾ in. thick on metal lath	1	—	—	—

Exterior Bearing Wall

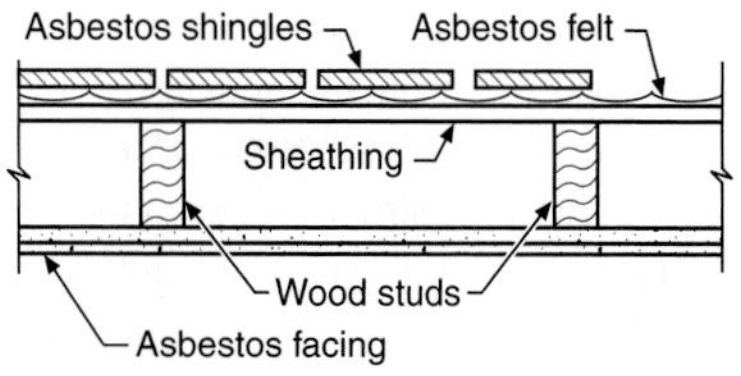

Material	Partition Hollow *hr*	Partition Hollow *min*	Mineral Wool* *hr*	Mineral Wool* *min*
Outside: Cement-asbestos shingles, 5/32 in. thick, on layer of asbestos felt on wood sheathing, ¾ in. thick, on wood studs; inside: Cement-asbestos facing, ⅛ in. thick on fiberboard, 7/16 in. thick	—	30	—	—
Outside: Gypsum sheathing, ½ in. thick; inside 1:2 gypsum-sand plaster, ½ in. thick on ⅜ in. perforated gypsum lath	1	30	—	—

*Mineral wool fill requires some degree of anchorage so as to be held in place after partition facing has been burned away.

For SI units: 1 in. = 25.4 mm; 1 lb = 0.454 kg; 1 ft^3 = 0.0283 m^3.

TABLE 19.2.13 Various Finishes over Wood Framing, One Side (Combustible) with Exposure on Finish Side

Material	*Fire Resistance Rating*[a] *(min)*
Fiberboard, ½ in. thick	5
Fiberboard, flameproofed, ½ in. thick	10
Fiberboard, ½ in. thick, with ½ in.-1:2, 1:2 gypsum-sand plaster	15
Gypsum wallboard, ⅜ in. thick	10
Gypsum wallboard, ½ in. thick	15
Gypsum wallboard, ⅝ in. thick	20
Gypsum wallboard, laminated, two ⅜ in.	28
Gypsum wallboard, laminated, one ⅜ in. plus one ½ in. thick	37
Gypsum wallboard, laminated, two ½ in. thick	47
Gypsum wallboard, laminated, two ⅝ in. thick	60
Gypsum lath, plain or indented, ⅜ in. thick, with ½ in.-1:2, 1:2 gypsum-sand plaster	20
Gypsum lath, perforated, ⅜ in. thick, with ½ in.-1:2, 1:2 gypsum-sand plaster	30
Gypsum-sand plaster, 1:2, 1:3, ½ in. thick, on wood lath	15
Lime-sand plaster, 1:5, 1:7.5, ½ in. thick, on wood lath	15
Gypsum-sand plaster, 1:2, 1:2, ¾ in. thick, on metal lath (no paper backing)	15
Neat gypsum plaster, ¾ in. thick on metal lath (no paper backing)[b]	30
Neat gypsum plaster, 1 in. thick, on metal lath (no paper backing)[b]	35
Lime-sand plaster, 1:5, 1:7.5, ¾ in. thick, on metal lath (no paper backing)	10
Portland cement plaster, ¾ in. thick, on metal lath (no paper backing)	10
Gypsum-sand plaster, 1:2, 1:3, ¾ in. thick, on paper-backed metal lath	20

[a]From National Bureau of Standards BMS-92.
[b]Unsanded wood-fiber plaster.
For SI units: 1 in. = 25.4 mm.

calculating the fire resistance ratings that are equivalent to the results obtained from the standard fire test method (NFPA 251, ASTM E119). The calculation methods in ASCE/SFPE 29 are used as an alternative to the laboratory test results. These calculation methods are applicable only to structural steel, plain and reinforced concrete, timber and wood, concrete masonry, and clay masonry. Limitations of applicability are also identified.

Calculation methods offer advantages in economy and better predictability over the traditional test approach. The calculation methods may be grouped into two categories: (1) calculation of the fire endurance that would have been obtained in the standard fire test and (2) calculation of structural or thermal performance in an actual building fire compartment. Careful consideration must be given when using the latter category. If

TABLE 19.2.14 Solid Partitions: Nonbearing

Materials	Fire Resistance Rating *hr*	*min*
Sheathing planks (tongue-and-groove), in 2 layers, each ¾ in. thick (1 in. nominal) and with joints staggered	—	15[a]
Same, with layer of 30 lb asbestos felt between planks	—	25[a]
Planking, pine (tongue-and-groove), 2 in. thick (nominal), wet vertically	—	12[a]
Wallboard, ⅜ in. gypsum, full height facings on two thicknesses ½-in. coreboard, full height, cemented with staggered vertical joints to form 1¾ in. thick partition, external joints finish taped	1	—
Wallboard, ⅝ in. gypsum, Type X[c], full height facings, cemented and nailed or screwed to ribs made of two thicknesses of ½ in. gypsumboard 3½ or 6½ in. wide and 1 in. by ⅝ in. wood runners top and bottom, external joints finish taped	1	—
Wallboard, ½ in. gypsum, full height, nailed and cemented to 1 in. thick coreboard factory laminated from two ½ in. thick by 24 in. wide coreboards with staggered edges, external joints staggered, butted and finish taped with joint finisher	2	—
Gypsum tile, 3 in. thick, cored	2	—
Gypsum tile, 4 in. thick, cored	2	—
Gypsum tile, 3 in. solid, no cores	3	—
Gypsum tile, 3 in. cored, ½ in. of 1:3 gypsum-sand plaster on each side	3	—
Gypsum tile, 4 in. cored, ½ in. of 1:3 gypsum-sand plaster on each side	4	—
Gypsum-vermiculite or perlite plaster, 1½:2, 1½:3 by vol., ¾ in. thick on each side of 1½ in. gypsum lath, vertical full height, tied to floor and ceiling runners, no studs	1	30
Gypsum-sand plaster, 1:2, 1:3 by wt, ¾ in. thick on each side of ½ in. gypsum lath vertical full height, tied to floor and ceiling runners, no studs	1	—
Partition tile, burned clay, 4 in. thick, 1 cell in thickness	—	10[b]
Cinder block, 4 in. thick, solid	1[b]	—
Cinder block, 6 in. thick, 1 cell in thickness	1	15[b]
Calcareous gravel concrete tile, 4 in. thick, 65 percent solid	—	45[c]
Calcareous gravel concrete tile, 8 in. thick, 55 percent solid	2	30

[a]Combustible.
[b]When plastered on both sides with ½ in. 1:3 gypsum-sand plaster, the tile partition described has 45 minute fire resistance and the cinder block and 4 in. concrete tile assemblies described have 2 hour fire resistance.
[c]Type X gypsum wallboard designates gypsum wallboard with a specially formulated core that provides greater fire resistance than regular gypsum wallboard of the same thickness.
For SI units: 1 in. = 25.4 mm; 1 lb = 0.454 kg.

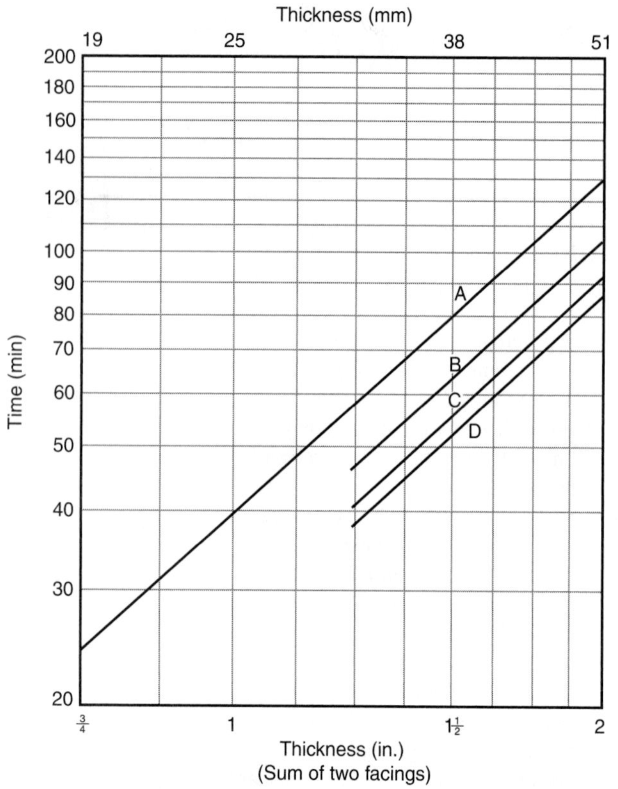

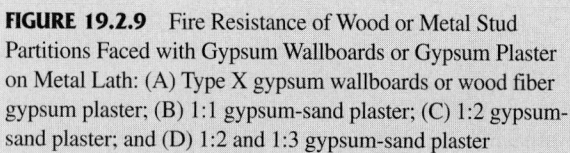

FIGURE 19.2.9 Fire Resistance of Wood or Metal Stud Partitions Faced with Gypsum Wallboards or Gypsum Plaster on Metal Lath: (A) Type X gypsum wallboards or wood fiber gypsum plaster; (B) 1:1 gypsum-sand plaster; (C) 1:2 gypsum-sand plaster; and (D) 1:2 and 1:3 gypsum-sand plaster

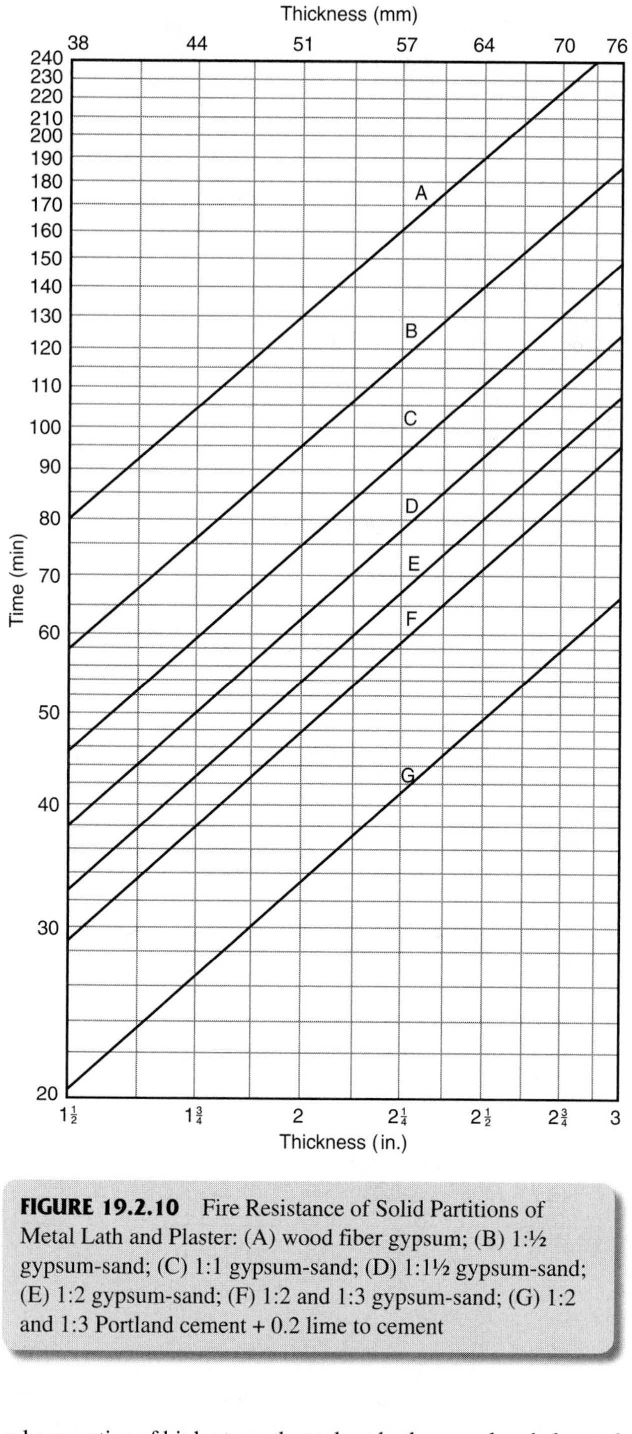

FIGURE 19.2.10 Fire Resistance of Solid Partitions of Metal Lath and Plaster: (A) wood fiber gypsum; (B) 1:½ gypsum-sand; (C) 1:1 gypsum-sand; (D) 1:1½ gypsum-sand; (E) 1:2 gypsum-sand; (F) 1:2 and 1:3 gypsum-sand; (G) 1:2 and 1:3 Portland cement + 0.2 lime to cement

a wall is calculated for a certain duration using a less severe fire (thermal) load and the occupancy changes (increased fire loading), the expected fire resistance of the wall with the new occupancy must be recalculated.

Building code requirements specify fire resistance ratings as reflected by the standard fire test. Consequently, it has been beneficial to develop methods to calculate the fire resistance that would have been obtained in the standard fire test. Illustrative equations and graphs for this type of evaluation are given later. A brief description of procedures to calculate performance in actual building fires is given at the end of this chapter.

Equivalent Fire Endurance of Structural Steel

As noted previously, fire testing has been ongoing for many years, yielding a large amount of data and experience. The procedures described here reflect the type of methods that will enable equivalent fire resistance to be calculated. It should be noted that many of these calculation methods are obtained from test data. Consequently, one should be critical when applying these methods to materials that have not been used in the tests that were the basis for the calculation procedures. For example, the data for structural steel has been based on testing of A7 or A36 structural steel. High-strength steels have become popular. The mechanical properties of high-strength steels at both normal and elevated temperatures are different from those of A7 and A36 steel. Consequently, for fire resistance calculations, when the term *structural steel* is used in this section, A7 and A36 steels are intended.

The fire resistance of structural steel beams and columns can be improved by insulating the members. Equation 1 calculates the fire resistance of steel columns protected by light insulation.[4,5] The members may be protected by boxing the slope or by a contour protection. The equation is:

$$R = \left(C_1 \frac{M}{D} + C_2\right) l \qquad (1)$$

where

R = Fire endurance (min)

M = Mass of the member (lb/ft)

D = Heated perimeter (in.)

l = Thickness of protection (in.)

C_1, C_2 = Constants that are empirically derived for the insulating units

In SI units:

$$R = \left(0.672C_1\frac{M}{D} + 0.039C_2\right)l \qquad (1m)$$

where

R = Fire endurance (min)

M = Mass of the member (kg/m)

D = Heated perimeter (mm)

l = Thickness of protection (mm)

C_1, C_2 = Empirical constants, the same as used for U.S. customary units

The heated perimeter, *D,* varies depending on whether the structural member is a column or beam. It also varies depending on the shape of the member and whether the coating is directly applied to the contour of the member, or in a box fashion.

Most commonly, insulating materials will have densities less than 20 lb/ft^3. For the cementitious material in UL Design Nos. X701, X704, X722 and X723, $C_1 = 69$ and $C_2 = 31$. For the mineral fiber material in UL Design Nos. X801, X807, X818, X821 and X822, $C_1 = 63$ and $C_2 = 42$.

Empirical coefficients that should be used for other coatings can be found in the AISC Steel Design Guide 19.[6] It should be noted that the version of the above formula used in that document calculates the fire resistance in hours instead of minutes (as done in the original derivation), so the values of the coefficients have been adjusted accordingly. The formula for determining the heated perimeter (*D,* in.) for beams and columns in contour or box profiles, can also be found in that document.

For insulating materials, such as mineral fibers, vermiculite, and perlite, having densities *r* in the range of 20 to 50 lb per ft^3 (32 to 80 kg/m^3), the factors C_1 and C_2 are:

$$C_1 = \frac{1200}{r}, \text{ and } C_2 = 30$$

For insulating materials of the same range of densities but incorporating cement pastes or gypsum, the factors C_1 and C_2 are:

$$C_1 = \frac{1200}{r}, \text{ and } C_2 = 72$$

To calculate the fire resistance of columns boxed with gypsum wallboard, the total weight of the column plus wallboard must first be calculated using the following formula:

$$W' = W + \frac{50\,(hD)}{144}$$

where

W' = Total weight of the column plus wallboard

W = Weight of steel shape (lb/ft)

h = Thickness of gypsum wallboard (in.)

D = Heated perimeter of column (in.)

Using W' (instead of W), the column fire resistance, R, is then calculated as follows:

$$R = 130\left[\frac{h(W'/D)}{2}\right]^{0.75}$$

Most columns normally used only offer a few minutes of fire resistance when unprotected. Very heavy, unprotected steel columns are capable of exhibiting some significant fire resistance. Equations 2, 3, 2m, and 3m can be used to predict the fire resistance of unprotected steel columns.[4]

$$R = 10.3\left(\frac{M}{D}\right)^{0.7} \quad \text{for} \quad \frac{M}{D} < 10 \qquad (2)$$

$$R = 8.3\left(\frac{M}{D}\right)^{0.8} \quad \text{for} \quad \frac{M}{D} > 10 \qquad (3)$$

where

R = Fire endurance (min)

M = Mass of the member (lb/ft)

D = Heated perimeter (in.)

In SI units:

$$R = 75.1\left(\frac{M}{D}\right)^{0.7} \quad \text{for} \quad \frac{M}{D} < 171 \qquad (2m)$$

$$R = 60.5\left(\frac{M}{D}\right)^{0.7} \quad \text{for} \quad \frac{M}{D} > 171 \qquad (3m)$$

where

R = Fire endurance (min)

M = Mass of the member (kg/m)

D = Heated perimeter (mm)

Beams with a larger *W/D* ratio can always be substituted for the structural member listed with a specific fire-resistive covering without changing the thickness of the covering.

Beams with different shapes than those listed in a fire-resistive assembly may be substituted for the listed shape as long as the coating thickness is adjusted as a function of the W/D ratio according to the following equation:

$$h_1 = \left(\frac{W_2/D_2 + 0.6}{W_1/D_1 + 0.6}\right)h_2$$

where

h = Thickness of the spray-applied fire protection (in.)

W = Weight of steel beam (lb/ft)

D = Heated perimeter of the steel beam (in.)

Subscript 1 refers to the substitute beam and required protection thickness

Subscript 2 refers to the listed beam and protection thickness

The following are the limitations of this formula:

1. W/D values must be 0.37 or greater.
2. h must be ⅜ in. (9.5 mm) or greater.
3. The unrestrained beam rating and restrained beam rating must both be at least 1 hour.
4. For restrained beams, the beam must be a "compact" section per AISC Steel Construction Manual.[7]

Equivalent Fire Endurance of Reinforced Concrete

Thermal and mechanical properties vary for all materials with the temperature of the material. Because the heat transmission through concrete is quite slow, the variability of properties throughout the member is quite nonuniform. As a result, the behavior of reinforced concrete in fire is very complex. Nevertheless, equations have been developed to predict the fire resistance of reinforced concrete columns. The resistance depends on the weight and aggregate of the concrete, the minimum dimension of the column, the area of vertical reinforcement in the column, and the effective length of the column.

The effective length of the column is equal to the length of the column multiplied by a factor. The factor can range from 0.65 to 2.1, depending on how the column is secured in the top and the bottom. If the exact method of securement is unknown, a factor of 1 can be used. When the column is constructed of normal-weight siliceous aggregate and columns 1 and 3 are used in Table 19.2.15, use Equation 4. When the column is constructed of normal-weight carbonate aggregate and columns 1 and 3 are used in Table 19.2.15, use Equation 5. When the column is constructed of normal-weight carbonate or siliceous aggregate and column 2 is used in Table 19.2.15, use Equation 6. When the column is constructed of lightweight aggregate and any column is used in Table 19.2.15, use Equation 7.

$$R = \frac{t}{3.2f} - 1 \tag{4}$$

$$R = \frac{t}{3.2f} - 0.75 \tag{5}$$

$$R = \frac{t}{4f} - 1 \tag{6}$$

$$R = \frac{t}{3f} - 1 \tag{7}$$

where

R = Fire resistance (hr)

t = Minimum dimension of the column (in.)

f = A factor that considers overdesign (Table 19.2.15 provides values for f)

In SI units:

$$R = \frac{t}{81.3f} - 1 \tag{4m}$$

$$R = \frac{t}{81.3f} - 0.75 \tag{5m}$$

$$R = \frac{t}{101.6f} - 1 \tag{6m}$$

$$R = \frac{t}{76.2f} - 1 \tag{7m}$$

where

R = Fire endurance (hr)

t = Minimum dimension of the column (mm)

f = A factor that considers overdesign (Table 19.2.15 provides values for f)

Equation 8 gives calculated fire endurance for normal-weight concrete slabs,[8,9]

$$R = 0.031\rho^{1.2}L^{1.85} \tag{8}$$

where

R = Fire resistance (hr)

ρ = Concrete density (lb/ft³)

L = Slab thickness (ft)

In SI units:

$$R = 0.031\rho^{1.2}L^{1.85} \tag{8m}$$

where

R = Fire resistance (min)

TABLE 19.2.15 Values for *f*

	f		
		Effective length, kL 12 ft < kL < 24 ft	
Overdesign Factor	Effective Length, kL (kL_{max} = 12 ft)	$\rho \le 0.03$ $t \le 12$ in.	All Other Cases
Column	*1*	*2*	*3*
1.00	1.0	1.2	1.0
1.25	0.9	1.1	0.9
1.50	0.8	1.0	0.8

For SI units: 1 in. = 25.4 mm; 1 ft = 0.305 m.
L = column length (feet).
k = effective length factor (dimensionless); if unknown, assume k = 1.

ρ = Concrete density (kg/m^3)

L = Slab thickness (m)

Equivalent Fire Endurance of Timber

When timber members are tested, they burn. As burning continues, a char layer is formed on the exposed surfaces. This char layer reduces the usable strength of the timber members. The time duration that elapses before the member reaches its critical failure load is the fire endurance. The fire endurance for wood beams is calculated by determining the breaking strength of the uncharred residual cross section. The time to reach a critical depth may be calculated using the applicable equations in ASCE/SFPE 29. The critical residual depth, *d,* can be obtained from Figures 19.2.11 and 19.2.12.[10]

STRUCTURAL MATERIALS AT ELEVATED TEMPERATURES

All structural materials used in building construction are adversely affected by the elevated temperatures caused by fire. The degree and significance of this adverse behavior depend primarily on the function of the elements and on the degree of protection afforded. The mechanical properties of strength and stiffness decrease as the temperature rises. Other adverse behavior, such as excessive expansion and accelerated creep, also develops with increasing temperatures. In general, however, the design parameters that are of concern at normal temperatures are the same parameters that are of concern at elevated temperatures.

Structural Steel

Property of Structural Steel. Steel is the backbone of modern building design. Whether it acts as the reinforcement for concrete or the skeleton framework for buildings, it constitutes the major load-carrying material in modern building construction. From the designer's viewpoint, steel possesses many qualities, such as high strength and good ductility, that make it an ideal structural material. However, steel, like all other materials, is adversely affected by fire.

Steel is noncombustible and does not contribute fuel to a fire. In the past, these properties have sometimes provided a false sense of security with regard to its durability in a fire because they overshadow the fact that steel loses strength when subjected to temperatures easily attained in a fire. The relative seriousness of the problem depends on several factors, such as the function of the steel element, its level of stress, the support conditions, its surface area and thickness, and the temperature within the steel itself. This temperature can be quite different from the ambient temperature in the compartment.

From a structural viewpoint, the yield stress of steel is the significant parameter in establishing load-carrying capacity. The tensile stress strain diagram for A36 steel at various temperatures is shown in Figure 19.2.13.[11] It can be seen that both the yield strength and the modulus of elasticity decrease

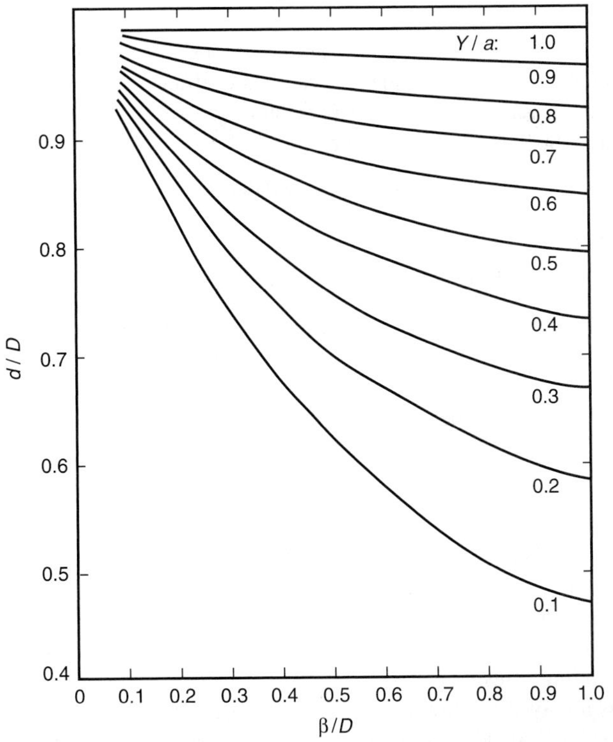

FIGURE 19.2.11 Critical Depth of Solid Timber Beams of Rectangular Cross Section Exposed on Three Sides to Fire

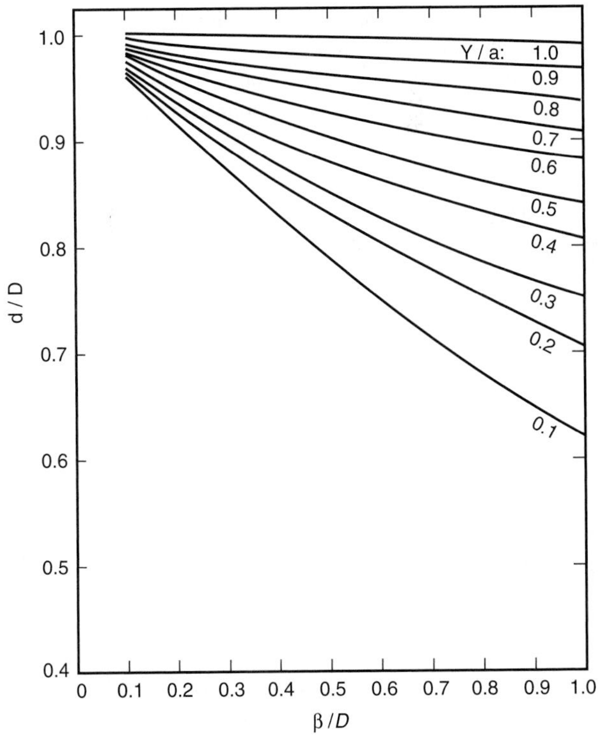

FIGURE 19.2.12 Critical Depth of Solid Timber Beams of Rectangular Cross Section Exposed on Four Sides to Fire

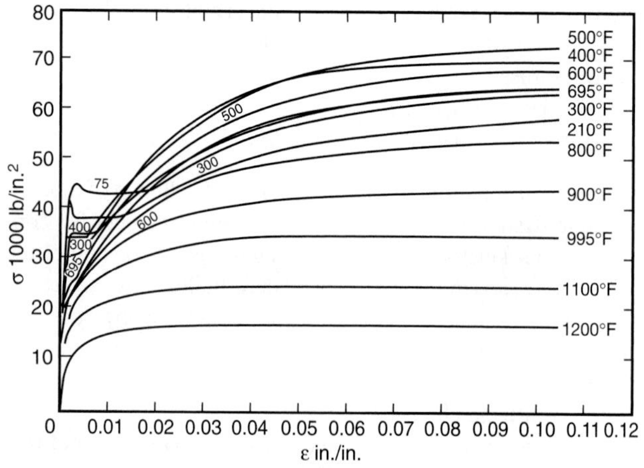

FIGURE 19.2.13 Stress-Strain Curves for an ASTM A36 Steel

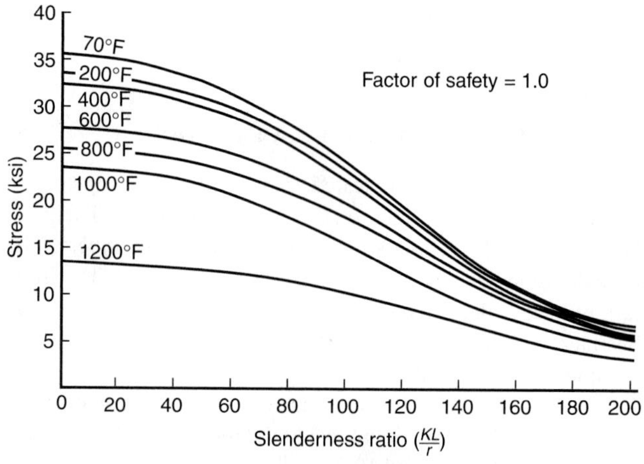

FIGURE 19.2.15 Critical Stress as a Function of the Slenderness Ratio for Various Temperatures—A36 Steel

with increasing temperatures. Figure 19.2.14 shows the ratios of modulus of elasticity and yield stress for A36 steel at various temperatures.[12] As can be seen, both values decrease with an increase in temperature.

This reduction in strength, combined with the reduction in the modulus of elasticity, causes compression members to be more sensitive to higher temperatures than tensile or flexural members. Figure 19.2.15 shows the influence of temperature on the critical stress of compression members of A36 steel.[12]

It should be recognized that the temperature considered for stress limitations is the temperature within the steel and not the ambient temperature. Because steel has a high thermal conductivity, it can transfer heat away from a localized heat source rather quickly. This property, in conjunction with its thermal capacity, enables steel to act as a heat sink. When the steel has an opportunity to transfer heat to cooler regions, it can take a relatively long time for a member to reach its critical value. On the other hand, an extensive fire that distributes heat simultaneously over a greater area reduces this time considerably.

Related to this thermal activity is the effect of mass and surface area of structural steel members. Heavy, thick sections have a far greater resistance to the effects of building fires than do lighter ones. Unprotected lightweight sections, such as those found in trusses and open-web joists, can collapse after 5 or 10 minutes of exposure.

Another property of steel that has an effect on its performance at elevated temperatures is its coefficient of expansion. The linear coefficient of expansion of steel at temperatures up to 1100°F (600°C) is given as:

$$\alpha = 0.0000061 = 0.0000022\Delta t$$

where

α = The coefficient of expansion

Δt = Temperature change in degrees Fahrenheit

In SI units:

α = The coefficient of expansion

Δt = Temperature change in degrees Celsius

$$\alpha = 6.1 \times 10^{-6} + 3.96 \times 10^{-9}\Delta t$$

This high coefficient affects the structure in two ways. If the ends of a structural member are axially restrained, the attempted expansion due to the heat causes thermal stresses to be induced in the member. These stresses combine with those of the normal loading, causing more rapid collapse. If the structural member is not axially restrained, the increased stresses described do not occur; instead, movement takes place. This movement causes the ends of steel columns to be moved laterally, producing an eccentrically loaded column. In other cases, walls can be moved to the point of collapse by expansion of beams. This creates an

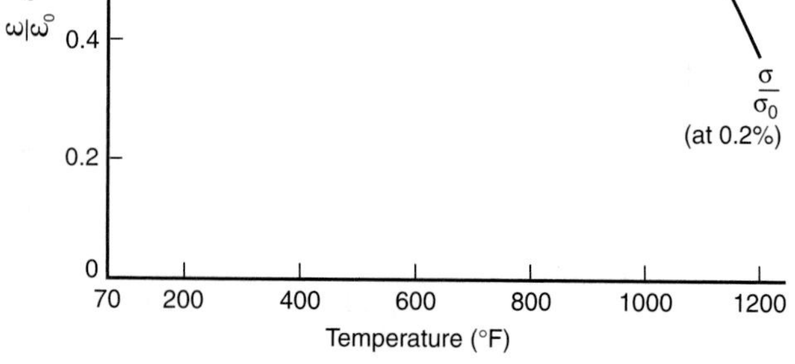

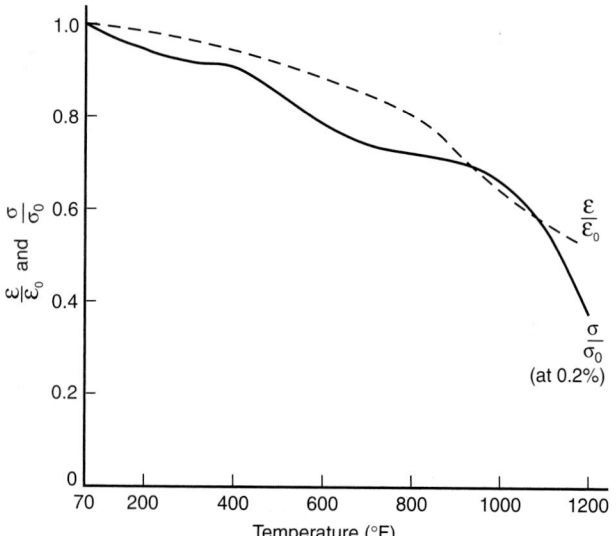

FIGURE 19.2.14 Ratio of Modulus and Yield Strength with Temperature—A36 Steel

extremely hazardous condition both for the building itself and for fire fighters.

In October 2006, NIST issued their final report on the September 11, 2001, collapse of the World Trade Center Towers.[13,14] In this report they note very limited test data that indicates that, all else being equal, as the length of a horizontal structural member increases, the fire endurance may be reduced. Insufficient data currently exists to either substantiate or quantify this relationship. The limited testing also leaves questions regarding benefits of restrained versus unrestrained conditions on fire endurance of protected steel structural members. The discussion of potential research studies began in 2006 to evaluate current fire endurance test methods to see if changes in test procedures, or adjustments to the thickness of a tested fire-resistive coating (to reflect an increase in length over the tested span), are needed.

To illustrate the magnitude of movement, consider a 50 ft (15.24 m) long steel beam that is heated uniformly over its length from 72 to 972°F (22.2 to 522°C). The average value for alpha is 0.0000073, and the increase in length, delta, becomes approximately

$$\delta = \alpha L \,\Delta t = (7.3 \times 10^{-6})(50 \times 12)(900)$$

Thus, $\delta = 3.9$ in.

In NFPA 251, alternate tests may be used to evaluate protection of steel beams and columns. These alternate tests evaluate the thermal protection of the insulating materials by measuring the temperature in the steel for the standard time-temperature exposure. In these alternate tests, failure occurs when the average temperature reaches 1000 to 1100°F (538 to 593°C).

If critical temperature for structural steel is intended to describe the steel temperature at which collapse is impending, temperatures in the range of 1000 to 1100°F (538 to 593°C) can be viewed as a reasonable failure criteria. The actual temperatures at which collapse will occur will likely differ from the 1000 to 1100°F range, depending on the load and support conditions, dimensions, and geometry of the structural member. The actual temperature at which collapse is likely to occur is the temperature at which the yield stress is reduced to the point where it is approximately equal to the stress the member was designed to have applied to it, at or near its full design load.[15] The yield stress is the force per unit area at which permanent deformation occurs. In other words, that temperature range is where the safety factor utilized in the structural design has been reduced to unity due to the reduction in strength.

The modulus of elasticity (E), or ratio of stress to strain, is also reduced at elevated temperatures. Since the deflection of a horizontal structural member is inversely proportional to E, all else being equal, deflection will increase with increased temperatures.

Rather than focus exclusively on temperature, it is more appropriate to focus on the load-carrying capacity of a member at different temperatures. For example, one may question, what is the load-carrying capacity of the structural member when the temperature reaches x°F? The related question may then be asked: What is the likelihood that the steel temperature will reach this value in a room fire? Modern calculation methods enable both of these questions to be addressed with a reasonable degree of confidence, although not yet as a simple, routine evaluation.

Fire Protection of Structural Steel. Because unprotected structural steel loses its strength at high temperatures, it must be protected from exposure to the heat produced by building fires. This protection, often referred to as "fireproofing," insulates the steel from the heat. The more common methods of insulating steel are encasement of the member and application of a surface treatment. Installation of a suspended ceiling as part of a floor-ceiling assembly has been used to increase the fire resistance of the assembly. Additional methods, such as sheet steel membrane shields around members and box columns filled with liquid, have been introduced.

Over the years, encasement of the structural steel member has been a very common and a very satisfactory method of insulating steel to increase its fire resistance. In floor systems of reinforced-concrete slabs supported by structural steel beams, the encasement can be placed monolithically with the floor. Figure 19.2.16 illustrates an older technique of encasement. The major disadvantage of this procedure is the cost, which is related both to the added formwork and concrete and to the increased weight of the supporting members due to the added dead load. To reduce the cost of encasement, systems utilizing lath and plaster or gypsumboard, or spray-on mineral fiber or cementitious coatings, have been developed, as shown in Figures 19.2.17[16] and 19.2.18.

Because of labor costs and the weight increases of encasement, surface treatments applied directly to the member have become quite popular. Low density (13 pcf) sprayed-on

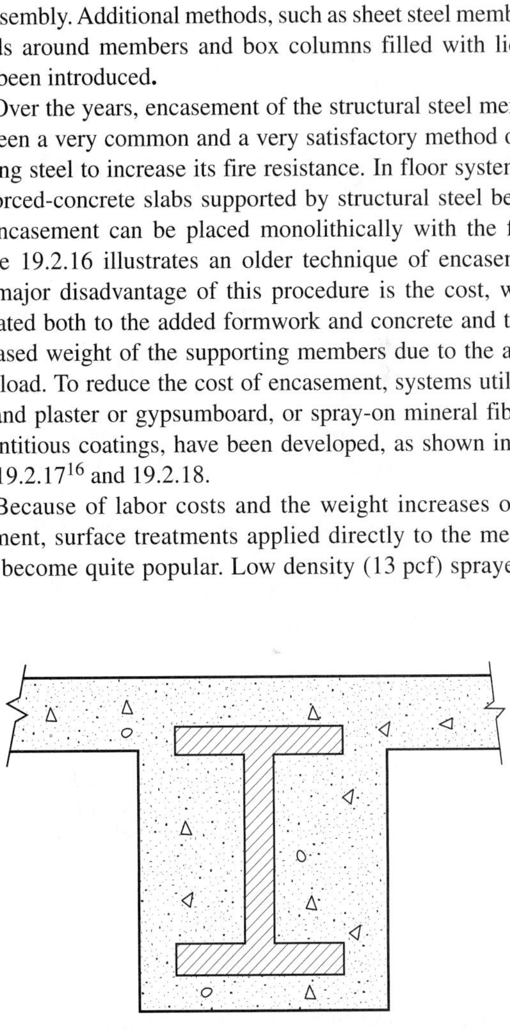

FIGURE 19.2.16 Encasement of a Steel Beam by Monolithic Casting of Concrete Around the Beam

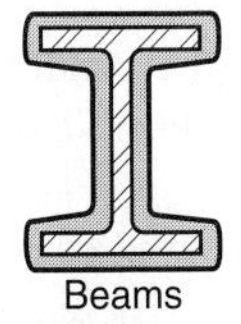

FIGURE 19.2.17 Spray-On Fireproofing

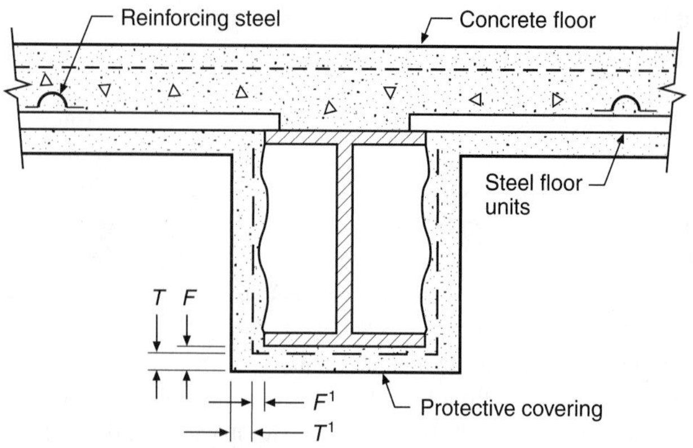

FIGURE 19.2.18 Furred Steel Beams with Noncombustible Protective Coverings

cementitious and mineral fiber coatings are widely used for protecting structural steel. While the protection is excellent if applied correctly, it can easily be scraped off the member during construction or renovations. Consequently, sprayed-on coatings are suspect in their effectiveness over long-term use.

Sprayed-on coverings can spall, and adhesion problems also have been experienced. Thus, effective application, complete coverage, and long-term maintenance are attributes that must be evaluated in considering sprayed-on applications. The application of sprayed-on material must be monitored. The material being applied has specific guidelines that must be met. Conditions that are too humid or too cold may cause the material to fail earlier than it normally would.

The proper surface condition of structural steel is important to assure adequate adhesion of sprayed fire-resistive materials (SFRM) to the steel. The steel surface must be free of dirt, grease, oil, and loose mill scale. Blast cleaning of the surface is generally not required. Also, for common SFRM, such as cementitious or mineral fiber type, the use of primer paint is generally not required or recommended. In most cases, the use of a primer paint will result in a considerable reduction in adhesive strength of the coating to the steel and, if a primer paint is to be used, it is imperative that it be approved for use with the specific SFRM that is to be used. Whether or not a primer is used, conducting field tests to assure adequate thickness, density, adhesion and cohesion is achieved in the actual installation is recommended. Guidance can be found in ASTM E 605 and E 736. The NIST WTC report[14] confirmed existing concerns regarding how surface preparation for structural steel affects the adhesion of spray-applied fire-resistive material. Prior to selecting a coating, lab test information should be reviewed to assure that the coating is appropriate for the conditions of service. Guidance on these tests can be found in ASTM E759, E760, E761, E859 and E937.

Intumescent coatings have been utilized to increase the fire endurance of structural steel. These coatings intumese, or swell, when heated, thus forming an insulation around the steel. Prolonged exposure to flame can destroy the char coating.

Suspended ceilings consisting of lath and plaster, gypsum panels, or acoustical tile supported on a grid system as part of a floor-ceiling assembly are a popular method of fireproofing. The grid system can be suspended from wire hangers or it can be attached directly to the bottom chord of joists or to the bottom flange of beams. Sometimes ceiling tiles are either mechanically fastened or fitted into splines to prevent the pressures that occur in building fires from lifting them out of place.

The overall effectiveness of this type of barrier protection, often called membrane protection, is questionable. This is due to experiences where a lack of control during construction resulted in improper installation procedures, such as inattention to expansion control in the suspension system. In addition, maintenance of ductwork and fixtures in the plenum area may be done by personnel who are not aware of the importance of the integrity of the ceiling to the fire protection system. Removed tiles are not replaced in a manner that will ensure their integrity during a building fire. Consequently, the unprotected steel in the plenum area is exposed to fire and hot gases, which significantly reduce its strength.

Structural steel members also can be protected by sheet steel membrane shields. The sheet steel holds inexpensive insulation materials in place, thus providing a greater fire resistance. In addition, polished sheet steel has been used in tests to protect spandrel girders. The shield reflects radiated heat and protects the load-carrying spandrel.

Reinforced Concrete

Concrete is often used as a protective covering for other materials, as well as a primary load-bearing structural material. Consequently, reinforced-concrete buildings give a sense of fire security. However, concrete as a material also is adversely affected by heat from a fire. Although collapse of reinforced-concrete structures is comparatively rare, there is some experience with collapse of such structures in a fire. Loss in strength, spalling, and other deleterious effects do occur. The collapse of several multistory reinforced concrete buildings during fire exposure is discussed in the report, NIST GRC 02-843.[17]

When the temperature of a reinforced-concrete member is raised, the member loses strength. The amount of strength reduction is influenced by a number of factors. Among the most significant from a structural viewpoint are the type of aggregate, moisture content, type of loading, and level of stress during the fire exposure.

One of the more significant factors in determining the change in strength and the thermal characteristics of concrete is the type of aggregate. Aggregate types can vary widely from region to region. Consequently, numerical values of strength properties are related to a percentage of the original strength, rather than a specific stress value. The qualitative behavior of concrete is generally accurate, however.

Lightweight concrete performs better at elevated temperatures than does normal-weight concrete. Not only does it retain more of its strength during heat buildup, but it also has a lower coefficient of thermal conductivity. Concrete using aggregates of vermiculite of perlite is particularly good at protecting structural steel from a heated environment.

Figures 19.2.19 and 19.2.20 illustrate the effect of aggregates on the fire resistance of reinforced-concrete slabs.[3] The lightweight aggregates, such as expanded shale and expanded slag, have considerably more fire resistance than do normal-weight concretes made from carbonate and siliceous aggregates.

The moisture content of concrete has a significant influence on its thermal performance. A considerable quantity of the heat energy of a fire is expended in vaporizing the absorbed and capillary moisture in concrete. In the case of horizontal members, the water vapor is driven upward and maintains a temperature at the top of the member of 212°F (100°C) until the water has been driven off. This increases the fire resistance, as it keeps the temperature on the unexposed side below that defined as the failure temperature. However, the voids caused by the evaporation of water contribute to shrinkage and a decrease in concrete strength.

The mechanical properties of concrete are significantly reduced at elevated temperatures. Figure 19.2.21 shows the effect on the compressive strength and modulus of elasticity by increasing the temperature.[3] There is some question about whether concrete completely regains its strength after exposure to high temperatures.

Concrete structures generally have less stringent requirements regarding expansion joints for normal thermal expansion.

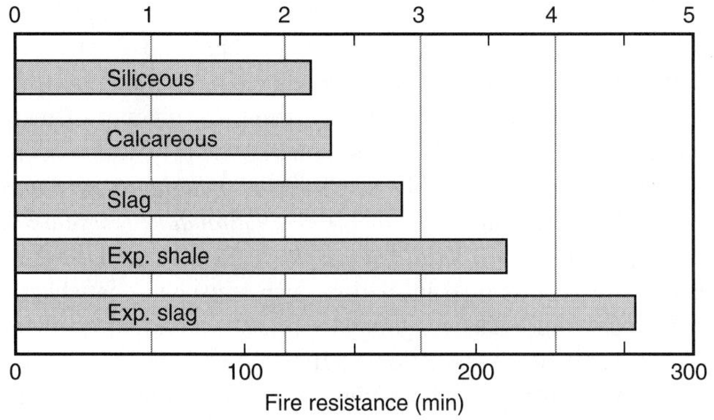

FIGURE 19.2.19 Effect of Various Types of Aggregate on the Fire Endurance of 4¾ in. (121 mm) Slabs

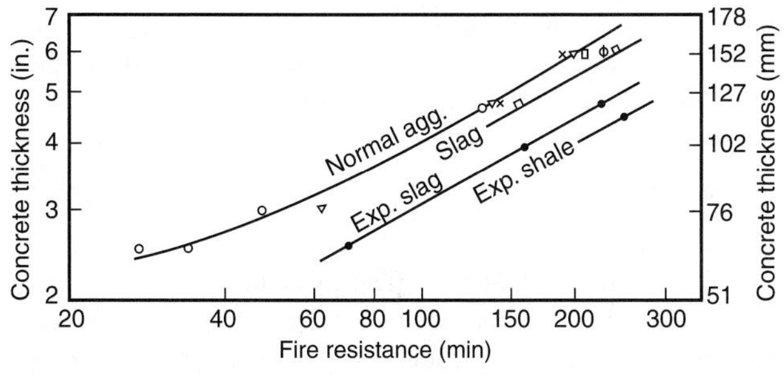

FIGURE 19.2.20 Relationship of Slab Thickness and Type of Aggregate to Fire Endurance

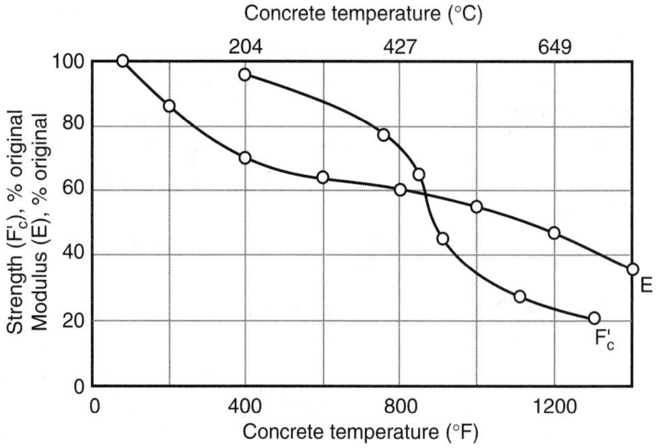

FIGURE 19.2.21 Effect of Temperature on Modulus of Elasticity and Compressive Strength. The curves are taken from two differing specimens.

Consequently, a large concrete structure exposed to an uncontrolled fire can experience large horizontal forces due to the expansion of beams, which can cause structural damage at the junction of beams and columns. In 1973, an uncontrolled fire occurred in a military personnel records storage center in Overland, Missouri. The building was 730 ft (222 m) long, but had no expansion joints. Floors, beams, and columns (20 in. × 20 in. [508 mm × 508 mm]) were made of reinforced concrete. An estimated 28 in. (700 mm) of horizontal expansion occurred during the fire, causing severe structural damage at the junction of the beams and columns, resulting in partial collapse.[18]

Prestressed Concrete

The factors that are significant in the behavior of prestressed concrete are similar to those that affect reinforced concrete. In addition to the influences of moisture content and aggregate, the higher strength concrete and the function and type of steel used for prestressing are important considerations. The concrete used for prestressed concrete is of a higher strength than that used in ordinary reinforced-concrete construction. The overall fire resistance of this concrete is somewhat better than the lower-strength concrete. The heat transmission is about the same for the two systems. However, there is a somewhat greater tendency for prestressed concrete to spall, thus exposing the prestressing steel.

The greatest problem of prestressed concrete subjected to elevated temperatures involves the prestressing steel. The fact that the steel is put under high initial stress, coupled with the fact that the reinforcing wires are high-carbon, cold-drawn, rather than low-carbon, hot-rolled steel, is the root of the problem. Normal prestressing losses due to deformation and creep are considered in prestressed concrete design. At elevated temperatures these losses are accelerated. Creep in the steel increases, and the modulus of elasticity of the prestressing wires is reduced by about 20 percent when the temperature reaches 600°F (316°C). These losses reduce the carrying capacity of the member.

Another problem of prestressed concrete relates to thermal expansion. Because of the prestress in the design procedures, the compressive stresses near the top of a beam are less than those for reinforced concrete design. The thermal expansion of the concrete at the bottom of a beam can induce an upward movement, resulting in an initial failure opposite in direction to that normally assumed in collapses.

The type of steel used for prestressing is more sensitive to elevated temperatures than the steel used in reinforced-concrete construction. Not only is its strength reduced at temperatures somewhat less than those for hot-rolled steel, but also that strength is not regained after cooling. Prestressing wires are permanently weakened when they reach a temperature of about 800°F (427°C).

Wood

Depending on its form, wood may or may not provide reasonable structural integrity in a fire. The important factors that influence fire resistance are the physical size and the moisture content of the members. Fire-retardant treatments may be used to delay ignition and retard combustion. This provides time for extinguishing procedures. However, all wood will burn.

The burning of wood produces a charcoal on the surface at an average rate of about 1/40 in. per minute (0.6 mm/min). This charcoal provides a protective coating that insulates the unburned wood and isolates it from the flame, thus retarding pyrolysis. Therefore, thick members provide much more structural integrity over the period of fire exposure than do thin ones.

Heavy timber construction has proved to be an excellent form of construction. It maintains its integrity during a fire for a relatively long time, providing an opportunity for extinguishment. When the fire is extinguished relatively soon, much of the original strength of the members is retained and reconstruction is possible.

Glued laminated frames, arches, and beams have become increasingly popular. These members also provide reserve strength during a fire, and, if the layer is not deep, the char may be removed by sandblasting to restore the aesthetic appearance.

Wood-frame construction utilizes structural members considerably smaller than mill construction. The exposed area is greater, relative to mass, and the fire resistance considerably reduced. When this type of construction is exposed to a fire, it offers relatively little structural integrity. Therefore, protective surfaces, such as gypsum wallboard or plaster, are important to provide fire resistance. Lightweight wood trusses, due to their connection design, usually offer very limited integrity during fire exposure. Several related articles are referenced in Section 19, Chapter 1, "Types of Building Construction."

FIRE BEHAVIOR OF OTHER BUILDING MATERIALS

Many materials other than steel, concrete, and wood are commonly used in modern building construction. They frequently make up a large volume and/or surface area of the structure. Nonbearing partitions, insulation, building services, and finish materials are all important parts of building construction. Some of the nonstructural, thermally inert materials are used as fireproofing. Others may contribute significant fuel to a potential fire.

Glass

Glass is utilized in three common ways in building construction. The most obvious is glazing for windows and doors. In this capacity the glass has little resistance to fire. It quickly cracks because of the temperature difference between the surfaces. Double glazing does not provide much improvement. Wire-reinforced glass is an improvement, as it provides somewhat greater integrity in a fire if it is properly installed. However, no glazing should be relied on to remain intact in a fire. Ordinary annealed glass has minimal resistance to fire and will break at heat fluxes near or below that required for piloted ignition of ordinary combustibles like wood. Fully tempered glass can resist higher heat fluxes but will break if engulfed in flames.

Glass block and ceramic glass also provide some duration (45 minutes or more) of endurance against fire, although the reduction of heat transmission is limited. The test standard for such assemblies is NFPA 257, *Standard on Fire Test for Window and Glass Block Assemblies.* Only certain types of glass significantly limit heat transmission, such as a special double or triple layer glass with a clear gel between layers of glass. When exposed to fire, the gel becomes opaque, reducing radiant heat transfer in addition to conductive heat transfer. Such insulating glass has been tested in NFPA 251.

A second common use of glass in buildings is in fiberglass insulation. The fiberglass does not burn and is an excellent insulator. Glass fiber is often coated with a combustible resin binder. When used as an insulation, the amount of resin binder and resultant fuel load is such that the insulation is considered limited-combustible (see NFPA 220, *Standard on Types of Building Construction,* and NFPA 259, *Standard Test Method for Potential Heat of Building Materials*). Facings used as vapor barriers over glass fiber insulation, such as asphalt-coated kraft paper and some plastics, generally present more potential for fire spread than the insulation itself.

A third form in which glass is found in buildings is as reinforcement for fiberglass-reinforced plastic building products. The products include translucent window panels, siding, and prefabricated bathroom units. They have distinct advantages of economy and aesthetic appeal. The fiberglass acts as reinforcement for a thermosetting resin, usually a polyester. The resin, combustible even with fire retardants incorporated in the composition, frequently comprises 50 percent or more of the material. Although the fiberglass itself is noncombustible, the products are quite combustible.

Gypsum

Gypsum products, such as plaster and plasterboard, are excellent fire protection materials. The gypsum has a high proportion of chemically combined water. Evaporation of this water requires a great deal of heat energy, making gypsum an excellent, inexpensive, fire-retardant building material. A detailed description of numerous fire-rated assemblies using gypsum can be found in the "Fire Resistance Design Manual" by the Gypsum Association.

Lightweight Concrete

Lightweight concrete, made with noncombustible aggregates, resists high temperatures extremely well without degradation. Vermiculite and perlite are the most common types of light concrete used for this purpose. Vermiculite is an inert aggregate made from weathered mica. The mica is crushed and roasted, which causes it to expand to form pellet-like aggregates. Perlite is a volcanic rock that is crushed and heat treated. The heat treatment causes the rock to expand in volume. During the process, water vapor is absorbed by the rock particles, and the perlite takes the form of glasslike, cellular-structured particles.

Asbestos

Asbestos is a mineral fiber that historically had been used in several forms in building construction. It was used with a cementitious binder and sprayed onto structural members to form an excellent fireproofing agent. Asbestos was combined with portland cement to make asbestos cement products. Although these products are noncombustible, they often shattered during the temperature buildup of a fire, thus reducing their effectiveness. Asbestos was also combined with materials other than portland cement to form products such as asbestos insulation board and asbestos wood. These products behaved quite well in fires, providing a great deal of fire resistance and protection. However, because of health hazards during application, construction, occupancy, and demolition, asbestos products are now banned. Nevertheless, it is still found in older buildings undergoing renovation.

Masonry

Brick, tile, and concrete masonry products behave well when subjected to the elevated temperatures of a fire. Hollow concrete blocks may crack from the heat, but they generally retain their integrity. Brick can withstand high temperatures without severe damage. The fire resistance of masonry can be determined based on the type of aggregate used and the equivalent thickness of material.[19]

Plastics

There is a wide range of plastic products used by the building industry. They provide numerous aesthetic, physical, and economic advantages in building applications. Their major disadvantage is that all plastics are combustible. Although there are certain treatments that increase ignition temperatures or inhibit flame spread, there is no known additive that will make them noncombustible.

CONTEMPORARY TRENDS IN STRUCTURAL FIRE PROTECTION

There is an increased interest internationally in the development of more rational methods of structural fire design. These methods attempt to establish a theoretical base for the design of structural members and assemblies that will predict their actual fire performance more accurately than present methods. This section briefly addresses some of these modern trends. A more detailed discussion is provided in Section 19, Chapter 5, "Approaches to Calculating Structural Fire Resistance."

Usual Structural Design Procedures for Fire Conditions

The standard fire resistance test, combined with building code requirements that specify fire resistance ratings for structural frames and barrier assemblies, is the usual basis for structural fire design. The building code identifies building construction classifications based on materials and fire resistance requirements for barriers and structural framing members. The code relates these construction classifications with use groups, the building height and area, and adjustments for fire protection features. These code requirements for fire resistance are the subjective judgments of the code-writing groups.

The numbers and assemblies are laboratory tested in accordance with a standard fire test. This test is the equivalent to NFPA 251 or ASTM E119 for the jurisdiction served by the code. An acceptable design occurs when the test results exceed the code requirements. Although this procedure is common, its validity is subject to increasing doubts. The fire test itself is being severely criticized. In addition to the concerns identified earlier in this chapter, considerable variation can occur for the same assembly when it is tested in different laboratories. The relationship between test results and field performance is subject to debate. The code requirements have a weak technical base. The procedure, however, is relatively easy to administer from a regulatory viewpoint, and many other code requirements can be related to the form of construction anticipated by the fire resistance ratings.

Analytical Methods of Design

Research has been conducted along two different but related aspects of structural fire design.[20] Both attempt to provide rational analytical procedures for predicting structural fire behavior. One procedure is to develop analytical methods by which the fire resistance of a member or assembly may be calculated. The American Society of Civil Engineers (ASCE) and the Society of Fire Protection Engineers (SFPE) jointly developed ASCE/SFPE 29, *Standard Calculation Methods for Structural Fire Protection.* ASCE/SFPE 29 can be used for the calculation of fire resistance of structural elements. The calculation method computes the fire resistance that one would expect from the standard fire test. This method uses structural characteristics of the members, thermal properties of the materials, heat transfer characteristics of the assembly, mechanical properties of structural materials and compartment, and design service loads. This method enables the important considerations of structural restraint to be taken into account more easily than the standard fire test. This procedure is identical to the traditional design procedure, except that calculated fire resistance ratings are substituted for fire test ratings.

The provisions of the American Concrete Institute and the Masonry Society standard ACI 216.1/ TMS 0216.1 can be used to calculate the fire resistance of concrete and masonry elements or assemblies. The two above references are acceptable to use for calculated fire resistance per the *NFPA 5000* building code.

Another approach to which considerable research effort has been devoted is an analytical design based on real fire-exposure characteristics. There are basically two methods in this approach. The first relates the time-temperature characteristics of real fires to the structural behavior at elevated temperatures. In connection with this approach, NFPA and SFPE have recently initiated two independent projects to establish fire loads for engineering design of structural fire resistance in buildings. The second method relates the properties of real fire development to an equivalent standard time-temperature curve. This method relates a theoretically equivalent time to experimental fire test results. It is important to understand that exposure fires estimated for the proposed occupancy will change with future occupancy changes.

Design Procedure

The Swedish Institute of Steel Construction publishes a design manual, entitled "Fire Engineering Design of Steel Structures."[21] A building designer has the option of designing the structural system in accordance with the traditional code or by the procedures described in the manual.

The manual describes a rational fire-engineering design process for steel structures on the basis of performance requirements. The manual consists of four parts. The first part is a relatively detailed description of fire energy impacts and structural behavior at elevated temperatures. This part provides the foundation for the design procedures. The second part presents the detailed design procedure. Design charts and curves which provide the numerical base are provided. Worked examples comprise the third part, and an alternate design method based on the concept of equivalent fire duration is given in the fourth.

The American Iron and Steel Institute (AISI) published *Firesafe Structural Steel, A Design Guide,*[22] for exterior structural members. Exterior members, of course, cannot be tested in the standard laboratory test. The guide provides a design procedure by which interior members can be designed for fire conditions. The design guide presents step-by-step procedures to arrive at a design. The basis for this design guide is *Design Guide for Fire Safety of Bare Exterior Structural Steel.*[23] Part One of the AISI guide presents the theory and validation of the method, while Part Two reviews the state of the art of relevant research programs conducted during the past 20 years.

The Prestressed Concrete Institute has published a procedure to analytically determine the fire resistance of prestressed concrete structures. This method is described in *PCI Design for Fire Resistance of Precast Prestressed Concrete.*[24] The method calculates fire resistance by obtaining temperatures at various locations for the various standard fire test times, using tables and diagrams based on test results. This information is then used to compute a fire resistance value.

SUMMARY

Two important considerations in designing for structural integrity of a building during a fire are the ability of the structure to avoid collapse and the ability of barriers to prevent the fire from spreading to adjacent spaces. Three approaches to structural frame and barrier design for fire resistance include (1) standard fire resistance testing and building code requirements; (2) analytical calculations to determine fire resistance; and (3) analytical structural methods based on real fire exposure characteristics. Currently, the first two approaches are accepted in building codes. Testing of structural assemblies determines the fire resistance rating, as well as the behavior of structural materials at elevated temperatures. Several methods are under development that would establish a more scientific base for the design of structural members and assemblies that will predict their fire performance under a broader range of conditions than the standard fire tests.

BIBLIOGRAPHY

References Cited

1. Clay, W., "Standard Fire Tests," *Proceedings* of the 13th Annual Meeting of the Building Officials' Conference of America, Chicago, IL, 1927, pp. 74–88.
2. Shaub, H., "Early History of Fire Endurance Testing in the United States," *ASTM Special Technical Publication 301,* American Society for Testing and Materials, Philadelphia, PA, 1961, pp. 1–9.
3. Benjamin, I. A., "Fire Resistance of Reinforced Concrete," *Symposium* on Fire Resistance of Concrete, American Concrete Institute, Detroit, MI, 1961, pp. 29 and 31.
4. Lie, T. T., and Stanzak, W. W., "Fire Resistance of Protected Steel Columns," *Engineering Journal,* Vol. 10, No. 3, 1973.
5. *Designing Fire Protection for Steel Columns,* American Iron and Steel Institute, Washington, DC, 1983.
6. Ruddy, J. L., Mario, J. P., Ioannides, S. A., and Alfawakhiri, F., "Fire Resistance of Structural Framing, Steel Design Guide 19," American Institute of Steel Construction, Chicago, IL, Dec. 2003.
7. *Steel Construction Manual,* 13th ed., American Institute of Steel Construction, Chicago, IL, 2006.
8. Harmathy, T. Z., "Thermal Performance of Concrete Masonry Walls and Fire," *Special Technical Publication 464,* American Society for Testing and Materials, Philadelphia, PA, 1970.
9. Allen, L. W., and Harmathy, T. Z., "Fire Endurance of Selected Concrete Masonry Units," *Journal of ACI,* Vol. 69, 1972.
10. Schaffer, E. W., "State of Structural Timber Fire Endurance," *Wood and Fiber,* Vol. 9, No. 2, 1977.
11. Harmathy, T. Z., and Stanzak, T. T., "Elevated-Temperature Tensile and Creep Properties of Some Structural and Prestressing Steels," *ASTM Special Technical Publication 464,* American Society for Testing and Materials, Philadelphia, PA, 1969, pp. 186–208.
12. DeFalco, F. D., "An Investigation of Modern Structural Steels at Fire Temperatures," Ph.D. Thesis, University of Connecticut, Storrs, CT, 1974.
13. "Final Report of the National Construction Safety Team on the Collapses of the World Trade Center Towers," NIST NCSTAR 1, National Institute of Standards and Technology, Gaithersburg, MD, Oct. 2005.
14. "Structural Fire Response and Probable Collapse Sequence of the World Trade Center Towers," NIST NCSTAR 1-6 , National Institute of Standards and Technology, Gaithersburg, MD, Oct. 2005.
15. Fields, B. A., and Fields, R. J., "Elevated Temperature Deformation of Structural Steel," NISTIR 88-3899, National Institute of Standards and Technology, Gaithersburg, MD, Mar. 1989.
16. Przetak, L., *Standard Details for Fire-Resistive Building Construction,* McGraw-Hill, New York, 1974.

17. Beitel, J. J., and Iwankiw, N. R., "Analysis of Needs and Existing Capabilities for Full Scale Fire Resistance Testing," NIST Report GCR 02-843, National Institute of Standards and Technology, Gaithersburg, MD, December, 2002.
18. Beitel, J. J., and Iwankiw, N. R., "Historical Survey of Multi-Story Building Collapses Due to Fire," *Designing Structures for Fire—Proceedings,* Society of Fire Protection Engineers, Bethesda, MD, and Structural Engineering Institute, Reston, VA, 2003.
19. Structural Engineering Institute, *Standard Calculation Methods for Structural Fire Protection: ASCE/SEI/SFPE 29-05,* American Society of Civil Engineers/Society of Fire Protection Engineers, 2007.
20. Pettersson, O., "Structural Fire Protection," *Fire and Materials,* Vol. 4, No. 1, 1980.
21. Pettersson, O., and Magnusson, S. E., et al., "Fire Engineering Design of Steel Structures," *Publication 50,* Swedish Institute of Steel Construction, Stockholm, Sweden, 1976.
22. *Firesafe Structural Steel, A Design Guide,* American Iron and Steel Institute, New York, 1979, 1983.
23. Law, M., *Design Guide for Fire Safety of Bare Exterior Structural Steel,* Ove Arup & Partners, London, UK, 1977.
24. Gustaferro, A. H., and Martin, L. D., *PCI Design for Fire Resistance of Precast Prestressed Concrete,* Prestressed Concrete Institute, Chicago, IL, 1989.

NFPA Codes, Standards, and Recommended Practices

Reference to the following NFPA codes, standards, and recommended practices will provide further information on structural integrity during fire discussed in this chapter. (See the latest version of The NFPA Catalog *for availability of current editions of the following documents.)*

NFPA 80, *Standard for Fire Doors and Other Opening Protectives*
NFPA 220, *Standard on Types of Building Construction*
NFPA 221, *Standard for High Challenge Fire Walls, Fire Walls, and Fire Barrier Walls*
NFPA 251, *Standard Methods of Tests of Fire Resistance of Building Construction and Materials*
NFPA 252, *Standard Methods of Fire Tests of Door Assemblies*
NFPA 257, *Standard on Fire Test for Window and Glass Block Assemblies*
NFPA 259, *Standard Test Method for Potential Heat of Building Materials*
NFPA 5000®, Building Construction and Safety Code®

References

ACI 216.1-97/TMS 0216.1, "Standard Method for Determining Fire Resistance of Concrete and Masonry Construction Assemblies," American Concrete Institute, The Masonry Society, Farmington Hills, MI, 1997.

ASTM E605-93, "Standard Test Methods for Thickness and Density of Sprayed Fire-Resistive Material Applied to Structural Members," ASTM International, W. Conshohocken, PA, 2006.

ASTM E736-00, "Standard Test Method for Cohesion/Adhesion of Sprayed Fire-Resistive Materials Applied to Structural Members," ASTM International, W. Conshohocken, PA, 2006.

ASTM E759-92, "Standard Test Method for Effect of Deflection on Sprayed Fire-Resistive Material Applied to Structural Members," ASTM International, W. Conshohocken, PA, 2005.

ASTM E760-92, "Standard Test Method for Effect of Impact on Bonding of Sprayed Fire-Resistive Material Applied to Structural Members," ASTM International, W. Conshohocken, PA, 2005.

ASTM E761-92, "Standard Test Method for Compressive Strength of Sprayed Fire-Resistive Material Applied to Structural Members," ASTM International, W. Conshohocken, PA, 2005.

ASTM E859-93, "Standard Test Method for Air Erosion of Sprayed Fire-Resistive Materials Applied to Structural Members," ASTM International, W. Conshohocken, PA, 2006.

ASTM E937-93, "Standard Test Method for Corrosion of Steel by Sprayed Fire-Resistive Material Applied to Structural Members," ASTM International, W. Conshohocken, PA, 2005.

Buchanan, A. H., *Structural Design for Fire Safety,* John Wiley & Sons, Chichester, UK, 2001.

DeStefano, J., "Fire Protection of Structural Steel," *Structure Magazine,* Nov. 2005.

Fire Resistance Design Manual, 17th ed., GA-600-03, Gypsum Association, Washington, DC, 2003.

Lie, T. T., "Structural Fire Protection," American Society of Civil Engineers, Reston, VA, 1992.

Mowrer, F. W., "Window Breakage Induced by Exterior Fires," NIST-GCR-98-751, National Institute of Standards and Technology, Gaithersburg, MD, 1998.

Structural Engineering Institute (SEI), *Designing Structures for Fire—Proceedings,* American Society of Civil Engineers/Society of Fire Protection Engineers, September 30–October 1, 2003.

Chapter 3

Structural Fire Safety in One- and Two-Family Dwellings

Revised by
Kuma Sumathipala

Chapter Contents

Key Terms

construction (Type III), construction (Type V), dwelling, manufactured home, structural integrity

According to the 2003 American Housing Survey data, 76.4 percent of occupied housing units were in single-family attached or detached dwellings, including manufactured homes.[1] Another 8.0 percent were in buildings having two to four housing units. Therefore, one- and two-family dwellings can be estimated to represent approximately 80 percent of all occupied U.S. housing units in 2003. This chapter addresses the structural elements of one- and two-family dwellings as they affect the fire safety of the structure. Manufactured homes are also included in the discussion of one- and two-family dwellings.

This chapter does not cover the influence of interior finish or energy conservation measures, the hazards of building facilities (heating and electrical installations), or the role of detection, extinguishing, or egress systems as fire and life safety features. Those subjects are included in other chapters of this handbook. See Section 1, Chapter 2, "Fundamentals of Structurally Safe Building Design"; Section 8, Chapter 13, "Electrical Systems and Appliances"; Section 10, Chapter 2, "Heating Systems and Appliances"; Section 14, Chapter 6, "Household Fire Warning Equipment"; Section 18, Chapter 2, "Interior Finish"; Section 20, Chapter 6, "One- and Two-Family Dwellings"; Section 20, Chapter 7, "Manufactured Housing"; and Section 21, Chapter 6, "Recreational Vehicles."

MODERN CONSTRUCTION

Various types of construction are used in the design and building of one- and two-family dwellings. Specific requirements are dictated by state and local building codes and, in the case of manufactured homes, by federal regulation, via the Manufactured Housing Consensus Committee administered by the National Fire Protection Association. In general, most one- and two-family residential buildings are built of Type V (frame) or Type III (ordinary) construction, as defined by building codes such as *NFPA 5000®, Building Construction and Safety Code®,* the International Residential Code, and NFPA 220, *Standard on Types of Building Construction.* There are, of course, exceptions: some dwellings are erected of Type I (fire resistive), Type II (noncombustible), or possibly Type IV (heavy timber) construction.

Type V (Frame) Construction

The principal categories of Type V construction are (1) platform or western, (2) balloon, (3) braced, (4) plank and beam, and (5) veneer (a combination of one of the previous four with a facing wythe of brick, concrete masonry units, or stone on the exterior walls). The buildings may be constructed on foundations that consist of slab on grade or which incorporate basements, cellars, or crawl spaces. Geographical peculiarities or the needs of the owner generally dictate which foundation type is used. Where basements, cellars, or crawl spaces are provided, they play a distinct role insofar as residential fire safety is concerned, since heating, air-conditioning, and water heating equipment

Kuma Sumathipala, Ph.D., P.E., is the senior manager of fire technology of the American Forest & Paper Association, Washington, DC.

are often installed in these spaces, and this equipment can be an ignition source. These spaces are also often used for storage of combustible materials by building occupants. Roof framing can be either of rafter or trusses. Where trusses are used, interior bearing partitions might not be required.

Platform or Western, Balloon, and Braced Framing. This construction type is often referred to as stick-built. The basic difference among platform or western, balloon, and braced framing is the manner in which the floor, roof, and bearing walls are supported and/or erected.

In platform or western framing (Figure 19.3.1), which is by far the most common type of framing, walls made of studs nailed to top and bottom plates are set on top of the floor sheathing and joists, with the joists bearing on sills at the foundation level and on beams or partitions at intermediate locations. Platform construction combines safety for framers working on a building with inherent firestopping qualities once the walls are sheathed. In both balloon and braced framing, the stud-bearing walls are set on sills at the foundation level.

In balloon framing (Figure 19.3.2), the studs in exterior-bearing walls extend for two stories, with the joists supported by 1 in. by 6 in. (25.4 mm by 152.4 mm) ledger strips or ribbon boards at the intermediate level.* Early house construction was balloon framed. Unless firestopping is added, fire within the wall can easily spread vertically, since there are no top plates in the wall cavity. Fire originating in the floor/ceiling assembly can spread horizontally and eventually vertically through the walls.

In braced framing, the bearing wall extends for only one story, with joists at the second level of bearing walls bearing on 4 in. × 6 in. (101.6 mm × 152.4 mm) girths. In both framing types, the interior bearing partitions are erected in one-story heights.

FIGURE 19.3.1 Platform Construction

Plank and Beam Framing. In plank and beam framing, a few larger structural members replace the more closely spaced smaller wood members used in typical wood framing. In other words, larger dimensional beams (4 in. × 10 in. or 5 in. × 12 in.) are spaced 4 ft or 6 ft on center. This arrangement is used rather than the standard floor and/or roof framing in which smaller dimensioned members such as 2 in. × 8 in. or 2 in. × 10 in. joists or rafters are spaced on 16 in. centers. The decking for floors and roofs is planking in nominal thicknesses of 2 in. or more, as opposed to ½ in., ⅝ in., or ¾ in. plywood sheeting. Instead of 2 in. × 4 in. bearing partitions supporting the floor or roof joist or rafter systems, the beams are supported by posts. Wood foundation walls are used for some homes, and crawl spaces can be utilized as return air plenums.

Veneer. The exterior wall finish of buildings of frame construction, except for masonry veneer, generally consists of stucco, wood, plastic siding, metal, or concrete siding over wood, foam plastic, or gypsum sheathing. Masonry veneer exteriors utilize one of the wood framing systems, with the addition of a wythe of masonry secured by metal ties to the wood frame exterior walls. Usually an insulating board of some type is provided between the studs and the masonry veneer. Although the exterior exposed surfaces can be of masonry, veneer construction is generally considered a combustible frame construction because the load-bearing members are usually wood.

Steel Framing. Steel framing for residential building is becoming more widely used. Steel framing has many similarities to conventional wood framing classified as either Type III or Type V construction. Steel framing methods are available for stick-built (balloon or platform), panelized, and pre-engineered building types. Steel, like the exterior masonry walls of Type III construction, is noncombustible. However, unprotected steel loses its structural capacity under severe exposure to heat. Extensive testing has been conducted on steel-framed assemblies. The Steel Framing Alliance has compiled a summary of fire resistance testing of floor-ceiling, roof-ceiling, and wall assemblies utilizing combinations of metal studs and other building products, such as concrete, plywood, and gypsum wallboard. This compilation is available at http://www.steelframing.org.

Type III (Ordinary) Construction

The significant difference between Type III (ordinary) and Type V (frame) construction lies mostly with the construction of the exterior walls. Whereas in Type V (frame) construction

*Nominal dimensions are used throughout this chapter. For comparison, 1 in. = 25.4 mm, 1 ft = 0.305 m, and 1 ft^2 = 0.0929 m^2.

FIGURE 19.3.2 Balloon Framing

the load-bearing components of the walls are usually of wood, in ordinary construction the exterior walls are masonry or other noncombustible materials. The interior partitions, floor, and roof framing systems are of wood and, in general, utilize either the platform or braced framing methods previously described.

Manufactured Home Construction

The structural system of the manufactured home comprises four major components or subassemblies: (1) chassis, (2) floor system, (3) wall system, and (4) roof system. Manufactured homes are designed specifically to meet the requirements of an efficient assembly-line production.

The chassis, the structural base of the manufactured home, receives all vertical loads from the walls and floor and transfers them to a substructure of either the wheel assembly (when the home is in transit) or to a foundation (when the home is installed at a permanent site). The chassis generally consists of two longitudinal steel beams, braced by steel cross members. Steel outriggers cantilevered from the outsides of the main beams bring the width of the chassis to the approximate overall width of the superstructure. The running gear used when the unit is in transit is also considered part of the chassis.

The floor system consists of its framing members, generally conventional 2 in. × 6 in. or 2 in. × 8 in. (50.8 mm × 152.4 mm or 50.8 mm × 203.2 mm) wood joists, with wood structural panels glued and nailed to the joists, glass fiber insulation blankets installed between the joists, and an asphalt-impregnated insulation board sealing the bottom of the floor system. Ductwork and piping are installed longitudinally within the floor system, often requiring the cutting of the joists. The floor finish is generally carpeting or resilient flooring, such as linoleum or tile.

The wall system sometimes utilizes the stressed-skin principle and consists of an interior skin of wood structural panels glued and nailed to wood studs and an exterior skin of aluminum siding. The actual sizing of members is dictated by the structural loads. Often, however, conventional 2 in. × 4 in. (50.8 mm × 101.6 mm) exterior bearing walls are used.

The roof system consists of either a rafter and ceiling joist system or a wood truss system. Roof decking is generally a rigid insulation board attached to the top of the roof rafters or trusses. Finished roofing is galvanized steel, aluminum decking, or asphalt shingles. The ceiling is either acoustical planks or gypsum wallboard attached directly to the bottom of the ceiling joists or the bottom chords of the trusses. Insulation blankets provide the roof insulation. Steel tie plates reinforce connections between wall and floor systems; diagonal steel strapping binds the floors, walls, and roof into a complete unit.

CONSTRUCTION CONSIDERATIONS FOR FIRE SAFETY

One- and Two-Family Dwellings

A dwelling unit is defined as a one or more rooms arranged for complete and independent housekeeping purposes, with space for eating, living, and sleeping; facilities for cooking; and provisions for sanitation. A one-family dwelling unit is generally defined as a building that consists solely of one dwelling unit with independent cooking and bathroom facilities. A two-family dwelling unit is a building that consists solely of two dwelling units with independent cooking and bathroom facilities.

In terms of size and occupant density, one- and two-family dwellings present lower overall occupant loads when compared to other building types. However, fire in single-family homes results in a significant portion of the overall life loss and injury statistics when compared to other building types.

Means of Escape. Some building regulation requirements concerning fire safety for one- and two-family dwellings differ substantially from those for other types of buildings. For example, depending upon certain conditions, single-family dwellings are required to have a primary means of escape that leads directly to the outside of the building. Single-family dwellings are also required, depending on certain conditions, to have a secondary means of escape. The secondary means is most often at least one escape window or outside door from basements with habitable spaces and from every sleeping room. Unlike office buildings, which require a certain number of means of egress, single-family homes require means of escape, which is a different egress concept.

Automatic Sprinklers. Building codes such as *NFPA 5000* limit the height of Type V unprotected one- and two-family dwellings that are not equipped with automatic sprinkler systems to two stories. The structural members in Type V unprotected construction do not possess any fire resistance rating.

Fire-Rated Separation. Within dwelling units, fire-rated separation between spaces is not generally required. However, attached garages are typically required to be separated from other parts of the dwelling by ½ in. (12.7 mm) gypsum wallboard on the garage side. In addition, doors to attached garages must be solid wood, steel, or 20 minute fire-rated doors. No door is permitted to connect garages and bedrooms. Within dwelling units, unrated gypsum wallboard, which is the most commonly used wall and ceiling material in the housing industry, affords a certain degree of passive fire protection.

Flame Spread Testing. The 2006 edition of *NFPA 5000* and the 2006 edition of NFPA *101*®, *Life Safety Code*®, no longer exempt materials less than 1/28 in. thick from flame spread testing. Wall and ceiling finishes must have a flame spread classification of not greater than 200. Wall and ceiling finishes must have a smoke developed index of not greater than 450. Testing must be done in accordance with NFPA 255, *Standard Method of Test of Surface Burning Characteristics of Building Materials. NFPA 5000* prohibits the use of foam plastic materials unless they are tested in a full-scale fire test or fire test that simulates conditions of actual use. There is an exemption in *NFPA 5000* for the limited use of cellular or foamed plastic.

Building Codes and Regulations. Building codes require that, with the exception of windows, doors, and moldings, wall and ceiling finishes have a flame spread classification of not greater than 200. As stated above, as of the 2006 editions, *NFPA 5000* and NFPA *101* no longer exempt materials less than 1/28 in. (0.91 mm) thick from flame spread testing. Wall and ceiling finishes must have a smoke developed index of not greater than 450. Testing must generally be done in accordance with NFPA 255 or ASTM E84, *Standard Test Method for Surface Burning Characteristics of Building Materials.* Building regulations also place limitations on foam plastic insulation, such as requiring it have a flame spread classification of not greater than 75 and be covered with ½ in. (12.7 mm) gypsum board or other thermal barrier to retard ignition and flame spread.

The majority of one- and two-family dwellings are built of frame or ordinary construction. The physical nature of these construction types necessitates the addition of certain features that will inhibit the spread of fire. The combustible materials in the structural framework of these construction types, in conjunction with the presence of voids and concealed spaces, create conditions that can contribute to the propagation and migration of fire throughout the concealed spaces of the structure. These conditions are addressed in building regulations by the requirement for the installation of draft stops, fire blocking, and firestopping materials.

Fire Blocking and Draft Stopping. In wood frame construction, fire blocking is generally required in walls at ceiling and floor levels; at 10 ft (3.05 m) intervals, both vertically and horizontally; at interconnections between concealed vertical and horizontal spaces such as occur at soffits, drop ceilings, and cove ceilings; at concealed spaces between stair stringers at the top and bottom of the stairs; at openings around vents, pipes, and ducts at ceiling and floor levels; at chimneys and fireplaces; and at cornices of a two-family dwelling at the line of dwelling unit separation.

Draft stopping is generally required within all open-web floor and ceiling systems and between a suspended ceiling and the floor or ceiling above it, to reduce the size of the concealed spaces to not more than 1000 ft^2 (92.9 m^2). The spaces must also be divided into nearly equal areas.

Construction Contributing to Flame Spread. A 1977 study of fires in multifamily residential buildings of frame or ordinary construction revealed a number of built-in contributing factors to the spread of fire that may also be relevant to some one- and two-family dwellings:[2]

1. *The use of nonrated soffit materials, both combustible and noncombustible, and the use of soffit or eave vents.* These practices can allow fires that break through an exterior wall opening to spread into the attic or roof space by the flue action of the attic or roof ventilation system (Figure 19.3.3).

2. *Mansard roofs extending below the top-story windows with the windows recessed.* The soffit extending from the face of the window to the edge of the roof is typical of nonrated materials. In addition, the wall construction is not extended in back of the plane of the mansard roof, thus providing an interconnected void. A fire breaking through the window impinges on this soffit, burning through in a relatively short time and involving the attic and roof spaces.

3. *Unfirestopped penetrations of the gypsum wallboard partitions by plumbing, mechanical, and electrical work.*

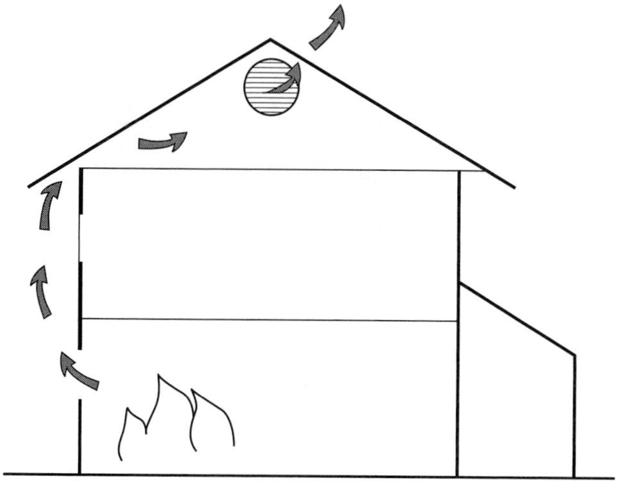

FIGURE 19.3.3 Attic Vents Under Eaves Presenting Serious Potential for Outside Extension of Fire into Attic Space

FIGURE 19.3.4 Soffits (arrow) over Kitchen Cabinets Connecting Wall Voids to Ceiling Voids, Permitting Fire Extension Both Vertically and Horizontally in Concealed Spaces

4. *The widespread use of wood-trussed roof and floor framing.* Such use precludes the need for the interior bearing partitions normally required where solid sawn joists and rafters are provided. Regulations typically required joists to be doubled under interior bearing partitions running parallel to joists and bridging to be installed under partitions running perpendicular to joists. This results in a minimum amount of firestopping of joist spaces. Current building codes compensate for this by requiring draft stopping of the trussed floor systems to reduce the spread of fire.

5. *Installing cabinets and other fixtures directly to stud framing, without an intervening protective diaphragm.* Such installation presents a situation where the only firestopping between a room fire and the concealed stud spaces are the materials that constitute the bottoms and backs of the cabinets or fixtures (Figure 19.3.4). This same practice exists in the installation of bathtubs or shower stalls.

Manufactured Housing

In 1999, manufactured homes constituted 6.6 percent of U.S. occupied housing units.[1] This share has generally been growing, as households sought more affordable housing in a rapidly increasing real estate market.

Over the years, the growth in popularity of manufactured housing was viewed with some concern within the fire service and the fire protection community, because manufactured homes were considered to pose a greater life safety risk than stick-built homes. In response to this concern, in 1976 the U.S. Department of Housing and Urban Development (HUD) promulgated "Mobile Home Construction and Safety Standards," later termed "Manufactured Home Construction and Safety Standards," which was then based on NFPA 501B, *Standard for Mobile Homes.* NFPA 501B has since been withdrawn and replaced by NFPA 501, *Standard for Fire Safety Criteria for Manufactured Home Installatinos, Sites, and Communities.* These standards have been amended several times to strengthen requirements for interior finish and firestopping and to identify acceptance criteria limiting the use of materials that generate smoke and gases more toxic than those produced by untreated wood.[3] Today HUD regulations depend heavily on the requirements in NFPA 501 and the recently published NFPA 225, *Model Manufactured Home Installation Standard.* In December 2000, the Manufactured Housing Improvement Act of 2000 (MHIM-2000) was passed by Congress. MHIM-2000 established a 21-person Federal Advisory Committee. This committee operates utilizing many of the principles for consensus standards development as outlined by the American National Standards Institute (ANSI). This Federal Advisory Committee has made numerous recommendations to the Secretary of the Department of Housing and Urban Development to improve both the quality and safety of manufactured homes. See Section 20, Chapter 7, "Manufactured Housing," for more discussion on fire and life safety of manufactured housing units.

SUMMARY

The structural elements of one- and two-family dwellings, including manufactured homes, affect the fire safety of those structures. Most one- and two-family residential buildings are of Type V (frame) or Type III (ordinary) construction, as defined in NFPA 220. Manufactured homes have four major components: chassis, floor system, wall system, and roof system. Building and life safety regulations concerning fire safety for one- and two- family dwellings differ from those for other types of buildings. Several factors may contribute to the impact of fires in one- and two-family dwellings, including attic vents, mansard roofs, unfirestopped penetration of gypsum wallboard partitions, wood-trussed roof and floor framing, and cabinets affixed directly to stud framing. Manufactured homes pose their own set of problems in relation to fire safety. However, standards established by HUD and NFPA continue to be updated to address these concerns.

BIBLIOGRAPHY

References Cited

1. American Housing Survey (AHS) website, http://www.census.gov/hhes/www/housing/ahs/ahs.html, Table 2–25, 2003.
2. Vogel, B. M., "A Study of Fire Spread in Multi-Family Residences: The Causes—The Remedies," NBSIR 76-1194, Center for Fire Research, National Bureau of Standards (NIST), Washington, DC, 1977.
3. HUD, "Manufactured Home Construction and Safety Standards," http://www.hud.gov/offices/hsg/sfh/mhs/mchss.cfm, U.S. Department of Housing and Urban Development, Washington, DC, 2002.

NFPA Codes, Standards, and Recommended Practices

Reference to the following NFPA codes, standards, and recommended practices will provide further information on structural fire safety for one- and two-family dwellings discussed in this chapter. (See the latest version of The NFPA Catalog *for availability of current editions of the following documents.)*

NFPA *101®*, *Life Safety Code®*
NFPA 220, *Standard on Types of Building Construction*
NFPA 225, *Model Manufactured Home Installation Standard*
NFPA 255, *Standard Method of Test of Surface Burning Characteristics of Building Materials*
NFPA 501, *Standard on Manufactured Housing*
NFPA 5000®, *Building Construction and Safety Code®*

Reference

"A Study of the HUD Minimum Property Standards for One- and Two-Family Dwellings," http://www.huduser.org/publications/polleg/mps_tsp.html, U.S. Department of Housing and Urban Development, Washington, DC, 2003.

Chapter 4

Analyzing Structural Fire Damage

Revised by
Stephen Pessiki

Chapter Contents

Key Terms

building code, building collapse, construction (type of), fire resistant, lateral load, prestressed concrete, structural steel, vertical load, World Trade Center

This chapter addresses several factors that should be considered in evaluating the integrity of structures for safe use and occupancy after exposure to fire. Initially, the focus will be on evaluating structural systems and identifying the structural damage that may affect overall and local structural stability. Subsequently, special attention is directed to the techniques for evaluating the postfire strengths and weaknesses of basic building materials—that is, steel, concrete, masonry, and wood—in structural assemblies; the use of plastic materials is also discussed. Finally, unique problems of fires at construction sites are considered.

All structural materials, whether classified as combustible or noncombustible, inherently possess a degree of fire resistance. However, they are adversely affected when exposed to elevated temperatures during a fire. The degree of damage varies with the different materials and building configurations. Where there is no visible cosmetic damage to the building after a fire, such as glass breakage, concrete spalling, or steel distortion, there is little chance of serious damage, although this is no guarantee. Thorough inspection is necessary to verify that no further damage has occurred due to the effects of excessive expansion, contraction upon cooling, and hidden deterioration. A building that is deemed safe for occupancy requires that the structural system and all its individual elements and their connections are able to safely support the structure's weight, contents, and environmental loads.

Other chapters in this handbook address structural fire protection and provide necessary background information. For topics related specifically to this chapter, see the following chapters: Section 11, Chapter 4, "Fire Hazards of Construction, Alteration, and Demolition of Buildings"; Section 18, Chapter 1, "Confinement of Fire in Buildings"; Section 19, Chapter 1, "Types of Building Construction"; Section 19, Chapter 2, "Structural Integrity During Fire"; and Section 19, Chapter 5, "Approaches to Calculating Structural Fire Resistance."

BUILDING TYPES

As discussed in Section 19, Chapter 1, building codes classify buildings by types (I, II, III, etc.) according to fire resistance. In general, the fire resistance of the construction varies from the most fire resistant for Type I to the least fire resistant for Type V. Though this classification system is useful in codifying levels of fire resistance, other more descriptive nomenclature could better differentiate a structure's performance during and after a fire. One would be better served by a more comprehensive system for identifying structures subjected to fire.

The text *Building Construction for the Fire Service*[1] discusses various aspects of the following construction and building arrangements:

1. Wood
2. Ordinary
3. Garden apartments

Stephen Pessiki, Ph.D., is professor of structural engineering and chairman of the Department of Civil and Environmental Engineering at Lehigh University in Bethlehem, Pennsylvania.

4. Steel
5. Concrete
6. High Rise

Each has unique characteristics relative to its susceptibility to fire damage and to the challenges that it presents to fire fighting. Here one can begin to appreciate that the fire performance of two structures built of the same construction type can differ—for example, a convention center versus a high-rise building, both of Type I construction. Differences in various building construction types are addressed in this book.

Dunn's book, *Collapse of Burning Buildings,*[2] addresses the collapse hazards of the five standard types of constructions when exposed to fire, but the work also expands to cover the following:

- Masonry wall and parapet collapse
- Wood floor collapse
- Wood roof collapse, including peaked, flat, and timber truss types
- Lightweight steel roof collapse
- Ceiling collapse
- Stairway and fire escape collapse
- Wood frame building collapse

This text is another comprehensive guide for building performance during and after a fire. The collapse types that Dunn covers are those that have caused the majority of fire fighter casualties in the recent past.

ATC-20, *Post Earthquake Safety Evaluation of Buildings,* and its companion Field Manual, ATC-20-1,[3] present a state-of-the-art guide for evaluating structures after devastating earthquakes. ATC-20 provides detailed guidance for evaluating various combinations of materials in structural types as indicated in Table 19.4.1 and addresses unique structural damage patterns. These structure types were originally presented in ATC-21, *Rapid Visual Screening of Buildings for Potential Seismic Hazards,*[4] and are referenced in NFPA 1670, *Standard on Operations and Training for Technical Search and Rescue Incidents,* Annex C.

It should be understood that some buildings may have structures that have elements of more than one category, such as wood buildings that are braced with shear walls and steel frames, or steel frame buildings with moment frames and diagonally braced frames. Also, the category URM usually indicates structures with exterior masonry walls and wood framed floors (ordinary construction).

The ATC-20-1 Field Manual has been especially helpful in enabling engineers to provide more consistent postearthquake evaluations since its introduction in 1989 (just prior to the Loma Prieta earthquake). Much can be learned from its systematic approach in providing guidelines that help differentiate between "significant" and "acceptable" degradation of structural systems when subjected to severe environmental loading. ATC has also published *Field Manual for Post Flood and Windstorm Safety Evaluation of Postal Buildings;* but, unfortunately, no similar publication is available to aid in postfire building evaluation. The authors strongly recommend that those involved in evaluating buildings after any type of event that could cause degradation should become familiar with the ATC-20 methodology.

TABLE 19.4.1 Combinations of Materials in Structural Types

Structural Type Identifier	*General Description*
W	Wood buildings of all types
S1	Steel moment-resisting frames
S2	Braced steel frames
S3	Light metal buildings
S4	Steel frames with cast-in-place concrete shearwalls
C1	Concrete moment-resisting frames
C2	Concrete shearwall buildings
C3/C5	Concrete or steel frame buildings with unreinforced masonry in-fill walls
TU	Tilt-up buildings
PC2	Precast concrete frame buildings
RM	Reinforced masonry
URM	Unreinforced masonry

Source: NFPA 1670, *Standard on Operations and Training for Technical Search and Rescue Incidents,* Table C.1, 2004, p. 1670-46.

STRUCTURAL SYSTEMS

Every building has some sort of a vertical and lateral load resisting system. Even though these systems may be poorly organized and difficult to determine, the essential first step in evaluating any structure is to define and assess the competency of these systems.

Vertical Load Resisting Systems

Vertical load resisting may be described using a plumbing analogy. Building loads derived from component weights, contents, occupants, and so on are collected by the smallest members in the horizontal planes, then collected by beams, and finally delivered by columns to the foundation. The connections of all components are required to competently transfer the loads. The failure of any member or its connection can cause a collapse.

Vertical load resisting systems may be framed systems consisting of a coherent system of beams and columns. They may also be unframed systems that have some beams and columns, but with bearing walls that provide most of the vertical support. The size of the collapse will be determined by the importance of the member or members that are compromised. In general, a framed system has a greater potential for a larger collapse. These easily understood concepts sometimes become lost in the chaos of a disaster situation.

Lateral Load Resisting Systems

Lateral load resisting systems (LLRS) may not be as apparent upon examination of a structure. They can be described using a "pushover" analogy. The structure must have elements and interconnections that will transfer lateral loadings, acting in any horizontal direction, into the foundation system. Without a competent system, the structure will rack; that is, rectangular spaces will become parallelograms, and possibly collapse to the ground. LLRS can be categorized as one of the following three types, or a combination of types:

1. Box buildings
2. Moment resistant frames
3. Diagonally braced frames

Box Buildings. The majority of buildings are box-type structures. They maintain their stability by having horizontal (roof and floor) planes that need to be strong, relatively rigid, and well interconnected. Plywood or solid wood diagonal sheathing on roof/floors usually performs this function in modern wood structures. Less desirable materials, such as parallel wood sheathing or decking, may be found in older and/or more poorly braced buildings. The floor sheathing provides lateral stability to joist and beams as well as transferring lateral forces to the walls. Wall sheathing, if adequately connected to the floors and wall structure, will keep the structure from racking as it transfers the forces to the foundation. The term *shear wall* is used to describe a wall that has this ability to prevent racking, which may also serve as a bearing wall. Again, plywood and diagonal wood sheathing are the most desirable sheathing types; but wallboard, plaster, and parallel sheathing may be the only type found on walls in marginally braced buildings. Box buildings may also be constructed with concrete or masonry shear walls/bearing walls. Also, floors of concrete or concrete-filled corrugated steel decking are normally strong enough to act as "floor diaphragms."

Moment Resistant Frame Structures. Moment resistant frame (MRF) structures are usually constructed using steel or reinforced concrete. The frames provide both vertical and lateral resistance. MRF structures require a competent floor plane (diaphragm) for lateral stability and load transfer. As previously stated, this is easily provided by a concrete or concrete-filled steel floor system. The interconnection of beam and column is the most critical feature of the MRF, since, in order to resist the repeated loading during high winds or earthquakes, the joints must exhibit great toughness and ductility. Prior to the 1970s, few concrete structures were capable of the required ductile performance. The 1994 Northridge earthquake demonstrated that the then standard welded joints did not possess the required ductility to reliably transfer severe earthquake stresses.[5] One needs to be aware of these difficulties when evaluating MRF structures after a severe fire. It is possible that connection damage caused by expansion or contraction forces could be hidden by fireproofing.

Diagonally Braced Frame Structures. Diagonally braced frame structures are similar to MRF, except that diagonal steel braces are strategically placed between columns to prevent racking by acting similarly to shear walls. In most occupied buildings, where rigidity is important, the diagonals are proportioned to resist both tension and compression forces. The toughness and rigidity of the diagonals and their connections are very important. Again, these members may be subjected to expansion or contraction damage during a prolonged fire.

In light industrial buildings, thin rods or small angles capable of only tension resistance are used as diagonal braces. They need to be configured as "X" bracing and need competent connections to function properly.

EVALUATING FIRE-DAMAGED STRUCTURES

Evaluation of structural damage to buildings following exposure to fire needs to be undertaken at any one or at all three time periods in the fire episode. The first would take place while the fire is still in progress, the second immediately after the fire, and the third somewhat later when the structure has been stabilized. The urgency and focus of an evaluation would be different in each of these conditions. Fire fighter safety is paramount in the first instance; public safety, including the protection of adjacent structures and their occupants, is the focus in the second; and safety issues involving long-term occupancy is the main consideration of the final, more detailed evaluation.

When considering damage incurred from fires, one must take into account deterioration of structural elements that accompanies normal aging. Wood is subjected to shrinkage/drying effects, rotting due to wetting/drying cycles, animal and insect infestations, corrosion of fasteners, and the effects of poor repair and maintenance practices. Steel may have deteriorated because of inadequate corrosion protection or thermal insulation.

Evaluation During a Fire

The primary purpose of evaluation during a fire is to ascertain whether it is safe for fire fighters to conduct control operations in or near the fire-involved building. Fire unit commanders need to quickly assess the risk of entry versus the likelihood of saving lives and property. Obviously there needs to be a different calculation for each. In some instances, such an early and preliminary evaluation can also be helpful in determining the necessary strategy for fighting the fire. As with all stages of structure evaluation, identification of building type along with vertical and lateral load resisting systems should be done immediately. Assessment should then be made based on a systematic approach to the problem. In some cases the choices may be very limited, as was the case in the 1991 fire at One Meridian Plaza in Philadelphia. There, based on inadequacy of available water supply, the decision was made to withdraw fire forces, with the result that the fire burned through ten floors prior to being controlled at an upper floor by sprinklers.

In noncombustible and significantly fire-protected structures, the decision to enter may be made with greater confidence than is the case in other buildings. Structure collapse is usually not an immediate problem. However, in the case of steel frame structures, thermal expansion may cause very high stresses in floor beams that are restrained by shear walls or diagonal braces. In addition, expansion in unrestrained floor systems can cause the enclosing walls to become dangerously out of plumb. Thermal expansion and material degradation may also cause damage to both cast-in-place as well as precast concrete structures.

At the opposite end of the spectrum, wood buildings, especially those with small member roof framing and trusses, provide the conditions that can lead to a collapse in minutes. Since these structures are relatively small and common, their performance should be well understood by most fire-fighting units. An NFPA review examined 69 incidents from 1985 through 1997 involving fire fighter deaths or injuries as a result of roof or floor collapses in wood frame buildings. Although the data being used were anecdotal rather than statistically representative or comprehensive, the report illustrates failure modes that have been reported. A number of the cited cases involved fires in attic spaces, where the structural elements can be directly exposed to fire.[6] It should be noted that most sloped, roofed wood structures with flat ceilings are framed with some sort of wood truss. These trusses may have been constructed in place in older structures or prefabricated using metal plate connectors in more modern ones, but all present a difficult problem for fire fighting.

Structures with Timber Trusses. Timber trusses have been constructed in the United States for more than one hundred years. They are a very efficient way of spanning large spaces. Most roof trusses have some sort of a sloped, top compression member (upper chord), a level, bottom tension member (lower chord), and a series of interconnected diagonal tension or compression members (webs). Flat roof and floor trusses usually have parallel upper and lower chords connected by the webs, and some sloped roof trusses (scissors trusses) have sloped bottom and top chords. Prior to the advent of the glued laminated beam in the early 1950s, large timber trusses were used in industrial and commercial structures to span up to 100 ft (30.5 m) and more, spaced 16 to 24 ft (4.9 to 7.3 m) apart, with wood joist infilling members. These trusses were configured in a bowstring shape, or had partly sloped and partly near flat upper chords that were interconnected with steel plates and bolts (strap and pin) or diagonal steel rods and vertical wood posts (rod and block). The lower chords in these trusses are most critical since they are highly stressed in tension and interconnected by bolts. Due to normal defects in sawn timber, these bolted connections may deteriorate with time, especially in hot attic spaces. They may be a disaster waiting to happen when exposed to fire, and they should be approached with extreme caution when fire-fighting tactics are considered. A single lower chord failure could result in a large collapse. Fortunately, these trusses are limited to older buildings. The informed observer should be able to easily recognize structures with these trusses.

Structures with Light Timber Trusses. Light timber trusses, spaced from 2 to 4 ft (0.6 to 1.2 m) on center have also been constructed for more than one hundred years. Since the 1960s, with the advent of the metal plate connection, they have been engineered using very small wood members for maximum economy. As roof trusses, they are often configured with a sloped top and a flat bottom (A trusses) or may be made as scissors trusses. When intended for floors or flat roofs, parallel chord trusses are used. Some parallel floor and roof trusses may use a combination of wood chords and tubular metal webs.

Unfortunately, the attributes that make light timber trusses economical and efficient construction elements can lead to sudden, catastrophic collapse during a fire. This type of construction has the undesirable properties of highly stressed, small, easily consumed wood members that are placed in concealed spaces where fire may grow and spread between members. Collapse can and has occurred within minutes. NFPA: Alert Bulletin #97-1 of the NFPA Fire Investigations Department states that 30 fire fighters were killed in 16 incidents involving wood trusses from 1977 to 1995. Before planning interior operations in wood structures, one must identify the type of roof and floor structures. It is most difficult to determine the presence of floor trusses, but it should be assumed that any building with a sloped roof and flat ceiling is framed with trusses until determined otherwise.

Heavy-Wall Buildings. Heavy wall buildings can present some difficult and dangerous problems for fire fighters, during and immediately following a fire. These buildings are characterized as structures that are surrounded by masonry or concrete walls and are framed with wood roof/floors, and include ordinary, URM, tilt-up, and various other classifications. Since the walls usually act to confine the fire, the roof and floors can rapidly lose strength and collapse. Older buildings have the potential of containing deteriorated wood members, and newer, long span structures have the potential for a large area collapse. Both conditions can lead to a sudden entrapment of fire fighters. The 1999 Worcester, Massachusetts, cold storage building fire is a tragic example of the catastrophic performance of this type of structure.

In some cases, masonry walls, even with "fire cut" ends (i.e., ends cut at an angle to allow the floor beam to collapse without levering the masonry wall over) on wood members, have been pulled in by the collapsing floors with lethal results. The potential for this type of collapse is even greater in the western United States earthquake regions, by the practice of mechanically tying masonry and concrete walls to the roof and floor structures to limit wall collapse during seismic events. Also, walls can be forced outward by the ladder-type forces generated when an interior collapse results in large floor or roof sections being angled up against the wall. As discussed earlier, structures of this type, built prior to the 1950s, may have large, long span roof trusses, with their associated risk of sudden collapse. For more information on assessing the potential for building collapse during a fire, see *Structural Fire Fighting*.[7]

Initial Postfire Evaluation

Depending on the severity of the fire, the number of victims, the type of collapse, and so on, the authority having jurisdiction (AHJ), fire chief, or building official may require that a recovery and stabilization operation be conducted. This is the essential first postfire requirement. In cases where building departments normally have jurisdiction over certification of whether a building is safe for occupancy, there will be instances in which the necessary technical competence and experience to conduct a postfire investigation is not available within such agencies. In such cases appropriate expert consultation must be engaged.

In cases where roof and/or floor burnout have occurred, the remaining unsupported structures may require stabilization. The public way and adjacent, occupied structures must be protected, since heavy, freestanding exterior walls can collapse due to high wind forces. If major supporting elements have been weakened or if parts of the structure have become misaligned, the building must be stabilized. The vertical and lateral load resisting systems need to be identified, and significant degradation needs to be addressed. A careful, well-documented, step-by-step evaluation should be performed. The investigator needs to identify and assess all structural systems and provide an adequate load path of resistance for all probable environmental loadings, including wind, water, and snow. To accomplish this, shoring may need to be constructed and/or safety evaluation and monitoring may be required. If the fire has produced trapped victims, recovery operations must be allowed to proceed safely and carefully. In addition, fire investigators also need time to do their essential work in a reasonably safe environment. All these operations may need to be performed prior to allowing the owner's engineer and insurance investigator access. This may appear to impede their investigations, and may cause complaints to be filed. However, safety should not be compromised at this time. If local fire and building officials do not have the necessary technical competence and experience to conduct the recovery operations or the postfire investigation within their agencies, it is imperative that expert help and consultation be engaged. This help may be available from federal, state, or local sources. The Federal Emergency Management Agency (FEMA) Urban Search and Rescue (US&R) system has developed coherent emergency shoring systems that are being taught to US&R teams throughout the United States. The U.S. Army Corps of Engineers, through its Readiness Support Center in San Francisco, California, has published *Structure Specialist Field Operations Guide,* which includes information and step-by-step procedures for constructing this emergency shoring. It also includes other information useful during rescue situations. The FEMA US&R system can also provide assistance. This system is composed of 28 locally based task forces made up of individuals with special search, rescue, engineering, communication, and medical skills (Figure 19.4.1).

CASE STUDY: Oakland, California. Following the 1992 firestorm in Oakland and at the request of the California Office of Emergency Services, a structural evaluation performed just prior to final search and recovery operations at a multibuilding apartment project. The original three-story wood apartment buildings, built over one-story concrete parking garages, had burned down to a deep pile of debris on top of the concrete structure. The parking structure was partly subterranean, and it was observed that large cracks had developed in the longitudinal, spaced shear/bearing walls of the 150 ft (46 m) long structures. The 10 in. (250 mm) thick slab was still warm to the touch a week after the fire. It was most probable that thermal expansion had caused the cracking in the restraining walls, but that the damage was not severe enough to preclude the recovery operation. Since the search could be completed within 4 hours, the risk of a major earthquake that could further compromise the walls was judged to be minimal. There was no possibility of live recovery, but there was little risk to search dogs and handlers, especially after formulating a good escape plan.

FIGURE 19.4.1 Location of the 28 FEMA US&R Task Forces

CASE STUDY: Worcester, Massachusetts. Immediately after the 1999 Worcester cold storage building fire, search and engineering elements from the FEMA Massachusetts US&R Task Force I (MA-TF-1) were dispatched to aid the Worcester Fire Department with the recovery operations involving six missing fire fighters. The search element included teams of canines with handlers that were experienced in forensic and cadaver search work. They were instrumental in locating all six victims.

The engineers deployed by MA-TF-1, known in the US&R system as structure specialists, provided initial analysis of the six-story high, unreinforced masonry walls. They then developed a safety strategy for the weeklong recovery operation that included 24 hour monitoring of the walls and the wind speed. Recommendations for safe deconstruction of the structure to aid recovery efforts were also provided by rigging experts from the task force.

CASE STUDY: Sacramento, California. In early 2001, structure specialists from the Sacramento US&R Task Force 7 provided initial evaluation of the fire hazard when a large truck rammed the state capitol building while the legislature was in session. Fortunately, in this case, there was only one casualty, the truck's driver.

Postfire Building Evaluation and Reoccupancy

Most often, inspection and evaluation of fire damage would be undertaken immediately after the fire department has extinguished the fire and declared the building stable and able to safely support an engineering investigation. There is a tendency for owners to quickly remove fire debris from the scene and thereby disturb evidence of interest in damage assessment. For this reason it is necessary that cleanup and repair operations be carefully monitored and controlled while the investigation of fire damage is underway. Some aspects of the fire damage evaluation process require that certain transient conditions regarding fire deterioration of materials and the loss of strength be allowed to take place prior to the initiation of detailed study. This is particularly true in the case of estimating residual strength of concrete materials, which may undergo cracking, calcination, layering, and discoloration in the weeks following exposure to fire temperatures.

It should also be noted that the work and reports of engineers engaged in the assessment of fire damage will often be of interest in litigation following severe and high-loss fires. For this reason, the methodology for conducting inspections, testing, and the manner of reporting should, as a minimum, follow the evaluation procedures outlined in ATC-20, and a report should be written that documents all observations made by the investigator and any physical tests that are performed. Owners or their insurance companies will normally pay for the reports and choose the engineer. However, tenants or their legal representatives, and even the local building official, may also be involved in the selection process.

A detailed engineering study will be necessary to determine the parameters for repair and/or partial replacement of the building. Damage to vertical and lateral load resistant systems as a whole, as well as to individual members, will need to be assessed and carefully tabulated. The determination of significant degradation versus cosmetic damage requires well-informed engineering judgment. A qualified professional engineer specializing in structures should conduct the evaluation, since the influence of distortion and residual stresses may have a significant negative effect on parts of the structure. Prudence and legal liability concerns may cause engineers to err on the conservative side. Insurance interests and the owner's needs for reoccupancy may argue for a greater acceptance of partly damaged structural elements. This natural conflict should be anticipated, and it may need to be emphasized that, since the building is being renewed at least in part, it needs to be at least as safe as in its prefire condition or satisfy current code requirements.

If a significant percentage of the structure needs to be rebuilt, the entire building may be required to meet current building codes. Some building codes, such as *NFPA 5000®*, *Building Construction and Safety Code,* specifically address building rehabilitation and include provisions for damaged and unsafe buildings. More specifically, Chapter 15 of *NFPA 5000®* indicates that where the structure of a building is damaged, an evaluation is to be conducted to determine whether such damage is substantial as defined by the code, and whether the building was structurally unsafe prior to the damage. *NFPA 5000®* determines that a building has substantial damage when either:

(a) The total strength of a structural element or group of elements, supporting more than 30 percent of the structure's vertical loads has been reduced by more than 25 percent from the pre-damaged condition, and the remaining capacity with respect to all dead and live loads is less than 75 percent of that required by this Code, or
(b) The combined lateral strength of resisting structural elements in any story has been reduced by more than 20 percent from the predamaged condition.

Depending on the degree of damage and the determination as to when the damage occurred, the building structure is to be restored to either conditions prior to the damage or into compliance with the Code. As indicated by the description of unsafe buildings in *NFPA 5000®*, the damage or unsafe structural condition can result from a number of events, including fire, explosion, wood-destroying pests, winds, earthquake, vehicular impact, or ground subsidence.

Some building codes might have requirements for "abatement of dangerous buildings" that are less restrictive than *NFPA 5000®*. Buildings that are significantly damaged by fire are considered dangerous. It should be noted that local building officials have considerable discretion in applying abatement requirements. Changed zoning requirements and economic considerations may also influence reconstruction. In some codes, buildings may be reconstructed according to prior regulations, providing the cost for renovation does not exceed a given percentage of the original cost.

Historic buildings may be treated somewhat differently. Many historic buildings do not meet current codes, and if significantly damaged by fire, they may not be able to be economically upgraded to current code requirements. Chapter 15 of *NFPA 5000®* has specific provisions that address historic buildings and structures. As a result of what preservationists considered unnecessary demolition following earthquakes, a guidebook, *Temporary Shoring and Stabilization of Earthquake Damaged Historic Buildings,*[8] was developed in 1998. It discusses the difficult issues facing local building, emergency, and other governmental officials regarding the saving of damaged historic buildings.

Finally, cooperation with the fire department is essential to establish the path and progress of fire, including the method of extinguishment. It may be possible to establish maximum temperatures reached during the fire by examining debris from melted material and by inspecting structural members for spalling, cracking, discoloration, deflection, and so on. The influence of temperature on the mechanical properties of structural materials raises the question of the usability of the material after it has cooled down to ambient temperature. The evaluation of the structural behavior of steel, concrete, masonry, and wood is described in general in the following section. A more detailed evaluation procedure and a case study of renovations is given in Chapters 12 and 13 of *A Complete Guide to Fire and Buildings.*[9]

EVALUATING DAMAGE TO SPECIFIC MATERIALS

Design of Structures Against Fire[10] contains useful information on the behavior of common building materials, including structural steel, reinforced concrete, and wood, when exposed to high temperatures. Of interest in this same publication is information on repair of fire-damaged structures that includes an assessment procedure for fire-damaged structures and a visual damage classification system for reinforced concrete elements. Also of interest to the fire investigator is the ASCE publication, *Guidelines for Failure Investigation.*[11] Here, the organization and details of postfire examinations are outlined in enough detail to better suit the rigors of forensic inquiries. NFPA 921, *Guide for Fire and Explosion Investigations,* is also a useful resource in this regard.

Structural Steel

Thermal and mechanical properties of steel are given in ASCE's manual of practice, entitled *Structural Fire Protection.*[12] This publication presents information on the modulus of elasticity at elevated temperatures, stress-strain curves for structural steel at various temperatures, and deformation properties. Most important for evaluating load-carrying capacity following exposure to fire is the loss of strength suffered as temperatures rise from about 212 to 1292°F (100 to 700°C). Steel loses significant stiffness above 600°F (316°C) and loses significant strength above 1000°F (538°C). A second factor that influences the behavior of steel during fire incidents is the coefficient of thermal expansion, which increases with increasing temperatures and reaches a value of approximately 0.008 in./in. at a temperature of 1112°F (600°C).

The use of several grades of steel in buildings and bridges is accepted in modern building codes and design standards. Although different grades of steel have a wide range of strengths, tensile and yield strengths of all steel grades are similarly affected by the temperatures that may be expected in building fires.

The behavior of beams or other members subject to bending stresses under fire conditions is complex (Figure 19.4.2). In a building fire, the steel temperature may vary considerably over a single cross section, as well as along the length of a structural member. Information relating to the strength properties of steel at elevated temperatures has been derived from the results of tests on small specimens heated so that the entire specimen was at or close to the measured temperature. Conclusions relating to strength characteristics from such small-scale tests may not be applicable to steel structural members. Moreover, plastic action results in the redistribution of stresses in steel members that are loaded close to the design limit. This characteristic permits steel members to sustain loads greater than those calculated to be safe on the base of yield strength alone; therefore, the strength of a given steel member cannot be determined only from isolated temperature data.

FIGURE 19.4.2 Unprotected Steel Damage on Floor of Office High Rise with Minimal Fire Load but Extensive Loss

In a building fire, parts of the structure may have been exposed to heating followed by abrupt cooling by water from hose streams. This temperature change is usually less severe than what accepted practice allows in heat-treating of steel during manufacture. Tests performed on structural steel specimens taken from buildings that experienced fire during and after construction have indicated that yield strengths did not drop below the specified minimums. However, when a postfire test is compared with the original mill tests, one can find that the original yield strength, usually at least 10 percent above minimum, has dropped to the minimum value. This can be explained as a loss in the nominal gain in strength that occurs during the rolling process. The members that exhibited scorched paint will most often suffer this loss. It then becomes the responsibility of the investigating engineer to determine if the loss is significant. Steel members that show some distortion due to heat, but that can be straightened, should have their physical properties thorougly evaluated. Connections between members should also be examined for cracks around fastener holes and welds.

Occasionally, steel exposed to a fire will have a somewhat roughened appearance due to excessive scaling and grain coarsening. The coarsening is caused by exposure of steel to temperatures around 1600°F (870°C) or higher. The steel will usually have a dark gray color, although other colors may be present if certain chemicals have been involved in the fire. Steel so modified is commonly called "burnt" steel. Members that have become burnt will usually be severely corroded as well, and their suitability for further use is a matter for individual judgment. The FEMA Report 403, "World Trade Center Performance Study,"[13] Appendix A, presents a detailed discussion on the effects of fire on steel structures. The NIST report on the collapses of the World Trade Center towers also includes an analysis of the structural fire response of steel.

Protective Coating on Structural Steel. Excluding other factors that affect fire growth, such as extinguishing systems, low fire loads, compartmentalization, and so on, damage to structural steel members may be minimized by application of protective coatings that provide a period of fire resistance. Generally, a mineral fiber or cementitious mixture is applied by spray application; however, the adherence and durability of such coatings, even under normal circumstances, has been the subject of some concern. Too often, questionable application resulted in unreliable fire resistance and subsequently, considerable structural damage. The absence of protective coatings over even relatively small areas of the flange or web of steel beams and columns can have a dramatic impact on the structural fire behavior of these elements.[14,15] The local heating of the structural steel at the exposed location can reduce the resistance of the beam or column. In contrast, even a small remnant thickness of protective coating can significantly improve the behavior of the structural element as compared to bare steel (Figure 19.4.3).

A large fire in a 50 story office building known as One New York Plaza occurred in 1970 in New York City and resulted in three fatalities. Much of the $10 million in physical damage

FIGURE 19.4.3 Large Unprotected Steel Girders Damaged Beyond Repair, Illustrating Vulnerability of Steel in a Fire

arose from failure of sprayed-on thermal insulation. This incident was instrumental in the passage of New York City's Local Law Number 5, which is a comprehensive approach to improving life safety in high-rise office buildings.

Sprayed-on protective coverings can be expected to be easily dislodged during fire-fighting and overhaul operations. Usually problems of this kind are easily detected, but a complete examination of the structure must be made to determine the extent of damage. Also, before occupancy is permitted, it is imperative to determine that fire damage to a specific section of a building does not impair the integrity of zones of safety, means of egress, and smoke towers, or the operation of fire doors, fire dampers, or other protective devices or systems in areas not damaged by fire.

Fire Tests. The principal fire test used to establish fire resistance for structural elements is NFPA 251, *Standard Methods of Tests of Fire Resistance of Building Construction and Materials,* or its ASTM equivalent, ASTM E119, *Standard Test Methods for Fire Tests of Building Construction and Materials.* In using test results, however, it is essential that architects and design engineers look closely at differences between standard test conditions and potential fire conditions the structure may be exposed to. Only with such a review can accurate and safe conclusions be drawn about the performance of a building design. At best it is a destructive comparative test with little relation to actual fire conditions.

For fire-resistive purposes, many floor/ceiling and roof/ceiling assemblies are considered as a single fire-resistive element. The ceiling by itself does not provide a specific fire resistance rating. It should be noted that many floor or roof and ceiling tests provide an assembly rating, as well as a beam rating. The beam rating should not be interpreted as a measure of protection afforded by the ceiling. Unfortunately, if the ceiling membrane does not provide fire resistance, structural components above the ceiling are subject to damage in a fire.

Cast Iron. The use of cast iron as structural material has all but ceased. If found, these buildings are undoubtedly archaic historical preservations. A number of such buildings may still be found in New York City and elsewhere. In some instances, only the facades are of cast iron; in other cases, both the structural elements and facades are of this material. The behavior of cast iron when exposed to fire temperatures is substantially different from that of steel. Cast iron exposed to temperatures of 800°F (427°C) will deteriorate and fracture if struck with water from a fire hose.

Concrete

In a fire lasting 1 to 2 hours, concrete will generally suffer only moderate damage, so routine cutting and patching procedures will usually be adequate for repairs. In intense and long-lasting fires, such as those that may occur in large, heavily stocked warehouses and department stores, severe damage to concrete may occur. Restoration may entail the removal of severely damaged areas and patching in areas less severely damaged. Experienced engineering judgment is required for evaluating the residual strength of those areas that are somewhere between moderately and severely damaged. An example of one approach to the problem of evaluating the residual strength of apparently marginally damaged concrete structural units can be found in the article "Prestressed Concrete Resists Fire" by Zollman and Garavaglin.[16]

Damage Analysis. Over the past two decades much progress has been made in the improvement of methods for analysis of properties and behavior of concrete exposed to elevated temperatures. Better understanding of the fire behavior of concrete is a result of full-scale test results, model studies, and analytical methodologies directed to long-standing issues, including influence of restraints on reinforced concrete columns, deformation behavior, and thermal damage. These developments offer valuable tools for estimating the extent of fire damage and residual strength following fire exposure of structural elements and systems. *Fire Safety Design & Concrete,*[17] discusses structural response of concrete elements to fire. This work presents basic engineering concepts for considering flexural elements, compression elements, and complex structures and frames.

The use of admixtures to produce various desired characteristics in concrete has increased over the years. There are now on the market dozens of products for strength enhancement, set acceleration and retardation, shrink reduction and flowability, early strength, reduced permeability, and other qualities. Long-term effects of some of these additives on strength and durability are not well researched, and the same is true for behavior of these concretes during and following exposure to fire conditions.

With the increasing use of high-performance concrete (HPC) with compressive strengths exceeding 16,000 psi (110,000 KPa), the matter of spalling at high temperatures has become of interest. Research in the United Kingdom and elsewhere indicates that *explosive spalling* greatly reduces the fire resistance of concrete and that increasing the strength of concrete can be expected under certain conditions to reduce fire performance.[18,19] The identification and control of unfavorable factors, such as curing and drying conditions, aggregate size and type, and concrete permeability, remain under investigation. Research indicates that the addition of polypropylene fibers to the concrete mixture will reduce spalling and improve the fire load behavior of high strength concrete columns.[20] Work on the characterization of high-performance concrete is underway at the National Institute of Standards and Technology (NIST), using quantitative image analysis to determine the macro- and microstructures of HPC in relation to the response to fire.

A waiting period of perhaps several weeks should elapse after the fire has been extinguished before careful study of structural damage is initiated. This delay will allow any damage to the concrete, such as cracking, layering, calcination, and discoloration change from the natural gray color to pink or brown, which is indicative of heating to temperatures in excess of 450°F (232°C), to become more discernible. The thickness of fire-damaged concrete in structural members can be determined by chipping with a pick or geologist's hammer. Unsound concrete may be colored and will be more or less soft and friable, whereas sound concrete will give a distinctive ring when struck with a pick or hammer. Cored concrete samples for compressive strength tests and reinforcing steel for tensile strength determinations will enable a closer evaluation of the residual strength of damaged members. Load tests may be applied but should only be conducted under the supervision of a registered structural engineer. ACI Committee Report 437R-03, "Strength Evaluation of Existing Buildings," provides guidance on the planning, conduct, and interpretation of load tests.[21]

A variety of nondestructive evaluation (NDE) test methods may be deployed to help evaluate the postfire condition of a concrete structure. A detailed explanation of these methods is beyond the scope of this chapter. Two ACI Committee Reports provide the state of the art on NDE methods for concrete. ACI Committee Report 228.1R, "In-Place Methods to Estimate Concrete Strength,"[22] describes procedures to estimate the in-place strength of concrete in existing construction, including methods that may be applicable to a postfire evaluation, such as rebound number penetration resistance and ultrasonic pulse velocity. The principle, inherent limitations, and repeatability of each method are reviewed, and procedures are presented for developing the relationship needed to estimate compressive strength from in-place results. A second report, ACI Committee Report 228.2R-98, "Nondestructive Test Methods for Evaluation of Concrete in Structures,"[23] reviews nondestructive test methods for evaluating the condition of concrete and steel reinforcement in structures. The methods discussed include visual inspection, stress-wave methods, nuclear methods, penetrability methods, magnetic and electrical methods, infrared thermography and ground-penetrating radar. The principle of each method is discussed and the typical instrumentation is described. In addition, the testing procedures are summarized and the data analysis methods are explained. Finally, the advantages and limitations of each of the methods are summarized. Severe exposure of heavy concrete sections to fire may cause layering, that is, partial separation of the outer 1 to 2 in. (25 to 51 mm) of concrete of a building member from the interior mass. Such layering can complicate the application of the NDE methods described in the ACI Committee 228 reports. Successful application of the methods described in the reports requires an experienced operator.

A complete report dealing with a survey of fire damage to a multistory reinforced-concrete building and the subsequent repair procedure can be found in the paper "Fire Damage to General Mills Building."[24]

CASE STUDY. A severe fire occurred in 1951 in an unsprinklered paper warehouse. This fire lasted for more than 44 hours, and it is estimated that heat intensities of more than 1600°F (870°C) existed for 3 hours or longer. Even after severe fire, the structure was still standing and the concrete floors prevented the spread of fire and major water damage. An inspection of the structure after the fire showed that the concrete roof and columns appeared to have suffered little damage, except that the roof showed deflection up to a maximum of approximately 2½ in. (64 mm) in a 20 ft (6.1 m) span. When holes were cut through the roof, it was found that the concrete was calcined and had a light brown color in varying depths. This damaged concrete had almost no strength and began to disintegrate after a period of several weeks. As a result, the portions of the roof slab that showed appreciable amounts of calcined concrete were replaced. Many of the columns required removal of the concrete down to the reinforcing steel spiral, and, in some cases, calcining appeared inside the spiral. In these cases, the entire column was replaced. The column caps were replaced completely if more than one-half of the column showed evidence of calcining. Reinforcing rods showed some reduction in tensile strength, but most were salvaged and reused and downgraded to about three-quarters of their original strength.

If a decision is made to repair the damage, the usual procedure is to shore up the structure, if necessary, and to remove the fire-damaged concrete, using a hammer, chisel, or a lightweight mechanical hammer. (Use of heavy hammers is discouraged, since they might aggravate the damage by inadvertently chipping good concrete.) The steel reinforcements are then cleaned and, if necessary, additional reinforcements are added and, finally, the concrete is built up with air-blown grout. Durable concrete repairs have been made with epoxy resins also (unfortunately, epoxy is subject to significant strength loss at temperatures above 150°F [66°C]).

The significant difference between conventional reinforced concrete and prestressed concrete in fires is the performance of the high-strength steel wire, strands, or rods used for prestressing. Under fire conditions, the prestressed steel concrete units are susceptible to rapid loss of strength at temperatures in excess of 752°F (400°C). A load test is recommended in postinspection for significant pronounced sag or an indication of excessive temperature in a range where stress loss may have been sufficient to seriously affect the strength.

Tilt-up construction is a popular, simple, and effective type of concrete construction. As the name implies, slabs are site precast adjacent to their final location and lifted into place. In older structures, dating from the 1950s and 1960s, the reinforcing steel projecting from adjoining wall panels was encased in cast-in-place concrete columns. These systems provided relatively reliable fire resistance. In more recent construction, the wall panels are connected by exposed steel weldments, which are vulnerable to fire damage. The joints in this type of newer "value engineered" construction are filled with flexible, combustible mastic instead of concrete.

Tilt-up construction does not normally allow the walls to be as well connected to the foundations as in normal cast-in-place construction. This can result in an even more potentially dangerous condition when the roof has been burned away. The then unsupported walls are quite vulnerable to tip-over in windy conditions. Some building codes require that this and similar "heavy wall" buildings be designed for "burn-out " conditions, and mandates more competent wall foundations. One should be especially aware of this inherent weakness, during and immediately after a fire.

Several fires on the West Coast have displayed these inherent weaknesses (Figure 19.4.4). Complete collapse and highly damaged panels precluded any effort of cost-effective repair.

Brick

During production, clay bricks are exposed to temperatures in excess of 2000°F (1093°C); hence their strength is retained in actual fires. Reinforcing steel embedded in the center of a clay brick wall would normally be protected by a minimum of 3 to 4 in. (76 to 102 mm) of brick and not be affected. Spalling should be expected, especially if hot bricks are drenched with water from a fire hose. In most cases, temporary repairs can be made with epoxy cement or air-blown grout. Permanent repairs are more appropriately made by replacement, in kind, of the defaced brick.

Wood

Wood is one of the oldest and most widely used building materials. Its behavior in fire conditions varies considerably, depending on the species of wood and the design configuration, that is, solid sawn lumber, glue laminates, plywood, wood chipboard, and so on. The effect of fire on glue laminates may be considered the same as that on solid sawn lumber (heavy timber), assuming that the adhesives used were not affected by heat and that metal plates joining members and their attachment are not damaged. Generally, the phenol-resorcinal and melamine adhesives are not affected by heat. Plywood and chipboard are also dependent on proper adhesives, the difference potentially being slow burning versus a hazardous flash fire caused by delamination.

FIGURE 19.4.4 Fire Damage to Building of Tilt-Up Construction (Source: Oakland, CA, Fire Department)

There are two primary aspects of the behavior of wood materials exposed to fire and other sources of ambient heat. The first involves loss of strength as a result of burning away of material. The second is its contribution to the energy released in a fire through its combustion. Time rates of loss of material and strength can be estimated in terms of char depth and direction of fire spread can be estimated by developing char depth contours. This was the procedure used to trace the extension of fire in the Happy Land Social Club that took 87 lives in New York City in 1991. Ignition temperatures and contributions to heat release in a specific fire depends on a number of factors, including species, density, and moisture content. Long-term exposure of wood to elevated ambient temperatures reduces strength and lowers ignition temperature. Both of these effects can be important in the overall investigation and evaluation of structural damage from fire.

ASCE's "Guide and Commentary for the Evaluation, Maintenance and Upgrading of Wood Structures"[25] provides detailed information on serviceability factors, inspection, evaluation of load-carrying capability of timber structures and methods of repair.

Redwood, found on the West Coast of the United States, withstands high fire exposures. It is reported that the high resistance is due to the lack of the usual volatile resins and oils found in other woods. Redwood forests have resisted fire for centuries.

When wood structural members are subjected to fire, the ability to withstand the imposed loads is dependent to a degree on the remaining undamaged cross-sectional area. The average rate of penetration of char when flame is impinged upon an exposed wood member is approximately 1½ in. (38 mm) per hour. Beyond the char area to a distance not more than ¼ in. (6 mm), the structural properties of wood may be affected by its exposure to high temperatures. The degree of strength loss in this small zone adjacent to the char is not exactly known but is presumed to be insignificant.

Fire tests made on two solid sawn wood joists, 4 × 14 in. (102 × 356 mm), nominal size, at the Southwest Research Institute showed that, after 13 minutes of fire exposure, 80 percent of the original wood section remained undamaged and available to carry the load. In another test of two 7 × 21 in. (178 × 533 mm) glued laminated beams, after a 30 minute fire exposure, 75 percent of the original wood section remained and continued to support the design load.[26]

The previous tests, as well as actual fire experience, substantiate the fact that large-dimension wood members will remain in place under fire conditions and continue to support design loads. It is usually in the larger or heavy timber members that char can be scraped clear and an evaluation made by a qualified engineer or architect to determine the remaining load-supporting capacity of the wood member. As previously discussed, trussed wood roof structures constructed with 2 × 4 and 2 × 6 members have a history of lethal, sudden collapse when exposed to fire.

The practice in older, wood frame buildings was to diagonally cut the tops of wood beams within the bearing wall pocket so that in the event of failure due to fire, the weight of the member would not tear out the wall masonry and/or cause collapse. Further, on reuse of older wood beams it was the practice to invert the beam, which then placed the cut in the pocket, resulting in a reduced bearing area and ability to take shear load. The notching of wood structural members can play an important role in determining the time for failure and the estimation of residual strength of structural timber constructions in fires. The inverting of these members on reuse can also contribute to early failure and collapse. Because of the large number of wood framed buildings in existence, the condition of floor and roof beams at bearing walls should be carefully examined following exposure to fire.

Unanticipated problems often arise following building conversions and other structural and spatial renovations, which may either conceal spaces that were originally open or expose spaces and structural members that were originally concealed and protected from fire. The latter can be particularly hazardous in unsprinklered buildings.

A good example of the complexity of restoration work following a fire is described in the paper "Saving the Exeter Street Theater."[27] This landmark building in Boston, Massachusetts, was constructed in 1885 and ravaged by fire in 1985. One of four 80 ft (24.4 m) long, 18 ft (5.5 m) deep wood trusses and the roof were severely damaged. Besides preserving the original character of the building, engineers were obliged to meet structural requirements of the modern building code. Among other conditions, designers were faced with serious truss decay at the bearing locations and distortion and shrinkage defects of the top and bottom chords. Restoration efforts plus changes in the useable spaces in the building required use of a full range of structural technology. The paper illustrates the importance of careful evaluation of all aspects of wear and aging in addition to fire damage that must be addressed when older buildings are to be repaired.

The special case of evaluating and predicting possibilities for collapse while a fire is still in progress is of interest to fire forces engaged in rescue and fire control operations. Here there is need for the evaluator to recognize early signs of impending failure of both structural and nonstructural elements and systems. Failure resulting in collapse of ceilings, sheathing, glass, and other elements of construction that do not directly affect structural integrity can endanger fire fighters and can contribute to the growth and extension of fire.

Plastics

Plastic construction has been limited to small structures, such as cabins and radomes. However, the use of plastics in building contents and as building materials has steadily increased,[28] as has the resultant fire load. The products of combustion of plastic can be very corrosive and can severely damage structural elements in buildings during a fire. The Munich Reinsurance Company reported extensive losses due to corrosion from gaseous decomposition of burning plastic. Twelve buildings were listed as having extensive corrosion-damaged structural steel members. In several cases, it was necessary to destroy the buildings. Steel members moderately damaged by corrosion may be sandblasted, but it is suggested that a stress analysis be conducted before repairs are started. Damage to reinforcement concrete is more complex, since corrosion, in time, is apt to penetrate to the reinforcing material. Preliminary analysis is necessary before power hammers are used to inspect the extent of damage to reinforcing steel.

FIRE DURING CONSTRUCTION

A dangerous practice is often found during the course of construction of steel-frame buildings; it is common during the application of fireproofing to structural steel members that the coating on the lower first and second stories is postponed until the final stages of construction. The application of fireproofing to these lower floors is often delayed due to the potential physical damage to the coating in these high-traffic areas. These heavy-working areas usually also contain storage of construction materials and equipment, much of which is highly combustible (Figure 19.4.5). The amount of combustible material can provide a fire load capable of destroying the building.

Buildings of reinforced concrete may depend on wood shoring supports and form work to support the fresh concrete pour and to retain their shape until the concrete gains sufficient strength to support its own weight and possibly portions of the floors above that are under construction (Figure 19.4.6). At this stage of construction the building is also highly vulnerable to fire damage. A fire before the concrete curing process is complete could result in a total loss.

Awareness of this problem was demonstrated at the reconstruction of St. Mary Cathedral in San Francisco, California. Built at a cost of \$10 million to replace a former church destroyed by fire, its cupola walls extended some 150 ft (46 m) above the ground floor. The supporting scaffolding filled the interior with 1½ million board feet (3500 m^3) of lumber at a cost of \$100,000. The chief building superintendent, aware of the fire loss potential, directed that a temporary sprinkler system be installed.

FIGURE 19.4.5 Lower Floor Used for Storage of Materials and Equipment

FIGURE 19.4.6 Timber Used as Shoring and Support of Reinforced-Concrete Construction, Essentially a Forest of Wood

SUMMARY

Several factors must be considered in the evaluation of the integrity of a structure after a fire. First, structural damage that may affect overall or local stability must be identified. Then the postfire strengths and weaknesses of the basic materials of the structural assembly must be assessed. Structural steel, concrete, brick, wood, and plastics exhibit different behaviors both during and after exposure to fire. The age and deterioration (e.g., from corrosion, animal infestation, or poor maintenance practices) of the individual materials must also be taken into account. Finally, thorough engineering studies are necessary to determine the parameters for repair and/or replacement of the building's structural elements, as well as to document insurance and litigation claims.

BIBLIOGRAPHY

References Cited

1. Brannigan, F. L., *Building Construction for the Fire Service,* 3rd ed., National Fire Protection Association, Quincy, MA, 1992.
2. Dunn, V., *Collapse of Burning Buildings,* Fire Engineering, New York, 1988.
3. ATC-20 and Field Manual ATC-20-1, *Post Earthquake Safety Evaluation of Buildings,* Applied Technology Council, Redwood City, CA, 1989.
4. ATC-21, "Rapid Visual Screening of Buildings for Potential Seismic Hazards," (FEMA-154), Applied Technology Council, Redwood City, CA, 1988.
5. FEMA 351, "Recommended Seismic Evaluation and Upgrade Criteria for Existing Welded-Steel Moment-Frame Buildings," Federal Emergency Management Agency, Washington, DC, July 2000.
6. "Special Data Package: Fire Fighter Casualties as a result of Roof or Floor Collapses," National Fire Protection Association One-Stop Data Shop, Quincy, MA, March 1998.
7. Klaene, B., and Sanders, R., *Structural Fire Fighting,* National Fire Protection Association, Quincy, MA, 2000.
8. Harthorn, R. W., *Temporary Shoring and Stabilization of Earthquake Damaged Historic Buildings,* California Building Officials, Sacramento, CA, 1998.
9. Marchant, E. W. (Ed.), *A Complete Guide to Fire and Buildings,* Barnes and Noble, New York, 1973.
10. Anchor, R. D., Malhotra, H. L., and Purkiss, J. A., *Design of Structures Against Fire,* Elsevier Applied Science Publishers, New York, 1986.
11. ASCE, *Guidelines for Failure Investigations,* American Society of Civil Engineers, Reston, VA, 1989.
12. Lie, T. T. (Ed.), Structural Fire Protection, American Society of Civil Engineers, Reston, VA, 1992.
13. FEMA 403, "World Trade Center Building Performance Study," Federal Emergency Management Agency, Washington, DC, May 2002.
14. Kang, Y., Hadjisophocleous, G. V., and Aik Khoo, H., "The Effect of Partial Fire Protection Loss on the Fire Resistance of Steel Beams," Fourth International Workshop, Structures in Fire, Aveiro, Portugal, 2006, pp. 63–74.
15. Pessiki, S., Kwon, K., and Lee, B. J., "Fire Load Behavior of Steel Building Columns with Damaged Spray-Applied Fire Resistive Material," Fourth International Workshop, Structures in Fire, Aveiro, Portugal, 2006, pp. 235–245.
16. Zollman, L., and Garavaglin, M., "Prestressed Concrete Resists Fire," *Civil Engineering,* 1960, pp. 36–41.
17. Harmathy, T. Z., *Fire Safety Design & Concrete,* Longman Group U.K. Limited, London, UK, 1982.
18. Ali, F. A., Connolly, R., and Sullivan, P. J. E., "Spalling of High Strength Concrete at Elevated Temperatures," *Journal of Applied Fire Science,* Vol. 6, No. 1, 1996–1997, pp. 3–14.
19. Sullivan, P. J. E., and Thiruchelvam, C., "High Strength Plastic Concrete at Elevated Temperatures," *Journal of Applied Fire Science,* Vol. 9, No. 2, 1999–2000, pp. 113–123.
20. Kodur, V. K. R., Cheng, F., Wang, T., and Sultan, M. A., "Effect of Strength and Fiber Reinforcement on Fire-Resistance of High-Strength Concrete Columns," *Journal of Structural Engineering,* ASCE, Feb. 2003, pp. 253–259.
21. ACI Committee 437, Committee Report 437R-03, "Strength Evaluation of Existing Buildings," American Concrete Institute, Farmington Hills, MI, 2003.
22. ACI Committee 228, Committee Report 228.1R-03, "In-Place Methods to Estimate Concrete Strength," American Concrete Institute, Farmington Hills, MI, 2003.
23. ACI Committee 228, Committee Report 228.2R-98, "Nondestructive Test Methods for Evaluation of Concrete in Structures," American Concrete Institute, Farmington Hills, MI, 1998.
24. Fruchtbaum, J., "Fire Damage to General Mills Building," *Proceedings* of American Concrete Institute, Detroit, MI, 1941.
25. ASCE, "Guide and Commentary for the Evaluation, Maintenance and Upgrading of Wood Structures," American Society of Civil Engineers, 1989.
26. "Comparative Fire Tests of Timber and Steel Beams," Technical Report No. 3, 1961, National Forest Products Association, Washington, DC.
27. Roberge, C. P., Dusenberry, D. O., Zagajeski, S. W., and Liepins, A. A., "Saving the Exeter Street Theater," *National Council of Structural Engineers Associations,* Fall 1999, pp. 17–21.
28. Schaden, S., "Loses and Loss Prevention," Munich Re-Insurance Co., Munich, Germany, Apr. 1968.

NFPA Codes, Standards, and Recommended Practices

Reference to the following NFPA codes, standards, and recommended practices will provide further information on the processes for analyzing structural fire damage discussed in this chapter. (See the latest version of The NFPA Catalog *for availability of the current editions of the following documents.)*

NFPA 220, *Standard on Types of Building Construction*
NFPA 251, *Standard Methods of Tests of Fire Resistance of Building Construction and Materials*
NFPA 921, *Guide for Fire and Explosion Investigations*
NFPA 1670, *Standard on Operations and Training for Technical Search and Rescue Incidents*
NFPA 5000®, Building Construction and Safety Code®

Chapter 5

Approaches to Calculating Structural Fire Resistance

Barbara Lane

This chapter provides an overview of structural fire resistance calculation techniques, developed over many years, to address the critical parameters that can affect structural performance in actual building fires. It concentrates on the international body of work on the subject. As discussed in the first few sections, determination of structural fire resistance is typically associated with standardized laboratory fire resistance testing, which finds its roots in the 19th century. However, over several decades, researchers have investigated structural response of building elements to real-world fire loads and postulated various theories for use in the design domain.

It is a misnomer to conclude that any standard fire resistance test can demonstrate or approximate the full-scale complex structural fire performance of building elements. Instead, standard test methods serve well as a comparative assessment method, providing valuable data on the relative performance of materials and small-scale assemblies for a specified fire load.

Concern with the limitations of these standardized tests in providing a comprehensive assessment of full-scale structural fire resistance and the use of these test results as the primary basis for fire-resistant design in building structures has led to the development of alternative assessment and calculation methods over the years. The primary concern is the reliance on the assumption that a structural system tested at a relatively short span, in a laboratory furnace, can robustly translate into a basis for design at the scale required in real buildings. Concerns also exist regarding the lack of assessment of the performance of structural connections as well as the universal application of a standardized fire load during the test.

Initially researchers concentrated on the concept of a standardized fire load (time-temperature curve) and whether it adequately represented the broad range of fire conditions that could be experienced in actual building fires. As such, initial efforts attempted to gain a better understanding of the heating regime that can occur in a compartment (enclosure containing a fire). These investigations concentrated on determining whether a common set of parameters affected overall fire loading such as duration of the fire, the peak temperatures and heat release rates attained in the enclosure, the rate of heating in the compartment once flashover had occurred, and so on. The section "Alternative Approaches to Fire Resistance" describes some of the techniques that address the fire resistance rating appropriate to specific compartment geometry and its contents.

Further clarification on the critical parameters to consider when specifying the fire load that forms the basis of a structural fire design are outlined in the section "Determining a Design Fire for a Structural Analysis" and result in temperature-time relationships that form the basis for calculating structural fire resistance that is not based on standardized tests.

Over time, it became apparent that not only was a better understanding of fire parameters required to understand real fire resistance, but also the performance of structural elements in these fires. As such, individual structural element response to the elevated temperatures that occur in fires was investigated. Analytical methods to capture these very specific responses to fire are presented in the section "Single Structural Element Analysis."

This growing understanding of basic structural response was further developed over the years in part by more critical observations during fires, as well as formal full-scale testing. The data produced

Barbara Lane, Ph.D., is the technical leader of Arup Fire in the firm's London office. She specializes in structural fire engineering design and implementation, with an international portfolio of completed projects.

Chapter Contents

Key Terms

aluminum, composite steel, concrete, design fire, fire resistance, fire test, heat transfer, postflashover fire, section factor, single element analysis, spalling, structural integrity, structural performance, structural steel, time-temperature curve, wood

have resulted in the creation of more advanced structural analysis techniques specifically targeted for fire conditions. The increasing work in this domain is resulting in a substantially greater understanding of true building structural performance in response to fire and is prompting the view that structural detailing and specific structural design for fire is the next and much needed step in optimizing building safety. Methodologies that exist to carry out such assessments are presented in the section "Use of Advanced Analysis in Global Structural Response to Fire."

It is increasingly clear that this important topic requires the attention of fire protection engineers and structural engineers, and that only through successful integration of the expertise in both professions can the result be a robust and commercially beneficial approach to improving the effectiveness of structural design for fire safety.

For related topics, see Section 19, Chapter 2, "Structural Integrity During Fire"; and Section 19, Chapter 4, "Analyzing Structural Fire Damage."

UNDERSTANDING STRUCTURAL RESPONSE TO FIRE

Standardized Fire Resistance Test and Refinements to Fireproofing Thickness

The standard fire resistance test (NFPA 251, *Standard Methods of Tests of Fire Resistance of Building Construction and Materials;* ASTM E119; ISO 834; BS 476; etc.) has formed the basis of fire resistance ratings in building codes worldwide for more than a century, resulting in structural fire resistance being treated separately from the concerns typically addressed by structural design. The implementation of the standardized fire resistance tests called for establishing adequate protection to the structural material with respect to limiting its temperature rise in fire. Time was the sole emphasis—providing fire resistance time to meet code requirements for building structure elements. See Section 19, Chapter 2, "Structural Integrity During Fire," for more discussion on the implementation of the standardized fire resistance test.

Typical building code requirements call for ratings appropriate to specific structural elements as a function of the building use, height, and area, and remain an established "best practice" approach to designing structures for fire resistance worldwide.

In brief, therefore, steel structures require varying amounts of applied fireproofing as a function of building height and use; concrete structures require varying amounts of cover for reinforcement; and timber structures require varying section sizes to allow for the loss of material in elevated temperatures. These measures, in the case of steel, were simply to limit the temperature rise beyond the material's estimated failure temperature of 550°C. For concrete, requirements sought to prevent the reinforcement bars from similarly exceeding these temperatures, whereas for timber, to ensure that the remaining timber portion could still carry its design loads once the charred portion of timber was no longer considered.

Small changes were made over the years, mainly coming from continuing strides to bring efficiency to fire protection costs. In the United Kingdom particularly, the ability of structural elements to sustain the load path in fire was increasingly studied to reduce the amount of fireproofing materials required. Refinements to the formulized fireproofing thicknesses were made, based on individual structural element failure temperatures rather than on the assumption of the generic 550°C concept. The refinements were also made based on the postulated theory that structural elements carry less of a load in the fire (fire limit state) relative to the "normal temperature" conditions (BS 5950-8: 2003). In addition, the sensitivity of section size to heat was incorporated via the heated perimeter to cross-sectional area concept.

Studies After Broadgate Building Fire

This refined single element approach served the design community well, albeit in the specialist domain only. More change was to come, however, after a real fire at the Broadgate building in London, where the steel structure was in essence unprotected and yet managed to survive the severe fire that occurred there. The steel industry in the UK and also in Australia started to question just how much real understanding of structural performance in fire existed and established a major program of full-scale fire tests on real-scale structures.[1–4] The findings caused a fundamental change in the understanding of steel structural performance in fire. It is worth noting that the concept of specific fire-related structural mechanisms is also being investigated and applied to other types of structural materials.

The studies after the Broadgate fire made it clear that the traditional emphasis on limiting temperature rise in materials to prevent degradation of strength was just one important parameter in the fire condition. Similarly, it became clear that refinements to fireproofing thickness based on generic reduced loading conditions for fire, and taking account of the specific strength of an individual structural element and therefore its unique failure temperature, were only touching the surface of what in fact was an incredibly complex problem. The effect of the expansion of structural materials in fire was shown to be of dominant concern, even at very low temperatures. Work such as the British Steel data from the Cardington fire tests,[5,6] the Cardington Fires Main Report from Edinburgh University,[7] and Usmani et al.[8] provide detailed background information on the test observations and structural mechanics in fire.

Although it is true that strength of steel structural materials decreases with increasing temperature, the geometry of the structural component itself also changes over the time of the fire due to the expansion of structural materials. This expansion effect is not just a function of very high temperatures experienced during a fully developed fire, but also a function of the span of the structural elements, their arrangement, and strength losses. These structural responses during fire were observed at temperatures as low as 100°C.

The results of the test program at both Cardington and William Street indicated that, for some structural arrangements, less fireproofing than expected was needed to provide structural stability as well as to maintain compartmentation (i.e., fire separation) requirements for the duration of a severe fire, including the cooling regime as the fire died out.[2]

To clarify this point, fire resistance is classified in two ways: (1) rating for the structural elements to maintain the structural stability of the building in fire and (2) rating for walls, floors, shaft walls, and so on, whose aim is to limit fire spread from one fire compartment to the next. For example, one story in a building may be one compartment, or, for a different use, one story may in fact contain several fire compartments. The work at Cardington looked at the effect of removing fireproofing from specific—namely, secondary—beams and observing whether (1) structural integrity was maintained (i.e., there was no overall building collapse) and (2) compartmentation was maintained. In other words, if the floor, for example, was deforming in the fire, it might not interfere with the overall stability of the building, but it could cause a breach in a compartment wall (as the result of the deforming floor pulling on the wall) and therefore could create a gap that allowed the fire to spread to another fire compartment.

Robust Response Analysis

Thus, there is a growing trend to apply this increasing understanding to real buildings, as well as carry on with investigations of full-scale structural response mechanisms in fire. Prior to the collapse of the World Trade Center, particularly in the United Kingdom and Europe, the emphasis for such detailed analysis of structures in fire and its practical implementation was very much on bringing efficiency to mostly steel design arrangements. However, since the collapse of the World Trade Center, robustness of response has formed the theme of this analysis, particularly for tall building structures. This means understanding the potential structural fire response mechanisms associated with a proposed structural design, and making refinements where weaknesses are identified that can result in global or local failures (either in the ability to maintain the design load or in the necessary compartmentation). Specifically, if structural designs are based on structural assemblies at a scale, span, or extent that have never been fire tested, there is an increasing onus on the profession to better approximate the design's performance in fire, particularly in buildings where the consequences of collapse are significant. For example, some long-span structures have shown through calculation methods to possess unsatisfactory fire performance because of the resulting effect they have on columns in fire. By conducting specific structural fire analysis and quantifying the structure's response, guidance can then be provided to enhance structural detailing needed to improve the performance of the columns during fire. In essence the future of structural design seems to be leading toward considering fire as a design load, similar to the approach taken for wind effects, snow effects, earthquake effects, or other environmental design events.

The standard fire resistance test, along with traditional fireproofing and fire resistance methods, will likely continue to serve as a fundamental basis for the design of structures, but will need to be supplemented with quantified structural responses during real fires, as the structural response of a building not only affects the stability of the structure but also the performance of compartmentation (or fire separation). This need requires the establishment of some fundamental performance objectives for structures in fire. For example, what are the acceptable behaviors that robustly confirm stability of the structural system itself during a fire? Then, to maintain compartmentation—to stair cores, to other stories in the building, or from compartment to compartment on the same story—what fundamental performance demonstrates that this stability is being maintained?

The need for risk-based design approaches should be considered as a way forward. Currently, some specialists in this structural fire engineering field design for absolute events, unlike earthquake design, for example, which addresses likely events. Earthquake designs that satisfy such requirements are deemed to be acceptable, safe, and best practice. Such confidence is not yet available in the regulatory environment for structural fire engineers.

A significant amount of work now remains to be done to firmly establish structural fire engineering knowledge and the techniques presented here as a mainstream part of any building and fire safety regulation. In the meantime, fundamental questions must be answered and substantial work is required to establish safe and reliable design techniques within the approvals process for the authorities having jurisdiction, as well as for building insurers and other key stakeholders. All of this is deemed necessary such that real structural performance in fire is no longer omitted from the design process. The techniques described in this chapter are presented as a first step in this process.

ALTERNATIVE APPROACHES TO FIRE RESISTANCE

Traditionally, standard temperature-time relationships, such as those described in ASTM E119,[9] NFPA 251, BS 476, Part 20,[10] or ISO 834,[11] have formed the basis of standard furnace tests to determine the structural response of building elements in fire conditions. However, it is well understood that the standard temperature-time curve does not always represent real postflashover fire (Law,[12] Thomas,[13] Malhotra[14]). This is due to the number of variables that can affect the heating regime in a compartment.

Postflashover fires can be more or less severe in terms of duration, rate of heating, and peak temperature than the standard temperature-time relationship in a furnace test. In addition, real fires are a function of fuel load and geometry, compartment dimensions, thermal properties of the compartment boundaries, and the quantity of unprotected openings that allow ventilation in a postflashover fire. In addition, in Europe—and to some extent New Zealand and Australia—active fire safety systems, compartment area, occupancy type, numbers of water supplies to the compartment, provisions for fire fighters, and even smoke extraction are assigned risk factors that increase or decrease the likelihood of a flashover and its possible extent. The resulting compartment fire is a complex mix of relationships. For structural fire resistance, this fire—the design fire—is the most important input variable, as it greatly influences the structural response. It is important, therefore, to understand its origin.

However, explicitly defining temperature-time relationships as a function of a specific compartment is a relatively new phenomenon in structural fire resistance calculations (also called structural fire engineering). Initially, research work concentrated on fire resistance periods and refining these periods as a function of the compartment in question.

Historically, therefore, due to concerns with the standard furnace test temperature-time relationship, work was carried out by Ingberg, Law, and Pettersson, among others, to determine what is known as *equivalent fire resistance* or *time-equivalent* methods. For these methods, the heating effect in a compartment is based on real compartment fire behavior and therefore takes into account fuel load density, ventilation openings, compartment dimensions, and enclosure thermal properties. This allows some improvement in the grading method, based on the standard furnace test that is currently assumed in building codes worldwide.

Time-equivalent methods can be described as methods that define the thermal exposure of a particular compartment fire in terms of the duration of the *equivalent standard fire.* This is important when engineers and designers want to use published fire resistance ratings from standard tests but based on estimates of real fire exposure.

Equivalence of thermal exposure has been defined in two ways:

1. *Fire load or equal area concept.* Equal areas under the temperature-time curves
2. *Equal temperature concept.* Equal temperatures at the critical part of the structural element

The two methods give similar results where the element selected has a fire resistance on the order of half an hour or more. Samples of both methods developed in the last 80 years, which form the basis of popular calculation methods internationally, are described in the following paragraphs. What these methods provide is an overall building rating, based on building-specific compartment factors.

It is important to note that time-equivalent methods do not assess local or global structural response mechanisms. They relate only to heating effects and their relationship with the standard furnace test. In addition, time-equivalent methods typically apply to protected steelwork but have been extended to include concrete. Some of these methods have recently also been applied to unprotected steelwork and timber construction, but their use with these building materials is not well validated. For unprotected steelwork, it is important to note that in general such elements can achieve 30 minutes standard fire resistance; attempts to extend use beyond this level result in the errors observed, for example, in the Natural Fire Safety Concept study.[15]

Fire Load or Equal Area Concept

By 1918 there was a widespread concern in the fire protection and code enforcement community[16] that there was no accepted method for establishing appropriate levels of fire endurance (now referred to as fire resistance) for buildings of different sizes and occupancies. The original work had been based on "fireproofing" large commercial buildings. It was recognized that these differed significantly from residential fires but it was not understood how their severity related to the conditions in the now formulated standard fire resistance test.

The Building Code recommended by the National Board of Fire Underwriters (NBFU), 1905 edition, contained a series of tables specifying certain wall thicknesses of buildings based on the use and number of stories. Sections 106 to 108 of this code specified other criteria for "fireproof" building construction, which was generally applicable to any structure more than 55 stories in height regardless of use.

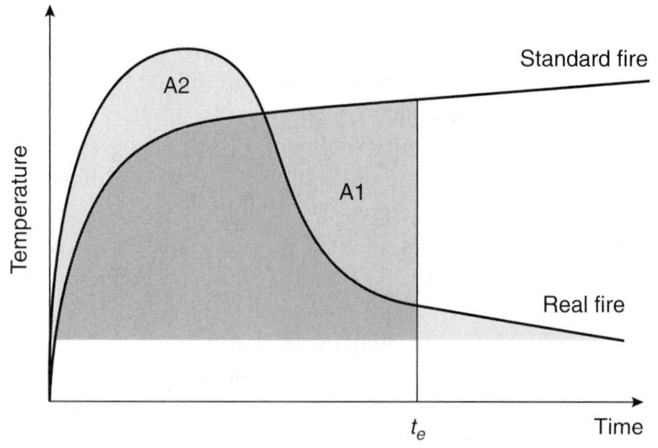

FIGURE 19.5.1 Fire Severity Concept (Source: A. H. Buchanan, *Structural Design for Fire Safety.* Copyright John Wiley and Sons Limited, 2001. Reproduced with permission.)

In order to develop a solution to this problem, in 1922 the National Bureau of Standards in the United States (now called the National Institute of Standards and Technology) investigated the nature of building fires under the direction of Simon Ingberg.[17] The main aim was to determine the intensity and duration of uncontrolled fires in particular occupancies resulting from different levels of fire load. Ingberg was also to investigate the validity of the standard time-temperature curve, which had been accepted as the basis for testing since 1918.

Ingberg investigated office and record storage type occupancies, including the effects of the building size and fire load, the effects of combustible and noncombustible flooring, and the effect of wood and steel furniture. As a result of these tests, Ingberg established a simple relationship between the average weight of combustible material within a room and the fire endurance necessary to withstand a complete burnout of the contents, known as the "fire load concept." It assumes that the area under any time-temperature curve from ignition through decay provides a comparative measure of fire severity, and that fire severity is a function of only the fire load.

Ingberg compared the area under the time-temperature curves generated in the burnout tests to an equivalent area under the standard time-temperature curve. The areas below a threshold temperature of about 300°C were not taken into account. The graph in Figure 19.5.1 shows the basis for Ingberg's work.

Ingberg developed the following relationship for time-equivalence:

$$t_e = k_1 L'' \tag{1}$$

where

t_e = *t*-equivalent (min)

L'' = Fire load (wood) per unit floor area

$k_1 = 1$ when L'' is in units of kg/m^2

$k_1 = 5$ when L'' is in units of lb/ft^2

Ingberg's work became widely accepted as the general basis for establishing fire endurance requirements. This method, however, neglects the effects of ventilation, fuel type, and fuel geometry on fire severity, and therefore its application and usefulness with engineered fire safety solutions is limited.

Equal Temperature Concept

The equal temperature concept is a more realistic method, where the equivalent fire severity is the time of exposure that a protected steel member would endure under the standard fire that would result in the same maximum temperature if it were exposed to a real postflashover fire. This concept was developed by Law,[12] Pettersson et al.,[18] and others and is applicable to insulating elements and materials with a limiting temperature such as wood with a charring temperature of 300°C.

The equal temperature concept is widely used, but can give misleading information if the maximum temperature of the structural element is not the limiting or failure temperature. Several factors, such as building geometry, section details, loading, connections, end conditions, continuity, and so on, can markedly influence the critical temperature for structural performance. This is discussed in more detail later in this chapter.

Kawagoe and Sekine. In 1963, after further small-scale tests and analysis, Kawagoe et al.[19] went on to show the importance of the ventilation parameter as follows:

$$\sqrt{h}\,\frac{A_B}{A_T} \tag{1}$$

where

h = Window height in the compartment (m)

A_B = Total area of windows (m^2)

A_T = Total area of inside compartment surfaces, including window area (m^2)

Kawagoe and Sekine also developed a formula for fire duration and defined it as the period from the beginning of temperature rise until the time the temperature drops after most of the combustible material is consumed. This time, T, is approximated as:

$$T = WA_F/5.5\sqrt{h}A_B \text{ (min)} \tag{2}$$

where

T = Time (min)

W = Fire load (kg/m^2)

A_F = Floor area (m^2)

h = Height of the window (m)

A_B = Area of the windows (m^2)

Law's Time Equivalent Method. In 1971, Law developed a time-equivalent formula based on the equal temperature concept.[12] This formula was based on small-scale compartment tests, as conducted by Thomas and Heselden,[20] and some large-scale compartment tests.[12]

The maximum temperature, which would be attained by a protected steel element in a real fire compartment, was chosen as a basis for comparison with the corresponding heating effect on the element if heated in a standard fire.

For a temperature-time curve, the maximum temperature obtained by a protected steel element in a compartment fire was calculated as:

$$\frac{d\theta_s}{dt} = \frac{\theta_f - \theta_s}{RC} \tag{3}$$

where

θ_s = Steel temperature (°C)

t = Time (sec)

θ_f = Fire temperature (°C)

R = Thermal resistance of the protective layer

C = Thermal capacity of the steel (J k^{-1})

The temperature of the heated surface of the protective material is assumed to be the same as the fire temperature. The heat transfer through the steel section can then be calculated.

For a given time-temperature curve the value RC was determined so that the maximum temperature of the protected member was 550°C. The time for the protected member to attain 550°C when exposed to the standard temperature-time curve then gives the value of time equivalent.

The best correlation was obtained from the product (L/A_v) and a term taking into account A_v and the solid surface to which heat is lost:

$$t_e = \frac{k_3 L}{\sqrt{A_v(A_t - A_F - A_v)}} \text{ (min)} \tag{4}$$

where

t_e = Time equivalent (min)

A_F = Floor area of the compartment (m^2)

L = Fire load (wood equivalent) (kg)

A_v = Area of ventilation opening (m^2)

k_3 = 1.3 to 1.5, depending on the stick spacing in the cribs used as fuel min m^2/kg

A_t = Area of internal envelope (walls, floor, ceiling, and openings) (m^2)

In this correlation, A_F was not included in the evaluation of solid surfaces because the floors were very well insulated. In all experiments, the openings were the full compartment height. The values of t-equivalent were found to be independent of scale and height of ventilation openings.

Law then analyzed temperature-time curves for a number of burn-out fires in larger brick and concrete compartments (approximately 3 m high) with fire loads ranging from wood cribs, furniture, and liquid fuels, and developed:[12]

$$t_e = k_4 L/[A_v(A_t - A_v)]^{1/2} \text{ (min)} \tag{5}$$

where k_4 is 1.0. This was due to the little effect fuel arrangement appeared to have in these larger-scale tests. In this correlation the floor area was included in the evaluation of solid surfaces to which heat is lost. The larger-scale data also showed no significant effect of ventilation opening height on t_e.

Law concluded that this Equation 5 was most suitable for engineering purposes for protected steel columns and went on to demonstrate that it gave good results for reinforced concrete also. She did discover that it overestimates the time prediction for tightly baled paper and cloth.

This formula is valid only for compartments with vertical openings in the walls, and cannot be used for rooms with openings in the roof.

Pettersson's Time Equivalent Method. Pettersson et al.[18] adopted Law's approach to *t*-equivalent but, instead of the experimental curves on which Law's work was based, used the family of calculated temperature-time curves for particular compartments, as derived by Magnusson and Thelandersson.[21] When the fuel load is expressed in mass (kg) of wood instead of "effective calorific value" (MJ), Pettersson's expression for *t*-equivalent is as follows:

$$t_e = 1.21L/(A_v\sqrt{h}A_t)^{1/2} \text{ (min)} \tag{6}$$

where

t_e = Time equivalent (min)

L = Fire load (wood equivalent) (kg)

h = Height of vertical opening (m)

A_t = Total area of internal envelope (walls, floor, ceiling, and openings) (m^2)

A_v = Area of ventilation opening (m^2)

Note that in his original heat balance work he excluded A_v appropriately, but for an unstated reason does not in his final equations presented in his design guide.[18] This equation includes $\sqrt{h}$ because of the input parameters in the method for calculating the temperature-time curves from Magnusson and Thelanderson,[21] on which this equation is based.

Equation 7 can be modified to take into account the thermal properties of the compartment enclosure by applying the factor k_f to each input parameter.

This yields

$$t_e = 1.21k_f^{1/2}L''A_F/(A_v\sqrt{h}A_t)^{1/2} \text{ (min)} \tag{7}$$

where

k_f = Factor applied to input parameters to take account of the thermal properties $k\rho c$ of the compartment enclosure expressed as a proportion of the $k\rho c$ for Pettersson's "standard" compartment. This standard compartment, defined in the Swedish Building Regulations in 1967, is where the surrounding structure has the thermal properties of an average of concrete, brick, and lightweight concrete of thickness 20 cm. (Note also the fire is ventilation controlled and with a cooling phase of 10°C/min.)

L'' = Fire load (wood equivalent) (kg/m^2)

A_F = Floor area of the compartment (m^2)

Eurocodes and British Standards

Eurocode 1: Actions on Structures—Part 1.2: General Actions—Actions on Structures Exposed to Fire, dated 2002,[22] has now also been adapted as a British Standard BS EN 1991-1-2:2002. It is understood that the time equivalent method defined within originates from the German standard DIN 18230, version 94.[23] The derivation of this formula has never been published but it is understood to have come from an empirical analysis of calculated steel temperatures in a large number of simulated fires computed by the German program "Multi Room Fire Code."[24] Though this German reference refers to an earlier published version of this Eurocode, the basic formulations remain and therefore this origin is believed to still apply. This method is dependent on ceiling height of the compartment but not the opening height. The fuel type assumed in the original work is unknown, although it is widely believed to be a cellulosic-type.

The time-equivalent is defined in Eurocode 1, Part 1.2[22] as:

$$t_e = q_{f,d}k_b w_f k_c \text{ (min)} \tag{8}$$

where

$q_{f,d}$ = Fire load density related to the floor area (MJ/m^2)

$$q_{f,d} = q_{f,k}m\delta_{q1}\delta_{q2}\delta_n \tag{9}$$

where

$q_{f,k}$ = Fire load density determined from a fire load classification of occupancies (see Table 19.5.1)

m = Combustion factor, which for cellulosic materials is defined as 0.8

δ_{q1} = Safety factor taking account of the fire activation risk due to the size of compartment (see Table 19.5.2)

δ_{q2} = Safety factor taking account of the fire activation risk due to the type of occupancy (see Table 19.5.3)

$\delta_n = \prod_{i=1}^{10}\delta_{ni}$ = A factor taking account of the different active fire-fighting measures such as sprinklers, detection, fire brigade, etc. (see Table 19.5.4)

k_b is a conversion factor and can be taken as 0.07 (min·m^2 /MJ) when no detailed assessment of the thermal properties of the boundary are pursued and when q_d is given in MJ/m^2. Otherwise k_b may be related to the thermal property $b = \sqrt{\rho c \lambda}$ in accordance with Table 19.5.5.

w_f is the ventilation factor and is calculated as

$$w_f = \left(\frac{6}{H}\right)^{0.3}\left[0.62 + \frac{90(0.4-\alpha_v)^4}{1+b_v\alpha_h}\right] \geq 0.5 \tag{10}$$

where

$\alpha_v = A_v/A_f$ = Area of vertical openings A_v in the facade related to the floor area of the compartment where the limit $0.025 \leq \alpha_v \leq 0.25$ should be observed

$\alpha_h = A_h/A_f$ = Area of horizontal opening in the roof related to the floor area of the compartment

$b_v = 12.5(1 + 10\alpha_v - \alpha_v^2) \geq 10$

H = Height of the compartment (m)

For small fire compartments (defined in the Eurocode as $A_f <$ 100 m^2) without openings in the roof, the factor w_f may also be calculated as

$$w_f = O^{-1/2}A_f/A_t \quad (11)$$

where

O = Opening factor = $A_v h^{1/2}/A_t$ with $0.02 \leq O \leq 0.20$ with the default value $k_b = 0.07$ and assuming 18 MJ/kg for wood, Equation 6 becomes the same as Equation 8

k_c = A newly incorporated correction factor, which is a function of the material composing structural cross sections and as defined as 13.7 × O for unprotected steel

Reinforced concrete and protected concrete remain as 1.

The basis of this method is that it should be verified that:

$$t_{e,d} < t_{fi,d} \quad (12)$$

where

$t_{fi,d}$ = The design value of the standard fire resistance of the members, assessed according to the relevant parts of the Eurocodes (Table 19.5.1 to Table 19.5.4)

Note according to the BS EN 1991-1-2[22] for "normal fire-fighting measures" such as safe access routes, fire-fighting devices, and smoke exhaust systems in staircases, the factors should be taken as 1.0. If these measures have not been fore-seen but provided, then the values can be taken as 1.5 (Table 19.5.5).

New Zealand Codes

The New Zealand *Fire Engineering Design Guides*[25] gives the same empirical expression for equivalent fire severity t_e (min) as the British Standards (BS EN 1991-1-2[22]). The upper and lower k_b values have been increased by a factor of 1.3 compared to the Eurocode due to what they declare are inherent uncertainties in the Eurocode formula, the use of fuels other than wood, application to structures other than steel, and deep compartment effects. If the properties of the linings are not known, a value of $k_b = 0.09$ is suggested. This formula is based on cellulosic-type fuels. The ventilation factor limits of use are retained, although the small compartment formula in the Eurocode does not form part of the New Zealand guidance.

Comparisons

Time-equivalent methods are an improvement on the grading method in building codes worldwide, which is based on the standard fire temperature-time relationship such as ASTM E119,[9] NFPA 251, BS 476, Part 20,[10] and ISO 834.[11] This is because they attempt to account for compartment geometry, ventilation openings, fuel load density, and compartment boundary materials in addition to fuel load density, which are the key factors that affect full-scale fire development. However, the temperatures calculated on these principles are then related back to

TABLE 19.5.1 Fire Load Densities $q_{f,k}$ (MJ/m^2) for Different Occupancies

Occupancy	*Average*	*80% Fractile*
Dwelling	780	948
Hospital (room)	230	280
Hotel (room)	310	377
Library	1500	1824
Office	420	511
Classroom	285	347
Shopping center	600	730
Theater (cinema)	300	365
Transport (public space)	100	122

Note: Gumbel distribution is assumed for the 80% fractile.

Source: British Standards Institute. Permission to reproduce extracts from British Standards is granted by BSI. British Standards can be obtained from BSI Customer Services, 389 Chiswick High Road, London W4 4AL. Tel: +44 (0)20 8996 9001. email: cservices@bsi-global.com.

TABLE 19.5.2 Factors for δ_{q1}

Compartment Floor Area A_f (m^2)	*Danger of Fire Activation (δ_{q1})*
25	1.10
250	1.50
2,500	1.90
5,000	2.00
10,000	2.13

Source: British Standards Institute. Permission to reproduce extracts from British Standards is granted by BSI. British Standards can be obtained from BSI Customer Services, 389 Chiswick High Road, London W4 4AL. Tel: +44 (0)20 8996 9001. email: cservices@bsi-global.com.

TABLE 19.5.3 Factors for δ_{q2}

Danger of Fire Activation (δ_{q2})	*Examples of Occupancies*
0.78	Art gallery, swimming pool
1.00	Offices, hotel, residential
1.22	Manufacturing for machinery and engines
1.44	Chemical lab, painting workshop
1.66	Manufacturing of fireworks or paints

Source: British Standards Institute. Permission to reproduce extracts from British Standards is granted by BSI. British Standards can be obtained from BSI Customer Services, 389 Chiswick High Road, London W4 4AL. Tel: +44 (0)20 8996 9001. email: cservices@bsi-global.com.

TABLE 19.5.4 Factors for δ_{ni}

δ_{ni} Function of Active Fire-Fighting Measures												
Automatic Fire Suppression				Automatic Fire Detection			Manual Fire Suppression					
Automatic Water Extinguishing System	Independent Water Supplies (δ_{n2})			Automatic Fire Detection and Alarm		Automatic Transmission to Fire Brigade	Work Fire Brigade	Off-Site Fire Brigade	Safe Access Routes	Fire-Fighting Devices	Smoke Exhaust System
				By Heat	*By Smoke*						
(δ_{n1})	*0*	*1*	*2*	(δ_{n3})	(δ_{n4})	(δ_{n5})	(δ_{n6})	(δ_{n7})	(δ_{n8})	(δ_{n9})	(δ_{n10})
0.61	1	0.87	0.7	0.87 or 0.73		0.87	0.61 or 0.78		0.9/1/1.5	1/1.5	1/1.5

Source: British Standards Institute. Permission to reproduce extracts from British Standards is granted by BSI. British Standards can be obtained from BSI Customer Services, 389 Chiswick High Road, London W4 4AL. Tel: +44 (0)20 8996 9001. email: cservices@bsi-global.com.

TABLE 19.5.5 Conversion Factor k_b Depending on the Thermal Properties of the Enclosure

$b = \sqrt{\rho c \lambda}$ ($J/m^2 sec^{1/2} K$)	k_b ($Min\text{-}m^2/MJ$)
$b > 2500$	0.04
$720 \le b \le 2500$	0.055
$b < 720$	0.07

Source: British Standards Institute. Permission to reproduce extracts from British Standards is granted by BSI. British Standards can be obtained from BSI Customer Services, 389 Chiswick High Road, London W4 4AL. Tel: +44 (0)20 8996 9001. email: cservices@bsi-global.com.

the standard time-temperature relationship. It is also important to note that they are based on specific compartment test data, rather than generalized heat balance solutions. They are therefore not entirely representative of natural temperature-time relationships, and, as such, are not independent of the standard fire resistance test formulation.

Drysdale describes a comparison Harmathy carried out where the Ingberg,[17] Pettersson,[18] and Harmathy equations for t_e were compared.[26] Drysdale rejects Ingberg's method as radiative heat flux T^4 makes simple scaling impossible when heat transfer is dominated by radiation. He concluded that Law and Harmathy provided more conservative solutions than the others. Note that Ingberg's method ignores ventilation, unlike the other methods presented here.

Law compared results using the time-equivalent relationships by Ingberg,[17] Kawagoe et al.[19] Pettersson, et al.,[18] Harmathy and Mehaffey,[27] plus the 1993 Eurocode formula[28] with experimental data from postflashover fires in full-scale compartments.[29] These consisted of small insulated compartments, 30 m^2 area, 2.5–3 m high, with brick or concrete enclosures and larger, deeper rooms 128 m^2 in area (depth to width ratio 4:1). Law concluded Pettersson, Harmathy, and Mehaffey were the most promising methods. See Figure 19.5.2 for Law's correlation compared with experimental data.

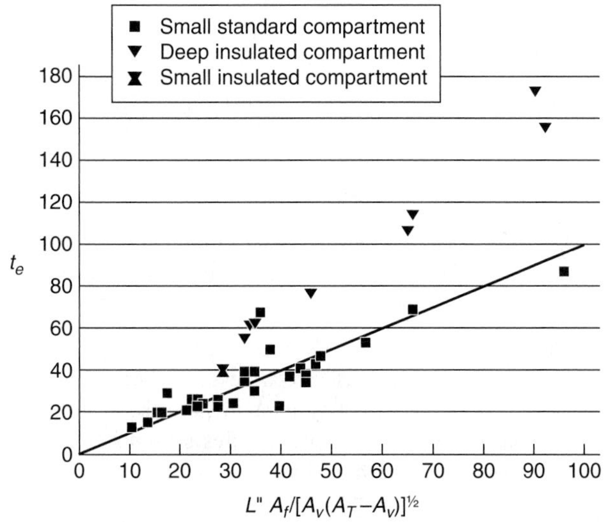

FIGURE 19.5.2 Law's Correlation Between Fire Resistance Requirements (t_e) and $L''A_f/(A_v(A_T - A_v)^{½}$ where
L'' = The fire load (kg/m^2)
A_f = The area of the floor
A_v = The area of the ventilation
A_T = The total internal surface area (m^2) of the compartment
(Courtesy of Margaret Law)

Limitations and Assumptions

There are several limitations, including the deep compartment* effect. Law examined deep compartments further, as all her derived time-equivalent formulae gave odd results when deep compartments were studied. Law also discovered that the 1993

*A deep compartment is defined by I. R. Thomas and I. D. Bennetts in *Fires in Enclosures with Single Ventilation Openings. Comparison of Long and Wide Enclosures,* 6th IAFSS Symposium, pp. 941–952, 1999 as the situation where the depth, *D,* is greater than the width, *W,* of the compartment.

Eurocode *t*-equivalent method gave poor correlation for both small and deep compartments. She concluded that the depth of the compartment has an effect on the time equivalent over and above that which can be allowed for by increase in insulation and in internal surface area A_r. Thomas and Heselden[20] had already shown that the ventilation-controlled rate of burning is affected by the compartment depth to width ratio. Recent research on this phenomenon has also resulted in the New Zealand codes recommending increased factors of safety to somehow account for this effect in their time-equivalent formula. Thomas and Bennetts[30] concluded that fire behavior and fuel mass loss rates in long and wide enclosures differ markedly if the width of the opening is less than the full width of the enclosures. However, it should be noted that they did not look at cross-ventilation. They demonstrated that mass loss in wide enclosures is greater than for deep enclosures that incorporate both full-width and partial-width openings. In their small-scale experiments the fire duration was double for deep compartments, relative to wide compartments with the same openings.

The Eurocode or BSEN formulae have caused considerable concern as Eurocode does not reference the source of the equation derivations, particularly regarding the ventilation factor, the correction factor to take account of cross section material types, as well as other factors of safety recommended for application to the calculated time-equivalent value. The Eurocode formula has also been extended to unprotected steelwork.

The k_c is defined for unprotected steel as 13.7 times the opening factor (O). Since $0.02 < O < 0.2$, this gives $0.27 < k_c < 2.7$ for unprotected steel. For small compartments $w_f = O^{-1/2} A_f / A_t$ and since $O = A_v h^{1/2} / A_t$, it can be written that the equivalent time for unprotected steel in small compartments is as follows:

$$t_e = 13.7\, q_{fd} \cdot k_b \cdot (A_v\, h^{1/2}/A_t\,)^{1/2} \cdot A_f/A_t$$

(fire load given as per unit floor area)

Pettersson calculated $t_e(h)$ for unprotected steel for values of opening factor ranging from 0.2 to 0.12 $m^{1/2}$ and various section factors (Tables 19.5.6 and 19.5.7). Law[31] compares Pettersson's time-equivalent formula with the Eurocode formula for $\varepsilon_r = 0.5$ for unprotected steel of various section factors in Table 19.5.8.

It can be seen that while the values of t_e tend to increase with increasing fuel load, they tend to decrease with ventilation factor. They are not independent of section factor. Yet when the Eurocode formula is used with $k_b = 0.055$ for Pettersson's compartment type A, for all sections, the following data is produced (Table 19.5.8).

The trends in the Eurocode are different and no explanation as to why has been provided. For unprotected steel, if the steel is assumed to be a perfectly stirred fluid, the postflashover fire temperatures are also perfectly stirred, and the temperature of the exposed surface is the same as the fire temperatures, which implies that the steel temperature is always the same as the fire temperature. Therefore, section factors of 100 m^{-1} or more would not be expected to survive a postflashover fire, but would survive a localized fire. Until suitable justification of such difference is made, it seems the original work of Pettersson or Law is best suited to this type of time-equivalent calculation.

Another limitation is that the *t*-equivalent methods do not address transient temperature gradients or associated load-bearing capacities. The ratings derived do not relate to actual frame performance in fire. These methods are quite simply refined versions of single element performance in fire, but only relative to the standard furnace test. They normally assume insulated structures only (protected steel or reinforced concrete). Although Pettersson's work does address uninsulated steel, these bare elements would not be expected to achieve a fire resistance of beyond 20 to 30 minutes.

A time-equivalent calculation does not apply if the preflashover calculations show that flashover will not occur—that is, the calculation is no longer relevant if flashover has not occurred. Then local heating effects are relevant, not temperatures in a uniformly heated compartment, as is assumed in time-equivalent analysis methods.

TABLE 19.5.6 Equivalent Time for Unprotected Steel with Section Factor = 50 m^{-1}

	$t_e(h)$			
	$A_v h^{1/2}/A_t (m^{1/2})$			
Q_{td} *(Fire Load)*	*0.02*	*0.04*	*0.08*	*0.12*
42	0.29	0.25	0.21	0.16
84	0.42	0.43	0.36	0.29
126	0.51	0.58	0.525	0.41

Source: Courtesy of Swedish Institute of Steel Construction.

TABLE 19.5.7 Equivalent Time for Unprotected Steel with Section Factor = 150 m^{-1}

	$t_e(h)$			
	$A_v h^{1/2}/A_t (m^{1/2})$			
Q_{td} *(Fire Load)*	*0.02*	*0.04*	*0.08*	*0.12*
42	0.21	0.23	0.19	0.16
84	0.27	0.37	0.38	0.30
126	0.30	NA	NA	NA

NA = Not available.
Source: Courtesy of Swedish Institute of Steel Construction.

TABLE 19.5.8 Equivalent Time for Unprotected Steel All Sections

	$t_e(h)$			
	$A_v h^{1/2}/A_t (m^{1/2})$			
Q_{td} *(Fire Load)*	*0.02*	*0.04*	*0.08*	*0.12*
42	0.07	0.11	0.15	0.18
84	0.15	0.21	0.30	0.37
126	0.22	0.32	0.45	0.55

Source: Arup.

In addition, t-equivalent methods are empirical formulae developed by regression analysis using a selected number of tests or calculations. Therefore, they have been developed for a certain range of structural steel sizes and thicknesses of insulation and so may not be appropriate outside this range. The methods are used for other materials, but beyond protected steel and reinforced concrete, very little is known of the accuracy in applying the methods to other materials. Note that all t-equivalent methods described here involve combustible solids only.

The time-equivalence method is a simple analytical method that is generally useful in the everyday design environment due to its relative ease of use and its time and cost efficiency. However, such methods are generally incapable of considering the numerous complex structural behavior issues and are highly dependent on the parameters and assumptions chosen by the designer.

Because of the limitations and uncertainties associated with time-equivalent methods, it is important that risk factors are considered in the analysis. Using a probabilistic model, the uncertainties in the concept of safety, fire, reliability of active and passive systems, structural stability, material behavior, and so on can be incorporated into a time-equivalent analysis to envelope the expected response. In this way, a numeric measure of risk can be assessed and compared to an accepted level of risk established by the governing codes.

The accepted level of risk varies from country to country and in many cases is not explicitly documented. In Europe, the acceptable level of risk is implicitly captured in the partial safety factors found in the National Annex for each country. Similar documents are also available in the U.S. codes, New Zealand codes, and other codes around the world. A discussion of risk assessment is given by Hall[32] and Baldwin.[33]

CASE STUDY: Outlining Use of the Time-Equivalent Method. This case study is based on a study of a 50 story high-rise office building in the United Kingdom, with a combination of several structural systems (a perimeter diagrid, a secondary bracing system, and internal columns). Based on the governing codes, the sprinklered building would be required to achieve a 120 minute fire resistance rating. However, an alternate rating was proposed for the design using the time-equivalent method for justification.

The main floor plate of the building consists of an open floor plan system as seen in Figure 19.5.3 (no subdivisions proposed). Because of this open floor layout, the entire floor was considered one single fire compartment. Due to the high variability in the building geometry/design and uncertainties in identifying a representative fire for the structure, a sensitivity study was conducted to provide a range of probable design fires.

Therefore, the factors forming the basis of the time-equivalent method—that is, the fire compartment geometry, the ventilation to the fire compartment, and the other significant fire parameters—were considered in a sensitivity analysis to determine a final equivalent time of fire resistance. In addition, several fire locations within the building itself were investigated in order to ensure that a reasonable worst-case fire scenario was determined. This was as an alternative to applying the code-required fire resistance ratings for individual structural elements.

The time-equivalent method described in the Eurocode[22] was used. Combining Equations 12 and 13, the equivalent time of fire exposure can be defined as:

$$t_{e,d} = mq_{f,k}\delta_{q1}\delta_{q2}\delta_{ni}w_f k_b k_c \quad \text{(min)} \tag{13}$$

Two floor levels (5th and 44th levels) were assessed to provide an upper and lower bound estimate for the equivalent time of fire exposure. This was because level 5 had the largest floor area of 1896 m^2 with the greatest amount of glazed facade, whereas level 44 had the smallest floor area of 694 m^2 and the least amount of glazed facade.

First, a sensitivity analysis was conducted to determine a range of possible design fire loads. The characteristic fuel load ($q_{f,k}$) was 511 MJ/m^2, the compartment floor area factor δ_{q1} was valued as 1.9, and the occupancy factor δ_{q2} was valued as 1.0, as recommended by the Eurocode for office buildings with compartment floor areas less than 2500 m^2. Assuming these values as constant, the combustion factor (m), the water extinguishing factor (δ_{ni}), the automatic detection factor (δ_{ni}), and the off-site fire brigade factor (δ_{ni}) were varied to determine their impact on resulting design fire loads:

$$q_{f,d} = mq_{f,k}\delta_{q1}\delta_{q2}\delta_{ni} \quad \text{(MJ/ m}^2\text{)} \tag{14}$$

Based on this sensitivity analysis a design fire load ranging from 270 to 971 MJ/m^2, as presented in Table 19.5.9, was obtained.

Next, a sensitivity analysis was conducted for each design fire load to determine a range of time-equivalent fire exposures based on the variation of the ventilation factor (w_f) in the following equation:

$$t_{e,d} = q_{f,d}w_f k_b k_c \quad \text{(min)} \tag{15}$$

The k_b and k_c terms were assumed constant at 0.07 min·m^2/MJ and 1.0, respectively.

Four different ventilation factors were determined by varying the area of ventilation openings in the facade from 25 percent to 100 percent. It was necessary to assess the lower levels of glazing failure (below 50%) due to the approving authority's concern with the concept of glazing breakage in fire and their lack of certainty that this would occur. The maximum openings for the 5th and 44th levels were 498 and 305 m^2, respectively. Note that there were no horizontal openings in the compartment.

The ventilation factor was calculated by the following equation taken from the Eurocode:

$$w_f = \left(\frac{6}{H}\right)^{0.3}\left[0.62 + \frac{90(0.4-\alpha_v)^4}{1+b_v\alpha_h}\right] \geq 0.5 \tag{16}$$

Based on this sensitivity analysis, a range of 16 different equivalent times of fire exposure were determined and are presented in Table 19.5.10 and Figure 19.5.4 for levels 5 and 44 of the building investigated.

The results of the time-equivalent sensitivity study range from a fire resistance rating of 15 to 138 minutes. The sole value greater than 90 minutes was an equivalent time of 138 minutes. This value occurs when the reduction in risk of a flashover due to active fire protection methods is not incorporated, but only

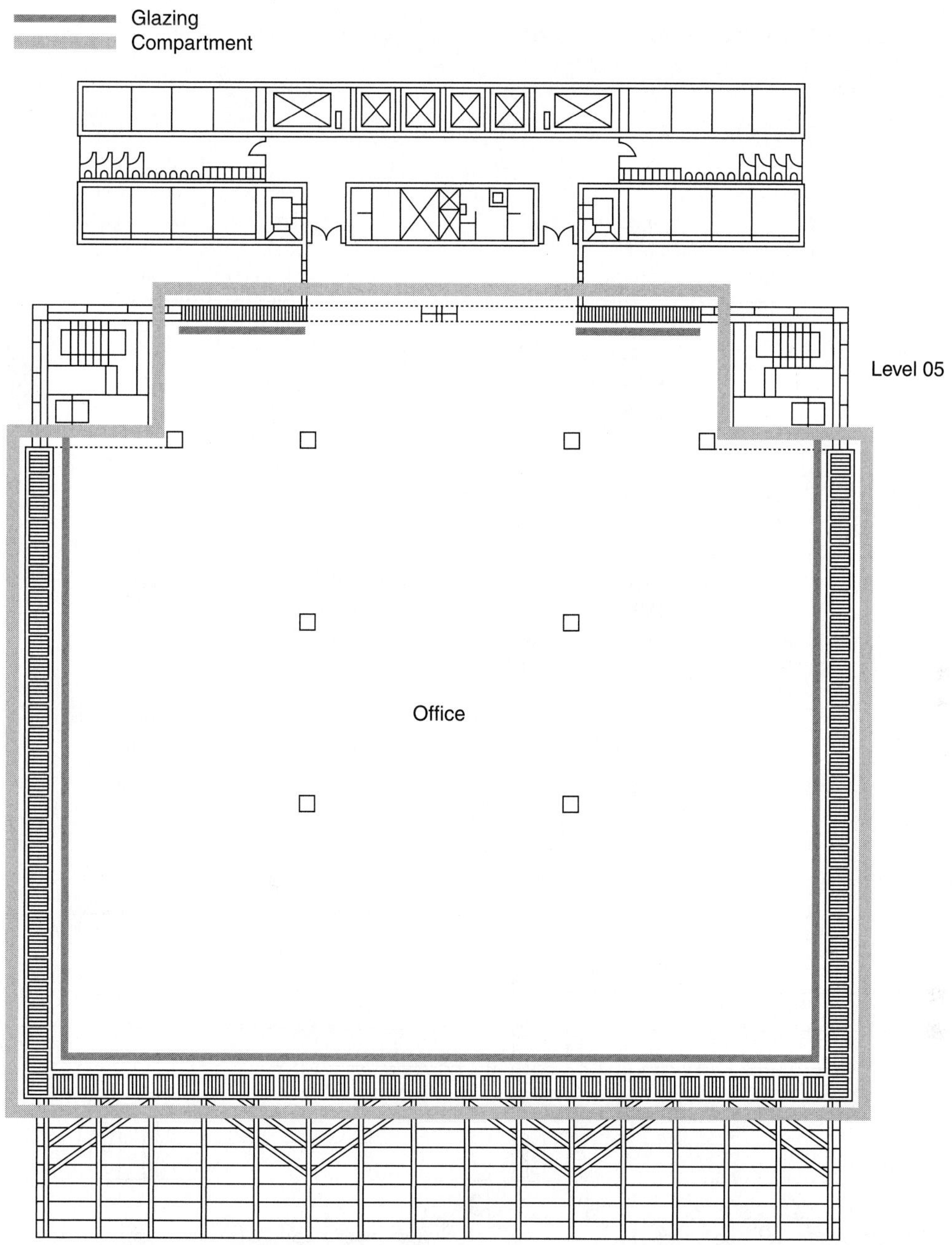

FIGURE 19.5.3 Level 5 Floor Plate, Compartmentation Arrangement, and Glazing (Source: Arup)

TABLE 19.5.9 Design Fire Loads for Sensitivity Study

	Characteristic Value	*Compartment Factor*	*Combustion Factor*	*Water Extinguishing Factor*	*Automatic Fire Detection*	*Off-Site Fire Brigade*	*Design Fire Load q_{fd} (MJ/m^2)*
Scenarios 1–4	511	1.9	0.8	0.61	0.73	0.78	270
Scenarios 5–8	511	1.9	1	1	1	1	971
Scenarios 9–12	511	1.9	1	0.61	1	1	593
Scenarios 13–16	511	1.9	1	0.61	0.73	0.78	338

Source: Arup.

TABLE 19.5.10 Sensitivity Study of Equivalent Time of Fire Exposure—Varying Fire Load, Ventilation, and Story for a Full Office Floor on Fire

	Level 5					Level 44			
	Design Fire Load q_{fd} *(MJ/m²)*	*Area of Ventilation Openings in Facade (m²)*	*Floor Area Compartment* (A_f) *(m²)*	$t_{e,d}$ *(min)*		*Design Fire Load* q_{fd} *(MJ/m²)*	*Area of Ventilation Openings in Facade (m²)*	*Floor Area Compartment (Af) (m²)*	$t_{e,d}$ *(min)*
Scenario 1	270	489	1896	15	Scenario 1	270	305	694	15
Scenario 2	270	367	1896	17	Scenario 2	270	229	694	15
Scenario 3	270	245	1896	24	Scenario 3	270	153	694	16
Scenario 4	270	122	1896	38	Scenario 4	270	76	694	28
Scenario 5	971	489	1896	52	Scenario 5	971	305	694	52
Scenario 6	971	367	1896	61	Scenario 6	971	229	694	52
Scenario 7	971	245	1896	86	Scenario 7	971	153	694	56
Scenario 8	971	122	1896	138	Scenario 8	971	76	694	99
Scenario 9	593	489	1896	32	Scenario 9	593	305	694	32
Scenario 10	593	367	1896	38	Scenario 10	593	229	694	32
Scenario 11	593	245	1896	53	Scenario 11	593	153	694	34
Scenario 12	593	122	1896	84	Scenario 12	593	76	694	60
Scenario 13	338	489	1896	18	Scenario 13	338	305	694	18
Scenario 14	338	367	1896	21	Scenario 14	338	229	694	18
Scenario 15	338	245	1896	30	Scenario 15	338	153	694	20
Scenario 16	338	122	1897	48	Scenario 16	338	76	694	34

Source: Arup.

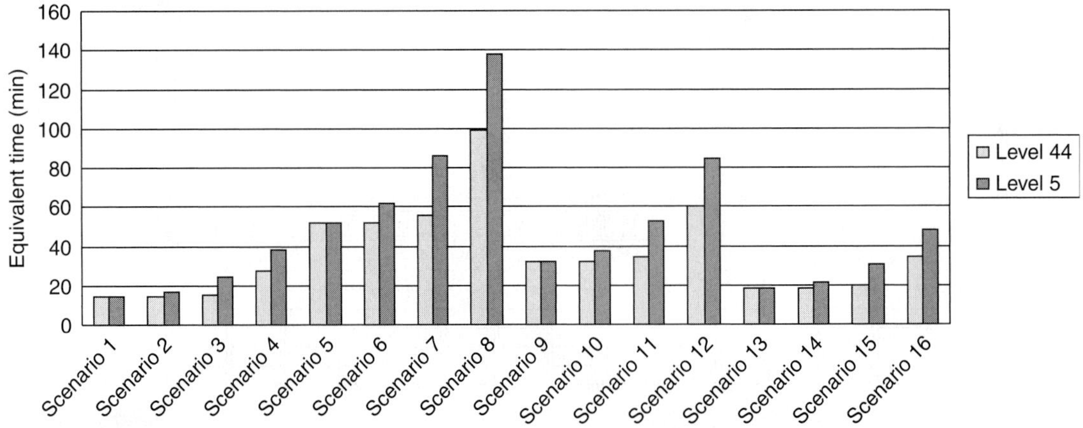

FIGURE 19.5.4 Graph of the Output Data from the Sensitivity Study (Source: Arup)

if a low glazing failure quantity is also assumed to occur. As it was agreed with the approving authorities that such a low level of glazing failure was not practically possible at the fire temperatures expected without active fire protection intervention, this value was deemed overly conservative.

The high variability in the upper and lower bound values illustrates the importance of performing such a sensitivity study, in order to appreciate the potential fire resistance ratings for a structure when using the time-equivalent method.

A reduction in the fire resistance of the building from 120 minutes to 90 minutes was proposed on the basis of this study, because the majority of cases fell well below this value.

DETERMINING A DESIGN FIRE FOR A STRUCTURAL ANALYSIS

Throughout the remainder of this chapter, as specific structural analysis techniques are presented, the important role of the heating regime on the structural element or elements is clear.

Specific references are provided to direct the reader to useful analytical models and formulae to represent fire.

Issues Involving Design of Fire Component

Before more detailed information is presented, it is useful to consider the issues involved with the fire component of a structural design. Unlike design basis fires for smoke control systems or as part of developing time to untenable conditions for purposes of egress, structures are usually most severely affected by postflashover fires. This is when the fire has moved beyond the incipient and growth phase to a point where it is consuming essentially all combustible contents of the enclosure. The resulting peak temperatures, duration, and overall fire severity are then a function of the available combustibles and the ventilation openings into the space. It is these postflashover fires that normally form the basis of a structural fire assessment.

When contemplating the occurrence of a postflashover fire, the sequence of events that must occur to allow such an event to take place is of importance. For example, in a fully sprinklered building, failure of the sprinkler system would have to be assumed to create a flashover condition. Another event is the effect of fire-fighting operations on the occurrence of flashover. Whatever assumptions are made, it is important to bear in mind the risks associated with such assumptions and the different consequences that may result depending on the building height, scale of occupancy, fuel content, use, and compartment extent. That is, the taller the building, the greater the consequence of failure of the structure, and so on.

Addressing Postflashover Events

Various methods are available to designers to address such a postflashover event, including the use of the standard temperature-time relationship on which the furnace tests are based; parametric temperature-time relationships derived from specific postflashover fire tests; or temperature-time relationships derived from resolving the heat balance system within a compartment.

The important question, then, is whether the temperature-time regime proposed represents (or even should represent) an absolute worst case or a reasonable worst-case scenario. In the Eurocodes, for example, designers are advised to use risk-based factors to apply to the fuel load content assumed in a compartment, such that the resulting heating regime is not absolute but also addresses the consequence of failure, the likelihood of occurrence of the fire, and the role of active fire safety systems (e.g., sprinklers) on the probability of a severe fire in a building.

There are concerns with the limitations of parametric fires specifically, as the equation now proposed, for example in the Eurocode, is in essence the result of a regression analysis of specific test data. How to justify the use of this outside the limits of the original test data remains an unresolved subject in the design domain. Although this is the case, engineers are relying on additional safety factors to ensure that design remains on a reasonably conservative side. The more theoretical approaches based on heat-balance relationships, such as Pettersson's, are less popular with code writers, but it may be prudent to revisit such approaches in order to resolve the design basis fire problem for structural fire engineering.

However, adopting a postflashover fire condition as a basis for design is not always the correct approach, as in the case, for example, of very large open spaces with specific pockets of fuel, such as in an airport terminal, where a postflashover fire is unlikely to occur. In such an arrangement, a severe localized fire may expose only one or two columns supporting a long-span structural roof system. For such design cases, specific formulae for local fire and smoke effects are available.[34–36]

Finally, if the structure in question is external to the building, the heating that results from internal and external flaming adjacent to the structural elements becomes the basis for design. Again guidance is provided in the following section on useful formulations to create temperature-time regimes for such events.

Once the design fire temperature-time regime is defined, the remaining steps in a structural fire assessment are possible. The following sections provide information on this. It is recommended that the authorities having jurisdiction are consulted and approve the design fire formulated prior to any time-consuming structural analysis.

SINGLE STRUCTURAL ELEMENT ANALYSIS

The analysis of a single structural element in isolation from the rest of the structural frame has formed the basis for structural fire engineering for many years, mainly because it is comparable with a standard furnace test and excludes calculations based on the nonlinear response of a whole frame or a significant subassembly to fire, both of which require extensive computations.

Single Element Analysis Defined

Single element analysis is useful as a first check of structural capacity at elevated temperature as a basis for design or before conducting a more complex analysis. It typically involves comparing the structural load that the member has to carry in the fire condition with the capacity of the member at elevated temperature. Axial force, bending, shear, and buckling, including lateral torsional buckling, all need to be considered as appropriate. The capacity of the associated connections also needs to be checked.

Single element analysis is a fast, effective technique that can bring substantial value to a design as it allows an understanding of the overcapacity or undercapacity of the member in the fire limit state. This can be used to formulate adequate fire resistance ratings and protection thicknesses for specific elements or to inform a change to the structural design to allow adequate capacity without any added fire protection. Using single element analysis is preferable for isolated structural element concerns in a building, rather than for forming a uniform design approach for all elements in a building. This is because single element checks cannot capture the full frame response, which can mean, in some construction forms, significant weaknesses in fire performance.

Specifically, it is not typical to consider thermal expansion in single element calculations; therefore, the forces experienced by the structural element in a fire when restrained by adjacent members in a structural frame are not adequately considered. However, in general, single element calculations can be assumed to be conservative because alternative load paths that can be present in a real frame during a fire are neglected.

Single element analysis techniques are codified in many countries worldwide. The approach is commonly applied to concrete, steel, and wood members. As with all structural fire engineering, single element analysis is generally based on a three-stage calculation process:

1. Definition of credible design fires
2. Heat transfer analysis to the structural member from the design fires
3. Structural analysis at the elevated member temperature calculated from the heat transfer

Design tools for heat transfer and structural analysis vary in complexity from empirical correlations, look-up tables, nomograms, and hand/spreadsheet calculations, to simple finite element analysis. The tools adopted by an engineer depend on the failure criteria to be identified. For example, a critical steel temperature of 1022°F (550°C) for column members may be sufficient as the basis of design; alternatively, determining the residual strength/stiffness could be more appropriate. However, a simple temperature comparison may not always be appropriate. In columns and beams that are unrestrained on their top flange, instability events such as buckling also need to be considered, because they occur at lower temperatures than the yield temperature of the constituent material. Guidance exists in several countries worldwide on how to approach this problem; several are identified in the following sections.

Design Fires

One approach to the design fire is to simply assume a heating regime in the compartment of interest identical to the standard temperature-time curve (e.g., ISO 834,[11] BS 476,[10] ASTM E119,[9] NFPA 251). Alternatively, a more rigorous approach to the heating regime from the design fire can be taken. The choice of design fire then depends on the location of the structure in relation to the fire compartment, available fuel load, available ventilation, compartment dimensions, and compartment enclosure material properties. Figure 19.5.5 produced for the One Stop Shop in Structural Fire Engineering website in the United Kingdom (MACE) highlights the range of design fires possible.

In addition, for countries outside the United States, it depends on whether failure of sprinklers must be assumed when calculating the fire for determining structural capacity of a single structural element. For example, external structures may only be exposed to flaming through specific window openings. In tall spaces with well-defined and specific locations for fire load, a local fuel-bed-controlled fire adjacent to a critical piece of structure might be appropriate as the basis of design. In areas of high fire load with ceiling heights of 3 to 4 m, a postflashover fire is likely to be the most appropriate fire case. Alternatively, the standard fire heating regime can be selected to carry out a comparative analysis of the structural element relative to code-based fire resistance recommendations.

Empirical equations and complex computer codes such as fire dynamics simulator (FDS) exist to calculate external fire exposures. A useful empirical approach is presented by Law and O'Brien.[37] Note this was also published in the United States by the AISC. FDS, which is well documented elsewhere,[38] can also be used to formulate, at a reasonably complex level, temperature changes with time for external flaming.

Empirical equations are available for considering local fire cases. In the United Kingdom, TM19[34] provides empirical correlations commonly used in the United Kingdom. The *SFPE Handbook of Fire Protection Engineering*[35] also describes correlations by many researchers, and these are used worldwide. The correlations generally enable the user to calculate flame heights, plume temperatures at various heights, and temperatures along ceiling jets. These data can then be used to calculate the heating effect to and through the structural element for the duration of the fire.

Many deterministic models of postflashover fires have been developed, starting in the 1960s. All postflashover models are based on the assumption that the gas temperature in the compartment is uniform. Walton and Thomas[39] provide a review of many of the available models in the *SFPE Handbook of Fire Protection Engineering.*

The models most often used in design internationally include the parametric temperature time curve given in Eurocode 1, Part 1.2[22] and the heat balance model developed by Magnusson and Thelandersson[21] (Figure 19.5.6). Note that in the United Kingdom, EC1-1-2 has been amended and adopted for use as BSEN1991-1-2:2002. Each country in Europe has similarly made various amendments based on local concerns and market, presented in National Application Documents (NAD) to the main Eurocode. This is true for each material type (steel, concrete, wood, aluminum) and for each calculation procedure or approach.

Computer zone models such as Ozone (University of Liege, Belgium) and CFAST (NIST) will also provide temperature-time curves for postflashover fires. All of the models developed to calculate postflashover fires are only strictly applicable for relatively small compartments, close to square in plan. They are not strictly applicable to large open plan spaces commonly found in real buildings, but they are the only tools available to engineers at the present time. For example, a typical commercial office floor in a tall building in London is approximately 1500 to 2000 m^2 per story, yet the EC1-1-2 limits compartment areas to 500 m^2. As such, the design theory continues to fall behind commercial design requirements and concerns.

The alternative is to use computational fluid dynamics (CFD) codes,[40] but these were originally developed for smoke movement studies and, therefore, consider small fuel-bed-controlled fires in large spaces. Work in defining realistic postflashover fires for use in large or rectangular spaces is ongoing and is considered urgent. Current CFD models will tend to overpredict compartment temperatures and must therefore be used with care when forming the basis of actual design. It is worth noting that NFPA's Technical Committee on Hazard

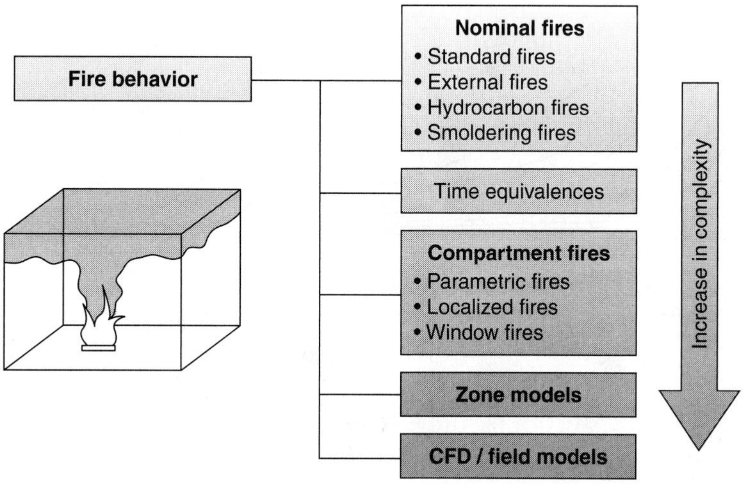

Fire Model	Nominal Fires	Time Equivalences	Compartment Fires: Parametric	Compartment Fires: Localized	Zone Models: One-Zone	Zone Models: Two-Zone	CFD / Field Models
Complexity	Simple	Intermediate			Advanced		
Fire Behavior	Postflashover fires			Preflashover fires	Postflashover fires	Preflashover/ localized fires	Complete temperature-time relationships
Temperature Distribution	Uniform in whole compartment			Nonuniform along plume	Uniform	Uniform in each layer	Time and space dependent
Input Parameters	Fire type No physical parameters	Fire load Ventilation conditions Thermal properties of boundary Compartment size		Fire load and size Height of ceiling	Fire load Ventilation conditions Thermal properties of boundary Compartment size Detailed input for heat and mass balance of the system		Detailed input for solving the fundamental equations of the fluid flow
Design Tools	BSEN1991-1-2				COMPF2 OZone SFIRE-4	CCFM CFAST OZone	FDS SMARTFIRE SOFIE
	PD7974-1		PD7974-1				
	Simple equations for hand calculations		Spreadsheet	Simple equations	Computer models		

FIGURE 19.5.5 Range of Design Fire Models (Courtesy of MACE One Stop Shop in Structural Fire Engineering, University of Manchester)

and Risk of Contents and Furnishings has recently initiated a project to better define fire loads for structural fire resistance calculations.

Heat Transfer

Once a temperature-time regime for the space containing the structural element or, in the case of a local fire or external fire, for the area immediately surrounding or adjacent to the structural element, the structural temperatures can be calculated using heat transfer equations. Various empirical and analytical equations exist in Europe; specifically, the lumped mass heat transfer equations to calculate average section temperatures in Eurocode 1, Part 1.2[22] and Eurocode 3, Part 1.2[41] or Law and O'Brien's[37] view factors to calculate radiative heat transfer to elements remote from a fire are typically used. All equations in codes and guidance documents are very similar because each one has to consider conduction, convection, and radiation in accordance with the principles of heat transfer.

For heat transfer analysis, the nonlinear values of conductivity, specific heat, density, and moisture content of the constituent materials are required to calculate heat transfer. Where available, these values should vary with increasing temperature to obtain an accurate result.

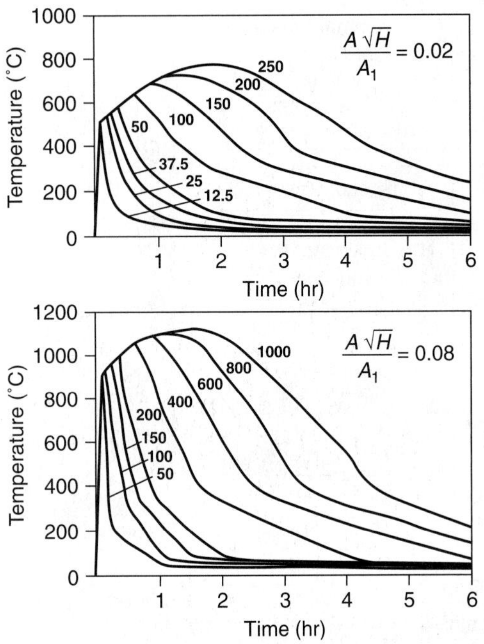

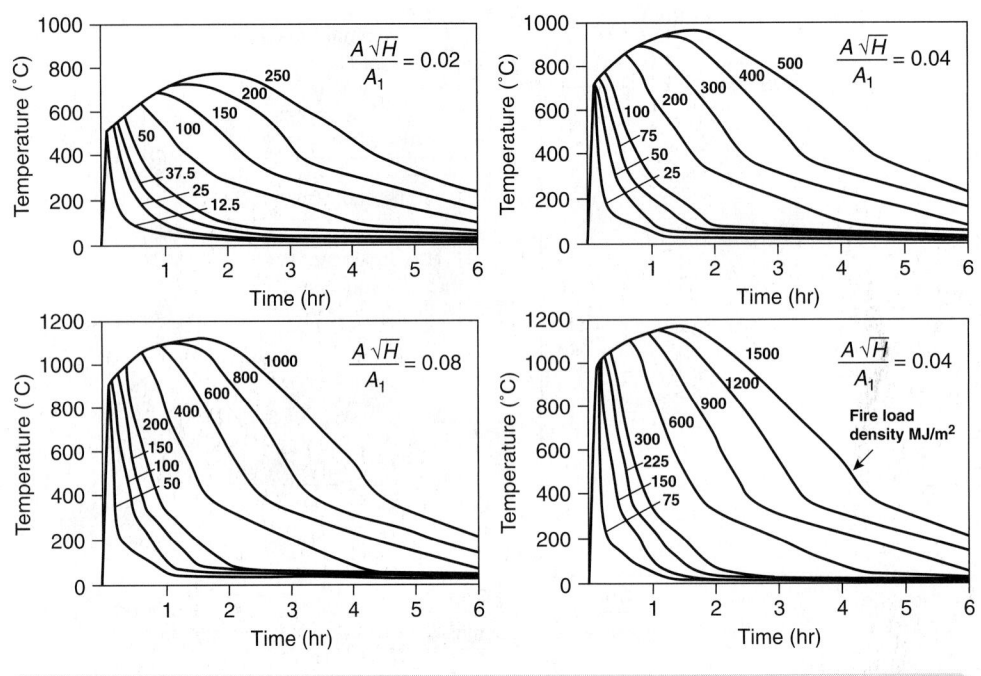

FIGURE 19.5.6 Postflashover Temperature-Time Curves (Courtesy of Swedish Institute of Steel Construction)

For single structural element analysis, some analytical design tools require the use of strength and stiffness properties at elevated temperatures. Where this is the case it is highlighted in the text in the following sections. Most international material codes provide values for stress-strain and Young's modulus with increasing temperature.

APPLICATION OF SINGLE STRUCTURAL ELEMENT ANALYSIS TO STEEL

There are numerous methods applicable to steel elements because the steel industry has spent many years of research optimizing steel design for fire. The main reason is that passive fire protection can significantly increase the cost of a steel frame solution. However, with modern fire protection materials, options for off-site application, particularly of intumescents, are on a rapid rise of use, mainly in Europe. These new approaches, which bring considerable time saving to a construction project and ensure a high quality of application and finish, along with performance-based design methods to optimize fire protection arrangements and thicknesses, mean steel frame solutions are cost effective and very popular in the United Kingdom, as well as in cities where high-rise construction is in demand internationally (e.g., Singapore, Beijing, Dubai).

Some steel-specific calculation methods follow.

Section Factor

The *Hp/A concept*, or *section factor*, is a key variable in single element analysis of steel members in fire. It provides a simple relationship between the surface area of the section exposed to fire and its cross-sectional area or thermal mass. The rate of temperature change in a steel section is a function of this relationship. Consequently, the concept is used by fire protection manufacturers as a factor in determining and specifying the necessary thickness of fire protection material for a particular member size. The value varies if the section is sprayed with fire protection or boxed, as shown in Figure 19.5.7.

Consider a unit length of a steel element where the end connections are ignored. A steel section with a larger surface area will receive more heat than one with a smaller surface area. Moreover, the greater the volume of the section, the greater is the heat sink. Typical values of section factor for structural steel members commonly used in building design are between 100 to 250 m^{-1}. At values of about 50 m^{-1}, a beam section can be assumed to have about 30 minutes inherent fire resistance[42] as a single element considering its thermal mass only.

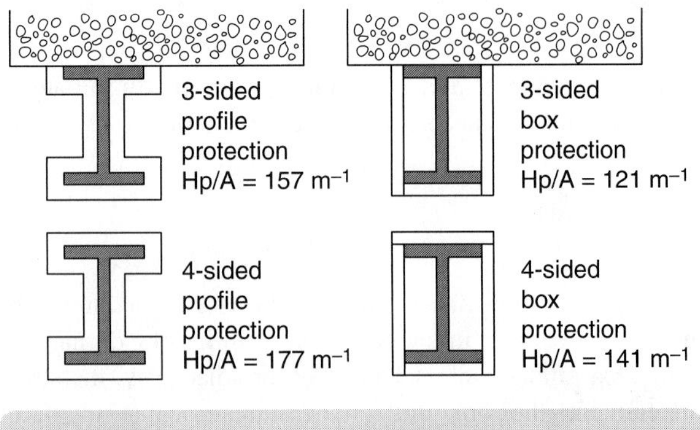

FIGURE 19.5.7 The Section Factor Concept (Courtesy of CORUS)

BS 5950-8[42] in the UK and Eurocode 3, Part 1.2[41] describe the Hp/A concept and how to calculate it for different steel sections and protection arrangements. Note that in the United States, the section factor is represented by the *W/D* (average weight/heated perimeter) *concept* where *W* is in pounds/ft and *D* is given in inches.

Section factors for common structural steel shapes are available from steel distributors worldwide, such as CORUS (the largest steel producer in Europe) and the Heavy Engineering Research Association (HERA), a nonprofit research organization dedicated to the needs of the metals-based industries in New Zealand. The American Institute of Steel Construction and various building codes provide reference to such information in the United States.

Once the section factor is known for a specific section, the average steel temperature development can then be evaluated using relatively simple lumped mass heat transfer formulae for protected and unprotected internal steelwork. The heat transfer analysis is based on the net heat flux to the surface of the member, including convection and radiation effects and conduction through the fire protection material and /or the steel. Equations are provided throughout the literature including the *SFPE Handbook of Fire Protection Engineering* and the following design codes: BS 5950-8,[42] EC 1-1-2,[22] and EC 3-1-2.[41] The lumped mass equations do not calculate temperature gradients through the depth of a steel section; they should, therefore, not be used when this is important for design—for example, if a protected column could fail as a result of thermal bowing. Heat transfer and structural stability have to be checked by finite element analysis or stability of the frame proven by showing the single element can be removed.

Note that the IBC[43] in the United States has many empirical correlations based on the *W/D* ratio to allow engineers to calculate the fire resistance of a particular steel section protected with different materials, including concrete, masonry, and type X gypsum board. It does not currently provide analytical methods for heat transfer analysis. *NFPA 5000®, Building Construction and Safety Code®*, allows for the use of analytical methods to determine the fire resistance of building assemblies. Specific reference is made to ASCE/SFPE 29, *Standard Calculation Methods for Structural Fire Protection,* and ACI 216.1/TMS 0216.1, *Standard Method for Determining Fire Resistance of Concrete and Masonry Assemblies.*

Fire Limit State Factors

Traditionally, single element analysis assumed failure of a steel member occurred at a temperature of 1022°F (550°C). This is because fire protection is typically applied to steel members to limit the temperature rise to 1022°F (550°C) for a prescribed fire resistance period and because steel has lost about 40 percent of its design strength at 1022°F (550°C). (Note that in more recent years in the United Kingdom, a limiting temperature of 620°C is now used for beams, with columns remaining at the traditional 550°C. It is important to ascertain for the specific fire protection being reviewed as part of the single element analysis what limiting temperatures have been assumed. For unprotected members, the limiting temperature should be clearly defined and used as the basis of the capacity checks.)

Often designers would not consider the load or structural actions on a steel member but simply assume failure at 1022°F (550°C). This was generally conservative, but analytical methods are now available to define critical steel temperatures more accurately, considering load, residual capacity of strength and stiffness, and structural failure mechanisms. What this means is that for some cases a higher limiting temperature is possible, but for others, a lower temperature should be assumed.

To determine the limiting steel temperature, load combinations for buildings exposed to fires must be considered. An important part of structural fire engineering is defining the applied load assumed to act on the structure during a fire event. It is common practice to assume that a fire is an unusual event, and, as such, that the safety factors applied to characteristic dead load, wind load, and live load can be reduced. (Dead load is a load of constant magnitude and position that acts permanently, including self-weight. Live load is load on a structure or member, other than wind load, produced by the external environment or the intended occupancy or use.) In general, dead load (DL) is multiplied by 1.0 and live load (LL) is multiplied by a factor ranging from 0.3 to 0.8, depending on the building occupancy type.[42]

Different countries adopt slightly different factors as discussed below. In the UK and Europe, partial safety factors for accidental loads in structural steel design are given by BS 5950-8[42] and Eurocode 0,[44] respectively, for the fire limit state. Table 19.5.11 shows the values for load factors at the fire limit state in BS 5950-8.[42]

The New Zealand Standard NZS 4203[45] adopts 1.0 DL + 0.6 LL or 1.0 DL + 0.4 LL for fire limit state. The live load factor 0.6 is used for storage occupancies and 0.4 for other

TABLE 19.5.11 Load Factors for γ_f at the Fire Limit State

Load	γ_f
Dead load	1.00
Imposed loads:	
a) Permanent:	
1) Those specifically allowed for in design, e.g., plant, machinery, and fixed partitions	1.00
2) In storage buildings or areas used for storage in other buildings (including libraries and designated filing areas)	1.00
b) Nonpermanent:	
1) In escape stairs and lobbies	1.00
2) In offices for general use	0.50
3) All other areas (imposed snow loads on roofs may be ignored)	0.80
Wind loads:	
a) Design for boundary conditions to control external fire spread	0.00
b) All other cases	0.33

Source: British Standards Institute. Permission to reproduce extracts from British Standards is granted by BSI. British Standards can be obtained from BSI Customer Services, 389 Chiswick High Road, London W4 4AL. Tel: +44 (0)20 8996 9001. email: cservices@bsi-global.com.

occupancies. The Australian Standard AS 1170[46] adopts the same factors as New Zealand for live load but a slightly higher factor (1.1) for dead load.

Ellingwood and Corotis[47] present a methodology for determining loads and load combinations for use in fire-resistant structural design in the United States. Loads and load combinations were found by using probabilistic load modeling techniques and modern load survey results. Since significant fires are rare, it was found that a reduced nominal live load combined with the structural action due to fire is appropriate for design. The load combination that they found is:

$$U_n = D_n + 0.5L_n + F \tag{17}$$

where D_n and L_n are the dead and live loads from the ANSI Standard A58.1[48] and F is the structural action due to fire.[47] ASCE 7-05, *Minimum Design Loads for Buildings and Other Structures,*[49] has adopted load combinations based on the work by Ellingwood and Corotis but applied a factor of 1.2 to dead load and a factor of 0.2 to wind load.

Single Element Calculation Methods Used in the United Kingdom and Europe

BS 5950-8[42] and the Eurocode series[22,41] are the main references for structural fire engineering of steel members. Both codes define methods for heat transfer analysis and single element structural analysis techniques. The codes also provide detailed information on the thermal and mechanical properties of steel at high temperatures necessary to conduct a single element calculation for a steel member.

A key factor in the introduction of BS 5950-8 was a series of loaded furnace tests conducted in the United Kingdom in the 1990s.[50] The tests showed that if a member was carrying less load than assumed in ambient design, then its failure temperature was shown to increase from the traditional 550°C typically assumed. As a result of these tests, BS 5950-8 was published and included the concept of the limiting temperature method. The limiting temperature method, also called the critical temperature method, relies on reduced dead and live loads in fire conditions (relative to the cold temperature design), as defined above, and allows the user to calculate a specific limiting temperature for the structural element on this basis, using the actual loads of the cold temperature structural design. Therefore, the resulting limiting temperature for the element is building-specific.

The limiting temperature method or critical temperature method therefore provides a simple way of relating the critical temperature to the load that the member actually supports in fire conditions. It does not require the engineer to consider reduced strength and stiffness properties at high temperature.

This approach has been commonly adopted in the United Kingdom, Europe, New Zealand, and Australia, where limit state design is used. In North America, however, working stress design is still preferred. This means that, in fire design, the structure's full dead and live design loads are assumed.

For beams under bending and having three or four sides fully exposed to the standard fire or to natural fires, BS 5950-8[42] defines the load ratio (R) as:

$$R = \frac{M_f}{M_c} \tag{18}$$

where M_f is the maximum bending moment under fire conditions (e.g., 1.0 DL + 0.5 LL in an office occupancy) and M_c is the bending moment capacity of the beams at ambient temperature.

If the beam fails by yielding of the steel, M_c is equal to the plastic bending moment capacity of the cross section of the beam. If lateral torsional buckling (LTB) governs design, M_c is the lateral torsional buckling capacity of the beam.

A similar equation is provided for columns or members in tension. For columns, axial load and bending in both directions is also considered.

All steel members lose strength in a similar manner, but because of aspects such as temperature gradients and instability effects (e.g., buckling) at elevated temperatures, it is not always appropriate to apply the same strength reduction to structural members as are applied to the steel itself. Therefore, BS 5950: Part 8 gives limiting temperatures for different types of member for a range of load ratios shown in Table 19.5.12.

The limiting temperature method is simple to use. However, if temperature distribution in a steel beam for the specific design fire is shown to be nonuniform and the beam is prevented from lateral torsional buckling, it may be more beneficial to use a more detailed method to calculate the bending capacity of the beam. Such calculations may be carried out using the bending moment capacity method in accordance with BS 5950–8.

For this approach the beam is divided into a number of sections (Figure 19.5.8) of approximately the same temperature. The number of elements will depend on the complexity of the member and its temperature gradient. The bending moment ca-

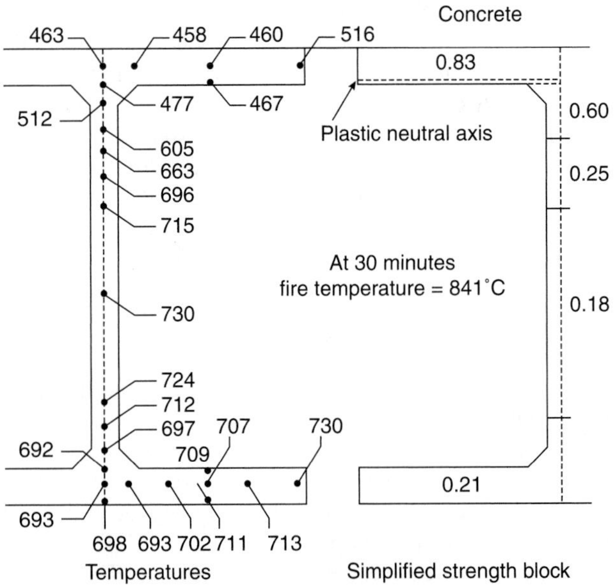

FIGURE 19.5.8 Example of Use of Moment Capacity for 838 × 292 × 194 UB (Courtesy of Steel Construction Institute, Silwood Park, Ascot, SL5 7QN, United Kingdom)

TABLE 19.5.12 Limiting Temperature for Design of Protected and Unprotected Hot Finished Members

	Limiting Temperature (°C) at a Load Ratio Of						
Description of Member	*0.7*	*0.6*	*0.5*	*0.4*	*0.3*	*0.2*	*0.1*
Members in compression, for a slenderness λ[a]:							
≤ 70	510	540	580	615	655	710	800
> 70 but ≤ 180	460	510	545	590	635	635	635
Noncomposite members in bending supporting concrete slabs or composite slabs:							
Unprotected members, or protected members complying with item (a) or (b) of 6.3[b]	590	620	650	680	725	780	880
Other protected members	540	585	625	655	700	745	800
Composite members in bending supporting concrete slabs or composite slabs:							
Unprotected members, or protected members complying with item (a) or (b) of 6.3[b]							
i) 100% degree of shear connection	550	580	610	645	685	470	840
ii) 40% degree of shear connection	575	600	635	665	700	760	865
Other protected members							
i) 100% degree of shear connection	495	530	570	610	650	705	785
ii) 40% degree of shear connection	530	560	595	630	675	725	795
Members in bending not supporting concrete slabs:							
Unprotected members, or protected members complying with item (a) or (b) of 6.3[b]	520	555	585	620	660	715	810
Other protected members	460	510	545	590	635	690	770
Members in tension: all cases	460	510	545	590	635	690	770

Note: For beams supporting a composite of slab the limiting temperatures only apply when the voids between the top of the beam and underside of the steel deck are filled with noncombustible void fillers. For guidance on limiting temperatures when void fillers are not used, see Association of Specialist Fire Protection (ASFP), *Fire Protection for Structural Steel in Buildings,* 3rd ed., ASFP and Steel Construction Institute, Hampshire, UK, June 2004.

[a]λ is the slenderness, i.e., the effective length divided by the radius of gyration.

[b]The 6.3 refers to the limiting strain level in the steel and the corresponding strain in any fire protection material. The following strains should not be exceeded: (a) composite members in bending that are unprotected or protected with fire protection materials that have demonstrated their ability to remain intact at a strain of 2.0 percent; (b) noncomposite members in bending that are unprotected or protected with fire protection materials that have demonstrated their ability to remain intact at a strain of 1.5 percent; (c) members not covered in (a) or (b) with a strain of 0.5.

Source: British Standards Institute. Permission to reproduce extracts from British Standards is granted by BSI. British Standards can be obtained from BSI Customer Services, 389 Chiswick High Road, London W4 4AL. Tel: +44 (0)20 8996 9001. email: cservices@bsi-global.com.

pacity of the cross section is calculated according to the reduced strength and stiffness of steel at the temperature of these sections. See Figure 19.5.7 and the SCI 080[51] for an example.

The bending moment capacity method requires more calculation work than the limiting temperature method. The benefit of using the more elaborate method is to explore possible benefits of the nonuniform temperature distribution in the cross section of the beam, particularly to optimize fire protection or to justify the use of unprotected steel.

EC3-1-2[41] gives two methods to calculate the bending capacity of a steel beam using reduced strength and stiffness properties for steel at high temperature. The first is identical to the bending moment capacity method in BS 5950-8,[42] which is described in the previous section.

Since this method requires many calculation steps, EC3 gives an alternative method that is simpler to use. In this simple method, the design bending moment resistance of the beam is given by

$$M_{fi,\theta,Rd} = \frac{k_{y,\theta} \cdot M_{Rd} \cdot \dfrac{\gamma_{m1}}{\gamma_{m,fi}}}{k_1 \cdot k_2} \tag{19}$$

where M_{Rd} is the bending moment capacity of the cross section ambient temperature and $k_{y,\theta}$ is the reduction factor in the effective yield strength of steel at the maximum temperature in the cross section. Adaptation factors k_1 and k_2 are used to account for nonuniform temperature distribution through the depth and along the length of the steel beam. γ_{m1} and $\gamma_{m,fi}$ are partial safety factors, which vary per country.

Although the bending resistance of a steel beam is usually controlled by the plastic bending capacity of the cross section, it is sometimes necessary to consider the lateral torsional buckling

(LTB) resistance of a steel beam in fire. In EC3, the lateral torsional buckling resistance of a steel beam is calculated the same way as at ambient temperature.

In EC3-1-2, calculations for the strength of a column in fire follow the procedure for design of cold columns in EC3, Part 1.1. An equation to calculate the column slenderness conditions under fire is given a buckling curve *c,* which is to be used to determine the reduced values for flexural stiffness. Although there are four column-buckling curves for column design at ambient temperature, for fire safety design in EC3-1-2, only column curve *c* is used regardless of the type of cross section and axis of buckling. Column buckling curve *c* gives relative conservative values of column buckling resistance. Reasons for using this low buckling curve in fire include the more severe influences of initial imperfections and additional bending moments in the fire case, due to possible nonuniform temperature distributions.[52] Application of BS 5950-8 for a postflashover design fire is presented in the following case study of the Rem Koolhaas CCTV Building in Beijing.

CASE STUDY: Rem Koolhaas CCTV Building, Beijing, China. At the request of the approving authorities in China, the fire resistance of the CCTV (Central China Television) building, Beijing, was calculated using performance-based engineering, despite the fact that that structure was proposed to be fully protected to code. This request was made because the structure was highly innovative, completely asymmetric, and, therefore, the approving authorities wanted to check that the performance was adequate in a real fire.

The CCTV building is a high-rise office building (Figure 19.5.9) with an internal structure consisting of a composite steel and concrete frame. The exterior structure consists of a lateral bracing system formed with tubular structural elements. This exterior lateral stability system comprises a series of axial members at many different orientations, forming a structural role as well as an architectural role. Each member is designed to carry load in axial compression and/or tension.

In collaboration with the structural engineer, the most highly loaded columns and bracing members were identified and checked against their respective failure criteria at the fire limit state using the limiting temperature method in BS 5950-8.[42] All of the steel members were to be protected to not exceed 540°C at the end of 2 or 3 hours heating, dependent on the prescriptive rating of the member in accordance with the local code.

In almost all cases the limiting temperature was shown to be greater than 540°C and therefore deemed to have passed the performance criterion. However, some members were considerably heavily loaded in compression, thereby lowering their limiting temperature to just below 540°C (see Table 19.5.13). A further check on stability was carried out by removing the critical member from the cold design structural model and assessing the performance of the rest of the frame. In all cases loads were able to redistribute to adjacent members without causing failure of adjacent members.

In order to carry out the analysis, credible postflashover design fires were proposed and calculated in accordance with

FIGURE 19.5.9 CCTV Building, Beijing, China (Source: Arup)

TABLE 19.5.13 Load Ratio Calculated for CCTV Building

Check Number	*Type*	*Load Type*	*Section*	*Load Ratio (R)*	*Limiting Temperature (°C)*	*Maximum Steel Temperature (°C)*	*Pass?*
C1	Steel column	Compression	EC5L-0.535	0.403290	615	540	Yes
C2	Steel column	Compression	EC6-0.106	0.311235	651	540	Yes
C3	Steel column	Compression	EC4-0.106	0.199308	710	540	Yes
C4	Steel column	Tension	EC6-0.093	0.147490	730	540	Yes
C5	Steel column	Compression	EC6-0.093	0.134998	773	540	Yes
C6	Steel column	Compression	EC6-0.093	0.342531	639	540	Yes
C7	Steel column	Compression	EC1-0.620	0.472994	590	540	Yes
C8	Steel column	Compression	EC1L-0.620	0.316175	647	540	Yes
C9	Steel column	Compression	EC3-0.323	0.587734	544	540	No
C10	Steel column	Compression	EC3-0.323	0.089909	800	540	Yes
BM1	Beam	Bending	EB1_ext	0.108341	794	540	Yes
BM2	Beam	Bending	EB1_ext	0.135486	778	540	Yes
BM5	Beam	Bending	EB5	0.067274	800	540	Yes
BR1	Brace	Compression	X3S60	0.374001	627	540	Yes
BR2	Brace	Compression	X35	0.374545	627	540	Yes
BR3	Brace	Compression	XH75Q	0.668774	519	540	No
BR4	Brace	Tension	X35Q	0.165109	714	540	Yes
BR5	Brace	Compression	X35	0.259566	677	540	Yes

Source: Arup.

the parametric equation in EC1-1-2, assuming no reduction of the fuel load as a result of sprinklers or other active systems (the parametric temperature-time curve and its limitations are discussed later in this chapter in the section "Use of Advanced Analysis in Global Structural Response to Fire"). The heat transfer from these design fires to the protected steel elements were then calculated using the lumped mass heat transfer equations in EC1-1-2 and EC3-1-2.

For the design fire case, all of the members passed their limiting temperature criterion because the design fires, although sometimes hotter than the standard fire, were of shorter duration than the standard fire resistance period required. The protected members, therefore, reached lower temperatures in response to the design fires than the 540°C at the end of the standard fire resistance test and also did not reach their limiting temperature.

Single Element Calculation Methods Used in Australia and New Zealand

Structural fire design is a rapidly developing subject in Australia and New Zealand. The New Zealand and the Australian standards are referenced in their building codes (AS 1170 and NZS 4203). The following fire engineering approach was developed in New Zealand and modified for Australia, but is still very similar. As with British and EC standards, the Australian and New Zealand standards determine a fire limit state load combination for fire emergency conditions.

Standards AS 4100[53] and NZS 3404[54] present a limiting temperature method. The simple design method is based on determining the limiting temperature of the steel member under consideration. The limiting steel temperature is the temperature at which the steel member would be expected to yield considering the strength of the steel and load ratio (load in fire/design capacity at ambient temperatures) of the member. The limiting temperature is directly related to the variation of material properties at elevated temperatures. The yield-stress ratio at elevated temperatures and Young's modulus degradation curve at elevated temperatures used in Australia and New Zealand is presented in Figure 19.5.10.

The standards specify the formula from European Convention for Constructional Steelwork[55] to predict the fire resistance time for protected and unprotected steel. Times are based on exposures to standard fire or on an equivalent time exposure.

Single Element Calculation Methods Used in the United States

ASCE/SFPE Standard 29-99, *Standard Calculation Methods for Structural Fire Protection,* provides calculation methods to find the fire resistance of selected structural member and barrier assemblies using structural steel, plain concrete, reinforced concrete, and wood. These methods are intended to produce fire resistance rating times equivalent to those found from ASTM E119, *Standard Test Methods for Fire Tests of Buildings Construction and Materials,* and to NFPA 251. Therefore, the results obtained from the calculations should be used in place of test results.

Chapter 5 of this standard covers the methods for determining the fire resistance of structural steel construction. It describes analytical procedures for determining the fire resistance rating of protected columns, beams, girders, and trusses.

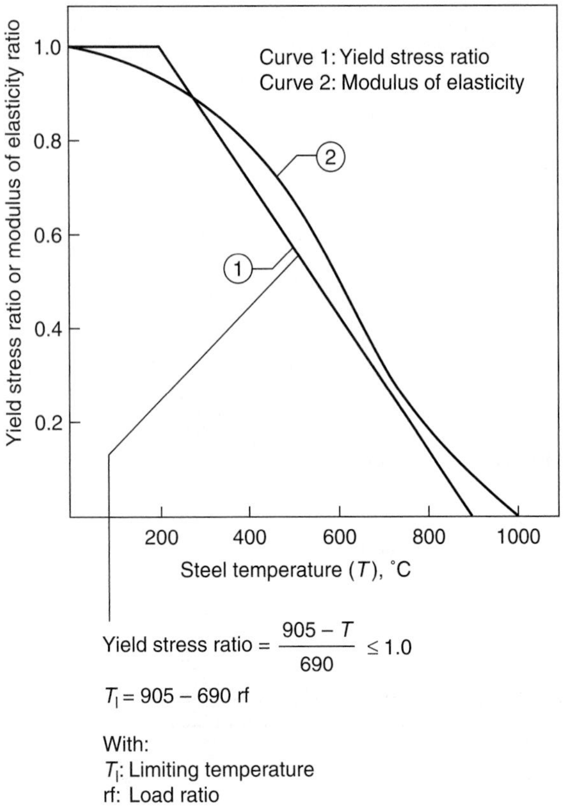

FIGURE 19.5.10 Australian and New Zealand Load Ratio and Limiting Temperatures Standards (Source: A. H. Buchanan, *Structural Design for Fire Safety.* Copyright John Wiley & Sons Limited, 2001. Reproduced with permission.)

The standard also provides calculation methods to find the fire resistance of structural steel beams and girders that differ in size from that specified in approved fire-resistant assemblies, as a function of the thickness of fire protection material and the weight (W) and heated perimeter (D) of the beam or girder. The W/D ratio is similar to the Hp/A concept used in the UK and Europe in that it is an indictor of heating rate.

The calculation methods apply to structural steel beams and girders protected with spray-applied cementitious or mineral fiber materials and a W/D ratio of 0.37 or greater (0.022 in SI units). In addition, the thickness of fire protection material is not to be less than ³⁄₈ in. (9.5 mm). For beams and girder meeting these criteria, the thickness of fire protection material can be found using the following equation:

$$h_2 = \left(\frac{W_1/D_1 + 0.60}{W_2/D_2 + 0.60}\right) h_1 \qquad (20a)$$

where

h = Thickness of spray-applied fire protection material (in.)

W = Weight of the structural steel beam or girder (lbs per linear ft)

D = Heated perimeter of the structural steel beam or girder (in.)

In SI units:

$$h_2 = \left(\frac{W_1/D_1 + 0.036}{W_2/D_2 + 0.036}\right) h_1 \qquad (20b)$$

where

h = Thickness of spray-applied fire protection material (mm)

W = Weight of the structural steel beam or girder (kg per m)

D = Heated perimeter of the structural steel beam or girder (mm)

Subscript 1 refers to the beam and fire protection thickness in the approved assembly and subscript 2 refers to the substitute beam or girder and the required fire protection thickness.[56]

The ASCE standard also provides a method for dealing with structural steel trusses. Although analytical tools for steel fire design are not included in the codes and standards in the United States, the *SFPE Handbook of Fire Protection Engineering* includes a chapter dedicated to analytical methods for determining fire resistance of steel members. This chapter describes three types of calculation methods used to determine fire resistance of steel structural members. Empirical correlations are given based on the analysis of data from performing the standard test, heat transfer analyses to determine the time required for the structural member to attain a predetermined critical temperature or to provide input to a structural analyses, and structural analyses similar to those conducted for structural engineering purposes, except that the material properties are evaluated at elevated temperatures.[57] Methods developed by Lie and Stanzak to calculate the critical temperature of beam and column sections are presented. As with the methods described in other countries, the members are generally assumed to be simply supported and unrestrained.

Milke[57] provides examples throughout the description of each method to illustrate the procedure. The section also provides various methods of protection used for steel structural members.

Calculation Methods Applicable to Steel Elements Exposed to Local Heating

In general, the single element structural checks discussed in the previous section for steel members exposed to postflashover fires can also be applied to steel elements exposed to local heating. This equivalence is because once the temperature of the steel section has been established by heat transfer, the same structural checks considering load ratio and limiting temperature or the reduction in strength and stiffness of the constituent materials are conservative, unless temperature gradient is an issue for stability (e.g., columns).

In the case of local fires, the heat transfer calculation is slightly more sophisticated than the lumped mass heat transfer calculations used in a postflashover fire presented previously. Lower emissivity values and view factors need to be used to calculate heat transfer from radiation when the flames (external through a window or door) or fire are remote from the steel member. For example, if a local fire is located under a floor slab supported by steel beams but the flames are not high enough to touch the steel, then the effects of convective and radiative heat transfer are reduced compared to a member in a compartment engulfed in a postflashover fire. In this case convective heat transfer to the steel member is a result of the temperature of the hot gases/smoke in the plume above the fire. Radiative heat transfer is largely dependent on the distance of the fire from the steel and is evaluated by using view factors.

Care should be taken when columns are likely to be exposed to a thermal gradient. In this instance the applicability of single element checks has not been validated. The gradient may result in significant thermal bowing and out-of-straightness that should be considered. For example, overall stability of the frame could be checked by removing the member from the ambient structural model that most structural engineers now generate for cold design and checking the resulting stability of the frame. The deflected shape of the structure is less important for fire limit state design, but the stresses generated in the rest of the frame, including the connections, should be shown as less than that required for failure. Once this assessment has been made, a single element approach is acceptable.

One form of local heating is external flaming from a compartment fire through openings or windows. Annex B of EC 1 gives thermal actions for external members. The equations and methodology in EC 1 are based on the external structural steel calculations originally developed by Law and O'Brien.[37]

The calculations consider the different fire exposure experienced by external structural members as compared to the same members in a fire compartment. The concept is shown in Figure 19.5.11. The calculations account for the following:

- The fire being within an adjacent compartment
- No heat buildup because the member is outside
- Cooling from surrounding air
- Heating based on flame size and position of member with respect to the facade
- Radiative heat flux from the fire compartment
- Radiative and convective heat flux from the external flames through the windows
- Radiative and convective heat loss from the steelwork to the ambient surroundings
- Size and location of the structural steelwork
- Through-draft conditions

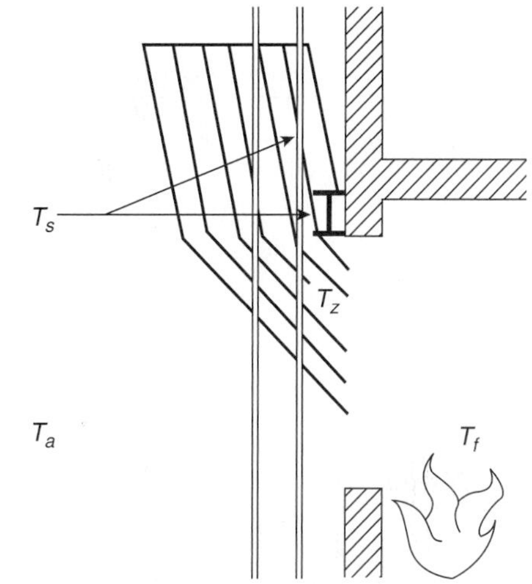

FIGURE 19.5.11 Concept of Thermal Actions on External Members (Courtesy of Steel Construction Institute, Silwood Park, Ascot, SL5 7QN, United Kingdom)

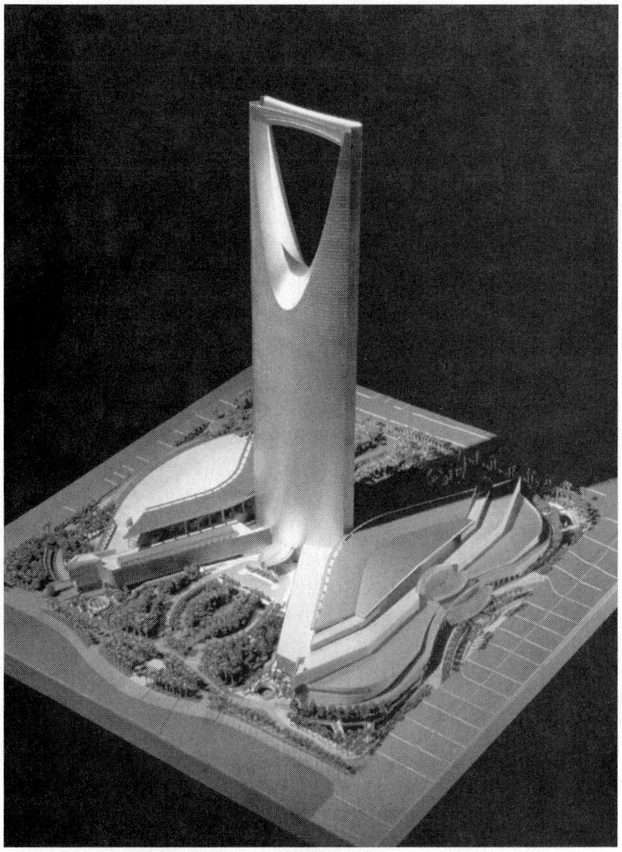

FIGURE 19.5.12 The Kingdom Centre, Riyadh, Saudi Arabia (Courtesy of Ellerbe Becket, Inc.)

CASE STUDY: Kingdom Centre, Riyadh, Saudi Arabia. The Kingdom Centre in Riyadh, Saudi Arabia, is an example of the application of Law and O'Brien's original external steel work calculations to an external flame–only design fire. The building is mainly office use with some retail and extends from grade to 180 m. At 180 m to 290 m, there is a raised observation deck (located at 290 m), a supporting structure containing lift/stair cores, and a steelwork "necklace." The observation deck, its supporting structure, and the nonstructural necklace are referred to as the "sculpture" (Figure 19.5.12 and 19.5.13).

The building structure was designed to meet the requirements of the Uniform Building Code, 1994. By code, it required a 3 hour rating, which meant the sculpture, which was not to contain any occupied floors other than the observation deck at the top, would be protected with passive fire protection. This passive fire protection requirement, however, had a negative impact

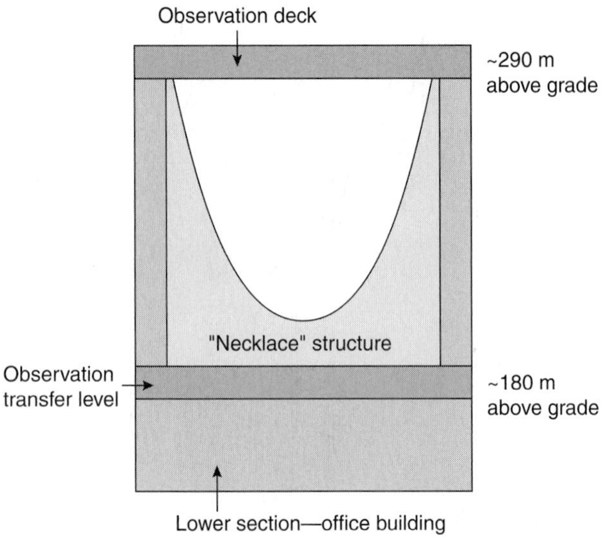

FIGURE 19.5.13 The Sculpture (Source: Arup)

on the aesthetic value of the sculpture and the construction program. In addition, the fire protection appeared to be redundant as it would be providing protection in an area of low fire load. A fire engineering study was, therefore, performed to reduce the areas of passive fire protection to the sculpture structure.

A number of fire scenarios were considered; failure was defined as a critical steel temperature of 550°C, when steel has lost about 40 percent of its ambient strength. This is conservative because it does not take advantage of the limiting temperature method presented previously, in which higher critical temperatures could have been calculated based on a reduced dead load, live load, and wind load at the fire limit state. For the sculpture this could have meant higher limiting temperatures of 600 to 700°C.

One of the fire scenarios considered for this project was the flame projection through the proposed windows and the resulting heating of the external steel members in proximity to the windows due to a postflashover fire on an office level. The flame projection (see Figure 19.5.14) from the office was determined for a range of ventilation conditions, and the heat transfer from the flames to the steel was calculated for the worst-case condition of flame length and temperature.

It was found by iteration that, at a vertical distances of greater than 10 m above the window opening, the heat flux from the flames would not heat the steel members to above 550°C, even after infinite exposure time. The steelwork immediately above the office floors was therefore protected for a height of 10 m, but the remainder of the structure above, including the observation desk, was unprotected. On the observation deck, credible local fires—for example, a large baggage fire—were investigated, assuming the same critical steel temperature of 550°C for failure criterion. Lower temperatures were shown as a result of heat transfer using the equations from the fire to the steel elements based on the work of Milke[57] from the *SFPE Handbook of Fire Protection Engineering*.

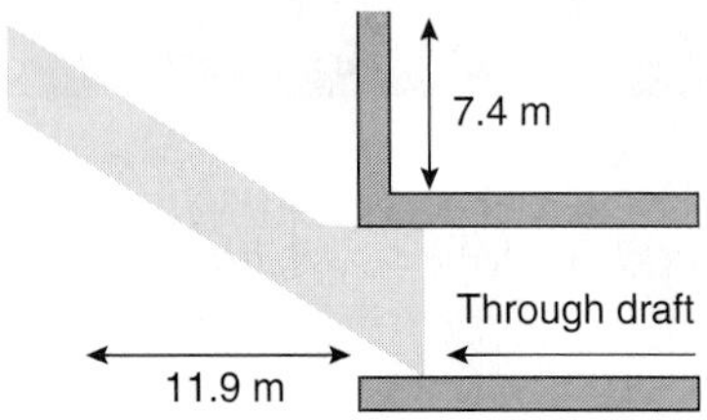

FIGURE 19.5.14 Summary of Flame Projection Calculations for the Office Level (Source: Arup)

Role of Connections in Single Element Design

Calculating the fire resistance of single members is only an acceptable design solution when the connections between the members are also considered. The fire resistance of connections in a steel frame is generally not well understood. The University of Sheffield in the United Kingdom has conducted some of the most significant research in this field.[58]

In addition, Scott, Lane, and Gibbons[59] discuss the behavior of connections in response to whole frame behavior and provide some insight into likely favorable and nonfavorable connection arrangements when considering the axial (compression and tension) forces placed on a connection as beams expand, pull, and push on connections in fire. Rotter et al.[60] state that connections should be designed for the tensile pulling force in the cooling phase of a fire when deflected steel beams try to contract to their original position but, because of plastic strains in the steel beam, cannot.

However, with respect to design recommendations in codes for single element analysis, it is generally assumed that a connection will be designed for ambient loads and then protected to the same standard as the adjoining member. If the adjoining member has been overdesigned so that it has more fire resistance, then the connection should also be overdesigned. This is always the approach when using the single element approach to design discussed in this chapter.

EC 3[41] and BS 5950-8[42] state that the fire resistance of a bolted or a welded connection may be assumed to be sufficient, as long as the fire protection on the connection provides the same thermal resistance to the joint as the fire protection on connecting members and the utilization of the joint is equal or less than the maximum value of the utilization of any of the connected members. BS 5950[42] further states that if the utilization of the connection is higher than the utilization of the connecting members, the protection to the connection should be increased to ensure that the connection does not fail first.

APPLICATION OF SINGLE STRUCTURAL ELEMENT ANALYSIS TO CONCRETE

The simplest and most common method of designing concrete structures in fire is to ascertain the required thickness and cover to reinforcement for the necessary fire resistance period, as specified in tabulated data in codes worldwide. When these tabulated data are applicable and are followed in the design of a concrete element, spalling prevention is generally assumed to heave been adequately addressed. There are a number of analytical methods to calculate the fire resistance of concrete members based on their capacity in fire, but the phenomenon of spalling must also be addressed when using these approaches.

Spalling

Detailed analysis of concrete members' response to fire, including the effect of spalling throughout the fire duration, is difficult due to the complexity of the factors that cause spalling and their nonlinear and unpredictable response to heat. Spalling prevention must therefore be demonstrated as provided prior to detailed analysis of concrete elements. Before the range of single element calculation methods available internationally for concrete are presented, a discussion of spalling and how it is treated by design codes in various countries is given.

Spalling is a complex process and, in general, not well understood, even by experts in the field. There are various different kinds of spalling (aggregate splitting, explosive, surface, corner separation, sloughing off, and cooling spalling). The most detrimental to a structural member in fire is explosive spalling. Explosive spalling (Figure 19.5.15) can occur at temperatures as low as 100°C and in some cases can fully expose the reinforcement to the full heat of a fire. Explosive spalling is thought to be primarily associated with evaporation of water in the concrete pores and the associated buildup of pore pressures. However, restraint to thermal expansion, the heating rate of the fire, the strength of the concrete, and the dimensions of the section also contribute.[61]

The risk of explosive spalling can be reduced by choice of aggregate, by limiting the concrete strength and moisture content where possible, and by the addition of polypropylene fibers. Arup Fire[61] conducted a research project to define the risk of spalling in normal weight-reinforced concrete exposed to hydrocarbon fires for the health and safety executive in the United Kingdom. Risk values (1 to 5) were assigned to all of the variables affecting spalling of concrete in a fire—for example, moisture content, restraint, and aggregate type. Risk categories associated with the combined or additive risk values for a particular concrete were assigned spalling rates defined by Arup Fire from evidence in the literature.

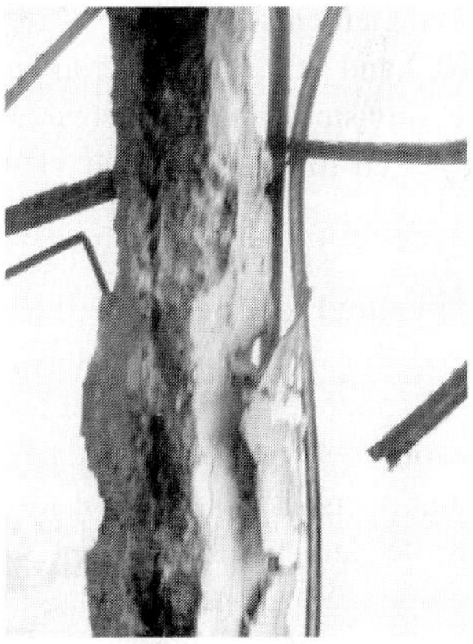

FIGURE 19.5.15 Example of Explosive Spalling of Concrete (Source: Arup)

Spalling Prevention Measures Used in the United Kingdom and Europe

BS 8110, Part 2[62] presents a tabulated approach to specifying cover and thickness of section required for different fire resistance periods for a range of concrete elements. Lennon[63] gives the background to these data and reports on spalling observed during standard fire tests and the adequacy of this guidance for cover to reinforcement given in the United Kingdom. Section 4 of BS 8110-2[62] gives additional measures necessary to reduce the risks of spalling at elevated temperatures. It is recommended that these additional measures also be implemented when the cover to reinforcement exceeds 40 to 50 mm.

The British standard discusses the key factors believed to influence spalling. It states that rapid rates of heating, large compressive stresses, or high moisture contents (over 5% by volume or 2% to 3% by mass of dense concrete) can lead to spalling of concrete cover at elevated temperatures, particularly for cover to reinforcement of thicknesses exceeding 40 to 50 mm. In addition it states that concretes made from limestone aggregates are less susceptible to spalling than concretes made from aggregates containing a higher proportion of silica, quartzites, and granites. Concrete made from manufactured lightweight aggregates are found to rarely spall.

Recommendations are given to designers to protect the concrete against spalling when the cover to reinforcement exceeds 40 to 50 mm. Acceptable measures are proposed as follows:

- An applied finish by hand or spray of plaster, vermiculite, and so forth
- The provision of a false ceiling as a fire barrier
- The use of lightweight aggregates
- The use of sacrificial tensile steel

The code states that welded steel fabric as supplementary reinforcement is sometimes used to prevent spalling; it is then placed within the cover at 20 mm from the concrete face.

General design rules concerning spalling are also mentioned in EC 2-1-2,[64] giving recommendations to limit explosive spalling and falling off of concrete. The main parameter considered by this design guidance is the moisture content. The code states that explosive spalling is unlikely to occur when the moisture content of the concrete is less than a certain amount with respect to the weight. This parameter is called k and is given as a percentage. The allowable percentage for each European nation is given by each individual National Annex. However, the recommended base value in EC 2-1-2[64] is 3 percent by weight of moisture content. (The United Kingdom has adopted 3%).

For normal-weight concrete, when using tabulated data to design section thickness and cover to reinforcement for the standard fire, the European code states that there is no further check required for spalling.

For beams, slabs, and tensile members, if the moisture content of the concrete is more than *k* percent by weight, the influence of explosive spalling on load-bearing function R may be assessed by assuming local loss of cover to one reinforcing bar or bundle of bars in the cross section and checking the reduced load–bearing capacity at the resulting high temperatures.

A specific section in the Eurocode addresses high strength concrete. For concrete grades C55/67 to C80/95 (where the two numerical values given after the C refer to the strengths measured in a cube and cylinder test), the rules as already described apply, provided that the maximum content of silica fume is less than 6 percent by weight of cement.

For higher contents of silica fume, further spalling prevention measures are proposed. For concrete grades 80/95 < C < 90/105, spalling is deemed as likely in any situation for concrete exposed directly to the fire and at least one of the following methods should therefore be provided:

- *Method A.* A reinforcement mesh with a nominal cover of 15 mm. This mesh should have wires with a diameter greater than or equal to 2 mm with a pitch less than or equal to 50 × 50 mm. The nominal cover to the main reinforcement should be greater than or equal to 40 mm.
- *Method B.* A type of concrete for which it has been demonstrated (by local experience or by testing) that no spalling of concrete occurs under fire exposure
- *Method C.* Protective layers for which it is demonstrated that no spalling of concrete occurs under fire exposure
- *Method D.* Include in the concrete mix more than 2 kg/m^3 of monofilament propylene fibers

Spalling Prevention Measures Used in New Zealand and Australia

The concrete code used in Australia is AS3600.[65] The existing code contains only a cautionary note about spalling, with no actual guidance; it reads as follows:

> SAA is not prepared at present to specify requirements for the prevention of spalling of concrete from beams or columns exposed to fire. However, reference may be made to Clauses 4.1.6 and 4.1.7 of BS8110 part 2, in relation to this matter.

The whole code is currently being redrafted. The reason for this exercise is to increase the maximum concrete grade addressed by the code and therefore more easily used in design from 65 MPa to 100 MPa. This further increases the risk of spalling. The current draft in circulation includes no guidance on spalling and the intention is to include some technical advice to prevent spalling, in the commentary only.

Spalling Prevention Measures Used in the United States

In the United States, the building codes and ACI Manual of Concrete Practice are silent on spalling prevention measures for fire other than specifying minimum levels of cover to reinforcement. In the *SFPE Handbook of Fire Protection Engineering,* Fleischmann and Buchanan[66] briefly discuss the merits of adding fine polypropylene fibers to the concrete mix but do not specify quantities for design.

Calculation Methods Applicable to Concrete Structures

In all the analytical methods presented here to determine the capacity of concrete elements in fire, engineers should also satisfy themselves that spalling has been adequately addressed by the design, through the meeting of tabulated code requirements for dimensions of section and cover or by prevention measures.

When designing concrete elements for fire protection, well-detailed reinforcement with adequate tying will generally perform well in that loads can be redistributed. It has been shown that continuity will enable redistribution of moments to hogging areas where steel is remote from the fire, enhancing the fire resistance of a slab or beam; if this is considered in design, however, then the detailing must allow for it.

Axial restraint will allow arch/membrane action to occur; some single element design methods take this into account to further increase the fire resistance that can be assumed to be achieved by a section in design, although it should be noted that this may also then increase the likelihood of spalling.

Calculation Methods for Concrete Used in the United Kingdom and Europe

The tabulated data in BS 8110 are based on furnace test data from the 1950s and are therefore relevant to design fire cases where a postflashover fire is assumed. Tables tend to be related to element type; tables for columns and beams, for example, are different. Similarly, separate tables exist for prestressed members as opposed to ordinary reinforced sections in BS 8110. The prestressed data are based on data for precast elements and their application, therefore, to modern posttensioned slabs is questionable, particularly bonded systems with very little passive reinforcement and the protection of anchorages in unbonded construction. Similar tables are available in Eurocode 2, Part 1.2, and these are also assumed to be applicable to the design fire case where flashover has occurred in the compartment containing the structural elements.

Both BS 8110-2 and EC2 give material properties for reinforcement, prestressing steel, and concrete at elevated temperature. These can be used for detailed analysis to determine the capacity of single concrete elements at elevated temperatures. Again a three-step process (design fire, heat transfer, capacity calculation) is required for concrete. When calculating heat transfer, there are no simple equations that can be used because the conductivity of concrete is low and concrete sections are thermally thick. Consequently, either predefined nomograms drawn for particular sections in response to the standard fire can be used, or a finite element heat transfer analysis is required to calculate the temperature gradient through the depth and/or along the length of a concrete section.

The most commonly applied design tool for concrete members in a compartment with a postflashover fire is the 932°F (500°C) isotherm method or reduced cross section method originally developed by Anderberg.[67] The approach is recognized by EC 2-1-2[64] and illustrated in Figure 19.5.16.

It is assumed that any concrete at a temperature greater than 500°C will not be able to support load in fire. Any concrete at a temperature less than 500°C can be assumed to have its full ambient design strength. These simple rules and the reduced strength of reinforcement are used to calculate the residual capacity of the section in response to fire. If this residual capacity is sufficient to carry the loads, factored for the fire limit state, the section is deemed to be acceptable.

Data are available in EC2 to predict the location of the 500°C isotherm in various sections at 30, 60, 90, and 120 minutes of the standard fire, usually in the form of nomograms. Alternatively, engineers can calculate a credible design fire and subsequent heat transfer through the particular concrete element to actually predict the isotherm. The methodology is generally applied to beams and columns, although it can also be applied to slabs, provided the section is not too thin that almost the entire section is at 500°C and, therefore, has to be ignored.

In addition to the 500°C isotherm method, Annex B of EC2-1-2 also provides the zone method for calculating the resistance to bending moments and axial forces. The zone method is recommended for use with small sections and slender columns fully engulfed in a postflashover fire, but is only valid when the standard fire is used as the design fire case.

The zone method requires more calculation but is of benefit to smaller sections because some strength in the concrete is considered even at high temperatures. The zone method splits the member into three or more zones of near equal temperature; then the material properties at elevated temperature are used to calculate that particular section capacity. A zone of damaged

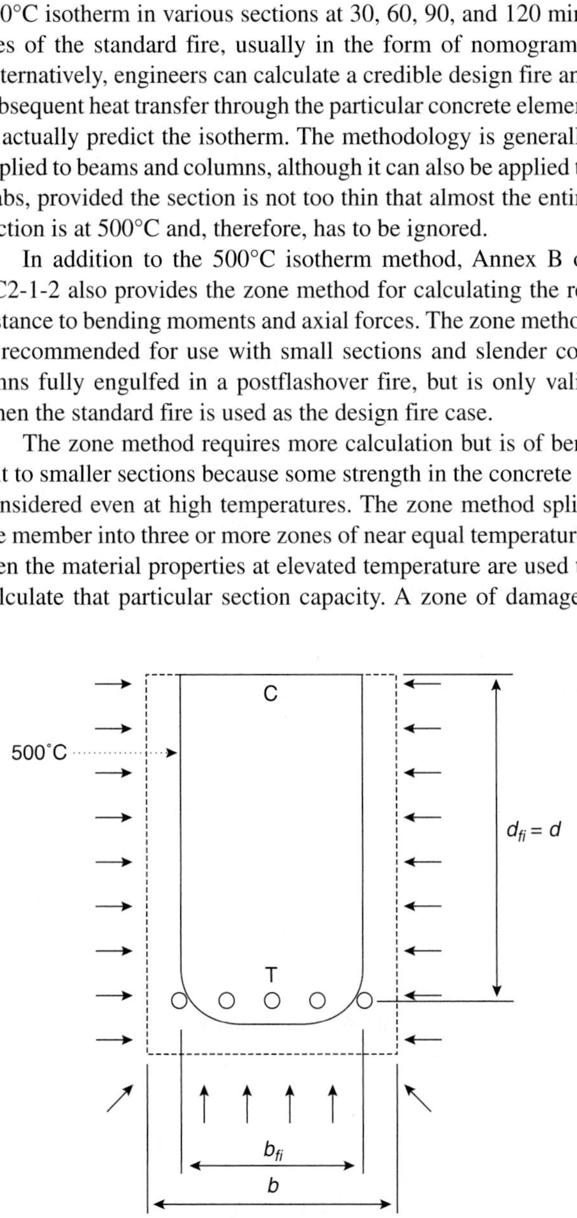

FIGURE 19.5.16 500°C Isotherm Method (Courtesy of British Standards Institute. Permission to reproduce extracts from British Standards is granted by BSI. British Standards can be obtained from BSI Customer Services, 389 Chiswick High Road, London W4 4AL. Tel: +44 (0)20 8996 9001. email: cservices@bsi-global.com.)

concrete at the surface is calculated and ignored in the capacity check. The capacity of the reduced section is then calculated by summing the capacity of each remaining zone.

For shear, torsion, and anchorage, Annex D provides a simplified calculation method, although failure of concrete is rare in this respect. Shear can be a problem in precast, pretensioned slabs with narrow webs.[68]

Simplified methods for the design of beams and slabs where the loading is predominantly uniformly distributed and where the design at normal temperature is based on linear analysis are provided in Annex E of the Eurocode. A method for simply supported slabs and beams and a method considering redistribution of load for continuous members are also provided. When considering the redistribution of load in continuous members in fire, the curtailment length of the reinforcement over the supports should be checked because the point of contra-flexure will have changed. A formula to calculate the required length is given by EC2.

The Eurocode does not provide a simplified calculation method for the analysis of axially restrained slabs/beams, unlike methods presented in the *SFPE Handbook of Fire Protection Engineering.*[66] This is conservative as restraint induces thrust, which will enhance the members' fire resistance because the thrust acts as additional reinforcement.

Calculation Methods for Concrete Used in New Zealand and Australia

The Australian Concrete Design Code, AS 3600,[65] provides dimensions for concrete sections to achieve periods of fire resistance like all other codes, assumed as applicable for postflashover fire conditions. In Section 5.9 of the code it states that fire resistance may be predicted by methods of calculation provided the relevant properties of materials at elevated temperature are used. New Zealand's NZS 3101 has a similar approach.

Calculation Methods for Concrete Used in the United States

Tabulated data for cover and thickness of concrete elements are given in building regulations ACI 216.1-97 in the ACI *Manual of Concrete Practice*[69] and ASCE/SFPE 29-99.[56] The main differences between U.S. data and tabulated data elsewhere are that U.S. codes differentiate between aggregate type, recognizing that carbonate concretes spall less than siliceous concretes. Dimensions and cover are given for restrained and unrestrained slabs and beams as a consequence of the restrained furnace test in ASTM E119. The data for prestressed members differ from the data for ordinary reinforced members.

Fleischmann and Buchanan[66] present analytical methods for determining the fire resistance of concrete members in the *SFPE Handbook of Fire Protection Engineering.* The chapter presents temperature nomograms for slabs and beams in the standard fire and equations for calculating the fire resistance of simply supported slabs and beams, continuous unrestrained flexural members, and those restrained against thermal expansion.

Continuous unrestrained members have longer fire endurance than simply supported members because they can redistribute moments. Usually the redistribution of moment through the depth of the member results in failure of the negative moment reinforcement over the supports. The chapter states that the American Concrete Institute warns against increasing this reinforcement as this could result in compression failure of the member, which is not desirable. Limitations are therefore placed on the negative reinforcement to ensure flexural failure in design. Equations to calculate the flexural strength at any point are given.

Equations are also given to account for the thermal thrust force that will occur in the axis of members heated from below and restrained from thermal expansion. The effect of the thermal thrust is the same as prestressing a concrete beam or slab. Therefore, the line of thrust can be considered a fictitious line of reinforcement in flexural design. To calculate the thrust moment, the midspan deflection must be calculated. Fleishmann gives an approximate equation for deflection.

Similar calculations to those presented by Fleischmann and Buchanan[66] are presented in ACI 216R-89, ACI *Manual of Concrete Practice.*[69]

Calculation Methods Applicable to Concrete Elements Exposed to Local Heating

As for steel design, local fires and external flaming can be considered as credible design fires to be resisted by the concrete element, in lieu of a standard fire or postflashover design fire, depending on the fuel load arrangement, quantity, and location (as outlined earlier, TM19[34] and Law[37] are useful references to determine such fire cases).

Heat transfer to concrete is more complex and will generally require a finite element computer code to calculate the temperature gradient through a concrete section.[68]

Spalling prevention measures should be addressed by the design if the concrete is exposed to direct flame impingement or if the concrete temperature in the cover to reinforcement exceeds 100°C. However, if overall frame stability can be shown when a single critical element is lost, then spalling prevention is not required. The capacity of the element in these local or external heating regimes can then be checked using the methods outlined from BS8110 Part 2 or EC2.

APPLICATION OF SINGLE STRUCTURAL ELEMENT ANALYSIS TO COMPOSITE STEEL AND CONCRETE MEMBERS

Composite steel and concrete members are generally concrete slabs connected to steel beams via shear studs, hollow steel sections filled with reinforced concrete, or hot rolled steel sections encased in concrete, all of which are designed at ambient temperature, taking into account composite action. In some cases steel hollow sections are filled with concrete to provide fire resistance, but the concrete fill is ignored by the ambient design. In this case there may be no composite action, and the concrete simply acts as heat sink, in which case there is a limit to the fire resistance that can be achieved (30 to 60 minutes maximum).

Composite steel frame construction generally has excellent fire resistance properties as a single member and as a whole frame. The main reason for this good performance is that when the steel member becomes hot and weak, there are alternative paths for the load into the colder concrete slab in a composite floor or the concrete core of a composite column.

As a consequence of the concrete, composite members experience large gradients through their depth; therefore, to obtain an accurate representation of this temperature gradient during a fire, a heat transfer analysis using a finite element method is usually required. A 2D analysis is sufficient if it is safe to assume there would be no gradient along the member.

For composite slabs it is reasonable to assume an average steel temperature from the fire for the entire protected or unprotected beam section, because it is the gradient between the steel beam and the concrete slab that tends to define performance. In this case, the simple lumped mass heat transfer equations can be used to calculate the average steel temperature. However, increased fire resistance could be achieved if the temperature gradient in the beam is also calculated.

As for all single element methods, the design fire must first be established (a standard fire; a postflashover fire calculated using, for example, a parametric equation; a local fire; or an external fire case). The heat transfer from this fire through the structural element can then be determined using a finite element analysis. Predefined nomograms based on standard furnace tests can also be used to obtain the temperature gradient. The capacity assessment methods, as follows, can then be used.

Composite Beams, Slabs, and Columns in the United Kingdom and Europe

The limiting temperature method discussed in the context of steel members previously can also be used for composite beams. The difference with the design methods for steel beams is that if the beam fails by yielding of the steel, M_c is equal to the plastic bending moment capacity of the cross section of the composite beam (steel and concrete). BS 5950-8[42] and Eurocode 4, Part 1.2,[70] therefore, give specific values for limiting temperature of composite steel beams.

An essential part of composite beams are the shear connectors or shear studs, which transfer the forces from steel beam into the concrete slab and vice versa. EC4-1-2[70] states that the design shear resistance in fire situation can be determined in accordance with the cold design in EC4-1-1,[71] except that in the fire circumstances, the variation of material properties with temperature and the different partial safety factor should also be taken into account. The temperature of the stud connector and concrete may be taken as 8 percent and 40 percent, respectively, of the temperature of the upper flange of the beam. Note BS 5950–8 does not consider the temperature of the shear stud.

However, both BS 5950-8 and EC4-1-2 differentiate between partial and full shear connection. Note that the limiting temperatures for partial shear connections are higher than for the 100 percent shear connection (Table 19.5.14) due to the fact that the partial shear connection determines the capacity of the beam. The shear connections remain relatively cold, because the studs are in the concrete slab. The limiting temperature for the rest of the cross section might therefore be higher. For the 100 percent shear connection, temperatures of the lower flange are determined to find the capacity of the composite beam in fire.

In addition to providing design methods for conventional composite beams, both design guides also present design meth-

TABLE 19.5.14 Limiting Temperature of Composite Beams

Description of Member		Limiting Temperature (°C) at a Ratio Of					
		0.7	*0.6*	*0.5*	*0.4*	*0.3*	*0.2*
Unprotected, or protected with fire protection that can undergo large strains	100% shear connection	550	580	610	645	685	740
	40% shear connection	575	600	635	665	700	760
Other protected members	100% shear connection	505	540	575	620	660	715
	40% shear connection	535	565	605	640	675	736

Source: Arup.

ods to determine the capacity of partially encased composite beams (as would occur when shelf angle floor beams are used and some of the beam is embedded in the slab).

When calculating the load-bearing resistance of a composite slab in fire using a single element approach, it is often assumed that it is one-way spanning, being effective only in the direction of the concrete rib. This is in contrast to the much stronger mechanism that occurs in reality—tensile membrane action—discussed later in this chapter in the subsection "Analytical Methods to Quantify Tensile Membrane Action in Fire." Consequently, a single element approach will tend to be on the conservative side.

For a continuous slab, a plastic design method may be used as defined in EC 4.[70] In this method, plastic hinges are assumed at the support and locations of the maximum bending moment in the slab. In order to guarantee sufficient deformation capacity for continuous slabs, there are limitations on the minimum amount of reinforcement at supports and midspan.

In sagging bending, since the temperature rise on the unexposed side of the slab is generally required to be below 284°F (140°C) to fulfill the insulation requirement in standard fire resistance testing, the concrete in compression can be assumed to be cold. Its cold strength may be used when calculating the sagging bending moment capacity of the slab. Contributions from the steel decking are usually ignored because the decking will be unprotected and might debond when under direct fire attack. Reinforcement in the ribs generally provides the tension force in fire. (See Figure 19.5.17 for visualization of the design method.) To calculate this tension force, the temperature distribution through the composite slab is required and can be obtained from calculation using finite element heat transfer models or nomograms provided in Eurocode 4.

Under a negative bending moment (Figure 19.5.18) in a continuous slab, the compression face of a composite slab is exposed to fire where there is a steep temperature gradient. When calculating the negative moment capacity, the composite slab, including the concrete ribs, should be divided into a number of layers, each of approximately the same temperature. The contribution of each layer should be evaluated separately using the reduced strength and stiffness properties of the materials and then integrated to give the total slab resistance. To simplify this calculation, a ribbed or trapezoidal slab may be converted into a flat slab with an effective flat slab depth, with its corresponding temperature distribution. This temperature distribution can be calculated using nomograms for the standard fire or finite element analysis for any fire type.

Composite Beams, Slabs, and Columns in New Zealand and Australia

In New Zealand and Australia, the limiting temperature method is used for composite beam members. Performance-based design assuming reduced strength and stiffness of composite columns and other structural members can also be performed within the performance-based framework in both New Zealand and Australia.

Composite Beams, Slabs, and Columns in the United States

Fleishmann and Buchanan[66] briefly discuss composite steel–concrete construction in the *SFPE Handbook of Fire Protection Engineering* but simply cross-reference Eurocode 4 for detailed analysis. ASCE/SEI/SFPE 29-99[56] provides empirical correlations to calculate the benefit of increased thermal mass when steel sections are filled or encased with concrete.

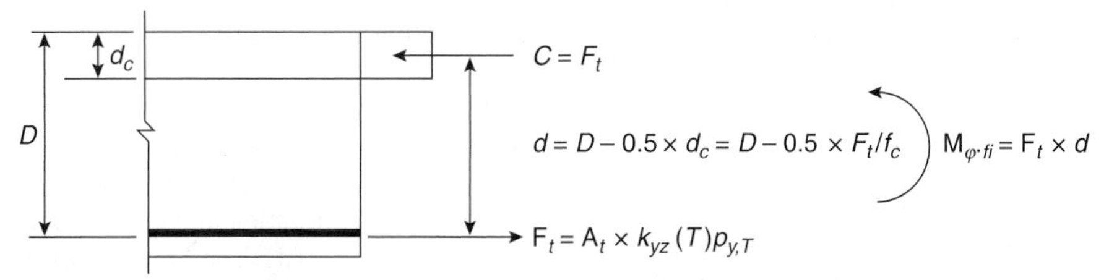

d_c
D
$C = F_t$
$d = D - 0.5 \times d_c = D - 0.5 \times F_t/f_c$
$M_{\varphi \cdot fi} = F_t \times d$
$F_t = A_t \times k_{yz}(T)p_{y,T}$

FIGURE 19.5.17 Calculation Method for Sagging Moment Capacity (Source: Arup)

$$\frac{1}{z} = \frac{1}{\sqrt{u_1}} + \frac{1}{\sqrt{u_2}} + \frac{1}{\sqrt{u_3}}$$

where u_1, u_2, u_3 are axial distances (mm) of the reinforcing bar to the profiled steel as specified in figure.

Additionally to the limitations given in the table, the use of this table is restricted to:

u_1 and $u_2 \geq 50$ mm
$u_3 \geq 35$ mm

Relation fire duration - temperature of the reinforcing steel

Standard Fire Resistance	*Temperature of Reinforcing Steel (°C)*
R 60	$\theta_z = 1175 - 350\,z \leq 810°C$ for ($z \leq 3{,}3$)
R 90	$\theta_z = 1285 - 350\,z \leq 880°C$ for ($z \leq 3{,}6$)
R 120	$\theta_z = 1370 - 350\,z \leq 930°C$ for ($z \leq 3{,}8$)
R 180	$\theta_z = 1490 - 350\,z \leq 1000°C$ for ($z \leq 4{,}0$)
R 240	$\theta_z = 1575 - 350\,z \leq 1500°C$ for ($z \leq 4{,}2$)

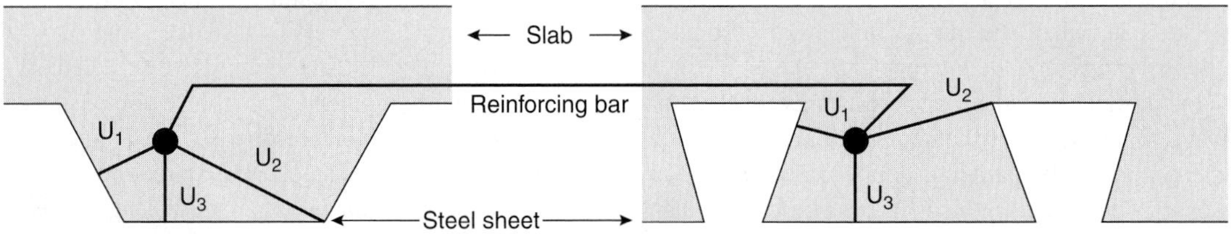

FIGURE 19.5.18 Calculation of the Negative Moment Resistance (Courtesy of British Standards Institute. Permission to reproduce extracts from British Standards is granted by BSI. British Standards can be obtained from BSI Customer Services, 389 Chiswick High Road, London W4 4AL. Tel: +44 (0)20 8996 9001. email: cservices@bsi-global.com.)

Calculation Methods for Concrete-Filled Hollow Steel Sections

Various existing calculation methods provide a cost-effective way to obtain columns with a high load-carrying capacity at ambient temperature and high fire resistance (Figure 19.5.19) without the addition of passive fire protection to the steel. When the column is designed as composite at ambient temperature and in fire the concrete filling has several beneficial effects. The concrete will act as a heat sink to slow the temperature rise of the steel column; the reinforced concrete can bear some or all of the axial load as the steel weakens; and the reinforced concrete fill can provide lateral stability to inhibit local buckling of the steel shell.

In some instances the hollow steel section is filled with concrete only and no benefit is taken from composite action in design, in which case the concrete simply acts as a heat sink. Low fire resistance periods of 30 to 60 minutes can be achieved.[72]

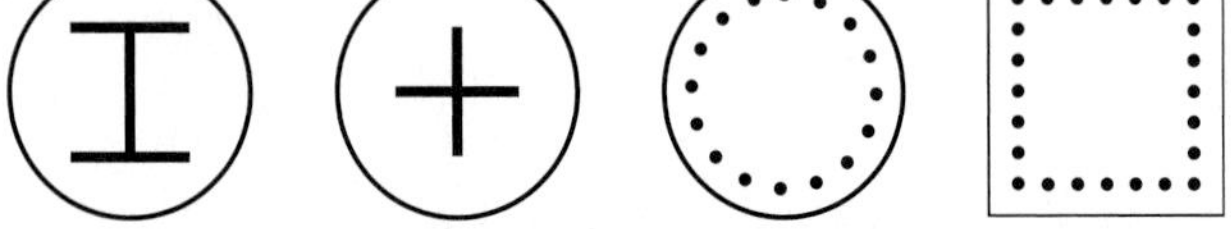

FIGURE 19.5.19 Example of Composite Column Sections (Source: F. Kettner, "Investigations on the Load Bearing Behavior of Composite Columns Under Fire Conditions," *1st International Ph.D. Workshop on Fire Protection Science and Engineering,* Hanover, Germany, 2005)

Composite Column Design Approaches

EC4-1-2 Design Approach. EC4-1-2 gives a more rigorous and detailed approach to composite column design than any other code worldwide. It introduces three design procedures for composite columns: (1) tabulated data, (2) simple calculation model, and (3) advanced calculation models.

The application of the tabulated approach is for a limited range of load ratios and steel section size and is only applicable to columns with a buckling length of less than 4.5 m. A more detailed calculation method is given in Annex H of EC4-1-2.[70] In this case the maximum buckling length permissible in order for the calculation to be valid is still 4.5 m as a consequence of the furnace tests the methodology is based on, but any section and any load ratio can theoretically be designed using this approach.

EC 4 also permits advanced analysis; a number of researchers have created software (Kettner,[73] CEC,[74] SCI,[51] and CORUS[72]) to calculate and extend the application of EC4-1-2 Annex H.[70] The software is still based on single element analysis but allows an accurate calculation of the through-depth thermal gradient and resulting differential strains in the steel casing, concrete, and reinforcement. Each code is based on an iterative process to obtain the squash load and rigidity of the composite column in fire. The calculation involves the determination of the temperature distribution in the cross section and the consequent residual rigidity (EI). The Steel Construction Institute (United Kingdom) and CORUS steel have produced software to make this calculation easy to use in design but this is also limited to a column buckling length of 4.5 m.[75]

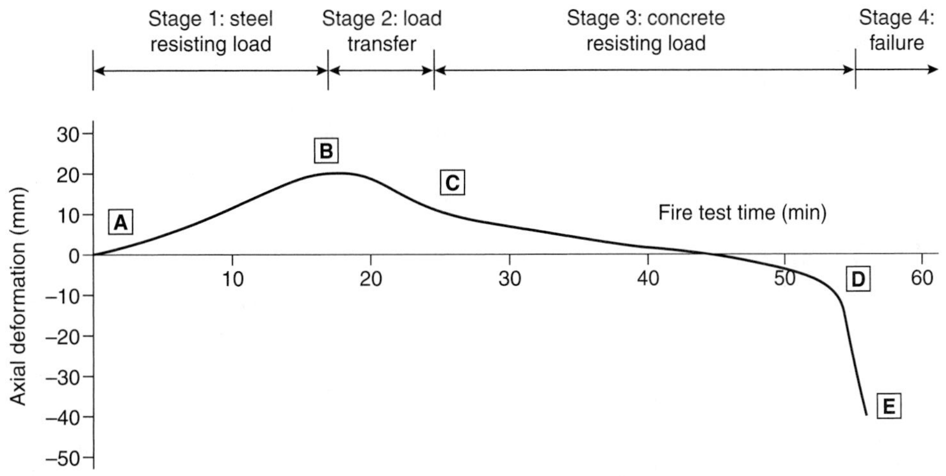

FIGURE 19.5.20 Axial Deformation Response as a Function of Time for a Typical Concrete-Filled Tube (Courtesy of V. K. R. Kodur and John C. Latour, National Research Council of Canada)

Canadian Fire Tests. In Canada a body of work exists on the response of concrete-filled steel sections. Over a number of years, the National Research Council of Canada (NRCC) carried out numerous fire tests on unprotected concrete-filled steel columns. The fire tests were carried out in a specially constructed fire testing furnace at the National Fire Laboratory.[76] The Canadian fire tests included different dimensions and thickness of circular and square hollow sections, a variety of concretes (plain, bar reinforced, high strength, and steel fiber reinforced with either siliceous or carbonate aggregates), and different levels of applied loads.[77–79] All the test columns were 3810 mm and the column ends were rotationally restrained at the ends. All fire tests were carried out with unprotected steel sections and fire exposure according to ASTM E119.[9]

Figure 19.5.20 shows a typical response of the recorded axial deformation-time relationship. It can be divided into four parts: (1) a phase of steady increase in the column expansion (A-B) is followed by (2) a sharp contraction (B-C) and (3) then gradual contraction (C-D) in the column axial deformation. (4) The columns experience another sharp contraction (D-E) before failure.

This type of behavior may be explained by considering the temperatures and resistances of the steel tube and concrete. Fire tests by others[74] on unprotected concrete-filled columns show similar results.

A design method for the calculation of the fire resistance of concrete-filled hollow steel columns was included in Appendix D of the National Building Code of Canada beginning with the 1995 edition and then later in a joint publication of the American Society of Civil Engineers and the Society of Fire Protection Engineers.[56]

CASE STUDY: Auditorium. The following case study demonstrates a single element analysis of unprotected circular hollow section (CHS) columns in a steel sway frame. The columns form part of the primary structural frame of an auditorium. The aim was to determine if the unprotected columns could achieve their necessary fire resistance rating as a result of composite action with reinforced concrete filling. The local code required a fire resistance rating of 2 hours, except where the columns support the roof, in which case a reduction to 1 hour was acceptable.

The simplified single element approach in Eurocode 4 for nonsway frames was deemed applicable for the sway frame of the auditorium because it was determined that the overall lateral stability could be provided by the global performance of the steel frame with four adjacent columns removed. Based on the fire load in the auditorium it was shown that only four columns are expected to be affected by fire simultaneously. Therefore, four adjacent columns were removed from the structural engineer's model and the stability of the frame in wind was shown to remain adequate. As global lateral stability was justified, the capacity of the columns under gravity loading in fire could be assessed individually.

The inherent fire resistance of the columns under axial load was checked in accordance with the simplified guidance in Eurocode 4 for single elements in a nonsway frame. The heating regime was assumed to be the standard temperature-time curve.[9] The calculations were performed using a combination of software developed by the steel producer CORUS[72] and spreadsheet calculations. The software assessed the temperature gradient in the section and then the capacity of the composite column using the properties of steel and concrete at elevated temperatures. It also considered the differential strains between the cool concrete and the hot steel casing. The resulting capacities were incorporated into a spreadsheet and compared to the demands.

The columns were analyzed with up to 6 percent reinforcement within the concrete fill with 1 in. (25.4 mm) cover throughout. The column capacities produced by the software were used to calculate the utilization (ratio of load to capacity) at 60 and 120 minutes of the standard fire for each column member. Failure was defined as a load ratio greater than one.

The effective length of the columns was assumed to be 1.0 and the safety factors applied to dead, snow, and live loads were taken as 1.0. These values are considered conservative because Eurocode 4 allows a reduction of 0.7 to 0.85 times the actual column length and a reduction in live load of 50 percent. These reductions are permitted because a hot column will be restrained by the cold structure at its ends and the ambient design live load is unlikely to be achieved in reality. It was shown that all columns met the code required rating.

APPLICATION OF SINGLE STRUCTURAL ELEMENT ANALYSIS TO WOOD ELEMENTS

Pyrolysis Behavior of Wood

The pyrolysis behavior of wood (Figure 19.5.21) is that of a charring material that deposits residue as it burns. This residue helps prevent further pyrolysis; it does, however, result in some loss of section. The thermal and mechanical properties of wood vary with respect to heat flux/exposure, exposure time, moisture content, wood species, and density.

Wood performance in fire is complex to predict. Heat transfer through this material is affected by phase change of moisture as well as opening/cracking of the increasing char layers, which then generate new paths for heat transfer. The mechanical properties of wood are known to be dependent on creep, moisture, the direction of the grain, and the presence of knots and other discontinuities.

However, fire is a short-term event; therefore, creep is of less concern. Indeed, because fire is a short-term event, BS 5268, Part 4[80] and other design codes allow the long-term stress values used for ambient design to be increased when checking the cold residual section after charring in fire design—that is, the strength properties of the cold residual section are assumed to be better in fire than ambient because the member will only carry the load for a short time. Due to charring, design codes generally recommend the reduced cross section method to calculate the residual capacity in fire in order to determine available fire resistance.

As for steel and concrete, the design fire must be first ascertained (standard fire, postflashover design fire, local fire, or external fire). However, unlike steel and concrete, a heat transfer analysis to determine the wood section temperature for the fire duration is not always required because most design methods assume the charred material should be ignored and the rest of the section has its full ambient design strength. Specific capacity checks, assuming the same equations as used at ambient, as outlined in the following sections can then be utilized.

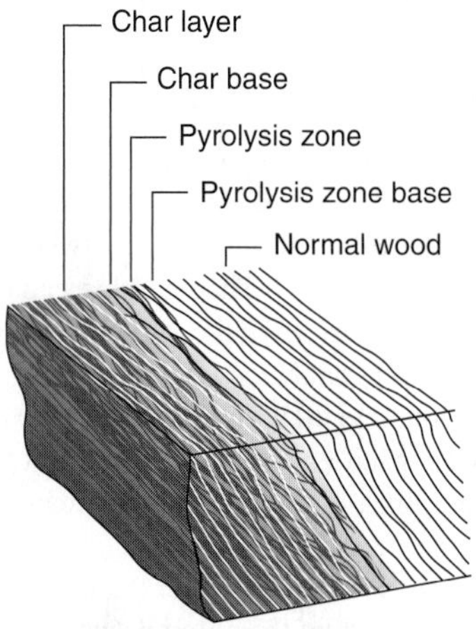

FIGURE 19.5.21 Charring of a Wood Section (Source: A. H. Buchanan, *Structural Design for Fire Safety.* Copyright John Wiley & Sons Limited, 2001. Reproduced with permission.)

Calculation Methods for Wood Used in the United Kingdom, Europe, Australia, and New Zealand

In the UK, BS 5268, Part 4[80] provides simple rules for designing wood members for fire. It treats solid members and glulams (glued laminated wood sections) in the same way, provided the glulam is laminated with certain phenolic and amnioplastic synthetic resin adhesives. Table 1 in the code lists charring rates to calculate the residual section of a wood member as a function of exposure of density. For example, the table has a higher char rate for western red cedar and a lower char rate for hardwoods with a density of 650 kg/m^3 or greater at 18 percent moisture content.

If wood sections are built up with metal fasteners, the charring rates given in BS 5268[80] can only be used on the whole section if the metal fasteners are fully protected against heat from the fire. Metal fasteners can be protected with passive fire protection or embedded in the wood so that they remain within the residual section (section not affected by charring).

To assess the fire resistance of a wood section, the following steps are proposed:

1. Calculate the residual cross section by subtracting the appropriate amount of lost wood, based on the defined charring rate for the fire resistance period under assessment. If the section has exposed corners, then rounding needs to be taken into account – that is, the corner will char more because it is exposed to heat on two sides.
2. Calculate the capacity of the resulting reduced section using cold design checks but assuming 2.25 × permissible long-term dry stresses.
3. For flexural, check that the deflection of the resulting reduced section does not exceed L/20 and does not impact the stability or integrity of other parts of the construction.
4. Check the stability in members subject to buckling, for example, columns or beams unrestrained by a slab.

Where connections are traditional wood joints, the same charring rates as for the main member can be adopted and its capacity in shear can be checked as it would be in ambient design.

The Hp/A of the wood section is important because fire-rated construction, for example, a ceiling, will shield wood sections and can have a significant impact on the resulting area of residual section for fire design. Figure 19.5.22 illustrates this concept. With shielding, considerably more area of residual section is possible, thereby increasing the fire resistance of the section.

Similar methods are given in Eurocode 5, Part 1.2[81] and design codes in Australia (SAA[82]) and New Zealand (NZS 3606[83]). The main difference is that BS 5628 and the methods in New Zealand ignore any reduction of wood strength below the char line (see Figure 19.5.21) whereas EC5 and SAA recommend considering it.

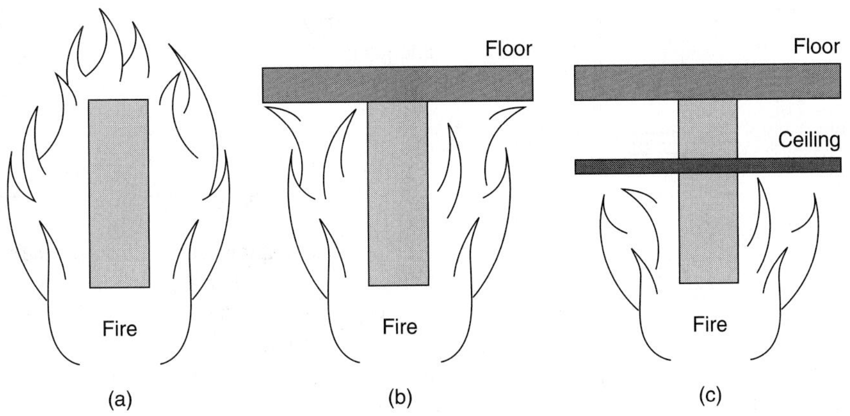

FIGURE 19.5.22 Heated Perimeter of a Wood Beam Shielded by a Fire-Rated Ceiling (Source: A. H. Buchanan, *Structural Design for Fire Safety.* Copyright John Wiley & Sons Limited, 2001. Reproduced with permission.)

Calculation Methods for Wood Used in the United States

White,[84] in Section 4, Chapter 11, of the *SFPE Handbook of Fire Protection Engineering,* discusses analytical methods for determining fire resistance of wood members. He reports on theoretical models for wood charring, many of which are based on the conservation of energy equation. The balance is between the heat stored in the wood, conduction away from or into the wood, and the fire and the energy absorbed when the wood undergoes pyrolysis. White also gives properties for wood at elevated temperatures and empirical models to calculate charring and the capacity of the residual cross sections.

For heavy wood members, ASCE/SFPE 29-99[56] provides analytical methods for calculating the fire resistance time (t) of beams and columns. The equations typically include load factor (z), initial dimensions of the section (b,d), and a constant (γ) with the units min/mm or min/in.

An example for beams exposed to fire on four sides is given in Equation 21.

$$t = \gamma z b\left[4 - 2\left(\frac{b}{d}\right)\right] \tag{21}$$

ASCE/SFPE 29-99[56] also presents values of fire resistance for various components of light frame wood construction. The additive method of calculation is proposed, which simply means adding together the fire resistance times assigned to each component as given in the code. For a stud wall, for example, the fire resistance time is equal to the total of all of the membrane elements on the fire exposed face plus the fire resistance time of the stud framing elements; the membrane on the unexposed face is ignored in the calculation.

Assessing Wood Connections in Fire

The collapse of traditional wood connections in fire scenarios is preceded by distinctive cracking and hissing noises due to the stresses in the wood. Visible deflections also become apparent before collapse, providing the fire services with notification that collapse is imminent.

New construction techniques involving steel connectors such as bolts or steel plates mean that the traditional bending and compressive forces in the wood joints have been largely replaced by localized shear forces surrounding the steel connectors.

Shear failure occurs when the lining within the wood section becomes heated and begins to act like a supercooled liquid. This change occurs at relatively low temperatures (~120°C) and causes the shear strength of the wood to change. This shear failure poses a catastrophic collapse mechanism during a fire because no prior warning of collapse is given under these circumstances. This area of fire engineering is being investigated by a number of researchers.[85,86] For now, metal connectors should be protected.

CASE STUDY: Residential Development, England. The following case study shows the application of single element calculation methods for wood using BS 5268 at a residential development in England. A structural assessment was undertaken of the existing wood beams within an old mill in the United Kingdom being converted to apartments. The structure required 60 minutes fire resistance according to the UK Building Regulations.

At ambient design, the wood members were being retrofitted with two steel plates, one on each side of the full length of the beam to resist bending. The beams were 190 mm wide by 390 mm deep plus partially shielded by a fire-rated ceiling 110 mm through its depth. The method in BS 5268[80] was used, assuming a total amount of charring of 40 mm for 60 minutes of the standard fire.

As an initial calculation, the residual section capacity after this section loss due to charring was calculated (Figure 19.5.23), assuming no benefit of the steel plates. This was done to determine if the steel plates might be left unprotected. The area of beam above the ceiling was assumed to not char because it is shielded from a fire. It was therefore assumed that the beam

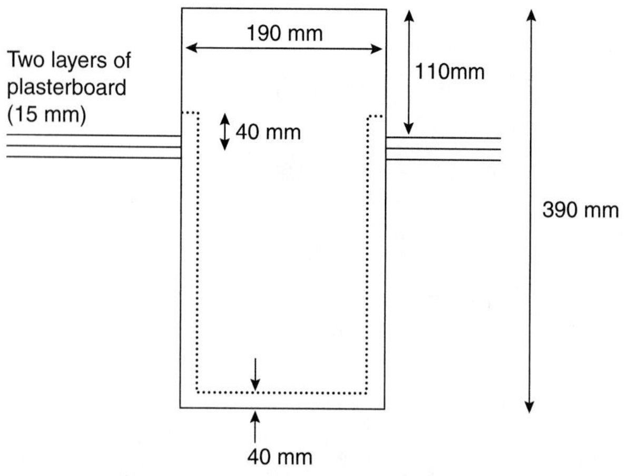

FIGURE 19.5.23 Residual Section After Char (Source: Arup)

would char on all three sides. The shear and bending capacity were checked, assuming the full strength of the residual cross section as permitted by BS 5268 [80].

From these assessments it was confirmed that the existing section would need additional provisions for 60 minutes fire resistance because the reduced section failed in bending. The following recommendations were therefore made:

- The wood section size to be extended to 430 mm deep from 390 mm, providing 40 mm sacrificial wood on the underside of the beam only (Figure 19.5.24)
- To provide two 280 mm × 12 mm S275 steel plates such that they extended the full depth of the exposed part of the beam, including the 40 mm additional depth proposed
- To protect the steel plates and bolt faces to a 60 minute applied fire protection, using a 550°C limiting temperature
- All connections exposed within the apartments to have 60 minutes applied fire protection because they are steel

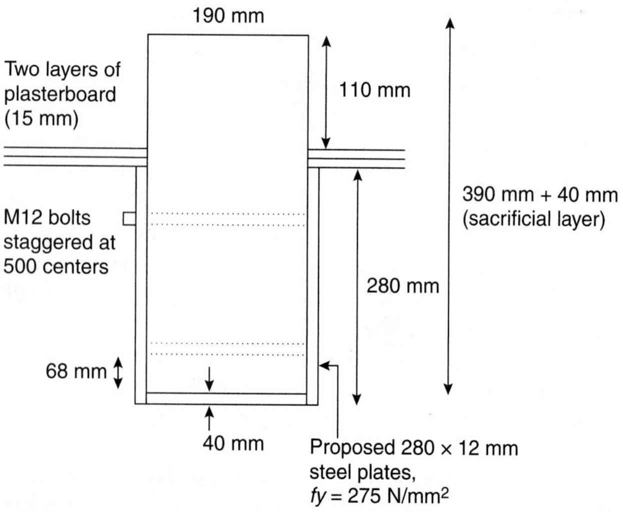

FIGURE 19.5.24 New Proposed Design Solution (Source: Arup)

The capacity of the new proposed section was shown to be adequate.

APPLICATION OF SINGLE STRUCTURAL ELEMENT ANALYSIS TO ALUMINUM

The sole design guidance available for the fire design of aluminum is Eurocode 9, Part 1.2, published in 2000.[87] In general the methods and principles are the same as for steel and the code looks very similar to EC3-1-2. Specific material properties (thermal and mechanical) at elevated temperatures are included.

USE OF ADVANCED ANALYSIS IN GLOBAL STRUCTURAL RESPONSE TO FIRE

Advanced Analysis Techniques

The current state of the art for structural fire assessments is to use advanced analysis techniques (Figure 19.5.25). These allow designers to quantify the global and local structural mechanisms throughout the duration of a fire. Therefore the stability of the structure in a severe fire can be determined, along with the quantification of the compartmentation response.

Such analysis can be used to assess a cold temperature structural design in specific fire events to determine if there are any particular areas of strength or, more importantly, weakness in the fire limit state. Fire-related responses are very different from any other form of cold temperature structural design concerns. So this form of analysis can prove a very useful tool to allow economical enhancements to be made to the areas of the structure underperforming in fire. For example, perhaps increasing the bottom flange thickness of a long span cellular beam is a more robust design measure in fire than applying thin-film intumescent paint.

Advanced analysis techniques also allow the development of refined passive fire protection strategies such that, in the case of steel structures, applied passive fire protection is proposed and installed in areas of the structure that require it, rather than providing "blanket" coverage, with its associated ongoing maintenance concerns throughout the lifetime of a structure. Of particular use is the ability, based on advanced analysis techniques, to quantify if compartmentation is being maintained, particularly at areas of concern, such as at egress stairs or fire fighter enclosures.

Advanced analysis models have undergone substantial validation for steel construction forms. Greater full-scale validation tests are now needed for other construction forms. Real-fire experience such as the Torre Windsor* in Madrid, Spain, on Feb-

*On the evening of Saturday, February 12, 2005, a fire broke out in the 32 story Windsor Tower, one of the tallest buildings in Madrid's commercial and banking center. The unsprinklered building had a concrete central core and a typical floor slab construction reinforced by bidirectional ribbed slabs spanning onto composite beams. Fire spread from the 21st floor, causing collapse of floors above the 17th, with significant deformation but no collapse of floors below the 17th.

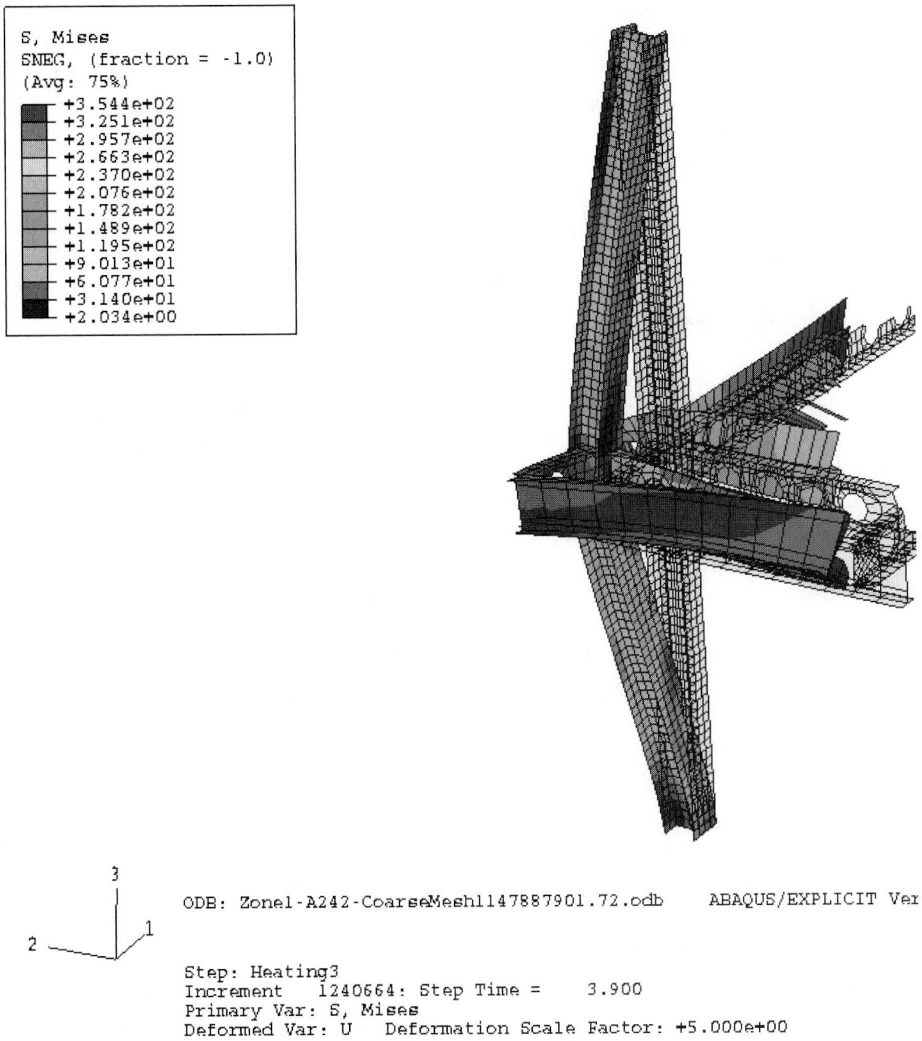

FIGURE 19.5.25 Example of Column Lateral Displacement from Advanced Analysis (Source: Arup)

ruary 12, 2005,[61] will provide substantial information on real performance of concrete structures. But a specific program of validation would be of great benefit for concrete, timber, and the increasingly popular long-span cellular beam construction forms.

This section addresses existing design methods, as well as a methodology for applying advanced finite element analysis techniques to real building design. This four-step technical process must always be accompanied by close consultation with the authorities having jurisdiction, and any other primary stakeholders, to ensure its real value is brought to a design.

Advanced analysis of steel/composite steel frames in fire was initiated in 2000. The Cardington experiments[6] and finite element modeling of the tests that followed[88–90] resulted in a number of design approaches for composite steel frame construction, taking advantage of tensile membrane action during high deflections in a fire. Two approaches are available: (1) design methods based on analytical methods derived from the Cardington data or (2) advanced thermomechanical analysis of the full structure using finite element analysis.

Analytical Methods to Quantify Tensile Membrane Action in Fire

In 2000, the Steel Construction Institute (SCI) in the United Kingdom produced relatively simple design guidance[91] based on work carried out by Bailey et al.,[92] as well as observations of the Cardington frame fire tests and similar building fire tests carried out in Australia and Europe. The guide is designed to allow secondary beams in composite steel-framed structures to be left unprotected, while achieving code-recommended fire resistances by capturing the strength enhancement of the composite slab in tensile membrane action. This occurs due to the high deflections in the slab during a fire.

Recommendations given in the new guide are restricted to structures that are similar to the Cardington eight-story composite steel frame—that is, nonsway frames with composite steel decks. The slab should comprise steel decking, reinforcing mesh, and normal-weight or lightweight concrete. The profile of the slab can be trapezoidal or re-entrant. The floor beams should act compositely (including the edge beams) and be designed to BS 5950 Part 3 or EC 4.[70] This method, therefore, does not apply to fabricated beams or beams with large openings, precast concrete slabs, or slim-floor construction. Slim-floor construction is a proprietary product in the United Kingdom where the beams are partially embedded in the depth of the concrete slab to achieve fire resistance with reduced passive fire protection on the steel.

The design method, derived from the principles of yield line theory for slabs, is simplified into a set of look-up tables that state whether a particular design will pass or fail given a certain combination of variables of beam span, reinforcement mesh, slab profile, and load. The design data assume the standard fire exposure (Figure 19.5.26) only. However, the full theoretical model[92] can be implemented with natural fire curves if created specially on a spreadsheet-based tool.

The maximum fire resistance that can be achieved using the guide is restricted to 60 minutes. Rules and guidelines for

Standard A-series mesh reinforcement
Reinforcement strength 500 N/mm²

R 90 R 120

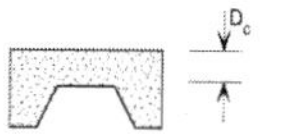

Design Table 2			Mesh size, beam design factor and additional beam load (kN) for fire resistance, concrete type and span 1											
			90 minutes fire resistance						120 minutes fire resistance					
			Normal weight concrete 80 mm concrete depth			Lightweight concrete 80 mm concrete depth			Normal weight Concrete 90 mm concrete depth			Lightweight concrete 90 mm concrete depth		
Span 2 (m)	Imposed Load (kN/m²)	Span 1 (m)	6.0	7.5	9.0	6.0	7.5	9.0	6.0	7.5	9.0	6.0	7.5	9.0
6.0	2.5 + 1.7	Mesh	A142	A193	A193	A142	A142	A193	A142	A193	A193	A142	A193	A193
		Beam	OK	OK	OK	OK	0.75	OK	OK	OK	0.99	OK	OK	OK
		Load	1	8	15	1	6	14	2	9	17	1	8	15
	3.5 + 1.7	Mesh	A142	A193	A193	A142	A193	A193	A142	A193	A252	A142	A193	A252
		Beam	OK	OK	0.99	OK	OK	OK	OK	OK	OK	OK	OK	OK
		Load	1	8	17	1	7	15	2	9	18	1	8	16
	5.0 + 1.7	Mesh	A142	A193	A252	A193	A193	A252	A193	A193	A252	A193	A193	A252
		Beam	0.83	OK	OK	OK	OK	OK	OK	0.89	OK	OK	0.84	OK
		Load	0	9	18	1	8	17	2	10	20	2	9	18
7.5	2.5 + 1.7	Mesh	A193	A142	A193	A142	A193	A193	A193	A193	A193	A193	A193	A193
		Beam	OK	0.80	OK	0.79	OK	OK	OK	OK	OK	OK	OK	0.98
		Load	6	14	26	4	13	23	7	17	28	6	15	25
	3.5 + 1.7	Mesh	A193	A193	A193	A193	A193	A193	A193	A193	A252	A193	A193	A252
		Beam	OK	OK	OK	OK	OK	0.86	OK	OK	OK	OK	OK	OK
		Load	6	16	28	5	14	24	7	18	30	6	16	27
	5.0 + 1.7	Mesh	A193	A193	A252	A193	A193	A252	A193	A193	A252	A193	A252	A252
		Beam	OK	OK	OK	OK	OK	OK	0.89	0.95	OK	0.84	OK	OK
		Load	7	18	31	6	16	28	7	20	34	6	18	31
9.0	2.5 + 1.7	Mesh	A193	A193	A193	A193	A193	A193	A193	A193	A193	A193	A193	A193
		Beam	OK	OK	OK	OK	OK	OK	OK	OK	OK	OK	0.98	OK
		Load	9	21	34	8	19	31	11	23	38	9	20	33
	3.5 + 1.7	Mesh	A193	A193	A193	A193	A193	A193	A252	A252	A252	A252	A252	A252
		Beam	0.99	OK	OK	OK	0.86	0.91	OK	OK	OK	OK	OK	OK
		Load	10	23	37	9	19	33	11	25	41	10	22	36
	5.0 + 1.7	Mesh	A252	A252	A252	A252	A252	A252	A252	A252	A252	A252	A252	A252
		Beam	OK	OK	OK	OK	OK	OK	OK	OK	OK	OK	OK	OK
		Load	11	25	41	10	23	38	13	28	45	11	25	41
12.0	2.5 + 1.7	Mesh	A252	A252	A252	A252	A252	A252	A393	A393	A252	A393	A393	A252
		Beam	0.76	OK	OK	OK	OK	OK	OK	OK	OK	OK	OK	0.85
		Load	14	30	48	13	27	43	17	33	52	15	29	45
	3.5 + 1.7	Mesh	A393	A393	A252	A393	A393	A252	A393	A393	A393	A393	A393	A393
		Beam	OK	OK	OK	OK	OK	0.78	OK	OK	OK	OK	OK	OK
		Load	16	33	52	14	29	44	18	36	56	16	32	51
	5.0 + 1.7	Mesh	A393	A393	A393	A393	A393	A393	A393	A393	A393	A393	A393	A393
		Beam	OK	OK	OK	OK	OK	OK	OK	OK	OK	OK	OK	OK
		Load	18	36	58	16	33	53	20	40	63	18	36	57

Notes:

Mesh indicates the minimum required mesh size.

Beam indicates the maximum beam design factor or utilization for the internal beams. If, in fire, the beam strength is adequate, 'OK' is shown. In other cases, the factor represents the maximum beam utilization at the ultimate limit state which ensures adequate performance in fire.

Load indicates the additional distributed load that must be applied to each of the boundary beams parallel to the internal beams at the fire limit state. The additional load from adjacent zones must be combined.

FIGURE 19.5.26 Example of a Look-Up Table for the Bailey Method (Courtesy of Steel Construction Institute, Silwood Park, Ascot, SL5 7QN, United Kingdom)

maximum spans, layout configurations, allowable deflections, and construction details are based on providing a final solution that brings no increased threat to the life safety of the occupants or fire fighters. Property protection is not addressed by U.K. legislation.

Excessive deflections that can occur in a fire should, therefore, be limited to prevent compartmentation breach. This ensures that the fire would not be able to spread horizontally or vertically as a result of deflections imposed by the heating regime. The guidance for the detailing of the slab to achieve adequate tensile membrane action in the fire limit state is, therefore, on this basis.

The method requires the building floor to be split into square or rectangular design zones (see example in Figure 19.5.27) or panels with each panel incorporating a number of unprotected beams surrounded by a square or rectangle of fully protected beams. The spans are restricted to 9 m. The edges of each panel must be vertically supported for the duration of the fire. Catenary action of the beams is conservatively ignored, although a revised version has recently been published that includes catenary of the beams. As a result of the slab membrane forces, beams at the boundaries of the floor design zones receive additional loading due to forces transferred from the slab, thus increasing the load ratio. This increase is addressed in the final design guidance provided.

Failure is defined in terms of a maximum allowable vertical displacement (L/30) and limits mechanical strains by assuming a maximum allowable stress for the reinforcement of $0.5f_y$. The equation for allowable vertical displacements should always give conservative results because of the various assumptions made and the fact that there was no failure observed in any of the Cardington tests.[6]

The enhancement in load-carrying capacity as a result of tensile membrane action is restricted by this limit. It is impossible to know how overconservative this method is because failure was not observed in the tests to validate the failure criterion assumed by the analytical model. Global failure can be modeled by finite element analysis; therefore, overconservatism can be avoided using a finite element approach. The method also includes options to enhance the strength of the slab if the load capacity is determined to be less than the applied load in the fire limit state, for instance, by increasing the mesh size or slab depth.

In 2005 the method was extended to include orthotropic reinforcement, recognizing that structural bays are sometimes longer in one direction and therefore require an orthotropic reinforcement mesh. The new method also includes catenary action of the steel beams, which was conservatively ignored in the earlier approach.

Usmani and Cameron[93] also developed a new concept for determining the limit capacity of rectangular reinforced concrete slab panels subjected to fire in tensile membrane action. In the context of performance-based design, this additional capacity of composite decks or reinforced concrete slabs can be exploited for providing structural stability in fire, given that a quantitative estimate of this capacity can be reliably made.

The difference between Usmani and Cameron's approach compared with the Bailey method is that the deflected shape of

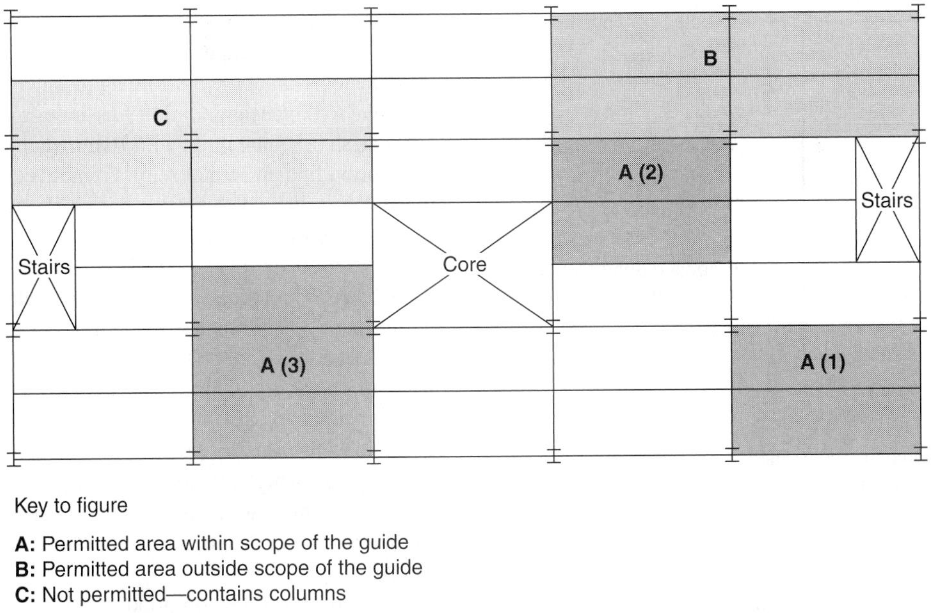

FIGURE 19.5.27 Example of a Suitable Structural Zone for the Bailey Method (Courtesy of Steel Construction Institute, Silwood Park, Ascot, SL5 7QN, United Kingdom)

the reinforced concrete slab is estimated using a cubic function before a calculation of tensile membrane effects is carried out. Usmani and Cameron[93] propose a three-stage process. First, the temperature distribution over the depth of the slab is estimated for a given fire scenario. Then, the deflected shape of the reinforced concrete slab and its membrane stress state is determined using an analytical method. Finally, an energy-based method is used to determine the maximum load that the slab could carry based on the geometric form and stress state determined in the previous steps. Failure is defined as a rupture of the reinforcing mesh at a given mechanical strain. There is no limit placed on deflection.

Heavy Engineering Research Association (HERA), a nonprofit research organization dedicated to the needs of the metals-based industries in New Zealand, has also published a design procedure to capture tensile membrane action in fire.[94] The design approach predicts the strength re-enhancement required from tensile membrane action to support the load based on work by Wang.[95] As tensile membrane action is a function of the maximum deflection of the slab and the extent of strength re-enhancement required is known, this is used to determine the slab deflection at elevated temperatures associated with the required level of strength reenhancement. Limits are applied to prevent undesirable failure of the slab and secondary beams—for example, fracture of the reinforcement. The guide considers all aspects of the frame, including pulling in of the columns when the slab is at high deflections in tensile membrane action, which is not addressed by Bailey[92] or Usmani and Cameron.[93]

All of the analytical methods presented require primary and edge beams to be protected. The protection reduces the edge/primary beam deflections and will generally allow the frame to survive longer in a fire. If the edge beams are unprotected, the relative displacement of the floor slab between the outside edges and the middle of the compartment would be smaller, reducing the development of tensile membrane action. It is important to note, however, that in order to address long-span floor systems and the stability of the columns, a finite element approach is required.

CASE STUDY: No. 1 Bradford Interchange, United Kingdom. The following case study uses the Bailey method to optimize the passive fire protection layout at No. 1 Bradford Interchange, United Kingdom.[96] Two design options were calculated, both of which allow unprotected secondary steel beams but consider different solutions for the slab profile and size of mesh reinforcement.

The office use building is four stories high. The structure is a composite steel frame with two configurations for the structural bays. The first is a 9 m × 7.5 m bay. Secondary beams are 9 m with secondary beam centers at 3.75 m. The second configuration is a 6 m × 7.5 m bay. Secondary beams are 6 m with secondary beam centers at 3.75 m. A typical structural bay is illustrated in Figure 19.5.28.

The structural bays described in Figure 19.5.27 are appropriate floor design zones for assessment using Bailey's method because they are rectangular and bounded by beams on all sides. Each zone contains beams spanning in one direction only. The columns are on the boundary of the zone—not within the zone—and all the beams connected to the columns are protected to 60 minutes fire resistance.

The calculations were carried out using a spreadsheet based on the original theory by Bailey,[92] rather than the tabulated data presented in the SCI guide.[91] The results were compared with the look-up tables in the SCI guide for consistency; although the

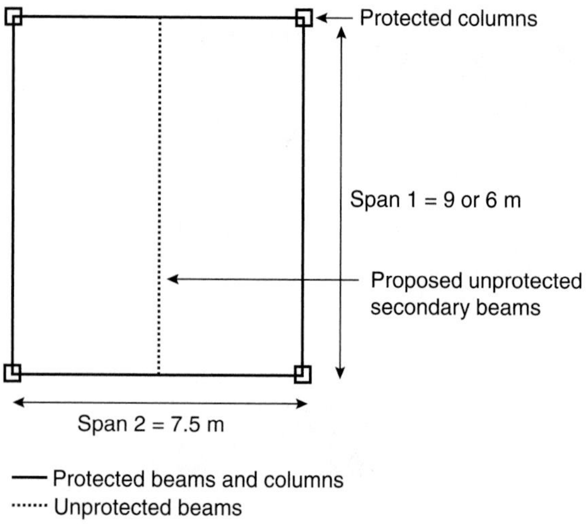

FIGURE 19.5.28 Schematic Plan View of a Structural Bay at Bradford Interchange (Source: Arup)

look-up tables are considered to be more conservative because the results are rounded up, they compared well.

The results of the design calculations for the 9 m span bay are given in Table 19.5.15. The use of re-entrant deck provides significantly better fire resistance because the ribs of the profile deck are bigger than in a trapezoidal deck, and therefore the reinforcement remains cooler. The reinforcing mesh required in a re-entrant deck slab is therefore less compared with the same design assuming a trapezoidal deck.

The location of the reinforcing mesh in the depth of the slab is critical to the design. Option 1 assumes a trapezoid deck with A393 mesh (a square mesh with 10 mm diameter bars at 200 mm pitch, providing an area of reinforcement equal to 393 mm^2/m); option 2 considers a re-entrant deck with A252 mesh (a square mesh with 8 mm diameter bars at 200 mm pitch, providing an area of reinforcement equal to 252 mm^2/m).

The additional load at the fire limit state on the edge beams parallel to the unprotected secondary beams is listed in Table 19.5.15 as a load ratio. The corresponding critical temperature in BS 5950, Part 8[42] is also listed. Where the critical temperature is less than 620°C (the normal assessment temperature for fire protection materials for beams), the beam must then be resized to incorporate a higher load-carrying capacity. In this case study, the critical temperatures for each beam size in each design option are all greater than 620°C; therefore, the beams did not need to be resized.

The method relies on good structural detailing; therefore, the following was written on the construction drawings:

1. All the steel beams should be composite with the slab through the use of shear studs.
2. The reinforcing mesh should be properly lapped and anchored in all areas of the slab as required for ambient design.
3. The location of the reinforcing mesh in the depth of the slab is critical to the design and should be marked on the construction drawings. For a trapezoid deck with A393 mesh, it should be 40 mm to 45 mm from the top surface of the slab. For a re-entrant deck with A252 mesh, it should be 65 mm from the top surface of the slab.
4. The mesh reinforcement should conform to the ductility limits of BS 4482[97] and BS EN 10080[98] for type B reinforcement. These limits are consistent with 12 percent elongation at failure.
5. Any cellular beams, including the beams immediately adjacent in the bay, are to be fire rated (i.e., no fire engineering).
6. All beams above a compartment wall (parallel or crossing the wall) should be fire protected to at least the same fire resistance standard as the compartment wall.

The use of Bailey's design method shows that unprotected steel secondary beams at Bradford Interchange were acceptable under the U.K. Building Regulations, which address life safety, while achieving structural stability for a 60 minute rating.

TABLE 19.5.15 Design options 9 m × 7.5 m Bays

	Option 1	*Option 2*
Span 1 (m)	9	9
Span 2 (m)	7.5	7.5
Unfactored dead load (kPa)	4	4
Unfactored live load (kPa)	4 + 1 = 5	4 + 1 = 5
Secondary beam spacing (m)	3.75	3.75
Mesh size	A393	A252
Slab profile	Trapezoid	Re-entrant
Reinforcement depth* (mm)	40–45	65
Concrete strength, f_{cu} (N/mm^2)	30	30
Concrete type	NWC	NWC
Secondary beam moment capacity (kNm)	640	640
Load ratio on edge beams parallel to secondary beams	0.33	0.32
Limiting temperature (Table 5 BS 5950 Part 8)	725	725
Resize edge beams for additional load?	No	No
Applied load at the fire limit state (kPa)	8	8
Capacity (kPa)	9.12	8.08
Capacity-load (kPa)	1.12	0.08

*The depth to reinforcement is measured from the top surface of the slab.
Source: Arup.

Design Methods Based on Finite Element Analysis

As a consequence of the Cardington Frame fire tests[6] and the savings that can be brought to a steel design project by using global structural analysis, composite steel frame structures are the most common construction form modeled using finite element techniques by design consultants. Performance-based codes in the United Kingdom, Europe, Hong Kong, Australia, and New Zealand state that design considering credible design fires, thermal heat transfer, and structural analysis using advanced finite element methods is an acceptable approach to fire design. There is currently no such guidance document in the United States. However, organizations like SFPE, NFPA, NIST, and AISC are gradually funding research and drafting documents that will assist engineers in carrying out structural fire engineering using finite element analysis in the future. It is expected that this process will take a number of years to enter the design domain.

Since the collapse of the World Trade Center towers, the finite element analysis technique is being increasingly used as a design tool to bring greater robustness to the response of a structure to fire. This is the only method that allows the quantification of the strengths and weaknesses in a cold temperature structural design to be quantified and identified; it can provide invaluable information to the structural team to allow changes to be made to enhance the performance of the cold temperature structure in the fire limit state. Currently almost no data exist for concrete or wood structures at a level that exists for steel structures. Hence finite element methods remain underutilized with these forms of construction.

In general, structural fire design codes will not provide guidance on how to perform an advanced structural fire analysis using finite element methods. They do, however, set out the principles that should be followed. They tend to state that the structural performance of steel may be assessed using calculation models that consider the fire exposure, thermal response, and structural response, provided that the models are based on acknowledged principles and assumptions of the theory of heat transfer and structural mechanics. Further, they stipulate that the governing elevated temperature response of thermal expansion and geometric nonlinearity have to be included in a structural model.

When using finite element analysis, a four-step process is recommended:[99] (1) determine credible design fires, (2) calculate the heat transfer from these fires to the elements in a representative structural model, (3) quantify the mechanical response of these elements for the duration of the fire, and (4) determine strengths and weaknesses in the global response of the structure when considering stability and compartmentation.

Typically, stability is deemed to be maintained once the columns continue to carry their design load for the duration of the fire and runaway failure of the beams or slab does not occur.[99] Note that an alternative view to this is to simply design to prevent deflections beyond that allowed in the standard fire test (L/20 as an example in the United Kingdom[10]).

For compartmentation, an assessment of strain in the slab and adjacent to protected escape stairs or, in countries such as the United Kingdom, adjacent to fire-fighting cores is necessary to ensure severe cracking is not causing breach of integrity or insulation.

Various methods, such as Eurocode 1, Part 1.2[22] or those described in the *SFPE Handbook of Fire Protection Engineering,* exist to determine design fires. However, their limitation, due to the small-scale nature of the testing carried out, means realistic compartment sizes as used in real buildings have not yet been validated. For empirical methods, this remains a concern. It is essential that a factor of safety is introduced in the design fire to overcome this concern. Methods based on a theoretical heat-balance approach are, therefore, preferred for adoption in compartment sizes that exceed the limits of empirical methods (i.e., the parametric equation in the Eurocode, derived from specific experimental data sets from Franssen,[100] NFSC1,[15] and NFSC2[101]).

An alternative approach is to assume the heating regime follows the standard temperature-time relationship as would be utilized in a furnace. However, when this is used, no cooling phase is incorporated, and so the specific structural response in this phase is then ignored. This can in some cases result in a nonconservative design, especially of connections that can fail in cooling as contracting beams pull on the connections.

One example of a methodology when using a finite element method is outlined in Eurocode 3. It gives similar performance-based objectives to other codes but also specific details about what should be included in advanced calculation methods. For example, when conducting a calculation of mechanical response, it states the following requirements, among others:

- The effects of thermally induced strains and stresses, both due to temperature rise and due to temperature differentials, should be considered.
- The deformations at ultimate limit state implied by the calculation method should be limited to ensure that compatibility is maintained between all parts of the structure.
- The design should take into account the ultimate limit state beyond which the calculated deformations of the structure would cause failure due to the loss of adequate support to one of the members.

Eurocode 3 also explicitly asks for validation of the computer model being used for the assessment, with whole frame fire tests.

In the United Kingdom, a new guide is being produced by the Institute of Structural Engineers that will identify the best practice for creating and using finite element models, plus suggested failure criteria to assess structural and compartmentation response in fire.

In Australia, the performance-based design framework permits structural fire engineering analysis using advanced modeling techniques. This is as a result of a series of full-scale fire tests to determine which elements were critical to the stability of the Williams Street building in Melbourne, Australia, as well as those elements critical for ensuring adequate protection during egress and fire fighting—for example, detailing of connections at protected cores.[102]

In Hong Kong and China, the finite element approach is not specifically codified, but is possible via performance-based options for design in the building codes there. However, currently the approach is most widely used in the United Kingdom.

In the United States, performance-based design is also permitted as an alternate means to the prescriptive requirements of the building codes; therefore, a finite element approach is permitted if the basis for the design can be agreed with the approving authorities. The finite element approach is not codified in the United States.

An alternative approach to this quantitative method for assessing structural response to fire is to use a risk-based method, such as outlined by Fontana. The main objective of Fontana's work is to develop a fire risk assessment framework that takes into account both risks associated with property damage and risks associated with injuries and fatalities. A generic model is developed, taking into account fire relevant parameters such as fire load, ventilation, and so on. The causal interrelations are modeled with Bayesian networks. The generic model is used for the calibration of already existing fire risk assessment frameworks—for example, the Swiss SIA Documentation 81.[103]

CASE STUDY: Kings Place Building, London, England. The following case study outlines the key steps and major considerations for a whole frame analysis using finite element analysis. The Kings Place building in London, England, is a composite steel-framed structure with eight stories above ground and three basement levels. The composite floors are constructed using 130 mm deep composite slabs with profiled steel decking attached by shear connectors to steel beams with circular web penetrations. The columns are universal steel column sections with two changes in size (at floor 2 and floor 6). Steel beam spans are 9 m or 12 m.

A finite element analysis of the structure was proposed in order to determine the response of the structure to fire. The aim of this nonlinear finite element analysis was to determine an optimized fireproofing strategy, along with an understanding of the strengths and weaknesses in the cold temperature design. This would allow specific advice to be determined for the structural team to incorporate enhancements, if required, specifically for the fire limit state.

Specific aims of the nonlinear analysis were to investigate the required fire rating of the structural elements and to determine if secondary steel beams could be left unprotected when only the columns and primary structure (edge beams and beams connected to columns) are protected. Based on the life safety requirements of the building regulations in the United Kingdom, acceptance criteria for the data produced by the analysis were structural stability (columns maintain their load-carrying capacity throughout the fire duration and no runaway deflections in beams or floors), compartment integrity, and compartment insulation (assessment of strain in the slab and adjacent to fire-rated enclosures to prevent any cracking).

For addressing the fire ratings, all structures forming the fire-fighting shafts were considered to remain at the standard 120 minutes. The time-equivalent method, as defined in BSEN 1991-1-2,[22] was then used to determine an overall building rating, utilizing risk factors that address only compartment size, occupancy type, and sprinkler provision. This resulted in an equivalent fire resistance rating of 90 minutes, based on calculation for an assumed compartment area of 4081 m², with a compartment height of 3.68 m, and percentage glazing failure of 100 percent. A sensitivity study considering 100 percent or 50 percent of the glazing breaking as well as the influence of reducing the floor area of the compartment involved in the fire was studied to obtain the longest period of fire resistance. This rating was utilized as the basis of the first model run, when any protected elements proposed that did not form part of the fire-fighting shafts and all compartment floors were assumed to be protected to a 90 minute standard. Should the finite element analysis reveal any concerns with this rating assumption, alterations could then be made. This is necessary as time-equivalent methods do not incorporate any form of structural response; they are purely simple methods based on possible heating regimes in a compartment only.

As a first step in the structural fire analysis, an assessment of credible design fires was necessary. This resulted in two design fires, quantified using the parametric equation in BS EN 1991-1-2:[22]

- *Short/hot fire.* Assuming 100 percent glazing failure to allow ventilation in the postflashover fire state, with a flashover fire acting over the whole floor plate. The peak temperature is about 1200°C.
- *Standard fire.* A long/cool fire relative to the parametric temperature-time curve described above, as specified in BS 476.[10] This was at the request of the approving authorities.

A short/hot fire, which results when the fire is well ventilated, was considered because of its high peak temperatures and its short duration, which together are known to induce large thermal gradients within structural elements, and also because it includes a cooling phase. The standard fire was chosen to investigate the effects of a longer-lasting fire, with a constant increase in temperature—that is, no cooling phase. All other credible postflashover fire scenarios, based on possible ventilation provision to the specific compartment dimensions and boundaries, were considered to fall within the boundaries of the two cases adopted.

The next step was to calculate the heat transfer from these fires to the structural elements in the proposed representative structural model. Different approaches were followed with regard to the concrete and steel materials. The heat transfer for the concrete slab was modeled using a 1D heat transfer model in ABAQUS 6.5.4.[104] The slab is modeled as a flat slab of equivalent thickness, although ribs in the dovetail slab are ignored. The same assumption is used in the structural model. This reflects the approach given in Section 4.4 of EC 4, Part 1.2.[70] Input data to the heat transfer model complied with the recommendations for siliceous concrete material properties in EC 2.[64] Moisture content in the concrete was ignored.

The heat transfer calculations for the steelwork were conducted using the lumped mass heat transfer model in EC 1, Part 1.2[22] and EC 3, Part 1.2[41] for the unprotected steel beams and protected columns. Material properties for the protection material were provided by the manufacturer and for the steel the values of conductivity, specific heat, and density in EC3, Part 1.2, were assumed.

In order to create a representative structural model, that is, a model with enough elements within it that it represented the full building, various modeling assumptions were made. When considering a single-story fire, the third floor was deemed to be the worst-case floor scenario in the building due to the highest column load ratio occurring on this floor. Therefore, it was considered to be representative of the entire floor plate on any story from Level 1 to Level 8 (Figure 19.5.29).

Worst-case boundary conditions were assumed for the structural models of each zone (see Figure 19.5.29). This means the resulting structural fire responses observed are on the conservative side, as less reliance is placed on the overall floor continuity available in the model.

The boundary conditions assumed for Zone 1 makes the portion of the building weaker with respect to the real case. The edge beam condition on the north side does not take advantage of continuity of the floor plate. Furthermore, the two symmetry conditions discount the model from the beneficiary effect of the concrete core and the continuity of the floor plate on the south side.

The boundary conditions of Zone 2 make the model act as an infinitely long strip of structural bays. In reality it is six bays long, and three of these are connected to structure that wraps around the core.

Zone 3 does not have boundary conditions. It has been considered as a structure itself, neglecting the decks that connect it to the rest of the building.

BS 5950-8[42] has been used to determine the factored design loads for the structural elements in the fire limit state. The factored gravity (1.0) and live load (0.5) were applied to the model throughout the analysis, using the applied loads provided by the structural engineers.

The materials adopted to represent the steel and concrete of the composite frame were taken from the appropriate Eurocodes (Table 19.5.16). Thermal expansion and full degradation of the stress-strain curves with temperature are allowed.

All connections were modeled in such way that they could not fail. For this reason the connection forces were checked at key stages in the fire to determine if the connection was being pulled in tension by the beam. (The protected steel-steel and steel-concrete core connections will therefore be designed on site to resist a tensile pull force of 60 kN when at a temperature achieved at 90 minutes of the standard fire, when protected.)

The software used to perform the finite element analyses (FEA) was ABAQUS.[104] The software is used throughout the world for stress, heat transfer, and other types of analysis in mechanical, structural, civil, and related engineering applications.

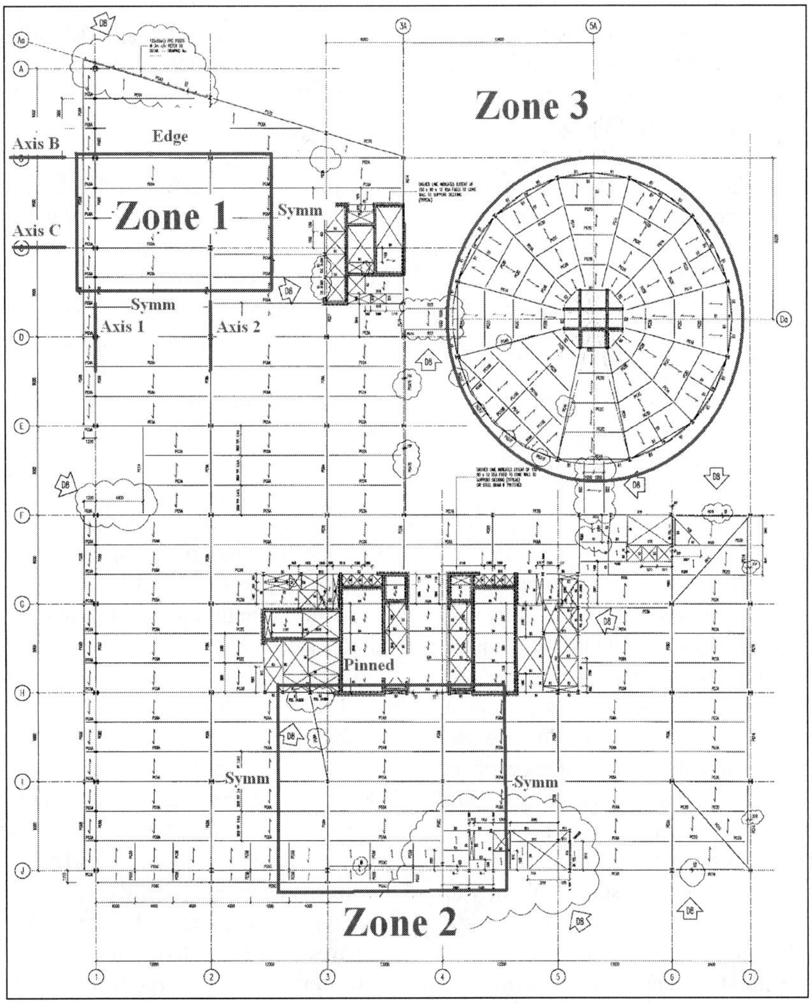

FIGURE 19.5.29 Third Floor Plan, Models Location, and Associated Boundary Conditions (Source: Arup)

TABLE 19.5.16 Material Properties

Material	*Grade*	*Model*
Steel (frame)	S355	Eurocode 3
Lightweight concrete (slab)	C35	Eurocode 2 with tensile strength equal to 5% of the compressive strength
Reinforcing mesh		A252, steel mat, 8 mm bars, spacing 200 mm

Source: Arup.

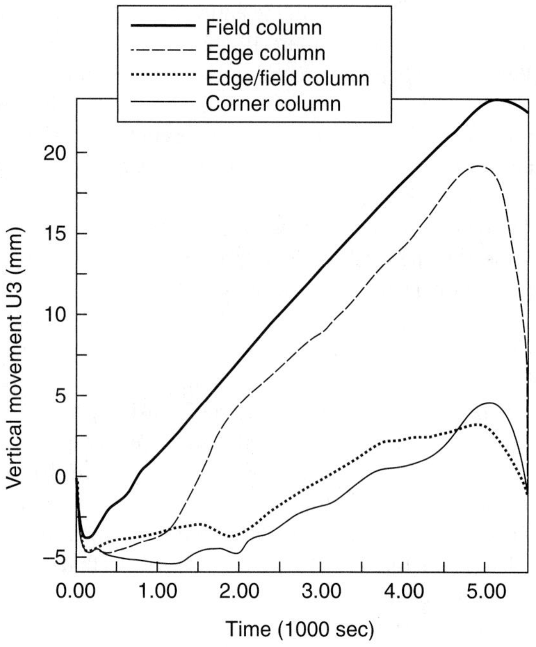

FIGURE 19.5.30 Vertical Displacement of Columns over Time During Standard Fire (Source: Arup)

The code has been validated extensively for many engineering problems and in particular by University of Edinburgh[7] and British Steel (now CORUS)[5,6] to model composite steel and lightweight concrete structures in fire.

The performance of all the models under the effects of the short/hot fire was found to be acceptable; stability and compartmentation were maintained throughout the duration of the fire. For the standard fire, however, various issues with respect to the response arose, as described in the following sections.

The main differences between the two fires are the length of the heating phase, the maximum temperature, and the cooling phase. The standard fire does not have a cooling phase; therefore, the elements are heated up throughout the analysis, with a steep initial increase and a rather flat evolution for the rest of the time. Eventually, in the standard fire, the elements reach hotter temperatures than in the short/hot fire, and this results in larger deflections as a consequence of more thermal expansion and also weaker material strengths, therefore leading to reduced structural performance. This would also be true of a parametric fire with limited ventilation—for example, 25 percent glazing failure.

An important outcome of the study was the finding that the Zone 1 model failed when subjected to the standard fire. Structural failure is assumed because rapid downward vertical displacement of the columns was observed. After the initial downward movement due to the load given by the above floors, the columns began to elongate when heated. The displacement reached values of about 25 mm before inverting its trend. At about 80 minutes, all the columns showed vertical runaway with a rapid increase in the downward movement while the temperature was still rising (Figure 19.5.30).

The column capacity is undermined by the lateral movement of the elements at the floor level causing bending stresses and P-Delta moments. Due to large thermal elongation of the long-span beams connected to the columns, and consequently large displacements, the column elements were required to sustain loads and actions they were not designed for in cold temperature conditions. Additional stresses/strains, along with material degradation, therefore undermined the structural stability. The structural model was considered unsafe under the effects of fire, and therefore methods of increasing the robustness were investigated.

A number of options are available to increase the robustness of the structure, such as increasing the column size, increasing the strength of the slab by adding more reinforcement, keeping the 12 m span beams cooler with additional fire protection, or increasing their load-bearing capacity by increasing the member size. In this project the latter choice was adopted in order to reach the best performance/cost-effective solution. Therefore, the bottom flange of the 12 m span secondary protected beams connected to the columns was increased from 16 to 25 mm. This means less reliance on fire protection and greater reliance on the structural system itself. This is considered to be a more robust approach as it is not reliant on maintenance.

When the Zone 1 analysis was carried out to check that the improvements adopted in the model were significantly changing the response of the structure, it was determined that the change meant no column failure and therefore greater robustness in the building. Throughout the fire, the columns exhibited a steady elongation along with the increasing temperatures (Figure 19.5.31). No vertical runaway was recorded in this case, and therefore the columns can be expected to maintain their stability.

Figure 19.5.32 shows the deflection contour of the slab at the end of the fire. The maximum deflection is 1600 mm at the mid-span of the corner bay. The stability of the structure is maintained thanks to the tensile membrane action developing within each structural bay.

A thorough investigation was made with regard to the total strains exhibited by the model. The software itself does not model reinforcement rupture, and therefore identification of this failure mode had to be considered by plotting the plastic strains in the structure.

Due to the high value of deflection, relatively large total strains are observed across the protected secondary beams, axis

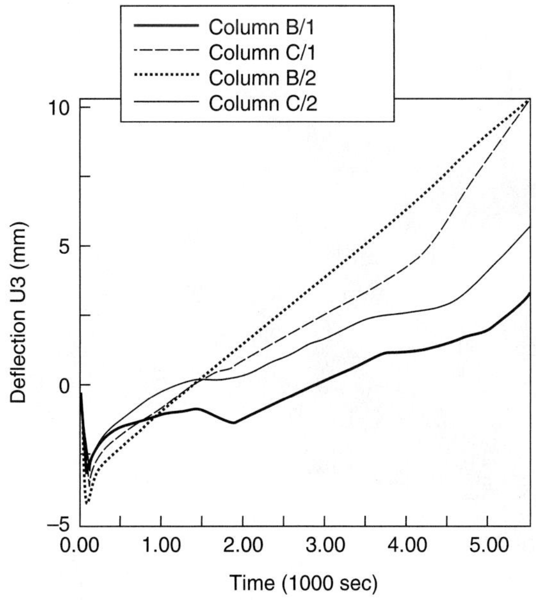

FIGURE 19.5.31 Vertical Displacement of the Column (Elongation) (Source: Arup)

C. The maximum observed strain is about 30 percent in the top of the slab and 25 percent in the reinforcement mesh (Figure 19.5.33).

It is assumed that these strains are likely to cause cracks at the top face of the composite slab. In addition, it is possible that the reinforcement may rupture locally over the support. To ensure stability is maintained, additional reinforcement was therefore proposed for the ribs of the dovetail profile over the protected primary beams.

For the Zone 2 model in the standard fire, there was generally better response than in Zone 1, mainly because Zone 1 represents the corner of the building and as such has two exterior edges, whereas Zone 2 represents an edge bay, which has more redundancies. However, as per the Zone 1 model, relatively large strains were observed at the core to slab interface. This has implications for compartmentation rather than stability. The connection between the concrete core and the dovetail slab was realized for this building using pull-out rebars that bond the core and the slab together. The concrete does not give continuity to the connection because it is poured in different stages, although a friction interaction might be assumed when the slab is heated and the edges are in close contact.

Given the aforementioned connection detail, the finite element model assumed a pinned connection between the concrete core and the slab. It is proposed that this assumption conservatively represents the connection at the early stages of the fire and better represents the behavior of the structure later in the analysis when the concrete slab may be cracked.

As highlighted in Figure 19.5.34, large strains up to a magnitude of 20 percent (neglecting the strains affected by the boundary conditions at the edges of the model) evolved at the concrete core, on the bottom side of the slab.

Initially, the underside of the slab will expand due to thermal elongation. Thus, high compressive strains will rise at the boundary with the slab pushing against the concrete core. Later, when the structural bays begin to deflect more, the edge of the slab will rotate significantly and concrete crushing is likely to occur on the lower portion and significant tension can be expected to develop in the rebars (Figure 19.5.35).

Compartmentation could be maintained due to geometrical rotation of the section, which is expected to tighten the lowermost portion of the concrete slab to the core. In addition, the rise in temperature throughout the extent of the fire will cause

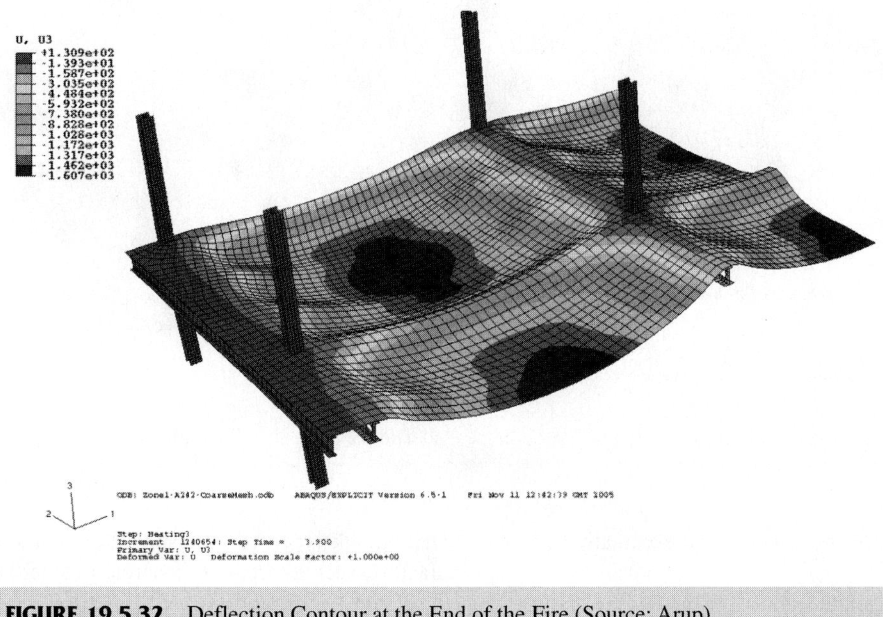

FIGURE 19.5.32 Deflection Contour at the End of the Fire (Source: Arup)

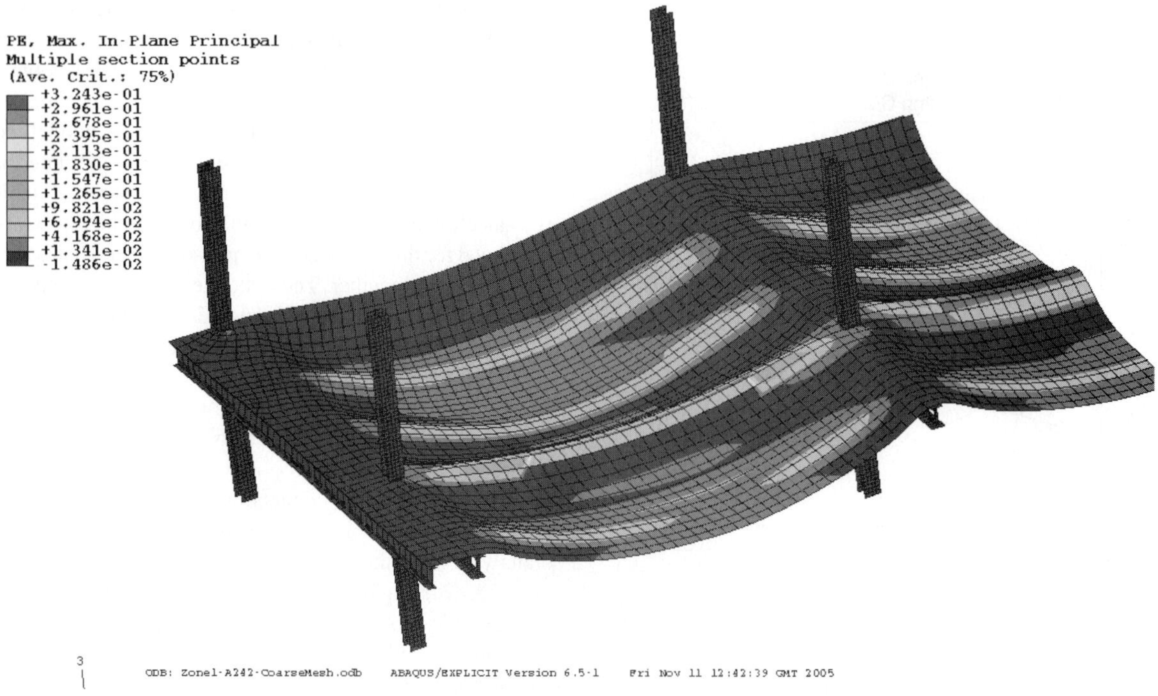

FIGURE 19.5.33 Maximum In-Plane Plastic Strains in the Reinforcement Mesh, Shorter Span Direction (Source: Arup)

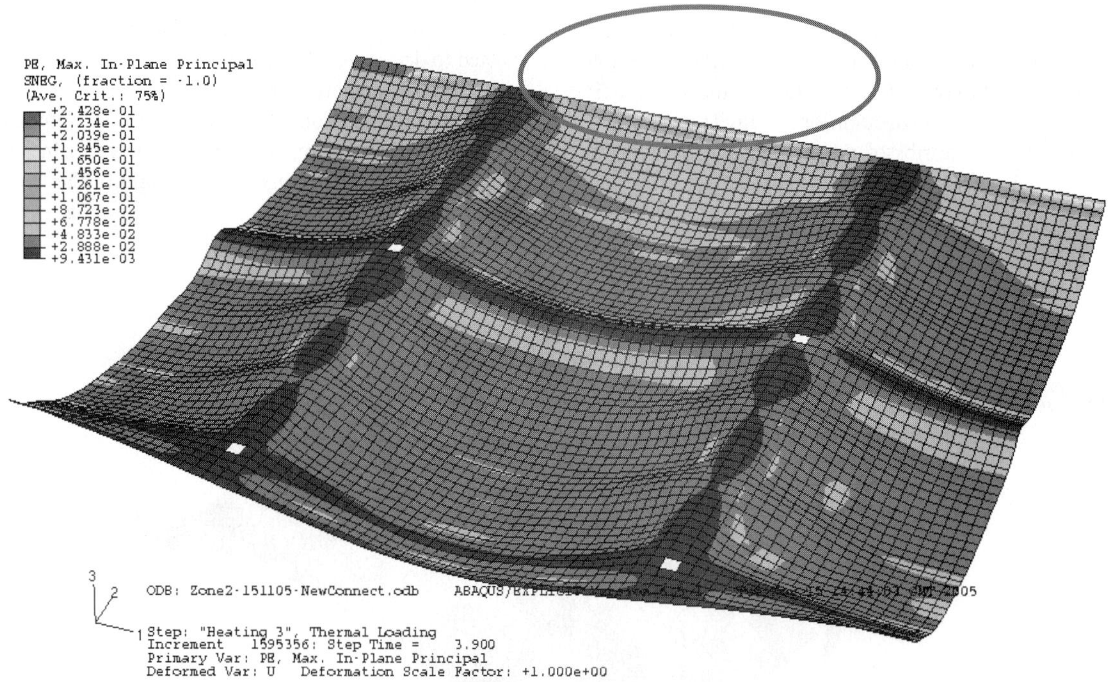

FIGURE 19.5.34 Maximum Resulting Plastic Strain on the Underside of the Slab at the End of the Fire (Source: Arup)

large elongation in the concrete, which will eventually help in closing the gap.

This interpretation of the matter is merely based on an understanding of the behavior of materials at high temperature and the likely structural response of an assembly in fire. Many factors, such as friction, concrete to steel bond, rebar anchorage, and temperature distribution are involved. Hence, a clear understanding of the phenomenon is not straightforward and to

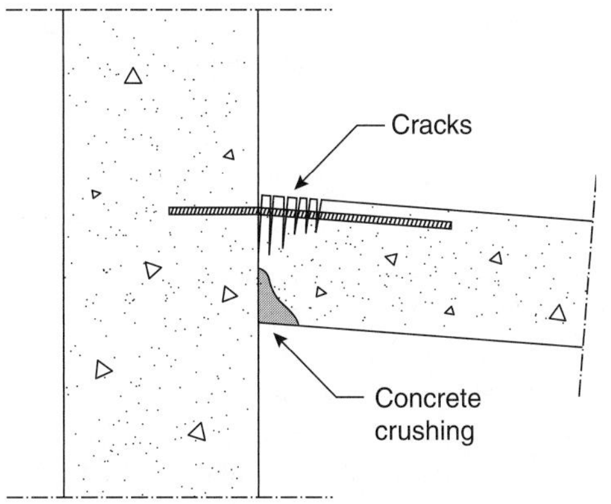

FIGURE 19.5.35 Likely Deformed Shape of the Structure at the Core Connection (Source: Arup)

obtain a more accurate understanding, specific detailed research is required. Detailing of connections and interfaces is becoming more and more important as the understanding of structures in fire evolves. It is important to note that this form of response is also true of fully protected structures.

Whether the current situation will cause a gap at the core to slab interface is highly debatable. On this subject, the approving authority has put forward a request for making further provisions to ensure compartmentation. To limit the effect of strains, a steel angle or similar vertical support was requested at the concrete core-to-floor interface to allow the slab to slide over the angle during a fire (Figure 19.5.36). The angle is fire protected and the length of the horizontal flange is at least 70 mm to accommodate an estimated horizontal displacement of the slab of 60 mm.

The analysis presented here was used to determine whether the structure could withstand an agreed set of credible design fires when secondary steel beams are left unprotected. This approach allowed a full quantification of the structural response of the building to fire.

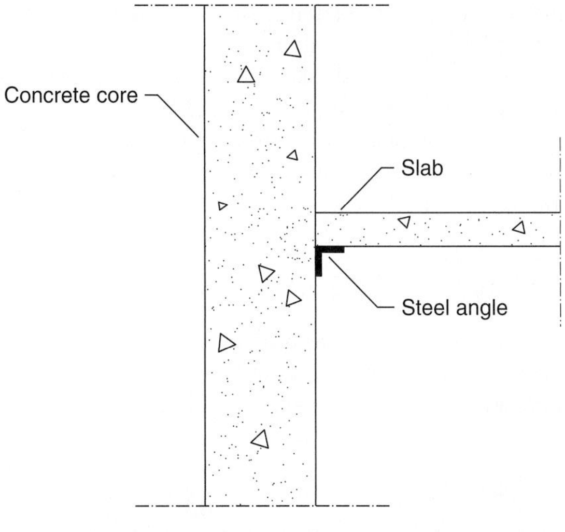

FIGURE 19.5.36 Detail of the Connection Between Slab and Concrete Core (Source: Arup)

The Kings Place case study has given rise to some important issues when considering stability and compartmentation of composite steel-framed buildings with long-span cellular beams. Leaving the secondary beams unprotected relies on secondary load-bearing mechanisms exhibited by the composite floor at the fire limit state. Minor mitigation measures were adopted to improve the structural performance in lieu of fire protection, including adding reinforcement locally and increasing the thickness of the lower flange of critical primary beams. Both are considered more robust than applied passive fire protection.

To improve compartmentation, a protected steel angle was proposed for the core walls to provide vertical support to the slab and allow the slab to slide over the angle during a fire. This provision is believed to avoid the fire breaching the floor-to-floor compartmentation of the building. The finite element analysis allowed such alterations to be determined.

This case study highlights the importance of checking that the cold temperature structural design has no intrinsic structural weaknesses in fire.

Advanced Analysis of Concrete Structures

Calculation of the whole frame response of concrete frames to fire is possible using finite element analysis. Eurocode 2 contains a method that specifically addresses concrete. However, none of the computer codes that currently exist and are used in fire design explicitly calculate spalling. Therefore the thickness of spalled material must be assumed and generally removed at the start of a structural or heat transfer analysis.

Most of the research in this field with regard to modeling concrete frames or sub-assemblies has been carried out in Europe, with some work in the United Kingdom after the full-scale Cardington frame fire test.[6] Most of the concrete finite element models in Europe have been validated against single element tests.[105,106]

Modeling tension cracking cannot be done without a code that includes fracture mechanics, which most do not because this calculation is labor intensive. In general, a smeared crack model is used to indicate areas of high tensile strain, which indicate that cracking will have occurred. Spalling is also an unknown; therefore, accurate concrete models are difficult to achieve.

The same four-step approach outlined for steel structures undergoing a finite element analysis can be used. Computer programs specifically written to quantify concrete frame response to fire include CONFIRE,[107] TCD,[108] FIRES-T3,[109] and SAFIR.[100]

As for any frame analysis in fire, concrete-specific codes must model nonlinear behavior of the structural elements and material properties, as well as include full degradation of material properties with temperature. An accurate representation of thermal gradients varying with time is particularly important for concrete elements as a consequence of concrete's poor conductivity. Nonlinear material properties of density, specific heat, and conductivity are required in a finite element model of the concrete structural element's cross section to calculate through-depth temperature gradients. If moisture content is ignored this will give conservative results because there will be no thermal lag as a result of latent heat of evaporation at 100°C. A temperature-time curve representing the design fire and associated boundary conditions (convection coefficient and emissivity) can then be applied to the appropriate faces of the finite element model. Design fires can be determined, as outlined earlier in this chapter.

Calculating the whole frame response of concrete frames to fire is rarely carried out in design. The main reason for this is the lack of full-scale test data to validate the use of finite element methods with concrete materials.

Of particular interest in the United Kingdom currently is the performance of prestressed concrete frames in fire, as they may be more susceptible to fire because the slabs are thinner, the prestressed tendons tend to be weaker than ordinary reinforcement at elevated temperature, and thermal expansion may reduce prestress. This results in an overall reduced level of performance. However, this remains to be confirmed.

Tabulated data exist for the dimensions and cover to reinforcement for prestressed slabs exposed to the standard fire, but they are based on limited test data. Ideally, a full-scale fire test of a concrete frame comprised of prestressed slabs/beams is desirable to check the tabulated data when the slab is restrained as in the real case; more spalling may occur because of this restraint. The test should be designed to identify alternative load paths such as compressive and tensile membrane action, which may support the load if prestressing is reduced by the tendons expanding in a fire. The test should also measure the reduction in prestress, if any, during the fire.

Advanced Analysis of Wood Elements

Design of wood elements in fire is also generally achieved by single element analysis throughout the world. However, Eurocode 5, Part 1.2[81] acknowledges that advanced models can be used for heat transfer analysis and or mechanical response. The complex phenomena associated with wood response to fire, as highlighted when single element methods of design were discussed, are also an issue for whole frame response; the recommendations in EC5-1-2[81] for conducting advanced analysis recognize these. For instance, it states that the thermal response model should take into account the variation of the thermal properties of the material with temperature, including phenomena such as increased heat transfer due to mass transport (e.g. due to the vaporization of moisture) or increased heat transfer due to cracking, which causes heat transfer by convection and/or radiation.

In advanced calculation methods for the structural response EC5-1-2[81] states that the user should take into account the changes of mechanical properties with temperature and moisture. In particular, the effects of transient thermal creep and transient states of moisture should be taken into account. One way of doing this is to use the mechanical properties of wood given in Annex B of EC5-1-2,[81] which include the effects of thermal creep and transient states of moisture. As for the advanced analysis of any structural frame, EC5-1-2[81] states that the structural response model should take into account the effects of nonlinear material properties and nonlinear geometry.

SUMMARY

This chapter outlined some of the design techniques available to assess structural fire resistance, with a specific focus on international approaches. The initial emphasis on the heating regime, which resulted in alternative approaches to fire resistance, was summarized. These do not address structural performance; rather, they address only heating regimes in real compartments and their duration relative to the standard fire resistance heating regime.

The three different forms that fire can take when forming the basis of a structural design include postflashover fires, local fires, and external fires. Guidance was provided on when these very distinctive scenarios are appropriate. Although work remains to be done on addressing the fire scenario in a risk-based framework appropriate for structural design, several design options are available for real building performance. Determining a fire scenario for a structural analysis should, therefore, serve as a useful framework for understanding the issues surrounding the most important parameter in structural fire assessments.

Specific design methods allow single structural element response to elevated temperatures to be quantified. Single structural element analysis techniques provide useful understanding of single element strength in fires under the reduced loading conditions associated with the fire limit state. They do not, however, incorporate any thermal expansion effects, which is one of the most important parameters that govern full-frame structural response.

The chapter concludes with a discussion on methodologies for using advanced structural fire models, as well as some current design methods derived from full-scale testing available in the public domain. Such techniques allow quantification of structural mechanics in elevated temperatures, including significant parameters such as degradation of strength and the alteration in geometry that takes place in a fire. A formal process for design and approvals within a risk-based framework is suggested as a useful way forward for the profession, along with the creation and education of skilled structural fire engineering professionals trained to address this essential component of robust design for all structural forms.

ACKNOWLEDGMENT

The author was assisted in the production of this chapter by her Arup colleagues Dr. Susan Lamont and Ms. Darlene Rini, both of whom are structural fire engineering specialists.

BIBLIOGRAPHY

References Cited

1. "The Behaviour of a Multi-Storey Steel Framed Building Subjected to Fire Attack Experimental Data," British Steel plc, 1998.

2. "Fire Safe Design: A New Approach to Multi-Storey Steel-Framed Buildings (Section Edition)," SCI Publication P288, Steel Construction Institute, Ascot, Berkshire, UK, 2006.
3. Client Report: Results and Observations from Full-Scale Fire Test at BRE Cardington, 16 January 2003, Building Research Establishment, Watford, UK, 2004.
4. Dayawansa, P. H., Goh, C. C., Bennetts, I. D., Poh, K. W., and Thomas, I. R., "Structural Evaluation of the 140 Williams St Office Building," Rep. No. BHPR/PPA/R/94/047/SG2C, BHP Melbourne Research Laboratories, Melbourne, Victoria, Australia, Feb. 1994.
5. Kirby, B. R., "Large Scale Fire Tests: The British Steel European Collaborative Research Program on the BRE 8-Storey Frame," *Fire Safety Science—Proceedings* of the 5th International Symposium, Melbourne, Australia, 1997.
6. Kirby, B. R., *British Steel Data on the Cardington Fire Tests,* technical report, British Steel, 2000.
7. "Main Report, Behavior of Steel Framed Structures Under Fire Conditions," PIT Project, University of Edinburgh, School of Civil and Environmental Engineering, Edinburgh, UK, June 2000.
8. Usmani, A. S., Rotter J. M., Lamont, S., Sanad, A. M., and Gillie, M., "Fundamental Principles of Structural Behavior Under Thermal Effects," *Fire Safety Journal,* Vol. 36, No. 8, 2001.
9. ASTM E 119—00a, *Standard Test Methods for Fire Tests of Building Construction and Materials,* American Society for Testing and Materials, W. Conshohocken, PA, 2000.
10. BS 476, Part 20: 1987, *Fire Tests on Building Materials and Structures,* British Standards Institute, London, UK, 1987.
11. ISO 834, *Fire-Resistance Tests—Elements of Building Construction—Part 8: Specific Requirements for Non-Load Bearing Vertical Separating Elements,* International Organization for Standardization, Geneva, Switzerland, 2002.
12. Law, M., "Prediction of Fire Resistance," Symposium No. 5, Fire Resistance Requirements for Buildings—A New Approach, Department of the Environment and Fire Office's Committee Joint Fire Research Organisation, London HMSO, 1973.
13. Thomas, P. H., *Fires in Model Rooms: CIB Research Programmes,* Current Paper CP 32/74, BRE, Borehamwood, UK, 1974.
14. Malhotra, H. L., *Design of Fire-Resisting Structures,* Surrey University Press, Glasgow, UK, 1982.
15. *Competitive Steel Buildings Through Natural Fire Safety Concept,* Final Report, NFSC1, CEC Agreement 7210-SA/125/126/213/214/323/423/522/623/839/937, Profil ARBED Research, Luxembourg, Mar. 1999.
16. *Fire Protection Through Modern Building Codes,* 5th ed., American Iron and Steel Institute, Washington, DC, 1981.
17. Ingberg, S. H., "Tests of the Severity of Building Fires," *NFPA Quarterly,* Vol. 22, No. 1, 1928, pp. 43–61.
18. Pettersson, O., Magnusson, S.E., Thor, J., *Fire Engineering Design of Steel Structures,* Swedish Institute of Steel Construction, Stockholm, Sweden, 1976.
19. Kawagoe, K., Takashi, S., and Sekine, T., *Estimation of Fire Temperature-Time Curve in Rooms,* Occasional Report No. 11, Building Research Institute of Japan, Tokyo, 1963.
20. Thomas, P. H., and Heselden, A. J. M., *Fully Developed Fires in Single Compartments,* A co-operative research program of the Conseil International du Batiment, CIB Report No. 20, Fire Research Station Research Note No. 923, 1972.
21. Magnusson, S. E., and Thelandersson, S., *Temperature-Time Curves of Complete Process of Fire Development—Theoretical Study of Wood Fuel Fires in Enclosed Spaces,* Civil Engineering and Building Construction Series, Technical Report 65, Acta Polytechnica Scandinavica, Stockholm, Sweden, 1970.
22. *Eurocode 1: Actions on Structures—Part 1.2: General Actions—Actions on Structures Exposed to Fire,* BS EN 1991-1-2:2002, British Standards Institute, London, UK, 2002.
23. DIN 18230-1, *Structural Fire Protection in Industrial Buildings—Part 1: Determining the Design Fire Resistance Time,* Beuth Verlag, Berlin, Germany, 1998.
24. Thomas, G. C., Buchanan, A. H., Fleischmann, C. M., "Structural Fire Design: The Role of Time Equivalence," *Fire Safety Science—Proceedings* of the 5th International Symposium, Melbourne, Australia, 1997, pp. 607–618.
25. *Fire Engineering Design Guides,* A. H. Buchanan (Ed.), report of a study group of the New Zealand Structural Engineering Society and the New Zealand National Fire Protection Association, endorsed by the Society of Fire Protection Engineers New Zealand Chapter, July 1994.
26. Drysdale, D., *An Introduction to Fire Dynamics,* 2nd ed., Wiley & Sons, Hoboken, NJ, 1999.
27. Harmathy, T. Z., and Mehaffey, J. R., "Post-Flashover Compartment Fires," *Fire and Materials,* Vol. 7, No. 2, 1983, pp. 49–61.
28. *Eurocode 1: Basis of Design and Actions on Structures. Part 2.7: Actions on Structures Exposed to Fire,* CEN/TC250/SC1/1993/N107, European Committee for Standardization, Brussels, Belgium, June 1993.
29. Law, M., "A Review of Formulae for *t*-Equivalent," *Fire Safety Science—Proceedings* of the Fifth International Symposium, March 3–7, 1997, Melbourne, Australia, International Association for Fire Safety Science, London, UK, 1997, pp. 985–996.
30. Thomas, I. R., and Bennetts, I. D., *Fires in Enclosures with Single Ventilation Openings. Comparison of Long and Wide Enclosures,* 6th IAFSS Symposium, Poitiers, France, 1999, pp. 941–952.
31. Law, M., Private correspondence, Nov. 2000.
32. Hall, J. R., "Fire Risk Analysis," *Fire Protection Handbook,* 18th ed., A. E. Cote (Ed.), National Fire Protection Association, Quincy, MA, 1997.
33. Baldwin, R., "A Statistical View of Fire Protection," Paper 05, Fire-Resistance Requirements for Buildings—A New Approach, Symposium No. 5, September 28, 1971, London, UK, Fire Research Station, Borehamwood, UK, 1971, pp. 39–46.
34. CIBSE Technical Memorandum TM19, "Relationships for Smoke Control Calculations," Chartered Institution of Building Services Engineers, London, UK, Sept. 1995.
35. Heskestad, G., "Fire Plumes, Flame Height, and Air Entrainment," *SFPE Handbook of Fire Protection Engineering,* 3rd ed., P. J. DiNenno et al. (Eds.), National Fire Protection Association, Quincy, MA, 2002.
36. Mulholland G. W., "Smoke Production and Properties," *SFPE Handbook of Fire Protection Engineering,* 3rd ed., P. J. DiNenno et al. (Eds.), National Fire Protection Association, Quincy, MA, 2002.
37. Law, M., and O'Brien, T., *Fire and Steel Construction: Fire Safety of Bare External Structural Steel,* The Steel Construction Institute, Ascot, Berkshire, UK, 1986.
38. McGrattan, K. B., Baum, H. R., Rehm, R. G., Hamins, A., Forney, G. P., Floyd, J. E., Hostikka, S., and Prasad, K., "Fire Dynamics Simulator (Version 3)—Technical Reference Guide," NIST, Gaithersburg, MD, 2002.
39. Walton, D., and Thomas, P. H., "Estimating Temperatures in Compartment Fires," *SFPE Handbook of Fire Protection Engineering,* 3rd ed., P. J. DiNenno et al. (Eds.), National Fire Protection Association, Quincy, MA, 2002.
40. Cox, G., and Suresh, K., "Modeling Enclosure Fires Using CFD," *SFPE Handbook of Fire Protection Engineering,* 3rd ed., P. J. DiNenno et al. (Eds.), National Fire Protection Association, Quincy, MA, 2002.
41. *Eurocode 3: Design of Steel Structures—Part 1.2: General Rules—Structural Fire Design,* BS EN 1993-1-2:1995, British Standards Institute, London, UK, 2001.
42. BS 5950-8: 2003, *Structural Use of Steelwork in Building—Part 8: Code of Practice for Fire Resistant Design,* British Standards Institute, London, UK, 2003.
43. *International Building Code,* International Code Council, Washington, DC, 2003.
44. *Eurocode 0: Basis of Structural Design,* BS EN:1990, British Standards Institute, London, UK, 2002.

45. NZS 4203: 1992, *Code of Practice for General Structural Design and Design Loadings for Buildings,* Standards New Zealand, Wellington, New Zealand, 1992.
46. AS/NZS 1170.1:2002, *Structural Design Actions, Part 1: Permanent, Imposed and Other Actions,* Australian/New Zealand Standard, 2002.
47. Ellingwood, B. R., and Corotis, R. B., "Load Combinations for Buildings Exposed to Fire," *American Institute of Steel Construction Engineering Journal,* First Quarter, 1991.
48. ANSI A58.1, *Minimum Design Load in Buildings and Other Structures,* American National Standards Institute, Washington, DC, 1982.
49. ASCE 7-05, *Minimum Design Loads for Buildings and Other Structures,* American Society of Civil Engineers, Reston, VA, 2005.
50. Kirby, B. R., "The Application of BS 5950: Part 8 on Fire Limit State Design to the Performance of 'Old' Structural Mild Steels," *Fire Safety Journal,* Vol. 20, No. 4, 1993, pp. 353–376.
51. Lawson, R. M., and Newman, G. M., *Fire-Resistant Design of Steel Structures—A Handbook to BS 5950,* Part 8, SCI Publication 080, The Steel Construction Institute, Berkshire, UK, 1990.
52. Wang, Y. C., *Steel and Composite Structures, Behavior and Design for Fire Safety,* Spon Press, London and New York, 2002.
53. AS 4100:1998, *Steel Structures,* Australian Code, Section 12, "Fire," Standards Australia, Sydney, Australia, 1998.
54. NZS 3404:1996, *Steel Structures Standard,* Standards New Zealand, Wellington, New Zealand, 1996.
55. ECCS, *Design Manual on the European Recommendations for Fire Safety of Steel Structures,* European Convention for Constructional Steelwork, Brussels, Belgium, 1985.
56. ASCE/SFPE 29-99, *Standard Calculation Methods for Structural Fire Protection,* American Society of Civil Engineers, Reston, VA, 2003.
57. Milke, J. A., "Analytical Methods for Determining Fire Resistance of Steel Members," *SFPE Handbook of Fire Protection Engineering,* 3rd ed., P. J. DiNenno et al. (Eds.), National Fire Protection Association, Quincy, MA, 2002.
58. Al-Jabri, K. S., Burgess, I. W., and Plank, R. J., "Prediction of the Degradation of Connection Characteristics at Elevated Temperature," *Journal of Constructional Steel Research,* No. 60, 2004, pp. 771–781.
59. Scott, D. M., Lane, B., and Gibbons C., "Fire Induced Progressive Collapse," *NIST Multihazard Mitigation Council, National Workshop on the Prevention of Progressive Collapse,* Chicago, July 2002.
60. Rotter, J. M., et al., "Structural Performance of Redundant Structures Under Local Fires," *Proceedings* of the Interflam '99 Conference, Edinburgh, UK, 1999, pp 1069–1080.
61. Arup Fire Report for the Health and Safety Executive, *Fire Resistance of Concrete Enclosures,* Work Packages 1–8, http://www.hse.gov.uk/research/nuclear/parts1and2.pdf, http://www.hse.gov.uk/research/nuclear/parts3and4.pdf, http://www.hse.gov.uk/research/nuclear/parts5to8.pdf, Arup, London, UK, Oct. 2005.
62. BS 8110–2:1985, *Structural Use of Concrete—Part 2: Code of Practice for Special Circumstances,* British Standards Institute, London, UK, 1985.
63. Lennon, T., *Fire Safety of Concrete Structures: Background to BS 8110 Fire Design,* BR 468, Building Research Establishment, Watford, UK, 2004.
64. *Eurocode 2: Design of Concrete Structures—Part 1.2: General Rules—Structural Fire Design,* BS EN 1992-1-2:1996, British Standards Institute, London, UK, 1995.
65. AS 3600:2001, *Concrete Structures,* Australian Code, Section 5, "Design for Fire Resistance," Standards Australia, Sydney, Australia, 2001.
66. Fleischmann, C., and Buchanan, A., "Analytical Methods for Determining the Fire Resistance of Concrete Members," *SFPE Handbook of Fire Protection Engineering,* 3rd ed., P. J. DiNenno et al. (Eds.), National Fire Protection Association, Quincy, MA, 2002.
67. Anderberg, Y., *Computer Simulations and a Design Method for Fire Exposed Concrete Columns,* Report 92-50, Fire Safety Design, Lund, Sweden, 1993.
68. Buchanan, A. H., *Structural Design for Fire Safety,* John Wiley and Sons, West Sussex, UK, 2001.
69. ACI 216R-89, "Guide for Determining the Fire Endurance of Concrete Elements," *Manual of Concrete Practice,* American Concrete Institute (ACI), Farmington Hills, MI, 2005.
70. *Eurocode 4—Design of Composite Steel and Concrete Structures—Part 1.2: General Rules—Structural Fire Design,* BS EN 1994-1-2:2005, British Standards Institute, London, UK, 2005.
71. British Standards Institution, "Eurocode 4: Design of Composite Steel and Concrete Structures General Rules—Structural Fire Design," BS EN 1994-1.2:2005, London, UK, 2005.
72. *Design Guide for SHS Concrete Filled Columns,* The Steel Construction Institute, Ascot, Berkshire, UK, 2002.
73. Kettner, F., "Investigations on the Load Bearing Behavior of Composite Columns Under Fire Conditions," 1st International PhD Workshop on Fire Protection Science and Engineering, Hanover, Germany, 2005.
74. *Computer Assisted Analysis of the Fire Resistance of Steel and Composite Concrete–Steel Structures,* REFAO-CAFIR, final report, CEC Agreement 7210-SA/502, Commission of the European Community (CEC), Luxembourg, 1987.
75. ConcFill, released by the Steel Construction Institute (UK) and Corus Group, plc, Corus Tubes, Corby, Northhamptonshire, UK, 2003.
76. Lie, T. T., "New Facility to Determine Fire Resistance of Columns," *Canadian Journal of Civil Engineering,* Vol. 7, No. 3, 1980, pp. 551–558.
77. Kodur, V. K. R., "Performance of High Strength Concrete-Filled Steel Columns Exposed to Fire," *Canadian Journal of Civil Engineering,* Vol. 25, 1998, pp. 975–981.
78. Lie, T. T., and Chabot, M., *Experimental Studies on the Fire Resistance of Hollow Steel Columns Filled with Plain Concrete,* Internal report No. 611, National Research Council of Canada, Ottawa, Ontario, 1992.
79. Lie, T. T., and Kodur, V. J. R., "Fire Resistance of Steel Columns Filled with Bar-Reinforced Concrete," *ASCE Journal of Structural Engineering,* Vol. 122, No. 1, 1996, pp. 30–36.
80. BS 5268, Part 4, *Structural Use of Timber—Part 4: Fire Resistance Design of Timber Structures,* Section 4.1, "Recommendations for Calculating Fire Resistance of Timber Members," British Standards Institute, London, UK, 1978.
81. *Eurocode 5: Design of Timber Structures—Part 1.2: General—Structural Fire Design,* BS EN 1995-1-2:2004, British Standards Institute, London, UK, 2004.
82. SAA, "Timber Structures, Part 4: Fire Resistance of Structural Timber Members," AS 1720.4-1990, Standards Association of Australia, North Sydney, New South Wales, Australia, 1990.
83. NZS 3606:1993, *Code of Practice for Timber Design,* Standards New Zealand, Wellington, New Zealand, 1993.
84. White, R. H., "Analytical Methods for Determining the Fire Resistance of Timber Members," *SFPE Handbook of Fire Protection Engineering,* 3rd ed., P. J. DiNenno et al. (Eds.), National Fire Protection Association, Quincy, MA, 2002.
85. Buchanan, A. H., and King, A. B., "Fire Performance of Gusset Connections in Glue Laminated Timber," *Fire and Materials,* Vol. 15, 1991, pp. 137–143.
86. White, R. H., and Cramer, S. M., "Improving the Fire Endurance of Wood Truss Systems," *Proceedings* of the Pacific timber engineering conference, Gold Coast, Australia, 1994, pp. 582–589.
87. British Standards Institution, "Eurocode 9: Design of Aluminium Structures—Structural Fire Design," BS EN 1999-1.2:2007, London, UK, 2007.
88. *Final Report of the DETR-PIT Project: Behaviour of Steel Framed Structures Under Fire Conditions,* Report R00-SM3, www.civ.ed.ac.uk/research/fire/public_html/Cardington/SM3.pdf, The University of Edinburgh, Edinburgh, UK, 2000.

89. Huang, Z., Burgess, I. W., and Plank, R. J., "Non-Linear Modeling of Three Full Scale Structural Fire Tests," 1st International Conference Structures in Fire, Copenhagen, June 2000.
90. Bailey, C. G., and Moore, D. B., "The Behavior of Full-Scale Steel Framed Buildings Subject to Compartment Fires," *The Structural Engineer,* Vol. 77, No. 8, 1999, pp. 15–21.
91. Newman, G., Robinson, J. T., and Bailey, C. G., *Fire Safe Design: A New Approach to Multi-Storey Steel Framed Buildings,* SCI Publication 288, Steel Construction Institute, Berkshire, UK, 2000.
92. Bailey, C. G., White, D. S., and Moore, D. B., "The Tensile Membrane Action of Unrestrained Composite Slabs Simulated Under Fire Conditions," *Engineering Structures,* Vol. 22, 2000, pp. 1583–1595.
93. Usmani, A. S., and Cameron, N. J. K., "Limit Capacity of Reinforced Concrete Floor Slabs in Fire," *Cement and Concrete Composites,* Vol. 26, No. 2, 2004, pp. 127–140.
94. Clifton, G. C., *Draft for Development: Design Procedure for the Inelastic Floor System Frame Response of Multi-Storey Steel Framed Buildings in Fully Developed Natural Fires,* Technical Report R4-90-DD, HERA (Heavy Engineering Research Association), Manukau City, New Zealand, 1998.
95. Wang, Y. C., "Tensile Membrane Action in Slabs and Its Application to the Cardington Fire Tests," *Proceedings* of the 2nd Cardington Conference. BRE, Cardington, UK, March 1996.
96. Arup Fire report, *Structural Fire Assessment of No.1 the Interchange Bradford,* Arup, London, UK, 2002
97. BS 4482, "Steel Wire for Reinforcement of Concrete Products—Specification," British Standards Institute, London, UK, 2005.
98. BS EN 10080, "Steel for Reinforcement of Concrete—Weldable Reinforcing Steel—General," British Standards Institute, London, UK, 2005.
99. Lamont, S., Lane, B., Flint, G., and Usmani, A. S., "Behavior of Structures in Fire and Real Design—A Case Study," *Journal of Fire Protection Engineering,* Vol. 16, No. 1, 2006.
100. Nwosu, D. I., Kodur, V. K. R., Franssen, J. M., and Hum, J. K., *User Manual for SAFIR: A Computer Program for Analysis of Structures at Elevated Temperature Conditions,* Int. Report 782, National Research Council of Canada, Ottawa, Canada, Oct. 1999.
101. NFSC2: CEC Agreement 7210-PA/PB/PC/PE/PF/PR-060, *Natural Fire Safety Concept—Full Scale Tests, Implementation in the Eurocodes and Development of a User Friendly Design Tool,* Final report, Profil ARBED Research, Luxembourg, Dec. 2000.
102. Owens, G. (Ed.), *Proceedings* of the 2nd World Conference on Steel in Construction, San Sebastián, Spain, May 11–13, 1998.
103. Gretner, M., *Fire Risk Evaluation,* Association of Cantonal Institutions for Fire Insurance, Society of Engineers and Architects and Fire Prevention Services for Industry and Trade, Zurich, Switzerland, 1980.
104. ABAQUS, Inc., Rising Sun Mills, 166 Valley Street, Providence, RI 02909-2499, USA.
105. Hurst, J. P., and Ahmed, G. N., "Validation and Application of a Computer Model for Predicting the Thermal Response of Concrete Slabs Subjected to Fire," *ACI Structural Journal,* Title no. 95-S42, Vol. 95, No. 5, Sept.–Oct. 1998.
106. Khoury, G. A., "Effect of Fire on Concrete and Concrete Structures," *Progress in Structural Engineering and Materials,* Vol. 2, No. 4, 2000, pp. 429–447.
107. Forsen, N. E., *A Theoretical Study of the Fire Resistance of Concrete Structures,* FCB-SINTEF Report STF65 A82062, Norwegian Institute of Technology, Trondheim, Norway, 1982.
108. Anderberg, Y., "Fire Engineering Design Based on PC," *Nordic Mini-Seminar on Fire Resistance of Concrete Structures,* Trondheim, Fire Safety Design, Lund, Sweden, 1989.
109. Nizamuddin, Z., Iding, R. H., and Bresler, B., "FIRES-T3—Computer Program for the Fire Response of Structures—Thermal (3-Dimensional Version), University of California, Berkeley, Oct. 1977.

NFPA Codes, Standards, and Recommended Practices

Reference to the following NFPA codes, standards, and recommended practices will provide further information on approaches to calculating structural fire resistance discussed in this chapter. (See the latest version of The NFPA Catalog *for availability of current editions of the following documents.)*

NFPA 251, *Standard Methods of Tests of Fire Resistance of Building Construction and Materials*
NFPA 255, *Standard Method of Test of Surface Burning Characteristics of Building Materials*

References

ACI 216.1-97/TMS 0216.1-97, "Standard Method for Determining Fire Resistance of Concrete and Masonry Construction Assemblies," *Manual of Concrete Practice,* American Concrete Institute (ACI), Farmington Hills, MI, 2005.
ACI 318-02/318R-02, *Building Code Requirements for Structural Concrete and Commentary,* ACI Committee 318, American Concrete Institute, Farmington Hills, MI, 2002.
AISC and UL, *Report on Development of Equation Relating W/D and Material Protection Thickness for Restrained Beams,* American Institute of Steel Construction, Chicago, IL, 2003.
Akio, H., "Analytical Method for High Temperature Collapse of a 3D Steel Frame," *Fire Science and Technology,* Vol. 23, No. 3, 2004, pp. 208–221.
AS/NZS 1170.0:2002, *Structural Design Actions, Part 0: General Principles,* Australian/New Zealand Standard, 2002.
ASFP (Ed.), *Fire Protection for Structural Steel in Buildings,* 3rd ed., Association for Specialist Fire Protection of Structural Steel and Buildings, Farnham, UK, 2004.
Babrauskas, V., and Williamson, R. B., "Post Flashover Compartment Fires: Basis of a Theoretical Model," *Fire and Materials,* No. 2, 1978, pp. 39–53.
Babrauskas, V., and Williamson, R. B., "Post Flashover Compartment Fires: Application of a Theoretical Model," *Fire and Materials,* No. 3, 1979, pp. 1–7.
Bailey, C., *Digest 462—Steel Structures Supporting Composite Floor Slabs: Design for Fire,* BRE Centre for Structural Engineering, 2001.
Bailey, C., *FBE Report 5—New Fire Design Method for Steel Frames with Composite Floor Slabs,* BRE Centre for Structural Engineering, Jan. 2003.
Bailey, C. G., *A Simple New Fire Design Method to Predict the Structural Response of Steel Frames with Composite Floors,* NSCC 2001, 9th Nordic Steel Construction Conference, Helsinki, Finland, June 18–20, 2001, pp. 557–564.
Bailey, C. G., and Moore, D. B., "The Structural Behavior of Steel Frames with Composite Floor Slabs Subject to Fire: Part 1: Theory and Part 2: Design," *The Structural Engineer,* Vol. 78, No. 11, 2000, pp. 19–33.
British Standards Institute, "Structural Use of Steelwork in Building Design in Composite Construction Code of Practice for Design of Simple and Continuous Composite Beams," BS 5950 Part 3, London, UK, 1990.
Building Code of Australia, Australian Building Codes Board, Canberra, ACT, Australia, 1996.
New Zealand Building Code, Building Industry Authority, Wellington, New Zealand, 1993.
Cadorin, J.-F., and Franssen, J.-M., *The One Zone Model OZone—Description and Validation Based on 54 Experimental Fire Tests,* unpublished report, 2006.
Cadorin, J.-F., Pintea, D., Dotreppe, J. C., and Franssen, J. M., "A Tool to Design Steel Elements Submitted to Compartment Fires—Ozone V2: Part 2 Methodology and Application," *Fire Safety Journal,* Vol. 38, 2003, pp. 429–451.
"CFAST: Consolidated Model of Fire Growth and Smoke Transport," http://www.bfrl.nist.gov, NIST, Gaithersburg, MD, 2005.
Choi, S. K., Burgess, I. W., Plank, R. J., "The Behavior of Lightweight Composite Floor Trusses in Fire," ASCE Specialty

Conference: Designing Structures in Fire, Baltimore, October 2003, pp. 24–32.
Clifton, G. C., *Draft for Development Revision 2: Design Procedure for the Inelastic Floor System/Frame Response of Multi-Storey Steel Framed Buildings in Fully Developed Natural Fires,* Technical Report R4-90-DD, HERA, Manukau City, New Zealand, 2000.
"Code of Practice for the Structural Use of Steel," http://www.bd.gov.hk, Buildings Department, Hong Kong, 2005.
Competitive Steel Buildings Through the Natural Fire Safety Concept, Final Report No. 32, CEC Agreement 7210-SA/125/126/213/214/323/423/522/623/839/937, Profil ARBED Research, Luxembourg, Mar. 1999.
"A Conceptual Approach Towards a Probability-Based Design Guide on Structural Fire Safety," Workshop report, Structural Fire Safety, *Fire Safety Journal,* Vol. 6, No. 1, 1983.
Design Guide for Fire Safety of Bare Exterior Structural Steel, American Iron and Steel Institute (AISI), Washington, DC, 1977.
Faber, M. H., Kübler, O., Fontana, M., and Knobloch, M., *Failure Consequences and Reliability Acceptance Criteria for Exceptional Building Structures,* IBK Report No. 285, vdf Hochschulverlag AG, Zurich, Switzerland, July 2004.
Feasey, R., and Buchanan, A., "Post-Flashover Fires for Structural Design," *Fire Safety Journal,* Vol. 37, 2002, pp. 83–105.
FEMA, *World Trade Center Building Performance Study: Data Collection, Preliminary Observations and Recommendations,* Report 403, FEMA, Washington, DC, 2003.
Foster, S. J., and Bailey, C., "Experimental Behavior of Concrete Floor Slabs at Large Displacements," *Engineering Structures,* Vol. 26, 2004, pp. 1231–1247.
Franssen, J. M., "Improvement of the Parametric Fire of Eurocode 1 Based on Experimental Tests Results," *Proceedings* of the 6th International Symposium on Fire Safety Science, M. Curtat (Ed.), IAFSS, Poitiers, France, 2000, pp. 927–938.
Gillie, M., Usmani, A. S., and Rotter, J. M., "A Structural Analysis of the Cardington British Steel Corner Test," *Journal of Constructional Steel Research,* Vol. 58, 2001, pp. 427–442.
Khoury, G. A., Grainger, B. N., and Sullivan, P. J. E., "Transient Thermal Strain of Concrete: Literature Review, Conditions Within Specimen and Behavior of Individual Constituents," *Magazine of Concrete Research,* Vol. 37, No. 132, 1985.
Kirby, B. R., Wainman, D. E., Tomlinson, L. H., Kay, T. R., and Peacock, B. N., *Natural Fires in Large Scale Compartments,* A British Steel Technical, Fire Research Station Collaborative project, British Steel Technical Swinden Laboratories, UK, June 1994.
Kodur, V. K. R., and Sultan, M. A., "Enhancing the Fire Resistance of Steel Columns Through Composite Construction," *Proceedings* of the 6th ASCCS International Conference on Steel-Concrete Composite Structures, Volume 1, Los Angeles, CA, March 22–24, 2000.
Kodur, V. K. R., and Wang, Y. C., "Performance of High Strength Concrete Filled Steel Columns at Ambient and Elevated Temperatures," *Tubular Structures IX,* R. Puthli and S. Heron (Eds.), Balkema Publishers, Lisse, Netherlands, 2001.
Lie, T. T., "Fire Temperature-Time Relationships," *SFPE Handbook of Fire Protection Engineering,* 3rd ed., P. J. DiNenno et al. (Eds.), National Fire Protection Association, Quincy, MA, 2002.
Lie, T. T., and Chabot, M., "Evaluation of Fire Resistance of Compression Members Using Mathematical Models," *Fire Safety Journal,* Vol. 20, 1993, pp. 135–149.
Maag, T., *Risikobasierte Beurteilung der Personensicherheit im Brandfall unter Verwendung von Bayes'schen Netzen,* Ph.D. Thesis No. 15366 and IBK report No. 282, vdf Hochschulverlag AG, Zurich, Switzerland, Mar. 2004.
Newman, G., Robinson, J. T., and Bailey, C. G., *Fire Safe Design, A New Approach to Multi-Storey Steel Framed Buildings,* SCI Publication 288, Berkshire, UK, 2000.
NZS 3101 1995, *Code of Practice for the Design of Concrete Structures,* Standards New Zealand, Wellington, New Zealand, 1995.
Partners in Technology Report, *Behavior of Steel Framed Structures Under Fire Conditions,* University of Edinburgh, UK, 2001.
Pettersson, O., Magnusson, S. E., and Thor, J., *Fire Engineering Design of Steel Structures,* Publication 50, Swedish Institute of Steel Construction, Stockholm, 1976.
Quintiere, J. G., Di Marzo, M., and Becker, R., "A Suggested Cause of the Fire-Induced Collapse of the World Trade Towers," *Fire Safety Journal,* Vol. 37, No. 7, 2002, pp. 707–716.
Schaffer, E. L., *Charring Rate of Selected Woods—Transverse to Grain,* U.S. Forest Service Research Paper FPL69, Forest Products Laboratory, Madison, WI, 1967.
SCI-P288, *Safe Design: A New Approach to Multi-Storey Steel-Framed Buildings,* 2nd ed., Steel Construction Institute, Ascot, Berkshire, UK, 2006.
SFPE Handbook of Fire Protection Engineering, 3rd ed., P. J. DiNenno et al. (Eds.), National Fire Protection Association, Quincy, MA, 2002.
Twilt, L., Hass, R., Klingsch, W., Edwards, M., and Dutta, D., *CIDECT Design Guide 4: For Structural Hollow Section Columns Exposed to Fire,* International Committee for Research and Technical Support for Hollow Section Structures, 1996
Usmani, A. S., and Lamont, S., "Key Events in the Structural Response of a Composite Steel Frame Structure in Fire," *Fire and Materials,* Vol. 28, 2004, pp. 281–297.
Wang, Y. C., *Tensile Membrane Action and Fire Resistance of Steel Framed Buildings,* Technical Report PD59/96, Building Research Establishment, Watford, UK, 1996.
Wickstrom, U., "Application of the Standard Fire Curve for Expressing Natural Fires for Design Purposes," *Fire Safety: Science and Engineering,* T. Z. Harmathy (Ed.), ASTM STP 882, American Society for Testing and Materials, Philadelphia, 1985, pp 145–159.

SECTION 20

Protecting Occupancies

Gregory E. Harrington

Section 20 of the *Fire Protection Handbook*® describes fire protection requirements and operating features for individual occupancies covered by NFPA *101*®, *Life Safety Code*®, and *NFPA 5000*®, *Building Construction and Safety Code*®. Many of the chapters also discuss the characteristics of the occupants typically found in the occupancies.

Chapter 1, "Assessing Life Safety in Buildings," sets the stage for the chapters that follow by previewing life safety concepts, goals, objectives, strategies, and tools such as the Fire Safety Concepts Tree and fire safety evaluation systems.

The next chapters deal with types of residential facilities. Chapter 2, "Board and Care Facilities," examines what makes alcohol and drug rehabilitation facilities, shelters, assisted living facilities, and other board and care facilities so susceptible to fire and loss of life and what must be done to improve the fire record. Chapter 3, "Hotels and University Housing," has undergone a major revision for the 20th edition. Chapter 4, "Apartment Buildings," also addresses residential condominiums. Chapter 5, "Lodging or Rooming Houses," provides information for facilities providing sleeping accommodations without separate cooking facilities for up to 16 persons who are capable of self-preservation.

The next two chapters also cover types of residences. Chapter 6, "One- and Two-Family Dwellings," concentrates on one- and two-family dwellings, defined as residential structures that contain not more than two dwelling units. Chapter 7, "Manufactured Housing," covers manufactured homes and their construction, fire safety features, installation, and associated utilities.

Chapter 8, "High-Rise Buildings," describes some of the code provisions and special features of the high-rise building, as well as presenting historical data on high-rise building fires.

Chapter 9, "Assembly Occupancies," addresses the fire safety issues of assembly occupancies, which generally can be defined as rooms, spaces, or structures in which groups of people gather for a purpose, such as deliberation, worship, entertainment, or to await transportation. Chapter 10, "Mercantile Occupancies," covers shopping malls and other shops and stores. Chapter 11, "Business Occupancies," includes a discussion of staged and total evacuation.

In previous editions of this handbook, information on educational occupancies and day-care occupancies were combined into a single chapter. In this edition, Chapter 12, "Educational Occupancies," addresses educational occupancies, which are generally defined as facilities in which six or more persons gather for purposes of formal or structured instruction through the twelfth grade. Chapter 13, "Day-Care Occupancies," addresses structures in which four or more clients receive care, maintenance, and supervision by other than their relatives or legal guardians for fewer than 24 hours per day.

Gregory E. Harrington, P.E., is principal fire protection engineer with NFPA's Building Fire Protection and Life Safety Division.

Chapter 14, "Detention and Correctional Occupancies," covers fire safety concerns in buildings and facilities in which persons are restrained for security purposes by locks they do not control.

Chapter 15, "Health Care Occupancies," describes fire protection needs in a variety of facilities that care for nonambulatory patients who are incapable of self-preservation.

Chapter 16, "Storage Occupancies," addresses fire protection for storage and warehouse operations, where intense fires can develop rapidly. Chapter 17, "Library and Museum Collections," summarizes the unique fire safety concerns, including damage limitation, in cultural properties such as historic buildings and sites.

Hazard assessment and prefire planning are among the topics considered in Chapter 18, "Industrial Occupancies." Chapter 19, "Motion Picture and Television Studios and Soundstages," includes a discussion of pyrotechnics before a proximate audience.

The section closes with Chapter 20, "Occupancies in Special Structures." For purposes of this chapter, special structures include limited access and underground structures, mall buildings, open parking structures, special amusement structures, piers and wharves, water-surrounded structures, membrane structures and tents, grandstands, towers, and open structures.

Chapter 1

Assessing Life Safety in Buildings

John M. Watts, Jr.

Assessment of life safety is the process of estimating the quality of security against fire and its effects. There is no universally accepted method of assessing life safety from fire in buildings. Life safety is a concept, and no formula can identify or guarantee that a building is safe from fire.

First of all, assessment requires an understanding of the fundamentals of the life safety concept. Life safety goals and objectives need to be reviewed and then an evaluation can be made of the parameters that create hazards to life and those that tend to offset or control a portion of the life hazard. A wide variety of tools have been devised to relate these parameters so as to assess life safety in buildings.

Every general type of fire safety practice and fire protection strategy discussed in this handbook may apply to life safety in buildings. Specific additional information that can be helpful in a life safety assessment is identified throughout this chapter.

See also Section 2, Chapter 1, "Physics and Chemistry of Fire"; Section 4, Chapter 1, "Human Behavior and Fire"; Section 4, Chapter 2, "Calculation Methods for Egress Prediction"; and Section 6, Chapter 2, "Combustion Products and Their Effects on Life Safety."

Chapter Contents

Key Terms

egress, evacuation capability, fire prevention, Fire Safety Concepts Tree, Fire Safety Evaluation Systems (FSES), fire scenario, life safety assessment, life safety concept, occupancy classification, occupant characteristics, occupant load, performance-based approach, travel distance, untenable condition

LIFE SAFETY CONCEPTS

Concern for life safety implies avoiding exposure to harmful levels of products of combustion. This goal is usually achieved by controlling the fire process or by separating endangered individuals from the harmful effects of fire by time, distance, or shielding. Thus, life safety is accomplished if endangered individuals can move away from potential danger or if harmful effects of fire can be delayed indefinitely from reaching people in the building.

Details of the fire's development, along with characteristics of exposed occupants, determine the magnitude of the hazard. In addition, specific safety measures may be employed to reduce the hazard. Understanding the interrelationships of these components is the first step in assessing life safety from fire in buildings.

Importance of Time

As a fire develops over time, smoke and heat build up to create an environment that is hazardous to life. The rate at which the environment deteriorates is difficult to predict, because a great many variables are involved. Figure 20.1.1 is a generalization of the way life hazard increases over time. At the time of ignition (lower left corner), the environment is normal. Most fires develop slowly, so the initial hazard is small. Eventually, fire intensity will increase more rapidly, building up the level of dangerous products of combustion.

After some period of time, the accumulation of products of combustion reaches a level at which the fire will be discovered by the occupants through sight or smell or by automatic fire detectors. The level of hazard at which discovery occurs corresponds to a specific time in the course

John M. Watts, Jr., Ph.D., is director of the Fire Safety Institute, a not-for-profit information, research, and educational corporation located in Middlebury, Vermont. He also serves as editor of NFPA's quarterly scientific journal, *Fire Technology.*

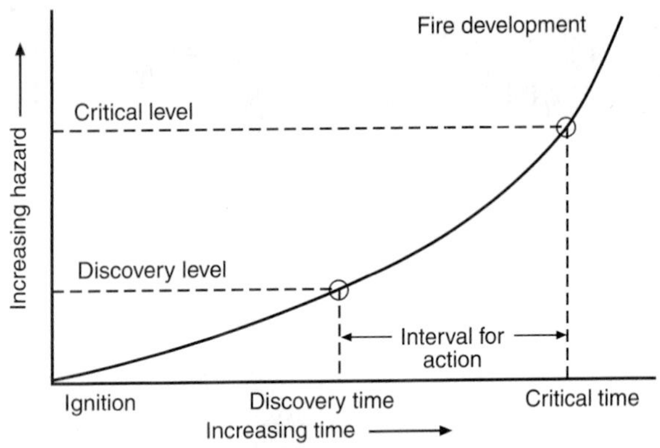

FIGURE 20.1.1 Representative Rate of Deterioration of the Environment as a Fire Progresses and the Interval of Time Available to Take Action to Prevent Death or Injury

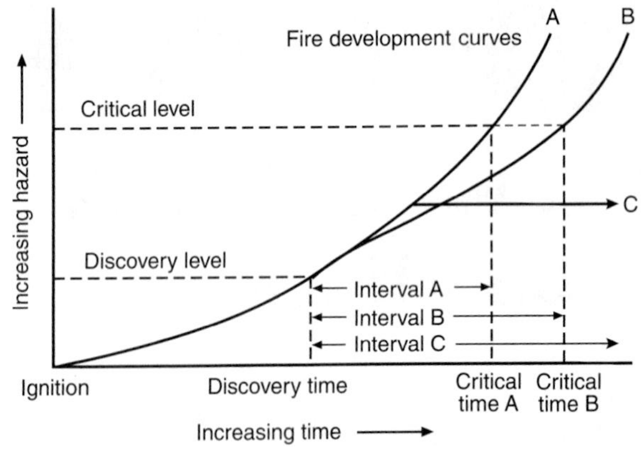

FIGURE 20.1.2 Difference in Deterioration Rates Between a Faster-Developing and a Slower-Developing Fire and Resulting Impact on the Interval for Action

of the fire. Figure 20.1.1 indicates a discovery level and a corresponding discovery time. If no actions are taken after discovery, eventually, the hazard will increase to a level that is lethal or incapacitating. In Figure 20.1.1 this is shown as the critical level and there is a corresponding critical time.

Fire Hazard

The critical time depends on the interaction of three sets of conditions: (1) elevated environmental temperatures, (2) toxic conditions resulting from pyrolysis or combustion products, and (3) preexisting or current psychophysiological attributes of the occupants. Elevated temperatures can cause burns or heat stress ranging from trivial to lethal. Specific chemical pyrolysis or combustion products, decreased oxygen concentration, or particulate smoke can cause toxic effects. The clinical consequences of these physical conditions also will reflect the psychophysiological conditions of the occupants. For example, preexisting heart disease has been established as a contributory factor in fire deaths.[1] Assessment of the variable interactions of these three sets of conditions is, obviously, extremely complicated.

Interval for Action

The interval between discovery and criticality is the time available to undertake action to prevent occupants from being exposed to the critical hazard level. This action may take various forms, such as activation of automatic equipment, evacuation of occupants, or both. Lowering the hazard level where discovery occurs, such as by automatic fire detection, will have a corresponding decrease in the time to discovery and, therefore, will increase the interval of time available for action. On the other hand, occupants with greater susceptibility and, hence, a lower personal critical level will have less time to react.

Fire growth and hazard are not the same in every fire. If conditions are insufficient to sustain a fast-spreading fire, the rate of deterioration of the environment is reduced, resulting in a decreased slope of the fire development curve. Figure 20.1.2 shows three different fire development curves. Curve A is the same fire as in Figure 20.1.1. Curve B represents a slower-developing fire than curve A. The curve starts at the same point of ignition but does not curve upward as quickly as curve A. This means it takes longer to reach the critical hazard level and, thus, has a resultant increase in the interval of time available for action. This could be affected by a decrease in the surface area or combustibility of interior finish materials.

Alternatively, curve C might represent the effect of a smoke control system or sprinkler system, which are two active systems that can stop or even reverse the developing severity of the fire. Curve C begins with ignition and then grows at the same rate as curve A, but at some point after discovery, the system is activated and it maintains the atmosphere below the critical level for an indefinite period of time.

LIFE SAFETY GOALS AND OBJECTIVES

Life safety goals and objectives identify what it is that we want to achieve. The primary difference between goals and objectives is that objectives are more specific to the problem being solved. Goals are always qualitative, whereas objectives may also be quantitative.

Life Safety Goals

A goal is a broad, qualitative expression of the overall, primary concern. Goals are nonspecific and are potentially measurable although only on a qualitative basis. They are stated in terms of conditions that are intrinsically desirable and do not rely on assumptions.

Goals relating to life safety are the most common and arguably the most important in fire and other emergency situations. The public trusts the built environment (that is, anyone involved in constructing buildings, structures, and other facilities—designers, engineers, code officials, and the like) to maintain some level of safety or protection from adverse conditions. Therefore, maintaining the health, safety, and welfare of building occupants is a basic goal.

NFPA *101*®, *Life Safety Code*®, has three stated goals to reduce the adverse impact of fire on people:

- Protection of occupants not in contact with the initial fire development
- Improvement of the survivability of occupants in contact with the initial fire development
- Provision of reasonably safe emergency crowd movement

Life Safety Objectives

A life safety objective is a requirement of the fire development, building, or occupants that needs to be accomplished in order to achieve a life safety goal. Objectives provide a greater level of qualitative detail than goals, are stated in more specific terms than goals, and are measured on a more quantitative rather than qualitative basis. In general, objectives define a series of actions necessary to make the achievement of a goal much more likely. If each life safety objective is accomplished for a building, then that building can be said to meet the life safety goals.

NFPA *101* has three objectives that address occupant protection, structural integrity, and system effectiveness:

- A structure shall be designed, constructed, and maintained to protect occupants who are not intimate with the initial fire development for the time needed to evacuate, relocate, or defend in place.
- Structural integrity shall be maintained for the time needed to evacuate, relocate, or defend in place occupants who are not intimate with the initial fire development.
- Systems utilized to achieve the goals shall be effective in mitigating the hazard or condition for which they are being used, shall be reliable, shall be maintained to the level at which they were designed to operate, and shall remain operational.

Life safety goals and objectives identify the fundamental purpose of assessing life safety in buildings. Meeting these goals and objectives is what the assessment is intended to help achieve.

CHARACTERISTICS OF OCCUPANTS

The most difficult component of life safety to evaluate is the population at risk (i.e., the occupants of the building). The difficulty is due to wide variations among building occupants. It is necessary to assess their susceptibility to fire and fire products and their ability to undertake and follow procedures necessary for their safety (i.e., anticipated response to a fire emergency). Indications of these abilities may be found in physical and mental characteristics of the occupants, as individuals and as a group. Four categories of occupant characteristics influence the ability to survive in a fire: (1) location, (2) response, (3) number, and (4) staff.[2]

Location

Assumptions generated by committees responsible for the development of NFPA *101* performance-based design option regarding the location of occupants dealt more with the density or concentration of people within a space rather than the actual location of individual occupants. However, the location of individual occupants may be inferred from the stated assumptions. For example, the Technical Committee on Board and Care Facilities assumed "full occupancy" and the Technical Committee on Residential Occupancies assumed "high-density (people per room) properties." These assumptions indicate that the maximum travel distance from any occupiable room or space within the building must be considered when designing and analyzing potential building designs.

The present prescriptive requirements in NFPA *101* and *NFPA 5000*®, *Building Construction and Safety Code*®, identify the location of occupants in regard to compliance with maximum allowable travel distances. Table 20.1.1 lists travel distance limits by type of occupancy and sprinkler protection as prescribed in NFPA *101* and *NFPA 5000.* These codes specify that the travel distance to an exit must be measured from the most remote point subject to occupancy. This has been interpreted as an assumption necessary for performance-based design as follows: "In every normally occupied room or area, at least one person shall be assumed to be located at the point most remote from the exit(s)." Although consistent with the prescriptive code, this is a conservative assumption and not necessarily representative of expected normal human behavior.

Another aspect of occupant location is the remoteness of exits when more than one is required. This is to ensure that multiple exits are not simultaneously blocked by a single fire. Current codes rely on a rule that says exits should be a straight-line distance apart not less than one-half the length of the maximum overall diagonal dimension of the building or area served. The rationale for this "one-half diagonal rule" is not obvious. There is no physical or logical reason to relate a building diagonal to the emergency egress of people. Furthermore, this approach permits configurations in which the exits might not intuitively be considered remote. For example, consider a space with a length of 100 ft (30.4 m) and a width of 60 ft (18.2 m) with both its exits at one of the narrow ends.

Remoteness of exits may be more logically a function of direction of travel than separation distance. A measure of this concept would be the angled distended between lines corresponding to routes from any point in a room or space to the exits or exit accesses. Figure 20.1.3 illustrates a situation where if the travel paths to two exits are different by at least 30°, the exits may be considered remote. That is, if the exits were closer together, the angle of remoteness would be less than 30°. There are also ways this concept can be adapted to include a common path of travel limitation.[3]

Response

In a performance evaluation of life safety, assumptions need to be made regarding the expected distribution of characteristics of a population appropriate to the use of the building. The four basic characteristics (i.e., sensibility, reactivity, mobility, and susceptibility) comprise a minimum, exhaustive set of mutually exclusive performance characteristics of people in buildings that can affect a fire safety system's ability to meet life

TABLE 20.1.1 Travel Distance Limits by Occupancy and Sprinkler Protection

Type of Occupancy	Travel Distance Limit: Unsprinklered ft	Unsprinklered m	Sprinklered ft	Sprinklered m
Assembly				
New	200	61[a]	250	76[a]
Existing	200	61[a]	250	76[a]
Educational				
New	150	45	200	61
Existing	150	45	200	61
Day Care				
New	150	45[b]	200	61[b]
Existing	150	45[b]	200	61[b]
Health Care				
New	NA	NA	200	61[b]
Existing	150	45[b]	200	61[b]
Ambulatory Health Care				
New	150	45[b]	200	61[b]
Existing	150	45[b]	200	61[b]
Detention and Correctional				
New—use condition II, III, IV	150	45[b]	200	61[b]
New—use condition V	150	45[b]	200	61[b]
Existing—use condition II, III, IV, V	150	45[b]	200	61[b]
Residential				
One- and two-family dwellings	NR	NR	NR	NR
Lodging or rooming houses	NR	NR	NR	NR
Hotels and dormitories				
New	175	53[b,c]	325	99[b,c]
Existing	175	53[b,d]	325	99[b,d]
Apartments				
New	175	53[b,c]	325	99[b,c]
Existing	175	53[b,c]	325	99[b,c]
Residential *(continued)*				
Board and care				
Small, new and existing	NR	NR	NR	NR
Large, new	NA	NA	325	99[b,c]
Large, existing	175	53[b,c]	325	99[b,c]
Mercantile				
Class A, B, C				
New	150	45	250	76
Existing	150	45	250	76
Open air	NR	NR	NR	NR
Mall				
New	150	45	400	120[e]
Existing	150	45	400	120[e]
Business				
New	200	61	300	91
Existing	200	61	300	91
Industrial				
General	200	61[f]	250	75[g]
Special purpose	300	91	400	122
High hazard	0	0	75	23
Aircraft servicing hangars, ground floor	[f]	[f]	[f]	[f]
Aircraft servicing hangars, mezzanine floor	75	23	75	23
Storage				
Low hazard	NR	NR	NR	NR
Ordinary hazard	200	61	400	122
High hazard	75	23	100	30
Parking structures, open	300	91	400	122
Parking structures, enclosed	150	45	200	60
Aircraft storage hangars, ground floor	[f]	[f]	[f]	[f]
Aircraft servicing hangars, mezzanine floor	75	23	75	23
Underground spaces in grain elevators	200	61	400	122

[a]NFPA *101* has special considerations for smoke-protected assembly seating in arenas and stadia.
[b]This dimension is for the total travel distance, assuming incremental portions have fully utilized their permitted maximums. For travel distance within the room, and from the room exit access door to the exit, see the appropriate occupancy chapter.
[c]See the appropriate occupancy chapter in NFPA *101* for special travel distance considerations for exterior ways of exit access.
[d]See the appropriate occupancy chapter in NFPA *101* for requirements for second exit access based on room area.
[e]NFPA *101* has special travel distance considerations in covered malls considered to be pedestrian ways.
[f]NFPA *101* has special requirements on spacing of doors in aircraft hangars.
[g]NFPA *101* has industrial occupancy special travel distance considerations.
NR = No requirement; NA = Not applicable.
Source: Adapted from Table A.7.6, NFPA *101,* 2006 edition.

safety objectives. They are briefly described in Table 20.1.2. In application, as with the use of computer evacuation models, assumptions may address a larger number of factors that are components of these basic performance characteristics.

Furthermore, occupant response assumptions vary depending on the type of facility being analyzed. For example, the committee dealing with theaters, nightclubs, concert halls, sports arenas, and so on assumed that patrons may be intoxicated. This

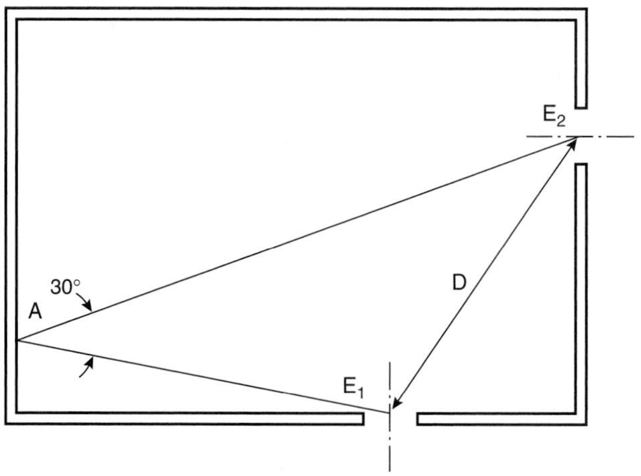

FIGURE 20.1.3 Travel Paths from Point A to Two Exits, E_1 and E_2, with 30° Difference (D = Safe separation distance)

assumption would affect the patrons' sensibility, reactivity, most likely their mobility, and possibly their susceptibility. Other occupancy committees made assumptions that fall into only one of the categories of Table 20.1.2: detention and correction facilities by their very purpose impair the mobility of the occupants; specific kinds of health care and board and care facilities may involve persons with limited sensibility, persons with limited reactivity, or persons having a wide range of susceptibility; and so on.

TABLE 20.1.2 Occupant Response Characteristics

Characteristic	*Description*
Sensibility	Sensibility to physical cues. Ability to sense the sounding of an alarm. May also include discernment and discrimination of visual and olfactory cues in addition to the sounds of the fire itself.
Reactivity	Reactivity is the ability to correctly interpret cues and take appropriate action. May be function of cognitive capacity, speed of instinctive reaction, or group dynamics. May need to consider reliability or likelihood of a wrong decision as in the influence of familiarity with the premises on wayfinding.
Mobility	Mobility is speed of movement. Determined by individual capabilities as well as crowding or congestion phenomena, such as "arching" at doorways.
Susceptibility	Susceptibility to products of combustion. Metabolism, lung capacity, pulmonary disease, allergies, or other physical limitations that may affect survivability in a fire environment.

There also may be a dynamic component to occupant response assumptions. Any facility in which occupants may be sleeping requires different sensibility and reactivity assumptions when occupants are expected to be awake than when occupants are expected to be sleeping.

One type of occupant response assumption that the occupancy committees made that is difficult to categorize has to do with an occupant's familiarity with the facility being analyzed. For example, occupants of an office building were assumed to have a high degree of familiarity with the building in which they work, whereas patrons in an assembly occupancy were assumed to be unfamiliar with their surroundings. Is "higher familiarity" manifested as greater mobility? Presumably, a higher degree of familiarity with a facility results in more correct decisions about the safest path to take to reach a place of safety and, therefore, an effectively higher degree of mobility. Certainly an argument may be made that those having less familiarity with a facility's exit locations and egress routes will have a lesser degree of mobility (i.e., take a longer time to evacuate). However, not enough is currently known to make an estimation of how much mobility should be degraded to account for poor decision making while evacuating a building.

Number

A critical factor in human behavior in fire is the number of occupants in a given space. NFPA *101* and *NFPA 5000* identify figures for the average maximum density of occupancy for the existing classifications. Table 20.1.3 shows occupant load factors for types of occupancies and functional spaces within the occupancies as prescribed in NFPA *101* and *NFPA 5000.* These figures represent acceptable estimates in the absence of preferable data.

Staff

When trained employees are explicitly or implicitly included as part of the fire safety system, assumptions regarding their capability need to be identified and documented. For example, in hospitals, staff characteristics such as number, location, quality, frequency of training, and so on should be considered. An aspect that is often overlooked is the potential effectiveness of staff in assembly occupancies such as art galleries and museums. Although staff may be present in a given occupancy, they often are not considered part of the fire safety system. A case in point is in most mercantile occupancies where staff are trained to aid customers in sales, not necessarily evacuation.

Additional information on human behavior in fire is found in Section 4, Chapter 1, "Human Behavior and Fire," and in the *SFPE Engineering Guide to Human Behavior in Fires.*[4]

NFPA 101A, *Guide on Alternative Approaches to Life Safety,* addresses some characteristics of occupants. The chapter on "Evacuation Capability Determination for Board and Care Occupancies" describes a method for determining evacuation capability for a specific type of occupancy. This method calculates an evacuation capability score using information on residents, staff, and vertical egress travel required. Rating of residents assesses several characteristics of occupants that are particularly important to board and care occupancies. Table 20.1.4

TABLE 20.1.3 Occupant Load Factor

Use	*(ft² per person)*[a]	*(m² per person)*[a]
Assembly Use		
Concentrated use, without fixed seating	7 net	0.65 net
Less concentrated use, without fixed seating	15 net	1.4 net
Bench-type seating	1 person/18 linear in.	1 person/455 linear mm
Fixed seating	Number of fixed seats	Number of fixed seats
Waiting spaces	See Sections 12.1.7.2 and 13.1.7.2 in NFPA *101*	See Sections 12.1.7.2 and 13.1.7.2 in NFPA *101*
Kitchens	100	9.3
Library stack areas	100	9.3
Library reading rooms	50 net	4.6 net
Swimming pools	50 (water surface)	4.6 (water surface)
Swimming pool decks	30	2.8
Exercise rooms with equipment	50	4.6
Exercise rooms without equipment	15	1.4
Stages	15 net	1.4 net
Lighting and access catwalks, galleries, gridirons	100 net	9.3 net
Casinos and similar gaming areas	11	1
Skating rinks	50	4.6
Educational Use		
Classrooms	20 net	1.9 net
Shops, laboratories, vocational rooms	50 net	4.6 net
Day-Care Use	35 net	3.3 net
Health Care Use		
Inpatient treatment departments	240	22.3
Sleeping departments	120	11.1
Ambulatory health care	100	9.3
Detention and Correctional Use	120	11.1
Residential Use		
Hotels and dormitories	200	18.6
Apartment buildings	200	18.6
Board and care, large	200	18.6
Industrial Use		
General and high-hazard industrial	100	9.3
Special-purpose industrial	NA	NA
Business Use	100	9.3
Storage Use		
In storage occupancies	NA	NA
In mercantile occupancies	300	27.9
In other than storage and mercantile occupancies	500	46.5
Mercantile Use		
Sales area on street floor[b,c]	30	2.8
Sales area on two or more street floors[c]	40	3.7
Sales area on floor below street floor[c]	30	2.8
Sales area on floors above street floor[c]	60	5.6
Floors or portions of floors used only for offices	See business use	See business use
Floors or portions of floors used only for storage, receiving, and shipping, and not open to general public	300	27.9
Mall buildings[d]	Per factors applicable to use of space[e]	Per factors applicable to use of space[e]

Note: The occupant load is the maximum probable number of occupants present at any time.

[a]All factors are expressed in gross area unless marked "net."

[b]For the purpose of determining occupant load in mercantile occupancies where, due to differences in grade of streets on different sides, two or more floors directly accessible from streets (not including alleys or similar back streets) exist, each such floor is permitted to be considered a street floor. The occupant load factor is one person for each 40 ft² (3.7 m²) of gross floor area of sales space.

[c]For the purpose of determining occupant load in mercantile occupancies with no street floor, as defined in Section 3.3.239 of NFPA *101,* but with access directly from the street by stairs or escalators, the floor at the point of entrance to the mercantile occupancy is considered the street floor.

[d]For any food court or other assembly use areas located in the mall that are not included as a portion of the gross leasable area of the mall building, the occupant load is calculated based on the occupant load factor for that use as specified in this table. The remaining mall area is not required to be assigned an occupant load.

[e]The portions of the mall that are considered a pedestrian way and not used as gross leasable area are not required to be assessed an occupant load based on this table. However, means of egress from a mall pedestrian way are required to be provided for an occupant load determined by dividing the gross leasable area of the mall building (not including anchor stores) by the appropriate lowest whole number occupant load factor from Figure 7.3.1.2(a) or Figure 7.3.1.2(b) of NFPA *101.*

Each individual tenant space is required to have means of egress to the outside or to the mall based on occupant loads calculated by using the appropriate occupant load factor from this table.

Each individual anchor store is required to have means of egress independent of the mall.

NA = Not applicable.

Source: Table 7.3.1.2, NFPA *101,* 2006 edition.

summarizes these characteristics and illustrates that for some types of building use more detailed information on occupants is necessary.

Surrogate Descriptors

Occupant age is often used as a surrogate descriptor for characteristics that determine life safety risk. Relatively easy to identify, age is often directly associated with characteristics such as mobility, awareness, and knowledge. Statistics showing that the very young and the very old suffer higher fatality rates from fire indicate variation of life risk with age.

NFPA *101, NFPA 5000,* and other model building codes categorize building use or occupancy classifications to simplify the application of regulations governing construction, fire protection, and other life safety requirements. In application, occupancy class, once determined, becomes the basis for most code requirements. In effect, we use occupancy classification as a surrogate for life safety risk. This generalization is inadequate for more performance-based assessment of life safety in buildings. NFPA *101* and *NFPA 5000* categorize buildings using the following occupancy classifications:

- Assembly
- Educational
- Day care
- Health care
- Detention and correctional
- One- and two-family dwellings
- Lodging or rooming houses
- Hotels and dormitories
- Apartment buildings
- Residential board and care

TABLE 20.1.4 Risk Factors for Rating Evacuation Capability of Residents in a Board and Care Occupancy (as addressed in NFPA 101A)

Risk Factor	*Description*
Risk of resistance	During an emergency evacuation, the resident might resist leaving the facility
Impaired mobility	Physical ability of the resident to leave the facility
Impaired consciousness	A resident could experience partial or total loss of consciousness in a fire emergency
Need for extra help	Possibility that more than one staff member might be needed to evacuate the resident
Response to instructions	Resident's ability to receive, comprehend, and follow simple instructions during a staff-directed evacuation
Waking response to alarm	Fire alarm might fail to awaken the resident

- Mercantile
- Business
- Industrial
- Storage

NFPA *101* further classifies occupancies as either new or existing.

LIFE SAFETY STRATEGIES

Ideally, building design considers the risk factors associated with occupants and fire, and it includes safety features to mitigate the risks. The discussion in this chapter is intended as a synthesis of the various safety measures that may be applied to reduce the danger of fire to occupants. Major categories of safety strategies have been identified by NFPA 550, *Guide to the Fire Safety Concepts Tree,* as (1) prevent fire, (2) manage fire, and (3) manage exposed (occupants). A simplified portion of the Fire Safety Concepts Tree showing the relationships of these strategies is presented as Figure 20.1.4.

Fire Prevention

No harm can come from fire if no fire takes place. Fire prevention, therefore, has the potential to eliminate the need for other fire safety measures. However, no fire prevention strategy is ever totally effective, so it is not prudent to rely on fire prevention alone.

Fire prevention considerations relate to heat energy sources, fuels, and the mechanisms that bring them together. For example, major potential ignition energy sources, such as electrical power, can be controlled largely through regulation, such as by following the requirements of NFPA 1, *Uniform Fire Code™,* and NFPA 70, *National Electrical Code®*. In addition, some fuels, such as flammable liquids and interior finish, also may be addressed by codes and standards. However, not all energy sources or all fuels can be regulated. This is also true of people, the primary causal factor of ignition. Assessment of the probability of

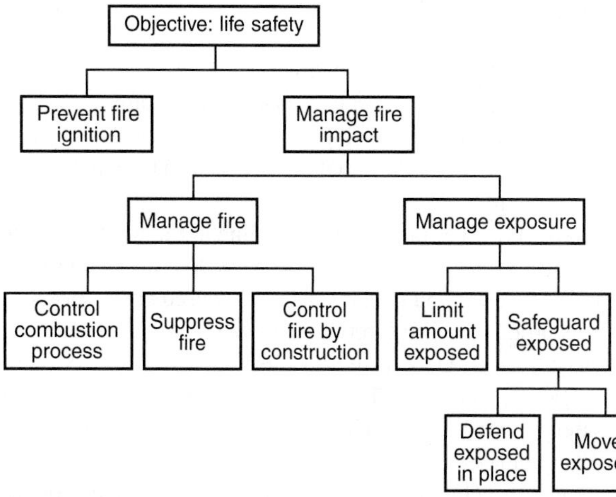

FIGURE 20.1.4 Simplified Portion of the Fire Safety Concepts Tree

fire occurrence involves analysis of ignition potential, especially in relation to the activities of building occupants, and of factors that will decrease the likelihood of ignition.

Fire Management

Since it is impossible to avoid all ignitions, managing fires that occur also is important. The strategies of fire management may be seen as reducing the slope of the fire development curves portrayed in Figures 20.1.1 and 20.1.2. These approaches strive to control the rate of smoke and heat production by altering fuel and/or the environment, controlling the combustion process by manual or automatic suppression, and controlling the products of combustion through venting and/or containment.

Objectives of the "manage fire" strategy are to reduce risks associated with fire growth and to reduce fire and smoke spread. Together, these reductions diminish the impact of a fire on building occupants.

Occupant Management

This life safety strategy (manage exposed) is the most complex, dealing with the risk factors of both fire and people. Occupant management involves undertaking emergency action appropriate to expected fire development and to characteristics of the occupants.

To initiate occupant management action, there first must be detection and alerting activities. Automatic equipment may perform these functions. Actions for managing exposed persons involve evacuation, refuge, or rescue. Evacuation is the most common approach when occupants are alert and mobile. In other cases, areas of refuge from fire and smoke within a building are employed, along with movement assisted by emergency personnel.

LIFE SAFETY ASSESSMENT TOOLS

The components of a generalized approach to assessment of life safety from fire in buildings are shown in Figure 20.1.5.

Step 1 is to identify the expected fire. This is depicted by the boxes to the left of the centerline in Figure 20.1.5. The expected fire is determined by the fire hazards that are present in the building, fire prevention measures implemented to prevent specific hazards from occurring, and fire management activities to control the severity of a fire if it does occur. The expected fire is input to step 2.

Step 2 is to the right of the centerline in Figure 20.1.5. The expected fire from step 1 is considered in conjunction with occupant risk factors and management of exposed occupants. This analysis produces a life safety assessment.

Step 3 is a return to the beginning to consider other expected fires or enhanced fire safety strategies. Thus, improving life safety in buildings is an iterative process of matching hazard and safety factors.

Specific techniques can be used in an assessment of life safety from fire in buildings including codes, exit analysis, fire safety evaluation systems (FSES), fire scenarios, evacuation models, and performance-based evaluation.

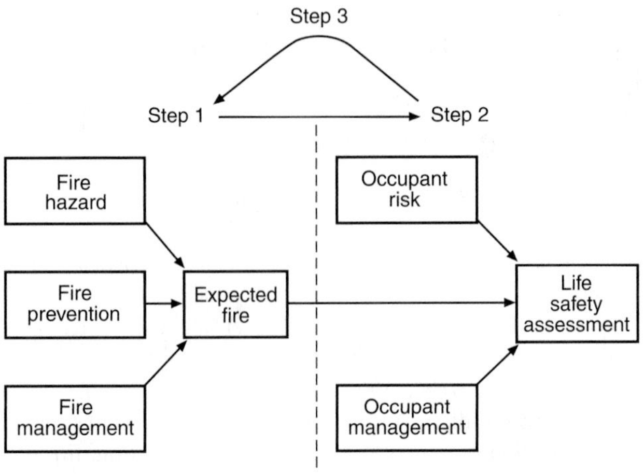

FIGURE 20.1.5 General Approach to Assessing Life Safety in Buildings

Codes

In the United States, NFPA *101* is the most widely used code for life safety from fire in buildings. The code has its origins in the 1912 *Exit Drills in Factories, Schools, Department Stores, and Theaters* that evolved as a result of the Triangle Shirtwaist factory fire in New York City that killed 146 workers in 1911. Requirements for factories and other occupancies were combined with specifications for building construction and automatic fire protection into the *Buildings Exit Code,* adopted and published in 1927. During the next 37 years, 18 revisions of this code were published, greatly expanding its content. In 1963, the document was reorganized and renamed the *Code for Safety to Life from Fire in Buildings and Structures,* or simply, the *Life Safety Code.* To date an additional thirteen editions have been published—the 2006 edition being the latest at the time this handbook was published.

NFPA *101* provides minimum requirements for the design, operation, and maintenance of buildings and other structures for safety to life from fire and similar emergencies. The code requires new and existing buildings to allow for "prompt escape" or to provide people with a reasonable degree of safety through other means.

The code meets its objectives by following two parallel approaches. First, it defines hazards, along with general requirements for the means of egress (a path of travel to a public way outside the building), fire protection features (such as fire doors), and building service and fire protection equipment (such as heating, ventilating, and air conditioning systems, sprinkler systems, and fire detection systems). Next, the code prescribes life safety requirements that vary with a building's use. Buildings used as one- and two-family dwellings, for example, have different life safety needs than hospitals and schools. Unique among fire safety codes, the provisions of the *Life Safety Code* depend on the type of occupancy and whether the occupancy is new or existing. The code can be used in conjunction with a building code or by itself in jurisdictions that have not adopted a building code.

NFPA *101* in particular and building codes in general are the predominant overall guides to life safety from fire in buildings in the United States. NFPA *101* identifies the following 10 fundamental requirements that are the basis for most of the specific provisions in the code. More information on these principles is found in Section 4, Chapter 3, "Concepts of Egress Design."

Multiple Safeguards. The design of every building or structure intended for human occupancy must be such that reliance for safety to life does not depend solely on any single safeguard. An additional safeguard(s) must be provided for life safety in case any single safeguard is ineffective due to inappropriate human actions or system failure.

Appropriateness of Safeguards. Every building or structure must be provided with means of egress and other safeguards of the kinds, numbers, locations, and capacities appropriate to the individual building or structure, with due regard to character of the occupancy, capabilities of the occupants, number of persons exposed, fire protection available, height and type of construction of the building or structure, and other factors necessary to provide occupants with a reasonable degree of safety.

Number of Means of Egress. Two means of egress, as a minimum, must be provided in every building or structure, section, and area where size, occupancy, and arrangement endanger occupants attempting to use a single means of egress that is blocked by fire or smoke. The two means of egress must be arranged to minimize the possibility that both might be rendered impassable by the same emergency condition.

Unobstructed Egress. In every occupied building or structure, means of egress from all parts of the building must be maintained free and unobstructed. No lock or fastening is permitted that prevents free escape from the inside of any building other than in health care occupancies and detention and correctional occupancies where staff are continually on duty and effective provisions are made to remove occupants in case of fire or other emergency. Means of egress must be accessible to the extent necessary to ensure reasonable safety for occupants having impaired mobility.

Awareness of Egress System. Every exit must be clearly visible, or the route to reach every exit must be conspicuously indicated. Each means of egress, in its entirety, must be arranged or marked so that the way to a place of safety is indicated in a clear manner.

Lighting. Where artificial illumination is needed in a building or structure, egress facilities must be included in the lighting design.

Occupant Notification. In every building or structure of such size, arrangement, or occupancy that a fire itself might not provide adequate occupant warning, fire alarm facilities must be provided where necessary to warn occupants of the existence of fire.

Vertical Openings. Every vertical opening between the floors of a building must be suitably enclosed or protected, as necessary, to afford reasonable safety to occupants while using the means of egress and to prevent spread of fire, smoke, or fumes through vertical openings from floor to floor before occupants have entered exits.

System Design/Installation. Any fire protection system, building service equipment, feature of protection, or safeguard provided for life safety must be designed, installed, and approved in accordance with applicable NFPA standards.

Maintenance. Whenever or wherever any device, equipment, system, condition, arrangement, level of protection, or any other feature is required for compliance with the provisions of the code, such device, equipment, system, condition, arrangement, level of protection, or other feature must thereafter be maintained unless the code exempts such maintenance.

Egress Analysis

Egress analysis is an important component of a life safety evaluation, as well as a tool for other forms of life safety assessment. The analysis uses anthropometric and biokinetic data on occupants, together with hydraulic flow analogies or other models, to calculate the time required to evacuate a building or space. The result can be compared to a calculated time for deterioration of the environment. Some basic engineering approaches to egress analysis have been developed and are presented in the *SFPE Handbook of Fire Protection Engineering.*[5,6] It is critical that results of egress analysis calculations, whether manual or computer, be examined with respect to the vagaries of human behavior that accompany an emergency.

Emergency egress systems should be assessed in terms of adequacy and reliability. Adequacy refers to structural components that determine the capacity to evacuate part or all of a building within a safe egress time span. Reliability considers how efficiently the egress capacity will be utilized. Factors of reliability include alerting messages and instructions, signage and emergency lighting, and protection of egress routes from fire, smoke, and toxic gases. Figure 20.1.6, a logic diagram, enumerates some features of egress adequacy and reliability.

Fire Safety Evaluation Systems (FSES)

NFPA 101A addresses fire safety evaluation systems (FSES). FSES is a fire risk indexing approach to determining equivalencies to NFPA *101* for certain occupancies. The FSES originally was created to provide a uniform method of evaluating health care facilities and to identify measures that would provide a level of fire safety equivalent to NFPA *101*.

Occupant Risk. Unlike NFPA *101,* the FSES for health care occupancies begins with a determination of relative risk derived from occupant characteristics. Variations of selected characteristics are assigned relative weights. Values were determined from the experienced judgment of a panel of fire safety professionals. Occupancy risk is then calculated as the

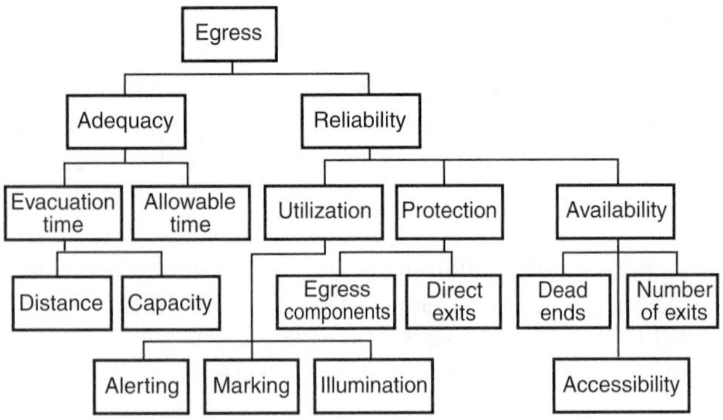

FIGURE 20.1.6 Logic Diagram of Egress Features

product of the risk factor values appropriate for the particular occupancy.

Safety Parameters. Safety features must offset this calculated risk. Thirteen possible safety parameters are considered. These parameters and their respective ranges of values for health care occupancies are based on opinions of the same expert panel.

Safety Strategies. An important concept of the FSES is reliability through redundancy by the simultaneous use of alternative safety strategies. Fire safety strategies considered in the FSES are containment, extinguishment, and people movement. Figure 20.1.7 indicates the expert panel's opinion of which safety parameters apply to each strategy. Values for a particular

Safety Parameters	Containment Safety (S_1)	Extinguishment Safety (S_2)	People Movement Safety (S_3)	General Safety (S_4)
1. Construction				
2. Interior Finish (Corr. and Exit)				
3. Interior Finish (Rooms)				
4. Corridor Partitions/Walls				
5. Doors to Corridor				
6. Zone Dimensions				
7. Vertical Openings				
8. Hazardous Areas				
9. Smoke Control				
10. Emergency Movement Routes				
11. Manual Fire Alarm				
12. Smoke Detection and Alarm				
13. Automatic Sprinklers			÷ 2 =	
Total Value	S_1 =	S_2 =	S_3 =	S_4 =

FIGURE 20.1.7 Individual Safety Evaluations for Fire Safety Evaluation of Health Care Occupancies. For use with NFPA 101A, *Guide on Alternative Approaches to Life Safety*, 2007, and NFPA *101*®, *Life Safety Code*®, 2006.

occupancy are entered in the appropriate places on Figure 20.1.7 and then added for each column. The resulting sums are compared to predetermined minimum values and to the occupancy risk previously calculated.

A method of minimizing the cost of retrofitting for compliance with the FSES for health care occupancies has been adapted for personal computers.[7] This approach is of practical interest to persons with fiscal responsibilities for health care facilities. The software includes the integrated code compliance optimizer, full-screen data editor, and file manager. ALARM 1.0 is available from the National Fire Protection Association (http://www.nfpa.org) through the One-Stop-Data-Shop. NFPA 101A includes FSESs for health care occupancies, correctional facilities, board and care facilities, business occupancies, and educational occupancies. One of the most widely used of these is Fire Safety Evaluation System for Business Occupancies. A PC-based computerized version has been developed. Fire risk indexing (FRI) models, such as the FSES, are powerful tools for assessing fire safety, especially in existing buildings. Designers can use FRI to determine the attributes needed to bring a building up to an acceptable level of fire safety. See the *SFPE Handbook of Fire Protection Engineering* for more information on this concept.

Fire Scenarios

In the theater, a scenario outlines the action of a play. Used in forecasting and political analysis, scenarios are sequences of events that lead to some specified circumstances. Scenarios are particularly suited to examining related conditions (such as building occupancy) and events (such as ignition). A fire scenario is a generalized, detailed description of an actual or hypothetical, but credible, fire incident. Such a scenario identifies a chain of events leading to deaths and other fire losses.

Each fire scenario includes all details relevant to a fire's development and the subsequent behavior of people and protection mechanisms. A properly developed fire scenario describes all essential elements of a fire incident. Scenario development is one of the most useful devices for anticipating a largely uncertain future. Fire protection engineering evaluation of a building or facility involves creating and analyzing fire scenarios. In the simplest form, a fire protection engineer hypothesizes plausible fire scenarios using professional experience and scientific principles of fire dynamics. A more sophisticated form uses computer models to predict fire scenario events.

Fire scenarios are particularly useful in assessing life safety in buildings. By considering various fire scenarios, it often is possible to identify and evaluate the potential for life loss. Plausible fire scenarios are an essential component of some other techniques of life safety assessment, such as the performance-based approach.

Evacuation Models

Computer models for the assessment of life safety in buildings are developing rapidly, concurrent with technical knowledge and hardware capability. These advances occur internationally in acknowledgment of their potential effect on reducing loss of life from fire.

Computer simulation is the process of representing item by item and step by step a system's essential features and then predicting what is likely to happen by running the model case by case. A great advantage of computer simulation is that by using computer-generated random numbers, the model can represent with desired precision processes for which satisfactory analytical approximations do not exist. A system that is not well enough understood to permit mathematical relations between variables to be formalized may often be modeled as a simulation. In studying behavioral systems, the need for simulation becomes acute. When objective data are very difficult to obtain, most predictions must be derived from vague, tentative, and intuitive conjectures. Such ill-defined structures and laborious analyses make computers indispensable tools.

The flexibility of simulation modeling and the complexity of the evacuation problem have resulted in numerous applications. These models differ in complexity, input requirements, underlying assumptions, specific application areas, and validation. Computer simulations of emergency egress range from simple travel time models to detailed representations of human decision making.

Performance-Based Approach

Most building codes maintain only an assumed, implicit relationship between fire safety requirements and fire safety objectives. For example, the number of exits has an intuitively positive correlation with life safety but no explicit relationship and no functional association for determining costs or benefits.

Performance-based evaluation focuses on fire safety objectives. This implies an examination of how all materials, products, components, and assemblies in a building work together as a system to meet fire safety objectives. For example, in determining adequacy of egress routes, it is desirable to consider the overall effect of number, size, length, and reliability of use, as well as the interdependencies among fire growth, fire resistance, and fire suppression.

The performance-based approach establishes fire safety objectives and leaves means for achieving objectives to the design professional. Carrying out this significant departure from traditional code practice requires the capability to determine whether fire safety objectives are being met.

NFPA *101* provides requirements for the evaluation of a performance-based life safety design. The evaluation process is summarized in Figure 20.1.8. On the left-hand side of Figure 20.1.8 is input from the code, life safety goals, the objectives necessary to achieve these goals, and the measures that are to be used to determine whether the objectives have been met.

At the top of Figure 20.1.8 is the input necessary to evaluate a life safety design. The design specifications are to include certain retained prescriptive requirements as specified in the code. All assumptions about the life safety design and the response of the building and its occupants to a fire need to be clearly stated. Fire scenarios are used to assess the adequacy of the design.

Appropriate methods for assessing performance are to be used and safety factors are to be applied to account for uncertainties in the assessment. If the resulting predicted outcome of the scenarios is bounded by the performance criteria, then the

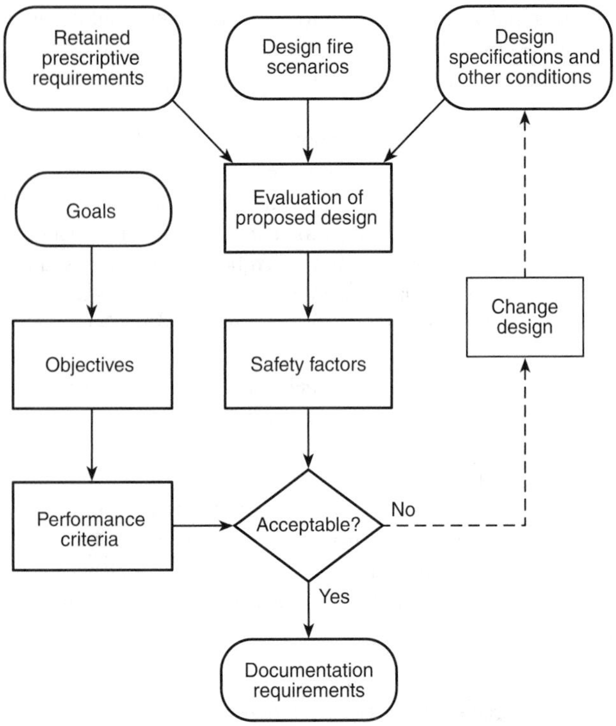

FIGURE 20.1.8 Performance-Based Life Safety Evaluation Process

objectives have been met and the life safety design is considered to be in compliance with the code. A design that fails to comply can be changed and reassessed as indicated on the right-hand side of Figure 20.1.8.

Although the performance option of this code contains goals, objectives, and performance criteria necessary to provide an acceptable level of risk to occupants, it does not describe how to meet the goals, objectives, and performance criteria. Professional design and engineering are needed to develop solutions that meet the performance provisions. Additional information on performance-based fire codes and standards is found in Section 3, Chapter 10, "Performance-Based Codes and Standards for Fire Safety," and the *SFPE Engineering Guide to Performance-Based Fire Protection Analysis and Design of Buildings.*[8]

SUMMARY

The main goals of life safety are to prevent fire, control fire if it happens, and to evacuate occupants. Many factors need to be evaluated when assessing life safety in buildings. The qualified evaluator must, therefore, have a good understanding of a range of concepts, including ignition potential, fire hazards, fire detection, fire suppression, emergency notification, building construction, occupant behavior, exit systems, and emergency management. Tools that can be used in the assessment process include fire code requirements, egress analysis, fire safety evaluation systems, fire scenarios, computer evacuation models, and the performance-based approach.

BIBLIOGRAPHY

References Cited

1. *Fire Deaths—Causes and Strategies for Control,* Technomic Publishing, Lancaster, PA, 1984, pp. 18, 21.
2. Beller, D. K., and Watts, J. M., Jr., "Occupancy Classification for Performance-Based Life Safety," *Fire and Materials,* Vol. 23, 1999, pp. 281–289.
3. Watts, J. M., Jr., "Angle of Exit Remoteness," *Fire Technology,* Vol. 32, No. 1, 1996, pp. 76–82.
4. *SFPE Engineering Guide to Human Behavior in Fires,* Society of Fire Protection Engineers, Bethesda, MD, 2004.
5. Proulx, G., "Movement of People," *The SFPE Handbook of Fire Protection Engineering,* 3rd ed., P. J. DiNenno, et al. (Eds.), National Fire Protection Association, Quincy, MA, 2002, pp. 3-342–3-366.
6. Nelson, H. E., and Mowrer, F. W., "Emergency Movement," *The SFPE Handbook of Fire Protection Engineering,* 3rd ed., P. J. DiNenno, et al. (Eds.), National Fire Protection Association, Quincy, MA, 2002, pp. 3-367–3-380.
7. Weber, S. F., and Lippiatt, B. C., "Cost-Effective Compliance with Life Safety Codes," *Fire Technology,* Vol. 32, No. 4, 1996, pp. 291–296.
8. Society of Fire Protection Engineers, *SFPE Engineering Guide to Performance-Based Fire Protection Analysis and Design of Buildings,* National Fire Protection Association, Quincy, MA, 2000.

NFPA Codes, Standards, and Recommended Practices

Reference to the following NFPA codes, standards, and recommended practices will provide further information on assessing life safety in buildings discussed in this chapter. (See the latest version of The NFPA Catalog *for availability of current editions of the following documents.)*

NFPA 1, *Uniform Fire Code™*
NFPA 70, *National Electrical Code®*
NFPA *101®, Life Safety Code®*
NFPA 101A, *Guide on Alternative Approaches to Life Safety*
NFPA 550, *Guide to the Fire Safety Concepts Tree*
NFPA 5000®, Building Construction and Safety Code®

References

Coté, R., and Harrington, G. E. (Eds.), *Life Safety Code® Handbook,* 10th ed., National Fire Protection Association, Quincy, MA, 2006.

Marchant, E. W., and Copping, A. G., "Fire Risk Assessment: Human Behavior Within Fire Safety Systems," *Fire Engineers Journal,* Vol. 61, No. 211, 2001, pp. 26–29.

Board and Care Facilities

Philip R. Jose

Chapter Contents

Key Terms

egress, evacuation capability, fuel control, ignition control, occupant characteristics, personal care, residential board and care occupancy, special hazards

Although it has been with us for more than a century, the residential board and care home has been a phenomenon in the United States since the 1970s. Reasons for the growth of this type of occupancy are numerous. The population of state hospitals was reduced sharply in the 10-year period from 1969 to 1979. Social, judicial, economic, and therapeutic pressures to remove patients from the restrictive environments of psychiatric hospitals, nursing homes, state schools, and other institutional settings helped create a need for board and care facilities. This occupancy provides the deinstitutionalized person with a more normal setting to live in and furnishes the support services the resident needs to cope with life's daily requirements.

Today's older adults often live alone, even after they are unable to care for all their own needs. They might need to be in a setting where someone can look after their nutrition, personal hygiene, and so on. In recent decades, the rapid growth of assisted living facilities has driven the overall growth in board and care facilities, a trend that will continue to accelerate due to the aging baby boom population.

Alcohol and drug rehabilitation programs often use the halfway house concept, in which the individual is somewhat sheltered from the pressures of returning too quickly to society for independent living. Shelters for battered persons, unwed mothers, and homeless children have also become more common.

The fire experience in what NFPA statistical analysts call board and care homes was striking during 1979–1983 and remains a concern today (Table 20.2.1). Many of the multiple-death fires reported in Table 20.2.1 killed over half the residents, and it is not unusual for the largest fires to totally destroy facilities. At the same time, these fires are becoming less frequent. Fires involving 10 or more fatalities in particular are declining, and this is a hopeful development.

This chapter examines what makes board and care facilities so susceptible to fire and loss of life and what must be done to improve the fire record.

See also Section 5, Chapter 5, "Reaching High-Risk Groups"; and Section 20, Chapter 1, "Assessing Life Safety in Buildings."

DEFINITION

A residential board and care occupancy is defined in NFPA *101*®, *Life Safety Code*®, and *NFPA 5000*®, *Building Construction and Safety Code*®, as a building or portion thereof that is used for lodging and boarding of four or more residents, not related by blood or marriage to the owners or operators, for the purpose of providing personal care services. The characteristic of providing personal care services distinguishes a board and care facility from a rooming house or dormitory.

In fire incident databases, a board and care facility is defined by its occupants' needs. It is important to keep the distinction between the code and database definitions in mind, because there is no guarantee that the occupants' needs match the care the facility provides. In particular, the care needs of occupants that qualify a property as a board and care facility for fire-reporting purposes will often be greater than the care delivered by a facility legitimately classified as a board and care facility under NFPA *101* and *NFPA 5000*. Therefore, Table 20.2.1 might not properly describe

---

Philip R. Jose, P.E., CSP, is a private consulting fire protection engineer. He chairs the Life Safety Code and Building Code Technical Committee on Board and Care Facilities and is a Life Safety Code seminar instructor for NFPA.

TABLE 20.2.1 North American Board and Care Home Fires Causing Five or More Deaths (1971–2005)

Date	*Occupancy**	*Civilians Killed*
1/73	Pleasantville, NJ	10
4/79	Farmington, MO	25
4/79	Washington, DC	10
4/79	Connellsville, PA	10
11/79	Pioneer, OH	14
7/80	Bradley Beach, NJ	24
11/80	Detroit, MI	5
1/81	Keansburg, NJ	31
10/82	Pittsburgh, PA	5
2/83	Eau Claire, WI	6
3/83	Gladstone, MI	5
4/83	Worcester, MA	7
8/83	Lawrenceville, GA	8
12/83	Cincinnati, OH	7
11/84	Lexington, KY	5
3/91	Colorado Springs, CO	10
9/91	St. Isidore, Quebec	5
6/92	Detroit, MI	10
10/94	Mobile, AL	6
12/94	Fort Lauderdale, FL	6
3/95	Mississauga, Ontario	7
3/96	Laurinburg, NC	8
8/96	Sainte Genevieve, Quebec	7
5/97	Harveys Lake, PA	10
4/98	Arlington, WA	8
1/04	Maryville, TN	5

*The classification as a board and care home is based on the needs of the occupants, specifically the presence of tenants who were over age 65 or had chronic mental illness. The classification is not based on the level of care the facility offered or the level of care it claimed to offer.

Source: NFPA Fire Incident Data Organization.

the fire experience of facilities that NFPA *101* and *NFPA 5000* would have classified as board and care homes or that claimed to be board and care homes.

The NFPA *101* and *NFPA 5000* definition could easily describe a hospital or a nursing home. The primary difference is in the definition of personal care. The care given in a hospital or a nursing home is certainly personal, but its primary purpose is to meet the medical needs of patients. In the board and care facility, the care provided is not medical in nature, nor does it require the services of doctors and nurses. It is generally a kind of assistance that can be rendered by laypersons who help residents cope with the rigors of daily living. This care might include looking after residents' personal hygiene, cleaning their living quarters, helping those who are physically handicapped to move around, preparing meals, looking after residents' financial matters, seeing that appointments are kept, reminding residents to take their medications, and numerous other tasks.

As this discussion implies, NFPA *101* and *NFPA 5000* seek to identify distinct populations in terms of needed levels of care and then define distinct categories of facilities that are established to provide the level of care required by a group of potential residents. A separate problem must be solved; making sure that residents are not put in facilities that are unable to or will not serve all their needs. This problem, implicit in most of the fires in Table 20.2.1, is one for enforcement authorities and probably the most important key to fire safety for all populations needing care.

Few board and care facilities call themselves by that name. Some facilities that fit into the definition of this occupancy include the following:

- Assisted living facilities
- Group homes for mentally retarded persons
- Group homes for released psychiatric patients
- Rest homes for older adults
- Foster care homes
- Orphanages
- Shelters for battered persons
- Shelters for unwed mothers
- Halfway houses for rehabilitated alcoholics
- Halfway houses for rehabilitated drug abusers
- Halfway houses for prison parolees
- Shelters for runaways
- Rescue missions with overnight accommodations

Whatever their names, a common thread ties these facilities together. They provide residents with more than just food and shelter. The residents usually are furnished some form of assistance, support, or care that is not of a medical nature.

The technical committee responsible for developing the board and care chapters of NFPA *101* and *NFPA 5000* has worked very hard to balance the need for a high level of fire safety with the financial constraints imposed on the owners and operators of the facilities. Many new small board and care facilities are existing residential structures that have been converted to this new occupancy. The owners and operators of these facilities are filling a significant need for this type of housing. The cost of upgrading these homes to meet board and care requirements is a major issue. The committee has allowed for certain code modifications to meet this concern. One such, often controversial, modification is the sprinkler exemption for conversions of existing buildings with a prompt evacuation capability and eight or fewer residents. It is important to note that by definition, a facility with a prompt rating houses a group of people with "the ability to move reliably to a point of safety in a timely manner that is equivalent to the capacity of a household in the general population." The committee feels with that restriction and the many other fire safety features required for this occupancy, a reasonable level of fire safety is provided.

CODE REQUIREMENTS FOR NEW BOARD AND CARE FACILITIES

Starting with the 2003 editions of NFPA *101* and *NFPA 5000,* the requirements for new board and care facilities are not dependent on the evacuation capability of the residents. For new facilities, one set of requirements applies, regardless of the evacuation capability. This new approach provides one level of safety for all new facilities. Not only does this simplify the application of code requirements for new facilities, it resolves the ongoing compliance problem presented by an aging resident population.

The code has always required that facilities upgrade to meet the requirements for new construction whenever the evacuation capability of the residents changed to a slower classification. This routinely occurs as residents grow older and less able to evacuate at the same rate. Owners can be faced with costly modifications, which might include the installation of automatic sprinklers. Possible alternatives are moving selected residents to other facilities or hiring additional staff. Now that new facilities are governed by one set of requirements, this issue needs to be addressed only in existing facilities.

This same approach is not realistically viable for existing board and care facilities, as nearly all structures would require significant costly modifications to meet the code requirements to provide a level of safety appropriate for all evacuation-capability classifications. The existing approach of providing increased levels of protection, dependent on the evacuation capability of the residents as a group, continues to be valid and reasonable for existing facilities.

CLASSIFYING BOARD AND CARE FACILITIES

Classifying a board and care facility is an extremely important first task when conducting an inspection or evaluating a facility for compliance with NFPA *101* or *NFPA 5000.* If a mistake is made here, most of the inspection or evaluation that follows will be invalid. Answers to three questions determine building requirements for board and care facilities:

- Is the facility new or existing?
- Is the facility large or small?
- If existing, what is the facility's evacuation capability?

New or Existing

If the structure is built new or if it is a conversion from another occupancy type other than health care, the requirements for new board and care facilities in NFPA *101* must be met. If not, the requirements for existing facilities apply.

Large or Small

Simply counting the number of available beds for residents determines the size of the facility. Staff or family members are not counted when making this determination. By definition, a resident is a person who is receiving personal care and resides in the board and care facility. It is only the total number of residents in the facility that determines if it is large or small. Small facilities are those that provide sleeping accommodations for not more than 16 residents. Large facilities are those that provide sleeping accommodations for 17 or more residents.

Evacuation Capability in Existing Facilities

All *occupants* of the building, as a group, are evaluated when determining the evacuation capability. *Everyone* in the structure is included when making this determination, not just the residents. Assistance by staff, if provided, is a key part of the evaluation. A group of residents who might otherwise be classified slow could be considered prompt when well-trained staff assist in the evacuation process. Remember, however, if staff assistance is used to enhance the rating, they must always be present in the facility to provide that assistance when needed.

There are three classifications of evacuation capability: prompt, slow, and impractical. The rating may be arrived at in one of three ways—using the definitions to come up with a subjective determination; using NFPA 101A, *Guide on Alternative Approaches to Life Safety;* or using a program of timed exit drills.

NFPA *101* requires that facility management furnish to the authority having jurisdiction (AHJ), on request, an evacuation capability determination using a procedure acceptable to the AHJ. If such documentation is not furnished, the evacuation capability is classified as impractical.

If timed drills are used to determine evacuation capability, NFPA *101* recommends that evacuation times of 3 minutes or less be used for classifying a facility as prompt, 3 minutes to 13 minutes slow, and greater than 13 minutes impractical. The slowest time should be used for classification. Evacuation time is measured from the time of alarm to the time the last occupant arrives at a *point of safety* as defined in NFPA *101.*

NFPA *101* requires that six fire drills be performed each year in all board and care facilities, with a minimum of two drills conducted at night when residents are sleeping. It is at this point in the evaluation process that judgment becomes critical. Common sense and experience must be used to look at the residents and staff as a group and determine if the recorded times for drills performed during the last year are realistic. To aid in the determination of evacuation capability, the AHJ might ask the facility owner to conduct a fire drill while he or she is present. Occupants' performance during the day can be observed and compared against the recorded times for night drills when residents are sleeping. Clearly, if the group is unable to evacuate the home within the previously recorded time frames during waking hours, night drills indicating equal or faster times may have been falsified.

Construction and egress arrangement requirements become more strict as evacuation capability decreases. For instance, windows may not be used for the secondary means of escape in a small facility with a slow evacuation rating. Classification of a board and care facility is the most important step in the evaluation process. Taking the necessary time to get it right is critical to the safety of the residents.

OCCUPANCY CHARACTERISTICS

Characteristics of Buildings

The contents of a board and care facility typically fall into the ordinary hazard category by the methods of evaluation under NFPA *101.* There are rarely any large concentrations of combustible materials and usually no use of flammable liquids or gases. No processes pose "special hazards." Ignition sources are typical of those found in residential occupancies, and fuel loads are generally light. The most significant fire threat in this occupancy is the enormous potential for loss of life.

Structural characteristics of buildings that house residential board and care facilities vary significantly. They range from single-family dwellings, in which a family takes in a few boarders, to high-rise, reinforced-concrete apartment buildings for the elderly operated by religious organizations, to commercial rest homes built for the purpose. Construction can be practically any type.

Characteristics of Residents

A description of the characteristics of the "typical" resident of a board and care facility is just as elusive as a description of a "typical" construction type. Residents of board and care facilities do not fit a stereotype—they may be children or elderly, physically impaired or physically sound, mentally handicapped or fully functioning. They may be capable of self-preservation or totally dependent on others to provide for their safety. No one description fits the residents of all board and care facilities. Variations that exist in the buildings and the range of residents' capabilities in these facilities pose the most significant challenge to fire protection professionals.

FIRE PROBLEMS

Problems of board and care facilities generally fall into two categories: structural and behavioral.

Structural Problems

Many board and care facilities are single-family dwellings or single-family dwellings to which space has been added to accommodate a number of boarders. Consequently, it is probable that many facilities are in structures built to standards intended for housing a "typical" family with normal abilities to detect, respond to, and escape from a fire. What follows are some of the specific fire safety characteristics for those kinds of facilities.

Building Construction. Board and care facilities that are converted dwellings reflect construction preferences for dwellings. Hence, many facilities are housed in one-, two-, and three-story wood-frame structures. In older buildings, balloon construction and unprotected wood structural members are common structural hazards. Under the best circumstances, wood-frame construction can offer some measure of protection, but fire endurance is limited and the combustible structure will eventually contribute fuel to a fire.

Egress Facilities. In converted dwellings, there is generally only a single route that occupants can use from any given room to get to safety outdoors. In converted two-story dwellings, this escape route typically includes an unenclosed stairway that might take escaping residents through the area of the house that is on fire. Often, the only alternate escape route is through a window, which in the case of a three-story building, may be more than 20 ft (6 m) above the ground. Typical of single-family dwellings, exit doors often are equipped with locking devices that impede egress, particularly for those unfamiliar with the locks or incapable of operating them.

Compartmentation. Separation of rooms from corridors and rooms from each other is sometimes nonexistent or of construction that provides little or no resistance to the passage of fire and smoke. If so, a fire in any room can quickly fill the entire building with smoke and toxic combustion products, limiting visibility and making the environment intolerable for human survival.

Vertical Openings. As with many multistory dwellings, the stairway, which also serves as the primary means of escape, normally is not enclosed. Stairs are usually open to the corridor on the upper floors and living spaces on the first floor. The spread of fire and smoke from one floor to the next can occur rapidly.

Interior Finishes. Walls and ceilings may be finished with paneling and acoustical ceiling tiles, without any thought to the combustibility of these materials. The facility owner, trying to improve the environment in which the residents live by providing attractive decor, may be placing them in jeopardy without knowing it. Highly combustible wall paneling and ceiling tiles can contribute to rapid horizontal and vertical fire spread and can be a major factor contributing to flashover. They can also contribute to the speed with which egress pathways become untenable.

Electrical Wiring and Appliances. Wiring is generally typical of the converted building's original use, which as noted is often that of a single-family dwelling. In older buildings, circuits may be inadequate in number and capacity, insulation may be old and deteriorating, fuses may be the wrong size for the circuits they protect, and wiring modifications, if any, may have been made by unqualified people. Use of extension cords, space heaters, and other residential-type electrical appliances may be common and contribute to the risk of fire.

Furnishings. The fire hazard posed by furniture and furnishings varies widely. Often, residents are permitted to bring an unlimited quantity of personal furnishings into the facility. Practically all such products can contribute fuel to a fire, with some, of course, being worse than others. Furniture that burns fiercely or gives off inordinately large quantities of smoke or toxic combustion products is a major hazard.

Behavioral Problems

Much concern over life safety in board and care facilities arises from the fact that they house a number of people who, in many cases, have diminished physical and/or mental capacity. Although this is not true of all facilities, or all residents of a given facility, the very fact that impaired people are residents of a facility that assists them in coping with daily life suggests that they may have problems fending for themselves in an emergency.

The impact that behavioral problems create generally falls into two categories: evacuation capability and safety consciousness.

Evacuation Capability. Because populations housed in board and care facilities differ widely, a broad statement describing evacuation capability in all such facilities cannot be made.

In the case of homes for older adults, some residents may be slow and unsteady, and unable to manage stairs, to see well, or to remember procedures to be followed in a fire. Some may be so incapacitated that they cannot be evacuated without a great deal of assistance. Residents of some facilities may be physically handicapped to such an extent that self-evacuation is not possible.

Evacuation capability can be affected by the facility's staff. In a facility housing deaf residents, for example, the presence of one staff member who can awaken and alert the residents to the emergency might be sufficient to normalize the evacuation capability of the group. In facilities housing more debilitated handicapped persons, a large staff might still be incapable of effecting a prompt evacuation.

Safety Consciousness. One risk factor that this occupancy has to a greater degree than other residential occupancies is that more of the residents tend to be unaware of or unconcerned with the dangers of their actions. This heightened risk applies to all the behaviors where errors lead to fires in ordinary homes, including smoking, use of space heaters, cooking, supervision of children who might play with fire, handling of appliances and electrical equipment, and even deliberate firesetting.

FIRE PROTECTION STRATEGIES

With respect to life safety, the fire problems in board and care facilities can be addressed by ignition control, fuel control, occupant protection, detection and suppression equipment, and planning and training operations. The systems approach to fire safety in correctional facilities can be modified to apply to board and care facilities as well. (See Section 20, Chapter 14, "Detention and Correctional Occupancies.")

Ignition Control

Smoking materials start many fatal fires in board and care facilities. Every facility must have a smoking policy to address such issues as where smoking is permitted and the proper disposal of smoking materials. Clearly, the policy should attempt to prevent ignitions that occupants cause by falling asleep while smoking or improperly disposing of smoking materials. Noncombustible safety-type ashtrays should be provided in areas where smoking is permitted. In those facilities that permit smoking, designated smoking areas that are supervised or in which an occupant is rarely alone can work well.

Other ignition sources, such as space heaters, cooking and other heat-producing appliances, and electrical equipment must be controlled and maintained properly. The use of such equipment should be limited to those who are capable of operating the appliance properly or to those who are being trained under supervision. Sufficient numbers of electrical outlets should be provided to eliminate the use of extension cords.

Fuel Control

In many board and care facilities, residents are permitted to bring their own furnishings into their sleeping rooms. Most of these furnishings have not been subjected to any type of test to indicate their ease of ignition or heat release rates. New drapes, curtains, upholstered furniture, and mattresses must meet specific NFPA test criteria. An exception is made for upholstered furniture and mattresses belonging to residents when placed in their sleeping room, provided a smoke alarm is installed in the room.

In facilities with existing furnishings that do not meet the referenced NFPA flammability criteria, other protection features, such as early detection, suppression, and compartmentation, should be evaluated to ensure that an acceptable level of protection is provided. Other fuel sources, such as interior finish materials, should also be evaluated with respect to their potential to spread fire.

Occupant Protection

Setting minimum criteria for the protection of life from fire in board and care occupancies is not simple. As indicated, this is not a homogeneous occupancy. Minimum protection in one facility may be overprotection or inadequate protection in another. In few, if any, other types of occupancies is it so difficult to ensure over time that there is a proper match between the care residents need and the care provided to them by the facility.

Evacuation capability is the most significant factor in determining the fire protection features needed to achieve an acceptable level of life safety. A facility that houses a group with a normal ability to respond may need little protection beyond that of other residential occupancies. In buildings housing people who respond slowly, a protection system that provides extra time to react and evacuate may be adequate. Groups that cannot be expected to evacuate to safety unaided may need a defend-in-place protection system.

One might suspect that, over a period of time, all facilities may house residents who are incapable of evacuation, so that protection for the worst situation should be provided. This approach is valid in the instance of homes for the aged, where deteriorating physical and mental conditions are predictable. However, many types of board and care facilities, because of their size and the nature of the services they provide, never deal with people incapable of self-preservation.

For a population with a relatively normal evacuation capability, the most basic system of protection consists of the following:

- Controls to prevent ignition
- Prompt detection
- Means to alert the residents
- Possibly a means of automatically suppressing the fire
- At least two routes of escape
- Prohibiting highly combustible interior finish materials (limiting the rate of fire spread and minimizing the risk of flashover)
- Enclosing vertical openings (limiting the vertical spread of fire and smoke)

For a population that is able to evacuate, but does so slowly or with difficulty, a reasonable system of protection would include all the items listed above, plus the following:

- Stricter controls to prevent ignition
- Early detection and alarm
- A greater need for automatically suppressing the fire
- Exits that are easier to use than those that might be adequate for a more capable population
- Stricter controls on the combustibility of interior finishes
- A greater degree of fire endurance to maintain building integrity during a longer evacuation period
- Compartmentation to confine fire and smoke, thus keeping egress pathways usable during the longer evacuation period
- Greater resistance to the vertical spread of fire and smoke

For a population that is not capable of evacuation, a defend-in-place protection concept would include all the features listed previously, plus the following:

- Sufficient structural fire endurance to allow the building and the internal compartmentation to outlast the fire
- A means of automatically suppressing the fire before it seriously threatens the structure and the compartmentation
- Strict control on furnishings

Note that the code requirements for new board and care facilities are predicated on the assumption that a facility's evacuation capability is impractical.

Fire Detection and Suppression

The means by which ignition and fuel controls are implemented, as well as the occupants' evacuation capability, are critical factors in determining the appropriate level of detection and suppression necessary. Residential sprinklers are the most effective means of increasing life safety. In accordance with NFPA *101* and *NFPA 5000,* a sprinkler system in accordance with one of the following standards may be used in board and care facilities, depending on the size of the facility and, for existing facilities, the evacuation capability of the occupants:

- NFPA 13, *Standard for the Installation of Sprinkler Systems*
- NFPA 13D, *Standard for the Installation of Sprinkler Systems in One- and Two-Family Dwellings and Manufactured Homes*
- NFPA 13R, *Standard for the Installation of Sprinkler Systems in Residential Occupancies up to and Including Four Stories in Height*

With respect to NFPA 13D, it should be recognized that the water supply duration depends on the evacuation capability rating of the facility and that domestic water demand is not necessarily included. Other exceptions permit sprinklers to be omitted from certain areas such as small closets, bathrooms, attics, and other areas in which fire loss data indicates that fatal fires are less likely to originate. NFPA 13 now mandates the use of either quick response or residential sprinklers for these and all other light-hazard occupancies.

Insurance carriers and applicable codes should be consulted before selecting detection and suppression systems. Preventive maintenance requirements for each type of system should also be considered during the selection and design process. Once installed, inspection, and testing and maintenance of these systems in accordance with applicable NFPA standards is mandatory.

Planning and Training Operations

The facility management must develop an emergency plan that addresses various emergencies or disasters, including fires. The plan should be realistic and capable of being implemented with the minimum resources that may be available, typically during the night. The plan should be coordinated with the local fire department to ensure that their expectations and those of the facility are consistent. The emergency plan must be amended or revised whenever a resident with special needs is admitted to the facility. All staff must understand their responsibilities in the plan and should formally review those responsibilities at least every 2 months.

Capable residents must participate in the training and drills. As discussed above, residents need to be familiar and comfortable with various egress paths available to them. Escape routes used by residents should be routinely alternated during drills so they become familiar with all ways out of the building. Residents should demonstrate the ability to use all egress routes. If windows are used as a secondary means of escape, residents must demonstrate the ability to open them unless staff or other residents are specifically assigned to assist. If assistance is needed, those so assigned must always be present when those needing assistance are present in the building. Local fire departments, fire training schools, and fire marshals' offices may have personnel and audiovisual materials that can assist in staff and resident training. It is important that the training be specific to the facility. This is one area in which board and care facilities have an advantage over other residential occupancies. There can be significantly better control over occupants in these facilities. When properly trained, board and care residents can perform above average during fire drills.

SUMMARY

The number of residential board and care facilities is steadily increasing. The move during the last half century toward reducing populations in psychiatric hospitals, nursing homes, and other types of institutional environments has created a greater need for board and care facilities. Hazards typical of board and care occupancies include structural problems, such as building construction and egress facilities, as well as behavioral problems. Fire protection strategies used in these facilities include ignition control, fuel control, occupant protection, detection and suppression activities, and planning and training operations.

BIBLIOGRAPHY

NFPA Codes, Standards, and Recommended Practices

Reference to the following NFPA codes, standards, and recommended practices will provide further information on board and care facilities discussed in this chapter. (See the latest version of The NFPA Catalog *for availability of current editions of the following documents.)*

NFPA 13, *Standard for the Installation of Sprinkler Systems*
NFPA 13D, *Standard for the Installation of Sprinkler Systems in One- and Two-Family Dwellings and Manufactured Homes*
NFPA 13R, *Standard for the Installation of Sprinkler Systems in Residential Occupancies up to and Including Four Stories in Height*
NFPA *101*®, *Life Safety Code*®
NFPA 101A, *Guide on Alternative Approaches to Life Safety*
NFPA 5000®, *Building Construction and Safety Code*®

References

"Code Change B7-97 Will Reduce Conflict Between FHAA Objectives and Fire Safety," *Building Official and Code Administrator,* Vol. 31, No. 5, 1997, pp. 16–19.

Comeau, E., "Board and Care, Arlington, Washington, April 27, 1998, Eight Fatalities," NFPA Fire Investigation Report, National Fire Protection Association, Quincy, MA, 1999.

Comeau, E., "Board and Care Fires," *NFPA Journal*, Vol. 92, No. 5, 1998, pp. 34–41.

"Inadequate Staff Training and Open Fire Doors Led to the Deaths of Six Residents in a U.S. Residential Care Home," *Fire Prevention,* No. 295, Dec. 1996, pp. 31–34.

Koffel, W. E., "Classifying Assisted-Living Facilities," *NFPA Journal*, Vol. 93, No. 4, 1999, p. 32.

Lake, J. D., Comeau, E., and Duval, R. F., "Board and Care Facility Fire, Harveys Lake, Pennsylvania, May 13, 1997," NFPA Fire Investigation Report, National Fire Protection Association, Quincy, MA, 1998.

Chapter 3

Hotels and University Housing

Revised by

April Berkol ❑ Byron Briese ❑ Ed Comeau

Key Terms

active fire protection systems, automatic sprinkler system, dormitory, false alarm, fire containment, fire-safe cigarette, Greek housing, hotel, Hotel and Motel Safety Act, lodging occupancy, nuisance alarm, occupancy characteristics, occupant characteristics, residence hall, smoke control system, university housing, unwanted alarm

In NFPA *101*®, *Life Safety Code*®, and *NFPA 5000*®, *Building Construction and Safety Code*®, requirements for hotels and dormitories are located in the same chapters. NFPA *101* and *NFPA 5000* definitions for hotel and dormitory are as follows:

Hotel—A building or groups of buildings under the same management in which there are sleeping accommodations for more than 16 persons and primarily used by transients for lodging with or without meals

The definition of *hotel* is further refined in NFPA *101* and *NFPA 5000* to include hotel, inn, club, motel, bed-and-breakfast, or any other structure meeting the foregoing definition of hotel.

Dormitory—A building or a space in a building in which group sleeping accommodations are provided for more than 16 persons who are not members of the same family in one room or a series of closely associated rooms under joint occupancy and single management, with or without meals, but without individual cooking facilities.

It is important to note that the definition for dormitory that is used by the National Fire Incident Reporting System (NFIRS) includes occupancies other than just the typical dormitory found on campuses across the country. It includes military barracks, monasteries, and nursing quarters. For this reason, the statistics generated since 2000 for "dormitories" are no longer only applicable to university housing.

As used in this chapter, *university housing* includes dormitories or residence halls and Greek housing (whether on or off campus) in addition to apartments and houses.

See also Section 20, Chapter 1, "Assessing Life Safety in Buildings"; and Section 20, Chapter 4, "Apartment Buildings."

FIRE SAFETY IN HOTELS

Hotel Fire Record

The May 1981 issue of *Fire Journal,* NFPA's membership publication now titled *NFPA Journal,* provided a bleak summary of multiple-fatality hotel fires in the United States reported to NFPA since 1934. The article also contained an analysis of the fire scenarios involved in 170 fatal hotel fires experienced in the previous decade.

April Berkol is director of environmental health, fire, and life safety at Starwood Hotels and Resorts Worldwide, Inc., headquartered in White Plains, New York, and is a member of the NFPA Board of Directors.

Byron Briese is a vice-president with Rolf Jensen and Associates in Fairfax, Virginia. He earned a bachelor of science degree in fire protection engineering at the University of Maryland and is a member of NFPA's Residential Occupancy Committee.

Ed Comeau is publisher of *Campus Firewatch,* a monthly electronic newsletter focusing on campus fire safety issues. He is the founder and former director of the Center for Campus Fire Safety and the former chief fire investigator for NFPA.

The *Fire Journal* article followed these four landmark hotel fire incidents in North America that occurred between November 1980 and February 1981:

- MGM Grand Hotel (Las Vegas, Nevada, November 1980)
- Stouffers Inn (Harrison, New York, December 1980)
- Inn on the Park (North York, Ontario, Canada, January 1981)
- Hilton Hotel (Las Vegas, Nevada, February 1981)

These four hotel fires resulted in 125 civilian deaths as well as injuries to hundreds of civilians and scores of fire fighters.

As shown in Table 20.3.1, fire deaths of this magnitude, within such a short period of time, had not occurred in North American hotels in almost four decades. Previously, between June 1946 and December 1946, nearly 200 fatalities were recorded in three notorious fatal hotel fires, including the LaSalle Hotel in Chicago and the Winecoff Hotel in Atlanta.

The large scale of the fire incidents in the early 1980s shook public confidence in the lodging industry and prompted industry experts and regulatory authorities to reconsider the life safety strategies used for hotel occupancies.

The review of fire scenarios clearly showed the need to emphasize protection of the sleeping-room areas of hotels. Smoking materials and intentionally set fires were the leading ignition factors in the data set of fires reviewed.

Unlike the period following the 1946 incidents, fire suppression and detection technology had evolved by the early 1980s to provide tools to effectively protect building occupants in the incipient stages of a fire. These technologies, complemented by cooperative fire safety research into industry-specific solutions, coupled with public expectations regarding fire safety, resulted in significant changes to building and fire safety codes in the United States, as applied to hotels.

Evolution of Life Safety Strategies for Hotels

Prior to the landmark fires of the early 1980s, little emphasis was placed on the use of automatic sprinklers in hotels. Reliable, commercially viable, early-warning fire detection technology did not exist until the latter part of the twentieth century. Further, although fire research had been ongoing for decades, application to residential settings was limited.

TABLE 20.3.1 Summary of Fire Incidents, Hotel Fires in the United States, as Reported to NFPA, with Ten or More Fatalities, 1934–2005

City	*Hotel*	*Date*	*Deaths*
Lansing, MI	Kerns Hotel	December 1934	32
Atlanta, GA	Terminal Hotel	May 1938	35
Minneapolis, MN	Marlborough Hotel	January 1940	19
Houston, TX	Gulf Motel	September 1943	54
Chicago, IL	LaSalle Hotel	June 1946	61
Dubuque, IA	Canfield Hotel	June 1946	19
Atlanta, GA	Winecoff Hotel	December 1946	119
Chicago, IL	Barton Hotel	February 1955	29
Atlantic City, NJ	Surfside Hotel	November 1963	25
Jacksonville, FL	Hotel Roosevelt	December 1963	22
St. Paul, MN	Hotel Carlton	January 1966	11
Boston, MA	Paramount Hotel	January 1966	11
Anchorage, AK	Lane Hotel	September 1966	14
Seattle, WA	Ozark Hotel	March 1970	20
Los Angeles, CA	Ponet Square Hotel	September 1970	19
Tucson, AZ	Pioneer International	December 1970	28
Tyrone, PA	Pennsylvania House Hotel	January 1972	12
Berkely Springs, WV	Washington House	August 1974	12
Portland, OR	Pomona Hotel	July 1975	11
Fremont, NE	Pathfinder Hotel	January 1976	20
Breckenridge, MN	Stratford Hotel	January 1977	17
Bay City, MI	Wenonah Park Hotel	December 1977	10
Kansas City, MO	Coates House Hotel	January 1978	20
Honesdale, PA	Allen Motor Inn	November 1978	12
Greece, NY	Holiday Inn	November 1978	10
Cambridge, OH	Holiday Inn	July 1979	10
Las Vegas, NV	MGM Grand Hotel	November 1980	85
Harrison, NY	Stouffers Inn	December 1980	26
Houston, TX	Hilton Hotel	March 1982	12
San Juan, PR	Dupont Plaza	December 1986	97

Source: NFPA's archive files, *The1984 Fire Almanac,* and NFPA's Fire Incident Data Organization database.

The January 1930 issue of *NFPA Quarterly* provided a summary of numerous hotel fires experienced within the United States during the prior 30-year period. Based on this experience, several hotel fire safety requisites were summarized by the *Quarterly,* including the need for fire-resistive construction, the provision of proper exits, the protection of vertical openings, the use of fire walls, and the provision of fire alarm facilities.

The article summarized nearly 100 hotel fire incidents that occurred between 1910 and 1928 where automatic sprinklers were present. Despite a significant success rate for control and suppression of fires (72 of 76 incidents where sprinklers activated were extinguished with not more than four sprinklers), sprinkler installation was listed below construction features in the summary of hotel fire safety requisites.

Automatic sprinklers were recommended for the entire building "where possible," but otherwise, complete coverage was only considered mandatory for buildings of combustible construction or in limited hazardous areas such as kitchens and basements.

By the mid-1980s the effectiveness of automatic sprinkler protection was recognized. In testimony provided to a science subcommittee of the U.S. House of Representatives in 1988, Rolf Jensen, in his capacity as president of the Society of Fire Protection Engineers, observed that the twentieth-century history of fatal fire incidents in hotels involved "fast fires," killing "large numbers of people in a single incident." Mr. Jensen's testimony detailed the progress that had been made to develop sprinkler technology that could be effectively applied to hotels as well as other residential structures.

Code and Legislative Developments Related to Sprinkler Systems in Hotels

The 1976 edition of NFPA *101* reflected the decades-old protective philosophy discussed previously and contained no specific requirement for automatic sprinklers in hotels. Requirements for smoke detection systems were limited to corridors in new facilities.

NFPA *101* was amended in 1988 to require the installation of automatic sprinklers in new and existing high-rise hotels. By 1990, each of the United States model building codes also required this level of protection, with the Uniform Building Code requiring new hotels with 20 or more sleeping rooms, regardless of height, to be protected with automatic sprinklers.

Three decades following the publication of the 1976 edition of NFPA *101*, the 2006 edition emphasizes the use of active fire protection systems, notably automatic sprinklers, in hotels. With limited exceptions for smaller properties or those hotels with guest-room entrances leading directly to the exterior, NFPA *101* and *NFPA 5000* require full sprinkler protection for new hotels.

Several states, including large tourism states such as Nevada and Florida, legislated retroactive fire protection requirements for certain existing lodging establishments, generally high-rise hotels. In the 1980s, the states of Alaska, California, and New Jersey exempted fire protection system installations from taxation by virtue of either a tax credit (Alaska) or a property tax exemption (California and New Jersey), thus easing the financial cost of such improvements in existing buildings including hotels.

In 1989, NFPA issued a new sprinkler standard, NFPA 13R, *Standard for the Installation of Sprinkler Systems in Residential Occupancies up to and Including Four Stories in Height,* aimed at making sprinkler protection more affordable for low-rise, residential-use buildings. NFPA 13R, combined with the development and listing of chlorinated polyvinyl chloride (CPVC) and polybutylene (PB) sprinkler pipe, reduced the cost of sprinkler installation, especially in existing hotels.

In 1990, Congress enacted the Hotel and Motel Fire Safety Act of 1990 (Public Law 101-391). This statute brought the power of the federal government's purse to bear on the lodging fire safety issue by limiting meetings in lodging establishments by federal agencies to hotels and motels that met the fire safety requirements outlined in the act. Individual federal employees on official travel were also limited, after a phase-in period, to staying only in lodging facilities that also met these requirements.

Industry Response to Hotel Fires

In addition to code and legislative changes, the hotel industry responded to the fire challenge experienced in the early 1980s. In 1987, in cooperation with leading hotel firms, NFPA formed the Lodging Industry Membership Section to provide a forum and focus within the association for the industry's voice and needs.

The automatic sprinkler industry developed equipment specifically devised for life safety protection. As new "quick-response" sprinkler technology and fire detection capability were developed, many hotel owners and operators voluntarily retrofitted new protective systems into existing buildings as well as new construction projects.

By 1988, and noted in the first large-scale study of fire safety in the lodging industry conducted by the American Hotel and Motel Association, now the American Hotel and Lodging Association, almost universal usage of smoke alarms within hotel guest rooms was reported. The study also noted that about half of all hotel rooms were equipped with automatic sprinklers, with the number rising to about two-thirds when only high-rise hotels were considered.[1]

As evidenced by Table 20.3.2 covering the years 1980 to 2002, there was a downward trend in reported lodging industry fire incidents, losses, and most importantly, casualty figures.

The effectiveness of automatic sprinklers in hotels can be seen in Table 20.3.3. For the years 1994 to 1998, estimates show a 100 percent reduction in fatalities per 1000 fires with automatic fire suppression systems present.

Improvements to fire loss statistics have occurred despite an unparalleled building boom in the 1990s when thousands of new hotels were constructed. (See *Lodging Profile.*[1])

Recent Lodging Industry Fire Experience

For the years 1999 to 2002, data developed by NFPA suggest that three factors—cooking equipment, smoking materials, and arson—are today's leading causes of fatal fires in hotels and motels. See Tables 20.3.4 and 20.3.5.

TABLE 20.3.2 Structure Fires in Hotels and Motels, by Year: 1980–2002

				Direct Property Damage (in Millions of Dollars)	
Year	*Fires*	*Civilian Deaths*	*Civilian Injuries*	*As Reported*	*In 2002 Dollars*
1980	12,530	80	752	63.7	139.2
1981	12,880	148	719	69.5	137.3
1982	10,240	52	587	42.2	78.6
1983	9,550	73	562	103.2	186.2
1984	9,670	34	538	65.6	113.4
1985	9,310	85	412	74.0	123.5
1986	8,790	57	416	74.4	122.2
1987	8,210	54	430	70.6	111.7
1988	8,230	35	382	85.1	129.5
1989	7,710	24	333	68.2	99.0
1990	7,090	54	496	70.3	96.9
1991	6,610	22	372	84.8	111.9
1992	6,530	26	395	63.5	81.4
1993	6,140	62	456	63.9	79.5
1994	5,890	28	349	59.3	72.0
1995	5,460	36	299	71.5	84.4
1996	5,610	43	332	110.6	126.9
1997	5,010	21	284	81.6	91.4
1998	4,750	24	257	55.3	61.1
1999	4,610	24	249	124.6	134.4
2000	4,830	11	170	82.8	86.6
2001	4,590	12	217	59.3	60.2
2002	4,180	16	138	77.1	77.1

Note: These are national estimates of fires reported to U.S. municipal fire departments and so exclude fires reported only to federal or state agencies or industrial fire brigades. National estimates are projections. Casualty and loss projections can be heavily influenced by the inclusion or exclusion of one unusually serious fire. Fires are rounded to the nearest ten; civilian deaths and injuries are rounded to the nearest one; and direct property damage is rounded to the nearest hundred thousand dollars.

Source: NFIRS and NFPA survey. Inflation adjustments were based on U.S. Census Bureau's *Statistical Abstract of the United States: 2006,* "Table 705, Purchasing Power of the Dollar."

TABLE 20.3.3 Automatic Suppression Systems in Hotel and Motel Fires Reported to Public Fire Departments: 1994–1998 Annual Averages

Percentage of fires in buildings with automatic suppression system	34%
Deaths per 1000 fires with automatic suppression system	0.0
Deaths per 1000 fires with no automatic suppression system present	7.7
Reduction in deaths per 1000 fires when automatic suppression systems were present	100%
Average loss per fire when automatic suppression system was present	$7,160
Average loss per fire with no automatic suppression system	$15,320
Reduction in loss per fire when automatic suppression systems were present	53%

Source: National estimates based on NFIRS and NFPA survey. 1998 is the most current data available.

Cooking Equipment. Changes to cooking equipment and oils have led to the development of more effective means to control cooking fires, notably advances in wet chemical fixed extinguishing systems. As with any commercial kitchen, hotel kitchens require the installation of fire suppression equipment effective for the hazard present.

Smoking Materials. For smoking, research[2] authorized by Congress pursuant to the 1990 Fire Safe Cigarette Act and undertaken by the National Institute of Standards and Technology (NIST) concluded that the commercial production of a relatively fire-safe cigarette was feasible. Although regulation at the federal level has not passed legislation, several states have introduced requirements limiting the sale of cigarettes to only those cigarettes that were deemed fire safe effective in January 2003.

Faced with the possibility of having to produce different cigarettes for different states, the nation's largest producer of cigarettes, the Altria Corporation (formerly Philip Morris) took the position that all such cigarettes should be fire safe.[3] With that

TABLE 20.3.4 Leading Causes of Structure Fires in Hotels and Motels: 1999–2002 Annual Averages

Cause	*Fires*		*Civilian Deaths*		*Civilian Injuries*		*Direct Property Damage (in Millions of Dollars)*	
Cooking equipment fire	1060	(23%)	0	(0%)	37	(19%)	14.0	(16%)
Identified cooking equipment	770	(17%)	0	(0%)	35	(18%)	10.2	(12%)
Confined cooking fire	290	(6%)	0	(0%)	2	(1%)	3.7	(4%)
Smoking materials	710	(16%)	9	(56%)	45	(23%)	7.0	(8%)
Intentional	530	(12%)	6	(37%)	35	(18%)	24.7	(29%)
Heating equipment	440	(10%)	3	(17%)	14	(7%)	4.1	(5%)
Identified heating equipment	380	(8%)	3	(17%)	13	(7%)	4.0	(5%)
Confined chimney or flue fire	30	(1%)	0	(0%)	0	(0%)	0.0	(0%)
Confined fuel burner or boiler malfunction or fire	30	(1%)	0	(0%)	1	(0%)	0.1	(0%)
Clothes dryer or washer	430	(9%)	0	(0%)	21	(11%)	1.9	(2%)
Electrical distribution or lighting equipment	360	(8%)	1	(7%)	15	(8%)	9.3	(11%)
Candle	120	(3%)	0	(0%)	10	(5%)	1.8	(2%)
Torch, burner, or soldering iron	80	(2%)	0	(0%)	6	(3%)	3.0	(3%)
Exposure to other fire	80	(2%)	0	(0%)	0	(0%)	4.7	(6%)
Contained trash fire	100	(2%)	0	(0%)	0	(0%)	0.0	(0%)

Note: These are the leading causes, obtained from the following list: intentional (from the NFIRS field "cause"); playing with fire (from factor contributing to ignition); confined heating (including confined chimney and confined fuel burner or boiler fires), confined cooking, and contained trash or rubbish (from incident type); identified heating, identified cooking, clothes dryer or washer, torch (including burner and soldering iron), electrical distribution and lighting equipment, medical equipment, and electronic, office, or entertainment equipment (from equipment involved in ignition); smoking materials, candles, lightning, and spontaneous combustion or chemical reaction (from heat source); and mobile property involved (from mobile property involved in ignition). Exposure fires include fires with an exposure number greater than zero, as well as fires identified by heat source or factor contributing to ignition when no equipment was involved in ignition that were not intentionally set. The same fire can be listed under multiple causes, based on multiple data elements.

These are national estimates of fires reported to U.S. municipal fire departments and so exclude fires reported only to federal or state agencies or industrial fire brigades. National estimates are projections. Casualty and loss projections can be heavily influenced by the inclusion or exclusion of one unusually serious fire. Fires are rounded to the nearest ten; civilian deaths and injuries are rounded to the nearest one; and direct property damage is rounded to the nearest hundred thousand dollars. Property damage has not been adjusted for inflation.

Source: NFIRS and NFPA survey.

change in position and with additional research by NIST,[4] new legislation[5] was introduced in April 2002 by Senators Richard Durbin (D-Ill.) and Sam Brownback (R-Kan.) and Rep. Edward Markey (D-Mass.) to effect such change. For current information about the changing status of legislation to require fire-safe cigarettes, see http://firesafecigarettes.org.

Arson. As for arson, its traditional rationales include arson for profit, revenge, and emotional disturbance. The 1990s saw a new dimension: arson as a weapon in domestic terrorism. Although yet to strike the hotel industry, arson as a means to express a political philosophy adds a new rationale for ensuring the reliability of fire protection equipment and systems and for a stronger hotel emergency team to ensure the security of lodging occupants and establishments. Arson is a difficult crime to prevent. Typically, the industry steps up its security measures in times of difficult labor relations, political unrest, when controversial individuals or groups meet or stay at a particular hotel, and so forth. Properties will add cameras to their perimeter surveillance systems and increase security patrols during such times.

ACTIVE FIRE PROTECTION SYSTEMS AND EQUIPMENT IN HOTELS

Industry experience, for nearly a century, underscores the need for the installation of adequately designed and maintained active fire protection systems and equipment in hotels. These systems can include fire alarm systems, automatic sprinkler systems, and smoke control systems, as well as smoke alarms and kitchen fire suppression systems. This chapter will briefly discuss fire alarm systems, automatic sprinkler systems, and smoke control systems for use in hotels. For information on smoke alarms, see Section 14. Also see Section 17, Chapter 2, "Chemical Extinguishing Agents and Application Systems."

Selection of the proper system or systems will depend in large measure on the size and configuration of the property.

Fire Alarm Systems

A fundamental design parameter for fire alarm systems in lodging occupancies is that most building occupants are transient

TABLE 20.3.5 Structure Fires in Hotels and Motels by Equipment Involved in Ignition: 1999–2002 Annual Averages

Equipment Involved	*Fires*		*Civilian Deaths*		*Civilian Injuries*		*Direct Property Damage (in Millions of Dollars)*	
No equipment involved	1780	(39%)	12	(76%)	88	(45%)	49	(58%)
Clothes dryer or washer	430	(9%)	0	(0%)	21	(11%)	2	(2%)
Range or cooking surface	430	(9%)	0	(0%)	16	(8%)	2	(2%)
Confined cooking fire	290	(6%)	0	(0%)	2	(1%)	4	(4%)
Lamp, bulb, or lighting	120	(3%)	0	(0%)	1	(0%)	2	(2%)
Wiring, switch, or outlet	120	(3%)	1	(7%)	3	(2%)	5	(6%)
Fixed area heater	120	(3%)	0	(0%)	4	(2%)	1	(1%)
Unclassified kitchen or cooking equipment	100	(2%)	0	(0%)	5	(3%)	4	(5%)
Contained trash or rubbish fire	100	(2%)	0	(0%)	0	(0%)	0	(0%)
Portable cooking or warming equipment	90	(2%)	0	(0%)	6	(3%)	0	(0%)
Torch, burner, or soldering iron	80	(2%)	0	(0%)	6	(3%)	3	(3%)
Oven or rotisserie	80	(2%)	0	(0%)	5	(2%)	0	(1%)
Unclassified heating, ventilating and air conditioning, other	80	(2%)	0	(0%)	5	(2%)	0	(1%)
Air conditioner	80	(2%)	0	(0%)	3	(1%)	0	(1%)
Unclassified equipment involved in ignition	60	(1%)	0	(0%)	3	(2%)	0	(1%)
Central heat or boiler	60	(1%)	0	(0%)	0	(0%)	0	(1%)
Water heater	60	(1%)	3	(17%)	4	(2%)	1	(1%)
Cord or plug	50	(1%)	0	(0%)	9	(5%)	1	(1%)
Fireplace or chimney	50	(1%)	0	(0%)	0	(0%)	0	(0%)
Confined chimney fire	30	(1%)	0	(0%)	0	(0%)	0	(0%)
Confined fuel burner or boiler fire or malfunction	30	(1%)	0	(0%)	1	(0%)	0	(0%)
Elevator or lift	30	(1%)	0	(0%)	0	(0%)	0	(0%)
Unclassified portable appliance designed to produce heat	20	(1%)	0	(0%)	1	(0%)	0	(0%)
Steam table or warming drawer or table	20	(1%)	0	(0%)	0	(0%)	0	(0%)
Other known equipment	230	(5%)	0	(0%)	14	(7%)	9	(10%)
Other confined fire	10	(0%)	0	(0%)	0	(0%)	0	(0%)
Total	4550	(100%)	16	(100%)	194	(100%)	86	(100%)

Note: These are national estimates of fires reported to U.S. municipal fire departments and so exclude fires reported only to federal or state agencies or industrial fire brigades. National estimates are projections. Casualty and loss projections can be heavily influenced by the inclusion or exclusion of one unusually serious fire. Fires are rounded to the nearest ten; civilian deaths and injuries are rounded to the nearest one; and direct property damage is rounded to the nearest million dollars. Property damage has not been adjusted for inflation.

Nonconfined fires in which the equipment involved in ignition was unknown or not reported have been allocated proportionally among fires with known equipment involved. Sums may not equal totals due to rounding errors.

Source: NFIRS and NFPA survey.

users of the buildings. Little detailed knowledge of the building should be assumed, as numerous guests use a given hotel for as little as a single night. In numerous labor markets within the United States, employee turnover rates can be significant, thereby also limiting the number of individuals within a hotel with detailed knowledge of the building.

High-rise hotels and large campus-type properties will require the use of addressable technology and voice technology to efficiently pinpoint fire incidents and effectively notify guests and employees of an emergency.

The installation of fire alarm systems in hotels will typically be subject to the requirements of *NFPA 72*®, *National Fire Alarm Code*®, which is widely referenced by model building codes. Notification devices, both audible and visual, must account for the fact that occupants may need to be alerted to a fire emergency from a deep-sleep condition.

Automatic Sprinkler Protection

With few exceptions, the installation of sprinkler protection throughout all portions of newly constructed hotels, regardless of their height, has become a general requirement in most building codes. Of particular importance for the protection of smaller hotels and dormitories is NFPA 13R, which may provide for more economical design and installation of automatic sprinkler systems in low-rise residential occupancies.

Once installed, automatic sprinkler protection should be inspected, tested, and maintained in strict accordance with NFPA 25, *Standard for the Inspection, Testing, and Maintenance of Water-Based Fire Protection Systems.* As automatic sprinkler systems age, it is imperative that piping, valves, and related hardware be maintained in working order, that fire pumps and water supplies remain within design tolerance, and that as modifications are made to the underlying building, sprinkler protection changes reflect these changes.

Smoke Control Systems

For high-rise and atrium hotels, smoke control concepts, including stairway pressurization and smoke exhaust, play an important role in mitigating initial smoke production from fires until sprinklers activate and make any staged evacuation tenable. NFPA *101* and *NFPA 5000* permit atria in hotels and dormitories, provided that they meet certain conditions. Included in these conditions are the requirements for properly designed automatic sprinkler protection and either an engineering analysis to show that the building is designed to keep the smoke layer interface above the highest unprotected opening to adjoining spaces, or 6 ft (183 cm) above the highest floor level of exit access open to the atrium, or that it has an engineered smoke control system that will do the same. The design parameters for smoke control systems and the engineering methods used for the analysis can be found in NFPA 92A, *Standard for Smoke-Control Systems Utilizing Barriers and Pressure Differences,* and NFPA 92B, *Standard for Smoke Management Systems in Malls, Atria, and Large Spaces.*

FIRE SAFETY IN UNIVERSITY HOUSING

Overview of University Housing

As used in this chapter, *university housing* includes dormitories (more accurately known as *residence halls*), university-owned apartments and houses (whether located on or off campus), and on- and off-campus Greek housing (whether owned by the university, fraternity, or sorority). For the purposes of this chapter, colleges and universities are generically referred to as "universities."

On-campus university housing consists of dormitories/residence halls, university-owned apartments, and houses. Some Greek houses are university owned, whereas others are owned by the fraternity or sorority. In some cases, the building may be privately owned and is rented by the local chapter. The capacity of residence halls at these institutions is approximately 15 percent of the 17 million students enrolled.[6]

According to the U.S. Department of Education, there were more than 4000 degree-granting colleges and universities in the United States[6] and it was projected that more than 17 million students enrolled in 2- and 4-year institutions in the fall of 2006.[7] For many of these students, this was their first time living away from home, meeting new friends, and having new experiences.

Fire Deaths in the University Environment

Unfortunately, over the years we have seen that tragedy can strike these students. According to information compiled by Campus Firewatch from January 2000 to April 2007, at least 109 people died in student housing fires. Over 80 percent of the fire deaths occurred in off-campus houses and apartments and the remainder occurred either in residence halls or fraternity houses (i.e., in Greek housing). Clearly, the predominant fire-death risk is in the off-campus environment (Table 20.3.6).

Occupancy and Occupant Characteristics

University years are a period when young adults have a sense of invulnerability. A number of factors come together in campus environments that create a potentially high-risk environment.

Close Quarters. There is a greater density of people living in close proximity to one another, both on and off campus. This creates a situation in which the actions of one person can potentially endanger a greater number of people than would otherwise be expected.

Risky Behavior. Young adults tend to engage in risky behaviors, such as drinking, that contribute to the incidence of fire. Alcohol consumption has long been connected with college campuses. Although the recent trend is toward educating students in more responsible behavior, the problem still exists. The connection between alcohol consumption, student behavior, and the incidence of fires in student housing, both on and off campus, is a serious concern.

Currently, there is no known research that definitively connects impaired judgment from alcohol consumption to fire risk in the student demographic. However, in speaking with fire chiefs across the country in college communities, there is no question that there is a definite correlation between the two. In a number of the incidents identified by Campus Firewatch, alcohol has played a factor. This is further reinforced in a study conducted by *USA TODAY* for an article on campus-related fires.[8]

Level of Scrutiny. Although on-campus housing facilities tend to be more regulated and monitored, off-campus housing facilities are subject to a lower level of scrutiny and a potentially lower level of fire safety.

Dormitories/Residence Halls

Note that in NFIRS, the classification "dormitories" includes school, college, and university dormitories; nurses' quarters;

TABLE 20.3.6 Summary of Fire Deaths in the University Environment

City	*University*	*Date*	*Type of Housing*	*Deaths*
East Orange, NJ	Seton Hall University	1/19/00	Residence hall	3 students
Bloomsburg, PA	Bloomsburg University	3/19/00	Fraternity	3 students
Cambridge, MA	Massachusetts Institute of Technology	4/10/00	Residence hall	1 student
Decatur, IL	Millikin University	6/8/00	Fraternity	1 student
Berkeley, CA	University of California	8/20/00	Off-campus	1 student and her 2 parents
Pittsburgh, PA	University of Pittsburgh	9/29/00	Off-campus	1 student
Baytown, TX	Lee College	11/16/00	Off-campus	1 student
New York, NY	New York University	11/22/00	Off-campus	1 student
Dayton, OH	University of Dayton	12/10/00	Residence hall	1 student
Morgantown, WV	West Virginia University	1/1/01	Off-campus	1 student
Athens, GA	University of Georgia Law School	1/19/01	Off-campus	1 student
Berkeley, CA	University of California	1/30/01	Off-campus	1 student
Binghamton, NY	Binghamton University	2/26/01	Off-campus	1 student
Austin, TX	University of Texas	5/1/01	Off-campus	1 student
Cleveland Heights, OH	John Carroll University	5/19/01	Off-campus	1 student
Athens, OH	Ohio University	5/19/01	Off-campus	1 student and 1 guest
Emporia, KS	Emporia State University	7/29/01	Off-campus	1 student and her son
Morgantown, WV	University of West Virginia	8/18/01	Off-campus	1 student
Anderson, IN	Anderson University	8/30/01	Off-campus	1 student
Lexington, KY	University of Kentucky	9/1/01	Off-campus	1 student
Fort Wayne, IN	Ivy Tech State College	9/30/01	Off-campus	1 student and her son
Salisbury, NC	Catawba College	10/28/01	Residence hall	1 student
Richmond, VA	Virginia Commonwealth University	11/2/01	Off-campus	1 student and her 2 children
Greensboro, NC	University of North Carolina–Greensboro	2/15/02	Off-campus	4 students
Narragansett, RI	University of Rhode Island	7/17/02	Off-campus	1 student
Houghton, MI	Michigan Tech University	8/13/02	Fraternity	1 student
Bloomington, IN	Indiana University	12/3/02	Off-campus	1 student
Medford, MA	Tufts University	1/18/03	Off-campus	1 student
Greenville, NC	Eastern Carolina University	2/18/03	Off-campus	2 students
Meadville, PA	Allegheny College	2/22/03	Off-campus	1 student
Cape Girardeau, MO	Southeast Missouri State University	3/11/03	Off-campus	1 student
Amherst, MA	University of Massachusetts	4/5/03	Off-campus	1 student
Columbus, OH	Ohio State University and Ohio University	4/13/03	Off-campus	5 students
Bowling Green, KY	Western Kentucky University	5/4/03	Residence hall	1 student
Minneapolis, MN	University of Minnesota–Twin Cities	9/20/03	Off-campus	3 students
Undetermined[a]	West Virginia University	9/22/03	Off-campus	1 student
Baton Rouge, LA	Louisiana State University	10/18/03	Off-campus	1 student
Ames, IA	Iowa State University	3/8/04	Off-campus	1 student
Bloomington, IN	Indiana University	5/22/04	Off-campus	3 students
College Station, TX	Texas A&M University	7/31/04	Residence hall (married student housing)	A student's daughter and mother
Savannah, GA	Savannah College of Art and Design	8/19/04	Off-campus	1 student
Oxford, MS	University of Mississippi	8/27/04	Fraternity	3 students
Washington, DC	Georgetown University	10/17/04	Off-campus	1 student
Oxford, OH	Miami University	4/10/05	Off-campus	3 students
State College, PA	Penn State	4/24/05	Off-campus	1 student
Collegedale, TN	Southern Adventist University	4/26/05	Residence hall	1 student

TABLE 20.3.6 Continued

City	*University*	*Date*	*Type of Housing*	*Deaths*
College Park, MD	University of Maryland	4/30/05	Off-campus	1 student
Chicago, IL	Conservatory of Recording Arts and Sciences (NOTE: The students were on an internship in Chicago.)	6/7/05	Off-campus	3 students
Raleigh, NC	North Carolina State University	10/7/05	Off-campus	2 students
Lawrence, KS	University of Kansas	10/7/05	Off-campus	1 student
College Park, MD	University of Maryland	1/24/06	Off-campus	1 student
Pittsburg, KS	Pittsburg State University	2/11/06	Off-campus	2 guests
Lincoln, NE	University of Nebraska–Lincoln	2/15/06	Off-campus	1 student and her child[b]
Anchorage, AK	University of Alaska	2/26/06	Off-campus	1 student and 1 nonstudent
Coos Bay, OR	Southwestern Oregon Community College	4/26/06	Academic building	1 student
Ithaca, NY	Cornell University	5/13/06	Off-campus	1 student
Stillwater, OK	Oklahoma State University	7/30/06	Off-campus	1 student
Pittsburgh, PA	University of Pittsburgh	11/4/06	Off-campus	1 student
Lincoln, NE	Nebraska Wesleyan University	11/17/06	Fraternity	1 student
St. Louis, MO	University of Missouri–St. Louis	11/29/06	Fraternity	1 student
Huntington, WV	Marshall University	1/13/07	Off-campus	3 students and 2 siblings who were visiting a student
Linwood, MS	University of Mississippi–Meridian	2/3/07	Off-campus	1 student, her husband, and her daughter
Weldon, NC	Halifax Community College	2/12/07	Off-campus	1 student
Boston, MA	Boston University	2/24/07	Off-campus	2 students
Farmville, VA	Longwood University	3/3/07	Off-campus	2 students
Boston, MA	Boston University	3/16/07	Off-campus	1 student[c]
Cincinnati, OH	Cincinnati State	4/21/07	Off-campus	1 student[d]

[a]The city where the death occurred could not be determined. The student was living in a trailer.
[b]The woman was scheduled to deliver her child three hours after the fire occurred. Since the fetus was full-term, the Lincoln Fire Department classified this as two fire deaths.
[c]The victim was from Bloomsburg University and was visiting two BU students when the fire occurred.
[d]The victim had been enrolled at Cincinnati State until the semester before the fire. He was reportedly taking this semester off and he stayed in Cincinnati, living in off-campus student housing.

convent, monastery, and other religious dormitories; and bunkhouses and workers' barracks. For this reason, statistics are not available specific to the occurrence of fires in university residence halls.

The types of dormitories/residence halls that are found on campuses can range from wood-frame renovated houses to noncombustible high-rise buildings. More schools are building third-party residence halls as a solution to providing housing. Third-party residence halls are buildings that are built and owned by a private developer but function as residence halls. One vendor, who has buildings on 39 campuses, estimates that there are approximately 30 companies building privately run residence halls.

Fires in residence halls pose a special risk because of the higher concentration of people who live in these buildings—one fire can quickly endanger a large number of occupants.

Residence halls tend to be occupied by younger students, such as freshmen and sophomores. Because housing is limited on a number of campuses, and as they get older, students tend to move off campus into Greek housing or rented houses and apartments.

Since residence halls are under the control of the university, it is possible to impose conditions that can dramatically improve the level of fire safety in these buildings as opposed to off-campus residential occupancies. These can include the following:

- Regulating the combustibility of contents such as furniture, wall, and floor finishings
- Regulating appliances such as microwaves, refrigerators, and so on
- Regulating the use of open flames, including candles, incense, and smoking

Many residence halls have staff assigned to them to help the students, often referred to as resident assistants, or RAs. This staff is generally made up of older students who live in the building and have received training in a variety of different areas. RAs can serve a vital role in fire safety since they are living in the building and can identify any potential hazards and assist in ensuring that students understand the importance of fire safety and the dangers of tampering with fire protection equipment.

The residence hall physical plant can be maintained to a consistent level of fire safety by the university as opposed to off-campus housing in the community. Dangerous conditions can be corrected properly.

Students who live in residence halls are subject to stricter behavior guidelines than off-campus students. When students move into a residence hall, they are often provided with information regarding expected behavior, what comprises a violation, and the penalties that can follow. Because of the presence of university staff in these buildings, it is more likely that violators can be identified and either counseled or penalized as necessary. If a student's actions are serious enough, the student can be removed from the residence hall altogether.

Apartments and Houses

Because of the lack of existing on-campus dormitory space, some institutions are either building or purchasing off-campus apartment complexes to provide student housing. In other cases, the school may be buying private houses to serve the same function. Although these structures may be "off campus," since the institution owns them, they should be provided the same fire protection as dormitories/residence halls.

Greek Housing

In the Greek system, the fire-death problem clearly lies within the fraternity community rather than the sororities. From 1990 to May 2006, there has been only 1 fire fatality in a sorority versus 27 within fraternities, according to information compiled by NFPA and Campus Firewatch.

Because of the recognized problem with fires in Greek occupancies, a number of communities, as well as the state of New Jersey, have passed ordinances and laws requiring that they be equipped with automatic fire sprinklers. Some fraternal organizations are taking it upon themselves to install sprinklers in their properties nationwide, recognizing the importance and value of these systems.

"Circle of Life" Approach to University Fire Safety

A comprehensive approach to fire safety for students living in residence halls and Greek housing is needed. As part of this approach, it is important to remember that the education and training that are provided will also give students the fire safety tools they need to protect them when they move off campus, where almost 80 percent of the fire fatalities do occur.

The solutions to fire safety problems in universities often are not unique. What is unique is the environment in which they must be employed. An approach developed by Campus Firewatch involves the four following components that are collectively known as the "Circle of Life" and includes:

- Prevention
- Detection
- Containment
- Suppression

FIRE PREVENTION ISSUES IN UNIVERSITY HOUSING

For general information on fire prevention, see Section 1, Chapter 5, "Fire Prevention and Code Enforcement."

There is a unique challenge in the campus environment to educate and train the students. People of this age have a sense of invulnerability that can be difficult to overcome and convince them of the risk they face from fire. For this reason and other reasons, it is important to ensure that the environment around them is as fire safe as possible, so if they should involve themselves in risk-taking behavior, or if a fire should occur, the effects of it can be minimized. For example, there should be sufficient exits that are properly marked and illuminated. If there are fire safety design features, such as fire doors that are routinely propped open for convenience, then the university or landlord should evaluate strategies to stop this practice from occurring.

The basic fire prevention strategies in university housing are to do the following:

- Reduce fuel load
- Reduce ignition sources
- Enforce good housekeeping
- Educate students about the fire protection features of their housing

Reducing Fuel Load

The fuel load in a fire comprises the structure, its interior finish materials, and the contents that are placed inside of the structure.

Structure. Many residence halls that are built today are made up of noncombustible materials. This construction helps to reduce the fire load significantly and also helps to compartmentalize the building, limiting fire spread. However, there are many older buildings, either built as residence halls or converted into residence halls, which are constructed of combustible materials. Reduced ignition sources, good housekeeping practices, and student fire safety education are particularly important in these combustible structures.

Interior Finish. For a general discussion of interior finish, see Section 18, Chapter 2, "Interior Finish."

Interior finish can, and has, played a significant role in the spread of fires in university housing. At the Chapel Hill fraternity fire, the wood paneling on the walls was identified as a significant contributing factor to the spread of the fire from the basement to the second floor. Universities and landlords should be cognizant of the materials used inside of the buildings and how they may contribute to the fire spread.

Contents. Furniture represents much of the fuel load in student housing. In an environment where it is possible to control the type of furniture, such as residence halls, appropriate flammability and combustibility criteria should be followed. Personal contents such as clothes and books that students bring cannot be regulated and should be considered a part of the normal fuel load in any student housing occupancy.

Students may personalize or decorate areas using combustible materials. This situation can especially be a problem during holidays. For example, at the Providence College fire in 1977 where 10 students were killed, the combustible decorations on the corridor walls were identified as a significant factor in the fire spread. A Halloween decorating contest at Seton Hall, months after the fatal fire at that university, was stopped by the fire department because of the accumulation of combustible materials, including hay, in the corridor.

Reducing Ignition Sources

In the university housing environment, control of smoking hazards, electrical hazards, and cooking hazards can be particularly helpful in reducing ignition sources.

Smoking. Many universities have implemented no-smoking policies in their residence halls, often in response to public health concerns. The fire safety professional should be concerned with students attempting to circumvent no-smoking regulations, especially during colder weather when people are more reluctant to go outside to smoke. In order to smoke in their rooms, students sometimes disable smoke detectors or find alternative locations to smoke within the building. This can lead to a fire breaking out in areas that may not normally be inhabited, such as stairwells or utility closets.

Electrical. Electrical equipment represents a significant concern in the university housing environment. Many residence halls and Greek houses were built prior to the advent of computers, microwaves, stereos, televisions, and other electrical equipment that students commonly possess. Two problems arise because of increased electrical needs.

First, a room, house, or facility may not have sufficient electrical capacity to provide the required power, which may cause the electrical system to overload. If circuit breakers continually trip, the occupants may try to circumvent such safety features to ensure that power is not interrupted. For example, occupants may run extension cords from other areas into their living space to power the equipment, leading to problems such as worn or frayed cords or overloaded circuits in another area.

Second, if there are not enough outlets, occupants are likely to use extension cords and power taps (commonly known as "power strips"). The use of such devices creates problems, such as the following:

- Overheated electrical cords that may be coiled or bunched up, creating a potential ignition source
- Physical damage—electrical cords that are run under carpet and around furniture in such a way that they can become damaged or worn, exposing bare conductors
- Overloading—even though occupants may use power strips equipped with individual circuit breakers, the circuit is not necessarily adequately protected

Halogen torchiere lamps have been a concern in residence halls and Greek housing because of the high temperature of the bulb. In recent years, manufacturers have implemented design changes to prevent combustible materials from contacting the bulb, helping to reduce the potential for ignition. Nonetheless, the use of torchiere lamps is discouraged by a number of universities, not only because of the fire hazard but also because of their high power demand.

Cooking. Cooking should be permitted only in specifically designated cooking areas. The use of hotplates and other cooking devices should be restricted or prohibited to minimize the potential for a fire. To regulate the size of microwaves and refrigerators in residence halls, some institutions specify a vendor to provide this equipment to the students and only use of specified equipment is permitted.

Enforcing Good Housekeeping

For general information, see Section 11, Chapter 2, "Housekeeping Practices."

Maintaining an environment that is relatively clean and orderly helps to reduce the amount of combustible fuel load that can potentially be ignited or serve as a fuel load to a fire. The 1996 fire in Chapel Hill was fueled in its initial stages by trash that had not been discarded following a party the evening before.

Recycling has created a challenge to good housekeeping. Recycling containers for paper and cardboard placed in buildings create two concerns. The first is that a container with a concentrated combustible fuel load may either be ignited (accidentally or deliberately) or may serve as a fuel package for an external fire. It is, therefore, important that recycling containers be emptied on a regular basis and that their placement be regulated with consideration given to fire safety.

The second concern is that recycling containers might be placed in a means of egress. The philosophy is that corridors and stairways should be kept clear of any such fuel loads because they may impact the safety and integrity of the escape route if they should become ignited. Also, these containers may serve as an obstruction along the egress route. Placement of these containers should be carefully monitored and controlled.

Educating Students About Fire Protection Features

A key component of any fire safety education program is ensuring that the occupants understand the importance of fire safety and how their actions can have a direct impact on the level of fire safety in their residence hall, fraternity, sorority, apartment, or house.

Students often are not fully aware of the fire protection features in the buildings they occupy and may inadvertently bypass them by, for example, propping open fire doors to facilitate pedestrian traffic flow. Students should understand the importance of fire protection systems, such as sprinkler and fire alarm systems, and the results of tampering with them. During an inspection at one university, audible notification appliances in some of the rooms were found to have been disabled by the students. In several fatal fires, smoke detectors were found to have been either disabled or removed entirely. The risks and penalties for tampering with fire protection systems should be communicated to every student and enforced.

Fire safety education and training for university students can be difficult to accomplish because of the regular turnover of students. Furthermore, any fire safety education program must compete for the attention of the student audience. The fire safety professional may have to be creative and tailor the message to appeal to the students.

Sample strategies include the following:

- *Audience-appropriate videos.* The U.S. Fire Administration's video "Get Out and Stay Alive" is one such program, among others.
- *Live fire training.* Students and/or staff can be given live fire training, such as fire extinguisher training that includes propane-fueled fires.
- *Fire academies.* The Boulder Fire Department and the University of Colorado, among a number of schools across the nation, hold annual fire academies for the resident assistants and the Greek leadership. Such intensive training programs stress the importance of student actions in fire safety. Training programs also motivate the students to look at their living areas with a more critical eye for fire safety dangers.

FIRE DETECTION ISSUES IN UNIVERSITY HOUSING

For general information on detection technology, see Section 14, "Detection and Alarm."

Unquestionably, smoke detection plays a critical role in any fire safety program. Properly installed, operating smoke detection systems or smoke alarms can literally make the difference between the occupants being able to escape from a fire and being trapped by the smoke and flames.

Unfortunately, in the university environment, smoke alarms are sometimes disabled. In a number of fatal fires, especially off campus, the batteries were removed from smoke alarms. In some cases, smoke alarms could not even be located following the fires. Steps should be taken to ensure that such fire protection features are properly maintained.

False or Unwanted Alarms

False or unwanted alarms are a particular problem in the university setting. Students can activate the fire alarm system as a prank, which causes the residents to become desensitized to the alarms and to not react when needed. The problem with unnecessary activation of the fire alarm system is it creates apathy among the students. The occupants will become "numb" to the sound of the fire alarm system and will begin to ignore it, which could have tragic consequences. For example, there had been a number of false alarms in the weeks leading up to the Seton Hall fire in January 2000. Because of this, several of the occupants of the building did not evacuate when the fire alarm system went into alarm on the night of January 19, 2000. This time, there really was a fire.

A *false alarm* is a situation in which someone has deliberately activated the fire alarm system, knowing that there is no danger. For example, a student activating a manual pull station when there is no fire would be classified as a *malicious false alarm.* An *unwanted alarm* or *nuisance alarm* is one when the fire alarm system is activated but not under conditions where a fire exists. For example, a smoke alarm placed in or near a shower and activated by the shower steam would be considered an unwanted or nuisance alarm.

In addition to creating apathy among the students, false or unwanted alarms place undue stress on the local responders. If they are continually responding to false or unwanted alarms at a building, they may develop a "cry wolf" syndrome. In addition, a false alarm takes these units out of service to respond to other emergencies.

The solution that some schools adopt to avoid overloading the local responders is to have the alarms investigated, often by security, before notifying the local fire department. This is a very dangerous procedure since it may allow a fire to grow to a point where it can be fatal. This was the case at Catawba College where a student was killed in a fire that occurred after a series of other smaller fires and false alarms. A clear distinction must be made between false alarms and unwanted alarms.

Engineering, Education, and Enforcement Strategies

Engineering, enforcement, and education are three strategies that can be employed to help reduce the number of false and unwanted alarms.

Engineering. Maintenance of the smoke detectors is critically important. By having an ongoing program of inspection and maintenance, the number of alarms caused by dirty smoke detectors can be reduced.

Using devices that cover the manual fire alarm boxes (pull stations) is an engineering solution to false alarms. When the device is lifted, a local alarm sounds, alerting people in the area. Such covers do not restrict access to the pull station, which can be activated if necessary.

The use of addressable fire alarm systems is beneficial in helping to identify problem areas. Detectors that are improperly located or are continuing to cause unwanted alarms can be identified and corrected.

Education. Educating the occupants and enforcing proper behavior are also important components when it comes to reducing the number of alarms. At one university, postings were put up in the buildings after every alarm advising students as to the cause of the alarm. If the alarm activation was accidental, they provided information on how to avoid future activations. If the alarm was malicious, then information about the incident as well as a reward was offered.

Enforcement. Universities may impose sanctions on resident students up to and including dismissal for maliciously activating a fire alarm. One university offers rewards to find offenders and has installed CCTV cameras to record violators in the act.

A particularly vexing problem is that of off-campus houses and apartments where the smoke alarms are not part of a fire alarm system that can monitor the condition of the devices. Disabled or missing smoke alarms can contribute substantially to the risk of fatality in a fire in any residential occupancy. Strategies include the following:

- Severe penalties for students who are caught activating the fire alarm needlessly
- Financial penalties being imposed on the floor or building where there is an ongoing problem of false alarms, leading to peer pressure to help reduce the problem

FIRE CONTAINMENT AND SUPPRESSION ISSUES IN UNIVERSITY HOUSING

Fire Containment

For general information, see Section 18, "Confining Fires."

A common violation of the principle of fire containment in university housing occurs when doors are propped open in corridors and stairwells. Even if they aren't designed to protect openings in a fire or smoke barrier, they will serve to stop the spread of the smoke, reduce the number of people who may be endangered, and also limit the amount of damage that may be caused by fire or smoke. Doors that are supposed to be kept closed to limit the spread of smoke and fire are frequently propped open simply for convenience. Educating the students and maintenance and cleaning staff about the importance of ensuring that barrier doors are kept closed can help to alleviate this problem.

Fire Suppression

Two types of fire suppression can be used: manual (by portable fire extinguishers or the fire department using hoselines) and automatic.

Fire Extinguishers. Fire extinguishers can play a valuable role in ensuring that the fire remains in the incipient stage. However, there are certain considerations, as discussed more extensively in Section 17, Chapter 5, "Fire Extinguisher Use and Maintenance."

First, the fire extinguisher should be matched to the probable hazard that will be encountered. Many of the fires that would be encountered in student housing would probably involve Class A combustibles such as wood, paper, and so on. A water-based fire extinguisher would probably be the best type to use in this environment. However, the occupants must be knowledgeable in the steps to take if a fire should occur. Training and education must be conducted prior to an incident to ensure that the occupants know what actions to take. This can be a time-consuming, yet important, responsibility of the university.

Fire extinguishers, especially those that are water based, can be inappropriately discharged as a "squirt gun" and then placed back on the wall. When such misuse occurs, the extinguisher is no longer operational. Constant vigilance by staff is necessary to ensure that the fire extinguishers are not tampered with and that they are promptly recharged when necessary.

Because of the need for ongoing occupant training and education in the use of fire extinguishers, one university has taken the step of removing them from all residence halls. This was done, however, only in fully sprinklered, noncombustible buildings.

Fire Department Response. When a fire does occur, time is critically important. The sooner the occupants of the building are alerted to the fire, the better their chances are of escape and survival. Also, the sooner that the fire department is notified of the fire, the faster it will be able to respond, suppress the fire, and rescue any trapped occupants. For this reason, it is important that procedures are in place to notify the fire department promptly whenever a fire alarm is sounding.

Automatic Sprinklers

Based on the occupancy and occupant characteristics (particularly in the residence halls and Greek environment), the need for sprinklers is paramount. For this reason, NFPA *101* requires automatic suppression systems for new construction.

Recognizing the importance of automatic fire sprinklers in life safety, a number of schools across the country are voluntarily installing these systems in their residence halls. Fire sprinklers provide a significant level of safety when used in concert with fire alarm systems and student education, especially given the risk presented by student behavior, actions, and lifestyle. In addition to protecting lives, sprinklers will minimize the property damage and the amount of time that students will be displaced. Often, they can re-enter the building almost immediately, except for the areas directly affected by the fire and water discharge.

In the wake of the Seton Hall fatal fire, legislation was introduced across the country calling for the installation of sprinkler systems in residence halls and Greek housing. The most sweeping legislation was enacted in 2000 by the State of New Jersey, which called for sprinkler systems to be installed within 4 years. All of the schools met this deadline, greatly increasing the level of fire safety for students across the state.

INSTITUTIONS AND ORGANIZATIONS INVOLVED IN UNIVERSITY HOUSING FIRE SAFETY

University and Fire Department Interaction

The university should work closely with the local fire department in all areas of fire protection. This effort should include not only the academic and support buildings and residence halls but also the off-campus Greek and private student housing. Especially in off-campus housing, the fire department is a critical component in helping to provide a fire-safe environment for the school's students.

Universities should not completely rely on the fire department for all fire safety needs. For example, fire prevention is ultimately the responsibility of the institution. The fire department cannot be expected to inspect the residence halls and other buildings for fire hazards as frequently as the university staff.

Depending on whether it is a public or private university, the fire department may or may not be legally required to conduct plan reviews. However, it is a good idea to always involve the fire department in any plan reviews of new construction or renovations. This coordination helps to build a stronger relationship between the university and the fire department; the university can gain valuable information on fire-safe design and the fire department can improve its familiarity with the different occupancies on campus.

Organizations Involved in University Housing Fire Safety

A number of organizations are active in various facets of campus fire safety. They are as follows:

Campus Firewatch
P.O. Box 1046
Belchertown, MA 01007
http://www.campus-firewatch.com

Campus Safety Health and Environmental Management Association
c/o National Safety Council
1121 Spring Lake Drive
Itasca, IL 60143
http://www.cshema.org

Center for Campus Fire Safety
P.O. Box 2358
Amherst, MA 01004
http://www.campusfire.org

National Association of State Fire Marshals (NASFM)
P.O. Box 8778
Albany, NY 12208-0778
http://www.firemarshals.org

National Fire Protection Association (NFPA)
One Batterymarch Park
Quincy, MA 02269
http://www.nfpa.org

National Fire Sprinkler Association (NFSA)
Robin Hill Corporate Park
Route 22
P.O. Box 1000
Patterson, NY 12563
http://www.nfsa.org

United States Fire Administration (USFA)
16825 S. Seton Avenue
Emmitsburg, MD 21727
http://www.usfa.fema.gov

SUMMARY

Since the late 1980s, building and fire codes have changed to require fire protection systems and equipment for lodging establishments. More recently, similar awareness and action have taken place in the area of university housing.

In both lodging and university housing, occupants have unique characteristics. For example, hotel occupants are in an unfamiliar environment. Students can be very familiar with their housing but engage in risky behavior. Hotels and university housing both feature high population density.

These occupant characteristics lead to the need for an effective emergency organization, automatic sprinklers, compartmentation, effective egress design, and detection and alarm systems. Regular fire drills will enhance survivability. Continued improvements in fire protection technology and related areas, such as fire-safe cigarettes, are expected to contribute to further decline in fires in hotels and university housing.

BIBLIOGRAPHY

References Cited

1. *Lodging Profile,* American Hotel and Lodging Association Annual Reports, Washington, DC, 1988–2000.
2. NIST PB94-108644INZ, "Test Methods for Quantifying the Propensity of Cigarettes to Ignite Soft Furnishings," National Institute of Standards and Technology, Gaithersburg, MD, Aug. 1993.
3. Zuckerbrod, N., "Fire Standard Sought for Cigarettes," *Harvard Law Journal,* Vol. 40, April 25, 2002.
4. "Relative Ignition Propensity of Test Market Cigarettes," NIST Technical Note 1436, Appendix D: Cigarette Extinction Method, National Institute of Standards and Technology, Gaithersburg, MD, Jan. 2001.
5. The Joseph Moakley Memorial Fire Safe Cigarette Act of 2002, H.R. 4607, 107th Congress, 2nd Session, Apr. 25, 2002.
6. "Degree-Granting Institutions, by Control and Type of Institution; Selected Years, 1949–50 through 2004–05," *Digest of Education Statistics Tables and Figures,* Table 243, National Center for Education Statistics, Washington, DC, 2005.
7. "Total Fall Enrollment in Degree-Granting Institutions by Attendance Status, Age, and Sex; Selected Years, 1970 through 2014," *Digest of Education Statistics Tables and Figures,* Table 172, National Center for Education Statistics, Washington, DC, 2005.
8. Davis, R., and Debarros, A., "Alcohol and Fire a Deadly Mix," *USA Today,* Aug. 30, 2006.

NFPA Codes, Standards, and Recommended Practices

Reference to the following NFPA codes, standards, and recommended practices will provide further information on hotels and university housing discussed in this chapter. (See the latest version of The NFPA Catalog *for availability of current editions of the following documents.)*

NFPA 13R, *Standard for the Installation of Sprinkler Systems in Residential Occupancies up to and Including Four Stories in Height*
NFPA 72®, National Fire Alarm Code®
NFPA *101®, Life Safety Code®*
NFPA 5000®, Building Construction and Safety Code®

Chapter 4

Apartment Buildings

Kenneth Bush

Chapter Contents

Key Terms

apartment building, condominium, hazard classification, means of egress, occupancy characteristic, occupancy hazard, public fire and life safety education, residential occupancy

Apartment buildings are those structures containing three or more living units with independent cooking and bathroom facilities, whether designated as apartment houses, tenements, condominiums, or garden apartments. Apartments differ from multi-unit residential occupancies that are not considered homes, such as hotels and boarding homes, by the provision of individual cooking facilities, the number of sleeping rooms, and the less transient nature of the occupants.

The adequate protection of residential buildings and their occupants from the effects of fire has historically been a major concern of fire protection professionals. The construction of multiple dwelling units makes this job more complex. Such construction not only adds to building size and occupant numbers but also adds major complexity due to building design, construction, and fire protection features.

See also Section 20, Chapter 2, "Board and Care Facilities"; Section 20, Chapter 3, "Hotels and University Housing"; Section 20, Chapter 5, "Lodging or Rooming Houses"; and Section 20, Chapter 6, "One- and Two-Family Dwellings."

OCCUPANCY CHARACTERISTICS

According to statistics compiled from the U.S. Census Bureau, there were an estimated 109,902,090 occupied housing units in the United States in 2004. Of that number, 21,136,883 units, or approximately 21 percent of the total number of such units, consisted of three or more units, meeting the definition of "apartment building" in NFPA *101*®, *Life Safety Code*®, and *NFPA 5000*®, *Building Construction and Safety Code*®. The breakdown of all housing units both occupied and vacant by size was 5,739,277 in structures with 3 or 4 units; 6,088,586 in structures with 5 to 9 units; 5,521,813 in structures with 10 to 19 units; and 9,526,484 in structures with 20 or more units.[1,2]

The U.S. population is aging. In 2000, approximately 12.4 percent of the U.S. population was age 65 or over, with an additional 22.1 percent of the population age 45 to 64. Projections from the U.S. Census Bureau indicate that by the year 2050, these figures will increase to 20.7 percent for the group of persons age 65 or over, including 5 percent age 85 or over, and an additional 22.2 percent of the population from 45 to 64 years of age. Coupled with these statistics comes an increasing need for housing units that are compact, economical, and require less individual maintenance. As land values continue to increase, there is little wonder why the design, construction, and occupancy of multi-unit buildings has become a popular issue with the U.S. public.

During 2004, approximately 1,550,500 fires were attended by public fire departments in the United States. Of that number, 526,000 fires occurred in structures, of which 410,500, a significant 78 percent of all structure fires, occurred in residential properties. Of these residential structure fires, 301,500, or 57.3 percent of all structural fires, occurred in one- and two-family dwellings and another 94,000 occurred in apartment buildings, accounting for 17.8 percent of all structural fires. This figure represents an increase of 2.7 percent of fires reported in apartments compared to 2003. This means that a fire occurred in a structure at the rate of one every 60 seconds, and in particular, a residential fire occurred every 77 seconds.[2]

For the period 1977 to 2004, the number of structure fires was at its peak in 1977 when 1,098,000 structure fires occurred. The number of structure fires then decreased quite steadily,

Kenneth Bush is a senior fire protection engineer with the Office of the Maryland State Fire Marshal. He is a member of five NFPA technical committees and a member of the Life Safety Code and Building Construction and Safety Code Technical Correlating Committees.

particularly in the 1980s, to 688,000 by the end of 1989, for an overall decrease of 37.3 percent from 1977. The number of structure fires continued to decrease at a steady rate following 1989 by an overall figure or 24.7 percent to 517,500 incidents by the end of 1998 and has remained in the vicinity of 526,000 fires per year from 1998 to 2004.

OCCUPANCY HAZARDS

The occupancy hazards of apartment buildings include all risk factors that may arise in particular segments of the population. Preschoolers and older adults, if present, have a higher risk of dying in fires because of the mental or physical limitations associated with their age. Older children and younger adults may be at risk if they are physically or mentally handicapped or as a result of drug or alcohol use. Fatal fires are more common at night when people are asleep.

Another important consideration for the protection of apartment buildings is the difference in causes attributed to fire incidents between this property classification and one- and two-family dwellings (Figure 20.4.1). This difference is most likely due to the centralized design and installation of systems typically found in most apartment buildings. Equipment fires are usually the result of poor maintenance or misuse; such equipment tends to have closer supervision in apartment buildings. The number of fires and related casualties caused by occupants, especially from cooking operations, remains high in all types of residential structures. This demonstrates the need to properly apply all required code provisions to these occupancy types, and it also demonstrates the importance of public education regarding the causes, prevention, and control of home fires.

There were 3900 civilian fire deaths in 2004 with almost 82 percent, or 3225 of these deaths occurring in a residential setting. Of these deaths, 510 occurred in apartment fires, a substantial increase of 24.4 percent from 2003. Home fire deaths were at their peak in 1978 when 6015 fire deaths occurred. These numbers slightly decreased during the period of 1979 to 1982, except for 1981, and further decreased a substantial 20 percent during the period to 4820 by the end of 1982. For the next six years, the number of home fire deaths remained consistent in the area of 4655 to 4955 deaths, except for 1984 when 4075 deaths occurred.

In addition, during 1984 there were 17,785 civilian fire injuries, with 14,175 injuries, or nearly 80 percent occurring in residential occupancies. Of the number of persons injured in residential properties, 3200 such injuries occurred in apartments. For the period from 1977 to 2003, the number of civilian injuries ranged from a high of 31,275 in 1983 to a low of 17,785 in 2004 for an overall decrease of 43 percent. It is recognized that these statistics may not represent the actual number of total injuries, as many such injuries occur at small fires where no fire department response is made, or where the responding fire department may not be aware of injured persons that do not require medical attention or are transported for treatment by private means (Table 20.4.1).

During 2004, fire caused an estimated $9.8 billion in property damage, with $5.9 billion attributed to fires in residential occupancies. The $5.9 billion residential property fire loss in 2004 represented a slight increase of 2.1 percent from 2003. The actual property loss from fires in apartments during 2004 totaled $885 million, a decrease of 1.3 percent from 2003. Fires in structures resulted in $8.3 billion in property damage, a moderate decrease of 5.3 percent. The average loss per structure fire

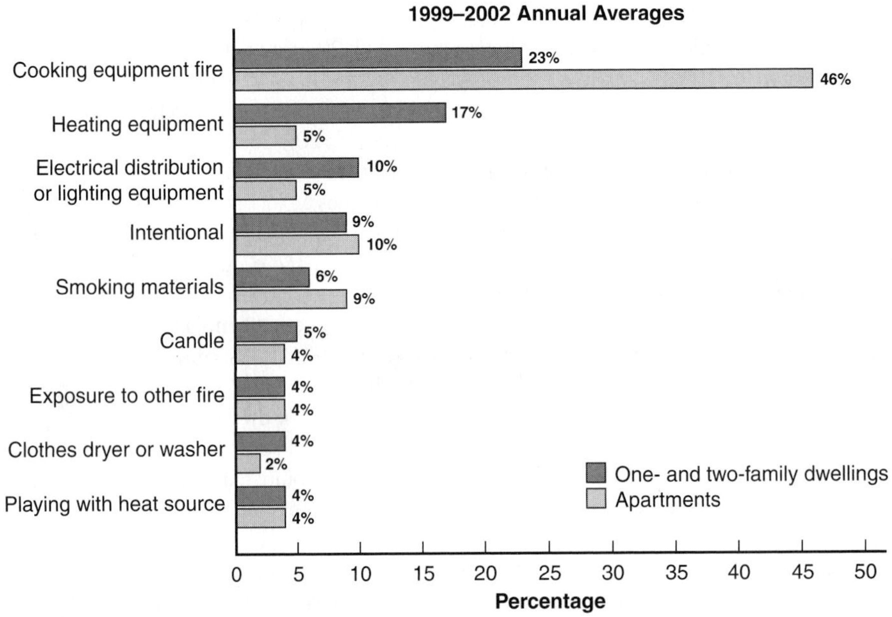

FIGURE 20.4.1 Leading Causes of Structure Fires in One- and Two-Family Dwellings and Apartments (Source: *U.S. Fires in Selected Occupancies*, NFPA, Mar. 2006)

TABLE 20.4.1 Estimates of 2005 Civilian Fire Deaths and Injuries by Property Use

	Civilian Deaths			Civilian Injuries		
Property Use	*Estimate*	*Percentage Change from 2004*	*Percentage of All Civilian Deaths*	*Estimate*	*Percentage Change from 2004*	*Percentage of All Civilian Injuries*
Residential (total)	3,055	–5.3	83.1	13,825	–2.5	77.1
One- and two-family dwellings[a]	2,570	–4.1	69.9	10,300	–1.9	57.5
Apartments	460	–9.8	12.5	3,000	–6.3	16.7
Other residential[b]	25	–28.6	0.7	525	+10.5	2.9
Nonresidential structures[c]	50	–37.5	1.4	1,500	+11.1	8.4
Highway vehicles	500	–3.8	13.6	1,450	+11.5	8.1
Other vehicles[d]	20	–33.3	0.5	200	0.0	1.1
All other[e]	50	+11.1	1.4	950	+11.8	5.3
Total	3,675	–5.8		17,925	+0.3	

Note: Estimates are based on data reported to the NFPA by fire departments that responded to the 2005 National Fire Experience Survey. Note that most changes were not statistically significant; considerable year-to-year fluctuation is to be expected for many of these totals because of their small size.

[a]This includes manufactured homes.

[b]Includes hotels and motels, college dormitories, boarding houses, etc.

[c]This includes public assembly, educational, institutional, store and office, industry, utility, storage, and special structure properties.

[d]This includes trains, boats, ships, farm vehicles, and construction vehicles.

[e]This includes outside properties with value, as well as brush, rubbish, and other outside locations.

Source: *Fire Loss in the United States During 2005,* Table 3, NFPA, Sept. 2006.

was $15,806, a decrease of 4.2 percent. During the reporting period of 1997 to 2004, the average loss per structure fire ranged from a low of $3757 to a high of $17,016 in 2001 for an overall increase of 353 percent. The increase in the average structure loss between 1977 and 2001 was 56 percent when adjusted for inflation. It should be noted that this overall property loss statistic represented a significant 20.5 percent decrease in the totals from the previous year, much of which was attributed to losses incurred by wildfires in Southern California during 2003 (Table 20.4.2).

Citing the number of fires and fire casualties that continue to dominate fire loss statistics, and considering the increased interest in multiple-unit building design, particularly among a growing elderly U.S. population, a number of fire safety initiatives targeted at the residential fire problem remain key to any reductions in these numbers. Currently, five major strategies exist to further reduce the numbers of fire incidents, contain property losses, and control the number of home fire deaths and injuries. First, more widespread public safety education is needed on how to prevent fires and how to avoid serious injury or death should a fire occur. A primary message of any such education must contain information on the common causes of fatal and significant loss fires.

Second, the use, including proper installation and maintenance, of smoke alarms, and the development and practice of home escape plans play another significant role in the control of overall fire losses. Third, accompanying this use of early warning devices comes a need for the aggressive pursuit of the installation and maintenance of approved residential sprinkler systems.

Fourth, additional means to improve the safety of household products should be sought. Recent regulations on the production of child-resistant lighters and research on self-extinguishing cigarettes are two excellent examples of such safe product initiatives. Acceptance of the manufacture, purchase, and use of upholstered furniture and mattresses that are more resistant to cigarette ignition, and to the use of decorations that have been made, or specially treated, to resist ignition represents another change that has already produced positive results and will continue to influence fire safety trends in the future. Lastly, there has to be special considerations for the fire safety needs of high-risk populations, especially very young children, older adults, and the poor.[3]

Smoke detectors and smoke alarms have been a great success in apartment buildings, as well as in private homes. Use of smoke alarms continues to grow, but more slowly since 1982. In 1995, 93 percent of all homes had at least one smoke alarm, and there was evidence that their use in apartments was higher still, probably because state and local laws requiring smoke alarms often have stronger requirements for apartments. However, NFPA studies indicate that when fire occurs, roughly one-third of apartment smoke alarms are not operational, the same share as for one- and two-family dwellings. These studies also indicate that smoke alarms cut the risk of dying in a home fire by roughly 40 percent. However, the estimated reduction is only 16 percent in apartments, townhouses, and condominiums based on fires that occurred between 1985 and 1994. Although available data do not lead to definite conclusions, it appears that the difference in effectiveness levels may be due to the fewer number or longer distance in apartment building escape routes, more success in early detection to prevent fires from growing large enough to report, or the delayed reaction of apartment dwellers to alarms outside of their unit.

TABLE 20.4.2 Estimates of 2005 Structure Fires and Property Loss by Property Use

	Structure Fires		Property Loss[a]	
Property Use	*Estimate*	*Percentage Change from 2004*	*Estimate*	*Percentage Change from 2004*
Public assembly	13,500	+3.9	$320,000,000	+1.3
Educational	6,000	–14.3	67,000,000	–1.5
Institutional	7,500	+15.4	40,000,000	+60.0**
Residential (total)	396,000	–3.5	6,875,000,000	+15.6**
One- and two-family dwellings[b]	287,000	–4.8*	5,781,000,000	+16.8**
Apartments	94,000	0.0	948,000,000	+7.1
Other residential[c]	15,000	0.0	146,000,000	+27.0*
Stores and offices	23,000	–2.1	687,000,000	+17.2*
Industry, utility, defense[d]	11,500	–4.2	376,000,000	–11.1
Storage in structures	30,000	–6.3	590,000,000	–21.1**
Special structures	23,500	+9.3	238,000,000	+19.0
Total	511,000	–2.9	$9,193,000,000	+10.6**

Note: The estimates are based on data reported to the NFPA by fire departments that responded to the 2005 National Fire Experience Survey.
[a]This includes overall direct property loss to contents, structure, a vehicle, machinery, vegetation, or anything else involved in a fire. It does not include indirect losses, e.g., business interruption or temporary shelter costs. No adjustment was made for inflation in the year-to-year comparison.
[b]This includes manufactured homes.
[c]Includes hotels and motels, college dormitories, boarding houses, etc.
[d]Incidents handled only by private fire brigades or fixed suppression systems are not included in the figures shown here.
*Change was statistically significant at the .05 level.
**Change was statistically significant at the .01 level.
Source: *Fire Loss in the United States During 2005,* Table 4, NFPA, Sept. 2006.

Once a potentially serious fire starts, apartment buildings can pose special problems to fire department suppression forces. The variety of these types of residences, as well as the architectural desire to make buildings aesthetically pleasing yet functional, creates an interesting combination of fire protection demands. Building designs, space considerations, and parking arrangements can create major access problems, particularly for fire-fighting apparatus (Figure 20.4.2). Long hose lays and blocked roadway access can create problems for fire-fighting operations in addition to existing problems, such as weather, personnel deficiencies, and hampered water supplies (Figure 20.4.3). Architectural designs may use false partitioning and veneered construction, giving an unrealistic impression of the type and magnitude of the actual building construction (Figure 20.4.4). Although NFPA *101* makes no special requirements for the construction of these buildings, many such requirements are found and enforced through model building codes, such as *NFPA 5000,* as well as through many local codes and ordinances currently in effect. Sometimes the location and construction of apartment buildings make egress for residents and access by fire fighters very difficult (Figure 20.4.5).

Apartment buildings are typically a collection of more than two self-contained dwelling units with independent living and cooking facilities. Model building codes, such as *NFPA 5000,* establish the criteria for separation between dwelling units in order for them to be classified as other occupancy types, most likely one- and two-family dwellings. These substantial separation requirements are intended to protect dwelling units from a fire in a neighboring unit, even if the fire severity causes collapse of the unit involved in fire. Residents of these buildings are typically less transient in nature and are more familiar with the building construction and arrangement, especially exiting patterns and levels of protection afforded such as the installation of smoke detection, fire alarms, and automatic sprinkler systems.

FIGURE 20.4.2 Apartment Building Designs and Parking Arrangements Creating Major Access Problems and Hindering Fire-Fighting Operations

FIGURE 20.4.3 Location and Lack of Access Routes for Many New Apartment Buildings Creating Major Fire Apparatus Placement and Fire-Fighting Operations Problems

FIGURE 20.4.4 Architectural Designs Using False Partitioning and Veneered Construction

The levels of protection required by most model codes take this level of familiarity into consideration when establishing reasonable levels of protection.

Whenever apartment units are utilized for other purposes, such as day-care homes, residential board and care facilities, or even business offices, the levels of protection and design considerations must be adjusted accordingly. Such modifications may affect only one or a limited number of apartment units, or may involve modification to the entire building. Earlier editions of NFPA *101* made some adjustments to its requirements based upon the advanced ages of building residents; however, that distinction no longer exists in more recent code editions. Many times, local statutes, such as zoning codes or license requirements, restrict the nature of occupancy, and the number and abilities of persons who may reside in an apartment building.

FIGURE 20.4.5 Limited Fire Department Access Due to Proximity of Waterway

Another important consideration to remember is that the term "condominium" refers to ownership, not occupancy. Therefore, the occupancy classification for residential occupancies is not dependent on property lines or ownership arrangements.

An additional problem arises in the location and combination of apartments with other occupancy types, particularly those above and behind mercantile and business occupancies (Figure 20.4.6). Where multiple occupancy classes occur in the same building and are so intermingled that separate safeguards are impractical, means of egress facilities, construction, protection, and other safeguards must comply with the most restrictive code requirements for the occupancies involved.

LIFE SAFETY CONCEPTS

The apartment fire death and injury problem is very complex, and several strategies must be presented to help solve it. The installation and proper maintenance of smoke alarms and quick-response residential sprinklers in sleeping areas provide an effective, low-cost, and widely available method of early warning so that evacuation, containment, and suppression can begin during the incipient stages of a fire.

FIGURE 20.4.6 Combination of Apartments with Other Occupancy Types

Public Education

The general public must be taught to protect themselves and others occupying the residential unit from fire through the safe use and installation of alternative heating devices, the proper storage and handling of flammable liquids, and the identification and correction of home fire hazards. In addition, stringent flammability standards for upholstered furniture, such as those previously issued by the U.S. Consumer Product Safety Commission (CPSC) for children's sleepwear and mattresses, will provide long-term fire safety benefits. Specially designed systems that are effective in terms of life safety should be installed to provide a high level of protection to occupants, particularly where large numbers of persons are present, such as in a high-rise apartment building, or where the occupants' ability to escape is hampered, such as in apartments for the elderly.

Design Considerations

Although such fire safety precautions are not always practical, particularly within an individual dwelling unit, a more concentrated effort must be made to confine the fire and its effects to a well-defined, limited area of the structure. This task is accomplished through the adoption of accepted fire safety and building construction codes, such as NFPA *101* and *NFPA 5000*. Since many current laws and regulations prevent fire inspection authorities from entering individual living units, adequate fire protection features must be designed and constructed during the initial phases of the project. The regulation of interior furnishings provides only a partial solution to the fire safety problem, although such consumer items are generally in use for many years before they are replaced. Futhermore, the individual habits and attitudes of building occupants can never be regulated and are difficult to change.

Additional requirements of *NFPA 5000* address fire safety requirements intended to promote property protection and to enhance the safety of fire fighters and other emergency personnel who must enter the building under varying degrees of fire conditions. Such levels of protection include detailed requirements for building construction and other structural features and the installation of standpipes and alarm and communication systems for fire service use. Although these requirements have been modeled from those recognized by NFPA *101* for occupant protection, *NFPA 5000* is intended to address other issues concerning property protection and emergency operation procedures.

One of the most important, yet sometimes most complicated considerations of adequate protection is the proper classification of occupancy. All residential occupancies, including apartment buildings, require occupancy by persons for more than 24 hours. However, the number and abilities of building occupants, particularly to be able to escape a fire without assistance, play vital roles in the classification of an occupancy, and hence, directly affect the design, construction, and arrangement of the building and associated levels of protection.

All occupants of an apartment building are expected to have the ability to recognize a direct fire threat, or the warning from a building alarm system, and be able to physically exit the building without obstruction, including locked egress doors. Where these criteria are not met, classification of the building as a different occupancy type, such as a health care facility, residential board and care facility, or detention and correctional occupancy, may be warranted. Even though it is recognized that reaction to a fire may be delayed while residents are asleep, it is assumed that they will be able to take appropriate actions for self-preservation when warned of potential danger.

Because apartment buildings are so diverse in size, configuration, and resident population, many regulatory codes pay particular attention to construction designs and fire protection features. NFPA *101* covers the presence of hazards such as cooking and heating equipment, as well as the occupant's degree of familiarity with his or her living space. NFPA *101* and *NFPA 5000* require most new apartment buildings to be protected by automatic sprinklers. However, sprinkler protection is not required where each apartment has a door directly to the outside at ground level, such as in townhouse-style apartments, or is served by an interior stair totally enclosed by fire-rated construction, or where an outside stair serves a maximum of two units located on the same level (Figure 20.4.7). NFPA *101* has a unique method of regulating the construction and design of existing apartment buildings based on the type and extent of automatic fire detection and/or fire suppression equipment provided. Recognizing equivalency provisions found elsewhere in NFPA *101,* the

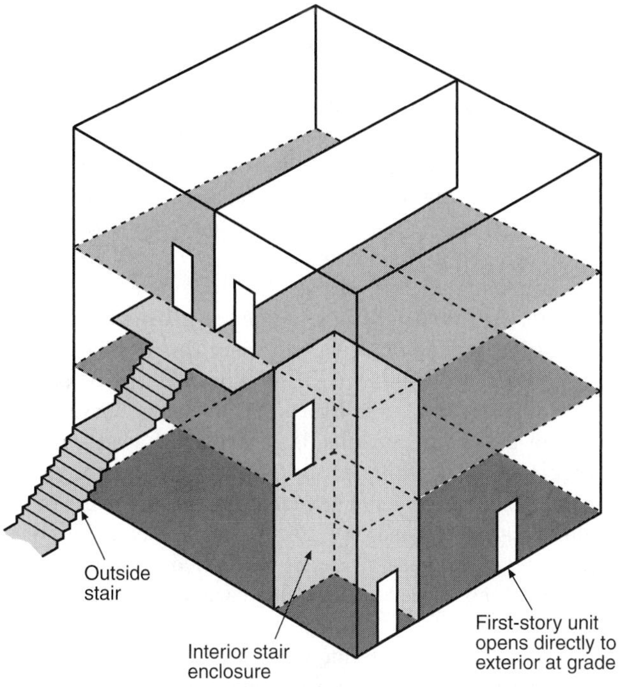

FIGURE 20.4.7 Required Exiting Arrangements for New Apartment Buildings Without Sprinkler Protection

FIGURE 20.4.8 Exits from Apartments Discharging to a Public Way, Protected from Fires in Exposure Occupancies, Particularly Parking Areas

technical committee on residential occupancies established four equivalent schemes to provide a high degree of flexibility. These designs provide a minimum level of life safety for apartments. Some systems have additional protective capability, permitting greater building heights and larger building areas.

This overall approach provides one of the first system design attempts to be codified. Whereas a total system would have many design approaches, this more limited system offers only four different approaches. Yet an evaluator can identify an appropriate method from the four approaches based on the building size, height, and arrangement. This allows the person evaluating the existing building to formulate a safety approach that best fits the building, rather than fitting the building to a single codified design criterion.

The contents of living units in residential occupancies fall into the ordinary-hazard classification as defined by NFPA *101* and *NFPA 5000*. Characteristics of these hazards include moderately rapid burning and considerable smoke generation (Figure 20.4.8). Under normal conditions, no unduly dangerous exposure should develop during the period necessary to escape from the fire area given prompt occupant notification of the fire. Generally, this classification represents conditions found in most buildings. Even with the introduction of plastics, foam materials, and other combustible materials in furnishings, the amount and configuration of such materials present a lower hazard than in other occupancies where they may be sold, stored, or displayed. NFPA 13, *Standard for the Installation of Sprinkler Systems,* classifies the contents of apartment buildings as "light hazard" for the design of extinguishing systems. This classification difference is based on the threat to life safety assumed in the ordinary classification versus that assumed where the extinguishing capability of the automatic sprinkler system results in the light-hazard classification.

Means of Egress

In designating the number and types of exits required for apartment buildings, NFPA *101* and *NFPA 5000* determine the occupant load on the basis of 1 person/200 ft^2 (18.6 m^2) of gross floor area, or the maximum probable population of any room or section under consideration, whichever is greater. Many buildings, such as dormitories, may produce a greater occupant load. However, even though some portions of these buildings are densely populated, the whole building may not necessarily exceed 1 person/200 ft^2 (18.6 m^2) of gross area, owing to the space taken for toilet facilities, hallways, closets, and living rooms. These requirements do not preclude the need for providing adequate exit capacities from concentrated use and sleeping areas based on the maximum probable population, rather than on the design figure. The capacities of required exits are as specified in NFPA *101* and *NFPA 5000.*

Travel within the individual dwelling unit need not comply with the requirements for means of egress, but must be arranged as means of escape. The differences between means of escape and means of egress have an impact on the size and type of escape components, especially doors and headroom of some occupiable spaces. Most of these requirements apply to the unit only, and not necessarily to the entire building.

Although seemingly contrary to the basic code requirements of two distinct, remote means of egress from all locations, several exceptions to this rule are found within the requirements for apartment occupancies. Whereas the traditional interior exit corridor arrangement commonly found in larger apartment buildings and condominiums requires two remote exits, several other options in apartment building configurations permit other arrangements. The common townhouse arrangement, which provides an exit directly to the street or yard at ground level or by way of an outside or enclosed stairway serving that apartment only, permits the front door to be the only required exit. Therefore, a rear door, which is often provided, would not be required and could be a sliding door to a porch or patio.

Another exit arrangement unique to apartment buildings permits an exception to the typical requirement for remoteness of exits from nonlooped exit access corridors in apartment buildings that have corridor doors from dwelling units arranged so that exits are located in opposite directions from such doors. In addition, a provision was introduced into the code to limit travel distances from areas of apartment buildings, other than those within living units, to a maximum of 200 ft (61 m) in unsprinklered buildings and a maximum of 250 ft (76 m) in sprinklered buildings.

In apartment buildings, travel distance does not typically include the means of escape within the dwelling unit; only the path of travel in the means of egress is considered. Likewise, common paths of travel are only considered outside the dwelling unit. Travel distance in nonsprinklered buildings is tacitly regulated by limiting any floor level of an individual dwelling unit to no more than one level above or below the entrance floor. In the event of multiple levels within a single dwelling unit, consideration must be given to the limitation of no more than two levels within a dwelling unit to be open to each other. Where a third level exists, it must be separated from the other two levels as required by other code provisions.

Another exception is a basic design approach for garden apartments where the apartment entrances are enclosed around a single protected stairway. This single stairway usually is open to the exterior or is glass enclosed. It must be separated from the building by construction of at least 1-hour fire resistance rating. The doors should be treated similarly. Note that this exception for a single exit is limited to buildings having four or fewer stories with not more than four living units per story and protected throughout by an approved, supervised automatic sprinkler system, and to existing buildings of three stories or less. Interestingly, the basic design of a typical garden-style apartment has influenced other chapters of NFPA *101*. Previous editions of NFPA *101* required that all exit stairways continuing beyond the floor of discharge be interrupted at that level by partitions, doors, or other effective means to make clear the direction of egress to the street. However, an exception to this requirement allows these stairways to continue one-half story beyond the level of discharge without such physical interruption. This exit arrangement is typically found in garden-style apartments that have apartments or service areas on the ground floor or terrace level. Based on this exception, stairways serving these levels need not be interrupted at the floor of exit discharge for fire safety reasons. Recently, fire escape ladders and alternating tread devices have been added as recognized means of egress components from apartment buildings. It must be recognized, however, that these types of means of egress components are acceptable in a very limited number of circumstances, such as from areas having low occupant loads of persons physically capable of using such devices.

In addition to the number and types of required exits, the arrangement and travel distance to these exits are regulated by the general requirements of NFPA *101* and *NFPA 5000*, with due consideration to the levels of fire protection features within the building. As in other occupancies, all exits must terminate directly at a public way or at an approved exit discharge (see Figure 20.4.8), unless certain additional protection features, such as automatic sprinkler protection and vestibule separation and/or enclosures, are provided to permit 50 percent of the required exit capacity to discharge through areas on the level of discharge. NFPA *101* and *NFPA 5000* also recognize the use of areas of refuge, particularly for spaces accessible to persons with severe mobility impairments. Because of the high level of satisfactory performance and response to fire conditions by supervised automatic sprinkler systems, any story of an apartment building equipped with this level of protection may be considered an area of refuge even if an occupant does not have access to any of the apartment units. Because locked apartment unit doors create inaccessibility to spaces other than the corridor, the corridor maintains its tenability due to the effectiveness of the automatic sprinklers and serves as the area of refuge. This does not preclude the demonstration of the corridor to maintain tenable conditions, especially if the aggregate area of the corrider is less than 1000 ft^2.

Minimum levels of illumination must be provided for public spaces, hallways, stairways, and other means of egress. Emergency lighting is required for apartment buildings that have more than 12 living units or are more than three stories high, except in buildings where every living unit has a direct exit to the outside at grade, such as in townhouses. Approved exit signs are required in all apartment buildings with more than one required exit. However, discretion should be used in placing such signs where exits are obvious or where all occupants are familiar with the building.

Because a higher degree of transient occupancy in some apartments is a definite possibility, special exiting considerations are made within the individual living units, in addition to those found in the public access spaces. All individual living units with two or more rooms must comply with the minimum provisions for operable exterior openings to be used as a secondary means of escape or with the specialized separation or protection requirements of NFPA *101* and *NFPA 5000*. Not only must these openings be of a minimum size, but they also must be accessible and easy to operate. In addition, every dwelling unit greater than 2000 ft^2 (180 m^2) or having a travel distance to the primary means of escape greater than 75 ft (22.5 m) must have two primary means of escape remote from each other, or it must be protected by an approved supervised automatic sprinkler system. Special multilevel units, such as penthouses, are permitted to have regular, curved, or spiral stairways that connect to one level above or below the entrance to the apartment.

Additional requirements prohibit any door in an apartment building, including individual unit doors, from being locked against egress while the building is occupied. This means that a door may be locked so that it can be opened from within the building but not from the outside. Ordinarily, dead bolts, double-cylinder locks, and chain locks would not meet these provisions. Multiple-death fires may occur if a key cannot be found to unlock the door or the chain is not removed. A concept that sets apartment buildings apart from other residential occupancies is a unique arrangement where a nontransient population is required to escape the building utilizing a common corridor egress system. In recognition of heightened security concerns, one additional operation is permitted to operate locks installed on doors between public spaces and individual dwelling units. This operation may include a sliding chain and catch or bolt, or any similar device such that no key or special knowledge or effort is necessary. Additional locks or latches may be installed provided that no more than two operations are required to open the door. In that case, one action must operate more than one locking or latching device. Note that in existing residential occupancies, NFPA *101* permits two additional releasing operations, for a total of three. The use of delayed egress locks, however, is permitted in apartment buildings protected throughout by automatic sprinkler systems or fire detection systems. The limitation of one such locking device in any one egress path and the 15- or 30-second delayed release provides the security needed for infrequently used doors but at the same time ensures that the door remains available for emergency use.

Another feature unique to apartment buildings permits stairway doors to be locked to prohibit building re-entry when such stairs are arranged as smokeproof enclosures. This requirement differs slightly from other occupancy types for which a number of restrictions exist to permit locking of doors from the exit stair to prevent re-entry onto a floor of the building (Figure 20.4.9).

FIGURE 20.4.9 Locked Stairway Doors Served by Smokeproof Enclosure

In apartment buildings, the protection of vertical openings, such as stairways, elevator shafts, and atria, follows the requirements found in NFPA *101* and *NFPA 5000*. Smokeproof enclosures are required in existing high-rise apartment buildings except those that are totally sprinklered. This limits the possibility of smoke contamination of exits and ensures a safe, protected means of egress. The protection from hazards, as well as the classification of interior finishes, is also based on the levels of fire detection and/or protection within the building.

The recognition of the limited fire hazard and fuel loading in apartment buildings permits a unique reduction for the fire resistance requirements for vertical openings. In apartment buildings protected throughout by automatic sprinklers, vertical openings are permitted to be enclosed by construction having a fire resistance rating of 1 hour regardless of the number of stories connected by the opening unless the building is a high-rise.

A relatively new provision of the model codes prohibits unenclosed vertical openings of any kind within new buildings or fire sections of new buildings served by a single exit. In addition, any new building with unprotected vertical openings is required to be protected throughout by an approved supervised automatic sprinkler system. However, convenience openings, which meet the special requirements found in other chapters of NFPA *101* and *NFPA 5000* are permitted without exception in apartment buildings.

A highly effective form of fire protection in a residential occupancy is early warning. All living units in an apartment building must be equipped with approved smoke alarms. These smoke alarms are usually located in hallways that have access to the sleeping areas although new unsprinklered apartment buildings must also be equipped with smoke alarms in every sleeping room. In multiple-level units, a smoke alarm also should be located at the tops of stairways. Detection systems must be installed in accordance with basic engineering practices. Special consideration should be given to room configuration, air movement, and stagnant air pockets that would reduce detector efficiency, and to cooking areas, fireplaces, or other normally smoke-producing appliances that cause an excess of nuisance alarms. All smoke alarms required for installation in multiple-dwelling units must be powered by the building's electrical system. In order to reduce the possibilities of unnecessary alarms due to ambient conditions, or where incipient incidents can be controlled without total building evacuation, smoke alarms within individual units are not required to sound the building fire alarm. This permits rapid notification of those persons most intimate with the fire without unnecessary evacuation of areas of the building not immediately affected by the incident. Secondary power sources are not required for single-station smoke alarms in existing buildings only. In addition, where a single apartment needs more than one smoke alarm, there is no requirement to interconnect multiple smoke alarms within a single unit. However, the audibility requirements of *NFPA 72*®, *National Fire Alarm Code*®, almost always require multiple smoke alarms within a single dwelling unit to be electrically interconnected such that when one detects smoke, all smoke alarms within the dwelling unit sound their audible (and visible, where applicable) alarms. Note that this type of detection system is required in addition to the requirements for any other detection or suppression system.

Manual fire alarm systems are required in apartment buildings according to the building's size and height. As building designs become higher and more complex, additional special features are required, such as annunciator panels, visible alarm signals, voice communications systems, and automatic transmission of building fire alarms to the fire department. Voice communications systems are often used as part of a multifaceted system that allows the fire department to provide verbal instructions to building occupants during a fire. Where levels of protection, such as automatic sprinkler protection or exit access directly to the exterior of the building, particularly at ground level, are suitable to maintain a safe egress system for a longer period of time, other fire protection features, such as fire alarm systems, are not required to be installed. This is in recognition of the benefits associated with a properly designed, installed, and maintained automatic sprinkler system in a type of occupancy in which fire casualties remain at a high level.

As mentioned before, NFPA *101* and *NFPA 5000* require almost all new apartment buildings to be protected by automatic sprinklers. In existing apartment buildings, the extent of automatic sprinkler protection is again governed by the building's size and height, as well as by the four protection options discussed in NFPA *101.* To the extent permitted by the applicable sprinkler system installation standard, the use of residential or quick-response sprinklers is required for new installations of sprinkler systems in dwelling units, apartments, and hotel guest rooms. The increased technology, cost-effectiveness, and appearance of these systems have provided numerous additional incentives for mandating this protection option. An exception permits the elimination of the draftstops and closely spaced sprinklers as required by NFPA 13 for convenience openings within dwelling units.

Continuing efforts have been made by the technical committees of the model building codes, NFPA *101,* and the sprinkler standards to coordinate the requirements for automatic sprinkler protection in buildings housing residential occupancies. Two examples are the levels of protection necessary for closets within individual dwelling units and for open parking structures in buildings protected by systems designed in accordance with NFPA 13.

Caution should be exercised when designing automatic sprinkler protection in buildings where residential and other occupancies are located. Often mercantile or business uses occupy the lower floors of a building, with residential units located on upper floors. These nonresidential spaces might pose an additional threat of a fire during nonbusiness hours, having the potential of affecting the tenability of egress routes from residential areas above. These buildings might be classified as mixed-use buildings, and do not fall within the scope of NFPA 13R, *Standard for* the *Installation of Sprinkler Systems in Residential Occupancies up to and Including Four Stories in Height,* for the design and installation of automatic sprinkler protection. Therefore, the sprinkler design for these types of structures must conform to the requirements of NFPA 13.

Designers of sprinkler systems for apartment buildings must pay particular attention to details, because residential and quick-response sprinklers cannot always be installed in a system that could normally be designed with standard sprinklers. There may also be other situations, such as vaulted ceilings or areas with special ambient temperature considerations, where residential sprinklers or quick-response sprinklers might not be listed for use. In all cases, the intent to obtain the quick response afforded by these types of sprinklers, as well as the high spray provided by residential sprinklers, serves to maintain tenability within the room of fire origin.

NFPA *101* requires portable fire extinguishers to be located in hazardous areas only, not throughout the entire building. Many building owners place these extinguishers in individual living units, under the direct responsibility of the occupant. In addition, a provision of NFPA *101* eliminates the need for portable fire extinguishers in buildings protected throughout by an approved supervised automatic sprinkler system. The possible ineffective use of such devices by persons not routinely trained in their operation, as well as the expense and effort to install and maintain portable extinguishers, especially in unsecured areas, is addressed by using early warning and suppression operations of smoke alarms and automatic sprinklers, especially those systems utilizing fast-response or residential sprinklers, to adequately notify building occupants and to control fires without the need for occupant intervention. It should be noted, however, that some fire prevention codes, including NFPA 1, *Uniform Fire Code*™, require the installation of portable fire extinguishers throughout apartment buildings. The requirements of NFPA 1 and NFPA *101* differ because the two codes have differing scopes, goals, and objectives.

The design, installation, and maintenance of all such fire detection and protection systems are based on referenced fire protection standards, as well as on sound engineering judgment. For residential occupancies of four or fewer stories, see NFPA 13R.

When fires cannot be confined to the area of origin, the means of egress must be sufficiently protected to allow all building occupants enough time for safe evacuation. This basic concern for providing safety for the occupant in a room during a fire led to a minimum corridor wall construction to keep fire in a corridor from entering a room or to keep fire in a room from entering the corridor. Doors protecting openings in these enclosures must provide a level of protection commensurate with the expected fuel load in the room and with the fire resistance of the corridor wall construction. Contrary to the general rule for door assembly considerations, the requirements for doors in residential occupancies apply to the leaf only, with a 1¾ in. (45 mm) solid, bonded, wood-core door considered equivalent to a door with a 20-minute fire protection rating. The door rating requirement establishes a minimum quality of construction and does not require a complete listed fire door assembly. However, the requirement that doors between apartments and corridors be self-closing reduces the risk of fire fatalities. Fire spread can occur mainly due to the door being left open as the occupant flees the fire. People may die after opening the door to a fully involved room, or after causing a room to become fully involved by opening a door and introducing oxygen to the fire. Under both circumstances, a door equipped with spring-loaded hinges or a door closer would prevent smoke or fire from spreading down the corridor and exposing other occupants. Since a fire and its effects can be adequately and quickly contained in spaces that are protected by residential or quick-response sprinklers, the installation of those styles of sprinklers now permits the elimination of corridor walls and doors separating exit access corridors from spaces not used as dwelling units or hazardous areas. Such spaces may include meeting rooms, lobbies, gift shops, offices, and other ancillary spaces found in a number of apartment buildings. Spaces where a higher fuel load, or where sources of ignition may exist, such as workshops, storage rooms, and laundries, are not permitted to use this corridor wall exception.

During a fire, the evacuation of all residents from a large apartment building is at best a time-consuming process. This problem is compounded by the introduction of larger and taller structures, complex and intricate building designs, and a larger population of residents who are incapable of rapid evacuation, especially by stairways. For these reasons, the most expedient movement of a sizable number of residents may be horizontally. The introduction of required areas of refuge serves three purposes fundamental to the protection of building occupants by (1) limiting the spread of fire and fire-produced contaminants, (2) limiting the number of occupants exposed to a single fire, and (3) providing for horizontal evacuation by creating safe and tenable space on the same level.

Accessible means of egress and associated areas of refuge are required in new apartment buildings based on the evacuation capabilities of the building's occupants and on the construction and design characteristics of the building and levels of fire protection features. Since the majority of apartment residents are assumed to be capable of vertical evacuation using stairways, the location of stairways provides both the required area of refuge as well as the required means of egress. Where travel time to stairways increases due to excessive horizontal distances and/or where a majority of residents have reduced mobility, specialized areas are required on the same floor level.

Typically, all building service equipment and utilities in apartment buildings are required to be designed and installed in accordance with sound engineering practices and all applicable NFPA standards. The use of a public corridor as part of the supply, return, or exhaust air system is not permitted in accordance with NFPA 90A, *Standard for the Installation of Air-Conditioning and Ventilating Systems.* In fact, in certain apartment building designs, these corridors must be pressurized against smoke movement. The standard requirements for the reliability of the means of egress and fire retardancy for interior furnishings and decorations, as well as the proper maintenance and testing of fire protection equipment also apply equally to apartment occupancies. With the advent of new innovations in gas heater technology and design, including automatic fuel shutoffs and oxygen-depletion alarms, the use of approved gas space heaters is now permitted under certain conditions commensurate with the listing of the heater.

Occupants of each living unit must be given emergency instructions on a yearly basis, indicating the location of alarms, exiting paths, and actions to be taken in response to a fire in the living unit and in response to the sounding of an alarm. However, other operating features, such as specialized fire safety training and fire exit drills, have been deleted due to the nontransient nature of most building occupants.

SUMMARY

The statistical data previously cited provide clear evidence that the fire problem in apartment buildings and in residential occupancies as a whole is complex, significant, and not easily solved. The increasing demand for adequate, yet low-cost, functional and aesthetically pleasing housing has led to an increasing demand for adequate, safe, and economical fire protection. The problem intensifies with the demand for higher and larger buildings with a higher density of occupants and with the demand for more personal services for building occupants. Although the solution to these fire problems undoubtedly requires much future study, the obvious short-term solution of effective code formulation, adoption, and enforcement is the immediate responsibility of every fire safety professional.

BIBLIOGRAPHY

References Cited

1. *U.S. Interim Projections by Age, Sex, Race, and Hispanic Origin,* Table 2a, U.S. Census Bureau, Washington, DC, 2004.
2. *Selected Housing Characteristics: 2004,* U.S. Census Bureau, Washington, DC, 2004.
3. Karter, M. J., Jr., *Fire Loss in the United States During 2004,* National Fire Protection Association, Quincy, MA, Sept. 2005.

NFPA Codes, Standards, and Recommended Practices

Reference to the following NFPA codes, standards, and recommended practices will provide further information on apartment buildings discussed in this chapter. (See the latest version of The NFPA Catalog *for availability of current editions of the following documents.)*

NFPA 1, *Uniform Fire Code™*
NFPA 13, *Standard for the Installation of Sprinkler Systems*
NFPA 13R, *Standard for the Installation of Sprinkler Systems in Residential Occupancies up to and Including Four Stories in Height*
NFPA 72®, National Fire Alarm Code®
NFPA 90A, *Standard for the Installation of Air-Conditioning and Ventilating Systems*
NFPA *101®, Life Safety Code®*
NFPA 5000®, Building Construction and Safety Code®

References

Comeau, E., and Duval, R., "Apartment Building Fire, Bremerton, Washington, November 13, 1997," NFPA Fire Investigation Report, National Fire Protection Association, Quincy, MA, 1999.
Proulx, G., "Evacuation Time and Movement in Apartment Buildings," *Fire Safety Journal,* Vol. 24, No. 3, 1995, pp. 229–246.
Proulx, G., and Fahy, R. F., "Time Delay to Start Evacuation: Review of Five Case Studies," *Proceedings* of the 5th International Symposium, Fire Safety Science, March 3–7, 1997, Melbourne, Australia, International Association for Fire Safety Science, Boston, 1997, pp. 783–794.
Proulx, G., and McQueen, C., "Evacuation Timing in Apartment Buildings. Internal Report," Internal Report 660, National Research Council of Canada, Ottawa, Ontario, June 1994.

Chapter 5

Lodging or Rooming Houses

Key Terms

bed-and-breakfast, occupancy characteristic, occupant characteristic, rooming house, self-preservation, university housing

Revised by
Richard R. Anderson

Lodging or rooming houses are defined by NFPA *101*®, *Life Safety Code*®, and *NFPA 5000*®, *Building Construction and Safety Code*®, as those buildings in which separate sleeping rooms are rented and sleeping accommodations are provided for 16 or fewer persons on either a transient or a permanent basis, with or without meals, but without separate cooking facilities for individual occupants.

Facilities with sleeping accommodations for more than 16 persons are classified as hotels and dormitories, and those with individual cooking facilities are classified as apartment buildings. Occupants must be capable of self-preservation. The presence of four or more occupants who are incapable of self-preservation reclassifies the facility as a health care, or possibly, a board and care facility. Based on these restrictions, the classification "lodging or rooming house" is effectively limited to facilities providing sleeping accommodations without separate cooking facilities for up to 16 persons who are capable of self-preservation.

Lodging or rooming houses can be in buildings of any construction type permitted by local building codes. NFPA *101* does not identify any minimum construction requirements for occupant life safety purposes. Because most lodging or rooming houses are located in converted dwellings or share space with mercantile operations, construction is generally found to be Type III or V, as defined by NFPA 220, *Standard on Types of Building Construction,* and *NFPA 5000*. The hazard of the contents is considered "ordinary," a trait consistent with most residential occupancies.

For related topics, see the following chapters in Section 20: Chapter 1, "Assessing Life Safety in Buildings"; Chapter 2, "Board and Care Facilities"; Chapter 3, "Hotels and University Housing"; Chapter 4, "Apartment Buildings"; and Chapter 6, "One- and Two-Family Dwellings."

OCCUPANT AND OCCUPANCY CHARACTERISTICS

How familiar occupants of lodging and rooming houses are with the layout of the houses they live in varies considerably. Permanent occupants of a rooming house have the advantage of being familiar with the layout of the building. Occupants of a campus lodging house, better known as a fraternity or sorority house, are not permanent; however, over the course of a semester they can become increasingly familiar with the layout of the building. Bed-and-breakfast guests, like hotel guests, are typically transient in nature.

Mixed occupancies generally are not encountered in lodging and rooming houses, except in cases in which mercantile-use spaces are located on the lower floor or floors and sleeping rooms are located above. Neither NFPA *101* nor *NFPA 5000* permits such an arrangement without specific protection requirements.

Rooming Houses

In the 1970s and 1980s, several new markets spurred a growth in the number and nature of lodging and rooming houses, which were once considered budget-conscious alternatives to expensive hotels. Landmark court decisions required that psychiatric patients capable of living in less

Richard R. Anderson, CFPS, is vice-president of Anderson Risk Consultants and chair of NFPA's Lodging Industry Section Executive Committee.

restrictive environments than psychiatric hospitals be released to live in the general population. Although many deinstitutionalized people do not require the assistance of support staff, such as might be found in residential board and care facilities, they prefer not to assume all the responsibilities of independent living, meal preparation, and the like and choose to live in rooming houses.

Due to the limited number of sleeping accommodations and the lack of separate cooking facilities for individual occupants, lodging or rooming houses are viewed, from a life safety standpoint, as falling above one- and two-family dwellings and below dormitories, hotels, and apartment buildings.

NFPA *101* and *NFPA 5000* requirements for lodging and rooming houses center on four key elements essential to life safety: means of escape, detection and alarm systems, separation of sleeping rooms, and automatic sprinkler protection. These four elements are covered in the sections that follow.

Bed-and-Breakfast Properties

Bed-and-breakfast properties are typically distinctly different from rooming houses, dormitories, or fraternity and sorority houses. They are typically owner-occupied, well kept, and often upscale accommodations. Bed-and-breakfasts and country inns have become increasingly popular in the United States as alternative travel accommodations to hotels. Many facilities known as bed-and-breakfasts meet the definition of hotel because they provide sleeping accommodations for more than 16 guests.

Fraternity/Sorority or University Housing

Fraternity houses, sorority houses, and university housing in converted dwellings are found on and around university campuses. These properties pose many of the same life safety hazards posed by rooming houses. In most cases, these properties are occupied by young adults who might be prone to risky behavior—for example, smoking, consuming alcohol, and using controlled substances—which can serve to increase the life safety hazard.

FIRE SAFETY

Because most fires involve behaviors and transitory hazards that may not be identified in an annual inspection, the property owner should be well versed in understanding fire hazards.

Inherent Hazards

The leading causes of fires in lodging and rooming houses during the 4-year period from 1999 to 2002 were cooking equipment (42%), smoking materials (16%), and arson (10%). Whereas cooking equipment was involved in 42 percent of all fires in rooming and boarding houses, 25 percent were confined to the cooking equipment.[1] Smoking in the guest rooms and common areas of bed-and-breakfast properties can be prohibited, and enforcement of a no-smoking policy can eliminate one of the leading causes of fires in these occupancies. However, smoking is typically allowed in rooming, fraternity, and sorority houses. Fire-retardant textiles, furniture, and mattresses can help slow the spread of fires caused by smoking materials.

Electrical Equipment

The original design of the electrical systems for homes converted to or used as bed-and-breakfast occupancies did not consider the use of modern-day appliances, such as 2000 watt hair dryers, 900 watt space heaters, coffee makers, and the like. If a property has undergone renovations to facilitate its use as a bed-and-breakfast, the electrical system might have been updated. However, if there were no renovations, electrical systems may be prone to improper use of extension cords and outlet strips due to the lack of sufficient receptacles. The use of extension cords and outlet strips should be limited due to the potential of overloading circuits. Where used, such devices should be listed, approved, and used according to the manufacturer's recommendations. From 1992 to 2002, electrical equipment represented the cause of 5 percent of structural fires in lodging and boarding houses.[1]

Building Systems

Due to the limited size of lodging or rooming house occupancies, building systems are typically not very sophisticated; however, it is not uncommon for them to have a central air and heating system. These systems might be required to be equipped with smoke dampers to isolate the air-handling equipment from the remainder of the system or smoke detectors in the ducts arranged to automatically shut down the system upon detection of smoke. See NFPA 90A, *Standard for the Installation of Air-Conditioning and Ventilating Systems,* for detailed requirements for such systems.

Heating and cooling systems should be installed by qualified installers and maintained in accordance with the manufacturer's recommendations. Inadequate heating can lead to the use of supplemental heating devices, such as portable electric, kerosene, or fixed-space heaters. Each represents a specific hazard and has its own accompanying set of requirements.

Appliances

Appliances in a lodging or rooming house occupancy include appliances similar to those found in a residence. However, the frequent use of clothes dryers to do laundry for up to 16 guests can lead to a dangerous buildup of lint that could result in a fire. In rooming houses some tenants may be permanent and are, therefore, likely to accumulate more electrical appliances than transient tenants, such as those in a bed-and-breakfast facility.

Open Flames

Sources of open flames in lodging or rooming houses include candles and fireplaces. The National Candle Association recommends that candles never be left unattended. Many bed-and-breakfast owners have instituted policies that prohibit the use of candles in the guest rooms or have replaced them with battery-operated candles. Battery-operated candles can actually flicker and appear very realistic, thus providing the desired ambiance without the danger.

Cooking Equipment

The presence of individual cooking facilities changes the type of occupancy, typically to an apartment building. However, a central kitchen is sometimes found in lodging or rooming house occupancies. The leading cause of fire incidents in U.S. lodging and room houses from 1999 to 2002 was cooking equipment, which resulted in 16 civilian injuries and $0.9 million in direct property damage.[1] Central kitchens are typically only accessible to staff. Cooking equipment in such central kitchens should be protected in accordance with NFPA 96, *Standard for Ventilation Control and Fire Protection of Commercial Cooking Operations.*

Fireplaces

Wood-burning fireplaces are common in bed-and-breakfast properties and are typically used more often than in private residences. Annual cleaning and inspection of the flue can prevent the buildup of flammable creosote and reveal defects in the flue or blockage, such as a nest.

Occupancy Conversion or Remodeling

Fire hazards may be inadvertently created during conversion or remodeling. Existing wall and ceiling finishes might be removed, exposing combustible structural components. Concealed combustible spaces may be created by installing drop ceilings and new wall finishes. Concealed combustible spaces can permit rapid fire development and spread and limit accessibility for fire fighting. The wall and ceiling finishes in new facilities are limited to Class A, B, or C as defined in NFPA *101* and *NFPA 5000*; however, wall and ceiling finish materials can exceed these limitations and significantly increase fire spread and smoke generation in existing buildings.

MEANS OF ESCAPE

In lodging or rooming houses, the egress system consists of means of escape, which, by definition, is a way out of a building or structure that does not conform to the strict definition of means of egress but does provide a safe way out.

Sleeping rooms and living areas above and below grade are required to have a primary and secondary means of escape, one of which must be either an enclosed interior stairway, an exterior stairway, a horizontal exit, or an existing fire escape. The primary means of escape must provide a safe path of travel from the building, one that does not expose occupants to an unprotected vertical opening, except in completely sprinklered buildings of three stories or fewer (Figures 20.5.1, 20.5.2, and 20.5.3). In buildings protected throughout by automatic sprinklers, secondary means of escape are not required.

The example in Figure 20.5.1 shows an enclosed interior stairway that discharges directly outside. Access to the interior stairway is by an interior corridor that is not exposed to an unprotected vertical opening. The secondary means of escape could be through windows of sufficient size to provide egress. The bottom of the stairway can be enclosed several ways; this is only one example. In the example of means of escape shown in Figure 20.5.2, the tenants reach the exterior stairway via an interior corridor that is not exposed to an unprotected vertical opening. The secondary means of escape is through windows.

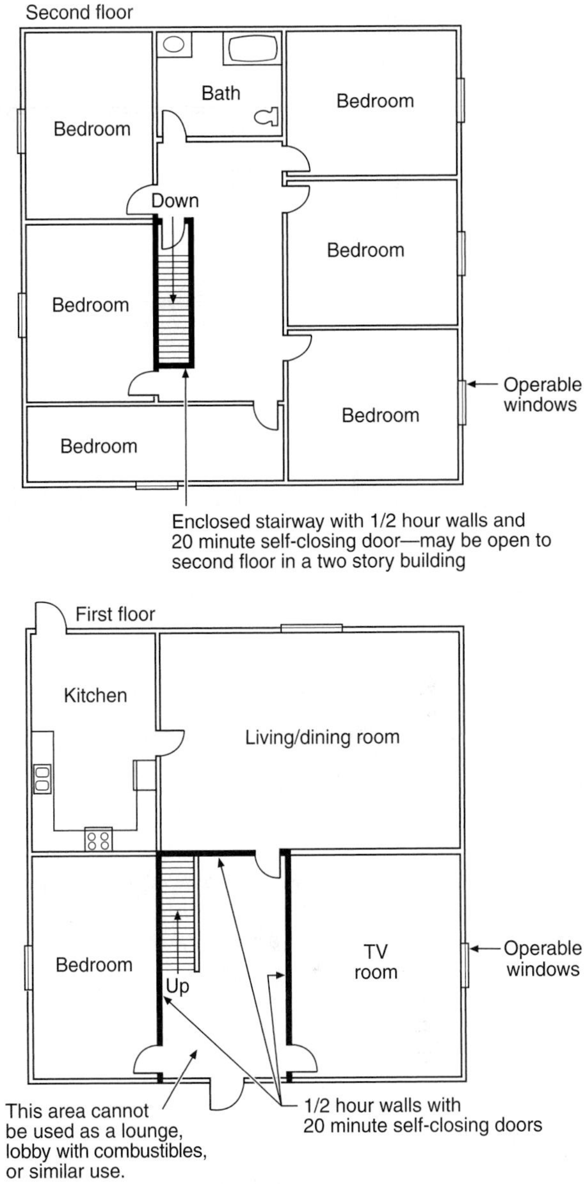

FIGURE 20.5.1 Means of Escape from a Lodging or Rooming House Using an Interior Stairway

In the example shown in Figure 20.5.3, access is not through an interior corridor, and the secondary means of escape is through the open interior stairway.

The specified means of escape should meet the requirements of NFPA *101* and *NFPA 5000*. Detailed requirements for secondary means of escape are provided in NFPA *101* and *NFPA 5000*; they include either a door or stairway that provides unobstructed travel to the outside of the building at street or ground level or an outside operable window located not more than 20 ft (6.1 m) above the ground. Note that a secondary means of escape is not required where the room has a door leading directly

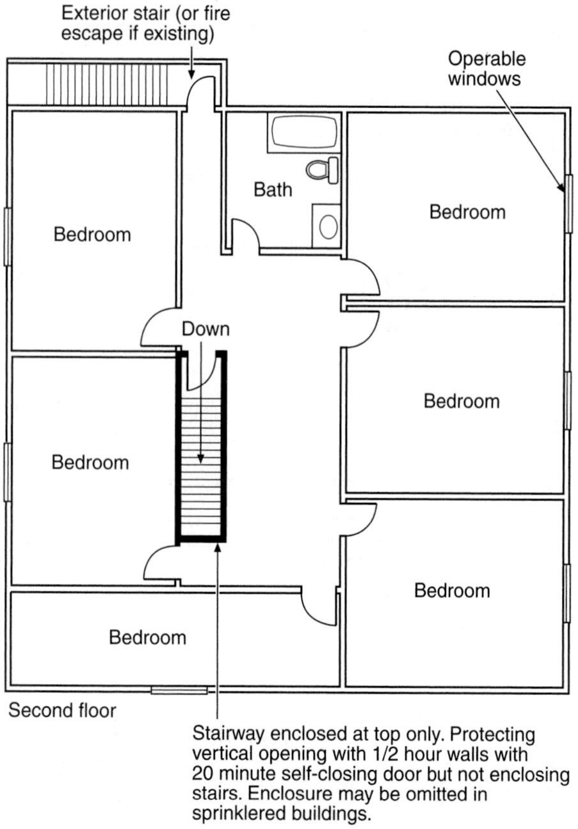

FIGURE 20.5.2 Means of Escape from a Lodging or Rooming House Using an Exterior Stairway

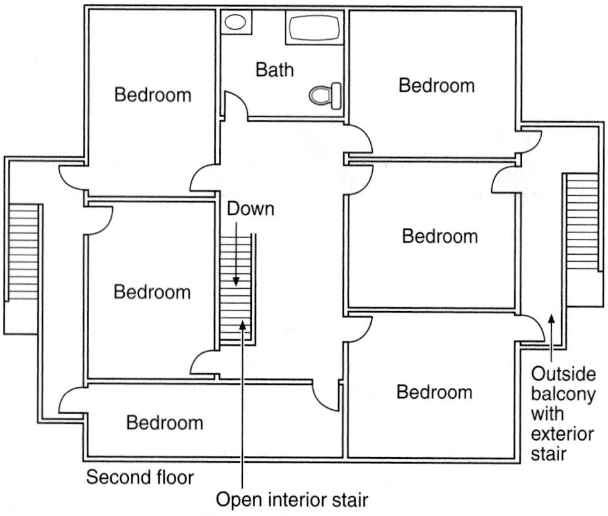

FIGURE 20.5.3 Means of Escape from a Lodging or Rooming House Using an Outside Stairway with Exterior Exit Access

outside at grade level or to an approved outside stair. No required means of escape may be routed through an area that is not under the control of the occupant who is leaving the building or be routed through a door that may be locked.

PASSIVE FIRE PROTECTION

Fire Doors

The installation of automatic or self-closing doors is an effective, relatively low-cost, and easy-to-maintain life safety feature. Fire-rated doors can help to confine a fire to the room of origin. Fire doors must not be blocked or otherwise secured in the open position, and they must positively latch when closed. See NFPA 80, *Standard for Fire Doors and Other Opening Protectives,* for details on the installation of fire doors.

Lack of Fire Blocking

Many older buildings lack fire blocking in walls and ceilings due to the lack of a building code or its enforcement at the time of construction. Such a lack of fire blocking, sometimes referred to as "balloon construction," can accommodate rapid, undetected spread of fire and smoke.

Separation of Sleeping Rooms

Sleeping rooms should be separated from corridors by smoke-resistant walls and self-closing doors. This feature helps prevent smoke from compromising the egress corridors in case of a fire in a room. In addition, if the corridor becomes smoke-logged before all occupants can escape, the smoke-resistant separation will allow occupants to remain within the room for a limited period of time.

Vertical Openings

Vertical openings, or "holes" in the floor that connect two or more contiguous stories, are not limited to stairs. They include shafts, floor penetrations for air ducts, heat grates, and other old floor openings that were never covered. Each represents a path for vertical fire and smoke spread. Unprotected vertical openings have been identified as significant contributing factors in many fatal fires.

CASE STUDY: Small Inn Fire. The fire that broke out on July 17, 2001, in a small inn in Allentown, New Hampshire, demonstrates how the lack of some of the passive fire protection measures mentioned in this section can result in tragedy. A three-alarm fire killed the innkeeper and destroyed the historic building that dated from 1760. Of the six guests who were occupying the premises, all survived, three by climbing to the roof of a portico. The NFPA fire investigation and analysis[2] revealed that the following played a significant role in the incident:

- There was only a single path of escape from the attic bedroom.

- No fire alarms or smoke detectors were functioning.
- There were unprotected vertical openings.

ACTIVE FIRE PROTECTION SYSTEMS AND EQUIPMENT

Detection and Alarm Systems

Detection and alarm systems in lodging or rooming houses play a critical role in the early warning and evacuation of occupants. A manual fire alarm system should be installed in accordance with *NFPA 72®, National Fire Alarm Code®*.

Smoke alarms installed in accordance with *NFPA 72* and powered by the building electrical service are required on each floor, including basements, but excluding crawl spaces and unfinished attics. When activated, the smoke alarms should be audible in all areas. This requirement can be satisfied by interconnecting smoke alarms with the manual fire alarm system. In addition to smoke alarms in the corridors on each level, a single-station smoke alarm powered by the building electrical system is required in each sleeping room to alert the occupant to a fire or smoke in the room. It is critical that the fire alarm system be audible in all sleeping rooms.

Automatic Sprinkler Protection

Automatic sprinkler systems are designed to operate during the early stages of fire development and minimize the fire's overall impact. If the room of fire origin is provided with a sprinkler system, flashover should be prevented, thus improving the opportunity to escape or be rescued and minimizing property damage. NFPA *101* and *NFPA 5000* require most new lodging or rooming houses to be protected by automatic sprinklers. Modifications to other requirements are permitted where sprinklers have been installed. In existing buildings, where automatic sprinkler protection is provided, the following code modifications are permitted:

- The lodging or rooming house is permitted to be located above another occupancy type.
- No secondary means of escape is required.
- It may be permissible for the primary escape stairway to remain unenclosed if each bedroom and living area has a secondary means of escape.

NFPA *101* and *NFPA 5000* recognize three standards for the installation of automatic sprinkler systems in lodging or rooming houses. For small, one- and two-family residences in which boarders are housed and rooming houses that are not part of a mixed occupancy, NFPA 13D, *Standard for the Installation of Sprinkler Systems in One- and Two-Family Dwellings and Manufactured Homes,* permits a simple, lower-cost system. For larger buildings of up to four stories in height, NFPA 13R, *Standard for the Installation of Sprinkler Systems in Residential Occupancies up to and Including Four Stories in Height,* may be used. For large buildings, especially those housing multiple occupancies, NFPA 13, *Standard for the Installation of Sprinkler Systems,* is the appropriate installation standard. Successful testing of water mist suppression systems in residential properties may offer a desirable protection strategy to owners of historic bed-and-breakfast occupancies containing irreplaceable antique contents and furnishings.

Staff Emergency Training

By combining the recognition of individual responsibilities to report fire-related hazards and how to initiate the appropriate actions should a fire occur, the risks to employees and the workplace can be reduced. Staff should be familiar with their responsibilities in the event of a fire including guiding guests or tenants in proper evacuation. NFPA *101* fire drill requirements for dormitories call for them to take place often enough so that the occupants are familiar with the emergency procedures, evacuation routes, alarm operation, and tone. In hotels, where guests are transient and may only be there for one night, the staff must be trained and prepared to assist the guests in the event of an incident. Although these code requirements do not directly apply to lodging or rooming house occupancies, the concepts can be readily applied to them to enhance a facility's life safety program.

SUMMARY

Lodging or rooming houses are defined as facilities providing sleeping accommodations without separate cooking facilities for up to 16 persons who are capable of self-preservation. Fire spread in these occupancies can be rapid due to lack of firestopping, unprotected vertical openings, storage of combustible materials, and the lack of automatic sprinkler protection. Primary fire hazards include electrical and other building service equipment, supplemental heating devices, smoking, and cooking.

Fire and life safety protection involves providing adequate means of escape, detection and alarm systems, bedrooms that are separated from corridors by smoke-resistant walls and self-closing doors, and automatic sprinkler systems.

BIBLIOGRAPHY

References Cited

1. Ahrens, M., *U.S. Fires in Selected Occupancies: Rooming and Boarding Houses,* National Fire Protection Association, Quincy, MA, Mar. 2006, p. 94.
2. Duval, R. F., *Bed and Breakfast, Allentown, NH,* National Fire Protection Association, Quincy, MA, 2002.

NFPA Codes, Standards, and Recommended Practices

Reference to the following NFPA codes, standards, and recommended practices will provide further information on lodging or rooming houses discussed in this chapter. (See the latest version of The NFPA Catalog *for availability of current editions of the following documents.)*

NFPA 13, *Standard for the Installation of Sprinkler Systems*
NFPA 13D, *Standard for the Installation of Sprinkler Systems in One- and Two-Family Dwellings and Manufactured Homes*

NFPA 13R, *Standard for the Installation of Sprinkler Systems in Residential Occupancies up to and Including Four Stories in Height*
NFPA 72®, National Fire Alarm Code®
NFPA 80, *Standard for Fire Doors and Other Opening Protectives*
NFPA 90A, *Standard for the Installation of Air-Conditioning and Ventilating Systems*
NFPA 96, *Standard for Ventilation Control and Fire Protection of Commercial Cooking Operations*
NFPA *101®*, *Life Safety Code®*
NFPA 220, *Standard on Types of Building Construction*
NFPA 255, *Standard Method of Test of Surface Burning Characteristics of Building Materials*
NFPA 5000®, Building Construction and Safety Code®

Chapter 6

One- and Two-Family Dwellings

James K. Lathrop

Chapter Contents

Key Terms

dwelling, evacuation, fire prevention, heating equipment, residential sprinkler system, smoking materials

One- and two-family dwellings are defined as residential structures in which not more than two families reside. These dwelling units may be attached to or detached from one another, and typical styles include detached single-family dwellings, townhouses, and duplexes. There are many different designs, such as the one-story ranch, two-story colonial, split-level, and three-level townhouse. Wood frame and masonry are the most common construction types.

In 2003, 70 percent of all housing units occupied year-round were single-family detached or attached units, and another 6 percent were manufactured housing. The figures for seasonal housing were comparable at 63 percent and 23 percent. Two-family houses were not tabulated separately, but housing units in buildings with two to four housing units accounted for another 8 percent of the total year-round housing and 3 percent of the total seasonal housing. Therefore, one- and two-family housing accounts for 75 to 84 percent of all housing in the United States. This total has not changed since the last edition of the *Fire Protection Handbook.*

Each year, the majority of all U.S. fire deaths occur in one- and two-family dwellings. During 1999–2002, 94 percent of the civilian structure fire deaths occurred in the home and 83 percent of those occurred in one- and two-family dwellings, a share comparable to their share of all housing units. Thus, it is important to consider every element of fire safety for its potential value in this setting. Unless otherwise indicated, all data contained in this chapter come from *Selections from U.S. Fires in Selected Occupancies—Homes,* by Marty Ahrens, NFPA Fire Analysis and Research Division, NFPA, March 2006.

NFPA *101*®, *Life Safety Code*®, and *NFPA 5000*®, *Building Construction and Safety Code*®, include requirements for one- and two-family dwellings. In particular, NFPA *101* addresses the need for two means of escape from every room for occupant evacuation; the selection of interior finish materials to prevent rapid early fire growth and spread and to protect occupant evacuation routes; and smoke alarms to provide early warning. Beginning with the 2006 edition of NFPA *101,* all new one- and two-family dwellings require sprinkler protection.

See also Section 4, Chapter 5, "Strategies for Occupant Evacuation during Emergencies"; Section 14, Chapter 6, "Household Fire Warning Equipment"; and Section 16, Chapter 6, "Residential Sprinkler Systems."

IMPORTANCE OF EVACUATION

The philosophy of life safety and fire protection for one- and two-family dwellings is based on evacuation of the building in the event of a fire. The defend-in-place concept used in other types of occupancies, which relies on fixed fire protection systems and fire-resistant construction, does not lend itself to one- and two-family dwellings. To allow residents time to evacuate, they must be alerted to a fire that has been detected at the incipient stage, they must know what action to take, and they must have adequate means of escape. Even with residential sprinkler systems, ocupants need to evacuate. NFPA 13D, *Standard for the Installation of Sprinkler Systems in One- and Two-Family*

James K. Lathrop is vice-president of Koffel Associates, Inc., and a fellow of the Society of Fire Protection Engineers. He is also assistant chief of the Niantic, Connecticut, fire department.

Dwellings and Manufactured Homes, permits a limited water supply, so defending in place is not an option in most cases.

Proper installation and use of smoke alarms can accomplish early warning. *NFPA 72®, National Fire Alarm Code®*, recommends smoke alarms be installed in all sleeping rooms, outside of each separate sleeping area, in the immediate vicinity of the sleeping rooms, and on each additional story of the dwelling including basements. Additional information on smoke alarms can be found in Section 14, Chapter 6, "Household Fire Warning Equipment."

Means of Escape

After the occupants have been alerted, they must promptly evacuate. A written fire escape plan should be made for each dwelling, showing two means of escape from every habitable room, especially the bedrooms, and this plan should be practiced by the entire family. Programs such as NFPA's Exit Drills in The Home (EDITH) explain how to write and practice a home fire escape plan.

Adequate means of escape from each room should be provided in accordance with the requirements of NFPA *101* and *NFPA 5000.* Two means of escape are required from each room. One must be a door or stairway, and the second way can be an operable window. Figure 20.6.1 illustrates means of escape from a three-bedroom single-family home. The bedroom in the upper left has no window, but it has a door directly to the outside. The alternate means of escape from the other bedroom is through windows and must comply with the requirements of NFPA *101* and *NFPA 5000.* Figure 20.6.2 shows the minimum

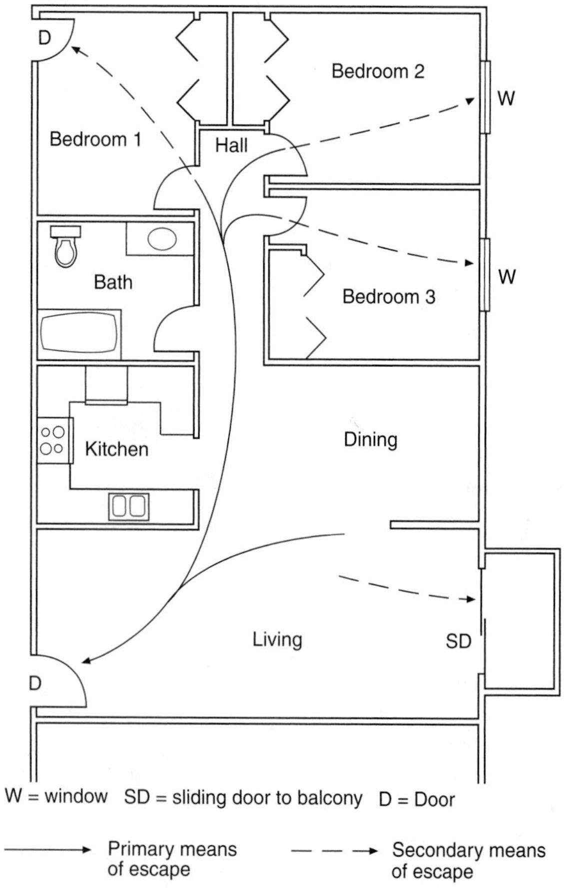

FIGURE 20.6.1 Means of Escape from Single-Family Home

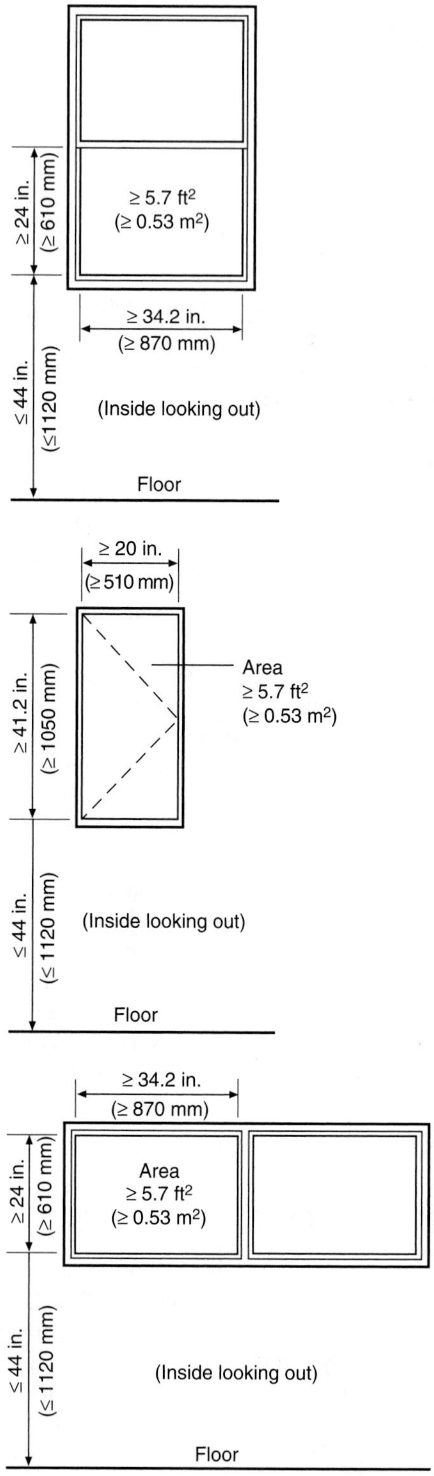

FIGURE 20.6.2 Escape Window Minimum Opening Dimensions

size and dimensions of outside windows used as a second means of escape.

Adequate means of escape also involves eliminating obstacles created by some security provisions. Escape may be slowed—possibly more than safe escape allows—by security measures like double-cylinder locks, which require a key to open from inside. Escape may be totally obstructed by security measures, either designed (such as burglar bars) or makeshift (such as nailing windows shut).

Residential Sprinklers

Residential-type automatic sprinkler systems provide a high degree of protection for one- and two-family dwellings. A growing number of communities require sprinklers in all new dwellings, as does the 2006 edition of the *Life Safety Code.* Even where they are not required, sprinklers are a valuable and effective fire safety choice. In any property, sprinklers reduce the chances of dying if fire occurs and the average property loss per fire by one-half to two-thirds. From 1994 through 1998 automatic suppression systems, usually sprinklers, were present in 1 percent of one- and two-family dwelling fires, 7 percent of the apartment fires, and in 2 percent of reported home fires overall. The fire death rate per 1000 fires was 77 percent lower and the average loss per fire was 85 percent lower in fires in which this equipment was present. Additional information on sprinkler systems in one- and two-family dwellings can be found in Section 16, Chapter 6, "Residential Sprinkler Systems."

FIRE AND LIFE SAFETY HAZARDS

Many other fire protection strategies are under discussion, but they have not yet been reduced to codes or regulations. These address the contribution of various types of contents, furnishings, and construction elements to fire growth, smoke and gas generation, and confinement after a fire begins.

Most fire fatalities in one- and two-family dwellings are a result of smoke inhalation, not burns, and most victims die in a room that is not the room of fire origin. In other words, they die as a result of a fire that has produced enough smoke to spread beyond the room in which the fire began. Prevention and early action are needed to control the development of these lethal conditions.

When studying fire data in one- and two-family dwellings, it is very important to understand that the statistics are significantly different between numbers of fires and numbers of fatal fires. For example the leading cause of fires in one- and two-family dwellings is cooking equipment, but by far the leading cause of fatal fires in dwellings is smoking materials. Table 20.6.1 demonstrates these differences.

TABLE 20.6.1 Leading Causes of Structure Fires in One- and Two-Family Dwellings, 1999–2002 Annual Averages

Cause	*Fires*		*Civilian Deaths*		*Civilian Injuries*		*Direct Property Damage (in Millions of Dollars)*	
Cooking equipment fire	63,400	(23%)	220	(9%)	2570	(24%)	357	(8%)
Identified cooking equipment	45,800	(16%)	220	(9%)	2300	(22%)	350	(8%)
Confined cooking fire	17,600	(6%)	0	(0%)	280	(3%)	7	(0%)
Heating equipment	48,900	(17%)	300	(12%)	1090	(10%)	571	(13%)
Identified heating equipment	36,100	(13%)	300	(12%)	1060	(10%)	563	(13%)
Confined chimney or flue fire	10,400	(4%)	0	(0%)	10	(0%)	7	(0%)
Confined fuel burner or boiler malfunction or fire	2,500	(1%)	0	(0%)	10	(0%)	1	(0%)
Electrical distribution or lighting equipment	27,900	(10%)	200	(8%)	770	(7%)	577	(14%)
Intentional	25,500	(9%)	410	(17%)	850	(8%)	515	(12%)
Smoking material	16,400	(6%)	640	(26%)	1150	(11%)	307	(7%)
Candle	14,400	(5%)	130	(5%)	1230	(12%)	304	(7%)
Exposure to other fire	11,800	(4%)	20	(1%)	70	(1%)	161	(4%)
Clothes dryer or washer	11,200	(4%)	10	(1%)	240	(2%)	90	(2%)
Playing with heat source	10,200	(4%)	180	(7%)	940	(9%)	175	(4%)

Note: These are national estimates of fires reported to U.S. municipal fire departments and so exclude fires reported only to federal or state agencies or industrial fire brigades. National estimates are projections. Casualty and loss projections can be heavily influenced by the inclusion or exclusion of one unusually serious fire. Fires are rounded to the nearest hundred, civilian deaths and injuries are rounded to the nearest ten, and direct property damage is rounded to the nearest million dollars. Property damage has not been adjusted for inflation.

Source: NFIRS and NFPA survey.

PREVENTION OF FIRE IGNITION

Leading Causes of Fire Fatalities

The leading cause of fire deaths in one- and two-family dwellings is smoking materials or lighted tobacco products (Tables 20.6.2 and 20.6.3). Fatal smoking material fires most often involve the ignition of upholstered furniture, mattresses, or bedding, which also rank highest as combustible items first ignited in all kinds of fatal fires. Because it is not unusual for a fire to smolder for hours before it progresses to open burning, many of these fatal fires occur at night when everyone is asleep. Although smoking material is the leading cause of fatal one- and two-family dwelling fires, it is fifth in list of causes of the total number of fires in one- and two-family dwellings.

A major change from the last edition of the *Fire Protection Handbook* is that intentional fires have moved to the second leading cause of fatal fires in one- and two-family dwellings. These fires previously ranked third. Intentional fires rank fourth as the cause of all fires in one- and two-family dwellings.

The third-ranking cause of fire deaths in one- and two-family homes is heating equipment. Heating equipment was also the second leading cause of fires. Heating equipment includes fixed or portable space heaters, chimneys, central heating units, fireplaces, and water heaters. Each type of heating appliance has its own rules for safe installation, maintenance, and use. NFPA 211, *Standard for Chimneys, Fireplaces, Vents, and Solid Fuel-Burning Appliances,* in particular, covers solid-fueled appliances. Maintaining adequate clearance to combustibles, whether fixed (e.g., walls and structural members) or moveable (e.g., furniture, bedding, and clothing), is a common problem for all types of portable and area heating equipment. Safe fueling practices are especially important for liquid-fueled units, as is adequate venting for gas-fueled units and regular inspection and cleaning for solid-fueled units.

Electrical distribution equipment ranked a very close fifth as a cause of fire deaths. Many people mistakenly believe that electrical system fires represent a larger share of fires, but the widespread and long-term use of NFPA 70, *National Electrical Code*®, has reduced them to a lower-order problem, usually involving some kind of failure to observe the code. Electrical distribution equipment fires can take many forms. Damaged components, such as frayed cords, broken switches, or plugs; bypassed protection systems, such as oversized fuses or pennies in place of fuses; overloaded cords, circuits, or outlets; and cords run through traffic areas or pinned by furniture, are all potential problems. Knowledgeable, experienced people should always perform repairs and modifications in strict accordance with applicable codes.

Cooking equipment ranked fifth as a cause of fire deaths but first in fires and fire injuries. Such equipment also accounts for a majority of unreported fires, which injure tens of thousands. Unattended cooking is a principal cause. Others include combustibles, such as rags, pot holders, or bags, placed too close to heat; failure to clean stove tops and ovens; and overhanging curtains, drapes, or clothing.

The sixth leading cause of fire deaths in one- and two-family dwellings was "playing with heat source, usually matches or

TABLE 20.6.2 Leading Causes of Structure Fires Resulting in Civilian Fire Deaths in One- and Two-Family Dwellings, 1999–2002 Annual Averages

Cause	*Fires*		*Civilian Deaths*	
Smoking material	16,400	(6%)	640	(26%)
Intentional	25,500	(9%)	410	(17%)
Heating equipment	48,900	(17%)	300	(12%)
Identified heating equipment	36,100	(13%)	300	(12%)
Confined chimney or flue fire	10,400	(4%)	0	(0%)
Confined fuel burner or boiler malfunction or fire	2,500	(1%)	0	(0%)
Cooking equipment fire	63,400	(23%)	220	(9%)
Identified cooking equipment	45,800	(16%)	220	(9%)
Confined cooking fire	17,600	(6%)	0	(0%)
Electrical distribution or lighting equipment	27,900	(10%)	200	(8%)
Playing with heat source	10,200	(4%)	180	(7%)
Candle	14,400	(5%)	130	(5%)
Exposure to other fire	11,800	(4%)	20	(1%)
Clothes dryer or washer	11,200	(4%)	10	(1%)

Note: These are national estimates of fires reported to U.S. municipal fire departments and so exclude fires reported only to federal or state agencies or industrial fire brigades. National estimates are projections. Casualty and loss projections can be heavily influenced by the inclusion or exclusion of one unusually serious fire. Fires are rounded to the nearest hundred and civilian deaths are rounded to the nearest ten.

Source: NFIRS and NFPA survey.

TABLE 20.6.3 Leading Causes of Civilian Injuries and Direct Property Damage in Structure Fires in One- and Two-Family Dwellings, 1999–2002 Annual Averages

Cause	*Civilian Injuries*		*Direct Property Damage (in Millions of Dollars)*	
Cooking equipment fire	2570	(24%)	357	(8%)
Identified cooking equipment	2300	(22%)	350	(8%)
Confined cooking fire	280	(3%)	7	(0%)
Candle	1230	(12%)	304	(7%)
Smoking material	1150	(11%)	307	(7%)
Heating equipment	1090	(10%)	571	(13%)
Identified heating equipment	1060	(10%)	563	(13%)
Confined chimney or flue fire	10	(0%)	7	(0%)
Confined fuel burner or boiler malfunction or fire	10	(0%)	1	(0%)
Playing with heat source	940	(9%)	175	(4%)
Intentional	850	(8%)	515	(12%)
Electrical distribution or lighting equipment	770	(7%)	577	(14%)
Clothes dryer or washer	240	(2%)	90	(2%)
Exposure to other fire	70	(1%)	161	(4%)

Note: These are national estimates of fires reported to U.S. municipal fire departments and so exclude fires reported only to federal or state agencies or industrial fire brigades. National estimates are projections. Casualty and loss projections can be heavily influenced by the inclusion or exclusion of one unusually serious fire. Civilian injuries are rounded to the nearest ten and direct property damage is rounded to the nearest million dollars. Property damage has not been adjusted for inflation.

Source: NFIRS and NFPA survey.

TABLE 20.6.4 Structure Fires in One- and Two-Family Dwellings by Area of Origin, 1999–2002 Annual Averages

Area of Origin	*Civilian Deaths*		*Fires*		*Civilian Injuries*		*Direct Property Damage (in Millions of Dollars)*	
Common room, living room, family room, lounge, or den	730	(30%)	18,900	(7%)	1,340	(13%)	481	(11%)
Bedroom	590	(24%)	34,800	(12%)	2,700	(25%)	702	(16%)
Kitchen or cooking area	390	(16%)	59,200	(21%)	2,850	(27%)	561	(13%)
Unclassified function area	100	(4%)	3,600	(1%)	240	(2%)	87	(2%)
Unclassified structural area	70	(3%)	4,600	(2%)	140	(1%)	106	(2%)
Garage or vehicle storage area	40	(2%)	9,600	(3%)	330	(3%)	304	(7%)
Crawl space or substructure space	40	(2%)	7,800	(3%)	240	(2%)	186	(4%)
Unclassified	40	(2%)	4,000	(1%)	110	(1%)	125	(3%)
Dining room, bar, or beverage area	40	(2%)	2,000	(1%)	120	(1%)	48	(1%)
Other known area	410	(15%)	137,100	(49%)	2,530	(25%)	1667	(41%)
Total	2450	(100%)	281,600	(100%)	10,600	(100%)	4267	(100%)

Note: These are national estimates of fires reported to U.S. municipal fire departments and so exclude fires reported only to federal or state agencies or industrial fire brigades. National estimates are projections. Casualty and loss projections can be heavily influenced by the inclusion or exclusion of one unusually serious fire. Fires are rounded to the nearest hundred, civilian deaths and injuries are rounded to the nearest ten, and direct property damage is rounded to the nearest million dollars. Property damage has not been adjusted for inflation. Nonconfined and noncontained structure fires in which the area of origin was unknown or not reported have been allocated proportionally among fires with known area of origin. Totals may not equal sums due to rounding errors.

Source: NFIRS and NFPA survey.

lighters." Children playing with fire also is the leading cause of fire deaths for children under age 6. Children must be monitored closely and taught at an early age that matches and lighters are tools for adults, not toys. These fire deaths have dropped sharply since the Consumer Product Safety Commission adopted regulations requiring butane lighters manufactured in the United States to be child-resistant in mid-1994. Matches and lighters must be kept out of the reach and sight of young children.

Location of Fire Fatalities

Nearly three-fourths of all fatal fires in one- and two-family dwellings begin in living rooms, family rooms, or dens; bedrooms; or kitchens (Table 20.6.4). These areas are also the leading areas for fires, injuries, and direct property damage. The number of one- and two-family dwelling fires has decreased over the last couple of decades as has the number of civilian deaths. This is seen in Table 20.6.5. However, the decrease appears to be leveling off, which indicates that we cannot sit back, but must be aggressive in attacking this problem

SUMMARY

The majority of U.S. fire deaths occur in one- and two-family dwellings, the most common form of housing in the United

TABLE 20.6.5 Structure Fires in One- and Two-Family Dwellings, by Year, 1980–2002

				Direct Property Damage (in Millions of Dollars)	
Year	*Fires*	*Civilian Deaths*	*Civilian Injuries*	*As Reported*	*In 2002 Dollars*
1980	595,800	4222	14,245	2457	5369
1981	573,500	4329	13,978	2338	4619
1982	545,700	3858	14,806	2732	5086
1983	518,600	3850	15,020	2644	4770
1984	494,000	3277	13,031	2714	4690
1985	483,800	3897	13,285	3026	5050
1986	448,400	3777	12,637	2758	4529
1987	421,600	3643	13,635	2831	4480
1988	421,800	3977	15,155	3024	4601
1989	386,000	3365	13,702	2953	4286
1990	346,700	3184	13,327	3221	4438
1991	357,400	2783	14,106	4262	5626
1992	347,900	2923	13,834	3006	3854
1993	347,700	2996	14,568	3827	4764
1994	334,500	2746	12,908	3291	3996
1995	317,300	2926	12,702	3368	3974
1996	316,900	3336	12,714	3854	4422
1997	299,600	2652	11,558	3512	3935
1998	282,600	2673	11,337	3471	3833
1999	274,300	2359	10,688	3839	4143
2000	274,600	2857	11,579	4328	4522
2001	288,600	2459	10,476	4264	4333
2002	288,900	2112	9,670	4635	4635

Note: These are national estimates of fires reported to U.S. municipal fire departments and so exclude fires reported only to federal or state agencies or industrial fire brigades. National estimates are projections. Casualty and loss projections can be heavily influenced by the inclusion or exclusion of one unusually serious fire. Fires are rounded to the nearest hundred, civilian deaths and injuries are rounded to the nearest one, and direct property damage is rounded to the nearest million dollars.

Source: NFIRS and NFPA survey. Inflation adjustments were based on U.S. Census Bureau, *Statistical Abstract of the United States: 2006,* "Table 705, Purchasing Power of the Dollar."

States. Fatalities are most often the result of smoke inhalation rather than burns. The requirements for one- and two-family dwellings are covered by NFPA *101* and *NFPA 5000*, which address the need for two means of escape from every room for occupant evacuation; the selection of interior finish materials to prevent rapid early fire growth and spread and to protect occupant evacuation routes; and smoke alarms to provide early warning. In new construction sprinkler protection must be installed, and it is also encouraged in existing homes. A written evacuation plan, adequate means of escape, and properly installed and functioning smoke alarms are critical to life safety. In recent years, residential-type automatic sprinkler systems have proved an effective means of fire suppression. Fire prevention measures should be taken to avoid ignition in the home. The most common sources of ignition of fatal fires in one- and two-family dwellings are smoking material, arson, heating equipment, cooking equipment, electrical equipment, children playing with heat sources, and candles.

BIBLIOGRAPHY

NFPA Codes, Standards, and Recommended Practices

Reference to the following NFPA codes, standards, and recommended practices will provide further information on one- and two-family dwellings discussed in this chapter. (See the latest version of The NFPA Catalog *for availability of current editions of the following documents.)*

NFPA 13D, *Standard for the Installation of Sprinkler Systems in One- and Two-Family Dwellings and Manufactured Homes*

NFPA 13R, *Standard for the Installation of Sprinkler Systems in Residential Occupancies up to and Including Four Stories in Height*

NFPA 70, *National Electrical Code®*

NFPA 72®, National Fire Alarm Code®

NFPA *101®, Life Safety Code®*

NFPA 211, *Standard for Chimneys, Fireplaces, Vents, and Solid Fuel-Burning Appliances*

NFPA 5000®, Building Construction and Safety Code®

References

Ahrens, M., *U.S. Fires in Selected Occupancies,* Fire Analysis and Research Division, National Fire Protection Association, Quincy, MA, Mar. 2006.

Dubay, C., *Automatic Sprinkler Systems for Residential Occupancies Handbook,* National Fire Protection Association, Quincy, MA, 2007.

Gustin, B., "Search and Rescue in Single Family Dwellings. Part 2," *Fire Engineering,* Vol. 151, No. 9, 1998, pp. 51–52.

Gustin, B., "Search and Rescue in Single Family Dwellings. Part 3," *Fire Engineering,* Vol. 151, No. 10, 1998, pp. 81–88.

One- and Two-Family Dwelling Code, International Code Council, Washington, DC.

Statistical Abstract of the United States 2000, U.S. Census Bureau, Washington, DC, Dec. 2003.

Chapter 7

Manufactured Housing

Kirsten M. Paoletti

Manufactured homes represent an important and affordable housing option for over 22 million people in the United States. By 2000 an estimated 10.5 million units made up the manufactured housing inventory, including those used year-round, either occupied or vacant, and used seasonally.[1] (The U.S. Census Bureau reported a lower figure of 8.9 million total units and a lower population served, apparently because of differences in definitions and labeling rules.[2]) During 2000, newly placed manufactured homes accounted for almost 23 percent (280,900 units) of the combined total of new privately owned (site-built) one-family houses completed and manufactured homes placed for residential use (1,242,000 total combined units). This share for manufactured homes represented an increase of over 17 percent in 1990, a recent low point in manufactured home placements, and roughly the same as 20 percent in 1980.[3]

Manufactured homes are getting larger. In 2000, some 70 percent of the 250,419 manufactured homes shipped were multisection units, and the remaining 30 percent were smaller single-section homes. The share of multisection units was just under 50 percent in 1991. Further, on an average square foot basis, multisection manufactured homes are becoming comparable in size to site-built homes. For example, in 2001 the average square footage of a multisection home was 1695 ft^2 (157.5 m^2), which was 74 percent of the average site-built home at 2282 ft^2 (212.0 m^2).[1,4]

Most new manufactured homes (68 percent) are located on private property with the remainder located in manufactured home communities. Manufactured homes are predominantly located in rural areas with a concentration in the southern regions of the United States. In 1997, 44 percent of manufactured homes were located in rural areas compared to 20 percent of detached single-family dwellings. Also, during 1997, over one-half of all occupied manufactured homes were located in the South compared to 37 percent of occupied single-family dwellings. During 1993, the five states receiving the greatest percentage of new manufactured homes were North Carolina, Texas, Florida, Georgia, and South Carolina.[5–8]

This chapter covers manufactured homes and their construction, fire safety features, installation, and associated utilities. The development of the HUD *Manufactured Home Construction and Safety Standards, 24 CFR, Part 3280* (HUD Code), which governs manufactured home construction in the United States, is discussed. The recent developments of NFPA standards, such as NFPA 501, *Standard on Manufactured Housing,* and NFPA 225, *Model Manufactured Home Installation Standard,* are addressed. Related manufactured home fire experience is also addressed.

See also Section 20, Chapter 6, "One- and Two-Family Dwellings."

Chapter Contents

Key Terms

HUD *Manufactured Home Construction and Safety Standards,* manufactured home, manufactured home construction, manufactured home safety, manufactured home site, manufactured housing, oil-burning equipment, residential fire sprinkler systems, smoke alarms

BACKGROUND ON MANUFACTURED HOUSING

Manufactured Home Defined

Amendments made in 1980 to the National Manufactured Housing Construction and Safety Standards Act of 1974 changed the definition of manufactured homes from "mobile" to "manufactured." Manufactured homes in the United States are built in accordance with the federal HUD Code,

Kirsten M. Paoletti is a fire protection and code consultant with Robson Woese, Inc., in Albany, New York. She is a former instructor for NFPA's Life Safety Code seminar and served as NFPA staff liaison for the Technical Committee on Fire Safety for Manufactured Housing.

which preempts state and local building codes. Manufactured homes are factory-assembled structures that can be transported in one or more sections. Sections are typically 8 ft (2.5 m) or more wide and 40 to 80 ft (12.2 to 24.4 m) long, each built on a permanent chassis. When assembled on site for occupancy as a dwelling, manufactured homes are connected to required utilities and placed on stabilizing devices, which may be piers and footings, or a permanent foundation. Manufactured homes are constructed in sections. A single-wide home is one that is made up of a single, transportable section. A multiwide home is one that is made up of two or more transportable sections, typically referred to as double-wide and triple-wide (Figure 20.7.1). The length of a manufactured home is the home's largest overall dimension in the traveling mode including cabinets and other projections that contain interior space. The final length, in terms of the outside dimensions of the living space, is typically 4 ft less than the traveling mode length. Although predominantly single-story structures, the single most important advancement since the late 1990s has been the development of two-story models. With recent innovations in chassis and transportation systems as well as improved architectural compatibility with existing homes in urban/suburban surroundings, multistory models, although still a small percentage of the overall housing market, have gained tremendous consumer interest and will likely translate into increased availability by manufacturers.[9] Figure 20.7.2 illustrates a multistory manufactured home.

HUD Code manufactured homes are not to be confused with modular homes. A modular home is built in a factory in units and transported to a site where the units are joined together on a permanent foundation. It is designed and constructed in accordance with a building code that has been adopted, administered, and enforced by a state or local regulatory agency. Further, some non–HUD Code factory-built, commercial modular units are used as temporary classrooms, construction site offices, or for business uses such as banks or fast-food restaurants. Depending on the application and local authorities having jurisdiction (AHJs), such structures typically must comply with state or local building codes.

FIGURE 20.7.1 Installed Double-Section Manufactured Home

FIGURE 20.7.2 Installed Multistory Manufactured Home (Source: Manufactured Housing Institute)

Manufactured Home Construction

HUD Code manufactured homes consist of four major components or subassemblies: the chassis, floor system, wall system, and roof system.

Chassis System. The chassis is the structural base of the manufactured home, which receives all of the vertical loads from the walls, roof, and floor and transfers them to stability devices, which may be piers, footings, or a permanent foundation. The chassis generally consists of two longitudinal steel beams braced by steel cross members. Steel outriggers extending from the outsides of the main beams bring the width of the chassis to the approximate overall width of the superstructure.

Floor System. The floor system consists of its framing members with sheet decking of particleboard, oriented strand board (OSB), or plywood, glued and nailed to the joists; glass fiber insulation blankets or cellulose insulation installed between the joists; and a bottom board material sealing the bottom of the floor. Trunk ducts and piping are often installed longitudinally within the floor system. The floor finish is generally carpeting, resilient flooring, linoleum, or tile.

Wall System. The exterior wall system consists of vinyl, wood, cement board, hardboard, or sometimes metal on wood studs applied over laminated fiberboard, insulative fiberboard, or OSB sheathing. The interior surfaces of exterior walls are most often constructed of gypsum wallboard, and fiberglass insulation blankets provide exterior wall insulation. Interior partitions are most often constructed of gypsum wallboard attached to wood studs.

Roof System. The roof system consists of either the framed wood roof rafter and ceiling joist system or a wood truss system. This roof decking generally consists of oriented strand board (OSB) or plywood attached to the top of the roof rafters or trusses. The finished roofing is most often composition shingles and infrequently metal without decking. Blown rockwool or cellulose insulation or fiberglass insulation blankets provide the roof insulation. The interior ceiling finish, which consists of gypsum wallboard, is attached directly to the bottom chords of trusses or joists. Steel strapping or brackets are used to reinforce connections between the walls and floor systems and between the walls and roof to make a complete transportable section (Figure 20.7.3).

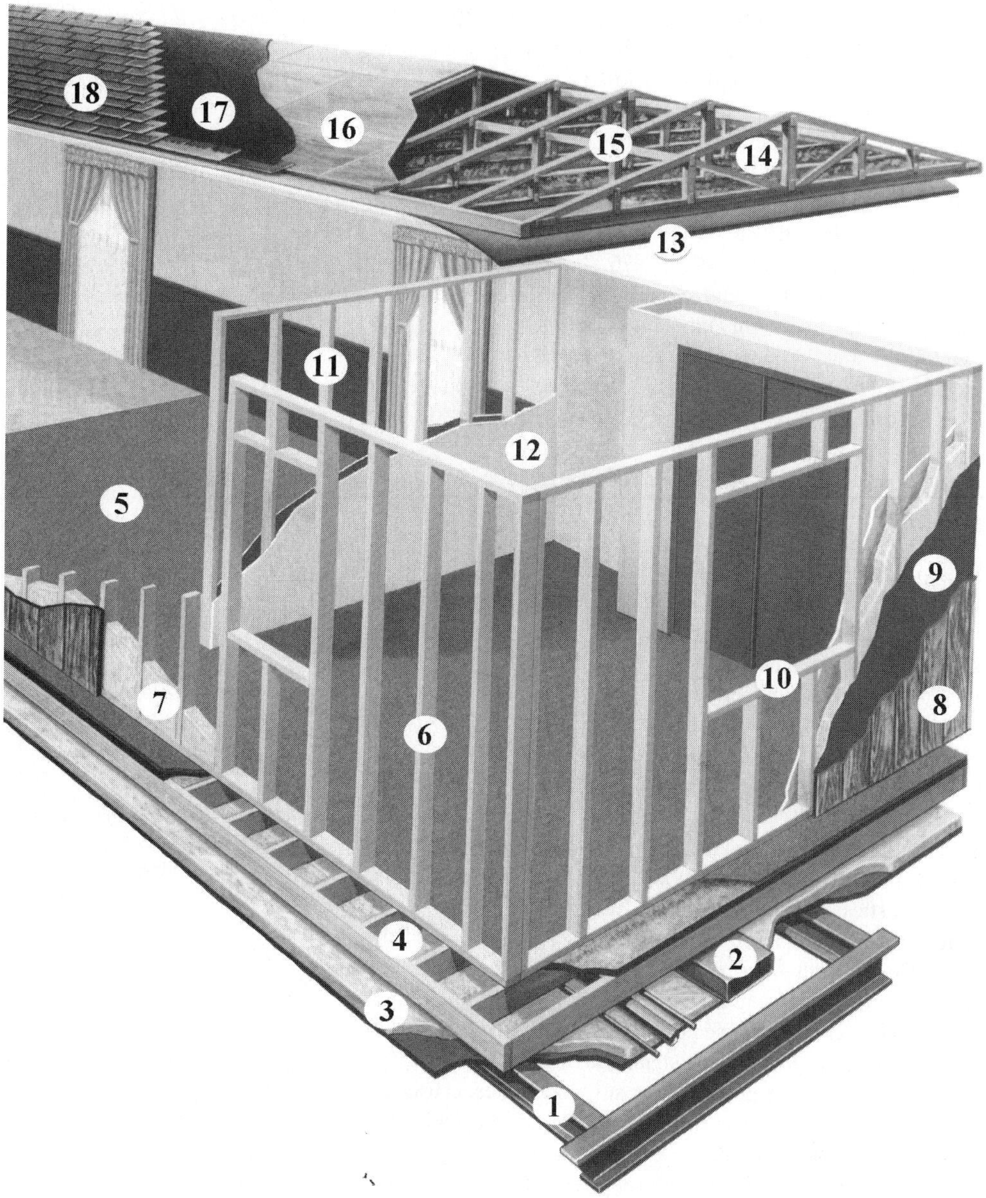

1. Steel chassis.
2. Heating ducts in floor cavities, normally sized for central air conditioning.
3. Fiberglass or cellulose insulation under the entire floor covered by a bottom board material that acts like a vapor barrier.
4. 2 in. × 6 in. (51 mm × 152 mm) wood floor joists spaced every 16 in. to 24 in. (406 mm to 610 mm). Joists are normally positioned and secured transverse to steel I-beams.
5. Decking of particleboard, oriented strand board (OSB), or plywood, under carpeting or vinyl rolled goods.
6. 2 in. × 6 in. (51 mm × 152 mm) or 2 in. × 4 in. (51 mm × 102 mm) wood studs spaced every 16 in. or 24 in. (406 mm or 610 mm) in exterior walls.
7. Fiberglass insulation in all exterior walls, plus a vapor barrier.
8. Vinyl, wood, hardboard, cement board, or metal exterior siding.
9. Laminated Kraft fiberboard, insulative fiberboard, or OSB.
10. Glass windows with screens. At least one egress window in each bedroom.
11. 2 in. × 4 in. (51 mm × 102 mm) or 2 in. × 3 in. (51 mm × 76 mm) wood studs in the interior walls.
12. Gypsum wallboard for interior wall paneling. Flame spread index shall not exceed 200, except for walls enclosing a furnace or water heater shall not exceed 25.
13. Gypsum wallboard on either cathedral or flat ceilings, flame spread index shall not exceed 75.
14. Fiberglass or cellulose roof insulation, plus a ceiling-area vapor barrier.
15. Load-tested, wood roof-rafter system normally 2 in. × 3 in. (51 mm × 76 mm) chords, for structural strength against wind and snow loads.
16. Plywood or OSB roof decking.
17. Roofing underlayment between shingles and roof decking.
18. Shingled pitched roof.

FIGURE 20.7.3 Typical Manufactured Home Construction Systems and Materials (Source: Champion Home Builders Co.)

HUD Code Manufactured Home Fire Experience

Post–HUD Code homes have much lower fire losses per fire incident compared to pre–HUD Code homes.* From 1989 to 1998, manufactured homes built after 1976 averaged 1.2 civilian fire deaths per 100 fires compared to 2.6 civilian fire deaths per 100 fires for manufactured homes built before 1976. The 54 percent lower fire death rate per 100 fires in post-1976 units was also strengthened by a significantly lower rate of reported fires per 1000 units, although precise calculations are not possible because the census reporting on year of manufacture breaks at 1974–1975 and not at 1976. Manufactured homes built after 1976 also averaged 4.3 civilian fire injuries per 100 fires, 22 percent lower than the 5.5 civilian fire injuries per 100 fires for manufactured homes built before 1976.[10]

Post–HUD Code manufactured home fire incident, death, and injury rates are roughly the same as rates for other one- and-two-family, stick-built dwellings relative to the number of occupied units.† Annual average statistics for the 1999–2002 period show that the fire death rate per 100 fires in HUD Code homes was 1.7 compared to 0.8 for one- and two-family dwellings. The fire injury rate was 3.9 per 100 fires in HUD Code homes and 3.8 in one- and two-family dwellings. There were 2.0 fires per 1000 housing units in HUD Code units, lower than the 3.2–3.5 fires per 1000 units in one- and two-family dwellings. HUD Code homes had 3.3 deaths per 100,000 housing units, a slightly higher rate, compared to 2.7–3.0 deaths for one- and two-family stick-built homes. The statistics for deaths and injury rates in pre–HUD Code manufactured homes are significantly higher than one- and two-family dwellings, 2.6 deaths per 100 fires and 5.5 injuries per 100 fires, respectively.[11]

Table 20.7.1, which compares pre– and post–HUD Code fire causes from 1999 to 2002, shows a continued downward shift in the share of electrical distribution and heating system fires in post–HUD Code manufactured homes when compared with statistics from 1989 to 1998. Electrical and heating systems must meet the installation and testing requirements of the HUD Code. Further, furnace and water heater compartments must meet the flame spread and combustibility construction requirements. In both pre– and post–HUD Code homes, occupant-related fire causes comprise a significant share of the total fire causes. These include incendiary or suspicious fires, caused by cooking, smoking materials, children playing, and open flame.

The dramatic difference in the injury and death rates is directly attributable to HUD's uniformly applying and enforcing the fire safety provisions of the HUD Code. Both the mandatory smoke alarm provision and the restrictions on flame spread ratings, throughout the unit and especially around heating and cooking equipment, are major contributors to the effects of the HUD Code. From 1999 to 2002, 45 percent of post-standard manufactured home fires were reported as having no smoke alarms present, a higher percentage than in 1997 and 1998. As noted in the NFPA report *Manufactured Home Fires in the U.S.*, "Because all post-standard manufactured homes are required to be sold with smoke alarms installed, this implies a disturbingly high rate of smoke alarm removal by occupants."[12]

When smoke alarms are not present in post–HUD Code homes, the fire death rate is significantly higher than in HUD Code homes where smoke alarms were recorded as present (1.3 deaths per 100 fires compared to 0.9 deaths per 100 fires). Every HUD Code home must have installed and tested smoke alarms, which are verified at the plant by approved quality control procedures. One study of manufactured home smoke alarm installation and testing practices found that nearly 100 percent of smoke alarms were installed, tested, and left in place at the factory. In a few cases, for special transportation-related reasons, smoke alarms were removed after testing, and reinstallation instructions were provided for those responsible for the setup of the home. In fire incident reports, a home recorded as not having smoke alarms most likely involves the removal of them by some party following the manufacturing process, or the devices were possibly not

TABLE 20.7.1 Structure Fires Reported to U.S. Fire Departments: Pre-Standard and Post-Standard Manufactured Home Fires, by Cause, 1999–2002

Cause	*Pre-Standard Percentage (Pre-1976)*	*Post-Standard Percentage (Post-1976)*
Electrical distribution	17	10
Heating	16	8
Intentional	13	10
Exposure (to other hostile fire)	10	16
Other equipment	9	21
Cooking	9	9
Open flame, candle, or torch	7	7
Appliance, tool, or air conditioning	7	5
Smoking material (i.e., lighted tobacco product)	4	5
Child playing	4	4
Other heat source	3	4
Natural causes	1	1
Total	100	100

Note: These are percentages of fires reported to U.S. municipal fire departments and so exclude fires reported only to federal or state agencies or industrial fire brigades. Only percentages are shown because so few fires have unitage coded after 1998. National estimates are projections. Casualty and loss projections can be heavily influenced by the inclusion or exclusion of one unusually serious fire. Totals may not equal sums because of rounding.

Changes in coding and analysis rules produced some shifts in shares by major cause, beginning in 1999 and growing thereafter. Major changes include (1) movement of unknown-equipment fires from "other equipment" to "unknown," where they are then statistically allocated; and (2) movement of playing fires where firestarter age is not recorded from "child playing" to the category for the heat source, primarily "open flame."

Source: NFIRS and NFPA survey.

*For statistical purposes, post–HUD Code homes refer to manufactured homes built after the year 1976. Pre–HUD Code refers to homes built before 1976.

†For statistical reasons in this data set only, post–HUD Code homes are those built in 1975 and later, and pre–HUD Code homes are those built before 1975.

found during a fire investigation. Nonworking smoke alarms are a concern in manufactured homes and other dwellings. The issue of nonworking smoke alarms was addressed in the Consumer Product Safety Commission's (CPSC) National Smoke Detector Project, which found that power supplies (batteries or ac power) were too often disconnected. The project found that the leading reason for nonoperability of home smoke alarms, when it occurs, is frustration over nuisance alarms, leading to occupants disabling the offending smoke alarms. Home manufacturers typically provide homeowners with the smoke alarm manufacturer's literature, which includes instructions for the inspection and testing of smoke alarms. Some manufacturers also provide additional fire safety information in their homeowner's manuals.[13–16]

The installation of smoke alarms alone is not enough. To ensure reasonable fire safety, homeowners need to practice fire prevention, periodically test and maintain smoke alarms, and develop and practice home escape plans. Clearly, with working smoke alarms and these fire safety practices, the manufactured home fire experience could be further improved.

MANUFACTURED HOUSING STANDARDS

HUD Code Development

Manufactured housing in the United States is built in accordance with the preemptive federal standard, *Manufactured Housing Construction and Safety Standards, 24 CFR, Part 3280* (HUD Code), which is administered by the U.S. Department of Housing and Urban Development (HUD). Effective mid-1976, the HUD Code was based on NFPA 501B, *Standard for Mobile Homes* (ANSI No. A119.1), which was the result of a cooperative NFPA and industry committee project developed under the NFPA consensus codes and standards-making process. In 1979, NFPA 501B was withdrawn following the federal legislation that established the HUD Code. Unique among built structures, the federal preemptive status sets a single construction and performance specification for all manufactured homes that are built in the United States. Neither state nor local jurisdictions can reduce or increase on the federal standards without a great deal of effort to amend the requirements.

In 1997, NFPA reinstituted the standard for manufactured housing as NFPA 501, based in part on the 1977 edition of NFPA 501B and the HUD Code, and it was updated to include current technology. The 1999 edition of NFPA 501 contained significant revisions to the smoke alarm requirements, and it was developed through the NFPA Manufactured Housing project consisting of the Technical Correlating Committee on Manufactured Housing and the six technical committees involved with specific areas of responsibility including administration, electrical, fire safety, mechanical, plumbing, and structural. The current edition of NFPA 501 incorporates significant revisions concerning the installation of smoke alarms; residential sprinkler installation requirements; updated electrical provisions; new heating, cooling, and fuel-burning system requirements; updated plumbing provisions; revised load testing for trusses; and updated referenced standards.

In 1998 HUD selected NFPA to develop proposals for revisions to the HUD Code, and NFPA submitted a proposal to HUD for the revision of smoke alarm requirements to reflect current state-of-the-art smoke alarm technology and installation practices. A notice of the proposed rulemaking, for HUD Code smoke alarm revisions, was published in the May 2000 *Federal Register* and the final rule was published in the March 2002 *Federal Register.* In addition, NFPA has submitted recommendations to HUD for changes to the HUD Code based on the 1997, 1999, 2000, and 2003 editions of NFPA 501.[17]

NFPA 501A, *Standard for Fire Safety Criteria for Manufactured Home Installations, Sites, and Communities,* was prepared by the same technical committees involved with the NFPA Manufactured Housing project. NFPA 501A provides state and local AHJs with the requirements for fire safety at manufactured home sites, including accessory buildings, structures, and communities.

NCSBCS/ANSI A225.1, *American National Standard, Manufactured Home Installations,* was published by the National Conference of States on Building Codes and Standards, Inc. (NCSBCS). In 2001, an agreement was reached between NCSBCS and NFPA that allowed transfer of the ANSI A225.1 standard to NFPA. The 1994 edition of NCSBCS/ANSI A225.1 formed the basis for the first edition of NFPA 225, *Model Manufactured Home Installation Standard.* This document was not only developed to pick up where the previous NCSBCS document left off, but it also became an integral part of providing another option, along with other state-sponsored installation standards, that could potentially be considered by HUD, the ultimate overseer of manufactured homes. NFPA 225, *Model Manufactured Home Installation Standard,* covers the installation of manufactured homes at sites or communities whenever the manufacturer's installation instructions are not available. This document is applicable to new installations of single-section and multisection homes, regardless of whether they are at new or existing manufactured housing sites. The criteria in NFPA 225 are intended to be adopted and enforced by the authority having jurisdiction when an alternative state standard does not exist. In addition to covering the basic administrative criteria, provisions are included for site preparation work, foundations, and procedures during on-site installation/erection, as well as management of appliances and utility connections. Requirements reflecting current design loads and practices associated with seismic, wind, and flood events have been included.

HUD Code and Regulatory Enforcement Program

NFPA standards activity regarding manufactured homes began in 1937 with publication of the first standard in 1940, and the documents have evolved over the years. The 1969 edition of NFPA 501B, ANSI A119.1 and its revisions through 1977, had become the guiding industry construction standard for manufactured homes. For example, the Mobile Home Manufacturers Association (MHMA), which became the Manufactured Housing Institute (MHI), required that its members meet NFPA 501B before the HUD Code became effective in June 1976. NFPA 501B was the basis for the HUD Code. It addressed the unique construction characteristics, or the body and frame design; plumbing systems; heating, cooling, and fuel-burning systems; and electrical systems of transportable homes. By the early 1970s, almost all states adopted the NFPA 501B standard for manufactured homes, and concerned federal agencies, such as the Federal Housing Administration and the Veterans Administration, used it in connection with home purchases under loan programs they administered.

However, both the manufactured housing industry and the federal government were concerned about the lack of enforcement by states, counties, and cities. To ensure a safe, low-cost form of housing of uniform quality throughout the United States, Congress passed the National Manufactured Housing (formerly Mobile Home) Construction and Safety Standards Act of 1974 (Title VI of the Housing and Community Development Act of 1974). This act established HUD as the sole source of standards governing the construction of these homes in the United States. It gave HUD the authority to establish procedural and enforcement regulations necessary to ensure that makers of manufactured homes uniformly met the construction standards.

HUD fully implemented the act in June 1976, substantially adopting NFPA 501B as the construction standard and naming the NCSBCS as the contract agent for ensuring uniform enforcement. The HUD manufactured housing program requires that manufacturers participate in a system of design approvals and inspections to ensure that a home complies with the HUD Code. The enforcement system includes preproduction design approval, production inspections, and postproduction consumer complaint handling. An independent, third-party design approval primary inspection agency (DAPIA) reviews and approves home designs and the manufacturer's quality assurance manuals. An independent, third-party production inspection primary inspection agency (IPIA) ensures that homes in the plant comply with the design, quality assurance manuals, and the HUD Code. Before production begins, the IPIA conducts a plant certification inspection, and during production, each home is inspected in at least one stage of its construction. During a plant visit, to assure quality control, the IPIA inspects each visible part of each home on the production line. A state with an approved state administrative agency (SAA) may act as the DAPIA or IPIA in that state.[18]

All transportable sections of each manufactured home sold in the United States must bear a HUD certification label, which certifies that the home has been inspected, has passed all of the quality assurance checks, and is in compliance with the HUD Code. These metal labels are attached to the exterior siding of the transportable sections of each home and bear a unique IPIA identification number for each section.

In 1984, some of the HUD Code fire safety provisions were revised following research on means of egress and fire growth and spread issues, conducted by the Center for Fire Research, National Bureau of Standards (NBS), now the National Institute of Standards and Technology (NIST). However, the HUD Code has not kept up with developing fire safety technology. In December 2000, the Manufactured Housing Improvement Act was passed, which provides for a more timely process of establishing new standards, updating the existing standards, and providing comments to HUD on related programs for consumer protection, regulatory enforcement, and similar programs that affect the industry. The act established a federal advisory committee that mostly conducts its business in accordance with ANSI procedures. Since its inception, the advisory committee, generally referred to as the Manufactured Housing Consensus Committee (MHCC), has made numerous recommendations to HUD on ways to keep the HUD Code up-to-date. The act provides a mechanism for HUD adoption and adaptation of requirements from private-sector, consensus standards such as NFPA 501. Also under the act, each state will be required to establish an installation program and a dispute resolution program. The MHCC has provided base guidelines to HUD that can be adopted by each state. Conversely, a state can establish its own program but the criteria must be at least as stringent as the federal criteria.[19]

Approximately 6.6 million manufactured homes have been built under the act. The infusion of safer new manufactured homes into the U.S. housing stock has dramatically affected life safety and fire incidents in manufactured homes built after June 1976.[20]

HUD CODE REQUIREMENTS

HUD Code Fire Safety Provisions

Since 1976, the HUD Code has required that the interior finish be regulated for flame spread characteristics and, in certain areas of the home, for combustibility. Fire blocking is required in concealed wall and partition spaces. At least two exterior doors are required, and they must be arranged to provide a means of unobstructed travel to the outside. The minimum width of doors is specified, as is the ability to operate locking mechanisms without a key from inside to facilitate egress. Each room designed expressly for sleeping, unless it has a door to the outside, must have at least one outside window large enough to permit emergency egress. The window must meet size and location specifications and must be able to be opened without the use of special tools or special knowledge.

In 1979 the Center for Fire Research, National Bureau of Standards (NBS), now NIST, issued a report following four years of fire tests in manufactured homes. The purpose was to provide experimental data on the potential growth and spread of fire in manufactured homes and recommend upgrades in the level of fire protection for kitchen areas and flame spread ratings for interior finishes.* The Center for Fire Research also conducted research and issued reports on emergency egress from manufactured homes. Following these reports, HUD issued the first update to its standard in 1984. HUD lowered the maximum height above the floor of the egress window latch from 60 to 54 in. (1.5 to 1.4 m). More importantly, HUD issued a stricter limit on ceiling interior finish flame spread—to a flame spread index of 75 from 200—and expanded its criteria on kitchen cabinet protection. Other minor changes included further clarification of fire-blocking construction techniques in concealed wall, ceiling, and floor construction; recognition of 5/16-in. (8-mm) thick gypsum wallboard as fire-blocking material; and clarification of smoke alarm placement instructions.[21–24]

The HUD Code also specifies the minimum construction requirement, thickness, and gauge of the metal ventilating hood

*These NBS (NIST) fire tests of over 25 years ago focused on major fire growth factors understood during the 1970s such as room geometry and combustible interior finish. Based on further NIST research during the 1980s, the role of combustible contents, including heat release rates, was also identified as having a significant influence on the rate of compartment fire growth leading to flashover.

to be installed over a kitchen range. In addition, the HUD Code limits the flame spread of the wall and cabinet finishes in the immediate vicinity of the kitchen range. This combination of requirements effectively negates or minimizes the direct exposure of the wall and cabinet surfaces nearest the kitchen range in the event of a cooking surface fire. Fire experience statistics show that these provisions produce smaller cooking and heating fires in post-1976 manufactured homes and that a much smaller share of such fires spread beyond the room of origin than in pre-1976 units.

HUD Code Utility Provisions

Manufactured homes requiring fuel-gas are required to be equipped with a natural gas piping system that is acceptable for LP-gas. The gas piping system must be designed for a pressure no more than 14 in. (3.4 kPa) water column and no less than 7 in. (1.7 kPa), and manufacturers are required to provide written instructions regarding the design pressure limitations for safe and effective operation. The HUD Code regulates piping materials, routing, sizing, joints, and anchoring. Tubing for gas piping systems cannot be run inside walls, floors, partitions, or roofs, and listed appliance connectors, when used, cannot run through walls, floors, ceilings, or partitions except cabinetry. Shutoff valves must be installed in the gas piping at appliances upstream of unions or connectors. Piping systems are to be tested at specified pressures before and after connection of gas appliances. Gas supply connections cannot be located beneath an exit door. Manufacturers are required to affix a permanent label on the outside of the home at the gas supply connection, providing supply requirements and precautions for installers. For fuel-gas systems the HUD Code references ANSI Z223.1/NFPA 54, *National Fuel Gas Code,* and NFPA 58, *Liquefied Petroleum Gas Code.*

Where oil is used as the heating fuel, there are specific requirements for oil tanks, fill and vent pipes, liquid level gauges, and shutoff valves. Materials for oil piping systems are specified as to size, type of joints, couplings, grading, hangers, and leakage tests. For oil-burning equipment the HUD Code references NFPA 31, *Standard for the Installation of Oil-Burning Equipment.*

A unique feature of the HUD Code concerns the installation of heat-producing appliances. Especially noteworthy is the requirement that all fuel-burning appliances except ranges, ovens, illuminating appliances, clothes dryers, solid fuel-burning fireplaces, and solid fuel-burning fireplace stoves be installed so that the combustion system is completely separate from the home's interior. Combustion air inlets and flue gas outlets must be listed or certified components of the appliance. The required separation may be obtained by installing direct vent systems (sealed combustion systems) or by installing the appliance within an enclosure so its appliance combustion and venting systems are separated from the manufactured home's interior.

No forced-air appliance, or its air return system, can allow the creation of a negative pressure that will affect either its combustion air supply or that of any other appliance, nor can the systems act to mix products of combustion with circulating air. Other requirements for heat-producing appliances include special provisions relating to solid fuel-burning fireplaces or fireplace stoves. The size and air tightness of circulating air duct materials are specified, and the design and combustibility of duct materials are regulated. Special provisions are included for registers and grills and ducts in expandable or multiple transportable section connections.

The HUD Code includes specific requirements for electrical installations. It concentrates on those provisions that differ from provisions applicable to all buildings under NFPA 70, *National Electrical Code*®. Some special features relate to the fact that manufactured homes are factory assembled, to the underchassis wiring requirements, to the wiring of expandable units with multiple transportable sections, to the need to bond metal parts, and to the grounding of services and appliances. For example, regarding electrical hookups at the site, manufacturer's installation instructions typically require a four-conductor service entrance (two hot conductors, a neutral, and a ground conductor); a grounding conductor must also be run from the electrical distribution panel to a grounding rod, and on the distribution side of the electrical system, the neutral bus in the electrical panel must be isolated from the grounding system. The HUD Code and approved quality control procedures require that at the factory the manufactured home electrical system be subjected to a continuity test to ensure metallic parts are properly bonded, an operational test to ensure that appliances are connected and working, and a polarity check to determine if connections have been properly made. Also, a dielectric strength test is conducted at 900 to 1079 V for 1 minute or alternatively at 1080 to 1250 V for 1 second to detect and correct electrical current leakage or short circuits.[25]

NFPA REQUIREMENTS

NFPA 501 Fire Safety Provisions

As discussed previously, NFPA 501 contains provisions impacting fire safety and reflecting state-of-the-art concepts and technology. Of particular note are the sections addressing the installation of smoke alarms and residential sprinklers. The Technical Committee on Fire Safety for Manufactured Housing had previously updated the smoke alarm requirements based on a 1998 research report, *Smoke Alarms in Manufactured Housing,* from the NIST Building and Fire Research Laboratory. These requirements are in harmony with other NFPA codes and standards, including *NFPA 72*®*, National Fire Alarm Code*®, and NFPA 13D, *Standard for the Installation of Sprinkler Systems in One- and Two-Family Dwellings and Manufactured Homes.*[26]

Smoke Alarms. Smoke alarms must be ac powered or powered by a nonreplaceable, 10 year battery, and they are permitted to be installed on flat ceilings, sloping ceilings, or walls, with specific requirements for each arrangement. Regarding location, smoke alarms are required in all sleeping rooms, outside each sleeping area, and on each additional story of the home. If installed within a 20 ft (6.1 m) horizontal path of a cooking appliance, they must have an alarm-silencing means or be of a photoelectric type. If stairs lead to other occupied levels, smoke alarms must be installed near the top of each stair. Smoke alarms are required to be interconnected so that the operation of one will sound all of the smoke alarms in the home. There are additional requirements for visual notification appliances if they are provided.

Following their installation at the manufactured home factory, smoke alarms must be functionally tested. Recognizing that smoke alarm testing is also a critical responsibility of others after the home leaves the factory, NFPA 501 requires that the home manufacturer provide testing instructions for the setup crews or other installers to use at the site and for the homeowner for periodic testing and maintenance. Further, the home manufacturer is to provide the homeowner with instructions to replace alarms if they fail to respond during tests and to replace smoke alarms after 10 years of service.

Residential Fire Sprinkler Systems. NFPA 501 contains minimum requirements for residential fire sprinkler systems if installed by the home manufacturer. The requirements are voluntary unless the AHJ requires fire sprinklers in all detached one- and two-family dwellings. When fire sprinkler systems are to be provided in the manufactured home, they are to be designed, installed, and tested in accordance with NFPA 13D, and the home manufacturer must affix a certificate adjacent to the home data plate. The certificate is to include information on the residential sprinkler system, such as sprinkler specifications, minimum water supply required, and control valves. The home manufacturer is required to provide setup crews or other installers with instructions for inspection and testing of the system. Further, when the system is connected at the home site, the water supply must be verified and tested, and those data added to the system certificate. The home manufacturer is also required to provide the homeowner with information about the automatic fire sprinkler system's operation, testing, and maintenance.

There are several other important fire safety provisions in NFPA 501, including definitions on interior finish and limited-combustible materials and requirements on the application of foam plastics. Means of egress provisions include design requirements for exterior doors, egress windows from sleeping rooms, and interior passage and room requirements.

NFPA 501 Utility Provisions

NFPA 501 addresses heating, cooling, and fuel-burning equipment installed within or external to a manufactured home and contains specific requirements for the various systems. The following NFPA codes and standards are referenced: ANSI Z223.1/NFPA 54, NFPA 58, NFPA 90B, *Standard for the Installation of Warm Air Heating and Air-Conditioning Systems,* and NFPA 31. Additionally, NFPA 501 contains requirements for electrical conductors and equipment installed within the home and service entrance equipment that connect the home to an electrical supply. In addition to NFPA 501 requirements, NFPA 70 applies to manufactured home electrical systems. It further states that service entrance equipment must be installed in accordance with NFPA 70 and that bonding and grounding of the service must meet NFPA 70 requirements.

NFPA 501A Provisions for Manufactured Home Installations, Sites, and Communities

NFPA 501A covers fire safety requirements for manufactured home installation, home sites, accessory buildings, structures, and communities. A manufactured home site is a parcel of land for one home and its supplemental structures. A manufactured home accessory building or structure is a supplemental structure such as an awning, cabana, garage, carport, or storage building. A community building is a nonresidential building used for manufactured home community purposes.

Fuel storage and supply systems for manufactured home sites and communities must meet the requirements of the referenced NFPA or federal standards, including ANSI Z223.1/NFPA 54, NFPA 58, and NFPA 31. The same requirements also apply to manufactured home community buildings. Electrical service equipment and installations must meet the applicable provisions of NFPA 70.

NFPA 501A includes manufactured home separation requirements for fire safety and requires that fire separation distances comply with local regulations. However, the fire separation distances mandated by *NFPA 5000®, Building Construction and Safety Code®*, must be used where local rules or regulations do not exist. Manufactured home installations must follow the printed instructions provided by home manufacturers, including the installation of the support system and utility connections.

NFPA 501A includes fire safety requirements for manufactured home community buildings, including construction, control of outdoor hazards, fire detection and alarm systems, and water supplies for fire protection. The posting of emergency information in conspicuous places is required for manufactured home communities. The standard also contains setback requirements for accessory buildings and exit requirements as well. The appendices of NFPA 501A provide manufactured home community management and manufactured home residents advisory material on fire safety responsibilities and procedures.

SUMMARY

In the United States, manufactured homes, which are factory-assembled structures that can be transported in one or more sections, are built in accordance with the federal HUD Code and NFPA codes and standards. These codes and standards cover many aspects of design, construction, and installations, including body and frame design; plumbing systems; heating, cooling, and fuel-burning systems; electrical systems; and smoke alarms. NFPA 501, *Standard on Manufactured Housing,* contains provisions impacting fire safety and reflecting state-of-the-art concepts and technology.

NFPA 225, *Model Manufactured Home Installation Standard,* addresses provisions for the installation of manufactured homes used as dwelling units. The criteria established by NFPA 225 govern single-section as well as multisection homes and provide requirements for everything from interconnection criteria for multisection homes to anchor provisions to restrict movement from wind loads, seismic events, and floods.

NFPA 501A, *Standard for Fire Safety Criteria for Manufactured Home Installations, Sites, and Communities,* covers fire safety requirements for manufactured home installation, home sites, accessory buildings, structures, and communities. To ensure fire safety, occupants must also practice fire prevention, periodically test and maintain smoke alarms, and develop and practice home escape plans.

BIBLIOGRAPHY

References Cited

1. *Quick Facts,* Manufactured Housing Institute, Arlington, VA, Mar. 2006.
2. *Statistical Abstract of the United States 2000,* U.S. Census Bureau, Table 1209, Washington, DC, Dec. 2000.
3. *Statistical Abstract of the United States 2006,* U.S. Census Bureau, Tables 932 and 937, Washington, DC, Dec. 2006.
4. *Quick Facts,* Manufactured Housing Institute, Arlington, VA, 1994/1995 and 2006.
5. *Quick Facts,* Manufactured Housing Institute, Arlington, VA, 2000/2001.
6. *A Look at Residential Energy Consumption in 1997,* U.S. Department of Energy, Washington, DC, 1999.
7. *Statistical Abstracts of the United States 1997,* U.S. Census Bureau, Table 1212, Washington, DC, 1999.
8. *Final Report,* National Commission on Manufactured Housing, Washington, DC, 1994.
9. *Understanding Today's Manufactured Housing,* Manufactured Housing Institute, Arlington, VA, 2004.
10. Hall, J. R., Jr., *Manufactured Home Fires in the U.S.,* National Fire Protection Association, Quincy, MA, Feb. 2005.
11. Hall, J. R., Jr., *Manufactured Home Fires in the U.S.,* National Fire Protection Association, Quincy, MA, Feb. 2005.
12. Hall, J. R., Jr., *Manufactured Home Fires in the U.S.,* National Fire Protection Association, Quincy, MA, Feb. 2005.
13. Hall, J. R., Jr., *Manufactured Home Fires in the U.S.,* National Fire Protection Association, Quincy, MA, Apr. 2001.
14. Willey, A. E., and Schudel, D., *A Study of Smoke Detectors in Manufactured Housing,* FIREPRO Incorporated, 1996.
15. CPSC *Fire Incident Study,* National Smoke Detector Project, Bethesda, MD, 1995.
16. Ahrens, M., *U.S. Experience with Smoke Alarms and Other Fire Alarms,* National Fire Protection Association Fire Analysis and Research Division, Jan. 2000.
17. "Notice of Proposed Rulemaking, Manufactured Home Construction and Safety Standards: Smoke Alarms" *Federal Register* 65FR31778, May 18, 2000; "Manufactured Home Construction and Safety Standards: Smoke Alarms," *Federal Register,* Vol. 67, No. 53, 2002.
18. "Final Report," National Commission on Manufactured Housing, Ch. 1, Washington, DC, 1994.
19. *Summary of the Manufactured Housing Improvement Act P.L. 106-569,* Manufactured Housing Institute, Arlington, VA, 2001.
20. Manufactured Housing Institute Estimate, 2001, based on NCS-BCS "Shipment Figures."
21. Budnick, E. K., and Klein, D. P., *Mobile Home Fire Studies Summary and Recommendations,* Center for Fire Research, National Bureau of Standards, Gaithersburg, MD, 1979.
22. Adler, S., *Evaluation of the Egress Provisions of the HUD Mobile Home Construction and Safety Standard,* Center for Fire Research, National Bureau of Standards, Gaithersburg, MD, 1977.
23. Pezoldt, V. J., *Emergency Egress from Mobile Homes: Anthropometric and Ergonomic Considerations,* Center for Consumer Product Technology, National Bureau of Standards, Gaithersburg, MD, 1980.
24. *Federal Register Notice,* HUD 24 CFR 3280, Manufactured Home Construction and Safety Standards, Final Rule, Office of the Federal Register, Washington, DC, Aug. 9, 1984.
25. *Part 3280, Manufactured Home Construction and Safety Standards,* Subparts H and I, U.S. Department of Housing and Urban Development, Washington, DC, Revised Apr. 1998.
26. Averill, J. D., and Bukowski, R. W., *Smoke Alarms in Manufactured Housing,* NIST Building and Fire Research Laboratory, Gaithersburg, MD, undated report.

NFPA Codes, Standards, and Recommended Practices

Reference to the following NFPA codes, standards, and recommended practices will provide further information on manufactured housing discussed in this chapter. (See the latest version of The NFPA Catalog *for availability of current editions of the following documents.)*

NFPA 13D, *Standard for the Installation of Sprinkler Systems in One- and Two-Family Dwellings and Manufactured Homes*
NFPA 31, *Standard for the Installation of Oil-Burning Equipment*
NFPA 54, *National Fuel Gas Code*
NFPA 58, *Liquefied Petroleum Gas Code*
NFPA 70, *National Electrical Code®*
NFPA 90B, *Standard for the Installation of Warm Air Heating and Air Conditioning Systems*
NFPA 225, *Model Manufactured Home Installation Standard*
NFPA 501, *Standard on Manufactured Housing*
NFPA 501A, *Standard for Fire Safety Criteria for Manufactured Home Installations, Sites, and Communities*
NFPA 5000®, Building Construction and Safety Code®

Chapter 8

High-Rise Buildings

James R. Quiter

Chapter Contents

Key Terms

egress, fire department access, fire resistance, high-rise building, National Institute of Standards and Technology (NIST), NFPA High-Rise Building Safety Advisory Committee, performance-based codes, smoke movement, stack effect, World Trade Center

The high-rise building has garnered significant attention in the fire safety world over the years, but perhaps never more so than since 2001. The public; the code bodies; the local, regional and federal governments; and the design, build, and ownership communities are all reviewing high-rise building safety and developing positions regarding the need (or lack of need) for additional protection in those buildings. This chapter describes some of the code provisions and special features of the high-rise building, as well as presenting historical data on high-rise building fires.

See also Section 1, Chapter 7, "Protecting Against Extreme Events"; Section 20, Chapter 1, "Assessing Life Safety in Buildings"; and Section 20, Chapter 3, "Hotels and University Housing."

DEFINITION AND BACKGROUND

High-Rise Building Defined

NFPA *101*®, *Life Safety Code*®, and *NFPA 5000*®, *Building Construction and Safety Code*®, define a high-rise building as a building where the floor of an occupiable story is greater than 75 ft (23 m) above the lowest level of fire department vehicle access. This definition is consistent with most U.S.-based model building codes but is not consistent around the world. Many local authorities having jurisdiction also use varying heights and measurement criteria to determine whether a building is a high-rise, with heights ranging from 40 ft (12 m) to as high as 150 ft (45 m). When evaluating whether a code requires a building to be treated as a high-rise, it is important to review the code, as well as any local amendments, to determine the method of measuring building height and what height threshold is used to define a high-rise.

Code application to high-rise buildings is also inconsistent. For many years, most of the U.S. model building codes limited high-rise provisions to business and residential buildings. NFPA *101* contained provisions for high-rise buildings that varied by occupancy. In 2006, most U.S. codes for high-rise apply to all high-rise buildings except open parking garages and some special use structures. Open parking garages are excluded because of the minimal risk imposed by the open structure.

Background

The original intent of the high-rise building provisions was to provide greater protection in buildings where rescue of occupants via ladders was no longer practicable. The 75 ft (23 m) threshold and the measurement of level of fire department vehicle access to the top occupied floor were intended to track with the maximum height that fire department ladders could reach. Many of the jurisdictions that lowered the threshold did so because their equipment was incapable of reaching such heights.

Extensive high-rise provisions first appeared in U.S. codes in the early 1970s. These provisions contained an option to either sprinkler the building or to separate each floor into 2-hour compartments. If the sprinkler option was chosen, several "construction modifications" were permitted.

James R. Quiter, P.E., FSFPE, leads the consulting practice for Arup in the Americas from the firm's San Francisco office. Arup is a global firm of designers and business consultants with over 7000 employees in over 30 countries. He is also chair of NFPA's Safety to Life Committee and the High Rise Building Safety Advisory Committee.

Over time, most codes have been changed to require automatic sprinklers, yet still allow some of the original "modifications" that were originally permitted.

Many codes outside the United States also address high-rise buildings, and many apply high-rise provisions at a building height of about 75 ft (23 m). Provisions similar to those found in U.S. codes apply in other countries. Codes from outside the United States may include more restrictive criteria, including the number and location of fire fighter lifts (elevators); the number, width, and travel distance to escape stairs; compartmentation requirements; and structural fire resistance. In parts of Asia, buildings over a certain height (often in the 15- to 30-story range) also require one or more open-air refuge floors.

In recent years in the United States, two problematic areas have gradually begun to be addressed. The first is that building codes typically apply to new buildings, yet there is a huge stock of existing buildings, particularly in older cities, to which building code requirements do not apply. Retrofit sprinkler ordinances have been passed in many U.S. cities, often after a local disaster. These retrofit laws are not consistent in the level of protection they require, in the types of buildings to which they apply (that is, office, hotel, apartment, condominium), or in the time allowed to complete the retrofit. NFPA *101* has gradually added to the types of existing high-rise buildings required to have automatic sprinklers, but it is not necessarily applied to all existing buildings. Therefore, the public has no easy way of knowing the level of protection they will be afforded in a high-rise building, particularly as they travel from city to city.

Another series of code changes has occurred more recently. Some codes require additional protection measures in some buildings as they get higher. Few people, when they walk into a 7- to 10-story building, picture that building as a high-rise. Yet the level of protection traditionally required is the same as that required in a 50- or 100-story building down the street. Similarities between two such buildings are that exterior rescue above 75 ft (23 m) is difficult if not impossible (depending on local fire department apparatus and access to the building). However, the dynamics of air movement (and therefore smoke movement), the viability of total evacuation versus staged evacuation, and the level of information needed by occupants and the fire service are clearly different in a very tall building compared to a mid-level (but still "high-rise" building). These ideas are beginning to be addressed in a piecemeal fashion in the codes but often with little technical analysis or evaluation of risk. NFPA has established a High-Rise Building Safety Advisory Committee to try to coordinate and guide the NFPA codes as they adapt to the new high-rise performance expectations of society.

FIRE LOSS HISTORY

The NFPA Fire Analysis and Research Division publishes an annual statistical report on high-rise fire incidents.[1] Table 20.8.1 is shown in five parts and is taken from the 2005 edition of the annual survey, with statistics through 2002. It shows, by year, the number of fires, deaths and injuries, property damage, and percentage of high-rise fires to total fires. Separate parts of Table 20.8.1 show results for apartment buildings, hotels, health care occupancies, offices, and all structures. The tables seem to show that there has been a general trend of improvement in all categories.

Table 20.8.1 reflects fires reported to U.S. municipal fire departments and so exclude fires reported only to federal or state agencies or industrial fire brigades. Fires are rounded to the nearest hundred, civilian injuries are rounded to the nearest ten, and direct property damage is rounded to the nearest million dollars; civilian deaths are not rounded. Property damage has been adjusted for inflation, using the Consumer Price Index, to 2002 dollars.

Significant High-Rise Fires

Throughout history, there have been many significant high-rise fires. Table 20.8.2 contains a summary of fires occurring from 1911 to 2004 that have resulted in 10 or more deaths. These fire incident reports include only those submitted to and documented by NFPA. Since not all fires are reported to NFPA, the information should not be considered complete.

Since 2000, several events have caused the fire protection community to refocus on whether we are adequately addressing high-rise protection, through mechanisms such as the NFPA High-Rise Building Safety Advisory Committee. Similar committees have been formed by government entities and professional associations around the world.

One of the recent events that has inspired this rethinking was the World Trade Center disaster of September 11, 2001. However, several other significant fires have also occurred.

Recent Events

Cook County Office Building. Chicago had two significant fires in existing high-rise buildings in the early 2000s. The first occurred at 69 West Washington Street in the Cook County office building on October 17, 2003. In this incident, the fire started in a storage room on the 12th floor of a nonsprinklered building. It was able to spread through the suite of origin, and because corridor walls were not full height, it also spread hot smoke and gases into the corridor system. A stair enclosure with a vestibule was located almost directly across the corridor from the area of fire origin. When the fire department responded and opened the doors from the corridor into the stairs, hot smoke and gases flowed into the stairwell. In this building, stairwell doors were locked from the stair side for security purposes, and no automatic or remote unlocking capability was provided. Six occupants, all who were trapped above the 12th floor, died in the stairwell. Those were the only fatalities in this event. The postfire analysis concluded that, if the stair doors had not been locked from the stair side, there would likely have been no fatalities. Similarly, if the building had been sprinklered, it is unlikely that the smoke and gases would have been as hot, as buoyant, or in the same quantities. Therefore, the fatalities (and much of the damage) could have been avoided by the presence of sprinklers. Perhaps the only lesson learned from this fire is that we ought to apply the knowledge that we already know. Sprinklers greatly increase the safety of buildings, and locked stairwells, even from the stair side, create a hazard.

TABLE 20.8.1 High-Rise Building Fire Experience for Selected Property Classes, by Year, 1985–2002 Structure Fires

				Direct Property Damage (in Millions of Dollars)		
Year	*Fires*	*Civilian Deaths*	*Civilian Injuries*	*Current Dollars*	*2002 Dollars*	*What Percentage of All Apartment Fires Were High-Rise?*
A. Apartment Buildings						
1985	11,700	54	470	15	26	10
1986	10,300	32	380	21	35	9
1987	8,900	46	520	22	34	8
1988	10,300	83	640	48	63	9
1989	11,000	97	610	30	44	10
1990	9,400	76	460	22	31	9
1991	9,900	23	590	129[a]	170[a]	9
1992	10,300	31	640	19	25	9
1993	9,600	43	600	41	51	9
1994	8,900	51	830	36	44	9
1995	7,700	53	530	31	36	8
1996	9,600	56	650	33	38	10
1997	9,200	27	480	30	33	10
1998	8,100	35	570	23	25	9
1999	9,900	27	430	42	46	10
2000	8,600	83	480	25	26	9
2001	7,400	23	320	24	24	8
2002	5,900	15	280	21	21	7
Adjusted Estimates[b]						
1999	10,200	25	430	44	47	11
2000	9,200	85	520	26	27	10
2001	9,800	32	330	19	19	11
2002	8,700	26	350	19	19	10
B. Hotels						
1985	1,800	0	70	2	3	21
1986	1,600	0	50	2	3	20
1987	1,500	5	40	6	10	20
1988	1,800	8	60	20	30	24
1989	1,600	5	60	4	6	22
1990	1,300	7	120	6	8	24
1991	1,300	0	90	6	8	21
1992	1,000	0	80	4	5	21
1993	900	0	60	6	8	17
1994	1,000	0	70	4	5	17
1995	1,100	0	70	5	6	20
1996	800	8	100	17	20	21
1997	800	6	40	9	10	18
1998	800	0	20	11	12	19
1999	900	0	30	19	21	18
2000	900	0	20	3	3	19
2001	900	0	10	13	13	21
2002	700	0	10	1	1	17
Adjusted Estimates						
1999	800	0	30	25	27	18
2000	1,000	0	30	4	4	21
2001	1,300	0	20	24	24	29
2002	1,200	0	40	5	5	28

(continued)

TABLE 20.8.1 Continued

				Direct Property Damage (in Millions of Dollars)		
Year	*Fires*	*Civilian Deaths*	*Civilian Injuries*	*Current Dollars*	*2002 Dollars*	*What Percentage of All Apartment Fires Were High-Rise?*
C. Hospitals and Other Facilities That Care for the Sick						
1985	2,400	11	120	2	3	38
1986	2,000	3	30	1	2	37
1987	1,700	0	70	1	2	32
1988	1,500	2	70	1	2	35
1989	1,400	9	110	3	4	34
1990	1,300	0	40	4	6	37
1991	1,100	0	50	4	5	36
1992	1,100	2	30	3	4	32
1993	1,000	0	30	3	4	32
1994	900	6	30	4	5	31
1995	800	2[c]	40	1	1	31
1996	900	0[c]	30	3	3	35
1997	800	0	20	1	1	29
1998	600	2	80	4	5	29
1999	700	0	20	1	1	24
2000	600	0	10	1	1	23
2001	500	0	10	1	1	23
2002	400	0	10	1	1	23
Adjusted Estimates						
1999	700	0	20	1	1	24
2000	600	0	10	1	1	23
2001	500	0	10	2	2	26
2002	500	0	20	2	2	30
D. Office Buildings						
1985	1,300	1	10	6	10	13
1986	1,100	1	80	28	28	12
1987	900	4	10	11	11	10
1988	1,000	0	20	50	50	13
1989	900	0	20	30	30	12
1990	900	0	10	22	22	14
1991	800	0	10	15	15	12
1992	1,000	1	80	62	62	12
1993	800	0	20	14	14	12
1994	700	0	20	18	18	10
1995	500	0	60	8	8	9
1996	500	0	20	18	18	9
1997	600	0	10	4	4	10
1998	500	0	10	4	4	9
1999	600	0	10	7	7	11
2000	500	0	10	3	3	10
2001	300	0	10	7	7	8
2002	300	0	0	3	3	7
Adjusted Estimates						
1999	600	0	10	7	7	12
2000	500	0	10	3	3	11
2001	600	0	10	19	20	13
2002	500	0	0	5	5	12

TABLE 20.8.1 Continued

				Direct Property Damage (in Millions of Dollars)	
Year	*Fires*	*Civilian Deaths*	*Civilian Injuries*	*Current Dollars*	*2002 Dollars*
E. Four Property Classes Combined					
1985	17,200	66	670	25	41
1986	15,000	37	550	41	68
1987	13,000	54	640	36	36
1988	14,600	94	780	102	102
1989	14,800	111	800	58	58
1990	13,300	84	620	48	48
1991	13,100	23	750	150	150
1992	13,600	34	830	75	75
1993	12,400	43	700	61	61
1994	11,500	57	950	59	59
1995	10,000	55	690	45	45
1996	12,100	64	790	69	69
1997	11,400	33	560	43	43
1998	10,000	37	680	41	41
1999	12,100	27	500	68	68
2000	10,600	83	520	32	32
2001	9,200	23	350	44	44
2002	7,300	15	300	26	26
Adjusted Estimates					
1999	12,400	25	490	76	82
2000	11,300	85	560	34	35
2001	12,300	32	360	64	65
2002	10,900	26	410	31	31

Note: Property damage figures for office buildings are underestimated in several years due to problems in handling some large-loss fires, such as the $325 million One Meridian Plaza fire in Pennsylvania in 1991 and the $230 million World Trade Center incident in 1993, whose more than 1000 injuries also are not properly reflected in national estimates. The events of September 11, 2001, are not reflected in these figures.

[a]Property damage figures for apartments in 1991 are inflated by problems in handling the Oakland wildfire in the estimates.

[b]The "Adjusted Estimates" are calculated using only NFIRS Version 4.1 data to estimate the percent of fires (and losses) that occurred in high-rise buildings. Use Adjusted Estimates for trend analysis, as they are more comparable in approach to pre-1999 data, but for any single year, use the main estimates, which are considered more accurate.

[c]Based on high-rise share of fires in 1995 and 1996, because all deaths were in buildings with unknown height.

Source: *High-Rise Building Fires,* NFPA Fire Analysis and Research Division, p. 5, August 2005. Original data from NFIRS and NFPA survey.

For a discussion of the evacuation from the Cook County office building, see Section 4, Chapter 1, "Human Behavior and Fire."

La Salle Bank Building. The second Chicago fire, on December 6, 2004, occurred at the La Salle Bank Building and had better results. Again it was a fire in a nonsprinklered high-rise building. This building had operable windows, and several occupants went to windows for fresh air. There were no fatalities in this fire although there were 37 injuries. The fire was notable nationally because it closely followed the 69 West Washington Street fire, making it the second significant high-rise fire in the same city in a short period of time. As with 69 West Washington, sprinklers in the building would have greatly reduced the amount of smoke and heat generated and therefore would probably not have required occupants to rely on operable windows for fresh air.

Chicago has since passed a retroactive high-rise sprinkler ordinance and has also outlawed door locks on stairwells, unless there is automatic and remote release.

Parque Central Building. In October 2004, a fire began on the 34th floor of the Parque Central Building in Caracas, Venezuela. This building was a 56-story government office building. The fire did more than $250 million (U.S.) in damage, burning the structure's contents from the 34th to the 50th floor. The building was fully sprinklered; however, the sprinkler system was inoperable. Postfire analysis indicated that had the sprinkler system been active, the fire would have been limited to the floor of

TABLE 20.8.2 International Listing of Fatal High-Rise Structure Fires, 1911–2004 (10 or More Deaths)

Date	*Building*	*Location*	*Number of Deaths*	*Floor of Origin*	*Height in Stories*
March 1911	Clothing manufacturer	New York	146	8	10
July 1945	Office building	New York	11	79	102
June 1946	Hotel (transient hotel)	Illinois	61	1	22
December 1946	Hotel (transient hotel)	Georgia	119	3	15
December 1961	Hospital	Connecticut	16	9	13
December 1963	Hotel	Florida	22	1	14
January 1966	Hotel (transient hotel)	Massachusetts	11	Basement	11
February 1967	Restaurant/apartment building	Alabama	25	11	11
December 1970	Hotel	Arizona	28	4	11
December 1971	Hotel	Korea	163	2	21
February 1972	Andraus building	Brazil	16	5	31
November 1972	Elderly apartments	Georgia	10	7	11
February 1974	Bank building	Brazil	179	12	25
June 1977	Detention center (jail)	New Brunswick, Canada	21	Sublevel	16
November 1980	Hotel	Nevada	85	1	23
March 1981	Office building	Chile	11 (1 FF)	12	15
February 1982	Hotel	Japan	32	9	10
March 1982	Hotel	Texas	12	4	13
January 1984	Hotel	Korea	38	4	10
October 1984	Hotel	New Jersey	15	3	9
November 1984	Hotel	Philippines	10	17	16
February 1986	Office building	Brazil	23	Unknown	13
September 1986	Hotel	Norway	14	1	13
December 1986	Hotel	Puerto Rico	96	1	20
October 1989	Plastic manufacturing plant	Texas	23	Unknown	20
April 1995	Office building	Oklahoma	168	Outside	9
November 1996	Office building	Hong Kong	40 (1 FF)	Basement	16
July 1997	Hotel	Thailand	90	1	17
March 2001	Oil rig	Brazil	10	Unknown	40
September 2001	Office building	New York	2791 (340 FF)	Bldg. 1: 94–98 Bldg. 2: 78–84	Bldg. 1: 110 Bldg. 2: 110
August 2003	Apartment building	Taiwan	13	Unknown	8
January 2004	Apartment building	Egypt	14 (8 FF)	Unknown	12

FF = fire fighter.

Source: *International Listing of Fatal High-Rise Structure Fires, 1911–2004,* National Fire Protection Association, 2005, http://www.nfpa.org.

origin. The lesson learned from this fire is that the systems that are provided in buildings should be maintained.

Madrid Office Building. On February 12, 2005, a nighttime fire in a Madrid office building resulted in significant fire and structural damage to the building, but no fatalities. Again, the fire was in a nonsprinklered building, and the results would likely have been very different in a sprinklered building. Therefore, although we may learn from the structural response to this fire, from a life safety point of view, sprinkler protection was likely the first and best protective measure that could have been provided.

Lessons Learned. The lessons learned from these fires are simple. The satisfactory protection of the structure, maintaining the integrity of the egress systems, and the compartmentation of high-rise buildings must be ensured. That is not enough, however. All high-rise buildings should be protected by automatic sprinklers; if they were, they would be significantly safer. It is recognized that there is no simple means of sprinklering existing high-rise buildings. Therefore, means to encourage sprinkler protection in those buildings, such as tax incentives on capital improvements and extended times for installation, need to be factored into the process of requiring automatic sprinklers. However, until such sprinklers are required, there is the risk of significant fire and risk to life safety in our stock of nonsprinklered high-rise buildings.

The World Trade Center

Much has been written and discussed about the World Trade Center (WTC) events of September 11, 2001. This chapter cannot address the event in any level of depth, given that the National Institute of Standards and Technology (NIST) has written reports totaling over 10,000 pages for WTC 1 and 2 and will have more to say about WTC 7. Neither of the NIST reports addresses all the fire protection design issues that must be considered. Before discussing the NIST recommendations, there are a couple of thoughts or concepts that bear serious consideration.

The first question is whether the incident involving WTC 1 and 2 is an event that should be considered in high-rise building design. Other questions include whether all buildings, or a subset of landmark buildings, are going to be designed to defend against terrorist threats and hostile acts. If so, which threats? What will this design cost, and can society afford it? Also, if buildings are designed to protect against these extreme events, will day-to-day life become more difficult, or will our reaction to more typical or equally severe but unusual threats become more hazardous? For instance, if we decide to fully evacuate all high-rise buildings for all events, will we end up with more injuries and deaths than we save?

For example, one common recommendation that has been heard coming out of the event is the need to harden stairwells. What does this mean? How hard should they be made? If they are hardened, what are the results? For instance, if a bomb were detonated in a hardened stairwell, is it better or worse than the traditional stairwell? The bottom line is we cannot react to a single event without understanding that there may be negative implications in the building's response to other events—the theory of unintended consequences. It is a difficult task to apply rigor to our thinking as we respond to events such as security threats that may be very unlikely, impossible to predict, and subject to emotion. If we do not, however, the overall performance of a building may be worsened rather than improved.

A second big question coming out of the WTC disaster is whether we, as a society, are comfortable with the performance of the rest of the WTC complex. There was significant damage to several of the buildings, including the collapse of WTC 7, a 47 story building. Although the ignition was due to the attacks on WTC 1 and 2 and the lack of water for both automatic sprinkler systems and manual fire-fighting efforts was also due to that event, the fuel and fire causing the collapse were all within the WTC 7 building. There may well be lessons to be learned from this event that can extend to typical high-rise buildings.

The NIST Recommendations

In 2005, NIST issued a series of recommendations on the collapse of the World Trade Center Towers.[2] The report included 30 recommendations in eight general groups. This paper does not attempt to address each of those recommendations. However, to gain a feel for the recommendations, the groupings are described as follows:

Group I: Increase Structural Integrity
Group II: Enhanced Fire Resistance of Structures
Group III: New Methods for Fire Resistance Design of Structures
Group IV: Improved Active Fire Protection
Group V: Improved Building Evacuation
Group VI: Improved Emergency Response
Group VII: Improved Procedure and Practices
Group VIII: Education and Training

These recommendations were issued in draft form and many organizations have responded with comments. Many of the recommendations were logical outgrowths of the event, but some others could lead to substantial changes in building design. NIST has offered to work with model code groups in developing code language to respond to these recommendations. Some of the far-reaching recommendations are considered controversial because they may not necessarily spring from the World Trade Center events or because the recommendation seems to stem from an event that occurred only because of the method of attack. Others will lead to long-term improvements in buildings or building operations, or perhaps will spur industry to develop new products. Still other recommendations can be accomplished quite easily with changes in operations or methods.

The NIST reports can be found on the NIST website (http://www.nist.gov or http://wtc.nist.gov). This includes all of the research reports that have led up to the recommendations, as well as the recommendations themselves.

HIGH-RISE FIRE RISK

Why do high-rise buildings require more protection than other buildings? Simply put, the risk of a significant hazardous event is greater than that associated with a non–high-rise building. This is because the number of people exposed is likely greater than normal; the building's floor area is likely greater than normal; the impact of an event is more likely to impact other floors and more people than an event in a large low-rise building; evacuation via building systems will take longer; the dynamics of smoke spread will encourage spread to upper floors; external evacuation is not practical; and a localized structural collapse could impact other portions of the building or of adjacent buildings. While codes do not explicitly define these risks, many of the code provisions do address them. For the designer, it is important that these risks be considered, rather than just assuming that the code has adequately covered them for any specific building.

UNIQUE FEATURES OF A HIGH-RISE

Some of the major issues that make high-rise buildings different from other buildings include fire department access, egress, smoke movement, and fire control.

Fire Department Access

Fire department accessibility, a major issue, takes several forms:

- The limitations of present-day fire apparatus in reaching upper floors from the exterior of the building
- The height of the fire and the number of personnel required to deliver adequate types and amounts of equipment to the fire area. (Due to the possible height of the fire area, equipment transport and force deployment efforts

could exact an exhaustive toll on fire-fighting forces before they can even mount a fire attack. This has a significant impact when available fire fighters and equipment are limited. This condition can also occur in a large low-rise building with the same distance problems as a high-rise, although the elevation difference in a high-rise exaggerates the problem.)

- Inherent delays in deploying equipment. (Delays in deploying equipment and fire fighters can indirectly affect fire growth, thereby resulting in a fire of greater magnitude by the time manual forces are in place to attack.)
- The height and location of a building. (The height and location of a building can further restrict the fire department's ability to approach the area of origin from more advantageous directions. As a result, the fire department may only be able to approach a fire area from below. In many cases where the area of origin has no automatic suppression and compartmentalization, the area of origin may not be approachable at all, resulting in a defensive approach that depends on fuel consumption for control and extinguishment. This approach typically results in a large or unacceptable loss.)
- Communication issues. (Fire department as well as other first responder radio transmitters struggle to work or do not work at all in the confines of a high-rise building. Delays in reporting real-time fire conditions, summoning more help to upper floors, or learning of imminent threats can jeopardize the fireground safety parameters.)

Egress

Egress and people movement systems within a high-rise building also make the building unique. In a low-rise building, it is typical to assume that total evacuation of the building can occur in a relatively short time. In a high-rise, however, full evacuation may take more than an hour. Also, because all occupants are using the same stairs, full evacuation in many circumstances may lead to slower evacuation of those most affected by the event. In addition, competition for stair use by first responders can further slow evacuation travel times. Because of these differences, a high-rise requires a well-conceived and delivered evacuation system which revolves around education and information. Therefore, written emergency plans, fire drills, and training are important factors regarding safety in a high-rise. Notification to occupants is typically provided by zone via voice communication, which allows those most directly affected to evacuate or relocate first and gives emergency responders the opportunity to communicate with others in the building, perhaps to initiate a full and orderly evacuation.

In tall buildings, relocation to other areas is often the first mode of evacuation. This may be by horizontal exit or relocation to other floors. Most events do not necessitate full evacuation of a building, and initial relocation to nearby areas may prevent slips and falls or exhaustion-related injuries. From the area of relocation, the authorities can decide whether evacuees should remain in place, use the elevators, or continue down the stairs in an organized manner.

Smoke Movement

The high-rise building often has natural forces affecting fire and smoke movement that are not normally significant in lower buildings. Stack effect and the impact of exterior winds can be very significant, and very different, in high-rise buildings.

Stack Effect. Stack effect results from the temperature differences between two areas, usually the inside and outside temperatures, which create a pressure difference that results in natural air movements within a building. In a high-rise building, this effect is increased due to the height of the building. Many high-rise buildings have a significant stack effect, capable of moving large volumes of heat and smoke through the building.

No manual fire-fighting techniques are known to counter stack effect or to mitigate its effect during a fire. Stack effect cannot be eliminated because of the temperature differences and building height. As a result, potential stack effect will exist and may vary with climatic conditions. The only way to mitigate the potential of stack effect is to design and construct the building to minimize the effect. A thorough review of available resources on the subject will enhance design and construction. Basic concepts include the following:

- Compartmentalization from floor to floor and wall to wall, which involves sealing penetrations and exterior building tightness
- Limiting continuous shaft heights or constructing vestibules on stairs, elevators, and other vertical shafts
- Use of vestibules and gasketing on exterior doors at both the bottom and top of a building
- Eliminating naturally ventilated shafts and floors that could contribute to stack effect during a fire (elevator shafts with normally open vents, which are commonly utilized, can significantly enhance stack effect)
- Zoning, compartmentalization, and control of mechanical systems, which could contribute to, or be affected by, stack effect

Winds. Winds can profoundly affect fire and smoke movement within a building. Wind patterns around high-rise buildings have been the subject of study due to their effect on structural issues, but very little has been studied with regard to fire protection. In high-rise buildings, winds can vary radically in intensity and direction at different floor levels or sections. It is known that wind velocity and direction can be very different at the street level than at upper sections of the structure, and there is no known method of predicting or preliminarily measuring their effects.

The primary design approach to mitigate the effect of wind on smoke movement is to make the exterior walls of a building as airtight as possible. This approach is highly dependent on the design criteria, materials chosen, and integrity of workmanship. The result should be that wind direction and velocity will have a reduced impact on air movement within the structure, thereby allowing conventional smoke management systems to overcome the effects of wind to some degree. It is noted that the degree of the smoke management system's ability to overcome the wind effect is based on many variables, including system design, system power, tightness of the building, wind velocity, and wind direction.

It is reasonable to assume that, if wind is not taken into consideration in the design and construction of the high-rise building and the exterior of the building is not reasonably tight, any fire may be significantly affected by wind velocity and direction. Wind direction can complicate the accessibility and preferred direction of fire attack and can increase fire and smoke impingement on areas of refuge, possibly exceeding their design criteria.

Even when heating, ventilating, and air conditioning (HVAC) systems are zoned and compartmentalized, they can share common exhaust shafts and fresh-air intake shafts. Such shafts and duct runs often penetrate multiple fire zones, requiring special attention to design and protection. Many high-rise buildings integrate smoke management systems with conventional HVAC systems. Although this is acceptable, and in many cases preferred, it requires special design considerations, including fail-safe devices and adequate controls, acceptance testing, and ongoing maintenance. See NFPA 92A, *Standard for Smoke-Control Systems Utilizing Barriers and Pressure Differences*, and NFPA 92B, *Standard for Smoke Management Systems in Malls, Atria, and Large Spaces*, for additional information on the design of smoke management systems.

Fire Control

Of special importance in a high-rise building is the ability to control a fire. With large numbers of people in a building, many of whom may be above the fire location, fire control is both a life safety and property protection issue. Fire control affects many of the features of the building including its overall fire resistance, compartmentation, automatic and manual suppression, and control of contents.

Most new high-rise buildings around the world are now required to have automatic sprinklers. This is a significant first step in fire control but may not be enough by itself. Codes require manual suppression capabilities in the form of standpipes and portable extinguishers. All of this may be inadequate, however, if the contents in the building become significantly more hazardous than were originally assumed for the building.

CODE REQUIRED FEATURES

NFPA *101* and *NFPA 5000* contain general high-rise building protection criteria in Chapters 11 and 33, respectively. The occupancy chapters use these as base criteria and add or subtract as deemed necessary for the particular occupancy. In Chapter 33 of *NFPA 5000,* the following criteria are addressed:

- Construction types and construction modifications
- Voice communication for fire alarm
- Two-way fire department communication systems
- Automatic sprinkler protection
- Smoke-proof exit enclosures
- Emergency lighting
- Standby power
- Emergency command center

These features are intended to address many of the unique features of a high-rise building. Over the past several years, code requirements such as these have caused the active protection of existing high-rise buildings to gradually improve. Tables 20.8.3 and 20.8.4 show the levels of automatic sprinkler, fire detection, and fire-resistive construction in hotel and office buildings from 1985 to 1998.

HIGH-RISE ISSUES TO CONSIDER

Areas to which the design and code community should give serious consideration with respect to high-rise buildings include risk evaluations, thresholds, and structural fire resistance.

Risk Evaluations

Very large buildings should not be designed using a "cookbook" approach. Rather, an integrated, holistic, and rational engineering approach should be used. Although there are not enough events in high-rise buildings to do statistical analysis of the risks, there are many ways to look at risk in relation to high-rise buildings. As a building gets taller, the number of occupants increases, and the potential for disaster increases. Engineering decisions should be based on such factors as potential occupant load; whether a building may be a target; potential contents and businesses within the building; the capability and effectiveness of built-in systems such as automatic sprinklers, emergency power, and other systems to protect the occupants and the structure; and supplemental, unique features in the building. Without such analysis, the rigor that the building demands and the public deserves will not be included in the design process. This rigor should lead to an informed, well-documented design, so that the thought process on which the design is based can be followed in the future. Only then will high-rise buildings be engineered rather than pieced together. Application of current codes to very or extremely tall buildings is worthy of scrutiny and discussion. Criteria that are virtually identical for a 10 story building and a 100 story building should be adjusted for the taller structures; the only question is how. Such an approach exists today in the form of performance-based codes, but their use in high-rise buildings has been limited, particularly in the United States.

Thresholds

Although codes are gradually grappling with the concept that not all high-rise buildings are the same, it may make sense to develop some thresholds of protection. For instance, high-rise requirements may start at 75 ft (23 m), or 7 or 8 stories, based on the reach of fire department apparatus. The next threshold may occur at about 20 stories, where full-building evacuation becomes unwieldy, and where stack effect can significantly affect smoke movement. Subsequent thresholds may be at 40, 60, or 100 stories, where the time to evacuate may exceed the fire resistance of a structure, where elevators may need to be considered in building evacuation, where special provisions for fire fighter access may be needed, where mechanical systems alone may not be able to overcome stack effect, and where people

TABLE 20.8.3 Fire Protection in Hotels and Motels, High-Rise Versus Other Buildings, 1985–1998 Structure Fires

Year of Fire	*Percentage of High-Rise Buildings*	*Percentage of Buildings That Are Not High-Rise*	*Percentage of All Buildings of Known Height*	*Year of Fire*	*Percentage of High-Rise Buildings*	*Percentage of Buildings That Are Not High-Rise*	*Percentage of All Buildings of Known Height*
A. Automatic Extinguishing Systems[a]				**B. Fire Detection Equipment**[b]			
1985	51	11	19	1985	74	54	58
1986	61	15	24	1986	82	60	64
1987	59	16	25	1987	82	63	67
1988	63	19	30	1988	85	65	70
1989	63	22	32	1989	87	70	74
1990	69	22	34	1990	86	69	73
1991	66	22	32	1991	86	74	76
1992	72	22	32	1992	91	73	77
1993	75	25	34	1993	90	73	76
1994	69	25	33	1994	92	76	79
1995	72	23	33	1995	87	74	77
1996	76	24	35	1996	89	76	79
1997	67	27	34	1997	91	78	80
1998	77	32	41	1998	87	76	78

Year of Fire	*Percentage of High-Rise Buildings*	*Percentage of Buildings That Are Not High-Rise*	*Percentage of All Buildings of Known Height*
C. Fire-Resistive Construction			
1985	57	13	22
1986	63	14	24
1987	52	15	22
1988	59	12	24
1989	54	14	23
1990	55	13	23
1991	48	13	21
1992	48	10	18
1993	52	12	19
1994	49	12	18
1995	43	11	17
1996	46	11	19
1997	51	13	20
1998	54	9	18

Note: These are fires reported to U.S. municipal fire departments and so exclude fires reported only to federal or state agencies or industrial fire brigades. "High-rise" means seven or more stories in height.

[a]Analysis limited to buildings of known height (number of stories), so statistics do not agree exactly with statistics for all buildings, including buildings with unreported height, as shown in Kimberly D. Rohr, *U.S. Experience with Sprinklers,* NFPA Fire Analysis & Research Division, Quincy, MA, Sept. 2001.

[b]Analysis limited to buildings of known height (number of stories), so statistics do not agree exactly with statistics for all buildings, including buildings with unreported height, as shown in Marty Ahrens, *U.S. Experience with Smoke Alarms,* NFPA Fire Analysis & Research Division, Quincy, MA, Sept. 2001.

Source: *High-Rise Building Fires,* NFPA Fire Analysis and Research Division, p. 23, August 2005. Original data from NFIRS and NFPA survey.

movement and psychology may have to be factored into how messages are transmitted and received. At one of these thresholds, it may well be that prescriptive codes no longer apply and that a performance-based approach using engineered systems is the only allowed alternative. Once this analysis is done, it may also be that requirements can be relaxed somewhat in the 7- to 20-story building range. As an example, in China, buildings over 820 ft (250 m) are considered as super-high-rise buildings, and approval involves the central government authorities.

Structural Fire Resistance

Although the current code methods of evaluating structural fire resistance are archaic, they still provide a very accurate and con-

TABLE 20.8.4 Fire Protection in Facilities That Care for the Sick, High-Rise Versus Other Buildings, 1985–1998 Reported Fires

Year of Fire	*Percentage of High-Rise Buildings*	*Percentage of Buildings That Are Not High-Rise*	*Percentage of All Buildings of Known Height*	*Year of Fire*	*Percentage of High-Rise Buildings*	*Percentage of Buildings That Are Not High-Rise*	*Percentage of All Buildings of Known Height*
A. Automatic Extinguishing Systems[a]				**B. Fire Detection Equipment**[b]			
1985	61	61	61	1985	85	80	82
1986	60	61	60	1986	88	86	87
1987	64	63	63	1987	89	85	86
1988	62	58	60	1988	90	85	87
1989	64	60	61	1989	90	85	87
1990	69	62	65	1990	92	87	89
1991	57	64	62	1991	87	87	87
1992	74	67	70	1992	91	88	89
1993	76	69	71	1993	93	86	88
1994	67	66	67	1994	94	88	90
1995	78	67	70	1995	96	88	90
1996	82	69	74	1996	94	89	91
1997	80	69	72	1997	96	89	91
1998	80	70	73	1998	92	89	90

Year of Fire	*Percentage of High-Rise Buildings*	*Percentage of Buildings That Are Not High-Rise*	*Percentage of All Buildings of Known Height*
C. Fire-Resistive Construction			
1985	73	58	64
1986	67	54	59
1987	66	48	54
1988	66	49	55
1989	57	47	51
1990	54	46	49
1991	53	43	47
1992	55	42	46
1993	57	42	46
1994	53	34	40
1995	48	36	40
1996	49	33	39
1997	51	38	42
1998	49	33	38

Note: These are fires reported to U.S. municipal fire departments and so exclude fires reported only to federal or state agencies or industrial fire brigades. "High-rise" means seven or more stories in height.

[a]Analysis limited to buildings of known height (number of stories), so statistics do not agree exactly with statistics for all buildings, including buildings with unreported height, as shown in Kimberly D. Rohr, *U.S. Experience with Sprinklers,* NFPA Fire Analysis & Research Division, Quincy, MA, Sept. 2001.

[b]Analysis limited to buildings of known height (number of stories), so statistics do not agree exactly with statistics for all buildings, including buildings with unreported height, as shown in Marty Ahrens, *U.S. Experience with Smoke Alarms,* NFPA Fire Analysis & Research Division, Quincy, MA, Sept. 2001.

Source: *High-Rise Building Fires,* NFPA Fire Analysis and Research Division, p. 25, August 2005. Original data from NFIRS and NFPA survey.

sistent model of expected performance. Simulation techniques are available that can reveal much more about a building's potential behavior than a 1-, 2-, or 3-hour rating. In the automotive industry, physical crashes and crash simulations are used on new car models to determine how a vehicle will respond to a series of events. Those same models can be used (and are starting to be used) in the building industry to judge structural and fire performance.

Another aspect of structural fire resistance in tall buildings is the need for a building to withstand an event for long periods of time. In a medium-height building, the current building codes reasonably match full evacuation time with structural fire resistance. As we get into very tall buildings, however, should we consider a change in fire resistance? If so, how much (given that fires will only burn a finite amount of time)? A balance on this item that has not yet emerged and needs to be found. Costs and acceptable end-points if sprinklers fail also need to be discussed. Surely, total building collapse is unacceptable, but is localized collapse or deflection over small areas acceptable in the rare event of a fire and sprinkler failure? With more stringent provisions come more costs.

SUMMARY

The high-rise building presents several challenges not found in traditional low-rise buildings. Those involved with the design and construction of high-rise buildings should recognize those challenges and address them accordingly. Although codes provide a basis for dealing with a high-rise, each building should be considered individually. Items to consider include height, occupancy, occupant load, unusual uses, availability of fire service, and the expectations of society.

BIBLIOGRAPHY

References Cited

1. *High-Rise Building Fires*, NFPA Fire Analysis and Research, August 2005.
2. NIST NCSTAR 1, *Federal Building and Fire Safety Investigation of the World Trade Center Disaster: Final Report of the National Construction Safety Team on the Collapses of the World Trade Center Towers,* National Institute of Standards and Technology, Gaithersburg, MD, 2005.

NFPA Codes, Standards, and Recommended Practices

Reference to the following NFPA codes, standards, and recommended practices will provide further information on high-rise buildings discussed in this chapter. (See the latest version of The NFPA Catalog *for availability of current editions of the following documents.)*

NFPA 92A, *Standard for Smoke-Control Systems Utilizing Barriers and Pressure Differences*

NFPA 92B, *Standard for Smoke Management Systems in Malls, Atria, and Large Spaces*

NFPA *101*®, *Life Safety Code*®

NFPA 5000®, *Building Construction and Safety Code*®

References

Averill, J. D., Mileti, D. S., Peacock, R. D., Kuligowski, E. D., Groner, N., Proulx, G., Reneke, P. A., and Nelson, H. E., *Federal Building and Fire Safety Investigation of the World Trade Center Disaster—Occupant Behaviour, Egress, and Emergency Communications,* NIST NCSTAR 1-7, National Institute of Standards and Technology, Gaithersburg, MD, 2005.

Butterworth, N., and Green, M., "Fire Safety Design of Tall Buildings: Application to the No. 1 City Square Building in Leeds," *Proceedings* of the 9th Fire Protection Seminar, Engineering Methods for Fire Safety, May 25–26, 2001, Munich, Germany, 2001, pp. 4/311–330.

Craighead, G., *High-Rise Security and Fire Life Safety,* 2nd ed., Elsevier Science, Amsterdam, Netherlands, 2003.

Emergency Evacuation Elevator Systems Guideline, Council on Tall Buildings and Urban Habitat, Chicago, 2004.

Evans, D. H., Weber, R. D., and Quiter, J. R., "Luxor Hotel and Casino: An Application of Performance-Based Fire Safety Design Methods," *Proceedings* of Pacific Rim Conference and 2nd International Conference on Performance-Based Codes and Fire Safety Design Methods, May 3–9, 1998, Maui, HI, International Code Council, Birmingham, AL, 1998, pp. 393–410.

Fahy, R. F., and Proulx G., "A Comparison of the 1993 and 2001 Evacuations of the World Trade Center," *Proceedings* of the 2002 Fire Risk and Hazard Assessment Symposium, National Fire Protection Research Foundation, July 24, 2002, Baltimore, MD, 2002, pp. 111–117.

Federal Building and Fire Safety Investigation of the World Trade Center Disaster: Final Report on the Collapse of the World Trade Center Towers, NIST NCSTAR 1, National Institute of Standards and Technology, Gaithersburg, MD, 2005.

Guo, D. G., Wong, K. H. L., Luo, M. C., Kang, L., and Shi B. B., "Lift Evacuation Design of Ultra High-Rise Building," *Proceedings* of the Fire Conference 2004—Total Fire Safety Concept, Hong Kong SAR, December 2004, Hong Kong Polytechnic University, Hong Kong, 2004, pp. 151–158.

He, Y., Horasan, M., Tayor, P., Ramsay, C., and Lai, D., "Probabilistic Fire Safety Engineering Assessment of Refurbished High Rise Office Building," *Proceedings* of International Conference, Engineered Fire Protection Design . . . Applying Fire Science to Fire Protection Problems, June 11–15, 2001, San Francisco, CA, Society of Fire Protection Engineers, Bethesda, MD, 2001, pp. 211–228.

International Listing of Fatal High-Rise Structure Fires, 1911–2004, National Fire Protection Association, http://www.nfpa.org.

Lovell, T., Hedges, A., and Bressington, P., "Kingdom Trade Centre Sculpture, Riyadh, Saudi Arabia," *Proceedings* of 9th International INTERFLAM Conference, INTERFLAM 2001, September 17–19, 2001, Edinburgh, UK, Interscience Communications Ltd., London, UK, 2001, pp. 371–381.

Moore, W. D., "High-Rise Speaker Circuit Survivability," *NFPA Journal*, Vol. 95, No. 3, 2001, p. 76.

Powell, P., *NFPA Ready Reference: Fire Safety in High-Rise Buildings,* National Fire Protection Association, Quincy, MA, 2003.

Proulx, G., *High-Rise Evacuation: A Questionable Concept,* NRCC-44675, National Research Council, Canada, 2001.

Quiter, J. R., "Application of Performance Based Concepts at the Stratosphere Tower, Las Vegas, Nevada," *Proceedings* of Fire Risk and Hazard Assessment Symposium, Research and Practice: Bridging the Gap, June 26–28, 1996, San Francisco, CA, National Fire Protection Research Foundation, Quincy, MA, 1996, pp. 118–126.

"Residential High-Rise North York, Ontario, Canada, January 6, 1995," *NFPA Fire Investigations*, National Fire Protection Association, Quincy, MA, 1996.

Wong, H. L. K., Hui, M. C., Guo, D. G., and Luo, M. C., "A Refined Concept on Emergency Evacuation by Lift," *Fire Safety Science—Proceedings* of 8th International Symposium, International Association for Fire Safety Science, September 18–23, 2005, Beijing, China, 2005, pp. 599–610.

SECTION 20

Chapter 9

Assembly Occupancies

Revised by

Gregory Miller ❑ Edward Roether

Chapter Contents

Key Terms

aisle accessway, assembly occupancies, continental seating, crowd management, dead-end aisles, festival seating, fire exit hardware, fixed seating, legitimate stage, life safety evaluation, normal seating, panic hardware, Station Nightclub fire

Assembly occupancies generally can be defined as rooms, spaces, or structures in which groups of people gather for a purpose, such as deliberation, worship, entertainment, or to await transportation. Examples of assembly occupancies are large meeting rooms, restaurants, nightclubs, dance halls, bars, cocktail lounges, auditoriums with fixed or loose chair seating, libraries, concert halls, theaters, cinemas, multipurpose rooms, exhibition halls, convention centers, sports facilities, field houses, places of worship, and passenger terminals for air or surface transportation.

Because the safety and hazards of large numbers of people gathered in one place are a specific concern with this type of occupancy, a minimum number of occupants must be reached to establish whether a room, space, or structure constitutes an assembly occupancy. Although this minimum number of occupants can vary between codes, NFPA *5000*®, *Building Construction and Safety Code*® and NFPA *101*®, *Life Safety Code*®, set the threshold at 50 persons. Occupancies with similar uses but having occupant loads less than 50 would be incidental within other occupancy classifications. An example might be a small meeting room in an office building (incidental assembly use in a business occupancy). NFPA *101* and *NFPA 5000* recommend, via annex notes, classifying small restaurants and drinking establishments with occupant loads of less than 50 as mercantile occupancies.

See also Section 4, Chapter 2, "Calculation Methods for Egress Prediction"; Section 4, Chapter 4, "Techniques of Crowd Management"; Section 4, Chapter 5, "Strategies for Occupant Evacuation During Emergencies"; and Section 20, Chapter 1, "Assessing Life Safety in Buildings."

OCCUPANCY CHARACTERISTICS

The density of the occupant population presents a unique concern for safety in assembly occupancies. No other occupancy experiences occupant loads of such density. The occupant load is dependent upon how the space is being used. Typically, one person per 15 ft^2 (1.4 m^2) of net area would be expected in less concentrated spaces, 7 ft^2 (0.65 m^2) of net area in concentrated spaces, and 5 ft^2 (0.46 m^2) of net area in very concentrated spaces.

Assembly occupancies are usually inhabited by persons who do not use the building frequently and, therefore, might not be familiar with exit locations, egress paths, or other safeguards present. In addition, many assembly occupancies, such as theaters, concert halls, nightclubs, lounges, and some restaurants, are used in conditions of low lighting levels. Such high occupant densities under these conditions impact physical movement and the behavior of people. The capacity and maintenance of the means of egress elements, fire resistance of building construction and interior finish materials, fire suppression systems, crowd management, and the method of alerting occupants of an emergency require proper attention.

All of these factors—high occupant density, unfamiliarity with the building, and low lighting levels—are common to the many and varied forms of assembly occupancies. Provisions must be made to deal with all of these factors to avoid panic and facilitate orderly egress when an emergency occurs. Despite these factors, sprinklered assembly occupancies have had a remarkably good fire

Gregory Miller is with Code Consultants, Inc., in St. Louis, Missouri.

Edward Roether is with the architectural firm of HOK Sport Venue Event in Kansas City, Missouri.

record. A fire on February 20, 2003, at the nonsprinklered Station Nightclub in West Warwick, Rhode Island, resulted in the loss of 100 lives (Figure 20.9.1).

Tables 20.9.1 and 20.9.2 provide data on structure fires in assembly occupancies.[1]

SPECIAL CONSIDERATIONS

Restaurants and Nightclubs

Both restaurants and nightclubs share common concerns, such as aisles that do not provide adequate access to exits. Adding tables in an effort to increase the number of occupants may simply be uncomfortable under normal conditions but can be disastrous in an emergency. Although nightclubs share this concern with restaurants, it is more acute with nightclubs due to increased consumption of alcohol.

Proper aisle access and aisles must be maintained to facilitate egress. Aisles should be wide enough to accommodate the movement of people, taking into consideration the position of chairs during normal use and during emergencies. Proper aisle access and aisle widths also provide more comfort and make table service easier and more efficient in restaurants. Nightclubs differ from restaurants in that there can be less focus on ease and efficiency in table service and the occupant load is more concentrated. Certain techniques, such as using small, round tables rather than larger, square tables, help achieve maximum patron capacity.

In both restaurants and nightclubs, the decor can be elaborate and thematic. Care and attention are required to assure that decor does not obstruct or obscure exits, exit markings, emergency lighting, automatic sprinkler systems, and other safety features. Absence of effective, well-understood procedures for alerting patrons to an emergency and notifying the fire department can have disastrous outcomes in these occupancies. Delayed notification shortens the available evacuation time in case of an emergency and delays fire department response. Reluctance to notify patrons and the fire department of an emergency before the last possible minute significantly reduces the likelihood of safe egress.

Fixed Seating

Occupancies that use fixed seating present the usual challenges, such as exit marking, emergency illumination, and occupant notification; however, there are some added unique considerations. Fixed seating arrangements have very concentrated occupant densities in a confined environment where there is limited ability to move. People exiting from their seats must move through the space between the rows of seats (called an *aisle accessway* in *NFPA 5000* and NFPA *101*) to reach an aisle, and then tra-

FIGURE 20.9.1 Overhead View of Smoldering Remains of Station Nightclub (Source: AP Photo by Tom Gilbert)

TABLE 20.9.1 Structure Fires in Eating and Drinking Establishments, 1999–2002 Annual Averages

Occupancy	*Fires*	*Civilian Deaths*	*Civilian Injuries*	*Direct Property Damage (in Millions of Dollars)*
Restaurant or cafeteria	7670	3	108	153
Bar or nightclub	1270	1	13	41
Unclassified or unknown-type eating or drinking place	960	1	12	20
Total	9910	4	133	214

Note: These are national estimates of fires reported to U.S. municipal fire departments and so exclude fires reported only to federal or state agencies or industrial fire brigades. National estimates are projections. Casualty and loss projections can be heavily influenced by the inclusion or exclusion of one unusually serious fire. Fires are rounded to the nearest ten, civilian deaths and injuries are rounded to the nearest one, and direct property damage is rounded to the nearest million dollars.

Source: National estimates based on NFIRS and NFPA survey.

TABLE 20.9.2 Structure Fires in Public Assembly Properties, Excluding Eating and Drinking Establishments and Religious and Funeral Properties, 1999–2002 Annual Averages

Occupancy	*Fires*	*Civilian Deaths*	*Civilian Injuries*	*Direct Property Damage (in Millions of Dollars)*
Fixed use amusement or recreation	710	0	6	15.2
Variable use amusement or recreation	930	1	6	11.9
Club	950	1	17	31.4
Library, museum, or courtroom	450	0	5	11.2
Passenger terminal	220	0	2	0.7
Theater or studio	270	0	6	3.2
Unclassified or unknown-type public assembly property	360	0	2	8.2
Total	3890	2	43	81.8

Note: These are national estimates of fires reported to U.S. municipal fire departments and so exclude fires reported only to federal or state agencies or industrial fire brigades. National estimates are projections. Casualty and loss projections can be heavily influenced by the inclusion or exclusion of one unusually serious fire. Fires are rounded to the nearest ten, civilian deaths and injuries are rounded to the nearest one, and direct property damage is rounded to the nearest hundred thousand dollars.

Source: National estimates based on NFIRS and NFPA survey.

verse the aisle to a cross-aisle, vomitory, vestibule, concourse, or corridor, and continue to an exit. Proper design of each exit access component for the fixed seating area is critical for safe egress of all occupants during an emergency.

Prior to the 1988 edition, NFPA *101* classified fixed seating into two types: (1) normal and (2) continental (Figures 20.9.2 and 20.9.3).

Normal seating is characterized by a limited number of seats, with cross-aisles limiting dead-end aisles. Continental seating is characterized by long rows of chairs discharging into side aisles, which, in turn, connect directly to exits from the room. In 1988, NFPA *101* was the first model code to adopt concepts for all seating in new assembly occupancies rather than dividing seating into two categories. These concepts can now be found in other model codes. This approach recognizes the advantages of continental seating, such as reduced egress time, and applies those principles comprehensively to all seating. Since the inception of this new approach, the requirements for

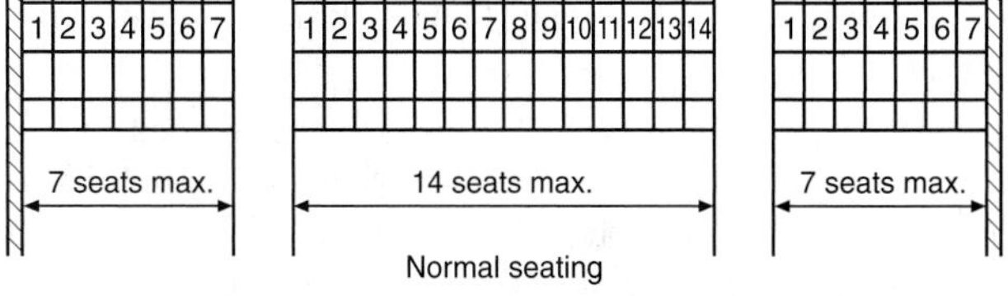

FIGURE 20.9.2 Arrangement of Seats and Aisles in an Assembly Occupancy with Normal Seating

assembly seating have been refined through the code development process.

NFPA 5000 and NFPA *101* utilize one approach for all assembly seating arrangements. Egress capacity factors are used to calculate minimum required clearances. Alternative factors

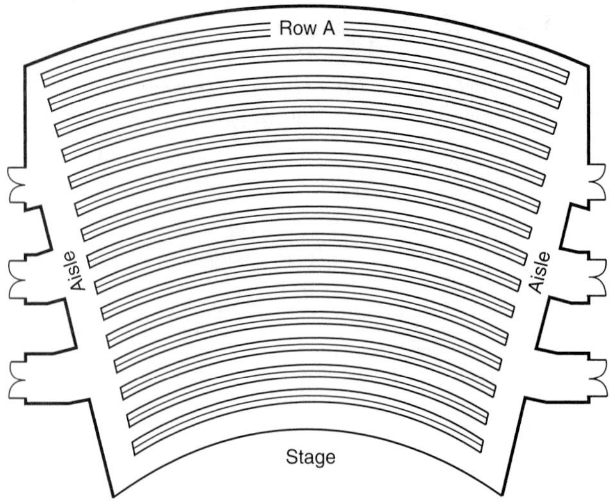

FIGURE 20.9.3 Arrangement of Seats and Aisles with Continental Seating

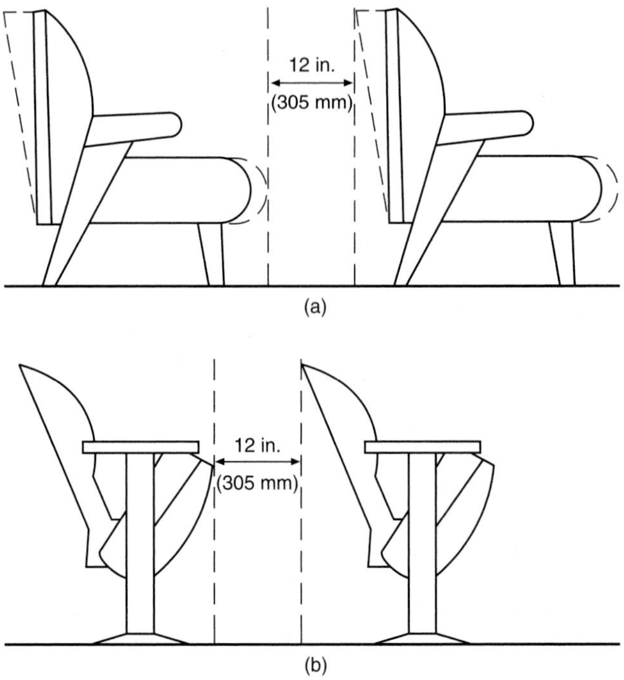

FIGURE 20.9.4 Correct Measurement of Minimum Spacing Between Rows of Seats (Aisle Accessway Width) (a) Without Self-Rising Seats and (b) With Self-Rising Seats

are utilized where the assembly seating is protected from smoke since more time to egress would be provided by such protection. However, an overall evaluation of life safety is necessary to support such modifications. Assembly seating requirements are summarized as follows:

1. Rows of seats are permitted to extend to 100 seats between aisles provided there is sufficient clearance between rows. However, rows would typically have fewer seats between aisles due to practical considerations.

2. The minimum clear width between rows of seats, called the *aisle accessway,* is determined by starting with 12 in. (355 mm) for an allocated number of seats, which is then increased proportionately for the number of additional seats up to a maximum width of 22 in. (560 mm) (Figure 20.9.4).

3. The length of *dead-end aisles,* an aisle exiting in only one direction, is limited unless the assembly seating is protected from smoke. However, the length of dead-end aisles in a smoke-protected assembly would be limited by the number of seats served by the aisle and the width of the aisle along with practical considerations.

4. The minimum width of aisles is determined by the greater of either a specified minimum width or a formula based on egress capacity factors, which take into account the riser height of the steps in a stepped aisle, the slope of a ramped aisle, and the locations of handrails.

5. The travel distance to an exit from assembly seating areas is limited to 200 ft (61 m) or 250 ft (76 m) if the occupancy is protected by an approved, supervised automatic sprinkler system. Greater distances are permitted where the occupancy is protected from smoke; it is permitted to be unlimited where the occupancy is smoke protected, the seating facility is of Type I or Type II construction as defined in *NFPA 5000,* and all portions of the means of egress are open to the outside.

Smoke-protected assembly seating is defined by NFPA *101* and *NFPA 5000* as seating served by a means of egress that is not subject to smoke accumulation within or under the structure. Smoke-protected assembly seating is typically achieved in indoor venues by providing an engineered smoke control system. NFPA *101* establishes conditions that must be assessed as part of a life safety evaluation when considering provisions for smoke-protected assembly seating. See the end of this chapter for a brief discussion of life safety evaluation. Where loose chairs are used in lieu of fixed seating, care must be taken to keep the chairs from being moved into a haphazard arrangement that could impair exit access. Generally, loose chairs must be arranged in a manner similar to fixed seating to maintain required aisle accessway and aisle widths. To prevent chair movement during use, most codes require loose chairs to be fastened together in groups to make them difficult to reposition in order to maintain egress paths. Many chair manufacturers produce chairs with interlocking features to meet this requirement. These features usually require no tools to join or separate the chairs, which can also be stacked for storage.

Festival Seating

A concept called *festival seating* is popular for certain entertainment events, particularly concerts. Festival seating is an audience or spectator accommodation in which no seating, other than the floor or ground surface, is provided for the audience gathered to observe a performance. This type of seating has the potential to result in overcrowding and high audience density that may compromise occupant safety. Also notable is the potential for injury prior to the actual event as patrons rush into the venue seeking the best locations. Festival seating should be used with caution. NFPA *101* requires the completion of a life safety evaluation for festival seating for more than 250 occupants; in addition, trained crowd managers are required for all assembly occupancies. See the end of this chapter for a discussion of a life safety evaluation.

Multipurpose Rooms

Ballrooms, meeting rooms, cafeterias, and gymnasiums are usually multipurpose rooms and may be used for dining, dancing, sporting events, exhibits, meetings, receptions, or other uses. In general, local codes contain requirements for each use. Overall, the key to occupant safety is adequate exiting. If movable walls or partitions subdivide large areas, each subdivision must have proper exit access and exits. Care must be taken to ensure that proper means of egress is designed into the arrangement.

Exhibit Halls

Exhibit halls are large assembly areas that are multipurpose in nature. Special diligence regarding control of display and chair arrangement must be exercised to ensure unimpeded egress and to maintain the proper travel distances to exits. Therefore, a permit process for the authority having jurisdiction's approval of display and seating layouts is recommended prior to each trade show or exhibition.

Exhibit halls might have excessive quantities of combustible materials unless provisions are made for remotely storing the packing materials needed to transport the displays and for surplus quantities of literature. The importance of this cannot be overemphasized, since failure to remove this heavy fuel load to proper storage areas, remote from the exhibit hall, can result in large, rapidly spreading fires. The McCormick Place fire of January 1967, in Chicago, Illinois, is an example of the fire potential of this type of occupancy.[2] Special attention must be paid to the travel distance within a larger exhibit booth or display to the aisle; this distance should be limited to 50 ft (15 m). Multilevel exhibit booths present problems with regard to both egress and fire protection. This type of booth, as well as large exhibit booths with ceilings, can shield the booth's contents from the building's automatic sprinkler system. In these cases, consideration should be given to providing sprinkler protection for the booth itself. In all cases, booths should be constructed of noncombustible, limited combustible, or fire-retardant-treated materials. NFPA *101* and *NFPA 5000* contain special requirements for exhibit halls. Because of the fuel load and the large number of occupants, moderate and larger size exhibit halls should be provided with automatic sprinkler systems in accordance with NFPA 13, *Standard for the Installation of Sprinkler Systems.*

Sports Facilities

Sports arenas, stadiums, ballparks, and field houses usually have fixed seating for large numbers of spectators, as well as large areas. It is not uncommon for such occupancies to hold more than 10,000 people. Smoke development during a fire can present a major threat to life safety when large numbers of people are evacuating a sports facility. Proper clearances between rows of seats, aisle width, and travel distances require proper care during the planning stage. Protecting the assembly seating and exit path from smoke provides more time for people to evacuate, thereby allowing adjustment in clearances and travel distances where smoke protected.

On the positive side, these occupancies usually include very large open areas, permitting smoke to be diluted or held above exiting occupants' heads in the early stages of a fire, keeping them reasonably safe for egress. Engineered smoke control systems can be designed to keep enclosed facilities protected from smoke similar to outdoor facilities. If they are used for exhibitions, the special considerations for exhibit halls must also be followed. Requirements for the design of smoke-control systems are provided in NFPA 92A, *Standard for Smoke-Control Systems Utilizing Barriers and Pressure Differences,* and NFPA 92B, *Standard for Smoke Management Systems in Malls, Atria, and Large Spaces.*

Care must be taken to prevent the accumulation of combustible waste under seating areas; such trash accumulation, along with combustible construction, contributed to the Bradford, England, soccer stadium fire of 1985, in which 56 spectators died.

Passenger Terminals

Passenger terminals require special consideration for fire safety because only general rules can be written for their regulation. Dense populations are localized, especially at departure and arrival gates. NFPA *101* and *NFPA 5000,* via annex notes, recommend special occupant load factors for airport terminals. As in most assembly occupancies, the occupants of passenger terminals are generally unfamiliar with the building, its egress routes, and its protection features. Proper marking of exits and egress routes and limiting travel distances to exits are particularly important.

The potential for significant loss of life from fire in passenger terminals that are not sprinklered has been tragically realized in recent years. On November 18, 1987, a fire originated within an escalator at the King's Cross Station—a subway station in London, England—leading to the deaths of 30 occupants and one fire fighter.[3] On April 11, 1996, workers using cutting torches inadvertently started a fire in a combustible concealed space in the ceiling of a terminal building at the airport in Düsseldorf, Germany. The ensuing fire spread rapidly and undetected in the void space. By the time it was noticed, a significant portion of the ceiling void was involved in fire. Delays in occupant notification resulted in numerous people trapped in spaces adjoining the main terminal area, such as airline clubrooms and lounges. Because these mezzanine areas were only provided with means of egress back through the main terminal area, and inadequate occupant notification was provided, 17 occupants lost their lives and 62 were injured.[4]

Passenger terminals must have their projected occupant loads carefully analyzed based on projected passenger operations; capacity of aircraft, vehicles, and trains utilized; and peak scheduling and possible delays, which involve embarking and disembarking passengers. A study of embarking and disembarking passengers with safety factors for delays should be performed. In addition certain sterile or secure areas and the people who must use these areas in a given time frame need to be analyzed. Unlike most other assembly facilities, the projected occupant load does not increase proportionally with increased floor area.

Special Amusement Buildings

Special amusement buildings are temporary, permanent, or mobile structures that contain a device or system conveying passengers, space for viewing a display, a walkway course in any direction, or any combination for the purposes of amusement. These structures are of particular concern because the egress path might not be readily apparent due to low lighting levels, visual or audio distractions, and intentionally confounded paths of travel. In addition, amusement displays can involve a large amount of combustibles. The Haunted Castle fire at the Great Adventure Amusement Park in Jackson Township, New Jersey, on May 11, 1984, is an example of all of these concerns that was not equipped with an automatic sprinkler system. Eight teenagers, ranging in age from 15 to 19 years, died in that fire.[5] Special amusement buildings require unique protection provisions. Consideration should be given to automatic sprinkler protection, special controls to increase lighting levels and turn off confusing or confounding sounds and visual displays when smoke is detected, the strategic placement of exit signs, and control of interior finish materials. NFPA *101* and *NFPA 5000* contain provisions for special amusement buildings that address all the above considerations.

Requirements for special amusement buildings in NFPA *101* and *NFPA 5000* include multilevel play structures, such as those found in children's play areas in fast-food restaurants. It is important to note that NFPA *101* and *NFPA 5000* classify special amusement buildings as assembly occupancies even when the occupant load is less than 50 persons; other assembly uses must meet the 50-occupant load threshold before they are classified as assembly occupancies.

OCCUPANCY HAZARDS

Cooking and Open Flames

Cooking is often associated with the use of assembly occupancies (Tables 20.9.3 and 20.9.4).[1] The hazards associated with cooking in traditional kitchens can be handled by automatic extinguishing systems and proper vapor removal, as outlined in NFPA 96, *Standard for Ventilation Control and Fire Protection of Commercial Cooking Operations.* The widespread use

TABLE 20.9.3 Leading Causes of Structure Fires in Eating and Drinking Establishments, 1999–2002 Annual Averages

Cause	*Fires*		*Civilian Deaths*		*Civilian Injuries*		*Direct Property Damage (in Millions of Dollars)*	
Cooking equipment fires	4500	(45%)	1	(27%)	68	(51%)	30	(14%)
Identified cooking equipment	3300	(33%)	1	(27%)	56	(42%)	28	(13%)
Confined cooking fire	1210	(12%)	0	(0%)	12	(9%)	2	(1%)
Electrical distribution and lighting equipment	1050	(11%)	0	(0%)	5	(4%)	42	(20%)
Heating equipment fires	790	(8%)	0	(11%)	8	(6%)	12	(6%)
Identified heating equipment fire	510	(5%)	0	(11%)	7	(5%)	12	(5%)
Confined heating equipment	280	(3%)	0	(0%)	2	(1%)	0	(0%)
Smoking materials	820	(8%)	4	(82%)	8	(6%)	19	(9%)
Intentional	760	(8%)	2	(54%)	12	(9%)	42	(20%)
Exposure to other fire	150	(2%)	0	(0%)	0	(0%)	6	(3%)
Contained trash or rubbish fire	180	(2%)	0	(0%)	1	(1%)	0	(0%)

Note: These are the leading causes, obtained from the following list: intentional (from the NFIRS field "cause"); playing with fire (from factor contributing to ignition); confined heating (including confined chimney and confined fuel burner or boiler fires), confined cooking, and contained trash or rubbish (from incident type); identified heating, identified cooking, clothes dryer or washer, torch (including burner and soldering iron), electrical distribution and lighting equipment, medical equipment, and electronic, office, or entertainment equipment (from equipment involved in ignition); smoking materials, candles, lightning, and spontaneous combustion or chemical reaction (from heat source); and mobile property involved (from mobile property involved in ignition). Exposure fires include fires with an exposure number greater than zero, as well as fires identified by heat source or factor contributing to ignition when no equipment was involved in ignition that were not intentionally set. The same fire can be listed under multiple causes, based on multiple data elements.

These are national estimates of fires reported to U.S. municipal fire departments and so exclude fires reported only to federal or state agencies or industrial fire brigades. National estimates are projections. Casualty and loss projections can be heavily influenced by the inclusion or exclusion of one unusually serious fire. Fires are rounded to the nearest ten, civilian deaths and injuries are rounded to the nearest one, and direct property damage is rounded to the nearest million. Property damage has not been adjusted for inflation.

Source: NFIRS and NFPA survey.

TABLE 20.9.4 Structure Fires in Eating and Drinking Establishments by Area of Origin, 1999–2002 Annual Averages

Area of Origin	*Fires*		*Civilian Deaths*		*Civilian Injuries*		*Direct Property Damage (in Millions of Dollars)*	
Kitchen or cooking area	4080	(41%)	1	(33%)	70	(52%)	57	(27%)
Confined cooking fire	1210	(12%)	0	(0%)	12	(9%)	2	(1%)
Exterior wall surface	450	(5%)	0	(0%)	1	(1%)	5	(2%)
Exterior roof surface	370	(4%)	0	(0%)	4	(3%)	4	(2%)
Attic or ceiling/roof assembly or concealed space	360	(4%)	0	(0%)	4	(3%)	19	(9%)
Lavatory, bathroom, locker room, or check room	270	(3%)	0	(0%)	5	(3%)	2	(1%)
Dining room, bar or beverage area, cafeteria	230	(2%)	1	(22%)	4	(3%)	12	(6%)
Heating equipment room	210	(2%)	0	(0%)	4	(3%)	3	(2%)
Wall assembly or concealed space	190	(2%)	0	(0%)	0	(0%)	3	(1%)
Storage of supplies or tools or dead storage	190	(2%)	0	(0%)	4	(3%)	7	(3%)
Duct for HVAC, cable, exhaust, heating, or air conditioning	130	(1%)	0	(0%)	1	(1%)	3	(1%)
Office	110	(1%)	1	(22%)	3	(2%)	5	(3%)
Confined chimney fire	100	(1%)	0	(0%)	1	(0%)	0	(0%)
Storage room, area, tank, or bin	90	(1%)	0	(0%)	1	(1%)	4	(2%)
Ceiling/floor assembly or concealed space	90	(1%)	0	(0%)	0	(0%)	6	(3%)
Unclassified	90	(1%)	0	(0%)	0	(0%)	2	(1%)
Crawl space or substructure space	90	(1%)	0	(0%)	0	(0%)	20	(9%)
Small assembly area, less than 100-person capacity	90	(1%)	1	(12%)	4	(3%)	4	(2%)
Common room, living room, family room, lounge, or den	80	(1%)	0	(0%)	2	(1%)	6	(3%)
Laundry room or area	80	(1%)	0	(0%)	3	(2%)	1	(1%)
Lobby or entrance way	80	(1%)	0	(0%)	1	(0%)	3	(1%)
Confined fuel burner or boiler fire	80	(1%)	0	(0%)	2	(1%)	0	(0%)
Unclassified equipment or service area	80	(1%)	0	(0%)	2	(1%)	2	(1%)
Trash or rubbish chute, area, or container	70	(1%)	0	(0%)	0	(0%)	1	(1%)
Awning	60	(1%)	0	(0%)	0	(0%)	1	(0%)
Unclassified storage area	60	(1%)	0	(0%)	1	(0%)	3	(2%)
Unclassified structural area	50	(1%)	0	(0%)	0	(0%)	4	(2%)
Chimney	50	(1%)	0	(0%)	0	(0%)	1	(0%)
Other known service or equipment area	110	(1%)	0	(0%)	1	(0%)	3	(1%)
Other known means of egress	90	(1%)	0	(0%)	1	(1%)	3	(1%)
Other known assembly or sales area	90	(1%)	0	(0%)	0	(0%)	3	(1%)

of "display cooking" presents new problems in vapor removal and in protecting the cooking surfaces and humans in case of fire. However, display cooking on properly designed and fixed equipment can be made reasonably safe with fixed systems, proper means of egress, and trained staff.

The use of portable cooking equipment must be carefully evaluated before it is permitted. Cooking equipment that uses LP-gas is common; however, large LP-gas cylinders, such as those commonly found on outdoor gas grills, must never be used indoors. A failure of the valve or connecting hose or other event could result in propane leakage and potentially result in a vapor cloud explosion. Such an event in an indoor assembly occupancy would obviously be catastrophic. Small LP-gas cylinders, similar in appearance to aerosol spray cans, can be used safely indoors with properly listed equipment. Details on the use of such equipment are found in NFPA 58, *Liquefied Petroleum Gas Code.*

The use of open-flame devices in tableside and flambé cooking should be carefully reviewed before it is permitted. Specially designed equipment and properly trained staff are necessary to ensure safety. The use of candles and other open flames requires the same degree of awareness as tableside cooking. Several commercial devices are available that make open-flame lighting safe, even in the event of a tip-over. Coordination between facility operators and the fire department can help maintain an acceptable level of safety.

Theatrical Stages

The distinctive fire hazards of theaters tend to revolve around the stage area. The 1903 Iroquois Theater fire in Chicago, Illinois, is probably the most vivid example of a stage fire and its tragic consequences.[6] The Iroquois Theater was not protected with automatic sprinklers and did not have many of today's code-required safeguards.

Traditional proscenium stages have scenery and lighting "flown" above the stage and scenery on the back and sides of the stage; shops along the back and sides of the stage; and storage, props, trap doors, and stage lifts under the stage floor. The potential for maximum fire severity is great with this combination of fuel and potential ignition sources. Since the Iroquois Theater fire, many safeguards have been required to control these hazards, including the following:

- Automatic sprinklers at the ceiling level, below the gridiron, in usable spaces under the stage, and in all auxiliary spaces surrounding the stage
- Ventilation over the stage, operable manually or automatically by fusible links
- An automatically closing fire-resistant curtain to cut off the stage from the audience chamber

All of these features are necessary with a full theatrical stage, defined in NFPA *101* and *NFPA 5000* as a *legitimate stage.*

Modern stages are generally modified versions of the classic theatrical stage. More scenery is now moved horizontally, eliminating the need for the high scene loft or fly space. Modern stages also tend to be variations of the traditional proscenium stage, thrusting the stage farther out into the audience or having it open to the audience on three sides, as in an arena theater—often called "theater in the round."

Whatever the arrangement of scenery on the stage, scenery handling equipment and allied shops need to be protected to prevent a large stage fire from threatening the audience, either directly or indirectly during evacuation.

Projection Booths

Projection booths refer to any booth housing equipment for the transmission of light onto a screen, curtain, or stage. The hazard is not with the projection of motion pictures or slides made on flammable film, as is commonly assumed, but with the mechanism used to project light. Electric arc, zenon, and other light sources generate hazardous gases, dust, or radiation and can fail with explosive force under certain circumstances. Where these light sources are used, a booth around the projection equipment is required to protect the audience. Proper ventilation also is required. Incandescent light sources do not produce the same hazard and, therefore, need not have the same enclosure. The enclosure of projection rooms in modern motion picture theaters is for sound control, not fire protection purposes.

Modern motion pictures and slides use safety film, which does not introduce the hazards of nitrocellulose found in early movies. Therefore, modern projection rooms are not designed for, and cannot safely project, non–safety film.

Storage

Improper storage practices present a hazard for fire and life safety in assembly occupancies, as in many other occupancies. Storage of tables and chairs, scenery, or supplies in aisles, exit access paths, or exits compromises not only life safety of a large number of occupants trying to evacuate but also fire department response. It is essential that space be allocated for proper storage of materials, supplies, props, tables, chairs, and other items associated with assembly occupancies to avoid the creation of unnecessary hazards.

LIFE SAFETY CONCEPTS FOR ASSEMBLY OCCUPANCIES

Many life safety features contribute to the protection of assembly occupancies, including construction, fire suppression, alarm systems, interior finish, and employee training (Tables 20.9.5 and 20.9.6).[1]

Construction

Assembly occupancies have a high occupant density under variable conditions, which, to one degree or another, makes alerting and evacuating the occupants more difficult than in other occupancies. Because of this, building construction is an important element in the life safety system.

In general, the building should be constructed to allow the structure to remain intact under fire conditions and not contribute significantly to the fire development for at least the time necessary for evacuation. Obviously, for a one-story building, this is relatively easy to accomplish when occupant loads are moderate in size (under 1000). But even a one-story building with proper exits may require structural protection and/or fire-resistant finish materials to ensure everyone's safety. The roof height and the required evacuation time, type of construction, finish materials, fire suppression, and means of egress need to be analyzed and considered specifically to the type of assembly occupancy.

As building heights increase, the level of construction and protection must increase accordingly to permit large assembly occupancies on higher stories. NFPA *101* and *NFPA 5000* specify sizes of assembly occupancies permitted in buildings based on construction, height of the assembly occupancy above the level of exit discharge, and fire protection provided (such as the presence of automatic sprinkler systems). Whereas *NFPA 5000* is generally limited to new construction, NFPA *101* applies to both new and existing assembly occupancies.

Alarm Systems

Prompt notification of occupants of an emergency cannot be overemphasized. However, the sounding of a fire alarm without

TABLE 20.9.5 Automatic Suppression Systems in Public Assembly Property Structure Fires Reported to Public Fire Departments Excluding Fires in Eating and Drinking Establishments and in Religious and Funeral Properties, 1994–1998 Annual Averages

Percentage of fires in buildings with automatic suppression system	26%
Deaths per 1000 fires with automatic suppression system present	0.0
Deaths per 1000 fires with no automatic suppression system present	1.1
Reduction in deaths per 1000 fires when automatic suppression systems were present	100%
Average loss per fire when automatic suppression system was present	$6,320
Average loss per fire with no automatic suppression system	$30,490
Reduction in loss per fire when automatic suppression systems were present	79%

Source: National estimates based on NFIRS and NFPA survey.

TABLE 20.9.6 Automatic Suppression Systems in Fires in Eating and Drinking Establishments Reported to Public Fire Departments, 1994–1998 Annual Averages

Percentage of fires in buildings with automatic suppression system	29%
Average loss per fire when automatic suppression system was present	$6,500
Average loss per fire with no automatic suppression system	$18,800
Reduction in loss per fire when automatic suppression systems were present	65%

Source: National estimates based on NFIRS and NFPA survey.

accompanying verbal instructions might introduce the threat of panic, or alternatively, delay in occupant response. To overcome these possibilities, an appropriate alarm system—perhaps one using prerecorded or electronically synthesized voice messages—can be installed. Such voice-evacuation systems are required by NFPA *101* and *NFPA 5000* in assembly occupancies that have occupant loads greater than 300 persons.

Panic Hardware or Fire Exit Hardware

Because of the threat of a large group of occupants rushing to an exit, leaning together on the door, and making use of traditional knob-activated latching devices difficult or impossible, assembly occupancies usually require panic hardware or fire exit hardware. Panic hardware and fire exit hardware consist of a door-latching assembly incorporating a wide barlike or push padlike device that releases the latch on application of force in the direction of egress travel. Security-conscious owners in the past have objected to panic hardware or fire exit hardware because of the potential for slipping the latch from the outside for purposes of gaining unauthorized entry. However, modern panic and fire exit hardware designs provide for both life safety and security.

There is no excuse for chained or padlocked doors, given the availability of secure exit hardware. Outdoor facilities using gates offer different challenges. Although panic devices or fire exit hardware can be installed on gates, they cannot be made secure due to practical considerations without potentially compromising the hardware's ability to reliably open under crowd pressures. Therefore, other means to secure gates are often taken regardless of whether gates are provided with secure exit hardware or not. Any measures to secure exit gates must be removed prior to occupancy when such outdoor facilities are opened to the public so that such gates will open on contact.

Interior Finish

Interior finish is a key element in providing fire control and life safety. Materials used in assembly occupancies must limit the rate of flame spread and smoke production. Generally, materials are limited to flame spreads of 75 or less (Class A or B), when tested in accordance with NFPA 255, *Standard Method of Test of Surface Burning Characteristics of Building Materials,* for all but the smallest assembly uses. Drapes, hangings, tapestries, and other decorative materials must be fire retardant when tested in accordance with NFPA 701, *Standard Methods of Fire Tests for Flame Propagation of Textiles and Films,* if they constitute a significant part of the decor or if they would provide a continuous path for fire travel. Ignition of such materials without fire retardant can lead to very rapid fire growth and spread, with the potential for a high death toll in densely occupied spaces, such as the 1942 Cocoanut Grove nightclub fire in Boston, Massachusetts, in which 492 people perished. Proper treatment to make materials fire retardant is necessary to avoid disaster.[7] For additional information on interior finish, see Section 18, Chapter 2, "Interior Finish."

The fire at the Station Nightclub in West Warwick, Rhode Island, on February 20, 2003, was ignited by the improper use of indoor pyrotechnics. It is believed that foam sound insulation surrounding the stage area that did not limit the rate of flame spread and smoke production contributed to the rapid spread of this deadly fire.

Employee Training

Employees of assembly occupancies are critically important to the life safety of patrons. If staff members are trained properly, they can prevent serious injury or death to many patrons. The Beverly Hills Supper Club fire in 1977 at Southgate, Kentucky, showed the importance of staff assistance in fire survival.[8] Although the building lacked proper exits and had no automatic fire sprinkler protection, staff members saved hundreds of lives by leading patrons to means of escape unknown to the patrons.

The management of every assembly occupancy should devise an emergency plan in conjunction with the local fire department, deal with the many contingencies associated with fires, and properly train staff members in safe emergency procedures.

Assembly occupancies can be safely occupied when the following conditions are avoided:

- Overcrowding
- Blocked or impaired exits or means of exit access
- Chained or locked exits
- Storage of combustibles in improper locations
- Improper use or insufficient control of open flames
- Disregard for fire characteristics of materials and decorations

Crowd Management

The 2006 edition of NFPA *101* requires "trained crowd managers" for all assembly occupancies regardless of occupant load. This is a significant revision compared to the prior (2003) edition of the code, which set the occupant load threshold at 1000 occupants before crowd managers were required. Where the occupant load exceeds 250, an additional trained crowd manager or supervisor is required for every 250 occupants. Assembly occupancies used exclusively for religious worship with an occupant load not exceeding 2000 are exempt from the requirement for crowd managers. For additional information, see Section 4, Chapter 4, "Techniques of Crowd Management."

Sprinkler Protection

In response to the tragic Station Nightclub fire, the 2006 editions of NFPA *101* and *NFPA 5000* require automatic sprinkler protection for all of the following new assembly occupancies regardless of occupant load:

- Bars with live entertainment
- Dance halls
- Discotheques
- Nightclubs
- Assembly occupancies with festival seating

In addition, NFPA *101* now requires those same existing assembly occupancies with an occupant load of greater than 100 to be protected with a supervised automatic sprinkler system. This new provision requires retrofitting such existing assembly occupancies with automatic sprinkler protection.

Other new assembly occupancies are required by NFPA *101* and *NFPA 5000* to be protected by automatic sprinklers where the occupant load is 300 or greater or where necessary based on the building's construction type.

MAIN ENTRANCE/EXIT CRITERIA

The 2006 edition of NFPA *101* requires the following new assembly occupancies main entrance/exit on each level to accommodate two-thirds of the occupant load of such levels:

- Bars with live entertainment
- Dance halls
- Discotheques
- Nightclubs
- Assembly occupancies with festival seating

As in the requirement for automatic sprinkler protection, the increase of accommodating two-thirds of the occupants from the previous one-half the occupant load at the main entrance was in reaction to the Station Nightclub fire in Warwick, Rhode Island, in 2003.

LIFE SAFETY EVALUATION

A *life safety evaluation* is a comprehensive report on the planned safety measures considering such things as the nature of the assembly event and participants, crowd management, medical emergencies, fire hazards, structural systems (e.g., temporary stages, rigging, etc.), severe weather, earthquakes, civil disturbances, and hazardous materials. It also considers the relationships between facility management, event participants, emergency responders, and others. When required, a life safety evaluation must be prepared by persons having experience with the conditions described and must be approved by the authority having jurisdiction.

A life safety evaluation is an ongoing exercise that requires periodic confirmation at appropriate times depending on the facility and/or events being held. A change in the type of events, operational practices, or the built environment would warrant an evaluation of life safety. Operational practices may not be fully known when an application for a building permit is submitted. Therefore, consideration should be given to those contingent items needing confirmation prior to issuance of a certificate of occupancy.

Detailed guidance on the development of life safety evaluations is included in NFPA *101.*

SUMMARY

Assembly occupancies, by their nature, pose unique life safety challenges. Typical characteristics include large numbers of people with a high occupant density and an emotional or raucous environment (such as during a sporting event or rock concert). Because of the large number of occupants, evacuation of the building can take longer when compared to other occupancies. To ensure rapid evacuation, sufficient means of egress systems must be provided and maintained. Prompt notification must be made to the occupants and clear directions provided. This requires a well-documented emergency plan, trained staff, and facility management who must not hesitate in implementing the emergency plan. Fire-resistive construction, automatic fire suppression systems, adequate means of egress, alarm and communications systems, and trained staff all contribute to the safety of assembly occupants.

Lessons learned from the tragedies described in this chapter have been incorporated into codes, such as NFPA *101*®, *Life Safety Code*®, and *NFPA 5000*®, *Building Construction and Safety Code*®. Codes alone, however, are not the entire solution—they must be enforced. In other words, incorporation of lessons learned into the codes and even code adoption do not ensure occupant safety. Codes must be enforced for the entire life of the facility. Facility management must commit to life safety by maintaining fire protection systems and conducting frequent staff training. An open line of communications with the local fire department and other emergency response agencies (police, emergency medical services, etc.) will help to keep assembly events safe. Every assembly event poses unique hazards and each should be evaluated carefully and mitigated.

NFPA members can download at no cost a number of investigation reports on public assembly fires from NFPA's website at http://www.nfpa.org. Nonmembers may order investigation reports through the NFPA library.

BIBLIOGRAPHY

References Cited

1. Ahrens, M., *The U.S. Fire Problem Overview Report,* National Fire Protection Association, Fire Analysis and Research Division, Quincy, MA, Mar. 2006.
2. Mayor's Committee to Investigate McCormick Place Fire, *Report of the Investigation of the McCormick Place Fire of Jan. 16, 1967,* Chicago, IL, 1967.
3. Fennell, D., *Investigation into the King's Cross Underground Fire,* Her Majesty's Stationary Office, London, UK, Nov. 1988.
4. Comeau, E., "Airport Terminal Fire. Düsseldorf, Germany, April 11, 1996," Fire Investigation Report, National Fire Protection Association, Quincy, MA.
5. Bouchard, J., "Fire in Haunted Castle Kills Eight," *Fire Journal,* Vol. 79, No. 5, 1985, pp. 45–81.
6. Ditzel, P., "Theater of Death. December 30, 1903: Chicago's Iroquois Theater Becomes a Stage for an Inferno That Kills 602," *Firehouse Magazine,* Vol. 7, No. 12, 1982, pp. 52–60.
7. Grant, C. C., "Last Dance at the Cocoanut Grove," *NFPA Journal,* Vol. 85, No. 3, 1990, pp. 74–86.
8. Best, R. L., *Reconstruction of a Tragedy: The Beverly Hills Supper Club Fire, Southgate, Kentucky, May 28, 1977,* National Fire Protection Association, Quincy, MA, 1977.

NFPA Codes, Standards, and Recommended Practices

Reference to the following NFPA codes, standards, and recommended practices will provide further information on assembly occupancies discussed in this chapter. (See the latest version of The NFPA Catalog *for availability of current editions of the following documents.)*

NFPA 13, *Standard for the Installation of Sprinkler Systems*
NFPA 58, *Liquefied Petroleum Gas Code*
NFPA 92A, *Standard for Smoke-Control Systems Utilizing Barriers and Pressure Differences*
NFPA 92B, *Standard for Smoke Management Systems in Malls, Atria, and Large Spaces*
NFPA 96, *Standard for Ventilation Control and Fire Protection of Commercial Cooking Operations*
NFPA *101®*, *Life Safety Code®*
NFPA 101A, *Guide on Alternative Approaches to Life Safety*
NFPA 255, *Standard Method of Test of Surface Burning Characteristics of Building Materials*
NFPA 701, *Standard Methods of Fire Tests for Flame Propagation of Textiles and Films*
NFPA 5000®, *Building Construction and Safety Code®*

References

Comeau, E., and Duval, R. F., "Dance Hall Fire, Gothenburg, Sweden, October 28, 1998, Sixty-Three Fatalities," *Fire Investigation Report,* National Fire Protection Association, Quincy, MA, 2000.

Grosshandler, W., Bryner, N., Madrzykowski, D., and Kuntz, K., *Report of the Technical Investigation of the Station Nightclub Fire,* NIST NCSTAR2, National Institute of Standards and Technology, Gaithersburg, MD, June 2005.

Howarth, D. J., and Kara-Zaitri, C., "Fire Safety Management at Passenger Interchanges. The Achilles Heel of Maintaining a Fire Safe Environment," *Fire Engineers Journal,* Vol. 59, No. 201, 1999, pp. 17–24.

Marchant, E. W., Copping, A., and Idris, M. F. M., "Fire Safety Evaluation: Schools and Churches," *Proceedings* of 8th International INTERFLAM Conference, INTERFLAM '99, June 29–July 1, 1999, Edinburgh, UK, Interscience Communications Ltd., London, UK, 1999, pp. 1229–1234.

Morgan, H. P., and DeSmedt, J. C., "Fire Safety Engineering Solutions for the Design of an Airport Terminal Building," *Fire Safety Engineering,* Vol. 7, No. 1, 2000, pp. 16–19.

Murphy, J., "Now We're Cooking," *Fire International,* No. 189, Sept. 2001, p. 28.

NFPA Ready Reference: Fire Safety in Assembly Occupancies, National Fire Protection Association, Quincy, MA, 2004.

Chapter 10

Mercantile Occupancies

Ed Schultz

Chapter Contents

Key Terms

accessory occupancy, exit, mall building, means of egress, mercantile occupancy, occupant load factor, smoke management, sprinkler system

This chapter addresses mercantile occupancies, from small stores operated by families to large shopping malls and multiuse projects. It also describes changes in building codes in response to the increased complexities of megaprojects.

Because in many instances a mercantile use may be an ancillary or accessory use in a building with a different occupancy classification, this chapter covers only those facilities whose primary occupancy classification is mercantile.

See also Section 20, Chapter 1, "Assessing Life Safety in Buildings."

MERCANTILE OCCUPANCY CLASSIFICATIONS

Mercantile occupancies are facilities in which a wide variety of goods and services are displayed and sold. Examples of such goods and services include clothing and footwear; jewelry; beauty, health, and fitness products; home furnishings; luggage, books, cards, and stationery; music, electronic equipment, and photography supplies; sport specialties; toys, hobbies, and pets; drugs, varieties, and tobacco; food and food specialties; and hardware.

Many items displayed in mercantile occupancies are combustible and spread over the available floor where customers circulate to view and purchase the items. Many mercantile occupants are in an unfamiliar environment that may be conducive to rapid fire development after a fire begins. This condition raises various levels of concern because the size of the mercantile occupancy and the number of occupants vary greatly. Therefore, it is important to categorize mercantile stores by size.

Small Mercantile Occupancies

In the past, smaller shops were constructed principally in cities and towns, along business thoroughfares, next to each other, often with basements for stock, and sometimes with an office or dwelling unit immediately above them. Many such stores still exist today, especially in older business sections of cities; they are sometimes called "ma and pa" stores because their proprietors often live in the dwelling units directly above them. However, this type of store is slowly fading out of existence.

Because of more restrictive zoning regulations, larger stores are now constructed without other occupancies above them, unless the mercantile occupancy serves an ancillary or accessory use such as a retail shop in a hotel lobby. In addition, basement space, even for stock space, is being phased out because stock space on the same level as the sales area is more efficient and functional. Also the retail merchandising concepts have changed to that of displaying as much of the available merchandise on the sales floor as possible. This decreases the amount of inventory held in stockrooms.

Originally, these stores were constructed primarily of wood- or masonry-bearing walls with wood joists, floors, and roofs. Subsequent establishment of fire districts in urban areas, plus the adoption of more stringent building code requirements, led to construction with noncombustible materials, such as masonry walls, load bearing or nonload bearing; steel joists; concrete floors; and metal roof decks.

Ed Schultz is founder and principal of Code Consultants, Inc., in St. Louis, Missouri.

Until recently, these small stores were seldom sprinklered. NFPA *101*®, *Life Safety Code*®, and *NFPA 5000*®, *Building Construction and Safety Code*®, currently require sprinkler protection based on height and area and, in certain instances, whether the stores are located below the level of exit discharge.

Medium Mercantile Occupancies

Medium-size mercantile occupancy stores, such as supermarkets and discount drugstores, did not become numerous until the mid- to late 1940s. In many areas, they replaced the neighborhood grocer and the corner druggist, who could not compete with high-volume chains.

Medium mercantile occupancy stores generally range in size from 10,000 to 40,000 ft^2 (2800 to 3700 m^2), are usually one story with mezzanine management offices, and are usually constructed of noncombustible unprotected construction. Until the mid-1970s sprinklers were not required in these stores.

These stores are generally freestanding buildings, unless they are part of a shopping center complex, and they may have relatively large contiguous parking areas surrounding them.

Medium-size mercantile occupancy stores usually have at least two principal areas: (1) the stock space or "back of the house" employee area and (2) the sales space or customer area. Approximately one-tenth to one-third of the total area is apportioned to stock and the remainder to sales. These stores typically include nonmercantile accessory uses, such as management offices, that occupy a small area in relation to sales and stock space. From a retailer's viewpoint, the distinction between retail stock space and storage space is important. Employees enter the retail stock areas frequently during the day to bring merchandise onto the sales floor. Storage areas, on the other hand, are less frequently accessed because goods are set aside in these areas for extended time periods. Today, if one corporation operates many stores, its storage areas are generally in a separate location, essentially a distribution warehouse. Again the new retail marketing concepts are reducing the amount of area used for stock and storage areas in favor of enlarging the sales area to display more merchandise.

Large Mercantile Occupancies

The multiple-category merchandise store, such as a department store and bulk merchandising retail buildings, is as common as other types of mercantile occupancies. Generally from one to three stories high, their area normally exceeds 40,000 ft^2 (3700 m^2).

Earlier department stores were constructed exclusively in business and retail districts in cities. Stores were typically either of exterior masonry-bearing wall construction with protected wood joists and floors or of reinforced concrete. Many had no sprinkler protection. Today, most newly or recently constructed department stores are of protected and unprotected noncombustible construction and are protected by complete automatic sprinkler systems.

As their name implies, department stores are divided into departments or sections for different kinds of merchandise, with or without partition walls. Departments are laid out in a particular way to influence customer movement patterns vertically and horizontally through the store according to a preconceived merchandising plan. Vertical movement in multistory stores is most effectively accomplished using escalators and stairs in open wells in highly visible and accessible areas.

At one time basements were quite commonly used as either sales or stock areas. This practice generally is no longer followed because basement space is not as desirable as the same area constructed at or above ground level.

Unlike the vast majority of small and medium mercantile occupancies where stock space is located in the rear of the store, stock space in large mercantile occupancies is often distributed throughout the store in many small stockrooms. These stockrooms often represent 10 to 15 percent of the total floor area, with the remaining area used for retail sales.

Another example of a large mercantile store is the discount store, which grew out of the well-known "five-and-dime" variety store. It is usually one story high and laid out like a retail food supermarket, with shopping carts, self-service, and checkout counters. However, the same sectioning of merchandise occurs as in a department store.

Over the last 20 years, bulk merchandising retail stores have come into existence. These facilities are a blend of warehouse operation and retail sales store. Typically, pallet or rack storage is used in a large portion of the building with other areas of the building designed in the more traditional retail display using fixtures and low-level racks or shelves to display merchandise. A large portion of the facility typically has shelving and rack storage that can extend to a height of 20 ft (6 m) or more. The retail merchandise is displayed on the lower portion of the rack and the stock is located directly above. This arrangement eliminates the separate stock areas that are typical to retail department stores.

Bulk merchandising retail stores generally have very limited interior finishes and are typically constructed as warehouse facilities with exposed concrete floors, masonry exterior walls, and unprotected steel columns and roof structures. These stores function as self-service facilities with shopping carts and they have checkout counters near the main entry of the facility.

Since this type of retail operation displays and sells a variety of commodities, many of the design standards that must be used are those used for storage (warehouse) facilities. See the chapters on new and existing mercantile occupancies that are listed in NFPA *101* for a listing of some of these design standards. These properties are sufficiently challenging in size and fuel load that they may require a specific engineering analysis to design, and confirm the adequacy of, built-in fire protection. See, for example, several research reports from the Fire Protection Research Foundation dealing with flammable and combustible liquid storage in wholesale/retail occupancies.

Accessory Occupancies

To round out the full range of goods and services a customer needs and expects, mercantile occupancies sometimes include accessory or ancillary occupancies, in addition to administrative office areas. Examples are restaurants, beauty shops, travel agencies, banks, and optometry services.

OCCUPANT AND FIRE LOADS

Occupant Load

Actual occupant load varies with the seasons, generally being higher before school begins, around holidays, and during occasional clearance sales. NFPA *101* and *NFPA 5000* take these primary merchandising seasons into account in establishing the occupant load factor for calculating egress requirements. The model construction codes, including NFPA *101* and *NFPA 5000,* require that occupant load for mercantile occupancies be calculated on the basis of a factor of one occupant per 30 ft^2 (2.8 m^2) of street floor or basement sales areas, and a factor of one occupant per 60 ft^2 (5.6 m^2) of other upper sales floors. These factors for occupant load vary based on the expected flow of customers into and out of these large stores. An increase in occupant load is also created by the retailer merchandising concepts of placing the higher-volume sales items on the main level to accommodate and benefit from the higher customer flow.

These factors have been recognized by some of the codes by addressing building designs that have main entrances on more than one floor level. In these design concepts, the customer flow (occupant load) is projected to be less than a single main floor design but more than a second-level sales floor. Therefore, the occupant load factor assumed for this type of design concept is one occupant per 40 ft^2 (3.7 m^2) for both of the floor levels having main entrances. The occupant load for stock or storage space that is not open to the public and other accessory occupancies is calculated using different factors, depending on the particular use.

Fire Load

As in most other occupancies, contents represent the major potential hazard. Sprinklers have proven effective as a means of combating fires in mercantile occupancies. In terms of life safety, NFPA *101* reflects cost-benefit considerations in the use of sprinklers. Its requirements for sprinklers, based on height and area limits, let many small shops be unsprinklered (unless they are accessory uses to an occupancy requiring sprinklers), while requiring medium and large mercantile occupancies to be protected with automatic sprinklers. In recent years, recognition has been given to the variety of contents of mercantile occupancies. The building and fire codes have now addressed the amounts of select contents that could be classified as hazardous that may be stored or displayed in areas of a mercantile occupancy. The maximum quantities permitted are generally limited to control area; this provides for separation of materials that are considered as presenting a physical hazard such that a single fire or other type of condition would only affect the materials in one control area.

MALL BUILDINGS

A mall is commonly defined as a covered or roofed interior area used as a pedestrian way, which connects buildings or portions of a building housing single and/or multiple tenants. Mall buildings became very popular in a relatively short time period, and today most large shopping centers either planned or under construction are of this type. In addition, many mall buildings are now being built in urban areas as multiuse projects in conjunction with parking decks, office buildings, hotels, recreational facilities, and public or private transit systems.

The mall may be considered as either (1) a way of exit access from the connected buildings or (2) a pedestrian way permitting an increase in the distance of travel from each of the tenant stores to a mall exit.

The first instance treats the entire complex as one building or one compartmented retail facility; the mall is simply an extension of the sales space. In terms of exit access, the mall is an aisle common to the various tenant stores that extends (continues) exit access aisles of tenant stores to mall exits. This treatment, in terms of NFPA *101* and *NFPA 5000,* leads to the strict application of all design factors as though the shopping center were a large single mercantile occupancy or department store.

The second instance employs a systems approach. The mall is considered to offer a higher degree of safety than a typical aisle serving as an exit access if certain minimum conditions and systems are provided. The mall should be of at least sufficient clear width to accommodate egress requirements for all mercantile tenants, but in no case less than 20 ft (6 m) wide at its narrowest dimension. The minimum width dimension of 20 ft (6 m) is particularly significant in terms of protecting occupants from direct exposure to a fire within a tenant store while those occupants utilize the exit access paths within the mall. Newly constructed malls with floor openings connecting more than two levels must be provided with an engineered smoke control system.

Design

The mall building is generally designed as one building connecting several sizable department stores and composed of numerous smaller specialty stores (mall tenant shops), all interconnected by a covered, climate-controlled, pedestrian way. The complex may also include ancillary occupancies, such as movie theaters, bowling lanes, ice arenas, food courts, project management offices, and other customer service areas accessed from the mall. Some even contain enclosed amusement parks.

The mall building may be designed as a single- or multilevel structure, depending on such factors as topography, size of the land parcel, and number and size of department stores and retail shops.

When a mall has two levels, the parking areas surrounding it usually are shaped to provide grade access to each level of the department stores and the small shops. This permits each level to serve as an entrance/exit, thus providing stores on all levels increased and equalized customer traffic as customers enter and leave the building (Figure 20.10.1). The two-level shopping center differs from the two-story shopping center in this important respect. When department stores are part of a two-level mall building, they are designed and merchandised in a similar manner.

Building codes have recognized that the construction of mall buildings up to a maximum of three stories high with floor openings within the pedestrian way (the mall) complying with the code mall provisions should not be considered atriums based on the special code provisions that address mall buildings.

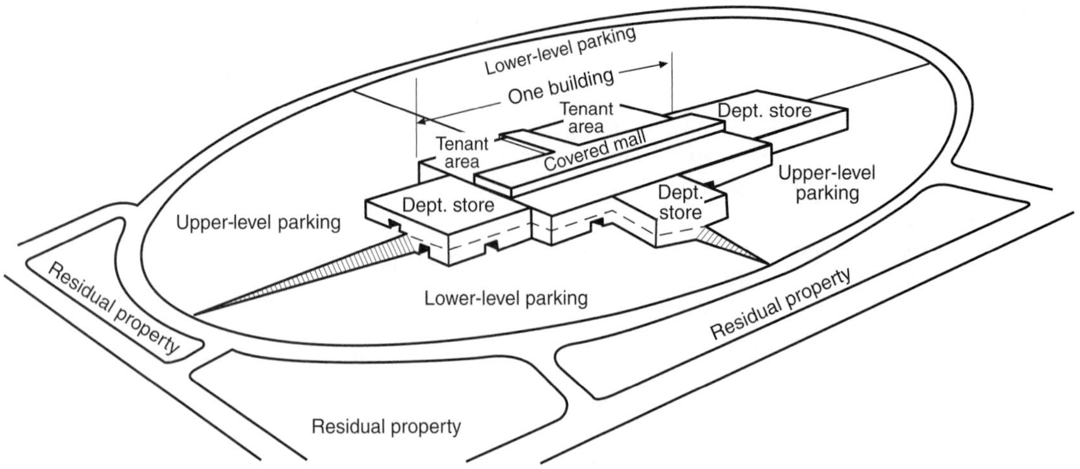

FIGURE 20.10.1 Two-Level Mall Building with Equal Distribution of Customer Traffic on All Levels

Exiting Concept. The mall proper is designed primarily to meet requirements for occupant flow and egress. Storefronts along the pedestrian way (the mall) must be designed to encourage unrestricted customer flow and traffic control from the mall to individual shops and to any connected department stores. This system of customer traffic flow and traffic control reflects the merchandising concept of mall buildings and the exiting concept of the codes. The exit concept is that the mall is an inherently safe space with controlled uses, adequate width, large volume, and high ceiling space that may also have smoke venting, and is protected with automatic sprinklers. This then allows egress capacity design to be based on the assumption that 100 percent of the occupants in the mall building will exit via the mall proper. This allows the back exit system for tenant shops to be sized for the most restrictive of the following:

1. The code-stated minimum dimension
2. The exit width required for the largest single tenant occupant flow exiting into the back exit system
3. The exit width required for occupants exiting from the mall, if the exit passageway also serves as a mall exit

This is the case even if the mall uses the same exit passageway that is used for a second exit by several mall tenant shops. Again this concept is based on the fact that occupants tend to exit the way they entered a store, via the mall itself. Therefore, the back exit system is truly a secondary exit system, and the mall is the primary egress path for mall building occupants.

Open storefronts between the mall and tenant mall shops are critical because swinging doors, whether glass or solid, not only make exiting more difficult but also promote what the retail industry calls "threshold resistance"—that is, customers' reluctance to push, pull, or slide doors to enter. The storefront closures ideally suited for maintaining after hours security are those that can be fully recessed, such as rolling overhead grilles, side-coiling grilles, and horizontal sliding doors. Because the ambient temperature in the mall and the tenant space is the same, the storefront closure only needs to satisfy a security requirement when the store is unoccupied.

Occupant Allowance Requirements. Mall buildings are constructed before tenants are known. When construction begins, the ultimate ratio of sales space to storage space for tenant stores and what changes may occur in the life of the building are also unknown. The use of each tenant space—for example, retail or assembly—is also typically unknown at the time of construction. Hence, occupant load must be projected to determine the required egress width well before negotiations with prospective tenants.

Egress width from the mall need only satisfy the calculated occupant load based on all connected tenant occupancies. It is not necessary to provide egress width from the mall commensurate with the minimum mall width. Doing so would unnecessarily result in wall-to-wall doors.

The occupant load factor used to determine egress width for the mall proper varies with the aggregate area of the connected stores. This sliding scale of occupant load factors reflects the relationship between an increase in a shopping center's size and an increase in its occupant load, which is not linear but parabolic, as Figure 20.10.2 shows. Once determined, the occupant load factor is applied to the gross leasable area (GLA) to calculate the covered mall building total occupant load for egress design. Again, this factor is not applied to gross building area. However, in mall buildings with large seating areas within the mall concourse that are part of a food court concept, the number of occupants for whom seating is provided is normally added to the occupant load that is calculated using the GLA of the mall building to establish the required egress width. Other types of assembly tenant spaces, such as restaurants with seating included within the tenant space, are considered as typical tenant spaces that are a portion of building's GLA.

Systems Approach

In most cases, two- or three-level covered malls are designed for visual communication among levels through openings in the floor of the upper level(s). Wherever practicable, visual com-

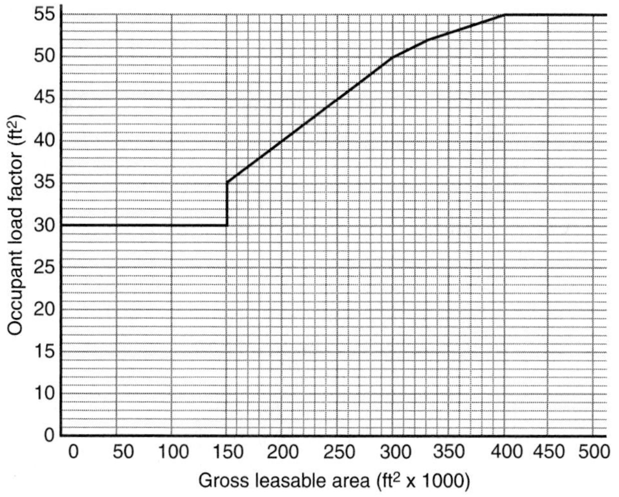

FIGURE 20.10.2 Relationship of an Increase in the Size of a Covered Mall to an Increase in the Occupant Load

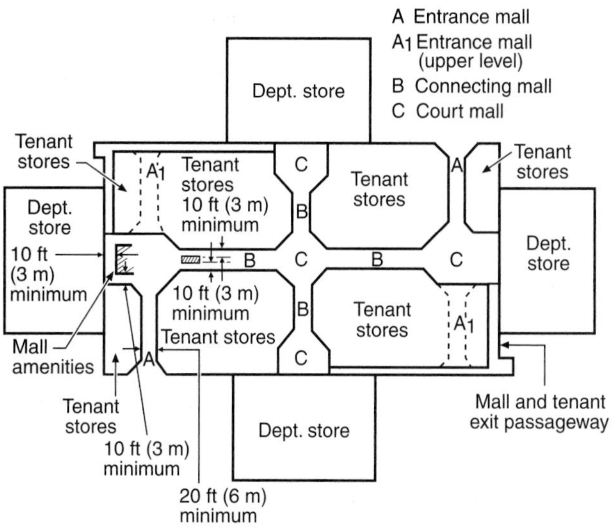

FIGURE 20.10.3 Typical Two-Level Shopping Center (Lower Level)

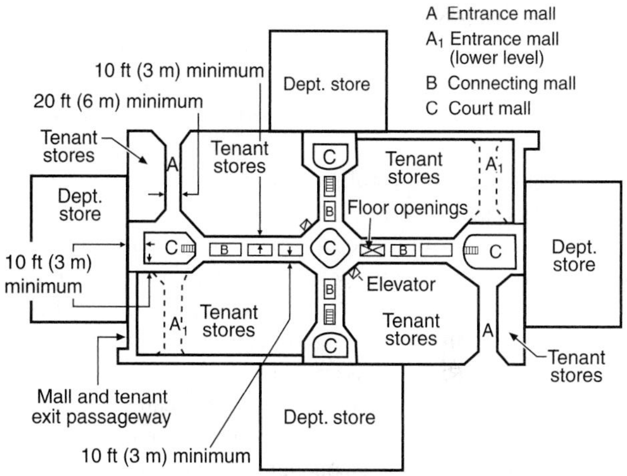

FIGURE 20.10.4 Typical Two-Level Shopping Center (Upper Level)

munication between levels is important in maximizing exposure of storefronts and merchandise to customer traffic. The floor areas between openings in the upper level(s) serve as bridges that promote cross-mall shopping convenience for the customer (Figures 20.10.3 and 20.10.4).

When construction starts, not everything about the shopping center is known, even to the developer. Mechanical, electrical, and fire protection systems are designed for main distribution only in the tenant store areas, with branch distribution added to the construction documents as lease agreements define tenant space.

The mall proper may contain other amenities for sales promotion, customer service, and convenience, such as seating areas, art objects, planting areas, food court seating areas, pools, specialty retail kiosks, directories, openings in upper levels of multilevel structures, and areas designed for promotional activities. Care must be exercised in locating these amenities so they do not interfere with, or encroach upon, required exit access. However, the width of the covered mall connecting courts at entrances to department stores generally is found well in excess of the 20 ft (6 m) minimum to provide for these amenities and at the same time provide for an aggregate of 20 ft (6 m) of exit access width (see Figure 20.10.3).

Stores located on either side of entrance malls and not along the direct path to department stores (commonly called "anchor stores" or "magnet stores" because of their greater customer attraction) do not enjoy as much customer exposure as those located along connecting malls. To compensate and maximize convenient cross-mall customer shopping, stores on opposite sides of the entrance mall are brought closer together by eliminating mall amenities that by themselves are not likely to generate traffic. The minimum mall width of 20 ft (6 m) is entirely compatible with this merchandising concept and does not impose an unreasonable burden on developers or merchants. This minimum width requirement has been applied successfully in shopping centers throughout the United States.

The mall should have an unobstructed exit access of not less than 10 ft (3 m) clear width on each side of the mall floor area, parallel and adjacent to the mall storefronts. The exit access should lead to an exit having a minimum of 66 in. (168 cm) of width. The purpose of requiring 10 ft (3 m) of clear exit access is to provide a higher degree of safety in the covered mall commensurate with its use as a continuation of exit access from the tenant stores. Safe, continuous, and unobstructed exit access from each tenant store is provided, while the owners' merchandising and operational requirements for mall amenities are recognized.

The minimum requirement of 10 ft (3 m) of clear exit access parallel and adjacent to the mall storefronts relates directly to the minimum mall width of 20 ft (6 m). None of the mall amenities mentioned earlier should encroach on this minimum dimension of 10 ft (3 m). In effect, this requirement precludes the installation of mall amenities in areas of the covered mall that are the minimum 20 ft (6 m) width. In life safety terms, this requirement has proven reasonable and workable and has the added advantage of not being unduly restrictive or burdensome to developers.

Sprinkler Protection

The mall and all its connected buildings must be provided with an electrically supervised automatic sprinkler system throughout. This has proven the most effective way to protect life and property from fire. Sprinklers allow the replacement of many passive long-standing code requirements by active systems in combination with specified design requirements. See NFPA 13, *Standard for the Installation of Sprinkler Systems,* for details on the design and installation of sprinkler systems.

Separation of Mall Tenant Stores

Walls dividing mall building stores from each other can extend from the floor to the underside of the roof deck or floor deck above or to the underside of a noncombustible ceiling. The purpose of this requirement is to help limit fire and smoke spread to its area of origin. No separation is required between a store and the covered mall. The engineering of a smoke-control system may require deletion of the tenant partitions above the ceilings so the system operates effectively to prevent smoke accumulation. Tenant separation walls are usually constructed of metal studs and gypsum board.

Any requirement for separation at the storefront would defeat the merchandising purpose of the mall: to optimize unrestricted customer flow between the mall and the tenant store. This form of compartmentation, in concert with an electrically supervised automatic sprinkler system, eliminates the need for any fire separation wall requirements at the mall storefronts. In shopping centers, additional fire separation is unnecessary and, in fact, burdensome from an operational standpoint. In the leasing and subsequent re-leasing of shopping centers, maximum flexibility to rearrange space is important to continued success.

Smoke Management

Smoke management has been evaluated over the 30 years that mall buildings have existed and several approaches to smoke management are used in these buildings. One approach is a method to remove smoke from the mall when smoke migrates into it, since the mall is a primary component of the means of egress system.

Another approach is to design an engineered smoke management system for both the mall and the tenant spaces. This approach reacts to smoke that develops in a tenant space to limit smoke migration to the mall.

A third approach is to use the expansive volume of the mall building space, including the volume of the mall proper, to act as a reservoir for the accumulation of combustion products. With this method, even if smoke develops and migrates into the mall area, it will represent little threat to life safety since the building is sprinklered throughout, and the smoke and combustion gases entering a large-volume space, such as an atrium or mall, can be expected to be maintained at the higher elevations of the mall, which are typically well above the occupants who are evacuating. Since the mall is typically a large open space, people can see the smoke developing from a distance and use one of the multiple egress paths available to evacuate the mall building, while moving away from the developing fire condition.

Construction codes recognize that active smoke removal or venting may not be necessary in one- or two-level mall buildings. Thus, the type of smoke management system used can vary depending on project design from active mechanical systems to that of a passive design concept. See NFPA 92A, *Standard for Smoke-Control Systems Utilizing Barriers and Pressure Differences,* and NFPA 92B, *Standard for Smoke Management Systems in Malls, Atria, and Large Spaces,* for details on smoke control system design.

General Requirements

In addition to the special code provisions, certain means of egress conditions should be present in all mall buildings:

1. Every floor and every store of a mall building, except those less than 100 ft (30 m) deep, should have at least two exits remotely located from each other. The two required exits may both be through the mall concourse if the exits from the tenant space are remotely located as required by the code.
2. Every mall should have unobstructed 10-ft (3-m) wide exit access parallel and adjacent to the connected tenant spaces. The exit access should extend to the mall exits.
3. Exits from the mall should be arranged so that travel distance from any mall storefront entrance to an exit is no more than 200 ft (61 m).

GENERAL LIFE SAFETY FACTORS APPLYING TO MERCANTILE OCCUPANCIES

A number of factors related to life safety are common to all types of mercantile facilities.

Prompt discovery is one of the most important factors associated with minimizing loss due to fire. This is especially important during nonbusiness hours, from late night to very early morning. Many fires occur in stock areas, as opposed to sales areas. Poor housekeeping and smoking are two significant concerns in stock areas. For example, workers may remove merchandise from cartons for display on the sales floor and not properly dispose of the cartons and packaging, thus increasing the hazard.

Properly engineered sprinkler systems can be expected to respond to a fire to control its development, if not extinguish it entirely. The exit concepts for all large mercantile occupancies, including bulk merchandising stores, require careful design to achieve the operational needs of the facility while ensuring safe evacuation of the occupants in the event of a fire or other emergency.

Some items to consider follow:

1. If the main entrances are in one wall of the store, the code may require 50 percent or more of the required egress capacity to be provided in the same exterior wall. If high racks or fixtures are used, occupants must be able to readily identify the direction to this main exit wall.
2. Do egress paths of travel conflict with merchandise and stock movement? Such could be the case if exit access passes through shipping and receiving areas without defined egress paths identified by floor markings or physical barriers.
3. Does exit access require travel through other use areas in which the egress path is not clear and direct? Exit access through stockrooms, back-of-house or employee areas, or exterior garden departments can be used effectively if a clear and defined egress path is available.

The need to renovate existing facilities as a result of new trends in fashion or store design may arise in mercantile facilities as may the need to reconstruct existing facilities when releasing space, especially in shopping centers. Extra care should be taken to mitigate the potential problem of fire during these times, since reconstruction and renovation are very likely to increase the hazard. See NFPA 241, *Standard for Safeguarding Construction, Alteration, and Demolition Operations,* for more information.

Certain accessory uses, such as food preparation areas in restaurants, often found in mercantile facilities and more particularly in department stores and shopping centers, warrant special attention. Such areas should be segregated with appropriate construction, if not sprinklered, and appropriate fire suppression systems should be installed in food preparation equipment. See NFPA 96, *Standard for Ventilation Control and Fire Protection of Commercial Cooking Operations,* for more information.

SUMMARY

An important purpose of this chapter on the nature of mercantile occupancy is to form a basis for considering or reconsidering code requirements that let the mercantile trade function optimally and yet provide the necessary degree of life safety for the facilities' occupants.

All requirement-related items discussed in this chapter have been practically applied in many stores and mall buildings throughout the United States. They have answered the need for life safety without imposing burdensome or unreasonable restrictions on either the developers or the merchandising needs of the mall buildings.

In addition to NFPA *101* and *NFPA 5000,* other model codes address the issues presented in this chapter in an effort to achieve codification of requirements for mall buildings. This effort's success will depend on how successfully the life safety concern is addressed in harmony with the retail merchandising purpose of the mall building.

Overreaction in the formulation of code requirements is possible if the fire record is not reviewed and used as a guide to the need for additional requirements. This is especially important when operational needs of the building type being considered are not fully understood. Therefore, code revisions should be tested to see if they are unreasonably restrictive or unfounded in terms of any real threat to life safety, compared to practicability in application and in terms of costs and benefits.

BIBLIOGRAPHY

NFPA Codes, Standards, and Recommended Practices

Reference to the following NFPA codes, standards, and recommended practices will provide further information on mercantile occupancies discussed in this chapter. (See the latest version of The NFPA Catalog *for availability of current editions of the following documents.)*

NFPA 13, *Standard for the Installation of Sprinkler Systems*
NFPA 92A, *Standard for Smoke-Control Systems Utilizing Barriers and Pressure Differences*
NFPA 92B, *Standard for Smoke Management Systems in Malls, Atria, and Large Spaces*
NFPA 96, *Standard for Ventilation Control and Fire Protection of Commercial Cooking Operations*
NFPA *101*®, *Life Safety Code*®
NFPA 241, *Standard for Safeguarding Construction, Alteration, and Demolition Operations*
NFPA 5000®, *Building Construction and Safety Code*®

References

Caldwell, C. A., "Ballantynes Department Store Performance Fire Design," *Proceedings* of Engineered Fire Protection Design . . . Applying Fire Science to Fire Protection Problems, June 11–15, 2001, San Francisco, CA, Society of Fire Protection Engineers, Bethesda, MD, 2001, pp. 54–65.
Comeau, E., and Duval, R., "Retail Store Fire, Mableton, Georgia (GA), October 26, 1997," Fire Investigation Report, National Fire Protection Association, Quincy, MA, 1998.
Comeau, E., Duval, R., and Dubay, C., "Bulk Retail Store Fire, Tempe, Arizona, March 19, 1998," *Fire Engineers Journal,* Vol. 58, No. 197, 1998, pp. 7–15.
Corbett, G. P., "Strip Malls: The Taxpayers of Today," *Fire Engineering,* Vol. 149, No. 5, 1996, pp. 58–62.
Johnson, P. F., and Timms, G. R., "Performance Based Design of Shopping Center Fire Safety," *Proceedings* of the 1st International Conference on Fire Science and Engineering, ASIAFLAM '95, March 15–16, 1995, Kowloon, Hong Kong, 1995, pp. 41–49.
McMillan, J., "Guideline for the Fire Design of Shopping Centres," Fire Engineering Research Report 00/16, University of Canterbury, Christchurch, New Zealand, Nov. 2000.
Shields, T. J., and Boyce, K. E., "Study of Evacuation from Large Retail Stores," *Fire Safety Journal,* Vol. 35, No. 1, 2000, pp. 25–49.
Shields, T. J., Boyce, K. E., and Silcock, G. W. N., "Towards the Characterization of Large Retail Stores," *Fire and Materials,* Vol. 23, No. 6, 1999, pp. 325–331.
Webb, B., Sr., "Evaluating Equivalencies to Code for a Four Level Shopping Mall," Rolf Jensen and Associates, Inc., Fairfax, VA, Video; Federal Fire Forum, Performance-Based Design Issues of Concern to the A/E Community, November 6, 1995, Gaithersburg, MD, 1995.
Webb, W. A., "Using FPETool to Evaluate Fire Safety of a Four-Level Shopping Mall," *Proceedings* of the International Conference on Fire Research and Engineering, September 10–15, 1995, Orlando, FL, Society of Fire Protection Engineers, Boston, 1995, pp. 365–370.

Chapter 11

Business Occupancies

Brian L. Marburger

Chapter Contents

Key Terms

defend in place, Fire Safety Evaluation System, fire scenario, means of egress, occupancy characteristic, relocation, staged evacuation, total evacuation

As the service side of the economy continues to grow, more and more of us have become part of the many industries that deal in information. For example, based on U.S. Census statistics, the seasonally adjusted annual rate of the value of construction put in place for "Offices" grew 4.2 percent from January 2005 to January 2006. This indicates a continued growth in the development and construction of office space. Record keeping, data processing, and information management are central to businesses that are physically located in office buildings, and office buildings are the prototype for the class of properties defined as business occupancies in NFPA *101*®, *Life Safety Code*®, and *NFPA 5000*®, *Building Construction and Safety Code*®.

Most of the fires each year in business occupancies occur specifically in general business offices (Tables 20.11.1 and 20.11.2). Large numbers of business occupancy fire problems also occur in college classroom and administrative buildings, medical offices, and bank buildings. Other examples of this occupancy class include city or town halls, courthouses, laboratories not involving hazardous chemicals, and some ambulatory outpatient clinics. In each of these properties, information storage has dominated the building's distinctive fuel load. However, in recent decades the increased use of desktop computers and peripheral equipment has added to the overall fuel load.

The business occupancy has long been considered a low-hazard occupancy and, therefore, not worthy of serious protection consideration. However, this is not the case, as this chapter will show. It examines building construction, occupancy characteristics, potential fire scenarios, means of egress, effects of sprinklers, effects of detection systems, and special cases of existing buildings.

Rather than recite requirements available for reference in codes and standards, this chapter approaches the subject of protecting life in a business occupancy from a more philosophical standpoint. It challenges the reader to look beyond the codes and to observe, measure, and understand the impact that building and occupancy conditions actually have on persons in them.

During the 1999–2002 period, the 4900 fires in office properties accounted for 0.9 percent of the 517,130 structure fires, 0.1 percent of the 3140 civilian structure fire deaths, 0.3 percent of the 17,730 civilian structure fire injuries, and 1.6 percent of the $8.6 billion in direct property loss. (The events of September 11, 2001, are excluded from these statistics.)[1]

In addition, fires in office properties fell 60 percent from 10,570 in 1980 to 4200 in 2002 (see Table 20.11.2). From 2001 to 2002, structure fires in these occupancies fell 14 percent. In comparison, structure fires of all types declined 51 percent from 1980 to 1999.[1]

What's driving the reduction in fires? Most industry experts attribute the loss reduction to a combination of improved application of safety codes and standards, increased public fire prevention and awareness, and increased effectiveness of life safety measures.

Office buildings have been terrorist targets in recent years. On February 23, 1993, a terrorist attack at the World Trade Center in New York City claimed six lives. On April 19, 1995, an explosion at a federal office building in Oklahoma City killed 168 people. On September 11, 2001, terrorist attacks on the twin towers of the World Trade Center in New York City and at the Pentagon in Virginia caused thousands of deaths.

NFPA members can download a number of investigation reports on office building fires, including the 1995 attack in Oklahoma City, the first World Trade Center attack in 1993, Philadelphia's One Meridien Plaza, Boston's Prudential Office Building, New York City's Rockefeller Center, and

Brian L. Marburger is a second vice-president with Travelers Insurance Group in Hartford, Connecticut.

TABLE 20.11.1 Structure Fires in Office Properties, 1999–2002 Annual Averages*

Occupancy	*Fires*	*Civilian Deaths*	*Civilian Injuries*	*Direct Property Damage (in Millions of Dollars)*
Business office	4060	4	42	114
Research or veterinary office	420	0	4	10
Bank	320	0	3	14
Post office or mailing firm	100	0	1	3
Total	4900	4	51	141

Note: These are national estimates of fires reported to U.S. municipal fire departments and so exclude fires reported only to federal or state agencies or industrial fire brigades. National estimates are projections. Casualty and loss projections can be heavily influenced by the inclusion or exclusion of one unusually serious fire. Fires are rounded to the nearest ten, civilian deaths and injuries are rounded to the nearest one, and direct property damage is rounded to the nearest million dollars. Property damage has not been adjusted for inflation.

*Excluding the events of September 11, 2001.

Source: NFIRS and NFPA survey.

TABLE 20.11.2 Structure Fires in Office Properties, by Year 1980–2002

				Direct Property Damage (in Millions of Dollars)	
Year	*Fires*	*Civilian Deaths*	*Civilian Injuries*	*As Reported*	*In 2002 Dollars*
1980	10,570	0	103	89	195
1981	11,330	3	142	141	278
1982	10,220	8	176	310	578
1983	9,040	14	157	121	218
1984	9,270	9	140	99	171
1985	9,830	8	93	150	250
1986	9,170	8	195	158	259
1987	8,680	4	107	109	172
1988	8,170	4	128	272	414
1989	7,330	2	82	114	166
1990	6,970	8	68	154	213
1991	7,030	2	99	134	177
1992	8,070	4	148	456	585
1993	6,430	3	113	127	158
1994	6,500	2	93	155	188
1995	5,390	0	90	83	98
1996	6,200	1	86	186	213
1997	5,760	0	73	106	119
1998	5,130	2	59	118	131
1999	5,530	5	62	116	125
2000	4,960	9	91	159	166
2001*	4,910	2	31	191	194
2002	4,200	0	19	100	100

Note: These are national estimates of fires reported to U.S. municipal fire departments and so exclude fires reported only to federal or state agencies or industrial fire brigades. National estimates are projections. Casualty and loss projections can be heavily influenced by the inclusion or exclusion of one unusually serious fire. Fires are rounded to the nearest ten, civilian deaths and injuries are rounded to the nearest one, and direct property damage is rounded to the nearest million dollars.

*Excluding the events of September 11, 2001.

Source: NFIRS and NFPA survey. Inflation adjustments were based on U.S. Census Bureau's *Statistical Abstract of the United States: 2006*, "Table 705, Purchasing Power of the Dollar."

Los Angeles's First Interstate Bank and Union Bank Building, at no cost from http://www.nfpa.org. Nonmembers may order these reports from the NFPA library.

A discussion of the terrorist threat to office buildings is provided here only as a point of reference to the changing landscape of risks in America. This chapter does not address the specific risks associated with terrorism.

To be aware of the concept of risk is to begin to understand the fire problem. The business occupancy is certainly of a lower hazard class than many industrial or hazardous materials handling operations. But when more people occupy a single building than reside in a small town, as is often the case in the modern high-rise, the magnitude of the challenge faced in protecting the building, its contents, and, most importantly, its occupants, is realized.

This chapter examines how the contents and the building itself affect fire growth and severity, how growth and severity affect notification and egress time of occupants, and how the conditions of occupants affect their abilities to escape. A format and issues for analysis are presented.

Additional information on determining necessary levels of protection can be found in Section 3, "Information and Analysis for Fire Protection." More information on fire-safe building design can be found in Section 1, Chapter 9, "Systems Approach to Fire-Safe Building Design." Information on interior finish can be found in Section 18, Chapter 2, "Interior Finish." Other relevant information can be found in Section 4, Chapter 5, "Strategies for Occupant Evacuation During Emergencies."

BUILDING CONSTRUCTION

Construction Type

Business occupancies can be found in a variety of building types. Although a two- or three-story noncombustible structure or a fire-resistant high-rise may be most familiar, many business occupancies are housed in ordinary wood frame, joisted masonry, and even heavy timber buildings.

Each construction type affects the business occupancy differently because fires behave differently in each. This discussion and its examples are confined to noncombustible and fire-resistive construction because it is most prevalent. The reader must understand that, in other construction types, the availability of fuel from the structure itself can increase fire severity, thereby decreasing potential structural integrity much more quickly.

Noncombustible Construction. In noncombustible construction, construction materials do not burn, thereby providing a measure of increased occupant safety. In reviewing the life safety needs of a business occupancy in a building of noncombustible construction, the designer or reviewing official can be primarily concerned with fuel load from the contents, furnishings, and interior finish, and with the means of egress. Although the potential fire's effect on the structure also must be assessed, this is usually simpler to do than it is in the case of combustible construction materials.

Fire-Resistive Construction. Fire-resistive structures are similar to noncombustible structures except that the material or combinations of materials used inherently resist failure due to fire or to the spread of fire. These characteristics help ensure sufficient time for persons to egress and/or receive other forms of assistance.

Interior Finish

Interior finish comprises the various aesthetic treatments to the structure that make it more comfortable to work in and more pleasing to the eye. Interior finish includes the materials used to cover walls, ceilings, and floors, such as paint, wallpaper, vinyl and textile wallcoverings, paneling, acoustic panels, hardwood floors, vinyl tile, terrazzo, and carpet.

The main fire performance measure of an interior wall or ceiling finish material is flame spread. This is the ability of the material to propagate a flame front across its surface. Wall and ceiling materials are ranked by relative ratings based on a value of 100 given for a specially prepared sample of red oak. Floor finishes are rated by the amount of heat energy imparted to the surface from an external source that is necessary to sustain combustion; this is called critical radiant flux. The better the flame-spread characteristics—that is, the lower the rating for wall and ceiling material, and the higher critical radiant flux for floor coverings—the more occupant protection can be assumed.

It is important to note that flame-spread ratings are based on tests of materials under controlled conditions and with specific backing materials. A wallcovering mounted on gypsum wallboard would be expected to perform differently than a wallcovering installed over brick or concrete block.

A most important but often overlooked point is that interior finish materials are also fuels. When materials are relatively thin—two coats of paint or one layer of vinyl wallcovering, for example—the additional fuel may be insignificant. In general, wallcovering materials with a thickness of 1/28 in. (0.91 mm) or less are typically exempt from testing on the actual substrate material. If they achieve a Class A rating when tested using fiber cement board as the substrate, they are not subject to the interior finish requirements of NFPA *101* and *NFPA 5000*. But when several layers of wallcovering, carpet, floor coverings, or other materials are present, the hazard and risk change dramatically. It should not be assumed that a low flame-spread rating alone results in a significant risk reduction. It is important to understand the impact this additional fuel has on the entire environment.

Furnishings and Contents

Furnishings and contents make up the bulk of the potential fuel load in a business occupancy. Furnishings, for the purpose of this discussion, include desks, chairs, sofas, and files.

Over the past decades, there have been many changes in the furnishings put into buildings. At one time, desks and chairs were routinely wood. Then metal became popular. Now, any combination of wood, metal, thermoplastics, and foamed plastics can be found. In addition, the increased use of computers has added to the fuel load.

Business occupancies are considered lower hazard than industrial or other occupancies handling hazardous materials. However, this perception sometimes confuses familiarity with safety. The quantity of combustible fuel in business occupancies can be a source of significant hazard, even if hazardous materials are not involved. In addition, some relatively benign materials may have burning characteristics—such as peak intensity of heat when fully involved in fire—comparable to some hazardous materials.

The designer and code official must be aware of the characteristics of the materials in a building, such as construction materials, interior finish materials, and furnishings. Each provides a degree of protection and a degree of hazard; their combined effect influences risk. Without understanding the potential fire behavior in a business occupancy, one cannot begin to understand its potential effect on people.

OCCUPANCY CHARACTERISTICS

Business occupants are generally characterized as awake, alert, and familiar with their surroundings. Although this is true of most offices, designers and code officials must assess the actual characteristics of a particular business occupancy, such as a doctor's office or an outpatient clinic, in which a minority of the occupants are familiar with the surroundings. In business occupancies, generalities do not always apply. The following three examples of different occupancy conditions emphasize the need for designers and code officials to evaluate the actual occupant conditions.

Support Services

Support services often are found within business occupancies. Each provides a challenge in the analysis of potential fire impact because these service areas present their own special hazards (Table 20.11.3). Examples include cafeterias, auditoriums, print shops, storage areas, parking facilities, small retail outlets,

TABLE 20.11.3 Structure Fires in Office Properties, by Area of Origin, 1999–2002 Annual Averages*

Area of Origin	*Fires*		*Civilian Deaths*		*Civilian Injuries*		*Direct Property Damage (in Millions of Dollars)*	
Office	750	(15%)	3	(68%)	17	(33%)	43	(30%)
Kitchen or cooking area	290	(6%)	1	(21%)	2	(4%)	1	(1%)
Exterior wall surface	260	(5%)	0	(0%)	0	(0%)	4	(2%)
Attic or ceiling/roof assembly or concealed space	220	(4%)	0	(0%)	1	(1%)	15	(10%)
Exterior roof surface	210	(4%)	0	(0%)	1	(1%)	3	(2%)
Lavatory, bathroom, locker room, or check room	190	(4%)	0	(0%)	0	(0%)	2	(1%)
Confined cooking fire	190	(4%)	0	(0%)	0	(0%)	0	(0%)
Heating equipment room	190	(4%)	0	(0%)	6	(11%)	3	(2%)
Machinery room or area or elevator machinery room	170	(3%)	0	(0%)	0	(0%)	9	(6%)
Storage of supplies or tools or dead storage	130	(3%)	0	(0%)	0	(0%)	6	(4%)
Computer room, control room, or center	110	(2%)	0	(0%)	1	(2%)	1	(1%)
Lobby or entrance way	110	(2%)	0	(0%)	1	(2%)	4	(3%)
Hallway, corridor, or mall	110	(2%)	0	(0%)	2	(5%)	1	(0%)
Wall assembly or concealed space	100	(2%)	0	(0%)	0	(0%)	2	(1%)
Crawl space or substructure space	80	(2%)	0	(0%)	2	(3%)	5	(4%)
Ceiling/floor assembly or concealed space	80	(2%)	0	(0%)	1	(1%)	3	(2%)
Trash or rubbish chute, area, or container	80	(2%)	0	(0%)	1	(2%)	1	(1%)
Switchgear area or transformer vault	70	(1%)	0	(0%)	3	(6%)	3	(2%)
Dining room, bar or beverage area, cafeteria	70	(1%)	0	(0%)	1	(1%)	0	(0%)
Unclassified	60	(1%)	0	(0%)	1	(1%)	5	(3%)
Unclassified equipment or service area	60	(1%)	0	(0%)	0	(0%)	1	(1%)
Unclassified structural area	60	(1%)	0	(0%)	0	(0%)	3	(2%)
Duct for HVAC, cable, exhaust, heating, or air conditioning	60	(1%)	0	(0%)	2	(5%)	0	(0%)
Common room, living room, family room, lounge, or den	60	(1%)	0	(0%)	1	(1%)	2	(1%)
Closet	50	(1%)	0	(0%)	1	(1%)	0	(0%)
Confined fuel burner or boiler fire	50	(1%)	0	(0%)	0	(0%)	0	(0%)
Records storage room or vault	50	(1%)	0	(0%)	1	(2%)	1	(1%)
Unclassified storage area	50	(1%)	0	(0%)	0	(0%)	2	(2%)
Storage room, area, tank, or bin	50	(1%)	0	(0%)	2	(4%)	4	(3%)

*Excluding the events of September 11, 2001.
Source: NFIRS and NFPA survey.

and banks or credit unions. People usually gather in these areas during certain times, often in large concentrations relative to the general occupant load for the entire building. Many service areas increase the potential for fire ignition because of their operation; one example is a cafeteria kitchen.

Child-Care Center

Another growing service area in business occupancies is the child-care center. With more families having both parents, or the only parent, working, employer-provided child care or contract day care is becoming more common. This poses special concerns: the occupants' ages, their lack of familiarity with their surroundings, mobility, and the fact that they sleep in the space from time to time. Special protection must be considered for child-care centers, including smoke detection, sprinkler protection, fire-resistive enclosures, location at grade level with direct access to the outside, and sufficient adult supervision.

Disabilities

Another high-risk segment of the population in business occupancies are people with disabilities. There are special requirements for access and acommodations for disabled people, as well as increasing awareness of the large number of people with ability limitations of some kind to some degree that could affect their response to fire. Disabilities cover a wide range, including sight, hearing, and mobility impairments. A disability also can be temporary or transient, such as a broken leg. Disabilities can increase the time needed to alert individuals or the time necessary to safely egress an area or the building. Designers and code officials must consider the presence of persons with known or hidden disabilities when evaluating a life safety system for a business occupancy.

POTENTIAL FIRE SCENARIOS

Fire safety design for a particular property must begin with a consideration of characteristics of most likely fires and the most serious fire the occupancy might encounter (Table 20.11.4). This may be done by defining potential fire scenarios to use as a basis for analysis.

Ignition Sources

Leading sources of heat for unintentional ignition include electrical distribution systems, portable and fixed space heating

TABLE 20.11.4 Leading Causes of Structure Fires in Office Properties, 1999–2002 Annual Averages*

Cause	*Fires*		*Civilian Deaths*		*Civilian Injuries*		*Direct Property Damage (in Millions of Dollars)*	
Electrical distribution and lighting equipment	930	(19%)	0	(0%)	22	(44%)	23	(16%)
Intentional	650	(13%)	0	(0%)	6	(12%)	41	(29%)
Heating equipment fires	520	(11%)	1	(33%)	5	(10%)	6	(4%)
Identified heating equipment	460	(9%)	1	(33%)	5	(10%)	6	(4%)
Confined heating equipment fire	60	(1%)	0	(0%)	0	(0%)	0	(0%)
Cooking equipment fires	500	(10%)	1	(33%)	4	(7%)	2	(1%)
Identified cooking equipment	310	(6%)	1	(33%)	4	(7%)	2	(1%)
Confined cooking fire	190	(4%)	0	(0%)	0	(0%)	0	(0%)
Smoking materials	490	(10%)	1	(25%)	1	(3%)	13	(9%)
Exposure to other fire	250	(5%)	0	(0%)	1	(1%)	10	(7%)
Torch (including burner or soldering iron)	240	(5%)	0	(0%)	4	(9%)	5	(3%)
Candle	120	(2%)	0	(0%)	1	(1%)	3	(2%)
Contained trash or rubbish fire	130	(3%)	0	(0%)	0	(0%)	0	(0%)

Note: These are the leading causes, obtained from the following list: intentional (from the NFIRS field "cause"); playing with fire (from factor contributing to ignition); confined heating (including confined chimney and confined fuel burner or boiler fires), confined cooking, and contained trash or rubbish (from incident type); identified heating, identified cooking, clothes dryer or washer, torch (including burner and soldering iron), electrical distribution and lighting equipment, medical equipment, and electronic, office, or entertainment equipment (from equipment involved in ignition); smoking materials, candles, lightning, and spontaneous combustion or chemical reaction (from heat source); and mobile property involved (from mobile property involved in ignition). Exposure fires include fires with an exposure number greater than zero, as well as fires identified by heat source or factor contributing to ignition when no equipment was involved in ignition that were not intentionally set. The same fire can be listed under multiple causes, based on multiple data elements.

These are national estimates of fires reported to U.S. municipal fire departments and so exclude fires reported only to federal or state agencies or industrial fire brigades. National estimates are projections. Casualty and loss projections can be heavily influenced by the inclusion or exclusion of one unusually serious fire. Fires are rounded to the nearest ten, civilian deaths and injuries are rounded to the nearest one, and direct property damage is rounded to the nearest million dollars. Property damage has not been adjusted for inflation.

*Excluding the events of September 11, 2001.

Source: NFIRS and NFPA survey.

equipment, other appliances, torch and other maintenance operations, matches and lighters, and smoking materials. The design professional and code official must know where potential ignition sources are and where they expose potential fuels.

Arson

One of the leading causes of fire in business occupancies is not unintentional, however; it is arson. Arson prevention is partly a matter of understanding the business and those who might wish to harm it, such as competitors, disgruntled employees, angry customers, or economically strapped owners. But arson more often occurs as a result of less direct motives, such as emotional disturbance, so it is important to emphasize security controls and arrangements, such as housekeeping, that will reduce the range of attractive and easy targets for potential arsonists. Also, the importance of arson underscores the limits of fire prevention as a strategy, so postignition fire protection provisions are needed, too.

The value at risk from a fire in a business occupancy can easily be underestimated, with the increase in regular use of computers, facsimile machines, copy machines, printers, and similar equipment, and the purchase of telephone systems for offices and buildings. The value of loss of business and other interruption costs, including the occupancy of temporary space and reduced employee productivity during space restoration, also must be considered.

The designer and code official must look carefully at the business occupancy for available fuels and potential ignition sources. The impact of fire on the occupancy and occupants can then be predicted. Computer models and other engineering tools can translate the occupancy's physical and occupant characteristics into a timeline of fire development and its effects on people and property.

MEANS OF EGRESS

In analyzing the potential fire scenario and choosing strategies to deal with the results of the analysis, it is useful to think in terms of major groups of fire protection provisions. Means of egress will be the first discussed here. Before the means of egress needs can be assessed, however, an objective must first be established: every occupant should be able to reach a safe location from anywhere in the building without incurring serious harm from fire, smoke, or other products of combustion along the way.

For a long time, this objective was fulfilled by evacuating building occupants when fire was discovered. As buildings get larger and taller, this came to be less practical. Some high-rise building populations are the size of a small town; total evacuation may take hours. Nor does it make sense to move people from the 40th floor of a building in response to a small trash fire on the 60th floor, especially if the fire is being controlled or extinguished by an automatic sprinkler system. Persons with severe mobility impairments may not have this option available without assistance.

One method of establishing an acceptable level of protection for persons from fire is the application of NFPA *101* or *NFPA 5000*. They provide requirements for determining occupant loads, arrangement of means of egress, capacity of means of egress, and exit travel distances, as well as requirements for the design of doors, stairs, and interior finish materials. NFPA *101* recognizes differences in existing buildings and new construction, and it provides different requirements for each. In fact, all codes and standards have equivalency clauses so as not to exclude sound engineering approaches that accomplish the same or similar results. The code official must be aware of the application of these equivalency clauses.

Total Evacuation

In a total evacuation, persons should be able to leave the building before conditions become untenable. Fire growth, temperature rise, and the production of toxic combustion products must be estimated. Then the time needed to evacuate the building must be estimated. The difference between the evacuation time and the time to untenable conditions is the time allowed for fire detection, notification of occupants, and occupant reaction.

The alarm system, either manual or automatic, must be chosen based on the time available to notify occupants. In most business occupancies, a manual alarm system is sufficient, but the designer and code official must be aware of conditions that warrant the use of an automatic detection and alarm system. If automatic sprinkler protection is provided, the designer should take advantage of its presence and use it as an alarm-initiating device.

Alternatives to Total Evacuation

If total evacuation is not practical, it is still necessary to ensure that occupants can get to an area of relative safety before conditions become untenable. This is commonly accomplished by a combination of four approaches.

Relocation. Fire conditions and necessary egress time must be estimated. The area of relative safety must then be chosen. This may be a trial-and-error design process because estimated fire conditions and the structure's ability to resist fire affect where the safer areas will most likely be. Furthermore, persons must be able to reach those areas in a reasonable time.

Other egress or occupant protection strategies are similar to relocation and include defend in place, staged evacuation, and use of horizontal exits.

Defend in Place. Defend-in-place strategies are generally used in health care occupancies where patients cannot be readily moved. Although not preferred for business occupancies, the existence of such strategies should be noted and understood.

Staged Evacuation. Staged evacuation can take several forms. One is staged total evacuation where the fire floor occupants are notified, and, after a determined time period, other occupants are notified. This allows those on the fire floor the first opportunity to escape. Persons in areas farther from the fire start to evacuate a bit later.

Another method of staged evacuation is the use of "hardened" areas, or areas of refuge, where persons may seek temporary refuge until they are able to egress. These staging areas pose several questions:

1. How should the area be hardened? Fire resistance is not enough. Ventilation and pressurization are critical to maintaining a tenable environment when the area is exposed to postflashover conditions or smoke migration.
2. How many people will use the area? These areas have been suggested for use by people with disabilities. With the population of mobility-impaired occupants growing in many business occupancies, a minimum number of such occupants must be able to be safely protected in such areas. NFPA *101* and *NFPA 5000* provide guidance on this topic.
3. How will people use these areas? Practice is the only answer. If provided, these areas must be addressed in the fire evacuation plan for the building. This fact would suggest that these staging areas have only limited impact on persons who are not familiar with the building.
4. How will persons eventually leave the building? These areas must not be considered as a place to wait until the fire is extinguished. Persons generally must leave the fire floor. These areas, if provided, should be adjacent to stairs or elevators so that fire department personnel or building fire wardens can assist persons in these areas to other areas of relative safety.

The use of this type of staging area takes much planning, practice, maintenance, and coordination. Unfortunately, it is of little benefit to persons unfamiliar with the building and its features. Therefore, a preferred method would be to establish a way to protect the occupants with little or no special instructions.

In potential impact and effectiveness of staging areas for occupants with disabilities, complete automatic sprinkler protection (properly designed, installed, and maintained) afforded occupants sufficient safety without actually needing to egress the floor (Table 20.11.5). If the sprinkler system uses quick-response sprinklers, there will likely be no perception of risk on the part of building occupants.

Horizontal Exit. Another method of staged evacuation is through horizontal exits. Horizontal exits can be provided by subdividing a building with specially designed fire barriers. Persons passing through doors in these walls move to an area of relative safety. In some cases, the horizontal exit alone may provide enough egress protection. In others, the horizontal exit may be used to provide enough protection to stage occupants, thereby allowing more time for total evacuation or assisted evacuation, as in the case of persons with disabilities.

In either relocation or staged evacuation, fire control is important. To ensure the success of the egress or occupant protection strategy, fire growth and combustion products must be held to a minimum. This can be done in several ways. Fuel can be limited, room geometry can be controlled, and ventilation of fire areas can be limited. A proven effective method of controlling fire growth and smoke production is through the use of automatic sprinklers. Therefore, where occupant relocation or staging is an intended strategy, the building should be protected with automatic sprinklers, although individual conditions dictate the actual protection necessary.

TABLE 20.11.5 Fire Protection Features in Office Property Structure Fires Reported to Public Fire Departments, 1994–1998 Annual Averages

Percent of fires in buildings with smoke or other fire alarms present	53.7%
Percent of fires in buildings having smoke or other fire alarms in which devices were operational	74.3%
Percent of fires in buildings with operational smoke or other fire alarms (product of first two statistics)	39.9%
Percent of fires in buildings with automatic suppression system	25.4%
Deaths per 1000 fires with automatic suppression system present	0.0
Deaths per 1000 fires with no automatic suppression system present	0.3
Reduction in deaths per 1000 fires when automatic suppression systems were present	100.0%
Average loss per fire when automatic suppression system was present	$11,311
Average loss per fire with no automatic suppression system	$28,091
Reduction in loss per fire when automatic suppression systems were present	59.7%

Source: National estimates based on NFIRS and NFPA survey; Marty Ahrens, *The U.S. Fire Problem Overview Report,* NFPA Fire Analysis and Research Division, Quincy, MA, June 2001.

EXIT LIGHTING

The means of egress should be continuously illuminated by a reliable lighting system. This usually means spacing lighting fixtures and providing primary and emergency power to ensure a lighting level of at least 1 footcandle (10 lux), measured at the floor level.

Emergency power can be provided in many ways: batteries, inverters, generators, separate building substations with automatic transfer switches, and power distribution system network grids. The concept behind emergency power for egress lighting is to ensure that the exit path is illuminated if a fire in the building disrupts the primary power source. Because a complete power failure at the utility would rarely occur at the same time a fire in the building would, it is sufficient to have only one of the recommended emergency power sources. However, other design arrangements may be necessary, depending on specific local conditions and utility reliability.

AUTOMATIC SPRINKLERS

As discussed, automatic sprinkler protection can increase the level of fire safety in a business occupancy. From the life safety standpoint, sprinklers limit fire growth and the production of smoke, thereby increasing the time available for persons to egress. If designed to do so, automatic sprinklers can even keep conditions in close proximity to the fire in a tenable range.

Another reason sprinklers should be considered is property protection. Fire department suppression capabilities may be limited by staffing issues, water supplies, or height of the fire above ground level. If fire fighters must rescue occupants, their fire suppression capability decreases. As property values and mission criticality increase, the typical business cannot afford this potential exposure.

The average loss per fire was cut almost in half when automatic suppression systems were present. Automatic suppression systems were present in only 25 percent of these fires from 1994 to 1998. The average estimated direct property damage was almost twice as high when no automatic suppression system was present. Because a code for undetermined system presence was not included in Version 5.0 of NFIRS until 2004, data on number of fires and loss rates cannot be confidently updated (Table 20.11.6).

Sprinkler protection automatically detects a fire and starts suppression actions, providing additional time for occupants to exit. The sprinkler system can even notify occupants of the fire when arranged to activate the fire alarm. Sprinklers also limit fire and water damage, thereby decreasing business interruption. With the expanded use of quick-response sprinklers, these occupant protection factors and property protection features can be expected to increase.

Retrofitting sprinkler systems is becoming easier with the use of special materials such as lightweight steel pipe, copper tube, and plastic pipe. In addition, sprinklers can be safely installed in buildings with sprayed-on asbestos containing fireproofing through a process of local encapsulation and control. See the additional readings for this chapter for more information on this subject.

EXISTING BUILDINGS

Business occupancies in existing buildings pose several concerns from a life safety standpoint. Many do not meet the requirements of codes, standards, or design practices for new construction. The question should not be, "Do they comply?" Rather, we should ask, "Is the occupant protection objective fulfilled?" In this case, occupant protection should be no different than that previously discussed. The objective is to get people to an area of relative safety before conditions become untenable.

TABLE 20.11.6 Automatic Suppression Systems in Office Property Structure Fires Reported to Public Fire Departments, 1994–1998 Annual Averages

Percent of fires in buildings with automatic suppression system	25%
Average loss per fire when automatic suppression system was present	$11,300
Average loss per fire with no automatic suppression system	$28,100
Reduction in loss per fire when automatic suppression systems were present	60%

Source: National estimates based on NFIRS and NFPA survey.

The difference is that an existing building constrains the protection strategy. Several resources can be used to help find solutions to egress problems in existing buildings.

NFPA *101* has a separate chapter for existing business occupancies. Requirements in that chapter are similar to those for new buildings, but they reflect the necessity of accepting those things that cannot be economically changed, provided a reasonable degree of safety is present.

Another good reference is NFPA 101A, *Guide on Alternative Approaches to Life Safety,* which includes a chapter on a Fire Safety Evaluation System (FSES) for business occupancies. FSES is a measuring system. It compares the level of safety provided by an arrangement of safeguards that differs from those specified in NFPA *101* to the level of safety provided in a building that conforms with the details of the code.

Other analytical methods exist that may be beneficial in evaluating the risk to life in an existing business occupancy. These include hand calculations and computer-based predictive fire models. (See Section 3, "Information and Analysis for Fire Protection.") In any event, the process is the same—determine the fire exposure, the time available for safe egress, and the time needed to egress.

A special category of existing buildings must be mentioned: historic or architecturally significant buildings. Society puts additional constraint on these structures as to the way alterations must be done. Here, historic preservation and life safety objectives must be carefully outlined and communicated. These objectives are not necessarily at cross purposes. Innovative design techniques and engineered performance-based solutions, rather than code compliance, are usually called for. A reference on the process and design tips is included in the list of additional readings following this chapter. Also see Section 20, Chapter 17, "Library and Museum Collections."

SUMMARY

Business occupancies comprise a large segment of the communities protected, and they can be found in a variety of building types. Construction type, occupancy characteristics, potential fire scenarios, means of egress, the effect of sprinklers, and existing conditions all affect the ability to protect occupants from the effects of fire. An objective has been set for protecting these occupants by keeping them in a tenable environment or by allowing them to escape to an area of relative safety before untenable conditions are reached. This area may be outside the building, on another floor, or through a horizontal exit.

The designer and code official must look deeper than codes and standards alone to understand actual conditions and measure exposures. They will then be able to recommend ways of fulfilling the objective of protecting occupants.

BIBLIOGRAPHY

Reference Cited

1. "Structure Fires in Office Properties," National Fire Protection Association, Quincy, MA, 2006.

NFPA Codes, Standards, and Recommended Practices

Reference to the following NFPA codes, standards, and recommended practices will provide further information on business occupancies discussed in this chapter. (See the latest version of The NFPA Catalog *for availability of current editions of the following documents.)*

NFPA *101*®, *Life Safety Code*®
NFPA 101A, *Guide on Alternative Approaches to Life Safety*
NFPA 5000®, *Building Construction and Safety Code*®

References

Brennan, P., "Impact of Social Interaction on Time to Begin Evacuation in Office Building Fires: Implications for Modelling Behavior," *Proceedings* of the 7th International INTERFLAM Conference, INTERFLAM '96, March 26–28, 1996, Cambridge, UK, Interscience Communications Ltd., London, UK, 1996, pp. 701–710.

Comeau, E. "Fire Investigation Report, Rescue Operations Report, Oklahoma City, OK," National Fire Protection Association, Quincy, MA, 1995.

Comeau, E., Ode, M. C., and Duval, R. F., "Office Building Fire, New York, New York, October 10, 1996," NFPA Fire Investigation Report, National Fire Protection Association, Quincy, MA, 1997.

Fahy, R. F., and Proulx, G., "Human Behavior in the World Trade Center Evacuation," *Proceedings* of the 5th International Symposium, Fire Safety Science, March 3–7, 1997, Melbourne, Australia, International Association for Fire Safety Science, Boston, 1997, pp. 713–724.

Hughes Associates, Incorporated, "Fire Safety Evaluation System (FSES) for Business Occupancies Software (ver 1.0 for Windows) Users' Manual," NIST-GCR-96-692, Hughes Associates, Inc., Baltimore, MD, National Institute of Standards and Technology, Gaithersburg, MD, General Services Administration, Washington, DC, Mar. 1996.

Klem, T. J. "Fire Investigation Report, First Interstate Bank Building Fire, Los Angeles, CA, May 4, 1988." National Fire Protection Association, Quincy, MA, 1998.

Koffel, W. E., "Common Code Issues in Office Buildings," *NFPA Journal*, Vol. 94, No. 1, 2000, p. 26.

Proulx, G., "Comparison of Occupant Behavior During Office and Apartment Evacuation Drills," IRC-ORAL-161, National Research Council of Canada, Ottawa, Ontario, 1996.

Proulx, G., and Hadjisophocleous, G., "Modelling Occupant Response and Evacuation in Apartment and Office Buildings," *Proceedings* of the Pacific Rim Conference and the 2nd International Conference on Performance-Based Codes and Fire Safety Design Methods, May 3–9, 1998, Maui, HI, International Code Council, Birmingham, AL, 1998, pp. 279–293.

Respondek, J., "Fire Safety Concept and Evacuation Procedure for a Modern Office Building," *Proceedings* of the 9th International INTERFLAM Conference, INTERFLAM 2001, September 17–19, 2001, Edinburgh, UK, Interscience Communications Ltd., London, UK, 2001, pp. 877–882.

Stroup, D. W., "Using Performance-Based Design Techniques to Evaluate Fire Safety in Two Government Buildings," *Proceedings* of Pacific Rim Conference and 2nd International Conference on Performance-Based Codes and Fire Safety Design Methods, May 3–9, 1998, Maui, HI, International Code Council, Birmingham, AL, 1998, pp. 429–439.

Yung, D., and Hadjisophocleous, G. V., "Cost-Effective Fire Safety Retrofits for Canadian Government Office Buildings," *International Journal on Engineering Performance-Based Fire Codes,* Vol. 1, No. 3, 1999, pp. 123–128.

Chapter 12

Educational Occupancies

Revised by
Alex L. Szachnowicz

Chapter Contents

Key Terms

educational occupancy, exit hardware, fire exit drills, means of egress, occupant characteristic, occupant load, open plan design, windows

This chapter addresses *educational occupancies,* which are generally defined as new or existing facilities in which six or more persons gather for purposes of formal or structured instruction. This chapter describes the nature of educational occupants as well as the hazards and life safety concepts relevant to this type of occupancy.

Examples of educational occupancies include public, private, and parochial schools, academies, kindergartens, and other facilities whose purpose is primarily educational, even though their students may be of preschool age. Educational occupancies are typically defined as places where students are present for formalized instruction for more than 4 hours per day, or more than 12 hours per week, through the twelfth grade. This is differentiated from day-care occupancies, which are generally defined as those facilities in which four or more clients receive care, maintenance, and supervision by other than their relatives or legal guardian for less than 24 hours per day. Colleges, universities, and postsecondary trade schools are typically excluded from educational occupancies as well. Furthermore, the definition of an educational occupancy excludes facilities in which instruction is incidental to some other occupancy. In such cases, the requirements of the predominant occupancy shall apply. Examples of excluded facilities include the following:

- Rooms located within places of worship used for purposes of religious education while services are being held in the building
- Rooms used for extracurricular purposes such as piano instruction, dance instruction, martial arts classes, or sport activities
- Classrooms and laboratories located within business or industrial occupancies

See also Section 20, Chapter 13, "Day-Care Occupancies."

FIRE PROBLEM IN EDUCATIONAL OCCUPANCIES

The U.S. fire problem in educational occupancies is outlined in Tables 20.12.1 through 20.12.4. As one can see, between 1999 and 2002, there was an annualized average of approximately 7070 structure fires in educational properties. These fires contributed to an average of 113 civilian injuries and $112 million in direct property damage per year during that period. Although educational occupancy fires can start in a variety of locations, the data indicate that the leading areas of origin tend to be in lavatories or locker rooms, with rubbish, trash, magazines, papers, and other waste products often the first items to be ignited. Almost half of the fires in educational occupancies were intentionally set or the result of fireplay. It is for this reason that traditional fire safety education messages should be augmented with juvenile firesetter programs in educational occupancies. It is important to note that these data are derived from the National Fire Incident Reporting System (NFIRS) and from information gleaned from an annual survey conducted by NFPA. As such, this information does contain some imbedded data garnered from day-care occupancies, colleges, universities, and other adult learner properties.

Table 20.12.5 presents the benefits of automatic suppression systems in educational properties. Note that automatic suppression systems were present in only 24 percent of the fires in educational

Alex L. Szachnowicz, P.E., is the director of facilities for Anne Arundel County Public Schools in Annapolis, Maryland. He is chair of the NFPA Technical Committee on Educational and Day Care Occupancies for NFPA *101®*, *Life Safety Code®*, and *NFPA 5000®*, *Building Construction and Safety Code®*.

TABLE 20.12.1 Structural Fires in Educational Properties, 1999–2002 Annual Averages

Occupancy	*Fires*	*Civilian Deaths*	*Civilian Injuries*	*Direct Property Damage (in Millions of Dollars)*
Nursery school through high school	5320	0	88	74
Preschool	210	0	1	1
Elementary school, including kindergarten	1380	0	13	27
High school, junior high, or middle school	3020	0	62	33
Unclassified nonadult school	700	0	12	13
Adult education center or college classroom	980	0	17	30
Day care	440	0	4	4
Unclassified educational	330	0	3	5
Total	7070	0	113	112

Note: These are fires reported to U.S. municipal fire departments and so exclude fires reported only to federal or state agencies or industrial fire brigades. Fires are rounded to the nearest ten, deaths and injuries to the nearest one, and direct property damage to the nearest million dollars. Sums may not equal totals due to rounding errors. Damage has not been adjusted for inflation.

Source: *U.S. Fires in Selected Occupancies,* National Fire Protection Association, March 2006. National estimates based on NFIRS and NFPA survey.

properties, and the average estimated direct property damage was almost five times higher when no automatic suppression system was present.

OCCUPANT CHARACTERISTICS

People in educational occupancies vary in their ability to deal with an emergency condition, depending on their age, mental and physical conditions, as well as the facility's physical characteristics. Generally, regulations concerning educational occupancies are based on the abilities of children in the third through eighth grades, with special provisions made for younger children. High school occupants gain an extra measure of protection because the fire safety design package is based on younger children's capabilities.

Children younger than those in the third grade require special consideration because of their limited ability to traverse

TABLE 20.12.2 Leading Causes of Structure Fires in Educational Occupancies: 1999–2002 Annual Averages

Cause	*Fires*		*Civilian Deaths*		*Civilian Injuries*		*Direct Property Damage (in Millions of Dollars)*	
Intentional	2650	(38%)	*	(*%)	27	(24%)	51.2	(46%)
Cooking equipment fires	930	(13%)	*	(*%)	8	(7%)	1.7	(2%)
Identified cooking equipment	570	(8%)	*	(*%)	6	(6%)	1.7	(2%)
Confined cooking fire	350	(5%)	*	(*%)	2	(2%)	0.0	(0%)
Electrical	550	(8%)	*	(*%)	23	(20%)	12.0	(11%)
Heating equipment fires	530	(8%)	*	(*%)	4	(3%)	6.6	(6%)
Identified heating equipment	450	(6%)	*	(*%)	4	(3%)	6.5	(6%)
Confined heating equipment fire	80	(1%)	*	(*%)	0	(0%)	0.1	(0%)
Playing with fire	520	(7%)	*	(*%)	0	(0%)	4.0	(4%)
Smoking materials	350	(5%)	*	(*%)	6	(6%)	3.5	(3%)
Torch (including burner or soldering iron)	220	(3%)	*	(*%)	10	(9%)	4.7	(4%)
Clothes dryer or washer	200	(3%)	*	(*%)	3	(3%)	0.5	(0%)
Contained trash or rubbish fire	550	(8%)	*	(*%)	4	(4%)	0.3	(0%)

Note: These are national estimates of fires reported to U.S. municipal fire departments and so exclude fires reported only to federal or state agencies or industrial fire brigades. National estimates are projections. Casualty and loss projections can be heavily influenced by the inclusion or exclusion of one unusually serious fire. Fires are rounded to the nearest ten, civilian deaths and injuries are rounded to the nearest one, and direct property damage is rounded to the nearest hundred thousand dollars. Property damage has not been adjusted for inflation.

*The cause of all the fatalities during this period was unknown or not reported.

Source: *U.S. Fires in Selected Occupancies,* Table 5, National Fire Protection Association, March 2006. Based on NFIRS and NFPA survey.

TABLE 20.12.3 Structure Fires in Educational Properties, by Area of Origin, 1999–2002 Annual Averages

Area of Origin	*Fires*		*Civilian Deaths*		*Civilian Injuries*		*Direct Property Damage (in Millions of Dollars)*	
Lavatory, bathroom, locker room, or check room	1330	(19%)	0	(0%)	23	(21%)	1	(1%)
Kitchen or cooking area	630	(9%)	0	(0%)	8	(7%)	15	(14%)
Hallway, corridor, or mall	440	(6%)	0	(0%)	2	(1%)	3	(3%)
Small assembly area, less than 100-person capacity	440	(6%)	0	(0%)	11	(10%)	15	(14%)
Confined cooking fire	350	(5%)	0	(0%)	2	(2%)	0	(0%)
Heating equipment room	200	(3%)	0	(0%)	1	(1%)	1	(1%)
Exterior wall surface	160	(2%)	0	(0%)	0	(0%)	2	(2%)
Laundry room or area	150	(2%)	0	(0%)	4	(4%)	1	(1%)
Exterior roof surface	150	(2%)	0	(0%)	2	(1%)	6	(5%)
Attic or ceiling/roof assembly or concealed space	130	(2%)	0	(0%)	2	(2%)	5	(4%)
Storage of supplies or tools or dead storage	130	(2%)	0	(0%)	1	(0%)	5	(5%)
Office	120	(2%)	0	(0%)	3	(3%)	7	(6%)
Unclassified	110	(2%)	0	(0%)	0	(0%)	5	(4%)
Trash or rubbish chute, area, or container	110	(2%)	0	(0%)	2	(1%)	0	(0%)
Bedroom	110	(1%)	1	(100%)	6	(6%)	1	(0%)
Laboratory	100	(1%)	0	(0%)	9	(8%)	2	(2%)
Large open room without fixed seats	90	(1%)	0	(0%)	1	(0%)	2	(2%)
Machinery room or area or elevator machinery room	80	(1%)	0	(0%)	1	(1%)	1	(1%)
Wall assembly or concealed space	80	(1%)	0	(0%)	1	(1%)	1	(1%)
Closet	70	(1%)	0	(0%)	1	(0%)	0	(0%)
Interior stairway or ramp	70	(1%)	0	(0%)	0	(0%)	0	(0%)
Unclassified storage area	70	(1%)	0	(0%)	1	(1%)	1	(1%)
Dining room, bar or beverage area, cafeteria	70	(1%)	0	(0%)	1	(1%)	1	(1%)
Common room, living room, family room, lounge, or den	70	(1%)	0	(0%)	0	(0%)	1	(1%)
Lobby or entrance way	70	(1%)	0	(0%)	1	(0%)	0	(0%)
Confined fuel burner or boiler fire	70	(1%)	0	(0%)	0	(0%)	0	(0%)
Large assembly area with fixed seats	60	(1%)	0	(0%)	0	(0%)	4	(4%)
Unclassified technical processing area	60	(1%)	0	(0%)	1	(1%)	0	(0%)
Duct for HVAC, cable, exhaust, heating, or air conditioning	60	(1%)	0	(0%)	1	(1%)	1	(1%)
Crawl space or substructure space	50	(1%)	0	(0%)	1	(1%)	0	(0%)
Unclassified equipment or service area	50	(1%)	0	(0%)	1	(1%)	1	(1%)
Ceiling/floor assembly or concealed space	50	(1%)	0	(0%)	0	(0%)	1	(0%)
Computer room, control room, or center	50	(1%)	0	(0%)	1	(1%)	4	(4%)
Maintenance or paint shop or area	50	(1%)	0	(0%)	2	(1%)	1	(1%)
Unclassified structural area	40	(1%)	0	(0%)	0	(0%)	1	(1%)
Unclassified function area	40	(1%)	0	(0%)	1	(1%)	1	(1%)
Storage room, area, tank, or bin	40	(1%)	0	(0%)	1	(0%)	3	(2%)
Multiple areas of origin	40	(1%)	0	(0%)	0	(0%)	6	(5%)
Exterior stairway, ramp, or fire escape	40	(1%)	0	(0%)	1	(1%)	0	(0%)
Switchgear area or transformer vault	40	(1%)	0	(0%)	8	(7%)	1	(1%)
Other known service or equipment area	90	(1%)	0	(0%)	3	(3%)	0	(0%)
Other known outside area	80	(1%)	0	(0%)	0	(0%)	1	(1%)
Other known technical processing area	60	(1%)	0	(0%)	6	(5%)	1	(1%)
Other known assembly or sales area	60	(1%)	0	(0%)	1	(0%)	5	(5%)
Other known area	140	(2%)	0	(0%)	2	(2%)	2	(2%)
Contained trash fire	550	(8%)	0	(0%)	4	(4%)	0	(0%)
Other confined fire	40	(1%)	0	(0%)	0	(0%)	0	(0%)
Total	7070	(100%)	1	(100%)	113	(100%)	112	(100%)

Note: These are national estimates of fires reported to U.S. municipal fire departments and so exclude fires reported only to federal or state agencies or industrial fire brigades. National estimates are projections. Casualty and loss projections can be heavily influenced by the inclusion or exclusion of one unusually serious fire. Fires are rounded to the nearest ten, civilian deaths and injuries are rounded to the nearest one, and direct property damage is rounded to the nearest million dollars. Property damage has not been adjusted for inflation. Nonconfined and noncontained structure fires in which the area of origin was unknown or not reported have been allocated proportionally among fires with known area of origin. Totals may not equal sums due to rounding errors.

Source: *U.S. Fires in Selected Occupancies,* Table 8, National Fire Protection Association, March 2006. Based on NFIRS and NFPA survey.

TABLE 20.12.4 Structure Fires in Educational Properties, by First Item Ignited: 1999–2002 Annual Averages

Item First Ignited	*Fires*		*Civilian Deaths*		*Civilian Injuries*		*Direct Property Damage (in Millions of Dollars)*	
Rubbish, trash, or waste	870	(12%)	0	(0%)	5	(4%)	3	(3%)
Unclassified	600	(9%)	0	(0%)	11	(10%)	9	(8%)
Electrical wire or cable insulation	600	(8%)	0	(0%)	15	(13%)	5	(5%)
Magazine, newspaper, or writing paper	570	(8%)	0	(0%)	3	(3%)	2	(2%)
Contained trash or rubbish fire	550	(8%)	0	(0%)	4	(4%)	0	(0%)
Cooking materials, including food	440	(6%)	0	(0%)	3	(3%)	1	(1%)
Confined cooking fire	350	(5%)	0	(0%)	2	(2%)	0	(0%)
Flammable or combustible liquid or gas, filter, or piping	190	(3%)	0	(0%)	11	(10%)	12	(11%)
Structural member or framing	180	(3%)	0	(0%)	1	(1%)	10	(9%)
Unclassified storage supplies	180	(2%)	0	(0%)	6	(5%)	1	(1%)
Multiple items first ignited	170	(2%)	0	(0%)	1	(1%)	17	(15%)
Rolled or wound material	170	(2%)	0	(0%)	8	(7%)	1	(1%)
Box, carton, bag, basket, or barrel	160	(2%)	0	(0%)	1	(1%)	1	(1%)
Clothing	150	(2%)	0	(0%)	4	(4%)	1	(1%)
Exterior roof covering or finish	130	(2%)	0	(0%)	2	(2%)	6	(5%)
Household utensils	120	(2%)	0	(0%)	4	(3%)	1	(1%)
Exterior wall covering or finish	110	(2%)	0	(0%)	1	(1%)	3	(3%)
Linen other than bedding	100	(1%)	0	(0%)	1	(1%)	2	(2%)
Appliance housing or casing	90	(1%)	0	(0%)	8	(7%)	1	(1%)
Interior wall covering, excluding drapes	80	(1%)	0	(0%)	1	(1%)	2	(2%)
Unclassified structural component or finish	80	(1%)	0	(0%)	2	(2%)	2	(2%)
Insulation within structural area	80	(1%)	0	(0%)	0	(0%)	2	(2%)
Dust, fiber, lint, sawdust, or excelsior	70	(1%)	0	(0%)	3	(3%)	0	(0%)
Confined fuel burner or boiler fire or malfunction	70	(1%)	0	(0%)	0	(0%)	0	(0%)
Cabinetry, including built-in	60	(1%)	0	(0%)	3	(3%)	3	(3%)
Book	60	(1%)	0	(0%)	1	(1%)	1	(1%)
Floor covering, rug, carpet, or mat	60	(1%)	0	(0%)	0	(0%)	0	(0%)
Transformer or transformer fluids	60	(1%)	0	(0%)	1	(1%)	0	(0%)
Interior ceiling cover or finish	50	(1%)	0	(0%)	0	(0%)	2	(2%)
Unclassified adornment, recreational material, or sign	50	(1%)	0	(0%)	1	(1%)	0	(0%)
Unclassified furniture or utensils	50	(1%)	0	(0%)	1	(1%)	1	(1%)
Upholstered furniture or vehicle seat	40	(1%)	0	(0%)	0	(0%)	1	(1%)
Exterior trim, including doors	40	(1%)	0	(0%)	0	(0%)	0	(0%)
Unclassified soft goods or wearing apparel	40	(1%)	0	(0%)	1	(1%)	0	(0%)
Mattress or bedding	40	(1%)	1	(100%)	4	(3%)	0	(0%)
Decoration	40	(1%)	0	(0%)	0	(0%)	0	(0%)
Agricultural crop, including fruits and vegetables	40	(1%)	0	(0%)	1	(1%)	0	(0%)
Other known item	280	(4%)	0	(0%)	7	(6%)	19	(17%)
Other confined fire	40	(1%)	0	(0%)	0	(0%)	0	(0%)
Total	7070	(100%)	1	(100%)	113	(100%)	112	(100%)

Note: These are national estimates of fires reported to U.S. municipal fire departments and so exclude fires reported only to federal or state agencies or industrial fire brigades. National estimates are projections. Casualty and loss projections can be heavily influenced by the inclusion or exclusion of one unusually serious fire. Fires are rounded to the nearest ten, civilian deaths and injuries are rounded to the nearest one, and direct property damage is rounded to the nearest million dollars. Property damage has not been adjusted for inflation. Nonconfined and noncontained structure fires in which the area of origin was unknown or not reported have been allocated proportionally among fires with known area of origin. Totals may not equal sums due to rounding errors.

Source: *U.S. Fires in Selected Occupancies,* Table 9, National Fire Protection Association, March 2006. Based on NFIRS and NFPA survey.

TABLE 20.12.5 Automatic Suppression Systems in Educational Property Structure Fires Reported to Public Fire Departments: 1994–1998 Annual Averages

Percentage of fires in buildings with automatic suppression system	24%
Average loss per fire when automatic suppression system was present	$2800
Average loss per fire with no automatic suppression system	$12,900
Reduction in loss per fire when automatic suppression systems were present	78%

Note: Because a code for undetermined system presence was not included in Version 5.0 of NFIRS until 2004, data on number of fires and fire loss rates cannot be confidently updated.

Source: National estimates based on NFIRS and NFPA survey.

stairs or evacuate effectively in an emergency. Because there is a potential for younger children to be overrun by older students and adults on stairs, most codes require that preschool, kindergarten, and first-grade students be located on a level of exit discharge to facilitate egress. Second-grade students are usually limited to one level above a level of exit discharge in recognition of their limited movement ability. NFPA *101* and *NFPA 5000* permit students younger than the third grade to use rooms or areas located on floor levels higher than the first or second level where provided with independent means of egress dedicated for use by the younger children. The codes recognize that these younger students, with the help of teachers and staff, can use stairs and ramps effectively if they do not have to compete with older, larger, and faster students.

DESIGN CONSIDERATIONS

Schools of only one story, with each room having a direct exit to the outside, represent the most conservative design for life safety. However, economics, site restrictions, or programmatic requirements often dictate other design considerations that can be accommodated and made safe by adhering to certain design principles noted elsewhere within this chapter, in NFPA *101,* and in *NFPA 5000.*

The need to accommodate physically and mentally challenged students within the general school population also affects school designs. Access and egress must be considered for these students by providing facilities such as elevators, ramps, horizontal exits, and areas of refuge in multiple-story buildings. Provisions must be made for using elevators or other special facilities to shelter and evacuate these students. It is important that local fire departments be aware of any special arrangements for evacuating physically disabled students and preplan for such scenarios, as their approach to rescue efforts might be affected by such arrangements.

Flexible and Open Plan Designs

Flexible and open plan design concepts used in some schools differ from conventional designs in that the walls may be demountable or easily moved without major reconstruction efforts. The ability to easily rearrange walls to suit changing programmatic or educational needs is valuable, but proper consideration to egress requirements and fire safety must be included in the planning process.

Open plan buildings delineate spaces and corridors by using movable fixtures and low-height partitions (usually maximum height of 5 ft [1.5 m]). Although this design provides greater flexibility, it diminishes the building's overall fire safety level by omitting features that could confine fire and smoke to a single, smaller compartment long enough to permit orderly evacuation. The compensating factor is the occupants' ability to observe the entire area over the low-height partitions and presumably detect any fire in its incipient stage. Because occupants are presumably awake and alert, their natural faculties can serve as fire and smoke detectors. Such early detection should make prompt evacuation and emergency forces notification possible.

Flexible and open plan buildings should be evaluated while all folding walls are extended and in use, as well as when they are in the retracted position. Flexible and open plan buildings shall also be permitted to periodically rearrange their walls and partitions if revised plans have been thoroughly reviewed and approved by the authority having jurisdiction.

Day-Care Occupancies

Requirements for educational occupancies are not applicable to most child, adult, or home day-care occupancies. As occupants of day-care facilities may not always be considered as being capable of self-preservation actions, a higher level of active and passive life safety measures is often prescribed for day-care occupancies. For more information on child, adult, and home day-care occupancies, see Section 20, Chapter 13, "Day-Care Occupancies."

College and Universities

Requirements for educational occupancies are not applicable to colleges, universities, postsecondary trade schools, or other forms of education beyond grade 12. Students at these levels are generally presumed to be capable of adult behavior because of their age and maturity levels. For more information on colleges and universities, see Section 20, Chapter 3, "Hotels and University Housing," and Section 20, Chapter 11, "Business Occupancies."

OCCUPANCY HAZARDS

Multiple Occupancies

Often more than one type of occupancy exists within or adjacent to an educational facility. Typical scenarios often include assembly and business occupancies as well as dormitories.

In multiple-occupancy situations where the occupancies are mixed as described in NFPA *101* and *NFPA 5000,* care must be taken to ensure that the fire and life safety provisions for all occupancies are met. It is important to provide sufficient protection to prevent the educational occupancy from being exposed to any hazards associated with other occupancies located within or adjacent to the educational facility.

Hazardous Areas and Arrangements

Areas such as laboratories, shops, kitchens, storage areas, janitor closets, laundries, mechanical rooms, and stages may often be separated from educational occupancies or otherwise protected. Usually, fire-rated walls and doors provide the necessary degree of protection unless the hazard is severe, in which case, automatic suppression systems may also be required. Kitchens should also be protected in accordance with NFPA 96, *Standard for Ventilation Control and Fire Protection of Commercial Cooking Operations.*

Clothing, personal effects, and other combustible materials should not be stored in corridors. However, if automatic smoke detection or suppression systems protect the corridors, or if metal lockers are used, clothing and personal effects can be stored in corridors. Metal lockers should not, however, reduce the required egress width.

Child-prepared artwork and teaching materials attached directly to walls should not cover more than 20 percent of the wall area in nonsprinklered buildings or more than 50 percent of the wall area in sprinklered buildings. It is advantageous to not only limit the quantity of artwork and teaching materials displayed but also to avoid placing such materials near a room's exit access doors. Because the artwork's combustibility cannot be effectively controlled, the quantity, in terms of the percentage of the overall wall area covered, is regulated to avoid creating a continuous combustible surface that will spread flames across the room. Hanging banners in rooms and corridors should also be avoided unless they meet the requirements for flame resistance as prescribed in NFPA 701, *Standard Methods of Fire Tests for Flame Propagation of Textiles and Films.* Because banners can frequently obstruct exit signs, emergency lights, and sprinklers, consideration should be given to problems associated with hanging such banners before allowing their use.

LIFE SAFETY CONCEPTS

Occupant Load

The occupant load, in terms of the number of persons for whom means of egress provisions are to be provided, is typically determined on the basis of the occupant load factors prescribed by NFPA *101* and *NFPA 5000.* The occupant load factors utilized should take into consideration the characteristics or actual use of the space being analyzed. NFPA *101* and *NFPA 5000* prescribe an occupant load factor of 20 net ft^2 (1.9 net m^2) per person for typical classrooms in educational occupancies. Shops, laboratories, and vocational rooms should utilize an occupant load factor of 50 net ft^2 (4.6 net m^2) per person. Areas for assembly uses and spaces utilized for business, storage, kitchens, and so on should utilize the occupant load factors appropriate to that specific function.

Means of Egress

There are no substitutes for properly designed and protected exit access paths, exits, and exit discharges. The total capacity of the means of egress for any story, level, or occupied area must be sufficient for the occupant load thereof. Travel distance requirements and dead-end restrictions are especially important in educational occupancies because of the age and nature of the occupants. Every room or space larger than 1000 ft^2 (93 m^2), or with an occupant load of more than 50 persons, must be provided with a minimum of two exit access doors. It is also important that no less than two separate and remote exits be provided and made accessible on every story, level, or mezzanine.

Proper exit and vertical opening enclosures are important to prevent smoke and heat contamination. Precautions must also be taken to prevent corridors from becoming untenable. The use of fire-rated corridor construction, generally with a fire resistance rating of 1 hour, is common practice in nonsprinklered educational occupancies. If the corridor ceiling is an assembly that has a 1-hour fire resistance rating (when tested as a wall), the corridor walls are normally permitted to terminate at the corridor ceiling. NFPA *101* and *NFPA 5000* do not require lavatories to be separated from corridors in educational occupancies, provided the building is protected throughout by an approved, supervised automatic sprinkler system, or the lavatories are separated from all other spaces by walls having a fire resistance rating of not less than 1 hour as shown in Figure 20.12.1. Proper door controls are also necessary to protect corridors, exits, and vertical openings. Although many codes require self-closing doors in these locations, operational necessities make them impractical in many schools. Therefore, integrated magnetic door hold-open devices and staff training are necessary to ensure doors are properly closed at the appropriate times, such as during emergency evacuation scenarios.

Additionally, exit access corridors may not be not less than 6 ft (1830 mm) wide, regardless of the required egress capacity. The intent of the 6 ft (1830 mm) corridor is to permit two files of students to move simultaneously with sufficient room for teachers or monitors to supervise. Short corridors serving only one or two rooms might warrant consideration for some reduction in required width. NFPA *101* and *NFPA 5000* are very exacting about limiting projections, such as drinking fountains, furniture, or lockers into these corridors.

Windows for Rescue

NFPA *101* and *NFPA 5000* require the installation of specially sized windows for fire department use for rescue (Figure

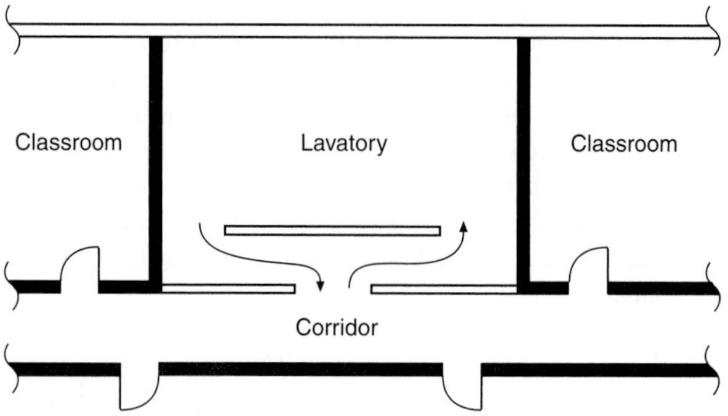

FIGURE 20.12.1 Lavatory Permitted to Be Open to Corridor

20.12.2). One such window is required in any room larger than 250 ft^2 (23.2 m^2) that is normally subject to occupancy by students, unless the building is protected by a supervised automatic sprinkler system. The minimum dimension requirement allows students to escape through the window and fire fighters wearing self-contained breathing apparatus to enter the room for rescue or fire suppression purposes. These windows must be accessible to fire department personnel but are not required on floors above the third story as fire department ground ladders cannot reliably reach these windows. Such taller structures are often protected throughout with automatic sprinklers, which eliminate the need for rescue windows. The requirement for such rescue windows does not apply to any room or space that has a door leading directly to the outside of the building.

Exit Hardware

All exit facilities should be inspected on a daily basis to ensure that they remain unobstructed and function properly. As we become increasingly attuned to safety and security considerations, additional care must be taken with respect to access-control devices and special locking arrangements. Any such locking devices must be approved by the authority having jurisdiction, listed for their intended use, and integrated with the overall life safety and fire protection plan for the building. In no instance are chains or padlocks permitted on exit doors when the building is occupied. If such security devices are used when the building is unoccupied, provisions for their removal must be made to the satisfaction of the local authorities. Any condition likely to interfere with safe egress should be reported to the proper authorities and corrected immediately.

In new educational occupancies, any door in a required means of egress from an area having an occupant load of 100 or more persons is permitted to be provided with a latch or lock only if it is outfitted with approved panic hardware or fire exit hardware. In existing educational occupancies, panic hardware or fire exit hardware is only mandated on required exit doors that are capable of locking or latching if the door's required egress capacity is 100 or more persons.

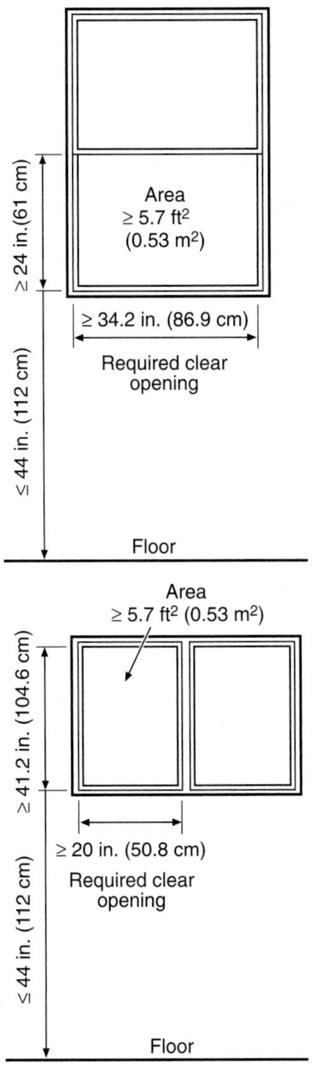

FIGURE 20.12.2 Minimum Dimensional Criteria for Rescue and Ventilation

Means of Egress Illumination and Marking

The means of egress must be properly illuminated any time that the conditions of occupancy require that the means of egress be available for use. Stairways should be provided with a minimum illumination level of 10 ft-candle (108 lux) when measured at the floor. Other walking surfaces along the means of egress route should be provided with a minimum illumination level of 1 ft-candle (10.8 lux) when measured at the floor. Suitable emergency lighting provisions must be provided to automatically illuminate the means of egress system in the event of any interruptions to the normal electrical power supply or building lighting circuitry. Exits should be marked with approved signs that are readily visible from any direction of exit access travel. The access paths leading to the exits should also be marked with approved signage where the route to reach the exit is not readily apparent to the occupants.

Alarm Systems

In general, schools require a manual fire alarm system as a minimum. Because of vandalism, fire alarm systems have sometimes been inappropriately turned off or otherwise disabled in order to prevent malicious or false alarms from disrupting the learning process. Recent changes in some codes permit the deletion of manual fire alarm boxes if the building is protected throughout by an approved automatic fire detection system or supervised automatic sprinkler system, and there is a continuously staffed central location where an evacuation signal can be manually activated. Emergency forces notification must also be provided to alert the fire department of any fire or other hazardous condition.

In school structures not over 1000 ft^2 (93 m^2) and that contain only a single classroom, fire alarm systems are not usually required. As with flexible and open plan design areas, the entire area can be readily observed and, therefore, a fire would likely be easily detected in its incipient state. A minimum separation distance of 30 ft (9.2 m) between the single classroom building and any other structure should be maintained.

Emergency Plans and Fire Exit Drills

Operators of educational occupancies should develop emergency plans in conjunction with the local fire department. The emergency plans should reflect procedures for the reporting of emergencies as well as the occupant and staff response to such emergencies. The local fire department needs to be made aware of the school's plan regarding evacuation of any students with disabilities or staff who might be incapable of self-preservation. Areas of refuge (as required by NFPA *101, NFPA 5000,* or other accessibility laws) should be easily identifiable from the exterior so that fire department personnel can readily access these areas. Emergency plans should be reviewed and updated periodically to reflect any new information or changes in condition.

Frequent fire exit drills are critical in achieving the proper response by occupants during an emergency. Fire exit drills should include the assignment of staff or more mature students to hold doors open in the line of march and to close doors where necessary to prevent the spread of fire or smoke; to search lavatories or other ancillary rooms; to properly account for all occupants; and to achieve a prompt, quiet, and orderly evacuation of the building or relocation to designated areas of refuge. Occupants should not be allowed to retrieve clothing or book bags after the alarm sounds due to the confusion that would result in forming lines, student accountability, and the danger of tripping over dragging apparel.

Fire exit drills should be held not less than once per month when the building is open for occupancy. In climates where winter weather is severe, additional drills should be run before bad weather starts. Everyone within the building should participate in such drills as this ensures that all staff and students understand the fire exit drill procedure. Drills should be unannounced and held at different hours of the day, during changing of classes, when the school is at assembly, and during recess or gym periods. As drills simulate an actual fire or emergency condition, the fire alarm signaling devices should be used so that occupants recognize the signal and respond appropriately. A separate and distinct recall signal should be developed to prevent a premature return to the building. Repetitive training in fire drills will also benefit the student later in life or when he or she is within another occupancy type.

Unfortunately, several high-profile school tragedies have given school officials pause with respect to conducting traditional fire exit drills. Schools should not be dissuaded from conducting these vital drills since delayed egress can lead to tragic consequences. However, some adjustments to previously established emergency evacuation and relocation drills may be advisable. One such alteration may be to involve law enforcement agents to supplement the role traditionally played by the fire service. School-based personnel may also be assigned to scan the school grounds and create a safety perimeter until the proper recall signal is sounded. Where building geometries and fire-resistive design features permit, consideration may also be given to utilizing horizontal exiting strategies and phased emergency evacuation scenarios to relocate students to predetermined safe locations in lieu of evacuating in the traditional sense. It is critical that any such adjustments be documented in the building's emergency plan, practiced frequently, and communicated to the appropriate first responders.

SUMMARY

Because of the nature of their occupants, educational facilities require specific life safety considerations. Educational occupancies can generally be characterized as public, private, and parochial schools for students from kindergarten through grade 12. Examples of educational occupancies include conventional schools, academies, kindergartens, and other facilities whose purpose is primarily educational, even though their students may be of preschool age. Fire protection measures should focus on building design principles, means of egress provisions, exit hardware, fire alarm systems, and emergency planning, staff training, and exit drills. Fire protection strategies must take into consideration the fact that the occupants may vary in their ability to cope with emergency situations. Hazardous areas such as laboratories, shops, kitchens, storage areas, janitor closets, laundries, mechanical rooms, and stages must often be separated from educational occupancies by fire-resistant construction or otherwise protected. In addition, special care must be taken to avoid hazardous arrangements such as the improper storage of clothing and the display of child artwork. In multiple-occupancy situations where the occupancies are mixed, care must be taken to ensure that the fire and life safety provisions for all occupancies are met.

BIBLIOGRAPHY

NFPA Codes, Standards, and Recommended Practices

Reference to the following NFPA codes, standards, and recommended practices will provide further information on educational occupancies discussed in this chapter. (See the latest version of The NFPA Catalog *for availability of current editions of the following documents.)*

NFPA 13, *Standard for the Installation of Sprinkler Systems*

NFPA 45, *Standard on Fire Protection for Laboratories Using Chemicals*

NFPA 54, *National Fuel Gas Code*

NFPA 72®, National Fire Alarm Code®

NFPA 96, *Standard for Ventilation Control and Fire Protection of Commercial Cooking Operations*

NFPA *101®, Life Safety Code®*

NFPA 101A, *Guide on Alternative Approaches to Life Safety*

NFPA 701, *Standard Methods of Fire Tests for Flame Propagation of Textiles and Films*

NFPA 5000®, Building Construction and Safety Code®

References

Berlin, G., Crowely, A., and Sweeney, R., "Manual for the Safe and Secure Schools Tools to Improve Hazardous Mitigation Planning for the Nation's School Systems," National Association of State Fire Marshals, Washington, DC, Mar. 2006.

Coté, R. (Ed.), *Life Safety Code Handbook,* 10th ed., National Fire Protection Association, Quincy, MA, 2006.

Dolan, T. G., "Life/Fire Safety," *School Planning and Management,* Vol. 43, No. 8, 2004, pp. 25–28.

"Indicators of School Crime and Safety—Executive Summary," National Council for Educational Statistics, U.S. Department of Education, Washington, DC, 2002.

Kroll, K., "Stay or Go," *NFPA Journal,* Vol. 97, No. 5, 2003, pp. 42–47.

Szachnowicz, A., "Balancing Safety and Security in the School Environment," *Fire Protection Engineering,* No. 20, Fall 2003, pp. 7–24.

Chapter 13

Day-Care Occupancies

Catherine L. Stashak

Chapter Contents

Key Terms

capable of self-preservation, day-care home, day-care occupancy, hazardous area, lockup, means of egress, occupant characteristics

This chapter addresses day-care occupancies, which are generally defined as structures in which four or more clients receive care, maintenance, and supervision, by other than their relatives or legal guardians for less than 24 hours per day. This chapter describes the nature of day-care occupants as well as the hazards and life safety concepts pursuant to the occupancy.

Examples of day-care occupancies include adult day-care occupancies, except where part of a health care occupancy; child day-care occupancies; day-care homes; and nursery schools. In areas where local schools offer half-day kindergarten programs only, many child day-care occupancies offer state-approved kindergarten classes for children who need full-day care. As these classes are normally incidental to the day-care occupancy, the requirements applicable to the day-care occupancy should be followed. The definition of day-care occupancy also excludes day-care occupancies that are incidental to some other occupancy. In such cases, the requirements of the predominant occupancy apply. Examples of excluded facilities include the following:

- Rooms located within places of worship used as nurseries or for supervision of children or religious education while services are being held in the building
- Rooms used for temporary child care during short-term recreational activities of the child's relative or guardian, such as within a health club

Table 20.13.1 summarizes structure fire loss in day-care occupancies.

See also Section 5, Chapter 5, "Reaching High-Risk Groups"; and Section 20, Chapter 1, "Assessing Life Safety in Buildings."

OCCUPANT CHARACTERISTICS

Day-care facilities have traditionally been associated with child care and have thus been historically considered as educational occupancies. Changes in society have indicated a need to expand the definition of day-care facilities to include facilities that care for older people. Because physical limitations that apply to children can also apply to older adults, this approach seems logical from fire protection and life safety standpoints. Design criteria for these facilities should focus less on age-group classifications and more on clients' ability to evacuate and staff members' ability to evacuate clients.

Capability of Self-Preservation

NFPA *101*®, *Life Safety Code*®, and *NFPA 5000*®, *Building Construction and Safety Code*®, use the term *capable of self-preservation,* which is defined as the ability of a client to evacuate a day-care occupancy without direct intervention by a staff member, in the chapters that address day-care occupancies. It is the intent of NFPA *101* and *NFPA 5000* to classify children under the age of 24 months as incapable of self-preservation. Children older than 24 months should be capable of navigating stairs without dropping to their knees and will also follow directions. Other examples of incapability of self-preservation for children and adults might be confinement to a wheelchair

Catherine L. Stashak is retired from the Des Plaines, Illinois, Fire Department and works as a fire protection specialist for the Illinois Office of the State Fire Marshal. She is a principal member on the NFPA Technical Committee on Educational and Day-Care Occupancies, which she chaired for 10 years.

TABLE 20.13.1 Structure Fires in Day-Care Occupancies, 1999–2002 Annual Averages

Occupancy	*Fires*	*Civilian Deaths*	*Civilian Injuries*	*Direct Property Damage (in Millions of Dollars)*
Day-care	440	0	4	4

Note: These are fires reported to U.S. municipal fire departments and so exclude fires reported only to federal or state agencies or industrial fire brigades. Fires are rounded to the nearest ten, deaths and injuries to the nearest one, and direct property damage to the nearest million dollars. Damage has not been adjusted for inflation.

Source: *U.S. Fires in Selected Occupancies,* March 2006. National estimates based on NFIRS and NFPA survey.

or other physical disability and clients who are unable to follow directions or a group to the outside due to mental or behavioral disorders. Examples of direct intervention by staff members include carrying a client, pushing a client in a wheelchair, and guiding a client by direct hand-holding or continued bodily contact. Another common method of evacuation used with infants is to place several infants in one crib and roll the crib out of the facility. If clients are unable to exit the building by themselves, with minimal intervention from staff members, such as verbal orders, classification as incapable of self-preservation should be considered. Client mobility is an important consideration in developing life safety requirements.

It should be recognized that some day-care facilities operate 24 hours per day to care for dependents of people who work at night. These facilities present the greatest hazard because their occupants will most likely be asleep when a fire starts. Therefore, day-care facilities that operate at night require special considerations. No matter what time of day, day-care staff members are required to be awake and alert at all times; however during a nap period it is possible that some staff may be asleep when an emergency occurs.

Lockups

It is possible that a day-care facility might have an area where clients are restrained, and such occupants are considered as incapable of self-preservation because of security measures not under the occupant's control. If this arrangement exists, these areas must comply with the requirements for lockups in NFPA *101* and *NFPA 5000*, which are located in the chapters that address detention and correctional occupancies.

CONSTRUCTION REQUIREMENTS

NFPA *101* prescribes location and construction type limitations for both new and existing day-care occupancies. The types of construction listed in Tables 20.13.2 and 20.13.3 are defined in NFPA 220, *Standard on Types of Building Construction,* and *NFPA 5000*. The types of construction permitted by the code depend on the location of the day-care occupancy in the building relative to the level of exit discharge (LED).

TABLE 20.13.2 Location and Construction Type Limitations for New Day-Care Occupancies

Location of Day-Care Occupancy	*Sprinklered Building*	*Construction Type*
1 story below LED	Yes	I (442), I (332), II (222), II (111), II (000), III (211), IV (2HH), V (111)
	No	NP
Level of exit discharge	Yes	Any type
	No	Any type
1 story above LED	Yes	Any type
	No	I (442), I (332), II (222)
2 or 3 stories above LED	Yes	I (442), I (332), II (222), II (111), II (000), III (211), V (111)
	No	NP
More than 3 stories above LED but not high-rise	Yes	I (442), I (332), II (222), II (111)
	No	NP
High-rise	Yes	I (442), I (332), or II (222)
	No	NP

LED = Level of exit discharge.
NP = Not permitted.
Source: NFPA *101,* 2006 edition, Table 16.1.6.1.

OCCUPANCY HAZARDS

Multiple Occupancy

Sometimes more than one type of occupancy exists in conjunction with a day-care facility. Where a day-care facility serves not more than 12 clients in an apartment building, it could be considered a day-care home; a corporate day-care center that serves more than 12 clients could be located within an office building, which is classified as a business occupancy. Where multiple occupancies are mixed, as described in NFPA *101* and *NFPA 5000*, care must be taken to ensure that the fire and life safety provisions for all occupancies are met. It is important to provide sufficient protection to prevent the day-care occupancy from being exposed to hazards of other occupancies in the structure. To be considered separate occupancies, the day-care occupancy must be separated from the other uses by fire barriers, and the occupancies must be provided with independent exit access.

TABLE 20.13.3 Location and Construction Type Limitations for Existing Day-Care Occupancies

Location of Day-Care Occupancy	*Sprinklered Building*	*Construction Type*
1 story below LED	Yes	I (442), I (332), II (222), II (111), II (000), III (211), IV (2HH), V (111)
	No	I (442), I (332), II (222), II (111), III (211), IV (2HH), V (111)
Level of exit discharge	Yes	Any type
	No	Any type
1 story above LED	Yes	Any type
	No	I (442), I (332), II (222)
	No	II (111)*, III (211)*, V (111)*
2 or 3 stories above LED	Yes	I (442), I (332), II (222)
	Yes	II (111)*, III (211)*, V (111)*
	No	I (442), I (332), II (222)
At or above 3 stories above LED but not high-rise	Yes	I (442), I (332), II (222)
	Yes	II (111)*
	No	I (442), I (332), II (222)
High-rise	Yes	I (442), I (332), II (222)
	No	NP

LED = Level of exit discharge.
NP = Not permitted.
*Permitted only if clients are capable of self-preservation.
Source: NFPA *101,* 2006 edition, Table 17.1.1.

Hazardous Areas and Arrangements

Areas such as storage areas and boiler and furnace rooms must be separated from day-care occupancies. Usually, fire-rated walls and doors provide the necessary degree of protection unless the hazard is severe, in which case automatic suppression systems may also be required. In some cases, the fire resistance rating is eliminated if the building is protected throughout with automatic sprinklers.

Clothing, personal effects and other combustible materials should not be stored in corridors. If automatic detection or suppression systems are provided in the corridors, or if metal lockers are used, clothing and personal effects can be stored in corridors. Metal lockers should not, however, reduce the required egress width.

Child-prepared artwork and teaching materials attached directly to walls should not cover more than 20 percent of the wall area in a building that is not protected throughout by an approved, supervised automatic sprinkler system. In a building that is protected throughout by an approved, supervised automatic sprinkler system, child-prepared artwork and teaching materials attached directly to walls should not cover more than 50 percent of the wall. It is advantageous not only to limit the quantity of child-prepared materials displayed but also to avoid placing such materials near a room's exit access doors. Because the artwork's combustibility cannot be effectively controlled, the quantity, in terms of percentage of the overall wall area covered, is regulated to avoid creating a continuous combustible surface that will allow flames to spread across the room.

Draperies, curtains, hanging banners, and other similar furnishings and decorations should meet the requirements for flame resistance when tested per NFPA 701, *Standard Methods of Fire Tests for Flame Propagation of Textiles and Films.* Care should be taken when installing hanging banners so that exit signs and automatic sprinklers are not obstructed.

LIFE SAFETY CONCEPTS

Means of Egress

There are no substitutes for properly designed exit access paths, exits, and exit discharges. Travel distance requirements and dead-end limits are especially important in day-care occupancies because of the nature of the occupants and the slower rate at which evacuation is completed. Proper exit enclosures are important to prevent contamination by smoke and heat. Means of egress requirements for day-care occupancies do not differ much from those for educational occupancies, except that 6 ft (1.8 m) corridors, which are required in educational occupancies, are not required in day-care occupancies.

NFPA *101* and *NFPA 5000* require the installation of specially sized windows for fire department use for rescue as shown in Figure 20.13.1. One such window is required in any room normally subject to client occupancy, other than bathrooms. These windows are not required if the building is protected by a supervised automatic sprinkler system or if the room or space has a door leading directly to the outside of the building or on floors above the third story. The minimum dimension requirement allows clients to escape through the window and fire fighters wearing self-contained breathing apparatus to enter the room for rescue or fire suppression purposes. These windows must be accessible to fire department personnel, so they are not required on floors above the third story as fire department ground ladders do not normally reach such windows.

Although the ability of staff to assist and participate in evacuation is part of the life safety package for day-care occupancies,

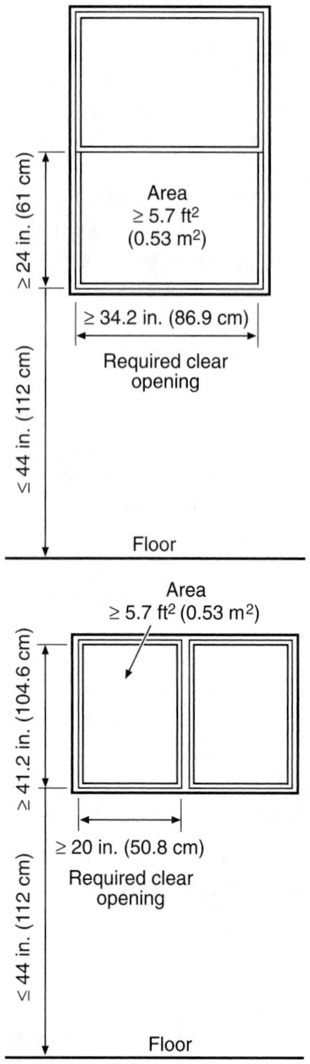

FIGURE 20.13.1 Minimum Dimensional Criteria for Rescue and Ventilation

neither NFPA *101* nor *NFPA 5000* mandates staff-to-client ratios because, from the standpoint of the local authority, ratios are very difficult to enforce. Most state licensing requirements include staff-to-client ratios; additional requirements are considered duplicate effort.

Precautions must be taken to prevent corridors from becoming untenable. The use of fire-rated corridor construction, generally with a rating of one hour, is common practice. If the corridor ceiling is an assembly that also has a 1-hour fire resistance rating (when tested as a wall assembly), the corridor walls are normally permitted to terminate at the corridor ceiling. This requirement is reduced if the building is protected throughout with automatic sprinklers or if rooms occupied by clients have a direct exit to the outside. Neither NFPA *101* nor *NFPA 5000* requires lavatories to be separated from corridors, provided the lavatories are separated from all other spaces by walls having a fire resistance of not less than one hour as shown in Figure 20.13.2.

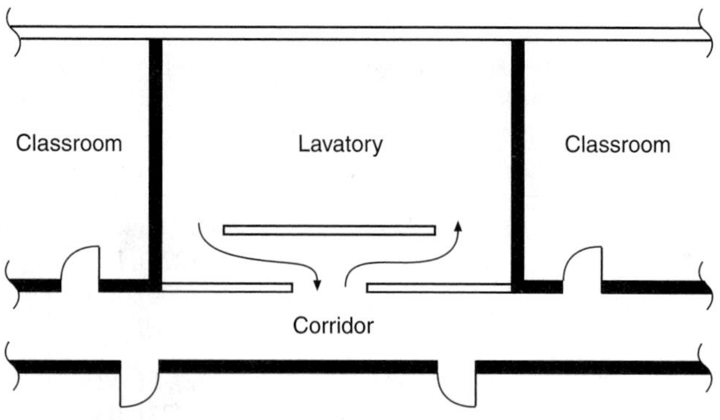

FIGURE 20.13.2 Lavatory Permitted to Be Open to Corridor

Exit Hardware

Any door within a required means of egress from an area having an occupant load of 100 or more should have panic hardware or fire exit hardware if equipped with a lock or latch. It should be noted that the requirement for panic hardware or fire exit hardware is based on the total occupant load of the area served and not the required capacity of the door. In no instance are chains or padlocks permitted on egress doors when the building is occupied.

Closet and Bathroom Doors

Closet Doors. Closet doors should be designed so that clients can open the door from inside the closet. The purpose of this requirement is to prevent arrangements where a client can be trapped in a closet. It is intended that this provision be broadly interpreted to include equipment such as refrigerators and freezers.

Bathroom Doors. Bathroom doors should be designed to allow the door to be unlocked from the outside by an opening device that is readily accessible to the staff. The purpose of this requirement is to permit access to a client in the bathroom should they become injured or sick.

Fire Alarm Systems

Fire alarm requirements for day-care occupancies are more stringent than those for most occupancies because it takes longer for day-care clients to evacuate—they could be asleep or they could be incapable of self-preservation. In day-care centers housed in more than one room, smoke detection is required so as to provide early warning for clients and staff not located in the room of fire origin. This early notification is especially important in centers that have clients incapable of self-preservation or clients that are asleep.

In day-care centers that are housed in one room, fire alarm systems are not usually required. The entire area can be observed; therefore, a fire can be easily detected in its incipient stage. An important part of a day-care occupancy's life safety plan is notification of the local fire department. The sooner fire department personnel arrive on the scene, the sooner they can assist with evacuation of clients.

Staff Training and Emergency Egress and Relocation Drills

Day-care occupancies should develop emergency plans in conjunction with the local fire department. The local fire department needs to be made aware of the day-care facility's plan regarding evacuation of clients who are incapable of self-preservation. Areas of refuge, as required by NFPA *101, NFPA 5000*, or any other accessibility laws, need to be identifiable from the exterior so fire department personnel can readily access these areas.

Frequent fire exit drills are critical in achieving proper response by occupants during an emergency. Fire exit drills should include assignment of staff to close doors where necessary to prevent spread of fire or smoke; to search the lavatories or other rooms; to account for all occupants; and to achieve a prompt, quiet, and orderly evacuation of the building or relocation to areas of refuge. Fire exit drills should be held not less than once per month when the building is open for occupancy. In climates where winter weather is severe, most drills should be run before bad weather starts. This ensures that staff and clients understand fire exit drill procedures.

Drills should be held at expected and unexpected times and at varying times that the day-care center is open, including during outdoor play time and even during nap periods. As drills simulate an actual fire condition, the fire alarm signaling devices should be activated so that occupants recognize the signal and respond appropriately. Repetitive training in fire drills will benefit the client when he or she is within another occupancy type. When a fire alarm is activated within the other occupancy, the day-care client should recognize the signal and respond appropriately.

DAY-CARE HOMES

Day-Care Home Defined

NFPA *101* and *NFPA 5000* provide requirements for smaller day-care occupancies. A *day-care home* is defined as a day-care occupancy that has not more than 12 clients. Day-care homes are further subdivided into family day-care homes that have 4 to 6 clients and group day-care homes that have 7 to 12 clients. NFPA *101* and *NFPA 5000* specify that the caregiver's own children or relatives under the age of six are to be included in the specified staff-to-client ratios for these day-care occupancies. The provisions found in NFPA *101* and *NFPA 5000* recognize that a typical day-care home is usually located in a residential setting. Because of this, it is difficult to mandate fire protection features that are as stringent as in a "full-size" day-care occupancy, such as one serving more than 12 clients.

Means of Escape in Day-Care Homes

In day-care homes, means of escape are permitted as the egress system. The concept of means of escape is well developed in the chapters that address one- and two-family dwellings in NFPA *101* and *NFPA 5000*. However NFPA *101* and *NFPA 5000* require that every room used for sleeping, living, or dining meet the following provisions:

- At least two means of escape must be provided, one of which needs to be a door or stairway providing travel to the outside of the building at street or ground level.
- The second means of escape is permitted to be a window under certain circumstances.
- No room or space that is accessible only by a ladder, folding stair, or through a trapdoor is permitted to be occupied for living or sleeping purposes.
- In group day-care homes, spaces used by clients on any story above the level of exit discharge must have access to at least one means of escape that discharges directly to the outside; the second means of escape can be a window under certain circumstances.
- Spaces used by clients below the level of exit discharge must be provided with not less than one means of escape that discharges directly to the outside, with vertical travel not more than 96 inches to the ground level; the second means of escape can be a window under certain circumstances (Figure 20.13.3).

Staff-to-Client Ratio

It is important that the staff-to-client ratios mandated by NFPA *101* and *NFPA 5000* for day-care homes be followed. Table 20.13.4 addresses the staff-to-client ratios mandated by NFPA *101* and *NFPA 5000* for day-care homes.

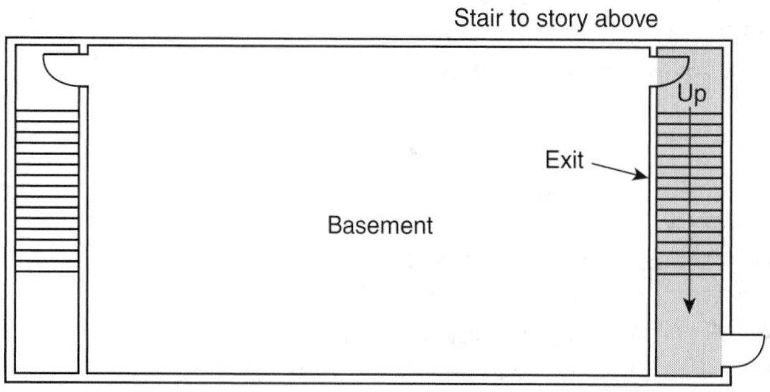

FIGURE 20.13.3 Egress Requirements from Group Day-Care Home Occupying Basement (Source: *Life Safety Code® Handbook*, NFPA, 2006 edition)

TABLE 20.13.4 Required Staff-to-Client Ratios in Day-Care Homes

Day-Care Home Type	*Staff-to-Client Ratios (Including Caregivers' Children)*	*Maximum Number of Clients Incapable of Self-Preservation*
Family day-care homes	1 staff for up to 6 clients	2
Group day-care homes	2 staff for up to 12 clients*	3

*Staff-to-client ratio is permitted to be modified by the authority having jurisdiction (AHJ) where safeguards in addition to those specified by code are provided.

Local authorities may not have knowledge of the full number of day-care homes within their jurisdictions. Parents who wish to earn money while staying home with their own children may simply advertise by word of mouth that they are willing to watch children. No notification may be given to the fire department, which will have to deal with multiple young children when the home is involved in fire. Local authorities may only find out about the day-care home if the owner obtains a license from the state.

SUMMARY

Because of the nature of their occupants, day-care facilities require specific life safety considerations. Day-care occupancies include both child and adult day-care occupancies, day-care homes, and nursery schools. Fire protection measures should focus on building design, means of egress, exit hardware, fire alarm systems, staff training, and emergency egress and relocation drills. The fact that the occupants, whether children, infants, the elderly, or disabled, vary in their abilities to cope with emergency situations should be taken into consideration. Hazardous areas such as janitor's closets, kitchens, storage areas, and furnace rooms should be separated from day-care occupancies or protected with automatic sprinklers. In addition, special care must be taken to avoid hazardous arrangements such as the improper storage of clothing or excessive display of child-prepared artwork.

BIBLIOGRAPHY

NFPA Codes, Standards, and Recommended Practices

Reference to the following NFPA codes, standards, and recommended practices will provide further information on day-care occupancies discussed in this chapter. (See the latest version of The NFPA Catalog *for availability of current editions of the following documents.)*

NFPA *101*®, *Life Safety Code*®
NFPA 220, *Standard on Types of Building Construction*
NFPA 701, *Standard Methods of Fire Tests for Flame Propagation of Textiles and Films*
NFPA 5000®, *Building Construction and Safety Code*®

References

Comoletti, J., "School Fire Drills," *NFPA Journal,* Vol. 93, No. 1, 1999, p. 80.
Coté, R., *Life Safety Code® Handbook,* National Fire Protection Association, Quincy, MA, 2006.
Cowan, D., and Kuenster, J., "To Sleep with the Angels: The Story of a Fire," Ivan R. Dee, Chicago, 1996.
Lynsky, R., and Winder, M. S., "ICS Goes to School," *Fire Chief,* Vol. 44, No. 3, 2000, p. 32.
Penney, G., "Schooling Seniors in Safety," *Fire Chief,* Vol. 41, No. 5, 1997, pp. 67–70.
Powers, D., "Installing Sprinklers in Existing School Buildings," *Fire Prevention,* No. 277, Mar. 1995, pp. 16–18.
Smith, J. P., "School Fires," *Firehouse,* Vol. 26, No. 6, 2001, p. 18.

Chapter 14

Detention and Correctional Occupancies

Thomas W. Jaeger

Chapter Contents

Key Terms

area of refuge, defend-in-place, detection, drills, emergency procedures, evacuation, fire emergency plan, fuel control, ignition control, lockup, occupant protection, suppression

Detention and correctional occupancies include buildings and facilities in which persons are restrained by locks they do not control. Such occupancies include adult correctional institutions, adult local detention facilities, adult community residential centers, juvenile detention facilities, juvenile training schools, juvenile community residential centers, adult and juvenile work camps, and adult and juvenile substance abuse centers. Some psychiatric and acute care hospitals may have similar security provisions, but this chapter addresses only facilities where controlled movements are not based entirely on health care considerations. Security is a major operational consideration in these facilities and must be included in the fire protection design process.

Lockups facilities in occupancies other than detention and correctional facilities are areas where building occupants are restrained for less then 24 hours and occupants are incapable of self preservation because of security measures not under their control. Lockups can be found in courthouses, police stations, international airports, sports arenas and stadiums, shopping malls, and other occupancies where it might be necessary to detain occupants for security purposes. Lockups are now specifically addressed in provisions that are new to the 2006 editions of NFPA *101*®, *Life Safety Code*®, and *NFPA 5000*®, *Building Construction and Safety Code*®.

Large correctional facilities may contain other occupancies, including industrial occupancies such as vocational shops; business occupancies such as classrooms and offices; assembly occupancies such as dining halls, auditoriums, and gymnasiums; and storage occupancies such as warehouses. The principal concern of Chapters 22 and 23 of NFPA *101* and Chapter 21 of *NFPA 5000* is the residential portion of correctional facilities. Except for the locking of doors, other uses within the detention and correctional occupancy must comply with the appropriate occupancy chapters of NFPA *101* and *NFPA 5000.* If locking of doors in these occupancies is required, Chapters 22 and 23 of NFPA *101* or Chapter 21 of *NFPA 5000* should be reviewed for guidance. These chapters of NFPA *101* do permit locking of doors in other use areas if staff is available to unlock the egress doors.

Additional information relevant to fire safety in correctional institutions can be found in Section 18, Chapter 2, "Interior Finish"; Section 18, Chapter 3, "Smoke Movement in Buildings"; and the discussion on portable fire extinguishers in Section 17, Chapter 5, "Fire Extinguisher Use and Maintenance."

OCCUPANCY CHARACTERISTICS

The major difference between detention and correctional occupancies and other residential occupancies is that the occupants are not capable of significant self-preservation actions until staff unlocks the doors. However, the occupants are capable of such actions when the doors are unlocked.

The degree of locking can have a significant impact on the risk to the occupants. For example, a facility with only two locks that can be remotely released to allow the occupants out of the building into a controlled exercise yard generally would present less risk to the occupants than

Thomas W. Jaeger, P.E., is president of Jaeger & Associates, LLC, a consulting fire protection engineering firm. He is chair of the NFPA Technical Committee on Detention and Correctional Occupancies.

one that required 15 locks to be unlocked manually with 10 different keys. Although the number of locks and the method of unlocking have an impact on the level of risk to the occupants, operations have even a greater impact. Because of the nature of the occupancy, there is a natural reluctance for staff to quickly unlock doors until adequate staff and security are present. This operational feature results in a delay in initiating the unlocking of doors and initiating evacuation or relocation.

Five types of restraint or locking systems are generally found in detention and correctional occupancies. These different locking conditions, referred to as "Use Conditions" by NFPA *101* and *NFPA 5000,* are illustrated in Figure 20.14.1 and defined below.

Use Condition I—Free Egress

In Use Condition I, free movement is allowed from sleeping areas and other spaces where access or occupancy is permitted to the exterior through means of egress meeting the requirements of NFPA *101* and *NFPA 5000.* For example, a work release center, where the doors are not locked, would be considered Use Condition I. Use Condition I facilities are permitted to comply with the requirements for Use Condition II facilities or with the requirements for the appropriate residential occupancy in NFPA *101* or *NFPA 5000.* Since a Use Condition I facility has no locks on doors in the means of egress, this type of facility can be treated as a residential occupancy.

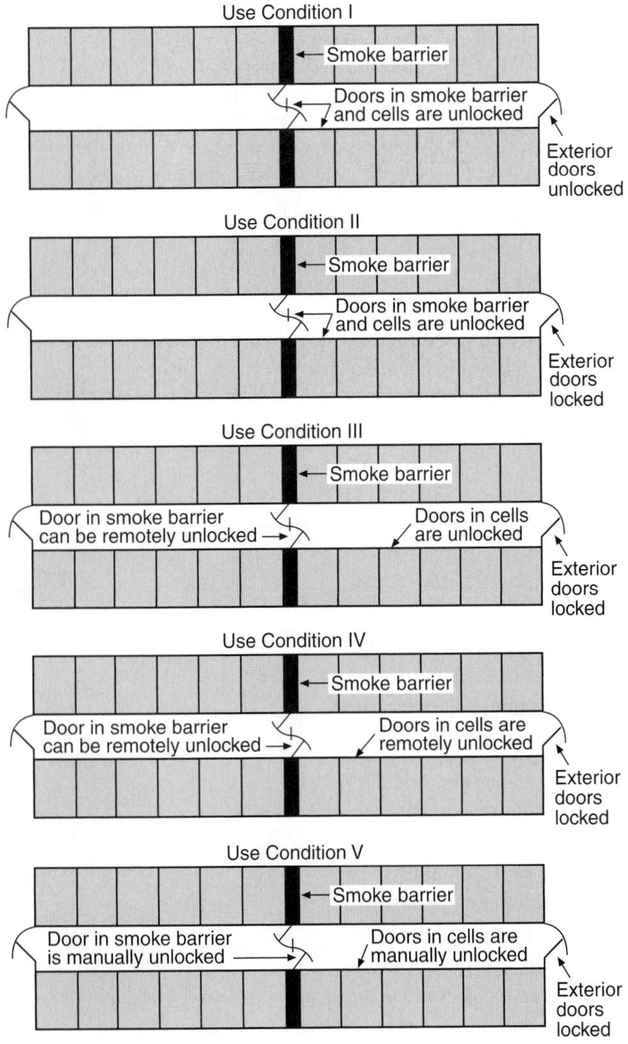

FIGURE 20.14.1 Classes of Restraint: Use Conditions I, II, III, IV, and V

Use Condition II—Zoned Egress

In Use Condition II, free movement is allowed from sleeping areas and any other occupied smoke compartments to other smoke compartments, but the exterior doors are locked.

The individual cell door may be locked from the inside by the occupant and can be unlocked by the occupant. Also, the individual cell door may be locked by the occupant when leaving the cell. This is sometimes done to provide security for the occupants' property while occupants are out of their cells.

Use Condition III—Zoned Impeded Egress

In Use Condition III, free movement is allowed within individual smoke compartments—for example, within a residential unit composed of individual sleeping rooms and within group activity space—with egress from that smoke compartment to another smoke compartment provided by the remote-control unlocking of doors. The exterior doors may be manually locked. Again, the individual cell doors may be locked by the occupant as noted in the Use Condition II section.

Use Condition IV—Impeded Egress

In Use Condition IV, free movement is restricted from an occupied space. Remote-control release is provided to permit movement from all sleeping rooms, activity spaces, and other occupied areas within the smoke compartment to other smoke compartment(s). Exterior doors may be manually locked. NFPA *101* and *NFPA 5000* allow up to a maximum of 10 manual release locks to be unlocked to relocate all occupants from one smoke compartment to an area of refuge for Use Condition IV. Unlocking of the manual release locks cannot require more than two separate keys, and the unlocking must occur as promptly as would occur if remote-control unlocking was used.

Use Condition V—Contained

In Use Condition V, free movement is restricted from an occupied space. Staff-controlled manual release at each door is provided to permit movement from all sleeping rooms, activity spaces, and other occupied areas within the smoke compartment to other smoke compartments.

When evaluating the degree of locking for determination of Use Condition, any operable locks, even those not normally used, need to be considered lockable.

The higher level of security provided, the more demanding the code requirements are for life safety because higher levels of security result in longer evacuation times, a more difficult population to evacuate, or a combination thereof.

THE FIRE PROBLEM IN DETENTION AND CORRECTIONAL FACILITIES

Each year NFPA statistically analyzes the fire problem in detention and correctional facilities.[1] The expanded version of this analysis, which appears in Tables 20.14.1, 20.14.2, and 20.14.3, identifies the significant common characteristics of correctional facility fires and groups them into several categories.

Most fires in detention and correctional facilities are incendiary or suspicious in nature. Motives can include the following:

- Increased chances of escape
- Malicious damage as a protest against conditions
- Show of force during a riot
- Suicide attempt
- Divert attention from other activities
- Weapon

In nearly all intentionally set fires for which the ignition source could be identified, the source was a match, smoking materials, or a cigarette lighter. These are the ignition sources most readily available to inmates. The typical correctional facility fire is incendiary in origin, starts in a cell, and involves bedding, trash, or papers.

Reported prison and jail fires fell 79 percent from 4180 in 1980 to 860 in 2002. It is encouraging to see that the fire data show both a reduction in the number of fires and the number of civilian deaths in detention and correctional occupancies in recent years even though the population of this occupancy has significantly increased during this same period. It should be pointed out that various detention and correctional agencies

TABLE 20.14.1 Structure Fires in Prisons and Jails by Year, 1980–2004, Structure Fires Reported to U.S. Municipal Fire Departments

				Direct Property Damage (in Millions of Dollars)	
Year	*Fires*	*Civilian Deaths*	*Civilian Injuries*	*As Reported*	*In 2004 Dollars*
1980	4200	0	190	4.6	10.6
1981	3900	5	420	14.9	30.8
1982	3600	8	210	4.4	8.6
1983	3000	0	260	5.8	11.1
1984	3000	0	140	4.3	7.8
1985	3300	2	80	2.6	4.5
1986	3200	0	110	3.2	5.5
1987	3200	2	70	5.0	8.3
1988	2900	0	180	5.6	8.9
1989	3100	5	210	15.7	23.9
1990	2500	0	140	7.1	10.3
1991	2600	0	210	29.2	40.4
1992	2300	1	150	8.1	10.8
1993	2200	1	190	8.3	10.8
1994	2300	0	200	3.5	4.5
1995	1900	0	70	2.2	2.8
1996	2100	0	70	1.2	1.5
1997	2400	0	50	6.9	8.2
1998	2200	0	50	6.9	7.9
1999*	1900	0	10	5.4	6.1
2000	1500	0	20	1.7	1.8
2001	1200	0	30	11.4	12.1
2002	900	0	20	0.8	0.8
2003	700	0	10	3.1	3.1
2004	700	0	60	1.1	1.1

Note: These are national estimates of fires reported to U.S. municipal fire departments and so exclude fires reported only to federal or state agencies or industrial fire brigades. National estimates are projections. Casualty and loss projections can be heavily influenced by the inclusion or exclusion of one unusually serious fire. Fires are rounded to the nearest hundred, direct property damage is rounded to the nearest hundred thousand dollars, and civilian deaths and injuries are not rounded. Confined fires are analyzed separately.

*From 1999, based on only fires reported in NFIRS Version 5.0.

Source: NFIRS and NFPA survey. Inflation adjustments were based on the consumer price indexes in the U.S. Census Bureau's *Statistical Abstract of the United States: 2006*, Table 705.

TABLE 20.14.2 Structure Fires in Prisons and Jails, by Area of Origin, Annual Average of 2000–2004 U.S. Structure Fires Reported to Municipal Fire Departments*

Area of Origin	*Fires*		*Civilian Deaths*		*Civilian Injuries*		*Direct Property Damage (in Millions of Dollars)*	
Bedroom	220	(26%)	0	(NA)	16	(58%)	0.8	(22%)
Laundry area	160	(19%)	0	(NA)	4	(16%)	0.5	(14%)
Kitchen	50	(5%)	0	(NA)	0	(2%)	0.0	(1%)
Duct	30	(3%)	0	(NA)	0	(0%)	0.0	(1%)
Unclassified equipment or service area	30	(3%)	0	(NA)	0	(0%)	0.0	(1%)
Unclassified area of origin	30	(3%)	0	(NA)	0	(0%)	0.0	(0%)
Unclassified function area	20	(3%)	0	(NA)	2	(7%)	0.0	(0%)
Office	20	(3%)	0	(NA)	0	(0%)	0.3	(7%)
Bathroom	20	(2%)	0	(NA)	0	(0%)	0.0	(0%)
Corridor	20	(2%)	0	(NA)	1	(2%)	0.0	(0%)
Wall assembly	20	(2%)	0	(NA)	0	(0%)	0.0	(1%)
Cell (intended to be test cell; possibly miscoded)	20	(2%)	0	(NA)	2	(8%)	0.0	(1%)
Attic or crawl space above top story	20	(2%)	0	(NA)	0	(0%)	0.0	(1%)
Lounge, living room, family room, or den	20	(2%)	0	(NA)	0	(0%)	0.2	(5%)
Unclassified service facility	10	(2%)	0	(NA)	0	(0%)	0.0	(0%)
Heating room or area	10	(2%)	0	(NA)	0	(0%)	1.0	(29%)
Exterior roof surface	10	(2%)	0	(NA)	0	(0%)	0.0	(1%)
Maintenance shop or area	10	(1%)	0	(NA)	0	(0%)	0.3	(8%)
Tool or supply storage room or area	10	(1%)	0	(NA)	0	(0%)	0.0	(1%)
Storage room, area, tank, or bin	10	(1%)	0	(NA)	0	(0%)	0.0	(0%)
Exterior wall surface	10	(1%)	0	(NA)	0	(0%)	0.0	(0%)
Entrance way or lobby	10	(1%)	0	(NA)	0	(0%)	0.0	(0%)
Other known area of origin	120	(14%)	0	(NA)	2	(7%)	0.2	(7%)
Total	860	(100%)	0	(NA)	27	(100%)	3.6	(100%)

Note: These are national estimates of fires reported to U.S. municipal fire departments and so exclude fires reported only to federal or state agencies or industrial fire brigades. National estimates are projections. Casualty and loss projections can be heavily influenced by the inclusion or exclusion of one unusually serious fire. Fires are rounded to the nearest ten, direct property damage is rounded to the nearest hundred thousand dollars, and civilian deaths and injuries are rounded to the nearest one. Prison and jail fires with area of origin unknown are proportionally allocated.

*Based on only fires reported in NFIRS Version 5.0, excluding fires reported as confined fires.

NA = Not applicable because total is zero.

Source: NFIRS and NFPA survey.

indicate "off-the-record" that a significant number of fires, up to 75 percent, in prisons and jails are small fires that go unreported to local fire departments due to security concerns.

SYSTEMS APPROACH TO FIRE SAFETY IN DETENTION AND CORRECTIONAL FACILITIES

To deal with the fire safety problem in correctional facilities, two concerns need to be addressed continually: security for the public and safety from fire for the inmates. Fire safety and security are not contradictory concepts, and there need not be an imbalance of emphasis for either in detention and correctional facilities. Neither absolute fire safety nor absolute security is attainable when considered independently, let alone when considered together. The systems approach seeks to guide the analysis and planning of correction toward achieving an economically feasible program that will attain an acceptable level of protection within the intent of the applicable codes and standards and good engineering practices and that is commensurate with the level of security provided.

The systems approach to fire safety helps to achieve these two objectives through a systematic analysis of each problem area and application of available technologies. Fire safety should be an integrated subsystem of building design, construction, and operation. This method of designing fire safety is known as the systems approach or systems concept of fire-safe building design. A system organizes interacting components in such a way that, working together, they perform a predetermined function or reach a specified objective. The use of the systems approach first requires that fire safety goals be clearly identified. These goals should describe the amount of protection a building should provide its occupants, contents, and operations. These goals should be quantified wherever possible. Once these fire safety goals are established, the methods used to achieve them should work collectively to achieve and maintain the prescribed level of fire safety.

TABLE 20.14.3 Structure Fires in Prisons and Jails, by Leading Major Cause, Annual Average of 2000–2004 U.S. Structure Fires Reported to Municipal Fire Departments*

Major Cause	*Fires*		*Civilian Deaths*		*Civilian Injuries*		*Direct Property Damage (in Millions of Dollars)*	
Intentional	350	(36%)	0	(NA)	22	(80%)	1.7	(48%)
Clothes dryer or washer	170	(17%)	0	(NA)	5	(19%)	0.2	(5%)
Cooking equipment fire	100	(10%)	0	(NA)	1	(3%)	0.0	(1%)
Identified cooking equipment	30	(3%)	0	(NA)	0	(0%)	0.0	(1%)
Confined cooking fire	70	(7%)	0	(NA)	1	(3%)	0.0	(0%)
Electrical distribution or lighting equipment	50	(5%)	0	(NA)	1	(4%)	0.1	(3%)
Smoking materials	50	(5%)	0	(NA)	0	(0%)	0.1	(3%)
Heating equipment	40	(4%)	0	(NA)	0	(0%)	0.2	(5%)
Identified heating equipment	20	(2%)	0	(NA)	0	(0%)	0.2	(5%)
Confined chimney or flue fire	0	(0%)	0	(NA)	0	(0%)	0.0	(0%)
Confined fuel burner or boiler fire	10	(1%)	0	(NA)	0	(0%)	0.0	(0%)
Playing with fire	40	(4%)	0	(NA)	0	(0%)	0.2	(5%)
Air conditioning or fan	20	(2%)	0	(NA)	0	(0%)	0.0	(0%)
Contained trash fire	40	(4%)	0	(NA)	0	(0%)	0.0	(0%)

Note: These are national estimates of fires reported to U.S. municipal fire departments and so exclude fires reported only to federal or state agencies or industrial fire brigades. National estimates are projections. Casualty and loss projections can be heavily influenced by the inclusion or exclusion of one unusually serious fire. Fires are rounded to the nearest ten, direct property damage is rounded to the nearest hundred thousand dollars, and civilian deaths and injuries are rounded to the nearest one. Candidate causes are examined separately; confined fires are analyzed separately. Major causes are defined by groupings from the data elements of cause, factor contributing to ignition, heat source, and equipment involved in ignition. Major causes are shown only if they accounted for at least 2 percent of fires.

*Based on only fires reported in NFIRS Version 5.0.

NA = Not applicable because total is zero.

Source: NFIRS and NFPA survey.

Goals of a Simplified Fire Safety System

The systems approach can be illustrated by the simplified fire safety system for correctional facilities. The box at the top of Figure 20.14.2 shows the four goals of the simplified fire safety system.

Life Safety. The protection of life is paramount in any fire. Occupants can be protected by providing a safe area of refuge from the fire within the building or by providing a safe and readily available path of travel to an outside secured area.

Property Protection. The protection of property is also of concern, particularly with today's higher replacement costs. Some areas may be considered more important than others—for example, a control room versus a storage room—and therefore require more protection.

Continuity of Operations. This involves providing protection to limit fire damage so an area can be returned to use quickly. This is a critical issue since there are generally no adequate alternative facilities available to house and provide services to displaced occupants.

Security. The primary function of a detention and correctional facility is to maintain a secure perimeter and protect the public from the occupants. Fire safety must be compatible with this function.

Objectives of a Simplified Fire Safety System

These goals are achieved through a series of objectives:

- Ignition control
- Fuel control
- Occupant protection
- Detection and suppression
- Planning and training

Success in meeting the overall goals depends on the degree of success in meeting these five objectives, and the relationships between goal success and objective success may be mathematically complex. In practical terms, however, no one objective is likely to be sufficient by itself to meet the goals, so it is safest to assume that all five objectives must be addressed. Some methods to attain each objective are listed beneath the objectives shown in Figure 20.14.2. For the objective of ignition control, for example, the methods available to reduce ignitions include the following:

- Controlling smoking materials
- Controlling electrical ignition sources
- Controlling occupant population mix to reduce intentionally set fires

When certain methods for achieving the objective are not practical or not particularly effective, other parts of the system may have to be enhanced to compensate. For example, when ignition sources cannot be effectively reduced, fuel control

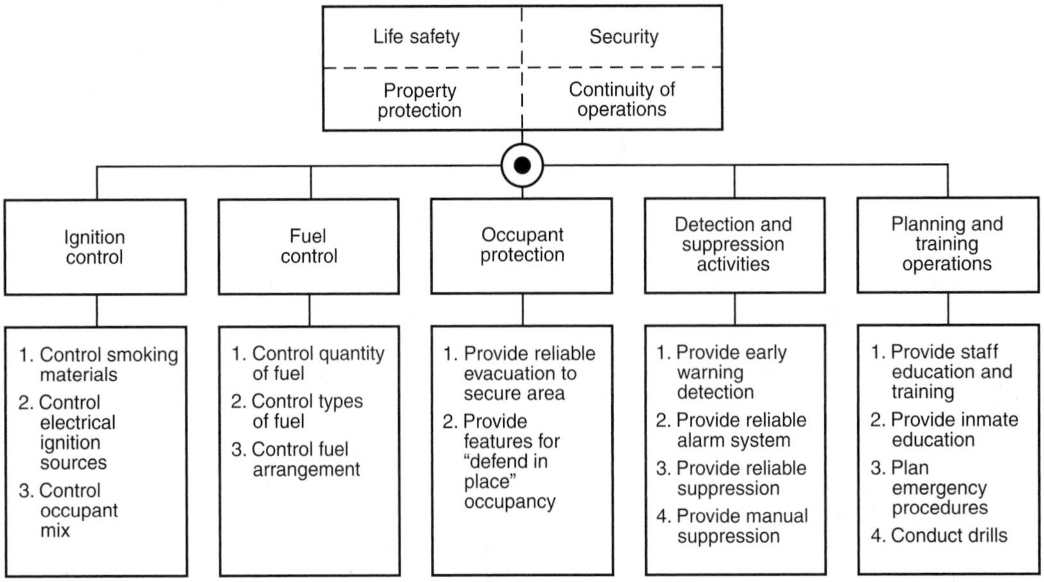

FIGURE 20.14.2 Simplified Fire Safety System for Detention and Correctional Facilities

becomes more important, or when the quantity of combustible materials cannot be effectively controlled, sprinklers may offset the hazard.

Because different objectives do not have an equal impact on the ultimate level of fire protection, the concept of equivalent protection, also known as tradeoffs, may be necessary. For example, under certain conditions, NFPA *101* and *NFPA 5000* permit the use of higher flame spread materials as interior finish if automatic sprinklers are provided. The systems approach provides for analysis of the interacting components of the fire safety system so that alternate means of protection can be evaluated. This evaluation may include initial costs, operational and maintenance costs, and impact on operations.

Ignition Control

Ignition control means greater and more dependable protection of heat sources and separation from fuel sources. In a property where most fires are deliberately set, this primarily means eliminating unnecessary heat sources. Unfortunately, total ignition control is nearly impossible to maintain and may therefore be the least effective fire defense measure. Sources of ignition are nearly always available because cigarettes and matches are, in most cases, available to inmates, and electrical appliances are generally allowed in cells. However, an effort must be made to control unwanted or unnecessary ignition sources. Some jails and prisons prohibit smoking for health reasons. This, of course, will also reduce smoking materials as an ignition source. If smoking is permitted, the types of lighters or matches can be specified. The overall use of electrical power must be carefully supervised. The number and type of heat-producing appliances, such as toasters, hot plates, and space heaters, must be controlled by the facility administrator to prevent overloading circuits. If electrical devices are allowed in cells, adequate electrical outlets should be provided to discourage the use of extension cords.

Fuel Control

Fuel control means controlling the type, arrangement, and burning characteristics of potential fuels. These fuels may include the building structural system, interior finish materials, and combustible contents, such as furnishings and inmates' personal property. Assuming that heat sources will be available, the likelihood of fire and the rate of fire growth can be controlled by limiting the type, quantity, and arrangement of the fuels available. Limiting the speed at which fire develops and spreads reduces its impact on life safety.

Achieving the goal of fuel control means keeping fuel quantity at a minimum, controlling the type of fuel, eliminating those fuels that are easy to ignite or result in fast fires, and separating fuels from readily available ignition sources. One part of fuel control is to eliminate highly combustible furnishings. Since mattresses and bedding are the fuel sources most readily available to inmates, they are most frequently involved in fires. Certain types of polyurethane foam mattresses can be a significant fuel source in prison fires because they can support fast fire development, high heat release, and heavy smoke production.

Mattresses can be made to resist ignition from cigarettes, which are a low-heat ignition source. The federal *Flammability Standard for Mattresses*[2] requires that mattresses resist ignition by cigarettes placed at 18 specified locations. This test does not include sheets or blankets on the mattress and does not indicate the resistance to ignition from open flames or the intensity of the resulting fire. A series of tests of mattresses by the U.S. Department of Agriculture[3] concluded that "the data show that mattresses containing polyurethane foam easily comply with the federal standard[2] where cigarettes are the igniting source; however, such mattresses present a significant hazard where the igniting source is an open flame. Mattresses containing 100 percent polyurethane foam usually burn vigorously until little char remains. Burning in such cases is accompanied by the release of copious amounts of black smoke."

In 1977, the National Bureau of Standards (now the National Institute of Standards and Technology) conducted fire tests of mattresses and issued a report,[4] which categorized mattresses into four groups in order of safety (Table 20.14.4).

These tests indicate that the best mattresses for use in correctional facilities are those with padding material of cotton treated with boric acid. Mattresses of cotton treated with boric acid pass the federal standard[2] and perform well when exposed to open-flame ignition sources. Such mattresses will burn but at a much slower rate than urethane foam mattresses.[5] Some other materials are entering the market for mattress padding, including treated neoprene. Because occupants of detention and correctional facilities frequently intentionally damage mattresses, operators of these facilities are reluctant to purchase expensive mattresses. Therefore, the most common mattresses found are fire-retardant-covered foam or cotton-treated mattresses.

Inmate possessions and furnishings in the cell must be controlled in order to limit the size of fire that can be expected. Books, clothing, and other combustible personal property allowed in cells should be stored in closable metal lockers or fire-resistant containers. Combustible decorations should be prohibited unless they have been treated with flame retardants. Although rarely used, draperies, curtains, or other decorative and acoustical materials should be noncombustible or rendered and maintained flame resistant according to NFPA 701, *Standard Methods of Fire Tests for Flame Propagation of Textiles and Films.* There is no maximum limit of combustibles permitted in NFPA *101* or *NFPA 5000.* The codes do, however, provide a cautionary statement for management to control the combustibles.

TABLE 20.14.4 Mattress Safety Categories

Group	*Safety Criteria*
A	Mattresses that did not exceed any of the tenability criteria for the duration of the 30 minute test. This group included two treated, cotton-batting mattresses.
B	Mattresses that only exceeded the smoke obscuration criterion. Two neoprene mattresses were in this category.
C	Mattresses that exceeded all tenability criteria, but did not cause full room involvement. This group included three polyurethane foam-core mattresses and one of mixed fiber construction. The best-performing polyurethane mattress was of the type associated with a multiple-life-loss prison fire.
D	Mattresses that exceeded all criteria. Included were one styrene-butadiene latex foam core and one polyurethane foam-core mattress. The latex mattress was of the type associated with a multiple-life-loss fire in a health care institution.

Interior finish materials can contribute fuel to a fire, they may accelerate room flashover, and they can result in rapid fire spread. Materials that have high flame spread rates or produce hazardous concentrations of smoke or noxious gases should not be used. This includes plastic wall finish material, fiberboard, thin paneling, and untreated plywood. Interior finish alternatives with good fire characteristics include paneling treated to provide Class A interior finish rating with a flame spread of 25 or less, painted steel, gypsum board, or masonry block.

Occupant Protection

Occupant protection means providing life safety to building occupants in case of fire. This may be accomplished either by evacuating them to a secure area or by defending them in place. This objective is the most controversial in the fire safety system for correctional facilities because "evacuation" is often interpreted by administrators and staff to mean "escape." Although this assumption is not valid, means of egress does directly affect security.

With reference to the evacuation of inmates, most detention and correctional facilities can be grouped into two general types, based on their physical arrangement. In the first group are larger institutions that have an outdoor secure area such as an outdoor exercise yard or courtyard. It is possible to evacuate inmates rapidly from the fire area to this outside area and still maintain security. In the second category are the inner city high rise facilities and the smaller city or county facilities where there are no separate, secure outdoor areas. In these facilities, which have no enclosed courtyards or other areas to evacuate inmates and still maintain security, it becomes necessary to defend the inmates in place from fire. Evacuating inmates outside the secured perimeter of a facility is as much a safety hazard to the general public as the fire itself.

Defend-in-Place Strategy. The defend-in-place protection strategy is a workable and accepted means of providing fire safety for building occupants and is commonly used to protect persons in hospitals and nursing homes. The technology exists to defend inmates in place so that only a few cells need to be evacuated—possibly only the cell of fire origin. A defend-in-place occupancy, as well as an occupancy using evacuation to a secure area of refuge, needs a reliable means of egress. Unique to detention and correctional facilities, because some occupant populations cannot be mixed with the general population for security reasons, there is often a need for multiple and separate areas of refuge for both inside and outside secured areas. Although means for defending the occupants in place are provided, it is always considered necessary to provide reliable exits. According to NFPA *101* and *NFPA 5000,* this means that two distinct paths of travel must be provided from each cell block or area. The exits should be remote from each other so that a single fire cannot readily block both. In addition, travel distances must not exceed those specified by NFPA *101* and *NFPA 5000.* The travel distance can be increased if the building is sprinklered. The exit access needs to be free and unobstructed, and it should not be circuitous. An exit access that requires travel through a room or an area containing a fire hazard higher than usual for the occupancy violates the principles of safe egress. Dead-end corridors are not good practice because a fire in a dead end between an exit and an occupant can prevent the occupant from reaching the exit. Means of egress need to be illuminated continuously, and emergency lighting must be provided. Exits and the paths to them should be clearly marked. However, NFPA *101* and *NFPA* 5000 permit the elimination of exit signs in inmate housing areas where no visitors are permitted. The rationale for this is that the inmates cannot leave until someone unlocks the doors and security staff, who are familiar with the locations of exits, direct the evacuation of inmates.

Compartmentation. Compartmentation is an important aspect of occupant protection, whether inmates are evacuated or defended in place. Compartmentation limits the number of persons exposed to a single fire. The walls, ceilings, and floors of fire compartment boundaries must be fire resistant. Openings must be protected with self-closing, fire-rated doors. The degree of fire protection these elements provide depends on the degree of hazard the occupancy presents, or its fuel loading, and the type of building construction—for example, fire resistive versus combustible—and the function served, such as a load-bearing or nonload-bearing wall. For more information on compartmentation, see Section 18, Chapter 1, "Confinement of Fire in Buildings."

Smoke Control. Controlling smoke means controlling the type and quantity of materials used in the building construction and building contents and providing a means of restricting smoke movement within the building. Dilution, which is reducing smoke concentration by introducing massive quantities of uncontaminated air into a building, is not always satisfactory when used alone. Smoke may be generated in such quantities that adequate dilution may not be obtained. Prudent use and placement of automatically opening vents can provide some relief from smoke and combustion products in small, one-story buildings or multitiered cell blocks. However, smoke confinement can best be achieved by providing a physical barrier, such as a wall with self-closing doors and dampers that restrict smoke movement, and by using pressure differences across the physical barrier to prevent smoke from entering the nonfire area. The building's heating, ventilating, and air-conditioning (HVAC) system can be designed to provide this pressurization. Physical barriers alone usually are not effective in controlling smoke movement because they have many penetrations, and the fire, the building HVAC, and/or the weather conditions create uncontrolled pressures. NFPA 92A, *Standard for Smoke-Control Systems Utilizing Barriers and Pressure Differences,* provides requirements for the design and installation of smoke-control systems. For more information on smoke control, see Section 18, Chapter 3, "Smoke Movement in Buildings."

Locking Systems. Since the primary objective of detention and correction facilities is security, reliable locking systems are essential. However, the inability to unlock doors has played a major role in some of the deadliest correctional fire tragedies. Whatever the type of locking system, the system must function reliably in emergencies, whether a facility is designed to evacuate its inmates or to defend them in place. Individual key locks are the most unreliable for several reasons, including the time required to unlock each door, the loss of keys or the breaking of a key in a lock during an emergency, heat and smoke prohibiting entry into the cell block, and confusion due to the number of keys required to release the inmates.

It is important that the number of keys needed to evacuate the occupants to the outside or to an area of refuge be limited to reduce the confusion. Also, all keys needed for evacuation should be marked by sight and touch for quick identification in an emergency.

CASE STUDY: Jail Fires. In two deadly jail fires, a major factor was the loss, early in the incident, of the only set of keys to the fire-involved area, combined with the lack of a secure area of refuge to which prisoners could be evacuated. Both facilities lacked sprinklers; at least one of the two facilities lacked detectors as well. In both facilities, exit problems were cited (in one, the two means of egress were too close together; in the other, the means of egress were blocked and inadequate in number). In one incident, the storage of urethane foam mattresses in an unsecured room was cited as a contributing factor.[6]

Detection and Suppression Activities

Detection and suppression activities deal directly with the fire—detecting its presence, sounding an alarm to alert occupants, and inhibiting fire growth by active fire suppression. To achieve this objective, the following must be provided: an early warning fire detection system, a reliable alarm system, and a reliable fire suppression system. All automatic detection and suppression systems and manual equipment need to be inspected and tested regularly. See NFPA 10, *Standard for Portable Fire Extinguishers*, NFPA 25, *Standard for the Inspection, Testing, and Maintenance of Water-Based Fire Protection Systems*, and *NFPA 72*®, *National Fire Alarm Code*®.

There are three separate stages of detection and suppression activities, each of which can be performed automatically or manually (Table 20.14.5). Automatic and manual systems can

TABLE 20.14.5 Stages of Detection and Suppression

Stage	*Manual*	*Automatic*
Detection	Inmate or guard detects fire	Smoke detectors or sprinklers detect fire
Alarm	Guard verbally transmits information to other guards	Fire alarm system activates audible and visible alarms
Suppression	Guards use extinguishers to suppress fire	Sprinklers begin extinguishing immediately

also be combined. For example, detection can be provided by smoke detectors installed throughout the facility with manual fire fighting by fire brigade personnel using a standpipe hose. However, any system needing manual intervention requires that someone make a decision, requires time for human action, and requires trained personnel with the necessary equipment to do the job. The human element is generally the most unreliable part of a fire safety system.

The effectiveness of fire detection and suppression systems depends on the rate of fire growth and the time from ignition until detection and, eventually, suppression activities begin. If the fuel available is capable of producing a fast fire, as it is in padded cells, the extinguishing agent, usually water, must be applied to the fire very quickly after ignition. This is very difficult to do with manual fire suppression even if early warning fire detection, such as automatic smoke detectors, is available. Automatic sprinklers provide reliable fire detection and suppression, and they need no human intervention. With an automatic sprinkler system, the extinguishment phase begins almost simultaneously with detection and alarm, a response difficult to achieve with manual suppression.

Detection and Alarm Activities. NFPA *101* and *NFPA 5000* require smoke detectors in the sleeping areas of detention and correctional occupancies. Smoke detectors may cause needless or nonfire emergency alarms. Therefore, in housing areas, they may alarm at a constantly attended location, such as a control room, and are not required to sound a general evacuation alarm or call the fire department. A manual fire alarm system is also required. NFPA *101* and *NFPA 5000* permit the manual fire alarm boxes to be locked, provided staff has keys. In addition, the alarm systems should be arranged to automatically notify the local fire department. Manual suppression ability should include portable fire extinguishers of the proper type and number, readily accessible fire hose stations for use by correctional officers, and a means to stretch fire hoses through double security gates, or sallyports, so the gates can be closed and security maintained.

Suppression Activities. Sprinklers have been, and are being, installed quite successfully in detention and correctional facilities throughout the United States and Canada. Contrary to some schools of thought, vandalism of sprinklers by inmates, especially in long-term facilities, is very low. It is recommended that institutional type sprinkler heads be used in areas occupied by and within easy reach of inmates. Sprinklers control fire development, thereby reducing the production of heat and smoke. They also give fire service personnel a better opportunity to begin rescue and extinguishment operations. Automatic sprinklers can reduce property loss and limit downtime. In addition, they offer several economic advantages:

- Insurance premiums may be reduced with the installation of sprinkler protection.
- Many building codes offer tradeoffs when sprinklers are used, thereby reducing building costs.
- Sprinklers may also result in fewer persons being evacuated and reduce the burden for manual fire fighting—in effect, increasing security.

NFPA *101* and *NFPA 5000* require the installation of automatic sprinkler systems in all new detention and correctional occupancies, other than those classified as Use Condition I. Prior to the 1997 edition of NFPA *101*, requirements for automatic sprinklers depended on the facility's construction type, number of stories, and use condition.

Planning and Training Operations

Planning and training mean conducting training activities among inmates and staff and planning emergency operating procedures. To achieve this objective, the following methods are used: staff education and training, inmate education, planning emergency procedures, and conducting drills. Planning and training require little capital investment in equipment, but they will make a big difference in reducing the impact of a potentially disastrous fire. In addition, planning and training are important to maintain a high level of security during a fire.

Because fire safety should be everyone's concern, both staff and inmates should be involved in a fire safety program. Each shift should practice the fire emergency plan at least quarterly, and new employees should be briefed routinely on the fire emergency plan. Inmates should be instructed in emergency procedures. Safety information can also be included in an inmate information booklet.

The fire safety program should be designed to meet the needs of the facility. The size and age of the facility and the security classification of the occupants, as well as its proximity to municipal fire departments, should be considered. All training programs should include a short description of the background and evolution of the problem; how to recognize, prevent, and reduce fire hazards; information on the fire protection technology available for application at the facility; hands-on training for staff and inmate fire brigades; emergency operating procedures; and identification of potential problems that affect fire safety.

Fire brigades should be equipped and trained to deal effectively with a fire emergency. Brigade responsibility and functions will vary with the size of the facility and the size and location of the nearest fire department, but they should include calling the fire department, safeguarding lives, providing manual suppression to control the fire until the fire department arrives, and protecting equipment. Fire department access into detention and correctional facilities will usually be delayed because of security.

Each building in a detention or correctional facility should have a written fire emergency response plan detailing staff action during a fire emergency. The plan provides a guide for evaluating the particular problems and coordinating the response of the fire brigade, fire department, staff, and inmates. Emergency response plans should be simple yet comprehensive, specific, flexible, and workable. Preparing the plan can be accomplished in these five steps:

- Define the potential fire protection problems in the particular detention and correctional facility.
- Determine the security needs of the facility.
- Set objectives for what can be accomplished with the plan in an emergency.

- Determine the facility's capability for controlling an emergency.
- Define the roles of the responding agencies, especially the fire department and fire brigade.
- Put the information in written form.

The local fire department should be involved in formulating the fire emergency plan and briefed on building conditions, contents, and fire-fighting equipment within the complex. Fire departments with correctional facilities within their jurisdictions should conduct site surveys and have their own prefire plans for each building.

LOCKUPS

For many years building officials, fire officials, and designers have looked for guidance in codes on how to treat and protect "lockup" areas of buildings. Lockups are holding areas for not more than 50 detainees, where individuals are detained for less than 24 hours. A lockup that has a holding area for more than 50 detainees or detains individuals for 24 hours or more is classified as a detention and correctional occupancy or health care occupancy. Lockups are commonly found in courthouses, international airports, sports arenas and stadiums, shopping malls and police stations. The 2006 editions of NFPA *101* and *NFPA 5000* contain, for the first time, requirements for such lockups.

The only real difference between a lockup area and a detention and correctional facility is that an occupant in a lockup area is detained for less than a 24 hour period and generally sleeping facilities are not provided in lockup areas. Occupants in lockups, like detention and correctional occupancies, are generally prevented from taking actions for self-preservation because of security measures not under the occupants' control.

Because occupants in lockups are generally incapable of self-preservation, the lockup areas require a higher level of life safety than other portions of the same building. Codes require that the lockup areas comply with the requirements of the predominant occupancy plus staff must be present to release locks and/or restraints within two minutes of the onset of a fire or similar emergency or the lockup areas must be provided with a complete smoke detection system and automatically notify the staff and the fire department.

SUMMARY

Providing balanced fire protection and security in detention and correctional facilities can be challenging and has two goals: security for the public and safety from fire for the inmates. The systems approach to fire safety helps to achieve these two goals through meeting a series of objectives, including ignition control, fuel control, occupant protection, detection and suppression, and planning and training. Ignition control involves greater and more dependable protection of heat sources and separation from fuel sources. Fuel control means controlling the type, arrangement, and burning characteristics of potential fuels. Occupant protection can be accomplished either by evacuating inmates to a secure area or by defending them in place. Detection and suppression of fire require an early warning fire detection system, a reliable alarm system, and a reliable fire suppression system. Planning and training include staff education and training, inmate education, emergency procedure planning, and emergency drills. When certain of these objectives cannot be met, other parts of the system may have to be enhanced to compensate. The fire safety program should be designed to meet the particular needs of the facility and should involve the participation of the local fire department.

BIBLIOGRAPHY

References Cited

1. Aherns, M., *U.S. Fires in Selected Occupancies*, National Fire Protection Association Fire Analysis and Research Division, Quincy, MA, March 2006.
2. FF4-72, *Flammability Standard for Mattresses*, U.S. Department of Commerce, Washington, DC, June 1973.
3. "Resistance of Mattresses Containing Boric Acid Treated Cotton Batting to Open Flame Ignition," *Journal of Consumer Product Flammability*, Vol. 4, 1977, pp. 169–188.
4. NBSIR-77-1290, "Combustion of Mattresses Exposed to Flaming Ignition Sources/Part I—Full-Scale Tests and Hazard Analysis," National Bureau of Standards, Washington, DC, 1977,
5. "Firesafety Bulletin on Penal Institutions," National Fire Protection Association, Quincy, MA, 1977.
6. Hall, J. R., Jr., et al., *Fire Code Inspections and Fire Prevention: What Methods Lead to Success,* National Fire Protection Association and the Urban Institute, Boston, MA, 1979.

NFPA Codes, Standards, and Recommended Practices

Reference to the following NFPA codes, standards, and recommended practices will provide further information on detention and correctional facilities discussed in this chapter. (See the latest version of The NFPA Catalog *for availability of current editions of the following documents.)*

NFPA 1, *Uniform Fire Code*™
NFPA 10, *Standard for Portable Fire Extinguishers*
NFPA 13, *Standard for the Installation of Sprinkler Systems*
NFPA 14, *Standard for the Installation of Standpipe and Hose Systems*
NFPA 25, *Standard for the Inspection, Testing, and Maintenance of Water-Based Fire Protection Systems*
NFPA 72®, *National Fire Alarm Code*®
NFPA 90A, *Standard for the Installation of Air-Conditioning and Ventilating Systems*
NFPA 92A, *Standard for Smoke-Control Systems Utilizing Barriers and Pressure Differences*
NFPA *101*®, *Life Safety Code*®
NFPA 204, *Standard for Smoke and Heat Venting*
NFPA 251, *Standard Methods of Tests of Fire Resistance of Building Construction and Materials*
NFPA 255, *Standard Method of Test of Surface Burning Characteristics of Building Materials*
NFPA 701, *Standard Methods of Fire Tests for Flame Propagation of Textiles and Films*
NFPA 5000®, *Building Construction and Safety Code*®

Chapter 15

Health Care Occupancies

Daniel J. O'Connor

Chapter Contents

Key Terms

automatic sprinkler system, disposable equipment and supplies, exit illumination, exit marking, interior finish, means of egress, portable fire extinguisher, smoke control, vertical openings

In today's business environment, health care, medical care, and personal care services have evolved such that there is a wide variety of facilities and business operations delivering health care to the general population. As a result, there are varying levels of risk among the facilities that offer health care and medical services. Within NFPA *101*®, *Life Safety Code*®, and *NFPA 5000*®, *Building Construction and Safety Code*®, there are several types of occupancies where people may receive some form of health care, medical, or personal care service. These include the following:

- Health care occupancies
- Ambulatory health care occupancies
- Residential board and care occupancies
- Business occupancies

The focus of this chapter is on those facilities that pose greater risks due to the impairment of occupants and/or lack of ambulatory capabilities of the occupants. Specifically, this chapter addresses health care occupancies and ambulatory health care occupancies; however, some brief discussion of residential board and care and business occupancies is warranted, as there are important distinctions that should be understood and considered when applying the requirements of NFPA *101* and *NFPA 5000.*

Health care facilities are used for the treatment or care of persons suffering from physical or mental illness, disease, or infirmity, and for the care of infants, convalescents, or aged persons. These facilities provide sleeping accommodations for occupants who may be incapable of self-preservation because of physical or mental disability or age. Some buildings that house health care occupants have security measures that limit freedom of movement.

In recent years, facilities—sometimes called ambulatory health care facilities—have been developed to provide medical treatment on an outpatient basis. Although patients might be placed under general anesthesia or other treatment that would render them incapable of self-preservation, they are not housed overnight. Occupants exhibit some characteristics of people in business occupancies and some characteristics typical of people in health care facilities.

Tremendous growth has occurred in recent years in residential board and care facilities. These facilities are commonly called assisted living facilities, personal care facilities, and so on. Residential board and care facilities provide personal care to occupants in a residential setting. The residents' abilities to respond to a fire threat differ greatly from patients in health care facilities. The safeguards appropriate for health care facilities should be applied only when a facility meets the definition in NFPA *101* and *NFPA 5000* of a health care facility.

In many facilities the presence of doctors providing diagnosis and treatment for patients may suggest that the facility is a health care occupancy. This may not be the case, as most doctor's offices and birthing centers are classified as business occupancies when meeting the definitions and criteria defined in NFPA *101* and *NFPA 5000.* Where doctor's offices solely provide outpatient care and are physically separated from facilities housing inpatient treatment and care areas, such offices can be classified as business occupancies, although associated with the operations and management of a health care occupancy.

Daniel J. O'Connor, P.E., is vice-president of Schirmer Engineering Corporation in Deerfield, Illinois. He is chair of the NFPA Technical Committee on Health Care Occupancies.

Additionally, in recent years there has been a significant growth in facilities known as birth centers. These facilities do not pose the risks associated with health care occupancies as they are intended for low-volume service for healthy, childbearing women and their families, who are capable of evacuating in the event of a fire. Such facilities should meet the definitions for birth center and business occupancy given in NFPA *101* and *NFPA 5000;* otherwise the facility may be a health care occupancy.

This chapter describes the characteristics and fire hazards of health care facilities. It specifically discusses the characteristics of the health care occupant and the fire safety features that all health care facilities should provide.

Additional information relating to health care facilities can be found in Section 8, Chapter 6, "Protection of Electronic Equipment"; Section 18, Chapter 1, "Confinement of Fire in Buildings"; Section 18, Chapter 2, "Interior Finish"; and Section 20, Chapter 2, "Board and Care Facilities."

OCCUPANCY CHARACTERISTICS

Occupants of health care facilities are generally presumed to be incapable of self-preservation. A significant percentage of occupants in hospitals and nursing homes are incapable of self-evacuation or are ambulatory but incapable of perceiving a fire threat and choosing a rational response.

There are three types of care in most modern hospitals: (1) ambulatory, (2) general, and (3) intensive care. Given proper directions, unless smoke or heat is intense, ambulatory patients can make their own way to safety. General care patients may be transported on stretchers or in wheelchairs with some difficulty; horizontal and even some vertical movement is generally possible, although independent evacuation is not. Patients in intensive care are likely to be connected to various life support devices, making movement for even short distances very difficult and evacuation almost impossible without further endangering these patients' lives.

Occupants of nursing homes vary from geriatric residents who are capable of evacuation with limited assistance to residents who are comatose and require close supervision with evacuation being very difficult. Today's nursing home resident is less ambulatory and requires more medical care than a resident of even 10 years ago. The significant increase in the number of assisted living facilities has made the typical intermediate care nursing home resident of yesterday an assisted living resident today.

Because some occupants are incapable of movement or slow to evacuate, a health care facility resembles a ship at sea: it is better to keep the fire from the patient than to remove the patient from the fire. Thus, occupants must be defended in place. As a result, health care facility design and operation must incorporate methods by which a fire can be detected early, contained, and fought rapidly and successfully. Accomplishing this requires careful planning of the health care facility and its day-to-day operation.

NFPA *101,* widely used to establish minimum requirements for life safety from fire within health care facilities, sets forth criteria based on the following general principles:

- Fire-resistive construction
- Subdivision of spaces, known as compartmentation
- Protection of vertical openings
- Provision of adequate means of egress
- Provision of exit marking, exit illumination, and emergency power
- Limits on the use of interior finish materials
- Fire alerting facilities
- Control of smoke movement
- Protection of hazardous areas
- Adequate protection of building service equipment
- Control of fuel loads
- Operational features

Total building fire protection for life safety is more necessary in health care facilities than in other occupancies because of the nature of the occupants. At the same time, exits are slightly less important. The first principle of designing a fire-safe health care facility is that safety must not depend wholly on any single safeguard.

IGNITION SOURCES

In the 1994–1998 period, smoking materials, both lighted tobacco products and implements used to light them, and incendiary and suspicious acts accounted for 75 percent of deaths and 45 percent of injuries in facilities that care for the sick and for 54 percent of deaths and 33 percent of injuries in facilities that care for older adults. These causes totally dominate the ignition side of the life safety problem in these properties, although other causes, notably failures in electrical distribution systems, appliances, and other equipment, are also important in property damage (Tables 20.15.1 through 20.15.4).

More and more health care facilities are establishing smoke-free environment policies. In addition, the Joint Commission on Accreditation of Healthcare Organizations (JCAHO) requires facilities to establish a no-smoking policy. As the result of prohibiting or controlling smoking in health care facilities, a new phenomenon has developed: visitors giving smoking materials to patients and residents without the health care staff's knowledge.

Most fatalities in health care fires are so close to the point of origin that their locations are coded as "intimate with ignition" (Table 20.15.5). Most fatalities that occur in the room where a fire begins turn out to have been intimate with ignition. Most intimate-with-ignition fire deaths begin on the victims' clothing or in the mattress, bedding, or upholstered furniture on which they were lying when the fire began.

FIRE LOADS

Studies show relatively low fuel loads within most spaces in health care facilities. Fire duration varies from approximately 20 minutes for patient areas to several hours, depending on the space involved.

A study by the National Bureau of Standards (now the National Institute of Standards and Technology [NIST]) conducted in 1942 involving three hospitals revealed an average fuel load

TABLE 20.15.1 Causes of Fires and Direct Property Damage, Structure Fires in Facilities That Care for the Sick, 1994–1998 Annual Averages (Unknown-Cause Fires Allocated Proportionally)

Cause	*Fires*		*Property Damage (in Millions of Dollars)*	
Other equipment	500	(20.2%)	1.8	(19.2%)
Electronic equipment	100	(3.6%)	0.4	(3.9%)
Separate motor or generator	100	(2.5%)	0.1	(1.0%)
Cooking equipment	500	(18.0%)	0.3	(2.9%)
Stove	100	(5.1%)	0.1	(1.5%)
Portable cooking or warming unit	100	(5.1%)	0.1	(0.6%)
Oven	100	(2.4%)	0.0	(0.3%)
Appliance, tool, or air conditioning	400	(15.6%)	1.4	(15.1%)
Dryer	200	(6.1%)	0.4	(4.7%)
Electrical distribution	300	(12.1%)	1.4	(15.4%)
Light fixture, lamp holder, ballast, or sign	100	(3.9%)	0.1	(0.7%)
Incendiary or suspicious	300	(10.5%)	2.1	(22.7%)
Smoking materials	200	(7.6%)	0.2	(2.6%)
Open flame, ember, or torch	200	(7.4%)	1.2	(12.6%)
Torch	100	(4.5%)	0.7	(8.1%)
Heating equipment	100	(5.1%)	0.4	(4.3%)
Other heat source	0	(1.3%)	0.2	(1.9%)
Natural causes	0	(1.2%)	0.2	(1.8%)
Exposure (to other hostile fire)	0	(0.7%)	0.1	(1.5%)
Child playing	0	(0.4%)	0.0	(0.0%)
Total	2600	(100.0%)	9.2	(100.0%)

Note: These are fires reported to U.S. municipal fire departments and so exclude fires reported only to federal or state agencies or industrial fire brigades. Fires are expressed to the nearest hundred and property damage is rounded to the nearest hundred thousand dollars. Property damage figures have not been adjusted for inflation. The 12 major cause categories are based on a hierarchy developed by the U.S. Fire Administration. Sums may not equal totals due to rounding errors.

Source: National estimates based on NFIRS and NFPA survey.

TABLE 20.15.2 Causes of Civilian Deaths and Injuries, Structure Fires in Facilities That Care for the Sick, 1994–1998 Annual Averages (Unknown-Cause Fires Allocated Proportionally)

Cause	*Civilian Deaths*		*Civilian Injuries*	
Open flame, ember, or torch	3	(55.9%)	14	(13.4%)
Match	2	(35.0%)	5	(4.9%)
Lighter	1	(20.0%)	8	(7.5%)
Other equipment	1	(24.6%)	16	(15.3%)
Biomedical equipment or device	1	(12.5%)	5	(4.3%)
Incendiary or suspicious	1	(14.2%)	26	(24.3%)
Smoking materials	0	(5.3%)	9	(8.0%)
Cooking equipment	0	(0.0%)	12	(11.5%)
Electrical distribution	0	(0.0%)	9	(8.4%)
Appliance, tool, or air conditioning	0	(0.0%)	8	(7.3%)
Natural causes	0	(0.0%)	6	(5.5%)
Heating equipment	0	(0.0%)	5	(4.6%)
Other heat source	0	(0.0%)	2	(1.7%)
Total	5	(100.0%)	107	(100.0%)

Note: These are fires reported to U.S. municipal fire departments and so exclude fires reported only to federal or state agencies or industrial fire brigades. Civilian deaths and injuries are rounded to the nearest one. The 10 major cause categories are based on a hierarchy developed by the U.S. Fire Administration. Sums may not equal totals due to rounding errors.

Source: National estimates based on NFIRS and NFPA survey.

TABLE 20.15.3 Causes of Fires and Direct Property Damage, Structure Fires in Facilities That Care for the Aged, 1994–1998 Annual Averages (Unknown-Cause Fires Allocated Proportionally)

Cause	*Fires*		*Property Damage (in Millions of Dollars)*	
Appliance, tool, or air conditioning	900	(30.5%)	1.3	(19.7%)
Dryer	600	(20.3%)	0.9	(14.0%)
Fixed area air conditioner	100	(2.1%)	0.1	(0.9%)
Cooking equipment	600	(19.3%)	0.9	(13.1%)
Stove	300	(8.9%)	0.7	(10.2%)
Portable cooking or warming unit	100	(3.3%)	0.0	(0.3%)
Oven	100	(3.0%)	0.1	(1.1%)
Heating equipment	300	(10.0%)	0.3	(4.9%)
Fixed area heater	100	(4.8%)	0.2	(2.3%)
Central heating unit	100	(2.1%)	0.1	(1.5%)
Smoking materials	300	(10.0%)	0.6	(8.9%)
Electrical distribution	300	(9.7%)	0.8	(12.1%)
Light fixture, lamp holder, ballast, or sign	100	(2.6%)	0.1	(0.8%)
Fixed wiring	100	(1.7%)	0.4	(5.5%)
Other equipment	300	(9.0%)	0.7	(10.6%)
Incendiary or suspicious	100	(4.8%)	0.8	(12.3%)
Open flame, ember, or torch	100	(2.8%)	0.9	(12.7%)
Natural causes	100	(1.9%)	0.1	(1.3%)
Other heat source	0	(1.3%)	0.2	(2.7%)
Exposure (to other hostile fire)	0	(0.5%)	0.1	(1.2%)
Child playing	0	(0.1%)	0.0	(0.5%)
Total	3000	(100.0%)	6.8	(100.0%)

Note: These are fires reported to U.S. municipal fire departments and so exclude fires reported only to federal or state agencies or industrial fire brigades. Fires are expressed to the nearest hundred and property damage is rounded to the nearest hundred thousand dollars. Property damage figures have not been adjusted for inflation. The 12 major cause categories are based on a hierarchy developed by the U.S. Fire Administration. Sums may not equal totals due to rounding errors.

Source: National estimates based on NFIRS and NFPA survey.

TABLE 20.15.4 Causes of Civilian Deaths and Injuries, Structure Fires in Facilities That Care for the Aged, 1994–1998 Annual Averages (Unknown-Cause Fires Allocated Proportionally)

Cause	*Civilian Deaths*		*Civilian Injuries*	
Smoking materials	5	(39.5%)	54	(22.6%)
Other equipment	3	(24.7%)	25	(10.3%)
Biomedical equipment or device	2	(18.0%)	2	(1.0%)
Unclassified special equipment	1	(6.0%)	5	(2.1%)
Open flame, ember, or torch	2	(18.7%)	12	(4.9%)
Lighter	1	(8.0%)	5	(1.9%)
Incendiary or suspicious	1	(6.9%)	21	(8.9%)
Cooking equipment	1	(6.1%)	11	(4.5%)
Stove	1	(6.1%)	6	(2.3%)
Other heat source	0	(4.1%)	2	(0.6%)
Appliance, tool, or air conditioning	0	(0.0%)	65	(27.1%)
Heating equipment	0	(0.0%)	29	(12.2%)
Electrical distribution	0	(0.0%)	20	(8.3%)
Child playing	0	(0.0%)	1	(0.5%)
Exposure (to other hostile fire)	0	(0.0%)	0	(0.2%)
Total	12	(100.0%)	241	(100.0%)

Note: These are fires reported to U.S. municipal fire departments and so exclude fires reported only to federal or state agencies or industrial fire brigades. Civilian deaths and injuries are rounded to the nearest one. The 11 major cause categories are based on a hierarchy developed by the U.S. Fire Administration. Sums may not equal totals due to rounding errors.

Source: National estimates based on NFIRS and NFPA survey.

TABLE 20.15.5 Locations of Victims of Fatal Health Care Facility Fires

Property Class	*Intimate with Ignition*	*Same Room as Fire but Not Intimate*	*Not Same Room as Fire*
Facilities that care for the sick	76%	6%	18%
Hospitals	75	5	20
Other or unknown type	86	14	0
Facilities that care for older adults	53	19	28
With nursing staff	60	15	25
Other or unknown type	39	27	33
All facilities combined	60	15	25

Source: NFPA analysis of data from 1980–1998 NFIRS and NFPA survey.

of 5.7 lb/ft^2 (30 kg/m^2).[1] Fuel loads for typical spaces are indicated in Table 20.15.6. A 1980 study of fuel loads in a U.S. Navy hospital confirms the relatively low fuel loads for general hospital areas but indicates that higher fuel loads may be anticipated in some spaces such as medical libraries, X-ray file rooms, linen storage, and general storage rooms. Further, the increased use of disposables and modern medical record storage practices are likely to result in above average fuel loads. These areas may contain fuel loads sufficient for fires from 1- to 3-hour duration. However, such spaces represent a small percentage of total floor area.

A major portion of the floor area of health care facilities is used for patient sleeping or treatment rooms. Fuel loads for such spaces are low. For example, fuel loads in nursing homes have been estimated at 2.5 to 3 lb/ft^2 (10 to 15 kg/m^2).[2] NIST surveys indicate that fuel loads for hospital patient rooms approximate 4 lb/ft^2 (20 kg/m^2) and that the combustible load in patient sleeping areas ranges from approximately 3 to 4.5 lb/ft^2 (15 to 23 kg/m^2). A study of a Navy hospital indicates fuel loads for sleeping rooms average 1 lb/ft^2 (5 kg/m^2) or less. Assuming standard time/temperature conditions, fire duration for patient areas and a majority of other occupied spaces would be less than 30 minutes.

Disposables

The use of combustible disposable equipment and supplies is common in health care facilities. Disposables include bedding, gowns, gloves, drapes, collection bags, tubing, dishes, glasses, syringes, needles, and many diagnostic and therapeutic instruments. All such items require packaging, which can add to the combustible load both before and after use.

Data Processing and Medical Records

Used to satisfy general business needs as well as to store patient records, data processing centers contain quantities of combustibles. These combustibles could expose high-value equipment, result in loss of vital records, and produce a fire that threatens occupants outside the data processing areas. Special protection should be considered for data processing centers.

Health care facilities generate and store medical files in considerable quantity. Files stored in closed steel cabinets do not represent any significant increase in hazard over that typical of most areas. However, files stored on open shelving create a serious fire hazard. Large quantities of open-file storage should be treated as a severe hazard and should be separated by fire-rated construction and protected by automatic sprinklers.

TABLE 20.15.6 Fuel Loads in Typical Health Care Facilities

	Average Combustible Contents (per ft^2)		
Location	*Movable Property*	*Exposed Woodwork and Floors*[a]	*Total*
Rooms (single)	0.5	3.2	3.7
Corridors	0.0	2.6	2.6
Waiting rooms	1.7	1.5	3.2
Janitors' closets and supplies	3.1	3.4	6.5
Doctors' offices	5.7	2.9	8.6
Nurses' offices and rooms	3.1	1.9	5.0
Nurses' infirmary	0.8	2.2	3.0
Diet kitchens and dining rooms	1.2	2.4	3.6
Laundries	4.4	0.6	5.0
Laundries and clothes storage	12.5	0.6	13.1
Dormitories	0.8	2.0	2.8
Pharmacy, dispensary, and stores	5.8	1.9	7.7
Lockers, toilets, and barber shops	0.2	1.2	1.4
Approximate average for entire usable floor area of three hospital buildings surveyed			5.7[b]

[a]Combustible floor finish, where present, was ¼ in. (6.35 mm) linoleum; it was assumed to be the equivalent of 1 lb (0.37 kg) of combustible material, such as wood, per ft^2 of floor area (4.88 kg/m^2). Doors, windows, trim, moldings, baseboards, and so on are included.

[b]This approximate average weight was computed from Table 16 on page 25 of the Bureau Report BMS 921. The value is somewhat high because the highest weight in each bracket of combustible contents was used in figuring it, that is, in the bracket "0 to 4.9 lb/ft^2 (23.9 kg/m^2)," the value 4.9 lb (2.22 kg) was applied to the indicated area, and so on.

FIRE SEVERITY

Determining relative fire hazard involves considerations beyond total fuel loads. The arrangement of combustibles, their chemical makeup, and their physical state are all factors to be evaluated in addition to room geometry, ventilation rates, fire compartment size, and fire protection facilities. Generally, the faster a fire develops, the greater its threat.

Although the total fuel load in patient rooms remains low, the nature of the combustibles is important. Foam plastic decubitus pads, upholstered furniture, and polyurethane foam mattresses may not affect the length of time a fire will burn, but such items have affected the rate of fire growth. These types of products can cause fire to grow to a large size quickly.

Fires that reach flashover produce acutely lethal atmospheres generating thousands of cubic feet of smoke per minute. Such fires threaten fire-rated barriers and produce enough energy to drive smoke to remote areas. A fire that grows to full room size in a health care facility represents an unacceptable level of risk; there is a high likelihood that such a fire will result in injuries or fatalities if its origin is in the patient sleeping area. Therefore, every effort should be made to recognize and eliminate or adequately protect fuel arrangements that might produce such fires.

Fire tests and actual fire experience have shown that certain common arrangements and types of fuels in patient rooms create especially hazardous situations because they are able to produce large fires in short time periods. In January 1976, for example, multiple-death fires in both the Wincrest and Cermak House nursing homes involved wooden wardrobes within patient sleeping rooms.[3,4] Tests show that combustible wardrobe fires can result in acutely hazardous environments in as little as 120 seconds.[5]

A 1989 fire in a Norfolk nursing home resulting in 12 deaths originated in a foam plastic decubitus pad on a mattress in a patient sleeping room. The fire grew to flashover in less than 5 minutes.[6] A 1985 fire in a Michigan hospice initially involved an upholstered chair. The fire caused eight deaths.[7] Analysis of this fire established that flashover could have occurred in the room of origin in under 4 minutes. See Figure 20.15.1 for documentation of the analysis for the hospice fire.

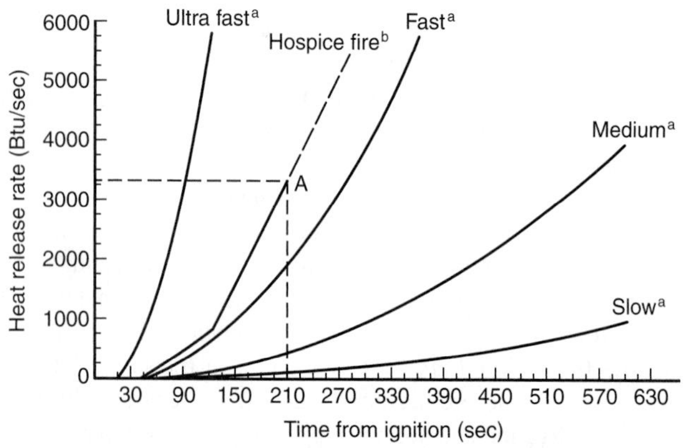

FIGURE 20.15.1 Comparison of the Hospice Fire to *NFPA 72®, National Fire Alarm Code®* Growth Curves. [a]From *NFPA 72®, National Fire Alarm Code®*. [b]From NFPA study of the hospice fire, Southfield, Michigan, December 1985 and CFR/NBS fire model analysis. A = Room flashover

Any combination of finishes, combustible building materials, or contents and furnishings that could result in full room involvement or flashover in 5 minutes or less represents a severe fire hazard in a health care facility. Such spaces should always be protected by automatic sprinklers and separated by fire-rated construction.

Computer fire models developed at NIST have been used to establish the rate of heat release required to produce flashover in a typical patient sleeping room. Under the "worst" circumstances—where the room door is partially open—a 1 MW fire can cause flashover. When the room door is fully open, approximately a 2 MW fire is necessary to cause flashover. NFPA *101* suggests that upholstered furniture, mattresses, and wardrobes be constructed to produce a maximum rate of heat release of 250 kW. It also has been determined that when a fire grows beyond 250 kW in size, hazard thresholds are exceeded, and patients must be removed from sleeping rooms.

Furnishings are frequently major contributors to fire growth. Recent developments make it possible to determine whether furnishings in a given environment can produce sufficient energy to cause full room involvement.

A simplified equation for estimating the rate of heat release required for flashover to occur in a room[8] is given by the expression

$$\dot{Q} \geq 750A\sqrt{h}$$

where

$\dot{Q}$ = Rate of heat release (kW)

A = Ventilation opening area (ft^2 [m^2])

h = The height of the opening (ft [m])

Once the heat release rate required to produce flashover is known for a typical room geometry, such information can be compared to actual heat release rates for typical furnishings, as determined by tests conducted in a calorimeter such as the NIST furniture calorimeter[9] or by Underwriters Laboratories (UL) Subject 1056, "Outline of Investigation for Upholstered Furniture." Figures 20.15.2 and 20.15.3 are idealized curves developed by NIST that illustrate the rate of heat release for typical furnishings as a function of time. Such information can be used to establish the probability of flashover; it also allows estimation of the time required to reach critical fire size.

Interior Finish

A successful fire protection strategy requires fires to remain small. Any large fire in a confined space creates a potentially lethal atmosphere. A fire's initial growth may be affected significantly by the interior finish of walls, ceilings, and floors. Interior finishes, therefore, deserve special attention. Combustible wall and ceiling finishes can act as a fuse, causing a fire to spread to objects remote from the fire origin. Wall and ceiling finishes also provide a large continuous surface over which fire may spread. Thus, an interior finish may, by releasing energy, cause a fire that would otherwise have remained small to become large.

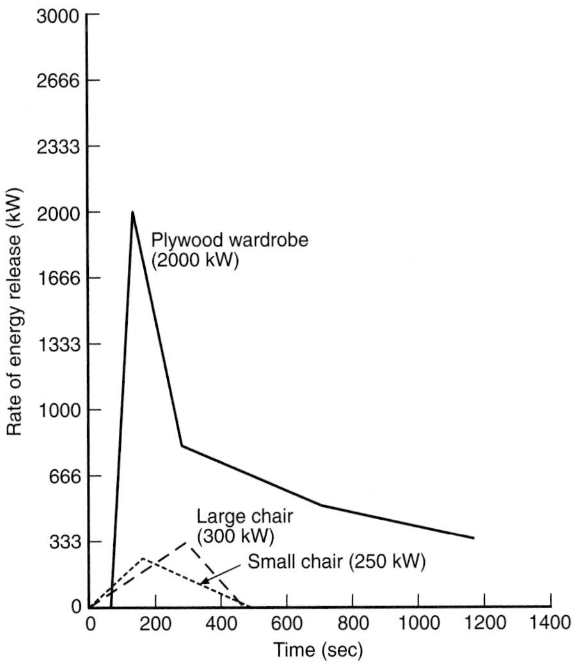

FIGURE 20.15.2 Heat Release Rates for Miscellaneous Furniture

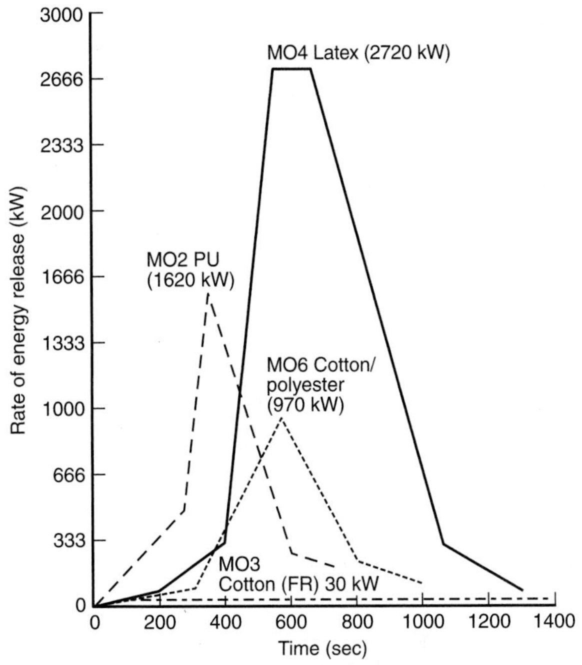

FIGURE 20.15.3 Heat Release Rates for Beds

The relative hazard of an interior finish is usually determined by a test conducted in accordance with NFPA 255, *Standard Method of Test of Surface Burning Characteristics of Building Materials,* commonly called the "tunnel test."

Interior finish on walls and ceilings within the means of egress and any room should be limited to Class A materials, which have a flame-spread rating of 25 or less. Class B materials, or those with a flame-spread rating of 25 to 75, are considered tolerable, but they should be limited to small rooms. Full-scale experiments show that automatic sprinklers can limit fire growth in rooms with Class C wall and Class D ceiling finishes.[2,5] Accordingly, in buildings with automatic sprinkler protection, it has been judged acceptable practice to allow the use of materials having higher flame-spread classifications than would otherwise be permitted. For example, Class B materials are sometimes used where Class A is normally specified and Class C materials where Class B is normally required. In new health care facilities, higher flame-spread classifications are permitted based on the mandatory requirement for sprinklers.

Further, it has been shown that the performance of interior finishes also is related to location.[10] Finishes on the upper portions of walls and ceilings contribute more significantly to flame propagation than finishes on the floor or on the lower half of a wall. Therefore, where finishes are limited to the lower half of a wall and are less than 4 ft (1.2 m) above floor level, materials having a higher flame-spread rating than would otherwise be allowed might be used without significantly affecting fire growth. For example, where Class A materials are judged necessary, a Class B material might be allowed on the lower portion of a wall.

In the past, floor finish materials were excluded from requirements for interior finishes, based on favorable experience and the assumption that limited exposure exists at the floor level during an actual fire. However, a fire on January 9, 1970, in the Harmer House Convalescent Home in Marietta, Ohio, significantly changed this attitude.[11] Thirty-two persons died in this fire. Carpeting with foam-rubber backing was judged to have played a significant role.

Interior floor finishes in the corridors of nonsprinklered health care facilities should be limited to Class A materials or those with a minimum critical radiant flux of 0.45 W/cm^2. Where automatic sprinklers are provided, interior floor finishes need not be regulated beyond the federal flammability standard.

BUILDING CONSTRUCTION

Because occupants of health care facilities must be defended in place, construction is an important factor, especially in multistory buildings. Buildings preferably should be constructed of noncombustible materials that resist the effects of fire and maintain structural integrity.

Buildings of two or more stories should be constructed of noncombustible materials with major structural members having at least a 2 hour fire resistance. Materials that either burn or support combustion, although less desirable, are considered acceptable if special precautions are taken. An automatic sprinkler system is an essential part of the total fire defense system for combusitble buildings.

Any evaluation of building materials should include consideration of their smoke-generating capabilities. In addition, plastic construction materials, which are becoming more common, are sometimes capable of generating large quantities of smoke.

Subdivision of Building Spaces

Mixed and Separated Occupancies. There are basically two ways to handle multiple occupancies in a building that houses a health care facility and other uses. One alternative is to separate the different occupancies. The second alternative is to treat the entire facility as a mixed occupancy and comply with the provisions that are the most stringent of the occupancies involved. When using the mixed occupancy design alternative, there are no specific fire-rated separation requirements. Fire-rated separation requirements, however, do apply in addition to other restrictions when adjacent occupancies are separated from health care occupancies. The health care occupancy chapters and the ambulatory health care occupancy chapters stipulate the fire-resistance separation requirements (2 and 1 hours, respectively) and other provisions when the health care facility is intended to be separated from adjacent occupancies.

Figure 20.15.4 shows health care and other occupancy areas intermingled without fire separations as a mixed occupancy facility. Figure 20.15.5 shows a health care occupancy (hospital) separated from an adjacent business occupancy and ambulatory health care occupancy. In this case, 2 hour fire-resistive separa-

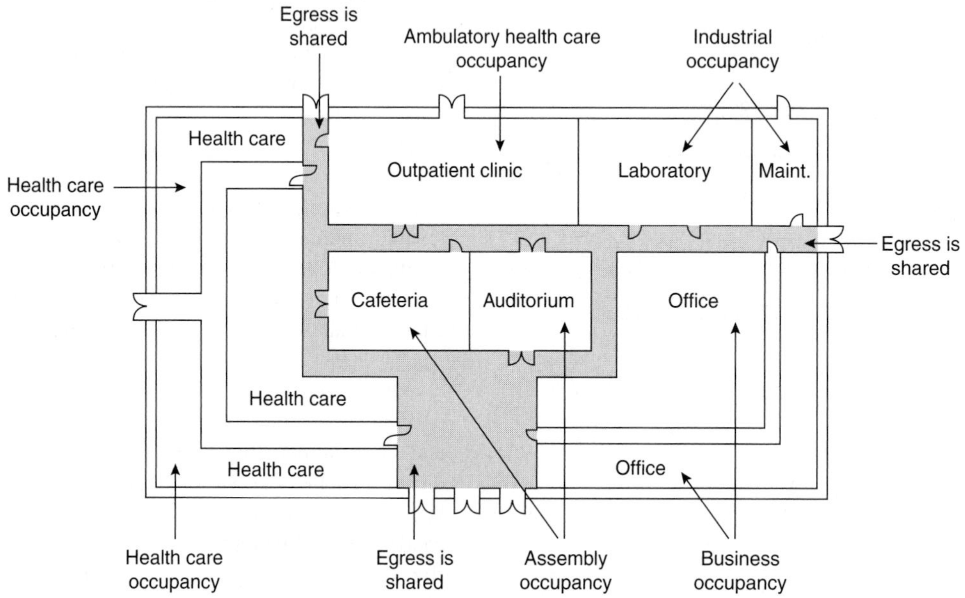

FIGURE 20.15.4 Multiple Occupancy with Mixed Uses

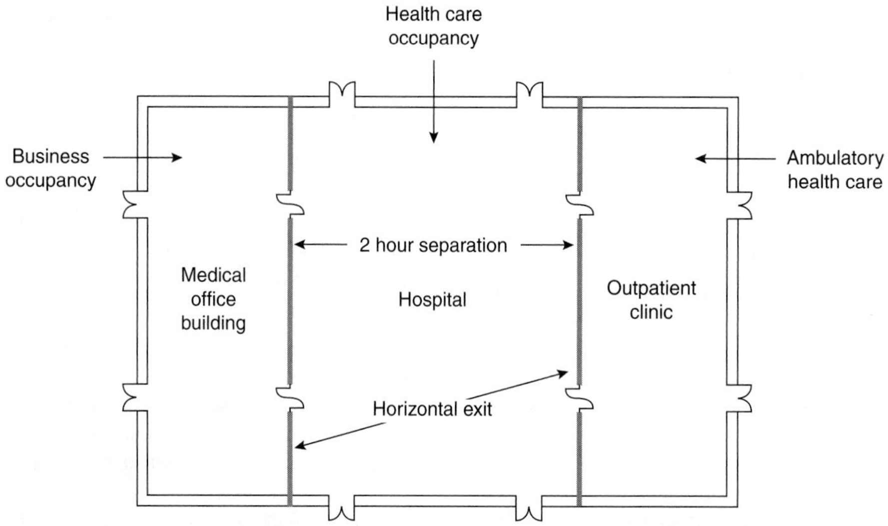

FIGURE 20.15.5 Multiple Occupancy with Separated Uses

tions are used to qualify the hospital, business, and ambulatory health care areas as separate occupancies.

Separation of Patient Sleeping Rooms. Because it may not be possible to remove occupants during a fire, sleeping rooms other than the room of fire origin sometimes must serve as temporary areas of refuge. Therefore, sleeping rooms should be isolated from all other building spaces by fire-rated construction. Partitions should be continuous from the floor slab to the floor or roof above through any concealed spaces, such as those above suspended ceilings. If the building is protected by sprinklers, NFPA *101* and *NFPA 5000* allow these walls to be nonrated, provided the walls resist the passage of smoke, and they are permitted to terminate at the ceiling, provided the ceiling resists the passage of smoke (see Figure 20.15.6 for typical floor plan for a health care facility).

There has been much discussion in the past about the operational considerations versus the fire safety considerations of equipping patient room doors with door closers. NFPA *101* and *NFPA 5000* do not require door-closing devices on patient room doors. The current opinion is that a health care facility's functional needs prevail, and other fire safety and operational features a health care facility provides are adequate alternatives to door-closing devices.

Any penetration of fire barriers by building service equipment should be protected in order to maintain the required fire resistance rating. All spaces around piping and duct penetrations should be sealed tightly with a noncombustible material having adequate fire resistance and capable of retarding the transfer of smoke. Transfer grills should not be used within such doors or partitions.

Smoke Barriers. Every floor used by inpatients should be subdivided into at least two compartments by smoke barriers that also have a 1-hour fire resistance rating. A horizontal exit, when constructed to satisfy the additional criteria imposed on construction of smoke barriers, is a desirable alternative. Smoke barriers and smoke compartments play a very important fire safety role in health care facilities. Subdividing each floor minimizes the

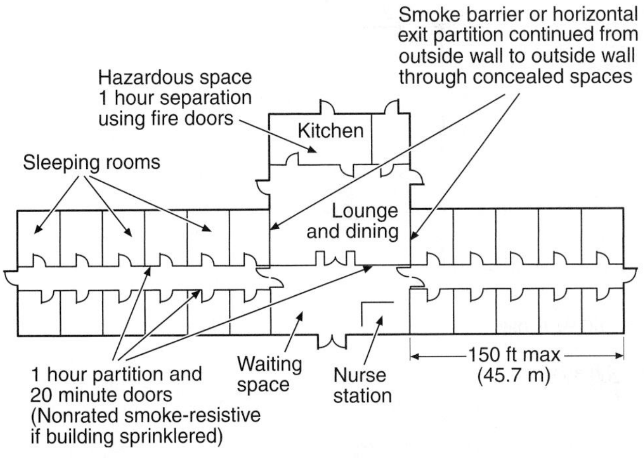

FIGURE 20.15.6 Typical Floor Plan for a Health Care Facility

number of occupants exposed to a single fire. More importantly, the barriers allow for horizontal evacuation of occupants to an area of refuge on the same floor. In a protect-in-place occupancy where evacuation is difficult, having the capability to evacuate horizontally is extremely important.

In new health care construction, smoke barriers are generally required to subdivide into at least two compartments every story used for inpatient sleeping and treatment and any story in the building, regardless of occupancy, that has an occupant load of greater than 50 people. In existing facilities, subdividing a space with a smoke barrier is required only on stories with patient sleeping areas that can accommodate more than 30 patients. Several exceptions to the general requirement for smoke barriers in new health care construction are found in NFPA *101* and *NFPA 5000.*

For stories that must be subdivided, there are two limitations on how large the smoke compartment formed can be related to area and travel distance from any point to a door in a smoke barrier. No smoke compartment can exceed 22,500 ft^2 (2100 m^2) nor can the travel distance from any part of a smoke compartment to the door in a smoke barrier exceed 200 ft (60 m). One exception for existing health care occupancies is that the travel distance to reach the smoke barrier door need not be limited where neither the length nor width of the smoke compartment exceeds 150 ft (45 m). Figures 20.15.7 and 20.15.8 illustrate the basic dimensional criteria and features that constitute an appropriate smoke compartment arrangement for new and existing health care facilities. In addition to the features shown in Figures 20.15.7 and 20.15.8, accumulation space must be provided on both sides of a smoke barrier to accommodate a certain number of people in an emergency based on factors that range from 30 net ft^2 (2.8 m^2) per patient for hospitals and nursing homes to as low as 3 net ft^2 (2.8 m^2) per person on floors with non–health care spaces.

Protection of Vertical Openings

Fire, smoke, and other toxic products of combustion tend to spread vertically within a building. Special effort is required to prevent fire on one level from threatening the occupants above; this is especially important in health care facilities.

All shafts should be provided with fire-rated enclosures. Vertical openings connecting not more than three floors should be enclosed with fire barriers having a minimum 1-hour fire resistance rating. Two-hour rated enclosures should be provided for vertical openings connecting more than three floors. Openings to shafts should be limited to those necessary, and such openings must be protected.

When designing partitions to enclose vertical shafts, consideration should be given to the varying durability of materials. In spaces where partitions may be subject to mechanical injury, materials used to provide floor-to-floor separation should be able to resist damage in order to maintain the required fire resistance.

Means of Egress Design

Exits in health care facilities should be limited to doors leading directly outside of the building, interior stairs and smokeproof

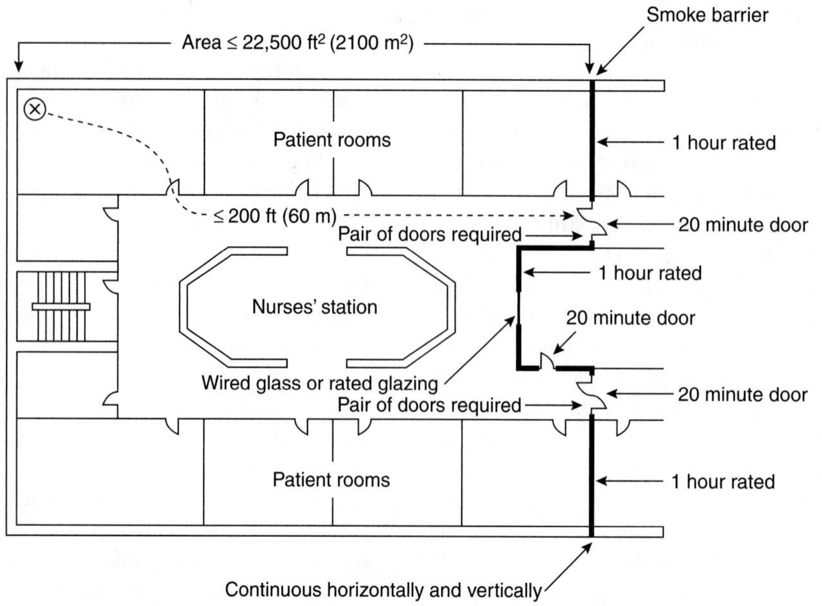

FIGURE 20.15.7 Smoke Compartment in a New Health Care Facility

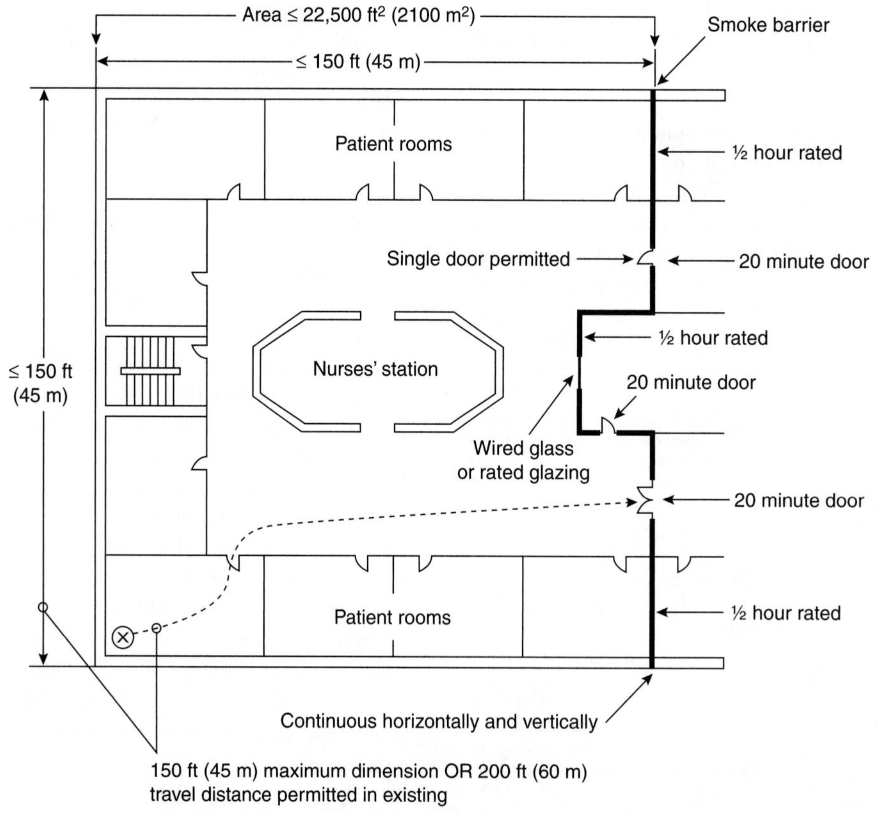

FIGURE 20.15.8 Smoke Compartment in an Existing Health Care Facility

enclosures, ramps, horizontal exits, outside stairs, and exit passageways.

Vertical evacuation of occupants within a health care facility is, at best, difficult and time consuming. Therefore, horizontal movement of patients is of primary importance.

Horizontal passageways and doors opening into corridors and rooms used for sleeping or treatment should be wide enough to allow the horizontal movement of occupants, even those in beds or on gurneys. Relocation of patients is a slow process, even under favorable staff-to-patient ratios. Because of the time required to move patients, exit access routes should be protected against fire effects. Spaces open to the corridor should not be used for patient sleeping or treatment rooms, nor should hazardous contents or activities be permitted within them. NFPA *101* and *NFPA 5000* provide detailed requirements for spaces open to corridors. Such requirements include the installation of smoke detection systems, quick-response sprinklers, direct visual supervision of the open space by staff, or a combination thereof.

Horizontal Exits. Horizontal exits are common in health care facilities. Partitions used as horizontal exits and smoke barriers should provide the fire resistance required for exits and, in addition, should satisfy the criteria for smoke barriers when appropriate. If possible, door openings should be limited to corridors, lobbies, or public spaces. The most desirable arrangement of mechanical systems is one in which the partitions forming the horizontal exit are not penetrated. If penetration by utilities or piping occurs, the space around the piping should be filled tightly with noncombustible materials and maintain the barrier's required fire resistance. If ducts penetrate partitions intended to be smoke barriers, combination fire/smoke dampers that close if smoke detectors within the duct activate should be provided.

Two-hour fire barrier walls must be used to create horizontal exits. Such barriers must be vertically continuous and must penetrate any ceiling and continue to the floor or roof deck above. NFPA *101* and *NFPA 5000* require such barriers to be continuous to the ground. The fire barrier is allowed to be omitted on any story below, provided the floor below the lowest level on which the barrier exists and all supporting members are of a 2 hour fire-resistive construction. Figure 20.15.9 illustrates the vertical continuity of walls forming horizontal exits.

Because a horizontal exit implies that occupants will be transferred from one side of a partition to the other (horizontal evacuation), adequate space must be available to house occupants after movement. In hospitals, at least 30 net ft^2 (2.79 m^2) per patient should be available on each side of the horizontal exit, allowing for accumulation of the total number of patients in adjoining compartments.

Interior Stairs. Exit stairs should be designed to satisfy the criteria for interior stairs. Stairs should be enclosed with fire barriers, and openings into stair enclosures should be limited to those necessary for access and discharge purposes. Stairs must be properly protected from the effects of fire.

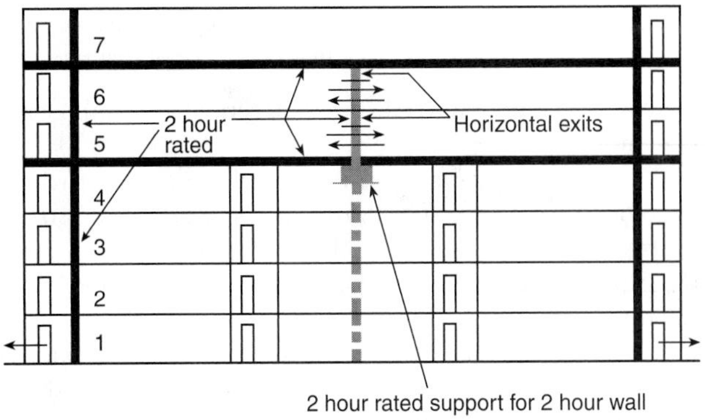

FIGURE 20.15.9 Building with Horizontal Exits on Some Floors

Exit Features

Life safety from fire in health care facilities relies on a "defend-in-place" principle. Horizontal exits or smoke barriers are required to subdivide each story of a health care facility to provide an area of refuge on each floor.

The original concept for the design of exits for health care facilities was derived from studies conducted in the early 1900s. A practice evolved of using exit stair enclosures as areas of refuge. Exit capacity for health care facilities was set conservatively to offset slow travel rates and to create space within exit enclosures for "storing" patients on litters and in wheelchairs.

Means for horizontal evacuation are provided for each story, using either a smoke barrier or a horizontal exit. A barrier subdivides each story to provide an area of refuge for patients without traversing stairs. Furthermore, it is common—indeed, it is required since the 1991 edition of NFPA *101*—to install automatic sprinklers throughout all new health care facilities. Automatic sprinklers limit fire size and complement the defend-in-place strategy currently in use.

Egress capacity in nonsprinklered health care facilities is set at 0.6 in. (15.24 mm) per person for travel over stairs, whereas the capacity through doors and level passageways is calculated at 0.5 in. (12.7 mm) per person. Where automatic sprinklers are provided throughout a building, exit capacity is increased to 0.3 in. (7.62 mm) per person for travel over stairs and 0.2 in. (5.08 mm) per person for travel over level passageways.

Capacity is calculated using a "flow rate" principle. Flow rates assumed are for able-bodied persons because it is presumed that evacuation over stairs will involve only staff, visitors, and ambulatory patients. Nonambulatory occupants are expected to remain in the building under the defend-in-place concept, with those patients on the floor of fire origin being moved horizontally to an adjoining smoke or fire compartment.

Limits on travel distance reflect anticipated slow movement. Travel distance normally should not exceed the following:

1. 100 ft (30 m) between an exit and any room door intended for use as an exit access
2. 150 ft (46 m) between an exit and any point in a room

3. 50 ft (15 m) between any point in a sleeping room or suite of sleeping rooms and the exit access door of that room

Increases in corridor travel distance are permitted in sprinklered buildings.

Because smoke barriers and areas of refuge play such an important role in fire safety, travel distances to smoke barriers is also restricted in NFPA *101*. Travel distance from any point on a floor to reach a door in a smoke barrier is limited to 200 ft (61 m).

Elevators are not permitted to serve as required exits in health care occupancies because they possess numerous shortcomings that may prevent their use during a fire. In the cases of critically ill patients, patients in body casts or balkan frames, and others who would be difficult to move, however, elevators provide the only practical evacuation method from upper stories of the facility. If separate banks of elevators are located in separate smoke compartments, and if the staff are well trained, it may be possible to devise a plan in which using elevators during fires is safe.

Suites

The design of suites has been addressed by NFPA *101* for many years. These requirements, however, were previously dispersed among several topic areas in the code. In the 2006 editions of NFPA *101* and *NFPA 5000,* the terms "suite," "non-sleeping suite," and "sleeping suite," were defined in the context of health care occupancies, and their requirements were consolidated under the provisions for means of egress arrangement.

The suite concept permits groups of rooms in health care occupancies to be treated as one large "room" subject to specified limitations. Normally, rooms in health care occupancies must be provided with direct access to a corridor without traveling through an intervening room. Rooms within suites are not subject to the usual corridor separation requirements, and the circulation spaces within suites are not subject to the strict use limitations imposed on corridors. The creation of suites has long been a cost-effective solution to address the needs of groups of patients having similar health issues or needing similar levels of staff monitoring and care. Suite configurations are often used for specialty care patient sleeping units, such as intensive care, cardiac care, or pediatric care units. Suites can also be used effectively for treatment areas such as a radiology department or operating room suite. In prior editions of NFPA *101* and *NFPA 5000,* sleeping suites were limited in size to 5000 ft^2 (460 m^2) and required direct visual supervision by staff.

Some facility designers and architects have attempted to create sleeping suites larger than 5000 ft^2 using alternative measures (equivalency) to substitute for the requirement of "direct visual supervision by staff" and as a means of providing a cost-effective environment for patients. Based on the prevalence of the suite size limitation issue, the 2006 editions of NFPA *101* and *NFPA 5000* have increased the sleeping suite area limitation from 5000 ft^2 (460 m^2) to 7500 ft^2 (700 m^2) if the suite is provided with smoke detection, sprinkler protection, and direct visual patient supervision by staff. Direct supervision is typically provided from a normally attended staff location. Separation by glass walls is permitted provided that staff can visually see into the patient sleeping room. The use of cubical curtains at patient beds is also permitted; solid walls and doors would not facilitate the required direct visual supervision.

The Technical Committee on Health Care Occupancies recognized that there are practical safety concerns pertaining to how good visual supervision is for patient sleeping rooms within suites. In sleeping suites that do not exceed 5000 ft^2 (460 m^2), any room that lacks direct visual supervision can be used for patient sleeping only where such room is provided with automatic smoke detection arranged to activate the fire alarm. This option only applies to suites that are 5000 ft^2 (460 m^2) or less. Sleeping suites exceeding 5000 ft^2 (460 m^2) are required to provide a total coverage automatic smoke detection system throughout the sleeping suite and provide direct visual patient supervision. It is important to note that although smoke detection can substitute for direct visual supervision in smaller sleeping suites, it is intended that staff are constantly present in the suite.

Several other revisions to the requirements for suites in NFPA *101* and *NFPA 5000* allow for design flexibility without compromising occupant safety. Where two means of egress from a suite are required because of its size, at least one must lead directly to a corridor. The second means of egress is permitted to lead through another suite. See NFPA *101* and *NFPA 5000* for additional details on suite arrangments.

Exit Marking and Exit Illumination

Readily visible signs should mark all exits. Where access to exits is not immediately visible, access routes also should be marked.

The entire means of egress must be continuously illuminated whenever the building is occupied. In some cases, normal street lighting is adequate for illumination of exit discharge. However, consideration should be given to the conditions that would result from a power failure.

Emergency power is also required to illuminate the means of egress and exit marking. In hospitals, this power should be supplied by the life safety branch of the hospitals' essential electrical system. Luminescent, fluorescent, or reflective material should not be substituted for required lighting.

Emergency power supplies should maintain illumination automatically in the event of a power failure without any appreciable interruption during the changeover from normal to emergency power. Where a generator is provided, the delay should not be more than 10 seconds. Where emergency power is supplied by a central system with an engine-driven generator, the design should minimize the probability of any single emergency simultaneously interrupting both normal and emergency power supplies. The switch(es) that transfers power from normal to emergency circuits is one place where normal and emergency circuits are required to merge. If this switch(es) is exposed to fire, it could simultaneously interrupt power to both normal and emergency circuits. The transfer switch and other electrical distribution panels and switch gear should be separated from the generator, as well as from the remainder of the building. See NFPA 99, *Standard for Health Care Facilities,* NFPA *101,* NFPA 110, *Standard for Emergency and Standby Power Systems,* and *NFPA 5000* for additional details on emergency power for health care occupancies.

Fire Alarms

Every health care facility should be equipped with a fire alarm system. When actuated, the system should sound alarms that can be heard above ambient noise levels throughout the facility. Visible alarm indicating devices are permitted in critical patient care areas in lieu of audible alarm devices. The fire alarm should also transmit automatically to the fire department. Any fire detection or fire suppression system that activates should automatically activate the building alarm system.

Alarm systems, including detection devices, should be provided with an emergency power supply and designed according to *NFPA 72®*.

The activation of any sprinkler system, manual fire alarm box, or detection device should provide automatically an alarm for staff and/or occupants within the affected zones initially. Means to notify staff and occupants in other zones as needed should be provided. In sprinklered health care facilities, positive alarm sequence in accordance with *NFPA 72* is permitted. Although the use of a general evacuation alarm is permitted, it may be more appropriate to use the private operating mode as described in *NFPA 72* because occupants may be incapable of evacuating without assistance. The private operating mode recognizes that health care facility staff will perform and direct evacuation procedures within patient areas affected by the fire. The private operating mode requires that the notification method for staff provide a means to identify the zone, area, floor, or building in need of evacuation.

FIRE SUPPRESSION EQUIPMENT

Automatic Sprinkler Systems

A proven effective, practical, and reliable approach to life safety in health care facilities is to use automatic fire suppression—in particular, automatic sprinkler systems. Although persons in the area of origin may still be seriously threatened, those in adjoining spaces—and, in a number of cases, in the same room—are protected.[2,3,7,12] NFPA *101* and *NFPA 5000* require all new health care facilities to be protected by automatic sprinklers.

The 1991 edition of NFPA *101* was the first to require sprinkler protection for all new health care facilities. Two multiple death nursing home fires occurred within seven months of each other in 2003—one in Hartford, Connecticut, on February 26, 2003, that resulted in 16 deaths, and another in Nashville, Tennessee, on September 25, 2003, that resulted in 15 deaths. These fires resulted in calls to require automatic sprinkler protection in all existing nursing homes. As a result, the 2006 edition of NFPA *101* became the first edition to retroactively require that all buildings containing nursing homes be protected throughout with electrically supervised automatic sprinkler systems.

Full sprinkler protection obviously increases the level of fire protection and life safety in nursing homes; however, the impact on scarce health care funding must also be addressed. Although the design, installation, and maintenance of sprinkler systems in nursing homes will have a measurable cost (which can be affected by the availability of an adequate water supply), there are associated savings, including the following:

- Some buildings of noncompliant construction types could "become" compliant, negating the need for equivalencies, other alternate means of protection, or waivers.
- Increased allowable travel distances permitted in sprinklered facilities could solve existing egress problems and/or facilitate building additions.
- Hazardous area enclosures would change from 1 hour fire barriers to smoke partitions—facilities might save money because firestopping of penetrations above the ceiling would no longer be necessary.
- Some areas would be allowed to be open to the corridor.
- Corridor walls would be required to be smoke resistant rather than fire rated—facilities might save money because firestopping of corridor wall penetrations above the ceiling would no longer be necessary.
- The requirement for smoke dampers in duct penetrations of smoke barriers in fully ducted HVAC systems would be eliminated—facilities could disconnect existing dampers, fix them in the open position, and save money on future testing and maintenance.
- Newly introduced upholstered furniture and mattresses could be less expensive because they would be exempted from ignition resistance and heat release rate standards.

The ability of automatic sprinklers to provide a survivable environment for building occupants has been debated at length. Full-scale tests have shown that standard sprinklers can extinguish many fires while maintaining a survivable atmosphere outside the room of fire origin.[2,5] In addition, sprinklers have been shown to be effective in limiting carbon monoxide to nonlethal levels outside the room. Tests have also shown that privacy curtains may interfere with sprinkler discharge.[13] To obtain full sprinkler effectiveness, the influence of any building design feature or furnishing that would impair sprinkler discharge should be evaluated carefully.

The quick-response or fast-response sprinkler has been shown in most instances to maintain a survivable atmosphere within the room of fire origin. Full-scale tests at NIST have documented this performance.[13]

Where fire defenses are based on automatic sprinkler systems, fast-response sprinklers should be considered for the entire building. At a minimum, fast-response sprinklers should be used throughout compartments having sleeping rooms. This is required for new health care facilities by NFPA *101*.

Automatic sprinkler systems should comply with NFPA 13, *Standard for the Installation of Sprinkler Systems*. Sprinkler operation should sound the building fire alarm automatically. The sprinkler system and components should be electrically supervised to ensure reliable operation and should include valve tamper switches with a local alarm at a constantly attended location when the valve is closed. If pressure tanks are the primary source of water, air pressure, water level, and temperature should be supervised. If fire pumps are provided, electrical supervision should monitor the fire pump in accordance with NFPA 20, *Standard for the Installation of Stationary Pumps for Fire Protection*.

Portable Fire Extinguishers

Portable fire extinguishers should be placed in all buildings, as they may provide an opportunity to control a fire during its early stages. In all cases, however, the fire department should be notified before or at the same time that occupants are attempting to fight the fire. Delayed alarms have allowed fires to grow to large scale and, in turn, threaten occupants before fire department notification and arrival.

Smoke Control

Although operable windows were required in every patient sleeping room for many years, neither NFPA *101* nor *NFPA 5000* requires them. Outside windows are required but need not be operable. Windows in atrium walls are considered to be equivalent to outside windows in health care facilities.

Special forced-air systems or, in some cases, the adaptation of conventional building air-handling systems can permit venting of products of combustion early in the fire. Such systems may also make it possible to create a pressure difference across physical barriers, such as floors or partitions, and prevent smoke transfer. The effectiveness of fire partitions often improves significantly by the use of such systems.

Where adaptation of the building air-handling system is contemplated for smoke removal, its design should be in accordance with NFPA 92A, *Standard for Smoke-Control Systems Utilizing Barriers and Pressure Differences.* Consideration should be given to alternative power supplies and electrical supervision of critical system components.

PROTECTION OF HAZARDOUS AREAS

Areas with contents more hazardous than those normally found in health care facilities should be arranged to minimize occupant exposure if a fire occurs. NFPA *101* and *NFPA 5000* address hazardous areas in general and also address hazardous areas in the specific occupancy chapters. The general provisions require one of the following:

1. Enclose the hazardous area with fire barriers having a 1-hour fire resistance rating and without windows.
2. Protect the area with an automatic extinguishing system.
3. Apply the protection of both (1) and (2) where the hazard is severe or where otherwise specified by the occupancy chapters.

When the 1 hour enclosure is used, the doors must be ¾ hour fire rated, self-closing, and positive-latching doors. Typically, in new construction and in any health care occupancy, when a hazardous area is sprinkler protected without having a fire resistance rated enclosure, the area must be protected with at least a smoke-resisting enclosure equipped with smoke-resisting self- or automatic-closing doors. In health care facilities, corridor doors are normally required to latch. Doors in hazardous areas are typically required to be self- or automatic-closing doors and self-latching.

The health care occupancy chapters of NFPA *101* and *NFPA 5000* detail the specific areas that must be addressed as hazardous areas; however, the listed areas are not intended to be all-inclusive, and the general provisions must be met if an area poses unusual fire hazards in the health care facility.

There are provisions related to other hazardous areas, including gift shops, laundry and trash chutes, cooking facilities, and laboratories. Gift shops must be protected as hazardous areas when they are used for storing or displaying combustibles in quantities considered hazardous. Trash chutes and linen chutes can pose significant fire risks for health care occupancies. These areas should comply with NFPA 82, *Standard on Incinerators and Waste and Linen Handling Systems and Equipment.* Laboratories, anesthetizing locations, and medical gas systems should comply with the provisions of NFPA 99, which relate to the protection of hazardous areas. New heliports must comply with NFPA 418, *Standard for Heliports.* Cooking facilities are required to be protected in accordance with NFPA 96, *Standard for Ventilation Control and Fire Protection of Commercial Cooking Operations.*

Building Service Equipment

Building service equipment should be installed and maintained in accordance with appropriate NFPA standards. Special consideration should be given to the design and installation of heating and air-conditioning systems.

Portable heating devices are unsafe in patient-occupied portions of health care facilities. All heating devices should be designed and installed to prevent ignition of combustible materials. Approved suspended unit heaters may be used, except in means of egress and patient sleeping areas, if they are high enough to be out of the reach of persons using the area.

Air for combustion and ventilation in boilers, incinerators, or heater rooms should be taken directly from, and discharged directly to, the outside of the buildings.

OPERATING FEATURES

Smokers cause many fires in health care facilities. Adoption and enforcement of suitable smoking regulations are essential.[7] Smoking should be prohibited in any room, ward, or compartment where flammable liquids, combustible gases, or oxygen is used or stored. Such areas should be posted with no-smoking signs. Smoking by patients who are under sedation or who are not considered responsible should be prohibited. Smoking should be permitted in a sleeping room only when authorized by medical staff and then only under direct staff supervision. Metal containers with self-closing covers should be available for disposal of smoking materials in all areas where smoking is allowed.

Most hospitals and many nursing homes have established no-smoking policies. JCAHO requires hospitals to be smoke free. Nursing homes are becoming smoke free on a voluntary basis. These are very positive steps in improving the level of fire safety in health care facilities.

Visitors sometimes give patients smoking materials without the staff's knowledge. Health care facilities need to address this serious issue. In 1989, 12 residents died in a Norfolk, Virginia, nursing home fire attributed to a visitor giving a resident smoking materials.

Window draperies and curtains should be made of noncombustible material or material that has been rendered and maintained flame retardant. These window hangings should be capable of passing NFPA 701, *Standard Methods of Fire Tests for Flame Propagation of Textiles and Films.* Furnishings, decorations, and other objects should not obstruct exits or exit access routes. Combustible decorations should be prohibited.

Exits and mechanical devices provided to control or limit fire should be maintained to ensure reliable operation. Inspections and tests should be performed, as required, to verify satisfactory performance.

In facilities with locked exits, adequate staff should always be present to release occupants and direct them away from the fire area to a place of safety during an emergency.

Care should be exercised during construction and repair operations to ensure that such activities do not reduce life safety.

EMERGENCY PLANNING

In no occupancy are staff training and emergency planning more important than a protect-in-place occupancy housing a significant number of occupants incapable of self-preservation. Every health care facility must have a fire and evacuation plan, including a disaster plan, with which all personnel must be familiar. NFPA 99 provides guidance for both internal and external disasters that affect health care facilities. In addition, personnel should be trained to use fire extinguishers and hose cabinet lines if provided. They must also know how to sound an alarm, move or evacuate patients, and contain the fire.

Each facility should have a safety officer whose primary responsibility is to recognize hazards, act as liaison with the fire service, and arrange for training personnel. While training health care personnel is straightforward and can be accomplished on the job, orienting members of the fire service to health care facility problems is more difficult.

Copies of the fire and evacuation plan should be available to all personnel. The plan should contain specific instructions for key—that is, supervisory—personnel if there is a fire. A copy of the plan also should be posted for reference. All employees should be periodically trained to ensure readiness.

Emergency drills should include transmission of a fire alarm signal and simulation of emergency conditions insofar as possible without jeopardizing occupants. Drills should be conducted on each shift at least quarterly, with at least 12 drills held every year. The drills should be varied to test the alertness of all shifts and, if possible, should be unannounced. Use of the building alarm during drills also verifies its normal operation.

The fire and evacuation plan should include the following fundamentals:

- Training personnel to use the alarm and alarm equipment
- Transmission of alarm to the fire department
- Details of the fire location
- Evacuation practices for all areas
- Preparation of building spaces for evacuation
- Fire extinguishment

During drills, emphasis should be on immediate notification of the fire department; many fires have spread because of delayed alarms.

FIRE SAFETY EVALUATION SYSTEM

NFPA codes contain the fundamental statement of the "equivalency concept," which provides for the use of alternatives to the methods, materials, devices, systems, and so on that are prescribed and/or specifically detailed by the codes. Key to the concept of equivalency is the submission of technical documentation acceptable to the authority having jurisdiction. One method of providing technical documentation for health care facilities is to appropriately apply and utilize the *Fire Safety Evaluation System for Health Care Occupancies (FSES),* which provides a formalized equivalency methodology specific to health care occupancies. The documentation and procedure for the use of this fire safety evaluation system are found in NFPA 101A, *Guide on Alternative Approaches to Life Safety.*

The *FSES for Health Care Occupancies* has, since the 1981 edition of NFPA *101,* provided a basis for developing alternatives that achieve a level of safety equivalent to that mandated by the *Life Safety Code.* The *FSES* was developed to provide a rational basis for achieving the level of safety intended by the *Life Safety Code* without necessarily meeting all of its prescriptive requirements. This can be especially important for existing buildings in which physical conditions may not allow strict compliance or where retroactive compliance may present an economic hardship.

The *FSES* involves the evaluation and comparison of the risk factors and safety features present or proposed for a health care occupancy. The *FSES* methodology for health care occupancies is based on the evaluation of individual "zones," which are generally the spaces separated by floors, horizontal exit barriers, or smoke barriers. The risks of a zone consider the number of people affected by a given fire, the density of the people in the zone, the mobility of the patients, the age of patients, the location of the zone, and the ratio of patients to staff in the given zone.

In addition to the risk aspects of the *FSES,* each zone must consider the ability of the building and its fire protection features to provide measures of safety commensurate with the risk. Safety parameters that are evaluated include building construction fire resistance, interior finish, corridor partitions/walls, corridor doors, zone dimensions, vertical openings, hazardous areas, smoke control, egress routes, fire alarms, fire detection, and automatic sprinklers. Redundancy of the safety features is an important aspect of the *FSES.* By evaluating the redundancy of safety features, the methodology intends to ensure that the failure of a single protection feature or device will not result in major failure of the entire system.

The approach is quantitative in that the *FSES* awards positive point values for strong life safety and fire protection features and negative point values for lesser conditions. With appropriated selection of alternative features a number of both positive and negative factors can be balanced in a manner that results in establishing a level of life safety equivalent to NFPA *101* without complying with all of its prescribed requirements.

The *FSES* methodology has a long and proven track record, but it is not the only approach available for establishing equivalency. NFPA *101* formally recognizes performance-based options for the design and analysis of alternatives to the prescriptive requirements of the code. Additional discussion of the performance-based option can be found in Section 3, Chapter 10, "Performance-Based Codes and Standards for Fire Safety."

AMBULATORY HEALTH CARE

The provisions for ambulatory health care facilities intend to fulfill the needs of facilities that do not pose the risks of 24 hour health care facilities such as hospitals but do pose a greater risk than medical office buildings (business occupancy) that provide for routine doctor visits.

The definition of an ambulatory health care occupancy has three key elements:

1. An ambulatory health care occupancy is a building or portion of a building used to provide services or treatment simultaneously to four or more patients.
2. The services or treatment provided is done solely on an outpatient basis and renders the patients incapable of taking action for self-preservation under emergency conditions without the assistance of others.
3. Anesthesia is provided solely on an outpatient basis and renders the patients incapable of taking action for self-preservation under emergency conditions without the assistance of others.

The distinguishing features of an ambulatory health care occupancy are that 24 hour sleeping accommodations are not provided and services are rendered solely on an outpatient basis. This effectively means that patients walk in and walk out of the facility but may be subject to treatment or anesthesia that temporarily renders them incapable of self-preservation, including postoperative recovery in a bed.

The life safety and fire protection features specified in NFPA *101* and *NFPA 5000* for ambulatory health care occupancies are a blend of those used for both health care occupancies and business occupancies. In fact, many of the provisions for ambulatory health care facilities are simply addressed by references to the provisions for business occupancies. Construction type requirements are less restrictive than those required for health care occupancies but more restrictive than allowed for business occupancies. Several egress requirements are more restrictive than those permitted for business occupancies. Also, there are specific provisions for mixed occupancies, smoke compartments, and fire alarm features that will affect the design of an ambulatory health care occupancy.

SUMMARY

Total building fire protection for life safety is more necessary in health care facilities than in other occupancies because of the nature of the occupants. A significant percentage of occupants in hospitals and nursing homes are incapable of self-evacuation or are ambulatory but incapable of perceiving a fire threat and choosing a rational response. Therefore, fire protection is based on a "defend-in-place" principle and cannot depend on any one safeguard. As a result, health care facility design and operation must incorporate methods by which a fire can be detected early, contained, and fought rapidly and successfully. Fire safety requirements include fire-resistive construction, compartmentation, fire-alerting facilities, and control of smoke movement. In addition, it is critical that every health care facility have a fire and evacuation plan, including a disaster plan, with which all personnel are familiar. Personnel should be trained in emergency procedures, including how to sound an alarm, move or evacuate patients, and contain the fire. Emergency drills should be conducted on each shift at least quarterly, with at least 12 drills held every year.

BIBLIOGRAPHY

References Cited

1. "Building Materials and Structures," Report BMS 92, National Bureau of Standards, Washington, DC, 1942.
2. "Full-Scale Fire Tests in a Nursing Home Patient Room," Report 7463, HEW Contract HSA 105-74-116, prepared by American Health Care Association, U.S. Department of Health, Education and Welfare, Washington, DC, 1975.
3. Best, R., "The Wincrest Nursing Home Fire," *Fire Journal,* Vol. 70, No. 5, 1976.
4. Best, R., "The Cermak House Fire," *Fire Journal,* Vol. 70, No. 5, 1976.
5. O'Neill, J. G., et al., "Full-Scale Fire Tests with Automatic Sprinklers in a Patient Room, Phase II," NBSIR 80-2097, National Bureau of Standards, Gaithersburg, MD, 1980.
6. Hall, J. R., Jr., "The Elderly, the Sick, and Health Care Facilities," *Fire Journal,* Vol. 84, No. 4, 1990.
7. NFPA Fire Analysis Division, "Fatal Fire Risks and Hazards in Health Care Facilities," *Fire Journal,* Vol. 81, No. 5, 1987.
8. Babrauskas, V., "Estimating Room Flashover Potential," *Fire Technology,* May 1980.
9. Babrauskas, V., et al., "Upholstered Furniture Heat Release Rates Measured with a Furniture Calorimeter," NBSIR 82-2604, National Bureau of Standards, Washington, DC, 1982.
10. Christian, W. J., and Waterman, T. E., "Flame Spread in Corridors: Effects of Location and Area of Wall Finish," *Fire Journal,* Vol. 65, No. 4, 1971.
11. Sears, A. B., Jr., "Nursing Home Fire, Marietta, OH," *Fire Journal,* Vol. 64, No. 3, 1970.
12. Boettcher, E. N., M.D., "Hospital Fire Defense: People and Sprinklers," *Fire Journal,* Vol. 61, No. 4, 1967, pp. 93–96.
13. Notarianni, K. A., "Five Small Flaming Fire Tests in a Simulated Hospital Patient Room Protected by Automatic Fire Sprinklers," Report of Test FR-3982, National Institute of Standards and Technology, Gaithersburg, MD, Oct. 31, 1990.

NFPA Codes, Standards, and Recommended Practices

Reference to the following NFPA codes, standards, and recommended practices will provide further information on health care facilities discussed in this chapter. (See the latest version of The NFPA Catalog *for availability of current editions of the following documents.)*

NFPA 13, *Standard for the Installation of Sprinkler Systems*
NFPA 20, *Standard for Installation of Stationary Pumps for Fire Protection*
NFPA 30, *Flammable and Combustible Liquids Code*
NFPA 55, *Standard for the Storage, Use, and Handling of Compressed Gases and Cryogenic Fluids in Portable and Stationary Containers, Cylinders, and Tanks*

NFPA 72®, National Fire Alarm Code®
NFPA 90A, *Standard for the Installation of Air-Conditioning and Ventilating Systems*
NFPA 92A, *Standard for Smoke-Control Systems Utilizing Barriers and Pressure Differences*
NFPA 96, *Standard for Ventilation Control and Fire Protection of Commercial Cooking Operations*
NFPA 99, *Standard for Health Care Facilities*
NFPA *101®*, *Life Safety Code®*
NFPA 255, *Standard Method of Test of Surface Burning Characteristics of Building Materials*
NFPA 701, *Standard Methods of Fire Tests for Flame Propagation of Textiles and Films*
NFPA 5000®, Building Construction and Safety Code®

References

Fischer, M., *NFPA Guide to Electrical Systems in Health Care Facilities,* National Fire Protection Association, Quincy, MA, 2006.
Isner, M. S., "Hospital Fire, Sprinkler Success, Weymouth, Massachusetts, January 24, 1993. Summary," Fire Investigation Report, National Fire Protection Association, Quincy, MA, 1993.
Isner, M. S., "Sprinklers Prevent Tragedy in Two Health Care Facility Fires," *NFPA Journal,* Vol. 87, No. 5, 1993, pp. 49–52, 54–55.
NFPA Ready Reference: Fire Safety in Health Care Facilities, National Fire Protection Association, Quincy, MA, 2003.
UL Subject 1056, "Outline of Investigation for Upholstered Furniture," Underwriters Laboratories Inc., Northbrook, IL.

Chapter 16

Storage Occupancies

Revised by
Jeffrey Moore

This chapter addresses fire protection for storage and warehouse operations. Due to the nature, quantity, and arrangement of inventory in these occupancies, intense fires can develop rapidly. Developing and implementing a comprehensive fire protection plan are essential to minimize the potential for significant fire loss and disruption of operations.

Modern storage practices aim to maximize storage efficiency by piling products high and leaving minimal aisle space between storage piles or racks. As a result, enormous volumes of combustible material are often located in a single fire area or building. In addition, many warehouses contain large quantities of plastics as both products in storage and as packing materials. Most plastics burn rapidly, have a high rate of heat release, and generate copious amounts of smoke, soot, and toxic products of combustion.

Most facilities have some sort of storage or warehousing area to store raw stock, in-process goods, or finished products. The area may be called a storeroom, parts crib, or central sterile supply, depending on the type of facility and the materials in storage. Fortunately, the incidence of fires in storage areas is relatively low compared to other occupancies. Unfortunately, when storage and warehousing fires do occur, they tend to be severe.

This chapter reviews basic fire protection principles for the protection of warehousing and storage areas. It presents an overview of the fire protection features that a comprehensive fire protection program needs and highlights materials and storage occupancies that pose unusual fire protection challenges.

See also Section 6, "Characteristics of Materials and Products"; Section 7, "Storage and Handling of Materials"; Section 9, Chapter 7, "Storage and Handling of Grain Mill Products"; and Section 18, Chapter 4, "Venting Practices."

NFPA STORAGE STANDARDS

NFPA has developed standards that provide an effective means of preparing fire protection plans for various types of storage occupancies. Design requirements for sprinkler system protection of general indoor storage, rack storage, rubber tires, roll paper, baled cotton, and other commodities have been consolidated into NFPA 13, *Standard for the Installation of Sprinkler Systems.*

The fire protection for commercial warehousing and storage occupancies depends on the type of storage and the methods of storage. In most cases, the protection standards contemplate dedicated storage areas with storage heights exceeding 12 ft (3.7 m). NFPA 13 addresses fire protection for miscellaneous storage not meeting this criteria, as well as the protection requirements for dedicated warehousing and storage areas of most commodities.

Miscellaneous storage typically does not exceed 12 ft (3.7 m) in height and is incidental to the primary operations in a facility. For example, small areas used for parts storage along an assembly line would generally be considered incidental storage. A storeroom in a business occupancy would also usually be considered incidental storage. NFPA 13 describes the various types of storage and the design of automatic sprinkler protection for each type and configuration of storage.

The requirements contained within NFPA standards, such as NFPA 13, are based on full-scale fire tests and past fire experience. The standards do not address storage arrangements where

Jeffrey Moore, P.E., is a senior fire protection engineer with Hughes Associates, Inc., in Cincinnati, Ohio.

Chapter Contents

Key Terms

aircraft hangar, automatic sprinkler system, bulk storage, characteristics of materials, cold storage warehouse, commodity, fire-fighting operations, flammable liquid, mixed storage, outdoor storage, pallet storage, parking garage, pier, portable fire extinguisher, pre-incident planning, private fire service main, rack storage, smoke venting, storage occupancy, warehouse

test data are not available or where valid conclusions could not be drawn from the extrapolation of available data, judgment, or experience. For storage arrangements beyond the scope of a specific NFPA document, engineering judgment and other sources should be utilized. In some cases this may require actual fire testing of the materials and configurations encountered or contemplated.

OCCUPANCY CHARACTERISTICS

A study of warehouse fires conducted by NFPA and several major property insurers showed that over a 4 year period, warehouse and storage fires comprised only 14 percent of the reported fires, but these fires caused nearly 40 percent of the damage incurred. The study further determined that, on average, a warehouse fire occurs every 22 hours, and that a warehouse fire that results in a loss of over $500,000 occurs every 11 days.[1]

Storage occupancies are buildings, or portions of a building, used to store or shelter goods, merchandise, products, vehicles, or animals. Storage facilities can be separate and distinct facilities or part of a multiple-use occupancy. Storage occupancies pose a wide range of fire protection challenges, including large open fire areas, high values concentrated in a relatively small area, limited access for fire suppression operations, and fuels arranged in arrays conducive to rapid fire development and spread. Examples of storage occupancies are warehouses, freight terminals, parking garages, aircraft hangars, grain elevators, and outdoor storage areas. Table 20.16.1 shows the estimated frequency of fires in various warehousing and storage occupancies.

NFPA 13 classifies storage occupancies as light-, ordinary-, or extra-hazard, or a combination of these where mixed commodities are stored together without separation. NFPA *101*®, *Life Safety Code*®, and *NFPA 5000*®, *Building Construction and Safety Code*®, divide storage occupancies into low-, ordinary- and extra-hazard. Factors affecting the hazard classification are burning characteristics of the material stored, combustibility of packaging, method of storage and packaging, and the quantity stored.

Current material handling technology permits storage in automated storage and retrieval systems to heights exceeding 100 ft (30 m). Computer-controlled stacker cranes are now being used to move and place commodities in rack storage areas. Distribution warehouses may cover several acres under one roof and may contain multilevel mezzanines. These large, open areas pose a major fire threat. Fortunately, storage occupancies usually have a limited number of occupants in relation to total floor area. The presence of fewer people generally translates into a lower incidence of fire. Although some warehouses with automatic storage and retrieval systems are fully automated, the workflow in most warehouses usually requires employees to move materials through the facility using industrial lift trucks.

Contents

The contents of storage occupancies may consist of raw materials, goods in an intermediate stage of production, or finished products. These materials may be found in bulk storage, solid piling, palletized storage, or rack storage arrangements. Bins and narrow shelves are also used, usually in stockrooms and small storage areas. The major difference between these storage arrangements is the exposed surface area of the storage. As the exposed surface area of the storage increases, the speed at which a fire develops increases. Other storage occupancies, such as parking garages, grain elevators, and aircraft hangars create other problems due to the nature of operations in the building. The problems posed by these and other storage operations are addressed later in this chapter.

Mini-Storage Facilities

Mini-storage facilities for rental to the general public consist of several small rental spaces ranging from 40 to 400 ft^2 (3.7 to 37 m^2) in one building or several adjacent buildings. These facilities pose some unique fire problems of their own. There is little control over the type and amount of materials that may be stored in rental areas because they are accessible to renters on a 24 hour basis. Automatic sprinklers are typically not installed in these buildings and fire-resistance-rated walls or barriers do not usually separate the individual rental spaces from each other.

HAZARDS ASSOCIATED WITH OCCUPANCY

Contents

In determining the hazard classification of storage, consideration should be given to the product, product container, and packaging materials. The fire hazard of a warehouse or storage occupancy is a function of the commodity or material in storage, the method of packaging, and the storage arrangement. Fire development in a storage area depends on the material, ease of ignition, flame spread rate, and the rate of heat release. All too often a judgment concerning the hazard of the storage is based on the commodity with little thought given to the methods of packaging and the storage arrangement. For example, a metal part stored on a wooden pallet poses a low threat of fire. However, if the same part is packaged inside a multilayer cardboard carton with expanded polystyrene foam packing material, the fire hazard is greatly increased. Plastics are increasingly used as part of the product as well as the packaging.

Package Commodity Storage. A packaged commodity must be considered as a whole—that is, the way it burns. For example, bottled beer would be considered a low hazard, but when stored in cardboard or wood containers, it becomes an ordinary-hazard commodity. Washing machines have very few combustible components. However, they can burn rapidly and produce large volumes of smoke where packaged in cardboard boxes and surrounded with plastic packing materials.

Mixed Storage. In areas with mixed storage, the hazard classification should be based on the most hazardous storage. This mixed condition is common in most warehouses supplying department stores, hardware stores, and automotive parts stores. High-hazard materials or materials that require special consideration can sometimes be segregated from other storage to keep

TABLE 20.16.1 Reported U.S. Structure Fires in Warehouse-Type Storage Properties, 1994–1998 Annual Averages

Type of Storage Facility	*Fires*	*Civilian Deaths*	*Civilian Injuries*	*Direct Loss (in Millions of Dollars)*
WAREHOUSE (excluding refrigerated storage)	5489	3	73	237.2
General item storage (excluding wharf or pier, ice storage)	2893	2	37	103.3
General warehouse	1338	1	25	77.3
Freight terminal	75	0	1	2.5
Coal or coke briquette or charcoal storage	13	0	0	0.5
Packaged mineral products storage	8	0	0	0.5
Other military or national defense storage	7	0	0	0.2
Bagged mineral products storage	6	0	0	0.0
Unclassified general item storage	885	0	6	11.1
Unknown-type general item storage	562	1	4	11.2
Agricultural products storage (containerized)	820	0	9	19.7
Agricultural supply storage	650	0	8	14.5
Boxed, crated, or packaged agricultural products storage	82	0	1	3.4
Loose or bagged agricultural products storage	57	0	0	1.1
Loose or baled tobacco storage	30	0	0	0.7
Wood or paper products storage (excluding timber or wood fuel)	663	1	12	35.7
Lumberyard or building materials storage	180	0	2	15.6
Paper or paper products storage	163	0	4	10.0
Wood products or furniture storage	112	0	3	2.8
Fiber products storage	27	0	0	1.2
Rolled paper storage	13	0	0	0.2
Unclassified wood or paper products storage	57	0	0	2.6
Unknown-type wood or paper products storage	110	0	2	3.3
Metal or metal products storage (excluding scrap yards)	498	0	3	18.3
Machinery storage	142	0	1	4.8
Hardware storage	110	0	0	4.3
Electrical appliance or supply storage	44	0	0	1.1
Basic metal form storage	39	0	0	1.9
Metal parts storage	38	0	1	1.9
Finished metal products storage	21	0	0	0.4
Unclassified metal or metal products storage	37	0	0	0.9
Unknown-type metal or metal products storage	66	0	0	3.1
Chemical or plastic or related products storage	270	1	8	49.2
Plastic or plastic product storage	43	0	0	4.1
Industrial chemical storage	42	0	2	31.7
Paint or varnish storage	38	0	1	2.3
Rubber or rubber products storage	35	0	1	2.2
Hazardous chemical storage	34	0	4	2.7
Fertilizer storage	15	0	0	0.3
Drug, cosmetic, or pharmaceutical storage	14	0	0	0.2
Photographic film storage	6	0	0	0.0
Unclassified chemical or plastic or related products storage	14	0	0	2.2
Unknown-type chemical or plastic or related products storage	29	0	0	3.4
Processed food or tobacco storage (not refrigerated)	172	0	3	4.0
Packaged foodstuff storage	76	0	1	1.8
Canned or bottled food or soft drink storage	29	0	1	0.7
Loose or bagged processed food storage	26	0	1	0.6
Packaged tobacco product storage	3	0	0	0.0
Bulk sugar storage	1	0	0	0.0
Bulk flour or starch storage	1	0	0	0.0
Unclassified processed food or tobacco storage	12	0	0	0.2
Unknown-type processed food or tobacco storage	24	0	0	0.6

continued

TABLE 20.16.1 Continued

Type of Storage Facility	*Fires*	*Civilian Deaths*	*Civilian Injuries*	*Direct Loss (in Millions of Dollars)*
Textile storage	140	0	1	5.6
Clothing or finished textile storage	47	0	0	0.6
Baled cotton storage	22	0	0	0.9
Cloth or yarn storage	12	0	0	0.2
Baled jute, flax, or mixed fiber storage	7	0	0	0.3
Leather or leather products storage	5	0	0	0.0
Baled silk or synthetic fiber storage	4	0	0	0.6
Fur, skin, or hair products storage	3	0	0	0.0
Baled wool or worsted storage	0	0	0	0.0
Unclassified textile storage	18	0	0	1.6
Unknown-type textile storage	22	0	0	1.3
Flammable or combustible gas or liquid storage (containerized)	34	0	0	1.4
Alcoholic beverage storage	18	0	0	0.5
Packaged petroleum products storage	16	0	0	0.9
REFRIGERATED STORAGE	63	0	0	3.6
Cold storage	46	0	0	2.0
Food locker plants	9	0	0	1.5
Ice storage	8	0	0	0.1
Total of warehouse-type properties	5552	3	73	240.8

Note: These are fires reported to U.S. municipal fire departments and so exclude fires reported only to federal or state agencies or industrial fire brigades. Fires, deaths, and injuries are estimated and direct property damage rounded to the nearest hundred thousand dollars. Sums may not equal totals due to rounding errors. Damage has not been adjusted for inflation.

Source: National estimates based on NFIRS and NFPA survey.

them from influencing the overall hazard classification. Examples of high-hazard materials are rubber tires, plastic products, combustible fibers, paper and paper products, hanging garments, carpeting, pesticides, flammable liquids and gases, and reactive chemicals. NFPA 13 details the specific sprinkler requirements for areas containing such commodities.

Flammable Aerosol Products. Flammable aerosol products pose an extreme hazard. When heated in a fire, the containers rupture, produce fireballs, and can rocket throughout the storage area. This results in the ignition of multiple fires that can quickly overwhelm the automatic sprinklers. Bulk storage of aerosols should meet the requirements of NFPA 30B, *Code for the Manufacture and Storage of Aerosol Products.* Smaller quantities of flammable aerosol storage should be segregated in a specially protected room or in flammable liquid storage cabinets.

A 1982 fire in a K-Mart distribution warehouse, located in Falls Township, Pennsylvania, vividly illustrated this hazard. The fire started in palletized storage of petroleum-liquid-based aerosol containers. Exploding aerosol cans quickly overwhelmed the automatic sprinklers and destroyed the 1.2 million ft^2 (111,500 m^2) distribution center.[2] The rapid spread of the fire was due in great part to rocketing aerosol cans that spread the fire throughout adjoining areas.

The 1982 K-Mart distribution warehouse fire is just one of many similar incidents that illustrates the need for proper segregation and protection of flammable aerosols. A single pallet of flammable aerosols is sufficient to burn a general storage warehouse to the ground. Such materials need to be stored in a special area with fire protection features designed in accordance with NFPA 30B.

Storage Arrangement

The arrangement of stored materials impacts the potential for fire spread. It also affects the efficiency of materials handling in the warehouse, and, unfortunately, this is where fire protection and materials-handling efficiency generally conflict with each other. Each feature that is desirable to enhance fire safety usually has a negative impact on the operating efficiency of the warehouse.

Aisles are required in storage areas to permit access by materials-handling equipment. For maximum storage efficiency, these aisles are normally as narrow as possible and spaced as far apart as possible. These same aisles provide access to the area for manual fire suppression operations during a fire and act as fire breaks between storage piles or racks. From a fire safety standpoint, wide aisles spaced at short intervals are preferred. Such arrangement permits maximum access to the area while decreasing the probability of fire spread across an aisle due to radiant heat or from a pile collapse. See Figure 20.16.1 for an example of a typical rack storage arrangement. Note that aisles

FIGURE 20.16.1 Typical Rack Storage Arrangement (Courtesy of Jeffrey Moore)

provide access for materials-handling equipment as well as acting as fire breaks between the storage racks.

Horizontal air spaces formed by the pallets in palletized storage create open channels that feed air into the center of the storage and serve as pathways for fire spread throughout the pile. Rack storage compounds this problem by exposing multiple surfaces of the storage, permitting them to burn simultaneously.

Storage height is another area where fire protection and materials-handling efficiency clash. In general, the higher the storage is stacked, the greater the fire control challenge. Higher storage means more surface area exposed to burning and a greater total quantity of fuel available. The rate of heat release will also be greater as the height of the storage is increased.

As storage expands and available warehouse space decreases, the trend is to increase the storage height. This can be done safely as long as the automatic sprinkler protection is designed to meet the additional challenge posed by the higher storage. Even one extra tier of storage can be enough to burn a warehouse to the ground if that extra tier increases the storage height beyond the protection capabilities of the sprinklers.

OPERATIONAL HAZARDS AND FIRE PREVENTION PRACTICES

Storage occupancies often encompass large open spaces occupied by only a few people. With few occupants in the area, fires in the incipient stage may go undetected for an extended time period, particularly in spaces not protected by automatic fire detection or suppression systems.

Common hazards and ignition sources generally associated with storage occupancies are incendiarism, hot work operations, failure of electrical equipment, careless disposal of smoking materials, and ignition from materials-handling equipment.

Incendiarism

Storage occupancies are vulnerable to incendiary acts because they often present an inviting target for those who wish to cause a great deal of damage and disruption. Often an arsonist can enter and start a fire without being detected. Even where security personnel are present but access is not tightly controlled, arsonists may ignite a fire in a location beyond their sight. Such fires can grow to disastrous proportions before detection, particularly if multiple fires are set.

Hot Work Operations

Hot work operations, such as cutting, welding, and grinding, should be prohibited in storage areas unless there is no other method of accomplishing the work. If hot work is conducted in a storage occupancy, extraordinary precautions must be taken to prevent ignition of the stored materials. Such operations should not begin until all combustible materials have been removed from the area or covered with a fire-retardant cover. Portable fire extinguishers or small hose lines should be ready for use before the operation begins. A fire watch must be present at all times during operation and for at least 30 minutes after its completion. Consideration should be given to using mechanical fastening devices and saws when repairing or replacing steel racks to avoid cutting or welding. All cutting and welding must be conducted in accordance with NFPA 51B, *Standard for Fire Prevention During Welding, Cutting, and Other Hot Work.*

Lighting and Heating Appliances

Sufficient clearance must be provided between storage and any lighting fixtures or heating appliances in the area. The appropriate NFPA standards, such as NFPA 70, *National Electrical Code*®, should be consulted to determine the minimum required distances from electrical equipment. Special care is needed when using temporary or portable lighting or heating appliances. Relevant NFPA codes and standards must be strictly observed for all types of heating and electrical distribution system equipment in storage areas.

Smoking

Smoking should be prohibited in storage areas. Effective implementation of a smoking control program requires facility management to conscientiously enforce the smoking prohibition and also provide a safe area for employees to smoke. Such areas should be confined to specific areas set aside from storage. The areas must be kept clean and appropriate disposal containers must be provided.

Housekeeping Practices

Proper housekeeping practices prevent the accumulation of combustible waste that can serve as the point of origin for a fire. Packing or unpacking operations generally result in the generation of significant quantities of loose packing materials such as paper, cardboard, and polystyrene beads or cocoons. Procedures must be in implemented to remove excess materials from the building before they pose a significant hazard.

Idle Pallet Storage

Piles of empty wooden pallets are an ideal configuration for rapid development of a fire. The pile is essentially multiple layers of combustible fuel each separated by a layer of air. The built-in flues provide a means for fire to spread throughout the pile and for air to carry oxygen to the layers of burning fuel. Their large surface area to mass ratio also makes the pallets easy to ignite. Plastic pallets and shipping containers present similar hazards. Empty pallet storage poses a severe threat of a fast-developing fire. Even where stored in areas protected by automatic sprinklers, idle pallet fires can cause extensive damage. Pallet pile sizes should be limited, and the pallets should preferably be stored outside, away from any buildings (Figure 20.16.2). If pallets must be stored inside the building, they should be in a segregated area with automatic sprinklers designed for such storage. NFPA 13 contains special provisions for the design of sprinklers to protect idle pallet storage.

Industrial (Lift) Trucks

Industrial trucks, also called lift trucks or forklifts, are an integral part of most storage occupancies. The trucks are usually electric or propane powered, although some may use other fuels. Misuse of the trucks can result in their being an ignition source.

FIGURE 20.16.2 Idle Pallet Storage Should Be Away from Buildings. Here the pallet storage poses a severe threat to the building. (Courtesy of Jeffrey Moore)

There have been many multimillion dollar losses caused by the improper use or application of industrial lift trucks.

The general hazards associated with the use of lift trucks are refueling operations, maintenance, and storage when not in use. Refueling operations should be conducted outside or in a segregated area of the storage building or warehouse. Fuel leakage during refueling operations has been the cause of many fires. Storage and dispensing of the fuel must comply with applicable NFPA codes and standards. Lift trucks used in areas where flammable or combustible liquids are stored must be specifically listed for use in such areas. NFPA 505, *Fire Safety Standard for Powered Industrial Trucks Including Type Designations, Areas of Use, Conversions, Maintenance, and Operations,* designates the type of truck that can be used in a hazardous area.

LIFE SAFETY CONSIDERATIONS

The life safety hazard in a storage occupancy depends on a number of factors. These include the materials stored, the storage configuration, construction of the building, the type and design of the fire protection systems provided, and the number, arrangement, and location of the exits provided. Fire in a storage area can develop and spread rapidly. Although the occupant load is generally light in a storage occupancy, the means of emergency egress is a concern. In single-story buildings with high ceilings, smoke and heat may have a place to accumulate before descending to a level that obscures or obstructs the means of egress. In buildings with low ceilings, the opposite occurs. In multilevel buildings, smoke and heat from fires below can rapidly block a means of egress on an upper level. (The thermal gradient normally causes the smoke and products of combustion to rise to the ceiling.) In buildings protected by automatic sprinklers, operation of the sprinklers may contain the spread of fire, but it also usually upsets the thermal gradient in the space. This can cause smoke to hang close to the floor, disrupting egress from the area.

In older multiple-floor warehouses, unprotected vertical openings for freight elevators and other materials-handling systems are common. These permit rapid smoke and heat spread to upper floors.

Egress Design

NFPA *101*®, *Life Safety Code*®, and *NFPA 5000*®, *Building Construction and Safety Code*®, address life safety from fire and similar emergencies. They detail the features required to provide the minimum level of fire safety to occupants of a storage or warehouse occupancy, including the number of exits required and the arrangement of the means of egress.

NFPA *101* and *NFPA 5000* classify the materials stored in a warehouse or storage occupancy as low-, ordinary-, or high-hazard based on the expected speed of fire development. The codes contain significantly different requirements for different hazard classifications. For example, the maximum travel distance to an exit in a warehouse with low-hazard contents is essentially unlimited, whereas the maximum travel distance to an exit in a warehouse with high-hazard contents is 100 ft (30 m) where sprinklers are provided, and 75 ft (23 m) where the building is nonsprinklered. Where a warehouse or storage area contains storage of different classifications in the same area, the requirements for the most hazardous classification apply. Sound judgment must be used when determining the hazard classification of the contents. NFPA *101* and *NFPA 5000* use ordinary-hazard as the basis for general requirements; most storage occupancies fall into this classification. Only rarely does storage fall into the low- or high-hazard classifications.

The requirements for the means of egress in storage occupancies are similar to other occupancies. The principal difference is that storage occupancies typically require fewer exits than other occupancies. Since storage areas and warehouses generally have few occupants, neither NFPA *101* nor *NFPA 5000* assigns occupant load factors to such uses. Rather, occupant load is based on the maximum probable number of occupants present at any time. NFPA *101* or *NFPA 5000* should be consulted to determine the specific arrangement of the means of egress.

Exit doors must remain unlocked from the egress side of the door when the building is occupied. In areas of low- and ordinary-hazard contents, special-listed delayed-egress locks are permitted if an approved automatic fire detection or supervised sprinkler system protects the entire building. Access controlled egress doors are permitted, provided they meet specific requirements in NFPA *101* and *NFPA 5000.* Egress doors from areas of high-hazard contents must swing in the direction of egress travel.

The continual movement of stock within a storage occupancy demands special attention to prevent blocking required means of egress aisles and doors.

Exit Identification

All required exits must be marked as required by NFPA *101* and *NFPA 5000.* The signs must identify the means of egress, exit locations, and be readily visible where the direction of exit access is not obvious. In areas with high-piled storage, exit identification can be a problem. In addition to signage, other means of egress marking may be necessary, such as painting egress travel paths on the floor.

Illumination of the means of egress is also required. This is particularly important in windowless buildings where natural light is not available during all occupied times. Emergency lights must be installed to provide illumination of required egress stairs, aisles, corridors, ramps, and passageways. NFPA *101* and *NFPA 5000* detail the specific requirements for means of egress illumination.

Vertical Openings

Vertical openings, such as conveyor openings in multistory buildings, must be provided with automatically closing fire doors, fire shutters, or fire dampers on each opening. Convenience openings are permitted provided they connect not more than two stories (they pierce only one floor), are separated by a fire barrier from unprotected vertical openings serving other floors, are separated from corridors, and do not serve as a required exit.

Fire Alarm Systems

Although a fire alarm system is often provided in a warehouse or storage occupancy due to property protection concerns, a fire alarm system is not generally required in warehouses to meet the requirements of NFPA *101* or *NFPA 5000,* unless the warehouse stores high-hazard commodities or exceeds 100,000 ft^2 (9300 m^2). However, due to the large areas and the limited number of employees that may be working in widely scattered areas of the building, a fire alarm system should be considered to alert all occupants in the event of a fire. A fire alarm system provides timely notification of building occupants who can then initiate emergency action and notify the fire department or private fire brigade.

Fire alarm systems for occupant notification must include audible and visible notification appliances installed in accordance with *NFPA 72®*, *National Fire Alarm Code ®*. Fire alarm system actuation may be manual, through the use of manual fire alarm boxes, or automatic, through the use of fire detectors or sprinkler waterflow alarms. Fire alarm systems must be installed, tested, and maintained in accordance with *NFPA 72*. The fire alarm signal must be separate and distinct from any other audible signals used in the facility. All new fire alarm systems must use the American National Standard evacuation signal to initiate evacuation as required by *NFPA 72*, unless otherwise permitted by the authority having jurisdiction.

BUILDING CONSTRUCTION AFFECTING HAZARDOUS CONDITIONS

Most construction types are suitable for a storage occupancy, although the use of noncombustible construction is preferred. Combustible construction, although permitted by most building codes, adds to the fire load and may contain combustible concealed spaces that contribute to rapid fire spread.

Materials

The combustibility, flame spread rate, smoke production, heat release potential, and structural stability of materials used in building construction should all be considered. Certain expanded plastic insulation core panel walls should be used only in buildings with automatic sprinkler protection, and the panels should be covered with fire-resistant material. Most building codes limit the use of exposed, expanded foam plastic insulation. Lightweight steel and wood truss construction now commonly used in newer buildings is susceptible to early structural collapse when exposed to an intense fire as is expected in most storage occupancies. Steel columns within storage racks over 15 ft (4.6 m) high may require additional protection, such as automatic sprinklers installed in the column web or enclosing the columns in fire-rated construction.

The rack structures used in automated storage and retrieval systems may double as the structural frame of the building. Properly designed, installed, and maintained automatic sprinkler protection is necessary to prevent extensive damage or total destruction of storage buildings using any of these lightweight methods of construction.

Buildings up to 100 ft (30 m) high used for such rack storage are not uncommon. Fully automated rack systems usually have narrow aisles between racks. Providing fire suppression within the racks may be difficult even in buildings protected by automatic sprinklers. Fires involving upper portions of high-rack storage present unusual problems and severe risks to fire suppression forces. Access to the upper portion for complete extinguishment and overhaul is limited. Using ground ladders inside buildings is difficult, dangerous, and generally limited to the length of a typical fire department ground ladder, about 35 ft (10.5 m). Storage damaged by the fire or wetted by sprinklers and hose streams often falls from the racks blocking aisles and posing a hazard to fire fighters.

Smoke and Heat Venting

Smoke and steam generated during a fire can obscure visibility, making it difficult for fire suppression forces to locate the fire. Venting aids in smoke removal, which, in turn, aids fire-fighting operations and rescue. Installation of heat and smoke vents in storage occupancies provides a method for fire fighters to vent accumulated heat and smoke from the building. The vents may be automatic or manually operated. Although there is some disagreement between various fire protection groups, the vents installed in buildings protected by automatic sprinklers should generally be arranged for manual operation because the sprinkler design criteria in NFPA 13 are based on a building without automatic venting. In buildings without automatic sprinkler protection, venting combined with draft curtains or curtain boards can reduce the horizontal smoke and heat spread along the ceiling. In some cases roof vents may be supplemented or replaced by mechanical heat and smoke exhaust systems. Special mechanical ventilation systems should be considered for large-area storage occupancies. The systems should be designed and installed in accordance with NFPA 92A, *Standard for Smoke-Control Systems Utilizing Barriers and Pressure Differences.* See Section 18, Chapter 4, "Venting Practices."

Smoke and heat venting facilities, as well as automatic sprinkler protection, are essential for life safety in windowless buildings and underground structures. The installation of smoke and heat venting should be in accordance with NFPA 204, *Standard for Smoke and Heat Venting.*

Separation

Buildings used for both manufacturing and warehousing should be separated by properly constructed fire walls with all openings protected by automatic closing fire doors. Incidental areas, such as boiler rooms, maintenance areas, and offices, should also be separated from storage areas by rated fire barriers. The rating depends on the requirements of the applicable codes and standards, and the site-specific fire risk management objectives.

AUTOMATIC SPRINKLER PROTECTION

Automatic sprinkler protection, supplemented by manual fire-fighting operations and sound storage and housekeeping practices, is a proven effective and practical means of protecting warehouse and storage occupancies from fire. The automatic sprinklers for a warehouse or storage occupancy must be specifically engineered to match the hazards posed by the storage, installed in accordance with NFPA 13, and inspected, tested, and maintained in accordance with NFPA 25, *Standard for the Inspection, Testing, and Maintenance of Water-Based Fire Protection Systems.*

Basic Approaches

Current automatic sprinkler technology provides three basic approaches to providing sprinkler protection of storage operations: standard spray sprinklers, large drop sprinklers, and early suppression fast response (ESFR) sprinklers.

Standard Spray Sprinklers. The standard spray sprinkler category includes standard orifice, large orifice, and extra large orifice (ELO) sprinklers. Any of these sprinklers may be equipped with fusible elements for standard response or fast response.

Large Drop Sprinklers. Large drop sprinklers produce much larger water droplets with more mass to better penetrate a fire plume and reach the seat of high-challenge fires, such as those involving rubber tires or roll paper. The standard spray sprinkler and large drop sprinkler are designed to control a fire and limit its spread until the arrival of a trained fire suppression force that can extinguish the fire.

EFSR Sprinklers. The ESFR sprinkler incorporates a fast response operating element and a large orifice. They are designed to operate at relatively high pressures and discharge up to 175 gpm (662 L/min) each during the initial stages of a fire. The ESFR sprinkler is the only sprinkler designed to extinguish a fire. Refer to Section 16, "Water-Based Fire Suppression Equipment," for more detailed discussions regarding the design and operation of the various types of sprinklers and sprinkler systems.

Most building codes require automatic sprinkler systems in high-hazard storage occupancies. Some codes require sprinkler protection when materials are stored in racks or piles more than 12 ft (3.7 m) high. Most building codes permit low- and ordinary-hazard storage buildings of unlimited floor area when they are protected by sprinkler systems.

Effective Sprinkler Operation

Properly designed automatic sprinkler protection is essential to control a fire and limit damage in a warehouse or storage occupancy. It follows then that a major factor contributing to large-loss fires in warehouses and storage areas is the inability of the sprinkler system to control the fire. This may result from a change in the type, volume, height, or configuration of storage that raises the hazard level beyond that for which the sprinkler system was designed. Any change in the storage or configuration must be accompanied by a comprehensive hazard analysis to assure the change does not outstrip the capabilities of the sprinkler system.

Impairment of the sprinkler system, such as broken piping, shut valve, or piping obstruction, may prevent the sprinklers from controlling the fire. Many serious fires have occurred during periods of sprinkler shutdown. Facility managers must implement an effective impairment-handling program that limits the number, extent, and duration of sprinkler system impairments. Complying with the requirements of NFPA 25 minimizes the probability of sprinkler system impairment when a fire occurs.

SUPPLEMENTAL FIRE PROTECTION

Although they are the most important fire protection feature, automatic sprinklers are not the only fire protection necessary for a fully protected warehouse or storage occupancy. Although sprinklers may extinguish a fire, most sprinkler systems are designed to control a fire until trained fire suppression personnel can extinguish it with portable fire extinguishers or hose lines. Other provisions, such as hose systems, portable extinguishers, and effective prefire planning and fire prevention efforts are essential ingredients of any complete warehouse fire safety program.

Large and Small Hose

Warehouses of moderate area close to public hydrants present no special manual fire suppression problems. Where the smaller dimension of a warehouse exceeds about 200 ft (61 m), hose lays from public hydrants to the far side of the building are difficult and time-consuming. Strategically located private hydrants on the building perimeter near building access doors are important to the overall facility fire protection plan. Private hydrant spacing of 250 ft (76 m) is common in such situations. NFPA 24, *Standard for the Installation of Private Fire Service Mains and Their Appurtenances,* provides guidance on the number and location of private hydrants.

Indoor hose connections are recommended in high-piled or rack storage buildings for use on incipient fires. Their relatively good reach and unlimited supply make them more effective than portable fire extinguishers in most situations. However, they do not eliminate the need for portable fire extinguishers. Although not a requirement, the supply for hose connections should come from a system separate from the automatic sprinklers protecting the area. This permits the hose connections to remain in service even if the sprinkler system must be shut down for inspection, testing, or repair.

Provision of interior hose connections requires that the connections, nozzles, and attached hose be inspected, tested, and maintained in accordance with NFPA 25. OSHA regulations require that occupants expected to use the hoses during a fire be trained in their use.

Multistory, large-area, and high-hazard warehouses should be equipped with a standpipe system. A Class III standpipe system provides 1½ in. (38 mm) hose lines for use by building occupants trained in their use and a 2½ in. (64 mm) connection for use by the fire department or a fire brigade. Connections should be located so that all portions of the area can be reached. Providing hose connections for high-rack systems, particularly automated storage and retrieval systems, requires special consideration. In addition to connections at floor level, additional connections may be needed at various heights to enable hose lines to reach all levels. Standpipe systems should be installed in accordance with NFPA 14, *Standard for the Installation of Standpipe and Hose Systems.*

Portable Fire Extinguishers

Portable fire extinguishers should be located throughout the premises in accordance with NFPA 10, *Standard for Portable Fire Extinguishers.* They can be effective during the incipient stages of a fire if used by properly trained operators. All employees should be familiar with the locations and use of portable fire extinguishers. Extinguishers should be in visible, readily accessible locations. Employee training should stress the importance of sounding an alarm and notifying the fire department before attempting to fight a fire with portable fire extinguishers. Up to half the required extinguishers may be replaced by hose connections equipped with hose and a nozzle.

Pre-Emergency Planning

Action in an emergency is seldom effective unless it is carefully planned and executed. Facility management must develop a program that identifies the types of fires and other emergencies likely to occur in the facility. The plans should detail how employees should respond to each type of incident. A program must then be implemented to train employees in the proper methods of response to each type of emergency.

In most cases, employees are not expected to respond to fires and participate in fire suppression operations beyond the incipient stage. Nevertheless, certain information will assist warehouse personnel to understand the interrelationship between fire protection systems and manual fire-fighting operations.

Fire tests and actual fire experience show that even when automatic sprinklers are properly designed and are successful in controlling a warehouse fire, they will not usually extinguish a fire. Personnel trained and equipped for manual fire suppression operations must accomplish final extinguishment. This may be the facility fire brigade, the public fire department, or a combination of the two. Even under the most favorable conditions this is a challenging task that requires careful planning, training of employees, and coordination with public response agencies.

OSHA regulations require that all facilities with more than ten employees have a written emergency action plan (EAP). The plan must identify and explain emergency egress routes and any required emergency procedures. Emergency procedures might include the shutdown of hazardous processes, closure of fire doors, or other operations that make the facility safer during a fire. If specific employees are designated to remain behind to complete critical tasks until their evacuation becomes necessary, the EAP must detail these requirements. The plan must also include procedures to account for employees after building evacuation. Employees must be given the names and contact information for individuals who have additional information about the plan. The employer is also required to review the plan with each employee at the time of development or at the time of initial job assignment. Facility managers should consult 29 CFR 1910 Subpart E for the complete OSHA requirements related to emergency planning.

All planning should be developed in coordination with the public agencies that respond to the facility during an emergency. Plans that are not developed and practiced with the cooperation of the public fire department are unlikely to be effective during an actual emergency. A later section of this chapter provides detailed information for use by fire brigades and public fire departments in developing prefire plans for warehouse and storage occupancies. NFPA 600, *Standard on Industrial Fire Brigades,* and NFPA 1620, *Recommended Practice for Pre-Incident Planning,* should be consulted for additional guidance.

Fire Prevention

Fire prevention efforts to eliminate common sources of ignition are the most effective method of limiting fire loss in warehouses and storage occupancies. Among the leading causes of fires in storage facilities are incendiarism or arson; open flames; exposure to fire from another structure, such as an adjoining building; malfunction or failure of electrical distribution equipment, particularly wiring; and heating equipment. Table 20.16.2 shows the leading causes of warehouse fires.

Fire prevention efforts should be directed toward reducing or eliminating any potential sources of ignition in the warehouse or storage area. This should include proper installation and maintenance of electrical equipment, prohibition of smoking and other sources of open flames, limiting access by unauthorized personnel, and proper installation and maintenance of heating equipment. Facility management should make routine tours of the warehouse to look for and correct any potential ignition sources.

SPECIAL STORAGE FACILITIES

Cold Storage

Cold-storage warehouses are used primarily for extended storage of food and other products at temperatures that prevent or retard spoilage. Products such as pharmaceuticals, antibiotics, and unstable chemicals may also require refrigerated storage.

Depending on the products or processes involved, cold-storage warehouse temperatures may reach a low of –50°F (–46°C) or lower. Despite low temperatures, cold-storage warehouses are not immune to fire hazards. Low temperatures present unusual fire prevention and control problems. Combustible materials in such warehouses include cork or expanded plastic insulation; wood dunnage, pallets, boxes, and baskets; fiberboard containers; paper and cloth wrapping; plastic containers and boxes; and grease- or wax-impregnated materials. These pose a large loss potential.

Construction. Refrigerated warehouses may be constructed of combustible or noncombustible material or a combination of both. The current trend is to build larger and higher buildings in which automated storage racks are structural units supporting the walls and roofs of the buildings. Such construction is acceptable if the rack structure supports wind and snow loads. Although the structural materials themselves are noncombustible, such buildings must be properly sprinklered to protect both the structure and the stored material. When cork or foam insulation ignites, it can generate temperatures high enough to weaken structural steel members.

Polyurethane foam, either in sheets or foamed-in-place, and polystyrene foam are two common insulation materials. When used in walls or ceilings, these materials should be protected by an approved thermal barrier or by a ½ in. (12.7 mm) coat of cement plaster on metal lath attached to the building's framing. For polystyrene, the barrier also may be either ½ in. (12.7 mm) Type X gypsum wallboard or ¾ in. (19 mm) fire-retardant plywood supported by studs or furring attached to the framing. To meet sanitary standards, these thermal barriers must be coated with a U.S. Department of Agriculture (USDA) approved washable finish. If used in the floor, the insulation should be covered with concrete and the joint between floor and wall provided with a cove or curb. Automatic sprinklers should be provided below suspended ceilings, and the space above the ceiling should be protected against fire spread and sprinklered if combustible.

Refrigerant Gases. Refrigerant gases present two basic hazards: toxicity and flammability. Sprinklers are very effective at mitigating the fire hazard because the spray dilutes, disperses, and cools escaping gases.

Storage Arrangements. As in other warehouses, storage arrangements in refrigerated warehouses can be in bulk, solid piling, palletized, or in racks. One exception to this arrangement is the hook storage of meat and poultry products awaiting further processing. This storage method poses a minimal fire hazard because of the absence of combustible packaging.

Sprinkler Protection. The same sprinkler system design used for nonrefrigerated buildings is appropriate for refrigerated storage, except that it must be a dry-pipe or other nonfreeze-type system. In chill rooms and coolers, sprinkler systems of the electrically operated pre-action type are preferable to dry-pipe systems. In freezers or holding rooms, systems are often a combination preaction/dry-pipe system. Figure 20.16.3 shows such a system. In this system, a ⅛ in. (3.2 mm) orifice in a bypass maintains water pressure under the dry-pipe valve. A deluge valve holds back the main water supply. A separate fire detection system electrically activates the valve. Where racks are used for storage, it may be necessary to use in-rack sprinklers.

All sprinklers in refrigerated warehouses should be designed and installed in accordance with NFPA 13. They should be designed so that they can be easily inspected and disassembled to remove ice plugs that commonly form due to moisture condensation in the piping.

The combination dry-pipe deluge system shown in Figure 20.16.3 minimizes the potential for filling the piping with water should there be accidental actuation of a dry-pipe valve. When this arrangement is used, note the following requirements:

1. The dry system should be manifolded to the deluge valve.
2. The protected area should not exceed 40,000 ft^2 (3716 m^2).
3. The distance between valves should be as short as possible.

TABLE 20.16.2 Reported U.S. General Warehouse Structure Fires, 1994–1998 Average Annual Values, by Form of Heat of Ignition

Form of Heat of Ignition	*Fires*	*Percentage*	*Civilian Deaths*	*Percentage*	*Civilian Injuries*	*Percentage*	*Direct Property Damage (in Millions of Dollars)*	*Percentage*
Electric-powered equipment	310	23.2	0	22.1	9	34.3	18.3	23.7
Exposure fire	196	14.6	0	0.0	0	0.0	3.1	4.0
Match	114	8.6	0	0.0	1	2.9	4.7	6.1
Lighted tobacco product	103	7.7	0	0.0	1	4.9	14.0	18.1
Torch	101	7.5	0	0.0	6	24.5	13.3	17.2
Unclassified or unknown-type open flame	80	6.0	0	0.0	0	1.0	3.3	4.3
Gas-fueled equipment	64	4.8	0	0.0	1	5.9	2.6	3.4
Open fire	63	4.7	0	0.0	0	2.0	1.8	2.3
Rekindle or reignition	40	3.0	0	0.0	0	0.0	1.2	1.5
Spontaneous ignition or chemical reaction	35	2.6	0	0.0	0	1.0	1.4	1.8
Lightning	29	2.1	0	0.0	0	0.0	2.4	3.1
Electric lamp	22	1.6	0	0.0	0	0.0	0.4	0.6
Solid-fueled equipment	20	1.5	0	0.0	0	0.0	0.3	0.5
Liquid-fueled equipment	19	1.4	1	77.9	0	2.0	0.1	0.1
Unclassified form of heat	17	1.3	0	0.0	0	0.0	0.6	0.8
Lighter	17	1.2	0	0.0	0	0.0	1.6	2.0
Incendiary device	16	1.2	0	0.0	0	0.0	1.9	2.5
Multiple forms of heat	16	1.2	0	0.0	1	3.9	5.3	6.8
Heat or spark from friction	14	1.1	0	0.0	0	0.0	0.4	0.5
Unclassified or unknown-type hot object	14	1.1	0	0.0	1	2.9	0.1	0.1
Hot ember or ash	12	0.9	0	0.0	1	3.9	0.0	0.0
Other or unknown-type fueled equipment	11	0.8	0	0.0	0	0.0	0.1	0.2
Molten or hot material	6	0.5	0	0.0	0	0.0	0.2	0.3
Other known form of heat of ignition	18	1.4	0	0.0	3	10.8	0.1	0.2
Total	1338	100.0	1	100.0	25	100.0	77.3	100.0

Note: These are fires reported to U.S. municipal fire departments and so exclude fires reported only to federal or state agencies or industrial fire brigades. Fires, deaths, and injuries are estimated and direct property damage rounded to the nearest hundred thousand dollars. Sums may not equal totals due to rounding errors. Percentages are based on the total number of fires reported between 1994 and 1998 and not on the total annual average in the table. Damage has not been adjusted for inflation.

Source: National estimates based on NFIRS and NFPA survey.

4. The chamber between deluge and dry-pipe valves should be pressurized from the supply side of the deluge valve.
5. An approved ball drip valve should be installed on the dry-pipe valve.

Properly located heat detectors in the protected area automatically actuate the deluge valve. An electrically actuated deluge valve is preferred.

Figure 20.16.4 shows an acceptable alternative to the deluge valve/dry-pipe valve combination. Approved equipment should be used throughout, and all electrical equipment should be compatible. The piping to the heat-actuated devices should be supervised. The control piping should be arranged so both loss of sprinkler piping air pressure and operation of a heat-actuated device occur before the deluge valve release mechanism operates.

Piers and Wharves

Warehouses often form the superstructure of piers and wharves. They may be called "sheds" and often project great distances over the water. They share the same general characteristics as other warehouses, but present more fire protection and suppression problems. Among these are reduced accessibility for land-based fire department vehicles; the usual combustible nature of the substructures, which can be exposed to floating burning debris

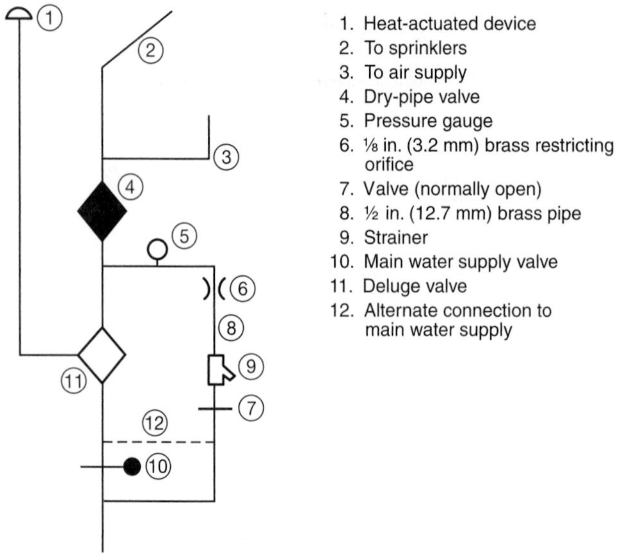

FIGURE 20.16.3 Piping to a Combination Dry-Pipe Preaction Sprinkler System

or flammable liquids; the danger of water supply mains freezing; and the hazard of ships colliding with piers. More favorably, commodities tend to be piled low because of the temporary, transfer nature of the storage—that is, ship-to-shore or shore-to-ship.

NFPA 307, *Standard for the Construction and Fire Protection of Marine Terminals, Piers, and Wharves,* requires a water supply for both hose streams and sprinkler systems to be available for at least 4 hours—about double the usual requirement. To protect the combustible underside of the pier, sprinklers should be either standard pendant sprinklers in the upright position or old-style sprinklers in the upright position to wet the undersurface of the substructure.

Parking Garages

There are two types of parking garages: those in which vehicles are parked exclusively by attendants or mechanical means and those in which customers park the vehicles. NFPA *101* and *NFPA 5000* address the egress requirements of garages in which the customer parks the vehicle.

For more information on parking garages, see NFPA 88A, *Standard for Parking Structures.*

Occupancy Characteristics. Parking garages may be several levels above or below grade and may be enclosed or open. A garage is considered open when there are uniformly distributed openings in exterior walls on not less than two sides totaling not less than 40 percent of the building perimeter.

Parking garages are often found in conjunction with other uses, such as hotels, apartments, and office buildings. In garages used for both parking and repairs, the repair area should be separated from the parking area and treated as an industrial occupancy.

Hazards Associated with Garages. Motor vehicles generally contain fast-burning fuels, including gasoline, diesel fuel,

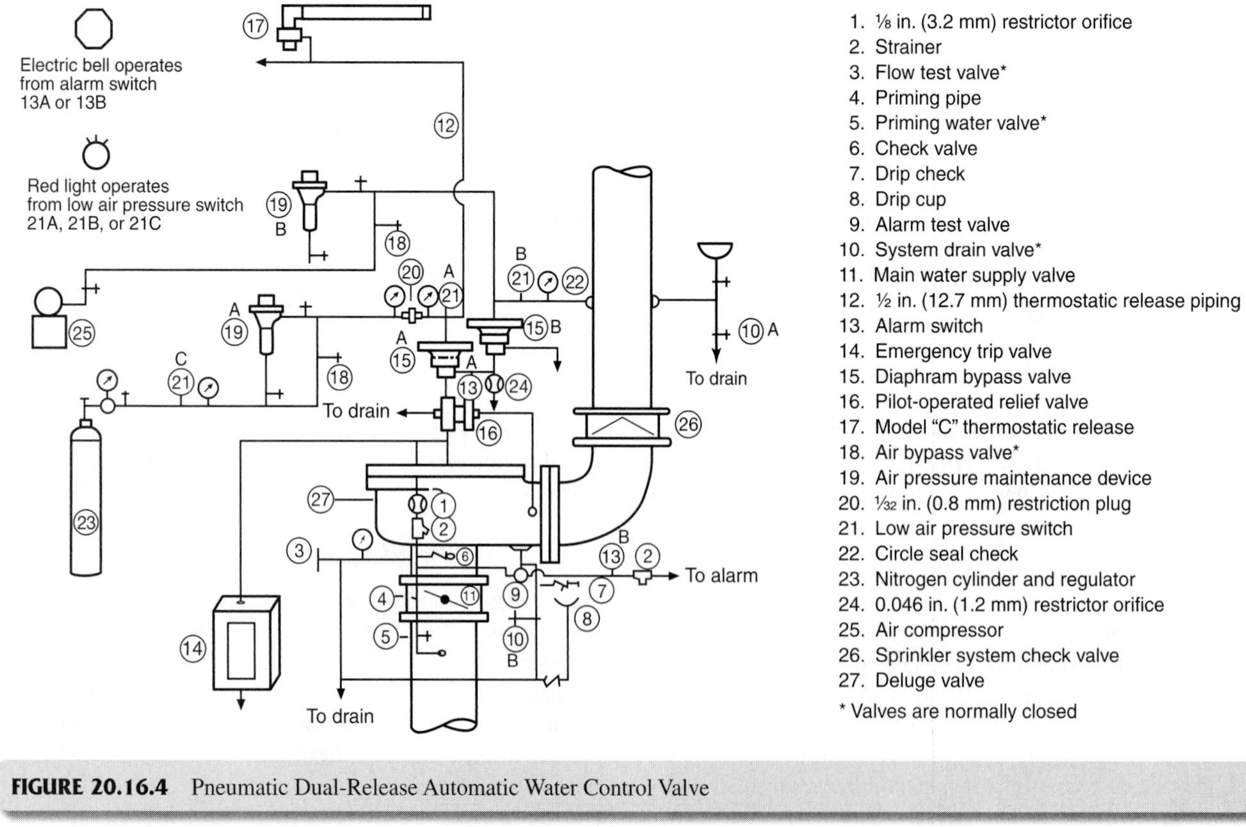

FIGURE 20.16.4 Pneumatic Dual-Release Automatic Water Control Valve

or LP-gas. Major parts of newer model vehicles are made of plastic. These materials can cause severe fires that produce copious amounts of smoke. Gasoline is dispensed in some garages. NFPA 30A, *Code for Motor Fuel Dispensing Facilities and Repair Garages,* and NFPA 88A list requirements for this type of operation. In addition, NFPA *101* and *NFPA 5000* contain special requirements for garages where gasoline is dispensed.

Only a few persons at any one time usually occupy parking garages. However, structures that are located near large assembly occupancies, such as civic centers or theaters, can be occupied by a large number of persons at one time after a show or event ends. During this time, many people move throughout the structure, either going to their vehicles or waiting in their vehicles to exit the parking garage.

Life Safety Considerations. Every floor level of a parking structure must have access to at least two separate exits, arranged so that the travel path is in two different directions. Vehicle ramps can serve as exit access under special conditions. The travel distance permitted to reach an exit depends on whether the building is open or enclosed and whether automatic sprinklers protect the garage.

Special consideration must be given to the location of fuel pumps to avoid trapping occupants if there is a fire or explosion at the pumps. Travel in any direction must lead to an outside exit at the same level or to properly arranged egress stairs. Where parking areas are located below gasoline dispensing pumps, each floor must have direct access to the outside. This arrangement minimizes the potential for gasoline vapor accumulation in enclosed exit stairs.

The means of egress should be provided with illumination and emergency lighting when the garage is used at night or has no natural lighting from windows or other openings during the day. Most people using a parking garage are unfamiliar with the location of exits. Exits and access to the exits must be marked and identified.

Enclosed parking garages must have a fire alarm system when the total aggregate floor area exceeds 100,000 ft^2 (9300 m^2). Open-air parking structures and parking structures protected throughout by an approved automatic sprinkler system do not require fire alarm systems. In general, automatic sprinkler protection is required in enclosed garages located below grade and in those over 75 ft (23 m) in height.

Grain and Other Bulk Storage Elevators

Grain and other bulk storage elevators structures move, store, and process grain, such as wheat, corn, oats, soybeans, and sunflower seeds (Figure 20.16.5). Commodities are stored in bulk form in concrete and steel silos, wooden bins, and steel tanks. Handling the commodity generates dust, making the grain stream susceptible to fire and explosion. NFPA 61, *Standard for the Prevention of Fires and Dust Explosions in Agricultural and Food Processing Facilities,* lists fire protection and

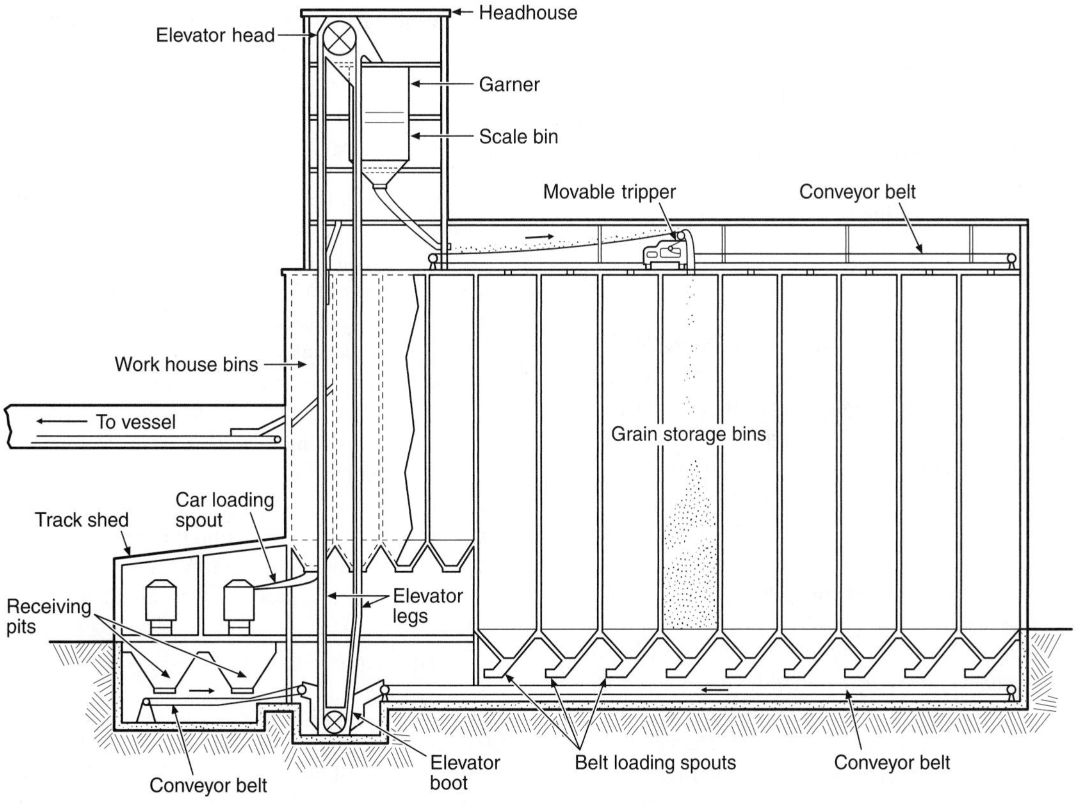

FIGURE 20.16.5 Grain and Bulk Storage Elevator

safety requirements for the installation and operation of grain elevators.

Structures of this type are unique and particularly dangerous. They pose serious life safety hazards for all occupants. Grain elevators account for some of the largest loss-of-life incidents in storage occupancies. In many dust explosions, the primary or only means of exiting from the upper parts of an elevator may be damaged or destroyed by the initial explosion, trapping workers on top of the structure.

NFPA *101* addresses life safety considerations based on the occurrence of fires. Basic life safety requirements require that at least two means of egress be available. The exits must be arranged to be remote from each other. These means of egress should be available from all working areas and from the headhouse located on top of the storage structure. All working areas should have access to at least one stairway leading to an exit discharge point at ground level. This stairway should be constructed within a dust- and fire-rated enclosure.

In addition to the stairway, an alternative means of escape is required. This secondary means should provide a continuous path to the ground from the top of the elevator structure, but it need not meet all provisions for a means of egress. This secondary escape can consist of exterior stairs or basket-type ladders accessible from all working levels of the headhouse. This escape means provides passage to the ground or to the top of adjoining structures.

An exterior stair or basket-type ladder should be provided from the top of storage structures such as silos, conveyors, galleries, and gantries. This secondary escape should be located at the end of the structure opposite the headhouse.

Most grain elevators have underground passages for conveyors beneath the silos. These spaces should have at least two means of egress without dead ends. One means of egress can be a ladder or other escape method that leads to a window, hatch, or panel that can be opened to permit escape.

For more information on grain elevators, see Section 9, Chapter 7, "Storage and Handling of Grain Mill Products."

Aircraft Hangars

An aircraft hangar is a structure for the storage or maintenance of aircraft. Because it is generally impractical to remove all fuel from aircraft before moving them into a hangar, large quantities of flammable or combustible liquids are usually present inside the structure. Some maintenance procedures use highly flammable solvents and unstable toxic chemicals. Fire during maintenance and servicing operations can pose hazards to personnel in the hangar and potentially endanger aircraft worth millions of dollars. Special precautions for ventilation and control of ignition sources are needed.

Aircraft hangars provide a particular challenge when designing adequate exiting and egress facilities. The large open area needed for aircraft, especially commercial airliners, requires extended travel distances to reach exits. The presence of flammable and combustible liquids compounds this problem. Exits must be located at intervals not exceeding 150 ft (46 m) along all exterior walls of the hangar. Each part of the hangar or servicing area must have access to at least two exit locations. If approved interior horizontal exits are provided, then exit locations along the wall must be provided at intervals not exceeding 100 ft (30 m). Since a large hangar door cannot be left open in poor weather, small access doors can be installed in hangar doors. Egress from mezzanines must be arranged so that an exit can be reached within a maximum travel distance of 75 ft (23 m). These exits must lead directly to an approved enclosed stairway that discharges directly to the outside, to another fire-separated area, or to outside stairs.

For life safety purposes, a fire alarm system is required in hangars not protected by automatic sprinkler systems if the total floor area exceeds 100,000 ft^2 (9300 m^2). For additional requirements related to constructing and protecting aircraft hangars from fire, refer to NFPA 409, *Standard on Aircraft Hangars.*

Isolated Storage Buildings

Some high-value warehouses are needed for only a few years, such as those for construction projects in remote areas. At times, these warehouses may contain large quantities of electrical and electronic equipment, wire, cables, fixtures, and production equipment. Experimental or mining sites may also have large warehouses. These remote areas often lack public water mains or fire departments. Several factors must be weighed, such as the importance of the building to the project and the time needed to replace vital contents. Standards and building codes do not apply rigidly in these situations. Good loss prevention and control practice is to separate unprotected warehouses into small units, to provide fully adequate private protection, or to compromise and use protection systems with a limited water supply. Increased vigilance over guard service, housekeeping, maintenance, and smoking control should accompany any compromised physical protection.

Underground Storage

Large underground warehouses can be a boon to energy conservation because rock caverns have a nearly constant temperature and humidity. In the United States, some caverns have stored compressed gas, and old mines are used for records storage. Caves used for warehousing and storage should be protected with automatic sprinklers.

In general, the problems associated with underground structures include egress, venting smoke and heat, and limited access for fire fighting. Automatic sprinkler protection installed under constructed floors and ceilings is vital to protect combustible storage and personnel. NFPA 520, *Standard on Subterranean Spaces,* provides minimum requirements for the design, operation, and maintenance of developed subterranean spaces for safety to life and property from fire and similar hazards.

Air-Supported Structures

For warehousing in temporary or remote locations, such as at construction sites, or as a low-cost adjunct to more permanent conventional buildings, large air-supported structures are sometimes used (Figures 20.16.6 and 20.16.7). These structures are plastic-coated fabric envelopes resembling balloons and are kept rigid by internal positive air pressure. Structures less than

FIGURE 20.16.6 Typical Air-Supported Structure Suitable for Warehouse Purposes (Source: Air Structures American Technologies, Inc.)

FIGURE 20.16.7 Interior of a 100 ft by 300 ft (30 m by 91 m) Air-Supported Warehouse Showing Storage (Source: Air Structures American Technologies, Inc.)

150 ft (46 m) in width or diameter should comply with NFPA 102, *Standard for Grandstands, Folding and Telescopic Seating, Tents, and Membrane Structures,* which deals with wind resistance, strength, load distribution, and pressurizing air-supported structures. A trend toward using a cable harness net system to encapsulate the envelope in all directions increases the structure's stability during wind loading.

Because these structures cannot support overhead piping, conventional automatic sprinkler protection is not generally feasible. Such buildings are unsuitable for long-term storage of high-value or hazardous materials. When reasons to use these structures are compelling, a number of separate smaller units are preferable to one large structure.

WAREHOUSE FIRE-FIGHTING OPERATIONS AND PRE-INCIDENT PLANNING

The following information is intended primarily for fire brigade officers and public fire officials who must develop and implement a pre-incident plan for a warehouse. It will also assist fire officials in command positions who are responsible for tactical and strategic decisions made on the fireground.

Because automatic sprinkler protection is the most effective—and in many instances, the only—method to successfully control a warehouse fire, all fire-fighting operations should be geared toward support of the sprinkler system where present. This support not only increases the likelihood of fire control but also maximizes fire fighter safety because it is unnecessary for fire fighters to be exposed to the hazards of an interior fire attack.

After effective support for the sprinklers has been established, the fire emergency can be considered stabilized. This provides sufficient time to carefully organize a safe and successful fire suppression operation. In addition, sprinklers buy time and help maximize safety and operational effectiveness—hurried fire-fighting operations are not only disorganized but are also unsafe and often ineffective.

The overall success of a warehouse fire-fighting operation is determined long before the first smoke is visible—in fact, it is determined before actual ignition occurs. The operation's success is determined as the warehouse pre-incident plan develops.

The pre-incident plan must be a cooperative effort among the building owner, plant emergency teams, and the public fire department expected to respond to the fire. Other agencies may also provide valuable input to the prefire plan. Such agencies include plant security forces, plant engineering staff, public utility companies, and the insurance carrier.

Developing a Pre-Incident Plan

The pre-incident planning process begins with a warehouse tour. Arrangements should be made with the building owner for someone with a working knowledge of the facility and its operations to accompany the fire department representatives on the tour. Building owners should cooperate fully with the public fire department when they develop a pre-incident plan. Architectural drawings and diagrams of the facility showing the building layout, construction, storage configurations, and the design of the fire protection systems and equipment should be provided for examination prior to the tour.

The tour's purpose is to gather information that the fire department will use to predict the type of fire anticipated and the possible complications encountered during fire suppression operations. Information gathered should include at least the following:

- Evaluation of building size and construction characteristics to determine a fire's probable effect. For example, a roof supported by lightweight steel bar joists or trusses can be expected to collapse early during a serious fire.

- Location of fire walls, fire barriers, and fire doors that separate the storage area from the surrounding operations. Fire doors should be checked for proper operation because they must be relied on during an emergency to inhibit the spread of the fire.
- Identification of the commodities stored within the warehouse. Knowledge of their burning characteristics is essential. For example, burning aerosol products, flammable liquids, or similar materials may be beyond the capabilities of the sprinkler system.
- Determination of the method of packaging materials in the warehouse. For example, cardboard cartons can be expected to collapse quickly into the aisle, and plastic straps attaching materials to pallets can be expected to melt quickly.
- Identification of storage method, for example, racks, solid piles on the floor, or palletized.
- Evaluation of normal and maximum storage levels. Stock levels must be assessed as to relative stability from season to season. Pre-incident plans should be based on the worst case. For example, the worst-case fire in a department store warehouse might occur in September or October when it is filled to capacity with holiday sale merchandise.
- Determination of the type and design of the automatic sprinkler systems. Obtaining complete information on the capability of the sprinkler systems is very important so it can be compared to the hazards the storage in the warehouse pose. If sprinkler design is inadequate for the storage type and arrangement, fire control is unlikely.
- Determination of minimum flow and pressure required to supply sprinkler systems. To evaluate the adequacy of the available water supplies, water supply demands for the sprinklers must be known. If the water supply is inadequate, sprinklers will not perform as designed. If current water supply test results are not available, tests should be conducted to obtain current information.
- Identification of the type and number of water supplies available for fire protection and information on how to start fire pumps so that fire fighters may start them manually, if necessary.
- Location of public hydrants and fire department sprinkler connections. Fire apparatus should not steal water from the sprinkler systems by connecting to yard hydrants. The location of suitable public hydrants and static water sources to supply fire apparatus must be noted and evaluated.
- Arrangement of interior standpipes and hose connections. Are they fed from overhead sprinklers? Can they remain in service with the sprinklers shut off? All hose connections must have the same hose threads as those used by the public fire department.
- Assessment of type, capacity, and method of operation of any automatic or manual heat and smoke venting facilities. How can exhaust fans be activated? How is the power supply to the fans arranged? Will power be lost when electric power for the warehouse shuts down during an emergency?
- Determination of primary and alternate means of access to the warehouse. What security features make access more difficult? Are security guards or guard dogs normally in the warehouse after normal working hours?
- Determination of type of training provided for the plant emergency organization. Also assess how many members will be available during a fire, and what procedures they follow in a fire.
- Assessment of types of manual fire suppression equipment available to the plant emergency organization and whether the public fire department can utilize this equipment.
- Assessment of general storage practices in the building. Are piles neat and orderly? Are they sloppy and in disarray, indicating poor housekeeping practices conducive to rapid fire spread?
- Investigation of aisle storage. Even so-called temporary storage blocks access to the aisles in an emergency and can cause rapid bridging of a fire across aisles.
- Determination of the materials-handling equipment available during overhaul operations to move stock out of the building. Will employees be available to operate the equipment or must fire fighters be trained to use the equipment?

After this basic information has been gathered, development of the actual pre-incident plan begins. The plan, of course, should be developed in conjunction with the building owner so that everyone knows their specific responsibilities during an emergency incident. Employees and the plant emergency organization should be instructed in the procedures for reporting a fire, making sure that employees are evacuated, checking to ensure that sprinkler control valves are open, and closing fire doors to prevent fire spread.

Strategic Fire-Fighting Considerations

The strategy employed in fighting structure fires is to confine the fire to the smallest possible area after arrival of the first fire department unit. In most cases, this means confining the fire to the room or compartment of origin. Even in large commercial buildings, fire fighters can usually depend on at least some degree of compartmentation to at least slow a fire's spread and intensity. When compartmentation works as intended, fires are "simple" room-and-contents fires.

Unfortunately, modern warehouses often lack such compartmentation. Warehouses with several hundred thousand square feet (100,000 ft^2 equals 9300 m^2) of floor area under a single roof with few, if any, true fire walls or fire barriers are not uncommon. Conveyor openings, drive-through doors, and holes for utilities to pass through often compromise existing fire walls and fire barriers. Firestopping or automatically closing fire doors may or may not properly protect these openings.

Sizing up a warehouse fire can, and most likely will, be very difficult. A serious fire may be burning in a large warehouse, but very little smoke may be visible from outside. Smoke visible from the building's exterior may not indicate the location of the fire within. Because most warehouses have few if any windows, there may be no easy method of determining the fire's size, location, or current status. This makes having an up-to-date pre-incident plan even more important.

Sprinkler System Support

Sprinklers begin fighting the fire before the fire department arrives, discharge water directly into the fire area, and are unaffected by poor visibility, heat, and toxic gases. The best course of action is to support the sprinkler system's operation by pumping into the fire department sprinkler connection at full capacity. The higher the pressure available to the sprinkler system, the more water discharged from the operating sprinklers and the better will be the chance of controlling the fire. After support for the sprinklers has been established, the fireground commander has time to carefully size up the situation to determine the best use of available resources.

To support sprinklers, the fire department must pump into the fire department sprinkler connections and ensure that proper pressures are maintained within the system. Steps must also be taken to ensure that water for manual fire suppression operations is not taken from the sprinklers or that fire apparatus connected to yard hydrant systems do not rob water from sprinklers. In cases where water supplies were marginal, fire departments have taken water from the system, causing pressure within the sprinkler system to drop to critically low levels. Fire fighters should understand that, although a flow of 1000 gpm (63 L/sec) may be a high rate of flow for many fire types, the sprinkler system in a warehouse may require from 1500 to over 3000 gpm (95 to 190 L/sec) to operate effectively.

Arriving fire companies may face a number of different situations that hinge mostly on the effectiveness of the automatic sprinkler system. Such situations are discussed in the following paragraphs.

No Sprinklers Provided. If the warehouse has no automatic sprinklers and the fire is beyond the incipient stage, controlling it will be very difficult. Saving anything in the compartment of origin may be unlikely, and efforts should be directed toward preventing the fire's spread beyond the compartment currently involved. This can be accomplished by closing fire doors, using hose lines to prevent the fire's spread through unprotected openings in fire walls and fire barriers, and using master streams through doorways to contain the fire. Entry into the fire area can be extremely dangerous due to the speed with which the fire spreads and the probability of early structural collapse. A good water supply should be secured as soon as possible to supply the large hose streams required to control the fire and protect exposures.

Sprinklers Provided but Not Operating. If sprinklers are provided but not yet operating when fire companies arrive, one of two situations has occurred:

- It is possible that the fire has not yet grown large enough to actuate any sprinklers. In this case, hose lines can be advanced into the area to control the fire.
- Sprinklers may not be operating because the sprinkler system is impaired. One or more valves may be closed for maintenance or repair. Also, someone may have intentionally closed the sprinkler valves in an incendiary incident. Personnel should always be assigned to verify sprinkler control valves and water supplies are in service. At least one engine company should be assigned to support the sprinkler systems by pumping into the sprinkler connection, which may be arranged to bypass closed valves.

Sprinklers Operating and Controlling the Fire. If sprinklers are operating on arrival and appear to be controlling the fire, a first arriving engine company should be assigned to pump into the sprinkler connection. Increasing the pressure available to the sprinklers results in quicker, more effective, fire control. After the sprinklers have controlled the fire, there will be time to plan operations needed for final extinguishment, overhaul, and salvage.

Sprinklers Operating but Not Controlling the Fire. If the sprinklers are not controlling the fire on arrival, pressure in the sprinkler system must be increased immediately by connecting to and pumping into the fire department sprinkler connection. There will be very little time to establish support for the sprinklers before the sprinkler systems are overwhelmed. If only one sprinkler connection is available, it should be used to maximum advantage by connecting multiple hose lines to it. Additional water can be supplied to the sprinkler systems by pumping into wall hydrants or private yard hydrants, if available.

Hazards Posed by Stock

Personnel at a warehouse fire must be familiar with specific hazards of stock in the warehouse. Materials such as flammable liquids, flammable aerosols, and toxic chemicals pose obvious hazards. Hazards of other materials are often overlooked. For example, baled materials, such as scrap paper or paper pulp, can be deadly. These materials absorb water from fire suppression operations and can collapse on fire fighters operating inside the building. Another hazard of materials as they absorb water is that they may expand when wet. If materials such as paper pulp are packed into a building against masonry walls, it is possible that, as the material expands, it may push walls outward, causing local or total collapse of the structure. When developing preincident plans, such possibilities must always be considered.

Materials stored in cardboard cartons also may collapse as the cartons become wet and weak. In fact, in some cases a pile collapse is considered advantageous from a fire control standpoint because it exposes fire in the pile's interior to discharge from the sprinkler system. Fire fighters should understand that fire protection engineers may want a pile in a warehouse to collapse to facilitate fire control.

An example of the hazards of collapsing stock occurred in Idaho where three members of an industrial fire department and two other employees died during a fire in a sprinklered paper warehouse. The noncombustible storage building was 46 ft by 72 ft (14 m by 23 m) and fully protected by automatic sprinklers. Part of a paper mill, it stored scrap paper baled for recycling to a height of about 15 ft (4.6 m). An employee discovered a fire started by welding and grinding operations, and the plant fire department was notified. Arriving fire fighters found the building heavily charged with smoke and sprinklers operating at the ceiling. They entered the building with hose lines to find the seat of the fire. One crew of fire fighters was only 10 to 12 ft (3 to

3.7 m) into the building when bales of paper collapsed on them and trapped two fire fighters. Other fire fighters and employees outside the building rushed in to assist the trapped fire fighters. A second collapse trapped seven would-be rescuers. By the time the incident ended, the collapsing bales killed two employees and three fire fighters. All victims died of suffocation. Seven other fire brigade members were injured in the incident. The NFPA investigative report on the incident said, "This fire clearly illustrates the hazard to fire fighters of the collapse of storage materials which expand with the absorption of water. The hazard is particularly acute in sprinklered warehouses and must be considered in the pre-incident plans of fire departments that protect plants or storage facilities involving such commodities."[3]

Personnel must also be aware of the potential of stock falling from racks. In many cases, racks may be over 30 ft (9.1 m) high. Some warehouses have storage heights exceeding 100 ft (30.5 m). Burning stock falling from such heights could easily be fatal to anyone unfortunate enough to be working in the aisles. Regardless of the type of stock, the storage arrangement, or the design of the fire protection systems, fire fighters should always be alert to the possibility of collapsing stock and protect themselves accordingly.

Visibility

Visibility inside a warehouse during a fire incident is usually limited. Most warehouses are built with limited access and few windows. Natural lighting may not exist, resulting in poor visibility, especially if electric power to the building is cut as often happens when a fire occurs. When smoke fills the building, visibility is reduced even further.

Like a hose line discharged into an enclosed area, sprinklers operating in the fire area disrupt the thermal layers normally present in a fire. Contrary to what some believe, sprinklers do not "drive" smoke to the floor. As they operate, steam forms and cools the atmosphere in the fire area. As every fire fighter knows, cool, damp smoke is difficult to vent. However, the automatic sprinklers should never be shut down in an attempt to improve visibility until it is verified the fire is extinguished or under control. A fire fighter should remain at the sprinkler control valve in case the system needs to be reactivated.

Ventilation

Ventilation is important in a warehouse fire, as in any other structure fire. Automatic smoke and heat vents or mechanical smoke exhaust systems may aid fire fighters. If no heat and smoke venting facilities are provided, ventilation may be accomplished by more traditional methods, such as opening the roof. Cross-ventilation may be accomplished by opening overhead doors or breaking eave-line windows, if they are present.

It is important that fire-fighting personnel not be committed to the roof of a steel-frame building unless the sprinklers have positively controlled the fire. If the fire is not under control, the lightweight steel structural members could quickly fail, causing the roof to collapse. Personnel should also never be committed to the roof of a wood-truss-supported structure. Wood-truss buildings can collapse quickly and without warning during a fire.

Charged hose lines should be available before venting because ventilation, although necessary to improve visibility, may increase fire intensity. As mentioned in the visibility discussion, properly operating sprinklers cause steam to form in the fire area, and smoke saturated with steam becomes difficult to move. Cross-ventilation may be the best method of clearing the building. Positive pressure ventilation may also be used.

Fire Fighter Orientation

Warehouses are typically large buildings. Aisles and storage pile arrangements can become confusing. If fire-fighting personnel are not careful, they can easily become disoriented and lost in the building, especially when visibility is limited. Personnel operating inside a warehouse should always maintain contact with a hose line or a lifeline that they can follow outside to safety.

Logistics

The logistics of a warehouse fire-fighting operation must not be underestimated. Even under ideal circumstances, successfully fighting a fire requires large numbers of personnel and supplies. Physical demands on fire fighters due to the sheer size of the building require regular rotation of personnel out of the fire area for rest and rehabilitation. Pre-incident plans should contain provisions for assembling a large pool of trained personnel to assist in fire-fighting operations.

Other required supplies include air cylinders. Most self-contained breathing apparatus (SCBA) have only a 30- to 45-minute rating and probably last only half that long during strenuous fire-fighting operations. Fire fighters who must walk 300 ft (91.5 m) into the building to the actual fire area may only be able to spend 5 to 7 minutes fighting the fire before they must replenish their air supplies.

Materials-handling equipment for moving stock during overhaul and salvage operations must also be available, as well as qualified personnel who can operate it under emergency conditions. This may require that the operators be trained to use SCBA so they can assist with overhaul operations.

Fire Control Priorities

After ensuring life safety, the primary problem confronting the fire department on arrival at a warehouse fire is controlling the fire. Establishing control simply means preventing the fire from spreading. Assuming that sprinklers are operating, water damage should not be a concern until the fire has been extinguished.

If building owners or tenants complain about water flowing into the building, fire fighters may feel pressure to shut off the sprinklers to prevent further water damage. They must ignore such pressure.

Overhaul

As effectively as sprinklers control a warehouse fire, final extinguishment must be accomplished manually. This means that personnel must break open smoldering pallets, extinguish residual fire inside loads, and then remove them from the warehouse. If possible, personnel should accomplish this under the protection of operating sprinklers. At the very least, multiple-charged hose lines must be available in the area.

Overhauling a warehouse fire can present several challenges, especially if rack storage is involved. For example, how can fire fighters and hose lines reach the 30 ft (9.1 m) or the 80 ft (24.4 m) level in a high-rack storage area for final extinguishment and overhaul? The pre-incident plan must address such problems and should be practiced during on-site drills.

Rekindling

Fire may rekindle during overhaul operations when cartons of stock are broken open. If the sprinklers are shut down, someone with a radio should be stationed at the sprinkler control valve(s) to restore the system quickly to service if rekindling occurs.

In general, basic rules for shutting down the sprinkler system are as follows:

- Do not shut the sprinklers off until fire extinguishment is positively determined. If there is any doubt, the sprinklers should remain in operation.
- Make available charged hose lines in the fire area(s) before sprinklers are shut down.
- Station someone with a radio at the sprinkler control valve(s) to reopen the valve(s) if rekindling occurs.
- Restore the sprinkler system to full operation as soon as possible.

Limitations of Manual Fire Suppression

The best method of protecting a warehouse is to install a properly designed automatic sprinkler system and maintain it in proper working order. If sprinklers are not provided or they are not in service due to poor maintenance, the chances of saving a warehouse involved in a fire are greatly reduced. Personnel should not be committed to dangerous positions in an attempt to control an uncontrollable fire. The best-equipped fire department can never compensate for the lack of an effective sprinkler system.

OUTDOOR STORAGE

Truly engineered fire protection is difficult to achieve for outdoor storage. Depending on the hazard, monetary value, and storage area, a basic fire protection plan can be developed. For small amounts of incidental and transitory outdoor storage, appropriate protection might consist merely of good security fencing and outdoor lighting. On the other hand, very large, high-value storage yards warrant more elaborate safeguards.

Choosing the Site

Size. The storage area should be large enough to hold the quantity of stored material, with allowance for spacing between piles. If the area is inadequate, additional sites should be found. Congestion can be a major factor in fire spread.

Terrain. The ground should be leveled, if possible. Sloping terrain is undesirable because it makes piles unstable and complicates fire-fighting operations.

Exposure. Adequate clearances to adjacent properties should be maintained to minimize mutual fire exposure. Zoning regulations often specify clear distances to a property line. If no such regulations exist, the nature of future development on adjacent property should be considered, as it may affect the size of the storage area.

Other exposure considerations include protection from grass, brush, or forest fires, as well as protection from potential ignition sources, such as sparks generated by rolling railroad equipment, incinerator stacks, electrical transformers on poles, or lighted cigarettes discarded from nearby cars.

Fire Protection. Because fixed automatic systems are usually not an option, manual fire protection features available dictate the arrangement of outdoor storage, including pile size and the clearances required from adjacent piles, buildings, and property boundary lines. Local fire protection features, such as public water supply and its reliability, the available fire flow, fire department location and travel time, and the means available for notifying the fire department, should be evaluated.

Floods and Windstorms. Areas subject to flooding or windstorms should be avoided. Windstorms present a particular problem in some coastal areas. Fires occurring during high winds pose an exposure problem against which protection is almost impossible. Winds can carry burning materials and brands over considerable distances, even though the fire may be confined to a relatively small area.

Preparing the Site

Site Clearance. Vegetation should be cleared away so that it cannot dry out and become fuel for ignition or fire spread. The site should be leveled as much as possible and then paved. If the entire yard is not surfaced, care should be taken to ensure that fire apparatus can easily maneuver throughout the yard. This requires properly developed roadways capable of supporting heavy trucks. Proper site drainage is also essential.

It is good practice to paint lines within the yard to show aisles and roadways, as well as the location of yard hydrants, extinguishers, and hose houses.

Site Layout. A site plan should be developed. It should detail where specific materials are stored, the proper separation distances between piles, and access points to all site areas, including fences and gates.

The density of stored materials influences the manner in which the material burns. Lumber stacked in solid, orderly piles to a height of 20 ft (6 m) does not present the same problem as lumber stored in "stickered" piles, or wood stacked with spaces between to enhance air flow. In the latter case, fire develops more rapidly because of air spaces in the piles. Pulpwood is sometimes stored in piles 200 ft (61 m) in diameter and 100 ft (30 m) high; the logs' rough and varied shapes create air spaces and pockets in the piles, which accelerate burning.

Certain materials burn quickly and produce a great deal of heat. Baled cotton, hay, lumber, packing materials, pallets, plywood, pulpwood, and rubber are examples of such materials, and considerable clearance should be provided between and around these piles. Aisle widths equal to the height of the pile are desirable for these types of commodities.

Both the yard itself and the piles within the yard must be easily accessible for fire fighting. Access to storage close to railroad spurs is often difficult because of boxcars and other railroad equipment left on the tracks. Driveways at least 15 ft (4.5 m) wide should be provided to permit fire department apparatus to reach all portions of the storage area. Aisles of 10 ft (3 m) or more should be provided to reduce the likelihood of fire spreading from pile to pile. In unusually large storage yards or moderate-size yards with valuable commodities, main aisles or firebreaks subdivide the storage much like firewalls do indoors. Overall, ideal aisle width depends on a number of factors, including the type of material, how it is stored, storage height, anticipated wind conditions, fire-fighting capabilities, and fire-fighting equipment.

In some cases, packaging and palletizing affect storage methods, particularly of irregularly shaped or small materials. Combustible pallets may present an added hazard. Some materials are packed in heavy crates. Usually, they do not increase hazard except after severe weathering or where handling has caused breakage or splintering. Tarpaulins and other weather-resistant materials used to cover stock should be of fire-retardant-treated material.

A stable pile under normal conditions may present a severe hazard in a fire. It is wise to anticipate how fire and water affect the stability of piles when planning their sizes and configurations. Collapsing piles may enhance fire spread and hamper fire-fighting operations.

Areas used to service and maintain equipment should be designated, marked, and separated from the storage. Flammable and combustible liquids, such as fuel for lift trucks, should be stored in accordance with NFPA 30, *Flammable and Combustible Liquids Code*. Fuel storage tanks should be located so spills do not flow under or around storage and, conversely, so that a fire in a storage area will not expose any flammable or combustible liquid storage area.

Installation of Fire Protection. Fire protection features and equipment should be installed during site preparation. Depending on the site's size and location, installing private water mains and hydrants throughout the yard may be necessary.

In planning for hydrants and yard mains, the water supply, whether from public mains or private sources, should be able to furnish the needed fire flow.

Properly marked portable fire extinguishers, preferably the nonfreezing water type, should be placed so that the distance to the nearest unit is 75 ft (23 m) or less. For active and normally occupied sites, fully equipped hose houses should be provided and personnel trained to use them in a fire.

A means to notify the fire department is essential. A system that directly signals the fire department is best; minimally, a telephone should be accessible.

Security Measures. Outdoor storage yards may have problems with trespassing, vandalism, and theft. Security measures, such as installing fencing and lighting, can minimize these problems. A fence, however, must not prevent ready access to the yard by the fire department. The fire department should be consulted about incorporating remote gates in the fencing to provide additional access under fire conditions.

Security guards can provide fire protection and loss control surveillance for outdoor storage yards. NFPA 601, *Standard for Security Services in Fire Loss Prevention,* covers the selection, duties, instruction, and training of such personnel.

Utilizing the Site

Management. When a yard is selected and laid out, the maximum amount of material to be stored in it is also established. Frequent inspections should monitor the quantity of the material and other fire prevention and protection features, including disposal of waste materials.

In general, management's attitude toward the yard's fire protection provides an example that employees are likely to follow.

Fire Protection and Prevention. All fire protection equipment, including hydrants, fire pumps, fire extinguishers, and any suppression, detection, or alarm systems on the storage site, must be properly inspected, tested, and maintained. All materials-handling equipment at the site should be equipped with a multipurpose portable fire extinguisher suitable for any type of fire.

The locations of all hydrants, hose houses, portable extinguishers, alarm boxes, and other fire protection equipment should be properly marked, preferably with elevated signs. Arrows and signs painted on the pavement are the minimum markings required.

If material to be torch cut or welded cannot be moved from the storage yard to a remote location, work should be done only after taking appropriate precautions (see NFPA 51B).

Smoking should be prohibited or restricted to specific areas that are remote from combustible storage. Adequate signs should be displayed and regulations strictly enforced.

A private fire brigade of employees can provide initial fire-fighting capabilities. If there are enough employees to organize a fire brigade, the availability and ability of a public fire department normally govern the level of organization, training, and equipment provided to the brigade. The larger the storage yard and the more valuable its contents, the greater the need for a private fire brigade for immediate response to an incident. NFPA 600 provides minimum requirements for their organization and training.

Maintenance and Housekeeping. Repairs to fencing, lighting, and the yard surface should be made promptly, and materials-handling equipment should be kept in good condition. Suitable safeguards should be provided to minimize the hazard of sparks from equipment, such as refuse burners, boiler stacks, vehicle exhausts, and locomotives.

Good housekeeping also includes controlling weeds and vegetation. Weeds, grass, and other vegetation should be sprayed with an acceptable herbicide or ground sterilizer. Dead vegetation should be removed.

In many instances, scrap lumber, broken pallets, broken containers, bales, or pieces of material stored on the site are discarded into the clear space around the yard. Daily checks should be made for such discarded materials; where found, they should be properly removed. Care should be taken to prevent the accumulation of windblown debris and other combustible materials around the storage.

Outdoor Storage of Specific Materials

A discussion of safe storage practices for a few common materials follows. As a source for good practices, see the NFPA publications previously referenced and industry or insurance company standards. Many times, the application of inside storage guidelines for a commodity is a good starting point for devising outdoor storage guidelines.

Wood and Wood Products. Because wood is moved from the forests only at certain times of the year, large quantities of logs are stored at sawmills, paper mills, and pulp mills. Large circular piles with logs dumped on the top are called "stacked piles." Logs stacked parallel, like matches in a box, are called "ranked piles." Stacked piles are usually much larger, with pile heights often approaching 100 ft (30.5 m). Ranked piles are usually 10- to 15-ft (3- to 5-m) high. Because maintaining separation and aisles is much easier for ranked piles, fire protection for them is also much easier (Figure 20.16.8).

Controlling log yard fires can require large quantities of water. This can require that many portable turrets and monitor nozzles, each discharging about 1000 gpm (3785 L/min) operate simultaneously. A looped underground fire main system with hydrants spaced throughout the yard is good practice. Monitor nozzles on towers are advantageous in log yards, especially those with high-stacked piles. Burrowing fires in large stacked piles are difficult to extinguish even after surface burning is under control.

Chip storage has replaced log storage at many pulp and paper mills. Two completely different types of fires occur in chip piles: surface fires and internal fires. The amount of water needed to control a chip pile fire varies, depending on the pile size. Weather conditions, operating methods, geographic location, wood chip type, and the degree to which wetting may be employed all influence fire conditions. Exposure to long periods of hot, dry weather with no regular surface wetting creates conditions under which fast-spreading surface fires occur.

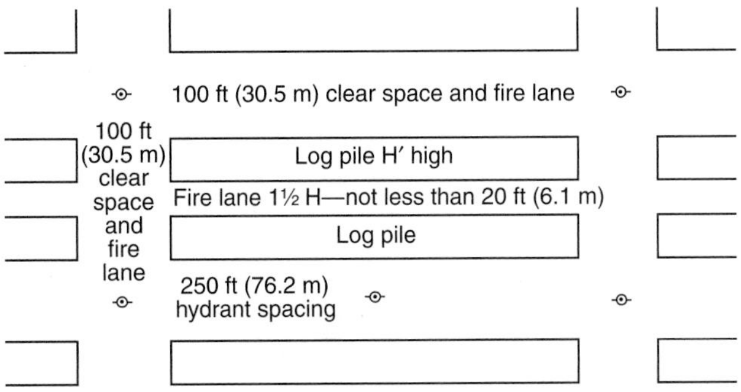

FIGURE 20.16.8 Good Layout for Ranked Piles of Logs in a Storage Yard

Frequency of pile turnover and operating methods influence the potential for fires. Piles built using methods that allow a concentration of fines (the dust and small pieces of material in the pile) are subject to internal heating, which, if undetected, can cause intense internal fires. This is also true of piles stored for long time periods with no turnover.

Paper and Paper Products. Some paper and paper products are stored outdoors. Roll paper is normally stored in large rolls weighing 2 tons (1814 kg) or more. Tightly wound paper is difficult to ignite; however, roll paper stored outdoors is more vulnerable. Once ignited, the rolls burn with great intensity as the paper exfoliates and exposes more paper to burning.

Baled wastepaper does not produce as intense a fire as roll paper does, but instead tends to produce burrowing fires. Broken bales are difficult to handle after wetting. A motorized vehicle with a shovel may be needed to move debris in order to complete extinguishment. Spontaneous ignition can occur in wastepaper if foreign materials subject to spontaneous heating become trapped in bales. Fire protection for wastepaper storage is generally the same as for other outdoor storage.

SUMMARY

Fires in warehousing and storage areas pose a number of fire protection challenges that must be addressed in a facility fire protection plan. The provision of a properly designed, installed, and maintained automatic sprinkler system is the best method of controlling a storage fire until it can be extinguished by the facility fire brigade or the public fire department. Effective action during a fire can limit the loss; such action must be carefully planed in advance. Ideally, the building owner and the public fire department must partner to develop an effective response plan.

BIBLIOGRAPHY

References Cited

1. *Before the Fire: Fire Prevention Strategies for Storage Occupancies*, National Fire Protection Association, Quincy, MA, 1988.
2. Best, R. L., "Kmart Corporation Distribution Center Fire, Falls Township, PA, June 21, 1982," National Fire Protection Association Investigation Report, National Fire Protection Association, Quincy, MA, 1982.
3. Best, R. L., "Storage Collapse Kills Five," *Fire Command,* Nov. 1980.

NFPA Codes, Standards, and Recommended Practices

Reference to the following NFPA codes, standards, and recommended practices will provide further information on general indoor and outdoor storage discussed in this chapter. (See the latest version of The NFPA Catalog *for availability of current editions of the following documents.)*

NFPA 10, *Standard for Portable Fire Extinguishers*
NFPA 11, *Standard for Low-, Medium-, and High-Expansion Foam*
NFPA 13, *Standard for the Installation of Sprinkler Systems*
NFPA 13E, *Recommended Practice for Fire Department Operations in Properties Protected by Sprinkler and Standpipe Systems*

NFPA 14, *Standard for the Installation of Standpipe and Hose Systems*
NFPA 24, *Standard for the Installation of Private Fire Service Mains and Their Appurtenances*
NFPA 25, *Standard for the Inspection, Testing, and Maintenance of Water-Based Fire Protection Systems*
NFPA 30, *Flammable and Combustible Liquids Code*
NFPA 30A, *Code for Motor Fuel Dispensing Facilities and Repair Garages*
NFPA 30B, *Code for the Manufacture and Storage of Aerosol Products*
NFPA 51B, *Standard for Fire Prevention During Welding, Cutting, and Other Hot Work*
NFPA 61, *Standard for the Prevention of Fires and Dust Explosions in Agricultural and Food Processing Facilities*
NFPA 70, *National Electrical Code®*
NFPA 72®, National Fire Alarm Code®
NFPA 80A, *Recommended Practice for Protection of Buildings from Exterior Fire Exposures*
NFPA 88A, *Standard for Parking Structures*
NFPA 92A, *Standard for Smoke-Control Systems Utilizing Barriers and Pressure Differences*
NFPA *101®, Life Safety Code®*
NFPA 102, *Standard for Grandstands, Folding and Telescopic Seating, Tents, and Membrane Structures*
NFPA 204, *Standard for Smoke and Heat Venting*
NFPA 307, *Standard for the Construction and Fire Protection of Marine Terminals, Piers, and Wharves*
NFPA 409, *Standard on Aircraft Hangars*
NFPA 434, *Code for the Storage of Pesticides*
NFPA 505, *Fire Safety Standard for Powered Industrial Trucks Including Type Designations, Areas of Use, Conversions, Maintenance, and Operations*
NFPA 520, *Standard on Subterranean Spaces*
NFPA 600, *Standard on Industrial Fire Brigades*
NFPA 601, *Standard for Security Services in Fire Loss Prevention*
NFPA 1620, *Recommended Practice for Pre-Incident Planning*
NFPA 5000®, Building Construction and Safety Code®

References

Beals, J. A., "Fire Test of Records Storage to 40 Feet," *Proceedings* of Fire Suppression and Detection Research Application Symposium, Research and Practice: Bridging the Gap, February 7–9, 2001, Orlando, FL, National Fire Protection Research Foundation, Quincy, MA, 2001, pp. 718–768.

Blume, G., and Hosser, D., "Design of Pesticide Warehouses Using Fire Simulation Tools," *Proceedings* of International Conference, Engineered Fire Protection Design, Applying Fire Science to Fire Protection Problems, June 11–15, 2001, San Francisco, CA, Society of Fire Protection Engineers, Bethesda, MD, 2001, pp. 31–41.

Carey, W. M., "Fire Testing of Warehouse Sprinklers for Storage Applications," *Proceedings* of Fire Suppression and Detection Research Application Symposium, Research and Practice: Bridging the Gap, February 23–25, 2000, Orlando, FL, National Fire Protection Research Foundation, Quincy, MA, 2000, pp. 88–131.

Golinveaux, J., "Under Pressure: How the K-17 and K-25 Sprinklers Performed in Rigorous Warehouse Conditions," *Proceedings* of Fire Suppression and Detection Research Application Symposium, Research and Practice: Bridging the Gap, February 23–25, 2000, Orlando, FL, National Fire Protection Research Foundation, Quincy, MA, 2000, pp. 282–317.

Lataille, J. (Ed.), *Fire Protection of Storage Facilities*, National Fire Protection Association, Quincy, MA, 2004.

Sheppard, D. T., and Torrey, B., "Burning and Suppression of Plastic Warehouse Pallets," *Proceedings* of Fire Suppression and Detection Research Application Symposium, Research and Practice: Bridging the Gap, February 23–25, 2000, Orlando, FL, National Fire Protection Research Foundation, Quincy, MA, 2000, pp. 255–258.

Standing, T., "Stocking Up On Safety," *Fire Prevention,* No. 335, Aug. 2000, pp. 18–20.

Troup, J. M. A., "Full-Scale Fire Tests: Warehouse Protection for Plastic-Wrapped (Uncartoned) Aerosols," *Proceedings* of Fire Suppression and Detection Research Application Symposium, Research and Practice: Bridging the Gap, February 23–25, 2000, Orlando, FL, National Fire Protection Research Foundation, Quincy, MA, 2000, pp. 156–166.

Chapter 17

Library and Museum Collections

Danny L. McDaniel

Chapter Contents

Key Terms

bookstack, compartmentation, cultural resource properties, historic building, means of egress, museum, place of worship

This chapter discusses the incidence of fire in cultural resource properties, analyzes the differences between fires in which large and minimal losses occur, and describes principles and practices for managing cultural resources to reduce the risk of fire occurring in them and to minimize losses when they do occur.

At first glance historic buildings, libraries, museums, and places of worship seem quite different because of the nature of their use, contents, and degree of public access. Nevertheless, most museums contain libraries, many libraries feature exhibits of art or other culturally significant objects, most museums and many libraries and places of worship are in historic buildings, many places of worship house important collections of artifacts, art objects, and library materials, and all contain archival records essential to understanding our cultural heritage. Moreover, the fire protection problems are similar. Cultural resource properties nearly always include large quantities of combustible, high-value, and often irreplaceable materials. Another striking similarity is that although places of worship, libraries, and museums are public assembly occupancies, the open construction and extraordinarily high fuel loads are more typical of warehouse occupancies.

From a fire protection viewpoint, places of worship, libraries, and museums are mixed-use occupancies with significant public assembly and storage components but also may include cooking and eating facilities, laboratories, child care facilities, and even sleeping accommodations. A popular program in museums, for example, is to allow groups, usually children, to camp overnight in a gallery. Such programs have long been part of the educational outreach offered by historic sites and living history museums, and, of course, some places of worship provide shelter for the homeless and other disadvantaged persons as part of their community outreach. The fire risk in these occupancies should not be underrated. Public areas, such as assembly areas, library reading rooms, and museum exhibit galleries, generally are no-smoking areas with low fuel loads and high standards of housekeeping, and they may be monitored by staff or security officers. Nevertheless, such areas regularly suffer costly fires.

Nonpublic areas, such as storerooms, bookstacks, collection storage, work areas, exhibit preparation areas, food preparation areas, and conservation laboratories, present additional special hazards. Fuel loads are much higher in these areas, and housekeeping and smoking are more difficult to control.

A review of fire experience in NFPA 909, *Code for the Protection of Cultural Resource Properties—Museums, Libraries, and Places of Worship,* and NFPA 914, *Code for Fire Protection of Historic Structures,* clearly demonstrates the risk to cultural resource properties. Recent fires worthy of special attention include those at the Los Angeles Central Public Library (two in 1986 and one in 1988); the Hampton Court Palace in Richmond on Thames, England, in 1986; the Louisiana State Museum in New Orleans in 1988; the Library of the USSR Academy of Sciences in St. Petersburg, Russia, in 1988; Windsor Castle in Berkshire, England, in 1992; the Hofburg Palace in Vienna, Austria, in 1992; the Norwich Central Library in Norwich, England, in 1994; La Fenice Opera House in Venice, Italy, in 1996; and the First Presbyterian Church in Lexington, Virginia, in 2000.

Danny L. McDaniel, CPP, CSP, ASSE, ASIS, ICOM, AAM, is director of security, safety, and transportation for the Colonial Williamsburg Foundation in Williamsburg, Virginia. He is a member of the NFPA Cultural Resources Committee.

See also Section 1, Chapter 6, "Premises Security"; Section 7, Chapter 2, "Storage of Flammable and Combustible Liquids"; Section 8, Chapter 13, "Electrical Systems and Appliances"; Section 9, Chapter 8, "Protection of Records"; Section 11, Chapter 2, "Housekeeping Practices"; Section 12, Chapter 9, "Fire and Emergency Services Protective Clothing and Protective Equipment"; Section 12, Chapter 18, "Pre-Incident Planning for Emergency Response"; Section 14, Chapter 2, "Automatic Fire Detectors"; Section 16, Chapter 2, "Automatic Sprinklers"; Section 16, Chapter 6, "Residential Sprinkler Systems"; Section 16, Chapter 8, "Water Mist Fire Suppression Systems"; Section 17, Chapter 5, "Fire Extinguisher Use and Maintenance"; Section 17, Chapter 6, "Halon and Halon Replacement Agents and Systems"; and Section 20, Chapter 1, "Assessing Life Safety in Buildings."

CAUSES OF CULTURAL PROPERTY FIRES

In 1999, the Federal Emergency Managment Agency implemented Version 5.0 of the National Fire Incident Reporting System, which changed some of the cause codes used in earlier versions. Therefore, only relative comparisons can be made between leading causes of fires from data collected before 1999 and data collected thereafter. Tables 20.17.1, 20.17.3, and 20.17.5 show leading cause data for fires in libraries, places of worship, and museums for the period 1980 through 1998. Tables 20.17.2, 20.17.4, and 20.17.6 show the same data for the period 1999 through 2002.

Arson is the leading cause of fires in libraries and places of worship (Tables 20.17.1, 20.17.2, 20.17.3, and 20.17.4), both in the number of fires and in the value of property damaged. Arson also was the second most frequent cause of fires in museums during the period 1980 through 1998 (Table 20.17.5) and the third leading cause in the period 1999 through 2002. From 1980 to 1998, arson accounted for 85 percent of the property loss in library fires, including the disastrous Los Angeles Central Public Library fire in 1986, and in the same period, arson accounted for 42 percent of the property loss in places of worship fires, and 26 percent of the fire losses in museums (see Table 20.17.5). In the period 1999 through 2002, arson accounted for 13 percent of the property losses in libraries and 20 percent in places of worship. The second most significant cause of fires in libraries and places of worship, and the third leading cause in museums in the period 1999 through 2002, have been failures in electrical distribution equipment. Electrical distribution equipment fires accounted for 13 percent of the property damage losses in libraries, places of worship, and museums during 1980 to 1998 and 21 percent in the period 1999 through 2002. Together, incendiary and suspicious causes and electrical distribution equipment problems accounted for nearly half the fires in cultural properties from 1980 through 1998 and about 33 percent of the fires from 1999 through 2002.

FIRE PREVENTION PRINCIPLES

Fire prevention is the cultural property's first line of defense against fire. Fire prevention consists of controlling and separating ignition sources from the supply of fuel.

Ignition Control

Ignition control involves identifying all sources of heat that could cause ignition in combustibles and isolating these sources from the fuel.

Arson. Arson is a difficult crime to prevent, and the arsonist is an unpredictable variable in the fire prevention program. A determined arsonist can circumvent even the most carefully defined fire prevention program. However, most arsonists are not so determined and have no special knowledge of fire or safety systems. Although preventing all deliberately set fires may be impossible, a fire prevention program that incorporates a strong security program can limit risk.

Fundamental precautions against arson are a strong access control program backed by detailed opening and closing procedures and strong measures to deter and detect unauthorized entry. At a minimum a security program should include the following:

1. A detailed, written, access control policy with two objectives: (1) to control (define) legitimate access and (2) to prevent illicit or unnecessary access. These objectives can be met by establishing levels of access to spaces and degrees of access to protected areas or objects. Legitimate access to grounds or buildings does not mean access to nonpublic areas. Access to storage does not necessarily mean access to protected objects. Likewise, access does not mean uncontrolled access. Visitor escorts are a legitimate means of access control.

   An effective access control policy includes the following provisions:

   - Identification of those who may obtain access (both routine and occasional) to nonpublic spaces and under what circumstances, for example, employees, scholars, researchers, visitors, service vendors, emergency response personnel, and others.
   - Procedures to obtain legitimate access to nonpublic areas. The policy should identify which staff can grant access, how much access they may grant, and on what basis. The policy should identify who must be escorted in nonpublic areas.
   - Responsibility for keeping access lists up-to-date and for making sure they are used routinely.
2. The best access and key control program is of little value if the facility is improperly opened or closed. Following written opening and closing procedures is the safest way to make the transition from one condition to the other. Standardizing how the facility is opened and closed establishes a baseline condition of the facility during each period. In the risk assessment process, these baseline conditions dictate the additional physical security tools needed to achieve acceptable security levels. Opening and closing procedures should:
   - Identify who may open or close. As the basis of the facility's access control program, designating, in writing, who has authority to open a building or controlled area establishes both the responsibility and authority to control access.

TABLE 20.17.1 Major Causes of U.S. Library Structure Fires, 1980–1998 Annual Averages

Major Cause	*Fires*		*Civilian Deaths*		*Civilian Injuries*		*Direct Property Damage (in Dollars)*	
Incendiary or suspicious	78	(40.0%)	0	(NA)	0	(24.5%)	4,018,200	(84.5%)
Electrical distribution	38	(19.6%)	0	(NA)	0	(10.0%)	281,400	(5.9%)
Other equipment	16	(8.3%)	0	(NA)	0	(0.0%)	16,700	(0.4%)
Open flame, ember, or torch	12	(6.2%)	0	(NA)	0	(10.3%)	17,800	(0.4%)
Smoking materials	11	(5.9%)	0	(NA)	0	(11.4%)	65,300	(1.4%)
Heating equipment	11	(5.7%)	0	(NA)	0	(32.5%)	143,200	(3.0%)
Cooking equipment	8	(4.0%)	0	(NA)	0	(0.0%)	14,900	(0.3%)
Appliance, tool, or air conditioning	7	(3.8%)	0	(NA)	0	(11.4%)	31,200	(0.7%)
Child playing	5	(2.3%)	0	(NA)	0	(0.0%)	56,600	(1.2%)
Natural causes	4	(2.0%)	0	(NA)	0	(0.0%)	30,900	(0.6%)
Exposure (to other hostile fire)	3	(1.3%)	0	(NA)	0	(0.0%)	78,100	(1.6%)
Other heat source	2	(0.9%)	0	(NA)	0	(0.0%)	300	(0.0%)
Total	195	(100.0%)	0	(NA)	1	(100.0%)	4,754,400	(100.0%)

Note: This table shows the causes of structure fires (incident type 11) in libraries (fixed property use 151). These are fires reported to U.S. municipal fire departments and so exclude fires reported only to federal or state agencies or industrial fire brigades. Fires, civilian deaths, and civilian injuries are expressed to the nearest one and property damage is rounded to the nearest hundred dollars. Sums may not equal totals due to rounding errors. Property damage figures have not been adjusted for inflation. The 12 major cause categories are based on a hierarchy developed by the U.S. Fire Administration. Fires in which the cause was unknown were allocated proportionally among fires of known cause.

Source: National estimates based on NFIRS and NFPA survey.

TABLE 20.17.2 Leading Causes of Structure Fires in Libraries, 1999–2002 Annual Averages

Cause	*Fires*		*Civilian Deaths*		*Civilian Injuries*		*Direct Property Damage (in Dollars)*	
Intentional	32	(26%)	0	(NA)	0	(NA)	171,000	(13%)
Electrical distribution and lighting equipment	17	(14%)	0	(NA)	0	(NA)	441,000	(33%)
Cooking equipment fires	11	(9%)	0	(NA)	0	(NA)	16,000	(0%)
Identified cooking equipment	4	(3%)	0	(NA)	0	(NA)	2,000	(0%)
Confined cooking fire	7	(6%)	0	(NA)	0	(NA)	2,000	(0%)
Heating equipment	8	(7%)	0	(NA)	0	(NA)	2,000	(1%)
Smoking materials	6	(5%)	0	(NA)	0	(NA)	34,000	(0%)
Torch	5	(4%)	0	(NA)	0	(NA)	2,000	(3%)
Contained trash or rubbish fire	10	(8%)	0	(NA)	0	(NA)	16,000	(0%)

Note: These are the leading causes, obtained from the following list: intentional (from the NFIRS field "cause"); playing with fire (from factor contributing to ignition); confined heating (including confined chimney and confined fuel burner or boiler fires), confined cooking, and contained trash or rubbish (from incident type); identified heating, identified cooking, clothes dryer or washer, torch (including burner and soldering iron), electrical distribution and lighting equipment, medical equipment, and electronic, office or entertainment equipment (from equipment involved in ignition); smoking materials, candles, lightning, and spontaneous combustion or chemical reaction (from heat source); and mobile property involved (from mobile property involved in ignition). Exposure fires include fires with an exposure number greater than zero, as well as fires identified by heat source or factor contributing to ignition when no equipment was involved in ignition that were not intentionally set. The same fire can be listed under multiple causes, based on multiple data elements.

These are national estimates of fires reported to U.S. municipal fire departments and so exclude fires reported only to federal or state agencies or industrial fire brigades. National estimates are projections. Casualty and loss projections can be heavily influenced by the inclusion or exclusion of one unusually serious fire. Fires, deaths, and injuries are rounded to the nearest one. Direct property damage is rounded to the nearest thousand. Property damage has not been adjusted for inflation.

Source: NFIRS and NFPA survey.

TABLE 20.17.3 Major Causes of U.S. Structure Fires in Churches, Chapels, Temples, or Mosques, 1980–1998 Annual Averages

Major Cause	*Fires*		*Civilian Deaths*		*Civilian Injuries*		*Direct Property Damage (in Millions of Dollars)*	
Incendiary or suspicious	510	(32.3%)	1	(52.3%)	3	(17.8%)	18.4	(41.5%)
Electrical distribution	230	(14.8%)	0	(0.0%)	2	(13.5%)	5.8	(13.1%)
Heating equipment	180	(11.7%)	0	(16.0%)	3	(14.3%)	5.9	(13.4%)
Open flame, ember, or torch	120	(7.3%)	0	(5.8%)	2	(8.5%)	2.0	(4.5%)
Other equipment	110	(7.1%)	0	(0.0%)	5	(25.0%)	3.6	(8.1%)
Natural causes	90	(5.5%)	0	(8.3%)	1	(4.6%)	4.0	(8.9%)
Exposure (to other hostile fire)	70	(4.6%)	0	(0.0%)	0	(0.4%)	0.7	(1.5%)
Cooking equipment	70	(4.5%)	0	(9.2%)	1	(7.6%)	0.4	(1.0%)
Appliance, tool, or air conditioning	60	(3.9%)	0	(0.0%)	0	(1.4%)	1.3	(2.9%)
Other heat source	50	(3.3%)	0	(0.0%)	1	(3.9%)	1.2	(2.6%)
Smoking materials	40	(2.8%)	0	(8.5%)	0	(0.9%)	0.6	(1.4%)
Child playing	40	(2.4%)	0	(0.0%)	0	(2.1%)	0.5	(1.1%)
Total	1580	(100.0%)	2	(100.0%)	18	(100.0%)	44.2	(100.0%)

Note: This table shows the causes of structure fires (incident type 11) in churches, chapels, temples, or mosques (fixed property use 131). These are fires reported to U.S. municipal fire departments and so exclude fires reported only to federal or state agencies or industrial fire brigades. Fires are rounded to the nearest ten, civilian deaths and civilian injuries are expressed to the nearest one, and property damage is rounded to the nearest hundred thousand dollars. Sums may not equal totals due to rounding errors. Property damage figures have not been adjusted for inflation. The 12 major cause categories are based on a hierarchy developed by the U.S. Fire Administration. Fires in which the cause was unknown were allocated proportionally among fires of known cause.

Source: National estimates based on NFIRS and NFPA survey.

TABLE 20.17.4 Leading Causes of Structure Fires in Places of Worship and Funeral Parlors, 1999–2002 Annual Averages

Cause	*Fires*		*Civilian Deaths*		*Civilian Injuries*		*Direct Property Damage (in Millions of Dollars)*	
Intentional	290	(17%)	0	(0%)	0	(0%)	19.6	(20%)
Electrical distribution and lighting equipment	290	(16%)	0	(0%)	2	(9%)	20.6	(21%)
Heating equipment	200	(12%)	0	(0%)	1	(4%)	8.5	(9%)
Identified heating equipment	180	(10%)	0	(0%)	1	(4%)	8.3	(9%)
Confined heating equipment fire	30	(2%)	0	(0%)	0	(0%)	0.1	(0%)
Cooking equipment fires	230	(13%)	1	(54%)	6	(29%)	2.4	(2%)
Identified cooking equipment	150	(8%)	1	(54%)	5	(26%)	2.4	(2%)
Confined cooking fire	80	(5%)	0	(0%)	1	(3%)	0.0	(0%)
Candle	110	(6%)	0	(0%)	2	(11%)	2.2	(2%)
Torch (including burner or soldering iron)	80	(4%)	0	(0%)	1	(4%)	2.2	(2%)
Lightning	80	(4%)	0	(0%)	0	(0%)	11.4	(12%)
Smoking materials	70	(4%)	1	(50%)	1	(6%)	10.7	(11%)
Exposure to other fire	60	(3%)	0	(0%)	0	(0%)	3.6	(4%)
Playing with fire	60	(3%)	0	(0%)	0	(0%)	3.6	(4%)
Contained trash or rubbish fire	40	(2%)	0	(0%)	1	(3%)	0.0	(0%)

Note: These are the leading causes, obtained from the following list: intentional (from the NFIRS field "cause"); playing with fire (from factor contributing to ignition); confined heating (including confined chimney and confined fuel burner or boiler fires), confined cooking, and contained trash or rubbish (from incident type); identified heating, identified cooking, clothes dryer or washer, torch (including burner and soldering iron), electrical distribution and lighting equipment, medical equipment, and electronic, office or entertainment equipment (from equipment involved in ignition); smoking materials, candles, lightning, and spontaneous combustion or chemical reaction (from heat source); and mobile property involved (from mobile property involved in ignition). Exposure fires include fires with an exposure number greater than zero, as well as fires identified by heat source or factor contributing to ignition when no equipment was involved in ignition that were not intentionally set. The same fire can be listed under multiple causes, based on multiple data elements.

These are national estimates of fires reported to U.S. municipal fire departments and so exclude fires reported only to federal or state agencies or industrial fire brigades. National estimates are projections. Casualty and loss projections can be heavily influenced by the inclusion or exclusion of one unusually serious fire. Fires are rounded to the nearest ten, civilian deaths and injuries are rounded to the nearest one, and direct property damage is rounded to the nearest hundred thousand dollars. Property damage has not been adjusted for inflation.

Source: NFIRS and NFPA survey.

TABLE 20.17.5 Major Causes of Structure Fires in U.S. Museums or Art Galleries, 1980–1998 Annual Averages

Major Cause	*Fires*		*Civilian Deaths*		*Civilian Injuries*		*Direct Property Damage (in Dollars)*	
Electrical distribution	21	(24.6%)	0	(NA)	0	(22.3%)	532,300	(27.2%)
Incendiary or suspicious	16	(18.3%)	0	(NA)	0	(0.0%)	502,200	(25.7%)
Other equipment	9	(10.9%)	0	(NA)	0	(6.1%)	263,600	(13.5%)
Open flame, ember, or torch	8	(9.1%)	0	(NA)	0	(14.3%)	38,400	(2.0%)
Heating equipment	7	(8.0%)	0	(NA)	0	(19.9%)	500,800	(25.6%)
Smoking materials	6	(7.5%)	0	(NA)	0	(0.0%)	12,700	(0.6%)
Cooking equipment	6	(7.1%)	0	(NA)	0	(0.0%)	24,800	(1.3%)
Exposure (to other hostile fire)	4	(4.3%)	0	(NA)	0	(0.0%)	51,600	(2.6%)
Natural causes	4	(4.1%)	0	(NA)	0	(0.0%)	21,800	(1.1%)
Appliance, tool, or air conditioning	3	(3.5%)	0	(NA)	0	(30.8%)	1,900	(0.1%)
Other heat source	1	(1.7%)	0	(NA)	0	(6.5%)	4,600	(0.2%)
Child playing	1	(0.7%)	0	(NA)	0	(0.0%)	0	(0.0%)
Total	86	(100.0%)	0	(NA)	1	(100.0%)	1,954,800	(100.0%)

Note: This table shows the causes of structure fires (incident type 11) in museums or art galleries (fixed property use 152). These are fires reported to U.S. municipal fire departments and so exclude fires reported only to federal or state agencies or industrial fire brigades. Fires, civilian deaths, and civilian injuries are expressed to the nearest one, and property damage is rounded to the nearest hundred dollars. Sums may not equal totals due to rounding errors. Property damage figures have not been adjusted for inflation. The 12 major cause categories are based on a hierarchy developed by the U.S. Fire Administration. Fires in which the cause was unknown were allocated proportionally among fires of known cause.

Source: National estimates based on NFIRS and NFPA survey.

TABLE 20.17.6 Leading Causes of Structure Fires in Museums, 1999–2002 Annual Averages

Cause	*Fires*		*Civilian Deaths*		*Civilian Injuries*		*Direct Property Damage (in Dollars)*	
Heating equipment	10	(16%)	0	(NA)	0	(0%)	65,000	(6%)
Identified heating equipment	9	(14%)	0	(NA)	0	(0%)	755,000	(74%)
Confined heating equipment fire	1	(2%)	0	(NA)	0	(0%)	114,000	(11%)
Cooking equipment fires	8	(13%)	0	(NA)	3	(100%)	114,000	(11%)
Identified cooking equipment	3	(6%)	0	(NA)	3	(100%)	0	(0%)
Confined cooking fire	4	(7%)	0	(NA)	0	(0%)	1,000	(0%)
Intentional	8	(8%)	0	(NA)	0	(0%)	1,000	(0%)
Electrical distribution and lighting equipment	4	(7%)	0	(NA)	0	(0%)	0	(0%)
Candle	3	(5%)	0	(NA)	0	(0%)	0	(0%)
Torch	3	(5%)	0	(NA)	0	(0%)	12,000	(1%)
Smoking materials	2	(3%)	0	(NA)	0	(0%)	0	(0%)
Contained trash or rubbish fire	3	(5%)	0	(NA)	0	(0%)	9,000	(1%)

Note: These are the leading causes, obtained from the following list: intentional (from the NFIRS field "cause"); playing with fire (from factor contributing to ignition); confined heating (including confined chimney and confined fuel burner or boiler fires), confined cooking, and contained trash or rubbish (from incident type); identified heating, identified cooking, clothes dryer or washer, torch (including burner and soldering iron), electrical distribution and lighting equipment, medical equipment, and electronic, office or entertainment equipment (from equipment involved in ignition); smoking materials, candles, lightning, and spontaneous combustion or chemical reaction (from heat source); and mobile property involved (from mobile property involved in ignition). Exposure fires include fires with an exposure number greater than zero, as well as fires identified by heat source or factor contributing to ignition when no equipment was involved in ignition that were not intentionally set. The same fire can be listed under multiple causes, based on multiple data elements.

These are national estimates of fires reported to U.S. municipal fire departments and so exclude fires reported only to federal or state agencies or industrial fire brigades. National estimates are projections. Casualty and loss projections can be heavily influenced by the inclusion or exclusion of one unusually serious fire. Fires, deaths, and injuries are rounded to the nearest one. Direct property damage is rounded to the nearest thousand. Property damage has not been adjusted for inflation.

Source: NFIRS and NFPA survey.

- Establish locking, unlocking, entry sequences, and paths. When opening or closing a building, a clearly defined entry and exit procedure should assure continuity and complete coverage. Opening and closing procedures should be designed so the person opening the building starts at one selected point and the person closing the building finishes at the same point. This procedure assures that all critical areas are consistently checked.
- Establish procedures to inspect the building for stay-behinds. Large buildings usually have many places where someone intent on remaining in the building can avoid detection. The first step in dealing with stay-behinds is to make it as difficult as possible for unauthorized persons to get into areas where they can hide. Nonpublic areas, such as utility closets, mechanical areas, office spaces, and the like, should be locked while visitors are in the building. In some cases isolated spaces should have local daytime intrusion detectors to alert staff if an unauthorized person enters one of them. At the end of the day, it is important to search the building in a systematic way, usually starting at the top and working down and out. If possible, lock or secure building areas as they are inspected to prevent an intruder from moving back into a space after inspection. Opening and closing procedures should highlight areas that are particularly vulnerable to stay-behinds for special consideration. Where installed, the intrusion detection system may be zoned so that it can be activated in sections to help keep cleared areas secure.
- Identify other specific features of concern in the building.

3. Windows and doors should be secured with good-quality locking devices. Panic hardware on emergency exit doors allows doors to be opened from the inside and remain locked from the outside. Doors into nonpublic areas should be kept locked to prevent uncontrolled access by the general public.
4. Windows and doors should be equipped to provide an alarm on any unauthorized opening. In some communities intrusion alarms may be connected directly to the police or fire department. Alarm monitoring services also are available from commercial organizations.
5. Closed-circuit television can be extremely useful for monitoring little used spaces, exhibit areas, print rooms, and other collection study facilities, as well as emergency exits. In addition, the presence of a camera often is a psychological deterrent to illegal behavior.
6. Exterior lighting is an important element in the security program. Illuminating concealed building areas, potential entry points, and large windows let police, security patrols, and others in the neighborhood observe activity around the building. Where public utilities do not provide it, lighting should be added at all concealed approaches to the building.
7. Libraries should eliminate book drops used for after-hours book return, isolate them from the building by fire-resistant construction, or equip them with an automatic fire suppression system. Book drops are favorite targets for arsonists and vandals.[1]
8. If feasible, security patrols should inspect the building along well-planned and monitored routes at irregular intervals.
9. Staff should regularly and closely inspect ashtrays, waste receptacles, soiled linen hampers, electric heating appliances, and other places that can support fire development. Although not specifically an arson prevention measure, this routine can uncover hazards that could involve incendiarism, such as a filled wastebasket hiding a time-delay igniter, or other unusual conditions.

Electrical System. Wiring installed in accordance with the requirements of NFPA 70, *National Electrical Code*®, is equipped with overcurrent protection that opens the circuit before current flow reaches a level that dangerously overheats the conductor or its insulation. Nevertheless, overcurrent devices may fail, and under some conditions overloaded or partially grounded wiring may generate enough heat to ignite combustibles without blowing fuses or tripping circuit breakers.[2] For example, circuits subjected to flooding when a water line breaks or a steam line leaks, must be thoroughly dried. Otherwise, water can partially ground the circuit, generating excessive heat when current is applied.[3] The most common example of problems leading to failure of overcurrent protection, however, involves improperly altering the circuit by installing an improperly sized fuse or circuit breaker.[4] A comprehensive preventive maintenance program for the building's electrical distribution system is an essential element in the fire prevention program.

The proliferation of information processing equipment (computer terminals, word processors, PCs, modems, printers, and facsimile and photocopying machines) adds significant electrical loads that can exceed the existing building wiring system's capacity. More often, however, the problem is either a shortage of electrical outlets to accommodate the equipment or a shortage of outlets where they are needed. The temptation is to make the existing arrangement work by adding multiple outlet adapters to expand the capacity of an existing outlet or to use extension cords to bring power from a less conveniently placed outlet. Neither solution is acceptable. Multiple outlet adapters encourage overloading of the electrical circuit and should never be permitted. Extension cords are not an acceptable substitute for fixed wiring for the following reasons: (1) they are subject to mechanical damage, and (2) they can be overloaded easily. Extension cords usually are made with smaller gauge wire than the fixed wiring in the building. Electrical resistance increases significantly as wire size decreases and length increases. Where permitted, extension cords must be for temporary, short-term use only. The conductor must be rated to carry the current load expected over the distance it will be used. In addition, where extension cords have multiple outlet assemblies, they should have a circuit breaker at the output end to provide overcurrent protection for the extension cord. Extension cords must be protected from mechanical damage and never concealed under carpets. (See Section 8, Chapter 13, "Electrical Systems and Appliances.")

Surface temperatures of incandescent lamps vary widely. Spotlights, for example, easily can reach the ignition temperature of paper or textiles. Incandescent bulbs near, or in contact with, combustible materials may ignite them even if their surface temperature is below the ignition temperature of the combustible material. Steady application of a heat source below a combustible material's ignition temperature can generate enough heat to ignite the material, given enough time.

The cooler surface temperatures of fluorescent lamps do not present the ignition hazards of incandescent bulbs. Nevertheless, ballasts in fluorescent light fixtures generate heat and are potential ignition sources, particularly when installed in a way that traps heat. For example, ballasts mounted flush against combustible, low density, cellulose fiberboard or other materials of similar combustibility present a potentially severe fire hazard. Fluorescent light ballasts also may be a source of ignition when they fail. At a minimum, a failing ballast may generate significant quantities of acrid smoke.

Heating Equipment. Heating equipment malfunction or misuse is an important potential cause of fires. Boilers and furnaces of central heating systems should be isolated in a fire-resistant enclosure, either separate from or attached to the cultural resource property. Fixed or portable space heaters and portable heaters should not be used in combustible collection storage areas.

Because cellulosic materials, such as wood, paper, or textiles, store heat, they may ignite after prolonged contact with hot objects that are well below the materials' usual ignition temperature. Such materials should not be in contact with steam piping, heat ducts, or other low-grade heat sources.

Appliances. If not prohibited entirely, space heaters, hot plates, microwave ovens, coffee makers, and other small appliances should be rigidly regulated and closely monitored. Where permitted, each appliance should satisfy the following conditions:

- Listed by an independent testing laboratory
- Placed on a noncombustible base
- Located so they are adequately separated from combustible materials
- Located where air circulation prevents heat buildup

Those responsible for closing the building or area should have a listing of the location of each heating appliance and should inspect them as part of the building closing procedure. The inspection should ensure that the appliance works properly, that combustible materials are not touching or close to the appliance, and that appliances not necessary for building protection are turned off. If the facility has security officers, they should also have a listing of each heating appliance and should check each appliance during their rounds. Where feasible, heating appliances should be unplugged when not in use.

Smoking. Most cultural resource buildings are smoke-free facilities. Where permitted, smoking should be limited to those places, such as administrative offices, staff rest areas, and designated visitor lounges, where fire-safe practices can be monitored and controlled. As more facilities ban smoking, however, it is important to recognize that a total ban may result in surreptitious smoking in unsupervised locations, thus actually reintroducing the risk of fire from smoking practices. Where smoking is banned inside the building, adequate facilities should be provided outside the building to accommodate those who wish to smoke.

Open Flame Devices. Open flames used in building repairs, laboratory operations, or in the interpretation of historic environments are severe ignition hazards, as are hot metal sparks or slag from welding and cutting. Candles are a large part of many worship services, including both lit candles fixed in place and lit candles carried by worshipers. Use of open flame devices should require the written approval of a responsible management official. Before signing such an authorization, the official should evaluate the risk to life safety and collection materials, and should prescribe protective measures as conditions of the authorization. Management conditions for authorization should include at least:

1. Relocating combustible materials, especially irreplaceable, valuable, sensitive materials as in an exhibit or collection, a safe distance from the ignition source.
2. Requiring a fire watch of one or more trained persons with appropriate fire-extinguishing equipment. The fire watch should be on site continuously, with no other duties, while the hazardous activity is performed and should remain in the area long enough to ensure the discovery of any hidden fire after interruption or termination of the activity. A fire watch should monitor the area for at least 30 minutes after welding and cutting torches have been used.

Fuel Control

Fuel control must include all combustible contents, including any collections and ancillary records, as well as furniture, interior finish, packaging materials, and flammable liquids. Control measures include arrangement of storage to limit fire spread and separation of fuel from ignition sources. Much of this can be accomplished through good housekeeping practices. (See Section 11, Chapter 2, "Housekeeping Practices.")

Flammable Liquid Storage and Handling. Where possible, flammable and combustible liquids should be stored in fire-resistant structures isolated from the building. Where this is not feasible, small quantities of flammable or combustible liquids may be stored in approved, self-closing, flammable liquid storage cabinets. All flammable or combustible liquids permitted inside the building should be contained in safety cans. When in use, only that quantity of flammable or combustible liquid required during an 8 hour shift should be permitted outside the flammable liquid storage cabinet. It must be in safety cans until actually used. Special attention is required to ensure adequate ventilation, and ignition sources must be eliminated or carefully controlled. (See Section 7, Chapter 2, "Storage of Flammable and Combustible Liquids.")

Spontaneous Heating. Oil- and solvent-soaked cloths and rags, such as those used with oil-based paint, mineral spirits, and some cleaning products, can heat spontaneously. They should be placed in a metal can with a tightly fitting metal top immediately after use and completely removed from the building no later than the end of each day.

Fuel Geometry and Overcrowding. A useful way to consider the combustible materials contained in a cultural resource building is to see them as arranged in fixed fuel packages: exhibit cases, bookstacks, desks, tables, chairs, pews, hymnals, heavy curtains or drapery, and so on. These fuel packages also may contain quantities of movable fuel, such as loose paper, which can vary the total fuel load and radically change the ignition characteristics of individual fuel packages. Although these fuel packages usually are not contiguous, and indeed may be housed in a noncombustible building shell, they may become contiguous because of combustible interior finishes. Increasing the distance between the fuel packages and using interior finish materials, such as carpet, wall coverings, and draperies, with a low flame spread rating, minimizes the risk of fire spreading from one package to another.

Interior Finish. Interior finish materials with high flame spread rates, such as fiberboard and some textile coverings (analogous in composition to carpet floor coverings) when vertically oriented, negate the effectiveness of distance as a tool to isolate fuel packages. For example, flame can spread in low-density cellulosic fiberboard and acoustic ceiling tile, as shown in Figure 20.17.1, as fast as people can run. Decades ago flame spread index ratings for low-density cellulosic fiberboard and acoustic ceiling tile products were reported to range from 225 to 350.[5,6]

Although building test fires in 1959 demonstrated this flame spread potential, these materials still may be found in some cultural resource properties across North America.[7] Where such low-density finish materials still exist, they should be replaced. During removal it is especially important to also remove any adhesive used to attach the tile to ceilings or walls. The adhesive has been identified as a key factor in the rapid flame spread over ceiling tiles.[8] If replacement is not feasible, these materials should be encapsulated behind fire-rated gypsum board. Treatment with intumescent paint may not provide the intended protection unless this application is approved by the listing laboratory and maintained as the manufacturer prescribes.[9] Textile coverings may present a similar hazard when used in exhibits or when applied to wall surfaces unless they are specifically tested to establish an acceptable rate of flame spread when vertically installed.

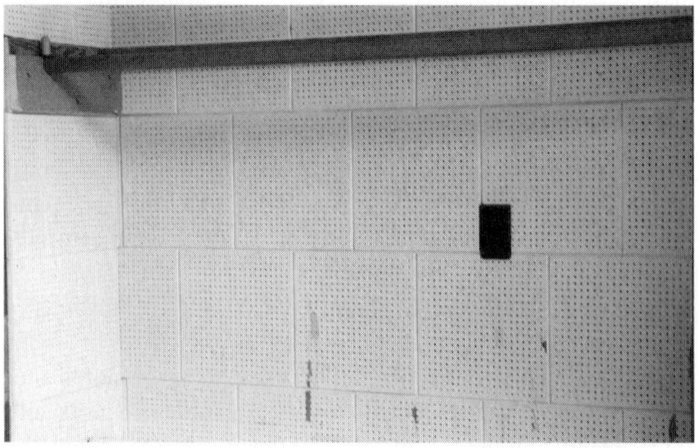

FIGURE 20.17.1 Typical Low-Density Cellulosic Acoustical Tile

Inadequate Space. Museums and libraries collect; therefore, growth of the collection is inevitable. As collections grow, staffing levels tend to grow also. Adding space is expensive and usually the last resort. These conditions cause overcrowding of both collections and staff, reducing the space between fuel packages. Overcrowding increases the risk that a fire will grow by spreading to adjacent fuel packages rather than burning itself out. Periods of overcrowding, therefore, require compensating emphasis on other elements of the fire prevention program, especially control of ignition sources.

FIRE PROTECTION FOR LIBRARY AND MUSEUM COLLECTIONS

Experience shows that early detection followed by quick action to stop fire growth can prevent large fire losses. A common element in most large-loss fires is the absence of automatic suppression systems to control or extinguish fire in its early stages. Some preservation specialists—museum curators, librarians, and archivists—believe water is a greater hazard to the building and collections than fire. They emphasize fire prevention almost exclusively, limiting fire protection to the installation of automatic detection systems. Cultural resource property fires continue to occur despite this heavy emphasis on fire prevention. Table 20.17.7 shows that 24 percent of all reported library fires occur between 9 p.m. and 9 a.m.; an additional 23 percent start between 5 p.m. and 9 p.m.—times when libraries have little or no staff on duty.[10] These off-hour periods also account for about half the property loss. However, fires have steadily declined in cultural resource properties (Tables 20.17.8, 20.17.9, and 20.17.10).

Total dependence on fire prevention and manual extinguishment places the cultural resource property at serious risk of catastrophic loss when prevention fails. The 1986 fire in the Los Angeles Central Library illustrates the point clearly. In this fire, smoke detectors warned building occupants, who evacuated safely. Nevertheless, despite timely notification to the Los Angeles Fire Department, lack of an automatic suppression system allowed the fire to spread. Bringing it under control took more than 7 hours. The fire destroyed more than 400,000 objects, and 700,000 wet books were placed in cold storage to await restoration.

Because fire prevention efforts can lessen, but not eliminate, the possibility of fire, knowledge of the options available to limit fire spread is essential. Local fire and building codes provide minimum requirements for the survival of the building and for the life safety of its occupants. Nevertheless, sole reliance on code provisions will not adequately preserve building contents, especially highly valuable collections. Fire protection features to protect the building contents are needed over and above minimum requirements that local codes impose.

Systems Approach to Fire Safety

A systems approach to fire safety is a useful management tool for selecting the appropriate level of fire protection to limit fire loss to an acceptable level. The systems approach uses decision tree analysis, failure modes and effects analysis, and other

TABLE 20.17.7 U.S. Library Structure Fires, by Time of Alarm, 1980–1998 Annual Averages

Time of Alarm	*Fires*		*Civilian Deaths*		*Civilian Injuries*		*Direct Property Damage (in Dollars)*	
12:01 a.m. to 1:00 a.m.	2	(1.2%)	0	(NA)	0	(0.0%)	4,900	(0.1%)
1:01 a.m. to 2:00 a.m.	3	(1.5%)	0	(NA)	0	(0.0%)	26,800	(0.6%)
2:01 a.m. to 3:00 a.m.	4	(2.3%)	0	(NA)	0	(0.0%)	691,900	(14.6%)
3:01 a.m. to 4:00 a.m.	2	(1.0%)	0	(NA)	0	(0.0%)	884,300	(18.6%)
4:01 a.m. to 5:00 a.m.	2	(0.8%)	0	(NA)	0	(0.0%)	115,100	(2.4%)
5:01 a.m. to 6:00 a.m.	2	(1.0%)	0	(NA)	0	(0.0%)	6,200	(0.1%)
6:01 a.m. to 7:00 a.m.	3	(1.6%)	0	(NA)	0	(0.0%)	8,800	(0.2%)
7:01 a.m. to 8:00 a.m.	4	(1.9%)	0	(NA)	0	(0.0%)	21,200	(0.4%)
8:01 a.m. to 9:00 a.m.	9	(4.5%)	0	(NA)	0	(0.0%)	44,100	(0.9%)
9:01 a.m. to 10:00 a.m.	9	(4.7%)	0	(NA)	0	(12.5%)	14,800	(0.3%)
10:01 a.m. to 11:00 a.m.	11	(5.6%)	0	(NA)	0	(25.0%)	1,993,900	(41.9%)
11:01 a.m. to Noon	10	(5.4%)	0	(NA)	0	(12.5%)	18,400	(0.4%)
12:01 p.m. to 1:00 p.m.	11	(5.8%)	0	(NA)	0	(6.3%)	14,200	(0.3%)
1:01 p.m. to 2:00 p.m.	13	(6.8%)	0	(NA)	0	(0.0%)	58,100	(1.2%)
2:01 p.m. to 3:00 p.m.	12	(5.9%)	0	(NA)	0	(0.0%)	148,000	(3.1%)
3:01 p.m. to 4:00 p.m.	14	(7.3%)	0	(NA)	0	(18.8%)	13,800	(0.3%)
4:01 p.m. to 5:00 p.m.	21	(10.8%)	0	(NA)	0	(0.0%)	38,000	(0.8%)
5:01 p.m. to 6:00 p.m.	15	(7.5%)	0	(NA)	0	(12.5%)	62,000	(1.3%)
6:01 p.m. to 7:00 p.m.	13	(6.6%)	0	(NA)	0	(0.0%)	297,400	(6.3%)
7:01 p.m. to 8:00 p.m.	9	(4.6%)	0	(NA)	0	(0.0%)	29,800	(0.6%)
8:01 p.m. to 9:00 p.m.	9	(4.8%)	0	(NA)	0	(12.5%)	21,600	(0.5%)
9:01 p.m. to 10:00 p.m.	6	(3.2%)	0	(NA)	0	(0.0%)	162,600	(3.4%)
10:01 p.m. to 11:00 p.m.	4	(2.2%)	0	(NA)	0	(0.0%)	8,800	(0.2%)
11:01 p.m. to Midnight	6	(3.0%)	0	(NA)	0	(0.0%)	69,600	(1.5%)
Total	195	(100.0%)	0	(NA)	1	(100.0%)	4,754,400	(100.0%)
Hourly average	8	(4.2%)	0	(NA)	0	(4.2%)	198,100	(4.2%)
9:01 a.m. to 5:00 p.m. Subtotal	102	(52.4%)	0	(NA)	1	(75.0%)	2,299,200	(48.4%)
9:01 a.m. to 5:00 p.m. Hourly average	13	(6.5%)	0	(NA)	0	(9.4%)	287,400	(6.0%)
5:01 p.m. to 9:00 p.m. Subtotal	46	(23.4%)	0	(NA)	0	(25.0%)	410,800	(8.6%)
5:01 p.m. to 9:00 p.m. Hourly average	11	(5.9%)	0	(NA)	0	(6.3%)	102,700	(2.2%)
9:01 p.m. to 9:00 a.m. Subtotal	47	(24.2%)	0	(NA)	0	(0.0%)	2,044,300	(43.0%)
9:01 p.m. to 9:00 a.m. Hourly average	4	(2.0%)	0	(NA)	0	(0.0%)	170,400	(3.6%)

Note: This table shows the alarm times for structure fires (incident type 11) in libraries (fixed property use 151). These are fires reported to U.S. municipal fire departments and so exclude fires reported only to federal or state agencies or industrial fire brigades. Fires, civilian deaths, and civilian injuries are expressed to the nearest one, and property damage is rounded to the nearest hundred dollars. Sums may not equal totals due to rounding errors. Property damage figures have not been adjusted for inflation.

Source: National estimates based on NFIRS and NFPA survey.

systems techniques to identify hazards, assess probability, establish maximum acceptable fire loss, and identify fire defense alternatives.

A critical element in the systems approach is to develop fire safety objectives for the facility based on life safety considerations, the value and vulnerability of the collections, and obligations for continuity of service. The fire safety objectives adopted by the Library of Congress in Washington, DC, may provide a useful reference point.[11] The General Firesafety Objectives and Critical Space Objectives, shown graphically in Figure 20.17.2, are similar to those the U.S. General Services Administration (GSA) originally adopted for federal office buildings nationwide.[12] This graph shows the fire safety objectives for Library of Congress buildings and represents the desired minimum probability of success in limiting a fire's growth from its start to full building involvement. Adoption of

TABLE 20.17.8 Structure Fires in Libraries by Year, 1980–2002

Year	Fires	Civilian Deaths	Civilian Injuries	Direct Property Damage (in Dollars)
1980	386	0	0	2,170,000
1981	266	0	0	215,000
1982	276	0	0	13,864,000
1983	194	0	0	3,557,000
1984	238	0	3	225,000
1985	279	0	0	1,424,000
1986	206	0	5	42,859,000
1987	197	0	0	15,163,000
1988	150	0	0	482,000
1989	151	0	0	1,916,000
1990	171	0	2	679,000
1991	175	0	0	118,000
1992	158	0	1	1,940,000
1993	124	0	0	2,264,000
1994	144	0	0	170,000
1995	131	0	0	927,000
1996	182	0	2	1,187,000
1997	140	0	0	341,000
1998	132	0	2	833,000
1999	153	0	0	2,195,000
2000	102	0	0	1,846,000
2001	115	0	0	1,015,000
2002	118	0	0	342,000

Note: This table shows the structure fire (incident type 11 through 1998 and incident types 110–129 in 1999–2002) experience by year in libraries (fixed property use 151). These are fires reported to U.S. municipal fire departments and so exclude fires reported only to federal or state agencies or industrial fire brigades. Fires, deaths, and injuries are rounded to the nearest one; direct property damage is rounded to the nearest thousand. Property damage has not been adjusted for inflation.

Source: National estimates based on NFIRS and NFPA survey.

TABLE 20.17.9 Structure Fires in Museums and Art Galleries, by Year, 1980–2002

Year	Fires	Civilian Deaths	Civilian Injuries	Direct Property Damage (in Dollars)
1980	98	0	0	880,000
1981	120	0	0	1,096,000
1982	105	0	0	544,000
1983	72	0	0	828,000
1984	117	0	7	4,702,000
1985	105	0	0	8,304,000
1986	137	0	2	2,045,000
1987	82	0	2	599,000
1988	86	0	0	363,000
1989	101	0	3	7,633,000
1990	64	0	0	397,000
1991	84	0	1	341,000
1992	79	0	3	694,000
1993	78	0	2	2,438,000
1994	59	0	2	3,708,000
1995	78	0	1	1,025,000
1996	59	0	2	734,000
1997	70	0	0	419,000
1998	42	0	0	390,000
1999	55	0	0	688,000
2000	71	0	14	414,000
2001	55	0	0	2,319,000
2002	59	0	0	658,000

Note: This table shows the structure fire (incident type 11 through 1998 and incident types 110–129 in 1999–2002) experience by year in museums or art galleries (fixed property use 152). These are fires reported to U.S. municipal fire departments and so exclude fires reported only to federal or state agencies or industrial fire brigades. Fires, deaths, and injuries are rounded to the nearest one; direct property damage is rounded to the nearest thousand. Property damage has not been adjusted for inflation.

Source: National estimates based on NFIRS and NFPA survey.

acceptable limits of fire loss should reconcile the cost of the fire defense system to achieve those limits with the resources available to the institution.[13]

Designing the Fire Safety System

The specific design selected for the fire protection system in a typical cultural resource property depends on the value of the exhibits, collections, or other unique contents and the value and characteristics of the building and its fuel load. At a minimum, the system should include fire detection, alarm notification, emergency communication, manual extinguishment, automatic fire suppression, protection for special hazards and other passive construction elements for safe occupant egress, limiting fire spread, and isolating hazardous operations and building systems.

Detection and Alarm. A fire detection and alarm system should be installed throughout the building. The system should include smoke detectors in all exhibit galleries, reading rooms, and collection storage areas; smoke, heat, or flame detectors, as appropriate, should be installed in other parts of the building. From 1994 to 1998, 39 percent of reported U.S. structure fires in churches and related properties and 70 percent in museums and libraries were reported with automatic fire detection present.

A detection and alarm system should alert building occupants of an unwanted fire before it becomes a threat. A properly designed and installed system will alert occupants in time to evacuate in an orderly manner. The system also will facilitate prompt notification of the fire service. Ideally the detection system also provides an opportunity for trained building staff to extinguish the fire before automatic fire suppression equipment activates or the fire service arrives. (Section 14 of this handbook describes types of detection and alarm systems.) Care and good judgment are imperative, however. Fire in concealed spaces can burn for a considerable period before activating detection equipment. In 1994–1998, roughly 10 percent of reported U.S.

TABLE 20.17.10 Structure Fires in Places of Worship and Funeral Parlors, by Year, 1980–2002

				Direct Property Damage (in Millions of Dollars)	
Year	*Fires*	*Civilian Deaths*	*Civilian Injuries*	*As Reported*	*In 2002 Dollars*
1980	3500	2	23	62.1	135.7
1981	3340	0	14	79.2	156.4
1982	3350	16	58	43.3	80.6
1983	2850	7	26	114.0	205.7
1984	2930	3	45	50.4	87.1
1985	3020	0	30	60.5	101.0
1986	2770	2	29	51.5	84.6
1987	2660	4	23	51.7	81.8
1988	2360	4	14	69.0	105.0
1989	2160	3	11	59.0	85.6
1990	2100	0	17	62.1	85.6
1991	2120	2	34	56.9	75.1
1992	2190	0	28	70.7	90.7
1993	2030	5	41	57.7	71.8
1994	2040	1	25	60.7	73.7
1995	1890	5	62	52.1	61.5
1996	2180	1	27	62.1	71.3
1997	1950	0	25	43.6	48.9
1998	1910	4	25	68.0	75.1
1999	2000	3	26	100.8	108.8
2000	1620	0	16	94.9	99.2
2001	1750	0	24	85.2	86.6
2002	1670	1	15	104.3	104.3

Note: These are national estimates of fires reported to U.S. municipal fire departments and so exclude fires reported only to federal or state agencies or industrial fire brigades. National estimates are projections. Casualty and loss projections can be heavily influenced by the inclusion or exclusion of one unusually serious fire. Fires are rounded to the nearest ten, civilian deaths and injuries are rounded to the nearest one, and direct property damage is rounded to the nearest hundred thousand dollars.

Source: NFIRS and NFPA survey. Inflation adjustments were based on U.S. Census Bureau's *Statistical Abstract of the United States: 2006,* "Table 705, Purchasing Power of the Dollar."

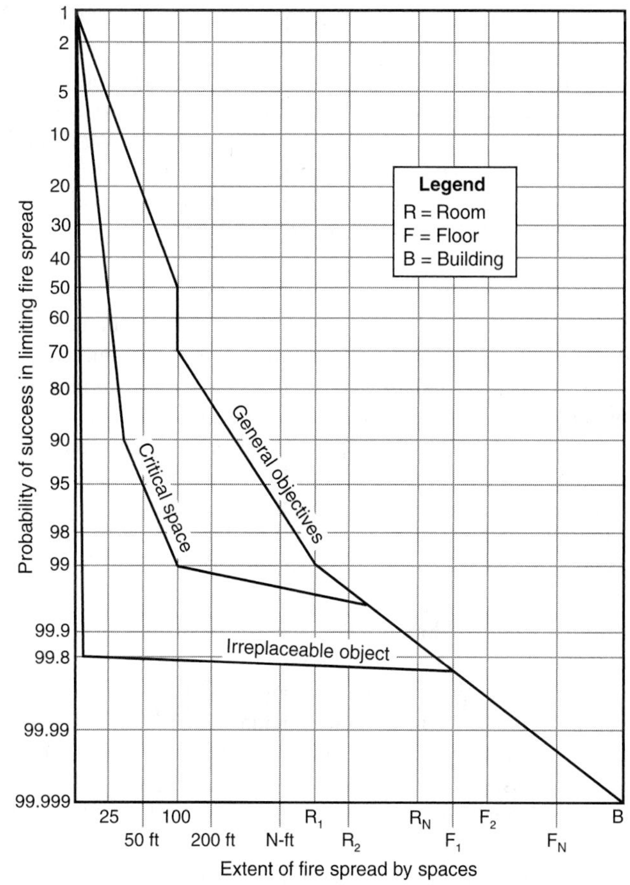

FIGURE 20.17.2 Illustrative Graphic Probability Analysis of Fire Safety Objectives

structure fires in libraries and museums and roughly 15 percent in places of worship began in concealed spaces. Those responding to investigate an alarm must be alert to signs that fire is well established. If there is any doubt, evacuate. Attempting to manually suppress a well-established, concealed space fire can lead to tragedy. When the fire breaks out of the concealed space, it can spread very quickly.

An automatic sprinkler system also can provide the alarm when the first sprinkler opens and water begins to flow in the system. However, this detection occurs at a later stage of fire development when fire and smoke may hamper orderly evacuation. Quick-response (QR) sprinklers may be an exception because they respond to heat at an earlier stage of fire development than standard sprinklers—in some configurations only seconds later than smoke detectors. For this reason some libraries, including the National Library of Canada, the National Library of Scotland, the New British Library, the U.S. Library of Congress, and the U.S. National Archives are installing QR sprinklers to protect their collection storage areas. (See Section 16, Chapter 6, "Residential Sprinkler Systems.")

In addition to sounding an alarm throughout the building, the detection and alarm system should be connected to a central station, the local fire department, or some other acceptable monitoring facility. The value of a detection system is as a communications tool. The detection system itself takes no action to control or extinguish fire. A local alarm may be adequate for evacuating building occupants, but a local alarm alone does not summon the fire department or other emergency assistance. This is particularly true when the building is unoccupied. For this reason connection of the detection system to a central station or equivalent is recommended.

A qualified fire protection specialist or engineer with experience in cultural resource property protection should design the fire detection and alarm systems to ensure proper building coverage and to minimize the risk of unwanted alarms. The designer must have knowledge of, and experience in, fire behavior in the type of facility to properly select fire detectors for the threat and the ambient environment. The designer must also be well versed in the requirements of applicable codes and standards.

After installation and acceptance tests have been completed, a regular test and maintenance program should be established. This is very important because testing is the only way to determine that no part of the detection and alarm system has failed.[14] Furthermore, because the sensitivity of smoke detectors can change as dust and dirt accumulate, periodic inspection and cleaning are needed to keep the detector working within its intended sensitivity range. (See Section 14, Chapter 2, "Automatic Fire Detectors.")

Communication. A public address system should be considered, especially in very large facilities, to provide emergency voice instructions and information to facilitate evacuation. Cultural resource properties can have complicated egress routes. If unfamiliar with the building layout, the general public may experience difficulty finding appropriate means of egress. Egress routes should be properly marked by illuminated exit signs as required by NFPA *101*®, *Life Safety Code*®, and *NFPA 5000*®, *Building Construction and Safety Code*®.

Manual Extinguishment. Portable extinguishers in the hands of trained users constitute an institution's first line of fire attack. To prevent the use of the wrong class of extinguisher on a particular fire, some institutions provide only multipurpose portable extinguishers. These should be appropriately located and regularly inspected and maintained, so they are fully charged and operational when needed. (See Section 17, Chapter 5, "Fire Extinguisher Use and Maintenance.")

Occupant-use standpipe hose lines require specific hands-on training and drills to avoid personal injury and unnecessary property damage. Hose lines must be inspected at least annually and should be service tested when doubtful conditions are identified. Unfortunately, because many building occupants are not trained to properly use a fire hose and because of a general tendency not to inspect and test hoses as required, municipal fire departments may arrive at a fire to find the occupant hose used ineffectively, sometimes dangerously, or not at all.

Obviously, the fire department also provides manual extinguishment. In buildings without automatic sprinkler systems, it follows occupant fire suppression efforts as the second and final line of fire suppression defense to control loss from fire. If the fire area has reached 2500 to 3000 ft^2 (232 to 279 m^2) at the time of water application, the fire may be confined but not readily extinguished. Figure 20.17.3 suggests that the probability of fire department success actually begins to drop rapidly when fire areas exceed 750 to 1500 ft^2 (70 to 140 m^2).[15]

The most significant concern with manual extinguishment is that once fire enters the free burning phase, fire damage increases exponentially until the fire is under control.[16] Fire protection systems that depend entirely on manual extinguishment risk disaster if human response is delayed or unavailable.

Automatic Sprinklers. As stated earlier, lack of an automatic suppression system is a major contributing factor to large-loss fires in cultural resource properties. Sprinkler systems have been shown to reliably and effectively minimize the risk of large-loss fires in cultural properties.[16] A Factory Mutual Research Corporation (FMRC, now FM Global Research) study found that the average dollar loss in fires with adequate sprinkler protection in the 5 year period 1984 through 1988 was 5.8 times less than the average loss during the same period in fires studied without adequate sprinkler protection. For this study, fires where adequate sprinkler protection existed were those reported to FMRC in which (1) sprinklers were in service, (2) there were no sprinkler system or water supply deficiencies, and (3) sprinkler density was appropriate for the risk.[17] In 1994–1998 U.S. structure fires reported to local fire departments, sprinklers were present on only 4 percent of fires in places of worship and 32 percent of library and museum fires. Average dollar loss per fire was reduced by sprinklers by 32 percent in places of worship and by 72 percent in libraries and museums. This is roughly consistent with the general finding that average loss is reduced by one-half to two-thirds.

For many years, cultural resource management professionals opposed automatic water sprinkler protection, fearing water damage even more than fire damage. Many library and museum planning references reflect this attitude.[18–20] Through the years libraries and museums have experienced water damage from various sources: roof leaks, storm damage, plumbing problems, rivers overflowing, and so on. By comparison, water damage from sprinklers is rare.

Water damage is more likely, however, when fire department hose lines are used to fight fires. Automatic sprinklers actually minimize the potential for water damage. An automatic sprinkler releases 20 to 25 gpm (76 to 95 L/min) in a spray pattern, in contrast to the 150 to 250 gpm (568 to 946 L/min) of pressurized water from each fire fighter's hose stream. Most fires in buildings with automatic sprinklers are controlled with fewer than five sprinklers opening, which collectively release less water per minute than one hose stream. Hoses can sweep materials from shelves and displays into a disorganized mass on a flooded floor. Prospects of salvaging wet materials that remained in place under the relatively gentle action of sprinklers are much better than for materials knocked to the floor, soaked, and possibly trampled on.

Another consideration is that sprinklers discharge water directly in the area of the fire. Sprinklers respond to heat, and only those in the direct fire area become sufficiently hot to open. Fire department hose streams, on the other hand, must be directed to the general area of the fire until smoke clears sufficiently for fire fighters to find and soak the concentration of fire. Therefore, whereas sprinklers tend to restrict damage to the room of origin, fire department hose streams can spread water damage much more widely.

Finally, sprinklers operate early in fire growth, reducing the amount of water needed to extinguish the fire. Fire department hose streams are used much later in the growth of the fire, usually after free burning begins. Therefore, extinguishing fire with a fire department hose stream requires significantly more water. The combination of more water flowing, more area to cover, and more water needed for extinguishment means that fire department hose streams pour huge quantities of water on a fire. This water has to go somewhere: it floods out of the fire area through every available drain and crack and drains to the building's lowest point. Therefore, fires on upper floors can result in extensive water damage to materials many floors below. The

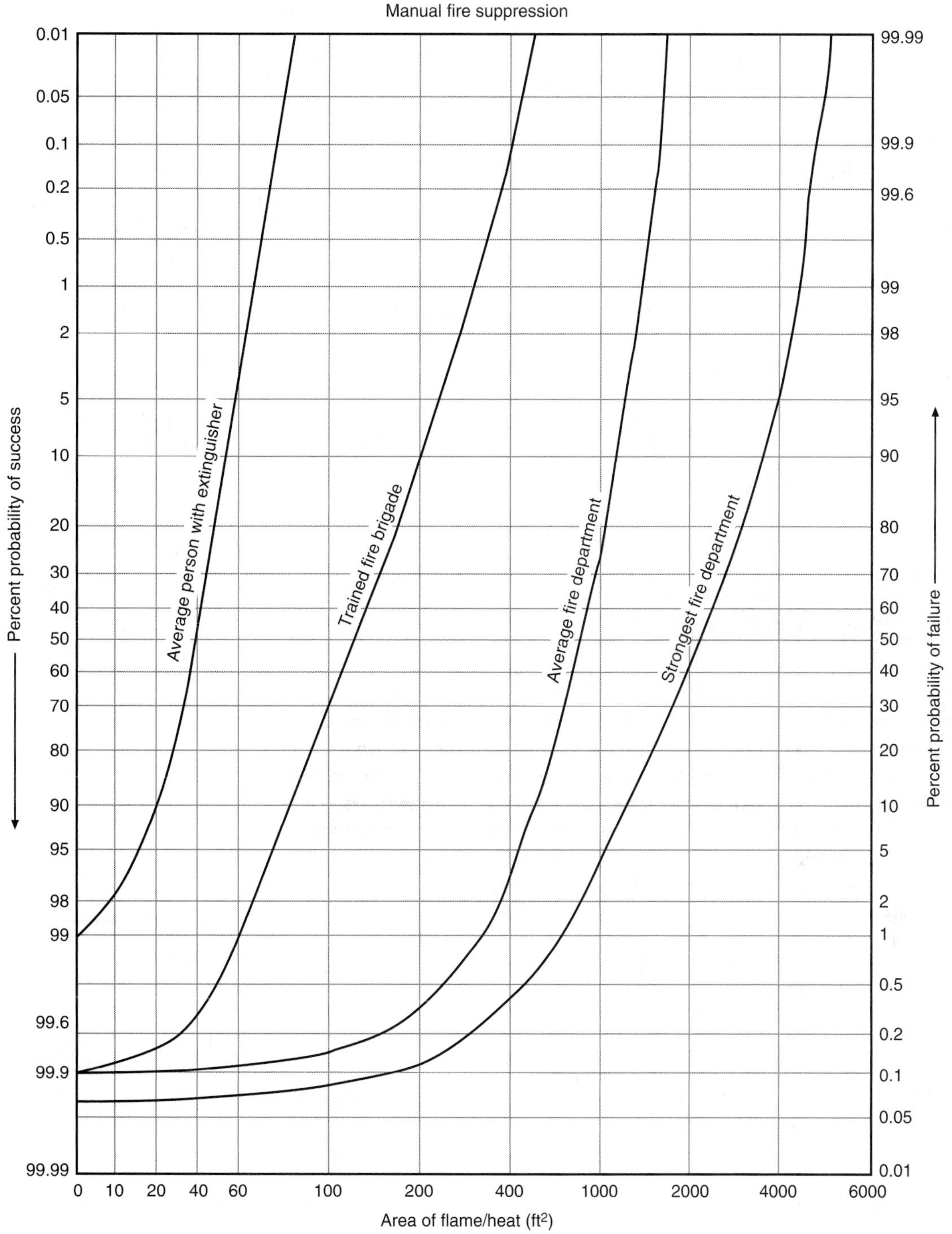

FIGURE 20.17.3 Illustrative Graph of Probability of Success at Different Levels of Manual Extinguishment

use of high-density compact storage modules on lower floors and in basements has magnified this problem in recent years. Compact movable storage modules for libraries significantly increase floor load requirements, and, especially in retrofits, only the ground floor or basement of a building has sufficient floor loading capacity. This concentrates collections in a building's lowest areas, so fighting a fire on an upper floor, or on the roof, can result in significant water damage.

Alternatives to the standard wet-pipe sprinkler system, such as on/off sprinklers and automatic recycling systems, minimize water damage after a fire has been extinguished.

Another alternative, the preaction sprinkler system, may be used where fear of water damage from damaged sprinklers or broken piping is a significant concern. The preaction sprinkler system piping is dry until a signal from an automatic fire detection system opens the water supply valve. Failure of the fire detection system, however, eliminates the automatic operation of a preaction sprinkler system and requires manual operation of the water supply valve. The fire detection system, then, is a single point of failure in a preaction system, reducing its reliability below that of a wet-pipe sprinkler system. Furthermore, preaction systems require higher levels of regular maintenance to preclude additional potential failure modes. This further reduces their reliability relative to wet-pipe systems. Higher installation and maintenance costs, and less reliability, are the trade-offs for any increased confidence that a preaction system is less likely to accidentally release water than a wet-pipe system. For reasons of reliability, maintainability, and cost, facility owners may elect to install wet-pipe sprinkler systems or even convert their preaction systems to wet pipe.

Corrosion damage in dry pipe and preaction sprinkler systems is emerging as a significant concern in museums and libraries. Oxidation caused by water trapped at low points in sprinkler piping, microbiologically influenced corrosion (MIC), or a combination thereof, can cause severe damage to pipe walls and joints in a relatively short time. Over the last 3 years, for example, one museum has replaced severely damaged systems in two of its buildings—one less than 10 years old and the other 20 years old. At a minimum, where such systems are installed, pipe interiors should be inspected regularly in accordance with NFPA 25, *Standard for the Inspection, Testing, and Maintenance of Water-Based Fire Protection Systems.*

Sprinkler systems retrofitted into operating cultural resource facilities can pose a problem when the system is initially charged with water. Final acceptance testing of a sprinkler system requires a 2-hour 200 psi (1034 kPa) hydrostatic test on all piping, fixtures, and sprinklers. Newly installed sprinkler systems can leak, at least a little, when the system is first charged. This is unacceptable where collections are still in place. One solution, used by the Office of the Architect of the U.S. Capitol in the installation of wet-pipe sprinkler systems in Library of Congress bookstacks, requires pneumatic testing of each system before proceeding with normally required hydrostatic testing.

Where sprinkler systems are used in special or high-value areas, those items especially vulnerable to water damage should be stored in cabinets, manuscript boxes, or other appropriate containers. This practice serves several purposes: (1) containerized materials are more difficult to ignite, (2) the containers not only shield contents from water spray in the event of sprinkler discharge but also from intrusion of water from other sources (for example, roof leaks, plumbing problems, etc.), and (3) containers protect contents from smoke damage.[21]

Since about 1970, a number of new and existing libraries and museums have installed automatic sprinkler systems to achieve fire safety objectives and to keep fire risk within manageable, and often insurable, limits. The reduction in insurance premiums can pay off the sprinkler system's installation cost in a few years.[22] Even if the presence of automatic sprinklers does not reduce insurance premiums, their presence may make the facility a more attractive and marketable risk. This can be a significant advantage in getting competitive bids on a facility's property insurance program. (See Section 16, Chapter 1, "Principles of Automatic Sprinkler System Performance," and Section 16, Chapter 2, "Automatic Sprinklers.")

Protection for Special Risks. Areas containing highly valuable or especially vulnerable collections or equipment, or areas essential for continuity of operations, may require a higher level of fire protection to minimize damage or to keep interruption of service within acceptable limits than the combination of a smoke detection system with automatic sprinklers can provide.[22] NFPA 550, *Guide to the Fire Safety Concepts Tree,* is an excellent tool to help managers assess the effectiveness of fire protection strategies, such as installing special fire protection systems or other techniques to achieve higher protection levels within the limits of affordability.[23]

In devising protection strategies for special risks, particular attention should be given to passive fire protection, for example, using special fire- and water-resistant vaults, cabinets, manuscript boxes, or other containers to protect highly valuable collection items. Passive features may be less expensive to install and maintain and may, over time, be more reliable than more complicated alternatives. Nevertheless, relatively low levels of heat can destroy film and other heat-sensitive materials. Therefore, passive features are not a substitute for timely detection and suppression; rather, a combination of active and passive fire protection elements increases the likelihood that sensitive, highly valuable contents, furnishings, and finishes can survive a fire intact. (See Section 9, Chapter 8, "Protection of Records.")

Some items may be so valuable, rare, or vulnerable that their protection becomes one of the institution's highest priorities: the only acceptable level of loss is zero. When this is true, the institution may opt for a special protection system in addition to automatic sprinklers to provide nearly instantaneous response. Such special systems may include sophisticated air-sampling smoke detection, flame detectors, linear heat detectors, or other rapid-detection devices that automatically activate special fire suppression systems, using a gaseous agent or a water mist system. Everything else being equal, a fire in a space protected with a special protection system will be extinguished in the first seconds of combustion, thus limiting damage to the lowest possible level.

Unless it at least matches the automatic sprinkler system's reliability and maintainability, the special system installed for this purpose should be used in combination with, and not as a substitute for, the sprinkler system. The installation cost of a special system to augment a standard automatic sprinkler system should be justified based on the extraordinary value and/or irreplaceability of the items it protects or because it is required for continuity of operations that cannot accept any downtime, such as in the control room for the facility fire protection/security systems and building utilities. The justification should demonstrate a need for a very high probability of success in confining fire growth to an area significantly smaller than would be possible using standard automatic sprinklers alone—for example, less than 100 ft^2 (9.3 m^2). A sprinkler system is a vital backup to the special protection system, however, if the special system fails to extinguish the fire.

Halon 1301 often was used to provide this extra level of protection. Cultural institutions found it particularly attractive because it could be used in normally occupied areas, rapidly extinguished the flaming portion of fires, left no residue, and was not known to harm objects chemically or physically. The environmental issues associated with halon 1301, however, have rendered its use impractical for the majority of applications. See Section 17, Chapter 6, "Halon and Halon Replacement Agents and Systems," for more information on halon 1301 and halon alternatives.

Water Mist. Water closely fits all requirements of the ideal fire suppression agent. It is safe for the environment and for people, it has excellent extinguishment properties, and it has the advantages of being both inexpensive and abundant. A relatively recent development in fire protection, water mist technology promises to provide all advantages of water with less subsidiary damage and much faster response. In addition, facilities in remote locations, where the cost of installing a water supply for a sprinkler system is prohibitive, may find that water mist systems with self-contained water supplies, or with relatively small water supply tanks, can provide cost-effective fire protection. For more information, see Section 16, Chapter 8, "Water Mist Fire Suppression Systems."

Other Special Hazards. Although the same fire safety principles are applicable to all cultural resource properties, several activities common to museums and some libraries require special attention. These include the following:

- Storing art and other valuable objects
- Packing and unpacking traveling exhibits
- Storing shipping crates and packing materials
- Cleaning and restoring art and other objects
- Constructing and renovating displays

Areas where these activities occur should be isolated and sprinklered. Good practice limits storage of combustible materials to the minimum required for the current exhibit(s) under preparation or being dismantled, with all other materials stored off-site.

Places of worship also house activities requiring special attention. These include the following:

- Storing combustible decorative materials used in services, lawn mowers, and other gasoline powered equipment, and candles
- Operating kitchen and cooking facilities
- Operating child-care and nursery facilities
- Operating temporary shelters for the homeless

These activities should be monitored carefully and the areas should be protected by an automatic fire suppression system. Storage should be controlled to limit the quantity of combustible materials, and all flammable materials or gasoline-powered equipment should be stored away from the structure.

CONSTRUCTION CONSIDERATIONS

Intrinsic design features should include fire safety aspects of site planning, fire-resistant construction, interior finish smoke control, water supply for fire protection, and special requirements for underground structures. Topics deserving special attention in this chapter are compartmentation, means of egress, lighting, and gallery flexibility.

Compartmentation

A well-protected building is subdivided into compartments where walls provide barriers to the spread of fire. Compartments should be as small as possible, and walls should be designed to resist the estimated fire duration, based on maximum fuel loads in the compartments. Where small fire compartments would restrict flexible use of space, the installation of automatic sprinkler systems permits larger compartment areas and compensates for heavy fuel loads in places like collection storage areas and bookstacks.

Smoke damages valuable contents and harms occupants. Fire barriers should confine smoke to the compartment of fire origin. Fire doors protecting openings in these walls must be self-closing or automatic-closing. Self-closing fire doors must never be propped open by wedges, "kick-down" doorstops, or other unapproved means. Where it may be necessary for efficient operations to hold open these doors, this may be done only where automatic devices, such as electromagnetic hold-open devices installed in compliance with NFPA *101,* and *NFPA 5000,* automatically release the door on a signal from a smoke detector or from the fire detection system. In the past, some building codes allowed fusible link assemblies to be used to hold doors open with automatic door closers. They are not acceptable for smoke control or life safety because they depend on heat at the door to release them. By the time the fusible link reaches its release temperature, the fire has already made the door opening unusable, and smoke, which precedes the fire, has already spread beyond the space.

High-hazard contents areas where large quantities of combustible material are used or stored should be separated by fire walls from areas with large exposure of people or sensitive, valuable contents, such as exhibit galleries, reading rooms, other public areas, bookstacks, and collection storage areas. These high-hazard contents areas include carpenter shops; display or exhibit preparation shops; research, restoration, and conservation laboratories; paint rooms; packing rooms; and restaurant kitchens, among other places. When possible, hazardous materials such as flammable liquids, including some paints, should be housed in a structure separate from the building. Fire barrier walls protecting high-hazard areas should be designed to withstand fires involving the maximum fuel loads they will enclose rather than the minimum building code requirements.

Means of Egress

Library and museum security arrangements commonly require all patrons and employees to enter and leave the building at one or two closely monitored points. Unfortunately, this often means that other doors required by NFPA *101* and *NFPA 5000* for exit access or egress are locked. This problem most often arises in museums and libraries with valuable collections and in libraries with heavily used reference collections, such as college and university libraries. Use of electromagnetic and electromechanical door locking systems is gaining acceptance as a way to resolve this conflict between life safety and security. Such systems should include features that provide a level of life safety equivalent to that NFPA *101* and *NFPA 5000* require.

NFPA *101* and *NFPA 5000* allow delayed release locks, with strict limitations, in assembly occupancies, provided automatic sprinklers or fire detectors protect the entire building. Also see NFPA 909 and NFPA 914. Places of worship typically lack the need for such close monitoring and may not limit the number of points of entry.

Attendance in exhibition galleries and reading rooms varies with the exhibit's popularity and the season. For example, a blockbuster museum exhibit draws thousands of visitors each day. Places of worship will see peak attendance in conjunction with religious holidays and certain events, such as weddings. During periods of high attendance, museums and libraries must control occupant loading of the building to ensure egress capacity is not exceeded.[24] Particularly at peak times, a complete emergency plan and a well-trained staff are critical. Staff must take the lead in helping visitors evacuate safely, especially those with disabilities that might make emergency evacuation difficult. As mentioned previously in this chapter, the use of voice communications should be considered for large facilities or those with high attendance or complex egress paths. Voice communications facilitate coordination and reduce occupants' fears and anxieties during evacuation.

Lighting

Art museums typically use as much natural light as possible. They often have features such as glass roofs, light-diffusing glass ceilings, and window walls, which all increase the museum's vulnerability to fire exposure. Conversely, to protect collections from ultraviolet radiation and achieve complete light control, some museums have minimal wall and roof openings. Complex wiring systems carrying unusually heavy electrical loads compensate for the absence of natural light in these buildings. In addition to general area lighting, museums use independent light sources for case and exhibit lighting. Therefore, museums need numerous electrical outlets in floors, walls, and ceilings to provide flexibility for frequent exhibit changes and to avoid dangerous use of extension cords. Electrical installations should comply with NFPA 70.

Gallery Flexibility

Movable walls, temporary furring, and lightweight partitions facilitate rearranging exhibit spaces and changing exhibits. Such features, however, should not be allowed to impede occupants' movement in an emergency, nor should materials used increase fire risk by adding significant quantities of combustible material to the building's fuel load.

FIRE EMERGENCY MANAGEMENT

Managing a cultural resource facility fire involves decisions and actions necessary to mitigate the consequences before, during, and immediately following an incident. Effective management includes continuous monitoring to ensure that fire protection systems and features are always operational and never degraded or defeated by space changes or other building modifications. This also includes providing emergency electric power to support emergency lighting, communications, security systems, and fire protection systems. (See Section 10, Chapter 1, "Emergency and Standby Power Supplies.")

At a minimum, a viable fire emergency plan should provide for planning with the fire department and pre-emergency training of all building staff in evacuation and salvage operations. (See Section 12, Chapter 18, "Pre-Incident Planning for Emergency Response.") The decision to establish fire brigades should depend on whether the building(s) are close enough to a municipal or county fire department for timely response and whether employees are expected to use portable fire extinguishers and standpipe hose lines. In deciding whether to require employees to use fire-fighting equipment, management must be prepared to comply with state and federal regulations for protective clothing, training, and maintenance of fire-fighting equipment.[25] (See Section 12, Chapter 9, "Fire and Emergency Services Protective Clothing and Protective Equipment.") In addition to safety considerations, emphasis should be placed on minimizing water damage and protecting or removing endangered, highly valuable collections. Prefire planning also must provide security for valuable materials after their removal from the building.

DAMAGE LIMITATION

Using freeze/vacuum drying techniques, library preservation specialists have been successful in limiting damage to water-soaked library, archival, and other collection materials. However, water is only one hazard to which collections are vulnerable during a fire. Others include smoke, acids contained in combustion products, and chemical agents used in fire fighting. These hazards perhaps endanger museum collections more than water.

Damage Limitation in Places of Worship and Museums

With much higher values per item and fewer items than libraries, museums and places of worship must concentrate damage limitation efforts on removing endangered collections from the fire area to a safe location as quickly and carefully as possible. Conservation-oriented fire-fighting strategies and techniques enhance salvage efforts and minimize collection losses.

The Winterthur Museum in Wilmington, Delaware, has developed fire-fighting techniques that other museums and libraries might adopt.[26,27] Fire-fighting efforts are divided into three concurrent phases that the fire marshal and staff direct: (1) collection protection and damage limitation operations, led by the housekeeping supervisor and staff; (2) security for collections removed from the fire area, which is the responsibility of the security supervisor and staff; and (3) overall coordination, provided by the building superintendent or a designee.

Damage Limitation in Libraries

The success and cost of limiting damage in water-soaked library collections depend on advance planning and how wet the materials are. Freeze/vacuum drying very effectively removes water and smoke odors, while using ethylene oxide, a sterilizing agent, during the process arrests the mold growth. Freeze/vacuum drying cannot, however, restore physical damage inflicted by hose streams, trampling, or mishandling.

Before the Fire. Planning for damage limitation efforts before a fire must include the following:

1. Establishing priorities. This facilitates decision making under emergency conditions by identifying, in advance, the items or collections to save first.
2. Identifying preservation specialists who can provide needed guidance
3. Identifying sources of materials, equipment, and facilities to support damage limitation that are available on short notice
4. Organizing and training employees who will be needed in the damage limitation effort during and after the fire
5. Orienting and training the fire service to understand where vulnerable or especially valuable collections or objects are stored. The fire department should prepare a prefire plan that takes these factors into account and provides ongoing damage limitation during fire suppression operations.

During the Fire. Damage limitation efforts during the fire include:

1. Removing endangered highly valued collections if this can be done without placing staff at risk. Where this is not possible, the fire service may perform this function with guidance.
2. Using tarpaulins or plastic sheeting to protect materials that remain in or near the fire area, but are not directly involved in the fire, from water. Here, too, staff must be alert to hazards and must not place themselves at risk to save objects. A well-developed fire department prefire plan will include provisions to accomplish these objectives.

After the Fire. Damage limitation efforts after the fire include:

1. Wrapping and freezing damaged articles
2. Obtaining guidance from a preservation specialist experienced in damage limitation
3. Determining appropriate restoration procedures

Much less damage limitation and restoration work should be needed in facilities protected by automatic sprinklers. Water absorption is minimized when materials are left on shelves undisturbed by the gentler action of automatic sprinklers, as opposed to hose streams' more forceful action. An automatic sprinkler system also greatly reduces the quantity of materials requiring restoration by limiting the size of the fire area to that covered by the operation of one or just a few sprinklers.[28]

FIRE SAFETY IMPLICATIONS OF AUTOMATION AND NEW TECHNOLOGY

Automation of Library Catalogs and Museum Accession Records

Automation has replaced traditional card catalogs and paper museum accession records in most libraries. Continuity of public service increasingly depends on computers and necessitates a high level of fire protection including automatic suppression to ensure continuity of operation. Duplicates of magnetic media containing a library's computer-based catalog or a museum's accession records should be maintained in a safe, remote, off-site location.

Bookstacks

Multitier Bookstacks. Bookstacks, modeled after those developed for the U.S. Library of Congress in 1893, have been used for several decades in many libraries (Figure 20.17.4). Typically, unprotected iron or steel columns and beams at intervals of 7 ft (2.14 m) support decks or tiers. Vertical openings between decks permit heating of bookstack areas by convection or air currents. (See "Deck slit" in Figure 20.17.5.) Under fire conditions, these same openings function as flues to accelerate vertical fire spread to the tiers above.

Smoke barriers should be installed in these vertical openings, or deck slits, to facilitate smoke detection on the tier or deck of fire origin. This was not done when the smoke detection system was installed in the multitier bookstack of the Los Angeles Central Public Library because a ducted ventilation system had not been installed for bookstacks. When an arsonist set a fire on the fifth tier, the first detectors to activate were on the sixth tier, one tier above the tier of fire origin. A delay in finding the fire resulted, and occupants lost the opportunity to stop the fire with portable extinguishers while it was small, with catastrophic results.[29] It took nearly 350 fire fighters and over 70 pieces of fire apparatus 7 hours to extinguish the ensuing inferno.[30]

Modern versions of these systems are still sold but without vertical openings in the modules (Figure 20.17.6). Unprotected steel support structures are vulnerable to collapse in a fire, however. Cast iron and steel structural members lose strength at high temperatures encountered in fires and may collapse. For this reason, the fire service may not be able to enter a multitier bookstack for manual fire suppression. This also applies to any variation on this bookstack design that uses exposed steel structural elements. Because it may be impossible for the fire service to provide manual fire suppression in bookstacks of this or similar design, it is essential that the bookstacks be equipped with automatic fire suppression systems to defend against fire.

In new library construction, multitier bookstacks replace freestanding bookstack ranges installed on structural fire-resistant floors. The difference in fuel load between multitier stacks and freestanding stacks is substantial. All levels in a multitier system are usually considered as one fire compartment, due to the absence of vertical fire barriers between tiers. Fire loads depend on the number of tiers in the bookstack. With shelf loading at 70 percent of capacity, the expected fire load in each tier would be 55 to 65 lb/ft^2 (268 to 317 kg/m^2). Thus, for a multitier bookstack with 10 tiers in a single fire compartment, fire duration is estimated at 70 to 85 hours. Conversely, a fire in a free-standing bookstack that is seven shelves high and set on a fire-resistant floor, would be limited to a single tier and a fire duration of 7 to 8 hours.

Compact Storage or Track Files. Bookstack shelving units, or ranges, mounted on carriages that roll on tracks are common in

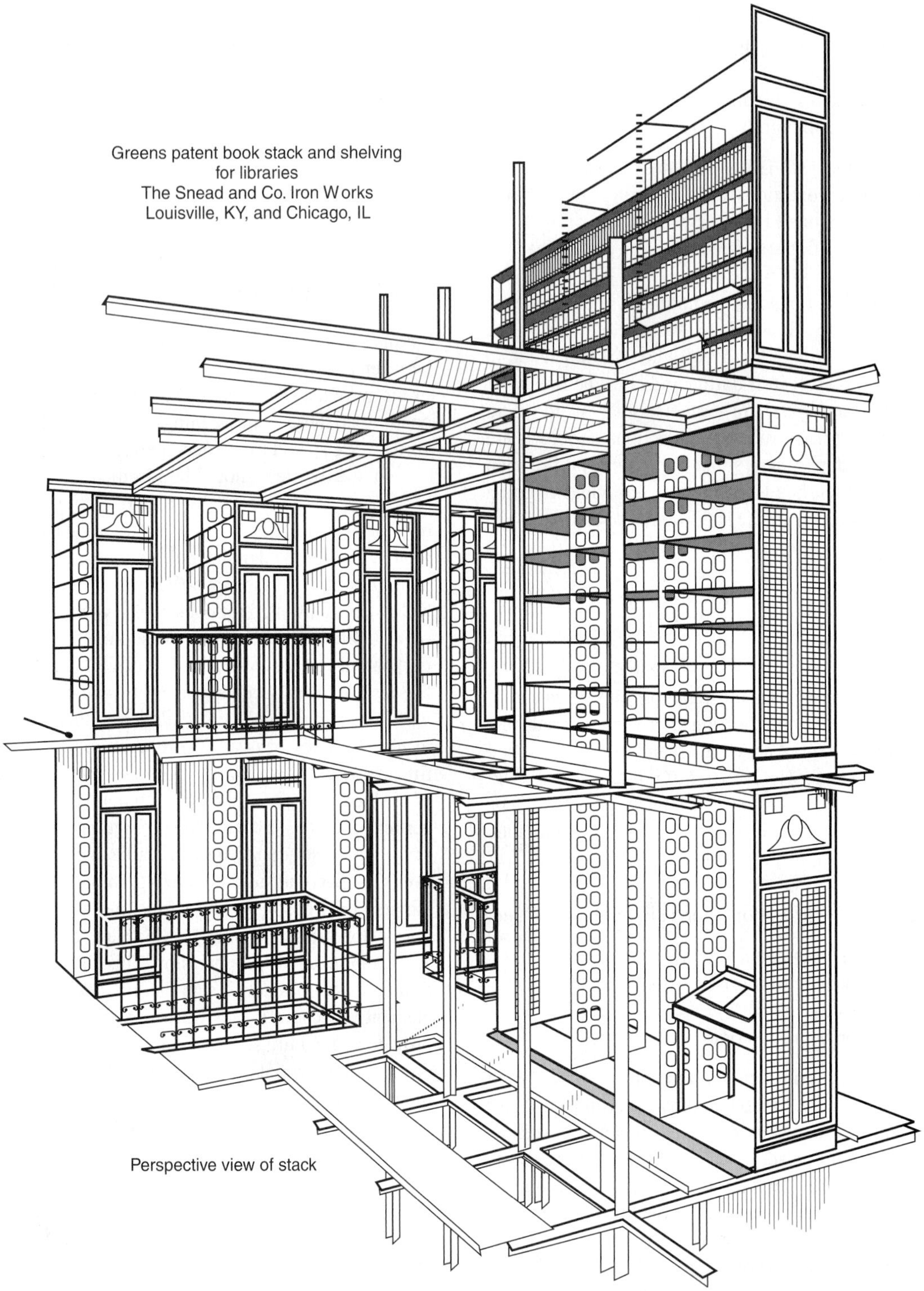

Greens patent book stack and shelving
for libraries
The Snead and Co. Iron Works
Louisville, KY, and Chicago, IL
Perspective view of stack

FIGURE 20.17.4 Multitier Bookstack as Installed in the Library of Congress, Circa 1893

new library and museum construction and in renovations. In this space-saving storage system, one moving aisle serves several ranges. The track systems are modular, with two or more mobile ranges between two fixed-end ranges in each module (Figure 20.17.7). This storage method can create fire loads exceeding 120 lb/ft^2 (586 kg/m^2) and fire durations exceeding 15 hours. This is more than enough to challenge the most fire-resistant barriers and construction prescribed by building and fire codes.

The NFPA Technical Committee on Protection of Cultural Resources recommends automatic sprinkler protection for compact storage installations. Without such protection, a fire in a facility with this type of storage system endangers not only the

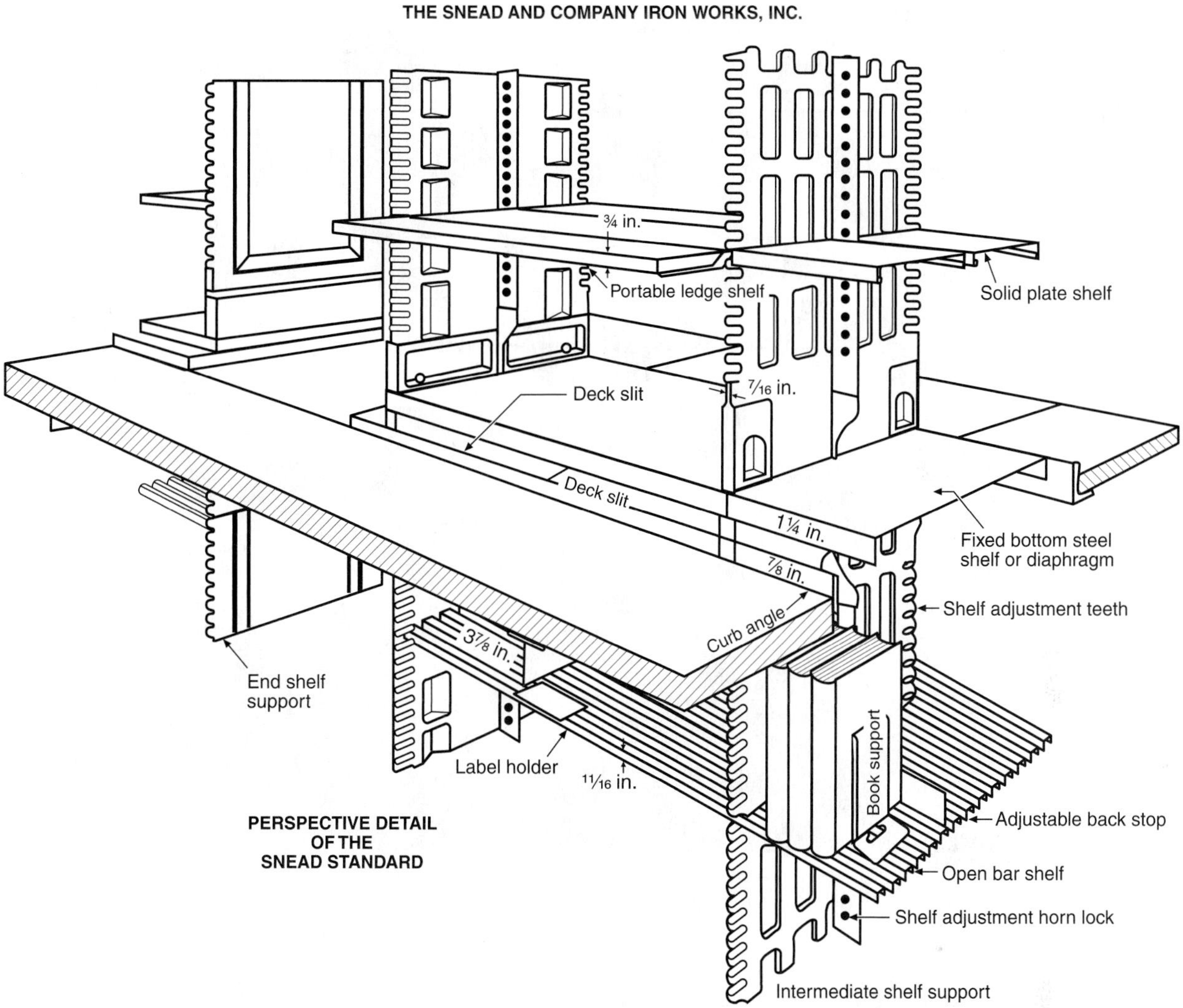

FIGURE 20.17.5 Multitier Bookstack—Showing Section Through Deck Flooring, Deck Slit, Fixed Bottom Shelf, and Adjustable Shelves

collection, but may cause severe structural failures and perhaps building collapse as well. An independent analysis[31] of fire tests conducted to evaluate sprinklers' effectiveness on a compact storage system[32] concluded that sprinklers, installed over a compact storage module, will most probably prevent a fire that originates in the module from damaging building structural elements outside the module. Furthermore, the tests showed (1) there is a good probability that sprinklers will prevent fire spread across 4 ft (1.22 m) aisles between compact storage modules, and (2) sprinklers may effectively prevent fire spread between back-to-back shelves of adjacent modules when a sheet metal panel with a 1 in. (25 mm) air space between adjacent panels backs each shelf. Thus, automatic sprinklers can be expected to limit fire development to that portion of the module of fire origin between the fixed-end range and the open aisle. Nevertheless, total loss of contents within that portion of the storage module is possible (see Figure 20.17.7).

Facility designers must carefully consider the following points in designing compact storage systems:

1. More efficient use of space results in greater density or concentration of values. That is, it increases the number of items subject to fire damage per unit volume of storage space. This risk should be considered in determining the maximum number of ranges to include in each module.
2. Existing automatic fire detection and fire suppression systems may have to be modified, and gaseous agents may be ineffective. In an existing facility with sprinkler protection where compact storage systems are retrofitted, particular attention must be given to water density, ceiling clearances, and structural features of the space. Tests conducted for the National Library of Canada clearly showed that for compact storage systems installed where "explicit compliance with current installation standards" is not possible, it may be necessary to go well beyond normal sprinkler design criteria to achieve adequate protection.[33]
3. Compact storage modules may conceal the origin of smoke, thereby compounding the difficulty in locating and extinguishing a fire.

FIGURE 20.17.6 Modern Multitier Bookstack Installation

TYPICAL INDIVIDUAL HALF SHELF IN INDIVIDUAL SECTION

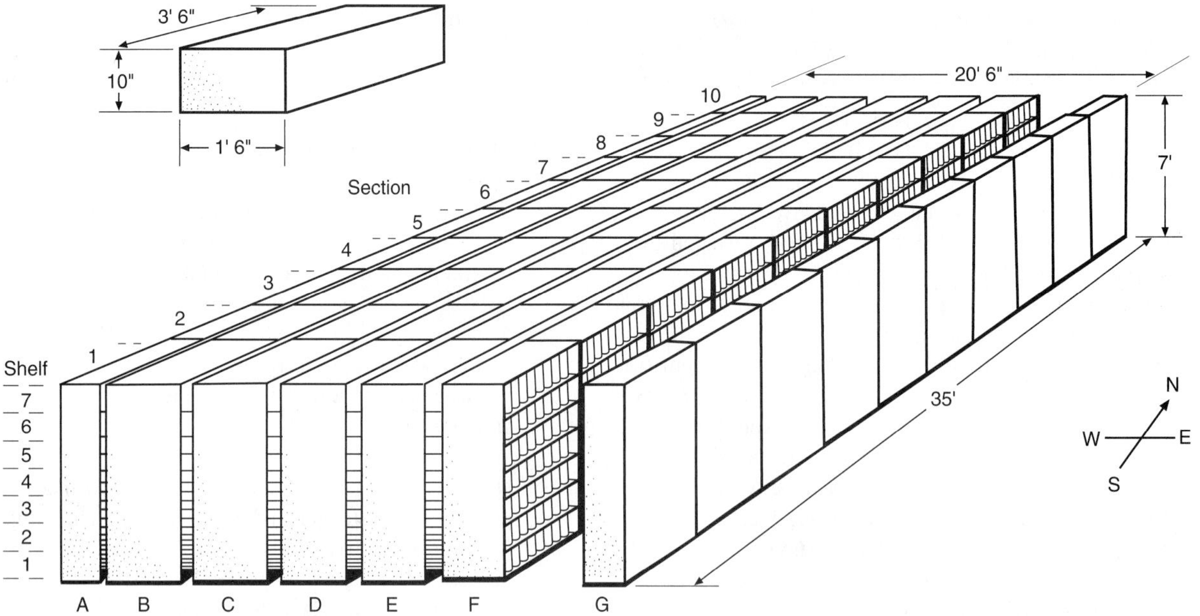

FIGURE 20.17.7 Compact Mobile Shelving

4. Compact storage modules prevent penetration of water from hose streams for fire extinguishment and delay detection by trapping smoke and heat. Consider designing the system so that ranges can be parked with a 5 in. (12.7 cm) gap between them during inactive storage periods. Underwriters Laboratories tested this arrangement with satisfactory results for the U.S. National Archives and Records Administration using quick response sprinklers. Paper record loss was limited to 10 ft^3 (0.28 m^3) and computer record loss to 3 ft^3 (0.08 m^3).[34]
5. Water mist fire suppression test results in bookstack scenarios show promise for special application to the burrowing fire problem in compact storage. It may be possible to design water mist systems for compact storage that limit fire and water damage loss even more effectively than the sprinkler system design tested for the U.S. National Archives and Records Administration.[34]
6. Bookstack ranges may be moved electrically or manually. In compact storage systems that are moved electrically, the electric motor in each bookstack range is a potential ignition source.

FIRE PROTECTION DECISIONS

The elapsed time between a fire's discovery and the beginning of effective manual suppression can easily be too long to prevent unacceptable loss, especially when the building is unoccupied. Faced with this reality, directors of museums and libraries and their governing bodies are deciding to incorporate automatic fire suppression systems as the primary defense against fire loss.

In a 1989 survey of museums of various sizes, including 30 of the largest in the United States, 77 percent reported that they use automatic sprinkler protection.[16] The list of museums that made this decision includes the 15 Smithsonian museums: National Air and Space Museum, National Museum of American History, National Museum of Natural History, National Portrait Gallery, the Sackler Gallery, National Museum of African Art, National Museum of the American Indian, and so on. It also includes the J. Paul Getty Museum, the High Museum of Art in Atlanta, the Phillips Gallery in Washington, DC, and the Dewitt Wallace Museum and Abby Aldrich Rockefeller Folk Art Museum in Williamsburg, Virginia, to name a few.

Similarly, the list of libraries, large and small, equipped to defend their collections against fire loss by installing automatic sprinkler systems continues to grow. Examples include city libraries in Atlanta; Dallas; Houston; Los Angeles; Portland, Maine; and Portland, Oregon, as well as many academic libraries, the State Library of Michigan, and national libraries, such as the Saudi Arabian National Library, the U.S. Library of Congress, the National Library of Canada, and the National Library of Scotland, and the British Library at St. Pancras.[35]

NFPA 909 and other chapters of this handbook provide guidance for procuring, installing, testing, and maintaining fire protection systems.

HISTORIC BUILDINGS AND SITES

Historic buildings house museums, places of worship, office buildings, residences, schools, libraries, restaurants, hotels, restaurants—to name a few. Historic sites include structures as small as covered bridges or as large as entire communities. Historic buildings and sites are often off the beaten path and at a considerable distance from organized fire-fighting services. Often it is as important to protect the structure of a historic building or site as it is to protect the contents. Fire can damage decorative architectural features quickly and burned historic building fabric is lost forever.

Life safety issues in historic buildings may be complicated as well. Historic structures may contain highly combustible structural materials and finishes, and means of egress may be inadequate by today's standards. Fire develops and spreads rapidly via open stairways or where fire and smoke barriers and other smoke and fire control features are absent.[36,37] Historic buildings may not have modern exit signs and emergency lighting, which may cause confusion in an emergency. Building managers must control the occupant load and have a well-developed evacuation plan where such conditions exist.[36]

Historic Building Fires

Fire service reports classify buildings by occupancy type, so data on the frequency or causes of fires in historic buildings are incomplete. Those that are coded as historic buildings experienced 35 U.S. structure fires per year reported to local fire departments from 1994 to 1998. Nevertheless, where data are available, the reported fire causes, in order of 1994–1998 frequency, are arson; electrical distribution equipment, such as fixed wiring; heating equipment; natural causes, such as lightning; cooking equipment; smoking; appliances; open flame; children playing; and exposure from newly burning structures, grass, and woodlands.[36,37] Historic buildings often contain outdated mechanical and electrical systems, and many historic building museums use candles, fireplaces, forges, stoves and other open-flame devices as interpretive aids.

Fire can grow and spread in historic buildings because of inadequate barriers, absence of sprinklers or other means of automatic protection, and delayed discovery and reporting of the fire. The first few minutes after ignition can be critical, particularly in historic buildings of combustible construction. Absence of automatic fire detection or other automatic protection leaves discovery of a fire to a night guard or to chance. Historic buildings require painstaking attention to details to preserve historic authenticity, but experience shows that it is possible to provide appropriate levels of fire protection for the structure and safety for staff and visitors while maintaining original construction or historical appearance.[38,39]

Historic Building Fire Safety

Each historic building or site is unique and the planner must address merits and problems individually. A fire protection plan that systematically achieves fire safety goals includes compartmentation, structural analysis, alarm and communications, means of egress, smoke control, fire suppression, water supply, ignition prevention, fuel control, and impact on authenticity.[38] Managing a historic building for fire safety includes the following:

- Examining the physical conditions and developing a fire defense plan

- Incorporating automatic detection and alarm or fixed extinguishing systems or both
- Providing or having available a trained, properly equipped fire-fighting and salvage organization
- Instituting management and operational practices that eliminate causes of fire, and promoting organized training of personnel so they act effectively when called on

Other Considerations

Chimneys. Flues should be examined for deteriorated mortar joints that may permit sparks or excessive heat to pass into wood framing or other combustible material. Chimneys should be lined and repointed before they are used. If the condition of a flue is questionable or if it cannot be repaired without seriously affecting the building structure around the chimney, then it should not be used.

Electrical Service. Electrical wiring should be approved. Old wiring systems may include deteriorated materials, fittings, and connections that do not meet current codes. A licensed electrician or engineer should inspect and evaluate electrical circuits and wiring. Inadequate or unsafe components should be replaced, and fuses and circuit breakers should be labeled to indicate the areas they control.

FIGURE 20.17.8 Typical Sprinkler Protection for Exposure Fires

Exposure Fires. The fire safety plan should consider exposure of the structure to outside fires. Structures in or adjacent to forests or tall grass must have fire lanes and cleared areas to protect the property from a forest or grass fire. Other nearby structures may present an exposure fire threat where insufficient clear space exists to reduce fire spread from one structure to another. If the historic building is wood frame construction, fire-resistive roofing and siding may help protect it, although eaves, cornices, and windows may still be exposed. Strategically located exterior sprinklers at window openings, along combustible cornices and walls, and on combustible roofs provide protection. See Figure 20.17.8 for an example of automatic sprinklers utilized for exposure fire protection. Fire doors or fire shutters that automatically close in a fire can protect openings in brick and masonry walls. Careful architectural planning can minimize the impact of these protective devices on the historic fabric or appearance of the structure.

Open Flames. Historic building museums use fireplaces and stoves for cooking and heating and to create the desired atmosphere and often use candles and lamps—oil, gas, and kerosene—for illumination. Any flame is a potential ignition source that must be safeguarded and monitored.

Housekeeping. Good housekeeping is a vital element in fire prevention. Clutter and waste invite fire. Rubbish and trash should be removed regularly and exterior housekeeping should be monitored. Debris, tall grass, brush, and fallen leaves that can cause fire to spread should be removed.

Fire Suppression. Even small communities usually have a fire department. However, if the structure is isolated or distant from a fire station, on-site emergency equipment and personnel training for its operation are prudent. The fire service must know the location of hydrants or alternative sources of water such as streams, rivers, ponds, or cisterns if hydrants are not available and must carefully plan how to use alternative sources effectively. It may be prudent to install a dry hydrant with the supply line beneath the frost line so the fire department can use an alternate water source.

Performance-Based Design

Designing fire protection systems in historic buildings requires imagination and innovation to minimize the intrusion on authenticity. A team that includes a fire safety professional with experience in protecting historic buildings, preservation specialists, the building owner or manager, and the authority having jurisdiction should evaluate the building and consider acceptable alternatives. The planning team may conclude that traditional codes and standards do not provide practical solutions to correcting the fire protection deficiencies. To meet this challenge, NFPA 914 contains performance-based alternatives for solving fire protection problems in historic buildings. NFPA 914 provides a road map, written in code language, for designers developing performance-based alternatives that may be acceptable to the authority having jurisdiction. It also includes provisions to include management operating systems as acceptable elements of the overall fire safety system.

SUMMARY

Places of worship, libraries, and museums are mixed-use occupancies that present unique fire protection challenges. Although the public areas of these cultural resource properties usually have low fuel loads and high standards of housekeeping, these areas do suffer costly fires. Fire prevention in cultural resource properties is the first line of defense against fire. Early detection and quick action to stop fire growth can prevent large fire losses. Useful fire protection features include a systems approach to fire safety and a specifically designed fire protection system. Construction considerations, such as compartmentation, means of egress, lighting, and gallery flexibility, must be considered in fire safety planning.

The effective fire emergency management of cultural resource facilities includes continuous monitoring of fire protection systems, providing emergency electric power to support fire protection systems, planning with the local fire department, and prefire training of all building staff.

BIBLIOGRAPHY

References Cited

1. Morris, J., "Is Your Library Safe From Fire?," *American School and University,* Apr. 1980, p. 61.
2. McElroy, F. E. (Ed.), *Accident Prevention Manual for Industrial Operations,* 7th ed., National Safety Council, Chicago, IL, 1974.
3. Factory Mutual Research Corp., *Handbook of Industrial Loss Prevention,* 2nd ed., McGraw-Hill, Inc., New York, 1967.
4. McKinnon, G. P. (Ed.), *Industrial Fire Hazards Handbook,* 1st ed., National Fire Protection Association, Quincy, MA, 1979.
5. *Fire Protection Handbook,* 12th ed., Table 80143, National Fire Protection Association, Quincy, MA, 1962, pp. 8–145.
6. Lathrop, J. K., "Building Under Construction," *Fire Journal,* Vol. 68, No. 5, 1974, pp. 37, 39.
7. *Operational School Burning: Official Report on a Series of School Fire Tests, Conducted April 16 to June 30, 1959, by the Los Angeles Fire Department,* National Fire Protection Association, Quincy, MA, 1959.
8. Brannigan, F. L., "Fire Growth," *Firehouse,* July 1995, pp. 80–85.
9. Juillerat, E., Jr., "The Hartford Hospital Fire," *NFPA Quarterly,* Vol. 55, No. 3, 1962, pp. 295–303.
10. Harvey, B., "Fire Hazards in Libraries: Part I—Clearing the Smoke," *Library Security Newsletter,* Vol. 1, No. 1, 1975.
11. Firepro, Inc., *Fire Defense Alternatives: Library of Congress,* Washington, DC, 1977, unpublished report.
12. *Building Firesafety Criteria,* PBS P5920.9, Appendix D, General Services Administration, Washington, DC, 1979.
13. Marchant, E. W., "Fire Engineering Strategies," *Fire Science and Technology,* Vol. 11, Nos. 1–2, 1991, pp. 13–19.
14. Zimmerman, C. E. (Ed.), *Fire Alarm Signaling Handbook,* NFPA SPP 82, National Fire Protection Association, Quincy, MA, 1987.
15. Fitzgerald, R. W., and Wilson, R., *The Systems Technique for Evaluating Building Firesafety,* Worcester Polytechnic Institute, Worcester, MA, 1976.
16. Wilson, J. A., "Fire Fighters," *Museum News,* Nov./Dec. 1989, pp. 68–72.
17. Kirsch, A., "Preserving Today's Treasures for Tomorrow," *Factory Mutual Record,* Vol. 76, No. 1, 1990, pp. 4–8.
18. Myller, R., *The Design of the Small Public Library,* Bowker, New York, 1966.
19. Thompson, G., *The Museum Environment,* Butterworths, London, UK, 1978.
20. Brawne, M., *Libraries: Architecture and Equipment,* Praeger, New York, 1970.
21. Johnson, E. V., and Horgan, J. C., *Museum Collection Storage,* United Nations Educational Scientific and Cultural Organization, Paris, France, 1979.
22. Thomas, S. (Ed.), "Retrofitting with Sprinklers for Added Protection," *Factory Mutual Record,* Vol. 59, No. 3, 1982, pp. 13–19.
23. Grant, C. C., P.E., "Life Beyond Halon," *Fire Journal,* Vol. 84, No. 3, 1990.
24. Shields, T. J., Dunlop, K. E., and Silcock, G. W. H., "Management Strategy to Establish Life Safety Equivalency for Historic Buildings," *Fire Science and Technology,* Vol. 11, Nos. 1–2, 1991, pp. 21–26.
25. 29 CFR 1910, *Occupational Safety and Health Standards,* Subparts E & L, U.S. Department of Labor, Occupational Safety and Health Administration (OSHA), Washington, DC, 1976.
26. Fennelly, L. J. (Ed.), *Museum, Archive and Library Security,* Butterworths, London, UK, 1983.
27. Cash, J., "Sophisticated System Protects Historic Museum," *NFPA Journal,* Vol. 86, No. 5, 1992, pp. 63–67.
28. Fuhlrott, R., and Dewey, M., *Library Interior Layout and Design,* Saur, Munich, Germany, 1982.
29. Morris, J., "Fire Protection for the Library," *The Construction Specifier,* Oct. 1989.
30. Isner, M. S., "Fire in Los Angeles Central Library Causes $22 Million Loss," *Fire Journal,* Vol. 81, No. 5, 1987.
31. Cutler, H. R., *Engineering Analysis of Compact Storage Fire Tests,* Library of Congress, Washington, DC, 1979.
32. Chicarello, P. J., et al., *Fire Tests in Mobile Storage Systems for Archival Storage,* General Services Administration, Washington, DC, 1978.
33. Lougheed, G. D., Mawhinney, J. R., and O'Neill, J., "Full-Scale Fire Tests and Development of Design Criteria for Sprinkler Protection for Mobile Shelving Units," *Fire Technology,* Vol. 30, No. 1, 1994.
34. Underwriters Laboratories Inc., "Report on Archives II Mobile High Density Shelving Fire Protection System." A copy of this report, dated Nov. 30, 1989, is available from the National Archives and Records Administration (NARA), Washington, DC 20408.
35. Cartwright, N. K., "Fire Protection at the New British Library," *Fire Prevention,* Vol. 203, Oct. 1987.
36. The United Kingdom Working Party on Fire Safety in Historic Buildings, *Heritage Under Fire,* Fire Protection Association, London, UK, 1990.
37. Maxwell, I., "Fire Protection Measures in Scottish Historic Buildings," *Fire Protection and the Built Heritage,* Historic Scotland, Edinburgh, UK, 1999, pp. 1–14.
38. Allwinkle, S., et al., *Technical Advice Note 11: Fire Protection Measures in Historic Buildings,* Historic Scotland, Edinburgh, UK, 1997.
39. The Fire Protection Association, *Technical Advice Note 14: The Installation of Sprinkler Systems in Historic Buildings,* Historic Scotland, Edinburgh, UK, 1998.

NFPA Codes, Standards, and Recommended Practices

Reference to the following NFPA codes, standards, and recommended practices will provide further information on library and museum collections discussed in this chapter. (See the latest version of The NFPA Catalog *for availability of current editions of the following documents.)*

NFPA 1, *Uniform Fire Code™*
NFPA 10, *Standard for Portable Fire Extinguishers*
NFPA 11, *Standard for Low-, Medium-, and High-Expansion Foam*
NFPA 12, *Standard on Carbon Dioxide Extinguishing Systems*
NFPA 12A, *Standard on Halon 1301 Fire Extinguishing Systems*
NFPA 13, *Standard for the Installation of Sprinkler Systems*
NFPA 14, *Standard for the Installation of Standpipe and Hose Systems*
NFPA 40, *Standard for the Storage and Handling of Cellulose Nitrate Film*
NFPA 45, *Standard on Fire Protection for Laboratories Using Chemicals*
NFPA 70, *National Electrical Code®*
NFPA *101®*, *Life Safety Code®*
NFPA 232, *Standard for the Protection of Records*
NFPA 550, *Guide to the Fire Safety Concepts Tree*
NFPA 600, *Standard on Industrial Fire Brigades*
NFPA 909, *Code for the Protection of Cultural Resource Properties—Museums, Libraries, and Places of Worship*
NFPA 914, *Code for Fire Protection of Historic Structures*

NFPA 2001, *Standard on Clean Agent Fire Extinguishing Systems*
NFPA 5000®, Building Construction and Safety Code®

References

Ahrens, M., "Selections from U.S. Fires in Selected Occupancies Religious and Funeral Properties," National Fire Protection Association, Quincy, MA, Feb. 2006.

Bowman, A., "Performance-Based Analysis of an Historic Museum, Arts and Industries Building: A Case Study," *Fire Protection Engineering,* No. 8, Fall 2000, pp. 36–38.

Brown, G., "Back to First Principles for Museum Fire Protection," *Fire Australia,* Aug. 2000, pp. 9–11.

Bush, S. E., "How a Library Can Overcome Its Fear of Frying," *Proceedings* of inFIRE, the international network for Fire Information and Reference Exchange and Society of Fire Protection Engineers and International Association of Fire Chiefs, Annual Conference, May 11–13, 1994, Fairfax, VA, 1994, pp. 41–51.

Catchpole, L., "Fast Response Sprinklers Protect the British Library," *Fire International,* No. 292, Sept. 1996, pp. 18–19.

Cavill, S., "On Guard at the Royal Armouries," *Fire,* Vol. 89, No. 1097, 1996, p. 39.

Comeau, E., "Capitol Challenge," *NFPA Journal,* Vol. 94, No. 6, 2000, pp. 57–61.

Comeau, E., "Fire Hits Washington Treasury During Renovation," *Fire Prevention,* No. 303, Oct. 1997, pp. 26–27.

Copping, A. G., "Application of a Systematic Fire Safety Evaluation Procedure in the Protection of Historic Property," *Proceedings* of International Conference, Engineered Fire Protection Design, Applying Fire Science to Fire Protection Problems, June 11–15, 2001, San Francisco, CA, Society of Fire Protection Engineers, Bethesda, MD, 2001, pp. 3–11.

Coppola, L., and Gecchele, G., "Fire Safety for Historical Buildings and Performance Criteria for Their Use," *Proceedings* of the 2nd International Symposium, Human Behavior in Fire: Understanding Human Behavior for Better Fire Safety Design, March 26–28, 2001, Boston, MA, Interscience Communications Ltd., London, UK, 2001, pp. 451–458.

Corneo, E., Gallina, G., and Mutani, G., "Fire Safety in a Historical Building: A Case History," *Proceedings* of Symposium '97 FORUM, Applications of Fire Safety Engineering, October 6–7, 1997, Tianjin, China, 1997, pp. 60–72.

Fan, W. C., and Weng, W. G., "Fire Protection of Chinese Historic Buildings," *Proceedings* of FORUM 2001 Symposium, Fire Safety in Buildings, October 23, 2001, Milan, Italy, 2001, pp. 15–23.

Fiameni, C., Gallina, G., and Mutani, G., "Fire Safety Performance Based Approach Applied to LaFenice Theatre in Venice (Italy)," *Proceedings* of FORUM 2000 Symposium, Fire Research Development and Application in the 21st Century, October 23–24, 2000, Taipei, Taiwan, 2000, pp. 1–19.

Forrest, R., "Old Meets New in the Great Court," *Fire Prevention,* No. 342, Mar. 2001, pp. 18–20.

Gallina, G., and Mutani, G., "People Evacuation in Historical Buildings," *Proceedings* of 1st International Symposium, Human Behavior in Fire, August 31–September 2, 1998, Belfast, UK, Textflow Ltd., UK, 1998, pp. 319–329.

Jason, N. H., "Preservation and Restoration of Library Collections from Fire," *Proceedings* of Fire Information for the 21st Century, May 4–8, 1998, Melbourne, Australia, International Network for Fire Information and Reference Exchange, Perth, Australia, 1998, pp. 9/1–7.

Kidd, S., "Historic Assessment," *Fire Prevention,* No. 342, Mar. 2001, pp. 24–27.

Kidd, S., "Managing Fire Safety in Heritage Premises," *Fire Protection,* Vol. 23, No. 2, 1997, pp. 12–17.

Koffel, W. E., "Preserving Historic Buildings," *NFPA Journal,* Vol. 93, No. 5, 1999, p. 28.

Marsella, S., "Performance-Based Codes and Prescriptive Rules in Fire Protection of Cultural Resources," *Proceedings* of FORUM 2001 Symposium, Fire Safety in Buildings, October 23, 2001, Milan, Italy, 2001, pp. 9–14.

Milke, J. A., "Comparison of the Performance of Water Mist System Designs for Library Stack Areas," *Journal of Applied Fire Science,* Vol. 5, No. 3, 1995/1996, pp. 185–201.

Mizukami, G., Hasemi, Y., Yamada, T., and Jin, T., "Study for the Fire Safety Planning of the Himeji-jo Castle: A World Heritage," *Proceedings* of 4th Asia-Oceania Symposium on Fire Science and Technology, May 24–26, 2000, Tokyo, Japan, 2000, pp. 227–238.

Moore, W. D., "Protecting Our Cultural Heritage," *NFPA Journal,* Vol. 94, No. 6, Nov./Dec. 2000, p. 28.

Moore, W. D., Rosenbaum, E. R., and Domnitch, C., "Preserving History and Lives," *Consulting-Specifying Engineer,* Vol. 29, No. 4, 2001, pp. 59–60.

Muraoka, K., and Sugahara, S., "Fire Problems and Fire Protection Management for Wooden Shrines and Temples in Japan," *Proceedings* of 4th Asia-Oceania Symposium on Fire Science and Technology, May 24–26, 2000, Tokyo, Japan, 2000, pp. 239–250.

O'Neill, J. G., and Bowman, A. B., "Fire Protection of a Landmark Historic Building: Performance Based Life Safety Analysis," *Proceedings* of Fire Suppression and Detection Research Application Symposium, Research and Practice: Bridging the Gap, February 23–25, 2000, National Fire Protection Research Foundation, Quincy, MA, 2000, pp. 180–203.

Papaioannou, K. K., "Fire Safety Design in Mount Athos, Greece," *NFPA Journal,* Vol. 94, No. 6, 2001, pp. 73–76.

Respondek, J., "Fire Safety Concept for a Modern University Library: Performance-Based Design," *Proceedings* of 3rd International Conference on Fire Research and Engineering (ICFRE3), October 4–8, 1999, Chicago, IL, Society of Fire Protection Engineers, Boston, 1998.

Respondek, J., "Fire Safety Concept for a Small Mediaeval Castle: Performance-Based Design Approach," *Proceedings* of the 8th International INTERFLAM Conference, INTERFLAM '99, June 29–July 1, 1999, Edinburgh, UK, Interscience Communications Ltd., London, UK, 1999, pp. 1373–1379.

Solomon, R. E., "Preserving History from Fire: Bridging the Gap between Safety Codes and Historic Buildings," *Old House Journal,* Vol. 28, No. 6, 2000, pp. 40–45.

Tamura, H., Tanaka, H., Nomura, S., Kozeki, D., and Yamashita, K., "Field Study on the Causes of False Alarms at Cultural Heritage Old Buildings," *Bulletin of Japan Association for Fire Science and Engineering,* Vol. 51, No. 2, 2001, pp. 13–20.

Twomey, E. R., "Structure Fires in Libraries," National Fire Protection Association, Quincy, MA, Mar. 2006.

Twomey, E. R., "Structure Fires in Museums and Art Galleries," National Fire Protection Association, Quincy, MA, Mar. 2006.

Watson, T. M., "Fire Protecting the Thatched Roof of Shakespeare's Globe Theatre," *Fire Safety Engineering,* Vol. 5, No. 4, 1998, pp. 19–22.

Watts, J. M., Jr., "Fire Protection Performance Evaluation for Historic Buildings," *Journal of Fire Protection Engineering,* Vol. 11, No. 4, 2001, pp. 197–208.

Watts, J. M., Jr., and Kaplan, M. E., "Development of an Historic Fire Risk Index," *Proceedings* of Fire Suppression and Detection Research Application Symposium, Research and Practice: Bridging the Gap, June 25–27, 1997, National Fire Protection Research Foundation, Quincy, MA, 1997, pp. 315–327.

Watts, J. M., Jr., and Kaplan, M. E., "Fire Risk Index for Historic Buildings," *Fire Technology,* Vol. 37, No. 2, 2001, pp. 167–180.

Watts, J. M., Jr., and Rosenbaum, E. R., "Fire Risk Assessment for Cultural Heritage," *Proceedings* of the 9th International INTERFLAM Conference, INTERFLAM 2001, September 17–19, 2001, Edinburgh, UK, Interscience Communications Ltd., London, UK, 2001, pp. 203–212.

Woodward, P., "BA London Eye: The Fire Engineering Challenges of Designing within a Large Heritage Building in London," *Fire Safety Engineering,* Vol. 7, No. 6, 2000, pp. 24–27.

Yates, S., "Traditional Recipe for Disaster," *Fire Prevention,* No. 314, Nov. 1998, pp. 36–37.

Chapter 18

Industrial Occupancies

David P. Demers

Chapter Contents

Key Terms

computer fire models, general industrial occupancy, high-hazard industrial occupancy, industrial occupancy, industrial fire brigade, special-purpose industrial occupancy

Industrial occupancies encompass a broad spectrum of purposes. Some employ many people to work in a single building. Other facilities house large items of equipment but have very few employees. Industrial occupancies are generally divided into two categories: general-purpose industrial, which are low- and moderate-hazard facilities, and high-hazard facilities. Examples of industrial occupancies include factories, power plants, refineries, and laundries.

This chapter discusses the loss history of industrial occupancies; general risk assessment; occupancy and occupant characteristics; fire protection features available; NFPA *101*®, *Life Safety Code*®, and *NFPA 5000*®, *Building Construction and Safety Code*®, criteria; and prefire planning.

For additional information relevant to life safety in industrial occupancies, see Section 11, Chapter 5, "Control of Electrostatic Ignition Sources"; Section 18, Chapter 1, "Confinement of Fire in Buildings"; Section 18, Chapter 2, "Interior Finish"; and Section 20, Chapter 20, "Occupancies in Special Structures." Explosion suppression devices are covered in Section 17, Chapter 8, "Explosion Prevention and Protection." Section 3, Chapter 5, "Introduction to Fire Modeling," provides information on computer fire models.

LOSS HISTORY

Industrial and manufacturing facilities experienced 11,400 structure fires reported to U.S. local fire departments in 2002, with associated losses of 11 civilian deaths, 342 civilian injuries, and $774 million in direct property damage.[1] The number of fires declined more than 73 percent from 1980, whereas civilian deaths declined by 50 percent (Table 20.18.1 and Figure 20.18.1). The variety of industrial and manufacturing activities is reflected in the loss history (Table 20.18.2), although certain activities stand out with larger shares of the fire problem.

Of the 25 costliest U.S. fires and explosions in history (as of the end of 2002), after adjusting for inflation, nine involved industrial or manufacturing facilities, and all but two of those occurred in the last decade and a half of the twentieth century—a 1989 Texas polyolefin plant fire (number 5 costliest of all time), a 1999 Michigan automobile manufacturing complex power plant fire (number 9), a 1995 Massachusetts textile mill fire (number 11), a 1947 Texas ship and chemical plant fire (number 13), a 1988 Louisiana petroleum refinery fire (number 14), a 1987 Texas chemical plant fire (number 21), a 1975 Alabama nuclear power plant fire (number 22), and a 1999 Louisiana aluminum plant fire (number 24).

The same 1989 Texas polyolefin plant fire and a 1991 North Carolina chicken processing plant fire are the most recent examples of the continued potential for major life loss in these facilities, as more than 20 people died in each incident.[2]

However, the deadliest recent industrial fire in the world by far occurred in a toy factory in Thailand in 1992.[3] That fire killed 188 workers, surpassing the death toll of 145 in the Triangle Shirtwaist Company fire of 1911, which is still the deadliest manufacturing plant incident not involving an explosion in U.S. history.

Another fire, this one in 1992 in China, occurred in a doll factory and took the lives of 81 occupants.[4] These and other less deadly incidents around the world underline the need for a higher standard of global industrial fire safety. Setting that standard starts with recognizing the many ways

---

David P. Demers, P.E., is president of Demers Associates, Inc., a fire protection consulting firm in Lunenburg, Massachusetts, and deputy chief of the Lunenburg Fire Department.

TABLE 20.18.1 Structure Fires in Industrial and Manufacturing Properties by Year, 1980–2002

				Direct Property Damage (in Millions of Dollars)	
Year	*Fires*	*Civilian Deaths*	*Civilian Injuries*	*As Reported*	*In 2002 Dollars*
1980	42,100	21	775	609	1331
1981	39,000	31	1322	659	1302
1982	35,000	50	1118	450	837
1983	29,900	51	1091	727	1312
1984	30,400	88	853	804	1389
1985	30,900	37	779	569	950
1986	26,400	24	821	516	847
1987	25,800	44	991	542	858
1988	24,100	30	847	676	1028
1989	21,700	60	783	1796	2606
1990	18,700	79	830	689	949
1991	18,300	21	641	647	854
1992	17,500	11	545	539	691
1993	16,400	13	893	566	705
1994	18,000	16	648	567	689
1995	16,300	32	587	1254	1479
1996	16,500	8	540	786	902
1997	17,800	16	485	709	795
1998	16,100	20	520	632	698
1999	17,200	29	609	1116	1204
2000	14,000	9	566	688	719
2001	12,700	17	321	846	859
2002	11,400	11	342	774	774

Note: These are national estimates of fires reported to U.S. municipal fire departments and so exclude fires reported only to federal or state agencies or industrial fire brigades. National estimates are projections. Casualty and loss projections can be heavily influenced by the inclusion or exclusion of one unusually serious fire. Fires are rounded to the nearest hundred, civilian deaths and injuries are rounded to the nearest one, and direct property damage is rounded to the nearest million dollars.

Source: NFIRS and NFPA survey. Inflation adjustments were based on the consumer price index found in the U.S. Census Bureau's *Statistical Abstract of the United States: 2006*, "Table 705, Purchasing Power of the Dollar."

in which serious fires can occur in industrial and manufacturing facilities. Table 20.18.3 shows the cause patterns for fires and associated property damage in industrial and manufacturing properties. The wide variety of potentially hazardous industrial and manufacturing process is clearly reflected in these figures, but so are more familiar hazards associated with heating, electrical service, arson, and smoking. Although the process or manufacturing area that defines the facility's activity and purpose is the leading area of fire origin, most fires and losses occur in fires that began somewhere else (Table 20.18.4).

Even when they occur, industrial fires need not be deadly and need not be costly. Many factors typically contributed to turn an industrial fire into a major loss of life or property. One common factor is the lack of functioning fire suppression systems in a structure. From 1994 to 1998, 59 percent of reported structure fires in industrial and manufacturing facilities were in properties without sprinklers. When sprinklers were present, the chances of dying were 30 percent lower and the average loss per fire was 66 percent lower.[1]

A factor that has contributed to large loss fires in sprinklered industrial occupancies is a change in the hazard for which the sprinkler systems were originally designed. When the hazard or fuel load changes, suppression systems need to be re-evaluated. Yet another factor is improperly designed egress systems. Unfortunately, locked exits still contribute to fatalities. Locked and blocked exits contributed to the 25 deaths in the 1991 North Carolina chicken processing plant fire. An important cause of the loss of life in the 1992 Thailand toy factory fire was inadequate exit arrangements. It is only one example of how major industrial fires tend to involve a failure to follow well-established fire safety requirements. NFPA *101* and *NFPA 5000* provide requirements for designing appropriate egress systems.

HAZARD ASSESSMENT AND EVALUATION

To provide adequate life safety for an industrial occupancy, the relative degree of fire and life safety risk must be evaluated. Since the industrial classification is so broad, the hazards involved vary greatly. The first concern is the amount of time available for evacuation. Both the contents of the building and the interior construction affect this, as well as the materials of the building itself if they contribute to the fire during occupant evacuation. Examples of items to consider are interior finish, rate of fire spread, burn rate, toxic fume evolvement, potential ignition sources, fuel load, and smoke generated. After employees evacuate, the problem becomes one of property protection.

Many resources exist to aid in hazard assessment. Examples include talking to plant operators, reviewing building blueprints, and so on. The NFPA codes contain valuable information on various hazards. Insurance companies and records of previous fires also provide useful information. Section 20, Chapter 1, "Assessing Life Safety in Buildings," describes methods for assessing life safety from fire in buildings.

Computer models can assist in assessing an occupancy's hazard. After determining the appropriate potential fire, a computer model can help predict the impact of fire on a facility. This is valuable in determining the possible time available for occupants to exit the area or facility before conditions become untenable. The ASET, FPETOOL, and CFAST models do this. (See Section 3, Chapter 5, "Introduction to Fire Modeling.") The assessment can be done in conjunction with egress analysis. Required safe egress time is a model to analyze egress. Combined models can evaluate whether there is sufficient time for the occupants to exit before conditions become untenable. This particular method of assessing hazard and evaluating life safety is common practice in code-enforcement systems that accept performance-based designs.

Because explosions are probably the most destructive industrial accidents in terms of life and property loss, they require special attention. Flammable dust, vapor, mist, or gas presents an explosion hazard. A carefully designed system is needed to ensure life safety from explosive forces. Two primary ap-

TABLE 20.18.2 Structure Fires in Industrial and Manufacturing Facilities, 1999–2002 Annual Averages

Occupancy	*Fires*	*Civilian Deaths*	*Civilian Injuries*	*Direct Property Damage (in Millions of Dollars)*
Utility, defense, agriculture, or mining	3,400	9	78	284
Energy production plant	200	3	31	174
Laboratory	300	0	8	5
Defense, computer, or communications center	100	0	4	3
Utility or distribution system	500	1	13	24
Agriculture	1,700	4	13	57
Forest, timberland, or woodland	100	0	3	1
Mine or quarry	100	0	1	9
Unclassified or unknown-type utility, defense, agriculture, or mining	400	1	5	13
Manufacturing or processing	10,500	7	382	571
Total	13,800	17	460	856

Note: These are national estimates of fires reported to U.S. municipal fire departments and so exclude fires reported only to federal or state agencies or industrial fire brigades. National estimates are projections. Casualty and loss projections can be heavily influenced by the inclusion or exclusion of one unusually serious fire. Fires are rounded to the nearest hundred, civilian deaths and injuries are rounded to the nearest one, and direct property damage is rounded to the nearest million dollars. Property damage has not been adjusted for inflation.

Source: NFIRS and NFPA survey.

proaches to the problem exist: prevent the explosion—obviously the better choice—and control the damage from the explosion. Specialized equipment designed to detect, suppress, and control damage from explosions is available. NFPA 69, *Standard on Explosion Prevention Systems,* provides additional information.

BUILDING CONSTRUCTION

NFPA *101* does not include construction requirements for industrial occupancies; however, *NFPA 5000* does. The varying types of industrial occupancies use many different types of construction. Smaller facilities might be constructed of unprotected wood, corresponding to Type V in NFPA 220, *Standard on Types of Building Construction,* and *NFPA 5000,* whereas larger buildings might be of fire-resistive construction, Type I. Additionally, buildings can range from totally enclosed high-rises and windowless buildings to open structures providing equipment protection from weather. The type of construction is generally based on local building codes for the type of use rather than on life safety concerns.

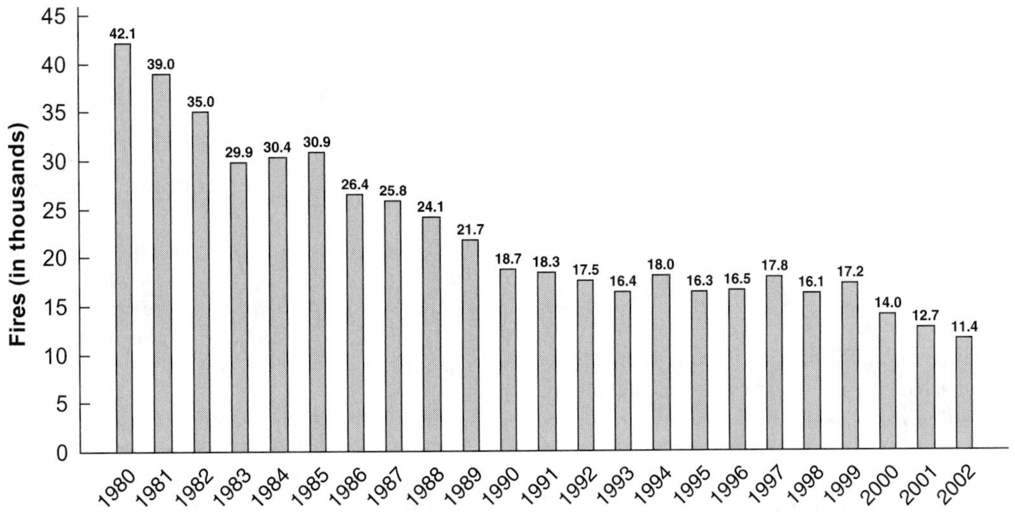

FIGURE 20.18.1 Structure Fires in Industrial and Manufacturing Properties by Year, 1980–2002 (Source: U.S. Fires in Selected Occupancies, NFPA, 2006)

TABLE 20.18.3 Leading Causes of Structure Fires in Industrial and Manufacturing Properties, 1999–2002 Annual Averages

Cause	*Fires*		*Civilian Deaths*		*Civilian Injuries*		*Direct Property Damage (in Millions of Dollars)*	
Shop tools or industrial equipment, except torches	3500	(25%)	3	(19%)	192	(42%)	167	(20%)
Electrical distribution and lighting equipment	1400	(10%)	4	(25%)	33	(7%)	94	(11%)
Heating equipment fires	1400	(10%)	0	(0%)	30	(6%)	47	(5%)
Identified heating equipment	1000	(7%)	0	(0%)	23	(5%)	46	(5%)
Confined heating equipment fire	400	(3%)	0	(0%)	6	(1%)	2	(0%)
Torch (including burner or soldering iron)	1000	(7%)	1	(6%)	51	(11%)	53	(6%)
Intentional	700	(5%)	6	(36%)	14	(3%)	73	(9%)
Cooking equipment fires	500	(4%)	0	(0%)	11	(2%)	17	(2%)
Identified cooking equipment	400	(3%)	0	(0%)	10	(2%)	13	(2%)
Confined cooking fire	100	(1%)	0	(0%)	1	(0%)	4	(0%)
Smoking materials	500	(4%)	0	(0%)	13	(3%)	29	(3%)
Spontaneous combustion or chemical reaction	500	(4%)	0	(0%)	11	(2%)	38	(4%)
Exposure to other fire	400	(3%)	0	(0%)	3	(1%)	15	(2%)
Contained trash or rubbish fire	500	(3%)	0	(0%)	2	(0%)	0	(0%)

Note: These are the leading causes, obtained from the following list: intentional (from the NFIRS field "cause"); playing with fire (from factor contributing to ignition); confined heating (including confined chimney and confined fuel burner or boiler fires), confined cooking, and contained trash or rubbish (from incident type); identified heating, identified cooking, clothes dryer or washer, torch (including burner and soldering iron), electrical distribution and lighting equipment, medical equipment, and electronic, office, or entertainment equipment (from equipment involved in ignition); smoking materials, candles, lightning, and spontaneous combustion or chemical reaction (from heat source); and mobile property involved (from mobile property involved in ignition). The statistics on smoking materials and candles include a proportional share of fires in which the heat source was heat from an unclassified open flame or smoking material. Exposure fires include fires with an exposure number greater than zero, as well as fires identified by heat source or factor contributing to ignition when no equipment was involved in ignition and the fires were not intentionally set. Because contained trash or rubbish fires are a scenario without causal information, they are shown at the bottom of the table if they account for at least 2 percent of the fires. Casual information is not routinely collected for these incidents. The same fire can be listed under multiple causes, based on multiple data elements.

These are national estimates of fires reported to U.S. municipal fire departments and so exclude fires reported only to federal or state agencies or industrial fire brigades. National estimates are projections. Casualty and loss projections can be heavily influenced by the inclusion or exclusion of one unusually serious fire. Fires are rounded to the nearest hundred, civilian deaths and injuries are rounded to the nearest one, and direct property damage is rounded to the nearest million. Property damage has not been adjusted for inflation.

Source: NFIRS and NFPA survey.

OCCUPANT CHARACTERISTICS

In general, occupants of an industrial facility are able-bodied adults. Statistically less at risk of injury from fire, they are ambulatory and capable of responding quickly to a fire. These occupants should be familiar with facility hazards and emergency exit locations. The likelihood also exists that employees in an industrial setting have received some emergency training. As density of the occupant load varies significantly, it must be considered in exit system design. Facilities employing many physically and mentally disabled people require supplemental prefire planning to ensure safe evacuation.

FIRE PROTECTION FEATURES

A primary life safety feature of an industrial occupancy should be an automatic sprinkler system. Originally developed as a property protection feature, it has proved effective in preventing loss of life. Automatic sprinklers mitigate the effects of fire, thereby allowing occupants sufficient time to evacuate the building. In addition, the sprinkler system waterflow alarm can alert building occupants of the fire earlier and thereby give them more time to react. Several sources have documented the effectiveness of sprinkler systems. The U.S. Department of Energy (DOE) reported on the effectiveness and reliability of the sprinkler systems protecting DOE facilities during the years 1952 to 1980.[5] Several conclusions resulted from the study:

- Sprinkler systems are over 98 percent effective in controlling or extinguishing fires.
- Considering only building fires, sprinklers reduce the loss by at least a factor of 5.
- About one-third of all fires may be completely extinguished with only one sprinkler head operating.

TABLE 20.18.4 Structure Fires in Industrial and Manufacturing Properties by Area of Origin, 1999–2002 Annual Averages

Area of Origin	*Fires*		*Civilian Deaths*		*Civilian Injuries*		*Direct Property Damage (in Millions of Dollars)*	
Process or manufacturing area or workroom	2500	(18%)	3	(18%)	167	(36%)	182	(21%)
Machinery room or area or elevator machinery room	1300	(10%)	3	(19%)	52	(11%)	73	(9%)
Storage room, area, tank, or bin	600	(5%)	0	(0%)	14	(3%)	50	(6%)
Maintenance or paint shop area	600	(4%)	1	(3%)	27	(6%)	58	(7%)
Duct for HVAC, cable, exhaust, heating, or air conditioning	500	(3%)	0	(0%)	8	(2%)	13	(2%)
Unclassified equipment or service area	500	(3%)	1	(4%)	20	(4%)	37	(4%)
Unclassified area	400	(3%)	2	(11%)	10	(2%)	48	(6%)
Heating equipment room	400	(3%)	1	(3%)	11	(2%)	16	(2%)
Attic or ceiling/roof assembly or concealed space	400	(3%)	0	(0%)	2	(1%)	18	(2%)
Exterior roof surface	400	(3%)	0	(0%)	5	(1%)	7	(1%)
Exterior wall surface	400	(3%)	0	(0%)	4	(1%)	9	(1%)
Unclassified storage area	400	(3%)	2	(11%)	21	(5%)	62	(7%)
Wall assembly or concealed space	300	(2%)	0	(0%)	2	(0%)	8	(1%)
Unclassified structural area	300	(2%)	1	(7%)	2	(1%)	18	(2%)
Trash or rubbish chute, area, or container	300	(2%)	0	(0%)	4	(1%)	6	(1%)
Storage of supplies or tools or dead storage	200	(2%)	0	(0%)	5	(1%)	16	(2%)
Kitchen or cooking area	200	(2%)	0	(0%)	5	(1%)	4	(0%)
Switchgear area or transformer vault	200	(1%)	1	(8%)	13	(3%)	18	(2%)
Confined chimney or flue fire	200	(1%)	0	(0%)	5	(1%)	0	(0%)
Shipping, receiving, or loading area	200	(1%)	0	(0%)	8	(2%)	59	(7%)
Ceiling/floor assembly or concealed space	200	(1%)	0	(0%)	0	(0%)	10	(1%)
Office	200	(1%)	1	(4%)	1	(0%)	11	(1%)
Confined fuel burner or boiler fire	200	(1%)	0	(0%)	1	(0%)	1	(0%)
Unclassified technical processing area	200	(1%)	0	(0%)	14	(3%)	7	(1%)
Conveyor	200	(1%)	0	(0%)	2	(1%)	13	(2%)
Laboratory	200	(1%)	0	(0%)	15	(3%)	6	(1%)
Computer room, control room or center	200	(1%)	0	(0%)	1	(0%)	8	(1%)
Lawn, field, or open area	100	(1%)	1	(4%)	0	(0%)	3	(0%)
Confined cooking fire	100	(1%)	0	(0%)	1	(0%)	4	(0%)
Conduit, pipe, utility, or ventilation shaft	100	(1%)	0	(0%)	2	(0%)	2	(0%)
Laundry room or area	100	(1%)	0	(0%)	1	(0%)	3	(0%)
Garage or vehicle storage area	100	(1%)	0	(0%)	2	(1%)	6	(1%)
Lavatory, bathroom, locker room, or check room	100	(1%)	0	(0%)	4	(1%)	4	(1%)
Confined compactor fire	100	(1%)	0	(0%)	0	(0%)	0	(0%)
Unclassified service facility	100	(1%)	0	(0%)	3	(1%)	6	(1%)
Confined incinerator fire	100	(1%)	0	(0%)	3	(1%)	2	(0%)
Dark room, printing, or photo room or area	100	(1%)	0	(0%)	2	(0%)	6	(1%)
Crawl space or substructure space	100	(1%)	0	(0%)	0	(0%)	3	(0%)
Chimney	100	(1%)	0	(0%)	0	(0%)	1	(0%)
Unclassified outside area	100	(1%)	0	(0%)	0	(0%)	6	(1%)
Other known service or equipment area	200	(1%)	0	(0%)	3	(1%)	12	(1%)
Other known assembly or sales area	100	(1%)	1	(4%)	1	(0%)	4	(0%)
Other known means of egress	100	(1%)	0	(0%)	5	(1%)	4	(1%)
Other known function area	100	(1%)	1	(4%)	3	(1%)	7	(1%)
Other known vehicle area	100	(1%)	0	(0%)	6	(1%)	4	(0%)
Other known area	200	(1%)	0	(0%)	5	(1%)	20	(2%)
Contained trash fire	500	(3%)	0	(0%)	2	(0%)	0	(0%)
Total	13,800	(100%)	17	(100%)	460	(100%)	856	(100%)

Note: These are national estimates of fires reported to U.S. municipal fire departments and so exclude fires reported only to federal or state agencies or industrial fire brigades. National estimates are projections. Casualty and loss projections can be heavily influenced by the inclusion or exclusion of one unusually serious fire. Fires are rounded to the nearest hundred, civilian deaths and injuries are rounded to the nearest one, and direct property damage is rounded to the nearest million dollars. Property damage has not been adjusted for inflation. Nonconfined and noncontained structure fires in which the area of origin was unknown or not reported have been allocated proportionally among fires with known area of origin. Totals may not equal sums due to rounding errors.

Source: NFIRS and NFPA survey.

Additionally, a book from the Australia Fire Protection Association on the performance of automatic sprinklers in Australia and New Zealand, 1886–1968,[6] includes a detailed analysis of fire involving different occupancies. The section on industrial occupancies is broken down into different categories. Sprinklers operated effectively over 98 percent of the time. Life loss in these facilities was minimal, nil in the majority of incidents.

Both these studies were limited to special groups of facilities in which design, usage, or maintenance may tend to be better than the average U.S. practice. As noted earlier, NFPA analysis of industrial and manufacturing facility fires reported to U.S. fire departments indicates sprinklers reduce the average loss per fire by two-thirds.

To be effective, a system must be operable. A closed sprinkler control valve was a contributing factor to a 1993 fire at a Newark, New Jersey, electrical power plant in which three workers died.[4] Programs must be in place to provide for inspection of control valves to ensure they are open and for maintenance of associated trim for alarm piping, dry-pipe valves, and preaction and deluge systems. For preaction and deluge systems, the associated detection systems must also be operational.

NFPA *101* AND *NFPA 5000*

Classification of Occupancy

To design the appropriate exit system for an industrial occupancy, the life safety industrial occupancy hazard classification per NFPA *101* and *NFPA 5000* must be established. The three basic classifications include general industrial, special-purpose industrial, and high-hazard industrial occupancy.

General-Purpose Industrial Occupancy. General-purpose industrial occupancies involve low- and ordinary-hazard industrial operations occurring in any type of building, be it single-story, multistory, or multiple tenant. These occupancies normally have a higher density of employees than other classifications. Examples are a laundry or a vehicle assembly plant having low- or moderate-hazard operations.

Special-Purpose Industrial Occupancy. Special-purpose industrial occupancies also involve low- and ordinary-hazard industrial operations. They are characterized by low employee density with most of the floor area occupied by equipment. An example is a structure built to protect large processing equipment from weather, where people associated with the process work in a separate control room, thereby reducing employee exposure to fire. These occupancies have slightly different egress requirements that are generally more lenient, such as an increase in the travel distance allowed. Also, egress is designed for the actual number of employees in the structure, rather than the calculated occupant load. A telephone switch building or a turbine generator building at a power plant meets the definition of low or moderate hazard and very reduced number of occupants.

High-Hazard Industrial Occupancy. A high-hazard industrial occupancy differs from low- and ordinary-hazard industrial occupancies by the materials used and the potential results and by-products of their use. High-hazard industrial occupancies include structures in which there are processes involving highly combustible, highly flammable, or explosive materials, or structures in which materials are likely to burn with extreme rapidity or to produce poisonous fumes or gases. Also included are industrial facilities in which flammable liquids are routinely handled, used, or stored in large quantities or those in which explosive dusts from grain, wood, flour, plastic, aluminum, magnesium, or other explosive-dust-generating materials are produced. Plants such as a grain handling facility or a gasoline refinery are examples of high-hazard industrial occupancies.

Structures with adequately protected, incidental high-hazard uses do not have to be classified as high-hazard facilities. These structures may include specific fire prevention measures such as a small flammable liquid storage room designed to meet NFPA 30, *Flammable and Combustible Liquids Code.* The restricted use of flammable liquids does not require a high-hazard classification. An example is a metalworking plant, normally classified as low hazard, that has a flammable solvent dip tank coater. Although adequate means of egress away from the coater are required, the classification of the entire facility does not change to high hazard.

The classification of the life safety hazard of an industrial occupancy must be carefully considered. The goal is to evaluate the hazard of the contents, process, and other factors affecting fire development. The time available for occupants to evacuate can be very much affected by the growth of the fire. Many resources are available to assist in the determination. Review of pertinent NFPA literature, including the codes and this handbook, is helpful. Officials in other jurisdictions with similar occupancies and plant operators can provide additional valuable information. Chapter 34 of *NFPA 5000* contains a comprehensive package of requirements for buildings that contain high-hazard contents.

Means of Egress Design Requirements

Designing the egress system for a building requires consideration of many factors. Some involve distance requirements, such as travel distance, common path of travel, and dead ends. These distances vary based on the life safety hazard classification and the absence or presence of automatic sprinklers. Egress distance limitations are shown in Table 20.18.5. To use some of the greater distances involves special requirements, such as application to one-story buildings only, with automatic sprinklers mandatory and smoke and heat venting.

High-hazard occupancies are very restrictive on means of egress distances allowed, with no dead ends or common paths of travel permitted. Generally, two exits are required from every story or section. However, NFPA *101* and *NFPA 5000* provide exceptions to this requirement. By careful design, the listed requirements can be met. The addition of exit tunnels, overhead passageways, or horizontal exits can aid in meeting prescribed distance limits.

Fire Alarm Systems

As illustrated by Figure 20.18.2, industrial and office park facilities coexist side by side and can be large and complex.

TABLE 20.18.5 Egress Distance Limitations

	Travel Distance			Dead End	Common Path of Travel	
Industrial Occupancy	*Unsprinklered ft (m)*	*Sprinklered ft (m)*	*Special ft (m)*	*ft (m)*	*Unsprinklered ft (m)*	*Sprinklered ft (m)*
General purpose	200 (61)	250 (76)	400 (122)*	50 (15)	50 (15)	100 (30)
Special purpose	300 (91)	400 (122)	—	50 (15)	50 (15)	100 (30)
High hazard	NP	75 (23)	—	0	0	0

*Special requirements in NFPA *101* and *NFPA 5000* for this travel distance in general-purpose industrial occupancies.
NP = Not permitted.

Due to the size and complexity of most industrial facilities, a fire alarm system is a valuable tool for life safety. It can alert designated personnel, such as an industrial fire brigade, to a fire and allow for prompt response to evacuate occupants, fight the fire, shut down equipment, and other actions, as required. NFPA *101* and *NFPA 5000* require a fire alarm system for most industrial occupancies. Exceptions are based on occupant load, where total capacity is less than 100 persons and fewer than 25 persons are located above or below the level of exit discharge. In low- and ordinary-hazard industrial occupancies, the fire alarm must sound an audible alarm at a continuously attended location to initiate emergency action. At high-hazard industrial occupancies, in addition to the foregoing, the fire alarm must initiate an occupant evacuation signal. In these occupancies, early notification can be critical to life safety.

PREFIRE PLANNING

Individual preplanning is appropriate for property protection. Training in the use of fire extinguishers for incipient fires must be provided if employees are expected to use them. Designated employees need to be trained to check that fire protection equipment is operating as designed—for example, that sprinkler control valves are open. The responding fire department should be made familiar with the facility, and an employee should be designated as their primary contact. Hazardous materials should be identified and their location noted on a building plan. Full participation in drills is necessary to completely test the plan.

The prefire plan should be evaluated routinely through simulated fire exercises. Such exercises are critical to identify deficiencies in the plan. If possible, request the participation of the responding fire department.

If there are industrial fire brigades at the site, they must be adequately trained. Training should include brigade organization and responsibility, the basics of fire behavior, special onsite fire and health hazards, and hands-on training with the fire equipment they are expected to use (see NFPA 600, *Standard on Industrial Fire Brigades*). Available equipment might include fire extinguishers, standpipes, hoses, and hydrants. Appropriate use of this equipment on incipient fires can contribute to a major reduction in the risk of fire loss and loss of life in industrial occupancies. Restricting the spread of fire also reduces the threat to life.

FIGURE 20.18.2 Fire at the Large River City Business Park in Iowa (Source: Davenport Fire Department)

SUMMARY

Industrial occupancies must be adequately evaluated to determine fire hazard. Fire hazard affects the potential for life loss and property damage. Loss history can be used to see whether current designs and requirements are effective. NFPA *101* and *NFPA 5000* requirements for industrial facilities are briefly discussed. It is important that building design and fire protection systems allow for safe occupant egress in the event of fire. The effectiveness of sprinklers has been documented from two sources in particular.

BIBLIOGRAPHY

References Cited

1. Ahrens, M., *U.S. Fires in Selected Occupancies,* NFPA Fire Analysis and Research Division, Quincy, MA, Mar. 2006.
2. Klem, T. J., "25 Die in Food Plant Fire," *Fire Journal,* Vol. 86, No. 1, 1992, pp. 29–35.
3. Grant, C. C., and Klem, T. J., "Toy Factory Fire in Thailand Kills 188 Workers," *NFPA Journal,* Vol. 88, No. 1, 1994, pp. 42–49.
4. Klem, T. J., and Grant, C. C., "Three Workers Die in Electrical Power Plant Fire," *NFPA Journal,* Vol. 87, No. 2, 1993, pp. 44–47.

5. "Automatic Sprinkler System Performance and Reliability in United States Department of Energy Facilities 1952–1980," DOE/EP-0052, UC-41, U.S. Department of Energy, Washington, DC, June 1982.
6. Marryatt, H. W., "General Occupancy Analysis," *Fire—Automatic Sprinkler Performance in Australia and New Zealand 1886–1968,* McCarron Bird Pty, Melbourne, Australia, 1971, pp. 103–118.

NFPA Codes, Standards, and Recommended Practices

Reference to the following NFPA codes, standards, and recommended practices will provide further information on the industrial occupancies discussed in this chapter. (See the latest version of The NFPA Catalog *for availability of current editions of the following documents.)*

NFPA 30, *Flammable and Combustible Liquids Code*
NFPA 69, *Standard on Explosion Prevention Systems*
NFPA *101®*, *Life Safety Code®*
NFPA 220, *Standard on Types of Building Construction*
NFPA 600, *Standard on Industrial Fire Brigades*
NFPA 5000®, *Building Construction and Safety Code®*

References

Fire Protection Guide to Hazardous Materials, 13th ed., National Fire Protection Association, Quincy, MA, 2000.
Zalosh, R. G., *Industrial Fire Protection Engineering,* John Wiley and Sons, Hoboken, NJ, 2003.

Chapter 19

Motion Picture and Television Studios and Soundstages

Raymond A. Grill

Chapter Contents

Key Terms

assembly occupancy, auxiliary heating, combustible load, hot work, industrial occupancy, proximate audience, pyrotechnics

NFPA 140, *Standard on Motion Picture and Television Production Studio Soundstages and Approved Production Facilities,* provides minimum requirements for the design, construction, operation, and maintenance of soundstages and approved production facilities, as defined here. Now in its second edition, the standard defines motion picture and television studios as buildings, portions of buildings, or groups of buildings designed and constructed for use by the entertainment industry to produce motion pictures, television shows, or commercials, or to broadcast television programs utilizing a soundstage. Although NFPA 140 covers all pre- and postproduction facilities including construction shops, warehouses, soundstages, control rooms, editing facilities, and other exterior filming locations on the studio property, the requirements of NFPA 140 are focused on soundstages and approved production facilities. An approved production facility is an existing building, portion of a building, or group of buildings that has been altered to be used for motion picture, television, or commercial production and that has been approved by the authority having jurisdiction (AHJ) for that purpose. Approved production facilities function as soundstages.

The motion picture and television industry is dynamic in nature, and soundstages and production facilities need to be flexible. As a result, the fire protection needs of these types of facilities must be evaluated based on the hazards present, which change from production to production, and the industry's operational needs. Many occupancies and hazards found at a studio are similar to those in typical light industrial facilities.

This chapter, therefore, focuses primarily on fire protection issues relating to soundstages and approved production facilities. It does not deal with locations or exterior production areas that might be found on a studio lot. For instance, construction shops for building sets contain the same hazards as many other shops or factories and should be treated as such. Warehouses on studio property can also be treated like other warehouses, while bearing in mind their contents' dynamic nature. Administrative areas, control rooms, and commissaries can also be treated from a fire protection and life safety standpoint like other similar occupancies. However, soundstages, which are specifically designed for filming or live broadcasts, have special operational needs, and an understanding of their specific fire protection hazards and features is required.

See also Section 20, Chapter 1, "Assessing Life Safety in Buildings"; Section 20, Chapter 9, "Assembly Occupancies"; and Section 20, Chapter 18, "Industrial Occupancies."

OCCUPANCY CHARACTERISTICS

A soundstage is a building or a portion of a building, usually insulated from outside noise and natural light, used to produce motion pictures, television shows, or commercials. Soundstages like the one shown in Figure 20.19.1 are specifically designed and constructed to create a controlled environment that can be isolated from exterior noise and light.

Raymond A. Grill is the fire area business leader for Ove Arup & Partners in the Americas.

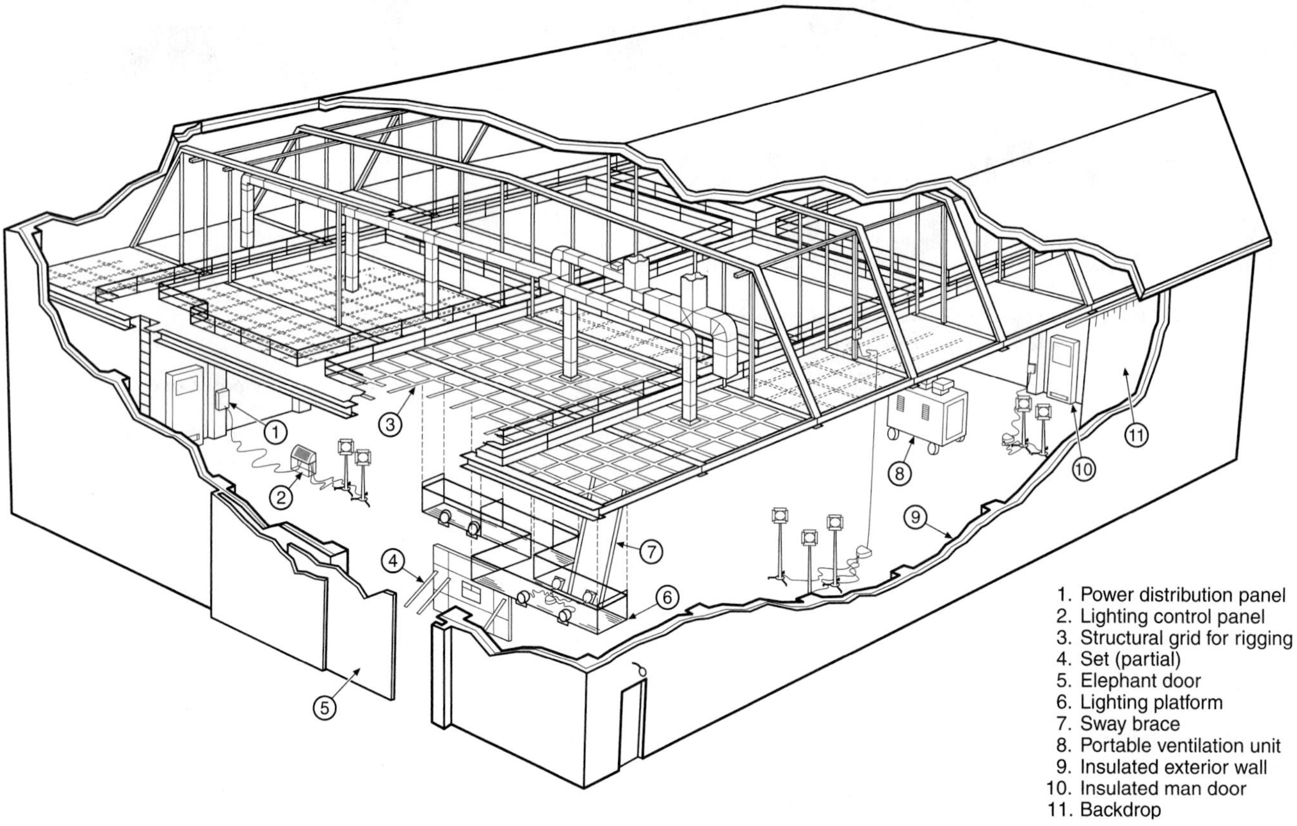

FIGURE 20.19.1 Typical Soundstage

Soundstages are often stand-alone buildings but can also be a room within a larger mixed-used building. Mixed use is often found in television production and broadcasting. Multiple soundstages can also be located within a single building.

The motion picture and television production industry commonly converts existing buildings to soundstages. This process may or may not include a change of occupancy classification for the existing facility. Vacant warehouses have been the primary type of existing facility converted into soundstages because of their openness. Its contents make a soundstage unique and the contents and configuration can change frequently to meet the needs of the production.

Live broadcast facilities, such as those for the production of network news broadcasts, incorporate production activities within other activities, such as newsrooms and offices. Some productions also include live audience environments within the soundstage. Introducing a live audience, depending on its size, can impact occupancy classification and other life safety and fire protection issues. These issues are discussed later in this chapter.

Sets within soundstages can be very elaborate. The duration of their use varies significantly from production to production. Some sets for television series may be used for years; others are specifically constructed for an episode. A set may be developed to simulate an entire building or series of buildings within the soundstage. Sets are typically constructed of wood and generally treated as temporary structures.

HISTORICAL FIRE EXPERIENCE

In 2006, the National Fire Protection Association Fire Analysis and Research Division analyzed fire losses in motion picture and television studios based on annual averages between 1999 and 2002.[1] The information gathered was based on data from NFPA's annual stratified random sample survey and the United States Fire Administration's National Fire Incident Reporting System (NFIRS).

Between 1999 and 2002, an estimated nine structure fires were reported annually to U.S. fire departments as occurring in motion picture studios and resulted in an average total fire loss of $65,000 in property damage per year. During the same period, an average of 18 reported structure fires in radio or television studios annually resulted in a yearly average of $71,000 in direct property damage. Due to the small number of fires, extreme caution should be used in interpreting these statistics.

Motion Picture Studios

Thirty-eight percent of the reported motion picture studio fires were unintentional, 27 percent were intentionally set, and 27 percent were caused by a failure of equipment or heat source. In 27 percent of these fires, electrical wire or cable insulation was the item first ignited; 18 percent of the fires began with upholstered furniture. Electrical arcing was the heat source in 27 percent of these fires.

Radio and Television Studios

Forty percent of the reported 1999–2002 radio or television studio fires were unintentional, 30 percent resulted from a failure of equipment or heat source, and 14 percent were intentionally set. Eleven percent of the fires were confined chimney or fuel burner fires; causal information is not routinely collected for these incidents. Electrical distribution equipment was involved in 18 percent of the fires in these properties. Including the confined fires, heating equipment was involved in 16 percent. Electrical wire or cable insulation was the item first ignited in 18 percent of these fires.

OCCUPANCY HAZARDS

Due to the unique nature of motion picture and television production, the contents of a soundstage and its combustible load vary from time to time. Soundstages themselves may also include combustible materials as part of their construction. Supplemental and temporary equipment, as well as set construction, contributes to the potential hazard within the soundstage. Introduction of occupants (performers and audiences) also needs to be addressed from a life safety exposure and egress perspective.

Combustible Fuel Load

Production sets can consist of simple platforms, backdrops, or very elaborate structures. Sets are typically constructed of wood framing. They may consist of a simple platform to provide for appropriate camera angles or may include walls and ceilings to simulate a room or building. Some model building codes generally exempt motion picture and television sets from permit requirements. Sets are typically considered temporary because changes occur regularly. *NFPA 5000®, Building Construction and Safety Code®*, mandates compliance with NFPA 140.

Set construction might obstruct sprinkler protection and other fire protection features. Ceilings of sets may be movable or built with materials that are not self-venting and, therefore, obstruct heat flow and sprinkler operation.

Set Construction/Hot Work

The use of arc welders, oxyacetylene torches, and grinders is common during set construction. NFPA 51B, *Standard for Fire Prevention During Welding, Cutting, and Other Hot Work,* provides comprehensive criteria for managing the potential hazards of these operations. Requirements include management responsibilities as well as operators' responsibilities. Fires caused by hot work can best be prevented by separating combustibles from ignition sources or by shielding combustibles. Regular inspections should be conducted to verify that compressed gas cylinders are adequately secured, hoses and cables are in good condition, combustible materials and flammable liquids are appropriately separated, and adequate fire-fighting equipment is provided.

Electrical Considerations

Electrical equipment and installations should comply with applicable sections of NFPA 70, *National Electrical Code®*. Specific articles in NFPA 70 address theaters, audience areas of motion picture and television studios, and similar locations. These articles include specific requirements for equipment, switchboards, lighting, and grounding. They address portable wiring, which is extensively used in motion picture and television production.

Mobile power generators are routinely used in motion picture production. Soundstages are not constructed to accommodate the temporary power needs of all production activities. Therefore, portable generators often supplement normal building power. When routing auxiliary power cables, care should be taken not to obstruct or interfere with fire ratings of walls, doors, or windows. NFPA 140 prohibits cables from being routed through fire-rated windows or doors. NFPA 140 allows cables to pass through fire-rated assemblies, when the penetrations are protected in accordance with NFPA 221, *Standard for High Challenge Fire Walls, Fire Walls, and Fire Barrier Walls.* Temporary electrical equipment can also obstruct egress and fire-fighting operations. When laying cables and locating portable generators, exit routes should be carefully avoided.

The location of portable generating equipment is subject to the approval of the AHJ based on NFPA 140.

The location of portable power-generating equipment should include consideration of the following:

- Potential exposure to the soundstage and adjacent structures
- Potential obstruction of egress or fire-fighting access
- Service and fueling needs

Portable power generators should be regularly inspected for leaks and adequate portable fire extinguishers should be available for use on this equipment.

Portable Heating, Venting, and Air Conditioning

Auxiliary heating, venting, and air-conditioning equipment often supplements the built-in capacity of a soundstage. These units should be listed by an approved testing laboratory and located so they do not obstruct egress or access. Flexible ducts used with these systems should be noncombustible and also arranged not to block egress and access.

Special Effects

Special effects might significantly impact the safety of soundstage occupants. Special effects may include pyrotechnic materials, gas, or other open flames, theatrical smoke, or fuel-powered vehicles. Clearly, special effects' impact is greater when there is an audience.

Pyrotechnics. Based on NFPA 140, use of pyrotechnic special effects is subject to the approval of the AHJ. Therefore, the proposed use of pyrotechnics on a soundstage must be reviewed with the AHJ prior to use.

NFPA 1126, *Standard for the Use of Pyrotechnics Before a Proximate Audience,* applies to the indoor display of pyrotechnic special effects in television and movie production only if the production is before a proximate audience. Special effects are partially defined as visible or audible effects for entertainment purposes, frequently an illusion. NFPA 1126 defines proximate audience as "an audience closer to pyrotechnic devices than allowed by NFPA 1123, *Code for Fireworks Display*." This NFPA standard contains requirements on storage, permits, operator qualifications, labeling of preloads and use of pyrotechnics. It should be consulted when pyrotechnic special effects will be used indoors before an audience.

NFPA *101*®, *Life Safety Code*®, addresses pyrotechnic devices in its chapters on assembly occupancies by requiring compliance with NFPA 1126.

Open Flame. Based on NFPA 140, use of open flames is subject to the approval of the AHJ. Therefore, the proposed use of open flames on a soundstage must be reviewed with the AHJ prior to use. NFPA *101* also addresses open-flame devices in assembly occupancies. It allows open flame on stages and platforms as a necessary part of a performance, when precautions satisfying the AHJ are taken to prevent ignition of combustible material or injury to occupants. It permits gas lights under similar conditions. Prior to the performance, use of open flame or gas lights before an audience should be worked out with the AHJ.

Smoke. Theatrical smoke used as a special effect should not obscure exit signs, particularly if an audience is present. If no audience is present, and dense smoke is integral to the production, those affected by the smoke should be trained and drilled regarding egress routes.

Decorations

Combustible drapes, drops, hangings, cycloramas, cut greenery, and other decorative materials are required by NFPA 140 to be maintained in a flame-retardant condition. Depending on the material and the duration of use, this may necessitate periodic reapplication of fire retardant.

Foam plastic materials used for decorative purposes, scenery, or props must be limited to materials with a maximum heat release rate of 100 kW when tested in accordance with UL 1975, *Standard for Fire Tests for Foam Plastics Used for Decorative Purposes.*

Housekeeping/Smoking

Combustible waste and other combustible materials should be stored in a manner that limits their potential of coming in contact with ignition sources. Approved self-closing metal containers should be provided for containing combustible waste. Housekeeping hazards include accumulated sawdust or wood scraps; accumulated litter; combustible storage below platforms; storage of props, equipment, and material that may block exits, fire protection equipment, and electrical equipment.

NFPA 140 prohibits smoking on soundstages unless it is required as part of a production.

LIFE SAFETY/EGRESS

A soundstage may have two separate and distinct uses, depending on the presence of an audience. If no audience is anticipated, the soundstage can be considered an industrial occupancy. Means of egress should meet the requirements of NFPA *101* and *NFPA 5000.* Soundstages exceeding 1500 ft^2 (139 m^2) are required by NFPA 140 to have an aisle along the perimeter, clear to 7 ft (2.1 m) above the floor. Motion picture soundstages often maintain a 4 ft (1.2 m) aisle, with that portion of the floor painted yellow to clearly indicate that it is to be kept open. NFPA 140 also limits the travel distance to an exit in a soundstage to 150 ft (46 m).

If an audience of 50 or more people may be present, the requirements for assembly occupancies of NFPA *101* and *NFPA 5000* apply. Other portions of this handbook, NFPA *101,* and NFPA *5000* address exiting from assembly spaces, and the reader should refer to them for guidelines and requirements on number of exits, stair and handrail criteria, aisle and seating arrangements, emergency lighting, and the need for sprinkler and alarm systems.

If an audience is present, maintaining clear and obvious egress paths is important, especially if special effects or other visual illusions are used.

FIRE PROTECTION

Soundstages should be provided with automatic sprinkler protection to control and suppress fires in their incipient stages. New soundstages and new approved production facilities are required by NFPA 140 to be provided with an approved, supervised automatic sprinkler system. The systems are required to be designed in accordance with NFPA 13, *Standard for the Installation of Sprinkler Systems,* and maintained in accordance with NFPA 25, *Standard for the Inspection, Testing, and Maintenance of Water-Based Fire Protection Systems.* The design of automatic sprinkler systems needs to consider the special circumstances created by platforms and solid-ceiling sets. In recognition of the temporary nature of platforms and sets it might be necessary to permit omission of sprinklers in these areas when alternative protective means are provided. Such means might include limiting the size of platforms and solid ceilings, limiting use below platforms, and installation of heat or smoke detectors in areas that are shielded from sprinklers. NFPA 140 also recognizes the potential for obstructions. When the design of the building's automatic sprinkler system is increased to Extra Hazard, Group 2 density and area of coverage, NFPA 140 allows obstructions to sprinkler discharge that can be created by construction of sets. When a fire is shielded from sprinklers, it might develop beyond its incipient stage before sprinkler activation. The Extra Hazard, Group 2 design criteria are necessary to control a fire of this type.

Soundstages have unique needs with respect to audible and visible alarms. Audible and visible notification appliances within soundstages are allowed by NFPA 140 to be deactivated during production provided the following conditions are met:

1. Alarm system activation causes notification appliances to activate at a constantly attended location.
2. The attendants of the location have a means of communicating with the building fire command center, if one is provided, and with the occupants of the soundstage.

3. Deactivation of notification appliances on the soundstage activates an appropriately labeled visible signal at an approved location that remains illuminated while notification appliances on the soundstage are deactivated.

This approach is most likely to be utilized in a soundstage that is part of another building having a fire alarm system.

Portable fire extinguishers should be provided throughout soundstages in accordance with the requirements of NFPA 10, *Standard for Portable Fire Extinguishers.*

OPERATING FEATURES

Several other NFPA standards may apply to soundstage operations. These include NFPA 1, *Uniform Fire Code*™, regarding maintenance of systems, waste, and refuge accumulation; and elimination or mitigation of hazards. NFPA 30, *Flammable and Combustible Liquids Code,* and NFPA 58, *Liquefied Petroleum Gas Code,* address flammable and combustible liquids and liquefied petroleum gases, respectively. Welding is addressed by NFPA 51, *Standard for the Design and Installation of Oxygen–Fuel Gas Systems for Welding, Cutting, and Allied Processes,* and NFPA 51B.

Of primary importance in the operation of a motion picture or television production facility is the need to continually monitor and maintain the fire protection provided. Occupancies, uses, and hazards can change daily. Thew operator should assign a person to maintain proper fire protection and life safety who can apply good fire protection practice and common sense to day-to-day operations. This person needs to interface effectively with AHJs and must have enough internal authority to correct or mitigate hazards as they arise.

SUMMARY

Motion picture and television studios and soundstages are part of a dynamic industry. Fire protection needs to take into account the fact that hazards, occupancies, and operational needs will change from production to production. Hazards typical of production facilities that need to be constantly monitored include combustible loading, set construction, hot work, electrical systems, portable heaters and air conditioners, and special effects. Fire protection and life safety measures include clearly marked exits, an alarm system, an automatic sprinkler system, and the presence of portable fire extinguishers.

BIBLIOGRAPHY

Reference Cited

1. NFPA Fire Analysis and Research Division.

NFPA Codes, Standards, and Recommended Practices

Reference to the following NFPA codes, standards, and recommended practices will provide further information on the motion picture and television studios and soundstages discussed in this chapter. (See the latest version of The NFPA Catalog *for availability of the current edition of the following documents.)*

NFPA 1, *Uniform Fire Code*™
NFPA 10, *Standard for Portable Fire Extinguishers*
NFPA 13, *Standard for the Installation of Sprinkler Systems*
NFPA 25, *Standard for the Inspection, Testing, and Maintenance of Water-Based Fire Protection Systems*
NFPA 30, *Flammable and Combustible Liquids Code*
NFPA 51, *Standard for the Design and Installation of Oxygen–Fuel Gas Systems for Welding, Cutting, and Allied Processes*
NFPA 51B, *Standard for Fire Prevention During Welding, Cutting, and Other Hot Work*
NFPA 58, *Liquefied Petroleum Gas Code*
NFPA 70, *National Electrical Code*®
NFPA *101*®, *Life Safety Code*®
NFPA 140, *Standard on Motion Picture and Television Production Studio Soundstages and Approved Production Facilities*
NFPA 221, *Standard for High Challenge Fire Walls, Fire Walls, and Fire Barrier Walls*
NFPA 1123, *Code for Fireworks Display*
NFPA 1126, *Standard for the Use of Pyrotechnics Before a Proximate Audience*
NFPA 5000®, *Building Construction and Safety Code*®

Chapter 20

Occupancies in Special Structures

Wayne D. Holmes

Chapter Contents

Key Terms

air-supported structures, below-grade fires, grandstands, Hartford circus fire, lighthouses, limited-access structures, mall buildings, marine terminals, membrane structures, offshore platforms, open structures, parking garages, piers, Six Flags Great Adventure Amusement Park fire, special amusement structures, tents, towers, underground structures, wharves, windowless structures

Every occupancy has unique needs for fire safety. Other chapters in this section describe fire protection techniques for various general occupancy types. For the most part, the fire protection techniques described in the other chapters are presented without regard to the type of structure. It is generally assumed that occupancies will be situated in "ordinary" structures with no unusual building features.

Some structures, because of their physical arrangement or construction methods, may present additional fire safety challenges that warrant additional protection measures, regardless of the occupancy. Special structures might present impediments to fire-fighting and rescue access, impediments to occupant egress, or fire and smoke management challenges. For purposes of this chapter, special structures include limited-access and underground structures, mall buildings, open parking structures, special amusement structures, piers and wharves, water-surrounded structures, membrane structures and tents, grandstands, towers, and open structures.

This chapter addresses some of the extraordinary fire safety aspects of special structures and presents some particular fire protection features that should be provided, regardless of the occupancy classification, in addition to the occupancy-based features that are described in other chapters in this section.

Another type of special structure, the high-rise building, is addressed in Section 20, Chapter 8, "High-Rise Buildings."

ACCEPTABLE DESIGN

Unique building arrangements of special structures are limited only by the designer's imagination. As a result, it is impossible for model codes, such as NFPA *101*®, *Life Safety Code*®, and *NFPA 5000*®, *Building Construction and Safety Code*®, to anticipate precisely all of the conditions and hazards that such a design could create. It is incumbent upon building owners, designers, and code officials to include those additional, beyond-the-codes, fire safety features that may be deemed necessary due to the uniqueness of the special structure and to the atypical fire safety problems that it may create.

Although the primary goals of fire protection will likely remain unchanged for occupancies in special structures, the prescriptive requirements of codes and standards, which typically apply to ordinary structures, might not be directly applicable. Thus, appropriate levels of fire protection for occupancies in special structures might require a special degree of sound design, engineering judgment, common sense, and cooperation between the designers and code officials.

When it is not possible to follow prescriptive requirements, alternative designs are necessary. Modern codes, including NFPA *101* and *NFPA 5000,* recognize performance-based options

Wayne D. Holmes, P.E., is vice-president of HSB Professional Loss Control, a fire protection engineering consulting firm. He is chair of the NFPA Technical Committee on Industrial, Storage, and Miscellaneous Occupancies; a member of the NFPA Technical Committee on Business and Mercantile Occupancies; a member of the NFPA Technical Committee on Fire Protection Features; a member of the NFPA Technical Committee on Fire Doors; and chair of the NFPA Technical Committee on Nuclear Facilities. He is also a fellow in the Society of Fire Protection Engineers.

as alternate means of achieving compliance. Both NFPA *101* and *NFPA 5000* include a "Performance-Based Option" chapter. Goals, objectives, and performance-based criteria are established, in conjunction with the codes' fundamental requirements, to achieve alternative means of complying with the codes' objectives. In order to develop an appropriate alternative design, basic information must be agreed on. The designer, building owner, and authority having jurisdiction (AHJ) together need to discuss design philosophy and specific performance requirements. The following should be considered:

- Minimum required fire protection systems and features
- Building characteristics
- Operational status and effectiveness of building systems and features
- Occupant characteristics
- Reasonable assumptions, limitations, and safety factors

All aspects of the performance-based design must be documented. NFPA *101* and *NFPA 5000* require that not less than eight design fire scenarios be considered with respect to initial fire location, rate of growth in fire severity, and smoke generation.

Finally, the proposed alternative design should be reviewed. Ultimately, the AHJ will determine if the provisions of NFPA *101* or *NFPA 5000* are met by the performance-based design. NFPA *101* and *NFPA 5000* permit the AHJ to require an approved, independent third party to review the proposed design and provide an evaluation of the design. If the AHJ is uncomfortable reviewing and accepting it, there are several options to consider. One is to have another competent fire protection engineer review the design. Perhaps the review cost can be included as part of the building permit fee. Or the AHJ could work jointly with another competent fire engineer on the review. The design could be sent elsewhere within the same jurisdiction for competent review. However it is done, the design, particularly one involving an extensive, complicated submittal, should be thoroughly reviewed prior to acceptance. The building owner is also required to annually certify compliance with the conditions and limitations of the performance-based design and submit a warrant of fitness acceptable to the AHJ.

Regardless of whether prescriptive code requirements are followed or performance-based fire safety practices are applied, occupancies in special structures should be afforded the same level of fire safety as similar occupancies in ordinary structures. The unique challenges of the special structure must be recognized, addressed, and overcome. This chapter describes some types of special structures and discusses some of the fire safety challenges presented in those structures.

LIMITED-ACCESS AND UNDERGROUND STRUCTURES

The hazards of underground and limited-access (known as "windowless" prior to the 2003 edition of NFPA *101*) structures are very similar. Both of these types of special structures present challenges with regard to smoke and heat venting, access for fire fighting and rescue, and, in some cases, for means of egress for occupants. Therefore, underground and limited-access structures pose similar concerns.

The feasibility of ventilating the structure should be considered in relationship to the classification, nature, and character of the occupancy. In the event that the occupancy is of such a character that a large number of occupants could be present, smoke control and smoke venting capabilities could have a significant impact on the overall level of life safety.

The following features of limited-access and underground buildings make them special structures:

- Due to the lack of windows, there are fewer points of entry into the building for manual fire suppression forces.
- Ventilation during emergencies and removal of products of combustion, such as heat and smoke, depend on mechanical systems and door openings. If there are no mechanical systems designed for ventilation and smoke removal, then emergency operations may be hindered or additional damage/downtime may occur, as compared to buildings with large numbers of access openings or windows.
- Natural illumination is limited or nonexistent. This issue has an impact on egress and emergency operations within the building.
- Limited-access and underground structures may make the fire department's initial size-up more difficult due to the lack of visibility from the exterior. Many times, size-up will be delayed until an initial interior observation can be made.

It is sometimes difficult to determine whether a building that appears to be windowless is a limited-access structure as defined by the codes. It is unusual to find a building that does not have at least a few access points and windows. It is necessary to review the definition of limited-access structures and to understand its intent in order to determine whether the structure meets the definition of a limited-access structure.

NFPA *101* and *NFPA 5000* define a limited-access structure as "a structure or portion of a structure lacking emergency openings." An emergency access opening is a window, panel, or similar opening of certain minimum dimensions and location that is readily identifiable from both the exterior and interior and readily openable from both the exterior and interior.

Emergency access panels provide fire-fighting access for fire control and rescue as well as a means for providing manual ventilation. With respect to emergency access panels, NFPA *101* and *NFPA 5000* state that a building need not be considered a limited-access structure if emergency access panels are provided on two sides of the first story, spaced not more than 125 ft (38 m) apart, and every story above the first floor is provided with emergency access panels on two sides of the building, spaced not more than 30 ft (9.1 m) apart.

Figure 20.20.1 provides an example of a structure that would not be considered a limited-access structure because openings meeting the dimensional and operational requirements of the codes are provided on two sides of the structure, where

$$D_1 \leq 125 \text{ ft } (38 \text{ m})$$

$$D_2 \leq 30 \text{ ft } (9.1 \text{ m})$$

$$x \geq 22 \text{ in. } (560 \text{ mm})$$

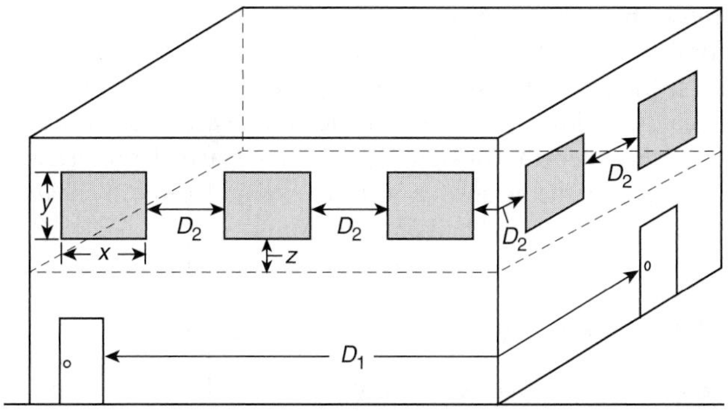

FIGURE 20.20.1 Emergency Access Openings (Source: *NFPA 5000® Handbook,* 2003, Figure 31.1, p. 731)

$$y \geq 24 \text{ in. } (610 \text{ mm})$$

$$z \leq 44 \text{ in. } (1120 \text{ mm})$$

Underground structures present additional problems not experienced in most other structures. The two primary issues are lack of accessibility and below-grade fires.

As with limited-access structures, it can be difficult to identify and classify underground structures. Many times, the difficulty occurs when a building or structure is constructed on a site with varying grades. This may result in some levels of the building being below grade on one or more sides and at, or above, grade on other sides. One example is a four-story structure built into the side of a steep hill. Although this arrangement might create a building in which more than 50 percent of the total wall surface is below ground, the building is not necessarily considered an underground structure provided that the levels of exit discharge and adequate accessibility are provided above grade.

NFPA *101* and *NFPA 5000* give specific guidance in determining when a building is considered an underground structure. The lowest floor used as a level of exit discharge may be considered the demarcation point for above and below grade. This may be true even if much of the wall surface of that floor is below grade. NFPA defines an underground structure as a structure or portion of a structure in which the floor level is below the level of exit discharge. A structure is not considered to be an underground structure if the story is provided with not less than 20 ft^2 (1.9 m^2) of emergency access opening entirely above the adjoining grade level in each 50 lineal ft (15 lineal m) of exterior enclosing wall area.

Exits from underground structures having an occupant load of more than 100 persons in the underground portions of the structure and having a floor used for human occupancy more than 30 ft (9.1 m) or more than one level below the lowest level of exit discharge should be arranged as follows:

- Exits should be cut off from the level of exit discharge.
- Exits should be provided with outside smoke-venting facilities or other means to prevent the exits from becoming charged with smoke from any fire in the areas served by the exits.

Furthermore, the underground portions of new underground structures should be provided with approved automatic smoke venting where the underground structure has the following:

- An occupant load of more than 100 persons in the underground portions of the structure
- A floor level used for human occupancy more than 30 ft (9.1 m) or more than one level below the lowest level of exit discharge
- Combustible contents, combustible interior finish, or combustible construction

From a practical standpoint, a limited-access structure has fire protection problems similar to an underground structure, but the windowless building can be constructed more easily to meet natural ventilation and rescue accessibility requirements. An underground structure must meet the requirements of a limited-access structure, and, in addition, some form of smoke management system must be provided. If a limited-access or windowless structure cannot meet the ventilation and rescue requirements, it should be considered equivalent to an underground structure, and the same code requirements should be applied.

Both underground and limited-access structures with occupant loads of more than 50 persons should be provided with approved, supervised automatic sprinkler systems throughout the underground or limited-access portions and all areas and floors traversed in traveling to the exit discharge.

Some examples of how occupancies and occupant loads affect code compliance for these special structures are helpful. For example, an underground space of 6000 ft^2 (560 m^2) housing an ordinary hazard industrial occupancy (occupant load factor of 100 ft^2 [9.3 m^2] per person) has an occupant load of 60 persons (6000/100 = 60). For this underground occupancy, NFPA *101* would require an approved, supervised automatic sprinkler system in all areas and floor levels traversed in traveling to the exit discharge.

For the same 6000 ft^2 (560 m^2) space housing a mercantile occupancy below grade and below the level of exit discharge (occupant load factor of 30 ft^2 [2.8 m^2] per person), the occupant load is 200 persons (6000/30 = 200). For this underground occupancy, NFPA *101* would require both an approved, supervised automatic sprinkler system in all areas and floor levels traversed in traveling to the exit discharge and an approved smoke venting system. It is important to consult specific code requirements for special provisions for occupancies in limited-access and underground structures.

Other general fire safety precautions should be observed for limited-access and underground structures. The use of combustible construction and other than Class A interior finish materials should be avoided. Foam plastics should not be left exposed; rather, they should be protected by a thermal barrier acceptable to the AHJ.

Compartmentation by fire barriers will help limit the extent of spread of fire and smoke. Barriers will help to reduce the severity of exposure to occupants and provide extended time for safe evacuation or relocation of occupants.

Manual fire-fighting equipment, such as standpipe and hose systems and portable fire extinguishers, can provide for quick suppression of small fires when handled by trained personnel.

Drainage of water from automatic sprinklers or from hose streams can be a significant problem in underground structures and requires preplanning. If drainage is required for reasons other than fire protection, it may be possible to use one drainage system for all purposes, provided that it is designed to handle the maximum flow.

For occupancies in underground caverns and similar subterranean spaces, refer to NFPA 520, *Standard on Subterranean Spaces*.

MALL BUILDINGS

Mall buildings are often associated with large shopping centers. However, mall buildings are increasingly being constructed for multiple uses. Mixed uses of mall buildings might include airport terminals, amusement and recreation operations, business operations, restaurants, broadcast studios, and other occupancies in addition to mercantile occupancies. Mall buildings are characterized by large, open areas under a single roof or multiple roofs that might include large populations of people and multiple occupancies. Mall buildings may or may not be subdivided into smaller spaces and are often constructed with multiple levels open to each other.

As used in NFPA documents, a mall is "a roofed or common pedestrian area within a mall building that serves as access for two or more tenants and does not exceed three levels open to each other." In the same context, a mall building is "a single building enclosing a number of tenants and occupancies wherein two or more tenants have a main entrance into one or more malls."

Like limited-access and underground structures, mall buildings can present challenges to smoke and heat venting and access for fire fighting and rescue. In fact, many malls may also be classified as limited-access or underground structures and may need to meet code requirements for such structures. Further, the large open spaces presented by many mall buildings can allow for extensive, uninterrupted spread of smoke and other fire products.

Mall buildings are typically large buildings with an extensive perimeter and may include multiple grade levels. This arrangement, often combined with vehicle parking facilities surrounding the mall building, limits fire department vehicular access to the mall building. There may also be limited building access points to the large enclosed area, which will contribute to the difficulty in providing fire-fighting access.

Large open areas can contribute to the spread of fire and smoke. Building code height and area requirements might limit the size of fire areas and require fire barrier walls to divide sections of the mall building, but openings to the pedestrian mall area may be allowed to be unprotected. Large areas are thus exposed to unimpeded spread of fire and smoke.

Because of the large, open areas, mall buildings should be provided with approved, supervised automatic sprinkler systems throughout the building to suppress fires before they grow to endanger occupants or cause significant property damage. Mall buildings with more than two interconnected levels should be provided with smoke control systems to reduce the danger to occupants in the event of a fire. See NFPA 92B, *Standard for Smoke Management Systems in Malls, Atria, and Large Spaces,* for details on designing smoke control systems for mall buildings. Means of egress, particularly means of egress alternate from the main entrances, should be properly identified by sufficient numbers of exit signs. Fire detection and alarm systems, with appropriate means for occupant notification, will enhance the fire safety of mall building occupants.

OPEN PARKING STRUCTURES

Parking garages that permit drivers to drive their own vehicles to a parking space have been the subject of recurring and ongoing fire safety concerns. The general concern has been for the survival of the structure's integrity when exposed to a fire potentially involving the fuel tank, tires, and other combustible elements and contents of more than one car parked near a structural element. However, research has consistently shown that the effect of permanently open exterior walls on the dissipation of smoke and heat prevents a serious threat to the structure, even with an unusually challenging initial fire scenario.

Numerous tests in the United States and elsewhere have demonstrated the validity of this conclusion. One such test, known as the "Scranton Fire Test," was conducted in 1972 by the American Iron and Steel Institute (AISI) in a multistory, open parking structure with exposed structural steel members.[1] Three automobiles parked next to each other, each with a fuel tank containing 10 gal (38 L) of gasoline, were used as the test ignition and fuel source. The center automobile was gutted 48 minutes after crumpled newspapers in the rear seat were ignited. The contents of its fuel tank were spilled or consumed, but the fire did not spread to the adjacent automobiles and the overhead structural steel was essentially unaffected. The temperature of the steel remained far below critical levels throughout the test. A similar test conducted by the British at the Borehamwood Fire Test Station yielded similar results.[2] These results do not necessarily apply to aboveground enclosed garages or to underground garages.

Building codes, such as *NFPA 5000,* recognize the test results and permit noncombustible parking structures of unlimited area up to 75 ft (23 m) high to have no structural fire protection, as long as they are used for no other purpose and have ample permanent wall openings for the free dissipation of smoke and gases. Applicable building codes should be consulted for minimum amounts of exterior wall openings and construction requirements. NFPA *101* contains means of egress requirements specific to parking structures and NFPA 88A, *Standard for Parking Structures,* contains fire protection requirements.

SPECIAL AMUSEMENT STRUCTURES

Special amusement structures, whether used to house permanent rides or exhibits (amusement parks), temporary rides or exhibits (fairs and carnivals), or seasonal exhibits (haunted houses), present unusual situations for fire and life safety. Such venues are often dark and intended to deceive or confuse occupants. The occupants often include young children with immature decision-making skills who are easily deceived. In some cases, the structure or interior details might be quickly and haphazardly constructed of light materials that can contribute to rapid fire spread. Unapproved temporary wiring, special lighting effects, pyrotechnics, or other ignition sources might be present. Paths of travel are often convoluted, and the means of egress might be obscured. Most of these structures can be classified also as limited-access structures. In some cases, special amusement buildings might be located on piers, which further complicates fire-fighting and rescue access.

NFPA defines a special amusement building as "a building that is temporary, permanent, or mobile that contains a device or system that conveys passengers or provides a walkway along, around, or over a course in any direction that is a form of amusement arranged so that the egress path is not readily apparent due to visual or audio distractions or an intentionally confounded egress path, or is not readily available due to the mode of conveyance through the building or structure." Special amusement buildings include multilevel play structures in a restaurant or shopping mall, Halloween haunted house displays, and large roller coaster rides located within a building.

History records many fires in special amusement buildings. One of the most significant fires occurred in a "haunted castle" amusement attraction, made up of 17 interconnected commercial trailers, at the Six Flags Great Adventure Amusement Park in Jackson Township, New Jersey, on May 11, 1984.[3] Eight visitors in the structure were unable to immediately exit and died in the rapidly developing fire. Major factors contributing to the loss of life were the lack of properly designed fixed detection and suppression systems, ignition of synthetic foam material from which fire spread to other combustible contents and interior finish, and the difficulty occupants had in trying to escape along a convoluted, smoke-filled path.

Special amusements, whether they are permanent or only intended to last for a few days, must be carefully planned to assure fire safety. Ignition sources must be controlled. Open flames and pyrotechnics should be prohibited. Permanent or temporary electrical wiring should be in strict compliance with NFPA 70, *National Electrical Code®*. Gasoline and gasoline-powered internal combustion engines should not be stored or used inside special amusement structures.

If possible, the structure housing the special amusement occupancy should be of noncombustible construction. All interior finish, contents, and furnishings should have appropriate fire ratings by applicable fire test methods. Exposed foam plastic and other combustible materials should be prohibited.

To provide prompt detection of any developing fire, special amusement buildings should be provided with an approved smoke detection system throughout that alarms to a constantly attended location on the premises. To suppress fires and allow for ample time for safe evacuation, an approved, supervised automatic sprinkler system should be installed throughout special amusement buildings. In addition to providing an alarm, actuation of the smoke detection system or sprinkler system should automatically increase lighting in darkened spaces and immediately terminate any sounds or visual effects that might serve to confuse occupants.

As in all structures, ample exits must be provided for special amusement structures. The exits should be readily identifiable with floor proximity exit signs. Special arrangements to identify the means of egress might be necessary in amusement spaces that include mirrors, mazes, and other confusing paths of travel. Lobby areas should not interfere with egress paths.

Amusement operators are urged to work closely with fire safety specialists and AHJs in the planning and operation of special amusements to help assure the fire safety of occupants.

PIERS AND WHARVES

When piers or related structures partially surrounded by water are used for places of amusement, for restaurants, for mercantile operations, or similar uses, they fall out of the normal use category—that is, mooring of vessels and handling of cargo—and into the special structure category. The question of fire and life safety is of primary concern, because these structures, which may contain large numbers of people, may have limited egress facilities and limited fire-fighting access due to their location or arrangement on the water.

Figure 20.20.2 illustrates Balboa Pier in Newport Beach, California, on which a restaurant is located.

NFPA 307, *Standard for the Construction and Fire Protection of Marine Terminals, Piers, and Wharves,* defines a pier as a structure, usually of greater length than width, projecting from the shore into a body of water with direct access from land that can be either open deck or provided with a superstructure. NFPA 307 deals mostly with property conservation features of piers and wharves and does not include explicit provisions for means of egress or safety to life. NFPA *101* and *NFPA 5000* specifically address the unique characteristics of piers. Any occupancy situated on a pier must meet the applicable

FIGURE 20.20.2 Balboa Pier, Newport Beach, California (Source: *NFPA 5000® Handbook,* 2003, Figure 31.4; © Ron Niebrugge/wildnatureimages.com)

occupancy-specific requirements of the code (for example, those for assembly occupancies in the case of a restaurant with an occupant load of 50 or more) in addition to the special provisions for piers.

Piers used exclusively to moor cargo vessels and to store materials are exempt from a number of means of egress requirements when provided with proper means of egress from structures thereon to the pier and a single means of access to the mainland, as appropriate for the pier's arrangement.

Piers occupied for other than cargo handling and storage and extending over 150 ft (45 m) from shore should also be provided with the following:

- The pier should be arranged to provide two separate ways to travel to shore, such as by two well-separated walkways or independent structures.
- The pier deck should be open, fire-resistive, and set on noncombustible supports.
- The pier should be open, unobstructed, and not less than 50 ft (15 m) in width if less than 500 ft (150 m) long, or its width should not be less than 10 percent of its length if more than 500 ft (150 m) long.
- The pier deck should be provided with an approved, supervised automatic sprinkler system for combustible substructures and superstructures.

WATER-SURROUNDED STRUCTURES

This category includes structures fully surrounded by water, including lighthouses and offshore platforms. Occupant loads could vary from a limited number of people in some cases to hundreds of people on offshore oil platforms. A large, water-surrounded structure could include areas that contain assembly, industrial, or residential occupancies. Egress from the entire structure is limited because of its location.

Other than the fact that the structure is surrounded by water, traditional occupancy requirements and fire protection features remain the same with respect to the actual occupancy classifications being evaluated. The occupancy should be addressed as if it was not surrounded by water, and the particular circumstances created by the special structure should then be applied. The special structure features should be evaluated as they relate to the occupancy at hand.

In some cases, either sufficient outside ground area, such as an island, is needed for refuge or a separate, fire-resistant platform should be provided for this purpose. A communications system and means of transportation for evacuating the occupants from the refuge area may be needed. Means of transportation might be limited to either boats or helicopters depending on the nature and location of these special structures. With limited fire-fighting access from the outside and limited means of egress, preplanning of emergency response for fire fighting and for occupant safety is imperative.

It is possible, as in the case with deep-water oil platforms, that a water-surrounded structure can be more than 100 miles from shore and very remote from any emergency response from outside of the structure. The world's worst water-surrounded structure disaster occurred in the North Sea in 1988. An explosion and ensuing fire on the Piper Alpha oil platform resulted in the deaths of 167 workers.[4]

The structure may be subject to severe environmental conditions, including wind, wave action, and heavy rain. NFPA *101* and *NFPA 5000* exempt water-surrounded structures from their provisions if the structure is under the jurisdiction of the U.S. Coast Guard and is in compliance with U.S. Coast Guard regulations. The additional regulations of the U.S. Coast Guard should be consulted for such facilities.

MEMBRANE STRUCTURES AND TENTS

Membrane Structures

NFPA defines a membrane structure as a building or portion of a building incorporating an air-inflated, air-supported, tensioned-membrane structure; a membrane roof; or a membrane-covered rigid frame to protect habitable or usable space. For cost-reduction, usability, and aesthetic purposes, membrane structures are being increasingly used in modern construction to house numerous types of occupancies. Membrane structures are used for both permanent and temporary structures.

Some membrane structures are of the air-inflated type, where the air pressure is within a series of tubes, which then form the structure and keep it upright. In this case, the occupants are not within a pressurized atmosphere. Others, such as the one shown in Figure 20.20.3 are air supported where the shape is maintained by air pressure and in which occupants are within the elevated pressure area. Also included as membrane structures are cable-supported membrane structures, such as some newer sports stadiums, where cables support the roof and air pressure may or may not be provided. In other types of structures, the membrane is tensioned, and weather protection is usually provided without enclosing walls (Figure 20.20.4). Finally, there are the framework-type structures in which the membrane is stretched over the frame to form enclosing walls and a roof.

The fire and life safety concerns with membrane structures include the combustibility of the membrane when exposed to ignition sources and the structural stability of the membrane

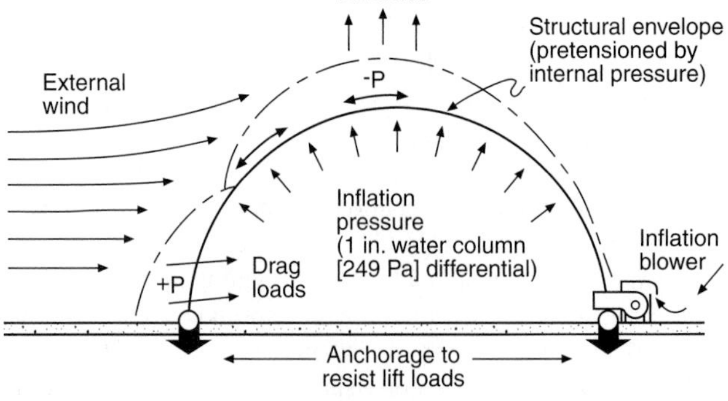

FIGURE 20.20.3 Loads on a Typical Single-Walled, Air-Supported Structure

FIGURE 20.20.4 Example of a Tensioned-Membrane Structure: Denver International Airport (Source: *NFPA 5000® Handbook,* 2003, Figure 32.2; courtesy of the Denver International Airport)

structure when exposed to fire. NFPA *101* and *NFPA 5000* address both of these concerns in their requirements. For permanent membrane structures, membrane materials cannot be used where fire resistance ratings are required for walls or roofs. Both permanent and temporary membrane structures are required to use flame-resistant membrane materials that are satisfactorily tested in accordance with NFPA 701, *Standard Methods of Fire Tests for Flame Propagation of Textiles and Films.* Membranes used in permanent membrane structures must be tested to provide a Class A flame-spread rating. All membrane materials must be tested as weathered-membrane materials. Blowers for air-supported and air-inflated membrane structures must meet special design requirements for reliability. Blowers must be provided with fully automatic standby power systems.

The area around temporary membrane structures must be clear of flammable and combustible materials and vegetation for a distance of at least 10 ft (3 m) to reduce potential fire exposures. Approved portable fire-extinguishing equipment must also be provided for temporary membrane structures.

Tents

The fire and life safety concerns associated with tents as places of assembly were made evident by a disastrous circus tent fire in Hartford, Connecticut, on July 6, 1944, in which 168 people died and 487 were injured.[5] The fire and life safety concerns for tents are similar to those for temporary membrane structures. As such, NFPA *101* applies the same requirements for tents as for temporary membrane structures for flame resistance, clear area around tents, and portable fire-extinguishing equipment. Tents should only be permitted on a temporary basis.

Additionally, tents should not cover more than 75 percent of the premises and stake lines should be not less than 10 ft (3 m) apart to help prevent fire propagation to adjacent tents. Additional spacing should be provided if needed to provide for adequate means of egress.

GRANDSTANDS

Grandstands are typical examples of structures found in places of outdoor and indoor assembly and are structures that can constitute a safety problem. These structures must have adequate aisles, proper distance between rows of seats, strong guard railings, and other means of egress features to ensure rapid and orderly evacuation to areas of safety. Requirements applicable to such installations are found in NFPA *101*. Grandstands should also be designed to withstand predetermined deadweight and live loads, as well as anticipated wind loads.

Since many grandstands are constructed entirely or partially of wood, basic fire protection principles of division of areas and separation from exposures apply. Long, combustible grandstands should be divided by fire partitions or be constructed in smaller sections with adequate separation between the sections.

Frequently, the space underneath a grandstand is used to store materials and for concession booths. The space underneath a grandstand might be become littered with combustible refuse. Refuse under the grandstand was a major factor in the soccer stadium fire in Bradford, England, on May 11, 1985, which claimed 56 lives.[6]

TOWERS

NFPA defines a tower as an enclosed, independent structure or portion of a building with elevated levels for support of equipment or occupied for observation, control, operation, signaling, or similar limited use where (1) the elevated levels are provided to allow adequate observation or line-of-sight for personnel or equipment, and (2) the levels within the tower below the observation level and equipment room for that level are not occupied. This definition does not include towers used for routine industrial, business, or assembly purposes. When a tower is used for these or other traditional occupancy purposes, it must comply completely with the appropriate occupancy classification and code provisions in NFPA *101, NFPA 5000,* and other applicable codes.

When a tower is being used in accordance with its definition, the special structures chapters of NFPA *101* and *NFPA 5000* apply. In some cases, the means of egress from a tower may be a single exit and, in some cases, may be only a ladder. If only one means of egress exists, caution must be taken to ensure that occupants cannot be trapped. In such cases, occupancy of the tower is limited to fewer than 25 persons, and the tower cannot be used for sleeping or living purposes.

Where a tower with a single means of egress is located above a building, special precautions must be taken to prevent the tower's single means of egress from being compromised by a fire in the building below. In Figure 20.20.5(a), the single exit stair enclosure for the tower is separated from the building by fire-resistance rated construction. Additionally, the single existing stair enclosure has no openings to the floors of the building above which the tower is positioned, thus preventing a fire in the building from rendering the stair unusable.

In Figure 20.20.5(b), the single exit stair positioned above the building serves the tower. It provides direct access to the

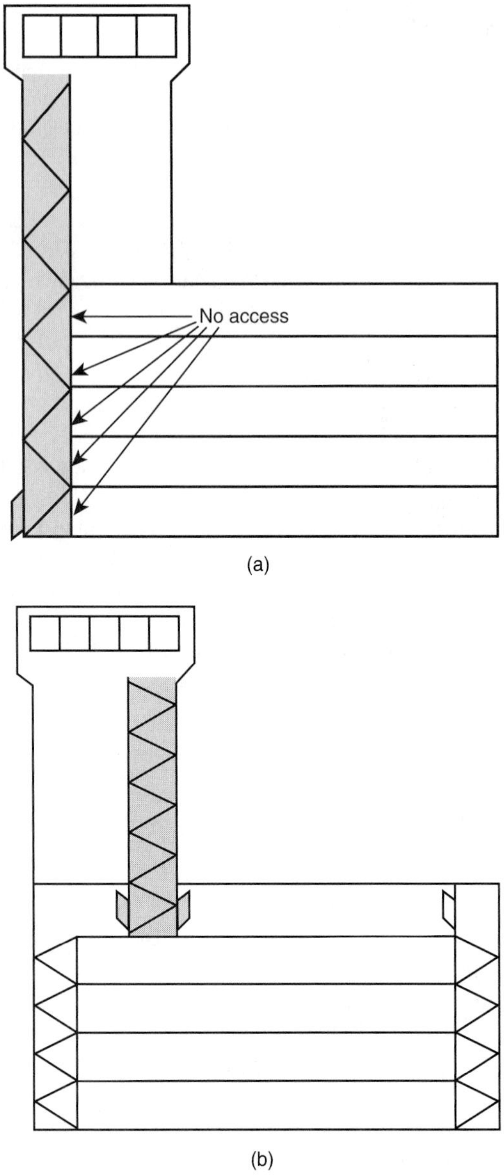

FIGURE 20.20.5 Single Exit from a Tower (Source: *NFPA 5000® Handbook,* 2003, Figure 31.3)

exit stair enclosure on the left, which also serves the building floors. If a fire prevents the use of the exit stair enclosure on the left, the tower stair permits tower occupants to traverse the top floor of the building and access a second exit stair enclosure on the right.

Fire-resistant or noncombustible construction should be used, with either Class A or B interior finish. There should be no high-hazard occupancies in the tower or immediate vicinity. If the tower is located above a building, the exit enclosure should be separated from the building or an exit enclosure should be provided leading directly to an exit enclosure serving the building and another door allowing access to the top floor of the building that provides access to a second exit serving that floor. Towers with 360 degree line-of-site requirements are permitted to have a single means of egress for a distance of travel not exceeding 75 ft (23 m) or 100 ft (30 m) if the tower is protected throughout by an approved, supervised automatic sprinkler system.

The amount of combustible materials in, under, or around a tower must be carefully controlled. Combustibles should be totally eliminated except for necessary furniture and operating supplies. Careful judgment should be used in determining what combustible materials to allow in the immediate vicinity of the tower. Similar care should be used in evaluating a tower located near high-hazard occupancies. The tower should be separated by a reasonable distance, especially when it has only a single means of egress.

Towers surrounded by water or offshore structures require special consideration and are strictly controlled by the U.S. Coast Guard. Coast Guard regulations and those of similar regulatory bodies in foreign countries normally take precedence over NFPA *101* and *NFPA 5000* requirements.

In small towers where there will be no more than three occupants at any one time, the means of egress may be a fire escape ladder. This might include forest fire observation or railroad signaling towers. Ladders should be arranged according to requirements of ANSI A-14.3, *Safety Requirements for Fixed Ladders,* and must provide continuous access to grade at all times. In towers with a single escape ladder, vertical openings need not be protected because such a requirement does not significantly increase protection for occupants.

In some special cases, towers subject to occupancy by not more than 90 persons are permitted to use elevators as the means of egress. This might include special operations such as aircraft control towers. NFPA *101* and *NFPA 5000* provide special provisions that apply to elevators when they are used as a second means of egress from towers. Among the limitations are the following:

- The tower and any attached structure must be protected throughout by an approved, supervised automatic sprinkler system.
- The primary means of egress must discharge directly to the outside.
- No high-hazard content areas may exist in the tower or attached structure.
- One hundred percent of the required egress capacity must be provided independent to the elevator(s).
- An evacuation plan, specifically including the use of the elevator, must be implemented and staff must be trained in elevator operations and procedures.
- The tower must not be used by the general public.

Further restrictions apply to the elevator, elevator lobby, controls, and operations, including the following:

- The elevator car must have a capacity of not less than eight persons.
- The elevator lobby must have a capacity of not less than 50 percent of the occupant load of the area being served by the lobby.
- On every floor served by the elevator, there must be an elevator lobby with a fire resistance rating of not less than 1 hour, with self-closing or automatically closing 1 hour

rated, temperature-rise-rated fire doors that close in the event of a fire alarm signal.

- Building elements must be used to restrict water exposure of elevator equipment.
- Power and control wiring for the elevator must be supplied from both normal and standby power and must be located and protected to ensure at least 1 hour of operation in the event of a fire.
- The elevators must be provided with fire fighter service controls in accordance with ASME A17.1, *Safety Code for Elevators and Escalators*.
- Elevators must have the capability of orderly shutdown during earthquakes where such shutdown is an option of ASME A17.1.

OPEN STRUCTURES

At the opposite extreme of the limited-access and underground structures are open structures. Whereas limited-access and underground structures are fully enclosed, thus making egress, access, and smoke venting more difficult, open structures are totally unenclosed.

Open structures are those that support equipment and operations not enclosed within building walls. Open structures are most often found in industrial operations, where the structure would come under the guidelines of an industrial occupancy (Figure 20.20.6). It is often difficult to determine whether the occupancy should be classified as general, special-purpose, or high-hazard industrial. The hazard classification usually is determined by the classification of the hazards of the contents that can be present. Occupancies in open structures are commonly classified under special-purpose industrial as defined in NFPA *101* and *NFPA 5000.*

NFPA *101* and *NFPA 5000* have several provisions for special-purpose industrial occupancies. The special-purpose industrial occupancy is typically characterized by a relatively low density of employee population, where most of a structure is occupied by machinery or equipment. Typically, the open structure facilitates access to the equipment by use of platforms, gratings, stairs, and ladders.

It is sometimes difficult to determine when a structure is open and when it is enclosed. An open structure may include a roof to provide some protection from the elements. Additionally, open structures may be provided with partial walls intended to shield the operations from environmental conditions or to segregate the operations. The AHJ must determine whether the open structure truly meets the definition of an open structure or whether the facility is a building. As a guide, the AHJ could determine whether the structure would react as an enclosed building in the event of fire.

Within a building, walls acting in conjunction with a roof enclose the combustion process and products of combustion, thereby allowing fire to spread both horizontally and vertically to other areas. The advantage of an open structure is that it allows the products of combustion to vent to the atmosphere, instead of spreading to unaffected areas of the structure. This depends on wind and climatic conditions in addition to the design of the structure.

If the roof and walls could direct or channel products of combustion to other unaffected portions of the structure, thereby preventing their free venting to the atmosphere, then that portion of the open structure could be considered a building. It is not uncommon to have buildings constructed within the framework of an open structure, resulting in a mixed classification.

Open structures that are occupied by not more than three persons are permitted to have a single exit provided that the exit can be reached within 200 ft (60 m) from any point. Fire escape ladders are permitted for open structures where the occupant load does not exceed three persons.

Open structures are exempt from NFPA *101* and *NFPA 5000* requirements for capacity of means of egress, travel distance, illumination, emergency lighting, marking of means of egress, protection of vertical openings, and detection and alarm systems.

FIGURE 20.20.6 Typical Industrial Open Structure

SUMMARY

Special structures, regardless of type, present out-of-the-ordinary fire protection challenges, independent of the hazards associated with the occupancy in the structure. Often, these challenges include impediments to fire-fighting access and rescue, impediments to means of egress, and impediments to smoke and heat venting. Special structures include limited-access and underground structures, mall buildings, open parking structures, special amusement structures, piers and wharves, water-surrounded structures, membrane structures and tents, grandstands, towers, and open structures.

The unique fire safety complexities of the special structure must be addressed in addition to the fire safety requirements for the occupancy. In some cases, occupancies might be housed in structures that could be classified as multiple types of special structures. For example, a shopping mall might be classified as both a covered mall and a limited-access or underground building. An amusement center might be located in a facility that could be a special amusement structure, a limited-access structure, and a pier structure. An airport terminal might be classified as a covered mall, a limited-access building, and a tower.

A combination of sound design and engineering judgment, common sense, and cooperation between the designers and code officials might be necessary to ensure an adequate level of life safety and property protection for the unique exposures of occupancies in special structures. Performance-based fire protection analysis and design methods can be useful in creating fire-safe special structures.

BIBLIOGRAPHY

References Cited

1. Gewain, R. G., "Fire Experience and Fire Tests in Automobile Parking Structures," *Fire Journal,* Vol. 67, No. 4, 1973.
2. Butcher, E. G., et al., "Fire and Car-Park Buildings," *Fire Note No. 10,* Ministry of Technology and Fire Offices' Committee/ Joint Fire Research Organization, London, UK, 1968
3. Bouchard, J., "NFPA Investigation Report: Fire in Haunted Castle Kills Eight," *Fire Journal,* Vol. 79, No. 5, 1985, pp. 45–81.
4. Tougher, H. E., "Safety at Sea," *NFPA Journal,* Vol. 95, No. 5, Sept./Oct. 2001, pp. 47–50.w
5. Kimball, W. J., "Hartford Circus Fire Holocaust," *The Quarterly,* July 1949, pp. 9–21.
6. Klem, T. J., "Investigation Report: 56 Die in English Stadium Fire," *Fire Journal,* Vol. 80, No. 3, 1986, pp. 128–147.

NFPA Codes, Standards, and Recommended Practices

Reference to the following NFPA codes, standards, and recommended practices will provide further information on occupancies in special structures discussed in this chapter. (See the latest version of The NFPA Catalog *for availability of current editions of the following documents.)*

NFPA 13, *Standard for the Installation of Sprinkler Systems*
NFPA 14, *Standard for the Installation of Standpipe and Hose Systems*
NFPA 25, *Standard for the Inspection, Testing, and Maintenance of Water-Based Fire Protection Systems*
NFPA 70, *National Electrical Code®*
NFPA 88A, *Standard for Parking Structures*
NFPA 92A, *Standard for Smoke-Control Systems Utilizing Barriers and Pressure Differences*
NFPA 92B, *Standard for Smoke Management Systems in Malls, Atria, and Large Spaces*
NFPA *101®*, *Life Safety Code®*
NFPA 307, *Standard for the Construction and Fire Protection of Marine Terminals, Piers, and Wharves*
NFPA 520, *Standard on Subterranean Spaces*
NFPA 701, *Standard Methods of Fire Tests for Flame Propagation of Textiles and Films*
NFPA 5000®, *Building Construction and Safety Code®*

SECTION 21

Transportation Fire Safety

Carl H. Rivkin

The 20th edition of the *Fire Protection Handbook®* concludes with Section 21 on transportation fire safety. Five of the eleven chapters in this section are new.

The first new chapter is Chapter 1, "Passenger Vehicle Fires," which discusses regulations and standards associated with passenger vehicle fire safety and presents relevant data and research. Also new is Chapter 2, "Fire Safety in Commercial Vehicles," addressing hazards and standards related to commercial vehicle fire safety.

The list of new chapters continues with Chapter 3, "Automotive and Marine Service Station Operations." Automotive and marine service stations, whose operations include both refueling and repairs, present a fire risk because of the storage of flammable and combustible liquids and the transfer and use of these liquids.

The next two chapters deal with the subject of alternative fuels. Chapter 4, "Vehicle Fueling Using Gaseous Fuels," considers the implications of the growing use of alternative fuels, such as compressed natural gas (CNG), liquefied natural gas (LNG), and liquefied petroleum gas (LP-gas). Chapter 5, "Fuel Cell Vehicles," is a new chapter that describes current fuel cell vehicles and operating features being developed to facilitate commercialization and acceptance by the general public and regulatory authorities.

Chapter 6, "Recreational Vehicles," is also new. This chapter discusses the types of recreational vehicles and their development and use, RV standards, the fire and life safety issues associated with RVs, their fire safety record, and existing oversight programs.

Chapter 7, "Fixed Guideway Transit and Light Rail Systems," describes system characteristics and explains underground trainways, underground stations, and surface-level and elevated transit systems.

Chapter 8, "Rail Transportation Systems," identifies different types of rail rolling equipment used by North American railroads, both freight and passenger, and discusses fire hazards associated with them. The chapter generally discusses the rail transportation of hazardous materials and discusses in detail the transportation of hazardous materials in rail tank cars and in intermodal tank containers.

Chapter 9, "Aviation," provides information on airport and aircraft fire safety and aircraft maintenance and servicing.

Fire safety on pleasure craft, small commercial boats, and commercial vessels is presented in Chapter 10, "Marine Vessels." Marine fire hazards and emergency response to ship fires are also discussed.

Chapter 11, "Road Tunnels and Bridges," addresses the unique fire protection and life safety considerations and challenges posed by road tunnels and road bridges. A road tunnel is defined as any enclosed facility through which road vehicles (cars, vans, buses, and trucks) travel. Emergency communications and tunnel fire tests are also discussed.

Carl H. Rivkin, P.E., is principal chemical engineer on the NFPA engineering staff.

Chapter 1

Passenger Vehicle Fires

R. T. Long, Jr. ❑ Jeff D. Colwell ❑ Rose Ray ❑
Helene L. Grossman ❑ Ben Thomas ❑ Robert Strassburger

Chapter Contents

Key Terms

Federal Motor Vehicle Safety Standard (FMVSS), National Highway Traffic Safety Administration (NHTSA), passenger vehicle, tenability

According to the Centers for Disease Control and Prevention, the reduction of the rate of fatalities[1] attributable to motor vehicle crashes in the United States "represents the successful public health response to a great technologic advance of the 20th century—the motorization of America."[2] More than six times as many people drive today as in 1925, and the number of motor vehicles in the country has increased 12-fold since then to approximately 246 million. The number of miles traveled in motor vehicles is 24 times higher than in the mid-1920s. The annual fatality rate has declined from 18 per 100 million vehicle miles traveled (VMT) in 1925 to 1.45 per 100 million VMT in 2005—a 92 percent decrease.[3]

Motor vehicle fire safety has also realized significant improvements over the past several decades. Comparing today's vehicles to model year 1978 and earlier vehicles, the risk of passenger vehicle fire fatality per one million vehicles in use has decreased more than 50 percent. If the comparison is restricted to new vehicles only (defined as 4 years old or newer), in order to eliminate effects attributable to vehicle age, then it is found that the risk of fire fatality per one million vehicles in use is about 25 percent lower for today's vehicles than for model year 1982 to 1986 vehicles.

This risk reduction is even more pronounced when the comparison is done per vehicle mile traveled. The risk of passenger vehicle fire fatality per one billion vehicle miles traveled is almost 70 percent lower for today's vehicles than for model 1978 and earlier vehicles. If only new vehicles (4 years old or newer) are considered, it is found that the risk of fire fatality per one billion vehicle miles traveled is about 30 percent lower for today's vehicles than for model year 1982 to 1986 vehicles.

In terms of total numbers, the number of highway vehicle fires and associated fatalities has decreased by approximately 25 percent over the past quarter century. This reduction has occurred despite the significant increase in exposure to fire risk. In the last 25 years the number of highway vehicles registered in the United States has grown by 60 percent and the number of vehicle miles traveled annually has nearly doubled, growing by 91 percent. The probability of fire increases with vehicle age. Beginning in 1975, people began to hold onto their vehicles longer and scrap them later. Prior analyses indicate that as the median age of vehicles increases, the number of motor vehicle fatalities with postcollision fires grows. Between 1980 and 2004, the median age of passenger cars rose by 50 percent to almost 9 years of age. Similarly, the median lifetime of passenger cars

R. T. Long, Jr., P.E., is a principal fire protection engineer with the thermal sciences practice of Exponent. Exponent is a multidisciplinary scientific and engineering consulting company.

Jeff D. Colwell, Ph.D., P.E., is a senior managing engineer in Exponent's thermal sciences practice and specializes in investigating the origin, cause, and propagation of motor vehicle fires.

Rose Ray, Ph.D., is a principal scientist with Exponent and specializes in data analysis and the application of statistical methods to the evaluation of passenger vehicle performance.

Helene L. Grossman, Ph.D., is a senior scientist in Exponent's statistical and data sciences practice and has experience in the assessment of passenger vehicle safety based on field performance data.

Ben Thomas, Ph.D., is a senior managing scientist in Exponent's health sciences practice and has over 30 years experience in toxicology, pathology, risk assessment, and risk management.

Robert Strassburger is the vice-president of vehicle safety and harmonization with the Alliance of Automobile Manufacturers.

increased by 47 percent to 16.9 years. Finally, the use of plastics and plastic composites in highway vehicles to replace metal materials has increased to 7.6 percent of total weight in 2004 from 5.0 percent in 1978. In 2004, the typical passenger car contained 258 pounds (117 kg) of plastic materials, up 78 pounds (35 kg) from 1978.[4] The increased use of plastics increases the amount of combustibles available to ignite and/or contribute to a fire.

Nevertheless, advancing motor vehicle safety remains a significant public health challenge—one that automakers are addressing daily. Automakers make huge investments in safer vehicle design and technology. According to recent data, in the United States, approximately 32,000 passenger vehicle occupants are fatally injured annually as a result of traffic crashes. Of these fatalities, approximately 1.2 percent (385) are attributable to postcollision fires. In addition, there are approximately 40 passenger vehicle fire fatalities per year that are not collision-related.

This chapter discusses regulations and standards associated with passenger vehicle fire safety and presents relevant data and research.

See also in Section 21: Chapter 2, "Fire Safety in Commercial Vehicles," Chapter 3, "Automotive and Marine Service Station Operations," and Chapter 6, "Recreational Vehicles."

FEDERAL REGULATION OF PASSENGER VEHICLE FIRE SAFETY

History of the National Highway Traffic Safety Administration

In 1966, the United States Congress passed the Highway Safety Act and the National Traffic and Motor Vehicle Safety Act (Vehicle Safety Act) which authorized the federal government to establish safety standards for motor vehicles. The Highway Safety Act created the National Highway Safety Bureau (NHSB), which later became the National Highway Traffic Safety Administration (NHTSA). The first director of the NHSB, Dr. William Haddon, defined a systematic approach to motor vehicle–related injury prevention. Haddon, a public health physician, recognized that standard public health methods and epidemiology could be applied to preventing motor vehicle–related and other injuries. He defined interactions between host (human), agent (motor vehicle), and environmental (highway) factors before, during, and after crashes resulting in injuries.

Shared Responsibilities for Vehicle Fire Safety

Many changes in both vehicle and highway design have followed since the passage of the Highway Safety Act. As such, safety features for vehicles (agents) have improved substantially over the years, as advancements have been made in air bag design, side impact protection, and fuel tank integrity, to name a few. Vehicles (agents) were built with new safety features including head rests, energy-absorbing steering wheels, shatter-resistant windshields, and safety belts. Roads (environment) were improved by better delineation of curves (i.e., edge and center-line stripes and reflectors), use of breakaway sign and utility poles, improved illumination, addition of barriers separating oncoming traffic lanes, and guardrails.

The fatality rate per 100,000 population dropped from 25.89 in 1966 to 16.46 in 1991 (25 years later) and to 15.86 in 1996 (30 years later). The traffic safety indicator (fatalities per 100 million VMT) dropped from 5.50 in 1966 to 1.91 in 1991 (25 years later) and to 1.69 in 1996 (30 years later).[5]

Changes in driver and passenger (host) behavior also have reduced motor vehicle crashes and injuries. Enactment and enforcement of traffic safety laws, reinforced by public education, have led to safer behavior choices. Examples include enforcement of laws against driving while intoxicated (DWI) and underage drinking, and enforcement of safety belt, child safety seat, and motorcycle helmet use laws.

Enhancing motor vehicle safety is a shared responsibility of government, industry, and consumers. Government and community recognition of the need for motor vehicle safety prompted initiation of programs by federal and state governments, academic institutions, community-based organizations, and industry. State and local governments have enacted and enforced laws that affect motor vehicle and highway safety, driver licensing and testing, vehicle inspections, and traffic regulations. Preventing motor vehicle–related injuries has required collaboration among many professional disciplines (e.g., biomechanics has been essential to vehicle design and highway safety features). Citizen and community-based advocacy groups have played important prevention roles in areas such as drinking and driving and child-occupant protection.

NHTSA FMVSS Standards

As part of its mandate, NHTSA is responsible for adopting and enforcing federal motor vehicle safety standards (FMVSS). These safety standards apply to the manufacture and sale of new motor vehicles and motor vehicle equipment (see 49 U.S.C. 30112). The FMVSS adopted by NHTSA encompass most aspects of motor vehicle safety performance and must be practicable, meet the need for motor vehicle safety, and be stated in objective terms.[6] States and localities are precluded by the Vehicle Safety Act from adopting and enforcing standards for motor vehicles that are inconsistent with these federal standards.

With respect to motor vehicle fires, NHTSA has promulgated a suite of standards to enhance fire safety as outlined below. The two principal federal motor vehicle safety standards addressing motor vehicle flammability, FMVSS 301, *Fuel System Integrity,* and FMVSS 302, *Flammability of Interior Materials,* were the first to be issued by the agency to address flammability issues.

FMVSS 301, *Fuel System Integrity.* Issued in 1968, FMVSS 301,* *specifies* requirements for the postcollision integrity of motor vehicle fuel systems. Its purpose is to reduce deaths and injuries occurring from fires that result from fuel spillage during

*FMVSS 301 was amended on December 1, 2003, to upgrade the rear impact test used to assess fuel system integrity. The final rule replaced the full rear impact test procedure that was conducted at a speed of 30 mph (48 km/h) with an offset rear impact test procedure conducted at 50 mph (80 km/h). See 68 Fed. Reg. 67068.

and after motor vehicle crashes. FMVSS 301 applies to passenger cars, multipurpose passenger vehicles, trucks, school buses and other buses with a gross vehicle weight rating (GVWR) of 4536 kg (10,000 lb) or less. The standard dictates a maximum fuel tank leakage of 28 g per minute after a collision.

FMVSS 302, *Flammability of Interior Materials.* Issued in 1972, FMVSS 302 specifies burn resistance requirements for materials used in the occupant compartments of motor vehicles. Its purpose is to reduce deaths and injuries to motor vehicle occupants caused by vehicle fires, especially those originating in the interior of the vehicle from sources such as matches or cigarettes. FMVSS 302 applies to passenger cars, multipurpose passenger vehicles, trucks, and buses. The standard dictates that all materials used in the passenger compartment should not allow a flame to propagate faster than 4 in./min (0.1 m/min), setting criteria for flammability performance. The test is performed on a sample of material in a horizontal orientation under controlled laboratory conditions.

FMVSS 303, *Fuel System Integrity of Compressed Natural Gas Vehicles.* FMVSS 303 specifies requirements for the integrity of motor vehicle fuel systems using compressed natural gas (CNG), including the CNG fuel systems of bifuel, dedicated, and dual-fuel CNG vehicles. The purpose of this standard is to reduce deaths and injuries from fires that result from fuel leakage during and after motor vehicle crashes. FMVSS 303 applies to passenger cars, multipurpose passenger vehicles, trucks, and buses that have a GVWR of 10,000 lb (4536 kg) or less and use compressed natural gas as a motor fuel, and school buses regardless of weight that use compressed natural gas as a motor fuel.

FMVSS 304, *Compressed Natural Gas Fuel Container Integrity.* FMVSS 304 specifies requirements for the integrity of compressed natural gas (CNG) motor vehicle fuel containers. The purpose of this standard is to reduce deaths and injuries from fires that result from fuel leakage during and after motor vehicle crashes. FMVSS 304 applies to containers designed to store CNG as motor fuel on board any motor vehicle.

PASSENGER VEHICLE FIRE DATA ANALYSIS

Every year in the United States, approximately 32,000 passenger vehicle occupants are fatally injured as a result of traffic accidents. Of these fatalities, approximately 1.2 percent (385) are attributed to postcollision fires. In addition, there are approximately 40 passenger vehicle fire fatalities per year that are not collision-related. There exist several data sources from which an estimate of the number of passenger vehicle fire fatalities may be derived. In this section, these data sources are identified and any differences reconciled to derive the estimate presented immediately above. These statistics illustrate that there are two main categories of interest in postcollision fires. The first category is postcollision fuel-fed fires, and the second category is postcollision fires that originate in the engine compartment and spread into the passenger compartment.

Passenger Vehicle Fire Fatalities

Using data from the U.S. Fire Administration's National Fire Incident Reporting System (NFIRS), the National Fire Protection Association's (NFPA's) annual survey of U.S. fire departments, and the NHTSA's Fatality Analysis Reporting System (FARS), an analysis of passenger vehicle fire injuries and fatalities can be conducted to examine such factors as the fuel involved in the fire, the point of origin of the fire, and the percentage of these fires associated with a crash.

NFPA survey data, as given in "Fire Loss in the United States," indicate that there are approximately 480 civilian fatalities per year due to highway vehicle fires (average for 1999–2004).[7] According to NFIRS data, approximately 88 percent of these fatalities, or 425 per year, are due to passenger vehicle fires. NFPA estimates of fire fatalities only include those that are judged by the fire department investigator to result from the fire itself, rather than related trauma such as a collision. All fatalities occurring up to a year following the fire are included, although tracking subsequent deaths is not always feasible.

These estimates differ from the estimate of 360 annual passenger vehicle fire fatalities for 1999–2003 presented in the NFPA report, "U.S. Vehicle Fire Trends and Patterns."[8] There are several reasons for this discrepancy. The analysis presented here used NFPA survey data directly to estimate highway vehicle fire fatalities. In contrast, the NFPA report used NFPA survey data to estimate *all vehicle* fire fatalities and then used NFIRS data to allocate the data into highway versus nonhighway vehicle fire fatalities. These two methods yield estimates of highway vehicle fire fatalities that differ by about 8 percent.* The advantage to using the direct NFPA survey estimate of highway vehicle fire fatalities is that the NFPA survey follows up on fatalities to distinguish those caused by the fire versus those caused by related trauma, whereas NFIRS does not conduct such follow-up. Hence, the direct NFPA estimate of highway vehicle fire fatalities may be more reliable.

Both the NFPA report and the analysis presented here used NFIRS to allocate highway vehicle fire fatalities into passenger vehicle versus nonpassenger vehicle fire fatalities. However, the NFPA report used NFIRS mobile property type "Passenger road vehicles," which includes passenger cars, buses, motorcycles, offroad recreational vehicles, and trailers, whereas the analysis presented here excludes some of those vehicles (motorcycles, offroad recreational vehicles, and trailers), but includes additional vehicles such as pickups and general-use trucks.

The estimates derived from NFPA/NFIRS data can be compared with those from the NHTSA's FARS. FARS is a census of all highway vehicle fatalities that occur on public roadways and for which the death is attributable to the accident and occurs within 30 days. A query of the FARS system indicates that there are approximately 1635 fatalities associated with highway vehicle fires each year, of which about 88 percent, or 1440 fatalities per year, involve passenger vehicles. The vast majority, approximately 99 percent, of passenger vehicle fires reported in FARS

*The fatality estimates given here are rounded to the nearest 5. The 8 percent difference between the NFPA/NFIRS and FARS estimates is calculated using nonrounded estimates rather than rounded estimates.

TABLE 21.1.1 Estimates of Passenger Vehicle Fire Fatalities from NFPA/NFIRS and FARS

	NFPA, NFIRS	FARS			
Year	*Civilian Fatalities Resulting from Passenger Vehicle Fires**	*Fatalities Where Fire Is Most Harmful Event for Passenger Vehicle*	*Fatalities Where Postcollision Fire Is Most Harmful Event for Passenger Vehicle*	*All Fatalities Associated with Passenger Vehicle Fires*	*All Fatalities Associated with Postcollision Passenger Vehicle Fires*
1999	385	300	295	1445	1440
2000	400	365	355	1515	1500
2001	415	360	350	1460	1445
2002	505	415	410	1495	1490
2003	385	425	410	1385	1375
2004	455	485	480	1335	1335
Average 1999–2004	425	390	385	1440	1430

Note: Numbers have been rounded to the nearest 5.
*NFPA estimates of highway vehicle fires are taken from NFPA's Fire Loss Series and are allocated into passenger vehicle fires/nonpassenger vehicle fires using NFIRS percentages.

are postcollision fires. However, the number of fatalities that result from the fire, rather than from collision-related trauma, is only about one-quarter of the total fatalities, approximately 390 annual deaths resulting from passenger vehicle fires, of which about 385 result from postcollision fires.* These numbers are averages for 1999 through 2004.

The estimates of fatalities associated with passenger vehicle fires of 425 and 390 per year from NFPA/NFIRS and FARS, respectively, are similar. The NFPA/NFIRS estimates are higher than the FARS estimates by about 8 percent, possibly because some fires that are not accident-related appear in the NFPA/NFIRS estimates, but do not occur on public roadways and are not included in the FARS database. Table 21.1.1 shows the NFPA and FARS estimates of passenger vehicle fire fatalities for 1999–2004.

For this analysis, NFIRS data were used to provide detailed information on the causes and ignition characteristics of fires. Because NFIRS only captures one-third to one-half of fire incidents in the United States, it was necessary to use the NFPA survey data to scale up the NFIRS data to obtain national estimates; the scaling factor depended on the category of interest (i.e., fires, deaths, injuries). Data were analyzed from the 6 year period 1999 through 2004 (2004 is the most recent year for which NFIRS data are publicly available). Fires for which a characteristic was unknown or not reported were allocated proportionally, assuming the same proportions as the fires with a known characteristic. The analyses and results that follow all pertain to passenger vehicle fires.

Based on the NFIRS and NFPA data, approximately half of passenger vehicle fire fatalities (about 220 fatalities per year) result from postcollision fires. However, according to the FARS analysis using the "most harmful event" code, there are approximately 385 fatalities per year resulting from postcollision passenger vehicle fires. It appears that the NFIRS data underestimate the proportion of fires and fatalities associated with collisions, probably due to factors other than "collision" being recorded as the factors contributing to ignition. This is further evidenced by the fact that roughly 50 percent of passenger vehicle fires do not have any factor contributing to ignition recorded (in the analysis discussed here, these unknowns were allocated proportionally). Therefore, the FARS estimate of postcollision fire fatalities and the NFPA/NFIRS estimate of total vehicle fire fatalities were used in this analysis to get a more conservative estimate of fatal passenger vehicle fires.

Results of the statistical analysis presented here are summarized in Figure 21.1.1. As shown in the leftmost part of the figure, the annual number of passenger vehicle fire fatalities is small compared to the total population of passenger vehicle fatalities due to traffic accidents. Of the fatalities due to fires, shown in the center chart, the vast majority are associated with postcollision fires.

Postcollision fires account for 90 percent of all passenger vehicle fire fatalities, while noncollision fires account for 10 percent. Of these noncollision fire fatalities, 5 percent are due to intentional fires and 95 percent are due to unintentional fires. Approximately 50 percent of the fatalities resulting from unintentional passenger vehicle fires involve the occupant being asleep or impaired by alcohol or other drugs prior to the fire.

Case studies of postcollision fires have indicated that there are two major categories: fuel-fed (gasoline) pool fires and engine compartment fires. Fuel-fed fires generally occur when collision damage causes a gasoline leak and then this fuel is the first material ignited. As shown in the rightmost chart of Figure 21.1.1, about 60 percent of postcollision passenger vehicle fire fatalities result from fires in which gasoline is the first material ignited.

Whereas more than half of postcollision fires involve gasoline as the first ignited material, almost half originate in the

*The "most harmful event" code in FARS was used to determine the fatalities resulting from fire. Different states code harmful events differently.

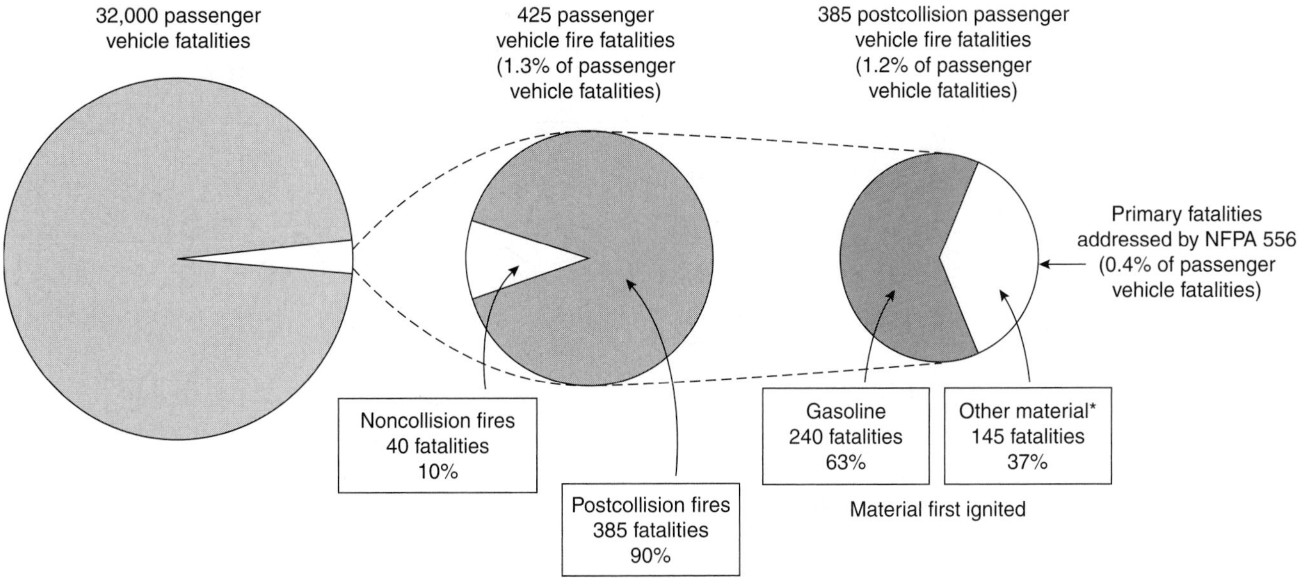

FIGURE 21.1.1 Summary of Statistical Analysis Results. *Includes the category "multiple types of fuels," so it is possible that gasoline was involved. (Sources: FARS, NFPA, and NFIRS 1999–2004 Annual Averages)

engine compartment, as shown in Figure 21.1.2. These facts indicate that fuel-fed fires and those that originate in the engine compartment are two of the most important passenger vehicle fire scenarios. These two fire scenarios have been the subject of extensive research and are discussed in more detail later.

Fire Risk Trends

Passenger vehicle fire safety has realized significant improvements over the past several decades. As shown in Figure 21.1.3, the risk of passenger vehicle fire fatalities per million vehicles in use has decreased from 3.7 per million registered vehicles per year for model year 1978 and earlier vehicles to an average of 1.8 per million registered vehicles per year for model year 1996 through 2004 vehicles, a more than 50 percent decrease.

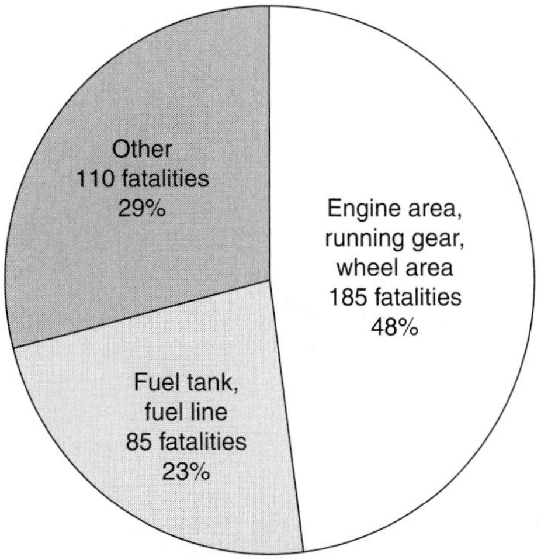

FIGURE 21.1.2 Area of Origin of Fatal Postcollision Fires (Sources: FARS, NFPA, and NFIRS, 1999–2004)

The observed increase in risk for model year 2004 vehicles may be an artifact of small sample size (only 40 fatalities listed in FARS). The lower bound on the 95 percent confidence interval for this risk is 1.8 fatalities per million registered vehicle years, which is equivalent to the average risk for model year 1996 through 2004 vehicles. Thus, the observed increase in risk for model year 2004 vehicles is not statistically significant.

Also shown in Figure 21.1.3 is the risk of passenger vehicle fire fatalities per million registered vehicles per year, restricted to new vehicles (vehicles aged 1 to 4 years). Although it appears that the risk increased between model years 1981 and 1982, the sample size is very small for model year 1981 vehicles aged 1 to 4 years (only 12 fatalities listed in FARS), so this increase is not statistically significant. The average risk for model year 1982 to 1986 vehicles aged 1 to 4 years was 2.2 fire fatalities per million registered vehicle years, whereas the average risk for model year 1996 to 2004 vehicles aged 1 to 4 years was 1.6 fire fatalities per million registered vehicle years. Thus, the fire fatality risk, restricted to new vehicles only, has decreased by about 25 percent between these time periods.

Figure 21.1.4 shows the risk of passenger vehicle fire fatalities per billion vehicle miles traveled. This risk has decreased from 0.42 per billion vehicle miles traveled for model year 1978 and earlier vehicles to an average of 0.13 per billion vehicle miles traveled for model year 1996 through 2004 vehicles, a decrease of almost 70 percent. This analysis takes into account decreases in annual mileage as vehicles age, as determined from the 1995 and 2001 National Household Travel Surveys.[9]

Figure 21.1.4 also shows the risk of passenger vehicle fire fatalities per billion vehicle miles traveled, restricted to new

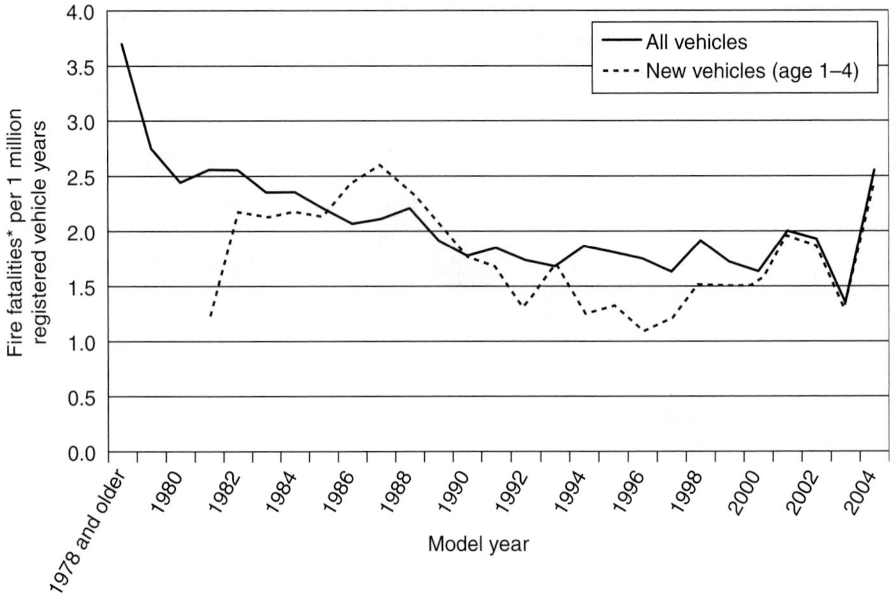

*Only includes fatalities when fire is coded as the most harmful event for the vehicle.

FIGURE 21.1.3 Passenger Car and Light Truck Fire Fatalities per 1 Million Registered Vehicle Years (RVY), by Model Year of Vehicle, 1978–2005. (Source: FARS and R. L. Polk, 1985–2005)

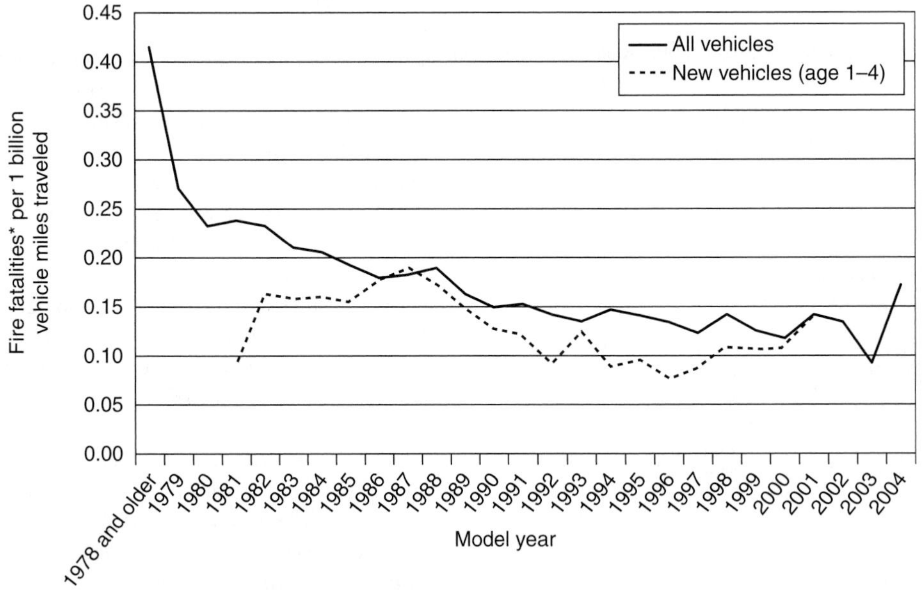

*Only includes fatalities when fire is coded as the most harmful event for the vehicle.

FIGURE 21.1.4 Passenger Car and Light Truck Fire Fatalities per 1 Billion Vehicle Miles Traveled (VMT), by Model Year of Vehicle, 1978–2005. (Source: FARS, 1985–2005, R. L. Polk, 1985–2005; National Household Travel Survey, 1995 and 2001)

vehicles (vehicles aged 1 to 4 years). As with the risk per registered vehicle year analysis, it appears that the risk increased between model years 1981 and 1982. As discussed previously, the sample size for new vehicles of model year 1981 is small (only 12 fatalities listed in FARS), so this increase is not statistically significant. The average risk for model year 1982 to 1986 vehicles, aged 1 to 4 years, was 0.16 fire fatalities per billion vehicle miles traveled, whereas the average risk for model year 1996 to 2004 vehicles, aged 1 to 4 years, was 0.11 fire fatalities per billion vehicle miles traveled. Thus, the fire fatality risk, restricted to new vehicles only, has decreased by about 30 percent.

PASSENGER VEHICLE FIRE RESEARCH

The statistical analysis demonstrates that, on average, there are 425 fatalities per year attributed to fires associated with passenger vehicles, and that a vast majority of these fatalities (90 percent) are associated with postcollision fires. Other key findings are that about 60 percent of postcollision passenger vehicle fire fatalities result from fuel-fed fires, and about 50 percent result from fires originating in the engine compartment. These findings are consistent with a report prepared for the Motor Vehicle Fire Research Institute (MVFRI),[10] which illustrated that of all the vehicle collision fires reported by the National Automotive Sampling System (NASS), the majority were caused by front-end collisions and were initiated in the engine compartment.

The following sections briefly describe recent research conducted on postcollision fires and a number of strategies to mitigate the risk to occupants of passenger vehicles involved in postcollision fires. The establishment of valid performance criteria is critical before creating a model or test method.

Postcollision Fire Research

One of the most challenging aspects of the research to better understand postcollision passenger vehicle fires is to reproduce the coupling between the impact damage, fire initiation, and fire propagation. Another key component and challenge is the ability to determine when, and by what mechanism, conditions within the passenger compartment become untenable.

A major milestone in research associated with postcollision fires occurred as part of the DOT/GM Settlement Agreement. This agreement resolved a defect investigation opened by NHTSA into the postcollision fuel tank integrity of General Motors' pickup trucks, model years 1973–1987. As part of the settlement, a 5 year/$10 million vehicle fire research program was initiated to better understand fire initiation and propagation following a vehicle collision.[11] This study is by far the most extensive and detailed study of its kind and provided valuable data related to both understanding postcollision fires as well as mitigating the fire hazard to motor vehicle occupants.

Crash Tests. Consistent with real-world postcollision passenger vehicle fires, the 11 crash tests conducted as part of this study were intended to be severe, providing substantial damage to the vehicle structure, electrical systems, fluid systems, and the fuel tank. Crash test configurations included a moving deformable barrier, similar to the barrier used to assess compliance with the requirements of FMVSS 214,[12] with the vehicle traveling at 53 mph (85 km/hr) for rear impacts and 65 mph (104.6 km/hr) for front impacts, at 34 mph (54.7 km/hr) for frontal pole impacts, and frontal at 37 mph (59.5 km/hr) for oblique barrier impacts (only one oblique test was conducted). The crash tests were conducted with all normal engine fluids (except for the main fuel tank which was filled with Stoddard solvent for the crash test) with the engine running, and were heavily instrumented to attempt to capture the mechanism of ignition and propagation, should a fire occur. Once the crash tests were conducted, carefully controlled and heavily instrumented burn tests were performed in a manner consistent with the expected method of fire causation for each crash test. The data collected from the burn test were then used to calculate the point in time in which conditions would have become untenable for any occupants within the passenger compartment.

Untenable Conditions. One of the important findings from this work was that the time at which untenable conditions were reached was strongly correlated to the time that flames entered the passenger compartment. Regardless of how or where flames entered the passenger compartment, conditions became untenable in a matter of several minutes. It should be noted that untenable conditions depend on where measurements were taken. In larger vehicles, tenable and untenable conditions may occur at the same time in different locations within a burning vehicle. In the case of the pool fire tests, flames from the pool fire underneath the vehicle penetrated into the passenger compartment though gaps around deformed doors or underbody seams created by crash-induced damage. The time to reach untenable conditions ranged from 1.6 to 4.0 minutes, a relatively short period for rescue by emergency personnel. For fires which initiated in the engine compartment, flames entered the passenger compartment in one of three manners: (1) through the windshield when it failed; (2) through the heating and air conditioning system vents; and/or (3) through pass-throughs in the bulkhead. A comparison of the times required to reach untenable conditions for both the pool fires and the engine compartment fires is shown in Figure 21.1.5.

It should be noted that a comparison of individual times to untenable conditions within a given test series must also be analyzed based on the manner and location in which the fire was initiated and the type of crash. Although pool fires are less common than engine compartment fires, they are responsible for a large number of fatalities. In the period from 1994 through 1998, NFPA data indicate that fuel-fed fires accounted for 27 percent of highway vehicle fires, but they were responsible for 56 percent of vehicle fire fatalities. Pool fires (or fuel-fed fires) differ from other vehicle fires in that the power output of the initial fire is controlled not by the material flammability characteristics of the vehicle components but by the size of the fuel pool.

Further, flame penetration times into the passenger compartment vary depending on the condition of the vehicle. Time to penetration can be reduced in postcollision fires, as the

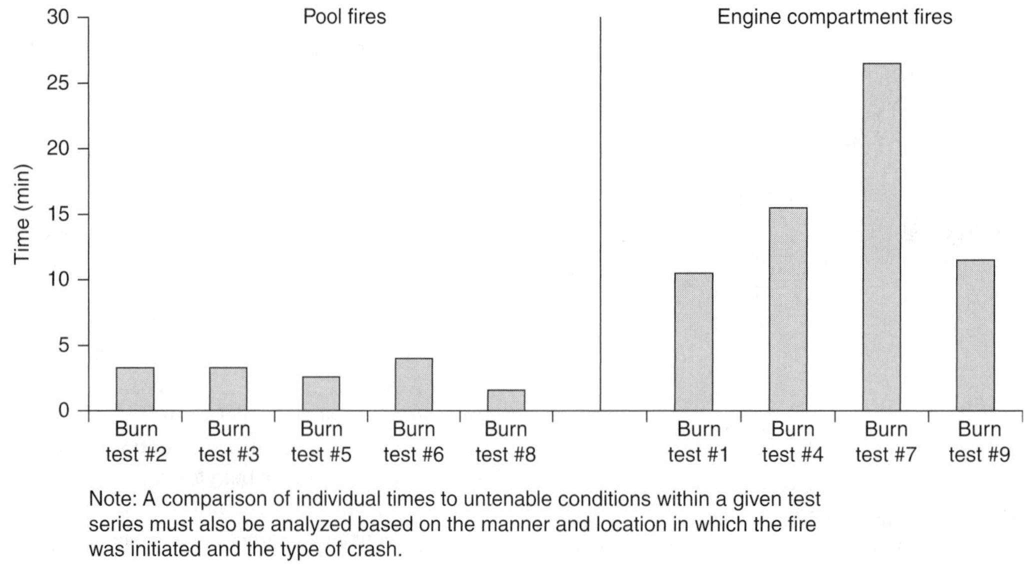

FIGURE 21.1.5 Time to Reach Untenable Conditions in Postcollision Fire Tests.

vehicle structure and metal panels can be torn or otherwise breached, allowing flames and smoke to more quickly enter the passenger compartment. As such, the onset of untenable conditions is linked to the condition of the vehicle and hence whether there has been a collision event. In the case of pool fires, untenable conditions that can cause injuries and fatalities can occur quickly, much quicker than the response times of emergency personnel. (See Figure 21.1.5 reference to NFPA report that has response time information.) Thus the strategies involving fire performance of materials and components inside the vehicle are not expected to have a significant effect on the outcome of a fuel-fed fire.[13]

Material Flammability Research

As part of the NHTSA's mandate to reduce deaths, injuries, and economic losses related to crashes and vehicle fire hazards, the NHTSA not only reviews existing standards internally and evaluates their effectiveness on a periodic basis, but also considers requests from any person or organization to develop new or revised standards. This standard development process incorporates the extensive technical expertise and resources available in the automotive industry. It also provides a mechanism to evaluate and compare the potential safety benefits of a new or revised standard with the associated cost to the public. Furthermore, this process assesses design and safety trade-offs associated with a wide range of interdependent technical issues, including crashworthiness, fire safety, human health, toxicology, environmental impact, and fuel economy.

Small-Scale Testing. As part of an effort to determine the feasibility and benefit of improving the FMVSS 302 test procedure, NHTSA recently funded a Southwest Research Institute (SwRI) study.[14] The purpose of this study was to identify or develop new small-scale test methodologies to rate automotive materials consistent with actual fire performance in full-scale vehicle burn tests and to explore levels of performance for this test methodology that would significantly increase survivability. The study, which addressed materials in the engine compartment, identified the cone calorimeter (ASTM E1354) as the most suitable bench-scale test apparatus to rate the flammability characteristics of automotive materials. The cone calorimeter is a small-scale, or bench-scale, flammability testing apparatus that subjects small 4 in. by 4 in. (100 mm by 100 mm) samples of a material or materials to an applied heat source. The heat source heats the material and the material, if possible, is ignited by means of a spark igniter. The equipment provides a measure of the material's heat release rate (HRR) and ignition time, and can be equipped to collect other data, including quantities of products of combustion produced as well as mass loss rate data, among other things. Using the cone calorimeter data, a model was formulated for evaluating the fire hazard of a particular engine component material. There was no validation of the proposed model, although validation was proposed as part of future work through full-scale vehicle burn tests. No specific performance criteria that would significantly alter the fire outcome in terms of injury or survivability were offered.

The difficulty of establishing a link between bench-scale test results and the performance of materials in full-scale vehicle tests was highlighted in several of the tests associated with the GM/DOT settlement described previously. To examine the influence of fire retardants, a test vehicle was identified from previous testing where the engine compartment fire penetrated into the passenger compartment through the HVAC unit and windshield.[15] These tests set out to examine if a flame-retardant HVAC unit would alter this behavior.

In these full-scale tests, one passenger vehicle was equipped with a factory supplied HVAC unit and the other otherwise identical vehicle was equipped with the fire-retardant HVAC. Each of these vehicles was crashed in identical crash tests. These crashed vehicles were then burned using identical ignition sources in identical locations within the engine compartment. The instrumentation associated with the burn tests was the same as used in previous burn tests in the GM/DOT research program, such that the time to untenable conditions could be evaluated for each vehicle.

In bench-scale tests, as expected, the polymer material treated with the fire retardant exhibited a significantly lower heat release rate.[16,17] The heat release rate of the material with untreated polypropylene exceeded 200 kW/m^2 whereas the heat release rate of the flame-retarded HVAC unit was approximately 5 kW/m^2.

Full-Scale Testing. Results from the full-scale vehicle burn tests demonstrated that the fire retardant was ineffective. The heat release rates from the two burn tests were essentially identical. As expected with very similar fire growth rates, the times to reach untenable conditions were also essentially identical. These results are in sharp contrast to the bench-scale cone calorimeter and intermediate-scale results described previously and indicate the difficulty in using bench-scale tests to predict behavior in full-scale vehicle burn tests. Not only did the fire retardant not produce an improvement in the time to untenable conditions, the addition of the fire retardant actually degraded fire safety by producing higher levels of toxic gases.

HAZARD MITIGATION STRATEGIES

Role of ASTM E1546

ASTM E1546, *Standard Guide for Development of Fire-Hazard-Assessment Standards,* describes the development of a fire hazard assessment. ASTM E1546 outlines the manner in which scientific data should be compiled in order to ensure that the information is relevant to the assessment of a fire hazard of a product under specific conditions of use.

According to ASTM E1546, the purpose of a fire hazard assessment is to reveal whether a product produces an increase, no increase, or a decrease in fire hazard for all scenarios relevant to the use of such product. As part of this assessment, it is necessary to first determine the nature of the product's involvement in a potential fire (i.e., initial heat source, initial fuel source, principal or largest fuel source, etc.). This factor is critical in assessing the role that the product plays in fire growth and spread, and how its material properties affect the evolution of the fire. Once this determination is made, it is possible to define the material properties that would provide a "significant variation" on the fire hazard of the product. Once the area of greatest concern is determined, it is then possible to define the test methods or calculation procedures that will measure the product's contribution to the fire hazard.

The environment in which the product is used is also of importance. ASTM E1546 states that it is possible to use data from fire tests of isolated parts. However, the relative importance, interaction, and relevance of the fire test response characteristics, individually and collectively, to the hazard posed by the product in real fires must be established by comparison to more thorough assessments, such as established scientific principles, large-scale tests, and analyses of real fires.

This requires that testing and/or analysis be performed not only for the isolated product (i.e., at the component level), but also as a component in a system (i.e., in actual vehicles under actual fire scenario conditions). Apart from the product analysis, it is also important to identify and measure the impact (i.e., reduction in injuries and fatalities) of the product's flammability properties on the outcome of a possible fire.

Application of ASTM E1546 to Vehicle Fire Safety

ASTM E1546 provides general guidelines for fire hazard assessments. In the case of vehicle fires, it is important to take into account the special circumstances involved and to use any available data on such incidents. In particular, emphasis should be placed on types of fires that are likely to result in injuries and fatalities. It is also important to have a clear understanding of the types of fires commonly involved in vehicle accidents and how such fires progress. This information must then be used to assess what factors play the largest role in the evolution and growth of vehicle fires. Only then can the major fire hazards be identified and quantified.

The fundamental requirement to prevent fatalities due to postcollision fires is that egress or extinguishment occurs before conditions become untenable in the passenger compartment. Mitigating the risk of injury to the occupants of passenger vehicles involved in postcollision fires can be accomplished by any combination of the four factors that follow:

1. Reduce the risk of ignition, that is, prevent the fire from occurring
2. Decrease the time necessary to egress or to be extricated
3. Decrease the time required to extinguish the fire
4. Increase the time until untenable conditions exist within the passenger compartment

Reducing the Ignition Probability. The most obvious way to reduce the number of postcollision fire injuries and deaths is to prevent fires from occurring. Limited research has been conducted to evaluate the mechanisms responsible for ignition of postcollision fires, particularly those that did not involve gasoline as the first material ignited. More research is necessary in this area to better understand the processes that cause ignition as a result of collisions and the methods that may be used to reduce the probability of ignition.

Decreasing the Time Required to Egress. In cases where the occupants of the vehicle are incapacitated or trapped, the time required to egress is related to the involvement of bystanders or emergency response personnel. Time to egress is also influenced by specific crash-induced damage to the vehicle and the ability of occupants to egress. The response of emergency personnel depends of a number of complex factors and has been studied extensively. In 1999, NHTSA funded a study to address the possibility of reducing the crash-to-notification times to 1 minute using an automated collision notification (ACN) system.[18] This system was expected to also shorten the notification-to-arrival time due to automated directions to the site. The system was evaluated by NHTSA,[19] with a program initiated in 1995, in order to assess its effectiveness. In the end, it was found that the ACN produced an unacceptable number of false alarms and was too complicated and costly.

Decreasing the Time Required to Extinguish the Fire. Excluding the possibility of bystanders extinguishing a postcollision fire, the two main methods to decrease the time required to extinguish the fire are decreasing the emergency personnel response time (and associated time to notify emergency responders) or designing and installing an effective on-board fire suppression system. Because fuel-fed fires can become untenable before emergency personnel arrive on scene, one of the leading hazard mitigation strategies in this scenario is an on-board fire suppression system.

The great diversity of collisions and the associated post-collision fires create a complex set of problems which must be overcome in developing a robust, on-board fire suppression system. Factors such as the amount of damage sustained to the vehicle, vehicle movement, wind direction and speed, and reignition after suppressant release can substantially reduce the effectiveness of an automatic suppression system in extinguishing a postcollision fire.[20] Overall, these technologies show some promise, but there is still much research required to improve their reliability and effectiveness in an actual postcollision vehicle fire. Tewarson et al. relayed in their work that one set of tests conducted produced results indicating that it is highly improbable that an on-board fire suppression system would be able to extinguish most engine compartment and underbody fires.[21]

Increasing Tenability Time. Another approach to hazard mitigation of postcollision fires (at least those which do not involve a fuel-fed fire) is to slow the spread of the fire into the passenger compartment. A strategy that has received significant attention is the use of fire retardants in plastic automotive components. Although bench-scale tests have shown that fire retardants can lower the heat release rate of plastics, the ability of fire retardants to increase the time to untenable conditions in the vehicle interior has not been demonstrated in full-scale tests. Whereas the benefits of using fire retardants are unclear, there are numerous potential negative consequences to using fire retardants, many of which are toxic to humans. These include toxic effects of the fire retardant coming into contact with people, the toxic gases produced by fire retardants when they burn, environmental concerns about disposing of these toxic materials at the end of a vehicle's life, and the potential adverse effects that fire retardants may have on the intended function of the component, such as energy absorption, strength, weight, wear, durability, and appearance. Additional research is necessary to evaluate the effectiveness of fire retardants on motor vehicle safety and to ensure that the toxic effects of fire retardants are not a detriment to the public.

DESIGN AND SAFETY CONSIDERATIONS

Other physical properties and component relationships related to vehicle safety other than flammability and fire response must be included in the hazard assessment in order to assess whether changes in component flammability or fire response will adversely affect other safety attributes of the components and the entire vehicle system (i.e., trade-offs).

From the standpoint of fire safety, all vehicle components could theoretically be made of noncombustible materials. This, however, is not feasible, as has been previously discussed in the literature.[22] In the case of a passenger vehicle, the choice of materials to be used in the vehicle should be driven by overall safety and function. For example, it would not be prudent to decrease the fire hazard related to automobile components while increasing the risk of injury during a crash.

Automobile components are specifically designed to be used for extended periods of time, under a variety of environmental conditions and (most importantly) be able to perform well during a crash. Before any additional requirements (such as changes in flammability performance) are suggested regarding vehicle components, it is necessary to determine that these new requirements are not detrimental to other safety properties of such materials. The following is a discussion of some possible considerations.

Need for a Systems Approach

Safe vehicle design requires a systems-level approach, instead of focusing solely on prescriptive, individual material performance requirements. Other physical properties related to the ability to manufacture a working component, the functionality of a finished component or assembly, the durability of the component, occupant protection in a crash, and other safety parameters, are necessary and equally important considerations in designing components for use in passenger vehicles. Changes to the formulation of combustible materials that result in improved flammability and/or fire response characteristics based on bench-scale tests alone could adversely affect other material physical properties and may negatively impact manufacturability, durability, functionality, and crash protection.

Physical Properties

Many of the components in today's vehicles are designed with specific material properties intended to increase the survivability of passengers during a collision or rollover. As an example, some fire mitigation strategies may have adverse and unwanted effects on FMVSS 201* performance such as energy absorption due to change in materials stiffness if new materials were substituted for current materials. Another example is the use of fire retardants that may compromise crash safety performance, because of the reduction in energy absorption due to the increase of material stiffness. In the case of very specialized components, such as airbags or seatbelts, the addition of fire retardants would

*FMVSS 201 specifies requirements for occupant protection in interior impacts.

have to be thoroughly evaluated and analyzed if the materials used in their construction were altered.

Although ordinary fire-retardant treatments have been shown to improve the flammability properties of polymer materials under bench-scale testing, their behavior under real fire conditions is currently not well understood. In one study of automotive material flammability, it was noted that "ordinary fire retardant treatments are not effective in preventing the flame to penetrate the passenger compartment and thus concepts based on modifying the fundamental thermo-physical-chemical and fire properties under high heat flux exposure conditions need to be utilized to enhance the fire retardancy of automotive polymers."[23]

Although the desired performance requirements may be met with the addition of fire retardants in automotive materials, an increase in time to ignition and a decrease in heat release rate performance may yield an increase in toxicity levels and provide no net benefit in overall fire safety. The smoke and fumes inside the passenger compartment during a fire should be considered in a fire hazard assessment. Toxic fumes could overcome passengers that have become entrapped or otherwise incapacitated inside the passenger compartment due to the use of fire-retardant chemicals.[24,25]

Health and Environmental Hazards

Potential health and environmental hazards also need to be evaluated. Next to homes and offices, we spend the most time inside automobiles, an average of 101 minutes per day.[26] During this time, we are exposed to the materials within the automobile in an enclosed space, increasing our contact with any volatiles or contaminated particulates. This means that care must be taken to reduce the toxicity of materials and/or reduce the use of toxic materials within an automobile. Chemicals within a passenger vehicle are exposed to extreme conditions, which may accelerate their decay. Summer air temperatures inside parked vehicles can reach 192°F (88.88°C), with dash surface temperatures of up to 248°F (120°C) recorded.[27] In addition, most vehicle windows transmit long-wave UV light, which can increase the rate of decomposition of materials.

The literature contains numerous papers addressing health and/or environmental concerns associated with the historical use of flame-retardant substances. Asbestos and PCBs are just two examples of materials adopted as flame retardants because of their chemico-physical properties. Only later did scientists and the industry develop an understanding of the biological consequences of that decision.

There are many different potential flame-retardant additives that can be used in plastics in order to meet specified performance requirements. Not all of these chemicals have been thoroughly investigated in terms of their human or ecological health hazard. Prior to their implementation, each of the various chemical options deserves to be assessed fully in order to characterize these hazards.

Another important concern is that when a flame retardant is brought into the marketplace, there is an abundance of opportunities for its distribution into the environment. People may be exposed during the manufacture of the flame retardant. Sometimes, particularly toxic chemicals are necessary to synthesize the agent. From there, the retardant needs to be placed in packages and then shipped. The areas of potential risk can be divided into three main categories: risk to workers, risk to consumers, and risk to the environment. Each area must be examined before making changes in material properties.

SUMMARY

Motor vehicle fire safety has realized significant improvements over the past several decades. Considering new vehicles only (4 years old or newer), to eliminate effects attributable to vehicle age, it is found that the risk of fire fatality per one billion vehicle miles traveled is about 30 percent lower for today's vehicles than for model year 1982 to 1986 vehicles. Nevertheless, advancing motor vehicle safety remains a significant public health challenge—one that automakers are addressing daily. According to recent data, in the United States, approximately 32,000 passenger vehicle occupants are fatally injured every year as a result of traffic accidents. Of these fatalities, approximately 1.2 percent (385) are attributed to postcollision fires. In addition, there are approximately 40 passenger vehicle fire fatalities per year that are not collision-related. These statistics indicate that the current standard has been empirically demonstrated to produce a low risk of fatality.

The complexities of passenger vehicle safety require a broad approach in order to ensure that efforts to increase fire safety performance do not undermine other important safety considerations. Any new motor vehicle fire hazard mitigation strategy must address safety trade-offs, such as the extent to which other critical safety features may be compromised if new strategies are implemented. Potential design changes, such as changing the flammability properties of individual components, will have an effect on other component properties, either immediately or over time.

Research to improve vehicle fire safety involving postcollision fires is in its infancy, and few full-scale vehicle burn tests have been conducted to validate new strategies. Significant additional research is necessary to develop robust, cost-effective hazard mitigation strategies for postcollision fires.

BIBLIOGRAPHY

References Cited

1. *Traffic Safety Facts 2005,* http://www-nrd.nhtsa.dot.gov/pdf/nrd-30/NCSA/TSFAnn/TSF2005.pdf, Table 2, NHTSA's National Center for Statistics and Analysis, U.S. Department of Transportation, Washington, DC, 2006, p. 15.
2. "Achievements in Public Health, 1900–1999, Motor Vehicle Safety: A 20th Century Public Health Achievement," Centers for Disease Control and Prevention, United States Department of Health and Human Services, *Morbidity and Mortality Weekly Report,* Vol. 48, 1999, pp. 369–374.
3. *Traffic Safety Facts 2005,* http://www-nrd.nhtsa.dot.gov/pdf/nrd-30/NCSA/TSFAnn/TSF2005.pdf, Table 2, NHTSA's National Center for Statistics and Analysis, U.S. Department of Transportation, Washington, DC, 2006, p. 15.
4. Analysis of data contained in "Motor Vehicle Facts and Figures 2005," Ward's Communications, p. 56, and "Motor Vehicle Facts and Figures 2002," Ward's Communications, p. 61.

5. *Traffic Safety Facts 2005,* http://www-nrd.nhtsa.dot.gov/pdf/nrd-30/NCSA/TSFAnn/TSF2005.pdf, Table 2, NHTSA's National Center for Statistics and Analysis, U.S. Department of Transportation, Washington, DC, 2006, p. 15.
6. "Laws/Regulations," http://www.nhtsa.gov/portal/site/nhtsa/menuitem.e649cd1b2b018c71d8eca01046108a0c, NHTSA, U.S. Department of Transportation, Washington, DC.
7. Karter, M. J., Jr., "Fire Loss in the United States," reports from 1999–2004, Fire Analysis & Research Division, National Fire Protection Association, Quincy, MA.
8. Ahrens, M., "U.S. Vehicle Fire Trends and Patterns," Fire Analysis and Research Division, National Fire Protection Association, Quincy, MA, Oct. 2006.
9. "National Household Travel Survey," http://nhts.ornl.gov, Federal Highway Administration, U.S. Department of Transportation, Washington, DC.
10. Tewarson, A., Quintiere, J. G., and Purser, D., "Fire Behavior of Materials in Vehicle Crash Fires and Survivability of the Passengers," 2005-01-1555, SAE International, Warrendale, PA, 2005.
11. Jensen, J. L., and Santrock, J., "Evaluation of Motor Vehicle Fire Initiation and Propagation, Vehicle Crash and Fire Propagation Test Program," NHTSA-1998-3588-38, General Motors Corporation, Internationl Technical Conference on the Enhanced Safety of Vehicles (ESV) paper number 98-S4-O-05, NHTSA, U.S. Department of Transportation, Washington, DC, 1998.
12. FMVSS 214, "Side Impact Protection," 60 Fed. Reg. 57838-39, NHTSA, U.S. Department of Transportation, Washington, DC, Nov. 22, 1995.
13. Carpenter, K., Huczek, J., Janssens, M., and Miller, M., "Development of a Method to Assess the Hazard of Plastic Components to Passengers Trapped in Post-Collision Motor Vehicle Fires," 2005-01-1556, SAE International, Warrendale, PA, 2005.
14. Battipaglia, K. C., Griffith, A. L., Huczek, J. P., Janssens, M. L., Miller, M. A., and Willson, K. R., "Comparison of Fire Properties of Automotive Materials and Evaluation of Performance Levels," SwRI Project No. 01.05804, Southwest Research Institute, San Antonio, TX, Oct. 2003.
15. Santrock, J., "Evaluation of Motor Vehicle Fire Initiation and Propagation, Part 7: Propagation of an Engine Compartment Fire in a 1997 Rear Wheel Drive Passenger Car," www.nhtsa.dot.gov, docket number 3588, document number NHTSA-1998-3588-178, NHTSA, U.S. Department of Transportation, Washington, DC, Aug. 12, 2002.
16. Ohlemiller, T. J., "The Effect of Polymer Resin Substitution on the Flammability of a Standardized Automotive Component in Laboratory Tests," NISTIR 6745, National Institute of Standards and Technology, Building and Fire Research Laboratory, Gaithersburg, MD, 2002.
17. Ohlemiller, T. J., "Influence of Flame-Retarded Resins on the Burning Behavior of a Heating, Ventilating and Air Conditioning Unit from a Sports Coupe," NISTIR 6748, NHTSA-98-3588-185, National Institute of Standards and Technology, Building and Fire Research Laboratory, Gaithersburg, MD, 2002.
18. Champion, H. R., Augenstein, J. S., Cushing, B., Digges, K. H., Hunt, R., Larkin, R., Malliaris, A. C., Sacco, W. J., and Siegel, J. H., "Reducing Highway Deaths and Disabilities with Automatic Wireless Transmission of Serious Injury Probability Ratings from Crash Recorders to Emergency Medical Service Providers," International Symposium on Transportation Recorders, May 1999.
19. "Automated Collision Notification Field Operational Tests," Report DOT HS-809-304, http://www-nrd.nhtsa.dot.gov/departments/nrd-12/ACNEvaluation, NHTSA, U.S. Department of Transportation, Washington, DC, Feb. 2001.
20. Santrock, J., and Hodges, S. E., "Evaluation of Automatic Fire Suppression Systems in Full Scale Vehicle Fire Tests and Static Vehicle Fire Tests," 2005-01-1788, SAE International, Warrendale, PA, 2005.
21. Tewarson, A., Quintiere, J. G., and Purser, D. A., "Post Collision Motor Vehicle Fires," Technical Report, Project ID 0003018009, Vol I, Motor Vehicle Fire Research Institute, Charlottesville, VA, Oct. 2005.
22. Hirschler, M. M. (Ed.), "Expert View: Dr. Vytenis Babrauskas," *Fire Safety & Technology Bulletin,* Vol. 1, No. 1, 2006, p. 3.
23. Tewarson, A., "Fire Behavior of Automotive Polymers," 8th International Fire and Materials Conference, January 27–28, San Francisco, CA, 2003.
24. Wichman, I. S., "A Review of the Literature of Material Flammability, Combustion and Toxicity Related to Transportation," NHTSA-98-3588-142, NHTSA, U.S. Department of Transportation, Washington, DC, 2002.
25. van Esch, G. J., "Flame Retardants: A General Introduction," WHO on Chemical Safety, http://www.inchem.org/documents/ehc/ehc/ehc192.htm#SubsectionNumber:6.3.2, World Health Organization, Geneva, Switzerland, 1997.
26. Dong, L., Block, G., Mandel, S., "Activities Contributing to Total Energy Expenditure in the United States: Results from the NHAPS Study," International Journal of Behavioral Nutrition and Physical Activity, Vol. 1, No. 4, 2004.
27. National Renewable Energy Laboratory, "Development of a Weather Correction Model for Outdoor Vehicle Testing," Golden, CO, Aug. 7, 2001.

NFPA Codes, Standards, and Recommended Practices

Reference to the following NFPA codes, standards, and recommended practices will provide further information on fire safety in passenger vehicles discussed in this chapter. (See the latest version of The NFPA Catalog *for availability of current editions of the following documents.)*

NFPA 30A, *Code for Motor Fuel Dispensing Facilities and Repair Garages*

NFPA 385, *Standard for Tank Vehicles for Flammable and Combustible Liquids*

NFPA 1192, *Standard on Recreational Vehicles*

Reference

Nicholson, J., "Vehicle Fire Problem," *NFPA Journal,* Jan./Feb. 2007.

Chapter 2

Fire Safety in Commercial Vehicles

Revised by
Brian Routhier

Chapter Contents

Key Terms

cargo tank, commercial vehicle, Federal Motor Vehicle Safety Standard (FMVSS), hazardous material, motor vehicle, National Transportation Safety Board (NTSB), road trailer, vehicle electrical system, vehicle fuel tank

Many factors influence motor vehicle fire safety. Among these are vehicle design and construction; materials from which a vehicle is constructed or which are carried by a vehicle, particularly upholstery, plastic, wood, fuel, and hazardous materials cargoes; vehicle maintenance, including safeguards against fire during vehicle repair; vehicle operation, including avoidance of collisions and of other accidents, such as those involving smoking materials; and garaging or storage of vehicles.

The degree of fire hazard depends on the vehicle type, such as passenger car, motorcycle, motor home, or tank truck; the use of the vehicle for pleasure driving, commercial service, or off-road; the climate and environment in which it is used; the age, condition, and maintenance of the vehicle; the material and construction standards to which it is built, particularly the fuel and electrical systems; and the type of fuel used—gasoline, diesel fuel, propane, natural gas, or alcohol—and the way the fuel is contained in the vehicle.

Research into causes of motor vehicle fires based on individual crash investigations and collections of crash and other loss data indicate the magnitude of the motor vehicle fire problem and some specific causal factors in motor vehicle fires.

Each year, the United States experiences approximately 6200 highway vehicle fires due to collision and 12.7 million on-the-road vehicle accidents. Yet serious injury from vehicle fires occurs overwhelmingly from crash-related fires—fires that occur at a rate of approximately 1 per 1000 crashes. Three-fifths of fire deaths in motor vehicle fires come in postcrash incidents.[1,2]

In 2000, there were an estimated 325,000 fires involving highway vehicles, causing 450 civilian deaths and 1325 civilian injuries. Table 21.2.1 presents information on the U.S. highway vehicle fire problem for the years 1980 to 2002.

For related topics, see the following chapters in Section 21: Chapter 1, "Passenger Vehicle Fires"; Chapter 3, "Automotive and Marine Service Station Operations"; Chapter 4, "Vehicle Fueling Using Gaseous Fuels"; and Chapter 6, "Recreational Vehicles." See also Section 13, Chapter 6, "Public Fire Protection and Hazmat Management"; and Section 13, Chapter 8, "Managing the Response to Hazardous Material Incidents."

NATURE OF VEHICLE FIRES

As with other fires, motor vehicle fires require a flammable substance, an ignition source, and oxygen. Virtually all motor vehicles carry flammable fuel—gasoline, gasohol, diesel fuel, or another hydrocarbon compound. Vehicle upholstery, insulating and sound-deadening materials, electrical wiring insulation, and plastic body and trim also can fuel a motor vehicle fire. Materials carried as cargo and fare in or on motor vehicles, particularly trucks, also may be flammable.

Ignition sources include electrical short circuits or other electrical malfunctions that cause excessive heating of conductors or components; sparks from an engine ignition system; hot exhaust system components; engine backfire; overheating of tires, brakes, and wheel bearings; friction-generated

Brian Routhier is an automotive engineer with the American Trucking Associations in Arlington, Virginia.

TABLE 21.2.1 U.S. Highway Vehicle Fire Problem, by Year: 1980–2002

Year	*Fires*	*Civilian Deaths*	*Civilian Injuries*	*Direct Property Damage (in Millions of Dollars)*	*Loss in 2002 Dollars (in Millions of Dollars)*
1980	411,300	600	3,350	478	1,044
1981	417,500	680	2,930	477	942
1982	398,400	570	2,850	409	761
1983	405,400	640	3,250	532	959
1984	411,600	550	3,080	592	1,024
1985	417,000	710	3,060	702	1,172
1986	417,600	740	3,180	608	998
1987	429,300	700	2,620	687	1,088
1988	416,000	730	2,520	728	1,108
1989	379,100	520	2,570	751	1,090
1990	383,000	590	2,920	792	1,092
1991	371,200	480	2,500	801	1,058
1992	335,700	590	2,510	758	971
1993	354,600	500	2,380	723	900
1994	330,100	460	1,960	779	946
1995	334,700	380	1,780	790	932
1996	327,800	470	1,520	774	888
1997	355,100	430	1,860	1,025	1,149
1998	313,600	420	1,610	1,010	1,115
1999*	288,000	350	1,150	911	984
2000	252,400	310	1,100	903	943
2001	257,500	390	1,440	1,064	1,081
2002	281,600	480	1,540	1,143	1,143
1980–2002 annual average	360,400	530	2,330	758	1,017
1999–2002 annual average	269,900	380	1,310	1,005	1,038

Note: These are national estimates of fires reported to U.S. municipal fire departments and so exclude fires reported only to federal or state agencies or industrial fire brigades. National estimates are projections. Casualty and loss projections can be heavily influenced by the inclusion or exclusion of one unusually serious fire. Fires are rounded to the nearest hundred, civilian deaths and injuries to the nearest ten, and direct property damage is rounded to the nearest million dollars.

*NFIRS data for 1999 and later was received in the Version 5.0 format. Due to the many coding changes, the 1999–2002 data can better be analyzed separately from data from previous years.

Source: NFIRS and NFPA survey; Table 697, "Purchasing Power of the Dollar" from U.S. Census Bureau's *Statistical Abstract of the United States: 2004–2005* (124th Edition).

sparks from a collision or from metal components scraping against the pavement; and careless use of cigarettes and other smoking materials. Generally, oxygen in the ambient atmosphere is sufficient for a motor vehicle fire.

Table 21.2.2 summarizes passenger and freight vehicle fires, by area of origin of fires, from 1999 to 2003. More detailed but dated analyses have been developed by the Federal Motor Carrier Safety Administration (FMCSA) of the U.S. Department of Transportation (DOT).

Death and injury in motor vehicle fires can result from direct exposure to heat and from inhalation of toxic combustion products. In major vehicle crashes involving fire, determining with certainty whether death resulted from the crash or from the fire may not be possible. In some cases, injury results from or is exacerbated by the inability of a vehicle's occupant to get out of the burning vehicle—doors or seats are jammed by a crash, or the occupant is injured or stunned.

Hazardous materials in motor vehicles present a particular fire problem. The National Transportation Safety Board (NTSB), the FMCSA, and NFPA all carried out a number of detailed accident investigations into such fires. These investigations led to changes in regulations for hazardous materials containers and in other aspects of the transportation of such cargoes. Despite such precautions, hazardous materials cargo fires and explosions occur.

The NTSB has issued investigative reports on accidents in which hazardous materials exploded or burned following a crash. (These and other NTSB reports are available from the National Technical Information Service, Springfield, Virginia 22161.) As a result of these and other highway crash investigations, the NTSB made numerous recommendations to the FMCSA, the Research and Special Programs Administration (RSPA) of DOT, and to other agencies concerning modification and enforcement of safety and hazardous materials regulations.

TABLE 21.2.2 U.S. Highway Vehicle Fires, by Area of Fire Origin, 1999–2003 Annual Averages

Area of Fire Origin	*Fires*		*Civilian Deaths*		*Civilian Injuries*		*Direct Property Damage (in Millions)*	
Engine area, running gear, or wheel area	212,000	(65%)	170	(39%)	740	(49%)	$618	(53%)
Operator or passenger area	53,800	(17%)	90	(20%)	270	(18%)	$264	(23%)
Unclassified vehicle area	14,400	(4%)	50	(11%)	70	(5%)	$55	(5%)
Exterior, exposed vehicle surface	10,200	(3%)	10	(2%)	50	(3%)	$33	(3%)
Cargo or trunk area	9,900	(3%)	10	(3%)	100	(7%)	$44	(4%)
Fuel tank or fuel line	5,400	(2%)	80	(17%)	150	(10%)	$41	(4%)
Unclassified area of origin	4,300	(1%)	10	(2%)	10	(1%)	$22	(2%)
On or near highway, parking lot, or street	4,100	(1%)	10	(3%)	10	(1%)	$17	(1%)
Separate operator or control area	3,200	(1%)	0	(1%)	10	(1%)	$18	(2%)
Other known area	7,900	(2%)	10	(3%)	80	(6%)	$44	(4%)
Total	325,100	(100%)	440	(100%)	1,500	(100%)	$1,156	(100%)

Note: These are national estimates of fires reported to U.S. municipal fire departments and so exclude fires reported only to federal or state agencies or industrial fire brigades. National estimates are projections. Casualty and loss projections can be heavily influenced by the inclusion or exclusion of one unusually serious fire. Fires are rounded to the nearest hundred, civilian deaths and injuries to the nearest ten, and direct property damage is rounded to the nearest million dollars. Sums may not equal totals due to rounding errors. Property damage figures are not adjusted for inflation. Percentages were calculated on the actual estimates, so two figures with the same rounded-off estimates may have different percentages. Fires in which the area or origin was unknown or not reported were allocated proportionally among fires with known area of origin. A proportional share of fires in which the mobile property type was unknown or not reported are included in this table.

Source: NFIRS and NFPA survey.

FEDERAL REGULATIONS AFFECTING MOTOR VEHICLE FIRE SAFETY

As you read the statistics in this section, note that the data were current at the time of writing. As always, it is wise to check Federal Motor Vehicle Safety Standards for the most current information.

Federal Motor Vehicle Safety Standards

The National Traffic and Motor Vehicle Safety Act of 1966 authorized the National Highway Traffic Safety Administration (NHTSA) of DOT to set minimum safety standards applicable to new motor vehicles, trailers, and motor vehicle equipment manufactured after the effective date of the standard, or any subsequent amendment. To date, only four fire-related standards have been issued for new vehicles, and none has been issued for vehicles in use. The NHTSA also has the authority to investigate motor vehicle defects, some of which may present fire hazards, and to order manufacturers to notify owners and repair defects.

Federal Motor Vehicle Safety Standard (FMVSS) 301 sets requirements for the fuel system integrity of passenger cars, trucks, buses, and multipurpose vehicles having a gross vehicle weight rating (GVWR) of 10,000 lb (4536 kg) or less. The standard also applies to school buses of more than 10,000 lb (4536 kg) GVWR using fuel with a boiling point of more than 32°F (0°C).

FMVSS 301 is intended specifically to reduce the fire hazard resulting from fuel leakage in crashes. It was first applied to passenger cars manufactured on and after January 1, 1968. Since that time, the standard has been made increasingly stringent.

Under provisions that became effective on September 1, 1977, all vehicles with a GVWR of 10,000 lb (4536 kg) or less must pass prescribed front, side, and rear crash barrier tests and a rollover test. Front tests are conducted at an impact speed of 30 mph (48 km/hr), rear tests at 50 mph (80 km/hr), whereas lateral impact speed is 33 mph (53 km/hr). In the crash barrier tests, fuel leakage cannot exceed 1 oz (28 g) by weight from impact until the vehicle stops moving, 5 oz (142 g) by weight in the 5 minutes following cessation of motion, or 1 oz (28 g) by weight per minute for 25 minutes.

In the rollover test, the vehicle is turned about its longitudinal axis in 90° increments and is held for 5 minutes in each position. Rotation occurs every 1 to 3 minutes. Fuel leakage cannot exceed 5 oz (142 g) by weight in the first 5 minutes of each segment or 1 oz (28 g) per minute for the remainder of the segment.

The school bus test procedure for buses over 10,000 lb (4536 kg) GVWR uses a special, moving, contoured barrier that strikes the test vehicle at the front, rear, and sides. No rollover test is prescribed for these buses. Maximum permissible fuel leakage is the same as indicated above for front, side, and rear barrier crash tests.

FMVSS 302 sets flammability limits for materials used in interiors of vehicles in the driver and passenger space. Its requirements are directed at reducing the hazards of interior fires caused by smoking and matches. Vehicle appointments specifically covered by the standard include seat cushions, seat backs, seat belts, headlining, arm rests, trim panels, compartment shelves, head restraints, floor covering, engine compartment covering, padding, and the surface of crash protection components.

FMVSS 302 specifies a horizontal flame test for all materials and incorporates detailed requirements for the test procedure. Material under test must not burn or transmit a flame across the surface at a rate exceeding 4 in. per minute (1.7 mm/s).

FMVSS 303, *Fuel System Integrity of Compressed Natural Gas Vehicles—Passenger Cars, Multipurpose Passenger Vehicles, Trucks, and Buses,* covers vehicles that have a gross vehicle weight rating of 10,000 lb (4536 kg) or less and use compressed natural gas as a motor fuel. FMVSS 303 also covers school buses (regardless of weight) that use CNG as a motor fuel.

FMVSS 303 specifies requirements for the integrity of motor vehicle fuel systems using CNG, including CNG fuel systems of bi-fuel, dedicated, and dual-fuel CNG vehicles. The purpose of the standard is to reduce deaths and injuries resulting from fires after fuel leakage during and after motor vehicle crashes.

FMVSS 304, *Compressed Natural Gas Container Integrity,* specified requirements for the integrity of CNG motor vehicle fuel containers. FMVSS 304 applies to containers designed to store CNG as motor fuel on board any motor vehicle.

Federal Motor Carrier Safety Regulations

FMCSA administers the Federal Motor Carrier Safety Regulations (FMCSRs), which can be found online at http://www.fmcsa.gov. These regulations apply to vehicles in use, as contrasted with the Federal Motor Vehicle Safety Standards promulgated by the National Highway Traffic Safety Administration (NHTSA) that apply to new vehicles.

The FMCSRs are set forth in Title 49 of the Code of Federal Regulations, Parts 325–399, and apply to commercial vehicles in interstate or foreign commerce. Because most states have adopted these regulations by reference, they also apply, *de facto,* to most commercial vehicles in intrastate commerce.

Provisions of these regulations that address fire safety issues for commercial vehicles include the following:

- A requirement for fire extinguishers and for the driver to check the extinguisher at the start of each trip
- A prohibition against attaching a flame-producing warning device to a vehicle and a prohibition against using flame-producing devices on vehicles transporting certain explosives and tank vehicles transporting flammable liquids or gases (loaded or empty), or any commercial vehicle using compressed gas as a fuel
- Fueling precautions including a prohibition against smoking, a requirement to maintain contact between the tank and the nozzle, and restrictions on fueling buses when passengers are aboard
- Standard for installing and protecting the electrical system, including the battery, and standards for constructing and testing fuel tanks
- Special driving and parking rules applicable to drivers transporting hazardous materials including requirements to periodically check for overheated tires, a requirement that someone be present at the nozzle when the vehicle is being fueled, and a prohibition against smoking in or within 25 ft (7.6 m) of a vehicle transporting specified classes of hazardous materials

Hazardous Materials Regulations

Federal hazardous materials regulations, other than those governing driving and parking, are published in Title 49, Code of Federal Regulations, Parts 105–180. By law, hazardous materials regulations apply to both intrastate and interstate transportation. Many provisions of these regulations have been promulgated specifically to meet the needs of emergency responders by providing essential information pertaining to the materials in transport and to warn the public of those vehicles transporting hazardous materials in excess of specified quantities. For further information on the federal hazardous materials regulations, refer to Section 13, Chapter 6, "Public Fire Protection and Hazmat Management"; and Section 13, Chapter 8, "Managing the Response to Hazardous Material Incidents."

Provisions of the hazardous materials regulations address the following:

- Preparation of shipping documents to facilitate the recognition and identification of hazardous materials including a 24 hour emergency telephone that can be contacted for additional information, if needed
- Job-specific training requirements for employees involved in transporting hazardous materials at any level
- Emergency instructions to be carried in vehicles and kept in motor carrier terminals where hazardous materials are handled
- Marking and labeling of hazardous materials packaging to identify its contents and to indicate that the packaging complies with applicable specifications
- Specifications for bulk packaging such as cargo tanks and portable tanks, and for nonbulk packaging such as cylinders, boxes, drums, and bags used for hazardous materials
- Requirements for shippers that specify the types of packaging to be used for hazardous materials shipments based on the commodity's specific hazard(s)

State Activity

Most states have adopted by reference the provisions of the Federal Motor Carrier Safety Regulations and the DOT hazardous materials regulations. A number of other states have regulations similar to the federal requirements. As these trends continue, they will foster increasing uniformity of legal requirements.

National Transportation Safety Board

The National Transportation Safety Board, an independent federal agency, oversees safety for all types of transportation. Probably best known for its investigations of aircraft accidents, the agency is also concerned with fire-related highway accidents. The NTSB is responsible for making recommendations for improved safety, based on its investigations. The majority of its recommendations deal with suggested changes in the regulations and practices of federal and state government agencies, but they may also be directed at others, such as vehicle manufacturers and users.

Role of Congress

In Congress, the responsibility for legislation and oversight of transportation rests with the Senate Committee on Commerce and the House Committee on Transportation and Infrastructure. These committees take a keen interest in the activities of the federal government in the field of motor vehicle safety. They regularly hold legislative and oversight hearings on FMCSA and NHTSA activities and occasionally on NTSB activities. Reports of these hearings are available from the U.S. Superintendent of Documents or from the committees.

NFPA AND RELATED STANDARDS ON MOTOR VEHICLES

Several NFPA standards contain requirements for transportation by truck of specific hazardous materials. NFPA 495, *Explosive Materials Code,* details fire and explosion prevention related to the transportation of explosive materials, including driver qualifications, vehicle design, placarding, fire-fighting equipment, and vehicle operation. This code is widely used as the basis for state regulations.

NFPA 385, *Standard for Tank Vehicles for Flammable and Combustible Liquids,* and NFPA 407, *Standard for Aircraft Fuel Servicing,* both contain requirements for design and construction of cargo tanks of tank vehicles, for auxiliary equipment, and for operation of tank vehicles. NFPA 407 covers only special requirements for aircraft fuel servicing tank vehicles and aircraft fuel servicing hydrant vehicles.

NFPA 58, *Liquefied Petroleum Gas Code,* contains requirements for transporting liquefied petroleum gases, including requirements for transporting portable containers, for cargo tanks, and for parking and garaging vehicles used to carry LP-gas. NFPA 58 also includes requirements for installing LP-gas systems in vehicles fueled by LP-gas. It has been adopted for regulatory purposes by 47 states and by the DOT for vehicles in interstate commerce.

NFPA 52, *Vehicular Fuel Systems Code,* covers design and installation of compressed natural gas (CNG) engine fuel systems on vehicles of all types and their associated fueling systems. NFPA 52 applies to the design, installation, operation, and maintenance of liquefied natural gas engine fuel systems on vehicles of all types and to their fueling facilities.

NFPA 58 covers parking and garaging of LP-gas cargo vehicles. Another NFPA standard includes provisions relating to parking trucks: NFPA 498, *Standard for Safe Havens and Interchange Lots for Vehicles Transporting Explosives.*

The dependence of the fire service upon motor vehicles is well recognized, and it is particularly important that fire apparatus be safely constructed. NFPA 1901, *Standard for Automotive Fire Apparatus,* and NFPA 414, *Standard for Aircraft Rescue and Fire-Fighting Vehicles,* detail practices that should be followed on these types of apparatus.

Underwriters Laboratories Inc.

Certain over-the-road motor vehicle components and signaling appliances have special fire hazard significance. Underwriters Laboratories Inc. tests and lists them in UL's *Accident, Automotive, and Burglary Protection Equipment* directory. Specific items listed include the following:

1. Electrical equipment such as automobile fuses and switches
2. Fill and vent fittings
3. Fuel equipment such as backfire deflectors, fuel feed systems, electric gasoline gages, automotive-type LP-gas accessories, automotive fuel tanks, and tubing
4. Automotive heaters of the combustion type
5. LP-gas automotive vehicles—that is, farm and road tractors incorporating fuel systems designed for use of LP-gas as engine fuel and LP overfill prevention
6. Mufflers for automobiles
7. Signals and signaling appliances or highway emergency signals

UL also has its own standard, UL 395, *Standard on Automotive Fuel Tanks,* for liquid fuel tanks mounted outside the frame or in other exposed locations on gasoline- or diesel-powered trucks, tractors, or trailers. It has issued UL 307(a), *Standard on Liquid Fuel-Burning Heating Appliances for Mobile Homes and Recreational Vehicles,* and UL 307(b), *Standard for Gas Burning Heating Appliances for Mobile Homes and Recreational Vehicles.*

Society of Automotive Engineers, Inc.

The Society of Automotive Engineers, Inc. (SAE) is concerned with any vehicle that moves under its own power. SAE's standardization program covers passenger cars, trucks and buses, farm and earth-moving machinery, marine propulsion units, aircraft, and space vehicles, as well as the materials and components that go into them. Content of the SAE standards is limited to environmental and operating problems with these vehicles. The *SAE Handbook* contains all the society's surface vehicle documents.

Other Organizations Interested in Highway Safety

American Petroleum Institute (API). Active in the field of truck transportation of petroleum products, API publishes a number of publications of interest and value from the fire safety viewpoint. More information is available at http://www.api.org.

American Trucking Associations, Inc. The association reproduces the federal hazardous materials regulations in their entirety as "Hazmat Transport Regs." The association's safety department sets trucking industry standards for selecting, training, and supervising employees and develops a variety of materials for the use of trucking companies dealing with general safety and safe transportation of hazardous materials. More information is available at http://www.truckline.com.

Canada Safety Council. The council is a national, nongovernmental organization that promotes public safety initiatives in English and French. See http://www.safety-council.org.

Center for Auto Safety. The center is a consumer advocate organization dedicated to improving the safety and value of automobiles, other motor vehicles, highways, and mobile homes. The center regularly issues reports, books, comments on federal rule making, and other materials. See http://www.autosafety.org.

American Chemistry Council. The council has an active technical service on transportation and packaging. It also operates the Chemical Transportation Emergency Center (Chemtrec), 1-800-262-8200, http://www.chemtrec.com, which provides information on hazardous materials involved in emergencies. For more information, see http://www.americanchemistry.com.

Compressed Gas Association, Inc. (CGA). CGA provides technical services on products of interest and concern to its membership. See www.cganet.org.

Consumers Union of U.S., Inc. (CU). A nonprofit consumer information organization with a large technical staff, CU regularly tests automobiles—and occasionally trucks and other motor vehicles—and publishes its findings monthly in *Consumer Reports* magazine. For more information, see http://www.consumersunion.org or http://www.consumerreports.org.

Cooperative Hazardous Materials Enforcement and Development (COHMED). COHMED develops and promotes training programs for personnel responding to hazardous materials emergencies. More information on COHMED, an outreach activity of the U.S. Department of Transportation, is available at http://hazmat.dot.gov/cohmed.htm. Other DOT sites and resources on hazardous materials include the following:

- DOT regulations at http://www.myregs.com/dotrspa
- DOT Hazmat Law at http://www.hazmat.dot.gov/regs/notices/dotbill.pdf
- DOT main page at http://www.dot.gov

Hazardous Materials Advisory Council. The council is concerned with all aspects of hazardous materials transportation affecting shippers, all modes of transportation, and manufacturers of packaging. It also conducts training in the safe transportation of hazardous materials. See http://www.hmac.org.

Insurance Institute for Highway Safety. The institute is an independent, nonprofit, scientific, and educational organization dedicated to reducing losses resulting from crashes on the nation's highways. See http://www.iihs.org.

National LP-Gas Association. This association develops LP-gas standards and provides safety programs for the general public. See http://www.pgas.com.

National Safety Council (NSC). A nonprofit organization dedicated to accident prevention, the council has an extensive program on highway safety geared principally to the motoring public. NSC produces numerous publications on transportation and highway safety. More information is available at http://www.nsc.org.

National Tank Truck Carriers, Inc. (NTTC). NTTC helps members, who are operators of tank truck fleets, solve problems associated with safe handling of flammable liquids, gases, and chemicals. See http://www.tanktruck.org.

Truck Trailer Manufacturers Association. A trade association of manufacturers of truck trailers, it cooperates, through its various committees and representatives, with NFPA, other allied industry associations, and governmental agencies in matters affecting tank transport design and fabrication. See http://www.ttma.net.

Trailer and Truck Box Design and Construction Safeguards

Currently there are no FMVSS, NHTSA, or FMCSA standards for fire retardance of cargo trailers or bodies. In large truck bodies and in freight-carrying trailers, wood is used as flooring. It withstands torsional stresses, impacts, and abrasions encountered in this type of service, and replacement of worn or damaged sections is relatively economical. Wood provides safety benefits because blocking and bracing can be nailed in place to prevent shifting of cargo. It offers a high coefficient of friction for safe forklift operation and a slip-resistant footing for personnel who handle cargo.

Plywood is used for interior lining material in van-bodied trucks and trailers because it effectively protects other structural components from damage that may occur during loading, unloading, and transportation of freight. As with wood flooring, replacing damaged sections is relatively inexpensive.

Plywood flooring is used in buses for essentially the same reasons. Metal flooring would create "tin canning" under torsional stress and a resulting noise level unacceptable to passengers.

These uses of wood do not create any significant fire hazards. In the forms used, the wood is relatively difficult to ignite and burns slowly. Specific provisions of the Federal Motor Carrier Safety Regulations require that flooring be in good condition. The use of flooring permeated with oil or gasoline is prohibited.

In major incidents involving fire, wood can be a contributing factor, but usually only in incidents so severe that their outcomes would have been little affected if wood had not been present.

When the cargo must be covered during transportation on flatbed, open-top, and other types of nonenclosed vehicles, the use of tarpaulins is the only practicable means of providing needed protection. Such tarpaulins normally are not given flame-retardant treatment, but they pose little risk of fire.

Vehicle Fuel Tanks and Systems

The location, construction, and security of fuel tanks are important design features for fire safety in motor vehicles. Liquid fuel tanks for general passenger car use are generally of plastic or thin-gauge steel of various shapes and dimensions, dependent upon other body and chassis characteristics. The vast majority of U.S.-built cars, trucks, and buses have liquid fuel tanks located at the rear of the vehicle, frequently in such a position that they are not entirely enclosed in the body. The greatest risk of loss of life and property from fire in vehicles, therefore, occurs in fires following rear-end collisions.

The Federal Motor Carrier Safety Administration (FMCSA) has developed fuel tank regulations applicable to commercial vehicles operating in interstate or foreign commerce. These regulations closely parallel Underwriters Laboratories (UL) standards. In 1973, requirements that previously had been limited to gasoline tanks were extended to include tanks for diesel fuel. This action also required protection for diesel fuel crossover lines located below the bottom of a tank or sump. The DOT regulations include requirements for tank construction and installation and for adequate fillpipe closure. Tanks must pass drop, rupture, vent, and spillage tests. Required safety vent systems must limit pressure rise to 50 psig (345 kPa) in a specified fire test.

Tanks must be marked by a manufacturer's certificate to indicate that they meet DOT-FMCSA specifications for side-mounted or non-side-mounted tanks, as applicable.

Efforts have been made to gain DOT approval for plastic fuel tanks for truck service. Despite certain advantages their manufacturers claim, doubts about the safety of such tanks in commercial vehicle operations have not been satisfactorily resolved.

Vehicles using flammable compressed gas as a motor fuel must be equipped with fuel systems constructed and installed in accordance with applicable provisions of NFPA 58 or NFPA 52. Likewise appropriate LNG tanks are required.

Fuel systems must be maintained so they are free of leaks. Fuel tanks must be capped, and connections must be checked regularly. Metal fuel lines are subject to vibration-induced fatigue, and flexible lines may deteriorate with age. Chafing, cutting, or proximity to hot surfaces also can damage lines. In a gasoline system, carburetor flooding due to dirt in the float valve or electric fuel pumps that do not shut down may cause gasoline to overflow onto a hot surface and result in a fire.

These problems are somewhat less critical on diesel-powered vehicles because diesel fuel has a higher flashpoint. Diesel engines are designed to operate at higher temperatures to control exhaust emissions. This, in turn, led to higher fuel temperature in the return flow line, thus making the fuel more prone to ignition if the warmed, leaking fuel contacts a hot surface.

PREVENTING MOTOR VEHICLE FIRES

Fire prevention in motor vehicles requires the attention of everyone involved. Vehicle designers must be aware of fire hazards in their products. Sources of heat and ignition must be kept away from flammable materials as much as possible. Consideration should be given to the vulnerability of fuel system components, in particular to their basic integrity, their location away from the perimeter of the vehicle and from crash-collapsible and intrusive parts, and their location away from potentially hot exhaust and electrical components.

Examples of location hazards were found in 1971–1976 Ford Pintos and 1975–1976 Mercury Bobcats. These cars' fuel filler necks and tanks could separate in a rear-end collision, resulting in fire. Manufacturers recalled 1.4 million of these vehicles for retrofitting of longer fuel filler necks and for installation of protective shields on the front of fuel tanks. Improperly routed fuel lines to the carburetor have been the subject of recalls because of potential rupture and underhood fires.

Because electrical system failures can cause fires resulting in property damage, particular attention must be paid to routing of wiring, aging of insulation and components, and failure modes of components.

To minimize potential fuel leakage in any crash, extraneous plumbing and openings should be eliminated in fuel and hazardous liquid and gaseous cargo containers. Necessary plumbing should be designed so it is protected from potential crash damage.

In vehicle construction, care must be taken to ensure that fuel and electrical lines are correctly routed and connections secure. In addition, location of sharp or pointed components near fuel or hazardous cargo tanks should be avoided.

A major hazard during the vehicle repair process is the use of torches, usually in the repair of exhaust systems and crash damage. Some items used in vehicle repair are particularly flammable, such as paint, solvents, adhesives, and oily rags.

Care must be taken when maintaining and rebuilding damaged vehicles to ensure that their fuel and electrical systems are free of hazards not present in the original vehicle.

Vehicle Electrical Systems

Automotive lighting and accessory circuits are usually 6 or 12 V, but vehicle ignition systems have high voltage and low amperage. Automobile electrical system fire safety is largely a matter of proper installation, fusing, and maintenance. Important checkpoints include the location and protection afforded the battery; battery cable integrity and protection of exposed battery terminals; adequate flame-retardant insulation on all wiring; proper fusing of normal lighting and accessory circuits; proper support, location, and security of all wiring, with adequate protection by rubber insulating bushings where wiring passes through metal; and good ignition system maintenance.

Electrical fires can be fed by oily deposits in and around the engine or by combustible materials, such as interior fabric linings and upholstery. In collision or upset, electrical short circuits can occur and may ignite fuel vapors. It is desirable, particularly on buses and trucks, to provide an approved type of manual battery/generator disconnect switch, preferably one incorporating short circuit supervision. However, use of such devices on vehicles is rare.

Miscellaneous Vehicle Hazards

Proper exhaust system installation is important because the system's hot surfaces can ignite nearby combustible components. Hot carbon particles and hot gases discharged from the exhaust can ignite flammable liquids, grease, or similar exposed materials, such as insulation on electrical wiring.

Catalytic converters in exhaust systems can cause wildland fires, if automobiles are driven through dry grass or vegetation.

Overuse of vehicle brakes can result in sufficient overheating to cause severe smoldering and sometimes fire. Improper adjustment that prevents full release of a brake can lead to similar conditions. Overheated brake drums or rotors can cause ignition of fuel if spillage occurs onto the brakes during refueling.

The problem of overheating brakes increases with the vehicle's size and gross weight. On long downgrades, a driver must rely on the braking effect of the engine for primary control of the vehicle, limiting brake use to slowing for sharp turns or unanticipated, localized, hazardous conditions, and to stop. The engine's maximum braking effect is achieved only in the transmission lower gears. Particularly on trucks and buses, it is essential for the driver to get into a low gear at the top of the grade before the vehicle reaches a speed at which downshifting is no longer possible. Engine braking devices are used on diesel-powered trucks, especially in mountainous regions. Other types of electrically and hydraulically operated retarders are used in special situations.

If one tire of a dual-tire installation runs flat or is seriously underinflated, flexing may cause sufficient internal heat to build up to cause ignition. This possibility also exists if tires are seriously overloaded and may be exacerbated by sustained high-speed operation and high ambient temperature. Occasionally, fire results if dual tires are spaced so closely together that they rub or chafe against each other when the vehicle is in motion.

Provisions of the Federal Motor Carrier Safety Regulations for all heating systems used on vehicles in interstate commerce have been upgraded. Reducing such fires has also been aided by technological advances in heaters.

Fire Hazards of Special Vehicles

Certain types of special vehicles, such as farm tractors, motorcycles, all-terrain vehicles, and others, have special problems resulting from the close spacing of such components as the fuel tank and other parts of the fuel system, the engine, the ignition system and other electrical components, and the exhaust, coupled with minimal protective bodywork that increases the susceptibility of these fire-sensitive components to damage.

The need for care to avoid fuel spillage and sparks from static electricity is especially important when refueling in the field from portable containers.

Vapor recovery nozzles on gasoline pumps introduced a potential fire hazard in fueling motorcycles and other vehicles with small fuel tanks. The depth to which the nozzle must be inserted in order to activate vapor recovery control and permit fuel flow is so great that effective refueling cannot be accomplished in the normal manner. It has become necessary to use a device to bridge the fill-pipe opening. Otherwise, the operator must pull back the bellows with one hand and activate the nozzle trigger with the other to obtain fuel.

Use of Fire Extinguishers

Commercial vehicles operating in interstate commerce must be equipped with fire extinguishers to comply with Federal Motor Carrier Safety Regulations. These regulations provide two minimum levels of protection: a 5-B:C extinguisher (or two 4-B:C extinguishers) is required if the power unit is not transporting hazardous materials in sufficient quantity to require marking or placarding the vehicle, and a 10-B:C extinguisher is required on a power unit used for transporting hazardous materials.

Many states have similar requirements for commercial vehicles, through adoption of applicable provisions of federal regulations or their own regulations. Some state laws require additional or larger extinguishers on tank vehicles transporting flammable liquids or gases, combustible liquids, or Class A and/or Class B explosives.

There are no legal requirements for carrying fire extinguishers in private passenger cars, vans, or light trucks, although many people do keep them in vans and motor homes. As a minimum, the vehicle owner should consider buying a portable extinguisher that can deal with Class B (flammable liquids) and Class C (electrical) fires. Also on the market are extinguishers using multipurpose agents for use on Class A fires (ordinary combustibles), as well as Class B and C fires. Anyone equipping a vehicle with a fire extinguisher must understand that the best chance for its successful use lies in prompt action in the fire's early stages and proper use to avoid wasting the agent and exhausting the extinguisher's contents prematurely. NFPA 10, *Standard for Portable Fire Extinguishers,* gives additional information on ratings and use of fire extinguishers.

Other Fire Hazards

While the vehicle is operating, the driver should be alert for any indication of fire or a fire hazard, such as the smell of something hot, of unusual fumes, or of leaking fuel or lubricant. The driver should check for conditions that can create sufficient heat buildup to cause a fire, such as exhaust leaks and dragging brakes.

Carrying extra gasoline in a can is extremely dangerous because of the possible accumulation of fumes. The hazard increases if glass or plastic containers are used, because they're more likely to break and leak.

Smoking by a driver or passengers presents the potential for fire if sparks, hot ashes, or incompletely extinguished matches get into upholstery or other interior materials. Water or an agent suitable for Class A fires can extinguish such fires; the burn area then must be watched in case it continues to smolder and eventually rekindles.

In an accident, the engines and all electrical accessories of all involved vehicles should be turned off to minimize the danger of fire. At night, headlights can be left on to protect the scene, but persons in the vicinity should be alert for indication of overheated wiring or fire. Smoking and all use of open flames or lights must cease, particularly if leaking fuel is detected. If a travel trailer or motor home is involved, the probable presence of liquefied petroleum gas should be kept in mind, smoking should be prohibited, and open flames and lights should be kept well away from the scene.

When a vehicle fire occurs, the following basic steps should be taken, regardless of the type of vehicle involved:

1. Shut off the engine and all electrical systems that can be reached.
2. Get everyone out of the burning vehicle and well away from it, preferably uphill and upwind. The potential for fire is one justification for quickly moving injured persons from the scene of an accident.
3. Summon the fire department by the best available means.
4. Attempt to fight the fire only if it can be done without endangering anyone's personal safety.

Basic principles to be observed in attempting to fight a vehicle fire with a portable fire extinguisher are:

1. First, see item 4 above. The fire should be fought from the windward side so that wind, if any, will help carry the fire extinguishing agent toward the fire and help blow smoke and flame away from the person attempting to extinguish it.
2. The fire extinguisher should be aimed at the base of the flames.
3. If leaking flammable liquid is involved, work toward the source of the leak in putting out the flames. Ultimate control may depend on the ability to shut off leaking fuel at its source.
4. If flammable gas is burning, allow it to continue to burn until the source of any leak is controlled. Otherwise, extinguishing the fire may permit leaking gas to accumulate, with later fire or explosion likely. If flames impinge on a flammable gas container, the container should be kept cool to avoid a flame-induced weakening and possible rupture or a boiling liquid expanding vapor explosion (BLEVE). If fire-fighting hose streams are not available, RUN. Leave IMMEDIATELY.
5. If no extinguisher is available, throw sand or dirt on a fire to control flames.
6. If stopping to help at the scene of a vehicle fire, park uphill, preferably upwind, and at a safe distance from the burning vehicle.
7. After a fire has been extinguished, do not operate the vehicle until all burned parts are cool and the cause of the fire has been corrected.
8. During an electrical fire, turn off the ignition switch and lights to try to cut off the flow of current and permit faster extinguishment. If tools are available and it can be done safely, disconnect the battery.
9. In fighting an underhood fire, use great care in opening the hood to avoid injury in case of a sudden flareup.
10. Inspect and recharge all extinguishers without delay.

The following special considerations apply to fires and potential hazards involving commercial vehicles:

1. Any hazardous situation should be evaluated to avoid endangering lives and wasting extinguishing agent.
2. If a vehicular combination unit is involved in a fire, the power unit should be unhooked and moved a safe distance away from the vehicle if it can be done safely.
3. Drivers must be alert for the hard pulling characteristics that may indicate dragging brakes and must readjust brakes before a fire develops.
4. A driver must examine each tire on a motor vehicle at the beginning of each trip and each time the vehicle is parked. FMCSA regulations require this practice for a vehicle placarded for transportation of hazardous materials.
5. Drivers should check rearview mirrors frequently for signs of smoke and must stop and investigate any smoke detected.
6. A hot or underinflated tire should be moved well away from the vehicle. As an alternative, the driver should remain with the vehicle until the tire is cool to the touch and then make repairs. If a vehicle is left with a hot tire, the tire may burst into flames, destroying the vehicle and its load. With proper tire-changing equipment and a pair of heavy leather gloves, a driver can safely remove a hot tire that has not burst into flames.
7. Because a tire fire results from internal heat buildup, portable extinguishers normally cannot do more than control open flames. The cooling effect of large quantities of water is required for extinguishment.
8. If fire is suspected inside a closed van body—usually indicated by smoke seeping out around the doors—the doors should be left closed until fire department assistance is at hand. Should the doors be opened, oxygen reaching the fire may cause a sudden flareup. As long as the doors are closed, the fire can only smolder from lack of oxygen.

In the interest of preventing cargo fires, motor carriers generally prohibit smoking while vehicles are being loaded or unloaded, so sparks or hot ashes do not lodge in the cargo and burst into flame later.

Federal Motor Carrier Safety Regulations prohibit smoking during refueling; while loading, unloading, or transporting explosives, flammable liquids, gases, or solids, or oxidizing materials requiring marking or placarding of the vehicle; and while driving an empty tank vehicle that last contained a flammable liquid or gas and that was required to be marked or placarded.

CARGO TANKS (TANK TRUCKS)

Cargo tanks and portable tanks are large containers for hauling liquids and gases in bulk. Cargo tanks are sometimes called "tank motor vehicles" or "tank trucks." Any person offering a hazardous material in a container for transportation must determine that the container used is authorized for the commodity. Specifications for cargo tanks, portable tanks, and all other hazardous materials packaging other than rail tank cars are in 49 CFR, Part 178. Authorized packaging is prescribed in 49 CFR, Part 173, the shipper regulations for the particular material, as listed in 49 CFR 172.101. If a carrier supplies a container, such as a cargo tank, the shipper still must determine that the tank supplied is a proper container for the material being offered. The shipper must either examine the manufacturer's specification marking on the tank or obtain papers from the carrier certifying that the tank is proper for the material, per 49 CFR, Part 173.22.

Cargo tanks are the most common transport vehicles used to move combustible, flammable, and corrosive liquids, as well as compressed gases, both flammable and nonflammable. Hazardous materials in powder or granular form are transported in hopper-type, dump-bodied vehicles. When these hazardous materials are transported in bulk containers, such as cargo tanks, and an accident occurs, the disaster potential is substantial.

To minimize risks involved in transporting hazardous materials and to reduce hazards should an accident occur, the federal government specifies requirements for the manufacture, operation, maintenance, inspection, testing, and repair of cargo tanks.

DOT's hazardous materials regulations apply to interstate and intrastate commerce and are enforced by both federal and state authorities. DOT phased in new cargo tank regulations designed to reduce spillage and to ensure that tanks are properly constructed, maintained in safe condition, and properly repaired. The new cargo tank regulations are designated in 49 CFR, Part 180.

Leakage is likely to occur in both contact and noncontact accidents, leading to high cost in terms of personal injury and property damage. The major causes of unintentional release of hazardous materials are poor maintenance and deviation from tank specifications.

Potential hazards to fire fighters dealing with cargo tanks transporting hazardous materials are as follows:

1. Multipurpose tanks holding improper commodities for the specific container
2. Multicompartment containers hauling materials in more than one hazard class (corrosive/flammable/poison/oxidizer)
3. Defective or missing safety controls
4. Release of large quantities of hazardous materials
5. Increase of potential fires—extra equipment required to fight fires and control spills
6. Potential for a boiling liquid expanding vapor explosion (BLEVE)
7. Incorrect or missing placarding and identification markings on exterior of cargo tank
8. Missing, incomplete, or incorrect shipping papers

Persons receiving a report of an actual or potential highway transportation hazardous materials emergency should obtain as much of the following information as possible:

1. Location of the emergency
2. Type of commercial vehicle(s) involved, such as cargo tank, flatbed, van, and so on
3. Class(es) of hazardous material(s) as indicated by placards, if visible, including the four-digit identification number, if visible
4. Proper shipping name(s), hazardous class(es), and identification number(s) of hazardous materials, if shipping papers are available
5. Nature of the emergency—Is it a fire? Is there leakage? Are persons affected or injured by hazardous materials?
6. Name and address of trucking company
7. Other vehicles and/or property involved
8. Weather conditions and wind direction
9. Type of area

Upon arriving at the scene, emergency responders should take time to assess the situation and make every effort to ascertain what type(s) of hazardous materials and packaging is involved. The scene should be approached from upwind. Responders must avoid contact with spilled or leaking materials that may penetrate protective or other clothing, resulting in death or injury.

Figures 21.2.1 through 21.2.6 display tank construction, denoting areas where leakage is most likely. All these diagrams

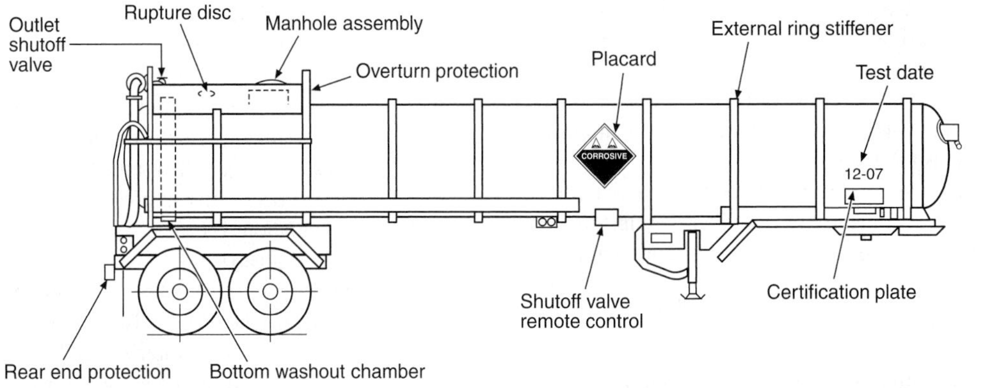

FIGURE 21.2.1 Corrosive Materials Cargo Tanks Equipped with an Internal Shutoff Valve for Unloading from the Bottom

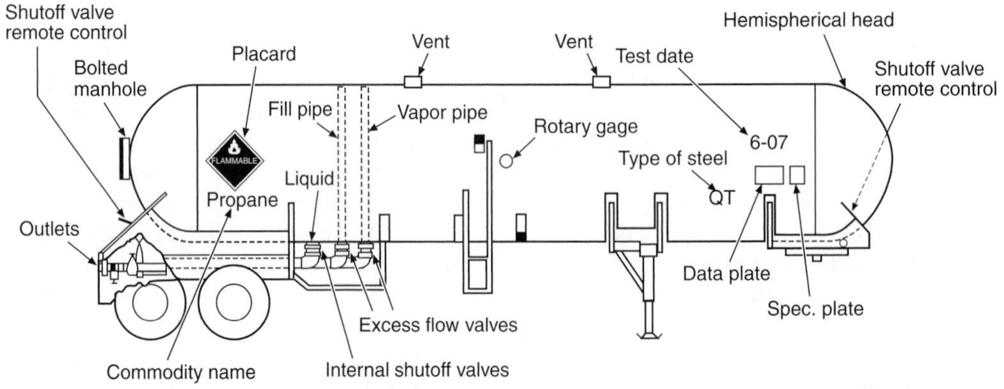

FIGURE 21.2.2 Compressed Gas Cargo Tanks Equipped with Internal Shutoff Valves at Liquid and Vapor Discharge Openings

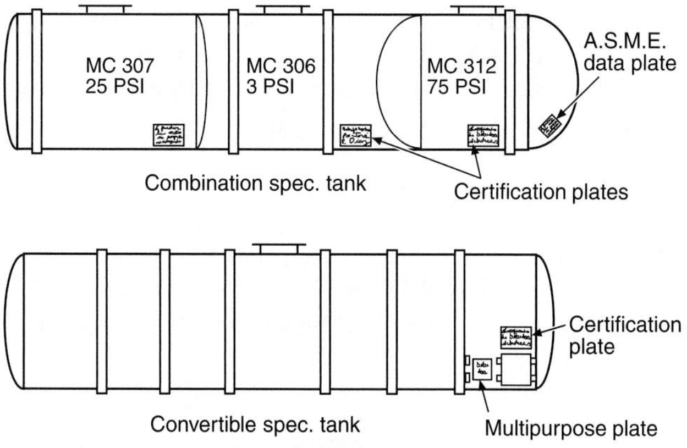

FIGURE 21.2.3 Profiles of Combination (Multiple-Compartment) and Convertible (Single-Compartment) Cargo Tanks

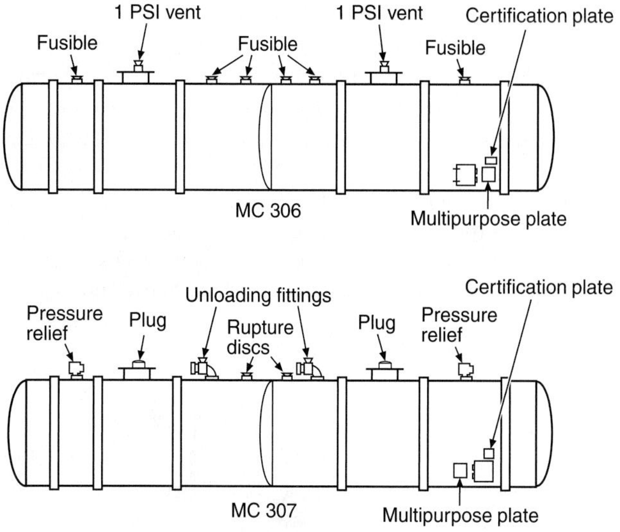

FIGURE 21.2.4 Profiles of Two-Compartment Convertible Cargo Tanks

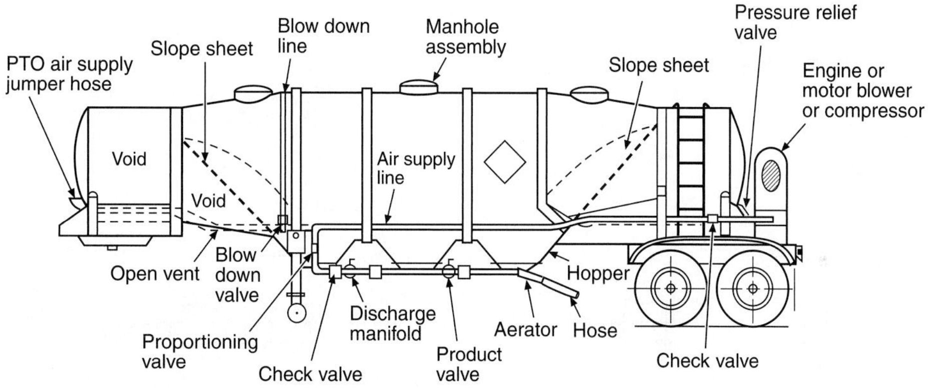

FIGURE 21.2.5 Profile of a Dry Bulk Cargo Tank Used to Transport Cargo Such as Ammonium Nitrate, an Oxidizer, or Corrosive Solids

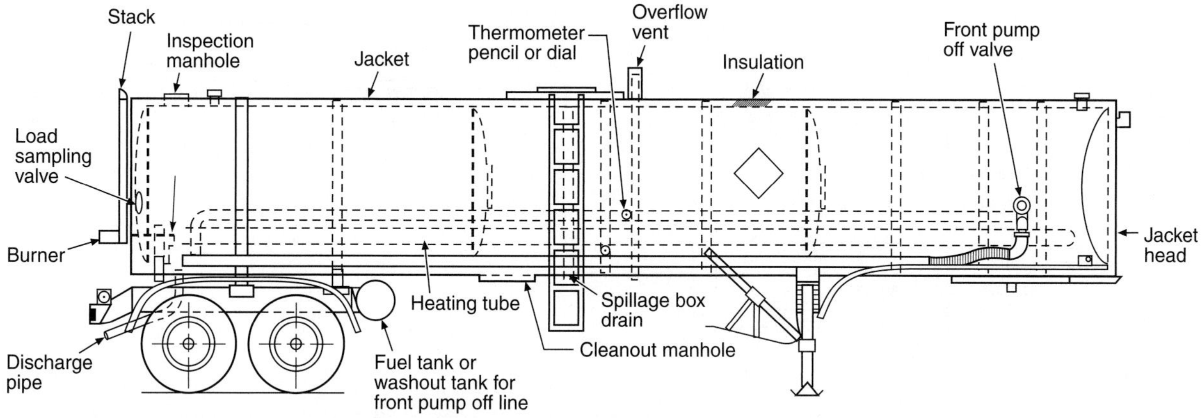

FIGURE 21.2.6 A Nonspecification Asphalt Cargo Tank

should be considered as guidelines rather than constants. Figures 21.2.7 and 21.2.8 show common tank shapes and internal/external inspection items. Emergency response personnel must be aware that many variations of road trailers, not illustrated here, are used for shipping chemical products. Suggested guides are for the most hazardous products that these trailer types may transport. Recommended guides should be considered as a last resort if the product cannot be identified by any other means.

Many tank vehicles contain hazardous materials of one or more types. These units, which include farm "nurse" tanks, tank trucks, tank trailers, and railroad tank cars, must be treated with equal respect. Each emergency must be sized up quickly and individually, taking into consideration the safety of every person at the scene.

SUMMARY

This chapter has described the magnitude of the problem of commercial motor vehicle fires in the United States and has outlined the several types of regulations and standards directed

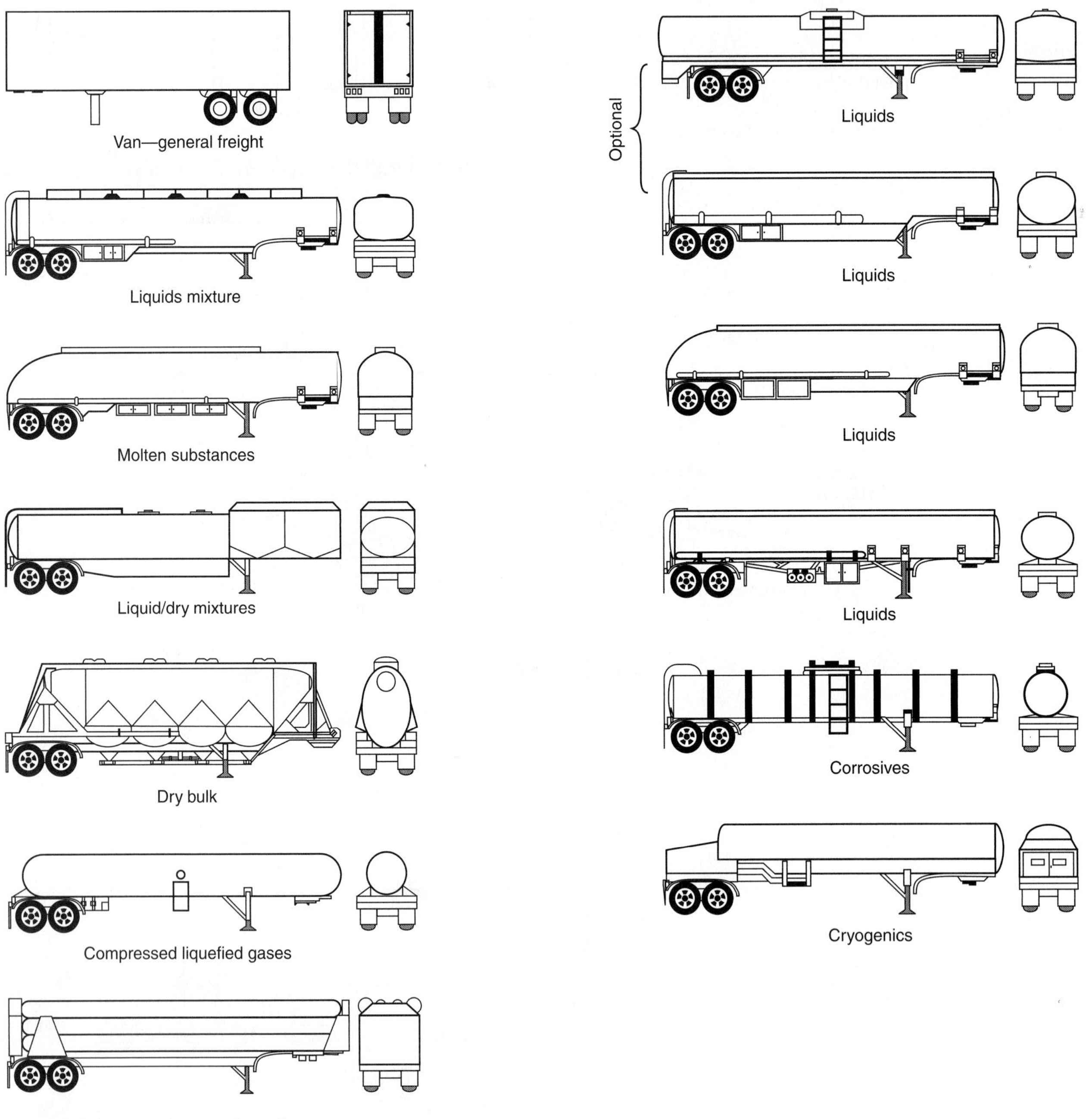

FIGURE 21.2.7 General Shapes of Road Trailers

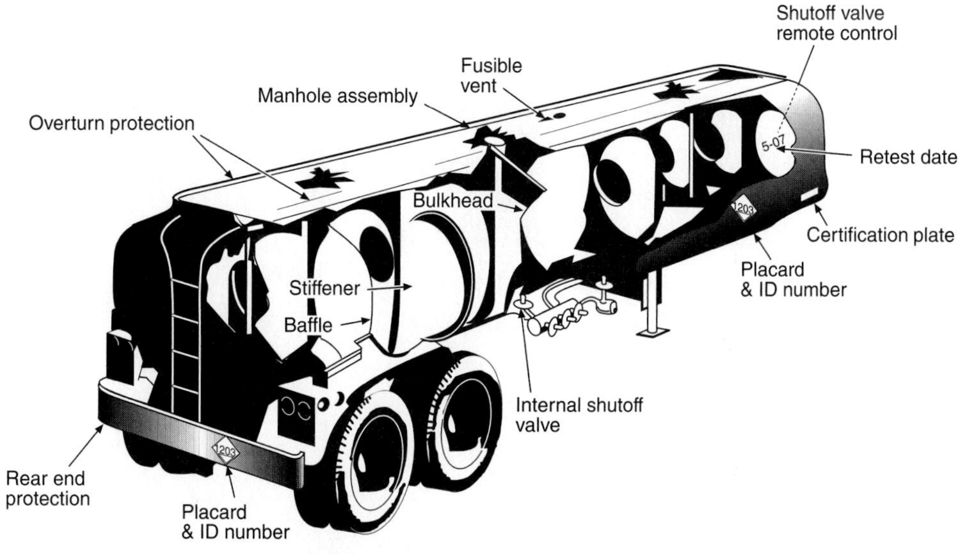

FIGURE 21.2.8 Cargo Tank Inspection Guide (MC 306)

at commercial motor vehicle fire safety. Organizations with an interest in highway safety have been identified. Hazards and safeguards have been outlined.

BIBLIOGRAPHY

References Cited

1. Ahrens, M., "U.S. Vehicle Fire Trends and Patterns," Fire Analysis and Research Division, National Fire Protection Association, Quincy, MA, Aug. 2001.
2. *Statistical Abstract of the United States 2000,* U.S. Census Bureau, Washington, DC, Dec. 2000.

NFPA Codes, Standards, and Recommended Practices

Reference to the following NFPA codes, standards, and recommended practices will provide further information on fire safety in commercial vehicles discussed in this chapter. (See the latest version of The NFPA Catalog *for availability of current editions of the following documents.)*

NFPA 10, *Standard for Portable Fire Extinguishers*
NFPA 52, *Vehicular Fuel Systems Code*
NFPA 58, *Liquefied Petroleum Gas Code*
NFPA 385, *Standard for Tank Vehicles for Flammable and Combustible Liquids*
NFPA 407, *Standard for Aircraft Fuel Servicing*
NFPA 414, *Standard for Aircraft Rescue and Fire-Fighting Vehicles*
NFPA 495, *Explosive Materials Code*
NFPA 498, *Standard for Safe Havens and Interchange Lots for Vehicles Transporting Explosives*
NFPA 1192, *Standard on Recreational Vehicles*
NFPA 1901, *Standard for Automotive Fire Apparatus*

Chapter 3

Automotive and Marine Service Station Operations

Carl H. Rivkin

Chapter Contents

Key Terms

automotive service station, flammable liquid, fuel dispensing system, fuel tank, hazardous material, marine service station, refueling, repair garage, service station

Automotive and marine service stations, whose operations include both refueling and repairs, present a fire risk because of the storage of flammable and combustible liquids and the transfer and use of these liquids. Many of these transfer operations involve the general public, which increases the risk associated with transfer. Unlike an industrial facility, in which personnel involved in flammable liquid* transfer operations can be restricted to those trained in the hazards of the materials and the operations, anyone can use the services of a public automotive or marine service station.

Also, the transfer operations at a service station occur more frequently than at an industrial facility. Service stations that include repair facilities also use flammable liquids in the repair and servicing of vehicles and these operations present additional risks. This chapter covers the hazards associated with flammable liquids at automotive and marine service stations.

For related topics, see Section 6, Chapter 12, "Flammable and Combustible Liquids"; Section 7, Chapter 2, "Storage of Flammable and Combustible Liquids"; Section 21, Chapter 4, "Vehicle Fueling Using Gaseous Fuels"; and Section 21, Chapter 5, "Fuel Cell Vehicles."

BASICS

Public Service Station Fire Data

NFPA analyzes fire data and prepares reports on topics of interest, including fires at public service stations.[1] Fire data from private service stations are not readily available. Data from public service stations indicate where the greatest fire risk at a service station lies. Over the period 1994 to 1998, 62 percent of fires at public service stations were categorized as vehicle fires. This does not mean that the fire involved the vehicle only. Several of these fires spread beyond the area where the vehicle was located to parts of the facility. Code requirements address vehicle activity in several areas and because vehicle fires account for such a large percentage of the fires documented, these requirements need to be examined.

Another factor potentially influencing the increased percentage of fires at service stations involving vehicles over the 1994 to 1998 time period is the change in the types of products sold at service stations. As of the year 2000, there were approximately 210,000 retail outlets selling motor fuel. Many of these motor fuel retail outlets also have repair facilities, but the trend in motor fuel retail facilities has been toward the sale of other merchandise as well as fuel and repairs. Many service stations are paired with convenience stores or food retail businesses. These new arrangements are bringing increased vehicle traffic through the service station area. Also, vehicles might

*Although "flammable liquids" is referred to throughout this chapter, the term is meant to encompass both flammable and combustible liquids.

Carl H. Rivkin, P.E., is principal chemical engineer on the NFPA engineering staff and the NFPA staff liaison to the Technical Committee on Automotive and Marine Service Stations. He has more than 20 years of engineering experience with hazardous materials safety.

be parked at the service station. These changes could be causing an increased number of vehicle fires at service stations.

Basic Service Station Refueling Components

Figures 21.3.1, 21.3.2, and 21.3.3 provide an overview of the basic refueling components at a service station. Figure 21.3.1 shows double-walled tanks and the associated safety and filling appurtenances for these tanks. The use of the safety devices illustrated in this figure is a code requirement, including pressure relief devices, cathodic protection, and the concrete foundation. The concrete foundation prevents damage to the tank from the supports settling or other movement of the supporting soil. The cathodic protection prevents the tank metal from corroding.

Figure 21.3.2 shows (a) standard installation of aboveground horizontal tank and (b) the basic components of a standard fuel dispenser. Figure 21.3.3 is an illustration of (a) a dispenser with (b) a below-grade cutaway showing the lines that feed the dispenser. Also shown are the breakaway valve at the dispensing nozzle and the shear valve on the fuel-feed line. Both of these valves limit the release of fuel in the event of a break in the fuel piping or hoses.

Properties of Hazardous Materials at Service Stations

Because flammable liquids have varying volatility, they will both vaporize at different rates and migrate at different rates to potential ignition sources. Table 21.3.1 lists flammable liquids commonly found at service stations and repair garages. The data provide indicators about how the material behaves when it is accidentally released and exposed to ignition sources. The information on each material includes the flashpoint, the class under NFPA 30, *Flammable and Combustible Liquids Code* (which is based on the flashpoint), the boiling point, and the minimum ignition temperature in air.

The *flashpoint* is the minimum temperature of a liquid at which sufficient vapor is given off to form an ignitable mixture with the air, near the surface of the liquid or within the vessel used, as determined by the appropriate test procedure and apparatus. NFPA 30 gives additional information about appropriate procedures for determining the flashpoint of a material.

The table data indicate why gasoline is more hazardous than other materials commonly used at service stations and repair garages. It has a flashpoint of –50°F (–40°C), which is 150°F (83°C) lower than that of diesel fuel #1. The flashpoint for gasoline is so low that only under severely cold conditions would it not have the potential to form an ignitable mixture.

DESIGN AND CONSTRUCTION

Design and construction safety requirements for the different refueling and repair components found at service stations are based on NFPA 30A, *Code for Motor Fuel Dispensing Facilities and Repair Garages.*

General Building Requirements

Code Requirements. Building construction requirements apply to general categories of structures in which flammable

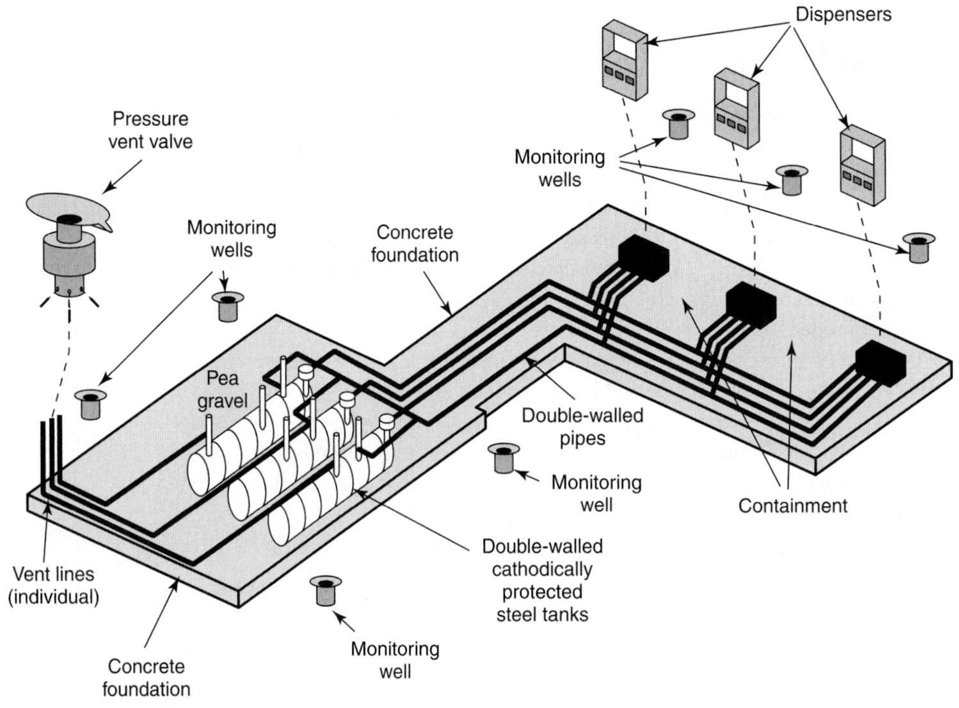

FIGURE 21.3.1 Fuel Dispensing System Assembly (Source: Based on information from Florida Department of Environmental Protection)

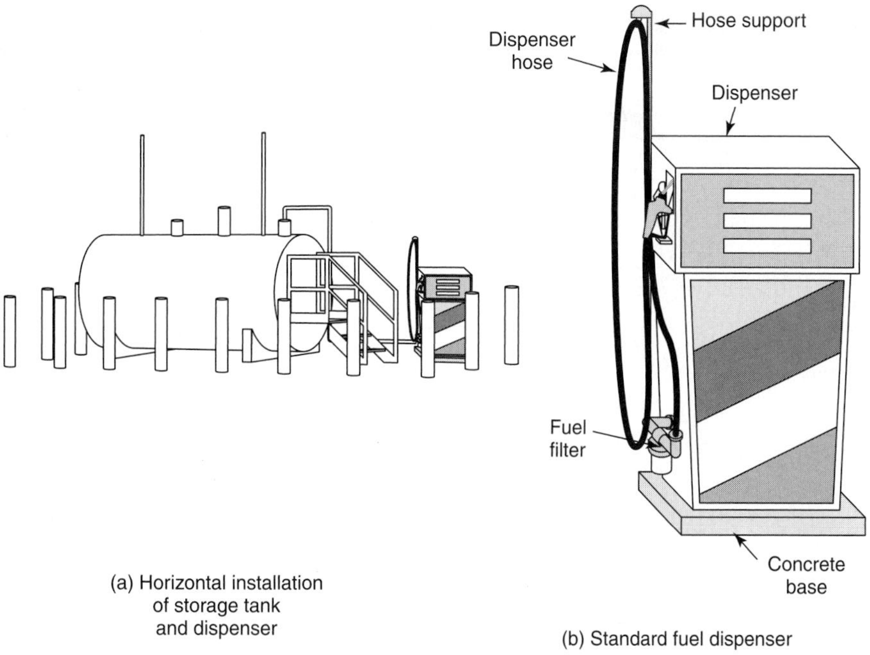

FIGURE 21.3.2 (a) Aboveground Fuel Dispensing System with Dispenser and (b) Standard Fuel Dispenser (Source: Based on information from Florida Department of Environmental Protection)

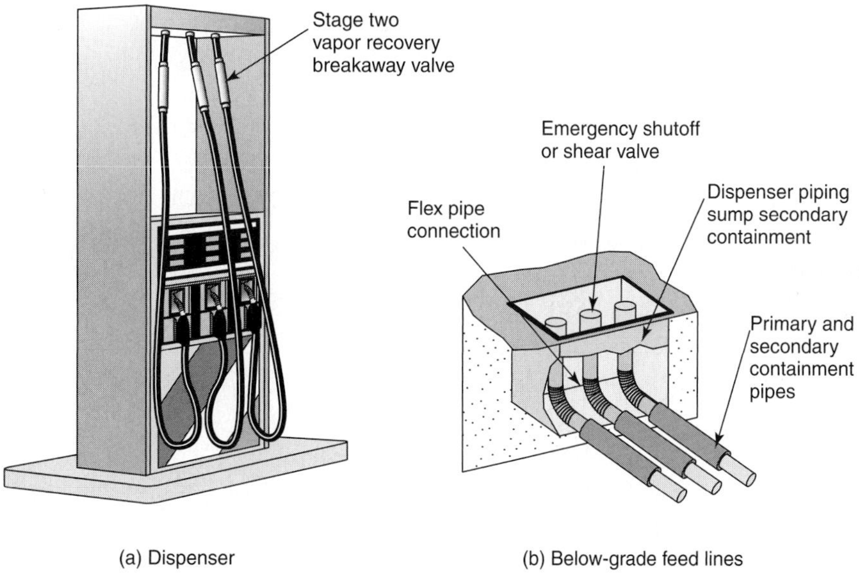

FIGURE 21.3.3 Dispenser Assembly with (a) Dispenser and (b) Below-Grade Feed Lines (Source: Based on information from Florida Department of Environmental Protection)

liquids present a hazard. The two types of structures of concern are buildings housing fuel dispensing operations and repair garages.

Structures that house refueling or repair operations must not have obstructions in egresses that restrict building evacuation. Specific requirements for egress can be found in NFPA *101*®, *Life Safety Code*®, in the chapter on industrial occupancies. Refueling facilities and repair garages are classified as special-purpose industrial occupancies. Such special-purpose industrial occupancies conduct ordinary and low-hazard industrial

TABLE 21.3.1 Properties of Flammable and Combustible Liquids Commonly Found in Service Stations

Liquid	*Flashpoint*	*NFPA 30 Class*	*Boiling Point*	*Minimum Ignition Temperature in Air*
Antifreeze	230°F (110°C)	IIIB	300°F (149°C)	—
Brake fluid	300°F (149°C)	IIIB	540°F (282°C)	—
Chassis grease	400°F (204°C)	IIIB	>800°F (>427°C)	>800°F (>427°C)
Crankcase drainings	—	IIIB	—	—
Diesel fuel no. 1	100°F (38°C)	II	—	—
Diesel fuel no. 2	125°F (52°C)	II	—	—
Diesel fuel no. 4	130°F (54°C)	II	—	—
Gasoline	–40 to –50°F (–40 to –46°C)	IB	100 to 400°F (38 to 204°C)	~825°F (~441°C)
Gear lubricant	395°F (202°C)	IIIB	>800°F (>427°C)	>800°F (>427°C)
Kerosene (fuel oil no. 1)	100°F (38°C)	II	303 to 574°F (151 to 301°C)	440°F (227°C)
Lithium-moly grease	380°F (193°C)	IIIB	>800°F (>427°C)	>900°F (>482°C)
Lubricating oils	300 to 450°F (149 to 232°C)	IIIB	—	—
Power steering fluid	350°F (177°C)	IIIB	>550°F (>288°C)	—
Dexron II transmission fluid	395°F (202°C)	IIIB	>800°F (>427°C)	>800°F (>427°C)
Type F transmission fluid	380°F (193°C)	IIIB	>800°F (>427°C)	>800°F (>427°C)
White grease	465°F (241°C)	IIIB	>800°F (>427°C)	>800°F (>427°C)
Windshield washer fluid (methanol/water mixtures)				
100% methanol	54°F (12°C)	IB	148°F (64°C)	725°F (385°C)
50% methanol	80°F (27°C)	IB	—	—
20% methanol	118°F (48°C)	II	—	—
5% methanol	206°F (97°C)	IIIB	—	—

operations in buildings designed for, and suitable only for, particular types of operations. Such occupancies are characterized by a relatively low density of employee population, with much of the area occupied by machinery or equipment.

Spill Control. Spill control must be provided to prevent fuels from flowing either through the floor or into other parts of the building. The drainage system must have an oil trap or separator if it connects to public sewers or waterways.

Fuel Dispensing Buildings

Hazards. Most public service stations do not have indoor fuel dispensing and, therefore, do not have fuel dispensing buildings. Occasionally parking garages include fuel dispensing. Buildings housing fuel dispensing areas present special hazards, and requirements have been developed to address these hazards. Fuel dispensing is more likely to produce a material release than are other components of the refueling system.

Construction, Design, and Location. Dispensing areas within the building must be separated from other portions of the building by 2-hour fire-resistant structures. Openings into the dispensing space must be designed to prevent a fire from moving to other parts of the building. This containment is accomplished by using fire doors and fire dampers.

Fuel dispensing areas must be located at street level, not more than 50 ft (15.2 m) from the building entrance or exit. This requirement prevents the release of material at a location that would be difficult for emergency responders to access. The dispensing areas are also limited to the size required to service four vehicles or fewer.

Safeguards and Controls. The dispensing area must have a dedicated mechanical exhaust system that is interlocked with the dispensing system. If the system were not dedicated, there would be the potential to transfer fuel vapors and vehicle exhaust to other parts of the facility. The system has to provide airflow across all portions of the floor of the fuel dispensing area to prevent the potential buildup of ignitable vapors. Serious accidents have occurred in which vapors released in a part of a facility free of ignition sources migrated into locations where ignition sources were present through pathways that had not been considered before the accident. For specific information on designing ventilation systems see NFPA 91, *Standard for Exhaust Systems for Air Conveying of Vapors, Gases, Mists, and Noncombustible Particulate Solids,* and the American Conference of Industrial Hygienists, *Industrial Ventilation: A Manual of Recommended Practice.*[2]

Repair Garages

Hazards. Repair garages present different hazards from those found in refueling operations because of the use of pits or below-grade areas required to work on vehicles. These areas normally have special ventilation requirements and fixed fire protection to allow personnel to function in the workspace.

Construction, Design, and Location. Pits and below-grade work areas must be constructed of noncombustible materials and be provided with ventilation and means of egress previously described. These areas, although not viewed as confined spaces, can present oxygen-deficient atmosphere risks under certain conditions such as restricted airflow or displacement of air. This is another reason why egress and ventilation are important.

Safeguards and Controls. Fixed fire protection is required for larger repair garages if any of the following situations exist:

- The garage is two or more stories in height, including basements, and any one floor exceeds 10,000 ft^2 (930 m^2).
- The garage is one story and exceeds 15,000 ft^2 (1400 m^2) in floor area.
- The garage is in the basement of a building.

The larger repair garages will likely handle more material, conduct more operations, and therefore present a greater fire risk.

Heating, ventilating, and air-conditioning (HVAC) for repair garages must be independent and designed to provide good airflow and mixing in the ventilated space. Air from below-grade areas should not be recirculated into the building HVAC system.

Heat-producing appliances present an ignition source hazard and must be carefully controlled in repair garages. In several incidents, heat-producing appliances were the ignition source the ignitable vapor eventually located. Cleaning floors with gasoline is a common unsafe practice that can lead to fires and explosions. Heat-producing appliances have to be of types approved for use in a repair garage. Solid fuel burning devices and space heaters are typically not considered an approved type of appliance. Heat-producing appliances must be separate from areas dispensing or transferring Class I liquids, such as gasoline. This separation can be accomplished by placing the device in another room or at least 8 ft (2.4 m) above the floor. At this height, the device should be above any flammable vapors.

Storage

General. All flammable liquids must be stored in either an approved closed container or a tank. In service stations, containers cannot exceed 60 gal (227 L) in volume. Tanks can be located underground, aboveground, or in vaults. A vault is a protective enclosure that does not allow the tanks to contact the ground even if installed below grade. Underground tanks present less fire hazard but they have a greater potential to impact the environment. Environmental regulations place more stringent requirements on underground tanks than aboveground tanks. Vaulted tanks present a potential solution to these conflicting concerns of fire safety and environmental impacts by allowing an above-grade installation with additional fire protection.

All tanks must be constructed to consensus-based construction standards. Underwriters Laboratories is an example of an organization that promulgates these types of tank construction standards.

Underground Tanks. Underground tanks require vent pipes of sufficient diameter to prevent blowback of vapor or liquid at the fill opening while the tanks are being filled. The vent pipes also should not be obstructed, which would effectively reduce their diameter. Undersized vent piping will impede the refilling process because it is more difficult to displace the air in the tank. The discharge point for vent pipes should be at least 12 ft (3.7 m) above ground level for tanks storing Class I liquids (gasoline) and higher than expected snow level for tanks storing Class II liquids (diesel fuel). The discharge point must also be located away from building openings and power ventilation air intakes. Allowing flammable materials to infiltrate a structure could possibly result in material in the flammable range being exposed to a source of ignition. The vent pipe must also be higher than the fill pipe to prevent spills during tank fill operations.

Underground tanks must be provided with external corrosion protection, either in the form of a cathodic protection system or corrosion-resistant materials. The type of protection employed must be determined on a location-by-location basis.

Underground tanks must be installed so that they are no less than 1 ft (0.3 m) from any wall of a basement or pit and 3 ft (0.91 m) from any property line that can be built on. The tanks must be set on a firm foundation and surrounded by noncorrosive material such as sand or gravel. They also must be buried sufficiently deep or be protected on the surface so that they are not subject to vehicle damage.

Aboveground Tanks. Aboveground tanks must be separated from the property line, important buildings, other fuel dispensing devices, public ways, and other tanks. These distances vary based on the size of the tank and the level of fire protection the tanks are constructed to meet. Aboveground tanks must be provided with spill protection. NFPA 30 provides options for spill control.

All aboveground tanks must be provided with an alarm that sounds when the level inside reaches 90 percent of tank capacity. All tanks must be provided with physical protection to prevent unauthorized access and to protect from vehicle impact. However, it is difficult to prevent all vehicle impact accidents because of the unpredictability of driving behavior and the tremendous force involved in high-speed impact. As an example of this problem, see the following case.

CASE STUDY: South Carolina. In South Carolina in 1991, a driver was killed when his pickup truck careened off the road, striking the piping for two 4000 gal (15,142 L) aboveground fuel tanks located at a convenience store. The collision broke the piping and resulted in the release of gasoline that quickly found an ignition source.

Vaulted Tanks. Gasoline tanks installed in vaults must have ventilation systems and vapor and liquid detection systems. The vapor detection system should sound an alarm when the concentration of vapor in the vault equals or exceeds 25 percent of the lower flammable limit (LFL) for the material.

Piping

Piping is one of the most vulnerable components in a fuel system because vehicle impacts can easily rupture pipes, corrosion can cause leaking, and stresses can cause cracking. Piping must be protected from mechanical damage. Piping that runs through buildings must be enclosed in fire-resistant material. All piping must be identified by color code or some other readily identifiable system to indicate the material contained in the pipe. There are significant differences in the physical characteristics of gasoline and diesel fuel, and confusing the two could result in damage to vehicles.

Fuel Dispensing Systems

The requirements for fuel dispensing systems cover the following seven areas:

1. Dispensing devices
2. Remote or submersible pumps (i.e., pumps not located at the device)
3. Hoses
4. Nozzles
5. Emergency electrical disconnects
6. Vapor recovery systems
7. Hazardous location electrical equipment

The requirements are structured to prevent the accidental release of material either from liquid or vapor leaks in the dispensing system or from overfilling of the container into which the system is feeding liquid.

General Requirements. Two general requirements apply to all fuel dispensing systems. The first is that all portions of the vehicle being refueled must be on the dispensing facility property. The reason for this is straightforward. The vehicle should not be in a position in which it could be struck by other vehicles while refueling. The second general requirement is that fuel not be dispensed by applying pressure to the container in which the fuel is stored but instead by means of pumps. The reason for this requirement is that containers are not constructed to allow external pressure to be used as a means for moving fuel out of the container.

Dispensing Devices. The requirements for dispensing devices address several points in the dispensing process which have the potential for the release of fuel. The first requirement is that the dispensing device not operate when the dispenser nozzle is in the holding bracket or routine rest position. This requirement prevents the release of material when no person is present to stop it.

The dispensing devices must be protected from physical damage that could cause the release of material. This protection should take the form of bolting the dispensing devices to a concrete island situated to keep vehicles not being refueled from passing through the refueling area. Because there are vehicles moving through a refueling area in close proximity to pedestrians (people refueling their vehicles), a major safety concern is vehicles striking pedestrians.

The dispensing devices must incorporate an emergency shutoff in the line that supplies fuel to the dispensing device. This emergency shutoff must be designed to be activated by severe impact or fire exposure. The purpose of the shutoff is to prevent fuel from flowing to the dispensing device in the event of an accident. When installed, the emergency shutoff device must be tested at least annually after the initial test.

CASE STUDY: Saint John, New Brunswick. In January 1974, a fire killed five people at a service station in Saint John, New Brunswick, Canada. A large amount of fuel was released because the emergency shutoff valve failed to operate when the dispenser was knocked over by a vehicle. The service station was located on the roof of a tire warehouse (the structure was located on a slope so that one side of the service station was on ground level) and the fuel released migrated into the warehouse where it was ignited and exploded. Because the explosion took place in the enclosed warehouse space, there was tremendous damage in addition to the loss of life.

Remote or Submersible Pumps. If fuel is transferred to the dispenser by a pump located outside of the dispenser, such as a submersible turbine pump located in the fuel storage tank, then the pump is subject to additional requirements. The pump must have a device that would detect whether there is a leak in the portion of the dispensing system upstream from the pump discharge. Pumps also must be located at least 5 ft (1.5 m) from building entrances and 10 ft (3 m) from property lines. These separation distances would reduce the risk of fuel being released into the building.

Hoses. Hoses must be listed by an independent testing organization for their intended use. The hose length should be no more than 18 ft (5.5 m). Although this is based on "weights and measures" laws, it also serves to reduce the chance of the hose being damaged or rupturing. If the hose is carrying gasoline, it should be constructed with a breakaway device that will retain the gasoline in the hose. This feature would prevent someone from releasing gasoline by accidentally driving away from a refueling area while the hose is still inserted in the vehicle fill pipe.

Nozzles. Hose nozzles for dispensing gasoline must have an automatic-closing valve to prevent the flow of gasoline when the valve-opening device is not depressed. This device combined with the hose breakaway device should prevent the release of anything but small amounts of gasoline if the person operating the dispenser either drives away from a refueling area with the hose nozzle still inserted in the vehicle fill pipe or neglects to shut off the flow valve for other reasons. Figure 21.3.4 illustrates a standard nozzle, pressure vent valves, and vent pipes.

Emergency Electrical Disconnects. Remotely located emergency electrical disconnects are a critical component in the fuel safety system for two reasons: (1) they will remove an ignition source from areas where there is the potential of an ignitable vapor mixture, and (2) they can stop the flow of liquid if other safety devices do not function, thereby preventing the release of large amounts of liquid.

The emergency disconnect must be located between 20 and 100 ft (6.1 and 30.5 m) from the fuel dispensing device. This range would create sufficient separation distance from the fuel dispensing device for the disconnect to be safely activated without being so far away that it could not be readily activated in an emergency situation. The emergency disconnect device must be interconnected so that if there are multiple emergency disconnects, the activation of any one disconnect device will

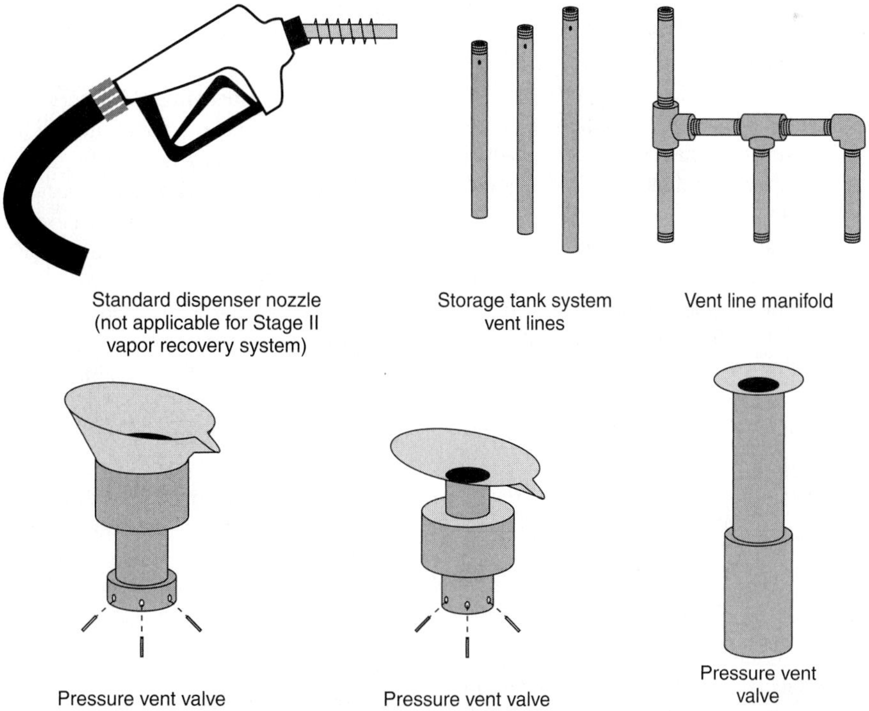

FIGURE 21.3.4 Dispenser Hose Nozzle, Pressure Vent Valves, and Vent Pipes (Source: Based on information from Florida Department of Environmental Protection)

cut off all power in hazardous locations surrounding the fuel dispensing devices.

Vapor Recovery Systems. Environmental regulations require vapor recovery systems in many locations. These devices must be listed for application as vapor recovery devices and must be designed to prevent the release of vapor when they are attached to the dispenser and not being used.

Hazardous Location Electrical Equipment. For a height 18 in. (0.5 m) above grade in a 20 ft (6.1 m) radius from refueling areas, special electrical equipment is required. The following case is an example of how electrical equipment not classified for use in a potentially dangerous area can be an ignition source.

CASE STUDY: Gadsden, Alabama. An explosion occurred at a gasoline station outside of Gadsden, Alabama, in August 1976. In this incident, a tank truck was filling aboveground storage tanks at the station using an electric pump that was missing a cover on the junction box. The lack of a cover allowed the pump to become an ignition source for fugitive vapor emissions lost during the transfer operation. These vapors were ignited, the fire spread to the truck, which exploded, and three responding fire fighters were killed in the explosion.

OPERATIONS SAFETY REQUIREMENTS

Many accidents are the result of improper use of properly designed equipment; therefore, it is important to understand how a construction safety feature is utilized through operational requirements. For example, the requirement that delivery vehicles must be separated from aboveground tanks is an operational requirement that directly connects to construction requirements. If the separation distance from property line and other exposures is met, the separation distance for the refueling vehicle should be less difficult to comply with.

Operations requirements can be divided into those requirements that apply to fueling operations and those that apply to repair operations. Fueling operations include both the filling of tanks at refilling facilities and the refueling of vehicles at these facilities. Because the refueling of vehicles is done so much more frequently than the refilling of storage tanks, these transfers account for a large percentage of the incidents at service stations. However, NFPA incident data have several accounts of serious accidents taking place during tank filling and servicing operations. The following case is an example of this type of incident.

CASE STUDY: Portland, Maine. A gas tank explosion occurred at an abandoned service station in Portland, Maine, in May 1986. This incident resulted from the ignition of vapors that were being removed with a vacuum pump from abandoned tanks at the service station. The vapors were being discharged at street level without any ventilation on a day when there was insufficient natural ventilation to dissipate the gasoline vapor withdrawn from the underground tanks. A vehicle that was allowed in the area where there was the potential for ignitable vapors provided the ignition source. The result was one fatality and three other people injured.

Filling and Fueling Operations

Mass Balance. Inventory records, which must be kept on a daily basis, indicate whether material is being lost from the system. The relatively simple process of performing a mass balance can reveal a small leak before it becomes a large leak and prevent the loss of significant amounts of material and subsequent safety and environmental problems. A mass balance is a comparison between the material going into a system and the material discharged from the system. The difference between these two numbers is the amount lost (leaked) from the system.

Tank Filling. For tank filling operations, 25 ft (7.6 m) must separate the delivery vehicle from any aboveground tank. All parts of the delivery vehicle must be on the premises when the delivery is made. This requirement prevents refilling from taking place at locations where the tank truck could block traffic in the public access road to the facility. Fill covers must identify the tanks that they service (Figure 21.3.5).

Portable Container Dispensing. Dispensing into portable containers is allowed, provided that the containers are approved and labeled and the dispensing is done manually. The container must be on the ground when being filled—not in or on the vehicle. If the container is not secured in the vehicle, a spill could result that would be very difficult to clean.

Motor Fuel Dispensing. Motor fuel–dispensing facilities can be divided into attended and unattended operations and many facilities offer both. Attended fueling operations theoretically have an increased level of safety because a human observer can detect problems that would not be observed at an unattended facility. Because of this difference, unattended facilities must have automatic-closing hose nozzles and a telephone or other device to notify the fire department.

Another potential problem in unattended facilities is that persons performing the refueling might reenter their vehicle during refueling and then remove the nozzle from the vehicle after they have built up a static charge from moving across the seat of the vehicle. Persons refueling at an unattended facility are required to stay outside of their vehicle throughout the duration of the refueling operation to prevent this static buildup, which could potentially ignite residual vapors released after the nozzle is removed from the vehicle fill pipe.

Repair Areas

Requirements for repair areas or facilities fall into the following four general categories:

1. Hot work
2. Spray painting and undercoating

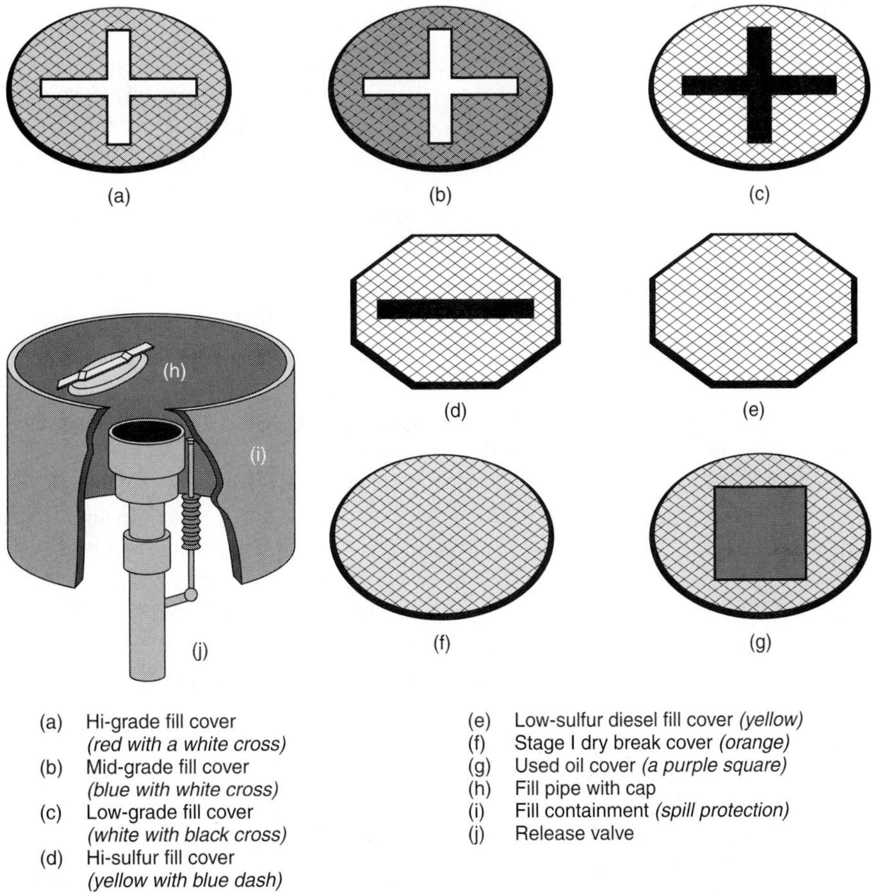

FIGURE 21.3.5 Fill Area Assembly with Color-Coded Covers (Source: Based on information from Florida Department of Environmental Protection)

3. Parts cleaning
4. Housekeeping

Hot Work. Hot work is defined in NFPA 51B, *Standard for Fire Prevention During Welding, Cutting, and Other Hot Work,* as "any work involving burning, welding, or similar operations that is capable of igniting fires or explosions." Hot work operations must be performed in specially designed areas, because they present excellent sources of ignition. Performing these operations in a defined, controlled area is the best way to reduce the risk that these operations will become an ignition source for a flammable vapor release.

Spray Painting and Undercoating. Spray painting operations are restricted to work on only small parts of a vehicle and these operations must be located at least 20 ft (6.1 m) from any potential ignition source.

Parts Cleaning. Parts cleaning operations can present a significant risk because they may involve relatively large amounts of heated solvent. To reduce this risk, nonflammable cleaning solvents should be used whenever possible. If flammable solvents must be used, they should be used only under conditions in which the opportunities for creating a flammable atmosphere are also controlled or eliminated. This means that ignition sources should be kept away from the areas where flammable atmospheres could be created. If the solvent is heated, it should have a shutoff device that prevents the solution from getting close to the temperature at which a flammable atmosphere would be created.

Housekeeping. Housekeeping requirements are extremely important for fire prevention. Mixing incompatible materials, such as oxidizing substances and flammable liquids, is one undesired outcome of poor housekeeping. There are some general organizational and cleaning procedures that should be followed to achieve good housekeeping.

The work area should be kept clean and free from obstructions. Materials should be stored in assigned areas and not allowed to be left in work areas as part of ongoing work projects. Combustible rubbish should be placed in covered metal receptacles until removed for disposal. These materials should not be allowed to accumulate. Personnel should know if combustible rubbish is in a waste receptacle to prevent adding an incompatible material to the receptacle.

Most important, a daily inspection should be conducted of the work area to identify and eliminate hazards. This daily inspection should give facility managers timely information about the storage of materials and the condition of equipment so that they can respond to a hazard before it causes a fire.

FIRE SUPPRESSION

Fixed Fire Protection

Fixed fire protection is often recommended for refueling areas at service stations. It is required at larger repair garages (as defined earlier) because these are facilities where people work and in which operations involving the transfer of flammable liquids occur routinely. These transfer operations are often not as well controlled as in vehicle refueling areas but instead can vary depending on the type of repair and specific vehicle being worked on.

Fire Extinguishers

Each motor fuel–dispensing facility should have one or more listed fire extinguishers that have a minimum capability of 40-B:C. A B:C fire extinguisher is one suitable for use on fires involving flammable liquids, combustible liquids, petroleum greases, tars, oils, oil-based paints, solvents, lacquers, and alcohols (Class B fires) or fires involving energized electrical equipment in which the electrical nonconductivity of the extinguishing media is of importance (Class C fires). The 40 number indicates the relative strength of the extinguisher—the greater the number, the greater the extinguishing power. The extinguishers should be located within 100 ft (30 m) of each pump, storage tank fill-pipe opening, and lubrication or service room.

Materials that obstruct access to fire-fighting equipment or important piping system control valves must not be placed on a pier. Where the pier is accessible to vehicular traffic, there should be an unobstructed roadway to the shore end of the wharf. This roadway is required for access by fire-fighting apparatus.

SPECIAL REQUIREMENTS FOR MARINE REFUELING FACILITIES

Many of the requirements for automotive refueling also apply to marine refueling, but because marine refueling is done on piers, special requirements apply. At marine refueling facilities, a fuel line is often run from a storage tank located on land to a dispensing device located on the pier, wharf, or floating dock. This run of pipe increases the risk for an accidental release of material. The additional safety requirements for marine refueling facilities focus on preventing a release of material from the fuel supply line that runs between the onshore storage tank and the dispenser.

Storage

Storage tanks for marine refueling have to comply with the same requirements that motor vehicle refueling must meet, with a few differences. Pumps that are not a part of the dispensing device must be placed on shore. The tank must have a device that would prevent the gravity flow of liquid if the supply hose were broken.

Piping Systems

Piping systems must be protected against movement that might occur because the dispenser is located on a structure in or at the water. The piping also must be protected against physical damage that could result from its being exposed. A valve is required in each pipeline at or near the approach to the pier and at the shore end of each marine refueling facility to shut off the liquid supply from shore.

Fuel Dispensing System

Dispensing hose must be listed and hose length should be kept to less than 18 ft (5.5 m), if possible. The dispensing device should be designed so that it does not prevent people from leaving the pier in an emergency situation.

Boats should not be berthed (parked) at a refueling area or attached to boats that are being refueled. Boats have several ignition sources and these must be kept away from the refueling area. Unlike automotive refueling, there should always be an attendant on duty when marine refueling is done because of the less routine nature of marine refueling. Fueling should not be undertaken at night except under well-lighted conditions.

Sources of Ignition

Electrical arcs and open flames are the most likely ignition sources in the marine refueling environment. Each dispensing unit must have a clearly identified electrical disconnect to shut off power to all pumps and motors in the dispensing system. All wiring should be located on the side of the structure opposite the piping to reduce the opportunity for the ignition of fugitive emissions from the piping.

During refueling, the fuel nozzle must be electrically bonded by contact to the vessel fill pipe throughout the refueling operation. This contact should reduce the opportunity for potential difference between the nozzle and another surface that would receive the charge and that could create an electrical arc.

Pipelines on piers must be bonded and grounded. In bonding, the pipeline is connected to an electrically conductive material. In grounding, this material is connected to a ground or a conductor that discharges to ground.

Smoking materials, including matches and lighters, should not be used within 20 ft (6 m) of areas used for fueling. The area should be marked to warn people not to use these materials.

Because people are less likely to shut off the motor of a boat during refueling, it is important that the attendant ensure that all motors are turned off during refueling. Hot engines have the potential to act as ignition sources.

Containers and Movable Tanks

Movable refueling tanks and portable containers present a greater fire risk than fixed installations because of the decreased control associated with mobile equipment. Because of this increased risk, the conditions under which movable tanks can be used are limited.

With the approval of the authority having jurisdiction, movable tanks can be used for dispensing fuel at locations inaccessible to the public. This additional level of approval should reduce the chance of releasing material during transfer operations.

Gasoline should not be put into a portable container unless the container is approved for the storage of gasoline. Only containers less than 12 gal (45.4 L) should be filled on vessels.

Marine Facilities

Marine motor fuel–dispensing facilities should have one or more listed fire extinguishers having a minimum classification of 40-B:C. An extinguisher should be within 100 ft (30 m) of each pump, each dispensing device, and each pier-mounted liquid storage tank.

Piers that extend more than 500 ft (152 m) in travel distance from shore should have a Class III standpipe. A standpipe system is an arrangement of piping, valves, hose connections, and allied equipment installed in a building or structure, with the hose connections located so that water can be discharged in streams or spray patterns through the attached hose and nozzles. This is accomplished by connections to municipal water supply systems or by pumps, elevated gravity tanks, and other equipment necessary to provide an adequate supply of water to the hose connections. A Class III standpipe system has a minimum flow rate for the hydraulically most remote standpipe of 500 gpm (1893 L/min) and a minimum flow rate for additional standpipes of 250 gpm (946 L/min). The total flow rate should not exceed 1250 gpm (4731 L/min).

SERVICE STATION MAINTENANCE AND INSPECTION

The checklist in Figure 21.3.6, which describes the different components of a service station and the applicable fire safety requirements, is designed to assist in a safety inspection of the facility. This checklist is not comprehensive and is intended only to make people aware of the areas of concern. State and federal regulations and codes and standards contain detailed requirements that address these various areas. The checklist parallels the material discussed in this chapter.

SUMMARY

Because the operations of automotive and marine service stations include both refueling and repair and, therefore, involve the storage, transfer, and use of flammable liquids, they present a distinct fire risk. The risk associated with the transfer of

	Dispensing System	*Tank*	*Repair Work Area*
Are hoses listed for use?			
Are pumps and nozzles listed for use?			
Are emergency shutoff devices installed correctly?			
Are ignition sources controlled?			
Are emergency shutoff switches present and properly located?			
Are required operating procedures and warnings posted?			
Is electrically safe equipment being used in areas classified for type of electrical equipment?			
Is physical protection in place for pumps and piping?			
Do tanks have adequate spill control?			
Are proper separation distances being followed for operations involving ignition sources and Class I liquids?			
Is housekeeping adequate?			
Is cleanup routinely performed after operations?			

(continued)

FIGURE 21.3.6 Service Station Inspection Checklist

	Dispensing System	*Tank*	*Repair Work Area*
Are flammable liquids stored properly?			
Are other hazardous materials stored in proximity to flammable liquids?			
Are required communication devices working properly?			
Is required egress obstructed?			
Are required fire extinguishers present and properly located?			
For larger repair garages, is sprinkler protection installed?			
Is piping properly color coded?			
Are below-grade work areas properly ventilated?			
Are fuel dispensing devices in buildings properly located?			
Is any flammable liquid waste properly stored and labeled?			
Are work areas free of combustible waste material?			
Are containers listed for use and properly labeled?			

FIGURE 21.3.6 Continued

flammable liquids is also increased because this operation involves the general public, who are not trained in the hazards of the materials.

This chapter covered construction, design, and location requirements for dispensing areas and repair facilities, including, for example, oil traps or separators for spill control; dedicated mechanical exhaust systems; container and tank storage requirements; as well as special requirements for piping, dispensing devices, hoses, and other system components. This chapter also covered operations safety requirements that include such items as performing a mass balance to detect leaks; dispensing into approved and labeled containers; and following specific requirements when performing hot work, spray finishing, and parts cleaning.

Fixed fire suppression is recommended for refueling areas at service stations and is required at larger repair garages. Each motor fuel–dispensing facility, including marine facilities, should have listed fire extinguishers on hand. Additional safety requirements for marine refueling facilities focus on preventing a release of material from the fuel supply line, controlling sources of ignition, and limiting conditions under which movable tanks can be used.

BIBLIOGRAPHY

References Cited

1. Ahrens, M., "Service Station Fires," *Trends, Causes, and Published Incidents On: Public Service Station Fires, Private Service Station Fires, Marine Service Station Fires, Motor Vehicle and Repair and Paint Shops,* Fire Analysis and Research Division, National Fire Protection Association, Quincy, MA, 2002.
2. *Industrial Ventilation: A Manual of Recommended Practice,* 23rd ed., American Conference of Governmental Industrial Hygienists, Cincinnati, OH, 1998.

NFPA Codes, Standards, and Recommended Practices

Reference to the following NFPA codes, standards, and recommended practices will provide further information on liquid fueling and repair operations at automotive and marine service stations discussed in this chapter. (See the latest version of The NFPA Catalog *for availability of current editions of the following documents.)*

NFPA 30, *Flammable and Combustible Liquids Code*
NFPA 30A, *Code for Motor Fuel Dispensing Facilities and Repair Garages*
NFPA 91, *Standard for Exhaust Systems for Air Conveying of Vapors, Gases, Mists, and Noncombustible Particulate Solids*
NFPA *101*®, *Life Safety Code*®

Chapter 4

Vehicle Fueling Using Gaseous Fuels

Carl H. Rivkin

The use of alternative fuels for vehicles is becoming more predominant. Forces driving their use are increasing air pollution and the United States' dependence on foreign oil. Federal regulations such as the Energy Policy Act (EPACT) of 1992 and the Clean Air Act Amendments (CAAA) of 1990 were specifically designed to increase the driving public's use of alternative-fueled vehicles to benefit the environment and to increase the use of natural resources available in North America. From 1992 to 2000, there was a 6.9 percent average annual percent increase in alternative fuel vehicles in use in the United States. As of 2000, they accounted for 0.2 percent of all registered motor vehicles in the United States.[1] This chapter discusses several areas, including properties and hazards associated with different alternative fuels, vehicle fueling stations, vehicle component designs and operation, emergency response to alternative fuel incidents, and federal regulations that may impact alternative fuels users.

For related topics, see the following chapters in Section 21: Chapter 1, "Passenger Vehicle Fires"; Chapter 2, "Fire Safety in Commercial Vehicles"; Chapter 4, "Vehicle Fueling Using Gaseous Fuels"; and Chapter 5, "Fuel Cell Vehicles."

Chapter Contents

Key Terms

alternative fuel, automotive exhaust, boiling liquid expanding vapor explosion (BLEVE), Clean Air Act, compressed natural gas (CNG), compressed natural gas (CNG) vehicle, fuel cell powered vehicle, liquefied natural gas (LNG), liquefied natural gas (LNG) vehicle, liquefied petroleum gas (LP-gas), liquefied petroleum gas (LP-gas) vehicle, odorization, particulate matter emissions, vehicle fueling station

INTRODUCTION TO THE USE OF ALTERNATIVE FUELS

Alternative Fuels Defined

A variety of alternative fuels are currently used in the United States. However, the review of alternative fuels in this chapter is limited to compressed natural gas (CNG), liquefied natural gas (LNG), and liquefied petroleum gas (LP-gas), specifically propane. The scope is limited to these three gaseous fuels because the hazards of alternative fuels, like flammable liquids (alcohols and reformulated gasoline), are better known and generally accepted. Hydrogen is the least used of these three fuels but hydrogen may become a more important alternative fuel as hydrogen vehicle applications and technology continue to develop. Gaseous fuels have recently gained popularity and more information is needed on their use as motor vehicle fuel.

Additionally, the three main alternative fuels are used by over 85 percent of the light alternative fuel vehicles and by over 95 percent of the heavy alternative fuel vehicles. Over 95 percent of the alternative fuel refueling sites are for CNG, LNG, or LP-gas[2] (Tables 21.4.1 through 21.4.13).

The Clean Air Act Amendments (CAAA) define alternative fuels as methanol, ethanol, and other alcohols; reformulated gasoline; reformulated diesel (for trucks only); natural gas; propane; hydrogen; or electricity. The Energy Policy Act (EPACT) includes all fuels listed under CAAA except for reformulated gasoline and diesel. EPACT also defines other alternative fuels, that is, fuels derived from biomass, liquid fuels derived from coal, and alcohol blended with other fuels containing at least 85 percent alcohol by volume.[3]

Carl H. Rivkin, P.E., is a principal chemical engineer in NFPA's Fire Protection Applications and Chemical Engineering Division. He is NFPA's staff liaison to the Technical Committee on Vehicular Alternative Fuel Systems.

TABLE 21.4.1 Estimated Number of Alternative-Fueled Vehicles in Use in the United States, by Fuel, 1995–2004

Fuel	*1995*	*1996*	*1997*	*1998*	*1999*	*2000*	*2001*	*2002*	(Projected) *2003*	(Projected) *2004*	*Average Annual Growth Rate (Percentage)*
Liquefied petroleum gases (LP-gas)	172,806	175,585	175,679	177,183	178,610	181,994	185,053	187,680	190,438	194,389	1.3
Compressed natural gas (CNG)	50,218	60,144	68,571	78,782	91,267	100,750	111,851	120,839	132,988	143,742	12.4
Liquefied natural gas (LNG)	603	663	813	1,172	1,681	2,090	2,576	2,708	3,030	3,134	20.1
Methanol, 85 percent (M85)[a]	18,319	20,265	21,040	19,648	18,964	10,426	7,827	5,873	4,917	4,592	–14.3
Methanol, neat (M100)	386	172	172	200	198	0	0	0	0	0	0.0
Ethanol, 85 percent (E85)[a,b]	1,527	4,536	9,130	12,788	24,604	87,570	100,303	120,951	133,776	146,195	78.8
Ethanol, 95 percent (E95)[a]	136	361	347	14	14	4	0	0	0	0	0.0
Electricity[c]	2,860	3,280	4,453	5,243	6,964	11,830	17,847	33,047	45,656	55,852	39.1
Non-LP-gas subtotal	74,049	89,421	104,526	117,847	143,692	212,670	240,404	283,418	320,367	353,515	19.0
Total	246,855	265,006	280,205	295,030	322,302	394,664	425,457	471,098	510,805	547,904	9.3

Note: Estimates for 2003 are based on plans or projections. Estimates for historical years may be revised in future reports if new information becomes available.

[a]The remaining portion of 85 percent methanol and both ethanol fuels is gasoline.

[b]In 1997, some vehicle manufacturers began including E85-fueling capability in certain model lines of vehicles. For 2002, the EIA estimated that the number of E85 vehicles that are capable of operating on E85, gasoline, or both, is about 4.1 million. Many of these alternative-fueled vehicles (AFVs) are sold and used as traditional gasoline-powered vehicles. In this table, AFVs in use include only those E85 vehicles believed to be intended for use as AFVs. These are primarily fleet-operated vehicles.

[c]Excludes gasoline-electric hybrids.

Sources: 1995: Science Applications International Corporation, "Alternative Transportation Fuels and Vehicles Data Development," unpublished final report prepared for the Energy Information Administration (McLean, VA, July 1996) and U.S. Department of Energy, Office of Energy Efficiency and Renewable Energy. 1996–2004: Energy Information Administration, Office of Coal, Nuclear, Electric, and Alternate Fuels. Beginning in 2000, federal data were derived from the DOE/GSA Federal Automotive Statistical Tool (FAST).

Alternative Fuel Users

Many entities such as private, state, federal, and local government fleets and the general public use alternative fuels to power their vehicles. Fleets using alternative fuels can be small or large and are typically located predominantly in urban areas.

The Clean Fleets Program established by CAAA states that by 1998, serious, severe, and extreme ozone nonattainment areas must purchase alternative fuel vehicles. This applies to fleets with 10 or more vehicles capable of being centrally refueled and located in an area with a population of 250,000 or more. The law excludes emergency, farm, construction, rental, demonstration, and privately garaged vehicles.[3]

EPACT, which took effect in 1992, mandates the purchase of alternative fuel vehicles, with the intent of reducing the United States' dependence on oil imports. Federal and state fleets, as well as private-sector companies that produce alternative fuels, are required to purchase alternative fuel vehicles as a percent of their annual vehicle acquisitions. This can be a phased schedule for fleets of 50 or more vehicles, with at least 20 that can be centrally refueled, and located in an area with a population of 250,000 or greater. The law can extend to include municipal and private fleet owners if the U.S. Environmental Protection Agency (EPA) determines that EPACT's goals cannot be met.

IMPACT OF CLEAN AIR ACT AMENDMENTS OF 1990 ON ALTERNATIVE FUEL USE

Alternative fuel use has increased since the EPA established maximum concentration levels called national ambient air quality standards (NAAQs) for certain pollutants in the ambient air. The standards targeted the following pollutants:

- Automotive exhaust pollutants such as volatile organic compounds (VOCs) that lead to the formation of ozone
- Nitrous oxides (NO_x)
- Carbon monoxide (CO)

TABLE 21.4.2 Estimated Number of Alternative-Fueled Vehicles in Use in the United States, by Fuel and Weight Category, 2001–2003

Fuel	Light Duty	Medium Duty	Heavy Duty	Total
	2001			
Liquefied petroleum gases (LP-gas)	124,790	53,634	6,629	185,053
Compressed natural gas (CNG)	84,077	15,041	12,733	111,851
Liquefied natural gas (LNG)	381	0	2,195	2,576
Methanol, 85 percent (M85)[a]	7,819	0	8	7,827
Methanol, neat (M100)	0	0	0	0
Ethanol, 85 percent (E85)[a,b]	100,287	15	1	100,303
Ethanol, 95 percent (E95)[a]	0	0	0	0
Electricity[c]	17,056	445	346	17,847
Non-LP-gas subtotal	209,620	15,501	15,283	240,404
Total	334,410	69,135	21,912	425,457
	2002			
Liquefied petroleum gases (LP-gas)	124,877	55,671	7,132	187,680
Compressed natural gas (CNG)	87,340	18,449	15,050	120,839
Liquefied natural gas (LNG)	452	0	2,256	2,708
Methanol, 85 percent (M85)[a]	5,865	0	8	5,873
Methanol, neat (M100)	0	0	0	0
Ethanol, 85 percent (E85)[a,b]	120,809	140	2	120,951
Ethanol, 95 percent (E95)[a]	0	0	0	0
Electricity[c]	31,926	671	450	33,047
Non-LP-gas subtotal	246,392	19,260	17,766	283,418
Total	371,269	74,931	24,898	471,098
	2003			
Liquefied petroleum gases (LP-gas)	125,110	57,873	7,455	190,438
Compressed natural gas (CNG)	91,231	24,525	17,232	132,988
Liquefied natural gas (LNG)	463	0	2,567	3,030
Methanol, 85 percent (M85)[a]	4,911	0	6	4,917
Methanol, neat (M100)	0	0	0	0
Ethanol, 85 percent (E85)[a,b]	133,634	140	2	133,776
Ethanol, 95 percent (E95)[a]	0	0	0	0
Electricity[c]	44,334	674	648	45,656
Non-LP-gas subtotal	274,573	25,339	20,455	320,367
Total	399,683	83,212	27,910	510,805

Note: Light duty includes vehicles less than or equal to 8500 gross vehicle weight rating (GVWR); medium duty includes vehicles 8501 to 26,000 GVWR; heavy duty includes vehicles 26,001 GVWR and over. Estimates for 2003 are based on plans or projections. Estimates for historical years may be revised in future reports if new information becomes available.

[a]The remaining portion of 85 percent methanol and both ethanol fuels is gasoline.

[b]In 1997, some vehicle manufacturers began including E85-fueling capability in certain model lines of vehicles. For 2002, the EIA estimated that the number of E85 vehicles that are capable of operating on E85, gasoline, or both, is about 4.1 million. Many of these alternative fuel vehicles (AFVs) are sold and used as traditional gasoline-powered vehicles. In this table, AFVs in use include only those E85 vehicles believed to be intended for use as AFVs. These are primarily fleet-operated vehicles.

[c]Excludes gasoline-electric hybrids.

Source: Energy Information Administration, Office of Coal, Nuclear, Electric, and Alternate Fuels and the DOE/GSA Federal Automotive Statistical Tool (FAST).

Other pollutants exhausted from diesel fuel in trucks and buses include sulfur dioxide (SO_2) and particulate matter (PM_{10}, which stands for particulate matter 10 microns or less in diameter, and $PM_{2.5}$, which stands for particulate matter 2.5 microns or less in diameter). The phase out of leaded gasoline is controlling lead, the sixth criteria pollutant. However, there are still some lead nonattainment areas in the western United States. *Criteria pollutants* are those for which EPA has

TABLE 21.4.3 Estimated Number of Alternative-Fueled Vehicles in Use in the United States, by Fuel and Census Region, 2001–2003

Fuel	Northeast	South	Midwest	West	Total
			2001		
Liquefied petroleum gases (LP-gas)	9,613	88,314	33,949	53,177	185,053
Compressed natural gas (CNG)	20,809	35,644	12,593	42,805	111,851
Liquefied natural gas (LNG)	0	834	0	1,742	2,576
Methanol, 85 percent (M85)[a]	315	379	331	6,802	7,827
Methanol, neat (M100)	0	0	0	0	0
Ethanol, 85 percent (E85)[a,b]	13,018	39,190	21,732	26,363	100,303
Ethanol, 95 percent (E95)[a]	0	0	0	0	0
Electricity[c]	5,505	3,996	1,187	7,159	17,847
Total	49,260	168,357	69,792	138,048	425,457
			2002		
Liquefied petroleum gases (LP-gas)	9,670	90,577	33,023	54,410	187,680
Compressed natural gas (CNG)	22,346	38,180	13,681	46,633	120,839
Liquefied natural gas (LNG)	0	895	0	1,813	2,708
Methanol, 85 percent (M85)[a]	237	284	249	5,103	5,873
Methanol, neat (M100)	0	0	0	0	0
Ethanol, 85 percent (E85)[a,b]	14,485	46,023	33,662	26,781	120,951
Ethanol, 95 percent (E95)[a]	0	0	0	0	0
Electricity[c]	10,178	7,395	2,121	13,353	33,047
Total	56,916	183,354	82,736	148,092	471,098
			2003		
Liquefied petroleum gases (LP-gas)	9,935	90,375	35,642	54,486	190,438
Compressed natural gas (CNG)	24,339	41,701	15,289	51,659	132,988
Liquefied natural gas (LNG)	0	986	0	2,044	3,030
Methanol, 85 percent (M85)[a]	198	239	209	4,271	4,917
Methanol, neat (M100)	0	0	0	0	0
Ethanol, 85 percent (E85)[a,b]	16,018	50,899	37,236	29,623	133,776
Ethanol, 95 percent (E95)[a]	0	0	0	0	0
Electricity[c]	13,955	10,196	2,957	18,549	45,657
Total	64,445	194,395	91,333	160,632	510,805

Note: Estimates for 2003 are based on plans or projections. Estimates for historical years may be revised in future reports if new information becomes available.

[a]The remaining portion of 85 percent methanol and both ethanol fuels is gasoline.

[b]In 1997, some vehicle manufacturers began including E85-fueling capability in certain model lines of vehicles. For 2002, the EIA estimated that the number of E85 vehicles that are capable of operating on E85, gasoline, or both, is about 4.1 million. Many of these alternative fuel vehicles (AFVs) are sold and used as traditional gasoline-powered vehicles. In this table, AFVs in use include only those E85 vehicles believed to be intended for use as AFVs. These are primarily fleet-operated vehicles.

[c]Excludes gasoline-electric hybrids.

Source: Energy Information Administration, Office of Coal, Nuclear, Electric, and Alternate Fuels and the DOE/GSA Federal Automotive Statistical Tool (FAST).

set national ambient air quality standards. States and other municipalities must measure ambient air according to an EPA-approved plan to determine whether they meet these ambient standards. Both mobile and stationary sources generate all of these pollutants. Aboveground storage tanks, industrial processes, and diesel-fueled generator sets introduce pollutants into the atmosphere.

A county or area can be designated a nonattainment area when concentrations of any one of these pollutants exceed NAAQ limits. The nonattainment categories are extreme, severe, and moderate. Ozone, PM_{10}, and CO nonattainment are the predominant nonattainment pollutants. Individual states are responsible for attaining each EPA NAAQ. States accomplish this by utilizing state implementation plans, which outline specific actions to reduce emissions. One method of reducing mobile sources of criteria pollutants is using alternative fuels instead of more traditional fuels such as gasoline or diesel.

TABLE 21.4.4 Estimated Number of Alternative-Fueled Vehicles in Use, by State, 2001–2003

State	*2001*	*2002*	*2003*	*State*	*2001*	*2002*	*2003*
Alabama	7,501	8,979	9,870	Nebraska	5,142	5,814	6,303
Alaska	1,288	1,277	1,433	Nevada	5,318	5,571	5,968
Arizona	11,046	11,771	13,303	New Hampshire	935	1,096	1,218
Arkansas	2,873	2,839	3,014	New Jersey	5,854	5,956	6,569
California	66,366	71,501	77,761	New Mexico	9,643	10,624	11,042
Colorado	11,120	11,925	12,447	New York	26,890	32,423	37,559
Connecticut	3,981	5,147	5,606	North Carolina	8,661	9,770	10,695
Delaware	679	1,378	1,492	North Dakota	1,818	1,819	2,133
District of Columbia	3,105	3,243	3,674	Ohio	8,296	9,939	11,097
Florida	15,959	16,542	17,829	Oklahoma	21,440	22,283	23,336
Georgia	12,959	15,567	17,912	Oregon	5,769	5,878	6,568
Hawaii	2,487	2,513	2,707	Pennsylvania	7,326	7,611	8,351
Idaho	2,759	5,233	5,821	Rhode Island	745	844	936
Illinois	12,912	15,401	16,521	South Carolina	6,018	7,460	7,992
Indiana	5,515	6,584	7,405	South Dakota	1,765	1,802	1,906
Iowa	3,163	4,139	4,823	Tennessee	5,430	6,654	7,343
Kansas	5,633	5,985	6,332	Texas	54,254	56,190	55,820
Kentucky	4,676	5,718	6,298	Utah	6,583	7,162	7,621
Louisiana	3,154	3,325	3,582	Vermont	675	748	844
Maine	376	390	417	Virginia	9,686	10,495	11,706
Maryland	9,031	9,157	9,791	Washington	9,122	9,166	9,764
Massachusetts	2,478	2,700	2,946	West Virginia	1,022	1,012	1,098
Michigan	10,675	12,307	14,335	Wisconsin	4,168	5,813	6,457
Minnesota	4,403	6,032	6,482	Wyoming	2,737	2,780	2,924
Mississippi	1,908	1,876	1,990	U.S. Total	425,457	471,098	510,805
Missouri	6,302	7,102	7,540				
Montana	3,812	3,557	4,228				

Note: Excludes gasoline-electric hybrids.Estimates for 2003 are based on plans or projections. Estimates for historical years may be revised in future reports if new information becomes available. Total may not equal sum of components due to independent rounding.

Source: Energy Information Administration, Office of Coal, Nuclear, Electric, and Alternate Fuels and the DOE/GSA Federal Automotive Statistical Tool (FAST).

Automotive Exhaust Pollutants

The use of alternative fuels significantly reduces the production of ozone. Alternative fuels can reduce ozone generation by reducing both the amount of volatile organic compounds (VOCs) in tailpipe emissions and the photochemical reactivity of VOC emissions. Hydrogen used in fuel cells produces no VOC emissions because there is no carbon in the fuel cell feed stream. Ozone is not a direct product of the combustion process but a result of atmospheric photochemical reactions between VOCs and the oxides of nitrogen (NO_x). NO_x is primarily produced when nitrogen and oxygen in combustion air combine at high temperatures. VOCs result from incomplete combustion of hydrocarbon fuels used in motor vehicles.[4]

Simple compounds such as methane and propane predominantly comprise LNG, CNG, and LP-gas fuels. The amount of VOCs these fuels generate is lower than the amount gasoline generates. Furthermore, ozone formation increases when constituents of tailpipe emissions have high photochemical reactivity.[4] Fuels composed of small molecules such as methane generate less ozone because they are unreactive in the atmosphere. Propane is more reactive than methane but significantly less reactive than large molecules of hydrocarbon fuels, such as the constituents of gasoline.

As of the year 2000, 26 states, the District of Columbia, and almost every major urban area in the United States had areas classified as nonattainment for ozone. One area, the South Coast Air Basin (which includes the city of Los Angeles and has a population of over 13,000,000 people), is classified as extreme. Approximately 100,000,000 people in the United States live in a nonattainment area for ozone.[5]

Carbon Monoxide Pollutants

As of the year 2000, there were eight areas classified as serious nonattainment areas for carbon monoxide: Anchorage, Alaska; Fairbanks, Alaska; Denver–Fort Collins, Colorado; Las Vegas, Nevada; Los Angeles–South Coast Basin, California; Phoenix, Arizona; and Spokane, Washington. Several other areas are in the moderate nonattainment class.[5] Approximately 80 percent of CO discharged to the atmosphere is from mobile sources, primarily from emissions from gasoline-powered vehicles. Alternative fuels composed of methane and propane emit much less CO than gasoline does because they have lower carbon to

TABLE 21.4.5 Estimated Number of Alternative-Fueled Vehicles in Use, by State and Fuel Type, 2002

State	*Liquefied Petroleum Gases*	*Natural Gas*	*Methanol*	*Ethanol*	*Electricity*	*Total*
Alabama	4,289	1,341	0	2,713	636	8,979
Alaska	145	401	0	720	11	1,277
Arizona	1,082	7,243	201	1,583	1,662	11,771
Arkansas	2,199	340	0	300	0	2,839
California	21,537	24,990	4,787	9,517	10,670	71,501
Colorado	5,611	2,694	3	3,491	126	11,925
Connecticut	379	2,762	1	1,849	156	5,147
Delaware	85	489	10	783	11	1,378
District of Columbia	7	1,462	50	1,408	316	3,243
Florida	4,171	4,152	6	7,856	357	16,542
Georgia	4,418	4,484	39	2,076	4,550	15,567
Hawaii	842	0	0	1,467	204	2,513
Idaho	1,581	3,412	0	240	0	5,233
Illinois	5,259	3,120	17	6,916	89	15,401
Indiana	1,426	3,397	0	1,670	91	6,584
Iowa	2,179	18	27	1,903	12	4,139
Kansas	3,565	748	1	1,649	22	5,985
Kentucky	2,214	1,191	0	2,313	0	5,718
Louisiana	1,117	896	3	1,309	0	3,325
Maine	158	77	0	134	21	390
Maryland	2,570	3,634	7	2,901	45	9,157
Massachusetts	249	1,006	36	1,331	78	2,700
Michigan	4,822	991	48	4,840	1,606	12,307
Minnesota	2,162	509	0	3,361	0	6,032
Mississippi	1,193	140	0	543	0	1,876
Missouri	2,642	476	95	3,878	11	7,102
Montana	2,980	268	0	309	0	3,557
Nebraska	4,338	370	0	1,095	11	5,814
Nevada	1,487	3,111	0	973	0	5,571
New Hampshire	718	42	0	169	167	1,096
New Jersey	358	2,723	4	2,681	190	5,956
New Mexico	6,069	1,969	11	2,140	435	10,624
New York	6,213	13,100	88	3,723	9,299	32,423
North Carolina	4,560	559	0	4,539	112	9,770
North Dakota	1,310	155	0	354	0	1,819
Ohio	2,487	2,647	26	4,537	242	9,939
Oklahoma	17,839	3,322	0	1,122	0	22,283
Oregon	3,084	1,034	20	1,528	212	5,878
Pennsylvania	1,107	2,299	108	4,008	89	7,611
Rhode Island	122	331	0	391	0	844
South Carolina	3,047	362	0	4,051	0	7,460
South Dakota	1,374	44	0	384	0	1,802
Tennessee	2,623	763	0	3,068	200	6,654
Texas	39,279	9,961	162	6,706	82	56,190
Utah	3,227	1,961	8	1,966	0	7,162
Vermont	366	5	0	199	178	748
Virginia	927	4,735	7	3,740	1,086	10,495
Washington	4,397	1,925	73	2,760	11	9,166
West Virginia	39	378	0	595	0	1,012
Wisconsin	1,459	1,207	35	3,075	37	5,813
Wyoming	2,368	303	0	87	22	2,780
U.S. Total	187,680	123,547	5,873	120,951	33,047	471,098

Note: Natural gas includes compressed natural gas (CNG) and liquefied natural gas (LNG). Methanol includes M85 and M100. Ethanol includes E85 and E95. Excludes gasoline-electric hybrids. Totals may not equal sum of components due to independent rounding.

Source: Energy Information Administration, Office of Coal, Nuclear, Electric, and Alternate Fuels and the DOE/GSA Federal Automotive Statistical Tool (FAST).

TABLE 21.4.6 Estimated Number of Alternative-Fueled Vehicles in Use by U.S. Private Entities, by Fuel and Weight Category, 2001–2003

Fuel	*Light Duty*	*Medium Duty*	*Heavy Duty*	*Total*
	2001			
Liquefied petroleum gases (LP-gas)	100,297	44,678	5,038	150,013
Compressed natural gas (CNG)	44,598	9,075	8,761	62,434
Liquefied natural gas (LNG)	264	0	2,020	2,284
Methanol, 85 percent (M85)[a]	4,010	0	0	4,010
Methanol, neat (M100)	0	0	0	0
Ethanol, 85 percent (E85)[a,b]	36,176	4	1	36,181
Ethanol, 95 percent (E95)[a]	0	0	0	0
Electricity[c]	11,939	91	262	12,292
Non-LP-gas subtotal	96,987	9,170	11,044	117,201
Total	197,284	53,848	16,082	267,214
	2002			
Liquefied petroleum gases (LP-gas)	100,926	46,498	5,539	152,963
Compressed natural gas (CNG)	47,417	11,465	10,338	69,220
Liquefied natural gas (LNG)	315	0	2,110	2,425
Methanol, 85 percent (M85)[a]	3,207	0	0	3,207
Methanol, neat (M100)	0	0	0	0
Ethanol, 85 percent (E85)[a,b]	43,521	40	2	43,563
Ethanol, 95 percent (E95)[a]	0	0	0	0
Electricity[c]	26,156	312	361	26,829
Non-LP-gas subtotal	120,616	11,817	12,811	145,244
Total	221,542	58,315	18,350	298,207
	2003			
Liquefied petroleum gases (LP-gas)	101,335	48,652	5,900	155,887
Compressed natural gas (CNG)	49,529	15,242	11,837	76,608
Liquefied natural gas (LNG)	321	0	2,414	2,735
Methanol, 85 percent (M85)[a]	2,456	0	0	2,456
Methanol, neat (M100)	0	0	0	0
Ethanol, 85 percent (E85)[a,b]	45,091	38	2	45,131
Ethanol, 95 percent (E95)[a]	0	0	0	0
Electricity[c]	35,482	313	520	36,315
Non-LP-gas subtotal	132,879	15,593	14,773	163,245
Total	234,214	64,245	20,673	319,132

Note: Light duty includes vehicles less than or equal to 8500 GVWR; medium duty includes vehicles 8501 to 26,000 GVWR; heavy duty includes vehicles 26,001 GVWR and over. Estimates for 2003 are based on plans or projections. Estimates for historical years may be revised in future reports if new information becomes available.

[a]The remaining portion of 85 percent methanol and both ethanol fuels is gasoline.

[b]In 1997, some vehicle manufacturers began including E85-fueling capability in certain model lines of vehicles. For 2002, the EIA estimated that the number of E85 vehicles that are capable of operating on E85, gasoline, or both, is about 4.1 million. Many of these alternative fuel vehicles (AFVs) are sold and used as traditional gasoline-powered vehicles. In this table, AFVs in use include only those E85 vehicles believed to be intended for use as AFVs. These are primarily fleet-operated vehicles.

[c]Excludes gasoline-electric hybrids.

Source: Energy Information Administration, Office of Coal, Nuclear, Electric, and Alternate Fuels.

TABLE 21.4.7 Estimated Number of Alternative-Fueled Vehicles in Use by Local Governments, by Fuel and Weight Category, 2001–2003

Fuel	*Light Duty*	*Medium Duty*	*Heavy Duty*	*Total*
	2001			
Liquefied petroleum gases (LP-gas)	17,700	7,884	889	26,473
Compressed natural gas (CNG)	19,114	3,889	3,755	26,758
Liquefied natural gas (LNG)	86	0	165	251
Methanol, 85 percent (M85)[a]	2,986	0	8	2,994
Methanol, neat (M100)	0	0	0	0
Ethanol, 85 percent (E85)[a,b]	6,384	0	0	6,384
Ethanol, 95 percent (E95)[a]	0	0	0	0
Electricity[c]	3,601	304	70	3,975
Non-LP-gas subtotal	32,171	4,193	3,998	40,362
Total	49,871	12,077	4,887	66,835
	2002			
Liquefied petroleum gases (LP-gas)	17,810	8,205	977	26,992
Compressed natural gas (CNG)	20,321	4,914	4,431	29,666
Liquefied natural gas (LNG)	106	0	136	242
Methanol, 85 percent (M85)[a]	2,501	0	8	2,509
Methanol, neat (M100)	0	0	0	0
Ethanol, 85 percent (E85)[a,b]	7,681	0	0	7,681
Ethanol, 95 percent (E95)[a]	0	0	0	0
Electricity[c]	3,921	331	76	4,328
Non-LP-gas subtotal	34,530	5,245	4,651	44,426
Total	52,340	13,450	5,628	71,418
	2003			
Liquefied petroleum gases (LP-gas)	18,063	8,322	991	27,376
Compressed natural gas (CNG)	21,227	6,532	5,073	32,832
Liquefied natural gas (LNG)	102	0	141	243
Methanol, 85 percent (M85)[a]	2,306	0	6	2,312
Methanol, neat (M100)	0	0	0	0
Ethanol, 85 percent (E85)[a,b]	8,122	0	0	8,122
Ethanol, 95 percent (E95)[a]	0	0	0	0
Electricity[c]	6,086	333	109	6,528
Non-LP-gas subtotal	37,843	6,865	5,329	50,037
Total	55,906	15,187	6,320	77,413

Note: Light duty includes vehicles less than or equal to 8500 GVWR; medium duty includes vehicles 8501 to 26,000 GVWR; heavy duty includes vehicles 26,001 GVWR and over. Estimates for 2003 are based on plans or projections. Estimates for historical years may be revised in future reports if new information becomes available.

[a]The remaining portion of 85 percent methanol and both ethanol fuels is gasoline.

[b]In 1997, some vehicle manufacturers began including E85-fueling capability in certain model lines of vehicles. For 2002, the EIA estimated that the number of E85 vehicles that are capable of operating on E85, gasoline, or both, is about 4.1 million. Many of these alternative fuel vehicles (AFVs) are sold and used as traditional gasoline-powered vehicles. In this table, AFVs in use include only those E85 vehicles believed to be intended for use as AFVs. These are primarily fleet-operated vehicles.

[c]Excludes gasoline-electric hybrids.

Source: Energy Information Administration, Office of Coal, Nuclear, Electric, and Alternate Fuels.

TABLE 21.4.8 Estimated Number of Alternative-Fueled Vehicles in Use by State Governments, by Fuel and Weight Category, 2001–2003

Fuel	*Light Duty*	*Medium Duty*	*Heavy Duty*	*Total*
	2001			
Liquefied petroleum gases (LP-gas)	6,395	1,019	629	8,043
Compressed natural gas (CNG)	5,063	303	96	5,462
Liquefied natural gas (LNG)	2	0	0	2
Methanol, 85 percent (M85)[a]	747	0	0	747
Methanol, neat (M100)	0	0	0	0
Ethanol, 85 percent (E85)[a,b]	18,218	10	0	18,228
Ethanol, 95 percent (E95)[a]	0	0	0	0
Electricity[c]	967	0	0	967
Non-LP-gas subtotal	24,997	313	96	25,406
Total	31,392	1,332	725	33,449
	2002			
Liquefied petroleum gases (LP-gas)	5,835	944	561	7,340
Compressed natural gas (CNG)	4,623	478	124	5,225
Liquefied natural gas (LNG)	2	0	0	2
Methanol, 85 percent (M85)[a]	83	0	0	83
Methanol, neat (M100)	0	0	0	0
Ethanol, 85 percent (E85)[a,b]	22,600	73	0	22,673
Ethanol, 95 percent (E95)[a]	0	0	0	0
Electricity[c]	1,004	0	0	1,004
Non-LP-gas subtotal	28,312	551	124	28,987
Total	34,147	1,495	685	36,327
	2003			
Liquefied petroleum gases (LP-gas)	5,418	877	521	6,816
Compressed natural gas (CNG)	4,829	635	142	5,606
Liquefied natural gas (LNG)	2	0	0	2
Methanol, 85 percent (M85)[a]	79	0	0	79
Methanol, neat (M100)	0	0	0	0
Ethanol, 85 percent (E85)[a,b]	27,787	73	0	27,860
Ethanol, 95 percent (E95)[a]	0	0	0	0
Electricity[c]	1,555	0	0	1,555
Non-LP-gas subtotal	34,252	708	142	35,102
Total	39,670	1,585	663	41,918

Note: Light duty includes vehicles less than or equal to 8500 GVWR; medium duty includes vehicles 8501 to 26,000 GVWR; heavy duty includes vehicles 26,001 GVWR and over. Estimates for 2003 are based on plans or projections. Estimates for historical years may be revised in future reports if new information becomes available.

[a]The remaining portion of 85 percent methanol and both ethanol fuels is gasoline.

[b]In 1997, some vehicle manufacturers began including E85-fueling capability in certain model lines of vehicles. For 2002, the EIA estimated that the number of E85 vehicles that are capable of operating on E85, gasoline, or both, is about 4.1 million. Many of these alternative fuel vehicles (AFVs) are sold and used as traditional gasoline-powered vehicles. In this table, AFVs in use include only those E85 vehicles believed to be intended for use as AFVs. These are primarily fleet-operated vehicles.

[c]Excludes gasoline-electric hybrids.

Source: Energy Information Administration, Office of Coal, Nuclear, Electric, and Alternate Fuels.

TABLE 21.4.9 Estimated Number of Alternative-Fueled Vehicles in Use by the U.S. Federal Government, by Fuel and Weight Category, 2001–2003

Fuel	*Light Duty*	*Medium Duty*	*Heavy Duty*	*Total*
		2001		
Liquefied petroleum gases (LP-gas)	398	53	73	524
Compressed natural gas (CNG)	15,302	1,774	121	17,197
Liquefied natural gas (LNG)	29	0	10	39
Methanol, 85 percent (M85)[a]	76	0	0	76
Methanol, neat (M100)	0	0	0	0
Ethanol, 85 percent (E85)[a]	39,509	1	0	39,510
Ethanol, 95 percent (E95)[a]	0	0	0	0
Electricity[b]	549	50	14	613
Non-LP-gas subtotal	55,465	1,825	145	57,435
Total	55,863	1,878	218	57,959
		2002		
Liquefied petroleum gases (LP-gas)	306	24	55	385
Compressed natural gas (CNG)	14,979	1,592	157	16,728
Liquefied natural gas (LNG)	29	0	10	39
Methanol, 85 percent (M85)[a]	74	0	0	74
Methanol, neat (M100)	0	0	0	0
Ethanol, 85 percent (E85)[a]	47,007	27	0	47,034
Ethanol, 95 percent (E95)[a]	0	0	0	0
Electricity[b]	845	28	13	886
Non-LP-gas subtotal	62,934	1,647	180	64,761
Total	63,240	1,671	235	65,146
		2003		
Liquefied petroleum gases (LP-gas)	294	22	43	359
Compressed natural gas (CNG)	15,646	2,116	180	17,942
Liquefied natural gas (LNG)	38	0	12	50
Methanol, 85 percent (M85)[a]	70	0	0	70
Methanol, neat (M100)	0	0	0	0
Ethanol, 85 percent (E85)[a]	52,634	29	0	52,663
Ethanol, 95 percent (E95)[a]	0	0	0	0
Electricity[b]	1,211	28	19	1,258
Non-LP-gas subtotal	69,599	2,173	211	71,983
Total	69,893	2,195	254	72,342

Note: Light duty includes vehicles less than or equal to 8500 GVWR; medium duty includes vehicles 8501 to 26,000 GVWR; heavy duty includes vehicles 26,001 GVWR and over. Estimates for 2003 are based on plans or projections. Estimates for historical years may be revised in future reports if new information becomes available.
[a]The remaining portion of 85 percent methanol and both ethanol fuels is gasoline.
[b]Excludes gasoline-electric hybrids.

Source: The DOE/GSA Federal Automotive Statistical Tool (FAST).

hydrogen ratios. In addition, alternative fuel vehicles do not need to run fuel rich during cold weather like gasoline-fueled vehicles do.[3] This reduced fuel consumption lowers CO emissions.

Particulate Matter (PM) Emissions

PM emissions can be reduced by using alternative fuels because the primary mobile source of these emissions is diesel-powered vehicles.[4] Diesel fuels' high sulfur content and aromatic hydrocarbons contribute to high PM emissions. In gaseous alternative fuels, sulfur is not present in appreciable amounts, and aromatic hydrocarbons are not present at all.

As of the year 2000, there were six serious nonattainment areas for PM_{10}: Clark County, Nevada; Coachella Valley, California; Los Angeles–South Coast Air Basin, California; Owens Valley, California; Phoenix, Arizona; and San Joaquin Valley, California. Additionally, many other areas are classified as moderate nonattainment areas.[5]

TABLE 21.4.10 Estimated Consumption of Vehicle Fuels in the United States, 1995–2004

Fuel	*1995*	*1996*	*1997*	*1998*	*1999*	*2000*	*2001*	*2002*	*2003* (Projected)	*2004* (Projected)
Alternative fuels										
Liquefied petroleum gases (LP-gas)[a]	232,701	239,158	238,356	241,386	209,817	212,576	215,876	223,143	230,486	242,368
Compressed natural gas (CNG)[a]	35,162	46,923	65,192	72,412	79,620	86,745	104,496	120,670	141,726	159,464
Liquefied natural gas (LNG)[a]	2,759	3,247	3,714	5,343	5,828	7,259	8,921	9,382	10,514	10,868
Methanol, 85 percent (M85)[b]	2,023	1,775	1,554	1,212	1,073	585	439	337	274	257
Methanol, neat (M100)	2,150	347	347	449	447	0	0	0	0	0
Ethanol, 85 percent (E85)[a,b]	190	694	1,280	1,727	3,916	12,071	14,623	17,783	20,092	22,405
Ethanol, 95 percent (E95)[b]	995	2,699	1,136	59	62	13	0	0	0	0
Electricity[c]	663	773	1,010	1,202	1,524	3,058	4,066	7,274	9,633	11,836
Subtotal[a]	276,643	295,616	312,589	323,790	302,287	322,307	348,421	378,589	412,725	447,198
Oxygenates										
Methyl tertiary butyl ether (MTBE)[d]	2,691,200	2,749,700	3,104,200	2,903,400	3,402,600	3,296,100	3,352,200	2,383,000	NA	NA
Ethanol in gasohol[a]	910,700	660,200	830,700	889,500	950,300	1,085,800	1,143,300	1,413,600	1,792,900	2,052,000
Biodiesel	NA	NA	NA	NA	NA	6,816	7,076	16,917	26,758	36,599
Total alternative and replacement fuels	3,878,543	3,705,516	4,247,489	4,116,690	4,655,187	4,711,023	4,850,997	4,192,106	2,232,383	2,535,797
Traditional fuels										
Gasoline[e]	115,943,000	117,783,000	119,336,000	122,849,000	125,111,000	125,720,000	127,768,000	131,299,000	132,961,000	136,374,000
Diesel	28,555,040	30,101,430	31,949,270	33,665,360	35,796,800	36,990,370	37,085,270	38,305,630	39,930,170	40,740,760
Total fuel consumption[a,f]	144,774,683	148,180,046	151,597,859	156,838,150	161,210,087	163,032,677	165,201,691	169,983,219	173,303,895	177,561,958

Note: Fuel quantities are expressed in a common base unit of gasoline-equivalent gallons to allow comparisons of different fuel types. Gasoline-equivalent gallons do not represent gasoline displacement. Gasoline equivalent is computed by dividing the lower heating value of the alternative fuel by the lower heating value of gasoline and multiplying this result by the alternative fuel consumption value. Lower heating value refers to the Btu content per unit of fuel excluding the heat produced by condensation of water vapor in the fuel. Totals may not equal sum of components due to independent rounding. Estimates for 2003 and 2004 are based on plans or projections. Estimates for historical years may be revised in future reports if new information becomes available.

[a] 1999 and 2002 estimates have been revised.

[b] The remaining portion of 85 percent methanol and both ethanol fuels is gasoline. Consumption data include the gasoline portion of the fuel.

[c] Excludes gasoline-electric hybrids.

[d] Includes a very small amount of other ethers, primarily Tertiary Amyl Methyl Ether (TAME) and Ethyl Tertiary Butyl Ether (ETBE).

[e] Gasoline consumption includes ethanol in gasohol and MTBE.

[f] Total fuel consumption is the sum of alternative fuel, gasoline, and diesel consumption. Oxygenate consumption is included in gasoline consumption.

NA = Not available.

Sources: 1993–2002 Oxygenate Consumption: Energy Information Administration, Petroleum Supply Monthly. 1993–2004 Traditional Fuel Consumption: Energy Information Administration, Petroleum Supply Annual, Volume 1 (June 2000). Highway use of gasoline was estimated as 97.1 percent of consumption, based on data in the Transportation Energy Data Book: Edition 16, prepared by Oak Ridge National Laboratory for the U.S. Department of Energy (July 1996). Diesel consumption was adjusted for highway use by multiplying by 0.568 derived from Energy Information Administration, Fuel Oil and Kerosene Sales 1999. 2002–2004 Oxygenate and Traditional Fuel Consumption: Energy Information Administration, Short Term Energy Outlook, September 2002. Alternative Fuel Consumption: Science Applications International Corporation 1992–1995, "Alternative Transportation Fuels and Vehicles Data Development." Unpublished final report prepared for the Energy Information Administration (McLean, VA, July 1996) and Energy Information Administration, Office of Coal, Nuclear, Electric and Alternate Fuels for 1996–2004.

TABLE 21.4.11 Estimated Share of Alternative Transportation Fuel Consumption, by Census Region, 2000, 2002, and 2004

Fuel	*Northeast*	*South*	*Midwest*	*West*
		2000		
Liquefied petroleum gases (LP-gas)	11	28	37	24
Compressed natural gas (CNG)	18	12	27	43
Liquefied natural gas (LNG)	0	1	50	49
Methanol, 85 percent (M85)*	5	7	6	82
Methanol, neat (M100)	0	0	0	0
Ethanol, 85 percent (E85)*	2	81	11	6
Ethanol, 95 percent (E95)*	0	0	0	0
Electricity	14	7	22	57
Total	8	23	26	43
		2002		
Liquefied petroleum gases (LP-gas)	11	28	37	24
Compressed natural gas (CNG)	18	12	27	43
Liquefied natural gas (LNG)	0	1	50	49
Methanol, 85 percent (M85)*	5	7	6	82
Methanol, neat (M100)	0	0	0	0
Ethanol, 85 percent (E85)*	2	81	11	6
Ethanol, 95 percent (E95)*	0	0	0	0
Electricity	14	7	22	57
Total	8	23	26	43
		2004		
Liquefied petroleum gases (LP-gas)	11	28	37	24
Compressed natural gas (CNG)	18	12	27	43
Liquefied natural gas (LNG)	0	1	50	49
Methanol, 85 percent (M85)*	5	7	6	82
Methanol, neat (M100)	0	0	0	0
Ethanol, 85 percent (E85)*	2	81	11	6
Ethanol, 95 percent (E95)*	0	0	0	0
Electricity	14	7	22	57
Total	8	23	26	43

Note: Estimates for 2002 are revised. Estimates for 2004 are based on plans or projections.
*The remaining portion of 85 percent methanol and both ethanol fuels is gasoline. Consumption data include the gasoline portion of the fuel.
Source: Energy Information Administration, Office of Coal, Nuclear, Electric, and Alternate Fuels.

As mentioned earlier, nonattainment of ozone, PM_{10}, and CO is the most widespread. Using alternative fuels such as CNG, LNG, and LP-gas can significantly reduce these pollutants.

PREVENTION OF UNINTENTIONAL RELEASES AND REQUIRED RISK MANAGEMENT PROGRAMS

The Prevention of Accidental Releases of CAAA of 1990, Title III, Section 112 R, aims to prevent inadvertent chemical releases at storage locations and to minimize their consequences. Section 112 R of Title III of CAAA exempts the following propane facilities from developing and submitting risk management plans:

- Propane facilities where the propane is stored for use as fuel at the facility
- Facilities that store 10,000 lb (4540 kg) of propane or less
- Facilities where the propane is held for sale and the facility itself is considered a retail facility (one at which more than half of the income is obtained from direct sales to end users or at which more than half the fuel sold, by volume, is sold through a cylinder exchange program)

The requirements of Title III, Section 112 R, apply to existing and new stationary sources in excess of threshold quantities. The list of regulated flammable substances includes methane and propane with threshold storage quantities of 10,000 lb (4540 kg). LNG is composed of 95 to 99 percent methane;

TABLE 21.4.12 Estimated Consumption of Alternative Transportation Fuels in the United States, by Fuel and Vehicle Weight, 2000, 2002, and 2004 (Thousand Gasoline-Equivalent Gallons)

	2000			2002			2004		
Fuel	*Light Duty*	*Medium/ Heavy Duty*	*Total*	*Light Duty*	*Medium/ Heavy Duty*	*Total*	*Light Duty*	*Medium/ Heavy Duty*	*Total*
Liquefied petroleum gases (LP-gas)	60,340	152,236	212,576	61,715	161,428	223,143	62,010	180,358	242,368
Compressed natural gas (CNG)	38,436	48,309	86,745	42,528	78,142	120,670	46,387	113,077	159,464
Liquefied natural gas (LNG)	278	6,981	7,259	358	9,024	9,382	412	10,456	10,868
Methanol, 85 percent (M85)*	576	9	585	330	7	337	254	3	257
Methanol, neat (M100)	0	0	0	0	0	0	0	0	0
Ethanol, 85 percent (E85)*	12,071	0	12,071	17,783	0	17,783	22,405	0	22,405
Ethanol, 95 percent (E95)*	0	13	13	0	0	0	0	0	0
Electricity	1,726	1,332	3,058	5,224	2,050	7,274	9,006	2,830	11,836
Total	113,427	208,880	322,307	127,938	250,651	378,589	140,474	306,724	447,198

Note: Light duty includes vehicles less than or equal to 8500 GVWR; medium duty includes vehicles 8501 to 26,000 GVWR; heavy duty includes vehicles 26,001 GVWR and over. Fuel quantities are expressed in a common base unit of gasoline-equivalent gallons to allow comparisons of different fuel types. Gasoline-equivalent gallons do not represent gasoline displacement. Gasoline equivalent is computed by dividing the lower heating value of the alternative fuel by the lower heating value of gasoline and multiplying this result by the alternative fuel consumption value. Lower heating value refers to the Btu content per unit of fuel excluding the heat produced by condensation of water vapor in the fuel. Totals may not equal sum of components due to independent rounding. Estimates for 2000 are revised. Estimates for 2002 are preliminary. Estimates for 2004 are based on plans or projections. Estimates for historical years may be revised in future reports if new information becomes available.

*The remaining portion of 85 percent methanol and both ethanol fuels is gasoline. Consumption data include the gasoline portion of the fuel.

LP-gas is predominantly propane. Assuming commercial automotive grades of LNG and LP-gas, facilities using stationary containers with capacities greater than 2780 gal (10.5 m^3) of LNG or 2380 gal (9.0 m^3) of LP-gas may be required to prepare a risk management plan. The rule should not impact most CNG fueling stations because storage is normally below the threshold storage quantity. Natural gas from a distribution line is usually compressed at the facility, so it is usually unnecessary to store large quantities. Hydrogen is also listed in table 3 to 40 CFR 68.30 of the Risk Management Plan list of regulated flammable materials with a threshold of 10,000 lb.

The risk management program and its implementation consist of three components: (1) a hazard analysis, (2) a program for preventing accidental releases, and (3) an emergency response program. A Risk Management Plan must be submitted to the implementing agency, the State Emergency Planning Committee, the Local Emergency Planning Committee, and the Chemical Safety and Hazard Investigation Board. The three elements of the risk management program must be summarized in a Risk Management Plan and submitted to the above organizations. The report must be reviewed every 5 years. *Risk Management Program Guidance for Propane Storage Facilities* (40 CFR Part 68) is available from the EPA to assist regulated facilities in complying with risk management programs.[6]

Hazard Analysis

Hazard assessment is a determination of the worst-case release scenario, identification of other more likely significant releases of propane or LNG, an analysis of the off-site consequences, and a history of unintentional releases of propane or LNG. Under 40 CFR 112.R, worst-case releases are determined by assuming that in an instantaneous release, all mitigation systems fail. Other more likely accidental releases can include failure of transfer hoses, excess flow valve, emergency shutoff controls, piping, and other significant equipment failures. The rule also states that consequences must be determined from the rate and quantity of the substance lost in the air, the event's duration, the distance to exposures such as single- and multiple-family dwellings, the populations within these distances, and the potential for environmental damage. The owner or operator must maintain a 5 year history that includes such information as the date and time of a release and its quantity and duration.

Program to Prevent Unintentional Releases of Propane

The prevention program's intent is to evaluate potential hazards present at a storage and dispensing station and to find the best way to control them. The program consists of a management system,

TABLE 21.4.13 Estimated Consumption of Alternative Transportation Fuels in the United States, by Vehicle Ownership, 2000, 2002, and 2004 (Thousand Gasoline-Equivalent Gallons)

Fuel	*Federal*	*State/ Local*	*Private*	*Total*
	2000			
Liquefied petroleum gases (LP-gas)	458	19,730	192,388	212,576
Compressed natural gas (CNG)	6,294	34,061	46,390	86,745
Liquefied natural gas (LNG)	101	6,031	1,127	7,259
Methanol, 85 percent (M85)*	2	193	390	585
Methanol, neat (M100)	0	0	0	0
Ethanol, 85 percent (E85)*	2,661	5,482	3,928	12,071
Ethanol, 95 percent (E95)*	0	13	0	13
Electricity	639	595	1,824	3,058
Total	10,155	66,105	246,047	322,307
	2002			
Liquefied petroleum gases (LP-gas)	213	20,097	202,833	223,143
Compressed natural gas (CNG)	6,142	52,482	62,046	120,670
Liquefied natural gas (LNG)	124	7,797	1,461	9,382
Methanol, 85 percent (M85)*	2	103	232	337
Methanol, neat (M100)	0	0	0	0
Ethanol, 85 percent (E85)*	3,495	9,215	5,073	17,783
Ethanol, 95 percent (E95)*	0	0	0	0
Electricity	191	1,165	5,918	7,274
Total	10,167	90,859	277,563	378,589
	2004			
Liquefied petroleum gases (LP-gas)	164	19,277	222,927	242,368
Compressed natural gas (CNG)	7,449	73,217	78,798	159,464
Liquefied natural gas (LNG)	146	9,035	1,687	10,868
Methanol, 85 percent (M85)*	1	82	174	257
Methanol, neat (M100)	0	0	0	0
Ethanol, 85 percent (E85)*	4,331	12,713	5,361	22,405
Ethanol, 95 percent (E95)*	0	0	0	0
Electricity	291	1,461	10,084	11,836
Total	12,382	115,785	319,031	447,198

Note: Fuel quantities are expressed in a common base unit of gasoline-equivalent gallons to allow comparisons of different fuel types. Gasoline-equivalent gallons do not represent gasoline displacement. Gasoline equivalent is computed by dividing the lower heating value of the alternative fuel by the lower heating value of gasoline and multiplying this result by the alternative fuel consumption value. Lower heating value refers to the Btu content per unit of fuel excluding the heat produced by condensation of water vapor in the fuel. Totals may not equal sum of components due to independent rounding. Estimates for 2004 are based on plans or projections. Estimates for historical years may be revised in future reports if new information becomes available.

*The remaining portion of 85 percent methanol and both ethanol fuels is gasoline. Consumption data include the gasoline portion of the fuel.

Source: Energy Information Administation, Office of Coal, Nuclear, Electric, and Alternate Fuels.

process hazard analysis, process safety information, standard operating procedures, training, maintenance, prestartup reviews, management of change, safety audits, and incident investigations.

The rule states that the process hazard analysis must be conducted by using quantitative or qualitative methodologies such as what-if, fault tree analysis, hazard and operability study (HAZOP), or other accepted practices. The process hazard analysis should address the hazards of the process; identify previous incidents that impacted off-site exposures, engineering, and administrative controls; predict the consequences of control or human failures, and stationary source sitting; and qualitatively evaluate possible safety and health effects if controls fail.

Emergency Response Program

Of particular importance to emergency response personnel is the rule that requires the owner or operator of an LNG or LP-gas fueling station to establish and implement an emergency response program for responding to and mitigating unintentional releases. The emergency response must include information on evacuation routes, employee instructions, descriptions of response and mitigation technologies at the fueling station, and procedures for informing the public and emergency response agencies of a release.

The rule states that procedures for the testing, maintenance, and use of response equipment must be established. In addition, the owner or operator is responsible for training employees in emergency response procedures and documenting all training activities. The rule states that drills or exercises will be conducted and documented, but does not specify the frequency of these drills. However, other regulations, such as those promulgated by OSHA, do establish the required frequency of emergency drills.

The emergency response program requires facilities storing LNG or LP-gas to document first aid and emergency medical treatment procedures necessary to treat persons exposed. The emergency response plan must coordinate with other local emergency response plans developed by the Local Emergency Planning Committee (LEPC) or other local emergency response agencies.

ANALYSIS OF THE CHEMICAL AND PHYSICAL PROPERTIES AND HAZARDS OF ALTERNATIVE FUELS

When a vehicle is being fueled or repaired, release from the vehicle to the fueling or repair facility is a reasonable scenario that requires fire fighters' consideration. The impact of potential releases can be analyzed using computer dispersion models that predict where the maximum ground level concentration for a specific release scenario would occur. The models (of which there are many variations) can predict concentrations at other distances from the release than the distance at which the maximum concentration would occur. A sensitivity analysis could be performed to show which parameter(s) would contribute most to the release impacts and potentially how best to reduce the impacts from a release.

Chemical and Physical Properties

The properties of each fuel require consideration in determining its potential hazard. Whether the hazard becomes "real" depends on various time-dependent conditions, the fuel system design, and the quality of the fuel system's manufacture and installation. This is due to the properties and hazards of the materials, whether release occurs inside or outside of a building, and the release scenario. This chapter discusses the relationships between identified properties and hazards of CNG, LNG, and LP-gas.

Compressed Natural Gas. Mixing and dispersion of gases depend on discharge velocities, vapor density, diffusion characteristics of the gas, and conditions and location of release. CNG can be expected to disperse readily, mix, and quickly form combustible mixtures. Under unconfined conditions, methane gas mixtures dilute rapidly to concentrations below the lower flammable limit. In contrast, the ability to form combustible mixtures rapidly generates a hazardous situation if fuel leaks in confined areas without significant ventilation.

Hydrogen. Hydrogen is used both as a liquid and a gas. Hydrogen has a molecular weight of approximately 1, but hydrogen occurs as a diatomic molecule with an approximate molecular weight of 2. Because of its extremely low density (0.07 relative to air), hydrogen typically is stored at much higher pressures than CNG. This is also the reason why some storage systems use liquid hydrogen with vaporizers to convert the hydrogen to a gas for the specific application. Gaseous hydrogen in the flammable range (4 to 75% by volume in air) can be easily ignited but because it is the lightest gas, it disperses rapidly. Because of its extremely low boiling point, liquid hydrogen boils rapidly if released. Liquid hydrogen releases can cause oxygen to condense out of the air and present this additional hazard.

Liquefied Natural Gas. LNG is natural gas liquefied by cryogenic refrigeration and stored at a temperature of –260°F (–162°C). The vapor cloud above a pool of released LNG is fairly difficult to ignite. However, the very low temperature of LNG causes normally buoyant methane to become heavier than air, creating large volumes of flammable methane-air mixtures that can spread significantly beyond the area of the initial spill. The possibility of ignition increases, and the potentially large volume of combustible gas mixture constitutes a major safety risk in substantial LNG spills.[7] When LNG vaporizes, the gas vapor cloud begins to warm and comes into thermal equilibrium with the atmosphere. LNG and CNG are primarily composed of natural gas; however, prior to liquefaction of LNG, constituents such as carbon dioxide, water, hydrogen sulfide, the odorant, and trace metal oxides are removed because they solidify at LNG storage temperatures.[8]

LP-Gas. One relative safety comparison of the three alternative fuels discussed here found that safety ranking of LP-gas appears to be similar to that of gasoline.[4] This can be attributed to heavier-than-air LP-gas vapors that do not disperse as quickly as those of other alternative fuels.

Automotive grade natural gas contains 95 to 99 percent methane and a mixture of several other gases.[8] Methane is the simplest hydrocarbon, with one carbon molecule bonded to four hydrogen molecules. Other hydrocarbons present include ethane, propane, and butane, in addition to trace amounts of metal oxides, nitrogen, carbon dioxide, water, helium, and hydrogen sulfide.

LP-gas can be either butane, propane, or a mixture of both. However, LP-gas used as an alternative fuel is composed of commercial propane. Commercial propane is not pure, but contains varying percentages of butane, ethane, ethylene, propylene, isobutane, and butylene. Propane is a straight-chain saturated hydrocarbon composed of three carbon atoms and eight hydrogen atoms. Propane is a gas at room temperature, but is liquefied when stored under a pressure equal to its vapor pressure.

Fire Hazards

The need to understand the fire hazards associated with CNG, LNG, and LP-gas grows as the number of alternative-fueled vehicles increases. For example, emergency response personnel need to recognize that these fuels present significantly different fire hazards than traditional fuels such as gasoline and diesel.

Table 21.4.14 summarizes chemical, physical, and fire hazard properties of the three alternative fuels. CNG and LNG have

TABLE 21.4.14 Properties of Fuels

Property	*Gasoline*	*No.2 Diesel Fuel*	*Methanol*	*Ethanol*	*MTBE*	*Propane*	*Compressed Natural Gas (CNG)*	*Hydrogen*
Chemical formula	C_4 to C_{12}	C_3 to C_{25}	CH_3OH	C_2H_5OH	$(CH_3)_3COCH_3$	C_3H_8	CH_4	H_2
Molecular weight	100–105[a]	≈200	32.04	46.07	88.15	44.1	16.04	2.02
Composition, weight percent								
Carbon	85–88[b]	84–87	37.5	52.2	66.1	82	75	0
Hydrogen	12–15[b]	33–16	12.6	13.1	13.7	18	25	100
Oxygen	0	0	49.9	34.7	18.2	—	—	0
Specific gravity, 60° F/60° F	0.72–0.78[b]	0.81–0.89[d]	0.796[c]	0.796[c]	0.744[m]	0.508	0.424	0.07[u]
Density, lb/gal at 60° F	6.0–6.5[b]	6.7–7.4[d]	6.63[b]	6.61[b]	6.19[m]	4.22	1.07[r]	—
Boiling temperature, °F	80–437[b]	370–650[d]	149[c]	172[c]	131[c]	–44	–259	–423[u]
Reid vapor pressure, psi	8–15[k]	0.2	4.6[o]	2.3[o]	7.8[e]	208	2,400	—
Octane no.[1]								
Research octane no.	90–100[u]	—	107	108	116[t]	112	—	130+
Motor octane no.	81–90[s]	—	92	92	101[t]	97	—	—
(R + M)/2	86–94[s]	N/A	100	100	108[t]	104	120+	—
Cetane no.[1]	5–20	40–55	—	—	—	—	—	—
Water solubility, at 70°F								
Fuel in water, volume percent	Negligible	Negligible	100[c]	100[b]	4.3[e]	—	—	—
Water in fuel, volume percent	Negligible	Negligible	100[c]	100[b]	1.4[e]	—	—	—
Freezing point, °F	–40[g]	–40–30[4]	–143.5	–173.2	–164[c]	–305.8	–296	–435[v]
Viscosity								
Centipoise at 60°F	0.37–0.44[3,p]	2.6–4.1	0.59[j]	1.19[j]	0.35[j]	—	—	
Flashpoint, closed cup, °F	–45[b]	165[d]	52[o]	55[o]	–14[e]	–100 to –150	–300	—
Autoignition temperature, °F	495[b]	≈600	867[b]	793[b]	815[e]	850–950	1,004	1,050–1,080[u]
Flammability limits, volume percent								
Lower	1.4[b]	1	7.3[o]	4.3[o]	1.6[e,k]	2.2	5.3	4.1[u]
Higher	7.6[b]	6	36[o]	19[o]	8.4[e,k]	9.5	15	74[u]
Latent heat of vaporization								
Btu/gal at 60°F	≈900[b]	≈700	3,340[b]	2,378[b]	863[5]	775	—	—
Btu/lb at 60°F	≈150[b]	≈100	506[b]	396[b]	138[5]	193.1	219	192.1[v]
Btu/lb air for stoichiometric mixture at 60°F	≈10[b]	≈8	78.4[b]	44[b]	11.8	—	—	—
Heating value[2]								
Higher (liquid fuel-liquid water) Btu/lb	18,800–20,400	19,200–20000	9,750[2]	12,800[q]	18,290[h]	21,600	23,600	61,002[v]
Lower (liquid fuel-water vapor) Btu/lb	18,000–19,000	18,000–19,000	8,570[b]	11,500[q]	15,100[h]	19,800	21,300	51,532[v]
Higher (liquid fuel-liquid water) Btu/gal	124,800	138,700	64,250	84,100	—	91,300	—	—
Lower (liquid fuel-water vapor) Btu/gal at 60°F	115,000	128,400	56,800[3]	76,000[3]	93,500[4]	84,500	19,800[6]	—

Heating value, stoichiometric mixture								
Mixture in vapor state, Btu/cubic foot at 68°F	95.2[b]	96.9[5,q]	92.5[b]	92.9[b]	—	—	—	—
Fuel in liquid state, Btu/lb or air	1,290[b]	—	1,330[b]	1,280[b]	—	—	—	—
Specific heat, Btu/lb °F	0.48[g]	0.43	0.6[j]	0.57[j]	0.5[j]	—	—	—
Stoichiometric air/fuel, weight	14.7[3]	14.7	6.45[l]	9[l]	11.7[j]	15.7	17.2	34.3[u]
Volume percent fuel in vaporized stoichiometric mixture	2[b]	—	12.3[b]	6.5[b]	2.7[j]	—	—	—

Notes:

1. Octane values are for pure components. Laboratory engine Research and Motor octane rating procedures are not suitable for use with neat oxygenates. Octane values obtained by these methods are not useful in determining knock-limited compression ratios for vehicles operating on neat oxygenates and do not represent octane performance of oxygenates when blended with hydrocarbons. Similar problems exist for cetane rating procedures.
2. The higher heating value is cited for completeness only. Since no vehicles in use, or currently being developed for future use, have power plants capable of condensing the moisture of combustion, the lower heating value should be used for practical comparisons between fuels.
3. Calculated.
4. Pour Point, ASTM D97 from Reference (c).
5. Based on cetane.
6. For compressed gas at 2400 psi.

Sources:

[a]The basis of this table and associated references was taken from American Petroleum Institute (API), Alcohols and Ethers, Publication No. 4261, 2nd ed. (Washington, DC, July 1988), Table B-1.

[b]"Alcohols: A Technical Assessment of Their Application as Motor Fuels," API Publication No. 4261, July 1976.

[c]*Handbook of Chemistry and Physics,* 62nd Edition, The Chemical Rubber Company Press, Inc., 1981.

[d]"Diesel Fuel Oils, 1987," Petroleum Product Surveys, National Institute for Petroleum and Energy Research, October 1987.

[e]ARCO Chemical Company, 1987.

[f]"MTBE, Evaluation as a High Octane Blending Component for Unleaded Gasoline," Johnson, R. T., Taniguchi, B. Y., Symposium on Octane in the 1980's, American Chemical Society, Miami Beach Meeting, September 10–15, 1979.

[g]"Status of Alcohol Fuels Utilization Technology for Highway Transportation: A 1981 Perspective," Vol. 1, *Spark-Ignition Engine,* May 1982, DOE/CE-56051–7.

[h]American Petroleum Institute Research Project 44, NBS C-461.

[i]*Lang's Handbook of Chemistry,* 13th Edition, McGraw-Hill Book Company, New York, 1985.

[j]"Data Compilation Tables of Properties of Pure Compounds," Design Institute for Physical Property Data, American Institute of Chemical Engineers, New York, 1984.

[k]Petroleum Product Surveys, Motor Gasoline, National Institute for Petroleum and Energy Research, Summer 1986, Winter 1986/1987.

[l]Based on isoctane.

[m]API Monograph Series, Publication 723, "Teri-Butyl Methyl Ether," 1984.

[n]BP America, Sohio Oil Broadway Laboratory.

[o]API Technical Data Book—Petroleum Refining, Volume I, Chapter I. Revised Chapter 1 to First, Second, Third and Fourth Editions, 1988.

[p]"Automotive Gasolines," SAE Recommended Practice, J312 May 1986, SAE Handbook, Volume 3, 1988.

[q]"Internal Combustion Engines and Air Pollution," Obert, E. F., 3rd Edition, Intext Educational Publishers, 1973.

[r]Value at 80 degrees F with respect to the water at 60 degrees F (Mueller & Associates).

[s]National Institute for Petroleum and Energy Research, Petroleum Product Surveys, Motor Gasolines, Summer 1992, NIPER-178 PPS 93/1 (Batlesville, OK, January 1993), Table 1.

[t]P. Dorn, A. M. Mourao, and S. Herbstman, "The Properties and Performance of Modern Automotive Fuels," Society of Automotive Engineers (SAE), Publication No. 861178 (Warrendale, PA), 1986, p. 53.

[u]C. Borusbay and T. Nejat Veziroglu, "Hydrogen as a Fuel for Spark Ignition Engines," Alternative Energy Sources VIII, Volume 2, Research and Development (New York: Hemisphere Publishing Corporation), 1989, pp. 559–560.

[v]Technical Data Book, Prepared by Gulf Research and Development Company, Pittsburgh, PA, 1962.

similar fire hazards because some natural gas properties do not change between the two different physical states. Flammability limits and autoignition temperature of natural gas are the same in the two physical storage states of CNG and LNG. Its flammable range is narrow, and its autoignition temperature is high. LP-gas produces a flammable mixture in air at lower concentrations than natural gas but has a narrower flammable range.

Fire Hazards of Compressed Natural Gas. Natural gas, which has a vapor density of less than 1, tends to rise at ambient conditions. This is one important property of natural gas to consider because vapor density varies under different temperatures. However, because of the extremely low boiling point of natural gas, the vapor density will be less than air under most conditions. CNG released into the atmosphere at normal temperatures and pressures rapidly rises and disperses into the air. CNG-fueled vehicles provide a high degree of safety if a release occurs outdoors because the compressed methane diffuses rapidly in unconfined locations. If a container relief valve operates or the fuel line piping breaks, the duration of the release is limited because the gas discharges at high pressures.

When CNG vents from a relief device or pipe opening, it forms a gas jet that "blows" into the atmosphere in the direction the hole faces, continually entraining and mixing with air. If the CNG encounters an ignition source, a flame jet of considerable length may form. Flame jets pose a thermal radiation hazard to the vehicle and persons nearby and are particularly hazardous if they impinge on the exterior of adjacent containers. This can lead to the operation of additional pressure-relief devices, increasing the fire's thermal flux. Compressed methane gas releases are of relatively short duration. The ensuing fire usually involves only combustibles on the vehicle because natural gas is rapidly consumed during the jet fire.

A CNG release in an enclosed space can present a higher risk for a deflagration because the contained gas may not readily diffuse. Because methane has a vapor density of 0.6, it rises rapidly and pools if contained by a ceiling. Light fixtures and air-handling equipment normally installed at a building's ceiling or roof can serve as potential ignition sources.

Studies have evaluated the deflagration hazard resulting from a leak in a CNG vehicle fuel system or relief device operation inside parking garages and transit tunnels.[9] A gas utility corporation commissioned a study that examined the consequences of a fuel pipe leak or the operation of a container pressure relief device inside a partially open public parking garage. The study found that a leak in the fuel piping was the most credible event, whereas the operation of the container relief valve was the worst-case event. Recognizing that the three model codes and NFPA 88A, *Standard for Parking Structures,* require a method for mechanically ventilating carbon monoxide exhaust, and that all parking garages have fairly open spaces, vapor dispersion models related to this study were created to evaluate selected leak scenarios. Analyses of the most probable event resulted in no flammable concentrations beyond the leak point's immediate vicinity. The leak did not result in accumulated flammable gas in the garage. The operation of the container relief valve did result in the brief formation of a gas puff that was within the flammable limits of methane. However, the vapor puff was effectively mitigated by the rapid diffusion of the gas in open space and its removal from the garage by the mechanical exhaust system. The study showed that a CNG vehicle poses no extraordinary risk; that is, the CNG vehicle's risk is equal to or less than the risk a gasoline-fueled vehicle poses.

One study[10] compared the flammable vapor clouds formed following a fuel line failure of a hypothetical CNG-powered and gasoline-powered van inside ventilated and unventilated tunnels with various types of ceiling construction. Depending on tunnel ventilation, the hypothetical CNG vehicle would be expected to produce both a smaller and shorter-lived flammable gas region than the equivalent gasoline van. Effective ventilation could be mechanical ventilation by fans or ventilation induced by a vehicle's motion. The study recommended that transportation authorities develop policies limiting the size of vehicles allowed in tunnels.

Fire Hazards of Liquefied Natural Gas. LNG is stored at an approximate temperature of –260°F (–162°C). Studies show that at temperatures less than –180°F (–118°C), LNG is more dense than air at 60°F (16°C).[8] Because LNG is a flammable cryogen, the integrity of the container and piping is of primary concern; a container or piping failure can result in a cryogen liquid spill. However, loss of liquid from a container requires that the outer steel shell, insulation, and inner vessel all fail. All three components are less likely to fail than are single-wall, atmospheric storage tanks found on conventional gasoline- or diesel-fueled vehicles. Nonetheless, the probability of a spill is still a consideration.

The liquid from an LNG spill begins to vaporize rapidly and forms a white cloud as cold vapors condense in air. Initially, the vapor is negatively buoyant and sinks to the ground until it warms to approximately –180°F (–118°C). At this temperature, the vapor becomes positively buoyant and begins to rise.

The vaporization rate and distance the gas cloud travels and disperses depends on the four following factors:

1. *Wind speed.* Wind speed is influential because as velocity increases, the LNG evaporation rate tends to increase. Increased wind velocity helps to induce mixing of methane vapors with air, causing the vapor cloud to disperse into smaller clouds, or puffs. This reduces the flammable atmosphere's area.
2. *Surface area of the spill.* The larger the spill area, the greater its vaporization rate. This can result in larger vapor clouds, increasing the boundary of the flammable atmosphere.
3. *Surface type.* The surface where the LNG spills influences its vaporization rate. Vaporization rates are high on wet surfaces, such as muddy soil, because water acts as a heat sink. Asphalt promotes vaporization because its dark color acts as a heat radiator. If LNG spills onto a good heat-insulating surface, boiling may eventually slow down, but the remaining liquid pool continues to evaporate rapidly. Evaporation maintains the remaining liquid near its boiling point as it absorbs heat from its surroundings.
4. *Time of the incident.* At night, lack of atmospheric heating by the sun and ground reduces the evaporation rate of LNG. While this influences the vaporization rate, it also influences the distance from the source spill in which the vapor

puff remains in its flammable range. At night, the distance is greater because the time needed to heat the vapor until it is lighter than air increases.

Fire fighters should remember that LNG vapor formed during the phase change is colorless and odorless at normal temperature and pressures. They cannot rely on visual or olfactory indicators to establish safe boundaries. Only gas detection equipment designed to detect methane can establish safe exclusion and operating zones when dealing with LNG releases.

Fire Hazards of LP-Gas. LP-gas is stored as a liquefied gas at its vapor pressure and at ambient temperature. At ambient conditions, propane's vapor density is 1½ times that of air. This means that propane released to the atmosphere sinks to the ground and forms a vapor cloud that can follow surface contours over a large area. Because of the vapor density and expansion ratio of LP-gas, this class of materials can challenge fire fighters. Incidents involving LP-gas containers can result in jet fires, vapor cloud ignition, or boiling liquid expanding vapor explosions (BLEVEs). Because the alternative-fueled vehicles on the road are predominantly LP-gas fueled, fire fighters can expect to respond to incidents involving LP-gas more than other alternative fuels.

Two types of LP-gas releases can occur: vapor phase release and liquid phase release. A vapor phase release can occur if a component installed above the liquid line is damaged or the container is punctured or otherwise damaged above the liquid line. During a vapor release, LP-gas vents at a high velocity from the opening, possibly creating some liquid droplets during the process. The velocity of the release reduces with time as boiling inside the container cools the liquid mass. The tank's surface forms a layer of frost due to the refrigeration effect of the liquid being cooled. The gas may continue venting for a considerable time until no liquid is left in the container.

A liquid phase release occurs if an LP-gas component installed below the liquid line is damaged or if the container is punctured or damaged below the liquid line. When the release occurs below the liquid level, the liquefied gas may jet from the hole. The velocity of the liquid discharge depends on the amount of liquid in the container and the gas vapor pressure. During a liquid phase release, large amounts of the liquid flash into gas or vapor. Depending on the temperature and pressure, a propane release in its liquid phase can discharge a large mass of vapor mixed with small droplets suspended as an aerosol. Sometimes, liquid propane pools on the ground surface and typically boils off into gas.

During a vapor phase or liquid phase release, volatile gases and vapors, if not ignited immediately, form a plume that moves downwind of the container. If the plume contacts an ignition source, and the vapor plume is within the flammable range, the flame may flash back toward the source of the release. Unprotected people within the cloud may be severely injured. If the velocity of the flame front is great enough, air, products of combustion, and unburned fuel can compress to a point where a vapor cloud explosion could occur. In this case, the deflagration's pressure can also impact persons and property.

Fire Hazards of Hydrogen Gas and Liquid Hydrogen. Hydrogen gas has a flammable range of 4 percent to 75 percent in air by volume. It can be easily ignited and if contained can explode. Hydrogen has a vapor density of 0.07 relative to air, so it will disperse rapidly. Hydrogen has a boiling point of –423°F (–253°C), which means that any liquid release will quickly vaporize. Liquid hydrogen released from a pipe will under many conditions vaporize before contacting the ground resulting in no free-flowing liquid hydrogen. Liquid hydrogen releases may cause oxygen to condense out of the air presenting the additional hazard of an oxygen-enriched environment.

BOILING LIQUID EXPANDING VAPOR EXPLOSIONS

A boiling liquid expanding vapor explosion (BLEVE) is defined as a major container failure, into two or more pieces, at the moment in time when the contained liquid is well above its normal boiling point at atmospheric pressure.[11] Gas and LNG containers are susceptible to BLEVEs. BLEVEs occur when liquids are stored in a container under pressure at a temperature above their boiling points.

LNG and LP-gas both possess high expansion ratios. For instance, 1 ft^3 (0.028 m^3) of LNG expands to 618 ft^3 (17.4 m^3) of natural gas at ambient conditions, and 1 ft^3 (0.028 m^3) of liquid propane expands to approximately 265 ft^3 (7.5 m^3) of propane gas at normal temperature and pressure. Expansion of a liquefied gas increases the pressure on tank walls if pressure relief valves fail to open or if relief valves are incapable of adequately relieving internal tank pressure. A puncture in the tank wall or heating of the container surface due to an exposure or pool fire could cause expansion. As the tank walls' strength decreases and liquefied gas within the tank continues to expand, the tank fails, breaking into two or more pieces. The flammable gas can ignite simultaneously with tank failure.

The insulation of LNG containers that are constructed according to ASME Boiler and Pressure Vessel code helps protect the inner tank from exposure to high temperatures resulting from flame impingement. Storage vessels used at LNG fueling sites are similar to those used for storing cryogenic liquids. LNG containers' outer metal jacket protects an insulating material maintained under a vacuum. This assembly surrounds an inner steel vessel that holds the cryogenic natural gas liquid. This outer jacket and insulation, combined with the liquid's extreme cold, are expected to provide substantial protection from radiant heat exposure due to a pool fire. Fire tests conclude that the pressure relief valves for an uninsulated cryogenic vessel activate within 1 hour. If the tank insulation and vacuum are intact, the relief valve does not actuate for several days.[12]

Additional information on BLEVEs involving LP-gases can be found in Section 6, Chapter 10, "Gases."

HEALTH AND SAFETY CONCERNS

Health Hazards

Health risks of the three alternative fuels discussed in this chapter generally result from two different exposure routes: (1) skin contact and (2) inhalation. Ingestion is usually not a likely route of exposure.

Potential for skin contact with CNG is very low. Almost immediate dispersion results when a container releases CNG stored at pressures in excess of 2400 psi (16,546 kPa). LNG, a cryogenic liquid stored at –260°F (–162°C), can cause burns or frostbite upon contact. Hypothermia can also occur from prolonged exposure to LNG vapor.

Asphyxiation occurs when other gases displace oxygen in the air and the oxygen concentration decreases to less than a tenable level. LNG vapor is not toxic; however, there is potential for lung damage or asphyxiation. Lung damage could occur from prolonged breathing of cold vapors. Neither CNG or LNG has an established time-weighted average because they are simple asphyxiates; LP-gas has a time-weighted average of 1000 ppm. All the gaseous alternative fuels may cause asphyxiation if released in a confined space.

Hydrogen does not present a toxicity hazard. However, liquid hydrogen storage systems operate at extremely low temperatures and present cryogen burn hazards. Also, gaseous hydrogen storage systems operate at extremely high pressures, and the potential energy of these high pressures presents a hazard.

Odorization

Odorization of odorless gas such as natural gas or propane is an important safety precaution. It indicates, by odor, a gas leak or a release event. Natural gas is odorized within the pipeline prior to general distribution. Natural gas is normally odorized at a level allowing detection at 20 to 25 percent of the lower flammable limit of methane. CNG taken from a distribution line and compressed contains the odorants typically added to natural gas. One major difference between CNG and LNG is that LNG has no odor. Consequently, LNG leaks cannot be detected by smell. San Diego Gas and Electric Company developed an odorization technique for LNG in the 1970s. The technique used the same odorants used in natural gas, but blended them with a carrier gas such as liquid propane. A Gas Research Institute study revealed that odorants such as ethyl mercaptan, *i*-propyl mercaptan, and *t*-butyl mercaptan could be used with carrier gases such as liquid propane and *i*-butane to odorize LNG.[13] Although the study indicates viable options for odorization of LNG, NFPA 59A, *Standard for the Production, Storage, and Handling of Liquefied Natural Gas (LNG),* does not require it.

LP-gas is odorized before delivery to a bulk plant.[14] Like natural gas, it is detectable by odor at a concentration in air at less than one-fifth of the lower flammability limit. Typical odorants used include ethyl mercaptan and thiophane.

It is not possible to warn everyone of a gas leak by using odorants. Odorants can fade in transmission lines and containers due to oxidization by oxygen, rust, or iron oxides. Furthermore, olfactory senses diminish with increasing age, allergies, and during smoking and eating.

Hydrogen is typically not odorized. Because hydrogen has a boiling point of –423°F (–253°C) most chemicals would be in the solid phase if mixed with liquid hydrogen. Gaseous hydrogen is often used in fuel cells where the odorants would contaminate the fuel cell catalysts and prevent the fuel cells from functioning. Therefore, odorants are not used in hydrogen. As hydrogen becomes more widely used in fuel cells, there may be odorants developed that would not contaminate the fuel cell. Research is being conducted on this topic.

APPLICABLE NFPA STANDARDS

NFPA standards have been developed for all alternative fuels described in this chapter. NFPA 52, *Vehicular Fuel Systems Code,* 2006 edition, contains requirements for the use of CNG, LNG, and hydrogen. NFPA 57, *Liquefied Natural Gas Vehicular Fuel Systems Code,* has been incorporated into NFPA 52 and no longer exists as an independent document. The 2006 edition of NFPA 52 contains new requirements for both liquefied and gaseous hydrogen. NFPA 58, *Liquefied Petroleium Gas Code,* contains requirements for LP-gas. NFPA 59, *Utility LP-Gas Plant Code,* has requirements for storing and constructing LNG containers. However, the standard was originally written for site-erected LNG containers similar to those found at peak-shaving plants. Conversely, LNG stations normally use shop-constructed containers. Many station designers and operators wanted a separate standard that specifically applies to vehicle fuel systems and LNG dispensing. The National Fire Protection Association responded by developing NFPA 57, which was incorporated into NFPA 52 in 2005.

VEHICLE FUELING STATIONS

There were over 5000 refueling sites in the United States in 2006. The majority of these sites (2771) are for LP-gas refueling (Table 21.4.15). There are 754 sites for CNG refueling, leaving approximately 1500 sites for all other types of alternative fuels. Of these approximately 1500 remaining sites, 37 are for LNG refueling. These sites are both public and private refueling sites, which may skew the distribution toward LP-gas; but even considering this possibility, it is clear that there is much greater access to LP-gas. Note that Alaska and Hawaii do not have CNG refueling facilities and that the majority of states do not have LNG refueling facilities. However, the number of refueling facilities has steadily increased, and if current trends in the increased use of alternative fuel vehicles continue, the number of refueling facilities should also increase.

Compressed Natural Gas Vehicle Fueling Stations

CNG fueling stations can be generally categorized according to the time needed to fuel. The method used depends on the filling time the user desires. Available equipment combinations result in facilities being categorized as either "fast-fill dispensing" or "slow-fill dispensing."

Refueling a standard passenger vehicle at slow-fill CNG stations can commonly take up to 8 hours. These stations connect to the natural gas service line that typically supplies fuel for building heat. CNG slow-filling systems use a small compressor, eliminating the need for high gas flow and large gas supply piping. The small compressor usually combines with the dispensing equipment to form a compact module mounted next to the vehicle's parking space. Typically, no storage containers

TABLE 21.4.15 Alternative Fueling Station Counts by State and Fuel Type, 2006

State	*CNG*	*E85*	*LPG*	*ELEC*	*BD*	*HY*	*LNG*	*Totals by State*
Alabama	1	0	74	0	0	0	0	75
Alaska	0	0	12	0	0	0	0	12
Arizona	30	4	74	18	4	1	4	135
Arkansas	4	0	57	0	0	0	0	61
California	179	3	257	405	17	9	30	900
Colorado	21	11	72	4	22	0	0	130
Connecticut	11	0	19	4	1	0	0	35
Delaware	1	0	3	0	3	0	0	7
Dist. of Columbia	1	0	0	0	0	1	0	2
Florida	23	2	70	7	4	0	0	106
Georgia	20	5	55	0	18	0	0	98
Hawaii	0	0	6	11	3	0	0	20
Idaho	8	1	28	0	2	0	1	40
Illinois	11	96	73	0	9	0	0	189
Indiana	11	18	42	0	10	0	0	81
Iowa	0	40	29	0	8	0	0	77
Kansas	3	7	49	0	4	0	0	63
Kentucky	0	5	36	0	6	0	0	47
Louisiana	8	0	14	0	0	0	0	22
Maine	1	0	6	0	2	0	0	9
Maryland	13	4	19	0	3	0	0	39
Massachusetts	9	0	28	28	1	0	0	66
Michigan	15	4	94	0	13	2	0	128
Minnesota	3	196	35	0	2	0	0	236
Mississippi	0	0	40	0	6	0	0	46
Missouri	6	21	88	0	2	0	0	117
Montana	2	5	31	0	6	0	0	44
Nebraska	1	26	23	0	1	0	0	51
Nevada	16	3	25	0	10	1	0	55
New Hampshire	3	0	13	10	10	0	0	36
New Jersey	15	0	11	0	1	0	0	27
New Mexico	8	3	60	0	2	0	0	73
New York	37	6	28	0	3	0	0	74
North Carolina	10	9	69	0	38	0	0	126
North Dakota	4	20	16	0	0	0	0	40
Ohio	13	6	77	0	16	0	0	112
Oklahoma	53	4	71	1	5	0	0	134
Oregon	14	1	34	4	14	0	0	67
Pennsylvania	31	1	64	0	11	0	0	107
Rhode Island	6	0	4	2	0	0	0	12
South Carolina	5	28	41	2	24	0	0	100
South Dakota	0	30	22	0	0	0	0	52
Tennessee	6	5	59	0	9	0	0	79
Texas	29	4	628	2	10	0	2	675
Utah	63	3	27	0	3	0	0	96
Vermont	1	0	6	10	5	0	0	22
Virginia	13	2	25	0	10	0	0	50
Washington	14	2	60	0	17	0	0	93
West Virginia	2	2	8	0	0	0	0	12
Wisconsin	18	12	56	0	2	0	0	88
Wyoming	11	3	33	0	13	0	0	60
Totals by fuel	754	592	2771	508	350	14	37	5026

Source: U.S. Department of Energy.

are associated with these units, which contributes to longer filling times. Mostly used for overnight fueling, slow-fill units are typically used by fleets of less than 30 vehicles that do not operate continuously. Compact unit design and smaller supply requirement makes slow-fill fueling possible at private residences, depending on local regulations. The installation shown in Figure 21.4.1 uses vehicle refueling appliances (VRAs) to fuel CNG-powered vans overnight. Average fill time for an automobile or van is 4 to 8 hours, depending on the size and number of cylinders.

Fast-fill CNG stations normally fuel a conventional passenger vehicle in less than 5 minutes. Sometimes, fixed storage vessels are used as supply sources and must be transfilled from a high-pressure transport tube trailer that is brought to the station site. More commonly, a connection to the nearest domestic natural gas distribution system supplies the natural gas. A pressure cascade system compresses and dispenses low pressure natural gas (60 to 100 psi [413 to 689 kPa]) at the higher pressures (2500 to 4500 psi [16,536 to 31,005 kPa]) the CNG vehicle requires. These systems can be found at locations typically serving more than 30 vehicles.

CNG Siting Considerations. CNG fueling is performed at public service stations, small private fleet operations, metropolitan mass transit facilities, school districts, cab companies, government agencies, and residences (if local regulations allow). CNG fueling typically is performed outdoors. CNG compression, storage, and dispensing systems should take into consideration setback distances from property lines, on-site adjacent buildings, overhead power lines, nonclassified overhead electrical lighting, and ignition sources. Protective canopies and open structures installed to protect equipment should be of noncombustible construction, with a roof design that ensures adequate ventilation and prohibits pocketing or collection of CNG due to the buoyancy of natural gas. Typical unintentional releases of CNG will be completed in a matter of seconds due to very high compression and storage pressures. The quick release and buoyancy of CNG minimize the potential threat from open-air flammable vapor cloud ignitions. Ignition of leaking high-pressure gas is possible, and the resulting jet fire can extend from 10 to 30 ft (3 to 9 m) in length, depending on the leak's size and CNG pressure. This makes the orientation of storage cylinders and relief valves an important site consideration. With the addition of protective measures and depending on local regulations, CNG fueling can be accomplished indoors. This is a potential consideration when weather- or freeze-protection is needed for the compression, storage, and dispensing systems. Indoor fueling with CNG can only be accomplished inside structures dedicated to this purpose or within rooms or additions provided with at least 2 hour fire-resistive walls as separation from other occupancies. When dispensing CNG indoors, overpressure protection, such as explosion venting, is necessary. Mechanical ventilation that is continuous or activated by a gas detection system must be installed. To allow for delays in the mechanical ventilation startup, the gas detection system should activate ventilation at a level not exceeding 20 percent of the lower flammable limit. An audible alarm should also sound at the 20 percent lower flammability level. Activation of the gas detection system must result in automatic shutdown of compression and dispensing equipment by placement of solenoid switches and automatic shutoff valves. Although not required by NFPA 52, some model building and fire codes may require the installation of an automatic sprinkler system for indoor dispensing and storage of CNG. Local approvals for indoor dispensing may vary, but public structures, such as parking garages, are commonly unacceptable for fueling of any type of conventional or alternative fuel.

When considering the siting of CNG fueling stations, the general public is probably most familiar with the hazard potential of natural gas. Their expectation or acceptance of hazard is commonly based on the low pressure natural gas used for home cooking and heating. Mentioning high-pressure natural gas used in CNG fueling is likely to conjure up consequences associated with large-diameter, high-pressure natural gas transmission pipelines. Major CNG fueling facilities that use large-capacity compressors sometimes require the extension of a larger and higher pressure natural gas pipeline. Those who live near large CNG fueling stations may question their safety and acceptability because they fear CNG fueling components and the increased size of natural gas mains in the public right-of-way.

FIGURE 21.4.1 Slow-Fill Vehicle Refueling Appliance (Source: Fuelmaker, Inc.)

CNG Compressor Components. The very large range of CNG compressors' capacity makes fill time vary. Small, slow-fill units with a compressor capacity of approximately 5 to 10 SCF/min are small enough to fit in the front seat of a car. NFPA 52 defines these compressors as residential refueling appliances or vehicle refueling appliances (see Figure 21.4.1). They generally require only a normal domestic natural gas supply line. Medium-sized, fast-fill compressors typically found at public fueling stations are capable of supplying approximately 1000 SCF/min (28.3 m^3/min). A normal domestic supply line can also supply these medium-sized compressors. Like the slow-fill units, these fast-fill compressor sets are sometimes packaged with other fueling components and are available as portable, premanufactured units that fit in the space required for a passenger vehicle. Large industrial compressors can compress approximately 5000 SCF/

min (142 m^3/min) at about 3600 psi (24,804 kPa) and can fill the space needed to park a bus. Depending on the number of large compressors needed, supply from a 6-in. (152-mm) diameter natural gas pipeline is not uncommon.

Compressors require pressure relief devices set for each stage pressure. A four-stage compressor might have relief valves set for 250, 1250, 1400, and 4150 psi (1724, 8618, 9652, and 28,610 kPa), depending on the compression chamber's size and associated piping into which they are installed. CNG compressors are also required to have automatic shutdown capability in the event of high discharge pressure or low suction pressure. Compressor controls must be manually reset if an automatic shutoff or power failure occurs. Internal combustion engines, modified to operate using natural gas, usually drive compressor sets. NFPA 52 requires the design, construction, and maintenance of these compressor drivers to be in accordance with NFPA 37, *Standard for the Installation and Use of Stationary Combustion Engines and Gas Turbines.*

CNG Storage Components. Pressure vessels are a common method of storing compressed natural gas. NFPA 52 requires pressure vessels to be constructed in accordance with the ASME Boiler and Pressure Vessel Code. Fast-fill dispensing transfers CNG from a bank of pressure vessels to the vehicle in a fairly short time, usually less than 5 minutes. These pressure vessel banks, or cascades, are usually multiple compressed gas cylinders, spherical vessels, or horizontal tubes. Normally, three pressure banks are involved in a cascade system (Figure 21.4.2). To "top off" a vehicle container, dispensing begins from a storage vessel having lower pressure until pressure equalizes, then automatic controls switch to a vessel of higher storage pressure. This automatic switching between cascade banks continues sequentially until vehicle fueling is complete. Subsequent vehicles can be filled until cascade pressure drops too low. Then the system automatically switches to the compressor. This, however, increases fill time, so the capacity of storage containers at a site usually reflects the number of vehicles to be served.

Bulk CNG storage is infrequently required when obtaining an on-site natural gas supply to compress is not possible or when the economics of installation does not justify the cost of a compressor. Bulk storage is usually accomplished by transporting gas compressed at another site, then transfilling from the transport tube trailer into pressure vessels. Bulk vessels do not draw down at the same rate when fueling a vehicle, but their automated systems operate like the cascade system. Bulk compressed gas is usually dispensed from at least three vessels (see Figure 21.4.2).

CNG cascade and bulk storage vessels must be adequately supported on no more than two longitudinal points and should be adequately protected from vehicle impact. A check valve should be installed so that backpressure cannot bleed back to the supply, and adequate pressure-relief devices must be installed in each vessel. The pressure-relief devices should be vertically vented and protected against weather. Pressure gauges installed on each vessel or pressure bank determine the fullness of a storage vessel. Sometimes, outlets for storage vessels are fitted with excess flow valves. These devices restrict flow from the vessel if the tubing or piping leaks. A check-type valve closes when flow exceeds that rated for the piping system. Usually, carbon or stainless steel tubing and piping connect the cascade or bulk vessels, and approved flexible metallic hose is installed for expansion, contraction, jarring, vibration, and settling where necessary.

CNG Dispenser Components. Dispensing equipment can look like conventional gasoline dispensing equipment, or it can simply be a hose and nozzle rated for high-pressure service and mounted on a post (Figure 21.4.3). Fuel dispensers should be provided with protection from vehicle impact, using islands, pipe bollards, or other appropriate designs.

If located at a public service station, the dispenser usually measures "equivalent gallons" of fuel; otherwise, the unit of measure varies depending on the owner's needs or local weights and measures standards. Underground piping usually connects

FIGURE 21.4.2 Pressure Vessels for Storing Compressed Natural Gas

FIGURE 21.4.3 CNG Dispensers

CNG dispensers to the storage and compression systems. Just as at a conventional service station, multiple CNG dispensers are not typically installed on one supply line. Instead, each has individual, dedicated piping from the storage or supply.

CNG dispensing systems require electronic or pneumatic controls that sense vehicle container fill pressure and automatically stop the flow. Settings for these controls are based on outside temperature. In addition, an emergency shutdown device commonly installed at the storage and compressor activates if there is a problem at the dispenser. Even so, a "quarter turn" manual shutoff valve is located at the dispenser just upstream from the dispensing hose and its required breakaway device. The hose breakaway device, located outside the dispenser end, closes if a vehicle moves away from the dispenser without breaking the vehicle fueling connection. CNG breakaway devices release and seal at approximately 44 lb (22 kg) of force from any direction.

The CNG fueling hose must be rated for the system's service pressures. Like the flammable liquids dispensing hose, the CNG hose must be nonconductive. A significant feature of the CNG fueling hose is the inclusion of a second hose, usually designed as integral to the supply hose. When fueling is complete, this second hose collects natural gas from the vehicle fueling connection and supply hose. Some dispensing units vent the hose automatically; others require a manual valve to accomplish this venting. In either case, the vehicle connection does not release until the connection and hose is depressurized. After CNG fueling is complete, vented gas returns to the dispenser and ultimately to storage or an approved vent stack, depending on local requirements. Typical CNG fueling hose is easy to handle and is approximately ½ to ¾ in. (1.27 to 1.91 cm) in diameter. CNG dispensing hose cannot be more than 25 ft (7.6 m) long and must be supported aboveground, usually by a retractable cord like those used on conventional fuel dispensers.

The CNG dispensing nozzle that connects the fueling hose to the vehicle is similar to a typical quick-connect coupling used on compressed air hoses, except it includes breakaway protection. The vehicle fueling receptacle, fuel control valve, and dispenser nozzle are designed in accordance with ANSI/American Gas Association NGV 1, *Basic Requirements for Compressed Natural Gas Vehicle Fueling Connection Devices.*[15] The NGV 1 standard includes requirements for the vehicle fueling receptacle, the dispenser nozzles, and the fuel control valve installed at the dispenser. Depending on the component's style, devices are rated for service pressure between 2400 and 3600 psig. The NGV 1 standard defines three types of nozzles:

- Type 1 nozzles use an integral valve operating mechanism that vents the gas between the vehicle's fill line check valve and the nozzle inlet valve and then disconnects the nozzle from the vehicle (Figure 21.4.4). CNG nozzles are similar to quick-connect couplings used on compressed air hoses. The Type 1 nozzle shown in Figure 21.4.4 has an integral valve that vents the gas between the vehicle's fill-line check valve and nozzle inlet before it can be disconnected from the vehicle.
- Type 2 nozzles use an external valve that must be vented before disconnection.

FIGURE 21.4.4 CNG Nozzle

- Type 3 nozzles use controls that automatically depressurize the fill line upon dispenser shutdown. They are normally found on vehicle refueling appliances or residential refueling appliances.

Each type must be designed so that the fueling system is depressurized before the nozzle can be removed.

Liquefied Natural Gas Vehicle Fueling Stations

LNG fueling stations can be characterized according to the method used for obtaining liquid transfer pressure. Some use gravity available from a vertical bulk storage vessel to fill a smaller transfer vessel at 75 to 100 psi (517 to 689 kPa). A portion of the LNG passes through a vaporizer and back into the smaller transfer vessel to warm the liquid. The 618:1 expansion ratio of the LNG in the smaller vessel increases the pressure to as much as 230 psi (1586 kPa) to force liquid into the LNG vehicle. Transfer rates of 40 to 50 gal/min (0.15 to 0.19 m^3/min) are not uncommon.

The other common type of LNG fueling station uses a centrifugal cryogenic pump supplied from a vertical or horizontal bulk LNG storage vessel. Centrifugal cryogenic pumps typically provide LNG fueling rates of 30 to 50 gal/min (0.11 to 0.19 m^3/min), depending on the LNG vehicle tank pressure required. The net positive suction head that the centrifugal pump requires is important. Some installations experience cavitation and poor performance when storage design does not provide enough suction head. Fueling stations that use underground LNG bulk storage vessels are available but not as common. Underground installations use a slow-action, positive-displacement pump that lifts LNG about 25 ft (7.6 m), provides 30 to 50 gal (0.11 to 0.19 m^3/min) of liquid per minute, and delivers at pressures as high as 200 psi (1379 kPa).[16] LNG fueling facilities that use cryogenic pumps typically operate on electricity.

LNG fueling facilities can also be designed to supply CNG vehicles. LNG fueling stations normally create some vapor due to external heat absorption of the stored LNG, priming of pumps, and temperature equalization of equipment. In addition to normal vaporization, LNG is sent to a vaporizer to create gas specifically for fueling CNG vehicles. Under some conditions, LNG to CNG fuel supply or liquefied-compressed natural gas (LCNG) may be cheaper than CNG supplied from domestic natural gas lines. Facilities that use vapor expansion for LNG fueling pressure provide a compressor and cascade system to fuel CNG vehicles. Systems with high-pressure LNG pumps combine LNG pump capacity and gas expansion, through the vaporizer, to fill the CNG cascade storage. The CNG must be odorized with an odor potent enough to be detected to down to a concentration in air of not over one-fifth of the lower limit of flammability.

LNG Siting Considerations. LNG vehicle fueling is typically associated with large fleet operations in heavily populated urban areas. These include such facilities as mass transit, cab companies, and government agencies. Some rural fleets that use large vehicles, such as mining operations or transport trucking, have also converted to LNG use. Because a significant number of fleet vehicles are necessary for LNG fueling to be economical, self-serve general public vehicle fueling with LNG is not expected to become commonplace.[12] In addition, indoor fueling with LNG is not typically performed. However, it has been proposed that this activity be limited to the use of less than 125 gal (0.47 m^3) containers when necessary gas detection, ventilation, fire protective, and building construction features are provided.

NFPA 57 sets distances from impoundment areas to building and property lines. These distances are based on the container volume and range from 0 for containers of 0.5 m^3 or less to 23 m for containers of 114–265 m^3. This range of 0.5–265 m^3 should include most LNG storage containers. Additionally, there are minimum distances between storage containers set in NFPA 57; these distances range from 0 for containers 0.5 m^3 or less to one-fourth of the diameter of adjacent container(s) for containers ranging from 114 to 265 m^3. There are also requirements for container seismic design that specify the horizontal and vertical forces that shop-built ASME containers must meet based on the amount of seismic activity at the location where the container is to be installed.

Normally buoyant, natural gas vaporizing from a supercooled liquid state remains initially heavier than air. While cool, the natural gas forms a vapor cloud that follows the ground surface until it heats sufficiently to regain its lighter-than-air characteristics. In addition to separation, site consideration should include containment of the fueling facility. Containment helps limit the surface area of an LNG spill, reduces the spill vaporization rate, and thereby reduces the distance a potential vapor cloud travels before becoming buoyant. Separation and containment are important requirements, particularly when locating an LNG fueling facility near other land uses that are densely populated or provide potential ignition sources.

LNG Storage Components. LNG storage and use is not something that very many communities have experienced. Members of the general public who are presently familiar with LNG facilities usually live in areas that have bulk LNG supply for domestic natural gas distribution or power plant peak shaving needs. Cryogenic gas storage and liquid transfer have a long history, but bulk storage and dispensing of LNG vehicle fueling is a relatively new use of an adapted technology. Compared with the other types of alternative fuels, LNG use in private vehicles does not seem to be as well demonstrated. This could result in hesitation to accept the additional hazards associated with LNG storage and vehicle fueling in densely populated urban areas or the costs associated with LNG systems versus CNG systems.

LNG is normally transported from a liquefaction plant to the fueling facility by cryogenic bulk transport trailers. Transfilling may occur at night because LNG-fueled fleets need to be filled before business hours. The number of vehicles to be filled and the capacity of on-site storage dictate the frequency of LNG transport and transfilling. Bulk LNG at typical fueling sites is stored in containers having a total capacity of approximately 15,000 gal (57 m^3). This quantity allows unloading of one transport that usually carries 11,000 to 13,000 gal (42 to 49 m^3) (Figure 21.4.5). Depending on delivery schedules and demand, more than one container might be located at a fueling site. Containers can be horizontal or vertical, depending on owner preference, aesthetics, and available space.

Siting of containers should be based on the requirements of NFPA 59A. Transfer of LNG from the supply truck trailer to bulk storage is accomplished by increasing the trailer's normal storage pressure of 10 psi (70 kPa) to approximately 40 to 50 psi (276 to 345 kPa). If a vertical bulk storage vessel is used, transfer pressure may be as high as 250 psi (1724 kPa). This is accomplished by boiling off some LNG in an auxiliary line and allowing it back into the trailer. A small amount of LNG may leak out of the hose connection to the bulk vessel because of the temperature difference between the inside and outside of the fueling connection. LNG bulk storage containers have liquid level gauges and a high liquid level alarm or indicator that warns the operator to stop filling the bulk vessel. When transfer is complete, a pump on the supply truck transfers any LNG remaining

FIGURE 21.4.5 A 13,500 gal (51 m^3) LNG Container Used for Vehicle Refueling

in the hose to the storage vessel. During transfer, a pressure differential of at least 15 psi is maintained between the transport trailer and the bulk storage vessel. In the event of a backfill condition, a backflow check valve is required on the transfer fill piping of an LNG bulk storage vessel.

LNG spill containment should include the following requirements:

- Impounding area that has the volumetric capacity to hold the greatest volume of LNG that could be discharged into the area during a 10 minute release from any single accidental leakage source
- Measures to prevent any release of LNG from the plant property and for surface water drainage
- Provisions to clear rain or other water from the impounding area
- Separating the point of transfer from the nearest important building not associated with the LNG facility by 25 ft (7.6 m)
- Selecting a design and materials appropriate for LNG
- Operating instructions identifying the location and operation of emergency controls

The use of insulated materials considerably reduces vapor dispersion distances. The containment system's design and the type of insulating material used can reduce the vaporization rate as much as 30 percent.[17] Equipment within the containment should be limited to LNG-related apparatus. CNG equipment such as compressors, vaporizers, and CNG storage cylinders should not be located within the LNG secondary containment, due to potential fire exposure and damage from high pressure.

Pressure-relief valves must be designed with a capacity to not only vent vaporized natural gas adequately if fire exposure occurs but also include capacity for the flow of liquid in the event an overfill of the bulk storage occurs. Pressure-relief valves are typically located in the storage vessel, the insulation space of the vessel, and any insulated piping that can be isolated between two block valves. Typically, a system of air-operated valves controls the flow of liquid for vehicle fueling. Air supply lines for the flow control valves commonly consist of low-melt-point plastic tubing. If exposed to fire, these air supply lines will melt and cause the valves to shut in a fail-safe manner.

LNG Dispenser Components. Dispensers available for LNG fueling can look like conventional fuel dispensers. Typically they do not. Instead they are an assembly of a cryogenic coupling nozzle, insulated cryogenic hose, shutoff valves, and panel or pole mounted gauges. Sometimes the fueling hose attaches to a rotating arm that supports the hose as it is attached to the vehicle. If not, a retractable stainless steel cable supports the cryogenic hose. LNG fueling hoses are insulated and can be 3 to 4 in. (7.6 to 10.2 cm) in diameter. They are fitted with a large cryogenic coupling, about 1 in. (2.5 cm) in diameter. Compared to conventional fuel hoses and nozzles, this assembly can be cumbersome.

A shutoff valve is attached on the open end of the cryogenic hose, just before the LNG coupling that connects to the vehicle. This coupling includes an interlock device that does not allow release during transfer. LNG couplings operate like sexless fittings commonly used on fire hose. A manual emergency shutoff valve is placed in the transfer system, near the connection to supply piping at the storage vessel. This manual shutoff valve must be readily accessible by the operator. Bleed or vent connections incorporated into the coupling let dispenser hoses be drained, depressurized, and sometimes purged with nitrogen. These connections usually drain to a vaporizer, and natural gas either vents or is transferred to a CNG fueling process. LNG dispensing units may have electronic level sensors that automatically activate the dispensing shutoff valve. More often, a level gauge provided on the vehicle requires the operator to measure the vehicle tank level and then manually stop dispensing. Even with these controls, providing drainage should be considered so that accidental LNG spills drain into the storage vessel secondary containment.

Liquefied Petroleum Gas Fueling Stations

Types of LP-Gas Fueling Stations. LP-gas used for vehicle fueling is typically propane. Propane has a long history of use in industrial applications and predominately rural areas as a home-and-business heating fuel. Although most domestic propane heating appliances use vapor as fuel, vehicle fueling transfers propane in liquid form. The equipment needed has been used for many years at bulk plant facilities for transfer to bobtail propane delivery trucks and for container filling. This equipment has also been extensively used for forklift truck fueling at manufacturing and storage occupancies.

Historically, propane vehicle fueling in the United States has been predominantly at bulk plant locations or with the other traditional propane supply services. Some consider LP-gas vehicle fueling the least complicated of the three alternative fuels discussed in this chapter. The mechanics of supplying liquefied gases for fueling vehicles does not vary significantly from the processes used for supplying LP-gas for heating. LP-gas at vehicle fueling locations is typically moved to the fueling site by highway transport truck and then transfilled into the bulk fueling storage container.

There are three common ways to transfer LP-gas in the liquid phase: (1) by use of an LP-gas pump, (2) by gravity, and (3) by use of a compressor. Using LP-gas pumps to transfer liquid is the most common method. This is because of the flexibility afforded by not having a required tank elevation or hazards associated with vessel pressurization. LP-gas pumping has been used extensively to fill LP-gas bobtail delivery trucks from bulk storage vessels. The same pump technology has been adapted for use in fueling vehicles with propane. Positive displacement pumps, such as sliding vane, gear pumps, or centrifugal pumps, are common with the pump discharge pressure limited to a maximum of 350 psig (2412 kPag). Electricity usually powers the LP-gas pumps used at vehicle fueling stations.

LP-gas vehicle fueling facilities can use horizontal, vertical, or, sometimes, underground pressure vessels. Vehicle fueling at LP-gas bulk storage operations is typically in horizontal pressure vessels. LP-gas vehicle fueling at locations with space limitations sometimes uses vertical pressure vessels. Underground pressure vessels dedicated for LP-gas vehicle fueling are not as common because of additional cost, maintenance responsibilities associated with corrosion protection, and, sometimes, prohibitive soil conditions.

LP-Gas Siting Considerations. Vehicle fueling with LP-gas should be limited to outdoors. The liquid–vapor expansion ratio of propane is approximately 270:1,[14] so an unintended liquid discharge releases a greater quantity of vapor than does a leak from the LP-gas vessel's vapor space. In addition, vapor release from emergency relief valves due to unintended container overfilling makes LP-gas vehicle fueling hard to justify as an enclosed, indoor activity. Even outdoors, propane tends to form a vapor cloud that, under the right conditions, can travel downwind at flammable concentrations until it encounters an ignition source. This is because LP-gas has a vapor density approximately 1.5 times that of air. Less common, but possible, is an LP-gas container BLEVE incident initiated by an emergency relief device failure or rapid container exposure to intense radiant heat.

Setback distances from adjoining property lines and adjacent buildings should be evaluated not only for building exposure from leaks at the LP-gas fueling station but also for building fire exposure on the fueling station. Considering mutual exposure is sometimes complicated. Many published setback requirements intend to prevent smaller, more common LP-gas vapor releases from reaching an ignition source. These distances also provide space to buy time for implementing emergency activities such as applying water to a propane pressure vessel to protect it from an adjacent fire's radiating heat. Typically these distances offer protection for releases, such as those from emergency relief valves, that result from container overfilling. A large, continuous liquid leak from a damaged or malfunctioning container connection, transfer piping, or pump casing can produce more serious vapor cloud, BLEVE, and shrapnel hazards. The hazards associated with these situations exceed the largest setback distances specified for LP-gas applications. The setback distances given in NFPA 58 should be considered minimum requirements to reduce risk. These distances should not be treated as safe distances that would eliminate all risk or eliminate the effect of all types of hazardous events associated with LP storage and transfer operations.

Historically, the location of LP-gas applications has been predominantly in rural or suburban areas, or in commercial or industrial areas. In these locations, hazards are commensurate with other hazardous operations and exposure to the public has been limited accordingly.[18] The addition of LP-gas vehicle fueling stations to heavily populated urban areas offers LP-gas suppliers new markets, sometimes near congested residential areas that historically supported conventional public fueling stations. Additional setbacks and protective equipment should be considered in these situations. These help limit urban public exposure to a risk level enjoyed before the alternative fuels market expanded. NFPA 58 gives a set of alternative provisions for the installation of American Society of Mechanical Engineers (ASME) containers, which includes additional safety requirements that allow for setback distance reductions. These provisions would allow the installation of ASME containers at locations, such as conventional refueling facilities, without increasing the risk that these installations create. These additional safety measures include low emission transfer and automatic shutdown of all primary valves in the event of a fire or hose pull-away. Figure 21.4.6 shows a fueling facility that stores and dispenses gasoline, CNG, and LP-gas in an urban area. A release or fire from such an aboveground fueling facility would impact surrounding fire exposures, the general public, and emergency responders.

LP-Gas Storage Components. LP-gas vehicle fueling has typically been accomplished at bulk storage facilities where large volumes are stored in horizontal pressure vessels. With LP-gas vehicle fueling increasing at existing industrial and commercial fleet sites, limited available land area has made the use of vertical pressure vessels more common. The size of pressure vessel used for storage varies because some installations are not dedicated solely to LP-gas vehicle fueling. Typically, installations dedicated for public vehicle fueling use storage pressure vessels having a water capacity of 1000 to 2000 gal (3.8 to 7.6 m^3).

These storage vessels must meet standards addressed in the *ASME Boiler and Pressure Vessel Code*[19] or the API-ASME *Code for Unfired Pressure Vessels for Petroleum Liquids and Gases.*[20] LP-gas pressure vessels must meet design or service pressures, which depend on the vapor pressure of the LP-gas stored. Propane storage vessels used for fueling require a minimum design pressure of 250 psig (1724 kPa). Structural support for LP-gas storage vessels containing propane can vary from

FIGURE 21.4.6 Fueling Facility Storing and Dispensing Gasoline, CNG, and LP-Gas in Densely Populated and Congested Urban Area

concrete saddles on horizontal vessels to structural metal supports protected with a fire-resistive coating on vertical tanks. LP-gas fueling vessels should be permanently fastened to paved surfaces or concrete pads, adequately protected from vehicle impact, and protected from tampering by chain-link fencing. Secondary containment is not provided at LP-gas vehicle fueling facilities because when spilled or released, nonrefrigerated liquid propane immediately vaporizes.

Bobtail tanker trucks with a capacity of 2000 to 4000 gal (7.6 to 15.2 m^3) most commonly supply LP-gas vehicle fueling stations. The operator transfers liquid by a pump mounted on the transport vehicle. A transfer hose connected to the pump discharge is attached to a threaded fill pipe connection located a short distance away from the storage vessel. This fill pipe allows the operator to top fill the fueling station storage container without having to climb on top. NFPA 58 has setback requirements for various types of exposures from the point of transfer if that point is not located on the container. For bulk LP-gas storage, transport hose connections at the fill pipe include breakaway protection. At bulk plants, bulkhead devices provide this protection with cable-activated or pneumatic emergency shutoff valves. On smaller vessels dedicated for LP-gas vehicle fueling, these are not typical. Instead, their design usually incorporates a breakaway valve in the vessel fill piping. In addition, a required backflow check valve at the inlet to the storage vessel prevents pressurized contents from flowing from the fill connection if the piping is damaged.

Filling the storage vessel proceeds until the operator notes that the liquid level has reached the maximum allowed. Several options exist for monitoring when the storage vessel is full. Using a fixed maximum liquid level gauge is a popular method. A No. 54 drill hole bleed valve in this device connects to an internal dip tube. When vessel filling is to begin, the valve is opened and normally vents invisible vapor. The operator notes refrigerated air moisture through the bleed valve when vaporizing liquid reaches the predetermined interior dip tube height. The operator then stops the liquid transfer. Variable liquid level gauges, such as a slip tube or rotary tube, operate similarly but indicate liquid height on a scale that the operator reads to determine when the vessel is properly filled.

Emergency shutoff valves are required at LP-gas vehicle fueling facilities. These consist of emergency devices associated with dispensing from storage into the vehicle. Manual shutoff valves, excess flow check valves, backflow check valves, and quick closing internal valves can be used at liquid bypass, vapor recycle, liquid withdrawal, and equalizing connections. Storage vessel discharge connections located at the bottom of the vessel can be provided with shear protection in the event the discharge piping is damaged. To protect the vessel against significant fire exposure in the event of a leak, a fusible link shutoff valve is commonly installed at the vessel liquid opening, usually in conjunction with an excess flow check valve.

The excess flow check valve for discharge from the vessel is usually installed internal to the vessel; some valves are manufactured to be installed in-line. A spring normally holds excess flow check valves open. The valves close automatically when the device's rated liquid flow is exceeded. Excess flow check valves operate only if a break in the vessel discharge line is sufficiently large for flow to exceed the rated valve setting. Pump bypass liquid lines and vapor equalization lines, commonly connected to LP-gas storage, also have excess flow check valves.

LP-gas storage vessels used for vehicle fueling must have one or more pressure relief devices installed in their vapor space. ASME vessels having a water capacity greater than 1200 gal (4.5 m^3) must have spring-loaded pressure-relief valves that directly communicate with the vessel vapor space. These self-actuated relief valves help to limit the accidental release of LP-gas because they normally close when excess pressure is relieved. Other devices, such as frangible or rupture disks, let the entire contents of the pressure vessel discharge and, therefore, are not used in LP-gas pressure vessels. In addition to spring-loaded relief valves, fusible plugs not exceeding ¼ in. (0.6 cm) diameter may be installed in pressure vessels with a water capacity lower than 1200 gal (4.5 m^3).

LP-Gas Dispenser Components. LP-gas dispensing devices typically include a meter, vapor separator, hydrostatic relief valves, check valve, solenoid valve, pressure differential valve, and manual shutoff valves. As with the other types of alternative fuels, dispensers can be the simple assemblies mounted on a post that are common at fleet operations or the manufactured dispensing units for public fueling locations. Manufactured dispensing units can look like those used for conventional gasoline or diesel fueling. Excess flow check valves in a shear plate are generally installed below the dispensing unit and function like shear valves under conventional flammable liquid fuel dispensers.

LP-gas dispensers can fill at a maximum rate of approximately 18 gal/min (0.07 m^3/min).[21] Pursuant to NFPA 30A, *Code for Motor Fuel Dispensing Facilities and Repair Garages,* LP-gas dispensers should be located at least 20 ft (6.1 m) from gasoline or diesel dispensers. LP-gas fuel hoses must be fitted with a listed emergency breakaway device to prevent propane releases in the event a driver pulls away while the fueling hose is still connected. The LP-gas vehicle fueling hose, commonly known as "wet" hose, is required to be continuously marked "LP-GAS," "Propane," and "350 PSI WORKING PRESSURE." Fueling hose typically connects to the vehicle via a U.S. standard 1¾ in. (4.5 cm) acme-threaded connection. These connectors are designed with a mechanism that prohibits liquid flow unless connected to a vehicle. A "quarter turn" valve located before the threaded connection controls flow. Flow control valves are available with a lever action similar to conventional gasoline-dispensing nozzles. The main difference is that LP-gas lever valves do not presently shut off automatically when the liquid level is full. Instead, an outage gauge or outage vent valve is located on the vehicle, near the hose connection.

The vehicle outage gauge operates like bulk vessel liquid level gauges. When the vehicle tank is approximately 80 percent full, a small amount of liquid propane is released through the outage vent. The operator recognizes that the vehicle container is full and manually disengages the dispensing flow valve. This venting to atmosphere at each refueling has been recognized as a potential problem. Automatic shutoff devices, such as a float valve inside the vehicle tank, are available, and computer-controlled overfill systems are being developed. When perfected, these systems might be required on all LP-gas vehicles or dispensers.

VEHICLE COMPONENTS, DESIGN, AND OPERATION

The appearance and shape of alternative-fueled vehicles are the same as conventional-fueled vehicles. In many cases, they are conventional-fueled vehicles that have been retrofitted to operate with alternative fuels. Several vehicle manufacturers are developing alternative-fueled versions of their popular conventionally fueled models. How the fuel is carried and consumed differs in the vehicles. Although vehicle storage containers and delivery systems differ for each type of fuel, the concept is the same for all hydrocarbon alternative fuels. CNG, LNG, and LP-gas vehicles store and consume a mixture of flammable gas. Understanding fuel storage and consumption is important from the perspectives of the vehicle's operator, the individual fueling the vehicle, and the emergency responder.

There are two types of alternative-fueled vehicles: (1) those converted from another fuel, called bi-fueled conversions, and (2) those designed to be exclusively powered by CNG, LNG, or LP-gas. Bi-fuel converted vehicles may operate on natural gas or propane and a conventional fuel, such as gasoline or diesel, because the liquid fuel system remains intact. CNG-, LNG-, or LP-gas-fueled vehicles can cost more than conventionally fueled vehicles because of the vehicle fuel tank expense.

Compressed Natural Gas Vehicles

CNG vehicles include conventional passenger vehicles, light- and medium-duty trucks, and heavy-chassis vehicles such as transit buses. CNG vehicles store natural gas compressed at pressures of 2500 to 4000 psig (17,235 to 27,576 kPa) in compressed gas cylinders equipped with a pressure relief device, a filling connection, and a shutoff valve. The vehicle fuel container connects to either a manifold or single fuel line equipped with a manual shutoff valve. Natural gas is dispensed to the engine via a pressure regulator that reduces the gas to the service pressure the engine uses. After its pressure is reduced, the gas enters a gas-air mixer to produce a flammable mixture that is injected into the internal combustion engine.

NFPA 52 applies to the design and installation of CNG fuel systems on all types of vehicles and their fuel dispensing systems. The standard's scope includes the CNG element of bi-fueled vehicles and vehicles originally manufactured to operate using CNG. Fuel is delivered from a CNG dispenser through its nozzle and introduced into the vehicle's container through the vehicle fueling receptacle. The attachment is like a typical quick-connect coupling used on compressed air hoses. Vehicle fueling receptacles are designed in accordance with ANSI/American Gas Association NGV 1.

CNG Fuel Containers. CNG fuel containers are designed to store compressed methane gas at high pressures. The gas is stored in a compressed state to increase the quantity that can be stored on board the vehicle, thus increasing the vehicle's driving range. American Natural Standards Institute/American Gas Association NGV2, *Basic Requirements for Compressed Natural Gas Vehicle Fuel Containers,*[22] addresses the design and construction of CNG fuel containers. NGV2 containers have service pressures between 2400 and 4350 psi (16,546 and 29,989 kPa) at 70°F (21°C), capacities not greater than 35.4 ft^3, and a service life of 15 years. NGV2 containers are either constructed of metal (NGV2–1), a metal liner reinforced with hoop-wrapped (NGV2–2) or full-wrapped (NGV2–3) resin-impregnated continuous filament, or a full-wrapped continuous filament with a nonmetallic liner (NGV2–4). All construction materials must be capable of operating throughout a temperature range of –40 to 180°F (–40 to 82°C). Containers installed in vehicles require identification using a label that reads "CNG ONLY." This label is required to prevent the installation of cylinders not designed for CNG service.

CNG vehicle fuel containers are subject to nondestructive pressure and leak tests. To achieve certification, metal containers and liners must successfully pass destructive tests that evaluate the materials yield strength, tensile strength, elongation, and its performance under mechanical impact. Other requirements that must be met include drop, fire exposure, gunfire, gas permeation, pressure cycling, and burst tests. These tests ensure the container maintains its integrity over its service life.

Vehicle containers can be located inside, below, or above the driver or passenger compartment, provided all connections to the container are either external or sealed and vented from the area where the driver or passengers sit. Containers are installed in a location that minimizes the probability of damage resulting from a collision. Neither containers nor container components can be located ahead of the vehicle's front axle or behind its rear bumper.

The mounting mechanism must secure the CNG vehicle fuel container to the vehicle's frame, body, or cargo box to prevent damage resulting from road hazards, container slippage, and loosening or rotating of the container. The method used for mounting the container must withstand a static force of eight times the weight of a fully pressurized cylinder applied in six directions of loading. When subjected to this load test, the container is allowed a maximum displacement of ½ in. (1.3 cm) in any direction of loading. Unless shielded, containers require a minimum 8 in. (20.3 cm) clearance from vehicle exhaust systems. If metallic clamps or clamping bands are used, they cannot be in direct contact with the container. This necessary provision protects the container from exterior corrosion resulting from moisture accumulation or mechanical vibration. To satisfy the requirement, a resilient, water-resistant material is commonly installed between the clamp and the container supports.

CNG Pressure-Relief Devices. Vehicle fuel containers are required to be fitted with one or more pressure-relief devices. Pressure-relief devices protect the container from catastrophic failure due to overpressure resulting from fire exposure.

Pressure-relief devices for CNG cylinders are constructed in accordance with Compressed Gas Association Pamphlet S-1.1, *Pressure Relief Device Standards, Part 1—Cylinders for Compressed Gases.*[23] Pressure-relief devices can be rupture disks, fusible plugs, a combination rupture disk/fusible plug, or a pressure-relief valve. A rupture disk is the component of a pressure-relief device designed to burst at a predetermined pressure and allow gas to discharge. Rupture disks are preformed metal designed to fail at a particular pressure or temperature. When a rupture disk operates, it vents the entire contents of the container. Rupture disks do not close. Fusible plug devices are also nonreclosing pressure-relief devices designed to function when a plug of fusible material melts at a suitable temperature. Fusible plugs are designed to operate at a nominal yield temperature of either 165°F or 212°F (74°C or 100°C), depending on the material selected.

Pressure-relief valves are safety valves designed to relieve excessive pressure. They reclose and reseal to prevent the further flow of gas from the container after the reseating pressure has been achieved. Pressure-relief devices are installed so the relief device is in direct communication with the fuel. Additionally, a shutoff valve should not be installed between the pressure-relief device and the cylinder, or after the pressure-relief devices.

When containers are installed inside vehicles, such as in the cargo trunk of a passenger car, these are the following requirements concerning how the pressure-relief device is installed and terminated to the vehicle's exterior:

- Installation in the same vehicle compartment of the container
- Termination to the exterior using piping or tubing of at least the same diameter as the pressure-relief device
- Termination of the vent opening so that road debris will not block it
- Enclosure of the container neck and all CNG fittings within a gastight compartment

Valves located at the container and the engine isolate the piping system from the container and the engine. A vehicle manual shutoff valve is also located along the frame rail. These valves are provided for the safety of the vehicle user, persons performing repairs, and emergency responders.

A valve is required for the vehicle container. The container valve can be operated manually or with a normally closed remotely activated shutoff valve. When the container has a remotely activated valve, the valve must be equipped with a means that allows the cylinder to be depressurized. Regardless of the valve type used, authorities having jurisdiction should ensure that personnel performing maintenance activities on CNG vehicles clearly understand the manufacturer's procedures for depressurizing a charged cylinder of CNG. In Texas in March 1993, the Austin Fire Department responded to a fire involving a CNG vehicle. The fire resulted from a mechanic improperly depressurizing the container by not electrically bonding the depressurizing tool to the vehicle frame. The high-pressure discharge of natural gas created a static accumulation and spark that ignited the gas jet, forming a flame jet approximately 15 ft (4.6 m) long, as witnessed by arriving fire fighters. Although the fire did not result in any fire fighter or civilian injuries, the vehicle of fire origin was destroyed and an exposed vehicle suffered damage from the thermal flux of the flame jet.[24]

A second valve is required between the engine and the fuel cylinder that permits fire fighters and repair personnel to isolate the containers from the remainder of the fuel system. This manual shutoff valve must be installed in an accessible location and can have no more than a 90° rotation from open to closed position. Labels or stencils stating "MANUAL SHUTOFF VALVE" identify the valve location. The manual shutoff valve requires protection from vibration and road hazards (Figure 21.4.7).

CNG Piping. Finally, a third valve is required in the fuel system that automatically prevents the flow of CNG when the engine is not running but the ignition switch is in the "ON" position. This ensures that methane does not flow during repairs while the vehicle's electrical system is energized.

Piping is used in a CNG fueling system because it offers a reliable, safe, and affordable method of moving high-pressure gas from the container to the engine. Normally, rigid or flexible stainless steel fuel lines connect the fuel containers, engine, and vehicle fueling receptacle. The use of certain materials for CNG piping service is prohibited: plastic piping and fittings for high-pressure service and galvanized piping and fittings. Even so, other considerations, such as temperature and vibration, must be taken into account.

Piping installed on vehicles is subjected to a fairly rigorous service life. As a result, the piping installed between the container and the secondary shutoff valve located along the vehicle's frame must capably withstand a hydrostatic pressure of at least four times the rated service pressure without structural failure. This generally results in only stainless steel tubing being used for CNG vehicle fuel lines.

Pipe connections can be welded, mechanically bent, or mechanically connected. When piping or tubing is threaded, the pipe sealing material must be impervious to natural gas and be applied to all male pipe threads before assembly. When mechanical joints or connections are used, joints must be located in an accessible location. Pipe routing must consider the effects of vibration, corrosion, damage from road objects and collisions, and normal service life wear and tear. Piping routed through engine compartment fire walls or other vehicle panels requires protection from abrasive wear through the use of grommets or other acceptable means.

When the engine requires fuel, the gas leaves the storage containers and flows to a high-pressure regulator. The gas pressure from the fuel container reduces to an intermediate pressure. As the gas expands from a fuel container pressure of 2500 to 4000 psig (17,235 to 27,576 kPa) to the intermediate pressure of 120 to 300 psig (827 to 2068 kPa), its temperature drops by

FIGURE 21.4.7 A Typical Label Identifying the Location of the Manual Shutoff Valve Between the Fuel Containers and Engine, as Required by NFPA 52

as much as 100°F (38°C). If the gas contains too much moisture, it can freeze and damage the fuel system and engine. Also, cold gas can harden pipe seals in the fuel system and result in leaks. For these reasons, most CNG vehicles have pressure regulators heated by engine coolant.

From the high-pressure regulator, the methane gas flows toward the engine through another line to the low-pressure regulator. Located in the engine compartment, the low-pressure regulator reduces gas pressure to approximately 100 psi (689 kPa). Engine coolant does not normally heat this regulator because the refrigeration effect is negligible. From the low-pressure regulator the gas flows to the engine, entering the fuel injectors and the cylinder's combustion chamber.

Liquefied Natural Gas Vehicles

LNG vehicles can be used for such applications as midsize and heavy-duty truck chassis vehicles, such as refuse trucks and transit vehicles. However, LNG is also a viable fuel for railroad locomotives and marine vessels. LNG vehicle fuel systems have several components, such as a pressure regulator and gas-air mixer, that are like those on CNG vehicles. Because engines cannot consume cryogenic fluids, the liquid must be converted to gas, which requires a heat exchanger.

NFPA 57 applies to the design and installation of LNG fuel systems on vehicles and their fuel-dispensing systems. The standard scope includes the CNG element of bi-fueled vehicles and vehicles originally manufactured to operate using LNG. Vehicles fueled by LNG have components designed to operate at temperatures and pressures encountered in cryogenic service. These components are on the system's liquid side. Major components on the cryogenic side of the fuel system include the vehicle's LNG storage tank and fuel lines. When LNG vaporizes into a gas, its components are designed for compressed gas service. Major components on the vapor phase side of the system include the heat exchanger and pressure regulator.

LNG Fuel Containers. LNG vehicle containers commonly use a vacuum-jacketed Dewar-type design, based on the Dewar flask. This double-walled vessel has reflective surfaces on the container's exterior where vacuum is maintained between the two walls. This helps prevent the LNG loss when the container and liquid become warm. An important consideration in LNG vehicle containers' design is hold time. Hold time is the length of time a vehicle can remain unused until pressure in its tank builds to a point that it must be vented. Hold time depends on the liquid/vapor ratio in the tank, as well as the tank's construction. The liquid/vapor ratio depends on the amount of tank ullage. Space is always required to allow for vaporization and liquid expansion that occurs as temperature and pressure increase. The ullage is typically 5 to 10 percent of the vehicle's tank volume. Ullage is necessary in the event the tank reaches a vent pressure. When the pressure-relief valve functions to relieve pressure, gas, not LNG, is discharged.[25]

LNG vehicle fuel containers are constructed with an inner tank and outer tank. The inner tank is normally constructed of stainless steel. Because it serves as a cryogenic pressure vessel, the inner tank's design meets Section VIII, Division 1 of the *ASME Boiler and Pressure Vessel Code* or U.S. DOT regulations 49 CFR 178, for example, DOT 4L tank. It normally contains a baffle and method of indicating the level of liquid in the container. The outer tank is constructed of either stainless or carbon steel. The inner tank connects to the outer tank with supports designed to minimize heat conduction but maintain the container's structural integrity. To minimize radiation heat transfer, insulation consisting of multiple layers of aluminum/polyester film separated by nylon netting is placed in the container's interstice. A vacuum drawn in the interstice minimizes the effect of convective heat transfer. Common LNG vehicle containers are cylindrically shaped with elliptical heads. The structural integrity of an LNG vehicle fuel container during normal operation and under fire or other abnormal stress is analyzed in the tank design. The structural integrity of the LNG container must be evaluated against vibration, acceleration, and shock loads to determine crashworthiness.

LNG vehicle fuel containers are required to have identification features for individuals performing repairs and emergency responders. With the exception of openings for pressure relief or liquid gauging, all openings are designated as to whether they open into the vapor or liquid space. The total volume of the container is identified, and signs indicate that the container can only be used for LNG service. Valves to control liquid and vapor flow must be readily accessible and operable without the use of tools.

Location of the LNG storage container on a vehicle is an important consideration. Containers should not be located ahead of the vehicle's front axle, beyond its rear bumper, or on its roof. Containers may be installed in the interior of vehicles, provided the compartment is not in direct communication with the driver, passenger, or any space containing radio transmitters or spark-producing equipment. This can be accomplished by providing gastight enclosures over the equipment and venting the enclosure outside the vehicle. When LNG is not odorized, a continuous monitoring methane gas detection system is required in the compartment holding the container. The detection system should be designed to sound an alarm when the atmosphere in the compartment exceeds 20 percent of the lower flammable limit for methane. The gas detection system is not required to stop the flow of fuel or turn off the engine's ignition.

LNG Pressure-Relief Devices. LNG storage containers require pressure-relief devices. Most vehicle containers are equipped with pressure-relief valves and rupture disks. Pressure-relief valves relieve the pressure that develops during the LNG hold time in the container. If the pressure-relief device fails, pressure increases until the rupture disk fails. The burst pressure of the disk is higher than the relief valve setting but lower than the container's design pressure. Unlike conventional relief valves, rupture disks are not designed to close. If a rupture disk operates, LNG vapor is released until the tank is empty. If the vehicle is involved in an incident in which the container is overturned and the rupture disk operates, LNG discharges from the pressure-relief opening.

LNG Heat Exchanger and Piping. LNG must be converted from liquid to gas for proper combustion in reciprocating engines. A heat exchanger performs the phase change. Commonly called a vaporizer, the heat exchanger raises the temperature of LNG vapors so that the phase change from liquid methane to methane gas is efficient. A commonly used heat-transfer medium is engine coolant recirculated between the heat exchanger and the engine's radiator. At maximum fuel flow rate, the heat exchanger must have the capacity to completely vaporize the LNG. In addition, it must heat the gas to the appropriate temperature before the gas enters the fuel regulator. Identifying the maximum allowable working pressure for heat exchangers is a necessity to protect the device against possible overpressurization resulting from the installation of an improperly sized relief device.

From an emergency response perspective, the heat exchanger is the component in the fuel system dividing the cryogenic side and the vapor phase, or noncryogenic side. A pressure regulator ahead of the heat exchanger controls the pressure of gas consumed at the mixer or carburetor.

Piping transfers LNG from the vehicle container's liquid withdrawal connection, through the heat exchanger and pressure regulator, to the carburetor or fuel injector. As LNG travels from the fuel container through the fuel line to the heat exchanger, it begins to warm, causing condensation on exterior surfaces. Most fuel lines are insulated to retard heat loss. Piping designed for LNG vehicles is required to withstand pressure of at least twice the container's maximum allowable working pressure. Typical construction materials for piping include stainless steel, brass, and copper that are fitted using threaded, welded, or brazed joints. Where valves are arranged such that LNG could be trapped between them, a pressure-relief device must be installed in the pipe section to relieve any excess pressure the warm LNG causes.

Liquefied Petroleum Gas Vehicles

LP-gas vehicles include industrial trucks, farm equipment, and vehicles ranging in size from automobiles to heavy-duty trucks. LP-gas has the longest history of all the alternative fuels. Propane used to heat rural homes has also been readily available on the farm for use as a vehicle fuel. According to the DOE's *Transportation Energy Data Book* (Edition 20-2000), approximately 270,000 vehicles in North America are fueled using LP-gas (see Table 21.4.1). This figure does not include off-road vehicles; including these vehicles would increase this number significantly.

LP-gas vehicles normally use propane, a flammable, liquefied petroleum gas stored at pressures of approximately 120 to 200 psig (827 to 1379 kPa), depending on its specific gravity and storage temperature. The vehicle container connects to either a manifold or single fuel line that dispenses propane to the engine via expansion of the liquefied gas. The gas enters a propane carburetor and produces a flammable mixture that is injected into the engine's combustion chamber.

NFPA 58 applies to the design, installation, and maintenance of LP-gas fuel systems on all vehicles and fuel dispensing systems. NFPA 58 covers the installation of fuel systems supplying engines used to propel vehicles such as passenger cars, taxicabs, multipurpose passenger vehicles, buses, recreational vehicles, trucks (including tractors, tractor semitrailer units, and truck trains), and farm appliances.

LP-Gas Containers. NFPA 58 regulates the design, fabrication, and construction of LP-gas containers designed for installation on vehicles. LP-gas vehicle fuel containers must meet either the requirements of *ASME Boiler and Pressure Vessel Code,* Section VIII, Division 1, "Rules for Construction of Unfired Pressure Vessels," or U.S. DOT requirements. Normally, pressure vessels used for LP-gas service have a minimum design pressure of 250 psig (1724 kPa), based on NFPA 58 and ASME requirements for gases with a vapor pressure of 215 psig (1482 kPa) at 100°F (38°C). However, when the pressure vessel is intended for installation on a motor vehicle, such as an automobile or bus, the minimum design pressure for the container increases to 312.5 psig (2154 kPa). The higher design pressure ensures that the pressure-relief device has an increased operating setting because the container may be subjected to operating temperatures not normally found at stationary LP-gas installations. In addition, premature operation of a relief valve on, for example, a school bus filled with children introduces a variety of concerns to vehicle operators and emergency responders. Establishing a higher starting pressure for opening a relief valve reduces the probability of premature LP-gas release.

Particular attention must be paid to the location of vehicle LP-gas containers. Containers must be located to minimize the possibility of damage to them and their fittings. Suitable locations may include the trunk of a passenger car, directly attached to the frame of a vehicle, or in the cargo box of a pickup truck. Containers should be installed in a location to minimize damage resulting from a collision. Containers and their components cannot be located ahead of the vehicle's front axle, behind its rear bumper, or on its roof.

A container installed inside a vehicle should be installed so that the driver or passengers are not exposed to any release of LP-gas, nor should it be within any space containing radio transmitters or other spark-producing equipment. NFPA addresses the three following options to satisfy this concern:

1. Locate the container and its appurtenances outside the passenger compartment.
2. Completely enclose the container appurtenances in a gas-tight enclosure or housing.
3. Store the container and its appurtenances in the trunk of an automobile and seal the compartment to form a separation from the passenger carrying space.

The size of the container on vehicles is also limited. Vehicles designed to transport passengers, such as buses or automobiles, are limited to an aggregate of not more than 200 gal (0.75 m^3) water capacity, or approximately 160 gal (0.6 m^3) of LP-gas. Vehicles not designed to carry passengers, such as farm machinery or mail trucks, may have an aggregate 300 gal (1.1 m^3) water capacity of volume, or approximately 240 gal (0.9 m^3) of LP-gas. In both instances, more than one tank can be used and manifolded, but the total volume cannot exceed the aggregate quantity.

A method of preventing the overfilling of vehicle LP-gas containers is required. Overfilled containers can be hazardous when liquid LP-gas expands to the point where the containers become liquid-full, causing the pressure-relief valve to open and discharge LP-gas. To minimize the hazard, containers manufactured after January 1, 1984, and installed in vehicles must be equipped with a device that prevents overfilling. Listed stop fill valves designed to satisfy this requirement are available. Other means, such as a solenoid valve, may be used.[26]

LP-Gas Pressure-Relief Devices. Vehicle LP-gas fuel containers require a method of relieving excess pressure resulting from an external heat source. Spring-loaded pressure-relief devices accomplish this. The relief valve is recessed or flush with the surface of the pressure vessel. For ASME containers, the relief valve is normally designed to meet the requirements of Underwriter Laboratories Standard 132, *Safety Relief Valves for Anhydrous Ammonia and LP-Gas,*[27] Section UG-125 of the *ASME Boiler Pressure Vessel Code,* or other standards acceptable to the authority having jurisdiction. DOT containers require spring-loaded pressure-relief valves in accordance with CGA Pamphlet S-1.1. NFPA 58 prohibits the use of relief devices that use fusible plugs because the vehicle container can be subjected to considerable heat while garaged or in use.

LP-gas pressure-relief devices must be installed in direct communication with the vapor space of the vehicle fuel container. The relief device must also be located at the container's uppermost point. When this is not possible, the device should be internally piped to the uppermost practical point in the container's vapor space. Because propane has an approximate expansion ratio of 1:260, any liquid discharge from a relief device results in the development of a gas vapor cloud. The requirement for locating the relief valve at either the uppermost point of the container or the vapor space is based on experience with relief valves located at or directly above the 80 percent liquid level, in which the relief valve sometimes discharged liquid LP-gas. When the container is installed inside the vehicle, its discharge outlet must terminate outside the vehicle. It must also be directed so that it does not directly impinge on the vehicle fuel containers, the exhaust system, or any other part of the vehicle; it cannot be directed into the passenger compartment.

A manual shutoff valve is required for LP-gas vehicle fuel containers. This valve has an additional protective feature known as the internal excess flow check valve. It closes and stops the flow of gas from the container in the event the shutoff valve is sheared or broken off the container. The excess flow check valve does not operate if the shutoff valve is only partially damaged. Also, the valve does not stop the flow of LP-gas if a fuel pipe leaks downstream of the valve. Manual shutoff valves are normally installed at the container's liquid and vapor openings. These valves must also be readily accessible so they can be shut off using tools or other means.

LP-Gas Piping. The construction materials for piping, hose, and fittings used to connect the fuel container to the vaporizer and carburetion equipment are the same as for fixed installations. Piping must be corrosion-resistant or protected against corrosive action, free of leaks, and securely mounted on the vehicle. Any fuel piping that passes through a vehicle's floor must be installed so that the pipe is beneath or adjacent to the container and connections are outside the vehicle. Hydrostatic relief valves are required between any section of pipe or hose in which LP-gas could be isolated between shutoff valves. Carburetion equipment for LP-gas vehicles is designed to complete the phase change of propane from liquefied phase to gas phase. Equipment is required to be listed for vehicle service and should be acceptable to the authority having jurisdiction. Carburetion equipment is normally rated with a design pressure of 250 psig (1724 kPa), although operating pressures are normally limited to 125 to 250 psig (862 to 1724 kPa). Like CNG and LNG fuel systems, LP-gas fuel systems require an automatic shutoff valve provided as close as practical to the inlet of the pressure regulator. The valve prevents the flow of fuel to the carburetor when the engine is not running but the ignition switch is in the "ON" position. Pressure-relief requirements for carburetion equipment are the same as for containers installed on vehicles: relief devices must be spring-loaded pressure-relief valves; fusible plugs are not acceptable.

Hydrogen-Fueled Vehicles

Hydrogen-fueled vehicles are addressed in Section 21, Chapter 5, "Fuel Cell Vehicles." Most of these vehicles are fuel cell powered, where the hydrogen acts as a fuel for the fuel cell. However, there are some internal combustion engine vehicles that run on hydrogen. These vehicles present hazards that are similar to those presented by CNG vehicles. In Section 21, Chapter 5, the section on physical properties and fire hazards explains some of the differences between the behavior of CNG and hydrogen and will help in understanding how the gases would behave in an accident.

EMERGENCY RESPONSE TO ALTERNATIVE FUEL INCIDENTS

Highway operation of vehicles that use CNG, LNG, and LP-gas is increasingly common. Fire fighters must be prepared to respond to incidents involving the release of these alternative fuels. Emergency response to a vehicle or fueling station releasing alternative fuel requires an understanding of the fuel's hazards, release mechanisms, methods available to safely stop the release, and, in the event an ignition source is introduced, how to safely and effectively initiate a successful fire attack. Three plausible scenarios for emergencies involving the release of alternative fuels are as follows:

1. The vehicle is being fueled.
2. The vehicle is involved in an accident.
3. The vehicle is under repair.

Identifying Alternative Fuel Vehicles

Components of alternative fuel vehicles are normally protected and hidden from view to protect these components in an accident. Fire fighters approaching alternative-fueled vehicles cannot usually distinguish these vehicles from those fueled with gasoline or diesel. Fortunately, measures have been taken to identify these vehicles to responding fire fighters.

All three NFPA standards require that vehicles be identified with a weather-resistant, diamond-shaped label on the exterior vertical surface on the lower right rear of the vehicle (Figure 21.4.8). Most labels are placed on the trunk lid or rear cowl; they cannot be affixed to the bumper because they may be covered by bumper stickers or damaged in minor vehicle accidents. For CNG vehicles, NFPA 52 requires white or silver letters "CNG" on a blue background. NFPA 58 and NFPA 57 require white or silver letters "propane" and "LNG," respectively, on a blue background. The retroreflective labels are visible at night or in fog.

Response to Vehicle Fires and Accidents

Many variables outside fire fighters' control impact how an emergency response will be handled. It is important to understand that alternative fuels have somewhat predictable characteristics when released to the atmosphere, and all the alternative fuels are flammable gases at normal temperatures and pressures. These facts, along with an understanding of the basics of fireground safety, will result in the safe conclusion of an incident.

Apparatus should be placed upwind of a vehicle on fire or involved in an incident. If the vehicle is LNG fueled, the apparatus should be located away from the path of flowing LNG. However, this is not as critical as wind direction because flammable LNG or LP-gas vapors can travel significant distances downwind. LNG vapors will eventually become positively buoyant. Conversely, LP-gas vapors always remain heavier than air due to the molecular weight of the gas. Fire fighters should also recognize that LNG is normally unodorized, but LP-gas is odorized.

Fire fighters should accurately assess the scene before initiating a fire attack. Maintaining an adequate distance, fire fighters should walk completely around the vehicle, observing it and paying special attention to the right rear so they can identify the fuel used. Fire fighters should look for the blue or black retroreflective diamond that identifies which fuel is used.

FIGURE 21.4.8 Diamond-Shaped Label That Identifies the Fuel Used by the Vehicle

For CNG and LP-gas vehicles, water from attack streams can be used to control fire and enhance vapor dispersion. However, for LNG releases, applying water from fire streams greatly increases the vaporization rate for a pool of liquid methane. Fire fighters should attack LNG fires with potassium bicarbonate, ammonium phosphate, or sodium bicarbonate dry chemical fire extinguishers until they confirm that the fire does not involve fuel.

Regardless of the fuel, the primary concern at vehicle crash sites is to ensure the safety of fire fighters and civilians. The strategy is to control or stop the release of fuel and eliminate ignition sources. If a vehicle fuel release has been ignited, stopping the release of additional fuel, if possible, is critical before further fire-fighting activities are undertaken.

The fuel systems for CNG, LNG, and LP-gas can be stabilized by closing the primary shutoff valve at the storage containers. CNG vehicles normally have a second fuel isolation valve installed along the frame rail. NFPA 52 requires a method of identifying this valve's location. All alternative fuel containers are required to vent outside the vehicle. The fire fighter assigned the task of closing the primary valve should also locate and inspect the tank vent line to ensure that it is not blocked.

Closing the primary valve may require the operation of the tank vent. Before fire fighters attempt to isolate the fuel supply on LNG vehicles, they should check the vehicle's on-board gas detection system to determine if fuel is leaking. Because a collision could damage this system, fire fighters should also survey the vehicle and accident scene using gas detection equipment. After checking the vehicle and scene for leaks, fire fighters can proceed to close the liquid product valve. LNG containers have two valves, one for liquid product and the other for the tank vent. The vent line should not be closed because it lets the LNG vehicle container vent gas if tank pressure increases, as it does in a fire. If labels are missing or obscured, fire fighters can always locate the liquid valve because it will be covered with ice and frost formed from moisture in the atmosphere. The vent valve will not be covered with ice or frost.

Hydrogen Fueling Facilities

Hydrogen fueling systems (Figure 21.4.9) typically do not have feed lines from off-site storage but employ on-site storage. Because of the low density of hydrogen gas, hydrogen is often stored as a cryogenic fluid. Hydrogen systems may also have vaporizers to convert the liquid hydrogen to gaseous hydrogen. Additionally, hydrogen fueling systems operate at higher pressures than natural gas fueling systems. Natural gas systems operate in the 3000 to 4000 psi (20,684 to 25,579 kPa) range as compared to hydrogen systems that may reach pressures of 10,000 psi (68,948 kPa). The reason for this difference is that the low density of hydrogen gas means that higher vehicle tank pressures are required to store enough fuel on the vehicle to give it a practical driving range.

Response to Vehicle Fueling Stations

Response considerations for fueling stations are the same as those for vehicles. The difference between the fueling station and vehicle is the amount of fuel stored at the site and the types of safety features.

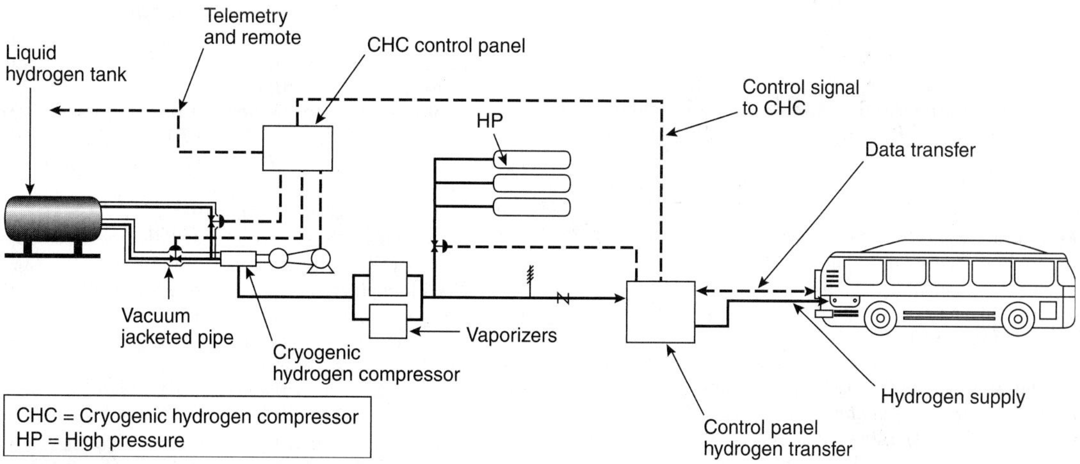

FIGURE 21.4.9 Compressed Hydrogen Gas Fueling System.

Fire fighters who might conceivably respond to a vehicle fueling station should prepare a written plan documenting how to manage and control the response to the facility in the event of a fire or fuel release. The pre-incident plan should consider points of access, required and available water supply, capabilities of fire department resources and personnel, buildings that could be exposed, safe evacuation of occupants, the location of fuel delivery valves and the method of closing them, and safety features or controls provided. The evaluation should also consider probable and worst-case event scenarios. For example, the overfilling of an LP-gas container or the operation of a relief valve on a pressure vessel storing compressed methane are not uncommon and will probably occur over the life of a facility. Conversely, worst-case scenarios can include a catastrophic container failure or a BLEVE. Although catastrophic incidents are rare, such an event can occur. Its consequences to the public and fire fighters must be considered before any response to the fueling station. Where available, fire fighters should consider using a vapor dispersion model such as CHARM (Chemical Hazard Airborne Release Model) to determine the anticipated size and boundary of the exclusion zones. Another resource is CAMEO (Computer-Aided Management of Emergency Operations). This software and supporting information is available at EPA's Chemical Emergency Preparedness and Prevention Office website (http://www.epa.gov/ceppo). CAMEO also has a specific support group website: http://www.CAMEOSupport.com.

The EPA's various guidance documents developed for implementing the Risk Management Program Rule can be used to give estimates of potentially affected areas resulting from an incident. Many of these documents are available through the EPA website, http://www.epa.gov.

All vehicle fueling stations require emergency shutoff devices. These can be simple electrical kill switches or valves designed with integral fusible-links that close if subjected to flame impingement or thermal flux. These devices' location and method of operation should be known and understood. LNG facilities normally require a gas detection system because of the lack of odorant. The gas detection system features and its sequence of operation should be included in the pre-incident plan.

Facility management should be cognizant of the hazards of the alternative fuel stored and should develop its own plan in the event of a release or fire. Further, the fire department and facility management should work jointly to prepare and communicate the pre-incident plan, so realistic action plans can be formulated and the consequences of probable and worst-case events are understood.

SUMMARY

The use of alternative fuels for vehicles has been increasing in the United States, as part of an effort to reduce air pollution and dependence on foreign oil. Compressed natural gas (CNG), liquefied natural gas (LNG), and liquefied petroleum gas (LP-gas) are the most commonly used alternative fuels in the United States. There is significant interest in using hydrogen as fuel for fuel cell powered vehicles. Although relatively few hydrogen-powered vehicles have been produced, there has been a good deal of development and research work done by automobile manufacturers, the U.S. Department of Energy, and other organizations that would play a role in the implementation of a hydrogen energy infrastructure. Hazards associated with these fuels are determined by their physical and chemical properties as well as by time-dependent conditions, the fuel system design, and the quality of the fuel system's manufacture and installation. NFPA codes and standards form the basis of many safety requirements concerning vehicle fueling, fuel storage, and vehicle fuel systems. Fire fighters must be prepared to respond to a vehicle or fueling station releasing alternative fuel and must have an understanding of the fuel's hazards, release mechanisms, ways to stop the release, and methods of conducting a successful fire attack if necessary.

BIBLIOGRAPHY

References Cited

1. Energy Information Administration, *Alternatives to Traditional Transportation Fuels,* U.S. Department of Energy, Washington, DC, 1999.
2. *Transportation Energy Data Book: Edition 20.* U.S. Department of Energy, Washington, DC, 2000.
3. J. E. Sinor Consultants, Inc., *Comparative Analysis of Transportation Fuels,* Clean Fuels Consulting, Inc., Canada, 1994.
4. Klausmier, R., "Assessment of Environment, Health, and Safety Issues Related to the Use of Alternative Transportation Fuels," Radian Corporation, Austin, TX, 1989.
5. EPA's Greenbook, U.S. Environmental Protection Agency, Washington, DC, http://www.epa.gov/oar/oaqps/greenbk.
6. *Risk Management Program Guidance For Propane Storage Facilities* (40 CFR Part 68), EPA-550-B-00-001, Environmental Protection Agency, Washington, DC. Available on EPA website.
7. Krupka, M. C., Peaslee, A. T., and Laquer, H. T., *Gaseous Fuel Safety Assessment for Light Duty Automotive Vehicles,* Los Alamos National Laboratory, Los Alamos, NM, Nov. 1983, p. 12.
8. *Introduction to LNG Vehicle Safety,* Gas Research Institute, Chicago, IL, Sept. 1992.
9. Grant, T. J., Shaaban, S., and Zalak, V., *Hazard Assessment of Natural Gas Vehicles in Public Parking Garages,* Ebasco Services, Inc., July 1991, pp. 53–55.
10. Zalosh, R., Pilette, Y., and Weining, W., *Hazard Analysis of Alternative Fueled Vehicles in Tunnels—Part 1: CNG Fueled Vehicles,* Center for Firesafety Studies, Worcester Polytechnic, Worcester, MA, Apr. 1994, pp. 8-1–8-2.
11. Walls, W., "Just What Is a BLEVE?" *Fire Journal,* Nov. 1978, p. 46.
12. Beale, J., "Natural Gas Liquefaction Primer," *Natural Gas Fuels,* Nov. 1993, p. 33.
13. Greene, T., Williams, T., and Blazek, C., *An Investigation of the Use of Odorants in Liquefied Natural Gas Used as a Vehicle Fuel,* Gas Research Institute, Chicago, IL, 1994.
14. Lemoff, T., *Liquefied Petroleum Gas Handbook,* National Fire Protection Association, Quincy, MA, 2001, p. 416.
15. NGV1-1998, "Compressed NGV Fueling Connection Devices," CSA International, Cleveland, OH.
16. Lewis, J., "LNG Explained," *Natural Gas Fuels,* May 1995, p. 59.
17. Moorhouse, J., and Roberts, P., "Cryogenic Spill Protection and Mitigation," *Cryogenics,* Dec. 1988, pp. 838–846.
18. Because of the cost of constructing natural gas pipelines, natural gas is generally available in more densely populated areas. LP-gas is typically used where natural gas is not available—less densely populated areas.
19. "Rules for the Construction of Unfired Pressure Vessels," Section VIII, ASME *Boiler and Pressure Vessel Code,* 1998.
20. API-ASME *Code for Unfired Pressure Vessels for Petroleum Liquids and Gases,* Pre-July 1, 1961.
21. *Butane-Propane News,* Mar. 1995, p. 24.
22. NGV2-2000, "Basic Requirements for Compressed Natural Gas Vehicles," CSA International, Cleveland, OH, 2000.
23. CGA Pamphlet S-1-1, "Pressure Relief Device Standards—Part 1: Cylinders for Compressed Gases," Compressed Gas Association, Chantilly, VA, 2002.
24. Incident Report, Austin, TX, Fire Department, 1993.
25. Powars, C., et al., *A White Paper: Preliminary Assessment of LNG Vehicle Technology, Economics and Safety Issues,* Gas Research Institute, Chicago, IL, Jan. 10, 1992, pp. 2–16.
26. Lemoff, T., *Liquefied Petroleum Gases Handbook,* National Fire Protection Association, Quincy, MA, June 1992, p. 169.
27. UL 132, *Safety Relief Valves for Anhydrous Ammonia and LP-Gas,* Underwriters Laboratories Inc., Northbrook, IL, 1997.

NFPA Codes, Standards, and Recommended Practices

Reference to the following NFPA codes, standards, and recommended practices will provide further information on alternative fuels for vehicles discussed in this chapter. (See the latest version of The NFPA Catalog *for availability of the current edition of the following documents.)*

NFPA 30A, *Code for Motor Fuel Dispensing Facilities and Repair Garages*

NFPA 37, *Standard for the Installation and Use of Stationary Combustion Engines and Gas Turbines*

NFPA 51, *Standard for the Design and Installation of Oxygen–Fuel Gas Systems for Welding, Cutting, and Allied Processes*

NFPA 52, *Vehicular Fuel Systems Code*

NFPA 54, *National Fuel Gas Code*

NFPA 58, *Liquefied Petroleum Gas Code*

NFPA 59, *Utility LP-Gas Plant Code*

NFPA 59A, *Standard for the Production, Storage, and Handling of Liquefied Natural Gas (LNG)*

NFPA 88A, *Standard for Parking Structures*

Chapter 5

Fuel Cell Vehicles

Glenn W. Scheffler ❑ William P. Collins

Chapter Contents

Key Terms

auxiliary power unit (APU), bus (transit), compressed hydrogen, electric drive system, fault management, fuel cell, fuel cell vehicle, hybrid car, hydrogen, hydrogen fueling station

The world's leading automakers, fuel cell developers, material and component suppliers, national laboratories, and universities are in a race to bring fuel cell vehicles (FCVs) to the marketplace. FCVs offer an alternative to the internal combustion engine that promises to increase efficiency, lower emissions, and reduce our dependency on foreign oil. The goal is to meet these objectives without compromising the vehicle performance, cost, and safety that consumers have come to expect.

Many of the leaders in fuel cell vehicle development are members of the U.S. Fuel Cell Council. The U.S. Fuel Cell Council is dedicated to being "the voice of the fuel cell industry" and its membership contributed to this chapter. The Transportation Working Group includes producers of fuel cells and equipment, automakers, hydrogen suppliers, and government entities and national laboratories that are actively developing FCVs and the infrastructure to fuel and maintain these vehicles.

FCVs are already on the road in demonstration programs in California and throughout the nation. The California Fuel Cell Partnership estimates that its members will have approximately 300 fuel cell cars and buses operating in demonstrations in the state by 2007. To support these demonstration vehicles, a number of hydrogen fuel stations have been installed in Northern and Southern California, and the state has launched the California Hydrogen Highway Network to help expand fuel stations to support more hydrogen vehicles. Other projects are proceeding in Michigan, Connecticut, New York, Florida, and Washington, DC.

This chapter describes current fuel cell vehicles and operating features being developed to facilitate commercialization and acceptance by the general public and regulatory authorities.

For related topics, see Section 21, Chapter 1, "Passenger Vehicle Fires"; Chapter 2, "Fire Safety in Commercial Vehicles"; and Chapter 4, "Vehicle Fueling Using Gaseous Fuels."

ADVANTAGES OF FUEL CELL VEHICLES

Operating fuel cell vehicles results in a number of advantages for the country. These advantages include but are not limited to reduced emissions and energy independence and diversity.

Emissions

Hydrogen-fueled FCVs are true "zero emissions vehicles." The exhaust is only steam. The EPA and the California Air Resource Board have already certified Honda's FCX as a zero emitting vehicle (ZEV). There are emissions associated with producing the hydrogen, but typical feed stocks being considered for producing the hydrogen would yield emissions that are extremely low in comparison to internal combustion engines (ICEs).

Glenn W. Scheffler has a B.S. in aerospace engineering from Pennsylvania State University and an M.S. in mechanical engineering from the University of Connecticut and has 36 years' experience in the fields of fuel cells and hydrogen. He is chairman of the SAE Fuel Cell Vehicles (FCV) Safety Working Group, vice-chairman of the FCV Standards Committee, chairman of the US-TAG for ISO TC22/SC21 for Electric (and Fuel Cell) Vehicles, and a member of the Hydrogen Industry Panel on Codes (HIPOC).

William P. Collins has a B.S. in mechanical engineering from the University of Connecticut and an M.S. in management from Rensselaer Polytechnic Institute and has 26 years' experience in the fields of power generation, fuel cells, and hydrogen. He is a member of the SAE Fuel Cell Vehicles Standards Committee, the NFPA Electrical Generating Committee, the ASME B31.12 working group, and the US-TAG for ISO TC197.

Energy Independence and Diversity

After a century of continuous improvements, the internal combustion engine still converts on average only about 16 percent of the energy in gasoline to turn the car's wheels. FCVs can achieve energy efficiencies of over 50 percent. Given this significant improvement in energy efficiency, FCVs offer higher mileage and substantial reductions in greenhouse gas emissions and other monitored pollutants.

Additionally, hydrogen can be generated from a number of domestic sources, helping the United States to reduce its dependence on foreign energy. Fueling vehicles with hydrogen also offers the possibility of using renewable energy sources to produce transportation fuel.

DESCRIPTION OF FUEL CELL VEHICLES

The "heart" of the FCV is the fuel cell. Fuel cells are electrochemical devices similar to a battery except that, rather than consuming chemical energy that has been stored with the battery, the fuel cell uses a supply of hydrogen to produce electric power on an ongoing basis.

Hydrogen Storage and Supply

FCV developers are considering several methods to store and supply hydrogen to fuel cells. Examples of methods to store hydrogen are as follows:

- Compressed hydrogen gas
- Liquefied hydrogen
- Hydrogen stored in reversible metal hydrides
- Hydrogen as a chemical hydride

Alternatively, hydrogen (or a hydrogen-rich gas) can be generated on board the vehicles from hydrocarbon fuels and alcohol within fuel-processing systems. Although all of these methods of storing and supplying hydrogen have been demonstrated in FCVs, most FCVs currently utilize compressed hydrogen gas that is stored at high pressure in containers on the vehicle.

For an FCV to be propelled, the electrical power produced by the fuel cell needs to be converted to mechanical energy through traction motors that, in turn, drive the wheels. In its simplest form, the electric drive system has (1) a power control to translate driver "throttle input" into modulated electric power from the fuel cell to the drive motors and (2) electric drive motors for vehicle propulsion.

An example of a typical FCV with compressed hydrogen storage to supply hydrogen to the fuel cells, fuel cells to convert the chemical energy of hydrogen into electric power, and an electric drive system (including a power control and motors) to propel the vehicle is shown in Figure 21.5.1.

In general practice, many current FCVs use a hybrid electric architecture that also includes regenerative braking to recover motive energy from the vehicle during braking and batteries or ultracapacitors to store the energy for future use. The hybrid architecture increases efficiency (i.e., raises mileage) and can improve vehicle response and acceleration.

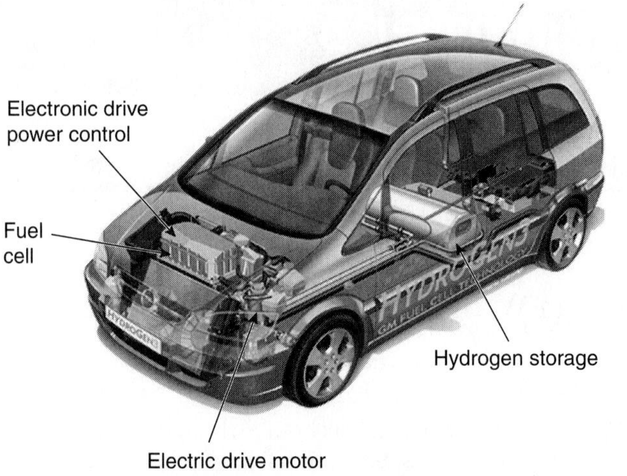

FIGURE 21.5.1 Typical Fuel Cell Vehicle (FCV) (Courtesy of General Motors Corporation)

In addition to propelling the vehicle, fuel cells typically provide electric power for vehicle auxiliary and ancillary systems, such as radios and air conditioners. On many FCVs, auxiliary and ancillary power is supplied by conventional 12 volt batteries or tapped off the fuel cell or electric drive bus; but, in some cases, dedicated power is provided from a separate fuel cell, called an auxiliary power unit (APU) (Figure 21.5.2). The typical power rating of an APU is between 3 and 10 kW.

Fuel cell vehicles are being developed by manufacturers throughout the world. FCVs range from 40 ft (12.2 m) transit buses down to motor scooters and fork trucks. Examples of buses and cars being developed by major vehicle manufacturers are provided in the following sections, along with a discussion of the design practices being employed for basic vehicle safety.

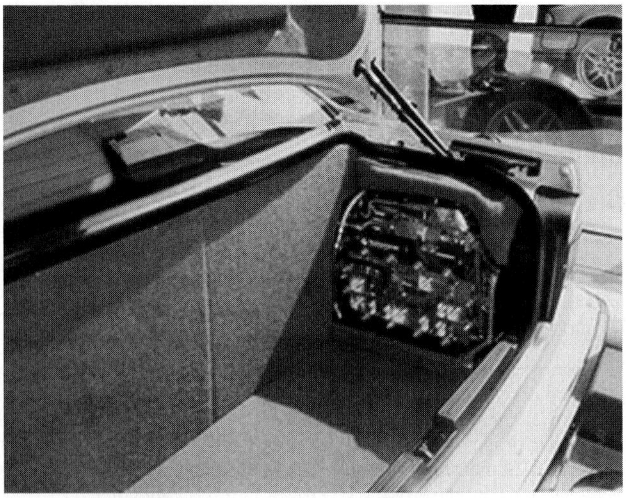

FIGURE 21.5.2 APU in Trunk of Passenger Vehicle (Courtesy of UTC Power)

Buses

Transit buses are widely viewed as a good early market for commercializing fuel cell vehicles. Many advantages have been identified regarding the use of transit buses as fuel cell platforms. Examples are as follows:

- Transit buses have well-defined duty cycles, centralized fueling and maintenance infrastructure, and dedicated maintenance personnel.
- Transit buses are large, providing ample room to install the fuel cell and related components.
- Many older diesel transit buses are noisy and polluting, providing fuel cells with an opportunity to make significant performance improvements.
- Transit agencies are subsidized by the government, thus helping to defray most of the risks and costs of technology development.
- Transit buses are highly visible in the community, providing an excellent showcase for fuel cells.

As a result, governments in North America, Europe, and Asia are supporting many demonstrations of fuel cell buses, causing the number of fuel cell buses to grow at an almost exponential pace (Figures 21.5.3 and 21.5.4).

Cars

A number of domestic car companies are actively developing FCVs. GM's HydroGen3 fuel cell minivan established a long distance driving record in 2004 by traveling 6200 miles from Norway to Portugal and is in service in Japan, California, and Washington, DC (Figure 21.5.5). Ford's Focus vehicles are used in California, Michigan, Florida, Canada, and Germany. DaimlerChrysler's A-class F-cells are in service in Germany, Singapore, Japan, and the United States (Figure 21.5.6).

Major Asian car companies are also very active. Honda's FCX is being used in demonstration programs in New York,

FIGURE 21.5.3 Van Hool Bus Powered by UTC Power's Fuel Cell (Courtesy of UTC Power)

FIGURE 21.5.5 General Motors FCV (Courtesy of General Motors and U.S. Postal Service)

FIGURE 21.5.4 DaimlerChrysler Citaro Bus Powered by Ballard Fuel Cells (Courtesy of DaimlerChrysler)

FIGURE 21.5.6 DaimlerChrysler FCV (Courtesy of DaimlerChrysler)

Nevada, California, and Japan. The company is also developing hydrogen fueling stations at customer sites. Toyota's Fuel Cell Hybrid Vehicle (FCHV) is in use in Japan and California (Figure 21.5.7). Nissan has X-Trail Fuel Cell Vehicles operating with both UTC Fuel Cells and Nissan stacks (Figure 21.5.8). Hyundai has introduced an improved version of its Tucson Fuel Cell Vehicle (FCV) using an advanced UTC Fuel Cells stack (Figure 21.5.9).

Most other automakers are also involved in public road tests with their fuel cell prototypes. For example, Mazda's Premacy FC-EV has undergone public road testing in Japan since 2001. Volkswagen's HyPower prototype has completed testing in cold temperatures and high altitudes in the Swiss Alps. The Mitsubishi FCV, based on the Grandis minivan, has been approved for road trials by Japan's Minister of Land, Infrastructure and Development. Suzuki's wagon R-FCV began Japanese road trials in 2005.

FIGURE 21.5.7 Toyota FCHV Fuel Cell Vehicle (Courtesy of Toyota Motor Company)

Design for Safety

The automotive industry is applying design practices developed over the past 100 years to ensure that FCV development and commercialization is successful and safe. Under normal and anticipated driving and vehicle scenarios, the vehicle and associated subsystems are designed with the objective that foreseeable single-point hardware or software failures do not result in an unreasonable safety risk to any person or uncontrolled vehicle behavior. This, in part, dictates the use of redundant safety features. Where this is not possible, a high safety factor is necessary to provide reasonable assurance that a component, such as a pressure vessel, will not fail.

A standard automotive industry approach to identifying and managing safety risks, particularly in new technologies and designs for higher volume products, is the use of a failure modes and effects analysis (FMEA).[1]

FIGURE 21.5.8 Nissan X-Trail FCV (Courtesy of Nissan Motor Company)

Hazardous conditions often depend on several conditions existing simultaneously. Prudent design, focused on the separation of hazards, prevents hazardous conditions from arising. Isolation and separation of hazards are approaches used to prevent cascading of failures and preclude unwanted or unexpected interactions.

Fail-safe design is a key philosophical approach. With regard to FCVs, automatic electrical disconnects should open and fuel shutoffs should close when de-energized. Utilizing this design philosophy, any interruption of this control signal (whether caused by accident, equipment failure, or human error) will cause isolation of electrical or fuel sources and minimize exposure of occupants, repair personnel, and emergency responders to hazards.

FIGURE 21.5.9 Hyundai FCEV Powered by UTC Power's Fuel Cell (Courtesy of UTC Power)

Fault Management

Faults that could result in a hazardous situation are detected and mitigated by control systems on the vehicle. When necessary, a staged warning and shutdown procedure is implemented to shut off the supply of fuel and open the electrical circuits to mitigate potential hazards. A staged warning and shutdown system is used when loss of vehicle power due to an automatic shutdown may, in itself, lead to a hazardous operating condition. In order to ensure the safety of the driver and the passengers in the vehicle, the sequence and rate of actions depends on the operating state of the vehicle.[2]

A main switch function is usually provided in demonstration vehicles so that the operator can disconnect all vehicle power sources by electrically isolating both poles of a fuel cell stack module, traction battery, and other high voltage sources (if equipped). This main switch, such as a conventional ignition switch, should be easily accessible and activated by the operator.

Typically, when the vehicle is involved in a crash detected by the crash sensors, the fuel is automatically shut off and the electrical system is disconnected. Additionally, to provide protection against electric shock by emergency responders, vehicles are designed to maintain proper electrical isolation following accidents.[3]

FUEL CELL SYSTEMS

In 1839, British scientist Sir William Robert Grove discovered that hydrogen and oxygen could be combined to produce water and an electric current. Fredrick Ostwald helped provide the theoretical foundations of fuel cells in the 1880s and was also able to experimentally determine the roles played by the different parts of Grove's fuel cell. In the late 1950s, Francis Bacon's research team developed a more advanced fuel cell. This design was used for NASA's Apollo moon missions and Skylab programs. Fuel cells also provide electrical power for space applications on board NASA's space shuttle orbiter. Today, fuel cell technology is being brought back to earth to power everything from cars and buses, to homes and businesses, and even cellular phones and laptop computers.

Fuel Cell Operation

Although there are several different types of fuel cells based on the type or state of the electrolyte used within the cell, almost all prototype fuel cell cars and buses use proton exchange membrane (PEM) fuel cells. Each PEM fuel cell is a thin wafer with a catalyst-coated membrane resembling a plastic film that is enclosed in electrically conducting graphite or metal plates (Figure 21.5.10). One side of the membrane acts as an anode and is fed hydrogen gas. The other side of the membrane serves as the cathode and is bathed in air to provide oxygen. At the anode, a catalytic reaction takes place with the hydrogen atoms releasing their electrons and becoming hydrogen ions (protons). The protons are transported through the membrane to reach the cathode. Another catalytic reaction takes place on the cathode where the protons combine with oxygen and electrons to produce water. The electric circuit is completed by connecting the cathode and anode to a load so that the electrons released from the anode can flow through the load to the cathode.

Fuel Cell Stack

In order to meet vehicular requirements, fuel cells are assembled in stacks to generate sufficient power and voltage for the electric drive system (Figure 21.5.11). Fuel cell stacks with electric capacities between 50 to 150 kilowatts are powering prototype passenger cars, minivans, sport utility vehicles, and transit buses. Tremendous improvements in stack efficiency, as well as weight and size reductions, have been achieved in recent years, but more remains to be done to make fuel cells affordable.

Balance of Plant

The fuel cell stack is just one component of the overall fuel cell system. The remainder of the fuel cell system, known as the "balance of plant," performs the following basic functions:

- Delivery of the hydrogen to the fuel cell stack and discharge of exhaust
- Delivery of fresh air to the cathodes of the cell stack
- Management of the fuel cell stack temperature and water

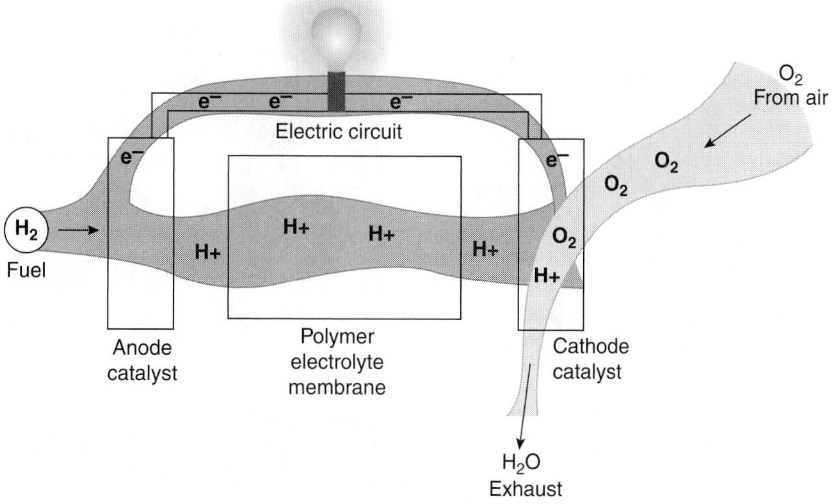

FIGURE 21.5.10 Operation of a PEM Cell (Courtesy of the U.S. Fuel Cell Council)

FIGURE 21.5.11 Fuel Cell Stack Installed in a Vehicle (Courtesy Nissan Motor Company)

To meet these functions, the balance of plant typically requires pumps, blowers or compressors, fans, heat exchangers, filters, and control valves. In many cases, standard off-the-shelf components are not suitable and specialized components must be designed and manufactured. Additionally, since many components in the balance of plant require electric power, the balance of plant often includes power conditioners to adjust fuel cell output power to an appropriate level for the component (Figures 21.5.12 and 21.5.13).

ELECTRIC DRIVE SYSTEMS

Operation of Electric Drive System

As described earlier in the chapter, the electric drive system converts the electric power from the fuel cell (and battery or ultracapacitor, if hybrid) into traction power for the FCV. Key functional elements of the system are shown in Figure 21.5.14 and described as follows:

1. The power control translates driver "throttle input" into modulated electric power from the fuel cell to the drive motors.
2. Electric drive motors convert the electric power into vehicle propulsion.
3. Batteries, ultracapacitors, or other methods of energy storage allow energy from regenerative braking to be captured for reuse and can provide improved vehicle response in hybrids.

A simplified electrical schematic is shown in Figure 21.5.15. The power control meets the driver's "throttle" request by varying the power from the fuel cell and the energy storage (if the vehicle is a hybrid) to meet in the propulsion requirement of the electric drive motor. Depending on the type of electric drive motor, the power control may also have to adjust the voltage level or convert the current from dc to ac. Additionally, in hybrid configurations, the power control also manages the recharge of the energy storage (i.e., batteries, ultracapacitors, or other devices) for optimum efficiency and performance of the vehicle.

Electrical Safety Elements

Typical voltages of the electric drive system range from 300 to 600 volts. Since the electrical system of a fuel cell vehicle is

FIGURE 21.5.12 NuCellSys HY-80 Engine with Ballard Fuel Cell (Courtesy of Ballard)

FIGURE 21.5.13 PureMotion™ Fuel Cell Power Plant Installed in a Van Hool Bus (Courtesy of UTC Power)

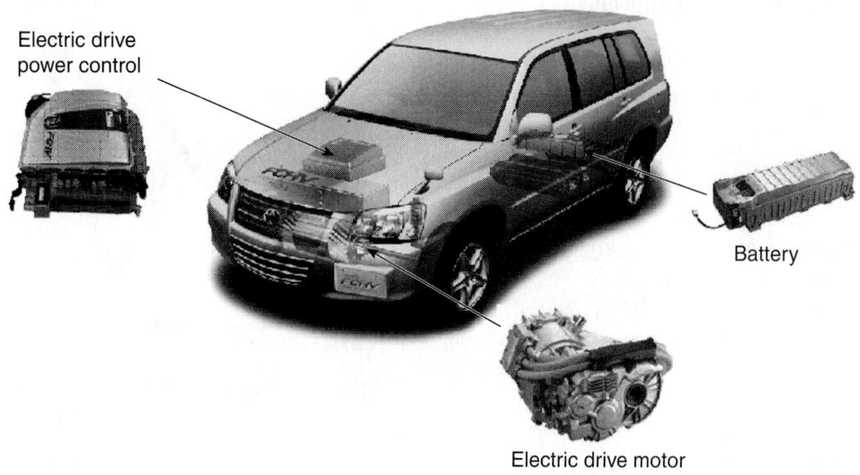

FIGURE 21.5.14 Key Components of the Electric Drive System in an FCV (Courtesy Toyota Motor Company)

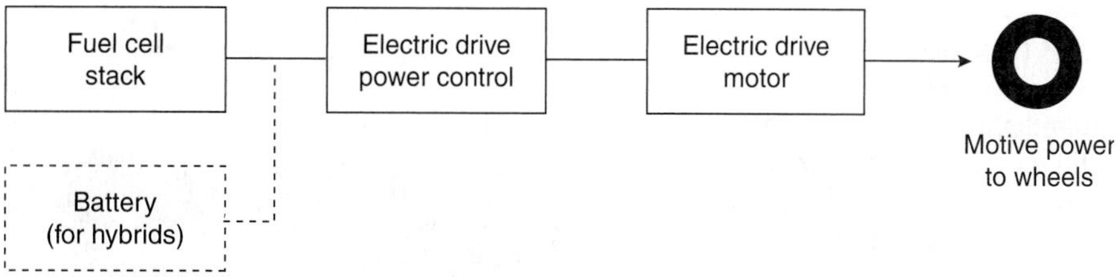

FIGURE 21.5.15 Simplified Schematic of the Electric Drive System

very similar to other electrical and hybrid vehicles, FCVs rely heavily on existing approaches from electric vehicles and hybrids to minimize hazards to vehicle occupants, repair workers, and emergency responders. Key elements of electrical safety include the following:

- *High voltage dielectric withstand capability.* Each high voltage system should demonstrate adequate dielectric strength of harnesses, bus bars, and connectors such that there is no indication of a dielectric breakdown or flashover after the application of voltage.[2,4]
- *Access to live parts.* An interlock, special fasteners, or other means should be provided on covers that are intended to prevent access to live parts with hazardous voltage.[2]
- *Electrical isolation.* Unlike low voltage circuits in vehicles that are bonded (or grounded) to the chassis of the vehicle, high voltage systems in current electric and hybrid vehicles as well as FCVs are isolated from the chassis. By so doing, the high voltage circuit can be touched in any single location without receiving an electric shock. This feature provides a second layer of protection in case the primary measures to prevent access to live parts are compromised by accident or repair activity.[2,3]
- *Fusing/overcurrent protection.* Like low voltage systems in vehicles, the high voltage system should be designed to prevent excessive current due to shorts or malfunctions from causing overheating and fires.[2,5]
- *High voltage wire identification.* High voltage cables and harnesses are visually identified with a permanent orange covering material (Figure 21.5.16).[2,6]
- *Labeling.* Hazardous voltage equipment or compartments containing hazardous voltage equipment should be identified

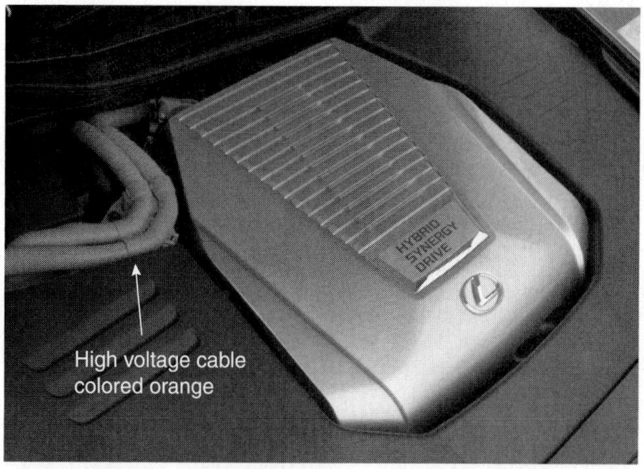

FIGURE 21.5.16 High Voltage Cable Identification as Shown Under the Hood of a Production Gasoline Hybrid Vehicle (Courtesy of Toyota Motor Company)

using the high voltage symbol, as shown in Figure 21.5.17, using black on a yellow background.[2,7]

- *Automatic disconnects.* An automatic disconnect function should provide a means of electrically isolating both poles of a fuel cell stack module, a traction battery, and other high voltage sources (if equipped) from external circuitry or components. This function would be activated by either the main switch or as an automatic triggering protection.[2]
- *Manual disconnects.* A means should be provided to disconnect both poles or de-energize the fuel cell module, a traction battery, and other high voltage sources (if equipped) from external circuitry or components. This function would be used for vehicle assembly, service, and maintenance operations.[2]

FIGURE 21.5.17 High Voltage Symbol

COMPRESSED HYDROGEN STORAGE SYSTEMS

Compressed hydrogen storage is the most common type of hydrogen storage on current FCVs. The technical challenge with compressed hydrogen is to store enough hydrogen on board the vehicle to achieve reasonable range between fuel refills. A typical FCV requires about 6 kg of hydrogen. To achieve this amount of hydrogen gas storage, manufacturers are increasing the storage pressures from the present level of 350 to 700 bar (5000 to 10,000 psig). Figure 21.5.18 illustrates a compressed hydrogen container installed on an FCV. A simplified process schematic for a compressed hydrogen system is shown in Figure 21.5.19.

Functions and Features

Key functions and features of the compressed hydrogen storage system are as follows:

1. A filling receptacle on the vehicle is used to connect to the filling station. The receptacle (such as an SAE J2600 design[8]) typically has a check valve function built into the

FIGURE 21.5.18 Compressed Hydrogen Container in FCV (Courtesy of Toyota)

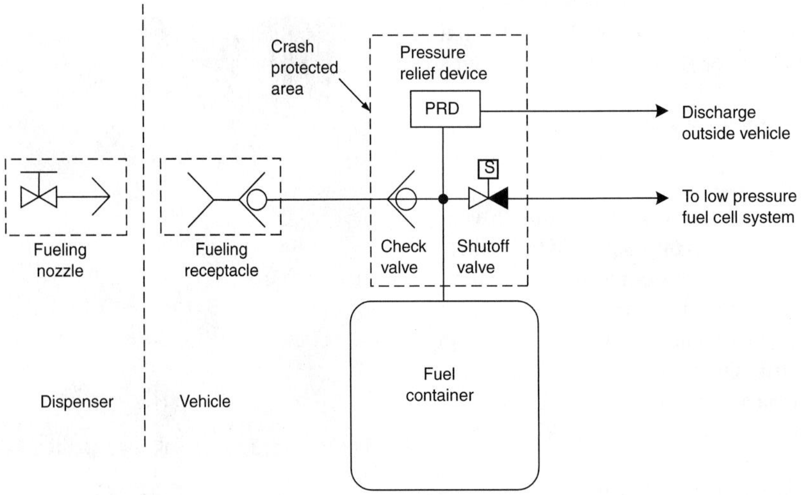

FIGURE 21.5.19 Compressed Hydrogen Storage System Process on FCVs

receptacle to prevent backflow leakage when the fill nozzle is disconnected. Additionally, there usually is a redundant check on the line between the nozzle and tank to meet design for safety requirements.
2. One or more containers on the vehicle store compressed hydrogen for use by the fuel cell.
3. Shutoff valves and pressure regulators are used to control the delivery of hydrogen to the fuel cells, as is done today with compressed natural gas vehicles.
4. One or more pressure relief devices (PRDs) are utilized to prevent tank burst in case the compressed hydrogen system is exposed to a fire due to an accident or other fault.

Safety Measures

The SAE is leading a cross-industry team of engineers from automotive, fuel cell, container, and component manufacturers, including technical experts from CSA (originally, Canadian Standards Organizations). The objective of this activity is to ensure the integrity of the hydrogen storage and fuel systems on the FCVs as well as other hydrogen vehicles that deliver hydrogen or hydrogen-rich gas to internal combustion engines. Guidance will be provided with regard to proper design and material selection. Systems-level, performance-based tests are being developed to demonstrate system integrity for normal operation and during fault management. The aim is to provide real-world system safety guidance while still facilitating rapid technology advances by the industry.

SAE recommendations for fuel cell and hydrogen vehicle safety are built on the excellent safety record for existing fuels. For example, labeling is very important for identifying unique items that are not on conventional vehicles and require special handling or awareness. Natural gas vehicles have historically been identified with a blue diamond with a "CNG" to convey to emergency responders and others that the fuel system on the vehicle is compressed natural gas. Based on the similarities to a natural gas fuel system, SAE has recommended vehicles with hydrogen fuel utilize a similar blue diamond. The difference with hydrogen vehicles would be that the diamond would indicate compressed hydrogen or another method used to store the hydrogen.

HYDROGEN SYSTEM SAFETY

Hydrogen is as safe as, if not safer than, other conventional fuels on the market today.[9] Experience has shown that hydrogen can be safely produced and transported; it has been in mass production and transportation for over 50 years in the United States. Ford Motor Company examined this issue under contract to the Department of Energy (DOE) and concluded in 1997 that "overall, [they] judge the safety of a hydrogen fuel cell vehicle system to be potentially better than the demonstrated safety record of gasoline or propane, and equal to or better than that of natural gas." A Norwegian study in 2002 reached a similar conclusion: "There are no technical or safety barriers that prevent the use of hydrogen for fuel in the transportation sector or as a medium for the storage and transportation of energy. It is possible to manufacture and utilize hydrogen just as safely as with today's gasoline systems."[10]

The automobile industry and government agencies have decades of experience in designing and testing for the safe use of fuels in motor vehicles. Fuels used in automobiles contain energy in a concentrated form. This same characteristic is why fuels must be handled appropriately. The past 100 years of experience with automobile fuels such as gasoline, diesel, and natural gas can be used and expanded upon for hydrogen as an automobile fuel.

The compressed hydrogen systems benefit from experience with compressed natural gas (CNG) and are designed to contain hydrogen and not burst. SAE is working to define performance-based standards for hydrogen systems designed to meet customer demand and use profiles of passenger and fleet vehicles.

Safety Measures

In the event that a leak does occur from the hydrogen system, SAE[2] has defined requirements to ensure that unintended hydrogen discharges do not cause a hazard within the vehicles. Discharges to any compartments within the vehicle that contain or may contain ignition sources are rendered nonflammable and the atmosphere in the passenger compartment is to be maintained nonhazardous through the use of active or passive barriers, dilution of potentially flammable gases, or the use of recombiners to eliminate flammable gases by catalytic reaction. If a leak is detected that exceeds the ability of these countermeasures to appropriately mitigate, then a staged warning and shutdown is executed following the guidance discussed in an earlier section (entitled "Fault Management") in this chapter.

Finally, vehicles are designed to protect the compressed hydrogen system during a crash. Typically, if a crash occurs, the hydrogen shutoff valves at the containers are closed to isolate the system, leaving only a small amount of hydrogen downstream of the shutoff valves as a minimal risk, given that the energy content is typically less than that in fuel lines on conventional gasoline vehicles. If the vehicle is exposed to a fire following the crash, pressure relief devices (PRDs) will thermally activate to release hydrogen and prevent a burst of the container.

Management of Discharges from FCVs

Successful commercialization of fuel cell and hydrogen vehicles requires that these vehicles be used in a manner consistent with current gasoline, internal combustion engine (ICE) vehicles. To achieve this objective, SAE[2] has defined recommended practices such that hydrogen vents, purges, leaks, and exhausts during operating and nonoperating states are consistent with usage in residential garages and commercial structures as well as general use outdoors and that safety is comparable to that presented by leaks and ruptures of fuel lines in present gasoline vehicles. To ensure that discharges are nonhazardous, the discharge is examined in two regions:

1. The local region where the discharge from the vehicle initially mixes with surrounding air
2. The atmosphere surrounding the vehicle after dispersal of the discharge

The local region where the discharges from the vehicle mix with the surrounding air should be locally unignitible at all times.

Discharges may be managed through dilution of potentially flammable gases, use of recombiners to eliminate flammable gases by catalytic reaction, or adjustment of process controls within the fuel cell or vehicle systems.

Hydrogen is potentially flammable in a gas mixture with oxygen and nitrogen (the primary constituents of air) when the concentration of hydrogen exceeds 4 percent (by volume) and the concentration of oxygen exceeds 5 percent (by volume). As shown in Figure 21.5.20, hydrogen discharges may or may not pass through regions of potential flammability during dispersal into the surrounding atmosphere, depending on the local concentration of hydrogen and oxygen concentration as the discharge mixes with the surrounding air. The situation is illustrated by two cases in Figure 21.5.20:

1. In the first case (indicated by the dotted line), the initial concentration of hydrogen is diluted to 5 percent with inerts before discharge. The discharge is always nonflammable as it mixes with surrounding air because the hydrogen concentration falls below 4 percent before the oxygen concentration reaches 5 percent.
2. In the second case (indicated by the dashed line), the initial hydrogen content is 100 percent at the point of discharge and a potentially flammable mixture is formed as the hydrogen mixes with surrounding air.

There is empirical evidence that discharges may not be ignitable even though the local concentration passes through the region of potential flammability. This is because the lower flammability limit (LFL) of hydrogen (4% in air) is based on testing a uniform mixture of gas in a quiescent state,[11] which is inconsistent with the mixing that occurs in the local region of discharge from the vehicle. Testing has shown that flow conditions and mixing during dispersal can actually suppress ignition and that hydrogen concentrations above 8 percent are typically required to ignite discharges.[12] A test method is being developed by the SAE to explore the areas of potential flammability (if they exist) with an ignition source. The objective of the test is to determine if there is a release of energy or the propagation of combustion into a standing flame that could represent a hazard to people or property. The local area of the discharge can therefore be demonstrated to be nonhazardous.

In order to complete the evaluation of hydrogen discharges from the vehicle, it is also necessary to look beyond the local region of discharge and evaluate the condition of the general atmosphere surrounding the vehicle. An approach was defined by the SAE[2] for assessing discharges when vehicles are being parked in residential garages[13] and being operated in mechanically ventilated commercial structures,[14] as well as when being operated out-of-doors.[15] The approach uses a combination of analysis and test for vehicle manufacturers to verify that the atmosphere surrounding the vehicle remains unclassified (see Article 500 of NFPA 70, *National Electric Code*®) and is therefore nonhazardous. By so doing, FCVs can be used and stored in the same manner as current gasoline-ICE-powered vehicles without modification to building codes.

Hydrogen Quality and Odorants

FCVs currently require a clean grade of hydrogen as a fuel. The industry is looking at a quality level that allows less than 1000 ppm of impurities. This is being done for several reasons. One reason is that a clean grade of fuel minimizes the buildup of noncondensable, nonhydrogen constituents. This buildup could reduce the operating efficiency of the fuel cell systems and result

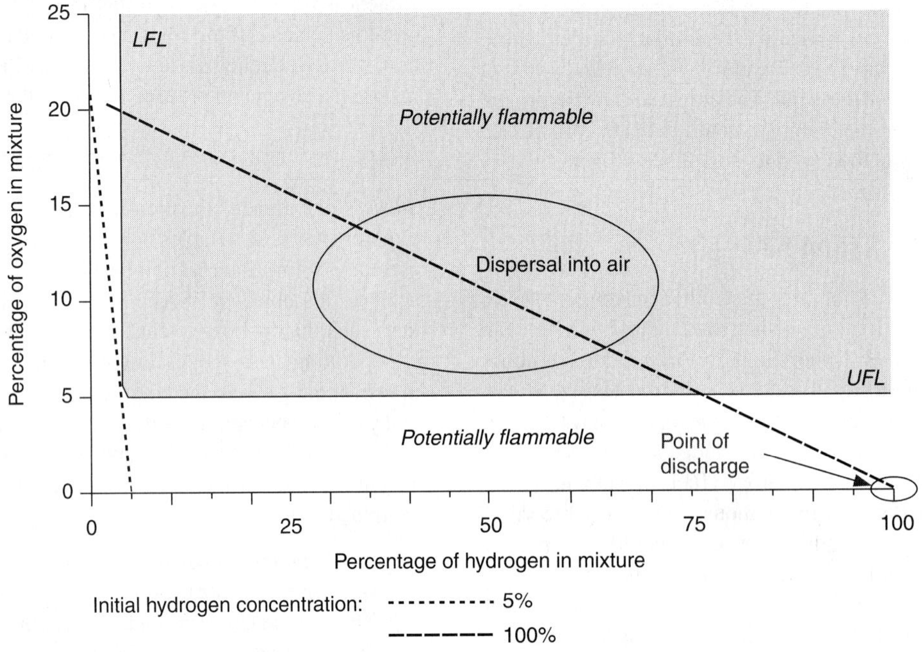

FIGURE 21.5.20 Potential Flammability of Hydrogen Discharges

in increased venting of hydrogen and these noncondensables. This venting would present additional emissions of flammable gases, which would have to be mitigated. Another reason is that some impurities are detrimental to both fuel cell components and fuel storage media. The removal of these impurities on the vehicle will add weight and cost to the vehicle, increase vehicle maintenance costs, and, in some cases, may not be technically practical.

Some parties have suggested odorizing the hydrogen fuel. Although this "low tech" approach has been used for nearly a century with natural gas, it is inconsistent with FCVs because fuel cells do not benignly consume (i.e., burn) the odorant as do internal combustion vehicles. The odorant either adversely reacts with components of the FCV or passes through the fuel cell system. If the odorant reacts with the system, the life and durability of the components will be severely limited. If it passes through the fuel cell system, it is concentrated by up to 500 times the original concentration in the hydrogen supply. This means that detection of a leak would be masked by the highly concentrated (and objectionable) odors emanating from the exhaust pipe.

Finally, the use of an odorant may be inconsistent with common types of hydrogen storage such as liquefied hydrogen and metal hydrides. With liquid hydrogen, for example, all compounds with the exception of helium are separated as solids at liquid hydrogen temperatures. This means that hydrogen could leak out of a containment system but the odorant would be retained inside the system, leaving the leaking gas not odorized and therefore not detected.

For these reasons, current FCVs are designed to operate with odorant-free fuel. As with a number of natural gas vehicle applications, if hydrogen is to be supplied to a filling station by pipeline, the fuel should be deodorized (if an odorant is present) before dispensing at the fueling station to hydrogen vehicles.

FIGURE 21.5.21 Hydrogen Fueling Station in Oakland, California (Courtesy of Chevron)

FIGURE 21.5.22 Hydrogen Fueling Station in Washington, DC (Courtesy of General Motors)

Vehicle Fueling

The commercialization of hydrogen fuel cell vehicles raises a "chicken-and-the-egg" question: Which comes first, mass-produced fuel cell vehicles or the hydrogen fueling infrastructure necessary to operate them? With a growing number of hydrogen fuel cell vehicles hitting public roads, the answer to this question may be getting clearer.

It is true that a supporting infrastructure for hydrogen fuel cell vehicles will be needed to make them practical. A fully integrated, fully deployed infrastructure is not, however, needed all at once. State and regional infrastructures are already planned and being developed. Recent examples include the California Hydrogen Highway and hydrogen station plans in the states of Florida and New York. Similar regional efforts are currently under way in Canada, Norway, Singapore, Germany, Japan, and other countries.[16]

These early hydrogen stations (Figures 21.5.21 and 21.5.22) serve to provide a limited infrastructure for fuel cell vehicle demonstrations and some commercial sales arrangements and also serve to research and demonstrate the various ways in which hydrogen can be produced and stored. The California Hydrogen Highway Plan serves to establish a baseline network of hydrogen fueling and electrical generating stations along California's interstate highways by 2010. The hydrogen from these fueling stations will be from various sources, including renewables, such as renewable methanol and ethanol, and nonrenewables, such as natural gas.

In today's society, the use of gasoline as an automobile fuel has become so common that the safe handling of the fuel is practically engrained into the culture of users. While refueling their vehicles, users are aware of the precautions and operate in a certain manner, such as not running their vehicle and not smoking. Users often take for granted that fuel distribution systems have built-in safety features. For example, the prevention of static electricity is designed into both the vehicle and the refueling station[2,17] (see NFPA 77, *Recommended Practice on Static Electricity*). Vehicles are designed to maintain a conductive path from the fueling neck to the tires. The refueling station is designed in a manner that a conductive path exists from the tire contact surface to the fueling nozzle. The result is a bonding and grounding path that prevents sparks that could ignite gasoline during filling. The countermeasures developed for gasoline fueling have been adapted to hydrogen fueling.

FCVs and other hydrogen vehicles will also depend on the filling station and dispenser to provide the following additional protective measures during vehicle filling[18] (see also NFPA 52, *Vehicular Fuel Systems Code*):

- Overpressure protection of the hydrogen storage system on the vehicle by relief valves on the filling station set to 1.38 times the nominal working pressure (service pressure)
- Provision for leak detection
- Emergency shutoff of hydrogen if a fault is detected
- Breakaway protection if the vehicle moves before the fueling nozzle is disconnected

Vehicle Maintenance and Service

Existing model building codes already address requirements for facilities conducting repairs on vehicles (NFPA 30A, *Code for Motor Fuel Dispensing Facilities and Repair Garages*). These requirements are adequate for FCVs, as long as work on the hydrogen storage system is not being conducted.

Additional countermeasures should be considered for areas conducting work on the hydrogen storage systems. For example, a vent system will probably be required to defuel (depressurize and purge) the hydrogen storage system on the vehicle before major repairs are conducted. Additionally, requirements for ventilation, gas and fire detection, electrical classification, HVAC interconnection with other areas of the building, and fire rating of interior walls and doors should be considered, following standard practices for hydrogen systems[19] (see also NFPA 52).

POSTCRASH CONSIDERATIONS

Fuel cells vehicles will be expected to have crashworthiness that is equivalent to or better than current motor vehicles, and the SAE Fuel Cell Standards Committee is developing standards that will allow vehicle manufacturers to evaluate their designs and demonstrate that expectations are fulfilled. In this regard, there are two keys to FCV safety following a crash.

The first postcrash consideration is that occupants or emergency responders must not be exposed to electrical shock hazards. The SAE Fuel Cell Committee has updated SAE J1766 for electrical safety following a crash to account for the unique characteristics of fuel cells and modern hybrid electric drive trains. High voltage electrical circuits are to be discharged or appropriately isolated from ground such that circuits can be touched without receiving a harmful shock.[3]

The second postcrash consideration is that the hydrogen fuel needs to be contained. Crash standards for both gasoline and compressed natural gas (CNG) vehicles were reviewed by the SAE Fuel Cell Standards Committee, and an approach was defined to demonstrate that compressed hydrogen systems will retain their contents and thereby minimize exposure to potentially hazardous events.[2]

Additionally, the fuel system needs to protect against secondary events (such as fire from another vehicle) following the accident. CNG vehicles use pressure-relief devices (PRDs) to vent gas in the event of a fire. By so doing, the fuel tanks can be depressurized by venting fuel, and a potentially hazardous event, such as a container burst, can be avoided. Fuel cell vehicle manufacturers have already adopted this practice, and the SAE Fuel Cell Standards Committee is addressing postcrash situations as part of new standards being developed.

FUEL CELL ORGANIZATIONS AND INITIATIVES

U.S. Fuel Cell Council

The U.S. Fuel Cell Council is the industry association of the fuel cell industry. The council's membership includes producers of all types of fuel cells, major suppliers, automakers, universities, fuel cell customers, hydrogen suppliers, government entities and national laboratories, and other associations. Formed in 1998, the U.S. Fuel Cell Council provides its members with an opportunity to develop industrywide policies and procedures, work with codes and standards developers, conduct education and marketing activities for the fuel cell industry, and collaborate on a wide range of technical subjects.

The U.S. Fuel Cell Council is dedicated to commercializing fuel cell technology. Members of the U.S. Fuel Cell Council are spending their own resources to achieve this goal and are also partnering with government initiatives.

Fuel Cell Initiatives

Two high profile examples of government initiatives are the FreedomCAR Partnership and the California Fuel Cell Partnership (CAFCP).

FreedomCAR Partnership. The FreedomCAR Partnership is a collaboration between the U.S. Department of Energy (DOE), the United States Council for Automotive Research (USCAR), and five large energy providers. The goal of this organization is "the development of emission- and petroleum-free cars and light trucks." The focus is on the high-risk research needed to develop the necessary technologies, such as fuel cells and advanced hybrid propulsion systems, to provide a full range of affordable cars and light trucks that are free of harmful emissions and that do not sacrifice freedom of mobility and freedom of vehicle choice. The FreedomCAR Partnership is not designed to produce any particular vehicle, but rather to accelerate the adoption of advanced automotive technologies. The program has established technology goals to be reached by 2010 in order to target areas for research and development.

California Fuel Cell Partnership (CAFCP). The California Fuel Cell Partnership (CaFCP) is a unique collaboration of auto manufacturers, energy companies, fuel cell technology companies, and government agencies. This organization is demonstrating hydrogen vehicle technology that could move the world toward practical and affordable environmental solutions.

In addition to demonstrating fuel cell vehicles, the CaFCP is examining fuel infrastructure issues and beginning to prepare the California market for this new technology.

Three California transit agencies have a few demonstration sites: Sunline Transit Agency in Coachella Valley, Santa Clara Valley Transportation Authority in Silicon Valley, and AC Transit in Northeast San Francisco Bay. In addition, Santa Clara VTA and AC Transit opened hydrogen fueling stations for their fleets in 2005. For more information see http://www.cafcp.org.

SUMMARY

Fuel cell vehicles (FCVs) are being developed in response to the worldwide need to lower emissions and decrease dependence on oil. A risk-based approach has been used to identify both electrical and fuel system hazards on FCVs, and approaches to mitigate these hazards have been and are being developed based on past automotive experience and sound engineering practice. Overall, a philosophy of mitigating credible single-point failures was utilized as a minimum standard.

Because the electrical system of a fuel cell vehicle is very similar to that of other electrical and hybrid vehicles, the practices and requirements rely heavily on previously published work in these areas. Correspondingly, hydrogen requirements are based on previous experience with gasoline and compressed natural gas (CNG) internal combustion vehicles with appropriate adjustments and expansions for fuel cell propulsion. The overall objective is to establish recommended practices such that FCVs can be used and stored in the same manner as conventional gasoline, internal combustion vehicles while still facilitating rapid advances by the industry.

BIBLIOGRAPHY

References Cited

1. SAE 1739, "Potential Failure Mode and Effects Analysis in Design (Design FMEA), Potential Failure mode and Effects Analysis in Manufacturing and Assembly Processes (Process FMEA), Potential Failure Mode and Effects Analysis for Machinery (Machinery FMEA)," SAE International, Warrendale, PA.
2. SAE J2578, "Recommended Practice for General Fuel Cell Vehicle Safety," SAE International, Warrendale, PA.
3. SAE J1766, "Recommended Practice for Electric and Hybrid Electric Vehicle Battery Systems Crash Integrity Testing," SAE International, Warrendale, PA.
4. SAE J1742, "Connections for High Voltage On-Board Road Vehicle Electrical Wiring Harnesses—Test Methods and General Performance Requirements," SAE International, Warrendale, PA.
5. SAE 2344, "Guidelines for Electric Vehicle Safety," SAE International, Warrendale, PA.
6. SAE J1654, "High Voltage Primary Cable," SAE International, Warrendale, PA.
7. IEC 60417, "Graphical Signals for Use on Equipment," International Electrotechnical Commission, Geneva, Switzerland.
8. SAE J2600, "Compressed Hydrogen Surface Vehicle Fueling Connection Devices," SAE International, Warrendale, PA.
9. Breakthrough Technologies Institute's (BTI) Hydrogen and the Law: Safety and Liability report available at: http://www.fuelcells.org.
10. Kruse, B., Grinna, S., and Buch, C., "Hydrogen Status og muligheter," *Bellona rapport,* No. 6, 2002, p. 15.
11. Coward, H. F., and Jones, G. W., *Limits of Flammability of Gases and Vapors,* Bulleting 503, Bureau of Mines, U.S. Department of the Interior, Washington, DC, 1952.
12. Swain, M., "Codes and Standards Analysis," DE-FC36-00GO10606, A007, University of Miami, Coral Gables, FL, 2004.
13. Mitiltsky, F., Weisberg, A. H., and Myers, B., "Vehicle Hydrogen Storage Using Lightweight Tank," *Proceedings* of the 2000 DOE Hydrogen Program Review, U.S. Department of Energy, Washington, DC, 2000.
14. *2000 International Mechanical Code (IMC),* Chapter 4, International Code Council, Inc., Falls Church, VA, 2000.
15. IEC 60079-10, "Electrical Apparatus for Explosive Gas Atmospheres—Part 10: Classification of Hazardous Areas," International Electrotechnical Commission, Geneva, Switzerland.
16. For chart outlining hydrogen fueling stations, go to: http://www.fuelcells.org/info/charts/h2fuelingstations.pdf.
17. API Recommended Practice 2003, "Protection Against Ignitions Arising out of Static, Lightning, and Stray Currents," API, Washington, DC.
18. SAE TIR 2760, "Technical Information Report for Pressure Terminology Used in Fuel Cells and Other Hydrogen Vehicle Applications," SAE International, Warrendale, PA.
19. *2006 International Fire Code (IFC),* Chapter 22, International Code Council, Inc., Falls Church, VA, 2006.

NFPA Codes, Standards, and Recommended Practices

Reference to the following NFPA codes, standards, and recommended practices will provide further information on fuel cell vehicles discussed in this chapter. (See the latest version of The NFPA Catalog *for availability of current editions of the following documents.)*

NFPA 30A, *Code for Motor Fuel Dispensing Facilities and Repair Garages*
NFPA 52, *Vehicular Fuel Systems Code*
NFPA 70, *National Electrical Code®*
NFPA 77, *Recommended Practice on Static Electricity*

Chapter 6

Recreational Vehicles

Bruce A. Hopkins

Chapter Contents

Key Terms

motor home, recreational vehicle, towable

Recreational vehicles (RVs) have been around since the beginning of motorized travel in the early 1900s. RVs are available in several styles, types, and sizes to offer people of all ages the opportunity to camp and travel to points of interest or special events and otherwise enjoy the great outdoors. Today nearly 8 million U.S. households own at least one RV—a 15 percent increase over the 4 years from 2001 to 2005 and a 58 percent rise since 1980, according to the 2003 edition of *Industry Profile: RVIA Year End Report.* One in twelve U.S. vehicle-owning households now owns at least one RV.[1]

This chapter discusses the types of recreational vehicles and their features, the development and use of RVs, the development of RV standards, the fire and life safety issues associated with RVs, their fire safety record, and the oversight programs that are in place to assist RV industry manufacturers in the safe production of these vehicles for recreation, travel, and seasonal use.

For related topics, see Section 21, Chapter 1, "Passenger Vehicle Fires"; and Section 21, Chapter 4, "Vehicle Fueling Using Gaseous Fuels."

OVERVIEW OF RECREATIONAL VEHICLES

Recreational Vehicle Defined

Based on the NFPA 1192, *Standard on Recreational Vehicles,* definition as refined by the Recreation Vehicle Industry Association (RVIA), a recreation vehicle (RV) is defined as a vehicle that combines transportation and temporary living quarters for travel, recreation, and camping. RVs may have their own motor power (as in the case of motor homes), may be mounted (as are truck campers), or may be towed by another vehicle (as are travel, fifth-wheel, and folding camping trailers). Not included in the RV definition are conversion vehicles, off-road vehicles, emergency living units, and manufactured housing for long-term residence (i.e., park trailers and mobile homes).

Types of Recreational Vehicles

The two main categories of RVs are *motor homes* (motorized RVs) and *towables* (RVs towed behind the family car, van, or pickup).[2]

Motor Homes. A motor home is a vehicle built on or as an integral part of a self-propelled motor vehicle chassis. It may provide kitchen, sleeping, and bathroom facilities, and it may be equipped with the ability to store and carry fresh water and sewage. Type A motor homes (Figure 21.6.1) are generally the largest, where the driving compartment is built by the RV manufacturer; Type B motor homes (Figure 21.6.2), or van campers, are the smallest and are built on vehicles where the chassis manufacturer provides the driving compartment and the entire exterior shell; and Type C motor homes have the driving compartment provided by the chassis manufacturer (Figure 21.6.3) and generally fall in between these two in size (see Table 21.6.1).

Bruce A. Hopkins is the vice-president of standards and education for the Recreation Vehicle Industry Association (RVIA) in Reston, Virginia. Mr. Hopkins has worked in the area of RV standards for 34 years, 28 of these with RVIA. He has been directly associated with the RV industry for over 40 years.

FIGURE 21.6.1 Type A Motor Homes—Generic Model and Actual Example (Source: Courtesy of RVIA)

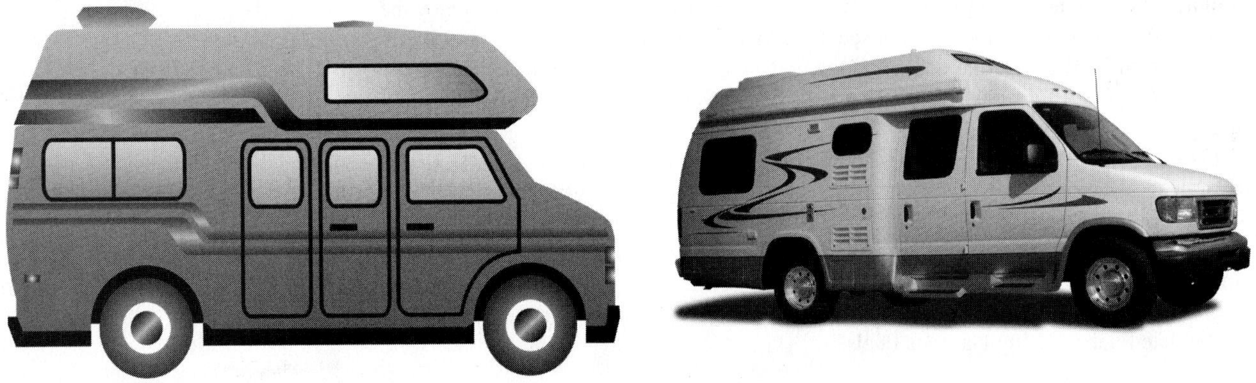

FIGURE 21.6.2 Type B Motor Homes—Generic Model and Actual Example (Source: Courtesy of RVIA)

FIGURE 21.6.3 Type C Motor Homes—Generic Model and Actual Example (Source: Courtesy of RVIA)

Towables. A towable RV is designed to be towed by a motorized vehicle (e.g., auto, van, or pickup truck) and of such size and weight as not to require a special highway movement permit. It does not require permanent on-site hook-up. Types of towable RVs are conventional travel trailers (Figure 21.6.4), sports utility RVs (Figure 21.6.5), travel trailers with expandable ends (Figure 21.6.6), fifth-wheel travel trailers (Figure 21.6.7), folding camping trailers (Figure 21.6.8), and truck campers (Figure 21.6.9).

Construction Techniques

RVs are manufactured on production lines similar to that of the automobile industry, but only a few RV manufacturers use fully automated assembly lines. In a typical RV manufacturing facility, the vehicles are generally pushed manually along the assembly line. The stations within a typical production line might include chassis, floors, interior walls, cabinetry, roofs and exterior coverings, installation of electrical/plumbing/propane-

TABLE 21.6.1 Recreational Vehicle Types and Features

Type	*Features*	*Sleeps*	*Price Range*
Motor home—Type A	• Constructed on a specially designed motor vehicle chassis • Kitchen, sleeping, bathroom, living facilities accessible from driver's area	2–6	$76,275–$1,350,000
Motor home—Type B (or van camper)	• Referred to as a "van camper" • Panel-type truck with kitchen, sleeping, and/or bathroom facilities • Freshwater storage, city water hook-up, and top extension for more head room	2–4	$41,000–$72,660
Motor home—Type C	• Constructed on automotive manufacture van frame with attached cab • Kitchen, sleeping, bathroom facilities • Living area behind and above cab	6–10	$48,450–$298,910
Towable—conventional travel trailer	• Towable by car, van, or pickup • Kitchen, sleeping, bathroom, dining, living facilities • 12–35 ft (3.66–10.67 m) long	4–8	$8,085–$79,510
Towable—sport utility RV	• Built-in "garage" for cycles, ATVs, other sports equipment	Up to 8	$21,000–$58,000
Towable—travel trailer with expandable ends	• Built for "fresh air" experience • Folds for lightweight towing	Up to 8	$9,000–$18,000
Towable—fifth-wheel travel trailer	• Equipped same as conventional travel trailer • Raised forward section, allowing bilevel floor plan • Towable by vehicle equipped with fifth-wheel hitch	Up to 8	$10,870–$120,350
Towable—folding camping trailer	• Lightweight with collapsible sides • Towable by family vehicle (even some compacts) • Kitchen, sleeping, dining, (often) bathroom facilities	Up to 8	$4,380–$12,800
Towable—truck camper	• Loaded onto bed or chassis of truck • Most with kitchen, sleeping, dining, bathroom facilities	2–6	$4,580–$22,590

Source: Data from *RVIA Types & Terms,* Recreational Vehicle Industry Association, Reston, VA, 2005.

fuel systems, installation of appliances or furniture, final finish, and testing.

RECREATIONAL VEHICLE DEVELOPMENT AND USE

History

Early Years. The recreational vehicle industry developed and grew from its early roots in camping, hunting, and other outdoor activities.[3] Tents, provisions, and cooking and sleeping equipment were loaded and pulled around the countryside on wagons, carts, and other conveyances long before the advent of the automobile.

The development of the automobile in the years around 1900 greatly increased the range of these campers and vagabonds, and mechanical power made it easier for them to take more supplies and comforts along on their adventures. Early "auto campers" simply piled their tents, equipment, and supplies in and on their vehicles. Later, they attached carts and trailers to the cars, increasing carrying capacity greatly. The earliest trailers were often modified horse-drawn carts with wooden cartwheels. The cartwheels were shortly replaced with heavier auto-type wheels. This relative ease of travel, with all the needed camping supplies, brought about the beginnings of what is now recognized as the RV industry and its related lifestyle.

In the early 1910s, trailers were being built not only to transport camping supplies and equipment, but to also be used as "house trailers," or mobile cabins. These earliest units, mostly homemade or custom built by local handymen or carriage makers, allowed for the storage of provisions, preparation of meals, and comfortable and relatively "bug-proof" sleeping. "Living rooms" and most daytime activities were relegated to the great outdoors.

From the mid-1910s to the mid-1920s, individual builders were creating one-of-a-kind "house cars" by motorizing their camping vehicles. Some were permanently built on auto or truck chassis; others were bolt-on structures added to a rigid frame and could be removed and exchanged. It is estimated that 15 million campers and RVers were on the nation's roads in 1922. In 1926, the Chenango Camp Trailer Co. introduced the first

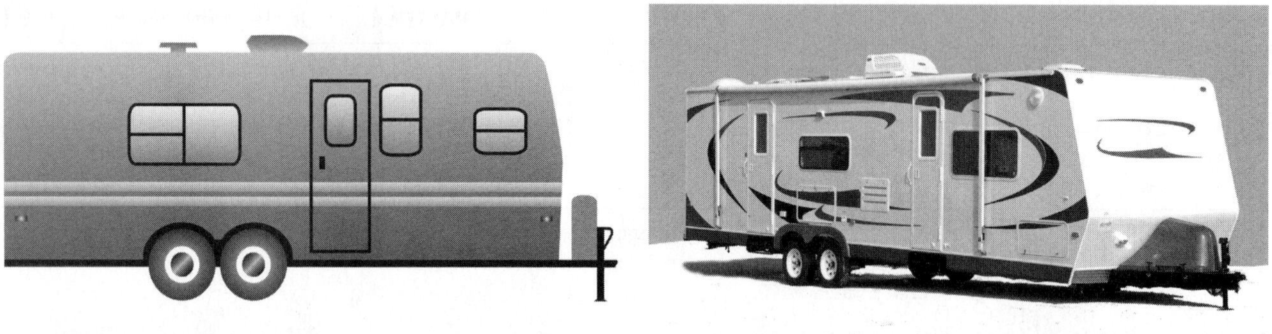

FIGURE 21.6.4 Conventional Travel Trailers—Generic Model and Actual Example (Source: Courtesy of RVIA)

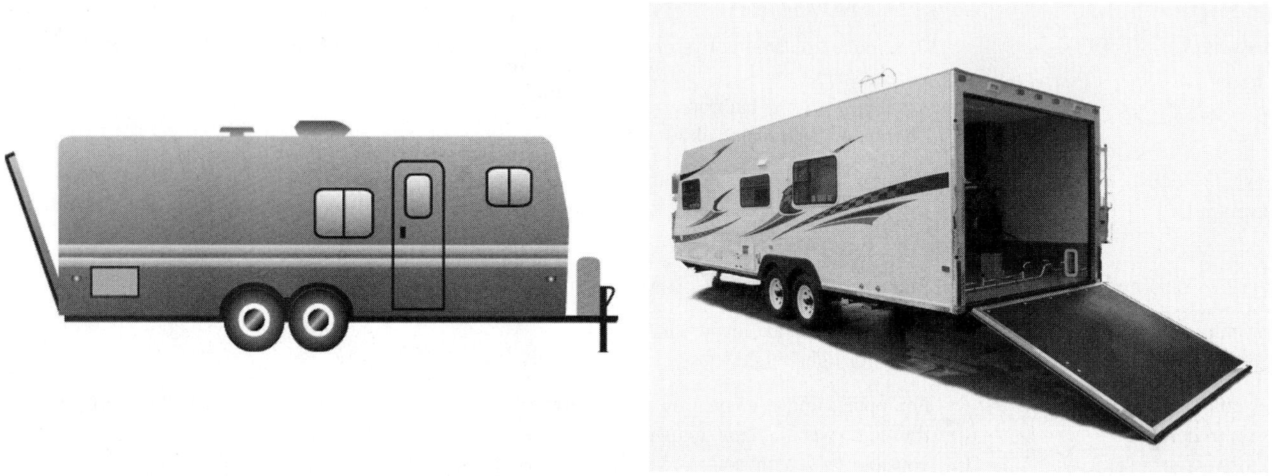

FIGURE 21.6.5 Sports Utility RVs—Generic Model and Actual Example (Source: Courtesy of RVIA)

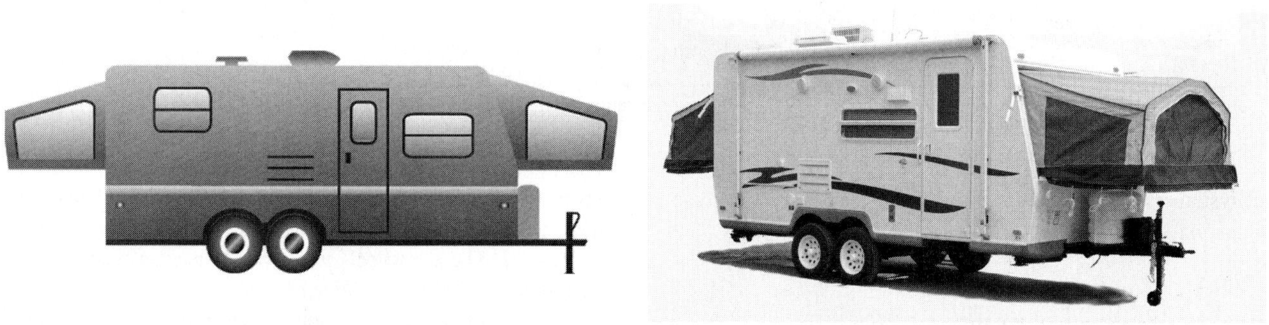

FIGURE 21.6.6 Travel Trailers with Expandable Ends—Generic Model and Actual Example (Source: Courtesy of RVIA)

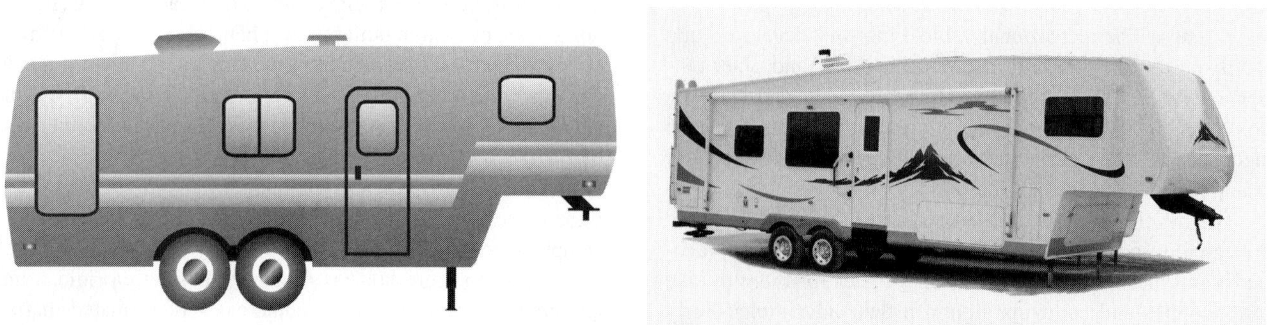

FIGURE 21.6.7 Fifth-Wheel Travel Trailers—Generic Model and Actual Example (Source: Courtesy of RVIA)

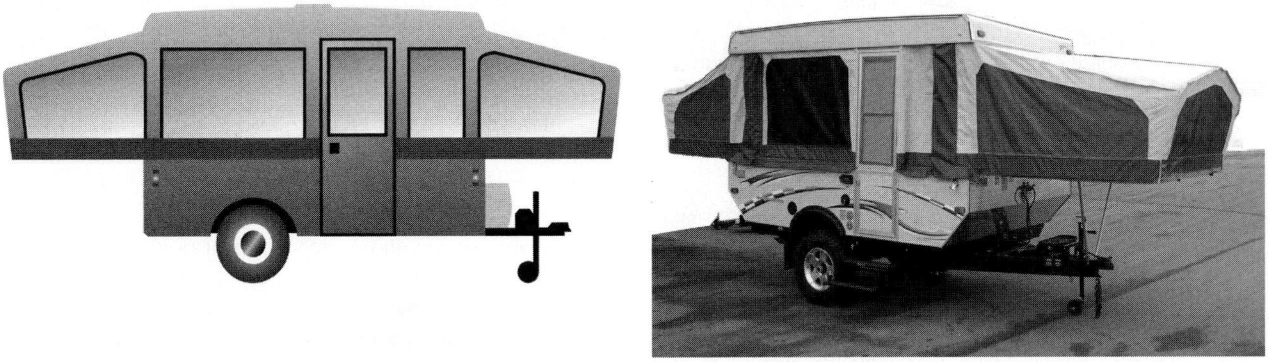

FIGURE 21.6.8 Folding Camping Trailers—Generic Model and Actual Example (Source: Courtesy of RVIA)

FIGURE 21.6.9 Truck Campers—Generic Model and Actual Example (Source: Courtesy of RVIA)

assembly-line-produced travel vehicle, a fold-up tent trailer. A few other manufacturers followed, offering multiple units for sale, and the rush was on.

The rapid growth in numbers of these early "auto campers" and their demands for safe and scenic places to camp and enjoy the outdoors were a primary motivation for the development and early growth of the U.S. National Park system in the early 1920s. City- and county-operated camping sites were also becoming popular in the early 1920s as communities began to realize that the travelers, in most cases, brought money with them and would spend it with local businesses.

The economic disaster of the 1929 stock market crash slowed the rise of the new industry, but not for long. By the mid-1930s, one manufacturer, The Covered Wagon Company of Mt. Clemons, Michigan, was building 40 to 50 units per 8-hour shift from a single factory. Industry production records indicate that, in 1936, one-sixth of the nation's total recorded trailer production came from that single Detroit area factory.

By 1939, there were well over 100 manufacturing companies and an even larger body of suppliers and parts distributors active in the rapidly growing trailer coach industry. Associations of manufacturers were becoming organized, and national and international organizations of trailer owners were proving to be very popular.

The earliest activity of NFPA in the field of mobile homes and recreational vehicles was the formation of the NFPA Committee on Trailers and Trailer Camps in 1937. The first standard was adopted in 1940 and revised in 1952.

Local and national retail and wholesale trailer shows were being organized. The Tin Can Tourists of the World, organized in 1919, had become by far the largest of the consumer groups, with hundreds of thousands of members from the United States and Canada. In 1936 a Tin Can Tourists rally recorded well over 1000 units and nearly 3000 participants in attendance and hosted one of the first large retail shows.

World War II to the Present. World War II caused a second major pause in the dynamic growth of the RV industry, primarily due to very strict material rationing and the conscription of many potential customers and workers. Some manufacturers converted their production to various war-related items and others produced units as temporary housing for workers at war production facilities and military bases. The late 1940s and early 1950s saw a great burst of technological advances and living comforts for trailers, such as portable propane or butane cylinders, allowing gas stoves and heaters to replace liquid-fueled models, on-board refrigeration replacing ice boxes for food preservation, hot and cold running water, as well as on-board toilets, showers, and 110-volt generators. With this growth came concerns regarding the safe installation of living systems, such as plumbing, LP-gas, and electrical. In the late 1950s, California introduced RV safety standards for the living systems and initiated a state-sponsored oversight program to ensure compliance. Many other Western states followed suit, often creating similar criteria, yet different enough to make manufacturing for multiple markets difficult.

Continued growth in the 1960s brought hundreds of new companies (many of today's industry giants) into the industry, as the baby boomers began to grow up and look for inexpensive recreational opportunities for their young families. In 1963, the Mobile Homes Manufacturers Association and the Trailer Coach Association worked together to create the *American Standard Installations of Plumbing, Heating and Electrical Systems in Travel Trailers* (A119.2–1963).

The growth of the RV industry, up to this point mostly trailer-based, was further enhanced with the advent and availability of affordable, assembly-line-produced motor homes. The development of modern pickup trucks also enabled the creation and popularization of the slide-in pickup carried campers and related Type C motor homes, which today are built mostly on van chassis rather than the original pickup truck chassis.

In the late 1960s, recognizing that these new motorized type products, different from travel trailers, were not included in the safety standards (A119.2-1963), the Mobile Homes Manufacturers Association, the National Fire Protection Association, the Recreational Vehicle Institute, and the Trailer Coach Association jointly sponsored the development of ANSI A119.2 and NFPA 501C, *A Standard for Recreational Vehicles,* 1970 edition. This standard also covered installation of plumbing, heating, and electrical systems. Additionally, definitions were added to clearly identify the product types known today as motor homes, travel trailers, camping trailers, and truck campers. This standard also assisted in defining the separation between mobile homes and recreational vehicles.

That 1960s boom in RV industry growth and the dramatic explosion of affordable motorized units was again nearly destroyed by the embargo-based fuel shortages and astronomically high interest rates of the 1970s, when almost half of the industry manufacturers either went out of business or merged into some of today's industry giants. Through the 1970s, the lifestyle was still primarily referred to as *camping,* and the rigs, whether motorized or towed, continued to be identified as *campers,* as they had been for over 50 years.

In the early 1980s, another dynamic change brought complete livability to the units. Many people with little interest in purely camping and nature-based outdoor activities became attracted to longer and larger rigs with living room space and the availability of features such as couches, recliners, TV, VCR, air-conditioning, and other homelike comforts. The lifestyle known today as RVing began to partially replace camping as the travel attraction, with many retirees and some families with itinerant-type jobs selling their real estate–based homes and residing full time on the road. Destination-oriented trips and not just family jaunts to favorite campsites became popular. This alteration in comforts and conveniences made the growth in popularity of "full-timing" possible. This change also forced the evaluation of fire safety standards developed in the late 1970s and adopted for the first time in the NFPA 501C and ANSI A119.2, *Standard for Recreational Vehicles,* in 1982. These requirements addressed interior finish, textile and film material flammability, exit facilities, fire detection equipment, and smoke alarms.

From the 1930s through the 1950s and into the early1960s, unit lengths were usually less than 20 ft (6.1 m) with 12 to 15 ft (3.66 to 4.57 m) long units very common. Most of the motorized as well as the towable units of the 1960s were less than 25 ft (7.62 m) long. With the improvement of both vehicles and highways, unit length began to grow through the 1970s, with RVs evolving into the common 30 to 40 ft (9.14 to 12.19 m) long units of today. It was this increase in length that allowed the addition of more homelike features to today's RVs.

Early unit pricing varied as widely as do prices today. Entry-level towable trailers in the Depression days of the 1930s were primarily sold in the $250 to $400 range with luxury trailers ranging as high as $1000. At the same time, luxury fifth-wheel rigs (which were often sold with a matching tow vehicle included) and "land yacht" motorized "house cars" up to 35 ft (10.67 m) long were being sold for $25,000 and up.

Today's RV lifestyle has come a long way from its earliest roots in the camping activities of the horse-and-buggy days and the early auto campers through the trailerites and Tin Can Tourists of the 1920s, 1930s, and 1940s. The medium-sized campers of the 1950s and 1960s began the move to modern conveniences and comforts, but the upsizing of vehicles and the resulting larger units of the 1970s and 1980s allowed campers to become RVers and made today's luxury RV lifestyle possible. This has attracted a completely new group of participants whose primary interest is not in camping and basic wilderness outdoor activities, but who enjoy the many benefits of self-contained travel both temporarily and full time.

From 1987 to 2005, NFPA 501C and ANSI A119.2 were updated every 3 years in an effort to harmonize safety and technology. Most of the changes through the mid-1990s were minor revisions and definitional improvements but also included substantive changes, such as requirements for increased exit sizes, requirements for carbon monoxide and LP-gas detectors, and provisions for RVs used for transporting or storing internal combustion vehicles. In 2005, NFPA 501c and ANSI A119.2 were combined to become NFPA 1192, *Standard on Recreational Vehicles.*

RV Ownership

U.S. ownership of RVs has reached record levels, according to a 2005 University of Michigan study.[4] Nearly one in twelve U.S. vehicle-owning households now owns an RV, almost 8 million households, or, as mentioned earlier, a 15 percent increase from 2001 to 2005 and a 58 percent gain from 1980 through 2005. The number of RV deliveries is also increasing, as seen in Table 21.6.2.[5]

Approximately 8.2 million RVs are on the nation's roads. RVIA, the national trade association for RV manufacturers and their component suppliers, estimates there are as many as 30 million RV enthusiasts, including RV renters, nationwide.

TABLE 21.6.2 Recreational Vehicle Shipment Totals, 1994–2006

Year	*Shipment*
1994	259,200
1995	247,000
1996	247,500
1997	254,500
1998	292,700
1999	321,200
2000	300,100
2001	256,800
2002	311,000
2003	320,800
2004	370,100
2005	384,400
2006	390,500

Source: *Industry Profile (RVIA Year End Report),* Recreational Vehicle Industry Association, Reston, VA, 2003.

DEVELOPMENT OF RECREATIONAL VEHICLE STANDARDS

Early NFPA RV Standards

The earliest activity of NFPA in the field of mobile homes and recreational vehicles was the formation of an NFPA Committee on Trailers and Trailer Camps in 1937. Its first standard, adopted in 1939, established a general overall outline of regulations for trailer camps. This edition was supplanted by the 1940 *Standard for Trailer Coaches and Trailer Coach Camps,* which expanded the requirements and addressed trailer vehicle construction, safety features pertaining to trailers in transit, and the regulation of trailers while not in transit. The standard, which applied to trailer coaches used as living quarters or for sleeping purposes, defined *trailer coach* as any structure intended for human habitation, mounted on wheels, and capable of being moved from place to place.

In 1952 the standard was revised into two parts and renamed *Standard for Fire Prevention and Fire Protection in Trailer Coaches and Trailer Courts.* Part A of this revised standard applied to trailer coaches intended for use as living quarters or for sleeping purposes. This part of the standard extended to awnings, porches, lean-tos, or other structures and equipment of a portable character designed to be carried in, on, or with the trailer and installed, assembled, or erected as appurtenances to the trailer when parked. Any structures built permanently in place in conjunction with a trailer were not considered as part of the trailer but considered as buildings and subject to the provisions of the building codes or other requirements.

Part B applied to trailer courts accommodating or providing a parking space for more than one trailer coach used for living or sleeping purposes. This part was limited to provisions affecting fire protection and prevention and was intended to be supplemented by municipal sanitary and public health codes. In addition, the standard recognized that local building codes were to be enforced if the wheels of a trailer were removed, if a trailer was permanently blocked up, or if the space beneath it was enclosed.

In 1960 NFPA approved a revised version of the standard, dividing it into two separate standards. NFPA 501A, *Standard for Fire Protection in Trailer Courts,* consisting of Chapters 10 through 19 of the 1952 standard, covered trailer courts intended to accommodate trailers designed (or intended) for living quarters. In 1961 NFPA 501B, *Standard for Fire Prevention and Fire Protection in Mobile Homes and Travel Trailers,* consisting of Chapters 1 through 9 of the original 1952 standard, was finalized.

In the early 1960s the Mobile Homes Manufacturers Association (MHMA) and the Trailer Coach Association (TCA) prepared, under the aegis of the American Standards Association (now American National Standards Institute, or ANSI), two standards that were subsequently approved as the *American Standard Installations of Plumbing, Heating and Electrical Systems in Travel Trailers* (A119.2–1963) and *Standard for Fire Prevention and Fire Protection in Mobile Homes and Travel Trailers* (A119.1–1963). In 1969 the Recreational Vehicle Institute (RVI) was added to the MHMA, NFPA, and TCA as a fourth cosponsor of the project. The first *Standard for Recreational Vehicles* developed under the consolidated efforts of NFPA, MHMA, TCA, and RVI was approved by NFPA in 1970 and by ANSI in 1971. This standard replaced ASA Standard A119.2–1963. In 1975 the MHMA and the TCA merged to become the Manufactured Housing Institute. Also in 1975 the Recreational Vehicle Institute absorbed the Recreational Vehicle Division of the Trailer Coach Association and was redesignated the Recreation Vehicle Industry Association.

This time period also saw the publication of two other NFPA standards: NFPA 501C, *Standard for Recreational Vehicles Installation of Plumbing, Heating and Electrical Systems,* and NFPA 501D, *Electrical Standard for Recreational Vehicle Parks.* Under various formats and titles, subsequent editions of the NFPA 501 series were published from 1972 through 1977, with only minor changes.

After 1977 NFPA withdrew as a cosponsor of the existing ANSI project and established its own ANSI-approved project, covering only the subject of fire safety for recreational vehicles. This committee, charged with developing a standard for fire safety for recreational vehicles and recreational vehicle parks, produced and revised three standards through the 1980s: NFPA 501A, *Standard for Fire Safety Criteria for Manufactured Home Installations, Sites, and Communities;* NFPA 501C, *Standard on Recreational Vehicles;* and NFPA 501D, *Standard for Recreational Vehicle Parks and Campgrounds.* These standards excluded all sections of the previous editions not considered within the committee scope, primarily plumbing and sanitary issues.

The standards continued through the 1990, 1993, and 1996 editions with only minor changes, including the size of alternate exits, clothes dryers, LP-gas detectors, and the expansion of provisions for recreational vehicles used for transporting or storing vehicles with internal combustion engines.

NFPA 1192, *Standard of Recreational Vehicles,* and NFPA 1194, *Standard for Recreational Vehicle Parks and Campgrounds*

In 1999 NFPA 501C was renumbered as NFPA 1192, *Standard on Recreational Vehicles,* and the requirements on LP-gas containers and connectors were updated. Changes also included modifications to requirements for exit facilities and special transportation provisions. Similarly, NFPA 501D was renumbered as NFPA 1194, *Standard for Recreational Vehicle Parks and Campgrounds.* NFPA 501A continues, most recently updated in 2005.

In 2002 there was a major editorial reorganization of both NFPA 1194 and NFPA 1192 in accordance with the NFPA *Manual of Style,* 2002 edition. Other changes occurred in the language of caution and warning labels.

In 2005 NFPA and RVIA once again merged the requirements from ANSI A119.2 into NFPA 1192, and ANSI A119.2 was no longer published. NFPA 1192 now contains minimum requirements for the installation of plumbing, fuel burning, electrical, and other safety-related systems in recreational vehicles. Technical changes to the standard include clarification of requirements for location and securing of propane containers, requirements for high-pressure piping, revision of requirements for fuel tank installation, and the inclusion of requirements for automatic generator starting systems.

NFPA 1192 Requirements. The following partial table of contents of NFPA 1192 shows the scope of this standard, which covers the fire and life safety criteria for recreational vehicles:

Chapter 4 General Requirements

4.1.1 Differing Standards
4.1.2 U.S. Federal Regulations
4.1.3 Exterior Labels
4.1.4 Electrical Requirements

Chapter 5 Fuel Systems and Equipment

5.1 Quality of Design and Installation
5.2 Propane Systems
5.3 Propane Piping Systems
5.4 Fuel-Burning Appliances
5.5 Venting, Ventilation, and Combustion Air
5.6 Marking Appliances (Installation and Operation Features)
5.7 Circulating Air Systems for Heating (Other Than Automotive Type)
5.8 Air Conditioning (Other Than Automotive Type)
5.9 Consumer Information
5.10 Gasoline or Diesel Fuel Systems
5.11 Propane Vehicle Propulsion Engine Installations

Chapter 6 Fire and Life Safety Provisions

6.1 Interior Finish and Textile or Film Materials
6.2 Recreational Vehicle Exit Facilities
6.3 Fire Detection Equipment
6.4 Other Considerations
6.5 Automatic Generator Starting System (AGS) Requirements

Chapter 7 Plumbing Systems

7.1 Plumbing System
7.2 Plumbing Fixtures
7.3 Water Distribution Systems
7.4 Drainage Systems
7.5 Waste Holding Tanks
7.6 Vents and Venting
7.7 Plumbing System Tests

NFPA 1194 Requirements. NFPA 1194, *Standard for Recreational Vehicle Parks and Campgrounds,* provides minimum construction requirements for safety and health for occupants using facilities supplied by recreational vehicle parks and campgrounds that offer temporary living sites for use by recreational vehicles, recreational park trailers, and other camping units. The following partial table of contents of NFPA 1194 shows the scope of this standard:

Chapter 4 General Requirements

4.1 Differing Standards
4.2 U.S. Federal Regulations
4.3 Electrical Requirements
4.4 Wildland/Urban Interface Areas
4.5 Recreational Park Trailers

Chapter 5 General Design Criteria for Recreational Vehicle Parks and Campgrounds

5.1 Park Design and Construction
5.2 Recreational Vehicle Site
5.3 Recreational Park Trailer Site
5.4 Camping Unit Site

Chapter 6 Fire Safety

6.1 Fire Detection and Alarm Services
6.2 Fire Safety Rules and Regulations for Recreational Vehicle Parks and Campgrounds—Posting of Emergency Information

Chapter 7 Environmental Health and Sanitation

7.1 General
7.2 Potable Water Supply and Distribution
7.3 Potable Water Connections at Individual Sites
7.4 Drinking Fountains
7.5 Sanitary Conveniences
7.6 Number, Location, and Arrangement of Toilets, Urinals, and Lavatories
7.7 Showers
7.8 Sewerage Facilities
7.9 Sanitary Disposal Stations
7.10 Potable Water Supply Stations
7.11 Refuse Disposal

RECREATIONAL VEHICLE FIRE AND LIFE SAFETY

Safety and Fire Data

As the industry has matured, so have its safety efforts. Over the years, RV safety has expanded. Interiors now have fire retardant requirements, fire extinguishers, propane detectors, CO detectors, and smoke alarms. The exit facilities have increased in size and their markings have improved to help occupants exit RVs in dangerous situations.

Fire and Life Safety Issues

Reasons for Decrease in Fatalities. Why deaths in RVs due to fire decreased between 1993 and 2002 is difficult to determine because records are limited and also because the manner of classifying vehicles in police accident reports is inconsistent. RVs are sometimes reported as mobile homes or manufactured homes, and motor homes and trailers are often referred to by brand names, such as Airstreams or Winnebagos, regardless of whether they are towable or motorized RVs. Also, other vehicles such as all-terrain vehicles and dune buggies are reported and documented as RVs, skewing the data available. All these reporting variables prevent the emergence of a true picture of how RVs perform over a specific period of time and of which factors affect the data.

RV Standard Changes Affecting Fire Safety Results. Some changes to the RV standards, beginning with the 1993 edition of NFPA 501C, that could be credited for enhanced fire and life safety resulting in fewer deaths by fire might include the following:

- The provisions for portable fire extinguishers mandated a size increase from 4B:C to 5B:C for towable RVs and later added the requirement for motorized RVs to have a 10B:C fire extinguisher.
- Carbon monoxide detectors were required in all RVs equipped with an internal combustion engine or designed with features to accommodate future installation of an internal combustion engine.
- Propane detectors were required in all RVs equipped with propane appliances and 120 volt ac systems.
- Emergency exit openings were increased in size and exit markings were added.
- Propane containers were required to be shielded from exhaust components and other high-heat sources.
- RVs designed for the transportation of internal combustion engine–type vehicles inside the RV required the transport area to have ventilation and vaportight separation from the living area, as well as requiring consumer information to be provided for guidance relating to fire and life safety.
- Low-voltage wire was required to have a minimum insulation rating of 90°C for interior applications and 125°C in an engine area.
- 30 A power supply assemblies were limited to a maximum of five branch circuits.
- RVs were required to have listed low-voltage lighting fixtures to reduce heat buildup at their mounting surfaces.
- Receptacles serving countertops with sinks were required to be provided with ground-fault circuit interrupter (GFCI) protection.
- RVs were limited to only one power supply assembly instead of two.

RV Manufacturer Compliance with Codes and Standards

The Recreation Vehicle Industry Association (RVIA), the national trade association representing more than 550 manufacturers and component suppliers that produce approximately 98 percent of all RVs and conversion vehicles manufactured in the United States, is headquartered in Reston, Virginia. Consumers shopping for an RV often look for the RVIA seal prominently displayed on the exterior of an RV. The seal means the manufacturer certifies compliance with more than 500 electrical, plumbing, heating, and fire and life safety requirements established under NFPA 1192. The oval-shaped RVIA seal comes in three colors, depending on RV type:

- Gold ovals with the word "MOTORHOME" for all Type A, B, and C motor homes
- Silver ovals with the words "TRAVEL TRAILER • FIFTH-WHEEL" for all conventional, hybrid, and fifth-wheel travel trailers
- White ovals with the words "TRUCK CAMPER • FOLDING CAMPING TRAILER" for all truck campers and folding camping trailers

As a condition of membership, all RVIA member manufacturers are subject to periodic, unannounced plant inspections by RVIA representatives to audit these member manufacturers' pledge to comply with NFPA 1192. Members who fail to maintain acceptable levels of compliance can be expelled from the association, thereby losing the right to display RVIA seals on their products.[6]

In addition to RVIA's oversight, which helps the manufacturers build safe RVs, the manufacturers must comply with the standards and regulations established by the U.S. Department of Transportation and with a variety of state regulations. All programs, both state and federal, are self-certification programs. There is no oversight by an outside agency to ensure compliance. However, compliance is of paramount importance to the manufacturer. Manufacturers are required by law to notify the government of all safety-related defects. Most safety-related defects require the manufacturer to conduct a recall campaign to fix the failed part or system. The federal government imposes the same program requirements on RV manufacturers as they do on the automotive industry.[6]

SUMMARY

Recreational vehicles (RVs) have been around since the beginning of motorized travel in the early 1900s. RVs, which are defined as vehicles that combine transportation and temporary living quarters for travel, recreation, and camping, may have their own motor power, as in the case of motor homes; be mounted, as in the case of truck campers; or be towable, as in the case of travel, fifth-wheel, and folding camping trailers. Discussed in this chapter are the types of recreational vehicles and their features; the historical development and use of RVs; and the development of the two main RV standards, NFPA 1192 and NFPA 1194. The chapter concludes with a discussion of the fire and life safety issues of RVs and the oversight programs that are in place to assist RV industry manufacturers in the safe production of RVs for recreation, travel, and seasonal use.

BIBLIOGRAPHY

References Cited

1. Recreation Vehicle Industry Association, http://www.rvia.org.
2. *RVIA Types & Terms,* Recreation Vehicle Industry Association, Reston, VA, 2005.
3. Hesselbart, A., *History of RVs,* RV/MH Heritage Foundation, Elkhart, IN, 2006.
4. *RV Consumer Demographic Profile,* University of Michigan Study, Recreation Vehicle Industry Association, Reston, VA, 2005.
5. *Industry Profile (RVIA Year End Report),* Recreation Vehicle Industry Association, Reston, VA, 2003.
6. *RVIA Manufacturing Member Overview,* Recreation Vehicle Industry Association, Reston, VA, 2006.

NFPA Codes, Standards, and Recommended Practices

Reference to the following NFPA codes, standards, and recommended practices will provide further information on recreational vehicles discussed in this chapter. (See the latest version of The NFPA Catalog *for availability of current editions of the following documents.)*

NFPA 1192, *Standard on Recreational Vehicles*
NFPA 1194, *Standard for Recreational Vehicle Parks and Campgrounds*

Chapter 7

Fixed Guideway Transit and Light Rail Systems

Revised by
Tom Peacock

Chapter Contents

Key Terms

elevated transit system, fixed guideway transit system, King's Cross Station fire, passenger rail system, point of safety, rail car, traction power, transit vehicle, underground (transit) station, underground (transit) system

The environment of a transit and passenger rail system (the system) lends itself to peculiar and difficult fire safety problems. Large numbers of people who move through these subterranean enclosures and elevated structures compound the life safety dangers. Fires within subways—such as the 1987 fire at King's Cross Station in London in which 31 people died—have attracted international attention over the years due to the danger facing passengers who must evacuate trains through smoke-filled trainways and other emergency exitways. Figure 21.7.1 illustrates the King's Cross fire.

Among the causes of fire in a system can be mechanical failure of undercar components, high-energy electrical short circuits, accumulation of combustible debris along the trainways and within vent shafts, accumulation of road film and oils on the transit vehicle underside, combustible materials in car components, combustible construction of trainways including crossties, and hazards associated with the human factor, such as criminal or terrorist acts.

This chapter covers areas in a transit system requiring special attention, including underground trainways, underground stations, and surface-level and elevated transit systems.

For related topics, see Section 21, Chapter 8, "Rail Transportation Systems."

SYSTEM CHARACTERISTICS

Although underground and elevated trainways and underground stations pose the most serious threat to transit users from fire, certain basic considerations must be recognized throughout the system.

Traction Power

Traction power provides the electrical energy needed to run trains and may be carried throughout the system by means of a third rail or overhead contact system and is typically a nominal 600 to 750 V dc. For transit systems with traction power provided by a third rail, a coverboard of electrical insulating material is often installed throughout the system to prevent people from inadvertently coming in contact with the energized rail. The coverboard should be strong enough to hold a 250 lb (113 kg) weight. Warning signs should be affixed to the coverboard in any area accessible to the public.

Disconnect switches should be located strategically throughout the system so traction power can be removed as quickly as possible under emergency conditions. Otherwise, alternative prompt and reliable means for disconnecting power should be provided.

Tom Peacock has graduate engineering degrees from the University of Maryland and Johns Hopkins University as well as 35 years of professional engineering experience. He previously headed the Federal Railroad Administration's Motive Power and Equipment group and currently serves as the director of operations and technical services for the American Public Transportation Association. He also heads the American Public Transportation Association's Transit Standards Program.

FIGURE 21.7.1 Remains of Booking Hall After Fire at King's Cross Underground Station

Egress from Stations

When determining required exit capacity, future occupancy needs must be considered. After a station has been constructed, it becomes very difficult, if not impossible, to place additional stairs or escalators where they best serve the public. Complying with required exit width may present major difficulty to designers. NFPA *101*®, *Life Safety Code*® as modified by NFPA 130, *Standard for Fixed Guideway Transit and Passenger Rail Systems,* contains basic requirements.

To establish required exit widths for any structure, it is first necessary to determine occupancy classification. For example, the State of California, other jurisdictions, and NFPA *101* determined that places where people await transportation should be classified as assembly occupancies. Effective June 1983, however, NFPA 130 established requirements for life and fire safety in system stations, trainways, vehicles, and outdoor vehicle maintenance areas. The dynamic exiting concept in NFPA 130 determines occupancy based on estimated numbers of patrons waiting in stations and alighting from trains. NFPA 130 considers only those stations accommodating passengers and employees of the system and incidental occupancies. Where large numbers of people other than transit patrons are involved, such as where stations are incorporated into shopping malls, sports facilities, or other occupancies, NFPA *101* sets exit requirements.

Because transit systems are designed to move people rapidly, most new systems have installed escalators as the primary means to enter and exit stations. Escalators that are designed to be reversible, depending on commute conditions, are acceptable as emergency exits. However, escalators should not account for more than the number of units of exit at any one level that are specified by NFPA 130.

When escalators are designed as required exits, their usability in evacuating a station under emergency conditions must be seriously studied. For example, provisions must be made to stop all platform-bound escalators so that they can be used as egress. Reversible escalators should be set to run in the exit direction. NFPA 130 contains requirements for methods of stopping escalators in a manner that prevents injuries to patrons.

In many instances, escalators penetrate two or more floor levels to access the intended platform. This can pose special design problems because many designers prefer to maintain an open environment throughout a station complex. Vertical penetration of more than one floor without enclosures has been accomplished in some systems by increasing other fire protection components.

Exit Barriers

Stations contain two basic areas to separate those individuals who have paid their fare from those who have not. These are commonly referred to as "paid areas" and "free areas." Patrons in the free area can move directly to the outside without encountering barriers. Patrons within the paid area may go through fare barriers to access the free area. During emergency evacuation, either all fare barriers should open automatically, allowing patrons to evacuate the station rapidly, or specially designed access gates should be installed for the same purpose. With increased emphasis being directed to patrons with disabilities, access gates become more useful in basic station design.

Procedures and methods that allow operators to quickly control or limit the number of patrons allowed into a station in the event of a delay or a malfunction are most important. A public address system that notifies and advises patrons during an emergency or a malfunction is also considered essential.

Grills or steel doors completely close off many stations after normal revenue hours. Installing small doors in the grills can provide easy access for fire department personnel, as well as serve as an acceptable means of exit for any employees who may be working in the station.

Emergency Procedures

Due to the variety of hazards involved in a fixed guideway transit and passenger rail system, local fire authorities must establish a direct line of communication with the system's top management. Good inspection techniques must be developed, and coordinated emergency response procedures planned. Access points to all parts of the system must be pinpointed, and engine and truck company response patterns tailored to meet special access problems. Information regarding the system, such as floor plans, electrification, vehicle design, structures, fire protection systems, and communications, is needed to plan emergency procedures properly. Specially developed map books, known as "Fire Maps," for fire department use have proven valuable. A wise course for a fire department is to assign one command officer the responsibility of coordinating all emergency activities required to protect against fires on rapid transit trains, on the right of way, and adjacent to the right of way.

Communication must also extend in the other direction. Fires and other emergencies in adjacent properties may require modified transit operation. In downtown areas, fire suppression activities in nearby buildings can cause water drainage into subways, or flammable liquid spills can endanger below-grade stations. Elevated structures can block fire department access to adjacent buildings. The American Public Transportation Association, RT-S-OP-007-0 Standard for Rail Transit System Emergency Management provides detailed guidance to rail transit systems on planning for emergency preparedness.

Transit and Passenger Rail Vehicle

The construction and use of the transit vehicle (the rail car) has received a great deal of attention regarding fire and life safety. With a reasonable degree of attention, all elements of the transit system—trainway, stations, wayside equipment, and maintenance facilities—can be designed with an acceptable level of fire protection. Construction materials and methods can provide a noncombustible, if not fire-resistive, profile. These elements are static, and many solutions for achieving a degree of fire resistance are already in use in related structures, such as buildings and bridges, and in support subsystems, such as elevators, escalators, and electrical and mechanical systems.

Because of performance and comfort considerations, the modern rail car has made extensive use of manufactured materials. The rail car includes many attractive and serviceable plastics, such as foams, fibers, and other synthetic materials. These are often quite combustible and may emit toxic combustion products while burning. These problems are not unique to the transit and passenger rail car. Combustible plastics are used in passenger compartments of other modes of transportation, including aircraft, buses, and the family car. However, transit vehicles can accommodate several thousand people—far more than even a jumbo jet—and this therefore presents the potential for great loss of life.

Much attention must be focused on the materials and finishes of every item that goes into each car, including insulation for propulsion motors and other electrical wiring. The rail car is typically a source of toxic smoke generated by, and fuel contributed to, a fire.

Therefore, the rail car is a primary concern in a fire and life safety program for a transit system. Unfortunately, many existing fire test methods used to measure performance of materials in fire test conditions have proven inadequate in predicting actual fire performance. NFPA 130 contains a table of required specific test methods and tests to be used for transit rail car materials. This table is based on a guideline for grantees developed by the Federal Transit Administration. The Federal Railroad Administration has incorporated a version of this table into the federal regulations that applies to commuter rail cars. The NFPA 130 requirements and the Federal Railroad Administration requirements are slightly different.

Considering all this, the complete fire hazard assessment for new or retrofitted cars should include fire propagation resistance, smoke emission, ease of ignition, and heat and smoke release rate. The cars' total combustible loading should be limited to as low a value as possible. Existing tests, such as those in NFPA 255, *Standard Method of Test of Surface Burning Characteristics of Building Materials;* NFPA 251, *Standard Methods of Tests of Fire Resistance of Building Construction and Materials;* ASTM E162; ASTM E84; and others can be used if results are interpreted in relation to the transit environment. With the sponsorship of the Volpe Transportation System, the National Institute of Standards and Technology is developing tests to better predict the performance of materials when subjected to elevated temperatures, especially with respect to the release of toxic products.

UNDERGROUND TRAINWAYS

Fires within the confines of an underground system, especially those in trainways, are among the most difficult to extinguish because fire fighters have limited room in which to operate. Access points for fire personnel, emergency exit locations for passengers, availability of water supply, and ventilation capabilities are among the fundamentals that must be considered in providing adequate safeguards for passengers and facilities for fire fighters responding to emergencies.

A direct liaison between system operating authorities and fire officials is essential to keep emergency forces apprised of current conditions in underground installations. Floor plans of stations and subways must be reviewed continually. Fire protection included in the original system design may have changed, thus requiring fire-fighting plans to be updated.

Ventilation

Ventilation of underground trainways in emergencies is of primary importance. The removal of smoke during fires must be seriously studied. Several commercially developed computer programs are available to model various smoke removal scenarios. Exiting schemes that allow passengers to exit rapidly into fresh air must also be developed. Some systems have installed fully reversible fans within vent shafts. They move large quantities of air by intake or exhaust, and thus purge smoke from the trainway in a predetermined direction so passengers can evacuate to the nearest station or exit. Ventilation shafts and fans are often placed at each end of an underground station and, in some instances, between stations. When vertical shafts are included in the ventilation construction, the possibility of flammable liquid spills entering the shaft at street level must be considered. Shafts should terminate in roadways only when absolutely no other alternative exists. Adequate sumps equipped with flammable vapor detectors must be developed to retain such spills. Ventilation equipment installed within shafts and fan rooms should meet requirements for expected fire exposure.

Transit systems need to develop safeguards to ensure that central control operators responsible for implementing fire emergency ventilation scenarios receive the correct initial information. Implementing the wrong scenario could move smoke to where the people are rather than away from them, resulting in disaster.

Access/Egress

Walkways. Primary consideration must be given to evacuation of large numbers of passengers to a point of safety if a train stopped between stations must be evacuated. A "point of safety" could be a station platform or direct access to the open air through vertical exitways. Some older systems evacuate passengers by having them descend from the train to the walkway, and then walk until they reach a vertical exit or station platform. In newer systems, passengers evacuate the rail car to a walkway constructed alongside the rail car opposite the third-rail power source (Figure 21.7.2). This arrangement lets passengers step directly from the train to the walkway.

For trainways separated by noncombustible walls and fire doors, the walkway system also provides easy access to a train on the opposite trainway and an acceptable horizontal exit path that remains relatively free of smoke and heat. Obviously, adequate underground trainway lighting must be provided to allow safe evacuation.

Many systems currently operate underground on trainways completely separated from each other by noncombustible walls and fire doors (Figure 21.7.3). As previously mentioned, this concept provides a refuge for passengers, as long as adequate train control and planning is practiced. Separation walls should have no less than a 2 hour fire resistance rating, and openings in them should be protected by 1½ hour fire doors. Openings through the wall, protected by fire doors, can provide an acceptable horizontal exit path from the trainway on which an accident has occurred to the other trainway, which remains relatively free of smoke and heat. Cross-passageways between trainways can be used in lieu of emergency exit stairways to the surface. When used, cross-passageways should not be farther than 800 ft (244 m) apart. Hardware normally used in the installation of fire doors and frames has been found inadequate for the pressures generated by a train moving through the trainway and for the damp environment found in trainways. Special study and consideration must be given to the type of door, frame, hinges, locking device, and method of securing the frame to the opening. Sliding fire doors with counterweights require special attention.

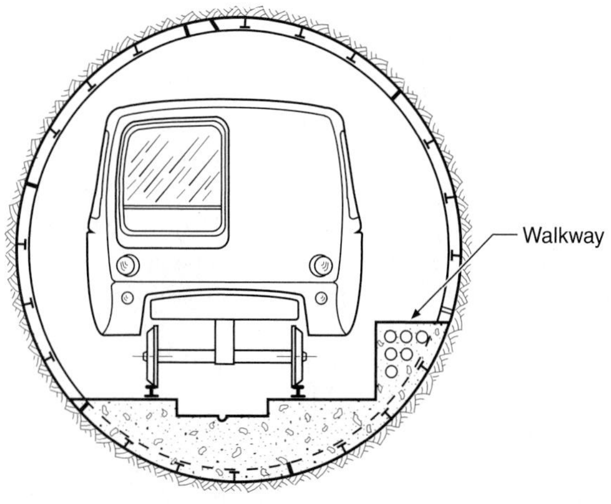

FIGURE 21.7.2 Sectional View of a Single-Tube Subway Tunnel, Showing Location of Emergency Passenger Walkway to Floor of the Car

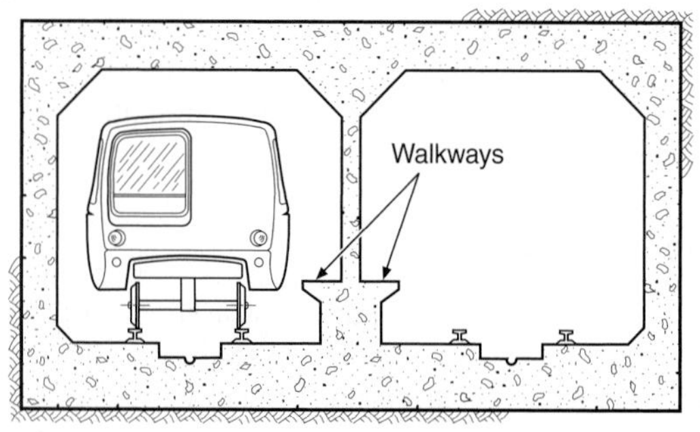

FIGURE 21.7.3 Sectional View of a Subway Tunnel Having Trainways Separated from Each Other by a Noncombustible Wall

Emergency Exits. Several factors must be considered to determine exit requirements from an underground subway system, including the following:

- Train length
- Depth of trainway below grade
- Accessibility to exit at grade
- Accessibility to exit at trainway
- Time and distance needed for people to exit to surface
- Available ventilation and controls
- Access to trainway for fire service

Due to transit systems' ability to control smoke using sophisticated ventilation systems, and since unlimited vertical shafts are impractical, NFPA 130 allows emergency exit shafts to be placed so that maximum travel distance does not exceed 1250 ft (381 m) in tunnels. The intent and basics of NFPA *101,* as modified by NFPA 130, should be followed in designing exit stairs. Hatches can be used at the surface, if there are provisions to prevent obstructions that would keep them from opening in an emergency.

Internally illuminated exit signs with two power supply sources should be installed at the trainway level to direct passengers, and emergency lighting should be provided within the exit enclosure.

Communication

Probably one of the most serious problems encountered during underground emergencies involves communications. Emergency telephones normally are identified throughout the underground system by a distinctive light: in most systems blue lights designate emergency phone locations. Communication from the trainway directly to a central control room is accomplished merely by picking up the phone.

Blue-light stations identifying the location of emergency telephones can also serve multiple purposes. For example, on the San Francisco Bay Area Rapid Transit (BART) System headquartered in Oakland, California, blue-light stations include a third-rail or power-disconnect button, a 110 V outlet, and a 20 lb (9 kg) multipurpose dry chemical extinguisher. Stations are spotted throughout the underground system at 1000 ft (30 m) intervals or in line of sight, whichever is shorter.

Communication (particularly radio communication) in an underground system is sometimes very difficult. Many newer subway systems have installed equipment to let fire department radios be used in underground stations and tunnels. Where this capability does not exist, fire authorities should make every effort to test their communication systems under actual conditions throughout the subway system. Consideration should be given to using hard-wired communication systems that may already exist. Portable radios or emergency phones with a direct line to the transit system's central headquarters or to train radios are both useful. Every system should have a radio network providing two-way communication connecting personnel on trains and other vehicles anywhere in the system.

During emergencies, radio frequencies and telephone lines quickly become overwhelmed. Portable hardwire telephones, dedicated to fire department use, should be available for point-to-point communications.

Fire Protection in Underground Trainways

A principal fire protection device in systems is the standpipe hose system. NFPA 14, *Standard for the Installation of Standpipe and Hose Systems,* provides good guidance for installations, and Class I or Class III service should be specified.

Standpipes. Standpipes should be located in stations and throughout the underground trainway system. Standpipes in tunnels should be at least 4 in. (101.6 mm) in diameter or sized by hydraulic calculations, and may be of the dry type. Generally speaking, local fire authorities determine locations of standpipe outlets, with consideration given to fire department access at tunnel level, available vertical access shafts for emergency forces, available street access to the fire department, and siamese connections at grade level.

Some systems require that dry standpipe outlets be no more than 200 ft (61 m) apart throughout the underground. Others have determined that maximum separation distances of 300, 400, and 500 ft (91, 122, and 152 m) are acceptable.

Some systems place bins or boxes containing 2½ in. (64 mm) hose near dry standpipe outlets and leave inspection and testing of such hose to system personnel. Fire authorities operating under this principle should seriously consider assigning personnel to witness hose inspections and required waterflow testing. Other systems and fire departments have agreed to only place hose and appliances in lockers at the base of access shafts. In areas where local fire authorities wish to use their own hose, provisions must be made to transport hose and other equipment to a fire site or to store necessary equipment in tunnels and stations.

Special Apparatus. In lieu of supplying the fire hose required at standpipe stations, some systems have taken innovative measures to ensure that hose is available when needed. BART, for example, with approval of fire authorities, removed all fire hose from its subway system, except the 1½ in. (38 mm) hose located within stations. In turn, BART provided five fully equipped, specially designed fire engines capable of traveling by street or rail to previously designated rendezvous points. The responding fire department then boards the apparatus and goes to the fire or emergency location within the underground. Each piece of apparatus includes, as part of its inventory, 1200 ft (366 m) of 2½ in. (64 mm) hose and 400 ft (122 m) of 1½ in. (38 mm) hose, as well as nozzles, a portable emergency generator, a power saw, a cutting torch, extension cords, floodlights, demand breathing apparatus, lifelines, miscellaneous tools, a high-expansion foam unit and nozzle, a 300 gal (1136 L) water tank, and a small pressure pump.

A more practical solution is manual pushcarts, designed to run on rails and stored in stations. These carts range from small commercially available maintenance carts to specially designed folding multilevel carts constructed using lightweight alloys. These pushcarts can also be used to evacuate stretcher cases.

Fire Department Operational Plans. Fire departments that respond to emergencies in underground systems must be extremely familiar with the layout, access, exit, communications, ventilation, and other special factors that must be part of an operational plan for both the fire department and the system. Such plans must be reviewed and practiced regularly, and all fire department members and system employees must be trained to respond appropriately to incidents.

Every fire fighter entering an underground system to fight a fire must have self-contained breathing apparatus (SCBA) to meet the requirements of NFPA 1500, *Standard on Fire Department Occupational Safety and Health Program.* One challenge facing the fire department is how to maintain an adequate supply of replacement air cylinders for members working below grade level. This may require long-duration breathing apparatus and trucks to refill or deliver quantities of SCBA air cylinders.

Fire Extinguishers. Fire extinguishers should be placed on board each car. In addition, fire extinguishers should be placed near fixed equipment throughout the underground system where ignition sources and/or combustibles exist. Locations should include electrical equipment, sumps, ventilation equipment, and so on. If the blue-light or the emergency station is suitably located, one or the other would be a preferred place for extinguishers. The size and type of exposure expected dictates the extinguisher's size and type.

Drainage. Adequate drainage of water accumulated during a fire requires careful consideration. Fire authorities should be made aware of the underground system's drainage capabilities and recognize that large amounts of water could seriously impair other required rescue operations. When fighting structural fires at street level near station entrances or street ventilation grills, fire officers should alert transit system officials that water intrusion into their system may be expected and take steps to prevent water intrusion using tarps.

UNDERGROUND STATIONS

Design and Construction of Underground Stations

Underground stations should be constructed of minimum approved noncombustible materials—that is, Type I, Type II, or combinations thereof—as outlined in NFPA 220, *Standard on Types of Building Construction.* Many modern systems use reinforced concrete construction for the station's outer shell and protected steel beams, girders, and columns within the shell.

This results in a structure with a very substantial fire-resistive capability.

Very few major fires have occurred within stations. A notable exception is the King's Cross Station fire, which occurred in London, England, on November 18, 1987.[1] Thirty patrons and one fire fighter were killed in that fire. Among the many possible causes of station fires are poor housekeeping or electrical fires in escalator machine rooms.

A significant fuel source at stations, other than the trains, is the concessions. Small concessions that sell newspapers and magazines normally have a low-risk classification, whereas major concessions, such as restaurants or theaters, have a high potential risk classification for smoke and heat development.

Newspaper and magazine concessions should be limited in size and must not block required exits. Automatic sprinkler protection should be installed to protect concession areas. Possible future expansion of the area should be considered in designing the fire protection system.

Station public areas should be separated from nontransit areas with a fire barrier having at least a 3 hour fire rating. Major concessions or openings from public areas of the station into existing commercial structures should be protected by fire door assemblies having a 1½ hour fire protection rating. Even if the system owns the commercial activity and the station, good separation between the two areas is needed. Fire barriers can be established by installing fire doors or automatic fire extinguishing systems to prevent fire and smoke spread from the commercial occupancy into the station or from the station into the commercial occupancy. Before making any opening into a station, existing conditions on both sides of the proposed opening must be reviewed carefully so that an effective fire protection plan can be developed.

Fire Protection for Underground Stations

An underground station may be compared to a multiple-basement structure, except that a station generally has a very low fire-loading factor when compared to that of a commercial basement. Because of the substantial cost of code-compliant fire protection and transit car design, these may be good applications for performance-based design, in which tests and calculations are used to show that innovative approaches and designs meet the intent of the code, if not the letter of the code. In late 2001, ASTM adopted a guide for fire hazard assessment of rail cars as a step in the direction of supporting performance-based innovation.

Automatic Sprinkler Systems. All areas in stations that are used for concessions, storage, and fare collection, and other similar areas with combustible loadings, as well as the steel truss area of all escalators in a single-entry station, should be protected by automatic sprinklers equipped with flow alarms and supervision. Trainways are excluded. NFPA 13, *Standard for the Installation of Sprinkler Systems,* should be used. Other approved fire extinguishing systems, such as clean agent extinguishing systems in train control rooms, could also be used in lieu of the automatic sprinkler system, but only with the approval of the authority having jurisdiction (AHJ).

Deluge Systems. In the event of a fire in undercar equipment, train operators are instructed to bring trains to stations for passenger evacuation whenever possible. Some newer systems have opted for undercar deluge systems. These systems consist of fixed piping connected to a water supply, with open sprinklers located between rails. They are activated manually from the station attendant's booth or at the ends of the platform.

An alternative is an overcar deluge system designed to create a water curtain between a burning train and the platform. The system can be activated automatically by heat detectors in the trainway or manually as described previously. Examples of both types of installations are found in the Baltimore Metro System.

Emergency Communications. Underground stations typically do not have traditional fire alarm systems with pull stations and bells. Instead, the public address system alerts and directs passengers in the event of an emergency. Passengers can report emergencies through emergency voice alarm reporting devices located on the platform and throughout the station. Emergency communication systems must conform to *NFPA 72*®, *National Fire Alarm Code*®.

Fire Detection Systems. All nonpublic areas commonly classified as support or ancillary areas, if not protected by an automatic fire suppression system, should be fully protected by a fire detection system conforming to *NFPA 72.* Listed smoke alarms are preferable, although rate-of-rise detectors may be used if authorized by the concerned fire authority.

It is good practice to provide supervision for all fire detection and automatic fire suppression systems. Supervisory signals should be received at the system's command center and annunciated by zone at the station agent's booth or kiosk.

Wet Standpipes. Where separate standpipe and automatic sprinkler systems are provided, wet standpipes usually are supplied by a piping system that is separate and distinct from that used for automatic sprinkler systems. Fire department siamese connections, properly labeled and installed at grade level, let the fire department supply additional water to either system.

Fire hose cabinets may contain 1½ in. (38 mm) and 2½ in. (64 mm) control valves, as recommended in NFPA 14. A maximum of 100 ft (30 m) of attached 1½ in. (38 mm) hose with nozzle and/or 2½ in. (64 mm) hose and a spanner wrench may be stored in cabinets for use by the fire department at the discretion of the local AHJ. A suitable fire extinguisher may also be placed in the cabinet. To reduce pilferage of fire equipment, cabinets should be locked and a breakaway glass panel installed to allow ready access under emergency conditions. Some systems have installed intrusion alarms, which send a signal to the station agent if a fire hose cabinet has been opened.

SURFACE-LEVEL AND ELEVATED TRANSIT SYSTEMS

Generally, combating fires in transit systems at or above grade is no more difficult than fighting any other type of fire at grade.

Primary consideration must always be given to the traction power. Even when assured that the power has been shut off, fire department personnel should operate under the assumption that the third rail or overhead wire is still energized.

Although fires in trains on surface track or elevated trainways present a less serious exposure to the public, design must address certain basic considerations, such as means of egress along elevated trainways. As always, communication is paramount in any emergency operation. The ability to direct emergency forces to the scene of an incident and to place the system in a safe condition for egress is necessary for patrons and emergency personnel.

Access to a trainway also may require special provisions. Locating trainways in a joint corridor with a railroad or freeway may limit access for long distances of the trainway. Trainways extending from population centers through undeveloped areas sometimes extend where surface roads and water mains do not exist. Trainways in congested areas, trainways elevated to unusual heights, and trainways in other sections not accessible to emergency vehicles or paramedic units could create other problems. Trainway construction can also cause problems of fire exposure and access to adjacent structures. For example, an elevated trainway above existing city streets and adjacent to existing buildings can interfere with fire department operations at those buildings.

Similar problems can exist at stations. However, permanent exits provide both passenger evacuation and emergency personnel access. Recent systems have incorporated stations in the lower elevations of high-rise buildings or within mall complexes that have divergent occupancies. In these cases, detailed plans for coordination and compatible design are necessary.

Stations that can be considered to be buildings would normally be reviewed through normal code procedures. If a transit system passes through more than one jurisdiction, particularly if different basic codes apply, development of a common set of requirements is desirable to achieve uniformity throughout the system.

Most existing building codes do not usually address the subject of trainways, however. The exception is NFPA *101*. Items that should be considered during a plan review of a guideway include the following:

1. Designated location markers to provide a response location for fire personnel
2. Locations where overhead trainways may intersect with known street locations
3. Egress gates allowing passengers to exit the system under authorized employee supervision
4. Available wayside communications allowing the fire department to communicate directly with the system's command center
5. Locations of substations, switching stations, gap breaker stations, or other major electrical installations of concern to local fire authorities

SUMMARY

Fire protection of fixed guideway transit and passenger rail systems is similar to fire protection of other occupancies in many respects. Prevention of ignition is of paramount importance, as are safe evacuation of occupants and the safety of responding fire fighters. However, the unique characteristics of fixed guideway transit and passenger rail systems are more challenging, particularly in underground trainways and stations.

BIBLIOGRAPHY

Reference Cited

1. Best, R. L., and Engleman, L. M., "Fact Sheet—King's Cross Station Fire," *Fire Command,* Jan. 1988.

NFPA Codes, Standards, and Recommended Practices

Reference to the following NFPA codes, standards, and recommended practices will provide further information on fixed guideway transit and light rail systems discussed in this chapter. (See the latest version of The NFPA Catalog *for availability of current editions of the following documents.)*

NFPA 10, *Standard for Portable Fire Extinguishers*
NFPA 13, *Standard for the Installation of Sprinkler Systems*
NFPA 14, *Standard for the Installation of Standpipe and Hose Systems*
NFPA 24, *Standard for the Installation of Private Fire Service Mains and Their Appurtenances*
NFPA 30, *Flammable and Combustible Liquids Code*
NFPA 33, *Standard for Spray Application Using Flammable or Combustible Materials*
NFPA 51B, *Standard for Fire Prevention During Welding, Cutting, and Other Hot Work*
NFPA 58, *Liquefied Petroleum Gas Code*
NFPA 70, *National Electrical Code®*
NFPA 72®, National Fire Alarm Code®
NFPA 80, *Standard for Fire Doors and Other Opening Protectives*
NFPA 90A, *Standard for the Installation of Air-Conditioning and Ventilating Systems*
NFPA 91, *Standard for Exhaust Systems for Air Conveying of Vapors, Gases, Mists, and Noncombustible Particulate Solids*
NFPA *101®*, *Life Safety Code®*
NFPA 130, *Standard for Fixed Guideway Transit and Passenger Rail Systems*
NFPA 220, *Standard on Types of Building Construction*
NFPA 241, *Standard for Safeguarding Construction, Alteration, and Demolition Operations*
NFPA 251, *Standard Methods of Tests of Fire Resistance of Building Construction and Materials*
NFPA 255, *Standard Method of Test of Surface Burning Characteristics of Building Materials*
NFPA 256, *Standard Methods of Fire Tests of Roof Coverings*
NFPA 505, *Fire Safety Standard for Powered Industrial Trucks Including Type Designations, Areas of Use, Conversions, Maintenance, and Operations*
NFPA 1500, *Standard on Fire Department Occupational Safety and Health Program*

ASTM Publications

Available from ASTM, 100 Barr Harbor Dr., West Conshohocken, PA 19428-2959.

Chapter 8

Rail Transportation Systems

Revised by
Charles J. Wright

Chapter Contents

Key Terms

freight car, hazardous material, intermodal tank, locomotive, passenger train, rail transportation, railroad, refrigerator car, right-of-way, rolling equipment, rolling stock, tank car

The rail industry as a whole considers safety a top priority. The federal government, through the Federal Railroad Administration (FRA) and the Federal Transit Administration (FTA), provides the basis of regulation, which may be enforced by either FRA inspectors or state inspectors using federal guidelines. Design standards and recommended practices for new or rehabilitated railroad infrastructure are prepared and maintained by organizations such as the Association of American Railroads (AAR), the American Railway Engineering and Maintenance of Way Association, and the American Public Transportation Association (APTA). In some instances, the Code of Federal Regulations (CFR) references these standards and in other cases it cites them as guidelines and encourages compliance as a condition of accepting capital grant money. The codes and standards of the NFPA are often incorporated by reference or serve as a design and/or maintenance basis for the safe and efficient operation of railroad properties. Railroad systems are classified into two broad groups. The first group consists of systems that operate on the general railway system of the United States. These systems are regulated by the FRA and include the freight carriers, intercity rail services (Amtrak), and commuter rail systems. The second group is the rapid transit and light rail (trolley) lines in metropolitan areas not connected to the general railway system. These systems are regulated by state and local bodies with FTA oversight.

This chapter addresses the first group of rail systems only and introduces the reader to physical aspects of the rail transportation industry. It identifies different types of rail rolling equipment used by North American railroads, both freight and passenger, and discusses fire hazards associated with them. It also identifies fire problems involving rights-of-way and specialized railroad facilities and presents safety precautions, both general and situation specific, that all persons should follow while on railroad properties or near rail activities. The chapter generally discusses the rail transportation of hazardous materials. It also discusses in detail the transportation of hazardous materials in rail tank cars and in intermodal tank containers and describes emergency response capabilities of the rail industry.

The business of rail transportation touches on a wide variety of topics. Most chapters in this handbook provide useful assistance in dealing with at least some aspect of the industry. However, the reader is specifically referred to these chapters for discussions of related topics:

Section 13, Chapter 6, "Public Fire Protection and Hazmat Management"; Section 13, Chapter 8, "Managing the Response to Hazardous Material Incidents"; and Section 21, Chapter 7, "Fixed Guideway Transit and Light Rail Systems."

OVERVIEW

Rail Transportation Systems

Rail Transportation Systems, a membership section of the National Fire Protection Association, was organized in 1963 as the Railroad section. It is dedicated to promoting interest in, and improving the methods of, fire prevention and protection in the railroad industry and to encouraging proper safeguards and recommended practices against fire through the interchange of ideas and

Charles J. Wright is manager of hazardous materials training at the Union Pacific Railroad in Omaha, Nebraska.

experience. The Rail Transportation System annual meeting is held each May in connection with the NFPA Annual World Fire Safety Congress and Exposition. This event provides an excellent forum for the exchange of ideas between the fire service and railroad fire safety specialists.

Terminology

Two important rail transportation terms are used in this chapter. *Rolling equipment,* or *rolling stock,* is an all-inclusive term that includes locomotives, freight cars of all types, cabooses, and on-rail track maintenance (maintenance-of-way) equipment. *Right-of-way* refers to the (usually) continuous strip of land on which tracks are laid and trains operate. Right-of-way also technically refers to the contiguous property areas on which shops, offices, switching yards, and other railroad facilities and activities are located or take place. The rail transportation company usually owns and maintains the right-of-way.

U.S. Freight and Commuter Railroads

According to the AAR,[1] the more than 562 freight railroads operating today in Canada, Mexico, and the United States are vital to North America's economic health. They form a seamless integrated system that provides the world's most efficient and cost-effective freight service. North American railroads operate over 140,806 (2005 data) miles of track and earn $42 billion in annual revenues.

Also, according to the AAR,[1] U.S. freight railroads fall into one of several classifications. *Class I* railroads, which comprise the largest classification, are those with operating revenue of at least $319.3 million in 2005. Currently there are seven Class I railroads. *Regional* railroads, of which there were 30 in 2005, are line-haul railroads that operate at least 350 miles of road and/or earn revenue between $40 million and the Class I threshold. *Local* railroads include freight railroads that are neither Class I nor regional; they operate less than 350 miles of road and earn less than $40 million. In 2005, there were 320 local railroads.

According to the APTA,[2] there are 20 commuter rail passenger systems associated with various transportation agencies in the United States. In addition, Amtrak provides intercity service.

Railroad Fire Losses

Since their inception, railroads have been associated with fires. Steam engines powered the earliest locomotives; burning wood made the steam. Engine exhaust sparks commonly ignited nearby dry vegetation. A published account of the first passenger train trip in the United States describes how these sparks ignited passengers' clothing and parasols. In the period from 1994 to 1998, rail vehicle fires that were reported to U.S. local fire departments averaged 650 per year, with associated losses of 6 civilian deaths, 12 civilian injuries, and $221.0 million in direct property damage per year.[3]

The rail transportation industry has fire risks primarily in the following three separate areas:

1. The company's fixed physical plant, which ranges from high-rise offices to locomotive heavy repair shops to diesel fuel storage and dispensing facilities
2. Fires on trains, involving locomotives, rolling stock, passengers, or cargo
3. Fires caused by trains or right-of-way maintenance activities that cause damage to railroad property or to adjacent, privately owned properties; railroads are unique in that they typically operate over a continuous right-of-way that they both own and maintain

Tank Car and Intermodal Tank Container Fire Hazards

Fire hazards of tank cars and intermodal tank containers are minimal unless a car is damaged in an accident. If a fire does occur, it is essential to learn the contents of the car or the container before attempting to fight the fire. A tank car or a container exposed to radiant energy from a fire, particularly direct flame impingement, should be approached cautiously. If a commodity absorbs too much heat, vapor pressure can build up and cause the pressure relief device to operate or the tank to rupture. If any of the commodity is released, personnel should be prepared to deal with corrosive, toxic, or otherwise harmful effects. Direct contact with vapors discharged from tank cars or containers under emergency conditions should be avoided, unless appropriate protective clothing and self-contained breathing apparatus are worn.

RAILROAD OPERATIONS AND FACILITIES

Technological Advances

Today, on all but the smallest of railroads, trains are dispatched from remote dispatching centers. On several of the largest railroads, one central dispatching center controls all trains on the entire system. Crews on the trains follow explicit instructions at all times and are in continual radio and electronic contact with a dispatcher. Some locomotives have full-time computer contact both with the dispatcher and with their company's central computer system. One railroad tracks its trains' locations by satellite.

Advances in electronics and their increased use permit other railroad operational efficiencies as well. One or more locomotives (the "locomotive consist") at the front of the train still pull most trains, but it is now practical in certain circumstances to place locomotives at the end of a train or at intervals throughout the train, providing important operational and control efficiencies. However, with such advances come potential problems: a train is no longer the predictable entity it used to be. The emergency responder faces more uncertainties as well as genuine benefits: advanced computer systems have made a tremendous amount of information on a train's cargo, its proper handling, and emergency response protocols instantly available even at remote locations. Thus, it is now more imperative than ever for nonrailroaders involved in rail transportation activities or responses to communicate with, and to coordinate their activities with, proper railroad officials.

Miscellaneous Railroad Facilities

Many railroad facilities are similar to industrial facilities with familiar hazards. However, other facilities are unique to the railroad industry, such as diesel locomotive running repair and heavy repair shops, freight car repair shops, paint shops, and locomotive fueling facilities. Hazards associated with a diesel locomotive repair shop include cutting, welding, poor housekeeping, and fuel leakage.

Fueling facilities need particular protection, not only because of the economic value of the systems and of the stored fuel but also because of the value of locomotives and the cost of interruption of service. Fuel pump houses should be of noncombustible construction and, preferably, equipped with automatic fire protection and with light fixtures and devices suitable for hazardous locations. Because leakage is a prime hazard, careful housekeeping and preventive maintenance are essential. Portable and wheeled dry chemical fire extinguishers should be located throughout the fueling area. It is most desirable to have a high-volume water supply nearby.

Other facilities are critical to railroad operation and, if involved in fire, could stop the movement of trains in a given territory. These facilities include computer centers, microwave communications facilities, centralized train control equipment, and the many support elements in classification yards. Private detection and protection systems should protect these facilities. Typical fire suppression systems range from sprinklers to carbon dioxide and other clean-agent designs. Nearby adequate water and hydrant systems are essential.

Bridges and Trestles

Fire prevention is the key to continued operation of bridges and trestles. Regular maintenance should be done to provide and maintain a 25 to 50 ft (7.5 to 15 m) clearance between combustible structures and nearby vegetation. Susceptibility to fire damage can be reduced by treating the structure with a fire retardant and by providing water barrels, fire detection systems, standby pipe and hose systems, and guard service.

At some particularly valuable and critical bridges, fireboats and water buckets that can be attached to helicopters have been provided, and noncombustible bridge segments have been constructed at regular intervals to limit damage should fire occur. Most railroads have been replacing combustible bridges and other track structures with noncombustible construction at every opportunity, thus reducing their exposure to fire-related losses.

Exposure Risks for Rail Equipment

Exposure fires that destroy loaded and unloaded freight equipment underscore the need for close analysis of terminal fire hazards. These fires can start both on and off railroad property. When classification or switching yards are designed, adequate fire protection, both private and public, should be a prime consideration.

Lack of nearby fire mains and hydrants can contribute to fire loss in large yards. In a major incident, fire-fighting activities should be confined to containment and protection of exposed property. A prefire plan should map fire mains and hydrants both in and near the yard, because protection in the yard may be rendered useless or inaccessible during a major event.

Railroad sidings present a similar exposure hazard, particularly at grain elevators, lumber yards, flammable liquid or LP-gas unloading facilities, and similar industrial properties.

Railroad Communications

Communication with railroads today is simple, effective, and very necessary. On most railroads, a call to any office can be quickly connected to any other, including dispatching centers, maintenance crews, railroad emergency response teams, and, often, even the train itself. Similarly, the crew on a train can immediately notify dispatchers of an emergency on or off railroad property and advise in detail as events unfold. Dispatchers are specially trained to make appropriate emergency contacts both inside and outside of their company. See the next section, "Hazardous Materials Transported by Rail," for information on railroad emergency response capabilities. Most railroads currently have a single telephone number to a central location for emergency situations. Personnel at these locations make notifications and provide appropriate information as necessary.

HAZARDOUS MATERIALS TRANSPORTED BY RAIL

Hazardous material shipments are strictly regulated by the U.S. Department of Transportation (DOT) through the Pipeline and Hazardous Materials Safety Administration (PHMSA). The FRA enforces these regulations.

Statistical Overview of Hazardous Shipments

The Bureau of Explosives[4] reports that in 2005 U.S. and Canadian railroads originated 1,587,469 hazardous material shipments. During rail transportation 859 nonaccidental and 27 accidental releases (U.S. only) of hazardous materials occurred for a total of 886 releases of hazardous materials for the year. Figure 21.8.1 shows AAR/Bureau of Explosives' depiction of the total numbers of hazardous material shipments for 3 years (2003 to 2005).[4] Table 21.8.1 shows a summary of hazardous material shipments by hazard class.[4]

It is interesting to note that in 2005, 25 commodities accounted for approximately 93 percent of all the hazardous material that was shipped by rail (Table 21.8.2).[4]

Emergency Response

With the increased danger associated with emergencies involving hazardous materials, shippers, carriers, and local, state, and federal agencies, that is, fire, police, health, and environmental agencies, respond. The immediate purpose of the response is to minimize harm that would otherwise occur: death, injury, property damage, environmental damage, and system disruption. To accomplish this task, responders must identify hazardous materials involved in the emergency.

Sources for detecting the presence of hazardous materials include placards, markings, and shipping papers. Placards may

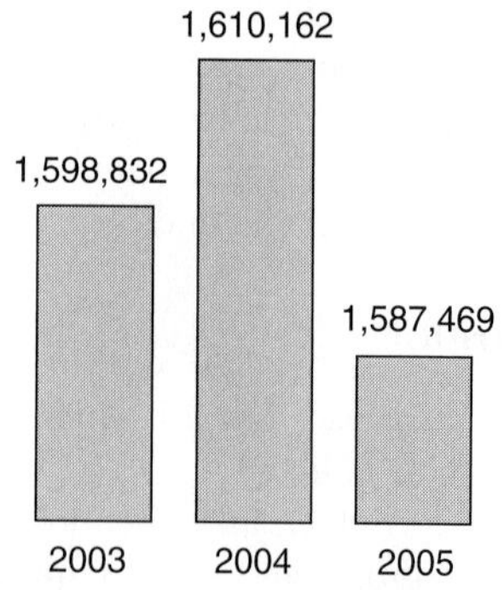

Note: The Bureau of Explosives' report breaks down these shipments by hazard class as follows: railroads transport hazardous materials in various types of rail cars, such as tank cars, covered hoppers, gondolas, box cars, and trailers and/or containers on flat cars (TOFC/COFC). The majority (85% in 2005) of rail shipments of hazardous materials move in tank cars.

FIGURE 21.8.1 Hazardous Material Shipments for the United States and Canada, 2003–2005

TABLE 21.8.1 Hazardous Material Shipments by Hazard Class for U.S. Originations, 2005

Hazard Class and Divisions	*All Rail HM Shipments*	*Tank Car HM Shipments*
Class 1 (explosives)	478	3
Division 2.1 (flammable gases)	229,355	229,132
Division 2.2 (nonflammable gases)	76,447	76,211
Division 2.3 (poison gases)	47,321	47,301
Class 3 (flammable liquids)	378,902	375,342
Combustible liquids	66,674	64,686
Division 4.1 (flammable solids)	22,407	22,307
Division 4.2 (spontaneously combustible)	1,482	1,293
Division 4.3 (dangerous when wet)	3,399	590
Division 5.1 (oxidizers)	50,329	15,448
Division 5.2 (organic peroxides)	6	0
Division 6.1 (poisonous materials)	31,615	31,037
Class 7 (radioactive materials)	11,074	0
Class 8 (corrosive materials)	278,763	276,772
Class 9	202,522	168,931
Mixed freight all kinds	139,103	660

be affixed to both sides and both ends of the rail car, trailer, or container. They alert response personnel to a hazardous material's presence and indicate the hazard class. The DOT identification number, which also may be found on both ends and both sides of the rail car, trailer, or container, will cross-reference the specific material involved, along with emergency response information. Another marking, the name of the contents, may be stenciled on the sides of the rail car, trailer, or container. Due to the orientation of the cars, placards and markings may not be visible in some emergencies. Because of the nature of the emergency, it may not be prudent to approach the car closely enough to read the placards and markings. Aided vision (binoculars, etc.) may be helpful in some cases. See the sections "Tank Car Markings" and "Tank Container Markings" for more information.

Shipping Papers

Rail cars, trailers, or containers transporting hazardous materials must be documented on shipping papers. Therefore, shipping papers are primary safety instruments in rail transportation for recognizing and identifying hazardous materials. The typical shipping paper for a train movement is a train consist or train list. This document lists the location of each rail car, trailer, or container in the train, including the location of each hazardous material in the train. The train consist/train list also includes emergency response information for each hazardous material on the train. It indicates the contents of each car, including the hazardous material shipments. Shipping papers may differ slightly among railroads; therefore, response personnel should be familiar with the railroads that move through their jurisdiction.

Shipping Paper Contents. The rail shipping paper typically includes the following entries: proper shipping name, hazard class, identification number, packing group, quantity, and hazardous material response codes (previously the 49 series Standard Transportation Commodity Code [STCC]). A 24 hour emergency response telephone number and detailed emergency response information are included with the shipping papers.

Shipping Paper Location. Shipping papers are available from the conductor on the train crew on-site or from the train dispatcher. Although traditionally found on the caboose, the conductor will be found in the lead locomotive of trains without cabooses. However, in an emergency involving hazardous material, the conductor and the rest of the train crew are likely to move to a safe location at least one-half mile upwind, uphill, or upstream of the problem.

Shipping Papers in Rescue Efforts. Upon notification of an accident or other occurrence involving rail equipment, response personnel should take the following actions:

1. Contact the responsible railroad. The telephone number should be identified in preemergency planning activities. Obtain a copy of the shipping papers and emergency response information, whether hard copy or from the railroad verbally.
2. Obtain as much information about the incident as is available: identify hazardous materials involved by name, DOT

TABLE 21.8.2 Top 25 Hazardous Materials in Rail Transportation, 2005

Rank	*Class*	*Commodity Name*	*Shipments*
1	2.1	Butane; liquefied petroleum gas; petroleum gases, liquefied; propylene; LP-gas; propane; isobutane; isobutylene; LP-gas (butylene/isobutane); LP-gas (butane/butylene); isopentane	166,310
2		Freight all kinds—hazardous materials	139,104
3	9	Elevated temperature liquid, N.O.S.	90,832
4	8	Sodium hydroxide solution (caustic soda)	82,892
5	8	Sulfuric acid	58,576
6	3	Alcohols, N.O.S.	75,057
7	4.1/9	Molten sulfur	62,261
8	3/CL	Diesel fuel	55,850
9	3/CL	Flammable liquid, N.O.S.	54,766
10	2.2	Anhydrous ammonia	52,634
11	3	Gasoline	47,362
12	2.3	Chlorine	36,475
13	3/CL	Fuel oil	31,452
14	8	Phosphoric acid	30,745
15	2.1	Vinyl chloride, stabilized	27,499
16	9	Environmentally hazardous substances, liquid, N.O.S.	26,182
17	3	Methanol (methyl alcohol)	22,641
18	9	Environmentally hazardous substances, solid, N.O.S.	22,401
19	8	Hydrochloric acid	22,154
20	2.2	Carbon dioxide, refrigerated liquid	20,245
21	5.1	Ammonium nitrate fertilizers	17,631
22	3	Styrene monomer, inhibited	17,279
23	2.1	Propylene	16,800
24	6.1	Petroleum distillates, N.O.S.	14,138
25	5.1	Sodium chlorate	14,043
Subtotal—top 25 commodities			1,218,656
Total—all hazardous commodities			1,587,469

identification number, or placard applied; determine the types of containers involved; determine the topography, bodies of water, population density, and so forth; obtain specific emergency location and best avenues of approach; ascertain whether any injuries have occurred; and determine when the emergency occurred.

3. Upon arrival at the scene, establish contact with the senior railroad official or representative before attempting to deal with the emergency.
4. Initiate command and control activities, including protecting yourself and others, initiating an incident command system, controlling access to the site, and making appropriate notifications.

In addition to the railroads, other organizations that can provide rail-oriented assistance include the following:

- AAR Bureau of Explosives (BOE)—BOE personnel will respond to major rail emergencies involving hazardous materials on request, typically from a railroad
- Carrier emergency response teams

Some carriers have developed emergency response capabilities to handle emergencies involving hazardous materials. Such teams are equipped with specialized tools and equipment to repair leaks and even transfer contents of damaged tank cars. For example, Union Pacific Railroad has two transfer vehicles equipped with tools and equipment to perform product removal activities as necessary (Figure 21.8.2).

Many rail carriers prepare guides and recommendations for handling rail emergencies involving hazardous materials and make them available to local emergency response agencies along their right-of-way. Railroads also present various training programs to local response agencies and assist at various local, state, and national fire school programs.

SAFETY ON RAILROAD PROPERTY

All who visit rail transportation properties under emergency or routine conditions need to exercise particular caution. The hazards are many and unfamiliar. The potential consequences are severe.

Taking Precautions

Always assume the tracks are "live"—expect a train to appear from either direction at any time. Rails are slippery—always

FIGURE 21.8.2 Union Pacific Railroad Transfer Vehicle Performing Multiple Liquid Transfers at an Incident

step over, not on, a rail, after first making sure the way is clear.

More and more often, a person at a distant dispatching center electrically operates track switches, the devices that physically move the rails and route a train from one track to another. Unlike the person who once stood near the switch and manually operated it, a remote operator cannot see the switch and is unaware of activities in its vicinity. Keep feet, hands, and equipment away from the moveable switch components.

Do not block tracks or place items across them without positive assurance from the railroad that all trains in the area have been stopped. Even then, minimize exposure to trains and clear the tracks as soon as practical. Hose lines laid across a railroad track can be cut by a passing train.

Until the railroad has given positive assurance that all trains in the area have been stopped, do not work around tracks or place equipment on or near tracks, until flaggers with red flags (in daylight) or red fusees (in darkness) have been deployed a minimum of 1½ miles (2.4 km) down the track in each direction. Where trains may be moving rapidly, an additional flagger should be placed a mile farther away in each direction. Fast-moving trains, freight or passenger, take at least that long to stop.

Rail emergencies on bridges and in tunnels with multiple tracks pose special hazards to the responder, as there usually is no work space except on tracks. Until positive assurance is received that all train activity in the area has stopped, there is no safe workplace for emergency activities and equipment and no safe haven for workers should a train appear on an adjacent track.

The railroad should be contacted at first opportunity whenever emergency activities occur on its property. This not only helps to maximize responder safety but it also activates the railroad's considerable emergency response capacity. Maintaining regular contact with each rail transportation entity in their area ensures that emergency responders are fully aware of the transportation company's emergency response resources that are available to them.

Self-Propelled Fire-Fighting and Derrick Equipment

Most carriers are well prepared to clear derailments and rerail freight equipment with their own forces or by standing arrangements with specialty contractors. They use lifting equipment with capacities ranging from 150 to 250 tons (136 to 227 metric tons). These may be mounted on a work train that also may carry water cars and fire pumps powered by the train air line or powered independently by an internal combustion engine. It is increasingly common to find wreck-clearing equipment with rubber tires or crawler tracks transported to the scene by highway. Carrier equipment usually includes fire hoses, nozzles, foam extinguishing compound, play pipes, and a quantity of extinguishers.

Work trains are especially valuable in incidents that occur in remote and inaccessible areas. Fire-fighting needs for such emergencies can be handled by driving a fire department pumper onto a flat car and taking it to the emergency by train.

Some railroads have self-propelled fire-fighting cars that can be used independently of the work train. The availability of such fire-fighting equipment is often overlooked in preemergency planning.

Rights-of-Way

A difficult problem is the right-of-way fire, or fire on railroad land adjacent to the roadbed. These fires can spread off railroad property. Such fires have occurred since the first days of railroading, but this risk has been greatly reduced by improved railroad equipment, controlled burning, chemical control of vegetation, and installation of fire breaks. Cooperation with the USDA Forest Service has led to development of spark arresters, spark arrester exhaust manifolds, and sparkless brake shoes. Planned vegetation, planting the right-of-way with fire-resistive vegetation, is a practice that, if properly maintained, can further reduce these fires.

PASSENGER TRANSPORTATION

Safety Precautions for Passenger Equipment

It is advisable to be aware of the following safety precautions, which are typically employed on passenger trains:

1. Passenger trains, including commuter trains, typically use 480 V ac power generated from a locomotive or a power car for onboard electrical systems, including heating, air conditioning, lighting, and food service. Generally, cables located beneath and between rail cars on both sides transmit this power. In an emergency situation, these cables may be damaged or loosened. Never attempt to disconnect any cables without assistance from the train crew. Never open any empty electrical receptacle until assured that the 480 V ac system has been deenergized. Contacts in the receptacle can be energized without the presence of cables and can produce an arc that can result in serious injury or death. Typically, 480 V ac systems are stepped down by transformers located under the car to provide 220/110 V ac power for onboard electrical equipment. Some electrical components use capaci-

tors, which store residual electrical energy for a time after the system has been shut down.

2. Typical passenger trains employ a 72 V dc emergency battery backup system for operation of lighting, electric doors, and public address systems when the 480 V ac power is lost. These batteries, typically nickel-cadmium and generally located under the car, can present a hazardous materials danger if damaged in an accident. In addition, train cars may be connected by 72 V dc jumper cables for public address and other systems. These cables must be approached with the same caution as 480 V ac cables.

3. Typical passenger trains also employ a pressurized air system, up to 140 psi (965 kPa), for operation of brakes, doors, and lavatories. Compressors in locomotives or power cars provide air pressure, and most passenger cars are equipped with at least one pressurized air reservoir. Some passenger cars ride on air-pressurized bellows instead of springs for improved passenger comfort. Emergency response personnel should be aware of the air pressure hazard and remain clear of any components where they hear the sound of leaking air, until assured that the system has been depressurized.

Passenger Equipment

Modern cars are constructed of steel and aluminum. Materials used for the interiors of today's passenger coaches, diners, and sleeping cars are, at the least, tested to the performance criteria outlined in Table 8.4.1 in NFPA 130, *Standard for Fixed Guideway Transit and Passenger Rail Systems.* Interiors designed to these criteria should show limited fire involvement when exposed to fire. Causes of fires on passenger trains include smoking materials, arson, and mechanical or electrical problems with equipment. However, extensive fire involvement can occur when cars have been exposed to an external fire source such as a flammable liquids fire. In diners, hazards include those inherent in stationary restaurants, such as grease and exhaust system fires. These, plus air-conditioning and heating systems, must be properly safeguarded, and regular preventive maintenance is essential.

Amtrak Trains

Amtrak sleeping cars are equipped with smoke detection systems that, when activated, shut down the HVAC system, sound an alarm within the car, and provide evacuation instructions to the car's passengers.

Amtrak high-speed trains operate along the Northeast Corridor from Washington, DC, to Boston, Massachusetts. These electric-powered trains operate as fixed train sets in which the individual cars are not typically separated. Each train set has a power car at each end. These train sets have some unique fire protection system features, such as the following:

- A deluge sprinkler system in the machine space of the locomotive, which is supplied with water through fire department connections located on each side of the unit
- A gaseous fire suppression system in some electric cabinets in the machine space, which is activated by a heat detection system connected to a control/releasing panel located in the cab of the engine
- On some units, an engineer's escape hatch in the roof of the cab of the power car; if the hatch is not present, there will be a marked "soft" spot in the roof of the cab
- The absence of drop steps on the passenger cars, which are present in older Amtrak cars; folding ladders are used for passenger evacuation, located in a marked compartment near each exit door
- A folded evacuation ramp stored beneath the train; the train crew is trained in the deployment of this ramp
- Every window in the car usable for evacuation; note that these windows are very heavy and care should be used when they are removed
- Presence of a marked "soft" spot located in the center of the roof of each passenger car; typical fire-fighting cutting equipment can be used to remove this soft spot to gain access to the car's interior

Emergency Response Efforts

Modern rail passenger equipment is designed to withstand the tremendous physical forces that would occur in a collision. This construction defeats typical rescue or forcible entry tools. Rescue and fire-fighting operations should be conducted through a car's doors and windows. The windows in passenger equipment generally are made of polycarbonate material that is far stronger and more flexible than safety glass—it cannot be smashed with an axe. Attempts to break windows can result in tool rebound, which can cause serious injury to the rescuer. Windows can be removed from inside or outside cars following the procedures given on labels or placards generally found adjacent to the windows.

Emergency response personnel must always assume that other trains are operating nearby. Modern passenger trains typically operate at up to 79 mph (127 kph) in most areas of the United States. In the Northeast Corridor, from Washington, DC, to Boston, trains operate at up to 125 mph (201 kph), with Amtrak's high-speed train operating at up to 150 mph (241 kph). The emergency stopping distance of a train traveling at 79 mph (127 kph) is approximately 1½ miles (2.4 km) after brakes are applied; at 125 mph (201 kph), it is 2½ miles (4 km); at 150 mph (241 kph), it is 3 to 3½ miles (4.8 to 5.6 km).

Emergency responders must protect the scene by providing flagging protection on the track in both directions from the incident at a distance of 1½ to 2 miles (2.4 to 3.2 km). In the high-speed corridor, this distance should be increased to 2½ to 3 miles (4 to 4.8 km). Flagging protection should be maintained until positive assurance has been received that the system operator or dispatcher knows that emergency response personnel are on the right-of-way and that other rail traffic has been notified. Even with these assurances, it is recommended that flagging protection be maintained for the event's duration.

Because of the weight and size of railroad passenger cars, stabilization in a derailment cannot be obtained using the highway-grade cribbing materials, portable rachet pullers, or air bags that emergency response personnel typically carry. It is strongly recommended that damaged or derailed cars be stabilized by using railroad ties (readily available at most derailment sites) or other suitably heavy-duty materials.

Most cars in a passenger train are those owned by the train's operator, usually Amtrak. Occasionally, however, privately owned passenger cars are attached to the train. Although most commercial passenger cars use electrical power for onboard lighting, food service, door operation, and heating/air-conditioning systems, privately owned passenger cars may employ liquefied petroleum gas (LP-gas) or diesel fuel for heating, cooking, or a generator system as an auxiliary power source. For this reason, responders must be prepared for such materials when dealing with a privately owned passenger car.

Rail transportation companies typically provide training for emergency response personnel on the proper procedures for dealing with a rail incident. Emergency responders with rail operations in their area should make certain that they take full advantage of the rail operators' training resources.

MOTIVE POWER

Diesel Electric Locomotives

What is generally referred to as a diesel locomotive is actually a diesel electric locomotive (Figure 21.8.3). The power is developed by the diesel engine, which drives a main traction generator (or alternator on ac locomotives). The output of this generator or alternator is then transmitted to the traction motors, which are mounted under the locomotive in massive frames called trucks and geared to the axles and wheels. The traction motors actually drive the locomotive. The numerous support systems of a locomotive include a battery that provides power to start the diesel engine, an auxiliary generator or alternator that charges the battery and supplies low-voltage current for control and lighting circuits, and an auxiliary alternator, mounted integrally with the main traction generator or alternator that furnishes field current for the main alternator and power for the radiator cooling fan motors and for a blower motor, which cleans the inertial carbody filters.

Main line locomotives have a normal service life of more than 30 years. Thousands of units still in service have operated far longer. Locomotives in main line service on a major railroad will average between 150,000 and 250,000 miles (241,403 and 402,338 km) per year.

The diesel electric locomotive is an enclosed, self-contained piece of equipment. Fire prevention in the engine room is almost exclusively limited to housekeeping and maintenance, which includes stopping and repairing fuel oil, lubricant oil, or exhaust leaks and ensuring that debris and products of leakage do not accumulate. Improved carbody filtration, through the development of self-cleaning inertial-type carbody filters and carbody pressurization, has also helped to improve engine room safety in modern diesel electric locomotives.

Improvements to electrical cabinets on newer locomotives include the use of fire-retardant wire and cable insulation and the practice of ventilating electrical cabinets with filtered air. This ventilation prevents flammable gases from collecting and keeps dirt out of the electrical cabinet. Other improvements include better wiring techniques, increased use of circuit breakers and fuses, and the pressurization of electrical cabinets. Design improvements, particularly in the extensive use of electronics throughout the locomotive, have also reduced fire hazards.

Fire protection for diesel locomotives includes the following:

Hot Engine Protection. To protect against excessive temperatures in the engine cooling system and hot engine oil, devices are installed to prevent excessive heat buildup in the engine and supporting systems.

Engine Crankcase Protection. This device is designed to detect a dangerous buildup of pressure in the engine and to shut down the engine when necessary.

High-Voltage Ground Protection. If a high-voltage fault develops on the locomotive and goes to ground, the ground relay detects the fault and disconnects the electrical load to the locomotive.

Emergency Fuel Cutoff Switches. In an emergency, the fuel supply to the engine can be stopped by pressing any one of three emergency fuel cutoff buttons. Two buttons are located on the

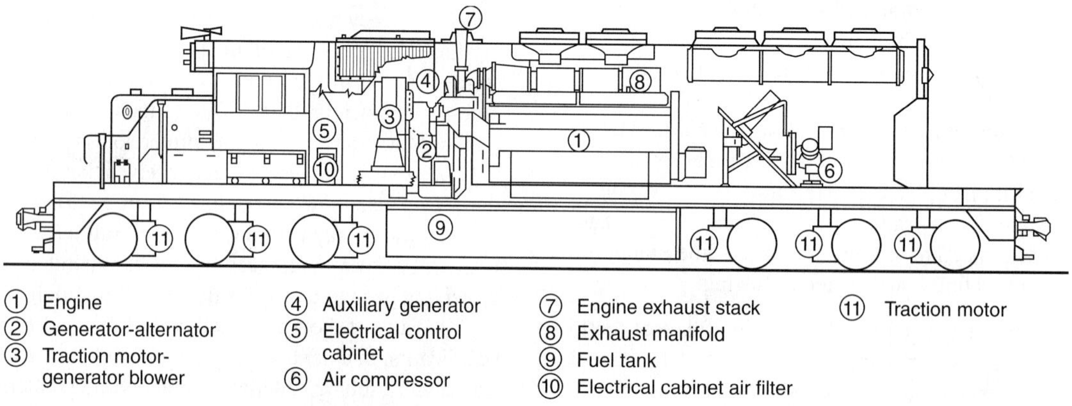

FIGURE 21.8.3 Diesel Electric Locomotive Showing the Location of Principal Components of the Power System

underframe near the fuel filler, one on either side of the locomotive, and a third is found on the engine control panel in the cab.

Main Battery Knife Switch. This large, single-throw knife switch is located in the engine cab at the lower portion of the fuse panel. It connects the battery to the locomotive low-voltage system.

Personnel Protection from High Voltage. Modern locomotives have their high-voltage electric componentry isolated in a labeled panel. This panel has interlocks and other design features to ensure that opening the panel door automatically de-energizes the electric components. Older units may not have this feature, however, so extreme caution is advised when working around locomotive electrical systems.

Portable Fire Protection Equipment. Each diesel electric locomotive is equipped with portable fire extinguisher protection, generally ordinary dry chemical. The quantity and type depend on the size of the locomotive and its use in yard, local, or main line service.

Preventive Maintenance and Inspections. Diesel electric locomotives are inspected, tested, and serviced on a regular schedule, based on life expectancy of component parts, empirical failure data, and Federal Railroad Administration (FRA) regulations.

Alternative Fuel Locomotives

The vast majority of locomotives operate on diesel fuel. The railroad industry is, after the federal government in the United States, the country's largest user of diesel fuel. Locomotive fuel is a significant element of a railroad's operating costs. Efforts are ongoing to reduce these costs, both the cost of the fuel itself as well as its storage, handling, and dispensing costs.

One railroad is now extending the range of some of its long-distance trains by placing a tank car of diesel fuel in its locomotive consist. This practice also permits the train to take on large quantities of fuel where the price is lowest. The larger quantity of locomotive fuel potentially involved in a train collision or derailment should be recognized by the fire community.

A few railroads are experimenting with liquefied natural gas (LNG) as a locomotive fuel. A handful of experimental units are in use on selected assignments. Some LNG locomotives designed only for use in switching yards use a relatively low-powered, spark-ignition engine that permits LNG to be the only fuel on board.

Other experimental LNG locomotives are high-horsepower units intended for long-distance hauling. They use engines with traditional diesel-type, compression-ignition technology. These units require that a percentage of diesel fuel be mixed with the LNG primary fuel to achieve combustion, so both diesel and LNG fuels are found on board. At present there is no uniformity of application: some units use high-pressure LNG technology; others use low-pressure designs.

Refueling arrangements for LNG units are also in the experimental stage. Installations and practices vary widely, both within a single railroad and between different companies. Some locations have fixed LNG fueling facilities operated by railroad personnel. At other locations fueling may be by a vendor's crew and tank truck.

The LNG-powered locomotive consists for long-distance service in use or contemplated now have this basic similarity: all have two high-horsepower locomotives with an LNG fuel tank car, or tender, between them. Equipment is well protected from all known hazards, including break-apart. The LNG in the tender is not considered to be in commerce; therefore, the LNG-containing tender is not subject to the DOT regulations and does not need to be placarded. All experimental locomotives and locomotive consists, along with LNG fueling operations, can be expected to be well marked.

Electric Locomotives

Electric locomotives today are used almost exclusively on passenger trains in major metropolitan areas.

Figure 21.8.4 illustrates the general arrangement of an electric locomotive. This particular unit can deliver 5100 hp (3.8 MW) at the rail and operates on 25,000 or 50,000 V alternating

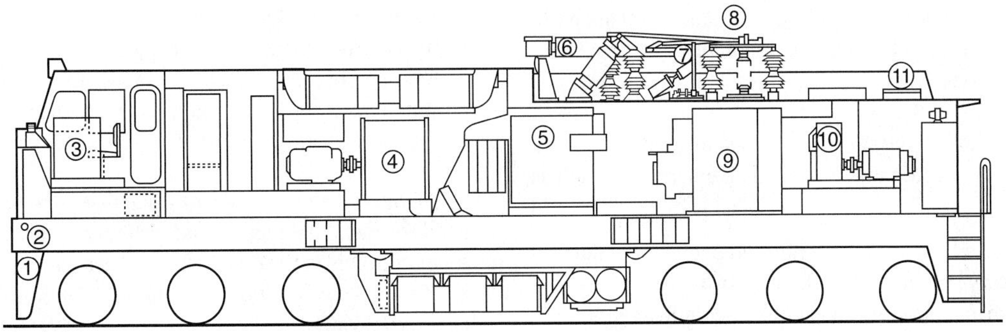

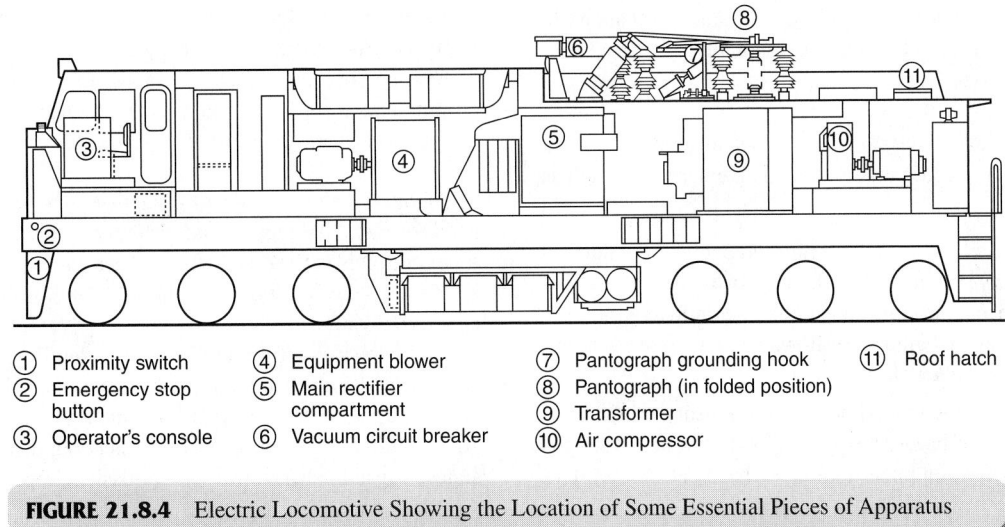

(1) Proximity switch
(2) Emergency stop button
(3) Operator's console
(4) Equipment blower
(5) Main rectifier compartment
(6) Vacuum circuit breaker
(7) Pantograph grounding hook
(8) Pantograph (in folded position)
(9) Transformer
(10) Air compressor
(11) Roof hatch

FIGURE 21.8.4 Electric Locomotive Showing the Location of Some Essential Pieces of Apparatus

current from an overhead wire. Because the electric locomotive derives its power from an electrical circuit, it is necessary to deenergize the circuit to extinguish any electrical fire safely.

Emergency Stop Buttons. These buttons, one on each side of the locomotive under the operator's cab, can be reached from the ground. Pushing either button trips the vacuum circuit breaker on the roofs of all locomotives in the consist and removes the power.

Manual Pantograph Grounding Switch. Usually located in the right rear of the locomotive, this switch grounds the pantograph before personnel perform maintenance or climb to the roof through the rear hatch. Grounding the pantograph (catenary), which is described in special instructions, varies depending on locomotive type and the overhead system employed. Fire fighters should obtain this information from railroad officials and include it in prefire plans.

Emergency Shutdown Switch. This switch, located on the master control housing, is used in emergencies to remove power from the locomotive during single-unit operation or to remove power from all units of the consist during multiple operation.

Electric locomotives, by their very nature, operate with voltages considerably higher than diesel locomotives. Modern electric locomotives have vacuum breakers that trip in cycles, thereby considerably reducing short circuits that could cause fires on older motive power.

Preventive Maintenance. Preventive maintenance is mandatory to preclude downtime caused by fire or equipment failure. Electrical circuits are tested for grounds or other defects when equipment is at major shops or at intervals of no more than 3 months. All tests and scheduled maintenance are performed in compliance with U.S. DOT rules, as a minimum.

Portable Fire Protection Equipment. Electric locomotives are equipped with portable fire extinguishers. Gaseous extinguishers are normally located in each cab and in the equipment compartment. The number of onboard extinguishers varies with equipment type and company policy. To minimize damage to delicate equipment found on electric locomotives, every effort should be made to use a gaseous agent to extinguish a fire.

Safety Precautions. Certain precautions must be observed when boarding an electric locomotive in an emergency, such as the following:

1. Never climb on top of any railroad equipment under an overhead catenary system until obtaining positive assurance that the wires have been deenergized and that locomotive grounding switches are engaged. Failure to follow this procedure can result in severe burns and even electrocution.

2. It is imperative that all persons on or near electric locomotives be aware of hazards associated with the high voltages involved. Electricity supplied by the overhead catenary system is typically 11,000 V ac and from the third rail, 600 V dc. Voltages within locomotive electrical cabinets are 600 V dc and 480 V ac. If the catenary wire falls on the train body, it energizes the entire train with high voltage. Do not assume that safety features on the power system or locomotive have functioned and deenergized the circuits. Make certain the power is off or use suitable precautions.

3. Unless human life is threatened, no fire-fighting activity should be undertaken on an electric locomotive until the catenary power has been removed and the overhead wire grounded by a qualified electric traction (ET) representative from the railroad. If action is required before an ET representative arrives, consult the train crew's conductor or engineer. These individuals are trained in the proper procedures to lower and secure the pantograph and to ground the electrical equipment.

4. Never enter any high-voltage compartment when the locomotive is energized.

5. Never touch motors, switches, protective barriers, or other electrical apparatus without knowing their exact purpose and function.

6. To protect against serious or fatal personal injury, be sure the pantograph is actually latched down before opening the roof hatch.

FREIGHT CARS AND EQUIPMENT

Freight cars account for the largest share of rail vehicle fires (Table 21.8.3). Major causes of fire in freight equipment, including motive equipment, are collision/derailment, suspected arson, electrical, brake shoe sparks or overheated brakes, welding and cutting, hot journals, and heating appliances. Tables 21.8.4 to 21.8.6 provide additional information on leading causes of rail vehicle fires.

Design advances and preventive maintenance are keys to reducing or eliminating fires caused by brake shoe sparks, exhaust sparks, hot journals or "hot boxes," electrical failures, and hot particles emitted from internal combustion engines. Design advances that should lessen the frequency of fires include increased use of turbochargers; renewed attention to the design and maintenance of eductor tubes, long a source of hot carbon particles on turbocharged locomotives; spark retention exhaust manifolds; nonsparking brake shoes; roller bearings; heat detectors, sensors, and indication lamps that supervise electrical circuits and components; and increased use and efficiency of trackside devices to detect overheated journals and dragging equipment.

Cotton bales are shrink-wrapped, which eliminates the need for metal bale bands and virtually eliminates the possibility of cotton bale fires. Bale fires can be caused by friction heat, which results when the bale bands rub against and ignite loose strands of cotton.

Fires resulting from collisions and derailments are a major concern of the railroad industry. To reduce these incidents, operating rules and safety programs are undergoing major revisions. An inventory of all grade crossings is being used by individual states to establish priorities for crossing improvements. This systemized approach to reducing crossing accidents, combined with the Federal Aid Highway Act of 1976 and the "Operation

TABLE 21.8.3 U.S. Rail Vehicle Transport Fire Problem, by Type of Vehicle, 1994–1998 Annual Averages

Vehicle Type	*Fires*		*Civilian Deaths*		*Civilian Injuries*		*Property Damage (in Millions of Dollars)*	
Freight, box, or hopper car	220	(33.8%)	0	(0.0%)	0	(0.0%)	2.8	(31.2%)
Locomotive or engine	200	(30.0%)	2	(37.9%)	4	(32.2%)	11.5	(54.7%)
Passenger or diner car	60	(8.6%)	3	(51.7%)	4	(33.9%)	1.2	(5.9%)
Maintenance equipment car	40	(6.2%)	0	(0.0%)	0	(3.4%)	0.5	(2.3%)
Self-powered car, trolley, or rapid-transit car	30	(4.4%)	0	(0.0%)	1	(6.8%)	0.1	(0.5%)
Container or piggyback car	20	(2.6%)	0	(0.0%)	1	(6.8%)	0.1	(0.7%)
Tank car	10	(1.4%)	0	(0.0%)	0	(3.4%)	0.9	(4.4%)
Unclassified or unknown-type rail transport vehicle	90	(13.1%)	1	(10.3%)	2	(13.6%)	3.8	(18.3%)
Total	650	(100.0%)	6	(100.0%)	12	(100.0%)	21.0	(100.0%)

Note: These are fires reported to U.S. municipal fire departments and so exclude fires reported only to federal or state agencies. Fires are rounded to the nearest ten, civilian deaths and injuries to the nearest one, and direct property damage to the nearest hundred thousand dollars. Sums may not equal totals due to rounding errors. Property damage figures are not adjusted for inflation. Percentages were calculated on the actual estimates, so two figures with the same rounded-off estimates may have different percentages.

Source: National estimates based on NFIRS and NFPA survey.

Lifesaver" educational program, is keeping the public alert to the dangers associated with railroad crossings.

Refrigerator Cars

Three types of cars commonly transport perishable and semiperishable commodities that require refrigeration, heater service, or protection from the extremes of heat or cold.

Standard Car. The standard ice car is virtually obsolete as a refrigerator car. Few railroads still furnish ice for shipment in such cars. However, some cars still may be used to keep commodities from freezing. Portable liquid fuel heaters that burn a mixture of methanol and isopropanol can be installed in the end ice bunkers. Alcohol foam is recommended as an extinguishing agent for these fuels because water may be ineffective.

Insulated Bunkerless Car. The insulated bunkerless car is widely used to protect semiperishable commodities such as canned goods, beer, grocery products, and drugs and medicines from extreme heat and cold. These cars provide no refrigeration, but they can be equipped with portable liquid fuel heaters. The heaters are usually suspended by chains from hooks, four per heater, in the ceiling of doorway areas. Heat shields protect the ceiling above each heater.

Refrigerated Car. The mechanically refrigerated car is the most modern and versatile of the freight cars used for perishables (Figure 21.8.5). It provides automatically controlled temperatures from 0 to 70°F (–18 to 21°C). Foamed-in-place polyurethane insulation helps to ensure consistent and dependable car temperatures. A compressor-evaporator is powered by a self-contained diesel-engine generator set located in a separate compartment within the car. The compressor-evaporator also can be powered directly from the alternator output of a diesel electric unit or from any suitable 220-V standby power supply. The fuel tank for the diesel engine is suspended below the car and normally carries 500 to 550 gal (1.9 to 2.1 m^3) of No. 1 or No. 2 diesel fuel oil. Fire fighting can be complicated by burning insulation and by the fact that fire fighters have not learned the location of the diesel engine stop control, which is clearly identified. Fire fighters should wear self-contained breathing apparatus when they enter a burning insulated or refrigerator car.

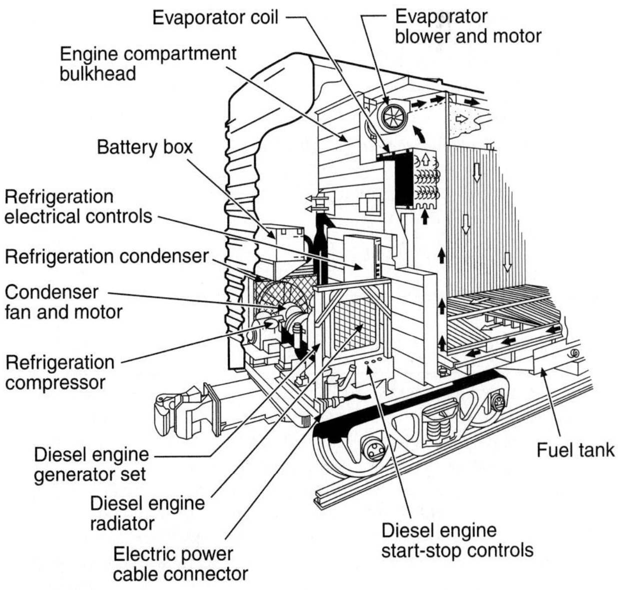

FIGURE 21.8.5 Engine Compartment of a Typical Mechanically Refrigerated Car. Note the start-stop control for the diesel engine at the lower left, mounted on the side of the car.

TABLE 21.8.4 U.S. Rail Transport Vehicle Fires, by Factor Contributing to Ignition Grouping, 1999–2002 Fires Reported to U.S. Fire Departments in NFIRS Version 5.0

Factor Contributing to Ignition	*Percentage of Fires*	*Percentage of Civilian Deaths*	*Percentage of Civilian Injuries*	*Percentage of Direct Property Damage*
Mechanical failure or malfunction	47	0	33	51
Unclassified mechanical failure or malfunction	27	0	0	27
Leak or break	13	0	33	23
Worn out	4	0	0	0
Backfire	2	0	0	0
Manual control failure	1	0	0	0
Misuse of material or product	19	0	0	7
Cutting or welding too close to combustible material	8	0	0	3
Heat source too close to combustible material	5	0	0	2
Abandoned or discarded material or product	2	0	0	0
Unclassified misuse of material or product	1	0	0	0
Flammable liquid used to kindle fire	1	0	0	0
Flammable liquid or gas spilled	1	0	0	1
Electrical failure or malfunction	15	0	67	6
Unclassified electrical failure or malfunction	8	0	0	2
Unspecified short circuit arc	3	0	0	0
Short circuit arc from defective, worn insulation	2	0	0	1
Arc or spark from operating equipment	1	0	0	0
Arc from faulty contact or broken conductor	1	0	67	0
Operational deficiency	7	100	0	7
Collision, knockdown, or overturn	1	100	0	0
Unclassified operational deficiency	1	0	0	1
Failure to clean	1	0	0	3
Overloaded equipment	1	0	0	0
Unattended equipment	1	0	0	2
Equipment not operated properly	1	0	0	0
Fire spread or control	5	0	0	32
Exposure fire	3	0	0	32
Rekindle	1	0	0	0
Unclassified fire spread or control	1	0	0	0
Design, manufacturing, or installation deficiency	2	0	0	0
Design deficiency	1	0	0	0
Manufacturing deficiency	1	0	0	0
Unclassified natural condition	2	0	0	0
Unclassified factor contributed to ignition	7	0	0	3

Note: These are national estimates of fires reported to U.S. municipal fire departments and so exclude fires reported only to federal or state agencies or industrial fire brigades. National estimates are projections. Casualty and loss projections can be heavily influenced by the inclusion or exclusion of one unusually serious fire. More than one factor contributing to ignition may be entered per incident. Fires in which the factor contributing to ignition was undetermined, not reported, or coded as "none" were allocated proportionally among fires with known factor contributing to ignition. Although this field is not required for fires that were coded as intentionally set or attributed to a cause of "other," the share of incidents with unreported data (fires—17%, deaths—0%, injuries—40%, property damage—54%) or fires with "none" (fires—27%, deaths—0%, injuries—0%, property damage—7%) generally exceeded those for undetermined (fires—11%, deaths—0%, injuries—0%, property damage—9%), suggesting that this type of allocation would be most appropriate.

Source: NFIRS and NFPA survey.

TABLE 21.8.5 U.S. Rail Transport Vehicle Fires, by Area of Fire Origin, 1999–2002 Fires Annual Averages

Area of Fire Origin	*Fires*		*Civilian Deaths*		*Civilian Injuries*		*Direct Property Damage (in Millions of Dollars)*	
Engine area, running gear, or wheel area	340	(45%)	0	(0%)	2	(2%)	6.0	(35%)
Cargo or trunk area of vehicle	120	(15%)	0	(0%)	2	(2%)	4.2	(24%)
Unclassified vehicle area	70	(9%)	0	(0%)	1	(1%)	3.1	(18%)
Exterior or exposed surface of vehicle	50	(6%)	0	(0%)	0	(0%)	1.0	(6%)
On or near railroad right-of-way	40	(6%)	0	(0%)	0	(0%)	1.6	(9%)
Operator or passenger area of vehicle	40	(5%)	5	(77%)	75	(95%)	0.5	(3%)
Unclassified area of origin	20	(2%)	0	(0%)	0	(0%)	0.1	(1%)
Separate operator or control area of vehicle	10	(2%)	0	(0%)	0	(0%)	0.0	(0%)
Fuel tank or fuel line	10	(1%)	1	(16%)	0	(0%)	0.1	(1%)
Storage room, area, tank, or bin	10	(1%)	0	(0%)	0	(0%)	0.2	(1%)
On or near highway, parking lot, or street	10	(1%)	0	(0%)	0	(0%)	0.0	(0%)
Unclassified storage area	10	(1%)	0	(0%)	0	(0%)	0.0	(0%)
Other known area	40	(5%)	0	(7%)	0	(0%)	0.4	(2%)
Total	770	(100%)	6	(100%)	79	(100%)	17.4	(100%)

Note: These are national estimates of fires reported to U.S. municipal fire departments and so exclude fires reported only to federal or state agencies or industrial fire brigades. National estimates are projections. Casualty and loss projections can be heavily influenced by the inclusion or exclusion of one unusually serious fire. Fires are rounded to the nearest ten, civilian deaths and injuries to the nearest one, and direct property damage is rounded to the nearest hundred thousand dollars. Sums may not equal totals due to rounding errors. Property damage figures are not adjusted for inflation. Percentages were calculated on the actual estimates, so two figures with the same rounded-off estimates may have different percentages. Fires in which the area of origin was unknown or not reported were allocated proportionally among fires with known area of origin.

Source: NFIRS and NFPA survey.

Box Cars

The design of all box cars is essentially the same; only the capacity, length, and details of the cars vary. Additions, such as special racks, dunnage devices, and nailable steel floors, are made to prevent vibration damage to the contents of the car without adding combustibility.

Special-Purpose Rail Cars

Equipment used to meet special shipping needs includes articulated cars, multilevel and enclosed cars for automobiles, "high cube" (large-capacity) box cars, 100 ton (90 metric ton) capacity covered hoppers, side-loading "all door" box cars, and aerated cars to handle bulk materials that require pneumatic loading and unloading mechanisms to "inhale" cargo at the loading point and "exhale" it at the destination.

"Intermodal service," in which specially designed flatcars carry loaded cargo containers, intermodal tank containers, or highway-type truck trailers, is an increasingly important part of the rail transportation business. Loaded and sealed, containers and trailers are delivered to the railroad at special intermodal terminals, where they are placed, usually by crane, onto the flatcar. Intermodal cars usually are part of a regular train, but intermodal-only trains are increasingly common. A single intermodal flatcar carrying two trailers, or as many as four cargo containers, usually has a wider variety of cargo than a single box car. Intermodal service also uses articulated cars of various designs and length for transporting containers and trailers.

Cabooses

Once every train had a locomotive at one end and a caboose at the other. The caboose was the traveling office of the conductor, the person in charge of the train, and a rear brakeman. Today, cabooses are a rarity; end-of-train electronic devices have taken over their "train-completion" function. Now only two or three persons riding in the lead locomotive customarily staff long-haul trains. Cabooses today are found only on an occasional branch-line or short-line train.

Cabooses' chief fire hazards are their combustible furnishings and heating systems. Most cabooses are heated with oil or coal. Fires can start because stoves and stovepipes do not have adequate clearances from combustible materials. Fire protection varies from water extinguishers to portable dry chemical extinguishers, although some carriers have discontinued this protection because of continuing problems with extinguisher theft.

RAIL TANK CARS

A tank car is a type of bulk packaging in which the tank is an integral part of a rail transport vehicle. More than 250,000 tank

TABLE 21.8.6 U.S. Rail Transport Vehicle Fires, by Item First Ignited, 1999–2002 Annual Averages

Item First Ignited	*Fires*		*Civilian Deaths*		*Civilian Injuries*		*Direct Property Damage (in Millions of Dollars)*	
Unclassified item first ignited	170	(22%)	2	(40%)	0	(0%)	2.1	(12%)
Flammable or combustible liquid or gas, including accelerants, aerosols, and atomized vapor	130	(17%)	2	(30%)	29	(37%)	8.0	(46%)
Electrical wire or cable insulation	120	(16%)	0	(0%)	50	(63%)	1.4	(8%)
Rubbish, trash, or waste	40	(5%)	0	(0%)	0	(0%)	0.1	(1%)
Multiple items first ignited	30	(4%)	0	(0%)	0	(0%)	1.5	(9%)
Upholstered sofa, chair, or vehicle seat	20	(2%)	2	(30%)	0	(0%)	0.2	(1%)
Agricultural crop, including fruits and vegetables	10	(2%)	0	(0%)	0	(0%)	0.1	(1%)
Unclassified flammable or combustible liquid, piping, or filter	10	(2%)	0	(0%)	0	(0%)	1.2	(7%)
Unclassified organic materials	10	(2%)	0	(0%)	0	(0%)	0.0	(0%)
Baled goods or material	10	(2%)	0	(0%)	0	(0%)	1.1	(6%)
Floor covering, rug, carpet, or mat	10	(2%)	0	(0%)	0	(0%)	0.1	(1%)
Grass or light vegetation, excluding crops	10	(2%)	0	(0%)	0	(0%)	0.0	(0%)
Interior wall covering excluding drapes	10	(2%)	0	(0%)	0	(0%)	0.0	(0%)
Railroad ties	10	(2%)	0	(0%)	0	(0%)	0.0	(0%)
Bulk storage	10	(2%)	0	(0%)	0	(0%)	0.0	(0%)
Box, carton, bag, basket, or barrel	10	(2%)	0	(0%)	0	(0%)	0.2	(1%)
Tire	10	(2%)	0	(0%)	0	(0%)	0.0	(0%)
Palletized material or material stored on pallets	10	(1%)	0	(0%)	0	(0%)	0.3	(2%)
Pipe, duct, conduit, hose, or associated covering	10	(1%)	0	(0%)	0	(0%)	0.0	(0%)
Unclassified general materials	10	(1%)	0	(0%)	0	(0%)	0.0	(0%)
Packing or wrapping material	10	(1%)	0	(0%)	0	(0%)	0.1	(0%)
Structural member or framing	10	(1%)	0	(0%)	0	(0%)	0.0	(0%)
Unclassified structural component or finish	10	(1%)	0	(0%)	0	(0%)	0.1	(1%)
Dust, fiber, or lint, including sawdust and excelsior	10	(1%)	0	(0%)	0	(0%)	0.0	(0%)
Magazine, newspaper, or writing paper	10	(1%)	0	(0%)	0	(0%)	0.0	(0%)
Rolled or wound paper or fabric	10	(1%)	0	(0%)	0	(0%)	0.3	(2%)
Conveyor belt, drive belt, or V-belt	10	(1%)	0	(0%)	0	(0%)	0.0	(0%)
Empty pallet or skid	10	(1%)	0	(0%)	0	(0%)	0.0	(0%)
Other known item	30	(4%)	0	(0%)	0	(0%)	0.3	(2%)
Total	770	(100%)	6	(100%)	79	(100%)	17.4	(100%)

Note: These are national estimates of fires reported to U.S. municipal fire departments and so exclude fires reported only to federal or state agencies or industrial fire brigades. National estimates are projections. Casualty and loss projections can be heavily influenced by the inclusion or exclusion of one unusually serious fire. Fires are rounded to the nearest ten, civilian deaths and injuries to the nearest one, and direct property damage is rounded to the nearest hundred thousand dollars. Sums may not equal totals due to rounding errors. Property damage figures are not adjusted for inflation. Percentages were calculated on the actual estimates, so two figures with the same rounded-off estimates may have different percentages. Fires in which the item first ignited was unknown or not reported were allocated proportionally among fires with known item first ignited.

Source: National estimates based on NFIRS and NFPA survey.

cars transport a diverse range of commodities—both hazardous and nonhazardous—including a variety of compressed and liquefied gases, liquids, and solids. The number and types of materials transported in a tank car depend on the size, construction, fittings, linings, and other physical features of the tank.

When faced with a tank car problem, communicating an accurate, detailed description of its contents, its condition, and other circumstances to tank car specialists not on the scene may be the most beneficial contribution an emergency responder can make. To help provide that information, one must understand tank car construction and features, tank car markings, types of tank cars, and tank car fittings.

Tank Car Construction and Features

Typically, tank cars are enclosed longitudinal cylinders (with or without compartments) with rounded ends called heads. Tank cars may or may not have underframes. If not, the tank must bear the stresses of train movement. Tank cars have railroad running gear and safety appliances. Figure 21.8.6 shows the shape and components of typical tank cars.

Tank cars may have such features as insulation, thermal protection, linings, and claddings. Manufacturers add these features to a basic tank, depending on the physical properties of commodities the tank is to carry. Safety features are applied to tank cars to reduce the potential for a release. Older tank cars have been retrofitted with these newer safety features.

Tank cars are built to mechanical standards common to all rail freight cars. In addition, they must meet the requirements of both the *Hazardous Materials Regulations of the Department of Transportation* (49 CFR, Part 179) and the AAR *Manual of Standards and Recommended Practices, Section C—Part III, Specifications for Tank Cars.* They also meet or exceed the ASME standards for pressure vessels. Builders must obtain design approval from the AAR Tank Car Committee before building a tank car. Transport Canada's *Regulations for the Transportation of Dangerous Commodities by Rail* contains Canadian tank car requirements.

Repairs of tank car tanks requiring welding, riveting, removal of damage, alterations, or conversions must occur only at AAR-certified facilities, using procedures and materials the AAR Tank Car Committee has approved.

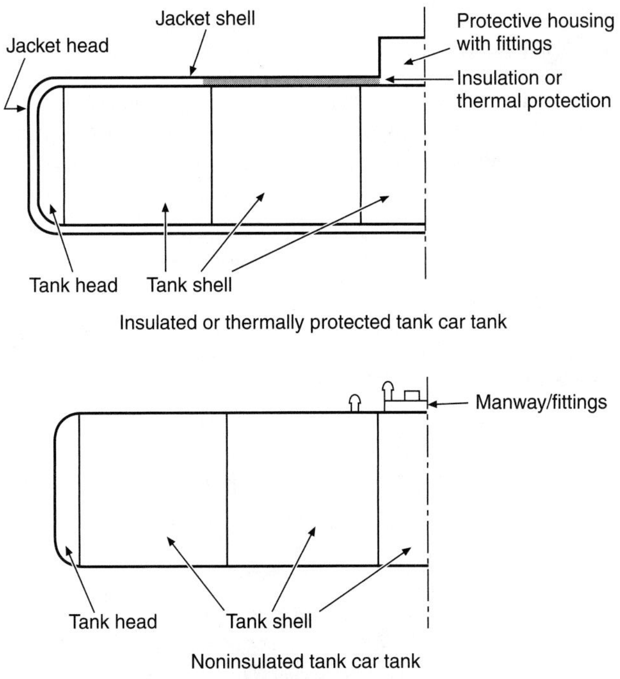

FIGURE 21.8.6 Tank Car Design and Nomenclature

Tank Car Tanks. Each tank car tank consists of a cylindrical shell closed at the ends by heads. The shell is constructed of two to seven rings formed from metal plates. Heads are made from plates pressed into a flanged-and-dished or an ellipsoidal shape; 2 to 1 ellipsoidal heads are the strongest. The rings and heads are fusion-welded together. In some older nonpressure tank cars, the tank parts are riveted together.

The completed tanks are heated to 1100°F (593°C) for 1 hour to relieve metal stresses caused by welding. Representative samples are X-rayed to identify possible flaws in the metal or the welds. Finally, they are hydrostatically tested.

Carbon steel is used in over 90 percent of tank car tanks, with aluminum making up most of the remainder. Stainless steel, referred to in the regulations as alloy steel, is used in a smaller number of cars. Nickel or nickel alloy is used for some tanks in acid or food services. Regulations specify the plate thickness of materials used to construct tank car tanks (Table 21.8.7).

TABLE 21.8.7 Minimum Tank and Jacket Plate Thickness

Minimum Plate Thickness After Forming	*Common Use of Plate Thickness*
Steel	
11 gauge (approximately 1/8 in.), also aluminum	Jacket of insulated tank cars, or jacket for thermally protected cars
7/16 in.	Tank for nonpressure tank cars, outer tank for nonpressure tank within a tank, or shell portion of outer tank for cryogenic liquid tank cars
1/2 in.	Head puncture resistance (head shield) or head portion of outer tank for cryogenic liquid tank cars
9/16 in.	Tank for steel pressure tank cars with tank test pressures of 200 psi and below
11/16 in.	Tank for steel pressure tank cars with tank test pressures of 300 psi and greater
3/4 in.	Tank for steel pressure tank cars in chlorine service
Aluminum	
1/2 in.	Tank for nonpressure aluminum tank cars
5/8 in.	Tank for aluminum pressure tank cars

Notes:
1. If high-tensile-strength steels are used, plate thickness for pressure tank car tanks may be reduced but in no case should that thickness be less than 1/2 in.
2. Plate thickness for nonpressure steel tank cars with expansion domes is a function of where the plate is used in the tank and the diameter of the tank. Thickness ranges from 1/4 to 1/2 in. For tank cars built after 1969, minimum plate thickness is 7/16 in., except for tank cars with a diameter of 12 to 122 in. where the thickness is 1/2 in.
3. For SI units: 1 in. = 2.54 cm; 1 psi = 6.9 kPa.

The capacities of tank car tanks vary from 4000 gal (15 m^3) to approximately 45,000 gal (170 m^3) in jumbo tank cars. Since 1970, however, the maximum capacity of new DOT specification tank cars transporting regulated hazardous materials is limited to 34,500 gal (130 m^3), or not more than 286,000 lb (119,295 kg) gross weight on rail.

Tank car tanks may be divided into as many as six compartments, each of which is actually a separate tank. Compartments may be of different capacities and may transport different commodities (Figure 21.8.7).

Car Structure. The completed tank is mounted on a car structure. The car structure consists of body bolsters attached to a framework (either continuous or stub sill). The framework rests on trucks at each end. The structure of the tank car includes the following components:

1. *Underframe.* Either a continuous underframe in which a one-piece assembly bridges the trucks of a tank car and assumes the draft and buff forces associated with train movement; or stub sill (underframeless), in which a short, longitudinal structural member welded to each end of the tank accommodates the coupler and draft gear assemblies and the attachment of the tank to its trucks
2. *Bolster.* In which a structural crossmember is mounted transversely to cradle the tank; tank cars have two body bolsters, one at each end of the tank
3. *Truck assembly.* Which consists of wheels, axles, sideframes, springs, truck bolster, and center bowl and pin; it supports one end of the car and allows it to be moved on the rail

Car Features. To increase their usefulness for a wide range of materials, tank cars may be equipped with various features, such as insulation, thermal protection, jackets, linings and claddings, and heater coils. These features have the following characteristics:

1. *Insulation.* Insulation is used on some tank cars to moderate the effects of temperature on the cars' contents. Fiberglass or polyurethane foams are the most common insulating materials. However, cork insulates tank cars carrying hydrocyanic acid, and perlite insulates cars transporting refrigerated liquid gases.

2. *Jacket.* Both insulation and jacketed thermal protection are held in place by a jacket, which also keeps out the elements. The jacket is constructed of a minimum of 11 gauge (approximately ⅛ in.) steel and serves as a heat-radiation shield. Metal brackets hold the jacket away from the tank. Jacketed cars can be recognized by a metal protective cover, or flashing, over the body bolster or tank bands; by the flattened appearance of the ends of the tank car; by flat sections on the sides of the car; or by the rough appearance of visible welds, even lap welds, which are generally thinner than the tank weld.

3. *Linings and claddings.* Some tank cars are lined to protect the tank from the corrosive or reactive effects of the contents or to maintain the contents' purity.

a. Lining materials and coatings are applied after the tank is constructed. Rubber is most commonly used in hazardous materials service, but glass, lead, nickel, polyurethane, polyvinyl chloride, and stainless steel are also used.
b. Cladding materials are applied to the tank base metal before the plate is formed. Nickel and stainless steel are used as cladding materials.

4. *Heater coils.* Some tank cars are equipped with heater coils, either inside or outside the tank. Steam, water, or hot oil from an external source runs through these coils to heat thick or solidified materials, such as asphalts, fused solids, heavy fuel oils, phenol, metallic sodium, or petroleum waxes to make them flow more easily when unloading. Outlets and inlets for interior heater coils have caps, which are in place when the car is loaded so that any damage to the coils does not release contents. Caps are off when the car is emptied and for cars equipped with external heat coils.

Safety Features

Various safety features have been instituted for tank cars to improve the safety of new and existing cars. The next four paragraphs provide examples of these programs.

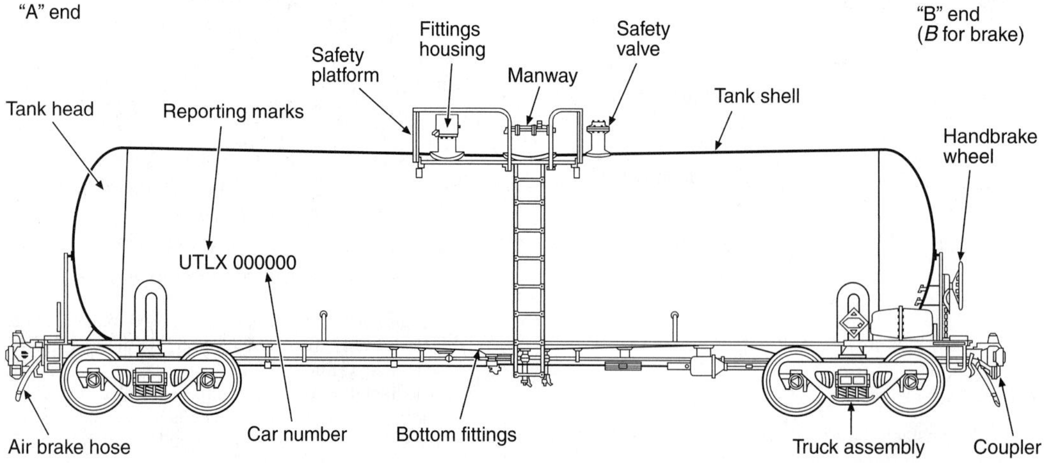

FIGURE 21.8.7 Typical Tank Car Tank with Some Basic Features Identified

Head Puncture Resistance (Head Shields). The head shield is applied to the lower portion of both ends or may cover the entire head to protect it against punctures. Some head shields are built into the jacket, whereas others are visible either as "half head" or trapezoidal-shaped plates of steel mounted on both ends of the tank car. Some head shields cover the entire head of the tank.

Top and Bottom Shelf Couplers. A top and bottom shelf coupler is a type of coupler with a vertical restraint mechanism, top and bottom, to reduce potential coupler disengagement in an accident.

Thermal Protection. Thermal protection, not to be confused with insulation, is used on some tank cars to protect the tank from flame impingement. It is designed to keep tank metal temperatures below 800°F (427°C) for 100 minutes (pool fire impingement) or 30 minutes (torch fire impingement). Thermal protection is used primarily on tank cars transporting liquefied flammable gases and on some nonpressure tank cars, such as the DOT-111J100W4 tank car for ethylene oxide. The following two types of thermal protection are used:

1. Jacketed thermal protection, in which mineral wool or various man-made ceramic fiber blankets are held in place by a metal jacket
2. Sprayed-on thermal protection, in which rough-textured coating sprayed onto the tanks or the jacket in some jacketed cars protects by expanding on exposure to fire

Bottom Discontinuity, or Skid, Protection. Skid protection is a safety device applied to the bottom of tank cars to protect bottom outlets, washouts, and sumps in a derailment.

Tank Car Markings

Various markings found on tank cars include initials, called reporting marks, and tank number; a specification marking; a DOT special permit (previously called an exemption) marking; tank and valve test dates; and tank identification plates.

Initials (Reporting Marks) and Tank Number. The car's initials and number identify the tank car, like any other freight car. The initials and number are found on both sides and both ends of a tank car. As one faces the side of the car, the initials and number are found on the left.

The initials indicate ownership of the car. An "X" as the last initial represents private ownership; that is, the railroad does not own the car. The number following the initials identifies the specific car. Most tank cars are owned by nonrailroad companies.

Using the car's initials and number, shippers, carriers, and emergency response personnel can identify a tank car's contents from the computer or shipping papers. The shipping papers indicate when the contents are hazardous.

Specification Marking. A specification marking identifies the standards to which a tank car is built. The specification marking is stamped into the head of the tank and stenciled on the car's sides. As one faces the side of the car, the specification number is to the right, opposite its initials and number.

The specification marking consists of a two- or three-letter prefix, followed by a series of numerals and/or letters. Specification markings may be as simple as DOT-103 or as detailed as DOT-111A60ALW1. A specification marking does not identify the car's contents but does indicate how the tank car was built. Specification information can be obtained from the railroad's computer using the car's initials and number (Figure 21.8.8).

Two- or three-letter prefixes of the specification marking include the following:

- DOT—Department of Transportation
- AAR—Association of American Railroads
- ICC—Interstate Commerce Commission (authority to DOT in 1966)
- CTC—Canadian Transport Commission
- TC—Transport Canada (replacing CTC)

Class. The *class* is the general designation of a tank car that may include several specifications (see Table 21.8.8). The term *class* designates a group of several specifications (e.g., Class DOT-112). The approving authority prefix and class number together indicate the class.

The specification is the specific designation of a tank car within a class (e.g., Specification DOT-112J340W).

Delimiter Letter. On most nonpressure tank cars, the letter *A* separates the class number from the tank test pressure and has no meaning. However, on pressure tank cars, cryogenic liquid tank cars, and some nonpressure tank cars, the letter indicates

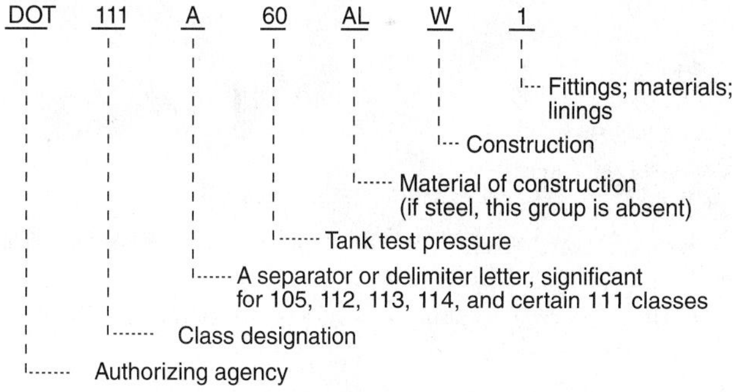

FIGURE 21.8.8 Explanation of Specification Marking

TABLE 21.8.8 Tank Car Classes

Nonpressure tank car classes
DOT-103 DOT-111 AAR-201 AAR-206
DOT-104 DOT-115 AAR-203 AAR-211

Pressure tank car classes
DOT-105 DOT-112 DOT-114 DOT-120
DOT-109

Cryogenic liquid tank car classes
DOT-113 AAR-204

how the car is equipped. The last number following the weld construction designator, if present, identifies special fittings, materials of construction (alloy steel), and linings.

You can get specification information from the railroad, shipper, car owner, or the Association of American Railroads (from the car's certificate of construction) by using the car's initials and number. The specification is the specific designation of a tank car within a class (e.g., Specification DOT-112J340W). The location of a specification marking is shown in Figure 21.8.9.

Capacity Stencil. The volume of the tank car tank, typically in gallons and liters, is stenciled on both ends of the car under the car's initials and number (Figure 21.8.10). The load limit, typically in pounds and kilograms, is stenciled on the sides of the car under the car's initials and number. *Load limit* means the same as *capacity.* Certain tank cars (e.g., DOT-111A100W4) have the water capacity (water weight) of the tank, typically in pounds and kilograms, stenciled on the sides of the tank near the center of the car.

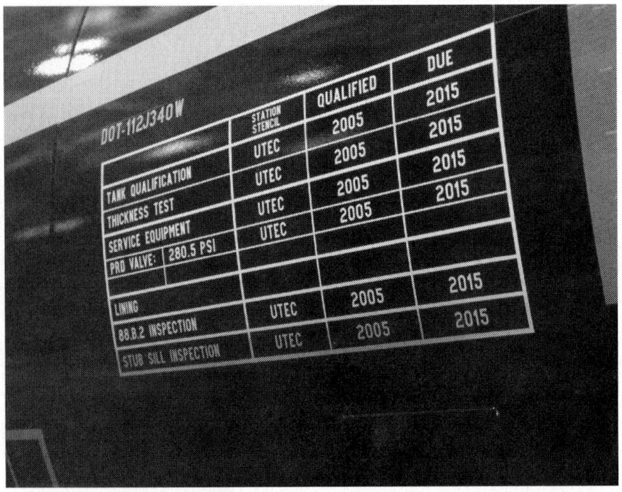

FIGURE 21.8.9 Location of Specification Marking on Tank Cars with Qualification Stencil

FIGURE 21.8.10 Capacity Stencil Marking Found on Heads of Tank Cars

DOT Special Permit (Previously Exemption) Marking. When special permits (exemptions) from the regulations for packages and containers and the preparation and offering of hazardous materials for shipment are made, the outside of each package must be plainly and durably marked DOT-SP (previously DOT-E) followed by the number assigned, such as DOT-SP8623 (previously DOT-E8623). On portable tanks, cargo tanks, and tank cars, the marking must be in 2 in. (50.8 mm) letters. This SP marking replaces the previously used E marking for an exemption from the regulations.

Tank Car Qualification Stencil. Tank and pressure-relief devices, if installed, have varying retest intervals, depending on the car's specification and/or age. Retest and test due dates must be marked or stenciled on the tank or on a dataplate. Interior coils are also tested (see Figure 21.8.9).

Tank Car Identification Plate. New tank cars will be equipped with two identical stainless steel identification plates. Plates (Figure 21.8.11) are permanently affixed in a visible location to the inboard surfaces of the AR and BL body bolster webs. The information on the dataplate includes the manufacturer, serial number, AAR certificate number, tank specification, shell and head material, insulation material, and date of manufacture.

Tank Car Types

Tank cars are classed according to their construction, features, and fittings. The tank's specification determines the product it may transport.

Nonpressure Tank Cars. Nonpressure tank cars, also known as general-service tank cars or acid-service tank cars, transport a wide variety of hazardous and nonhazardous materials at low pressures. Nonpressure tank cars transport hazardous materials, such as flammable and combustible liquids, flammable solids, oxidizers, organic peroxides and poison, corrosive materials, and molten solids. They also transport nonhazardous materials, such as tallow, clay slurry, corn syrup, and other food products.

Tank test pressures for nonpressure tank cars range from 60 to 100 psi (430 to 689 kPa). Capacities range from 4000 to 45,000 gal (15 to 181 m^3).

Nonpressure tank car tanks are cylindrical with rounded heads. Newer nonpressure tank cars have at least one manway to allow access to the car's interior. Some older nonpressure tank cars have at least one expansion dome with a manway (Figures 21.8.12 and 21.8.13). Fittings for loading and unloading, pressure and/or vacuum relief, gauging, and other purposes are visible at the top and/or bottom of the car.

Nonpressure "Tank-Within-a-Tank" Tank Cars. This nonpressure tank car is built as a tank within a tank. It consists of an inner tank of steel, alloy steel, or aluminum covered with thick insulation and enclosed within an outer tank. This tank car transports temperature-sensitive materials, such as food products.

FIGURE 21.8.11 Tank Identification Plate

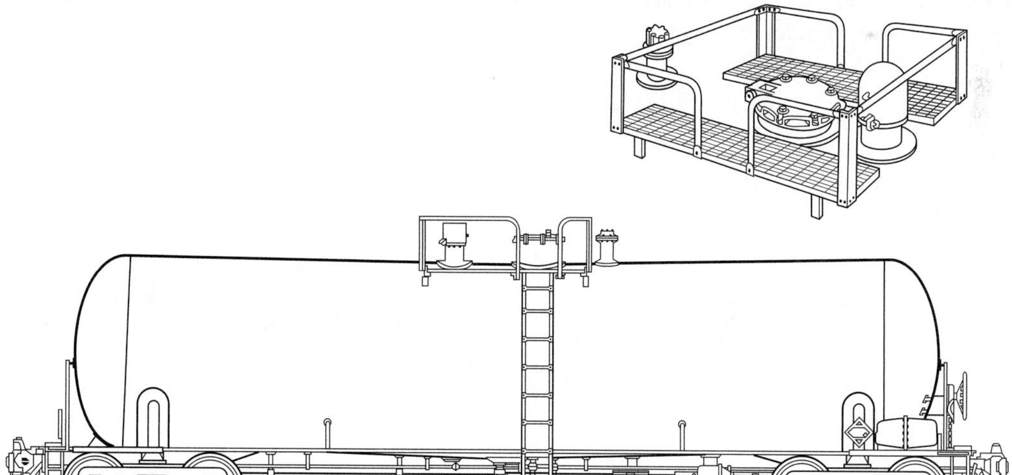

FIGURE 21.8.12 Typical Nonpressure Tank Car (DOT-111)

Tank Train®. The Tank Train is a series of nonpressure tank cars interconnected with flexible hoses that allow the cars to be loaded and unloaded from one end. A spring-loaded butterfly valve arrangement on each car is controlled pneumatically from the loading/unloading point. After loading, hoses are purged of liquid, and valves close automatically, isolating each car. The Tank Train transports hazardous and nonhazardous materials, including gasoline, fuel, oil, caustic soda, and pesticides.

Multicompartmented Nonpressure Tank Cars. Multicompartmented nonpressure tank cars have up to six compartments. Each compartment is considered a separate tank because of its

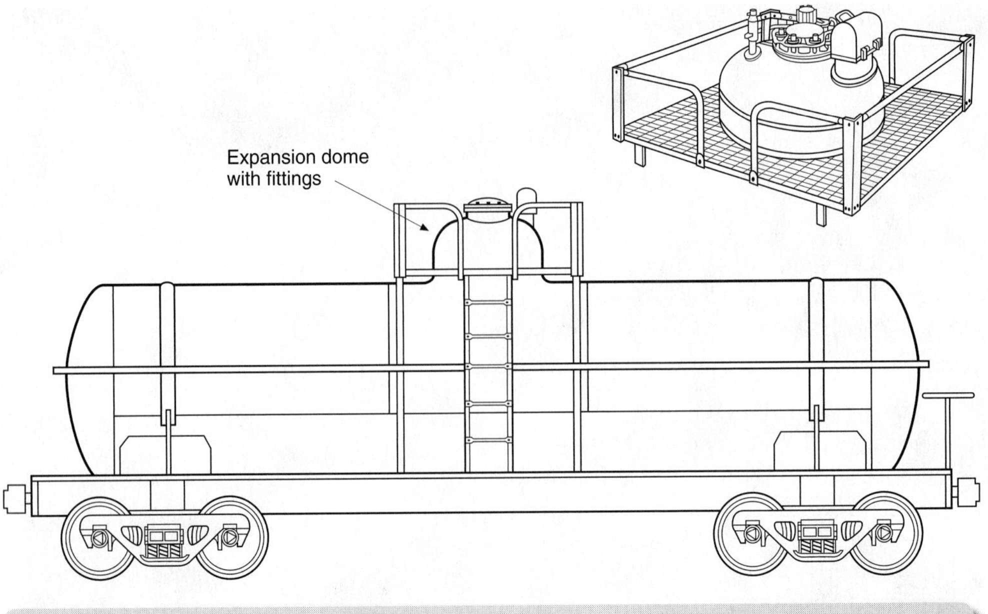

FIGURE 21.8.13 Typical Older-Style Nonpressure Tank Car (DOT-103) with an Expansion Dome

construction. Compartments may be of different capacities and may contain different materials. Each compartment has its own loading and unloading fittings.

Pressure Tank Cars. Pressure tank cars typically transport hazardous materials, including flammable, nonflammable, or poisonous gases at higher pressures. However, pressure tank cars can transport other commodities, depending on the characteristics of the product or the process for loading and unloading the tank. Other products transported in pressure tank cars are ethylene oxide, pyrophoric liquids, sodium metal, motor fuel antiknock compounds, bromine, anhydrous hydrofluoric acid, and acrolein (Figure 21.8.14).

Tank test pressures for these tank cars range from 100 to 600 psi (689 to 4137 kPa). Pressure tank cars range in capacity from 4000 to 45,000 gal (15 to 170 m^3).

Pressure tank cars are cylindrical, noncompartmented steel or aluminum tanks with rounded heads. They are top-loading,

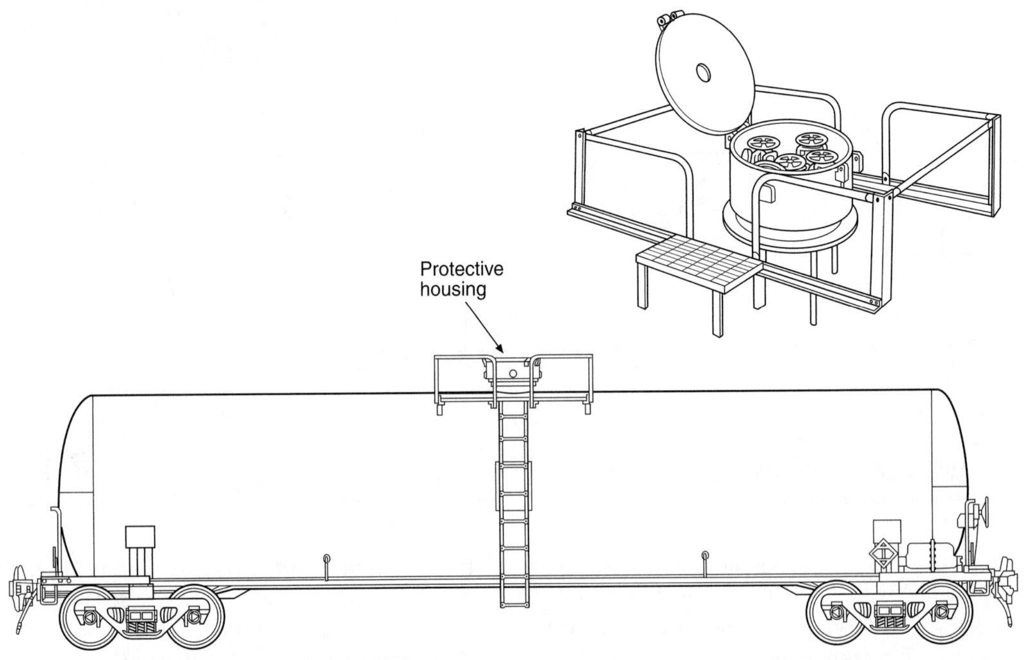

FIGURE 21.8.14 Typical Pressure Tank Car with Protective Housing

with fittings for loading and unloading, pressure relief, and gauging located inside protective housing mounted on a single manway.

Pressure tank cars may be insulated and/or thermally protected. The top two-thirds of pressure tank cars without insulation and without jacketed thermal protection will be painted white or another reflective color.

Cryogenic Tank Cars. Cryogenic tank cars carry low-pressure—usually 25 psi (172 kPa) or lower—cold liquids refrigerated to –155°F (–104°C) and below. Typical contents of these tanks are argon, ethylene, hydrogen, nitrogen, and oxygen (Figure 21.8.15).

Cryogenic tank car tanks (DOT-113) are of the tank-within-a-tank style with an alloy (stainless or nickel) steel inner tank inside an outer tank. The space between the inner tank and the outer tank is filled with insulation and under a vacuum. The combined vacuum and insulation protect the contents for only 30 days, making shipments in these cars time sensitive.

Fittings for loading and unloading, pressure relief, and venting are located in ground-level cabinets at diagonal corners of the car or in the center of one end of the car. Built to tank car specifications, the pneumatically unloaded covered hopper cars are covered hopper cars, which are unloaded through pressure differential, or pneumatics, by applying air pressure. Even though the pressure is used only during unloading, tank test pressures for the car range from 20 to 80 psi (138 to 551 kPa). Dry caustic soda is one commodity transported in this type of car (Figure 21.8.16).

Tank Car Fittings

Numerous fittings used on tank cars allow for loading and unloading and provide for safe transportation of their contents. All fittings are not found on all tank cars. This section addresses tank car fittings for nonpressure and pressure tank cars from a very general standpoint.

Fittings for Loading and Unloading Tank Cars. Various fittings are used to load and unload tank cars, including the following.

Manway. This large opening on top of the tank car allows access to the tank's interior. It is closed either with a permanently mounted cover plate with fittings attached or with a hinged-and-bolted cover opened for loading the car.

Liquid or Vapor Valves. These valves control the passage of liquid or vapor into or out of the tank in pressure tank cars (Figure 21.8.17).

Liquid valves, usually two, are used to load or unload liquids from tank cars. Unloading occurs as a result of pressure generated by the contents or when the tank is pressurized with air, nitrogen, or other gas. An eduction pipe reaches from the liquid valve to the tank's bottom.

One or two vapor valves are used to remove vapor from the tank or to pressurize the tank. On pressure tank cars, they are called vapor valves; on nonpressure tank cars, they are called air inlets or air valves. (Note: Excess flow valves found under various fittings shut when flow exceeds a predetermined amount.)

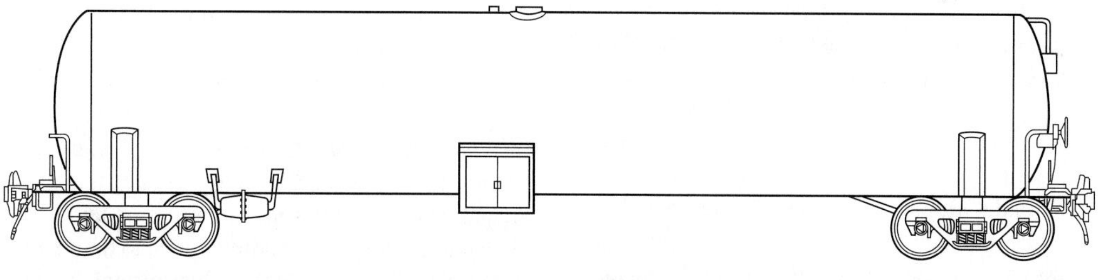

FIGURE 21.8.15 Typical Cryogenic Liquid Tank Car (DOT-113)

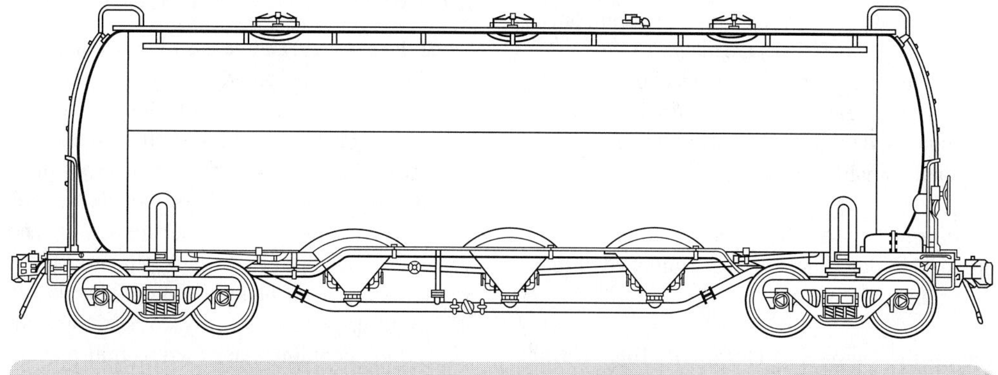

FIGURE 21.8.16 Pneumatically Unloaded Covered Hopper Car

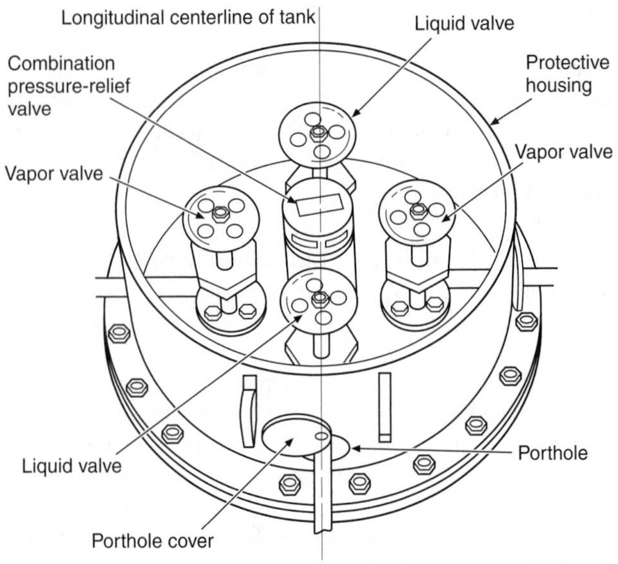

FIGURE 21.8.17 Fitting Arrangement in the Protective Housing on a Liquid Chlorine Tank Car

Bottom Outlet Valves. These valves are used to unload the tank from the bottom. Examples are a plug-type valve operated from the top of the tank, called a "top-operated bottom unloading valve"; a ball-type valve either external to or inside the tank and operated from ground level; or a wafersphere, or butterfly valve, mounted outside the tank.

Pressure-Relief Devices. These devices reduce the buildup of excess internal pressure that commodity vaporization and expansion cause. Pressure-relief valves are set at either 75 percent of the tank's test pressure or 33 percent of the tank's burst pressure.

Pressure-Relief Valve. This relief device has an operating part held closed by one spring or multiple springs. It is designed to open and reclose at predetermined pressures. The device can be mounted with the spring inside or outside the tank. It is typically set to activate when 75 percent of the tank test pressure is reached.

Safety Vent. This device uses a frangible disk, called a rupture disk, that seals the vent opening under normal conditions. The disk is designed to rupture at predetermined pressures and, once ruptured, does not reclose. Rupture disks are made of steel, plastic, rubber, or a combination of metal, plastic, or rubber. Lead is no longer authorized. Relief vents are used on certain nonpressure tank cars. Cars equipped with relief vents will be stenciled "Not for poisonous or flammable liquids."

Combination Pressure-Relief Device. This combination device uses a rupture disk and/or a breaking pin combined with a spring-operated pressure-relief valve.

Fittings for Gauging the Inage and Outage in Tank Cars. Gauging devices are used to determine the amount of lading in a tank. These devices allow one to measure the amount of liquid in the tank, such as liquefied or cryogenic gases (inage), or the amount of vapor space left in the tank (outage). Gauging devices usually measure outage. The following are two types of gauging devices:

1. *Open-type gauging devices.* These devices eject liquid once the liquid level reaches the bottom of a fixed- or adjustable-length tube; they read outage
2. *Closed-type gauging devices.* These devices use a float, coupled with a magnet on a measuring rod or a dial indicator, to show the liquid level of the commodity

Another method of determining the amount of lading in a tank car is to insert a measuring pole while using the appropriate inage/outage tables. Outage is also determined by gauge bars or "T" bars on most nonpressure cars.

Other Fittings. Various other fittings may be found on tank cars.

Sample Line. This device is used to obtain a sample of the commodity without opening the tank.

Thermometer Well. This closed tube, filled with a permanent-type antifreeze, extends into the tank. By inserting a thermometer into the tube, the temperature of the lading inside may be determined.

Bottom Washout. This bolted and flanged opening in the bottom of the tank car is used only when a tank is cleaned. There is no way to control the lading flow once the closure is removed.

Sump. This closed projection in the bottom of the tank allows the liquid eduction pipe to extend slightly below the bottom of the tank to unload the tank more completely.

Vacuum Relief Valve. This valve is designed to prevent excessive internal vacuum buildup (greater than 0.75 psi [5.5 kPa]) negative pressure in some nonpressure tanks. The vacuum relief valve used during unloading opens to admit air when a vacuum occurs and then recloses after normal conditions have been restored.

INTERMODAL TANK CONTAINERS

Since the early 1980s, the use of tank containers throughout the world has increased greatly. Factors accounting for this increase are improved safety, portability, lower transportation costs, and benefits of a multimodal transport system.

Advantages over alternative methods of transport, such as drums, tank trucks, and trailers, include reduction in the amount of handling required, faster transfer at ports and terminals, convenient storage options at the destination, and ready use of conventional container-handling equipment already in place.

Built according to many domestic and international standards, tank containers are used to transport diverse commodities, including an increasing number of hazardous materials.

Problems involving tank containers are best handled by giving an accurate, detailed description of the contents and condition of the tank container, and the circumstances to those with specialized knowledge and skills necessary to help handle the problem.

Tank Container Construction and Features

Tank containers consist of a single metal tank mounted inside a sturdy metal supporting frame. This unique frame structure, built to international standards, makes tank containers multimodal (intermodal). Thus, they are used interchangeably in two or more modes of transport, such as rail, highway, or water. Tank containers may be equipped with a variety of features.

Tank Container Tank. The tank container tank is generally built as a cylinder enclosed at the ends by heads. Other tank shapes—rectangular tanks—and configurations—tube modules—exist but are rare. Tanks with multiple compartments, each built as a separate tank, are also rare. A tank's capacity does not ordinarily exceed 6340 gal (about 24 m^3).

Ninety percent or more of the tanks are built of stainless steel; the rest are constructed of mild steel. Stainless steel is used because it resists cold temperatures. Aluminum and magnesium alloy tanks are available, but they cannot be used in water transport mode.

Minimum head and shell thickness is measured in terms of "equivalent thickness in mild steel" after forming. For steel tanks, the minimum thickness for nonregulated commodities is ¼ in. (6.35 mm). For regulated materials, the minimum thickness is ⅜ in. (9.5 mm). For stainless steel tanks, the minimum thickness for nonregulated materials is slightly less than ⅛ in. (3.2 mm). For regulated commodities, the minimum thickness is just under 3⁄16 in. (4.8 mm).

Most tanks are built according to the pressure-vessel standards of ASME, and the welds are X-rayed. Welds on carbon steel tanks are postweld heat-treated.

Supporting Frame. The supporting frame of a tank container protects the tank and provides for stacking, lifting, and securing the container. It also supports the walkways and ladders. Like other types of freight containers, supporting frames are built to the requirements of the International Standards Organization (ISO).

The most common size of supporting frame is 20 ft (6 m) long, 8 or 8½ ft (2.4 or 2.55 m) wide, and from 8 to 9½ ft (2.4 to 2.85 m) high. Except for the half-height tube modules and some cryogenic tank containers, some of which are 35 ft (10.5 m) long, very few tanks longer than 20 ft (6 m) are used in the United States.

There are two basic supporting frame types: the box type, which encloses the tank in a cagelike framework and the "beam type," which uses frame structures only at the ends of the tank.

Corner Casting. Supporting frames for all intermodal containers, including tank containers, are built with standard corner fittings, called corner castings. They are used to secure the tank and to lift it with standard container-handling equipment. Corner castings must conform to ISO standards. Cast-iron corner castings are prohibited. In an accident where proper lifting devices are not available, the corner castings may be used to lift or move the tank only after consulting the tank's owner or manufacturer.

Features. To increase their use for a wide range of cargoes, tank containers may be equipped with various features, such as linings that protect the tank from the lading, refrigeration units, electrical or steam heating, and insulation to maintain the desired temperature of the contents.

Foamed plastic, both polyurethane and polystyrene, is the predominant insulating material. However, mineral wool and fiberglass are also used. Insulation, generally 3 to 4 in. (76.2 to 101.6 mm) thick, is always covered with a weathertight jacket. Jackets are made of metal, at least 1⁄32 in. (1 mm) thick or of an equivalent thickness of plastic reinforced with either glass or fiber.

Tank Container Markings

Various markings may be found on tank containers, including the tank initials and number, the specification marking, the DOT exemption marking, the AAR 600 marking, the country and size/type markings, the dataplate, and the tank and valve test dates (Figure 21.8.18).

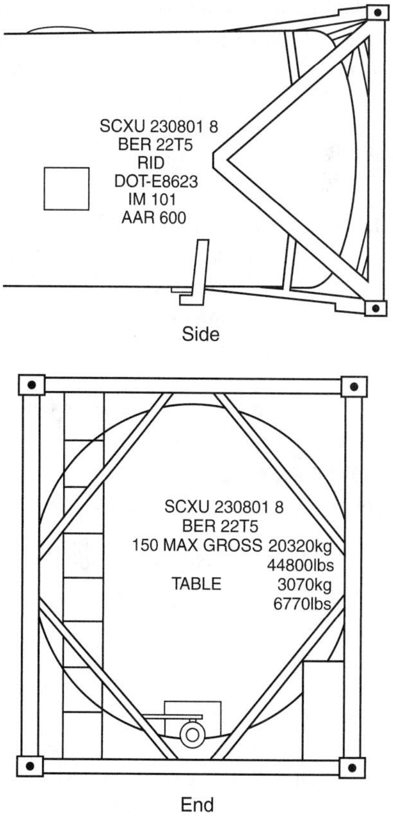

FIGURE 21.8.18 Typical Markings on Tank Containers

Tank Initials and Number. Tank containers must be registered with the International Container Bureau in France. They must be marked with initials, or reporting marks, and with a tank number. The initials indicate the tank's ownership, and the tank number identifies the specific tank.

The initials and tank number are generally on the right side of the tank, as one faces it from either side, and on both ends. They may be displayed either on the tank itself or on the frame.

With this information, shippers, carriers, and emergency response personnel can identify the tank's contents, using shipping papers or computer data. They can then determine if the contents are hazardous.

Specification Marking. The design, construction, and use of tank containers must conform to strict standards and regulations of many agencies, both in the United States and abroad. Markings on the tank container indicate the standards to which the tank was built.

In the United States, tank containers must meet the design, construction, and safety standards set forth by the DOT. Tanks meeting these standards have the specification markings or an exemption number displayed on both sides (generally the tank's initials and number). Examples of specification markings are IM 101 (IMO Type 1), IM 102 (IMO Type 2), and Spec. 51 (IMO Type 5 or IMO Type 7).

DOT Special Permit (Previously Called Exemption) Marking. When DOT grants special permits (previously exemptions) from the regulations governing packages and containers, and the preparation and offering of hazardous materials for shipment, the outside of each package must be plainly and durably marked in 2 in. (50.8 mm) letters and numbers—that is, DOT-SP (previously DOT-E) followed by the number assigned, such as DOT-SP 8623 (previously DOT-E8623).

AAR-600 Marking. For interchange purposes in rail transportation, tank containers should conform to the requirements of Section 600, "Specification for Acceptability of Tank Containers" of the AAR *Manual of Standards and Recommended Practices, Section C—Part III, Specification for Tank Cars.* Tanks meeting these requirements display the AAR 600 markings in 2 in. (50.8 mm) letters on both sides, near the tank's initials and number. The AAR-600 marking identifies tanks that can be used for regulated materials, whereas the AAR-600NR marking identifies tanks that cannot be used for regulated materials.

Country and Size Type Markings. In addition to the initials and number and the specification marking, the tank also displays a country code and a size/type code. When displayed, the two- or three-letter country code indicates the tank's country of registry.

The four-character size/type code follows the country code. Its first two characters (digits) jointly indicate the container's length and height. The second pair of characters (T + a digit) is the type code, which indicates the tank's pressure range.

Dataplate. For further technical, approval, and operational data, dataplates are permanently attached to the tank containers' tanks or frames.

Tank and Valve Test Dates. Tanks and pressure-relief devices, if installed, must have a retest interval not greater than 5 years. Retest and test due dates must be marked or stenciled on the tank or on the dataplate.

General Classes of Tank Containers

Tank containers are classed according to the specification of the tank and fittings. The classification of a tank container determines which products it may carry.

Nonpressure Tank Containers. Also called intermodal portable tanks or IM portable tanks, nonpressure tank containers comprise over 90 percent of the total (Figure 21.8.19). They usually transport liquid and solid materials at maximum allowable working pressures (MAWP) of up to 100 psi (690 kPa). Tanks are tested to at least 1.5 times the MAWP. In the United States, the following two groups of nonpressure tank containers are common:

1. *IM 101 portable tanks.* These tanks are built to withstand MAWP of from 25.4 to 100 psi (175 to 690 kPa). They may transport both nonhazardous and hazardous materials, including toxics, corrosives, and flammables, with flashpoints below 32°F (0°C). Internationally, an IM 101 portable tank is called an IMO type 1 tank container.

2. *IM 102 portable tanks.* These tanks are designed to handle lower MAWP—that is, from 14.5 to 25.4 psi (100 to 175 kPa). They transport materials such as liquor, alcohols, some corrosives, pesticides, insecticides, resins, industrial solvents, and flammables with flashpoints between 32 and 140°F (0 and 60°C). More often they transport various nonregulated materials, such as food-grade commodities. Internationally, an IM 102 tank is called an IMO type 2 tank container.

Pressure Tank Containers. Also known as DOT Spec. 51 portable tanks, these containers are less common in transport. Designed to handle internal pressures ranging from 100 to 500

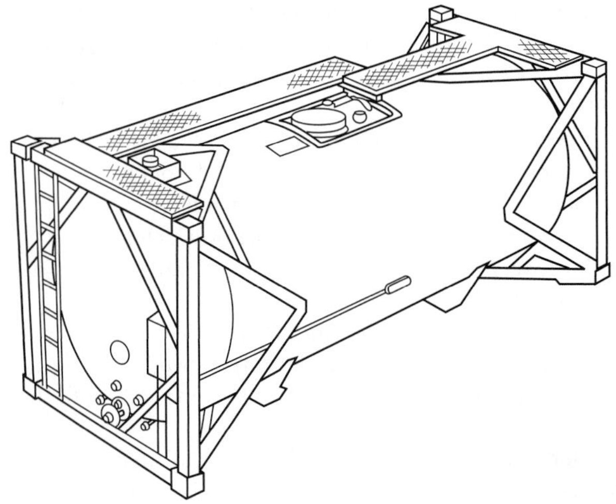

FIGURE 21.8.19 Nonpressure Tank Container

psi (690 to 3450 kPa), they generally transport gases liquefied under pressure, such as LP-gas and anhydrous ammonia. They may also carry liquids, such as motor fuel antiknock compounds or aluminum alkyls. Internationally, they are called IMO type 5 tank containers (Figure 21.8.20).

Specialized Tank Containers. There are several other variations of tank-type containers. Among them are the following:

1. *Cryogenic tank containers.* These containers carry refrigerated liquid gases, such as argon, oxygen, and helium, and are built to DOT Spec. 51 standards. Internationally, they are called IMO type 7 tank containers.
2. *Tube modules.* These containers transport gases in high-pressure 3T cylinders tested to 3000 or 5000 psi (20,700 or 34,500 kPa), permanently mounted within a full or half-height ISO frame (Figure 21.8.21).

Tank Container Fittings

Nonpressure Tank Container Fittings. Various fittings make nonpressure tank containers functional and safe.

Spillbox. On nonpressure tanks, a spillbox encloses the top fittings. It protects the tank's shell from any spillage. Any spilled material, as well as rainwater in the spillbox, drains through an open pipe.

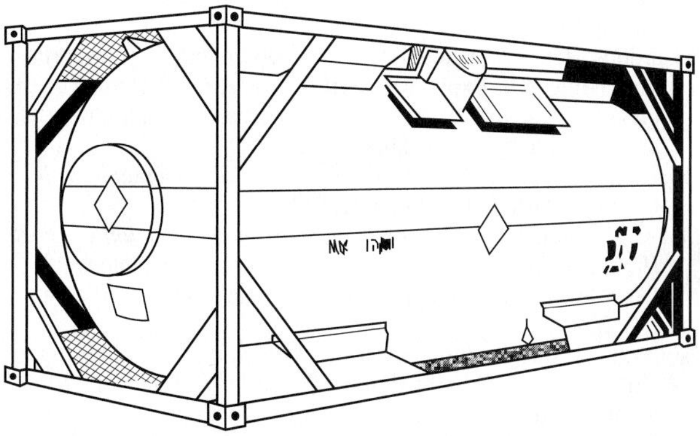

FIGURE 21.8.20 Typical Pressure Tank Container

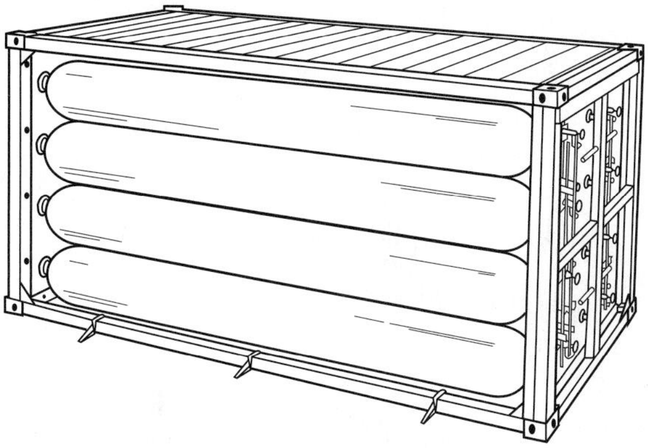

FIGURE 21.8.21 Tube Module

Manhole, Cover, and Dipstick. The manhole, located on the top center of the tank, is secured by six or eight wing nuts on a hinged and bolted lid fitted with a replaceable gasket.

The dipstick may be inside the manhole. Used in conjunction with a calibration chart, known as a strapping chart, it measures the amount of commodity in the tank. For liquids other than compressed gases, a minimum outage of 2 percent of total tank capacity must be provided in rail transportation.

Top-Loading Valves. Top-loading valves attached to a removable eduction pipe—dip leg, dip tube, or siphon tube—run into the tank.

Bottom-Outlet Valves. When tank containers are used for hazardous materials, two externally operated, bottom-outlet valves are required. Connected in series with a replaceable gasket between them, they are located at one end of the tank, the so-called discharge end. A liquidtight closure on the external valve is also required. It may be a blind flange, which is required on international shipments; a screw cap; or a cam-lock cap attached to the external valve. A positive lock is required on the external bottom valve to keep it closed.

In an emergency, the internal valve, or foot valve, can be shut off from a remote location. As one faces the discharge end of the tank, the emergency shutoff is on the right side near the far end.

Air-Line Connection. An air-line connection, located on the tank's top, can be used for pressure unloading, vapor return, and blanketing contents with an inert gas. On occasion, blind flanges may replace the top-loading valve and air-line connection. In this situation, the shipper or supplier of the tank must provide appropriate fittings for loading and unloading.

Pressure/Vacuum Relief Devices. Generally found in pairs on nonpressure tank containers, a combination pressure/vacuum relief device serves dual purposes of protecting the tank from both overpressure and from a vacuum of more than 0.75 psi (5 kPa) negative pressure. In many cases, this relief valve has a rupture, or bursting, disk between the pressure-relief valve spring and the commodity. It protects the spring from the commodity.

Thermometer. Some tanks have a built-in thermometer to measure the temperature of the lading.

Pressure Tank Container Fittings. Like nonpressure tank containers, pressure tank containers are equipped with various fittings to make them functional and safe. A wide variety of fitting arrangements exists for pressure tank containers. Pressure intermodal tanks may have fittings on top, at the end, or on the bottom. Generally, fittings are recessed or enclosed with a cover to protect them from mechanical damage.

Loading/Unloading Valves. Liquid and vapor valves are used to fill and empty the tank. The liquid valve reaches into the lading by means of an eduction pipe, which may be fitted with an excess-flow check valve. Vapor valves, which also may have an excess-flow check valve, are used to remove vapor from the tank or to pressurize the tank for unloading.

Pressure-Relief Devices. Pressure-relief valves, mounted on top, protect the tank from overpressure under abnormal conditions. In many cases, a rupture disk between the pressure-relief valve spring and the commodity protects the spring from the contents.

Gauging Devices. Gauging devices may be installed to measure how much liquid is in the tank.

Other Fittings. A sample line for sampling the lading and a thermometer well for measuring lading temperature may also be installed.

SUMMARY

Fire hazards in rail transportation systems exist in principally three areas: physical plants, ranging from office buildings to diesel fuel storage and dispensing facilities; trains, involving locomotives, rolling stock, passengers, or cargo; and adjacent, privately owned properties that can be damaged by a train or right-of-way fire. Fire protection for diesel, electrical, and other locomotives and for freight and other types of cars, together with fittings and equipment, includes proper design, preventive maintenance, protective equipment, and safe operations. Identification and proper documentation of the hazardous material are essential. Many rail carriers provide guidelines and training for responding to rail emergencies involving hazardous materials. Fire protection for fueling facilities and other railroad buildings and structures includes noncombustible construction, proper maintenance, fire suppression systems, and adequate water and hydrant systems. Measures that reduce the risk of right-of-way fires include improved railroad equipment, controlled burning, chemical control of vegetation, and installation of fire breaks.

BIBLIOGRAPHY

References Cited

1. Association of American Railroads, http://www.aar.org.
2. American Public Transportation Association, http://www.apta.com.
3. Ahrens, M., *U.S. Vehicle Fire Trends and Patterns,* National Fire Protection Association Fire Analysis and Research Division, Aug. 2001.
4. Bureau of Explosives, "Annual Report of Hazardous Materials Transported by Rail—2005," Report BOE-05-1, Association of American Railroads, Washington, DC, Oct. 2006.

NFPA Codes, Standards, and Recommended Practices

Reference to the following NFPA codes, standards, and recommended practices will provide further information on rail transportation systems discussed in this chapter. (See the latest version of The NFPA Catalog *for availability of current editions of the following document.)*

NFPA 130, *Standard for Fixed Guideway Transit and Passenger Rail Systems*

References

Bureau of Explosives, "Annual Report of Hazardous Materials Transported by Rail—2005," Association of American Railroads, Washington, DC, Oct. 2006.

"Collision and Derailment of Maryland Rail Commuter MARC Train 286 and National Railroad Passenger Corporation Amtrak Train 29, Near Silver Spring, Maryland on February 16, 1996," NTSB Number RAR-97102, NTIS Number B97-916302, National Transportation Safety Board, Washington, DC, 1997.

GATX Tank and Freight Car Manual, 6th ed., General American Transportation Company, Chicago, IL, 1994.

General Guide to Tank Cars, Union Pacific Railroad, Omaha, NE, 2006.

General Guide to Tank Container Operation, Sea Containers Group, London, UK, 1983.

General Guide to Tank Containers, Union Pacific Railroad, Omaha, NE, 2006.

"Hazardous Material Regulations of the Department of Transportation," Bureau of Explosive Tariff No. BOE-6000, Bureau of Explosives, Association of American Railroads, Washington, DC, revised annually and updated quarterly.

Inspection, Repair, and Test Requirements for Tank Containers, Sea Container Group, London, UK, 1983.

Manual of Standards and Recommended Practices, Section C—Part III, Specification for Tank Cars, Operation and Maintenance Department, Association of American Railroads, Washington, DC, 2003.

Maty, A. D., "Guide to the Identification of Tank Cars and Fittings Utilized for the Transportation of Hazardous Materials," 1985, unpublished.

Tank Car Book, Union Tank Car Company, Chicago, IL, 2005.

Chapter 9

Aviation

Revised by
Brian Boucher

Chapter Contents

Key Terms

aircraft, aircraft cabin, aircraft fire fighting, aircraft fuel, aircraft loading walkway, aircraft power plant, aircraft rescue, airport terminal building, air transport, aviation fuel, dangerous goods, hangar, hazardous materials, restricted articles

Aviation fire hazards develop from the energy of motion, the conversion of fuel to propulsive power, and the machinery necessary for the creation of a life-supporting environment above the surface of the earth. Complex system safety analysis and procedures are conducted to prevent problems from developing and to limit consequences of failures and mishaps that do occur. Most nations have extensive design, builder, and operator criteria for aircrews and maintenance personnel. A cohesive and comprehensive approach to safety during the operational phase of flight servicing must include training of baggage and cargo handlers, cabin clean-up crews, and customer contact personnel about their role in the safety management system and in response to a major accident or occurrence.

Airborne and ground navigational aids, weather monitoring, air traffic control, runways and overruns, taxiway design, the proper maintenance of such equipment including maintenance of clear approach, departure, and taxi paths are beyond the scope of this chapter.

For related topics, see Section 13, Chapter 7, "Aircraft Rescue and Fire Fighting (ARFF)"; and Section 17, Chapter 6, "Halon and Halon Replacement Agents and Systems."

AIRPORT SAFETY WORLDWIDE

Commercial aircraft internal fire safety features do not vary greatly worldwide since the choice of metals, composites, fuels, and interior furnishings are led by technical considerations and by major manufacturers throughout the world. Because builders must have their products accepted in worldwide markets, the degree of fire safety is uniformly high.

There are diverse approaches to fire safety goals in aviation ground facilities worldwide. In passenger terminals there may be only spot use of fire sprinklers and large areas of low risk may be unsprinklered. Although terminal buildings are rarely over five stories in height (except for towers), restaurant fires and fires in baggage-handling areas have contributed to serious smoke problems in passenger common areas.

For aircraft hangars, the design and construction materials may differ depending on the owner's and user's view of what is at risk: the aircraft or the building. Air-supported unconventional structures have received some attention. Military considerations, however, have brought about reinforced concrete shelters that provide internal aircraft fueling, maintenance, loading facilities, and electronic system testing. Because of the hazards associated with these activities, the hangars are equipped with ultrafast fire detection and suppression systems.

Aircraft loading walkways have been used that feature glass sidewalls. Although aircraft fires, both internal and external to the aircraft, at the loading walkways are rare, such incidents do occur.

Aircraft rescue and fire-fighting strategy and tactics, equipment, and personnel do not vary much from one major airport to another. The International Civil Aviation Organization (ICAO), NATO, and various pilots' unions tend to drive a high degree of competence. As in the United

---

Captain Brian Boucher is a fire protection engineer and has also been an airline pilot for the past 30 years. He spent 25 years as a municipal structural fire fighter holding the rank of chief of training for 8 years. He has been a member of the NFPA's ARFF Technical Committee for over 20 years and has served as chair for the past 10 years.

States, however, third-tier airports in other countries may depend on local or regional funding mechanisms and this usually translates into less than ideal personnel, equipment, and training. The most common and effective aircraft rescue and firefighting agent in the United States is an aqueous film-forming foam based on military specifications. In much of Europe, however, other formulas are favored.

AIRCRAFT FIRE SAFETY

Fire safety in aircraft starts on the drawing board, and aeronautical engineers bear the brunt of responsibility for fire prevention and control. Aircraft require large quantities of fuel, lubricating oils, hydraulic fluids, and Class A combustibles, which are in proximity to potential ignition sources such as power plants, auxiliary power units, electrical systems, and heaters. Many aircraft carry oxygen systems (liquefied and gaseous), and some use oxidizers for auxiliary power units or are equipped with small rocket units for additional takeoff thrust. Consequently, aircraft fire safety requires skillful blending of reasonable safeguards that are lightweight and do not interfere unduly with the use and mission of the particular aircraft.

Most nations that have a major aircraft production industry also have extensive regulations governing the use and arrangement of the foregoing items, and it is extremely important that the designer be thoroughly versed in the letter and intent of these regulations.

Installed fire detection and extinguishing equipment are normally required for those aircraft areas that possess inherent fire hazards and ignition potentials. Other fire prevention techniques used are the following:

- Compartmentation of fire hazard areas from critical structural components and flight control systems
- Judicious use of other materials that are fire or heat resistive or of very low flammability
- Separations of systems containing flammable fluids from potential ignition sources. For example, all aircraft have fire protection systems in washrooms because of the high risk of passengers smoking and placing their cigareete butts in the garbage. Also, aircraft that fly with only two engines follow the guidelines of Extended Twin Operations (ETOPS). Such aircraft must have fire protection systems that will suppress a fire for a minimum of 60 minutes (up to 207 minutes).

Because fires inflight pose tragic life hazard potentials, inflight fire prevention and control must receive high priority. Fires following impact accidents can result in the loss of many lives. Fires during maintenance can have consequences that range from the obviously disastrous to high monetary loss from small and simple fires. Even a very short fire exposure can result in delamination of honeycomb structures.

In commercial, light general aviation, and military reciprocating engine aircraft, the lightweight structure needed to allow the aircraft to perform its mission also permits impact energy to be transmitted to the aircraft occupants. Thus, more deaths occur due to impact trauma than due to fire.

In large turbine aircraft that operate in a more demanding flight envelope, heavier gauge metals, advanced composite materials, and computer-assisted design techniques strengthen airframe structures. These aircraft structures absorb a greater amount of impact energy, thereby transmitting less of it to the occupants. Subsequently, in accidents involving this type of aircraft, the postaccident fire is a more significant cause of serious injuries or death to the occupants.

As a result of aircraft accident investigations, there has been ongoing research on methods of minimizing aircraft fatalities. Improved seat belt design, heat-resistant evacuation slides, elimination of injury-causing projections, floor mounted emergency lighting systems, fire blocking seat materials and wall furnishings, stronger seats that withstand up to 16 g's, and overhead storage bins are some developments that improve occupants' chances of survival when an aircraft accident occurs.[1]

Many methods are being studied to reduce the hazard of postimpact fires. They include, but are not limited to, the following:

1. Segregating flammable-fluid containers and systems from ignition sources
2. Improving fueling systems and fuel containment methods
3. Reducing the rate of evaporation and the speed of flame spread over the surface of the spilled fuel
4. Improving the materials used for interior decor, insulation, sound attenuation, and cushioning to reduce ease of ignition, flame spread, and smoke and toxic gas generation
5. Compartmentation with lightweight fire walls in the occupied portions of the cabin, blind spaces, lavatories, and trash containers
6. Onboard cabin fire suppression systems using a variety of extinguishing agents
7. Early warning fire/smoke detection systems in occupied portions of the fuselage
8. Inerting fuel tank vapor space to reduce the possibility of explosion from static electrical discharge and lightning strikes. This can be effective in flight but does little to contain the postimpact fire, because the inert atmosphere would be lost almost immediately on impact, with the disruption of the tank structure

See Berg,[2] Diehl,[3] and Murray[4] for related information.

Aircraft Power Plants

Civil aircraft in the United States are subject to extensive federal regulation through the U.S. Department of Transportation (DOT), Federal Aviation Administration (FAA). The Code of Federal Regulations (CFR) Title 14, "Aeronautics and Space," contains the Federal Air Regulations. Other nations have similar requirements. The following list summarizes the regulations that apply to aircraft power plants:

1. All reciprocating engines, auxiliary power units, fuel-burning heaters, or other combustion devices intended for operation in flight must be separated from other areas of the aircraft by fire walls, shrouds, or equivalent means so that no hazardous quantities of air, fluid, or flame can pass from these compartments to other portions of the aircraft. These regulations also

apply to the combustion, turbine, and tailpipe sections of turbine engines. The fire walls and shrouds must be made of a material that withstands heat at least as well as steel. When applied to power plants, the material must perform under the most severe conditions of fire and duration likely to occur in such zones. All openings in fire walls and shrouds must be sealed with close-fitting fire-resistive grommets, bushings, or fittings. In engine nacelles, a fire seal or bulkhead is used to isolate the engine power section and exhaust system. In addition, a main fire wall segregates the complete engine assembly (power section, exhaust system, and accessory section) from the remainder of the nacelle section and, as applicable, the wheel well. In gas turbines, the fire seal or bulkhead separates the combustion, turbine, and tailpipe section from the compressor and accessory section. An additional main fire wall isolates the engine assembly from the support pylon or remainder of the aircraft, as applicable.

2. The cowling and nacelle skin are designed to prevent fire from circumventing the fire seals and main fire walls.

3. Tanks containing a flammable fluid cannot be located in a fire zone except when it can be proved that construction, connecting lines, controls, and shutoff means provide protection equivalent to segregation. A specified air gap is required between flammable fluid tanks and a fire wall, and materials that can absorb flammable fluids are prohibited from the area of the tank or any other system containing flammable fluids.

4. Emergency fuel shutoffs are required for each engine, auxiliary power unit, or combustion heater. The emergency shutoffs must be fire resistive or located so that a fire in any fire zone does not affect their operation. Operation of the emergency shutoff must not affect other emergency functions or the operation of any other engine.

5. Flammable liquid lines in fire zones must be fire resistive and, where required, flexible. This also applies to drain and vent lines for flammable fluids or vapor.

6. Reciprocating and turbine engine air inlets must be arranged to prevent backfire flames from entering the fire zone and designed so discharge from vents and drains cannot enter the air induction system.

7. Exhaust systems must discharge in a safe manner, not expose any portion of a flammable fluid system, and be provided with heat shields wherever they may impinge on other potions of the aircraft.

8. Drains must be provided for all fire zones, with the discharge arranged so that drained fluids will not be reingested into any portion of the aircraft.

Aviation Fuels

The fire hazard properties of aviation fuels are identified according to ease of ignition, flashpoints, flammability limits, distillation range (initial and end boiling point), and electrostatic susceptibility. (Note: Octane rating has no relation to the degree of fire hazard of a fuel.) Table 21.9.1 summarizes characteristics of more common aviation fuels. NFPA 407, *Standard for Aircraft Fuel Servicing,* requires that the same fire safety precautions apply to all types.

The following factors must be considered when evaluating fuel in an operating aircraft and when fuel stored in a tank at a bulk plant is being evaluated:

- Because an aircraft travels at different altitudes and through varying ambient temperatures, conditions of flammability in the tank vapor space can change rapidly. Thus, a fuel type such as

TABLE 21.9.1 Summary Data on the Fire Hazard Properties of Aviation Fuels

Characteristics	*Gasoline AVGAS*	*Kerosene Grades JET A, JET A-1, JP-5, JP-6, and JP-8*	*Blends of Gasoline and Kerosene JET B and JP-4*
Freeze point[a]	–76°F	–40°F to –58°F	–60°F
Vapor pressure[b] (Reid-ASTM D323-58)	5.5 to 7.0 psi	0.1 psi	2.0 to 3.0 psi
Flashpoint[a] (by closed-cup method at sea level)	–50°F	+95°F to +145°F	–10°F to +30°F
Flashpoint[a] (by air saturation method)	–75°F to –85°F	None	–60°F
Flammability limits			
Lower limit	1.4%	0.74%	1.16%
Upper limit	7.6%	5.32%	7.63%
Temp. range for flam. mixtures[a]	–50°F to +30°F	+95°F to +165°F	–10°F to +100°F
Autoignition temperature[a]	+825°F to +960°F	+440°F to +475°F	+470°F to +480°F
Boiling points[a]			
Initial	110°F	325°F	135°F
End	325°F	450°F	485°F
Pool rate of flame spread[c,d]	700–800 fpm	100 fpm (or less)	700–800 fpm

Note: Figures vary for some of these values.
[a] $5/9(°F - 32) = °C$.
[b] 1 psi = 6.9 kPa.
[c] 1 fpm = 0.3 m/min.
[d] In mist foam, rate of flame spread in all fuels is very rapid.

Jet A—which is normally too lean in a tank vapor space at sea level with a fuel temperature of 70°F (21°C)—can move into the flammable range as the aircraft gains altitude. Other factors contribute to this change, such as aircraft skin heating from air friction, outgassing of dissolved oxygen, and sloshing of the fuel from air turbulence. Figure 21.9.1 illustrates changes in flammability limits of aircraft fuels in tank vapor space due to altitude and temperature changes.

- After an impact when major structural damage occurs to aircraft fuel tanks, the fuel may be released as a mist due to forward momentum, splashing, and wind shearing. Regardless of the type of fuel involved, this mist can ignite easily from disrupted electrical circuits, hot engine surfaces, or ignition sources on the ground. The resulting fireball then acts as the ignition source for other combustibles in the area, including pools of high flashpoint Jet A fuel. In some aircraft crashes where deceleration forces are low, liquid fuel flowing from ruptured fuel tanks or broken fuel lines can be vaporized and ignited by hot engine surfaces, hot brakes, heavy electrical arcs, and so forth.
- Reciprocating engines present a fire hazard for a short period after shutdown. However, turbine engine tailpipe fires are fairly common and in crash situations turbine engines may be an ignition source for many minutes after a nominal "shutdown."

Relative Safety of Jet Fuels. The kerosene-type turbine fuels offer a safety advantage over other types of aviation fuels especially during fueling operations and aircraft fuel system maintenance. Fires are less likely in impact-survivable accidents when the aircraft involved has class Jet A fuel in the tanks. However, once ignition occurs, all fuels exhibit similar behavior, and control measures must be instituted quickly to prevent injury and fatalities.

In some portions of the world, Jet A (kerosene grade) fuel is not readily available, and Jet B (JP-4) is used. Some nations also have reduced the minimum flashpoint of Jet A to increase yield of aviation fuel per barrel; the minimum flashpoint has been in the 80°F (27°C) range. The actual flashpoint has been above 100°F (38°C).

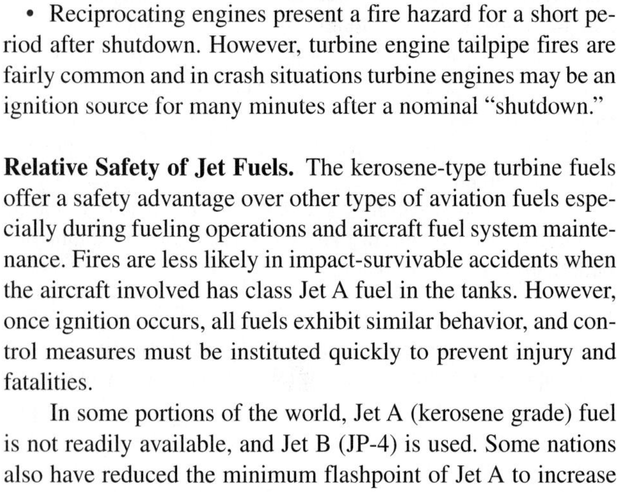

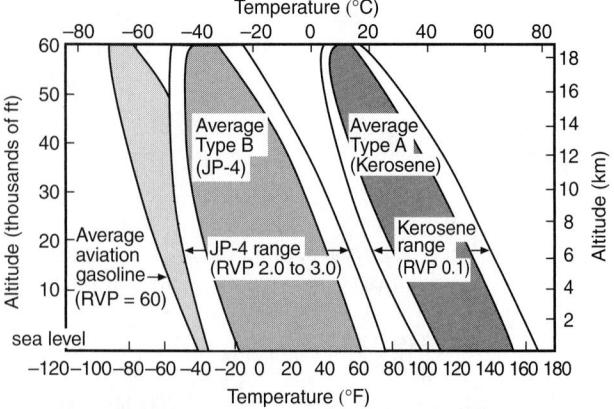

FIGURE 21.9.1 Flammable Ranges of Aviation Gasoline and Jet A (Kerosene) and Jet B (JP-4) Turbine Fuels, Showing Variations with Altitude

Electrostatic Susceptibility and Autoignition. The degree to which a static charge may be acquired by aviation fuels depends on many factors: the amount and type of residual impurities, dissolved water, the linear velocity through piping systems, and the types of filters and water separators used. Jet A and Jet B fuels are better static generators than AVGAS. Although all fuels generate static charges, the electrical conductivity of the fuel directly relates to the speed of charge relaxation (dissipation).

Antistatic additives increase static charge. However, rather than preventing the formation of static charges, they actually increase fuel conductivity, thus considerably shortening relaxation time. The charge generation increases as fuel passes through filter/water separators and other equipment. An unbonded object in the vicinity of the charge generation point before the charge has an opportunity to relax can act as a collector and cause high-energy static discharge.

Although possibly misnamed, antistatic additives have greatly increased the safety of aircraft fueling operations although there are some circumstances that are exceptions (e.g., the unbonded collector in close proximity to the static generation point). Autoignition in fuel cells/tanks can result if the internal fuel pumps run hot and/or dry.

Aircraft Fuel Systems. Most aircraft make extensive use of the internal wing volume to store fuel. In larger aircraft and newer general aviation aircraft, the wing structure is sealed and forms the fuel tank. This is commonly called integral tank, or wet wing, construction. Older and light aircraft may incorporate a flexible bladder to contain the fuel within the wing structure, using the wing structure only for support. Separate metal tanks or fiber-reinforced nonmetallic tanks are not widely used but can be found on aircraft that need extended fuel range when ferrying long distances.

With integral tank construction, and only to a slightly lesser extent with thin-wall bladder tanks, disruption of the wing structure by ground impact or other damage typically results in the release of fuel and potential for ignition. This can occur even though occupied portions of the aircraft may be only slightly damaged. If so, fire becomes a threat to the occupants. Figure 21.9.2 illustrates typical fuel-occupied spaces in a large turbo jet powered aircraft. The reserve tanks and Nos. 1, 2, 3, and 4 are integral tanks in this particular airplane, and the wing center section tank is of the bladder type.

One approach proposed is crash-resistant fuel tank construction with dry break fittings and automatic fuel shutoffs. Although the technology to develop this tank has been highly advanced, it has not been widely adopted due to weight limitations and reduction in volume available for fuel storage in long-range, military, and commercial aircraft. However, certain helicopters operated by the U.S. Army are equipped with such crashworthy fuel systems.

Open-celled plastic foam blocks, cut to fit and placed in the tank, are used on some military aircraft. Although primarily intended for explosion protection after projectile penetration (incendiary bullets, etc.) of the vapor space, they also improve the postcrash fire situation. Tests showed some resulting improvement, but the problems of removal and replacement for tank

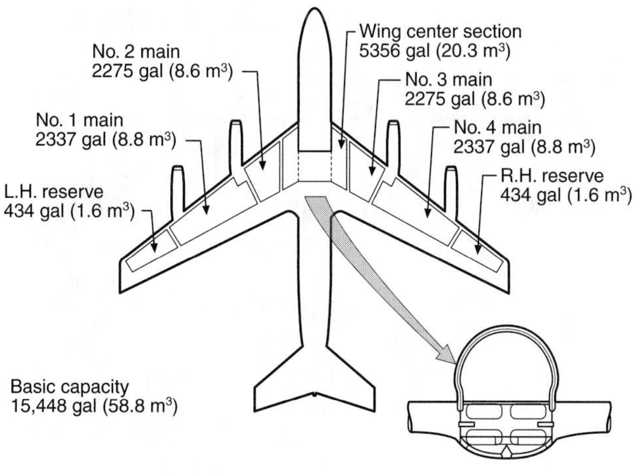

FIGURE 21.9.2 Arrangement of Fuel Tanks in a Typical Turbine-Powered Air Carrier Aircraft

interior maintenance and loss of available fuel volume preclude their use in large, long-range civil and military aircraft.

Aircraft equipped with these foam blocks can have internal fuel tank fires. Foam increases the static charging tendency and/or acts as the unbonded collector. However, the presence of the remaining foam in the tank vapor space prevents further propagation of the fire/explosion.

Many aircraft use the wing center section (where it passes through the fuselage) for additional fuel storage. In some aircraft, such as the Boeing 727 and DC-9, this is an integral tank with a bladder liner. Newer aircraft designs use a double-wall tank of metal with a honeycomb core. Although such tanks are well protected by the center wing section box structure (the heaviest on the aircraft), they directly expose the fuselage interior. To extend normal operating range, some aircraft use fuselage fuel tankage of the double-wall type outside of the wing center section box, and thus are deprived of heavy structural protection. As a reasonable compromise, all fuel tanks (at least those within the fuselage) should be crash-resistant with dry break fittings and automatic shutoff valves.

Certain models of existing aircraft contain fuel tanks well forward or aft in the fuselage. Fuel storage in the horizontal stabilizer and vertical fin is being used on certain aircraft to extend range.

Other Design Considerations

The Federal Air Regulations mention several design principles that affect basic aircraft fire safety and crashworthiness (excluding cabin furnishings and evacuation systems):

1. When the same structure supports fuel tanks and landing gear, shear pins must be incorporated in the landing gear support structure, allowing the gear to be wiped off without applying structural loads to the fuel tanks.
2. The metal aircraft structure must have electrical continuity to prevent accumulation of static electrical charges, particularly in the fuel tank areas. This is extremely important when designing an all-metal aircraft, since the aircraft structure acts as a Faraday Cage, shielding all contents from lightning strikes.
3. Static discharge devices and lightning divertors must be located and installed correctly.
4. Fuel lines supplying rear fuselage-mounted engines must be designed to ensure proper fire resistance and have the flexibility to resist rupture in a crash situation.
5. Fuel lines and main electrical leads must be segregated.
6. Main electrical power cables in the fuselage must be shrouded in fire-resistive flexible conduit.
7. The hydraulic system must be designed properly and use fire-resistive fluids. Such fluids presently in use have autoignition temperatures in excess of 1000°F (538°C) and are only slightly flammable. (Older types of mineral oil-based hydraulic fluids are still widely used, particularly in the military.)

Aircraft Cabin Fires

Cabin fires in flight are infrequent and usually discovered in their incipient stage and rapidly extinguished. The potential life loss, however, is severe if fire progresses beyond the point of control by use of handheld fire extinguishers. The fire reaction of aircraft cabin interior materials, once ignited, is crucial from a life safety viewpoint and can result in severe structural damage or loss of the aircraft, as was the case of Swiss Air 111 over the North Atlantic.

Prior to the mid-1940s, few, if any, regulations concerned the flammability of cabin furnishings. Old aircraft at air shows and in museums show wicker chairs, gauze fabric curtains, and other combustibles. Following World War II, a qualification test was required that involved igniting small horizontally mounted samples by a short exposure to a Bunsen burner flame. If a sample did not continue to burn after removal of the igniting flame, or burned less than a specified distance in the specified time, it was classified as self-extinguishing or slow burning. Although this test procedure was developed for laboratory comparisons, it created a widespread impression in the aviation industry that cabin furnishings were fire resistive. They were not.

In the 1950s and 1960s, research began to improve the fire resistance criteria. Various public and private organizations conducted tests that proved the inadequacies of the existing fire resistance criteria and, further, disclosed the problem of heavy smoke and toxic gas.

In the late 1960s and early 1970s, the fire resistance criteria were upgraded to require a material sample to be self-extinguishing when tested in the vertical position, with exceptions such as floor carpeting. Although flame spread of compliant materials was reduced, there is room for further improvement, and the problem of toxic smoke may need to be addressed directly.

In the late 1970s and early 1980s, researchers developed a method of "fire blocking" aircraft seat cushions. Inserted between the cushion, which is usually made of polyurethane foam and decorative upholstery, this fire-blocking layer is intended to delay or prevent seat cushion involvement in a cabin fire. The FAA now requires all commercial aircraft seat cushions to be fire blocked.

In addition to fire blocking, research is continuing toward the development of an improved, fire-resistant aircraft cabin window material to delay or prevent postimpact fire entry into the fuselage via the windows. These transparencies/windows are complicated design challenges because they must resist heat, cold, vibration, and substantial internal air pressure variations as the aircraft moves from ground level to heights of 40,000 ft (12,500 m) or more.

Many aircraft carry supplemental oxygen for the potential failure of cabin pressurization and in portable cylinders for first-aid purposes. In a crash, localized fire intensification can be expected if the oxygen cylinder fuse plug operates due to fire exposure and releases oxygen in the cabin atmosphere. In addition to potential oxygen release from high-pressure cylinders, some aircraft carry chemical oxygen generators. Improper packaging and transport of such devices in a cargo bay resulted in a disastrous inflight fire over the Florida Everglades.

Possible causes of aircraft cabin fires include the following:

1. Ignition of the cabin interior from a postimpact fuel fire or a fire resulting from a fueling operation malfunction. In such a fire, although the interior materials have a certain fire resistance, heat from the exposing fire overwhelms the materials' resistance.
2. Electrical failure and electrical arcing within concealed spaces, often behind the cabin decorative liner. Such fire can remain undetected for a considerable time period and grow beyond control of handheld fire extinguishers before it is discovered. Flight deck fires (or as often described "smoke in the cockpit") are a threat for several reasons: obscuration of pilot's vision, loss of instrumentation, and incapacitation of the flight deck crew. Radar, radios, life support systems, and motors to operate flight controls require tremendous electrical power. The wiring to serve them is subject to embrittlement, abrasion, vibration, and cracking. Events in the 1990s have resulted in more attention to electrical wiring.
3. Improper use of flammable liquids during cabin cleaning and refurbishing
4. Improper use or disposal of smoking materials (which should decrease due to prevalence of "no smoking" flights). Aircraft lavatories aboard all carriers are now required to be equipped with smoke detectors specifically designed for those areas. In addition to its functional purpose, the requirement deters persons who might wish to smoke in a lavatory. Tampering with or rendering aircraft lavatory smoke detectors inoperational is a serious offense. Figure 21.9.3 shows a UPS DC-8 cargo aircraft that landed successfully in Philadelphia after the pilots reported smoke in the cockpit.

NFPA 424, *Guide for Airport/Community Emergency Planning;* NFPA 415, *Standard on Airport Terminal Buildings, Fueling Ramp Drainage, and Loading Walkways;* and NFPA 402, *Guide for Aircraft Rescue and Fire Fighting Operations,* provide guidance concerning such fires. For more information on aircraft cabin fires and materials for use in aircraft cabins, see Babrauskas[5] and McCaffrey.[6]

FIGURE 21.9.3 Safe Landing of a DC-8 After Report of Cockpit Smoke

Air Transport of Dangerous Goods

Hazardous cargoes (hazardous materials, nuclear materials, and restricted articles) can present a problem to aircraft in flight, on the ground, during ground handling, and in a postcrash situation. This is an international problem, since many shipments cross national boundaries. Many agencies regulate hazardous cargoes, including the U.S. Department of Transportation, the International Air Transport Association, the International Civil Aviation Organization (an agency of the United Nations), and others.

The regulations cover the type of cargo that may be shipped, quantities allowed, packaging method, and aircraft type (passenger or cargo only) in which this material may be carried. Flight crews must be informed of the presence of hazardous cargoes on the manifest and, in some cases, the captain can refuse to carry the material.

If the rules are followed rigidly, there is little hazard to safety of flight or to ground personnel, whether in normal handling or a postcrash situation. Problems arise when the shipper, either in ignorance or in willful contempt of the regulations, misrepresents the contents of the shipment to a carrier or does not package the material adequately to ensure containment during transit.

After several serious crashes in the 1980s and early 1990s, the regulations were revised and further restrictions adopted. Better training is now required for each carrier's receiving agents, standard labels have been adopted, and penalties are assessed against shippers who violate the law. Detailed information regarding the air transport of dangerous goods and a listing of the United Nations warning label system can be found in Appendix B of NFPA 402.

Aircraft Fire Detection and Extinguishing Systems

Fire detection and extinguishing systems are required in certain zones of the aircraft, notably the power plant areas. These systems are defined in design regulations of the nation of aircraft origin.

The systems are similar to those used in ground installations, but there are significant differences. In most aircraft installations, the flight crew manually activates the extinguishing system. The detection system must be very sensitive, very stable (i.e., free of false alarms), and able to withstand extremes of the environment in which it must function—temperature, vibration, high airflows, and structural flexing. The system must also reset automatically to notify the flight crew when the fire has been extinguished, or when the temperature in the protected zone drops below the set point. System response must be within seconds of the beginning of abnormal conditions.

Extinguishing agent hardware must be lightweight, rugged, and, to overcome the high flows of flight, capable of higher rates of agent discharge than would be expected in a similar ground installation.

The most common extinguishing agents used in aircraft are bromotrifluoromethane (Halon 1301) and bromochlorodifluoromethane (Halon 1211). Due to the ozone depletion characteristics of the halogenated hydrocarbons, these chemicals are being phased out in accordance with international treaties. The development of suitable replacement agents is under way. See Section 17, Chapter 6, "Halon and Halon Replacement Agents and Systems." Older aircraft still use carbon dioxide, methyl bromide, and chlorobromomethane. All are somewhat effective on flammable liquid and electrical fires.

Cargo Compartment Fire Detection and Extinguishing Systems. Cargo compartments in passenger aircraft often are equipped with fire detection systems. Air starvation is one of the more common techniques used in fire extinguishment in cargo spaces. Upon actuation of fire detection systems, all ventilation to the compartment is sealed off and the fire is allowed to self-extinguish due to lack of oxygen. Fire extinguishing systems traditionally using Halon 1301 or Halon 1211 will need to switch to treaty-compliant halon alternatives.

Recent regulations have been adopted to improve the fire resistance and fire penetration-resisting capabilities of cargo compartment liners. An upper limit has been placed on the volume of a cargo compartment; above this limit, a fire suppression system must be installed regardless of compartment construction. For more information, see Bennett[7] and Grosshandler.[8]

Figure 21.9.4 shows an electric fire that occurred inflight over Canada. The fire was caused by an electrical arcing of a heater ribbon tape. The aircraft landed safely and ARFF crews quickly extinguished the fire.

FIGURE 21.9.4 Results of an In-Flight Electrical Fire

Aircraft Hand Fire Extinguishers

The FAA requires portable hand fire extinguishers in all air transport category aircraft. In some smaller general aviation aircraft, they are recommended but not required.

NFPA 408, *Standard for Aircraft Hand Portable Fire Extinguishers,* requires portable hand fire extinguishers on all aircraft and describes the type, quantity, minimum capacity, installation, location, and spacing of the extinguishers.

Although the FAA recognizes carbon dioxide, water, dry chemical, Halon 1211, Halon 1301, and halon combinations, at least two extinguishers installed on large transport aircraft must be of the Halon 1211 or combination Halon 1211/1301 type. Due to environmental problems associated with halogenated agents, their use is prohibited except in specific circumstances.

NFPA 408 no longer recognizes carbon dioxide and dry chemical as suitable for use on aircraft. Carbon dioxide is not recognized as suitable for the following reasons:

1. Ineffectiveness on Class A materials
2. Chilling effect of solid carbon dioxide (snow) may damage delicate electronic components
3. Weight of container and agent versus similar agent capacities of the halon type
4. Required dwell time and concentration for Class A fires is not compatible with human life

Dry chemical has long been banned from aircraft in NFPA 408 for the following reasons:

1. Obscuration of the operator's vision, particularly in confined spaces
2. Possibility of an insulating chemical layer forming on delicate electrical contacts, which could affect continued safety in flight
3. Dry chemical can irritate the eyes and mucous membranes even though it is not considered toxic
4. If not immediately cleaned up, certain types of dry chemical can be highly corrosive to aircraft metals

Means of Egress from Aircraft

In aircraft, emergency exit facilities are particularly important because postcrash fire exposure can be severe and safe evacuation time for the occupants is limited.

U.S. Federal Air Regulations set the number of exits required in transport category aircraft, depending on passenger capacity. The manufacturer or operator must demonstrate that evacuating a full load of passengers can be accomplished in 90 seconds or less, with half the available exits inoperative. These simulations require that the test subjects represent an average passenger load, with certain percentages of able-bodied males and females, elderly, children, and disabled. Tests are accomplished without normal cabin lighting; emergency lighting, however, is functional. The exits to be blocked are not preannounced to crew or occupants.

The simulations have some shortcomings:

1. Smoke, which could obscure emergency lights or exit signs, is not used.
2. The test subjects know this is an emergency exit certification test and will seek any usable exit. (In real life, most passengers may pay little attention to preflight announcements and, consequently, tend to attempt leaving the aircraft by the same door through which they entered.)
3. Again, many test subjects have taken part in previous demonstrations and although there is a required minimum time period since last participation, retain a certain knowledge of "what to do in the test."
4. Actual crash experience has shown considerable obstruction of egress because of failure of overhead storage bins, presence of carry-on luggage, and beverage/food service carts.

Escape Systems and Devices. It is acceptable and permissible to use the normal entrance and passenger service doors as part of the emergency exit system. If the door is power assisted in its normal mode of operation and operates relatively slowly, it is equipped with a high-speed power assist for the emergency mode.

Modern passenger aircraft are equipped with inflatable evacuation slides at all emergency exits that have a normal door sill height that exceeds 5 ft (1.5 m). The distance from door sill to ground level, however, can drastically change in the event of a collapse of the main gear or nose gear. (A deployed slide under these conditions would not provide an effective angle for safe descent.) FAA regulations require the slide to deploy and inflate automatically when an exit door opens in emergency mode. In many instances evacuation slides can also serve as life rafts. Figure 21.9.5 shows evacuation slides used in an emergency passenger evacuation in Lajes, Azores, after an AirBus 330 aircraft ran out of fuel and landed successfully without engines. The 300 passengers sustained only minor injuries.

FIGURE 21.9.5 AirBus 330 That Landed Without Engine Power

The openings designated as emergency exits must be operable from the outside and designed to resist jamming due to fuselage distortion. The slides must deploy properly regardless of wind direction or other influences.

The fire resistance of the slide material used to be very low, and even slight exposure to flame caused deflation of the slide. However, slide material has now been developed that incorporates a reflective coating, reducing the possibility of damage and deflation caused by radiant heat. At present, not all aircraft have been upgraded with this new material.

Emergency escape slides that are enabled during flight operations are deactivated when the aircraft reaches the terminal/parking spot. Consequently these systems are not available for food servicing, cleaning, and toilet service personnel.

Obscuration of exit signs and emergency exit lighting by smoke can seriously impede evacuation of the aircraft. All air transport aircraft are required to have exit signs installed at a lower level and the exit access must be visible from a minimum distance of 35 ft (11 m), assuming a smoke level above the seat back height. In addition, illuminated exit path lights installed in aisle seat armrests or in the floor must be provided.

Aircraft Construction Materials

Aircraft from small personal and business reciprocating engine powered to the largest and fastest of commercial and military jet aircraft use an amazing smorgasbord of metals, organic fibers, gases, and fluids. Metals such as aluminum, magnesium, and titanium can and do burn if heated sufficiently. Composites are used for structural components and for body, wing, and control surfaces. The organic binder and fiber matrix of these metal replacements can fracture under crash conditions and release physiologically dangerous materials to nearby occupants and rescue personnel. Protective clothing and personal breathing equipment should be worn at all times until it can be determined that there is no further risk to rescue personnel.

Pressure hazards range from tires inflated to 250 psi or more to pressure vessels both metal and fiber reinforced plastic wrapped that accumulate pressures of 3000 psi or more. These aspects of aircraft rescue and fire fighting are discussed in NFPA 402.

Aircraft Rescue and Fire Fighting

Aviation fire protection is an enterprise of wide challenge for economic, social, and technical reasons. In aircraft, a firewall can be a thin sheet of metal, an egress path can be an aluminized fabric slide, and survival from fire may be measured in seconds. Generally, survival from fire in exposed intact large aircraft can be as little as 3 minutes. Aluminum skin can burn through in 60 seconds, and windows and insulation may burn through in a few additional seconds. Fortunately, major airfield fires are rare, but it is clear that ready and competent rescue and fire-fighting teams are essential (see NFPA 403, *Standard for Aircraft Rescue and Fire-Fighting Services at Airports,* and NFPA 405, *Standard for the Recurring Proficiency of Airport Fire Fighters*).

Three distinct types of ground incidents can occur within the flight environment of the aircraft (excluding fires from fueling incidents, malfunction of ground servicing equipment, or fires originating during maintenance procedures).

The first type of ground incident is the high-speed and/or high-angle impact with the ground or other object that results in such structural breakup of the aircraft that survival of the occupants is highly unlikely (i.e., all or nearly all fatalities occur due to impact trauma).

The second incident type involves relatively low-speed and/or shallow ground impact angles. In this type of incident, occupant survival rate can be very high, especially if there is no postcrash fire or if the fire is controlled quickly in the area immediately surrounding the occupied portion of the aircraft.

The third incident type occurs when an aircraft in a landing/takeoff/taxiing mode impacts with another aircraft or other object such as a maintenance vehicle or construction equipment.

Fire can be anticipated in almost all abnormal aircraft landings as well as incidental occurrences such as overheated brakes or undetected fuel leaks. It is essential that airports maintain a well-equipped and trained rescue and fire-fighting capability during all hours that flight operations are in progress. At smaller airports, the response team is often made up of persons having other airport duties such as security, fueling operations, maintenance, or baggage handling. However staffed, personnel need to participate in frequent and meaningful training sessions, be equipped with proper protective gear, and be provided with the means to respond immediately to the scene of any emergency on or adjacent to the airport.

The term *rescue* used in the context of aircraft rescue and fire fighting means the control of life-threatening fire in the critical area during the time necessary for all physically able aircraft occupants to self-evacuate. The continuance of fire control is necessary in order to permit the extrication of those who are severely injured or pinned in the wreckage. Assisted rescue of individuals from small aircraft is often routine; however, in aircraft having a large number of occupants, such assistance is usually not possible in the time available. NFPA 403 mandates that responding units have specialized equipment and manpower for interior fire fighting operating within 5 minutes of notice of an accident.

Survivable accidents tend to occur within a certain area related to the runway centerline and threshold lights. This *critical rescue and fire-fighting access area* (CRFFAA) is clearly defined and illustrated in NFPA 402 (Figure 21.9.6).

To be considered effective, the demonstrated response time of the first responding fire-fighting vehicle to reach any point on the operational runway must be 2 minutes or less, and to any point remaining in the CRFFAA, 2.5 minutes or less. These conditions must be met when flight operations are in progress; however, NFPA 402 recognizes that mitigating circumstances can make it impossible to meet these times.

More accidents tend to occur during inclement weather and this can result in longer response times. In recent years the use of global positioning satellites and forward looking infrared optical devices help locate aircraft more speedily when visibility is poor.

Preplanning for declared emergency landings on airports is extremely important. Prepositioning of personnel and vehicles greatly reduces response time and increases the chance of survival of the aircraft occupants should the landing become a major emergency. Figure 21.9.7 illustrates one system of preplanning for this type of emergency.

Specialized vehicles have been developed that have the ability to transport rescue and fire-fighting personnel, equipment, and extinguishing agents to the scene of aircraft accidents within the required response time despite terrain surface or condition. Detailed information regarding such vehicles is contained in NFPA 414, *Standard for Aircraft Rescue and Fire-Fighting Vehicles.* The number and size of response vehicles and the amounts of extinguishing agents required at a given airport depends on the types of aircraft used and the frequency of air carrier operations.

Part 139 of Title 14 of the Code of Federal Regulations (CFR) contains these minimum levels. In addition, the FAA Advisory Circular 150/5210-6B[9] gives recommended levels of

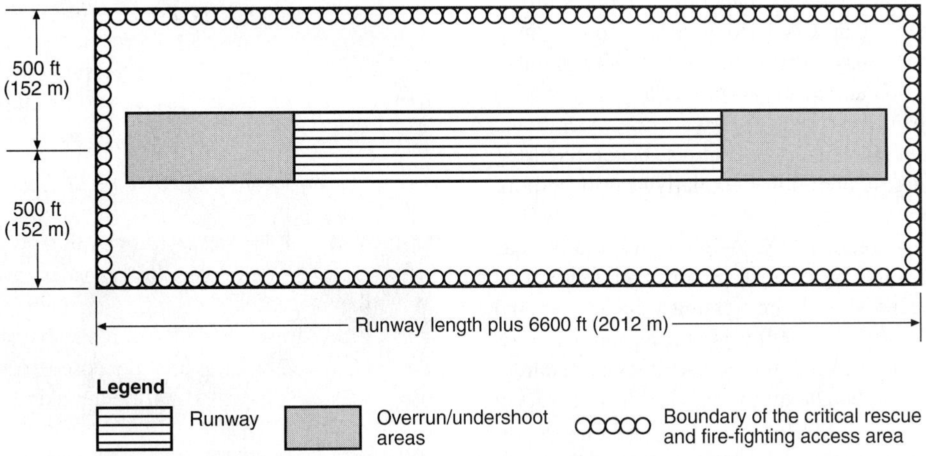

FIGURE 21.9.6 Critical Rescue and Fire-Fighting Access Area (CRFFAA)

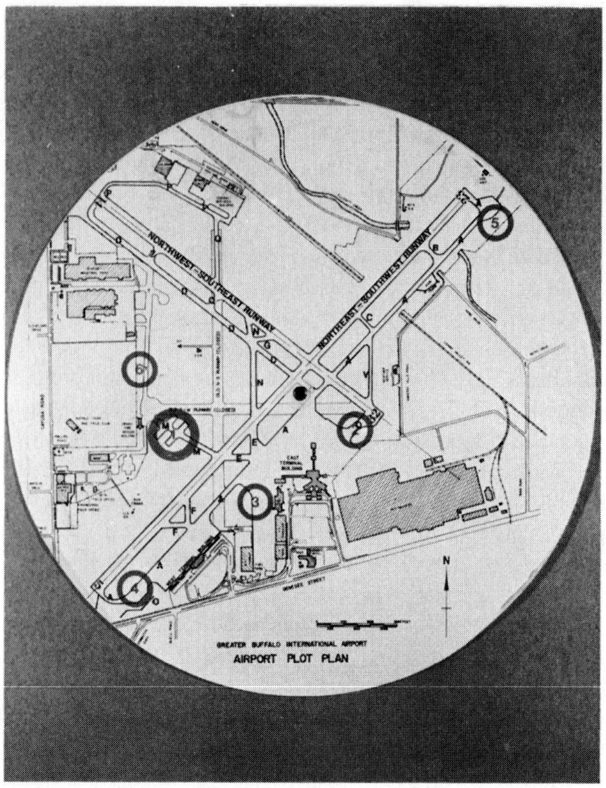

FIGURE 21.9.7 Typical Airport Plot Plan Indicating Preplanned Standby Positions for Rescue and Fire-Fighting (RFF) Vehicle

airport protection that are considerably higher than the minimum levels in Part 139.

Other information on the subject of aircraft rescue and fire-fighting protection is published in NFPA 403 and the International Civil Aviation Organization (ICAO) Annex 14 (Aerodromes) to the Convention on Civil Aviation.

There are interesting similarities of requirements among NFPA, ICAO, and the FAA Advisory Circular 150/5210-6B, as compared to the minimums of CFR Part 139. One major difference among the three is that ICAO and the FAA allow a remission factor so an airport may drop to a lower index if the number of movements (takeoffs and landings) of the largest aircraft to use the airport is below a certain daily or yearly operational level. NFPA does not recognize the remission factor, requiring protection for the largest aircraft that regularly uses the airport, regardless of operational levels.

The term "index" (e.g., 1–5, 6, 7–10), as used in the aircraft rescue and fire-fighting context, provides an approximation of the number and size of fire-fighting vehicles required for problems with the larger aircraft using the airport regularly. However, this system (FAA, ICAO, NFPA) does not address the manpower needed to handle the myriad aspects of a rescue/crash response. See NFPA 424 for insight and detail concerning manpower and organizational demands. For a more detailed discussion of aircraft rescue and fire fighting see Section 13, Chapter 7, "Aircraft Rescue and Fire Fighting (ARFF)."

Rescue and Fire-Fighting Personnel, Training, and Safety

After requirements for an airport's rescue and fire-fighting protection have been determined, the next major consideration is the selection of qualified personnel. Airport fire fighters should, at a minimum, meet standards set forth in NFPA 1003, *Standard for Airport Fire Fighter Professional Qualifications.* Candidates should be in top physical condition, and the department should maintain a required physical conditioning program to ensure the best possible performance of its personnel. Physical and mental stresses encountered when dealing with a major aircraft accident can be very demanding, and efficient performance is crucial.

In addition to physical conditioning, frequently scheduled and meaningful training sessions covering all phases of aircraft rescue and fire fighting are extremely important. Such sessions are necessary to maintain a high degree of competence and readiness (see NFPA 405).

Training of attendants proved important in the AirBus 340-300 crash pictured in Figure 21.9.8. Attendants were credited with the successful evacuation of all passengers. The aircraft was consumed by fire.

In addition to the physiological and psychological preparation of responders as individuals, the exercise serves to test communication, command, and control when noise level is high, visibility is poor, and dimensions of the problem may not be fully known.

"Live fire" training using hydrocarbon fuels and other flammable liquids has been suspended at many airports due to local environmental constraints. The FAA, the U.S. military, and private industry are all in the process of developing alternative "live fire" training exercises to duplicate realistic fuel fire atmospheres and at the same time, meet all necessary environmental requirements.

Special aircraft informational charts developed by airframe manufacturers are available to airport fire fighters as well as mutual aid fire departments adjacent to an airport. These charts

FIGURE 21.9.8 Overrun of Toronto, Canada, Runway by AirBus 340-300 in August 2005

indicate locations and operation of emergency exits, areas that normally contain flammable and hazardous materials, oxygen storage, and other pertinent information. Combined with preincident planning inspections of aircraft that normally use the airport, periodic review of the charts keeps fire fighters current on pertinent information on various types and models of aircraft. Most airline operators encourage familiarization with their aircraft and schedule tours when flight schedules permit. A variety of aircraft information charts are contained in NFPA 402.

The potential for extreme danger exists anywhere in the vicinity of operating aircraft, especially with regard to rotating propellers and rotors and jet engines. Severe injuries can occur when persons do not remain alert and do not maintain the necessary safe distance. Figure 21.9.9 depicts typical jet engine intake and exhaust danger areas.

Overheated brakes may cause wheel disintegration, control surfaces may deploy unexpectedly, and extremely-high-pressure tanks may rupture under fire conditions. The results of a brake fire and explosion in France can be seen in Figure 21.9.10. The protective fire fighter hoods restrict vision and hearing. NFPA 402 discusses these concerns.

Ground Environment Safety Factors

Serious crashes can occur off the ends of runways due to insufficient clearance from various objects. The problem may be compounded where zoning regulations permit construction in these areas. Dikes, structures supporting navigational aids, and blast fences can be struck by aircraft operating in conditions of poor visibility.

Atmospheric conditions also contribute to serious aircraft incidents. Fog, rain, sleet, and snow all adversely affect runway surfaces, aircraft performance, and visibility from the flight deck. Abnormal wind conditions, particularly the phenomenon called windshear, also can be factors. Normally, unusual atmospheric conditions are handled routinely. When they are involved in combination with other factors, incidents can occur more easily.

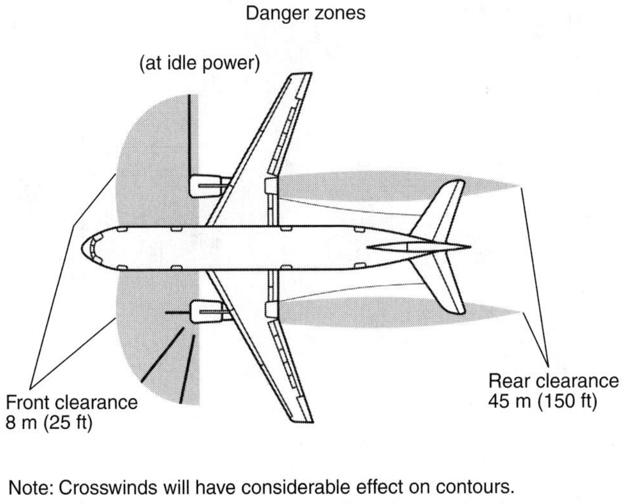

FIGURE 21.9.9 Engine Run Dangerous Areas

FIGURE 21.9.10 Brake Fire That Occurred During Certification Testing of an AirBus 340-600

During airport construction and repair, especially on movement areas, presence of construction and resurfacing equipment can be a factor in accidents. Another principal area where incidents can occur is in the overrun portions of runways when aircraft are unable to brake effectively, running off the runway, striking airport boundary fences, or bogging down while traversing unimproved ground surfaces. Unimproved ground surfaces between runways can result in aircraft being inaccessible to fire and rescue equipment, especially equipment not specifically designed for off-highway use.

Heliports present special problems because they are frequently located in congested areas of cities, on roofs of buildings, near hospitals, and on piers adjacent to water. NFPA 418, *Standard for Heliports,* covers landing deck construction, drainage, egress, and fire protection requirements.

Preplanning for Aircraft Incident Emergencies

All commercial airports serving passenger aircraft are required to develop and maintain an emergency plan that can be immediately activated should an aircraft incident occur on or near the airport. The plan needs to be flexible and encompass all aspects of the most difficult anticipated emergencies. All local emergency services, civic organizations, and resources need to be included in the plan. To be effective, a full-scale exercise of the plan should be conducted regularly to test and update its effectiveness.

Both tabletop and full-scale exercises are necessary because of personnel turnover in prime and supporting agencies. Physical changes in and about the airport need to be considered before, during, and after the construction period. Refer to NFPA 424 for further guidance.

Airports located adjacent to large bodies of water must give special consideration to the possibility that an aircraft incident could occur in the water. In these instances, special watercraft equipment dependent on the specific need should be provided. In addition, mutual aid agreements should be established with all local water rescue resources such as the Coast Guard, Navy, and fireboats.

AIRPORT FACILITIES

Hangars

An aircraft hangar is simply a building built to provide weather protection and shop space during aircraft maintenance and storage. Hangars pose unusual fire protection problems due to their occupancy's special nature. Since removing all fuel from an aircraft before moving it into a hangar is often impractical and economically unsound, potential exists for having large quantities of flammable liquids, mainly aviation fuel, inside the hangar. Quite often, aircraft contained in the hangar, particularly large aircraft, are several times more valuable than the hangar, necessitating some measure of protection for the aircraft as well as the hangar structure.

Aircraft hangars are divided into Types I, II, or III, which roughly correspond to the size and type of aircraft they house and their anticipated fuel loading. NFPA 409, *Standard on Aircraft Hangars,* defines these types and outlines requirements for construction, protection, drainage, fire cutoffs, and other provisions for each type of hangar. Innovative air/steel frame supported tents have been used at a few airfields. Consensus for exact fire protection measures have not been achieved, but it is clear that due to the value of housed aircraft and life hazards, an installed fire protection system will be warranted. Such steel-framed membrane-covered structures are recognized in several building codes.

Fixed hangar fire protection systems of the past provided protection for the hangar structure and consisted mainly of water-type sprinkler systems using the extra-hazard pipe schedule, or hydraulically calculated systems, primarily of the deluge type. In aircraft hangars, these water systems are no longer recognized as viable protection by NFPA 409. With increased size and fuel loading of the aircraft, foam-water deluge sprinkler systems are now common practice. Current designs incorporate foam-producing and oscillating monitor nozzles at (nominal) floor level in conjunction with previously mentioned systems, to provide fire control/extinguishment for the shadow area beneath the wings of large aircraft.

Adequate protection of the hangar structure can be achieved as well as providing increased protection for the aircraft, primarily due to more rapid fire control and/or extinguishment.

In older hangars being modernized, a different technique has more recently been used with the approval of the authority having jurisdiction (AHJ). This technique uses overhead closed-head type sprinkler systems hydraulically designed to deliver a specified minimum water density over a specified area. It is capable of delivering aqueous film-forming foam (AFFF) solution through standard (nonaspirating) sprinklers by using wide-range proportioning devices. Scheffey provides more insight on AFFF in an airport environment.[10]

Primary fire-extinguishing capability affording some degree of aircraft protection is provided by oscillating monitors that completely blanket the floor of the entire hangar with foam within 20 to 30 seconds of actuation.

Whether the foam delivery system is used only for shadow area protection or total floor coverage, foam monitor location, oscillation speed, foam pattern, and nozzle barrel centerline height above the floor are critical. Monitors should be located so that all areas to be covered can be easily reached. Depending on the arc of coverage, no more than 15 seconds should be necessary for a complete cycle. The foam pattern should be dispersed rather than a straight stream. This minimizes turbulence at the point of stream impact with objects or the floor. Figure 21.9.11 shows a typical monitor installation.

Due to hangar sizes or multiple aircraft positions, monitor nozzles can be mounted at the bottom of the roof truss space to provide coverage for these void spaces. Arrangements should be made to exercise and test the oscillating mechanism from the hangar floor or other easily accessible locations (Figure 21.9.12).

The principal means of fire detection for actuation of overhead sprinkler systems in hangars has been rate-of-rise type devices; however, as hangar roof heights have increased to as much as 150 ft (46 m) from the floor to the roof deck, the ability of this type of device to perform within the time required to minimize aircraft damage is limited. In climates with moderate to severe winter conditions, it is difficult to maintain stability of such systems, due to the opening and closing of hangar doors and the installation of high-recovery-rate heating systems, and still maintain the sensitivity necessary for rapid fire detection. Optical-type detectors of ultraviolet/infrared type or dual function can be used for high-speed detection of relatively small fires and actuation of monitor nozzles. Rapid temperature changes do not affect those devices.

FIGURE 21.9.11 Foam Monitor Nozzle (Source: United Airlines)

FIGURE 21.9.12 Monitor Nozzle Mounted Beneath the Roofwork to Fill Void Areas Unreachable from Monitors Located Near the Walls. Centerline of the barrel is approximately 65 ft (20 m) above the floor. Control valves are located at the floor line along the hangar wall. The small-diameter lines illustrated are for testing and exercising the water-powered oscillating mechanism. (Source: United Airlines)

Care must be taken in selecting the type of detector and control devices for optical detection. They must have demonstrated operational integrity, yet not be overly sensitive and subject to false or unwanted operation. Considerable progress has been made recently in developing optical detection systems that ignore or are insensitive to routine aircraft maintenance procedures involving welding, high-intensity lights, boroscopes, radioisotopes, X-ray inspections, and so on. Whenever an optical system is installed, its sensitivity to fire should be tested. Further, a recording device should be attached to provide a hard-copy record of what detectors "see" during routine aircraft maintenance operations. During the initial period after installation (usually 60 to 90 days), the detection systems should be in the "alarm only" mode and a careful record made of the recording device printout. Aircraft maintenance records can often determine what operation affected the optical detectors.

Floor drainage is another portion of the hangar fire protection system. The drainage system removes excess fire protection water and also removes large quantities of liquid fuel from the fire scene. These systems should be flushed thoroughly with high volumes of water at least annually. Oil/water separators should be meticulously maintained to prevent pollution of lakes and streams and to reduce hazards in the airport drainage system to which the hangar system may be connected.

In recent years environmental concerns have necessitated more restrictions on the disposal of AFFF solution subsequent to discharge. Therefore, new system designs should consider the provision of bypasses and retentional areas for initial and periodic system testing.

Airport Terminal Buildings

Airport terminal buildings include any fully enclosed extensions that function as passenger concourses (sometimes called fingers or piers) and satellite buildings that serve passenger-handling functions. The satellite building may be connected to the main terminal building via tunnels beneath the aircraft operating ramp or via people-mover transit systems operating on a fixed guideway, above or below ground level. Terminals also contain airline-related businesses, such as offices, restaurants, and gift shops. Quaglia and Grubits have discussed the fire safety design of airport terminals.[11]

Special attention is given to airport terminal buildings in NFPA 415. These buildings have a severe fire exposure potential from immediately adjacent aircraft fueling and servicing operations and the high-occupancy (people) load in terminals.

Walls and glass areas of terminal buildings and other airport structures that may be exposed to jet blast or explosion require design for wind loads in excess of that which building codes normally require.

Although NFPA 415 primarily addresses the terminal building interface with the aircraft ramp, a variety of other NFPA codes apply to areas such as restaurants, baggage handling systems, and important electronic and computer installations.

Aircraft Loading Bridges or Walkways

This equipment is frequently installed at the terminal area for passenger convenience and to protect passengers from the weather while they move from the terminal loading gate area to the aircraft. Loading equipment also increases safety by reducing ramp congestion and segregating passengers from the aircraft servicing equipment and personnel.

In the event of fire caused by a fueling malfunction or other reason, a loading bridge or walkway can serve as a means of egress from the aircraft to a safe refuge, for example, the terminal building. Most people naturally tend to exit an area (aircraft or building) the same way they entered. Because the emergency situation requiring evacuation may occur before the preflight safety and evacuation briefing, the loading bridge may be the only means of egress familiar to passengers. For this reason, NFPA 415 requires 5 minutes of safe passage from the aircraft to the terminal. Construction features, special fire protection, or a combination of both may accomplish this. Safe egress must be provided during severe fire exposure to the bridge.

Doors, if any, at the terminal end of the bridge should be equipped with panic hardware and swing in the direction of travel from the aircraft to the terminal. The loading bridge should not be considered part of the terminal egress system, unless a vestibule and stairs conforming to NFPA *101*®, *Life Safety Code*®, are provided at the terminal end, even though auxiliary stairs may be located near the aircraft end. Auxiliary stairs are strictly for the use of aircraft servicing personnel or flight crew.

Training of loading bridge operators in positioning the equipment and obtaining the best possible "seal" with the aircraft in all weather conditions is very important. Unless the bridge and closure curtain are properly positioned and utilized, the integrity of the loading bridge as a means of egress from the aircraft is seriously compromised. The operator must be aware that the closure curtain is a safety item, not merely weather protection.

Since escape slides aboard the aircraft are normally deactivated during the loading, unloading, and maintenance cleanup phases of activity, the loading bridge/walkway is a critical element in the fire safety system. It is essential that this egress path not be blocked by wheelchairs, trash carts, and so on.

Aircraft Fueling Ramp Drainage

The large amounts of combustible/flammable liquids (in the form of fuel) handled on aircraft servicing ramps demand that special attention be paid to the drainage system provided to prevent exposing the terminal or aircraft unnecessarily in the event of unintentional release. NFPA 415 specifies the amount of slope and direction regarding ramp geometry, location of drainage system inlets, water seal traps, and oil/water separators.

AIRCRAFT MAINTENANCE AND SERVICING

Aircraft Maintenance

To keep an aircraft airworthy, every part must be inspected, repaired, or overhauled periodically. The frequency of these procedures varies. Operations may be performed all at once in a single maintenance visit, or as part of a progressive overhaul system where a certain portion of a total overhaul is conducted periodically. In addition, periodic inspections are required between major overhauls to repair minor discrepancies, inspect critical structures, and test various components. Nonroutine maintenance can occur at any time to replace or repair a defective or prematurely failed part.

Many maintenance procedures involve the use of highly flammable solvents, sometimes unstable or toxic chemicals, and personnel entry into integral fuel tanks. When situations such as these occur, special procedures must be developed to ensure the safety of the operation. It is sometimes possible to pressurize equipment housings with shop air, using appropriate power/pressure interlock to prevent penetration of flammable vapors. Localized ventilation and curtailment of operations utilizing flammable or combustible liquids are also helpful. In any event, each potentially hazardous procedure should be developed or reviewed by a person who is thoroughly familiar with the basics of fire safety and aircraft maintenance requirements and procedures. NFPA 410, *Standard on Aircraft Maintenance,* should be used to develop local procedures for the more common hazardous aircraft maintenance operations, such as welding, spray painting, fuel tank ventilation, and so forth.

NFPA 70, *National Electrical Code®*, defines certain areas in hangars and around aircraft as Class I, Group D, Division I or II locations. In this age of sophisticated testing using electronics, eddy currents, X-rays, and so on, it is often impossible to design or obtain equipment listed or approved for these locations. Injuries and fires can occur due to the complexity of aircraft and associated electrical test equipment. Induced current, capacitor-type discharges, errant electromagnetic radiation, and simple poor electrical continuity are some of the electrical fire and safety hazards that can occur during aircraft maintenance. Welding (usually inert gas-shielded arc) is frequently performed on installed engines or aircraft structures.

Testing fuel tanks for system leaks is commonly performed in hangars using high flashpoint Jet A fuel or a special, usually combustible, test fluid. Toward this end, many hangars have a fixed system to load and unload fuel or test fluid. It has also been a practice to park a standard fuel servicing tank truck outside the hangar and run long hoses to the aircraft connection points. This practice is to be discouraged, because the hose is the weak point in any system. Although hoses are necessary for flexible connections, they should be kept as short as possible.

Painting the interior and exterior of aircraft is also accomplished in hangars. Although a few hangars have been constructed specifically for aircraft exterior painting, it is more common to control ignition sources and rely on the sheer volume of the hangar and natural ventilation to dissipate flammable vapors. Latex paints, which contain little, if any, solvent, are being used for aircraft interiors. Interior panel partitions and equipment can be painted in place rather than removed to a standard paint spray booth. Whenever using flammable paints inside an aircraft is necessary, special precautions for ventilation and control of ignition sources must be followed.

Aircraft Fueling

The potential exists for spills and fires each time an aircraft is fueled. Preventing such incidents is aided by reference to NFPA 407, a document accepted worldwide. The standard outlines specific precautions to control the extent of this hazard and gives recommendations on the design of aircraft fueling hose, aircraft fuel servicing tank vehicles, airport fixed fueling systems utilizing fuel hydrants, hydrant vehicles (to connect the fuel hydrant to the aircraft), as well as safety procedures to follow in the event of an accidental spill. A common type of spill is at the aircraft tank vent point, when an aircraft internal shutoff valve fails or closes slowly, allowing an overfill condition to develop.

Aircraft postincident defueling safety is important due to the possibility of injury to technicians, loss of salvage value, and potential environmental impact. Fuel system damage due to impact, inversion, or fire may result in a variety of aircraft balance, wiring, switch, plumbing, pump, tank, or other component irregularities that must be addressed by competent technicians. Only then can restoration of the incident sites be accomplished.

SUMMARY

Civil aircraft in the United States are subject to extensive federal regulation. Aeronautical engineers blend fire prevention and control safeguards with the use and mission of a particular aircraft. Fire detection and extinguishing equipment is normally required for aircraft areas possessing inherent fire hazards and ignition potentials, notably the power plant areas. The extinguishing agents most commonly used in aircraft are Halon 1301 and Halon 1211, although these chemicals are currently being phased out and replacement agents developed. Another key design element is emergency exit facilities, since postcrash fire exposure can be severe and safe evacuation time for the occupants is limited. Aircraft rescue and fire-fighting preplanning for emergency landings is extremely important. Airport facilities, including hangars, terminal buildings, loading bridges, and walkways, all require appropriate safeguards. In addition, special procedures must be developed to ensure the safety of inspection and maintenance operations and aircraft fueling.

BIBLIOGRAPHY

References Cited

1. Civil Aviation Authority, "Improving Passenger Survivability in Aircraft Fires: A Review," CAP 586, Civil Aviation Authority, London, UK, Apr. 1991.
2. Berg, H. D., "Future Needs in the Development of Materials for Aircraft Interiors and Equipment," Deutsche Aerospace Airbus GmbH, West Germany, DOT/FAA/CT-93/3, International Conference for the Promotion of Advanced Fire Resistant Aircraft Interior Materials, February 9–11, 1993, Atlantic City, NJ, 1993, pp. 333–337.
3. Diehl, R. G., "Applications of Continuous Fiber Reinforced Thermoplastics in Aircraft Interiors," Fokker Aircraft B.V., Amsterdam, Netherlands, DOT/FAA/CT-93/3, International Conference for the Promotion of Advanced Fire Resistant Aircraft Interior Materials, February 9–11, 1993, Atlantic City, NJ, 1993, pp. 93–104.
4. Murray, T. M., "Airplane Accidents and Fires," *Proceedings* of Improved Fire- and Smoke-Resistant Materials for Commercial Aircraft Interiors, November 8–10, 1994, Washington, DC, National Academy Press, Washington, DC, 1994, pp. 7–23.
5. Babrauskas, V., "Role of Aircraft Panel Materials in Cabin Fires and Their Properties," DOT/FAA/CT-84/30, Department of Transportation, Washington, DC, June 1985.
6. McCaffrey, B. J., et al., "Model Study of the Aircraft Cabin Environment Resulting from In-Flight Fires. Final Report," Maryland Univ., College Park, National Institute of Standards and Technology, Gaithersburg, MD, DOT/FAA/CT-90/22, Federal Aviation Administration, Atlantic City International Airport, NJ, Nov. 1992.
7. Bennett, M., "Halon Replacement for Aviation Systems," *Proceedings* of the 1992 International CFC and Halon Alternatives Conference, Stratospheric Ozone Protection for the 90's, September 29–October 1, 1992, Washington, DC, 1992, pp. 667–670.
8. Grosshandler, W. L., et al., "Assessing Halon Alternatives for Aircraft Engine Nacelle Fire Suppression," *Journal of Heat Transfer,* Vol. 117, May 1995, pp. 489–494.
9. *Aircraft Fire and Rescue Facilities and Extinguishing Agents,* FAA Advisory Circular 150/5210-6B, Federal Aviation Administration, U.S. Department of Transportation, Washington, DC, Jan. 25, 1973.
10. Scheffey, J. L., et al., "Comparative Analysis of Film Forming Fluoroprotein Foam (FFFP) and Aqueous Film Forming Foam (AFFF) for Aircraft Rescue and Fire Fighting Services," Hughes Associates, Inc., Wheaton, MD, Report 2108-A01-90, Naval Research Lab, Washington, DC, Naval Sea Systems Command, Washington, DC, June 1990.
11. Quaglia, C., and Grubits, S. J., "Fire-Safety Engineering Design of Airport Terminals," *Proceedings* of the 1st International Conference on Fire Science and Engineering, ASIAFLAM '95, March 15–16, 1995, Kowloon, Hong Kong, 1995, pp. 561–567.

NFPA Codes, Standards, and Recommended Practices

Reference to the following NFPA codes, standards, and recommended practices will provide further information on the safeguards for aviation discussed in this chapter. (See the latest version of The NFPA Catalog *for availability of current editions of the following documents.)*

NFPA 10, *Standard for Portable Fire Extinguishers*
NFPA 11, *Standard for Low-, Medium-, and High-Expansion Foam*
NFPA 12A, *Standard on Halon 1301 Fire Extinguishing Systems*
NFPA 13, *Standard for the Installation of Sprinkler Systems*
NFPA 20, *Standard for the Installation of Stationary Pumps for Fire Protection*
NFPA 70, *National Electrical Code®*
NFPA 72®, National Fire Alarm Code®
NFPA *101®, Life Safety Code®*
NFPA 402, *Guide for Aircraft Rescue and Fire Fighting Operations*
NFPA 403, *Standard for Aircraft Rescue and Fire-Fighting Services at Airports*
NFPA 405, *Standard for the Recurring Proficiency of Airport Fire Fighters*
NFPA 407, *Standard for Aircraft Fuel Servicing*
NFPA 408, *Standard for Aircraft Hand Portable Fire Extinguishers*
NFPA 409, *Standard on Aircraft Hangars*
NFPA 410, *Standard on Aircraft Maintenance*
NFPA 412, *Standard for Evaluating Aircraft Rescue and Fire-Fighting Foam Equipment*
NFPA 414, *Standard for Aircraft Rescue and Fire-Fighting Vehicles*
NFPA 415, *Standard on Airport Terminal Buildings, Fueling Ramp Drainage, and Loading Walkways*
NFPA 418, *Standard for Heliports*
NFPA 422, *Guide for Aircraft Accident/Incident Response Assessment*
NFPA 424, *Guide for Airport/Community Emergency Planning*
NFPA 1003, *Standard for Airport Fire Fighter Professional Qualifications*

Chapter 10

Marine Vessels

Randall Eberly

Key Terms

CNG marine fuel, commercial boat, International Convention for the Safety of Life at Sea (SOLAS), International Maritime Organization (IMO), LNG carrier, LP-gas marine fuel, marine engine, marine vessel, *Morro Castle* fire, performance-based design, pleasure craft, U.S. Coast Guard

According to industry statistics, fires and explosions continue to contribute to the fatalities and injuries experienced in marine vessel casualties. This chapter discusses marine fire hazards on small pleasure craft, small commercial boats, and commercial vessels, as well as the design, construction, and shipboard fire prevention systems normally installed to deal with them. It first covers pleasure and small commercial craft and then devotes the balance of the chapter to large commercial vessels.

Additional information about extinguishing systems suitable for use on vessels is found in the following chapters: Section 16, Chapter 3, "Automatic Sprinkler Systems"; Section 16, Chapter 9, "Water Spray Protection"; Section 17, Chapter 1, "Carbon Dioxide and Application Systems"; Section 17, Chapter 4, "Foam Extinguishing Agents and Systems"; Section 17, Chapter 5, "Fire Extinguisher Use and Maintenance"; and Section 17, Chapter 6, "Halon and Halon Replacement Agents and Systems."

PLEASURE AND SMALL COMMERCIAL BOATS

The latest boating safety statistics from the U.S. Coast Guard (USCG) indicate there are nearly 13 million pleasure and small commercial boats in the United States.[1] Statistics for the 5 year period from 2001 to 2005 show that annually there were approximately 5500 accidents, 700 fatalities, and 3800 injuries involving such boats. The fatality rate for this period is down an average of almost 50 per year (or about 6%) below that for the previous 5 years. The report indicates that approximately 225 fire and explosion accidents caused, on average, about 5 fatalities and 93 injuries per year. These accidents also resulted in a 5 year total property damage of almost $54 million.

The introduction of the 1960 edition of NFPA 302, *Fire Protection Standard for Pleasure and Commercial Motor Craft,* stated, "There are few other uses of petroleum fuels by the public in which the fire and explosion hazards parallel those possible in motor craft." In spite of technical developments since that time, the statement remains true today.

Overview

Boats and vessels of all sizes are constructed to create a form that is closed on the bottom and on all sides. This basic hull form is necessary for the boat to float. In the case of trains, aircraft, and all land vehicles (other than amphibious types), openings can be provided where needed to permit both liquid fuel leakage and heavier-than-air vapors to drain by gravity to the open atmosphere. Gasoline is commonly used for both propulsion engines and for onboard generators, and liquefied petroleum gas (LP-gas) is commonly used for cooking. Any leakage of these fuels and any gas or vapors released as a result of using those fuels is retained inside the hull. The two means of discharging gas and/or vapor "overboard" are (1) the slow process of natural ventilation, which requires airflow over the boat (from boat motion or wind speed), and (2) mechanical ventilation, which is used before starting any engine. Exhaust blowers tend to be effective in only the general area of the exhaust blower pickup. By comparison, automobiles and trucks are normally completely open on the bottom, providing effective ventilation in all areas of the fuel system. Seepage of liquid fuel and vapors can freely drain to the open atmosphere along the road from any point in the system.

Randall Eberly, P.E., is a staff fire protection engineer in the Lifesaving and Fire Safety Standards Division at U.S. Coast Guard Headquarters.

Aircraft, likewise, have drains in their engine nacelles and under their wings, allowing vapors to be dispelled to the atmosphere inflight or on the ground.

Since bottom drains are not possible in a boat, safety on boats depends on a carefully maintained, leak-free fuel system and on ventilation capable of discharging heavier-than-air fuel vapors overboard. When vapors are discharged overboard from lower levels, fresh air is automatically introduced into the hull's upper levels. The fresh air tends to dilute vapors in the upper level. An adequate removal and dilution process keeps the vapor and/or gas mixture below the lower explosive limit.

Consider that 1 oz (0.3 L) of gasoline fuel can create about 11 ft^3 (0.3 m^3) of explosive vapor. Gasoline vapor is approximately four times as heavy as air and tends to sink to the bottom of the bilge. Natural or mechanical ventilation cannot render a boat safe in any reasonable time if any liquid leakage occurs. An operating marine exhaust blower with a pickup duct placed 1 ft (0.3 m) above an open container of gasoline does not materially reduce the time required for the fuel to evaporate. Because an exhaust blower, or any ventilation, does not materially accelerate the fuel's vaporization rate, power ventilation should not be used when liquid fuel is known to be present. Ventilation, in addition to removing some flammable vapors in the duct intake areas, introduces fresh air that can bring an overly rich mixture into the explosive range. Whenever liquid fuel is present, no electrical circuit should be turned on or off. The battery should not be connected or disconnected. An arc can occur when making or breaking a circuit.

Boat Hulls

The hull of a pleasure boat or small commercial vessel must be arranged so that all compartments are as accessible as practicable for inspection and maintenance. Access must always be provided to sea cocks for emergency use. There must be two means of escape from all accommodation spaces in case fire in the engine space or the galley blocks one means of egress. Escape hatches must be unobstructed, readily accessible, and adequately sized and shaped for their designed purposes. Congestion of an engine compartment is unsafe; it may make sea cocks inaccessible and discourages adequate inspection and maintenance of engines and equipment. Adding internal combustion auxiliary machinery increases ventilation requirements.

Engine spaces (for propulsion engines, generators, and other auxiliary engines) must be separated from accommodation spaces by fore, aft, and transverse bulkheads and decks. The separation must serve as an effective fire barrier and minimize the escape of fire-extinguishing media that may be discharged into the space. Unsealed bulkheads with a ¼ in. (6.4 mm) annular space around items penetrating the bulkhead are considered adequate for ignition-protection purposes and for confining fire-extinguishing agents. However, these same bulkheads do not prevent carbon monoxide that may be present in the engine space from passing through the bulkhead to accommodation spaces.

Materials

Boat hulls, bulkheads, and superstructures are constructed of a wide variety of materials, including aluminum, steel, reinforced fiberglass laminates (FRP), and wood. In addition to solid fiberglass laminates, there are fiberglass laminates with balsa wood or plastic honeycomb core materials and wooden structures that have been covered with a fiberglass laminate on both sides, making a sandwich construction. The combustibility, flame spread rate, smoke production, and heat release characteristics of these various flammable materials have not been investigated and classified for use on boats. Thinner outer laminations of cored construction burn through relatively quickly, exposing core materials. Choice of material is determined by boat size, type, intended service, and cost. Horizontal deck surfaces, such as the deck above the engines, are very quickly involved in fire spread because of the low height and small volume of the compartments above which the decks are located. To minimize fire spread, fire-retardant resins and fire-retardant coatings suitable for marine service may be used. Because fire-retardant resins may reduce the structural strength of the laminate in which they are used, changes may be needed to compensate for strength differences. Upholstery and carpeting used in cockpits and accommodation spaces might have high flame spread ratings. The flame spread ratings of all materials and fire-retardant coatings used should be carefully considered. As in engine spaces, ceiling heights in accommodation spaces are low compared to those in buildings, and the height reduction effectively accelerates horizontal flame spread.

Ventilation

Ventilation is defined as the positive changing of air, by natural or mechanical means, within a compartment. Boat ventilation is primarily designed to remove heavier-than-air flammable vapors from the bottom of the compartment. When air is removed from the compartment, fresh air is simultaneously introduced at the upper level. The fresh air dilutes the flammable vapors in the upper levels where the intake ducts terminate.

Natural ventilation's effectiveness depends on outside air velocity and direction. Without wind or boat motion, there is virtually no natural ventilation other than that created by thermal air currents. The most important factors affecting air movement inside a hull are (1) the shape of the boat's superstructure (cabin or, in small open boats, the windshield), (2) the location of the boat cabin or windshield, and (3) the type and location of the ventilation fittings. With a bow wind, a boat cabin's shape makes it function like a ventilating clam shell, reducing pressure under the cabin. In runabouts, pressure is reduced behind the windshield. Reduced pressure results in an airflow to that area. For maximum ventilation efficiency, the engine space airflow that ventilating fittings create should be used to reinforce the airflow the cabin creates. Neither natural nor power ventilation effectively removes the hazard of vapors created by the presence of liquid gasoline because flammable vapors can be generated faster than they can be removed. Airflow created by the ventilating system only slightly affects the time necessary to evaporate liquid gasoline. Therefore, in the presence of liquid gasoline leakage, introducing fresh air by operating blowers may create, rather than eliminate, an explosive mixture. The boat's blowers should not be used.

Ventilation in an engine space plays an important role in controlling heat levels in that space. Ventilation for temperature control depends on natural airflow into the engine space when the boat is under way and on the efficiency of external ventilating fittings and ducts. These fittings and ducts must be large enough to supply the air required for the engines. The compartment pressure depression must be measured with all engines operating at full power. Exhaust blowers are not used to control temperature or to supply air to the compartment. The engines operate with block temperatures of about 140 to 180°F (60 to 80°C). Because of anticipated high engine room temperatures, electrical conductors are derated in those spaces.

Of all cooking fuels, LP-gas creates the greatest ventilation problem because the gas is approximately 1.6 the density of air. It tends to sink and must be removed with positive ventilation.

Ventilation and Carbon Monoxide

Carbon monoxide (CO) is a flammable, gaseous poison having the same vapor density as that of air. Large quantities of CO are produced as a component of gasoline engine exhausts and, to a lesser degree, from diesel exhausts. Cooking appliances produce smaller quantities. This gas must be kept out of accommodation spaces to the greatest degree possible. Control of CO depends on awareness of the following basic factors:

1. The separation of the engine exhaust system discharge fittings from ventilation system fittings, scuppers, drains, and any other openings into the hull is vital to prevent the gas from reentering the boat. The direction and velocity of airflow over the boat must be considered. It affects the flow of air into and from all the ventilation intakes and exhausts.
2. It is not possible to prevent CO gas from reentering the boat under some operating conditions. One common condition, for instance, would be when a boat is operated at slow speed with a following wind. The operator must recognize and avoid these conditions.
3. Even engine room bulkheads that meet the ignition protection requirements of USCG regulation 33 CFR 183.410 do not effectively prevent CO gas from moving from the engine space into accommodation spaces.
4. A CO detector can help warn the boater of the presence of CO. CO is a flammable gas, but its greatest danger is that it combines with blood hemoglobin in the same manner as oxygen. CO is the leading cause of gas poisoning deaths in the United States.
5. In 2000, the USCG became aware of another dangerous condition involving CO on recreational boats. On boats with gasoline-powered generators and transom exhaust ports, lethal concentrations of CO have been documented and pose a threat to any swimmers using stern swimming platforms. The Coast Guard issued an advisory and the National Marine Manufacturers Association (NMMA) distributed a safety pamphlet on the hazard.

Lightning Protection

Lightning hits many boats every year. USCG statistics consistently show that people killed by lightning on boats are usually in small open motorboats, not sailboats. Even if a sailboat does not have a complete lightning system, its metallic mast inherently serves as the major down conductor. It tends to conduct the lightning past the occupants.

The probability of a lightning strike on a boat varies with geographic location and season. Lightning protection can be provided on a boat that has a conductive mast with a conductivity equal to a No. 4 AWG conductor and enough height that an imaginary line drawn at a 45 degree angle from its tip does not intersect any part of the boat. A pointed lightning rod should be installed at the tip. The mast's base must be connected vertically and as directly as possible to an external grounding plate or grounding strip, located below the lightning mast. An external rectangular (1 ft^2 [0.09 m^2] or larger) grounding plate or an external horizontal grounding strip of the same approximate area may be used, running fore and aft from below the lightning mast to a position aft below the engine(s). Large metallic masses, such as metallic guard rails, engines, and tanks near the lightning ground conductor, should be connected to the grounding strip to prevent side flashes. If the mast being used is stepped on deck, the connection between the mast and the external grounding plate or strip should be made with a No. 4 AWG conductor or two parallel No. 6 conductors routed on both sides of an opening. The normal horizontal electrical system bonding conductor in a boat may be connected to a lightning conductor system, but should not be relied on as a lightning conductor. To be effective, lightning conductors must provide an essentially vertical path to the ground plate or strip.

Figures 21.10.1 through 21.10.4 show normal boat lightning protection systems. Spiral wrapped radio transmitter antennas will not function as lightning masts, but steel antennas may help, provided the antennas' coils are bypassed with a lightning arrester. If an external grounding strip is used, as illustrated in Figure 21.10.2, the sharp edges of the grounding strip should not be rounded. In both sailing auxiliaries and cruising power boats, the external grounding strip most effectively connects items in the boat to the ground without long horizontal conductors inside the boat. The mast and bow rails can be connected to the forward end, and the engine and back stay (sailboats) to the aft end of the strip. In larger boats it is difficult to avoid installing a number of horizontal lightning conductors to connect large metal masses to the system. Instead, an equalization bus may be installed inside the boat parallel to the external lightning grounding strip. The internal equalization bus and external grounding strip are interconnected at the forward and aft ends and must be connected to the lightning ground system. They must never be connected so that they become part of the main down conductor. If a seacock or through-hull fitting carries the full lightning current, any water in the seacock turns to steam instantaneously, breaking the fittings and possibly sinking the boat.

Occasionally, a sailboat's aluminum mast hits an overhead power line, and the question arises whether masts or sections of masts should be made of a nonconductive material to avoid such accidents. The answer is that a boat's lightning system should be maintained.

Engines

Liquid-Cooled Engine. Liquid-cooled marine gasoline and diesel engines may be cooled directly by seawater or with fresh water using a raw water-cooled heat exchanger. Liquid-cooled

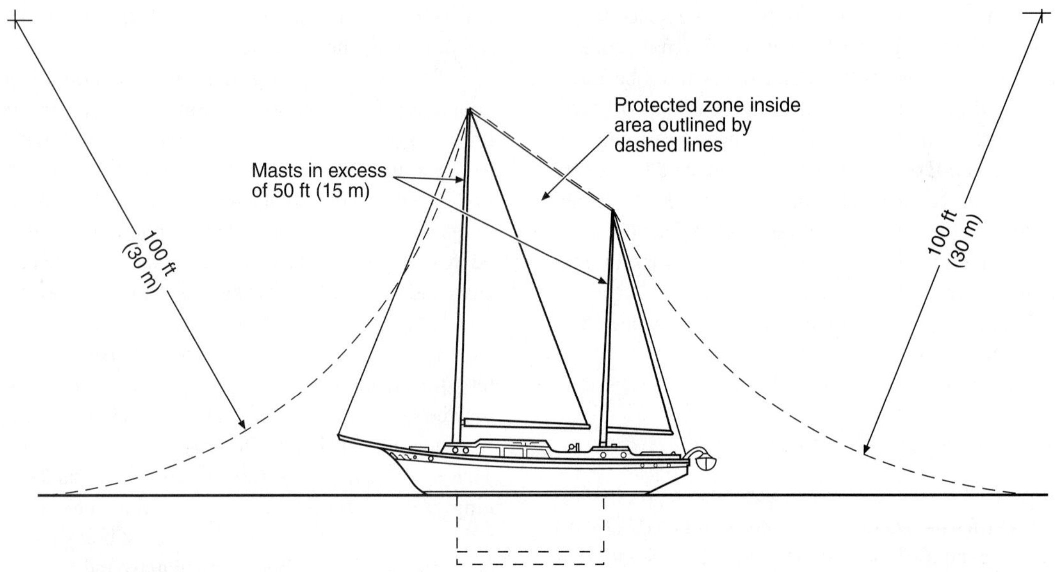

FIGURE 21.10.1 Proper Lightning Protection for a Boat with Masts More Than 50 ft (15 m) Above the Water. Protection is based on a lightning striking distance of 100 ft (30 m).

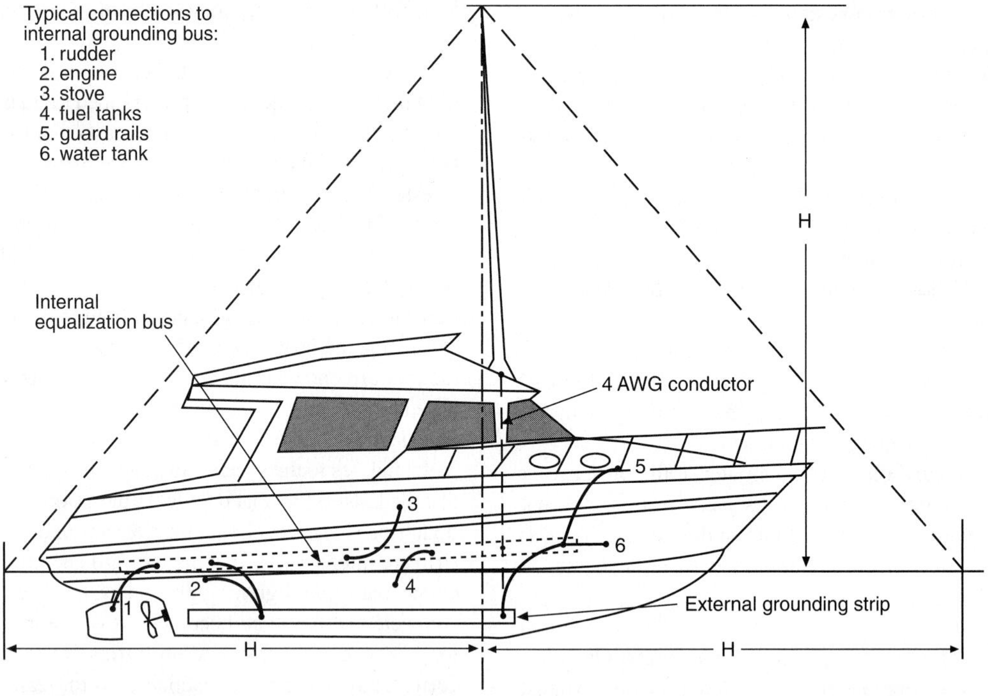

FIGURE 21.10.2 Boat with Mast Not More Than 50 ft (15 m) Connected to External Ground Strip, with Optional Equalization Bus

engines use water-jacketed blocks, heads, and exhaust manifolds. A self-priming, engine-driven pump circulates the cooling water. In a raw water-cooled engine, water circulates through the engine and then discharges into the exhaust pipe to create a raw water-cooled exhaust. The water discharges into the exhaust pipe through a water-jacketed riser at the engine. The riser's design prevents water from backing up into the engine through the exhaust manifold. Fresh water-cooled engines using a heat exchanger require two separate water pumps. One pump recirculates the fresh cooling water through the engine, and the second circulates water through the heat exchanger and provides raw water for the water-cooled exhaust. Fresh water-cooled

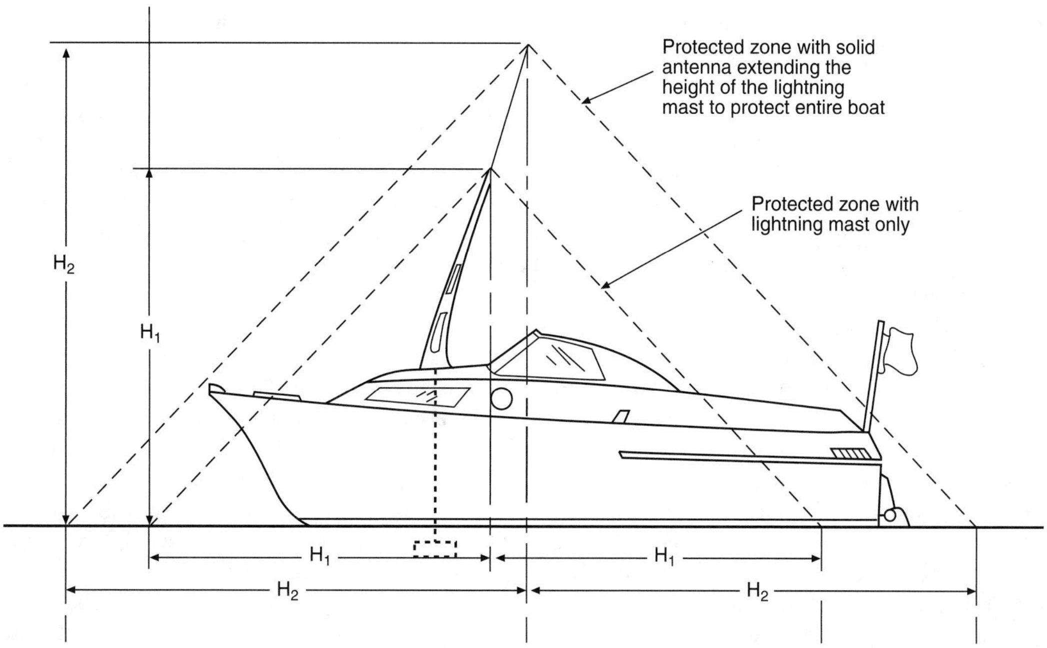

FIGURE 21.10.3 Proper Lightning Protection for a Small Sailboat with a Mast Not More Than 50 ft (15 m) Above the Water

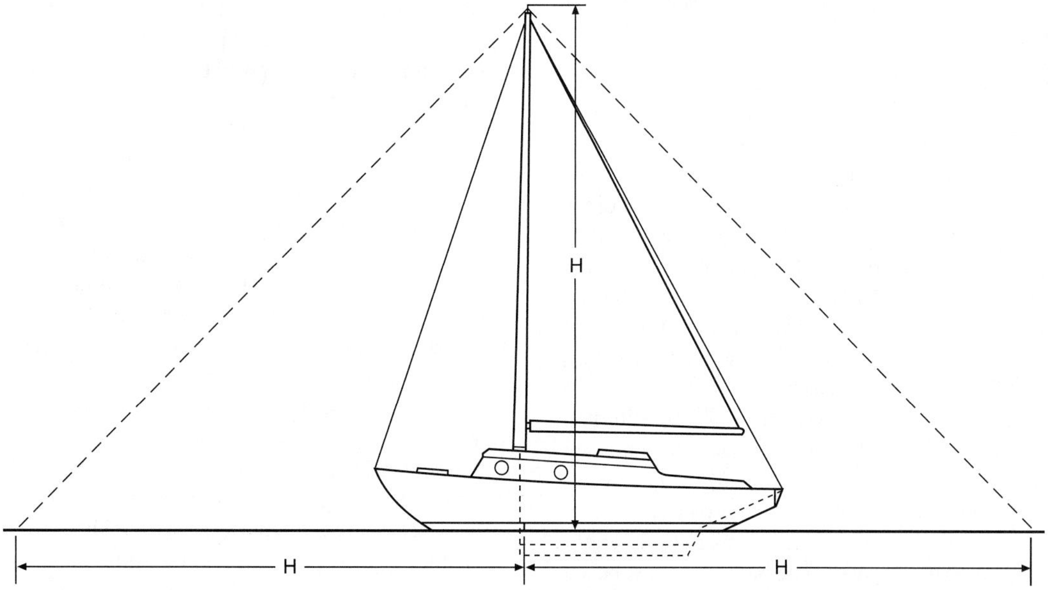

FIGURE 21.10.4 Proper Lightning Protection for a Boat with a Mast Not More Than 50 ft (15 m) Above the Water

engines can operate efficiently at approximately 180°F (82°C), whereas raw water-cooled engines, using seawater, must operate less efficiently at 140°F (60°C). The lower temperature prevents excessive salt precipitation in the block, manifold, and head of the engine. Raw water-cooled engines and engines using a heat exchanger can overheat if the pump fails or the water intake becomes blocked. Means to indicate loss of engine cooling water must be provided at all helm positions for propulsion engines. Nonpropulsion engines must automatically shut down with the loss of lubricating oil pressure, excessive engine temperature, and excess heat in the exhaust system.

Air-cooled engines are not recommended. However, if they are used in an enclosed space, a separate air duct must be provided for effective cooling. Because these ducts are large, they must be located to minimize the intake of excessive seawater, which could affect boat stability. A device must be provided to warn of excessive temperatures.

Fuel Injection. Technical advancement in automotive and marine engines has caused rapid replacement of carburetion with fuel injection. The more efficient fuel injection systems eliminate boilover and float-leakage problems of carburetors but are still subject to rap or lock. However, injection systems with return fuel lines present a major hazard not encountered in carburetor engines. Fuel injection gasoline engines and diesel engines may use a return fuel line that is warm and under pressure. In comparison, fuel in the distribution line from the fuel tank to the engine operates at reduced pressure, minimizing the hazard. When the engine is not running and the distribution line is at a reduced pressure, a pinhole may not leak any fuel at all. When the engine is running, a pinhole leak in the return line will tend to spray fuel, creating an immediate hazard. Consider that the return line can totally fail and not affect engine operation. The operator may be unaware of fuel spilling into the bilge unless there is an operating vapor detector. The fuel line requirements remain the same for distribution and return lines.

Backfire flame arresters are still required to meet the same requirements, but they no longer require a USCG approval number. Diaphragm fuel pumps must be designed and installed to prevent the release of fuel to the bilge in case of diaphragm failure. All electrical equipment in the engine space must be ignition protected.

Ignition Protection

All ac and dc electrical equipment in a gasoline engine space and any space with fuel line fittings must be ignition protected. Ignition-protected equipment has the same performance objective as hazardous location (explosionproof) equipment on shore and on commercial vessels. However, the requirements for ignition protection are less stringent and do not require hazardous location wiring. Accident statistics indicate that ignition protection has effectively reduced explosions in boats. Unfortunately, investigations of fire and explosion accidents have revealed that ignition-protected equipment is frequently replaced with non-ignition-protected equipment, eliminating the protection originally provided.

To eliminate the need for ignition-protected equipment in accommodation spaces, a bulkhead must separate the engine space from accommodation spaces. The bulkhead must be watertight for 12 in. (30.5 cm) or one-third the bulkhead height, whichever is less. Above that level the annular space around anything passing through the bulkhead (wires, cables, ducts, etc.) must not exceed ¼ in. (6.3 mm).

Fuel Systems

In aircraft and land vehicles, gravity drains liquid leakage, thereby preventing accumulation; this is not possible in a boat. Because both liquid fuel leakage and fuel vapors accumulate in a boat, fuel system components' design must resist vibration and shock failure, corrosion, and chemical deterioration. The system must be designed, installed, and maintained so as to be liquidtight and vaportight to the hull interior at all times. All fuel system parts should be capable of withstanding exposure to free-burning gasoline for 2.5 minutes without fuel leakage. Hose used instead of copper tubing must be USCG Type A1 or A2 fire-resistant hose. (Fire-resistant fuel distribution lines, however, are not required if less than 5 oz [150 mL] of fuel will leak when the distribution line is cut at the lowest point.) When fire resistance is not required, a USCG Type B1 or B2 hose can be used. Metallic fuel fill fittings must be electrically bonded to the engine negative terminal to dissipate static electrical charges. Fill hoses must be double-clamped.

Diesel fuel systems and gasoline fuel injection systems require the installation of efficient fuel filters and water separators to prevent dirt and water from reaching the fuel injector pump. Diesel and some gasoline fuel injector systems have pressurized return lines to the tank that must meet the same requirements as the fuel distribution line to the engine. Heated return fuel will gradually raise the temperature of the fuel in the tank. At normal temperatures, diesel fuel does not vaporize and create an explosive fuel air mixture, but diesel fuel has a greater tendency to accumulate in the bilges and create a fire hazard. Pressurized gasoline lines create an immediate hazard at any leakage level.

Appliances

Open flame appliances must be designed specifically for marine use and be installed to minimize personal and physical hazards. They must also be designed for attended use. The manufacturer must furnish printed instructions for their proper installation, operation, and maintenance. Portable devices and any device that cannot be secured in position when in use or stored are not permitted. A durable and permanently legible instruction sign describing safe operation and maintenance must be provided. The sign should be installed on or adjacent to the appliance where it can be quickly read. Air consumption and exhaust product venting from galley stoves and other appliances must be considered in the design and layout of compartments where they are installed. Lack of permanently open vents to supply air to the appliances can result in oxygen depletion in the compartment. Exposed materials around galley stoves and other heat-producing appliances must have a flame spread index (rating) of less than 75. Fabrics must not be used within 39 in. (1 m) of a galley stove.

Pilot lights and other automatic igniters are prohibited unless they are used in sealed combustion chamber type devices with outside air supply and exhaust discharge. Gas-fueled appliances must be equipped with flame failure devices to prevent gas flow if the flame is extinguished. Unattended devices, such as water heaters, refrigerators, and cabin heaters, cannot have automatic ignition unless they are of the sealed combustion chamber type, with the internal flame completely separated from accommodation spaces. Open flame water heaters and refrigerators are not permitted because they could be left on during fueling and because undetected leaks could occur in the fuel system. Gasoline is not permitted for use as a galley fuel.

Coal, charcoal, and wood-burning stoves must be installed on a hollow tile base or mounted on a noncombustible base with a clearance of 5 in. (13 cm) between the stove bottom and any deck. The deck must be sheathed with a noncombustible material. The sides and back of a stove must have a clearance of not less than 9 in. (23 cm) and must have a flame spread index of not more than 75.

Liquefied Petroleum Gas and Compressed Natural Gas Systems

The properties of both liquefied petroleum gas (LP-gas) and compressed natural gas (CNG) must be understood to ensure their safe use. Both are frequently used in the galley for cooking and are popular because they do not require priming like pressure alcohol stoves. At ambient temperatures, LP-gas can be liquefied at well under 250 psig (1724 kPa), the rated pressure of an LP-gas cylinder. CNG does not liquefy at ambient temperatures and is stored in cylinders under a pressure of about 2000 psig (13,790 kPa). LP-gas is a two-phase (liquid/vapor) fuel with a higher calorific value than CNG. LP-gas, when released as a gas, has approximately 1.6 times the density of air, and tends to sink to a boat's bilges. CNG is released as a lighter-than-air gas and tends to collect at the top of a compartment if not vented. When confined to a space, the gases will fill that space in a short time through diffusion. Diffusion and convection cause the gases to pass through and over bulkheads in all directions. An odorant added to both gases facilitates detection. A pressure regulator lowers the stored pressure of both gases to a system working pressure. LP-gas, normally stored at a pressure of 150 psig (1034.35 kPa) or less, is delivered to the appliance at approximately 14 in. (36 cm) water column, or about 0.735 psig (5.0 kPa gauge). CNG is reduced to about 6 in. (15 cm) water column, or about 0.22 psig (1.5 kPa gauge) at the appliance.

NFPA 302 permits LP-gas and CNG containers and regulators to be located on an open deck or on a cabin top in a housing, open at the top and bottom so escaping gas does not reenter the hull or accumulate in a cockpit or any enclosed space. The housing must protect the valves and the regulator assembly from mechanical damage. If not located on an upper deck or cabin top, the LP-gas containers and regulator assemblies must be located in a vaportight locker. The locker must be located above the waterline, be vaportight to the hull interior, be provided with a latched gasketed cover, and be vented overboard. It must be located so that when the cover is open, escaping vapor does not flow to the bilges, machinery spaces, accommodation spaces, or other enclosed spaces. Normal locations are along the side of the cabin in a molded-in locker or in an open cockpit in a vaportight locker. LP-gas lockers are vented with a ½ in. (13 mm) line led overboard with traps. The locker vent discharge must be separated from any hull opening and from any exhaust discharge fittings. Because CNG is lighter than air, CNG lockers must be vented with a ½ in. (13 mm) vent to the open atmosphere at a level above the cylinders and regulator assembly. CNG tanks, like LP-gas tanks, may be installed on an open deck, in a vaportight locker with an overboard vent or in a compartment that has no openings to an engine space above the level of the regulator. Engine room bulkheads that meet the ignition-protection requirements are not vaportight and therefore might communicate with other spaces.

Low-pressure distribution lines from the system regulator assembly to an appliance may be either copper tubing or hose. Copper tubing can be used with LP-gas without a problem, but copper tubing used with CNG must be internally tinned. LP-gas hose with permanently attached fittings must meet the requirements of UL Standard 21. CNG hose must meet the requirements of NFPA 52, *Vehicular Fuel Systems Code.* Distribution lines must be installed in continuous lengths from the regulator assembly to the appliance. The only exception is the installation of a flexible hose connection between copper tubing or copper piping and a gimbaled appliance.

Standards prohibit the use of pilot lights or other automatic ignition forms on gas-consuming appliances, but do permit a flame control for an oven in use. The flame control must be off when the oven control is off. All gas-fueled appliances must have a flame failure control to prevent gas flow if the flame is extinguished. Stoves with gas containers having less than 8 oz (0.24 L) of fuel are exempt from this requirement.

LP-gas or CNG systems installed in accordance with NFPA 302 can be simply, quickly, and positively checked for leakage in about 10 minutes. The method, which requires a pressure gauge, should be used frequently. The standard leakage check should be done after the system has been serviced, after the containers have been changed, and after any storm or grounding that might affect the system. NFPA 302 recommends that the check be done at the start of any cruise or voyage during which the system will or may be used. The standard specifies the following procedure:

- With the appliance valves closed and all other valves open, note the pressure on the gauge.
- Close the container valve.
- Observe the pressure to ensure that it remains constant for at least 10 minutes.
- If pressure drops, locate leakage by applying a soapy water solution at all connections.
- Repeat test for each container in multicontainer systems.
- *Never use flame to check for leaks.*
- *Never use soap containing ammonia.*

Electrical Systems Under 50 V

A boat's low-voltage dc system is intended to be a two-wire system with insulated conductors running parallel to each other to and from the power source, to each item of electrical equipment. The two-wire system minimizes the creation of magnetic fields that can affect the compass and other magnetically sensitive equipment and also minimizes the chances for stray dc current flow between metallic underwater components. Negative ground has been adopted as standard for dc systems, and the engine negative terminal is established as the single point for the dc system ground. When stray dc current flows between any two metallic components in contact with an electrolyte, such as seawater, the more positive (anodic) metal suffers accelerated corrosion. The more negative (cathodic) metal tends to be protected. Making the engine's lower unit or propeller and shaft purposely more negative or cathodic protects them and any other metallic objects connected to the same ground from accelerated corrosion due to stray currents. Although a true two-wire system would best serve the boating industry, most marine engines use converted automotive single-wire components. The automotive industry uses a common chassis ground return system so that all engine-mounted components have a negative conductor grounded to the frame. Because of the engine, the two-wire dc system on a boat is something of a compromise: mostly a two-wire system, it remains a single-wire system at and near the engine. The single-wire system has been extended off the engine by permitting an accessory negative bus for accessories near the engine. Accessories connected to a panelboard may have their negative conductors connected to the accessory bus near the engine, instead of the panelboard negative terminal strip. Whenever the system becomes a single-wire system and the feed and return conductors are not run in a pair, a magnetic loop forms. Standards do permit a completely ungrounded system, provided the engine's electrical components are all ungrounded.

Even though the engine's system is single wire, metal hulls and boat bonding systems must never be used as ground return paths. The boat bonding system—used to connect the non-current-carrying metal housing of dc equipment to the engine negative terminal—serves three functions:

1. Because the non-current-carrying parts of dc electrical equipment are connected to the engine negative terminal, stray current leaking from this equipment returns to the engine negative terminal (and battery negative) on the bonding conductor inside the hull. Electrical flow inside the hull minimizes current flow outside the hull between metallic appendages that would result in stray current corrosion of the equipment. A stray current leak of less than an ampere through a 1 in. (2.5 cm) through-hull fitting can destroy the fitting and sink the boat in 3 days.
2. A boat bonding system may be interconnected with and become part of the lightning protection system. When used in the lightning protection system to interconnect large metallic objects, the conductor size must be at least a No. 6 AWG conductor.
3. The bonding system conductor connects underwater metallic hardware to a galvanic anode (zinc) for galvanic protection.

If a boat has two or more propulsion engines and more than one battery bank, its engine blocks must be interconnected with two conductors capable of carrying the cranking current of the largest engine. The conductors prevent heavy damaging stray current corrosion due to current flow between propellers and shafts or outdrives when cranking one engine from the battery of another. Positive interconnection of all engines also prevents a current path through metallic fuel lines and control cables.

All dc conductors in the boat, except cranking motor conductors, require overcurrent protection at the power source for any circuit, generally within 7 in. (17.8 cm) of the source. USCG regulations and NFPA 302 permit a wire that is directly attached to the battery to be 72 in. (1.8 m) long without overcurrent protection. Using this exception is not recommended. NFPA 302 specifically requires the underground battery charger leads to be protected at the battery point of connection to the dc system. Under the regulations and NFPA 302, it is also possible to extend an unprotected sheathed wire's length from 7 in. (17.8 cm) to 40 in. (101.6 cm). The exception is used between the engine cranking motor solenoid hot terminal and the engine circuit breaker to position the circuit breaker high on the engine.

Boats have a special problem because many dc motors used on boats have no internal thermal protectors and by design cannot have the equivalent impedance protection. Lacking internal protection against overload, branch-circuit breakers or fuses must protect these motor-operated devices (pumps, blowers, etc.) against a "locked-rotor" condition. A locked-rotor condition exists if the pump becomes jammed and cannot turn. The motor manufacturer cannot easily specify the branch-overcurrent protection because it depends on the total wire length in that branch circuit.

Electrical Systems over 50 V

Three different sources may power the 120/240 V ac electrical system on a boat: (1) shore power, (2) an onboard ac generator, or (3) an onboard dc to ac inverter. Using shore power invites a special problem because the ac grounded neutral conductor is grounded to the earth on shore, but must never be grounded on the boat. When powered from shore, ac leakage currents return to the earth ground on shore. In contrast, both the onboard ac generators and the onboard inverters are grounded on the boat so that all leakage current remains on the boat. When two or all three sources of ac power are available, a switching arrangement must be provided to prevent any two sources of power from feeding the same circuit at the same time. This switch must disconnect one ac power source before connecting the circuits to another power source.

As on shore, under NFPA 70, *National Electrical Code®*, a green grounding-wire system keeps the non-current-carrying housings of ac appliances and ac equipment at ground potential to prevent electrical shock. When ac current is from an ac generator or an inverter on the boat, the green grounding-wire connects to the generator or inverter ground on the boat. With shore power, the green ac grounding-wire to the boat engine's negative terminal connects the underwater hardware of the boat (propellers, shaft, outdrivers, etc.) to other boats or any grounded metal on shore. Accordingly, aluminum- and steel-hulled boats and boats with aluminum outboard engines or aluminum stern drives suffer accelerated corrosion when connected to more noble metals (cathodic materials) on other boats or the dock. The interconnection with other boats or the dock can result in severe continuous galvanic corrosion of the anodic metals. This interboat corrosion could be stopped by not connecting the green grounding-wire to the boat engines, but any ac leakage on the boat can charge the surrounding water, electrocuting any swimmer near the boat. The solution requires the installation of a marine "galvanic isolator" or the installation of an isolation transformer in accordance with NFPA 302. The galvanic isolator is a device installed in series with the green grounding-wire on the boat. The device blocks the flow of dc galvanic currents while permitting the flow of ac current in the grounding conductor. The galvanic isolator must be sized to carry the system's full current because if it fails, the green grounding-wire stops working.

Fire Extinguishers

Testing laboratories normally evaluate the fire extinguishment potentials of portable fire extinguishers. The USCG also classifies portable fire extinguishers based on the Underwriters Laboratories Inc. classification of fires, but uses a different method to indicate extinguishment potential. Table 21.10.1 lists these designations.

PLEASURE AND SMALL COMMERCIAL BOAT OPERATIONS

General Maintenance

Operation and maintenance of pleasure and small commercial boats rely on general good housekeeping practices. Safety requires periodic inspection and maintenance of all equipment. When checks are conducted, unprotected electric lights should not be taken into areas of possible vapor accumulation from gasoline or liquids used for cleaning. The following, and other inspections and tests, are needed:

1. *Rags.* Clean rags should be kept in covered metal containers. Dirty waste and rags should be kept in separate covered metal containers. These should be disposed of each time the boat is docked.
2. *Fuel system.* The entire fuel system, from the fuel tank to the engine, must be visually examined periodically. The fuel tank should be checked to determine whether it shows any evidence of corrosion or leakage. Once a year the entire system should be pressure checked at 3 psi (20.7 kPa). The fuel hoses should be checked to determine that the connections (fittings and clamps, etc.) are tight and that hoses show no signs of deteriorating or cracking. The fuel pump should be checked to determine that it is a marine type, with a hose back to the intake manifold or carburetor in case of diaphragm failure. Fuel filters should be checked to determine that they are clean and not leaking. Used gaskets should be replaced with appropriate new ones whenever a fuel filter is cleaned.
3. *Detectors.* All detectors must be checked to determine whether they are working.
4. *Exhaust blowers.* Ventilating ducts should be checked to determine that they are installed without excessive bends and are neither kinked nor torn. Overcurrent protection should be checked to determine that it includes locked-rotor protection.
5. *Ignition protection.* All electrical equipment in the engine space and any space with fuel line fittings should be checked to determine that it is ignition protected. Replacement with automotive parts eliminates such protection.
6. *Painting.* When interior areas are repainted, fire-retardant paints should be used.

Proper maintenance and sensible fuel system operation, used together with ignition-protected electrical equipment, are probably a boat owner's most important fire prevention duties.

Fueling

Utmost care must be exercised during fueling operations. The following are general guidelines to be observed during fueling operations:

1. Fueling should not be undertaken at night, except under well-lighted conditions.
2. Smoking must be forbidden on board the boat and in the area of the fuel pumps and hose.

TABLE 21.10.1 Number and Distribution of Fire Extinguishers

Boat Type	*No. of Extinguishers*	*Minimum ANSI/UL Rating*[a,b]	*Minimum USCG Rating*[c]	*Location*
Open boats under 16 ft (4.8 m) with fiberglass or metal hulls and a light load of flammable Class A materials	1	5 B:C	B-1	Steering position
Open boats under 16 ft (4.8 m)	1	1A: 10B:C	B-1	Steering position
Boats 16 ft (4.8 m) up to, but not including, 26 ft (8 m)	2	1A: 10B:C	B-1	Steering position and galley, when on board, or cockpit
Open boats 16 ft (4.8 m) up to, but not including, 26 ft (8 m)	2	1A: 10B:C	B-1	Steering position and galley or cockpit
Boats 26 ft (8 m) up to, but not including, 40 ft (12 m)	3	1A: 10B:C	B-1	Outside engine compartment, steering position, and near galley or passenger cockpit
Boats 40 ft (12 m) up to, but not including, 65 ft (20 m)	4	1A: 10B:C	B-1	Outside engine compartment, steering position, crew quarters, and galley, when on board, or cockpit

[a]If a discharge port is installed, a USCG Type B-1 portable fire extinguisher might not be adequate.
[b]Extinguishers intended for machinery space protection are not required to have a Class A rating.
[c]Boats under 26 ft (8 m) in length without enclosed accommodation spaces or enclosed galleys shall be permitted to be equipped with a bucket with attached lanyard in lieu of Class A-rated portable fire extinguishers.

3. Before opening fuel tanks,
   a. Shut down all engines, motors, and fans
   b. Extinguish all open flames
   c. Close all ports, windows, doors, and hatches
   d. Determine the quantity of fuel to be taken aboard before fueling operations start
   e. Point out to the fuel attendant the correct deck fuel fitting for each tank
4. The fuel delivery nozzle must be in contact with the fuel fill deck fitting before fuel delivery begins. This contact should be maintained continuously until flow has stopped. Static discharge is a serious hazard if this rule is not followed. The fuel-fill fitting must be of a material that conducts electricity and must be electrically connected to the engine's negative terminal to ground the static charge.
5. Fuel tanks should never be completely filled because fuel expands. A minimum of 5 percent tank space must be allowed for expansion.
6. After fuel flow stops,
   a. Tightly secure the fill fitting cap
   b. Completely wipe up spillage
   c. Ventilate all spaces and check for gasoline vapors before starting any engine or operating any appliance

Storage Between Voyages

Before storing a boat, even for a short time period, several precautionary actions should be taken. The entire vessel should be thoroughly inspected. All combustible trash and rags should be removed, as well as any paint or other flammable liquids. Bilges should be inspected and pumped dry. All underwater hardware, including propellers, outdrives, rudders, through-hull fittings, and the hull should be checked and necessary repairs made. All seacocks should be checked and operated to make sure they can operate in an emergency. Liquid level of batteries and specific gravity of battery cells should be checked. If possible, lockers and bilge hatches should be secured in a partially open position to ventilate the spaces.

COMMERCIAL VESSELS

Code of Federal Regulations (CFR)

Ships and offshore marine structures present a wide range of potential fire risks that could threaten the safety of the public and our environment. The U.S. Congress has assigned the task of developing and instituting marine fire protection regulations to the United States Coast Guard, through the various laws governing marine inspection in the United States Code (USC). These laws delegate the authority to enforce all applicable federal laws on the high seas and on the waters subject to the jurisdiction of the United States for the safety of life and property. They are enforced through the application of detailed technical regulations for fire-fighting equipment and other precautionary measures guarding against fire, including the number, type, size, capacity, details of construction, methods of operation, stowage, maintenance, and drills and exercises necessary to assure proper functioning of the fire protection measures. The fire protection regulations are listed in the *Code of Federal Regulations* (CFR) under Title 46, *Shipping*. The regulations are further broken down into the various parts of Title 46, which address the different types of vessels and the types of fire hazards related to their normal operation. The transportation of hazardous materials on ships, or dangerous goods as they are called internationally, is regulated by the U.S. Department of Transportation (DOT) rules in Title 49 of the CFR Parts 171–180, *Hazardous Materials Regulations,* and by the Coast Guard at Title 46, Parts 147–148, *Dangerous Cargoes,* and Parts 150–154, *Certain Bulk Dangerous Cargoes.*

The regulations covering U.S. flag commercial vessels are contained in the following parts of the *Code of Federal Regulations:*

46 CFR Parts 24–28, *Uninspected Vessels*
46 CFR Parts 30–40, *Tank Vessels*
46 CFR Parts 70–80, *Passenger Vessels*
46 CFR Parts 90–105, *Cargo and Miscellaneous Vessels*
46 CFR Parts 107–109, *Mobile Offshore Drilling Units*
46 CFR Parts 114–122, *Small Passenger Vessels Carrying More Than 150 Passengers or with Overnight Accommodations for More Than 49 Passengers*
46 CFR Parts 125–134, *Offshore Supply Vessels*
46 CFR Parts 166–169, *Nautical Schools*
46 CFR Parts 175–185, *Small Passenger Vessels (under 100 gross tons)*
46 CFR Parts 188–196, *Oceanographic Research Vessels*

International Ship Fire Safety Requirements

The United States is a signatory nation to the International Convention for the Safety of Life at Sea treaty (SOLAS), which establishes regulations for fire protection on vessels that engage in international voyages to countries outside of the United States. The SOLAS convention is maintained by the International Maritime Organization (IMO), a specialized agency of the United Nations headquartered in London, England. IMO is the repository of all treaties dealing with commercial vessel safety, and has developed mandatory requirements as well as recommended codes and standards of practice relating to specialized maritime subjects. Under the terms of the SOLAS convention, all signatory countries are obligated to accept a SOLAS safety certificate, issued by another member country, as evidence of a ship's compliance with the convention. The use of mutually accepted safety certificates ensures a minimum level of safety and permits ships to operate freely between nations. The SOLAS regulations are sometimes written in very general terms to allow the use of equipment that is commonly accepted and approved by one member state, but which may be unfamiliar in other geographic locations. In some cases, SOLAS wording is intentionally vague, resulting from an inability to reach international agreement on more precise terms. As a result, there may be different interpretations between the member states regarding the SOLAS regulations. The convention has provisions permitting the countries where ships call to perform additional inspections, if needed, to ensure compliance with SOLAS. These inspections are called port state inspections, whereas those conducted by the ship's country of registry are called flag state inspections.

The Coast Guard regulations contained in the CFR are consistent with many of the SOLAS requirements, except that the CFR lifesaving and fire protection equipment and material requirements are much more detailed. Historically, SOLAS did not contain any type approval or testing requirements for the required fire protection measures, relying instead on nationally accepted procedures of the flag states. In 1998, a new Fire Test Procedures (FTP) Code was adopted that lists mandatory testing procedures for structural fire protection measures.

U.S. flag ships that engage only in domestic routes do not need to comply with the SOLAS requirements. Vessels that engage in international trade, however, must comply with SOLAS.

The SOLAS convention currently in effect is SOLAS 1974, as amended. This convention became effective for ships built after May 25, 1980, and has been amended several times since it was accepted. The large number of unrelated amendments and interpretations to SOLAS following its adoption made the convention difficult to apply. The International Maritime Organization, therefore, decided to perform a comprehensive review of the fire protection regulations in SOLAS and to update and reorganize the document to make it more user friendly. This updated version was adopted in the 2000 SOLAS amendments.

The update included several key changes. It incorporated the existing amendments and interpretations directly into the text of the Convention and included a new performance-based option. It was also decided that the fire extinguishing and fire detection system design and installation requirements in SOLAS should be removed from the convention and placed into a new mandatory standard called the International Code for Fire Safety Systems (FSS Code). Finally, new requirements were introduced for the carriage of emergency escape breathing devices (EEBDs), supplemental local application fire-fighting systems for the protection of high-hazard areas within machinery spaces, and a new Part E which contains requirements for the operational readiness of fire protection systems.

The performance-based option required changes to the Chapter II-2 regulations to include defined fire safety objectives and functional requirements within each regulation. In addition, a new regulation II-2/17 was developed to provide a methodology for approving alternate design and arrangements. Thus, owner/operators have the option of specifying ships that comply with either the prescriptive criteria listed in SOLAS, or specifying ships with performance-based designs that are demonstrated to achieve the stated fire safety objectives.

United States Domestic Ship Fire Safety Requirements

The fire safety regulations for vessels in domestic U.S. service are based on the principle of passive fire safety. Noncombustible fire boundaries and limited use of combustible materials are intended to limit fires to their space of origin. The different vessel regulations in the CFR are intended to provide a consistent level of fire protection safety to the many types of vessels common to the maritime industry. Ships may travel on different routes, have more passengers, engage in operations with varying levels of risk, or carry cargoes of varying fire hazard. The regulations, therefore, look at each class of ships separately, considering key fire protection and life safety risk factors. The regulations are based on many years of operating experience, compliance with international requirements, and lessons learned from casualty investigations.

The following service-related factors have been considered in the development of the vessel regulations:

- Relative size of the vessel
- Quantity, stowage arrangement, fire risk, and packaging of the cargoes carried
- Level of protection offered by the vessel's hull in collisions and groundings
- Number of passengers carried
- Length of a typical voyage
- Ship's means of propulsion and fuel type
- Route the ship will follow, as affected by weather issues and day or night operations

The following general vessel descriptions are provided to clarify the application of the regulations.

Uninspected Vessels. Uninspected vessels are generally smaller ships, such as tugboats, charter fishing boats, motorboats, or recreational boats (Figure 21.10.5). The fire risks are limited because the vessels carry limited cargoes, are limited in size, and carry only a small number of passengers. Vessels that are under 100 gross tons and carry less than six passengers for hire fit into this category. 46 CFR 28 contains regulations that specifically apply to commercial fishing, fish processing, and fish tender vessels. These vessels not only catch fish but may also include large refrigerated storage holds and processing facilities to cut, package, and flash-freeze the fish while at sea.

Tank Vessels. Tank vessels are vessels and barges that are designed to carry bulk liquid cargoes, mainly liquid petroleum products, that are usually flammable or combustible in nature. Because of the quantity and hazard of the cargoes carried, this class of vessels is subject to significant fire safety requirements, both in their design and operation. Tank vessels also include ships that carry hazardous chemicals and pressurized

FIGURE 21.10.5 Uninspected Tugboat Towing an Open Hopper Type Barge

or liquefied gases. Liquefied natural gas (LNG) or liquefied propane gas (LP-gas) carriers are included in this category.

Passenger Vessels. Passenger vessels are vessels that carry passengers for hire. Passengers for hire are defined as passengers who have either paid fares or contributed other consideration, as a condition of carriage on the vessel, whether directly or indirectly flowing to the owner, charterer, operator, agent, or any other person having an interest in the vessel. Passenger vessels may be further divided into five distinct classes:

1. *Uninspected passenger vessels less than 100 gross tons carrying 6 or fewer passengers.* Charter sailing vessels, charter fishing boats, and small water taxis are in this category.
2. *Uninspected passenger vessels more than 100 gross tons carrying 12 or fewer passengers.* Large luxury charter yachts are the best-known representatives of this class of vessels.
3. *Small passenger vessels less than 100 gross tons carrying more than 6 passengers.* Examples of this class include inflatable dive boats, passenger submarines, small ferries, dinner and tour boats, charter fishing headboats, and various types of sailing vessels. These vessels are also called "T boats," because their regulations are found in Subchapter T of 46 CFR.
4. *Small passenger vessels less than 100 gross tons carrying more than 150 daytime passengers or more than 49 overnight.* Typical examples include larger dinner cruise boats, casino vessels, and ferries. With their regulations located in Subchapter K of 46 CFR, these vessels are also called "K boats."
5. *Passenger vessels more than 100 gross tons carrying more than 12 passengers.* Examples of these type vessels are very large casino vessels and riverboats, as well as large oceangoing cruise ships. The regulations for these vessels are in Subchapter H of 46 CFR.

The majority of the passenger vessels in U.S. domestic service are Subchapter T and K boats. (Note that Subchapter T and K vessels that engage in international service must also comply with SOLAS.) Large oceangoing cruise ships are Subchapter H vessels if they are U.S. flag vessels. The majority of cruise ships are not U.S. flag vessels. They are foreign flag ships subject to the SOLAS regulations and U.S. port state inspection.

Cargo and Miscellaneous Vessels. Cargo and miscellaneous vessels are ships designed to carry general freight for hire, either in bulk, breakbulk, or containerized form. Breakbulk cargo is a nautical term that refers to cargoes that are baled, palletized, or placed in packaging for shipment and are consigned by various owners for delivery to different purchasers, yet are stowed in a common hold for shipment. Bulk cargoes are those that are loaded in loose condition, such as ores, grains, and coal. Breakbulk cargoes are loaded into the ship's holds by cranes, whereas bulk cargoes are usually loaded into the holds using conveyor belts, blowers, or grab buckets. This vessel category also includes container ships carrying multimodal freight containers that can be loaded directly onto railcars or truck chassis to continue their voyage. Vehicles carried as cargo can be driven on and off specialized cargo ships known as roll-on/roll-off or just ro-ro ships.

Mobile Offshore Drilling Units (MODUs). MODUs are special marine vessels designed for exploratory drilling operations on the ocean subfloor for possible offshore oil and gas well locations. These units must be mobile, because they are moved from site to site to look for new resources. Once a well is drilled and found to be satisfactory, a production platform is constructed at the site. Production platforms routinely pump thousands of barrels of oil daily, whereas MODUs only find productive well sites. The production platforms are thus exposed to greater fire risks. Production platforms are either connected to a pipeline through which oil is pumped to a refinery, or the oil is stored on the platform until it can be loaded onto a tank ship to be taken to the refinery terminal. Among the common types of MODUs are the following:

- *Jackup rigs:* These are mobile drilling rigs that float, so they can be moved or towed into position. A jackup rig has a series of self-elevating legs that are lowered to the seafloor to anchor the unit and lift the drilling platform out of the water. These rigs are generally used where the water depth is less than 400 ft (122 m).
- *Submersible rigs:* These are mobile drilling rigs that can be moved or towed into position. The rig has a hull that allows the unit to float. When the rig is in position, the lower section of the hull is flooded, causing it to settle onto the seabed, but keeping the work platform above the water. Submersibles provide very stable drilling platforms, but can only be used in limited water depths.
- *Semisubmersible rigs:* These are similar to submersible units; however, when the hull is flooded, the rig does not settle on the seabed, but floats beneath the surface of the water, keeping the working platform above the water. These types of rigs can be used in very deep water, as their submerged section assists in stabilizing the rig in heavy seas.
- *Drilling ships and barges:* These rigs are easily moved, as they are designed with similar hull shapes as oceangoing vessels. They are used to drill wells in remote locations. The limitation of these rigs is their lack of stability in very rough weather. They are, therefore, mainly used in locations where calm seas are enjoyed most of the time.

There are several types of production platforms in use, depending primarily on the water depth at the well site and the distance to the refinery:

- *Rigid steel platforms:* These are rigid platforms with a tubular steel foundation or jacket that is supported on piles driven into the seabed. The steel jacket is usually so large that it is towed to the site in a horizontal position and partially flooded to tip it into a vertical position and lower it onto the pilings. The crew quarters, the drilling rig, and all support equipment are then put on a platform positioned at the top of the jacket.
- *Rigid concrete platforms:* These are rigid platforms that resemble steel platforms, except the platform is supported

on large hollow concrete caissons. The entire rig is constructed and towed to the site, and then the caissons are flooded to anchor the unit to the seabed. Because of the tremendous weight of the concrete caissons, the rig does not have to be attached to the bottom with pilings. The hollow caissons are used to store the oil until it can be offloaded into tankers for delivery to the refinery. Because of their weight, these platforms are very stable in rough seas and are common in the North Sea.

- *Tension leg platforms:* Rigid platforms are limited in application to water depths less than roughly 1000 ft (305 m). For deeper water, a type of production rig called a tension leg platform (TLP) is used. Resembling semisubmersible drilling rigs, TLPs are moved into location and are then anchored to the seabed with tensioned steel tubes or cables. The working platform floats on the surface but is stabilized by the steel tensioning apparatus.
- *SPAR platforms:* Designed for very deep waters, SPAR platforms consist of a large cylindrical tube that floats vertically, anchored to the seafloor. Water ballast in the lower end of the tube keeps the SPAR deep in the water for stability in adverse sea conditions. The end of the cylinder above the water supports production and accommodation facilities. Newer SPARs are large enough to also accommodate a drilling rig for drilling new wells. Oil and gas processed on the SPAR are pumped into an underwater pipeline system.
- *Single point buoy mooring system (SPBM):* In locations in which a pipeline from the well to a refinery is neither economical nor practical to construct, a special mooring system can be built to allow oil tankers to load oil directly from the wells or from an underwater pipeline system serving several wells. A piping riser is constructed from the ocean floor to a mooring buoy that floats on the surface of the water. The oil tankers tie up to this buoy using a single line from the bow of the ship, hence the name. Some buoy systems also have a permanently attached tanker that is used for oil storage. These facilities are called floating production, storage, and offloading (FPSO) systems.

Offshore Supply Vessels. Offshore supply vessels are small cargo ships specifically designed to carry equipment, supplies, and workers to and from oil production platforms and drilling rigs. Special regulations were developed because these vessels are part cargo ship, part tanker, and part passenger ship, and they generally travel in limited geographic regions. The regulations were adapted to the specialized service of these vessels.

Nautical School Ships. Nautical school ships are training vessels used by merchant marine academies to provide their students with actual maritime operating experience. Although nautical school ships may be designed as cargo ships, they are provided with additional safety measures because the students carried on board are not licensed mariners, and there are generally more students on board than would be expected on a typical merchant ship.

Oceanographic Research Vessels. Oceanographic research vessels are vessels that are similar to small passenger vessels that have onboard laboratories to conduct research of water quality, marine life, or environmental science. The accommodation areas on these type ships are typically larger than those on board cargo vessels, because they need sufficient berthing capacity for the normal ship's crew plus the scientific complement. The laboratory areas are required to be separated from the accommodation areas by fire-rated bulkhead and decks, since flammable and combustible liquids may be used for the experiments.

MARINE FIRE PROTECTION CONSIDERATIONS

The application of fire protection engineering principles to ships and offshore marine structures is based on much of the technology used for the protection of buildings, warehouses, industrial plants, tank farms, and similar shoreside installations. Because the design and operating environment of ships are quite different from that of buildings, the basic fire protection principles have been adapted to suit the different marine-related circumstances.

Layout and Configuration

The basic layout and configuration of ships must be different from that of buildings because of their movement and the effects of the wind and wave forces they must endure. Ships cannot easily be designed with numerous deck levels without affecting their stability or their natural ability to remain upright. Similar to a building, a resting ship floating in calm water is subject to only the vertical force of the ship's weight acting through its center of gravity in a downward direction and the upward force of the water's buoyancy. Buildings, however, are designed as nonmoving structures, able to resist wind and weather forces without movement. Ships float and are propelled through the water. The directional forces caused by ships' engines and the wind and waves causes them to roll and pitch in the water. If more deck levels are added to a ship, its center of gravity is raised upward. The center of gravity is the chief force that keeps the ship in an upright position, and if the center of gravity is located too high on the vessel relative to its center of buoyancy, its righting ability is limited. Ships must be built in a horizontal rather than a vertical aspect because of this.

Multistory buildings have a similar footprint on each floor, which simplifies the design and layout of sprinkler and detection system devices. This common arrangement also greatly simplifies the arrangement of fire barriers and the means of egress. The main fire subdivisions in buildings are formed by the floor/ceiling assemblies, which prevent vertical fire spread. In contrast, the decks of a ship may vary considerably in shape and configuration on each level. The deck construction prevents vertical fire spread, but additional fire barriers must be provided to limit horizontal fire spread. The decks on some passenger vessels can be over 200 m in length. Horizontal fire barriers are only seen in very large buildings where the floor area exceeds that allowed by the building codes. The regulations for passenger ships require a 1-hour-rated fire barrier every 40 m fore and aft to subdivide them into fire areas called main vertical zones (MVZs).

Construction Materials and Design

The materials and design of fire barriers used in shipboard construction are quite different from those in buildings. The origin of modern shipboard fire barrier design can be traced to 1934, when the U.S. passenger ship *Morro Castle* burned off the coast of New Jersey, taking 124 lives. The combustible wooden construction and open stairways were determined to be the cause of the rapid fire spread throughout the vessel.[2] Outrage over this massive loss of life prompted the U.S. Senate Committee on Commerce to create a special Subcommittee on Fireproofing and Fire Prevention to develop recommendations for enhanced fire protection measures aboard ships.

The subcommittee procured a surplus ship, the *S.S. Nantasket,* from the Maritime Administration's reserve fleet moored on Virginia's James River and used it for a series of full-scale fire tests. Conducted in 1936, these tests showed the superior performance of steel bulkheads insulated with asbestos blanket insulation and joinerwork bulkheads constructed of noncombustible asbestos cement board panels.[2] The testing program also compared the temperatures developed in the full-scale *S.S. Nantasket* fires to those developed in the ASTM Standard E119 laboratory furnace to determine how other construction materials might be accepted.

At the conclusion of the *S.S. Nantasket* test series, the subcommittee report to Congress recommended the use of only noncombustible materials of construction.[2] The nearly exclusive use of noncombustible materials for shipboard fire protection has resulted in the development of methods and materials that are unique to ships. Although there have been many advances in the materials used for shipboard construction, the requirement for noncombustible materials remains the cornerstone of the structural fire protection system.

The majority of modern ships are constructed of steel. The regulations have, therefore, only needed to address one type of construction. Thus, they do not prescribe height and area limitations based on the type of construction, as is customary with the various building codes. Recent trends in construction methods are advancing the use of aluminum and composite materials for shipbuilding; however, the regulations have not fully recognized these materials, except in the development of the IMO High Speed Craft Code. This code was developed for the construction of lightweight high-speed vessels that cannot be constructed of steel without affecting their performance. These ships use lighter weight materials of construction such as aluminum alloys and fiberglass composites.

Fire Extinguishing and Fire Detection Systems Design

The design of fire extinguishing and fire detection systems on board ships also merits special consideration. Fire protection systems installed on board seagoing ships are more susceptible to environmental and operationally induced failures than those installed in buildings because of their continual exposure to salt water, humidity, shock, and vibration.

Because ships are moving structures, the installed equipment is regularly exposed to the vessel's motions and opposing wind and wave forces. Wiring connections may come loose from the constant vibration, so ring type connectors are used instead of spade connectors. Wiring nuts and solid conductor wiring, commonly used in building fire alarm systems, are not acceptable on ships because exposure of these components to vibration may result in circuit failure. Vibration is also a concern for the mounting brackets and equipment used to secure high-pressure cylinders employed in fire-extinguishing systems and portable fire extinguishers. The cylinders must be properly mounted to prevent vibration from causing damage to them or from causing their inadvertent operation.

The quality of the water supply used for fire protection is another matter that affects shipboard systems. Most ships sail in salt water. Those that do not, sail in river water that contains mud, sediment, and debris. Both fresh and salt water may contain biological organisms such as barnacles, Asiatic clams, or Zebra mussels. The fire main and sprinkler system suction arrangements must be designed with positive features to prevent clogging from these contaminants. Moreover, shipboard automatic sprinkler systems must be kept charged with potable fresh water to avoid marine growth in their branch lines. A very limited onboard fresh water supply is provided that automatically switches to a seawater pump during a fire to provide sufficient duration for the sprinkler protection.

The use of common shoreside materials such as anodized aluminum for fire hose couplings and nozzles is not realistic on ships because of corrosion-related failures. Fire-fighting equipment made from brass, bronze, or galvanized steel must be used to prevent corrosion problems. Stainless steel can be used in some applications, except that stainless steel fire extinguisher shells cannot be used on board ships because of their history of stress-corrosion cracking when exposed to saltwater environments.

Oceangoing ships can regularly be miles from the nearest port of refuge. It is essential that the installed fire protection equipment is rugged and reliable. Ships cannot depend on fire-fighting aid from a local fire department, so they must carry their own equipment and trained fire fighters. Fire-fighting tactics on ships are quite different from those used to attack fires in buildings. Ships are compartmentalized by steel bulkheads and decks. The fire brigade cannot ventilate a space before entering it by cutting openings in the overhead. The fire fighters entering confined areas may therefore be exposed to temperature extremes. As previously noted, stability is a significant concern, and the unlimited application of fire-fighting water on the upper decks must be controlled to keep the ship upright. This is compounded by the inability to readily drain water out of fire-affected compartments because floor drains and exterior doorways are not always available. Accumulated water can threaten the stability of the ship, so bilge pumps need to be operating when a significant amount of water has been used in fire-fighting efforts.

Evacuation

The evacuation of passenger ships is much more complex than the evacuation of a building. Ships have emergency evacuation components that are rarely, if ever, used for normal building occupancy. Passengers normally board cruise ships in port via gangways that connect the dock to the main deck of the ship. The capacity and configuration of the ship's main access corridors and stairways are planned to facilitate passenger movement across the gangways.

If a fire occurs while the vessel is in port, the gangways can be used for emergency evacuation of the ship. If a fire occurs at sea, the paths to the dock are no longer available, and the only means available to evacuate the ship are the survival craft (lifeboats, inflatable life rafts, etc.). The egress paths to the survival craft are through totally different routes from those used to board the ship.

Because passenger ships have multiple types of occupancies, emergency evacuations are further complicated by the possibility of two distinct initial passenger distribution conditions. The daytime condition considers that most of the passengers will be distributed throughout the public assembly spaces such as the restaurants, lounges, and theaters. During the nighttime condition the majority of the passengers are expected to be in their staterooms asleep. This variation is similar to that expected in a large shoreside hotel; however, unlike a hotel, passenger ships do not have direct exits on the ground floor to evacuate the public spaces. Passengers exiting from the public spaces to the open deck may have to reenter the ship to travel to the survival craft. For either the daytime or the nighttime condition, the passengers must assemble and move to the survival craft, which may be located several decks above the public spaces. On many ships, an emergency evacuation requires the passengers to ascend stairways. This action may seem foreign to many passengers, who are accustomed to exiting buildings by descending the exit stairways.

Ships are considered their own best lifeboat and are only evacuated if it appears that sinking is imminent. Evacuation procedures initially move passengers from the fire-affected spaces on the ship to areas of safe refuge called assembly stations. These are usually areas where there is ready access to the survival craft. When the passengers ultimately discharge from the exit system on board the ship, they are not at a safe location. Passenger ship exit systems discharge to the assembly stations, and if necessary, the occupants are put into the survival craft and lowered to the water (Figure 21.10.6). Depending on the weather, time of year, and location, the sea could be a much more hazardous environment than the ship. Thus, evacuation of a ship is only done when the ship is in peril. Shipboard evacuations must be possible in adverse sea states, with ship movements and even the possibility that one side of the ship might be inaccessible (due to listing or rolling to one side, for example).

Regulatory Review

Ships may be subject to regulatory review by different authorities having jurisdiction (AHJ) throughout their lifetime. Owners of vessels on international voyages must have their ship design and operation approved by the maritime authority of the country where the ship is registered (flag state), which is primarily responsible for ensuring that the ship meets international standards. Authorities of the countries to which the ship sails have the right to examine the ship to confirm compliance with international standards (port state control). This sometimes results

FIGURE 21.10.6 Enclosed Survival Craft Being Launched

in difficulty dealing with differing interpretations of the same regulations. Even ships limited to U.S. domestic service come under the jurisdiction of different Coast Guard authorities when they change their home port. Different local conditions and interpretations can mean that some aspect of ship design or operation acceptable in one port will not be acceptable in another. This is not the case for buildings, which are usually within the same jurisdiction for the life of the building.

The ship's crew can also include residents of many different countries, who may not all speak or understand the language of the flag state. Some ships may also be built in shipyards located outside of the flag state. For these reasons, there may be significant language issues to overcome in order to ensure that the entire crew understands the emergency procedures to follow in a fire emergency. The crew may also need supplemental training in the operation and maintenance of the installed fire protection equipment to ensure that it is properly serviced and remains operable at all times.

MARINE FIRE HAZARDS

General Fire Hazard Analysis

The general fire hazards on board ships can be analyzed looking at the three major occupancies common to all ships: (1) the engine room, which contains the propulsion machinery and auxiliary equipment; (2) the cargo holds or cargo tanks depending on the service of the vessel; and (3) the accommodation and service areas where the crew and/or passengers are berthed.

The U.S. Coast Guard maintains a database that is used to track casualty information relating to accidents investigated by the Coast Guard.[3] The database has been in use since 1985 and is useful to show trends in fire-related casualties. From an overall fire damage perspective, roughly 60 percent of all shipboard fires occur in the engine room. The remaining 40 percent of the total number of fires are split evenly between the cargo area and the accommodation area.

Engine Rooms. The engine rooms on modern ships usually have one or more large diesel engines and related auxiliary equipment for the propulsion of the ship. Some vessels may also have steam boilers for propulsion or auxiliary purposes. Engineering support systems include electrical generators and distribution systems, hydraulic systems, ventilation systems, and lubricating oil systems. The diesel engines are supplied with fuel from small capacity day tanks located in the engine room, which are filled by fuel pumps that take suction from large fuel storage tanks located outside the engine room. Casualty data shows that the majority of engine room fires are caused by broken fuel or lube oil lines spraying onto hot surfaces such as exhaust manifolds, turbochargers, or engine casings.[3] The next most likely engine room fire cause is attributable to shipboard electrical systems, usually a short circuit or failure of an electrical component or device. Although not seen as frequently, engine crankcase, clutch, and turbocharger explosions may occur, usually due to wear on the equipment. Human error is also a noted contributor to engine room fires, primarily cutting and welding operations that are not safely performed.[3]

Cargo Holds. The cargo holds on general cargo ships and container ships are nothing more than a series of large separated warehouse spaces. These ships could be used to transport general cargo in packages, multimodal containers, or portable tanks; vehicles; or flammable liquids or gases. Vehicle carrier holds are similar to general cargo holds except that they may have internal elevators or power-operated doors and may run the entire length of the vessel without subdivision. The vehicles carried may have gasoline in their tanks, which requires the cargo hold electrical system to be suitable for use in hazardous atmospheres. Bulk liquid cargo tanks on tank vessels are used to carry a variety of flammable and combustible liquids and are segregated from the accommodations areas aft where sources of ignition could be present. Electrical shorts and sparking are listed as the most frequently identified fire cause of shipboard cargo areas, followed by cutting and welding, contact with hot surfaces, human error/discarded cigarettes, static electricity/lightning, explosions, and chemical reactions.[3]

Accommodation and Service Areas. Shipboard accommodation and service areas include the staterooms and berthing areas, galleys, mess rooms, pantries, ship's offices, laundry facilities, navigating bridge, and radio room. The fire hazards in these areas are typical for light or ordinary hazard occupancies. Casualty statistics[3] show the leading causes of fires in these areas to be electrical in nature, followed by galley and cooking fires, human error/cigarettes, cutting and welding, portable heaters, and contact with hot surfaces.

Detailed Fire Hazard Analysis

Engine Rooms. Shipboard engine rooms or machinery spaces typically occupy the aft (rear) section of the ship up to the main deck, with the machinery space casing extending up through the accommodation area to the top of the vessel. The casing is a narrowing vertical trunk, similar to a pipe chase, which contains the engine exhaust pipes and ventilation equipment. A typical engine room has multiple levels separated only by steel gratings and ladders. The engineer's control room and various workshops could also be included within the engine room boundaries. Engine rooms are separated from the remainder of the ship by steel bulkheads and decks, with all openings and penetrations sealed to prevent the migration of hydrocarbon vapors to adjacent occupied areas.

The primary fire hazard in the engine room is the fuel oil used to supply the engines or boilers. This is usually marine diesel fuel, which is similar to # 2 fuel oil, or it may be a heavy oil called bunker C, which is similar to # 6 fuel oil. If heavy fuel oils are used, they must be heated in order to be transferred. Fuel and lube oil systems are the principal causes of fires in shipboard engine rooms.[3] Failures may occur in the fuel line piping and fittings from the continual exposure to vibration or because components were replaced with substandard parts not qualified for the intended service. Many ships are also fitted with duplex fuel strainers, which have two separate filter chambers that allow the crew to manually switch between them to clear the operating filter without stopping the engines. A significant number of fires occur in these filters because they are normally operated while the fuel system is under pressure.[4] Most ships will also have one or more day tanks that feed fuel to the engine room under a gravity head.

If an engine room fire occurs, the fuel in the tanks could continue to leak into the engine room until the tanks are empty. Because of this, fuel lines have remotely operated shutoff valves to allow the fuel tanks to be isolated from outside the engine room in the event of a fire. Beginning in 2002, the SOLAS convention required additional fuel system safeguards on new vessels. Specifically, all high-pressure fuel piping is required to be double jacketed, and any fuel lines that could spray onto hot surfaces must be suitably shielded or guarded.

Engine crankcase explosions are another recognized fire source in shipboard machinery spaces.[5] These explosions can occur when the engine's piston rings or related components become worn and allow fuel oil to be forced from the combustion chambers into the crankcase. Rigorous maintenance programs to replace worn equipment are the most effective way to prevent crankcase explosions. Pressure-relief vents are also provided on engine blocks to mitigate the effects of explosions. Recent advancements in oil mist detection technology show promise in their use for recognizing component wear before an explosion occurs.[5]

Because of the fire hazards inherent to engine rooms, the Coast Guard regulations require them to be protected by a total flooding carbon dioxide or clean agent fire-extinguishing system. Detection systems are not required except when the engine room is automated and when engineers are not continually present. The extinguishing systems are required to have a manual means of release to guard against unintentional discharges. The inadvertent discharge of an automatic engine room extinguishing system will cause the engines to shut down, leading to the loss of propulsion and steering. This could place a moving vessel in an extremely dangerous situation, depending on its location.

The SOLAS regulations allow the use of water spray or high-expansion foam protection for engine rooms in lieu of a total flooding gaseous system; however, these types of systems are currently not accepted for use aboard U.S. flag vessels. Water mist systems are the only water-based system accepted by the Coast Guard for the total flooding protection of engine rooms. Type approval for total flooding systems is based on IMO MSC/

Circ. 1165, *Revised Guidelines for the Approval of Equivalent Water-Based Fire-Extinguishing Systems for Machinery Spaces and Cargo Pump-Rooms.*

Galleys. Ships' galleys are similar to commercial restaurant kitchens. As a result they are vulnerable to the same fire hazards (Figure 21.10.7). Ship galley fires are often attributable to the buildup of grease in the galley hood and exhaust ducts, or from malfunctions in the cooking appliances themselves. Galley range tops and cooking appliances are designed with battens or guardrails to keep the cookware in place on the burners when the ship is in motion. The restraints prevent personnel injury and also guard against the heated cookware contacting adjacent combustibles. Galleys on domestic passenger vessels are required to have either a dry chemical or wet chemical extinguishing system for the protection of the hood. SOLAS vessels must have a fixed means of extinguishing a fire in the galley exhaust duct. On all vessels, the galley exhaust ducts must be separated from adjacent combustibles; however, fires still occur because crew members improperly store trash and other combustibles in void spaces or in lockers adjacent to the galley exhaust ducts.

Breakbulk General Cargo. Breakbulk cargo consists of general commodities in separate packaging that is stowed in a hold and tracked by separate bills of lading, as opposed to bulk cargoes such as coal or gain. Cargo holds designed for the carriage of breakbulk general cargoes typically comprise three or more levels: a lower hold, a 'tween deck, and an upper 'tween deck. 'Tween deck is a nautical term referring to the mezzanine levels between the bottom and top of a hold. Each cargo hold level has a fixed peripheral area, called the wing area, while the center area of the hold is open and is covered by removable hatch covers to allow vertical loading of the cargo by overhead cranes. The cargo is normally loaded into the center of each level by cranes, and then the stevedores move the cargo into the wing areas with forklifts until the hold is completely filled. The only other access to the holds is through small manholes and ladders. Breakbulk cargo is not loaded with any access aisles or storage racks in order to maximize the ship's carrying capacity. The cargo pile height is usually near the overhead, and may range from 10 to 20 ft (3 to 6 m) in height on each deck. At sea, the cargo holds are rarely accessed.

FIGURE 21.10.7 Typical Galley on Board a Large Passenger Ship

Many ships also have provisions for on-deck stowage, which is generally reserved for hazardous materials or bulky items. The materials carried on cargo ships are as varied as those in any general storage warehouse and routinely include hazardous chemicals, explosives, oxidizers, and flammable liquids and gases. The segregation and stowage of incompatible materials must be carefully controlled to minimize the risks of fire or explosion. The U.S. Department of Transportation (DOT) regulations in Title 49 of the Code of Federal Regulations and the IMO International Maritime Dangerous Goods (IMDG) Code provide highly specific packaging, stowage, ventilation, and segregation requirements for the loading of hazardous materials.

Breakbulk cargo holds are large open warehouse type spaces surrounded by steel bulkheads and decks. For efficiency in loading, and to maximize the quantity of goods that may be loaded, the decks and surrounding bulkheads are made as smooth and regularly shaped as possible. Lighting and ventilation systems are the main support equipment normally found in cargo holds. Some ships may have battery chargers for the forklifts as well as electrical systems that allow the stowage of refrigerated containers. Fires in cargo holds are mainly attributable to electrical sources, although there have been some cases reported of spontaneous combustion occurring in the cargo.[6] The tight stowage of the cargo in the holds limits the air available for combustion; if a fire does occur, it is generally a deep-seated, slowly developing event.

The standard protection for cargo holds consists of smoke detection and total flooding carbon dioxide systems. Because the cargo handling operations in the holds could damage or impair the function of electrical fire detection devices, an air-sampling detection system (called a sample extraction system in SOLAS regulations) is used. There are no smoke detectors in the holds; they are located in the system control cabinet. Cargo hold detection systems are combined with the carbon dioxide system discharge piping. The system control cabinet is located outside the cargo area and arranged to take suction through the carbon dioxide system discharge piping in each hold. The air samples are aspirated from each hold individually and then routed in sequence through an optical smoke detection chamber. If the system goes into alarm, valves are provided to isolate the discharge piping from the detection system prior to the release of the extinguishing gas. The carbon dioxide system is designed to provide a quantity of extinguishing agent intended for fire control until the ship can make it to a port of refuge. Because of the tight stowage arrangements and the likelihood of deep-seated fires, it is not considered realistic to expect the system to extinguish the fire.

Container Holds. Cargo holds designed for the carriage of shipping containers are similar to those on breakbulk ships; thus the same fire protection measures are provided. Unlike general cargo ships, however, container ship cargo holds are designed with very large hatch covers and do not have 'tween decks. This arrangement permits the entire hold to be loaded by the overhead gantry cranes, without movement of the cargo below decks. The containers are lifted into the holds and aligned and restrained by vertical cell guides. The clearances between the rows of containers is only several inches, making access to the loaded hold impossible. The fire hazards and protection for container holds is the same as for general cargoes. The steel, aluminum, or fiberglass shipping containers further segregate the combustible material and may restrict the spread of fire. However, they can also act as a shield to limit the application of extinguishing agents. The fire risks presented by containerized cargo are considered equivalent to those involved with the breakbulk shipment of commodities.

Bulk Cargo Holds. Bulk cargoes are loose commodities such as grain, ores, minerals, and coal, which are usually loaded and unloaded using conveyor belts, blowers, or grab buckets. The likely fire hazards involving these cargoes are very limited and may involve dust explosions and self-heating of some agricultural commodities. Detection and suppression systems would provide limited benefit and are therefore not required.

Some bulk cargo ships are self-unloaders, with a conveyor belt running beneath the cargo holds. These systems are common on both U.S. and Canadian vessels on the Great Lakes. The holds are hopper-shaped and have doors at the bottom to discharge the cargo onto the belt. At the end of the belt, another set of belts lifts the cargo above the deck and onto a conveyor boom, which can be turned to either side of the vessel to discharge the cargo. These conveyor systems with their numerous rollers, motors, and gearboxes can be the source of fires and should be protected with detection and suppression systems.

Vehicle Holds. Cargo ships designed for the carriage of vehicles can have a variety of different hold arrangements. These ships commonly transport automobiles, trucks, trains, military vehicles, or trailers. There are two basic loading arrangements for these ships. The vehicles may either be lifted on and off the ship by cranes, or they may be driven onto and off of the ship. Lift on/lift off (lo-lo) cargo holds designed for vehicles are similar in configuration to general cargo holds. Cargo holds designed for driving, or roll-on/roll-off (ro-ro) service, have multiple 'tween decks generally with only enough overhead clearance for one level of vehicles, to maximize the load-out of the ship.

If the vehicles are lifted on and off of the ship or if the vehicles are tractor-trailer trucks (briefly driven onto the ship just to deposit the trailer), there is no fuel in the vehicles, in which case the vehicles pose no greater fire hazard than general cargoes. If the vehicles are driven on and off of the ship and contain gasoline and charged batteries, additional fire protection is required. A higher concentration of carbon dioxide is specified by the regulations because the expected fires in the vehicle holds are not slow-developing, deep-seated fires, but flammable liquid fires. Additionally, protected electrical fixtures and mechanical ventilation systems are provided to protect against the ignition of explosive gasoline vapors.

Cargo Tanks. Tank vessels are designed for the carriage of bulk liquids, including crude oil, refined petroleum products, vegetable oils, alcohols, and chemicals. The most common types of tank vessels are designed for the carriage of petroleum products such as crude oil, heating oil, or gasoline. The greatest fire risk on tankships is the chance of flammable cargo vapors coming into contact with an ignition source. To protect against this, the ships are provided with restricted ventilation systems and are often arranged with a cargo pump room located between the engine room and the first row of tanks (in the aft portion of the vessel), to isolate the cargo from the ignition hazards in the engine room. Additionally, all deckhouses and machinery must be located aft of the cargo tank area to minimize contact of flammable vapors with possible ignition sources. Furthermore, the forward-facing portions of the deckhouse that face the cargo area are constructed of fire-rated bulkheads, with closeable steel covers over the windows.

Crude oil carriers are perhaps the most common type of oceangoing tankships. Crude oil carriers are generally designed with a series of large tanks of similar volume. The fire hazards of crude oil vary due to its elemental makeup and the geographic region where it was obtained. Crude oil contains all of the products that are separated during the refining process; thus crude oil includes volatile elements (such as gasoline) that have very low flashpoints. The fire risk of petroleum products is based on the flashpoint and volatility of the liquid. The volatile gases rising from the surface of the petroleum are the fire hazard, and burning gases produce the visible flames. The rate at which the gases are given off is expressed by the product's Reid vapor pressure. In order for the petroleum to burn, it must be mixed with air in the correct ratio. The flammable range for typical petroleum products carried on tankships is between 1 and 10 percent by volume in air. Air spaces in the cargo tanks and piping systems are inerted to further guard against the possibility of a cargo fire. Tankships have inert gas generators or use treated flue gas to provide the oxygen-deficient atmosphere that is needed for this purpose.

The cargo tanks may be connected with the ship's hull, in which case a grounding or collision is likely to result in an explosion and fire involving the cargo, or they may be independent from the hull. The public reaction over the *Exxon Valdez* oil spill in March 1989, where the cargo tanks were connected, resulted in the Oil Pollution Act of 1990. This law requires new tankers built after June 1995 to have independent cargo tanks separated from the hull by a void space. Existing single hull tankers must be retrofitted with double hulls over a 20 year period that began in 1995 and terminates in 2015. The required date of compliance is based on the original build date or date of major conversion of the tankship. The void space between the outer hull and the cargo tank provides added protection against damage in a grounding.

Fire protection of the cargo tank deck area is provided by manually operated deck foam systems that discharge through fixed monitors. The foam system controls, pumps, and concentrate storage tanks are located in a protected room aft in the deckhouse. In the event of a fire, the system can be started from the protected location and aligned to supply foam solution into the mains. The monitors are arranged to allow the crew to fight the fire from aft to forward.

Chemical tankers differ from oil tankers because they carry a variety of different chemical cargoes in varying lot sizes. These ships have numerous smaller tanks, generally of unequal capacity. The deck foam system must be specifically designed to protect against the different chemical and fire hazard properties of the chemicals. In some cases, the chemicals may be water soluble, requiring specialized "polar solvent" foam concentrates. Protection of chemical tankers can be further complicated by the use of cargo heating systems and the use of specialized piping materials. Compatibility of cargo represents an additional factor that complicates chemical tanker protection. Criteria have been established that restrict certain products from being stored in adjacent tanks.[7]

Liquefied natural gas (LNG) carriers are another type of specialized tank vessel seeing expanded service in the United States. Current vessel designs have a capacity sufficient to hold approximately 4.4 million ft^3 (125,000 m^3) of LNG, but tankers with larger capacities are in the design stages. The liquefied natural gas is contained in specially insulated cargo tanks at a temperature of approximately –256°F (–161°C) at atmospheric pressure. By cooling the gas to cryogenic temperatures, the volume of the cargo can be reduced by a factor of 600 for more cost-effective transport. LNG carriers do not have onboard refrigeration capability to keep the liquid cargo cold. Instead, the cargo tanks are heavily insulated; however, a small amount of the liquid will boil off during the voyage. This gas must either be reliquefied or used as fuel in the ship's boilers.

The composition of natural gas depends on the geographic location where it is produced, but consists primarily of methane with small amounts of other hydrocarbons such as ethane, pentane, and butane. When the natural gas is cooled and liquefied, any of the constituent elements that solidify must be removed to prevent damage to the gas compressors and cargo pumps. As a result, the liquefied cargo being carried on the ship is primarily methane. There are two customary LNG cargo tank designs: freestanding spherical tanks and prismatic membrane tanks.

Freestanding spherical tanks are constructed of either aluminum or nickel steel and are mounted inside the steel hull of the ship with the top half of the tank exposed above the main deck. A double hull arrangement is provided with several feet of separation between the tank and the ship's outer hull to protect the tanks from damage in the event of a collision or grounding. The tanks are surrounded by highly efficient insulation, and a metal weather cover is installed over the exposed parts of the sphere.

Membrane tanks conform to the shape of the hull and consist of an inner membrane constructed of a special nickel-iron alloy that has a very low coefficient of thermal expansion at cryogenic temperatures. A second metal or composite outer membrane is provided that is separated from the inner barrier by several layers of insulation. The space between the two barriers is inerted with nitrogen and monitored for leakage. Similar to the spherical tank design, a double hull is provided to protect the tanks in the event of a collision. Membrane tanks are fitted, for the most part, within the hull, allowing such vessels a lower overhead clearance than spherical tank designs.

For both types of LNG tank designs, fixed dry chemical monitors or hand hose lines are required for the protection of the cargo area. The dry chemical system is intended for the protection of the above-deck cargo area, tank domes, exposed cargo piping, and the cargo handling manifolds. In addition, a fixed water spray system is required for cooling the exposed cargo tank domes, the cargo manifolds, and the boundaries of any superstructures facing the cargo area.

Cargo Pumprooms. Tank vessels have cargo pumprooms that are used to convey the cargo onto and off the ship. On some vessels, deep-well pumps are installed in the cargo tanks, eliminating the need for a dedicated pumproom. The electrical equipment located in the pumproom must be electrically safe for hazardous atmospheres. The cargo pumps are usually arranged with electric motors in the engine room and the pump shafts passing through packing glands in the aft pumproom bulkhead. This arrangement eliminates the need for qualified electric motors in the pumproom. The standard protection for cargo pumprooms is a total flooding gaseous agent system. Some tankers may also have a water spray system or a foam system.

Cargo Ship Accommodation Areas. Accommodation areas are the part of the ship where the officers and crew are housed, and may include sleeping, galley, dining, laundry, and recreation areas. The typical crew staffing level on a modern cargo or tankship is about 20 to 30 persons. The officers and higher-ranking crew members have private rooms, whereas the remainder of the crew is assigned to rooms suitable for two to four occupants. U.S. Coast Guard regulations specify that the materials of construction in these areas must be noncombustible. The expected fire risks are limited to furnishings and personal articles placed in the berthing areas. Casualty statistics[6] show that the predominant fire risk in these areas is attributable to electrical sources, followed by failure to observe proper fire prevention practices.

U.S. flag cargo and tank vessels in domestic service are not required to have automatic sprinkler systems or fire detection systems for the protection of the crew accommodation areas. The primary fire protection measure is the use of noncombustible materials of construction. SOLAS allows three options for the design of cargo ship accommodation areas. They may be constructed of noncombustible materials (Method IC); or they may be constructed of limited combustible materials in conjunction with an automatic sprinkler system and a smoke detection system for the protection of all corridors, stairways, and escape routes (Method IIC); or they may be constructed of limited combustible materials in conjunction with an areawide detection system (Method IIIC). Only Method IC is accepted for U.S. flag vessels.

Passenger Ship Accommodation Areas. The fire risks anticipated in the accommodation areas on passenger vessels are the same as those on cargo ships; however, passenger ships have many more passengers who are not familiar with the vessel and there are public spaces such as casinos, restaurants, spas, movie theaters, and lounges in addition to the berthing areas. These larger public spaces present a higher level of risk because of the greater number of occupants that would have to be evacuated in an emergency. The furnishings in many of the public spaces also have the potential for a higher rate of heat release than those found in a berthing area—for example, a theater that has upholstered seating or a sales shop with combustible merchandise. SOLAS requires areawide automatic sprinkler protection and smoke detector coverage of all of the accommodation areas. The U.S. domestic vessel regulations vary depending on the size of the ship and the number of passengers carried. The individual vessel regulations should be consulted for these requirements.

Small domestic passenger vessels (Subchapter T and K vessels) are sometimes used for dinner cruises. The public spaces on these vessels may have a buffet line set up with portable, solid alcohol food warming equipment. Some vessels may also have casino gaming machines that are constructed with combustible materials and are electrically powered. The higher level of potential fire risk on these vessels is addressed by two additional provisions in the regulations. A limit on the allowable combustible load in the public spaces is applied to restrict the fuel load. For general public spaces, the maximum combustible load is limited to 7.5 lb/ft^2 (37.5 kg/m^2), considering the total volume of all construction and outfitting materials, furniture, furnishings, carpets, draperies, interior finish materials, electrical cable insulation, plastic light diffusers, mattresses, and similar materials. In addition, all accommodation, service, and control spaces must be equipped with a smoke detection system.

Passenger vessels may be designed with architectural features such as balconies and atriums (Figure 21.10.8). The domestic passenger vessel regulations permit atriums if they are of sufficient size for the occupants to be able to observe the outbreak of a fire at any location in the atrium. This concept is based on the minimum opening dimensions taken from the NFPA *101*®, *Life Safety Code*®, requirements for buildings. In addition, areawide automatic sprinklers, smoke detection, and a smoke control system are specified. The smoke control system must be designed to clear all of the smoke from the atrium within 10 minutes.

FIRE PREVENTION ON SHIPS

The basic fire protection philosophy applied to ships is to limit the use of combustible materials of construction, thereby restricting the available fire growth rates. This concept is applied to the materials of construction used for the decks, bulkheads, ceilings, interior finish materials, and any items incidental to the construction of the ship. There is still the possibility, however, that the vessel's furnishings, galley supplies, trash, and similar items can add up to a significant fire risk if safe operational practices are not followed. Although the regulations are not specific regarding housekeeping and fire prevention issues, good marine practice dictates that the handling and use of combustible materials, flammable liquids, and ignition sources be controlled. It is essential that the storage of consumable goods and their packaging be controlled to isolate combustible materials from sources of ignition.

FIGURE 21.10.8 Typical Atrium on a Passenger Ship

Important changes to the international regulations were adopted in 1997 that make fire prevention training mandatory for licensed seafarers serving onboard SOLAS vessels. This is intended to make the crew aware of the need to follow safe practices in the day-to-day operation of the ship. The International Convention on Standards of Training, Certification, and Watchkeeping for Seafarers (STCW), 1978, sets qualifications for masters, officers, and watchkeeping personnel on seagoing merchant ships. These requirements became effective on February 1, 1997, and require candidates for licenses and other certificates to establish competence through both subject-area examinations and demonstration of skills in basic safety training.

Controlling Flammable and Combustible Liquids Storage

The control of flammable and combustible liquids used for daily maintenance and repair activities is an important marine fire prevention practice. Steel lockers should be provided for the storage of paint and other flammable liquids. Hazardous liquids should be stored in the approved lockers at the end of each work shift. It is particularly important to store these materials in protected lockers on fiberglass and wooden hull vessels. The preferred location for these lockers is on the open deck, although the engineer's stores (such as lubricants and solvents) are ordinarily kept inside an approved flammable liquids cabinet in the engine room. Stowage of ordinary combustibles in paint and flammable liquid lockers should not be permitted. In the engine room, lube oil and fuel spills should be routinely cleaned up to keep the bilges from accumulating waste oils. Oily wiping rags should be stowed in sealed metal containers to guard against their spontaneous combustion.

Controlling Fuel Oil Transfers

Fuel oil transfers introduce the possibility of flammable or combustible vapors being released at the dock and in the vicinity of the fuel manifolds on board the ship. Precautions also need to be taken prior to and during fueling operations to lessen the chance of a fuel spill, caused by a fuel hose leak or the overfilling of a tank on the ship. All smoking, open lights, and other ignition sources should be prohibited in the vicinity of the fuel manifold, and only authorized personnel should be allowed to remain in the area. All open doors and windows near the manifold should be closed. The mooring lines should be confirmed tight before fueling is begun. An effective means of communication should be available at all times to permit the rapid shutdown of the fuel pumps in case of an emergency. A calibrated means of determining tank levels should be continuously available to prevent overfilling the ship's fuel tanks. If there are language difficulties between the crew and the fuel terminal, prior agreement should be made on the verbal expressions to be used for the transfer operations. Appropriate lighting should be readily available in the vicinity of the manifold in the event of a fuel spill.

Controlling Flammable and Combustible Cargo Vapors

On tank vessels, there is a significant fire risk from the release of flammable or combustible cargo vapors. To minimize vapor production, tankships have an inert gas system that maintains an inert atmosphere in the cargo tank and piping system vapor spaces, except when the tanks are required to be gas-free. Inert gas systems are designed to inert empty cargo tanks by displacing the atmospheric air in the tanks with inert gas. When the tanks have been inerted, the cargo can be loaded without the fear of an explosion. During the voyage, the inert gas system supplies makeup volume to maintain the oxygen content in the cargo tank air spaces below 8 percent oxygen by volume, at a positive pressure. When the cargo is offloaded, additional inert gas is supplied to the tank to keep the atmosphere out of the flammable range.

If any work is to be done inside of the cargo tanks, they must first be cleaned and gas-freed. This operation poses a particular risk because the inert gas blanket is pumped out of the tank and air is introduced. In the process, the tank atmosphere changes from a fuel-rich condition to a condition that will not support combustion. The danger of this is the intermediate condition when the tank atmosphere is between the upper and lower flammable limits. An ignition source or static discharge while the tank is in the explosive range could have serious results. Ships in port or a shipyard must engage a marine chemist to certify tanks as being safe for workers or safe for hot work as the job requirements dictate.

NFPA 306, *Standard for the Control of Gas Hazards on Vessels,* provides further technical details on the role of marine chemists. Marine chemists are certificated to perform this service through an industry-sponsored certification program that is administered by NFPA. Basically, the marine chemist must verify that the concentration of oxygen is sufficient to support life and that the concentration of flammable or combustible vapors is below their flammable limits. The marine chemist also verifies that toxic vapors or substances that are harmful to humans are not present in significant concentrations. If any tank or void space entry is to be done while the vessel is at sea, the ships' crew must first verify that the tanks are safe for entry following similar confined space safe practices to those of the marine chemist. In all cases, portable gas analyzers are used to verify that oxygen levels are adequate and cargo vapors are below their flammable range.

STRUCTURAL FIRE PROTECTION

Domestic Service Vessels

The origins of shipboard structural fire protection measures can be traced to the 1930s, when the U.S. Department of Commerce first established regulations for vessel construction in the wake of the *Morro Castle* disaster and the U.S. Senate investigation that followed. The regulations mandated the use of noncombustible insulation and bulkhead panels to protect the steel structure of passenger ships. The laboratory fire test method originally used to approve these materials was ASTM E119, which, with minor modifications, is still used today. In the years that have followed, additional laboratory test methods have been developed for noncombustibility of materials, flame spread on interior finishes, and the fire resistance of deck coverings.

Shipboard structural fire protection is based on the use of fire barriers that are rated for either 60 minutes of structural integrity (designated A-class divisions) or 30 minutes of structural integrity (designated B-class divisions). Marine fire barriers are further classified in terms of their ability to limit temperature rise on the unexposed side of the barrier. Alphanumeric fire ratings are assigned to barriers to indicate their tested temperature rise limitation. For example, an A-0 division provides structural integrity for 60 minutes but provides no temperature rise limitation on the unexposed side of the barrier. Such barriers are typically used for exterior bulkheads that separate interior spaces from the weather decks. An A-30 division provides 60 minutes of structural integrity and will also prevent the average temperature rise on the unexposed side of the barrier from exceeding 284°F (140°C) above ambient for at least 30 minutes. The highest fire rating used is A-60. These barriers can be used to form main vertical zones, separate stair towers from adjacent accommodation areas, or to separate engine rooms from accommodation areas.

The present Coast Guard regulations for fire protection materials are contained in 46 CFR 164. These regulations detail the necessary fire tests that must be conducted for a material to be Coast Guard type-approved for use on U.S. flag vessels. The Coast Guard does not perform the actual fire testing of the materials. The manufacturer is required to have their materials tested to the Coast Guard criteria at an independent testing laboratory that has been accepted by the Coast Guard. Materials that successfully pass the required tests are issued a type approval certificate and the product is added to the list of approved materials posted on the Coast Guard's website.

The current list of approved structural fire protection materials is broken down into the following five categories:

- Deck coverings 46 CFR 164.006
- Structural insulation 46 CFR 164.007
- Bulkhead panels 46 CFR 164.008
- Noncombustible materials 46 CFR 164.009
- Interior finishes 46 CFR 164.012

The Coast Guard publishes Navigation and Vessel Inspection Circular (NVIC) 9-97, which explains the use of these materials for ship construction in detail.

The IMO International Code for Application of Fire Test Procedures (FTP Code) became mandatory for all international service vessels constructed after December 2003. Thus, materials type approved under the categories in the previous list are no longer acceptable for use on board U.S. flag vessels in international service. They may only be used on board domestic service vessels.

Deck Coverings. Deck coverings provide A-60 fire resistance for steel decks. As the name implies, these materials are installed on the top of the steel structure. The test method for deck coverings contains three specific test criteria: limited organic (carbon) content, limited smoke generation, and fire resistance and integrity. Although these requirements are not identical to the noncombustibility test, the resulting performance is very close. Therefore, it is assumed that the materials approved under 164.006 are noncombustible when used in their intended purpose as deck coverings. A limited amount of combustible content is permitted for deck coverings to allow the use of materials better suited as flooring surfaces. Deck coverings are typically cementitious materials, such as oxychloride cements, that are troweled in place.

Structural Insulations. Structural insulations form the primary fire boundaries that separate galleys and machinery spaces from accommodation areas. They are also used to form main vertical zone (MVZ) boundaries on passenger ships. Because the major subdivisions on board ships consist of steel bulkheads (walls) and decks (floors), a system has been devised that uses the steel structure as a component of the required fire separations—hence the term *structural insulation.* The fire test method described in 46 CFR 164.007 requires a 40 in. by 60 in. (100 cm by 150 cm) test sample to be attached to a 0.19 in. (5 mm) thick steel plate, which is considered representative of typical shipboard construction practice. The test specimen is then mounted in a vertical furnace with the insulation on the exposed surface of the test specimen. The assembly is then subjected to the standard time-temperature curve described in ASTM E119 for a 60 minute period. During the test, the average temperature rise on the unexposed side of the plate must not exceed 250°F (140°C) at the end of 60 minutes and the temperature at any one point cannot rise more than 325°F (180°C) above ambient.

A steel plate 0.19 in. (5 mm) thick will pass the standard fire test for a 60 minute period, however, without any limit on the unexposed surface temperature. A bare steel bulkhead is designated an A-0 class barrier. If approved structural insulation is applied, the thickness of insulation tested will limit the temperature rise of the steel boundary for 60 minutes. An insulated fire barrier with this amount of protection is designated an A-60 barrier. It has been found that 75 percent of this thickness will provide at least 30 minutes of fire endurance (A-30 barrier), and 50 percent of this thickness provides at least 15 minutes of protection (A-15 barrier). Structural insulations can be field applied to either side of a bulkhead or to the underside of a deck to form A-class boundaries, based on their testing under 46 CFR 164.007. Structural insulations are typically fibrous batts, or blankets, which may be faced with foil or other noncombustible materials. Calcium silicate panels and spray-on mixtures are also typical.

Bulkhead Panels. The secondary fire separations on ships are formed by non-load-bearing bulkhead panels used to enclose individual rooms and corridors. This construction technique is similar to the use of gypsum board panels in buildings, except that the panels are joined together by a system of metal tracks and connector hardware instead of wooden studs, because only noncombustible materials may be used. The connection system is traditionally called a joinerwork system. B-class bulkheads are typically either 0.75 in. (19 mm) thick homogeneous mineral board panels or 2 in. (50 mm) thick steel-faced, mineral wool sandwich panels. B-class bulkheads are intended to be installed in a single thickness, except where they are used as a component of A-60 class barriers. In such a case, there could be multiple layers of the B-class panels combined with structural insulations.

A variety of laminates and decorative covers can be used to conceal the joiner system and cover the panel surfaces. The tape and spackling system used for buildings is not practical on board ships because of vibration-induced cracking. The bulkhead panels used in this system are approved using the fire test method described in 46 CFR 164.008, which is intended to test the panel and its joinerwork as a complete system. This test is conducted in a vertical furnace, similar to that used for structural insulations; however, the sample size is 50 ft^2 (4.65 m^2) with a height of at least 8 ft (2.44 m).

Bulkhead panels are usually installed on ships with penetrations for lights, receptacles, switches, and controls. Because of this, the laboratory tests generally include a specimen with representative electrical fittings. Bulkhead panels that pass the required fire tests for a 30 minute period are designated B-0 bulkheads. Panels that pass the fire integrity tests for 30 minutes and also provide at least 15 minutes of limited temperature rise on the unexposed surface of the barrier are designated B-15 bulkheads. B-15 bulkheads are qualified to be used as a component of steel A-class construction to offer 60 minutes of fire endurance when combined with other insulating materials.

Noncombustible Materials. The materials used in shipboard construction must be qualified as noncombustible materials before they are subjected to the furnace testing used to establish their fire resistance. Materials that are approved as noncombustible materials must either pass the fire test method in 46 CFR 164.009 or be inherently noncombustible. The test requires a 4.88 in.^{3} (80 cm^3) sample to be lowered into the test apparatus, which has been preheated to 1382°F (750°C). The pass/fail criteria include maximum temperature rise, flaming conditions, and a percent mass loss as follows:

- No more than 122°F (50°C) furnace temperature rise
- No more than 122°F (50°C) specimen surface temperature rise
- No more than 10 seconds total duration of flaming
- No more than 50 percent weight loss

This test is very stringent and thus, low flame spread and fire-resistant materials will not pass the test and do not qualify as noncombustible materials.

The Coast Guard considers the following materials as inherently noncombustible and no fire tests are required:

- Glass, clay, ceramics, or uncoated glass fiber
- All metals except magnesium or magnesium alloys
- Portland cement, gypsum, concrete with aggregates of only sand, gravel, vermiculite, silica, perlite, or pumice
- Woven or knitted glass fabric containing not more than 2.5 percent lubricant by mass

Interior Finishes. Interior finishes are coatings, overlays, or veneers that are used for decorative purposes. Interior finishes are normally applied to the exposed surfaces of bulkheads, ceilings, and decks, including exposed surfaces in concealed spaces. The two types of interior finishes used on domestic service vessels are approved finishes and combustible finishes. An approved interior finish is required to have a limited flame spread and smoke developed rating; a combustible interior finish may be a material with an unlimited flame spread or smoke developed rating.

Approved interior finishes are required in corridors and stairway enclosures as well as in concealed spaces within accommodation, service, and safety areas. They are also required in low-fire-risk accommodation spaces, which are sometimes required on board passenger ships. Combustible finishes may be installed in all other areas subject to thickness and volume restrictions. On all ships, the maximum allowed thickness of a combustible veneer is 0.075 in. (2 mm). On passenger ships, an additional volume limitation is imposed to restrict the volume of the installed veneer plus any moldings, trim, or decorations to a maximum of 0.1 in. (2.5 mm) times the aggregate surface area of the walls and ceilings in the space. This allows the use of decorative trim pieces of irregular shape. If thicker veneers or trim are installed, they must pass the noncombustibility test of 46 CFR 164.009.

Approved interior finishes must comply with 46 CFR 164.012, which requires the materials to be subjected to either ASTM E84 or NFPA 255, *Standard Method of Test of Surface Burning Characteristics of Building Materials.* The acceptance criteria for either test method is a flame spread of 20 or less and a smoke developed rating of 10 or less. The interior finish materials must be tested using the same mounting method or adhesives that are intended for use in the shipyard.

In addition to the type-approved material categories for deck coverings, structural insulations, bulkhead panels, noncombustible materials, and interior finishes, the Coast Guard has developed accepted construction specifications for the design of fire doors, fire dampers, and electrical and piping penetrations. These construction specifications are based on standard shipyard practices, and, as a result, the materials are not required to be fire tested. The details of these construction requirements are listed in the various subchapters applicable to each vessel category. Type approvals are not issued for these materials.

International Service Vessels

CFRs historically contained the requirements for Coast Guard approval of structural fire protection materials and assemblies aboard U.S. flag vessels on both domestic and international routes. Coast Guard approved materials were accepted for vessels on international voyages, because SOLAS did not include fire testing procedures. The IMO Subcommittee on Fire Protection recently decided that uniformly applied fire test procedures should be developed and made mandatory to assure that structural fire protection materials do not deviate significantly among the member states. Effective July 1, 1998, the fire test methods in the International Code for the Application of Fire Test Procedures (FTP Code) were made a mandatory part of SOLAS. All U.S. flag ships that require a SOLAS safety certificate must now use structural fire protection materials that have been tested in accordance with the FTP Code instead of the CFR. The fire test procedures in the FTP Code cover more types of materials than the CFR does, and require the completion of complex fire test protocols using test apparatus that is newer than that used for domestic service materials.

The FTP Code is divided into parts, each dealing with a specific set of performance criteria as follows:

- Part 1: Noncombustibility test
- Part 2: Smoke and toxicity test
- Part 3: Test for Class A and Class B divisions
- Part 4: Test for fire door control systems
- Part 5: Test for surface flammability
- Part 6: Test for primary deck coverings
- Part 7: Test for vertically supported textiles and films
- Part 8: Test for upholstered furniture
- Part 9: Test for bedding components

To implement the new FTP Code requirements, the Coast Guard established the following type approval categories:

• Deck assemblies	164.105
• Primary deck coverings	164.106
• Structural insulations	164.107
• Bulkhead panels	164.108
• Noncombustible materials	164.109
• Structural ceilings	164.110
• Draperies, curtains, and suspended textiles	164.111
• Interior finishes	164.112
• Floor coverings	164.117
• Fire doors	164.136
• Windows	164.137
• Penetration seals (firestops)	164.138
• Fire dampers	164.139
• Bedding components	164.142
• Upholstered furniture	164.144
• Fire-restricting materials for high-speed craft	164.201
• Fire-resisting divisions for high-speed craft	164.207

U.S. flag ships that engage only in domestic voyages have the option of using structural fire protection materials that comply with either the CFRs or the FTP Code, because the FTP Code approval tests requirements are deemed to be more stringent. U.S. flag vessels that engage in international service must meet the FTP Code.

There are many differences between the FTP Code tests and the existing Coast Guard regulations. One major variation is between the Coast Guard's deck covering test and the FTP Code's primary deck covering test. The FTP Code defines primary deck covering as the first layer of a floor construction that is applied directly on top of the deck plating and is inclusive of any primary coat, anticorrosive compound, or adhesive that is necessary to provide protection or adhesion to the deck plating. Primary deck coverings may be installed beneath a floor covering such as tile or carpet, in which case they are tested for ignitability. If the primary deck covering will be used as an exposed surface, it must be tested for surface flammability and smoke and toxic gas production. Primary deck coverings are not tested for their fire-resisting ability. This category has no counterpart in the CFR.

The FTP Code requires structural insulations to be tested in the orientation in which the material will be installed, that is, materials to be installed on both bulkheads and decks must be tested in vertical and horizontal orientations. The bulkhead insulation being tested must be installed on the side of the steel bulkhead not facing the fire (i.e., on the cold side), and deck insulation must be installed on the hot side (i.e., below the steel deck). Insulation tested on only one side is issued a restricted approval, limiting the installation to locations where there is no fire hazard from the uninsulated side.

The FTP Code requires a steel core to be part of a B-class bulkhead panel test assembly for panels that are to be used as a component of A-class construction. To receive an unrestricted approval, two separate tests must be conducted: one test with the B-class bulkhead facing the fire and one test with the steel core facing the fire.

Interior finish materials tested to the FTP Code must pass a flame spread test using a radiant panel test apparatus that differs from the apparatus used to test interior finishes for U.S. domestic approval. In addition, they must pass smoke and toxicity testing in accordance with ISO 5659:1994.

The Coast Guard has not previously issued type approval certificates for fire doors, windows, or fire dampers. However, since the FTP Code requires these materials to meet the referenced fire resistance tests, the Coast Guard has established approval categories for these items.

Coast Guard type approval of structural fire protection materials requires the establishment of a follow-up inspection program monitored by an independent testing laboratory or other accepted organization to ensure that the materials shipped from the factory are representative of the test specimens. If production changes occur because of refinements in the base materials or the dimensions of the approved materials, additional fire testing must be conducted to confirm that the fire performance of the material has not been reduced.

High-Speed Craft

In the latter part of the twentieth century, the maritime industry began developing high-speed vessels for applications such as for use as rapid commuter ferries. Unfortunately, the prescriptive fire protection regulations in SOLAS did not allow the freedom to design and build fast ships that were cost effective. The traditional fire protection materials required by SOLAS add too much weight to a high-speed vessel's design. In response, IMO has developed the High Speed Craft Code (HSC Code) as a valid alternative to SOLAS for designers, builders, and operators to use for ships that meet the definition of a high-speed craft (HSC). HSCs are typically vessels 131 to 328 ft (40 to 100 m) in length, used to transport people, automobiles, and cargo at speeds generally in excess of 20 knots and, in some cases, up to 50 knots. Among other differences from SOLAS, the HSC Code allows the use of lighter-weight materials for the ship's structure, compartment divisions, bulkhead and ceiling linings, and furniture components. Materials of construction must be either noncombustible as defined by SOLAS or fire restricting. Fire-restricting materials are defined by the HSC Code as having low flame-spread characteristics, limited rate of heat release, and low smoke and toxic gas production. Fire-restricting materials are qualified using the ISO 9705 room corner test for ship's structures and compartment linings and the ISO 5660 cone calorimeter test for furniture components (not including upholstery).

Coast Guard Type Approval Program

All structural fire protection materials installed on U.S. flag vessels must be Coast Guard type approved. There are two methods for obtaining type approval; the type approval can be issued by the U.S. Coast Guard, or a European Community representative can issue the approval on behalf of the Coast Guard.

For a Coast Guard–issued type approval, the manufacturer is required to submit the product to a Coast Guard accepted independent laboratory for testing. When the laboratory testing is completed, the test report, pertinent component drawings, installation instructions, and the follow-up services agreement are submitted to the Coast Guard for review. If the appropriate acceptance criteria are satisfied, a type approval certificate is issued and the product is added to the list of approved materials on the Coast Guard website.

Coast Guard–issued type approvals are required to be under a production control or follow-up program conducted by the testing laboratory. The laboratory is required to visit the factory to witness the fabrication of the test specimen prior to conducting the approval tests. After the type approval certificate is issued, the laboratory is required to make periodic factory visits to ensure that the raw materials and production methods for the approved materials have not changed and that the materials being produced remain representative of the specimen that was tested.

The other means for obtaining type approval is to have the material tested at a European Community recognized laboratory. On February 27, 2004, the United States entered into a Mutual Recognition Agreement (MRA) with the European Community (EC) that recognizes type approvals issued by either party. Under the terms of the agreement, manufacturers can obtain a Coast Guard type approval directly from a European Community Notified Body.

MRA type approvals are issued by the EC Notified Body without any review or approval by the Coast Guard. The materials are tested at laboratories specified by the Notified Bodies, using test methods that follow the FTP Code. The Coast Guard does not maintain a listing of MRA approved materials.

FIRE PROTECTION SYSTEMS

The Coast Guard's philosophy on shipboard fire protection emphasizes the use of noncombustible materials and limited fire loads to control the magnitude and severity of expected fires. The use of flammable and combustible liquid fuels and cargoes could result in fires that require supplemental fire-extinguishing systems. The CFR, therefore, specifies protection of engine rooms, larger generator rooms, cargo holds and tanks, certain galley areas, and cargo pumprooms with fixed fire-extinguishing systems. Most of these systems are designed for manual activation to prevent an inadvertent discharge from adversely impacting operation of the ship.

Fire Main System

A fire pump and fire main system are required for the general protection of all shipboard areas. The fire main is intended as the primary means of fire protection in the accommodation and service areas. It is considered a supplemental system for the protection of the machinery spaces and the cargo areas, which are provided with other specialized fire-extinguishing systems. The fire pumps can be sized to supply the fire main and other water-based extinguishing systems such as foam systems, sprinkler systems, or water spray systems. The fire main is required to be arranged so that effective hose station coverage is available in all areas of a vessel. In the fire hose station on board a cruise ship shown in Figure 21.10.9, note the preconnected hose and nozzle, gate valve, and spanner wrench.

Each part of 46 CFR lists specific requirements for the number and capacity of fire pumps. The water supply capacity is based on the expected fire-fighting needs for vessels of the size and service regulated by that part of the rules. Typically, the main fire pump is an independently driven electric motor pump located in the main machinery space, although diesel engine and steam-driven pumps may be encountered. If multiple pumps are required, the pumps must be located in separate fire areas to prevent damage from a fire or accident from impacting all of the pumps.

In addition to separation of the pumps, the regulations also specify that the arrangement of sea connections and sources of power shall be such as to ensure that a fire in any one space will not put all of the fire pumps out of operation. Fire pumps take their suction from an opening in the hull of the ship, called a sea connection. It is common for ships to have several sea connections to supply water pumps for cooling of the machinery, as well as the fire pump.

Because of the many different hose coupling dimensions and thread patterns found worldwide, it is likely that the fire hoses on a ship may not easily connect to those in the various ports visited by the ship. To provide a backup means of supplying fire-fighting water to vessels in port, a universal adapter flange, called an international shore connection, was developed. International shore connections are required on all SOLAS vessels; they consist of a flat-bolted flange that can be attached to the ship's fire main.The flange has a flat face on one side and a permanently attached coupling that fits the ship's hydrants and hose connections on the other side. The international shore connection is bolted to a mating flange from the port using a gasket suitable for 150 psi (1034 kPa) service, together with four ⅝ in. (16 mm) bolts, 2 in. (50 mm) long through a predrilled bolt pattern (Figure 21.10.10).

Automatic Sprinkler Systems

Until recently, automatic sprinkler systems were required on large passenger vessels for the protection of only cargo spaces considered accessible during the voyage. In 1993, the domestic commercial vessel industry expressed an interest in constructing casino gambling vessels and dinner cruise vessels, using alternative designs that featured large, open public areas. Some proposed designs also incorporated atriums that connected multiple decks. The structural fire protection regulations require main vertical zone bulkheads every 131 ft (40 m), which effectively prevent the use of this "open space" concept. For design flexibility, the Coast Guard developed a method to permit the use of this new concept without main vertical zones if areawide automatic sprinklers are installed. In 1996, NFPA 13, *Standard for the Installation of Sprinkler Systems,* was modified to include a Coast Guard–sponsored chapter on marine sprinkler systems, which is used for the design of sprinkler systems on board domestic service vessels. NFPA 13 may also be used to design sprinkler systems for SOLAS vessels, provided the SOLAS requirements for automatic sprinklers, which may exceed those in NFPA 13, are also satisfied.

Marine sprinkler systems are arranged differently from those in buildings because of the quality of the water supply. In buildings, potable fresh water from tanks or the public water supply mains is generally available, whereas the water supply on ships is usually taken from salt water, or water which may contain sediment or other foreign materials. Because of this, clogging and corrosion of the sprinkler system piping and components can occur if they are not designed to accommodate

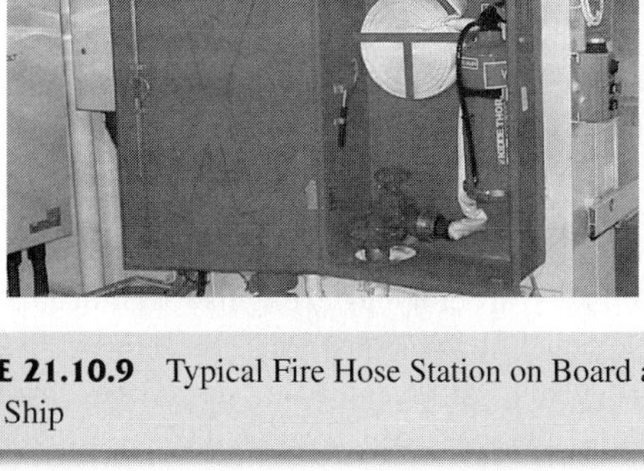

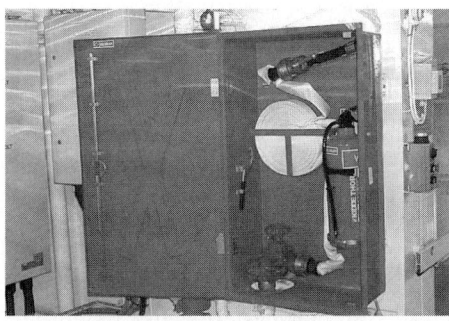

FIGURE 21.10.9 Typical Fire Hose Station on Board a Cruise Ship

FIGURE 21.10.10 Typical International Shore Connection Manifold Arrangement

raw water supplies. Additional components are thus required to maintain wet pipe marine sprinkler systems filled with potable fresh water. A limited capacity tank is also provided to supply the system for a short period, until the seawater pumps can pressurize the system. In the event the system operates, the sprinkler piping is flushed with fresh water before it is put back into service to prevent degradation. The limited exposure to salt water does not adversely affect the system piping.

Manual Sprinkler Systems

Manual sprinkler systems are intended for the protection of partially enclosed vehicle decks where the use of total flooding carbon dioxide is not practical. The systems use open head 3/8 or 0.375 in. (9.5 mm) sprinkler heads, arranged to discharge on the manual activation of a deluge or control valve. The systems are arranged to protect zones of approximately equal size on each deck area. The zones are overlapped so the end sprinklers on adjacent zones protect the same deck area.

Water Mist Systems

Marine water mist extinguishing systems were originally developed as a replacement for total flooding Halon 1301 systems in engine rooms. However, it was learned that they could be used as an alternative to automatic sprinklers for the protection of light-hazard accommodation and service occupancies. Because of their much lower flow rates, water mist system pipe sizes can be reduced, yielding measurable savings in cost and weight. The lesser amounts of water expelled by mist systems also benefit the overall stability of a vessel. Water mist systems require specialized strainers, components, and piping due to the very small orifices in the discharge nozzles.

Design and approval information regarding water mist systems intended for the protection of accommodation and service areas is contained in IMO Resolution A.800 (19), adopted in November 1995. This guide includes component testing information for water mist nozzles that is based on UL standard 199. It also contains four different fire test protocols using stateroom, corridor, public space, and shopping and storage area fuel packages. The tests are conducted in mock-up full-scale rooms that are considered representative of shipboard hazards. The acceptance criteria are based on maximum ceiling temperatures or a combination of maximum temperatures and damage to simulated furniture placed in the test rooms. Additional information about water mist system design is contained in NFPA 750, *Standard on Water Mist Fire Protection Systems.*

Design and approval information for total flooding water mist systems for the protection of machinery spaces and pump-rooms is based on IMO MSC/Circ. 1165, *Revised Guidelines for the Approval of Equivalent Water-Based Fire-Extinguishing Systems for Machinery Spaces and Cargo Pump-Rooms.* This test procedure contains three separate elements: component test standards that evaluate the suitability of the water mist nozzles for use in the marine environment, fire-extinguishing tests that confirm the nozzle's ability to extinguish a variety of fuel oil and heptane pan and spray fires, and thermal management tests that determine the nozzle's ability to cool the test enclosure to less than 212°F (100°C) no later than 5 minutes after the activation of the system. Test experience with total flooding water mist systems has shown that it is not currently possible to positively extrapolate design parameters from a tested volume to a larger protected space; however, advances with computer modeling may allow this in the future. As a result, Coast Guard type approvals for total flooding systems are limited to installation in protected shipboard spaces with a volume no larger than that tested.

The 2000 SOLAS amendments require ships with engine rooms larger than 17,650 ft^3 (500 m^3) to have a fixed local application fire-fighting system in addition to a total flooding system. Casualty data has shown that fuel oil leaks and pressurized sprays striking heated surfaces are the leading causes of engine room fires. The requirement for a local application system is intended to provide a system capable of immediate release to cool the machinery space and limit fire damage until the engineering staff can be evacuated and the total flooding system is activated. Design and approval information for fixed local application water mist systems for the protection of high-hazard areas in machinery spaces is based on IMO MSC/Circ. 913, *Guidelines for the Approval of Fixed Water-Based Local Application Fire-Fighting Systems for Use in Category A Machinery Spaces.* Although the local application system is not intended to have the capability of extinguishing typical flammable liquid fires, its early activation can many times lead to extinguishment before the total flooding system is discharged. On ships with a total flooding water mist system, a branch of the total flooding system can be arranged with appropriate section valves to act as the local application system, provided the nozzles have successfully passed the required MSC/Circ. 913 fire testing.

Foam Systems

Foam fire-fighting systems are approved for tank vessel deck protection, machinery space boiler flat protection, and helicopter deck protection on mobile offshore drilling rigs and offshore supply vessels. Foam systems intended for marine use are required to be Coast Guard type approved as a system, because standard industrial foam system products installed on board ships may not provide effective protection. The primary concern is the tankship structure and piping systems that can be heated to temperatures significantly above the breakdown temperature of the foam blanket. The mass of steel components on ships is much greater than that typically involved with shoreside foam system applications. Thus, marine foam concentrates are tested to ensure that they provide superior breakdown resistance when in contact with hot metal surfaces, and that they continue to provide a seal adjacent to heated metal surfaces for an extended cooling period.

Another significant concern with tankship fires is the large quantities of flammable liquids available for combustion. The laboratory testing of marine foam liquid concentrates, therefore, evaluates their capability to extinguish significant, in-depth flammable liquid fires.

A third concern is the use of seawater to supply the foam system. Standard fire-fighting foams used by municipal fire departments are only tested for their fire-extinguishing capability using fresh water. When they are mixed with salt water, these foam concentrates do not have equal fire-extinguishing effectiveness. The Coast Guard approval tests thus require the use of synthetic seawater.

The final concern is a foam concentrate's ability to contain reignited areas of the fuel after sections of the foam blanket have been disturbed. Coast Guard–approved foam liquids are approved by using a small-scale laboratory test derived from Federal Specification O-F-555C, which is no longer in print. The test standard currently appears in Annex F of NFPA 11, *Standard for Low-, Medium-, and High-Expansion Foam.* Breakdown of the foam on contact with heated surfaces is judged by the use of a square 10 ft by 10 ft (3 m by 3 m) steel test pan, 3 ft (0.9 m) in height. The fuel in the test pan is ignited and allowed to burn for 60 seconds before foam application is started. The fire-fighting effectiveness of the foam is evaluated by the use of 75 gal (284 L) of gasoline as the test fuel. The sealability of the foam is determined by the use of a square test pan instead of a round one, in conjunction with a torch test. The foam being tested is required to cover the entire fuel surface, including corners, in 2 minutes. It must also extinguish the test fire within 5 minutes. A burning torch is then passed over the foam blanket beginning 10 minutes after the start of foam application. The torch is eventually touched into the blanket to ensure that an effective seal remains present. The burnback resistance is determined at the end of the test by removing a 6 in. by 6 in. (152 mm by 152 mm) square section of the foam blanket and igniting the exposed fuel. The area of the burning fuel cannot increase beyond an opening measuring 20 in. by 20 in. (508 mm by 508 mm) after 5 minutes of burning.

During the laboratory fire testing, the quality of the foam is measured through a determination of its expansion ratio and its ability to retain water. The foam expansion ratio is measured by comparing the weight of a fixed volume of aerated foam to the weight of the same volume of nonaerated foam solution. Most of the foam concentrates approved for shipboard use have an expansion ratio between 6 to 1 and 12 to 1. The foam's ability to retain water is measured by determining the amount of time it takes for one-quarter of the water to drain out of an aerated foam sample. This measurement is called the foam's 25 percent drainage time.

The quality of the foam used to successfully pass the laboratory fire tests is characterized by its expansion ratio and 25 percent drainage time. The system discharge nozzles and monitors are flow tested to ensure that they produce foam that is comparable to that measured in the laboratory fire tests, thereby ensuring that the foam produced on the ship will be of the same quality. The construction of all devices used in an approved foam system must ensure that they will operate under the extreme environmental conditions likely in the marine environment. Foam system components are installed at exposed locations on deck, where they are routinely exposed to salt spray. Because of this, only corrosion-resistant materials, including stainless steel, brass, or bronze, are acceptable.

In addition to the usual petroleum products, some ships may carry chemical cargoes such as polar solvents, ethers, alcohols, and ketones. Protection of the cargo areas on these ships requires a different design approach because these types of cargoes are partially or completely miscible with water. Such cargoes require an alcohol-resistant foam concentrate capable of forming a barrier between the foam and the cargo. Significantly increased foam application rates may be necessary, depending on the fire hazard of the product. As a result, it is essential that the chemical properties and stowage locations of the cargo are known, to allow the design limitations of the system to be established. Systems may be designed either to protect against the "worst-case" product stored in any tank on the vessel or to protect specific chemicals located only in designated tanks. Because of the large amounts of foam required for "worst-case" products, designing for specific products or a group of products with similar fire-extinguishing requirements is a more typical situation. For further technical information regarding marine foam systems, see NFPA 11.

Carbon Dioxide Systems

The regulations in 46 CFR require the installation of total flooding carbon dioxide systems for the protection of machinery spaces and similar enclosed spaces where there is a possibility of a fire involving flammable or combustible liquids. Carbon dioxide extinguishing systems are also required for the protection of cargo holds whenever combustible Class A materials are carried.

For the successful use of shipboard total flooding carbon dioxide systems, it is necessary to discharge the system and then allow a "soak" time for the heated structures surrounding the space to cool below the reignition temperature of the fuel. Shipboard carbon dioxide systems are designed for a single application. After the system is discharged, there is no backup quantity of agent available. It is critical that the protected space be kept sealed until the danger of reignition is past. For machinery space systems, the discharge of carbon dioxide will likely extinguish the combustible liquid fire in a matter of minutes. However, the potential for reignition exists until all of the heated metal surfaces and other materials have cooled below the autoignition temperature of the fuel. This usually requires a waiting period of several hours after complete extinguishment before a machinery space can be reentered.

In contrast, cargo-hold extinguishing systems are designed to contain the fire until the vessel can make it to port. This is a result of the different combustion properties of solid materials versus liquids. With burning solids, the physical properties of the material and configuration of the surface can vary greatly, allowing combustion to penetrate into the core portions of the material and become a "deep-seated fire." The physical structure of the material then shields the active combustion zone from the surrounding air and causes a lower rate of heat loss. Complete extinguishment of burning Class A materials is very difficult using carbon dioxide and requires very high concentrations of agent.

Cargo-hold systems are not intended to completely extinguish a fire but to provide a reasonable degree of control. They are designed for an initial application of agent followed by periodic release of cylinders to maintain the extinguishing concentration. The system should keep the fire under control until port is reached and extinguishment is completed by the local fire authorities. If the cargo hold is entered after the carbon dioxide is discharged, there is a serious concern that the fire could rekindle from the introduction of fresh air. There is also a significant risk to personnel attempting to enter the space. The hatches should be left secured until the vessel makes port. In cases where it appears that the fire has been extinguished by the system, the hatches should be kept sealed and regular checks of the temperature of the surrounding bulkheads made for at least 24 hours after extinguishment before reentry is attempted. Even in such cases, it is recommended that the hold not be entered until the vessel reaches port.

Marine carbon dioxide systems are designed to be self-contained. No power source on the ship is needed to discharge the system. The pressure to discharge the gas and operate the warning sirens and the interlocked ventilation and fuel shutoff equipment is provided by the internal pressure in the cylinders.

Shipboard fire-extinguishing systems are designed for a minimum concentration of 34 percent carbon dioxide by volume. A carbon dioxide concentration of 6 to 7 percent is considered the maximum level that humans can be exposed to without harmful effects. Because the quantity of carbon dioxide required for fire-extinguishing systems is well above that which can cause serious injury or death to humans, spaces that are protected by such systems must be evacuated before the extinguishing agent is released. Careful attention must also be paid to areas where carbon dioxide could be inadvertently discharged. Specific safety precautions must be followed whenever carbon dioxide systems are being inspected or serviced. The 2005 edition of NFPA 12, *Standard on Carbon Dioxide Extinguishing Systems,* requires that manually operated total flooding systems installed for the protection of normally occupied engine rooms must have a system lockout valve, a pneumatic time delay with pneumatic predischarge warning sirens, and two independent manual release controls.

The Coast Guard approves both high- and low-pressure total flooding carbon dioxide systems. Low-pressure systems are usually specified where a large quantity of extinguishing agent is needed. The decision to install a high-pressure system or a low-pressure system is generally made on an economic basis.

Two types of system releasing arrangements are approved. A manually released configuration is used on the majority of systems and heat detectors are used to automatically release small systems. Coast Guard regulations permit automatically released carbon dioxide systems only for the protection of unoccupied spaces that are less than 6000 ft^3 (170 m^3) and have a suitable means of horizontal escape.

All manually released systems must be located in a protected storage room outside of the protected space. This requirement ensures that the equipment is not damaged by the fire and that if the remote releasing controls are inoperable, crewmembers can still access the carbon dioxide storage room and discharge the system by using the local manual controls. Automatically released systems that protect unoccupied spaces that are less than 6000 ft^3 (170 m^3) may be located inside the protected space. Additional information on the design of carbon dioxide systems can be found in NFPA 12.

Clean Agent Systems

The Coast Guard regulations specify that machinery spaces and pumprooms must be protected by gaseous-type fire-extinguishing systems. Traditionally, total flooding carbon dioxide systems have been used for this purpose. In the 1970s, the use of Halon 1301 systems became common because of concerns with the accidental discharge of carbon dioxide in occupied areas. Later, unease over the global warming potential of fluorocarbons led to the Montreal Protocol of 1987, which placed functional limits on the use of Halon 1301 as a fire-extinguishing agent. Because of the deterioration of the earth's ozone layer, the use of Halon 1301 in total flooding systems was effectively banned. It is specifically prohibited in SOLAS. As a result, new types of environmentally friendly halogenated and inert gas fire-extinguishing agents were developed. Although these agents are considered safe for use in occupied areas, their chemical properties require that they be used within defined safety parameters.

The U.S. Environmental Protection Agency is responsible for regulating the use of substances that are harmful to the environment. In 1994, new regulations were issued to establish the Significant New Alternatives Policy (SNAP) program. This program is intended to identify acceptable alternatives to known ozone-depleting substances that do not have adverse affects on human health or the environment. FM-200, FE-241, NOVEC 1230, and Inergen are SNAP-approved alternatives to Halon 1301 that are used in Coast Guard–approved systems. NFPA 2001, *Standard on Clean Agent Fire Extinguishing Systems,* provides detailed information on the design of these systems.

FIRE DETECTION SYSTEMS

Marine fire detection systems are Coast Guard approved to the criteria listed in 46 CFR 161.002. Basically, shipboard detection systems are identical to those used in buildings, except that the circuit boards, wiring, and connectors are designed to handle the corrosion and vibration common to shipboard installations. Fire alarm control panels are tested to typical industry standards such as UL 864, and the panels must undergo supplemental testing for exposure to increased levels of humidity and vibration. The control panels must also be shown to function properly when inclined. Coast Guard approved detection systems have specific circuit testing and power transfer features that differ from those found on standard panels. Coast Guard approval is granted for complete detection systems; the mixing of components between different approved systems is not permitted.

Initiating devices used for detection systems include heat, smoke and flame detectors, and manual pull stations. Notification appliances can be either audible or visual. The Coast Guard has no particular approval tests for these devices and relies instead on independent laboratory approval and listing. The vessel regulations specify which type of device is to be installed for the protection of specific hazards.

Fire detection systems on large passenger vessels are complex due to the large number of detection devices required throughout the ship. Typical systems monitor several thousand devices. The fire alarm control panels are usually located on the navigating bridge or in a continuously attended fire control station. It is typical for these systems to be designed with a presignal feature that allows the crew to investigate the fire before an evacuation signal is given. This arrangement is preferred because the evacuation procedures on passenger ships require careful coordination of the crew members to channel passengers to the correct embarkation stations and survival craft. The time delay between notification of the crew and sounding of the general evacuation alarm enables the crew to assemble and make necessary preparations. However, a series of casualties in the 1990s revealed that immediately evacuating passengers from the fire-affected area while the crew investigates may be advantageous.[8] Many of the major cruise lines have since voluntarily decided to supplement the required SOLAS fire alarm system with spot-type smoke detectors that give immediate occupant notification in the local area.

LIFE SAFETY CONSIDERATIONS

The following discussion focuses on the means of egress requirements for large passenger ships. The means of egress requirements for smaller passenger ships (Subchapter T and K), cargo ships, and tankers are much less complex. The individual vessel regulations should be consulted for more information on these type ships.

Means of Egress

The means of egress from occupied shipboard spaces is based on many of the fundamental principles inherent in NFPA *101*, with a number of characteristic differences relating to the design and operation of ships. All ships are required to be designed with two means of egress from occupied areas. However, the arrangement of the means of egress, the components of the means of egress, and the evacuation procedures used in an emergency can vary significantly. Cruise ships usually carry passengers with a broader diversity of physical abilities, cognitive skills, and languages than are found in most buildings, which may cause confusion and delays during an evacuation. However, trained crew members are always present to respond to emergencies and assist the occupants. The trained crew has the potential to rapidly suppress the fire, limiting its effect on the passengers. The crew can also assist in speeding the evacuation by taking control of the situation and directing the passengers to the correct exits. The use of a directed evacuation eliminates many of the human behavioral delays associated with the public response to an unanticipated fire emergency.

The exit system on ships is not designed to move passengers to the public way, since the water surrounding the ship is not considered a safe refuge area. The occupants are, instead, directed to refuge areas called *assembly stations.* (These areas are also referred to as muster stations on some ships.) The assembly stations are adjacent to or near the location where the survival craft are boarded. If a fire occurs that requires a general evacuation, the passengers are first moved to the protected assembly stations while the crew fights the fire. The ship is evacuated only if it is likely to sink.

General Life Safety Requirements. The goals and objectives for occupant life safety on ships are similar to those in buildings, namely, the construction features must be arranged to provide two safe escape routes for the passengers and crew, the escape routes must be maintained in a safe condition clear of obstacles, and additional aids must be provided to clearly identify and illuminate the escape paths. Two means of egress must be available from all areas, and they must be separated to the extent necessary that a single fire will not block both paths. On passenger ships, however, there are additional considerations not relevant to building construction. For example, the bulkheads and decks below the waterline must be watertight to limit the possible extent of flooding during an accident. Any openings in these watertight bulkheads are fitted with heavy steel watertight doors, which are either power operated or manually secured by multiple latching dogs. In Figure 21.10.11, which shows a typical watertight sliding door installation, the door is on the left of the doorway and the hydraulic mechanism and its operating lever for closing and opening the door are located on the right side of the doorway. Watertight doors cannot always be opened in a reasonable time period. The regulations thus specify that one of the means of egress must be independent of watertight doors to prevent unnecessary delays in evacuation times.

Means of Egress Components. Shipboard means of egress components are similar to those in buildings. Doors, ramps, and stairs commonly provided are similar to their land-based counterparts. However, because of space limitations on ships, the effective width of the components is usually less than that permitted by NFPA *101*. Another design consideration is the prospect that the ship could list or roll to one side, which would seriously impair the occupants' ability to rapidly traverse corridors and stairways. SOLAS thus requires stairways intended for use by more than 90 occupants to be situated in a fore and aft direction. In this configuration, the stair treads are parallel to the width of the ship. If the ship lists to one side, the angle of inclination of the stair remains fixed. Fire doors are also designed to close against a 3.5 degree opposing angle for the same reason.

Arrangement of Means of Egress. The stairways on ships are not required to be remotely located based on a diagonal dimension criterion, similar to NFPA *101*. This sort of requirement is

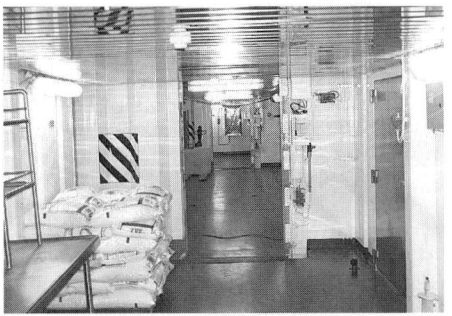

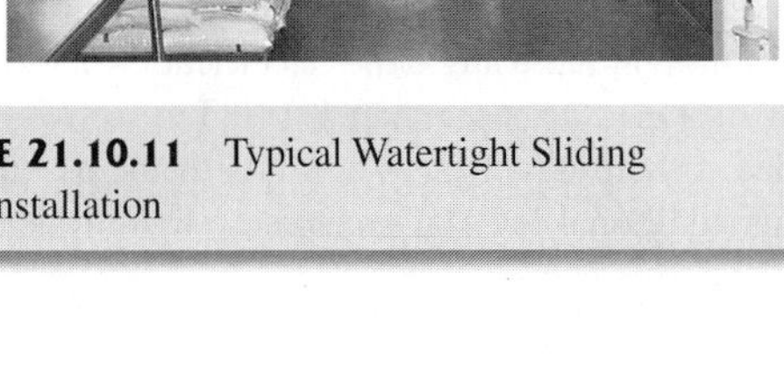

FIGURE 21.10.11 Typical Watertight Sliding Door Installation

not practical to implement on ships due to their horizontal arrangement and varying deck areas. Because the decks on a ship are usually not the same length, the stairways may not serve all areas on each deck. It is common to have a vessel design where some of the stairways end before they reach the level of the assembly stations. In such cases, horizontal means of egress are provided to allow the occupants to access an adjacent stairway to continue toward the assembly stations.

Measurement of Travel Distance. SOLAS requires large passenger ships to be divided into fire areas by the installation of 1-hour-rated main vertical zone bulkheads every 131 ft (40 m). Each main vertical zone is required to have two means of egress, which essentially limits the maximum travel distance to an exit. The requirement for main vertical zones is applicable to all areas on the ship, notwithstanding the type of occupancy. The vessel regulations, therefore, do not contain provisions for maximum travel distances.

Discharge from Exits. The exit discharge provisions on passenger ships are significantly different from those required for buildings. Emergency response procedures do not call for an immediate evacuation. Ships operate at sea, where the ship and its survival craft are the only buoyant platforms available for the safe refuge of the occupants. The ship is designed to safely and comfortably transport the passengers and crew in almost any weather or sea state. The survival craft are a last recourse for the occupants, if the sinking of the ship is imminent. Consequently, if a fire occurs, the occupants are initially marshaled to areas of safe refuge on the ship. The assembly stations may be near the survival craft or in large public restaurants or theaters. The direction of travel from the assembly stations to the survival craft could ultimately be different from the direction of travel the passengers originally followed to reach the assembly areas. The structural fire protection features and installed fire detection and suppression systems are designed to allow the crew to control the fire, making evacuation unnecessary except in extreme situations.

Emergency Lighting

Passenger ships are fitted with emergency lighting systems to illuminate the egress paths along the normal corridors and stairways to the assembly stations and survival craft areas. In addition, emergency lighting is provided to illuminate the survival craft boarding areas and the sides of the ship, including the water below. This is different from emergency lighting in typical buildings. Most building codes do not require illumination of the public way, only the egress paths leading to the public way. Additional emergency lighting is needed on ships to coordinate the launching of the survival craft and, if necessary, the rescue of persons who may have fallen or jumped into the water. The regulations also call for a specialized emergency lighting and exit marking system throughout the accommodation areas. Low-location lighting, using either electrical or photoluminescent strips installed no more than 1 ft (0.3 m) above the deck, is provided to help direct the occupants to the assembly stations. This additional level of emergency lighting is intended to supplement the overhead lighting during a power failure and also allows the occupants to more readily recognize the location of the exits if the corridors become smoke-filled.

IMO has recognized a new development in evacuation guidance systems that uses sound signals to identify evacuation routes. Although the low-location lighting is required to be mounted close to the deck, there is the possibility that smoke obscuration could reduce its effectiveness. The directional sound guidance system consists of strategically placed speakers that produce a broadband sound pattern optimized to allow the occupants to distinguish the direction of exit travel despite visibility. Performance standards for such systems have been developed and are listed in IMO MSC/Circ. 1168, *Interim Guidelines for the Testing, Approval and Maintenance of Evacuation Guidance Systems Used as an Alternative to Low-Location Lighting Systems*. Systems that successfully pass the testing criteria may be substituted for the required low-location lighting system.

Evacuation of Large Passenger Ferries

Passenger ferries have particular stability concerns attributable to the design of their vehicle carrying decks. The vehicle decks on ferries are usually large open spaces, without the benefit of main vertical zones or other means of subdivision. Past casualty experience has shown that an accident that causes flooding of the vehicle decks may cause the ship to capsize or sink much more rapidly than is the case in a standard passenger ship.[9] To offset this, SOLAS requires that the evacuation routes of all roll-on/roll-off passenger vessels built on or after July 1, 1999, be evaluated by an evacuation analysis during the design process. Typical ferry-loading operations have the passengers drive their vehicles on board and park in the designated lanes. The passengers then leave their vehicles and proceed to the accommodation or waiting areas of the ship for the duration of the voyage.

Depending on the duration of the trip, the passengers may wait in large public waiting areas, or, if the voyage is overnight, the passengers may be assigned to individual cabins. The evacuation analysis is intended to identify possible areas where congestion could slow the escape process. The analysis is also used to evaluate the flexibility of the egress design by simulating the blockage of one of the two required escape paths. Similar evacuation analysis requirements will be applied to all passenger ships in the future.

PERFORMANCE-BASED DESIGN

CFR and SOLAS fire protection regulations contain prescriptive requirements based on many years of practical operating knowledge, combined with lessons learned from marine casualty investigations. The regulations address typical ship designs and the expected fire risks on standard cargo, passenger, and tankships. The shipbuilding industry is continually developing novel and unique ship designs to carry different cargoes, to carry cargoes more economically, or to provide passengers with more luxury and entertainment options. Unconventional ship designs must be fit into these few basic regulatory categories. Unfortunately, the regulations offer no mechanism to determine if the prescriptive level of fire protection required is adequate or overly excessive for the particular arrangement.

A positive step in the advancement of alternative ship design and arrangements was taken by IMO in the 2000 revision of SOLAS. A new regulation was included that allows the use of fire safety engineering to show that alternative design and arrangements offer an equivalent level of safety as the prescriptive regulations. This new regulation allows ship designers to use industry-accepted fire safety engineering principles such as the *SFPE Engineering Guide to Performance-Based Fire Protection Analysis and Design of Buildings* and comparable guides for this purpose.

There is one major point in the application of this concept that differs significantly from land-based projects. If a building is approved using a performance-based design approach, it does not need to be reevaluated by the AHJ unless it changes occupancy. The SOLAS Convention permits ships open access to ports around the world, because all signatory countries are obligated to accept a SOLAS safety certificate as evidence of a ship's compliance with the convention. If the port state was not a participant in the review of the alternative design concept for a particular ship, compliance to the prescriptive regulations may be expected and the ship could be denied entry. To remedy this, IMO has issued guidelines that describe the necessary steps that should be followed to approve an alternative design. The guidelines also include suggested levels of documentation to carry on board the ship at all times for the use of port state inspectors.

EMERGENCY RESPONSE TO SHIP FIRES

Fires on board ships present a number of unique circumstances that must be carefully considered before a fire department reacts to a marine emergency. Fire departments in port cities must respond to ship fires, yet they may have limited experience in the differences between building fires and ship fires. Careful pre-incident planning of the roads and water supplies to the port, the vessels using the port, and the expected cargoes being handled is essential to ensuring an effective response.

Comprehensive training, operational information, and guidance for shoreside responders to shipboard fires are contained in NFPA 1405, *Guide for Land-Based Fire Fighters Who Respond to Marine Vessel Fires.* Despite the information the standard provides, many shoreside fire fighters are ill prepared for the complexity of fighting a shipboard fire, as found in the accident investigation of the tankship *Seal Island,* which occurred in the U.S. Virgin Islands on October 8, 1994.[10] Ships' decks and main bulkheads are steel, retain the heat of combustion for a long period of time, and can make locating the fire more difficult; spaces and access are more restricted than is the case in buildings, thus making fire fighting and retreating confusing; and the accumulation of water on decks can worsen the situation.

Most importantly, the command structure for fighting a shipboard fire is not always understood. At sea, only the crew is available to respond to fire emergencies; in port, shoreside fire fighters are likely to be called by the Coast Guard.

One readily available piece of information critical for fire fighting is located aboard the ship. All U.S. vessels of 1000 gross tons and over and all vessels subject to SOLAS must permanently display a fire-fighting plan or fire control plan of the ship. Although the plan's primary purpose is to guide shipboard personnel, it should contain the following information to assist port fire-fighting groups:

- Fire control stations for each deck
- Sections enclosed by fire-resistive divisions
- Fire alarms, detection systems, and sprinkler systems
- Fire-extinguishing appliances
- Access to different compartments, decks, and so on
- Ventilating systems, including master fan controls, positions of dampers, location of remote controls, and identification numbers of ventilating fans serving each section

Instead of being posted on a plan, the information listed can be described in a fire-fighting booklet. The booklet is required to be aboard ship at all times. Whether posted as a fire-fighting plan or presented in booklet form, information should be available on all watertight compartments, openings therein, and means of closure, controls, and arrangements for correcting any list due to flooding.

SOLAS '74 requires that a duplicate set of fire control plans be permanently stowed in a prominently marked, weathertight enclosure outside the deckhouse to assist shoreside fire-fighting personnel. Figure 21.10.12 illustrates a fire-fighting plan for the aft end of a super tanker.

The international community has also agreed on standard symbols for fire control plans (Figure 21.10.13). Most symbols are to be shown in red on the general arrangement plan to highlight their location for shipboard and shoreside fire fighters.

NFPA MARINE STANDARDS

In 1994, the U.S. Coast Guard and the marine community embarked on an ambitious project to shift development and maintenance of fire protection regulations applicable to U.S. flagged commercial ships to consensus standards-making organizations. The cornerstone of this effort is NFPA 301, *Code for Safety to Life from Fire on Merchant Vessels,* a "life safety code" for ships. Additionally, chapters on marine application have been added to NFPA 11, NFPA 12, NFPA 13, NFPA 750, and NFPA 2001.

Other NFPA standards relating to marine vessels are contained in NFPA 306; see also NFPA 312, *Standard for Fire Protection of Vessels During Construction, Conversion, Repair, and Lay-Up.* NFPA 306 describes the conditions necessary for safety before repairing any vessel carrying or having carried fuel as cargo, combustible or flammable liquids, flammable compressed gases, and bulk chemicals. NFPA 306 is also the basis for confined space safety in the maritime industry and must be followed by the NFPA-certificated marine chemist. It also contains a section on flammable cryogenic liquid carriers. NFPA 312 covers measures for preventing and controlling fires on vessels in the building or repair yard or on vessels that are laid up. Provisions for each circumstance appear separately in the standard.

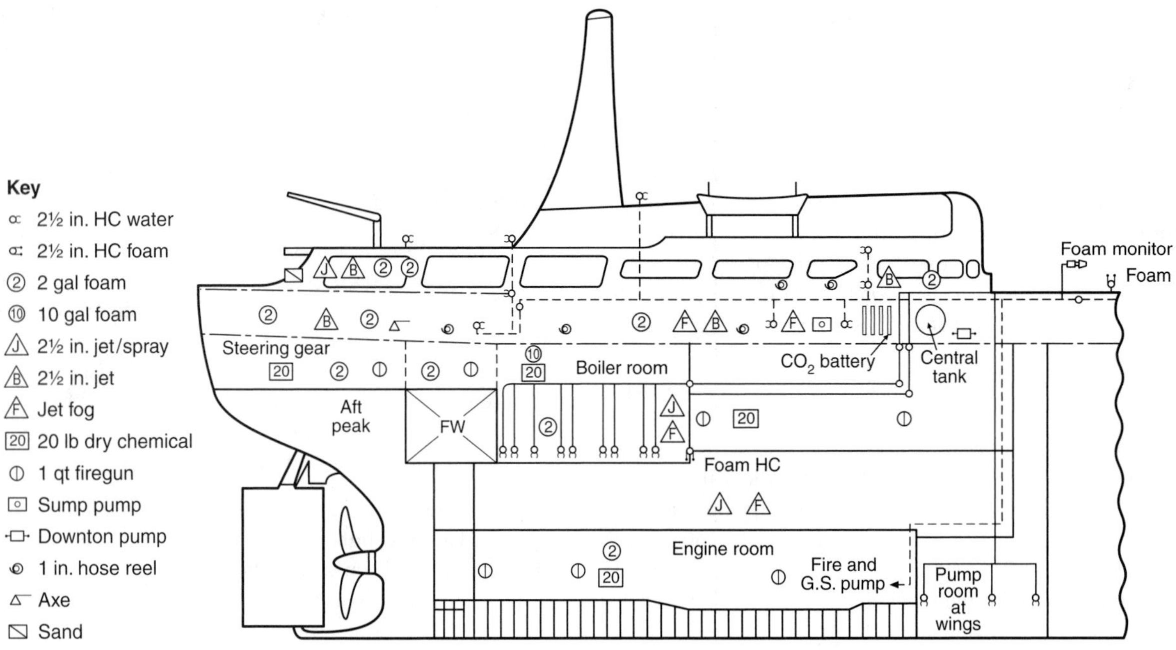

FIGURE 21.10.12 Fire-Fighting Plans for the Aft End of a Super Tanker

OTHER ORGANIZATIONS CONTRIBUTING TO MARINE FIRE SAFETY

American Bureau of Shipping

The American Bureau of Shipping (ABS) is the American classification society whose technical committees develop rules for the dimensions and use of materials in the construction and conversion of marine vessels. After a vessel is completed according to the rules and under the constant supervision of an ABS field inspector, the bureau classes and lists it as having met all design and structural safety requirements.

American Petroleum Institute

In the area of marine fire fighting and fire protection, the American Petroleum Institute (API) is active in developing domestic and international standards, codes, and regulations. Under the policy direction of the API Central Committee on Transportation by Water, most actions are directed by the API Committee on Tank Vessels. Ad hoc groups are sometimes formed for special studies of a nonrepetitive nature.

Marine Chemist Association, Inc.

Established in May 1938 as the Marine Chemists' Subsection of the NFPA Marine Section, the Marine Chemists organized its present association in 1948 after the Marine Section disbanded. This professional organization of chemists is certificated for marine work by NFPA in accordance with provisions of NFPA 306.

National Cargo Bureau, Inc.

The National Cargo Bureau is a nationwide, nonprofit membership organization established in 1952 as a private, nongovernmental agency that formulates recommendations to various governments for regulating the safe stowage of dangerous goods and other cargoes and for regulating related cargo-handling gear.

National Transportation Safety Board

The National Transportation Safety Board (NTSB) is an independent federal agency dedicated to promoting aviation, marine, railroad, highway, pipeline, and hazardous materials safety. Established in 1967, the agency is mandated by Congress through the Independent Safety Board Act of 1974 to investigate transportation accidents, including those involving fire, explosion, and pollution; determine the probable cause of accidents; issue safety recommendations; study transportation safety issues; and evaluate the safety effectiveness of government agencies involved in transportation. The Safety Board makes public its actions and decisions through accident reports, safety studies, special investigation reports, safety recommendations, and statistical reviews.

USCG Advisory Committee on Hazardous Materials

This committee of the National Academy of Sciences, National Research Council, is charged with advising the U.S. Coast Guard on scientific and technical matters relating to safe maritime transportation of hazardous materials.

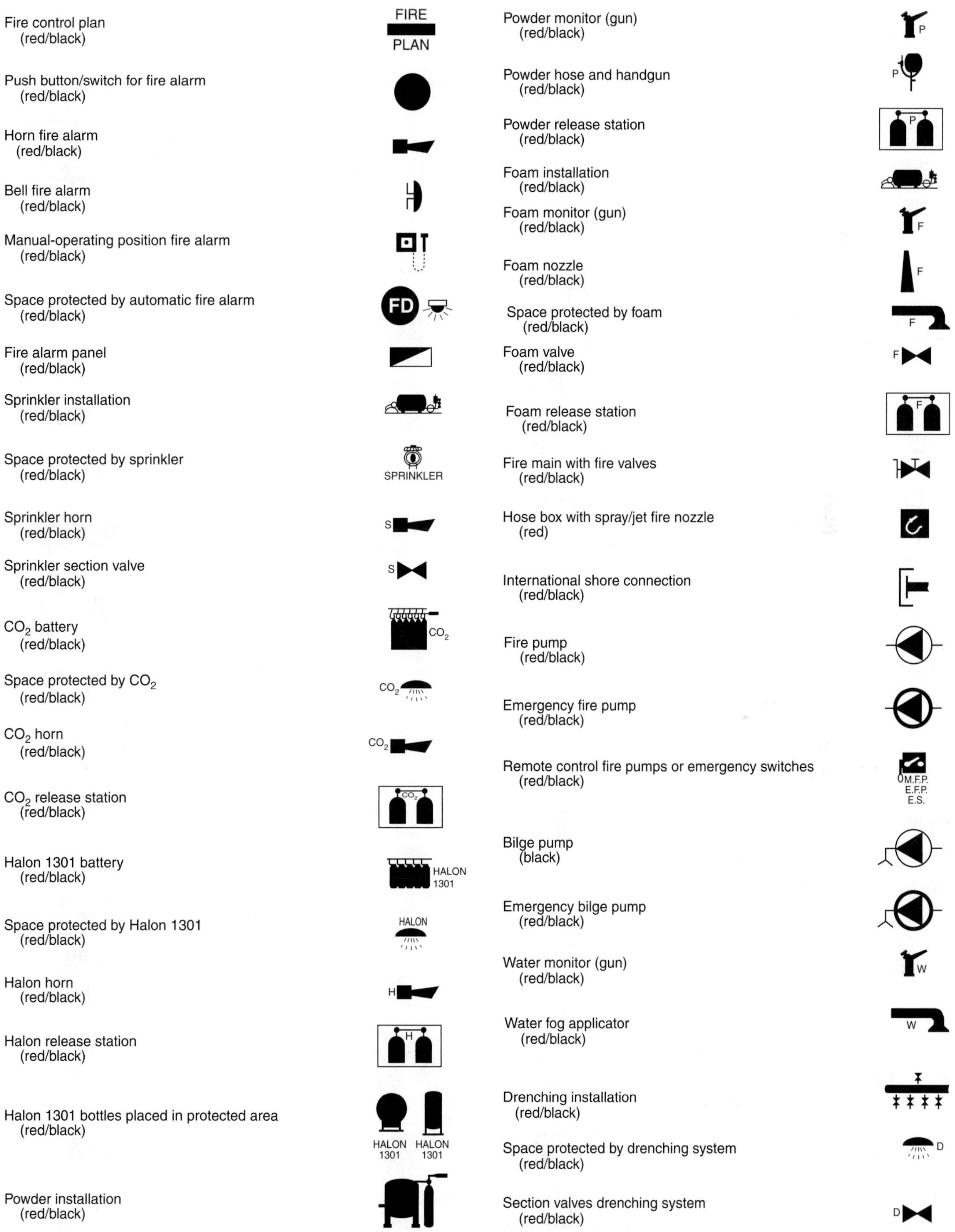
Fire control plan (red/black)
FIRE
PLAN
Push button/switch for fire alarm (red/black)
Horn fire alarm (red/black)
Bell fire alarm (red/black)
Manual-operating position fire alarm (red/black)
Space protected by automatic fire alarm (red/black)
FD
Fire alarm panel (red/black)
Sprinkler installation (red/black)
Space protected by sprinkler (red/black)
SPRINKLER
Sprinkler horn (red/black)
S
Sprinkler section valve (red/black)
S
CO2 battery (red/black)
CO2
Space protected by CO2 (red/black)
CO2
CO2 horn (red/black)
CO2
CO2 release station (red/black)
CO2
Halon 1301 battery (red/black)
HALON 1301
Space protected by Halon 1301 (red/black)
HALON
Halon horn (red/black)
H
Halon release station (red/black)
H
Halon 1301 bottles placed in protected area (red/black)
HALON 1301
HALON 1301
Powder installation (red/black)
Powder monitor (gun) (red/black)
P
Powder hose and handgun (red/black)
P
Powder release station (red/black)
P
Foam installation (red/black)
Foam monitor (gun) (red/black)
F
Foam nozzle (red/black)
F
Space protected by foam (red/black)
F
Foam valve (red/black)
F
Foam release station (red/black)
F
Fire main with fire valves (red/black)
Hose box with spray/jet fire nozzle (red)
International shore connection (red/black)
Fire pump (red/black)
Emergency fire pump (red/black)
Remote control fire pumps or emergency switches (red/black)
M.F.P.
E.F.P.
E.S.
Bilge pump (black)
Emergency bilge pump (red/black)
Water monitor (gun) (red/black)
W
Water fog applicator (red/black)
W
Drenching installation (red/black)
Space protected by drenching system (red/black)
D
Section valves drenching system (red/black)
D

(continued)

FIGURE 21.10.13 Symbols for Use in Accordance with Regulation 11-2/20 of the 1974 SOLAS Convention as Amended

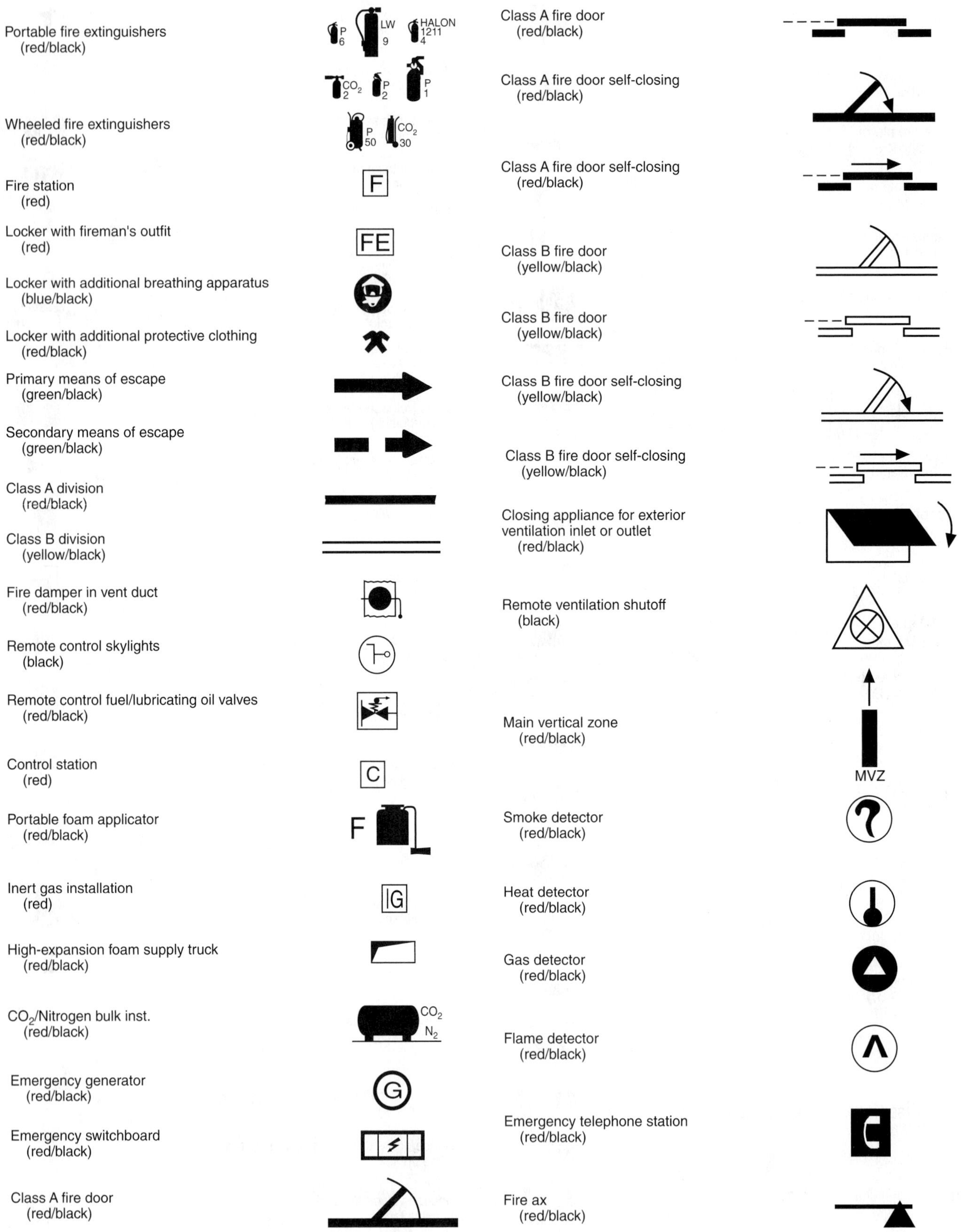
Portable fire extinguishers (red/black)
P 6
LW 9
HALON 1211 4
CO2 2
P 2
P 1
Wheeled fire extinguishers (red/black)
P 50
CO2 30
Fire station (red)
F
Locker with fireman's outfit (red)
FE
Locker with additional breathing apparatus (blue/black)
Locker with additional protective clothing (red/black)
Primary means of escape (green/black)
Secondary means of escape (green/black)
Class A division (red/black)
Class B division (yellow/black)
Fire damper in vent duct (red/black)
Remote control skylights (black)
Remote control fuel/lubricating oil valves (red/black)
Control station (red)
C
Portable foam applicator (red/black)
F
Inert gas installation (red)
IG
High-expansion foam supply truck (red/black)
CO2/Nitrogen bulk inst. (red/black)
CO2
N2
Emergency generator (red/black)
G
Emergency switchboard (red/black)
Class A fire door (red/black)
Class A fire door (red/black)
Class A fire door self-closing (red/black)
Class A fire door self-closing (red/black)
Class B fire door (yellow/black)
Class B fire door (yellow/black)
Class B fire door self-closing (yellow/black)
Class B fire door self-closing (yellow/black)
Closing appliance for exterior ventilation inlet or outlet (red/black)
Remote ventilation shutoff (black)
Main vertical zone (red/black)
MVZ
Smoke detector (red/black)
Heat detector (red/black)
Gas detector (red/black)
Flame detector (red/black)
Emergency telephone station (red/black)
Fire ax (red/black)

FIGURE 21.10.13 Continued

SUMMARY

Fires and explosions are frequent contributors to marine vessel injuries and fatalities. In pleasure and small commercial boats, gasoline is commonly used for both propulsion engines and onboard generators, and liquefied petroleum gas (LP-gas) is commonly used for cooking. Boats are constructed in such a way that they are closed on the bottom and on all sides, resulting in less effective ventilation than found in other types of vehicles such as trains and aircraft. Means of fire protection include leak-free fuel systems, ventilating systems, unobstructed areas and escape hatches, fire-retardant coatings for flammable materials, lightning protection, proper installation of electrical systems, and fire extinguishers. Safety procedures include thorough maintenance, inspection, and testing, careful fueling operations, and proper storage of the boat when not in use.

Fire protection regulations for commercial ships and offshore marine vessels are covered by the *Code of Federal Regulations* (CFR) and, for international voyages, the International Convention for the Safety of Life at Sea (SOLAS). The regulations are specific to different types of vessels, such as passenger ships, cargo vessels, and supply vessels. Marine fire protection considerations include construction materials and design, fire-extinguishing and fire detection systems, and evacuation. Fire hazards should be analyzed and controlled in the three major occupancies common to all ships: the engine room, the cargo holds or tanks, and the accommodation and service areas. Fire prevention measures include limiting the use of combustible construction materials and the safe handling and use of combustible materials, flammable liquids, and ignition sources.

BIBLIOGRAPHY

References Cited

1. *Boating Statistics—2005,* COMDTPUB P16754.19, U.S. Department of Transportation, United States Coast Guard, Washington, DC, Aug. 31, 2006.
2. Senate Report 184, 75th Congress, 1st Session, Mar. 17, 1937, pp. 8–9.
3. U.S. Coast Guard, Marine Safety Information System (MSIS) database for reportable marine casualties.
4. *Investigation of Fuel Oil/Lube Oil Spray Fires on Board Vessels,* Report No. CG-D-O1-99, U.S. Coast Guard Research and Development Center, Groton, CT, Nov. 1998.
5. SOLAS regulation II-1/47.2.
6. MSIS database.
7. *The International Code for the Construction and Equipment of Ships Carrying Chemicals in Bulk,* IBC Code, International Maritime Organization, London, UK, 1998.
8. *Fire on Board the Panamanian Passenger Ship* Universe Explorer *in the Lynn Canal Near Juneau, Alaska, July 27, 1996,* NTSB Report No. MAR-98-02, National Transportation Safety Board, Washington, DC, Apr. 14, 1998.
9. *Report of the Panel of Experts on Ro-Ro Ferry Safety to the Steering Committee on Ro-Ro Ferry Safety,* MSC 65/4 Rev 1, Maritime Safety Committee, International Maritime Organization, London, UK, Apr. 21, 1995.
10. *Engineroom Fire on Board the Liberian Tankship* Seal Island *While Moored at the Amerada Hess Oil Terminal in St. Croix, U.S. Virgin Islands, October 8, 1994,* NTSB Report No. MAR-95-04, National Transportation Safety Board, Washington, DC, Dec. 12, 1995.

NFPA Codes, Standards, and Recommended Practices

Reference to the following NFPA codes, standards, and recommended practices will provide further information on marine fire hazards discussed in this chapter. (See the latest version of The NFPA Catalog *for availability of the current edition of the following documents.)*

NFPA 11, *Standard for Low-, Medium-, and High-Expansion Foam*
NFPA 12, *Standard on Carbon Dioxide Extinguishing Systems*
NFPA 13, *Standard for the Installation of Sprinkler Systems*
NFPA 30A, *Code for Motor Fuel Dispensing Facilities and Repair Garages*
NFPA 52, *Vehicular Fuel Systems Code*
NFPA *101*®, *Life Safety Code*®
NFPA 301, *Code for Safety to Life from Fire on Merchant Vessels*
NFPA 302, *Fire Protection Standard for Pleasure and Commercial Motor Craft*
NFPA 303, *Fire Protection Standard for Marinas and Boatyards*
NFPA 306, *Standard for the Control of Gas Hazards on Vessels*
NFPA 312, *Standard for Fire Protection of Vessels During Construction, Conversion, Repair, and Lay-Up*
NFPA 750, *Standard on Water Mist Fire Protection Systems*
NFPA 1405, *Guide for Land-Based Fire Fighters Who Respond to Marine Vessel Fires*
NFPA 2001, *Standard on Clean Agent Fire Extinguishing Systems*

Chapter 11

Road Tunnels and Bridges

Arthur G. Bendelius

Chapter Contents

Key Terms

emergency communication, emergency planning, fire model, fire pump, fire test, point of safety, portable fire extinguisher, road bridge, road tunnel, smoke management, standpipe, tenability, ventilation (mechanical), ventilation (natural), ventilation system, water supply

This chapter addresses the unique fire protection and life safety considerations and challenges posed by road tunnels and road bridges. A road tunnel is defined as any enclosed facility through which road vehicles (cars, vans, buses, and trucks) travel. These vehicles are typically powered by internal combustion engines using traditional fuels such as gasoline and diesel. However, in recent years vehicles powered by alternative fuels such as CNG, LP-gas, LNG, or one of the blends of gasoline and feedstock fuel such as ethanol are becoming prevalent in the vehicle fleet.[1]

Road tunnels are usually constructed to overcome an obstacle, such as a mountain or a body of water. However, several new road tunnels result from the developmental benefits of the real estate created by putting roadways below the surface and developing the air rights above. Road tunnels are therefore typically catagorized, based on the obstacle encountered, as follows: mountain tunnel, subaqueous (underwater) tunnel, urban tunnel, or air-rights tunnel.

Fire protection for road tunnels requires a unique application of common fire protection, fire fighting, and fire suppression systems and techniques. The fire load in a tunnel is continuously changing and is basically unpredictable. The potential always exists, however, for fires to occur that are of significant scale in comparison to most commercial structures. Also, unlike commercial or industrial buildings and facilities, road tunnels do not offer any compartmentalization, making evacuation and rescue far more difficult. The entire population to be rescued will most likely be in the same "compartment" as the fire, and because a tunnel is essentially a linear structure, the fire must be fought from a position in the same compartment. This chapter addresses the unique aspects of road tunnel fire protection and explores the application of standard fire protection, fire suppression, and fire-fighting system practices and techniques to road tunnels.

Similar to road tunnels, bridges designed to carry vehicle traffic offer very limited access to emergency responders and can therefore pose unique challenges in the ability to ensure motorist life safety protection in the case of a fire. This chapter addresses the fire protection considerations for bridges built to transport road vehicles over another road, a railroad, a waterway, or a valley.

For related topics, see Section 12, Chapter 15, "Public Emergency Services Alarm, Dispatch, and Communications Systems"; and Section 16, Chapter 8, "Water Mist Fire Suppression Systems."

ROAD TUNNELS

History of Road Tunnel Fires

There are more than 150 road tunnels in the United States and several thousand more throughout the world. Table 21.11.1 lists some of the major operating U.S. road tunnels and their categories, length, and ventilation systems.

There have been over 30 reported serious road tunnel fires since the first one occurred over 60 years ago in New York's Holland Tunnel in 1949.[2] Serious road tunnel fires are those in which there

Arthur G. Bendelius, P.E., is president and principal consultant at A&G Consultants, Inc. He has served as a senior vice-president and technical director at Parsons Brinckerhoff. His technical expertise is in tunnel services, primarily in tunnel ventilation and fire protection systems. He has served as chair of the Technical Committee for NFPA 502, *Standard for Road Tunnels, Bridges, and Other Limited Access Highways,* and currently serves as animateur of World Road Association (PIARC) Working Group's "Ventilation Fire and Smoke Control in Road Tunnels."

TABLE 21.11.1 Selected U.S. Operating Road Tunnels

Tunnel	*Date Opened*	*Category*	*Location*	*Length (ft)*	*Length (m)*	*Bores/ Lanes*	*Ventilation System*
Anton Anderson*	2000	Mountain	Alaska	13,727	4184	1/1	Longitudinal
Brooklyn Battery	1950	Subaqueous	New York	9,210	2807	2/4	Full transverse
Ted Williams	1995	Subaqueous	Massachusetts	8,957	2730	2/4	Full transverse
Holland	1927	Subaqueous	New York-New Jersey	8,530	2600	2/4	Full transverse
Lincoln	1937	Subaqueous	New York-New Jersey	8,216	2504	3/6	Full transverse
	1945			8,005	2440		
	1957			7,484	2281		
Eisenhower	1973	Mountain	Colorado	8,148	2484	1/2	Full transverse
Central Artery-I93	2003	Urban	Massachusetts	8,100	2469	2/6	Full transverse w/ longitudinal on some ramps
Baltimore Harbor	1957	Subaqueous	Maryland	7,710	2350	2/4	Full transverse
Hampton Roads	1958	Subaqueous	Virginia	7,470	2277	2/4	Full transverse
	1975			7,314	2229		
Fort McHenry	1985	Subaqueous	Maryland	7,215	2199	4/8	Full transverse
Queens Midtown	1940	Subaqueous	New York	6,400	1951	2/4	Full transverse
Allegheny	1940	Mountain	Pennsylvania	6,073	1851	2/4	Semitransverse
	1966						
Liberty	1924	Mountain	Pennsylvania	5,905	1800	2/4	Longitudinal
Thimble Shoal	1964	Subaqueous	Virginia	5,740	1750	1/2	Full transverse
East River	1974	Mountain	Virginia-West Virginia	5,661	1726	2/4	Full transverse
Sumner	1934	Subaqueous	Massachusetts	5,657	1724	1/2	Full transverse
Baltimore Channel	1961	Subaqueous	Virginia	5,450	1661	1/2	Full transverse
Bankhead	1941	Subaqueous	Alabama	5,390	1643	1/2	Semitransverse
Tuscarora	1960	Mountain	Pennsylvania	5,328	1624	2/4	Semitransverse
	1968						
Central Artery-I90 Extension	2003	Urban	Massachusetts	5,300	1615	4/7	Full transverse w/ longitudinal on some ramps
Harano	1997	Mountain	Hawaii	5,165	1574	2/4	Full transverse
				4,890	1491		
Detroit Windsor	1930	Subaqueous	Michigan-Ontario	5,125	1562	1/2	Full transverse
Callahan	1961	Subaqueous	Massachusetts	5,085	1550	1/2	Full transverse
Monitor Merrimac	1992	Subaqueous	Virginia	4,783	1458	2/4	Full transverse
Kittatinny	1940	Mountain	Pennsylvania	4,728	1441	2/4	Semitransverse
	1968						
Cumberland Gap	1996	Mountain	Kentucky-Tennessee	4,600	1402	2/4	Longitudinal
Lehigh	1940	Mountain	Pennsylvania	4,462	1360	2/4	Semitransverse
	1991			4,380	1335		Longitudinal
Blue Mountain	1940	Mountain	Pennsylvania	4,340	1323	2/4	Semitransverse
Big Walker	1972	Mountain	Virginia	4,229	1289	2/4	Full transverse
Squirrel Hill	1953	Mountain	Pennsylvania	4,225	1288	2/4	Semitransverse
Elizabeth River-Midtown	1962	Subaqueous	Virginia	4,194	1278	1/2	Full transverse
Fort Pitt	1960	Mountain	Pennsylvania	3,603	1098	2/4	Semitransverse
Posey	1928	Subaqueous	California	3,545	1081	1/2	Full transverse
Mount Baker Ridge	1989	Urban	Washington	3,501	1067	3/8	Full transverse
Mall	1973	Urban	District of Columbia	3,400	1036	2/8	Full transverse
Mobile River	1972	Subaqueous	Alabama	3,380	1030	1/2	Longitudinal
Elizabeth River	1954	Subaqueous	Virginia	3,350	1021	2/4	Full transverse
Downtown	1986			3,814	1163		Semitransverse
Caldecott	1982	Subaqueous	California	3,350	1021	3/6	Full transverse
Webster Street	1963	Urban	California	3,350	1021	1/2	Full transverse
Mercer Island	1999	Urban	Washington	2,999	914	3/8	Full transverse
Wilson	1960	Mountain	Hawaii	2,813	857	2/4	Semitransverse
				2,775	846		
Lowry Hill	1971	Urban	Minnesota	1,496	456	3/6	Semitransverse
Battery Street	1952	Urban	Washington	2,100	671	2/4	Hybrid supply
Pali	1961	Mountain	Hawaii	1,577	481	2/4	Natural
	1957			1,500	457		

*A combined road/rail tunnel.

has been loss of life or significant property damage to either vehicles or tunnel structure. Table 21.11.2 lists selected road tunnel fires involving either loss of life, damage to vehicles, or damage to a significant portion of the tunnel, beginning with the 1949 Holland Tunnel fire.[2] In 1999 and 2001 several extremely serious road tunnel fires occurred. Three of these occurred in long single-bore, bidirectional trafficked, Alpine tunnels. (As illustrated in Figure 21.11.1, a bore is defined as a longitudinal compartment of a tunnel, either in a separate structure or in a single structure divided by a solid wall or rock.) The first of these Alpine tunnel fires occurred in the Mont Blanc Tunnel between France and Italy on March 24, 1999,[3,4] the second occurred in the Austrian Tauern Tunnel on May 29, 1999,[4] and the third occurred in the Swiss St. Gotthard Tunnel in October 2001.[4] Details of these three serious road tunnel fires are shown in Table 21.11.3.

Unknown Fire Loads

One of the major factors to be considered in the fire protection of a road tunnel is the unknown nature of the potential fire load. In other transportation tunnels, such as transit tunnels, the potential fire load can be estimated with reasonable accuracy, since both the vehicles and the passenger load are controlled by the operating agency. Such is not the case for the typical road tunnel, where an innocent-looking truck may be carrying a load that is capable of supporting a fast-growing, potentially lethal fire, but that is not necessarily "classified" as hazardous cargo.

TABLE 21.11.2 Selected Serious Road Tunnel Fires

	Tunnel Length								
Tunnel	*ft*	*m*	*Opening Date*	*Country*	*Fire Date*	*Fatalities*	*Injuries*	*Vehicles*	*Tunnel Damage*
Holland	8,180	2,550	1927	United States	1949	0	66	23	Serious
Moorfleet	797	243	—	Germany	1968	0	0	1	Serious
Guadarrama	10,731	3,345	1972	Spain	1975	0	0	1	Serious
Velser	2,470	770	1957	Netherlands	1978	5	5	6	Serious
Nihonzaka	6,560	2,045	1978	Japan	1979	7	2	173	Serious
Kajiwara	2,374	740	1963	Japan	1980	1	0	2	Serious
Sakai	1,472	459	—	Japan	1980	5	5	NA	Serious
Caldecott	3,298	1,028	1964	United States	1982	7	2	8	Serious
Percoile	2,124	662	1967	Italy	1983	8	22	10	Limited
Frejus	41,367	12,895	1980	France/Italy	1983	0	1	1	Serious
St. Gotthard	54,273	16,918	1980	Switzerland	1984	0	0	1	Serious
Felbertauren	17,015	5,304	1967	Austria	1984	0	0	1	Serious
L'Arme	3,625	1,105	1979	France	1986	3	5	5	Limited
Gumefens	1,100	343	1981	Switzerland	1987	2	5	3	Slight
Tanzenberg	7,847	2,446	1983	Austria	1987	0	1	NA	Serious
Brenner	2,634	803	1971	Italy	1989	2	9	NA	Serious
Serra Ripoli	1,418	442	—	Italy	1993	4	4	15	Limited
Huguenot	12,556	3,914	—	South Africa	1994	1	28	1	Serious
St. Gotthard	54,273	16,918	1980	Switzerland	1994	0	0	2	Serious
Pfänder	21,555	6,719	1980	Austria	1995	3	4	4	Serious
Isola delle Femine	475	148	—	Italy	1996	5	20	20	Serious
Gleinalm	26,691	8,320	1978	Austria	1998	0	0	1	Serious
Mont Blanc	37,213	11,600	1965	France/Italy	1999	39	NA	27	Serious
Tauren	20,534	6,401	1975	Austria	1999	12	49	40	Serious
Seljestad	4,081	1,272	1964	Norway	2000	0	6	NA	Serious
Gleinalm	26,691	8,320	1978	Austria	2001	5	4	2	—
Guldborgsund	1,476	460	1988	Denmark	2001	5	6	NA	—
St. Gotthard	54,273	16,918	1980	Switzerland	2001	11	0	2	Serious
Ostwaldiberg	1,476	460	1988	Austria	2002	1	NA	1	Serious
Baregg	4,459	1,390	1970	Switzerland	2004	1	1	2	Serious
Frejus	41,367	12,895	1980	France/Italy	2005	2	NA	5	Serious

Note: NA = not available.

TABLE 21.11.3 Details of Recent Road Tunnel Fires

Tunnel (Country)	*Opening Date (Fire Date)*	Tunnel Length		*Number of Bores*	*Persons Dead*	*Vehicles Destroyed*	Serious Tunnel Damage	
		ft	*m*				*ft*	*m*
Mont Blanc (France, Italy)	1965 (March 1999)	38,058	11,600	1	39 27 in own vehicles 2 in other vehicles 2 in refuge shelter 7 outside of vehicles 1 postincident	34 20 tractor-trailers 1 pickup truck 9 passenger cars 1 motorcycle 2 ATMB vehicles	2,953	900
Tauren (Austria)	1974 (May 1999)	20,997	6,400	1	12 8 in accident 1 upon return to his truck 2 in own vehicle 1 fleeing from fire	34 14 trucks 20 passenger cars	1,640	500
St. Gotthard (Switzerland)	1980 (October 2001)	55,512	16,920	1	8 5 in vehicles 3 walking and not finding emergency exits	23 13 trucks 10 passenger cars	2,297	700

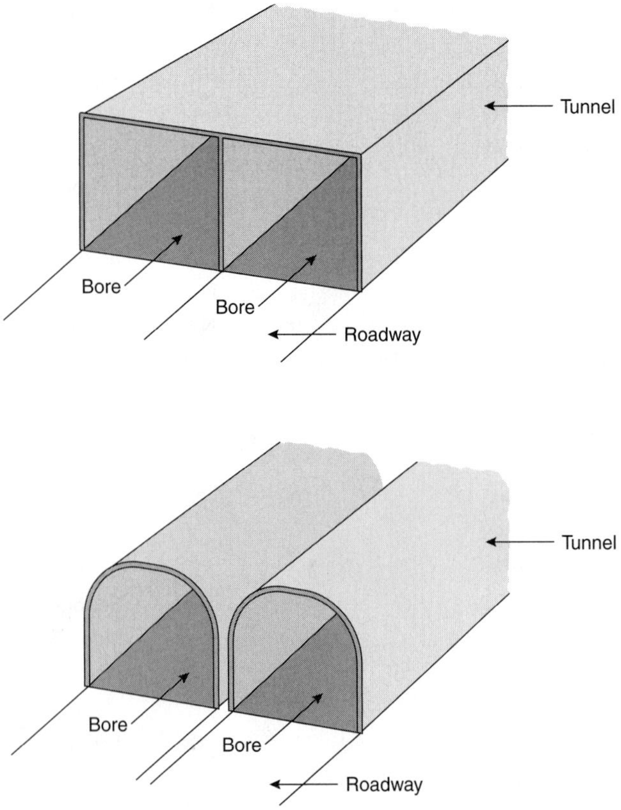

FIGURE 21.11.1 Tunnel with Two Bores

TABLE 21.11.4 Typical Tunnel Fire Incident Vehicle Loads

Tunnel Fire	*Year*	*Vehicle Load*
Holland	1949	Carbon bisulfate
Moorfleet	1968	Polyethylene bags
Guadarrama	1975	Pine resin
B6	1976	Polyester bundles
Kajiwara	1980	Paint in cans
Caldecott	1982	Petrol
Percoile	1983	Fish
Frejus	1983	Plastic materials
St. Gotthard	1984	Rolls of plastic
Mont Blanc	1990	Cotton
Serra Repoli	1993	Rolls of paper
St. Gotthard	1994	Cartons
St. Gotthard	1994	Plastic wrapping
Isola delle Femmine	1996	Liquid gas
Mont Blanc	1999	Margarine
Mont Blanc	1999	Flour
Tauern	1999	Aerosol paint cans
Prapontin	2001	Beets
St. Gotthard	2001	Tires
Frejus	2005	Tires
Frejus	2005	Cheese
Frejus	2005	Glue

A good example is the primary cargo—margarine and flour—in the incident truck involved in the Mont Blanc fire in 1999. Table 21.11.4 contains a list of the materials carried by the incident vehicle for many of the tunnel fires shown in Table 21.11.2.

Global Guidelines and Standards

Guidelines and standards for road tunnel fire protection have been published worldwide by both international organizations and individual countries. Both the National Fire Protection Association (NFPA) and the World Road Association (PIARC) publish standards and guidelines on road tunnel fire protection. Table 21.11.5 provides a sample list of some of the more pertinent global guidelines and standards.

Three NFPA standards address the fire protection requirements for the underground environment: NFPA 130, *Standard for Fixed Guideway Transit and Passenger Rail Systems;* NFPA 502, *Standard for Road Tunnels, Bridges, and Other Limited Access Highways;* and NFPA 520, *Standard on Subterranean Spaces.* The definitive standard for road tunnels is NFPA 502. Although the other two standards contain material that may be applicable to road tunnels, the NFPA Technical Committee on Road Tunnels and Highway Fire Protection has reviewed all of the material contained in these two documents and has applied what was determined to be truly pertinent and included references where appropriate. Elements of several other NFPA codes and standards may be applied to fire protection systems within road tunnels; these codes and standards are appropriately referenced in NFPA 502 and also appear at the end of this chapter. The fire protection requirements prescribed by NFPA Standard 502 are graphically displayed in Table 21.11.6. These prescribed fire protection requirements vary based on tunnel length. PIARC has published a number of documents particularly in the technical area of ventilation and fire and smoke control. The most important document is *Fire and Smoke Control* published in 1999.[5]

KEY ELEMENTS OF ROAD TUNNEL FIRE PROTECTION

The following are the primary objectives of road tunnel fire protection:

- Permit and encourage escape and evacuation of all motorists (i.e., motor vehicle occupants including the driver and passengers) from the tunnel
- Facilitate the entrance of fire-fighting personnel into the tunnel to combat the fire
- Protect the tunnel structure and facilities

TABLE 21.11.5 Road Tunnel Fire Safety Standards and Guidelines

Individual Countries	
Australia	*Road Tunnel Design Guideline, Fire Safety Design,* Parts 1–3, Roads and Traffic Authority (RTA), Australia, 2007
Austria	*Design Guidelines Tunnel Ventilation,* RVS 9261:9262, Austria, 1997
Croatia	*Regulations on Technical Standards and Conditions for Design and Construction of Tunnels on Roads,* Croatia, 1991
Czech Republic	*Design of Road Tunnels,* Standard ČSN 73 7507
	Road Tunnel Equipment—Technical Specifications—Guideline TP 98
France	*Inter-Ministry Circular No. 2000-63—Safety in the Tunnels of the National Highways Network,* Ministry of the Establishment, Transport and Housing, France, 2000
Germany	Forschungsgesellschaft für Strassen- and Verkehrswesen, Richtlinien fuer Ausstattung und Betrieb von Strassentunneln (RABT), Germany, 2006
Japan	*National Safety Standard of Emergency Facilities on Road Tunnels,* Japan Road Association, Japan, 2001
Netherlands	*Recommendations: Ventilation of Road Tunnels,* RWS Bouwdienst, Steunpunt Tunnelveiligheid, 2005
Norway	*Norwegian Design Guide—Road Tunnels,* Public Roads Administration, Norway, 1990
Nordic countries	*Ventilation of Road Tunnels,* Sub-Committee 61, Report No. 6, Nordisk Vejteknisk Forbund (NVF), 1993
Sweden	*Tunnel 2004—General Technical Specification for New Tunnels and Upgrading of Old Tunnels,* Publ. 2004, 124, Swedish National Road Administration, Sweden, 2004
Switzerland	*Ventilation for Road Tunnels,* Swiss Federal Roads Authority (FEDRO), 2004
United Kingdom	*Design Manual for Roads and Bridges,* Part 9, BD 78/99, Design of Road Tunnels, 1999
United States	*Road Tunnel Design Guidelines,* FHWA-IF-05-023, Federal Highway Administration, 2004
International Organizations	
NFPA	NFPA 502, *Standard for Road Tunnels, Bridges, and Other Limited Access Highways,* National Fire Protection Association, Quincy, MA, 2008
PIARC	*Fire and Smoke Control in Road Tunnels,* World Road Association (PIARC), Paris, 1999
	Systems and Equipment for Fire and Smoke Control in Road Tunnels, World Road Association (PIARC), Paris, 2007
European Union	Directive 2004/54/EC of the European Parliament and of the Council on minimum safety requirements for tunnels in the trans-European road network, 29 April 2004
United Nations	Economic Council, Economic Commission for Europe, Inland Transport Committee, Recommendations of the Group of Experts on Safety in Road Tunnels, 10 December 2001

TABLE 21.11.6 Road Tunnel Fire Protection Requirements

Tunnel Categories		X	A	B	C	D	
Fire Protection Systems	*NFPA 502 Sections*	*7.2(1)*	*7.2(2)*	*7.2(3)*	*7.2(4)*	*7.2(5)*	*Notes*
Fire Detection							
Manual fire alarm boxes	7.4.1.2			¤	¤	¤	
CCTV	7.4.1.3 7.4.1.4.6			¤	¤	¤	
Automatic fire detectors	7.4.1.4			¤	¤	¤	
Fire control panel	7.4.2			¤	¤	¤	
Communication							
Radio	7.5			¤	¤	¤	
Telephone	7.5			¤	¤	¤	
Traffic Control							
Stop traffic approaching tunnel portal	7.6.1		¤				
Stop traffic from entering tunnel's direct approaches	7.6.2			¤	¤	¤	
Fire Protection							
Fire apparatus	Annex J		+	+	+	+	Not mandatory to be at tunnel, however, they must be near to minimize response time
Fire standpipe	7.7 9.1		¤	¤	¤	¤	
Water supply	7.7 9.2		¤	¤	¤	¤	
Fire department connections	9.3		¤	¤	¤	¤	
Hose connections	9.4		¤	¤	¤	¤	
Fire pumps	9.5		+	+	+	¤	If required, must follow Section 9.5 in NFPA 502
Portable fire extinguisher	7.8			¤	¤	¤	
Water-based fixed fire fighting system	7.9		+	+	+	+	If installed, must follow Section 7.10 in NFPA 502
Emergency ventilation	7.10			#	#	¤	Section 10.1 in NFPA 502 allows engineering analysis to determine requirements
Drainage system	7.11			¤	¤	¤	
Hydrocarbon detector	7.11.7			¤	¤	¤	
Egress							
Emergency egress	7.14.1.1		¤	¤	¤	¤	
Exit identification	7.14.1.2		¤	¤	¤	¤	
Tenable environment	7.14.2		¤	¤	¤	¤	
Emergency exits	7.14.6		¤	¤	¤	¤	
Cross passageways	7.14.7		¤	¤	¤	¤	
Electrical							
Emergency lighting	11.6		¤	¤	¤	¤	
Emergency power	11.4		¤	¤	¤	¤	
Redundant power	11.5					¤	
Security plan	11.7		¤	¤	¤	¤	
Emergency response plan	12.3		¤	¤	¤	¤	

Legend: ¤ Mandatory requirement + Not mandatory requirement—see Notes # Conditionally mandatory—see Notes

Tunnel Categories. For the purpose of the 2008 edition of NFPA 502, tunnel length shall dictate the minimum fire protection requirements, as follows:

X—Where tunnel length is less than 300 ft (90 m), the provisions of this standard shall not apply.

A—Where tunnel length is 300 ft (90 m) or greater, standpipe systems and traffic control systems shall be installed in accordance with the requirements of Chapter 9 and Section 7.6, respectively, in NFPA 502.

B—Where tunnel length equals or exceeds 800 ft (240 m) and where the maximum distance from any point within the tunnel to a point of safety exceeds 400 ft (120 m), all provisions of this standard shall apply.

C—Where the tunnel length equals or exceeds 1000 ft (300 m), all provisions of this standard shall apply unless noted otherwise in this document.

D—Where the tunnel length equals or exceeds 3280 ft (1000 m), all provisions of this standard shall apply.

Source: Adapted from NFPA 502, *Standard for Road Tunnels, Bridges, and Other Limited Access Highways,* 2008 edition, Table 7.2, p. 502-10.

An effective road tunnel fire protection system program must contain the following elements:

- Fire identification, verification, and detection
- Emergency communications
- Smoke management
- Fire suppression
- Emergency response planning
- Evacuation and rescue

Traffic control, which is another element in an effective road tunnel fire protection system program, is not addressed in this chapter.

A road tunnel's fire protection system must be able to readily identify, verify, and locate a fire anywhere within the tunnel. Determining the location of the fire is critical to safe evacuation, since the success of many companion fire and life safety systems such as smoke control (ventilation) depend on knowing where the fire is within the tunnel to permit the appropriate operational response.

The mission during the initial phase of a tunnel fire-based emergency is to establish safe evacuation and rescue options for those persons within the tunnel. Safe evacuation and rescue requires the establishment of a tenable environment for the entire evacuation path. If the fire incident occurs relatively near one of the tunnel portals, the path to the portal may be the shortest route to a safe area. When the fire incident occurs deeper into the tunnel, the evacuation path will be through an emergency stairway to the surface or a cross passage to a parallel bore (Figure 21.11.2). The entrance to a typical cross passage to a parallel tunnel bore is shown in Figure 21.11.3. The tenable environment in the evacuation path is typically created by the operation of a smoke control or ventilation system. When all of the motorists in the tunnel have been either evacuated or rescued, the responding fire department must proceed with the necessary efforts to extinguish the fire.

FIGURE 21.11.3 Typical Cross Passage Entrance

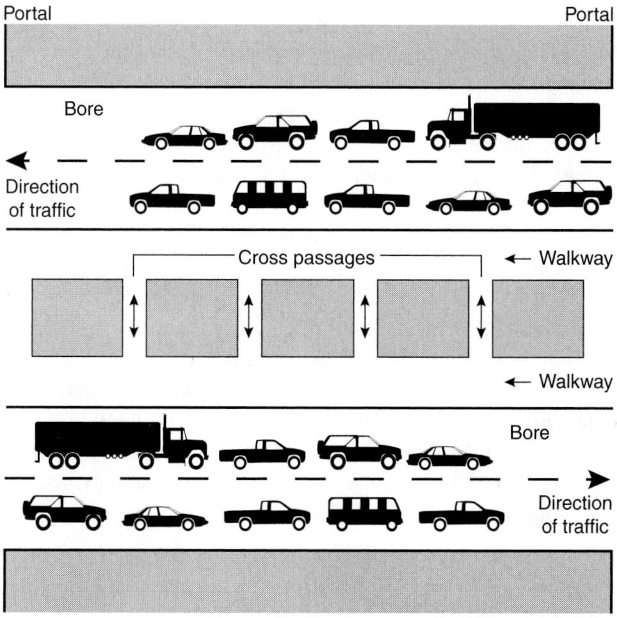

FIGURE 21.11.2 Cross Passages Leading to a Parallel Tunnel Bore

IDENTIFICATION, VERIFICATION, AND LOCATION OF FIRES

As previously stated, quick response is critical to the effective management of a fire emergency in a road tunnel. Once a fire has been detected and its location verified, it may take several minutes to fully initiate all necessary emergency response systems and procedures. Therefore, a reliable means to identify, verify, and locate a fire incident is required by NFPA 502 in all road tunnels over 1000 ft (300 m). There are several practical methods considered acceptable within NFPA 502 as a reliable means to identify, verify, and locate a fire within a road tunnel.

Visual Identification

Closed circuit television (CCTV), although not a listed fire detection device, has proven to be one of the most effective means for identifying and verifying a fire within a road tunnel. NFPA

502 considers CCTV monitoring an acceptable means of fire detection if the tunnel is fully monitored by dedicated staff on a 24 hour basis.

Manual Detection

Pull Box. The manual pull-box alarm is a common device used in most building fire protection systems. In a road tunnel, the installation of a pull box provides an opportunity for motorists within the tunnel to send a manual alarm in the event of an emergency, without relying on voice communication. NFPA 502 requires manual pull-box alarms (Figure 21.11.4) to be spaced at 300 ft (90 m) intervals within a road tunnel.

Emergency Telephone. Emergency telephones, generally located adjacent to where the main pull-box alarms are installed (they are at 300 ft [90 m] spacing), provide another means for sending an alarm manually, although the noise level within the tunnel roadway may prohibit clear voice communications. A number of European road tunnel owners have installed telephone booths to combat the problem of high ambient noise. However, the concept is not universally accepted because many believe that motorists might view the enclosure as a point of safety, which is not the case, unless the booths are designed specifically as a refuge with an appropriate fire-rated enclosure and environmental control system.

FIGURE 21.11.4 Fire Alarm Pull Box

Mobile Telephone. It is becoming more and more common for road tunnels to provide capability for signal reception for the use of mobile telephones. As such, the universal popularity of mobile phones provides another manual means for motorists to report an emergency within the tunnel.

Automatic Detection

Heat detectors, flame detectors, and digital imaging systems (using CCTV) are the most applicable forms of automatic fire detection systems for road tunnels. The most prevalent type of detector used in road tunnels worldwide is the heat detector—more specifically the linear heat detector. Flame detectors are found predominantly in Japanese road tunnels. CCTVs using digital imaging are a relatively new technology compared to linear heat detectors.

Linear Heat Detectors. Linear heat detectors are designed to sense an increase in temperature anywhere along the detector's length, to send a signal to a control center, and with this signal to identify the specific location of the alarm site within the tunnel. They are usually installed in zones (generally correlated with the ventilation zones) along the entire length of the road tunnel. The types of linear heat detectors that have been utilized in a road tunnel include the following:

- Electrical cable
- Fiber optic cable
- Thermocouple cable
- Gas-filled cable

Linear heat detectors have not yet received universal approval for application in road tunnels primarily due to their ensuing maintenance needs and their tendency to provide false and late alarms. To be effective, linear heat detectors must be installed directly above the travel lanes. Maintenance of any device mounted over the traveled roadway is always a more costly process, due to the need to close one or two lanes of traffic and use a unique maintenance vehicle with an elevating overhead platform.

Spot Heat Detectors. Spot heat detectors have been installed in a number of tunnels worldwide. However, one of the major drawbacks of spot heat detectors is the number of individual detectors necessary to locate the fire site as quickly and as precisely as possible. This required precision creates the need for a system with a number of spot detectors that may become unmanageable.

Other Detection Systems

Flame Detectors. Flame detectors were installed in over 60 tunnels in Japan beginning in the early 1960s. The early installed versions of the flame detector suffered from false alarm problems. As the products evolved in the ensuing years, flame detectors were developed to a point where the false alarms were limited. Some of the design modifications were believed to result in more sensitive detectors and the need for fewer detectors per length of tunnel. The most recent designs allow addressing individual detectors in order to identify the fire location within 75 ft (25 m).

Digital Imaging. A recent development is the ability of CCTV systems to automatically detect a fire through digital image analysis. CCTV surveillance systems are typically installed in road tunnels; therefore, the ability of this system to automatically detect and locate a fire in a road tunnel is extremely attractive. This capability, coupled with the existing capability of the CCTV systems to automatically monitor traffic, would enhance the ability of the tunnel operator to respond to a fire in a timely fashion. However, this technology has not yet been proven in the road tunnel environment, although it continues to be tested in trial tunnel installations.

Gas Detectors. Gas detectors, primarily for detection of carbon monoxide (CO), are used in almost all road tunnels to monitor vehicle emission levels during normal tunnel operations. They have not been used for fire detection in road tunnels primarily due to the difficulty in differentiating between concentrated vehicle exhaust and the hot gases from a fire.

Smoke Alarms. Smoke alarms are designed to sense the presence of particles of combustion, either by photoelectric or by ionization sensors. These systems are not designed for outdoor application and would not perform well in a tunnel environment due to a tendency for false alarms caused by heavy diesel engine exhaust.

Visibility Detectors. Visibility measurements are conducted in some road tunnels to monitor for safe operating conditions and in a limited number of tunnels to control the ventilation system during normal operation. These units can also be utilized for detection of a fire. An alarm is triggered once the preset limit value is attained. These detectors are based on either diffused light or illumination.

Research

A study to investigate the performance of fire detection systems in road tunnels was initiated by the Fire Protection Research Foundation (FPRF) in 1999. For Phase II the FPRF has teamed with the National Research Council of Canada (NRCC) and with the Port Authority of New York and New Jersey (PANYNJ). A Technical Advisory Group consisting of fire and transportation officials, engineering firms, researchers, and system manufacturers was formed to oversee the project.

The following are the goals of this research:

- Investigate the performance attributes of current fire detection technologies for road tunnel protection
- Develop performance criteria for fire and smoke detection systems in road tunnel applications
- Optimize technical specifications and installation requirements for this application

The first phase of this project, literature review of past and current research and application of fire detection systems for road tunnels, has been completed.[6] The second phase of the research program will include the following tasks performed at the following locations:

- Laboratory tests—NRCC Fire Research Facilities
- Laboratory tunnel tests—Carleton University–NRCC Test Facility
- Computation modeling—NRCC
- Field fire tests—operating tunnel in Montreal (Viger Tunnel)
- Environmental monitoring – PANYNJ operating tunnel (Lincoln Tunnel)
- Simulated fire tests—PANYNJ operating tunnel (Lincoln Tunnel)

The benefits of this research will be a better understanding of the reliability of various types of fire detection systems and how the operational and environmental factors within a road tunnel influence their performance.

EMERGENCY COMMUNICATIONS

Emergency communications permit the operator to communicate with the motorists within the tunnels and permit emergency responders to communicate with each other during an emergency in the tunnel. Emergency communication devices should have the following features:

- Conspicuous by means of indicating lights or other suitable markers
- Identified by a readily visible number plate or other appropriate device
- Posted with suitable instructions for use by motorists

Loudspeakers

Loudspeakers are prevalent in many European road tunnels. These systems are used to alert the motorists of an emergency situation and to provide directions and guidance. The use of loudspeakers in road tunnels is not a universally accepted safety concept. There are several problems with their application to the tunnel environment, including the following:

- Hard surfaces within the tunnel roadway that make it extremely difficult to understand most announcements
- Motorists' vehicles moving
- Vehicle windows closed (due to air conditioning)
- Potential language barriers

Therefore, the use of loudspeakers within a road tunnel is not a recommended means of reliable communication for emergencies.

Radio

Radio communication systems, such as highway advisory radio (HAR) and AM/FM commercial station overrides can be an effective means to communicate an emergency to motorists and to provide them with direction.

Regardless of type, all communications and messaging systems used within road tunnels should be capable of real-time composition and selection by the emergency response authority, and should not be of the recorded type. All areas planned for use of emergency refuge or assembly should be equipped with reliable two-way voice communication with the emergency response authority.

SMOKE MANAGEMENT

In a road tunnel, smoke management requires either direct extraction at the fire site or the generation of a longitudinal velocity in the tunnel capable of transporting the smoke and heated gases in the desired direction to a point of extraction or discharge from the tunnel. Without a smoke management system, the direction and rate of movement of the smoke and heated gases will be determined by fire size, tunnel grade, prefire tunnel conditions, and external meteorological conditions.

The primary purpose for controlling smoke in a tunnel is to protect life and to permit safe evacuation of the tunnel. This involves creating a safe path of egress for both motorists and any operating personnel located within the tunnel when the fire starts. The secondary purpose of smoke control ventilation is to assist fire fighters in accessing the fire site, by again providing a clear path to the fire site if possible.

The tunnel ventilation system is not specifically designed to protect property, although the effect of ventilation in diluting smoke and heated gases, thus removing some of the heat, results in reduced damage to the facilities and vehicles. The primary method of smoke management is the tunnel ventilation system, which provides the means for controlling smoke movement in the event of a fire incident. The approach used for smoke management varies depending on the type of ventilation system being used and whether the tunnel is serving unidirectional or bidirectional traffic.

Road Tunnel Ventilation System Types

The primary purpose of tunnel ventilation systems in a tunnel fire emergency is to control and/or remove the heated gases and smoke from the egress path. In essentially all emergency cases, protection of motorists and employees is enhanced by prompt activation of emergency ventilation procedures as planned in advance. The effectiveness of an emergency ventilation system in providing a sufficient quantity of uncontaminated air and in minimizing the hazard of smoke backlayering (i.e., the movement of smoke and hot gases contrary to the direction of the ventilation airflow) in an evacuation pathway is a function of the fire load (Figure 21.11.5).

Ventilation is required in many road tunnels to limit the concentrations of vehicle-emitted contaminants to acceptable levels during normal traffic operations. The ventilation systems can also be used to control smoke and heated gases generated during a fire emergency in the tunnel. There are many short tunnels that are ventilated naturally (without fans); such tunnels, however, may still require mechanical ventilation to assist in a fire emergency.

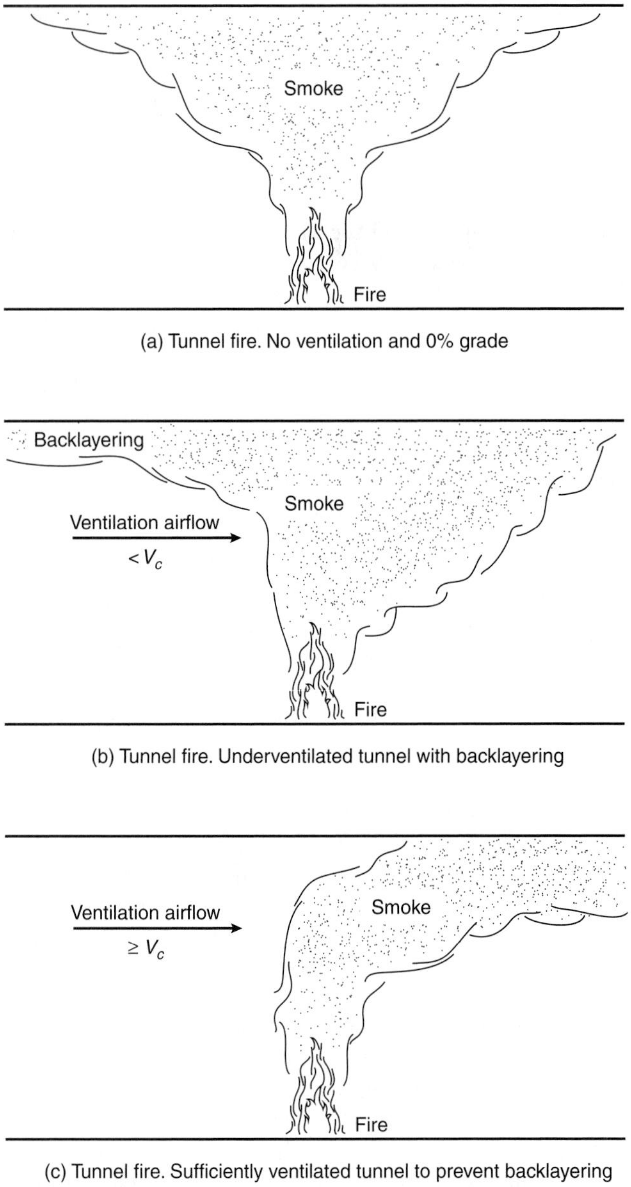

FIGURE 21.11.5 Backlayering of Smoke and Hot Gases

Natural Ventilation

Tunnels with natural ventilation only (no fans) rely chiefly on both the ambient meteorological conditions and on the piston effect generated by the moving traffic to maintain a satisfactory environment within the tunnel during normal operations (Figure 21.11.6). However, to handle a fire-based emergency within the naturally ventilated tunnel, an emergency ventilation system may be needed. NFPA 502 requires the consideration of emergency ventilation for all road tunnels over 1000 ft (300 m) in length. Given the lack of a mechanical ventilation system, the smoke and heated gases will, in the case of a tunnel without a grade (level) and without external wind, flow out of both portals. If the tunnel has a grade, the smoke will most likely flow toward the higher portal unless

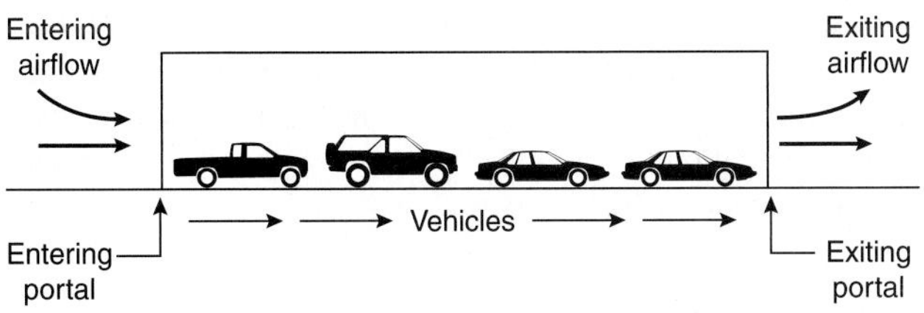

FIGURE 21.11.6 Natural Ventilation

there are abnormal meteorological conditions at the time of the incident.

Mechanical Ventilation

The systems used for mechanical, or fan-driven, ventilation can be classified as longitudinal or transverse. The longitudinal ventilation system achieves its objectives through the longitudinal flow of air within the roadway; the transverse system achieves its objectives by the uniform distribution and/or collection of air continuously throughout the length of the tunnel. The transverse ventilation system also experiences some longitudinal airflow, with the quantity dependent on the type of system.

Longitudinal Ventilation. Longitudinal ventilation is a system in which the air is introduced into or removed from the tunnel roadway at a limited number of points (such as at a portal or a shaft), thus creating a longitudinal flow of air within the roadway discharging at the exiting portal. Longitudinal ventilation systems can be further classified into those using central fans and those using local, or jet, fans.

Central fan longitudinal ventilation systems employ centrally located fans to inject air into the roadway usually through a high-velocity, or Saccardo, nozzle (Figure 21.11.7). The injection of air can take place at the entering portal or in midtunnel. Both concepts can provide the required longitudinal ventilation within the tunnel. An exhaust shaft may be combined with the injection nozzle to increase the quantity of air introduced into the tunnel. Jet fan–based longitudinal ventilation employs a series of axial fans mounted at the ceiling level of the tunnel roadway. These fans, through the effects of the high-velocity

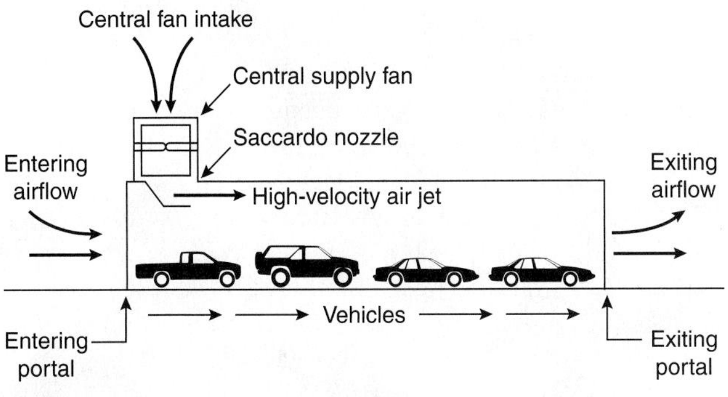

FIGURE 21.11.7 Longitudinal Ventilation with Saccardo Nozzle

discharge thrust, induce a total longitudinal airflow through the length of the tunnel (Figure 21.11.8).

Longitudinal ventilation can only be used in a unidirectional tunnel. In all longitudinal systems the smoke and heated gases (or pollutants during normal operations) will discharge from the exit portal. To achieve the required longitudinal movement of smoke, the longitudinal velocity must be sufficient to prevent backlayering of smoke over the stopped vehicles. The critical velocity must be achieved with the tunnel cross section (discussed later in the section "Engineering Analysis"). Longitudinal ventilation systems do not require a longitudinal duct with the tunnel, and systems employing jet fans do not require a ventilation building.

Transverse Ventilation. Transverse ventilation systems, which can be used in either bidirectional or unidirectional trafficked tunnels, are those that feature the uniform collection and/or distribution of air throughout the length of the tunnel. There are full transverse and semitransverse systems. In addition, there are both supply and exhaust versions of semitransverse systems.

Full transverse ventilation systems have both supply and exhaust systems throughout the length of the tunnel (Figure 21.11.9). When a full transverse system is employed, the majority of the smoke and heated gases (or pollutants during normal operations) will be discharged through a stack with a portion

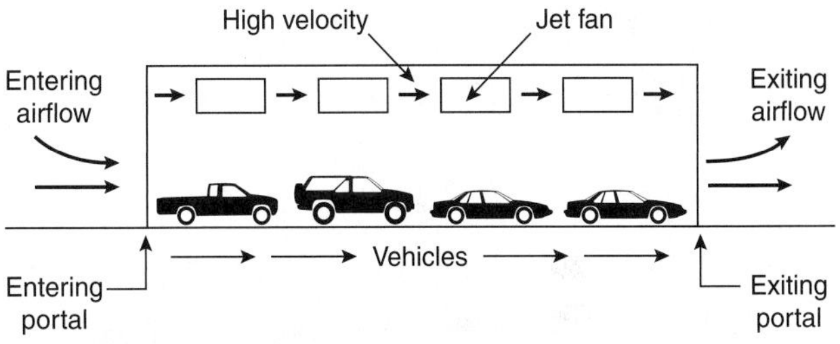

FIGURE 21.11.8 Longitudinal Ventilation with Jet Fans

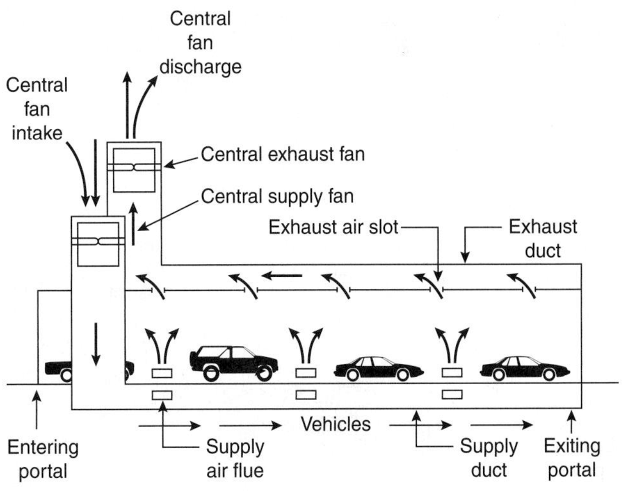

FIGURE 21.11.9 Full Transverse Ventilation

of the smoke exiting through the portals. A full transverse ventilation system can be either balanced (exhaust equals supply) or unbalanced (exhaust is greater than supply). Semitransverse systems are those that have only supply (Figure 21.11.10) or exhaust elements (Figure 21.11.11). The effluent exhaust from the tunnel is discharged at either the portals (supply system) or through ventilation stacks (exhaust system).

Smoke and heated gases from a tunnel fire can be mitigated in a tunnel outfitted with transverse ventilation in one of the following methods:

- Dilution
- Longitudinal airflow
- Extraction

Dilution was shown to be effective only up to a 20 MW fire and not effective beyond that.[7] Longitudinal airflow is an extremely effective method of controlling smoke and heated gases during a tunnel fire. Longitudinal airflow can be achieved in a multizone full transverse system by varying the operation mode between supply and exhaust for different zones.

Extraction is also an excellent method to control the smoke and heated gases within a tunnel. This concept will work with a transverse system with an overhead exhaust duct by outfitting the exhaust duct with a limited number of operable dampered openings. When a fire is identified and located, the control system can open the damper or dampers nearest the fire and extract the smoke and heated gases as close to the fire site as possible, thus removing most of the smoke. The capacity of the emergency ventilation system must be based on the design fire size selected for each specific tunnel.

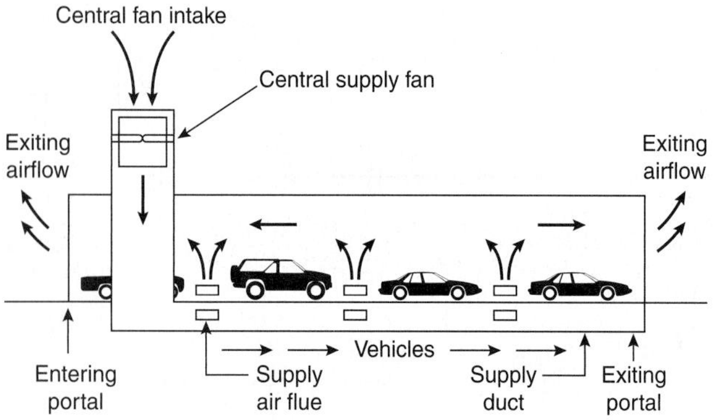

FIGURE 21.11.10 Semitransverse Supply Ventilation

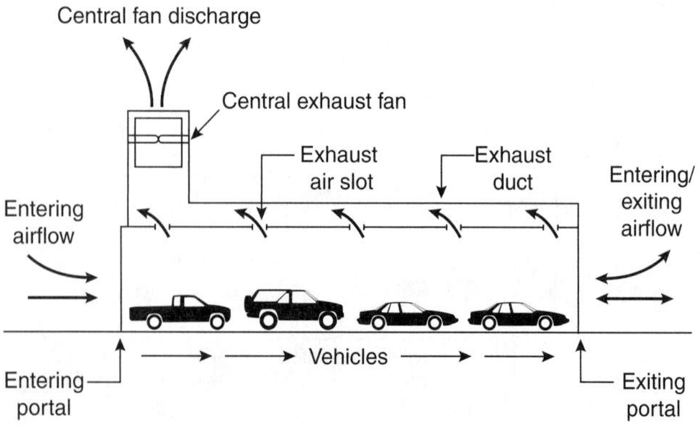

FIGURE 21.11.11 Semitransverse Exhaust Ventilation

FIRE SUPPRESSION

Portable Fire Extinguishers

NFPA 502 requires portable fire extinguishers to be located in the tunnel roadway in wall cabinets at 300 ft (90 m) spacing (Figure 21.11.12). The size and type of portable extinguishers are defined as 2-A:20-B:C and 20 lb (9 kg) as defined in NFPA 10, *Standard for Portable Fire Extinguishers*. It is prudent to install a device to provide the operator with an alarm indication that a fire extinguisher has been removed from its station. This signal could be an indication either of a fire within the tunnel or of the theft of an extinguisher (a common occurrence in some locations).

Standpipe

According to NFPA 502, a Class 1 standpipe system is required in all road tunnels over 300 ft (90 m) in length. The system should be of the wet type. However, if a wet-type system is not possible due to climatic conditions, a dry system is acceptable, provided that the system fill time is less than 10 minutes.

As specified in NFPA 502, the road tunnel standpipe system must be designed to provide support to a minimum of two fire hose streams delivering 250 gpm (16 L/sec) each. The standpipe system must be installed in accordance with NFPA 14, *Standard for the Installation of Standpipe and Hose Systems*.

Water Supply

The water supply system, whether municipal or private, should have adequate waterflow and pressure along with the required system integrity. The water supply system considered should have a minimum supply capacity of 1 hour of fire fighting as

FIGURE 21.11.12 Portable Fire Extinguisher in Cabinet

prescribed by NFPA 502 and should be configured in accordance with NFPA 14. If a storage tank is required to meet the water supply capacity, it should be installed in accordance with NFPA 22, *Standard for Water Tanks for Private Fire Protection.*

Hose Connections

According to NFPA 502, standpipe hose connections or hose valves should be installed in the road tunnel, so that no point on the protected tunnel roadway is more than 150 ft (45 m) from an active hose valve. The spacing of the standpipe hose valves should not be greater than 275 ft (85 m), and the hose connection should be equipped with 2½ in. (65 mm) external threads (see NFPA 1963, *Standard for Fire Hose Connections*). Figure 21.11.13 illustrates a diagram of a typical hose valve installation in a cabinet with a portable fire extinguisher. Figure 21.11.14 shows an actual installation of hose valves in a road tunnel. A fire cabinet with hose valves is shown in Figure 21.11.15.

Fire Hose

Some tunnels outside the United States provide a fire hose within the tunnel at each hose valve location. In many circumstances, this is a small diameter first aid hose. However, in the United States, fire departments are reluctant to use hose that they have not maintained. Consequently, in the United States, fire hose is not placed or stored in the tunnel but carried on the responding fire apparatus.

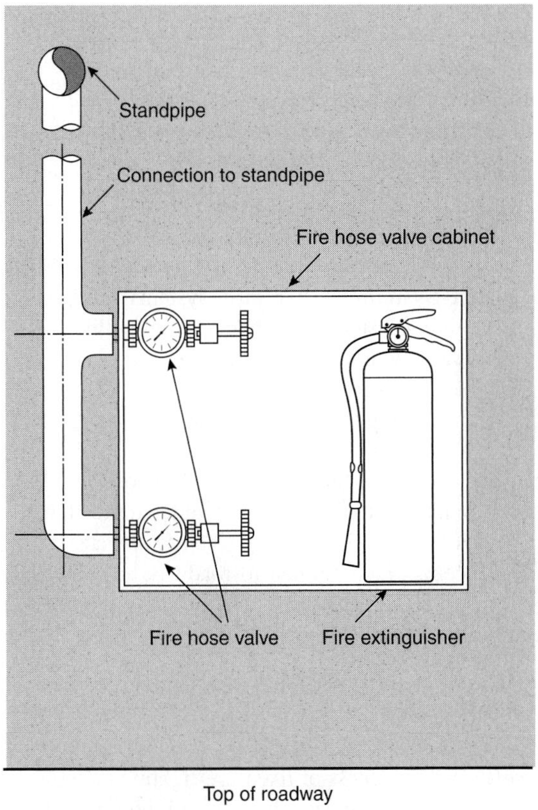

FIGURE 21.11.13 Typical Hose Valve Cabinet

Fire Pumps

When fire pumps are required to provide the necessary flow capacity and pressure in the road tunnel standpipe system, they should be installed in accordance with NFPA 20, *Standard for*

FIGURE 21.11.14 Hose Valves

FIGURE 21.11.15 Hose Valves in Fire Cabinet

the Installation of Stationary Pumps for Fire Protection. Figures 21.11.16 and 21.11.17 show typical installations of fire pumps and controls in a road tunnel application.

Fire Department Connection

Fire department connections are required to allow the fire department to charge the standpipe line. Two connections should be provided for every standpipe system and installed in accordance with NFPA 14. Each fire department connection should be installed within 100 ft (30.5 m) of an active hydrant that is tied into an approved water supply. A typical road tunnel fire department connection (FDC) and its active hydrant are shown in Figure 21.11.18.

Fixed Fire-Fighting Systems (FFFSs)

In road tunnels, fixed fire-fighting systems are defined as consisting of fire-fighting equipment, permanently attached to the tunnel, consisting of a piping system with a fixed supply of water or extinguishing agent which, when operated, has the intended effect of reducing the heat release and fire growth rates by discharging the water or extinguishing agent directly on the fire. Examples of fixed fire-fighting systems include sprinkler and deluge systems.

FIGURE 21.11.18 Fire Department Connection (FDC) with Hydrant

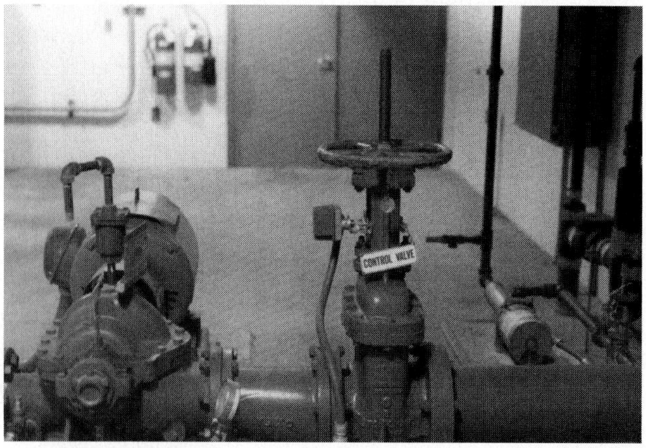

FIGURE 21.11.16 Fire Pump

FIGURE 21.11.17 Fire Pump Control Cabinet

Sprinkler Systems. These are fixed fire-fighting systems consisting of an integrated system of piping designed in accordance with fire protection engineering standards. The system is designed for each sprinkler head to be activated individually by heat from a fire itself so as to dispense water in the areas where it is needed to ensure rapid suppression of the fire.

Deluge Systems. These are fixed fire-fighting systems employing open nozzles that are attached to a zoned piping system that is connected to a water supply through a valve that is opened either manually or automatically. When this valve opens, water flows into the piping system and discharges from all nozzles in the designated zone.

Water Mist Systems. Water mist systems are pressurized fixed fire-fighting systems that operate by propelling very small droplets of water with high momentum which absorbs the fire's energy, cools the surrounding hot air and gases, and prevents oxygen from entering the combustion area.

Additives. Additives such as AFFF (aqueous film-forming foam) are being considered for in-tunnel fixed fire-fighting systems in lieu of water-only systems. The use of water only poses several concerns when applied to roadway tunnels. The high water demand rate needs to be available from the local supply, and this demand requires that in-tunnel drainage piping, storage, and pumping systems all become much larger.

History

The use and effectiveness of fixed fire-fighting systems in road tunnels has not been universally accepted; however, the recent severe fires in road tunnels in Europe have focused attention on the issue of fixed fire-fighting systems in road tunnels. NFPA

502 states that "the use of sprinklers (FFFS) in road tunnels generally is not recommended" (2004), and the World Road Association (PIARC) states that "sprinklers (FFFS) are generally not considered as cost effective and are not recommended in usual road tunnels"[4] (1999). Australia and Japan routinely install FFFS in their road tunnels. In addition, Austria, the Netherlands, Spain, and the United States have installed such systems in tunnels or are planning to do so in the near future. There are currently five U.S. road tunnels that have been equipped with fixed fire-fighting systems as shown in Table 21.11.7. Full-scale tests of fixed fire-fighting systems are or have been conducted by France, the Netherlands, Norway, and Spain.

Design and Control

System Design. When a fixed fire-fighting system is designed and installed in a road tunnel, the system should be designed as a manually activated deluge system to help ensure against accidental discharge of a sprinkler system. The system piping should be arranged using interval zoning so that the discharge can be focused in the zone or zones of incident without necessitating discharge for the entire length of the tunnel. Each zone should be equipped with its own proportioning valve set to control the appropriate water/foam mixture percentage if a water additive is being employed. Discharge heads should provide an open deluge and be spaced so that coverage extends to roadway shoulders and, if applicable, maintenance/patrol walkways. The system should be designed with enough water (and/or foam) capacity to allow operation of at least two zones adjacent to the incident zone. Zone length should be based on activation time as determined by the authority having jurisdiction (AHJ). Piping should be designed to allow drainage of the fixed fire-fighting systems after flow is stopped.

System Control. A full-time attended control room should be available for any road tunnel facility in which safe passage necessitates fixed fire-fighting system protection. Therefore, consideration should be given to human interaction in the system control and activation design to minimize false alarms and accidental discharges. Any automatic mode of operation should include a discharge delay to allow incident verification and assessment of in-tunnel conditions by trained operators. An integrated graphic display of the sprinkler system zones, fire detection system zones, tunnel ventilation system limits, and emergency access and egress locations should be provided at the control room to allow tunnel operators and responding emergency personnel to make appropriate initial response decisions.

Standards and Guidelines

NFPA 502 currently addresses road tunnel–based fixed fire-fighting systems as follows:

> Where sprinklers (fixed fire-fighting systems) are installed in road tunnels, the sprinkler systems (fixed fire-fighting systems) shall be installed, inspected and maintained in accordance with NFPA 13.

The catastrophic tunnel fires experienced in Europe during the last several years have prompted industry experts to revisit the potential benefit of fixed fire-fighting system applications in road tunnels. Research and test initiatives have been, and continue to be, performed by various organizations in both Europe and Japan that have provided new insight on the effectiveness of various FFFS technologies and their advantages and disadvantages under varying in-tunnel fire scenarios.

The technical committee for NFPA 502 has continued to monitor these programs and has acknowledged that when properly designed and maintained, FFFS can offer a potential life safety benefit in some road tunnel applications. As such the 2008 edition of NFPA 502 will reflect the latest technical considerations on the benefits of FFFS in road tunnels and will permit the installation of an FFFS where it can be shown by engineering analysis that the current level of safety can be equaled or exceeded by the use of fixed fire-fighting systems. As part of an integrated approach to the management of safety, such systems will be permitted in accordance with an engineering installation, inspection, and maintenance schedule using the design parameters for a particular tunnel which demonstrate that the level of performance provided by the fire-fighting systems will be maintained.

TABLE 21.11.7 Fixed Fire-Fighting Systems in U.S. Road Tunnels

Tunnel	*Location*	*Route*	*Opened to Traffic*	*Length ft*	*Length m*	*Bores/Lanes*	*Fixed Fire-Fighting System Type*	*System Zones*
CANA Northbound	Boston, Massachusetts	US 1	1990	1540	470	1/3	Deluge foam	15
CANA Southbound	Boston, Massachusetts	US 1	1990	900	275	1/3	Deluge foam	9
Mercer Island	Seattle, Washington	I-90	1989	2800	853	3/8	Deluge foam	37
Mt. Baker Ridge	Seattle, Washington	I-90	1989	3500	1067	3/8	Deluge foam	50
Battery Street	Seattle, Washington	Battery Street	1952	2140	652	2/4	Deluge water	14
I-5 Convention Center	Seattle, Washington	I-5	1988	547	167	1/12	Deluge foam	9

Source: Adapted from NFPA 502, *Standard for Road Tunnels, Bridges, and Other Limited Access Highways,* 2008 edition, Table E.3, p. 502-28.

In addition where fixed fire-fighting systems are installed in road tunnels, the fixed fire-fighting system should be installed, inspected, and maintained in accordance with other NFPA standards such as the following:

- NFPA 11, *Standard for Low-, Medium-, and High-Expansion Foam*
- NFPA 15, *Standard for Water Spray Fixed Systems for Fire Protection*
- NFPA 16, *Standard for the Installation of Foam-Water Sprinkler and Foam-Water Spray Systems*
- NFPA 18, *Standard on Wetting Agents*
- NFPA 25, *Standard for the Inspection, Testing, and Maintenance of Water-Based Fire Protection Systems*
- NFPA 750, *Standard on Water Mist Fire Protection Systems*

The reader is referred to Annex D of NFPA 502 for an extensive discussion on the use of fixed fire-fighting systems (sprinklers) in road tunnels. In addition, the subject of fixed fire-fighting systems is addressed by the World Road Association (PIARC) in their technical reports titled *Fire and Smoke Control in Road Tunnels,*[5] *Systems and Equipment for Fire and Smoke Control in Road Tunnels,*[8] and *Road Tunnels: An Assessment of Fixed Fire Fighting Systems.*[9]

Tunnel Drainage

A tunnel drainage system of sufficient capacity must be provided in any road tunnel to collect and discharge the water from seepage, rain, and fire-fighting activities, including the deployment of fixed fire-fighting systems. This system can be either gravity or pumped and should be designed, installed, and maintained in accordance with NFPA 502.

EMERGENCY RESPONSE PLANNING

The operation of any road tunnel includes many operation elements, but one of the most important from a safety viewpoint is the operation of the tunnel facility during a fire emergency. Key components necessary to be prepared for an emergency incident are the development of an integrated emergency response plan, the training of all participants, and the conducting of regularly scheduled exercises.

Emergency Response Plan Participants

An effective emergency response plan includes the interaction of not only the operators of the tunnel but of all outside agencies that might become active in an emergency response to a tunnel incident. Some or all of the following external agencies could be included:

- Police department
- Fire department (brigade)
- Civil defense
- Emergency medical services
- U.S. Department of Transportation (USDOT)
- Local private firms (equipment)
- Department of Public Works
- Water company
- U.S. Coast Guard
- U.S. Federal Emergency Management Agency (FEMA)
- Power company
- Telephone company

NFPA 502 contains a sample outline of a typical emergency response plan in Annex F.

Training and Exercises

A regular training program, which must be included as a part of an emergency response plan, should be scheduled for and should involve all operating personnel and all anticipated responders from external agencies. Because staff assignments within the responding agencies can change frequently, training should be continuous. Retraining of personnel should also be considered because the opportunity to participate in an actual response in a specific road tunnel may be infrequent.

Full-scale exercises should be conducted at least once a year and preferably twice a year. All potential responding external agencies should participate in these exercises so that all external agency representatives become familiar with the unique aspects of a road tunnel emergency response. Tabletop exercises, although extremely beneficial, do not replace the need for full-scale exercises.

Mutual-Aid Response

Arrangements for the response of nearby fire companies and emergency squads should be made a part of the emergency response planning process. Means of access that allows the entrance of outside aid companies to the facility should be provided, and procedures for utilizing such access need to be included in the emergency response plan. Appropriate precautions should be taken at the points of entry to alert and control traffic to allow safe entrance by emergency equipment.

Fire Apparatus

Fire apparatus suitable for fighting fires within road tunnels should be available within the general facility area, thus permitting a rapid response to a fire emergency. This apparatus should be equipped to deal effectively with flammable liquid and hazardous material fires. The responding fire apparatus should be appropriately equipped to fight fire within the road tunnel for a minimum of 30 minutes. If water supply is not available, suitable arrangements are needed to transport water so that the required apparatus delivery rate at the fire can be maintained for an additional 45 minutes. These fire-fighting units should carry multipurpose dry chemical extinguishers and an extinguishing agent for Class D metal fires.

Where the road tunnel is a high-capacity facility in a congested urban area, it may be appropriate to house such apparatus at the tunnel portal or portals. It may also be appropriate at these urban tunnels to combine the fire apparatus with the apparatus provided to effect retrieval and removal of disabled vehicles from the tunnel. Provisions should be taken to permit operation of vehicles and fire fighters in a potentially hazardous smoke and high-temperature gas-laden environment that may also have insufficient oxygen.

EVACUATION AND RESCUE

Point of Safety

A *point of safety* is defined by NFPA 502 as a location outside the incident structure that affords adequate protection for the motorist. Thus in the case of a road tunnel, the potential points of safety are the outside, the parallel nonincident bore (if it is a multibore facility), and a safety refuge (if one is provided). The potential egress paths would include the roadway, the cross passages, the emergency exits, and the safety refuge as shown in Figure 21.11.19. The egress path must be provided with a tenable environment for a sufficient period of time to permit motorist evacuation from the incident bore.

Tenable Environment Criteria

To a large extent, the quantitative aspect of the criteria for emergency situations is arbitrary because there are no universally accepted tolerance limits pertaining to air temperature and velocity. In fact, tolerance limits vary with age, health, weight, sex, and acclimatization.

Air Temperature Criteria. Motorists should not be exposed to maximum air temperatures exceeding 140°F (60°C) during emergencies. It is anticipated that the 140°F (60°C) air temperature will place a physiological burden on a few motorists, but the exposure also is anticipated to be brief and to produce no lasting harmful effects.

Air Velocity Criteria. When ventilation air is needed in evacuation routes to control smoke and heated gases, it might be necessary to expose motorists to high air velocities. The only upper limit to the ventilation rate occurs when the air velocity becomes great enough to create a hazard to persons walking in that airstream. According to the descriptions of the effects of various air velocities given in the Beaufort scale, motorists

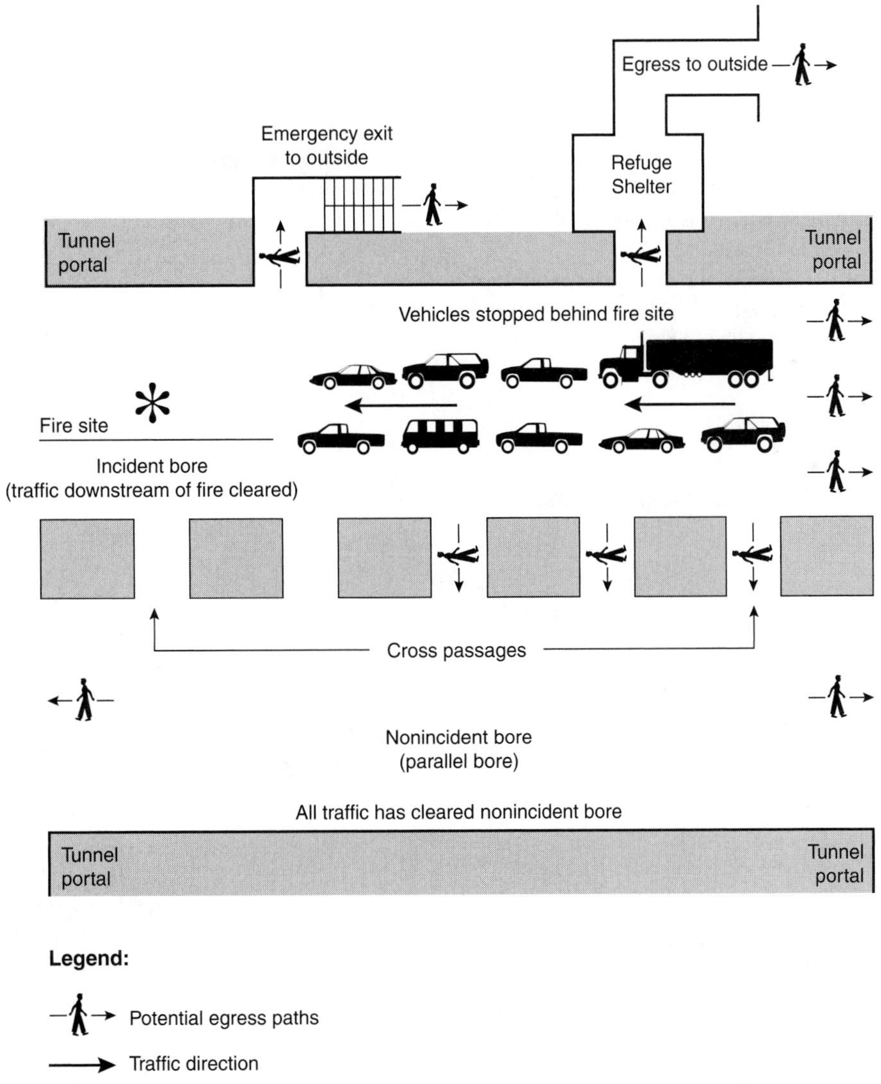

FIGURE 21.11.19 Typical Tunnel Means of Egress

under emergency conditions can tolerate as much as 2200 ft/min (11 m/sec).

ENGINEERING ANALYSIS

Engineering analysis is one of the key elements of the evaluation, development, and approval of any tunnel fire protection system. Many of the design concepts developed must be evaluated and their applicability and capacity demonstrated to the AHJ prior to approval. These analyses may be performed manually or by use of a computer program.

Calculations

Fire Heat Release Rate—Design Fire. The first design issue to be resolved is the selection of the design fire or fires—that is, the value of heat released that will provide the basis for the design of the emergency ventilation system. In a road tunnel, the vehicle fire load is either unknown or inconsistent. As a result, the review of data, such as those contained in Table 21.11.8, is extremely useful in the establishment of the design fire or fires.

Critical Velocity. The minimum air velocity within the tunnel section experiencing the fire emergency should be sufficient to mitigate backlayering of the smoke. The simultaneous solution of Equation 1 and Equation 2, by iteration, determines the critical velocity. The grade in these equations is taken in the direction of the airflow as shown in Figure 21.11.20.

The critical velocity (Figure 21.11.21) is the minimum steady-state velocity of the ventilation air moving toward the fire that is necessary to prevent backlayering:

TABLE 21.11.8 Typical Design Fire Size Data

Cause of Fire	*Peak Fire Heat Release Rate (MW)*
Passenger car	5–10
Multiple passenger cars (2–4 vehicles)	10–20
Bus	20–30
Heavy goods truck	70–200
Tanker*	200–300

Notes:
1. The designer should consider the rate of fire development (peak heat release rates may be reached within 10 minutes), the number of vehicles that could be involved in the fire, and the potential for the fire to spread from one vehicle to another.
2. Temperatures directly above the fire can be expected to be as high as 1832 to 2552°F (1000 to 1400°C).

*Flammable and combustible liquids for the tanker fire design should include adequate drainage to limit the area of the pool fire and its duration. The heat release rate may be greater than in the table if more than one vehicle is involved.

Source: Adapted from NFPA 502, *Standard for Road Tunnels, Bridges, and Other Limited Access Highways,* 2008 edition, Table A.10.5.1, p. 502-23.

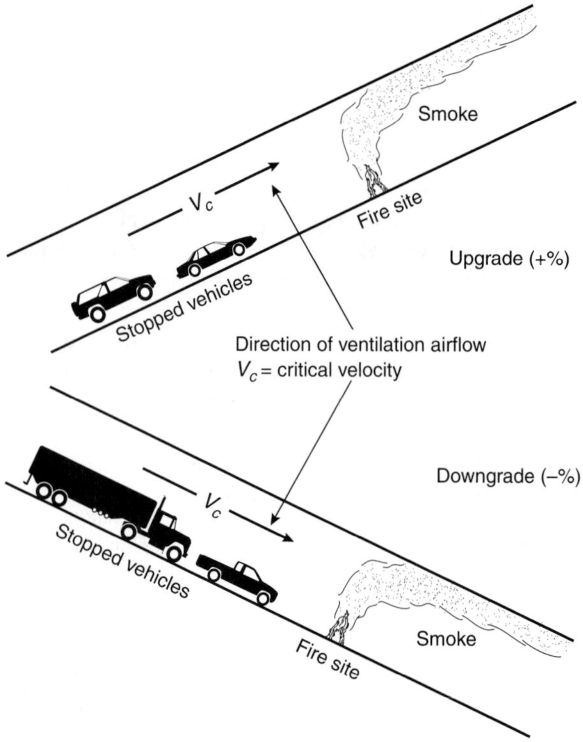

FIGURE 21.11.20 Grade Determination

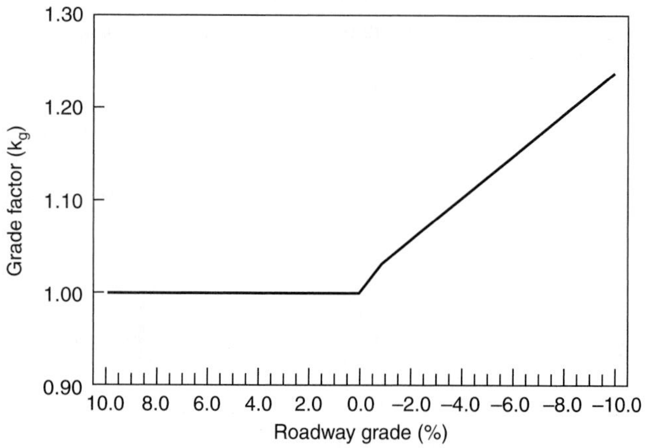

FIGURE 21.11.21 Critical Velocity Grade Factor

$$V_c = K_1 K_g \left(\frac{gHQ}{\rho C_p A T_f} \right)^{1/3} \qquad (1)$$

$$T_f = \left(\frac{Q}{\rho C_p A V_c} \right) + T \qquad (2)$$

where

A = Area perpendicular to the flow (ft^2 [m^2])

C_p = Specific heat of air (Btu/lb R [kJ/kg K])

g = Acceleration caused by gravity (ft/sec^2 [m/sec^2])
H = Height of the tunnel at the fire site (ft [m])
K_1 = 0.606
K_g = Grade factor (Figure 21.11.21)
Q = Heat the fire is adding directly to the air at the fire site (Btu/sec [MW])
T = Temperature of the approach air (degrees R [K])
T_f = Average temperature of the fire site gases (degrees R [K])
V_c = Critical velocity (ft/min [m/sec])
ρ = Average density of the approach (upstream) air (lb/ft^3 [kg/m^3])

Fire Models as Analytical Tools

The three following types of fire models can be applied to the road tunnel environment:

- One-dimensional models
- Zone models
- Field models

One-dimensional models are extremely useful and effective if the bulk results (i.e., the average values for results like airflow and temperature) are satisfactory. The zone models developed for use in buildings, which utilize room configurations, do not lend themselves to a linear configuration such as a road tunnel. Field models or computational fluid dynamics (CFD) will provide detailed results, including temperature and smoke profiles, and are therefore ideally suited to perform analyses for road tunnels. However, CFD simulation can be expensive to conduct.

A number of computer-based analytical tools have been developed that are applicable to road tunnels. Models are available to evaluate smoke control and ventilation requirements as well as emergency egress. Ventilation analyses have moved from the one-dimensional models developed 20 to 30 years ago to the three-dimensional aspects of computational fluid dynamics. CFD has been in use in other industries for many years, but only in the last 10 years has it begun to be used in tunnel fire protection applications.

SES. An excellent example of a one-dimensional model used in the analysis of road tunnel emergency ventilation requirements is the Subway Environment Simulation (SES) program. The SES is a one-dimensional network model that is extremely effective in the evaluation of tunnel/shaft configurations.

The SES program, which is essentially a one-dimensional, incompressible, turbulent, slug-flow model, comprises a series of interdependent computation subprograms to address vehicle performance, aerodynamics, temperature/humidity, heat sink, environmental control, and fire. The SES computer model provides a dynamic simulation of bidirectional traffic in a road tunnel and permits continuous reading of the average air velocity, temperature, and humidity throughout any arrangement of tunnels, ventilation buildings, and shafts.

The SES fire model, which has the ability to model the aerodynamic and thermodynamic effects of a tunnel fire, was designed to simulate the overall effects of a tunnel fire on the ventilation system. This level of detail is considered sufficient for evaluating the adequacy of an emergency ventilation system. The input/information required by the program and the outputs produced are tailored for use by design engineers concerned with practical environmental problems. The SES model[10] is available from the Volpe Transportation Center in Cambridge, Massachusetts.

TUNVEN. The TUNVEN computer program[11] solves the coupled one-dimensional steady-state road tunnel aerodynamics and advection equations to obtain the longitudinal air velocities and pollutant concentrations for a given road tunnel design, traffic load, and ventilation rate. The effect of ambient conditions external to the tunnel, such as portal winds and local pollutant levels, can also be included. This program can be used to determine ventilation requirements for natural, longitudinal, semitransverse, and full transverse ventilation systems.

A road tunnel is modeled in the TUNVEN computer program as a one-dimensional longitudinal air duct with inflow and outflow at each end and along its length. Airflow through the tunnel is caused by a pressure differential between the ends, by the piston action of the vehicles, and by addition or removal of air through the ventilation system. The forces generated by these effects are balanced in the steady-state case by opposing friction forces along the tunnel walls and flow entrance and exit losses.

Vehicles traveling through the tunnel also emit pollutants, which are diluted by the tunnel air to a concentration that depends on the pollutant sources in the upstream sections of the tunnel and on the local airflow velocity. The dependence on pollutant sources couples the aerodynamic and advection (or concentration) equations, making it necessary to compute the flow field before the concentrations can be determined. The TUNVEN model is available from National Technical Information Services (NTIS).

SOLVENT. SOLVENT[12] is a computational fluid dynamics model developed as a part of the Memorial Tunnel Fire Ventilation Test Program, for the simulation of fluid flow, heat transfer, and smoke transport in road tunnels. SOLVENT can be applied to all of the ventilation systems deployed in road tunnels, including longitudinal ventilation using jet fans, transverse ventilation, and natural ventilation.

The primary objective for the model is the ability to simulate the interactive effects of a tunnel fire and the ventilation system to determine the unsafe regions of the tunnel, where the hazardous effects of the fire (smoke and high temperature) are confined, and how these regions are affected by the ventilation system configuration, capacity, and operation.

For transverse ventilation systems, a flow network model is used to predict the flow rates, temperatures, and pressures in the ducts. The ventilation ducts and the tunnel (which uses the CFD model) are coupled via boundary conditions. SOLVENT is being applied to develop the emergency ventilation operating mode matrix for the many operating road tunnels. The matrix identifies how each ventilation zone is to be operated as a function of fire incident location and traffic direction. Figure 21.11.22 is a copy of the animation of the SOLVENT output

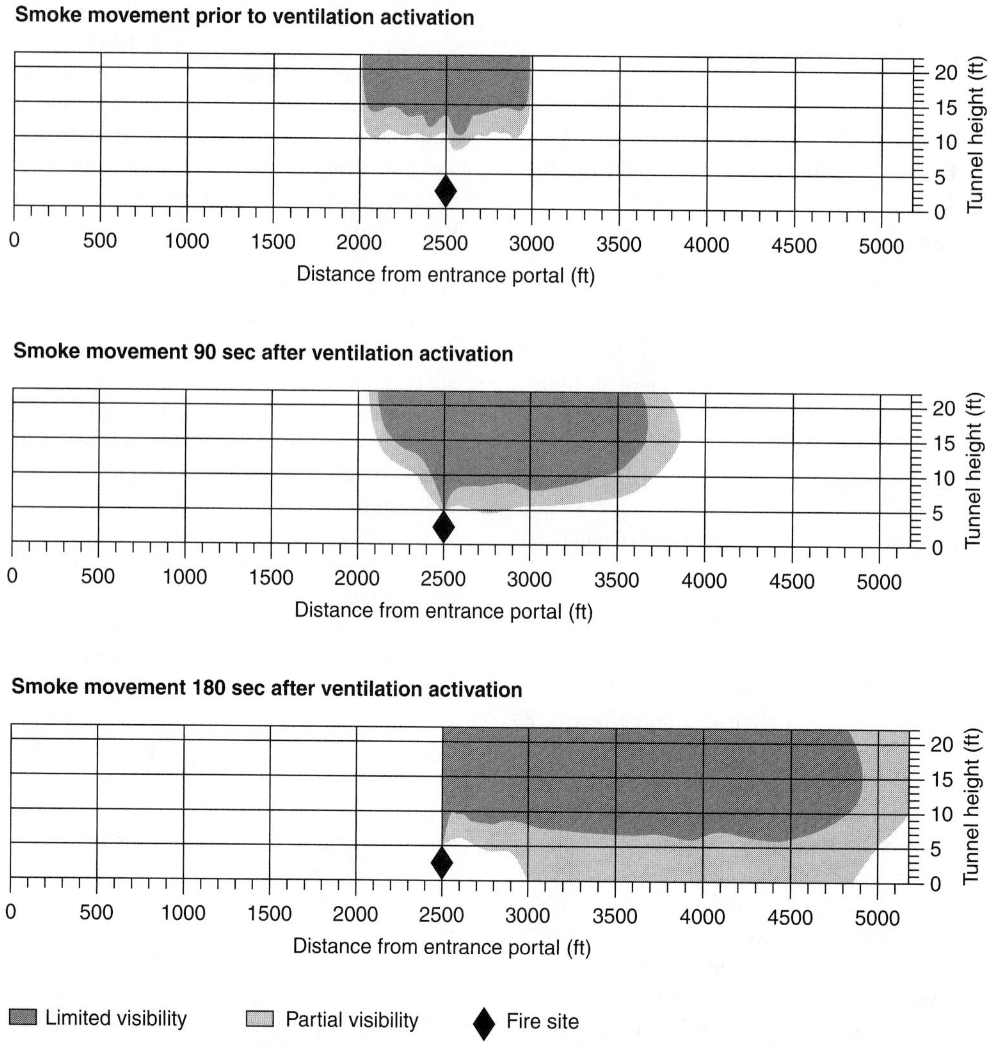

FIGURE 21.11.22 Smoke Movement Simulation

from simulations for a road tunnel with a longitudinal ventilation system. These graphics show the movement of the smoke before and after ventilation activation. They clearly show the progressive movement of the smoke and the ultimate elimination of any backlayering.

The SOLVENT model has been validated against the data compiled from the Memorial Tunnel Fire Ventilation Test Program.[12] The SOLVENT model is available, under license, from Parsons Brinckerhoff Quade & Douglas, Inc., in New York and Innovative Research, Inc., in Minneapolis.

Emergency Egress Models

Evacuation modeling software, such as SIMULEX, can be employed to simulate the escape movement of people to a point of safety during incidents within road tunnels. The algorithms for the movement of individuals are based on real-life data. The program shows the evacuation process graphically on the screen, with the plan view of passengers moving toward emergency exits or cross passages, and predicts where the exiting choke points occur within the tunnel. The egress times computed by this program can be used to evaluate alternative distances between emergency exits and can allow comparisons among alternative sizes of cross-passageways, exit stairways, and walkways. The program has been upgraded to simulate walkways in road tunnels and people walking at the 200 fpm (1 m/sec) exiting speed (the design speed for exiting passengers) specified in NFPA 130.

Current applicable standards for road tunnels require emergency exits and cross-passageways be provided throughout the tunnels and spaced so that the distance between exits is not greater than the limit specified in the standard. There is an ongoing interest to determine the most appropriate distance between emergency exits, minimum size of exit stairways, and widths of walkways in road and rail tunnels, which will ultimately lead to the development of more performance-based codes. The output in Figure 21.11.23 is a printout of an emergency egress simulation for a road tunnel employing SIMULEX. This figure shows the motorists in the process of leaving their vehicles and subsequently entering an emergency exit enclosure leading to an emergency exit stairway. The SIMULEX model is available, under license, from Integrated Environmental Solutions

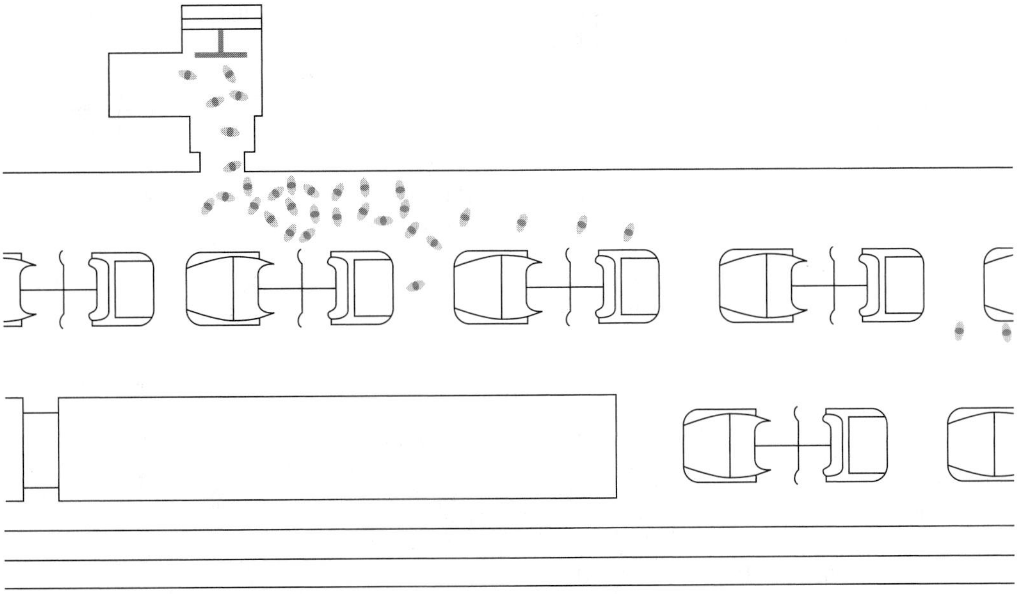

FIGURE 21.11.23 Emergency Egress Model Output

(IES) of Glasgow, Scotland.[13] There are other egress models currently being applied to tunnel egress such as STEPS, Exodus, and Legion.

TUNNEL FIRE TESTS

Over the past 40 years, a series of full-scale tunnel fire tests have been conducted to permit fire protection and ventilation engineers to better understand the phenomenon of fire and smoke within a tunnel. These tests were conducted in Switzerland, Austria, Japan, Norway, and the United States, as shown in Table 21.11.9. The most recent of these were the Eureka Project 499 FIRETUN, conducted in an abandoned mining tunnel in northern Norway by nine European countries;[14] the Memorial Tunnel Fire Ventilation Test Program (MTFVTP),[7] conducted in the United States; and the Runehamer tests,[15] conducted in Norway in 2003.

The most significant to the tunnel industry in the United States were the tests conducted at the Memorial Tunnel, an

TABLE 21.11.9 Full-Scale Tunnel Fire Tests

Fire Test Program	*Country*	*Year(s)*	*Test Tunnel Type*	*Number of Tests*	Test Tunnel Length *(ft)*	*(m)*	*Fire Type*	*Pan Fuel*
Ofenegg	Switzerland	1965	Railway	11	623	190	Pan	Gasoline
Zwenberg	Austria	1975	—	30	—	—	Pan	Diesel
PWRI[a]	Japan	1980	Road	8	9843	3000	Pan and vehicle	—
PWRI	Japan	1980	Test facility[b]	16	2297	700	Pan and vehicle	Heptane
Eureka[c] Project 499 FIRETUN	Norway[d]	1990–1992	Mining	21	7218	2200	Pan and vehicle	Wood cribs
Memorial Tunnel	United States	1993–1995	Road	98	2800	854	Pan	Diesel
Runehamar	Norway	2003	Road	4	5413	1650	Vehicle[e]	—

[a]Public Works Research Institute.
[b]A tunnel test facility built by PWRI.
[c]Eureka tests were conducted in the Repparfjord Tunnel in Norway.
[d]Although the Eureka tests were conducted in Norway, nine European countries conducted the specific tests.
[e]The fuel used was as follows for each of the four tests:

- Wood and plastic pallets
- Wood pallets and mattresses
- Furniture and tires
- Plastic cups in cardboard cartons

abandoned road tunnel in West Virginia. This comprehensive test program, which began with the initial fire tests in September 1993 and concluded with the final tests in March 1995, produced data that were acquired in a full-size facility, under controlled conditions, and over a wide range of system parameters.

Hot-Smoke Testing in Tunnels

Hot-smoke tests were initially conducted as a means of verifying smoke modeling predictions. More recently it has become common practice to use a hot-smoke test to actually test the smoke management systems of a completed tunnel. These tests have become valuable as a commissioning tool, allowing testing of the integrational functioning of all systems related to the fire life safety of the tunnel, including the detection, ventilation, smoke exhaust, dampers, fire-fighting systems, and fire control panels.[16]

Memorial Tunnel Fire Ventilation Test Program

The Memorial Tunnel Fire Ventilation Test Program[7] represented a unique opportunity to evaluate and develop design methods and operational strategies leading to safe road tunnels. The purpose of this test program was to develop a database that provides tunnel design engineers and operators with an experimentally proven means to determine the ventilation rates and ventilation system configurations that provide effective smoke control management during a tunnel fire emergency. It was even more important to establish specific operational strategies to permit effective reconfiguration of ventilation operational parameters for existing tunnel facilities.

The Memorial Tunnel, a two-lane, 2800 ft (854 m) road tunnel located near Charleston, West Virginia, was built in 1953 as part of the West Virginia Turnpike and abandoned in 1987 when it was bypassed by an open-cut section of a new six-lane interstate highway. The tunnel has a 3.2 percent uphill grade from the south to the north tunnel portal. The existing ventilation equipment was replaced with new variable speed, reversible, axial flow central ventilation fans. Fires were produced in roadway-level steel pans, with average fire heat release rates as shown in Table 21.11.10.

The ventilation systems, tested under varying flow rates and varying heat release rates with one or two zones of ventilation, included the following:

- Natural ventilation
- Longitudinal ventilation with jet fans
- Longitudinal ventilation with central fans and Saccardo nozzles
- Transverse ventilation
- Transverse ventilation with point extraction and oversized exhaust ports

TABLE 21.11.10 MTFVTP Test Fire Sizes

Nominal Fire Heat Release Rate (MW)	*Vehicle Incident Equivalent*
10	Two passenger cars
20	Bus or truck
50	Large truck
100	Petrol tanker

Source: "Memorial Tunnel Fire Ventilation Test Report."[7]

Suppression System. A fire suppression system employing a 3 percent aqueous film-forming foam (AFFF) solution was installed in the Memorial Tunnel primarily to suppress the test fire in an emergency; however, it was also used during several tests to evaluate the impact of horizontal roadway ventilation airflow on the operation of a foam suppression system.

The effectiveness of the foam suppression system tested was not diminished by operation in high-velocity longitudinal airflow (825 fpm [4.2 m/sec]). The time for the suppression system to extinguish the open pan fire with the nozzles located at the ceiling, 14 ft (4.3 m) above the roadway, ranged from 5 to 25 seconds for a 50 MW fire. This was the configuration for the transverse tests.

When the longitudinal ventilation tests with jet fans were conducted, the nozzles were located on the west wall, 7 ft (2.1 m) above the roadway. In this configuration the time to extinguishment was 102 seconds (50 MW) and 11 seconds (100 MW). The results of these suppression tests are shown in Table 21.11.11.

Video Recording System. The CCTV system included seven video cameras, two located within the tunnel with water-cooled enclosures, one roadway-level camera north of the fire to secure added video footage of smoke movement, two located at the tunnel portals, and two located on the north and south meteorological towers. This system provided essential video footage of smoke behavior during the fires.

Findings and Conclusions of the Memorial Tunnel Fire Ventilation Test Program. *Natural ventilation* resulted in extensive spread of smoke and heated gases upgrade of the fire but relatively clear conditions downgrade of the fire. Other conclusions related to natural ventilation included the following:

TABLE 21.11.11 Foam Suppression Tests

Ventilation System	*Fire Size (MW)*	*Air Velocity Across Fire (fpm)*	*Air Velocity Across Fire (m/sec)*	*Time to Extinguish (sec)*
Full transverse	50	115	0.6	5
Semitransverse—exhaust	50	210	1.1	8
Exhaust—single port	50	825	4.2	25
Longitudinal—jet fans	50	500	2.5	102
Longitudinal—jet fans	100	400	2.0	111

Source: "Memorial Tunnel Fire Ventilation Test Report."[7]

- The spread of smoke and heated gases during a 50 MW fire was considerably greater than during a 20 MW fire. The depth of the smoke layer increased with fire size.
- The time for the smoke layer to descend to a point where it posed an immediate life safety threat was dependent on the fire size and tunnel geometry, specifically the tunnel height.
- In the Memorial Tunnel, smoke traveled between 950 and 1200 ft (290 and 365 m) along the arched tunnel roof before cooling and descending into the roadway.
- The restriction to visibility caused by the movement of smoke occurred more quickly than did a temperature high enough to be debilitating.
- Exposure to high levels of carbon monoxide was never more critical than smoke or temperature for any test.

Longitudinal Ventilation System. A longitudinal ventilation system employing jet fans was highly effective in managing the direction of the spread of smoke for fires sizes tested up to 100 MW in a 3.2 percent grade tunnel. Jet fans located downgrade from the fire site were subjected to the temperatures shown in Table 21.11.12.

Transverse Ventilation. It was demonstrated in the MTFVTP that dilution as a sole means for temperature and smoke control was not very effective. Some means of extraction should be incorporated. Extraction and longitudinal airflow when combined can significantly increase the effectiveness of a road tunnel ventilation system to manage and control the movement of smoke.

Single-zone balanced full transverse ventilation systems operated at 100 cubic feet per minute per lane foot (cfm/lf) (0.155 cubic meters per second per lane meter [m^3/sec/lm]) were ineffective in the management of smoke and heated gases for fire sizes 20 MW and larger. Single-zone unbalanced full transverse ventilation systems generate some longitudinal airflow in the roadway. The result of this longitudinal airflow was to offset some of the effects of buoyancy for a 20 MW fire. The effectiveness of unbalanced full transverse ventilation systems is sensitive to the fire location, since there is no control over the airflow direction.

The tested two-zone transverse ventilation system provided control over the direction and magnitude of the longitudinal airflow. Airflow rates of 100 cfm/lf (0.155 m^3/sec/lm) contained high temperatures from a 20 MW fire within 100 ft (31 m) of the fire in the lower elevations of the roadway and smoke within 200 ft (61 m). The maximum temperatures experienced at the inlet to the central fans closest to the fire are shown in Table 21.11.13.

Smoke and Heated Gas Movement. The time for the smoke layer to descend to a point where it poses an immediate life safety threat is dependent on the fire size and tunnel geometry, specifically the tunnel height. As noted under the section on natural ventilation, smoke traveled between 950 and 1200 ft (290 and 365 m) along the arched tunnel roof before cooling and descending into the roadway. Selected smoke movement data for a naturally ventilated tunnel with a 3.2 percent grade is shown in Table 21.11.14.

Fan Operation Delays. The spread of hot gases and smoke was significantly greater with a longer fan response time. Hot smoke

TABLE 21.11.12 Temperatures at Jet Fans

Nominal Fire Size (MW)	Maximum Temperature (°F)	Maximum Temperature (°C)
20	400	204
50	630	332
100	1250	677

Note: The jet fans subjected to these maximum temperatures during the Memorial Tunnel Fire Ventilation Test Program were located 170 ft (51.8 m) downgrade of the fire site.

Source: "Memorial Tunnel Fire Ventilation Test Report."[7]

TABLE 21.11.13 Temperatures at Central Fan Inlet

Nominal Fire Size (MW)	Maximum Temperature (°F)	Maximum Temperature (°C)
20	225	107
50	255	124
100	325	163

Note: The central fans exposed (subjected) to these maximum temperatures during the Memorial Tunnel Fire Ventilation Test Program were located approximately 700 ft (213 m) from the fire site.

Source: "Memorial Tunnel Fire Ventilation Test Report."[7]

TABLE 21.11.14 Smoke Movement in a Naturally Ventilated Tunnel

Test Number	Fire Heat Release Rate: Nominal *10^6 Btu/hr*	Nominal *MW*	Peak *10^6 Btu/hr*	Peak *MW*	*Smoke Layer Begins Descent (min)*	*Smoke Fills Tunnel Roadway (min)*	Peak Smoke Velocity *fpm*	Peak Smoke Velocity *m/sec*
501	68	20	99	29	3+	5	1200	6.1
502	171	50	195	57	1+	3	1600	8.1

Source: "Memorial Tunnel Fire Ventilation Test Report."[7]

layers were observed to spread very quickly—1600 to 1900 ft (490 to 580 m) in the initial 2 minutes of a fire.

Ventilation System Enhancements. The ability to extract smoke quickly and as close as possible to the fire location can significantly reduce smoke and heat migration in undesired directions and facilitate two-way traffic operations. This localized extraction is possible with the application of single-point extraction openings (SPE) to a transverse ventilation system. SPE systems are applicable to two-way traffic flow with a dependency on the location, size, and spacing of the SPE openings. Smoke and heat drawn from the fire to the SPE could pass over or possibly around stalled traffic and vehicle occupants. An SPE located upgrade of the fire is very effective in temperature and smoke management. With the SPE located downgrade of the fire, only minimal improvement in temperature and smoke conditions over a single-zone partial transverse exhaust system was achieved. A single-point opening of 300 ft^2 (27.9 m^2) was most effective in temperature and smoke management of the SPE sizes tested. Significantly greater smoke and heat spread was observed with a 100 ft^2 (9.3 m^2) opening compared to the 300 ft^2 (27.9 m^2) opening.

For 20 MW fires, partial transverse ventilation exhaust ventilation operated with 100 cfm/lf (0.155 m^3/sec/lm) and supplemented with a large (300 ft^2 [27.9 m^2]) single-point opening limited smoke and heated gases migration to 200 ft (61 m) from the fire. A partial transverse exhaust system supplemented with oversized exhaust ports and operated with 85 cfm/lf (0.132 m^3/sec/lm) limited high temperatures to an area extending 100 ft (31 m) from the fire and sustained the stratified smoke layer above the occupied zone. For 50 MW fires, partial transverse ventilation exhaust ventilation operated with 110 cfm/lf (0.170 m^3/sec/lm) and supplemented with a large (300 ft^2 [27.9 m^2]) single-point opening limited smoke and heated gases migration to 280 ft (85 m) from the fire.

ROAD BRIDGES

The 2004 version of NFPA 502 provides the fire protection requirements for road bridges spanning more than 400 ft (122 m). A fire occurring on a bridge is a much less serious situation than that posed by the same fire size in a tunnel for the very basic reason that the resulting heat and smoke is not contained within the same confined space as the motorists. However, depending on the severity and location (on or under the bridge) of the fire, the risk to structure may threaten the life safety of motorists traveling both on and below the bridge. Similar to a tunnel, most bridges afford only limited access for emergency responders; therefore, emergency response planning for longer span bridges is recommended. Further, the fact that cargo restrictions are far less stringent on bridges (and likely nonexistent beneath bridges) than in tunnels suggests that the potential for a large-scale fire is far greater on such structures. This issue of structure fire resistance and methods for fire protection on bridges is likely to become an increasingly important consideration as more lightweight and double-decked bridges are built.

Recent Road Bridge Fires

Fires on or under road bridges can be devastating to the integrity of the bridge support structure. Examples of several such fires that have occurred on Interstate 95 (I-95) are briefly described as follows:

- A fire broke out under the elevated section of I-95 in Pennsylvania, near Philadelphia, in 1996, between Westmoreland Street and Tioga Street and caused three spans of the 26-span, 1707 ft (520 m) Westmoreland Viaduct to buckle. The cause of the fire was a stack of discarded tires in an illegal dump underneath the viaduct.
- A tanker truck loaded with 8700 gal (33,000 L) of gasoline was traveling on I-95 in Pennsylvania in 1998. While swerving to avoid a passing car, the tanker truck jumped the Jersey barrier and exploded after striking a pickup truck in the southbound lanes. Both drivers died at the scene. Nine steel support girders, each 6 ft (2 m) long and 8 in. (20 cm) tall, and between 65 and 80 ft (20 and 24 m) of the bridge crossing the Chester Creek, were damaged.[17]
- In 2004 a tanker truck carrying 12,000 gal (45,500 L) of fuel oil collided with another vehicle and caught fire on Interstate 95 near Bridgeport, Connecticut. The resulting blaze was hot enough to melt steel support beams on the southbound side of the bridge over Howard Avenue. I-95 was closed in both directions.

Recommendations for Road Bridge Fire Protection

Currently, NFPA 502 provides that the following fire protection system elements be considered for application on long span road bridges:

- Emergency communications
- Signage
- Traffic control
- Fire suppression
- Drainage
- Control of hazardous materials
- Emergency response planning

Emergency Communications. Emergency communications, where required by the AHJ, will be provided by the installation of outdoor-type telephone boxes, coded alarm telegraph stations, radio transmitters, or other approved devices. These devices should have all of the following features:

- Made conspicuous by means of indicating lights or other approved markers
- Identified by a readily visible number plate or other approved device
- Posted with instructions for use by motorists
- Located in approved locations so that motorists can park vehicles clear of the travel lanes

Signage. Signs, mile markers, or other approved location reference markers will be installed along the highway to allow motorists to provide authorities with accurate locations for accident or emergency areas.

Traffic Control. A traffic control procedure will be established so that vehicles either stop or proceed with caution. Traffic will not be permitted to block or otherwise interfere with the response of emergency and fire apparatus.

Fire Suppression System. Where the distance from an acceptable water supply source to any point on the bridge exceeds 400 ft (120 m), the bridge will be provided with a Class I standpipe system in accordance with NFPA 14. The maximum flow of the standpipe system will be 500 gpm (1920 L/min) for one hour. Standard hose connections will be provided so that no location on the roadway is more than 150 ft (45 m) from the hose connection; however, the spacing will not exceed 275 ft (85 m). Two standard fire department connections (FDC) will be provided for each independent standpipe system.

Drainage. Drainage systems on bridges will be designed to channel and collect spilled hazardous or flammable liquids to drain areas that cannot cause additional hazards. Expansion joints will be designed to prevent spillage to the area below the bridge.

Control of Hazardous Materials. Control of hazardous materials will be in accordance with the requirements of Chapter 13 of NFPA 502.

Emergency Response Plan. The designated agency (operating) will carry out a complete and coordinated program of fire protection that will include written preplanned emergency response procedures and standard operating procedures. Emergency response procedures and the development of an emergency response plan will comply with the requirements of Chapter 12 of NFPA 502.

SUMMARY

Road tunnels, which include mountain tunnels, underwater tunnels, urban tunnels, and air-rights tunnels, represent a unique challenge in fire protection. The linear shape, limited accessibility, and lack of compartmentalization of road tunnels make fire fighting and evacuation difficult. For most road tunnels, the potential fire load is unknown because of the variety of vehicles and cargoes that pass through. The primary objectives of a road tunnel fire protection system are to permit evacuation, facilitate the entrance of fire fighters, and protect the tunnel structure and facilities. The key elements of road tunnel fire protection are fire identification, verification, and location; emergency communications; smoke management; fire suppression; emergency response planning; and evacuation and rescue.

Means of fire identification, verification, and detection include closed circuit television, pull boxes, emergency telephones, and detection systems such as heat, flame, and smoke detectors. Emergency communications can be transmitted by radio, whereas the use of loudspeakers is not recommended. Smoke management can be achieved by a variety of ventilation systems. Fire suppression systems include portable fire extinguishers, standpipes, hoses, fire pumps, and sprinklers. The emergency response plan should include the interaction of all potential responders such as nearby fire companies and emergency squads. For evacuation and rescue, potential egress paths are the roadway, the cross passages, the emergency exits, and the safety refuge. When developing an effective fire protection system for a road tunnel, an engineering analysis, performed manually or by use of a computer program, is essential.

Road bridges, providing long span crossings of waterways, railroads, and other roadways, would appear to pose minimum life safety risk since they are not enclosed as is a tunnel. However, there are significant motorist life safety risks created by the potential for much larger-scale fires due to the less restrictive regulation of cargo and the failure of the bridge supporting structure from a fire located either on or under the bridge. Double-decked bridges create the additional risk of a fire developing on the lower level and ultimately impacting the integrity of the support structure of the upper level. In addition to proper methods for fire resistance protection of the bridge structure and the provision of minimal fire protection systems as required by NFPA 502, bridge operators and emergency responders must also develop an emergency response plan similar to that recommended for road tunnels.

BIBLIOGRAPHY

References Cited

1. "Alternative Fuels," NFPA 502, *Standard for Road Tunnels, Bridges, and Other Limited Access Highways,* 2008, Annex G, pp. 502-29–502-30.
2. *The Holland Tunnel Chemical Fire,* National Board of Fire Underwriters (NBFU), New York, 1949.
3. *Preliminary Report—Task Force for Technical Investigation of the 24 March 1999 Fire in the Mont Blanc Road Tunnel Fire, 13 April 1999,* Joint Report of the French and Italian Government Technical Investigation Teams Relative to the Accident That Occurred in the Mont Blanc Tunnel on 24 March 1999, France/Italy, 1999.
4. "A Comparative Analysis of the Mont Blanc, Tauern and Gotthard Tunnel Fires," *Routes/Roads,* No. 324, World Road Association (PIARC), Paris, France, 2004.
5. *Fire and Smoke Control in Road Tunnels,* World Road Association (PIARC), Paris, France, 1999.
6. "International Road Tunnel Fire Detection Research Project—Phase 1: Review of Prior Tests and Tunnel Fires," The Fire Protection Research Foundation, Quincy, MA, Nov. 2003.
7. "Memorial Tunnel Fire Ventilation Test Program Text Report," Massachusetts Highway Department, Boston, MA, 1995.
8. *Systems and Equipment for Fire and Smoke Control in Road Tunnels,* World Road Association (PIARC), Paris, France, 2007.
9. *Road Tunnels: An Assessment of Fixed Fire Fighting Systems,* World Road Association (PIARC), Paris, France, 2007.
10. Subway Environmental Handbook, Volume II—Subway Environment Simulation Computer Program—SES Version 4, Part 1, User's Manual, Parsons Brinckerhoff Quade & Douglas, Inc. for United States Department of Transportation, Federal Transit Administrator, Washington, DC, 1997.
11. *Users Guide for the TUNVEN and Duct Programs,* Report No. FHWA-RD-78-187, Federal Highway Administration, Offices of Research and Development, Washington, DC, 1980.

12. Bechtel/Parsons Brinckerhoff, "Memorial Tunnel Fire Test Ventilation Program—Phase IV Report," prepared for Massachusetts Highway Department/Federal Highway Administration, Boston, MA, 1999.
13. *SIMULEX Users Manual,* Integrated Environmental Solutions, Limited (IES), Glasgow, UK, 1998.
14. EUREKA Project EU 499: FIRETUN, Fires in Transport Tunnels, Report on Full Scale Test, edited by Studiengesellschaft Stahlanwendung e. V., Dusseldorf, Germany, 1995.
15. Ingason, H., and Lönnermark, A., *"Large Scale Fire Tests in the Runehamar Tunnel—Heat Release Rate,"* International Seminar on Catastrophic Tunnel Fires, Boras, Sweden, 2003.
16. *Hot-Smoke Testing in Australian Tunnels,* Building Innovation & Construction Technology, Number 9, Australia, 1999.
17. Bai, Y., Burkett, W. R., and Nash, P. T., "Rapid Bridge Replacement Under Emergency Situation: Case Study," *ASCE Journal of Bridge Engineering,* 2006.

NFPA Codes, Standards, and Recommended Practices

Reference to the following NFPA codes, standards, and recommended practices will provide further information on road tunnels and bridges discussed in this chapter. (See the latest version of The NFPA Catalog *for availability of current editions of the following documents.)*

NFPA 10, *Standard for Portable Fire Extinguishers*
NFPA 11, *Standard for Low-, Medium-, and High-Expansion Foam*
NFPA 13, *Standard for the Installation of Sprinkler Systems*
NFPA 14, *Standard for the Installation of Standpipe and Hose Systems*
NFPA 15, *Standard for Water Spray Fixed Systems for Fire Protection*
NFPA 16, *Standard for the Installation of Foam-Water Sprinkler and Foam-Water Spray Systems*
NFPA 18, *Standard on Wetting Agents*
NFPA 20, *Standard for the Installation of Stationary Pumps for Fire Protection*
NFPA 22, *Standard for Water Tanks for Private Fire Protection*
NFPA 25, *Standard for the Inspection, Testing, and Maintenance of Water-Based Fire Protection Systems*
NFPA 30, *Flammable and Combustible Liquids Code*
NFPA 70, *National Electrical Code®*
NFPA 72®, National Fire Alarm Code®
NFPA *101®*, *Life Safety Code®*
NFPA 130, *Standard for Fixed Guideway Transit and Passenger Rail Systems*
NFPA 241, *Standard for Safeguarding Construction, Alteration, and Demolition Operations*
NFPA 259, *Standard Test Method for Potential Heat of Building Materials*
NFPA 502, *Standard for Road Tunnels, Bridges, and Other Limited Access Highways*
NFPA 520, *Standard on Subterranean Spaces*
NFPA 750, *Standard on Water Mist Fire Protection Systems*
NFPA 1963, *Standard for Fire Hose Connections*

References

ASHRAE Handbook—Applications, American Society of Heating, Refrigerating and Air-Conditioning Engineers (ASHRAE), Atlanta, GA, 2007.
Beard, A., and Carvel, R., *The Handbook of Tunnel Fire Safety,* Thomas Telford, London, UK, 2005.
Bendelius, A. G., "What Is the Role of Full Scale Fire Testing in the Design and Management of Tunnels?" *Tunnel Management International,* Apr. 1999.
Bickel, J. O., Kuesel, T. R., and King, E. H., *Tunnel Engineering Handbook,* 2nd ed., Chapman & Hall, New York, 1996.
Caserta, A. S., and Bendelius, A. G., *The Memorial Tunnel Fire Ventilation Test Program—Phase IV,* World Road Congress, World Road Association (PIARC), Kuala Lumpur, Malaysia, 1999.
Kennedy, W. D., Cihak, F., and Bendelius, A. G., *The Role of Fire-Life Safety Standards in Tunnel Design and Operations,* 3rd International Conference on Safety in Road and Rail Tunnels, Nice, France, March 1998.
Road Safety in Tunnels, World Road Association (PIARC), Paris, France, 1995.
Schachenmayr, M. P., and Bendelius, A. G., *Review of the Application Guidelines for the Egress Element for the Fire Protection Standard for Fixed Guideway Transit Systems,* International Seminar on Tunnel Fires, International Tunnelling and Underground Space Association (ITA), Lyon, France, May 1999.
Subway Environmental Design Handbook, Vol. I, *Principles and Applications,* 2nd ed., Associated Engineers, A Joint Venture: Parsons Brinckerhoff Quade & Douglas, Inc.; Deleuw Cather and Company; Kaiser Engineers, under the direction of Transit Development Corporation, Inc., 1976.

Index

– E –

– F –

– G –

– P –

– S –

– V –

– X –

– Y –

– Z –

Brief Contents

VOLUME I

See front endsheets for Volume II Brief Contents